G000128907

 Sports Collectors Digest *Voice for the Hobby*

2001 Standard Catalog of

FOOTBALL CARDS

4TH EDITION

Published by

krause
publications

700 E. State Street • Iola, WI 54990-0001
Telephone: 715/445-2214

Please call or write for our free catalog.
Our toll-free number to place an order or obtain a free catalog is 800-258-0929
or please use our regular business telephone 715-445-2214
for editorial comment and further information.

Library of Congress Catalog Number: 97-73033
ISBN: 0-87341-651-1

Printed in the United States of America

The Official Site of whatever sports stuff you collect.

Ask for what you want and sellers come to you.
Or, if you have something to sell, meet people asking for it.

eWanted.com™

Turning Auctions Upside Down.™

TABLE OF CONTENTS

M

N

O

P

U

CFL

The "Click" of the Trade.

"The <u>Card Collector</u> is the ultimate software program for collectors and dealers... I've been using it for over 5 years."

Rob Veres
Owner of Burbank Sports Cards
and a Lifelong Collector

Get control of your card collection.

- Track your favorite players, teams and inserts
- Get complete checklists for all sets, inserts and rookie cards
- Flag the cards you have and the ones you want
- Includes all sports and manufacturers
- Monthly pricing and checklist updates available*

For the first time available at your favorite Hobby Store

#1 Dealer Recommended

visit us on the web at www.apbagames.com

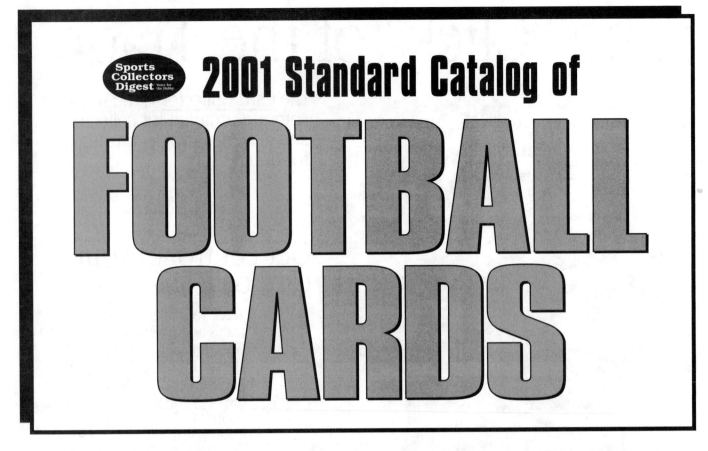

Sports Collectors Digest Voice for the Hobby

2001 Standard Catalog of FOOTBALL CARDS

WELCOME!

Thank you for purchasing the fourth edition of Standard Catalog of Football Cards.

This book is the most comprehensive annual football card price guide in the industry, complete with listings for more than 325,000 cards and checklists for more than 2,300 sets. The entire Sports Collectors Digest price guide staff contributed to this book, including coordinator Jason Stonelake and staff members Steve Bloedow, Joe Clemens and Bert Lehman.

Krause Publications' Standard Catalog of Baseball Cards is widely accepted in the sports card hobby as the most comprehensive annual price guide, containing current values for over 425,000 cards and checklists of over 7,600 sets. Authored each year by Bob Lemke, the Standard Catalog of Baseball Cards is a standard tool of the trade for the serious baseball card dealer and collector.

Given the outstanding performance of the Standard Catalog of Baseball Cards and the rising popularity of football cards, it was only natural for the price guide staff to extend the successful formula for its baseball catalog to the Standard Catalog of Football Cards.

It is our hope that this book enhances both your collection and your enjoyment of the sports card hobby.

HOW TO USE THIS CATALOG

This catalog has been uniquely designed to serve the needs of beginning and advanced football card collectors. It provides a comprehensive guide to more than 80 years of sports card issues, arranged so that even the novice collector can use it with confidence and ease.

The following explanations summarize the general practices used in preparing this catalog's listings. However, because of specialized requirements which may vary from card set to card set, these explanations should not be considered ironclad, but used as guidelines.

ARRANGEMENT

Because the most important feature in identifying and pricing a sports card is its set of origin, this catalog has been alphabetically arranged according to the name by which the set is most popularly known.

Those sets that were issued for more than one year are then listed chronologically, from earliest to most recent.

Within each set, the cards are listed by their designated card number, or in the absence of card numbers, alphabetically according to the last name of the player pictured.

IDENTIFICATION

While the date and issue of most modern sports cards are well identified on front, back, or both, such has not always been the case. In general, the back of the card is more useful in identifying the set of origin than the front. The issuer or sponsor's name will usually appear on the back since, after all, sports cards were first produced as a promotional item to stimulate sales of other products. As often as not, that issuer's name is the name by which the set is known to collectors and under which it will be found listed in this catalog.

In some difficult cases identifying a sports card's general age, if not specific year of issue, can be fixed by studying the biological or statistical information on the back of the card. The last year mentioned in either the biography or stats is usually the year which preceded the year of issue.

PHOTOGRAPHS

A photograph of the front of at least one representative card from virtually every set listed in this catalog has been incorporated into the listings to aid in identification.

Photographs have been printed in reduced size. The actual size of cards in each set is given in the introductory text preceding its listing, unless the card is the standard size 1-1/2" by 3-1/2".

DATING

The dating of sports cards by year of issue on the front or back of the card itself is a relatively new phenomenon. In most cases, to accurately determine a date of issue for an unidentified card, it must be studied for clues. As mentioned, the biography, career summary or statistics on the back of the card are the best way to pinpoint a year of issue. In most cases, the year of issue will be the year after the last season mentioned on the card.

Luckily for today's collector, earlier generations have done much of the research in determining your year of issue for those cards which bear no clues. The painstaking task of matching players' listed and/or pictured teams against their career records often allowed an issue date to be determined.

In some cases, particular card sets were issued over a period of more than one calendar year, but since they are collected together as a single set, their specific year of issue is not important. Such sets will be listed with their complete known range of issue years.

NUMBERING

While many sports card issues as far back as the early 1900s have contained card numbers assigned by the issuer to facilitate the collecting of a complete set, the practice has by no means been universal. Even today, not every set bears card numbers.

Logically, those sports cards which were numbered by their manufacturer are presented in that numerical order within the listings of this catalog. The many unnumbered issues, however, have been assigned Sports Collectors Digest Sports Card Price Guide numbers to facilitate their universal identification within the hobby, especially when buying and selling by mail.

In all cases, numbers which have been assigned or which otherwise do not appear on the card through error or by design, are shown in this catalog within parentheses. In virtually all cases, unless a more natural system suggested itself by the unique matter of a particular set, the assignment of Sports Collectors Digest Sports Card Price Guide numbers by the cataloging staff has been done by alphabetical arrangement of the players' last names or the card's principal title.

Significant collectible variations for any particular card are noted within the listings by the application of a suffix letter within parentheses. In instances of variations, the suffix "a" is assigned to the variation which was created first.

NAMES

The identification of a player by full name on the front of his sports card has been a common practice only since the 1940s. Prior to that, the player's name and team were the usual information found on the card front.

As a general practice, the listings in the Sports Collectors Digest Sports Card Price Guide present the player's name as it is more commonly known. If the player's name only appears on the back, rather than on the front of the card, the listing corresponds to that designation.

In cases where only the player's last name is given on the card, the cataloging staff has included the first name by which he was most often known for ease of identification.

Cards which contain misspelled first or last names, or even wrong initials, will have included in their listings the in-

correct information, with a correction accompanying in parentheses. This extends, also, to cases where the name on the card does not correspond to the player actually pictured.

GRADING

The vast majority of cards in this book were issued between 1981 and 1999 and feature NFL players only. The term "card" is used rather loosely as in this context it is construed to include virtually any series of cardboard or paper product, of whatever size and/or shape, depicting football players. Further, "cards" printed on wood, metal, plastic and other materials are either by their association with other issues or by their compatibility in size with the current 2-1/2" x 3-1/2" card standard also listed here.

Because modern cards are generally not popularly collected in lower grades, cards in this section carry only a Mint (MT) value quote. In general, post-1980 cards which grade Near Mint (NM) will retail at about 75% of the Mint price, while Excellent (EX) condition cards bring 40%.

Here is a more detailed look at grading procedures:

Mint (MT): A perfect card. Well-centered, with parallel borders which appear equal to the naked eye. Four sharp, square corners. No creases, edge dents, surface scratches, paper flaws, loss of luster, yellowing or fading, regardless of age. No imperfectly printed card - out of register, badly cut or ink flawed - or card stained by contact with gum, wax or other substances can be considered truly Mint, even if new out of the pack.

Near Mint (NR MT): A nearly perfect card. At first glance, a Near Mint card appears perfect; upon a closer examination, however, a minor flaw will be discovered. On well-centered cards, three of the four corners must be perfectly sharp; only one corner shows a minor imperfection upon close inspection. A slightly off-center card with one or more borders being noticeably unequal - but still present - would also fit this grade.

Excellent (EX): Corners are still fairly sharp with only moderate wear. Card borders may be off center. No creases. May have very minor gum, wax or product stains, front or back. Surfaces may show slight loss of luster from rubbing across other cards.

Very Good (VG): Show obvious handling. Corners rounded and/or perhaps showing minor creases. Other minor creases may be visible. Surfaces may exhibit loss of luster, but all printing is intact. May show major gum, wax or other packaging stains. No major creases, tape marks or extraneous markings or writing. Exhibit honest wear.

Good (G - generally 50% of the VG price): A well-worn card, but exhibits no intentional damage or abuse. May have major or multiple creases. Corners rounded well beyond the border.

Fair (F - generally 50% of the Good price): Shows excessive wear, along with damage or abuse. Will show all the wear characteristics of a Good card, along with such damage as thumb tack holes in or near margins, evidence of having been taped or pasted, perhaps small tears around the edges, or creases so heavy as to break the cardboard. Backs may show minor added pen or pencil writing, or be missing small bits of paper. Still, basically a complete card.

Poor (P): A card that has been tortured to death. Corners or other areas may be torn off. Card may have been trimmed, show holes from a paper punch or have been used for BB gun practice. Front may have extraneous pen or pencil writing, or other defacement. Major portions of front or back design may be missing. In other words, not a pretty sight.

In addition to these terms, collectors may encounter intermediate grades, such as VG-EX or EX-MT. These cards usually have characteristics of both the lower and higher grades, and are generally priced midway between those two values.

VALUATIONS

Values quoted in this book represent the current retail market and are compiled from recommendations provided and verified through the authors' daily involvement in the publication of the hobby's leading advertising periodicals, as well as the input of specialized consultants.

It should be stressed, however, that this book is intended to serve only as an aid in evaluating cards; actual market conditions are constantly changing. This is especially true of the cards of current players, whose on-field performance during the course of a season can greatly affect the value of their cards - upwards or downward.

Publication of this book is not intended as a solicitation to buy or sell the listed cards by the editors, publishers or contributors.

Again, the values here are retail prices - what a collector can expect to pay when buying a card from a dealer. The wholesale price, that which a collector can expect to receive from a dealer when selling cards, will be significantly lower.

Most dealers operate on a 100 percent mark-up, generally paying about 50 percent of a card's retail value. On some high demand cards, dealers will pay up to 75 percent or even 100 percent or more of retail value, anticipating continued price increases. Conversely, for many low-demand cards, such as common players' cards of recent years, dealers may pay 25 percent or even less of retail.

SETS

Collectors may note that the complete set prices for newer issues quoted in these listings are usually significantly lower than the total of the value of the individual cards which comprise the set. This reflects two factors in the sports card market. First, a seller is often willing to take a lower composite price for a complete set as a "volume discount" and to avoid inventorying a large number of common player or other lower-demand cards.

Second, to a degree, the value of common cards can be said to be inflated as a result of having a built-in overhead charge to justify the dealer's time in sorting cards, carrying them in stock and filling orders. This accounts for the fact that even brand new sports cards, which cost the dealer around 1 cent each when bought in bulk, carry individual price tags of 3 cents or higher.

ERRORS/VARIATIONS

It is often hard for the beginning collector to understand that an error on a sports card, in and of itself, does not usually add premium value to that card. It is usually only when the correcting of an error in the subsequent printing creates a variation that premium value attaches to an error.

Minor errors, such as wrong stats or personal data, create a variation that attaches to an error. Misspellings, inconsistencies, etc. - usually affecting the back of the card - are very common, especially in recent years. Unless a corrected variation was also printed, these errors are not noted in the listings of this book because they are not generally perceived by collectors to have premium value.

On the other hand, major effort had been expended to include the most complete listings ever for collectible variation cards. Many scarce and valuable variations are included in these listings because they are widely collected and often have significant premium value.

COUNTERFEITS/REPRINTS

As the value of sports cards has risen in the past 10-20 years, certain cards and sets have become too expensive for the average collector to obtain. This, along with changes in the technology of color printing, has given rise to increasing numbers of counterfeit and reprint cards.

While both terms describe essentially the same thing - a modern day copy which attempts to duplicate as closely as possible an original sports card - there are differences which are important to the collector.

Generally, a counterfeit is made with the intention of deceiving somebody into believing it is genuine, and thus paying large amounts of money for it. The counterfeiter takes every pain to try to make his fakes look as authentic as possible.

A reprint, on the other hand, while it may have been made to look as close as possible to an original card, is made with the intention of allowing collectors to buy them as substitutes for cards they may never be otherwise able to afford. The big difference is that a reprint is generally marked as such, usually on the back of the card.

In other cases, like the Topps 1952 baseball reprint set, the replicas are printed in a size markedly different from the originals. Collectors should be aware, however, that unscrupulous persons will sometimes cut off or otherwise obliterate the distinguishing word - "Reprint," "Copy" - or modern copyright date on the back of a reprint card in an attempt to pass it as genuine.

A collector's best defense against reprints and counterfeits is to acquire a knowledge of the look and feel of genuine sports cards of various eras and issues.

UNLISTED CARDS

Readers who have cards or sets which are not covered in this edition are invited to correspond with the editor for purposes of adding to the compilation of work now in progress. Address: SCD's Standard Catalog of Football Cards, 700 E. State St., Iola, WI 54990. Contributors will be acknowledged in future editions.

COLLECTOR ISSUES

Many cards do not fall under the scope of this catalog because they were issued solely for the collector market. Known as, "collector issues," these cards and sets are distinguished from "legitimate" issues by not having been created as a sales promotional item for another product - bubble gum, soda, snack cakes, dog food, cigarettes, gasoline, etc.

Because of their nature - the person issuing them is always free to print and distribute more if they should ever attain any real value - collector issues are generally regarded as having little or no premium value.

NEW ISSUES

Because new sports cards are being issued all the time, the cataloging of them is an ongoing challenge. Readers are invited to submit news of new issues, especially limited-edition or regionally issued cards, to the editors. Address: SCD's Standard Catalog of Football Cards, 700 E. State St., Iola, WI 54990.

ACKNOWLEDGMENTS

The editors wish to thank the many collectors, dealers and hobbyists who helped us compile, list and price the data in this edition.

HISTORY OF FOOTBALL CARDS

THE EARLY YEARS

The history of football cards started more than 100 years ago with the 1890 Mayo Cut Plug set. That set consists of 36 cards of college football players from Yale, Harvard and Princeton. It looks like any other small tobacco issue of the era, except the players are wearing hooded sweatshirts or turtlenecks with big letters on them instead of uniforms. There are no big names in the set, but it is still very significant for its historical perspective.

The next major football set came nearly a half-century later. The 1935 National Chicle set also has 36 cards, but the cards are beautiful full-color renditions - much like the Diamond Stars baseball set - of better-known football players, with some very well-known names (Knute Rockne, Bronko Nagurski) and a few more Hall of Famers (Dutch Clark, Cliff Battles, Clarke Hinkle).

The 1948 Leaf set introduced football cards to the postwar generation. The set consists of 98 hand-colored cards that closely resemble the Leaf baseball sets of the era. It contains the cards of Hall of Famers: Sid Luckman, Bulldog Turner, Doak Walker, Bobby Layne, Steve Van Buren, Bob Waterfield, Sammy Baugh, Leo Nomellini, George Connor, Pete Pihos and George McAffee.

Leaf also issued a "slip-numbered" 49-card set in 1949 that contains the rookie card of Chuck Bednarik.

BOWMAN

Bowman was also on the scene in 1948 and issued a 108-card football set that has "short prints" scattered throughout the set. Key cards include Baugh, Waterfield, Alex Wojciechowicz, Pihos, Bill Dudley, Luckman and Van Buren.

Bowman failed to issue a football set in 1949, but returned in 1950 with a football card set that bears a very close resemblance to the 1949 Bowman baseball set, with 144 hand-colored player pictures on card fronts and player information on card backs. Its 144 cards contain an astonishing number of Hall of Famers, and are among the loveliest renditions of sports figures on pasteboard ever. Key cards in the set include Lou Groza, Y.A. Tittle, Bobby Layne, Joe Perry, Tom Fears, Glenn Davis and Elroy Hirsch.

The 144-card 1951 Bowman set does not closely resemble the 1951 Bowman baseball set. All other Bowman football sets from this point deviate even more markedly from their baseball counterparts. Norm Van Brocklin, Ernie Stautner and Emlen Tunnell are the key cards in the set.

Two sets of 1952 Bowman cards were issued. The 1952 Bowman "small" set has 144 cards; the 1952 Bowman "large" has the same number of cards - the same cards, in fact. The difference? Cards in the small set measure 2-1/16" by 3-1/8,", while cards in the large set measure 2-1/2" by 3-3/4". The large set is scarcer, and therefore more expensive - in fact it is the single most expensive football set in this catalog. Key cards include Otto Graham, Frank Gifford, Gino Marchetti, Kyle Rote, Hugh McElhenny, Ollie Matson, Yale Lary, Tom Landry and Jim Lansford.

Set size was decreased to 96 cards in the 1953 Bowman set, while the card size remained large - Bowman-sized, in

other words. Trimmed cards are plentiful in this and subsequent Bowman sets.

The 128-card 1954 Bowman set was issued in four series of 32 cards each, with the third series being scarcest. Its key cards are the George Blanda rookie and a card of Whizzer White which actually shows Wilford White instead of the future Supreme Court justice. The set is the most common of all the Bowman sets.

Bowman's swan song as a company was the 160-card 1955 Bowman set. The company was purchased by Topps late in 1955 after it produced this set, which includes the rookie cards of Pat Summerall and John Henry Johnson. It was a scarce high-number series. Topps revived the Bowman name in 1991 and has had a set each year except for 1996 and 1997.

TOPPS

The trading card giant, Topps, entered the football card market in 1951 with its Topps Magic set, featuring 75 contemporary college football players.

The 1955 Topps All-American set also shows college football players, but in an all-time great format. Certain cards in the 100-card set were short-printed, a common practice in Topps football sets. Notable cards include Don Hutson, Knute Rockne, Jim Thorpe, Red Grange and Amos Alonzo Stagg.

There's a quirk in the 1956 Topps set: cards of St. Louis Cardinals and Washington Redskins are scarcer than other cards in the set. The set's key cards are Roosevelt Brown and Lenny Moore.

The 154-card 1957 Topps set has an unusual "splitscreen" format. High numbers are slightly scarcer.

Key cards are Bart Starr, John Unitas, Dick Lane, Ray Berry, Paul Hornung, Lenny Moore and Bob St. Clair.

Jim Brown's rookie card is far and away the key card in the 132-card 1958 Topps set, though there are others, most notably Sonny Jurgensen.

The 1959 Topps set has 176 cards, a high-number series and the rookie cards of Alex Karras and Sam Huff.

AFL and NFL players were included in the 198-card 1961 Topps set. AFL players are slightly scarcer in the set, which has the first cards of John Brodie, Don Maynard, Jim Otto and Lionel Taylor.

It was back to NFL-only status and a split-screen format for the 1962 Topps set, which contains a bundle of shortprinted cards along with the rookie cards of Ernie Davis, Don Meredith and Mike Ditka. The black-bordered set is exceptionally tough to find in top grade.

Topps' last NFL set for a while was the 1963 Topps set, which short-printed many Cleveland Browns and all New York Giants and Dallas Cowboys, including the Bob Lilly rookie. The rookie cards of Ray Nitschke, Willie Wood, Deacon Jones, and Jim Marshall are also in the 170-card set.

Short-prints were everywhere in the 1964 Topps set, which has 176 cards of AFL players. There are no special key cards in the set (Buck Buchanan and Bobby Bell are about it), but 86 short prints present quite a challenge in completing the 175-card set.

Probably the most unusual Topps set, and certainly one of the most significant and attractve, the 1965 Topps set has 175 tall (4-11/16,") cards, along with the normal batch of short prints. The key card here, and perhaps the key card of the 1960s, is the Joe Namath rookie. The set also has rookie cards of Willie Brown and Fred Biletnikoff.

With a "television" design borrowed from the 1955 Bowman baseball set, the 132-card 1966 Topps set has no short-prints, but one unusually scarce card - a checklist that everyone seemed to get in their packs but nobody saved.

The last of Topps' AFL-only sets, the 1967 Topps set, has no short prints and few significant rookie cards, save for the card of linebacker turned pro-wrestler Wahoo McDaniel. The set has 132 cards.

With Philadelphia Gum gone, Topps had the football card market all to itself, and responded with a 219-card set. First series cards have blue backs; key cards are the Jim Hart and Bob Griese cards.

One of the Topps' last classic football card sets, the 163-card 1969 Topps set was again split into two series, with an important distinction between the series: first-series cards have white borders; second-series cards have pictures that bleed out to the card edges. The set has Brian Piccolo's only card.

O.J. Simpson's rookie card is a highlight of the 263-card 1970 Topps set. There are no other significant cards (except for rookies of Alan Page, Jan Stenerud and Bubba Smith) in the set, which was issued in two series. The second series is slightly scarcer.

The 263-card 1971 Topps set was again split into two series, with the second series being slightly tougher to find. No cards are exceptionally scarce, though the set is notable for the rookie cards of Terry Bradshaw and Joe Greene.

Topps' most ambitious set to date, and one of its most interesting, the 351-card 1972 Topps set was split into three series: a common, low-number series, a slightly scarcer middle-number series, and a very scarcer high number series. The set also has rookie cards of Jim Plunkett, Lyle Alzado, Gene Upshaw, John Riggins, Ted Hendricks and Roger Staubach.

Topps sets through the rest of the 1970s fell into a relatively standard format. Set sizes were big, card sizes were uniform and designs followed a pattern. Key cards in the 528-card 1973 set include Franco Harris, Jack Ham and Art Shell. The 1974 set had the same number of cards and the rookie cards of Ahmad Rashad, Harold Carmichael, Ray Guy and John Matuszak. It was deja vu all over again with the 1975 set, which features the rookie cards of Mel Blount and Dan Fouts. The key card in the 1976 set, and maybe of the decade, is Walter Payton. The set also has rookie cards of Harvey Martin, Russ Francis, Randy White and Steve Grogan.

The 1977 set also has a key rookie card of Steve Largent, which accounts for about one-fourth of the total price. Similarly, the 1978 set contains the rookie card of Tony Dorsett.

The big rookie in the 528-card 1979 set is Earl Campbell. There were really no key rookie cards in the 1980 Topps set.

The string of flat sets with no key rookie cards changed in 1981 with the arrival of Joe Montana in a 528-card set that also features the rookie card of future Hall of Famer Art Monk and possible Hall of Famer Dan Hampton. Despite the big bucks you have to pump into the set for Montana, the set's a good buy for the secondary rookies and the added headroom left Montana.

Topps' last 528-card set was issued in 1982 and may be an even better buy than the 1981 set, considering it contains the rookie cards of Ronnie Lott, Lawrence Taylor, Cris Collinsworth and Anthony Munoz, in addition to Montana's second-year card.

The 1983 set represents a dip in both set size (328 cards) and interest. The top rookies are Mike Singletary and Marcus Allen. It's different with the 1984 set, which features the best assortment of rookies of any set of the 1980s, including John Elway, Eric Dickerson, Dan Marino and Roger Craig.

Topps also issued a 132-card set for the USFL in 1984, which includes rookie cards of Jim Kelly, Anthony Carter,

Reggie White and Herschel Walker, and is expensive because of its limited production.

Topps' 1985 NFL set is great-looking but a lot less significant, unless you attach a lot of importance to second-year cards. The biggest cards are second-year cards of Marino and Elway and the rookie cards of Richard Dent and Warren Moon. Its black-bordered, big-type design makes it hard to find in perfect shape. Topps issued another 132-card USFL set in 1985, that includes Doug Flutie's first card.

Jerry Rice's rookie card accounts for half of the value of the 1986 Topps set. Other top rookies include Boomer Esiason, Bernie Kosar and Steve Young.

The 396-card 1987 Topps set includes rookie cards of Jim Everett and Randall Cunningham.

There's no shortage of top running back rookies in the 1988 set. In addition to the first football card of Bo Jackson, the set features rookies of Christian Okoye, Neal Anderson, Chris Doleman, Vinny Testaverde and Cornelius Bennett.

An update set added some excitement to Topps' 1989 set, which is keyed by the rookie cards of John Taylor, Keith Jackson, Sterling Sharpe, Thurman Thomas, Anthony Miller and the update rookies of Troy Aikman, Barry Sanders, Michael Irvin and Eric Metcalf.

The 1990 Topps set was a big one: 528 cards, including several subsets highlighted by a series of 25 draft picks. A 132-card update set was also issued. An update set was not issued in 1991, but the regular set jumped to 660 cards, the largest ever at that point. The company topped that mark in 1992, issuing 759 cards over three series. In 1993, Topps reverted to a 660-card set.

The company's premium issue, under the name Stadium Club, debuted in 1991 with a 500-card glossy set. In 1992 the set jumped to 700 cards, issued over three series. The 1993 effort had two 250-card series.

Topps' Finest brand surfaced in 1992 with a 44-card set, while the first full set of Finest arrived two years later with 220 cards. While Topps, Stadium Club and Finest name brands have continued through 1998, Topps has also tried several brands like FantaSports in 1993, Archives in 1994 and Gilt Edge and Laser in 1996 that were not continued.

Topps also added Topps Chrome to its lineup of football cards in 1996, and that brand has become a mainstay in all sports. The product essentially reprints cards from Topps produce, but adds a chromium finish to the front and also adds Refractor parallels.

FLEER

Fleer issued football cards sets for four years (1960-63) and then again beginning in 1990. Fleer jumped from a 132-card set to a high of 220 and then down to two sets of 88 cards each, and featured the AFL exclusively three out of the four years.

The 1960 Fleer set contains 132 cards, including Ron Mix, Jack Kemp, George Blanda, Sid Gillman and Hank Stram.

Fleer showed both AFL and NFL players for the only time in this 1961 set. It's the most appealing of the four Fleer sets; it has the best photography and cards of players from both leagues. The 220-card set has several rookie cards - Don Meredith, Jim Otto, Johnny Robinson and Don Maynard and a scarce 87-card run of AFL players.

The 88-card 1962 Fleer set shows nothing but AFL players, most notably Gino Cappelletti. All cards in this set are relatively scarce, which accounts for its high price tag.

Fleer stayed at 88 cards for its 1963 football set, another rough set with two very scarce short prints - Charlie Long and Bob Dougherty This set also has a handful of significant rookie cards - Nick Buoniconti, Cookie Gilchrist, Keith Lincoln, Len Dawson and Lance Alworth. This set, like its 1961 and 1962 predecessors, is difficult to find in Mint condition at any price.

The company returned its line of football cards again in 1990 and has continued them. Fleer introduced its premium set, Fleer Ultra, in 1991, and has continued that label also. The 1992 and 1993 cards are glossy.

In 1995, Fleer purchased SkyBox, which had produced football since 1992, when it broke in with Impact and Primetime. Once under the Fleer/SkyBox umbrella, SkyMotion was issued in 1996 and Impact Rookies in 1997.

In 1997, Fleer renamed its Flair brand, which hadn't appeared in 1996, to Flair Showcase and mixed up the format with 120 players featured on three different frontal designs. Fleer/SkyBox also produced two series of Goudey Football in 1997 under the SkyBox name as well as 1997 SkyBox EX2001. In addition, NFL Autographics debuted in 1997 with autograph cards being inserted into all SkyBox releases for the season.

PHILADELPHIA

Philadelphia Gum's four sets chronicle the history of the NFL in, if not the Golden Age of pro football, the age from which many present and future Hall of Famers will come. These are the key years of the storied men in the trenches: Lombardi, Karras, Starr, Unitas, Brown, Olsen, Gifford, Ditka and Jurgensen. The sets are attractive, all more than 20 years old, and considerably underpriced compared to more modem issues. Their prices generally match the Topps sets of the same years, and yet contain more popular NFL players.

Philly's first set, the clean-lined, attractive 1964 Philadelphia set, has 198 cards and no short prints. However, it does have the first cards of Herb Adderly, Willie Davis, Henry Jordan, Willie Wood, Merlin Olsen and Roman Gabriel.

The key card in the 198-card 1965 Philadelphia set - a virtual clone of the 1964 set - is Paul Warfield, though the set also has the first cards of Deacon Jones, Charlie Taylor, Paul Krause and Mel Renfro.

The 1966 Philadelphia set is another fine-looking set, noteworthy for two big rookies: Gale Sayers and Dick Butkus. However, the set also has Jim Brown's last card, as well as Bob Hayes' first card.

Philly's last set, the 1967 Philadelphia set, has an easy-to-spot yellow border, first cards for Tommy Nobis and Lee Roy Jordan, and no scarcities.

PRO SET

Pro Set entered the football card market along with Score in 1989, injecting a much-needed shot of excitement and marketing savvy. Pro Set kicked off the year with a set that checked in at 615 cards, making it the largest football set. The set consists of a 440-card first series; a 100-card second series, including 30 announcer cards; 23 Super Bowl insert cards; and a 20-card "Final Update" set, which includes cards of Sterling Sharpe, Dave Meggett and Raiders coach Art Shell. The set has a handful of scarce variations as well as the rookie cards of Barry Sanders, Troy Aikman and Deion Sanders.

Pro Set produced full sets up until 1993, when their chronic over-production finally caught up with them and killed collector interest. Their final offering was a seven-card (eight with header) National Promo set in 1994.

UPPER DECK

Upper Deck produced its first football card set in 1991, after debuting in baseball in 1989. The 1991 set included 700 cards, which were issued in two series, as well as factory sets. Series I had 500 cards, while Series II (called High Series) had 200.

In 1993, Upper Deck added SP to its football product line. SP featured super-premium cards and one insert, called All-Pros. The SP line erupted with popularity in 1993, with rookies like Drew Bledsoe, Natrone Means and Rick Mirer. In 1994, SP added Holoviews and Die-cut Holoviews to its mix. The popularity of the Holoview technology also eventually led to an SPx brand, which featured a 50-card, all Holoview die-cut set.

In 1994, Collector's Choice also entered Upper Deck's mix. Collector's Choice was a base brand, tailored toward kids with its 99-cent pack price.

SPx was introduced by Upper Deck in 1996 with a 50-card set issued in one-card packs. This brand continued in 1997. SP Authentic debuted in 1997 with a 198-card set that was oriented toward autographs and memorabilia.

PLAYOFF

Playoff entered the football card market in 1992 with its Tekchrome finish. Its inaugural set featured 150 cards on thicker-than-usual card stock. Playoff added Contenders to its lineup in 1993, with 150 cards in the regular-issue set.

In 1995, Playoff split its product into Absolute (hobby) and Prime (retail). Although the checklist was identical, the photos were slightly different for each product, and the inserts were different, with some being totally unique to the product and others split into both.

In 1997, Playoff produced Absolute, Contenders, Zone and 1st & 10.

In recent years Collector's Edge, Pacific, Motion Vision, Sage, Press Pass and many other companies have been added to the mix. In 1996 alone there were 11 companies that produced major football issues, including Topps, Fleer/SkyBox, Upper Deck, Pinnacle, Donruss/Leaf, MotionVision, Press Pass, Score Board, Playoff, Pacific, Collector's Edge.

Score Board went backrupt in 1997 to reduce the number of licensees to 10.

Product releases have grown at an even greater rate than the number of manufacturers. In 1989, for example, there were only three football card releases - Topps, Score and Pro Set. In 1990, this number doubled to six, and in 1991, it doubled again to 12. In 1992, there were 22 football card releases, in 1993 there were 24, in 1994 it was 31 and in 1995 it was 46.

In 1996 there were 64 football card releases, and those products contained 363 insert sets. In 1997 the number of products jumped to 66, and contained a mind-boggling 451 insert sets.

1987 Ace Fact Pack Chicago Bears

Ace Fact Pack in West Germany printed card sets for 12 National Football League teams. The cards, which have rounded corners, were distributed throughout Great Britain and England. They were designed to look like a deck of playing cards and are unnumbered. There were 33 cards created for each of the 12 teams, which are listed below alphabetically. Twenty-two cards are players; 11 are informational. All but the cards for the Chicago Bears (2-1/2" x 3-1/2") measure 2-1/4" x 3-5/8".

		MT
Complete Set (33):		175.00
Common Player:		4.00
(1)	Todd Bell	5.00
(2)	Mark Bortz	4.00
(3)	Kevin Butler	5.00
(4)	Jim Covert	6.00
(5)	Richard Dent	10.00
(6)	Dave Duerson	4.00
(7)	Gary Fencik	5.00
(8)	Willie Gault	8.00
(9)	Dan Hampton	10.00
(10)	Jay Hilgenberg	4.00
(11)	Wilber Marshall	6.00
(12)	Jim McMahon	10.00
(13)	Steve McMichael	6.00
(14)	Emery Moorehead	4.00
(15)	Keith Ortega	4.00
(16)	Walter Payton	70.00
(17)	William Perry	8.00
(18)	Mike Richardson	4.00
(19)	Mike Singletary	10.00
(20)	Matt Suhey	5.00
(21)	Keith Van Horne	4.00
(22)	Otis Wilson	5.00
(23)	Bears Helmet	4.00
(24)	Bears Information	4.00
(25)	Bears Uniform	4.00
(26)	Game Record Holders	4.00
(27)	Season Record Holders	4.00
(28)	Career Record Holders	4.00
(29)	Bears 1967-86	4.00
(30)	1986 Team Statistics	4.00
(31)	All-Time Greats	4.00
(32)	Roll of Honour	4.00
(33)	Soldier Field	4.00

1987 Ace Fact Pack Denver Broncos

Measuring 2-1/4" x 3-5/8", the 33-card set features 22 player cards and 11 organizational cards. The front showcases the team's logo and player's name at the top, with a photo and the player's bio filling the remainder of the card front. The opposite side of the card has a playing card design. The cards are unnumbered. The set was released in Great Britain.

		MT
Complete Set (33):		175.00
Common Player:		4.00
(1)	Keith Bishop	4.00
(2)	Bill Bryan	4.00
(3)	Mark Cooper	4.00
(4)	John Elway	90.00
(5)	Steve Foley	5.00
(6)	Mike Harden	4.00
(7)	Rick Hunley	4.00
(8)	Vance Johnson	5.00
(9)	Rulon Jones	5.00
(10)	Rich Karlis	4.00
(11)	Clarence Kay	5.00
(12)	Ken Lanier	5.00
(13)	Karl Mecklenburg	8.00
(14)	Chris Norman	4.00
(15)	Jim Ryan	4.00
(16)	Dennis Smith	5.00
(17)	Dave Studdard	4.00
(18)	Andre Townsend	4.00
(19)	Steve Watson	5.00
(20)	Gerald Wilhite	4.00
(21)	Sammy Winder	5.00
(22)	Louis Wright	5.00
(23)	Team Helmet	4.00
(24)	Team Information	4.00
(25)	Broncos Uniform	4.00
(26)	Game Record Holders	
(27)	Season Record Holders	4.00
(28)	Career Record Holders	4.00
(29)	Record 1967-86	4.00
(30)	Roll of Honour	4.00
(31)	All-Time Greats	4.00
(32)	1986 Team Statistics	4.00
(33)	Denver Mile High Stadium	4.00

1987 Ace Fact Pack Dallas Cowboys

Measuring 2-1/4" x 3-5/8", the 33-card set follows the same design as the Bears and Broncos. The set was released in Great Britain. It has 22 player cards in the set and 11 organizational cards. The cards are unnumbered.

		MT
Complete Set (33):		200.00
Common Player:		4.00
(1)	Bill Bates	5.00
(2)	Doug Cosbie	5.00
(3)	Tony Dorsett	25.00
(4)	Michael Downs	4.00
(5)	John Dutton	5.00
(6)	Ron Fellows	4.00
(7)	Mike Hegman	4.00
(8)	Tony Hill	6.00
(9)	Jim Jeffcoat	5.00
(10)	Ed "Too Tall" Jones	12.00
(11)	Crawford Ker	4.00
(12)	Eugene Lockhart	5.00
(13)	Phil Pozderac	5.00
(14)	Tom Rafferty	5.00
(15)	Jeff Rohrer	4.00
(16)	Mike Sherrard	6.00
(17)	Glen Titensor	5.00
(18)	Mark Tuinei	5.00
(19)	Herschel Walker	15.00
(20)	Everson Walls	5.00
(21)	Danny White	8.00
(22)	Randy White	16.00
(23)	Cowboys Helmet	4.00
(24)	Cowboys Information	
(25)	Cowboys Uniform	4.00
(26)	Game Record Holders	4.00
(27)	Season Record Holders	4.00
(28)	Career Record Holders	4.00
(29)	1967-86 Team Record	4.00
(30)	1986 Team Statistics	4.00
(31)	All-Time Greats	4.00
(32)	Roll of Honour	4.00
(33)	Texas Stadium	4.00

1987 Ace Fact Pack Miami Dolphins

Measuring 2-1/4" x 3-5/8", the 33-card set follows the same design as the others. It was released in Great Britain. There are 22 player cards and 11 highlight cards. The cards are unnumbered.

		MT
Complete Set (33):		300.00
Common Player:		4.00
(1)	Bob Baumhower	5.00
(2)	Woody Bennett	4.00
(3)	Doug Betters	5.00
(4)	Glenn Blackwood	5.00
(5)	Bud Brown	4.00
(6)	Bob Brudzinski	4.00
(7)	Mark Clayton	7.00
(8)	Mark Duper	7.00
(9)	Roy Foster	4.00
(10)	Jon Giesler	4.00
(11)	Hugh Green	6.00
(12)	Lorenzo Hampton	4.00
(13)	Bruce Hardy	4.00
(14)	William Judson	4.00
(15)	Greg Koch	4.00
(16)	Paul Lankford	4.00
(17)	George Little	4.00
(18)	Dan Marino	175.00
(19)	John Offerdahl	5.00
(20)	Dwight Stephenson	6.00
(21)	Don Strock	5.00
(22)	T.J. Turner	4.00
(23)	Dolphins Helmet	4.00
(24)	Team Information	4.00
(25)	Dolphins Uniform	4.00
(26)	Game Record Holders	
(27)	Season Record Holders	4.00
(28)	Career Record Holders	4.00
(29)	Dolphins 1967-86	4.00
(30)	1986 Team Statistics	4.00

1987 Ace Fact Pack San Francisco 49ers

Measuring 2-1/4" x 3-5/8", this 33-card set was released in Great Britain. The design follows the same format of the other teams in the set. There are 22 player cards and 11 highlights cards. The cards are unnumbered.

		MT
Complete Set (33):		400.00
Common Player:		4.00
(1)	John Ayers	4.00
(2)	Dwaine Board	4.00
(3)	Michael Carter	6.00
(4)	Dwight Clark	12.00
(5)	Roger Craig	12.00
(6)	Joe Cribbs	5.00
(7)	Randy Cross	5.00
(8)	Riki Ellison	4.00
(9)	Jim Fahnhorst	4.00
(10)	Keith Fahnhorst	4.00
(11)	Russ Francis	5.00
(12)	Don Griffin	5.00
(13)	Ronnie Lott	14.00
(14)	Milt McColl	4.00
(15)	Tim McKyer	5.00
(16)	Joe Montana	175.00
(17)	Bubba Paris	4.00
(18)	Fred Quinlan	4.00
(19)	Jerry Rice	150.00
(20)	Manu Tuiasosopo	4.00
(21)	Keena Turner	6.00
(22)	Carlton Williamson	4.00
(23)	49er Helmet	4.00
(24)	49er Information	4.00
(25)	49er Uniform	4.00
(26)	Game Record Holders	
(27)	Season Record Holders	4.00
(28)	Career Record Holders	4.00
(29)	49ers History 1967-86	4.00
(30)	1986 Team Statistics	
(31)	All-Time Greats	4.00
(32)	Roll of Honour	4.00
(33)	Candlestick Park	4.00

1987 Ace Fact Pack New York Giants

Measuring 2-1/4" x 3-5/8", the 33-card set follows the same design as the other teams in the series. Released in Great Britain, the set includes 22 player cards and 11 highlight cards. The cards are unnumbered.

		MT
Complete Set (33):		150.00
Common Player:		4.00
(1)	Billy Ard	4.00
(2)	Carl Banks	8.00
(3)	Mark Bavaro	5.00
(4)	Brad Benson	4.00
(5)	Harry Carson	8.00
(6)	Maurice Carthon (misspelled Morris)	5.00
(7)	Mark Collins	5.00
(8)	Chris Godfrey	4.00
(9)	Kenny Hill	4.00
(10)	Erik Howard	5.00
(11)	Bobby Johnson	4.00
(12)	Leonard Marshall	6.00
(13)	George Martin	5.00
(14)	Joe Morris	5.00
(15)	Karl Nelson	4.00
(16)	Bart Oates (misspelled Oakes)	5.00
(17)	Gary Reasons	5.00
(18)	Stacy Robinson	4.00
(19)	Phil Simms	20.00
(20)	Lawrence Taylor	30.00
(21)	Herb Welch	4.00
(22)	Perry Williams	4.00
(23)	Giants Helmet	4.00
(24)	Giants Information	4.00
(25)	Giant Uniforms	4.00
(26)	Game Record Holders	
(27)	Season Record Holders	4.00
(28)	Career Record Holders	4.00
(29)	Giants 1967-86	4.00
(30)	1986 Team Statistics	
(31)	All-Time Greats	4.00
(32)	Roll of Honour	4.00
(33)	Giants Stadium	4.00

(31) Dolphin Greats 4.00
(32) Roll of Honour 4.00
(33) Joe Robbie Stadium 4.00

1987 Ace Fact Pack New York Jets

Measuring 2-1/4" x 3-5/8", the 33-card set follows the same design as the other teams in the series. Released in Great Britain, there are 22 player cards and 11 highlight cards. The cards are unnumbered.

		MT
Complete Set (33):		120.00
Common Player:		4.00
(1)	Dan Alexander	4.00
(2)	Tom Baldwin	4.00
(3)	Barry Bennett	4.00
(4)	Russell Carter	5.00
(5)	Kyle Clifton	6.00
(6)	Bob Crable	5.00
(7)	Joe Fields	5.00
(8)	Rusty Guilbeau	4.00
(9)	Harry Hamilton	5.00
(10)	Johnny Hector	7.00
(11)	Jerry Holmes	4.00
(12)	Gordon King	4.00
(13)	Lester Lyles	4.00
(14)	Marty Lyons	5.00
(15)	Kevin McArthur	4.00
(16)	Freeman McNeil	8.00
(17)	Ken O'Brien	7.00
(18)	Tony Paige	6.00
(19)	Mickey Shuler	5.00
(20)	Jim Sweeney	4.00
(21)	Al Toon	8.50
(22)	Wesley Walker	9.50
(23)	Jets Helmet	4.00
(24)	Jets Team Information	
(25)	Jets Uniform	4.00
(26)	Game Record Holders	4.00
(27)	Season Record Holders	
(28)	Career Record Holders	
(29)	1967-86 Team Record	4.00
(30)	1986 Team Statistics	
(31)	Jets 1967-86	4.00
(32)	All-Time Greats	4.00
(33)	Roll of Honour	4.00
	Giants Stadium	4.00

1987 Ace Fact Pack Detroit Lions

Measuring 2-1/4" x 3-5/8", the 33-card set follows the same design as the other teams in the series. Issued in Great Britain, the set includes 22 player cards and 11 highlight cards. The cards are unnumbered.

		MT
Complete Set (33):		120.00
Common Player:		4.00
(1)	Nolan Cromwell	6.00
(2)	Eric Dickerson	18.00
(3)	Reggie Doss	4.00
(4)	Carl Ekern	4.00
(5)	Henry Ellard	10.00
(6)	Jim Everett	10.00
(7)	Jerry Gray	5.00
(8)	Dennis Harrah	5.00
(9)	David Hull	4.00
(10)	Kevin House	5.00
(11)	LeRoy Irvin	5.00
(12)	Mark Jerue	4.50
(13)	Shawn Miller	4.00
(14)	Tom Newberry	5.00
(15)	Vince Newsome	4.50
(16)	Mel Owens	5.00
(17)	Irv Pankey	4.00
(18)	Doug Reed	5.00
(19)	Doug Smith	5.00
(20)	Jackie Slater	6.00
(21)	Charles White	6.00
(22)	Mike Wilcher	4.00
(23)	Rams Helmet	4.00
(24)	Rams Information	4.50
(25)	Rams Uniform	4.00
(26)	Game Record Holders	
(27)	Season Record Holders	
(28)	Career Record Holders	5.00
(29)	Team Record 1967-86	4.00
(30)	1986 Team Statistics	
(31)	All-Time Greats	4.00
(32)	Rams Roll of Honour	4.50
(33)	Anaheim Stadium	4.00

1987 Ace Fact Pack Los Angeles Rams

Measuring 2-1/4" x 3-5/8", the 33-card set follows the same design as the other teams in the series. Issued in Great Britain, it contains 22 player cards and 11 highlight cards, which are unnumbered.

(Lions list appears in column — see Detroit Lions entry above)

same design as the other teams in the series. Issued in Great Britain, there are 22 player cards and 11 highlight cards. The cards are unnumbered.

		MT
Complete Set (33):		120.00
Common Player:		4.00
(1)	John Anderson	6.00
(2)	Robbie Bosco	5.00
(3)	Don Bracken	4.00
(4)	John Cannon	5.00
(5)	Alphonso Carreker	4.00
(6)	Kenneth Davis	8.00
(7)	Al Del Greco	5.00
(8)	Gary Ellerson	4.00
(9)	Gerry Ellis	5.00
(10)	Phillip Epps	6.00
(11)	Ron Hallstrom	4.00
(12)	Mark Lee	5.00
(13)	Bobby Leopold	4.00
(14)	Charles Martin	4.00
(15)	Brian Noble	5.00
(16)	Ken Ruettgers	5.00
(17)	Randy Scott	5.00
(18)	Walter Stanley	5.00
(19)	Ken Stills	4.00
(20)	Keith Uecker	5.00
(21)	Ed West	5.00
(22)	Randy Wright	5.00
(23)	Packer Helmet	4.00
(24)	Packer Information	4.00
(25)	Packer Uniform	4.00
(26)	Game Record Holders	
(27)	Season Record Holders	
(28)	Career Record Holders	
(29)	1967-86 Team Record	4.00
(30)	1986 Team Statistics	4.00
(31)	All-Time Greats	4.00
(32)	Roll of Honour	4.00
(33)	Lambeau Field/Milwaukee County Stadium	4.00

1987 Ace Fact Pack Washington Redskins

Measuring 2-1/4" x 3-5/8", the 33-card set follows the same design as the other teams in the series. Issued in Great Britain, the set is broken up into

22 player cards and 11 highlight cards, which are unnumbered.

		MT
Complete Set (33):		175.00
Common Player:		4.00
(1)	Jeff Bostic	5.00
(2)	Dave Butz	6.00
(3)	Gary Clark	20.00
(4)	Monte Coleman	5.00
(5)	Vernon Dean	4.00
(6)	Clint Didier	5.00
(7)	Darryl Grant	4.00
(8)	Darrell Green	7.50
(9)	Russ Grimm	6.00
(10)	Joe Jacoby	6.00
(11)	Curtis Jordan	4.00
(12)	Dexter Manley	5.00
(13)	Charles Mann	6.00
(14)	Mark May	5.00
(15)	Rich Milot	4.00
(16)	Art Monk	30.00
(17)	Neal Olkewicz	4.00
(18)	George Rogers	8.00
(19)	Jay Schroeder	8.00
(20)	R.C. Thielemann	4.00
(21)	Alvin Walton	4.00
(22)	Don Warren	4.00
(23)	Redskin Helmet	4.00
(24)	Redskin Information	4.00
(25)	Redskin Uniforms	4.00
(26)	Game Record Holders	4.00
(27)	Season Record Holders	
(28)	Career Record Holders	
(29)	Redskins 1867-86	4.00
(30)	1986 Team Statistics	
(31)	All-Time Redskins	4.00
(32)	Roll of Honour	4.00
(33)	Robert F. Kennedy Stadium	4.00

1987 Ace Fact Pack Seattle Seahawks

Measuring 2-1/4" x 3-5/8", the 33-card set follows the same design as the other teams in the series. Issued in Great Britain, the set is broken up into 22 player and 11 highlight cards, which are unnumbered.

		MT
Complete Set (33):		150.00
Common Player:		4.00
(1)	Edwin Bailey	4.00
(2)	Dave Brown	6.00
(3)	Jeff Bryant	4.00
(4)	Blair Bush	5.00
(5)	Keith Butler	4.00
(6)	Kenny Easley	5.00
(7)	Greg Gaines	4.00
(8)	Jacob Green	6.00
(9)	Norm Johnson	5.00
(10)	Dave Krieg	8.00
(11)	Steve Largent	30.00
(12)	Reggie Kinlaw	4.00
(13)	Ron Mattes	4.00
(14)	Bryan Millard	4.00
(15)	Eugene Robinson	5.00
(16)	Bruce Scholtz	4.00
(17)	Terry Taylor	4.00
(18)	Mike Tice	5.00
(19)	Daryl Turner	5.00
(20)	Curt Warner	7.50
(21)	John L. Williams	12.00
(22)	Fredd Young	5.00
(23)	Seattle Helmet	4.00
(24)	Seahawk Information	4.00
(25)	Seahawk Uniform	4.00
(26)	Game Record Holder	4.00
(27)	Season Record Holders	
(28)	Career Record Holders	
(29)	1977-86 Team Record	4.00
(30)	1986 Team Statistics	
(31)	All-Time Greats	4.00
(32)	Roll of Honour	4.00
(33)	Kingdome	4.00

1989 Action Packed Prototypes

These cards were produced as prototypes before Action Packed released its 1989 30-card test set. The gold-bordered front has a raised color action photo on it; the back has stats, a head shot, notes, a card number and a space for an autograph. These cards, numbered 72 and 101, can be distinguished from the

1987 Ace Fact Pack Green Bay Packers

Measuring 2-1/4" x 3-5/8", the 33-card set follows the

test set by where the card number appears. On these cards, they are on the same side as the mug shot; on the test cards they are on the opposite side.

		MT
Complete Set (2):		75.00
Common Player:		45.00
72	Freeman McNeil	45.00
101	Phil Simms	45.00

1989 Action Packed Test

These 30 cards are standard size and were packaged in packs of six. Ten players from the Chicago Bears, New York Giants and Washington Redskins are represented in the set, which was copyrighted by Hi-Pro Marketing of Northbrook, Ill. Each front has a gold-border and a raised color action photo; the back has a head shot, statistics, informational notes, a card number and a space for an autograph.

		MT
Complete Set (30):		25.00
Common Player:		.50
Wax Box:		30.00
1	Neal Anderson	4.00
2	Trace Armstrong	.60
3	Kevin Butler	.50
4	Richard Dent	.75
5	Dennis Gentry	.50
6	Dan Hampton	.75
7	Jay Hilgenberg	.50
8	Thomas Sanders	.60
9	Mike Singletary	.75
10	Mike Tomczak	.75
11	Raul Allegre	.50
12	Ottis Anderson	.75
13	Mark Bavaro	.60
14	Terry Kinard	.50
15	Lionel Manuel	.50
16	Leonard Marshall	.60
17	Dave Meggett	4.50
18	Joe Morris	.75
19	Phil Simms	1.00
20	Lawrence Taylor	1.75
21	Kelvin Bryant	.75
22	Darrell Green	1.00
23	Dexter Manley	.60
24	Charles Mann	.60
25	Wilber Marshall	.60
26	Art Monk	1.50
27	Jamie Morris	.60
28	Tracy Rocker	.60
29	Mark Rypien	12.00
30	Ricky Sanders	1.00

1990 Action Packed

BARRY SANDERS — LIONS™

Action Packed was released in two series over the summer, with the first available in June and the second available in August. The total of 280 cards was randomly split up between the two series. In the first series, 126 players were issued; 154 come out in Series II. A factory set was also issued. The cards are embossed, with a gold foil and rounded corners. Special cards included those honoring the retired Reggie Williams and Steve Largent; a card back for Christian Okoye with a phrase written in Nigerian; and a Braille card featuring the retired Jim Plunkett.

		MT
Complete Set (280):		20.00
Complete Factory (281):		20.00
Common Player:		.10
Minor Stars:		.20
Wax Box:		25.00
1	Aundray Bruce	.10
2	Scott Case	.10
3	Tony Casillas	.10
4	Shawn Collins	.10
5	Marcus Cotton	.10
6	Bill Fralic	.10
7	Tim Green	.10
8	Chris Miller	.20
9	Deion Sanders	1.25
10	John Settle	.10
11	Cornelius Bennett	.20
12	Shane Conlan	.10
13	Kent Hill	.10
14	Jim Kelly	.50
15	Mark Kelso	.10
16	Scott Norwood	.10
17	Andre Reed	.20
18	Fred Smerlas	.10
19	Bruce Smith	.20
20	Thurman Thomas	.50
21	Neal Anderson	.20
22	Kevin Butler	.10
23	Richard Dent	.20
24	Dennis Gentry	.10
25	Dan Hampton	.20
26	Jay Hilgenberg	.10
27	Steve McMichael	.10
28	Brad Muster	.10
29	Mike Singletary	.20
30	Mike Tomczak	.10
31	James Brooks	.10
32	Rickey Dixon	.10
33	Boomer Esiason	.20
34	David Fulcher	.10
35	Rodney Holman	.10
36	Tim Krumrie	.10
37	Tim McGee	.10
38	Anthony Munoz	.20
39	Reggie Williams	.10
40	Ickey Woods	.10
41	Thane Gash	.10
42	Mike Johnson	.10
43	Bernie Kosar	.20
44	Reggie Langhorne	.10
45	Clay Matthews	.10
46	Eric Metcalf	.10
47	Frank Minnifield	.10
48	Ozzie Newsome	.10
49	Webster Slaughter	.10
50	Felix Wright	.10
51	Troy Aikman	2.00
52	James Dixon	.10
53	Michael Irvin	.50
54	Jim Jeffcoat	.10
55	Ed Jones	.10
56	Eugene Lockhart	.10
57	Danny Noonan	.10
58	Paul Palmer	.10
59	Everson Walls	.10
60	Steve Walsh	.20
61	Steve Atwater	.10
62	Tyrone Braxton	.10
63	John Elway	2.00
64	Bobby Humphrey	.10
65	Mark Jackson	.10
66	Vance Johnson	.10
67	Greg Kragen	.10
68	Karl Mecklenburg	.10
69	Dennis Smith	.10
70	David Treadwell	.10
71	Jim Arnold	.10
72	Jerry Ball	.10
73	Bennie Blades	.10
74	Mel Gray	.10
75	Richard Johnson	.10
76	Eddie Murray	.10
77	Rodney Peete	.10
78	Barry Sanders	5.00
79	Chris Spielman	.10
80	Walter Stanley	.10
81	Dave Brown	.10
82	Brent Fullwood	.10
83	Tim Harris	.10
84	Johnny Holland	.10
85	Don Majkowski	.10
86	Tony Mandarich	.10
87	Mark Murphy	.10
88	Brian Noble	.10
89	Ken Ruettgers	.10
90	Sterling Sharpe	.20
91	Ray Childress	.10
92	Ernest Givins	.10
93	Alonzo Highsmith	.10
94	Drew Hill	.10
95	Bruce Matthews	.10
96	Bubba McDowell	.10
97	Warren Moon	.50
98	Mike Munchak	.10
99	Allen Pinkett	.10
100	Mike Rozier	.10
101	Albert Bentley	.10
102	Duane Bickett	.10
103	Bill Brooks	.10
104	Chris Chandler	.10
105	Ray Donaldson	.10
106	Chris Hinton	.10
107	Andre Rison	.20
108	Keith Taylor	.10
109	Clarence Verdin	.10
110	Fredd Young	.10
111	Deron Cherry	.10
112	Steve DeBerg	.10
113	Dino Hackett	.10
114	Albert Lewis	.10
115	Nick Lowery	.10
116	Christian Okoye	.10
117	Stephone Paige	.10
118	Kevin Ross	.10
119	Derrick Thomas	.20
120	Mike Webster	.10
121	Marcus Allen	.20
122	Eddie Anderson	.10
123	Steve Beuerlein	.20
124	Tim Brown	.50
125	Mervyn Fernandez	.10
126	Willie Gault	.10
127	Bob Golic	.10
128	Bo Jackson	.50
129	Howie Long	.20
130	Greg Townsend	.10
131	Willie Anderson	.10
132	Greg Bell	.10
133	Robert Delpino	.10
134	Henry Ellard	.20
135	Jim Everett	.20
136	Jerry Gray	.10
137	Kevin Greene	.20
138	Tom Newberry	.10
139	Jackie Slater	.10
140	Doug Smith	.10
141	Mark Clayton	.10
142	Jeff Cross	.10
143	Mark Duper	.10
144	Ferrell Edmunds	.10
145	Jim Jensen	.10
146	Dan Marino	3.50
147	John Offerdahl	.10
148	Louis Oliver	.10
149	Reggie Roby	.10
150	Sammie Smith	.10
151	Joey Browner	.10
152	Anthony Carter	.10
153	Chris Doleman	.10
154	Steve Jordan	.10
155	Carl Lee	.10
156	Randall McDaniel	.10
157	Keith Millard	.10
158	Herschel Walker	.20
159	Wade Wilson	.10
160	Gary Zimmerman	.10
161	Hart Lee Dykes	.10
162	Irving Fryar	.20
163	Steve Grogan	.10
164	Maurice Hurst	.10
165	Fred Marion	.10
166	Stanley Morgan	.10
167	Robert Perryman	.10
168	John Stephens	.10
169	Andre Tippett	.10
170	Brent Williams	.10
171	John Fourcade	.10
172	Bobby Hebert	.20
173	Dalton Hilliard	.10
174	Rickey Jackson	.10
175	Vaughan Johnson	.10
176	Eric Martin	.10
177	Robert Massey	.10
178	Rueben Mayes	.10
179	Sam Mills	.10
180	Pat Swilling	.10
181	Ottis Anderson	.20
182	Carl Banks	.10
183	Mark Bavaro	.10
184	Mark Collins	.10
185	Leonard Marshall	.10
186	Dave Meggett	.10
187	Gary Reasons	.10
188	Phil Simms	.20
189	Lawrence Taylor	.50
190	Odessa Turner	.10
191	Kyle Clifton	.10
192	James Hasty	.10
193	Johnny Hector	.10
194	Jeff Lageman	.10
195	Pat Leahy	.10
196	Erik McMillan	.10
197	Ken O'Brien	.10
198	Mickey Shuler	.10
199	Al Toon	.10
200	JoJo Townsell	.10
201	Eric Allen	.10
202	Jerome Brown	.10
203	Keith Byars	.10
204	Cris Carter	1.00
205	Wes Hopkins	.10
206	Keith Jackson	.20
207	Seth Joyner	.10
208	Mike Quick	.10
209	Andre Waters	.10
210	Reggie White	.50
211	Rich Carmillo	.10
212	Roy Green	.10
213	Ken Harvey	.10
214	Gary Hogeboom	.10
215	Tim McDonald	.10
216	Stump Mitchell	.10
217	Luis Sharpe	.10
218	Vai Sikahema	.10
219	J.T. Smith	.10
220	Ron Wolfley	.10
221	Gary Anderson	.10
222	Bubby Brister	.10
223	Merril Hoge	.10
224	Tunch Ilkin	.10
225	Louis Lipps	.10
226	David Little	.10
227	Greg Lloyd	.10
228	Dwayne Woodruff	.10
229	Rod Woodson	.20
230	Tim Worley	.10
231	Marion Butts	.10
232	Gill Byrd	.10
233	Burt Grossman	.10
234	Jim McMahon	.20
235	Anthony Miller	.20
236	Leslie O'Neal	.10
237	Gary Plummer	.10
238	Billy Ray Smith	.10
239	Tim Spencer	.10
240	Lee Williams	.10
241	Mike Cofer	.10
242	Roger Craig	.20
243	Charles Haley	.10
244	Ronnie Lott	.20
245	Guy McIntyre	.10
246	Joe Montana	2.50
247	Tom Rathman	.10
248	Jerry Rice	2.00
249	John Taylor	.20
250	Michael Walter	.10
251	Brian Blades	.10
252	Jacob Green	.10
253	Dave Krieg	.10
254	Steve Largent	.20
255	Joe Nash	.10
256	Rufus Porter	.10
257	Eugene Robinson	.20
258	Paul Skansi	.10
259	Curt Warner	.10
260	John L. Williams	.10
261	Mark Carrier	.10
262	Reuben Davis	.10
263	Harry Hamilton	.10
264	Bruce Hill	.10
265	Donald Igwebuike	.10
266	Eugene Marve	.10
267	Kevin Murphy	.10
268	Mark Robinson	.10
269	Lars Tate	.10
270	Vinny Testaverde	.50
271	Gary Clark	.10
272	Monte Coleman	.10
273	Darrell Green	.20
274	Charles Mann	.10
275	Wilbur Marshall	.10
276	Art Monk	.20
277	Gerald Riggs	.10
278	Mark Rypien	.20
279	Rickey Sanders	.10
280	Alvin Walton	.10
NNO	Jim Plunkett BR (Braille)	4.00
NNO	Checklist	.10

1990 Action Packed Rookie Update

CHRIS WARREN — SEAHAWKS™

Issued in November 1990, the Update set includes each of the 1990 first-round draft choices, rookie prospects, and traded players. Randall Cunningham, who did not appear in the regular 1990 Action Packed set, signed a late contract with the NFL Players Association and does not appear in the Update set. Cards were issued in both wax packs and factory sets.

		MT
Complete Set (84):		20.00
Complete Factory (84):		20.00
Common Player:		.10
Minor Stars:		.20
Wax Box:		50.00
1	Jeff George	2.00
2	Richmond Webb	.20
3	James Williams	.10
4	Tony Bennett	.20
5	Darrell Thompson	.10
6	Steve Broussard	.20
7	Rodney Hampton	.75
8	Rob Moore	3.00
9	Alton Montgomery	.10
10	Leroy Butler	.50
11	Anthony Johnson	.50
12	Scott Mitchell	1.00
13	Mike Fox	.10
14	Robert Blackmon	.10
15	Blair Thomas	.20
16	Tony Stargell	.10
17	Peter Tom Willis	.10
18	Harold Green	.50
19	Bernard Clark	.10
20	Aaron Wallace	.10
21	Dennis Brown	.10
22	Johnny Johnson	.20
23	Chris Calloway	.50
24	Walter Wilson	.10
25	Dexter Carter	.20
26	Percy Snow	.10
27	Johnny Bailey	.10
28	Mike Bellamy	.10
29	Ben Smith	.10
30	Mark Carrier	.50
31	James Francis	.10
32	Lamar Lathon	.10
33	Bern Brostek	.10
34	Emmitt Smith	15.00
35	Andre Collins	.10
36	Alexander Wright	.10
37	Fred Barnett	.75
38	Junior Seau	3.00
39	Cortez Kennedy	.50
40	Terry Wooden	.10
41	Eric Davis	.10
42	Fred Washington	.10
43	Reggie Cobb	.10
44	Andre Ware	.20
45	Anthony Smith	.10
46	Shannon Sharpe	8.00
47	Harlon Barnett	.10
48	Greg McMurtry	.10
49	Stacey Simmons	.10
50	Calvin Williams	.20
51	Anthony Thompson	.10
52	Ricky Proehl	.50
53	Tony James	.10
54	Ray Agnew	.10
55	Tom Hodson	.10
56	Ron Cox	.10
57	Leroy Hoard	1.00
58	Eric Green	.50
59	Barry Foster	.10
60	Keith McCants	.10
61	Oliver Barnett	.10
62	Chris Warren	1.00
63	Pat Terrell	.10
64	Renaldo Turnbull	.10
65	Chris Chandler	.20
66	Everson Walls	.10
67	Alonzo Highsmith	.10
68	Gary Anderson	.10
69	Fred Smerlas	.10
70	Jim McMahon	.50
71	Curt Warner	.10
72	Stanley Morgan	.10
73	Dave Waymer	.10
74	Billy Joe Tolliver	.20
75	Tony Eason	.10
76	Max Montoya	.10
77	Greg Bell	.10
78	Dennis McKinnon	.10
79	Raymond Clayborn	.10
80	Broderick Thomas	.10
81	Timm Rosenbach	.10
82	Tim McKyer	.10
83	Andre Rison	.50
84	Randall Cunningham	.75

1990 Action Packed All-Madden

This 58-card set pictures players selected by CBS analyst and former coach John Madden. Cards were released in late February of 1991. Cards were issued in six-card wax packs and in complete sets. The set features Action Packed's first borderless set, previewing the 1991 set. Cards are standard-sized, embossed, and feature Madden's comments about each player on the back.

		MT
Complete Set (58):		20.00
Common Player:		.25
Wax Box:		20.00
1	Joe Montana	3.00
2	Jerry Rice	3.00
3	Charles Haley	.40
4	Steve Wisniewski	.25
5	Dave Meggett	.40
6	Ottis Anderson	.40
7	Nate Newton	.25
8	Warren Moon	1.00
9	Emmitt Smith	6.00
10	Jackie Slater	.25
11	Pepper Johnson	.25
12	Lawrence Taylor	.75
13	Sterling Sharpe	1.00
14	Sean Landeta	.25
15	Richard Dent	.40
16	Neal Anderson	.50
17	Bruce Matthews	.25
18	Matt Millen	.25
19	Reggie White	.50
20	Greg Townsend	.25
21	Troy Aikman	3.00
22	Don Mosebar	.25
23	Jeff Zimmerman	.25
24	Rod Woodson	.50
25	Keith Byars	.40
26	Randall Cunningham	.75
27	Reyna Thompson	.40
28	Marcus Allen	.60
29	Gary Clark	.50
30	Anthony Carter	.40
31	Bubba Paris	.25
32	Ronnie Lott	.50
33	Erik Howard	.25
34	Ernest Givins	.25
35	Mike Munchak	.25
36	Jim Lachey	.25
37	Merril Hoge	.25
38	Darrell Green	.25
39	Pierce Holt	.25
40	Jerome Brown	.25
41	William Perry	.25
42	Michael Carter	.25
43	Keith Jackson	.40
44	Kevin Fagan	.25
45	Mark Carrier	.40
46	Fred Barnett	.75
47	Barry Sanders	3.00
48	Pat Swilling	.50
49	Sam Mills	.25
	Vaughan Johnson	
50	Jacob Green	.25
51	Stan Brock	.25
52	Dan Hampton	.25
53	Brian Noble	.25
54	John Elliott	.25
55	Matt Bahr	.25
56	Bill Parcells	.25
57	Art Shell	.25
58	All-Madden Team Trophy	.25

1991 Action Packed

IRVING FRYAR-WR

Action Packed issued a borderless card with a gold stripe protecting the back seam, both improving on the previous year's design. Cards are arranged in alphabetical order by city and player. Two unnumbered prototype cards were also created, for Randall Cunningham and Emmitt Smith. The cards are labeled on the back as being 1991 prototypes. Cunningham's is valued at $10; Smith's is $15. Eight Braille cards, numbers 281-288, were also produced. The cards, similar in design to the regular issue, feature statistical leaders but have different photos than the players' regular cards. The backs are written in Braille. The Braille cards were only available in factory sets.

		MT
Complete Set (280):		30.00
Complete Factory (291):		30.00
Common Player:		.10
Minor Stars:		.20
Wax Box:		20.00
1	Steve Broussard	.10
2	Scott Case	.10
3	Brian Jordan	.20
4	Darion Conner	.10
5	Tim Green	.10
6	Chris Miller	.20
7	Andre Rison	.50
8	Mike Rozier	.10
9	Deion Sanders	1.00
10	Jessie Tuggle	.10
11	Leonard Smith	.10
12	Shane Conlan	.10
13	Kent Hull	.10
14	Keith McKeller	.10
15	James Lofton	.20
16	Andre Reed	.20
17	Bruce Smith	.20
18	Darryl Talley	.10
19	Steve Tasker	.10
20	Thurman Thomas	.50
21	Neal Anderson	.20
22	Trace Armstrong	.10
23	Mark Bortz	.10
24	Mark Carrier (Chi.)	.10
25	Wendell Davis	.10
26	Richard Dent	.20
27	Jim Harbaugh	.20
28	Jay Hilgenberg	.10
29	Brad Muster	.10
30	Mike Singletary	.20
31	Harold Green	.20
32	James Brooks	.10
33	Eddie Brown	.10
34	Boomer Esiason	.20
35	James Francis	.10

36	David Fulcher	.10
37	Rodney Holman	.10
38	Tim McGee	.10
39	Anthony Munoz	.10
40	Ickey Woods	.10
41	Rob Burnett	.10
42	Thane Gash	.10
43	Mike Johnson	.10
44	Brian Brennan	.10
45	Reggie Langhorne	.10
46	Kevin Mack	.10
47	Clay Matthews	.10
48	Eric Metcalf	.20
49	Anthony Pleasant	.10
50	Ozzie Newsome	.10
51	Troy Aikman	2.00
52	Issiac Holt	.10
53	Michael Irvin	.50
54	Jimmie Jones	.10
55	Eugene Lockhart	.10
56	Kelvin Martin	.10
57	Ken Norton Jr.	.10
58	Jay Novacek	.10
59	Emmitt Smith	4.00
60	Daniel Stubbs	.10
61	Steve Atwater	.10
62	Michael Brooks	.10
63	John Elway	2.00
64	Simon Fletcher	.10
65	Bobby Humphrey	.10
66	Mark Jackson	.10
67	Vance Johnson	.10
68	Karl Mecklenburg	.10
69	Dennis Smith	.10
70	Greg Kragen	.10
71	Jerry Ball	.10
72	Lomas Brown	.10
73	Robert Clark	.10
74	Michael Coper	.10
75	Mel Gray	.10
76	Richard Johnson	.10
77	Rodney Peete	.20
78	Barry Sanders	4.00
79	Chris Spielman	.10
80	Andre Ware	.10
81	Matt Brock	.10
82	Leroy Butler	.10
83	Tim Harris	.10
84	Perry Kemp	.10
85	Don Majkowski	.10
86	Mark Murphy	.10
87	Brian Noble	.10
88	Sterling Sharpe	.20
89	Darrell Thompson	.10
90	Ed West	.10
91	Ray Childress	.10
92	Ernest Givins	.10
93	Drew Hill	.10
94	Haywood Jeffires	.10
95	Richard Johnson	.10
96	Sean Jones	.10
97	Bruce Matthews	.10
98	Warren Moon	.20
99	Mike Munchak	.10
100	Lorenzo White	.10
101	Albert Bentley	.10
102	Duane Bickett	.10
103	Bill Brooks	.10
104	Jeff George	.50
105	Jon Hand	.10
106	Jeff Herrod	.10
107	Jessie Hester	.10
108	Mike Prior	.10
109	Rohn Stark	.10
110	Clarence Verdin	.10
111	Steve Deberg	.10
112	Dan Saleaumua	.10
113	Albert Lewis	.10
114	Nick Lowery	.10
115	Christian Okoye	.10
116	Stephone Paige	.10
117	Kevin Ross	.10
118	Dino Hackett	.10
119	Derrick Thomas	.20
120	Barry Word	.10
121	Marcus Allen	.25
122	Mervyn Fernandez	.10
123	Willie Gault	.10
124	Bo Jackson	.25
125	Terry McDaniel	.10
126	Don Mosebar	.10
127	Jay Schroeder	.10
128	Greg Townsend	.10
129	Aaron Wallace	.10
130	Steve Wisniewski	.10
131	Willie Anderson	.10
132	Henry Ellard	.10
133	Jim Everett	.20
134	Cleveland Gary	.10
135	Jerry Gray	.10
136	Kevin Greene	.10
137	Buford McGee	.10
138	Vince Newsome	.10
139	Jackie Slater	.10
140	Frank Stams	.10
141	Jeff Cross	.10
142	Mark Duper	.10
143	Ferrell Edmunds	.10
144	Dan Marino	3.00
145	Louis Oliver	.10
146	John Offerdahl	.10
147	Tony Paige	.10
148	Sammie Smith	.10
149	Richmond Webb	.10
150	Jarvis Williams	.10
151	Joey Browner	.10
152	Anthony Carter	.10
153	Chris Doleman	.10
154	Hassan Jones	.10
155	Steve Jordan	.10
156	Carl Lee	.10
157	Randall McDaniel	.10
158	Mike Merriweather	.10
159	Herschel Walker	.20
160	Wade Wilson	.10
161	Ray Agnew	.10
162	Bruce Armstrong	.10
163	Marv Cook	.10
164	Hart Lee Dykes	.10
165	Irving Fryar	.10
166	Tom Hodson	.10
167	Ronnie Lippett	.10
168	Fred Marion	.10
169	John Stephens	.10
170	Brent Williams	.10
171	Morten Andersen	.10
172	Gene Atkins	.10
173	Craig Heyward	.10
174	Rickey Jackson	.10
175	Vaughan Johnson	.10
176	Eric Martin	.10
177	Rueben Mayes	.10
178	Pat Swilling	.10
179	Renaldo Turnbull	.10
180	Steve Walsh	.10
181	Ottis Anderson	.10
182	Rodney Hampton	.20
183	Jeff Hostetler	.20
184	Pepper Johnson	.10
185	Sean Landeta	.10
186	Dave Meggett	.10
187	Bart Oates	.10
188	Phil Simms	.10
189	Lawrence Taylor	.20
190	Reyna Thompson	.10
191	Brad Baxter	.10
192	Dennis Byrd	.10
193	Kylce Clifton	.10
194	James Hasty	.10
195	Pat Leahy	.10
196	Erik McMillan	.10
197	Rob Moore	.50
198	Ken O'Brien	.10
199	Mark Boyer	.10
200	Al Toon	.10
201	Fred Barnett	.10
202	Jerome Brown	.10
203	Keith Byars	.10
204	Randall Cunningham	.50
205	Wes Hopkins	.10
206	Keith Jackson	.10
207	Seth Joyner	.10
208	Heath Sherman	.10
209	Reggie White	.50
210	Calvin Williams	.10
211	Roy Green	.10
212	Ken Harvey	.10
213	Luis Sharpe	.10
214	Ernie Jones	.10
215	Tim McDonald	.10
216	Freddie Joe Nunn	.10
217	Ricky Proehl	.10
218	Timm Rosenbach	.10
219	Anthony Thompson	.10
220	Lonnie Young	.10
221	Gary Anderson	.10
222	Bubby Brister	.10
223	Eric Green	.10
224	Merril Hoge	.10
225	Carnell Lake	.10
226	Louis Lipps	.10
227	David Little	.10
228	Greg Lloyd	.10
229	Gerald Williams	.10
230	Rod Woodson	.10
231	Marion Butts	.10
232	Gill Byrd	.10
233	Burt Grossman	.10
234	Courtney Hall	.10
235	Ronnie Harmon	.10
236	Anthony Miller	.10
237	Leslie O'Neal	.10
238	Junior Seau	.50
239	Billy Joe Tolliver	.10
240	Lee Williams	.10
241	Dexter Carter	.10
242	Kevin Fagan	.10
243	Charles Haley	.10
244	Brent Jones	.10
245	Ronnie Lott	.20
246	Guy McIntyre	.10
247	Joe Montana	2.50
248	Jerry Rice	2.00
249	John Taylor	.10
250	Roger Craig	.10
251	Brian Blades	.10
252	Derrick Penner	.10
253	Nesby Glasgow	.10
254	Jacob Green	.10
255	Tommy Kane	.10
256	Dave Krieg	.10
257	Rufus Porter	.10
258	Eugene Robinson	.10
259	Cortez Kennedy	.10
260	John L. Williams	.10
261	Gary Anderson	.10
262	Mark Carrier	.10
263	Steve Christie	.10
264	Reggie Cobb	.10
265	Paul Gruber	.10
266	Wayne Haddix	.10
267	Bruce Hill	.10
268	Keith McCants	.10
269	Vinny Testaverde	.50
270	Broderick Thomas	.10
271	Earnest Byner	.10
272	Gary Clark	.10
273	Darrell Green	.10
274	Jim Lachey	.10
275	Chip Lohmiller	.10
276	Charles Mann	.10
277	Wilber Marshall	.10
278	Art Monk	.20
279	Mark Rypien	.10
280	Alvin Walton	.10
281	Randall Cunningham (Braille)	.50
282	Warren Moon (Braille)	.20
283	Barry Sanders (Braille)	5.00
284	Thurman Thomas (Braille)	.50
285	Jerry Rice (Braille)	2.00
286	Haywood Jeffires (Braille)	.20
287	Charles Haley (Braille)	.20
288	Derrick Thomas (Braille)	.20
289	NFC Logo Card	.20
290	AFC Logo Card	.20
291	Checklist	.10

1991 Action Packed 24K Gold

These cards were randomly issued in foil packs of 1991 Action Packed cards. Cards feature the regular-issue fronts, but the stripe has been done in 24k gold. Cards have also been stamped 24k on the front and are numbered 1G-42G on the back. It's estimated that less than 8,000 were made of each card. Generally, the cards are valued at about 15 times the amount of the corresponding regular Action Packed card.

		MT
Complete Set (42):		500.00
Common Player:		5.00
Minor Stars:		10.00
1	Andre Rison	10.00
2	Deion Sanders	20.00
3	Andre Reed	5.00
4	Bruce Smith	5.00
5	Thurman Thomas	10.00
6	Neal Anderson	5.00
7	Mark Carrier	5.00
8	Mike Singletary	5.00
9	Boomer Esiason	5.00
10	James Francis	5.00
11	Anthony Munoz	5.00
12	Troy Aikman	40.00
13	Emmitt Smith	60.00
14	John Elway	40.00
15	Bobby Humphrey	5.00
16	Barry Sanders	80.00
17	Don Majkowski	5.00
18	Sterling Sharpe	10.00
19	Warren Moon	10.00
20	Jeff George	10.00
21	Christian Okoye	5.00
22	Derrick Thomas	10.00
23	Barry Word	5.00
24	Marcus Allen	10.00
25	Bo Jackson	10.00
26	Jim Everett	5.00
27	Cleveland Gary	5.00
28	Dan Marino	60.00
29	Herschel Walker	5.00
30	Ottis Anderson	5.00
31	Rodney Hampton	5.00
32	Dave Meggett	5.00
33	Marion Butts	5.00
34	Randall Cunningham	10.00
35	Reggie White	10.00
36	Jerry Rice	40.00
37	Eric Green	5.00
38	Charles Haley	5.00
39	Ronnie Lott	5.00
40	Joe Montana	60.00
41	Vinny Testaverde	10.00
42	Gary Clark	5.00

1991 Action Packed Rookie Update

This set features the first 26 top draft picks among its 74 rookie cards, plus 10 traded and update cards. Each card has an embossed helmet with a white "R" inside to indicate the player is a rookie. The backs are written in red and have the player's collegiate statistics. An Emmitt Smith prototype card was included in each case of 1991 Action Packed Rookie/Update foil or factory set ordered. Special 24K gold cards were also made for the 26 first-round draft picks. They were inserted into update packs.

		MT
Complete Set (84):		15.00
Complete Factory (84):		15.00
Common Player:		.05
Minor Stars:		.10
Wax Box:		25.00
1	Herman Moore	3.00
2	Eric Turner	.10
3	Mike Croel	.10
4	Alfred Williams	.05
5	Stanley Richard	.05
6	Russell Maryland	.25
7	Pat Harlow	.05
8	Alvin Harper	.10
9	Mike Pritchard	.25
10	Leonard Russell	.25
11	Jarrod Bunch	.10
12	Dan McGwire	.05
13	Bobby Wilson	.05
14	Vinnie Clark	.05
15	Kelvin Pritchett	.05
16	Harvey Williams	.25
17	Stan Thomas	.05
18	Todd Marinovich	.10
19	Antone Davis	.05
20	Greg Lewis	.05
21	Brett Favre	8.00
22	Wesley Carroll	.05
23	Ed McCaffrey	3.00
24	Reggie Barrett	.05
25	Chris Zorich	.05
26	Kenny Walker	.05
27	Aaron Craver	.05
28	Browning Nagle	.05
29	Nick Bell	.05
30	Anthony Morgan	.05
31	Jesse Campbell	.05
32	Eric Bieniemy	.10
33	Ricky Ervins	.05
34	Kanavis McGhee	.05
35	Shawn Moore	.05
36	Todd Lyght	.10
37	Eric Swann	.25
38	Henry Jones	.05
39	Ted Washington	.05
40	Charles McRae	.05
41	Randal Hill	.10
42	Huey Richardson	.05
43	Roman Phifer	.05
44	Ricky Watters	2.00
45	Esera Tuaolo	.05
46	Michael Jackson	.25
47	Shawn Jefferson	.05
48	Tim Barnett	.05
49	Chuck Webb	.05
50	Moe Gardner	.05
51	Mo Lewis	.05
52	Mike Dumas	.05
53	Jon Vaughn	.05
54	Jerome Henderson	.05
55	Harry Colon	.05
56	David Daniels	.05
57	Phil Hansen	.05
58	Ernie Mills	.05
59	John Kasay	.05
60	Darren Lewis	.05
61	James Joseph	.05
62	Robert Wilson	.05
63	Lawrence Dawsey	.05
64	Mike Jones	.05
65	Dave McCloughan	.05
66	Eric Pegram	.05
67	Aeneas Williams	.25
68	Reggie Johnson	.05
69	Todd Scott	.05
70	James Jones	.05
71	Lamar Rogers	.05
72	Darryll Lewis	.05
73	Bryan Cox	.25
74	Leroy Thompson	.05
75	Mark Higgs	.05
76	John Friesz	.25
77	Tim McKyer	.05
78	Roger Craig	.10
79	Ronnie Lott	.25
80	Steve Young	1.00
81	Percy Snow	.05
82	Cornelius Bennett	.05
83	Johnny Johnson	.10
84	Blair Thomas	.05

1991 Action Packed Rookie Update 24K Gold

These insert cards were randomly included in 1991 Action Packed Rookie Update foil packs and are devoted to first-round draft picks. Each card front has an embossed color photo, plus gold foil stamping. A "24K" is also stamped on the card to distinguish it as an insert card. The card back is in a horizontal format and includes the player's collegiate statistics, a color mug shot, a panel for an autograph, and a card number. The card is numbered according to the order the player was drafted and uses a "G" suffix.

		MT
Complete Set (26):		300.00
Common Player:		10.00
Minor Stars:		20.00
1	Russell Maryland	20.00
2	Eric Turner	10.00
3	Mike Croel	10.00
4	Todd Lyght	10.00
5	Eric Swann	20.00
6	Charles McRae	10.00
7	Antone Davis	10.00
8	Stanley Richard	10.00
9	Herman Moore	40.00
10	Pat Harlow	10.00
11	Alvin Harper	10.00
12	Mike Pritchard	10.00
13	Leonard Russell	10.00
14	Huey Richardson	10.00
15	Dan McGwire	10.00
16	Bobby Wilson	10.00
17	Alfred Williams	10.00
18	Vinnie Clark	10.00
19	Kelvin Pritchett	10.00
20	Harvey Williams	20.00
21	Stan Thomas	10.00
22	Randal Hill	10.00
23	Todd Marinovich	10.00
24	Ted Washington	10.00
25	Henry Jones	10.00
26	Jarrod Bunch	10.00

1991 Action Packed NFLPA Awards

1990 NFL award winners are recognized in this 16-card set produced by Action Packed. The cards, similar in design to the regular 1991 issue, were available as a boxed set; 5,000 individually-numbered sets were produced. Each box has the set number on it, plus "NFLPA/MDA Awards Dinner March 12, 1991" inscribed on it. Each card back has the award he won listed under his name.

		MT
Complete Set (16):		75.00
Common Player:		4.00
1	Jim Lachey	4.00
2	Anthony Munoz	5.00
3	Bruce Smith	6.00
4	Reggie White	6.00
5	Charles Haley	4.00
6	Derrick Thomas	6.00
7	Albert Lewis	4.00
8	Mark Carrier	5.00
9	Reyna Thompson	5.00
10	Steve Tasker	4.00
11	James Francis	6.00
12	Mark Carrier	7.50
13	Johnny Johnson	7.50
14	Eric Green	7.50
15	Warren Moon	9.00
16	Randall Cunningham	9.00

1991 Action Packed Whizzer White Greats

The 25 winners of the Justice Byron "Whizzer" White Humanitarian Award from 1967 to 1991 were pictured in this special Action Packed set issued in conjunction with the 1991 awards banquet in Chicago. The White award is given annually to a single NFL player who serves his team, community and country in the spirit of former NFL player and U.S. Supreme Court Justice Byron White. The card set features Action Packed's 1991 gold standard design with full color, embossed action photos. For the first time, however, the indicia is silver with the award year inscribed in a silver helmet. The card backs feature a color head shot, player biographical information, career and community contributions. A total of 3,500 sets were distributed at the dinner; another 5,000 were made available to collectors through Rotman Productions.

		MT
Complete Set (25):		75.00
Common Player:		2.00
1	Bart Starr (1967)	15.00
2	Willie Davis (1968)	4.00
3	Ed Meador (1969)	2.00
4	Gale Sayers (1970)	15.00
5	Kermit Alexander (1971)	2.00
6	Ray May (1972)	2.00
7	Andy Russell (1973)	3.00
8	Floyd Little (1974)	3.00
9	Rocky Bleier (1975)	3.00
10	Jim Hart (1976)	4.00
11	Lyle Alzado (1977)	4.00
12	Archie Manning (1978)	4.00
13	Roger Staubach (1979)	25.00
14	Gene Upshaw (1980)	4.00
15	Ken Houston (1981)	4.00
16	Franco Harris (1982)	10.00
17	Doug Dieken (1983)	2.00
18	Rolf Benirschke (1984)	2.00
19	Reggie Williams (1985)	2.00
20	Nat Moore (1986)	2.00
21	George Martin (1987)	2.00
22	Deron Cherry (1988)	2.00
23	Mike Singletary (1989)	5.00
24	Ozzie Newsome (1990)	4.00
25	Mike Kenn (1991)	2.00

1991 Action Packed All-Madden

This 52-card set is John Madden's second issue featuring the All-Madden team. The borderless fronts feature embossed color photos with gold and aqua border stripes. Cards, which are standard size, have the Madden logo and team helmet on the front. The back, which is numbered, has stats and a mug shot.

		MT
Complete Set (52):		25.00
Common Player:		.20
Wax Box:		15.00
1	Mark Rypien	.40
2	Erik Kramer	1.00
3	Jim McMahon	.40
4	Jesse Sapolu	.20
5	Jay Hilgenberg	.20
6	Howard Ballard	.20
7	Lomas Brown	.20
8	John Elliott	.20
9	Joe Jacoby	.20
10	Jim Lachey	.20
11	Anthony Munoz	.30
12	Nate Newton	.20
13	Will Wolford	.20
14	Jerry Ball	.20
15	Jerome Brown	.20
16	William Perry	.25
17	Charles Mann	.20
18	Clyde Simmons	.20
19	Reggie White	1.50
20	Eric Allen	.20
21	Darrell Green	.25
22	Bennie Blades	.20
23	Chuck Cecil	.20
24	Rickey Dixon	.30
25	David Fulcher	.20
26	Ronnie Lott	.75
27	Emmitt Smith	6.00
28	Neal Anderson	.30
29	Robert Delpino	.30

30	Barry Sanders	4.00
31	Thurman Thomas	1.00
32	Cornelius Bennett	.35
33	Rickey Jackson	.15
34	Seth Joyner	.20
35	Wilber Marshall	.20
36	Clay Matthews	.20
37	Chris Spielman	.20
38	Pat Swilling	.25
39	Fred Barnett	.50
40	Gary Clark	.40
41	Michael Irvin	1.50
42	Art Monk	.50
43	Jerry Rice	2.50
44	John Taylor	.50
45	Tom Waddle	.20
46	Kevin Butler	.20
47	Bill Bates	.20
48	Greg Manusky	.20
49	Elvis Patterson	.20
50	Steve Tasker	.20
51	John Daly	1.00
52	All-Madden Trophy	1.50

1992 Action Packed Prototypes

These standard-size cards are prototypes featuring the basic design for Action Packed's 1992 regular set. Each card has a card number (92) on the back, plus a suffix (A, N or P). The cards made their debut at the 1992 Super Bowl Show in Minneapolis and are labeled on the back as being prototypes.

		MT
Complete Set (3):		35.00
Common Player:		10.00
A	Thurman Thomas	10.00
N	Emmitt Smith	15.00
P	Barry Sanders	20.00

1992 Action Packed

These standard-size cards feature embossed photos on the front, with gold and red border stripes for AFC players or aqua and gold for NFC players. The cards are numbered alphabetically by team, by player. The set has two subsets - eight Braille cards (#s 281-288) featuring league leaders and two logo cards (#s 289-290). There were 42 24K gold insert cards made, too.

		MT
Complete Set (280):		30.00
Complete Factory (292):		35.00
Common Player:		.15
Minor Stars:		.30
Wax Box:		20.00
1	Steve Broussard	.15
2	Michael Haynes	.15
3	Tim McKyer	.15
4	Chris Miller	.30
5	Andre Rison	.50
6	Jessie Tuggle	.15
7	Mike Pritchard	.30
8	Moe Gardner	.15
9	Brian Jordan	.30
10	Mike Kenn,	.15
	Chris Hinton	
11	Steve Tasker	.15
12	Cornelius Bennett	.30
13	Shane Conlan	.15
14	Darryl Talley	.15
15	Thurman Thomas	.50
16	James Lofton	.30
17	Don Beebe	.15
18	Jim Ritcher	.15
19	Keith McKeller	.15
20	Nate Odomes	.15
21	Mark Carrier	.15
22	Wendell Davis	.15
23	Richard Dent	.15
24	Jim Harbaugh	.30
25	Jay Hilgenberg	.15
26	Steve McMichael	.15
27	Tom Waddle	.15
28	Neal Anderson	.15
29	Brad Muster	.15
30	Shaun Gayle	.15
31	Jim Breech	.15
32	James Brooks	.15
33	James Francis	.15
34	David Fulcher	.15
35	Harold Green	.15
36	Rodney Holman	.15
37	Anthony Munoz	.30
38	Tim Krumrie	.15
39	Tim McGee	.15
40	Eddie Brown	.15
41	Kevin Mack	.15
42	James Jones	.15
43	Vince Newsome	.15
44	Ed King	.15
45	Eric Metcalf	.15
46	Leroy Hoard	.30
47	Stephen Braggs	.15
48	Clay Matthews	.15
49	David Brandon	.15
50	Rob Burnett	.15
51	Larry Brown	.15
52	Alvin Harper	.15
53	Michael Irvin	.50
54	Ken Norton Jr.	.15
55	Jay Novacek	.15
56	Emmitt Smith	4.00
57	Tony Tolbert	.15
58	Nate Newton	.15
59	Steve Beuerlein	.15
60	Tony Casillas	.15
61	Steve Atwater	.15
62	Mike Croel	.15
63	Gaston Green	.15
64	Mark Jackson	.15
65	Greg Kragen	.15
66	Karl Mecklenberg	.15
67	Dennis Smith	.15
68	Steve Sewell	.15
69	John Elway	2.00
70	Simon Fletcher	.15
71	Mel Gray	.15
72	Barry Sanders	4.00
73	Jerry Ball	.15
74	Bennie Blades	.15
75	Lomas Brown	.15
76	Erik Kramer	.30
77	Chris Spielman	.15
78	Ray Crockett	.15
79	Willie Green	.15
80	Rodney Peete	.15
81	Sterling Sharpe	.50
82	Tony Bennett	.15
83	Chuck Cecil	.15
84	Perry Kemp	.15
85	Brian Noble	.15
86	Darrell Thompson	.15
87	Mike Tomczak	.15
88	Vince Workman	.15
89	Esera Tuaolo	.15
90	Mark Murphy	.15
91	William Fuller	.15
92	Ernest Givins	.15
93	Drew Hill	.15
94	Al Smith	.15
95	Ray Childress	.15
96	Haywood Jeffires	.15
97	Cris Dishman	.15
98	Warren Moon	.50
99	Lamar Lathon	.15
100	Mike Munchak,	.15
	Bruce Matthews	
101	Bill Brooks	.15
102	Duane Bickett	.15
103	Eugene Daniel	.15
104	Jeff Herrod	.15
105	Jessie Hester	.15
106	Donnell Thompson	.15
107	Anthony Johnson	.15
108	Jon Hand	.15
109	Rohn Stark	.15
110	Clarence Verdin	.15
111	Derrick Thomas	.50
112	Steve DeBerg	.15
113	Deron Cherry	.15
114	Chris Martin	.15
115	Christian Okoye	.15
116	Dan Saleaumua	.15
117	Neil Smith	.15
118	Barry Word	.15
119	Tim Barnett	.15
120	Albert Lewis	.15
121	Ronnie Lott	.30
122	Marcus Allen	.50
123	Todd Marinovich	.15
124	Nick Bell	.15
125	Tim Brown	.50
126	Ethan Horton	.15
127	Greg Townsend	.15
128	Jeff Gossett,	.15
	Jeff Jaeger	
129	Scott Davis	.15
130	Steve Wisniewski,	.15
	Don Mosebar	
131	Kevin Greene	.15
132	Roman Phifer	.15
133	Tony Zendejas	.15
134	Pat Terrell	.15
135	Willie Anderson	.15
136	Robert Delpino	.15
137	Jim Everett	.30
138	Larry Kelm	.15
139	Todd Lyght	.15
140	Henry Ellard	.15
141	Mark Clayton	.15
142	Jeff Cross	.15
143	Mark Duper	.15
144	John Offerdahl	.15
145	Louis Oliver	.15
146	Pete Stoyanovich	.15
147	Richmond Webb	.15
148	Mark Higgs	.15
149	Tony Paige	.15
150	Bryan Cox	.15
151	Anthony Carter	.15
152	Cris Carter	1.00
153	Rich Gannon	.15
154	Steve Jordan	.15
155	Mike Merriweather	.15
156	Henry Thomas	.15
157	Herschel Walker	.30
158	Randall McDaniel	.15
159	Terry Allen	.50
160	Joey Browner	.15
161	Leonard Russell	.30
162	Bruce Armstrong	.15
163	Vincent Brown	.15
164	Hugh Millen	.15
165	Andre Tippett	.15
166	Jon Vaughn	.15
167	Pat Harlow	.15
168	Marv Cook	.15
169	Irving Fryar	.30
170	Maurice Hurst	.15
171	Pat Swilling	.15
172	Vince Buck	.15
173	Rickey Jackson	.15
174	Sam Mills	.15
175	Bobby Hebert	.15
176	Vaughan Johnson	.15
177	Floyd Turner	.15
178	Fred McAfee	.15
179	Morten Andersen	.15
180	Eric Martin	.15
181	Rodney Hampton	.30
182	Pepper Johnson	.15
183	Leonard Russell	.15
184	Stephen Baker	.15
185	Mark Ingram	.15
186	Dave Meggett	.15
187	Bart Oates	.15
188	Mark Collins	.15
189	Myron Guyton	.15
190	Jeff Hostetler	.30
191	Jeff Lageman	.15
192	Brad Baxter	.15
193	Mo Lewis	.15
194	Chris Burkett	.15
195	James Hasty	.15
196	Rob Moore	.50
197	Kyle Clifton	.15
198	Terance Mathis	.15
199	Marvin Washington	.15
200	Lonnie Young	.15
201	Reggie White	.50
202	Eric Allen	.15
203	Fred Barnett	.30
204	Keith Byars	.15
205	Seth Joyner	.15
206	Clyde Simmons	.15
207	Jerome Brown	.15
208	Wes Hopkins	.15
209	Keith Jackson	.15
210	Calvin Williams	.15
211	Aeneas Williams	.15
212	Ken Harvey	.15
213	Ernie Jones	.15
214	Freddie Joe Nunn	.15
215	Rich Camarillo	.15
216	Johnny Johnson	.30
217	Tim McDonald	.15
218	Eric Swann	.15
219	Eric Hill	.15
220	Anthony Thompson	.15
221	Hardy Nickerson	.15
222	Barry Foster	.30
223	Louis Lipps	.15
224	Greg Lloyd	.15
225	Neil O'Donnell	.30
226	Jerrol Williams	.15
227	Eric Green	.15
228	Rod Woodson	.15
229	Carnell Lake	.15
230	Dwight Stone	.15
231	Marion Butts	.15
232	Jim Friesz	.30
233	Burt Grossman	.15
234	Ronnie Harmon	.15
235	Gill Byrd	.15
236	Rod Bernstine	.15
237	Courtney Hall	.15
238	Nate Lewis	.15
239	Joe Phillips	.15
240	Henry Rolling	.15
241	Keith Henderson	.15
242	Guy McIntyre	.15
243	Bill Romanowski	.15
244	Don Griffin	.15
245	Dexter Carter	.15
246	Charles Haley	.30
247	Brent Jones	.15
248	John Taylor	.15
249	Steve Young	1.50
250	Larry Roberts	.15
251	Brian Blades	.15
252	Jacob Green	.15
253	John Kasay	.15
254	Cortez Kennedy	.30
255	Rufus Porter	.15
256	John L. Williams	.15
257	Tommy Kane	.15
258	Eugene Robinson	.15
259	Terry Wooden	.15
260	Chris Warren	.50
261	Lawrence Dawsey	.15
262	Mark Carrier	.15
263	Keith McCants	.15
264	Jesse Solomon	.15
265	Vinny Testaverde	.50
266	Rickey Reynolds	.15
267	Broderick Thomas	.15
268	Gary Anderson	.15
269	Reggie Cobb	.15
270	Tony Covington	.15
271	Darrell Green	.30
272	Charles Mann	.15
273	Wilber Marshall	.15
274	Gary Clark	.15
275	Chip Lohmiller	.15
276	Earnest Byner	.15
277	Jim Lachey	.15
278	Art Monk	.30
279	Mark Rypien	.30
280	Mark Schlereth	.15
281	Mark Rypien (Braille)	.15
282	Warren Moon (Braille)	.30
283	Emmitt Smith (Braille)	2.00
284	Thurman Thomas (Braille)	.30
285	Michael Irvin (Braille)	.30
286	Haywood Jeffires (Braille)	.15
287	Pat Swilling (Braille)	.15
288	Ronnie Lott (Braille)	.15
289	NFC logo	.15
290	AFC Logo	.15

> Post-1980 cards in Near Mint condition will generally sell for about 75% of the quoted Mint value. Excellent-condition cards bring no more than 40%.

1992 Action Packed 24K Gold

These cards have a color embossed photo on the front, with gold foil stamping and a team helmet. The back has statistics, a mug shot, a biography and a caption which describes the photo on the front. A panel is also included for an autograph. Cards are numbered on the back, using a "G" suffix, and are checklisted alphabetically by team name. Cards were randomly inserted in foil packs. Detroit Lions star Barry Sanders autographed 1,000 of his card (#13G); they were randomly inserted in packs.

		MT
Complete Set (42):		650.00
Common Player:		7.00
Minor Stars:		14.00
1	Michael Haynes	7.00
2	Chris Miller	7.00
3	Andre Rison	14.00
4	Cornelius Bennett	7.00
5	James Lofton	7.00
6	Thurman Thomas	14.00
7	Neal Anderson	7.00
8	Michael Irvin	20.00
9	Emmitt Smith	75.00
10	Mike Croel	7.00
11	John Elway	50.00
12	Gaston Green	7.00
13	Barry Sanders	100.00
14	Sterling Sharpe	14.00
15	Ernest Givins	7.00
16	Drew Hill	7.00
17	Haywood Jeffires	7.00
18	Warren Moon	14.00
19	Christian Okoye	7.00
20	Derrick Thomas	14.00
21	Ronnie Lott	7.00
22	Todd Marinovich	7.00
23	Henry Ellard	7.00
24	Mark Clayton	7.00
25	Herschel Walker	7.00
26	Irving Fryar	7.00
27	Leonard Russell	7.00
28	Pat Swilling	7.00
29	Rodney Hampton	14.00
30	Rob Moore	14.00
31	Seth Joyner	7.00
32	Reggie White	20.00
33	Eric Green	7.00
34	Rod Woodson	7.00
35	Marion Butts	7.00
36	Charles Haley	7.00
37	John Taylor	7.00
38	Steve Young	40.00
39	Earnest Byner	7.00
40	Gary Clark	7.00
41	Art Monk	7.00
42	Mark Rypien	7.00

1992 Action Packed Rookie Update

ANTHONY MILLER-WR

Twenty-five first-round draft picks are featured in their new teams' uniforms in this 84-card update set, which has 51 rookies in all and 33 NFL stars. The cards have a black-and-gold foil stripe along the side, and a red helmet with an "R" on the front. There were also 35 24K gold insert cards featuring ten NFL quarterbacks and 25 first-round draft picks. A special "Neon Deion Sanders" card, numbered 84N, was also made and features neon fluorescent orange.

		MT
Complete Set (84):		15.00
Common Player:		.15
Minor Stars:		.30
Wax Box:		20.00
1	Steve Emtman	.30
2	Quentin Coryatt	.30
3	Sean Gilbert	.30
4	John Fina	.15
5	Alonzo Spellman	.30
6	Amp Lee	.30
7	Robert Porcher	.30
8	Jason Hanson	.15
9	Ty Detmer	.50
10	Ray Roberts	.15
11	Bob Whitfield	.15
12	Greg Skrepenak	.15
13	Vaughn Dunbar	.15
14	Siran Stacy	.15
15	Mark D'Onofrio	.15
16	Tony Sacca	.15
17	Dana Hall	.15
18	Courtney Hawkins	.30
19	Shane Collins	.15
20	Tony Smith	.15
21	Rod Smith	.15
22	Troy Auzenne	.15
23	David Klingler	.30
24	Darryl Williams	.15
25	Carl Pickens	2.00
26	Ricardo McDonald	.15
27	Tommy Vardell	.30
28	Kevin Smith	.30
29	Rodney Culver	.15
30	Jimmy Smith	4.00
31	Robert Jones	.15
32	Tommy Maddox	.30
33	Shane Dronett	.15
34	Terrell Buckley	.50
35	Santana Dotson	.50
36	Edgar Bennett	1.00
37	Ashley Ambrose	.15
38	Dale Carter	.50
39	Chester McGlockton	.15
40	Steve Israel	.15
41	Marc Boutte	.15
42	Marco Coleman	.30
43	Troy Vincent	.30
44	Mark Wheeler	.15
45	Darren Perry	.15
46	Eugene Chung	.15
47	Derek Brown	.15
48	Phillippi Sparks	.15
49	Johnny Mitchell	.30
50	Kurt Barber	.15
51	Leon Searcy	.15
52	Chris Mims	.30
53	Keith Jackson	.30
54	Charles Haley	.30
55	Dave Krieg	.15
56	Dan McGwire	.15
57	Phil Simms	.30
58	Bobby Humphrey	.15
59	Jerry Rice	2.50
60	Joe Montana	3.00
61	Junior Seau	.50
62	Leslie O'Neal	.30
63	Anthony Miller	.30
64	Timm Rosenbach	.15
65	Herschel Walker	.15
66	Randal Hill	.15
67	Randall Cunningham	.75
68	Al Toon	.15
69	Browning Nagle	.15
70	Lawrence Taylor	.50
71	Dan Marino	4.00
72	Eric Dickerson	.30
73	Harvey Williams	.30
74	Jeff George	.50
75	Russell Maryland	.30
76	Troy Aikman	1.00
77	Michael Dean Perry	.30
78	Bernie Kosar	.30
79	Boomer Esiason	.30
80	Mike Singletary	.30
81	Bruce Smith	.15
82	Andre Reed	.30
83	Jim Kelly	.50
84	Deion Sanders	1.00
84N	Deion Sanders Neon	10.00

1992 Action Packed Rookie Update 24K Gold

Quarterbacks and first-round draft picks are featured on these insert cards, randomly included in 1992 Action Packed Rookie Update foil packs. Cards have 24K gold foil-stamping on them.

		MT
Complete Set (35):		450.00
Common Player:		7.00
Minor Stars:		14.00
1	Steve Emtman	7.00
2	Quentin Coryatt	14.00
3	Sean Gilbert	14.00
4	Terrell Buckley	14.00
5	David Klingler	7.00
6	Troy Vincent	14.00
7	Tommy Vardell	14.00
8	Leon Searcy	7.00
9	Marco Coleman	14.00
10	Eugene Chung	7.00
11	Derek Brown	7.00
12	Johnny Mitchell	7.00
13	Chester McGlockton	7.00
14	Kevin Smith	7.00
15	Dana Hall	7.00
16	Tony Smith	7.00
17	Dale Carter	14.00
18	Vaughn Dunbar	7.00
19	Alonzo Spellman	14.00
20	Chris Mims	7.00
21	Robert Jones	7.00
22	Tommy Maddox	14.00
23	Robert Porcher	7.00
24	John Fina	7.00
25	Darryl Williams	7.00
26	Jim Kelly	20.00
27	Randall Cunningham	20.00
28	Dan Marino	75.00
29	Troy Aikman	40.00
30	Boomer Esiason	14.00
31	Bernie Kosar	14.00
32	Jeff George	20.00
33	Phil Simms	14.00
34	Ray Roberts	7.00
35	Bob Whitfield	7.00

1992 Action Packed NFLPA Mackey Awards

These standard-size 24K-gold cards were produced for those who attended the 1992 NFLPA Mackey Awards Banquet. Only 2,000 cards of each player were produced.

		MT
Complete Set (3):		125.00
(1)	John Mackey	35.00
(2)	Reggie White	65.00
(3)	Jack Kemp	85.00

1992 Action Packed 24K NFLPA MDA Awards

The 1991 NFL Players of the Year are honored in this 16-card set produced by Action Packed for distribution to those who attended the NFLPA/MDA Awards Dinner, March 5, 1992. The sets were packed in a black box and were stamped "Banquet Edition." The cards feature 24K gold stamping. Cards for players from the AFC are red and have the Action Packed logo in the upper left corner. Cards for the NFC players are blue and have the logo in the upper right corner. Only 1,000 sets were produced.

		MT
	Complete Set (16):	375.00
	Common Player:	15.00
1	Steve Wisniewski	15.00
2	Jim Lachey	15.00
3	Reggie White	25.00
4	William Fuller	15.00
5	Derrick Thomas	35.00
6	Pat Swilling	25.00
7	Darrell Green	25.00
8	Ronnie Lott	25.00
9	Steve Tasker	15.00
10	Mel Gray	15.00
11	Aeneas Williams	15.00
12	Mike Croel	35.00
13	Leonard Russell	50.00
14	Lawrence Dawsey	25.00
15	Barry Sanders	90.00
16	Thurman Thomas	75.00

1992 Action Packed All-Madden

This third John Madden set includes a card of the famed Madden Cruiser. Cards are standard size and were also made into 24K gold insert versions, too.

		MT
	Complete Set (55):	20.00
	Common Player:	.15
	Wax Box:	18.00
1	Emmitt Smith	6.50
2	Reggie White	.75
3	Deion Sanders	1.25
4	Wilber Marshall	.15
5	Barry Sanders	3.00
6	Derrick Thomas	.50
7	Troy Aikman	3.50
8	Eric Allen	.15
9	Cris Carter	.15
10	Jerry Rice	2.50
11	Rickey Jackson	.15
12	Bubba McDowell	.15
13	Jack Del Rio	.15
14	Nate Newton	.15
15	John Elliott	.15
16	Fred Barnett	.40
17	Mike Singletary	.15
18	Lawrence Taylor	.40
19	Bruce Matthews	.15
20	Pat Swilling	.40
21	Charles Haley	.15
22	Andre Rison	1.25
23	Seth Joyner	.15
24	Steve Young	1.75
25	Gary Clark	.25
26	Jerry Ball	.15
27	Michael Irvin	1.50
28	Haywood Jeffires	.30
29	Kevin Ross	.15
30	Chris Doleman	.15
31	Vai Sikahema	.15
32	Ricky Watters	2.00
33	Henry Thomas	.15
34	Mike Kenn	.15
35	Erik Williams	.15
36	Neil Smith	.15
37	Mark Schlereth	.15
38	Steve Wallace	.15
39	Randall McDaniel	.15
40	Kurt Gouveia	.15
41	Al Noga	.15
42	Tom Rathman	.15
43	Harris Barton	.15
44	Mel Gray	.15
45	Keith Byars	.15
46	Todd Scott	.15
47	Brent Jones	.15
48	Audray McMillian	.15
49	Ray Childress	.15
50	Dennis Smith	.15
51	Mark McMillian	.15
52	Sean Gilbert	.15
53	Pierce Holt	.15
54	Daryl Johnston	.40
55	Madden Cruiser	.50

1993 Action Packed Troy Aikman Promos

The two-card, standard-size set highlights Dallas quarterback Troy Aikman, after he won the MVP award in Super Bowl XXVII. Aikman's name is printed along the left border. The card back has "1993 Prototype" printed over Aikman's statistics. The cards are numbered TA2 and TA3 as they were originally part of an 11-card promo sheet.

		MT
	Complete Set (2):	40.00
	Common Player:	20.00
2	Troy Aikman (Running with ball)	20.00
3	Troy Aikman (Pitching the ball)	20.00

1993 Action Packed Emmitt Smith Promos

The five-card, standard-size set features five Emmitt Smith cards to promote the All-Madden Team set. The word "Prototype" is printed on the card back and each card has the prefix "ES". ES1 and ES4 were available at the Super Bowl Card Show in 1993. ES5 was available to members of the Tuff Stuff Buyers Club.

		MT
	Complete Set (5):	40.00
	Common Player:	5.00
1	Emmitt Smith (Receiving handoff from quarterback; side view)	5.00
2	Emmitt Smith	10.00
3	Emmitt Smith	10.00
4	Emmitt Smith (Cutting to right to elude tackler; ball cradled in left arm)	5.00
5	Emmitt Smith (Running to right; ball in left arm)	10.00

1993 Action Packed Prototypes

The six-card, standard-size set previewed the 1993 regular series. The player's last name is printed vertically on the card edge in gold foil. The card backs feature "1993 Prototype" and the prefix "FB". The bottom of the back includes a blank space for an autograph.

		MT
	Complete Set (6):	40.00
	Common Player:	5.00
1	Emmitt Smith	15.00
2	Thurman Thomas	5.00
3	Steve Young	8.00
4	Barry Sanders	10.00
5	Barry Foster	5.00
6	Warren Moon	6.00

1993 Action Packed

This 204-card set features 162 regular cards and 42 subset cards. The 42 subset cards are three types, each with its own numbering prefix - the "Quarterback Club" (18, with a QB prefix), "Moving Targets" (12, with an MT prefix) and 1,000-yard rushers (12, with an RB prefix). Each of these subset cards also has a 24K gold equivalent, with a G suffix. The Quarterback Club cards were also done in Braille (B suffix) and as Mint versions (500 each). The 1993 Rookie/Update set begins where the regular set ended, excluding subsets, by starting with #163. These cards have a gold, silver and bronze design theme designating the first three rounds of the NFL draft. First-rounders have gold foil accents, seconds have silver, and thirds have bronze. Prominent players who have been traded have also been included in the set; the year they were drafted is on the front of the card. There were six standard-size 1993 prototype cards also produced.

		MT
	Complete Set (222):	75.00
	Complete Series 1 (162):	45.00
	Complete Series 2 (60):	30.00
	Common Player:	.15
	Minor Stars:	.25
	Series 1 Wax Box:	45.00
	Rook/Up. Wax Box:	42.00
1	Michael Haynes	.15
2	Chris Miller	.15
3	Andre Rison	.25
4	Jim Kelly	.50
5	Andre Reed	.25
6	Thurman Thomas	.15
7	Jim Harbaugh	.15
8	Harold Green	.15
9	David Klingler	.25
10	Bernie Kosar	.25
11	Troy Aikman	3.00
12	Michael Irvin	.50
13	Emmitt Smith	5.00
14	John Elway	1.50
15	Barry Sanders	4.00
16	Brett Favre	5.00
17	Sterling Sharpe	.75
18	Ernest Givins	.15
19	Haywood Jeffires	.15
20	Warren Moon	.50
21	Lorenzo White	.15
22	Jeff George	.50
23	Joe Montana	3.00
24	Jim Everett	.25
25	Cleveland Gary	.15
26	Dan Marino	4.00
27	Terry Allen	.15
28	Rodney Hampton	.50
29	Phil Simms	.15
30	Fred Barnett	.15
31	Randall Cunningham	.50
32	Gary Clark	.15
33	Barry Foster	.50
34	Neil O'Donnell	.50
35	Stan Humphries	.50
36	Anthony Miller	.15
37	Jerry Rice	3.00
38	Ricky Watters	.50
39	Steve Young	2.00
40	Chris Warren	1.00
41	Reggie Cobb	.15
42	Mark Rypien	.15
43	Deion Sanders	1.50
44	Henry Jones	.15
45	Bruce Smith	.15
46	Richard Dent	.15
47	Tommy Vardell	.15
48	Charles Haley	.15
49	Ken Norton	.15
50	Jay Novacek	.15
51	Simon Fletcher	.15
52	Pat Swilling	.15
53	Tony Bennett	.15
54	Reggie White	.40
55	Ray Childress	.15
56	Quentin Coryatt	.15
57	Steve Emtman	.15
58	Derrick Thomas	.25
59	James Lofton	.15
60	Marco Coleman	.15
61	Bryan Cox	.15
62	Troy Vincent	.15
63	Chris Doleman	.15
64	Audray McMillian	.15
65	Vaughn Dunbar	.15
66	Rickey Jackson	.15
67	Lawrence Taylor	.25
68	Ronnie Lott	.15
69	Rob Moore	.15
70	Browning Nagle	.15
71	Eric Allen	.15
72	Tim Harris	.15
73	Clyde Simmons	.15
74	Steve Beuerlein	.15
75	Randal Hill	.15
76	Darren Perry	.15
77	Rod Woodson	.25
78	Marion Butts	.15
79	Chris Mims	.15
80	Junior Seau	.50
81	Cortez Kennedy	.15
82	Santana Dotson	.15
83	Earnest Byner	.15
84	Charles Mann	.15
85	Pierce Holt	.15
86	Mike Pritchard	.15
87	Cornelius Bennett	.15
88	Neal Anderson	.15
89	Carl Pickens	1.50
90	Eric Metcalf	.15
91	Michael Dean Perry	.15
92	Alvin Harper	.25
93	Robert Jones	.15
94	Steve Atwater	.15
95	Rod Bernstine	.15
96	Herman Moore	1.50
97	Chris Spielman	.15
98	Terrell Buckley	.15
99	Dale Carter	.15
100	Terry McDaniel	.15
101	Tim Brown	.25
102	Gaston Green	.15
103	Howie Long	.15
104	Todd Marinovich	.15
105	Anthony Smith	.15
106	Willie Anderson	.15
107	Henry Ellard	.15
108	Mark Higgs	.15
109	Keith Jackson	.15
110	Irving Fryar	.15
111	Cris Carter	.25
112	Leonard Russell	.15
113	Wayne Martin	.15
114	Mark Jackson	.15
115	David Meggett	.15
116	Brad Baxter	.15
117	Boomer Esiason	.15
118	Johnny Johnson	.15
119	Seth Joyner	.15
120	Kevin Greene	.15
121	Ronnie Harmon, Greg Lloyd	.15
122	Brent Jones	.15
123	Amp Lee	.15
124	Tim McDonald	.15
125	Darrell Green	.15
126	Art Monk	.15
127	Tony Smith	.15
128	Bill Brooks	.15
129	Kenneth Davis	.15
130	Donnell Woolford	.15
131	Derrick Fenner	.15
132	Michael Jackson	.15
133	Mark Clayton	.15
134	Al Smith	.15
135	Curtis Duncan, Rodney Culver	.15
137	Harvey Williams	.15
138	Neil Smith	.15
139	Marcus Allen	.25
140	Eric Dickerson	.15
141	Sean Gilbert	.15
142	Shane Conlan	.15
143	Todd Scott	.15
144	Vincent Brown	.15
145	Andre Tippett	.15
146	Jon Vaughn	.15
147	Marv Cook	.15
148	Morten Anderson	.15
149	Sam Mills	.15
150	Mark Collins	.15
151	Heath Sherman	.15
152	Johnny Bailey	.15
153	Eric Green	.15
154	Gill Byrd	.15
155	Leslie O'Neal	.15
156	Rufus Porter	.15
157	Eugene Robinson	.15
158	Broderick Thomas	.15
159	Lawrence Dawsey	.15
160	Anthony Munoz	.15
162	Wilber Marshall	.15
163	Drew Bledsoe	8.00
164	Rick Mirer	.50
165	Garrison Hearst	3.00
166	Marvin Jones	.25
167	John Copeland	.25
168	Eric Curry	.25
169	Curtis Conway	2.50
170	William Roaf	.15
171	Lincoln Kennedy	.15
172	Jerome Bettis	3.00
173	Dan Williams	.15
174	Patrick Bates	.25
175	Brad Hopkins	.15
176	Steve Everitt	.25
177	Wayne Simmons	.15
178	Tom Carter	.25
179	Ernest Dye	.15
180	Lester Holmes	.15
181	Irv Smith	.25
182	Robert Smith	3.00
183	Darrien Gordon	.25
184	Deon Figures	.25
185	Leonard Renfro	.15
186	O.J. McDuffie	2.00
187	Dana Stubblefield	1.00
188	Todd Kelly	.15
189	Thomas Smith	.15
190	George Teague	.25
191	Wilber Marshall	.15
192	Reggie White	.25
193	Carlton Gray	.15
194	Chris Slade	.50
195	Ben Coleman	.15
196	Ryan McNeil	.15
197	Demetrius DuBose	.15
198	Coleman Rudolph	.15
199	Tony McGee	1.00
200	Troy Drayton	.25
201	Natrone Means	3.00
202	Glyn Milburn	1.00
203	Chad Brown	.50
204	Reggie Brooks	.25
205	Kevin Williams	2.50
206	Michael Barrow	.15
207	Roosevelt Potts	.25
208	Victor Bailey	.25
209	Qadry Ismail	1.00
210	Vincent Brisby	1.00
211	Billy Joe Hobert	1.00
212	Lamar Thomas	.25
213	Jason Elam	.15
214	Andre Hastings	1.00
215	Terry Kirby	1.00
216	Joe Montana	3.00
217	Derrick Lassic	.25
218	Mark Brunell	8.00
219	Vaughn Hebron	.25
220	Troy Brown	.15
221	Derek Brown	.15
222	Raghib Ismail	.25

1993 Action Packed 24K Gold

These cards are identical in format to the regular 1993 Action Packed cards, except they have "24K" written under the Action Packed logo on the card front. The cards use a "G" suffix for numbering; the card number appears on the back. Cards were random inserts in 1993 Action Packed foil packs and feature 24K versions of three insert sets - Quarterback Club (1G-18G), Moving Targets (19G-30G) and 1,000 Yard Rushers (31G-42G), plus 30 others.

		MT
	Complete Set (72):	2000.
	Complete Series 1 (42):	1200.
	Complete Series 2 (30):	800.00
	Common Player:	20.00
	Minor Stars:	30.00
1	Troy Aikman	75.00
2	Randall Cunningham	20.00
3	John Elway	50.00
4	Jim Everett	20.00
5	Brett Favre	125.00
6	Jim Harbaugh	20.00
7	Jeff Hostetler	20.00
8	Jim Kelly	30.00
9	David Klingler	20.00
10	Bernie Kosar	20.00
11	Dan Marino	125.00
12	Chris Miller	20.00
13	Boomer Esiason	20.00
14	Warren Moon	30.00
15	Neil O'Donnell	30.00
16	Mark Rypien	20.00
17	Phil Simms	20.00
18	Steve Young	75.00
19	Fred Barnett	20.00
20	Gary Clark	20.00
21	Mark Clayton	20.00
22	Ernest Givins	20.00
23	Michael Haynes	20.00
24	Michael Irvin	30.00
25	Haywood Jeffires	20.00
26	Anthony Miller	20.00
27	Andre Reed	20.00
28	Jerry Rice	75.00
29	Andre Rison	20.00
30	Sterling Sharpe	30.00
31	Terry Allen	20.00
32	Reggie Cobb	20.00
33	Barry Foster	20.00
34	Cleveland Gary	20.00
35	Harold Green	20.00
36	Rodney Hampton	30.00
37	Barry Sanders	90.00
38	Emmitt Smith	125.00
39	Thurman Thomas	30.00
40	Chris Warren	30.00
41	Ricky Watters	30.00
42	Lorenzo White	20.00
43	Drew Bledsoe	75.00
44	Rick Mirer	35.00
45	Garrison Hearst	40.00
46	Marvin Jones	20.00
47	John Copeland	20.00
48	Eric Curry	20.00
49	Curtis Conway	35.00
50	William Roaf	20.00
51	Lincoln Kennedy	20.00
52	Jerome Bettis	35.00
53	Dan Williams	20.00
54	Patrick Bates	20.00
55	Brad Hopkins	20.00
56	Steve Everitt	20.00
57	Wayne Simmons	20.00
58	Tom Carter	20.00
59	Ernest Dye	20.00
60	Lester Holmes	20.00
61	Irv Smith	20.00
62	Robert Smith	35.00
63	Darrien Gordon	20.00
64	Deon Figures	20.00
65	Leonard Renfro	20.00
66	O.J. McDuffie	30.00
67	Dana Stubblefield	30.00
68	Todd Kelly	20.00
69	Thomas Smith	20.00
70	George Teague	20.00
71	Wilber Marshall	20.00
72	Reggie White	30.00

1993 Action Packed Moving Targets

These 12 cards were random inserts and are numbered with an "MT" prefix. The "Moving Targets" logo appears on each card front, plus a full-bleed embossed photo, along with the player's name in gold foil. The back has a painted football scene, plus a color head shot of the player and career stats. An autograph slot is also included. There were also 24K versions created for these cards; they are random inserts and are numbered with a "G" prefix.

		MT
	Complete Set (12):	12.00
	Common Player:	.50
	Minor Stars:	1.00
1	Fred Barnett	.50
2	Gary Clark	.50
3	Mark Clayton	.50
4	Ernest Givins	.50
5	Michael Haynes	.50
6	Michael Irvin	1.00
7	Haywood Jeffires	.50
8	Anthony Miller	.50
9	Andre Reed	.50
10	Jerry Rice	4.00
11	Andre Rison	1.00
12	Sterling Sharpe	1.00

1993 Action Packed Quarterback Club

These subset cards, numbered on the back using a "QB" prefix, were included in 1993 Action Packed boxes at the same rate as the set's regular cards, but 24K versions were randomly inserted in fewer quantities. The gold versions have a "G" suffix after the card number. "Quarterback Club" cards follow the same format as the regular cards, but have the set logo on the front to distinguish them.

		MT
	Complete Set (18):	20.00
	Common Player:	.50
	Minor Stars:	1.00
1	Troy Aikman	4.00
2	Randall Cunningham	2.00
3	John Elway	3.00

		MT
4	Jim Everett	.50
5	Brett Favre	6.00
6	Jim Harbaugh	1.00
7	Jeff Hostetler	.50
8	Jim Kelly	1.00
9	David Klingler	.50
10	Bernie Kosar	.50
11	Dan Marino	6.00
12	Chris Miller	.50
13	Boomer Esiason	.50
14	Warren Moon	1.00
15	Neil O'Donnell	1.00
16	Mark Rypien	.50
17	Phil Simms	.50
18	Steve Young	4.00

1993 Action Packed Quarterback Club Braille

These 18 cards, which each have a "B" suffix after the card number, are identical to their regular version counterparts, except they are done in Braille. They are generally about two or three times more valuable than the regular cards. Cards were random inserts; some were donated to more than 400 schools for the blind.

		MT
Complete Set (18):		60.00
Common Player:		1.25
1	Troy Aikman	15.00
2	Randall Cunningham	4.00
3	John Elway	8.00
4	Jim Everett	1.25
5	Brett Favre	10.00
6	Jim Harbaugh	1.25
7	Jeff Hostetler	1.25
8	Jim Kelly	5.00
9	David Klingler	2.00
10	Bernie Kosar	2.00
11	Dan Marino	12.00
12	Chris Miller	1.25
13	Boomer Esiason	3.00
14	Warren Moon	3.50
15	Neil O'Donnell	3.00
16	Mark Rypien	1.25
17	Phil Simms	3.00
18	Steve Young	6.00

1993 Action Packed Rookies Previews

The three-card, standard-size set features Troy Aikman, Brett Favre and Neil O'Donnell. The round the quarterback was drafted in is done in gold (first round), silver (second) or bronze (third) on the card front. The card back has "1993 Prototype" printed with the prefix "RU." The set was available as a topper in select hobby boxes.

		MT
Complete Set (3):		6.00
Common Player:		1.00
1	Troy Aikman	2.00
2	Brett Favre	4.00
3	Neil O'Donnell	1.00

1993 Action Packed Rushers

Players who gained 1,000 or more yards rushing during the previous season are featured in this Action Packed insert set. Cards have a "1000 Yard Rushers" logo on the front, plus a full-bleed photo and the player's name in gold foil. Backs have a color head shot of the player and statistics for his team's single-

season rushing leaders. Card backs have an autograph slot, and are numbered with an "RB" prefix. There were also 24K versions created of these cards; they are numbered with a "G" suffix and were random inserts.

		MT
Complete Set (12):		15.00
Common Player:		.50
Minor Stars:		1.00
1	Terry Allen	.50
2	Reggie Cobb	.50
3	Barry Foster	.50
4	Cleveland Gary	.50
5	Harold Green	.50
6	Rodney Hampton	.50
7	Barry Sanders	4.00
8	Emmitt Smith	6.00
9	Thurman Thomas	1.00
10	Chris Warren	1.00
11	Ricky Watters	1.00
12	Lorenzo White	.50

1993 Action Packed NFLPA Awards

Outstanding players from the 1992 NFL season are honored in this 17-card Action Packed set. The cards, issued in a special box, have an embossed front; backs have a head shot, career summary and the position the player was selected as being the best at in 1992. A card number is also on the back. The cards were distributed at the 20th annual NFLPA banquet on March 4, 1993, in Washington, D.C. The District of Columbia's Special Olympics was the beneficiary.

		MT
Complete Set (17):		60.00
Common Player:		3.00
1	Randall McDaniel	3.00
2	Bruce Matthews	3.00
3	Richmond Webb	3.00
4	Cortez Kennedy	7.00
5	Clyde Simmons	3.00
6	Wilber Marshall	4.00
7	Junior Seau	8.00
8	Henry Jones	4.00
9	Audray McMillian	3.00
10	Mel Gray	4.00
11	Steve Tasker	3.00
12	Marco Coleman	6.00
13	Santana Dotson	6.00
14	Vaughn Dunbar	7.00
15	Carl Pickens	7.00
16	Barry Foster	8.00
17	Steve Young	10.00

1993 Action Packed All-Madden

This 42-card set marks the 10th Anniversary All-Madden team and features the all-time favorites from the last 10 years as selected by the charismatic broadcaster and former coach, John Madden. Players' names are stamped in gold foil on a stone background. A 12-card insert was also done in a 24K gold equivalent. These cards have the suffix "G" used in their numbering. A five-card Emmitt Smith prototype set was also issued as a promotional for the All-Madden set. The All-Madden logo appears on each card front; the back is labeled as a prototype and is numbered ES1-ES5. Cards ES1 and ES4 were giveaways at the 1993 Super Bowl card show; ES5 was a giveaway

to members of the Tuff Stuff Buyers Club.

		MT
Complete Set (42):		18.00
Common Player:		.15
1	Troy Aikman	3.00
2	Bill Bates	.15
3	Mark Bavaro	.15
4	Jim Burt	.15
5	Gary Clark	.15
6	Richard Dent	.15
7	Gary Fenciik	.15
8	Darryl Green	.15
9	Roy Green	.15
10	Russ Grimm	.15
11	Charles Haley	.20
12	Dan Hampton	.15
13	Lester Hayes	.15
14	Michael Haynes	.50
15	Jay Hilgenberg	.15
16	Michael Irvin	.50
17	Joe Jacoby	.15
18	Steve Largent	.15
19	Howie Long	.15
20	Ronnie Lott	.25
21	Dan Marino	3.00
22	Jim McMahon	.15
23	Matt Millen	.15
24	Art Monk	.20
25	Joe Montana	2.50
26	Anthony Munoz	.15
27	Nate Newton	.15
28	Walter Payton	.50
29	William Perry	.15
30	Jack Reynolds	.15
31	Jerry Rice	1.50
32	Barry Sanders	3.00
33	Sterling Sharpe	1.00
34	Mike Singletary	.20
35	Jackie Slater	.15
36	Emmitt Smith	4.00
37	Pat Summerall	.25
38	Lawrence Taylor	.40
39	Jeff Van Note	.15
40	Reggie White	.40
41	Otis Wilson	.15
42	Jack Youngblood	.15

1993 Action Packed All-Madden 24K Gold

These 24K gold cards are identical in design to the regular 10th Anniversary All-Madden cards, except they use 24Kt. Gold stamped on the card front in gold foil. They were random inserts in 1993 Action Packed 10th Anniversary All-Madden Team packs and are numbered on the card back using a "G" suffix.

		MT
Complete Set (12):		500.00
Common Player:		20.00
1	Troy Aikman	125.00
2	Michael Irvin	70.00
3	Ronnie Lott	20.00
4	Dan Marino	75.00
5	Joe Montana	100.00
6	Walter Payton	30.00
7	Jerry Rice	100.00
8	Barry Sanders	90.00
9	Sterling Sharpe	30.00
10	Emmitt Smith	135.00
11	Lawrence Taylor	20.00
12	Reggie White	25.00

1993 Action Packed Monday Night Football Prototypes

The six-card, standard-size set promoted the Monday Night Football set with highlights from the 1992 season. The date of each game is printed on on each side border while the ABC logo is located in the bottom right corner. Helmets from each team from the Monday Night Game are found on the top corners. The card backs have "1993 Prototype" printed and feature the "MN" prefix.

		MT
Complete Set (6):		45.00
Common Player:		5.00
1	Barry Sanders	8.00
2	Steve Young	7.00
3	Emmitt Smith	15.00
4	Thurman Thomas	5.00
5	Barry Foster	5.00
6	Warren Moon	5.00

A card number in parentheses ( ) indicates the set is unnumbered.

1993 Action Packed Monday Night Football

December 20, 1993

The 1993 Monday Night Football schedule is chronicled in this 81-card Action Packed set. The cards preview top players slated to appear in each game, plus ABC's game announcers. Each card gives the date of the game, along with helmets of the two opposing teams participating. A key player from one of the teams is featured on each card front. The back has a mug shot of the player and provides a summary of his performance against that particular opponent. A Monday Night Football trivia fact is also given. Each foil pack also had the chance of obtaining a randomly included gold mint card; there were 250 gold mint cards produced for each card in the set.

		MT
Complete Set (81):		22.00
Common Player:		.15
Wax Box:		25.00
1	Michael Irvin	1.25
2	Charles Haley	.15
3	Art Monk	.15
4	Earnest Byner	.15
5	Tom Rathman	.15
6	John Taylor	.30
7	Bernie Kosar	.15
8	Clay Matthews	.15
9	Simon Fletcher	.15
10	John Elway	.50
11	Joe Montana	2.00
12	Derrick Thomas	.40
13	Rod Woodson	.20
14	Gary Anderson	.15
15	Chris Miller	.15
16	Andre Rison	.50
17	Mark Rypien	.25
18	Charles Mann	.15
19	Mark Duper	.15
20	Pete Stoyanovich	.15
21	Warren Moon	.50
22	Lorenzo White	.15
23	Haywood Jeffires	.40
24	Andre Reed	.40
25	Darryl Talley	.15
26	Tim Brown	.15
27	Howie Long	.15
28	Steve Atwater	.15
29	Karl Mecklenburg	.15
30	Chris Doleman	.15
31	Terry Allen	.40
32	Richard Dent	.15
33	Neal Anderson	.15
34	Darrell Green	.15
35	Chip Lohmiller	.15
36	Jim Kelly	.75
37	Cornelius Bennett	.15
38	Brett Favre	3.00
39	Sterling Sharpe	1.00
40	Reggie White	.40
41	Neil Smith	.15
42	Nick Lowery	.15
43	Thurman Thomas	1.50
44	Bruce Smith	.20
45	Barry Foster	.90
46	Neil O'Donnell	.90
47	Rickey Jackson	.15
48	Morten Andersen	.15
49	Brent Jones	.15
50	Ricky Watters	1.50
51	Leslie O'Neil	.15
52	Marion Butts	.15
53	Anthony Miller	.15
54	Jeff George	.25
55	Steve Emmtem	.75
56	Herschel Walker	.15
57	Randall Cunningham	.50
58	Clyde Simmons	.15
59	Emmitt Smith	4.00
60	Ken Norton	.15
61	Troy Aikman	2.00
62	Eric Green	.15
63	Greg Lloyd	.15
64	Bryan Cox	.15
65	Mark Higgs	.15
66	Phil Simms	.15
67	Lawrence Taylor	.30
68	Rodney Hampton	.75
69	Wayne Martin	.15
70	Vaughn Dunbar	.15
71	Keith Jackson	.15
72	Dan Marino	1.00
73	Junior Seau	.50
74	Stan Humphries	.15
75	Fred Barnett	.40
76	Seth Joyner	.15
77	Steve Young	1.00
78	Jerry Rice	1.25
79	Dan Dierdorf	.40
80	Frank Gifford	.40
81	Al Michaels	.40
82	All Three Together	.40

1993 Action Packed Monday Night Football Mint

Each 1993 Action Packed Monday Night Football pack had the random chance of including a certificate good for one of 250 gold mint cards produced for each card in the set.

		MT
Complete Set (78):		3000.
Common Player:		40.00
1	Michael Irvin	60.00
2	Charles Haley	40.00
3	Art Monk	40.00
4	Earnest Byner	40.00
5	Tom Rathman	40.00
6	John Taylor	40.00
7	Bernie Kosar	40.00
8	Clay Matthews	40.00
9	Simon Fletcher	40.00
10	John Elway	40.00
11	Joe Montana	275.00
12	Derrick Thomas	40.00
13	Rod Woodson	40.00
14	Gary Anderson	40.00
15	Chris Miller	40.00
16	Andre Rison	75.00
17	Mark Rypien	40.00
18	Charles Mann	40.00
19	John Offerdahl	40.00
20	Pete Stoyanovich	40.00
21	Warren Moon	60.00
22	Lorenzo White	40.00
23	Haywood Jeffires	40.00
24	Andre Reed	40.00
25	Darryl Talley	40.00
26	Tim Brown	40.00
27	Howie Long	40.00
28	Steve Atwater	40.00
29	Karl Mecklenburg	40.00
30	Chris Doleman	40.00
31	Terry Allen	65.00
32	Richard Dent	40.00
33	Neal Anderson	40.00
34	Darrell Green	40.00
35	Chip Lohmiller	40.00
36	Jim Kelly	150.00
37	Cornelius Bennett	40.00
38	Brett Favre	175.00
39	Sterling Sharpe	100.00
40	Reggie White	40.00
41	Neil Smith	40.00
42	Nick Lowery	40.00
43	Thurman Thomas	150.00
44	Bruce Smith	40.00
45	Barry Foster	90.00
46	Neil O'Donnell	100.00
47	Rickey Jackson	40.00
48	Morten Anderson	40.00
49	Brent Jones	40.00
50	Ricky Watters	95.00
51	Leslie O'Neal	40.00
52	Marion Butts	40.00
53	Anthony Miller	40.00
54	Jeff George	40.00
55	Steve Emtman	95.00
56	Herschel Walker	40.00
57	Randall Cunningham	40.00
58	Clyde Simmons	40.00
59	Emmitt Smith	300.00
60	Ken Norton	40.00
61	Troy Aikman	40.00
62	Eric Green	40.00
63	Greg Lloyd	40.00
64	Bryan Cox	40.00
65	Mark Higgs	40.00
66	Phil Simms	40.00
67	Lawrence Taylor	40.00
68	Rodney Hampton	100.00
69	Wayne Martin	40.00
70	Vaughn Dunbar	40.00
71	Keith Jackson	40.00
72	Dan Marino	250.00
73	Junior Seau	50.00
74	Stan Humphries	40.00
75	Fred Barnett	40.00
76	Seth Joyner	40.00
77	Steve Young	185.00
78	Jerry Rice	200.00

A player's name in *italic type* indicates a rookie card.

1994 Action Packed Prototypes

These 12 promotional cards preview Action Packed's 1994 design for its regular, subset and insert cards (the type of card is included in the checklist below). Each card is numbered on the back, using one of three different prefixes (FB, MNF or RU). The back is also labeled as a prototype. These cards were given to dealers and to those who attended the Super Bowl 28 card show. A set, which excluded Barry Foster's card, was also produced in its own display frame.

		MT
Complete Set (12):		70.00
Common Player:		3.00
FB941	(Troy Aikman) (1994 Action Packed)	15.00
FB942	Jeff Hostetler (Quarterback Challenge)	3.00
FB943	Emmitt Smith (Warp Speed)	12.00
FB944	(Jerry Rice) (Catching Fire)	7.00
FB945	(Barry Foster) (Fantasy Forecast Subset)	6.00
MNF941	(Steve Young) (Monday Night Football)	6.00
MNF942	(Steve Young) (Monday Night Moment)	6.00
MNF943	(Barry Foster) (Monday Night Moment)	6.00
RU941	(Drew Bledsoe) (Rookie Update)	10.00
RU942	(Derrick Lassic) (Rookie Update)	3.00
RU943	Rick Mirer (Golden Domers)	8.00
RU944	Jerome Bettis (Golden Domers)	8.00

1994 Action Packed

This 120-card set features Action Packed's regular sculptured texture, showing a full-bleed color photo on the card front, along with the player's name burnished in gold. Each card back has a metallic, foil background, a head shot of the player, 1993 statistics and an "Action Note." Insert sets include Quarterback Club, Catching Fire, Warp Speed, and Fantasy Forecast. There were 12 prototype cards made - each one says prototype on the back, and uses either an FB, MNF or RU prefix for the card number.

		MT
Complete Set (198):		60.00
Complete Series 1 (120):		35.00

Complete Series 2 (78):		25.00
Common Player:		.20
Minor Stars:		.40
Braille Cards:		2x
Gold Signature Cards:		3x
Inserted 1:1 Retail		
Series 1 Wax Box:		45.00
Series 2 Wax Box:		35.00

1	Michael Haynes	.20
2	Andre Rison	.75
3	Mike Pritchard	.20
4	Erric Pegram	.20
5	Deion Sanders	1.00
6	Jim Kelly	.75
7	Andre Reed	.40
8	Thurman Thomas	.75
9	Bruce Smith	.20
10	Cornelius Bennett	.20
11	Nate Odomes	.20
12	Richard Dent	.20
13	Donnell Woolford	.20
14	Harold Green	.20
15	David Klingler	.20
16	Eric Metcalf	.20
17	Michael Dean Perry	.20
18	Michael Jackson	.40
19	Vinny Testaverde	.75
20	Troy Aikman	2.50
21	Michael Irvin	.75
22	Emmitt Smith	4.00
23	Jay Novacek	.20
24	Alvin Harper	.40
25	Charles Haley	.20
26	John Elway	3.00
27	Shannon Sharpe	.40
28	Rod Bernstine	.20
29	Simon Fletcher	.20
30	Barry Sanders	5.00
31	Herman Moore	1.00
32	Pat Swilling	.20
33	Chris Spielman	.20
34	Brett Favre	5.00
35	Sterling Sharpe	.40
36	Reggie White	.75
37	Jackie Harris	.20
38	Tony Bennett	.20
39	LeRoy Butler	.20
40	Warren Moon	.75
41	Ernest Givins	.20
42	Haywood Jeffires	.20
43	Webster Slaughter	.20
44	Ray Childress	.20
45	Gary Brown	.40
46	Jeff George	.75
47	Roosevelt Potts	.20
48	Quentin Coryatt	.20
49	Joe Montana	3.00
50	Derrick Thomas	.40
51	Neil Smith	.20
52	Marcus Allen	.75
53	Willie Davis	.20
54	Jerome Bettis	1.00
55	Sean Gilbert	.20
56	Chris Miller	.20
57	Jeff Hostetler	.40
58	Tim Brown	.75
59	Anthony Smith	.20
60	Greg Townsend	.20
61	Terry McDaniel	.20
62	Dan Marino	4.00
63	Irving Fryar	.20
64	Keith Jackson	.20
65	Terry Kirby	.20
66	Bryan Cox	.20
67	Chris Doleman	.20
68	Cris Carter	1.00
69	John Randle	.40
70	Drew Bledsoe	3.00
71	Ben Coates	.40
72	Vincent Brisby	.20
73	Rickey Jackson	.20
74	Eric Martin	.20
75	Renaldo Turnbull	.20
76	Rodney Hampton	.40
77	Mike Sherrard	.20
78	Phil Simms	.40
79	Keith Hamilton	.20
80	Rob Moore	.75
81	Brad Baxter	.20
82	Boomer Esiason	.40
83	Johnny Johnson	.20
84	Ronnie Lott	.40
85	Randall Cunningham	.75
86	Herschel Walker	.20
87	Eric Allen	.20
88	Clyde Simmons	.20
89	Seth Joyner	.20
90	Calvin Williams	.20
91	Garrison Hearst	1.00
92	Steve Beuerlein	.20
93	Ricky Proehl	.20
94	Ron Moore	.20
95	Barry Foster	.20
96	Neil O'Donnell	.40
97	Eric Green	.20
98	Rod Woodson	.40
99	Greg Lloyd	.20
100	Kevin Greene	.20
101	Stan Humphries	.40
102	Anthony Miller	.20
103	Junior Seau	.40
104	Leslie O'Neal	.20
105	Ronnie Harmon	.20
106	Jerry Rice	2.50
107	Ricky Watters	.75
108	Steve Young	2.00
109	Brent Jones	.20
110	John Taylor	.20
111	Rick Mirer	.40
112	Chris Warren	.20
113	Cortez Kennedy	.20
114	Brian Blades	.20
115	Eugene Robinson	.20
116	Reggie Cobb	.20
117	Hardy Nickerson	.20
118	Reggie Brooks	.20
119	Darrell Green	.20
120	Troy Aikman	2.50
121	Dan Wilkinson	.40
122	Marshall Faulk	7.00
123	Heath Shuler	.75
124	Willie McGinest	.40
125	Trev Alberts	.40
126	Trent Dilfer	4.00
127	Bryant Young	.75
128	Sam Adams	.40
129	Antonio Langham	.40
130	Jamir Miller	.20
131	John Thierry	.40
132	Aaron Glenn	.40
133	Joe Johnson	.20
134	Bernard Williams	.20
135	Wayne Gandy	.20
136	Charles Johnson	.75
137	DeWayne Washington	.40
138	Todd Steussie	.40
139	Tim Bowens	.40
140	Johnnie Morton	2.00
141	Rob Fredrickson	.40
142	Shante Carver	.40
143	Thomas Lewis	.40
144	Greg Hill	.75
145	Henry Ford	.20
146	Jeff Burris	.40
147	William Floyd	.75
148	Derrick Alexander	.75
149	Darnay Scott	2.50
150	Isaac Bruce	6.00
151	Errict Rhett	1.00
152	Kevin Lee	.40
153	Chuck Levy	.40
154	David Palmer	1.00
155	Ryan Yarborough	.40
156	Charlie Garner	2.50
157	Mario Bates	.75
158	Bert Emanuel	2.00
159	Bucky Brooks	.40
160	Donnell Bennett	1.00
161	Tydus Winans	.40
162	Andre Coleman	.40
163	Calvin Jones	.40
164	LeShon Johnson	.40
165	Doug Brien	.20
166	Bam Morris	.75
167	Lake Dawson	.75
168	Perry Klein	.40
169	Doug Nussmeier	.40
170	Lamont Warren	.20
171	Gus Frerotte	1.00
172	Troy Aikman	1.50
173	Randall Cunningham	.40
174	John Elway	1.50
175	Jim Everett	.20
176	Drew Bledsoe	1.50
177	Jim Kelly	.40
178	Dan Marino	2.00
179	Chris Miller	.20
180	Warren Moon	.20
181	Rick Mirer	.20
182	Jeff Hostetler	.20
183	Brett Favre	3.00
184	Steve Young	1.00
185	Anthony Miller	.20
186	Michael Haynes	.20
187	Mike Pritchard	.20
188	Jeff George	.20
189	Lewis Tillman	.20
190	Ken Norton	.20
191	Erik Kramer	.20
192	Richard Dent	.20
193	Rick Mirer	.20
194	Jerome Bettis	.40
195	Reggie Brooks	.20
196	Tom Carter	.20
197	Irv Smith	.20
198	Rocket Ismail	.20

1994 Action Packed 24K Gold

Action Packed made 24K gold versions for each of its insert sets - Quarterback Club (G1-G20); Catching Fire (G21-G30); and Warp Speed (G31-G42). These Quarterback Club cards feature gold foil fronts rather than in silver like the regular ones.

		MT
Complete Set (55):		1000.
Complete Series 1 (42):		700.00
Complete Series 2 (13):		300.00
Common Player:		5.00
Minor Stars:		10.00
Inserted 1:96		
1	Troy Aikman	30.00
2	Randall Cunningham	15.00
3	John Elway	40.00
4	Boomer Esiason	5.00
5	Jim Everett	5.00
6	Brett Favre	60.00
7	Jerry Rice	30.00
8	Jeff Hostetler	5.00
9	Jim Kelly	10.00
10	David Klingler	5.00
11	Bernie Kosar	5.00
12	Dan Marino	45.00
13	Chris Miller	5.00
14	Warren Moon	10.00
15	Neil O'Donnell	10.00
16	Michael Irvin	10.00
17	Phil Simms	5.00
18	Steve Young	20.00
19	Rick Mirer	10.00
20	Drew Bledsoe	30.00
21	Jerry Rice	30.00
22	Sterling Sharpe	10.00
23	Michael Irvin	10.00
24	Anthony Miller	5.00
26	Tim Brown	10.00
27	Andre Reed	5.00
28	Herman Moore	10.00
29	Irving Fryar	5.00
30	Shannon Sharpe	10.00
31	Emmitt Smith	45.00
32	Barry Sanders	60.00
33	Thurman Thomas	10.00
34	Jerome Bettis	10.00
35	Barry Foster	5.00
36	Ricky Watters	10.00
37	Rodney Hampton	5.00
38	Chris Warren	10.00
39	Erric Pegram	5.00
40	Reggie Brooks	5.00
41	Marcus Allen	10.00
42	Ron Moore	5.00
43	Troy Aikman	30.00
44	Randall Cunningham	10.00
45	John Elway	40.00
46	Jim Everett	5.00
47	Drew Bledsoe	30.00
48	Jim Kelly	10.00
49	Dan Marino	45.00
50	Chris Miller	5.00
51	Warren Moon	10.00
52	Rick Mirer	10.00
53	Jeff Hostetler	5.00
54	Brett Favre	60.00
55	Steve Young	20.00

1994 Action Packed Catching Fire

The NFL's top 10 wide receivers are featured in this insert set. The "Catching Fire" logo is on the card front, which shows the player surrounded by metallic foil flames. Card backs are numbered with an "R" prefix; except for 24K gold versions which were also created; they are numbered G21-G30.

		MT
Complete Set (10):		10.00
Common Player:		.50
Minor Stars:		1.00
1	Jerry Rice	5.00
2	Sterling Sharpe	1.00
3	Michael Irvin	1.00
4	Andre Rison	1.00
5	Anthony Miller	.50
6	Tim Brown	1.00
7	Andre Reed	.50
8	Herman Moore	2.00
9	Irving Fryar	.50
10	Shannon Sharpe	1.00

1994 Action Packed Quarterback Challenge

The 12-card, regular-size set was inserted in each retail pack that was available at Foot Action stores. The card fronts feature the quarterback's face - outlined in silver, while the backs include information from the Quarterback Challenge competition. All cards are numbered with the "FA" prefix.

		MT
Complete Set (12):		15.00
Common Player:		.25
Minor Stars:		.50
1	Steve Young	2.00
2	John Elway	3.00
3	Troy Aikman	2.50
4	Randall Cunningham	.75
5	Warren Moon	.50
6	Brett Favre	5.00
7	Rick Mirer	.25
8	Drew Bledsoe	3.00
9	Boomer Esiason	.25
10	Jeff Hostetler	.25
11	Jim Kelly	.50
12	Dan Marino	3.50

Values quoted in this guide reflect the retail price of a card — the price a collector can expect to pay when buying a card from a dealer. The wholesale price — that which a collector can expect to receive when selling cards — will be significantly lower, depending on desirability and condition.

1994 Action Packed Fantasy Forecast

This Fantasy Forecast insert set provides a scouting report for 42 top NFL players. Each card front features the player with a football that is covered with heat-sensitive ink. Touching the football reveals how high you should draft the player if you were picking a fantasy football team. Cards are numbered FF1-FF42.

		MT
Complete Set (42):		15.00
Common Player:		.25
Minor Stars:		.50
1	Rodney Hampton	.50
2	Steve Young	1.50
3	Michael Irvin	.50
4	Emmitt Smith	3.00
5	Troy Aikman	2.00
6	Jerry Rice	2.00
7	Brett Favre	4.00
8	Jerome Bettis	.50
9	Reggie Brooks	.50
10	John Elway	2.50
11	Jim Kelly	.50
12	Dan Marino	3.00
13	Randall Cunningham	.50
14	Sterling Sharpe	.50
15	Chris Warren	.50
16	Andre Rison	.50
17	Mike Pritchard	.50
18	Barry Sanders	4.00
19	Marcus Allen	.50
20	Thurman Thomas	.50
21	Erric Pegram	.25
22	Barry Foster	.25
23	Anthony Miller	.25
24	Shannon Sharpe	.50
25	Tim Brown	.50
26	Ricky Watters	.50
27	Ernest Givins	.25
28	Cris Carter	.50
29	Willie Davis	.50
30	Warren Moon	.50
31	Joe Montana	2.50
32	Herman Moore	.50
33	Terry Kirby	.50
34	Eric Green	.25
35	Michael Jackson	.25
36	Johnny Johnson	.25
37	Calvin Williams	.25
38	Michael Haynes	.25
39	Irving Fryar	.25
40	Gary Brown	.25
41	Jeff Hostetler	.25
42	Keith Jackson	.25

1994 Action Packed Quarterback Club

These Action Packed cards are printed with a silver foil front similar to, but far more sturdier and attractive, than Topps 1965 Embossed insert set. Cards were random inserts in 1994 packs and are numbered with a "QB" prefix. They feature the player's embossed portrait on the front. There were also 24K gold versions made for each Quarterback Club card. These cards feature gold foil on the front instead of silver.

		MT
Complete Set (20):		15.00
Common Player:		.25
Minor Stars:		.50
1	Troy Aikman	2.50
2	Randall Cunningham	.75
3	John Elway	3.00
4	Boomer Esiason	.50
5	Jim Everett	.25
6	Brett Favre	5.00
7	Jerry Rice	2.50
8	Jeff Hostetler	.25
9	Jim Kelly	.50
10	David Klingler	.25
11	Bernie Kosar	.25
12	Dan Marino	3.50
13	Chris Miller	.25
14	Warren Moon	.50
15	Neil O'Donnell	.50
16	Michael Irvin	.50
17	Phil Simms	.25
18	Steve Young	2.00
19	Rick Mirer	.50
20	Drew Bledsoe	3.00

1994 Action Packed Warp Speed

These 1994 Action Packed inserts feature 12 of the NFL's top running backs. Card fronts are printed using a colored foil design and have the "Warp Speed" and player's name in foil, too. Cards are numbered with a "WS" prefix. Gold versions were also made and are numbered G31-G42.

		MT
Complete Set (12):		15.00
Common Player:		.25
Minor Stars:		.50
1	Emmitt Smith	4.00
2	Barry Sanders	6.00
3	Thurman Thomas	.50
4	Jerome Bettis	1.00
5	Barry Foster	.25
6	Ricky Watters	.50
7	Rodney Hampton	.50
8	Chris Warren	.25
9	Erric Pegram	.25
10	Reggie Brooks	.25
11	Marcus Allen	.50
12	Ron Moore	.25

1994 Action Packed All-Madden

The 11th Annual All-Madden Team is a 41-card set from Action Packed that showcases Madden's hand-picked All-Pro Team. The fronts have a borderless design and incorporates a band-aid logo, exemplifying the toughness that was required to be selected by Madden. All 41 cards also have a 24kt gold equivalent, of which there is one per every box of the product. Cards were sold in packs of six. Each pack includes a "Smash Mouth" scratch-and-win game card which offers various prizes, including different television sets and 24kt gold cards.

		MT
Complete Set (41):		20.00
Common Player:		.15
Wax Box:		35.00
1	Emmitt Smith	4.00
2	Jerome Bettis	1.00
3	Steve Young	2.00
4	Jerry Rice	2.50
5	Richard Dent	.15
6	Junior Seau	.50
7	Harris Barton	.15
8	Steve Wallace	.15
9	Keith Byars	.15
10	Michael Irvin	1.00
11	Joe Montana	2.50
12	Jesse Sapolu	.15
13	Rickey Jackson	.15
14	Ronnie Lott	.50
15	Donnell Woolford	.15
16	Reggie White	1.50
17	John Taylor	.25
18	Bruce Matthews	.15
19	Ron Moore	.15
20	Bill Bates	.15
21	Steve Hendrickson	.15
22	Eric Allen	.25
23	Monte Coleman	.15
24	Mark Collins	.15
25	Barry Sanders	3.00
26	Erik Williams	.15
27	Phil Simms	.25
28	Chris Zorich	.15
29	Troy Aikman	3.00
30	Charles Haley	.15
31	Darrell Green	.15
32	Sean Gilbert	.15
33	Kevin Gogan	.15
34	Rodney Hampton	1.00
35	Chris Doleman	.15
36	Nate Newton	.15
37	Jackie Slater	.15
38	Ricky Watters	1.00
39	LeRoy Butler	.15
40	Gary Clark	.15
41	Sterling Sharpe	.50

1994 Action Packed All-Madden 24k Gold

Each of the 41 cards in the 11th Annual All-Madden Team was created in a 24kt gold version for this parallel set. There was one 24kt gold card in each All-Madden product box.

		MT
Complete Set (41):		1000.
Common Player:		20.00
1	Emmitt Smith	150.00
2	Jerome Bettis	50.00
3	Steve Young	80.00
4	Jerry Rice	95.00
5	Richard Dent	20.00
6	Junior Seau	28.00
7	Harris Barton	20.00
8	Steve Wallace	20.00
9	Keith Byars	20.00
10	Michael Irvin	50.00
11	Joe Montana	95.00
12	Jesse Sapolu	20.00
13	Rickey Jackson	20.00
14	Ronnie Lott	28.00
15	Donnell Woolford	20.00
16	Reggie White	75.00
17	John Taylor	25.00
18	Bruce Matthews	20.00
19	Ron Moore	20.00
20	Bill Bates	20.00
21	Steve Hendrickson	20.00
22	Eric Allen	25.00
23	Monte Coleman	20.00
24	Mark Collins	20.00
25	Barry Sanders	95.00
26	Erik Williams	20.00
27	Phil Simms	25.00
28	Chris Zorich	20.00
29	Troy Aikman	95.00
30	Charles Haley	20.00
31	Darrell Green	20.00
32	Sean Gilbert	20.00
33	Kevin Gogan	20.00
34	Rodney Hampton	50.00
35	Chris Doleman	20.00
36	Nate Newton	20.00
37	Jackie Slater	20.00
38	Ricky Watters	50.00
39	LeRoy Butler	20.00
40	Gary Clark	20.00
41	Sterling Sharpe	28.00

1994 Action Packed Monday Night Football

Action Packed released a 71-card, silver foil, football set celebrating 25 years of Monday Night Football. This set includes a randomly inserted .999 pure silver foil insert set and 25 certificates for a sterling silver card with Emmitt, Troy Aikman and Michael Irvin. The card fronts feature a tight shot of each player. The back casts the player in moonlight and discusses specific challenges that player faced in the upcoming Monday night match-up. The set primarily consisted of players expected to shine in 1994 Monday Night match-ups. Also, as part of the 25th anniversary promotion, Action Packed included members of the announcing cast, such as Howard Cosell and Meredith.

		MT
Complete Set (71):		25.00
Common Player:		.20
Minor Stars:		.40
Wax Box:		35.00
1	Jeff Hostetler	.20
2	Terry McDaniel	.20
3	Steve Young	2.00
4	Jerry Rice	2.00
5	Donnell Woolford	.20
6	Eric Allen	.20
7	Herschel Walker	.20
8	Barry Sanders	3.00
9	Herman Moore	.75
10	Emmitt Smith	4.00
11	Michael Irvin	1.00
12	John Elway	1.00
13	Jim Kelly	.40
14	Andre Reed	.40
15	Gary Brown	.20
16	Ernest Givins	.20
17	Barry Foster	.20
18	Rod Woodson	.20
19	Warren Moon	.40
20	Cris Carter	.40
21	Rodney Hampton	.40
22	Derrick Thomas	.20
23	Marcus Allen	.40
24	Shannon Sharpe	.20
25	Cody Carlson	.20
26	Haywood Jeffires	.20
27	Randall Cunningham	.20
28	Calvin Williams	.20
29	Brett Favre	2.00
30	Sterling Sharpe	.40
31	Chris Zorich	.20
32	Dante Jones	.20
33	Mike Sherrard	.20
34	Keith Hamilton	.20
35	Charles Haley	.20
36	Thurman Thomas	.40
37	Bruce Smith	.20
38	Greg Lloyd	.20
39	Michael Brooks	.20
40	Jumbo Elliott	.20
41	Ray Childress	.20
42	Bruce Matthews	.20
43	Ricky Watters	.40
44	Brent Jones	.20
45	Morten Andersen	.20
46	Tim Brown	.40
47	Anthony Smith	.20
48	Natrone Means	1.50
49	Junior Seau	.40
50	Joe Montana	2.50
51	Neil Smith	.20
52	Dan Marino	4.00
53	Keith Jackson	.20
54	Troy Aikman	1.50
55	Jay Novacek	.20
56	Rickey Jackson	.20
57	John Taylor	.20
58	Tim McDonald	.20
59	John Randle	.20
60	Henry Thomas	.20
61	Prime Time Players	.20
62	The Don & Howard Show	.20
63	The Entertainers	.20
64	I Never Played the Game	.20
65	Monday Night Madness	.20
66	Whoa Nellie	.20
67	Dandy Don Meredith	.20
68	Speaking of Sports	.20
69	Donning a Dierdorf	.20
70	Half-Time Highlights	.20
71	Return to the Field	.20

1994 Action Packed Monday Night Football Silver

Action Packed randomly inserted a 12-card set into its foil packs, called .999 pure silver foil cards. These are comparable to the 24k gold cards randomly inserted into Action Packed's usual gold foil products.

		MT
Complete Set (12):		650.00
Common Player:		20.00
1	Steve Young	75.00
2	Jerry Rice	75.00
3	Barry Sanders	75.00
4	Emmitt Smith	100.00
5	John Elway	40.00
6	Jim Kelly	30.00
7	Warren Moon	20.00
8	Randall Cunningham	20.00
9	Brett Favre	75.00
10	Dan Marino	100.00
11	Troy Aikman	75.00
12	Speaking of Sports	20.00

1994 Action Packed Badge of Honor Pins

This set consists of 25 pins measuring 1-1/2" x 1".

The front of each pin features a color player portrait with a gold border on a bronze background. The player's last name and Action Packed logo are also on the front. Each box of Action Packed contained three packs of four pins and one of five black pin albums to store five pins. Each pack of pins came in a cardboard holder with the set checklist on the back. A 24K Gold parallel of each pin was created and randomly seeded in packs.

		MT
Complete Set (25):		40.00
Common Pin:		.75
*24K Gold Pins:		10x-20x
1	Troy Aikman	3.00
2	Drew Bledsoe	3.00
3	Bubby Brister	.75
4	Randall Cunningham	1.00
5	John Elway	2.00
6	Boomer Esiason	1.00
7	Jim Everett	.75
8	Brett Favre	6.00
9	Jim Harbaugh	1.50
10	Jeff Hostetler	.75
11	Michael Irvin	1.50
12	Jim Kelly	1.50
13	David Klingler	.75
14	Bernie Kosar	.75
15	Dan Marino	5.00
16	Chris Miller	.75
17	Rick Mirer	.75
18	Warren Moon	1.00
19	Neil O'Donnell	1.00
20	Jerry Rice	3.00
21	Mark Rypien	.75
22	Barry Sanders	4.00
23	Phil Simms	1.00
24	Emmitt Smith	5.00
25	Steve Young	2.00

1994 Action Packed CoaStars

The set of 25 coaster cards were sold in six-pack packs. Each coaster has rounded corners and measures 3-1/4" x 3-1/4". The front of the coaster features the player's name and position, while the back has an action shot with 1993 statistics.

		MT
Complete Set (25):		25.00
Common Player:		.25
1	Troy Aikman	2.50
2	Drew Bledsoe	2.50
3	Bubby Brister	.25
4	Randall Cunningham	.25
5	John Elway	1.25
6	Boomer Esiason	.40
7	Jim Everett	.40
8	Brett Favre	5.00
9	Jim Harbaugh	.50
10	Jeff Hostetler	.40
11	Michael Irvin	.50
12	Jim Kelly	.50
13	David Klingler	.25
14	Bernie Kosar	.40
15	Dan Marino	5.00
16	Rick Mirer	1.00
17	Chris Miller	.40
18	Warren Moon	.50
19	Neil O'Donnell	.50
20	Jerry Rice	2.50
21	Mark Rypien	.40
22	Barry Sanders	2.50
23	Phil Simms	.40
24	Emmitt Smith	5.00
25	Steve Young	1.50

Post-1980 cards in Near Mint condition will generally sell for about 75% of the quoted Mint value. Excellent-condition cards bring no more than 40%.

1994 Action Packed Mammoth

This large set (7-1/2" x 10-1/2") was offered to dealers by Action Packed. Each card has an "MM" prefix on the back and while it is a 25-card set, it's numbered from 1 to 26 as there is no card 25. Series 2 cards of Troy Aikman, Emmitt Smith and Michael Irvin are also included, while three prototypes, including two 24kt gold cards, were randomly inserted. Reportedly, only 25,000 of each base card was produced while less than 2,500 of the Aikman and Smith gold cards were issued.

		MT
Complete Set (25):		120.00
Common Player:		4.00
1	Troy Aikman	10.00
2	Drew Bledsoe	10.00
3	Barry Sanders	10.00
4	Chris Miller	4.00
5	Randall Cunningham	4.00
6	John Elway	6.00
7	Boomer Esiason	4.00
8	Jim Everett	4.00
9	Brett Favre	16.00
10	Jim Harbaugh	4.00
11	Jeff Hostetler	4.00
12	Michael Irvin	4.00
13	Jim Kelly	4.00
14	David Klingler	4.00
15	Bernie Kosar	4.00
16	Dan Marino	16.00
17	Rick Mirer	4.00
18	Warren Moon	4.00
19	Neil O'Donnell	4.00
20	Jerry Rice	10.00
21	Mark Rypien	4.00
22	Phil Simms	4.00
23	Emmitt Smith	16.00
24	Steve Young	6.00
26	Bubby Brister	4.00
2MM1	Troy Aikman (Series 2 card numbered MM1-2)	10.00
2MM2	Michael Irvin (Series 2 card numbered MM2-2)	4.00
2MM6	Emmitt Smith (Series 2 card numbered MM6-2)	16.00
P1	Troy Aikman (Prototype Numbered MMP)	10.00
P2	Emmitt Smith (Prototype 24K Gold Numbered MMP1G reportedly 2500 made)	60.00
P3	Troy Aikman (Prototype 24K Gold Numbered MMP2G reportedly 1000 made)	35.00

1995 Action Packed Promos

The four-card, standard-size set was issued as a preview for the 126-card base set. The set included two regular cards, one Armed Forces insert card and one advertisement card. The card fronts are the same as the base set, but the backs have a "Promo" stamp.

		MT
Complete Set (4):		10.00
Common Player:		.50
1	Jerry Rice	2.50
2	Emmitt Smith	5.00
AF4	Steve Young	1.75
NNO	Action Packed Ad Card (Armed Forces card)	.50

1995 Action Packed

Action Packed Football returned in 1995 under new ownership, Pinnacle, which repeated the existing embossed technology and added its own improvements. The 126-card set captures game action and candid shots with embossed highlights. All 126 cards were also repeated in a metallized silver foil parallel (Quick Silver) set (one per every six packs). The regular cards feature an action shot on the front, with the player's team helmet in the upper right corner. The player's last name is written in gold foil down the side, with Action Packed and 1995 written below the name. The card back is horizontal, with a mug shot, statistics and a brief career summary included. A panel at the bottom includes his name, biographical information and a team logo. The card number is in the upper right corner. Insert sets include Armed Forces, which are also featured on a parallel Braille set, Rocket Men, G-Force and 24k Gold cards.

		MT
Complete Set (126):		25.00
Common Player:		.10
Minor Stars:		.20
Complete Silver Set (126):		300.00
Wax Box:		50.00
1	Jerry Rice	1.50
2	Emmitt Smith	3.00
3	Drew Bledsoe	2.00
4	Ben Coates	.20
5	Jim Everett	.10
6	Warren Moon	.20
7	Herman Moore	.75
8	Deion Sanders	.75
9	Rick Mirer	.20
10	Natrone Means	.50
11	*Jeff Blake*	1.00
12	William Floyd	.20
13	Steve Young	1.00
14	John Elway	.75
15	Brett Favre	3.00
16	Marshall Faulk	.75
17	Heath Shuler	.20
18	Ricky Watters	.50
19	Michael Haynes	.10
20	Troy Aikman	1.25
21	Dan Marino	3.00
22	Bam Morris	.10
23	Marcus Allen	.20
24	Carl Pickens	.20
25	Rodney Hampton	.10
26	Dave Brown	.10
27	Jerome Bettis	.50
28	Jim Kelly	.50
29	Andre Reed	.20
30	Michael Irvin	.50
31	Barry Sanders	3.00
32	Chris Warren	.20
33	Jeff Hostetler	.10
34	Alvin Harper	.10
35	Rob Moore	.20
36	*Steve McNair*	5.00
37	*Rashaan Salaam*	.50
38	*Joey Galloway*	5.00
39	*J.J. Stokes*	2.00
40	*Michael Westbrook*	1.75
41	*Kerry Collins*	2.00
42	*Ki-Jana Carter*	1.00
43	Boomer Esiason	.10
44	Chris Spielman	.10
45	Vinny Testaverde	.10
46	Kevin Williams	.10
47	Ronnie Harmon	.10
48	Fred Barnett	.10
49	Harvey Williams	.10
50	Reggie White	.50
51	Brent Jones	.10
52	Henry Ellard	.10
53	Cris Carter	.50
54	Leroy Hoard	.10
55	Trent Dilfer	.75
56	Desmond Howard	.10
57	Garrison Hearst	.50
58	Lewis Tillman	.10
59	Mark Brunell	1.50
60	Bruce Smith	.20
61	Lake Dawson	.20
62	Bert Emanuel	.20
63	Eric Green	.10
64	Barry Foster	.10
65	Jeff Graham	.10
66	Curtis Conway	.20
67	Herschel Walker	.10
68	Edgar Bennett	.10
69	Mario Bates	.20
70	Irving Fryar	.10
71	Gary Brown	.10
72	Cortez Kennedy	.10
73	John Taylor	.10
74	Jeff George	.50
75	Shannon Sharpe	.50
76	Andre Rison	.50
77	Mike Sherrard	.10
78	Errict Rhett	.20
79	Junior Seau	.50
80	Willie Davis	.10
81	Craig Erickson	.10
82	Torrance Small	.10
83	Randall Cunningham	.50
84	Robert Brooks	.10
85	Terance Mathis	.10
86	Rod Woodson	.20
87	Anthony Miller	.20
88	Stan Humphries	.20
89	Chris Miller	.10
90	Steve Beuerlein	.10
91	Steve Bono	.20
92	Frank Reich	.10
93	Corey Fleming	.10
94	Isaac Bruce	.50
95	Dave Meggett	.10
96	Jackie Harris	.10
97	J.J. Birden	.10
98	Willie Anderson	.10
99	Johnnie Morton	.10
100	Michael Timpson	.10
101	Derek Brown	.10
102	Ricky Ervins	.10
103	*Derrick Alexander*	.20
104	*Dave Barr*	.20
105	*Tony Boselli*	.50
106	*Kyle Brady*	.75
107	*Mark Bruener*	.75
108	*Kevin Carter*	.50
109	Neil O'Donnell	.10
110	*Derrick Alexander*	.20
111	*Charlie Garner*	.20
112	*Darnay Scott*	.20
113	*Scott Mitchell*	.20
114	*Charles Johnson*	.20
115	*Greg Hill*	.20
116	*Ty Law*	.20
117	*Frank Sanders*	1.75
118	*James Stewart Tenn*	2.00
119	*James Stewart Miami*	.50
120	*Kordell Stewart*	6.00
121	*Rob Johnson*	3.00
122	*John Walsh*	.25
123	*Stoney Case*	.50
124	*Tyrone Wheatley*	.50
125	*Sherman Williams*	.50
126	*Ray Zellars*	.50

1995 Action Packed Quick Silver

The 126-card, regular-size set was a parallel release to the 1995 base set, inserted every six packs. The cards have a silver-foil card front while the backs have "Quick Silver" printed.

		MT
Complete Set (126):		450.00
Common Player:		1.50
Quick Silver Cards:		4x-8x

Post-1980 cards in Near Mint condition will generally sell for about 75% of the quoted Mint value. Excellent-condition cards bring no more than 40%.

1995 Action Packed 24K Gold

Twenty-one of the best cards from Action Packed's 1995 regular football set are show-cased in this 24K Gold insert set. Inserts, which have special gold foil stamping, could be found one per every 72 packs. They are numbered using a "G" suffix.

		MT
Complete Set (21):		450.00
Common Player:		7.50
Minor Stars:		15.00
Inserted 1:72		
1	Jerry Rice	30.00
2	Emmitt Smith	45.00
3	Drew Bledsoe	30.00
4	Warren Moon	7.50
5	Deion Sanders	20.00
6	Natrone Means	7.50
7	Steve Young	25.00
8	John Elway	45.00
9	Brett Favre	60.00
10	Marshall Faulk	15.00
11	Heath Shuler	7.50
12	Troy Aikman	30.00
13	Dan Marino	45.00
14	Jerome Bettis	15.00
15	Jim Kelly	15.00
16	Michael Irvin	15.00
17	Barry Sanders	60.00
18	Steve McNair	30.00
19	Rashaan Salaam	15.00
20	Kerry Collins	15.00
21	Ki-Jana Carter	7.50

1995 Action Packed Armed Forces

These 1995 Action Packed inserts feature 12 of the hottest arms in the NFL Quarterback Club. The cards were randomly included one per every 24 packs. The front is a horizontal design which features a full color or raised photo in the center, flanked by the insert set logo and the set logo in the upper corners. The player's name appears in gold below his name, which is adjacent to a team logo in the lower left corner. The card back, numbered using an "AF" prefix, is vertical and includes a close-up shot of the player, plus a brief career summary. A panel along the right side of the card includes an action shot. A paral-lel Braille version set was also created for the Armed Forces set (1 in 96 packs).

		MT
Complete Set (12):		100.00
Common Player:		5.00
Complete Braille Set (12):		150.00
Braille Cards:		1x-2x
1	Drew Bledsoe	10.00
2	Dan Marino	20.00
3	Troy Aikman	10.00
4	Steve Young	10.00

5	Brett Favre	20.00
6	Heath Shuler	5.00
7	Dave Brown	5.00
8	Jeff Blake	7.00
9	John Elway	8.00
10	Rick Mirer	5.00
11	Kerry Collins	10.00
12	Steve McNair	10.00

1995 Action Packed G-Force

Some of the NFL's best run-ning backs are featured on these 1995 Action Packed inserts. The 12 cards, random inserts one per every 24 packs, have a hori-zontal front format. The card front has two photos on it; one is an action shot, the other is a close-up profile. The player's name, in gold foil, and the in-sert set logo are on the left side of the card. The back, numbered with a "GF" prefix, contains a color photo and recap of the player's accomplishments in 1994. A panel on the left side has the in-sert set logo at the top, with the player's name and his yards per carry average underneath.

		MT
Complete Set (12):		75.00
Common Player:		5.00
1	Emmitt Smith	20.00
2	Barry Sanders	10.00
3	Marshall Faulk	5.00
4	Natrone Means	5.00
5	Chris Warren	5.00
6	Jerome Bettis	5.00
7	Errict Rhett	5.00
8	Bam Morris	5.00
9	Ki-Jana Carter	5.00
10	Mario Bates	5.00
11	Ricky Watters	5.00
12	Tyrone Wheatley	5.00

1995 Action Packed Rocket Men

These horizontally-de-signed inserts feature 18 of the NFL's top stars. Cards were ran-dom inserts in 1995 Action Packed football, one every 12 jumbo packs. The card front has a color embossed photo with a swirled background. "Rocket Man" is written along the left side of the card, with the player's name and team logo along the bottom, below the photo. The vertical back, numbered using an "RM" prefix, has a panel on the right which includes the play-er's name, team logo, card num-ber and "Rocket Man." An action photo and a closeup photo are also included on the back, which includes a quote from another player about the "Rocket Man."

		MT
Complete Set (18):		175.00
Common Player:		5.00
1	Marshall Faulk	5.00
2	Emmitt Smith	20.00
3	Barry Sanders	12.00
4	Natrone Means	5.00
5	Errict Rhett	5.00
6	Ki-Jana Carter	5.00
7	Tyrone Wheatley	5.00
8	Drew Bledsoe	10.00
9	Dan Marino	20.00
10	Steve Young	10.00
11	Troy Aikman	10.00
12	Brett Favre	20.00
13	Kerry Collins	10.00
14	Steve McNair	10.00
15	Heath Shuler	5.00
16	Jerry Rice	10.00
17	Michael Irvin	5.00
18	Herman Moore	5.00

1995 Action Packed Monday Night Football Promos

The four-card, standard-size set was issued as a preview to the 126-card Monday Night Football set. The set includes two base is-sues, one Night Flights insert card and one advertisement card. The card fronts are identical to the base set, but the backs have "Pro-mo" printed.

		MT
Complete Set (4):		10.00
Common Player:		.50
1	Steve Young	2.00
3A	Troy Aikman	4.00
3B	Drew Bledsoe	4.00
NNO	NMFB Ad Card (Night Flights card)	.50

1995 Action Packed Monday Night Football

Action Packed's 1995 Monday Night Football set con-tains 26 cards, plus a parallel Highlights set which uses a prismatic foil background. These cards, found one per ev-ery six packs, have "High-lights" written in gold foil on the card back. The regular cards feature a full-bleed photo with a raised image of the play-er. A gold band runs across the top of the card; it includes the player's last name in black, alongside a gold team logo. The Monday Night Football icon appears in the lower right corner. The horizontal card back has a mug shot, statistics, biographical information and a brief player profile. A black band with the various sponsor logos runs across the bottom

of the card. Insert sets include Night Flights, 24KT Team and Reverse Angle.

		MT
Complete Set (126):		25.00
Common Player:		.10
Minor Stars:		.20
Wax Box:		50.00
1	Jerry Rice	1.00
2	Barry Sanders	2.00
3	Troy Aikman	1.00
4	Jerome Bettis	.40
5	Tim Brown	.20
6	Marcus Allen	.20
7	Jeff Blake	2.00
8	Rodney Hampton	.20
9	Reggie White	.20
10	Warren Moon	.20
11	William Floyd	.40
12	Cris Carter	.20
13	Stan Humphries	.20
14	Herschel Walker	.10
15	Dave Brown	.10
16	Jim Everett	.10
17	Mario Bates	.40
18	Terance Mathis	.10
19	Chris Spielman	.10
20	Neil O'Donnell	.20
21	Anthony Miller	.10
22	Steve Bono	.30
23	Henry Ellard	.10
24	Dave Meggett	.10
25	Flipper Anderson	.10
26	Rocket Ismail	.10
27	Leroy Hoard	.10
28	Steve Young	1.00
29	Marshall Faulk	2.00
30	Dan Marino	2.50
31	Errict Rhett	1.50
32	Michael Irvin	.20
33	Bam Morris	.20
34	Heath Shuler	1.00
35	Jim Kelly	.20
36	Deion Sanders	.50
37	Jeff Hostetler	.20
38	Jeff George	.20
39	Alvin Harper	.10
40	Barry Foster	.10
41	Craig Erickson	.10
42	Vinny Testaverde	.10
43	Andre Reed	.10
44	Eric Green	.10
45	Bruce Smith	.10
46	Frank Reich	.10
47	Shannon Sharpe	.10
48	Chris Miller	.10
49	Darnay Scott	.50
50	Eric Metcalf	.10
51	Mike Sherrard	.10
52	Lorenzo White	.10
53	Scott Mitchell	.20
54	Jay Novacek	.10
55	Emmitt Smith	2.50
56	Drew Bledsoe	1.00
57	Natrone Means	.75
58	John Elway	.50
59	Herman Moore	.30
60	Brett Favre	1.00
61	Ricky Watters	.20
62	Andre Rison	.10
63	Junior Seau	.20
64	Randall Cunningham	.10
65	Chris Warren	.20
66	Garrison Hearst	.10
67	Ben Coates	.10
68	Rick Mirer	.40
69	Johnny Mitchell	.10
70	Trent Dilfer	.40
71	Carl Pickens	.25
72	Craig Heyward	.10
73	Greg Lloyd	.10
74	Boomer Esiason	.10
75	Greg Hill	.30
76	Lewis Tillman	.10
77	Willie Davis	.10
78	Brent Jones	.10
79	Michael Haynes	.10
80	Darryl Johnston	.10
81	Steve Beuerlein	.10
82	Ki-Jana Carter (The Night is Young)	.75
83	Steve McNair (The Night is Young)	4.00
84	Michael Westbrook (The Night is Young)	2.50
85	Kerry Collins (The Night is Young)	4.00
86	Joey Galloway (The Night is Young)	4.00
87	Kyle Brady (The Night is Young)	.40
88	J.J. Stokes (The Night is Young)	3.00
89	Tyrone Wheatley (The Night is Young)	.75
90	Rashaan Salaam (The Night is Young)	3.00
91	Napoleon Kaufman (The Night is Young)	1.50
92	Frank Sanders (The Night is Young)	1.25

93	Stoney Case (The Night is Young)	.50
94	Todd Collins (The Night is Young)	.50
95	James Stewart (The Night is Young)	1.50
96	Kordell Stewart (The Night is Young)	3.00
97	Joe Aska (The Night is Young)	.20
98	Terrell Fletcher (The Night is Young)	.20
99	Rob Johnson (The Night is Young)	1.50
100	Steve Young (Monday Night Classics)	.50
101	Jerry Rice (Monday Night Classics)	.50
102	Emmitt Smith (Monday Night Classics)	1.00
103	Barry Sanders (Monday Night Classics)	1.00
104	Marshall Faulk (Monday Night Classics)	.50
105	Drew Bledsoe (Monday Night Classics)	.50
106	Dan Marino (Monday Night Classics)	1.00
107	Troy Aikman (Monday Night Classics)	.40
108	John Elway (Monday Night Classics)	.30
109	Brett Favre (Monday Night Classics)	.50
110	Michael Irvin (Monday Night Classics)	.20
111	Heath Shuler (Monday Night Classics)	.40
112	Warren Moon (Monday Night Classics)	.20
113	Chris Warren (Monday Night Classics)	.20
114	Natrone Means (Monday Night Classics)	.30
115	Errict Rhett (Monday Night Classics)	.75
116	Bam Morris (Monday Night Classics)	.20
117	Randall Cunningham (Monday Night Classics)	.20
118	Jim Kelly (Monday Night Classics)	.20
119	Jeff Hostetler (Monday Night Classics)	.10
120	Barry Foster (Monday Night Classics)	.10
121	Jim Everett (Monday Night Classics)	.10
122	Neil O'Donnell (Monday Night Classics)	.10
123	Jerome Bettis (Monday Night Classics)	.20
124	Ricky Watters (Monday Night Classics)	.20
125	Joe Montana (Monday Night Classics)	.75
126	Howard Cosell (Monday Night Classics)	.20

Values quoted in this guide reflect the retail price of a card — the price a collector can expect to pay when buying a card from a dealer. The wholesale price — that which a collector can expect to receive from a dealer when selling cards — will be significantly lower, depending on desirability and condition.

1995 Action Packed Monday Night Football Highlights

The 126-card, regular-size set was parallel to the 1995 base set and were inserted ev-ery six packs. The card fronts feature a silver foil background.

	MT
Complete Set (126):	275.00
Common Player:	1.00
Highlight Cards:	5x-10x

1995 Action Packed Monday Night Football 24KT Gold Team

These inserts provide a golden rendition of 12 regular is-sue cards with micro-etched highlights on rainbow holo-graphic foil with an exclusive gold logo that includes genuine gold leafing. The cards, randomly included in every 72 packs of 1995 Action Packed Monday Night Football, features members of the 24KT Team. Fewer than 2,000 sets were made. The card front is horizontal and includes a smaller photo in the forefront, with a larger image of the same photo in the background. The card back, numbered 1 of 12, etc., has a player photo and brief recap of a game in which the player had a key role. A vertical format is used for the back, which has the appropriate logos in a panel on the right.

		MT
Complete Set (12):		400.00
Common Player:		20.00
1	Emmitt Smith	50.00
2	Barry Sanders	70.00
3	Marshall Faulk	40.00
4	Dan Marino	60.00
5	Steve Young	40.00
6	Drew Bledsoe	40.00
7	Troy Aikman	35.00
8	John Elway	50.00
9	Brett Favre	70.00
10	Ki-Jana Carter	20.00
11	Steve McNair	30.00
12	Kerry Collins	35.00

Post-1980 cards in Near Mint condition will generally sell for about 75% of the quoted Mint value. Excellent-condition cards bring no more than 40%.

1995 Action Packed Monday Night Football Night Flights

These 1995 Action Packed Monday Night Football inserts feature 12 members of the Quarterback Club on Dufex cards of textured gold foil. Each card front has a colored raised image, with the player's last name running in a gold strip along the left side of the card, which has the MNF logo at its bottom. The Night Flight logo is at the bottom of the card. The back is horizontal, with a mug shot, card number (1 of 12, etc.), and 1994 season recap.

		MT
Complete Set (12):		80.00
Common Player:		5.00
1	Steve Young	10.00
2	Dan Marino	17.00
3	Drew Bledsoe	10.00
4	Troy Aikman	10.00
5	John Elway	8.00
6	Brett Favre	10.00
7	Heath Shuler	8.00
8	Dave Brown	5.00
9	Steve McNair	10.00
10	Kerry Collins	12.00
11	Warren Moon	5.00
12	Jeff Hostetler	5.00

1995 Action Packed Monday Night Football Reverse Angle

These 18 insert cards could be found one per every 24 hobby packs of 1995 Action Packed Monday Night Football. They feature 18 NFL stars. Fewer than 1,500 sets of Reverse Angle inserts were made. The front has a raised color image, along with the set, insert set and MNF logos, against a metallic background. The player's name runs along the left side of the card. The back has a black panel along the left side, which also has his name and card number (1 of 18, etc.). A photo and brief player profile are also included on the back. Cards were random inserts, one per every 24 hobby packs.

		MT
Complete Set (18):		50.00
Common Player:		3.00
1	Emmitt Smith	12.00
2	Barry Sanders	8.00
3	Steve Young	7.00
4	Marshall Faulk	10.00
5	Randall Cunningham	3.00
6	Deion Sanders	5.00
7	John Elway	5.00

8	Brett Favre	7.00
9	William Floyd	5.00
10	Ricky Watters	3.00
11	Ben Coates	3.00
12	Rod Woodson	3.00
13	Marcus Allen	3.00
14	Eric Metcalf	3.00
15	Keith Byars	3.00
16	Jerry Rice	7.00
17	Alvin Harper	3.00
18	Eric Green	3.00

1995 Action Packed Rookies/Stars

Action Packed's 1995 Rookies and Stars set features the NFL's top rookie draft choices, along with a parallel foiled Stargazers set (one card per six packs). The regular cards have a raised full-bleed color photo on the front, with the set name in the upper left corner and the player's team logo in the bottom left corner. The player's name is stamped in gold foil at the bottom. The horizontal back has a photo on two thirds of the card, with a player profile paragraph next to it. A black band at the bottom of the card contains the player's 1994 and career statistics. Insert sets include 24K Gold Team, Bustout, Closing Seconds and Instant Impressions.

		MT
Complete Set (105):		25.00
Common Player:		.10
Minor Stars:		.20
Inserted 1:6		
Wax Box:		65.00
1	Steve Young	1.00
2	Steve Bono	.30
3	Natrone Means	.50
4	Steve Beuerlein	.10
5	Neil O'Donnell	.10
6	Marshall Faulk	1.00
7	Ricky Watters	.20
8	Gary Brown	.10
9	Jeff Hostetler	.10
10	Robert Brooks	.25
11	Johnny Mitchell	.10
12	Barry Sanders	2.00
13	Dave Brown	.10
14	John Elway	2.00
15	Garrison Hearst	.10
16	Jim Everett	.10
17	Michael Irvin	.20
18	Dan Marino	2.50
19	Jeff George	.20
20	Ben Coates	.10
21	Charles Johnson	.30
22	Carl Pickens	.25
23	Deion Sanders	.75
24	Errict Rhett	.75
25	Steve Walsh	.10
26	Bruce Smith	.10
27	Andre Rison	.20
28	Warren Moon	.10
29	Terry Allen	.10
30	Desmond Howard	.10
31	Shannon Sharpe	.10
32	Dave Krieg	.10
33	Bam Morris	.20
34	Rodney Hampton	.10
35	Scott Mitchell	.20
36	Alvin Harper	.10
37	Robert Smith	.10
38	Troy Aikman	1.00
39	William Floyd	.40
40	Randall Cunningham	.10
41	Mario Bates	.30
42	Reggie White	.20
43	Chris Chandler	.10
44	Erik Kramer	.10
45	Emmitt Smith	2.50
46	Irving Fryar	.10
47	Jeff Blake	.50
48	Drew Bledsoe	1.50
49	Anthony Miller	.10
50	Marcus Allen	.20
51	Leroy Hoard	.10
52	Stan Humphries	.20
53	Eric Green	.10

54	Herschel Walker	.10
55	Junior Seau	.20
56	Terance Mathis	.10
57	Boomer Esiason	.10
58	Lorenzo White	.10
59	Tim Brown	.20
60	Brett Favre	3.00
61	Craig Erickson	.10
62	Rod Woodson	.10
63	Frank Reich	.10
64	Cris Carter	.20
65	Jerry Rice	1.00
66	Greg Hill	.30
67	Andre Reed	.10
68	Trent Dilfer	.40
69	Eric Metcalf	.10
70	Jim Kelly	.20
71	Herman Moore	.50
72	Vinny Testaverde	.10
73	Jeff Graham	.10
74	Edgar Bennett	.10
75	Jerome Bettis	.30
76	Heath Shuler	.75
77	Chris Warren	.20
78	Reggie Brooks	.10
79	Rick Mirer	.40
80	Chris Miller	.10
81	*Napoleon Kaufman*	3.00
82	*Christian Fauria*	.20
83	*Todd Collins*	.20
84	*J.J. Stokes*	1.00
85	*Mark Bruener*	.40
86	*Frank Sanders*	1.00
87	*Chad May*	.20
88	*Kordell Stewart*	4.00
89	*Ki-Jana Carter*	.50
90	*Curtis Martin*	3.00
91	*Sherman Williams*	.20
92	*Terrell Davis*	12.00
93	*Chris Sanders*	.50
94	*Kyle Brady*	.40
95	*Tyrone Wheatley*	.50
96	*Rodney Thomas*	.50
97	*James Stewart*	1.50
98	*Kerry Collins*	1.00
99	*Rashaan Salaam*	.75
100	*Stoney Case*	.20
101	*Steve McNair*	3.00
102	*Joey Galloway*	3.00
103	*Michael Westbrook*	1.00
104	*Eric Zeier*	.75
105	*Ray Zellars*	.50

1995 Action Packed Rookies & Stars Stargazers

The 105-card, regular-size set was issued as a parallel release to the 1995 Rookies/Stars base set, inserted every six packs. The background of the card fronts contain silver while the backs each have a "Stargazers" stamp.

		MT
Complete Set (105):		475.00
Common Player:		.75
Stargazers:		6x-12x

1995 Action Packed Rookies/Stars 24K Gold

These 14 cards were the most exclusive of the 1995 Action Packed Rookies & Stars inserts, available at one per every 72 packs. Each card front has a raised color image on it, with part of it against a black background, and most of it against a gold foil panel along the right side of the card. "24 KT Gold Team" is inside the gold panel. The set logo is in the gold in the bottom right corner, opposite the player's name. The horizontal card back has mostly a black background which contains a mug shot and brief summary of the player's accomplishments. A jagged gold panel at the top of the card contains the words "24 KT Gold Team." A card number is in the lower right corner.

		MT
Complete Set (14):		575.00
Common Player:		10.00
Minor Stars:		20.00
Inserted 1:72		
1	Steve Young	30.00
2	Brett Favre	80.00
3	Rashaan Salaam	20.00
4	Tyrone Wheatley	10.00
5	Marshall Faulk	20.00
6	Rick Mirer	10.00
7	Troy Aikman	40.00
8	John Elway	60.00
9	Dan Marino	60.00
10	Barry Sanders	80.00
11	Jerry Rice	40.00
12	Emmitt Smith	60.00
13	Michael Irvin	20.00
14	Drew Bledsoe	40.00

1995 Action Packed Rookies/Stars Bustout

These insert cards were available in 12-card jumbo packs of 1995 Action Packed Rookies and Stars. The 12 cards, numbered on the back, feature top NFL running backs. The card front has a raised color photo against a metallic background. The player's name and the set logo are on the left side of the card. The player's name, card number and a team helmet are in a black strip along the left side of the card back; a photo is on the opposite side, along with an example of when the player "busted out" and had a big game.

		MT
Complete Set (12):		45.00
Common Player:		2.00
Minor Stars:		4.00
Inserted 1:12		
1	Marshall Faulk	5.00
2	Barry Sanders	20.00
3	Emmitt Smith	15.00
4	Natrone Means	4.00
5	Errict Rhett	2.00
6	Bam Morris	2.00
7	Terry Allen	4.00
8	Rodney Hampton	2.00
9	Ricky Watters	4.00
10	Chris Warren	2.00
11	Jerome Bettis	4.00
12	Gary Brown	2.00

> Post-1980 cards in Near Mint condition will generally sell for about 75% of the quoted Mint value. Excellent-condition cards bring no more than 40%.

1995 Action Packed Rookies/Stars Closing Seconds

These 12 1995 Action Packed Rookies & Stars inserts feature players who pulled out victories for their teams in the final seconds. A raised color photo is on the front, with a ghosted, rainbow holographic-foiled larger image of the same photo as a background. "Closing Seconds" is written in gold foil. The player's name and set name are in the top corners. The card back has a black panel along the left side which contains a number and accounts of the game he helped win in the final seconds. A photo also appears on the back. Cards were exlusive to hobby packs, one per every 36 packs.

		MT
Complete Set (12):		125.00
Common Player:		3.00
Minor Stars:		6.00
Inserted 1:36 Hobby		
1	Dan Marino	18.00
2	Steve Young	10.00
3	Jerry Rice	12.00
4	Emmitt Smith	18.00
5	Barry Sanders	25.00
6	Brett Favre	25.00
7	Drew Bledsoe	12.00
8	Troy Aikman	12.00
9	John Elway	18.00
10	Dave Brown	3.00
11	Warren Moon	6.00
12	Jim Kelly	6.00

1995 Action Packed Rookies/Stars Instant Impressions

These 1995 Action Packed Rookies & Stars inserts have 12 rookies highlighted on Dufex cards. The front has a raised color image against a strobelight-like background. The set and insert set logos are in the upper corners; the player's name is at the bottom in gold foil. The back has a colored panel on the left side which contains the player's name, position and card number. A smaller horizontal picture is on the right side, with a brief player profile sandwiched between it and the colored panel. Cards were available one per every 24 packs.

		MT
Complete Set (12):		75.00
Common Player:		1.25
Minor Stars:		2.50
Inserted 1:24		
1	Ki-Jana Carter	2.50
2	Steve McNair	12.00

3	Kerry Collins	5.00
4	Michael Westbrook	4.00
5	Joey Galloway	10.00
6	J.J. Stokes	5.00
7	Rashaan Salaam	2.50
8	Tyrone Wheatley	1.25
9	Eric Zeier	4.00
10	Curtis Martin	12.00
11	Napoleon Kaufman	12.00
12	Kyle Brady	1.25

1996 Action Packed Promos

The four-card, regular-size set was released as a preview for the 1996 base set and includes three regular cards and one Studs card. The card fronts are identical to the regular issue cards, but "Promo" is printed on the back.

		MT
Complete Set (4):		12.00
Common Player:		1.00
1	Emmitt Smith	4.50
3	Jerry Rice (Studs Card)	6.00
16	Steve Young	2.00
105	Neil O'Donnell	1.00

1996 Action Packed

Action Packed's 1996 football set has 126 regular cards, plus a parallel Artist's Proofs set (one in 24 packs). Each card front has a set logo in the upper left corner, with the player's name, in a black bar, and his team logo stamped in gold foil at the bottom. The full-bleed color action photo on the front uses the company's raised photo format. The card back has a closeup photo of the player on the left, with his name and position below, followed by biographical information and statistics. A colored panel along the right side has a brief player profile. The card number is in the upper left corner. Insert sets include 24k Team, Studs, Sculptor's Proofs, Ball Hog and the Longest Yard.

		MT
Complete Set (126):		35.00
Common Player:		.20
Minor Stars:		.40
Wax Box:		70.00
1	Emmitt Smith	3.00
2	Dan Marino	3.00
3	Isaac Bruce	.40
4	Eric Zeier	.20
5	Ben Coates	.20
6	Jim Kelly	.20
7	Rodney Hampton	.20
8	Greg Lloyd	.20
9	Reggie White	.20
10	Derrick Thomas	.20
11	Jerry Rice	1.50
12	Drew Bledsoe	1.50
13	Cris Carter	.20
14	Troy Aikman	1.50
15	Steve McNair	1.50
16	Steve Young	1.50

17	Ricky Watters	.20
18	Brett Favre	3.00
19	Michael Westbrook	.40
20	Charles Haley	.20
21	Heath Shuler	.40
22	Tim Brown	.20
23	Kerry Collins	2.00
24	Hugh Douglas	.20
25	Marcus Allen	.40
26	Steve Bono	.20
27	Curtis Martin	3.00
28	Wayne Chrebet	.20
29	Dave Brown	.20
30	James Stewart	.20
31	Chris Sanders	.20
32	Deion Sanders	1.00
33	Rodney Thomas	.40
34	Rashaan Salaam	.40
35	Curtis Conway	.20
36	Harvey Williams	.20
37	William Floyd	.20
38	Carl Pickens	.40
39	Herman Moore	.40
40	Stan Humphries	.20
41	Orlanda Thomas	.20
42	Bert Emanuel	.20
43	Yancey Thigpen	1.00
44	Darick Holmes	.40
45	Mario Bates	.20
46	Greg Hill	.20
47	Errict Rhett	.40
48	Erik Kramer	.20
49	Garrison Hearst	.40
50	Jim Everett	.20
51	Barry Sanders	2.50
52	Eric Metcalf	.20
53	Marshall Faulk	1.50
54	Junior Seau	.20
55	Bruce Smith	.20
56	Kordell Stewart	2.00
57	Edgar Bennett	.20
58	Joey Galloway	1.50
59	Jeff Hostetler	.20
60	Frank Sanders	.40
61	John Elway	.75
62	Tyrone Wheatley	.20
63	Jeff George	.20
64	Ken Norton Jr.	.20
65	Bryan Cox	.20
66	Bryce Paup	.20
67	Larry Centers	.20
68	Bernie Parmalee	.20
69	Jeff Graham	.20
70	Rick Mirer	.20
71	Chris Warren	.40
72	Charlie Garner	.20
73	Robert Brooks	.20
74	Jim Harbaugh	.20
75	Tamarick Vanover	.40
76	Napoleon Kaufman	.40
77	Warren Moon	.20
78	Vincent Brisby	.20
79	Ki-Jana Carter	.40
80	Michael Irvin	.40
81	Trent Dilfer	.20
82	Bam Morris	.20
83	Mark Brunell	1.50
84	Jeff Blake	1.00
85	Kevin Williams	.20
86	Rod Woodson	.20
87	Andre Reed	.20
88	Erric Pegram	.20
89	Anthony Miller	.20
90	Gus Frerotte	.20
91	Quinn Early	.20
92	Daryl Johnston	.20
93	Tony Martin	.20
94	Terrell Davis	6.00
95	Brent Jones	.20
96	Mark Chmura	.40
97	Kyle Brady	.20
98	J.J. Stokes	.40
99	Rodney Peete	.20
100	Natrone Means	.40
101	Sherman Williams	.20
102	Brian Blades	.20
103	Brett Perriman	.20
104	Antonio Freeman	.20
105	Neil O'Donnell	.20
106	Craig Heyward	.20
107	Derek Loville	.20
108	Jay Novacek	.20
109	Scott Mitchell	.20
110	Bill Brooks	.20
111	Shannon Sharpe	.20
112	Jake Reed	.20
113	Derrick Moore	.20
114	Steve Atwater	.20
115	Darren Woodson	.20
116	Junior Seau	.20
117	Quentin Coryatt	.20
118	Bruce Smith	.20
119	Rod Woodson	.20
120	Charles Haley	.20
121	Derrick Thomas	.20
122	Ken Norton	.20
123	Steve Atwater	.20
124	Greg Lloyd	.20
125	Reggie White	.20
126	Bryan Cox	.20

1996 Action Packed Artist's Proof

The 126-card, regular-size set was issued as a parallel re-lease to the 1996 base set. The cards were inserted every 24 hobby and retail packs and every 30 magazine packs. The cards have "Artist's Proof" printed on the fronts.

	MT
Complete Set (126):	1200.
Common Player:	5.00
Artist's Proof Cards:	15x-30x

1996 Action Packed 24kt Gold

These insert cards feature the standard raised photo on the front, against a "Prime Frost" background with 24kt gold foil stamping used for the 24kt gold logo. The card back has the number at the top of a panel along the left side of the card. The player's name and po-sition are also in the panel. The right side of the card has a mug shot at the top, along with an action photo. A recap of a mem-orable game from the previous season is underneath, along with the player's team name. Cards were seeded one per ev-ery 72 packs of 1996 Action Packed football.

		MT
Complete Set (14):		500.00
Common Player:		15.00
1	Brett Favre	80.00
2	Michael Irvin	15.00
3	Drew Bledsoe	45.00
4	Jerry Rice	45.00
5	Troy Aikman	45.00
6	Dan Marino	80.00
7	Errict Rhett	15.00
8	Curtis Martin	65.00
9	Steve Young	45.00
10	Barry Sanders	50.00
11	Marshall Faulk	30.00
12	Isaac Bruce	30.00
13	John Elway	30.00
14	Emmitt Smith	80.00

1996 Action Packed Ball Hog

This 12-card 1996 Action Packed insert set highlights play-ers who always seem to have the ball in their hands. The cards, seeded one per every 23 packs, use an embossed leather-looking print technology. The card front has a raised action photo against a football background. "Ball Hog" is written along the right side. The brand logo is stamped in gold in the upper left corner; the player's name and his team's name are stamped in gold in the bottom left corner. The back has the player's name written in a panel along the

---

lease to the 1996 base set. The cards were inserted every 24 hobby and retail packs and every 30 magazine packs. The cards have "Artist's Proof" printed on the fronts.

	MT
Complete Set (126):	1200.
Common Player:	5.00
Artist's Proof Cards:	15x-30x

1996 Action Packed 24kt Gold

These insert cards feature the standard raised photo on the front, against a "Prime Frost" background with 24kt gold foil stamping used for the 24kt gold logo. The card back has the number at the top of a panel along the left side of the card. The player's name and po-sition are also in the panel. The right side of the card has a mug shot at the top, along with an action photo. A recap of a mem-orable game from the previous season is underneath, along with the player's team name. Cards were seeded one per ev-ery 72 packs of 1996 Action Packed football.

1996 Action Packed Jumbo Inserts

These cards were inserted one per retail box as a boxtop-per insert. They are a parallel of each player's base set card ex-cept they are oversized and numbered differently.

		MT
Complete Set (4):		20.00
Common Player:		4.00
1	Emmitt Smith	6.00
2	Drew Bledsoe	4.00
3	Troy Aikman	4.00
4	Brett Favre	8.00

1996 Action Packed Longest Yard

The 12-card, regular-sized set was inserted every 24 maga-zine packs of 1996 Action Packed.

		MT
Complete Set (12):		180.00
Common Player:		5.00
1	Brett Favre	35.00
2	Tamarick Vanover	5.00
3	Joey Galloway	12.00
4	Kerry Collins	20.00
5	Jeff Blake	10.00
6	Jerry Rice	20.00
7	Barry Sanders	30.00
8	Rodney Thomas	5.00
9	Herman Moore	7.00
10	Emmitt Smith	35.00
11	Terrell Davis	20.00
12	Cris Carter	7.00

1996 Action Packed Sculptor's Proof

Sculptor's Proofs inserts are pewter metal-card rendi-tions of 14 players' regular is-sue cards, except the card numbers on the back corre-spond to the checklist. These cards were available to con-sumers through a randomly-in-serted redemption card found one per every 192 packs.

		MT
Complete Set (14):		1000.
Common Player:		30.00
1	Dan Marino	150.00
2	Deion Sanders	50.00
3	Joey Galloway	50.00
4	Brett Favre	150.00
5	Barry Sanders	80.00
6	Michael Irvin	30.00
7	Drew Bledsoe	75.00
8	Emmitt Smith	150.00
9	Curtis Martin	100.00
10	Steve Young	50.00
11	John Elway	50.00
12	Jerry Rice	75.00
13	Errict Rhett	40.00
14	Troy Aikman	75.00

1996 Action Packed Studs

These 1996 Action Packed insert cards feature six NFL stars and their diamond stud earrings. Studs cards contain a genuine diamond chip and are found one per every 161 packs. There were 1,500 sets pro-duced. Each card front, in a hor-izontal format, has the set name in the upper right corner in gold foil; the player's name and "Studs" are in gold along the

---

top, with a brief player profile and a player mug shot below.

		MT
Complete Set (12):		100.00
Common Player:		4.00
1	Carl Pickens	4.00
2	Terrell Davis	14.00
3	Jerry Rice	12.00
4	Barry Sanders	12.00
5	Marshall Faulk	6.00
6	Isaac Bruce	6.00
7	Michael Irvin	4.00
8	Cris Carter	4.00
9	Rashaan Salaam	6.00
10	Herman Moore	4.00
11	Chris Warren	4.00
12	Emmitt Smith	25.00

1997 Action Packed Promos

This three-card set was is-sued to promote sales of 1997 Action Packed. It included two base cards and one Studs in-sert. All three cards contained the words "Promo" in a black box across the back.

		MT
Complete Set (3):		5.00
Common Player:		.50
28	Kordell Stewart	1.50
45	Jim Harbaugh	.50
4 of 9	Jerry Rice (Studs)	4.00

1997 Action Packed

The 125-card set features a brown football pebble grain at the bottom of the card front. The player's photo is printed at the top, with the player em-bossed below. The Pinnacle Action Packed logo is at the bottom center, with the player's name printed directly below. The card backs have a player photo with a ghosted photo in the back-ground. The player's bio is list-ed along the upper right border. The player's name, position and stats are printed at the bottom left. The First Impressions sil-ver-foil parallel of the base set was inserted 1:15 packs, while the Gold Impressions parallel set, which includes gold foil, was seeded 1:44 packs. A 15-card Down "N" Dirty subset was included as part of the base set.

		MT
Complete Set (125):		40.00
Common Player:		.10
Minor Stars:		.20
Wax Box:		60.00
1	Jerry Rice	2.00
2	Troy Aikman	2.00
3	Ricky Watters	.20
4	Dan Marino	4.00
5	Emmitt Smith	4.00

---

bottom. The card back is also horizontal. An action photo of the player is on the right, with his name, position, team logo and card number in a panel above. The left side of the card has a recap of a memorable game in the player's career, plus his team name in a black strip.

		MT
Complete Set (6):		325.00
Common Player:		20.00
1	Emmitt Smith	150.00
2	Deion Sanders	60.00
3	Jerry Rice	75.00
4	Michael Irvin	20.00
5	Kordell Stewart	75.00
6	Ricky Watters	20.00

6	Warren Moon	.20
7	Rashaan Salaam	.50
8	Drew Bledsoe	2.00
9	Eddie George	2.00
10	John Elway	1.25
11	Robert Brooks	.10
12	Scott Mitchell	.10
13	Isaac Bruce	.50
14	Marshall Faulk	.75
15	Steve Bono	.10
16	Barry Sanders	3.00
17	Brett Favre	4.00
18	Curtis Martin	3.00
19	Keyshawn Johnson	.75
20	Dave Brown	.10
21	Frank Sanders	.10
22	Gus Frerotte	.10
23	Eric Metcalf	.10
24	Thurman Thomas	.20
25	Steve Young	1.25
26	Alvin Harper	.10
27	Mark Brunell	2.00
28	Kordell Stewart	2.00
29	Terry Glenn	.30
30	Junior Seau	.20
31	Karim Abdul-Jabbar	.30
32	Jeff Hostetler	.10
33	Rodney Hampton	.10
34	Irving Fryar	.10
35	Cris Carter	.10
36	James Stewart	.10
37	Marcus Allen	.20
38	Napoleon Kaufman	.20
39	Shannon Sharpe	.10
40	LeShon Johnson	.10
41	Tony Banks	.50
42	Lawrence Phillips	.20
43	Kerry Collins	.30
44	Curtis Conway	.10
45	Jim Harbaugh	.10
46	Garrison Hearst	.10
47	Trent Dilfer	.20
48	Terance Mathis	.10
49	Jerome Bettis	.30
50	Chris Sanders	.10
51	Deion Sanders	1.00
52	Herman Moore	.30
53	Elvis Grbac	.10
54	O.J. McDuffie	.10
55	Ben Coates	.10
56	Jim Kelly	.20
57	J.J. Stokes	.10
58	Terrell Davis	3.00
59	Stan Humphries	.10
60	Carl Pickens	.20
61	Neil O'Donnell	.10
62	Edgar Bennett	.10
63	Yancey Thigpen	.10
64	Bert Emanuel	.10
65	Amani Toomer	.10
66	Jeff Blake	.20
67	Eddie Kennison	.75
68	Jason Dunn	.10
69	Rob Moore	.10
70	Andre Rison	.10
71	Vinny Testaverde	.10
72	Henry Ellard	.10
73	Dale Carter	.10
74	Tony Martin	.10
75	Jim Everett	.10
76	Joey Galloway	.50
77	Mike Alstott	.20
78	Kevin Hardy	.10
79	Jake Reed	.10
80	Tim Brown	.20
81	Sean Dawkins	.10
82	Bobby Engram	.10
83	Michael Irvin	.20
84	Rickey Dudley	.20
85	Chris Chandler	.10
86	Keith Jackson	.10
87	Muhsin Muhammad	.20
88	Tamarick Vanover	.10
89	Chris Warren	.10
90	Johnnie Morton	.10
91	Terry Allen	.10
92	Stanley Pritchett	.10
93	Charles Johnson	.10
94	Chris T. Jones	.10
95	Winslow Oliver	.10
96	Anthony Miller	.10
97	Tyrone Wheatley	.10
98	Robert Smith	.10
99	Eric Moulds	.10
100	Hardy Nickerson	.10
101	Derrick Alexander	.10
102	Michael Haynes	.10
103	Jamal Anderson	.20
104	Marvin Harrison	.75
105	Antonio Freeman	.20
106	Dorsey Levens	.20
107	Natrone Means	.20
108	Keenan McCardell	.10
109	Mark Chmura	.10
110	Darren Woodson	.10
111	Brett Favre	2.00
112	Emmitt Smith	2.00
113	Junior Seau	.10
114	Jerry Rice	1.00
115	Barry Sanders	1.50
116	Bruce Smith	.10
117	Troy Aikman	1.00
118	Bryan Cox	.10
119	Zach Thomas	.30
120	Reggie White	.10
121	Ben Coates	.10
122	Jerome Bettis	.10
123	Michael Irvin	.10

124	Quentin Coryatt	.10
125	Checklist	.10

1997 Action Packed First Impressions

This 125-card parallel fea-tured each card from the regu-lar- issue set printed in a silver foil. First Impressions parallels were inserted one per 12 packs.

	MT
Complete Set (125):	400.00
First Impression Cards:	5x-10x

1997 Action Packed Gold Impressions

Gold Impressions was a 125-card parallel set to Action Packed that featured the bottom, football-textured part of each base card printed in gold foil. Each card featured a blue "Gold Impressions" logo and they were inserted one per 35 packs.

	MT
Complete Set (125):	800.00
Gold Cards:	10x-20x

1997 Action Packed Crash Course

Inserted 1:23 packs, the 18-card set includes the Crash Course logo at the bottom cen-ter. The Action Packed logo is in the upper right. The player's name is printed vertically along the upper right side.

		MT
Complete Set (18):		200.00
Common Player:		5.00
Minor Stars:		10.00
1	Dan Marino	35.00
2	Troy Aikman	20.00
3	Barry Sanders	25.00
4	Emmitt Smith	35.00
5	Brett Favre	40.00
6	John Elway	15.00
7	Keyshawn Johnson	10.00

8	Jim Harbaugh	5.00
9	Kerry Collins	20.00
10	Karim Abdul-Jabbar	15.00
11	Eddie Kennison	10.00
12	Curtis Martin	20.00
13	Tony Banks	10.00
14	Dorsey Levens	5.00
15	Jerome Bettis	10.00
16	Drew Bledsoe	20.00
17	Marvin Harrison	10.00
18	Jerry Rice	20.00

1997 Action Packed Studs

Numbered as one of 1,500 sets, the nine-card chase set was inserted 1:167 packs. The cards include a real diamond chip in the ears of the player on the card front.

		MT
Complete Set (9):		800.00
Common Player:		35.00
1	Deion Sanders	60.00
2	Barry Sanders	120.00
3	Eddie George	130.00
4	Jerry Rice	110.00
5	Kordell Stewart	80.00
6	Emmitt Smith	225.00
7	Terrell Davis	100.00
8	Keyshawn Johnson	35.00
9	Robert Smith	35.00

1997 Action Packed 24K Team

The 15-card chase set was inserted 1:71 packs. The top of the card front has a gold banner, which includes "24KT Gold." The player's name is printed directly below the banner. The player's photo is superimposed over a gold background and silver rays. The Action Packed logo is printed at the bottom center.

		MT
Complete Set (15):		550.00
Common Player:		15.00
1	Brett Favre	90.00
2	Steve Young	35.00
3	Terrell Davis	45.00
4	Barry Sanders	45.00
5	Isaac Bruce	25.00
6	Deion Sanders	30.00
7	Dan Marino	80.00
8	Jim Harbaugh	15.00
9	Jerry Rice	45.00
10	John Elway	35.00
11	Herman Moore	15.00
12	Troy Aikman	45.00
13	Emmitt Smith	80.00
14	Drew Bledsoe	45.00
15	Eddie George	50.00

1991 All-World Troy Aikman Promos

The six-card, regular size set used the same Troy Aikman photo, but with different crops and biography versions (English, French and Spanish). Each card is numbered with a "1" and A-F is used to distinguish the cards.

		MT
Complete Set (6):		15.00
Common Player:		2.50
1A	Troy Aikman (Green border, English bio)	2.50
1B	Troy Aikman (Green border, French bio)	2.50
1C	Troy Aikman (Green border, Spanish bio)	2.50
1D	Troy Aikman (Speckled border, English bio)	2.50
1E	Troy Aikman (Speckled border, French bio)	2.50
1F	Troy Aikman (Speckled border, Spanish bio)	2.50

A card number in parentheses ( ) indicates the set is unnumbered.

1992 All-World

The 1992 All World set, which included 300 regular-size cards, was sold in 12-card packs and 26-card rack packs. The front of each card features an American flag on the top. Two insert sets, Greats/Rookies and Legends/Rookies were randomly inserted in packs, as were autographed cards from Joe Namath, Jim Brown and Desmond Howard. Subsets in the base set included Legends in the Making (LM), and Greats of the Game (GG).

		MT
Complete Set (300):		18.00
Common Player:		.05
1	Emmitt Smith (LM)	.75
2	Thurman Thomas (LM)	.10
3	Deion Sanders (LM)	.25
4	Randall Cunningham (LM)	.10
5	Michael Irvin (LM)	.10
6	Bruce Smith (LM)	.10
7	Jeff George (LM)	.10
8	Derrick Thomas (LM)	.10
9	Andre Rison (LM)	.20
10	Troy Aikman (LM)	.40
11	Quentin Coryatt	.25
12	Carl Pickens	1.50
13	Steve Emtman	.10
14	Derek Brown (TE)	.10
15	Desmond Howard	.75
16	Troy Vincent	.20
17	David Klingler	.20
18	Vaughn Dunbar	.10
19	Terrell Buckley	.10
20	Jimmy Smith	.50
21	Marquez Pope	.05
22	Kurt Barber	.05
23	Robert Harris	.05
24	Tony Sacca	.10
25	Alonzo Spellman	.20
26	Shane Collins	.10
27	Chris Mims	.20
28	Siran Stacy	.10
29	Edgar Bennett	.40
30	Sean Gilbert	.20
31	Eugene Chung	.05
32	Levon Kirkland	.10
33	Chuck Smith	.05
34	Chester McGlockton	.20
35	Ashley Ambrose	.10
36	Phillippi Sparks	.05
37	Darryl Williams	.10
38	Tracy Scroggins	.10
39	Mike Gaddis	.05
40	Tony Brooks	.05
41	Steve Israel	.05
42	Patrick Rowe	.05
43	Shane Dronett	.05
44	Mike Pawlawski	.05
45	Dale Carter	.20
46	Tyji Armstrong	.05
47	Kevin Smith	.20
48	Courtney Hawkins	.10
49	Marco Coleman	.10
50	Tommy Vardell	.10
51	Ray Ethridge	.05
52	Robert Porcher	.05
53	Todd Collins	.10
54	Robert Jones	.10
55	Tommy Maddox	.10
56	Dana Hall	.05
57	Leon Searcy	.10
58	Robert Brooks	2.00
59	Darren Woodson	.20
60	Jeremy Lincoln	.05
61	Sean Jones	.05
62	Howie Long	.10
63	Rich Gannon	.10
64	Keith Byars	.05
65	John Taylor	.10
66	Burt Grossman	.05
67	Chris Hinton	.05
68	Brad Muster	.05
69	Cris Dishman	.05
70	Russell Maryland	.10
71	Harvey Williams	.20
72	Broderick Thomas	.05
73	Louis Lipps	.05
74	Erik Kramer	.10
75	David Fulcher	.05
76	Andre Tippett	.05
77	Timm Rosenbach	.05
78	Mark Rypien	.10
79	James Lofton	.10
80	Dan Saleaumua	.05
81	John L. Williams	.05
82	Kevin Fagan	.05
83	Flipper Anderson	.05
84	Michael Dean Perry	.10
85	Mark Higgs	.05
86	Pat Swilling	.05
87	Pierce Holt	.05
88	John Elway	.75
89	Bill Brooks	.10
90	Rob Moore	.10
91	Junior Seau	.30
92	Wendell Davis	.05
93	Brian Noble	.05
94	Ernest Givins	.10
95	Phil Simms	.10
96	Eric Dickerson	.20
97	Bennie Blades	.05
98	Gary Anderson (RB)	.05
99	Errict Rhett	.20
100	Hart Lee Dykes	.05
101	Charles Haley	.10
102	Bruce Smith	.20
103	Nick Lowery	.05
104	Webster Slaughter	.05
105	Ray Childress	.05
106	Gene Atkins	.05
107	Bruce Armstrong	.05
108	Anthony Miller	.20
109	Eric Thomas	.05
110	Greg Townsend	.05
111	Anthony Carter	.10
112	James Hasty	.05
113	Chris Miller	.10
114	Sammie Smith	.05
115	Bubby Brister	.10
116	Mark Clayton	.10
117	Richard Johnson	.05
118	Bernie Kosar	.10
119	Lionel Washington	.05
120	Gary Clark	.20
121	Anthony Munoz	.05
122	Brent Jones	.10
123	Thurman Thomas	.25
124	Lee Williams	.05
125	Jessie Hester	.05
126	Andre Ware	.10
127	Patrick Hunter	.05
128	Erik Howard	.05
129	Keith Jackson	.10
130	Troy Aikman	.75
131	Mike Singletary	.10
132	Carnell Lake	.05
133	Jeff Hostetler	.10
134	Alonzo Highsmith	.05
135	Vaughn Johnson	.05
136	Louis Oliver	.05
137	Mel Gray	.05
138	Al Toon	.10
139	Bubba McDowell	.05
140	Ronnie Lott	.10
141	Deion Sanders	.50
142	Jim Harbaugh	.20
143	Gary Zimmerman	.05
144	Ernie Jones	.05
145	Cortez Kennedy	.10
146	Jeff Cross	.05
147	Floyd Turner (UER-Bio says he was drafted in 4th round)	.05
148	Mike Tomczak	.10
149	Lorenzo White	.10
150	Mark Carrier (DB)	.10
151	John Stephens	.05
152	Jerry Rice	.75
153	Jim Kelly	.25
154	Al Smith	.05
155	Duane Bickett	.05
156	Brett Perriman	.10
157	Boomer Esiason	.10
158	Neil Smith	.20
159	Eddie Anderson	.05
160	Browning Nagle	.10
161	John Friesz	.10
162	Robert Delpino	.05
163	Darren Lewis	.05
164	Roger Craig	.10
165	Keith McCants	.05
166	Stephone Paige	.05
167	Steve Broussard	.05
168	Gaston Green	.05
169	Ethan Horton	.05
170	Lewis Billups	.05
171	Mike Merriweather	.05
172	Randall Cunningham	.10
173	Leonard Marshall	.05
174	Jay Novacek	.20
175	Irving Fryar	.10
176	Randal Hill	.05
177	Keith Henderson	.05
178	Brad Baxter	.10
179	William Fuller	.05
180	Leslie O'Neal	.05
181	Steve Smith	.05
182	Joe Montana (UER-Born 1956, not 1965)	.75
183	Eric Green	.10
184	Rodney Peete	.10
185	Lawrence Dawsey	.10
186	Brian Mitchell	.10
187	Rickey Jackson	.05
188	Christian Okoye	.05
189	David Wyman	.05
190	Jessie Tuggle	.05
191	Ronnie Harmon	.10
192	Andre Reed	.20
193	Chris Doleman	.10
194	Leroy Hoard	.10
195	Mark Ingram	.05
196	Willie Gault	.10
197	Eugene Lockhart	.05
198	Jim Everett	.10
199	Doug Smith	.05
200	Clarence Verdin	.05
201	Steve Bono	1.00
202	Mark Vlasic	.05
203	Fred Barnett	.20
204	Henry Thomas	.05
205	Shaun Gayle	.05
206	Rod Bernstine	.05
207	Harold Green	.10
208	Dan McGwire	.05
209	Marv Cook	.05
210	Emmitt Smith	1.50
211	Merril Hoge	.05
212	Darion Conner	.05
213	Mike Sherrard	.10
214	Jeff George	.25
215	Craig Heyward	.10
216	Henry Ellard	.10
217	Lawrence Taylor	.20
218	Gary Ball	.05
219	Tom Rathman	.05
220	Warren Moon	.20
221	Ricky Proehl	.05
222	Sterling Sharpe	.20
223	Earnest Byner	.05
224	Jay Schroeder	.05
225	Vance Johnson	.05
226	Cornelius Bennett	.10
227	Ken O'Brien	.05
228	Ferrell Edmunds	.05
229	Eric Allen	.05
230	Derrick Thomas	.20
231	Cris Carter	.20
232	Jon Vaughn	.05
233	Eric Metcalf	.10
234	William Perry	.10
235	Vinny Testaverde	.05
236	Chip Banks	.05
237	Brian Blades	.10
238	Calvin Williams	.10
239	Andre Rison	.20
240	Neil O'Donnell	.25
241	Michael Irvin	.25
242	Gary Plummer	.05
243	Nick Bell	.05
244	Ray Crockett	.05
245	Sam Mills	.05
246	Haywood Jeffires	.10
247	Steve Young	.50
248	Martin Bayless	.05
249	Dan Marino	1.50
250	Carl Banks	.05
251	Keith McKeller	.05
252	Aaron Wallace	.05
253	Lamar Lathon	.05
254	Derrick Fenner	.05
255	Vai Sikahema	.05
256	Keith Sims	.05
257	Rohn Stark	.05
258	Reggie Roby	.05
259	Tony Zendejas	.05
260	Harris Barton	.05
261	Checklist 1-100	.05
262	Checklist 101-200	.05
263	Checklist 201-300	.05
264	Rookies Checklist	.05
265	Greats Checklist	.05
266	Joe Namath (GG)	.10
267	Joe Namath (GG)	.10
268	Joe Namath (GG)	.10
269	Joe Namath (GG)	.10
270	Joe Namath (GG)	.10
271	Jim Brown (GG)	.10
272	Jim Brown (GG)	.10
273	Jim Brown (GG)	.10
274	Jim Brown (GG)	.10
275	Jim Brown (GG)	.10
276	Vince Lombardi (GG)	.05
277	Jim Thorpe (GG)	.05
278	Tom Fears (GG)	.05
279	Jim Henry Johnson (GG)	.05
280	Gale Sayers (GG)	.10
281	Willie Brown (GG)	.05
282	Doak Walker (GG)	.05
283	Dick Lane (GG)	.05
284	Otto Graham (GG)	.10
285	Hugh McElhenny (GG)	.05
286	Roger Staubach (GG)	.10
287	Steve Largent (GG)	.20
288	Otis Taylor (GG)	.05
289	Sam Huff (GG)	.05
290	Harold Carmichael (GG)	.05
291	Steve Van Buren (GG)	.05
292	Gino Marchetti (GG)	.05
293	Tony Dorsett (GG)	.05
294	Leo Nomellini (GG)	.05
295	Jack Lambert (GG)	.05
296	Joe Theismann (GG)	.05
297	Bobby Layne (GG)	.05
298	John Stallworth (GG)	.05
299	Paul Hornung (GG)	.05
300	Don Maynard (GG)	.05
A1	Desmond Howard (AU-Certified autograph)	75.00
A2	Jim Brown (AU-Certified autograph)	125.00
A3	Joe Namath (AU-Certified autograph)	175.00
P1	Desmond Howard (Promo)	3.00
TRI	Desmond Howard, Jim Brown, Joe Namath (Triplefolder)	5.00

1992 All-World Greats & Rookies

The 20-card, regular-size set was randomly inserted in the 1992 base set. The set features 15 current (as of 1992) players in color and five older players in black and white. The cards maintain the American flag card fronts, but with gold-foil embossed stars. The card backs lead with the "SG" prefix.

		MT
Complete Set (20):		12.00
Common Greats:		.50
Common Rookies:		.25
1	Troy Aikman	3.50
2	Thurman Thomas	1.00
3	Andre Rison	.50
4	Emmitt Smith	6.00
5	Derrick Thomas	.75
6	Joe Namath	.75
7	Jim Brown	.75
8	Roger Staubach	.50
9	Gale Sayers	.50
10	Jim Thorpe	.50
11	Quentin Coryatt	.50
12	Carl Pickens	3.50
13	Steve Emtman	.25
14	Derek Brown (TE)	.25
15	Desmond Howard	1.00
16	Troy Vincent	.25
17	David Klinger	.25
18	Vaughn Dunbar	.25
19	Terrell Buckley	.25
20	Jimmy Smith	.75

1992 All-World Legends & Rookies

The 20-card, standard-size set was randomly inserted in 1992 All-World packs. The first ten cards of the set feature Legends in the Making parallels (with gold stars) while cards 11-20 feature top rookies, also with gold stars on the card front's American flag. The card backs lead with the "L" prefix.

		MT
Complete Set (20):		25.00
Common Legends:		1.00
Common Rookies:		1.00
1	Emmitt Smith	10.00
2	Thurman Thomas	2.00
3	Deion Sanders	4.00
4	Randall Cunningham	1.00
5	Michael Irvin	1.50
6	Bruce Smith	1.00
7	Jeff George	1.50
8	Derrick Thomas	1.50
9	Andre Rison	1.00
10	Troy Aikman	6.00
11	Quentin Coryatt	1.00
12	Carl Pickens	6.00
13	Steve Emtman	1.00
14	Derek Brown (TE)	1.00
15	Desmond Howard	2.00
16	Troy Vincent	1.00
17	David Klinger	1.00
18	Vaughn Dunbar	1.00
19	Terrell Buckley	1.00
20	Jimmy Smith	2.00

1966 American Oil All-Pro

Released in 1966, the 15/16" x 1-1/8" 20-stamp set could be affixed to an 8-1/2" x 11" collection sheet. American Oil dealers distributed the stamps and collectors could win cash prizes and a 1967 Ford Mustang as a top prize. The stamps feature headshots of top players such as Bob Lilly, Deacon Jones, Alex Karras, Johnny Unitas and Gale Sayers.

		NM
Complete Set (15):		220.00
Common Player:		10.00
1	Herb Adderley (Winner 5.00)	
2	Gary Ballman	10.00
3	Dick Butkus (Winner 250.00)	
4	Gary Collins (Winner Car)	
5	Willie Davis	20.00
6	Tucker Frederickson	10.00
7	Sam Huff	28.00
8	Charlie Johnson	10.00
9	Deacon Jones	30.00
10	Alex Karras	30.00
11	Bob Lilly	35.00
12	Lenny Moore	35.00
13	Tommy Nobis	20.00
14	Dave Parks	10.00
15	Pete Retzlaff	10.00
16	Frank Ryan	10.00
17	Gale Sayers	45.00
18	Mick Tinglehoff	10.00
19	Johnny Unitas (Winner 25.00)	
20	Wayne Walker (Winner 1.00)	
NNO	Saver Sheet	25.00

1968 American Oil Mr. and Mrs.

The 32-card, 2-1/8" x 3-7/16" set featured 16 players and their wives. The cards were distributed by American Oil stations and collectors could win cash or a 1969 Ford. The player card fronts feature a horizontal action shot with the wife cards in domestic-type poses.

		NM
Complete Set (16):		100.00
Common Player:		5.00
Common Wife:		2.50
1	Kermit Alexander (Winner 100.00)	
2	Mrs. Kermit Alexander (Jogging with Family)	2.50
3	Jim Bakken	5.00
4	Mrs. Jim Bakken (Winner 1.00)	
5	Gary Collins (Winner 500.00)	
6	Mrs. Gary Collins (Enjoying the Outdoors)	2.50
7	Jim Grabowski (Winner 1969 Ford)	
8	Mrs. Jim Grabowski (At the Fireside)	2.50
9	Earl Gros (Winner 1.00)	
10	Mrs. Earl Gros (At the Park)	2.50
11	Deacon Jones	20.00
12	Mrs. Deacon Jones (Winner 500.00)	
13	Billy Lothridge (Winner 10.00)	
14	Mrs. Billy Lothridge and Baby Daughter	2.50
15	Tom Matte	10.00
16	Mrs. Tom Matte (Winner 50 cents)	
17	Bobby Mitchell (Winner 5.00)	
18	Mrs. Bobby Mitchell (At a Backyard Barbecue)	2.50
19	Joe Morrison	10.00
20	Mrs. Joe Morrison (Winner 1969 Ford)	
21	Dave Osborn	5.00
22	Mrs. Dave Osborn (Winner 5.00)	
23	Dan Reeves (Winner 50 cents)	
24	Mrs. Dan Reeves (Enjoying the Children)	2.50
25	Gale Sayers	30.00
26	Mrs. Gale Sayers (Winner 100.00)	
27	Norm Snead	5.00
28	Mrs. Norm Snead (On the Family Boat)	2.50
29	Steve Stonebreaker	5.00
30	Mrs. Steve Stonebreaker (Winner 10.00)	
31	Wayne Walker (Winner 50 cents)	
32	Mrs. Wayne Walker (At a Family Picnic)	2.50

1988 Athletes in Action

The 12-card, regular-sized set features six Dallas Cowboys and six Texas Rangers from 1988. The card fronts have a color action shot while the backs contain a player quote, a religious message and the player's favorite Bible verse. The top card in the set is Dallas head coach Tom Landry, featured one year before leaving the Cowboys after 29 years.

		MT
Complete Set (12):		10.00
Common Player:		.50
1	Pete O'Brien	.50
2	Scott Fletcher	.50
3	Oddibe McDowell	.75
4	Steve Buechele	.50
5	Jerry Browne	.50
6	Larry Parrish	.50
7	Tom Landry (CO)	3.00
8	Steve Pelluer	.50
9	Gordon Banks	.50
10	Bill Bates	.75
11	Doug Cosbie	.50
12	Herschel Walker	1.50

B

1990 Bandits Smokey

The Fresno Bandits, a semi-pro team, are featured in this 25-card set. The fronts feature a black-and-white player photo with the Smokey the Bear logo in the upper left and the team logo in the bottom right. The card backs have a black-and-white photo of the player with Smokey and a safety message.

		MT
Complete Set (25):		30.00
Common Player:		1.25
1	Allan Blades	1.25
2	Corey Clark	1.25
3	Darryl Duke	1.25
4	Heikoti Fakava	1.25
5	Charles Frazier	1.25
6	Chris Geile	1.25
7	Mike Henson	1.25
8	James Hickey	1.25
9	Anthony Howard	1.25
10	Derrick Jinks	1.25
11	Anthony Jones	1.25
12	Marvin Jones	1.25
13	Mike Jones	1.25
14	Steve Loop	1.25
15	Thomas Ireland	1.25
16	Jay Lynch	1.25
17	Sheldon Martin	1.25
18	Chuckie McCutchen	1.25
19	Lance Oberparleiter	1.25
20	Darrell Rosette	1.25
21	Fred Sims	1.25
22	Bryan Turner	1.25
23	Jim Woods CO	1.25
24	Rick Zumwalt	1.25
25	Coaching Staff	1.25

1959 Bazooka

These cards were found on the backs of Bazooka Bubble Gum boxes in 1959. The un-numbered cards are blank-backed and are checklisted alphabetically. Each card measures 2-13/16" x 4-15/16" and is part of the display box. Intact boxes are worth more than if the cards have been cut out.

		NM
Complete Set (18):		5000.
Common Player:		150.00
(1)	Alan Ameche	190.00
(2)	Jon Arnett	150.00
(3)	Jim Brown	675.00
(4)	Rick Casares	150.00
(5A)	Charley Connerly (error, Baltimore Colts)	450.00
(5B)	Charley Conerly (correct, New York Giants)	325.00
(6)	Howard Ferguson	150.00
(7)	Frank Gifford	450.00
(8)	Lou Groza	475.00
(9)	Bobby Layne	325.00
(10)	Eddie LeBaron	200.00
(11)	Woodley Lewis	150.00
(12)	Ollie Matson	250.00
(13)	Joe Perry	250.00
(14)	Pete Retzlaff	150.00
(15)	Kyle Rote	225.00
(16)	Y.A. Tittle	325.00
(17)	Tom Tracy	300.00
(18)	Johnny Unitas	500.00

1971 Bazooka

These cards were issued on the backs of Bazooka Bubble Gum as panels of three. The panels are 2-5/8" x 5-7/8"; each individual card is 1-15/16" x 2-5/8". The card front has a number, plus a color head shot of the player. The back is blank. Panels generally command a premium price which would be greater than the total of the three players combined. Individual card prices are listed.

		NM
Complete Set (36):		200.00
Common Player:		3.00
1	Joe Namath	35.00
2	Larry Brown	5.00
3	Bobby Bell	5.00
4	Dick Butkus	15.00
5	Charlie Sanders	3.00
6	Chuck Howley	4.00
7	Gale Gillingham	3.00
8	Leroy Kelly	6.00
9	Floyd Little	6.00
10	Dan Abramowicz	3.50
11	Sonny Jurgensen	15.00
12	Andy Russell	3.00
13	Tommy Nobis	3.00
14	O.J. Simpson	30.00
15	Tom Woodeshick	3.00
16	Roman Gabriel	4.50
17	Claude Humphrey	3.00
18	Merlin Olsen	8.00
19	Daryle Lamonica	4.00
20	Fred Cox	3.00
21	Bart Starr	16.00
22	John Brodie	8.00
23	Jim Nance	3.00
24	Gary Garrison	3.00
25	Fran Tarkenton	17.00
26	Johnny Robinson	3.00
27	Gale Sayers	18.00
28	John Unitas	20.00
29	Jerry LeVias	3.00
30	Virgil Carter	3.00
31	Bill Nelsen	3.00
32	Dave Osborn	3.00
33	Matt Snell	3.00
34	Larry Wilson	6.00
35	Bob Griese	15.00
36	Lance Alworth	8.00

1972 Bazooka Official Signals

The 12-card, 6-1/4" x 2-7/8" set was issued by Bazooka on the bottoms of its bubble gum boxes in 1972. The first eight cards define football lingo for juveniles while cards 9-12 describe the responsibilities of the referees.

		NM
Complete Set (12):		85.00
Common Player:		8.00
1	Football Lingo (Automatic through Bread and Butter Play)	8.00
2	Football Lingo (Broken-Field Runner through Dive)	8.00
3	Football Lingo (Double-Coverage through Interference)	8.00
4	Football Lingo (Game Plan through Lateral Pass)	8.00
5	Football Lingo (Interception through Man-to-Man Coverage)	8.00
6	Football Lingo (Killing the Clock through Punt)	8.00
7	Football Lingo (Belly Series through Quick Whistle)	8.00
8	Football Lingo (Prevent Defense through Primary Receiver)	8.00
9	Officials' Duties (Reveree through Line Judge)	8.00
10	Officials' Duties	8.00
11	Officials' Signals	8.00
12	Officials' Signals	8.00

1976 Bears Coke Discs

The 24 circular-card set was issued in 1976 as part of a local Coca-Cola promotion in Chicago. Each one of the 3-3/8" (diameter) discs feature Chicago Bears players, including a noteworthy disc of Walter Payton, whose rookie Topps card was also issued in 1976. The card front features the Coca-Cola logo and a Bears helmet while the back has another Coca-Cola logo and the "Coke adds life to ... halftime fun."

		NM
Complete Set (24):		60.00
Common Player:		1.50
1	Lionel Antoine	1.50
2	Bob Avellini	3.00
3	Waymond Bryant	1.50
4	Doug Buffone	2.00
5	Wally Chambers	2.00
6A	Craig Clemons (Yellow border)	1.50
6B	Craig Clemons (Orange border)	1.50
7	Allan Ellis	1.50
8	Roland Harper	2.50
9	Mike Hartenstine	1.50
10	Noah Jackson	2.50
11	Virgil Livers	1.50
12	Jim Osborne	1.50
13	Bob Parsons	1.50
14	Walter Payton	45.00
15	Dan Peiffer	1.50
16A	Doug Plank (Yellow border)	3.00
16B	Doug Plank (Green border)	3.00
17	Bo Rather	1.50
18	Don Rives	1.50
19	Jeff Sevy	1.50
20	Ron Shanklin	1.50
21	Revie Sorey	1.50
22	Roger Stillwell	1.50

1981 Bears Police

64 - Ted Albrecht

The 24-card, 2-5/8" x 4-1/8" set was released in 1981 and sponsored by the Kiwanis Club, the local law enforcement agency and the Chicago Bears. The card fronts feature an action shot while the backs have a Bears helmet and tips geared toward younger fans.

		MT
Complete Set (24):		25.00
Common Player:		.50
1	Ted Albrecht	.50
2	Neil Armstrong CO	.50
3	Brian Baschnagel	.50
4	Gary Campbell	.50
5	Robin Earl	.50
6	Allan Ellis	.50
7	Vince Evans	2.00
8	Gary Fencik	1.50
9	Dan Hampton	5.00
10	Roland Harper	.75
11	Mike Hartenstine	.50
12	Tom Hicks	.50
13	Noah Jackson	.75
14	Dennis Lick	.50
15	Jerry Muckensturm	.50
16	Dan Neal	.50
17	Jim Osborne	.50
18	Alan Page	3.50
19	Walter Payton	18.00
20	Doug Plank	.50
21	Terry Schmidt	.50
22	James Scott	.50
23	Revie Sorey	.50
24	Rickey Watts	.50

1994 Bears 75th Anniversary Sheets

The 10-card, 10-3/4" x 7-5/8" set was inserted into game programs for the 1994 75th anniversary season for the Chicago Bears. Each card in the set could be found on a perforated sheet for the eight regular-season Bears home games and two preseason home games. The card backs feature a WGN AM radio advertisement while the fronts have a light blue face with action shots of past Chicago Hall of Famers.

		MT
Complete Set (10):		50.00
Common Player:		2.50
1	George Halas OWN/CO (vs. Eagles; 8/5/94)	6.00
2	Doug Atkins, George Connor, George Blanda (vs. Giants; 8/27/94)	2.50
3	Walter Payton (vs. Bucs; 9/4/94)	8.00
4	Dan Fortmann, Mike Ditka, Paddy Driscoll (vs. Vikings; 9/18/94)	5.00
5	Dick Butkus (vs. Bills; 10/2/94)	7.00
6	Bill George, Red Grange, Ed Healey (vs. Saints; 10/9/94)	4.00
7	Gale Sayers (vs. Packers; 10/31/94)	7.00
8	Bill Hewitt, Stan Jones, Sid Luckman (vs. Lions; 11/20/94)	3.00
9	Link Lyman, George Musso, George McAfee (vs. Rams; 12/18/94)	2.50
10	Bronko Nagurski, Bulldog Turner, Joe Stydahar, George Trafton (vs. Patriots; 12/24/94)	4.00

1994 Bears Toyota

The two-card, standard-size set was sponsored by Toyota and commemorates October 31, 1994, the day Dick Butkus and Gale Sayers had their jerseys retired by the Bears. The card fronts have a Bears logo in the upper left corner and have a color action shot. The card backs feature a color headshot with a career summary and highlights.

		MT
Complete Set (2):		16.00
Common Player:		8.00
1	Dick Butkus	8.00
2	Gale Sayers	8.00

1995 Bears Program Sheets

The eight-sheet, 8" x 10" set was inserted in Bears game programs during the 1995 season to commemorate the 10th anniversary of Chicago's Super Bowl XX victory in January of 1986. The fronts contained color or action shots of players including Walter Payton, Jim McMahon and Mike Singletary.

		MT
Complete Set (8):		40.00
Common Player:		4.00
1	Mike Ditka (9/3/95 vs. Vikings)	6.00
2	Walter Payton (9/11/95 vs. Packers)	8.00
3	Jim McMahon (10/8/95 vs. Panthers)	5.00
4	Mike Singletary, Gary Fencik (10/22/95 vs. Oilers)	5.00
5	Richard Dent (11/5/95 vs. Steelers)	5.00
6	William Perry (11/19/95 vs. Lions)	5.00
7	Otis Wilson (12/17/95 vs. Buccaneers)	4.00
8	Wilber Marshall (12/24/95 vs. Eagles)	4.00

1995 Bears Super Bowl XX 10th Anniversary Kemper

The 20-card, regular-sized set released in 1995, commemorates the Chicago Bears Super Bowl XX win. Issued in conjunction with Kemper Mutual Funds, the fronts feature color action shots with the player's name, position and uniform number along the left border. The card backs have a player closeup with bio statistical information.

		MT
Complete Set (20):		25.00
Common Player:		1.00
1	Mark Bortz	1.00
2	Kevin Butler	1.00
3	Jim Covert	1.00
4	Richard Dent	1.50
5	Dave Duerson	1.00
6	Gary Fencik	1.00
7	Willie Gault	1.00
8	Dan Hampton	1.00
9	Jay Hilgenberg	1.00
10	Wilber Marshall	1.00
11	Dennis McKinnon	1.00
12	Jim McMahon	2.00
13	Steve McMichael	1.00
14	Walter Payton	4.00
15	William Perry	1.50
16	Mike Singletary	1.50
17	Matt Suhey	1.00
18	Tom Thayer	1.00
19	Keith Van Horne	1.00
20	Otis Wilson	1.00

1995 Bears Super Bowl XX Montgomery Ward Cards

The eight-card, regular-sized set was released in conjunction with Montgomery Ward stores and commemorates Chicago's 10th anniversary of a win in Super Bowl XX. The card fronts have a color action shot with a diagonal blue and orange stripe which states the player's name and position. The card backs contain a checklist for the eight cards.

		MT
Complete Set (8):		12.00
Common Player:		1.00
1	Mike Ditka ('85 Super Bowl)	2.00
2	Kevin Butler	1.00
3	Dan Hampton	1.00
4	Richard Dent	1.50
5	Gary Fencik	1.00
6	Walter Payton	2.50
7	Jim McMahon	1.00
8	Mike Ditka	1.75

1995 Bears Super Bowl XX Montgomery Ward Coins

The eight-coin set was released in 1995 in conjunction with Montgomery Ward stores to commemorate Chicago's 10th anniversary of its Super Bowl XX victory. The coins parallel the eight-card set, also released in 1995. The coin fronts depict the player's name and uniform number while the backs have the Super Bowl XX logo.

		MT
Complete Set (8):		10.00
Common Player:		1.00
1	Kevin Butler	1.00
2	Richard Dent	1.25
3	Mike Ditka CO	1.75
4	Gary Fencik	1.00
5	Dan Hampton	1.00
6	Jim McMahon	1.50
7	Walter Payton	2.50
8	Super Bowl Trophy	1.00

1996 Bears Illinois State Lottery

These cards were Illinois State Lottery scratch-and-win tickets. The tickets feature a color or photo of the player. They are usually found scratched.

		MT
Complete Set (5):		3.00
Common Player:		.25
1	Richard Dent	.50
2	Mike Ditka	1.00
3	Dan Hampton	.50
4	William Perry	.25
5	Gale Sayers	1.00

1968 Bengals Team Issue

The Cincinnati Bengals team-issued set consisted of 8-1/2" x 11" cards with a black and white player photo. The player's name and position are below the photo.

		NM
Complete Set (7):		35.00
Common Player:		5.00
1	Frank Buncom	5.00
2	Sherrill Headrick	5.00
3	Warren McVea	5.00
4	Fletcher Smith	5.00
5	John Stofa	7.00
6	Dewey Warren	5.00
7	Ernie Wright	7.00

1969 Bengals Tresler Comet

The 20-card, standard-size cards were distributed by Tresler Comet gas stations. The card fronts feature a simulated autograph while the backs contain bio and career highlights. The card backs are not numbered and Bob Johnson's card is unusually higher in value than the other 19 because of its scarcity. Also, future Bengals' coach Sam Wyche is included along with football announcer Bob Trumpy.

		NM
Complete Set (20):		300.00
Common Player:		5.00
1	Al Beauchamp	5.00
2	Bill Bergey	10.00
3	Royce Berry	5.00
4	Paul Brown CO	35.00
5	Frank Buncom	5.00
6	Greg Cook	10.00
7	Howard Fest SP	25.00
8	Harry Gunner SP	20.00
9	Bobby Hunt	5.00
10	Bob Johnson SP	125.00
11	Charley King	5.00
12	Dale Livingston	5.00
13	Warren McVea SP	25.00
14	Bill Peterson	5.00
15	Jess Phillips	5.00
16	Andy Rice	5.00
17	Bill Staley	5.00
18	Bob Trumpy	20.00
19	Ernie Wright	5.00
20	Sam Wyche	25.00

1960 Bills Team Issue

Issued by the team, this set of 40 black and white 5" x 7" cards were delivered to the

1960 Buffalo Bills season tick-etholders. The photos are not numbered and were frequently found autographed.

		NM
Complete Set (40):		180.00
Common Player:		5.00
1	Bill Atkins	5.00
2	Bob Barrett	5.00
3	Phil Blazer	5.00
4	Bob Brodhead	5.00
5	Dick Brubacher	5.00
6	Bernie Burzinski	5.00
7	Wray Carlton	8.00
8	Don Chelf	5.00
9	Monte Crockett	5.00
10	Bob Dove	5.00
11	Elbert Dubenion	10.00
12	Fred Ford	5.00
13	Dick Gallagher	5.00
14	Darrell Harper	5.00
15	Harvey Johnson	5.00
16	John Johnson	5.00
17	Billy Kinard	5.00
18	Joe Kulbacki	5.00
19	John Laraway	5.00
20	Richie Lucas	10.00
21	Archie Matsos	8.00
22	Richie McCabe	8.00
23	Dan McGrew	5.00
24	Chuck McMurtry	5.00
25	Ed Meyer	5.00
26	Ed Muelhaupt	5.00
27	Tom O'Connell	5.00
28	Harold Olson	5.00
29	Buster Ramsey CO	5.00
30	Floyd Reid	5.00
31	Tom Rychlec	5.00
32	Joe Schaeffer	5.00
33	John Scott	5.00
34	Bob Sedlock	5.00
35	Carl Smith	5.00
36	Jim Sorey	5.00
27	Lavern Torczon	5.00
38	Jim Wagstaff	5.00
39	Ralph Wilson OWN	8.00
40	Mack Yoho	5.00

1963 Bills Jones Dairy

The 40-card, circular cards were available as cardboard cut-outs on milk cartons. The 1" (diameter) discs are frequently found miscut and off-centered and are not numbered.

		NM
Complete Set (40):		1000.
Common Player:		20.00
1	Ray Abruzzese	20.00
2	Art Baker	20.00
3	Stew Barber	20.00
4	Glenn Bass	20.00
5	Dave Behrman	20.00
6	Al Bemiller	20.00
7	Wray Carlton	20.00
8	Carl Charon	20.00
9	Monte Crockett	20.00
10	Wayne Crow	20.00
11	Tom Day	20.00
12	Elbert Dubenion	25.00
13	Jim Dunaway	20.00
14	Booker Edgerson	20.00
15	Cookie Gilchrist	30.00
16	Dick Hudson	20.00
17	Frank Jackunas	20.00
18	Harry Jacobs	20.00
19	Jack Kemp	375.00
20	Roger Kochman	20.00
21	Daryle Lamonica	85.00
22	Charley Leo	20.00
23	Marv Matuszak	20.00
24	Bill Miller	20.00
25	Leroy Moore	20.00
26	Harold Olson	20.00
27	Herb Paterra	20.00
28	Ken Rice	20.00
29	Henry Rivera	20.00
30	Ed Rutkowski	20.00
31	George Saimes	25.00
32	Tom Sestak	25.00
33	Billy Shaw	25.00
34	Mike Stratton	20.00
35	Gene Sykes	20.00
36	John Tracey	20.00
37	Ernie Warlick	20.00
38	Willie West	20.00
39	Mack Yoho	20.00
40	Sid Youngelman	20.00

1965 Bills Super Duper Markets

The 10-card, 8-1/2" x 11" set was offered as a giveaway from Super Duper food stores in 1965. The fronts contain black and white action (posed) photos and the set is not numbered.

		NM
Complete Set (10):		180.00
Common Player:		5.00
1	Glenn Bass	5.00
2	Elbert Dubenion	10.00
3	Billy Joe	10.00
4	Jack Kemp	100.00
5	Daryle Lamonica	30.00
6	Tom Sestak	5.00
7	Billy Shaw	10.00
8	Mike Stratton	5.00
9	Ernie Warlick	5.00
10	Team Photo	25.00

1967 Bills Jones-Rich Milk

Through a special mail-in offer, Jones-Rich Milk offered the set of six Buffalo Bills 8-1/2" x 11" cards in 1967.

		NM
Complete Set (6):		100.00
Common Player:		15.00
1	George (Butch) Byrd	20.00
2	Wray Carlton	20.00
3	Hagood Clarke	15.00
4	Paul Costa	20.00
5	Jim Dunaway	20.00
6	Jack Spikes	20.00

1974 Bills Team Issue

The 12-card, 8-1/2" x 11" photo cards were issued through concession sales at Rich Stadium in Buffalo during the 1974 season.

		NM
Complete Set (12):		80.00
Common Player:		5.00
1	Jim Braxton	5.00
2	Bob Chandler	8.00
3	Jim Cheyunski	5.00
4	Earl Edwards	5.00
5	Joe Ferguson	12.00
6	Dave Foley	5.00
7	Robert James	5.00
8	Reggie McKenzie	5.00
9	Jerry Patton	5.00
10	Walt Patulski	5.00
11	John Skorupan	5.00
12	O.J. Simpson	30.00

1976 Bills McDonald's

The three-card set was issued by McDonald's in conjunction with WBEN-TV and was given away free with a purchase of a Quarter Pounder hamburger at particpating restaurants. The 8" x 10" color photos included statistical information on the backs.

		NM
Complete Set (3):		30.00
Common Player:		8.00
1	Bob Chandler	10.00
2	Joe Ferguson	15.00
3	Reggie McKenzie	8.00

1979 Bills Bell's Market

The 11-card, 7-5/8" x 10" photo cards were issued weekly by Bell's Markets during the 1979 season. The cards were printed on thin stock and are not numbered.

		NM
Complete Set (11):		50.00
Common Player:		4.00
(1)	Curtis Brown	4.00
(2)	Bob Chandler	5.00
(3)	Joe DeLamielleure	4.00
(4)	Joe Ferguson	10.00
(5)	Reuben Gant	4.00
(6)	Dee Hardison	4.00
(7)	Frank Lewis	4.00
(8)	Reggie McKenzie	5.00
(9)	Terry Miller	4.00
(10)	Shane Nelson	4.00
(11)	Lucius Sanford	4.00

1980 Bills Bell's Market

The 20-card, regular-sized set was issued by Bell's Markets

in 1980 and arrived in 20-card packs or two-pack perforation sets. The card fronts contain color shots while the backs have career statistics.

		NM
Complete Set (20):		9.00
Common Player:		.40
1	Curtis Brown	.40
2	Shane Nelson	.40
3	Jerry Butler	.40
4	Joe Ferguson	1.25
5	Joe Cribbs	1.00
6	Reggie McKenzie	.75
7	Joe Devlin	.40
8	Ken Jones	.40
9	Steve Freeman	.40
10	Mike Kadish	.40
11	Jim Haslett	.40
12	Isiah Robertson	.40
13	Frank Lewis	.40
14	Jeff Nixon	.40
15	Nick Mike-Mayer	.40
16	Jim Ritcher	.40
17	Charles Romes	.40
18	Fred Smerlas	.75
19	Ben Williams	.40
20	Roland Hooks	.40

1986 Bills Sealtest

The six-card, 3-5/8" x 7-5/8" set was issued on sides of half-gallon Sealtest milk containers. The Freeman and Marve cards were found on vitamin D cartons while the Kelly and Romes cards appeared on lowfat (2%) cartons. The cards featured a black and white player headshot with bio information and stats.

		MT
Complete Set (6):		30.00
Common Player:		1.50
1	Greg Bell SP	5.00
2	Jerry Butler SP	5.00
3	Steve Freeman	1.50
4	Jim Kelly	20.00
5	Eugene Marve	1.50
6	Charles Romes	1.50

1987 Bills Police

The eight-card, 2-5/8" x 4-1/8" set was sponsored by the Bills, Erie and Niagara County Sheriff's Departments, Louis Rich Turkey products and WBEN radio. The black and white photos on the card fronts were taken by Robert L. Smith, the Bills' official team photographer.

		MT
Complete Set (8):		12.00
Common Player:		1.00
1	Marv Levy CO	1.50
2	Bruce Smith	2.00
3	Joe Devlin	1.00
4	Jim Kelly	5.00
5	Eugene Marve	1.00
6	Andre Reed	2.00
7	Pete Metzelaars	1.00
8	John Kidd	1.00

1988 Bills Police

The eight-card, 2-5/8" x 4-1/8" set was sponsored by the Bills, Erie and Niagara County Sheriff's Departments, Louis Rich Turkey Products and WBEN radio. The fronts feature an action photo while the backs have bio and stat information.

		MT
Complete Set (8):		8.00
Common Player:		.75
1	Steve Tasker	1.50
2	Cornelius Bennett	2.00
3	Shane Conlan	1.25
4	Mark Kelso	.75
5	Will Wolford	.75
6	Chris Burkett	.75
7	Kent Hull	1.25
8	Art Still	.75

1989 Bills Police

The eight-card, regular-sized set was issued in conjunction with the Bills, Erie County Sheriff's Department and Louis Rich Turkey Products. The card fronts feature an action shot

while the backs contain bio and stat information.

		MT
Complete Set (8):		10.00
Common Player:		.75
1	Leon Seals	.75
2	Thurman Thomas	6.00
3	Jim Ritcher	.75
4	Scott Norwood	.75
5	Darryl Talley	1.50
6	Nate Odomes	.75
7	Leonard Smith	.75
8	Ray Bentley	.75

1990 Bills Police

The eight-card, 4" x 6" set was sponsored by Blue Shield of New York. The card fronts feature a color action photo and the card backs contain highlights and career statistics.

		MT
Complete Set (8):		10.00
Common Player:		.50
1	Carlton Bailey	.50
2	Kirby Jackson	.50
3	Jim Kelly	5.00
4	James Lofton	1.50
5	Keith McKeller	.50
6	Mark Pike	.50
7	Andre Reed	2.50
8	Jeff Wright	.50

1991 Bills Police

The eight-card, regular-sized set was sponsored by Blue Shield of New York. The card fronts feature an action shot and bio information while the backs contain highlights and career statistics.

		MT
Complete Set (8):		5.00
Common Player:		.75
1	Howard Ballard	.75
2	Don Beebe	1.50
3	John Davis	.75
4	Kenneth Davis	1.00
5	Mark Kelso	.75
6	Frank Reich	1.50
7	Butch Rolle	.75
8	J.D. Williams	.75

1992 Bills Police

The seven-card, 4" x 6" set was sponsored by Blue Shield of New York. The card fronts feature an action photo and bio information while the backs have highlights and stats.

		MT
Complete Set (7):		5.00
Common Player:		.50
1	Carlton Bailey	.50
2	Steve Christie	.50
3	Shane Conlan	.75
4	Phil Hansen	.50
5	Henry Jones	.75
6	Chris Mohr	.50
7	Thurman Thomas	3.00

1994 Bills Police

The six-card, 3" x 5" set was sponsored by the Erie County Sheriff's Office and Coca-Cola. The card fronts feature color action shots with the Bills logo in the lower left corner. The backs feature a headshot with biographical and statistical information with "Tips from the Sheriff."

		MT
Complete Set (6):		5.00
Common Player:		.50
1	Bill Brooks	1.25
2	Kenneth Davis	1.00
3	John Fina	.50
4	Phil Hansen	.75
5	Pete Metzelaars	1.00
6	Marvcus Patton	.75

1995 Bills Police

The six-card, 4" x 6" set was sponsored by the Erie County Sheriff's Office and Coca-Cola. The card fronts feature a color action shot with the Bills logo in the upper left cor-

ner. The card backs have a headshot with bio and stat information and a safety tip.

		MT
Complete Set (6):		5.00
Common Player:		.50
1	Jeff Burris	.50
2	Joe Ferguson (All-Time Great)	1.50
3	Kent Hull	.50
4	Adam Lingner	.50
5	Glenn Parker	.50
6	Andre Reed	2.50

1996 Bills Police

Coca-Cola and the Erie County Sheriff's Office sponsored this five-card set of the Buffalo Bills. The cards are 4" x 6" and feature a color player photo and the sponsors' logos on the front.

		MT
Complete Set (5):		4.00
Common Player:		.75
24	Kurt Schulz	.75
55	Mark Maddox	.75
79	Ruben Brown	1.25
94	Mark Pike	.75
95	Bryce Paup	1.50

1993-94 Bleachers Troy Aikman Promos

The four-card, standard-size promo set highlights the Dallas Cowboys quarterback in his UCLA uniform. Ten-thousand sets were produced and the card backs feature the same card-front image ghosted behind a text of career highlights. Card #4 was an exclusive promo for the 1994 Houston Tri-Star show and features "Houston 1994" in gold foil.

		MT
Complete Set (4):		10.00
Common Player:		2.50
1	Troy Aikman (Exclusive promo)	2.50
2	Troy Aikman (UCLA)	2.50
3	Troy Aikman (UCLA, Comicfest '93)	2.50
4	Troy Aikman (UCLA, Houston '94)	2.50

1993 Bleachers 23K Troy Aikman

This three-card set is sequentially-numbered to 10,000. The cards feature color photos of Aikman, a facsimile autograph printed in gold foil and golden borders. A promo card with Aikman pictured in his Cowboy uniform was also produced.

		MT
Complete Set (3):		20.00
Common Player:		5.00
1	Troy Aikman (Oklahoma)	5.00
2	Troy Aikman (UCLA)	5.00
3	Troy Aikman (Cowboys)	5.00
P1	Troy Aikman Promo (Cowboys)	5.00

1994 Bleachers 23K Troy Aikman

The three-card, standard-sized set features the Dallas Cowboys quarterback in collegiate color photos (#1 and #2) and a pro shot with Dallas (#3). The card fronts have a gold-foil border along with his name, team and position in gold on the bottom edge. The card backs are numbered in production "x of 10,000" and in the set "x of 3" and feature a facsimile Aikman autograph.

		MT
Complete Set (3):		15.00
Common Player:		5.00
1	Troy Aikman (Oklahoma)	5.00

| 2 | Troy Aikman (UCLA) | 5.00 |
| 3 | Troy Aikman | 5.00 |

1995 Bleachers 23K Emmitt Smith

The four-card, regular-sized set features the Dallas Cowboys running back in high school (#1), college (#2) and Dallas (#3). The card fronts feature a gold border while the card backs are numbered in production as "x of 10,000." A promo card, not numbered, featured Smith in his collegiate uniform.

		MT
Complete Set (3):		30.00
Common Player:		10.00
1	Emmitt Smith (Escambia High School)	10.00
2	Emmitt Smith (Florida Gators)	10.00
3	Emmitt Smith	10.00
NNO	Emmitt Smith (Promo, Escambia High School)	3.00

1983 Blitz Chicago

The eight-sheet, 10" x 8" set featured the United States Football League team. One set contains the coaching staff, including head coach George Allen, while the other seven feature the players. The sheets are unnumbered and the individual photos on the sheets are approximately 2-1/4" x 2-1/2".

		MT
Complete Set (8):		35.00
Common Player:		4.50
1	Coaching Staff (George Allen, Joe Haering, Paul Lanham, John Payne, John Teerlink, Dick Walker, Charlie	4.50
2	Luther Bradley, Eddie Brown, Virgil Livers, Frank Minnifield, Lance Sheilds, Don Schwartz, Maurice Tyler, Ted	4.50
3	Mack Boatner, Frank Collins, Frank Corral, Doug Cozen, Doug Dennison, John Roveto, Jim Stone, Tim Wrightman	4.50
4	Robert Barnes, Bruce Branch, Nick Eyre, Tim Norman, Wally Pesuit, Mark Stevenson, Rob Taylor, Steve Tobin	4.50
5	Junior Ah You, Mark Buben, Bob Cobb, Joe Ehrmann, Kit Lathrop, Karl Lorch, Troy Thomas	4.50
6	Jim Fahnhorst, Joe Federspiel, Doak Field, Bruce Gheesling, Andy Melontree, Ed Smith, Stan White, Kari	4.50
7	Marcus Anderson, Larry Douglas, Mark May, Pat Schmidt, Lenny Willis, Warren Anderson, Chris Pagnucco, Bruce Allen	4.50

1948 Bowman

Considered to be the first true football set of the modern era, the 1948 Bowman set included only players from the National Football League (the first set to do so). Each of the 108 cards measures 2-1/16" x 2-1/2" and shows a player photo on the front with no name or team name. Backs have biographical information. This set was printed on three separate sheets, with the first sheet being plentiful, the second a little scarcer, and the third very difficult to find. So cards numbered 1, 4, 7, 10, etc., are easiest to find; cards numbered 2, 5, 8, 11, etc., are somewhat harder, and those divisible by three (3, 6, 9, 12, etc.) are extremely tough to find. Rookie cards in this set include Hall of Famers Steve Van Buren, Charley Trippi, Sammy Baugh, Bob Waterfield, Bulldog Turner, Alex Wojciechowicz, Pete Pihos, Bill Dudley, George McAfee and Sid Luckman. Other star rookie cards include Johnny Lujack and Charlie Conerly.

		NM
	Complete Set (108):	6000.
	Common Player:	20.00
	SP Cards:	50.00
1	Joe Tereshinski	150.00
2	Larry Olsonoski	20.00
3	John Lujack	320.00
4	Ray Poole	20.00
5	Bill DeCorrevont	20.00
6	Paul Briggs	20.00
7	Steve Van Buren	150.00
8	Kenny Washington	50.00
9	Nolan Luhn	20.00
10	Chris Iversen	20.00
11	Jack Wiley	20.00
12	Charlie Conerly	320.00
13	Hugh Taylor	20.00
14	Frank Seno	20.00
15	Gil Bouley	100.00
16	Tommy Thompson	30.00
17	Charlie Trippi	100.00
18	Vince Banonis	20.00
19	Art Faircloth	20.00
20	Clyde Goodnight	20.00
21	Bill Chipley	100.00
22	Sammy Baugh	425.00
23	Don Kindt	20.00
24	John Koniszewski	100.00
25	Pat McHugh	20.00
26	Bob Waterfield	200.00
27	Tony Compagno	100.00
28	Paul Governali	20.00
29	Pat Harder	40.00
30	Vic Lindskog	100.00
31	Salvatore Rosato	20.00
32	John Mastrangelo	20.00
33	Fred Gehrke	100.00
34	Bosh Pritchard	20.00
35	Mike Micka	20.00
36	Bulldog Turner	250.00
37	Len Younce	20.00
38	Pat West	20.00
39	Russ Thomas	100.00
40	James Peebles	20.00
41	Bob Skoglund	20.00
42	Wat Stickle	100.00
43	Whitey Wistert	20.00
44	Paul Christman	45.00
45	Jay Rhodemyre	100.00
46	Skip Minisi	20.00
47	Bob Mann	20.00
48	Mal Kutner	100.00
49	Dick Poillon	20.00
50	Charles Cherundolo	20.00
51	Gerald Cowhig	100.00
52	Neil Armstrong	30.00
53	Frak Maznicki	20.00
54	John Sanchez	100.00
55	Frank Reagan	20.00
56	Jim Hardy	20.00
57	John Badaczewski	100.00
58	Robert Nussbaumer	20.00
59	Marvin Pregulman	20.00
60	Elbert Nickel	125.00
61	Alex Wojciechowicz	75.00
62	Walt Shclinkman	20.00
63	Pete Pihos	220.00
64	Joseph Sulaitis	20.00
65	Mike Holovak	50.00
66	Cecil Souders	100.00
67	Paul McKee	20.00
68	Bill Moore	20.00
69	Frank Minini	100.00
70	Jack Ferrante	20.00
71	Leslie Horvath	40.00
72	Ted Fritsch, Sr.	100.00
73	Tex Coulter	20.00
74	Boley Dancewicz	100.00
75	Dante Mangani	20.00
76	James Hefti	20.00
77	Paul Sarringhaus	20.00
78	Joe Scott	20.00
79	Bucko Kilroy	30.00
80	Bill Dudley	100.00
81	Marshall Goldberg	100.00
82	John Cannady	20.00
83	Perry Moss	20.00
84	Harold Crisler	100.00
85	Bill Gray	20.00
86	John Clement	20.00
87	Dan Sandifer	20.00
88	Ben Kish	20.00
89	Herbert Banta	20.00
90	Bill Garnaas	100.00
91	Jim White	20.00
92	Frank Barzilauskas	20.00
93	Vic Sears	100.00
94	John Adams	20.00
95	George McAfee	100.00
96	Ralph Heywood	20.00
97	Joe Muha	20.00
98	Fred Enke	20.00
99	Harry Gilmer	160.00
100	Bill Miklich	20.00
101	Joe Gottieb	20.00
102	Bud Angsman	100.00
103	Tom Farmer	20.00
104	Bruce F. Smith	50.00
105	Bob Cifers	20.00
106	Ernie Steele	20.00
107	Sid Luckman	220.00
108	Buford Ray	350.00

1950 Bowman

After a one-year absence, Bowman returned to football cards with the first of four straight 144-card sets. As with the '48 Bowman set, cards showed only the player on the front without any identification. Cards again measured 2-1/16" x 2-1/2". Rookie cards in this set include Y.A. Tittle, Lou Groza, Tony Canadeo, Joe Perry, Marion Motley, Otto Graham, Tom Fears, Elroy Hirsch, Dante Lavelli, Tobin Rote and Dub Jones.

		NM
	Complete Set (144):	4250.
	Common Player:	20.00
1	Doak Walker	175.00
2	John Greene	20.00
3	Bob Nowasky	20.00
4	Jonathan Jenkins	20.00
5	Y.A. Tittle	300.00
6	Lou Groza	180.00
7	Alex Agase	20.00
8	Mac Speedie	35.00
9	Tony Canadeo	55.00
10	Larry Craig	20.00
11	Ted Fritsch, Sr.	20.00
12	Joe Goldring	20.00
13	Martin Ruby	20.00
14	George Taliaferro	20.00
15	Tank Younger	50.00
16	Glenn Davis	130.00
17	Bob Waterfield	75.00
18	Val Jansante	20.00
19	Joe Geri	20.00
20	Jerry Nuzum	20.00
21	Elmer Angsman	20.00
22	Billy Dewell	20.00
23	Steve Van Buren	60.00
24	Cliff Patton	20.00
25	Bosh Pritchard	20.00
26	John Lujack	60.00
27	Sid Luckman	80.00
28	Bulldog Turner	45.00
29	Bill Dudley	45.00
30	Hugh Taylor	20.00
31	George Thomas	20.00
32	Ray Poole	20.00
33	Travis Tidwell	20.00
34	Gail Bruce	20.00
35	Joe Perry	160.00
36	Frankie Albert	35.00
37	Bobby Layne	190.00
38	Leon Hart	30.00
39	Bob Hoernschemeyer	20.00
40	Dick Barwegan	20.00
41	Adrian Burk	20.00
42	Barry French	20.00
43	Marion Motley	130.00
44	Jim Martin	20.00
45	Otto Graham	450.00
46	Al Baldwin	20.00
47	Larry Coutre	20.00
48	John Rauch	20.00
49	Sam Tamburo	20.00
50	Mike Swistowicz	20.00
51	Tom Fears	80.00
52	Elroy Hirsch	150.00
53	Dick Huffman	20.00
54	Bob Cage	20.00
55	Bob Tinsley	20.00
56	Bill Blackburn	20.00
57	John Cochran	20.00
58	Bill Fischer	20.00
59	Whitey Wistert	20.00
60	Clyde Scott	20.00
61	Walter Barnes	20.00
62	Bob Perina	20.00
63	Bill Wightkin	20.00
64	Bob Goode	20.00
65	Al Demao	20.00
66	Harry Gilmer	20.00
67	Bill Austin	20.00
68	Joe Scott	20.00
69	Tex Coulter	20.00
70	Paul Salata	20.00
71	Emil Sitko	20.00
72	Bill Johnson	20.00
73	Don Doll	20.00
74	Dan Sandifer	20.00
75	John Panelli	20.00
76	Bill Leonard	20.00
77	Bob Kelly	20.00
78	Dante Lavelli	80.00
79	Tony Adamle	20.00
80	Dick Wildung	20.00
81	Tobin Rote	35.00
82	Paul Burris	20.00
83	Lowell Tew	20.00
84	Barney Poole	20.00
85	Fred Naumetz	20.00
86	Dick Hoerner	20.00
87	Bob Reinhard	20.00
88	Howard Hartley	20.00
89	Darrell Hogan	20.00
90	Jerry Shipkey	20.00
91	Frank Tripucka	20.00
92	Garrard Ramsey	20.00
93	Pat Harder	20.00
94	Vic Sears	20.00
95	Tommy Thompson	20.00
96	Bucko Kilroy	20.00
97	George Connor	35.00
98	Fred Morrison	20.00
99	Jim Keane	20.00
100	Sammy Baugh	200.00
101	Harry Ulinski	20.00
102	Frank Spaniel	20.00
103	Charlie Conerly	60.00
104	Dick Hensley	20.00
105	Eddie Price	20.00
106	Ed Carr	20.00
107	Leo Nomellini	60.00
108	Verl Lillywhite	20.00
109	Wallace Triplett	20.00
110	Joe Watson	20.00
111	Cloyce Box	20.00
112	Billy Stone	20.00
113	Earl Murray	20.00
114	Chet Mutryn	20.00
115	Ken Carpenter	20.00
116	Lou Rymkus	20.00
117	Dub Jones	20.00
118	Clayton Tonnemaker	20.00
119	Walt Schlinkman	20.00
120	Billy Grimes	20.00
121	George Ratterman	20.00
122	Bob Mann	20.00
123	Buddy Young	50.00
124	Jack Zilly	20.00
125	Tom Kalmanir	20.00
126	Frank Sinkovitz	20.00
127	Elbert Nickel	20.00
128	Jim Finks	45.00
129	Charlie Trippi	45.00
130	Tom Wham	20.00
131	Ventan Yablonski	20.00
132	Chuck Bednarik	75.00
133	Joe Muha	20.00
134	Pete Pihos	45.00
135	Washington Serini	20.00
136	George Gulyanics	20.00
137	Ken Kavanaugh	20.00
138	Howie Livingston	20.00
139	Joe Tereshinski	20.00
140	Jim White	20.00
141	Gene Roberts	20.00
142	William Swiacki	20.00
143	Norm Standlee	20.00
144	Knox Ramsey	60.00

1951 Bowman

Bowman's third set was again 144 cards, but cards were increased in size to 2-1/16" x 3-1/8". Cards bear a close similarity to this year's Bowman baseball set on both fronts and backs. Rookies in this set include Norm Van Brocklin, Tom Landry, Arnie Weinmeister, Bill Walsh, Emlen Tunnell, and Ernie Stautner.

		NM
	Complete Set (144):	3500.
	Common Player:	18.00
1	Weldon Humble	60.00
2	Otto Graham	150.00
3	Mac Speedie	18.00
4	Norm Van Brocklin	250.00
5	Woodley Lewis	18.00
6	Tom Fears	35.00
7	George Musacco	18.00
8	George Taliaferro	18.00
9	Barney Poole	18.00
10	Steve Van Buren	60.00
11	Whitey Wistert	18.00
12	Chuck Bednarik	60.00
13	Bulldog Turner	40.00
14	Bob Williams	18.00
15	John Lujack	50.00
16	Roy "Rebel" Steiner	18.00
17	Earl "Jug" Girard	18.00
18	Bill Neal	18.00
19	Travis Tidwell	18.00
20	Tom Landry	500.00
21	Arnie Weinmeister	40.00
22	Joe Geri	18.00
23	Bill Walsh	18.00
24	Fran Rogel	18.00
25	Doak Walker	50.00
26	Leon Hart	18.00
27	Thurman McGraw	18.00
28	Buster Ramsey	18.00
29	Frank Tripucka	18.00
30	Don Paul	18.00
31	Alex Loyd	18.00
32	Y.A. Tittle	120.00
33	Verl Lillywhite	18.00
34	Sammy Baugh	150.00
35	Chuck Drazenovich	18.00
36	Bob Goode	18.00
37	Horace Gillom	18.00
38	Lou Rymkus	18.00
39	Ken Carpenter	18.00
40	Bob Waterfield	60.00
41	Vitamin Smith	18.00
42	Glenn Davis	50.00
43	Dan Edwards	18.00
44	John Rauch	18.00
45	Zollie Toth	18.00
46	Pete Pihos	30.00
47	Russ Craft	18.00
48	Walter Barnes	18.00
49	Fred Morrison	18.00
50	Ray Bray	18.00
51	Ed Sprinkle	18.00
52	Floyd Reid	18.00
53	Billy Grimes	18.00
54	Ted Fritsch, Sr.	18.00
55	Al DeRogatis	18.00
56	Charlie Conerly	50.00
57	Jon Baker	18.00
58	Tom McWilliams	18.00
59	Jerry Shipkey	18.00
60	Lynn Chandnois	18.00
61	Don Doll	18.00
62	Lou Creekmur	35.00
63	Bob Hoernschemeyer	18.00
64	Tom Wham	18.00
65	Bill Fischer	18.00
66	Robert Nussbaumer	18.00
67	Gordon Soltau	18.00
68	Visco Grgich	18.00
69	John Strzykalski	18.00
70	Pete Stout	18.00
71	Paul Lipscomb	18.00
72	Harry Gilmer	18.00
73	Dante Lavelli	40.00
74	Dub Jones	18.00
75	Lou Groza	70.00
76	Elroy Hirsch	60.00
77	Tom Kalmanir	18.00
78	Jack Zilly	18.00
79	Bruce Alford	18.00
80	Art Weiner	18.00
81	Brad Ecklund	18.00
82	Bosh Pritchard	18.00
83	John Green	18.00
84	H. Ebert Van Buren	18.00
85	Fred Davis	18.00
86	Julie Rykovich	18.00
87	John Hoffman	18.00
88	Tobin Rote	18.00
89	Paul Burris	18.00
90	Tony Canadeo	30.00
91	Emlen Tunnell	100.00
92	Otto Schnellbacher	18.00
93	Ray Poole	18.00
94	Darrell Hogan	18.00
95	Frank Sinkovitz	18.00
96	Ernie Stautner	70.00
97	Elmer Angsman	18.00
98	Jack Jennings	18.00
99	Jerry Groom	18.00
100	John Prchlik	18.00
101	J. Robert Smith	18.00
102	Bobby Layne	120.00
103	Frankie Albert	18.00
104	Gail Bruce	18.00
105	Joe Perry	60.00
106	Leon Heath	18.00
107	Ed Quirk	18.00
108	Hugh Taylor	18.00
109	Marion Motley	50.00
110	Tony Adamle	18.00
111	Alex Agase	18.00
112	Tank Younger	18.00
113	Bob Boyd	18.00
114	Jerry Williams	18.00
115	Joe Goldring	18.00
116	Sherman Howard	18.00
117	John Wozniak	18.00
118	Frank Reagan	18.00
119	Vic Sears	18.00
120	Clyde Scott	18.00
121	George Gulyanics	18.00
122	Bill Wightkin	18.00
123	Chuck Hunsinger	18.00
124	Jack Cloud	18.00
125	Abner Wimberly	18.00
126	Dick Wildung	18.00
127	Eddie Price	18.00
128	Joe Scott	18.00
129	Jerry Nuzum	18.00
130	Jim Finks	40.00
131	Bob Gage	18.00
132	William Swiacki	18.00
133	Joe Watson	18.00
134	Ollie Cline	18.00
135	Jack Lininger	18.00
136	Fran Polsfoot	18.00
137	Charlie Trippi	40.00
138	Ventan Yablonski	18.00
139	Emil Sitko	18.00
140	Leo Nomellini	50.00
141	Norm Standlee	18.00
142	Eddie Saenz	18.00
143	Al Demao	18.00
144	Bill Dudley	75.00

1952 Bowman Large

The player selection in the "Large" set exactly matches Bowman's 1952 "Small" issue. The card size, however, was increased from 2-1/16" x 3-1/8" to 2-1/2" x 3-3/4". A problem surfaced for Bowman while trying to produce the larger set: the company could not fit all the larger cards on one sheet the way it could with the smaller set. So certain cards were pulled. The short-printed cards are those with a factor of nine plus the card immediately following that number. In addition, the second series was issued in lesser quantities than the first. The 1952 Bowman Large set is easily the most valuable football card set ever produced. Card #144, Jim "Buck" Lansford, is practically impossible to find in mint condition, first because it was an odd number on the last sheet, second because it was the last card in the set.

		NM
	Complete Set (144):	12000.
	Common Player (1-72):	25.00
	Common Player (73-144):	35.00
1	Norm Van Brocklin	425.00
2	Otto Graham	275.00
3	Doak Walker	75.00
4	Steve Owen	50.00
5	Frankie Albert	30.00
6	Laurie Niemi	25.00
7	Chuck Hunsinger	25.00
8	Ed Modzelewski	25.00
9	Joe Spencer (SP)	75.00
10	Chuck Bednarik (SP)	175.00
11	Barney Poole	25.00
12	Charlie Trippi	50.00
13	Tom Fears	50.00
14	Paul Brown	225.00
15	Leon Hart	30.00
16	Frank Gifford	475.00
17	Y.A. Tittle	175.00
18	Charlie Justice (SP)	150.00
19	George Connor (SP)	125.00
20	Lynn Chandnois	25.00
21	Bill Howton	35.00
22	Kenneth Snyder	25.00
23	Gino Marchetti	200.00
24	John Karras	25.00
25	Tank Younger	30.00
26	Tommy Thompson	25.00
27	Bob Miller (SP)	285.00
28	Kyle Rote (SP)	140.00
29	Hugh McElhenny (SP)	200.00
30	Sammy Baugh	350.00
31	Jim Dooley	25.00
32	Ray Matthews	25.00
33	Fred Cone	25.00
34	Al Pollard	25.00
35	Brad Ecklund	25.00
36	John Lee Hancock	350.00
37	Elroy Hirsch (SP)	150.00
38	Keever Jankovich	25.00
39	Emlen Tunnell	60.00
40	Steve Dowden	25.00
41	Claude Hipps	25.00
42	Norm Standlee	25.00
43	Dick Todd	25.00
44	Babe Parilli	30.00
45	Steve Van Buren (SP)	225.00
46	Art Donovan (SP)	350.00
47	Bill Fischer	25.00
48	George Halas	275.00
49	Jerrell Price	25.00
50	John Sandusky	35.00
51	Ray Beck	25.00
52	Jim Martin	25.00
53	Joe Back	25.00
54	Glen Christian (SP)	75.00
55	Andy Davis (SP)	75.00
56	Tobin Rote	30.00
57	Wayne Millner	70.00
58	Zollie Toth	25.00
59	Jack Jennings	25.00
60	Bill McColl	25.00
61	Les Richter	30.00
62	Walt Michaels	35.00
63	Charlie Conerly (SP)	475.00
64	Howard Hartley (SP)	75.00
65	Jerome Smith	25.00
66	James Clark	25.00
67	Dick Logan	25.00
68	Wayne Robinson	25.00
69	James Hammond	25.00
70	Gene Schroeder	25.00
71	Tex Coulter	25.00
72	John Schweder (SP)	500.00
73	Vitamin Smith (SP)	150.00
74	Joe Campanella	35.00
75	Joe Kuharich	35.00
76	Herman Clark	35.00
77	Dan Edwards	35.00
78	Bobby Layne	225.00
79	Bob Hoernschemeyer	35.00
80	John Carr Blount	35.00
81	John Kastan (SP)	150.00
82	Harry Minarik (SP)	130.00
83	Joe Perry	80.00
84	Ray Parker	35.00
85	Andy Robustelli	175.00
86	Dub Jones	40.00
87	Mal Cook	35.00
88	Billy Stone	35.00
89	George Taliaferro	35.00
90	Thomas Johnson (SP)	150.00
91	Leon Heath (SP)	100.00
92	Pete Pihos	75.00
93	Fred Benners	35.00
94	George Tarasovic	35.00
95	Lawrence Shaw	35.00
96	Bill Wightkin	35.00
97	John Wozniak	35.00
98	Bobby Dillon	35.00
99	Joe Stydahar (SP)	575.00
100	Dick Alban (SP)	150.00
101	Arnie Weinmeister	55.00
102	Robert Joe Cross	35.00
103	Don Paul	35.00
104	Buddy Young	50.00
105	Lou Groza	100.00
106	Ray Pelfrey	35.00
107	Maurice Nipp	35.00
108	Hubert Johnston	625.00
109	Volney Quinlan (SP)	150.00
110	Jack Simmons	35.00
111	George Ratterman	35.00
112	John Badaczewski	35.00
113	Bill Reichardt	35.00
114	Art Weiner	35.00
115	Keith Flowers	35.00
116	Russ Craft	35.00
117	Jim O'Donahue (SP)	150.00
118	Darrell Hogan (SP)	100.00
119	Frank Ziegler	35.00
120	Deacon Dan Towler	40.00
121	Fred Williams	35.00
122	Jimmy Phelan	35.00
123	Eddie Price	35.00
124	Chet Ostrowski	35.00
125	Leo Nomellini	70.00
126	Steve Romanik (SP)	300.00
127	Ollie Matson (SP)	300.00
128	Dante Lavelli	75.00
129	Jack Christiansen	150.00
130	Dom Moselle	35.00
131	John Rapacz	35.00
132	Chuck Ortman	35.00
133	Bob Williams	35.00
134	Chuck Ulrich	35.00
135	Gene Ronzani (SP)	625.00
136	Bert Rechichar (SP)	150.00
137	Bob Waterfield	120.00
138	Bobby Walston	40.00
139	Jerry Shipkey	35.00
140	Yale Lary	150.00
141	Gordon Soltau	40.00
142	Tom Landry	600.00
143	John Papit	35.00
144	Jim Lansford (SP)	2800.

1952 Bowman Small

This set was issued in two sizes, large and small, with the large size being much more scarce and expensive. The Bowman Small set measures 2-1/16" x 3-1/8", and cards feature a flag motif, with flags pointing to the right (two years later, Bowman would use about the same theme, with flags pointing left). This 144-card set features an abundance of rookie cards. They include Steve Owen, Paul Brown, Frank Gifford, Gino Marchetti, Kyle Rote, Hugh McElhenny, George Halas, Wayne Millner, Walt Michaels, Andy Robustelli, Joe Stydahar, Ollie Matson and Yale Lary.

		NM
	Complete Set (144):	5000.
	Common Player (1-72):	20.00
	Common Player (73-144):	25.00
1	Norm Van Brocklin	200.00
2	Otto Graham	125.00
3	Doak Walker	35.00
4	Steve Owen	35.00
5	Frankie Albert	20.00
6	Laurie Niemi	20.00
7	Chuck Hunsinger	20.00
8	Ed Modzelewski	20.00
9	Joe Spencer	20.00
10	Chuck Bednarik	60.00
11	Barney Poole	20.00
12	Charlie Trippi	30.00
13	Tom Fears	30.00
14	Paul Brown	125.00
15	Leon Hart	17.50
16	Frank Gifford	325.00
17	Y.A. Tittle	80.00
18	Charlie Justice	30.00
19	George Connor	30.00
20	Lynn Chandnois	20.00
21	Bill Howton	30.00
22	Kenneth Snyder	20.00

#	Player	Price
23	*Gino Marchetti*	100.00
24	John Karras	20.00
25	Tank Younger	25.00
26	Tommy Thompson	25.00
27	Bob Miller	20.00
28	*Kyle Rote*	50.00
29	*Hugh McElhenny*	125.00
30	Sammy Baugh	200.00
31	Jim Dooley	25.00
32	Ray Matthews	20.00
33	Fred Cone	20.00
34	Al Pollard	20.00
35	Brad Ecklund	20.00
36	John Lee Hancock	20.00
37	Elroy Hirsch	50.00
38	Keever Jankovich	20.00
39	Emlen Tunnell	35.00
40	Steve Dowden	20.00
41	Claude Hipps	20.00
42	Norm Standlee	20.00
43	Dick Todd	20.00
44	Babe Parilli	25.00
45	Steve Van Buren	45.00
46	Art Donovan	150.00
47	Bill Fischer	20.00
48	George Halas	150.00
49	Jerrell Price	20.00
50	John Sandusky	20.00
51	Ray Beck	20.00
52	Jim Martin	20.00
53	Joe Back	20.00
54	Glen Christian	20.00
55	Andy Davis	20.00
56	Tobin Rote	25.00
57	*Wayne Millner*	35.00
58	Zollie Toth	20.00
59	Jack Jennings	20.00
60	Bill McColl	20.00
61	*Les Richter*	25.00
62	*Walt Michaels*	25.00
63	Charlie Conerly	50.00
64	Howard Hartley	20.00
65	Jerome Smith	20.00
66	James Clark	20.00
67	Dick Logan	20.00
68	Wayne Robinson	20.00
69	James Hammond	20.00
70	Gene Schroeder	20.00
71	Tex Coulter	20.00
72	John Schweder	20.00
73	Vitamin Smith	25.00
74	Joe Campanella	25.00
75	Joe Kuharich	25.00
76	Herman Clark	25.00
77	Dan Edwards	25.00
78	Bobby Layne	90.00
79	Bob Hoernschemeyer	25.00
80	John Carr Blount	25.00
81	John Kastan	25.00
82	Harry Minarik	25.00
83	Joe Perry	60.00
84	Ray Parker	25.00
85	*Andy Robustelli*	100.00
86	Dub Jones	25.00
87	Mal Cook	25.00
88	Billy Stone	25.00
89	George Taliaferro	25.00
90	Thomas Johnson	25.00
91	Leon Heath	25.00
92	Pete Pihos	40.00
93	Fred Benners	25.00
94	George Tarasovic	25.00
95	Lawrence Shaw	25.00
96	Bill Wightkin	25.00
97	John Wozniak	25.00
98	*Bobby Dillon*	25.00
99	*Joe Stydahar*	25.00
100	Dick Alban	25.00
101	Arnie Weinmeister	35.00
102	Robert Joe Cross	25.00
103	Don Paul	25.00
104	Buddy Young	30.00
105	Lou Groza	50.00
106	Ray Pelfrey	25.00
107	Maurice Nipp	25.00
108	Hubert Johnston	25.00
109	Volney Quinlan	25.00
110	Jack Simmons	25.00
111	George Ratterman	25.00
112	John Badaczewski	25.00
113	Bill Reichardt	25.00
114	Art Weiner	25.00
115	Keith Flowers	25.00
116	Russ Craft	25.00
117	Jim O'Donahue	25.00
118	Darrell Hogan	25.00
119	Frank Ziegler	25.00
120	Deacon Dan Towler	30.00
121	Fred Williams	25.00
122	Jimmy Phelan	25.00
123	Eddie Price	25.00
124	Chet Ostrowski	25.00
125	Leo Nomellini	50.00
126	Steve Romanik	25.00
127	Ollie Matson	120.00
128	Dante Lavelli	40.00
129	*Jack Christiansen*	75.00
130	Dom Moselle	25.00
131	John Rapacz	25.00
132	Chuck Ortman	25.00
133	Bob Williams	25.00
134	Chuck Ulrich	25.00
135	*Gene Ronzani*	28.00
136	Bert Rechichar	25.00
137	Bob Waterfield	60.00
138	*Bobby Walston*	30.00
139	Jerry Shipkey	25.00
140	*Yale Lary*	80.00
141	Gordon Soltau	25.00
142	Tom Landry	300.00
143	John Papit	25.00
144	*Jim Lansford*	125.00

1953 Bowman

The "name in a football" theme was one that would next be used by Topps in its 1960 set and again in the 1976 set. Bowman was the only company to issue football cards, but only a 96-card issue was produced and 24 of those were short-printed.

		NM
Complete Set (96):		3200.
Common Player:		25.00
SP Cards:		40.00
1	Eddie LeBaron	100.00
2	John Dottley	25.00
3	Babe Parilli	25.00
4	Bucko Kilroy	25.00
5	Joe Tereshinski	25.00
6	Doak Walker	50.00
7	Fran Polsfoot	25.00
8	Sisto Averno	25.00
9	Marion Motley	50.00
10	Pat Brady	25.00
11	Norm Van Brocklin	80.00
12	Bill McColl	25.00
13	Jerry Groom	25.00
14	Al Pollard	25.00
15	Dante Lavelli	40.00
16	Eddie Price	25.00
17	Charlie Trippi	40.00
18	Elbert Nickel	25.00
19	George Taliaferro	25.00
20	Charlie Conerly	50.00
21	Bobby Layne	100.00
22	Elroy Hirsch	60.00
23	Jim Finks	35.00
24	Chuck Bednarik	60.00
25	Kyle Rote	30.00
26	Otto Graham	135.00
27	Harry Gilmer	25.00
28	Tobin Rote	25.00
29	Billy Stone	25.00
30	Buddy Young	25.00
31	Leon Hart	25.00
32	Hugh McElhenny	60.00
33	Dale Samuels	25.00
34	Lou Creekmur	25.00
35	Tom Catlin	25.00
36	Tom Fears	40.00
37	George Connor	35.00
38	Bill Walsh	25.00
39	Leo Sanford (SP)	40.00
40	Horace Gillom	25.00
41	John Schweder (SP)	40.00
42	Tom O'Connell	25.00
43	Frank Gifford (SP)	350.00
44	Frank Continetti (SP)	40.00
45	John Olszewski (SP)	40.00
46	Dub Jones	25.00
47	Don Paul (SP)	40.00
48	Gerald Weatherly (SP)	40.00
49	Fred Bruney (SP)	40.00
50	Jack Scarbath	25.00
51	John Karras	25.00
52	Al Conway	25.00
53	Emlen Tunnell (SP)	100.00
54	Gern Nagler (SP)	40.00
55	Kenneth Snyder (SP)	40.00
56	Y.A. Tittle	100.00
57	John Rapacz (SP)	40.00
58	Harley Sewell	25.00
59	Don Bingham	25.00
60	Darrell Hogan	25.00
61	Tony Curcillo	25.00
62	*Ray Renfro* (SP)	50.00
63	Leon Heath	25.00
64	Tex Coulter	40.00
65	Dewayne Douglas	25.00
66	J. Robert Smith (SP)	40.00
67	Bob McChesney (SP)	40.00
68	Dick Alban (SP)	40.00
69	Andy Kozar	25.00
70	Merwin Hodel (SP)	40.00
71	Thurman McGraw	25.00
72	Cliff Anderson	25.00
73	Pete Pihos	25.00
74	Julie Rykovich	25.00
75	John Kreamcheck (SP)	40.00
76	Lynn Chandnois (SP)	25.00
77	Cloyce Box (SP)	40.00
78	Ray Matthews	25.00
79	Bobby Walston	25.00
80	Jim Dooley	25.00
81	Pat Harder (SP)	40.00
82	Jerry Shipkey	25.00
83	Bobby Thomason	25.00
84	Hugh Taylor	25.00
85	George Ratterman	25.00
86	Don Stonesifer	25.00
87	John Williams (SP)	40.00
88	Leo Nomellini	45.00
89	Frank Ziegler	25.00
90	Don Paul	25.00
91	Tom Dublinski	25.00
92	Ken Carpenter	25.00
93	*Ted Marchibroda*	40.00
94	Chuck Drazenovich	25.00
95	Lou Groza (SP)	100.00
96	William Cross (SP)	75.00

1954 Bowman

This 128-card set has a flag motif that points left, almost a reversal of the 1952 theme. Issued in four series of 32 cards, numbers 65-96 are much tougher to find than the other three. Rookies in this set include Doug Atkins, George Blanda, Hawg Hanner and Whizzer White (actually not Whizzer White; see below). There's an error and a variation in this set. The error is on card #125 "Whizzer" White, his rookie card. It shows not the future Supreme Court Justice, but Wilford White. The variation involves #97, Tom Finnan. On the scarcer error version, his name was incorrectly spelled "Finnin." This was corrected.

		NM
Complete Set (128):		1600.
Common Player (1-64):		6.00
Common Player (65-96):		25.00
Common Player (97-128):		6.00
1	Ray Matthews	25.00
2	John Huzvar	6.00
3	Jack Scarbath	6.00
4	*Doug Atkins*	45.00
5	Bill Stits	6.00
6	Joe Perry	30.00
7	Kyle Rote	12.00
8	Norm Van Brocklin	45.00
9	Pete Pihos	20.00
10	Babe Parilli	10.00
11	Zeke Bratkowski	25.00
12	Ollie Matson	25.00
13	Pat Brady	6.00
14	Fred Enke	6.00
15	Harry Ulinski	6.00
16	Bobby Garrett	6.00
17	Bill Bowman	6.00
18	Leo Rucka	6.00
19	John Cannady	6.00
20	Tom Fears	20.00
21	Norm Willey	6.00
22	Floyd Reid	6.00
23	*George Blanda*	180.00
24	Don Doheney	6.00
25	John Schweder	6.00
26	Bert Rechichar	6.00
27	Harry Dowda	6.00
28	John Sandusky	6.00
29	*Les Bingaman*	10.00
30	Joe Arenas	6.00
31	Ray Wietecha	8.00
32	Elroy Hirsch	30.00
33	Harold Giancanelli	6.00
34	Bill Howton	10.00
35	Fred Morrison	6.00
36	Bobby Cavazos	6.00
37	Darrell Hogan	6.00
38	Buddy Young	7.00
39	Charlie Justice	14.00
40	Otto Graham	75.00
41	Doak Walker	25.00
42	Y.A. Tittle	50.00
43	Buford Long	6.00
44	Volney Quinlan	6.00
45	Bobby Thomason	7.00
46	Fred Cone	6.00
47	Gerald Weatherly	6.00
48	Don Stonesifer	6.00
49	Lynn Chandnois	6.00
50	George Taliaferro	6.00
51	Dick Alban	6.00
52	Lou Groza	25.00
53	Bobby Layne	50.00
54	Hugh McElhenny	30.00
55	Frank Gifford	100.00
56	Leon McLaughlin	6.00
57	Chuck Bednarik	30.00
58	Art Hunter	6.00
59	Bill McColl	6.00
60	Charlie Trippi	25.00
61	*Jim Finks*	10.00
62	Bill Lange	6.00
63	Laurie Niemi	6.00
64	Ray Renfro	6.00
65	Dick Chapman	25.00
66	Bob Hantla	25.00
67	Ralph Starkey	25.00
68	Don Paul	25.00
69	Kenneth Snyder	25.00
70	Tobin Rote	25.00
71	Arthur DeCarlo	25.00
72	Tom Keane	25.00
73	Hugh Taylor	25.00
74	*Warren Lahr*	25.00
75	Jim Neal	25.00
76	Leo Nomellini	50.00
77	Dick Yelvington	25.00
78	Les Richter	25.00
79	Bucko Kilroy	25.00
80	John Martinkovic	25.00
81	*Dale Dodrill*	25.00
82	Ken Jackson	25.00
83	Paul Lipscomb	25.00
84	John Bauer	25.00
85	Lou Creekmur	50.00
86	Eddie Price	25.00
87	Kenneth Farragut	25.00
88	*Dave Hanner*	25.00
89	Don Boll	25.00
90	Chet Hanulak	25.00
91	Thurman McGraw	25.00
92	*Don Heinrich*	25.00
93	Dan McKown	25.00
94	Bob Fleck	25.00
95	Jerry Hilgenberg	25.00
96	Bill Walsh	25.00
97	Tom Finnin	50.00
98	Paul Barry	6.00
99	Harry Jagade	6.00
100	Jack Christiansen	20.00
101	Gordon Soltau	6.00
102	Emlen Tunnell	20.00
103	Stan West	6.00
104	Jerry Williams	6.00
105	Veryl Switzer	6.00
106	Billy Stone	6.00
107	Jerry Watford	6.00
108	Elbert Nickel	6.00
109	Ed Sharkey	6.00
110	Steve Meilinger	6.00
111	Dante Lavelli	20.00
112	Leon Hart	14.00
113	Charlie Conerly	30.00
114	Richard Lemmon	6.00
115	Al Carmichael	6.00
116	George Conner	15.00
117	John Olszewski	6.00
118	Ernie Stautner	20.00
119	Ray Smith	6.00
120	Neil Worden	6.00
121	Jim Dooley	6.00
122	Arnold Galiffa	6.00
123	Kline Gilbert	6.00
124	Bob Hoernschemeyer	6.00
125	*Whizzer White*	15.00
126	Art Spinney	6.00
127	Joe Koch	6.00
128	*John Lattner*	75.00

1955 Bowman

An excellent run of football cards ended after this year when the Bowman Co. released its last set of 160 cards. (Its competitor, Topps Chewing Gum Co., bought it early in 1956.) The first 64 cards are relatively easy to find, compared to numbers 65-160. Rookies in this set include Hall of Famers Mike McCormick, Len Ford, John Henry Johnson, Bob St. Clair, Jim Ringo, and Frank Gatski. Other rookies include Pat Summerall and Alan Ameche.

		NM
Complete Set (160):		1500.
Common Player (1-64):		4.50
Common Player (65-160):		6.00
1	Doak Walker	50.00
2	*Mike McCormack*	30.00
3	John Olszewski	4.50
4	Dorne Dibble	4.50
5	Lindon Crow	4.50
6	Hugh Taylor	4.50
7	Frank Gifford	75.00
8	*Alan Ameche*	30.00
9	Don Stonesifer	4.50
10	Pete Pihos	12.50
11	Bill Austin	4.50
12	Dick Alban	4.50
13	Bobby Walston	4.50
14	*Len Ford*	30.00
15	Jug Girard	4.50
16	Charlie Conerly	25.00
17	Volney Peters	4.50
18	Max Boydston	4.50
19	Leon Hart	4.50
20	Bert Rechichar	4.50
21	Lee Riley	4.50
22	Johnny Carson	4.50
23	Harry Thompson	4.50
24	Ray Wietecha	4.50
25	Ollie Matson	25.00
26	Eddie LeBaron	8.00
27	Jack Simmons	4.50
28	Jack Christiansen	12.50
29	Bucko Kilroy	4.50
30	Tom Keane	4.50
31	Dave Leggett	4.50
32	Norm Van Brocklin	35.00
33	Harlon Hill	4.50
34	Robert Haner	4.50
35	Veryl Switzer	4.50
36	Dick Stanfel	6.00
37	Lou Groza	24.00
38	Tank Younger	5.00
39	Dick Flanagan	4.50
40	Jim Dooley	4.50
41	Ray Collins	4.50
42	*John Henry Johnson*	40.00
43	Tom Fears	15.00
44	Joe Perry	25.00
45	Gene Brito	6.00
46	Bill Johnson	4.50
47	Deacon Dan Towler	6.00
48	Dick Moegle	4.50
49	Kline Gilbert	4.50
50	Les Gobel	4.50
51	Ray Krouse	4.50
52	*Pat Summerall*	55.00
53	Ed Brown	8.00
55	Joe Heap	4.50
56	John Hoffman	4.50
57	Howard Ferguson	4.50
58	Bobby Watkins	4.50
59	Charlie Ane	4.50
60	*Ken MacAfee*	6.00
62	George Blanda	70.00
63	Kenneth Snyder	4.50
64	Chet Ostrowski	4.50
65	Buddy Young	5.00
67	Eddie Bell	6.00
68	*Ben Agajanian*	8.00
69	Tom Dahms	6.00
70	*Jim Ringo*	35.00
71	Bobby Layne	60.00
72	Y.A. Tittle	60.00
73	Bob Gaona	6.00
74	Tobin Rote	10.00
76	Hugh McElhenny	20.00
77	John Kreamcheck	6.00
78	Al Dorow	6.00
79	Bill Wade	9.00
80	Dale Dodrill	6.00
81	Chuck Drazenovich	6.00
82	*Billy Wilson*	10.00
83	Les Richter	6.00
84	Pat Brady	6.00
85	Bob Hoernschemeyer	6.00
86	Joe Arenas	6.00
87	Len Szafaryn	6.00
88	*Rick Casares*	16.00
89	Leon McLaughlin	6.00
90	Charley Toogood	6.00
91	Tom Bettis	6.00
92	John Sandusky	6.00
93	Bill Wightkin	6.00
94	Darrell Brewster	6.00
95	Marion Campbell	8.00
96	Floyd Reid	6.00
97	Harry Jagade	6.00
98	George Taliaferro	6.00
99	Carleton Massey	6.00
100	Fran Rogel	6.00
101	Alex Sandusky	6.00
102	*Bob St. Clair*	35.00
103	Al Carmichael	6.00
104	Carl Taseff	8.00
105	Leo Nomellini	18.00
106	Tom Scott	6.00
107	Ted Marchibroda	16.00
108	Art Spinney	6.00
109	Wayne Robinson	6.00
110	Jim Ricca	6.00
111	Lou Ferry	6.00
112	Roger Zatkoff	6.00
113	Lou Creekmur	6.00
114	Kenny Konz	6.00
115	Doug Eggers	6.00
116	Bobby Thomason	6.00
117	Bill McPeak	6.00
118	William Brown	6.00
119	Royce Womble	6.00
120	Jim Finks	8.00
121	Andy Robustelli	20.00
122	Bobby Dillon	6.00
123	Leo Sanford	6.00
124	Elbert Nickel	6.00
125	Wayne Hansen	6.00
126	Buck Lansford	6.00
127	Gern Nagler	6.00
128	Jim Salsbury	6.00
129	Dale Atkeson	6.00
130	John Schweder	6.00
131	Dave Hanner	6.00
132	Eddie Price	6.00
133	Vic Janowicz	20.00
134	Ernie Stautner	20.00
135	James Parmer	6.00
136	Emlen Tunnell	20.00
137	Kyle Rote	14.00
138	Norm Willey	6.00
139	Charlie Trippi	18.00
140	Bill Howton	8.00
141	Bobby Clatterbuck	6.00
142	Bob Boyd	6.00
143	*Bob Toneff*	8.00
144	Jerry Helluin	6.00
145	Adrian Burk	6.00
146	Walt Michaels	8.00
147	Zillie Toth	6.00
148	*Frank Varrichione*	8.00
149	Dick Bielski	6.00
150	George Ratterman	6.00
151	Mike Jarmoluk	6.00
152	Tom Landry	175.00
153	Ray Renfro	6.00
154	Zeke Bratkowski	7.50
155	Jerry Norton	6.00
156	Maurice Bassett	6.00
157	Volney Quinlan	6.00
158	Chuck Bednarik	25.00
159	Don Colo	6.00
160	*L.G. Dupre*	30.00

1991 Bowman

CHRIS DOLEMAN

Topps produced this 561-card set in 1991 under the Bowman name. The standard-size cards have color photos on the front, with blue and orange borders. The player's name is in white in a purple stripe at the bottom. The grey backs, in green and black type, have a player profile, biography and statistics. The cards are numbered alphabetically by team, beginning with Atlanta and ending with Washington. Subsets include League Leaders (#s 273-283), Rookie Superstars (#s 1-11), and Road to the Super Bowl (#s 547-557). These 33 subset cards are gold-foil embossed, with one appearing in every pack.

		MT
Complete Set (561):		10.00
Common Player:		.03
Wax Box:		10.00
1	Jeff George (RS)	.10
2	Richmond Webb (RS)	.03
3	Emmitt Smith (RS)	1.00
4	Mark Carrier (RS)	.05
5	Steve Christie (RS)	.03
6	Keith Sims (RS)	.03
7	Rob Moore (RS)	.15
8	Johnny Johnson (RS)	.10
9	Eric Green (RS)	.03
10	Ben Smith (RS)	.03
11	Tory Epps (RS)	.03
12	Andre Rison	.25
13	Shawn Collins	.03
14	Chris Hinton	.03
15	Deion Sanders	.50
16	Darion Conner	.03
17	Michael Haynes	.30
18	Chris Miller	.03
19	Jessie Tuggle	.03
20	Scott Fulhage	.03
21	Bill Fralic	.03
22	Floyd Dixon	.03
23	Oliver Barnett	.03
24	Mike Rozier	.03
25	Tory Epps	.03
26	Tim Green	.03
27	Steve Broussard	.03
28	Bruce Pickens	.03
29	*Mike Pritchard*	.50
30	Andre Reed	.10
31	Darryl Talley	.03
32	Nate Odomes	.03
33	Jamie Mueller	.03
34	Leon Seals	.03
35	Keith McKeller	.03
36	Al Edwards	.03
37	Butch Rolle	.03
38	Jeff Wright	.10
39	Will Wolford	.03
40	James Williams	.03
41	Kent Hull	.03
42	James Lofton	.03
44	Bruce Smith	.03
45	Thurman Thomas	.50
46	Leonard Smith	.03
47	Shane Conlan	.03
48	Steve Tasker	.03
49	Ray Bentley	.03
50	Cornelius Bennett	.05
51	Stan Thomas	.03
52	Shaun Gayle	.03
53	Wendell Davis	.10
54	James Thornton	.03
55	Mark Carrier	.03
56	Richard Dent	.05
57	Ron Morris	.03
58	Mike Singletary	.10
59	Jay Hilgenberg	.03
60	Donnell Woolford	.03
61	Jim Covert	.03
62	Jim Harbaugh	.05
63	Neal Anderson	.10
64	Brad Muster	.03
65	Kevin Butler	.03
66	Trace Armstrong	.03
67	Ron Cox	.03

No.	Player	MT
68	Peter Tom Willis	.03
69	Johnny Bailey	.03
70	Mark Bortz	.03
71	Chris Zorich	.25
72	Lamar Rogers	.03
73	David Grant	.03
74	Lewis Billups	.03
75	Harold Green	.15
76	Ickey Woods	.03
77	Eddie Brown	.03
78	David Fulcher	.03
79	Anthony Munoz	.03
80	Carl Zander	.03
81	Rodney Holman	.03
82	James Brooks	.03
83	Tim McGee	.03
84	Boomer Esiason	.15
85	Leon White	.03
86	James Francis	.10
87	Mitchell Price	.03
88	*Ed King*	.10
89	*Eric Turner*	.25
90	*Rob Burnett*	.10
91	Leroy Hoard	.10
92	Kevin Mack	.03
93	Thane Gash	.03
94	Gregg Rakoczy	.03
95	Clay Matthews	.03
96	Eric Metcalf	.03
97	Stephen Braggs	.03
98	Frank Minnifield	.03
99	Reggie Langhorne	.03
100	Mike Johnson	.03
101	Brian Brennan	.03
102	Anthony Pleasant	.03
103	Godfrey Myles	.03
104	*Russell Maryland*	.50
105	*James Washington*	.10
106	Nate Newton	.03
107	Jimmie Jones	.03
108	Jay Novacek	.15
109	Alexander Wright	.10
110	Jack Del Rio	.03
111	Jim Jeffcoat	.03
112	Mike Saxon	.03
113	Troy Aikman	1.00
114	Issiac Holt	.03
115	Ken Norton	.03
116	Kelvin Martin	.03
117	Emmitt Smith	2.00
118	Ken Willis	.03
119	Daniel Stubbs	.03
120	Michael Irvin	.15
121	Danny Noonan	.03
122	*Alvin Harper*	.50
123	*Reggie Johnson*	.10
124	Vance Johnson	.03
125	Steve Atwater	.03
126	Greg Kragen	.03
127	John Elway	.40
128	Simon Fletcher	.03
129	Wymon Henderson	.03
130	Ricky Nattiel	.03
131	Shannon Sharpe	.10
132	Ron Holmes	.03
133	Karl Mecklenburg	.03
134	Bobby Humphrey	.03
135	Clarence Kay	.03
136	Dennis Smith	.03
137	Jim Juriga	.03
138	Melvin Bratton	.03
139	Mark Jackson	.03
140	Michael Brooks	.03
141	Alton Montgomery	.03
142	*Mike Croel*	.15
143	Mel Gray	.03
144	Michael Cofer	.03
145	Jeff Campbell	.03
146	Dan Owens	.03
147	Robert Clark	.03
148	Jim Arnold	.03
149	William White	.03
150	Rodney Peete	.03
151	Jerry Ball	.03
152	Bennie Blades	.03
153	Barry Sanders	1.50
154	Andre Ware	.10
155	Lomas Brown	.03
156	Chris Spielman	.03
157	Kelvin Pritchett	.03
158	*Herman Moore*	3.50
159	Chris Jacke	.03
160	Tony Mandarich	.03
161	Perry Kemp	.03
162	Johnny Holland	.03
163	Mark Lee	.03
164	Anthony Dilweg	.03
165	Scott Stephen	.03
166	Ed West	.03
167	Mark Murphy	.03
168	Darrell Thompson	.15
169	James Campen	.03
170	Jeff Query	.03
171	Brian Noble	.03
172	Sterling Sharpe	.15
173	Robert Brown	.03
174	Tim Harris	.03
175	LeRoy Butler	.03
176	Don Majkowski	.03
177	Vinnie Clark	.03
178	Esera Tuaolo	.03
179	Lorenzo White	.10
180	Warren Moon	.25
181	Sean Jones	.03
182	Curtis Duncan	.03
183	Al Smith	.04
184	Richard Johnson	.03
185	Tony Jones	.03

No.	Player	MT
186	Bubba McDowell	.03
187	Bruce Matthews	.03
188	Ray Childress	.03
189	Haywood Jeffires	.25
190	Ernest Givins	.03
191	Mike Munchak	.03
192	Greg Montgomery	.03
193	*Cody Carlson*	.30
194	Johnny Meads	.03
195	Drew Hill	.03
196	Mike Dumas	.03
197	*Darryll Lewis*	.10
198	Rohn Stark	.03
199	Clarence Verdin	.03
200	Mike Prior	.03
201	Eugene Daniel	.03
202	Dean Biasucci	.03
203	Jeff Herrod	.03
204	Keith Taylor	.03
205	Jon Hand	.03
206	Pat Beach	.03
207	Duane Bickett	.03
208	Jessie Hester	.03
209	Chip Banks	.03
210	Ray Donaldson	.03
211	Bill Brooks	.03
212	Jeff George	.30
213	Tony Siragusa	.03
214	Albert Bentley	.03
215	Joe Valerio	.03
216	Chris Martin	.03
217	Christian Okoye	.03
218	Stephone Paige	.03
219	Percy Snow	.03
220	David Scott	.03
221	Derrick Thomas	.25
222	Todd McNair	.03
223	Albert Lewis	.03
224	Neil Smith	.03
225	Barry Word	.10
226	Robb Thomas	.03
227	John Alt	.03
228	Jonathan Hayes	.03
229	Kevin Ross	.03
230	Nick Lowery	.03
231	Tim Grunhard	.03
232	Dan Saleaumua	.03
233	Steve DeBerg	.03
234	*Harvey Williams*	.50
235	*Nick Bell*	.15
236	Mervyn Fernandez	.03
237	Howie Long	.03
238	Marcus Allen	.03
239	Eddie Anderson	.03
240	Ethan Horton	.03
241	Lionel Washington	.03
242	Steve Wisniewski	.03
243	Bo Jackson	.25
244	Greg Townsend	.03
245	Jeff Jaeger	.03
246	Aaron Wallace	.03
247	Garry Lewis	.03
248	Steve Smith	.03
249	Willie Gault	.03
250	Scott Davis	.03
251	Jay Schroeder	.03
252	Don Mosebar	.03
253	*Todd Marinovich*	.10
254	Irv Pankey	.03
255	Flipper Anderson	.03
256	Tom Newberry	.03
257	Kevin Greene	.03
258	Mike Wilcher	.03
259	Bern Brostek	.03
260	Buford McGee	.03
261	Cleveland Gary	.03
262	Jackie Slater	.03
263	Henry Ellard	.03
264	Alvin Wright	.03
265	*Darryl Henley*	.10
266	Damone Johnson	.03
267	Frank Stams	.03
268	Jerry Gray	.03
269	Jim Everett	.03
270	Pat Terrell	.03
271	Todd Lyght	.15
272	Aaron Cox	.03
273	Barry Sanders (LL)	.50
274	Jerry Rice (LL)	.40
275	Derrick Thomas (LL)	.10
276	Mark Carrier (LL)	.05
277	Warren Moon (LL)	.15
278	Randall Cunningham (LL)	.10
279	Nick Lowery (LL)	.03
280	Clarence Verdin (LL)	.03
281	Thurman Thomas (LL)	.25
282	Mike Horan (LL)	.03
283	Flipper Anderson (LL)	.03
284	John Offerdahl	.03
285	Dan Marino	2.00
286	Mark Clayton	.03
287	Tony Paige	.03
288	Keith Sims	.03
289	Jeff Cross	.03
290	Pete Stoyanovich	.03
291	Ferrell Edmunds	.03
292	Reggie Roby	.03
293	Louis Oliver	.03
294	Jarvis Williams	.03
295	Sammie Smith	.03
296	Richmond Webb	.03
297	J.B. Brown	.03
298	Jim Jensen	.03
299	Mark Duper	.03

No.	Player	MT
300	David Griggs	.03
301	*Randal Hill*	.35
302	*Aaron Craver*	.10
303	Keith Millard	.03
304	Steve Jordan	.03
305	Anthony Carter	.03
306	Mike Merriweather	.03
307	*Audray McMillian*	.35
308	Randall McDaniel	.03
309	Gary Zimmerman	.03
310	Carl Lee	.03
311	Reggie Rutland	.03
312	Hassan Jones	.03
313	Kirk Lowdermilk	.03
314	Herschel Walker	.08
315	Chris Doleman	.03
316	Joey Browner	.03
317	Wade Wilson	.03
318	Henry Thomas	.03
319	Rich Gannon	.08
320	Al Noga	.03
321	*Pat Harlow*	.03
322	Bruce Armstrong	.03
323	Maurice Hurst	.03
324	Brent Williams	.03
325	Chris Singleton	.03
326	Jason Staurovsky	.03
327	Marvin Allen	.03
328	Hart Lee Dykes	.03
329	Johnny Rembert	.03
330	Andre Tippett	.03
331	Greg McMurtry	.03
332	John Stephens	.03
333	Ray Agnew	.03
334	Tommy Hodson	.03
335	Ronnie Lippett	.03
336	Marv Cook	.03
337	*Tommy Barnhardt*	.08
338	Dalton Hilliard	.03
339	Sam Mills	.03
340	Morten Andersen	.03
341	Stan Brock	.03
342	Brett Maxie	.03
343	Steve Walsh	.03
344	Vaughan Johnson	.03
345	Rickey Jackson	.03
346	Renaldo Turnbull	.03
347	Joel Hilgenberg	.03
348	*Toi Cook*	.10
349	Robert Massey	.03
350	Pat Swilling	.03
351	Eric Martin	.03
352	Rueben Mayes	.03
353	Vince Buck	.03
354	Brett Perriman	.03
355	*Wesley Carroll*	.25
356	*Jarrod Bunch*	.10
357	Pepper Johnson	.03
358	Dave Meggett	.03
359	Mark Collins	.03
360	Sean Landeta	.03
361	Maurice Carthon	.03
362	Mike Fox	.03
363	Jeff Hostetler	.15
364	Phil Simms	.08
365	Leonard Marshall	.03
366	Gary Reasons	.03
367	Rodney Hampton	.50
368	*Greg Jackson*	.08
369	Jumbo Elliott	.03
370	*Bob Kratch*	.08
371	Lawrence Taylor	.10
372	Erik Howard	.03
373	Carl Banks	.03
374	Stephen Baker	.03
375	Mark Ingram	.03
376	*Browning Nagle*	.25
377	Jeff Lageman	.03
378	Ken O'Brien	.03
379	Al Toon	.03
380	Joe Prokop	.03
381	Tony Stargell	.03
382	Blair Thomas	.10
383	Erik McMillan	.03
384	Dennis Byrd	.03
385	Freeman McNeil	.03
386	Brad Baxter	.08
387	Mark Boyer	.03
388	Terance Mathis	.10
389	Jim Sweeney	.03
390	Kyle Clifton	.03
391	Pat Leahy	.03
392	Rob Moore	.15
393	James Hasty	.03
394	Blaise Bryant	.03
395	Jesse Campbell (Error-Photo actually Dan McGwire, see 509 Corrected)	.03
396	Keith Jackson	.15
397	Jerome Brown	.03
398	Keith Byars	.03
399	Seth Joyner	.03
400	Mike Bellamy	.03
401	Fred Barnett	.20
402	Reggie Singletary	.03
403	Reggie White	.15
404	Randall Cunningham	.05
405	Byron Evans	.03
406	Wes Hopkins	.03
407	Ben Smith	.03
408	Roger Ruzek	.03
409	Eric Allen	.03
410	Anthony Toney	.03
411	Clyde Simmons	.03
412	Andre Waters	.03

No.	Player	MT
413	Calvin Williams	.15
414	*Eric Swann*	.15
415	Eric Hill	.03
416	Tim McDonald	.03
417	Luis Sharpe	.03
418	Ernie Jones	.03
419	Ken Harvey	.03
420	Ricky Proehl	.15
421	Johnny Johnson	.25
422	Anthony Bell	.03
423	Timm Rosenbach	.03
424	Rich Camarillo	.03
425	Walter Reeves	.03
426	Freddie Joe Nunn	.03
427	Anthony Thompson	.03
428	Bill Lewis	.03
429	*Jim Wahler*	.08
430	Cedric Mack	.03
431	*Michael Jones*	.08
432	Ernie Mills	.08
433	Tim Worley	.03
434	Greg Lloyd	.03
435	Dermontti Dawson	.03
436	Louis Lipps	.03
437	Eric Green	.08
438	Donald Evans	.03
439	David Johnson	.03
440	Tunch Ilkin	.03
441	Bubby Brister	.08
442	Chris Calloway	.03
443	David Little	.03
444	Thomas Everett	.03
445	Carnell Lake	.03
446	Rod Woodson	.05
447	Gary Anderson	.03
448	Merril Hoge	.03
449	Gerald Williams	.03
450	*Eric Moten*	.08
451	Marion Butts	.03
452	Leslie O'Neal	.03
453	Ronnie Harmon	.03
454	Gill Byrd	.03
455	Junior Seau	.25
456	*Nate Lewis*	.25
457	Leo Goeas	.03
458	Burt Grossman	.03
459	Courtney Hall	.03
460	Anthony Miller	.06
461	Gary Plummer	.03
462	Billy Joe Tolliver	.03
463	Lee Williams	.03
464	Arthur Cox	.03
465	John Kidd	.03
466	Frank Cornish	.03
467	John Carney	.03
468	*Eric Bieniemy*	.10
469	Don Griffin	.03
470	Jerry Rice	1.00
471	Keith DeLong	.03
472	John Taylor	.10
473	Brent Jones	.03
474	Pierce Holt	.03
475	Kevin Fagan	.03
476	Bill Romanowski	.03
477	Dexter Carter	.03
478	Guy McIntyre	.03
479	Joe Montana	1.00
480	Charles Haley	.03
481	Mike Cofer	.03
482	Jesse Sapolu	.03
483	Eric Davis	.03
484	Mike Sherrard	.03
485	Steve Young	.75
486	Darryl Pollard	.03
487	Tom Rathman	.03
488	Michael Carter	.03
489	*Ricky Watters*	1.50
490	*John Johnson*	.08
491	Eugene Robinson	.03
492	Andy Heck	.03
493	John L. Williams	.03
494	Norm Johnson	.03
495	David Wyman	.03
496	Derrick Fenner	.10
497	Rick Donnelly	.03
498	Tony Woods	.03
499	*Derek Loville*	.75
500	Dave Krieg	.03
501	Joe Nash	.03
502	Brian Blades	.03
503	Cortez Kennedy	.25
504	Jeff Bryant	.03
505	Tommy Kane	.03
506	Travis McNeal	.03
507	Terry Wooden	.03
508	Chris Warren	.50
509	*Dan McGwire* (Error-Photo actually Jesse Campbell; see 395 Corrected)	.50
510	Mark Robinson	.03
511	Ron Hall	.03
512	Paul Gruber	.03
513	Hary Hamilton	.03
514	Keith McCants	.03
515	Reggie Cobb	.25
516	Steve Christie	.03
517	Broderick Thomas	.03
518	Mark Carrier	.03
519	Vinny Testaverde	.10
520	Ricky Reynolds	.03
521	Jesse Anderson	.03
522	Reuben Davis	.03
523	Wayne Haddix	.03
524	Gary Anderson	.03
525	Bruce Hill	.03
526	Kevin Murphy	.03

No.	Player	MT
527	*Lawrence Dawsey*	.25
528	*Ricky Ervins*	.35
529	Charles Mann	.03
530	Jim Lachey	.03
531	Mark Rypien	.10
532	Darrell Green	.03
533	Stan Humphries	.40
534	Jeff Bostic	.03
535	Earnest Byner	.08
536	Art Monk	.08
537	Don Warren	.03
538	Darryl Grant	.03
539	Wilber Marshall	.03
540	*Kurt Gouveia*	.10
541	Markus Koch	.03
542	Andre Collins	.03
543	Chip Lohmiller	.03
544	Alvin Walton	.03
545	Gary Clark	.10
546	Ricky Sanders	.03
547	Redskins vs. Eagles (Gary Clark)	.03
548	Bengals vs. Oilers (Cody Carlson)	.03
549	Dolphins vs. Chiefs (Mark Clayton)	.03
550	Bears vs. Saints (Neal Anderson)	.03
551	Bills vs. Dolphins (Thurman Thomas)	.10
552	49ers vs. Redskins (Line Play)	.03
553	Giants vs. Bears (Ottis Anderson)	.03
554	Raiders vs. Bengals (Bo Jackson)	.10
555	AFC Championship (Andre Reed)	.03
556	NFC Championship (Jeff Hostetler)	.03
557	Super Bowl XXV (Ottis Anderson)	.03
558	Checklist 1-140	.03
559	Checklist 141-280	.03
560	Checklist 281-420	.03
561	Checklist 421-561	.03

1992 Bowman

SAM MILLS

These standard-size cards have color action photos against a white border. The upper left has a red "B" on a green stripe, while the player's name is at the bottom in an orange-yellow stripe. There are 45 subset cards within the regular set - 28 Team Leader cards, 12 Playoff Star cards and five cards commemorating the longest plays of the 1991 season (punt, kick return, field goal, run and reception). These cards have gold-foil engraved borders and were randomly inserted one per 15-card pack.

	MT
Complete Set (573):	160.00
Common Player:	.25
Minor Stars:	.50
Wax Box:	140.00

No.	Player	MT
1	Reggie White	1.00
2	Johnny Meads	.25
3	Chip Lohmiller	.25
4	James Lofton	.50
5	Ray Horton	.25
6	Rich Moran	.25
7	Howard Cross	.25
8	Mike Horan	.25
9	Erik Kramer	.50
10	Steve Wisniewski	.25
11	Michael Haynes	.25
12	Donald Evans	.25
13	Michael Irvin (FOIL)	1.00
14	Gary Zimmerman	.25
15	John Friesz	.50
16	Mark Carrier	.25
17	Mark Duper	.25
18	James Thornton	.25
19	Jon Hand	.25
20	Sterling Sharpe	1.00
21	Jacob Green	.25
22	Wesley Carroll	.25
23	Clay Matthews	.25
24	Kevin Greene	.50
25	Brad Baxter	.25
26	Don Griffin	.25

No.	Player	MT
27	Robert Delpino (FOIL SP)	1.50
28	Lee Johnson	.25
29	Jim Wahler	.25
30	Leonard Russell	.50
31	Eric Moore	.25
32	Dino Hackett	.25
33	Simon Fletcher	.25
34	Al Edwards	.25
35	Brad Edwards	.25
36	James Joseph	.25
37	Rodney Peete	.50
38	Ricky Reynolds	.25
39	Eddie Anderson	.25
40	Ken Clarke	.25
41	Tony Bennett (FOIL)	.50
42	Larry Brown	.25
43	Ray Childress	.25
44	Mike Kenn	.25
45	Vestee Jackson	.25
46	Neil O'Donnell	1.00
47	Bill Brooks	.25
48	Kevin Butler	.25
49	Joe Phillips	.25
50	Cortez Kennedy	.50
51	Rickey Jackson	.25
52	Vinnie Clark	.25
53	Michael Jackson	.50
54	Ernie Jones	.25
55	Tom Newberry	.25
56	Pat Harlow	.25
57	Craig Taylor	.25
58	Joe Prokop	.25
59	Warren Moon (FOIL SP)	2.00
60	Jeff Lageman	.25
61	Neil Smith	.50
62	Jim Jeffcoat	.25
63	Bill Fralic	.25
64	Mark Schlereth	.25
65	Keith Byars	.25
66	Jeff Hostetler	.50
67	Joey Browner	.25
68	Bobby Hebert (FOIL SP)	1.50
69	Keith Sims	.25
70	Warren Moon	1.00
71	*Pio Sagapolutele*	.25
72	Cornelius Bennett	.50
73	Greg Davis	.25
74	Ronnie Harmon	.25
75	Ron Hall	.25
76	Howie Long	.25
77	Greg Lewis	.25
78	Carnell Lake	.25
79	Ray Crockett	.25
80	Tom Waddle	.25
81	Vincent Brown	.25
82	Bill Brooks (FOIL)	.50
83	John L. Williams	.25
84	Floyd Turner	.25
85	Scott Radecic	.25
86	Anthony Munoz	.50
87	Lonnie Young	.25
88	Dexter Carter	.25
89	Tony Zendejas	.25
90	Tim Jorden	.25
91	LeRoy Butler	.50
92	*Richard Brown*	.25
93	Erric Pegram	.50
94	Sean Landeta	.25
95	Clyde Simmons	.25
96	Martin Mayhew	.25
97	Jarvis Williams	.25
98	Barry Word	.25
99	John Taylor (FOIL)	.50
100	Emmitt Smith	12.00
101	Leon Seals	.25
102	Marion Butts	.25
103	Mike Merriweather	.25
104	Ernest Givins	.25
105	Wymon Henderson	.25
106	Robert Wilson	.25
107	Bobby Hebert	.25
108	Terry McDaniel	.25
109	Jerry Ball	.25
110	John Taylor	.25
111	Rob Moore	1.00
112	Thurman Thomas (FOIL)	1.00
113	Checklist 1	.25
114	Brian Blades	.25
115	Larry Kelm	.25
116	James Francis	.25
117	Rod Woodson	.50
118	Trace Armstrong	.25
119	Eugene Daniel	.25
120	Andre Tippett	.25
121	Chris Jacke	.25
122	Jessie Tuggle	.25
123	Chris Chandler	1.00
124	Tim Johnson	.25
125	Mark Collins	.25
126	Aeneas Williams (FOIL SP)	2.00
127	James Jones	.25
128	George Jamison	.25
129	Deron Cherry	.25
130	Mark Clayton	.25
131	Keith DeLong	.25
132	Marcus Allen	1.00
133	Joe Walter	.25
134	Reggie Rutland	.25
135	Kent Hull	.25
136	Jeff Feagles	.25
137	Ronnie Lott (FOIL SP)	1.50

138	Henry Rolling	.25
139	Gary Anderson	.25
140	Morten Andersen	.50
141	Cris Dishman	.25
142	David Treadwell	.25
143	Kevin Gogan	.25
144	James Hasty	.25
145	Robert Delpino	.25
146	Patrick Hunter	.25
147	Gary Anderson	.25
148	Chip Banks	.25
149	Dan Fike	.25
150	Chris Miller	.25
151	Hugh Millen	.25
152	Courtney Hall	.25
153	Gary Clark	.25
154	Michael Brooks	.25
155	Jay Hilgenberg	.25
156	Tim McDonald	.25
157	Andre Tippett (FOIL)	.50
158	Doug Riesenberg	.25
159	Bill Maas	.25
160	Fred Barnett	.50
161	Pierce Holt	.25
162	Brian Noble	.25
163	Harold Green	.25
164	Joel Hilgenberg	.25
165	Mervyn Fernandez	.25
166	John Offerdahl	.25
167	Shane Conlan	.25
168	Mark Higgs (FOIL SP)	1.50
169	Bubba McDowell	.25
170	Barry Sanders	12.00
171	Larry Roberts	.25
172	Herschel Walker	.50
173	Steve McMichael	.25
174	Kelly Stouffer	.25
175	Louis Lipps	.25
176	Jim Everett	.50
177	Tony Tolbert	.25
178	Mike Baab	.25
179	Eric Swann	.25
180	Emmitt Smith (FOIL SP)	35.00
181	Tim Brown	1.00
182	Dennis Smith	.25
183	Moe Gardner	.25
184	Derrick Walker	.25
185	Reyna Thompson	.25
186	Esera Tuaolo	.25
187	Jeff Wright	.25
188	Mark Rypien	.50
189	Quinn Early	.25
190	Christian Okoye	.25
191	Keith Jackson	.50
192	Doug Smith	.25
193	John Elway (FOIL)	12.00
194	Reggie Cobb	.25
195	Reggie Roby	.25
196	Clarence Verdin	.25
197	Jim Breech	.25
198	Jim Sweeney	.25
199	Marv Cook	.25
200	Ronnie Lott	.50
201	Mel Gray	.25
202	Maury Buford	.25
203	Lorenzo Lynch	.25
204	Jesse Sapolu	.25
205	Steve Jordan	.25
206	Don Majkowski	.25
207	Flipper Anderson	.25
208	Ed King	.25
209	Tony Woods	.25
210	Ron Heller	.25
211	Greg Kragen	.25
212	Scott Case	.25
213	Tommy Barnhardt	.25
214	Charles Mann	.25
215	David Griggs	.25
216	Kenneth Davis (FOIL SP)	1.50
217	Lamar Lathon	.25
218	Nate Odomes	.25
219	Vinny Testaverde	1.00
220	Rod Bernstine	.25
221	Barry Sanders (FOIL)	20.00
222	Carlton Haselrig	.25
223	Steve Beuerlein	.25
224	John Alt	.25
225	Pepper Johnson	.25
226	Checklist 2	.25
227	Irv Eatman	.25
228	Greg Townsend	.25
229	Mark Jackson	.25
230	Robert Blackmon	.25
231	Terry Allen	2.50
232	Bennie Blades	.25
233	Sam Mills (FOIL)	.50
234	Richmond Webb	.25
235	Richard Dent	.50
236	Alonzo Mitz	.25
237	Steve Young	6.00
238	Pat Swilling	.25
239	James Campen	.25
240	Earnest Byner	.25
241	Pat Terrell	.25
242	Carwell Gardner	.25
243	Charles McRae	.25
244	Vince Newsome	.25
245	Eric Hill	.25
246	Steve Young (FOIL)	8.00
247	Nate Lewis	.25
248	William Fuller	.25
249	Andre Waters	.25
250	Dean Biasucci	.25
251	Andre Rison	1.00
252	Brent Williams	.25
253	Todd McNair	.25
254	Jeff Davidson	.25
255	Art Monk	1.00
256	Kirk Lowdermilk	.25
257	Bob Golic	.25
258	Michael Irvin	1.00
259	Eric Green	.25
260	David Fulcher (FOIL)	.50
261	Damone Johnson	.25
262	Marc Spindler	.25
263	Alfred Williams	.25
264	Donnie Elder	.25
265	Keith McKeller	.25
266	Steve Bono	2.00
267	Jumbo Elliott	.25
268	Randy Hilliard	.25
269	Rufus Porter	.25
270	Neal Anderson	.25
271	Dalton Hilliard	.25
272	Michael Zordich	.25
273	Cornelius Bennett (FOIL)	.75
274	Louie Aguiar	.25
275	Aaron Craver	.25
276	Tony Bennett	.25
277	Terry Wooden	.25
278	Mike Munchak	.25
279	Chris Hinton	.25
280	John Elway	6.00
281	Randall McDaniel	.25
282	Brad Baxter (FOIL)	.50
283	Wes Hopkins	.25
284	Scott Davis	.25
285	Mark Tuinei	.25
286	Broderick Thompson	.25
287	Henry Ellard	.25
288	Adrian Cooper	.25
289	Don Warren	.25
290	Rodney Hampton	1.00
291	Kevin Ross	.25
292	Mark Carrier	.25
293	Ian Beckles	.25
294	Gene Atkins	.25
295	Mark Rypien (FOIL)	.75
296	Eric Metcalf	.25
297	Howard Ballard	.25
298	Nate Newton	.25
299	Dan Owens	.25
300	Tim McGee	.25
301	Greg McMurtry	.25
302	Walter Reeves	.25
303	Jeff Herrod	.25
304	Darren Comeaux	.25
305	Pete Stoyanovich	.25
306	Johnny Holland	.25
307	Jay Novacek	.50
308	Steve Broussard	.50
309	Darrell Green	.50
310	Sam Mills	.25
311	Tim Barnett	.25
312	Steve Atwater	.25
313	Tom Waddle (FOIL)	.50
314	Felix Wright	.25
315	Sean Jones	.25
316	Jim Harbaugh	1.00
317	Eric Allen	.25
318	Don Mosebar	.25
319	Rob Taylor	.25
320	Terance Mathis	1.00
321	Leroy Hoard	1.00
322	Kenneth Davis	.25
323	Guy McIntyre	.25
324	Deron Cherry (FOIL)	.50
325	Tunch Ilkin	.25
326	Willie Green	.50
327	Darryl Henley	.25
328	Shawn Jefferson	.25
329		
330	John Roper	.25
331	Bill Lewis	.25
332	Rodney Holman	.25
333	Bruce Armstrong	.25
334	Robb Thomas	.25
335	Alvin Harper	.50
336	Brian Jordan	1.00
337	Morten Andersen (FOIL)	.75
338	Dermontti Dawson	.25
339	Checklist 3	.25
340	Louis Oliver	.25
341	Paul McJulien	.25
342	Karl Mecklenburg	.25
343	Lawrence Dawsey	.25
344	Kyle Clifton	.25
345	Jeff Bostic	.25
346	Cris Carter	2.50
347	Al Smith	.25
348	Mark Kelso	.25
349	Art Monk (FOIL)	1.00
350	Michael Carter	.25
351	Ethan Horton	.25
352	Andy Heck	.25
353	Gill Fenerty	.25
354	David Brandon	.25
355	Anthony Johnson	.25
356	Mike Golic	.25
357	Ferrell Edmunds	.25
358	Dennis Gibson	.25
359	Gill Byrd	.25
360	Todd Lyght	.25
361	Jayice Pearson	.25
362	John Rade	.25
363	Keith Van Horne	.25
364	John Kasay	.25
365	Broderick Thomas (FOIL SP)	1.50
366	Ken Harvey	.25
367	Rich Gannon	.25
368	Darrell Thompson	.25
369	Jon Vaughn	.25
370	Jesse Solomon	.25
371	Erik McMillan	.25
372	Bruce Matthews	.25
373	Wilber Marshall	.25
374	Brian Blades (FOIL SP)	1.50
375	Vance Johnson	.25
376	Eddie Brown	.25
377	Don Beebe	.50
378	Brent Jones	.50
379	Matt Bahr	.25
380	Dwight Stone	.25
381	Tony Casillas	.25
382	Jay Schroeder	.25
383	Byron Evans	.25
384	Dan Saleaumua	.25
385	Wendell Davis	.25
386	Ron Holmes	.25
387	George Thomas	.25
388	Ray Berry	.25
389	Eric Martin	.25
390	Kevin Mack	.25
391	Natu Tuataagaloa	.25
392	Bill Romanowski	.25
393	Nick Bell (FOIL)	1.50
394	Grant Feasel	.25
395	Eugene Lockhart	.25
396	Lorenzo White	.25
397	Mike Farr	.25
398	Eric Bieniemy	.25
399	Kevin Murphy	.25
400	Luis Sharpe	.25
401	Jessie Tuggle (FOIL SP)	1.50
402	Cleveland Gary	.25
403	Tony Mandarich	.50
404	Bryan Cox	.25
405	Marvin Washington	.25
406	Fred Stokes	.25
407	Duane Bickett	.25
408	Leonard Marshall	.25
409	Barry Foster	.50
410	Thurman Thomas	1.00
411	Willie Gault	.25
412	Vinson Smith	.25
413	Mark Bortz	.25
414	Johnny Johnson	.25
415	Rodney Hampton (FOIL)	1.00
416	Steve Wallace	.25
417	Fuad Reveiz	.25
418	Derrick Thomas	.50
419	Jackie Harris	.50
420	Derek Russell	.25
421	David Grant	.25
422	Tommy Kane	.25
423	Stan Brock	.25
424	Haywood Jeffires	.50
425	Broderick Thomas	.25
426	John Kidd	.25
427	Shawn McCarthy (FOIL)	.50
428	Jim Arnold	.25
429	Scott Fulhage	.25
430	Jackie Slater	.25
431	Scott Galbraith	.25
432	Roger Ruzek	.25
433	Irving Fryar	.50
434A	Derrick Thomas (FOIL ERR)	1.00
434B	Derrick Thomas (FOIL COR)	1.00
435	David Johnson	.25
436	Jim Jensen	.25
437	James Washington	.25
438	Phil Hansen	.25
439	Rohn Stark	.25
440	Jarrod Bunch	.25
441	Todd Marinovich	.25
442	Brett Perriman	1.00
443	Eugene Robinson	.50
444	Robert Massey	.25
445	Nick Lowery	.25
446	Rickey Dixon	.25
447	Jim Lachey	.25
448	Johnny Hector (FOIL)	.50
449	Gary Plummer	.25
450	Robert Brown	.25
451	Gaston Green	.25
452	Checklist 4	.25
453	Darion Conner	.25
454	Mike Cofer	.25
455	Craig Heyward	.25
456	Anthony Carter	.25
457	Pat Coleman	.25
458	Jeff Bryant	.25
459	Mark Gunn	.25
460	Stan Thomas	.25
461	Simon Fletcher (FOIL SP)	1.50
462	Ray Agnew	.25
463	Jessie Hester	.25
464	Rob Burnett	.25
465	Mike Croel	.25
466	Mike Pitts	.25
467	Darryl Talley	.25
468	Rich Camarillo	.25
469	Reggie White (FOIL)	1.50
470	Nick Bell	.25
471	Tracy Hayworth	.25
472	Eric Thomas	.25
473	Paul Gruber	.25
474	David Richards	.25
475	T.J. Turner	.25
476	Mark Ingram	.25
477	Tim Grunhard	.25
478	Marion Butts (FOIL)	.50
479	Tom Rathman	.25
480	Brian Mitchell	.25
481	Bryce Paup	.50
482	Mike Pritchard	.25
483	Ken Norton Jr.	.25
484	Roman Phifer	.25
485	Greg Lloyd	.50
486	Brett Maxie	.25
487	Richard Dent (FOIL SP)	1.50
488	Curtis Duncan	.25
489	Chris Burkett	.25
490	Travis McNeal	.25
491	Carl Lee	.25
492	Clarence Kay	.25
493	Tom Thayer	.25
494	Erik Kramer (FOIL SP)	2.00
495	Perry Kemp	.25
496	Jeff Jaeger	.25
497	Eric Sanders	.25
498	Burt Grossman	.25
499	Ben Smith	.25
500	Keith McCants	.25
501	John Stephens	.25
502	John Rienstra	.25
503	Jim Ritcher	.25
504	Harris Barton	.25
505	Andre Rison (FOIL SP)	2.00
506	Chris Martin	.25
507	Freddie Joe Nunn	.25
508	Mark Higgs	.25
509	Norm Johnson	.25
510	Stephen Baker	.25
511	Ricky Sanders	.25
512	Ray Donaldson	.25
513	David Fulcher	.25
514	Gerald Williams	.25
515	Toi Cook	.25
516	Chris Warren	1.00
517	Jeff Gossett	.25
518	Ken Lanier	.25
519	Haywood Jeffires (FOIL SP)	1.50
520	Kevin Glover	.25
521	Mo Lewis	.25
522	Bern Brostek	.25
523	Bo Orlando	.25
524	Mike Saxon	.25
525	Seth Joyner	.25
526	John Carney	.25
527	Jeff Cross	.25
528	Gary Anderson (FOIL SP)	1.50
529	Chuck Cecil	.25
530	Tim Green	.25
531	Kevin Porter	.25
532	Chris Spielman	.25
533	Willie Drewrey	.25
534	Chris Singleton	.25
535	Matt Stover	.25
536	Andre Collins	.25
537	Erik Howard	.25
538	Steve Tasker	.25
539	Anthony Thompson	.25
540	Charles Haley	.50
541	Mike Merriweather (FOIL)	.50
542	Henry Thomas	.25
543	Scott Stephen	.25
544	Bruce Kozerski	.25
545	Tim McKyer	.25
546	Chris Doleman	.25
547	Riki Ellison	.25
548	Mike Prior	.25
549	Dwayne Harper	.25
550	Bubby Brister	.25
551	Dave Meggett	.25
552	Greg Montgomery	.25
553	Kevin Mack (FOIL)	.50
554	Mark Stepnoski	.25
555	Wayne Walker	.25
556	Eric Moten	.25
557	Michael Stewart	.25
558	Calvin Williams	.25
559	Johnny Hector	.25
560	Tony Paige	.25
561	Tim Newton	.25
562	Brad Muster	.25
563	Aeneas Williams	.50
564	Herman Moore	8.00
565	Checklist 5	.25
566	Jerome Henderson	.25
567	Danny Copeland	.25
568	Alexander Wright (FOIL)	.50
569	Tim Harris	.25
570	Jonathan Hayes	.25
571	Tony Jones	.25
572	Carlton Bailey	.25
573	Vaughan Johnson	.25

1993 Bowman

The 1993 Bowman set cut back to 423 cards with a numbered subset of 27 special foil-designed cards. These cards feature nine 1993 rookies, nine former #1 draft picks and nine superstars. Each pack of 1993 Bowman contains 14 cards, plus one special foil insert card. The regular cards are glossy and feature full-color photos on premium stock.

	MT
Complete Set (423):	75.00
Common Player:	.15
Minor Stars:	.30
Wax Box:	70.00

No	Player	Price
1	Troy Aikman	4.00
2	John Parella	.15
3	*Dana Stubblefield*	1.00
4	Mark Higgs	.15
5	*Tom Carter*	.30
6	Nate Lewis	.15
7	*Vaughn Hebron*	.30
8	Ernest Givins	.15
9	Vince Buck	.15
10	Levon Kirkland	.15
11	J.J. Birden	.15
12	Steve Jordan	.15
13	Simon Fletcher	.15
14	Willie Green	.15
15	Pepper Johnson	.15
16	Roger Harper	.15
17	Rob Moore	.15
18	David Lang	.15
19	David Klingler	.15
20	*Garrison Hearst*	4.00
21	Anthony Johnson	.15
22	*Eric Curry*	.30
23	Nolan Harrison	.15
24	Earl Dotson	.15
25	Leonard Russell	.15
26	Doug Riesenberg	.15
27	Dwayne Harper	.15
28	Richard Dent	.30
29	*Victor Bailey*	.30
30	Junior Seau	.30
31	Steve Tasker	.15
32	Kurt Gouveia	.15
33	Renaldo Turnbull	.15
34	Dale Carter	.15
35	Russell Maryland	.15
36	Dana Hall	.15
37	Marco Coleman	.15
38	Greg Montgomery	.15
39	*Deon Figures*	.30
40	*Troy Drayton*	.50
41	Eric Metcalf	.30
42	Michael Husted	.15
43	Harry Newsome	.15
44	Kelvin Pritchett	.15
45	Andre Rison	.50
46	*John Copeland*	.30
47	Greg Biekert	.15
48	Johnny Johnson	.15
49	Chuck Cecil	.15
50	*Rick Mirer*	.50
51	Rod Bernstine	.15
52	Steve McMichael	.15
53	*Roosevelt Potts*	.30
54	Mike Sherrard	.15
55	Terrell Buckley	.15
56	Eugene Chung	.15
57	*Kimble Anders*	1.00
58	Daryl Johnston	.15
59	Harris Barton	.15
60	Thurman Thomas	.30
61	Eric Martin	.15
62	*Reggie Brooks*	.75
63	Eric Bieniemy	.15
64	John Offerdahl	.15
65	Wilber Marshall	.15
66	Mark Carrier	.15
67	Merril Hoge	.15
68	Cris Carter	.30
69	Marty Thompson	.15
70	Randall Cunningham	.30
71	Winston Moss	.15
72	Doug Pelfrey	.15
73	Jackie Slater	.15
74	Pierce Holt	.15
75	Hardy Nickerson	.15
76	Chris Burkett	.15
77	Michael Brandon	.15
78	Tom Waddle	.15
79	Walter Reeves	.15
80	Lawrence Taylor	.30
81	*Wayne Simmons*	.30
82	Brent Williams	.15
83	Shannon Sharpe	.30
84	Robert Blackmon	.15
85	Keith Jackson	.15
86	A.J. Johnson	.15
87	*Ryan McNeil*	.15
88	Michael Dean Perry	.15
89	*Russell Copeland*	.30
90	Sam Mills	.15
91	Courtney Hall	.15
92	*Gino Torretta*	.30
93	*Artie Smith*	.15
94	David Whitmore	.15
95	Charles Haley	.15
96	Rod Woodson	.15
97	Lorenzo White	.15
98	Tom Scott	.15
99	Tyji Armstrong	.15
100	Boomer Esiason	.30
101	Raghib Ismail	.15
102	Mark Carrier	.15
103	Broderick Thompson	.15
104	Bob Whitfield	.15
105	Ben Coleman	.15
106	Jon Vaughn	.15
107	Marcus Buckley	.15
108	Cleveland Gary	.15
109	Ashley Ambrose	.15
110	Reggie White	.30
111	*Arthur Marshall*	.30
112	Greg McMurtry	.15
113	Mike Johnson	.15
114	Tim McGee	.15
115	John Carney	.15
116	Neil Smith	.15
117	Mark Stepnoski	.15
118	Don Beebe	.15
119	Scott Mitchell	.30
120	Randall McDaniel	.15
121	Chidi Ahanotu	.15
122	Ray Childress	.15
123	*Tony McGee*	.30
124	Marc Boutte	.15
125	Ronnie Lott	.30
126	*Jason Elam*	.30
127	*Martin Harrison*	.30
128	Leonard Renfro	.15
129	Jesse Armstead	.15
130	Quentin Coryatt	.15
131	Luis Sharpe	.15
132	Bill Maas	.15
133	Jesse Solomon	.15
134	Kevin Greene	.30
135	*Derek Brown*	.30
136	Greg Townsend	.15
137	Neal Anderson	.15
138	John Williams	.15
139	*Vincent Brisby*	.50
140	*Barry Sanders*	6.00
141	Charles Mann	.15
142	Ken Norton	.15
143	Eric Moten	.15
144	John Alt	.15
145	*Dan Footman*	.15
146	Bill Brooks	.15
147	James Thornton	.15
148	Martin Mayhew	.15
149	Andy Harmon	.15
150	Dan Marino	7.00
151	Michael Barrow	.15
152	Flipper Anderson	.15
153	Jackie Harris	.15
154	Todd Kelly	.15
155	*Dan Williams*	.15
156	Harold Green	.15
157	David Treadwell	.15
158	Chris Doleman	.15
159	Eric Hill	.15
160	*Lincoln Kennedy*	.30
161	Devon McDonald	.15
162	*Natrone Means*	4.00
163	Rick Hamilton	.15
164	Kelvin Martin	.15
165	Jeff Hostetler	.15
166	*Mark Brunell*	15.00
167	Tim Barnett	.15
168	Ray Crockett	.15
169	William Perry	.15
170	Michael Irvin	.30
171	Marvin Washington	.15
172	Irving Fryar	.15
173	Scott Sisson	.15
174	Gary Anderson	.15
175	Bruce Smith	.15
176	Clyde Simmons	.15
177	Russell White	.15
178	*Irv Smith*	.30
179	Mark Wheeler	.15
180	Warren Moon	.30
181	Del Speer	.15
182	Henry Thomas	.15
183	Keith Kartz	.15
184	Ricky Ervins	.15
185	Phil Simms	.30
186	Tim Brown	.30
187	Willis Peguese	.15
188	Rich Moran	.15
189	Robert Jones	.15
190	Craig Heyward	.15
191	Ricky Watters	.30
192	Stan Humphries	.30
193	Larry Webster	.15
194	Brad Baxter	.15

A card number in parentheses ( ) indicates the set is unnumbered.

No.	Name	MT
195	Randal Hill	.15
196	Robert Porcher	.15
197	Patrick Robinson	.15
198	Ferrell Edmunds	.15
199	Melvin Jenkins	.15
200	Joe Montana	4.00
201	Marv Cook	.15
202	Henry Ellard	.15
203	Calvin Williams	.15
204	Craig Erickson	.15
205	Steve Atwater	.15
206	Najee Mustafaa	.15
207	Darryl Talley	.15
208	Jarrod Bunch	.15
209	Tim McDonald	.15
210	*Patrick Bates*	.30
211	Sean Jones	.15
212	Leslie O'Neal	.15
213	Mike Golic	.15
214	Mark Clayton	.15
215	Leonard Marshall	.15
216	Curtis Conway	3.00
217	*Andre Hastings*	.50
218	Barry Word	.15
219	Will Wolford	.15
220	Desmond Howard	.30
221	Rickey Jackson	.15
222	Alvin Harper	.15
223	William White	.15
224	Steve Broussard	.15
225	Aeneas Williams	.15
226	Michael Brooks	.15
227	Reggie Cobb	.15
228	Derrick Walker	.15
229	Marcus Allen	.30
230	Jerry Ball	.15
231	J.B. Brown	.15
232	Terry McDaniel	.15
233	LeRoy Butler	.15
234	Kyle Clifton	.15
235	Henry Jones	.15
236	Shane Conlan	.15
237	*Michael Bates*	.30
238	Vincent Brown	.15
239	William Fuller	.15
240	Ricardo McDonald	.15
241	Gary Zimmerman	.15
242	Fred Barnett	.15
243	Elvis Grbac	4.00
244	Myron Baker	.15
245	Steve Emtman	.15
246	Mike Compton	.15
247	Mark Jackson	.15
248	Santo Stephens	.15
249	Tommie Agee	.15
250	Broderick Thomas	.15
251	Fred Baxter	.15
252	Andre Collins	.15
253	Ernest Dye	.15
254	Raylee Johnson	.15
255	Rickey Dixon	.15
256	Ron Heller	.15
257	Joel Steed	.15
258	Everett Lindsay	.15
259	Tony Smith	.15
260	Sterling Sharpe	.30
261	Tommy Vardell	.15
262	Morten Andersen	.15
263	Eddie Robinson	.15
264	*Jerome Bettis*	6.00
265	Alonzo Spellman	.15
266	Harvey Williams	.15
267	Jason Belser	.15
268	Derek Russell	.15
269	*Derrick Lassic*	.30
270	Steve Young	3.00
271	*Adrien Murrell*	5.00
272	Lewis Tillman	.15
273	*O.J. McDuffie*	3.00
274	Marty Carter	.15
275	Ray Seals	.15
276	Earnest Byner	.15
277	Marion Butts	.15
278	Chris Spielman	.15
279	Carl Pickens	2.00
280	*Drew Bledsoe*	14.00
281	Mark Kelso	.15
282	Eugene Robinson	.15
283	Eric Allen	.15
284	Ethan Horton	.15
285	Greg Lloyd	.15
286	Anthony Carter	.15
287	Edgar Bennett	.30
288	Bobby Hebert	.15
289	Haywood Jeffires	.15
290	Glyn Milburn	1.00
291	Bernie Kosar	.15
292	Jumbo Elliott	.15
293	Jessie Hester	.15
294	Brent Jones	.15
295	Carl Banks	.15
296	Brian Washington	.15
297	Steve Beuerlein	.15
298	John Lynch	.15
299	Troy Vincent	.15
300	Emmitt Smith	7.00
301	Chris Zorich	.15
302	Wade Wilson	.15
303	*Darrien Gordon*	.30
304	Fred Stokes	.15
305	Nick Lowery	.15
306	Rodney Peete	.15
307	Chris Warren	.30
308	Herschel Walker	.15
309	Aundray Bruce	.15
310	Barry Foster	.15
311	*George Teague*	.30
312	Darryl Williams	.15

No.	Name	MT
313	*Thomas Smith*	.30
314	Dennis Brown	.15
315	*Marvin Jones*	.30
316	Andre Tippett	.15
317	*Demetrius Dubose*	.15
318	Kirk Lowdermilk	.15
319	Shane Dronett	.15
320	*Terry Kirby*	1.00
321	*Qadry Ismail*	.50
322	Lorenzo Lynch	.15
323	Willie Drewrey	.15
324	Jessie Tuggle	.15
325	Leroy Hoard	.15
326	Mark Collins	.15
327	Darrell Green	.15
328	Anthony Miller	.30
329	Brad Muster	.15
330	Jim Kelly	.50
331	Sean Gilbert	.15
332	Tim McKyer	.15
333	Scott Mersereau	.15
334	Willie Davis	.15
335	Brett Favre	8.00
336	Kevin Gogan	.15
337	Jim Harbaugh	.15
338	James Trapp	.15
339	Pete Stoyanovich	.15
340	Jerry Rice	4.00
341	Gary Anderson	.15
342	*Carlton Gray*	.15
343	Dermontti Dawson	.15
344	Ray Buchanan	.15
345	Derrick Fenner	.15
346	Dennis Smith	.15
347	Todd Rucci	.15
348	Seth Joyner	.15
349	Jim McMahon	.30
350	Rodney Hampton	.30
351	Al Smith	.15
352	Steve Everitt	.15
353	Vinnie Clark	.15
354	Eric Swann	.15
355	Brian Mitchell	.15
356	Will Shields	.15
357	Cornelius Bennett	.15
358	*Darrin Smith*	.30
359	Chris Mims	.15
360	Blair Thomas	.15
361	Dennis Gibson	.15
362	Santana Dotson	.15
363	Mark Ingram	.15
364	Don Mosebar	.15
365	Ty Detmer	.30
366	Bob Christian	.15
367	Adrian Hardy	.15
368	Vaughan Johnson	.15
369	Jim Everett	.15
370	Ricky Sanders	.15
371	Jonathan Hayes	.15
372	Bruce Matthews	.15
373	Darren Drozdov	.15
374	Scott Brumfield	.15
375	Cortez Kennedy	.15
376	Tim Harris	.15
377	Neil O'Donnell	.30
378	*Robert Smith*	4.00
379	Mike Caldwell	.15
380	Burt Grossman	.15
381	Corey Miller	.15
382	Kevin Williams	.50
383	Ken Harvey	.15
384	Greg Robinson	.15
385	Harold Alexander	.15
386	Andre Reed	.30
387	Reggie Langhorne	.15
388	Courtney Hawkins	.15
389	James Hasty	.15
390	Pat Swilling	.15
391	Chris Slade	.30
392	Keith Byars	.15
393	Dalton Hilliard	.15
394	David Williams	.15
395	Terry Obee	.15
396	Heath Sherman	.15
397	John Taylor	.15
398	Irv Smith	.15
399	Johnny Holland	.15
400	John Elway	3.00
401	Clay Matthews	.15
402	Dave Meggett	.15
403	Eric Green	.15
404	Bryan Cox	.15
405	Jay Novacek	.15
406	Kenneth Davis	.15
407	*Lamar Thomas*	.30
408	Lance Gunn	.15
409	Audray McMillian	.15
410	Derrick Thomas	.30
411	Rufus Porter	.15
412	Coleman Rudolph	.15
413	Mark Rypien	.15
414	Duane Bickett	.15
415	Chris Singleton	.15
416	Mitch Lyons	.15
417	Bill Fralic	.15
418	Gary Plummer	.15
419	Ricky Proehl	.15
420	Howie Long	.15
421	*Willie Roaf*	.30
422	Checklist 1 of 2	.15
423	Checklist 2 of 2	.15

> A card number in parentheses ( ) indicates the set is unnumbered.

1994 Bowman

This 360-card set features 116 of this year's draft picks, plus a 30-card rookie subset (#s 215-244). Each card front has a glossy full-color action photo of the player, with a borderless design. Gold-foil stamped yard markers run across the bottom, while the Bowman logo appears in the lower left corner. The player's name is stamped in gold in the opposite corner. The card back has a smaller picture of the player on the left side; statistics are on the right side on top of a football background. The card number is in white in a red triangle in the upper right corner.

No.	Name	MT
	Complete Set (390):	80.00
	Common Player:	.10
	Minor Stars:	.20
	Wax Box:	70.00
1	Dan Wilkinson	.20
2	Marshall Faulk	20.00
3	Heath Shuler	.75
4	Willie McGinest	.20
5	Trent Dilfer	6.00
6	*Brent Jones*	.20
7	*Sam Adams*	.20
8	*Randy Baldwin*	.20
9	*Jamir Miller*	.20
10	*John Thierry*	.20
11	*Aaron Glenn*	.20
12	*Joe Johnson*	.20
13	*Bernard Williams*	.20
14	*Wayne Gandy*	.20
15	*Aaron Taylor*	.20
16	*Charles Johnson*	1.50
17	*Dewayne Washington*	.20
18	Bernie Kosar	.10
19	*Johnnie Morton*	1.50
20	*Rob Fredrickson*	.20
21	*Shante Carver*	.20
22	*Thomas Lewis*	.20
23	Greg Hill	.75
24	Cris Dishman	.10
25	*Jeff Burris*	.20
26	*Isaac Davis*	.20
27	Bert Emanuel	2.00
28	*Allen Aldridge*	.20
29	*Kevin Lee*	.20
30	*Chris Brantley*	.20
31	*Rich Braham*	.20
32	Ricky Watters	.20
33	Quentin Coryatt	.10
34	Hardy Nickerson	.10
35	Johnny Johnson	.10
36	Ken Harvey	.10
37	Chris Zorich	.10
38	Chris Warren	.20
39	*David Palmer*	.20
40	Chris Miller	.20
41	Ken Ruettgers	.20
42	*Joe Panos*	.20
43	*Mario Bates*	.30
44	Harry Colon	.10
45	Barry Foster	.10
46	Steve Tasker	.10
47	Richmond Webb	.10
48	*James Folston*	.20
49	Erik Williams	.10
50	Rodney Hampton	.20
51	Derek Russell	.10
52	Greg Montgomery	.10
53	Anthony Phillips	.10
54	Andre Coleman	.10
55	Gary Brown	.10
56	Neil Smith	.10
57	Myron Baker	.10
58	*Sean Dawkins*	.50
59	Marvin Washington	.10
60	Steve Beuerlein	.10
61	*Brenston Buckner*	.20
62	William Gaines	.10
63	*LeShon Johnson*	.20
64	*Errict Rhett*	2.00
65	Jim Everett	.10
66	Desmond Howard	.10
67	Jack Del Rio	.10
68	*Isaac Bruce*	20.00
69	Van Moore	.20
70	Jim Kelly	.20

No.	Name	MT
71	Leon Lett	.10
72	Greg Robinson	.10
73	Ryan Yarborough	.20
74	Terry Wooden	.10
75	Eric Allen	.10
76	Ernest Givins	.10
77	*Marcus Spears*	.20
78	*Thomas Randolph*	.20
79	Willie Clark	.20
80	John Elway	1.50
81	*Aubrey Beavers*	.20
82	Jeff Cothran	.10
83	Norm Johnson	.10
84	*Donnell Bennett*	.20
85	Phillippi Sparks	.10
86	Scott Mitchell	.10
87	*Bucky Brooks*	.20
88	Courtney Hawkins	.10
89	Kevin Greene	.10
90	*Doug Nussmeier*	.20
91	Floyd Turner	.10
92	Anthony Newman	.10
93	Vinny Testaverde	.10
94	Ronnie Lott	.10
95	Troy Aikman	3.00
96	John Taylor	.10
97	Henry Ellard	.10
98	Carl Lee	.10
99	Terry McDaniel	.10
100	Joe Montana	3.00
101	David Klingler	.10
102	*Bruce Walker*	.20
103	Rick Cunningham	.10
104	Robert Delpino	.10
105	Mark Ingram	.10
106	Leslie O'Neal	.10
107	Darrell Thompson	.10
108	David Meggett	.10
109	Chris Gardocki	.10
110	Andre Rison	.10
111	Kelvin Martin	.10
112	Marcus Robertson	.10
113	*Jason Gildon*	.20
114	Mel Gray	.10
115	Tommy Vardell	.10
116	Dexter Carter	.10
117	*Scottie Graham*	.20
118	Horace Copeland	.10
119	Cornelius Bennett	.10
120	*Chris Maumalanga*	.20
121	Mo Lewis	.10
122	*Toby Wright*	.20
123	*George Hegamin*	.20
124	Chip Lohmiller	.10
125	*Calvin Jones*	.20
126	*Steve Shine*	.20
127	*Chuck Levy*	.20
128	Sam Mills	.10
129	Terance Mathis	.10
130	Randall Cunningham	.20
131	John Fina	.10
132	*Reggie White*	.20
133	Tom Waddle	.10
134	Chris Calloway	.10
135	*Kevin Mawae*	.20
136	*Lake Dawson*	.50
137	*Alai Kalaniubalu*	.20
138	Tom Nalen	.20
139	Cody Carlson	.10
140	Dan Marino	5.00
141	Harris Barton	.10
142	Don Mosebar	.10
143	Romeo Bandison	.10
144	Bruce Smith	.20
145	Warren Moon	.20
146	David Lutz	.10
147	Dermontti Dawson	.10
148	Ricky Proehl	.10
149	*Lou Benfatti*	.20
150	Craig Erickson	.10
151	Sean Gilbert	.10
152	*Zefros Moss*	.20
153	*Darnay Scott*	3.00
154	Courtney Hall	.10
155	Brian Mitchell	.10
156	*Joe Burch*	.20
157	*Terry Mickens*	.20
158	Jay Novacek	.10
159	Chris Gedney	.10
160	Bruce Matthews	.10
161	*Marlo Perry*	.10
162	Vince Buck	.10
163	Michael Bates	.10
164	Willie Davis	.10
165	Mike Pritchard	.10
166	Doug Riesenberg	.10
167	Herschel Walker	.10
168	*Tim Ruddy*	.20
169	*William Floyd*	1.50
170	John Randle	.10
171	Winston Moss	.10
172	Thurman Thomas	.20
173	*Eric England*	.20
174	Vincent Brisby	.20
175	Greg Lloyd	.10
176	Paul Gruber	.10
177	*Brad Ottis*	.20
178	George Teague	.10
179	*Willie Jackson*	.20
180	Barry Sanders	4.00
181	Brian Washington	.10
182	Michael Jackson	.10
183	*Jason Mathews*	.20
184	Chester McGlockton	.10
185	*Tydus Winans*	.20
186	Michael Haynes	.10
187	Erik Kramer	.10

No.	Name	MT
188	Chris Doleman	.10
189	Haywood Jeffires	.10
190	*Larry Whigham*	.20
191	Shawn Jefferson	.10
192	Pete Stoyanovich	.10
193	Rod Bernstine	.10
194	William Thomas	.10
195	Marcus Allen	.20
196	Dave Brown	.10
197	*Harold Bishop*	.20
198	Lorenzo Lynch	.10
199	Dwight Stone	.10
200	Jerry Rice	3.00
201	Raghib Ismail	.10
202	LeRoy Butler	.10
203	Glenn Parker	.10
204	Bruce Armstrong	.10
205	Shane Conlan	.10
206	Russell Maryland	.10
207	Herman Moore	1.00
208	Eric Martin	.10
209	John Friesz	.10
210	Boomer Esiason	.10
211	Jim Harbaugh	.10
212	Harold Green	.10
213	*Perry Klein*	.20
214	Eric Metcalf	.10
215	Steve Everitt	.10
216	Victor Bailey	.10
217	Lincoln Kennedy	.10
218	Glyn Milburn	.10
219	John Copeland	.10
220	Drew Bledsoe	3.00
221	Kevin Williams	.20
222	Roosevelt Potts	.10
223	Troy Drayton	.10
224	Terry Kirby	.10
225	Ron Moore	.10
226	Tyrone Hughes	.10
227	Wayne Simmons	.10
228	Tony McGee	.10
229	Derek Brown	.10
230	Jason Elam	.10
231	Qadry Ismail	.10
232	O.J. McDuffie	.20
233	Mike Caldwell	.10
234	Reggie Brooks	.10
235	Rick Mirer	.20
236	Steve Tovar	.10
237	Patrick Robinson	.10
238	Tom Carter	.10
239	Ben Coates	.20
240	Jerome Bettis	1.25
241	Garrison Hearst	1.00
242	Natrone Means	.75
243	Dana Stubblefield	.20
244	William Roaf	.10
245	Cortez Kennedy	.10
246	*Todd Steussie*	.20
247	Pat Coleman	.10
248	David Wyman	.10
249	Jeremy Lincoln	.10
250	Carlester Crumpler	.10
251	Dale Carter	.10
252	Corey Raymond	.10
253	Bryan Cox	.10
254	*Charlie Garner*	5.00
255	Jeff Hostetler	.20
256	Shane Bonham	.10
257	Thomas Everett	.10
258	John Jackson	.10
259	*Terry Irving*	.20
260	*Corey Sawyer*	.20
261	Rob Waldrop	.10
262	Curtis Conway	.30
263	*Winfred Tubbs*	.20
264	Sean Jones	.10
265	James Washington	.10
266	*Lonnie Johnson*	.20
267	Rob Moore	.10
268	Willie Anderson	.10
269	Jon Hand	.10
270	*Joe Patton*	.20
271	Howard Ballard	.10
272	*Fernando Smith*	.20
273	Jessie Tuggle	.10
274	John Alt	.10
275	Corey Miller	.10
276	*Gus Frerotte*	5.00
277	Jeff Cross	.10
278	Kevin Smith	.10
279	*Corey Louchiey*	.20
280	Michael Barrow	.10
281	*Jim Flanigan*	.30
282	Calvin Williams	.10
283	Jeff Jaeger	.10
284	*John Reece*	.20
285	Jason Hanson	.10
286	*Kurt Haws*	.20
287	Eric Davis	.10
288	Maurice Hurst	.10
289	Kirk Lowdermilk	.10
290	Rod Woodson	.10
291	Andre Reed	.10
292	Vince Workman	.10
293	Wayne Martin	.10
294	*Keith Lyle*	.20
295	Brett Favre	6.00
296	*Doug Brien*	.20
297	Junior Seau	.10
298	Randall McDaniel	.10
299	Johnny Mitchell	.10
300	Emmitt Smith	5.00
301	Michael Brooks	.10
302	Steve Jackson	.10
303	Jeff George	.20
304	Irving Fryar	.10
305	Derrick Thomas	.10

No.	Name	MT
306	Dante Jones	.10
307	Darrell Green	.10
308	Mark Bavaro	.10
309	Eugene Robinson	.10
310	Shannon Sharpe	.20
311	Michael Timpson	.10
312	Kevin Mitchell	.10
313	Stevon Moore	.10
314	Eric Swann	.10
315	James Bostic	.10
316	Robert Brooks	1.00
317	Pete Pierson	.10
318	Jim Sweeny	.10
319	Anthony Smith	.10
320	Rohn Stark	.10
321	Gary Anderson	.10
322	Robert Porcher	.10
323	Darryl Talley	.10
324	Stan Humphries	.20
325	Shelly Hammonds	.10
326	Jim McMahon	.10
327	Lamont Warren	.10
328	*Chris Penn*	.20
329	Tony Woods	.10
330	*Raymont Harris*	2.00
331	*Mitch Davis*	.20
332	Michael Irvin	.20
333	Kent Graham	.10
334	Brian Blades	.10
335	Lomas Brown	.10
336	Willie Drewrey	.10
337	Russell Freeman	.10
338	*Eric Zomalt*	.20
339	Santana Dotson	.20
340	Sterling Sharpe	.20
341	*Ray Crittenden*	.20
342	*Perry Carter*	.20
343	*Austin Robbins*	.20
344	*Mike Wells*	.20
345	Toddrick McIntosh	.10
346	Mark Carrier	.10
347	Eugene Daniel	.10
348	*Tre Johnson*	.20
349	D.J. Johnson	.10
350	Steve Young	1.50
351	Jim Pyne	.10
352	Jocelyn Borgella	.10
353	Pat Carter	.10
354	*Sam Rogers*	.20
355	*Jason Sehorn*	.20
356	Darren Carrington	.10
357	*Lamar Smith*	.20
358	James Burton	.10
359	Darrin Smith	.10
360	Marco Coleman	.10
361	Webster Slaughter	.10
362	Lewis Tillman	.10
363	David Alexander	.10
364	*Bradford Banta*	.20
365	Erric Pegram	.10
366	Mike Fox	.10
367	Jeff Lageman	.10
368	Kurt Gouveia	.10
369	Tim Brown	.20
370	Seth Joyner	.10
371	Irv Eatman	.10
372	*Dorsey Levens*	20.00
373	Anthony Pleasant	.10
374	Henry Jones	.10
375	Cris Carter	.20
376	Morten Andersen	.10
377	Neil O'Donnell	.10
378	Tyronne Drakeford	.10
379	John Carney	.10
380	Vincent Brown	.10
381	J.J. Birden	.10
382	Chris Spielman	.10
383	Mark Bortz	.10
384	Ray Childress	.10
385	Carlton Bailey	.10
386	Charles Haley	.10
387	Shane Dronett	.10
388	Jon Vaughn	.10
389	Checklist 1	.10
390	Checklist 2	.10

1995 Bowman

Bowman's 1995 set features many of the league's top draft picks and emerging young stars among its 357-card lineup. The set features 220 top players, 110 Draft Picks and 27 all-foil Expansion Team theme cards. Two insert sets were also made. Expansion Team cards are showcased utilizing an etched gold foil process with an embossed border (one per 12 packs), while 1st-Round Draft Picks highlights 22 players utilizing gold diffraction foil stamping (one per 12 packs). Each regular card in the set has a color action photo of the player on the right, with a smaller mirror image on a brown-shaded panel on the left. A team logo is in the lower left corner. The player's name is in the lower right corner, with his last name stamped in gold foil. The Bowman logo is in the upper right corner, stamped in red foil. The horizontal card back has biographical info, 1994 game-by-game stats and the player's name on one side; a color photo, team name, position and card number run along the right border.

	MT
Complete Set (357):	125.00
Common Player:	.10
Minor Stars:	.20
Expansion Foils (221-247):	.25
First Rounds:	1x-2x
Expansion Golds:	2x-4x
Wax Box:	95.00

1	Ki-Jana Carter (1st Round Draft Picks)	1.00
2	Tony Boselli (1st Round Draft Picks)	.50
3	Steve McNair (1st Round Draft Picks)	10.00
4	Michael Westbrook (1st Round Draft Picks)	3.00
5	Kerry Collins (1st Round Draft Picks)	4.00
6	Kevin Carter (1st Round Draft Picks)	.50
7	Mike Mamula (1st Round Draft Picks)	.10
8	Joey Galloway (1st Round Draft Picks)	6.00
9	Kyle Brady (1st Round Draft Picks)	.50
10	J.J. Stokes (1st Round Draft Picks)	2.00
11	Derrick Alexander (1st Round Draft Picks)	.10
12	Warren Sapp (1st Round Draft Picks)	.50
13	Mark Fields (1st Round Draft Picks)	.10
14	Ruben Brown (1st Round Draft Picks)	.10
15	Ellis Johnson (1st Round Draft Picks)	.10
16	Hugh Douglas (1st Round Draft Picks)	.50
17	Mike Pelton (1st Round Draft Picks)	.10
18	Napoleon Kaufman (1st Round Draft Picks)	8.00
19	James Stewart (1st Round Draft Picks)	5.00
20	Luther Elliss (1st Round Draft Picks)	.10
21	Rashaan Salaam (1st Round Draft Picks)	1.00
22	Tyrone Poole (1st Round Draft Picks)	.10
23	Ty Law (1st Round Draft Picks)	.10
24	Korey Stringer	.25
25	Billy Milner	.10
26	Devin Bush	.10
27	Mark Bruener	.75
28	Derrick Brooks	.10
29	Blake Brockermeyer	.10
30	Alundis Brice	.10
31	Trezelle Jenkins	.10
32	Craig Newsome	.40
33	Fred Barnett	.10
34	Ray Childress	.10
35	Chris Miller	.10
36	Charles Haley	.10
37	Ray Crittenden	.10
38	Gus Frerotte	.50
39	Jeff George	.20
40	Dan Marino	3.00
41	Shawn Lee	.10
42	Herman Moore	.50
43	Chris Calloway	.10
44	Jeff Graham	.10
45	Ray Buchanan	.10
46	Doug Pelfrey	.10
47	Lake Dawson	.25
48	Glenn Parker	.10
49	Terry McDaniel	.10
50	Rod Woodson	.10
51	Santana Dotson	.10
52	Anthony Miller	.10
53	Bo Orlando	.10
54	David Palmer	.10
55	William Floyd	.50
56	Edgar Bennett	.10

57	Jeff Blake	1.00
58	Anthony Pleasant	.10
59	Quinn Early	.10
60	Bobby Houston	.10
61	Terrell Fletcher	.50
62	Gary Brown	.10
63	Dwayne Sabb	.10
64	Roman Phifer	.10
65	Sherman Williams	.50
66	Roosevelt Potts	.10
67	Darnay Scott	.40
68	Charlie Garner	.10
69	Bert Emanuel	.40
70	Herschel Walker	.10
71	Lorenzo Styles	.10
72	Andre Coleman	.10
73	Tyronne Drakeford	.10
74	Jay Novacek	.10
75	Raymont Harris	.10
76	Tamarick Vanover	.50
77	Tom Carter	.10
78	Eric Green	.10
79	Patrick Hunter	.10
80	Jeff Hostetler	.20
81	Robert Blackmon	.10
82	Anthony Cook	.10
83	Craig Erickson	.10
84	Glyn Milburn	.10
85	Greg Lloyd	.20
86	Brent Jones	.10
87	Barrett Brooks	.10
88	Alvin Harper	.10
89	Sean Jones	.10
90	Cris Carter	.10
91	Russell Copeland	.10
92	Frank Sanders	3.00
93	Mo Lewis	.10
94	Michael Haynes	.10
95	Andre Rison	.10
96	Jesse James	.10
97	Stan Humphries	.10
98	James Hasty	.10
99	Ricardo McDonald	.10
100	Jerry Rice	1.50
101	Chris Hudson	.10
102	David Meggett	.10
103	Brian Mitchell	.10
104	Mike Johnson	.10
105	Kordell Stewart	20.00
106	Michael Brooks	.10
107	Steve Walsh	.10
108	Eric Metcalf	.10
109	Ricky Watters	.20
110	Brett Favre	3.00
111	Aubrey Beavers	.10
112	Brian Williams	.10
113	Eugene Robinson	.10
114	Matt O'Dwyer	.10
115	Michael Barrow	.10
116	Raghib Ismail	.10
117	Scott Gragg	.10
118	Leon Lett	.10
119	Reggie Roby	.10
120	Marshall Faulk	1.00
121	Jack Jackson	.10
122	Keith Byars	.10
123	Eric Hill	.10
124	Todd Sauerbrun	.10
125	Dexter Carter	.10
126	Vinny Testaverde	.10
127	Shane Conlan	.10
128	Terrance Shaw	.10
129	William Roaf	.10
130	Jim Kelly	.20
131	Neil O'Donnell	.20
132	Ray McElroy	.10
133	Ed McDaniel	.10
134	Brian Gelzheiser	.10
135	Marcus Allen	.20
136	Carl Pickens	.20
137	Mike Verstegen	.10
138	Chris Mims	.10
139	Darryl Pounds	.10
140	Emmitt Smith	3.00
141	Mike Frederick	.10
142	Henry Ellard	.10
143	Willie McGinest	.10
144	Michael Roan	.10
145	Chris Spielman	.10
146	Darryl Talley	.10
147	Randall Cunningham	.10
148	Andrew Greene	.10
149	George Teague	.10
150	Tyrone Hughes	.10
151	Ron Davis	.10
152	Stevon Moore	.10
153	Merton Hanks	.10
154	Darren Perry	.10
155	Dave Brown	.10
156	Mike Morton	.10
157	Seth Joyner	.10
158	Bryan Cox	.10
159	Corey Fuller	.10
160	John Elway	.50
161	Dewayne Washington	.10
162	Chris Warren	.25
163	Jeff Kopp	.10
164	Sean Dawkins	.10
165	Mark Carrier	.10
166	Andre Hastings	.10
167	Derek West	.10
168	Glenn Montgomery	.10
169	Trent Dilfer	.40
170	Rob Johnson	8.00
171	Todd Scott	.10
172	Charles Johnson	.25

173	Kez McCorvey	.10
174	Rob Fredrickson	.10
175	Corey Sawyer	.10
176	Brett Perriman	.20
177	Ken Dilger	.40
178	Dana Stubblefield	.10
179	Eric Allen	.10
180	Drew Bledsoe	1.50
181	Tyrone Davis	.10
182	Reggie Brooks	.10
183	Dale Carter	.10
184	William Henderson	.10
185	Reggie White	.20
186	Lorenzo White	.10
187	Leslie O'Neal	.10
188	Stoney Case	.50
189	Jeff Burris	.10
190	Leroy Hoard	.10
191	Thomas Randolph	.10
192	Rodney Thomas	.40
193	Quentin Coryatt	.10
194	Terry Wooden	.10
195	David Sloan	.25
196	Bernie Parmalee	.25
197	Zack Crockett	.25
198	Troy Aikman	1.50
199	Bruce Smith	.10
200	Eric Zeier	.20
201	Anthony Smith	.10
202	Jake Reed	.10
203	Hardy Nickerson	.10
204	Patrick Riley	.10
205	Bruce Matthews	.10
206	Larry Centers	.10
207	Troy Drayton	.10
208	John Burrough	.10
209	Jason Elam	.10
210	Donnell Woolford	.10
211	Sam Shade	.10
212	Kevin Greene	.10
213	Ronald Moore	.10
214	Shane Hannah	.10
215	Jim Everett	.10
216	Scott Mitchell	.20
217	Antonio Freeman	15.00
218	Tony McGee	.10
219	Clay Matthews	.10
220	Neil Smith	.10
221	Mark Williams (Expansion Team)	.25
222	Derrick Graham (Expansion Team)	.25
223	Mike Hollis (Expansion Team)	.25
224	Darion Conner (Expansion Team)	.25
225	Steve Beuerlein (Expansion Team)	.25
226	Rod Smith (Expansion Team)	.25
227	James Williams (Expansion Team)	.25
228	Bob Christian (Expansion Team)	.25
229	Jeff Lageman (Expansion Team)	.25
230	Frank Reich (Expansion Team)	.25
231	Harry Colon (Expansion Team)	.25
232	Carlton Bailey (Expansion Team)	.25
233	Mickey Washington (Expansion Team)	.25
234	Shawn Bouwens (Expansion Team)	.25
235	Don Beebe (Expansion Team)	.25
236	Kelvin Pritchett (Expansion Team)	.25
237	Tommy Barnhardt (Expansion Team)	.25
238	Mike Dumas (Expansion Team)	.25
239	Brett Maxie (Expansion Team)	.25
240	Desmond Howard (Expansion Team)	.25
241	Sam Mills (Expansion Team)	.25
242	Keith Goganious (Expansion Team)	.25
243	Bubba McDowell (Expansion Team)	.25
244	Vinnie Clark (Expansion Team)	.25
245	Lamar Lathon (Expansion Team)	.25
246	Bryan Barker (Expansion Team)	.25
247	Darren Carrington (Expansion Team)	.25
248	Jay Barker	.10
249	Eric Davis	.10
250	Heath Shuler	1.00
251	Donta Jones	.10
252	LeRoy Butler	.10
253	Michael Zordich	.10
254	Cortez Kennedy	.10
255	Brian McCray	.10
256	Randal Hill	.10
257	Michael Irvin	.50
258	Natrone Means	1.00
259	Linc Harden	.10
260	Jerome Bettis	.50
261	Tony Bennett	.10
262	Dameian Jeffries	.10
263	Cornelius Bennett	.10

264	Chris Zorich	.10
265	Bobby Taylor	.10
266	Terrell Buckley	.10
267	Troy Dumas	.10
268	Rodney Hampton	.10
269	Steve Everitt	.10
270	Mel Gray	.10
271	Antonio Armstrong	.10
272	Jim Harbaugh	.10
273	Gary Clark	.10
274	Tau Pupua	.10
275	Warren Moon	.20
276	Corey Croom	.10
277	Tony Berti	.10
278	Shannon Sharpe	.10
279	Boomer Esiason	.10
280	Aeneas Williams	.10
281	Lethon Flowers	.10
282	Derek Brown	.10
283	Charlie Williams	.10
284	Dan Wilkinson	.10
285	Mike Sherrard	.10
286	Evan Pilgrim	.10
287	Kimble Anders	.10
288	Greg Jefferson	.10
289	Ken Norton	.10
290	Terance Mathis	.10
291	Torey Hunter	.10
292	Ken Harvey	.10
293	Irving Fryar	.10
294	Michael Reed	.10
295	Andre Reed	.10
296	Vencie Glenn	.10
297	Corey Swinson	.10
298	Harvey Williams	.10
299	Willie Davis	.10
300	Barry Sanders	3.00
301	Curtis Martin	10.00
302	Johnny Mitchell	.10
303	Daryl Johnston	.10
304	Lorenzo Lynch	.10
305	Christian Fauria	.50
306	Sean Gilbert	.10
307	Ray Zellars	.50
308	William Strong	.10
309	Jack Del Rio	.10
310	Junior Seau	.20
311	Justin Armour	.10
312	Eric Bjorson	.10
313	Vincent Brown	.10
314	Darius Holland	.10
315	Chad May	.50
316	Simon Fletcher	.10
317	Roell Preston	.10
318	John Thierry	.10
319	Orlanda Thomas	.10
320	Zach Wiegert	.10
321	Derrick Alexander	.10
322	Chris Cowart	.10
323	Chris Sanders	1.50
324	Robert Brooks	.25
325	Todd Collins	.50
326	Ken Irvin	.10
327	Erric Pegram	.10
328	Damien Covington	.10
329	Brendan Stai	.10
330	James Stewart	.50
331	Jessie Tuggle	.10
332	Marco Coleman	.10
333	Steve Young	1.50
334	Greg Hill	.40
335	Darryl Williams	.10
336	Calvin Williams	.10
337	Cris Dishman	.10
338	Anthony Morgan	.10
339	Renaldo Turnbull	.10
340	Rick Mirer	.50
341	Tim Brown	.20
342	Dennis Gibson	.10
343	Brad Baxter	.10
344	Henry Jones	.10
345	Johnny Bailey	.10
346	Qadry Ismail	.10
347	Richmond Webb	.10
348	Robert Jones	.10
349	Garrison Hearst	.20
350	Errict Rhett	1.00
351	Steve Atwater	.10
352	Joe Cain	.10
353	Ben Coates	.10
354	Aaron Glenn	.10
355	Antonio Langham	.10
356	Eugene Daniel	.10
357	Tim Bowens	.10

1995 Bowman's Best

Ninety veterans, 90 rookies

and 15 Mirror Image cards make up the debut set of Bowman's Best Football. Bowman's Best 1995 is divided into three subsets - Black Series (90 veterans), Blue Series (90 rookies) and Mirror Images, which show off one of this year's first-round draft choices on one side and last year's corresponding first-round pick on the other (1 per every four packs). The entire set was also done in a refractor version. Black and Blue Series Refractors could be found one per six packs, while Mirror Images Refactors were seeded one per 36 packs. The Black and Blue Series cards have the same format, except the L-shaped border containing the player's team name and his last name are in the corresponding color. An action photo completes the card front color. The back has an action photo, with biographical information, best skills, best stats and the player's name against the corresponding subset color. Mirror Images cards use a black background for the 1994 first-round picks and a blue background for the 1995 selections. A circle with the overall number the player was drafted at is also included.

	MT
Complete Set (180):	220.00
Common Player:	.50
Minor Stars:	1.00
Inserted 1:6	
Wax Box:	275.00

V1	Rob Moore	.50
V2	Craig Heyward	.50
V3	Jim Kelly	1.00
V4	John Kasay	.50
V5	Jeff Graham	.50
V6	Jeff Blake	2.50
V7	Antonio Langham	.50
V8	Troy Aikman	4.00
V9	Simon Fletcher	.50
V10	Barry Sanders	8.00
V11	Edgar Bennett	.50
V12	Ray Childress	.50
V13	Ray Buchanan	.50
V14	Desmond Howard	.50
V15	Dale Carter	.50
V16	Troy Vincent	.50
V17	David Palmer	.50
V18	Ben Coates	.50
V19	Derek Brown	.50
V20	Dave Brown	.50
V21	Mo Lewis	.50
V22	Harvey Williams	.50
V23	Randall Cunningham	.50
V24	Kevin Greene	.50
V25	Junior Seau	1.00
V26	Merton Hanks	.50
V27	Cortez Kennedy	.50
V28	Troy Drayton	.50
V29	Hardy Nickerson	.50
V30	Brian Mitchell	.50
V31	Raymont Harris	.50
V32	Keith Goganious	.50
V33	Andre Reed	.50
V34	Terance Mathis	.50
V35	Garrison Hearst	1.00
V36	Glyn Milburn	.50
V37	Emmitt Smith	6.00
V38	Vinny Testaverde	.50
V39	Darnay Scott	1.00
V40	Mickey Washington	.50
V41	Craig Erickson	.50
V42	Chris Chandler	.50
V43	Brett Favre	8.00
V44	Scott Mitchell	.50
V45	Chris Slade	.50
V46	Warren Moon	1.00
V47	Dan Marino	6.00
V48	Greg Hill	.50
V49	Raghib Ismail	.50
V50	Bobby Houston	.50
V51	Rodney Hampton	.50
V52	Jim Everett	.50
V53	Rick Mirer	1.00
V54	Steve Young	3.00
V55	Dennis Gibson	.50
V56	Rod Woodson	.50
V57	Calvin Williams	.50
V58	Tom Carter	.50
V59	Trent Dilfer	1.00
V60	Shane Conlan	.50
V61	Cornelius Bennett	.50
V62	Eric Metcalf	.50
V63	Frank Reich	.50
V64	Eric Hill	.50
V65	Erik Kramer	.50
V66	Michael Irvin	1.00
V67	Tony McGee	.50
V68	Andre Rison	.50
V69	Shannon Sharpe	.50
V70	Quentin Coryatt	.50
V71	Robert Brooks	1.50

V72	Steve Beuerlein	.50
V73	Herman Moore	2.00
V74	Jack Del Rio	.50
V75	David Meggett	.50
V76	Pete Stoyanovich	.50
V77	Neil Smith	.50
V78	Corey Miller	.50
V79	Tim Brown	1.00
V80	Tyrone Hughes	.50
V81	Boomer Esiason	.50
V82	Natrone Means	1.00
V83	Chris Warren	1.00
V84	Byron Morris	.50
V85	Jerry Rice	4.00
V86	Michael Zordich	.50
V87	Errict Rhett	2.00
V88	Henry Ellard	.50
V89	Chris Miller	.50
V90	John Elway	3.00
R1	Ki-Jana Carter	2.00
R2	Tony Boselli	1.00
R3	Steve McNair	18.00
R4	Michael Westbrook	4.00
R5	Kerry Collins	5.00
R6	Kevin Carter	1.00
R7	Mike Mamula	1.00
R8	Joey Galloway	18.00
R9	Kyle Brady	1.50
R10	Ray McElroy	.50
R11	Derrick Alexander	.50
R12	Warren Sapp	1.50
R13	Mark Fields	.50
R14	Ruben Brown	.50
R15	Ellis Johnson	.50
R16	Hugh Douglas	1.50
R17	Alundis Brice	.50
R18	Napoleon Kaufman	15.00
R19	James Stewart	8.00
R20	Luther Elliss	.50
R21	Rashaan Salaam	2.00
R22	Tyrone Poole	.50
R23	Ty Law	.50
R24	Korey Stringer	1.00
R25	Billy Milner	.50
R26	Roell Preston	.50
R27	Mark Bruener	1.00
R28	Derrick Brooks	.50
R29	Blake Brockermeyer	.50
R30	Mike Frederick	.50
R31	Trezelle Jenkins	.50
R32	Craig Newsome	1.00
R33	Matt O'Dwyer	.50
R34	Terrance Shaw	.50
R35	Anthony Cook	.50
R36	Darick Holmes	2.00
R37	Cory Raymer	.50
R38	Zach Wiegert	.50
R39	Sam Shade	.50
R40	Brian DeMarco	.50
R41	Ron Davis	.50
R42	Orlanda Thomas	.50
R43	Derek West	.50
R44	Ray Zellars	1.50
R45	Todd Collins	1.50
R46	Linc Harden	.50
R47	Frank Sanders	2.00
R48	Ken Dilger	1.50
R49	Barrett Robbins	.50
R50	Bobby Taylor	.50
R51	Terrell Fletcher	1.50
R52	Jack Jackson	.50
R53	Jeff Kopp	.50
R54	Brendan Stai	.50
R55	Corey Fuller	.50
R56	Todd Sauerbrun	.50
R57	Damien Jeffries	.50
R58	Troy Dumas	.50
R59	Charlie Williams	.50
R60	Kordell Stewart	20.00
R61	Jay Barker	.50
R62	Jesse James	.50
R63	Shane Hannah	.50
R64	Rob Johnson	10.00
R66	Darius Holland	.50
R66	William Henderson	.50
R67	Chris Sanders	2.00
R68	Darryl Pounds	.50
R69	Melvin Tuten	.50
R70	David Sloan	.50
R71	Chris Hudson	.50
R72	William Strong	.50
R73	Brian Williams	.50
R74	Curtis Martin	18.00
R75	Mike Verstegen	.50
R76	Justin Armour	.50
R77	Lorenzo Styles	.50
R78	Oliver Gibson	.50
R79	Zack Crockett	1.00
R80	Tau Pupua	.50
R81	Tamarick Vanover	1.25
R82	Steve McLaughlin	.50
R83	Sean Harris	.50
R84	Eric Zeier	1.00
R85	Rodney Young	.50
R86	Chad May	1.00
R87	Evan Pilgrim	.50
R88	James Stewart	1.50
R89	Torey Hunter	.50
R90	Antonio Freeman	25.00

A card number in parentheses ( ) indicates the set is unnumbered.

1995 Bowman's Best Refractors

Each of the 195 cards in Bowman's Best football was done in a Refractor version. Black and Blue Series Refractors were seeded one per six packs; Mirror Images Refractors were seeded one per 36 packs. Each Refractor, which has a shiny, rainbow effect, has the same format as its regular counterpart, except it is labeled on the back with the card number as being a Refractor.

		MT
Complete Set (180):		1200.
Common Player:		4.00
Minor Stars:		8.00
V1	Rob Moore	4.00
V2	Craig Heyward	4.00
V3	Jim Kelly	8.00
V4	John Kasay	4.00
V5	Jeff Graham	4.00
V6	Jeff Blake	8.00
V7	Antonio Langham	4.00
V8	Troy Aikman	30.00
V9	Simon Fletcher	4.00
V10	Barry Sanders	60.00
V11	Edgar Bennett	4.00
V12	Ray Childress	4.00
V13	Ray Buchanan	4.00
V14	Desmond Howard	4.00
V15	Dale Carter	4.00
V16	Troy Vincent	4.00
V17	David Palmer	4.00
V18	Ben Coates	4.00
V19	Derek Brown	4.00
V20	Dave Brown	4.00
V21	Mo Lewis	4.00
V22	Harvey Williams	4.00
V23	Randall Cunningham	4.00
V24	Kevin Greene	4.00
V25	Junior Seau	8.00
V26	Merton Hanks	4.00
V27	Cortez Kennedy	4.00
V28	Troy Drayton	4.00
V29	Hardy Nickerson	4.00
V30	Brian Mitchell	4.00
V31	Raymont Harris	10.00
V32	Keith Goganious	4.00
V33	Andre Reed	4.00
V34	Terance Mathis	4.00
V35	Garrison Hearst	10.00
V36	Glyn Milburn	4.00
V37	Emmitt Smith	50.00
V38	Vinny Testaverde	4.00
V39	Darnay Scott	8.00
V40	Mickey Washington	4.00
V41	Craig Erickson	4.00
V42	Chris Chandler	4.00
V43	Brett Favre	60.00
V44	Scott Mitchell	8.00
V45	Chris Slade	4.00
V46	Warren Moon	8.00
V47	Dan Marino	50.00
V48	Greg Hill	8.00
V49	Raghib Ismail	4.00
V50	Bobby Houston	4.00
V51	Rodney Hampton	4.00
V52	Jim Everett	4.00
V53	Rick Mirer	8.00
V54	Steve Young	20.00
V55	Dennis Gibson	4.00
V56	Rod Woodson	4.00
V57	Calvin Williams	4.00
V58	Tom Carter	4.00
V59	Trent Dilfer	8.00
V60	Shane Conlan	4.00
V61	Cornelius Bennett	4.00
V62	Eric Metcalf	4.00
V63	Frank Reich	4.00
V64	Eric Hill	4.00
V65	Erik Kramer	4.00
V66	Michael Irvin	8.00
V67	Tony McGee	4.00
V68	Andre Rison	4.00
V69	Shannon Sharpe	4.00
V70	Quentin Coryatt	4.00
V71	Robert Brooks	8.00
V72	Steve Beuerlein	4.00
V73	Herman Moore	10.00
V74	Jack Del Rio	4.00
V75	David Meggett	4.00

V76	Pete Stoyanovich	4.00
V77	Neil Smith	4.00
V78	Corey Miller	4.00
V79	Tim Brown	8.00
V80	Tyrone Hughes	4.00
V81	Boomer Esiason	4.00
V82	Natrone Means	10.00
V83	Chris Warren	8.00
V84	Byron Morris	4.00
V85	Jerry Rice	30.00
V86	Michael Zordich	4.00
V87	Errict Rhett	8.00
V88	Henry Ellard	4.00
V89	Chris Miller	4.00
V90	John Elway	50.00
R1	Ki-Jana Carter	8.00
R2	Tony Boselli	8.00
R3	Steve McNair	60.00
R4	Michael Westbrook	35.00
R5	Kerry Collins	20.00
R6	Kevin Carter	8.00
R7	Mike Mamula	4.00
R8	Joey Galloway	60.00
R9	Kyle Brady	8.00
R10	Ray McElroy	4.00
R11	Derrick Alexander	8.00
R12	Warren Sapp	8.00
R13	Mark Fields	4.00
R14	Ruben Brown	4.00
R15	Ellis Johnson	4.00
R16	Hugh Douglas	4.00
R17	Alundis Brice	4.00
R18	Napoleon Kaufman	40.00
R19	James Stewart	40.00
R20	Luther Elliss	4.00
R21	Rashaan Salaam	10.00
R22	Tyrone Poole	4.00
R23	Ty Law	4.00
R24	Korey Stringer	8.00
R25	Billy Milner	4.00
R26	Roell Preston	4.00
R27	Mark Bruener	4.00
R28	Derrick Brooks	4.00
R29	Blake Brockermeyer	4.00
R30	Mike Frederick	4.00
R31	Trezelle Jenkins	4.00
R32	Craig Newsome	8.00
R33	Matt O'Dwyer	4.00
R34	Terrance Shaw	4.00
R35	Anthony Cook	4.00
R36	Darick Holmes	10.00
R37	Cory Raymer	4.00
R38	Zach Wiegert	4.00
R39	Sam Shade	4.00
R40	Brian DeMarco	4.00
R41	Ron Davis	4.00
R42	Orlanda Thomas	4.00
R43	Derek West	4.00
R44	Ray Zellars	8.00
R45	Todd Collins	8.00
R46	Linc Harden	4.00
R47	Barry Sanders	15.00
R48	Ken Dilger	8.00
R49	Barrett Robbins	4.00
R50	Bobby Taylor	4.00
R51	Terrell Fletcher	8.00
R52	Jack Jackson	4.00
R53	Jeff Kopp	4.00
R54	Brendan Stai	4.00
R55	Corey Fuller	4.00
R56	Todd Sauerbrun	4.00
R57	Dameian Jeffries	4.00
R58	Troy Dumas	4.00
R59	Charlie Williams	4.00
R60	Kordell Stewart	60.00
R61	Jay Barker	4.00
R62	Jesse James	4.00
R63	Shane Hannah	4.00
R64	Rob Johnson	25.00
R65	Darius Holland	4.00
R66	William Henderson	10.00
R67	Chris Sanders	8.00
R68	Darryll Pounds	4.00
R69	Melvin Tuten	4.00
R70	David Sloan	4.00
R71	Chris Hudson	4.00
R72	William Strong	4.00
R73	Brian Williams	4.00
R74	Curtis Martin	60.00
R75	Mike Verstegen	4.00
R76	Justin Armour	4.00
R77	Lorenzo Styles	4.00
R78	Oliver Gibson	4.00
R79	Zack Crockett	8.00
R80	Tau Pupua	4.00
R81	Tamarick Vanover	8.00
R82	Steve McLaughlin	4.00
R83	Sean Harris	4.00
R84	Eric Zeier	8.00
R85	Rodney Young	4.00
R86	Chad May	8.00
R87	Evan Pilgrim	4.00
R88	James Stewart	8.00
R89	Torey Hunter	4.00
R90	Antonio Freeman	60.00

Post-1980 cards in Near Mint condition will generally sell for about 75% of the quoted Mint value. Excellent-condition cards bring no more than 40%.

1995 Bowman's Best Mirror Images

These cards feature one of 1995's first-round draft picks on one side, with the corresponding 1994 pick on the other. The 1994 picks use black for the background; the 1995 picks use blue. A circle with the overall number the player was selected at is also included on both sides. Regular Mirror Images cards were seeded one per four packs of 1995 Bowman's Best football. Mirror Images Refractors were seeded one per 36 packs.

		MT
Complete Set (15):		35.00
Common Player:		1.00
Minor Stars:		2.00
Inserted 1:4		
Refractor Cards:		3x-6x
Inserted 1:36		
1	Ki-Jana Carter, Dan Wilkinson	2.00
2	Marshall Faulk, Tony Boselli	2.00
3	Steve McNair, Heath Shuler	8.00
4	Michael Westbrook, Willie McGinist	3.00
5	Kerry Collins, Trev Alberts	3.00
6	Trent Dilfer, Kevin Carter	2.00
7	Mike Mamula, Bryant Young	1.00
8	Joey Galloway, Sam Adams	6.00
9	Kyle Brady, Antonio Langham	1.00
10	J.J. Stokes, Jamir Miller	3.00
11	Derrick Alexander, John Thierry	1.00
12	Warren Sapp, Aaron Glenn	1.00
13	Mark Fields, Joe Johnson	1.00
14	Ruben Brown, Bernard Williams	1.00
15	Ellis Johnson, Wayne Gandy	1.00

1996 Bowman's Best

Bowman's Best contained 135 key veterans on gold designs and 45 1996 NFL draft picks on silver designed cards. All 180 cards are also found in a parallel Refractors and Atomic Refractors insert. The cards show the player in front of a fake field with yard markers running down the length of the card. The player's name and team logo are near the bottom. Bowman's Best had three inserts - Mirror Images, Best Bets and Best Cuts.

		MT
Complete Set (180):		110.00
Common Player:		.25
Minor Stars:		.50
Wax Box:		110.00
1	Emmitt Smith	6.00
2	Kordell Stewart	4.00
3	Mark Chmura	.25
4	Sean Dawkins	.25
5	Steve Young	3.00
6	Tamarick Vanover	1.00
7	Scott Mitchell	.25
8	Aaron Hayden	.25
9	William Thomas	.25
10	Dan Marino	6.00
11	Curtis Conway	.25
12	Steve Atwater	.25
13	Derrick Brooks	.25
14	Rick Mirer	.25
15	Mark Brunell	3.00
16	Garrison Hearst	.25
17	Eric Turner	.25
18	Mark Carrier	.25
19	Darnay Scott	.25
20	Steve McNair	4.00
21	Jim Everett	.25
22	Wayne Chrebet	.25
23	Ben Coates	.25
24	Harvey Williams	.25
25	Michael Westbrook	.50
26	Kevin Carter	.25
27	Dave Brown	.25
28	Jake Reed	.25
29	Thurman Thomas	.50
30	Jeff George	.25
31	Carnell Lake	.25
32	J.J. Stokes	.50
33	Jay Novacek	.25
34	Brett Perriman	.25
35	Robert Brooks	.25
36	Neil Smith	.25
37	Chris Zorich	.25
38	Michael Barrow	.25
39	Quentin Coryatt	.25
40	Kerry Collins	.75
41	Aeneas Williams	.25
42	James Stewart	.25
43	Warren Moon	.25
44	Willie McGinest	.25
45	Rodney Hampton	.25
46	Jeff Hostetler	.25
47	Darrell Green	.25
48	Warren Sapp	.25
49	Troy Drayton	.25
50	Junior Seau	.25
51	Mike Mamula	.25
52	Antonio Langham	.25
53	Eric Metcalf	.25
54	Adrian Murrell	.25
55	Joey Galloway	1.00
56	Anthony Miller	.25
57	Carl Pickens	.25
58	Bruce Smith	.25
59	Merton Hanks	.25
60	Troy Aikman	3.00
61	Erik Kramer	.25
62	Tyrone Poole	.25
63	Michael Jackson	.25
64	Rob Moore	.25
65	Marcus Allen	.25
66	Orlando Thomas	.25
67	David Meggett	.25
68	Trent Dilfer	.25
69	Herman Moore	.75
70	Brett Favre	8.00
71	Blaine Bishop	.25
72	Eric Allen	.25
73	Bernie Parmalee	.25
74	Kyle Brady	.25
75	Terry McDaniel	.25
76	Rodney Peete	.25
77	Yancey Thigpen	.25
78	Stan Humphries	.25
79	Craig Heyward	.25
80	Rashaan Salaam	.75
81	Shannon Sharpe	.25
82	Jim Harbaugh	.25
83	Vinnie Clark	.25
84	Steve Bono	.25
85	Drew Bledsoe	3.00
86	Ken Norton	.25
87	Brian Mitchell	.25
88	Hardy Nickerson	.25
89	Todd Lyght	.25
90	Barry Sanders	5.00
91	Robert Blackmon	.25
92	Larry Centers	.25
93	Jim Kelly	.25
94	Lamar Lathon	.25
95	Cris Carter	.25
96	Hugh Douglas	.25
97	Michael Strahan	.25
98	Lee Woodall	.25
99	Michael Irvin	.25
100	Marshall Faulk	1.00
101	Terance Mathis	.25
102	Eric Zeier	.25
103	Marty Carter	.25
104	Steve Tovar	.25
105	Isaac Bruce	1.00
106	Tony Martin	.25
107	Dale Carter	.25
108	Terry Kirby	.25
109	Tyrone Hughes	.25
110	Bryce Paup	.25
111	Errict Rhett	.75
112	Ricky Watters	.50
113	Chris Chandler	.25
114	Edgar Bennett	.25
115	John Elway	3.00
116	Sam Mills	.25
117	Seth Joyner	.25
118	Jeff Lageman	.25
119	Chris Calloway	.25
120	Curtis Martin	4.00
121	Ken Harvey	.25
122	Eugene Daniel	.25
123	Tim Brown	.25
124	Mo Lewis	.25
125	Jeff Blake	.75
126	Jessie Tuggle	.25
127	Vinny Testaverde	.25
128	Chris Warren	.25
129	Terrell Davis	8.00
130	Greg Lloyd	.25
131	Deion Sanders	2.00
132	Derrick Thomas	.25
133	Darryll Lewis	.25
134	Reggie White	.50
135	Jerry Rice	3.00
136	Tony Banks	4.00
137	Derrick Mayes	3.00
138	Leeland McElroy	1.00
139	Bryan Still	.25
140	Tim Biakabutuka	2.00
141	Rickey Dudley	2.00
142	Troy James	.25
143	Lawyer Milloy	.25
144	Mike Ulufale	.25
145	Bobby Engram	2.00
146	Willie Anderson	.25
147	Terrell Owens	30.00
148	Jonathan Ogden	.25
149	Darrius Johnson	.25
150	Kevin Hardy	.50
151	Simeon Rice	1.00
152	Alex Molden	.25
153	Cedric Jones	.25
154	Duane Clemons	.25
155	Karim Abdul-Jabbar	5.00
156	Dedric Mathis	.25
157	John Michels	.25
158	Winslow Oliver	.25
159	Stepfret Williams	.25
160	Eddie Kennison	1.00
161	Marcus Coleman	.25
162	Tedy Bruschi	.25
163	Detron Smith	.25
164	Ray Lewis	.25
165	Marvin Harrison	15.00
166	Je'Rod Cherry	.25
167	Jerris McPhail	.25
168	Eric Moulds	10.00
169	Walt Harris	.25
170	Eddie George	20.00
171	Jermaine Lewis	4.00
172	Jeff Lewis	.25
173	Ray Mickens	.25
174	Amani Toomer	.25
175	Zach Thomas	1.50
176	Lawrence Phillips	6.00
177	John Mobley	.25
178	Anthony Dorsett Jr.	.25
179	DeRon Jenkins	.25
180	Keyshawn Johnson	10.00

1996 Bowman's Best Refractors

All 180 cards in Bowman's Best Football had parallel Refractor versions, inserted every 12 packs. The fronts feature a refractive foil, while the backs contain the word "Refractor" within the white card number box.

	MT
Refractors:	5x-10x

1996 Bowman's Best Atomic Refractors

All 180 cards in Bowman's Best Football also had Atomic Refractor parallel versions, inserted every 48 packs. Atomic Refractors featured a prismatic refractive foil on the card fronts and the words "Atomic Refrac-

tor" on the back within the white card number box.

	MT
Atomic Refractors:	15x-30x

1996 Bowman's Best Mirror Images

Bowman's Best Mirror Images was a nine-card insert that featured four players per card, with two on each side. Regular versions are seeded every 48 packs, Refractors are found every 96 packs and Atomic Refractors are seeded every 192 packs. Card No. 7 has Jerry Rice on the front with Isaac Bruce with him, but lists running back as their position. This card was an uncorrected error.

		MT
Complete Set (9):		175.00
Common Player:		12.00
Refractors:		2x
Atomic Refractors:		4x
1a	Steve Young, Kerry Collins	40.00
1b	Dan Marino, Mark Brunell	40.00
2a	Brett Favre, Elvis Grbac	40.00
2b	John Elway, Drew Bledsoe	40.00
3a	Troy Aikman, Gus Frerotte	20.00
3b	Jim Harbaugh, Jeff Blake	20.00
4a	Emmitt Smith, Errict Rhett	40.00
4b	Chris Warren, Curtis Martin	40.00
5a	Barry Sanders, Rashaan Salaam	25.00
5b	Thurman Thomas, Terrell Davis	25.00
6a	Rodney Hampton, Lawrence Phillips	12.00
6b	Marcus Allen, Marshall Faulk	12.00
7a	Jerry Rice, Isaac Bruce	20.00
7b	Tim Brown, Joey Galloway	20.00
8a	Cris Carter, Curtis Conway	12.00
8b	Carl Pickens, Keyshawn Johnson	12.00
9a	Robert Brooks, Michael Westbrook	12.00
9b	Anthony Miller, O.J. McDuffie	12.00

1996 Bowman's Best Best Cuts

Bowman's Best Cuts displays 15 of the top players in the NFL on die-cut chromium cards. The player's name runs along the right side, with the majority of the die-cutting on that side. Regular versions are found every 24 packs, Refractors are seeded every 48 packs and Atomic Refractor versions are found every 96 packs.

		MT
Complete Set (15):		250.00
Common Player:		5.00
Refractors:		2x
Atomic Refractors:		4x
1	Dan Marino	40.00
2	Emmitt Smith	40.00
3	Rashaan Salaam	5.00
4	Herman Moore	5.00
5	Brett Favre	40.00
6	Marshall Faulk	10.00
7	John Elway	12.00
8	Curtis Martin	25.00
9	Deion Sanders	12.00
10	Jerry Rice	20.00
11	Terrell Davis	20.00
12	Kerry Collins	8.00
13	Steve Young	15.00
14	Troy Aikman	20.00
15	Barry Sanders	20.00

1996 Bowman's Best Best Bets

Bowman's Best Bets highlighted nine top rookies on a borderless design with "screws" in all four corners as if the card was in a screw-down holder. Regular versions are seeded every 12 packs, Refractors are found every 48 packs and Atomic Refractors every 96 packs.

		MT
Complete Set (9):		45.00
Common Player:		2.00
Refractors:		2x
Atomic Refractors:		4x
1	Keyshawn Johnson	10.00
2	Lawrence Phillips	4.00
3	Tim Biakabutuka	5.00
4	Eddie George	20.00
5	John Mobley	2.00
6	Eddie Kennison	6.00
7	Marvin Harrison	10.00
8	Amani Toomer	2.00
9	Bobby Engram	4.00

1997 Bowman's Best

Bowman's Best Football is a 125-card set featuring 95 NFL veterans with a gold design and 30 rookies with a silver design. The base cards also come in Refractor (1:12) and Atomic Refractor (1:24) parallels. The insert sets include Bowman's Best Autographs, Laser Cuts and Mirror Image. Each of the insert cards has a Refractor and Atomic Refractor version. Bowman's Best Football was sold in six-card packs.

	MT
Complete Set (125):	100.00

		MT
Common Player:		.25
Minor Stars:		.50
Refractor Stars:		4x-8x
Refractor Rookies:		2x-4x
Atomic Ref. Stars:		8x-16x
Atomic Ref. Rookies:		4x-8x
Wax Box:		100.00
1	Brett Favre	8.00
2	Larry Centers	.25
3	Trent Dilfer	.50
4	Rodney Hampton	.25
5	Wesley Walls	.25
6	Jerome Bettis	.50
7	Keyshawn Johnson	1.00
8	Keenan McCardell	.25
9	Terry Allen	.25
10	Troy Aikman	4.00
11	Tony Banks	1.50
12	Ty Detmer	.25
13	Chris Chandler	.25
14	Marshall Faulk	.50
15	Heath Shuler	.25
16	Stan Humphries	.25
17	Bryan Cox	.25
18	Chris Spielman	.25
19	Derrick Thomas	.25
20	Steve Young	2.50
21	Desmond Howard	.25
22	Jeff Blake	.50
23	Michael Jackson	.25
24	Cris Carter	.50
25	Joey Galloway	1.00
26	Simeon Rice	.25
27	Reggie White	.50
28	Dave Brown	.25
29	Mike Alstott	1.50
30	Emmitt Smith	7.00
31	Anthony Johnson	.25
32	Mark Brunell	4.00
33	Ricky Watters	.50
34	Terrell Davis	4.00
35	Ben Coates	.25
36	Gus Frerotte	.25
37	Andre Reed	.25
38	Isaac Bruce	.50
39	Junior Seau	.50
40	Eddie George	6.00
41	Adrian Murrell	.25
42	Jake Reed	.25
43	Karim Abdul-Jabbar	.75
44	Scott Mitchell	.25
45	Ki-Jana Carter	.25
46	Curtis Conway	.50
47	Jim Harbaugh	.25
48	Tim Brown	.50
49	Mario Bates	.25
50	Jerry Rice	4.00
51	Byron Morris	.25
52	Marcus Allen	.50
53	Errict Rhett	.25
54	Steve McNair	3.00
55	Kerry Collins	.75
56	Bert Emanuel	.25
57	Curtis Martin	4.00
58	Bryce Paup	.25
59	Brad Johnson	.50
60	John Elway	2.50
61	Natrone Means	.50
62	Deion Sanders	2.00
63	Tony Martin	.25
64	Michael Westbrook	.25
65	Chris Calloway	.25
66	Antonio Freeman	.50
67	Rick Mirer	.50
68	Kent Graham	.25
69	O.J. McDuffie	.25
70	Barry Sanders	4.00
71	Chris Warren	.25
72	Kordell Stewart	4.00
73	Thurman Thomas	.50
74	Marvin Harrison	1.00
75	Carl Pickens	.25
76	Brent Jones	.25
77	Irving Fryar	.25
78	Neil O'Donnell	.25
79	Elvis Grbac	.25
80	Drew Bledsoe	4.00
81	Shannon Sharpe	.25
82	Vinny Testaverde	.25
83	Chris Sanders	.25
84	Herman Moore	.50
85	Jeff George	.50
86	Bruce Smith	.25
87	Robert Smith	.25
88	Kevin Hardy	.25
89	Kevin Greene	.25
90	Dan Marino	7.00
91	Michael Irvin	.50
92	Garrison Hearst	.25
93	Lake Dawson	.25
94	Lawrence Phillips	.50
95	Terry Glenn	.75
96	Jake Plummer	10.00
97	Byron Hanspard	2.00
98	Bryant Westbrook	.50
99	Troy Davis	1.00
100	Danny Wuerffel	3.00
101	Tony Gonzalez	2.00
102	Jim Druckenmiller	4.00
103	Kevin Lockett	.25
104	Renaldo Wynn	.25
105	James Farrior	.25
106	Rae Carruth	3.00
107	Tom Knight	.25
108	Corey Dillon	7.00
109	Kenny Holmes	.25
110	Orlando Pace	.50
111	Reidel Anthony	4.00
112	Chad Scott	.25
113	Antowain Smith	5.00
114	David LaFleur	2.00
115	Yatil Green	1.50
116	Darrell Russell	.25
117	Joey Kent	1.00
118	Darnell Autry	1.00
119	Peter Boulware	.50
120	Shawn Springs	.25
121	Ike Hilliard	3.00
122	Dwayne Rudd	.25
123	Reinard Wilson	.25
124	Michael Booker	.25
125	Warrick Dunn	5.00

1997 Bowman's Best Autographs

This 10-card set features autographed versions of 10 base set cards. The cards were inserted 1:131. Refractor (1:1578) and Atomic Refractor (1:4733) parallels are also available.

		MT
Complete Set (10):		500.00
Common Player:		20.00
22	Jeff Blake	20.00
44	Scott Mitchell	20.00
47	Jim Harbaugh	20.00
99	Troy Davis	20.00
102	Jim Druckenmiller	80.00
113	Antowain Smith	80.00
114	David LaFleur	30.00
120	Shawn Springs	20.00
121	Ike Hilliard	50.00
125	Warrick Dunn	150.00

1997 Bowman's Best Cuts

Best Cuts features 20 players on die-cut cards. The top of the cards says Best Cuts and the letters are die-cut. Best Cuts was inserted once per 24 packs. Refractor (1:48) and Atomic Refractor (1:96) parallels were also created. They are numbered with the "BC" prefix.

		MT
Complete Set (20):		200.00
Common Player:		3.00
Refractors:		2x
Atomic Refractors:		2x-4x
1	Orlando Pace	3.00
2	Eddie George	16.00
3	John Elway	8.00
4	Tony Gonzalez	3.00
5	Brett Favre	25.00
6	Shawn Springs	3.00
7	Warrick Dunn	20.00
8	Troy Aikman	12.00
9	Terry Glenn	6.00
10	Dan Marino	20.00
11	Jake Plummer	8.00
12	Ike Hilliard	8.00
13	Emmitt Smith	20.00
14	Steve Young	8.00
15	Barry Sanders	18.00
16	Jim Druckenmiller	10.00
17	Drew Bledsoe	12.00
18	Antowain Smith	8.00
19	Mark Brunell	12.00
20	Jerry Rice	12.00

Values quoted in this guide reflect the retail price of a card — the price a collector can expect to pay when buying a card from a dealer. The wholesale price — that which a collector can expect to receive from a dealer when selling cards — will be significantly lower, depending on desirability and condition.

1997 Bowman's Best Mirror Images

The 10, double-sided cards in Mirror Images showcase four top players from the same position. Two NFC players and two AFC players are featured on each card. The chromium cards (1:48) also had Refractor (1:96) and Atomic Refractor (1:192) parallels. They are numbered with the "MI" prefix.

		MT
Complete Set (10):		180.00
Common Player:		5.00
Refractors:		2x
Atomic Refractors:		2x-4x
1	Brett Favre, Gus Frerotte, John Elway, Mark Brunell	40.00
2	Steve Young, Tony Banks, Dan Marino, Drew Bledsoe	35.00
3	Troy Aikman, Kerry Collins, Vinny Testaverde, Kordell Stewart	20.00
4	Emmitt Smith, Dorsey Levens, Marcus Allen, Eddie George	35.00
5	Barry Sanders, Errict Rhett, Thurman Thomas, Curtis Martin	25.00
6	Ricky Watters, Jamal Anderson, Chris Warren, Terrell Davis	20.00
7	Jerry Rice, Isaac Bruce, Tony Martin, Marvin Harrison	20.00
8	Herman Moore, Curtis Conway, Tim Brown, Terry Glenn	15.00
9	Michael Irvin, Eddie Kennison, Carl Pickens, Keyshawn Johnson	5.00
10	Wesley Walls, Jason Dunn, Shannon Sharpe, Rickey Dudley	5.00

1998 Bowman

Bowman contained 220 cards, including 150 veterans and 70 rookies. Prospects were featured on a silver and blue design while veterans are shown on a silver and red design. Rookies contain a "Bowman Rookie Card" gold foil stamp. The set is paralleled in Inter-State and Golden Anniversary sets. Three insert sets are included in packs: Bowman Autographs, which come in blue, silver and gold foil versions, Scout's Choice and Bowman Chrome Preview.

		MT
Complete Set (220):		100.00
Common Player:		.25
Minor Stars:		.50
Common Rookie:		.25
Golden Ann. Stars:		50x-100x
Golden Ann. Rookies:		10x-20x
Inserted 1:180		
Production 50 Sets		
Wax Box:		90.00
1	Peyton Manning	15.00
2	Keith Brooking	.50
3	Duane Starks	.50
4	Takeo Spikes	.50
5	Andre Wadsworth	2.00
6	Greg Ellis	1.00
7	Brian Griese	10.00
8	Germane Crowell	3.00
9	Jerome Pathon	2.00
10	Ryan Leaf	7.00
11	Fred Taylor	12.00
12	Robert Edwards	4.00
13	Grant Wistrom	.50
14	Robert Holcombe	4.00
15	Tim Dwight	3.00
16	Jacquez Green	4.00
17	Marcus Nash	3.00
18	Jason Peter	.50
19	Anthony Simmons	.50
20	Curtis Enis	5.00
21	John Avery	3.00
22	Patrick Johnson	.50
23	Joe Jurevicius	2.00
24	Brian Simmons	2.00
25	Kevin Dyson	3.00
26	Skip Hicks	3.00
27	Hines Ward	3.00
28	Tavian Banks	3.00
29	Ahman Green	4.00
30	Tony Simmons	.50
31	Charles Johnson	.25
32	Freddie Jones	.75
33	Joey Galloway	.75
34	Tony Banks	.50
35	Jake Plummer	1.50
36	Reidel Anthony	.25
37	Steve McNair	.75
38	Michael Westbrook	.50
39	Chris Sanders	.25
40	Isaac Bruce	.50
41	Charlie Garner	.25
42	Wayne Chrebet	.25
43	Michael Strahan	.25
44	Brad Johnson	.50
45	Mike Alstott	.50
46	Tony Gonzalez	.50
47	Johnnie Morton	.25
48	Darnay Scott	.25
49	Rae Carruth	.25
50	Terrell Davis	2.50
51	Jermaine Lewis	.25
52	Frank Sanders	.25
53	Byron Hanspard	.25
54	Gus Frerotte	.25
55	Terry Glenn	.50
56	J.J. Stokes	.25
57	Will Blackwell	.25
58	Keyshawn Johnson	.50
59	Tiki Barber	.25
60	Dorsey Levens	.50
61	Zach Thomas	.25
62	Corey Dillon	1.25
63	Antowain Smith	1.00
64	Michael Sinclair	.25
65	Rod Smith	.25
66	Trent Dilfer	.50
67	Warren Sapp	.25
68	Charles Way	.25
69	Tamarick Vanover	.25
70	Drew Bledsoe	1.50
71	John Mobley	.25
72	Kerry Collins	.50
73	Peter Boulware	.25
74	Simeon Rice	.25
75	Eddie George	1.50
76	Fred Lane	.50
77	Jamal Anderson	.50
78	Antonio Freeman	.75
79	Jason Sehorn	.25
80	Curtis Martin	.75
81	Bobby Hoying	.25
82	Garrison Hearst	.25
83	Glenn Foley	.25
84	Danny Kanell	.25
85	Kordell Stewart	1.50
86	O.J. McDuffie	.25
87	Marvin Harrison	.75
88	Bobby Engram	.25
89	Chris Slade	.25
90	Warrick Dunn	1.50
91	Ricky Watters	.50
92	Rickey Dudley	.25
93	Terrell Owens	.50
94	Karim Abdul-Jabbar	.50
95	Napoleon Kaufman	.75
96	Darrell Green	.25
97	Levon Kirkland	.25
98	Jeff George	.50
99	Andre Hastings	.25
100	John Elway	2.00
101	John Randle	.25
102	Andre Rison	.25
103	Keenan McCardell	.25
104	Marshall Faulk	.75
105	Emmitt Smith	3.00
106	Robert Brooks	.25
107	Scott Mitchell	.25
108	Shannon Sharpe	.50
109	Deion Sanders	.75
110	Jerry Rice	2.00
111	Erik Kramer	.25
112	Michael Jackson	.25
113	Aeneas Williams	.25
114	Terry Allen	.25
115	Steve Young	1.25
116	Warren Moon	.50
117	Junior Seau	.50
118	Jerome Bettis	.50
119	Irving Fryar	.25
120	Barry Sanders	4.00
121	Tim Brown	.50
122	Chad Brown	.25
123	Ben Coates	.25
124	Robert Smith	.25
125	Brett Favre	4.00
126	Derrick Thomas	.25
127	Reggie White	.50
128	Troy Aikman	2.00
129	Jeff Blake	.25
130	Mark Brunell	1.50
131	Curtis Conway	.25
132	Wesley Walls	.25
133	Thurman Thomas	.50
134	Chris Chandler	.25
135	Dan Marino	3.00
136	Larry Centers	.25
137	Shawn Jefferson	.25
138	Andre Reed	.25
139	Jake Reed	.25
140	Cris Carter	.50
141	Elvis Grbac	.25
142	Mark Chmura	.50
143	Michael Irvin	.50
144	Carl Pickens	.50
145	Herman Moore	.50
146	Marvin Jones	.25
147	Terance Mathis	.25
148	Rob Moore	.25
149	Bruce Smith	.25
150	Checklist	.25
151	Leslie Shepherd	.25
152	Chris Spielman	.25
153	Troy McGee	.25
154	Kevin Smith	.25
155	Bill Romanowski	.25
156	Stephen Boyd	.25
157	James Stewart	.25
158	Jason Taylor	.25
159	Troy Drayton	.25
160	Mark Fields	.25
161	Jessie Armstead	.25
162	James Jett	.25
163	Bobby Taylor	.25
164	Kimble Anders	.25
165	Jimmy Smith	.25
166	Quentin Coryatt	.25
167	Bryant Westbrook	.25
168	Neil Smith	.25
169	Darren Woodson	.25
170	Ray Buchanan	.25
171	Earl Holmes	.25
172	Ray Lewis	.25
173	Steve Broussard	.25
174	Derrick Brooks	.25
175	Ken Harvey	.25
176	Darryll Lewis	.25
177	Derrick Rodgers	.25
178	James McKnight	.25
179	Cris Dishman	.25
180	Hardy Nickerson	.25
181	Charles Woodson	5.00
182	Randy Moss	30.00
183	Stephen Alexander	.50
184	Samari Rolle	.50
185	Jamie Duncan	.50
186	Lance Schulters	.50
187	Tony Parrish	.50
188	Corey Chavous	.50
189	Jammi German	.50
190	Sam Cowart	.50
191	Donald Hayes	.50
192	R.W. McQuarters	1.00
193	Az-Zahir Hakim	2.00
194	Chris Fuamatu-Ma'afala	2.00
195	Allen Rossum	.50
196	Jon Ritchie	.50
197	Blake Spence	.50
198	Brian Alford	.50
199	Fred Weary	.50
200	Rod Rutledge	.50
201	Michael Myers	.50
202	Rashaan Shehee	2.00
203	Donovin Darius	.50
204	E.G. Green	2.00
205	Vonnie Holliday	2.00
206	Charlie Batch	8.00
207	Michael Pittman	.50
208	Artrell Hawkins	.50
209	Jonathan Quinn	.50
210	Kailee Wong	.50
211	Deshea Townsend	1.00
212	Patrick Surtain	.50
213	Brian Kelly	.50
214	Tebucky Jones	.50
215	Pete Gonzalez	1.00
216	Shaun Williams	.50
217	Scott Frost	.50
218	Leonard Little	.50
219	Alonzo Mayes	1.00
220	Cordell Taylor	.50

1998 Bowman Inter-State

All 220 cards were reprinted in Inter-State parallel versions and seeded one per pack. These are printed on silver foil and included a background map of where the player was born on the front and a vanity plate on the back.

	MT
Inter-State Cards:	3x
Inter-State Rookies:	2x

1998 Bowman Blue Autographs

Eleven different players signed cards to be inserted into packs of Bowman. Card rarity was differentiated by blue (1:360 packs), silver (2,401) or gold foil Topps Certified Autograph Issue stamps (1:7,202).

	MT
Complete Set (11):	700.00
Common Player:	20.00
Inserted 1:360	
Silver Cards:	2x
Inserted 1:2,401	
Gold Cards:	4x
Inserted 1:7,202	
1 Peyton Manning	140.00
2 Andre Wadsworth	20.00
3 Brian Griese	50.00
4 Ryan Leaf	75.00
5 Fred Taylor	100.00
6 Robert Edwards	60.00
7 Randy Moss	250.00
8 Curtis Enis	60.00
9 Kevin Dyson	40.00
10 Charles Woodson	60.00
11 Tim Dwight	40.00

1998 Bowman Chrome Preview

This 10-card insert set previewed the upcoming Bowman Chrome set. It included five veterans and five rookies, with regular versions seeded one per 12 packs and Refractors every 48 packs.

	MT
Complete Set (10):	50.00
Common Player:	4.00
Inserted 1:12	
Refractors:	2x
Inserted 1:48	
1 Peyton Manning	10.00
2 Curtis Enis	5.00
3 Charles Woodson	4.00
4 Robert Edwards	6.00
5 Ryan Leaf	7.00
6 Brett Favre	12.00
7 John Elway	6.00
8 Barry Sanders	12.00
9 Kordell Stewart	4.00
10 Terrell Davis	8.00

1998 Bowman Scout's Choice

This 14-card insert set showcased the top rookies according to the Bowman Scouts. Cards featured a borderless, double-etched foil design and were inserted one per 12 packs.

	MT
Complete Set (14):	60.00
Common Player:	2.00
Inserted 1:12	
SC1 Peyton Manning	15.00
SC2 John Avery	3.00
SC3 Grant Wistrom	2.00
SC4 Kevin Dyson	3.00
SC5 Andre Wadsworth	3.00
SC6 Joe Jurevicius	2.00
SC7 Charles Woodson	6.00
SC8 Takeo Spikes	2.00
SC9 Fred Taylor	10.00
SC10 Ryan Leaf	8.00
SC11 Robert Edwards	6.00
SC12 Randy Moss	20.00
SC13 Patrick Johnson	2.00
SC14 Curtis Enis	6.00

1998 Bowman's Best

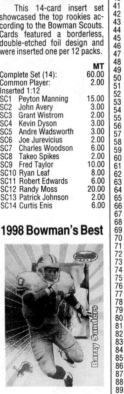

This super-premium set has a 125-card base set that is made up of 100 veterans and 25 rookies. Each veteran card has a gold design, while the rookies are in silver. Each card has a Refractor version that is sequentially numbered to 400 and inserted 1:25 packs. Each player also has a parallel Atomic Refractor version that is numbered to 100 and inserted 1:103 packs.

	MT
Complete Set (125):	140.00
Common Player:	.25
Minor Stars:	.50
Common Rookie:	2.00
Inserted 1:2	
Refractor Cards:	8x-16x
Refractor Rookies:	3x-6x
Inserted 1:25	
Production 400 Sets	
Atomic Ref. Cards:	25x-50x
Atomic Ref. Rookies:	10x-20x
Inserted 1:103	
Production 100 Sets	
Wax Box:	90.00
1 Emmitt Smith	4.00
2 Reggie White	.75
3 Jake Plummer	2.00
4 Ike Hilliard	.25
5 Isaac Bruce	.50
6 Trent Dilfer	.50
7 Ricky Watters	.50
8 Jeff George	.50
9 Wayne Chrebet	.50
10 Brett Favre	6.00
11 Terry Allen	.50
12 Bert Emanuel	.25
13 Andre Reed	.50
14 Andre Rison	.50
15 Jeff Blake	.50
16 Steve McNair	1.50
17 Joey Galloway	1.00
18 Irving Fryar	.25
19 Dorsey Levens	.75
20 Jerry Rice	3.00
21 Kerry Collins	.75
22 Michael Jackson	.25
23 Kordell Stewart	2.00
24 Junior Seau	.50
25 Jimmy Smith	.75
26 Michael Westbrook	.25
27 Eddie George	2.50
28 Cris Carter	1.00
29 Jason Sehorn	.25
30 Warrick Dunn	2.00
31 Garrison Hearst	.75
32 Erik Kramer	.25
33 Chris Chandler	.50
34 Michael Irvin	.50
35 Marshall Faulk	1.00
36 Warren Moon	.50
37 Rickey Dudley	.25
38 Drew Bledsoe	2.50
39 Antowain Smith	1.00
40 Terrell Davis	5.00
41 Gus Frerotte	.25
42 Robert Brooks	.25
43 Tony Banks	.50
44 Terrell Owens	1.50
45 Edgar Bennett	.25
46 Rob Moore	.50
47 J.J. Stokes	.50
48 Yancey Thigpen	.25
49 Elvis Grbac	.25
50 John Elway	3.00
51 Charles Johnson	.25
52 Karim Abdul-Jabbar	.75
53 Carl Pickens	.50
54 Peter Boulware	.25
55 Chris Warren	.25
56 Terance Mathis	.25
57 Andre Hastings	.25
58 Jake Reed	.25
59 Mike Alstott	1.00
60 Mark Brunell	2.50
61 Herman Moore	.75
62 Troy Aikman	3.00
63 Fred Lane	.50
64 Rod Smith	.75
65 Terry Glenn	.75
66 Jerome Bettis	.75
67 Derrick Thomas	.25
68 Marvin Harrison	.50
69 Adrian Murrell	.50
70 Curtis Martin	1.25
71 Bobby Hoying	.25
72 Darrell Green	.25
73 Sean Dawkins	.25
74 Robert Smith	.50
75 Antonio Freeman	1.50
76 Scott Mitchell	.25
77 Curtis Conway	.50
78 Rae Carruth	.25
79 Jamal Anderson	1.50
80 Dan Marino	4.00
81 Brad Johnson	1.00
82 Danny Kanell	.25
83 Charlie Garner	.25
84 Rob Johnson	.50
85 Natrone Means	.50
86 Tim Brown	.75
87 Keyshawn Johnson	1.00
88 Ben Coates	.50
89 Derrick Alexander	.25
90 Steve Young	2.00
91 Shannon Sharpe	.50
92 Corey Dillon	1.50
93 Bruce Smith	.25
94 Errict Rhett	.25
95 Jim Harbaugh	.50
96 Napoleon Kaufman	1.25
97 Glenn Foley	.50
98 Tony Gonzalez	.25
99 Keenan McCardell	.50
100 Barry Sanders	6.00
101 Charles Woodson	6.00
102 Tim Dwight	4.00
103 Marcus Nash	4.00
104 Joe Jurevicius	3.00
105 Jacquez Green	5.00
106 Kevin Dyson	4.00
107 Keith Brooking	2.00
108 Andre Wadsworth	2.50
109 Randy Moss	25.00
110 Robert Edwards	6.00
111 Robert Edwards	2.50
112 Peyton Manning	15.00
113 Duane Starks	2.00
114 Grant Wistrom	2.00
115 Anthony Simmons	2.00
116 Takeo Spikes	2.00
117 Tony Simmons	3.00
118 Jerome Pathon	3.00
119 Ryan Leaf	8.00
120 Skip Hicks	5.00
121 Curtis Enis	5.00
122 Germane Crowell	4.00
123 John Avery	4.00
124 Hines Ward	2.00
125 Fred Taylor	12.00

1998 Bowman's Best Autographs

Ten players are in this set with each having two different cards. The only difference is the suffix "A" or "B" after the card number. Each of the 20 cards has a "Certified Autograph Issue" stamp on the fronts. Singles are found 1:158 packs, while Refractor versions are 1:840 and Atomic Refractors are 1:2,521.

	MT
Complete Set (20):	850.00
Common Player:	20.00
Inserted 1:158	
Refractor Cards:	2x
Inserted 1:840	
Atomic Ref. Cards:	3x
Inserted 1:2,521	
1A Jake Plummer	100.00
1B Jake Plummer	100.00
2A Jason Sehorn	20.00
2B Jason Sehorn	20.00
3A Corey Dillon	80.00
3B Corey Dillon	80.00
4A Tim Brown	40.00
4B Tim Brown	40.00
5A Keenan McCardell	30.00
5B Keenan McCardell	30.00
6A Kordell Stewart	100.00
6B Kordell Stewart	100.00
7A Peyton Manning	150.00
7B Peyton Manning	150.00
8A Danny Kanell	20.00
8B Danny Kanell	20.00
9A Ryan Leaf	85.00
9B Ryan Leaf	85.00
10A Curtis Enis	50.00
10B Curtis Enis	50.00

1998 Bowman's Best Mirror Image Fusion

This insert is made up of 20 double-sided cards that feature two top players at the same position. Singles are found 1:48 packs, while the parallel Refractors are sequentially numbered to 100 and inserted 1:630. Atomic Refractors are numbered to 25 and found 1:2,521.

	MT
Complete Set (20):	280.00
Common Player:	4.00
Minor Stars:	8.00
Inserted 1:48	
Refractor Cards:	3x-5x
Inserted 1:630	
Production 100 Sets	
Atomic Ref. Cards:	6x-12x
Inserted 1:2,521	
Production 25 Sets	
MI1 Terrell Davis, John Avery	35.00
MI2 Emmitt Smith, Curtis Enis	35.00
MI3 Barry Sanders, Skip Hicks	50.00
MI4 Eddie George, Robert Edwards	12.00
MI5 Jerome Bettis, Fred Taylor	20.00
MI6 Mark Brunell, Ryan Leaf	20.00
MI7 John Elway, Brian Griese	25.00
MI8 Dan Marino, Peyton Manning	25.00
MI9 Brett Favre, Charlie Batch	50.00
MI10 Drew Bledsoe, Jonathan Quinn	20.00
MI11 Tim Brown, Kevin Dyson	10.00
MI12 Herman Moore, Germane Crowell	10.00
MI13 Joey Galloway, Jerome Pathon	8.00
MI14 Cris Carter, Jacquez Green	12.00
MI15 Jerry Rice, Randy Moss	60.00
MI16 Junior Seau, Takeo Spikes	4.00
MI17 John Randle, Jason Peter	4.00
MI18 Reggie White, Andre Wadsworth	8.00
MI19 Peter Boulware, Anthony Simmons	4.00
MI20 Derrick Thomas, Brian Simmons	4.00

1998 Bowman's Best Performers

This insert showcases the top rookies who came up in '98. Singles were inserted 1:12 packs, while Refractors are numbered to 200 and can be found 1:630. Atomic Refractors are numbered to 50 and found 1:2,521.

	MT
Complete Set (10):	60.00
Common Player:	2.00
Inserted 1:12	
Refractor Cards:	3x-6x
Inserted 1:630	
Production 200 Sets	
Atomic Ref. Cards:	10x-20x
Inserted 1:2,521	
Production 50 Sets	
BP1 Peyton Manning	15.00
BP2 Charles Woodson	6.00
BP3 Skip Hicks	4.00
BP4 Andre Wadsworth	2.00
BP5 Randy Moss	25.00
BP6 Marcus Nash	5.00
BP7 Ahman Green	4.00
BP8 Anthony Simmons	2.00
BP9 Tavian Banks	4.00
BP10 Ryan Leaf	8.00

1998 Bowman's Best Super Bowl Show

This 16-card set was available exclusively at the NFL Experience Card Show at Super Bowl XXXII. It features 4" x 5 1/2" Bowman's Best cards, with the Super Bowl logo on the front near the middle. Refractor versions of each of these cards was also available randomly. The cards were obtained by exchanging wrappers of Topps products at the Topps booth.

	MT
Complete Set (16):	350.00
Common Player:	8.00
Refractors:	2x
1 Brett Favre	75.00
2 Barry Sanders	60.00
3 Emmitt Smith	60.00
4 John Elway	30.00
5 Tim Brown	8.00
6 Eddie George	30.00
7 Troy Aikman	30.00
8 Drew Bledsoe	30.00
9 Dan Marino	60.00
10 Jerry Rice	30.00
11 Junior Seau	8.00
12 Antowain Smith	20.00
13 Warrick Dunn	30.00
14 Jim Druckenmiller	20.00
15 Terrell Davis	30.00
16 Curtis Martin	25.00

1998 Bowman Chrome

Bowman Chrome football is a 220-card base set that includes 150 veterans and 70 rookies. There are also Refractor parallel cards of every regular card in the set that are randomly inserted 1:12 packs. Rookies are designated with a silver and blue logo design, while the veteran cards are shown with a silver and red design.

	MT
Complete Set (220):	550.00
Common Player:	.30
Minor Stars:	.60
Common Rookie:	3.50
Refractor Cards:	3x-6x
Refractor Rookies:	3x
Inserted 1:12	
Inter-State Cards:	3x
Inter-State Rookies: 1.	2x
Inserted 1:4	
I.S. Refractor Cards:	5x-10x
I.S. Refractor Rookies:	3x
Inserted 1:24	
Golden Ann. Stars:	30x-60x
Golden Ann. Rookies:	2x-4x
Inserted 1:138	
Production 50 Sets	
Wax Box:	175.00
1 Peyton Manning	60.00
2 Keith Brooking	7.00
3 Duane Starks	5.00
4 Takeo Spikes	7.00
5 Andre Wadsworth	7.00
6 Greg Ellis	3.50
7 Brian Griese	25.00
8 Germane Crowell	15.00
9 Jerome Pathon	7.00
10 Ryan Leaf	30.00
11 Fred Taylor	45.00
12 Robert Edwards	10.00
13 Grant Wistrom	3.50
14 Robert Holcombe	10.00
15 Tim Dwight	10.00
16 Jacquez Green	10.00
17 Marcus Nash	10.00
18 Jason Peter	3.50
19 Anthony Simmons	3.50
20 Curtis Enis	15.00
21 John Avery	10.00
22 Patrick Johnson	7.00
23 Joe Jurevicius	7.00
24 Brian Simmons	4.00
25 Kevin Dyson	10.00
26 Skip Hicks	10.00
27 Hines Ward	10.00
28 Tavian Banks	7.00
29 Ahman Green	10.00
30 Tony Simmons	8.00
31 Charles Johnson	.30
32 Freddie Jones	.30
33 Joey Galloway	1.00
34 Tony Banks	.60
35 Jake Plummer	2.50
36 Reidel Anthony	.30
37 Steve McNair	1.00
38 Michael Westbrook	.60
39 Chris Sanders	.30
40 Isaac Bruce	.60

41	Charlie Garner	.30
42	Wayne Chrebet	.60
43	Michael Strahan	.30
44	Brad Johnson	1.00
45	Mike Alstott	1.00
46	Tony Gonzalez	.60
47	Johnnie Morton	.30
48	Darnay Scott	.30
49	Rae Carruth	.30
50	Terrell Davis	4.50
51	Jermaine Lewis	.30
52	Frank Sanders	.30
53	Byron Hanspard	.30
54	Gus Frerotte	.30
55	Terry Glenn	.60
56	J.J. Stokes	.60
57	Will Blackwell	.30
58	Keyshawn Johnson	1.00
59	Tiki Barber	.60
60	Dorsey Levens	.60
61	Zach Thomas	.30
62	Corey Dillon	1.50
63	Antowain Smith	1.00
64	Michael Sinclair	.30
65	Rod Smith	.60
66	Trent Dilfer	.60
67	Warren Sapp	.60
68	Charles Way	.30
69	Tamarick Vanover	.30
70	Drew Bledsoe	2.50
71	John Mobley	.30
72	Kerry Collins	.30
73	Peter Boulware	.30
74	Simeon Rice	.30
75	Eddie George	2.50
76	Fred Lane	.60
77	Jamal Anderson	1.50
78	Antonio Freeman	1.00
79	Jason Sehorn	.30
80	Curtis Martin	1.00
81	Bobby Hoying	.30
82	Garrison Hearst	1.00
83	Glenn Foley	.60
84	Danny Kanell	.30
85	Kordell Stewart	2.50
86	O.J. McDuffie	.60
87	Marvin Harrison	.60
88	Bobby Engram	.30
89	Chris Slade	.30
90	Warrick Dunn	2.00
91	Ricky Watters	.60
92	Rickey Dudley	.30
93	Terrell Owens	1.00
94	Karim Abdul-Jabbar	.60
95	Napoleon Kaufman	1.00
96	Darrell Green	.30
97	Levon Kirkland	.30
98	Jeff George	.60
99	Andre Hastings	.30
100	John Elway	3.00
101	John Randle	.30
102	Andre Rison	.30
103	Keenan McCardell	.30
104	Marshall Faulk	1.00
105	Emmitt Smith	4.50
106	Robert Brooks	.30
107	Scott Mitchell	.30
108	Shannon Sharpe	.60
109	Deion Sanders	1.00
110	Jerry Rice	3.00
111	Erik Kramer	.30
112	Michael Jackson	.30
113	Aeneas Williams	.30
114	Terry Allen	.60
115	Steve Young	1.75
116	Warren Moon	.60
117	Junior Seau	.60
118	Jerome Bettis	.60
119	Irving Fryar	.30
120	Barry Sanders	6.00
121	Tim Brown	.60
122	Chad Brown	.30
123	Ben Coates	.30
124	Robert Smith	.60
125	Brett Favre	6.00
126	Derrick Thomas	.30
127	Reggie White	1.00
128	Troy Aikman	3.00
129	Jeff Blake	.60
130	Mark Brunell	2.50
131	Curtis Conway	.60
132	Wesley Walls	.30
133	Thurman Thomas	.60
134	Chris Chandler	.30
135	Dan Marino	4.50
136	Larry Centers	.30
137	Shawn Jefferson	.30
138	Andre Reed	.30
139	Jake Reed	.30
140	Cris Carter	1.00
141	Elvis Grbac	.30
142	Mark Chmura	.60
143	Michael Irvin	.60
144	Carl Pickens	.60
145	Herman Moore	.60
146	Marvin Jones	.30
147	Terance Mathis	.30
148	Rob Moore	.60
149	Bruce Smith	.30
150	Checklist	.30
151	Leslie Shepherd	.30
152	Chris Spielman	.30
153	Tony McGee	.30
154	Kevin Smith	.30
155	Rob Romanowski	.30
156	Stephen Boyd	.30
157	James Stewart	.30
158	Jason Taylor	.30

159	Troy Drayton	.30
160	Mark Fields	.30
161	Jessie Armstead	.30
162	James Jett	.30
163	Bobby Taylor	.30
164	Kimble Anders	.30
165	Jimmy Smith	.60
166	Quentin Coryatt	.30
167	Bryant Westbrook	.30
168	Neil Smith	.30
169	Darren Woodson	.30
170	Ray Buchanan	.30
171	Earl Holmes	.30
172	Ray Lewis	.30
173	Steve Broussard	.30
174	Derrick Brooks	.30
175	Ken Harvey	.30
176	Darryll Lewis	.30
177	Derrick Rodgers	.30
178	James McKnight	.30
179	Cris Dishman	.30
180	Hardy Nickerson	.30
181	*Charles Woodson*	20.00
182	*Randy Moss*	85.00
183	*Stephen Alexander*	7.00
184	*Samari Rolle*	3.50
185	*Jamie Duncan*	3.50
186	*Lance Schulters*	3.50
187	*Tony Parrish*	3.50
188	*Corey Chavous*	3.50
189	*Jammi German*	7.00
190	*Sam Cowart*	3.50
191	*Donald Hayes*	6.00
192	*R.W. McQuarters*	6.00
193	*Az-Zahir Hakim*	6.00
194	*Chris Fuamatu-Ma'afala*	7.00
195	*Allen Rossum*	3.50
196	*Jon Ritchie*	7.00
197	*Blake Spence*	3.50
198	*Brian Alford*	3.50
199	*Fred Weary*	3.50
200	*Rod Rutledge*	3.50
201	*Michael Myers*	3.50
202	*Rashaan Shehee*	7.00
203	*Donovin Darius*	3.50
204	*E.G. Green*	7.00
205	*Vonnie Holliday*	7.00
206	*Charlie Batch*	35.00
207	*Michael Pittman*	7.00
208	*Artrell Hawkins*	3.50
209	*Jonathan Quinn*	10.00
210	*Kailee Wong*	3.50
211	*Deshea Townsend*	3.50
212	*Patrick Surtain*	3.50
213	*Brian Kelly*	3.50
214	*Tebucky Jones*	3.50
215	*Pete Gonzalez*	6.00
216	*Shaun Williams*	3.50
217	*Scott Frost*	6.00
218	*Leonard Little*	3.50
219	*Alonzo Mayes*	6.00
220	*Cordell Taylor*	3.50

1999 Bowman

RANDY MOSS

Bowman Football was a 220-card set that included 70 players who made their first appearance. Each of the rookie cards has the "Rookie Card Logo" on the front of the singles and are printed with a silver and blue logo design. The veterans are shown with a silver and red design. Parallel sets include the Inter-State and Gold singles. Other insert sets include: Autographs (Gold, Silver and Blue), Late Bloomers/Early Risers and Scout's Choice. Nine-card packs had an SRP of $3.00.

		MT
Complete Set (220):		85.00
Common Player:		.15
Minor Stars:		.30
Common Rookie:		.75
Wax Box:		60.00
1	Dan Marino	2.00
2	Michael Westbrook	.30
3	Yancey Thigpen	.15
4	Tony Martin	.15
5	Michael Strahan	.15
6	Dedric Ward	.15
7	Joey Galloway	.50
8	Bobby Engram	.15

9	Frank Sanders	.15
10	Jake Plummer	1.50
11	Eddie Kennison	.15
12	Curtis Martin	.50
13	Ryan Leaf	.30
14	Trent Dilfer	.15
15	Tim Biakabutuka	.15
16	Elvis Grbac	.15
17	Charlie Batch	1.00
18	Takeo Spikes	.15
19	Tony Banks	.30
20	Doug Flutie	1.00
21	Ty Law	.15
22	Isaac Bruce	.30
23	James Jett	.15
24	Kent Graham	.15
25	Derrick Mayes	.15
26	Amani Toomer	.15
27	Ray Lewis	.15
28	Shawn Springs	.15
29	Warren Sapp	.15
30	Jamal Anderson	.50
31	Byron Morris	.15
32	Johnnie Morton	.15
33	Terance Mathis	.15
34	Terrell Davis	2.00
35	John Randle	.15
36	Vinny Testaverde	.30
37	Junior Seau	.30
38	Reidel Anthony	.15
39	Brad Johnson	.50
40	Emmitt Smith	2.00
41	Mo Lewis	.15
42	Terry Glenn	.50
43	Dorsey Levens	.50
44	Thurman Thomas	.50
45	Rob Moore	.30
46	Corey Dillon	.50
47	Jessie Armstead	.15
48	Marshall Faulk	.50
49	Charles Woodson	.50
50	John Elway	2.00
51	Kevin Dyson	.30
52	Tony Simmons	.15
53	Keenan McCardell	.15
54	O.J. Santiago	.15
55	Jermaine Lewis	.15
56	Herman Moore	.50
57	Gary Brown	.15
58	Jim Harbaugh	.30
59	Mike Alstott	.50
60	Brett Favre	3.00
61	Tim Brown	.30
62	Steve McNair	.75
63	Ben Coates	.30
64	Jerome Pathon	.15
65	Ray Buchanan	.15
66	Troy Aikman	1.50
67	Andre Reed	.30
68	Bubby Brister	.30
69	Karim Abdul	.30
70	Peyton Manning	2.00
71	Charles Johnson	.15
72	Natrone Means	.30
73	Michael Sinclair	.15
74	Skip Hicks	.30
75	Derrick Alexander	.15
76	Wayne Chrebet	.30
77	Rod Smith	.30
78	Carl Pickens	.30
79	Adrian Murrell	.30
80	Fred Taylor	1.50
81	Eric Moulds	.50
82	Erik Kramer	.15
83	Marvin Harrison	.50
84	Cris Carter	.50
85	Ike Hilliard	.15
86	Hines Ward	.30
87	Terrell Owens	.50
88	Ricky Proehl	.15
89	Bert Emanuel	.15
90	Randy Moss	3.00
91	Aaron Glenn	.15
92	Robert Smith	.30
93	Andre Hastings	.15
94	Jake Reed	.15
95	Curtis Enis	.50
96	Andre Wadsworth	.30
97	Ed McCaffrey	.50
98	Zach Thomas	.30
99	Kerry Collins	.30
100	Drew Bledsoe	1.25
101	Germane Crowell	.30
102	Bryan Still	.15
103	Chad Brown	.15
104	Jacquez Green	.30
105	Garrison Hearst	.30
106	Napoleon Kaufman	.30
107	Ricky Watters	.30
108	O.J. McDuffie	.30
109	Keyshawn Johnson	.50
110	Jerome Bettis	.50
111	Duce Staley	.30
112	Curtis Conway	.30
113	Chris Chandler	.30
114	Marcus Nash	.30
115	Stephen Alexander	.15
116	Darnay Scott	.15
117	Bruce Smith	.15
118	Priest Holmes	.30
119	Mark Brunell	1.25
120	Jerry Rice	1.50
121	Randall Cunningham	.50
122	Cameron Cleeland	.30
123	Antonio Freeman	.50
124	Kordell Stewart	.75
125	Jon Kitna	.75

126	Ahman Green	.30
127	Warrick Dunn	.75
128	Robert Brooks	.15
129	Derrick Thomas	.30
130	Steve Young	1.00
131	Peter Boulware	.15
132	Michael Irvin	.30
133	Shannon Sharpe	.30
134	Jimmy Smith	.30
135	John Avery	.15
136	Fred Lane	.15
137	Trent Green	.30
138	Andre Rison	.15
139	Antowain Smith	.30
140	Eddie George	.75
141	Jeff Blake	.30
142	Raghib Ismail	.15
143	Rickey Dudley	.15
144	Courtney Hawkins	.15
145	Mikhael Ricks	.15
146	J.J. Stokes	.30
147	Levon Kirkland	.15
148	Deion Sanders	.50
149	Barry Sanders	3.00
150	Tiki Barber	.15
151	*David Boston*	4.00
152	*Chris McAlister*	1.50
153	*Peerless Price*	3.00
154	*D'Wayne Bates*	1.50
155	*Cade McNown*	6.00
156	*Akili Smith*	6.00
157	*Kevin Johnson*	3.00
158	*Tim Couch*	12.00
159	*Sedrick Irvin*	3.00
160	*Chris Claiborne*	1.50
161	*Edgerrin James*	12.00
162	*Michael Cloud*	1.50
163	*Cecil Collins*	6.00
164	*James Johnson*	3.00
165	*Rob Konrad*	1.50
166	*Daunte Culpepper*	6.00
167	*Kevin Faulk*	3.00
168	*Donovan McNabb*	6.00
169	*Troy Edwards*	4.00
170	*Amos Zereoue*	3.00
171	*Karsten Bailey*	1.50
172	*Brock Huard*	2.00
173	*Joe Germaine*	2.00
174	*Torry Holt*	4.00
175	*Shaun King*	5.00
176	*Jevon Kearse*	3.00
177	*Champ Bailey*	2.50
178	*Ebenezer Ekuban*	1.50
179	*Andy Katzenmoyer*	2.00
180	*Antoine Winfield*	1.50
181	*Jermaine Fazande*	.75
182	*Ricky Williams*	12.00
183	*Joel Mackovicka*	.75
184	*Reginald Kelly*	.75
185	*Brandon Stokley*	.75
186	*Shawn Bryson*	.75
187	*Marty Booker*	1.50
188	*Jerry Azumah*	.75
189	*Craig Yeast*	.75
190	*Scott Covington*	1.50
191	*Rahim Abdullah*	.75
192	*Darrin Chiaverini*	.75
193	*Dat Nguyen*	.75
194	*Wane McGarity*	1.50
195	*Al Wilson*	1.50
196	*Travis McGriff*	1.50
197	*Aaron Gibson*	1.50
198	*Antwan Edwards*	.75
199	*Aaron Brooks*	2.00
200	*De'Mond Parker*	.75
201	*Dee Miller*	.75
202	*John Tait*	.75
203	*Jim Kleinsasser*	1.50
204	*Michael Bishop*	3.00
205	*Joe Montgomery*	1.50
206	*Sean Bennett*	1.50
207	*Dameane Douglas*	.75
208	*Na Brown*	.75
209	*Jerame Tuman*	.75
210	*Malcolm Johnson*	.75
211	*Dre Bly*	.75
212	*Terry Jackson*	.75
213	*Tai Streets*	.75
214	*Autry Denson*	1.50
215	*Darnell McDonald*	1.50
216	*Charlie Rogers*	.75
217	*Reggie McGrew*	.75
218	*Tony Bryant*	.75
219	*Larry Parker*	.75
220	*Martay Jenkins*	.75

1999 Bowman Gold

This was a 220-parallel to the base set with the team name stamped in gold foil. Each card was sequentially numbered to 99 and inserted 1:68 packs.

	MT
Gold Cards:	20x-40x
Gold Rookies:	5x-10x
Production 99 Sets	

A card number in parentheses ( ) indicates the set is unnumbered.

1999 Bowman Interstate

PEYTON MANNING

This was a 220-card parallel to the base set. The card fronts have a scenic landmark from the player's home state and the card backs feature a custom-tailored vanity plate from that state. Singles were inserted into every pack.

	MT
Complete Set (220):	250.00
Interstate Cards:	3x
Interstate Rookies:	1.5x
Inserted 1:1	

1999 Bowman Autographs

Antoine Winfield

The 32-card autograph set was divdided into three sections with the first six cards in Gold and found 1:850 packs. The next 15 cards were printed in Silver and inserted 1:212 packs. The last 11 singles were in Blue and found 1:180 packs.

		MT
Complete Set (32):		1850.
Common Gold (1-6):		100.00
Inserted 1:850		
Common Silver (7-21):		20.00
Inserted 1:212		
Common Blue (22-32):		12.00
Inserted 1:180		
1	Randy Moss G	250.00
2	Akili Smith G	150.00
3	Edgerrin James G	275.00
4	Ricky Williams G	275.00
5	Torry Holt G	100.00
6	Daunte Culpepper G	150.00
7	Donovan McNabb S	85.00
8	Tim Couch S	175.00
9	Champ Bailey S	40.00
10	David Boston S	50.00
11	Chris Claiborne S	20.00
12	Chris McAlister S	20.00
13	Rob Konrad S	20.00
14	Michael Cloud S	20.00
15	Jermaine Fazande S	20.00
16	Brock Huard S	30.00
17	Joe Germaine S	30.00
18	Sedrick Irvin S	40.00
19	Cecil Collins S	80.00
20	Karsten Bailey S	20.00
21	Antoine Winfield S	20.00
22	Cade McNown B	60.00
23	Troy Edwards B	40.00
24	Jevon Kearse B	35.00
25	Andy Katzenmoyer B	20.00
26	Kevin Johnson B	40.00
27	James Johnson B	30.00
28	Kevin Faulk B	30.00
29	Shaun King B	25.00
30	Peerless Price B	30.00
31	D'Wayne Bates B	12.00
32	Amos Zereoue B	30.00

A player's name in *italic* type indicates a rookie card.

1999 Bowman Late Bloomers/ Early Risers

This 10-card set includes five Late Bloomers and five Early Risers. The Late Bloomer theme includes the best late-round selections and the Early Risers include impact players from past NFL Drafts. Singles were found 1:12 packs.

		MT
Complete Set (10):		20.00
Common Player:		1.00
Inserted 1:12		
1	Fred Taylor (Early Risers)	3.00
2	Peyton Manning (Early Risers)	4.00
3	Dan Marino (Early Risers)	4.00
4	Barry Sanders (Early Risers)	5.00
5	Randy Moss (Early Risers)	5.00
6	Mark Brunell (Late Bloomers)	2.00
7	Jamal Anderson (Late Bloomers)	1.00
8	Curtis Martin (Late Bloomers)	1.00
9	Wayne Chrebet (Late Bloomers)	1.00
10	Terrell Davis (Late Bloomers)	4.00

1999 Bowman Scout's Choice

This 21-card set included the top rookies from the 1999 Draft. Each card was borderless and printed on double-etched foil board. Singles were inserted 1:12 packs.

		MT
Complete Set (21):		50.00
Common Player:		1.00
Minor Stars:		2.00
Inserted 1:12		
1	David Boston	4.00
2	Champ Bailey	2.50
3	Edgerrin James	10.00
4	Michael Cloud	1.00
5	Kevin Faulk	3.00
6	Troy Edwards	4.00
7	Joe Germaine	2.00
8	Peerless Price	3.00
9	Torry Holt	4.00
10	Rob Konrad	2.00
11	Akili Smith	6.00
12	Daunte Culpepper	6.00
13	D'Wayne Bates	2.00
14	Donovan McNabb	6.00
15	James Johnson	3.00
16	Cade McNown	6.00
17	Kevin Johnson	4.00
18	Ricky Williams	10.00
19	Karsten Bailey	1.00
20	Tim Couch	10.00
21	Shaun King	3.00

1999 Bowman's Best

Bowman's Best Football was a 133-card set that had each single printed on 26-pt. Serillusion stock. The set breakdown was 90 Star Veterans that were printed on gold stock and 10 Best Performance cards. The last 33 cards were rookies and they were printed on silver stock and included the "Bowman's Best Rookie Logo". Rookies were found one-per-pack. Parallel sets included Refractors and Atomic Refractors. Other inserts included: Autographs, Franchise Best, Franchise Favorites, Franchise Favorite Autographs, Future Foundations, Honor Roll, Legacy, Legacy Autographs, Locker Room Autographs and Locker Room Jerseys. Six-card packs had an SRP of $5.00.

		MT
Complete Set (133):		100.00
Common Player:		.20
Minor Stars:		.40
Common Rookie:		1.00
Wax Box:		85.00
1	Randy Moss	3.00
2	Skip Hicks	.40
3	Robert Smith	.75
4	Drew Bledsoe	1.25
5	Tim Brown	.40
6	Marshall Faulk	.75
7	Terance Mathis	.20
8	Sean Dawkins	.20
9	Ed McCaffrey	.50
10	Jamal Anderson	.75
11	Antonio Freeman	.75
12	Terry Kirby	.20
13	Vinny Testaverde	.40
14	Eddie George	1.00
15	Ricky Watters	.50
16	Johnnie Morton	.20
17	Natrone Means	.50
18	Terry Glenn	.75
19	Michael Westbrook	.50
20	Doug Flutie	1.25
21	Jake Plummer	1.25
22	Darnay Scott	.40
23	Andre Rison	.40
24	Jon Kitna	1.00
25	Dan Marino	2.00
26	Ike Hilliard	.20
27	Warrick Dunn	.75
28	Jerome Bettis	.75
29	Curtis Conway	.40
30	Emmitt Smith	2.00
31	Jimmy Smith	.75
32	Isaac Bruce	.75
33	Jerry Rice	1.50
34	Curtis Martin	.75
35	Steve McNair	1.00
36	Jeff Blake	.40
37	Rob Moore	.40
38	Dorsey Levens	.75
39	Terrell Davis	2.00
40	John Elway	2.00
41	Trent Dilfer	.50
42	Joey Galloway	.75
43	Keyshawn Johnson	.75
44	O.J. McDuffie	.40
45	Fred Taylor	1.50
46	Andre Reed	.40
47	Frank Sanders	.40
48	Keenan McCardell	.40
49	Elvis Grbac	.40
50	Barry Sanders	3.00
51	Terrell Owens	.75
52	Trent Green	.50
53	Brad Johnson	.75
54	Rich Gannon	.40
55	Randall Cunningham	.75
56	Tony Martin	.20
57	Rod Smith	.50
58	Eric Moulds	.75
59	Yancey Thigpen	.40
60	Brett Favre	3.00
61	Cris Carter	.75
62	Marvin Harrison	.75
63	Chris Chandler	.40
64	Antowain Smith	.50
65	Carl Pickens	.40
66	Shannon Sharpe	.50
67	Mike Alstott	.75
68	J.J. Stokes	.40
69	Ben Coates	.40
70	Peyton Manning	2.00
71	Duce Staley	.50
72	Michael Irvin	.40
73	Tim Biakabutuka	.40
74	Priest Holmes	.75
75	Steve Young	1.25
76	Jerome Pathon	.20
77	Wayne Chrebet	.75
78	Bert Emanuel	.20
79	Curtis Enis	.75
80	Mark Brunell	1.25
81	Herman Moore	.75
82	Corey Dillon	.75
83	Jim Harbaugh	.40
84	Gary Brown	.40
85	Kordell Stewart	.75
86	Garrison Hearst	.50
87	Raghib Ismail	.20
88	Charlie Batch	1.25
89	Napoleon Kaufman	.75
90	Troy Aikman	1.50
91	Brett Favre	1.50
92	Randy Moss	1.50
93	Terrell Davis	1.00
94	Barry Sanders	1.50
95	Peyton Manning	1.00
96	Troy Edwards	.75
97	Cade McNown	2.00
98	Edgerrin James	6.00
99	Torry Holt	.75
100	Tim Couch	3.50
101	Chris Claiborne	1.50
102	Brock Huard	2.00
103	Amos Zereoue	2.00
104	Sedrick Irvin	2.50
105	Kevin Faulk	2.50
106	Ebenezer Ekuban	1.00
107	Daunte Culpepper	6.00
108	Rob Konrad	2.00
109	James Johnson	2.50
110	Kurt Warner	25.00
111	Mike Cloud	2.00
112	Andy Katzenmoyer	2.00
113	Jevon Kearse	3.50
114	Akili Smith	6.00
115	Edgerrin James	20.00
116	Cecil Collins	4.00
117	Chris McAlister	1.00
118	Donovan McNabb	6.00
119	Kevin Johnson	4.00
120	Torry Holt	4.00
121	Antoine Winfield	1.00
122	Michael Bishop	2.00
123	Joe Germaine	2.00
124	David Boston	4.00
125	D'Wayne Bates	1.00
126	Champ Bailey	2.50
127	Cade McNown	6.00
128	Shaun King	6.00
129	Peerless Price	3.00
130	Troy Edwards	4.00
131	Karsten Bailey	1.50
132	Tim Couch	12.00
133	Ricky Williams	12.00

1999 Bowman's Best Refractors

This was a parallel to the base set except that each single was printed on metalized refractor board. Singles were sequentially numbered to 400 and were inserted 1:17 packs.

	MT
Complete Set (133):	550.00
Refractor Cards:	5x-10x
Refractor Rookies:	2x-4x
Inserted 1:17	
Production 400 Sets	

Post-1980 cards in Near Mint condition will generally sell for about 75% of the quoted Mint value. Excellent-condition cards bring no more than 40%.

1999 Bowman's Best Atomic Refractors

This was a parallel to the base set except that each single was printed on iridescent refractor foil board. Singles were sequentially numbered to 100 and inserted 1:69 packs.

	MT
Atomic Cards:	15x-30x
Atomic Rookies:	8x-16x
Inserted 1:69	
Production 100 Sets	

1999 Bowman's Best Autographs

Each of the three autographs in this set include the stamp "Certified Autograph Issue" as well as the Topps-3M authentication sticker on the backs of the cards. The Fred Taylor and Jake Plummer singles were inserted 1:915 packs and the Randy Moss card was inserted 1:9,129 packs.

		MT
Complete Set (3):		300.00
Common Player:		50.00
Inserted 1:915		
Inserted 1:9,129 (Moss)		
1	Fred Taylor	50.00
2	Jake Plummer	50.00
ROY1	Randy Moss	200.00

1999 Bowman's Best Franchise Best

This 9-card insert included the top players in the NFL and pictured them on die-cut cards. Singles were inserted 1:20 packs.

		MT
Complete Set (9):		60.00
Common Player:		3.00
Inserted 1:20		
1	Dan Marino	10.00
2	Fred Taylor	6.00
3	Emmitt Smith	10.00
4	Terrell Davis	10.00
5	Brett Favre	12.00
6	Tim Couch	12.00
7	Peyton Manning	10.00
8	Eddie George	3.00
9	Randy Moss	12.00

Values quoted in this guide reflect the retail price of a card — the price a collector can expect to pay when buying a card from a dealer. The wholesale price — that which a collector can expect to receive from a dealer when selling cards — will be significantly lower, depending on desirability and condition.

1999 Bowman's Best Franchise Favorites

Singles from this insert set include both current and retired stars. Each is printed on prismatic holographic board with two players on each card. Singles were inserted 1:153 packs.

		MT
Complete Set (2):		30.00
Common Player:		10.00
Inserted 1:153		
1	Tony Dorsett, Roger Staubach	10.00
2	Randy Moss, Fran Tarkenton	20.00

1999 Bowman's Best Franchise Favorites Autographs

Each of the singles in this 6-card set are autographed and found at different ratios. The odds for the singles are as follows: #1 (1:4,599), #2, 5 (1:1,017) and #3, 4, 6 (1:9,129).

		MT
Complete Set (6):		600.00
Common Player:		70.00
Inserted 1:703		
1	Tony Dorsett	70.00
2	Roger Staubach	100.00
3	Tony Dorsett, Roger Staubach	150.00
4	Randy Moss	150.00
5	Fran Tarkenton	70.00
6	Randy Moss, Fran Tarkenton	200.00

1999 Bowman's Best Future Foundations

This 18-card insert set included the top rookies from the 1999 NFL Draft. Each card was printed on prismatic holographic stock with a die-cut pattern. Singles were inserted 1:20 packs.

		MT
Complete Set (18):		50.00
Common Player:		1.00
Minor Stars:		2.00
Inserted 1:20		
1	Tim Couch	10.00
2	David Boston	3.00
3	Donovan McNabb	5.00
4	Troy Edwards	3.00
5	Ricky Williams	10.00
6	Daunte Culpepper	5.00
7	Torry Holt	3.00
8	Cade McNown	5.00
9	Akili Smith	5.00
10	Edgerrin James	15.00
11	Cecil Collins	3.00
12	Peerless Price	2.00
13	Kevin Johnson	3.00
14	Champ Bailey	2.00
15	Michael Cloud	1.00
16	D'Wayne Bates	1.00
17	Shaun King	5.00
18	James Johnson	2.00

1999 Bowman's Best Honor Roll

This 8-card insert set included only Heisman winners or first overall Draft Picks. Singles were found 1:40 packs.

		MT
Complete Set (8):		35.00
Common Player:		3.00
Inserted 1:40		
1	Peyton Manning	10.00
2	Drew Bledsoe	5.00
3	Doug Flutie	4.00
4	Tim Couch	12.00
5	Charles Woodson	3.00
6	Ricky Williams	12.00
7	Tim Brown	3.00
8	Eddie George	4.00

1999 Bowman's Best Legacy

This 3-card insert set included Texas legends and Heisman Trophy winners. Singles were inserted 1:102 packs.

		MT
Complete Set (3):		40.00
Common Player:		10.00
Inserted 1:102		
1	Ricky Williams	15.00
2	Earl Campbell	10.00
3	Ricky Williams, Earl Campbell	15.00

1999 Bowman's Best Legacy Autographs

This was a parallel to the Best Legacy insert. Each single is autographed and includes the "Certified Autograph Issue" stamp on the fronts and the Topps-3M sticker on the backs. Card #1 was found 1:4,599, card #2 was found 1:2,040 and card #3 was found 1:18,108.

		MT
Complete Set (3):		425.00
Common Player:		75.00
#1 Inserted 1:4,599		
#2 Inserted 1:2,040		
#3 Inserted 1:18,108		
1	Ricky Williams	150.00
2	Earl Campbell	75.00
3	Ricky Williams, Earl Campbell	250.00

1999 Bowman's Best Rookie Class Photo

This single card included the 1999 NFL Rookie Class with a group shot photo. It was inserted 1:100 packs.

		MT
Inserted 1:100		
Refractor:		8x
Inserted 1:7,429		
Production 125 Sets		
Atomic Refractor:		20x
Inserted 1:26,880		
Production 35 Sets		
C1	Rookie Class Photo	12.00

1999 Bowman's Best Rookie Locker Room Autographs

This 5-card insert set included autographs of the top

rookies from 1999. Each card included the Topps "Certified Autograph Issue" stamp on the card fronts and the Topps-3M authentication sticker on the backs. Cards #1, 4 & 5 were inserted 1:305 packs and cards #2 & 3 were found 1:915 packs.

		MT
Complete Set (5):		300.00
Common Player:		25.00
#1,4,5 Inserted 1:305		
#2,3 Inserted 1:915		
1	Tim Couch	100.00
2	Donovan McNabb	60.00
3	Edgerrin James	200.00
4	David Boston	25.00
5	Torry Holt	25.00

1999 Bowman's Best Rookie Locker Room Jerseys

This 4-card set insert included rookies from 1999. Each card included the Topps-3M sticker on the card backs. Some of the singles could only be found through redemption cards. Singles were found 1:229 packs.

		MT
Complete Set (4):		225.00
Common Player:		50.00
Inserted 1:229		
1	Kevin Faulk	50.00
2	Donovan McNabb	75.00
3	Ricky Williams	100.00
4	Torry Holt	50.00

1999 Bowman Chrome

Bowman Chrome Football was a 220-card set that paralleled the regular Bowman issue. The set included 150 veterans and 70 rookies. Each rookie card had the "Bowman Chrome Rookie Card" logo. Parallel sets included: Refractors, Gold, Gold Refractors, Interstate and Interstate Refractors. Other insert sets included: Scout's Choice, Scout's Choice Refractors, Stock in the Game and Stock in the Game Refractors. Four-card packs had an SRP of $3.00.

		MT
Complete Set (220):		300.00
Common Player:		.25
Minor Stars:		.50
Common Rookie:		2.00
Wax Box:		200.00
1	Dan Marino	3.00
2	Michael Westbrook	.50
3	Yancey Thigpen	.50
4	Tony Martin	.25
5	Michael Strahan	.25
6	Dedric Ward	.25
7	Joey Galloway	1.00
8	Bobby Engram	.25

9	Frank Sanders	.50
10	Jake Plummer	2.00
11	Eddie Kennison	.25
12	Curtis Martin	1.00
13	Chris Spielman	.25
14	Trent Dilfer	1.00
15	Tim Biakabutuka	.50
16	Elvis Grbac	.50
17	Charlie Batch	1.50
18	Takeo Spikes	.25
19	Tony Banks	1.00
20	Doug Flutie	1.50
21	Ty Law	.25
22	Isaac Bruce	1.00
23	James Jett	.25
24	Kent Graham	.25
25	Derrick Mayes	.50
26	Amani Toomer	.50
27	Ray Lewis	.25
28	Shawn Springs	.25
29	Warren Sapp	.50
30	Jamal Anderson	1.00
31	Byron Morris	.25
32	Johnnie Morton	.50
33	Terance Mathis	.25
34	Terrell Davis	3.00
35	John Randle	.50
36	Vinny Testaverde	1.00
37	Junior Seau	.75
38	Reidel Anthony	.50
39	Brad Johnson	1.00
40	Emmitt Smith	3.00
41	Mo Lewis	.25
42	Terry Glenn	1.00
43	Dorsey Levens	1.00
44	Thurman Thomas	.75
45	Rob Moore	.50
46	Corey Dillon	1.00
47	Jessie Armstead	.25
48	Marshall Faulk	1.00
49	Charles Woodson	1.00
50	John Elway	3.00
51	Kevin Dyson	.50
52	Tony Simmons	.50
53	Keenan McCardell	.50
54	O.J. Santiago	.25
55	Jermaine Lewis	.50
56	Herman Moore	1.00
57	Gary Brown	.25
58	Jim Harbaugh	.50
59	Mike Alstott	1.00
60	Brett Favre	4.00
61	Tim Brown	.75
62	Steve McNair	1.00
63	Ben Coates	.50
64	Jerome Pathon	.50
65	Ray Buchanan	.25
66	Troy Aikman	2.00
67	Andre Reed	.50
68	Bubby Brister	.50
69	Karim Abdul	.50
70	Peyton Manning	3.00
71	Charles Johnson	.25
72	Natrone Means	.75
73	Michael Sinclair	.25
74	Skip Hicks	.50
75	Derrick Alexander	.25
76	Wayne Chrebet	1.00
77	Rod Smith	1.00
78	Carl Pickens	1.00
79	Adrian Murrell	.50
80	Fred Taylor	2.00
81	Eric Moulds	1.00
82	Erik Kramer	.25
83	Marvin Harrison	1.00
84	Cris Carter	1.00
85	Ike Hilliard	.50
86	Hines Ward	.75
87	Terrell Owens	1.00
88	Ricky Proehl	.25
89	Bert Emanuel	.25
90	Randy Moss	4.00
91	Aaron Glenn	.25
92	Robert Smith	1.00
93	Andre Hastings	.25
94	Jake Reed	.50
95	Curtis Enis	1.00
96	Andre Wadsworth	.50
97	Ed McCaffrey	1.00
98	Zach Thomas	.50
99	Kerry Collins	.50
100	Drew Bledsoe	1.50
101	Germane Crowell	.75
102	Bryan Still	.25
103	Chad Brown	.25
104	Jacquez Green	.50
105	Garrison Hearst	.50
106	Napoleon Kaufman	1.00
107	Ricky Watters	.50
108	O.J. McDuffie	.50
109	Keyshawn Johnson	1.00
110	Jerome Bettis	1.00
111	Duce Staley	1.00
112	Curtis Conway	.50
113	Chris Chandler	.50
114	Marcus Nash	.50
115	Stephen Alexander	.25
116	Darnay Scott	.50
117	Bruce Smith	.25
118	Priest Holmes	1.00
119	Mark Brunell	1.50
120	Jerry Rice	2.00
121	Randall Cunningham	1.00
122	Cameron Cleeland	.50
123	Antonio Freeman	1.00
124	Kordell Stewart	1.00
125	Jon Kitna	1.00
126	Ahman Green	.50

127	Warrick Dunn	1.00
128	Robert Brooks	.25
129	Derrick Thomas	.50
130	Steve Young	1.50
131	Peter Boulware	.25
132	Michael Irvin	.50
133	Shannon Sharpe	.50
134	Jimmy Smith	1.00
135	John Avery	.50
136	Fred Lane	.50
137	Trent Green	.50
138	Andre Rison	.50
139	Antowain Smith	.50
140	Eddie George	1.25
141	Jeff Blake	.75
142	Raghib Ismail	.50
143	Rickey Dudley	.25
144	Courtney Hawkins	.25
145	Mikhael Ricks	.25
146	J.J. Stokes	.50
147	Levon Kirkland	.25
148	Deion Sanders	1.00
149	Barry Sanders	4.00
150	Tiki Barber	.50
151	David Boston	10.00
152	Chris McAlister	3.00
153	Peerless Price	8.00
154	D'Wayne Bates	3.00
155	Cade McNown	25.00
156	Akili Smith	25.00
157	Kevin Johnson	10.00
158	Tim Couch	50.00
159	Sedrick Irvin	6.00
160	Chris Claiborne	3.00
161	Edgerrin James	80.00
162	Michael Cloud	3.00
163	Cecil Collins	10.00
164	James Johnson	6.00
165	Rob Konrad	3.00
166	Daunte Culpepper	25.00
167	Kevin Faulk	6.00
168	Donovan McNabb	25.00
169	Troy Edwards	10.00
170	Amos Zereoue	4.00
171	Karsten Bailey	3.00
172	Brock Huard	6.00
173	Joe Germaine	5.00
174	Torry Holt	10.00
175	Shaun King	20.00
176	Jevon Kearse	8.00
177	Champ Bailey	6.00
178	Ebenezer Ekuban	3.00
179	Andy Katzenmoyer	4.00
180	Antoine Winfield	3.00
181	Jermaine Fazande	4.00
182	Ricky Williams	50.00
183	Joel Mackovicka	3.00
184	Reginald Kelly	2.00
185	Brandon Stokley	2.00
186	L.C. Stevens	2.00
187	Marty Booker	4.00
188	Jerry Azumah	2.00
189	Ted White	2.00
190	Scott Covington	3.00
191	Tim Alexander	2.00
192	Darrin Chiaverini	3.00
193	Dat Nguyen	3.00
194	Wane McGarity	3.00
195	Al Wilson	3.00
196	Travis McGriff	3.00
197	Stacey Mack	2.00
198	Antwan Edwards	3.00
199	Aaron Brooks	4.00
200	De'Mond Parker	6.00
201	Jed Weaver	2.00
202	Madre Hill	4.00
203	Jim Kleinsasser	4.00
204	Michael Bishop	4.00
205	Michael Basnight	2.00
206	Sean Bennett	3.00
207	Dameane Douglas	2.00
208	Na Brown	2.00
209	Patrick Kerney	2.00
210	Malcolm Johnson	2.00
211	Dre Bly	3.00
212	Terry Jackson	3.00
213	Eugene Baker	2.00
214	Autry Denson	4.00
215	Darnell McDonald	4.00
216	Charlie Rogers	3.00
217	Joe Montgomery	4.00
218	Cecil Martin	3.00
219	Larry Parker	2.00
220	Mike Peterson	2.00

ed on refractor board. Singles were sequentially numbered to 25 and found 1:253 packs.

	MT
Complete Set (220):	3500.
Gold Ref. Cards:	35x-70x
Gold Ref. Rookies:	3x-6x
Inserted 1:253	
Production 25 Sets	

1999 Bowman Chrome Interstate

This set was a parallel to the base. The card fronts featured an image that related to that player's home state. The backs had a custom- tailored vanity plate from that state. Singles were found 1:4 packs.

	MT
Complete Set (220):	450.00
Interstate Cards:	2x-4x
Interstate Rookies:	1.5x
Inserted 1:4	

1999 Bowman Chrome Interstate Refractors

This was a parallel to the Interstate insert except that each single is printed on refractor board. Singles were sequentially numbered to 100 and found 1:63 packs.

	MT
Complete Set (220):	2200.
Interstate Ref. Cards:	15x-30x
Interstate Ref. Rookies:	3x
Inserted 1:63	
Production 100 Sets	

1999 Bowman Chrome Refractors

This was a parallel to the base set except that each single was printed on refractor board. Singles were found 1:12 packs.

	MT
Complete Set (220):	800.00
Refractor Cards:	4x-8x
Refractor Rookies:	2x
Inserted 1:12	

1999 Bowman Chrome Gold

This was a parallel to the base set with each single printed in gold ink. Singles were found 1:24 packs.

	MT
Complete Set (220):	1000.
Gold Cards:	4x-8x
Gold Rookies:	2x
Inserted 1:24	

1999 Bowman Chrome Gold Refractors

This is a parallel to the Gold set except that each card is print-

1999 Bowman Chrome Scout's Choice

This 21-card set includes all of the top rookies from the 1999 NFL Draft. Each single was borderless and printed on double-etched foil board. Singles were found 1:12 packs.

		MT
Complete Set (21):		60.00
Common Player:		1.00
Minor Stars:		2.00
Inserted 1:12		
1	David Boston	3.00
2	Champ Bailey	2.00
3	Edgerrin James	15.00
4	Michael Cloud	1.00
5	Kevin Faulk	2.00
6	Troy Edwards	3.00
7	Cecil Collins	3.00
8	Peerless Price	2.00
9	Torry Holt	3.00
10	Rob Konrad	1.00
11	Akili Smith	5.00
12	Daunte Culpepper	5.00
13	D'Wayne Bates	1.00
14	Donovan McNabb	5.00
15	James Johnson	2.00
16	Cade McNown	5.00
17	Kevin Johnson	3.00
18	Ricky Williams	10.00
19	Karsten Bailey	1.00
20	Tim Couch	10.00
21	Shaun King	5.00

1999 Bowman Chrome Scout's Choice Refractors

This was a parallel to the Scout's Choice insert. Singles were inserted 1:60 packs.

	MT
Refractor Cards:	2x
Inserted 1:60	

1999 Bowman Chrome Stock in the Game

This 18-card set was an exclusive to the Bowman Chrome

line. The set was divided into three categories. I.P.O. included six rookies not found in the Scout's Choice insert. The Growth section included six young stars and the Blue Chips included six of the game's veterans. Singles were found 1:21 packs.

		MT
Complete Set (18):		40.00
Common Player:		2.00
Inserted 1:21		
1	Joe Germaine	2.00
2	Madre Hill	2.00
3	Sedrick Irvin	2.00
4	Brock Huard	2.00
5	Amos Zereoue	2.00
6	Andy Katzenmoyer	2.00
7	Randy Moss	8.00
8	Jake Plummer	3.00
9	Keyshawn Johnson	2.00
10	Fred Taylor	4.00
11	Eddie George	2.00
12	Peyton Manning	6.00
13	Dan Marino	6.00
14	Terrell Davis	6.00
15	Brett Favre	8.00
16	Jamal Anderson	2.00
17	Steve Young	3.00
18	Jerry Rice	4.00

1999 Bowman Chrome Stock in the Game Refractors

This was a parallel to the Stock in the Game insert. Each single was printed on refractor board and was found 1:105 packs.

	MT
Refractors:	3x
Inserted 1:105	

1952 Bread For Health

These early 1950s bread end labels feature 32 NFL players. The cards, which measure 2-3/4" x 2-3/4", were found in loaves of Fisher's Bread (New Jersey, New York and Pennsylvania) and NBC Bread in Michigan. The cards are unnumbered and are blank-backed. A B.E.B. copyright is on the card front, along with an informational note.

		NM
Complete Set (32):		4300.
Common Player:		90.00
(1)	Frankie Albert	120.00
(2)	Elmer Angsman	90.00
(3)	Dick Barwegen	90.00
(4)	Sammy Baugh	350.00
(5)	Charley Conerly	200.00
(6)	Glenn Davis	150.00
(7)	Don Doll	90.00
(8)	Tom Fears	150.00
(9)	Harry Gilmer	100.00
(10)	Otto Graham	350.00
(11)	Pat Harder	110.00
(12)	Bobby Layne	300.00
(13)	Sid Luckman	200.00
(14)	Johnny Lujack	175.00
(15)	John Panelli	90.00
(16)	Barney Poole	90.00
(17)	George Ratterman	90.00
(18)	Tobin Rote	125.00
(19)	Jack Russell	90.00
(20)	Lou Rymkus	90.00
(21)	Joe Signiago	90.00
(22)	Mac Speedie	120.00
(23)	Bill Swiacki	90.00
(24)	Tommy Thompson	120.00
(25)	Y.A. Tittle	300.00
(26)	Clayton Tonnemaker	90.00
(27)	Charlie Trippi	110.00
(28)	Clyde Turner	150.00
(29)	Steve Van Buren	150.00
(30)	Bill Walsh	90.00
(31)	Bob Waterfield	200.00
(32)	Jim White	90.00

1992 Breyers Bookmarks

Breyers Bookmarks contained 66 bookmarks measuring 2" x 8". The set was used to promote reading in the city of 11 featured teams. Card fronts feature a cut-out of the player against a yellow background with books. Cards are numbered on the front and arranged in order by teams.

		MT
Complete Set (66):		150.00
Common Player:		1.50
1	Greg Townsend	1.50
2	Steve Wisniewski	1.50
3	Art Shell (CO)	2.50
4	Jeff Jaeger	1.50
5	Lisa O'Day (Cheerleader)	1.50
6	Los Angeles Raiders (Helmet and SB trophies)	1.50
7	Jerry Rice	12.00
8	Don Griffin	1.50
9	John Taylor	3.00
10	Joe Montana	18.00
11	Mike Walker	1.50
12	San Francisco 49ers (Helmet)	1.50
13	Junior Seau	3.00
14	John Friesz	1.50
15	Ronnie Harmon	1.50
16	Marion Butts	1.50
17	Gill Byrd	1.50
18	San Diego Chargers (Helmet)	1.50
19	Kelly Stouffer	1.50
20	John Kasay	1.50
21	Andy Heck	1.50
22	Jacob Green	1.50
23	Eugene Robinson	1.50
24	Seattle Seahawks (Helmet)	1.50
25	Pat Swilling	1.50
26	Vaughn Johnson	1.50
27	Bobby Hebert	1.50
28	Floyd Turner	1.50
29	Rickey Jackson	1.50
30	New Orleans Saints (Helmet)	1.50
31	Harvey Williams	1.50
32	Derrick Thomas	3.00
33	Bill Maas	1.50
34	Tim Grunhard	1.50
35	Jonathan Hayes	1.50
36	Kansas City Chiefs (Mascot)	1.50
37	Rich Gannon	1.50
38	Tim Irwin	1.50
39	Audray McMillian	1.50
40	Gary Zimmerman	1.50
41	Hassan Jones	1.50
42	Minnesota Vikings (Helmet)	1.50
43	Eric Green	1.50
44	Louis Lipps	1.50
45	Rod Woodson	1.50
46	Merril Hoge	1.50
47	Gary Anderson (RB)	1.50
48	Pittsburgh Steelers (60-Season Emblem)	1.50
49	Anthony Johnson	1.50
50	Bill Brooks	1.50
51	Jeff Herrod	1.50
52	Mike Prior	1.50
53	Jeff George	3.00
54	Indianapolis Colts (Ted Marchibroda) (CO)	1.50
55	Troy Aikman	12.00
56	Jay Novacek	1.50
57	Emmitt Smith	20.00
58	Michael Irvin	3.00
59	Dorie Braddy (Cheerleader)	1.50
60	Dallas Cowboys (Super Bowl trophy)	1.50
61	Clay Matthews	1.50
62	Tommy Vardell	1.50
63	Eric Turner	1.50
64	Mike Johnson	1.50
65	James Jones	1.50
66	Cleveland Browns (Helmet)	1.50

1990 British Petroleum

This 36-card set featured color fronts and black backs (with either contest rules or advertising). The cards were handed out two at a time in California, with the goal of the game to collect two adjacent numbers (1-2, 3-4). One of the two was difficult to find, with the contest expiring in October of 1991. There were also five instant win cards: Andre Tippett, Freeman McNeil, Clay Matthews, Tim Harris and Deion Sanders. Numbers 1, 3, 6, 8 and 10 had six different possible players.

		MT
Complete Set (36):		45.00
Common Player:		.50
1A	John Elway	3.00
1B	Boomer Esiason	.50
1C	Jim Everett	.50
1D	Bernie Kosar	.50
1E	Karl Mecklenburg	.50
1F	Bruce Smith	.50
2	Deion Sanders	
3A	Roger Craig	.50
3B	Randall Cunningham	
3C	Keith Jackson	.50
3D	Dan Marino	10.00
3E	Freddie Joe Nunn	.50
3F	Jerry Rice	5.00
3G	Vinny Testaverde	.50
3H	John L. Williams	.50
4	Tim Harris	
5	Clay Matthews	
6A	Neal Anderson	.50
6B	Duane Bickett	.50
6C	Ronnie Lott	.50
6D	Anthony Munoz	.50
6E	Christian Okoye	.50
6F	Barry Sanders	5.00
7	Freeman McNeil	
8A	Cornelius Bennett	.50
8B	Anthony Carter	.50
8C	Jim Kelly	1.00
8D	Louis Lipps	.50
8E	Phil Simms	.50
8F	Billy Ray Smith	.50
8G	Lawrence Taylor	1.00
9	Andre Tippett	
10A	Bo Jackson	1.50
10B	Howie Long	.50
10C	Don Majkowski	.50
10D	Art Monk	1.00
10E	Warren Moon	1.00
10F	Mike Singletary	1.00
10G	Al Toon	.50
10H	Herschel Walker	1.00
10I	Reggie White	1.50

1968-70 Broncos

This 53-card set contains black and white photos and black and white card backs. The cards measure 5" x 7" and include mostly posed shots.

		NM
Complete Set (53):		130.00
Common Player:		2.00
1	Bob Anderson	4.00
2	Tom Beer	4.00
3	Phil Brady	2.00
4	Sam Brunelli	3.00
5	George Burrell	2.00
6	Carter Campbell	2.00
7	Grady Cavness	3.00
8	Barney Chavous	6.00
9	Dave Costa	3.00
10	Ken Criter (Head shot)	2.00
11	Ken Criter (Head-and-shoulders)	2.00
12	Carl Cunningham	2.00
13	Mike Current (Left-side shot)	4.00
14	Mike Current (Right-side shot)	4.00
15	Joe Dawkins	4.00
16	Al Denson (Offensive end)	4.00
17	Al Denson (Wide receiver)	4.00
18	Wallace Dickey	2.00
19	John Embree	2.00
20	Fred Forsberg	2.00
21	Jack Gehrke	2.00
22	Cornell Gordon	3.00
23	John Grant	2.00
24	Charlie Greer (Head shot)	2.00
25	Charlie Greer (Head-and-shoulders)	2.00
26	Dwight Harrison	2.00
27	Walter Highsmith	2.00
28	Gus Hollomon	2.00
29	Larron Jackson (Left-side shot)	2.00
30	Larron Jackson (Right-side shot)	2.00
31	Calvin Jones	4.00
32	Larry Kaminski (Left-side shot)	2.00
33	Larry Kaminski (Right-side shot)	2.00
34	Bill Laskey	2.00
35	Pete Liske	4.00
36	Fran Lynch	2.00
37	Tom Lyons (Guard on front)	2.00
38	Tommy Lyons (Center on front)	2.00
39	Rex Mirich	2.00
40	Randy Montgomery (Left-side shot)	2.00
41	Randy Montgomery (Right-side shot)	2.00
42	Tom Oberg	2.00
43	Steve Ramsey	6.00
44	Frank Richter	2.00
45	Mike Schnitker	2.00
46	Roger Shoals	2.00
47	Jerry Simmons (Looking toward upper left corner of picture)	4.00
48	Jerry Simmons (Head turned slightly toward right)	4.00
49	Paul Smith (Head shot)	4.00
50	Paul Smith (Head-and-shoulders)	4.00
51	Olen Underwood	2.00
52	Dave Washington	2.00
53	Bob Young	2.00

1980 Broncos Stamps Police

This unnumbered set contains nine different stamps, with each stamp containing two players with a Broncos logo in between. The stamps were given away (one per week) at Albertson's food stores in the Denver area. The set measures 3" x 3" and is tri-sponsored by Albertson's, the Kiwanis Club and local police. There is a poster that the stamps fit on that sold at the time for 99 cents.

		NM
Complete Set (9):		12.00
Common Player:		1.00
1	Barney Chavous, Rubin Carter	1.00
2	Bernard Jackson, Haven Moses	1.00
3	Tom Jackson, Riley Odoms	3.00
4	Brison Manor, Steve Foley	1.00
5	Claudie Minor, Randy Gradishar	1.00
6	Craig Morton, Tom Glassic	2.00
7	Jim Turner, Bob Swenson	1.00
8	Rick Upchurch, Billy Thompson	1.00
9	Louis Wright, Joe Rizzo	1.00

1982 Broncos Police

Measuring 2-5/8" x 4-1/8", the 15-card set boasts the player's jersey number, name, position, team and Broncos' helmet under a photo. The unnumbered card backs feature Broncos Tips inside a box, which is topped by a Broncos' helmet. The set's sponsor is listed at the bottom center.

		MT
Complete Set (15):		150.00
Common Player:		2.00
7	Craig Morton	8.00
11	Luke Prestridge	2.00
20	Louis Wright	4.00
24	Rick Parros	2.00
36	Bill Thompson	4.00
41	Rob Lytle	2.00
46	Dave Preston (SP)	2.00
51	Bob Swenson	2.00
53	Randy Gradishar (SP)	45.00
57	Tom Jackson	12.00
60	Paul Howard	2.00
68	Rubin Carter	2.00
79	Barney Chavous (SP)	45.00
80	Rick Upchurch	8.00
88	Riley Odoms (SP)	12.00

1984 Broncos KOA

Handed out at Safeway or Dairy Queen stores, this 24-card set was part of the KOA Match 'N Win and KOA/Denver Broncos Silver Anniversary Sweepstakes. Measuring 2" x 4", with a bottom tab measuring 1-1/8", the card fronts showcase a black-and-white photo, with the player's name, number and position inside a banner under the photo. The American Football League and various sponsor logos appear under the photo. The card's tab featured three silver footballs that could be scratched off with a coin. The card backs feature the sweepstakes' rules. Besides the player's jersey number, the cards are unnumbered.

		MT
Complete Set (24):		90.00
Common Player:		1.00
7	Craig Morton	5.00
11	Bob Anderson (SP)	10.00
12	Charlie Johnson	4.00
15	Jim Turner	2.00
21	Gene Mingo	1.00
22	Fran Lynch	2.00
23	Goose Gonsoulin	2.00
24	Otis Armstrong	4.00
25	Willie Brown	6.00
36	Haven Moses	2.00
42	Billy Thompson	2.00
44	Bill Van Heusen	2.00
44	Floyd Little (SP)	16.00
53	Randy Gradishar (SP)	14.00
71	Claudie Minor (SP)	5.00
72	Sam Brunelli	1.00
74	Mike Current	1.00
75	Eldon Danenhauer	1.00
81	Marv Montgomery	1.00
81	Billy Masters	1.00
82	Bob Scarpitto	1.00
87	Lionel Taylor	2.00
87	Rich Jackson	1.00
88	Riley Odoms	2.00

1987 Broncos Orange Crush

This standard sized nine-card set honors former Denver Broncos players who are featured in the stadium's Ring of Fame. The card fronts feature a black-and-white photo bordered with blue and orange. The Orange Crush logo is on an angle at the top of the card front. The player's number, name, position and years played with the Broncos are printed underneath the photo. The Broncos' Ring of Fame logo is located at the bottom right. The backs feature "1st Annual Collector's Edition Ring of Famer" at the top, with his name, number, position, years played and highlights printed below. The info is packaged inside a box, which is topped by a Broncos' helmet, with the Crush logo appearing at the bottom. The KOA Radio logo is printed at the very bottom of the card back. The cards were handed out for three weeks at 7-11 and Albertsons stores in the Denver area.

1986 Brownell Heisman

Measuring 7-15/16" x 10", the black-and-white cards feature Art Brownell artwork of Heisman Trophy winners. The blank-backed cards are unnumbered. The cards are listed in chronological order. Even though Archie Griffin won the Heisman in both 1974 and 1975, he is featured on only one card. The fronts feature the year the player won the Heisman, plus a short write-up.

backed cards. The set was housed in an off-white envelope with brown and orange trim. "Cleveland Browns Photographs" is also printed on the envelopes.

		MT
Complete Set (50):		250.00
Common Player:		5.00
1	Jay Berwanger	4.00
2	Larry Kelley	4.00
3	Clint Frank	4.00
4	Davey O'Brien	4.00
5	Niles Kinnick	10.00
6	Tom Harmon	5.00
7	Bruce Smith	4.00
8	Frank Sinkwich	4.00
9	Angelo Bertelli	4.00
10	Les Horvath	4.00
11	Doc Blanchard	8.00
12	Glenn Davis	8.00
13	Johnny Lujack	12.00
14	Doak Walker	10.00
15	Leon Hart	4.00
16	Vic Janowicz	10.00
17	Dick Kazmaier	4.00
18	Billy Vessels	4.00
19	John Lattner	8.00
20	Alan Ameche	6.00
21	Howard Cassady	5.00
22	Paul Hornung	18.00
23	John David Crow	4.00
24	Pete Dawkins	4.00
25	Billy Cannon	4.00
26	Joe Bellino	4.00
27	Ernie Davis	30.00
28	Terry Baker	4.00
29	Roger Staubach	35.00
30	John Huarte	4.00
31	Mike Garrett	4.00
32	Steve Spurrier	15.00
33	Gary Beban	4.00
34	O.J. Simpson	20.00
35	Steve Owens	5.00
36	Jim Plunkett	10.00
37	Pat Sullivan	4.00
38	Johnny Rodgers	4.00
39	John Cappelletti	4.00
40	Archie Griffin	6.00
41	Tony Dorsett	18.00
42	Earl Campbell	18.00
43	Billy Sims	8.00
44	Charles White	4.00
45	George Rogers	4.00
46	Marcus Allen	10.00
47	Herschel Walker	8.00
48	Mike Rozier	4.00
49	Doug Flutie	8.00
50	Bo Jackson	10.00

1946 Browns Sears

Measuring 2-1/2" x 4", the eight-card set was released by Sears and Roebuck. The set showcases players from the Cleveland Browns' initial season. Card fronts boast a black-and-white photo of the player and a slogan to follow the Browns and shop at Sears. The cards are unnumbered.

		NM
Complete Set (8):		280.00
Common Player:		35.00
(1)	Ernie Blandin	35.00
(2)	Jim Daniell	35.00
(3)	Fred Evans	35.00
(4)	Frank Gatski	50.00
(5)	Otto Graham	150.00
(6)	Dante Lavelli	75.00
(7)	Mel Maceau	35.00
(8)	George Young	35.00

1950 Browns Team Issue

Measuring 6-1/2" x 9", the five-card set showcases a black-and-white posed player photo, which is bordered in white. The player's name, printed in cursive, also is on the front of the blank-backed and unnumbered cards.

		NM
Complete Set (5):		75.00
Common Player:		10.00
1	Frank Gatski	15.00
2	Tommy James	10.00
3	Don Moselle	10.00
4	Marion Motley	30.00
5	Derrell F. Palmer	10.00

1951 Browns White Border

Measuring 6-1/2" x 9", the 25-card team-issued set was anchored by a posed black-and-white photo on the front, bordered in white. The player's name is printed in cursive on the front of the unnumbered and blank-

		MT
Complete Set (25):		250.00
Common Player:		5.00
1	Tony Adamle	8.00
2	Alex Agase	8.00
3	Rex Bumgardner	5.00
4	Emerson Cole	5.00
5	Len Ford	12.00
6	Frank Gatski	12.00
7	Horace Gillom	5.00
8	Ken Gorgal	5.00
9	Otto Graham	45.00
10	Forrest Gregg	5.00
11	Lou Groza	20.00
12	Hal Herring	5.00
13	Lin Houston	5.00
14	Weldon Humble	5.00
15	Tommy James	5.00
16	Dub Jones	8.00
17	Warren Lahr	5.00
18	Dante Lavelli	20.00
19	Cliff Lewis	5.00
20	Marion Motley	20.00
21	Lou Rymkus	8.00
22	Mac Speedie	10.00
23	Tommy Thompson	5.00
24	Bill Willis	15.00
25	George Young	15.00

1954-55 Browns White Border

Measuring 8-1/2" x 10", the 20-card set showcases posed player shots on the front, which are bordered in white. The unnumbered and blank-backed cards feature the player's name and position at the bottom inside a white border.

		NM
Complete Set (20):		125.00
Common Player:		5.00
1	Maurice Bassett	5.00
2	Harold Bradley	5.00
3	Darrell Brewster	5.00
4	Don Colo	5.00
5	Len Ford	12.00
6	Bob Gain	5.00
7	Frank Gatski	10.00
8	Abe Gibron	5.00
9	Tommy James	5.00
10	Dub Jones	7.00
11	Ken Konz	5.00
12	Warren Lahr	5.00
13	Dante Lavelli	15.00
14	Carlton Massey	5.00
15	Mike McCormack	10.00
16	Walt Michaels	5.00
17	Chuck Noll	25.00
18	Don Paul	5.00
19	Ray Renfro	10.00
20	George Ratterman	5.00

1955 Browns Carling Beer

Measuring 8-1/2" x 11-1/2", the 10-card set featured a large black-and-white photo on the front of the white-bordered cards. Carling's Black Label Beer and team name are printed below the photo in black. "DBL 54" is printed in the bottom right corner.

		NM
Complete Set (10):		200.00
Common Player:		10.00
1	Darrell Brewster	10.00
2	Tom Catlin	10.00
3	Len Ford	20.00
4	Otto Graham	45.00
5	Lou Groza	30.00
6	Kenny Konz	10.00
7	Dante Lavelli	25.00
8	Mike McCormack	20.00
9	Fred Morrison	10.00
10	Chuck Noll	45.00

1955 Browns Color Postcards

These six postcards, which measure 6" x 9", boast a full-bleed color photo on the front. The unnumbered backs have the player's name and team at the top left, with the "place stamp here" box in the upper left and "Giant Post Card" cen-tered on the right. The cards feature rounded corners.

		NM
Complete Set (6):		120.00
Common Player:		10.00
1	Mo Bassett	10.00
2	Don Colo	10.00
3	Frank Gatski	20.00
4	Lou Groza	45.00
5	Dante Lavelli	30.00
6	George Ratterman	15.00

1959 Browns Carling Beer

Measuring 8-1/2" x 11-1/2", the nine-card set featured a black-and-white posed photo, which was bordered in white. The player's name and position are printed in black inside a white rectangle inside the photo. Printed under the photo are "Carling Black Label Beer" and "The Cleveland Browns." The backs are usually blank, but can be stamped with "Henry M. Barr Studios, Berea, Ohio BE4-1330." The card fronts are numbered in the lower right corner, except for Jim Brown's photo card. The set was also reprinted in the late 1980s on thinner paper and most likely show the Henry M. Barr stamp on the back. Some sources say the Brown photo is only available in the reprint set.

		NM
Complete Set (9):		130.00
Common Player:		10.00
A	Leroy Bolden	10.00
B	Vince Costello	10.00
C	Galen Fiss	10.00
E	Lou Groza	30.00
F	Walt Michaels	15.00
G	Bobby Mitchell	30.00
J	Bob Gain	10.00
K	Billy Howton	15.00
NNO	Jim Brown (DP)	8.00

1961 Browns Carling Beer

Measuring 8-1/2" x 11-1/2", the 10 black-and-white cards feature posed photos on the front, with the player's name and position printed inside a white rectangle inside the photo. "Carling Back Label Beer" and "The Cleveland Browns" are printed underneath the photo on the card front. The card numbers appear in the lower right corner on the front, while the backs are blank.

		NM
Complete Set (10):		200.00
Common Player:		10.00
A	Milt Plum	10.00
B	Mike McCormack	20.00
C	Bob Gain	10.00
D	John Morrow	10.00
E	Jim Brown	80.00
F	Bobby Mitchell	35.00
G	Bobby Franklin	10.00
H	Jim Ray Smith	10.00
K	Jim Houston	18.00
L	Ray Renfro	15.00

1961 Browns National City Bank

Measuring 2-1/2" x 3-9/16", the 36-card set was released in sheets of six cards. Each sheet was numbered, while each individual card was numbered. The card fronts feature "Quarterback Club Brownie Card 1961 Cleveland Browns" at the top. The posed photos anchor the front, with "issued in 1961 by Cleveland's Oldest Bank National City Bank" printed underneath. The card backs are numbered at the top with a set number and a player (card) number. The player's name, position, bio and write-up are also on the back. The bottom of the card back includes the National City Bank logo.

		NM
Complete Set (36):		2000.
Common Player:		40.00
1	Mike McCormack	80.00
2	Jim Brown	575.00
3	Leon Clarke	40.00
4	Walt Michaels	40.00
5	Jim Ray Smith	40.00
6	Quarterback Club Membership Card	220.00
7	Len Dawson	225.00
8	John Morrow	40.00
9	Bernie Parrish	40.00
10	Floyd Peters	40.00
11	Paul Wiggin	40.00
12	John Wooten	40.00
13	Ray Renfro	40.00
14	Galen Fiss	40.00
15	Dave Lloyd	40.00
16	Dick Schafrath	40.00
17	Ross Fichtner	40.00
18	Gern Nagler	40.00
19	Rich Kreitling	40.00
20	Duane Putnam	40.00
21	Vince Costello	40.00
22	Jim Shofner	40.00
23	Sam Baker	40.00
24	Bob Gain	40.00
25	Lou Groza	100.00
26	Don Fleming	40.00
27	Tom Watkins	40.00
28	Jim Houston	40.00
29	Larry Stephens	40.00
30	Bobby Mitchell	100.00
31	Bobby Franklin	40.00
32	Charlie Ferguson	40.00
33	Johnny Brewer	40.00
34	Bob Crespino	40.00
35	Milt Plum	40.00
36	Preston Powell	40.00

1961 Browns
White Border

Measuring 8-1/2" x 10-1/2", the 20-card set showcased black-and-white photos on the front, with the player's name and position listed inside a white box inside the photo. The fronts are bordered in white. The cards are unnumbered and blank-backed.

		NM
Complete Set (20):		160.00
Common Player:		5.00
1	Jim Brown	75.00
2	Galen Fiss	5.00
3	Don Fleming	5.00
4	Bobby Franklin	5.00
5	Bob Gain	5.00
6	Jim Houston	5.00
7	Rich Kreitling	5.00
8	Dave Lloyd	5.00
9	Mike McCormack	12.00
10	Bobby Mitchell	16.00
11	John Morrow	5.00
12	Bernie Parrish	5.00
13	Milt Plum	5.00
14	Ray Renfro	5.00
15	Dick Schafrath	5.00
16	Jim Shofner	5.00
17	Jim Ray Smith	5.00
18	Tom Watkins	5.00
19	Paul Wiggin	5.00
20	John Wooten	5.00

1963 Browns
White Border

Measuring 7-1/2" x 9-1/2", the 26-card set showcases black-and-white photos on the front. The card backs are blank. Each card is unnumbered.

		NM
Complete Set (26):		120.00
Common Player:		5.00
1	Johnny Brewer	5.00
2	Monte Clark	5.00
3	Gary Collins	10.00
4	Vince Costello	5.00
5	Bob Crespino	5.00
6	Ross Fichtner	5.00
7	Galen Fiss	5.00
8	Bob Gain	5.00

9	Bill Glass	5.00
10	Ernie Green	10.00
11	Lou Groza	16.00
12	Gene Hickerson	7.00
13	Jim Houston	5.00
14	Tom Hutchinson	5.00
15	Rich Kreitling	5.00
16	Mike Lucci	5.00
17	John Morrow	5.00
18	Jim Ninowski	5.00
19	Frank Parker	5.00
20	Bernie Parrish	5.00
21	Ray Renfro	5.00
22	Dick Schafrath	5.00
23	Jim Shofner	5.00
24	Ken Webb	5.00
25	Paul Wiggin	5.00
26	John Wooten	5.00

1985 Browns
Coke/Mr. Hero

Measuring 2-3/4" x 3-1/4", the 48-card set was released on six sheets of eight cards. The card fronts are anchored by a photo, with the player's name and position listed at the bottom center. The player's jersey number is printed in large numerals in the lower left. The unnumbered card backs spotlight the player's name, position, bio and career highlights. Coupons were included on each complete sheet.

		MT
Complete Set (48):		25.00
Common Player:		.50
7	Jeff Gossett (4)	.75
9	Matt Bahr (1)	.75
16	Paul McDonald (4)	.50
18	Gary Danielson (4)	.50
19	Bernie Kosar (6)	2.50
20	Don Rogers (4)	.50
22	Felix Wright (2)	.50
26	Greg Allen (3)	.50
27	Al Gross (2)	.50
29	Hanford Dixon (5)	.50
30	Boyce Green (1)	.50
31	Frank Minnifield (1)	.50
34	Kevin Mack (3)	1.00
37	Chris Rockins (1)	.50
38	Johnny Davis (5)	.50
44	Earnest Byner (2)	1.25
47	Larry Braziel (4)	.50
50	Tom Cousineau (6)	.50
51	Eddie Johnson (2)	.50
55	Curtis Weathers (1)	.50
56	Chip Banks (6)	.75
57	Clay Matthews (5)	1.75
58	Scott Nicolas (1)	.50
61	Mike Baab (4)	.50
62	George Lilja (5)	.50
63	Cody Risien (6)	.50
65	Mark Krerowicz (3)	.50
68	Robert Jackson (4)	.50
72	Dan Fike (2)	.50
74	Dave Puzzuoli (1)	.50
77	Paul Farren (2)	.50
77	Rickey Bolden (1)	.50
78	Carl Hairston (2)	.50
79	Bob Golic (6)	.50
80	Willis Adams (5)	.50
81	Harry Holt (3)	.50
82	Ozzie Newsome (3)	1.75
83	Fred Banks (3)	.50
84	Glen Young (1)	.50
85	Clarence Weathers (6)	.50
86	Brian Brennan (5)	.50
87	Travis Tucker (6)	.50
88	Reggie Langhorne (5)	.50
89	John Jefferson (4)	1.00
91	Sam Clancy (4)	.50
96	Reggie Camp (5)	.50
99	Keith Baldwin (6)	.50
NNO	Action Photo (Clay Matthews tackling Eric Dickerson, 3)	1.75

1987 Browns
Louis Rich

Louis Rich produced this set to be a promotion in its products. After the cards were printed the promotion was pulled. After the set's cancellation, Oscar Mayer gave collectors who stopped into the Cleveland corporate office a set. The cards measure 5" x 7-1/8".

		MT
Complete Set (5):		45.00
Common Player:		5.00
1	Jim Brown, Bobby Mitchell	22.00
2	Otto Graham	15.00
3	Lou Groza	10.00
4	Dante Lavelli (Question Mark)	5.00
5	Marion Motley	5.00

1992 Browns
Sunoco

NFL Properties produced this 24-card set as a promotion at Ohio-area Sunoco gas stations. Spotlighting Browns who have been inducted into the Hall of Fame, the player card fronts feature a full-bleed photo. The player's last name is printed in large orange letters at the bottom of the card, with a small Sunoco logo printed over the top of the name. The player card backs feature the player's career highlights and name printed over a ghosted image of the player. Logos for radio stations WMMS and WHK are printed at the bottom of the card backs. Player cards are numbered on the bottom right. The set was sold in three-card cello packs which included a cover card, player card and sweepstakes entry card. Randomly inserted in packs were autographed cards. The cover card fronts had "The Cleveland Browns' Collection" at the top, with a Browns' helmet at the center and the player's name underneath. The cover card backs showcase the sponsors' and Pro Football Hall of Fame logos. Cover card backs are not numbered. In addition, albums were issued to hold the set.

		MT
Complete Set (24):		16.00
Common Player (1-12):		.75
Common Cover (1C-12C):		.25
1	Otto Graham (Player card)	2.50
1C	Otto Graham (Cover card)	.25
2	Paul Brown (CO, Player card)	1.50
2C	Paul Brown (CO, Cover card)	.25
3	Marion Motley (Player card)	1.25
3C	Marion Motley (Cover card)	.25
4	Jim Brown (Player card)	4.00
4C	Jim Brown (Cover card)	.50
5	Lou Groza (Player card)	1.25
5C	Lou Groza (Cover card)	.25
6	Dante Lavelli (Player card)	1.00
6C	Dante Lavelli (Cover card)	.25
7	Len Ford (Player card)	1.00
7C	Len Ford (Cover card)	.25
8	Bill Willis (Player card)	1.00
8C	Bill Willis (Cover card)	.25
9	Bobby Mitchell (Player card)	1.50
9C	Bobby Mitchell (Cover card)	.25
10	Paul Warfield (Player card)	1.50
10C	Paul Warfield (Cover card)	.25
11	Mike McCormack (Player card)	1.00
11C	Mike McCormack (Cover card)	.25
12	Frank Gatski (Player card)	1.00
12C	Frank Gatski (Cover card)	.25

1980 Buccaneers
Police

Measuring 2-5/8" x 4-1/8", the 56-card set boasts a photo on the front, with the player's name, position and bio underneath on the left. The Bucs' helmet is printed in the lower right. The unnumbered card backs have "Kids and Kops tips from the Buccaneers" at the top. A definition of a football term and a safety tip are included, while the Coca-Cola logo is printed above the various sponsor names at the bottom. Cards including the Paradyne Corp.

name on the back are scarce variations, which are valued at two to three times more.

		NM
Complete Set (56):		150.00
Common Player:		3.00
1	Ricky Bell	8.00
2	Rick Berns	3.00
3	Tom Blanchard	3.00
4	Scot Brantley	3.00
5	Aaron Brown	3.00
6	Cedric Brown	3.00
7	Mark Cotney	3.00
8	Randy Crowder	3.00
9	Gary Davis	3.00
10	Johnny Davis	3.00
11	Tony Davis	3.00
12	Jerry Eckwood	5.00
13	Chuck Fusina	3.00
14	Jimmie Giles	3.00
15	Isaac Hagins	3.00
16	Charley Hannah	3.00
17	Andy Hawkins	3.00
18	Kevin House	3.00
19	Cecil Johnson	3.00
20	Gordon Jones	3.00
21	Curtis Jordan	3.00
22	Bill Kollar	3.00
23	Jim Leonard	3.00
24	David Lewis	3.00
25	Reggie Lewis	3.00
26	David Logan	3.00
27	Larry Mucker	3.00
28	Jim O'Bradovich	3.00
29	Mike Rae	3.00
30	Dave Reavis	3.00
31	Danny Reece	3.00
32	Greg Roberts	3.00
33	Gene Sanders	3.00
34	Dewey Selmon	3.00
35	Lee Roy Selmon	15.00
36	Ray Snell	3.00
37	Dave Stalls	3.00
38	Norris Thomas	3.00
39	Mike Washington	3.00
40	Doug Williams	10.00
41	Steve Wilson	3.00
42	Richard Wood	3.00
43	George Yarno	3.00
44	Garo Yepremian	6.00
45	Logo Card	3.00
46	Team Photo	5.00
47	Hugh Culverhouse (OWN)	3.00
48	John McKay (CO)	3.00
49	Mascot Capt. Crush	3.00
50	Cheerleaders: Swash-Buc-Lers	3.00
51	Swash-Buc-Lers (Buzz)	3.00
52	Swash-Buc-Lers (Check with me)	3.00
53	Swash-Buc-Lers (Gap Two)	3.00
54	Swash-Buc-Lers (Gas)	3.00
55	Swash-Buc-Lers (Pass Protection)	3.00
56	Swash-Buc-Lers (Post Pattern)	3.00

1982 Buccaneers
Shell

Measuring 1-1/2" x 2-1/2", the 32-card set boasts a full-bleed color photo on the front, with a white stripe at the bottom which includes the Buccaneers' helmet on the left, the player's name in the center and Shell logo on the right. The card backs are blank and unnumbered.

		MT
Complete Set (32):		30.00
Common Player:		.50
1	Theo Bell	.75
2	Scot Brantley	.75
3	Cedric Brown	.50
4	Bill Capece	.50
5	Neal Colzie	.75
6	Mark Cotney	.50
7	Hugh Culverhouse	.75
8	Jeff Davis	.75
9	Jerry Eckwood	.50
10	Sean Farrell	.75
11	Jimmie Giles	1.00
12	Hugh Green	1.50
13	Charley Hannah	.50
14	Andy Hawkins	.50
15	John Holt	.50
16	Kevin House	1.00
17	Cecil Johnson	.50
18	Gordon Jones	.50
19	David Logan	.75
20	John McKay	1.50
21	James Owens	1.00
22	Greg Roberts	.50
23	Gene Sanders	.50
24	Lee Roy Selmon	4.00
25	Ray Snell	.50
26	Larry Swider	.50
27	Norris Thomas	.50
28	Mike Washington	.50
29	James Wilder	1.50
30	Doug Williams	2.00
31	Steve Wilson	.50
32	Richard Wood	1.00

1984 Buccaneers
Police

Measuring 2-5/8" x 4-1/8", the 56-card set boasts a photo on the card front, with the player's name, position and bio on the bottom left. The Bucs' helmet is located in the lower right. The unnumbered card backs have "Kids and Kops tips from the Buccaneers" at the top, with a football term definition and safety tip below it. The various sponsors are listed at the bottom.

		MT
Complete Set (56):		65.00
Common Player:		1.00
1	Swash-Buc-Lers	2.00
2	Hugh Culverhouse (OWN)	1.75
3	John McKay (25 Years as Head Coach)	1.50
4	John McKay (CO)	1.50
5	Defensive Action	1.25
6	Fred Acorn	1.00
7	Obed Ariri	1.00
8	Adger Armstrong	1.00
9	Jerry Bell	1.00
10	Theo Bell	2.50
11	Byron Braggs	1.00
12	Scot Brantley	1.00
13	Cedric Brown	1.00
14	Keith Browner	1.50
15	John Cannon	1.00
16	Jay Carroll	1.00
17	Gerald Carter	1.00
18	Melvin Carter	1.00
19	Jeremiah Castille	1.50
20	Mark Cotney	1.00
21	Steve Courson	1.50
22	Jeff Davis	1.00
23	Steve DeBerg	5.00
24	Sean Farrell	1.75
25	Frank Garcia	1.00
26	Jimmie Giles	2.50
27	Hugh Green	3.00
28	Hugh Green (1A)	1.50
29	Randy Grimes	1.50
30	Ron Heller	1.50
31	John Holt	1.00
32	Kevin House	2.00
33	Noah Jackson	2.00
34	Cecil Johnson	1.00
35	Ken Kaplan	1.00
36	Blair Kiel	1.50
37	David Logan	1.50
38	Brison Manor	1.00
39	Michael Morton	1.00
40	James Owens	1.00
41	Beasley Reece	1.50
42	Gene Sanders	1.00
43	Lee Roy Selmon	5.00
44	Lee Roy Selmon (1A)	3.00
45	Danny Spradlin	1.00
46	Kelly Thomas	1.00
47	Norris Thomas	1.00
48	Jack Thompson	1.50
49	Perry Tuttle	1.00
50	Chris Washington	1.00
51	Mike Washington	1.00
52	James Wilder	2.50
53	James Wilder (1A)	1.25
54	Steve Wilson	1.00
55	Mark White	1.00
56	Richard Wood	1.00

1989 Buccaneers
Police

Measuring 2-5/8" x 4-1/8", the 10-card set showcases a color action photo at the top, with the player's name, position and team, along with the Bucs' helmet printed inside a box under the photo. The card backs have the Polk County Sheriff's name at the top, with the card number underneath. Located in the center of the card back are the player's name, number, bio, highlights and stats. A safety tip and IMC Fertilizer are listed at the bottom of the card back.

		MT
Complete Set (10):		20.00
Common Player:		1.50
1	Vinny Testaverde	6.00
2	Mark Carrier (WR)	4.00
3	Randy Grimes	1.50
4	Paul Gruber	3.00

5	Ron Hall	2.00
6	William Howard	1.50
7	Curt Jarvis	1.50
8	Ervin Randle	1.50
9	Ricky Reynolds	1.50
10	Rob Taylor	1.50

1976 Buckmans
Discs

Measuring 3-3/8 inches in diameter, the 20-disc set features a black-and-white headshot of the player on the front, with four stars printed at the top. The player's name is printed on the right side of the photo, with his team name on the left. His position is printed under the photo. A colored border surrounds the disc, except where the stars are at the top. Printed inside the border are the player's bio and "National Football League Players 1976." The unnumbered disc backs have "A collectors and traders item" at the top, with Buckmans and its address and phone number underneath.

		NM
Complete Set (20):		45.00
Common Player:		.50
1	Otis Armstrong	1.00
2	Steve Bartkowski	1.00
3	Terry Bradshaw	10.00
4	Doug Buffone	.50
5	Wally Chambers	.50
6	Chuck Foreman	1.00
7	Roman Gabriel	1.00
8	Mel Gray	1.00
9	Franco Harris	7.00
10	James Harris	.50
11	Jim Hart	.50
12	Gary Huff	.50
13	Billy Kilmer	1.00
14	Terry Metcalf	.50
15	Jim Otis	.50
16	Jim Plunkett	1.50
17	Greg Pruitt	.50
18	Roger Staubach	10.00
19	Jan Stenerud	1.00
20	Roger Wehrli	.50

C

1960 Cardinals
Mayrose Franks

Measuring 2-1/2" x 3-1/2", the 11-card set showcases a black-and-white photo printed over a red background. A box in the upper left includes the Cardinals' logo and card number. The player's name, position and bio are printed under the photo. The card backs describe the Mayrose Franks football contest. The cards are coated in plastic because they were inserted in hot dog and bacon packages. The cards feature rounded corners.

		NM
Complete Set (11):		100.00
Common Player:		8.00
1	Don Gillis	8.00
2	Frank Fuller	8.00
3	George Izo	10.00
4	Woodley Lewis	8.00
5	King Hill	12.00
6	John David Crow	16.00
7	Bill Stacy	8.00
8	Ted Bates	8.00
9	Mike McGee	8.00
10	Bobby Joe Conrad	12.00
11	Ken Panfil	8.00

1961 Cardinals
Jay Publishing

Measuring 5" x 7", the 12-card set spotlights posed black-and-white photos on the front, while the backs were blank and unnumbered. The set was sold in 12-card packs for 25 cents in 1961.

		NM
Complete Set (12):		50.00
Common Player:		5.00
1	Joe Childress	5.00
2	Sam Etcheverry	5.00
3	Ed Henke	5.00
4	Jimmy Hill	5.00
5	Bill Koman	5.00
6	Roland McDole	5.00
7	Mike McGee	5.00
8	Dale Meinert	5.00
9	Jerry Norton	5.00
10	Sonny Randle	5.00
11	Joe Robb	5.00
12	Billy Stacy	5.00

1965 Cardinals Big Red Biographies

Half-gallon milk cartons from St. Louis' Adams Dairy featured these biographies on side panels. When cut from the carton, the panels measure 3-1/16" x 5-9/16". The panels spotlight "Big Red Biographies" in the upper left, with the Cardinals' logo in the upper right. The player's photo is printed on the left panel, with his name, number, position and bio listed on the right. His highlights are printed under the photo. "Enjoy Cardinal Football get your tickets now!" and the team's address are printed at the bottom. The card backs are blank.

		NM
Complete Set (17):		1000.
Common Player:		50.00
1	Monk Bailey	50.00
2	Jim Bakken	100.00
3	Jim Burson	50.00
4	Willis Crenshaw	50.00
5	Bob DeMarco	50.00
6	Pat Fischer	100.00
7	Billy Gambrell	50.00
8	Ken Gray	75.00
9	Irv Goode	50.00
10	Mike Melinkovich	50.00
11	Bob Reynolds	50.00
12	Marion Rushing	50.00
13	Carl Silvestri	50.00
14	Dave Simmons	50.00
15	Jackie Smith	150.00
16	Bill (Thunder) Thornton	50.00
17	Herschel Turner	50.00

1965 Cardinals Team Issue

Measuring 7-3/8" x 9-3/8", the 10-card set is anchored by a black-and-white photo inside a white border on the front. The player's name, position and team are listed in the white border at the bottom. The unnumbered backs are also blank.

		NM
Complete Set (10):		40.00
Common Player:		4.00
1	Don Brumm	4.00
2	Bobby Joe Conrad	5.00
3	Bob DeMarco	4.00
4	Charley Johnson	7.00
5	Ernie McMillan	5.00
6	Dale Meinert	4.00
7	Luke Owens	4.00
8	Sonny Randle	4.00
9	Joe Robb	4.00
10	Jerry Stovall	4.00

1980 Cardinals Police

Measuring 2-5/8" x 4-1/8", the 15-card set showcases the player's name, jersey number, position, bio and team name under the photo. The Cardinals' helmet is printed in the lower left. The card backs feature Cardinal Tips inside a box, with the Cards' helmet at the top of it. The various sponsors are listed, along with their logos, at the bottom of the unnumbered card backs.

		NM
Complete Set (15):		16.00
Common Player:		.75
17	Jim Hart	2.00
22	Roger Wehrli	1.00
24	Wayne Morris	.75
32	Ottis Anderson	2.00
33	Theotis Brown	.75
37	Kevin Green	.75
55	Eric Williams	.75

56	Tim Kearney	.75
59	Calvin Favron	.75
68	Terry Stieve	.75
72	Dan Dierdorf	2.50
73	Mike Dawson	.75
82	Bob Pollard	.75
83	Pat Tilley	1.50
85	Mel Gray	2.00

1988 Cardinals Holsum

The standard sized 12-card set showcases the Holsum logo in the upper left, with "1988 Annual Collectors' Edition" in the upper right. The color headshot anchors the front, with the player's name and team listed in a box at the bottom. The backs have the player's facsimile autograph at the top, along with his jersey number, bio and card number. His stats are listed in the center. The NFLPA, MSA and Holsum logos are printed at the bottom of the card backs.

		MT
Complete Set (12):		50.00
Common Player:		4.00
1	Roy Green	7.00
2	Stump Mitchell	6.00
3	J.T. Smith	5.00
4	E.J. Junior	5.00
5	Cedric Mack	4.00
6	Curtis Greer	4.00
7	Lonnie Young	4.00
8	David Galloway	4.00
9	Luis Sharpe	4.00
10	Leonard Smith	4.00
11	Ron Wolfley	4.00
12	Earl Ferrell	4.00

1989 Cardinals Holsum

The standard-sized 16-card set showcases the Holsum logo in the upper left, with "1989 Annual Collectors' Edition" in the upper right. The player's name and team are printed inside a stripe underneath the photo. The card backs have the player's name, jersey number, card number, position and bio at the top. His stats are listed in the center, while the NFLPA logo is in the lower left.

		MT
Complete Set (16):		6.00
Common Player:		.25
1	Roy Green	1.00
2	J.T. Smith	.50
3	Neil Lomax	1.00
4	Stump Mitchell	.50
5	Vai Sikahema	.25
6	Lonnie Young	.25
7	Robert Awalt	.25
8	Cedric Mack	.25
9	Earl Ferrell	.25
10	Ron Wolfley	.25
11	Bob Clasby	.25
12	Luis Sharpe	.25
13	Steve Alvord	.25
14	David Galloway	.25
15	Freddie Joe Nunn	.25
16	Niko Noga	.25

1989 Cardinals Police

Measuring 2-5/8" x 4-3/16", the 15-card set has a photo bordered in white. The player's name and position are printed under the photo on the left, with his jersey number on the right. The bottom of the card front features the Phoenix Cardinals' logo. The unnumbered card backs feature the Cardinals' logo at the top, with his jersey number, name, position, bio and career highlights listed. The Cardinal Rule is listed inside a box. The KTSP-TV and Louis Rich logos also appear at the bottom. The cards are listed here by uniform number. Two cards were distributed each week. Overall, 100,000 of each card was produced.

		MT
Complete Set (15):		25.00

1990 Cardinals Police

Measuring 2-5/8" x 4-1/4", the 16-card set is bordered in maroon, with the Cardinals' logo in the upper left and NFL shield in upper right. Underneath the photo are the player's name, position and jersey number. The unnumbered card backs feature the Phoenix Cardinals' logo at the top, with the player's name, position, bio highlights underneath. The center of the card back has the Cardinal Rule in a box. KTSP, McGruff the Crime Dog and Louis Rich logos are printed at the bottom.

		MT
Complete Set (16):		10.00
Common Player:		.25
1	Anthony Bell	.25
2	Joe Bugel (CO)	.50
3	Rich Camarillo	.25
4	Roy Green	1.25
5	Ken Harvey	1.00
6	Eric Hill	1.25
7	Tim McDonald	.50
8	Tootie Robbins	.25
9	Timm Rosenbach	.75
10	Luis Sharpe	.50
11	Vai Sikahema	.50
12	J.T. Smith	.75
13	Lance Smith	.25
14	Jim Wahler	.25
15	Ron Wolfley	.25
16	Lonnie Young	.25

1992 Cardinals Police

The standard-sized 16-card set features a photo on the front that is bordered on the left by a stripe that changes from red to yellow. The NFL shield is in the upper left of the photo, with the player's jersey number and position on a scoreboard in the lower left. The Phoenix Cardinals' logo and player name and number are printed in red and white, respectively, at the bottom right of the photo. The unnumbered card backs have the player's name, jersey number and position at the top, with his bio printed under a stripe. The Cards' logo is ghosted in the center. A red box at the bottom of the card includes a safety tip and sponsor logos.

		MT
Complete Set (16):		12.00
Common Player:		.50
1	Joe Bugel (CO)	.75
2	Rich Camarillo	.50
3	Ed Cunningham	.50
4	Greg Davis	.75
5	Ken Harvey	.75
6	Randal Hill	1.50
7	Ernie Jones	.50
8	Mike Jones	.50
9	Tim McDonald	1.00
10	Freddie Joe Nunn	.50
11	Ricky Proehl	1.00
12	Timm Rosenbach	.75
13	Tony Sacca	.75
14	Lance Smith	.50
15	Eric Swann	1.50
16	Aeneas Williams	1.00

1994 Cardinals Police

Collectors believe this set only contains four cards. The

card fronts have a maroon and orange border, with a color photo, player name and number. The card backs are unnumbered and carry the player's name, number and bio.

		MT
Complete Set (4):		12.00
Common Player:		3.00
1	Greg Davis	3.00
2	Anthony Edwards	3.00
3	Terry Hoage	3.00
4	Aeneas Williams	4.00

1989 CBS Television Announcers

Measuring 2-3/4" x 3-7/8", this 10-card set showcases the 1989 CBS NFL announcers. The card fronts spotlight a color action shot from the announcer's pro career. The photo is bordered in orange and placed over a green and white football field. "Going the extra yard" is printed in red at the top. "NFL on CBS" is located in the bottom right. The horizontal card backs feature a black-and-white head shot of the announcer, with his bio and highlights bordered in red. Approximately 500 sets, which were divided into two five-card series, were given to CBS affiliates.

		MT
Complete Set (10):		250.00
Common Player:		10.00
1	Terry Bradshaw	50.00
2	Dick Butkus	45.00
3	Irv Cross	10.00
4	Dan Fouts	25.00
5	Pat Summerall	15.00
6	Gary Fencik	15.00
7	Dan Jiggetts	10.00
8	John Madden	45.00
9	Ken Stabler	35.00
10	Hank Stram	15.00

1961 Chargers Golden Tulip

The 22-card, 2" x 3" set was found in bags of Golden Tulip potato chips. The cards featured top players from the San Diego Chargers in black and white with brief bio information also on the card fronts. The back explains how to upgrade to an 8" x 10" photo and win tickets to a Chargers home game. The set was also sponsored by XETV, an independent television station in San Diego.

		NM
Complete Set (22):		1500.
Common Player:		40.00
1	Ron Botchan	40.00
2	Howard Clark	40.00
3	Fred Cole	40.00
4	Sam DeLuca	40.00
5	Orlando Ferrante	40.00
6	Charlie Flowers	40.00
7	Dick Harris	40.00
8	Emil Karas	40.00
9	Jack Kemp	550.00
10	Dave Kocourek	40.00
11	Bob Laraba	40.00
12	Paul Lowe	60.00
13	Paul Maguire	70.00
14	Charlie McNeil	40.00
15	Ron Mix	100.00
16	Ron Nery	40.00
17	Don Norton	40.00
18	Volney Peters	40.00
19	Don Rogers	40.00
20	Maury Schleicher	40.00
21	Ernie Wright	40.00
22	Bob Zeman	40.00

1962 Chargers Union Oil

The 14-card, 6" x 8" set, sponsored by Union 76, features black and white player sketches by the artist, "Patrick." The card backs include a player bio and the Union 76 logo.

		NM
Complete Set (14):		450.00
Common Player:		8.00
1	Chuck Allen	10.00

2	Lance Alworth	100.00
3	John Hadl	30.00
4	Dick Harris	10.00
5	Bill Hudson	8.00
6	Jack Kemp	225.00
7	Dave Kocourek	8.00
8	Ernie Ladd	25.00
9	Keith Lincoln	18.00
10	Paul Lowe	18.00
11	Charlie McNeil	10.00
12	Ron Mix	25.00
13	Ron Nery	8.00
14	Team Photo	25.00

1966 Chargers White Border

The 50-card, 5-1/2" x 8-1/2" set was issued by the team and features black and white headshots of top players, such as Lance Alworth, with facsimile autographs. With the exception of card No. 16 (George Gross), the card backs are blank.

		NM
Complete Set (50):		225.00
Common Player:		3.00
1	Chuck Allen	5.00
2	James Allison	3.00
3	Lance Alworth	30.00
4	Tom Bass	3.00
5	Joe Beauchamp	3.00
6	Frank Buncom	5.00
7	Richard Degen	3.00
8	Steve DeLong	5.00
9	Les Duncan	3.00
10	John Farris	3.00
11	Gene Foster	3.00
12	Willie Frazier	5.00
13	Gary Garrison	5.00
14	Sid Gillman (CO)	10.00
15	Kenny Graham	3.00
16	George Gross	3.00
17	Sam Gruineisen	3.00
18	Walt Hackett (CO)	3.00
19	John Hadl	15.00
20	Dick Harris	5.00
21	Dan Henning	10.00
22	Bob Horton	3.00
23	Harry Johnston (CO)	3.00
24	Howard Kindig	3.00
25	Keith Lincoln	5.00
26	Paul Lowe	5.00
27	Jacque MacKinnon	3.00
28	Joseph Madro (CO)	3.00
29	Ed Mitchell	3.00
30	Bob Mitinger	3.00
31	Ron Mix	10.00
32	Fred Moore	3.00
33	Don Norton	3.00
34	Terry Owen	3.00
35	Bob Petrich	3.00
36	Dave Plump	3.00
37	Rick Redman	3.00
38	Houston Ridge	3.00
39	Pat Shea	3.00
40	Walt Sweeney	5.00
41	Sammy Taylor	3.00
42	Steve Tensi	3.00
43	Herb Travenio	3.00
44	John Travis	3.00
45	Dick Van Raaphorst	3.00
46	Charlie Waller (CO)	3.00
47	Bud Whitehead	3.00
48	Nat Whitmyer	3.00
49	Ernie Wright	3.00
50	Bob Zeman	3.00

1976 Chargers Dean's Photo

The 10-card, 5" x 8" set was sponsored by Dean's Photo Service and featured top Chargers players such as Dan Fouts and Joe Washington. The card fronts are black and white while the Chargers helmet in the lower left corner is in color. The backs are blank.

		NM
Complete Set (10):		28.00
Common Player:		2.00
1	Pat Currin	2.00
2	Chris Fletcher	2.00
3	Dan Fouts	12.00
4	Gary Garrison	2.00
5	Louie Kelcher	3.00
6	Joe Washington	3.00
7	Russ Washington	2.00
8	Doug Wilkerson	2.00
9	Don Woods	2.00
10	Schedule Card	2.00

1981 Chargers Police

The 24-card, 2-5/8" x 4-1/8" set was sponsored by San Diego

law enforcement, Pepsi and Kiwanis. The card fronts feature an action shot with the player's name and position, along with the Chargers team logo. The backs contain a law enforcement tip. The Fouts and Winslow cards have two versions with different safety tips. The cards are numbered by the player's jersey number.

		MT
Complete Set (24):		50.00
Common Player:		1.00
6	Rolf Benirschke	2.00
14A	Dan Fouts (After a team...)	14.00
14B	Dan Fouts (Once you've...)	7.00
18	Charlie Joiner	4.00
25	John Cappelletti	2.00
28	Willie Buchanon	1.00
29	Mike Williams	1.00
43	Bob Gregor	1.00
44	Pete Shaw	1.00
46	Chuck Muncie	2.00
51	Woodrow Lowe	1.00
57	Linden King	1.00
59	Cliff Thrift	1.00
62	Don Macek	1.00
63	Doug Wilkerson	1.00
66	Billy Shields	1.00
67	Ed White	1.00
68	Leroy Jones	1.00
70	Russ Washington	1.00
74	Louie Kelcher	1.00
79	Gary Johnson	1.00
80A	Kellen Winslow (Go all out...)	14.00
80B	Kellen Winslow (The length of ...)	7.00
NNO	Don Coryell (CO)	2.00

1982 Chargers Police

The 16-card, 2-5/8" x 4-1/8" set is nearly identical in design with the 1981 Chargers Police set. The card fronts feature a Chargers player with his postion and San Diego helmet. The backs contain a law enforcement tip and are sponsored by San Diego law enforcement, Pepsi and Kiwanis.

		MT
Complete Set (16):		45.00
Common Player:		2.00
1	Rolf Benirschke	2.00
2	James Brooks	4.00
3	Wes Chandler	5.00
4	Dan Fouts	10.00
5	Tim Fox	2.00
6	Gary Johnson	2.00
7	Charlie Joiner	8.00
8	Louie Kelcher	2.00
9	Linden King	2.00
10	Bruce Laird	2.00
11	David Lewis	2.00
12	Don Macek	2.00
13	Billy Shields	2.00
14	Eric Sievers	2.00
15	Russ Washington	2.00
16	Kellen Winslow	10.00

1985 Chargers Kodak

The 15-card, 5-1/2" x 8-1/2" set, sponsored by Kodak, features color action shots and San Diego helmet in the lower left corner. The backs contain bio information.

		MT
Complete Set (15):		40.00
Common Player:		2.00
1	Carlos Bradley	2.00
2	Wes Chandler	6.00
3	Chuck Ehin	2.00
4	Mike Green	2.00
5	Pete Holohan	2.00
6	Lionel James	2.00
7	Charlie Joiner	12.00
8	Woodrow Lowe	2.00
9	Dennis McKnight	2.00
10	Miles McPherson	2.00
11	Derrie Nelson	2.00
12	Vince Osby	2.00
13	Billy Ray Smith	2.00
14	Danny Walters	2.00
15	Ed White	2.00

1986 Chargers Kodak

The 36-card, 5-1/2" x 8-1/2" set are similar to the 1985

Kodak Chargers cards, but have blank backs. The bio information is featured on the card fronts below the player's name and between the Chargers helmet and the Kodak logo.

		MT
Complete Set (36):		45.00
Common Player:		1.00
1	Curtis Adams	1.00
2	Gary Anderson (RB)	3.00
3	Jesse Bendross	1.00
4	Gill Byrd	1.00
5	Sam Claphan	1.00
6	Don Coryell (CO)	2.00
7	Jeffery Dale	1.00
8	Wayne Davis	1.00
9	Jerry Doerger	1.00
10	Chris Faulkner	1.00
11	Mark Fellows	1.00
12	Dan Fouts	8.00
13	Mike Guendling	1.00
14	John Hendy	1.00
15	Mark Hermann	1.00
16	Lionel James	1.00
17	Trumaine Johnson	1.00
18	David King	1.00
19	Linden King	1.00
20	Jim Lachey	2.00
21	Don Macek	1.00
22	Buford McGee	1.00
23	Dennis McKnight	1.00
24	Ralf Mojsiejenko	1.00
25	Ron O'Bard	1.00
26	Fred Robinson	1.00
27	Eric Sievers	1.00
28	Tony Simmons	1.00
29	Billy Ray Smith	1.00
30	Lucious Smith	1.00
31	Alex G. Spanos (PRES)	1.00
32	Tim Spencer	1.00
33	Rich Umphrey	1.00
34	Ed White	1.00
35	Lee Williams	1.00
36	Earl Wilson	1.00

1987 Chargers Junior Coke Tickets

The 12-card, 1-7/8" x 4-1/4" set was issued to members of the Coca-Cola Junior Chargers. The cards are in the form of a ticket, which was exchanged by members for actual game tickets. The card fronts included a color action photo, and had imitation ticket information, such as section, row and seat number. The card backs contain a Chargers logo and a description of how to exchange the coupon for a real ticket.

		MT
Complete Set (12):		12.00
Common Player:		1.00
1	Gary Anderson (RB)	1.50
2	Rolf Benirschke	1.00
3	Wes Chandler	1.75
4	Jeffery Dale	1.00
5	Dan Fouts	3.00
6	Pete Holohan	1.00
7	Lionel James	1.00
8	Don Macek	1.00
9	Dennis McKnight	1.00
10	Al Saunders (CO)	1.00
11	Billy Ray Smith	1.00
12	Kellen Winslow	3.00

1987 Chargers Police

The 21-card, 2-5/8" x 4-1/8" set, sponsored by the Chargers, Oscar Meyer and San Diego law enforcement, features top players from the 1987 Chargers squad. Even though the cards are numbered, there was no card No. 13 issued and card Nos. 3 and 17 were pulled during distribution. The card fronts feature an action shot and bio information while the backs have a brief player description with a safety tip.

		MT
Complete Set (22):		20.00
Common Player:		.75
1	Alex G. Spanos (OWN)	.75
2	Gary Anderson (RB)	1.00
3	Rolf Benirschke (SP)	5.00
4	Gill Byrd	1.00
5	Wes Chandler	1.50
6	Sam Claphan	.75
7	Jeffery Dale	.75
8	Pete Holohan	.75
9	Lionel James	.75
10	Jim Lachey	.75
11	Woodrow Lowe	.75
12	Don Macek	.75

14	Dan Fouts	3.50
15	Eric Sievers	.75
16	Billy Ray Smith	.75
17	Danny Walters (SP)	4.00
18	Lee Williams	.75
19	Kellen Winslow	2.50
20	Al Saunders (CO)	.75
21	Dennis McKnight	.75
22	Chip Banks	.75

1987 Chargers Smokey

The 48-card, 5-1/2" x 8-1/2" sets were issued by the California Forestry Department and fronted color action shots. The card backs contain a safety tip cartoon with Smokey The Bear. Coach Don Coryell's card was pulled after the initial distribution after he was replaced. Also, the cards of Donald Brown, Mike Douglas and Fred Robinson were pulled after they were cut.

		MT
Complete Set (48):		100.00
Common Player:		8.00
1	Curtis Adams	1.00
2	Ty Allert	1.00
3	Gary Anderson (RB)	2.50
4	Rolf Benirschke	2.00
5	Thomas Benson	1.00
6	Donald Brown (SP)	8.00
7	Gill Byrd	1.50
8	Wes Chandler	4.00
9	Sam Claphan	1.00
10	Don Coryell (CO, SP)	10.00
11	Jeffery Dale	1.00
12	Wayne Davis	1.00
13	Mike Douglass (SP)	8.00
14	Chuck Ehin	1.00
15	James Fitzpatrick	1.00
16	Tom Flick	1.00
17	Dan Fouts	12.00
18	Dee Hardison	1.00
19	Andy Hawkins	1.00
20	John Hendy	1.00
21	Mark Hermann	1.00
22	Pete Holohan	1.00
23	Lionel James	1.00
24	Trumaine Johnson	1.00
25	Charlie Joiner	8.00
26	Gary Kowalski	1.00
27	Jim Lachey	1.50
28	Jim Leonard	1.00
29	Woodrow Lowe	1.00
30	Don Macek	1.00
31	Buford McGee	1.00
32	Dennis McKnight	1.00
33	Ralf Mojsiejenko	1.00
34	Derrie Nelson	1.00
35	Leslie O'Neal	5.00
36	Gary Plummer	1.00
37	Fred Robinson (SP)	8.00
38	Eric Sievers	1.00
39	Billy Ray Smith	1.50
40	Tim Spencer	1.50
41	Kenny Taylor	1.00
42	Terry Unrein	1.00
43	Jeff Walker	1.00
44	Danny Walters	1.00
45	Lee Williams	1.50
46	Earl Wilson	1.00
47	Kellen Winslow	8.00
48	Kevin Wyatt	1.00

1988 Chargers Police

The 12-card, 2-5/8" x 4" set features white and blue borders with color action shots. The card backs have career highlights and safety tips.

		MT
Complete Set (12):		12.00
Common Player:		.50
1	Gary Anderson (RB)	.75
2	Rod Bernstine	1.00
3	Gill Byrd	.75
4	Vencie Glenn	.75
5	Lionel James	.75
6	Babe Laufenberg	.75
7	Don Macek	.50
8	Mark Malone	1.00
9	Dennis McKnight	.50
10	Anthony Miller	5.00
11	Billy Ray Smith	.75
12	Lee Williams	.75

1988 Chargers Smokey

The 52-card, 5" x 8" set features color action shots on the card fronts and a forestry safety tip, along with a Smokey The Bear cartoon on the back. Two Alex Spanos cards exist, one stating incorrectly that he purchased the Chargers in 1987, and one stating the correct 1984. Also, 18 of the cards were short printed (Nos. 9, 23, 27, 36, 55, 56, 57, 74, 77, 78, 79, 81, 88, 89, 92, 96 and 98) as some of the players were cut, traded or put on injured reserve.

		MT
Complete Set (52):		45.00
Common Player:		.50
2	Ralf Mojsiejenko	.50
9	Mark Hermann (SP)	1.50
10	Vince Abbott	.50
13	Mark Vlasic	.50
14	Dan Fouts	4.00
22	Barry Redden	.50
23	Gill Byrd	.75
25	Danny Walters (SP)	1.50
25	Vencie Glenn	.50
26	Lionel James	.75
27	Daniel Hunter (SP)	1.50
34	Elvis Patterson	.50
36	Mike Davis (SP)	1.50
40	Gary Anderson (RB)	.75
42	Curtis Adams	.50
43	Tim Spencer	.50
44	Martin Bayless	.50
52	Gary Plummer	.50
52	Jeff Jackson	.50
54	Billy Ray Smith	.50
55	Steve Busick (SP)	1.50
56	Chip Banks (SP)	2.00
57	Thomas Benson (SP)	1.50
58	David Brandon	.50
60	Dennis McKnight	.50
61	Ken Dallafior	.50
62	Don Macek	.50
64	Gary Kowalski	.50
69	Les Miller	.50
70	James Fitzpatrick	.50
71	Mike Charles	.50
72	Karl Wilson	.50
74	Jim Lachey (SP)	2.00
75	Joe Phillips	.50
76	Broderick Thompson	.50
77	Sam Claphan (SP)	1.50
78	Chuck Ehin (SP)	1.50
79	Curtis Rouse (SP)	1.50
80	Kellen Winslow	4.00
81	Timmie Ware (SP)	1.50
82	Rod Bernstine	.75
85	Eric Sievers	.50
86	Jamie Holland	.50
88	Pete Holohan (SP)	1.50
89	Wes Chandler (SP)	4.00
92	Dee Hardison (SP)	1.50
94	Randy Kirk	.50
96	Keith Baldwin (SP)	1.50
98	Terry Unrein (SP)	1.50
99	Lee Williams	.50
NNO	Al Saunders (CO)	.50
NNO	Alex G. Spanos (ERR SP Chairman of the Board, Purchased team 1987)	4.00
NNO	Alex G. Spanos (COR Chairman of the Board, Purchased team 1984)	.50

1989 Chargers Junior Ralph's Tickets

The 12-card, 1-7/8" x 3-5/8" set was delivered in a perforated sheet which had all 12 cards. The set was sponsored by Ralph's and XTRA and the backs of the cards had coupons to local attractions. The fronts have a color action shot with the coupon description.

		MT
Complete Set (12):		10.00
Common Player:		.50
1	Gary Anderson (RB)	.75
2	Gill Byrd	.75
3	Quinn Early	1.50
4	Vencie Glenn	.75
5	Jamie Holland	.50
6	Don Macek	.50
7	Dennis McKnight	.50
8	Anthony Miller	5.00
9	Ralf Mojsiejenko	.50
10	Leslie O'Neal	1.75
11	Billy Ray Smith	.50
12	Lee Williams	.50

A player's name in italic type indicates a rookie card.

1989 Chargers Police

The 12-card, 2-5/8" x 4-3/16" set has white borders with color action shots while the backs have bio information, career highlights and safety messages and are sponsored by Louis Rich. The cards were distributed in two, six-card sheets on Oct. 22 and Nov. 5 at Chargers home games.

		MT
Complete Set (12):		10.00
Common Player:		.50
1	Tim Spencer	.50
2	Vencie Glenn	.75
3	Gill Byrd	.75
4	Jim McMahon	1.50
5	David Richards	.50
6	Don Macek	.50
7	Billy Ray Smith	.75
8	Gary Plummer	.75
9	Lee Williams	.50
10	Leslie O'Neal	1.00
11	Anthony Miller	3.00
12	Broderick Thompson	.50

1989 Chargers Smokey

The 48-card, 5" x 8" set has white borders with color action shots while the backs have bio information, career highlights and safety tips.

		MT
Complete Set (48):		45.00
Common Player:		1.00
2	Ralf Mojsiejenko	1.00
6	Steve DeLine	1.00
10	Vince Abbott	1.00
13	Mark Vlasic	1.00
16	Mark Malone	1.00
20	Barry Redden	1.00
22	Gill Byrd	1.00
23	Roy Bennett	1.00
25	Vencie Glenn	1.00
26	Lionel James	1.00
30	Sam Seale	1.00
34	Leonard Coleman	1.00
34	Elvis Patterson	1.00
40	Gary Anderson (RB)	1.50
42	Curtis Adams	1.00
43	Tim Spencer	1.00
44	Martin Bayless	1.00
48	Pat Miller	1.00
51	Gary Plummer	1.00
52	Cedric Figaro	1.00
52	Jeff Jackson	1.00
54	Chuck Faucette	1.00
54	Billy Ray Smith	1.00
57	Keith Browner	1.00
58	David Brandon	1.00
59	Ken Woodard	1.00
60	Dennis McKnight	1.00
65	Ken Dallafior	1.00
65	David Richards	1.00
66	Dan Rosado	1.00
69	Les Miller	1.00
70	James Fitzpatrick	1.00
71	Mike Charles	1.00
72	Karl Wilson	1.00
73	Darrick Brilz	1.00
75	Joe Phillips	1.00
76	Broderick Thompson	1.00
82	Rod Bernstine	1.50
83	Anthony Miller	6.00
86	Jamie Holland	1.00
87	Quinn Early	1.50
88	Arthur Cox	1.00
89	Darren Flutie	2.50
91	Leslie O'Neal	2.50
93	Tyrone Keys	1.00
97	Joe Campbell	1.00
97	George Hinkle	1.00
99	Lee Williams	1.00

1990 Chargers Police

The 12-card, 2-5/8" x 4-1/8" set was sponsored by Louis Rich Meats. The card fronts have blue borders with color action shots while the backs have player descriptions and bio information, along with a safety tip.

		MT
Complete Set (12):		10.00
Common Player:		.75
1	Martin Bayless	.75
2	Marion Butts	1.25
3	Gill Byrd	.75
4	Burt Grossman	.75
5	Ronnie Harman	1.00

6	Anthony Miller	3.00
7	Leslie O'Neal	1.50
8	Joe Phillips	.75
9	Gary Plummer	.75
10	Billy Ray Smith	.75
11	Billy Joe Tolliver	1.00
12	Lee Williams	.75

1990 Chargers Smokey

The 36-card, 5" x 8" set was similar to the 1989 set with a fire safety cartoon and brief bio information on the back.

		MT
Complete Set (36):		30.00
Common Player:		.75
11	Billy Joe Tolliver	1.25
13	Mark Vlasic	.75
15	David Archer	1.50
20	Darrin Nelson	.75
22	Gill Byrd	1.00
24	Lester Lyles	.75
25	Vencie Glenn	1.25
30	Sam Seale	.75
31	Craig McEwen	.75
35	Marion Butts	1.25
43	Tim Spencer	.75
44	Martin Bayless	.75
46	Joe Caravello	.75
51	Gary Plummer	.75
51	Cedric Figaro	.75
53	Courtney Hall	.75
54	Billy Ray Smith	1.00
58	David Brandon	.75
59	Ken Woodard	.75
60	Dennis McKnight	.75
65	David Richards	.75
69	Les Miller	.75
75	Joe Phillips	.75
76	Broderick Thompson	.75
78	Joel Patten	.75
79	Joey Howard	.75
80	Wayne Walker	.75
82	Rod Bernstine	1.00
83	Anthony Miller	5.00
87	Andy Parker	.75
90	Quinn Early	1.75
92	Arthur Cox	.75
92	Leslie O'Neal	1.75
92	Burt Grossman	.75
97	George Hinkle	.75
99	Lee Williams	.75

1991 Chargers Vons

The twelve standard-sized cards were distributed by Vons in three-card sheets (6-5/8" x 3-1/2") with each sheet containing one card, one Junior Chargers Official Membership Card and a Sea World of California discount coupon. The card fronts have a color action shot with a white border while the backs have bio and stat information.

		MT
Complete Set (12):		10.00
Common Player:		.75
1	Rod Berstine	.75
2	Gill Byrd	1.00
3	Burt Grossman	.75
4	Ronnie Harman	1.00
5	Anthony Miller	2.00
6	Leslie O'Neal	1.50
7	Gary Plummer	.75
8	Junior Seau	2.50
9	Billy Ray Smith	.75
10	Broderick Thompson	.75
11	Billy Joe Tolliver	1.00
12	Lee Williams	.75

1992 Chargers Louis Rich

The 52-card, 5" x 8" set, distributed by Louis Rich, had glossy color fronts with the backs containing the Louis Rich logo.

		MT
Complete Set (52):		30.00
Common Player:		.50
1	Sam Anno	.50
2	Johnnie Barnes	.50
3	Rod Bernstine	.75
4	Eric Bieniemy	.75
5	Anthony Blaylock	.50
6	Brian Brennan	.50
7	Marion Butts	1.00
8	Gill Byrd	.75
9	John Carney	1.00
10	Darren Carrington	.50
11	Robert Claborne	.50
12	Floyd Fields	.50
13	Donald Frank	.50
14	Bob Gagliano	.50
15	Leo Goeas	.50
16	Burt Grossman	.50
17	Courtney Hall	.50
18	Delton Hall	.50
19	Ronnie Harman	1.00
20	Steve Hendrickson	.50
21	Stan Humphries	3.00
22	Shawn Jefferson	1.00
23	John Kidd	.50
24	Shawn Lee	.50
26	Nate Lewis	.50
26	Eugene Marve	.50
27	Deems May	.50
28	Anthony Miller	2.00
29	Chris Mims	1.00
30	Eric Moten	.50
31	Kevin Murphy	.50
32	Pat O'Hara	.50
33	Leslie O'Neal	1.50
34	Gary Plummer	.50
35	Marquez Pope	.50
36	Alfred Pupunu	.50
37	Stanley Richard	.75
38	David Richards	.50
39	Henry Rolling	.50
40	Bobby Ross (CO)	1.00
41	Junior Seau	2.50
42	Harry Swayne	.75
43	Broderick Thompson	.50
44	George Thornton	.50
45	Peter Tuipulotu	.50
46	Sean Vanhorse	.50
47	Derrick Walker	.50
48	Reggie E. White	.50
49	Curtis Whitley	.50
50	Blaise Winter	.50
51	Duane Young	.50
52	Mike Zandofsky	.50

1993 Chargers Police

The 32-card, regular-sized set was sponsored by the highway patrol and contained the rookie card of running back Natrone Means. The fronts feature team color borders and the backs have bio information with a safe driving tip appearing in the lower right corner.

		MT
Complete Set (32):		12.00
Common Player:		.25
1	Darren Gordon	.50
2	Natrone Means	3.00
3	John Friesz	.75
4	Stan Humphries	1.75
5	Anthony Miller	1.50
6	Marion Butts	.75
7	Ronnie Harman	.75
8	Stanley Richard	.50
9	Leslie O'Neal	1.00
10	Harry Swayne	.25
11	Junior Seau	1.75
12	Courtney Hall	.25
13	Gary Plummer	.25
14	Eric Moten	.25
15	Chris Mims	.75
16	Burt Grossman	.25
17	Blaise Winter	.25
18	Donald Frank	.25
19	Sean Vanhorse	.25
20	John Carney	.25
21	Floyd Fields	.50
22	Gill Byrd	.50
23	Shawn Jefferson	.50
24	Shawn Lee	.25
25	Alfred Pupunu	.25
26	Marquez Pope	.25
27	Darren Carrington	.25
28	Duane Young	.25
29	Derrick Walker	.25
30	Deems May	.25
31	Nate Lewis	.25
32	Bobby Ross CO, Clarence Tuck (CHP Chief)	.75

1994 Chargers Castrol Promos

The six-card, 5" x 8" set was sponsored by Pepboys

and Castrol. The card fronts feature a color photo with the backs containing bio information and sponsor logos over the NFL emblem.

		MT
Complete Set (6):		6.00
Common Player:		.50
1	Courtney Hall	.50
2	Ronnie Harmon	.50
3	Stan Humphries	1.50
4	Natrone Means	2.50
5	Leslie O'Neal	1.00
6	Junior Seau	1.50

1994 Chargers Castrol

The 52-card, 5" x 8" set, as with the Promos set, was sponsored by Pepboys and Castrol with the card fronts containing a color shot. The card backs are similar to the Promos set, with bio information and sponsor logos over the NFL emblem.

		MT
Complete Set (52):		30.00
Common Player:		.50
1	Johnnie Barnes	.50
2	Eric Bieniemy	.75
3	David Binn	.50
4	Stan Brock	.50
5	Jeff Brohm	.50
6	Lewis Bush	.50
7	John Carney	1.00
8	Darren Carrington	.50
9	Eric Castle	.50
10	Willie Clark	.50
11	Joe Cocozzo	.50
12	Andre Coleman	.75
13	Rodney Culver	.75
14	Isaac Davis	.50
15	Reuben Davis	.50
16	Greg Engel	.50
17	Dennis Gilbert	.50
18	Gale Gilbert	.50
19	Darrien Gordon	1.00
20	David Griggs	.50
21	Courtney Hall	.50
22	Ronnie Harmon	1.00
23	Dwayne Harper	.50
24	Rodney Harrison	.50
25	Steve Hendrickson	.50
26	Stan Humphries	3.00
27	Shawn Jefferson	1.50
28	Raylee Johnson	.50
29	Eric Jonassen	.50
30	Aaron Laing	.50
31	Shawn Lee	.50
32	Deems May	.50
33	Natrone Means	3.50
34	Joe Milinichik	.50
35	Doug Miller	.50
36	Chris Mims	1.00
37	Shannon Mitchell	.50
38	Leslie O'Neal	1.50
39	Vaughn Parker	.50
40	John Parrella	.50
41	Alfred Pupunu	.75
42	Stanley Richard	.75
43	Junior Seau	3.50
44	Mark Seay	1.75
45	Harry Swayne	.50
46	Cornell Thomas	.50
47	Sean Vanhorse	.50
48	Bryan Wagner	.50
49	Reggie E. White	.50
50	Curtis Whitley	.50
51	Duane Young	.50
52	Lonnie Young	.50

1994 Chargers Pro Mags/Pro Tags

The 12-card, 2-1/8" x 3-3/8" set (with rounded corners) was issued in 750 boxes that contained six magnets and six "tag"

cards. The magnet-card fronts feature the player's name and Super Bowl XXIX logo in gold foil, as do the tag cards which also have a closeup photo and a player profile on the backs.

		MT
Complete Set (12):		20.00
Common Player:		1.50
1	Stan Humphries	3.00
2	Tony Martin	3.00
3	Natrone Means	4.00
4	Leslie O'Neal	2.00
5	Junior Seau	3.00
6	Mark Seay	1.50
7	Stan Humphries	3.00
8	Tony Martin	3.00
9	Natrone Means	4.00
10	Leslie O'Neal	2.00
11	Junior Seau	3.00
12	Mark Seay	1.50

1964-69 Chiefs Fairmont Dairy

The 19-card, 3-3/8" x 2-3/8" set was available on milk cartons by Fairmont Dairy between the years 1964-69. Most cards are printed in red ink, with some cards printed in black (3-7/16" x 1-9/16"). Although there are 19 cards listed below, there could have been more than that produced in the 1960s. The card fronts feature a player closeup with brief bio information, as well as a Chiefs schedule.

		NM
Complete Set (19):		1800.
Common Player:		75.00
1	Fred Arbanas (Red printing)	75.00
2	Bobby Bell (Red printing)	175.00
3	Buck Buchanan (Black print)	160.00
4	Chris Burford (Red printing)	75.00
5	Len Dawson (Red printing)	260.00
6	Dave Grayson (Red printing)	75.00
7	Abner Haynes (Red printing)	100.00
8	Sherrill Headrick (Red printing)	100.00
9	Bobby Hunt (Red printing)	75.00
10	Frank Jackson (Red printing)	75.00
11	Curtis McClinton (Red printing)	75.00
12	Bobby Ply (Red printing)	75.00
13	Al Reynolds (Red printing)	75.00
14	Johnny Robinson (Red printing)	125.00
15	Noland Smith (Red printing)	75.00
16	Smokey Stover (Red printing)	75.00
17	Otis Taylor (Red printing)	150.00
18	Jim Tyrer (Red printing)	100.00
19	Jerrel Wilson (Red printing)	75.00

1969 Chiefs Kroger

The eight-card, 8" x 9-3/4" set was sponsored by Kroger and features card fronts with color paintings by artist John Wheeldon. The backs have biographical and statistical information and a brief note about the artist.

		NM
Complete Set (8):		75.00
Common Player:		5.00
1	Buck Buchanan	10.00
2	Len Dawson	25.00
3	Mike Garrett	10.00
4	Willie Lanier	15.00
5	Jerry Mays	5.00
6	Johnny Robinson	10.00
7	Jan Stenerud	15.00
8	Jim Tyrer	5.00

1971 Chiefs Team Issue

The 10-card, 7" x 10" set features Chiefs players in black and white headshots with white borders. The backs contain bio

information and career highlights and limited statistics.

		NM
Complete Set (10):		45.00
Common Player:		5.00
1	Bobby Bell	10.00
2	Wendell Hayes	5.00
3	Ed Lothamer	5.00
4	Jim Lynch	5.00
5	Jack Rudnay	5.00
6	Sid Smith	5.00
7	Bob Stein	5.00
8	Jan Stenerud	12.00
9	Otis Taylor	10.00
10	Jim Tyrer	5.00

1973-74 Chiefs Team Issue

The 18-card, 5" x 7" set features black and white photos on the card fronts with white borders. The card backs are blank.

		NM
Complete Set (18):		50.00
Common Player:		3.00
1	Robert Briggs	3.00
2	Larry Brunson	3.00
3	Gary Butler	3.00
4	Dean Carlson	3.00
5	Tom Condon	3.00
6	George Daney	3.00
7	Andy Hamilton	3.00
8	Dave Hill	3.00
9	Jim Kearney	3.00
10	Mike Livingston	3.00
11	Jim Marsalis	3.00
12	Barry Pearson	3.00
13	Francis Peay	3.00
14	Kerry Reardon	3.00
15	Mike Sensibaugh	3.00
16	Bill Thomas	3.00
17	Marvin Upshaw	3.00
18	Clyde Werner	3.00

1979 Chiefs Police

The 10-card, 2-5/8" x 4-1/8" set was issued by Hardee's Restaurants, the Chiefs and the Kansas City Police Department. The card fronts feature an action shot with the backs offering a safety tip.

		NM
Complete Set (10):		10.00
Common Player:		1.00
1	Bob Grupp	1.00
4	Steve Fuller	1.00
22	Ted McKnight	1.00
24	Gary Green	1.00
28	Gary Barbaro	1.50
32	Tony Reed	1.00
58	Jack Rudnay	1.00
67	Art Still	1.50
73	Bob Simmons	1.00
NNO	Marv Levy (CO)	3.00

1980 Chiefs Police

The 10-card, 2-5/8" x 4-1/8" set, sponsored by Frito-Lay, Kiwanis and area law enforcement, features action fronts with "Chiefs Tips" on the backs. The Stenerud card was limited in distribution.

		NM
Complete Set (10):		12.00
Common Player:		1.00
1	Bob Grupp	1.00
3	Jan Stenerud (SP)	3.00
32	Tony Reed	1.00
53	Whitney Paul	1.00
59	Gary Spani	1.00
67	Art Still	1.75
86	J.T. Smith	1.00
99	Mike Bell	1.00
NNO	Defensive Team	1.50
NNO	Offensive Team	1.50

1981 Chiefs Police

The 10-card, 2-5/8" x 4-1/8" set, sponsored by Frito-Lay, Kiwanis and local law enforcement, features action shots on the card fronts and "Chiefs Tips" on the backs.

		MT
Complete Set (10):		6.00
Common Player:		.50
1	Warpaint and Carla (Mascots)	.50
2	Art Still	.75
3	Steve Fuller, Jack Rudnay	.75

4	Gary Green	.50
5	Tom Condon, Marv Levy (CO)	1.00
6	J.T. Smith	.75
7	Gary Spani, Whitney Paul	.50
8	Nick Lowery, Steve Fuller	.75
9	Gary Barbaro	.50
10	Henry Marshall	.50

1982 Chiefs Police

The 10-card, 2-5/8" x 4-1/8" set, sponsored by Frito-Lay, Kiwanis and local law enforcement, features action fronts while the backs contain cartoons in addition to "Chiefs Tips." Some of the card fronts feature two players (card Nos. 1 and 2).

		MT
Complete Set (10):		6.00
Common Player:		.50
1	Bill Kenney, Jack Rudnay	.75
2	Steve Fuller, Nick Lowery	.75
3	Matt Herkenhoff	.50
4	Art Still	.75
5	Gary Spani	.50
6	James Hadnot	.50
7	Mike Bell	.50
8	Carol Canfield (Chiefette)	.50
9	Gary Green	.50
10	Joe Delaney	.75

1983 Chiefs Police

The 10-card, 2-5/8" x 4-1/8" set, sponsored by Frito-Lay, KCTV-5, Kiwanis and local law enforcement, features action fronts with "Crime Tip" cartoons on the backs.

		MT
Complete Set (10):		6.00
Common Player:		.50
1	John Mackovic (CO)	.75
2	Tom Condon	.50
3	Gary Spani	.50
4	Carlos Carson	.75
5	Brad Budde	.50
6	Lloyd Burruss	.50
7	Gary Green	.50
8	Mike Bell	.50
9	Nick Lowery	.75
10	Sandi Byrd (Chiefette)	.50

1984 Chiefs Police

The 10-card, 2-5/8" x 4-1/8" set, sponsored by Frito-Lay and KCTV, features a "Chiefs Tip" and "Crime Tip" on the card backs.

		MT
Complete Set (10):		6.00
Common Player:		.50
1	John Mackovic (CO)	.50
2	Deron Cherry	.75
3	Bill Kenney	.50
4	Henry Marshall	.50
5	Nick Lowery	.50
6	Theotis Brown	.50
7	Stephone Paige	1.00
8	Gary Spani, Art Still	.75
9	Albert Lewis	.75
10	Carlos Carson	.75

1984 Chiefs QuikTrip

The 16-card, 5" x 7" set was sponsored by QuickTrip and features black and white fronts with blank backs.

		MT
Complete Set (16):		48.00
Common Player:		2.00
1	Mike Bell	2.00
2	Todd Blackledge	3.00
3	Brad Budde	2.00
4	Lloyd Burruss	2.00
5	Carlos Carson	2.00
6	Gary Green	2.00
7	Anthony Hancock	2.00
8	Eric Harris	2.00
9	Lamar Hunt (OWN)	2.00
10	Bill Kenney	3.00
11	Ken Kremer	2.00
12	Nick Lowery	4.50
13	John Mackovic (CO)	3.00
14	J.T. Smith	3.00
15	Gary Spani	2.00
16	Art Still	3.00

1985 Chiefs Police

The 10-card, 2-5/8" x 4-1/8" set, sponsored by Frito-Lay, KCTV and local law enforcement, features a "Chiefs Tip" and "Crime Tip" on the card backs.

		MT
Complete Set (10):		6.00
Common Player:		.50
1	John Mackovic (CO)	.75
2	Herman Heard	.50
3	Bill Kenney	.75
4	Deron Cherry, Lloyd Burruss	.75
5	Jim Arnold	.50
6	Kevin Ross	.50
7	David Lutz	.50
8	Chiefettes Cheerleaders	.75
9	Bill Maas	.75
10	Art Still	1.00

1986 Chiefs Police

The 10-card, 2-5/8" x 4-1/8" set was sponsored by Frito-Lay, KCTV and local law enforcement and features "Chiefs Tip" and "Crime Tip" on the backs.

		MT
Complete Set (10):		6.00
Common Player:		.50
1	John Mackovic	.50
2	Willie Lanier (Hall of Fame)	1.50
3	Stephone Paige	1.00
4	Brad Budde	.50
5	Nick Lowery	.75
6	Scott Radecic	.50
7	Mike Pruitt	.50
8	Albert Lewis	.75
9	Todd Blackledge	.75
10	Deron Cherry	1.25

1987 Chiefs Police

The 10-card, 2-5/8" x 4-1/8" set, sponsored by Frito-Lay, US Sprint, KCTV and local law enforcement, features a "Chiefs Tip" and "Crime Tip" on the backs.

		MT
Complete Set (10):		5.00
Common Player:		.50
1	Frank Gansz (CO)	.50
2	Tim Cofield	.50
3	Deron Cherry, Albert Lewis	.75
4	Chiefs Cheerleaders	.50
5	Jeff Smith	.50
6	Rick Donnalley	.50
7	Lloyd Burruss, Kevin Ross	.50
8	Dino Hackett	.50
9	Bill Maas	.50
10	Carlos Carson	.75

1988 Chiefs Police

The 10-card, 2-5/8" x 4-1/8" set was sponsored by Frito-Lay, KCTV, US Sprint and local law enforcement and has "Chiefs Tip" and "Crime Tip" on the backs.

		MT
Complete Set (10):		6.00
Common Player:		.50
1	Frank Gansz (CO)	.50
2	Bill Kenney	.75
3	Carlos Carson	.75
4	Paul Palmer	.50
5	Christian Okoye	1.00
6	Mark Adickes	.50
7	Bill Maas	.50
8	Albert Lewis	.75
9	Deron Cherry	.75

10	Stephone Paige	.75

1989 Chiefs Police

The 10-card, 2-5/8" x 4-1/8" set, sponsored by Western Auto, KCTV and local law enforcement, features a "Chiefs Tip" and "Crime Tip" on the card backs.

		MT
Complete Set (10):		5.00
Common Player:		.50
1	Marty Schottenheimer (CO)	1.00
2	Irv Eatman	.50
3	Kevin Ross	.50
4	Bill Maas	.50
5	Chiefs Cheerleaders	.50
6	Carlos Carson	.75
7	Steve DeBerg	1.00
8	Jonathan Hayes	.50
9	Deron Cherry	.75
10	Dino Hackett	.50

1997 Chiefs Pocket Schedules

This 22-card set featured a Chiefs player on one side with the Kansas City Chiefs 1997 schedule on the other side. Pocket schedules were distributed in the Kansas City area early in the 1997 season.

		MT
Complete Set (22):		7.00
Common Player:		.25
	Marcus Allen	2.00
	Kimble Anders	.25
	Vaughn Booker	.25
	John Browning	.25
	Dale Carter	.50
	Anthony Davis	.25
	Troy Dumas	.25
	Donnie Edwards	.25
	Elvis Grbac	1.00
	Tim Grunhard	.25
	James Hasty	.25
	Greg Hill	.75
	Chris Penn	.25
	Will Shields	.25
	Tracy Simien	.25
	Pete Styoyanovich	.25
	Dave Szott	.25
	Derrick Thomas	1.00
	Reggie Tongue	.25
	Tamarick Vanover	.50
	K.C. Wolf	.25
	Jerome Woods	.25

1972 Chiquita NFL Slides

The 13-slide, 3-9/16" x 1-3/4" set features two players on each slide. The slides have a slide image in each of the four corners with a player summary in the middle. The top two images are of the same player, while the bottom two are of the second player. A yellow viewer was also issued.

		NM
Complete Set (13):		325.00
Common Player:		20.00
1	Joe Greene, Bob Lilly (2)	50.00
3	Bill Bergey, Gary Collins (4)	30.00
5	Walt Sweeney, Bubba Smith (6)	30.00
7	Larry Wilson, Fred Carr (8)	20.00
9	Mac Percival, John Brodie (10)	30.00
11	Lem Barney, Ron Yary (12)	30.00
13	Curt Knight, Alvin Haymond (14)	20.00
15	Floyd Little, Gerry Philbin (16)	30.00
17	Jim Mitchell, Paul Costa (18)	20.00
19	Jake Kupp, Ben Hawkins (20)	20.00
21	Johnny Robinson, George Webster (22)	20.00
23	Mercury Morris, Willie Brown (24)	40.00
25	Ron Johnson, Jon Morris (26)	20.00
NNO	Yellow Viewer	30.00

1970 Clark Volpe

The 66-card, 7-1/2" x 9-15/16" set includes cards for eight of the teams in the league in 1970. The Chicago Bears (1-8), Cincinnati Bengals (9-14), Cleveland Browns (15-21), Detroit Lions (22-30), Green Bay Packers (31-39), Kansas City Chiefs (40-48), Minnesota Vikings (49-57) and St. Louis Cardinals (58-66). Cards with the mail tabs measure 7-1/2" x 14" and the backs have mail-in offers for other merchandise while the fronts feature player drawings by artist Nicholas Volpe.

		NM
Complete Set (66):		325.00
Common Player:		3.00
1	Ron Bull	3.00
2	Dick Butkus	18.00
3	Lee Roy Caffey	3.00
4	Bobby Douglass	6.00
5	Dick Gordon	3.00
6	Bennie McRae	3.00
7	Ed O'Bradovich	3.00
8	George Seals	3.00
9	Bill Bergey	6.00
10	Jess Phillips	3.00
11	Mike Reid	6.00
12	Paul Robinson	3.00
13	Bob Trumpy	8.00
14	Sam Wyche	12.00
15	Erich Barnes	3.00
16	Gary Collins	6.00
17	Gene Hickerson	3.00
18	Jim Houston	3.00
19	Leroy Kelly	12.00
20	Ernie Kellerman	3.00
21	Bill Nelsen	6.00
22	Lem Barney	10.00
23	Mel Farr	6.00
24	Larry Hand	3.00
25	Alex Karras	12.00
26	Mike Lucci	6.00
27	Bill Munson	6.00
28	Charlie Sanders	6.00
29	Tommy Vaughn	3.00
30	Wayne Walker	6.00
31	Lionel Aldridge	3.00
32	Donny Anderson	6.00
33	Ken Bowman	3.00
34	Carroll Dale	6.00
35	Jim Grabowski	6.00
36	Ray Nitschke	15.00
37	Dave Robinson	6.00
38	Travis Williams	6.00
39	Willie Wood	10.00
40	Fred Arbanas	3.00
41	Bobby Bell	10.00
42	Aaron Brown	3.00
43	Buck Buchanan	10.00
44	Len Dawson	16.00
45	Jim Marsalis	3.00
46	Jerry Mays	3.00
47	Johnny Robinson	6.00
48	Jim Tyrer	6.00
49	Bill Brown	6.00
50	Fred Cox	6.00
51	Gary Cuozzo	6.00
52	Carl Eller	10.00
53	Jim Marshall	10.00
54	Dave Osborn	6.00
55	Alan Page	12.00
56	Mick Tingelhoff	6.00
57	Gene Washington	6.00
58	Pete Beathard	6.00
59	John Gilliam	6.00
60	Jim Hart	8.00
61	Johnny Roland	6.00
62	Jackie Smith	10.00
63	Larry Stallings	3.00
64	Roger Wehrli	6.00
65	Dave Williams	3.00
66	Larry Wilson	10.00

1991 Classic Promos

Raghib "Rocket" Ismail WR

These promotional cards preview Classic's design for its debut set in 1991. The card back only has trademark infor-

mation, plus the words "For Promotional Purposes Only! Not For Resale." The five cards were also featured together on a 7-1/2" x 7-1/8" promo sheet which was made available to collectors who attended the 12th National Sports Collectors Convention in Anaheim, Calif., in July 1991. Each sheet is serially-numbered (1 of 10,000, etc.) and is labeled on the back as being a promotional sheet.

		MT
Complete Set (7):		15.00
Common Player (1-5):		1.50
1	Antone Davis	1.50
2A	Raghib Rocket Ismail	5.00
2B	Raghib Rocket Ismail	5.00
3A	Todd Lyght	2.00
3B	Todd Lyght	2.00
4	Russell Maryland	2.00
5	Eric Turner	2.00

1991 Classic

Mike Pritchard

Classic's first venture into the football field resulted in this 50-card boxed set released in June. Classic reportedly paid several players for exclusive rights to appear in the set, including Raghib Ismail. No team names or college names are listed on the cards, which have a grey marble-like border on the front, plus the Classic logos. Each back has biographical information, plus a player profile.

		MT
Complete Set (50):		6.00
Common Player:		.05
1	Rocket Ismail	.50
2	Russell Maryland	.30
3	Eric Turner	.30
4	Bruce Pickens	.10
5	Mike Croal	.10
6	Todd Lyght	.10
7	Eric Swann	.30
8	Antone Davis	.10
9	Stanley Richard	.10
10	Pat Harlow	.10
11	Alvin Harper	.50
12	Mike Pritchard	.30
13	Leonard Russell	.10
14	Dan McGwire	.10
15	Bobby Wilson	.10
16	Alfred Williams	.10
17	Vinnie Clark	.10
18	Kelvin Pritchett	.10
19	Harvey Williams	.50
20	Stan Thomas	.10
21	Randal Hill	.25
22	Todd Marinovich	.10
23	Henry Jones	.05
24	Jarrod Bunch	.05
25	Mike Dumas	.05
26	Ed King	.05
27	Reggie Jackson	.05
28	Roman Phifer	.10
29	Mike Jones	.10
30	Brett Favre	2.00
31	Browning Nagle	.10
32	Esera Tualolo	.10
33	George Thornton	.10
34	Dixon Edwards	.10
35	Darryl Lewis	.10
36	Eric Bieniemy	.20
37	Shane Curry	.10
38	Jerome Henderson	.10
39	Wesley Carroll	.10
40	Nick Bell	.10
41	John Flannery	.05
42	Ricky Watters	1.00
43	Jeff Graham	.50
44	Eric Moten	.05
45	Jesse Campbell	.05
46	Chris Zorich	.20
47	Doug Thomas	.05
48	Phil Hansen	.10
49	Kanavis McGhee	.05
50	Reggie Barrett	.10

1992 Classic Promos

The six-card, standard-size set was issued by Classic to preview the upcoming 1992 NFL Draft set. The card fronts contain black borders while the backs have collegiate summaries. The photos on the card fronts of the six promos differ from their card counterparts in the 100-card set.

		MT
Complete Set (6):		8.00
Common Player:		.50
1	Desmond Howard	2.00
2	David Klingler	.50
3	Quentin Coryatt	.50
4	Carl Pickens	4.00
5	Derek Brown	.50
6	Casey Weldon	.50

1992 Classic

Carl Pickens

This set features 100 of the top collegiate players expected to be selected in the NFL draft. The card front has a color glossy photo surrounded by a black border. The player's name and position are at the bottom, along with a set logo. The card back has a summary of the player's collegiate successes and a color mug shot. Statistics, biographical information and a card number are also given. The background is a blurred image of a running back hitting the hole. These cards were sold in foil packs. Cards using the same design and card numbers, but different photos, were also sold in blister packs. There were six promo cards made, previewing the 1992 design but using different photos from the regular cards. Nuances in the card backs are what distinguishes these cards as promos - they are labeled as "For Promotional Purposes Only" and have an ad in place of a career summary.

		MT
Complete Set (100):		8.00
Common Player:		.05
1	Desmond Howard	.30
2	David Klingler	.20
3	Quentin Coryatt	.30
4	Bill Johnson	.05
5	Eugene Chung	.05
6	Derek Brown	.10
7	Carl Pickens	1.50
8	Chris Mims	.10
9	Charles Davenport	.05
10	Ray Roberts	.05
11	Chuck Smith	.05
12	Joe Bowden	.05
13	Mirko Jurkovic	.05
14	Tony Smith	.05
15	Ken Swilling	.05
16	Greg Skrepenak	.05
17	Phillippi Sparks	.05
18	Alonzo Spellman	.20
19	Bernard Dafney	.05
20	Edgar Bennett	1.00
21	Shane Dronett	.05
22	Jeremy Lincoln	.15
23	Dion Lambert	.05
24	Siran Stacy	.05
25	Tony Sacca	.10
26	Sean Lumpkin	.05
27	Tommy Vardell	.05
28	Keith Hamilton	.05
29	Ashley Ambrose	.05
30	Sean Gilbert	.75
31	Casey Weldon	.20
32	Marc Boutte	.05
33	Santana Dotson	.05
34	Ronnie West	.05
35	Michael Bankston	.05
36	Mike Pawlawski	.05
37	Dale Carter	.10
38	Carlos Snow	.05
39	Corey Barlow	.05
40	Mark D'Onofrio	.05
41	Matt Blundin	.05
42	George Rooks	.05
43	Patrick Rowe	.10
44	Dwight Hollier	.05
45	Joel Steed	.05
46	Erick Anderson	.05
47	Rodney Culver	.10
48	Chris Hakel	.05
49	Luke Fisher	.05
50	Kevin Smith	.05
51	Robert Brooks	1.00
52	Bucky Richardson	.05
53	Steve Isreal	.05
54	Marco Coleman	.40
55	Johnny Mitchell	.20
56	Scottie Graham	.30
57	Keith Goganious	.05
58	Tommy Maddox	.20
59	Terrell Buckley	.20
60	Dana Hall	.05
61	Ty Detmer	.25
62	Darryl Williams	.10
63	Jason Hanson	.30
64	Leon Searcy	.10
65	Gene McGuire	.05
66	Will Furrer	.10
67	Darren Woodson	.10
68	Tracy Scoggins	.10
69	Corey Widmer	.05
70	Robert Harris	.05
71	Larry Tharpe	.05
72	Lance Olberding	.05
73	Stacey Dillard	.05
74	Anthony Hamlet	.05
75	Tommy Jeter	.05
76	Mike Evans	.05
77	Shane Collins	.05
78	Mark Thomas	.05
79	Chester McGlockton	.10
80	Robert Porcher	.10
81	Marquez Pope	.10
82	Rico Smith	.05
83	Tyrone Williams	.05
84	Rod Smith	.05
85	Tyrone Legette	.05
86	Wayne Hawkins	.05
87	Derrick Moore	.25
88	Tim Lester	.05
89	Calvin Holmes	.05
90	Reggie Dwight	.05
91	Eddie Robinson	.05
92	Robert Jones	.05
93	Ricardo McDonald	.05
94	Howard Dinkins	.05
95	Todd Collins	.10
96	Eddie Blake	.05
97	Classic Quarterbacks	.05
98	Back to Back	.10
99	Checklist	.05
100	Checklist	.05

1992 Classic Draft Blister

These 60 cards feature the top prospects entering the 1992 NFL draft. Each card front has a black border surrounding a glossy color action photo. The player's name and position are at the bottom of the card, along with the Classic logo. The back has a blurred action photo for a background, and gives collegiate statistics and a summary of the player's accomplishments at that level. Bio information, a mug shot, and a card number are also on the back. The cards have the same numbers as those in Classic's regular 100-card main set, but the photos on the front are different. The backgrounds on the backs of these cards also have a richer color tone, too; the regular cards' backgrounds are ghosted. These cards were sold in blister packs.

		MT
Complete Set (60):		7.00
Common Player:		.05
1	Desmond Howard	.75
2	David Klingler	.75
3	Quentin Coryatt	.75
4	Bill Johnson	.07
5	Eugene Chung	.10
6	Derek Brown	.50
7	Carl Pickens	.75
8	Chris Mims	.30
9	Charles Davenport	.12
10	Ray Roberts	.10
11	Chuck Smith	.10
12	Joe Bowden	.07
13	Mirko Jurkovic	.05
14	Tony Smith	.25
15	Ken Swilling	.05
16	Greg Skrepenak	.10
17	Phillippi Sparks	.07
18	Alonzo Spellman	.25
19	Bernard Dafney	.07
20	Edgar Bennett	.75
21	Shane Dronett	.15
22	Jeremy Lincoln	.12
23	Dion Lambert	.07
24	Siran Stacy	.07
25	Tony Sacca	.12
26	Sean Lumpkin	.07
27	Tommy Vardell	.50
28	Keith Hamilton	.25
29	Ashley Ambrose	.12
30	John Rays	.07
31	Casey Weldon	.30
32	Marc Boutte	.12
33	Santana Dotson	.25
34	Ronnie West	.05
35	Michael Bankston	.10
36	Mike Pawlawski	.10
37	Dale Carter	.25
38	Carlos Snow	.07
39	Corey Barlow	.07
40	Mark D'Onofrio	.07
41	Matt Blundin	.20
42	George Rooks	.05
43	Patrick Rowe	.07
44	Dwight Hollier	.12
45	Joel Steed	.07
46	Erick Anderson	.10
47	Rodney Culver	.15
48	Chris Hakel	.07
49	Luke Fisher	.05
50	Kevin Smith	.25
51	Robert Brooks	.12
52	Bucky Richardson	.05
53	Steve Israel	.05
54	Tyrone Ashley	.05
55	Johnny Mitchell	.75
56	Scottie Graham	.50
57	Keith Goganious	.07
58	Tommy Maddox	.50
59	Terrell Buckley	.30
60	Dana Hall	.12

1992 Classic LPs

Matt Blundin QB

These gold-foiled stamps were randomly included inside 1992 Classic Draft Picks packs. Approximately 40,000 of each card was produced. Each is numbered on the back using LP 1/10, etc.. The players in the set were projected as top picks in the 1992 NFL draft.

		MT
Complete Set (10):		10.00
Common Player:		.75
1	Desmond Howard	2.00
2	David Klingler	1.25
3	Siran Stacy	.75
4	Casey Weldon	1.25
5	Sean Gilbert	3.00
6	Matt Blundin	1.25
7	Tommy Maddox	1.25
8	Derek Brown	.75
9	Tony Smith	.75
10	Tony Sacca	.75

1992 Classic NFL Game

These standard-size cards were included as part of Classic's 1992 NFL football game. The card front has a color action photo framed by rose and dark blue borders. The player's name is also on the front, in a black panel at the bottom, along with a Classic logo at the top. The card back has a player profile, action photo, a card number and five trivia questions. The game included a game board, die, player markers, a scoreboard, rules, and plays which could be used in the game. Two unnumbered cards - Cris Dish-

man and Andre Ware - had the game's rules on the back.

		MT
Complete Set (62):		10.00
Common Player:		.15
1	Steve Atwater	.15
2	Louis Oliver	.15
3	Ronnie Lott	.25
4	Reggie White	.50
5	Cortez Kennedy	.30
6	Derrick Thomas	.40
7	Pat Swilling	.20
8	Cornelius Bennett	.25
9	Mark Rypien	.20
10	Todd Marinovich	.15
11	Steve Young	1.00
12	Warren Moon	.30
13	Mirko Jurkovic	.15
14	Hugh Millen	.15
15	John Friesz	.25
16	John Elway	.75
17	Chris Miller	.25
18	Jim Everett	.25
19	Emmitt Smith	2.00
20	Johnny Johnson	.25
21	Thurman Thomas	.60
22	Leonard Russell	.25
23	Rodney Hampton	.50
24	Marion Butts	.30
25	Neal Anderson	.25
26	Barry Sanders	1.00
27	Dexter Carter	.15
28	Gaston Green	.15
29	Barry Word	.15
30	Eric Bieniemy	.15
31	Nick Bell	.20
32	Reggie Cobb	.15
33	Jay Novacek	.30
34	Keith Jackson	.30
35	Eric Green	.30
36	Lawrence Dawsey	.20
37	Mike Pritchard	.20
38	Michael Haynes	.20
39	James Lofton	.25
40	Art Monk	.25
41	Herman Moore	.40
42	Andre Rison	.40
43	Wendell Davis	.15
44	Sterling Sharpe	.60
45	Fred Barnett	.20
46	Rob Moore	.30
47	Gary Clark	.25
48	Wesley Carroll	.15
49	Michael Irvin	.75
50	John Taylor	.25
51	Robert Brooks	.15
52	Ray Bentley	.15
53	Eric Swann	.20
54	Amp Lee	.20
55	Darryl Williams	.15
56	Wilbur Marshall	.15
57	Siran Stacy	.15
58	Chip Lohmiller	.15
59	Rodney Culver	.15
60	Tommy Vardell	.25
----	Cris Dishman (Rules on back)	.15
----	Andre Ware (Rules on back)	.20

1993 Classic Gold Promos

The two-card, standard-size set was made available to Classic Collectors Club members. The fronts feature color action shots while the backs contain another action photo, biography and player profile. The cards are stamped as "x of 5,000" and are numbered with the "PR" prefix.

		MT
Complete Set (2):		7.00
Common Player:		2.00
1	Terry Kirby	2.00
2	Jerome Bettis	5.00

1993 Classic Preview

DREW BLEDSOE QB

The one-card, standard size promo was issued as a preview

to the base 1993 Classic set. The card, depicting Drew Bledsoe, has the same design as cards in the 1993 base set, although the Bledsoe photo is different from the base card photo.

	MT
Complete Set (1):	6.00
Common Player:	6.00
1 Drew Bledsoe	6.00

1993 Classic

These Classic cards feature blue marble-like borders around color action photos. The players name and position are at the bottom of the card in a yellow stripe which contains the set logo. The Classic logo appears in the upper left corner. The back is numbered and is designed in a horizontal manner. Another action photo, collegiate summary, statistics, biographical information and the logo for the team which selected the player in the draft are also included. Inserts within the main set included 1993 Basketball Draft Pick Preview cards, 1,000 cards autographed by Dallas Cowboy quarterback Troy Aikman, 1993 Classic Pro Line Preview cards, and LP cards. Classic also made three types of promo cards - Classic Draft Preview; C3 Presidential Club; and Classic Draft Gold promos. There were 5,000 Gold promos made, each having the words "1 of 5,000" and set logo stamped in gold foil on the front. The back indicates the card is for "Promotional Purposes Only." These cards previewed Classic's gold version set, which parallels its main set. The gold cards were issued in a factory set box and included a certificate of authenticity. There were 5,000 sets made; star gold cards are three to six times more valuable than the regular cards. Drew Bledsoe and Rick Mirer also signed 5,000 of their cards.

	MT
Complete Set (100):	8.00
Common Player:	.05
Comp. Gold Set (102):	180.00
Gold Cards:	3x-6x
Drew Bledsoe Auto/5000	75.00
Rick Mirer Auto/5000	45.00
1 Drew Bledsoe	2.00
2 Rick Mirer	1.00
3 Garrison Hearst	.75
4 Marvin Jones	.10
5 John Copeland	.10
6 Eric Curry	.10
7 Curtis Conway	.75
8 Willie Roaf	.10
9 Lincoln Kennedy	.10
10 Jerome Bettis	.75
11 Mike Compton	.05
12 John Gerak	.05
13 Will Shiellds	.10
14 Ben Coleman	.05
15 Ernest Dye	.05
16 Lester Holmes	.05
17 Brad Hopkins	.05
18 Everett Lindsay	.05
19 Todd Rucci	.05
20 Lance Gunn	.05
21 Elvis Grbac	.40
22 Shane Matthews	.10
23 Rudy Harris	.05
24 Rich Anderson	.05
25 Derek Brown	.10
26 Roger Harper	.05
27 Terry Kirby	.30
28 Natrone Means	1.25
29 Glyn Milburn	.40
30 Adrian Murrell	1.00
31 Lorenzo Neal	.10
32 Roosevelt Potts	.20
33 Kevin Williams	.10
34 Russell Copeland	.10
35 Fred Baxter	.05
36 Troy Drayton	.25
37 Chris Gedney	.10
38 Irv Smith	.10
39 Olanda Truitt	.05
40 Victor Bailey	.20
41 Horace Copeland	.05
42 Ron Dickerson Jr.	.05
43 Willie Harris	.05
44 Tyrone Hughes	.10
45 Qadry Ismail	.25
46 Reggie Brooks	.75
47 Sean LaChapelle	.05
48 O.J. McDuffie	.75
49 Larry Ryans	.05
50 Kenny Shedd	.05
51 Brian Stablein	.05
52 Lamar Thomas	.10
53 Kevin Williams	.75
54 Othello Henderson	.05
55 Kevin Henry	.05
56 Todd Kelly	.05
57 Devon McDonald	.05
58 Michael Strahan	.05
59 Dan Williams	.05
60 Gilbert Brown	.05
61 Mark Caesar	.05
62 Ronnie Dixon	.05
63 John Parrella	.05
64 Leonard Renfro	.05
65 Coleman Rudolph	.05
66 Ronnie Bradford	.05
67 Tom Carter III	.10
68 Deon Figures	.10
69 Derrick Frazier	.05
70 Darrien Gordon	.10
71 Carlton Gray	.10
72 Adrian Hardy	.05
73 Mike Reid	.05
74 Thomas Smith	.05
75 Robert O'Neal	.05
76 Chad Brown	.40
77 Demetrius DuBose	.20
78 Reggie Givens	.05
79 Travis Hill	.05
80 Rich McKenzie	.05
81 Barry Minter	.05
82 Darrin Smith	.10
83 Steve Tovar	.10
84 Patrick Bates	.05
85 Dan Footman	.05
86 Ryan McNeil	.05
87 Danan Hughes	.05
88 Mark Brunell	1.00
89 Ron Moore	.15
90 Antonio London	.10
91 Steve Everitt	.10
92 Wayne Simmons	.20
93 Robert Smith	.50
94 Dana Stubblefield	.30
95 George Teague	.20
96 Carl Simpson	.10
97 Billy Joe Hobert	.20
98 Gino Torretta	.15
99 Checklist No. 1	.05
100 Checklist No. 2	.05
AU1 Troy Aikman Auto/1000	150.00

1993 Classic Draft Stars

1993 Classic Football jumbo packs each contained one of these random inserts. The card front indicates the card is 1 of 20,000 made; the card back uses a DS prefix for the card number. The front has a color full-bleed photo and foil stamping for the player's name, position and set logo. The card back has biographical information, a mug shot and a congratulatory note indicating the card is one of 20,000 made for each player. The logo of the team which selected the player is also on the card back. A Mirer/Bledsoe jumbo card, available one per every other box, was also produced.

	MT
Complete Set (20):	24.00
Common Player:	.50
DS1 Drew Bledsoe	7.00
DS2 Rick Mirer	4.00
DS3 Garrison Hearst	3.00
DS4 Marvin Jones	.50
DS5 John Copeland	.50
DS6 Eric Curry	.50
DS7 Curtis Conway	2.00
DS8 Jerome Bettis	3.00
DS9 Patrick Bates	.50
DS10 Tom Carter	.50
DS11 Irv Smith	.50
DS12 Robert Smith	2.00
DS13 O.J. McDuffie	2.00
DS14 Roosevelt Potts	.75
DS15 Natrone Means	4.00
DS16 Glyn Milburn	1.00
DS17 Reggie Brooks	.75
DS18 Kevin Williams	1.50
DS19 Qadry Ismail	1.00
DS20 Billy Joe Hobert	.50
---- Drew Bledsoe, Rick Mirer	12.00

Post-1980 cards in Near Mint condition will generally sell for about 75% of the quoted Mint value. Excellent-condition cards bring no more than 40%.

1993 Classic LPs

These inserts were randomly included in 1993 Classic football packs. The card front has a blue-gray border which frames a color action photo. The Classic logo is at the top of the card; the player's name, position and set logo are at the bottom in a gold foil stripe. "LP" and "1 of 45,000" are also stamped in gold foil at the bottom. The card back is horizontal and includes another action photo, career summary and card number. The logo of the team which selected the player in the draft is also on the back.

	MT
Complete Set (10):	35.00
Common Player:	1.50
1 Drew Bledsoe	12.00
2 Rick Mirer	6.00
3 Garrison Hearst	5.00
4 Marvin Jones	1.50
5 John Copeland	1.50
6 Eric Curry	1.50
7 Curtis Conway	4.00
8 Jerome Bettis	4.00
9 Reggie Brooks	2.00
10 Qadry Ismail	3.00

1993 Classic Superhero Comic

These cards were random inserts in 1993 Classic Football packs. Each card front has a comic-book style drawing of the featured player, as illustrated by artist Neal Adams. The drawing is full-bleed and in color and includes the player's name and position at the bottom in a yellow bar. The card back is numbered with an "SH" prefix and features a ghosted image of the front photo as its background. A second color action photo and career summary are also included. There were 15,000 cards of each player made.

	MT
Complete Set (4):	50.00
Common Player:	7.00
1 Troy Aikman	20.00
2 Drew Bledsoe	20.00
3 Rick Mirer	12.00
4 Garrison Hearst	7.00

1993 Classic TONX

The 150-card, 1-5/8" in diameter set features color action shots on the circular fronts with the player's name, team helmet logo and NFL and Classic logos on the back.

	MT
Complete Set (150):	12.00
Common Player:	.05
1 Troy Aikman	1.00
2 Eric Allen	.05
3 Terry Allen	.25
4 Morten Anderson	.05
5 Neal Anderson	.05
6 Flipper Anderson	.05
7 Steve Atwater	.05
8 Carl Banks	.05
9 Patrick Bates	.05
10 Cornelius Bennett	.10
11 Rod Bernstine	.05
12 Jerome Bettis	.75
13 Steve Beuerlein	.05
14 Bennie Blades	.05
15 Brian Blades	.05
16 Drew Bledsoe	1.00
17 Tim Brown	.10
18 Terrell Buckley	.05
19 Marion Butts	.05
20 Mark Carrier (DB)	.05
21 Anthony Carter	.05
22 Cris Carter	.10
23 Dale Carter	.05
24 Ray Childress	.05
25 Gary Clark	.05
26 Reggie Cobb	.05
27 Marco Coleman	.05
28 Curtis Conway	.30
29 John Copeland	.05
30 Quentin Coryatt	.10
31 Randall Cunningham	.10
32 Eric Curry	.05
33 Lawrence Dawsey	.05
34 Chris Doleman	.05
35 Vaughn Dunbar	.05
36 Henry Ellard	.05
37 John Elway	.75
38 Steve Emtman	.05
39 Ricky Ervins	.05
40 Jim Everett	.05
41 Brett Favre	2.00
42 Barry Foster	.05
43 Gary Cleveland	.05
44 Jeff George	.10
45 Sean Gilbert	.05
46 Ernest Givins	.05
47 Harold Green	.05
48 Kevin Greene	.05
49 Paul Gruber	.05
50 Charles Haley	.05
51 Rodney Hampton	.05
52 Jim Harbaugh	.10
53 Ronnie Harmon	.05
54 Michael Haynes	.05
55 Garrison Hearst	.50
56 Randal Hill	.05
57 Merril Hoge	.05
58 Pierce Holt	.05
59 Jeff Hostetler	.05
60 Stan Humphries	.10
61 Michael Irvin	.15
62 Keith Jackson	.05
63 Rickey Jackson	.05
64 Haywood Jeffires	.05
65 Pepper Johnson	.05
66 Brent Jones	.05
67 Marvin Jones	.05
68 Seth Joyner	.05
69 Jim Kelly	.15
70 Cortez Kennedy	.05
71 David Klingler	.05
72 Bernie Kosar	.05
73 Reggie Langhorne	.05
74 Mo Lewis	.05
75 Howie Long	.10
76 Ronnie Lott	.10
77 Charles Mann	.05
78 Dan Marino	2.00
79 Todd Marinovich	.05
80 Eric Martin	.05
81 Clay Matthews	.05
82 Ed McCaffrey	.05
83 O.J. McDuffie	.30
84 Steve McMichael	.05
85 Audray McMillian	.05
86 Greg McMurtry	.05
87 Karl Mecklenburg	.05
88 Dave Meggett	.05
89 Eric Metcalf	.05
90 Anthony Miller	.10
91 Chris Miller	.05
92 Sam Mills	.05
93 Rick Mirer	.50
94 Johnny Mitchell	.05
95 Art Monk	.10
96 Joe Montana	1.00
97 Warren Moon	.15
98 Rob Moore	.05
99 Brad Muster	.05
100 Browning Nagle	.05
101 Ken Norton Jr.	.05
102 Jay Novacek	.05
103 Neil O'Donnell	.10
104 Leslie O'Neal	.05
105 Louis Oliver	.05
106 Rodney Peete	.05
107 Michael Dean Perry	.05
108 Carl Pickens	.30
109 Ricky Proehl	.05
110 Andre Reed	.10
111 Jerry Rice	1.00
112 Andre Rison	.10
113 Leonard Russell	.10
114 Mark Rypien	.05
115 Barry Sanders	1.00
116 Deion Sanders	.50
117 Junior Seau	.10
118 Shannon Sharpe	.10
119 Sterling Sharpe	.10
120 Clyde Simmons	.05
121 Wayne Simmons	.05
122 Phil Simms	.10
123 Bruce Smith	.05
124 Emmitt Smith	2.00
125 Alonzo Spellman	.05
126 Pat Swilling	.05
127 John Taylor	.05
128 Lawrence Taylor	.15
129 Broderick Thomas	.05
130 Derrick Thomas	.10
131 Thurman Thomas	.15
132 Andre Tippett	.05
133 Jessie Tuggle	.05
134 Tommy Vardell	.05
135 Jon Vaughn	.05
137 Clarence Verdin	.05
138 Herschel Walker	.10
139 Andre Ware	.05
140 Chris Warren	.05
141 Ricky Watters	.20
142 Lorenzen White	.05
143 Reggie White	.15
144 Alfred Williams	.05
145 Calvin Williams	.05
146 Harvey Williams	.05
147 John L. Williams	.05
148 Rod Woodson	.15
149 Barry Word	.05
150 Steve Young	.75

1994 Classic Previews

The five-card, standard-size set was issued by Classic to preview its 1994 NFL Draft Pick set. The card fronts feature the same design as the base set with the backs containing a congratulatory message for pulling the card, which was limited to "1 of 1,950" sets. They are numbered with the "PR" prefix.

	MT
Complete Set (5):	16.00
Common Player:	2.00
1 Heath Shuler	7.00
2 Trent Dilfer	4.00
3 Dan Wilkinson	2.00
4 David Palmer	2.00
5 Johnnie Morton	4.00

1994 Classic Promos

The three-card, standard-size set previewed the release of the 1994 base set. The card fronts feature the same design as the base set - as do the backs. The cards are numbered with the "PR" prefix.

	MT
Complete Set (3):	10.00
Common Player:	4.00
1 Marshall Faulk	5.00
2 Heath Shuler	4.00
3 Heath Shuler	4.00

1994 Classic

This 105-card set features the first licensed cards of 93 NFL rookies. Each card front has a full-bleed color action photo, the player's name and position, the set logo, and a helmet of the team which drafted him. The card back has a ghosted image of the player, except for the player's head, which is full-color. Biographical information, stats, a card number and collegiate summary are also included. The set is limited to just under 10,000 cases. A parallel gold foil card was also made for each card in the set; one card was included in each pack. Other inserts included 1,994 autographed Jerry Rice cards; 9,994 numbered cards honoring Rice's records; sweepstakes Rookie of the Year cards, Classic LPs, Pro Line previews, Basketball previews and Classic Stars. There were also three Classic Draft promo cards produced, using the same design as the main cards also produced, and labeled with a "PR" prefix. The front format is similar to the regular and promo cards, but the back is different; it has a congratulatory message indicating the card is one of five of the 1,950 sets produced.

	MT
Complete Set (105):	10.00
Common Player:	.05
Wax Box:	24.00
1 Heath Shuler	1.00
2 Trent Dilfer	.75
3 Marshall Faulk	2.00
4 Errict Rhett	1.25
5 Charlie Garner	.40
6 Sam Adams	.10
7 Shante Carver	.05
8 Dwayne Chandler	.05
9 Andre Coleman	.05
10 Carlester Crumpler	.05
11 Charles Johnson	.40
12 David Palmer	.10
13 Dan Wilkinson	.20
14 LeShon Johnson	.10
15 Mario Bates	.50
16 Glenn Foley	.05
17 William Gaines	.05
18 Wayne Gandy	.05
19 Jason Gildon	.05
20 Eric Gant	.05
21 Tre Johnson	.05
22 Calvin Jones	.05
23 Jake Kelchner	.05
24 Perry Klein	.05
25 Chuck Levy	.10
26 Corey Louchiey	.05
27 Chris Maumalanga	.05
28 Jamir Miller	.10
29 Jim Miller	.05
30 Johnnie Morton	.30
31 Doug Nussmeier	.05
32 Vaughn Parker	.05
33 Darnay Scott	.40
34 Fernando Smith	.05
35 Lamar Smith	.05
36 Marcus Spears	.05
37 Irving Spikes	.25
38 Todd Steussie	.10
39 Aaron Taylor	.10
40 John Thierry	.10
41 Dewayne Washington	.05
42 Jason Winrow	.05
43 Ronnie Woolfork	.05
44 Bryant Young	.30
45 Arthur Bussie	.05
46 Derrick Alexander	.25
47 Larry Allen	.05
48 Aubrey Beavers	.05
49 James Bostic	.10
50 Jeff Burris	.05
51 Lindsey Chapman	.05
52 Isaac Davis	.05
53 Lake Dawson	.30
54 Tyrone Drakeford	.05
55 William Floyd	.50
56 Henry Ford	.05
57 Rob Fredrickson	.20
58 Aaron Glenn	.05
59 Shelby Hill	.20
60 Willie Jackson	.20
61 Joe Johnson	.05
62 Aaron Laing	.05
63 Kevin Lee	.05
64 Eric Mahlum	.05
65 Steve Matthews	.05
66 Willie McGinest	.20
67 Kevin Mitchell	.05
68 Bam Morris	.75
69 Thomas Randolph	.05
70 Tony Richardson	.05
71 Corey Sawyer	.05
72 Jason Sehorn	.05
73 Rob Waldrop	.05
74 Jay Walker	.05
75 Bernard Williams	.05
76 Marvin Goodwin	.05
77 Romeo Bandison	.05
78 Bucky Brooks	.05
79 James Folston	.05
80 Donnell Bennett	.05
81 Charlie Ward	.20
82 Antonio Langham	.10
83 Greg Hill	.40
84 Darnay Scott	.05
85 Winfred Tubbs	.05
86 Trev Alberts	.10
87 Tim Bowens	.25
88 Thomas Lewis	.25
89 Allen Aldridge	.05
90 Bert Emanuel	.25
91 Ryan Yarborough	.10

92	Lonnie Johnson	.05
93	Isaac Bruce	1.00
94	Checklist #1	.05
95	Checklist #2	.05
96	Troy Aikman	.25
97	Steve Young	.25
98	Rick Mirer	.15
99	Drew Bledsoe	.40
100	Jerry Rice	.25
101	Heath Shuler	.75
102	Marshall Faulk	1.50
103	Trent Dilfer	.30
104	Dan Wilkerson	.10
105	David Palmer	.10
JR1	Jerry Rice Special	12.00
NNO	Jerry Rice Auto/1994	125.00

1994 Classic Football Gold

This set is a parallel to Classic's main 1994 Draft set; the cards are the same as the regular ones, except the set logo is stamped in gold foil on the card front. One gold card was in each pack.

	MT
Complete Set (105):	40.00
Common Player:	.15
Gold Cards:	2x

1994 Classic Draft Stars

These cards feature a full-bleed color action photo on the front, along with the set logo. The player's name, position and helmet of the team which drafted him are at the bottom. The card back has another color photo, part of which is ghosted to allow for the player's name and biographical information.

		MT
Complete Set (20):		12.00
Common Player:		.25
1	Trev Alberts	.50
2	Jeff Burris	.25
3	Shante Carver	.25
4	Trent Dilfer	2.00
5	Marshall Faulk	5.00
6	William Floyd	1.50
7	Aaron Glenn	.25
8	Greg Hill	.50
9	Charles Johnson	.50
10	Calvin Jones	.25
11	Antonio Langham	.25
12	Thomas Lewis	.25
13	Willie McGinest	.50
14	Jamir Miller	.25
15	Johnnie Morton	.75
16	David Palmer	.50
17	Darnay Scott	1.00
18	Heath Shuler	2.00
19	Dan Wilkinson	.50
20	Bryant Young	.75
NNO	Rick Mirer Special	10.00

1994 Classic Picks

These limited-edition cards were randomly included in Classic Draft football packs. Only 20,000 of each card was made, as noted in blue on the card back. The card front features a color action photo against a metallic background. The player's name appears in the upper left corner. The back has a player mug shot, collegiate highlights, and bio notes, all against a ghosted image of the photo on the front. A card number, using an "LP" prefix, is also included. An LP card was in every box.

	MT
Complete Set (5):	40.00
Common Player:	4.00
1 Heath Shuler	10.00
2 Trent Dilfer	7.00
3 Johnnie Morton	6.00
4 David Palmer	4.00
5 Marshall Faulk	20.00

1994 Classic ROY Sweepstakes

These 20 sweepstakes cards, issued approximately 5 per case, feature players who were in the running for the NFL's 1994 Rookie of the Year Award. Collectors who obtained a card of the winner could redeem it for an autographed football of the player.

		MT
Complete Set (20):		100.00
Common Player:		2.50
1	Trent Dilfer	5.00
2	Mario Bates	4.00
3	Darnay Scott	4.00
4	Johnnie Morton	3.00
5	William Floyd	5.00
6	Errict Rhett	12.00
7	Greg Hill	5.00
8	Lake Dawson	4.00
9	Charlie Garner	5.00
10	Heath Shuler	10.00
11	Derrick Alexander	4.00
12	LeShon Johnson	2.50
13	Kevin Lee	2.50
14	David Palmer	2.50
15	Charles Johnson	5.00
16	Chuck Levy	2.50
17	Calvin Jones	2.50
18	Thomas Lewis	2.50
19	Marshall Faulk	25.00
20	"Field" card	2.50

1994 Classic Game Cards

The 10-card, regular-sized set was inserted in every jumbo pack of 1994 Classic. The card fronts have "Game Card" printed along the left border with a scratch-off section on the back. An unnumbered Drew Bledsoe card was randomly inserted as well, and winning cards could be redeemed for an uncut Gold NFL Draft sheet or a 1994 NFL Draft Day set. The cards are numbered with the "GC" prefix.

		MT
Complete Set (10):		10.00
Common Player:		.25
Scratched Cards:		.5x
DB1	Drew Bledsoe Special	12.00
1	Trent Dilfer	.75
2	Marshall Faulk	3.50
3	Heath Shuler	1.75
4	Dan Wilkinson	.25
5	Antonio Langham	.25
6	Willie McGinest	.50
7	Greg Hill	.50
8	Trev Alberts	.25
9	Charles Johnson	.50
10	Errict Rhett	2.50

1994 Images

Only 1,994 cases of Classic Images Football were produced, with each card in the 125-card set printed on a specially designed 18-point, micro-lined foil board. The card front has an action shot on a foil background. The player's name is in a stripe at the bottom, with the Images logo

in the middle. The card back has stats from the 1993 season and the player's career totals, plus a color photo and card number. Inserts were from two types - All-Pros and All-Pro Prospects cards, and NFL Experience Sneak Preview cards.

		MT
Complete Set (125):		60.00
Common Player:		.25
Wax Box:		150.00
1	Emmitt Smith	4.00
2	Reggie White	.40
3	Michael Haynes	.25
4	Chris Warren	.40
5	Jeff George	.40
6	Sean Gilbert	.25
7	Ricky Watters	.40
8	Eric Metcalf	.25
9	Randall Cunningham	.40
10	Tim Brown	.40
11	Trent Dilfer	1.00
12	Marshall Faulk	7.00
13	David Klingler	.25
14	Barry Foster	.40
15	John Elway	1.50
16	Joe Montana	4.00
17	Rodney Hampton	.40
18	Todd Steussie	.40
19	Bruce Smith	.25
20	Wayne Gandy	.25
21	Anthony Miller	.25
22	Reggie Brooks	.25
23	Johnny Johnson	.25
24	Byron Morris	1.00
25	Drew Bledsoe	4.00
26	Jeff Hostetler	.25
27	Alvin Harper	.25
28	Cris Carter	.25
29	Bert Emanuel	2.00
30	Errict Rhett	1.00
31	Scott Mitchell	.25
32	Deion Sanders	1.50
33	Lewis Tillman	.25
34	Tim Bowens	.75
35	Charles Haley	.25
36	Stan Humphries	.40
37	Haywood Jeffires	.25
38	Andre Reed	.25
39	Charles Johnson	1.00
40	Ron Moore	.25
41	Jim Everett	.25
42	Greg Hill	1.00
43	Thurman Thomas	.50
44	Willie McGinest	1.00
45	Aaron Glenn	.40
46	Erric Pegram	.25
47	Terry Kirby	.25
48	Warren Moon	.40
49	Clyde Simmons	.25
50	Eric Turner	.25
51	Heath Shuler	.75
52	Rickey Jackson	.25
53	Johnnie Morton	1.00
54	Charlie Garner	3.00
55	Mark Collins	.25
56	Mike Pritchard	.25
57	Bryant Young	1.00
58	Joe Johnson	.40
59	Erik Kramer	.25
60	Barry Sanders	3.00
61	Rod Woodson	.40
62	Dave Brown	.25
63	Gary Brown	.25
64	Brett Favre	4.00
65	Isaac Bruce	5.00
66	Boomer Esiason	.25
67	Jim Harbaugh	.25
68	Jackie Harris	.25
69	Art Monk	.25
70	Jamir Miller	.40
71	Neil O'Donnell	1.00
72	Neil Smith	.25
73	Junior Seau	.40
74	Jerome Bettis	1.50
75	Bernard Williams	.25
76	Jeff Burris	.75
77	Henry Ellard	.25
78	Reggie Cobb	.25
79	Shante Carver	.40
80	Terry Allen	.25
81	Cortez Kennedy	.25
82	Trev Alberts	.50
83	Michael Irvin	1.00
84	Herschel Walker	.25
85	Dan Marino	4.00
86	Dave Meggett	.25
87	Herman Moore	1.00
88	Darnay Scott	2.00
89	Dewayne Washington	.50
90	Rob Fredrickson	.50
91	Rick Mirer	.50
92	Thomas Lewis	.75
93	Chris Miller	.25
94	Marion Butts	.25
95	Sam Adams	.75
96	Jerry Rice	2.50
97	Ben Coates	.50
98	David Palmer	1.00
99	Antonio Langham	.40
100	Curtis Conway	1.50
101	Derrick Thomas	.40
102	Ken Norton	.25
103	Ronnie Lott	.25
104	Sterling Sharpe	.40
105	Troy Aikman	3.00
106	Shannon Sharpe	.40
107	Natrone Means	1.00
108	Derek Brown	.40
109	Dan Wilkinson	.75
110	Andre Rison	.40
111	Quentin Coryatt	.25
112	Cody Carlson	.25
113	William Floyd	.75
114	Marcus Allen	.40
115	Steve Young	2.50
116	Jim Kelly	.40
117	LeShon Johnson	.50
118	Irving Fryar	.25
119	Carl Pickens	1.00
120	Keith Jackson	.25
121	John Thierry	.40
122	Vinny Testaverde	.25
123	Derrick Alexander	1.00
124	Seth Joyner	.25
125	Checklist	.25
TP1	Drew Bledsoe (NFL EX)	50.00
NNO	Emmitt Smith (NFL EX)	15.00

1994 Images All-Pro

These cards were randomly included in packs of 1994 Classic Images football, either one card per box or two All-Pro packs per case. Each card in this 25-card set is sequentially numbered up to 2,600. All-Pros have a colored foil stripe across the bottom which includes the Images logo. The player's name, his conference and All-Pro logo are in a box in the lower left corner. The card back has the sequential number, a color action photo, and card number, which uses an "A" prefix.

		MT
Complete Set (25):		350.00
Common Player:		7.00
1	Heath Shuler	10.00
2	Steve Young	25.00
3	Trent Dilfer	10.00
4	Troy Aikman	25.00
5	Emmitt Smith	50.00
6	Barry Sanders	30.00
7	Jerome Bettis	12.00
8	Errict Rhett	15.00
9	Jerry Rice	25.00
10	Michael Irvin	7.00
11	Andre Rison	7.00
12	Sterling Sharpe	7.00
13	Reggie White	7.00
14	Rick Mirer	10.00
15	Drew Bledsoe	20.00
16	John Elway	15.00
17	Joe Montana	30.00
18	Dan Marino	50.00
19	Thurman Thomas	10.00
20	Marshall Faulk	20.00
21	Marcus Allen	7.00
22	Charles Johnson	7.00
23	Tim Brown	7.00
24	Anthony Miller	7.00
25	Derrick Thomas	7.00

1994 Images Update

The 10-card, standard-size set was randomly inserted in retail packs of 1995 Classic Images 4-Sport. The cards' numbering starts at No. 126 as an addition to the 1994 Images set.

		MT
Complete Set (10):		100.00
Common Player:		4.00
126	Emmitt Smith	25.00
127	Troy Aikman	12.00
128	Steve Young	10.00
129	Deion Sanders	10.00
130	Ben Coates	4.00
131	Natrone Means	8.00
132	Drew Bledsoe	12.00
133	Cris Carter	5.00
134	Marshall Faulk	10.00
135	Errict Rhett	8.00

1994 Classic NFL Experience Promos

The six-card, standard-size set was issued to preview the 100-card 1994 Classic NFL Experience set. The fronts feature full-bleed action shots with "For Promotional Purposes Only" printed on the card backs.

		MT
Complete Set (6):		18.00
Common Player:		1.25
1	Troy Aikman	5.00
2	Jerry Rice	5.00
3	Emmitt Smith	10.00
4	Derrick Thomas	1.25
5	Thurman Thomas	2.50
6	Rod Woodson	1.25

1994 Classic NFL Experience

This limited-print 100-card set features the NFL's impact players and highlights 23 top rookies, along with 16 members of the NFL Quarterback Club. Each card front has a borderless color photo of the player, the set logo, and the player's name in a color bar at the bottom. The back has a color photo, a summary of the player's accomplishments during the 1993 season, and a card number. Both sides are UV coated. Classic produced only 1,500 numbered cases, available only through hobby dealers, in conjunction with Super Bowl XXVIII. A 10-card limited-print set of rookies was produced as inserts, as were 1,994 Troy Aikman Super Bowl MVP cards. Six promo cards were also produced to showcase the company's main set. The cards were given away during a Super Bowl card show.

		MT
Complete Set (100):		12.00
Common Player:		.06
Wax Box:		24.00
1	Checklist 1	.06
2	Checklist 2	.06
3	Bobby Hebert	.10
4	Erric Pegram	.25
5	Andre Rison	.30
6	Deion Sanders	.15
7	Cornelius Bennett	.08
8	Jim Kelly	.25
9	Andre Reed	.10
10	Bruce Smith	.10
11	Thurman Thomas	.40
12	Curtis Conway	.30
13	Jim Harbaugh	.06
14	John Copeland	.10
15	David Klingler	.20
16	Carl Pickens	.10
17	Eric Metcalf	.15
18	Vinny Testaverde	.10
19	Eric Turner	.08
20	Tommy Vardell	.08
21	Troy Aikman	1.00
22	Michael Irvin	.45
23	Emmitt Smith	2.00
24	Kevin Williams	.10
25	John Elway	.40
26	Glyn Milburn	.15
27	Shannon Sharpe	.10
28	Herman Moore	.25
29	Rodney Peete	.06
30	Barry Sanders	1.25
31	Pat Swilling	.10
32	Brett Favre	1.00
33	Sterling Sharpe	.10
34	Reggie White	.15
35	Haywood Jeffires	.10
36	Warren Moon	.15
37	Webster Slaughter	.06
38	Lorenzo White	.06
39	Quentin Coryatt	.06
40	Jeff George	.10
41	Roosevelt Potts	.06
42	Marcus Allen	.10
43	Joe Montana	1.25
44	Neil Smith	.08
45	Derrick Thomas	.20
46	Tim Brown	.25
47	Jeff Hostetler	.08
48	Raghib Ismail	.15
49	Anthony Smith	.06
50	Jerome Bettis	.50
51	Jim Everett	.08
52	T.J. Rubley	.06
53	Keith Jackson	.10
54	Terry Kirby	.45
55	Dan Marino	2.00
56	O.J. McDuffie	.25
57	Scott Mitchell	.35
58	Cris Carter	.10
59	Chris Doleman	.08
60	Robert Smith	.10
61	Drew Bledsoe	1.50
62	Vincent Brisby	.45
63	Derek Brown	.20
64	Willie Roaf	.08
65	Irv Smith	.06
66	Renaldo Turnbull	.06
67	Rodney Hampton	.35
68	Phil Simms	.10
69	Lawrence Taylor	.10
70	Boomer Esiason	.06
71	Marvin Jones	.06
72	Ronnie Lott	.10
73	Johnny Mitchell	.10
74	Rob Moore	.10
75	Victor Bailey	.10
76	Randall Cunningham	.10
77	Ken O'Brien	.06
78	Steve Beuerlein	.08
79	Garrison Hearst	.50
80	Ron Moore	.30
81	Ricky Proehl	.08
82	Deon Figures	.06
83	Barry Foster	.20
84	Neil O'Donnell	.12
85	Rod Woodson	.10
86	Natrone Means	.50
87	Anthony Miller	.25
88	Junior Seau	.06
89	Jerry Rice	.75
90	Ricky Watters	.20
91	Steve Young	1.00
92	Brian Blades	.06
93	Cortez Kennedy	.10
94	Rick Mirer	.50
95	Reggie Cobb	.06
96	Eric Curry	.06
97	Craig Erickson	.10
98	Reggie Brooks	.40
99	Desmond Howard	.10
100	Mark Rypien	.06

1994 Classic NFL Experience LPs

This limited-print 10-card set features 10 top NFL prospects. Only 2,400 of each card was produced, and each includes an embossed gold logo of Super Bowl XXVIII on the front. The card front also has a color action photo, the set logo, the player's name and "Classic Rookies" on it. The back, numbered using an "LP" prefix, has another color photo and brief player profile. Cards were random inserts in 1994 Classic NFL Experience packs.

		MT
Complete Set (10):		90.00
Common Player:		3.00
Minor Stars:		6.00
1	Jerome Bettis	6.00
2	Drew Bledsoe	25.00
3	Reggie Brooks	3.00
4	Garrison Hearst	12.00
5	Derek Brown	3.00
6	Terry Kirby	6.00
7	Natrone Means	12.00
8	Glyn Milburn	3.00
9	Rick Mirer	12.00
10	Robert Smith	6.00

1995 Classic NFL Rookies

Each of these cards features the 1995 NFL Draft logo and the logo of the team the player was selected by during the draft, along with a full-bleed color action photo on the front. The player's name is in white at the bottom of the card; the Classic logo is in an upper corner. The back has the player's name, position, NFL team name, biographical information and collegiate statistics toward the top; a recap of the player's collegiate accomplishments and a color action photo are on the bottom half. The card number is in the upper left corner in an arrow. Two subsets were also created within the main set - NFL Draft Retro cards and Award Winners. Three parallel sets were also produced - a Silver Series (cards printed on silver foil board; one per pack); a Printer's Proof Series (one per 18 hobby); and a Printer's Proof Silver Series (one in 36 packs). An abbreviated Die-Cut Printer's Proof 1st Round Picks set of the first 32 cards was also made; only 97 sets were made. Only 595 of each regular card appears in a Printer's Proof format, while only 297 of each card was done in a Printer's Proof Silver Series format. Three insert sets were made - Rookie of the Year Redemption, Pro Line Game Breakers and oversized bonus rookie cards. Production of 1995 NFL Classic Rookies was limited to 2,950 hobby and 2,950 retail cases.

		MT
Complete Set (110):		15.00
Common Player:		.05
1	Ki-Jana Carter	1.00
2	Tony Boseli	.25
3	Steve McNair	1.00
4	Michael Westbrook	.50
5	Kerry Collins	1.25
6	Kevin Carter	.25
7	Mike Mamula	.25
8	Joseph Galloway	1.25
9	Kyle Brady	.20
10	J.J. Stokes	1.25
11	Derrick Alexander	.25
12	Warren Sapp	.30
13	Mark Fields	.25
14	Ruben Brown	.05
15	Ellis Johnson	.25
16	Hugh Douglas	.40
17	Tyrone Wheatley	.75
18	Napoleon Kaufman	.75
19	James Stewart	.50
20	Luther Elliss	.20
21	Rashaan Salaam	1.50

22	Tyrone Poole	.10
23	Ty Law	.10
24	Korey Stringer	.10
25	Billy Milner	.10
26	Devin Bush	.10
27	Mark Bruener	.30
28	Derrick Brooks	.20
29	Blake Brockermeyer	.10
30	Craig Powell	.05
31	Trezelle Jenkins	.10
32	Craig Newsome	.20
33	Thomas Bailey	.05
34	Chad May	.10
35	J.J. Smith	.05
36	Lorenzo Styles	.05
37	Brian Williams	.05
38	Damien Covington	.05
39	Steve Stenstrom	.05
40	Darius Holland	.05
41	Pete Mitchell	.05
42	Todd Collins	.25
43	Kordell Stewart	1.00
44	Eric Zeier	.75
45	Frank Sanders	.50
46	Ben Talley	.05
47	Billy Williams	.05
48	Chris Jones	.05
49	Tamarick Vanover	.50
50	Jimmy Hitchcock	.05
51	Chris Hudson	.05
52	Terrell Fletcher	.20
53	Brent Moss	.05
54	Terrell Davis	1.00
55	Rodney Thomas	.50
56	Larry Jones	.10
57	Ray Zellars	.20
58	David Sloan	.05
59	Brandon Bennett	.05
60	Brian DeMarco	.05
61	Bryan Schwartz	.05
62	Jack Jackson	.05
63	Bobby Taylor	.05
64	Kevin Hickman	.05
65	Matt O'Dwyer	.05
66	Patrick Riley	.05
67	Ki-Jana Carter	1.00
68	Kerry Collins	1.25
69	Steve McNair	1.00
70	Tyrone Wheatley	.75
71	Antonio Freeman	.40
72	Clifton Abraham	.05
73	Kez McCorvey	.10
74	Lovell Pinkney	.05
75	Lee DeRamus	.05
76	John Walsh	.10
77	Cory Raymer	.10
78	Corey Fuller	.10
79	Tyrone Davis	.10
80	David Dunn	.10
81	Dana Howard	.05
82	Melvin Johnson	.05
83	Robert Baldwin	.05
84	Curtis Martin	1.50
85	Zack Crockett	.10
86	Jay Barker	.10
87	Christian Fauria	.25
88	Zach Wiegert	.05
89	Barrett Brooks	.05
90	Ken Dilger	.25
91	James Stewart	.20
92	Ed Hervey	.05
93	Torey Hunter	.05
94	Sherman Williams	.40
95	Shawn King	.05
96	Dave Barr	.05
97	Rob Johnson	.10
98	Stoney Case	.25
99	Checklist 1 (Ki-Jana Carter)	.25
100	Checklist 2 (Steve McNair)	.25
101	Rashaan Salaam	.75
102	Kerry Collins	.75
103	Rashaan Salaam	.75
104	Kerry Collins	.75
105	Jay Barker	.10
106	Drew Bledsoe	.50
107	Marshall Faulk	.50
108	Steve Young	.50
109	Troy Aikman	.50
110	Emmitt Smith	.75

1995 Classic NFL Rookies Silver

The 110-card, standard-size set is a parallel to the base set and features the same front and back designs as the base set, with the cards being printed on silver-foil stock. The cards were inserted one per pack.

	MT
Complete Set (110):	40.00
Common Player:	.10
Silver Cards:	3x

1995 Classic NFL Rookies Printer's Proofs

The 110-card, regular-sized set was a parallel set to the 1995 Classic NFL Rookies set. Limited to 595 each, the cards feature "Printer's Proofs" printed across the front, which are the same fronts as found in the base set. The backs are also identical.

	MT
Complete Set (110):	280.00
Common Player:	1.00
Printer's Proofs:	10x-20x

1995 Classic NFL Rookies Printer's Proofs Silver

The 110-card, regular-sized set was a parallel set to the Printer's Proofs inserts, with the difference being "Printer's Proofs" is printed in silver foil across the card fronts. Each card was limited to 297 issues.

	MT
Complete Set (110):	425.00
Common Player:	1.50
Silver Cards:	15x-30x

1995 Classic NFL Rookies Die Cuts

The 32-card, regular-size set featured the 32 players selected in the 1995 NFL Draft's first round. The cards are die cut in the form of a No. 1 and are sequentially numbered to 4,500. Cards in the set were inserted twice per box.

	MT
Complete Set (32):	85.00
Common Player:	.50
1 Ki-Jana Carter	6.00
2 Tony Boselli	1.50
3 Steve McNair	10.00
4 Michael Westbrook	4.00
5 Kerry Collins	12.00
6 Kevin Carter	1.00
7 Mike Mamula	1.00
8 Joey Galloway	10.00
9 Kyle Brady	1.00
10 J.J. Stokes	6.00
11 Derrick Alexander	1.00
12 Warren Sapp	1.50
13 Mark Fields	.50
14 Ruben Brown	.50
15 Ellis Johnson	.50
16 Hugh Douglas	2.00
17 Tyrone Wheatley	4.00
18 Napoleon Kaufman	4.00
19 James O. Stewart	2.00
20 Luther Ellis	1.00
21 Rashaan Salaam	8.00
22 Tyrone Poole	1.00
23 Ty Law	1.00
24 Korey Stringer	1.00
25 Billy Miner	.50
26 Devin Bush	.50
27 Mark Bruener	1.50
28 Derrick Brooks	1.00
29 Blake Brockermeyer	.50
30 Craig Powell	.50
31 Trezelle Jenkins	.50
32 Craig Newsome	2.00

1995 Classic NFL Rookies Die Cuts Printer's Proofs

The 32-card, regular-sized set, inserted every hobby case, paralleled the 1995 NFL Rookies Die Cut set with the exception being "Printer's Proofs" printed on the card fronts.

	MT
Complete Set (32):	1300.
Common Player:	10.00
Die-Cut Printer's Proofs:	8x-16x

1995 Classic NFL Rookies Die Cuts Silver Signatures

The 32-card, standard-size set paralleled the NFL Rookies set, except for the facsimile autographs stamped on each card front. Cards in the set were inserted every 48 packs and are sequentially numbered to 1,750.

	MT
Complete Set (32):	250.00
Common Player:	2.00

1995 Classic NFL Rookies Instant Energy

The 20-card, standard-sized set was inserted every

1995 Classic NFL Rookies Bonus Card Jumbos NFL Team's

As a special dealer bonus for Classic's 1995 NFL Rookies set, each hobby case of the product contains at least one of these three oversized rookie cards. Each card is sequentially numbered up to 2,500. The front has a photo of the player in his college uniform, with his NFL's team logo in the background. The brand logo is in the upper left corner; the player's name, position and team name are at the bottom. Cards are ticket size, measuring 4-3/4" x 2-1/2". They are printed on micro-lined foil board.

		MT
Complete Set (3):		30.00
Common Player:		10.00
1	Ki-Jana Carter	10.00
2	Steve McNair	12.00
3	Kerry Collins	10.00

1995 Classic NFL Rookies Draft Review

The first 14 cards of Draft Review were handed out to the media on NFL Draft Day, and were also later reissued in retail packs of Classic NFL Rookies, every one per three packs. Card No. 14, which was a checklist when first issued, was replaced by an Emmitt Smith card, while the eight additional cards updated team selections. The 14-card set that the media received came with a certificate of authenticity numbered up to 19,995 sets. Since it was not known which team would draft certain players, some are pictured in multiple pro uniforms, and updated in the final eight cards of this 22-card set.

		MT
Complete Set (23):		20.00
Common Player:		.25
1	Steve McNair (Oilers)	3.00
2	Steve McNair (Vikings)	1.50
3	Steve McNair (Jaguars)	1.50
4	Ki-Jana Carter (Panthers)	1.00
5	Ki-Jana Carter (Jaguars)	1.00
6	Kerry Collins (Bills)	1.75
7	Kerry Collins (Colts)	1.75
8	Kerry Collins (Cardinals)	1.75
9	John Walsh (Panthers)	.25
10	John Walsh (Vikings)	.25
11	John Walsh (Dolphins)	.25
12	J.J. Stokes (Seahawks)	1.00
13	J.J. Stokes (Rams)	1.00
14A	Checklist (John Walsh, Steve McNair, Kerry Collins)	1.75
14B	Emmitt Smith	2.50
15	Steve Young	1.00
16	Marshall Faulk	1.00
17	Troy Aikman	1.50
18	Ki-Jana Carter (Bengals)	1.50
19	Kerry Collins (Panthers)	3.50
20	J.J. Stokes (49ers)	1.50
21	Michael Westbrook (Redskins)	1.00
22	Kyle Brady (Jets)	.50

rack pack of 1995 Classic NFL Rookies. The card fronts feature a color player image over a lightning background with the backs containing another player shot with a profile, also over a lightning background. They cards are numbered with the "IE" prefix.

		MT
Complete Set (20):		18.00
Common Player:		.50
1	Ki-Jana Carter	1.00
2	Steve McNair	3.00
3	Michael Westbrook	1.00
4	Joey Galloway	3.00
5	Tyrone Wheatley	1.00
6	Napoleon Kaufman	1.25
7	Warren Sapp	.75
8	Kevin Carter	.50
9	Todd Collins	.75
10	Rob Johnson	.50
11	Chad May	.50
12	Mike Mamula	.50
13	Sherman Williams	.50
14	Tony Boselli	.75
15	Kerry Collins	3.00
16	J.J. Stokes	1.50
17	Rashaan Salaam	2.00
18	Kordell Stewart	3.00
19	Derrick Brooks	.50
20	Frank Sanders	1.00

1995 Classic NFL Rookies ROY Redemption

The top 19 offensive players and a field card are featured on these 1995 Classic NFL Rookies inserts. Each card in this set is limited to 2,500 produced and was inserted at a rate of one per every three boxes. Cards depicting the January 1996 NFL Offensive Rookie of the Year are redeemable for a $50 phone card of the player. The card front is horizontal, with "1 of 2,500" and "Rookie of the Year" on it. The back has the contest rules. The cards are numbered with "ROY" prefix.

		MT
Complete Set (20):		180.00
Common Player:		3.00
1	Ki-Jana Carter	10.00
2	Tony Boselli	4.00
3	Steve McNair	12.00
4	Michael Westbrook	8.00
5	Kerry Collins	18.00
6	Joseph Galloway	18.00
7	Kyle Brady	4.00
8	J.J. Stokes	12.00
9	Tyrone Wheatley	10.00
10	Napoleon Kaufman	10.00
11	Rashaan Salaam	16.00
12	Kordell Stewart	10.00
13	James Stewart	5.00
14	Frank Sanders	8.00
15	Ray Zellars	5.00
16	Zack Crockett	3.00
17	Tamarick Vanover	8.00
18	Chad May	3.00
19	Eric Zeier	10.00
20	Field Card	20.00

1995 Classic NFL Rookies Rookie Spotlight

The 30-card, standard-size set features a color action shot on the card fronts while the backs contain a color headshot with a player profile. The cards were inserted in every rack pack. The cards are numbered with the "RS" prefix.

		MT
Complete Set (30):		28.00
Common Player:		.50
Holographic Cards:		3x-6x
1	Ki-Jana Carter	1.50
2	Steve McNair	3.00
3	Michael Westbrook	1.00
4	Joey Galloway	3.00
5	Tyrone Wheatley	1.00
6	Napoleon Kaufman	1.00
7	Kordell Stewart	3.00
8	Frank Sanders	1.00
9	Zack Crockett	.50
10	Tamarick Vanover	1.00
11	Chad May	.50
12	Eric Zeier	.50
13	Mike Mamula	.50
14	Warren Sapp	.75
15	Kevin Carter	.50

16	Derrick Brooks	.50
17	Todd Collins	.50
18	Rob Johnson	.50
19	Chris T. Jones	1.00
20	Terrell Fletcher	.50
21	Sherman Williams	.50
22	Tony Boselli	.75
23	Kerry Collins	3.00
24	J.J. Stokes	1.50
25	Rashaan Salaam	2.00
26	James O. Stewart	1.00
27	Rodney Thomas	.50
28	Jack Jackson	.50
29	Lovell Pinkney	.50
30	Ruben Brown	.50

1995 Classic Draft Day Jaguars

The five-card, standard-size set was issued on Draft Day in 1995 to honor the Jacksonville Jaguars first NFL Draft. The card fronts feature color action photos of top 1995 NFL picks in their collegiate uniforms while the backs have the NFL Draft emblem, along with the Jaguars logo. The cards are numbered with the "JJ" prefix.

		MT
Complete Set (5):		20.00
Common Player:		2.00
1	Kerry Collins	6.00
2	Steve McNair	5.00
3	Tony Boselli	2.00
4	Kevin Carter	2.00
5	Ki-Jana Carter	5.00

1995 Classic Images Previews

These five micro-lined insert cards preview the design Classic used for its 1995 NFL Images set. Cards were seeded one per every 18 packs of 1995 Classic Pro Line II product.

		MT
Complete Set (5):		50.00
Common Player:		8.00
1	Emmitt Smith	20.00
2	Steve Young	8.00
3	Drew Bledsoe	10.00
4	Kerry Collins	10.00
5	Marshall Faulk	8.00

1995 Images Limited/Live

Classic's 1995 NFL Images Limited set has two versions - a hobby version called Limited and a retail version called Live. Both contain 125 cards in the regular issue, with an identical checklist, but slightly different designs. The set showcases top NFL veterans and 35 rookies in their pro uniforms. Limited card fronts have a slightly raised image against a metallic background. The player's team name and position are in the upper right corner, while the Images Limited logo is in the bottom left corner. The player's name runs along the bottom. The card back has the number in the upper left corner, with the player's name running along the left side of the card. A full-bleed color action photo is in the center, with 1994 and career statistics underneath. The Live versions have a slightly raised image with a metallic background. The player's

name, team and position are at the bottom. The set icon is in the upper left corner. "Live" repeats itself along the left border. The card back has a photo in the center with a white frame. The player's name and position are underneath, followed by his 1994 and career statistics. The card number is in the upper left corner, while a team logo is in the upper right corner. Images Limited features a 20-card Icons insert set that is printed on fabric. Other insert sets include: DC Images, Silks, NFL Experience Sculpted Previews, Focused and Untouchables.

		MT
Complete Set (125):		30.00
Common Player:		.20
Minor Stars:		.40
Wax Box:		75.00
1	Emmitt Smith	3.00
2	Steve Young	1.00
3	Drew Bledsoe	1.50
4	Dan Marino	3.00
5	John Elway	.75
6	Barry Sanders	2.00
7	Brett Favre	3.00
8	Troy Aikman	1.50
9	Jim Kelly	.40
10	Marshall Faulk	1.00
11	Jerry Rice	1.50
12	Warren Moon	.40
13	Jim Everett	.20
14	Rodney Hampton	.20
15	Jeff Hostetler	.20
16	Errict Rhett	.50
17	Jerome Bettis	.50
18	Byron Morris	.20
19	Randall Cunningham	.20
20	Rick Mirer	.50
21	Natrone Means	.75
22	Jeff George	.40
23	Garrison Hearst	.40
24	Michael Irvin	.75
25	Cris Carter	.40
26	Irving Fryar	.20
27	Jeff Blake	.75
28	Bruce Smith	.20
29	Shannon Sharpe	.20
30	Steve Beuerlein	.20
31	Stan Humphries	.40
32	Chris Warren	.40
33	Ben Coates	.20
34	Boomer Esiason	.20
35	Trent Dilfer	.75
36	Chris Miller	.20
37	Dave Brown	.20
38	Herman Moore	.75
39	Anthony Miller	.20
40	Andre Reed	.20
41	Reggie White	.40
42	Darnay Scott	.50
43	Erik Kramer	.20
44	Leroy Hoard	.20
45	Fred Barnett	.20
46	Junior Seau	.40
47	Vinny Testaverde	.20
48	Gus Frerotte	.50
49	William Floyd	.50
50	Mo Lewis	.20
51	Tim Brown	.40
52	Greg Lloyd	.20
53	Chester McGlockton	.20
54	Heath Shuler	.75
55	Rod Woodson	.20
56	Don Beebe	.20
57	Carl Pickens	.40
58	Charles Haley	.20
59	Steve Bono	.50
60	Harvey Williams	.20
61	Greg Hill	.50
62	Eric Metcalf	.20
63	Mario Bates	.50
64	Terry Allen	.20
65	Michael Timpson	.20
66	Mark Stepnoski	.20
67	Jeff Lageman	.20
68	Robert Smith	.20
69	Eric Allen	.20
70	Ricky Watters	.40
71	Derek Loville	.20
72	Bernie Parmalee	.40
73	Bryce Paup	.20
74	Frank Reich	.20
75	Henry Thomas	.20
76	Craig Erickson	.20
77	Eric Green	.20
78	Dave Meggett	.20
79	Deion Sanders	1.00
80	Herschel Walker	.20
81	Andre Rison	.40
82	Ki-Jana Carter	.75
83	Tony Boselli	.40
84	Steve McNair	4.00
85	Michael Westbrook	1.00
86	Kerry Collins	1.50
87	Kevin Carter	.20
88	Warren Sapp	.40
89	Joey Galloway	2.50
90	J.J. Stokes	1.00
91	Derrick Brooks	.40
92	Kyle Brady	.75

93	Napoleon Kaufman	2.00
94	Tyrone Wheatley	.75
95	Mike Mamula	.40
96	Desmond Howard	.20
97	James Stewart	2.00
98	Craig Newsome	.20
99	Ty Law	.20
100	Ellis Johnson	.20
101	Hugh Douglas	.50
102	Mark Bruener	.75
103	Tyrone Poole	.20
104	Luther Elliss	.20
105	Mark Fields	.20
106	Frank Sanders	.75
107	Rashaan Salaam	.75
108	Craig Powell	.20
109	Sherman Williams	.40
110	Chad May	.40
111	Rob Johnson	1.50
112	Todd Collins	.40
113	Terrell Davis	12.00
114	Eric Zeier	.40
115	Curtis Martin	4.00
116	Kordell Stewart	5.00
117	Troy Vincent	.20
118	Ray Zellars	.40
119	Dave Krieg	.20
120	Mike Sherrard	.20
121	Willie Davis	.20
122	Robert Brooks	.40
123	Chris Sanders	.75
124	Drew Bledsoe CL	.50
125	Emmitt Smith CL	1.00

1995 Images Limited/Live Die-Cuts

These 1995 NFL Images Limited die-cut cards were seeded one per every 99 packs. The card front has a color action photo on the left side, with the "Images" logo repeated throughout the background. An insert set logo is in the lower left corner. The right side of the card has a black panel with the player's name in it; the panel is die-cut like a puzzle piece. The card back repeats the die-cut design on the left side, with a color action photo on the right against a colored background which has the Images icon throughout it. A white box at the top has numbers which indicate the card is "x of 965" made. The cards are numbered with the "DC" prefix.

		MT
Complete Set (30):		450.00
Complete Series 1 (15):		225.00
Complete Series 2 (15):		225.00
Common Player:		7.00
1	Jim Kelly	10.00
2	Kerry Collins	35.00
3	Michael Irvin	10.00
4	Troy Aikman	25.00
5	John Elway	15.00
6	Barry Sanders	35.00
7	Marshall Faulk	10.00
8	James Stewart	7.00
9	Drew Bledsoe	25.00
10	Herman Moore	10.00
11	Bam Morris	7.00
12	Jerry Rice	25.00
13	Joey Galloway	25.00
14	Rick Mirer	7.00
15	Errict Rhett	10.00
16	Rob Moore	7.00
17	Jeff George	7.00
18	Rashaan Salaam	10.00
19	Andre Rison	7.00
20	Emmitt Smith	50.00
21	Brett Favre	50.00
22	Dan Marino	50.00
23	Warren Moon	10.00
24	Dave Brown	7.00
25	Napoleon Kaufman	10.00
26	Natrone Means	10.00
27	Steve Young	25.00
28	Reggie White	10.00
29	Jerome Bettis	10.00

30	Michael Westbrook	10.00

1995 Images Limited/Live Focused

These plastic cards were seeded one per every 24 packs of 1995 NFL Images Limited football. The horizontal front shows two teammates against a background of two wheel cogs. The Images logo is in the upper right corner. A "Focused" icon is in the center of the card at the bottom, sandwiched between the players' names. The card back has ghosted, reversed images of the photos from the front, plus a card number, which is in the upper left corner. The number uses an "F" prefix.

		MT
Complete Set (30):		140.00
Common Player:		5.00
1	Erik Kramer, Rashaan Salaam	8.00
2	Frank Reich, Kerry Collins	10.00
3	Jim Kelly, Andre Reed	5.00
4	Jeff George, Craig Heyward	5.00
5	Garrison Hearst, Dave Krieg	5.00
6	Barry Sanders, Herman Moore	10.00
7	John Elway, Shannon Sharpe	7.00
8	Troy Aikman, Emmitt Smith	20.00
9	Andre Rison, Leroy Hoard	5.00
10	Jeff Blake, Carl Pickens	7.00
11	Steve Bono, Willie Davis	5.00
12	James Stewart, Steve Beuerlein	5.00
13	Marshall Faulk, Craig Erickson	14.00
14	Steve McNair, Chris Chandler	7.00
15	Brett Favre, Reggie White	20.00
16	Dave Brown, Rodney Hampton	5.00
17	Jim Everett, Mario Bates	5.00
18	Drew Bledsoe, Ben Coates	12.00
19	Warren Moon, Cris Carter	5.00
20	Dan Marino, Irving Fryar	20.00
21	Stan Humphries, Natrone Means	8.00
22	Bam Morris, Kevin Greene	5.00
23	Randall Cunningham, Ricky Watters	5.00
24	Jeff Hostetler, Tim Brown	5.00
25	Boomer Esiason, Kyle Brady	5.00
26	Terry Allen, Michael Westbrook	5.00
27	Errict Rhett, Trent Dilfer	8.00
28	Jerome Bettis, Kevin Carter	5.00
29	Steve Young, Jerry Rice	13.00
30	Rick Mirer, Joey Galloway	7.00

Post-1980 cards in Near Mint condition will generally sell for about 75% of the quoted Mint value. Excellent-condition cards bring no more than 40%.

1995 Images Limited/Live Icons

These 20 cards, numbered on the back using an "I" prefix, are printed on fabric cards which are extremely limited; they are seeded one per every 20 boxes of 1995 Classic NFL Images Limited. The set logo is in the upper right corner; the insert set icon is in the lower right corner, opposite the player's name. A full-bleed fabric action photo comprises the front. The back has the card number in the upper left corner, with a photo on the top half of the card. The player's name is below the photo, at the top of a box which includes a recap of the player's professional accomplishments.

		MT
Complete Set (20):		150.00
Common Player:		5.00
1	Jim Kelly	5.00
2	Rashaan Salaam	7.00
3	Andre Rison	5.00
4	Troy Aikman	12.00
5	Emmitt Smith	25.00
6	John Elway	7.00
7	Barry Sanders	12.00
8	Brett Favre	25.00
9	Marshall Faulk	10.00
10	Irving Fryar	5.00
11	Dan Marino	25.00
12	Drew Bledsoe	12.00
13	Rodney Hampton	5.00
14	Ricky Watters	5.00
15	Byron Morris	5.00
16	Natrone Means	7.00
17	Steve Young	12.00
18	Jerry Rice	12.00
19	Errict Rhett	7.00
20	Michael Westbrook	5.00

1995 Images Limited/Live Sculpted Previews

These five insert cards preview the 1996 Classic NFL Experience Sculpted insert cards. Cards, seeded one per every 24 packs, are numbered using an "NX" prefix. The cards, with a foil background, are die-cut around the top. The team logo is incorporated into the background, with an action photo in the forefront. "Sculpted" is written across the top of the card; the player's name is in the bottom right corner in red foil. The back has the player's name at the top, along with a card number. An action photo is on the right, a recap of the player's 1994 season is on the left.

	MT
Complete Set (5):	40.00

1995 Images Limited/Live Silks

Common Player:		5.00
1	Emmitt Smith	15.00
2	Drew Bledsoe	10.00
3	Steve Young	7.00
4	Rashaan Salaam	5.00
5	Marshall Faulk	5.00

These 10 cards were extremely limited; they are seeded one per every 375 packs of 1995 Classic Images Limited/Live football. The card front has a fabric or "silk" action figure cutout of the player against an orange football helmet background. The rest of the card is black, and has a silk set logo in the upper left corner and the player's name in white silk along the bottom. The back, with a number using an "S" prefix in the upper left corner, has an action photo of the player on the right; his name and a summary of his career are on the left. S1-S5 were in Live Images packs; S6-S10 were in Limited packs.

		MT
Complete Set (10):		550.00
Complete Series 1 (5):		250.00
Complete Series 2 (5):		300.00
Common Player:		20.00
1	Troy Aikman	75.00
2	Marshall Faulk	50.00
3	Drew Bledsoe	75.00
4	Bam Morris	25.00
5	James Stewart	25.00
6	Steve Young	60.00
7	Rashaan Salaam	45.00
8	Natrone Means	35.00
10	Michael Westbrook	20.00

1995 Images Limited/Live Untouchables

These 25 cards feature some of the NFL's "untouchable" players. Cards were random inserts in 1995 Classic Images Limited/Live packs. The fronts have a large and small photo against a ghosted action background. The player's name and insert set icon are along the left side of the card. A brand logo is in the upper right corner. The back has a photo, stats, career recap, and card number, which uses a "U" prefix.

		MT
Complete Set (25):		180.00
Common Player:		3.00
1	Jim Kelly	3.00
2	Kerry Collins	8.00
3	Rashaan Salaam	6.00
4	Troy Aikman	12.00
5	Emmitt Smith	25.00
6	John Elway	6.00
7	Barry Sanders	20.00
8	Reggie White	3.00
9	Steve McNair	10.00
10	Marshall Faulk	8.00
11	Dan Marino	25.00
12	Drew Bledsoe	12.00
13	Ben Coates	3.00
14	Tyrone Wheatley	3.00
15	Chester McGlockton	3.00
16	Ricky Watters	3.00
17	Junior Seau	3.00
18	Natrone Means	3.00
19	Steve Young	12.00
20	Jerry Rice	12.00
21	Rick Mirer	3.00
22	Jerome Bettis	6.00
23	Warren Sapp	3.00
24	Michael Westbrook	3.00
25	Heath Shuler	3.00

1995 Classic NFL Experience

Classic limited production on these cards to 1,995 sequentially-numbered cases. Each card front shows an action shot of the player bordered by his team's colors. His team's name runs along the right side; the player's name is in a small pennant in the lower left corner. The set logo also appears on the card front. The back side has another color photo, a card number and highlights from the first 10 weeks of the 1994 season. Each pack included one gold card, which is part of a parallel set. Other inserts include Throwbacks, 1994 Classic Rookies, a Miami Dolphins commemorative card, an Emmitt Smith "Emmitt Zone" card, and an interactive game card awarding prizes based on the Super Bowl's final score.

		MT
Complete Set (110):		10.00
Common Player:		.05
Minor Stars:		.10
Wax Box:		35.00
1	Seth Joyner	.05
2	Clyde Simmons	.05
3	Ron Moore	.05
4	Andre Rison	.10
5	Bert Emanuel	.05
6	Jeff George	.10
7	Terance Mathis	.10
8	Jim Kelly	.15
9	Thurman Thomas	.20
10	Andre Reed	.10
11	Bruce Smith	.05
12	Cornelius Bennett	.05
13	Steve Walsh	.05
14	Lewis Tillman	.05
15	Chris Zorich	.05
16	Jeff Blake	1.00
17	Darnay Scott	.25
18	Dan Wilkinson	.10
19	Eric Metcalf	.05
20	Antonio Langham	.05
21	Pepper Johnson	.05
22	Eric Turner	.05
23	Leroy Hoard	.05
24	Vinny Testaverde	.05
25	Troy Aikman	.75
26	Emmitt Smith	1.00
27	Michael Irvin	.20
28	Alvin Harper	.10
29	Charles Haley	.05
30	John Elway	.25
31	Leonard Russell	.05
32	Shannon Sharpe	.10
33	Herman Moore	.10
34	Barry Sanders	1.00
35	Brett Favre	1.00
36	Sterling Sharpe	.15
37	Reggie White	.10
38	Gary Brown	.05
39	Haywood Jeffires	.05
40	Quentin Coryatt	.05
41	Marshall Faulk	1.00
42	Tony Bennett	.05
43	Joe Montana	1.00
44	Marcus Allen	.10
45	Derrick Thomas	.10
46	Neil Smith	.05
47	Tim Brown	.10
48	Jeff Hostetler	.05
49	Terry McDaniel	.05
50	Jerome Bettis	.30
51	Sean Gilbert	.05
52	Dan Marino	1.50
53	Irving Fryar	.05
54	Keith Jackson	.05
55	Bernie Parmalee	.30
56	Tim Bowens	.05
57	Cris Carter	.10
58	Terry Allen	.05
59	Warren Moon	.15
60	John Randle	.05
61	Jake Reed	.05
62	Drew Bledsoe	1.00
63	Marion Butts	.05
64	Ben Coates	.05
65	Derek Brown	.05
66	Jim Everett	.05
67	Michael Haynes	.05
68	Darion Conner	.05
69	Rodney Hampton	.10
70	Dave Meggett	.05
71	Boomer Esiason	.05
72	Johnny Johnson	.05
73	Ronnie Lott	.05
74	Rob Moore	.05
75	Mo Lewis	.05
76	Randall Cunningham	.10
77	Herschel Walker	.10
78	Charlie Garner	.05
79	Calvin Williams	.05
80	Fred Barnett	.05
81	William Fuller	.05
82	Eric Allen	.05
83	Barry Foster	.10
84	Neil O'Donnell	.05
85	Rod Woodson	.05
86	Kevin Greene	.05
87	Byron Morris	.30
88	Darren Perry	.05
89	Greg Lloyd	.05
90	Steve Young	.40
91	Ricky Watters	.10
92	Jerry Rice	.60
93	Ken Norton	.05
94	Deion Sanders	.50
95	Stan Humphries	.10
96	Natrone Means	.50
97	Junior Seau	.10
98	Leslie O'Neal	.05
99	Chris Mims	.05
100	Rick Mirer	.40
101	Chris Warren	.05
102	Brian Blades	.05
103	Trent Dilfer	.40
104	Errict Rhett	.50
105	Heath Shuler	.50
106	Henry Ellard	.05
107	Ken Harvey	.05
108	Gus Frerotte	.25
109	Checklist 1	.05
110	Checklist 2	.05
MD1	Dan Marino, Don Shula	10.00
NNO	Zone 95 (Emmitt Smith)	80.00

1995 Classic NFL Experience Gold

The 110-card, regular-sized set is a parallel to the 1995 NFL Experience base set, inserted one per hobby pack. The player's name is printed in gold foil on the card fronts, distinguishing it from the base cards.

	MT
Complete Set (110):	45.00
Common Player:	.25
Gold Cards:	2x-3x

1995 Classic NFL Experience Rookies

Ten rookies are showcased on these inserts, which were randomly included four per box of product. Each player is displayed on a horizontal design, with a grey border on the top and bottom and a foil embossed Super Bowl XXIX logo.

		MT
Complete Set (10):		20.00
Common Player:		1.00
1	Marshall Faulk	6.00
2	Bert Emanuel	1.00
3	Charlie Garner	4.00
4	Errict Rhett	4.00
5	Byron Morris	4.00
6	Heath Shuler	3.00
7	Trent Dilfer	3.00
8	Darnay Scott	2.00
9	Tim Bowens	1.00
10	Antonio Langham	1.00

1995 Classic NFL Experience Super Bowl Game

1995 Classic NFL Experience jumbo packs each had one of 20 of these inserts, based on an interactive game regarding the final score of Super Bowl XXIX. Each card has either an AFC or NFC logo, plus a number (0-9). If the last digit of the final score from the game corresponds with the conference and number of a card found by a collector, he could qualify for an assortment of prizes if he sent the card in by mail by March 6, 1995. The grand prize was to be a trip to Super Bowl XXX in Phoenix in 1996. Game cards submitted to Classic were not returned. The back had the rules and prizes for the game listed.

		MT
Complete Set (20):		20.00
Common Player:		.50
0	AFC (Marshall Faulk)	2.50
1	AFC (Natrone Means)	1.25
2	AFC (Thurman Thomas)	.50
3	AFC (Joe Montana)	2.00
4	AFC (John Elway)	1.00
5	AFC (Rick Mirer)	1.00
6	AFC (Drew Bledsoe)	2.00
7	AFC (Dan Marino)	3.00
8	AFC (Jim Kelly)	.50
9	AFC (Marcus Allen)	.50
0	NFC (Troy Aikman)	2.00
1	NFC (Steve Young)	2.00
2	NFC (Jerome Bettis)	1.00
3	NFC (Barry Sanders)	2.00
4	NFC (Randall Cunningham)	.50
5	NFC (Andre Rison)	.50
6	NFC (Jerry Rice)	2.00
7	NFC (Emmitt Smith)	3.00
8	NFC (Michael Irvin)	1.00
9	NFC (Sterling Sharpe)	1.00

1995 Classic NFL Experience Throwbacks

These 28 insert cards are printed on parchment to give each card a look and feel of an old-time card. This was done to commemorate the NFL's 75th anniversary. The set features one player from each team in his throwback uniform, bordered by a white frame. A brief history of the NFL franchise and the reason why the team chose that particular uniform are given on the back. The card number uses a "T" prefix. These inserts were included two per box.

		MT
Complete Set (28):		130.00
Common Player:		3.00
Minor Stars:		6.00
1	Seth Joyner	3.00
2	Andre Rison	6.00
3	Thurman Thomas	6.00
4	Lewis Tillman	3.00
5	Dan Wilkinson	6.00
6	Eric Metcalf	6.00
7	Emmitt Smith	20.00
8	John Elway	7.00
9	Barry Sanders	12.00
10	Reggie White	6.00
11	Haywood Jeffires	3.00

		MT
12	Marshall Faulk	12.00
13	Joe Montana	12.00
14	Jeff Hostetler	3.00
15	Jerome Bettis	6.00
16	Dan Marino	20.00
17	Warren Moon	6.00
18	Drew Bledsoe	12.00
19	Jim Everett	3.00
20	Dave Meggett	3.00
21	Ronnie Lott	3.00
22	Randall Cunningham	6.00
23	Rod Woodson	6.00
24	Natrone Means	10.00
25	Rick Mirer	6.00
26	Steve Young	12.00
27	Trent Dilfer	8.00
28	Henry Ellard	3.00

1996 Classic NFL Draft Day

The 15-card, regular-sized set was distributed by Classic in New York on the 1996 NFL Draft Day. The first nine cards feature the top three players in the draft with three different teams each. The final six cards feature former first-round draft picks.

		MT
Complete Set (15):		25.00
Common Player:		1.00
1A	Keyshawn Johnson (Jets)	2.50
1B	Keyshawn Johnson (Jaguars)	2.50
1C	Keyshawn Johnson (Redskins)	2.50
2A	Kevin Hardy (Jaguars)	1.25
2B	Kevin Hardy (Redskins)	1.25
2C	Kevin Hardy (Cardinals)	1.25
3A	Terry Glenn (Patriots)	2.00
3B	Terry Glenn (Giants)	2.00
3C	Terry Glenn (Jets)	2.00
4	Eddie George	5.00
5	Emmitt Smith	3.50
6	Troy Aikman	2.00
7	Drew Bledsoe	2.00
8	Kerry Collins	2.00
9	Title Card (Checklist back)	1.00

1996 Classic NFL Rookies

Classic's 1996 NFL Rookies set features top players in the 1996 NFL Draft, including two subsets called All-Americans and NFL Greats. Each card front has a full-bleed color action photo of the player in his college uniform, but his pro team's name is at the top, along with a team helmet at the bottom, next to his name. Backs have a color close-up photo of the player in a square which has his name, team name, position and draft selection number along the four sides. Below the photo is a ghosted body shot from the same closeup shot. A recap of his collegiate accomplishments are on one side; statistics and biographical information are on the other. A card number is in the upper left corner in a blue square. Hobby pack insert cards were Rookie of the Year Interactive, NFL Road Jerseys and Rookie Lasers. Retail pack inserts include Rookie #1 Die-Cuts and NFL Home Jerseys.

		MT
Complete Set (100):		10.00
Common Player:		.05
Minor Stars:		.10
1	Keyshawn Johnson	1.50
2	Jonathan Ogden	.20
3	Kevin Hardy	.20
4	Leeland McElroy	.30
5	Terry Glenn	1.00
6	Tim Biakabutuka	.50
7	Tony Brackens	.05
8	Duane Clemons	.10
9	Willie Anderson	.05
10	Karim Abdul-Jabbar	.75
11	Daryl Gardener	.05
12	Simeon Rice	.20
13	Eddie George	2.00
14	Andre Johnson	.05
15	Jon Runyan	.05
16	Jevon Langford	.05
17	Derrick Mayes	.40
18	Stephen Davis	.75
19	Ray Farmer	.05
20	Chris Doering	.10
21	Jimmy Herndon	.05
22	Jerome Woods	.05
23	Scott Greene	.05
24	Jamin Stephens	.05
25	Tommie Frazier	.20
26	Dusty Zeigler	.05
27	Alex Molden	.05
28	Dietrich Jells	.05
29	Brian Roche	.05
30	Danny Kanell	.50
31	Roman Oben	.05
32	Chris Darkins	.20
33	Christian Peter	.05
34	Jeff Hartings	.05
35	Bobby Hoying	.50
36	Steve Taneyhill	.05
37	Lance Johnstone	.05
38	Zach Thomas	.25
39	Donnie Edwards	.05
40	Eric Moulds	1.25
41	Amani Toomer	.40
42	Scott Slutzker	.05
43	Matt Stevens	.05
44	Randall Godfrey	.05
45	Orpheus Roye	.05
46	Jason Odom	.05
47	Jerod Cherry	.05
48	Jeff Lewis	.20
49	Mike Alstott	1.25
50	Tony Banks	.75
51	Stepfret Williams	.05
52	Michael Cheever	.05
53	Bryant Mix	.05
54	James Ritchey	.10
55	Marcus Coleman	.05
56	Sedric Clark	.05
57	Kyle Wachholz	.05
58	Johnny McWilliams	.10
59	Lawyer Milloy	.10
60	Alex Van Dyke	.30
61	Stanley Pritchett	.20
62	Ray Mickens	.10
63	Toraino Singleton	.05
64	Richard Huntley	.05
65	Eddie George	.75
66	Terry Glenn	.25
67	Keyshawn Johnson	.30
68	Jonathan Ogden	.05
69	Tommie Frazier	.10
70	Kevin Hardy	.05
71	Zach Thomas	.10
72	Tony Brackens	.05
73	Lawyer Milloy	.05
74	Leeland McElroy	.10
75	Emmitt Smith	.50
76	Steve McNair	.30
77	Kerry Collins	.10
78	Drew Bledsoe	.25
79	Marshall Faulk	.20
80	Pete Kendall	.05
81	Regan Upshaw	.05
82	Mercury Hayes	.05
83	Dou Innocent	.05
84	DeRon Jenkins	.05
85	Marco Battaglia	.10
86	John Mobley	.10
87	Cedric Jones	.05
88	Marvin Harrison	.50
89	Israel Ifeanyl	.05
90	Reggie Brown	.05
91	Jermain Mayberry	.05
92	Brian Dawkins	.05
93	Tedy Bruschi	.05
94	Terrell Owens	2.00
95	Jermaine Lewis	.05
96	Sean Boyd	.05
97	Phillip Daniels	.05
98	Lawrence Phillips	1.00
99	Keyshawn Johnson (Checklist 1)	.50
100	Terry Glenn (Checklist 2)	.25

1996 Classic NFL Rookies Rookie #1 Die-Cuts

Thirty top rookies are featured on these 1996 Classic NFL Rookies inserts, seeded ran-domly in retail packs. The cards use a metallic stock and are die-cut around the number 1.

		MT
Complete Set (30):		300.00
Common Player:		5.00
1	Keyshawn Johnson	20.00
2	Kevin Hardy	5.00
3	Simeon Rice	5.00
4	Jonathan Ogden	5.00
5	Cedric Jones	5.00
6	Lawrence Phillips	10.00
7	Terry Glenn	25.00
8	Tim Biakabutuka	7.00
9	Emmitt Smith	25.00
10	Willie Anderson	5.00
11	Alex Molden	5.00
12	Regan Upshaw	5.00
13	Kerry Collins	10.00
14	Eddie George	60.00
15	John Mobley	5.00
16	Duane Clemons	5.00
17	Reggie Brown	5.00
18	Marshall Faulk	10.00
19	Marvin Harrison	10.00
20	Daryl Gardener	5.00
21	Pete Kendall	5.00
22	Joey Galloway	7.00
23	Jeff Hartings	5.00
24	Eric Moulds	5.00
25	Jermain Mayberry	5.00
26	Steve McNair	20.00
27	Kyle Brady	5.00
28	Jerome Woods	5.00
29	Jamin Stephens	5.00
30	Andre Johnson	5.00

1996 Classic NFL Rookies NFL Home Jerseys

These 30 cards were exclu-sive inserts to 1996 Classic NFL Rookies retail packs, one per every 15 packs. The card front is horizontal and shows the player in action while he was in college, alongside a home jersey of his new NFL team. Card backs are numbered using an "HJ" prefix.

		MT
Complete Set (30):		120.00
Common Player:		3.00
1	Keyshawn Johnson	30.00
2	Kevin Hardy	8.00
3	Jonathan Ogden	3.00
4	Terry Glenn	17.00
5	Tim Biakabutuka	10.00
6	Karim Abdul-Jabbar	10.00
7	Simeon Rice	8.00
8	Eric Moulds	8.00
9	Mike Alstott	7.00
10	Leeland McElroy	5.00
11	Daryl Gardener	3.00
12	Eddie George	17.00
13	Amani Toomer	8.00
14	Johnny McWilliams	3.00
15	Derrick Mayes	3.00
16	Duane Clemons	3.00
17	Chris Darkins	7.00
18	Ray Farmer	3.00
19	Danny Kanell	7.00
20	Bobby Hoying	10.00
21	Zach Thomas	3.00
22	Tony Banks	3.00
23	Alex Van Dyke	3.00
24	Stepfret Williams	3.00
25	Chris Doering	3.00
26	Lance Johnstone	3.00
27	Stephen Davis	3.00
28	Scott Greene	3.00
29	Tony Brackens	3.00
30	Jevon Langford	3.00

1996 Classic NFL Rookies NFL Road Jerseys

Each of these horizontally-designed cards shows the play-er on the front in his college uni-form, and adjacent to a road jersey of the NFL team which drafted him in 1996. The cards were random inserts in 1996 Classic NFL Rookies packs, one per 15 packs. Card backs are numbered using an "RJ" prefix and have a color closeup photo, plus a recap of the player's col-legiate accomplishments. Silver foil stamping is used on the front for the player's name and brand logo.

		MT
Complete Set (30):		120.00
Common Player:		3.00
1	Keyshawn Johnson	30.00
2	Kevin Hardy	8.00
3	Jonathan Ogden	3.00
4	Terry Glenn	17.00
5	Tim Biakabutuka	10.00
6	Karim Abdul-Jabbar	10.00
7	Simeon Rice	8.00
8	Eric Moulds	8.00
9	Mike Alstott	7.00
10	Leeland McElroy	10.00
11	Daryl Gardener	3.00
12	Eddie George	17.00
13	Amani Toomer	8.00
14	Marvin Harrison	3.00
15	Derrick Mayes	3.00
16	Dietrich Jells	3.00
17	Chris Darkins	7.00
18	Ray Farmer	3.00
19	Danny Kanell	7.00
20	Bobby Hoying	10.00
21	Zach Thomas	3.00
22	Kyle Wachholz	3.00
23	Alex Van Dyke	3.00
24	Stepfret Williams	3.00
25	Chris Doering	3.00
26	Lance Johnstone	3.00
27	Stephen Davis	3.00
28	Scott Greene	3.00
29	Tony Brackens	3.00
30	Jevon Langford	3.00

1996 Classic NFL Rookies Rookie Lasers

Rookie Lasers cards were seeded one per every 100 packs of 1996 Classic NFL Rookies hobby packs. The cards feature 10 of the best rookies and are numbered using an "RL" prefix.

		MT
Complete Set (10):		150.00
Common Player:		7.00
1	Keyshawn Johnson	45.00
2	Jonathan Ogden	7.00
3	Eddie George	35.00
4	Terry Glenn	35.00
5	Tommie Frazier	25.00
6	Karim Abdul-Jabbar	15.00
7	Duane Clemons	7.00
8	Leeland McElroy	25.00
9	Tim Biakabutuka	30.00
10	Kevin Hardy	10.00

1996 Classic NFL Rookies Rookie of the Year Contenders

The 10-card, regular-sized set was randomly inserted in retail packs of 1996 Classic NFL. Both the card fronts and backs feature action shots of the players with the player's name appearing in the lower right corner of the fronts. The cards are numbered with the "C" prefix.

		MT
Complete Set (10):		65.00
Common Player:		1.50
1	Keyshawn Johnson	15.00
2	Jonathan Ogden	1.50
3	Eddie George	20.00
4	Terry Glenn	16.00
5	Eric Moulds	4.00
6	Karim Abdul-Jabbar	14.00
7	Leeland McElroy	6.00
8	Tim Biakabutuka	10.00
9	Bobby Hoying	3.00
10	Stephen Davis	3.00

1996 Classic NFL Rookies Rookie of the Year Interactive

These interactive insert cards were randomly seeded in hobby packs of 1996 Classic NFL Rookies product. The cards feature 20 leading candidates to win the NFL Offensive Rookie of the Year award. If the player on the card wins, it is redeemable for an autographed collectible of the player. The card front has a full-bleed color action photo, with the player's name towards the bottom of the card. "Rookie of the Year" and "Interactive" are spelled out along the right side of the card. Card backs, numbered using an "ROY" prefix, explain the rules of the redemption program.

		MT
Complete Set (20):		150.00
Common Player:		3.00
1	Keyshawn Johnson	30.00
2	Jonathan Ogden	3.00
3	Steve Taneyhill	3.00
4	Leeland McElroy	10.00
5	Terry Glenn	20.00
6	Tim Biakabutuka	15.00
7	Karim Abdul-Jabbar	10.00
8	Eddie George	20.00
9	Johnny McWilliams	3.00
10	Eric Moulds	8.00
11	Bobby Hoying	8.00
12	Chris Darkins	10.00
13	Derrick Mayes	10.00
14	Mike Alstott	3.00
15	Chris Doering	10.00
16	Danny Kanell	10.00
17	Stephen Davis	3.00
18	Amani Toomer	10.00
19	Dietrich Jells	3.00
20	Field Card	10.00

1996 Score Board Laser National Promos

Distributed at the Classic booth at the 1996 National Card Collector's Convention, this five-card set was available separately or in a lucite holder, which was numbered of 300.

		MT
Complete Set (5):		25.00
Complete Framed Set (5):		35.00
Common Player:		3.00
1	Kordell Stewart	5.00
2	Troy Aikman	5.00
3	Emmitt Smith	10.00
4	Lawrence Phillips	3.00
5	Keyshawn Johnson	4.00

1996 Score Board NFL Lasers

This 100-card set features some of the NFL's top stars, including seven who have autographed special inserts. The regular card front has a color action photo on it against a metallic background. The left frame of the card is green; the upper right and lower right corners are gold, with NFL Lasers and the player's team name in them. The player's name and position are above the bottom frame. The card back has a card number and the player's name at the top, with biographical information below. The right border has the player's name at the top, with his team name running horizontally toward the bottom. 1995 and career stats are along the bottom. A photo completes the back. The autographed cards, available at a rate of two per case, come in two versions - regular (400 each, one per 150 packs), and die-cuts (100 each, one per 930 packs). The other inserts are Laser Images and Sunday's Heroes.

7	Carl Pickens	.10
8	Cris Carter	.10
9	Curtis Martin	2.00
10	Dan Marino	2.50
11	Dave Brown	.10
12	Drew Bledsoe	1.00
13	Edgar Bennett	.30
14	Herman Moore	.30
15	Jeff Blake	.30
16	Jerry Rice	1.25
17	Jim Kelly	.20
18	John Elway	.75
19	Junior Seau	.10
20	Kerry Collins	1.25
21	Kordell Stewart	1.00
22	Leonard Russell	.10
23	Mark Brunell	.50
24	Marshall Faulk	.30
25	Mike Tomczak	.10
26	Reggie White	.20
27	Ricky Watters	.20
28	Rod Woodson	.10
29	Rodney Peete	.10
30	Stan Humphries	.10
31	Steve McNair	.75
32	Terry Allen	.10
33	Thurman Thomas	.20
34	Troy Aikman	1.25
35	Vinny Testaverde	.10
36	Chris T. Jones	.10
37	Deion Sanders	.75
38	Eric Metcalf	.10
39	Erik Kramer	.10
40	Emmitt Smith	2.50
41	Gus Frerotte	.10
42	Jeff George	.10
43	Jerome Bettis	.20
44	Jim Harbaugh	.10
45	Isaac Bruce	.50
46	Jeff Hostetler	.10
47	Ki-Jana Carter	.20
48	Marcus Allen	.20
49	Neil O'Donnell	.10
50	Rashaan Salaam	.40
51	Robert Brooks	.10
52	Steve Bono	.10
53	Scott Mitchell	.10
54	Terrell Davis	1.50
55	Tim Brown	.10
56	Troy Vincent	.10
57	Warren Moon	.10
58	Tony Martin	.10
59	Rodney Hampton	.10
60	Steve Young	1.00
61	Rick Mirer	.10
62	Mark Chmura	.10
63	Larry Centers	.10
64	Ken Dilger	.10
65	Joey Galloway	1.00
66	Jim Everett	.10
67	Chris Chandler	.10
68	James Stewart	.10
69	Robert Smith	.10
70	Tamarick Vanover	.50
71	Wayne Chrebet	.10
72	*Keyshawn Johnson*	*2.00*
73	*Kevin Hardy*	*.20*
74	*Lawrence Phillips*	*.50*
75	*Jonathan Ogden*	*.20*
76	*Terry Glenn*	*.50*
77	*Tim Biakabutuka*	*1.00*
78	*Eddie George*	*3.00*
79	*Eric Moulds*	*1.50*
80	*John Mobley*	*.10*
81	*Amani Toomer*	*.20*
82	*Marvin Harrison*	*2.00*
83	*Leeland McElroy*	*.30*
84	*Rickey Dudley*	*.30*
85	*Tony Banks*	*.50*
86	*Zach Thomas*	*.75*
87	*Alex Molden*	*.10*
88	*Daryl Gardener*	*.10*
89	*Jamal Anderson*	*5.00*
90	*Karim Abdul-Jabbar*	*.50*
91	*Simeon Rice*	*.20*
92	*Walt Harris*	*.10*
93	*Bobby Engram*	*.30*
94	Kevin Williams	.10
95	Sean Gilbert	.10
96	Kevin Greene	.10
97	Regan Upshaw	.10
98	Marcus Jones	.10
99	Ray Lewis	.10
100	Checklist	.10

1996 Score Board NFL Lasers Laser Images

These cards are seeded one per every 30 packs of 1996 Score Board NFL Lasers. The card front has a color action photo of the player, with a ghosted black laser image of the player in the background, which is metallic. The card has gold foil stamped around three sides as a border; the player's name is also in gold foil on the right side. The Laser Images logo is also on the front. The card back has a color photo of the laser image from the front, with a column down the left side which has a recap of the player's accomplishments and a team logo at the bottom. The card number, using an "I" prefix, is in the upper left corner. The player's name is in a rectangle in the upper right corner. His last name is in scripted letter along the left side of the card.

		MT
Complete Set (100):		30.00
Common Player:		.10
Minor Stars:		.20
Wax Box:		80.00
1	Brett Favre	2.50
2	Chris Warren	.10
3	J.J. Stokes	.25
4	Barry Sanders	1.25
5	Ben Coates	.10
6	Bryan Cox	.10

		MT
Complete Set (30):		250.00
Common Player:		3.00
1	Steve Bono	3.00
2	Kerry Collins	20.00
3	Tim Biakabutuka	6.00
4	Rashaan Salaam	3.00
5	Jeff Blake	6.00
6	Emmitt Smith	30.00
7	Troy Aikman	20.00
8	Deion Sanders	12.00
9	John Elway	12.00
10	Herman Moore	3.00
11	Brett Favre	20.00
12	Eddie George	20.00
13	Marvin Harrison	12.00
14	Mark Brunell	12.00
15	Dan Marino	20.00
16	Karim Abdul-Jabbar	15.00
17	Cris Carter	3.00
18	Drew Bledsoe	15.00
19	Curtis Martin	20.00
20	Keyshawn Johnson	10.00
21	Chris T. Jones	15.00
22	Kordell Stewart	15.00
23	Junior Seau	3.00
24	Steve Young	15.00
25	Jerry Rice	15.00
26	Joey Galloway	12.00
27	Lawrence Phillips	12.00
28	Jonathan Ogden	3.00
29	Jim Harbaugh	3.00
30	Neil O'Donnell	3.00

1996 Score Board NFL Lasers Sunday's Heroes

These cards, numbered using an "S" prefix, capture 25 stars on a thicker, embossed surface. Cards were seeded one per every 22 packs of 1996 Score Board NFL Lasers product.

		MT
Complete Set (25):		450.00
Common Player:		8.00
1	Tim Brown	8.00
2	Kerry Collins	30.00
3	Tim Biakabutuka	15.00
4	Rashaan Salaam	12.00
5	Jeff Blake	15.00
6	Ki-Jana Carter	12.00
7	Emmitt Smith	50.00
8	Troy Aikman	30.00
9	Deion Sanders	20.00
10	Terrell Davis	30.00
11	Barry Sanders	30.00
12	Brett Favre	50.00
13	Reggie White	12.00
14	Marshall Faulk	20.00
15	Mark Brunell	20.00
16	Kevin Hardy	8.00
17	Dan Marino	50.00
18	Drew Bledsoe	25.00
19	Curtis Martin	40.00
20	Keyshawn Johnson	20.00
21	Kordell Stewart	25.00
22	Steve Young	25.00
23	Jerry Rice	30.00
24	Chris Warren	8.00
25	Karim Abdul-Jabbar	30.00

1996 Score Board NFL Lasers Autographs

Seven players have autographed these 1996 Score Board inserts - Emmitt Smith, Troy Aikman, Keyshawn Johnson, Marshall Faulk, Drew Bledsoe, Steve Young and Kordell Stewart. The cards were available at a rate of two per case, in two different versions. Regular versions (400 each) were seeded one per 150 packs. Die-cut versions (100 each) were seeded one per 930 packs.

		MT
Complete Set (7):		850.00
Common Player:		3.00
1	Troy Aikman	150.00
2	Kerry Collins	—
3	Steve Young	120.00
	Kordell Stewart	150.00
	Keyshawn Johnson	100.00
	Emmitt Smith	250.00
	Marshall Faulk	100.00
	Drew Bledsoe	150.00

1996 Score Board NFL Lasers Die-Cut Autographs

Also included in packs of NFL Lasers were die-cut versions of each of the seven players. Die-cut versions were limited to only 100 of each.

		MT
Complete Set (7):		1700.
	Troy Aikman	300.00
	Steve Young	240.00
	Kordell Stewart	300.00
	Keyshawn Johnson	200.00
	Emmitt Smith	500.00
	Marshall Faulk	200.00
	Drew Bledsoe	300.00

1996 Classic NFL Experience

This 125-card 1996 Classic NFL Experience set is geared toward players who participated in the postseason. Each card front has a full-bleed color action photo on glossy stock. The Classic logo is in an upper corner; the player's name and position are in an arch at the bottom. Three-fourths of the card back has a format similar to the design used for the card front, except a number has been added in an upper corner. The bottom fourth of the card contains a 1995 recap. Insert sets include: Sculpted, Super Bowl game cards, three oversized bonus cards, Emmitt Zone and The "X." 1996 Classic NFL Experience also continues the Hot Box program. There is an average of one Hot Box every five sealed cases, with each pack in a Hot Box containing 20-percent inserts. Each card in the regular set is also reprinted as part of a Printer's Proof parallel set. Only 499 of each card is printed, with an insert ratio of one per 10 packs.

		MT
Complete Set (125):		10.00
Common Player:		.05
Minor Stars:		.10
Wax Box:		38.00
1	Emmitt Smith	2.00
2	Jerry Rice	1.00
3	Carl Pickens	.15
4	Curtis Conway	.10
5	Isaac Bruce	.10
6	Marshall Faulk	.10
7	Errict Rhett	.10
8	Troy Aikman	.75
9	Jeff Hostetler	.05
10	Dan Marino	2.00
11	Barry Sanders	1.00
12	Drew Bledsoe	.50
13	Ricky Watters	.10
14	Natrone Means	.20
15	Chris Warren	.10
16	Jim Kelly	.10
17	Jeff George	.05
18	Garrison Hearst	.10
19	Brett Favre	2.00
20	John Elway	.50
21	Robert Smith	.05
22	Steve Bono	.10
23	Byron Morris	.20
24	Jim Everett	.05
25	Steve Young	.50
26	Rodney Hampton	.05
27	Terry Allen	.05
28	Chris Chandler	.05
29	Mark Carrier	.05
30	Desmond Howard	.05
31	Erik Kramer	.05
32	Irving Fryar	.05
33	Jeff Blake	.50
34	Vinny Testaverde	.05
35	Stan Humphries	.05
36	Tim Brown	.05
37	Trent Dilfer	.10
38	Jim Harbaugh	.05
39	Warren Moon	.10
40	Ben Coates	.05
41	Boomer Esiason	.05
42	Rodney Peete	.05
43	Gus Frerotte	.05
44	Jerome Bettis	.10
45	Dave Brown	.05
46	William Floyd	.05
47	Andre Rison	.05
48	Robert Brooks	.10
49	Marcus Allen	.05
50	Rick Mirer	.10
51	Alvin Harper	.05
52	Chris Miller	.05
53	Eric Metcalf	.05
54	Dave Krieg	.05
55	Darnay Scott	.10
56	Cris Carter	.05
57	Lake Dawson	.05
58	Haywood Jeffires	.05
59	Herman Moore	.20
60	Michael Irvin	.20
61	Anthony Miller	.05
62	Troy Vincent	.05
63	Jake Reed	.05
64	Michael Haynes	.05
65	Scott Mitchell	.05
66	Roman Phifer	.05
67	Harvey Williams	.05
68	Darren Perry	.05
69	Brian Mitchell	.05
70	Derek Loville	.05
71	Junior Seau	.10
72	Bruce Smith	.05
73	Willie Davis	.05
74	Charles Haley	.05
75	Mike Sherrard	.05
76	Pat Swilling	.05
77	Yancey Thigpen	.25
78	Bryce Paup	.05
79	Eric Green	.05
80	Deion Sanders	.40
81	Mario Bates	.05
82	John Randle	.05
83	Charlie Garner	.05
84	Chris Doleman	.05
85	Robert Porcher	.05
86	Rob Moore	.05
87	Anthony Pleasant	.05
88	Bryan Cox	.05
89	Greg Hill	.05
90	Reggie White	.10
91	Shannon Sharpe	.05
92	Leroy Hoard	.05
93	John Copeland	.05
94	Tony Martin	.05
95	Greg Lloyd	.05
96	Tony Bennett	.05
97	Alonzo Spellman	.05
98	Wayne Martin	.05
99	Craig Heyward	.05
100	Leslie O'Neal	.05
101	Andy Harmon	.05
102	Edgar Bennett	.05
103	Derrick Moore	.05
104	Terrell Davis	.75
105	Kerry Collins	.75
106	Rodney Thomas	.25
107	Mark Brunell	.50
108	Curtis Martin	2.00
109	Tyrone Wheatley	.20
110	Rashaan Salaam	.10
111	Kevin Carter	.10
112	Joey Galloway	.75
113	Mike Mamula	.10
114	Kyle Brady	.10
115	James Stewart	.10

116	Michael Westbrook	.10
117	J.J. Stokes	.10
118	Wayne Chrebet	.10
119	Warren Sapp	.10
120	Hugh Douglas	.05
121	Jim Flanigan	.10
122	Chester McGlockton	.05
123	Shawn Lee	.05
124	Checklist Card 1	.25
125	Checklist Card 2	.25

1996 Classic NFL Experience Printer's Proofs

The 125-card, standard-size set is a parallel set to the 1996 NFL Experience base set, inserted every 20 packs. The card fronts are numbered as "x of 499."

	MT
Complete Set (125):	225.00
Common Player:	.75
Printer's Proofs Cards:	10x-20x

1996 Classic NFL Experience Super Bowl Gold/Red

The 125-card, regular-size set is a parallel to the 1996 NFL Experience set. The gold cards are numbered as "x of 799" while the red cards are numbered as "x of 150."

	MT
Complete Gold Set (125):	125.00
Common Gold Player:	.50
Gold Cards:	5x-10x
Complete Red Set (125):	550.00
Common Red Player:	2.00
Red Cards:	25x-50x

1996 Classic NFL Experience Class of 1995

This five-card set was included one per every 1996 Classic NFL Experience factory set. Cards are numbered using an "FI" prefix and have the set icon on the card front.

		MT
Complete Set (5):		10.00
Common Player:		1.00
1	Steve Young	2.00
2	Emmitt Smith	4.00
3	Deion Sanders	1.50
4	Rashaan Salaam	1.00
5	Kerry Collins	2.00

1996 Classic NFL Experience Emmitt Zone

The five-card, standard-size set was randomly inserted in packs of 1996 NFL Experi-

ence. Smith's name is printed down the card front's left border while "Emmitt Zone" appears in the lower right corner. A $5 "Emmitt Zone" phone card was also inserted every 375 Super Bowl packs.

		MT
Complete Set (5):		250.00
Common Player:		50.00
1	Emmitt Smith (1990-91 ROY)	50.00
2	Emmitt Smith (1992 NFL Leading Rusher)	50.00
3	Emmitt Smith (1993 3rd NFL Rushing Title)	50.00
4	Emmitt Smith (1994 Leader in League Touchdowns)	50.00
5	Emmitt Smith (1995 Best Season Ever)	50.00

1996 Classic NFL Experience Oversized Bonus Cards

These cards, one of which is randomly placed in each case of 1996 Classic NFL Experience product, complete the company's bonus program for its 1995 NFL-licensed products. The cards feature Emmitt Smith, Michael Westbrook and Reggie White.

		MT
Complete Set (15):		15.00
Common Player:		2.00
13	Emmitt Smith	10.00
14	Michael Westbrook	2.00
15	Reggie White	5.00

1996 Classic NFL Experience Super Bowl Die Cut Promos

The 10-card, regular-sized set, given away at the Super Bowl Card Show in Tempe, Ariz., featured players from the NFL Experience Die Cut matched inserts. The card backs contain rules for prize giveaways and "Show Promo." The cards are numbered with the "C" suffix.

	MT
Complete Set (10):	45.00

Common Player:		2.00
1	Jim Kelly	3.00
2	Dan Marino	12.00
3	Greg Lloyd	2.00
4	Marcus Allen	3.00
5	Tim Brown	2.00
6	Emmitt Smith	12.00
7	Steve Young	4.00
8	Rashaan Salaam	3.00
9	Brett Favre	12.00
10	Isaac Bruce	4.00

1996 Classic NFL Experience Super Bowl Die Cut Contest

The 20-card, regular-size set features 10 players on two cards each and was inserted in every 12 packs of the Card Show version of 1996 NFL Experience. The cards are numbered 1A through 10A and 1B through 10B. When the cards are put together, they form the Super Bowl XXX logo. The card backs contain rules on how to redeem the cards for a prize.

		MT
Complete Set (20):		160.00
Common Player:		2.50
1A	Jim Kelly	5.00
1B	Jim Kelly	5.00
2A	Dan Marino	20.00
2B	Dan Marino	20.00
3A	Greg Lloyd	2.50
3B	Greg Lloyd	2.50
4A	Marcus Allen	4.00
4B	Marcus Allen	4.00
5A	Tim Brown	2.50
5B	Tim Brown	2.50
6A	Emmitt Smith	20.00
6B	Emmitt Smith	20.00
7A	Steve Young	8.00
7B	Steve Young	8.00
8A	Rashaan Salaam	6.00
8B	Rashaan Salaam	6.00
9A	Brett Favre	20.00
9B	Brett Favre	20.00
10A	Isaac Bruce	8.00
10B	Isaac Bruce	8.00

1996 Classic NFL Experience Super Bowl Game Cards

These interactive cards are based on the final score of Super Bowl XXX in 1996. The 20 cards were inserted one per pack of 1996 Classic NFL Experience product; each card has either an AFC or NFC logo, plus a number (0-9). If the last digit of the final score from the game corresponds with the conference and number of a card found by a collector, he could qualify for an assortment of prizes if he sent it in by March 8, 1996. The grand prize was to be a trip to Super Bowl XXXI in 1997 in New Orleans. Game cards submitted to Classic were not returned. Each card front has a silver metallic background, with a color action shot. The Super Bowl XXX logo is in the upper left corner. The player's name and conference logo/card number are at the bottom. The back has a set checklist, list of rules and prizes, and the card number again. The Super Bowl logo repeats itself in the background.

	MT
Complete Set (20):	2.50
Common Player:	.75

		MT
A0	Drew Bledsoe	2.50
A1	John Elway	1.25
A2	Harvey Williams	.75
A3	Marshall Faulk	2.50
A4	Jim Kelly	.75
A5	Carl Pickens	.75
A6	Stan Humphries	.75
A7	Dan Marino	6.00
A8	Steve Bono	.75
A9	Napoleon Kaufman	.75
N0	Isaac Bruce	2.50
N1	Steve Young	2.50
N2	Michael Westbrook	2.50
N3	Troy Aikman	3.00
N4	Barry Sanders	3.00
N5	Rashaan Salaam	2.00
N6	Emmitt Smith	6.00
N7	Jerry Rice	3.00
N8	Deion Sanders	2.50
N9	Kerry Collins	3.00

1996 Classic NFL Experience Sculpted

These die-cut foil-board insert cards were seeded one per every 15 packs of 1996 Classic NFL Experience. Cards were limited to 2,400 of each card. The card has a color action photo against a tan background which has the team logo incorporated into it. "Sculpted" is written at the top; the player's name is at the bottom. The card back has a color action photo on one side, with the player's name at the top in his team's primary color. A brief player profile, also using the team color, is given, as is a card number, which uses an "S" prefix.

	MT
Complete Set (20):	180.00
Common Player:	3.00
Minor Stars:	6.00

1	Kerry Collins	12.00
2	Jeff Blake	8.00
3	Vinny Testaverde	3.00
4	Emmitt Smith	20.00
5	Troy Aikman	10.00
6	Deion Sanders	8.00
7	John Elway	6.00
8	Barry Sanders	12.00
9	Brett Favre	20.00
10	Marshall Faulk	10.00
11	Steve Bono	6.00
12	Dan Marino	20.00
13	Robert Smith	3.00
14	Drew Bledsoe	10.00
15	Natrone Means	6.00
16	Steve Young	10.00
17	Jerry Rice	10.00
18	Isaac Bruce	10.00
19	Errict Rhett	6.00
20	Michael Westbrook	6.00

1996 Classic NFL Experience X

This 1996 Classic NFL Experience insert set exposes col-

lectors to everything exceptional about the game. Each card is seeded one per every 45 packs; there were only 1,500 of each produced. The card front features a silver stamp, plus a color photo of the player and the set icon, an X. Backs are numbered using an "X" prefix.

	MT
Complete Set (10):	300.00
Common Player:	20.00

1	Kerry Collins	25.00
2	Rashaan Salaam	20.00
3	Michael Westbrook	20.00
4	Terrell Davis	40.00
5	Joey Galloway	20.00
6	Deion Sanders	20.00
7	Steve Young	30.00
8	Dan Marino	60.00
9	Drew Bledsoe	30.00
10	Emmitt Smith	60.00

1996 Classic SP Autographs

The eight-card, regular-sized set was available as a mail-in from Score Board Inc. and Scott Paper Company. Each card was originally sold for $7.95 with two UPCs or $10.95 without UPC labels. The autographed cards came with Score Board's certificate of authenticity and the entire set was available for $64.95, or $54.95 with eight UPC labels. The cards are numbered with the "SP" prefix.

	MT
Complete Set (8):	80.00
Common Player:	12.00

1	Kyle Brady	12.00
2	Kerry Collins	16.00
3	Ron Jaworski	12.00
4	Napoleon Kaufman	12.00
5	Jim Kiick	12.00
6	Steve McNair	14.00
7	Jim Plunkett	12.00
8	Randy White	12.00

1997 Score Board NFL Experience

The 100-card, regular-sized set was sold in six-card packs. The card fronts feature a color action photo with the player's name and position printed on the bottom edge. The team's logo appears in the lower left corner. The card backs include another photo, a short highlight and a trivia question with answer. The base cards are printed on vintage-style cards. Inserts include Foundations, Teams Of The 90's and NFL Vintage cards.

	MT
Complete Set (100):	12.00
Common Player:	.05
Minor Stars:	.10
Wax Box:	35.00

1	Emmitt Smith	1.50
2	Kordell Stewart	.75
3	Antonio Freeman	.05
4	William Thomas	.05
5	Simeon Rice	.25
6	Drew Bledsoe	.75
7	Elvis Grbac	.05
8	Ken Dilger	.05
9	John Elway	.50
10	Curtis Conway	.25
11	Adrian Murrell	.05
12	Karim Abdul-Jabbar	.25
13	Terry Allen	.05
14	Lawrence Phillips	.05
15	Barry Sanders	1.25
16	Shannon Sharpe	.05
17	Troy Aikman	.75

18	Kevin Greene	.05
19	Cris Carter	.05
20	Jim Kelly	.05
21	Eric Metcalf	.05
22	Joey Galloway	.50
23	Eddie George	1.00
24	Scott Mitchell	.05
25	Neil O'Donnell	.05
26	Ben Coates	.05
27	Andre Reed	.05
28	Michael Jackson	.05
29	Keith Jackson	.05
30	J.J. Stokes	.20
31	Rickey Dudley	.25
32	Ricky Watters	.10
33	Marcus Allen	.10
34	Brett Favre	1.25
35	Kevin Hardy	.05
36	Jim Everett	.05
37	Zach Thomas	.25
38	Lamar Lathon	.05
39	LeShon Johnson	.05
40	Bruce Smith	.05
41	Junior Seau	.05
42	Tony Banks	.50
43	Brian Mitchell	.05
44	Chris T. Jones	.05
45	Ty Detmer	.05
46	Robert Brooks	.05
47	Derrick Thomas	.05
48	Dan Wilkinson	.05
49	Michael Sinclair	.05
50	Dave Brown	.05
51	Carl Pickens	.05
52	Jim Harbaugh	.05
53	Wayne Chrebet	.05
54	Warren Moon	.05
55	Steve Young	.50
56	Sean Gilbert	.05
57	Jerome Bettis	.10
58	Dan Marino	1.50
59	Terrell Davis	.75
60	Mark Brunell	.20
61	Kent Graham	.05
62	Rashaan Salaam	.25
63	Tony Martin	.05
64	Robert Smith	.05
65	Thurman Thomas	.10
66	Marshall Faulk	.40
67	Dale Carter	.05
68	Stan Humphries	.05
69	Isaac Bruce	.40
70	Warren Sapp	.05
71	Kerry Collins	.25
72	Jamal Anderson	.40
73	Chris Chandler	.05
74	Herman Moore	.20
75	Rodney Hampton	.05
76	Tim Brown	.05
77	Keenan McCardell	.05
78	Anthony Miller	.05
79	Jake Reed	.05
80	Earnest Byner	.05
81	Chris Warren	.05
82	Deion Sanders	.50
83	Mike Tomczak	.05
84	Curtis Martin	1.00
85	John Friesz	.05
86	Gus Frerotte	.05
87	Vinny Testaverde	.05
88	Jason Dunn	.05
89	James Stewart	.05
90	Steve Bono	.05
91	Levon Kirkland	.05
92	Merton Hanks	.05
93	Marvin Harrison	.60
94	Reggie Brooks	.05
95	Reggie White	.10
96	Jeff Blake	.30
97	Terry Glenn	.25
98	Jerry Rice	.75
99	Keyshawn Johnson	.75
100	Checklist	.05

1997 Score Board NFL Experience Bayou Country

	MT
Complete Set (10):	150.00
Common Player:	5.00

1	Terry Allen	5.00
2	Emmitt Smith	30.00
3	Troy Aikman	15.00
4	Brett Favre	35.00
5	Jerry Rice	15.00
6	Curtis Martin	15.00
7	John Elway	12.00
8	Jerome Bettis	8.00
9	Kevin Greene	5.00
10	Karim Abdul-Jabbar	12.00

1997 Score Board NFL Experience Foundations

The 30-card, regular-sized set was inserted every 12 packs of Score Board's 1997 NFL Experience. The cards feature a key player from each of the league's 30 franchises. The card backs feature another player photo, imaged over a pedestal blueprint, and are numbered with an "F" prefix.

		MT
Complete Set (30):		150.00
Common Player:		2.00
1	Ray Lewis	2.00
2	Bruce Smith	2.00
3	Jeff Blake	6.00
4	Terrell Davis	10.00
5	Steve McNair	8.00
6	Marshall Faulk	8.00
7	Mark Brunell	5.00
8	Derrick Thomas	2.00
9	Karim Abdul-Jabbar	4.00
10	Curtis Martin	15.00
11	Keyshawn Johnson	8.00
12	Tim Brown	2.00
13	Kordell Stewart	10.00
14	Junior Seau	2.00
15	Joey Galloway	10.00
16	Simeon Rice	2.00
17	Jessie Tuggle	2.00
18	Kerry Collins	4.00
19	Rashaan Salaam	4.00
20	Emmitt Smith	20.00
21	Barry Sanders	10.00
22	Brett Favre	15.00
23	Cris Carter	2.00
24	Jim Everett	2.00
25	Amani Toomer	2.00
26	Ricky Watters	2.00
27	Tony Banks	5.00
28	Jerry Rice	10.00
29	Warren Sapp	2.00
30	Terry Allen	2.00

1997 Score Board NFL Experience Hard Target

Hard Target cards were distributed at the 1997 NFL Experience in New Orleans. The front of these 5" x 7" cards featured an NFL player and the backs described Score Board's Wrapper Redemption program. A different player was available each day of the show.

		MT
Complete Set (5):		20.00
Common Player:		3.00
1	Terrell Davis	4.00
2	Brett Favre	6.00
3	Eddie George	6.00
4	Keyshawn Johnson	3.00
5	Emmitt Smith	5.00

1997 Score Board NFL Experience Season's Heroes

Season's Heroes is a 20-card insert seeded 1:18. Each card features the Super Bowl XXXI logo and football-textured panel on the front. The cards are numbered with the "SH" prefix.

		MT
Complete Set (20):		150.00
Common Player:		3.00
1	Gus Frerotte	3.00
2	Terry Allen	3.00
3	Troy Aikman	12.00

4	Emmitt Smith	25.00
5	Ricky Watters	3.00
6	Brett Favre	30.00
7	Reggie White	5.00
8	Steve Young	10.00
9	Jerry Rice	12.00
10	Kevin Greene	3.00
11	Anthony Johnson	3.00
12	Thurman Thomas	5.00
13	Bruce Smith	3.00
14	Jerome Bettis	5.00
15	Rod Woodson	3.00
16	Eddie George	15.00
17	Terrell Davis	12.00
18	John Elway	10.00
19	Drew Bledsoe	12.00
20	Junior Seau	3.00

1997 Score Board NFL Experience Teams of the 90's

The 15-card, regular-sized set highlights players who have starred in Super Bowls of the 1990s. The cards are inserted in every 100 packs of Score Board's 1997 NFL Experience. The cards are die-cut into the shape of an oval ring. The card fronts feature the player over a common Super Bowl ring while the backs have another player shot with a short bio. The cards are numbered with the "T" prefix.

		MT
Complete Set (15):		300.00
Common Player:		15.00
1	Emmitt Smith	120.00
2	Bruce Smith	15.00
3	Steve Young	50.00
4	Thurman Thomas	15.00
5	Kordell Stewart	60.00
6	Ricky Watters	15.00
7	Ken Norton	15.00
8	Jeff Hostetler	15.00
9	Jim Kelly	15.00
10	Troy Aikman	60.00
11	Jerry Rice	60.00
12	Mark Rypien	15.00
13	Stan Humphries	15.00
14	Deion Sanders	40.00
15	Andre Reed	15.00

1995 Cleo Quarterback Club Valentines

The eight-card, regular-sized set was available through 38-card boxes of Cleo Valentines. The fronts feature a color action shot with a valentine heart with a catchy message. The set was found in perforated sheets with two rows of two cards each. The backs are blank.

		MT
Complete Set (8):		5.00
Common Player:		.25
1	Troy Aikman	1.00
2	John Elway	.50
3	Brett Favre	1.50
4	Jim Kelly	.25
5	Dan Marino	1.50
6	Warren Moon	.25
7	Phil Simms	.25
8	Steve Young	.50

1996 Cleo Quarterback Club Valentines

These eight cards were sold in 40-card boxes. The cards are 2-1/2" x 5" (except the Marcus Allen card which mea-

sures 3-3/4" x 5"), feature a color photo with a white border and are unnumbered. Each box had two cards on the bottom which are identical to cards in the set.

		MT
Complete Set (10):		2.50
Common Player:		.15
1	Troy Aikman	.40
2	Marcus Allen	.15
3	Drew Bledsoe	.40
4	John Elway	.30
5	Jim Kelly	.25
6A	Junior Seau (Valentine)	.15
6B	Junior Seau (box bottom card)	.25
7A	Emmitt Smith (Valentine)	.60
7B	Emmitt Smith (box bottom card)	.75
8	Steve Young	.30

1981 Coke

Players from seven NFL teams are represented in this 84-card set produced by Topps for Coca-Cola. Each card is numbered from 1-11 within its own team, but has been check-listed below using #s 1-77, plus seven unnumbered header cards (one for each team). The Coca-Cola logo appears on both sides of the card, making it identifiable from the regular 1981 Topps card, which the set is patterned after.

		MT
Complete Set (77):		50.00
Common Player:		.20
(1)	Raymond Butler	.40
(2)	Roger Carr	.30
(3)	Curtis Dickey	.40
(4)	Nesby Glasgow	.20
(5)	Bert Jones	1.00
(6)	Bruce Laird	.20
(7)	Greg Landry	.40
(8)	Reese McCall	.20
(9)	Don McCauley	.20
(10)	Herb Orvis	.20
(11)	Ed Simonini	.20
(12)	Pat Donovan	.20
(13)	Tony Dorsett	2.50
(14)	Billy Joe DuPree	.40
(15)	Tony Hill	.40
(16)	Ed "Too Tall" Jones	.75
(17)	Harvey Martin	.35
(18)	Robert Newhouse	.30
(19)	Drew Pearson	.40
(20)	Charlie Waters	.30
(21)	Danny White	.70
(22)	Randy White	1.75
(23)	Mike Barber	.30
(24)	Elvin Bethea	.30
(25)	Gregg Bingham	.20
(26)	Robert Brazile	.30
(27)	Ken Burrough	.30
(28)	Rob Carpenter	.30
(29)	Leon Gray	.30
(30)	Vernon Perry	.20
(31)	Mike Renfro	.30
(32)	Carl Roaches	.30
(33)	Morris Towns	.20
(34)	Harry Carson	.75
(35)	Mike Dennis	.20
(36)	Mike Friede	.20
(37)	Earnest Gray	.20
(38)	Dave Jennings	.30
(39)	Gary Jeter	.30
(40)	George Martin	.20
(41)	Roy Simmons	.20
(42)	Phil Simms	2.50
(43)	Billy Taylor	.20
(44)	Brad Van Pelt	.30
(45)	Ottis Anderson	1.50
(46)	Rush Brown	.20
(47)	Theotis Brown	.30
(48)	Dan Dierdorf	.75
(49)	Mel Gray	.30
(50)	Ken Greene	.20
(51)	Jim Hart	.50
(52)	Doug Marsh	.20
(53)	Wayne Morris	.20
(54)	Pat Tilley	.20
(55)	Roger Wehrli	.30
(56)	Rolf Bernirschke	.30
(57)	Fred Dean	.30
(58)	Dan Fouts	1.25
(59)	John Jefferson	.40
(60)	Gary Johnson	.30
(61)	Charlie Joiner	.75
(62)	Louie Kelcher	.30
(63)	Chuck Muncie	.30
(64)	Doug Wilkerson	.20
(65)	Clarence Williams	.20
(66)	Kellen Winslow	1.75
(67)	Coy Bacon	.20
(68)	Wilbur Jackson	.20
(69)	Karl Lorch	.20
(70)	Rich Milot	.20

(71)	Art Monk	20.00
(72)	Mark Moseley	.30
(73)	Mike Nelms	.30
(74)	Lemar Parrish	.30
(75)	Joe Theismann	1.25
(76)	Ricky Thompson	.20
(77)	Joe Washington	.30

1993 Coke Monsters of the Gridiron

The 30-card, standard-size set, sponsored by Coca-Cola, was available as a complete set at the Super Bowl Card Show in Atlanta. The card fronts feature players in uniforms, but with scary monster makeup. The card backs contain career highlights with the player's scary monster nickname. The set was available to the first 10,000 collectors who redeemed 10 1993 NFL-licensed trading card wrappers.

		MT
Complete Set (30):		20.00
Common Player:		.25
1	Title Card (Checklist)	.50
2	Cornelius Bennett (Big Bear)	.25
3	Terrell Buckley (Tiger)	.25
4	Tony Casillas (Conde (Count))	.25
5	Reggie Cobb (Crossbones)	.25
6	Marco Coleman (Cobra)	.25
7	Shane Conlan (Conlan the Barbarian)	.25
8	Randall Cunningham (Rocket Man)	.50
9	Chris Doleman (Dr. Doomsday)	.25
10	Steve Emtman (Beast-Man)	.25
11	Harold Green (Slime)	.25
12	Michael Haynes (Moonlight Flyer)	.25
13	Garrison Hearst (Hearse)	2.00
14	Craig Heyward (Iron Head)	.25
15	Rickey Jackson (The Jackal)	.25
16	Joe Jacoby (Frankenstein)	.25
17	Sean Jones (Ghost)	.25
18	Cortez Kennedy (Tez Rex)	.25
19	Howie Long (Howlin')	.75
20	Ronnie Lott (The Rattler)	.75
21	Karl Mecklenburg (Midnight Marauder)	.25
22	Neil O'Donnell (Knight Raider)	.50
23	Tom Rathman (Psycho)	.25
24	Junior Seau (Stealth)	1.00
25	Emmitt Smith (Lone Star Sheriff)	10.00
26	Pat Swilling (Chillin')	.25
27	Lawrence Taylor (Six Gun)	.75
28	Derrick Thomas (Attack Cat)	.75
29	Andre Tippett (Andre the Terrible)	.25
30	Eric Turner (Bad Bone)	.25

1994 Coke Monsters of the Gridiron

Coca-Cola and Classic teamed up for the promotion and distribution of Monsters of the Gridiron, which is a 30- card set featuring one player from each team transformed into a bizarre, supernatural creature. Two cards were inserted into specially marked multi-packs of Coca-Cola Classic, diet Coke, caffeine-free diet Coke and Sprite. The two additional cards feature a logo of the expansion Panthers and Jaguars. Classic used this promotion to launch its new line of pins

called PINHEADS. These pins were also offered in a parallel set to the cards.

		MT
Complete Set (30):		12.00
Common Player:		.25
(1)	Eric "The Red" Swann	.25
(2)	Jessie " Tarantula" Tuggle	.25
(3)	Cornelius "Big Bear" Bennett	.25
(4)	Team mascot (Panther)	.25
(5)	Chris "Zorro" Zorich	.25
(6)	Dan Wilkinson	.50
(7)	Eric "Bad Bone" Turner	.25
(8)	Emmitt "Lone Star Sheriff" Smith	3.50
(9)	Steve "The Bandit" Atwater	.25
(10)	Pat "Chillin" Swilling	.25
(11)	Sean "Ghost" Jones	.25
(12)	Ray "Scarecrow" Childress	.25
(13)	Marshall "The Missile" Faulk	3.00
(14)	Team mascot (Jaguar)	.25
(15)	Derrick "Attack Cat" Thomas	.50
(16)	Chester "Renegade Raider" McGlockton	.25
(17)	Shane "The Barbarian" Conlan	.25
(18)	Marco "Cobra" Coleman	.25
(19)	John "Runaway Train" Randle	.25
(20)	Bruce "The Pile Driver" Armstrong	.25
(21)	Renaldo "Raging" Turnbull	.25
(22)	John "Jumbo" Elliot	.25
(23)	Ronnie "The Rattler" Lott	.50
(24)	Randall "Rocket Man" Cunningham	.25
(25)	Neil "Knight Rider" O'Donnell	.25
(26)	Junior "Stealth" Seau	.50
(27)	Ken "Commando" Norton Jr.	.25
(28)	Cortez "Tez Rex" Kennedy	.25
(29)	Hardy "Hyena" Nickerson	.25
(30)	Ken "Jackhammer" Harvey	.25

1994 Collector's Choice

Upper Deck's Collector's Choice set was issued in one 384-card series, marking this brand's football debut. Each card has a color action photo on the front with a white frame. The set logo is in the upper left corner; a position icon is in the lower right corner. The player's name and team is in white letters along the bottom of the card. The card back has another photo, player profile, stats and a card number. All cards are UV coated and have the Upper Deck security hologram. Subsets within the main set include: 1994 Rookie Class, Images of '93, Traditions of Excellence, and Expansion cards. Two parallel sets to the main issue were also produced - silver-foil cards, one per pack, and gold-foil cards, one every 35 packs. Instant win "Crash the Game" cards were also made as random inserts. A Joe Montana prototype card was also produced to preview the regular set's design. The back, numbered 19, is somewhat different; the card back has a ghosted picture for its background and only has statistics.

		MT
Complete Set (384):		25.00
Common Player:		.05
Minor Stars:		.10
Wax Box:		30.00
1	Antonio Langham	.50
2	Aaron Glenn	.25
3	Sam Adams	.25
4	DeWayne Washington	.20

5	Dan Wilkinson	.40
6	Bryant Young	.50
7	Aaron Taylor	.10
8	Willie McGinest	.50
9	Trev Alberts	.25
10	Jamir Miller	.25
11	John Thierry	.20
12	Heath Shuler	.50
13	Trent Dilfer	2.00
14	Marshall Faulk	4.00
15	Greg Hill	.50
16	William Floyd	.30
17	Chuck Levy	.25
18	Charlie Gardner	.50
19	Mario Bates	.20
20	Donnell Bennett	.25
21	LeShon Johnson	.40
22	Calvin Jones	.25
23	Darnay Scott	1.00
24	Charles Johnson	.50
25	Johnnie Morton	.50
26	Shante Carver	.15
27	Derrick Alexander	.50
28	David Palmer	.50
29	Ryan Yarborough	.25
30	Errict Rhett	.75
31	Sterling Sharpe	.05
32	Sterling Sharpe	.10
33	Drew Bledsoe	.50
34	Eric Allen	.10
35	Jerome Bettis	.30
36	Joe Montana	.50
37	John Carney	.05
38	Emmitt Smith	1.00
39	Chris Warren	.05
40	Reggie Brooks	.05
41	Gary Brown	.05
42	Tim Brown	.10
43	Errict Pegram	.05
44	Ron Moore	.10
45	Jerry Rice	.50
46	Ricky Watters	.10
47	Joe Montana	.75
48	Reggie Brooks	.05
49	Rick Mirer	.50
50	Raghib Ismail	.10
51	Curtis Conway	.10
52	Junior Seau	.10
53	Mark Carrier	.05
54	Ronnie Lott	.05
55	Marcus Allen	.10
56	Michael Irvin	.15
57	Bennie Blades	.10
58	Randal Hill	.05
59	Brian Blades	.05
60	Russell Maryland	.05
61	Jim Kelly	.15
62	Arthur Marshall	.05
63	Webster Slaughter	.05
64	Dave Krieg	.05
65	Steve Jordan	.05
66	Neil O'Donnell	.10
67	Andre Reed	.10
68	Mike Croel	.05
69	Al Smith	.05
70	Joe Montana	1.00
71	Randall McDaniel	.05
72	Greg Lloyd	.05
73	Thomas Smith	.05
74	Glyn Milburn	.10
75	Lorenzo White	.05
76	Neil Smith	.05
77	John Randle	.05
78	Rod Woodson	.10
79	Russell Maryland	.05
80	Rodney Peete	.05
81	Jackie Harris	.05
82	James Jett	.05
83	Rodney Hampton	.10
84	Bill Romanowski	.05
85	Ken Norton Jr.	.05
86	Barry Sanders	1.25
87	Johnny Holland	.05
88	Terry McDaniel	.05
89	Greg Jackson	.05
90	Dana Stubblefield	.10
91	Jay Novacek	.05
92	Chris Spielman	.05
93	Ken Ruettgers	.05
94	Greg Robinson	.05
95	Mark Jackson	.05
96	John Taylor	.10
97	Roger Harper	.05
98	Jerry Ball	.05
99	Keith Byars	.05
100	Morten Andersen	.05
101	Eric Allen	.05
102	Marion Butts	.05
103	Michael Haynes	.05
104	Rob Burnett	.05
105	Marco Coleman	.05
106	Derek Brown	.10
107	Andy Harmon	.05
108	Darren Carrington	.05
109	Bobby Hebert	.05
110	Mark Carrier	.05
111	Bryan Cox	.05
112	Toi Cook	.05
113	Tim Harris	.05
114	John Friesz	.05
115	Neal Anderson	.05
116	Jerome Bettis	.50
117	Bruce Armstrong	.05
118	Brad Baxter	.05
119	Johnny Bailey	.05
120	Brian Blades	.05
121	Mark Carrier	.05
122	Shane Conlan	.05

#	Player	Price		#	Player	Price
123	Drew Bledsoe	1.00		240	Steve Young	.50
124	Chris Burkett	.05		241	Steve Tovar	.05
125	Steve Beuerlein	.05		242	Jason Belser	.05
126	Ferrell Edmunds	.05		243	Ray Seals	.05
127	Curtis Conway	.10		244	Earnest Byner	.05
128	Troy Drayton	.05		245	Ricky Proehl	.05
129	Vincent Brown	.05		246	Rich Miano	.05
130	Boomer Esiason	.05		247	Alfred Williams	.05
131	Larry Centers	.05		248	Ray Buchannan	.05
132	Carlton Gray	.05		249	Hardy Nickerson	.05
133	Chris Miller	.05		250	Brad Edwards	.05
134	Eric Metcalf	.05		251	Jerrol Williams	.05
135	Mark Higgs	.05		252	Marvin Washington	.05
136	Tyrone Hughes	.05		253	Tony McGhee	.05
137	Randall Cunningham	.10		254	Jeff George	.10
138	Ronnie Harmon	.05		255	Ron Hall	
139	Andre Rison	.10		256	Tim Johnson	.05
140	Eric Turner	.05		257	Willie Roaf	.05
141	Terry Kirby	.05		258	Andre Tippett	.05
142	Eric Martin	.05		259	Richardo McDonald	.05
143	Seth Joyner	.05		260	Jeff Herrod	.05
144	Stan Humphries	.05		261	Demetrius Dubose	.05
145	Deion Sanders	.50		262	Ricky Sanders	.05
146	Vinny Testaverde	.05		263	John L. Williams	.05
147	Dan Marino	2.00		264	John Lynch	.05
148	Renaldo Turnbull	.05		265	Lance Gurn	.05
149	Herschel Walker	.05		266	Jessie Hester	.05
150	Anthony Miller	.10		267	Mark Wheeler	.05
151	Richard Dent	.05		268	Chip Lohmiller	.05
152	Jim Everett	.05		269	Eric Swann	.05
153	Ben Coates	.20		270	Byron Evans	.05
154	Jeff Lageman	.05		271	Gary Plummer	.05
155	Garrison Hearst	.50		272	Roger Duffy	.05
156	Kelvin Martin	.05		273	Irv Smith	.05
157	Dante Jones	.05		274	Todd Collins	.05
158	Sean Gilbert	.05		275	Robert Blackmon	.05
159	Leonard Russell	.05		276	Reggie Roby	.05
160	Ronnie Lott	.05		277	Russell Copeland	.05
161	Randal Hill	.05		278	Simon Fletcher	.05
162	Rick Mirer	.50		279	Ernest Givins	.05
163	Alonzo Spellman	.05		280	Tim Barnett	.05
164	Todd Lyght	.05		281	Chris Doleman	.05
165	Chris Slade	.05		282	Jeff Graham	.05
166	Johnny Mitchell	.05		283	Kenneth Davis	.05
167	Ron Moore	.20		284	Vance Johnson	.05
168	Eugene Robinson	.05		285	Haywood Jeffires	.05
169	Chris Hinton	.05		286	Todd McNair	.05
170	Dan Footman	.05		287	Daryl Johnston	.05
171	Keith Jackson	.05		288	Ryan McNeil	.05
172	Ricky Jackson	.05		289	Terrell Buckley	.05
173	Heath Sherman	.05		290	Ethan Horton	.05
174	Chris Mims	.05		291	Corey Miller	.05
175	Erric Pegram	.05		292	Marc Logan	.05
176	Leroy Hoard	.05		293	Lincoln Coleman	.10
177	O.J. McDuffie	.20		294	Derrick Moore	.05
178	Wayne Martin	.05		295	Leroy Butler	.05
179	Clyde Simmons	.05		296	Jeff Hostetler	.05
180	Leslie O'Neal	.05		297	Qadry Ismail	.10
181	Mike Pritchard	.05		298	Andre Hastings	.05
182	Michael Jackson	.05		299	Henry Jones	.05
183	Scott Mitchell	.10		300	John Elway	.50
184	Lorenzo Neal	.05		301	Warren Moon	.15
185	William Thomas	.05		302	Willie Davis	.05
186	Junior Seau	.20		303	Vencie Glenn	.05
187	Chris Gedney	.05		304	Kevin Green	.05
188	Tim Lester	.05		305	Marcus Buckley	.05
189	Sam Gash	.05		306	Tim McDonald	.05
190	Johnny Johnson	.05		307	Michael Irvin	.30
191	Chuck Cecil	.05		308	Herman Moore	.20
192	Cortez Kennedy	.10		309	Brett Favre	2.00
193	Jim Harbaugh	.05		310	Raghib Ismail	.10
194	Roman Phifer	.05		311	Jerrod Bunch	.05
195	Pat Harlow	.05		312	Don Beebe	.05
196	Rob Moore	.05		313	Steve Atwater	.05
197	Gary Clark	.05		314	Gary Brown	.05
198	John Vaughn	.05		315	Marcus Allen	.10
199	Craig Heyward	.05		316	Terry Allen	.05
200	Michael Stewart	.05		317	Chad Brown	.05
201	Greg McCurty	.05		318	Cornelius Bennett	.05
202	Brian Washington	.05		319	Rod Bernstine	.05
203	Ken Harvey	.05		320	Greg Montgomery	.05
204	Chris Warren	.05		321	Kimble Anders	.05
205	Bruce Smith	.05		322	Charles Haley	.05
206	Tom Rouen	.05		323	Mel Gray	.05
207	Cris Dishman	.05		324	Edgar Bennett	.05
208	Keith Cash	.05		325	Eddie Anderson	.05
209	Carlos Jenkins	.05		326	Derek Brown	.05
210	Levon Kirkland	.05		327	Steve Bono	.10
211	Pete Metzelaars	.05		328	Alvin Harper	.10
212	Shannon Sharpe	.10		329	Willie Green	.05
213	Cody Carlson	.05		330	Robert Brooks	.05
214	Derrick Thomas	.10		331	Patrick Bates	.05
215	Emmitt Smith	2.00		332	Anthony Carter	.05
216	Robert Porcher	.05		333	Barry Foster	.10
217	Sterling Sharpe	.20		334	Bill Brooks	.05
218	Anthony Smith	.05		335	Jason Elam	.05
219	Mike Sherrard	.05		336	Ray Childress	.05
220	Tom Rathman	.05		337	J.J. Birden	.05
221	Nate Newton	.05		338	Cris Carter	.10
222	Pat Swilling	.05		339	Deion Figures	.10
223	George Teague	.05		340	Carlton Bailey	.05
224	Greg Townsend	.05		341	Brent Jones	.05
225	Eric Guliford	.20		342	Troy Aikman	1.00
226	Leroy Thompson	.05		343	Rodney Holman	.05
227	Thurman Thomas	.20		344	Tony Bennett	.10
228	Dan Williams	.05		345	Tim Brown	.05
229	Bubba McDowell	.05		346	Michael Brooks	.05
230	Tracy Simien	.05		347	Martin Harrison	.05
231	*Scottie Graham*	.25		348	Jerry Rice	1.00
232	Eric Green	.05		349	John Copeland	.05
233	Phil Simms	.05		350	Kerry Cash	.05
234	Ricky Watters	.10		351	Reggie Cobb	.05
235	Kevin Williams	.40		352	Brian Mitchell	.05
236	Brett Perriman	.05		353	Derrick Fenner	.05
237	Reggie White	.10		354	Roosevelt Potts	.05
238	Steve Wisniewski	.05		355	Courtney Hawkins	.05
239	Mark Collins	.05		356	Carl Banks	.05

357	Harold Green	.05
358	Steve Emtman	.05
359	Santana Dotson	.05
360	Reggie Brooks	.10
361	Terry Obee	.05
362	David Klingler	.05
363	Quentin Coryatt	.05
364	Craig Erickson	.05
365	Desmond Howard	.05
366	Carl Pickens	.05
367	Lawrence Dawsey	.05
368	Henry Ellard	.05
369	Shaun Gayle	.05
370	David Lang	.05
371	Anthony Johnson	.05
372	Darnell Walker	.10
373	Pepper Johnson	.05
374	Kurt Gouveia	.05
375	Louis Oliver	.05
376	Lincoln Kennedy	.05
377	Anthony Pleasant	.05
378	Irving Fryar	.05
379	Carolina Panthers	.25
380	Jacksonville Jaguars	.25
381	Checklist	.05
382	Checklist	.05
383	Checklist	.05
384	Checklist	.05

1994 Collector's Choice Silver

The 384-card, standard-sized set, parallel to the 1994 Collector's Choice base set, was available one per hobby pack, two per retail pack and three per jumbo pack. Unlike the base set, the Silver set has the team's name on the card front in silver foil.

	MT
Complete Set (384):	75.00
Common Player:	.20
Silver Cards:	2x-4x

1994 Collector's Choice Gold

This 384-card set features each card in the base set, but includes a gold border around the card and the team name is printed in gold foil. Gold parallel cards were seeded every 35 packs of Collector's Choice.

	MT
Complete Set (384):	1500.
Common Player:	2.00
Minor Stars:	4.00

#	Player	Price
1	*Antonio Langham*	10.00
2	*Aaron Glenn*	6.00
3	*Sam Adams*	6.00
4	*DeWayne Washington*	6.00
5	*Dan Wilkinson*	8.00
6	*Bryant Young*	10.00
7	*Aaron Taylor*	8.00
8	*Willie McGinest*	10.00
9	*Trev Alberts*	6.00
10	*Jamir Miller*	6.00
11	*John Thierry*	6.00
12	*Heath Shuler*	5.00

#	Player	Price		#	Player	Price
13	*Trent Dilfer*	30.00		131	Larry Centers	2.00
14	*Marshall Faulk*	100.00		132	Carlton Gray	2.00
15	*Greg Hill*	15.00		133	Chris Miller	2.00
16	*William Floyd*	35.00		134	Eric Metcalf	2.00
17	*Chuck Levy*	6.00		135	Mark Higgs	2.00
18	*Charlie Gardner*	10.00		136	Tyrone Hughes	2.00
19	*Mario Bates*	25.00		137	Randall Cunningham	4.00
20	*Donnell Bennett*	6.00		138	Ronnie Harmon	2.00
21	*LeShon Johnson*	8.00		139	Andre Rison	4.00
22	*Calvin Jones*	6.00		140	Eric Turner	2.00
23	*Darnay Scott*	30.00		141	Terry Kirby	2.00
24	*Charles Johnson*	20.00		142	Eric Martin	2.00
25	*Johnnie Morton*	6.00		143	Seth Joyner	2.00
26	*Shante Carver*	4.00		144	Stan Humphries	4.00
27	*Derrick Alexander*	15.00		145	Deion Sanders	20.00
28	*David Palmer*	10.00		146	Vinny Testaverde	2.00
29	*Ryan Yarborough*	6.00		147	Dan Marino	60.00
30	*Errict Rhett*	60.00		148	Renaldo Turnbull	2.00
31	James Washington	2.00		149	Herschel Walker	4.00
32	Sterling Sharpe	4.00		150	Anthony Miller	4.00
33	Drew Bledsoe	20.00		151	Richard Dent	2.00
34	Eric Allen	4.00		152	Jim Everett	2.00
35	Jerome Bettis	15.00		153	Ben Coates	8.00
36	Joe Montana	20.00		154	Jeff Lageman	2.00
37	John Carney	2.00		155	Garrison Hearst	10.00
38	Emmitt Smith	35.00		156	Kelvin Martin	2.00
39	Chris Warren	2.00		157	Dante Jones	2.00
40	Reggie Brooks	2.00		158	Sean Gilbert	2.00
41	Gary Brown	2.00		159	Leonard Russell	2.00
42	Tim Brown	4.00		160	Ronnie Lott	2.00
43	Erric Pegram	2.00		161	Randal Hill	2.00
44	Ron Moore	4.00		162	Rick Mirer	6.00
45	Jerry Rice	25.00		163	Alonzo Spellman	2.00
46	Ricky Watters	4.00		164	Todd Lyght	2.00
47	Joe Montana	30.00		165	Chris Slade	2.00
48	Reggie Brooks	2.00		166	Johnny Mitchell	2.00
49	Rick Mirer	15.00		167	Ron Moore	6.00
50	Raghib Ismail	4.00		168	Eugene Robinson	2.00
51	Curtis Conway	4.00		169	Chris Hinton	2.00
52	Junior Seau	4.00		170	Dan Footman	2.00
53	Mark Carrier	2.00		171	Keith Jackson	2.00
54	Ronnie Lott	2.00		172	Ricky Jackson	2.00
55	Marcus Allen	2.00		173	Heath Sherman	2.00
56	Michael Irvin	6.00		174	Chris Mims	2.00
57	Bennie Blades	4.00		175	Erric Pegram	2.00
58	Randal Hill	2.00		176	Leroy Hoard	2.00
59	Brian Blades	2.00		177	O.J. McDuffie	8.00
60	Russell Maryland	2.00		178	Wayne Martin	2.00
61	Jim Kelly	6.00		179	Clyde Simmons	2.00
62	Arthur Marshall	2.00		180	Leslie O'Neal	2.00
63	Webster Slaughter	2.00		181	Mike Pritchard	2.00
64	Dave Krieg	2.00		182	Michael Jackson	2.00
65	Steve Jordan	2.00		183	Scott Mitchell	4.00
66	Neil O'Donnell	4.00		184	Lorenzo Neal	2.00
67	Andre Reed	4.00		185	William Thomas	2.00
68	Mike Croel	2.00		186	Junior Seau	8.00
69	Al Smith	2.00		187	Chris Gedney	2.00
70	Joe Montana	40.00		188	Tim Lester	2.00
71	Randall McDaniel	2.00		189	Sam Gash	2.00
72	Greg Lloyd	2.00		190	Johnny Johnson	2.00
73	Thomas Smith	2.00		191	Chuck Cecil	2.00
74	Glyn Milburn	4.00		192	Cortez Kennedy	4.00
75	Lorenzo White	2.00		193	Jim Harbaugh	2.00
76	Neil Smith	2.00		194	Roman Phifer	2.00
77	John Randle	2.00		195	Pat Harlow	2.00
78	Rod Woodson	4.00		196	Rob Moore	2.00
79	Russell Maryland	2.00		197	Gary Clark	2.00
80	Rodney Peete	2.00		198	John Vaughn	2.00
81	Jackie Harris	2.00		199	Craig Heyward	2.00
82	James Jett	2.00		200	Michael Stewart	2.00
83	Rodney Hampton	4.00		201	Greg McCurty	2.00
84	Bill Romanowski	2.00		202	Brian Washington	2.00
85	Ken Norton Jr.	2.00		203	Ken Harvey	2.00
86	Barry Sanders	75.00		204	Chris Warren	2.00
87	Johnny Holland	2.00		205	Bruce Smith	2.00
88	Terry McDaniel	2.00		206	Tom Rouen	2.00
89	Greg Jackson	2.00		207	Cris Dishman	2.00
90	Dana Stubblefield	4.00		208	Keith Cash	2.00
91	Jay Novacek	2.00		209	Carlos Jenkins	2.00
92	Chris Spielman	2.00		210	Levon Kirkland	2.00
93	Ken Ruettgers	2.00		211	Pete Metzelaars	2.00
94	Greg Robinson	2.00		212	Shannon Sharpe	4.00
95	Mark Jackson	2.00		213	Cody Carlson	2.00
96	John Taylor	4.00		214	Derrick Thomas	4.00
97	Roger Harper	2.00		215	Emmitt Smith	60.00
98	Jerry Ball	2.00		216	Robert Porcher	2.00
99	Keith Byars	2.00		217	Sterling Sharpe	8.00
100	Morten Andersen	2.00		218	Anthony Smith	2.00
101	Eric Allen	2.00		219	Mike Sherrard	2.00
102	Marion Butts	2.00		220	Tom Rathman	2.00
103	Michael Haynes	2.00		221	Nate Newton	2.00
104	Rob Burnett	2.00		222	Pat Swilling	2.00
105	Marco Coleman	2.00		223	George Teague	2.00
106	Derek Brown	4.00		224	Greg Townsend	2.00
107	Andy Harmon	2.00		225	Eric Guliford	5.00
108	Darren Carrington	2.00		226	Leroy Thompson	2.00
109	Bobby Hebert	2.00		227	Thurman Thomas	8.00
110	Mark Carrier	2.00		228	Dan Williams	2.00
111	Bryan Cox	2.00		229	Bubba McDowell	2.00
112	Toi Cook	2.00		230	Tracy Simien	2.00
113	Tim Harris	2.00		231	*Scottie Graham*	6.00
114	John Friesz	2.00		232	Eric Green	2.00
115	Neal Anderson	2.00		233	Phil Simms	2.00
116	Jerome Bettis	25.00		234	Ricky Watters	4.00
117	Bruce Armstrong	2.00		235	Kevin Williams	4.00
118	Brad Baxter	2.00		236	Brett Perriman	2.00
119	Johnny Bailey	2.00		237	Steve Young	25.00
120	Brian Blades	2.00		238	Steve Wisniewski	2.00
121	Mark Carrier	2.00		239	Mark Collins	2.00
122	Shane Conlan	2.00		240	Steve Young	25.00
123	Drew Bledsoe	40.00		241	Steve Tovar	2.00
124	Chris Burkett	2.00		242	Jason Belser	2.00
125	Steve Beuerlein	2.00		243	Ray Seals	2.00
126	Ferrell Edmunds	2.00		244	Earnest Byner	2.00
127	Curtis Conway	4.00		245	Ricky Proehl	2.00
128	Troy Drayton	2.00		246	Rich Miano	2.00
129	Vincent Brown	2.00		247	Alfred Williams	2.00
130	Boomer Esiason	2.00				

#	Player	Price
248	Ray Buchannan	2.00
249	Hardy Nickerson	2.00
250	Brad Edwards	2.00
251	Jerrol Williams	2.00
252	Marvin Washington	2.00
253	Tony McGhee	2.00
254	Jeff George	4.00
255	Ron Hall	2.00
256	Tim Johnson	2.00
257	Willie Roaf	2.00
258	Andre Tippett	2.00
259	Richardo McDonald	2.00
260	Jeff Herrod	2.00
261	Demetrius Dubose	2.00
262	Ricky Sanders	2.00
263	John L. Williams	2.00
264	John Lynch	2.00
265	Lance Gurn	2.00
266	Jessie Hester	2.00
267	Mark Wheeler	2.00
268	Chip Lohmiller	2.00
269	Eric Swann	2.00
270	Byron Evans	2.00
271	Gary Plummer	2.00
272	Roger Duffy	2.00
273	Irv Smith	2.00
274	Todd Collins	2.00
275	Robert Blackmon	2.00
276	Reggie Roby	2.00
277	Russell Copeland	2.00
278	Simon Fletcher	2.00
279	Ernest Givins	2.00
280	Tim Barnett	2.00
281	Chris Doleman	2.00
282	Jeff Graham	2.00
283	Kenneth Davis	2.00
284	Vance Johnson	2.00
285	Haywood Jeffires	2.00
286	Todd McNair	2.00
287	Daryl Johnston	2.00
288	Ryan McNeil	2.00
289	Terrell Buckley	2.00
290	Ethan Horton	2.00
291	Corey Miller	2.00
292	Marc Logan	2.00
293	Lincoln Coleman	4.00
294	Derrick Moore	2.00
295	Leroy Butler	2.00
296	Jeff Hostetler	4.00
297	Qadry Ismail	4.00
298	Andre Hastings	2.00
299	Henry Jones	2.00
300	John Elway	50.00
301	Warren Moon	6.00
302	Willie Davis	2.00
303	Vencie Glenn	2.00
304	Kevin Green	2.00
305	Marcus Buckley	2.00
306	Tim McDonald	2.00
307	Michael Irvin	10.00
308	Herman Moore	8.00
309	Brett Favre	80.00
310	Raghib Ismail	4.00
311	Jerrod Bunch	2.00
312	Don Beebe	2.00
313	Steve Atwater	2.00
314	Gary Brown	2.00
315	Marcus Allen	4.00
316	Terry Allen	2.00
317	Chad Brown	2.00
318	Cornelius Bennett	2.00
319	Rod Bernstine	2.00
320	Greg Montgomery	2.00
321	Kimble Anders	2.00
322	Charles Haley	2.00
323	Mel Gray	2.00
324	Edgar Bennett	2.00
325	Eddie Anderson	2.00
326	Derek Brown	2.00
327	Steve Bono	4.00
328	Alvin Harper	2.00
329	Willie Green	2.00
330	Robert Brooks	2.00
331	Patrick Bates	2.00
332	Anthony Carter	2.00
333	Barry Foster	4.00
334	Bill Brooks	2.00
335	Jason Elam	2.00
336	Ray Childress	2.00
337	J.J. Birden	2.00
338	Cris Carter	4.00
339	Deion Figures	2.00
340	Carlton Bailey	2.00
341	Brent Jones	2.00
342	Troy Aikman	40.00
343	Rodney Holman	2.00
344	Tony Bennett	2.00
345	Tim Brown	4.00
346	Michael Brooks	2.00
347	Martin Harrison	2.00
348	Jerry Rice	40.00
349	John Copeland	2.00
350	Kerry Cash	2.00
351	Reggie Cobb	2.00
352	Brian Mitchell	2.00
353	Derrick Fenner	2.00
354	Roosevelt Potts	2.00
355	Courtney Hawkins	2.00
356	Carl Banks	2.00
357	Harold Green	2.00
358	Steve Emtman	2.00
359	Santana Dotson	2.00
360	Reggie Brooks	4.00
361	Terry Obee	2.00
362	David Klingler	2.00
363	Quentin Coryatt	2.00
364	Craig Erickson	2.00

365	Desmond Howard	2.00
366	Carl Pickens	2.00
367	Lawrence Dawsey	2.00
368	Henry Ellard	2.00
369	Shaun Gayle	2.00
370	David Lang	2.00
371	Anthony Johnson	2.00
372	Darnell Walker	4.00
373	Pepper Johnson	2.00
374	Kurt Gouveia	2.00
375	Louis Oliver	2.00
376	Lincoln Kennedy	2.00
377	Anthony Pleasant	2.00
378	Irving Fryar	2.00
379	Carolina Panthers	6.00
380	Jacksonville Jaguars	6.00
381	Checklist	2.00
382	Checklist	2.00
383	Checklist	2.00
384	Checklist	2.00

1994 Collector's Choice Crash the Game

These instant-win sweepstakes cards were randomly inserted in 1994 Upper Deck Collector's Choice packs, one every 36th pack. More than 300,000 prizes were to be given away, including a grand prize of a $10,000 football card and memorabilia shopping spree at Upper Deck and Upper Deck Authenticated, plus an afternoon with Joe Montana.

		MT
Complete Set (30):		75.00
Common Player:		1.00
Minor Stars:		2.00
Bronze Cards:		.2x
Silver Cards:		.3x
Gold Cards:		.5x
1	Steve Young	2.50
2	Troy Aikman	3.00
3	Rick Mirer	1.00
4	Trent Dilfer	2.00
5	Dan Marino	6.00
6	John Elway	4.00
7	Heath Shuler	1.00
8	Joe Montana	4.00
9	Drew Bledsoe	3.00
10	Warren Moon	1.00
11	Marshall Faulk	4.00
12	Thurman Thomas	1.00
13	Barry Foster	1.00
14	Gary Brown	1.00
15	Emmitt Smith	6.00
16	Barry Sanders	6.00
17	Rodney Hampton	1.00
18	Jerome Bettis	2.00
19	Ricky Watters	1.00
20	Ron Moore	1.00
21	Jerry Rice	3.00
22	Andre Rison	1.00
23	Michael Irvin	1.00
24	Sterling Sharpe	2.00
25	Shannon Sharpe	1.00
26	Darnay Scott	1.00
27	Andre Reed	1.00
28	Tim Brown	1.00
29	Charles Johnson	1.00
30	Irving Fryar	1.00

1994 Collector's Choice Then and Now

The eight-card, regular-sized set was available to collectors by sending in a redemption card. The horizontal card fronts feature a current top player with a former great in a holographic image. The backs feature color shots of each player with highlights of each player.

	MT
Complete Set (8):	10.00
Common Player:	.50

1	Eric Dickerson, Jerome Bettis	1.00
2	Fred Biletnikoff, Tim Brown	.50
3	Len Dawson, Joe Montana	2.00
4	Joe Montana, Steve Young	3.00
5	Bob Griese, Dan Marino	4.00
6	Jim Zorn, Rick Mirer	.50
NNO	Header Card (Joe Montana)	2.00
NNO	Then/Now Exch. Card	.50
NNO	Checklist (Eric Dickerson)	.50

1994-95 Collector's Choice Crash Super Bowl XXIX

The eight-card, standard-sized set, produced specifically for Super Bowl XXIX, were available at the NFL Experience card show in Miami, as well as other media outlets. The set features four players from the San Diego Chargers and four from the San Francisco 49ers. If a player featured in the set scored a touchdown in the Super Bowl, the card was redeemable for a special nine-card set.

		MT
Complete Set (9):		12.00
Common Player:		.50
1	Steve Young (WIN)	3.00
2	Jerry Rice (WIN)	4.00
3	Brent Jones	.50
4	Ricky Watters (WIN)	1.00
5	Stan Humphries (WIN)	1.00
6	Natrone Means (WIN)	1.50
7	Ronnie Harmon (WIN)	.50
8	Tony Martin (WIN)	.50
NNO	Header Card	.50

1995 Collector's Choice

Upper Deck's 1995 Collector's Choice 348-card set includes 296 regular cards, plus 30 1995 Rookie Class and 20 Did You Know cards. Each regular card front has a color photo with a white frame. The brand logo is in the upper left corner; the player's name, team name and position are at the bottom. The card back has that information at the top, along with biographical information and a card number. The middle of the card has another action photo, with statistics and a brief summary of the player's accomplishments. Two parallel sets were also created - Players Club, which uses a silver stamp (one card every pack) and Platinum Players Club, which reproduces each card on silver-foil paper (one in 35 packs). Other inserts include eight of 20 Joe Montana Trilogy cards, and You Crash the Game cards. Once again, Collector's Choice features Crash Packs, which contain all types of insert cards. These packs are inserted one per 144 packs.

	MT
Complete Set (348):	25.00
Common Player:	.05
Minor Stars:	.10

Wax Box:		20.00
1	Ki-Jana Carter	.30
2	Tony Boselli	.10
3	Steve McNair	2.50
4	Michael Westbrook	1.00
5	Kerry Collins	1.00
6	Kevin Carter	.10
7	Mike Mamula	.10
8	Joey Galloway	2.00
9	Kyle Brady	.40
10	J.J. Stokes	1.00
11	Derrick Alexander	.20
12	Warren Sapp	.20
13	Mark Fields	.10
14	Tyrone Wheatley	.30
15	Napoleon Kaufman	2.50
16	James Stewart	1.25
17	Luther Elliss	.10
18	Rashaan Salaam	.30
19	Ty Law	.10
20	Mark Bruener	.20
21	Derrick Brooks	.10
22	Christian Fauria	.10
23	Ray Zellars	.10
24	Todd Collins	.10
25	Sherman Williams	.10
26	Frank Sanders	1.00
27	Rodney Thomas	.10
28	Rob Johnson	1.75
29	Steve Stenstrom	.20
30	James Stewart	.10
31	Barry Sanders	1.00
32	Marshall Faulk	.20
33	Darnay Scott	.10
34	Joe Montana	.50
35	Michael Irvin	.10
36	Jerry Rice	.50
37	Errict Rhett	.20
38	Drew Bledsoe	.50
39	Dan Marino	.75
40	Terance Mathis	.10
41	Natrone Means	.20
42	Tim Brown	.10
43	Steve Young	.40
44	Mel Gray	.05
45	Jerome Bettis	.20
46	Aeneas Williams	.05
47	Charlie Gardner	.05
48	Deion Sanders	.20
49	Ken Harvey	.05
50	Emmitt Smith	.75
51	Andre Reed	.10
52	Sean Dawkins	.15
53	Irving Fryar	.05
54	Vincent Brisby	.05
55	Rob Moore	.05
56	Carl Pickens	.05
57	Vinny Testaverde	.05
58	Webster Slaughter	.05
59	Eric Green	.05
60	Anthony Miller	.05
61	Lake Dawson	.20
62	Tim Brown	.10
63	Stan Humphries	.10
64	Rick Mirer	.40
65	Gary Clark	.05
66	Troy Aikman	1.00
67	Mike Sherrard	.05
68	Fred Barnett	.05
69	Henry Ellard	.05
70	Terry Allen	.05
71	Jeff Graham	.05
72	Herman Moore	.10
73	Brett Favre	2.00
74	Trent Dilfer	.40
75	Derek Brown	.05
76	Andre Rison	.10
77	Willie Anderson	.05
78	Jerry Rice	1.00
79	Thurman Thomas	.20
80	Marshall Faulk	.50
81	O.J. McDuffie	.05
82	Ben Coates	.05
83	Johnny Mitchell	.05
84	Darnay Scott	.40
85	Derrick Alexander	.20
86	Michael Barrow	.05
87	Charles Johnson	.20
88	John Elway	1.00
89	Willie Davis	.05
90	James Jett	.05
91	Mark Seay	.05
92	Brian Blades	.05
93	Ricky Proehl	.05
94	Charles Haley	.05
95	Cris Calloway	.05
96	Calvin Williams	.05
97	Ethan Horton	.05
98	Cris Carter	.10
99	Curtis Conway	.05
100	Lomas Brown	.05
101	Edgar Bennett	.05
102	Craig Erickson	.05
103	Jim Everett	.05
104	Terance Mathis	.05
105	Wayne Gandy	.05
106	Brent Jones	.05
107	Bruce Smith	.05
108	Roosevelt Potts	.05
109	Dan Marino	1.50
110	Michael Timpson	.05
111	Boomer Esiason	.05
112	David Klingler	.05
113	Eric Metcalf	.05
114	Lorenzo White	.05
115	Neil O'Donnell	.10
116	Shannon Sharpe	.10
117	Joe Montana	1.00
118	Jeff Hostetler	.10
119	Ronnie Harmon	.05
120	Chris Warren	.10
121	Randal Hill	.05
122	Alvin Harper	.10
123	Dave Brown	.05
124	Randall Cunningham	.10
125	Heath Shuler	.50
126	Jake Reed	.05
127	Donnell Woolford	.05
128	Scott Mitchell	.05
129	Reggie White	.05
130	Lawrence Dawsey	.05
131	Michael Haynes	.05
132	Bert Emanuel	.20
133	Troy Drayton	.05
134	Merton Hanks	.05
135	Jim Kelly	.10
136	Tony Bennett	.05
137	Terry Kirby	.05
138	Drew Bledsoe	1.00
139	Johnny Johnson	.05
140	Dan Wilkinson	.05
141	Leroy Hoard	.05
142	Gary Brown	.05
143	Barry Foster	.05
144	Shane Dronett	.05
145	Marcus Allen	.10
146	Harvey Williams	.05
147	Tony Martin	.05
148	Rod Stephens	.05
149	Ronald Moore	.05
150	Michael Irvin	.20
151	Rodney Hampton	.05
152	Herschel Walker	.05
153	Reggie Brooks	.05
154	Qadry Ismail	.05
155	Chris Zorich	.05
156	Barry Sanders	2.00
157	Sean Jones	.05
158	Errict Rhett	.10
159	Tyrone Hughes	.05
160	Jeff George	.10
161	Chris Miller	.05
162	Steve Young	.75
163	Cornelius Bennett	.05
164	Trev Alberts	.05
165	Marco Coleman	.05
166	Marion Butts	.05
167	Aaron Glenn	.05
168	James Francis	.05
169	Eric Turner	.05
170	Darryll Lewis	.05
171	John L. Williams	.05
172	Simon Fletcher	.05
173	Neil Smith	.05
174	Chester McGlockton	.05
175	Natrone Means	.40
176	Michael Sinclair	.05
177	Larry Centers	.05
178	Daryl Johnston	.05
179	Dave Meggett	.05
180	Greg Jackson	.05
181	Ken Harvey	.05
182	Warren Moon	.10
183	Steve Walsh	.05
184	Chris Spielman	.05
185	Bryce Paup	.05
186	Courtney Hawkins	.05
187	Willie Roaf	.05
188	Chris Doleman	.05
189	Jerome Bettis	.40
190	Ricky Watters	.10
191	Henry Jones	.05
192	Quentin Coryatt	.05
193	Bryan Cox	.05
194	Kevin Turner	.05
195	Siupeli Malamala	.05
196	Louis Oliver	.05
197	Rob Burnett	.05
198	Cris Dishman	.05
199	Bam Morris	.40
200	Ray Crockett	.05
201	Jon Vaughn	.05
202	Nolan Harrison	.05
203	Leslie O'Neal	.05
204	Sam Adams	.05
205	Eric Swann	.05
206	Jay Novacek	.05
207	Keith Hamilton	.05
208	Charlie Garner	.05
209	Tom Carter	.05
210	Henry Thomas	.05
211	Lewis Tillman	.05
212	Pat Swilling	.05
213	Terrell Buckley	.05
214	Hardy Nickerson	.05
215	Mario Bates	.20
216	D.J. Johnson	.05
217	Robert Young	.05
218	Dana Stubblefield	.05
219	Jeff Burris	.05
220	Floyd Turner	.05
221	Troy Vincent	.05
222	Willie McGinest	.05
223	James Hasty	.05
224	Jeff Blake	1.00
225	Stevon Moore	.05
226	Ernest Givins	.05
227	Greg Lloyd	.05
228	Steve Atwater	.05
229	Dale Carter	.05
230	Terry McDaniels	.05
231	John Carney	.05
232	Cortez Kennedy	.05
233	Clyde Simmons	.05
234	Emmitt Smith	1.50
235	Thomas Lewis	.05
236	William Fuller	.05
237	Ricky Ervins	.05
238	John Randle	.05
239	John Thierry	.05
240	Mel Gray	.05
241	George Teague	.05
242	Charles Wilson	.05
243	Joe Johnson	.05
244	Chuck Smith	.05
245	Sean Gilbert	.05
246	Bryant Young	.05
247	Bucky Brooks	.05
248	Ray Buchanan	.05
249	Tim Bowens	.05
250	Vincent Brown	.05
251	Marcus Turner	.05
252	Derrick Fenner	.05
253	Antonio Langham	.05
254	Cody Carlson	.05
255	Kevin Greene	.05
256	Leonard Russell	.05
257	Donnell Bennett	.05
258	Raghib Ismail	.05
259	Alfred Pupunu	.20
260	Eugene Robinson	.05
261	Seth Joyner	.05
262	Darren Woodson	.05
263	Phillipi Sparks	.05
264	Andy Harmon	.05
265	Brian Mitchell	.05
266	Fuad Reveiz	.05
267	Mark Carrier	.05
268	Johnnie Morton	.05
269	LeShon Johnson	.05
270	Eric Curry	.05
271	Quinn Early	.05
272	Elbert Shelley	.05
273	Roman Phifer	.05
274	Ken Norton	.05
275	Steve Tasker	.05
276	Jim Harbaugh	.05
277	Aubrey Beavers	.05
278	Chris Slade	.05
279	Mo Lewis	.05
280	Alfred Williams	.05
281	Michael Dean Perry	.05
282	Marcus Robertson	.05
283	Rod Woodson	.10
284	Glyn Milburn	.05
285	Greg Hill	.25
286	Rob Fredrickson	.05
287	Junior Seau	.10
288	Rick Tuten	.05
289	Aeneas Williams	.05
290	Darrin Smith	.05
291	John Booty	.05
292	Eric Allen	.05
293	Reggie Roby	.05
294	David Palmer	.05
295	Trace Armstrong	.05
296	Dave Krieg	.05
297	Robert Brooks	.05
298	Brad Culpepper	.05
299	Wayne Martin	.05
300	Craig Heyward	.05
301	Isaac Bruce	.15
302	Deion Sanders	.40
303	Matt Darby	.05
304	Kirk Lowdermilk	.05
305	Bernie Parmalee	.20
306	Leroy Thompson	.05
307	Ronnie Lott	.05
308	Steve Tovar	.05
309	Michael Jackson	.05
310	Al Smith	.05
311	Chad Brown	.05
312	Elijah Alexander	.05
313	Kimble Anders	.05
314	Anthony Smith	.05
315	Andre Coleman	.05
316	Terry Wooden	.05
317	Garrison Hearst	.10
318	Russell Maryland	.05
319	Michael Brooks	.05
320	Bernard Williams	.05
321	Andre Collins	.05
322	DeWayne Washington	.05
323	Raymont Harris	.15
324	Brett Perriman	.05
325	LeRoy Butler	.05
326	Santana Dotson	.05
327	Irv Smith	.05
328	Ron George	.05
329	Marquez Pope	.05
330	William Floyd	.25
331	Mickey Washington	.05
332	Keith Goganious	.05
333	Derek Brown	.05
334	Steve Beuerlein	.05
335	Reggie Cobb	.05
336	Jeff Lageman	.05
337	Kelvin Martin	.05
338	Darren Carrington	.05
339	Mark Carrier	.05
340	Willie Green	.05
341	Frank Reich	.05
342	Don Beebe	.05
343	Lamar Lathon	.05
344	Tim McKyer	.05
345	Pete Metzelaars	.05
346	Vernon Turner	.05
347	Checklist 1-174	.05
348	Checklist 175-348	.05

1995 Collector's Choice Player's Club

The 348-card, regular-size parallel set was inserted in each pack of 1995 Collector's Choice. The card fronts have a silver border with a silver "Player's Club" logo.

	MT
Complete Set (348):	45.00
Common Player:	.20
Player's Club Cards:	2x

1995 Collector's Choice Player's Club Platinum

The 348-card, regular-sized parallel set was inserted every 35 packs of Collector's Choice. The card fronts feature a silver "Platinum Player's Club" logo, as well as a silver border.

	MT
Complete Set (348):	750.00
Common Player:	1.00
Player's Club Platinum:	10x-20x

1995 Collector's Choice Crash The Game

These 30 cards feature an action photo of a player, with a silver or gold foil date stamped into the design. If the player pictured scored a touchdown during his team's game on the date on the card front, a collector could redeem the card for a complete 30-card set. Odds of finding a silver version were one per every five packs; gold cards were inserted one per every 50 packs. The back of the card is numbered using a "C" prefix and includes the rules of the game.

		MT
Complete Silver Set (90):		60.00
Common Player:		.25
Minor Stars:		.50
Inserted 1:5		
Gold Cards:		3x
Inserted 1:50		
Silver Red. Cards:		.5x
Gold Red. Cards:		2x
1	Dan Marino	2.00
2	John Elway	2.00
3	Kerry Collins	.50
4	Stan Humphries	.25
5	Steve Young	1.00
6	Brett Favre	2.50
7	Troy Aikman	1.25
8	Warren Moon	.50
9	Drew Bledsoe	1.25

10	Steve McNair	1.00
11	Chris Warren	.25
12	Natrone Means	.50
13	Thurman Thomas	.50
14	Barry Sanders	2.50
15	Emmitt Smith	2.00
16	Jerome Bettis	.50
17	Ki-Jana Carter	.50
18	Napoleon Kaufman	1.00
19	Marshall Faulk	.75
20	Errict Rhett	.25
21	Cris Carter	.75
22	Jerry Rice	1.25
23	Tim Brown	.25
24	Andre Reed	.25
25	Andre Rison	.50
26	Ben Coates	.25
27	Michael Irvin	.50
28	Terance Mathis	.50
29	Michael Westbrook	.50
30	Herman Moore	.50

1995 Collector's Choice Marino Chronicles

The 10-card, regular-sized set was inserted in specially marked retail packs and features Marino highlight cards. The card fronts feature an aqua border with "Marino" in gold foil. The cards are numbered with the "DM" prefix.

		MT
Complete Set (10):		10.00
Common Player:		1.25
1	Dan Marino (Rookie of the Year)	1.25
2	Dan Marino (5000 Yards Passing)	1.25
3	Dan Marino (48 TD Passes)	1.25
4	Dan Marino (Super Bowl XIX)	1.25
5	Dan Marino (30,000 Yards Passing)	1.25
6	Dan Marino (4000 Yard Season)	1.25
7	Dan Marino (40,000 Yards Passing)	1.25
8	Dan Marino (Marino's Back)	1.25
9	Dan Marino (300th TD Pass)	1.25
10	Dan Marino (More Records to Fall)	1.25

1995 Collector's Choice Montana Trilogy

Eight of 20 Joe Montana Trilogy cards were included in packs of 1995 Upper Deck Collector's Choice football cards. These cards are numbered 1-8, using an "MT" prefix. Cards recap Montana's career, and were included one per every 12 packs. A Montana Trilogy header card was also produced.

		MT
Complete Set (9):		30.00
Common Player:		4.00
Header Card:		5.00
1	1977 NCAA Champs	4.00
2	1978 Cotton Bowl	4.00
3	The 1978 NFL Draft	4.00
4	The Catch	4.00
5	Super Bowl XVI	4.00
6	Super Bowl XVI MVP	4.00
7	Super Bowl XIX	4.00
8	Super Bowl XIX MVP	4.00
CCH	Trilogy Header	5.00

1995 Collector's Choice Update

The 1995 Upper Deck Collector's Choice set has 225 cards, including 103 regular player cards (featuring free agents, traded players and rookies in the uniforms of their new teams), 60 "Rookie Collection" cards (picturing first-year players in their NFL uniforms), 30 cards featuring players from the expansion team Carolina

Panthers and Jacksonville Jaguars, two checklists and 30 "The Key" cards (describing what NFL teams do to stop "key" players on each team). The set is numbered U1-U225. Gold and silver parallel sets were made for two of the subsets; silver Rookie Collection cards are found one per three packs, while gold versions are one in every 35. Silver "The Key" cards are seeded one per every five packs, while gold ones are one per every 52. Also included as inserts are Stick-Ums, restickable stickers the size of a trading card which picture top stars, rookies and team helmets. Each one has either four mini-stickers on it, a large "superstar" sticker, or one with three players and a team helmet. One of these 90 cards was seeded in every pack of 1995 Upper Deck Collector's Choice Update product. Six different Stick-Ums sticker booklets were also available through a wrapper mail-in offer. A new version of the "You Crash the Game" interactive cards were redesigned for the playoffs. "You Crash the Playoffs" cards were randomly inserted every 18th pack; if the player on the card scored a touchdown during the playoffs the card could be redeemed for various prizes.

		MT
Complete Set (225):		20.00
Common Player:		.05
Minor Stars:		.10
Wax Box:		30.00
1	Roell Preston	.05
2	Lorenzo Styles	.05
3	Todd Collins	.10
4	Darick Holmes	.75
5	Justin Armour	.10
6	Tony Cline	.05
7	Tyrone Poole	.05
8	Kerry Collins	.50
9	Sean Harris	.05
10	Steve Stenstrom	.05
11	Rashaan Salaam	.30
12	Ki-Jana Carter	.30
13	Craig Powell	.05
14	Eric Zeier	.50
15	Ernest Hunter	.05
16	Sherman Williams	.10
17	Terrell Davis	12.00
18	Luther Elliss	.05
19	Craig Newsome	.05
20	Steve McNair	1.00
21	Chris Sanders	.30
22	Rodney Thomas	.30
23	Ellis Johnson	.05
24	Ken Dilger	.40
25	Zack Crockett	.20
26	Tony Boselli	.10
27	Rob Johnson	1.00
28	James O. Stewart	.20
29	Pete Mitchell	.05
30	Tamarick Vanover	.20
31	Napoleon Kaufman	1.00
32	Kevin Carter	.05
33	Steve McLaughlin	.05
34	Lovell Pinkney	.05
35	James A. Stewart	.05
36	Chad May	.30
37	Derrick Alexander	.05
38	Curtis Martin	2.50
39	Will Moore	.05
40	Ty Law	.05
41	Ray Zellars	.05
42	Mark Fields	.05
43	Tyrone Wheatley	.30
44	Kyle Brady	.05
45	Mike Mamula	.05
46	Bobby Taylor	.05
47	Chris Jones	.30
48	Frank Sanders	.50
49	Stoney Case	.25
50	Mark Bruener	.05
51	Kordell Stewart	3.50
52	Jimmy Oliver	.05
53	Terrance Shaw	.05
54	Terrell Fletcher	.30
55	J.J. Stokes	.50
56	Christian Fauria	.05
57	Joey Galloway	1.00
58	Warren Sapp	.05
59	Derrick Brooks	.05
60	Michael Westbrook	.50
61	Emmitt Smith	.75
62	Barry Sanders	1.00
63	Marshall Faulk	.30
64	Troy Aikman	.50
65	Steve Young	.40
66	Junior Seau	.10
67	John Elway	.50
68	Dan Marino	.75
69	Drew Bledsoe	.50
70	Errict Rhett	.30

71	Natrone Means	.10
72	Deion Sanders	.30
73	Brett Favre	1.00
74	Cris Carter	.25
75	Ben Coates	.05
76	Jerome Bettis	.20
77	Reggie White	.05
78	Stan Humphries	.05
79	Michael Westbrook	.30
80	Steve McNair	.75
81	Kevin Greene	.05
82	Joey Galloway	.50
83	Napoleon Kaufman	.50
84	Jerry Rice	.50
85	Andre Rison	.05
86	Eric Metcalf	.05
87	Kerry Collins	.20
88	Chris Warren	.10
89	Irving Fryar	.05
90	Michael Irvin	.10
91	Don Beebe	.05
92	Pete Metzelaars	.05
93	Mark Carrier	.05
94	Frank Reich	.05
95	Randy Baldwin	.05
96	Bob Christian	.05
97	John Kasay	.05
98	Lamar Lathon	.05
99	Sam Mills	.05
100	Carlton Bailey	.05
101	Darrion Conner	.05
102	Blake Brockermeyer	.05
103	Gerald Williams	.05
104	Willie Green	.05
105	Derrick Graham	.05
106	Desmond Howard	.05
107	Harry Colon	.05
108	Steve Beuerlein	.05
109	Reggie Cobb	.05
110	Jeff Lageman	.05
111	Mark Brunell	1.00
112	Darren Carrington	.05
113	Brian DeMarco	.05
114	Ernest Givins	.05
115	LeShia Maston	.05
116	Willie Jackson	.05
117	Keith Goganious	.05
118	Kelvin Pritchett	.05
119	Ryan Christopherson	.05
120	Brian Schwartz	.05
121	Dave Kreig	.05
122	Darryl Talley	.05
123	Bryce Paup	.05
124	Anthony Johnson	.05
125	Eric Bieniemy	.05
126	Andre Rison	.05
127	Rodney Peete	.05
128	Aaron Craver	.05
129	Henry Thomas	.05
130	Antonio Freeman	3.00
131	Chris Chandler	.05
132	Craig Erickson	.05
133	Roell Preston	.05
134	Brian Washington	.05
135	Eric Green	.05
136	Broderick Thomas	.05
137	Dave Meggett	.05
138	Eric Allen	.05
139	Herschel Walker	.05
140	Dexter Carter	.05
141	Kerry Cash	.05
142	Kelvin Martin	.05
143	Erric Pegram	.05
144	Bo Orlando	.05
145	Ricky Ervins	.05
146	John Friesz	.05
147	Alexander Wright	.05
148	Alvin Harper	.05
149	Gus Frerotte	.25
150	Duval Love	.05
151	Eric Metcalf	.05
152	Ruben Brown	.05
153	Marty Carter	.05
154	James Joseph	.05
155	Steve Emtman	.05
156	Wade Wilson	.05
157	Britt Hager	.05
158	Mark Schlereth	.05
159	Corey Schlesinger	.05
160	Mark Ingram	.05
161	Mark Stepnoski	.05
162	Willie Anderson	.05
163	Donta Jones	.05
164	James Hasty	.05
165	Gary Clark	.05
166	David Sloan	.05
167	Jeff Dallenbach	.05
168	Rufus Porter	.05
169	Mike Croel	.05
170	Charles Wilson	.05
171	Pat Swilling	.05
172	Kurt Gouveia	.05
173	Norm Johnson	.05
174	Shawn Gayle	.05
175	Marquez Pope	.05
176	Tyrone Stowe	.05
177	Anthony Parker	.05
178	Kenneth Gant	.05
179	James Washington	.05
180	Rob Moore	.05
181	Alundis Brice	.05
182	Lamont Warren	.05
183	Michael Timpson	.05
184	Lorenzo White	.05
185	Charlie Williams	.05
186	Ed McCaffrey	.05

187	James Jones	.05
188	Derrick Fenner	.05
189	Mel Gray	.05
190	James Williams	.05
191	Jeff Criswell	.05
192	Randal Hill	.05
193	Terry Allen	.05
194	Joel Smeenge	.05
195	Ricky Watters	.10
196	Don Sasa	.05
197	Steve Bono	.10
198	Steve Broussard	.05
199	Carlos Jenkins	.05
200	Reggie Roby	.05
201	Stanley Richard	.05
202	Vince Workman	.05
203	Eric Guliford	.05
204	Lionel Washington	.05
205	Brian Williams	.05
206	Ronnie Lott	.05
207	Corey Harris	.05
208	Harlon Barnett	.05
209	Bubby Brister	.05
210	Darren Bennett	.05
211	Winston Moss	.05
212	Leonard Russell	.05
213	Ronald Davis	.05
214	Curtis Whitley	.05
215	Webster Slaughter	.05
216	Korey Stringer	.05
217	Don Davey	.05
218	Mark Rypien	.05
219	Chad Cota	.05
220	Tim Ruddy	.05
221	Corey Fuller	.05
222	Mike Dumas	.05
223	Eddie Murray	.05
224	Checklist	.05
225	Checklist	.05

1995 Collector's Choice Update Silver

The 90-card, regular-sized set was inserted every three packs of Collector's Choice Update and paralleled the first 90 cards of the set with the card name in silver foil.

	MT
Complete Set (90):	45.00
Common Player:	.15
Silver Cards:	1.5x-3x

1995 Collector's Choice Update Gold

The 90-card, regular-size set was inserted every 35 packs of Collector's Choice Update and paralleled the first 90 cards of the Update set.

	MT
Complete Set (90):	475.00
Common Player:	1.50
Gold Cards:	15x-30x

1995 Collector's Choice Update Crash the Playoffs

Upper Deck's "You Crash the Game" interactive cards were redesigned for the 1995 Upper Deck Collector's Choice Update set to spotlight the playoffs. Called "You Crash the Playoffs," the cards allow fans holding the cards to redeem them for special card sets if any of the players pictured on the cards is involved in a scoring play during the playoffs (catching or throwing a touchdown pass, running for one). Each card pictures five players at one position (either quarterback, running back or wide receiver) for each division. The winning cards were redeemable for a 20-card set which highlights the playoffs and Super Bowl XXX. Two versions were made – silver (good for a silver set; one in five packs), or gold (good for a gold set; one in 50 packs). The cards are numbered with the "CP" prefix.

		MT
Complete Set (18):		20.00
Common Player:		.50
Minor Stars:		1.00
Inserted 1:5		
Gold Cards:		3x
Inserted 1:50		

		MT
1	AFC East QB	3.00
2	AFC Central QB	1.50
3	AFC West QB	2.00
4	NFC East QB	1.50
5	NFC Central QB	3.00
6	NFC West QB	1.50
7	AFC East RB	2.50
8	AFC Central RB	.50
9	AFC West RB	3.00
10	NFC East RB	1.00
11	NFC Central RB	.50
12	NFC West RB	.50
13	AFC East WR	.50
14	AFC Central WR	.50
15	AFC West WR	1.00
16	NFC East WR	1.00
17	NFC Central WR	3.00
18	NFC West WR	1.50

1995 Collector's Choice Update Post Season Heroics

The 20-card, standard-size set was available by redeeming a winning Collector's Choice Update Crash The Playoffs silver or gold card. The cards are similar to the base set cards with "Post Season Heroics" printed along the card fronts in silver or gold foil.

		MT
Complete Set (20):		10.00
Common Player:		.25
Minor Stars:		.50
Gold Cards:		3x
1	Stan Humphries	.50
2	Natrone Means	.50
3	Tony Martin	.25
4	Neil O'Donnell	.25
5	Byron "Bam" Morris	.25
6	Charles Johnson	.25
7	Jim Harbaugh	.50
8	Darick Holmes	.50
9	Sean Dawkins	.25
10	Steve Young	1.50
11	Craig Heyward	.25
12	Jerry Rice	2.00
13	Brett Favre	4.00
14	Edgar Bennett	.25
15	Robert Brooks	.50
16	Troy Aikman	2.00
17	Emmitt Smith	3.00
18	Michael Irvin	.50
19	Byron "Bam" Morris	.25
20	Larry Brown	.25

1995 Collector's Choice Update Stick-Ums

These 1995 Upper Deck Collector's Choice inserts were seeded one per every pack. The 90 restickable stickers are the size of a trading card and picture some of the NFL's biggest stars and top rookies, plus team helmets. Cards have either four mini-stickers on it, one large full-size superstar sticker, or three players and a team helmet sticker. Six different Stick-Ums booklets (one for each division) were also made to display the stickers. Each booklet, which contains team trivia and important dates in team history, were available as a mail-in offer for $2 and two Collector's Choice Update foil wrappers.

		MT
Complete Set (90):		10.00
Common Player:		.10
Minor Stars:		.20
Inserted 1:1		
1	Jeff George	.20
2	Kerry Collins	.20
3	Jerome Bettis	.20
4	Mario Bates	.10
5	Steve Young	.50
6	Rashaan Salaam	.20
7	Barry Sanders	1.00
8	Brett Favre	1.00
9	Warren Moon	.20
10	Errict Rhett	.20
11	Emmitt Smith	.75
12	Rodney Hampton	.10
13	Ricky Watters	.20
14	Garrison Hearst	.20
15	Michael Westbrook	.20
16	Jim Kelly	.20
17	Marshall Faulk	.30
18	Dan Marino	.75
19	Drew Bledsoe	.50
20	Kyle Brady	.10
21	Ki-Jana Carter	.10
22	Andre Rison	.20

23	Steve McNair	.50
24	James O. Stewart	.20
25	Bam Morris	.10
26	John Elway	.75
27	Marcus Allen	.20
28	Tim Brown	.20
29	Natrone Means	.20
30	Chris Warren	.20
31	Terance Mathis, Mark Carrier, Chris Miller, Jim Everett	.10
32	Bert Emanuel, Pete Metzelaars, Isaac Bruce, Dana Stubblefield	.20
33	Chris Doleman, Frank Reich, Derek Brown, Jerry Rice	.30
34	Jessie Tuggle, Roman Phifer, Tyrone Hughes, Bryant Young	.30
35	Sam Mills, Kevin Carter, Michael Haynes, Brent Jones	.10
36	Falcons (Eric Metcalf, Tyrone Poole, Lovell Pinkney)	.10
37	Panthers (Morten Andersen, John Kasay, Troy Drayton)	.10
38	Vikings (Sean Gilbert, Mark Fields, J.J. Stokes)	.10
39	Saints (Darion Conner, Willie Roaf, Ken Norton)	.10
40	49ers (Craig Heyward, Renaldo Turnbull, William Floyd)	.10
41	Raymont Harris, Herman Moore, Edgar Bennett, Cris Carter	.10
42	Jeff Graham, Henry Thomas, Reggie White, Trent Dilfer	.10
43	Curtis Conway, Scott Mitchell, Scottie Graham, Alvin Harper	.10
44	Steve Walsh, Sean Jones, Qadry Ismail, Hardy Nickerson	.10
45	John Randle, Mark Carrier, Chris Spielman, John Jurkovic	.10
46	Bears (John Thierry, Luther Elliss, LeRoy Butler)	.10
47	Lions (Johnnie Morton, Robert Brooks, Jake Reed)	.10
48	Packers (LeShon Johnson, DeWayne Washington, Jackie Harris)	.10
49	Vikings (Donnell Woolford, James A. Stewart, Eric Curry)	.10
50	Buccaneers (Mark Carrier, Chris Spielman, Warren Sapp)	.10
51	Troy Aikman, Mike Sherrard, Fred Barnett, Dave Kreig	.30
52	Michael Irvin, Chris Calloway, Calvin Williams, Henry Ellard	.10
53	Sherman Williams, Dave Brown, Rob Moore, Heath Shuler	.10
54	Charles Haley, Randall Cunningham, Eric Swann, Ken Harvey	.10
55	Thomas Lewis, Charlie Garner, Clyde Simmons, Tom Carter	.10
56	Cowboys (Tyrone Wheatley, Bobby Taylor, Daryl Johnston)	.10
57	Giants (Mike Croel, Byron Evans, Aeneas Williams)	.10
58	Eagles (Mike Mamula, Larry Centers, Brian Mitchell)	.10

59	Cardinals (Jay Novacek, Frank Sanders, Terry Allen)	.10
60	Redskins (Deion Sanders, Herschel Walker, Sterling Palmer)	.20
61	Henry Jones, Craig Erickson, Terry Kirby, Ben Coates	.10
62	Andre Reed, Willie Anderson, Irving Fryar, Johnny Mitchell	.10
63	Russell Copeland, Sean Dawkins, Vincent Brisby, Boomer Esiason	.10
64	Bruce Smith, O.J. McDuffie, Willie McGinest, Ryan Yarborough	.10
65	Roosevelt Potts, Keith Byars, Curtis Martin, Brad Baxter	.75
66	Bills (Cornelius Bennett, Ray Buchanan, Marco Coleman)	.10
67	Colts (Quentin Coryatt, Bryan Cox, Chris Slade)	.10
68	Dolphins (Eric Green, Ty Law, Marvin Washington)	.10
69	Patriots (Todd Collins, Vincent Brown, Ronald Moore)	.10
70	Jets (Jeff Burris, Floyd Turner, Aaron Glenn)	.10
71	Carl Pickens, Vinny Testaverde, Haywood Jeffires, Desmond Howard	.10
72	Darnay Scott, Eric Turner, Gary Brown, Neil O'Donnell	.10
73	David Klingler, Leroy Hoard, Tony Boselli, Charles Johnson	.10
74	Steve Tovar, Al Smith, Derek Brown, John L. Williams	.10
75	Lorenzo White, Rodney Thomas, Steve Beuerlein, Kevin Greene	.10
76	Bengals (Jeff Blake, Derrick Alexander, Ray Childress)	.10
77	Browns (Eric Zeier, Mel Gray, Reggie Cobb)	.10
78	Oilers (Todd McNair, Jeff Lageman, Greg Lloyd)	.10
79	Jaguars (Dan Wilkinson, Rob Johnson, Rod Woodson)	.30
80	Steelers (Eric Bieniemy, Antonio Langham, Mark Bruener)	.10
81	Shannon Sharpe, Willie Davis, Jeff Hostetler, Stan Humphries	.10
82	Rod Bernstine, Ronnie Lott, Harvey Williams, Rick Mirer	.10
83	Anthony Miller, Neil Smith, Junior Seau, Brian Blades	.10
84	Mike Pritchard, Napoleon Kaufman, Leslie O'Neal, Sam Adams	.20
85	Greg Hill, Raghib Ismail, Alfred Pupunu, Cortez Kennedy	.10
86	Broncos (Steve Atwater, Tamarick Vanover, Chester McGlockton)	.10
87	Chiefs (Steve Bono, Rob Fredrickson, Tony Martin)	.10
88	Raiders (Terry McDaniel, Jimmy Oliver, Christian Fauria)	.10
89	Chargers (Glyn Milburn, John Carney, Joey Galloway)	.20
90	Seahawks (Simon Fletcher, Keith Cash, Eugene Robinson)	.10

1996 Collector's Choice

Upper Deck's 1996 Collector's Choice Series I contains 375 cards - broken down into 294 regular cards, 45 Rookie Class cards, two checklists and 34 Season to Remember cards. Each regular card front has a color action photo on it, with a brand logo in the upper right corner. The left side of the card has a team color-coded panel with the player's name and team helmet at the bottom; the top portion, which is black, has the player's position in it. The card back has biographical information at the top, along with a card number. A color action photo is underneath, followed by statistics and a football quiz. The right side of the card has a color-coded panel with the player's name at the bottom and the player's team name and position at the top. Insert sets created are MVPs (in gold and silver versions) and You Crash the Game redemption cards. Play Action Stick-Ums also return from the previous year's Update set. These re-stickable die-cut stickers allow collectors to create a football scene. The set consists of 30 NFL athletes and is seeded one per every three packs.

		MT
	Complete Set (375):	25.00
	Common Player:	.05
	Minor Stars:	.10
	Wax Box:	20.00
1	Keyshawn Johnson	1.50
2	Kevin Hardy	.10
3	Simeon Rice	.10
4	Jonathan Ogden	.10
5	Cedric Jones	.05
6	Lawrence Phillips	1.00
7	Tim Biakabutuka	.50
8	Terry Glenn	1.00
9	Rickey Dudley	.50
10	Regan Upshaw	.05
11	Walt Harris	.05
12	Eddie George	3.00
13	John Mobley	.05
14	Duane Clemons	.05
15	Marvin Harrison	2.00
16	Daryl Gardener	.05
17	Pete Kendall	.05
18	Marcus Jones	.05
19	Eric Moulds	1.50
20	Ray Lewis	.05
21	Alex Van Dyke	.10
22	Leeland McElroy	.20
23	Mike Alstott	1.50
24	Lawyer Milloy	.05
25	Marco Battaglia	.05
26	Je'Rod Cherry	.05
27	Israel Ifeanyi	.05
28	Bobby Engram	.50
29	Jason Dunn	.25
30	Derrick Mayes	.75
31	Stepfret Williams	.05
32	Bobby Hoying	.75
33	Karim Abdul-Jabbar	1.00
34	Danny Kanell	.50
35	Chris Darkins	.10
36	Charlie Jones	.05
37	Tedy Bruschi	.05
38	Stanley Pritchett	.05
39	Donnie Edwards	.05
40	Jeff Lewis	.50
41	Stephen Davis	2.50
42	Winslow Oliver	.05
43	Mercury Hayes	.05
44	Jon Runyan	.05
45	Steve Taneyhill	.05
46	Eric Metcalf	.05
47	Bryce Paup	.05
48	Kerry Collins	.40
49	Rashaan Salaam	.25
50	Carl Pickens	.05
51	Emmitt Smith	1.00
52	Michael Irvin	.50
53	Troy Aikman	.50
54	Terrell Davis	.30
55	John Elway	.15
56	Herman Moore	.25
57	Brett Favre	.50
58	Rodney Thomas	.05
59	Jim Harbaugh	.05
60	Mark Brunell	.25
61	Marcus Allen	.05
62	Tamarick Vanover	.15
63	Steve Bono	.05
64	Dan Marino	1.00
65	Warren Moon	.05
66	Curtis Martin	.75
67	Tyrone Hughes	.05
68	Rodney Hampton	.05
69	Hugh Douglas	.05
70	Tim Brown	.05
71	Ricky Watters	.05
72	Kordell Stewart	.30
73	Andre Coleman	.05
74	Jerry Rice	.50
75	Joey Galloway	.30
76	Isaac Bruce	.40
77	Errict Rhett	.40
78	Michael Westbrook	.25
79	Brian Mitchell	.05
80	Aeneas Williams	.05
81	Andre Reed	.05
82	Brett Maxie	.05
83	Jim Flanigan	.05
84	Jeff Blake	.30
85	Mike Frederick	.05
86	Michael Irvin	.05
87	Aaron Craver	.05
88	Barry Sanders	1.00
89	Keith Jackson	.05
90	Chris Sanders	.25
91	Marshall Faulk	.75
92	Bryan Schwartz	.05
93	Tamarick Vanover	.20
94	Troy Vincent	.05
95	Robert Smith	.05
96	Drew Bledsoe	.75
97	Quinn Early	.05
98	Wayne Chrebet	.05
99	Tim Brown	.05
100	Charlie Garner	.05
101	Yancey Thigpen	.30
102	Isaac Bruce	.75
103	Natrone Means	.10
104	Jerry Rice	1.00
105	Chris Warren	.10
106	Errict Rhett	.50
107	Heath Shuler	.40
108	Eric Swann	.05
109	Jeff George	.10
110	Steve Tasker	.05
111	Sam Mills	.05
112	Jeff Graham	.05
113	Carl Pickens	.10
114	Vinny Testaverde	.05
115	Emmitt Smith	2.00
116	John Elway	.25
117	Henry Thomas	.05
118	LeRoy Butler	.05
119	Blaine Bishop	.05
120	Floyd Turner	.05
121	Jeff Lageman	.05
122	Kimble Anders	.05
123	Bryan Cox	.05
124	Qadry Ismail	.05
125	Ted Johnson	.05
126	Wesley Walls	.05
127	Rodney Hampton	.05
128	Adrian Murrell	.05
129	Daryl Hobbs	.05
130	Ricky Watters	.10
131	Carnell Lake	.05
132	Toby Wright	.05
133	Darren Bennett	.05
134	J.J. Stokes	.50
135	Eugene Robinson	.05
136	Eric Curry	.05
137	Tom Carter	.05
138	Dave Krieg	.05
139	Eric Metcalf	.05
140	Bill Brooks	.05
141	Pete Metzelaars	.05
142	Kevin Butler	.05
143	John Copeland	.05
144	Keenan McCardell	.05
145	Larry Brown	.05
146	Jason Elam	.05
147	Willie Clay	.05
148	Robert Brooks	.05
149	Chris Chandler	.05
150	Quentin Coryatt	.05
151	Pete Mitchell	.05
152	Martin Bayless	.05
153	Pete Stoyanovich	.05
154	Cris Carter	.10
155	Jimmy Hitchcock	.05
156	Mario Bates	.05
157	Mike Sherrard	.05
158	Boomer Esiason	.05
159	Chester McGlockton	.05
160	Bobby Taylor	.05
161	Kordell Stewart	.60
162	Kevin Carter	.05
163	Junior Seau	.10
164	Derek Loville	.05
165	Brian Blades	.05
166	Jackie Harris	.05
167	Michael Westbrook	.50
168	Rob Moore	.05
169	Jessie Tuggle	.05
170	Darick Holmes	.05
171	Tim McKyer	.05
172	Erik Kramer	.05
173	Harold Green	.05
174	Stevon Moore	.05
175	Deion Sanders	.40
176	Anthony Miller	.05
177	Herman Moore	.20
178	Brett Favre	2.00
179	Rodney Thomas	.30
180	Ken Dilger	.05
181	Mark Brunell	.50
182	Marcus Allen	.10
183	Dan Marino	2.00
184	John Randle	.05
185	Ben Coates	.05
186	Tyrone Hughes	.05
187	Dave Brown	.05
188	Johnny Mitchell	.05
189	Harvey Williams	.05
190	Andy Harmon	.05
191	Kevin Greene	.05
192	D'Marco Farr	.05
193	Andre Coleman	.05
194	Bryant Young	.05
195	Rick Mirer	.05
196	Horace Copeland	.05
197	Leslie Shepherd	.05
198	Jamir Miller	.05
199	Bert Emanuel	.05
200	Steve Christie	.05
201	Kerry Collins	.75
202	Rashaan Salaam	.50
203	Steve Tovar	.05
204	Michael Jackson	.05
205	Kevin Williams	.05
206	Glyn Milburn	.05
207	Johnnie Morton	.05
208	Antonio Freeman	.05
209	Cris Dishman	.05
210	Ellis Johnson	.05
211	Cedric Tillman	.05
212	Steve Bono	.10
213	Eric Green	.05
214	David Palmer	.05
215	Vincent Brisby	.05
216	Michael Haynes	.05
217	Chris Calloway	.05
218	Kyle Brady	.05
219	Terry McDaniel	.05
220	Calvin Williams	.05
221	Greg Lloyd	.05
222	Jerome Bettis	.05
223	Stan Humphries	.05
224	Lee Woodall	.05
225	Robert Blackmon	.05
226	Warren Sapp	.05
227	Brian Mitchell	.05
228	Garrison Hearst	.05
229	Terance Mathis	.05
230	Bryce Paup	.05
231	Derrick Moore	.05
232	Curtis Conway	.05
233	Darnay Scott	.05
234	Andre Rison	.05
235	Jay Novacek	.05
236	Terrell Davis	.60
237	David Sloan	.05
238	Reggie White	.05
239	Todd McNair	.05
240	Ray Buchanan	.05
241	Steve Beuerlein	.05
242	Dan Saleaumua	.05
243	Bernie Parmalee	.05
244	Warren Moon	.05
245	Ty Law	.05
246	Torrance Small	.05
247	Philippi Sparks	.05
248	Mo Lewis	.05
249	Jeff Hostetler	.05
250	Rodney Peete	.05
251	Bam Morris	.05
252	Chris Miller	.05
253	Tony Martin	.05
254	Eric Davis	.05
255	Joey Galloway	.60
256	Derrick Brooks	.05
257	Ken Harvey	.05
258	Frank Sanders	.10
259	Morten Andersen	.05
260	Marlon Kerner	.05
261	Mark Carrier	.05
262	Mark Carrier	.05
263	Tony McGee	.05
264	Eric Zeier	.05
265	Darren Woodson	.05
266	Shannon Sharpe	.05
267	Brett Perriman	.05
268	Edgar Bennett	.05
269	Darryll Lewis	.05
270	Jim Harbaugh	.05
271	Desmond Howard	.05
272	Derrick Thomas	.05
273	Irving Fryar	.05
274	Jake Reed	.05
275	Curtis Martin	1.50
276	Eric Allen	.05
277	Thomas Lewis	.05
278	Hugh Douglas	.05
279	Pat Swilling	.05
280	William Thomas	.05
281	Norm Johnson	.05
282	Roman Phifer	.05
283	Chris Mims	.05
284	Steve Young	1.00
285	Cortez Kennedy	.05
286	Trent Dilfer	.05
287	Terry Allen	.05
288	Clyde Simmons	.05
289	Craig Heyward	.05
290	Jim Kelly	.05
291	Tyrone Poole	.05
292	Chris Zorich	.05
293	Dan Wilkinson	.05
294	Antonio Langham	.05
295	Troy Aikman	1.00
296	Steve Atwater	.05
297	Scott Mitchell	.05
298	Mark Chmura	.20
299	Steve McNair	.50
300	Tony Bennett	.05
301	Willie Jackson	.05
302	Neil Smith	.05
303	Terry Kirby	.05
304	Orlanda Thomas	.05
305	Willie McGinest	.05
306	Wayne Martin	.05
307	Michael Brooks	.05
308	Marvin Washington	.05
309	Nolan Harrison	.05
310	William Fuller	.05
311	Willie Williams	.05
312	Troy Drayton	.05
313	Shawn Lee	.05
314	Ken Norton	.05
315	Terry Wooden	.05
316	Hardy Nickerson	.05
317	Gus Frerotte	.05
318	Oscar McBride	.05
319	Merton Hanks	.05
320	Justin Armour	.05
321	Willie Green	.05
322	Roger Jones	.05
323	Leroy Hoard	.05
324	Chris Boniol	.05
325	Jason Hanson	.05
326	Sean Jones	.05
327	Roosevelt Potts	.05
328	Greg Hill	.05
329	O.J. McDuffie	.05
330	Amp Lee	.05
331	Chris Slade	.05
332	Jim Everett	.05
333	Tyrone Wheatley	.10
334	Charles Wilson	.05
335	Napoleon Kaufman	.10
336	Fred Barnett	.05
337	Neil O'Donnell	.05
338	Sean Gilbert	.05
339	Aaron Hayden	.30
340	Brent Jones	.05
341	Christian Fauria	.05
342	Alvin Harper	.05
343	Henry Ellard	.05
344	Willie Davis	.05
345	Charles Haley	.05
346	Chris Jacke	.05
347	Allen Aldridge	.05
348	Jeff Herrod	.05
349	Raghib Ismail	.05
350	Leslie O'Neal	.05
351	Marquez Pope	.05
352	Brock Marion	.05
353	Ernie Mills	.05
354	Larry Centers	.05
355	Chris Doleman	.05
356	Bruce Smith	.05
357	John Kasay	.05
358	Donnell Woolford	.05
359	David Dunn	.05
360	Eric Turner	.05
361	Sherman Williams	.05
362	Chris Spielman	.05
363	Craig Newsome	.05
364	Sean Dawkins	.05
365	James O. Stewart	.05
366	Dale Carter	.05
367	Marco Coleman	.05
368	Dave Meggett	.05
369	Irv Smith	.05
370	Mike Mamula	.05
371	Erric Pegram	.05
372	Dana Stubblefield	.05
373	Terrance Shaw	.05
374	Jerry Rice CL	.25
375	Dan Marino CL	.25

1996 Collector's Choice A Cut Above

This 10-card set was seeded one per special retail pack and included 10 different players.

		MT
	Complete Set (10):	10.00
	Common Player:	.20
	Minor Stars:	.40
	Inserted 1:1 Special Retail	
1	Terrell Davis	3.00
2	Tim Biakabutuka	.20
3	Drew Bledsoe	1.00
4	Emmitt Smith	1.50
5	Marshall Faulk	.40
6	Brett Favre	2.00
7	Keyshawn Johnson	.75
8	Deion Sanders	.40
9	Curtis Martin	1.00
10	Jerry Rice	1.00

Values quoted in this guide reflect the retail price of a card — the price a collector can expect to pay when buying a card from a dealer. The wholesale price — that which a collector can expect to receive from a dealer when selling cards — will be significantly lower, depending on desirability and condition.

1996 Collector's Choice Crash The Game

These inserts were available in 1996 Upper Deck Collector's Choice packs. If the player on the card throws for, runs for or catches a touchdown pass on the date specified, that card is redeemable for an exclusive Light F/X card of that player. Two versions were made - silver (one per five packs) and gold (one per 50). The basic card front design has a color action photo in the center, with the brand logo in the upper left corner. The player's name, team name and position are in the upper right corner. The bottom has a black panel which has the set icon in silver foil, along with the game date for the contest. The back, numbered using a "CG" prefix, has the rules of the redemption program.

		MT
	Complete Set (90):	75.00
	Common Player:	.50
	Minor Stars:	1.00
	Comp. Silver Redemption (22):	75.00
	Silver Redemptions:	1.5x-3x
1	Dan Marino	6.00
2	John Elway	3.00
3	Jeff Blake	1.00
4	Drew Bledsoe	3.00
5	Steve Young	4.00
6	Brett Favre	6.00
7	Jim Kelly	2.00
8	Scott Mitchell	.50
9	Jeff George	.50
10	Erik Kramer	.50
11	Jerry Rice	3.00
12	Michael Irvin	.50
13	Joey Galloway	3.00
14	Cris Carter	.50
15	Carl Pickens	.50
16	Herman Moore	.50
17	Isaac Bruce	2.00
18	Tim Brown	.50
19	Keyshawn Johnson	3.00
20	Terry Glenn	2.50
21	Emmitt Smith	6.00
22	Rodney Hampton	.50
23	Chris Warren	.50
24	Marshall Faulk	3.00
25	Curtis Martin	4.00
26	Barry Sanders	3.00
27	Rashaan Salaam	.50
28	Leeland McElroy	2.50
29	Tim Biakabutuka	2.50
30	Lawrence Phillips	2.50

1996 Collector's Choice Crash The Game Gold

You Crash the Game Golds ran parallel to the 90 cards in the silver version, but were inserted one per 50 packs. As the name indicates, gold versions are gold foil stamped instead of the silver foil used on regular versions. Similar to the rules for silver versions, if the player on the gold version throws for, runs for or catches a touchdown pass on the date specified, that card is redeemable for a gold Light F/X card of that player. Thirty different players are featured in this insert, with each having three specified dates.

	MT
Complete Set (90):	300.00
Gold Cards:	2x-4x
Gold Redemptions:	5x-10x

1996 Collector's Choice Cut Above Dan Marino

This 10-card insert features Miami Dolphins quarterback Dan Marino and highlights different moments in his Hall of Fame career. One Marino A Cut Above insert was found in each special retail pack of Collector's Choice Series I. The cards are numbered with the "CA" prefix.

		MT
Complete Set (10):		15.00
Common Player:		1.50
1	Dan Marino	1.50
2	Dan Marino	1.50
3	Dan Marino	1.50
4	Dan Marino	1.50
5	Dan Marino	1.50
6	Dan Marino	1.50
7	Dan Marino	1.50
8	Dan Marino	1.50
9	Dan Marino	1.50
10	Dan Marino	1.50

1996 Collector's Choice Jumbos

This nine-card set consists of enlarged versions (3-1/2" x 5") of the players' Season to Remember subset cards from the regular 1996 Collector's Choice set. The cards were inserted one per retail blister pack, which also included a team set and a foil pack of 1996 Collector's Choice.

		MT
Complete Set (9):		30.00
Common Player:		2.00
48	Kerry Collins	3.00
49	Rashaan Salaam	2.00
51	Emmitt Smith	5.00
57	Brett Favre	6.00
60	Mark Brunell	3.00
64	Dan Marino	5.00
70	Tim Brown	2.00
72	Kordell Stewart	3.00
74	Jerry Rice	3.00

1996 Collector's Choice MVPs

This set highlights the MVP and co-MVP of each NFL team in two different versions - gold or silver. The card has a marble-like background for the front, in either gold or silver. A player color photo is in the center. MVP is stamped into the upper left corner; the player's name is stamped in the lower left corner. A brand logo is in the upper right corner, while a circle towards the bottom has the player's position and team name inside it. Part of the circle's diameter is stamped in silver dots; the other is in the same color used to shadow the frame around the picture on the front. The back has biographical information, 1995 stats and a card number, which uses an "M" prefix. Gold versions were seeded one every 35 packs of 1996 Upper Deck Collector's Choice product; silver cards were in every pack.

		MT
Complete Set (45):		12.00
Common Player:		.20
Minor Stars:		.40
1	Larry Centers	.20
2	Jeff George	.20
3	Jim Kelly	.20
4	Bryce Paup	.20

5	Kerry Collins	.50
6	Erik Kramer	.20
7	Rashaan Salaam	.75
8	Jeff Blake	.75
9	Carl Pickens	.20
10	Vinny Testaverde	.20
11	Michael Irvin	.40
12	Emmitt Smith	2.00
13	John Elway	.50
14	Terrell Davis	1.00
15	Herman Moore	.40
16	Barry Sanders	1.50
17	Brett Favre	2.00
18	Edgar Bennett	.20
19	Rodney Thomas	.40
20	Jim Harbaugh	.20
21	Marshall Faulk	.75
22	Mark Brunell	1.00
23	Steve Bono	.20
24	Marcus Allen	.20
25	Dan Marino	2.00
26	Bryan Cox	.20
27	Cris Carter	.20
28	Drew Bledsoe	1.00
29	Curtis Martin	1.50
30	Jim Everett	.20
31	Rodney Hampton	.20
32	Adrian Murrell	.20
33	Tim Brown	.20
34	Rodney Peete	.20
35	Ricky Watters	.20
36	Yancey Thigpen	.75
37	Greg Lloyd	.20
38	Isaac Bruce	.75
39	Tony Martin	.20
40	Junior Seau	.20
41	Steve Young	1.00
42	Jerry Rice	1.00
43	Chris Warren	.40
44	Errict Rhett	.40
45	Brian Mitchell	.20

1996 Collector's Choice MVP Golds

This insert paralleled the MVP set, and is inserted every 35 packs of Series I. While regular versions are printed on silver foil, MVP Gold are printed on gold foil.

	MT
Complete Set (45):	120.00
Gold Cards:	5x-10x

1996 Collector's Choice Stick-Ums

Stick-Ums featured 30 top NFL players on re-stickable, die-cut stickers. The stickers offer removable players, names, footballs, referees, yardage markers and play calls. One Stick-Ums insert is found in every three packs of Series I. The cards are numbered with the "S" prefix.

		MT
Complete Set (30):		10.00
Common Player:		.25
Minor Stars:		.50
1	Dan Marino	2.00
2	Mike Mamula	.25
3	Errict Rhett	.50
4	Drew Bledsoe	1.00
5	Anthony Smith	.25
6	Brett Favre	2.00
7	Morten Andersen	.25
8	Deion Sanders	.75
9	Jeff George	.25
10	Erik Kramer	.25
11	Jerry Rice	1.00
12	Michael Irvin	.50
13	Greg Lloyd	.25
14	Cris Carter	.25
15	Ken Norton	.25
16	Natrone Means	.50
17	Robert Brooks	.50
18	Action Words-Bomb	.25
19	Kordell Stewart	1.00
20	Referee	.25
21	Emmitt Smith	2.00

22	Reggie White	.50
23	Eric Metcalf	.25
24	Jesse Sapolu	.25
25	Curtis Martin	1.50
26	Neil Smith	.25
27	Junior Seau	.25
28	Action Words-TD	.25
29	Accessories-Yardmarkers	.25
30	Terry McDaniel	.25

1996 Collector's Choice Update

The 200-card, regular-sized set was issued as an update to the 375-card Collector's Choice set in 1996. The Update set included a 60-card rookies subset and 30 Franchise Play Makers subset. The base card fronts included the player's team colors along the left border with the player's position and team helmet. Inserts included were Play Action Stick-Ums, Play Action Stick-Ums Base Cards, Record-Breaking Trio, You Make The Play and Meet The Stars Trivia Game Cards.

		MT
Complete Set (200):		15.00
Common Player:		.05
Minor Stars:		.10
Wax Box:		20.00
1	Zack Thomas	.75
2	Simeon Rice	.10
3	Jonathan Ogden	.05
4	Eric Moulds	.20
5	Tim Biakabutuka	.20
6	Walt Harris	.10
7	Willie Anderson	.05
8	Rickey Whittle	.05
9	John Mobley	.05
10	Reggie Brown	.05
11	John Michels	.05
12	Eddie George	1.00
13	Marvin Harrison	.50
14	Kevin Hardy	.10
15	Kavika Pittman	.05
16	Daryl Gardener	.05
17	Duane Clemons	.05
18	Terry Glenn	.75
19	Alex Molden	.05
20	Cedric Jones	.05
21	Keyshawn Johnson	.60
22	Rickey Dudley	.20
23	Jason Dunn	.05
24	Jermain Stephens	.05
25	Lawrence Phillips	.60
26	Bryan Still	.05
27	Isreal Ifeanyi	.05
28	Pete Kendall	.05
29	Regan Upshaw	.05
30	Andre Johnson	.05
31	Leeland McElroy	.20
32	Ray Lewis	.05
33	Sean Moran	.05
34	Mushin Muhammad	.50
35	Bobby Engram	.20
36	Marco Battaglia	.05
37	Stepfret Williams	.05
38	Jeff Lewis	.05
39	Derrick Mayes	.05
40	Reggie Tongue	.05
41	Tory James	.05
42	Tony Banks	.75
43	Tedy Bruschi	.05
44	Mike Alstott	.50
45	Anthony Dorsett Jr.	.05
46	Tony Brackens	.30
47	Bryant Mix	.05
48	Karim Abdul-Jabbar	.75
49	Moe Williams	.05
50	Lawyer Milloy	.05
51	Je'Rod Cherry	.05
52	Amani Toomer	.30
53	Alex Van Dyke	.05
54	Lance Johnstone	.05
55	Bobby Hoying	.05
56	John Wittman	.05
57	Eddie Kennison	.50
58	Brian Roche	.05
59	Terrell Owens	3.00

60	Stephen Davis	1.25
61	Jeff George	.05
62	Darick Holmes	.05
63	Kerry Collins	.40
64	Rashaan Salaam	.05
65	Jeff Blake	.20
66	Emmitt Smith	.75
67	Troy Aikman	.40
68	John Elway	.30
69	Terrell Davis	.50
70	Barry Sanders	1.00
71	Herman Moore	.05
72	Brett Favre	.75
73	Robert Brooks	.05
74	Steve McNair	.20
75	Marshall Faulk	.20
76	Marcus Allen	.05
77	Dan Marino	.75
78	Warren Moon	.05
79	Drew Bledsoe	.40
80	Curtis Martin	.50
81	Mario Bates	.05
82	Tim Brown	.05
83	Charlie Garner	.05
84	Kordell Stewart	.40
85	Isaac Bruce	.20
86	Tony Martin	.05
87	Jerry Rice	.40
88	J.J. Stokes	.05
89	Joey Galloway	.20
90	Errict Rhett	.15
91	Mike Pritchard	.05
92	Jerome Bettis	.10
93	Winslow Oliver	.05
94	David Klingler	.05
95	Lawrence Dawsey	.05
96	Charlie Jones	.05
97	Dave Krieg	.05
98	Chris Spielman	.05
99	Stanley Pritchett	.05
100	Sean Gilbert	.05
101	Tommy Vardell	.05
102	DeRon Jenkins	.05
103	Larry Bowie	.05
104	Kyle Wachholz	.05
105	Brady Smith	.05
106	Steve Walsh	.05
107	Wesley Walls	.05
108	Kevin Ross	.05
109	Willie Clay	.05
110	Olanda Truitt	.05
111	Calvin Williams	.05
112	Chris Doleman	.05
113	Irving Fryar	.05
114	Jimmy Spencer	.05
115	Reggie Barlow	.05
116	Reggie Brown	.05
117	Dixon Edwards	.05
118	Haywood Jeffires	.05
119	Santana Dotson	.05
120	Herschel Walker	.05
121	Darryl Williams	.05
122	Bryan Cox	.05
123	Lamar Thomas	.05
124	Hendrick Lusk	.05
125	Jahine Arnold	.05
126	Boomer Esiason	.05
127	Willie Davis	.05
128	Pete Stoyanovich	.05
129	Bill Romanowski	.05
130	Tim McKyer	.05
131	Patrick Sapp	.05
132	Natrone Means	.05
133	Quinn Early	.05
134	Leslie O'Neal	.05
135	Mark Seay	.05
136	Pete Metzelaars	.05
137	Jay Leuwenberg	.05
138	Buster Owens	.05
139	Todd McNair	.05
140	Eugene Robinson	.05
141	Sean Salisbury	.05
142	Eugene Robinson	.05
143	Jerris McPhail	.05
144	Ray Farmer	.05
145	Garrison Hearst	.05
146	Leonard Russell	.05
147	Ray Barker	.05
148	Larry Brown	.05
159	Webster Slaughter	.05
150	Roman Oben	.05
151	LeShon Johnson	.05
152	Patrick Bates	.05
153	Iheanyi Uwaezuoke	.05
154	Scott Slutzker	.05
155	John Jurkovic	.05
156	Brian Milne	.05
157	Mike Sherrard	.05
158	Neil O'Donnell	.05
159	Roger Harper	.05
160	Desmond Howard	.05
161	Alfred Williams	.05
162	Ronnie Harmon	.05
163	Sammie Burroughs	.05
164	Keenan McCardell	.05
165	Shane Dronett	.05
166	Jeff Graham	.05
167	Bill Brooks	.05
168	Shawn Jefferson	.05
169	Detron Smith	.05
170	Danny Kanell	.05
171	Jevon Langford	.05
172	Russell Maryland	.05
173	Scott Milanovich	.05
174	Eric Davis	.05
175	Ernie Conwell	.05
176	Kurt Gouveia	.05
177	Andre Rison	.05

178	Harold Green	.05
179	Frank Reich	.05
180	Glyn Milburn	.05
181	Nilo Silvan	.05
182	Cornelius Bennett	.05
183	Freddie Solomon	.05
184	Pat Terrell	.05
185	Miles Mecik	.05
186	Bo Orlando	.05
187	Kelvin Martin	.05
188	Todd Kinchen	.05
189	Reggie Brooks	.05
190	Steve Beuerlein	.05
191	Marco Coleman	.05
192	Johnnie Johnson	.05
193	Dedric Mathis	.05
194	Leon Searcy	.05
195	Kevin Greene	.05
196	Daniel Stubbs	.05
197	Ray Mickens	.05
198	Devin Wyman	.05
199	Lorenzo Lynch	.05
200	Checklist	.20

1996 Collector's Choice Update Record Breaking Trio

The four-card, regular-sized, die-cut set was inserted every 100 packs of Collector's Choice 1996 Update. The cards feature Joe Montana, Dan Marino, Jerry Rice and a fourth card including all three. The cards are numbered with the "RS" prefix.

		MT
Complete Set (4):		60.00
Common Player:		10.00
1	Joe Montana	10.00
2	Dan Marino	25.00
3	Jerry Rice	15.00
4	Joe Montana, Dan Marino, Jerry Rice	10.00

1996 Collector's Choice Update You Make The Play

You Make the Play is an interactive card deck that allows collectors to play a football game through cards. The deck contains 90 cards and is found at a rate of one per pack.

		MT
Complete Set (90):		20.00
Common Player:		.10
Minor Stars:		.20
1	Norm Johnson	.10
2	Jerry Rice	1.00
3	Dan Marino	2.00
4	Marshall Faulk	.30
5	Neil Smith	.10
6	Herman Moore	.20
7	Brett Favre	2.00
8	Curtis Martin	1.50
9	Reggie White	.20
10	Cris Carter	.20
11	Rick Tuten	.10
12	Steve Young	.75
13	Barry Sanders	2.00

14	Deion Sanders	.50
15	Isaac Bruce	.30
16	Troy Aikman	1.00
17	Emmitt Smith	2.00
18	Junior Seau	.10
19	Joey Galloway	.30
20	Drew Bledsoe	1.00
21	Jason Elam	.10
22	Edgar Bennett	.10
23	Greg Lloyd	.10
24	Tamarick Vanover	.20
25	John Elway	.75
26	Larry Centers	.10
27	Derrick Thomas	.10
28	Michael Irvin	.10
29	Jeff George	.10
30	Thurman Thomas	.10
31	Darren Bennett	.10
32	Ken Norton	.10
33	Carl Pickens	.10
34	Jeff Blake	.20
35	Craig Heyward	.10
36	Aeneas Williams	.10
37	Terance Mathis	.10
38	Jim Kelly	.20
39	Marcus Allen	.20
40	Tim McDonald	.10
41	Jason Hanson	.10
42	Scott Mitchell	.10
43	Tim Brown	.10
44	Kordell Stewart	1.00
45	Eric Metcalf	.10
46	Norm Johnson	.10
47	Jerry Rice	1.00
48	Dan Marino	2.00
49	Marshall Faulk	.30
50	Neil Smith	.10
51	Herman Moore	.30
52	Brett Favre	2.00
53	Curtis Martin	1.50
54	Reggie White	.20
55	Cris Carter	.10
56	Rick Tuten	.10
57	Steve Young	.75
58	Barry Sanders	2.00
59	Deion Sanders	.50
60	Isaac Bruce	.30
61	Troy Aikman	1.00
62	Emmitt Smith	2.00
63	Junior Seau	.20
64	Joey Galloway	.30
65	Drew Bledsoe	1.00
66	Jason Elam	.10
67	Edgar Bennett	.10
68	Greg Lloyd	.10
69	Tamarick Vanover	.20
70	John Elway	.75
71	Larry Centers	.10
72	Derrick Thomas	.10
73	Michael Irvin	.20
74	Jeff George	.10
75	Thurman Thomas	.20
76	Darren Bennett	.10
77	Ken Norton	.10
78	Carl Pickens	.10
79	Jeff Blake	.20
80	Craig Heyward	.10
81	Aeneas Williams	.10
82	Terance Mathis	.10
83	Jim Kelly	.20
84	Marcus Allen	.20
85	Tim McDonald	.10
86	Jason Hanson	.10
87	Scott Mitchell	.10
88	Tim Brown	.10
89	Kordell Stewart	1.00
90	Eric Metcalf	.10

1996 Collector's Choice Update Stick-Ums

The 30-card Stick-Ums set was inserted every four packs of Collector's Choice 1996 Update. The regular-sized set came with peel-off stickers of the player, team helmet and name. Thirty base cards were also inserted every four packs. The base cards feature a white outline of the corresponding player and contain clues as to which player's sticker goes with which base card. The cards are numbered with the "S" prefix.

		MT
Complete Set (30):		15.00
Common Player:		.25
Minor Stars:		.50
1	Jeff George	.25
2	Darren Bennett	.25
3	Marcus Allen	.50
4	Brett Favre	2.00
5	Carl Pickens	.25
6	Troy Aikman	1.00
7	John Elway	.75
8	Steve Young	.75
9	Norm Johnson	.25
10	Kordell Stewart	1.00
11	Drew Bledsoe	1.00
12	Jim Kelly	.50
13	Dan Marino	2.00
14	Joey Galloway	.50
15	Lawrence Phillips	.50
16	Reggie White	.50
17	Kevin Hardy	.25
18	Isaac Bruce	.50
19	Keyshawn Johnson	.50
20	Barry Sanders	1.50
21	Deion Sanders	.75
22	Emmitt Smith	2.00
23	Chris Warren	.25
24	Tim Biakabutuka	.50
25	Terry Glenn	1.00
26	Marshall Faulk	.50
27	Tamarick Vanover	.25
28	Curtis Martin	1.50
29	Terrell Davis	1.50
30	Jerry Rice	1.00

1996 Collector's Choice Update Stick-Ums Mystery Base

Each Stick-Ums card in Collector's Choice Update has a corresponding Mystery Base card. It is printed on cardboard stock like regular-issue cards and have a background of an action shot, with a white space where the player is supposed to be. The sticker is supposed to be used with the Mystery Base base to complete the football action scene. One Mystery Base card is included in every four packs of Collector's Choice Update.

	MT
Complete Set (30):	7.50
Mystery Base Cards:	.5x

1996 Collector's Choice Packers

This 90-card set was exclusively available in ShopKo stores and contained all Green Bay Packers including current players and all-time greats. The set featured several different subsets, including A Season to Remember and Legends of the Green and Gold. The regular-issue set contained the first 69

cards, while the final 21 cards, called Leaders of the Pack, is considered an insert set. The cards are numbered with the "GB" prefix.

		MT
Complete Set (69):		14.00
Common Player:		.10
1	Brett Favre	1.50
2	Mark Chmura	.25
3	Edgar Bennett	.25
4	Robert Brooks	.50
5	Antonio Freeman	.25
6	Travis Jervey	.10
7	Craig Newsome	.10
8	Reggie White	.75
9	Sean Jones	.10
10	LeRoy Butler	.10
11	Chris Jacke	.10
12	Derrick Mayes	1.00
13	Chris Darkins	.10
14	Anthony Morgan	.10
15	Terry Mickens	.10
16	Dorsey Levens	.40
17	Jim McMahon	.10
18	Craig Hendricks	.10
19	George Koonce	.10
20	William Henderson	.10
21	Doug Evans	.10
22	Mike Prior	.10
23	Wayne Simmons	.10
24	Darius Holland	.10
25	Gilbert Brown	.10
26	Aaron Taylor	.10
27	Frank Winters	.10
28	Ken Ruettgers	.10
29	Earl Dotson	.10
30	Eugene Robinson	.10
31	Brett Favre (Season to Remember)	1.50
32	Brett Favre (Season to Remember)	1.50
33	Brett Favre (Season to Remember)	1.50
34	Edgar Bennett (Season to Remember)	.25
35	Edgar Bennett (Season to Remember)	.25
36	Robert Brooks (Season to Remember)	.50
37	Robert Brooks (Season to Remember)	.50
38	Mark Chmura (Season to Remember)	.25
39	Mark Chmura (Season to Remember)	.25
40	LeRoy Butler (Season to Remember)	.10
41	LeRoy Butler (Season to Remember)	.10
42	Craig Newsome (Season to Remember)	.10
43	Craig Newsome (Season to Remember)	.10
44	Reggie White (Season to Remember)	.75
45	Reggie White (Season to Remember)	.75
46	Sean Jones (Season to Remember)	.10
47	Sean Jones (Season to Remember)	.10
48	Antonio Freeman (Season to Remember)	.25
49	Chris Jacke (Season to Remember)	.10
50	Offensive Line (Season to Remember)	.10
51	Forrest Gregg (Legends of the Green & Gold)	.10
52	Paul Hornung (Legends of the Green & Gold)	.50
53	Jim Taylor (Legends of the Green & Gold)	.10
54	Vince Lombardi (Legends of the Green & Gold)	.50
55	Ray Nitschke (Legends of the Green & Gold)	.30
56	Willie Wood (Legends of the Green & Gold)	.10
57	Don Hutson (Legends of the Green & Gold)	.10
58	Don Majkowski (Legends of the Green & Gold)	.10
59	Bryce Paup (Legends of the Green & Gold)	.10
60	Sterling Sharpe (Legends of the Green & Gold)	.40
61	Ted Hendricks (Legends of the Green & Gold)	.10
62	Lynn Dickey (Legends of the Green & Gold)	.10
63	James Lofton (Legends of the Green & Gold)	.20
64	Brett Favre (Legends of the Green & Gold)	1.50
65	Edgar Bennett (Legends of the Green & Gold)	.25
66	Reggie White (Legends of the Green & Gold)	.75
67	John Jurkovic (Legends of the Green & Gold)	.20
68	Mike Holmgren (Legends of the Green & Gold)	.30
69	Ron Wolf (Legends of the Green & Gold)	.10

1996 Collector's Choice Leaders of the Pack

Leaders of the Pack consisted of the final 21 cards of the Collector's Choice Packers set that was exclusively available at ShopKo stores. Although it's numbered consecutively with the regular-issue set, it was considered an insert and seeded one per pack. The cards are identified by a thick gold-foil border across the top with the words "Leaders of the Pack." In addition, a color shot of the featured player is shown over a black-and-white dotted background, with a bold yellow strip at the bottom that contains the player's name.

		MT
Complete Set (21):		8.00
Common Player:		.15
70	Forrest Gregg	.15
71	Paul Hornung	1.50
72	Jim Taylor	.15
73	Ray Nitschke	.15
74	Willie Wood	.15
75	Don Hutson	.15
76	Sterling Sharpe	1.25
77	Don Majkowski	.15
78	Ted Hendricks	.15
79	Lynn Dickey	.15
80	James Lofton	.50
81	Brett Favre	4.50
82	Edgar Bennett	.75
83	Robert Brooks	1.50
84	Mark Chmura	.75
85	Reggie White	2.50
86	Sean Jones	.15
87	Chris Jacke	.15
88	LeRoy Butler	.15
89	Craig Newsome	.15
90	Checklist	.25

1997 Collector's Choice

The 565-card set features white borders on the front. The player's name and team are printed inside a stripe at the top, while his position is located inside a rectangle at the upper right. The Collector's Choice logo is printed in the lower left on the front. The backs have a photo on the left, with the player's bio, "Did you know?" and stats along the right side. The cards feature a dual numbering system that helps collectors put players from their favorite team together. Series I also features a 45-card Rookie Class subset and a 40-card Names of the Game subset. Series II includes Checklist/Collector Info cards, 30 NFL Mini Standees and the StarQuest insert.

		MT
Complete Set (565):		40.00
Complete Series 1 (310):		25.00
Complete Series 2 (255):		15.00
Common Player:		.05
Minor Stars:		.10
Series 1 Wax Box:		40.00
Series 2 Wax Box:		40.00
1	Orlando Pace	.25
2	Darrell Russell	.05
3	Shawn Springs	.25
4	Peter Boulware	.05
5	Bryant Westbrook	.10
6	Tom Knight	.05
7	Ike Hilliard	1.00
8	James Farrior	.05
9	Chris Naeole	.05
10	Michael Booker	.05
11	Warrick Dunn	1.50
12	Tony Gonzalez	.75
13	Reinard Wilson	.05
14	Yatil Green	.75
15	Reidel Anthony	1.00
16	Kenard Lang	.05
17	Kenny Holmes	.05
18	Tarik Glenn	.05
19	Dwayne Rudd	.05
20	Renaldo Wynn	.05
21	David LaFleur	.20
22	Antowain Smith	1.50
23	Jim Druckenmiller	1.25
24	Rae Carruth	1.00
25	Jared Tomich	.05
26	Chris Canty	.05
27	Jake Plummer	4.00
28	Troy Davis	.50
29	Sedrick Shaw	.50
30	Jamie Sharper	.05
31	Tiki Barber	1.00
32	Byron Hanspard	.75
33	Darnell Autry	.50
34	Corey Dillon	1.75
35	Joey Kent	.30
36	Nathan Davis	.05
37	Will Blackwell	.30
38	Kim Herring	.05
39	Pat Barnes	.30
40	Kevin Lockett	.20
41	Trevor Pryce	.05
42	Matt Russell	.05
43	Greg Jones	.05
44	Antonio Anderson	.05
45	George Jones	.10
46	Steve Young	.20
47	Jerry Rice	.35
48	Curtis Conway	.05
49	Jeff Blake	.05
50	Carl Pickens	.05
51	Bruce Smith	.05
52	John Elway	.20
53	Terrell Davis	.50
54	Shannon Sharpe	.05
55	Junior Seau	.05
56	Darren Bennett	.05
57	Jim Harbaugh	.05
58	Marshall Faulk	.05
59	Emmitt Smith	.75
60	Troy Aikman	.35
61	Deion Sanders	.20
62	Dan Marino	.75
63	Ricky Watters	.05
64	Mark Brunell	.35
65	Keenan McCardell	.05
66	Keyshawn Johnson	.20
67	Barry Sanders	.50
68	Herman Moore	.50
69	Eddie George	.50
70	Steve McNair	.25
71	Brett Favre	1.00
72	Reggie White	.05
73	Edgar Bennett	.05
74	Kerry Collins	.35
75	Kevin Greene	.05
76	Drew Bledsoe	.35
77	Terry Glenn	.40
78	Curtis Martin	.50
79	Jeff Hostetler	.05
80	Napoleon Kaufman	.25
81	Isaac Bruce	.05
82	Terry Allen	.05
83	Joey Galloway	.35
84	Kordell Stewart	.20
85	Jerome Bettis	.05
86	Dana Stubblefield	.05
87	Merton Hanks	.05
88	Terrell Owens	.50
89	Brent Jones	.05
90	Ken Norton Jr.	.05
91	Jerry Rice	.75
92	Terry Kirby	.05
93	Bryant Young	.05
94	Raymont Harris	.05
95	Jeff Jaeger	.05
96	Curtis Conway	.10
97	Walt Harris	.05
98	Bobby Engram	.10
99	Donnell Woolford	.05
100	Rashaan Salaam	.10
101	Jeff Blake	.10
102	Tony McGee	.05
103	Ashley Ambrose	.05
104	Dan Wilkinson	.05
105	Jevon Langford	.05
106	Darnay Scott	.05
107	David Dunn	.05
108	Eric Moulds	.05
109	Darrick Holmes	.05
110	Thurman Thomas	.05
111	Quinn Early	.05
112	Jim Kelly	.25
113	Bryce Paup	.05
114	Bruce Smith	.05
115	Todd Collins	.05
116	Tory James	.05
117	Anthony Miller	.05
118	Terrell Bass	1.00
119	Tyrone Braxton	.05
120	John Mobley	.05
121	Bill Romanowski	.05
122	Vaughn Hebron	.05
123	Mike Alstott	.15
124	Errict Rhett	.10
125	Trent Dilfer	.10
126	Courtney Hawkins	.05
127	Hardy Nickerson	.05
128	Donnie Abraham	.05
129	Regan Upshaw	.05
130	Kent Graham	.05
131	Rob Moore	.05
132	Simeon Rice	.05
133	LeShon Johnson	.05
134	Frank Sanders	.05
135	Leeland McElroy	.05
136	Seth Joyner	.05
137	Andre Coleman	.05
138	Stan Humphries	.05
139	Charlie Jones	.05
140	Junior Seau	.05
141	Rodney Harrison	.05
142	Darrien Gordon	.05
143	Terrell Fletcher	.05
144	Tamarick Vanover	.10
145	Greg Hill	.05
146	Marcus Allen	.10
147	Lake Dawson	.05
148	Dale Carter	.05
149	Kimble Anders	.05
150	Chris Penn	.05
151	Sean Dawkins	.05
152	Ken Dilger	.05
153	Marvin Harrison	.40
154	Jeff Herrod	.05
155	Jim Harbaugh	.05
156	Cary Blanchard	.05
157	Aaron Bailey	.05
158	Deion Sanders	.40
159	Jim Schwantz	.05
160	Michael Irvin	.10
161	Herschel Walker	.05
162	Emmitt Smith	1.50
163	Chris Boniol	.05
164	Eric Bjornson	.05
165	Karim Abdul-Jabbar	.60
166	O.J. McDuffie	.05
167	Troy Drayton	.05
168	Zach Thomas	.40
169	Irving Spikes	.05
170	Shane Burton	.05
171	Stanley Pritchett	.05
172	Ty Detmer	.05
173	Chris T. Jones	.05
174	Troy Vincent	.05
175	Brian Dawkins	.05
176	Irving Fryar	.05
177	Charlie Garner	.05
178	Bobby Taylor	.05
179	Jamal Anderson	.05
180	Terance Mathis	.05
181	Craig Heyward	.05
182	Cornelius Bennett	.05
183	Jessie Tuggle	.05
184	Devin Bush	.05
185	Dave Brown	.05
186	Danny Kanell	.05
187	Rodney Hampton	.05
188	Tyrone Wheatley	.05
189	Amani Toomer	.05
190	Phillippi Sparks	.05
191	Thomas Lewis	.05
192	Jimmy Smith	.05
193	Pete Mitchell	.05
194	Natrone Means	.10
195	Mark Brunell	.75
196	Kevin Hardy	.05
197	Tony Brackens	.05
198	Aaron Beasley	.05
199	Chris Hudson	.05
200	Wayne Chrebet	.05
201	Keyshawn Johnson	.40
202	Adrian Murrell	.05
203	Neil O'Donnell	.05
204	Hugh Douglas	.05
205	Mo Lewis	.05
206	Glenn Foley	.05
207	Aaron Glenn	.05
208	Johnnie Morton	.05
209	Reggie Brown	.05
210	Barry Sanders	1.25
211	Glyn Milburn	.05
212	Bennie Blades	.05
213	Steve McNair	.40
214	Frank Wycheck	.05
215	Chris Sanders	.05
216	Blaine Bishop	.05
217	Willie Davis	.05
218	Darryll Lewis	.05
219	Marcus Robertson	.05
220	Robert Brooks	.10
221	Antonio Freeman	.30
222	Keith Jackson (Retired)	.05
223	Mark Chmura	.05
224	Brett Favre	1.75
225	Sean Jones	.05
226	Reggie White	.10
227	LeRoy Butler	.05
228	Craig Newsome	.05
229	Wesley Walls	.05
230	Mark Carrier	.05
231	Muhsin Muhammad	.05
232	John Kasay	.05
233	Anthony Johnson	.05
234	Kerry Collins	.75
235	Kevin Greene	.05
236	Sam Mills	.05
237	Ben Coates	.05
238	Terry Glenn	.75
239	Willie McGinest	.05
240	Ted Johnson	.05
241	Lawyer Milloy	.05
242	Drew Bledsoe	.75
243	Willie Clay	.05
244	Chris Slade	.05
245	Tim Brown	.05
246	Daryl Hobbs	.05
247	Rickey Dudley	.05
248	Joe Aska	.05
249	Chester McGlockton	.05
250	Rob Fredrickson	.05
251	Terry McDaniel	.05
252	Tony Banks	.25
253	Lawrence Phillips	.10
254	Isaac Bruce	.15
255	Eddie Kennison	.25
256	Kevin Carter	.05
257	Roman Phifer	.05
258	Keith Lyle	.05
259	Vinny Testaverde	.05
260	Derrick Alexander	.05
261	Ray Lewis	.05
262	Jermaine Lewis	.05
263	Bam Morris	.05
264	Stevon Moore	.05
265	Antonio Langham	.05
266	Brian Mitchell	.05
267	Henry Ellard	.05
268	Leslie Shepherd	.05
269	Michael Westbrook	.05
270	Jamie Asher	.05
271	Ken Harvey	.05
272	Gus Frerotte	.05
273	Michael Haynes	.05
274	Ray Zellars	.05
275	Jim Everett	.05
276	Tyrone Hughes (Bears)	.05
277	Joe Johnson	.05
278	Eric Allen	.05
279	Brady Smith	.05
280	Mario Bates	.05
281	Torrance Small	.05
282	John Friesz	.05
283	Brian Blades	.05
284	Chris Warren	.05
285	Joey Galloway	.25
286	Michael Sinclair	.05
287	Lamar Smith	.05
288	Mike Pritchard	.05
289	Jerome Bettis	.10
290	Charles Johnson	.05
291	Mike Tomczak	.05
292	Levon Kirkland	.05
293	Carnell Lake	.05
294	Erric Pegram	.05
295	Kordell Stewart	.50
296	Greg Lloyd	.05
297	Dixon Edwards	.05
298	Cris Carter	.05
299	Brad Johnson	.05
300	Qadry Ismail	.05
301	John Randle	.05
302	Orlanda Thomas	.05
303	DeWayne Washington	.05
304	Jake Reed	.05
305	Derrick Alexander	.05
306	Eddie George	1.25
307	Dan Marino	1.50
308	Curtis Martin	1.00
309	Troy Aikman	.75
310	Marcus Allen	.75
311	Jim Druckenmiller	1.00
312	Greg Clark	.05
313	Darnell Autry	.30
314	Reinard Wilson	.05
315	Corey Dillon	1.50
316	Antowain Smith	.75
317	Trevor Pryce	.05
318	Warrick Dunn	1.75
319	Reidel Anthony	1.75
320	Jake Plummer	1.75
321	Tom Knight	.05
322	Freddie Jones	.10
323	Tony Gonzalez	.30
324	Pat Barnes	.30

325	Kevin Lockett	.05
326	Tarik Glenn	.05
327	David LaFleur	.30
328	Antonio Anderson	.05
329	Yatil Green	.40
330	Jason Taylor	.05
331	Brian Manning	.05
332	Michael Booker	.05
333	Byron Hanspard	.40
334	Ike Hilliard	.40
335	Tiki Barber	.05
336	Renaldo Wynn	.05
337	Damon Jones	.05
338	James Farrior	.05
339	Dedric Ward	.05
340	Bryant Westbrook	.05
341	Matt Russell	.05
342	Joey Kent	.05
343	Kenny Holmes	.05
344	Darren Sharper	.05
345	Rae Carruth	.40
346	Chris Canty	.05
347	Darrell Russell	.05
348	Orlando Pace	.05
349	Peter Boulware	.05
350	*Danny Wuerffel*	.75
351	Troy Davis	.40
352	Shawn Springs	.05
353	Walter Jones	.05
354	Will Blackwell	.05
355	Dwayne Rudd	.05
356	Cardinals	.05
357	Falcons	.05
358	Ravens	.05
359	Bills	.05
360	Panthers	.05
361	Bears	.05
362	Bengals	.05
363	Cowboys	.05
364	Broncos	.05
365	Lions	.05
366	Packers	.05
367	Oilers	.05
368	Colts	.05
369	Jaguars	.05
370	Chiefs	.05
371	Dolphins	.05
372	Vikings	.05
373	Patriots	.05
374	Saints	.05
375	Jets	.05
376	Giants	.05
377	Raiders	.05
378	Eagles	.05
379	Steelers	.05
380	Chargers	.05
381	49ers	.05
382	Seahawks	.05
383	Rams	.05
384	Buccaneers	.05
385	Redskins	.05
386	William Floyd	.05
387	Steve Young	.75
388	Lee Woodall	.05
389	J.J. Stokes	.05
390	Marc Edwards	.05
391	Rod Woodson	.05
392	Jim Schwantz	.05
393	Garrison Hearst	.05
394	Rick Mirer	.05
395	Alonzo Spellman	.05
396	Tom Carter	.05
397	Bryan Cox	.05
398	John Allred	.05
399	Ricky Proehl	.05
400	Tyrone Hughes	.05
401	Carl Pickens	.05
402	Tremain Mack	.05
403	Boomer Esiason	.05
404	Ki-Jana Carter	.05
405	Steve Tovar	.05
406	Billy Joe Hobert	.05
407	Andre Reed	.05
408	Marcelius Wiley	.05
409	Steve Tasker	.05
410	Chris Spielman	.05
411	Alfred Williams	.05
412	John Elway	.75
413	Shannon Sharpe	.05
414	Steve Atwater	.05
415	Neil Smith	.05
416	Darrien Gordon	.05
417	Jeff Lewis	.05
418	Flipper Anderson	.05
419	Willie Green	.05
420	Jackie Harris	.05
421	Steve Walsh	.05
422	Anthony Parker	.05
423	Ronde Barber	.05
424	Warren Sapp	.05
425	Aeneas Williams	.05
426	Larry Centers	.05
427	Eric Swann	.05
428	Kevin Williams	.05
429	Darren Bennett	.05
430	Tony Martin	.05
431	John Carney	.05
432	Jim Everett	.05
433	William Fuller	.05
434	Latario Rachel	.05
435	Erric Pegram	.05
436	Eric Metcalf	.05
437	Jerome Woods	.05
438	Derrick Thomas	.05
439	Elvis Grbac	.05
440	Terry Wooden	.05
441	Andre Rison	.05
442	Brett Perriman	.05
443	Roosevelt Potts	.05
444	Robert Blackman	.05
445	Carlton Gray	.05
446	Chris Gardocki	.05
447	Marshall Faulk	.10
448	Sammie Burroughs	.05
449	Quentin Coryatt	.05
450	Troy Aikman	1.00
451	Daryl Johnston	.05
452	Tony Tolbert	.05
453	Brock Marion	.05
454	Billy Davis	.05
455	Dexter Coakley	.05
456	Anthony Miller	.05
457	Dan Marino	2.00
458	Jerris McPhail	.05
459	Terrell Buckley	.05
460	Daryl Gardener	.05
461	George Teague	.05
462	Qadry Ismail	.05
463	Fred Barnett	.05
464	Darrin Smith	.05
465	Michael Timpson	.05
466	Jon Harris	.05
467	Jason Dunn	.05
468	Bobby Hoying	.05
469	Ricky Watters	.10
470	Derrick Witherspoon	.05
471	Chris Chandler	.05
472	Ray Buchanan	.05
473	Michael Haynes	.05
474	Nathan Davis	.05
475	Morten Andersen	.05
476	Bert Emanuel	.05
477	Chris Calloway	.05
478	Jason Sehorn	.05
479	John Jurkovic	.05
480	Keenan McCardell	.05
481	James O. Stewart	.05
482	Rob Johnson	.05
483	Mike Logan	.05
484	Deon Figures	.05
485	Kyle Brady	.05
486	Alex Van Dyke	.05
487	Jeff Graham	.05
488	Jason Hanson	.05
489	Herman Moore	.10
490	Scott Mitchell	.05
491	Tommy Vardell	.05
492	Derrick Mason	.05
493	Rodney Thomas	.05
494	Ronnie Harmon	.05
495	Eddie George	1.50
496	Edgar Bennett	.05
497	William Henderson	.05
498	Dorsey Levens	.10
499	Gilbert Brown	.05
500	Steve Bono	.05
501	Derrick Mayes	.05
502	*Fred Lane*	.50
503	Ernie Mills	.05
504	Tshimanga Biakabutuka	.05
505	Michael Bates	.05
506	Winslow Oliver	.05
507	Ty Law	.05
508	Shawn Jefferson	.05
509	Vincent Brisby	.05
510	Henry Thomas	.05
511	Tedy Bruschi	.05
512	Curtis Martin	.75
513	Jeff George	.05
514	Desmond Howard	.05
515	Napoleon Kaufman	.10
516	Kenny Shedd	.05
517	Russell Maryland	.05
518	Lance Johnstone	.05
519	Chad Levitt	.05
520	Dexter McLeon	.05
521	Craig Heyward	.05
522	Ryan McNeil	.05
523	Mark Rypien	.05
524	Mike Jones	.05
525	Jamie Sharper	.05
526	Tony Siragusa	.05
527	Michael Jackson	.05
528	Floyd Turner	.05
529	Eric Green	.05
530	Michael McCrary	.05
531	Jay Graham	.05
532	Terry Allen	.05
533	Sean Gilbert	.05
534	Scott Turner	.05
535	Cris Dishman	.05
536	Jeff Hostetler	.05
537	Chris Mims	.05
538	Alvin Harper	.05
539	Daryl Hobbs	.05
540	Wayne Martin	.05
541	Heath Shuler	.05
542	Andre Hastings	.05
543	Jared Tomich	.05
544	Nicky Savoie	.05
545	Cortez Kennedy	.05
546	Warren Moon	.05
547	Chad Brown	.05
548	Willie Williams	.05
549	Bennie Blades	.05
550	Darren Perry	.05
551	Yancey Thigpen	.05
552	Courtney Hawkins	.05
553	Chad Scott	.05
554	George Jones	.05
555	Robert Tate	.05
556	Torrian Gray	.05
557	Robert Griffith	.05
558	Robert Griffith	.05
559	Leroy Hoard	.05
560	Robert Smith	.05
561	Randall Cunningham	.05
562	Darrell Russell CL	.05
563	Troy Aikman CL	.25
564	Dan Marino CL	.40
565	Jim Druckenmiller CL	.25

1997 Collector's Choice Crash the Game

This 30-card chase set was inserted 1:5 packs. If the player featured on the front scored on the date shown on the card, the collector won a redemption card of the player. This insert appeared only in Series I.

		MT
Complete Set (30):		25.00
Common Player:		.50
Minor Stars:		1.00

Each player has three cards with 3 different dates.

#	Player	Price
1	Troy Aikman	1.50
2	Dan Marino	3.00
3	Steve Young	1.25
4	Brett Favre	3.50
5	Drew Bledsoe	1.50
6	Jeff Blake	1.00
7	Mark Brunell	1.00
8	John Elway	1.25
9	Vinny Testaverde	.50
10	Steve McNair	1.25
11	Jerry Rice	1.50
12	Terry Glenn	1.00
13	Michael Jackson	.50
14	Tony Martin	.50
15	Isaac Bruce	1.00
16	Cris Carter	1.00
17	Shannon Sharpe	.50
18	Rae Carruth	1.00
19	Ike Hilliard	1.00
20	Yatil Green	.75
21	Terry Allen	.50
22	Emmitt Smith	3.00
23	Karim Abdul-Jabbar	1.00
24	Barry Sanders	1.50
25	Terrell Davis	1.50
26	Jerome Bettis	1.00
27	Ricky Watters	1.00
28	Curtis Martin	1.25
29	Byron Hanspard	1.00
30	Warrick Dunn	2.00

1997 Collector's Choice Mini-Standee

Inserted 1:5, the 30-card Mini Standee insert appeared in Series II. The cards can be folded into a football shaped stand-up card. The cards are numbered with the "ST" prefix.

		MT
Complete Set (30):		25.00
Common Player:		.25
Minor Stars:		.50

#	Player	Price
1	Jerry Rice	1.50
2	Rashaan Salaam	.25
3	Jeff Blake	.50
4	Antowain Smith	1.25
5	John Elway	1.25
6	Errict Rhett	.25
7	Jake Plummer	1.25
8	Junior Seau	.25
9	Marcus Allen	.50
10	Marvin Harrison	.50
11	Emmitt Smith	3.00
12	Dan Marino	3.00
13	Ricky Watters	.50
14	Jamal Anderson	.25
15	Rodney Hampton	.25
16	Mark Brunell	1.50
17	Keyshawn Johnson	.50
18	Barry Sanders	2.00
19	Eddie George	2.00
20	Brett Favre	3.50
21	Kerry Collins	1.00
22	Drew Bledsoe	1.50
23	Napoleon Kaufman	.50
24	Sean Dawkins	.50
25	Vinny Testaverde	.25
26	Terry Allen	.25
27	Mario Bates	.25
28	Joey Galloway	.50
29	Jerome Bettis	.50
30	Robert Smith	.25

1997 Collector's Choice Star Quest

StarQuest is a four-tiered insert available in Series II. The tiers are indicated by the number of stars on the card - one per tier. Tier one includes 45 cards and were inserted 1:1. Tier two includes 20 cards inserted 1:21. The 15 tier three cards were inserted 1:71. Tier four had 10 cards and was inserted 1:145. The insert set totaled 90 cards, featuring the top players in the game. The cards are numbered with the "SQ" prefix.

		MT
Complete Set (90):		500.00
Common Player (1-45):		.25
Common Player (46-65):		2.00
Common Player (66-80):		5.00
Common Player (81-90):		10.00

#	Player	Price
1	Frank Sanders	.25
2	Jamal Anderson	.50
3	Bam Morris	.25
4	Thurman Thomas	.50
5	Muhsin Muhammad	.25
6	Bobby Engram	.25
7	Carl Pickens	.25
8	Deion Sanders	.75
9	Shannon Sharpe	.50
10	Herman Moore	.50
11	Robert Brooks	.25
12	Steve McNair	1.50
13	Marshall Faulk	.50
14	Keenan McCardell	.25
15	Tamarick Vanover	.25
16	Fred Barnett	.25
17	Orlanda Thomas	.25
18	Drew Bledsoe	1.50
19	Mario Bates	.25
20	Keyshawn Johnson	.50
21	Rodney Hampton	.25
22	Darrell Russell	.25
23	Irving Fryar	.25
24	Charles Johnson	.25
25	Stan Humphries	.25
26	Terrell Owens	.50
27	Chris Warren	.25
28	Isaac Bruce	.50
29	Warrick Dunn	2.50
30	Gus Frerotte	.25
31	Raghib Ismail	.25
32	Natrone Means	.50
33	Chris Sanders	.25
34	Vinny Testaverde	.25
35	Ken Norton	.25
36	Kevin Greene	.25
37	Marcus Allen	.50
38	Zach Thomas	.25
39	Derrick Thomas	.25
40	Tyrone Wheatley	.25
41	Dorsey Levens	.50
42	Darnay Scott	.25
43	Scott Mitchell	.25
44	Marvin Harrison	.50
45	Eddie Kennison	.50
46	Jake Reed	2.00
47	Andre Reed	2.00
48	Neil Smith	2.00
49	Anthony Johnson	2.00
50	Napoleon Kaufman	4.00
51	Terance Mathis	2.00
52	Tony Martin	2.00
53	Adrian Murrell	4.00
54	Bryant Westbrook	2.00
55	Errict Rhett	2.00
56	Kerry Collins	10.00
57	Curtis Conway	2.00
58	Eric Swann	2.00
59	Michael Jackson	2.00
60	Ty Detmer	2.00
61	Michael Irvin	4.00
62	Andre Coleman	2.00
63	Brian Mitchell	2.00
64	Tony Banks	4.00
65	Eddie George	20.00
66	Kordell Stewart	20.00
67	Greg Hill	5.00
68	Karim Abdul-Jabbar	12.00
69	Cris Carter	5.00
70	Terry Glenn	15.00
71	Emmitt Smith	60.00
72	Jim Harbaugh	5.00
73	Jeff Blake	8.00
74	Rashaan Salaam	5.00
75	Ricky Watters	5.00
76	Joey Galloway	8.00
77	Junior Seau	5.00
78	Dave Brown	5.00
79	Tim Brown	5.00
80	Troy Aikman	25.00
81	Dan Marino	70.00
82	Brett Favre	75.00
83	John Elway	30.00
84	Steve Young	25.00
85	Mark Brunell	35.00
86	Barry Sanders	40.00
87	Jerome Bettis	10.00
88	Terrell Davis	35.00
89	Curtis Martin	30.00
90	Jerry Rice	35.00

1997 Collector's Choice Stick-Ums

Inserted 1:3 packs in Series I, these 30 stickers featured a photo of the player on the front, the Stick-Ums logo, his name and team helmet which could be peeled off. The sticker number is printed on the upper left of the back. Directions on how to use the stickers are on the left of the back, while the checklist is on the right. Each of the stickers' numbers included an "S" prefix.

		MT
Complete Set (30):		15.00
Common Player:		.25
Minor Stars:		.50

#	Player	Price
1	Kerry Collins	.75
2	Troy Aikman	1.25
3	Steve Young	.75
4	Ricky Watters	.50
5	Cris Carter	.25
6	Terry Allen	.25
7	Bobby Engram	.50
8	Simeon Rice	.25
9	Mike Alstott	.50
10	Rodney Hampton	.25
11	Eddie Kennison	.50
12	Jamal Anderson	.50
13	Jim Everett	.25
14	Curtis Martin	.50
15	Keenan McCardell	.25
16	Kordell Stewart	1.00
17	John Elway	.75
18	Terrell Davis	1.25
19	Thurman Thomas	.50
20	Marshall Faulk	.50
21	Marcus Allen	.50
22	Tony Martin	.25
23	Dan Marino	2.00
24	Karim Abdul-Jabbar	1.00
25	Carl Pickens	.25
26	Eddie George	1.50
27	Joey Galloway	.50
28	Napoleon Kaufman	.25
29	Vinny Testaverde	.25
30	Keyshawn Johnson	.50

1997 Collector's Choice Turf Champions

The 90-card chase set was broken up into four tiers. Tier one and two both contain 30 cards, while Tier three has 20. Tier four includes 10. The Tiers were inserted as follows: one (every pack), two (1:21), three (1:71) and four (1:145). The holofoil cards have a green-marble border at the top and bottom. The Collector's Choice logo is in the upper left, with the Turf Champions' logo in the lower left. The player's name, position and team are listed at the bottom center. The backs, which are numbered with a "TC" prefix, have the player's highlights printed over a green area on the left, with his achievement printed vertically in the center. The right has a photo and quote. Turf Champions appeared in Series I.

		MT
Complete Set (90):		650.00
Complete Tier 1 (30):		10.00
Complete Tier 2 (30):		100.00
Complete Tier 3 (30):		250.00
Complete Tier 4 (10):		300.00
Common Player (1-30):		.20
Common Player (31-60):		.50
Common Player (61-80):		5.00
Common Player (81-90):		6.00

#	Player	Price
1	Kerry Collins	1.00
2	Scott Mitchell	.20
3	Jim Schwantz	.20
4	Orlando Pace	.40
5	Troy Davis	1.25
6	Vinny Testaverde	.20
7	Raghib Ismail	.20
8	Henry Ellard	.20
9	Kevin Turner	.20
10	Bobby Engram	.20
11	Keyshawn Johnson	.40
12	Trent Dilfer	.20
13	Elvis Grbac	.20
14	Trev Alberts	.20
15	Kevin Hardy	.20
16	Warren Sapp	.20
17	Chris Hudson	.20
18	Antonio Langham	.20
19	Jonathan Ogden	.20
20	Bruce Smith	.20
21	Marcus Allen	.40
22	Desmond Howard	.20
23	Eric Metcalf	.20
24	Terance Mathis	.20
25	LeShon Johnson	.20
26	Kevin Greene	.20
27	Alex Van Dyke	.20
28	Jeff Jaeger	.20
29	Jason Elam	.20
30	Thomas Lewis	.20
31	Rick Mirer	4.00
32	Warren Moon	4.00
33	Jim Kelly	4.00
34	Junior Seau	4.00
35	Jeff Hostetler	2.00
36	Neil O'Donnell	2.00
37	Jeff Blake	2.00
38	Kordell Stewart	14.00
39	Terry Glenn	12.00
40	Simeon Rice	2.00
41	Jimmy Smith	2.00
42	Natrone Means	4.00
43	Tony Martin	2.00
44	Charles Johnson	2.00
45	Napoleon Kaufman	4.00
46	Dale Carter	2.00
47	Brett Perriman	2.00
48	Cortez Kennedy	2.00
49	Bryce Paup	2.00
50	Greg Lloyd	2.00
51	Bryant Young	2.00
52	Steve McNair	14.00

		MT
53	Garrison Hearst	2.00
54	John Copeland	2.00
55	Eric Curry	2.00
56	Reggie White	4.00
57	Rod Woodson	2.00
58	Andre Rison	2.00
59	Herschel Walker	2.00
60	John Kasay	2.00
61	Emmitt Smith	60.00
62	Dan Marino	60.00
63	Michael Irvin	10.00
64	Drew Bledsoe	30.00
65	Mark Brunell	30.00
66	Jim Harbaugh	5.00
67	Herman Moore	10.00
68	Rashaan Salaam	10.00
69	Ty Detmer	5.00
70	Cris Carter	5.00
71	Chris Warren	5.00
72	Thurman Thomas	5.00
73	Ricky Watters	10.00
74	Tim Brown	5.00
75	Marshall Faulk	10.00
76	Jerome Bettis	5.00
77	Karim Abdul-Jabbar	20.00
78	Deion Sanders	14.00
79	Ben Coates	5.00
80	Andre Reed	5.00
81	Brett Favre	75.00
82	Troy Aikman	35.00
83	Barry Sanders	40.00
84	Jerry Rice	35.00
85	Steve Young	20.00
86	John Elway	20.00
87	Terrell Davis	35.00
88	Carl Pickens	6.00
89	Curtis Martin	35.00
90	Eddie George	35.00

1992 Collector's Edge Prototypes

BERNIE KOSAR
QUARTERBACK

Two different versions of this six-card prototype set were issued. One version had a removable piece of paper glued to the card back, while the other version was not sticky. The paper-covered backs are tougher to find. Edge produced 8,000 of each card. The card fronts are bordered in black, with a color photo. The Edge '92 logo is in the upper left. The player's name and position are in the lower left. The player's team's helmet is located on the lower right of the card back. The backs have a player headshot at the top, with his name, position, team, bio and stats listed below. The cards are numbered in the upper right with a "prototype" suffix.

		MT
Complete Set (6):		25.00
Common Player:		2.00
1	Jim Kelly	3.00
2	Randall Cunningham	4.00
3	Warren Moon	2.00
4	John Elway	10.00
5	Dan Marino	10.00
6	Bernie Kosar	2.00

1992 Collector's Edge

ALONZO SPELLMAN
ROOKIE DEFENSIVE END

Each card in this 175-card

set is individually numbered from 1-100,000. The standard-size cards are printed on a plastic stock and feature color action shots with black borders. A team helmet is on the lower right-hand corner. Backs, which have the card front image ghosted through, have a mug shot, statistics and a biography. John Elway and Ken O'Brien autographed 2,500 cards which were randomly inserted in factory sets and foil packs. Rookie/Update cards begin with #176 and are considered a second series. There were also 2,500 Ronnie Lott autographed cards in the series, plus 20,000 cards each for Terrell Buckley and Tommy Maddox.

		MT
Complete Set (250):		40.00
Complete Series 1 (175):		25.00
Complete Series 2 (75):		15.00
Common Player:		.10
Minor Stars:		.20
Elway Auto:		100.00
Lott Auto:		40.00
O'Brien Auto:		20.00
Series 1 Wax Box:		15.00
Rookie/Update Box:		15.00
1	Chris Miller	.10
2	Steve Broussard	.10
3	Mike Pritchard	.20
4	Tim Green	.10
5	Andre Rison	.30
6	Deion Sanders	1.00
7	Jim Kelly	.50
8	James Lofton	.10
9	Andre Reed	.10
10	Bruce Smith	.10
11	Thurman Thomas	1.00
12	Cornelius Bennett	.10
13	Jim Harbaugh	.10
14	William Perry	.10
15	Mike Singletary	.10
16	Mark Carrier	.10
17	Kevin Butler	.10
18	Tom Waddle	.10
19	Boomer Esiason	.20
20	David Fulcher	.10
21	Anthony Munoz	.10
22	Tim McGee	.10
23	Harold Green	.10
24	Rickey Dixon	.10
25	Bernie Kosar	.10
26	Michael Dean Perry	.10
27	Mike Baab	.10
28	Brian Brennan	.10
29	Michael Jackson	.20
30	Eric Metcalf	.10
31	Troy Aikman	3.00
32	Emmitt Smith	6.00
33	Michael Irvin	1.00
34	Jay Novacek	.10
35	Issiac Holt	.10
36	Ken Norton	.10
37	John Elway	1.25
38	Gaston Green	.10
39	Charles Dimry	.10
40	Vance Johnson	.10
41	Dennis Smith	.10
42	David Treadwell	.10
43	Michael Young	.10
44	Bennie Blades	.10
45	Mel Gray	.10
46	Andre Ware	.10
47	Rodney Peete	.10
48	*Toby Caston*	.10
49	Herman Moore	2.00
50	Brian Noble	.10
51	Sterling Sharpe	.50
52	Mike Tomczak	.10
53	Vinnie Clark	.10
54	Tony Mandarich	.10
55	Ed West	.10
56	Warren Moon	.30
57	Ray Childress	.10
58	Haywood Jeffires	.10
59	Al Smith	.10
60	Cris Dishman	.10
61	Ernest Givins	.10
62	Richard Johnson	.10
63	Eric Dickerson	.10
64	Jessie Hester	.10
65	Robin Stark	.10
66	Clarence Verdin	.10
67	Dean Biasucci	.10
68	Duane Bickett	.10
69	Jeff George	.30
70	Christian Okoye	.10
71	Derrick Thomas	.30
72	Stephone Paige	.10
73	Dan Saleaumua	.10
74	Deron Cherry	.10
75	Kevin Ross	.10
76	Barry Word	.10
77	Ronnie Lott	.30
78	Greg Townsend	.10
79	Willie Gault	.10
80	Howie Long	.10
81	Winston Moss	.10
82	Steve Smith	.10
83	Jay Schroeder	.10

84	Jim Everett	.20
85	Willie Anderson	.10
86	Henry Ellard	.10
87	Tony Zendejas	.10
88	Robert Delpino	.10
89	Pat Terrel	.10
90	Dan Marino	5.00
91	Mark Clayton	.10
92	Jim Jensen	.10
93	Reggie Roby	.10
94	Sammie Smith	.10
95	Tony Martin	.10
96	Jeff Cross	.10
97	Anthony Carter	.10
98	Chris Doleman	.10
99	Wade Wilson	.10
100	Cris Carter	.20
101	Mike Meriweather	.10
102	Gary Zimmerman	.10
103	Chris Singleton	.10
104	Bruce Armstrong	.10
105	Marv Cook	.10
106	Andre Tippet	.10
107	Tom Hodson	.10
108	Greg McMurtry	.10
109	Jon Vaughn	.10
110	Vaughan Johnson	.10
111	Craig Heyward	.10
112	Floyd Turner	.10
113	Pat Swilling	.10
114	Ricky Jackson	.10
115	Steve Walsh	.10
116	Phil Simms	.10
117	Carl Banks	.10
118	Mark Ingram	.10
119	Bart Oates	.10
120	Lawrence Taylor	.20
121	Jeff Hostetler	.30
122	Rob Moore	.20
123	Ken O'Brien	.10
124	Bill Pickel	.10
125	Irv Eatman	.10
126	Browning Nagle	.10
127	Al Toon	.10
128	Randall Cunningham	.20
129	Eric Allen	.10
130	Mike Golic	.10
131	Fred Barnett	.10
132	Keith Byars	.10
133	Calvin Williams	.10
134	Randal Hill	.10
135	Ricky Proehl	.10
136	Lance Smith	.10
137	Ernie Jones	.10
138	Timm Rosenbach	.10
139	Anthony Thompson	.10
140	Bubby Brister	.10
141	Merril Hoge	.10
142	Louis Lipps	.10
143	Eric Green	.10
144	Gary Anderson	.10
145	Neil O'Donnell	.40
146	Rod Bernstine	.10
147	John Friesz	.10
148	Anthony Miller	.10
149	Junior Seau	.50
150	Leslie O'Neal	.10
151	Nate Lewis	.10
152	Steve Young	3.00
153	Kevin Fagan	.10
154	Charles Haley	.10
155	Tom Rathman	.10
156	Jerry Rice	3.00
157	John Taylor	.10
158	Brian Blades	.10
159	Patrick Hunter	.10
160	Cortez Kennedy	.20
161	Vann McElroy	.10
162	Dan McGwire	.10
163	John L. Williams	.10
164	Gary Anderson	.10
165	Broderick Thomas	.10
166	Vinny Testaverde	.20
167	Lawrence Dawsey	.10
168	Paul Gruber	.10
169	Keith McCants	.10
170	Mark Rypien	.10
171	Gary Clark	.10
172	Earnest Byner	.10
173	Brian Mitchell	.10
174	Monte Coleman	.10
175	Joe Jacoby	.10
176	*Tommy Vardell*	.20
177	*Troy Vincent*	.25
178	*Robert Jones*	.20
179	*Marc Boutte*	.10
180	*Marco Coleman*	.30
181	*Chris Mims*	.50
182	*Tony Casillas*	.10
183	*Shane Dronett*	.20
184	*Sean Gilbert*	.40
185	*Siran Stacy*	.10
186	*Tommy Maddox*	.20
187	*Steve Israel*	.10
188	*Brad Muster*	.10
189	*Shane Collins*	.10
190	*Terrell Buckley*	.25
191	*Eugene Chung*	.10
192	*Leon Searcy*	.10
193	*Chuck Smith*	.10
194	*Patrick Rowe*	.10
195	*Bill Johnson*	.10
196	*Gerald Dixon*	.10
197	*Robert Porcher*	.25
198	*Tracy Scroggins*	.40
199	*Jason Hanson*	.30

200	*Corey Harris*	.20
201	*Eddie Robinson*	.10
202	*Steve Emtman*	.30
203	*Ashley Ambrose*	.20
204	*Greg Skrepenak*	.20
205	*Todd Collins*	.20
206	*Derek Brown*	.25
207	*Kurt Barber*	.20
208	*Tony Sacca*	.20
209	*Mark Wheeler*	.20
210	*Kevin Smith*	.30
211	*John Fina*	.10
212	*Johnny Mitchell*	.50
213	*Dale Carter*	.20
214	*Bobby Spitulski*	.10
215	*Phillippi Sparks*	.10
216	*Levon Kirkland*	.20
217	*Mike Sherrard*	.10
218	*Marquez Pope*	.10
219	*Courtney Hawkins*	.30
220	*Tyji Armstrong*	.20
221	*Keith Jackson*	.20
222	*Clayton Holmes*	.20
223	*Quentin Coryatt*	.30
224	*Troy Auzenne*	.20
225	*David Klingler*	.25
226	*Darryl Williams*	.25
227	*Carl Pickens*	1.50
228	*Jimmy Smith*	3.50
229	*Chester McGlockton*	.50
230	*Robert Brooks*	2.00
231	*Alonzo Spellman*	.50
232	*Darren Woodson*	.30
233	*Lewis Billups*	.10
234	*Edgar Bennett*	.75
235	*Vaughn Dunbar*	.20
236	*Steve Bono*	1.00
237	*Clarence Kay*	.10
238	*Chris Hinton*	.10
239	*Jimmie Jones*	.10
240	*Vai Sikahema*	.10
241	*Russell Maryland*	.10
242	*Neal Anderson*	.10
243	*Charles Mann*	.10
244	*Hugh Millen*	.10
245	*Roger Craig*	.10
246	*Rich Gannon*	.10
247	*Ricky Ervins*	.10
248	*Leonard Marshall*	.10
249	*Eric Dickerson*	.20
250	*Joe Montana*	3.00

1992 Collector's Edge Special

Produced to promote Tuff Stuff's Buyer's Club, one of the four cards was inserted in all copies of the November 1992 magazine. Over 250,000 cards were issued of the first card. The other three cards were printed in quantities of approximately 40,000 each. One of each of the three cards were given as a bonus with each paid membership. The Elway card was also printed as "Proto 1," "John Elway Dealerships" and "Elway Foundation." Reportedly, less than 50,000 of these cards were issued. The card fronts have a dark blue border, with a color photo, the player's name and position in the lower left and his team's helmet in the lower right. The card backs are numbered with a "TS" prefix for the Buyer's Club. "Proto 1" is numbered as such, while the Elway Foundation and Elway Dealerships are not numbered. The card backs have a headshot, player's name, bio, position and stats. The card number is in the upper right.

		MT
Complete Set (4):		12.00
Common Player:		2.00
1	John Elway	2.00
2	Ronnie Lott	5.00
3	Jim Everett	3.00
4	Bernie Kosar	3.00
PROT1	John Elway	10.00
NNO	Elway Foundation	30.00
NNO	Elway Dealerships	25.00

Values quoted in this guide reflect the retail price of a card — the price a collector can expect to pay when buying a card from a dealer. The wholesale price — that which a collector can expect to receive from a dealer when selling cards — will be significantly lower, depending on desirability and condition.

1993 Collector's Edge Prototype

RANDALL CUNNINGHAM
QUARTERBACK

These cards, which promote the 1993 Collector's Edge set, are numbered from 1 to 40,000 on the backs. Each card front has a blue marble-like border and an action photo. The back uses a green marble-like border and also indicates that the card is a "Proto." In addition to these cards, there were 8-1/2" x 11" versions of these cards made, too. They, however, are not numbered and were included in dealer cases. They are generally two to four times more valuable than the smaller versions.

		MT
Complete Set (6):		25.00
Common Player:		4.00
1	John Elway	7.00
2	Derrick Thomas	4.00
3	Randall Cunningham	
4	Thurman Thomas	6.00
5	Warren Moon	5.00
6	Barry Sanders	8.00

1993 Collector's Edge RU Prototypes

Blue-marble borders highlight the front of this five-card Rookie/Update set. The Edge logo is in the upper left, with his name and position in the lower left. His team's helmet is printed in the lower right. The card backs have the player's headshot on the upper left, with his team's logo, name, team, position, jersey number and card number, prefixed with "RU." The card's serial number is printed in the center above the player's bio and stats.

		MT
Complete Set (5):		6.00
Common Player:		1.00
1	Garrison Hearst	1.50
2	Reggie White	2.00
3	Boomer Esiason	1.00
4	Rod Bernstine	1.00
5	Dana Stubblefield	1.50

1993 Collector's Edge

MARVIN JONES
LINEBACKER

The second set from Collector's Edge uses the same features as its first set in 1992 - the cards are plastic and are each individually numbered from 1-100,000. The fronts have an action photo with against a blue marble background. A team helmet is at the bottom of the card, while the

Collector's Edge logo is at the top. The backs have statistics, a career summary and a mug shot. Rookie/Update cards are numbered from #251-325. Ten John Elway prism inserts were randomly included in packs; E1-E5 were in late packs; while S1-S5 were in early packs. Twenty-five Collector's Edge Rookies FX cards were randomly inserted in Rookie/Update packs and are numbered with an "FX" prefix. Five Collector's Edge checklists were also made and were randomly inserted in regular packs. Six promo cards were also made featuring Elway, Derrick Thomas, Randall Cunningham, Thurman Thomas, Warren Moon and Barry Sanders. There were 40,000 cards produced for each player.

		MT
Complete Set (325):		20.00
Complete Series 1 (250):		10.00
Complete Series 2 (75):		10.00
Common Player:		.05
Minor Stars:		.10
Comp. Checklists (5):		2.00
Series 1 Wax Box:		13.00
Rookie/Up. Wax Box:		16.00
1	Atlanta Team	.05
2	Michael Haynes	.05
3	Chris Miller	.05
4	Mike Pritchard	.05
5	Andre Rison	.10
6	Deion Sanders	.50
7	Chuck Smith	.05
8	Drew Hill	.05
9	Bobby Hebert	.05
10	Buffalo Team	.05
11	Matt Darby	.05
12	John Fina	.05
13	Jim Kelly	.15
14	*Marcus Patton*	.10
15	Andre Reed	.10
16	Thurman Thomas	.15
17	James Lofton	.05
18	Bruce Smith	.05
19	Chicago Team	.05
20	Neal Anderson	.05
21	Troy Auzenne	.05
22	Jim Harbaugh	.05
23	Alonzo Spellman	.05
24	Tom Waddle	.05
25	Darren Lewis	.05
26	Wendell Davis	.05
27	Will Furrer	.05
28	Cincinnati Team	.05
29	David Klingler	.15
30	Ricardo McDonald	.05
31	Carl Pickens	.40
32	Harold Green	.05
33	Anthony Munoz	.05
34	Darryl Williams	.05
35	Cleveland Team	.05
36	Michael Jackson	.05
37	Pio Sagapolutele	.05
38	Tommy Vardell	.05
39	Bernie Kosar	.05
40	Michael Dean Perry	.05
41	Bill Johnson	.05
42	Vinny Testaverde	.05
43	Dallas team	.05
44	Troy Aikman	.75
45	Alvin Harper	.20
46	Michael Irvin	.10
47	Russell Maryland	.05
48	Emmitt Smith	2.00
49	Kenneth Gant	.05
50	Jay Novacek	.05
51	Robert Jones	.05
52	Clayton Holomes	.05
53	Denver Team	.05
54	Mike Croel	.05
55	Shane Dronett	.05
56	Kenny Walker	.05
57	Tommy Maddox	.05
58	Dennis Smith	.05
59	John Elway	.40
60	Karl Mecklenberg	.05
61	Steve Atwater	.05
62	Vance Johnson	.05
63	Detroit team	.05
64	Barry Sanders	1.25
65	Andre Ware	.05
66	Pat Swilling	.05
67	Jason Hanson	.05
68	Willie Green	.05
69	Herman Moore	.50
70	Rodney Peete	.05
71	Erik Kramer	.05
72	Robert Porcher	.10
73	Green Bay team	.05
74	Terrell Buckley	.05
75	Reggie White	.10
76	Brett Favre	2.00
77	Don Majkowski	.05
78	Edgar Bennett	.10
79	Ty Detmer	.05
80	Sanjay Beach	.05
81	Sterling Sharpe	.05
82	Houston team	.05
83	Gary Brown	.10

84	Ernest Givins	.05
85	Haywood Jeffires	.05
86	Corey Harris	.05
87	Warren Moon	.15
88	Eddie Robinson	.05
89	Lorenzo White	.05
90	Bo Orlando	.05
91	Indianapolis team	.05
92	Quentin Coryatt	.05
93	Steve Emtman	.05
94	Jeff George	.10
95	Jessie Hester	.05
96	Rohn Stark	.05
97	Ashley Ambrose	.05
98	John Baylor	.05
99	Kansas City team	.05
100	Tim Barnett	.05
101	Derrick Thomas	.10
102	Barry Word	.05
103	Dale Carter	.05
104	Jayice Pearson	.05
105	Tracy Simien	.05
106	Harvey Williams	.15
107	Dave Krieg	.05
108	Christian Okoye	.05
109	Joe Montana	1.00
110	Miami team	.05
111	J.B. Brown	.05
112	Marco Coleman	.05
113	Dan Marino	2.00
114	Mark Clayton	.05
115	Mark Higgs	.05
116	Bryan Cox	.05
117	Chuck Klingbeil	.05
118	Troy Vincent	.10
119	Keith Jackson	.10
120	Bruce Alexander	.05
121	Minnesota team	.05
122	Terry Allen	.10
123	Rich Gannon	.05
124	Todd Scott	.05
125	Cris Carter	.10
126	Sean Salisbury	.05
127	Jack Del Rio	.05
128	Chris Doleman	.05
129	Anthony Carter	.05
130	New England team	.05
131	Eugene Chung	.05
132	Todd Collins	.05
133	Tom Hodson	.05
134	Leonard Russell	.05
135	Jon Vaughn	.05
136	Andre Tippet	.05
137	New Orleans team	.05
138	Wesley Carroll	.05
139	Richard Cooper	.05
140	Vaughn Dunbar	.05
141	Fred McAfee	.05
142	Torrance Small	.05
143	Steve Walsh	.05
144	Vaughan Johnson	.05
145	New York Giants team	.05
146	Jarrod Bunch	.05
147	Phil Simms	.05
148	Carl Banks	.05
149	Lawrence Taylor	.10
150	Rodney Hampton	.10
151	Phillippi Sparks	.05
152	Derek Brown	.05
153	New York Jets team	.05
154	Boomer Esiason	.10
155	Johnny Mitchell	.05
156	Rob Moore	.05
157	Ronnie Lott	.05
158	Browning Nagle	.05
159	Johnny Johnson	.05
160	Dwayne White	.05
161	Blair Thomas	.05
162	Philadelphia team	.05
163	Randall Cunningham	.10
164	Fred Barnett	.05
165	Siran Stacy	.05
166	Keith Byars	.05
167	Calvin Williams	.05
168	Jeff Sydner	.05
169	Tommy Jeter	.05
170	Andre Waters	.05
171	Phoenix team	.05
172	Steve Beuerlein	.10
173	Randal Hill	.05
174	Timm Rosenbach	.05
175	Ed Cunningham	.05
176	Walter Reeves	.05
177	Michael Zordich	.05
178	Gary Clark	.05
179	Ken Harvey	.05
180	Pittsburgh team	.05
181	Barry Foster	.05
182	Neil O'Donnell	.15
183	Leon Searcy	.05
184	Bubby Brister	.05
185	Merril Hoge	.05
186	Joel Steed	.05
187	Los Angeles Raiders team	.05
188	Nick Bell	.05
189	Eric Dickerson	.05
190	Nolan Harrison	.05
191	Todd Marinovich	.05
192	Greg Skrepenak	.05
193	Howie Long	.05
194	Jay Schroeder	.05
195	Chester McGlockton	.05
196	Los Angeles Rams team	.05

197	Jim Everett	.05
198	Sean Gilbert	.05
199	Steve Israel	.05
200	Marc Boutte	.05
201	Joe Milinichik	.05
202	Henry Ellard	.05
203	Jackie Slater	.05
204	San Diego team	.05
205	Eric Bieniemy	.05
206	Marion Butts	.05
207	Nate Lewis	.05
208	Junior Seau	.15
209	Steve Hendrickson	.05
210	Chris Mims	.05
211	Harry Swayne	.05
212	Marquez Pope	.05
213	Donald Frank	.05
214	Anthony Miller	.05
215	Seattle team	.05
216	Cortez Kennedy	.10
217	Dan McGwire	.05
218	Kelly Stouffer	.05
219	Chris Warren	.20
220	Brian Blades	.05
221	Rod Stephens	.05
222	San Francisco team	.05
223	Jerry Rice	1.00
224	Ricky Watters	.20
225	Steve Young	1.00
226	Tom Rathman	.05
227	Dana Hall	.05
228	Amp Lee	.10
229	Brian Bollinger	.05
230	Keith DeLong	.05
231	John Taylor	.05
232	Tampa Bay team	.05
233	Tyji Armstrong	.05
234	Lawrence Dawsey	.05
235	Mark Wheeler	.05
236	Vince Workman	.05
237	Reggie Cobb	.05
238	Tony Mayberry	.05
239	Marty Carter	.05
240	Courtney Hawkins	.05
241	Ray Seals	.05
242	Mark Carrier	.05
243	Washington Team	.05
244	Mark Rypien	.05
245	Ricky Ervins	.05
246	Gerald Riggs	.05
247	Art Monk	.10
248	Mark Schlereth	.05
249	Monte Coleman	.05
250	Wilber Marshall	.05
251	Ben Coleman	.05
252	Curtis Conway	1.25
253	Ernest Dye	.05
254	Todd Kelly	.05
255	Patrick Bates	.10
256	George Teague	.10
257	Mark Brunell	3.00
258	Adrian Hardy	.05
259	Dana Stubblefield	.50
260	William Roaf	.10
261	Irv Smith	.10
262	Drew Bledsoe	3.00
263	Dan Williams	.05
264	Jerry Ball	.05
265	Mark Clayton	.05
266	John Stephens	.05
267	Reggie White	.10
268	Jeff Hostetler	.05
269	Boomer Esiason	.05
270	Wade Wilson	.05
271	Steve Beuerlein	.05
272	Tim McDonald	.05
273	Craig Heyward	.05
274	Everson Walls	.05
275	Stan Humphries	.10
276	Carl Banks	.05
277	Brad Muster	.05
278	Tim Harris	.05
279	Gary Clark	.05
280	Joe Milinichik	.05
281	Leonard Marshall	.05
282	Joe Montana	1.00
283	Rod Bernstine	.05
284	Mark Carrier	.05
285	Michael Brooks	.05
286	Marvin Jones	.10
287	John Copeland	.20
288	Eric Curry	.10
289	Steve Everitt	.10
290	Tom Carter	.10
291	Deon Figures	.15
292	Leonard Renfro	.10
293	Thomas Smith	.10
294	Carlton Gray	.10
295	Demetrius DeBose	.10
296	Coleman Rudolph	.05
297	John Parrella	.05
298	Glyn Milburn	.30
299	Reggie Brooks	.20
300	Garrison Hearst	1.00
301	John Elway	.40
302	Brad Hopkins	.05
303	Darrien Gordon	.20
304	Robert Smith	.60
305	Chris Slade	.25
306	Ryan McNeil	.10
307	Michael Barrow	.10
308	Roosevelt Potts	.10
309	Qadry Ismail	.50
310	Reggie Freeman	.10
311	Vincent Brisby	.30
312	Rick Mirer	.30
313	Billy Joe Hobert	.25
314	Natrone Means	1.00

315	Gary Zimmerman	.05
316	Bobby Hebert	.05
317	Don Beebe	.05
318	Wilber Marshall	.05
319	Marcus Allen	.10
320	Ronnie Lott	.05
321	Ricky Sanders	.05
322	Charles Mann	.05
323	Simon Fletcher	.05
324	Johnny Johnson	.05
325	Gary Plummer	.05
326	Carolina Panthers	30.00

1993 Collector's Edge Elway Prisms

This five-card chase set was randomly seeded in 1993 Collector's Edge packs. The cards are bordered with blue prism foil. The photo of Elway is placed over a silver prism background. The Edge logo is in the upper left, while the Broncos' helmet is in the lower right. The cards have an action shot at the top, with the card's serial number underneath it. Elway's highlights are printed inside a box in the center of the card. The cards are numbered with an "E" prefix. Two versions of each card were produced. Those cards with the "S" prefix were inserted in early packs, and tougher to locate. The "E" prefix cards were inserted in later runs. The backgrounds are different on the different versions of cards. Five "S" prefix cards were included with each box of All-Star Collection Manager software from Taurus Technologies. Approximately 500 sets were produced for this offer. Elway's best two-minute marches are featured in this Two-Minute Warning set.

		MT
Complete Set (5):		5.00
Common Player:		1.00
E1	John Elway (Both arms outstretched)	1.00
E2	John Elway (Passing, orange jersey)	1.00
E3	John Elway (Running, orange jersey)	1.00
E4	John Elway (Passing, white jersey)	1.00
E5	John Elway (Running, white jersey)	1.00
S1	John Elway (Both arms outstretched)	3.00
S2	John Elway (Passing, orange jersey)	3.00
S3	John Elway (Running, orange jersey)	3.00
S4	John Elway (Passing, white jersey)	3.00
S5	John Elway (Running, white jersey)	3.00
PRO1	John Elway (AU/3000)	80.00

Post-1980 cards in Near Mint condition will generally sell for about 75% of the quoted Mint value. Excellent-condition cards bring no more than 40%.

1993 Collector's Edge Rookies FX

These inserts, randomly available in 1993 Collector's Edge Rookie Update foil packs, feature top rookies. Each card is clear plastic and features a color action photo within a maroon border. A team helmet, in the lower right corner, and player's name, in white letters in the upper right, are also given on the card front. A card number, using an "F/X" prefix, is also on the front. The card back is clear; the reverse image from the front photo can be seen. Cards with gold backgrounds also exist; they are generally about 10 to 20 times more valuable than the regular inserts.

		MT
Complete Set (25):		15.00
Common Player:		.25
Minor Stars:		.50
Comp. Gold Set (25):		150.00
Gold Stars:		5x-10x
1	Garrison Hearst	2.00
2	Glyn Milburn	.50
3	Demetrius Debose	.25
4	Joe Montana	3.00
5	Thomas Smith	.25
6	Mark Clayton	.25
7	Curtis Conway	1.00
8	Drew Bledsoe	3.00
9	Todd Kelly	.25
10	Stan Humphries	.75
11	John Harbor	.50
12	Troy Aikman	3.00
13	Marion Butts	.25
14	Alvin Harper	.50
15	Drew Hill	.50
16	Michael Irvin	1.00
17	Warren Moon	.50
18	Andre Reed	.25
19	Andre Rison	.50
20	Emmitt Smith	4.00
21	Thurman Thomas	.75
22	Ricky Watters	.75
23	Calvin Williams	.25
24	Steve Young	1.50
25	Howie Long	.25

1994 Collector's Edge Boss Rookies Update Promos

Printed on green plastic stock, the six-card set promoted the upcoming series. The cards have a photo of the player superimposed over the clear background. The player's name, position and Edge logo are included inside a stripe near the bottom of the card. The card number is located on the upper right of the card front. The cards are prefixed with either a "P" or "SHR." The card backs have the player's bio inside the stripe, along with the various logos.

		MT
Complete Set (6):		12.00
Common Player:		.50
1	Trent Dilfer	1.00
2	Marshall Faulk	4.00
3	Heath Shuler	3.00
4	Errict Rhett	3.00
5	Johnnie Morton	1.00
6	Charlie Garner	.50

1994 Collector's Edge

Once again, Collector's Edge has used plastic for its card stock for this 200-card set. Each card front has a full-color action shot, framed by a thin black border. The set logo appears in the upper right corner. The player's name and a team logo appear in a panel at the bottom of the card. Each card back has a player mug shot and statistics at the top of the page, with a stadium shot underneath. A serial number and card number are also on the back. A parallel 1st Day Production set was also created; these cards have a gold-foil stamp for the logo. Insert cards were Boss Squad, F/X player and F/X gold checklist cards, and Boss Rookies.

		MT
Complete Set (200):		17.00
Common Player:		.10
Retail Wax Box:		30.00
Silver Wax Box:		50.00
Gold Wax Box:		70.00
Pop Warner Box:		50.00
1	Mike Pritchard	.12
2	Erric Pegram	.10
3	Michael Haynes	.12
4	Bobby Hebert	.10
5	Deion Sanders	.75
6	Andre Rison	.20
7	Don Beebe	.10
8	Mark Kelso	.10
9	Darryl Talley	.10
10	Cornelius Bennett	.10
11	Jim Kelly	.40
12	Andre Reed	.15
13	Bruce Smith	.10
14	Thurman Thomas	.50
15	Craig Heyward	.10
16	Chris Zorich	.10
17	Alonzo Spellman	.10
18	Tom Waddle	.10
19	Neal Anderson	.10
20	Kevin Butler	.10
21	Curtis Conway	.30
22	Richard Dent	.10
23	Jim Harbaugh	.10
24	Derrick Fenner	.10
25	Harold Green	.10
26	David Klingler	.10
27	Daniel Stubbs	.10
28	Alfred Williams	.10
29	John Copeland	.10
30	Mark Carrier	.10
31	Michael Jackson	.10
32	Eric Metcalf	.10
33	Vinny Testaverde	.10
34	Tommy Vardell	.10
35	Alvin Harper	.12
36	Ken Norton	.10
37	Tony Casillas	.10
38	Leon Lett	.10
39	Jay Novacek	.10
40	Kevin Smith	.10
41	Troy Aikman	1.00
42	Michael Irvin	.50
43	Russell Maryland	.10
44	Emmitt Smith	2.00
45	Robert Delpino	.10
46	Simon Fletcher	.10
47	Greg Kragen	.10
48	Arthur Marshall	.10
49	Steve Atwater	.10
50	Rod Bernstine	.10
51	John Elway	1.00
52	Glyn Milburn	.20

53	Shannon Sharpe	.10
54	Bennie Blades	.10
55	Mel Gray	.10
56	Herman Moore	.15
57	Pat Swilling	.10
58	Chris Spielman	.10
59	Rodney Peete	.10
60	Andre Ware	.10
61	Brett Perriman	.10
62	Erik Kramer	.10
63	Barry Sanders	1.25
64	Mark Clayton	.10
65	Chris Jacke	.10
66	Terrell Buckley	.10
67	Ty Detmer	.10
68	Sanjay Beach	.10
69	Brian Noble	.10
70	Edgar Bennett	.10
71	Brett Favre	2.00
72	Sterling Sharpe	.55
73	Reggie White	.12
74	Ernest Givins	.10
75	Al Del Greco	.10
76	Chris Dishman	.10
77	Curtis Duncan	.10
78	Webster Slaughter	.10
79	Spencer Tillman	.10
80	Warren Moon	.10
81	Wilber Marshall	.10
82	Haywood Jeffires	.10
83	Lorenzo White	.10
84	Gary Brown	.10
85	Reggie Langhorne	.10
86	Dean Biasucci	.10
87	Steve Emtman	.10
88	Jessie Hester	.10
89	Quentin Coryatt	.10
90	Roosevelt Potts	.10
91	Jeff George	.10
92	Nick Lowery	.10
93	Willie Davis	.10
94	Joe Montana	1.00
95	Neil Smith	.10
96	Marcus Allen	.15
97	Derrick Thomas	.10
98	Greg Townsend	.10
99	Willie Gault	.10
100	Ethan Horton	.10
101	Jeff Hostetler	.10
102	Tim Brown	.12
103	Raghib Ismail	.25
104	Shane Conlan	.10
105	Henry Ellard	.10
106	T.J. Rubley	.10
107	Sean Gilbert	.10
108	Troy Drayton	.20
109	Jerome Bettis	.50
110	Terry Kirby	.15
111	Mark Ingram	.10
112	John Offerdahl	.10
113	Louis Oliver	.10
114	Irving Fryar	.10
115	Dan Marino	2.00
116	Keith Jackson	.10
117	O.J. McDuffie	.40
118	Jim McMahon	.10
119	Sean Salisbury	.10
120	Randell McDaniel	.10
121	Jack Del Rio	.10
122	Cris Carter	.10
123	Chris Doleman	.10
124	John Randle	.10
125	Vincent Brisby	.20
126	Greg McMurtry	.10
127	Drew Bledsoe	1.00
128	Leonard Russell	.10
129	Michael Brooks	.10
130	Mark Jackson	.10
131	Pepper Johnson	.10
132	Doug Riesenberg	.10
133	Phil Simms	.10
134	Rodney Hampton	.35
135	Leonard Marshall	.10
136	Rob Moore	.10
137	Chris Burkett	.10
138	Boomer Esiason	.10
139	Johnny Johnson	.10
140	Ronnie Lott	.10
141	Brad Muster	.10
142	Renaldo Turnbull	.10
143	William Roaf	.20
144	Ricky Jackson	.10
145	Morton Anderson	.10
146	Vaughn Dunbar	.10
147	Wade Wilson	.10
148	Eric Martin	.10
149	Seth Joyner	.10
150	Calvin Williams	.10
151	Vai Sikahema	.10
152	Herschel Walker	.10
153	Eric Allen	.10
154	Fred Barnett	.10
155	Randall Cunningham	.25
156	Steve Beuerlein	.10
157	Gary Clark	.10
158	Anthony Edwards	.10
159	Randall Hill	.10
160	Freddie Joe Nunn	.10
161	Garrison Hearst	.50
162	Ricky Proehl	.10
163	Eric Green	.10
164	Levon Kirkland	.10
165	Joel Steed	.10
166	Deon Figures	.10
167	Leroy Thompson	.10
168	Barry Foster	.35
169	Neil O'Donnell	.10

170	Junior Seau	.10
171	Leslie O'Neil	.10
172	Stan Humphries	.10
173	Marion Butts	.10
174	Anthony Miller	.10
175	Natrone Means	.50
176	Odessa Turner	.10
177	Dana Stubblefield	.25
178	John Taylor	.10
179	Ricky Watters	.15
180	Steve Young	1.00
181	Jerry Rice	1.00
182	Tom Rathman	.10
183	Brian Blades	.10
184	Patrick Hunter	.10
185	Rick Mirer	.20
186	Chris Warren	.12
187	Cortez Kennedy	.12
188	Reggie Cobb	.10
189	Craig Erickson	.10
190	Hardy Nickerson	.10
191	Lawrence Dawsey	.10
192	Broderick Thomas	.10
193	Ricky Sanders	.10
194	Carl Banks	.10
195	Ricky Ervins	.10
196	Darrel Green	.10
197	Mark Rypien	.10
198	Desmond Howard	.15
199	Art Monk	.10
200	Reggie Brooks	.10

1994 Collector's Edge Silver

Randomly inserted into packs, this 200-card set was a parallel to the 1994 Edge base set. The card fronts have a silver-foil stamp on the front. The card backs resemble the base card backs.

	MT
Complete Set (200):	25.00
Common Player:	.10
Silver Cards:	1x

1994 Collector's Edge Gold

A parallel of the regular Collector's Edge set, the 200-card set features a gold-foil "First Day" logo on the front of the card. The backs resemble the base card backs.

	MT
Complete Set (200):	45.00
Common Player:	.15
Gold Cards:	2x

1994 Collector's Edge Pop Warner

This 200-card set was produced as a fund-raiser for Pop Warner football teams. The cards were available from participating dealers and Pop Warner players. Edge printed 1,000 cases of the product. An updated 25-card Boss Rookie chase set, printed on Edge-Glo card stock, was randomly seeded.

	MT
Complete Set (200):	25.00
Common Player:	.10
Pop Warner Cards:	1x

1994 Collector's Edge Pop Warner 22K Gold

The 200-card set was a parallel to the Edge Pop Warner base cards. The cards showcase the Pop Warner logo and a gold-foil helmet (with 22K printed under the helmet) on the card fronts.

	MT
Complete Set (200):	100.00
Common Player:	.40
Pop Warner 22K Cards:	2x-4x

1994 Collector's Edge Boss Rookies

Top rookies are featured on these insert cards, which were randomly included in 1994 Collector's Edge packs. The cards are similar to the format used by the Boss Squad insert cards; "Boss Rookies" is written in the upper left corner and the card number, Rookie 1, etc., is in the upper right corner. The player's name, position and Collector's Edge logo are at the bottom of the card. The back of the card shows a reverse image of the photo on the front.

		MT
Complete Set (19):		15.00
Common Player:		.25
Minor Stars:		.50
Inserted 1:2		
1	Isaac Bruce	1.75
2	Jeff Burris	.25
3	Shante Carver	.25
4	Lake Dawson	.50
5	Bert Emanuel	.75
6	William Floyd	.75
7	Wayne Gandy	.25
8	Aaron Glenn	.25
9	Chris Maumalanga	.25
10	David Palmer	.50
11	Errict Rhett	.75
12	Heath Shuler	.75
13	DeWayne Washington	.25
14	Bryant Young	.50
15	Dan Wilkinson	.25
16	Rob Fredrickson	.25
17	Calvin Jones	.25
18	James Folston	.25
19	Marshall Faulk	4.00

1994 Collector's Edge Boss Rookies Update

Randomly seeded in 1994 Pop Warner packs, this 25-card set was printed on Edge-Glo green plastic. The card fronts feature a purple Pop Warner logo in the upper left corner.

		MT
Complete Set (25):		30.00
Common Player:		.75
Minor Stars:		1.50
Diamond Cards:		2x
Green Cards:		1x
Inserted 1:3 Pop Warner		
1	Trent Dilfer	4.00
2	Jeff Burris	.75
3	Shante Carver	.75
4	Lake Dawson	1.50
5	Bert Emanuel	1.50
6	Marshall Faulk	7.00
7	William Floyd	1.50
8	Charlie Garner	1.50
9	Rob Fredrickson	.75
10	Wayne Gandy	.75
11	Aaron Glenn	.75
12	Greg Hill	1.50
13	Isaac Bruce	3.00
14	Charles Johnson	1.50
15	Johnnie Morton	1.50
16	Calvin Jones	.75
17	Tim Bowens	.75
18	David Palmer	1.50
19	Errict Rhett	1.50
20	Darnay Scott	2.50
21	Heath Shuler	1.50
22	John Thierry	.75
23	Bernard Williams	.75
24	Dan Wilkinson	.75
25	Bryant Young	1.50
NNO	Diamond Exch. Expired	1.50

1994 Collector's Edge Boss Squad Promos

Previewing the 1994 Edge Boss Squad insert, this six-card transparent plastic promo set showcases a cutout photo of a player over a background of lines which make a 3-D effect. The player's name, position and Edge logo are printed inside a stripe near the bottom of the front of the card. The card number is printed on the top right of the card front, prefixed by "Boss." The set was released on two uncut sheets.

		MT
Complete Set (6):		10.00
Common Player:		1.00
1	Marshall Faulk	4.00
2	Jerome Bettis	2.50
3	Erric Pegram	1.25
4	Sterling Sharpe	1.25
5	Shannon Sharpe	1.25
6	Leonard Russell	1.00

1994 Collector's Edge Boss Squad

This transparent set features eight top quarterbacks, running backs and receivers for this insert set titled Boss Squad. If the player on the card finished the 1994 season in first or second place in statistics for that position, the card could be redeemed for prizes. Receptions were used for receivers, rushing yards were used for running backs, and quarterback ratings were used for quarterbacks. Cards are numbered with a "Boss" prefix. The card back shows a reversed image of the photo on the front.

		MT
Complete Set (24):		20.00
Common Player:		.50
Minor Stars:		1.00
Inserted 1:2		
Silver Cards:		1x
Inserted 1:2 Pop Warner		
Bronze EQII Cards:		1x
Gold Helmet Cards:		1x
1	John Elway	2.50
2	Joe Montana	2.50
3	Vinny Testaverde	1.00
4	Boomer Esiason	.50
5	Steve Young	1.50
6	Troy Aikman	2.00
7	Phil Simms	.50
8	Bobby Hebert	.50
9	Thurman Thomas	1.00
10	Leonard Russell	.50
11	Chris Warren	1.00
12	Gary Brown	.50
13	Emmitt Smith	3.00
14	Jerome Bettis	1.00
15	Erric Pegram	.50
16	Barry Sanders	2.50
17	Reggie Langhorne	.50
18	Anthony Miller	.50
19	Shannon Sharpe	1.00
20	Tim Brown	1.00
21	Sterling Sharpe	1.00
22	Jerry Rice	2.00
23	Michael Irvin	1.00
24	Andre Rison	1.00

1994 Collector's Edge EdgeQuest

Randomly seeded in packs and offered as a dealer promotion, the nine-card set showcased a letter on the front, with EdgeQuest II printed inside a bar near the bottom of the card. The "Q" card was released in smaller numbers in packs. The cards were redeemable for prizes. Card backs include the rules of the contest. The identical cards with a clear background were inserted into Pop Warner packs.

		MT
Complete Set (10):		4.00
Comm. Pack Insert (A/B/D/U):		.40
Comm. Box Insert (E/G/O/S):		.40
Clear Cards:		1x
A	Letter A	.40
B	Letter B	.40
D	Letter D	.40
E	Letter E	.40
G	Letter G	.40
O	Letter O	.40
Q	Letter Q (SP, Expired)	1.00
S	Letter S	.40
U	Letter U	.40
WC	Clear Star Wild Card	1.00

1994 Collector's Edge FX

Two versions of these insert cards were made - a regular F/X card and a gold version. Seven top players are featured on these cards, which were random inserts.

		MT
Complete Set (7):		20.00
Common Player:		.75
Minor Stars:		1.50
Inserted 1:7 Gold		
Gold Shield Cards:		2x
Inserted 1:200 Gold		
White Back Cards:		1x
Inserted 1:7 Retail		
Silver Shield Cards:		5x
Inserted 1:200 Retail		
Silver Back Cards:		.5x
Inserted 1:7 Silver		
Gold Back Cards:		3x
Inserted 1:200 Silver		
Silver Letter Cards:		1x
Inserted 1:7 Pop Warner		
Gold Letter Cards:		2x
Inserted 1:200 Pop Warner		
Red Letter Cards:		1x
1	John Elway	5.00
2	Joe Montana	5.00
3	Troy Aikman	4.00
4	Emmitt Smith	6.00
5	Jerome Bettis	1.50
6	Anthony Miller	.75
7	Sterling Sharpe	1.50

A player's name in *italic type* indicates a rookie card.

1994 Collector's Edge Excalibur Elway Promos

This three-card set previewed the 1994 Excalibur set. Each of the cards featured John Elway. The Excalibur logo is printed in silver foil at the top, with his name and position printed in silver foil at the bottom to the right of the Edge logo. The backs have his headshot inside a shield design on the left, which also includes his position and jersey number. The shield in the right corner has his name, the Broncos' logo and card number "of 3" prefixed by "SL." A quote about Elway from Dick Butkus is included above his stats. The card's serial number is printed under the stats.

		MT
Complete Set (3):		15.00
Common Player:		5.00
1	John Elway	5.00
2	John Elway (Looking to pass)	5.00
3	John Elway (Running with football)	5.00

1994 Excalibur

This 75-card NFL All-Star set involves a medieval theme and features the company's unique plastic cards. Each card front has a full-bleed action photo and silver foil on the front for the player's name and position. The card back has a statement about the player by Hall of Famer Dick Butkus. The set's theme is based on Excalibur, the sword pulled from the stone in the legend of King Arthur. A player mug shot also appears on the card back, along with a medieval shield containing his name. A knight is ghosted in the background. All of the teams in the NFL are represented in the set, except for the Minnesota Vikings. Insert cards randomly included in Excalibur packs are: EdgeQuest cards, Excalibur FX, and Excalibur Knights of the NFL.

		MT
Complete Set (75):		30.00
Common Player:		.25
Minor Stars:		.50
Wax Box:		150.00
1	Bobby Hebert	.25
2	Deion Sanders	1.00
3	Andre Rison	.75
4	Cornelius Bennett	.25
5	Jim Kelly	.75
6	Andre Reed	.50
7	Bruce Smith	.25
8	Thurman Thomas	.75
9	Curtis Conway	.50
10	Richard Dent	.25
11	Jim Harbaugh	.50
12	Troy Aikman	2.50
13	Michael Irvin	.75
14	Russell Maryland	.25
15	Emmitt Smith	4.00
16	Steve Atwater	.25
17	Rod Bernstine	.25
18	John Elway	3.00
19	Glyn Milburn	.25
20	Shannon Sharpe	.75
21	Barry Sanders	5.00
22	Edgar Bennett	.25
23	Brett Favre	5.00
24	Sterling Sharpe	.75
25	Reggie White	.75
26	Warren Moon	.50
27	Wilber Marshall	.25
28	Haywood Jeffires	.25
29	Lorenzo White	.25
30	Quentin Coryatt	.25
31	Roosevelt Potts	.25
32	Jeff George	.75
33	Joe Montana	3.00
34	Neil Smith	.25
35	Marcus Allen	.75
36	Derrick Thomas	.50
37	Jeff Hostetler	.25
38	Tim Brown	.75
39	Raghib Ismail	.25
40	Howie Long	.25
41	Jerome Bettis	1.00
42	Dan Marino	4.00
43	Keith Jackson	.25
44	O.J. McDuffie	.50
45	Drew Bledsoe	3.00
46	Leonard Russell	.25
47	Wade Wilson	.25
48	Eric Martin	.25
49	Phil Simms	.25
50	Lawrence Taylor	.75
51	Rodney Hampton	.50
52	Boomer Esiason	.25
53	Johnny Johnson	.25
54	Ronnie Lott	.50
55	Fred Barnett	.25
56	Leroy Thompson	.25
57	Barry Foster	.50
58	Neil O'Donnell	.50
59	Stan Humphries	.25
60	Marion Butts	.25
61	Anthony Miller	.25
62	Natrone Means	1.00
63	Dana Stubblefield	.50
64	John Taylor	.25
65	Ricky Watters	.75
66	Steve Young	2.00
67	Jerry Rice	2.50
68	Tom Rathman	.25
69	Rick Mirer	.50
70	Chris Warren	.50
71	Cortez Kennedy	.25
72	Mark Rypien	.25
73	Desmond Howard	.25
74	Art Monk	.50
75	Reggie Brooks	.25

1994 Excalibur 22K

These 22K gold cards feature a color photo on the front against a background with a knight in shining armor. A gold sword appears at the top of the card; the player's name and position are at the bottom. The card back has a knight with a sword and shield as a background. The player's name and a team logo are in the forefront. Cards were random inserts in 1994 Collector's Edge foil packs. The set is titled Knights of the NFL.

		MT
Complete Set (25):		85.00
Common Player:		.75
Minor Stars:		1.50
Inserted 1:2		
1	Troy Aikman	4.00
2	Michael Irvin	1.50
3	Emmitt Smith	6.00
4	Edgar Bennett	.75
5	Brett Favre	8.00
6	Sterling Sharpe	1.50
7	Rodney Hampton	.75

8	Jerome Bettis	1.50
9	Jerry Rice	4.00
10	Steve Young	3.00
11	Ricky Watters	1.50
12	Thurman Thomas	1.50
13	John Elway	5.00
14	Shannon Sharpe	1.50
15	Joe Montana	5.00
16	Marcus Allen	1.50
17	Tim Brown	1.50
18	Raghib Ismail	.75
19	Barry Foster	.75
20	Natrone Means	1.50
21	Rick Mirer	1.50
22	Dan Marino	6.00
23	AFC Card	.75
24	NFC Card	.75
25	Excalibur card	.75

1994 Collector's Edge Excalibur EdgeQuest

Designed as a contest, this nine-card set was both inserted into packs and provided to dealers as a premium. The card fronts featured a letter and "EdgeQuest" at the bottom. The letter X was inserted in smaller quantities and was issued in both gold-foil and silver-foil versions. The letters C, E, L and U were printed as case promos for dealers. If a collector spelled out "Excalibur" with the cards, they could redeem the cards for a prize. A single card could be exchanged for a promo card. A gold version of "Excalibur" could be redeemed for an uncut sheet of 22K Gold insert cards. The card backs have the rules for the contest.

		MT
Complete Set (9):		5.00
Common Insert (A/B/I/R):		.50
Common Dealer (C/E/L/U):		.50
A	Letter A	.50
B	Letter B	.50
C	Letter C	.50
E	Letter E	.50
I	Letter I	.50
L	Letter L	.50
R	Letter R	.50
U	Letter U	.50
X	Letter X SP Expired	2.00

1994 Excalibur FX

These acetate cards were random inserts in 1994 foil packs. The front has a photo of a player inside a shield. His name, team helmet, position and card number are in the bottom right corner. Cards are numbered on the front using an "FX" prefix. Special gold versions of each card were also made and are generally eight to 10 times more valuable than the regular inserts.

		MT
Complete Set (7):		30.00
Common Player:		1.00
Minor Stars:		2.00
Inserted 1:7		
FX Gold Shield Cards:		4x
Inserted 1:170		
EQ Gold Shield Cards:		1x
EQ Silver Shield Cards:		1x
1	Emmitt Smith	10.00
2	Rodney Hampton	1.00
3	Jerome Bettis	2.00
4	Steve Young	5.00
5	Rick Mirer	2.00
6	John Elway	8.00
7	Troy Aikman	7.00

1994 Collector's Edge Excalibur Redemption

These nine EdgeQuest insert redemption cards were randomly included in 1994 Collector's Edge Excalibur packs. Each of the nine cards is numbered using a letter from the word EXCALIBUR, not a number. The object of the game is to get each different letter insert, to spell out Excalibur. Those who obtained all nine cards could redeem them for an F/X subset or uncut press sheet. The A, B, I, R and X cards were randomly inserted into every ninth foil pack. The C, E, L and U cards were given to dealers who purchased a case of the Excalibur cards.

		MT
Complete Set (9):		4.50
Common Player:		4.50
1	Dealer promo	4.50
2	Foil Pack Insert	4.50
3	Dealer promo	4.50
4	Foil Pack Insert	4.50
5	Dealer promo	4.50
6	Foil Pack Insert	4.50
7	Dealer promo	4.50
8	Dealer promo	4.50
9	Foil Pack Insert	4.50

1995 Collector's Edge Junior Seau Promos

Each card in the five-card set showcased a full-bleed photo of Seau on the front, with his last name running along the left border of the card. "Seau" is printed in large letters, while "Junior" is in a stripe. The card backs feature a head shot, the player's name, team, position, bio and stats. The cards are numbered "/5," with a promo prefix. "Promo '95" is printed in a white stripe along the right side of the card back.

		MT
Complete Set (5):		5.00
Common Player:		1.00
1	Rookie Season 1990	1.00
2	Second Season 1991	1.00
3	Third Season 1992	1.00
4	Fourth Season 1993	1.00
5	Super Bowl Season 1994	1.00

1995 Collector's Edge

The 1995 Collector's Edge football set is a 200-card retail set, with a Black Label hobby version also issued. The main cards in the set have a full-bleed color photo on the front, with the player's name along the left side and his position and team nickname along the right side. The horizontal back has a mug shot of the player in the upper right corner, and a ghosted image of him with his stats and biographical information superimposed over them. Two parallel sets were also made - a die-cut version (one per every 24 packs) and a gold foil-based set (one per every 20 packs). Insert sets include TimeWarp Match-ups, Rookies, EdgeTech, and EdgeQuest 12th Man cards. Retail cards have the same card numbers as the hobby versions, but different photos and designs are used, plus a Black Label logo is foil-stamped into the hobby cards. This set has the same insert sets as the hobby brand does.

		MT
Complete Set (205):		15.00
Common Player:		.10
Minor Stars:		.20
Comp. EdgeQuest 12th Man (7):		15.00
Common EdgeQuest:		2.50
Hobby Wax Box:		40.00
Retail Wax Box:		30.00
1	Anthony Edwards	.10
2	Garrison Hearst	.20
3	Seth Joyner	.10
4	Dave Krieg	.10
5	Chuck Levy	.10
6	Rob Moore	.10
7	J.J. Birden	.10
8	Jeff George	.20
9	Craig Heyward	.10
10	Norm Johnson	.10
11	Terance Mathis	.10
12	Eric Metcalf	.10
13	Chuck Smith	.10
14	Darryl Talley	.10
15	Cornelius Bennett	.10
16	Steve Christie	.10
17	Kenneth Davis	.10
18	Phil Hansen	.10
19	Jim Kelly	.20
20	Bryce Paup	.10
21	Andre Reed	.10
22	Bruce Smith	.10
23	Eric Ball	.10
24	Don Beebe	.10
25	Mark Carrier	.10
26	Tim McKyer	.10
27	Pete Metzelaars	.10
28	Sam Mills	.10
29	Jack Trudeau	.10
30	Mark Carrier	.10
31	Curtis Conway	.10
32	Eric Kramer	.10
33	Lewis Tillman	.10
34	Michael Timpson	.10
35	Steve Walsh	.10
36	Chris Zorich	.10
37	*Jeff Blake*	1.00
38	Harold Green	.10
39	David Klinger	.10
40	Carl Pickens	.20
41	Tom Waddle	.10
42	Dan Wilkinson	.10
43	Leroy Hoard	.10
44	Michael Jackson	.10
45	Antonio Langham	.10
46	Andre Rison	.20
47	Vinny Testaverde	.10
48	Eric Turner	.10
49	Tommy Vardell	.10
50	Troy Aikman	.75
51	Charles Haley	.10
52	Michael Irvin	.25
53	Daryl Johnston	.10
54	Leon Lett	.10
55	Jay Novacek	.10
56	Emmitt Smith	1.50
57	Kevin Williams	.10
58	Steve Atwater	.10
59	John Elway	.30
60	Simon Fletcher	.10
61	Glyn Milburn	.10
62	Anthony Miller	.10
63	Leonard Russell	.10
64	Shannon Sharpe	.10
65	Scott Mitchell	.10
66	Herman Moore	.20
67	Johnnie Morton	.10
68	Brett Perriman	.10
69	Barry Sanders	1.25
70	Edgar Bennett	.10
71	Brett Favre	1.50
72	Mark Ingram	.10
73	Chris Jacke	.10
74	Guy McIntyre	.10
75	Reggie White	.20
76	Gary Brown	.10
77	Ernest Givins	.10
78	Mel Gray	.10

79	Haywood Jeffires	.10
80	Webster Slaughter	.10
81	Craig Erickson	.10
82	Marshall Faulk	1.00
83	Jim Harbaugh	.10
84	Roosevelt Potts	.10
85	Floyd Turner	.10
86	Steve Beuerlein	.10
87	Reggie Cobb	.10
88	Jeff Lageman	.10
89	Mazio Royster	.10
90	Marcus Allen	.20
91	Steve Bono	.10
92	Willie Davis	.10
93	Lake Dawson	.25
94	Ronnie Lott	.10
95	Eric Martin	.10
96	Chris Penn	.10
97	Tim Brown	.20
98	Derrick Fenner	.10
99	Rob Fredrickson	.10
100	Nolan Harrison	.10
101	Jeff Hostetler	.10
102	Raghib Ismail	.10
103	James Jett	.10
104	Chester McGlockton	.10
105	Anthony Smith	.10
106	Harvey Williams	.10
107	Jerome Bettis	.25
108	Troy Drayton	.10
109	Chris Miller	.10
110	Robert Young	.10
111	Keith Byars	.10
112	Gary Clark	.10
113	Bryan Cox	.10
114	Jeff Cross	.10
115	Irving Fryar	.10
116	Randall Hill	.10
117	Terry Kirby	.10
118	Dan Marino	1.50
119	O.J. McDuffie	.10
120	Bernie Parmalee	.25
121	Terry Allen	.10
122	Cris Carter	.20
123	Qadry Ismail	.10
124	Warren Moon	.25
125	John Randle	.10
126	Jake Reed	.10
127	Fuad Reveiz	.10
128	Broderick Thomas	.10
129	Drew Bledsoe	1.00
130	Vincent Brisby	.10
131	Ben Coates	.10
132	David Meggett	.10
133	Chris Slade	.10
134	Leroy Thompson	.10
135	Eric Allen	.10
136	Mario Bates	.30
137	Quinn Early	.10
138	Jim Everett	.10
139	Michael Haynes	.10
140	Torrance Small	.10
141	Dave Brown	.10
142	Chris Calloway	.10
143	Keith Hamilton	.10
144	Rodney Hampton	.10
145	Mike Sherrard	.10
146	David Treadwell	.10
147	Herschel Walker	.10
148	Boomer Esiason	.10
149	Erik Howard	.10
150	Johnny Johnson	.10
151	Mo Lewis	.10
152	Johnny Mitchell	.10
153	Fred Barnett	.10
154	Randall Cunningham	.20
155	William Fuller	.10
156	Charlie Garner	.10
157	Greg Jackson	.10
158	Ricky Watters	.20
159	Calvin Williams	.10
160	Barry Foster	.10
161	Kevin Greene	.10
162	Greg Lloyd	.10
163	Bam Morris	.40
164	Neil O'Donnell	.10
165	Erric Pegram	.10
166	John L. Williams	.10
167	Rod Woodson	.10
168	John Carney	.10
169	Stan Humphries	.20
170	Natrone Means	.40
171	Chris Mims	.10
172	Leslie O'Neal	.10
173	Alfred Pupunu	.20
174	Junior Seau	.20
175	Mark Seay	.10
176	William Floyd	.40
177	Jerry Rice	.75
178	Deion Sanders	.40
179	Dana Stubblefield	.10
180	John Taylor	.10
181	Steve Young	.50
182	Bryant Young	.10
183	Brian Blades	.10
184	Cortez Kennedy	.10
185	Kelvin Martin	.10
186	Rick Mirer	.30
187	Ricky Proehl	.10
188	Michael Sinclair	.10
189	Chris Warren	.10
190	Trent Dilfer	.40
191	Alvin Harper	.10
192	Jackie Harris	.10
193	Hardy Nickerson	.10
194	Errict Rhett	.75

195	Reggie Roby	.10
196	Henry Ellard	.10
197	Ricky Ervins	.10
198	Darrell Green	.10
199	Brian Mitchell	.10
200	Heath Shuler	.50

1995 Collector's Edge Die Cuts

These 205 die-cut cards were a parallel to the base cards in the regular set. The top of each card was die-cut. The Edge logo is printed in silver foil on card fronts.

		MT
Complete Set (205):		150.00
Common Player:		.30
Die Cut Cards:		3x-6x

1995 Collector's Edge Gold Logo

Randomly inserted into hobby and retail packs, the 205-card set was a parallel to the base cards. The card fronts each showcase a gold-foil Edge logo at the bottom right.

		MT
Complete Set (205):		18.00
Common Player:		.05
Gold Cards:		1x

1995 Collector's Edge 22K Gold

Randomly inserted into retail packs, the 205-card set was a parallel to the base set. Each card front has a gold-foil 22K logo on it.

		MT
Complete Set (205):		2200.
Common Player:		3.00
22K Gold Cards:		35x-70x

1995 Collector's Edge EdgeTech

This insert set features 36 of the premier players in the game on cards with a prismatic background. Cards came in four versions - 22k Gold and Circular Prisms (in Edge packs) and Quantum and Die-Cuts (in Black Label packs).

		MT
Complete Set (36):		70.00
Common Player:		1.50
Black Label Same Price		
Comp. 22K Gold Set (36):		300.00
22K Gold Cards:		1x-3x
Comp. Quantum Set (36):		600.00
Quantum Cards:		2x-4x
Comp. Quantum Die Cut (36):		800.00
Quantum Die Cuts:		4x-8x
Comp. Circular Prisms (36):		50.00
Circular Prisms: Half Value		
1	Dan Marino	12.00
2	Steve Young	4.00
3	Rick Mirer	2.50
4	Emmitt Smith	12.00
5	John Elway	4.00
6	Neil O'Donnell	1.50
7	Marshall Faulk	3.00
8	Deion Sanders	3.00
9	Terance Mathis	1.50
10	Kevin Greene	1.50
11	Ricky Watters	2.00
12	Tim Brown	1.50
13	Antonio Langham	1.50
14	Lake Dawson	1.50
15	Jay Novacek	1.50
16	Herman Moore	2.50
17	Mark Seay	1.50
18	Bernie Parmalee	1.50
19	Drew Bledsoe	6.00
20	Troy Aikman	6.00
21	Brett Favre	12.00
22	Jerry Rice	6.00
23	Barry Sanders	6.00
24	Heath Shuler	2.50
25	Errict Rhett	2.50
26	Cris Carter	1.50
27	Jerome Bettis	2.50
28	Reggie White	2.00
29	Chris Warren	1.50
30	Ben Coates	1.50
31	Bryant Young	1.50
32	Mel Gray	1.50
33	Darryl Talley	1.50
34	Mike Sherrard	1.50
35	William Floyd	2.00
36	Alvin Harper	1.50

1995 Collector's Edge Rookies

These 1995 Collector's Edge inserts come in three versions - two in the retail packs, including a gold version, and one in the hobby Black Label packs. The cards feature 25 of the top 1995 NFL draft picks. The front has a photo of the player in his college uniform, along with a set logo in the upper right corner. The horizontal card back has a closeup shot of the player, biographical information, and a synopsis of the player's selection in the draft.

		MT
Complete Set (24):		35.00
Common Player:		.50
Minor Stars:		1.00
Comp. 22K Gold Set (24):		120.00
22K Gold Cards:		2x-4x
Black Label Same Price		
1	Derrick Alexander	.50
2	Tony Boselli	1.00
3	Ki-Jana Carter	3.00
4	Kevin Carter	.50
5	Kerry Collins	5.00
6	Steve McNair	4.00
7	Billy Milner	.50
8	Rashaan Salaam	4.00
9	Warren Sapp	1.50
10	James Stewart	.50
11	J.J. Stokes	3.00
12	Bobby Taylor	.50
13	Tyrone Wheatley	1.00
14	Derrick Brooks	.50
15	Reuben Brown	.50
16	Mark Bruener	1.00
17	Joey Galloway	4.00
18	Napolean Kaufman	1.00
19	Ty Law	.50
20	Craig Newsome	.50
21	Kordell Stewart	5.00
22	Korey Stringer	.50
23	Zach Weigert	.50
24	Michael Westbrook	2.00

1995 Collector's Edge TimeWarp

These 1995 Collector's Edge

inserts feature one star from today matched up against a former NFL star in game action, through the magic of computers. Three versions were made - two for Edge retail packs, including a gold version, and one for the hobby Black Label packs. Card fronts have a TimeWarp logo in the upper right corner, and show the two players competing against each other. The card back has mug shots of each player, with biographical information underneath. A quote from Hall of Fame linebacker Dick Butkus, the company's spokesman, is also given regarding the matchup.

	MT
Complete Set (20):	70.00
Common Player:	2.50
Minor Stars:	5.00
Comp. 22K Gold Set (20):	280.00
22K Gold Cards:	2x-4x
Black Label Same Price	
1 Emmitt Smith, Dick Butkus	14.00
2 Troy Aikman, Gino Marchetti	7.00
3 Natrone Means, Ray Nitschke	5.00
4 Chris Zorich, Steve Van Buren	2.50
5 Barry Sanders, Deacon Jones	14.00
6 Kevin Greene, Paul Hornung	2.50
7 Charles Haley, Len Dawson	2.50
8 Marshall Faulk, Willie Lanier	5.00
9 Ronnie Lott, Gale Sayers	5.00
10 Cris Carter, Jack Ham	2.50
11 Junior Seau, Gale Sayers	2.50
12 Reggie White, Otto Graham	2.50
13 Leslie O'Neil, Y.A. Tittle	2.50
14 Drew Bledsoe, Ted Hendricks	7.00
15 Heath Shuler, Bob Lilly	2.50
16 Ricky Watters, Daryle Lamonica	2.50
17 Marshall Faulk, Dick Butkus	5.00
18 Deion Sanders, Raymond Berry	7.00
19 Steve Young, Jack Youngblood	6.00
20 Bruce Smith, Sammy Baugh	2.50

1995 Collector's Edge TimeWarp Jumbos

Measuring 8 x 10 inches, the 42-card set has full-bleed photos on the front, with Time Warp in the upper right. The Time Warp logo also is in the lower right, with an Edge logo in the lower left. The cards resemble the regular sized Time Warp cards which were inserted into 1995 Collector's Edge. The backs have headshots of each featured player, along with the Time Warp logo, at the top. Each player's bio appears under the photo. A Dick Butkus quote appears in the lower center of the back. Overall, 5,000 of each card were issued and given to hobby dealers. Signed editions of each card were produced and autographed by a Hall of Famer. The cards were also offered through a 1996 Edge retail pack mail-in offer for $3.95 each with 12 wrappers.

	MT
Complete Set (42):	450.00
Common Player:	8.00
1 Dick Butkus, Emmitt Smith	20.00
2 Dick Butkus, Emmitt Smith	20.00
3 Gino Marchetti, Troy Aikman	14.00
4 Gino Marchetti, Troy Aikman	14.00
5 Ray Nitschke, Natrone Means	10.00
6 Ray Nitschke, Natrone Means	10.00
7 Steve Van Buren, Chris Zorich	8.00
8 Steve Van Buren, Chris Zorich	8.00
9 Deacon Jones, Barry Sanders	14.00

10 Deacon Jones, Barry Sanders	14.00
11 Paul Hornung, Kevin Greene	10.00
12 Paul Hornung, Kevin Greene	10.00
13 Len Dawson, Charles Haley	8.00
14 Len Dawson, Charles Haley	8.00
15 Willie Lanier, Marshall Faulk	12.00
16 Willie Lanier, Marshall Faulk	12.00
17 Gale Sayers, Ronnie Lott	10.00
18 Gale Sayers, Ronnie Lott	10.00
19 Jack Ham, Cris Carter	8.00
20 Jack Ham, Cris Carter	8.00
21 Gale Sayers, Junior Seau	10.00
22 Gale Sayers, Junior Seau	10.00
23 Otto Graham, Reggie White	10.00
24 Otto Graham, Reggie White	10.00
25 Y.A. Tittle, Leslie O'Neal	10.00
26 Y.A. Tittle, Leslie O'Neal	10.00
27 Daryle Lamonica, Ricky Watters	8.00
28 Daryle Lamonica, Ricky Watters	8.00
29 Dick Butkus, Marshall Faulk	12.00
30 Dick Butkus, Marshall Faulk	12.00
31 Raymond Berry, Deion Sanders	12.00
32 Raymond Berry, Deion Sanders	12.00
33 Jack Youngblood, Steve Young	12.00
34 Jack Youngblood, Steve Young	12.00
35 Sammy Baugh, Bruce Smith	10.00
36 Sammy Baugh, Bruce Smith	10.00
37 Ted Hendricks, Dan Marino	20.00
38 Bob Lilly, Dan Marino	20.00
39 Ted Hendricks, Drew Bledsoe	12.00
40 Bob Lilly, Heath Shuler	10.00
41 Dick Butkus, Jeff Blake	12.00
42 Dick Butkus, Michael Westbrook	12.00

1995 Collector's Edge TimeWarp Sunday Ticket

Offered for $19.95 per set through a mail order offer, the five-card set had a full-bleed photo on the front, with the Edge logo in the upper left and NFL Sunday Ticket logo in the lower right. The card backs resemble the Time Warp Jumbo backs, except the background has a prism effect. Overall, 2,500 sets were produced.

	MT
Complete Set (5):	15.00
Common Player:	2.00
1 Paul Hornung, Chris Zorich	2.00
2 Gale Sayers, Kevin Greene	2.00
3 Ted Hendricks, Ricky Watters	3.00
4 Sammy Baugh, Bruce Smith	3.00
5 Dick Butkus, Marshall Faulk	7.00

Values quoted in this guide reflect the retail price of a card — the price a collector can expect to pay when buying a card from a dealer. The wholesale price — that which a collector can expect to receive from a dealer when selling cards — will be significantly lower, depending on desirability and condition.

1995 Collector's Edge 12th Man Redemption

This redemption set was available through 1995 Black Label and retail version packs. If a collector compiled all the cards which spelled "12th Man," they could exchange them plus $19.95 for this complete 25-card set. The cards carry a 1996 copyright date, but are part of the 1995 set. The card fronts feature a cutout photo of the player over a multi-colored background, with "12th Man" printed at the top of the card. The card backs include a headshot, player name, bio and highlight. The card number is printed in the upper right.

	MT
Complete Set (25):	45.00
Common Player:	.50
Comp. Letters Set (7):	2.50
1 Dan Marino	8.00
2 Jeff Blake	2.00
3 Steve Bono	1.00
4 Brett Favre	8.00
5 Steve Young	3.00
6 Scott Mitchell	1.00
7 Chris Warren	1.00
8 Marshall Faulk	2.00
9 Byron "Bam" Morris	.50
10 Emmitt Smith	8.00
11 Barry Sanders	4.00
12 Rashaan Salaam	2.00
13 Carl Pickens	1.00
14 Anthony Miller	.50
15 Tim Brown	1.00
16 Jerry Rice	4.00
17 Herman Moore	2.00
18 Isaac Bruce	2.00
19 Ben Coates	1.00
20 Shannon Sharpe	1.00
21 Alfred Pupunu	.50
22 Jackie Harris	.50
23 Jay Novacek	.50
24 Brent Jones	.50
25 Checklist	.50

1995 Collector's Edge Black Label

This was the hobby version of the Collector's Edge set. The 205-card set was sold in six-card packs. The card fronts spotlight a full-bleed photo, with the player's last name at the bottom. The Black Label logo is printed in the top left. Showcased on the horizontal card backs are the player's headshot and an action photo in the background. The player's bio and stats are on the back, too.

	MT
Complete Set (205):	25.00
Common Player:	.05
Black Label Cards:	1x

1995 Collector's Edge Black Label 22K Gold

This parallel of the base set featured the Black Label logo in gold foil, along with a 22K logo, on the front of each card in the 205-card set.

	MT
Complete Set (205):	2200.
Common Player:	3.00
BL 22K Gold Cards:	35x-70x

1995 Collector's Edge Black Label Silver Die Cuts

Randomly seeded one per 24 packs, the 205-card set was a parallel of the base set. Each front showcased a Black Label logo in silver foil. The top of each card was die-cut.

	MT
Complete Set (205):	325.00
Common Player:	.50
Silver Die Cuts:	7x-14x

1995 Excalibur

1995 Collector's Edge Excalibur was issued in two 75-card series - I, called the Sword, and II, called the Stone. The regular cards have a full-bleed color action photo on the front, with a Collector's Edge logo in the upper left corner. The player's name is in silver foil along the right side of the card, with a silver-foiled sword next to it. The card back indicates at the top which series the card is from and includes a mug shot of the player. Each player is addressed as "Sir" and has his statistics from 1991-1994 listed, along with a team logo. Each card was also reprinted in a die-cut version resembling a castle (one in every nine packs). Insert sets in

both series include Rookie Roundtable and Knights of the NFL. Sword Challengers Draft Day Redemption cards were exclusive to Series I packs, while DragonSlayers could be found only in Series II packs. EdgeTech cards in Series I were continued in Series II, but were called Tek-Tech and had a different design. "Stone" and "Sword" game cards were also randomly included in their respective series' packs.

	MT
Complete Set (150):	30.00
Comp. Series 1 (75):	15.00
Comp. Series 2 (75):	15.00
Common Player:	.20
Minor Stars:	.40
Series 1 Wax Box:	100.00
Series 2 Wax Box:	100.00
1 Gary Clark	.20
2 Randall Hill	.20
3 Anthony Edwards	.20
4 Terrance Mathis	.40
5 Erric Pegram	.40
6 Jeff George	.40
7 Pete Metzelaars	.20
8 Jim Kelly	.40
9 Andre Reed	.40
10 Lewis Tillman	.20
11 Curtis Conway	.50
12 Steve Walsh	.20
13 Derrick Fenner	.20
14 Harold Green	.20
15 Michael Jackson	.20
16 Eric Metcalf	.20
17 Antonio Langham	.20
18 Troy Aikman	3.00
19 Alvin Harper	.40
20 Jay Novacek	.20
21 John Elway	4.00
22 Glyn Milburn	.20
23 Steve Atwater	.20
24 Mel Gray	.20
25 Herman Moore	.75
26 Scott Mitchell	.40
27 Guy McIntyre	.20
28 Edgar Bennett	.20
29 Sterling Sharpe	.40
30 Gary Brown	.20
31 Haywood Jeffires	.20
32 Marshall Faulk	.75
33 Roosevelt Potts	.20
34 Marcus Allen	.40
35 Willie Davis	.20
36 Lake Dawson	.75
37 Jeff Hostetler	.20
38 Raghib Ismail	.20
39 Troy Drayton	.20
40 Jerome Bettis	.75
41 Dan Marino	5.00
42 Mark Ingram	.20
43 O.J. McDuffie	.20
44 Warren Moon	.40
45 Qadry Ismail	.20
46 Jake Reed	.20
47 Ben Coates	.20
48 Vincent Brisby	.20
49 Michael Timpson	.20
50 Brad Daluiso	.20
51 Rodney Hampton	.20
52 Chris Calloway	.20
53 Rob Moore	.20
54 Boomer Esiason	.20
55 Michael Haynes	.20
56 Vaughn Dunbar	.20
57 Calvin Williams	.20
58 Herschel Walker	.20
59 Charlie Garner	.20
60 Neil O'Donnell	.40
61 Deon Figures	.20
62 Bam Morris	1.50
63 Junior Seau	.40
64 Leslie O'Neil	.20
65 Natrone Means	1.75
66 Jerry Rice	3.00
67 Deion Sanders	1.50
68 William Floyd	1.00
69 Chris Warren	.40
70 Cortez Kennedy	.20
71 Hardy Nickerson	.20
72 Craig Erickson	.20
73 Heath Shuler	1.00
74 Reggie Brooks	.20
75 Henry Ellard	.20
76 Garrison Hearst	.20
77 Steve Beuerlein	.20
78 Seth Joyner	.20
79 Andre Rison	.20
80 Norm Johnson	.20
81 Craig Hayward	.20
82 Thurman Thomas	.40
83 Kenny Davis	.20
84 Bruce Smith	.20
85 Tom Waddle	.20
86 Erik Kramer	.20
87 Alonzo Spellman	.20
88 Dan Wilkinson	.20
89 *Jeff Blake*	2.00
90 Vinny Testaverde	.20
91 Tommy Vardell	.20
92 Mark Carrier	.20
93 Emmitt Smith	5.00

94 Michael Irvin	.75
95 Daryl Johnston	.20
96 Shannon Sharpe	.20
97 Anthony Miller	.20
98 Leonard Russell	.20
99 Barry Sanders	5.00
100 Brett Perriman	.40
101 Johnnie Morton	.20
102 Brett Favre	5.00
103 Bryce Paup	.40
104 Jackie Harris	.20
105 Ernest Givins	.20
106 Webster Slaughter	.20
107 Jim Harbaugh	.40
108 Joe Montana	4.00
109 J.J. Birden	.20
110 Tim Burnett	.20
111 James Jett	.20
112 Tim Brown	.40
113 Rob Frederickson	.20
114 Chris Miller	.20
115 Bernie Parmalee	.50
116 Terry Kirby	.20
117 Keith Jackson	.20
118 Irving Fryer	.20
119 Terry Allen	.20
120 Cris Carter	.40
121 Fuad Reveiz	.20
122 Drew Bledsoe	3.00
123 Greg McMurtry	.20
124 Dave Brown	.20
125 David Meggett	.20
126 Johnnie Johnson	.20
127 Ronnie Lott	.20
128 Johnny Mitchell	.20
129 Eric Martin	.20
130 Jim Everett	.20
131 Randall Cunningham	.20
132 Fred Barnett	.20
133 Eric Allen	.20
134 Barry Foster	.20
135 Kevin Greene	.20
136 Eric Green	.20
137 Stan Humphries	.40
138 Mark Seay	.20
139 *Alfred Pupunu*	.50
140 Steve Young	2.00
141 John Taylor	.20
142 Ricky Watters	.50
143 Brian Blades	.20
144 Rick Mirer	.75
145 Cortez Kennedy	.20
146 Errict Rhett	2.00
147 Trent Dilfer	1.25
148 Brian Mitchell	.20
149 Ricky Ervins	.20
150 Desmond Howard	.20

1995 Excalibur Die Cuts

This 150-card set paralleled the base Excalibur set, and was inserted in packs at a rate of one per nine. Similar to the Excalibur set in 1995, this die-cut set was issued in two, 75-card series.

	MT
Complete Set (150):	400.00
Complete Sword Set (75):	200.00
Complete Stone Set (75):	200.00
Common Sword Card (1-75):	3.00
Common Stone Card (76-150):	3.00
Die Cuts:	4x-8x

Values quoted in this guide reflect the retail price of a card — the price a collector can expect to pay when buying a card from a dealer. The wholesale price — that which a collector can expect to receive from a dealer when selling cards — will be significantly lower, depending on desirability and condition.

1995 Excalibur 22K Gold

This 22K Knights of the NFL insert set was issued in two 25-card subsets; cards 1-25 were randomly included one per every 35 packs of Excalibur Series I product, while #s 26-50 were in Excalibur Series II packs at the same ratio. In addition to the regular versions, there were also limited editions of each card created in a prism format. The card front has "Excalibur 22K" stamped in gold foil at the top, with a colorful swirly-patterned background. The card back has a shield with the player's name and team logo in it, also against a background of a knight holding a football.

	MT
Complete Set (50):	1100.
Comp. Series 1 (25):	500.00
Comp. Series 2 (25):	600.00
Common Player:	10.00
Comp. Prism Set (50):	3600.
Comp. Prisms Ser. 1 (25):	1800.
Comp. Prisms Ser. 2 (25):	1800.
Prism Cards:	2x-3x
1 Steve Young	60.00
2 Barry Sanders	60.00
3 John Elway	30.00
4 Warren Moon	20.00
5 Chris Warren	10.00
6 Jim Kelly	20.00
7 Troy Aikman	60.00
8 Jerome Bettis	20.00
9 Marcus Allen	20.00
10 William Floyd	20.00
11 Terance Mathis	10.00
12 Antonio Langham	10.00
13 Sterling Sharpe	20.00
14 Leonard Russell	10.00
15 Drew Bledsoe	60.00
16 Rodney Hampton	10.00
17 Herschel Walker	10.00
18 Jim Everett	10.00
19 Eric Allen	10.00
20 Junior Seau	20.00
21 Natrone Means	30.00
22 Deion Sanders	30.00
23 Charlie Garner	10.00
24 Marshall Faulk	60.00
25 Ben Coates	10.00
26 Emmitt Smith	120.00
27 Jerry Rice	60.00
28 Stan Humphries	10.00
29 Joe Montana	75.00
30 Thurman Thomas	20.00
31 Eric Metcalf	10.00
32 Jay Novacek	10.00
33 Brett Favre	100.00
34 Dan Marino	120.00
35 Bam Morris	20.00
36 Heath Shuler	25.00
37 Trent Dilfer	20.00
38 Errict Rhett	25.00
39 Herman Moore	20.00
40 Terry Allen	10.00
41 Cris Carter	20.00
42 Ronnie Lott	10.00
43 Randall Cunningham	10.00
44 Barry Foster	10.00
45 John Taylor	10.00
46 Rick Mirer	20.00
47 Jerry Rice	60.00
48 Michael Irvin	30.00
49 Ricky Watters	20.00
50 Andre Rison	10.00

Post-1980 cards in Near Mint condition will generally sell for about 75% of the quoted Mint value. Excellent-condition cards bring no more than 40%.

1995 Excalibur Challengers Draft Day Rookie Redemption

Each of these 1995 Collector's Edge Excalibur Series I Sword inserts could be exchanged for a card of its respective team's top draft choice. Cards were seeded one per every four Series I packs. The front shows the team's helmet three times; a larger one dominates the center of the card, while smaller ones appear in the upper right and lower left corners. The team name is printed into the background, too. The card back states the rules of the redemption program.

	MT
Complete Set (31):	45.00
Common Player:	1.00
Minor Stars:	2.00
Gold Cards:	1x
1 Derrick Alexander	2.00
2 Tony Boselli	2.00
3 Kyle Brady	1.00
4 Mark Bruener	1.00
5 Jamie Brown	1.00
6 Ruben Brown	1.00
7 Devin Bush	1.00
8 Kevin Carter	1.00
9 Ki-Jana Carter	2.00
10 Kerry Collins	3.00
11 Kordell Stewart	10.00
12 Mark Fields	1.00
13 Joey Galloway	6.00
14 Trezelle Jenkins	1.00
15 Ellis Johnson	1.00
16 Napoleon Kaufman	6.00
17 Ty Law	2.00
18 Mike Mamula	1.00
19 Steve McNair	8.00
20 Billy Milner	1.00
21 Craig Newsome	2.00
22 Craig Powell	1.00
23 Rashaan Salaam	2.00
24 Frank Sanders	3.00
25 Warren Sapp	2.00
26 Terrance Shaw	1.00
27 J.J. Stokes	3.00
28 Michael Westbrook	2.00
29 Tyrone Wheatley	2.00
30 Sherman Williams	2.00

1995 Excalibur Dragon Slayers

These 1995 Collector's Edge Excalibur Series II inserts were made by members of the art departments of hobby price guide editors, so each card has a different design. Fourteen players were spotlighted on the cards, which were random inserts one per every 12 packs.

	MT
Complete Set (14):	65.00
Common Player:	2.00
Minor Stars:	4.00

1	Troy Aikman	5.00
2	Jerome Bettis	4.00
3	Ricky Watters	4.00
4	Barry Sanders	6.00
5	Emmitt Smith	10.00
6	Marshall Faulk	5.00
7	Drew Bledsoe	5.00
8	Errict Rhett	5.00
9	Joe Montana	5.00
10	Junior Seau	4.00
11	Deion Sanders	5.00
12	Bam Morris	2.00
13	Jerry Rice	5.00
14	Natrone Means	4.00

1995 Excalibur EdgeQuest

Designed as an insert and a dealer promotion, the set was printed on clear acetate. The fronts have a large letter and EdgeQuest at the bottom. Collectors who spelled "Sword" or "Stone" with the cards could redeem them for prizes. The D, R and W cards were in Sword packs. The E, N and T cards were in Stone packs. The S and O cards were given to hobby dealers. "Sword" cards could be exchanged for a Rookie Roundtable set, while "Stone" cards could be exchanged for a Challengers Rookie set.

	MT
Complete Set (9):	5.00
Common Box Insert (O/S):	.40
Common Sword Insert (D/R/W):	.40
Common Stone Insert (E/N/T):	.40
1 Letter D	.40
2 Letter E	.40
3 Letter N	.40
4 Letter T	.40
5 Letter O	.40
6 Letter R	.40
7 Letter S	.40
8 Letter W	.40
9 Ampersand	1.50

1995 Excalibur EdgeTech

These 1995 Collector's Edge Excalibur Series I inserts were the rarest, seeded one per every 75 packs. The cards are continued as a TekTech series in Excalibur Series II packs, starting with #13, but the designs remain different.

	MT
Complete Set (12):	375.00
Common Player:	15.00
Minor Stars:	20.00
1 Emmitt Smith	100.00
2 Errict Rhett	40.00
3 Steve Young	50.00
4 Jerry Rice	50.00
5 Ben Coates	15.00
6 Marcus Allen	20.00
7 John Elway	40.00
8 Keith Jackson	15.00
9 Garrison Hearst	25.00
10 Natrone Means	25.00
11 Michael Haynes	15.00
12 Bam Morris	20.00

1995 Excalibur Rookie Roundtable

These 25 inserts, featuring the top sophomores heading into the 1995 season, were is-sued in both 1995 Collector's Edge Excalibur series packs. Cards 1-13 were seeded one per every nine packs in Series I; cards 14-25 were in every ninth Series II pack. The card front has the Rookie Roundtable banner stamped in silver foil in the upper left corner; the player's name is along the bottom. The card back has a mug shot of the player, with biographical information beside it, plus his 1994 statistics and a quote from Hall of Fame linebacker Dick Butkus, the company's spokesman. The player's team helmet is in the upper right corner.

	MT
Complete Set (25):	50.00
Comp. Series 1 (13):	15.00
Comp. Series 2 (12):	35.00
Common Player:	2.00
1 Sam Adams	2.00
2 Joe Johnson	2.00
3 Tim Bowens	2.00
4 Bryant Young	2.00
5 Aubrey Beavers	2.00
6 Willie McGinnest	2.00
7 Rob Frederickson	2.00
8 Lee Woodall	2.00
9 Antonio Langham	2.00
10 DeWayne Washington	2.00
11 Darryl Morrison	2.00
12 Keith Lyle	2.00
13 Antonio Langham	2.00
14 Darnay Scott	6.00
15 Derrick Alexander	2.00
16 Todd Steussie	2.00
17 Larry Allen	2.00
18 Anthony Redmon	2.00
19 Joe Panos	2.00
20 Kevin Mawae	2.00
21 Andrew Jordan	2.00
22 Heath Shuler	6.00
23 Marshall Faulk	8.00
24 Errict Rhett	6.00
25 Marshall Faulk	8.00

1995 Excalibur TekTech

Like the Series I inserts, these cards were seeded one per 75 packs of 1995 Collector's Edge Excalibur Series II packs. The cards pick up where the first series left off, at #13, but have different designs from that series. The card front has a prism-like background, which contains ghosted images of the player in the background. The back has a mug shot of the player, with his name running down the left side of the card. Brief biographical information is underneath the photo.

	MT
Complete Set (12):	100.00
Common Player:	2.50
Minor Stars:	5.00
1 Ricky Watters	5.00
2 Rick Mirer	2.50
3 Drew Bledsoe	15.00
4 Barry Sanders	20.00
5 Junior Seau	2.50
6 Dan Marino	30.00
7 Edgar Bennett	2.50
8 Haywood Jeffires	2.50
9 Deion Sanders	7.00
10 Tim Brown	2.50
11 Jerome Bettis	5.00
12 Marshall Faulk	5.00

A card number in parentheses ( ) indicates the set is unnumbered.

1995 Collector's Edge Instant Replay

The 51-card set showcased the player's last name and team helmet at the top of the card fronts. The Edge logo is in the lower right. The card backs have the player's name, team, position and jersey number, along with a head shot, at the top. His bio is printed underneath. A quote is printed about the player's team logo background. Logos included on the back are Team NFL, Pop Warner and Edge. There is a Prism parallel of the set, which were seeded one per two packs. A Micro Mini set, an eight-card set of Black Label base cards, were found one per 14 packs. Each card showcased 50 mini-cards with 25 on each side.

	MT
Complete Set (51):	15.00
Common Player:	.05
Minor Stars:	.10
Prism Cards:	2x
Inserted 1:2	
1 Jeff George	.10
2 Eric Metcalf	.05
3 Jim Kelly	.20
4 Jeff Blake	.20
5 Andre Rison	.10
6 Troy Aikman	.75
7 Michael Irvin	.10
8 Emmitt Smith	1.00
9 John Elway	1.00
10 Terrell Davis	8.00
11 Herman Moore	.20
12 Barry Sanders	1.50
13 Brett Favre	1.50
14 Marshall Faulk	.30
15 Steve Beuerlein	.05
16 Steve Bono	.10
17 Tim Brown	.10
18 Jeff Hostetler	.05
19 Jerome Bettis	.20
20 Dan Marino	1.00
21 Cris Carter	.20
22 Drew Bledsoe	.75
23 Ben Coates	.20
24 Randall Cunningham	.20
25 Terry Kirby	.05
26 Ricky Watters	.10
27 Kyle Brady	.05
28 Byron "Bam" Morris	.05
29 Neil O'Donnell	.10
30 Natrone Means	.20
31 Junior Seau	.10
32 William Floyd	.10
33 Jerry Rice	.75
34 Deion Sanders	.40
35 Steve Young	.50
36 Rick Mirer	.10
37 Chris Warren	.10
38 Trent Dilfer	.20
39 Errict Rhett	.10
40 Heath Shuler	.10
41 Ki-Jana Carter	.10
42 Kerry Collins	.75
43 Steve McNair	2.00
44 Rashaan Salaam	.20
45 James O. Stewart	.20
46 J.J. Stokes	.50
47 Tyrone Wheatley	.20
48 Joey Galloway	1.50
49 Napoleon Kaufman	2.00
50 Michael Westbrook	.75
NNO Checklist	.05

A card number in parentheses ( ) indicates the set is unnumbered.

1995 Collector's Edge Instant Replay Edge Tech Die Cuts

Randomly seeded one per four regular retail packs and one per special retail pack, the 13-card set showcased a die-cut in the shape of a helmet on the top of the card. The player's name is printed at the bottom of the card. A helmet also appears in the background. The card backs have "EdgeTech" at the top, with the player's headshot inside a circle. The player's name and bio are inside a stripe underneath his picture.

	MT
Complete Set (13):	10.00
Common Player:	.25
1 Troy Aikman	1.50
2 Drew Bledsoe	1.50
3 Tim Brown	.50
4 Ben Coates	.25
5 Marshall Faulk	.75
6 William Floyd	.25
7 Dan Marino	3.00
8 Errict Rhett	1.00
9 Deion Sanders	1.25
10 Emmitt Smith	3.00
11 Ricky Watters	.50
12 Steve Young	1.25
NNO Checklist	.25

1995 Collector's Edge Instant Replay Quantum Motion

Cards Nos. 1-10 of the 22-card set were seeded one per 12 packs, while the remaining 11 cards were offered through a mail-in redemption. Card Nos. 1-10 include game action on the lenticular card fronts, with "Quantum Motion" printed at the bottom. The card backs have a headshot in the upper left, with the player's team's helmet on the right. The player's name and highlights are listed inside a box in the center of the card. The cards are numbered "of 21."

	MT
Complete Set (22):	55.00
Complete Series 1 (11):	30.00
Complete Series 2 (11):	25.00
Common Player:	1.00
1 Troy Aikman	5.00
2 Drew Bledsoe	5.00
3 Marshall Faulk	3.00
4 Michael Irvin	2.00
5 Dan Marino	10.00
6 Jerry Rice	5.00
7 Rod Smith	1.00
8 Emmitt Smith	10.00
9 Michael Westbrook	2.50
10 Steve Young	3.50
11 Erik Kramer	1.00

		MT
12	Jeff Blake	3.00
13	Eric Metcalf	1.00
14	Steve Bono	1.00
15	Carl Pickens	2.00
16	Isaac Bruce	3.00
17	Errict Rhett	3.00
18	Kerry Collins	5.00
19	Rashaan Salaam	3.00
20	Gus Frerotte	1.00
21	Terry Kirby	1.00
NNO	Checklist	1.00

1996 Collector's Edge Promos

This six-card set gave a sampling of the Collector's Edge set for 1996. It included three regular-issue cards and a sampling of inserts that resemble that of the regular-issue series.

		MT
Complete Set (4):		2.50
Common Player:		.25
P1	Errict Rhett	1.00
P2	Junior Seau	.75
P3	Terry Kirby	.50
NNO	Cover Card	.25

1996 Collector's Edge

1996 Collector's Edge Series I football has 240 cards, consisting of veterans and rookies. Each regular card is also reprinted as part of a parallel Holofoil set, found one per every six packs. Three insert sets were also made - Quantum, Ripped and Too Cool Rookies.

		MT
Complete Set (240):		20.00
Common Player:		.05
Minor Stars:		.10
Wax Box:		35.00
1	Larry Centers	.05
2	Garrison Hearst	.10
3	Dave Krieg	.05
4	Rob Moore	.05
5	Frank Sanders	.05
6	Eric Swann	.05
7	Morten Andersen	.05
8	Chris Doleman	.05
9	Bert Emanuel	.05
10	Jeff George	.10
11	Craig Heyward	.05
12	Terance Mathis	.05
13	Clay Matthews	.05
14	Eric Metcalf	.05
15	Bill Brooks	.05
16	Todd Collins	.05
17	Russell Copeland	.05
18	Jim Kelly	.10
19	Bryce Paup	.05
20	Andre Reed	.05
21	Bruce Smith	.05
22	Mark Carrier	.05
23	Kerry Collins	.30
24	Willie Green	.05
25	Eric Guliford	.05
26	Brett Maxie	.05
27	Tim McKyer	.05
28	Derrick Moore	.05
29	Curtis Conway	.05
30	Jim Flanigan	.05
31	Jeff Graham	.05
32	Robert Green	.05
33	Erik Kramer	.05
34	Rashaan Salaam	.50
35	Alonzo Spellman	.05
36	Donnell Woolford	.05
37	Chris Zorich	.05
38	Eric Bieniemy	.05
39	Jeff Blake	.50
40	Ki-Jana Carter	.25
41	John Copeland	.05
42	Harold Green	.05
43	Tony McGee	.05
44	Carl Pickens	.10
45	Darnay Scott	.05
46	Bracey Walker	.05
47	Dan Wilkinson	.05
48	Rob Burnett	.05
49	Leroy Hoard	.05
50	Earnest Hunter	.05
51	Michael Jackson	.05
52	Stevon Moore	.05
53	Anthony Pleasant	.05
54	Andre Rison	.05
55	Vinny Testaverde	.05
56	Eric Zeier	.05
57	Troy Aikman	1.00
58	Bill Bates	.05
59	Shante Carver	.05
60	Michael Irvin	.10
61	Daryl Johnston	.05
62	Jay Novacek	.05
63	Deion Sanders	.50
64	Emmitt Smith	2.00
65	Sherman Williams	.05
66	Terrell Davis	.50
67	John Elway	.50
68	Ed McCaffrey	.05
69	Glyn Milburn	.05
70	Anthony Miller	.05
71	Michael Dean Perry	.05
72	Shannon Sharpe	.05
73	Willie Clay	.05
74	Scott Mitchell	.05
75	Herman Moore	.25
76	Johnnie Morton	.05
77	Brett Perriman	.05
78	Barry Sanders	1.25
79	Tracy Scroggins	.05
80	Edgar Bennett	.05
81	Robert Brooks	.10
82	Brett Favre	2.00
83	Dorsey Levens	.10
84	Craig Newsome	.05
85	Wayne Simmons	.05
86	Reggie White	.10
87	Chris Chandler	.05
88	Anthony Cook	.05
89	Mel Gray	.05
90	Haywood Jeffires	.05
91	Darryll Lewis	.05
92	Steve McNair	.50
93	Todd McNair	.05
94	Rodney Thomas	.20
95	Trev Alberts	.05
96	Tony Bennett	.05
97	Quentin Coryatt	.05
98	Sean Dawkins	.05
99	Ken Dilger	.05
100	Marshall Faulk	.75
101	Jim Harbaugh	.05
102	Ronald Humphrey	.05
103	Floyd Turner	.05
104	Steve Beuerlein	.05
105	Tony Boselli	.05
106	Mark Brunell	.75
107	Willie Jackson	.05
108	Jeff Lageman	.05
109	James Stewart	.05
110	Cedric Tillman	.05
111	Marcus Allen	.05
112	Kimble Anders	.05
113	Steve Bono	.05
114	Dale Carter	.05
115	Willie Davis	.05
116	Lake Dawson	.05
117	Dan Saleaumua	.05
118	Neil Smith	.05
119	Derrick Thomas	.05
120	Tamarick Vanover	.30
121	Marco Coleman	.05
122	Bryan Cox	.05
123	Steve Emtman	.05
124	Irving Fryar	.05
125	Eric Green	.05
126	Terry Kirby	.05
127	Dan Marino	2.00
128	O.J. McDuffie	.05
129	Bernie Parmalee	.05
130	Troy Vincent	.05
131	Cris Carter	.05
132	Jack Del Rio	.05
133	Qadry Ismail	.05
134	Amp Lee	.05
135	Warren Moon	.05
136	John Randle	.05
137	Jake Reed	.05
138	Robert Smith	.05
139	Drew Bledsoe	.75
140	Vincent Brisby	.05
141	Ben Coates	.05
142	Curtis Martin	1.50
143	David Meggett	.05
144	Will Moore	.05
145	Chris Slade	.05
146	Mario Bates	.05
147	Quinn Early	.05
148	Jim Everett	.05
149	Michael Haynes	.05
150	Tyrone Hughes	.05
151	Wayne Martin	.05
152	Renaldo Turnbull	.05
153	Dave Brown	.05
154	Chris Calloway	.05
155	Rodney Hampton	.05
156	Mike Sherrard	.05
157	Michael Strahan	.05
158	Herschel Walker	.05
159	Tyrone Wheatley	.05
160	Kyle Brady	.05
161	Wayne Chrebet	.05
162	Hugh Douglas	.05
163	Adrian Murrell	.05
164	Todd Scott	.05
165	Charles Wilson	.05
166	Tim Brown	.05
167	Aundray Bruce	.05
168	Andrew Glover	.05
169	Jeff Hostetler	.05
170	Napoleon Kaufman	.05
171	Terry McDaniel	.05
172	Chester McGlockton	.05
173	Pat Swilling	.05
174	Harvey Williams	.05
175	Fred Barnett	.05
176	Randall Cunningham	.05
177	William Fuller	.05
178	Charlie Garner	.05
179	Andy Harmon	.05
180	Rodney Peete	.05
181	Ricky Watters	.05
182	Calvin Williams	.05
183	Chad Brown	.05
184	Kevin Greene	.05
185	Greg Lloyd	.05
186	Bam Morris	.05
187	Neil O'Donnell	.05
188	Eric Pegram	.05
189	Kordell Stewart	.75
190	Yancey Thigpen	.25
191	Rod Woodson	.05
192	Darren Bennett	.05
193	Ronnie Harmon	.05
194	Stan Humphries	.05
195	Tony Martin	.05
196	Natrone Means	.05
197	Leslie O'Neil	.05
198	Junior Seau	.10
199	Mark Seay	.05
200	William Floyd	.05
201	Merton Hanks	.05
202	Brent Jones	.05
203	Derek Loville	.05
204	Ken Norton Jr.	.05
205	Gary Plummer	.05
206	Jerry Rice	1.00
207	J.J. Stokes	.30
208	Dana Stubblefield	.05
209	John Taylor	.05
210	Bryant Young	.05
211	Steve Young	.75
212	Brian Blades	.05
213	Joey Galloway	.50
214	Carlton Gray	.05
215	Cortez Kennedy	.05
216	Rick Mirer	.10
217	Chris Warren	.05
218	Jerome Bettis	.05
219	Isaac Bruce	.40
220	Troy Drayton	.05
221	D'Marco Farr	.05
222	Sean Gilbert	.05
223	Chris Miller	.05
224	Roman Phifer	.05
225	Trent Dilfer	.05
226	Santana Dotson	.05
227	Alvin Harper	.05
228	Jackie Harris	.05
229	John Lynch	.05
230	Hardy Nickerson	.05
231	Errict Rhett	.50
232	Warren Sapp	.05
233	Terry Allen	.05
234	Henry Ellard	.05
235	Gus Frerotte	.05
236	Ken Harvey	.05
237	Brian Mitchell	.05
238	Heath Shuler	.05
239	James Washington	.05
240	Michael Westbrook	.30

1996 Collector's Edge Die Cuts

Randomly seeded one per retail pack, the die-cut had a pink front, with a front that was similar to base set cards, except for the die-cut.

		MT
Complete Set (240):		75.00
Common Player:		.25
Die-Cut Cards:		2x-4x

1996 Collector's Edge Holofoil

Seeded one per 48 retail, hobby or Cowboybilia packs, the 240-card set was a parallel to the Edge base cards.

	MT
Complete Set (240):	500.00
Common Player:	2.00
Holofoil Cards:	15x-30x

1996 Collector's Edge All-Stars

This 13-card set (includes a checklist) was done on plastic stock and features two photos of the player on the front.

		MT
Complete Set (13):		35.00
Common Player:		2.00
1	Junior Seau	3.00
2	Drew Bledsoe	6.00
3	Marshall Faulk	3.00
4	John Elway	5.00
5	Jerry Rice	6.00
6	Errict Rhett	2.00
7	Jerome Bettis	2.00
8	Deion Sanders	4.00
9	Byron "Bam" Morris	2.00
10	Cris Carter	3.00
11	Terrell Davis	6.00
12	Terance Mathis	2.00
---	Checklist Card	1.00

1996 Collector's Edge Big Easy

Big Easy cards were inserted in various 1996 Collector's Edge packs. Each card is numbered one of 2,000. A gold foil parallel was released through mail order. Each card in the parallel is numbered one of 3,100.

		MT
Complete Set (19):		200.00
Common Player:		5.00
1	Kerry Collins	14.00
2	Rashaan Salaam	5.00
3	Troy Aikman	16.00
4	Deion Sanders	10.00
5	Emmitt Smith	30.00
6	Terrell Davis	16.00
7	Barry Sanders	16.00
8	Brett Favre	35.00
9	Marshall Faulk	8.00
10	Tamarick Vanover	8.00
11	Dan Marino	30.00
12	Drew Bledsoe	16.00
13	Curtis Martin	16.00
14	J.J. Stokes	8.00
15	Joey Galloway	8.00
16	Isaac Bruce	8.00
17	Errict Rhett	5.00
18	Carl Pickens	5.00
---	Checklist Card	1.50

1996 Collector's Edge Draft Day Redemption

This 30-card set features one 1996 draft pick from each NFL team. One card could be obtained via that team's redemption card. The redemption cards were inserted 1:8.

		MT
Complete Set (30):		100.00
Common Player:		2.00
Trade Cards:		.10
1	Simeon Rice	2.00
2	Richard Huntley	2.00
3	Jonathan Ogden	2.00
4	Eric Moulds	4.00
5	Tim Biakabutuka	4.00
6	Walt Harris	2.00
7	Marco Battaglia	2.00
8	Stepfret Williams	2.00
9	John Mobley	2.00
10	Reggie Brown LB	2.00
11	Derrick Mayes	2.00
12	Eddie George	8.00
13	Marvin Harrison	4.00
14	Kevin Hardy	3.00
15	Jerome Woods	2.00
16	Karim Abdul-Jabbar	6.00
17	Duane Clemons	2.00
18	Terry Glenn	7.00
19	Ricky Whittle	2.00
20	Amani Toomer	2.00
21	Keyshawn Johnson	5.00
22	Rickey Dudley	3.00
23	Bobby Hoying	4.00
24	Jahine Arnold	2.00
25	Tony Banks	5.00
26	Bryan Still	2.00
27	Terrell Owens	5.00
28	Reggie Brown RB	2.00
29	Mike Alstott	4.00
30	Stephen Davis	3.00

1996 Collector's Edge Proteges

The cards in this 12-card insert feature an established star on one side and a young player with similar skills on the other. They were inserted 1:164 in 1996 Collector's Edge packs.

		MT
Complete Set (13):		200.00
Common Player:		8.00
1	Eric Metcalf, Joey Galloway	12.00
2	Herman Moore, Michael Westbrook	12.00
3	Emmitt Smith, Errict Rhett	30.00
4	Kordell Stewart, John Elway	20.00
5	Terrell Davis, Marshall Faulk	20.00
6	Rashaan Salaam, Marcus Allen	12.00
7	Dan Marino, Drew Bledsoe	30.00
8	Brett Favre, Kerry Collins	30.00
9	Tim Brown, Isaac Bruce	12.00
10	Cris Carter, Chris Sanders	8.00
11	Curtis Martin, Chris Warren	18.00
	Tamarick Vanover, Brian Mitchell	10.00
---	Checklist Card	2.00
P1	Rashaan Salaam Promo, Terry Kirby Promo	2.00

A card number in parentheses ( ) indicates the set is unnumbered.

1996 Collector's Edge Ripped

These 1996 Collector's Edge Series I inserts feature 36 of the NFL's top stars. Cards were seeded one per 18 packs of Series I product.

		MT
Complete Set (36):		100.00
Complete Hobby (18):		50.00
Complete Retail (18):		50.00
Common Player:		2.00
1	Jeff Blake	3.00
2	Steve Bono	2.00
3	Terrell Davis	7.00
4	John Elway	4.00
5	Marshall Faulk	4.00
6	Brett Favre	12.00
7	Jeff Hostetler	2.00
8	Erik Kramer	2.00
9	Dan Marino	12.00
10	Natrone Means	2.00
11	Eric Metcalf	2.00
12	Anthony Miller	2.00
13	Herman Moore	3.00
14	Errict Rhett	2.00
15	Andre Rison	2.00
16	Barry Sanders	6.00
17	Yancey Thigpen	2.00
18	Michael Westbrook	2.00
19	Troy Aikman	6.00
20	Drew Bledsoe	6.00
21	Tim Brown	2.00
22	Mark Brunell	6.00
23	Cris Carter	2.00
24	Kerry Collins	3.00
25	Joey Galloway	3.00
26	Michael Irvin	2.00
27	Terry Kirby	2.00
28	Curtis Martin	8.00
29	Carl Pickens	2.00
30	Jerry Rice	6.00
31	Rashaan Salaam	3.00
32	Deion Sanders	4.00
33	Emmitt Smith	12.00
34	Kordell Stewart	6.00
35	Ricky Watters	2.00
36	Steve Young	4.00

1996 Collector's Edge Too Cool Rookies

The NFL's top 25 rookies from 1995 are featured on these 1996 Collector's Edge Series I inserts. Cards were seeded one per every 25 packs of Series I product.

		MT
Complete Set (25):		75.00
Common Player:		2.00
1	Tony Boselli	2.00
2	Kyle Brady	2.00
3	Ki-Jana Carter	4.00
4	Kerry Collins	4.00
5	Todd Collins	2.00
6	Terrell Davis	6.00
7	Hugh Douglas	2.00
8	Joey Galloway	6.00
9	Darius Holland	2.00
10	Napoleon Kaufman	4.00
11	Mike Mamula	2.00
12	Curtis Martin	10.00
13	Steve McNair	6.00
14	Billy Milner	2.00
15	Rashaan Salaam	5.00

16	Frank Sanders	2.00
17	Warren Sapp	2.00
18	James Stewart	2.00
19	Kordell Stewart	7.00
20	J.J. Stokes	5.00
21	Tamarick Vanover	3.00
22	Michael Westbrook	5.00
23	Tyrone Wheatley	2.00
24	Sherman Williams	2.00
25	Eric Zeier	2.00

1996 Collector's Edge Quantum

These 24 cards were seeded one per 36 packs of 1996 Collector's Edge Series I football. The cards change images; NFL stars are shown in their current pro team's uniform and also in their college uniforms.

		MT
Complete Set (24):		300.00
Common Player:		7.00
1	Troy Aikman	20.00
2	Jeff Blake	15.00
3	Drew Bledsoe	20.00
4	Steve Bono	7.00
5	Tim Brown	7.00
6	Isaac Bruce	14.00
7	Mark Brunell	18.00
8	Kerry Collins	10.00
9	Marshall Faulk	10.00
10	Brett Favre	40.00
11	Jeff George	7.00
12	Terry Kirby	7.00
13	Dan Marino	40.00
14	Natrone Means	10.00
15	Carl Pickens	7.00
16	Errict Rhett	10.00
17	Rashaan Salaam	10.00
18	Deion Sanders	15.00
19	Barry Sanders	20.00
20	Emmitt Smith	40.00
21	Kordell Stewart	20.00
22	Yancey Thigpen	10.00
23	Michael Westbrook	10.00
24	Steve Young	20.00

1996 Collector's Edge Advantage Promos

This three-card promo set featured one regular-issue card (EA1), one Role Models insert (RM1) and one Edge Video (PR1). The cards detailed what the Edge Advantage set for 1996 would look like.

		MT
Complete Set (3):		8.00
Common Player:		2.50
EA1	Jeff Blake	3.00
PR1	Rashaan Salaam	3.00
RM1	Michael Westbrook	2.50

1996 Collector's Edge Advantage

Collector's Edge's 1996 Advantage set includes 150 cards,

including 25 cards of rookies in their NFL uniforms. Each card front and back is gold foil stamped and embossed, with the rookie cards featuring extra foil stamping. The base set is also paralleled by Perfect Play Holofoil inserts; these cards, seeded one per two packs, use prism art technology. Five other insert sets were also produced - Role Models, Edge Video, Crystal Cuts, Game Ball and Super Bowl Game Ball. Portions of the proceeds made from the sale of this product were donated to the Pop Warner Football program.

		MT
Complete Set (150):		25.00
Common Player:		.10
Minor Stars:		.20
Wax Box:		55.00
1	Drew Bledsoe	1.00
2	Chris Warren	.10
3	*Eddie George*	3.50
4	Barry Sanders	1.75
5	Scott Mitchell	.10
6	Carl Pickens	.10
7	Tim Brown	.10
8	John Elway	.75
9	Michael Westbrook	.20
10	Cris Carter	.10
11	Troy Aikman	1.25
12	Ben Coates	.10
13	Brett Favre	2.50
14	Marshall Faulk	.40
15	Steve Young	1.00
16	Terrell Davis	2.00
17	*Keyshawn Johnson*	3.00
18	Mario Bates	.10
19	Steve McNair	.75
20	Kerry Collins	.30
21	Natrone Means	.10
22	Kordell Stewart	1.25
23	Jeff George	.10
24	Rick Mirer	.10
25	Herman Moore	.20
26	Rodney Peete	.10
27	Isaac Bruce	.50
28	Errict Rhett	.20
29	Jerry Rice	1.25
30	Rashaan Salaam	.50
31	Eric Metcalf	.10
32	Jim Kelly	.20
33	Jerome Bettis	.20
34	Deion Sanders	.75
35	J.J. Stokes	.20
36	Neil O'Donnell	.10
37	Marcus Allen	.20
38	Thurman Thomas	.20
39	Dan Marino	2.50
40	*Rickey Dudley*	.75
41	Napoleon Kaufman	.10
42	Kyle Brady	.10
43	Emmitt Smith	2.50
44	Tyrone Wheatley	.10
45	Jeff Blake	.20
46	Reggie White	.20
47	Joey Galloway	1.00
48	Antonio Langham	.10
49	Craig Heyward	.10
50	Curtis Martin	1.75
51	*Karim Abdul-Jabbar*	1.00
52	Antonio Freeman	.10
53	Ki-Jana Carter	.20
54	Willie Davis	.10
55	Jim Everett	.10
56	Gus Frerotte	.10
57	Daryl Gardener	.10
58	Charles Haley	.10
59	Michael Irvin	.20
60	Keith Jackson	.10
61	Cortez Kennedy	.10
62	Greg Lloyd	.10
63	Tony Martin	.10
64	Ken Norton Jr.	.10
65	Leslie O'Neal	.10
66	Bryce Paup	.10
67	Jake Reed	.10
68	Frank Sanders	.10
69	Vinny Testaverde	.10
70	Regan Upshaw	.10
71	Tamarick Vanover	.50
72	Walt Harris	.10
73	John Randle	.10
74	Ricky Watters	.20
75	Terry Allen	.10
76	Edgar Bennett	.10
77	Larry Centers	.10
78	Chris Penn	.10
79	*Bobby Engram*	.75
80	Irving Fryar	.10
81	Charlie Garner	.10
82	Rodney Hampton	.10
83	Michael Jackson	.10
84	O.J. McDuffie	.10
85	Shannon Sharpe	.10
86	Aaron Hayden	.10
87	*Mushin Muhammad*	1.00
88	Rodney Woodson	.10
89	Levon Kirkland	.10
90	Chad Brown	.10
91	Junior Seau	.10
92	Terry Kirby	.10
93	*Zach Thomas*	1.00

94	Harvey Williams	.10
95	Robert Brooks	.10
96	Darrell Green	.10
97	Chester McGlockton	.10
98	Neil Smith	.10
99	Eric Swann	.10
100	*Mike Alstott*	1.50
101	*Tim Biakabutuka*	1.00
102	Mark Brunell	1.00
103	Chris Doleman	.10
104	Sean Gilbert	.10
105	Jim Harbaugh	.10
106	Chris T. Jones	.10
107	Tyrone Hughes	.10
108	*Amani Toomer*	.40
109	Larry Brown	.10
110	Kevin Greene	.10
111	John Mobley	.10
112	*Danny Kanell*	.75
113	*Kevin Hardy*	.40
114	Brett Perriman	.10
115	Simeon Rice	.40
116	Chris Sanders	.10
117	Dave Brown	.10
118	Bryan Cox	.10
119	Yancey Thigpen	.10
120	Terance Mathis	.10
121	Warren Moon	.10
122	Derrick Thomas	.10
123	Trent Dilfer	.10
124	*Terry Glenn*	2.00
125	Jeff Hostetler	.10
126	*Leeland McElroy*	.50
127	Hardy Nickerson	.10
128	Steve Bono	.10
129	Stanley Pritchett	.10
130	Dana Stubblefield	.10
131	Andre Coleman	.10
132	Anthony Miller	.10
133	Stan Humphries	.10
134	Robert Smith	.10
135	Curtis Conway	.10
136	Derrick Holmes	.10
137	Pat Swilling	.10
138	Andre Rison	.10
139	Erik Kramer	.10
140	Jason Dunn	.10
141	Torrance Small	.10
142	Cedric Jones	.10
143	Derek Loville	.10
144	Brian Mitchell	.10
145	*Eric Moulds*	2.00
146	James Stewart	.10
147	Bruce Smith	.10
148	Keenan McCardell	.10
149	Warren Sapp	.10
150	*Marvin Harrison*	3.00

1996 Collector's Edge Advantage Perfect Play Holofoil

Perfect Play Holofoil cards put a prismatic finish on all 150 cards in the Advantage set. These parallel cards were inserted every two packs.

	MT
Complete Set (150):	150.00
Holofoil Cards:	3x-6x

1996 Collector's Edge Advantage Game Ball

These 1996 Collector's Edge

Advantage inserts feature a medallion cut from an authentic game-used NFL football, with highlights of the game in which the ball was used. The card front has a color photo on it, plus foil stamping. The background of the card has a football field, with smaller color photos along the left side. Each card back contains a statement of authentication for the ball and game in which it was used. The cards are limited to 400 individually dual-numbered cards, seeded one per 72 packs.

		MT
Complete Set (36):		1600.
Common Player:		25.00
1	Kordell Stewart	75.00
2	Emmitt Smith	150.00
3	Brett Favre	150.00
4	Steve Young	50.00
5	Barry Sanders	120.00
6	John Elway	40.00
7	Drew Bledsoe	60.00
8	Dan Marino	150.00
9	Keyshawn Johnson	40.00
10	Eddie George	85.00
11	Kevin Hardy	25.00
12	Terry Glenn	75.00
13	Michael Westbrook	25.00
14	Joey Galloway	25.00
15	John Mobley	25.00
16	Curtis Martin	80.00
17	Rashaan Salaam	25.00
18	J.J. Stokes	25.00
19	Kerry Collins	60.00
20	Deion Sanders	50.00
21	Shannon Sharpe	25.00
22	Terry Allen	25.00
23	Rickey Watters	25.00
24	Marshall Faulk	40.00
25	Tim Biakabutuka	25.00
26	Troy Aikman	60.00
27	Jerry Rice	60.00
28	Chris Warren	25.00
29	Jeff Blake	25.00
30	Carl Pickens	25.00
31	Isaac Bruce	35.00
32	Terrell Davis	80.00
33	Mark Brunell	75.00
34	Karim Abdul-Jabbar	50.00
35	Herman Moore	25.00
36	Cris Carter	25.00

1996 Collector's Edge Advantage Super Bowl Game Ball

Collector's Edge obtained several footballs from the Super Bowl to create these 1996 inserts. Each card has a medallion cut from an authentic NFL Super Bowl game-used ball, with highlights of the game in which the ball was used. The 36 cards were limited to 200 individually-numbered cards each, with odds of one per 164 packs.

		MT
Complete Set (36):		2200.
Common Player:		30.00
1	Emmitt Smith	325.00
2	Troy Aikman	180.00
3	Michael Irvin	50.00
4	Deion Sanders	130.00
5	John Elway	160.00
6	Dan Marino	325.00
7	Marcus Allen	80.00
8	Kordell Stewart	180.00
9	Steve Young	130.00
10	Ricky Watters	50.00
11	Jerry Rice	180.00
12	Jim Kelly	80.00
13	Thurman Thomas	50.00
14	Bruce Smith	30.00
15	Stan Humphries	30.00
16	Junior Seau	50.00
17	Natrone Means	30.00
18	Neil O'Donnell	30.00
19	Rod Woodson	30.00
20	Andre Reed	30.00

21	Jeff Hostetler	30.00
22	Dave Meggett	30.00
23	Greg Lloyd	30.00
24	Kevin Green	30.00
25	Yancey Thigpen	30.00
26	Charles Haley	30.00
27	Bam Morris	30.00
28	Alvin Harper	30.00
29	Ken Norton Jr.	30.00
30	William Floyd	30.00
31	Leslie O'Neal	30.00
32	Jay Novacek	30.00
33	Irvin Fryar	30.00
34	Leon Lett	30.00
35	Tony Martin	30.00
36	Mark Collins	30.00

1996 Collector's Edge Advantage Role Models

These 1996 Collector's Edge Advantage inserts were seeded one per 12 packs. Each card front has an action shot on it, on a die-cut, embossed metallized card. A smaller photo is in the background of the card front, which has the Collector's Edge logo stamped in gold foil.

		MT
Complete Set (12):		60.00
Common Player:		2.50
1	John Elway	7.00
2	Dan Marino	16.00
3	Jerry Rice	8.00
4	Emmitt Smith	16.00
5	Chris Warren	2.50
6	Tim Brown	2.50
7	Jeff George	2.50
8	Tyrone Wheatley	2.50
9	Steve Bono	2.50
10	Kerry Collins	5.00
11	Jerome Bettis	5.00
12	Steve Beuerlein	2.50

1996 Collector's Edge Advantage Edge Video

These 1996 Collector's Edge Advantage inserts depict real game action with an over-laid photograph. The card front has a stand-out player shot with a state-of-the-art "Edge Video" background showing actual in-motion footage. The cards, each limited to 1,200, were seeded one per 36 packs.

		MT
Complete Set (25):		200.00
Common Player:		4.00
1	Brett Favre	35.00
2	Keyshawn Johnson	10.00
3	Deion Sanders	10.00
4	Marcus Allen	4.00
5	Rashaan Salaam	8.00
6	Thurman Thomas	4.00
7	Emmitt Smith	35.00
8	Isaac Bruce	6.00
9	Michael Westbrook	4.00

10	Cris Carter	4.00
11	Marshall Faulk	6.00
12	Jerry Rice	17.00
13	Tim Brown	4.00
14	Steve Young	12.00
15	Eric Metcalf	4.00
16	Chris Warren	4.00
17	Drew Bledsoe	17.00
18	Barry Sanders	20.00
19	Herman Moore	6.00
20	Rodney Peete	4.00
21	Troy Aikman	17.00
22	Jerome Bettis	4.00
23	Errict Rhett	6.00
24	Dan Marino	35.00
25	Natrone Means	4.00

1996 Collector's Edge Advantage Crystal Cuts

These 1996 Collector's Edge Advantage die-cut inserts are printed on clear plastic stock. The cards, dual numbered up to 5,000, were seeded one per eight packs. The card front has a color photo on it, with a background which makes the card look like a filmstrip. The player's name, position, number and team name are in gold foil and form a circle at the bottom of the card. The Collector's Edge logo is stamped in gold foil in the middle.

		MT
Complete Set (25):		125.00
Common Player:		2.50
1	Barry Sanders	8.00
2	Eddie George	12.00
3	Curtis Martin	12.00
4	J.J. Stokes	5.00
5	Kyle Brady	2.50
6	Chris Warren	2.50
7	Jerry Rice	7.00
8	Ben Coates	2.50
9	Terrell Davis	8.00
10	Marcus Allen	2.50
11	John Elway	6.00
12	Joey Galloway	5.00
13	Dan Marino	14.00
14	Napoleon Kaufman	2.50
15	Emmitt Smith	14.00
16	Eric Metcalf	2.50
17	Kerry Collins	7.00
18	Troy Aikman	7.00
19	Rickey Watters	3.00
20	Steve McNair	6.00
21	Steve Young	6.00
22	Isaac Bruce	4.00
23	Kordell Stewart	7.00
24	LeShon Johnson	2.50
25	Scott Mitchell	2.50

1996 Collector's Edge Cowboybilia

Each of the 25 cards, except Troy Aikman, were signed by the featured player. They were seeded one per 2.5 packs in Cowboybilia. Other packs included a certificate for signed Cowboys items like jerseys, helmets, photos, footballs and pennants. In addition, 24K Prism parallel cards of Deion Sanders, Troy Aikman, Emmitt Smith and Michael Irvin were seeded four per case (one of each player per case). A Roger Staubach/Drew Pearson autographed Hail Mary card was found one per 192 packs. The cards are numbered with the "DC" prefix.

		MT
Complete Set (25):		450.00
Common Player:		8.00
1	Chris Boniol (4000)	8.00

2	John Jett (4000)	8.00
3	Sherman Williams (4000)	8.00
4	Chad Hennings (4000)	8.00
5	Larry Allen (4000)	10.00
6	Jason Garrett (4000)	8.00
7	Tony Tolbert (4000)	8.00
8	Kevin Williams (4000)	20.00
9	Mark Tuinei (4000)	8.00
10	Larry Brown (4000)	10.00
11	Kevin Smith (4000)	10.00
12	Darrin Smith (4000)	8.00
13	Robert Jones (4000)	8.00
14	Nate Newton (4000)	12.00
15	Darren Woodson (4000)	12.00
16	Leon Lett (4000)	12.00
17	Russell Maryland (4000)	10.00
18	Erik Williams (4000)	12.00
19	Bill Bates (4000)	12.00
20	Daryl Johnston (2300)	20.00
21	Jay Novacek (2300)	20.00
22	Charles Haley (2300)	20.00
23	Troy Aikman (600 all cards unsigned)	18.00
24	Michael Irvin (500)	60.00
25	Emmitt Smith (500)	175.00
NNO	Roger Staubach, Drew Pearson (Hail Mary Pass numbered of 1000)	200.00

1996 Collector's Edge Cowboybilia 24K Holofoil

Randomly seeded one per 48 1995 Edge Cowboybilia packs, the four cards parallel the players' 1995 Edge Holofoil card. The Cowboybilia 24K Holofoil cards have a 24K logo and are numbered with the "CB" prefix.

		MT
Complete Set (4):		200.00
Common Player:		20.00
57	Troy Aikman	50.00
60	Michael Irvin	20.00
63	Deion Sanders	30.00
64	Emmitt Smith	100.00

1996 Collector's Edge President's Reserve Promos

The 1996 Edge President's Reserve set was hyped by this six-card set, which included one card from each of the upcoming set's regular and chase sets. The cards each are numbered with the "PR" prefix.

		MT
Complete Set (6):		7.00
Common Player:		.50
1	Jeff Blake, Errict Rhett (Running Mates)	2.50
2	Dick Butkus, Steve Bono (TimeWarp)	2.50
3	Philadelphia Eagles (Candidates Rookie Redemption)	.50
4	Rashaan Salaam (New Regime)	1.00
5	Junior Seau (Base Brand)	.50
6	Michael Westbrook (Air Force One)	1.00

1996 Collector's Edge President's Reserve

1996 Collector's Edge President's Reserve Series I contains 200 cards. The cards replace the Excalibur series of the previous year. There were only 20,000 boxes made (1,000 cases). Boxes could be purchased by invitation only, with collectors being limited to one box and dealers to two. Consumers who were invited to purchase the product were to order through an authorized President's Reserve dealer, who displays a marker in his store shop window. The cards are plastic, with gold foil used for the brand name, player's name and card trimmings and borders. An action photo is set against a color square. The card back uses that square as a base for biographical and statistical information about the player, plus a mug shot. Insert sets include: Air Force One; New Regime; Tan, Rested and Ready (Pro Bowl '96); Running Mates; Time Warp; and Candidates rookie redemption cards. These cards have a team logo on the front, with the team's colors as a background. The insert set and President's Reserve logos are also on the front. The back has the rules, which indicate the card can be returned for a set of "long shot" cards of players signed by the corresponding team pictured on the front. These cards, included in every fourth pack, were limited to 6,000 each.

		MT
Complete Set (400):		110.00
Complete Series 1 (200):		60.00
Complete Series 2 (200):		50.00
Common Player:		.25
Minor Stars:		.50
Wax Box:		75.00
1	Larry Centers	.25
2	Frank Sanders	.50
3	Clyde Simmons	.25
4	Eric Swann	.25
5	Morten Andersen	.25
6	Lester Archambeau	.25
7	J.J. Birden	.25
8	Bert Emanuel	.50
9	Jumpy Geathers	.25
10	Jeff George	.50
11	Craig Heyward	.25
12	Bill Brooks	.25
13	Steve Christie	.25
14	Todd Collins	.50
15	Darick Holmes	.50
16	Andre Reed	.25
17	Bryce Paup	.25
18	Bruce Smith	.25
19	Blake Brockermeyer	.25
20	Mark Carrier	.25
21	Kerry Collins	.75
22	Darion Conner	.25
23	Eric Guliford	.25
24	Lamar Lathon	.25
25	Derrick Moore	.25
26	Frank Reich	.25
27	Kevin Butler	.25
28	Tony Carter	.25
29	Curtis Conway	.50
30	Robert Green	.25
31	Jay Leeuwenburg	.25
32	Alonzo Spellman	.25
33	Chris Zorich	.25
34	Eric Bieniemy	.25
35	Jeff Blake	2.00
36	Tony McGee	.25
37	Carl Pickens	.50
38	Rob Burnett	.25
39	Earnest Byner	.25
40	Michael Jackson	.25
41	Antonio Langham	.25
42	Anthony Pleasant	.25
43	Vinny Testaverde	.25
44	Troy Aikman	3.00
45	Larry Allen	.25
46	Bill Bates	.25
47	Chris Boniol	.25
48	Charles Haley	.25
49	Michael Irvin	.50
50	Robert Jones	.25
51	Leon Lett	.25
52	Russell Maryland	.25
53	Nate Newton	.25
54	Deion Sanders	2.00
55	Sherman Williams	.50
56	Darren Woodson	.25
57	Aaron Craver	.25
58	Terrell Davis	3.50
59	Jason Elam	.25
60	Simon Fletcher	.25
61	Anthony Miller	.25
62	Shannon Sharpe	.25
63	Tracy Scroggins	.25
64	Antonio London	.25
65	Scott Mitchell	.25
66	Johnnie Morton	.25
67	Barry Sanders	3.00
68	Edgar Bennett	.25
69	Mark Chmura	.25
70	Brett Favre	6.00
71	Mark Ingram	.25
72	Dorsey Levens	.50
73	Wayne Simmons	.25
74	Gary Brown	.25
75	Anthony Cook	.25
76	Al Del Greco	.25
77	Haywood Jeffires	.25
78	Steve McNair	3.00
79	Rodney Thomas	.50
80	Trev Alberts	.25
81	Quentin Coryatt	.25
82	Ken Dilger	.25
83	Jim Harbaugh	.25
84	Floyd Turner	.25
85	Lamont Warren	.25
86	Steve Beuerlein	.25
87	Mark Brunell	1.50
88	Eugene Chung	.25
89	Jeff Lageman	.25
90	Willie Jackson	.25
91	Kimble Anders	.25
92	Steve Bono	.50
93	Derrick Thomas	.25
94	Willie Davis	.25
95	Greg Hill	.25
96	Neil Smith	.25
97	Tamarick Vanover	.50
98	James Hasty	.25
99	Gary Clark	.25
100	Marco Coleman	.25
101	Steve Emtman	.25
102	Irving Fryar	.25
103	Randal Hill	.25
104	Terry Kirby	.25
105	Dan Marino	6.00
106	Cris Carter	.25
107	Jack Del Rio	.25
108	David Palmer	.25
109	Jake Reed	.25
110	Robert Smith	.25
111	Korey Stringer	.25
112	Orlanda Thomas	.25
113	Drew Bledsoe	3.00
114	Vincent Brisby	.25
115	Ted Johnson	.25
116	Curtis Martin	7.00
117	Chris Slade	.25
118	Jim Dombrowski	.25
119	Vaughn Dunbar	.25
120	Quinn Early	.25
121	Wesley Walls	.25
122	Wayne Martin	.25
123	Irv Smith	.25
124	Torrance Small	.25
125	Dave Brown	.25
126	Chris Calloway	.25
127	John Elliott	.25
128	Rodney Hampton	.25
129	Tyrone Wheatley	.50
130	Kyle Brady	.25
131	Hugh Douglas	.25
132	Todd Scott	.25
133	Adrian Murrell	.25
134	Wayne Chrebet	.25
135	Aundray Bruce	.25
136	Andrew Glover	.25
137	Daryl Hobbs	1.00
138	Napoleon Kaufman	.50
139	Chester McGlockton	.25
140	Rob Fredrickson	.25
141	Guy McIntyre	.25
142	Bobby Taylor	.25
143	Fred Barnett	.25
144	William Fuller	.25
145	Rodney Peete	.25
146	Daniel Stubbs	.25
147	Charlie Garner	.25
148	Myron Bell	.25
149	Rod Woodson	.25
150	Charles Johnson	.25
151	Ernie Mills	.25
152	Levon Kirkland	.25
153	Carnell Lake	.25
154	Kevin Greene	.25
155	Neil O'Donnell	.50
156	Erric Pegram	.25
157	Ray Seals	.25
158	Willie Williams	.25
159	Kordell Stewart	4.00
160	Yancey Thigpen	2.00
161	Darren Bennett	.25
162	Andre Coleman	.25
163	Aaron Hayden	1.00
164	Tony Martin	.25
165	Chris Mims	.25
166	Shawn Lee	.25
167	Junior Seau	.50
168	Merton Hanks	.25
169	Rickey Jackson	.25
170	Derek Loville	.25
171	Gary Plummer	.25
172	J.J. Stokes	.50
173	John Taylor	.25
174	Bryant Young	.25
175	Antonio Edwards	.25
176	Joey Galloway	.50
177	Carlton Gary	.25
178	Rick Mirer	.25
179	Winston Moss	.25
180	Jerome Bettis	.25
181	Troy Drayton	.25
182	Wayne Gandy	.25
183	Sean Gilbert	.25
184	Jessie Hester	.25
185	Sean Landeta	.25
186	Roman Phifer	.25
187	Alberto White	.25
188	Santana Dotson	.25
189	Jerry Ellison	.25
190	Jackie Harris	.25
191	Courtney Hawkins	.25
192	Horace Copeland	.25
193	Hardy Nickerson	.25
194	Warren Sapp	.25
195	Terry Allen	.25
196	Henry Ellard	.25
197	Gus Frerotte	.50
198	John Gesek	.25
199	Jim Lachey	.25
200	Brian Mitchell	.25
201	Garrison Hearst	.25
202	Dave Krieg	.25
203	Rob Moore	.25
204	Aeneas Williams	.25
205	Chris Doleman	.25
206	Terance Mathis	.25
207	Clay Matthews	.25
208	Eric Metcalf	.25
209	Jessie Tuggle	.25
210	Cornelius Bennett	.25
211	Ruben Brown	.25
212	Russell Copeland	.25
213	Phil Hansen	.25
214	Jim Kelly	.50
215	Don Beebe	.25
216	Willie Green	.25
217	Howard Griffith	.25
218	John Kasay	.25
219	Brett Maxie	.25
220	Tim McKyer	.25
221	Sam Mills	.25
222	Jim Flanigan	.25
223	Jeff Graham	.25
224	Erik Kramer	.25
225	Rashaan Salaam	.50
226	Steve Walsh	.25
227	Donnell Woolford	.25
228	Ki-Jana Carter	1.50
229	John Copeland	.25
230	Harold Green	.25
231	Doug Pelfrey	.25
232	Darney Scott	.25
233	Bracey Walker	.25
234	Dan Wilkinson	.25
235	Leroy Hoard	.25
236	Earnest Hunter	.25
237	Keenan McCardell	.25
238	Steven Moore	.25
239	Andre Rison	.25
240	Eric Zeier	.50
241	Larry Brown	.25
242	Shante Carver	.25
243	Chad Hennings	.25
244	John Jett	.25
245	Daryl Johnston	.25
246	Derek Kennard	.25
247	Brock Marion	.25
248	Jay Novacek	.25
249	Emmitt Smith	6.00
250	Tony Tolbert	.25
251	Mark Tuinei	.25
252	Erik Williams	.25
253	Kevin Williams	.25
254	John Elway	2.00
255	Ed McCaffrey	.25
256	Glyn Milburn	.25
257	Michael Dean Perry	.25
258	Mike Pritchard	.25
259	Willie Clay	.25
260	Jason Hanson	.25
261	Herman Moore	.75
262	Brett Perriman	.25
263	Lomas Brown	.25
264	Chris Spielman	.25
265	Henry Thomas	.25
266	Robert Brooks	.25
267	Sean Jones	.25
268	John Jurkovic	.25
269	Anthony Morgan	.25
270	Craig Newsome	.25
271	Reggie White	.25
272	Chris Chandler	.25
273	Mel Gray	.25
274	Darryll Lewis	.25
275	Bruce Matthews	.25
276	Todd McNair	.25
277	Chris Sanders	1.00
278	Mark Stepnoski	.25
279	Ashley Ambrose	.25
280	Tony Bennett	.25
281	Zack Crockett	.25
282	Sean Dawkins	.25
283	Marshall Faulk	3.00
284	Ronald Humphrey	.25
285	Tony Siragusa	.25
286	Roosevelt Potts	.25
287	Bryan Barker	.25
288	Tony Boselli	.25
289	Keith Goganious	.25
290	Desmond Howard	.25
291	Jeff Lageman	.25
292	Corey Mayfield	.25
293	James Stewart	.25
294	Cedric Tillman	.25
295	Marcus Allen	.50
296	Dale Carter	.25
297	Lake Dawson	.25
298	Darren Mickell	.25
299	Dan Saleaumua	.25
300	Webster Slaughter	.25
301	Keith Cash	.25
302	Bryan Cox	.25
303	Jeff Cross	.25
304	Eric Green	.25
305	O.J. McDuffie	.25
306	Bernie Parmalee	.25
307	Billy Milner	.25
308	Pete Stoyanovich	.25
309	Troy Vincent	.25
310	Qadry Ismail	.25
311	Amp Lee	.25
312	Warren Moon	.50
313	Scottie Graham	.25
314	John Randle	.25
315	Fuad Reveiz	.25
316	Broderick Thomas	.25
317	Ben Coates	.25
318	Willie McGinest	.25
319	David Meggett	.25
320	Will Moore	.25
321	Dave Wohlabaugh	.25
322	Mario Bates	.25
323	Jim Everett	.25
324	Tyrone Hughes	.25
325	William Roaf	.25
326	Renaldo Turnbull	.25
327	Michael Haynes	.25
328	Mike Sherrard	.25
329	Michael Strahan	.25
330	Herschel Walker	.25
331	Charles Wilson	.25
332	Otis Smith	.25
333	Mo Lewis	.25
334	Marvin Washington	.25
335	Tim Brown	.25
336	Greg Skrepenak	.25
337	Kevin Gogan	.25
338	Jeff Hostetler	.25
339	Terry McDaniel	.25
340	Anthony Smith	.25
341	Pat Swilling	.25
342	Harvey Williams	.25
343	Tom Hutton	.25
344	Mike Mamula	.25
345	Randall Cunningham	.25
346	Ricky Watters	.25
347	Andy Harmon	.25
348	William Thomas	.25
349	Calvin Williams	.25
350	Mark Breunner	.25
351	Dermotne Dawson	.25
352	Greg Lloyd	.25
353	Norm Johnson	.25
354	Bam Morris	.25
355	Thomas Newberry	.25
356	Darren Perry	.25
357	Rohn Stark	.25
358	Joel Steed	.25
359	Brenden Stal	.25
360	Justin Strzelczyk	.25
361	Leon Searcy	.25
362	Chad Brown	.25
363	John Carney	.25
364	Rodney Culver	.25
365	Ronnie Harmon	.25
366	Stan Humphries	.25
367	Leslie O'Neal	.25
368	Natrone Means	.75
369	Mark Seay	.25
370	William Floyd	.25
371	Brent Jones	.25
372	Tim McDonald	.25
373	Ken Norton Jr.	.25
374	Jerry Rice	3.00
375	Dana Stubblefield	.25
376	Steve Young	3.00
377	Brian Blades	.25
378	Cortez Kennedy	.25
379	Michael Sinclair	.25
380	Lamar Smith	.25
381	Chris Warren	.50
382	Johnny Bailey	.25
383	Isaac Bruce	.50
384	Kevin Carter	.25
385	Shane Conlan	.25
386	D'Marco Farr	.25
387	Todd Kinchen	.25
388	Chris Miller	.25
389	Lonnie Marts	.25
390	Trent Dilfer	.25
391	Alvin Harper	.25
392	John Lynch	.25
393	Errict Rhett	.50
394	Darnell Stephens	.25
395	Ken Harvey	.25
396	Eddie Murray	.25
397	Heath Shuler	1.50
398	Matt Turk	.25
399	Michael Westbrook	1.00
400	James Washington	.25

1996 Collector's Edge President's Reserve Air Force One

These 18 cards, randomly inserted into 1996 Collector's Edge President's Reserve packs, feature top wide receivers and quarterbacks in the NFL. Cards were seeded one per 16 packs. The card front has a color action photo, with the set icon at the bottom. The player's team logo is in the upper left corner, with the team name running down the side. The player's name is in the upper right corner. The back has a color action photo, plus a color panel on one side which includes the player's name, team logo, biographical information, a card number and recap of the player's achievements. There were only 2,500 of each card made.

		MT
Complete Set (36):		300.00
Complete Series 1 (18):		150.00
Complete Series 2 (18):		150.00
Common Player:		3.00
Jumbo Cards:		1.5x
1	Brett Favre	30.00
2	Neil O'Donnell	3.00
3	Steve Young	15.00
4	Dan Marino	30.00
5	Kerry Collins	6.00
6	Scott Mitchell	3.00
7	Deion Sanders	15.00
8	Cris Carter	3.00
9	Tim Brown	3.00
10	Joey Galloway	15.00
11	Robert Brooks	3.00
12	Tony Martin	3.00
13	Michael Westbrook	6.00
14	Eric Metcalf	3.00
15	Vincent Brisby	3.00
16	Anthony Miller	3.00
17	J.J. Stokes	6.00
18	Kordell Stewart	15.00
19	Troy Aikman	15.00
20	Drew Bledsoe	15.00
21	Jeff Blake	10.00
22	John Elway	12.00
23	Jim Harbaugh	3.00
24	Erik Kramer	3.00
25	Herman Moore	6.00
26	Carl Pickens	3.00
27	Michael Irvin	6.00
28	Jerry Rice	15.00
29	Isaac Bruce	3.00
30	Yancey Thigpen	6.00
31	Brett Perriman	3.00
32	Ben Coates	3.00
33	Jay Novacek	3.00
34	Tamarick Vanover	3.00
35	Terrell Davis	25.00
36	Jeff Graham	3.00

Values quoted in this guide reflect the retail price of a card — the price a collector can expect to pay when buying a card from a dealer. The wholesale price — that which a collector can expect to receive from a dealer when selling cards — will be significantly lower, depending on desirability and condition.

1996 Collector's Edge P.R. Candidates Top Picks

This 30-card set was available through the mail in exchange for team logo cards, which were inserted one per four President's Reserve Series II packs. Overall, 6,000 of each card was produced. According to the company, eight of these 30 cards were completed in time to be inserted directly into packs, including Simeon Rice, Tim Biakabutuka, Jonathan Ogden, John Mobley, Eddie George, Keyshawn Johnson, Daryl Gardener and Kevin Hardy. The card fronts feature the rookie on draft day holding his new team jersey, while the backs feature the rookie in college action and information about the draft pick.

		MT
Complete Set (30):		100.00
Common Player:		2.00
Minor Stars:		4.00
1	Simeon Rice	4.00
2	Shannon Brown	2.00
3	Willie Anderson	2.00
4	Tim Biakabutuka	4.00
5	Eric Moulds	4.00
6	Kavika Pittman	2.00
7	Jonathan Ogden	2.00
8	Reggie Brown	2.00
9	John Mobley	2.00
10	John Michels	2.00
11	Walt Harris	2.00
12	Eddie George	10.00
13	Marvin Harrison	6.00
14	Kevin Hardy	2.00
15	Jerome Woods	2.00
16	Duane Clemons	2.00
17	Daryl Gardener	2.00
18	Terry Glenn	8.00
19	Alex Molden	2.00
20	Cedric Jones	2.00
21	Rickey Dudley	4.00
22	Keyshawn Johnson	5.00
23	Jermaine Mayberry	2.00
24	Jermain Stephens	2.00
25	Lawrence Phillips	4.00
26	Bryan Still	2.00
27	Isreal Ifeanyi	2.00
28	Pete Kendall	2.00
29	Regan Upshaw	2.00
30	Andre Johnson	2.00

1996 Collector's Edge P.R. Candidates Long Shots

This 30-card set was available through the mail in exchange for redemption cards which were inserted one per four packs in President's Reserve Series I. According to the company, 6,000 of each card was produced. The cards feature an action shot of the rookie in the NFL, while the backs feature the rookie in college action and information about the draft pick.

		MT
Complete Set (30):		75.00
Common Player:		2.00
Minor Stars:		4.00
1	Leeland McElroy	4.00
2	Richard Huntley	4.00
3	Ray Lewis	2.00
4	Sean Moran	2.00
5	Muhsin Muhammad	4.00
6	Bobby Engram	4.00
7	Marco Battaglia	2.00
8	Stepfret Williams	2.00
9	Jeff Lewis	4.00
10	Ryan Stewart	2.00
11	Derrick Mayes	4.00
12	Terry Killens	2.00
13	Scott Slutzker	2.00
14	Reggie Barlow	2.00
15	Joe Horn	2.00
16	Karim Abdul-Jabbar	5.00
17	Moe Williams	2.00
18	Kantroy Barber	2.00
19	Je'Rod Cherry	2.00
20	Amani Toomer	4.00
21	Alex Van Dyke	4.00
22	Tim Hall	2.00
23	Bobby Hoying	5.00
24	Jahine Arnold	2.00
25	Tony Banks	5.00
26	Freddie Bradley	2.00
27	Stephen Pitts	2.00
28	Reggie Brown	2.00
29	Mike Alstott	6.00
30	Stephen Davis	4.00

1996 Collector's Edge President's Reserve New Regime

These 1996 Collector's Edge President's Reserve cards were seeded one per every five packs. There were 12,000 cards produced for each of the 12 players in the set. The card front is die-cut around the words "New Regime," which appear along the left side of the card. The player's name, position, team name and set logo appear on the right, with a ghosted closeup shot of the player in the background. A set icon is stamped in gold foil in the lower right corner. An action photo is in the center of the card. The card back has a closeup shot of the player, with 1995 and career stats under it. To the right is biographical information, a brief player profile, plus the limited-edition number of 12,000.

		MT
Complete Set (24):		60.00
Complete Series 1 (12):		30.00
Complete Series 2 (12):		30.00
Common Player:		1.00
Minor Stars:		2.00
1	Tamarick Vanover	2.00
2	Kerry Collins	4.00
3	J.J. Stokes	2.00
4	Napoleon Kaufman	2.00
5	Steve McNair	6.00
6	Todd Collins	1.00
7	Frank Sanders	2.00
8	Warren Sapp	1.00
9	Tony Boselli	1.00
10	Curtis Martin	6.00
11	Ki-Jana Carter	2.00
12	Zack Crockett	1.00
13	Joey Galloway	3.00
14	Terrell Davis	10.00
15	Chris Sanders	2.00
16	Rashaan Salaam	2.00
17	Michael Westbrook	2.00
18	Hugh Douglas	1.00
19	Eric Zeier	1.00
20	Kordell Stewart	8.00
21	Ted Johnson	1.00
22	Ken Dilger	1.00
23	Derrick Holmes	2.00
24	Wayne Chrebet	1.00

1996 Collector's Edge President's Reserve Honor Guard

This set was a bonus redemption from President's Reserve. Collectors could redeem wrappers from a Jumbo Running Mates card and receive one Honor Guard card as a bonus. Each Honor Guard card is numbered one of 1,000 with an "HG" prefix.

1996 Collector's Edge President's Reserve Running Mates

These double-sided inserts feature two teammates per card. Cards, limited to 2,000 each, were randomly inserted into every 33rd pack of 1996 Collector's Edge President's Reserve. The cards match up a top NFL quarterback with a top running back from his team on the opposite side.

		MT
Complete Set (24):		400.00
Complete Series 1 (12):		200.00
Complete Series 2 (12):		200.00
Common Player:		8.00
Minor Stars:		16.00
1	Troy Aikman, Emmitt Smith	45.00
2	Jim Harbaugh, Marshall Faulk	16.00
3	John Elway, Terrell Davis	60.00
4	Stan Humphries, Natrone Means	16.00
5	Erik Kramer, Rashaan Salaam	8.00
6	Chris Miller, Jerome Bettis	16.00
7	Trent Dilfer, Errict Rhett	16.00
8	Jeff George, Craig Heyward	8.00
9	Gus Frerotte, Terry Allen	8.00
10	Drew Bledsoe, Curtis Martin	30.00
11	Jeff Blake, Ki-Jana Carter	16.00
12	Rick Mirer, Chris Warren	8.00
13	Brett Favre, Edgar Bennett	50.00
14	Neil O'Donnell, Bam Morris	8.00
15	Scott Mitchell, Barry Sanders	50.00
16	Steve Young, Derek Loville	25.00
17	Warren Moon, Robert Smith	8.00
18	Heath Shuler, Brian Mitchell	8.00
19	Rodney Peete, Ricky Watters	8.00
20	Kerry Collins, Derrick Moore	25.00
21	Dan Marino, Terry Kirby	50.00

		MT
Complete Set (30):		75.00
Common Player:		2.00
1	Troy Aikman	5.00
2	Michael Irvin	3.00
3	Emmitt Smith	10.00
4	Brett Favre	12.00
5	Steve Young	4.00
6	Tim Brown	2.50
7	Errict Rhett	2.50
8	Curtis Martin	5.00
9	Carl Pickens	3.00
10	Herman Moore	3.00
11	Robert Brooks	2.00
12	Michael Westbrook	2.00
13	Leon Lett	2.00
14	Russell Maryland	2.00
15	Eric Swann	2.00
16	John Elway	4.00
17	Barry Sanders	5.00
18	Dan Marino	10.00
19	Drew Bledsoe	5.00
20	Jerry Rice	5.00
21	Deion Sanders	3.50
22	Rashaan Salaam	2.00
23	Marshall Faulk	2.50
24	Napoleon Kaufman	2.00
25	Ki-Jana Carter	2.00
26	Cris Carter	2.00
27	Joey Galloway	3.00
28	Eric Metcalf	2.00
29	Derrick Thomas	2.00
30	Bruce Smith	2.00

		MT
Complete Set (30):		75.00
Common Player:		2.00
22	Steve Bono, Marcus Allen	16.00
23	Jim Kelly, Darick Holmes	16.00
24	Kordell Stewart, Eric Pegram	40.00

1996 Collector's Edge President's Reserve Pro Bowl '96

These cards feature participants in the 1996 Pro Bowl. Cards were seeded one per eight packs of 1996 Collector's Edge President's Reserve packs. The metallic card front has palm trees in the background, with the player in the center wearing his Pro Bowl uniform. The President's Reserve logo is stamped in gold at the bottom of the card. The player's name is written in a rectangle at the bottom which is flanked on each side by the appropriate football conference logo. The back has biographical information and a brief player profile on the left side, with 1995 and career stats below. A player close-up shot is on the right, along with the limited-edition number (1 of 7,500).

		MT
Complete Set (24):		100.00
Complete Series 1 (12):		50.00
Complete Series 2 (12):		50.00
Common Player:		2.00
1	Jeff Blake	5.00
2	Jim Harbaugh	2.00
3	Brett Favre	16.00
4	Steve Young	6.00
5	Emmitt Smith	16.00
6	Ricky Watters	2.00
7	Michael Irvin	2.00
8	Carl Pickens	2.00
9	Tim Brown	2.00
10	Anthony Miller	2.00
11	Darren Bennett	2.00
12	Yancey Thigpen	4.00
13	Bryce Paup	2.00
14	Warren Moon	2.00
15	Barry Sanders	8.00
16	Herman Moore	4.00
17	Cris Carter	2.00
18	Chris Warren	4.00
19	Marshall Faulk	6.00
20	Curtis Martin	12.00
21	Ben Coates	2.00
22	Brent Jones	2.00
23	Shannon Sharpe	2.00
24	Brian Mitchell	2.00
25	Ken Harvey	2.00

1996 Collector's Edge President's Reserve TimeWarp

These cards feature a former NFL star matched up

against a current NFL star, whose picture is superimposed into an action scene of the former star. The matchups are different from those produced last year. These cards were inserted one every 64th 1996 Collector's Edge President's Reserve pack and were limited in production to 2,000 each.

		MT
Complete Set (12):		300.00
Complete Series 1 (6):		150.00
Complete Series 2 (6):		150.00
Common Player:		8.00
1	Jack Kemp, Greg Lloyd	8.00
2	Sonny Jurgensen, Marshall Faulk	8.00
3	Fran Tarkenton, Bryce Paup	8.00
4	Roger Staubach, Emmitt Smith	50.00
5	Jack Lambert, Curtis Martin	25.00
6	Jack Youngblood, Brett Favre	60.00
7	Fran Tarkenton, Reggie White	8.00
8	Art Donovan, Steve Bono	8.00
9	Bobby Mitchell, Troy Aikman	25.00
10	Larry Csonka, Kordell Stewart	40.00
11	Dick Butkus, Deion Sanders	20.00
12	Deacon Jones, Dan Marino	50.00

1997 Collector's Edge Excalibur

The 150-card base set appears in two versions. The base set includes a space-motif Excalibur dragon in the top corner, with the tail filling the bottom right of the card. The premium parallel set featured a gold-foil stamped dragon. The backs have the player's headshot on the left over an outer space background. An Excalibur medallion is pictured in the upper right, along with the card number, player's name and bio. His stats appear in six sword blades near the bottom of the card back.

		MT
Complete Set (150):		30.00
Common Player:		.10
Minor Stars:		.20
Wax Box:		85.00
1	Larry Centers	.10
2	Leeland McElroy	.20
3	Simeon Rice	.20
4	Eric Swann	.10
5	Jamal Anderson	.30
6	Bert Emanuel	.10
7	Eric Metcalf	.10
8	Ray Lewis	.10
9	Derrick Alexander	.10
10	Michael Jackson	.10
11	Vinny Testaverde	.10
12	Todd Collins	.20
13	Jim Kelly	.20
14	Eric Moulds	.20
15	Andre Reed	.10
16	Bruce Smith	.20
17	Thurman Thomas	.20
18	Tim Biakabutuka	.20
19	Kerry Collins	.30
20	Kevin Greene	.10
21	Anthony Johnson	.10
22	Lamar Lathon	.10
23	Muhsin Muhammad	.10
24	Curtis Conway	.20
25	Bryan Cox	.10
26	Walt Harris	.10
27	Erik Kramer	.10
28	Rick Mirer	.10
29	Rashaan Salaam	.20
30	Jeff Blake	.30
31	Ki-Jana Carter	.20
32	Carl Pickens	.20
33	Troy Aikman	1.50
34	Michael Irvin	.20
35	Daryl Johnston	.10
36	Emmitt Smith	2.50
37	Broderick Thomas	.10
38	Terrell Davis	1.50
39	John Elway	1.00
40	Anthony Miller	.10
41	John Mobley	.10
42	Shannon Sharpe	.10
43	Neil Smith	.10
44	Scott Mitchell	.10
45	Herman Moore	.30
46	Brett Perriman	.10
47	Barry Sanders	4.00
48	Edgar Bennett	.10
49	Robert Brooks	.20
50	Brett Favre	3.00
51	Antonio Freeman	.30
52	Dorsey Levens	.20
53	Reggie White	.20
54	Eddie George	1.75
55	Darryll Lewis	.10
56	Steve McNair	1.25
57	Chris Sanders	.10
58	Marshall Faulk	.10
59	Jim Harbaugh	.10
60	Marvin Harrison	.75
61	Jimmy Smith	.10
62	Tony Brackens	.10
63	Mark Brunell	1.50
64	Kevin Hardy	.10
65	Keenan McCardell	.10
66	Natrone Means	.20
67	Marcus Allen	.20
68	Elvis Grbac	.10
69	Derrick Thomas	.10
70	Tamarick Vanover	.10
71	Karim Abdul-Jabbar	.30
72	Terrell Buckley	.10
73	Irving Fryar	.10
74	Dan Marino	2.50
75	O.J. McDuffie	.10
76	Zach Thomas	.50
77	Terry Kirby	.10
78	Cris Carter	.20
79	Brad Johnson	.10
80	John Randle	.10
81	Jake Reed	.10
82	Robert Smith	.10
83	Drew Bledsoe	1.50
84	Ben Coates	.10
85	Terry Glenn	.30
86	Ty Law	.10
87	Curtis Martin	1.50
88	Willie McGinest	.10
89	Mario Bates	.10
90	Jim Everett	.10
91	Wayne Martin	.10
92	Heath Shuler	.10
93	Torrance Small	.10
94	Ray Zellars	.10
95	Dave Brown	.10
96	Jason Sehorn	.10
97	Amani Toomer	.10
98	Tyrone Wheatley	.10
99	Hugh Douglas	.10
100	Aaron Glenn	.10
101	Jeff Graham	.10
102	Keyshawn Johnson	.75
103	Adrian Murrell	.10
104	Neil O'Donnell	.10
105	Tim Brown	.10
106	Jeff George	.10
107	Jeff Hostetler	.10
108	Napoleon Kaufman	.20
109	Chester McGlockton	.10
110	Fred Barnett	.10
111	Ty Detmer	.10
112	Chris T. Jones	.10
113	Ricky Watters	.20
114	Bobby Engram	.20
115	Jerome Bettis	.20
116	Charles Johnson	.10
117	Greg Lloyd	.10
118	Kordell Stewart	1.50
119	Yancey Thigpen	.10
120	Rod Woodson	.10
121	Stan Humphries	.10
122	Tony Martin	.10
123	Leonard Russell	.10
124	Junior Seau	.10
125	Chad Brown	.10
126	John Friesz	.10
127	Joey Galloway	.40
128	Cortez Kennedy	.10
129	Warren Moon	.10
130	Chris Warren	.10
131	Garrison Hearst	.10
132	Terrell Owens	1.00
133	Jerry Rice	1.50
134	Dana Stubblefield	.10
135	Bryant Young	.10
136	Steve Young	1.00
137	Tony Banks	.75
138	Isaac Bruce	.30
139	Eddie Kennison	.75
140	Keith Lyle	.10
141	Lawrence Phillips	.20
142	Mike Alstott	.75
143	Hardy Nickerson	.10
144	Errict Rhett	.10
145	Warren Sapp	.10
146	Gus Frerotte	.10
147	Sean Gilbert	.10

148	Ken Harvey	.10
149	Terry Allen	.10
150	Michael Westbrook	.20

1997 Collector's Edge Excalibur 22K Knights

The 25-card set includes a player photo superimposed over a foil background on the card front. The player's name is printed in gold foil at the top, while the "Excalibur 22k" logo is printed at the bottom center. The backs have the player's name printed vertically along the left border of the card. The player's head shot appears in the center, with his bio in the lower right. Edge produced 2,000 of each card. The cards were inserted 1:20 packs. A 22k Black Magnum Knights parallel version, which includes a prism logo printed above the Excalibur 22k logo on the card front, was inserted 1:75 packs in super premium boxes.

		MT
Complete Set (25):		200.00
Common Player:		2.50
Magnum Cards:		2x-3x
Supreme Edge Cards:		5x
Production 50 Sets		
1	Troy Aikman	15.00
2	John Elway	12.00
3	Brett Favre	30.00
4	Dan Marino	25.00
5	Barry Sanders	30.00
6	Emmitt Smith	25.00
7	Mark Brunell	15.00
8	Jerry Rice	15.00
9	Terrell Davis	15.00
10	Natrone Means	2.50
11	Joey Galloway	5.00
12	Keyshawn Johnson	2.50
13	Curtis Martin	10.00
14	Herman Moore	2.50
15	Eddie George	15.00
16	Terry Glenn	5.00
17	Steve McNair	8.00
18	Marshall Faulk	2.50
19	Ricky Watters	2.50
20	Karim Abdul-Jabbar	5.00
21	Gus Frerotte	2.50
22	Terry Allen	2.50
23	Andre Reed	2.50
24	Jerome Bettis	2.50
25	Tim Brown	2.50

1997 Collector's Edge Excalibur Crusaders

The 25 acetate die-cut cards have the player's photo superimposed over a chess piece background on the front. The Edge logo is printed in the upper left, with an Excalibur sword printed in the background on the right side. The

player's name is printed inside a gold-foil "plaque" at the bottom of the front. The chess piece is printed in purple in the background. The backs are a reverse of the front, with the card number inside a diamond in the upper right. The card's individual number is printed at the bottom center. Edge produced 750 of each card.

		MT
Complete Set (25):		250.00
Common Player:		5.00
1	Brett Favre	50.00
2	Mark Brunell	25.00
3	Jim Kelly	10.00
4	Michael Westbrook	5.00
5	Emmitt Smith	40.00
6	Marshall Faulk	5.00
7	Kerry Collins	10.00
8	Jeff Hostetler	5.00
9	Rashaan Salaam	5.00
10	Garrison Hearst	5.00
11	Tamarick Vanover	5.00
12	Rodney Hampton	5.00
13	Leeland McElroy	5.00
14	Tony Banks	15.00
15	Deion Sanders	15.00
16	Errict Rhett	5.00
17	Thurman Thomas	10.00
18	Chris Warren	5.00
19	Andre Reed	5.00
20	Napoleon Kaufman	10.00
21	Terry Allen	5.00
22	Carl Pickens	5.00
23	Marvin Harrison	10.00
24	Lawrence Phillips	5.00
25	Troy Aikman	25.00

1997 Collector's Edge Excalibur Game Gear

The 19 Game Gear chase cards are hard to miss, as they are as thick as six base cards. The fronts include a photo of the player along with a circular piece of the player's game-used helmet. Edge produced 500 of each card, which were inserted one per 60 packs. Autographed Game Gear cards were inserted one per 350 packs.

		MT
Complete Set (25):		900.00
Common Player:		12.00
1	Brett Favre	100.00
2	Mark Brunell	50.00
3	Barry Sanders	120.00
4	John Elway	40.00
5	Emmitt Smith	90.00
6	Drew Bledsoe	50.00
7	Troy Aikman	50.00
8	Dan Marino	90.00
9	Eddie George	60.00
10	Terry Glenn	25.00
11	Keyshawn Johnson	30.00
12	Terrell Davis	50.00
13	Curtis Martin	50.00
14	Steve McNair	40.00
15	Muhsin Muhammad	12.00
16	Antonio Freeman	20.00
17	Ricky Watters	12.00
18	Jerome Bettis	12.00
19	Herman Moore	12.00
20	Isaac Bruce	20.00
21	Deion Sanders	25.00
22	Cris Carter	12.00
23	Tim Biakabutuka	12.00
24	Karim Abdul-Jabbar	25.00
25	Mike Alstott	12.00

1997 Collector's Edge Excalibur Gridiron Sorcerers

Featuring the top 25 players from the 1997 draft, these

chase cards include a photo superimposed over a purple background filled with lightning. "1997 NFL Draft" is printed at the top of the front, with the player's team helmet printed at the top center. His name appears across the bottom of the front. The backs have the team name at the top, with the logo in the background on the left. The card number is in the top right. The player's name and bio is printed in the lower left, with his photo appearing on the right center. The card's individual number is printed at the bottom right. Edge produced 1,000 of each card.

		MT
Complete Set (25):		125.00
Common Player:		2.00
1	Orlando Pace	2.00
2	Peter Boulware	2.00
3	Darrell Russell	2.00
4	Shawn Springs	2.00
5	Yatil Green	5.00
6	Jim Druckenmiller	7.00
7	Bryant Westbrook	2.00
8	Dwayne Rudd	2.00
9	David LaFleur	5.00
10	Rae Carruth	5.00
11	Corey Dillon	10.00
12	Antowain Smith	8.00
13	Tiki Barber	7.00
14	Marcus Harris	2.00
15	Warrick Dunn	15.00
16	Chris Canty	2.00
17	Tony Gonzalez	5.00
18	Danny Wuerffel	5.00
19	Ike Hilliard	5.00
20	James Farrior	2.00
21	Reidel Anthony	6.00
22	Jake Plummer	15.00
23	Troy Davis	5.00
24	Pat Barnes	5.00
25	Darnell Autry	5.00

1997 Collector's Edge Excalibur Gridiron Wizards

Similar to the Gridiron Sorcerers, this 25-card set included the top players from the 1997 draft. Like the Sorcerers cards, the Wizard cards were inserted one per 20 packs, the only difference being the Wizard cards were seeded in super premium boxes and the Sorcerers cards were inserted in premium packs.

		MT
Complete Set (25):		140.00
Common Player:		2.50
1	Orlando Pace	5.00
2	Peter Boulware	2.50
3	Darrell Russell	2.50
4	Shawn Springs	5.00
5	Yatil Green	5.00
6	Jim Druckenmiller	10.00
7	Bryant Westbrook	2.50
8	Dwayne Rudd	2.50
9	David LaFleur	5.00
10	Rae Carruth	6.00
11	Corey Dillon	12.00
12	Antowain Smith	8.00
13	Tiki Barber	6.00
14	Marcus Harris	2.50
15	Warrick Dunn	12.00
16	Chris Canty	2.50
17	Tony Gonzalez	5.00
18	Danny Wuerffel	5.00
19	Ike Hilliard	6.00
20	James Farrior	2.50
21	Reidel Anthony	6.00
22	Jake Plummer	15.00
23	Troy Davis	5.00
24	Pat Barnes	5.00
25	Darnell Autry	5.00

1997 Collector's Edge Excalibur Marauders

The 25-card set featured 50 players, as two appeared on each double-front card. The player's photo is superimposed over a blue lenticular background, which featured vertical black lines moving from side-to-side. The team's logo appears in the upper left inside a shield, while the team name and his position are printed in gold foil in the upper right. The player's last name is printed inside a gold-foil stripe in the upper right. The appropriate logos appear in the lower left, while "Marauders" and the card number are printed in the lower right in dark blue. The cards were inserted in one of 20 super premium packs.

		MT
Complete Set (25):		200.00
Common Player:		3.00
Supreme Edge Cards:		5x
Production 50 Sets		
1	Antonio Freeman, Tony Banks	8.00
2	Heath Shuler, Tim Biakabutuka	3.00
3	Brett Favre, Eddie Kennison	30.00
4	Marcus Allen, Todd Collins	3.00
5	Dan Marino, Shannon Sharpe	25.00
6	Desmond Howard, Napoleon Kaufman	6.00
7	Dorsey Levens, Muhsin Muhammad	3.00
8	Drew Bledsoe, Mike Alstott	15.00
9	Emmitt Smith, Michael Westbrook	25.00
10	Heath Shuler, Marvin Harrison	3.00
11	Jeff Blake, Marshall Faulk	3.00
12	Jeff George, Lawrence Phillips	3.00
13	Tony Martin, Edgar Bennett	3.00
14	Jerry Rice, Karim Abdul-Jabbar	15.00
15	Jim Harbaugh, Terrell Owens	6.00
16	John Elway, Isaac Bruce	15.00
17	Dave Brown, Eric Metcalf	3.00
18	Junior Seau, Eddie Kennison	6.00
19	Mark Brunell, Eddie George	15.00
20	Cris Carter, Deion Sanders	6.00
21	Steve Young, Eric Moulds	10.00
22	Ben Coates, Chris Warren	3.00
23	Robert Brooks, Carl Pickens	3.00
24	Tim Brown, Bobby Engram	3.00
25	Troy Aikman, Ben Coates	15.00

Post-1980 cards in Near Mint condition will generally sell for about 75% of the quoted Mint value. Excellent-condition cards bring no more than 40%.

1997 Collector's Edge Excalibur Overlords

The 25-card set, which is printed on acetate, features a die-cut design in the shape of a dragon. The player's photo is superimposed over a orange and red dragon in the background on the front. The player's last name is printed in large capital letters at the bottom, with his first name printed in white in small letters. The team's logo is printed to the left of the player's name on the front. The backs have the player's headshot in the left center, with the team logo, his name and bio to the right of the photo. The top and bottom of the back have a brick design. The card's individual number appears at the bottom right. Edge produced 750 of each card.

		MT
Complete Set (25):		225.00
Common Player:		4.00
Minor Stars:		8.00
Inserted 1:30		
Production 750 Sets		
Castle Cards:		1x
Production 750 Sets		
1	Jeff Blake	4.00
2	Mark Brunell	25.00
3	Bobby Engram	4.00
4	Joey Galloway	8.00
5	Eddie Kennison	4.00
6	Terrell Davis	40.00
7	Joey Galloway	8.00
8	Hardy Nickerson	4.00
9	Errict Rhett	4.00
10	Emmitt Smith	35.00
11	Kordell Stewart	20.00
12	Steve Young	15.00
13	Marcus Allen	8.00
14	Edgar Bennett	4.00
15	Robert Brooks	4.00
16	Kerry Collins	8.00
17	Todd Collins	4.00
18	Brett Favre	50.00
19	Gus Frerotte	4.00
20	Elvis Grbac	4.00
21	Jeff Hostetler	4.00
22	Tony Martin	4.00
23	Terrell Owens	15.00
24	Dorsey Levens	8.00
25	Thurman Thomas	8.00

1997 Collector's Edge Extreme

Extreme includes a 180-card base set. Three different parallel sets were made. Extreme Base Parallel 1 (1:2) parallels 108 base cards with a flat silver foil stamp. Extreme Base Parallel II (1:12) adds a gold foil stamp to 36 base cards redone on a silver card. Base Parallel III (1:36) parallels the other 36 base cards with a diamond

etched foil stamp on a silver, die-cut card. The inserts include Force, Finesse, Fury, Forerunners and Gamegear Quads.

		MT
Complete Set (180):		30.00
Common Player:		.10
Minor Stars:		.20
1	Larry Centers	.10
2	Leeland McElroy	.10
3	*Jake Plummer*	4.00
4	Simeon Rice	.10
5	Eric Swann	.10
6	Jamal Anderson	.20
7	Bert Emanuel	.10
8	*Byron Hanspard*	.75
9	Derrick Alexander	.10
10	Peter Boulware	.10
11	Michael Jackson	.10
12	Ray Lewis	.10
13	Vinny Testaverde	.10
14	Todd Collins	.10
15	Eric Moulds	.10
16	Bryce Paup	.10
17	Andre Reed	.10
18	Bruce Smith	.10
19	*Antowain Smith*	1.25
20	Chris Spielman	.10
21	Thurman Thomas	.20
22	Tim Biakabutuka	.10
23	*Rae Carruth*	.75
24	Kerry Collins	.30
25	Anthony Johnson	.10
26	Lamar Lathon	.10
27	Muhsin Muhammad	.10
28	*Darnell Autry*	.50
29	Curtis Conway	.20
30	Bryan Cox	.10
31	Bobby Engram	.10
32	Walt Harris	.10
33	Erik Kramer	.10
34	Rashaan Salaam	.10
35	Jeff Blake	.20
36	Ki-Jana Carter	.10
37	*Corey Dillon*	1.50
38	Carl Pickens	.20
39	Troy Aikman	1.00
40	Dexter Coakley	.10
41	Michael Irvin	.20
42	Daryl Johnston	.10
43	*David LaFleur*	.50
44	Anthony Miller	.10
45	Deion Sanders	.50
46	Emmitt Smith	2.00
47	Broderick Thomas	.10
48	Terrell Davis	1.00
49	John Elway	.75
50	John Mobley	.10
51	Shannon Sharpe	.10
52	Neil Smith	.10
53	Checklist	.10
54	Scott Mitchell	.10
55	Herman Moore	.20
56	Barry Sanders	1.25
57	Edgar Bennett	.10
58	Robert Brooks	.20
59	Mark Chmura	.20
60	Brett Favre	2.25
61	Antonio Freeman	.20
62	Dorsey Levens	.20
63	Reggie White	.20
64	Eddie George	1.50
65	Darryll Lewis	.10
66	Steve McNair	.75
67	Chris Sanders	.10
68	Marshall Faulk	.20
69	Jim Harbaugh	.20
70	Marvin Harrison	.20
71	Tony Brackens	.10
72	Mark Brunell	1.00
73	Kevin Hardy	.10
74	Rob Johnson	.20
75	Keenan McCardell	.10
76	Natrone Means	.20
77	Jimmy Smith	.10
78	Marcus Allen	.20
79	Pat Barnes	.50
80	*Tony Gonzalez*	1.00
81	Elvis Grbac	.10
82	Brett Perriman	.10
83	Andre Rison	.20
84	Derrick Thomas	.10
85	Tamarick Vanover	.10
86	Karim Abdul-Jabbar	.50
87	Fred Barnett	.10
88	Terrell Buckley	.10
89	*Yatil Green*	.40
90	Dan Marino	2.00
91	O.J. McDuffie	.10
92	Jason Taylor	.10
93	Zach Thomas	.20
94	Cris Carter	.10
95	Brad Johnson	.20
96	John Randle	.10
97	Jake Reed	.10
98	Robert Smith	.10
99	Drew Bledsoe	1.00
100	Chris Canty	.10
101	Ben Coates	.20
102	Terry Glenn	.30
103	Ty Law	.10
104	Curtis Martin	1.00
105	Willie McGinest	.10
106	*Troy Davis*	.30
107	Wayne Martin	.10
108	Heath Shuler	.10
109	*Danny Wuerffel*	.75

110	Ray Zellars	.10
111	*Tiki Barber*	1.00
112	Dave Brown	.10
113	Checklist	.10
114	*Ike Hilliard*	.75
115	Jason Sehorn	.10
116	Amani Toomer	.10
117	Tyrone Wheatley	.10
118	Hugh Douglas	.10
119	Aaron Glenn	.10
120	Jeff Graham	.10
121	Keyshawn Johnson	.20
122	Adrian Murrell	.20
123	Neil O'Donnell	.10
124	Tim Brown	.10
125	Jeff George	.10
126	Desmond Howard	.10
127	Napoleon Kaufman	.20
128	Chester McGlockton	.10
129	Darrell Russell	.10
130	Ty Detmer	.10
131	Irving Fryar	.10
132	Chris T. Jones	.10
133	Ricky Watters	.20
134	Jerome Bettis	.20
135	Charles Johnson	.10
136	George Jones	.10
137	Greg Lloyd	.10
138	Kordell Stewart	.75
139	Yancey Thigpen	.10
140	Jim Everett	.10
141	Stan Humphries	.10
142	Tony Martin	.10
143	Eric Metcalf	.10
144	Junior Seau	.10
145	*Jim Druckenmiller*	1.50
146	Kevin Greene	.10
147	Garrison Hearst	.10
148	Terry Kirby	.10
149	Terrell Owens	.50
150	Jerry Rice	1.00
151	Dana Stubblefield	.10
152	Rod Woodson	.10
153	Bryant Young	.10
154	Steve Young	.50
155	Chad Brown	.10
156	John Friesz	.10
157	Joey Galloway	.20
158	Cortez Kennedy	.10
159	Warren Moon	.10
160	*Shawn Springs*	.20
161	Chris Warren	.10
162	Tony Banks	.50
163	Isaac Bruce	.20
164	Eddie Kennison	.20
165	Keith Lyle	.10
166	*Orlando Pace*	.20
167	Lawrence Phillips	.10
168	Checklist	.10
169	Mike Alstott	.50
170	*Reidel Anthony*	1.00
171	*Warrick Dunn*	1.75
172	Hardy Nickerson	.10
173	Errict Rhett	.10
174	Warren Sapp	.10
175	Terry Allen	.10
176	Gus Frerotte	.10
177	Sean Gilbert	.10
178	Ken Harvey	.10
179	Jeff Hostetler	.10
180	Michael Westbrook	.10

1997 Collector's Edge Extreme Foil

Collector's Edge ran three parallel sets to its Extreme set. The first parallel simply included a silver foil stripe up the left side and contained all 180 cards with an insert rate of one per two packs. The second parallel contained only 36 of the cards and featured a gold and silver strip on the left side, with the rest of the card done with a silver finish. These gold parallels are inserted every 12 packs. The third parallel level included a gold, silver and blue foil strip up the left side and was die-cut around the entire perimeter. The card fronts also featured a silver finish, with the cards inserted one per 36 packs. All three lev-

els were numbered on the back with a "P" prefix.

	MT
Silver Cards:	2x
Gold Cards:	2x-4x
Die-Cut Stars:	8x-16x
Die-Cut Rookies:	4x-8x

1997 Collector's Edge Extreme Finesse

This 19-card insert is done on frosted, clear, foil-stamped cards. The cards were inserted 1:60 packs of Extreme.

		MT
Complete Set (25):		400.00
Common Player:		5.00
Minor Stars:		10.00
1	Troy Aikman	30.00
2	Marcus Allen	10.00
3	Ben Coates	5.00
4	Tony Banks	10.00
5	Jeff Blake	10.00
6	Tim Brown	5.00
7	Mark Brunell	30.00
8	Todd Collins	5.00
9	Terrell Davis	30.00
10	Jim Druckenmiller	20.00
11	John Elway	25.00
12	Marshall Faulk	10.00
13	Brett Favre	60.00
14	Antonio Freeman	10.00
15	Joey Galloway	10.00
16	Eddie George	40.00
17	Terry Glenn	15.00
18	Marvin Harrison	10.00
19	Garrison Hearst	5.00
20	Warrick Dunn	35.00
21	Muhsin Muhammad	5.00
22	Jerry Rice	30.00
23	Barry Sanders	40.00
24	Emmitt Smith	55.00
25	Shawn Springs	5.00

1997 Collector's Edge Extreme Force

Force features 26 players on silver cards with flow etched designs. Force was inserted 1:8 packs of Extreme.

		MT
Complete Set (25):		75.00
Common Player:		.50
Minor Stars:		1.00
1	Marcus Allen	1.00
2	Chris Canty	.50
3	Jerome Bettis	1.00
4	Carl Pickens	.50
5	Drew Bledsoe	6.00
6	Robert Brooks	1.00
7	Shannon Sharpe	.50
8	Tim Brown	.50
9	Mark Brunell	6.00
10	Ben Coates	.50
11	Todd Collins	.50
12	Terrell Davis	6.00
13	John Elway	4.00
14	Brett Favre	12.00

15	Antonio Freeman	1.00
16	Joey Galloway	1.00
17	Warrick Dunn	6.00
18	Terry Glenn	3.00
19	Marvin Harrison	1.00
20	Dan Marino	10.00
21	Jerry Rice	6.00
22	Junior Seau	.50
23	Tony Banks	3.00
24	Emmitt Smith	10.00
25	Napoleon Kaufman	1.00

1997 Collector's Edge Extreme Forerunners

This 25-card redemption subset was made on clear two-way view cards with a large head shot on the back visible from the front. Gold foil was also added to the cards. The cards were available by redemption through instant win cards, of which 250 were made.

		MT
Complete Set (25):		300.00
Common Player:		5.00
Minor Stars:		10.00
1	Karim Abdul-Jabbar	10.00
2	Marcus Allen	5.00
3	Jerome Bettis	10.00
4	Drew Bledsoe	20.00
5	Robert Brooks	5.00
6	Mark Brunell	20.00
7	Todd Collins	5.00
8	Terrell Davis	20.00
9	John Elway	15.00
10	Brett Favre	45.00
11	Joey Galloway	5.00
12	Eddie George	30.00
13	Terry Glenn	12.00
14	Marvin Harrison	10.00
15	Keyshawn Johnson	10.00
16	Rob Johnson	5.00
17	Eddie Kennison	10.00
18	Dorsey Levens	10.00
19	Dan Marino	40.00
20	Steve McNair	15.00
21	Terrell Owens	10.00
22	Carl Pickens	5.00
23	Jerry Rice	20.00
24	Emmitt Smith	40.00
25	Kordell Stewart	20.00

1997 Collector's Edge Extreme Fury

Fury is an 18-card insert with top players featured on a Deep Metal card with chromium finish. Fury was inserted 1:48 packs of Extreme.

		MT
Complete Set (18):		200.00
Common Player:		3.00
Minor Stars:		6.00
1	Jerome Bettis	6.00
2	Terry Glenn	12.00
3	Drew Bledsoe	20.00
4	Mark Brunell	20.00
5	Terrell Davis	20.00
6	Troy Davis	6.00
7	Marshall Faulk	6.00
8	Brett Favre	40.00
9	Antonio Freeman	6.00
10	Joey Galloway	6.00
11	Eddie George	30.00
12	Eddie Kennison	6.00
13	Errict Rhett	3.00
14	Rashaan Salaam	3.00
15	Emmitt Smith	35.00
16	Kordell Stewart	20.00
17	Danny Wuerffel	6.00
18	Steve Young	15.00

A card number in parentheses ( ) indicates the set is unnumbered.

1997 Collector's Edge Masters

The 270 standard-sized cards include 240 player cards and 30 team flag cards. The fronts have a player photo superimposed over a background of etched foil that is in a "burst" design. The player's last name is printed in gold at the top center, while the Edge Masters' logo is located at the bottom center and printed in gold. The card backs have the player's headshot in the upper left, with the card number in the upper right. The player's name and bio runs vertically along the right side of the back. The stats are printed horizontally inside stripes along the left side of the back. All of the information is printed over a teal ghosted image of a Wilson football.

		MT
Complete Set (270):		25.00
Common Player:		.05
Minor Stars:		.10
Wax Box:		70.00
1	Arizona Cardinals	.05
2	Larry Centers	.05
3	Rob Moore	.05
4	Frank Sanders	.05
5	Eric Swann	.05
6	Atlanta Falcons	.05
7	Morten Andersen	.05
8	Bert Emanuel	.05
9	Jeff George	.05
10	Craig Heyward	.05
11	Terance Mathis	.05
12	Clay Matthews	.05
13	Eric Metcalf	.05
14	Baltimore Ravens	.05
15	Rob Burnett	.05
16	Leroy Hoard	.05
17	Earnest Hunter	.05
18	Michael Jackson	.05
19	Stevon Moore	.05
20	Anthony Pleasant	.05
21	Vinny Testaverde	.05
22	Eric Zeier	.05
23	Buffalo Bills	.05
24	Todd Collins	.05
25	Russell Copeland	.05
26	Quinn Early	.05
27	Jim Kelly	.10
28	Bryce Paup	.05
29	Andre Reed	.05
30	Bruce Smith	.05
31	Carolina Panthers	.05
32	Steve Beuerlein	.05
33	Mark Carrier	.05
34	Kerry Collins	.30
35	Willie Green	.05
36	Kevin Greene	.05
37	Eric Guliford	.05
38	Brett Maxie	.05
39	Tim McKyer	.05
40	Derrick Moore	.05
41	Chicago Bears	.05
42	Curtis Conway	.05
43	Bryan Cox	.05
44	Jim Flanigan	.05
45	Robert Green	.05
46	Erik Kramer	.05
47	Dave Krieg	.05
48	Rashaan Salaam	.10
49	Alonzo Spellman	.05
50	Donnell Woolford	.05
51	Chris Zorich	.05
52	Cincinnati Bengals	.05
53	Eric Bieniemy	.05
54	Jeff Blake	.20
55	Ki-Jana Carter	.05
56	John Copeland	.05
57	Garrison Hearst	.05
58	Tony McGee	.05
59	Carl Pickens	.05
60	Darnay Scott	.05
61	Bracey Walker	.05
62	Dan Wilkinson	.05
63	Dallas Cowboys	.05
64	Troy Aikman	1.00
65	Bill Bates	.05

66	Shante Carver	.05
67	Michael Irvin	.10
68	Daryl Johnston	.05
69	Jay Novacek	.05
70	Deion Sanders	.50
71	Emmitt Smith	2.00
72	Herschel Walker	.05
73	Sherman Williams	.05
74	Denver Broncos	.05
75	Terrell Davis	1.50
76	John Elway	.75
77	Ed McCaffrey	.05
78	Anthony Miller	.05
79	Michael Dean Perry	.05
80	Shannon Sharpe	.05
81	Mike Sherrard	.05
82	Detroit Lions	.05
83	Scott Mitchell	.05
84	Glyn Milburn	.05
85	Herman Moore	.20
86	Johnnie Morton	.05
87	Brett Perriman	.05
88	Barry Sanders	2.00
89	Tracy Scroggins	.05
90	Green Bay Packers	.05
91	Edgar Bennett	.05
92	Robert Brooks	.05
93	Santana Dotson	.05
94	Brett Favre	2.00
95	Dorsey Levens	.10
96	Craig Newsome	.05
97	Wayne Simmons	.05
98	Reggie White	.10
99	Houston Oilers	.05
100	Chris Chandler	.05
101	Anthony Cook	.05
102	Willie Davis	.05
103	Mel Gray	.05
104	Ronnie Harmon	.05
105	Darryll Lewis	.05
106	Steve McNair	1.00
107	Todd McNair	.05
108	Rodney Thomas	.05
109	Indianapolis Colts	.05
110	Trev Alberts	.05
111	Tony Bennett	.05
112	Quentin Coryatt	.05
113	Sean Dawkins	.05
114	Ken Dilger	.05
115	Marshall Faulk	.25
116	Jim Harbaugh	.05
117	Ronald Humphrey	.05
118	Floyd Turner	.05
119	Jacksonville Jaguars	.05
120	Tony Boselli	.05
121	Mark Brunell	1.00
122	Willie Jackson	.05
123	Jeff Lageman	.05
124	Natrone Means	.05
125	Andre Rison	.05
126	James Stewart	.05
127	Cedric Tillman	.05
128	Kansas City Chiefs	.05
129	Marcus Allen	.10
130	Kimble Anders	.05
131	Steve Bono	.05
132	Dale Carter	.05
133	Lake Dawson	.05
134	Dan Salesaumua	.05
135	Neil Smith	.05
136	Derrick Thomas	.05
137	Tamarick Vanover	.15
138	Miami Dolphins	.05
139	Fred Barnett	.05
140	Steve Emtman	.05
141	Eric Green	.05
142	Dan Marino	2.00
143	O.J. McDuffie	.05
144	Bernie Parmalee	.05
145	Minnesota Vikings	.05
146	Cris Carter	.05
147	Jack Del Rio	.05
148	Qadry Ismail	.05
149	Amp Lee	.05
150	Warren Moon	.05
151	John Randle	.05
152	Jake Reed	.05
153	Robert Smith	.05
154	New England Patriots	.05
155	Drew Bledsoe	1.00
156	Vincent Brisby	.05
157	Willie Clay	.05
158	Ben Coates	.05
159	Curtis Martin	1.50
160	Dave Meggett	.05
161	Will Moore	.05
162	Chris Slade	.05
163	New Orleans Saints	.05
164	Mario Bates	.05
165	Jim Everett	.05
166	Michael Haynes	.05
167	Tyrone Hughes	.05
168	Haywood Jeffires	.05
169	Wayne Martin	.05
170	Renaldo Turnbull	.05
171	New York Giants	.05
172	Dave Brown	.05
173	Chris Calloway	.05
174	Rodney Hampton	.05
175	Michael Strahan	.05
176	Tyrone Wheatley	.05
177	New York Jets	.05
178	Kyle Brady	.05
179	Wayne Chrebet	.05
180	Hugh Douglas	.05
181	Jeff Graham	.05

182	Adrian Murrell	.05
183	Neil O'Donnell	.05
184	Oakland Raiders	.05
185	Tim Brown	.05
186	Aundray Bruce	.05
187	Andrew Glover	.05
188	Jeff Hostetler	.05
189	Napoleon Kaufman	.05
190	Terry McDaniel	.05
191	Chester McGlockton	.05
192	Pat Swilling	.05
193	Harvey Williams	.05
194	Philadelphia Eagles	.05
195	Randall Cunningham	.05
196	Irving Fryar	.05
197	William Fuller	.05
198	Charlie Garner	.05
199	Andy Harmon	.05
200	Rodney Peete	.05
201	Mark Seay	.05
202	Troy Vincent	.05
203	Ricky Watters	.10
204	Calvin Williams	.05
205	Pittsburgh Steelers	.05
206	Jerome Bettis	.10
207	Chad Brown	.05
208	Greg Lloyd	.05
209	Bam Morris	.05
210	Erric Pegram	.05
211	Kordell Stewart	1.00
212	Yancey Thigpen	.05
213	Rod Woodson	.05
214	San Diego Chargers	.05
215	Darren Bennett	.05
216	Marco Coleman	.05
217	Stan Humphries	.05
218	Tony Martin	.05
219	Junior Seau	.05
220	San Francisco 49ers	.05
221	Chris Doleman	.05
222	William Floyd	.05
223	Merton Hanks	.05
224	Brent Jones	.05
225	Terry Kirby	.05
226	Derek Loville	.05
227	Ken Norton Jr.	.05
228	Gary Plummer	.05
229	Jerry Rice	1.00
230	J.J. Stokes	.10
231	Dana Stubblefield	.05
232	John Taylor	.05
233	Bryant Young	.05
234	Steve Young	.75
235	Seattle Seahawks	.05
236	Brian Blades	.05
237	Joey Galloway	.30
238	Carlton Gray	.05
239	Cortez Kennedy	.05
240	Rick Mirer	.05
241	Chris Warren	.05
242	St. Louis Rams	.05
243	Isaac Bruce	.20
244	Troy Drayton	.05
245	D'Marco Farr	.05
246	Harold Green	.05
247	Chris Miller	.05
248	Leslie O'Neal	.05
249	Roman Phifer	.05
250	Tampa Bay Buccaneers	.05
251	Trent Dilfer	.10
252	Alvin Harper	.05
253	Jackie Harris	.05
254	John Lynch	.05
255	Hardy Nickerson	.05
256	Errict Rhett	.20
257	Warren Sapp	.05
258	Todd Scott	.05
259	Charles Wilson	.05
260	Washington Redskins	.05
261	Terry Allen	.05
262	Bill Brooks	.05
263	Henry Ellard	.05
264	Gus Frerotte	.05
265	Sean Gilbert	.05
266	Ken Harvey	.05
267	Brian Mitchell	.05
268	Heath Shuler	.05
269	James Washington	.05
270	Michael Westbrook	.10

1997 Collector's Edge Masters '96 Rookies

Inserted in retail packs, this

chase set included a color photo of the player in the top center of the front. The photo is surrounded by holographic foil, with the Rookie Year '96 logo printed in the upper right. Printed at the bottom of the front is "'96 Rookies." The player's name is printed in yellow at the top center of the card. The backs have the player's name printed in yellow in the top center, followed by the team logo, his bio and stats. The card number is printed in the upper right. Each card is serial numbered, which is located along the left of the back. All the information on the back is printed over a ghosted image of a football player. Overall, 2,000 of each card was produced by Edge.

		MT
Complete Set (25):		45.00
Common Player:		1.00
1	Simeon Rice	1.00
2	Jonathan Ogden	1.00
3	Eric Moulds	2.00
4	Tim Biakabutuka	3.00
5	Walt Harris	1.00
6	John Mobley	1.00
7	Reggie Brown	1.00
8	Derrick Mayes	1.00
9	Eddie George	10.00
10	Marvin Harrison	4.00
11	Kevin Hardy	1.00
12	Jerome Woods	1.00
13	Karim Abdul-Jabbar	7.00
14	Duane Clemons	1.00
15	Terry Glenn	8.00
16	Rickey Whittle	1.00
17	Amani Toomer	1.00
18	Keyshawn Johnson	5.00
19	Rickey Dudley	1.00
20	Bobby Hoying	1.00
21	Eddie Kennison	4.00
22	Bryan Still	1.00
23	Terrell Owens	6.00
24	Reggie Brown	1.00
25	Mike Alstott	2.00

1997 Collector's Edge Masters Crucibles

Inserted one per six hobby packs, the chase set includes a color photo of the player on the right. The left side of the front is printed in holographic foil, with a "rolled over" effect in the center. The player's name and position are in the upper left, while the team logo is in the center left and the team name printed directly underneath. "Crucibles" is printed in large capital letters along the bottom front, with "1997 NFL Draft" in red over "Crucibles." The backs have the player's write-up along the left and right, with his name, team helmet and bio printed in the center over a ghosted gray background. The card's serial number is printed in the lower right. Edge produced 3,000 of each card in the chase set.

		MT
Complete Set (25):		75.00
Common Player:		1.50
Minor Stars:		3.00
1	Jake Plummer	3.00
2	Byron Harnspard	4.00
3	Peter Boulware	1.50
4	Jay Graham	1.50
5	Antowain Smith	5.00
6	Rae Carruth	4.00
7	Darnell Autry	3.00
8	Corey Dillion	5.00
9	Bryant Westbrook	3.00
10	Joey Kent	3.00
11	Kevin Lockett	3.00
12	Pat Barnes	3.00
13	Tony Gonzalez	3.00
14	Yatil Green	3.00
15	Danny Wuerffel	6.00
16	Troy Davis	3.00
17	Tiki Barber	6.00
18	Ike Hilliard	6.00
19	Darrell Russell	1.50
20	Leon Johnson	1.50
21	Jim Druckenmiller	7.00
22	Shawn Springs	3.00
23	Orlando Pace	3.00
24	Warrick Dunn	10.00
25	Reidel Anthony	6.00

1997 Collector's Edge Masters Night Games

Inserted one per 20 packs, the 25-card chase set features a color photo of the player superimposed over a black and brown computer-generated background. The player's name is printed in gold foil at the top, while the Night Games' logo is printed at the bottom center. The backs have the player's name running vertically along the left. The player's bio runs vertically along the right border. The card number is in the upper right. A color photo of the player is located at the bottom center printed over a colored ghosted image of the player. The card's serial number is printed in the lower right. Edge produced 1,500 of each card in the chase set. A Prism parallel set was inserted 1:60 packs. Edge produced 250 of each Prism card.

		MT
Complete Set (25):		175.00
Common Player:		2.00
1	Terry Glenn	8.00
2	Eddie George	10.00
3	Ricky Watters	2.00
4	Barry Sanders	20.00
5	Curtis Martin	15.00
6	Brett Favre	20.00
7	Emmitt Smith	20.00
8	John Elway	8.00
9	Keyshawn Johnson	4.00
10	Kordell Stewart	8.00
11	Drew Bledsoe	10.00
12	Kerry Collins	5.00
13	Terrell Davis	15.00
14	Karim Abdul-Jabbar	7.00
15	Jerome Bettis	2.00
16	Antonio Freeman	2.00
17	Dorsey Levens	2.00
18	Herman Moore	2.00
19	Jerry Rice	10.00
20	Mark Brunell	10.00
21	Mike Alstott	2.00
22	Napoleon Kaufman	2.00
23	Terry Allen	2.00
24	Tony Banks	2.00
25	Vinny Testaverde	2.00

1997 Collector's Edge Masters Nitro-Hobby

This chase set was split between hobby and retail packs. The fronts resemble the base cards with a player photo superimposed over an etched-foil background. The player's name is printed in gold at the top, while a gold-foil burst is printed at bottom of the card and includes the Nitro logo and the player's outstanding stat. The backs are identical to the base cards.

		MT
Complete Set (18):		20.00
Common Player:		.75
2	Larry Centers	.75
24	Todd Collins	.75
34	Kerry Collins	1.25
59	Carl Pickens	.75
71	Emmitt Smith	5.00
76	John Elway	1.50
88	Barry Sanders	6.00
116	Jim Harbaugh	.75
121	Mark Brunell	2.50
137	Tamarick Vanover	.75
159	Curtis Martin	3.50
189	Napoleon Kaufman	.75
206	Jerome Bettis	1.00
211	Kordell Stewart	2.00
229	Jerry Rice	2.50
237	Joey Galloway	1.25
243	Isaac Bruce	1.25
264	Gus Frerotte	.75

1997 Collector's Edge Masters Nitro-Retail

This chase set was split between hobby and retail packs. The fronts are identical to the base cards, except for a gold-foil burst at the bottom of the card front. The Nitro logo and outstanding player stats are printed inside the burst. The backs are identical to the base cards.

		MT
Complete Set (18):		20.00
Common Player:		.75
18	Michael Jackson	.75
30	Bruce Smith	.75
36	Kevin Green	.75
64	Troy Aikman	2.50
75	Terrell Davis	3.50
85	Herman Moore	1.25
94	Brett Favre	5.00
98	Reggie White	1.00
106	Steve McNair	2.50
126	Derrick Thomas	.75
142	Dan Marino	5.00
155	Drew Bledsoe	2.50
167	Tyrone Huges	.75
203	Ricky Watters	.75
207	Chad Brown	.75
218	Tony Martin	.75
234	Steve Young	1.50
261	Terry Allen	.75

1997 Collector's Edge Masters Playoff Game Ball

Inserted one per 72 packs, the 19-card set features two player photos on the front. The horizontal cards have a gold-foil background at the top, with the NFC or AFC logo in the top center. The two teams which matched up in the playoff game are printed in black over the logo. A piece of a game-used ball from the contest is embedded into the card in the bottom center. The bottom half of the card front has a Wilson football background. The player's names are printed over their respective photos in the lower corners of the front. The backs have a photo of each of the players, their names, game summary, score and date. All of the information is printed over a football background. Edge produced 250 of each of the cards in the chase set.

		MT
Complete Set (19):		1000.
Common Player:		15.00
1	Natrone Means, Thurman Thomas	15.00
2	Tony Boselli, Bruce Smith	15.00
3	Jerome Bettis, Marshall Faulk	15.00
4	Kordell Stewart, Jim Harbaugh	35.00
5	Natrone Means, Terrell Davis	50.00
6	Mark Brunell, John Elway	80.00
7	Curtis Martin, Jerome Bettis	50.00
8	Drew Bledsoe, Mark Brunell	100.00
9	Terry Glenn, Keenan McCardell	45.00
10	Troy Aikman, Brad Johnson	40.00
11	Steve Young, Ty Detmer	15.00
12	Jerry Rice, Irving Fryer	60.00
13	Dorsey Levens, Terry Kirby	15.00
14	Brett Favre, Steve Young	110.00
15	Andre Rison, Jerry Rice	60.00
16	Reggie White, Ken Norton Jr.	15.00
17	Kerry Collins, Troy Aikman	70.00
18	Kerry Collins, Brett Favre	120.00
19	Kevin Green, Reggie White	15.00

1997 Collector's Edge Masters Radical Rivals

The 12-card set features two players on each card, one on each side. A player photo is superimposed over a background of the two players' teams' helmets. The player's name and team are printed at the top in gold, while "Radical Rivals" and the card number are printed vertically along the left. The card's serial number is printed along the left border on one side of the card. Edge produced 1,000 of each card. The cards were inserted one per 30 hobby packs.

		MT
Complete Set (12):		130.00
Common Player:		2.00
1	Emmitt Smith, Eddie George	25.00
2	Brett Favre, Kerry Collins	25.00
3	Jerry Rice, Antonio Freeman	12.00
4	Ricky Watters, Napoleon Kaufman	2.00
5	Herman Moore, Keyshawn Johnson	6.00
6	Dan Marino, John Elway	25.00
7	Jerome Bettis, Karim Abdul-Jabbar	10.00
8	Isaac Bruce, Carl Pickens	2.00
9	Barry Sanders, Terry Allen	25.00
10	Terry Glenn, Joey Galloway	10.00
11	Mark Brunell, Steve Young	12.00
12	Terrell Davis, Curtis Martin	18.00

> Post-1980 cards in Near Mint condition will generally sell for about 75% of the quoted Mint value. Excellent-condition cards bring no more than 40%.

1997 Collector's Edge Masters Ripped

This retail-only chase set continues where the 1996 Ripped set left off, beginning with No. 19. The card fronts have the "Ripped" logo in the upper left, with the player's name printed vertically in black along the lower left border. A color photo of the player is superimposed over a background of red and blue prism-effect foil. The Edge logo is in the lower right of the front. The backs have the card number in gold in the upper right, with a quote about the player from Dick Butkus printed at the top. The player's head shot is printed in the right center, with the team's helmet and player's name, team, position and number printed to the left.

		MT
Complete Set (18):		150.00
Common Player:		3.00
19	Troy Aikman	15.00
20	Drew Bledsoe	15.00
21	Tim Brown	3.00
22	Mark Brunell	15.00
23	Cris Carter	6.00
24	Kerry Collins	5.00
25	Barry Sanders	20.00
26	Michael Irvin	3.00
27	Jeff Hostetler	3.00
28	Curtis Martin	20.00
29	Carl Pickens	3.00
30	Marshall Faulk	6.00
31	Rashaan Salaam	6.00
32	Deion Sanders	8.00
33	Emmitt Smith	30.00
34	Kordell Stewart	10.00
35	Ricky Watters	3.00
36	Steve Young	10.00

1997 Collector's Edge Masters Super Bowl XXXI Game Ball

Included with each card in this chase set was a circular piece of a game-used football from Super Bowl XXXI. Featured on the fronts are photos of one New England player and one Green Bay player (one on each side of the front). The Super Bowl XXXI logo appears in the top center in gold foil. The football piece is embedded in the card in the lower center of the front. The players' names are printed in the bottom corners. The Superdome is printed in the background of the lower part of the front. The backs have the player photos over the Super Bowl logo on the left. On the right over gold foil are the players' names, game score, date, game summary and team logos. Edge produced 250 of each card. One card was inserted per 350 packs.

		MT
Complete Set (6):		475.00
Common Player:		30.00
1	Brett Favre, Drew Bledsoe	300.00
2	Dorsey Levens, Curtis Martin	125.00
3	Desmond Howard, Dave Meggett	30.00
4	Antonio Freeman, Terry Glenn	100.00
5	Keith Jackson, Ben Coates	30.00
6	Reggie White, Willie McGinest	30.00

1998 Collector's Edge Advantage

Edge Advantage was a 180-card set that included three different parallel sets and five insert sets. The base cards contain the words "Advantage '98" written in script across the top, with the player's name, team logo and position in the bottom left corner. An action shot of the player is on the left part of the card with a close-up head shot on the right side, with all of this over another closer shot of the player in the background. Advantage also has a silver parallel (one per two packs) that has the front in a silver foil, a gold parallel (one per six) that has the front printed on gold foil and a 50-point stock parallel (one per pack) with the words "Advantage '98" printed in gold foil. Advantage Football included five insert sets: Livin' Large, Memorable Moments, Personal Victory, Prime Connection and Showtime.

		MT
Complete Set (200):		90.00
Common Player:		.25
Minor Stars:		.50
Wax Box:		85.00
1	Larry Centers	.25
2	Kent Graham	.25
3	LaShon Johnson	.25
4	Leeland McElroy	.25
5	Jake Plummer	2.50
6	Jamal Anderson	.50
7	Chris Chandler	.25
8	Bert Emanuel	.25
9	Byron Hanspard	.50
10	O.J. Santiago	.25
11	Derrick Alexander	.25
12	Peter Boulware	.25
13	Eric Green	.25
14	Michael Jackson	.25
15	Bam Morris	.25
16	Vinny Testaverde	.25
17	Todd Collins	.25
18	Quinn Early	.25
19	Jim Kelly	.50
20	Andre Reed	.25
21	Antowain Smith	1.75
22	Steve Tasker	.25
23	Thurman Thomas	.50
24	Steve Beuerlein	.25
25	Rae Carruth	.50
26	Kerry Collins	.25
27	Anthony Johnson	.25
28	Ernie Mills	.25
29	Wesley Walls	.25
30	Curtis Conway	.50
31	Bobby Engram	.25
32	Raymont Harris	.25
33	Erik Kramer	.25
34	Rick Mirer	.25
35	Darnay Scott	.25
36	Tony McGee	.25

37	Jeff Blake	.50
38	Corey Dillon	2.00
39	Carl Pickens	.25
40	Troy Aikman	2.50
41	Billy Davis	.25
42	David LaFleur	.50
43	Anthony Miller	.25
44	Emmitt Smith	4.00
45	Herschel Walker	.25
46	Sherman Williams	.25
47	Flipper Anderson	.25
48	Terrell Davis	2.50
49	Jason Elam	.25
50	John Elway	2.00
51	Darrien Gordon	.25
52	Ed McCaffrey	.25
53	Shannon Sharpe	.25
54	Neil Smith	.25
55	Rod Smith	.25
56	Maa Tanuvasa	.25
57	Glyn Milburn	.25
58	Scott Mitchell	.25
59	Herman Moore	.50
60	Johnnie Morton	.25
61	Barry Sanders	3.00
62	Tommy Vardell	.25
63	Bryant Westbrook	.25
64	Robert Brooks	.25
65	Mark Chmura	.50
66	Brett Favre	5.00
67	Antonio Freeman	.50
68	Dorsey Levens	.50
69	*Bill Schroeder*	4.00
70	Marshall Faulk	.50
71	Jim Harbaugh	.25
72	Marvin Harrison	.50
73	Derek Brown	.25
74	Mark Brunell	2.00
75	Rob Johnson	.50
76	Keenan McCardell	.50
77	Natrone Means	.50
78	Jimmy Smith	.25
79	James Stewart	.25
80	Marcus Allen	.50
81	Pat Barnes	.50
82	Tony Gonzalez	.50
83	Elvis Grbac	.25
84	Greg Hill	.25
85	Kevin Lockett	.25
86	Andre Rison	.25
87	Karim Abdul-Jabbar	.50
88	Fred Barnett	.25
89	Troy Drayton	.25
90	Dan Marino	4.00
91	Irving Spikes	.25
92	Cris Carter	.25
93	Matthew Hatchette	.25
94	Brad Johnson	.50
95	Jake Reed	.25
96	Robert Smith	.25
97	Drew Bledsoe	2.50
98	Keith Byars	.25
99	Ben Coates	.25
100	Terry Glenn	1.00
101	Shawn Jefferson	.25
102	Curtis Martin	2.00
103	Dave Meggett	.25
104	Troy Davis	.50
105	Danny Wuerffel	.25
106	Ray Zellers	.25
107	Tiki Barber	1.25
108	Rodney Hampton	.25
109	Ike Hilliard	.50
110	Danny Kanell	.25
111	Tyrone Wheatley	.25
112	Kyle Brady	.25
113	Wayne Chrebet	.25
114	Aaron Glenn	.25
115	Jeff Graham	.25
116	Keyshawn Johnson	.50
117	Adrian Murrell	.25
118	Neil O'Donnell	.25
119	Heath Shuler	.25
120	Tim Brown	.50
121	Rickey Dudley	.25
122	Jeff George	.25
123	Desmond Howard	.25
124	James Jett	.25
125	Napoleon Kaufman	.50
126	Chad Levitt	.25
127	Darrell Russell	.25
128	Ty Detmer	.25
129	Irving Fryar	.25
130	Charlie Garner	.25
131	Kevin Turner	.25
132	Ricky Watters	.50
133	Jerome Bettis	.50
134	Will Blackwell	.25
135	Mark Bruener	.25
136	Charles Johnson	.25
137	George Jones	.25
138	Kordell Stewart	2.50
139	Yancey Thigpen	.25
140	Gary Brown	.25
141	Jim Everett	.25
142	Terrell Fletcher	.25
143	Stan Humphries	.25
144	Freddie Jones	.25
145	Tony Martin	.25
146	Jim Druckenmiller	1.50
147	Garrison Hearst	.25
148	Brent Jones	.25
149	Terrell Owens	.50
150	Jerry Rice	2.50
151	J.J. Stokes	.25
152	Steve Young	1.50
153	Steve Broussard	.25
154	Joey Galloway	.50
155	Jon Kitna	.50
156	Warren Moon	.50
157	Shawn Springs	.25
158	Chris Warren	.25
159	Tony Banks	.50
160	Isaac Bruce	.50
161	Eddie Kennison	.50
162	Orlando Pace	.25
163	Lawrence Phillips	.25
164	Mike Alstott	.50
165	Reidel Anthony	1.25
166	Horace Copeland	.25
167	Trent Dilfer	.50
168	Warrick Dunn	3.00
169	Hardy Nickerson	.25
170	Karl Williams	.25
171	Eddie George	2.50
172	Ronnie Harmon	.25
173	Joey Kent	.25
174	Steve McNair	2.00
175	Chris Sanders	.25
176	Terry Allen	.25
177	Jamie Asher	.25
178	Stephen Davis	.25
179	Gus Frerotte	.25
180	Leslie Shepherd	.25
181	*Victor Reilly*	.50
182	*Curtis Enis*	2.00
183	*Brian Griese*	3.50
184	*Eric Brown*	.50
185	*Jacquez Green*	1.50
186	*Andre Wadsworth*	.75
187	*Ryan Leaf*	1.50
188	*Rashaan Shehee*	.75
189	*Peyton Manning*	8.00
190	*Flozell Adams*	.50
191	*Fred Taylor*	5.00
192	*Charlie Batch*	3.00
193	*Kevin Dyson*	1.50
194	*Charles Woodson*	2.00
195	*Ahman Green*	.75
196	*Randy Moss*	10.00
197	*Robert Edwards*	.75
198	*Reidel Anthony*	1.00
199	*Jerome Pathon*	.75
200	*Samari Rolle*	.50

1998 Collector's Edge Advantage Gold

The 180-card Advantage base set has a lacquered gold parallel version. The cards were inserted one per six packs.

	MT
Gold Cards:	5x

1998 Collector's Edge Advantage 50-Point

This parallel of the 180-card Advantage base set was printed on 50-point card stock and seeded one per pack.

	MT
50-Point Cards:	3x

1998 Collector's Edge Advantage Silver

A parallel of the 180-card Advantage base set was printed on embossed silver stock and inserted 1:2.

	MT
Silver Cards:	4x

1998 Collector's Edge Advantage Livin' Large

Livin' Large was a 22-card insert that was printed on plastic with a die-cut out of the top of the card. Inserted every 12 packs, these inserts featured a head shot of the player, with a football over his head with the insert name inside. The player's name, position and team logo was printed across the bottom, with the background colors related to that team. Holofoil versions of each card were also printed with a stated print run of 100 sets.

		MT
Complete Set (22):		150.00
Common Player:		2.00
Minor Stars:		4.00
Holofoil Cards:		5x-10x
1	Leeland McElroy	2.00
2	Jamal Anderson	4.00
3	Antowain Smith	8.00
4	Emmitt Smith	20.00
5	John Elway	12.00
6	Barry Sanders	20.00
7	Elvis Grbac	2.00
8	Dan Marino	20.00
9	Cris Carter	2.00
10	Drew Bledsoe	12.00
11	Curtis Martin	12.00
12	Troy Davis	4.00
13	Ike Hilliard	4.00
14	Adrian Murrell	2.00
15	Tim Brown	2.00
16	Kordell Stewart	12.00
17	Jerry Rice	12.00
18	Tony Banks	4.00
19	Mike Alstott	5.00
20	Trent Dilfer	4.00
21	Eddie George	12.00
22	Steve McNair	8.00

Values quoted in this guide reflect the retail price of a card — the price a collector can expect to pay when buying a card from a dealer. The wholesale price — that which a collector can expect to receive from a dealer when selling cards — will be significantly lower, depending on desirability and condition.

1998 Collector's Edge Advantage Personal Victory

This six-card set was also individually numbered to 200 on the back and contained a piece of a game-used ball on the front. The front has three shots of the player - one on each side of a large gold foil "V" and another inside the "V." The player's name is stamped across the bottom, with the piece of game ball above it with the words "Personal Victory" over the game ball. A dull finish is used on the back of the card along with a shot of the game in which the featured player achieved his personal victory.

		MT
Complete Set (6):		800.00
Common Player:		150.00
1	John Elway	200.00
2	Barry Sanders	300.00
3	Brett Favre	400.00
4	Mark Brunell	150.00
5	Drew Bledsoe	150.00
6	Jerry Rice	200.00

1998 Collector's Edge Advantage Prime Connection

Prime Connection spotlights the top tandems of 25 NFL teams on a double-sided, metallic looking card. Each side has an action shot of a player on the right side, with the player's name, position and team on the left side, along with the Prime Connection's logo in the upper left corner. The cards are numbered on both sides in the upper right corner and were inserted every 36 packs of Advantage.

		MT
Complete Set (25):		500.00
Common Player:		5.00
1	LeShon Johnson, Leeland McElroy	5.00
2	Peter Boulware, Michael Jackson	5.00
3	Andre Reed, Antowain Smith	20.00
4	Rae Carruth, Anthony Johnson	10.00
5	Herschel Walker, Emmitt Smith	50.00
6	Terrell Davis, John Elway	40.00
7	Ed McCaffrey, Shannon Sharpe	5.00
8	Herman Moore, Barry Sanders	40.00
9	Brett Favre, Antonio Freeman	60.00
10	Mark Brunell, James Stewart	25.00
11	Marcus Allen, Elvis Grbac	10.00
12	Karim Abdul-Jabbar, Dan Marino	50.00
13	Drew Bledsoe, Ben Coates	25.00
14	Terry Glenn, Curtis Martin	25.00
15	Troy Davis, Danny Wuerffel	10.00
16	Ike Hilliard, Danny Kanell	10.00
17	Aaron Glenn, Adrian Murrell	5.00
18	Tim Brown, Napoleon Kaufman	10.00
19	Mark Bruener, Jerome Bettis	10.00
20	Jim Druckenmiller, Terrell Owens	20.00
21	Garrison Hearst, Steve Young	20.00
22	Tony Banks, Eddie Kennison	15.00
23	Mike Alstott, Reidel Anthony	15.00
24	Hardy Nickerson, Warrick Dunn	30.00
25	Eddie George, Steve McNair	30.00

1998 Collector's Edge Advantage Showtime

This 23-card insert set was seeded one per 18 packs of Advantage Football. Card fronts featured an action shot of the player, with his name written across the bottom. The background was printed in team colors and was supposed to look like jersey material, with the player's position in large letters behind him. Holofoil versions of these cards also exist and were limited in print run to 100 sets.

		MT
Complete Set (23):		250.00
Common Player:		3.00
Minor Stars:		6.00
Holofoils:		3x-6x
1	LeShon Johnson	3.00
2	Peter Boulware	3.00
3	Jim Kelly	6.00
4	Rae Carruth	6.00
5	Kerry Collins	10.00
6	Troy Aikman	20.00
7	Terrell Davis	20.00
8	Shannon Sharpe	3.00
9	Brett Favre	40.00
10	Mark Brunell	20.00
11	Keenan McCardell	3.00
12	Marcus Allen	6.00
13	Terry Glenn	8.00
14	Danny Wuerffel	6.00
15	Danny Kanell	3.00
16	Aaron Glenn	3.00
17	Napoleon Kaufman	8.00
18	Mark Bruener	3.00
19	Jim Druckenmiller	10.00
20	Terrell Owens	8.00
21	Steve Young	12.00
22	Reidel Anthony	3.00
23	Warrick Dunn	20.00

1998 Collector's Edge First Place

Singles from this base set feature large action shots of each of the 250 players in this set. Each single has a parallel 50-Point card that are found one per pack. Also, each player has a 50-Point Silver issue that is sequentially numbered to 125 and found 1:24 packs.

		MT
Complete Set (250):		70.00
Common Player:		.10
Minor Stars:		.20
50-Point Cards:		2x-4x
50-Point Rookies:		2x
Inserted 1:1		
50-Point Gold Cards:		15x-30x
50-Point Gold Rookies:		5x-10x
Inserted 1:24		
Production 125 Sets		
Wax Box:		80.00
1	Karim Abdul-Jabbar	.50
2	*Flozell Adams*	.50
3	Troy Aikman	1.50
4	Robert Smith	.20
5	*Stephen Alexander*	1.00
6	*Harold Shaw*	.50
7	Marcus Allen	.20
8	Terry Allen	.20
9	Mike Alstott	.50
10	Jamal Anderson	.50
11	Reidel Anthony	.20
12	Jamie Asher	.10
13	Darnell Autry	.10
14	Phil Savoy	.50
15	*Jon Ritchie*	1.00
16	Tony Banks	.20
17	Tiki Barber	.20
18	Pat Barnes	.20
19	*Charlie Batch*	8.00
20	*Mikhael Ricks*	2.00
21	Jerome Bettis	.20
22	Tim Biakabutuka	.10
23	*Roosevelt Blackmon*	.50
24	Jeff Blake	.20
25	Drew Bledsoe	1.50
26	Tony Boselli	.10
27	Peter Boulware	.10
28	Tony Brackens	.10
29	*Corey Bradford*	2.50
30	*Michael Pittman*	1.00
31	*Keith Brooking*	1.00
32	Robert Brooks	.10
33	Derrick Brooks	.10
34	*Ken Oxendine*	1.50
35	*R.W. McQuarters*	1.00
36	Tim Brown	.20
37	Chad Brown	.10
38	Isaac Bruce	.20
39	Mark Brunell	1.50
40	Chris Canty	.10
41	Mark Carrier	.10
42	Rae Carruth	.10
43	Ki-Jana Carter	.10
44	Cris Carter	.20
45	Larry Centers	.10
46	Corey Chavous	.50
47	Mark Chmura	.10
48	*Cameron Cleeland*	2.00
49	Dexter Coakley	.10
50	Ben Coates	.10
51	*Jonathon Linton*	1.00
52	Todd Collins	.10
53	Kerry Collins	.20
54	*Tebucky Jones*	.50
55	Curtis Conway	.20
56	*Sam Cowart*	.50
57	Bryan Cox	.10
58	Randall Cunningham	.50
59	Terrell Davis	2.00
60	Troy Davis	.10
61	*Patrick Johnson*	.50
62	Trent Dilfer	.20
63	*Vonnie Holliday*	2.00
64	Corey Dillon	1.00
65	Hugh Douglas	.10
66	Jim Druckenmiller	.10
67	Warrick Dunn	1.50
68	*Robert Edwards*	3.00
69	*Greg Ellis*	1.00
70	John Elway	1.50
71	Bert Emanuel	.10
72	Bobby Engram	.10
73	*Curtis Enis*	4.00
74	Marshall Faulk	.50
75	Brett Favre	3.00
76	Doug Flutie	1.50
77	Glenn Foley	.10
78	Antonio Freeman	.50
79	Gus Frerotte	.10
80	John Friesz	.10
81	Irving Fryar	.10
82	Joey Galloway	.50
83	Rich Gannon	.10
84	Charlie Garner	.10
85	Jeff George	.20
86	Eddie George	1.25
87	Sean Gilbert	.10
88	Terry Glenn	.20
89	Aaron Glenn	.10
90	Tony Gonzalez	.10
91	Jeff Graham	.10
92	Elvis Grbac	.10
93	*Jacquez Green*	3.00
94	Kevin Greene	.10
95	*Brian Griese*	5.00
96	Byron Hanspard	.10
97	Jim Harbaugh	.10
98	Kevin Hardy	.10
99	Walt Harris	.10
100	Marvin Harrison	.20
101	Rodney Harrison	.10
102	Jeff Hartings	.10
103	Ken Harvey	.10
104	Garrison Hearst	.20

105 Ike Hilliard .10
106 Jeff Hostetler .10
107 Bobby Hoying .20
108 Michael Jackson .10
109 Anthony Johnson .10
110 Brad Johnson .50
111 Keyshawn Johnson .20
112 Charles Johnson .10
113 Daryl Johnston .10
114 Chris Jones .10
115 George Jones .10
116 Donald Hayes 1.50
117 Danny Kanell .10
118 Napoleon Kaufman .50
119 Cortez Kennedy .10
120 Eddie Kennison .20
121 Levon Kirkland .10
122 Jon Kitna .10
123 Erik Kramer .10
124 David LaFleur .10
125 Lamar Lathon .10
126 Ty Law .10
127 *Ryan Leaf* 6.00
128 Dorsey Levens .20
129 Ray Lewis .10
130 Darryl Lewis .10
131 *Matt Hasselbeck* 6.00
132 Greg Lloyd .10
133 Kevin Lockett .10
134 Keith Lyle .10
135 *Peyton Manning* 10.00
136 Dan Marino 2.00
137 Wayne Martin .10
138 *Ahman Green* 3.00
139 Tony Martin .10
140 *E.G. Green* 1.50
141 Derrick Mayes .10
142 Ed McCaffrey .20
143 Keenan McCardell .10
144 O.J. McDuffie .10
145 Leeland McElroy .10
146 Willie McGinest .10
147 Chester McGlockton .10
148 Steve McNair .50
149 Natrone Means .20
150 Eric Metcalf .10
151 Anthony Miller .10
152 Rick Mirer .10
153 Scott Mitchell .10
154 John Mobley .10
155 Warren Moon .50
156 Herman Moore .10
157 *Randy Moss* 15.00
158 Eric Moulds .20
159 Muhsin Muhammad .10
160 Adrian Murrell .10
161 *Marcus Nash* 3.00
162 Hardy Nickerson .10
163 Ken Norton .10
164 Neil O'Donnell .10
165 Terrell Owens .50
166 Orlando Pace .10
167 *Jammi German* 1.50
168 Erric Pegram .10
169 *Jason Peter* .50
170 Carl Pickens .20
171 Jake Plummer 1.50
172 John Randle .10
173 Andre Reed .10
174 Jake Reed .10
175 Errict Rhett .10
176 Simeon Rice .10
177 Jerry Rice 1.50
178 Andre Rison .20
179 Darrell Russell .10
180 Rashaan Salaam .10
181 Deion Sanders .50
182 Barry Sanders 3.00
183 Chris Sanders .10
184 Warren Sapp .10
185 Junior Seau .20
186 Jason Sehorn .10
187 Shannon Sharpe .20
188 Sedrick Shaw .10
189 Heath Shuler .10
190 *Chris Floyd* .50
191 *Terry Fair* 1.50
192 *Kevin Dyson* 3.00
193 Torrance Small .10
194 Antowain Smith .75
195 Bruce Smith .10
196 Tarik Smith .50
197 Emmitt Smith 2.00
198 Neil Smith .10
199 Jimmy Smith .20
200 Chris Spielman .10
201 Danny Wuerffel .10
202 Irving Spikes .10
203 Shawn Springs .10
204 *Duane Starks* .50
205 Kordell Stewart 1.50
206 J.J. Stokes .20
207 Eric Swann .10
208 Steve Tasker .10
209 *Tim Dwight* 2.00
210 Jason Taylor .10
211 Vinny Testaverde .20
212 Thurman Thomas .20
213 Broderick Thomas .10
214 Derrick Thomas .10
215 Zach Thomas .10
216 *Germane Crowell* 2.50
217 Amani Toomer .10
218 Tamarick Vanover .10
219 Ross Verba .10
220 *Andre Wadsworth* 1.50
221 Ray Zellars .10
222 Chris Warren .10
223 Steve Young 1.00
224 Tyrone Wheatley .10
225 Reggie White .50
226 *John Avery* 2.50
227 *Charles Woodson* 4.00
228 *Takeo Spikes* 1.50
229 Bryant Young .10
230 *Tavian Banks* 2.50
231 *Fred Beasley* .50
232 *Chris Ruhman* .50

1998 Collector's Edge First Place Game Gear Jersey

Jerseys present at the NFL Draft Day Ceremonies and worn during the pre-season were used to make these cards. Singles were found 1:480 packs.

	MT
Complete Set (2):	300.00
Common Player:	100.00
Inserted 1:480	

1 Peyton Manning 200.00
2 Ryan Leaf 100.00

1998 Collector's Edge First Place Peyton Manning

Edge produced a five-card insert of Manning and inserted them 1:24 packs.

	MT
Complete Set (5):	40.00
Common Player:	8.00
Inserted 1:24	

1998 Collector's Edge First Place Rookie Ink

This set features autographed cards from the top 1998 rookies. Cards are enhanced with silver foil and each card back contains a certificate of authenticity. Singles are signed in blue ink and are found 1:24 packs. Red signatures also exist and are limited to 50 each.

	MT
Complete Set (31):	750.00
Common Player:	8.00
Inserted 1:24	
Red Signatures:	3x
Production 50 Sets	

1 Brian Griese 45.00
2 Adrian Murrell 12.00
3 Marvin Harrison 20.00
4 Tavian Banks 25.00
5 Mike Alstott 18.00
6 Joe Jurevicius 12.00
7 Tim Dwight 18.00
8 Derrick Mayes 12.00
9 Kevin Greene 8.00
10 Marcus Nash 25.00
11 Charlie Batch 75.00
12 Cris Carter 25.00
13 Randy Moss 175.00
14 Tiki Barber 12.00
15 Ahman Green 12.00
16 Terrell Owens 20.00
17 Jim Druckenmiller 12.00
18 Reidel Anthony 12.00
19 Jacquez Green 25.00
20 Skip Hicks 20.00
21 Terry Allen 12.00
22 Fred Lane 12.00
23 Robert Holcombe 20.00
24 Jeremy Newberry 8.00
25 Fred Taylor 80.00
26 Mark Bruener 8.00
27 Hines Ward 20.00
28 Stephen Davis 12.00
29 Justin Armour 8.00
30 Peyton Manning 125.00
31 Ryan Leaf 50.00

1998 Collector's Edge First Place Rookie Markers

Each single in this 30-card set has a special embossed foil icon that recognizes the player's draft pick number. Singles were inserted 1:24 packs.

	MT
Complete Set (30):	175.00
Common Player:	2.00
Minor Stars:	4.00

Inserted 1:24
1 Michael Pittman 2.00
2 Andre Wadsworth 4.00
3 Keith Brooking 2.00
4 Patrick Johnson 2.00
5 Jonathon Linton 2.00
6 Donald Hayes 4.00
7 Mark Chmura 2.00
8 Terry Allen 2.00
9 Brian Griese 8.00
10 Marcus Nash 8.00
11 Germane Crowell 8.00
12 Roosevelt Blackmon 2.00
13 Peyton Manning 30.00
14 Tavian Banks 8.00
15 Fred Taylor 20.00
16 Jim Druckenmiller 4.00
17 John Avery 8.00
18 Randy Moss 40.00
19 Robert Edwards 10.00
20 Cameron Cleeland 6.00
21 Joe Jurevicius 4.00
22 Charles Woodson 10.00
23 Terry Allen 2.00
24 Ryan Leaf 12.00
25 Chris Ruhman 2.00
26 Ahman Green 8.00
27 Jerome Pathon 4.00
28 Jacquez Green 8.00
29 Kevin Dyson 8.00
30 Skip Hicks 6.00

1998 Collector's Edge First Place Ryan Leaf

Edge produced a five-card insert set of Leaf and inserted them 1:24 packs.

	MT
Complete Set (5):	25.00
Common Player:	5.00
Inserted 1:24	

1998 Collector's Edge First Place Successors

Only the top players in the NFL are in this 25-card set. Singles are featured on mirror silver with gold foil. Cards were inserted 1:8 packs.

	MT
Complete Set (25):	75.00
Common Player:	1.00
Minor Stars:	2.00

Inserted 1:8
1 Troy Aikman 4.00
2 Jerome Bettis 2.00
3 Drew Bledsoe 4.00
4 Tim Brown 1.00
5 Mark Brunell 4.00
6 Cris Carter 2.00
7 Terrell Davis 6.00
8 Robert Edwards 4.00
9 John Elway 8.00
10 Brett Favre 8.00
11 Eddie George 3.00
12 Brian Griese 3.00
13 Napoleon Kaufman 2.00
14 Ryan Leaf 5.00
15 Dorsey Levens 2.00
16 Peyton Manning 10.00
17 Dan Marino 6.00
18 Jim Druckenmiller 2.00
19 Herman Moore 2.00
20 Randy Moss 15.00
21 Jake Plummer 3.00
22 Barry Sanders 8.00
23 Emmitt Smith 6.00
24 Rod Smith 1.00
25 Fred Taylor 7.00

1998 Collector's Edge First Place Triple Threat

Three different levels to this 40-card insert. The first being Bronze that are found 1:12 packs. The next level is Silver that are inserted 1:24. The toughest is the Gold which are inserted 1:36.

	MT
Complete Set (40):	185.00
Common Bronze:	1.50
Inserted 1:12	
Common Silver:	2.50
Inserted 1:24	
Common Gold:	4.00
Inserted 1:36	

1 Robert Brooks 1.50
2 Troy Aikman 7.00
3 Randy Moss 20.00
4 Tim Brown 1.50
5 Brad Johnson 3.00
6 Kevin Dyson 4.00
7 Mark Chmura 1.50
8 Joey Galloway 3.00
9 Eddie George 6.00
10 Napoleon Kaufman 3.00
11 Dan Marino 12.00
12 Ed McCaffrey 3.00
13 Herman Moore 3.00
14 Carl Pickens 1.50
15 Emmitt Smith 12.00
16 Drew Bledsoe 7.00
17 Andre Wadsworth 3.00
18 Charles Woodson 7.00
19 Terrell Davis 12.00
20 Yancey Thigpen 2.50
21 Drew Bledsoe 7.00
22 Keith Brooking 2.50
23 Mark Brunell 7.00
24 Terrell Davis 12.00
25 Antonio Freeman 3.00
26 Peyton Manning 15.00
27 Jerry Rice 7.00
28 Takeo Spikes 3.00
29 Danny Wuerffel 1.50
30 Jerome Bettis 3.00
31 Cris Carter 4.00
32 Jim Druckenmiller 4.00
33 Warrick Dunn 4.00
34 John Elway 10.00
35 Brett Favre 20.00
36 Ryan Leaf 8.00
37 Dorsey Levens 4.00
38 Terrell Owens 6.00
39 Barry Sanders 20.00
40 Kordell Stewart 10.00

1998 Collector's Edge First Place Triumph

Each Triumph card is printed on clear acetate stock with a large action shot in the foreground with a head shot in the background. The 25 different singles were inserted 1:12 packs.

	MT
Complete Set (25):	85.00
Common Player:	2.00
Inserted 1:12	

1 Troy Aikman 5.00
2 Jerome Bettis 2.00
3 Drew Bledsoe 5.00
4 Tim Brown 2.00
5 Mark Brunell 4.00
6 Cris Carter 2.00
7 Terrell Davis 7.00
8 Jim Druckenmiller 2.00
9 Robert Edwards 4.00
10 John Elway 5.00
11 Brett Favre 10.00
12 Eddie George 4.00
13 Brian Griese 4.00
14 Napoleon Kaufman 4.00
15 Ryan Leaf 6.00
16 Dorsey Levens 2.00
17 Peyton Manning 10.00
18 Dan Marino 7.00
19 Herman Moore 2.00
20 Randy Moss 15.00
21 Jake Plummer 4.00
22 Barry Sanders 10.00
23 Emmitt Smith 7.00
24 Rod Smith 2.00
25 Fred Taylor 7.00

1998 Collector's Edge Masters

This is the first super-premium product that Edge has released. Every card in this set is sequentially numbered to 5,000, with double-thick parallel levels. The first being the 50-Point cards that are numbered to 3,000 and inserted one-per-pack. The 50-Point Gold singles are numbered to 150 and inserted 1:20 packs. HoloGold cards are numbered to 10 and found 1:300 packs.

	MT
Complete Set (199):	325.00
Common Player:	.25
Minor Stars:	.50
Common Rookie:	1.50
Production 5,000 Sets	
50-Point Cards:	1.5x
Inserted 1:1	
Production 3,000 Sets	
50-Point Gold Cards:	7x-14x
50-Point Gold Rookies:	2x-4x
Inserted 1:20	
Production 150 Sets	
Hologold Cards:	50x-100x
Hologold Rookies:	8x-16x
Inserted 1:300	
Production 10 Sets	
Wax Box:	100.00

1 Rob Moore .50
2 Adrian Murrell .25
3 Jake Plummer 3.00
4 *Michael Pittman* 1.50
5 Frank Sanders .50
6 *Andre Wadsworth* 3.00
7 Jamal Anderson 1.00
8 Chris Chandler .50
9 *Tim Dwight* 7.50
10 Tony Martin .25
11 Terance Mathis .25
12 *Ken Oxendine* 3.00
13 Jim Harbaugh .50
14 *Priest Holmes* 15.00
15 Michael Jackson .25
16 *Pat Johnson* 3.00
17 Jermaine Lewis .25
18 Eric Zeier .25
19 Doug Flutie 2.00
20 Rob Johnson .50
21 Eric Moulds 1.00
22 Andre Reed .50
23 Antowain Smith 1.00
24 Bruce Smith .25
25 Thurman Thomas .25
26 Steve Beuerlein .25
27 Kevin Greene .25
28 Raghib Ismail .25
29 Fred Lane .25
30 Muhsin Muhammad .25
32 Edgar Bennett .25
33 Curtis Conway .50
34 Bobby Engram .25
35 *Curtis Enis* 7.50
36 Erik Kramer .25
37 Chris Penn .25
38 Jeff Blake .50
39 Corey Dillon 2.00
40 Neil O'Donnell .25
41 Carl Pickens .50
42 Darnay Scott .25
43 *Damon Gibson* 1.50
44 Troy Aikman 3.00
45 Billy Davis .25
46 Michael Irvin .50
47 Ernie Mills .25
48 Deion Sanders 1.00
49 Emmitt Smith 4.50
50 Chris Warren .50
51 Bubby Brister .25
52 Terrell Davis 4.50
53 John Elway 4.50
54 *Brian Griese* 10.00
55 Ed McCaffrey .75
56 *Marcus Nash* 5.00
57 Shannon Sharpe .50
58 Rod Smith .50
59 *Charlie Batch* 12.00
60 *Germane Crowell* 5.00
61 Scott Mitchell .25
62 Johnnie Morton .25
63 Herman Moore .75
64 Barry Sanders 6.00
65 Robert Brooks .25
66 Brett Favre 6.00
67 Antonio Freeman 1.00
68 Raymont Harris .25
69 Dorsey Levens 1.00
70 Reggie White 1.00
71 Marshall Faulk 1.00
72 Marvin Harrison 1.00
73 *Peyton Manning* 25.00
74 *Jerome Pathon* 3.00
75 *Tavian Banks* 4.00
76 Mark Brunell 3.00
77 Keenan McCardell .25
78 Jimmy Smith .75
79 *Fred Taylor* 20.00
80 Derrick Alexander .25
81 Donnell Bennett .25
82 Rich Gannon .25
83 Elvis Grbac .50
84 Andre Rison .50
85 Rashaan Shehee 1.50
86 Karim Abdul .75
87 *John Avery* 5.00
88 *Oronde Gadsden* 5.00
89 Dan Marino 4.50
90 O.J. McDuffie .50
91 Zach Thomas .50
92 Cris Carter 1.00
93 Randall Cunningham 1.00
94 Brad Johnson .75
95 *Randy Moss* 50.00
96 Jake Reed .25
97 Robert Smith .50
98 Drew Bledsoe 3.00
99 Ben Coates .50
100 *Robert Edwards* 7.50
101 Terry Glenn .75
102 Shawn Jefferson .25
103 Ty Law .25
104 *Cameron Cleeland* 4.00
105 Kerry Collins .50
106 Sean Dawkins .25
107 Andre Hastings .25
108 Lamar Smith .25
109 Danny Wuerffel .25
110 Gary Brown .25
111 Chris Calloway .25
112 Ike Hilliard .25
113 *Joe Jurevicius* 3.00
114 Danny Kanell .25
115 Wayne Chrebet .75
116 Glenn Foley .50
117 Keyshawn Johnson 1.00
118 Leon Johnson .25
119 Curtis Martin 1.00
120 Vinny Testaverde .50
121 Tim Brown .50
122 Jeff George .25
123 James Jett .25
124 Napoleon Kaufman 1.00
125 *Charles Woodson* 7.50
126 Irving Fryar .25
127 Jeff Graham .25
128 Bobby Hoying .25
129 Duce Staley .75
130 Jerome Bettis .75
131 *Chris Fuamatu-Ma'afala* 3.00
132 Courtney Hawkins .25
133 Charles Johnson .25
134 Kordell Stewart 2.00
135 *Hines Ward* 3.00
136 Tony Banks .50
137 Isaac Bruce .50
138 *Robert Holcombe* 5.00
139 Eddie Kennison .50
140 *Ryan Leaf* 12.00
141 Natrone Means .50
142 *Mikhael Ricks* .50
143 Junior Seau .50
144 Bryan Still .25
145 Garrison Hearst .75
146 *R.W. McQuarters* 1.00
147 Terrell Owens 1.00
148 Jerry Rice 3.00
149 J.J. Stokes .50
150 Steve Young 2.00
151 Joey Galloway 1.00
152 *Ahman Green* 5.00
153 Warren Moon .50
154 Shawn Springs .25
155 Ricky Watters .50
156 Mike Alstott .50
157 Reidel Anthony .50
158 Trent Dilfer .50
159 Warrick Dunn 2.00
160 *Jacquez Green* 5.00
161 *Kevin Dyson* 5.00
162 Eddie George 2.00
163 Steve McNair 1.00
164 Yancy Thigpen .25
165 Frank Wycheck .25
166 Terry Allen .50
167 Gus Frerotte .50
168 Trent Green .50
169 *Skip Hicks* 5.00
170 Michael Westbrook .50
171 Jamal Anderson .50
172 Carl Pickens .25
173 Deion Sanders .50
174 Emmitt Smith 2.00
175 Terrell Davis 2.00
176 John Elway 2.00
177 *Charlie Batch* 7.50
178 Herman Moore .25
179 Barry Sanders 3.00
180 Brett Favre 3.00
181 Antonio Freeman .50
182 Marshall Faulk .50
183 Peyton Manning 15.00
184 Mark Brunell 1.50
185 Dan Marino 2.00
186 Randy Moss 30.00
187 Drew Bledsoe 1.50
188 Robert Edwards 3.00
189 Curtis Martin .50
190 Charles Woodson 3.00
191 Jerome Bettis .25
192 Robert Holcombe 2.00
193 Ryan Leaf 7.50
194 Natrone Means .50
195 Jerry Rice 1.50
196 Steve Young 1.00
197 Warrick Dunn 1.00
198 Eddie George 1.00
199 Peyton Manning CL 7.50
200 Ryan Leaf CL 4.00

1998 Collector's Edge Masters Legends

This 30-card set includes the top players from '98. Each card is sequentially numbered to 2,500 and inserted 1:8 packs.

	MT
Complete Set (30):	85.00
Common Player:	1.50
Minor Stars:	3.00
Inserted 1:8	
Production 2,500 Sets	

1 Jake Plummer 6.00
2 Doug Flutie 4.00
3 Corey Dillon 3.00
4 Carl Pickens 1.50
5 Troy Aikman 6.00
6 Deion Sanders 3.00
7 Emmitt Smith 10.00
8 Terrell Davis 10.00
9 John Elway 10.00
10 Herman Moore 3.00
11 Barry Sanders 12.00
12 Brett Favre 12.00
13 Antonio Freeman 3.00
14 Marshall Faulk 3.00

		MT
15	Mark Brunell	5.00
16	Dan Marino	10.00
17	Cris Carter	3.00
18	Drew Bledsoe	5.00
19	Keyshawn Johnson	3.00
20	Curtis Martin	3.00
21	Napoleon Kaufman	3.00
22	Jerome Bettis	3.00
23	Kordell Stewart	5.00
24	Natrone Means	3.00
25	Jerry Rice	6.00
26	Steve Young	4.00
27	Joey Galloway	3.00
28	Warrick Dunn	4.00
29	Eddie George	5.00
30	Terry Allen	1.50

1998 Collector's Edge Masters Main Event

Main Event singles are sequentially numbered to 2,000 and inserted 1:16 packs.

		MT
Complete Set (20):		160.00
Common Player:		2.50
Minor Stars:		5.00
Inserted 1:16		
Production 2,000 Sets		
1	Troy Aikman	8.00
2	Jamal Anderson	5.00
3	Charlie Batch	12.00
4	Jerome Bettis	2.50
5	Mark Brunell	6.00
6	Terrell Davis	12.00
7	Warrick Dunn	5.00
8	Robert Edwards	7.00
9	John Elway	12.00
10	Brett Favre	16.00
11	Doug Flutie	5.00
12	Eddie George	6.00
13	Dan Marino	12.00
14	Curtis Martin	5.00
15	Randy Moss	50.00
16	Carl Pickens	2.50
17	Jake Plummer	8.00
18	Barry Sanders	16.00
19	Emmitt Smith	12.00
20	Fred Taylor	25.00

1998 Collector's Edge Masters Rookie Masters

This 30-card set is made up of the top rookies from the class of '98. Each card is sequentially numbered to 2,500 and inserted 1:8 packs.

		MT
Complete Set (30):		125.00
Common Player:		1.50
Minor Stars:		3.00
Inserted 1:8		
Production 2,500 Sets		
1	Peyton Manning	25.00
2	Ryan Leaf	10.00
3	Charlie Batch	12.00
4	Brian Griese	8.00
5	Randy Moss	40.00
6	Jacquez Green	4.00
7	Kevin Dyson	4.00
8	Mikhael Ricks	3.00
9	Jerome Pathon	3.00
10	Joe Jurevicius	3.00
11	Germane Crowell	4.00
12	Tim Dwight	6.00
13	Pat Johnson	3.00
14	Hines Ward	4.00
15	Marcus Nash	4.00
16	Damon Gibson	1.50
17	Robert Edwards	5.00
18	Robert Holcombe	4.00
19	Tavian Banks	3.00
20	Fred Taylor	20.00
21	Skip Hicks	4.00
22	Curtis Enis	6.00
23	Ahman Green	4.00
24	John Avery	4.00
25	Chris Fuamatu-Ma'afala	3.00
26	Rashaan Shehee	1.50
27	Cameron Cleeland	4.00
28	Charles Woodson	6.00
29	R.W. McQuarters	3.00
30	Andre Wadsworth	3.00

1998 Collector's Edge Masters Sentinels

This 10-card set is made up of the top 10 most collectible superstars in the NFL. Each card is sequentially numbered to 500 and found 1:120 packs.

	MT
Complete Set (10):	275.00
Common Player:	15.00
Inserted 1:120	
Production 500 Sets	

1	John Elway	30.00
2	Brett Favre	40.00
3	Barry Sanders	40.00
4	Terrell Davis	30.00
5	Dan Marino	30.00
6	Emmitt Smith	30.00
7	Randy Moss	75.00
8	Peyton Manning	40.00
9	Robert Edwards	15.00
10	Fred Taylor	35.00

1998 Collector's Edge Masters Super Masters

We have the checklist at 23 players for a complete set. Ten of the players also have signed versions of their insert card. Insert odds are 1:10 packs for the regular insert and the Autographs vary.

	MT
Complete Set (23):	75.00
Common Player:	1.50
Minor Stars:	3.00
Inserted 1:10	
Production 2,000 Sets	
Set Price Doesn't Include Autographs	
Troy Aikman	8.00
Edgar Bennett	1.50
Robert Brooks	1.50
Dwight Clark	3.00
Dwight Clark AUTO	15.00
Roger Craig	3.00
Roger Craig AUTO	15.00
Terrell Davis	12.00
Len Dawson	3.00
Len Dawson AUTO	40.00
John Elway	12.00
Brett Favre	16.00
Antonio Freeman	3.00
Jack Ham	3.00
Jack Ham AUTO	15.00
Michael Irvin	3.00
Butch Johnson AUTO	10.00
Drew Pearson	3.00
Drew Pearson AUTO	15.00
Jerry Rice	8.00
Deion Sanders	3.00
Shannon Sharpe	3.00
Emmitt Smith	12.00
Rod Smith	3.00
John Stallworth	3.00
John Stallworth AUTO	15.00
Bart Starr	10.00
Bart Starr AUTO	325.00
Johnny Unitas	8.00
Johnny Unitas AUTO	300.00
Steve Young	5.00
Reggie White	3.00

1998 Collector's Edge Odyssey

The base set is made up of 250 cards and is broken down into four tiers or quarters. The first 150 cards are from the 1st Quarter subset. Cards 151-200 are 2nd Quarter and are inserted 1:1.5 packs. Cards 201-230 are 3rd Quarter and are found 1:3 packs. Cards 231-250 are the 4th Quarter singles and are the toughest to find at 1:18 packs.

	MT
Complete Set (250):	450.00
Common 1st Quarter:	.10
Minor Stars:	.20
Common Rookie:	1.50
Inserted 1:1.5	
Common 2nd Quarter:	.50
Common 3rd Quarter:	.75
Inserted 1:3	
Common 4th Quarter:	3.00
Inserted 1:18	
Wax Box:	85.00

1	Terance Mathis	.10
2	Tony Martin	.10
3	Chris Chandler	.20
4	Jamal Anderson	.50
5	Jake Plummer	.75
6	Adrian Murrell	.10
7	Rob Moore	.10
8	Frank Sanders	.10
9	Larry Centers	.10
10	Andre Wadsworth	1.50
11	Jim Harbaugh	.20
12	Errict Rhett	.10
13	Jermaine Lewis	.10
14	Michael Jackson	.10
15	Eric Zeier	.10
16	Rob Johnson	.20
17	Antowain Smith	.50
18	Andre Reed	.10
19	Bruce Smith	.10
20	Doug Flutie	.50
21	Thurman Thomas	.20
22	Kerry Collins	.20
23	Fred Lane	.20
24	Muhsin Mohammed	.10
25	Rae Carruth	.10
26	Raghib Ismail	.10
27	Kevin Greene	.10
28	Curtis Enis	3.00
29	Curtis Conway	.20
30	Erik Kramer	.10
31	Edgar Bennett	.10
32	Neil O'Donnell	.20
33	Jeff Blake	.20
34	Carl Pickens	.20
35	Corey Dillon	.50
36	Troy Aikman	1.00
37	Jason Garrett	.10
38	Emmitt Smith	1.50
39	Deion Sanders	.50
40	Michael Irvin	.20
41	Chris Warren	.10
42	John Elway	1.00
43	Terrell Davis	1.50
44	Shannon Sharpe	.20
45	Rod Smith	.10
46	Marcus Nash	2.50
47	Brian Griese	4.00
48	Barry Sanders	2.00
49	Herman Moore	.20
50	Scott Mitchell	.10
51	Johnnie Morton	.10
52	Rashaan Shehee	1.50
53	Charlie Batch	5.00
54	Brett Favre	2.00
55	Dorsey Levens	.20
56	Antonio Freeman	.50
57	Reggie White	.50
58	Robert Brooks	.10
59	Raymont Harris	.10
60	Peyton Manning	10.00
61	Marshall Faulk	.50
62	Jerome Pathon	2.00
63	Marvin Harrison	.20
64	Mark Brunell	.75
65	Fred Taylor	5.00
66	Jimmy Smith	.20
67	James Stewart	.20
68	Keenan McCardell	.10
69	Andre Rison	.10
70	Elvis Grbac	.10
71	Donnell Bennett	.10
72	Rich Gannon	.10
73	Derrick Thomas	.10
74	Dan Marino	1.50
75	Karim Abdul-Jabbar	.50
76	John Avery	3.00
77	O.J. McDuffie	.10
78	Oronde Gadsden	2.00
79	Zach Thomas	.20
80	Randy Moss	15.00
81	Cris Carter	.50
82	Jake Reed	.10
83	Robert Smith	.20
84	Brad Johnson	.50
85	Drew Bledsoe	1.00
86	Robert Edwards	4.00
87	Terry Glenn	.50
88	Troy Brown	.10
89	Shawn Jefferson	.10
90	Danny Wuerffel	.10
91	Dana Stubblefield	.10
92	Derrick Alexander	.10
93	Ray Zellars	.10
94	Andre Hastings	.10
95	Danny Kanell	.10
96	Tiki Barber	.10
97	Ike Hilliard	.10
98	Charles Way	.10
99	Chris Calloway	.10
100	Curtis Martin	.50
101	Glenn Foley	.20
102	Vinny Testaverde	.10
103	Keyshawn Johnson	.50
104	Wayne Chrebet	.20
105	Leon Johnson	.10
106	Jeff George	.20
107	Charles Woodson	3.00
108	Tim Brown	.20
109	James Jett	.10
110	Napoleon Kaufman	.50
111	Charlie Garner	.10
112	Bobby Hoying	.10
113	Duce Staley	.10
114	Irving Fryar	.10
115	Kordell Stewart	.75
116	Jerome Bettis	.50
117	Charles Johnson	.10
118	Randall Cunningham	.50
119	Courtney Hawkins	.10
120	Tony Banks	.50
121	Isaac Bruce	.50
122	Robert Holcombe	2.50
123	Greg Hill	.10
124	Ryan Leaf	5.00
125	Mikhael Ricks	2.50
126	Natrone Means	.50
127	Junior Seau	.20
128	Jerry Rice	1.00
129	Terrell Owens	.75
130	Garrison Hearst	.20
131	Steve Young	.75
132	J.J. Stokes	.20
133	Warren Moon	.20
134	Joey Galloway	.50
135	Ricky Watters	.20
136	Ahman Green	2.50
137	Trent Dilfer	.20
138	Mike Alstott	.50
139	Warrick Dunn	.75
140	Reidel Anthony	.20
141	Jacquez Green	2.50
142	Steve McNair	.50
143	Eddie George	.75
144	Yancey Thigpen	.20
145	Kevin Dyson	2.50
146	Trent Green	.20
147	Gus Frerotte	.10
148	Terry Allen	.20
149	Michael Westbrook	.20
150	Jim Druckenmiller	.20
151	Jake Plummer	1.50
152	Adrian Murrell	.50
153	Rob Johnson	.50
154	Antowain Smith	.75
155	Kerry Collins	.50
156	Curtis Enis	5.00
157	Carl Pickens	.50
158	Corey Dillon	1.00
159	Troy Aikman	1.50
160	Emmitt Smith	2.00
161	Deion Sanders	.50
162	Michael Irvin	.50
163	John Elway	1.50
164	Terrell Davis	2.00
165	Shannon Sharpe	.50
166	Rod Smith	.50
167	Barry Sanders	3.00
168	Herman Moore	.50
169	Brett Favre	3.00
170	Dorsey Levens	.50
171	Antonio Freeman	.75
172	Peyton Manning	14.00
173	Marshall Faulk	.50
174	Mark Brunell	1.00
175	Fred Taylor	7.00
176	Dan Marino	2.00
177	Randy Moss	25.00
178	Cris Carter	.50
179	Drew Bledsoe	1.00
180	Robert Edwards	6.00
181	Curtis Martin	.50
182	Napoleon Kaufman	.50
183	Kordell Stewart	1.00
184	Jerome Bettis	.50
185	Tony Banks	.50
186	Isaac Bruce	.50
187	Ryan Leaf	8.00
188	Natrone Means	.50
189	Jerry Rice	1.50
190	Terrell Owens	.75
191	Garrison Hearst	.50
192	Steve Young	.75
193	Warren Moon	.50
194	Joey Galloway	.50
195	Trent Dilfer	.50
196	Mike Alstott	.50
197	Warrick Dunn	1.50
198	Steve McNair	.75
199	Eddie George	1.00
200	Terry Allen	.50
201	Jake Plummer	2.00
202	Curtis Enis	8.00
203	Carl Pickens	.75
204	Corey Dillon	1.00
205	Troy Aikman	2.00
206	Emmitt Smith	3.00
207	John Elway	2.00
208	Terrell Davis	3.00
209	Barry Sanders	4.00
210	Brett Favre	4.00
211	Antonio Freeman	.75
212	Peyton Manning	25.00
213	Mark Brunell	1.50
214	Fred Taylor	12.00
215	Dan Marino	3.00
216	Randy Moss	35.00
217	Drew Bledsoe	1.50
218	Robert Edwards	8.00
219	Curtis Martin	.75
220	Kordell Stewart	1.50
221	Jerome Bettis	.75
222	Tony Banks	.75
223	Ryan Leaf	12.00
224	Jerry Rice	2.00
225	Steve Young	1.00
226	Warren Moon	.75
227	Trent Dilfer	.75
228	Warrick Dunn	2.00
229	Steve McNair	1.00
230	Eddie George	1.50
231	Curtis Enis	15.00
232	Carl Pickens	3.00
233	Troy Aikman	6.00
234	Emmitt Smith	8.00
235	John Elway	6.00
236	Terrell Davis	10.00
237	Barry Sanders	12.00
238	Brett Favre	12.00
239	Peyton Manning	35.00
240	Fred Taylor	18.00
241	Dan Marino	8.00
242	Randy Moss	65.00
243	Drew Bledsoe	5.00
244	Kordell Stewart	5.00
245	Jerome Bettis	3.00
246	Ryan Leaf	20.00
247	Jerry Rice	6.00
248	Steve Young	4.00
249	Warren Moon	3.00
250	Eddie George	5.00

1998 Collector's Edge Odyssey Galvanized

Each base card has a parallel Galvanized single that is also tiered four ways. Each single has the letter "G" on the back and has a foil front. Cards 1-150 are inserted 1:3 packs, Cards 151-200 were found 1:15 packs, 201-230 at 1:29 and 231-250 at 1:59.

	MT
Complete Set (250):	1000.
1st Quarter Cards:	3x
1st Quarter Rookies:	1.5x
Inserted 1:3	
2nd Quarter Cards:	4x
2nd Quarter Rookies:	2x
Inserted 1:15	
3rd Quarter Cards:	3x
3rd Quarter Rookies:	1.5x
Inserted 1:29	
4th Quarter Cards:	4x
4th Quarter Rookies:	2x
Inserted 1:144	

1998 Collector's Edge Odyssey HoloGold

HoloGold is the second parallel set to the base and is also tiered four different ways. These singles have the letter "H" on the backs and also have foil fronts. Cards 1-150 are numbered to 150 and inserted 1:34 packs, cards 151-200 are numbered to 50 and found 1:307, cards 201-230 are limited to 30 and found 1:840 and the last tier are cards numbered 231-250 with a production run of 20 and inserted 1:1,920.

	MT
1st Quarter Cards:	20x-40x
1st Quarter Rookies:	5x-10x
Inserted 1:34	
Production 150 Sets	

1998 Collector's Edge Odyssey Leading Edge

Leading Edge features 30 of the NFL's top stars in an attractive foil set. Singles were inserted 1:7 packs.

	MT
Complete Set (30):	75.00
Common Player:	1.00
Inserted 1:7	

1	Jake Plummer	2.00
2	Rob Johnson	1.00
3	Curtis Enis	3.00
4	Carl Pickens	1.00
5	Troy Aikman	3.00
6	Emmitt Smith	4.50
7	John Elway	3.00
8	Terrell Davis	4.50
9	Shannon Sharpe	1.00
10	Barry Sanders	6.00
11	Brett Favre	6.00
12	Antonio Freeman	1.50
13	Peyton Manning	10.00
14	Marshall Faulk	1.50
15	Mark Brunell	2.00
16	Dan Marino	4.50
17	Randy Moss	20.00
18	Cris Carter	1.50
19	Robert Edwards	4.00
20	Curtis Martin	1.50
21	Ryan Leaf	5.00
22	Terrell Owens	1.50
23	Garrison Hearst	1.50
24	Steve Young	1.50
25	Joey Galloway	1.50
26	Mike Alstott	1.50
27	Warrick Dunn	2.50
28	Eddie George	2.50
29	Kevin Dyson	2.00
30	Terry Allen	1.00

1998 Collector's Edge Odyssey Prodigies

ROBERT HOLCOMBE

The Prodigies insert is made up of autographs from young talent and rookies from '98. Singles were inserted 1:24 packs. A parallel of Red Signatures exist with most signing between 50 to 80.

	MT
Complete Set (32):	1000.
Common Player:	10.00
Minor Stars:	20.00
Inserted 1:24	
John Avery	30.00
Tavian Banks	20.00
Charlie Batch	75.00
Blaine Bishop	10.00
Robert Brooks	30.00
Tim Brown	50.00
Mark Brunell	100.00
Wayne Chrebet	30.00
Jim Druckenmiller	20.00
Robert Edwards	45.00
Doug Flutie	60.00
Glenn Foley	10.00
Oronde Gadsden	30.00
Joey Galloway	20.00
Garrison Hearst	20.00
Robert Holcombe	20.00
Joey Kent	10.00
Jon Kitna	30.00
Herman Moore	20.00
Randy Moss	200.00
Terrell Owens	30.00
Mikhael Ricks	20.00
Rashaan Shehee	30.00
Antowain Smith	20.00
Emmitt Smith	180.00
Robert Smith	20.00
Rod Smith	20.00
J.J. Stokes	20.00
Fred Taylor	60.00
Derrick Thomas	20.00
Chris Warren	10.00
Eric Zeier	10.00

1998 Collector's Edge Odyssey S.L. Edge

Super Limited Edge singles includes 12 of the game's most collectible superstars and were found 1:99 packs.

	MT
Complete Set (12):	275.00
Common Player:	10.00
Inserted 1:99	

1	Emmitt Smith	45.00
2	Deion Sanders	15.00
3	John Elway	30.00
4	Brett Favre	60.00
5	Antonio Freeman	15.00

6 Peyton Manning 30.00
7 Mark Brunell 25.00
8 Dan Marino 45.00
9 Randy Moss 70.00
10 Joey Galloway 10.00
11 Mike Alstott 10.00
12 Eddie George 25.00

1998 Collector's Edge Supreme

Supreme Season Review consists of a 200-card base set, with 170 veterans and 30 redemption cards for the top draft pick from each NFL team. The player's name and Collector's Edge logo are printed in gold foil on the front. The base set is paralleled by Gold Ingots. Inserts include Markers, T-3 Triple Threat and Pro Signatures Authentic. Two 1-of-1 inserts were also created: Memorable Moments and the 200-card Personal Collection, which features photos from Super Bowl XXXII.

	MT
Complete Set (200):	75.00
Common Player:	.20
Minor Stars:	.40
Wax Box:	60.00

1 Larry Centers .20
2 Jake Plummer 2.00
3 Simeon Rice .20
4 Arizona Draft Pick 1.00
5 Jamal Anderson .40
6 Bert Emanuel .20
7 Byron Hanspard .40
8 Atlanta Draft Pick 1.00
9 Derrick Alexander .20
10 Peter Boulware .20
11 Michael Jackson .20
12 Ray Lewis .20
13 Vinny Testaverde .40
14 Baltimore Draft Pick 1.00
15 Todd Collins .20
16 Jim Kelly .40
17 Andre Reed .20
18 Antowain Smith 1.00
19 Bruce Smith .20
20 Thurman Thomas .40
21 Buffalo Draft Pick 1.00
22 Tim Biakabutuka .20
23 Rae Carruth .40
24 Kerry Collins .40
25 Anthony Johnson .20
26 Lamar Lathon .20
27 Carolina Draft Pick .20
28 Curtis Conway .40
29 Bryan Cox .20
30 Bobby Engram .20
31 Erik Kramer .20
32 Rick Mirer .20
33 Rashaan Salaam .40
34 Chicago Draft Pick 3.00
35 Jeff Blake .40
36 Ki-Jana Carter .20
37 Corey Dillon 1.50
38 Carl Pickens .40
39 Cincinnati Draft Pick 1.00
40 Troy Aikman 2.00
41 Daryl Johnston .20
42 David LaFleur .40
43 Anthony Miller .20
44 Deion Sanders 1.00
45 Emmitt Smith 3.00
46 Broderick Thomas .20
47 Dallas Draft Pick 1.00
48 Terrell Davis 2.00
49 John Elway 2.00
50 Ed McCaffrey .20
51 John Mobley .20
52 Bill Romanowski .20
53 Shannon Sharpe .20
54 Neil Smith .20
55 Rod Smith .20
56 Maa Tanuvasa .20
57 Denver Draft Pick 6.00
58 Scott Mitchell .20
59 Herman Moore .40
60 Barry Sanders 3.00
61 Detroit Draft Pick 1.00
62 Robert Brooks .40
63 Mark Chmura .20
64 Brett Favre 4.00
65 Antonio Freeman .40
66 Dorsey Levens .40
67 Derrick Mayes .20
68 Ross Verba .20
69 Reggie White .40
70 Green Bay Draft Pick 1.00
71 Marshall Faulk .40
72 Jim Harbaugh .40
73 Marvin Harrison .40
74 Indianapolis Draft Pick 10.00
75 Tony Brackens .20
76 Mark Brunell 2.00
77 Rob Johnson .20
78 Keenan McCardell .20
79 Natrone Means .20
80 Jimmy Smith .20
81 Jacksonville Draft Pick 2.00
82 Marcus Allen .40
83 Tony Gonzalez .40
84 Elvis Grbac .20
85 Derrick Thomas .20
86 Tamarick Vanover .20
87 Kansas City Draft Pick 1.00
88 Karim Abdul-Jabbar .40
89 Fred Barnett .20
90 Dan Marino 3.00
91 O.J. McDuffie .20
92 Brett Perriman .20
93 Irving Spikes .20
94 Zach Thomas .20
95 Miami Draft Pick 2.00
96 Cris Carter .20
97 Brad Johnson .40
98 John Randle .20
99 Jake Reed .20
100 Robert Smith .20
101 Minnesota Draft Pick 20.00
102 Drew Bledsoe 2.00
103 Chris Canty .20
104 Ben Coates .20
105 Terry Glenn .40
106 Curtis Martin 1.50
107 Willie McGinest .20
108 Sedrick Shaw .20
109 New England Draft Pick 1.50
110 Mario Bates .20
111 Heath Shuler .20
112 Danny Wuerffel .40
113 New Orleans Draft Pick 1.00
114 Ray Zellars .20
115 Tiki Barber .40
116 Dave Brown .20
117 Ike Hilliard .40
118 Danny Kanell .20
119 Jason Sehorn .20
120 Amani Toomer .20
121 New York Giants Draft Pick 1.00
122 Wayne Chrebet .20
123 Hugh Douglas .20
124 Jeff Graham .20
125 Keyshawn Johnson .40
126 Adrian Murrell .40
127 Neil O'Donnell .20
128 New York Jets Draft Pick 1.00
129 Tim Brown .40
130 Jeff George .40
131 Desmond Howard .20
132 Napoleon Kaufman .40
133 Darrell Russell .20
134 Oakland Draft Pick 3.00
135 Ty Detmer .20
136 Irving Fryar .20
137 Bobby Hoying .40
138 Chris T. Jones .20
139 Ricky Watters .40
140 Philadelphia Draft Pick 1.00
141 Jerome Bettis .40
142 Charles Johnson .20
143 George Jones .20
144 Greg Lloyd .20
145 Kordell Stewart 2.00
146 Yancey Thigpen .20
147 Pittsburgh Draft Pick 1.00
148 Stan Humphries .20
149 Tony Martin .20
150 Eric Metcalf .20
151 Junior Seau .40
152 San Diego Draft Pick 2.50
153 Jim Druckenmiller .40
154 William Floyd .40
155 Garrison Hearst .20
156 Kevin Greene .20
157 Ken Norton .20
158 Terrell Owens .40
159 Jerry Rice 2.00
160 J.J. Stokes .20
161 Dana Stubblefield .20
162 Rod Woodson .20
163 Bryant Young .20
164 Steve Young .40
165 San Francisco Draft Pick 1.00
166 Steve Broussard .20
167 Chad Brown .20
168 Joey Galloway .40
169 Jon Kitna .20
170 Warren Moon .40
171 Chris Warren .20
172 Seattle Draft Pick 2.00
173 Tony Banks .40
174 Isaac Bruce .40
175 Eddie Kennison .40
176 Keith Lyle .20
177 Lawrence Phillips .20
178 St. Louis Draft Pick 1.00
179 Mike Alstott .40
180 Anthony Reidel .40
181 Trent Dilfer .40
182 Warrick Dunn 2.00
183 Hardy Nickerson .20
184 Errict Rhett .20
185 Warren Sapp .20
186 Tampa Bay Draft Pick 2.00
187 Eddie George 2.00
188 Darryll Lewis .20
189 Steve McNair 1.00
190 Chris Sanders .20
191 Tennessee Draft Pick 1.00
192 Terry Allen .40
193 Jamie Asher .20
194 Stephen Davis .20
195 Gus Frerotte .40
196 Sean Gilbert .20
197 Ken Harvey .20
198 Jeff Hostetler .20
199 Michael Westbrook .20
200 Washington Draft Pick 1.00

1998 Collector's Edge Supreme Gold Ingots

Gold Ingots is a full parallel of the Supreme Season Review base set. The cards are printed on 48-point card stock and have "Gold Ingots" printed in gold foil on the front.

	MT
Gold Ingots Cards:	2x-4x
Gold Ingots Rookies:	2x

1998 Collector's Edge Supreme Markers

Markers is a 30-card insert seeded one per 24 packs. The cards are printed on 48-point stock. The player's last name, position and team are listed at the top. An embossed gold-foil logo denotes which statistical "marker" the player has acheived.

	MT
Complete Set (30):	375.00
Common Player:	5.00
Minor Stars:	10.00

1 Jamal Anderson 5.00
2 Corey Dillon 20.00
3 Emmitt Smith 40.00
4 Terrell Davis 25.00
5 John Elway 25.00
6 Rod Smith 5.00

7 Herman Moore 10.00
8 Barry Sanders 40.00
9 Robert Brooks 5.00
10 Brett Favre 50.00
11 Antonio Freeman 10.00
12 Dorsey Levens 10.00
13 Marshall Faulk 10.00
14 Mark Brunell 20.00
15 Karim Abdul-Jabbar 10.00
16 Dan Marino 40.00
17 Cris Carter 5.00
18 Drew Bledsoe 20.00
19 Curtis Martin 15.00
20 Adrian Murrell 5.00
21 Tim Brown 5.00
22 Jeff George 5.00
23 Napoleon Kaufman 10.00
24 Jerome Bettis 10.00
25 Kordell Stewart 20.00
26 Yancey Thigpen 5.00
27 Garrison Hearst 5.00
28 Steve Young 15.00
29 Joey Galloway 10.00
30 Eddie George 25.00

1998 Collector's Edge Supreme Pro Signatures Authentic

Seven players signed cards for the Pro Signatures Authentic insert (1:800). Collector's Edge also obtained rookie draft-day jerseys and put swatches on Draft Day Jersey cards.

		MT
Common Player:		100.00
TA	Troy Aikman	450.00
DH	Desmond Howard	100.00
JR	Jerry Rice	500.00
MA	Marcus Allen	200.00
TD	Terrell Davis	500.00
RL	Ryan Leaf	150.00
PM	Peyton Manning	150.00

1998 Collector's Edge Supreme T-3 Triple Threat

T-3 Triple Threat is a 30-card insert. The set features 10 quarterbacks (1:36), 10 running backs (1:24) and 10 wide receivers (1:12). The front has a color player image which is repeated on the left and right. The team's logo is in the upper right and the player's name and T-3 logo are at the bottom.

	MT
Complete Set (29):	225.00
Common WR:	2.50
Common RB:	4.00
Common QB:	6.00
Card #18 Never Issued	

1 Rae Carruth 2.50
2 Carl Pickens 2.50
3 Troy Aikman 15.00
4 Emmitt Smith 20.00
5 Terrell Davis 12.00
6 John Elway 15.00
7 Herman Moore 5.00
8 Barry Sanders 20.00
9 Robert Brooks 2.50
10 Brett Favre 30.00
11 Antonio Freeman 5.00
12 Dorsey Levens 4.00
13 Rob Johnson 6.00
14 Jerry Rice 10.00
15 Dan Marino 25.00
16 Cris Carter 2.50
17 Drew Bledsoe 15.00
19 Adrian Murrell 4.00
20 Tim Brown 2.50
21 Napoleon Kaufman 4.00
22 Jerome Bettis 5.00
23 Kordell Stewart 15.00
24 Joey Galloway 5.00
25 Jim Druckenmiller 6.00

26 Terrell Owens 2.50
27 Jake Plummer 12.00
28 Warrick Dunn 12.00
29 Eddie George 12.00
30 Steve McNair 8.00

1999 Collector's Edge Advantage

Edge Advantage is a 190-card set that is made up of 150 veterans, 38 draft pick rookies and 2 checklists. Each card has three different parallels that include Gold Ingot, Galvanized and HoloGold. Other inserts in the product include Rookie Autographs, Jumpstarters, Memorable Moments, Overture, Prime Connection, Shockwaves and Showtime.

	MT
Complete Set (190):	65.00
Common Player:	.15
Minor Stars:	.30
Common Rookie:	.50
Wax Box:	75.00

1 Larry Centers .15
2 Rob Moore .30
3 Adrian Murrell .15
4 Jake Plummer 1.25
5 Frank Sanders .15
6 Jamal Anderson .50
7 Chris Chandler .30
8 Tim Dwight .50
9 Tony Martin .15
10 Terance Mathis .15
11 O.J. Santiago .15
12 Jim Harbaugh .30
13 Priest Holmes .75
14 Jermaine Lewis .30
15 Rod Woodson .15
16 Eric Zeier .15
17 Doug Flutie .75
18 Sam Gash .15
19 Rob Johnson .30
20 Eric Moulds .50
21 Andre Reed .30
22 Antowain Smith .50
23 Bruce Smith .15
24 Thurman Thomas .30
25 Steve Beuerlein .15
26 Kevin Greene .15
27 Raghib Ismail .15
28 Fred Lane .15
29 Muhsin Muhammad .15
30 Edgar Bennett .15
31 Curtis Conway .30
32 Bobby Engram .15
33 Curtis Enis .50
34 Erik Kramer .15
35 Jeff Blake .30
36 Corey Dillon .75
37 Neil O'Donnell .30
38 Carl Pickens .30
39 Takeo Spikes .15
40 Troy Aikman 1.25
41 Billy Davis .15
42 Michael Irvin .30
43 Deion Sanders .50
44 Emmitt Smith 1.75
45 Darren Woodson .15
46 Bubby Brister .30
47 Terrell Davis 1.75
48 John Elway 1.75
49 Ed McCaffrey .30
50 Bill Romanowski .15
51 Shannon Sharpe .30
52 Rod Smith .30
53 Charlie Batch 1.00
54 Germane Crowell .30
55 Herman Moore .50
56 Johnnie Morton .15
57 Barry Sanders 2.50
58 Robert Brooks .15
59 Brett Favre 2.50
60 Antonio Freeman .50
61 Dorsey Levens .50
62 Roell Preston .15
63 Darick Holmes .50
64 Marshall Faulk .50
65 E.G. Green .15
66 Marvin Harrison .30
67 Peyton Manning 2.00
68 Jerome Pathon .15
69 Mark Brunell 1.00
70 Kevin Hardy .15
71 Keenan McCardell .15
72 Jimmy Smith .30
73 Fred Taylor 1.25
74 Alvis Whitted .15
75 Kimble Anders .15
76 Donnell Bennett .15
77 Rich Gannon .15
78 Elvis Grbac .15
79 Bam Morris .15
80 Andre Rison .30
81 Karim Abdul .30
82 John Avery .30
83 Oronde Gadsden .30
84 Sam Madison .30
85 Dan Marino 1.75
86 O.J. McDuffie .30
87 Zach Thomas .30
88 Cris Carter .50
89 Randall Cunningham .50
90 Brad Johnson .50
91 Randy Moss 3.00
92 John Randle .30
93 Jake Reed .15
94 Robert Smith .50
95 Drew Bledsoe 1.00
96 Ben Coates .30
97 Robert Edwards .50
98 Terry Glenn .50
99 Ty Law .15
100 Cam Cleeland .30
101 Kerry Collins .30
102 Gary Brown .15
103 Kent Graham .15
104 Ike Hilliard .30
105 Joe Jurevicius .30
106 Danny Kanell .15
107 Wayne Chrebet .50
108 Aaron Glenn .15
109 Keyshawn Johnson .50
110 Curtis Martin .50
111 Vinny Testaverde .30
112 Tim Brown .30
113 Jeff George .30
114 James Jett .15
115 Napoleon Kaufman .50
116 Charles Woodson .50
117 Koy Detmer .15
118 Duce Staley .50
119 Jerome Bettis .50
120 Charles Johnson .15
121 Kordell Stewart .75
122 Tony Banks .30
123 Isaac Bruce .50
124 June Henley .15
125 Ryan Leaf .75
126 Natrone Means .50
127 Mikhael Ricks .30
128 Craig Whelihan .15
129 Garrison Hearst .50
130 Terrell Owens .75
131 Jerry Rice 1.25
132 J.J. Stokes .30
133 Steve Young 1.00
134 Joey Galloway .50
135 Ahman Green .30
136 Jon Kitna .75
137 Ricky Watters .50
138 Mike Alstott .50
139 Reidel Anthony .30
140 Trent Dilfer .30
141 Warrick Dunn .75
142 Jacquez Green .30
143 Kevin Dyson .50
144 Eddie George .75
145 Steve McNair .75
146 Yancey Thigpen .30
147 Terry Allen .30
148 Trent Green .30
149 Skip Hicks .30
150 Michael Westbrook .30
151 Rahim Abdullah 1.00
152 Champ Bailey 2.00
153 Marlon Barnes 1.00
154 D'Wayne Bates 1.00
155 Michael Bishop 2.50
156 Dre' Bly 1.00
157 David Boston 3.00
158 Chris Claiborne 1.50
159 Tim Couch 12.00
160 Daunte Culpepper 5.00
161 Autrey Denson 1.75
162 Jared DeVries 1.00
163 Troy Edwards 2.50
164 Kris Farris .50
165 Kevin Faulk 3.00
166 Martin Gramatica .50
167 Torry Holt 3.00
168 Brock Huard 2.00
169 Sedrick Irvin 1.75
170 Edgerrin James 12.00
171 James Johnson 2.00
172 Kevin Johnson 1.75
173 Andy Katzenmoyer 1.50
174 Jevon Kearse 2.00
175 Shaun King 4.00
176 Rob Konrad 1.00
177 Chris McAlister 1.00
178 Darnell McDonald 1.50
179 Donovan McNabb 6.00
180 Cade McNown 6.00
181 Dat Nguyen 1.50
182 Peerless Price 2.50
183 Akili Smith 5.00
184 Tai Streets 1.50

185	Cuncho Brown	1.00
186	Ricky Williams	12.00
187	Craig Yeast	1.00
188	Amos Zereoue	2.50
189	Checklist	.15
190	Checklist	.15

1999 Collector's Edge Advantage Galvanized

Galvanized singles are printed on silver foil board with gold foil stamping. Each has a Galvanized stamp on the front and are sequentially numbered on the back. Veterans are numbered to 500 and rookies to 200.

	MT
Galvanized Cards:	4x-8x
Production 500 Sets	
Galvanized Rookies:	3x-6x
Production 200 Sets	

1999 Collector's Edge Advantage Gold Ingot

Each Gold Ingot single is identical to the base card except for the foil is in gold rather than silver and each has a Gold Ingot stamp on the fronts of the cards. It is a parallel to the base and singles were inserted 1:1 packs.

	MT
Complete Set (190):	100.00
Gold Ingot Cards:	2x
Gold Ingot Rookies:	1.5x
Inserted 1:1	

1999 Collector's Edge Advantage HoloGold

HoloGold singles are printed on holographic foil board with veterans numbered to 50 and rookies to 20.

	MT
HoloGold Cards:	40x-80x
Production 50 Sets	
HoloGold Rookies:	20x-40x
Production 20 Sets	

1999 Collector's Edge Advantage Jumpstarters

Each of the singles in this set are printed on clear acetate and offer commentary of each player from Peyton Manning. Each card was sequentially numbered to 500.

	MT
Complete Set (10):	75.00
Common Player:	5.00
Production 500 Sets	
1 Champ Bailey	5.00
2 David Boston	10.00

3	Tim Couch	25.00
4	Daunte Culpepper	12.00
5	Torry Holt	10.00
6	Donovan McNabb	12.00
7	Cade McNown	12.00
8	Peerless Price	7.00
9	Brock Huard	5.00
10	Ricky Williams	25.00

1999 Collector's Edge Advantage Memorable Moments

Each card in this set highlights a memorable moment from 1998. Each is printed on silver foil and they were found 1:24 packs.

	MT
Complete Set (10):	85.00
Common Player:	5.00
Inserted 1:24	
1 Terrell Davis	12.00
2 Randy Moss	15.00
3 Peyton Manning	12.00
4 Emmitt Smith	12.00
5 Keyshawn Johnson	5.00
6 Dan Marino	12.00
7 John Elway	12.00
8 Doug Flutie	7.00
9 Jerry Rice	10.00
10 Steve Young	8.00

1999 Collector's Edge Advantage Overture

Ten of the NFL's superstars are featured in this foil set with gold foil stamping. Singles were inserted 1:24 packs.

	MT
Complete Set (10):	100.00
Common Player:	5.00
Inserted 1:24	
1 Jamal Anderson	5.00
2 Terrell Davis	12.00
3 John Elway	12.00
4 Brett Favre	15.00
5 Peyton Manning	12.00
6 Dan Marino	12.00
7 Randy Moss	15.00
8 Jerry Rice	10.00
9 Barry Sanders	15.00
10 Emmitt Smith	12.00

Values quoted in this guide reflect the retail price of a card — the price a collector can expect to pay when buying a card from a dealer. The wholesale price — that which a collector can expect to receive from a dealer when selling cards — will be significantly lower, depending on desirability and condition.

1999 Collector's Edge Advantage Prime Connection

Current and future NFL stars were included in this 20-card set. Singles were inserted 1:4 packs.

	MT
Complete Set (20):	65.00
Common Player:	1.50
Minor Stars:	3.00
Inserted 1:4	
1 Ricky Williams	12.00
2 Fred Taylor	4.00
3 Tim Couch	12.00
4 Peyton Manning	5.00
5 Daunte Culpepper	5.00
6 Drew Bledsoe	3.50
7 Torry Holt	4.00
8 Keyshawn Johnson	1.50
9 Champ Bailey	1.50
10 Charles Woodson	1.50
11 Brock Huard	1.50
12 Jake Plummer	4.00
13 Donovan McNabb	6.00
14 Steve Young	3.50
15 Edgerrin James	7.00
16 Jamal Anderson	1.50
17 Cade McNown	6.00
18 Mark Brunell	3.50
19 Peerless Price	3.50
20 Randy Moss	6.00

1999 Collector's Edge Advantage Rookie Autographs

Each of the autographs are printed on holographic foil board with the signature found on the fronts of each card. Singles were inserted on average of 1:24 packs.

	MT
Common Player:	6.00
Minor Stars:	12.00
Inserted 1:24	
151 Rahim Abdullah	12.00
152 Champ Bailey	15.00
153 Marlon Barnes	12.00
154 D'Wayne Bates	12.00
155 Michael Bishop	20.00
156 Dre Bly	6.00
157 David Boston	30.00
158 Cuncho Brown	6.00
159 Chris Claiborne	12.00
160 Tim Couch	100.00
161 Daunte Culpepper	45.00
162 Autry Denson	12.00
163 Jared DeVries	12.00
164 Troy Edwards	20.00
165 Kris Farris	6.00
166 Kevin Faulk	30.00
167 Martin Gramatica	6.00
168 Torry Holt	25.00
169 Brock Huard	15.00
170 Sedrick Irvin	15.00
171 Edgerrin James	60.00
172 James Johnson	15.00

173	Kevin Johnson	15.00
174	Andy Katzenmoyer	15.00
175	Jevon Kearse	18.00
176	Shaun King	15.00
177	Rob Konrad	12.00
178	Chris McAlister	15.00
179	Darnell McDonald	15.00
180	Donovan McNabb	45.00
181	Cade McNown	45.00
182	Dat Nguyen	12.00
183	Peerless Price	20.00
184	Akili Smith	40.00
185	Tai Streets	15.00
186	Ricky Williams	100.00
187	Craig Yeast	12.00
188	Amos Zereoue	20.00

1999 Collector's Edge Advantage Shockwaves

This 20-card set was printed on foil board with gold foil stamping. They were inserted 1:12 packs.

	MT
Complete Set (20):	120.00
Common Player:	3.50
Inserted 1:12	
1 Jamal Anderson	3.50
2 Jake Plummer	8.00
3 Eric Moulds	3.50
4 Troy Aikman	8.00
5 Emmitt Smith	12.00
6 Marshall Faulk	3.50
7 Jerome Bettis	3.50
8 Barry Sanders	16.00
9 Brett Favre	16.00
10 Peyton Manning	12.00
11 Mark Brunell	6.00
12 Fred Taylor	8.00
13 Randall Cunningham	3.50
14 Randy Moss	16.00
15 Drew Bledsoe	6.00
16 Keyshawn Johnson	3.50
17 Curtis Martin	3.50
18 Steve Young	5.00
19 Warrick Dunn	5.00
20 Eddie George	5.00

1999 Collector's Edge Advantage Showtime

Each of the 15 cards in this insert are printed on clear acetate with gold foil stamping. Each was sequentially numbered to 500.

	MT
Complete Set (15):	125.00
Common Player:	5.00
Production 500 Sets	
1 Troy Aikman	10.00
2 Jamal Anderson	5.00
3 Mark Brunell	8.00
4 Terrell Davis	15.00
5 Warrick Dunn	7.00
6 Brett Favre	20.00
7 Doug Flutie	7.00
8 Eddie George	7.00
9 Keyshawn Johnson	5.00
10 Peyton Manning	15.00
11 Dan Marino	15.00
12 Randy Moss	20.00
13 Jake Plummer	10.00
14 Jerry Rice	10.00
15 Barry Sanders	20.00

Post-1980 cards in Near Mint condition will generally sell for about 75% of the quoted Mint value. Excellent-condition cards bring no more than 40%.

1999 Collector's Edge First Place

First Place Football was a 200-card set printed on 20-pt. stock. The set included 148 veterans, 50 rookies and 2 checklists. The Kurt Warner #201 was added late to the print run and each was hand-numbered to 500. Parallel sets included Galvanized, Gold Ingot and HoloGold. Other insert sets included: Adrenalin, Excalibur, Future Legends, Loud & Proud, Pro Signature Authentics, Rookie Game Gear and Successors. SRP was $3.99 for 12-card packs.

	MT
Complete Set (200):	60.00
Common Player:	.15
Minor Stars:	.30
Common Rookie:	.50
Wax Box:	70.00
1 Adrian Murrell	.15
2 Rob Moore	.30
3 Jake Plummer	1.25
4 Simeon Rice	.15
5 Frank Sanders	.15
6 Jamal Anderson	.75
7 Chris Calloway	.15
8 Chris Chandler	.30
9 Tim Dwight	.75
10 Terance Mathis	.15
11 Jessie Tuggle	.15
12 Tony Banks	.30
13 Priest Holmes	.50
14 Jermaine Lewis	.15
15 Scott Mitchell	.15
16 Doug Flutie	1.00
17 Eric Moulds	.75
18 Andre Reed	.30
19 Antowain Smith	.50
20 Bruce Smith	.15
21 Thurman Thomas	.30
22 Steve Beuerlein	.30
23 Tim Biakabutuka	.30
24 Kevin Greene	.15
25 Muhsin Muhammad	.30
26 Edgar Bennett	.15
27 Curtis Conway	.30
28 Bobby Engram	.15
29 Curtis Enis	.75
30 Erik Kramer	.15
31 Jeff Blake	.30
32 Corey Dillon	.75
33 Carl Pickens	.30
34 Darnay Scott	.15
35 Takeo Spikes	.15
36 Ty Detmer	.15
37 Terry Kirby	.15
38 Leslie Shepherd	.15
39 Chris Spielman	.15
40 Troy Aikman	1.50
41 Michael Irvin	.30
42 Raghib Ismail	.15
43 Ernie Mills	.15
44 Deion Sanders	.75
45 Emmitt Smith	2.00
46 Chris Warren	.15
47 Bubby Brister	.30
48 Terrell Davis	2.00
49 Brian Griese	1.25
50 Ed McCaffrey	.50
51 Shannon Sharpe	.30
52 Rod Smith	.50
53 Charlie Batch	1.00
54 Terry Fair	.15
55 Herman Moore	.75
56 Johnnie Morton	.15
57 Barry Sanders	3.00
58 Robert Brooks	.15
59 Brett Favre	3.00
60 Mark Chmura	.30
61 Antonio Freeman	.75
62 Dorsey Levens	.75
63 Derrick Mayes	.30
64 Marvin Harrison	.75
65 Peyton Manning	2.00
66 Jerome Pathon	.15
67 Mark Brunell	1.25
68 Keenan McCardell	.30
69 Jimmy Smith	.75
70 Fred Taylor	1.50
71 Derrick Alexander	.15

72	Kimble Anders	.15
73	Elvis Grbac	.30
74	Warren Moon	.30
75	Bam Morris	.15
76	Andre Rison	.30
77	Karim Abdul	.30
78	Dan Marino	2.00
79	Tony Martin	.15
80	O.J. McDuffie	.30
81	Zach Thomas	.30
82	Cris Carter	.75
83	Randall Cunningham	.75
84	Jeff George	.75
85	Randy Moss	3.00
86	Jake Reed	.30
87	Robert Smith	.75
88	Drew Bledsoe	1.25
89	Ben Coates	.30
90	Terry Glenn	.75
91	Ty Law	.15
92	Shawn Jefferson	.15
93	Cameron Cleeland	.30
94	Andre Hastings	.15
95	Billy Joe Hobert	.15
96	Eddie Kennison	.15
97	Gary Brown	.15
98	Kerry Collins	.30
99	Kent Graham	.15
100	Ike Hilliard	.30
101	Joe Jurevicius	.15
102	Wayne Chrebet	.75
103	Aaron Glenn	.15
104	Keyshawn Johnson	.75
105	Mo Lewis	.15
106	Curtis Martin	.75
107	Vinny Testaverde	.50
108	Tim Brown	.30
109	Rich Gannon	.30
110	James Jett	.15
111	Napoleon Kaufman	.75
112	Charles Woodson	.75
113	Koy Detmer	.15
114	Charles Johnson	.15
115	Duce Staley	.50
116	Jerome Bettis	.75
117	Courtney Hawkins	.15
118	Levon Kirkland	.15
119	Kordell Stewart	.75
120	Isaac Bruce	.75
121	Marshall Faulk	.75
122	Trent Green	.50
123	Amp Lee	.15
124	Jim Harbaugh	.30
125	Charlie Jones	.15
126	Freddie Jones	.30
127	Ryan Leaf	.75
128	Natrone Means	.50
129	Junior Seau	.30
130	Garrison Hearst	.50
131	Terrell Owens	.75
132	Jerry Rice	1.50
133	J.J. Stokes	.30
134	Steve Young	1.00
135	Joey Galloway	.75
136	Jon Kitna	.75
137	Ricky Watters	.50
138	Mike Alstott	.75
139	Reidel Anthony	.30
140	Trent Dilfer	.50
141	Warrick Dunn	.75
142	Kevin Dyson	.30
143	Eddie George	1.00
144	Steve McNair	1.00
145	Frank Wycheck	.30
146	Skip Hicks	.30
147	Brad Johnson	.50
148	Michael Westbrook	.30
149	Checklist	.15
150	Checklist	.15
151	David Boston	2.50
152	Patrick Kerney	.50
153	Chris McAlister	1.00
154	Peerless Price	2.00
155	Antoine Winfield	1.00
156	D'Wayne Bates	1.00
157	Cade McNown	4.00
158	Akili Smith	4.00
159	Rahim Abdullah	.50
160	Tim Couch	7.00
161	Kevin Johnson	4.00
162	Ebenezer Ekuban	1.00
163	Dat Nguyen	.50
164	Al Wilson	.50
165	Chris Claiborne	1.00
166	Sedrick Irvin	1.50
167	Antwan Edwards	1.00
168	Aaron Brooks	1.00
169	De'Mond Parker	1.50
170	Edgerrin James	10.00
171	Fernando Bryant	1.00
172	Michael Cloud	1.00
173	John Tait	.50
174	Cecil Collins	2.50
175	J.J. Johnson	1.50
176	Rob Konrad	1.50
177	Daunte Culpepper	4.00
178	Jim Kleinsasser	1.00
179	Dimitrius Underwood	1.00
180	Michael Bishop	1.75
181	Kevin Faulk	1.75
182	Andy Katzenmoyer	1.00
183	Ricky Williams	7.00
184	Joe Montgomery	1.00
185	Donovan McNabb	4.00
186	Troy Edwards	2.50
187	Amos Zereoue	1.50

188	*Joe Germaine*	1.00
189	*Torry Holt*	2.50
190	*Jermaine Fazande*	1.00
191	*Reggie McGrew*	.50
192	*Karsten Bailey*	1.00
193	*Lamar King*	.50
194	*Autry Denson*	1.00
195	*Martin Gramatica*	1.00
196	*Shaun King*	4.00
197	*Darnell McDonald*	1.00
198	*Anthony McFarland*	.50
199	*Jevon Kearse*	2.00
200	*Champ Bailey*	1.50
201	*Kurt Warner/500*	400.00

1999 Collector's Edge First Place Galvanized

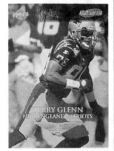

This was a 200-card parallel to the base set. Each single had the Galvanized stamp on the front of the card. Veterans were sequentially numbered to 500 and rookies to 100.

	MT
Galvanized Cards:	3x-6x
Production 500 Sets	
Galvanized Rookies:	5x-10x
Production 100 Sets	

1999 Collector's Edge First Place Gold Ingot

This was a 200-card parallel to the base set. Each single had the Gold Ingot stamp on the front of the card. Singles were found one- per-pack.

	MT
Gold Ingot Cards:	2x
Gold Ingot Rookies:	1.5x
Inserted 1:1	

1999 Collector's Edge First Place HoloGold

This was a 200-card parallel to the base set. Each single had the HoloGold stamp on the front of the card. Veterans were sequentially numbered to 50 and rookies to 10.

	MT
HoloGold Cards:	30x-60x
Production 50 Sets	
HoloGold Rookies:	25x-50x
Production 10 Sets	

1999 Collector's Edge First Place Adrenalin

This 20-card insert set included high impact players. Each single was sequentially numbered to 1,000 and printed on clear vinyl stock.

		MT
Complete Set (20):		100.00
Common Player:		4.00
Production 1,000 Sets		
1	Jake Plummer	6.00
2	Jamal Anderson	4.00
3	Eric Moulds	4.00
4	Emmitt Smith	10.00
5	Terrell Davis	10.00
6	Barry Sanders	15.00
7	Brett Favre	15.00
8	Antonio Freeman	4.00
9	Peyton Manning	10.00
10	Mark Brunell	6.00
11	Fred Taylor	8.00
12	Dan Marino	10.00
13	Cris Carter	4.00
14	Randy Moss	15.00
15	Keyshawn Johnson	4.00
16	Curtis Martin	4.00
17	Jerome Bettis	4.00
18	Terrell Owens	4.00
19	Joey Galloway	4.00
20	Eddie George	4.00

1999 Collector's Edge First Place Excalibur

Excalibur was a 25-card set that was a cross-brand program. Singles were found in First Place, Odyssey and Masters. Nine of the singles appeared in First Place and were found 1:24 packs.

		MT
Complete Set (9):		50.00
Common Player:		3.00
Inserted 1:24		
2	Torry Holt	6.00
5	Edgerrin James	15.00
7	Brett Favre	12.00
17	Peyton Manning	10.00
17	Randy Moss	12.00
19	Terrell Davis	10.00
20	Mark Brunell	5.00
22	Eddie George	3.00
24	Doug Flutie	5.00

Post-1980 cards in Near Mint condition will generally sell for about 75% of the quoted Mint value. Excellent-condition cards bring no more than 40%.

1999 Collector's Edge First Place Future Legends

This 20-card insert set included all of the top rookies from 1999. Singles were found 1:6 packs.

		MT
Complete Set (20):		45.00
Common Player:		.75
Minor Stars:		1.50
Inserted 1:6		
1	Tim Couch	10.00
2	Donovan McNabb	5.00
3	Akili Smith	5.00
4	Edgerrin James	12.00
5	Ricky Williams	10.00
6	Torry Holt	3.00
7	Champ Bailey	1.50
8	David Boston	3.00
9	Daunte Culpepper	5.00
10	Cade McNown	5.00
11	Troy Edwards	3.00
12	Chris Claiborne	1.50
13	Jevon Kearse	2.50
14	Shaun King	5.00
15	Kevin Faulk	2.00
16	James Johnson	1.50
17	Peerless Price	2.00
18	Kevin Johnson	3.00
19	Brock Huard	1.50
20	Joe Germaine	.75

1999 Collector's Edge First Place Loud and Proud

This 20-card insert set included the top stars in the NFL. Singles were found 1:12 packs.

		MT
Complete Set (20):		45.00
Common Player:		2.00
Inserted 1:12		
1	Jamal Anderson	2.00
2	Emmitt Smith	6.00
3	Terrell Davis	6.00
4	Barry Sanders	8.00
5	Fred Taylor	4.00
6	Randy Moss	8.00
7	Antonio Freeman	2.00
8	Curtis Martin	2.00
9	Terrell Owens	2.00
10	Eddie George	2.00
11	Dan Marino	6.00
12	Brett Favre	8.00
13	Jerry Rice	4.00
14	Steve Young	3.00
15	Doug Flutie	3.00
16	Jake Plummer	3.00
17	Troy Aikman	4.00
18	Mark Brunell	3.00
19	Jon Kitna	2.00
20	Charlie Batch	3.00

A player's name in *italic* type indicates a rookie card.

1999 Collector's Edge First Place Pro Signatures

This 29-card insert set included autographed cards from both rookies and veterans. Singles were found 1:24 packs. A parallel Blue version was made with each single sequentially numbered to 40. A Red version was also made with each single numbered to 10.

		MT
Complete Set (29):		425.00
Common Player:		6.00
Minor Stars:		12.00
Inserted 1:24		
Blue Cards:		3x
Production 40 Sets		
Red Cards:		
Production 10 Sets		
	Rahim Abdullah	6.00
	Kimble Anders	6.00
	Dre Bly	12.00
	David Boston	25.00
	Cuncho Brown	6.00
	Gary Brown	6.00
	Ray Buchanan	6.00
	Tim Couch	75.00
	Autry Denson	12.00
	Jared DeVries	6.00
	Bobby Engram	6.00
	Terry Fair	6.00
	Kevin Faulk	20.00
	Joey Galloway	20.00
	Rich Gannon	12.00
	Marvin Harrison	20.00
	Andre Hastings	6.00
	Courtney Hawkins	6.00
	Brock Huard	15.00
	Edgerrin James	100.00
	Shaun King	40.00
	Chris McAlister	12.00
	Keenan McCardell	12.00
	Dat Nguyen	12.00
	Andre Reed	12.00
	Jimmy Smith	20.00
	Akili Smith	35.00
	Duce Staley	20.00
	Craig Yeast	12.00

1999 Collector's Edge First Place Rookie Game Gear

This 10-card insert set included only rookies from 1999. Each single was sequentially numbered to 500.

		MT
Complete Set (10):		220.00
Common Player:		10.00
Production 500 Sets		
1	Tim Couch	60.00
2	Donovan McNabb	30.00
3	Akili Smith	30.00
4	Daunte Culpepper	30.00
5	Ricky Williams	60.00
6	Kevin Johnson	20.00
7	Cade McNown	30.00
8	Torry Holt	20.00
9	Champ Bailey	10.00
10	David Boston	20.00

Values quoted in this guide reflect the retail price of a card — the price a collector can expect to pay when buying a card from a dealer. The wholesale price — that which a collector can expect to receive from a dealer when selling cards — will be significantly lower, depending on desirability and condition.

1999 Collector's Edge First Place Successors

This 15-card insert set included a top rookie and a top NFL star from the same position and matched them up on the same card. Singles were found 1:12 packs.

		MT
Complete Set (15):		65.00
Common Player:		2.00
Minor Stars:		4.00
Inserted 1:12		
1	David Boston, Cris Carter	4.00
2	Peerless Price, Eric Moulds	2.00
3	Cade McNown, Brett Favre	8.00
4	Akili Smith, Charlie Batch	5.00
5	Tim Couch, Peyton Manning	10.00
6	Keyshawn Johnson, Joey Galloway	
7	Edgerrin James, Emmitt Smith	12.00
8	James Johnson, Curtis Martin	2.00
9	Daunte Culpepper, Dan Marino	6.00
10	Kevin Faulk, Barry Sanders	8.00
11	Ricky Williams, Marshall Faulk	8.00
12	Donovan McNabb, Steve Young	5.00
13	Troy Edwards, Kevin Johnson	4.00
14	Torry Holt, Jerry Rice	5.00
15	Shaun King, Jake Plummer	5.00

1999 Collector's Edge Fury

Edge Fury is a 200-card set with 148 veteran players, two checklists and 50 seeded rookies found one-per-pack. The product includes three parallel sets with Gold Ingot, Galvanized and HoloGold inserts. Other inserts include: Extreme Team, Fast and Furious, Forerunners, Game Ball, Heir Force and Xplosive.

		MT
Complete Set (200):		70.00
Common Player:		.15
Minor Stars:		.30
Common Rookie:		.50
Inserted 1:1		
Wax Box:		60.00
1	Checklist	.15
2	Checklist	.15
3	Karim Abdul	.30
4	Troy Aikman	1.50
5	Derrick Alexander	.15
6	Mike Alstott	.50
7	Jamal Anderson	.50

8	Reidel Anthony	.30
9	Tiki Barber	.15
10	Charlie Batch	1.00
11	Edgar Bennett	.15
12	Jerome Bettis	.50
13	Steve Beuerlein	.15
14	Tim Biakabutuka	.30
15	Jeff Blake	.30
16	Drew Bledsoe	1.00
17	Bubby Brister	.30
18	Robert Brooks	.15
19	Gary Brown	.15
20	Tim Brown	.30
21	Isaac Bruce	.30
22	Mark Brunell	1.00
23	Chris Calloway	.15
24	Cris Carter	.50
25	Larry Centers	.15
26	Chris Chandler	.30
27	Wayne Chrebet	.50
28	Cam Cleeland	.30
29	Kerry Collins	.30
30	Curtis Conway	.30
31	Germane Crowell	.30
32	Randall Cunningham	.50
33	Terrell Davis	2.00
34	Koy Detmer	.15
35	Ty Detmer	.30
36	Trent Dilfer	.50
37	Corey Dillon	.50
38	Warrick Dunn	.75
39	Tim Dwight	.50
40	Kevin Dyson	.30
41	John Elway	2.00
42	Bobby Engram	.15
43	Curtis Enis	.50
44	Terry Fair	.15
45	Marshall Faulk	.50
46	Brett Favre	3.00
47	Doug Flutie	.75
48	Antonio Freeman	.50
49	Joey Galloway	.50
50	Rich Gannon	.15
51	Eddie George	.75
52	Jeff George	.30
53	Terry Glenn	.50
54	Elvis Grbac	.15
55	Ahman Green	.30
56	Jacquez Green	.30
57	Trent Green	.50
58	Kevin Greene	.15
59	Brian Griese	1.00
60	Az-Zahir Hakim	.30
61	Jim Harbaugh	.30
62	Marvin Harrison	.50
63	Courtney Hawkins	.15
64	Garrison Hearst	.50
65	Ike Hilliard	.30
66	Billy Joe Hobert	.15
67	Priest Holmes	.50
68	Michael Irvin	.30
69	Raghib Ismail	.15
70	Shawn Jefferson	.15
71	James Jett	.15
72	Brad Johnson	.50
73	Charles Johnson	.15
74	Keyshawn Johnson	.50
75	Pat Johnson	.15
76	Joe Jurevicius	.15
77	Napoleon Kaufman	.50
78	Eddie Kennison	.30
79	Terry Kirby	.15
80	Jon Kitna	.75
81	Erik Kramer	.15
82	Fred Lane	.15
83	Ty Law	.15
84	Ryan Leaf	.75
85	Amp Lee	.15
86	Dorsey Levens	.50
87	Jermaine Lewis	.30
88	Sam Madison	.15
89	Peyton Manning	2.00
90	Dan Marino	2.00
91	Curtis Martin	.50
92	Tony Martin	.15
93	Terance Mathis	.15
94	Ed McCaffrey	.30
95	Keenan McCardell	.15
96	O.J. McDuffie	.30
97	Steve McNair	.75
98	Natrone Means	.30
99	Herman Moore	.50
100	Rob Moore	.30
101	Bam Morris	.15
102	Johnnie Morton	.15
103	Randy Moss	3.50
104	Eric Moulds	.50
105	Muhsin Muhammad	.15
106	Adrian Murrell	.30
107	Terrell Owens	.50
108	Jerome Pathon	.15
109	Carl Pickens	.30
110	Jake Plummer	1.25
111	Andre Reed	.15
112	Jake Reed	.15
113	Jerry Rice	1.50
114	Mikhael Ricks	.15
115	Andre Rison	.30
116	Barry Sanders	3.00
117	Deion Sanders	.50
118	Frank Sanders	.30
119	O.J. Santiago	.15
120	Darnay Scott	.15
121	Junior Seau	.30
122	Shannon Sharpe	.30
123	Leslie Shepherd	.15
124	Antowain Smith	.50

125	Bruce Smith	.15
126	Emmitt Smith	2.00
127	Jimmy Smith	.30
128	Robert Smith	.50
129	Rod Smith	.30
130	Chris Spielman	.15
131	Takeo Spikes	.15
132	Duce Staley	.30
133	Kordell Stewart	.75
134	Bryan Still	.15
135	J.J. Stokes	.30
136	Fred Taylor	1.50
137	Vinny Testaverde	.30
138	Yancey Thigpen	.30
139	Thurman Thomas	.30
140	Zach Thomas	.30
141	Amani Toomer	.15
142	Hines Ward	.30
143	Chris Warren	.30
144	Ricky Watters	.30
145	Michael Westbrook	.30
146	Alvis Whitted	.15
147	Charles Woodson	.50
148	Rod Woodson	.15
149	Frank Wycheck	.15
150	Steve Young	1.00
151	*Rabih Abdullah*	1.00
152	*Champ Bailey*	2.00
153	*D'Wayne Bates*	1.50
154	*Michael Bishop*	2.50
155	*Dre' Bly*	1.50
156	*David Boston*	3.00
157	*Fernando Bryant*	.50
158	*Chris Claiborne*	1.50
159	*Mike Cloud*	1.50
160	*Cecil Collins*	3.00
161	*Tim Couch*	12.00
162	*Daunte Culpepper*	5.00
163	*Antwan Edwards*	.50
164	*Troy Edwards*	2.50
165	*Ebenezer Ekuban*	1.00
166	*Kevin Faulk*	3.00
167	*Joe Germaine*	2.00
168	*Aaron Gibson*	.50
169	*Martin Gramatica*	.50
170	*Torry Holt*	2.50
171	*Brock Huard*	2.00
172	*Sedrick Irvin*	1.50
173	*Edgerrin James*	12.00
174	*James Johnson*	1.75
175	*Kevin Johnson*	1.50
176	*Andy Katzenmoyer*	1.50
177	*Jevon Kearse*	2.50
178	*Patrick Kerney*	.50
179	*Lamar King*	.50
180	*Shaun King*	4.00
181	*Jim Kleinsasser*	.50
182	*Rob Konrad*	1.00
183	*Chris McAlister*	1.00
184	*Anthony McFarland*	1.00
185	*Karsten Bailey*	1.00
186	*Donovan McNabb*	5.00
187	*Cade McNown*	5.00
188	*Joe Montgomery*	1.50
189	*Dat Nguyen*	1.50
190	*Luke Petitgout*	.50
191	*Peerless Price*	2.00
192	*Akili Smith*	5.00
193	*Matt Stinchcomb*	.50
194	*John Tait*	.50
195	*Jermaine Fazande*	.50
196	*Ricky Williams*	12.00
197	*Al Wilson*	1.00
198	*Antoine Winfield*	1.00
199	*Damien Woody*	.50
200	*Amos Zereoue*	2.50

1999 Collector's Edge Fury Galvanized

This 200-card parallel is identical to the Gold Ingot parallel except for the Galvanized stamp on the front of the card in silver and each card is sequentially numbered on the back. Veterans are numbered to 500 and rookies to 100.

	MT
Complete Set (200):	550.00

Galvanized Cards:	3x-6x
Production 500 Sets	
Galvanized Rookies:	5x-10x
Production 100 Sets	

1999 Collector's Edge Fury Gold Ingot

This is a 200-card parallel to the base set that was inserted 1:1 packs. The photo is the same as the base except for it's printed on foil board and the foil on the front is gold rather than silver. Each also has a Gold Ingot gold stamp on the fronts of the cards.

	MT
Complete Set (200):	140.00
Gold Ingot Cards:	2x
Gold Ingot Rookies:	1.5x
Inserted 1:1	

1999 Collector's Edge Fury HoloGold

Each card in this 200-card parallel set are printed on prismatic silver foil board. Each card front has the HoloGold stamp in gold foil. Veterans are printed to 50 and rookies to 10.

	MT
HoloGold Cards:	40x-80x
Production 50 Sets	
HoloGold Rookies:	25x-50x
Production 10 Sets	

1999 Collector's Edge Fury Extreme Team

Each card in this 10-card set is printed on micro-etched gold holographic foil board. Singles were inserted 1:24 packs.

		MT
Complete Set (10):		60.00
Common Player:		4.00
Inserted 1:24		
1	Keyshawn Johnson	4.00
2	Emmitt Smith	12.00
3	John Elway	12.00
4	Terrell Davis	12.00
5	Barry Sanders	15.00
6	Brett Favre	15.00
7	Peyton Manning	12.00
8	Fred Taylor	8.00
9	Dan Marino	12.00
10	Randy Moss	15.00

A player's name in *italic* type indicates a rookie card.

1999 Collector's Edge Fury Fast and Furious

This 25-card insert is sequentially numbered to 500 and is printed on plastic card stock with gold foil stamping.

		MT
Complete Set (25):		100.00
Common Player:		2.00
Minor Stars:		4.00
Production 500 Sets		
1	Jake Plummer	8.00
2	Jamal Anderson	4.00
3	Eric Moulds	4.00
4	Curtis Enis	4.00
5	Emmitt Smith	12.00
6	Deion Sanders	4.00
7	Terrell Davis	12.00
8	Barry Sanders	15.00
9	Herman Moore	4.00
10	Charlie Batch	5.00
11	Marshall Faulk	4.00
12	Mark Brunell	6.00
13	Fred Taylor	8.00
14	Randy Moss	15.00
15	Cris Carter	4.00
16	Robert Edwards	2.00
17	Keyshawn Johnson	4.00
18	Curtis Martin	4.00
19	Charles Woodson	4.00
20	Jerome Bettis	4.00
21	Kordell Stewart	5.00
22	Steve Young	6.00
23	Jerry Rice	8.00
24	Warrick Dunn	5.00
25	Eddie George	5.00

1999 Collector's Edge Fury Forerunners

This 15-card set includes the top running backs in the NFL. Each card is printed on holographic foil board with gold foil stamping. Singles were inserted 1:8 packs.

		MT
Complete Set (15):		40.00
Common Player:		1.00
Minor Stars:		2.00
Inserted 1:8		
1	Jamal Anderson	2.00
2	Curtis Enis	2.00
3	Corey Dillon	2.00
4	Emmitt Smith	8.00
5	Barry Sanders	10.00
6	Terrell Davis	8.00
7	Marshall Faulk	2.00
8	Fred Taylor	6.00
9	Robert Smith	2.00
10	Curtis Martin	2.00
11	Jerome Bettis	2.00
12	Garrison Hearst	2.00
13	Warrick Dunn	4.00
14	Eddie George	4.00
15	Ricky Watters	1.00

1999 Collector's Edge Fury Game Ball

Each card in this 43-card set includes a piece of a game-used football that the player used. Singles were found 1:24 packs.

		MT
Complete Set (43):		600.00
Common Player:		6.00
Minor Stars:		12.00
Inserted 1:24		
	Troy Aikman	25.00
	Mike Alstott	12.00
	Charlie Batch	20.00
	Jerome Bettis	20.00
	Mark Brunell	20.00
	Cris Carter	12.00
	Terrell Davis	40.00
	Corey Dillon	12.00
	Warrick Dunn	15.00
	John Elway	40.00
	Curtis Enis	12.00
	Marshall Faulk	12.00
	Brett Favre	50.00
	Antonio Freeman	12.00
	Joey Galloway	12.00
	Eddie George	15.00
	Garrison Hearst	12.00
	Michael Irvin	6.00
	Rob Johnson	12.00
	Napoleon Kaufman	12.00
	Ryan Leaf	15.00
	Dorsey Levens	12.00
	Peyton Manning	40.00
	Curtis Martin	12.00
	Steve McNair	15.00
	Natrone Means	12.00
	Warren Moon	12.00
	Herman Moore	12.00
	Randy Moss	50.00
	Adrian Murrell	12.00
	Terrell Owens	12.00
	Carl Pickens	6.00
	Jake Plummer	25.00
	Jerry Rice	25.00
	Barry Sanders	50.00
	Deion Sanders	12.00
	Shannon Sharpe	6.00
	Antowain Smith	12.00
	Emmitt Smith	35.00
	Rod Smith	6.00
	Kordell Stewart	15.00
	Fred Taylor	25.00
	Steve Young	20.00

1999 Collector's Edge Fury Heir Force

This 20-card set includes the top rookies and were inserted 1:6 packs. Each card was printed on holographic foil board with gold foil stamping.

		MT
Complete Set (20):		45.00
Common Player:		1.00
Inserted 1:6		
1	Rahim Abdullah	1.00
2	Champ Bailey	2.00
3	D'Wayne Bates	1.00
4	Michael Bishop	2.50
5	David Boston	3.00
6	Chris Claiborne	1.50
7	Tim Couch	12.00
8	Daunte Culpepper	5.00
9	Kevin Faulk	3.00
10	Torry Holt	2.50
11	Brock Huard	2.00
12	Edgerrin James	8.00
13	Andy Katzenmoyer	1.50
14	Shaun King	1.75
15	Rob Konrad	1.00
16	Donovan McNabb	5.00
17	Cade McNown	5.00
18	Peerless Price	2.00
19	Akili Smith	4.00
20	Ricky Williams	12.00

1999 Collector's Edge Fury X-Plosive

Each card is printed on explosive micro-etched holofoil with foil stamping. Singles from this 20-card set were found 1:12 packs.

		MT
Complete Set (20):		100.00
Common Player:		1.50
Minor Stars:		3.00
Inserted 1:12		
1	Jake Plummer	8.00
2	Doug Flutie	5.00
3	Eric Moulds	3.00
4	Troy Aikman	8.00
5	John Elway	12.00
6	Charlie Batch	6.00
7	Herman Moore	3.00
8	Brett Favre	15.00
9	Antonio Freeman	3.00
10	Peyton Manning	12.00
11	Mark Brunell	6.00
12	Dan Marino	12.00
13	Randy Moss	15.00
14	Drew Bledsoe	6.00
15	Keyshawn Johnson	3.00
16	Vinny Testaverde	1.50
17	Kordell Stewart	4.00
18	Terrell Owens	3.00
19	Jerry Rice	8.00
20	Steve Young	6.00

1999 Collector's Edge Masters

Edge Masters was a 200-card set that had every single card sequentially numbered. Veterans were numbered to 5,000 and rookies to 2,000. Each card was printed on micro-etched holographic foil board. Two parallel sets were issued as HoloSilver and HoloGold. Insert sets included Excalibur, Master Legends, Main Event, Majestic, Pro Signature Authentics, Quest, Rookie Masters and Sentinels. Three-card packs had an SRP of $5.59.

		MT
Complete Set (200):		500.00
Common Player:		.25
Minor Stars:		.50
Production 5,000 Sets		
Common Rookie:		3.00
Production 2,000 Sets		
Wax Box:		125.00
1	*David Boston*	15.00
2	*Marc Cody*	6.00
3	*Chris Griesen*	6.00
4	*Joel Makovicka*	6.00
5	Adrian Murrell	.25
6	Jake Plummer	1.50
7	Frank Sanders	.50
8	Jamal Anderson	1.00
9	Chris Chandler	.50
10	Reggie Kelly	.50
11	*Patrick Kerney*	3.00
12	Terance Mathis	.25
13	*Jeff Paulk*	6.00
14	Stoney Case	.50
15	Qadry Ismail	.25

16	Chris McAlister	6.00
17	Errict Rhett	.50
18	Brandon Stokley	6.00
19	Doug Flutie	1.50
20	Kamil Loud	6.00
21	Eric Moulds	1.00
22	*Peerless Price*	10.00
23	Andre Reed	.50
24	Antowain Smith	1.00
25	*Antoine Winfield*	6.00
26	Steve Beuerlein	.50
27	Tim Biakabutuka	.50
28	*Dameyune Craig*	6.00
29	*Patrick Jeffers*	25.00
30	Muhsin Muhammad	.50
31	*D'Wayne Bates*	6.00
32	*Marty Booker*	6.00
33	Bobby Engram	.25
34	Curtis Enis	1.00
35	*Ty Hallock*	6.00
36	Shane Matthews	1.00
37	*Cade McNown*	25.00
38	Marcus Robinson	2.00
39	*Scott Covington*	6.00
40	Corey Dillon	1.00
41	*Damon Griffin*	6.00
42	Carl Pickens	.50
43	Darnay Scott	.50
44	*Akili Smith*	20.00
45	*Craig Yeast*	6.00
46	*Darrin Chiaverini*	6.00
47	*Tim Couch*	40.00
48	*Phil Dawson*	3.00
49	*Kevin Johnson*	15.00
50	*Terry Kirby*	.25
51	*Wali Ranier*	3.00
52	*Troy Aikman*	2.00
53	*Ebenezer Ekuban*	6.00
54	Michael Irvin	.50
55	Raghib Ismail	.25
56	*Wane McGarity*	6.00
57	*Dat Nguyen*	6.00
58	Deion Sanders	1.00
59	Emmitt Smith	3.00
60	Byron Chamberlain	.50
61	*Andre Cooper*	3.00
62	Terrell Davis	3.00
63	*Olandis Gary*	25.00
64	Brian Griese	2.00
65	Ed McCaffrey	.50
66	*Travis McGriff*	6.00
67	Shannon Sharpe	.50
68	Rod Smith	.50
69	Al Wilson	6.00
70	Charlie Batch	1.50
71	*Chris Claiborne*	6.00
72	Germane Crowell	.50
73	Greg Hill	.25
74	*Sedrick Irvin*	8.00
75	Herman Moore	1.00
76	Johnnie Morton	.25
77	Barry Sanders	4.00
78	*Aaron Brooks*	8.00
79	*Antwan Edwards*	6.00
80	Brett Favre	4.00
81	Antonio Freeman	1.00
82	Dorsey Levens	1.00
83	Bill Schroeder	.25
84	E.G. Green	.25
85	Marvin Harrison	1.00
86	*Edgerrin James*	75.00
87	Peyton Manning	3.00
88	Mark Brunell	1.50
89	Jay Fiedler	.50
90	Keenan McCardell	.50
91	Jimmy Smith	1.00
92	James Stewart	.50
93	Fred Taylor	2.00
94	Derrick Alexander	.25
95	*Michael Cloud*	6.00
96	Elvis Grbac	.50
97	Bam Morris	.25
98	Andre Rison	.50
99	*Cecil Collins*	10.00
100	Damon Huard	1.50
101	*J.J. Johnson*	10.00
102	Rob Konrad	6.00
103	Dan Marino	3.00
104	O.J. McDuffie	.50
105	Cris Carter	1.00
106	*Daunte Culpepper*	25.00
107	Randall Cunningham	1.00
108	Jeff George	1.00
109	*Jim Kleinsasser*	6.00
110	Randy Moss	4.00
111	Robert Smith	1.00
112	Terry Allen	.50
113	*Michael Bishop*	10.00
114	Drew Bledsoe	1.50
115	*Kevin Faulk*	10.00
116	Terry Glenn	1.00
117	*Andy Katzenmoyer*	6.00
118	*Billy Joe Hobert*	.25
119	Eddie Kennison	.25
120	*Ricky Williams*	40.00
121	Tiki Barber	.50
122	*Sean Bennett*	6.00
123	Gary Brown	.25
124	Kent Graham	.25
125	Ike Hilliard	.25
126	*Joe Montgomery*	8.00
127	Amani Toomer	.50
128	Wayne Chrebet	1.00
129	Keyshawn Johnson	1.00
130	Curtis Martin	1.00
131	*Ray Lucas*	10.00
132	Vinny Testaverde	1.00

133	Tim Brown	.50
134	*Tony Bryant*	3.00
135	*Scott Dreisbach*	6.00
136	Rich Gannon	.25
137	Tyrone Wheatley	.50
138	Charles Woodson	1.00
139	*Na Brown*	3.00
140	Charles Johnson	.25
141	Cecil Martin	6.00
142	*Donovan McNabb*	25.00
143	Doug Pederson	.25
144	Duce Staley	1.00
145	Jerome Bettis	1.00
146	Kris Brown	6.00
147	*Troy Edwards*	15.00
148	Kordell Stewart	1.00
149	Hines Ward	.50
150	*Amos Zereoue*	8.00
151	Dre Bly	6.00
152	Isaac Bruce	1.00
153	Marshall Faulk	1.00
154	*Joe Germaine*	8.00
155	*Az-Zahir Hakim*	.50
156	*Torry Holt*	15.00
157	Kurt Warner	100.00
158	*Justin Watson*	6.00
159	*Jermaine Fazande*	8.00
160	Jeff Graham	.25
161	Jim Harbaugh	.50
162	*Steve Heiden*	3.00
163	Erik Kramer	.25
164	Natrone Means	.50
165	Mikhael Ricks	.50
166	Junior Seau	.50
167	*Jeff Garcia*	15.00
168	Charlie Garner	.50
169	*Terry Jackson*	6.00
170	Terrell Owens	1.00
171	Jerry Rice	2.00
172	Steve Young	1.25
173	*Karsten Bailey*	6.00
174	Joey Galloway	1.00
175	Brock Huard	8.00
176	Jon Kitna	1.00
177	Derrick Mayes	.50
178	*Charlie Rogers*	6.00
179	Ricky Watters	.50
180	*Rabih Abdullah*	3.00
181	Mike Alstott	1.00
182	Reidel Anthony	.50
183	Trent Dilfer	.50
184	Warrick Dunn	1.00
185	*Martin Gramatica*	6.00
186	Shaun King	25.00
187	*Darnell McDonald*	6.00
188	*Yo Murphy*	3.00
189	*Kevin Daft*	6.00
190	Kevin Dyson	.50
191	Eddie George	1.25
192	*Jevon Kearse*	15.00
193	Steve McNair	1.25
194	Yancey Thigpen	.50
195	*Champ Bailey*	10.00
196	Albert Connell	.50
197	Stephen Davis	1.00
198	Skip Hicks	.50
199	Brad Johnson	1.00
200	Michael Westbrook	.50

1999 Collector's Edge Masters HoloSilver

This was a 200-card parallel to the base set. Each card was sequentially numbered to 3,500.

	MT
HoloSilver Cards:	2x
HoloSilver Rookies (2,000):	50%
HoloSilver Rookies (5,000):	75%
Production 3,500 Sets	

1999 Collector's Edge Masters HoloGold

This was a 200-card parallel to the base set. Each single was sequentially numbered to 25.

	MT
HoloGold Cards:	25x-50x
HoloGold Rookies:	2x-4x
Production 25 Sets	

1999 Collector's Edge Masters Excalibur

Excalibur was a 25-card set that was a cross-brand program. Singles were found in First Place, Odyssey and Masters. Eight of the singles were inserted into Masters and were sequentially numbered to 5,000.

		MT
Complete Set (8):		35.00
Common Player:		2.00
Production 5,000 Sets		
3	Dan Marino	8.00
6	Champ Bailey	2.00
8	Barry Sanders	10.00
10	Brett Favre	10.00
12	Tim Couch	10.00
14	Akili Smith	5.00
18	Steve Young	4.00
21	Curtis Martin	2.00

1999 Collector's Edge Masters Main Event

This 10-card insert set included the key matchups from the 1999 NFL season. Each card included two players whose teams went head-to-head in big games. Each single was printed on clear plastic and was sequentially numbered to 1,000.

		MT
Complete Set (10):		45.00
Common Player:		3.00
Production 1,000 Sets		
1	Randy Moss, Jamal Anderson	15.00
2	Mark Brunell, Eddie George	6.00
3	Terrell Davis, Cecil Collins	8.00
4	Rocket Ismail, Stephen Davis	3.00
5	Troy Edwards, Kevin Johnson	7.00
6	Antonio Freeman, Charlie Batch	5.00
7	Terry Glenn, Marvin Harrison	3.00
8	Keyshawn Johnson, Doug Flutie	6.00
9	Cade McNown, Ricky Williams	15.00
10	Steve Young, Marshall Faulk	6.00

A player's name in *italic* type indicates a rookie card.

1999 Collector's Edge Masters Majestic

This 30-card insert set included the most popular and collectible stars and featured them on a clear vinyl card. Singles were sequentially numbered to 3,000.

		MT
Complete Set (30):		100.00
Common Player:		1.00
Minor Stars:		2.00
Production 3,000 Sets		
1	Jake Plummer	4.00
2	David Boston	4.00
3	Doug Flutie	4.00
4	Eric Moulds	2.00
5	Peerless Price	2.50
6	Tim Biakabutuka	2.00
7	Troy Aikman	6.00
8	Olandis Gary	8.00
9	Brian Griese	4.00
10	Charlie Batch	3.00
11	Antonio Freeman	2.00
12	Peyton Manning	8.00
13	Edgerrin James	15.00
14	Marvin Harrison	2.00
15	Fred Taylor	6.00
16	Daunte Culpepper	6.00
17	Terry Glenn	2.00
18	Keyshawn Johnson	2.00
19	Curtis Martin	2.00
20	Donovan McNabb	6.00
21	Kordell Stewart	2.00
22	Torry Holt	4.00
23	Marshall Faulk	2.00
24	Kurt Warner	25.00
25	Jerry Rice	6.00
26	Jon Kitna	2.50
27	Eddie George	3.00
28	Champ Bailey	2.00
29	Brad Johnson	2.00
30	Stephen Davis	2.00

1999 Collector's Edge Masters Master Legends

This 20-card insert set included the best players in football and pictured them on a clear card. Singles were sequentially numbered to 3,000.

		MT
Complete Set (20):		150.00
Common Player:		3.00
Production 1,000 Sets		
1	Doug Flutie	6.00
2	Troy Aikman	8.00
3	Emmitt Smith	10.00
4	Terrell Davis	10.00
5	Charlie Batch	5.00
6	Barry Sanders	15.00
7	Brett Favre	15.00
8	Antonio Freeman	4.00
9	Peyton Manning	10.00
10	Mark Brunell	6.00
11	Fred Taylor	8.00
12	Dan Marino	10.00
13	Randy Moss	15.00
14	Drew Bledsoe	6.00
15	Kurt Warner	35.00
16	Marshall Faulk	3.00

1999 Collector's Edge Masters Pro Signature Authentics

This 3-card insert set included some of the top names in the NFL. Each single was numbered to 500. The Manning 1B was a mail-in redemption and was numbered to 445.

		MT
Complete Set (3):		300.00
Common Player:		20.00
Production 500 Sets		
-	Stephen Davis	20.00
1A	Peyton Manning 500	100.00
1B	Peyton Manning 445	125.00
-	Kurt Warner	200.00

1999 Collector's Edge Masters Quest

This 20-card insert set included players who had the Super Bowl in their sights. Each single had a vinyl background and was sequentially numbered to 3,000.

		MT
Complete Set (20):		40.00
Common Player:		1.00
Minor Stars:		2.00
Production 3,000 Sets		
1	Jake Plummer	4.00
2	Eric Moulds	2.00
3	Curtis Enis	2.00
4	Emmitt Smith	7.00
5	Brian Griese	4.00
6	Dorsey Levens	2.00
7	Marvin Harrison	2.00
8	Mark Brunell	4.00
9	Fred Taylor	6.00
10	Cris Carter	2.00
11	Terry Glenn	2.00
12	Keyshawn Johnson	2.00
13	Isaac Bruce	2.00
14	Terrell Owens	2.00
15	Jon Kitna	2.50
16	Natrone Means	1.00
17	Warrick Dunn	2.00
18	Steve McNair	2.00
19	Brad Johnson	2.00
20	Stephen Davis	2.00

1999 Collector's Edge Masters Rookie Masters

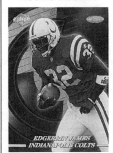

EDGERRIN JAMES INDIANAPOLIS COLTS

This 30-card insert set included the hottest rookies from the 1999 Draft. Each single was sequentially numbered to 3,000.

	MT
Complete Set (30):	75.00

17	Steve Young	6.00
18	Jerry Rice	8.00
19	Jon Kitna	4.00
20	Eddie George	4.00

Common Player: 1.00
Minor Stars: 2.00
Production 3,000 Sets

1	David Boston	4.00
2	Chris McAlister	1.00
3	Peerless Price	3.00
4	D'Wayne Bates	2.00
5	Cade McNown	6.00
6	Akili Smith	5.00
7	Tim Couch	10.00
8	Kevin Johnson	4.00
9	Wane McGarity	1.00
10	Chris Claiborne	1.00
11	Sedrick Irvin	2.00
12	Edgerrin James	15.00
13	Michael Cloud	2.00
14	Cecil Collins	3.00
15	J.J. Johnson	2.50
16	Rob Konrad	2.00
17	Daunte Culpepper	6.00
18	Kevin Faulk	2.50
19	Andy Katzenmoyer	2.00
20	Ricky Williams	10.00
21	Donovan McNabb	6.00
22	Troy Edwards	4.00
23	Amos Zereoue	2.00
24	Joe Germaine	4.00
25	Torry Holt	4.00
26	Karsten Bailey	2.00
27	Brock Huard	2.50
28	Shaun King	6.00
29	Jevon Kearse	4.00
30	Champ Bailey	2.50

1999 Collector's Edge Masters Sentinels

DONOVAN McNABB Philadelphia

This 20-card set included the 10 hottest veterans and the 10 hottest rookies from 1999. Each single was sequentially numbered to 500.

		MT
Complete Set (20):		250.00
Common Player:		5.00
Production 500 Sets		
1	Troy Aikman	15.00
2	Emmitt Smith	20.00
3	Terrell Davis	20.00
4	Barry Sanders	30.00
5	Brett Favre	30.00
6	Peyton Manning	20.00
7	Dan Marino	20.00
8	Randy Moss	30.00
9	Drew Bledsoe	10.00
10	Isaac Bruce	5.00
11	Kurt Warner	50.00
12	David Boston	5.00
13	Cade McNown	12.00
14	Akili Smith	10.00
15	Tim Couch	20.00
16	Edgerrin James	30.00
17	Ricky Williams	20.00
18	Donovan McNabb	12.00
19	Troy Edwards	5.00
20	Torry Holt	8.00

1999 Collector's Edge Odyssey

This 193-card set was supposed to be a 195-card set, but cards #21 and #55 were never produced. The first 150 cards

were 1st Quarter singles. Cards #151-170 were 2nd Quarter singles and were inserted 1:4 packs. Cards #171-185 were 3rd Quarter singles and they were found 1:8 packs. Cards #186-195 were 4th Quarter singles and they were found 1:24 packs. Insert sets included: Two Minute Warning, Overtime, Cut 'n' Ripped, Cutting Edge, Excalibur, End Zone, Game Gear, Old School, Pro Signature Authentics and Super Limited Edge. Ten-card packs had an SRP of $3.99.

	MT
Complete Set (193):	175.00
Common Player:	.15
Minor Stars:	.30
Common Rookie:	.50
Common Player (151-170):	1.00
Inserted 1:4	
Common Player (171-185):	2.50
Inserted 1:8	
Common Player (186-195):	5.00
Inserted 1:24	
#21 and 55 never produced	
Wax Box:	55.00
1	Checklist	.15
2	Checklist	.15
3	David Boston	1.75
4	Rob Moore	.30
5	Adrian Murrell	.30
6	Jake Plummer	1.00
7	Frank Sanders	.30
8	Jamal Anderson	.50
9	Chris Calloway	.15
10	Chris Chandler	.30
11	Tim Dwight	.50
12	Terance Mathis	.15
13	Tony Banks	.30
14	Priest Holmes	.50
15	Jermaine Lewis	.30
16	*Chris McAlister*	.50
17	Scott Mitchell	.15
18	Doug Flutie	.75
19	Eric Moulds	.50
20	*Peerless Price*	1.25
22	Antowain Smith	.50
23	*Antoine Winfield*	.50
24	Steve Beuerlein	.30
25	Tim Biakabutuka	.30
26	Rae Carruth	.15
27	Muhsin Muhammad	.30
28	*D'Wayne Bates*	1.00
29	Bobby Engram	.15
30	Curtis Enis	.50
31	Shane Matthews	.30
32	*Cade McNown*	3.00
33	Jeff Blake	.30
34	Corey Dillon	.50
35	Carl Pickens	.30
36	Darnay Scott	.30
37	*Akili Smith*	2.50
38	*Tim Couch*	5.00
39	*Kevin Johnson*	2.00
40	Terry Kirby	.15
41	Leslie Shepherd	.15
42	Troy Aikman	1.25
43	Michael Irvin	.30
44	Raghib Ismail	.15
45	Deion Sanders	.50
46	Emmitt Smith	1.75
47	Bubby Brister	.30
48	Terrell Davis	1.75
49	Brian Griese	1.00
50	Ed McCaffrey	.50
51	Shannon Sharpe	.30
52	Rod Smith	.50
53	Charlie Batch	.75
54	*Chris Claiborne*	.50
56	Herman Moore	.50
57	Johnnie Morton	.15
58	Ron Rivers	.15
59	Brett Favre	2.50
60	Mark Chmura	.30
61	Antonio Freeman	.50
62	Dorsey Levens	.50
63	E.G. Green	.15
64	Marvin Harrison	.50
65	*Edgerrin James*	8.00
66	Peyton Manning	1.75
67	Mark Brunell	1.00
68	Keenan McCardell	.30
69	Jimmy Smith	.50
70	Fred Taylor	1.25
71	Derrick Alexander	.15
72	Kimble Anders	.15
73	*Michael Cloud*	.50
74	Elvis Grbac	.30
75	Andre Rison	.30
76	Karim Abdul	.30
77	Cecil Collins	1.00
78	J.J. Johnson	1.00
79	Rob Konrad	.30
80	Dan Marino	1.75
81	O.J. McDuffie	.50
82	Cris Carter	.50
83	*Daunte Culpepper*	3.00
84	Randall Cunningham	.50
85	Randy Moss	2.50
86	Jake Reed	.30
87	Robert Smith	.50
88	Terry Allen	.30
89	Drew Bledsoe	1.00

90	Ben Coates	.30
91	Kevin Faulk	1.25
92	Terry Glenn	.50
93	Andy Katzenmoyer	.50
94	Cameron Cleeland	.30
95	Billy Joe Hobert	.15
96	Eddie Kennison	.15
97	Ricky Williams	5.00
98	Sean Bennett	.75
99	Gary Brown	.15
100	Kerry Collins	.30
101	Kent Graham	.15
102	Ike Hilliard	.15
103	Wayne Chrebet	.50
104	Keyshawn Johnson	.50
105	Curtis Martin	.50
106	Rick Mirer	.30
107	Tim Brown	.30
108	Rich Gannon	.30
109	Napoleon Kaufman	.50
110	Charles Woodson	.50
111	Charles Johnson	.15
112	Donovan McNabb	3.00
113	Doug Pederson	.15
114	Duce Staley	.50
115	Jerome Bettis	.50
116	Troy Edwards	1.75
117	Kordell Stewart	.50
118	Amos Zereoue	.75
119	Isaac Bruce	.50
120	Marshall Faulk	.50
121	Joe Germaine	1.00
122	Torry Holt	1.75
123	Kurt Warner	20.00
124	Jim Harbaugh	.30
125	Erik Kramer	.15
126	Natrone Means	.30
127	Junior Seau	.30
128	Terrell Owens	.50
129	Lawrence Phillips	.30
130	Jerry Rice	1.25
131	J.J. Stokes	.30
132	Steve Young	.75
133	Karsten Bailey	.50
134	Joey Galloway	.50
135	Brock Huard	1.25
136	Jon Kitna	.50
137	Ricky Watters	.30
138	Reidel Anthony	.30
139	Trent Dilfer	.30
140	Warrick Dunn	.50
141	Shaun King	3.00
142	Jevon Kearse	2.00
143	Kevin Dyson	.30
144	Eddie George	.75
145	Steve McNair	.75
146	Champ Bailey	1.25
147	Stephen Davis	.50
148	Skip Hicks	.30
149	Brad Johnson	.50
150	Michael Westbrook	.30
151	Chris McAlister	1.00
152	Peerless Price	1.75
153	Antoine Winfield	1.00
154	D'Wayne Bates	1.00
155	Kevin Johnson	3.00
156	Chris Claiborne	1.00
157	Sedrick Irvin	1.00
158	Michael Cloud	1.00
159	Cecil Collins	1.50
160	J.J. Johnson	1.50
161	Rob Konrad	1.00
162	Daunte Culpepper	3.50
163	Andy Katzenmoyer	1.00
164	Amos Zereoue	1.00
165	Joe Germaine	1.00
166	Karsten Bailey	1.00
167	Brock Huard	1.50
168	Shaun King	4.00
169	Jevon Kearse	2.50
170	Champ Bailey	1.50
171	Jake Plummer	2.50
172	Doug Flutie	2.50
173	Troy Aikman	4.00
174	Emmitt Smith	5.00
175	Terrell Davis	5.00
176	Barry Sanders	7.00
177	Brett Favre	7.00
178	Peyton Manning	7.00
179	Mark Brunell	2.50
180	Fred Taylor	4.00
181	Dan Marino	5.00
182	Randy Moss	7.00
183	Drew Bledsoe	2.50
184	Jerry Rice	5.00
185	Steve Young	2.50
186	David Boston	6.00
187	Cade McNown	12.00
188	Akili Smith	10.00
189	Tim Couch	20.00
190	Edgerrin James	30.00
191	Kevin Faulk	5.00
192	Ricky Williams	20.00
193	Donovan McNabb	12.00
194	Troy Edwards	6.00
195	Torry Holt	8.00

Post-1980 cards in Near Mint condition will generally sell for about 75% of the quoted Mint value. Excellent-condition cards bring no more than 40%.

1999 Collector's Edge Odyssey Two Minute Warning

This insert was a 45-card partial parallel to the base set. Cards #151-170 were sequentially numbered to 600. Cards #171-185 were numbered to 300 and cards #186-195 were numbered to 100.

	MT
Common Player (151-170):	3.50
Rookies:	4x
Production 600 Sets	
Common Player (171-185):	7.50
Stars:	3x
Production 300 Sets	
Common Player (186-195):	20.00
Rookies:	4x
Production 100 Sets	

1999 Collector's Edge Odyssey Overtime

This was a 45-card partial set parallel to the base set. Cards #151-170 were sequentially numbered to 60. Cards #171-185 were numbered to 30 and cards #186-195 were numbered to 10.

	MT
Common Player (151-170):	25.00
Rookies:	12x-24x
Production 60 Sets	
Common Player (171-185):	75.00
Stars:	15x-30x
Production 30 Sets	
Common Player (186-195):	100.00
Rookies:	10x-20x
Production 10 Sets	

1999 Collector's Edge Odyssey Cut'n'Ripped

This 15-card insert set included the top rookies from the 1999 class. Each was photographed in the weight room and singles were found 1:12 packs.

		MT
Complete Set (15):		20.00
Common Player:		1.00
Inserted 1:12		
1	Chris McAlister	1.00
2	Kevin Johnson	2.00
3	Chris Claiborne	1.00
4	Sedrick Irvin	1.00
5	Edgerrin James	8.00
6	Michael Cloud	1.00
7	J.J. Johnson	1.50
8	Rob Konrad	1.00

9	Daunte Culpepper	4.00
10	Andy Katzenmoyer	1.00
11	Amos Zereoue	1.00
12	Torry Holt	2.00
13	Shaun King	4.00
14	Jevon Kearse	2.50
15	Champ Bailey	1.50

1999 Collector's Edge Odyssey Cutting Edge

This 10-card set had each single printed on holographic foil with foil stamping. Singles were found 1:18 packs.

		MT
Complete Set (10):		30.00
Common Player:		2.50
Inserted 1:18		
1	Akili Smith	4.00
2	Tim Couch	7.00
3	Brian Griese	3.50
4	Charlie Batch	2.50
5	Brett Favre	8.00
6	Peyton Manning	6.00
7	Mark Brunell	2.50
8	Dan Marino	6.00
9	Drew Bledsoe	2.50
10	Steve Young	2.50

1999 Collector's Edge Odyssey End Zone

This 20-card insert set included the top players in the NFL. Singles were inserted 1:9 packs.

		MT
Complete Set (20):		30.00
Common Player:		1.00
Minor Stars:		2.00
Inserted 1:9		
1	Jamal Anderson	2.00
2	Priest Holmes	2.00
3	Doug Flutie	3.00
4	Eric Moulds	2.00
5	Charlie Batch	3.00
6	Barry Sanders	8.00
7	Antonio Freeman	2.00
8	Fred Taylor	4.00
9	Cris Carter	2.00
10	Randy Moss	8.00
11	Keyshawn Johnson	2.00
12	Curtis Martin	2.00
13	Vinny Testaverde	1.00
14	Kordell Stewart	2.00
15	Jerry Rice	4.00
16	Terrell Owens	2.00
17	Jon Kitna	2.00
18	Warrick Dunn	2.00
19	Eddie George	2.00
20	Steve McNair	2.50

A card number in parentheses ( ) indicates the set is unnumbered.

1999 Collector's Edge Odyssey Excalibur

Excalibur was a 25-card set that was a cross-brand program. Singles were inserted into First Place, Odyssey and Masters. Eight of the singles were found in Odyssey at 1:24 packs.

		MT
Complete Set (8):		35.00
Common Player:		5.00
Inserted 1:24		
2	Cade McNown	7.00
5	David Boston	5.00
7	Daunte Culpepper	6.00
8	Troy Edwards	5.00
11	Donovan McNabb	7.00
15	Ricky Williams	10.00
20	Troy Aikman	6.00
25	Emmitt Smith	8.00

1999 Collector's Edge Odyssey Game Gear

This 8-card insert set included a swatch of a game-used football. Each card was sequentially numbered and odds were 1:360 packs.

		MT
Complete Set (8):		300.00
Common Player:		25.00
Inserted 1:360		
1	Terrell Davis 500	40.00
2	Curtis Enis 338	25.00
3	Marshall Faulk 247	35.00
4	Brian Griese 500	25.00
5	Skip Hicks 315	25.00
6	Randy Moss 415	60.00
7	Lawrence Phillips 406	25.00
8	Fred Taylor 85	85.00

1999 Collector's Edge Odyssey Old School

Each card in this 25-card set is in black and white and has an Old School theme to it. Players are photographed in throwback jerseys, leather helmets and in Heisman-style poses. Singles were inserted 1:8 packs.

		MT
Complete Set (25):		45.00
Common Player:		1.00
Minor Stars:		2.00
Inserted 1:8		
1	David Boston	3.00
2	Chris McAlister	1.00
3	Peerless Price	1.00
4	D'Wayne Bates	2.00
5	Cade McNown	5.00
6	Akili Smith	3.00
7	Tim Couch	8.00
8	Kevin Johnson	4.00
9	Chris Claiborne	1.00

10	Sedrick Irvin	2.00
11	Edgerrin James	12.00
12	Michael Cloud	1.00
13	J.J. Johnson	2.50
14	Rob Konrad	1.00
15	Daunte Culpepper	4.00
16	Kevin Faulk	2.50
17	Donovan McNabb	5.00
18	Troy Edwards	3.00
19	Amos Zereoue	2.00
20	Joe Germaine	2.00
21	Torry Holt	3.00
22	Karsten Bailey	2.00
23	Shaun King	5.00
24	Jevon Kearse	3.50
25	Champ Bailey	2.00

1999 Collector's Edge Odyssey Pro Signature Authentics

This 18-card set included autographs from the rookies of 1999. Each player had signed a different amount of cards and each was sequentially numbered. They were inserted 1:36 packs.

		MT
Complete Set (18):		425.00
Common Player:		8.00
Minor Stars:		16.00
Inserted 1:36		
DB	D'Wayne Bates 1450	16.00
MB	Michael Bishop 2200	16.00
CC	Chris Claiborne 1120	8.00
DC	Daunte Culpepper 450	45.00
JD	Jared DeVries 290	16.00
JG	Jeff Garcia 2110	16.00
MG	Martin Gramatica 1950	16.00
TH	Torry Holt 1115	25.00
BH	Brock Huard 350	25.00
SI	Sedrick Irvin 1240	16.00
EJ	Edgerrin James 435	125.00
KJ	Kevin Johnson 1920	25.00
SK	Shaun King 920	45.00
RK	Rob Konrad 1420	8.00
DM	Darnell McDonald 2435	8.00
PP	Peerless Price 825	20.00
AS	Akili Smith 111	100.00
AZ	Amos Zereoue 1450	8.00

1999 Collector's Edge Odyssey Super Limited Edge

This 30-card insert set included football's biggest stars and featured them on a clear, vinyl card with foil stamping. Each single was sequentially numbered to 1,000.

		MT
Complete Set (30):		100.00
Common Player:		3.00
Production 1,000 Sets		
1	Jake Plummer	5.00
2	Jamal Anderson	3.00

3	Doug Flutie	4.00
4	Eric Moulds	3.00
5	Troy Aikman	8.00
6	Emmitt Smith	10.00
7	Terrell Davis	10.00
8	Charlie Batch	4.00
9	Herman Moore	3.00
10	Barry Sanders	12.00
11	Brett Favre	12.00
12	Antonio Freeman	3.00
13	Dorsey Levens	3.00
14	Peyton Manning	10.00
15	Mark Brunell	4.00
16	Fred Taylor	8.00
17	Dan Marino	10.00
18	Cris Carter	3.00
19	Randall Cunningham	3.00
20	Randy Moss	12.00
21	Drew Bledsoe	4.00
22	Ricky Williams	12.00
23	Keyshawn Johnson	3.00
24	Curtis Martin	3.00
25	Jerome Bettis	3.00
26	Jerry Rice	8.00
27	Terrell Owens	3.00
28	Jon Kitna	4.00
29	Eddie George	4.00
30	Steve Young	4.00

1999 Collector's Edge Supreme

The 170-card base set includes 40 rookie cards. A few errors in the set with two different Tim Couch cards #141. The error is the rarest to find without stats on the back. The corrected versions are numbered TC and include stats. Michael Wiley was suppose to be #166, but chose to stay in college and they had to be pulled from the set. Some still found their way into packs. The #166B Edgerrin James Trade card was inserted late and tough to find. Two parallel sets with Gold Ingot and Galvanized. Other inserts include: Future, Homecoming, Markers, PSA 10 Redemptions, Route XXXIII, Supremacy and T3.

		MT
Complete Set (170):		150.00
Common Player:		.20
Minor Stars:		.40
Common Rookie:		1.00
Card #166A not part of set price		
Wax Box:		100.00
1	Randy Moss CL	1.50
2	Peyton Manning CL	.75
3	Rob Moore	.40
4	Adrian Murrell	.20
5	Jake Plummer	1.50
6	Andre Wadsworth	.20
7	Jamal Anderson	.75
8	Chris Chandler	.40
9	Tony Martin	.20
10	Terance Mathis	.20
11	Jim Harbaugh	.40
12	Priest Holmes	.75
13	Jermaine Lewis	.20
14	Eric Zeier	.20
15	Doug Flutie	.75
16	Eric Moulds	.75
17	Andre Reed	.40
18	Antowain Smith	.75
19	Steve Beuerlein	.20
20	Kevin Greene	.20
21	Raghib Ismail	.20
22	Fred Lane	.20
23	Edgar Bennett	.20
24	Curtis Conway	.40
25	Curtis Enis	.75
26	Erik Kramer	.20
27	Corey Dillon	.75
28	Neil O'Donnell	.40
29	Carl Pickens	.40
30	Darnay Scott	.20
31	Troy Aikman	1.50
32	Michael Irvin	.40
33	Deion Sanders	.75
34	Emmitt Smith	2.00
35	Chris Warren	.40

36	Terrell Davis	2.00
37	John Elway	2.00
38	Ed McCaffrey	.75
39	Shannon Sharpe	.40
40	Rod Smith	.40
41	Charlie Batch	1.25
42	Herman Moore	.40
43	Johnnie Morton	.20
44	Barry Sanders	3.00
45	Robert Brooks	.20
46	Brett Favre	3.00
47	Antonio Freeman	.75
48	Darick Holmes	.20
49	Dorsey Levens	.75
50	Reggie White	.40
51	Marshall Faulk	.75
52	Marvin Harrison	.40
53	Peyton Manning	2.50
54	Jerome Pathon	.40
55	Tavian Banks	.40
56	Mark Brunell	1.25
57	Keenan McCardell	.20
58	Fred Taylor	2.00
59	Derrick Alexander	.20
60	Donnell Bennett	.20
61	Rich Gannon	.20
62	Andre Rison	.40
63	Karim Abdul	.40
64	John Avery	.40
65	Oronde Gadsden	.40
66	Dan Marino	2.00
67	O.J. McDuffie	.20
68	Cris Carter	.75
69	Randall Cunningham	.75
70	Brad Johnson	.40
71	Randy Moss	5.00
72	Jake Reed	.20
73	Robert Smith	.40
74	Drew Bledsoe	1.25
75	Ben Coates	.40
76	Robert Edwards	.75
77	Terry Glenn	.40
78	Cameron Cleeland	.40
79	Kerry Collins	.40
80	Sean Dawkins	.20
81	Lamar Smith	.20
82	Gary Brown	.20
83	Chris Calloway	.20
84	Ike Hilliard	.20
85	Danny Kanell	.20
86	Wayne Chrebet	.75
87	Keyshawn Johnson	.75
88	Curtis Martin	.75
89	Vinny Testaverde	.40
90	Tim Brown	.40
91	Jeff George	.40
92	Napoleon Kaufman	.75
93	Charles Woodson	.75
94	Irving Fryar	.20
95	Bobby Hoying	.20
96	Duce Staley	.20
97	Jerome Bettis	.40
98	Courtney Hawkins	.20
99	Charles Johnson	.20
100	Kordell Stewart	1.00
101	Hines Ward	.40
102	Tony Banks	.40
103	Isaac Bruce	.40
104	Robert Holcombe	.40
105	Ryan Leaf	1.00
106	Natrone Means	.40
107	Mikhael Ricks	.40
108	Junior Seau	.40
109	Garrison Hearst	.40
110	Terrell Owens	.75
111	Jerry Rice	1.50
112	J.J. Stokes	.40
113	Steve Young	1.00
114	Joey Galloway	.75
115	Jon Kitna	1.00
116	Warren Moon	.40
117	Ricky Watters	.40
118	Mike Alstott	.40
119	Reidel Anthony	.40
120	Warrick Dunn	1.00
121	Trent Dilfer	.40
122	Jacquez Green	.40
123	Kevin Dyson	.40
124	Eddie George	1.00
125	Steve McNair	.75
126	Frank Wycheck	.20
127	Terry Allen	.40
128	Trent Green	.40
129	Skip Hicks	.40
130	Michael Westbrook	.20
131	*Rahim Abdullah*	2.00
132	*Champ Bailey*	4.00
133	*Marlon Barnes*	2.00
134	*D'Wayne Bates*	2.00
135	*Michael Bishop*	4.00
136	*Dre' Bly*	1.00
137	*David Boston*	5.00
138	*Cuncho Brown*	1.00
139	*Na Brown*	1.00
140	*Tony Bryant*	1.00
141	*Tim Couch ERROR*	100.00
141TC	*Tim Couch*	25.00
142	*Chris Claiborne*	3.00
143	*Daunte Culpepper*	7.00
144	*Jared DeVries*	1.00
145	*Troy Edwards*	3.00
146	*Kris Farris*	1.00

147	*Kevin Faulk*	3.00
148	*Joe Germaine*	4.00
149	*Aaron Gibson*	1.00
150	*Torry Holt*	5.00
151	*Brock Huard*	3.00
152	*Sedrick Irvin*	3.00
153	*James Johnson*	2.00
154	*Kevin Johnson*	3.00
155	*Andy Katzenmoyer*	3.00
156	*Jevon Kearse*	4.00
157	*Shaun King*	6.00
158	*Rob Konrad*	2.00
159	*Chris McAlister*	2.00
160	*Darnell McDonald*	1.00
161	*Donovan McNabb*	7.00
162	*Cade McNown*	7.00
163	*Peerless Price*	5.00
164	*Akili Smith*	10.00
165	*Matt Stinchcomb*	1.00
166A	Michael Wiley	350.00
166B	Edgerrin James Trade	200.00
167	*Ricky Williams*	15.00
168	*Antoine Winfield*	2.00
169	*Craig Yeast*	2.00
170	*Amos Zereoue*	2.00

1999 Collector's Edge Supreme Galvanized

This 169-card set is a parallel to the base minus the cards of Michael Wiley and Edgerrin James #166. Each card is printed on silver foil board and is sequentially numbered. Veterans are printed to 500 and rookies to 250.

	MT
Complete Set (169):	800.00
Galvanized Cards:	3x-6x
Production 500 Sets	
Galvanized Rookies:	5x
Production 250 Sets	

1999 Collector's Edge Supreme Gold Ingot

The 169-card set is a parallel to the base minus the Michael Wiley and Edgerrin James cards #166. The cards are the same as the base except for the foil in gold and the Gold Ingot stamp on the fronts. They were inserted one-per-pack.

	MT
Complete Set (169):	300.00
Gold Ingot Cards:	2x
Gold Ingot Rookies:	1x
Inserted 1:1	

A player's name in *italic* type indicates a rookie card.

1999 Collector's Edge Supreme Future

Each card in this 10-card set is printed on micro-etched foil board and was inserted 1:24 packs.

		MT
Complete Set (10):		60.00
Common Player:		2.00
Inserted 1:24		
1	Ricky Williams	20.00
2	Tim Couch	20.00
3	Daunte Culpepper	7.00
4	Torry Holt	5.00
5	Edgerrin James	10.00
6	Brock Huard	2.00
7	Donovan McNabb	7.00
8	Joe Germaine	4.00
9	Cade McNown	7.00
10	Michael Bishop	4.00

1999 Collector's Edge Supreme Homecoming

Each card in this 20-card set includes two players on the front who went to the same college. A rookie from the 1999 draft and a veteran. Singles were inserted 1:12 packs.

		MT
Complete Set (20):		60.00
Common Player:		1.50
Inserted 1:12		
1	Ricky Williams, Priest Holmes	15.00
2	Andy Katzenmoyer, Eddie George	4.00
3	Daunte Culpepper, Shawn Jefferson	5.00
4	Torry Holt, Erik Kramer	4.00
5	Edgerrin James, Vinny Testaverde	8.00
6	Chris Claiborne, Junior Seau	1.50
7	Brock Huard, Mark Brunell	4.00
8	Champ Bailey, Terrell Davis	8.00
9	Donovan McNabb, Rob Moore	6.00
10	David Boston, Joey Galloway	4.00
11	Cade McNown, Troy Aikman	6.00
12	Kevin Faulk, Eddie Kennison	1.50
13	Sedrick Irvin, Andre Rison	1.50
14	Rob Konrad, Darryl Johnston	1.50
15	Amos Zereoue, Adrian Murrell	1.50
16	Peerless Price, Peyton Manning	10.00
17	Kevin Johnson, Marvin Harrison	3.00
18	Jevon Kearse, Emmitt Smith	7.00
19	Antoine Winfield, Shawn Springs	1.50
20	Tony Bryant, Andre Wadsworth	1.50

1999 Collector's Edge Supreme Markers

The cards are printed on clear vinyl stock with foil stamping. The set features 15 NFL stars and focuses on record-setting performances and milestones reached in the 1998 NFL season. They were sequentially numbered to 5,000.

		MT
Complete Set (15):		60.00
Common Player:		1.00
Minor Stars:		2.00
Production 5,000 Sets		
1	Terrell Davis	6.00
2	John Elway	5.00
3	Dan Marino	6.00
4	Peyton Manning	7.00
5	Barry Sanders	8.00
6	Emmitt Smith	6.00
7	Randy Moss	12.00
8	Jake Plummer	4.00
9	Cris Carter	1.00
10	Brett Favre	8.00
11	Drew Bledsoe	3.00
12	Charlie Batch	4.00
13	Curtis Martin	1.00
14	Mark Brunell	3.00
15	Jamal Anderson	2.00

1999 Collector's Edge Supreme PSA 10 Redemptions

Each card in this set was a redemption card for the player that was on it. You could then redeem it for a PSA 10 graded rookie of that player. The redemption cards were limited to 1,999.

		MT
Complete Set (3):		250.00
Common Player:		75.00
Production 1,999 Sets		
1	Ricky Williams	100.00
2	Tim Couch	100.00
3	Daunte Culpepper	75.00

1999 Collector's Edge Supreme Route XXXIII

This set includes the top stars from the 1998 NFL playoffs. Each player in the 10-card set is sequentially numbered to 1,000.

		MT
Complete Set (10):		150.00
Common Player:		8.00
Production 1,000 Sets		
1	Randy Moss	55.00
2	Jamal Anderson	8.00
3	Jake Plummer	15.00
4	Steve Young	12.00
5	Fred Taylor	20.00
6	Dan Marino	20.00
7	Keyshawn Johnson	8.00
8	Curtis Martin	12.00
9	John Elway	20.00
10	Terrell Davis	20.00

1999 Collector's Edge Supreme Supremacy

This set features 5 players from Super Bowl XXXIII. Each is printed on foil board with foil stamping and is sequentially numbered to 500.

	MT
Complete Set (5):	75.00

		MT
Common Player:		10.00
Production 500 Sets		
1	John Elway	25.00
2	Terrell Davis	25.00
3	Ed McCaffrey	10.00
4	Jamal Anderson	15.00
5	Chris Chandler	10.00

1999 Collector's Edge Supreme T3

This 30-card set is tiered into three levels with 10 wide receivers (foil board with bronze foil stamping), running backs (foil board with silver foil stamping) and quarterbacks (foil board with gold foil stamping). The receivers were the easiest to find at 1:8, running backs at 1:12 and the quarterbacks the toughest to get at 1:24.

		MT
Complete Set (30):		180.00
Common WR:		1.50
Inserted 1:8		
Common RB:		2.50
Inserted 1:12		
Common QB:		5.00
Inserted 1:24		
1	Doug Flutie (QB)	5.00
2	Troy Aikman (QB)	10.00
3	John Elway (QB)	15.00
4	Jake Plummer (QB)	10.00
5	Brett Favre (QB)	20.00
6	Mark Brunell (QB)	8.00
7	Peyton Manning (QB)	15.00
8	Dan Marino (QB)	15.00
9	Drew Bledsoe (QB)	8.00
10	Steve Young (QB)	7.00
11	Jamal Anderson (RB)	3.00
12	Emmitt Smith (RB)	8.00
13	Terrell Davis (RB)	10.00
14	Barry Sanders (RB)	10.00
15	Robert Smith (RB)	2.50
16	Robert Edwards (RB)	3.00
17	Curtis Martin (RB)	3.00
18	Jerome Bettis (RB)	2.50
19	Fred Taylor (RB)	10.00
20	Eddie George (RB)	5.00
21	Michael Irvin (WR)	1.50
22	Eric Moulds (WR)	3.00
23	Herman Moore (WR)	1.50
24	Reidel Anthony (WR)	1.50
25	Randy Moss (WR)	12.00
26	Cris Carter (WR)	1.50
27	Keyshawn Johnson (WR)	3.00
28	Jacquez Green (WR)	1.50
29	Jerry Rice (WR)	7.00
30	Terrell Owens (WR)	4.00

1999 Collector's Edge Triumph

Triumph was a 180-card set that included 40 rookie cards found one-per-pack. Insert sets included: Commissioner's Choice, Fantasy Team, Future Fantasy Team, Heir Supply, K-Klub Y3K, Pack Warriors and Signed, Sealed, Delivered. Packs contained eight cards.

	MT
Complete Set (180):	55.00
Common Player:	.15
Minor Stars:	.30
Common Rookie:	.50
Inserted 1:1	
Wax Box:	50.00

1	Jamal Anderson	.50
2	Jerome Bettis	.50
3	Terrell Davis	1.75
4	Corey Dillon	.50
5	Warrick Dunn	.50
6	Marshall Faulk	.50
7	Eddie George	.75
8	Garrison Hearst	.30
9	Skip Hicks	.30
10	Napoleon Kaufman	.50
11	Dorsey Levens	.50
12	Curtis Martin	.50
13	Natrone Means	.30
14	Adrian Murrell	.30
15	Barry Sanders	2.50
16	Antowain Smith	.50
17	Emmitt Smith	1.75
18	Robert Smith	.50
19	Fred Taylor	1.25
20	Ricky Watters	.30
21	Cameron Cleeland	.30
22	Ben Coates	.30
23	Shannon Sharpe	.30
24	Frank Wycheck	.15
25	Derrick Alexander	.15
26	Reidel Anthony	.30
27	Robert Brooks	.15
28	Tim Brown	.30
29	Cris Carter	.50
30	Wayne Chrebet	.30
31	Curtis Conway	.30
32	Tim Dwight	.50
33	Kevin Dyson	.30
34	Antonio Freeman	.50
35	Joey Galloway	.50
36	Terry Glenn	.50
37	Marvin Harrison	.50
38	Ike Hilliard	.30
39	Michael Irvin	.50
40	Keyshawn Johnson	.50
41	Jermaine Lewis	.15
42	Terance Mathis	.15
43	Ed McCaffrey	.50
44	Keenan McCardell	.30
45	O.J. McDuffie	.30
46	Herman Moore	.30
47	Rob Moore	.30
48	Randy Moss	2.50
49	Eric Moulds	.50
50	Muhsin Muhammad	.30
51	Terrell Owens	.50
52	Jerome Pathon	.15
53	Carl Pickens	.30
54	Andre Reed	.30
55	Jake Reed	.30
56	Jerry Rice	1.25
57	Andre Rison	.30
58	Jimmy Smith	.50
59	Rod Smith	.50
60	Michael Westbrook	.30
61	Morten Andersen	.15
62	Gary Anderson	.15
63	Doug Brien	.15
64	Chris Boniol	.15
65	John Carney	.15
66	Steve Christie	.15
67	Richie Cunningham	.15
68	Brad Daluiso	.15
69	Al Del Greco	.15
70	Jason Elam	.15
71	John Hall	.15
72	Jason Hanson	.15
73	Mike Hollis	.15
74	Norm Johnson	.15
75	Olindo Mare	.15
76	Doug Pelfrey	.15
77	Wade Richey	.15
78	Pete Stoyanovich	.15
79	Mike Vanderjagt	.15
80	Adam Vinatieri	.15
81	Ray Buchanan	.15
82	Jim Flanigan	.15
83	Darrell Green	.15
84	Kevin Greene	.15
85	Ty Law	.15
86	Ken Norton Jr.	.15
87	John Randle	.15
88	Bill Romanowski	.15
89	Deion Sanders	.50
90	Junior Seau	.30
91	Michael Sinclair	.15
92	Bruce Smith	.15
93	Takeo Spikes	.15
94	Michael Strahan	.15
95	Derrick Thomas	.30
96	Zach Thomas	.30
97	Andre Wadsworth	.15
98	Charles Woodson	.50
99	Checklist	.15
100	Checklist	.15
101	Troy Aikman	1.25
102	Tony Banks	.30
103	Charlie Batch	.75
104	Steve Beuerlein	.30

105	Jeff Blake	.30
106	Drew Bledsoe	1.00
107	Bubby Brister	.30
108	Mark Brunell	1.00
109	Chris Chandler	.30
110	Kerry Collins	.30
111	Randall Cunningham	.50
112	Koy Detmer	.15
113	Ty Detmer	.15
114	Trent Dilfer	.30
115	John Elway	1.75
116	Brett Favre	2.50
117	Doug Flutie	.75
118	Rich Gannon	.30
119	Jeff Garcia	4.00
120	Jeff George	.30
121	Kent Graham	.15
122	Elvis Grbac	.30
123	Brian Griese	1.00
124	Trent Green	.30
125	Jim Harbaugh	.30
126	Billy Joe Hobert	.15
127	Brad Johnson	.30
128	Rob Johnson	.30
129	Jon Kitna	.50
130	Erik Kramer	.15
131	Ryan Leaf	.50
132	Peyton Manning	1.75
133	Dan Marino	1.75
134	Steve McNair	.75
135	Scott Mitchell	.15
136	Warren Moon	.30
137	Jake Plummer	1.00
138	Kordell Stewart	.50
139	Vinny Testaverde	.30
140	Steve Young	.75
141	Champ Bailey	2.00
142	Karsten Bailey	1.00
143	D'Wayne Bates	1.00
144	David Boston	3.00
145	Cuncho Brown	.50
146	Dat Nguyen	.50
147	Chris Claiborne	1.00
148	Michael Cloud	1.00
149	Cecil Collins	1.50
150	Tim Couch	8.00
151	Daunte Culpepper	5.00
152	Autry Denson	1.00
153	Troy Edwards	3.00
154	Ebenezer Ekuban	.50
155	Kevin Faulk	2.00
156	Jermaine Fazande	1.00
157	Joe Germaine	1.00
158	Martin Gramatica	1.00
159	Torry Holt	3.50
160	Brock Huard	2.00
161	Sedrick Irvin	1.00
162	Edgerrin James	12.00
163	James Johnson	2.00
164	Kevin Johnson	3.50
165	Andy Katzenmoyer	3.00
166	Jevon Kearse	3.00
167	Patrick Kerney	.50
168	Shaun King	5.00
169	Jim Kleinsasser	1.00
170	Rob Konrad	1.00
171	Chris McAlister	1.00
172	Donovan McNabb	5.00
173	Cade McNown	5.00
174	Joe Montgomery	1.00
175	Peerless Price	1.00
176	Akili Smith	4.00
177	Ricky Williams	8.00
178	Larry Parker	.50
179	Antoine Winfield	.50
180	Amos Zereoue	1.00

1999 Collector's Edge Triumph Commissioner's Choice

		MT
Complete Set (10):		45.00
Common Player:		2.00
Inserted 1:15		
Gold Cards:		2x
Production 500 Sets		
1	Tim Couch	8.00
2	Donovan McNabb	5.00
3	Cade McNown	5.00
4	Daunte Culpepper	4.00
5	Akili Smith	4.00
6	Ricky Williams	8.00
7	Edgerrin James	12.00
8	Torry Holt	3.50
9	David Boston	3.50
10	Champ Bailey	2.00

1999 Collector's Edge Triumph Fantasy Team

This 10-card insert set included the top players in the NFL and inserted them 1:10 packs.

		MT
Complete Set (10):		45.00
Common Player:		3.50
Inserted 1:10		
1	Terrell Davis	6.00
2	John Elway	6.00
3	Brett Favre	8.00
4	Peyton Manning	6.00
5	Dan Marino	6.00
6	Randy Moss	8.00
7	Jake Plummer	3.50
8	Barry Sanders	8.00
9	Emmitt Smith	6.00
10	Fred Taylor	3.50

1999 Collector's Edge Triumph Future Fantasy Team

This 20-card insert set included the top rookies from 1999. Singles were inserted 1:6 packs.

		MT
Complete Set (20):		45.00
Common Player:		1.00
1	Champ Bailey	1.50
2	D'Wayne Bates	1.00
3	David Boston	2.00
4	Tim Couch	6.00
5	Daunte Culpepper	3.00
6	Troy Edwards	2.00
7	Kevin Faulk	1.50
8	Torry Holt	2.00
9	Brock Huard	1.50
10	Sedrick Irvin	1.50
11	Edgerrin James	10.00
12	James Johnson	1.50
13	Kevin Johnson	2.00
14	Rob Konrad	1.00
15	Donovan McNabb	3.00
16	Cade McNown	3.00
17	Peerless Price	2.00
18	Akili Smith	2.00
19	Ricky Williams	5.00
20	Amos Zereoue	1.50

1999 Collector's Edge Triumph Commissioner's Choice

This 10-card insert set included the top rookies from the 1999 Draft. Singles were inserted 1:15 packs. A parallel Gold version was also made and each card was sequentially numbered to 500.

1999 Collector's Edge Triumph Heir Supply

This 15-card insert set included the top rookies from the 1999 Draft. Singles were inserted 1:3 packs.

		MT
Complete Set (15):		25.00
Common Player:		.75
Minor Stars:		1.50
Inserted 1:3		
1	Ricky Williams	5.00
2	Tim Couch	5.00
3	Cade McNown	3.00
4	Donovan McNabb	3.00
5	Akili Smith	2.50
6	Daunte Culpepper	3.00
7	Torry Holt	2.00
8	Edgerrin James	7.00
9	David Boston	2.00
10	Troy Edwards	2.00
11	Peerless Price	1.50
12	Champ Bailey	1.50
13	D'Wayne Bates	.75
14	Kevin Faulk	.75
15	Amos Zereoue	.75

1999 Collector's Edge Triumph K-Klub Y3K

This 50-card insert set included both young and veteran players. Singles were sequentially numbered to 1,000.

		MT
Complete Set (50):		100.00
Common Player:		1.50
Minor Stars:		3.00
Production 1,000 Sets		
1	Kareem Abdul-Jabbar	1.50
2	Jamal Anderson	3.00
3	Jerome Bettis	3.00
4	Isaac Bruce	3.00
5	Cris Carter	3.00
6	Terrell Davis	8.00
7	Corey Dillon	3.00
8	Warrick Dunn	3.00
9	Curtis Enis	3.00
10	Marshall Faulk	3.00
11	Antonio Freeman	3.00
12	Joey Galloway	3.00
13	Eddie George	3.00
14	Terry Glenn	3.00
15	Garrison Hearst	1.50
16	Keyshawn Johnson	3.00
17	Napoleon Kaufman	1.50
18	Curtis Martin	3.00
19	Rob Moore	1.50
20	Herman Moore	1.50
21	Eric Moulds	3.00
22	Randy Moss	12.00
23	Adrian Murrell	1.50
24	Carl Pickens	1.50
25	Jerry Rice	6.00
26	Barry Sanders	12.00
27	Antowain Smith	1.50
28	Emmitt Smith	8.00
29	Fred Taylor	6.00
30	Ricky Watters	1.50
31	Troy Aikman	6.00
32	Charlie Batch	4.00
33	Drew Bledsoe	5.00
34	Mark Brunell	5.00
35	Chris Chandler	1.50
36	Randall Cunningham	3.00
37	Trent Dilfer	1.50
38	John Elway	8.00
39	Brett Favre	12.00
40	Doug Flutie	4.00
41	Brad Johnson	3.00
42	Jon Kitna	3.00
43	Ryan Leaf	3.00
44	Peyton Manning	8.00
45	Dan Marino	8.00
46	Steve McNair	3.00
47	Jake Plummer	5.00
48	Kordell Stewart	3.00
49	Vinny Testaverde	1.50
50	Steve Young	4.00

1999 Collector's Edge Triumph Pack Warriors

This 15-card insert set included veteran players. Singles were inserted 1:4 packs.

		MT
Complete Set (15):		30.00
Common Player:		1.00
Inserted 1:4		
1	Jamal Anderson	1.00
2	Jake Plummer	2.00
3	Emmitt Smith	3.50
4	Troy Aikman	3.00
5	Terrell Davis	3.00
6	John Elway	3.50
7	Barry Sanders	5.00
8	Brett Favre	5.00
9	Peyton Manning	3.50
10	Randy Moss	5.00
11	Dan Marino	3.50
12	Keyshawn Johnson	1.00
13	Fred Taylor	3.00
14	Jerry Rice	3.00
15	Jerome Bettis	1.00

1999 Collector's Edge Triumph Signed, Sealed, Delivered

This was a 40-card set that included autographs from the top rookies of 1999. Singles were inserted 1:32 packs. A parallel Blue version was issued and each was sequentially numbered to 40. A parallel Red version was also made and each of those singles was numbered to 10.

	MT
Complete Set (40):	550.00
Common Player:	5.00
Minor Stars:	10.00
Inserted 1:32	
Blue Cards:	4x
Production 40 Sets	
Red Cards:	
Production 10 Sets	

Champ Bailey	15.00
Karsten Bailey	10.00
D'Wayne Bates	10.00
David Boston	20.00
Cuncho Brown	5.00
Dat Nguyen	5.00
Chris Claiborne	10.00
Michael Cloud	10.00
Cecil Collins	15.00
Tim Couch	70.00
Daunte Culpepper	30.00
Autry Denson	10.00
Troy Edwards	20.00
Ebenezer Ekuban	5.00
Kevin Faulk	15.00
Jermaine Fazande	10.00
Joe Germaine	10.00
Martin Gramatica	10.00
Torry Holt	20.00
Brock Huard	15.00
Sedrick Irvin	15.00
Edgerrin James	100.00
James Johnson	15.00
Kevin Johnson	20.00
Andy Katzenmoyer	15.00
Jevon Kearse	20.00
Patrick Kerney	5.00
Shaun King	30.00
Jim Kleinsasser	10.00
Rob Konrad	10.00
Chris McAlister	10.00
Donovan McNabb	30.00
Cade McNown	30.00
Joe Montgomery	10.00
Peerless Price	15.00
Akili Smith	25.00
Ricky Williams	60.00
Larry Parker	5.00
Antoine Winfield	5.00
Amos Zereoue	10.00

1961 Colts Jay Publishing

Measuring 5" x 7", the 12-card set showcases black-and-white posed photos on the front. The 12 cards were included in a package and sold for 25 cents. The backs are blank and unnumbered.

		NM
Complete Set (12):		80.00
Common Player:		5.00
1	Raymond Berry	14.00
2	Art Donovan	12.00
3	Weeb Ewbank (CO)	5.00
4	Alex Hawkins	5.00
5	Gino Marchetti	10.00
6	Lenny Moore	12.00
7	Jim Mutscheller	5.00
8	Steve Myhra	5.00
9	Jimmy Orr	5.00
10	Jim Parker	7.00
11	Joe Perry	10.00
12	Johnny Unitas	25.00

1967 Colts Johnny Pro

Measuring 4-1/8" x 2-7/8", each player punchout featured a color photo, with the player's name, number and position inside a white box near the bottom. By inserting the punchout into a stand, which was included with each punchout, the player punchout stood upright. The punchouts are unnumbered.

		NM
Complete Set (41):		750.00
Common Player:		15.00
1	Sam Ball	15.00
2	Raymond Berry	40.00
3	Bob Boyd	15.00
4	Ordell Braase	15.00
5	Barry Brown	15.00
6	Bill Curry	15.00
7	Mike Curtis	20.00
8	Norman Davis	15.00
9	Jim Detwiler	15.00
10	Dennis Gaubatz	15.00
11	Alvin Haymond	15.00
12	Jerry Hill	15.00
13	Roy Hilton	15.00
14	David Lee	15.00
15	Jerry Logan	15.00
16	Tony Lorick	15.00
17	Lenny Lyles	15.00
18	John Mackey	30.00
19	Tom Matte	20.00
20	Lou Michaels	15.00
21	Fred Miller	15.00
22	Lenny Moore	40.00
23	Jimmy Orr	20.00
24	Jim Parker	30.00
25	Ray Perkins	15.00
26	Glenn Ressler	15.00
27	Willie Richardson	20.00
28	Don Shinnick	15.00
29	Billy Ray Smith	20.00
30	Bubba Smith	40.00
31	Charlie Stukes	15.00
32	Andy Stynchula	15.00
33	Dan Sullivan	15.00
34	Dick Szymanski	15.00
35	Johnny Unitas	75.00
36	Bob Vogel	15.00
37	Rick Volk	20.00
38	Bob Wade	15.00
39	Jim Ward	15.00
40	Jim Welch	15.00
41	Butch Wilson	15.00

1978 Colts Team Issue

Measuring 5" x 7", the 28-photo set featured a player photo on the front, with the player's name, team and position listed under the photo. The blank backs are also unnumbered.

		NM
Complete Set (28):		45.00
Common Player:		1.50
1	Mack Alston	2.00
2	Ron Baker	1.50
3	Mike Barnes	1.50
4	Tim Baylor	1.50
5	Randy Burke	1.50
6	Glenn Doughty	2.00
7	Joe Ehrmann	1.50
8	Wade Griffin	1.50
9	Don Hardeman	1.50
10	Dwight Harrison	1.50
11	Ken Huff	1.50
12	Marshall Johnson	1.50
13	Bert Jones	8.00
14	Bruce Laird	1.50
15	Roosevelt Leaks	2.50
16	David Lee	1.50
17	Ron Lee	1.50
18	Toni Linhart	1.50
19	Derrel Luce	1.50
20	Reese McCall	1.50
21	Ken Mendenhall	1.50
22	Don Morrison	1.50
23	Lloyd Mumphord	1.50
24	Calvin O'Neal	1.50
25	Robert Pratt	1.50
26	Mike Siani	1.50
27	Bill Troup	1.50
28	Stan White	1.50

1985 Colts Kroger

Measuring 5-1/2" x 8-1/2", the 17-photo set spotlighted a large photo on the front, with the Colts' helmet, player name, position, number and Kroger logo underneath from left to right. The card backs have the Indianapolis Colts at the top, with the player's name, position, number and bio underneath. The NFL logo and Kroger logos are also printed on the backs. The cards are unnumbered.

		MT
Complete Set (17):		30.00
Common Player:		1.00
1	Karl Baldischwiler	1.00
2	Pat Beach	1.00
3	Albert Bentley	2.00
4	Duane Bickett	3.00
5	Matt Bouza	1.00
6	Nesby Glasgow	1.00
7	Chris Hinton	2.00
8	Lamonte Hunley	1.00
9	Barry Krauss	1.00
10	Orlando Lowry	1.00
11	Tate Randle	1.00
12	Tim Sherwin	1.00
13	Ron Solt	1.00
14	Rohn Stark	1.50
15	Ben Utt	1.00
16	Brad White	1.00
17	Anthony Young	1.50

1988 Colts Police

Measuring 2-5/8" x 4-1/8", the eight-card set boasts a large photo, with the photo credit, player's name, number, position and bio beneath it. The Colts' helmet and name are at the bottom of the card front. The card backs feature two cartoon drawings -- one is a Colts Tip, while the other is a Crime Stoppers Tip. The card backs are numbered "of 8." Oscar Mayer and WTHR-TV logos are printed at the bottom of the card backs.

		MT
Complete Set (8):		8.00
Common Player:		1.00
1	Eric Dickerson	3.00
2	Barry Krauss	1.00
3	Bill Brooks	1.50
4	Duane Bickett	1.00
5	Chris Hinton	1.00
6	Eugene Daniel	1.00
7	Jack Trudeau	1.00
8	Ron Meyer (CO)	1.00

1989 Colts Police

Measuring 2-5/8" x 4-1/8", the nine-card set showcases a photo on the front, with a photo credit, player's name, number, position, bio, Colts' helmet and "Indianapolis Colts" printed beneath the photo. The card backs feature two cartoon drawings -- one being a Colts Tip and the other a Crime Stoppers Tip. The cards are numbered. The Indiana Law Enforcement, Louis Rich and WTHR logos are at the bottom of the card backs.

		MT
Complete Set (9):		8.00
Common Player:		.50
1	Colts Team Card	.50
2	Dean Biasucci	.50
3	Andre Rison	1.75
4	Chris Chandler	1.25
5	O'Brien Alston	.75
6	Ray Donaldson	.75
7	Donnell Thompson	.50
8	Fredd Young	.50
9	Eric Dickerson	1.50

1990 Colts Police

Measuring 2-5/8" x 4-1/8", the eight-card set features a large photo on the front, with a photo credit, player's name, position, bio, Colts' helmet and "Indianapolis Colts" printed underneath. The card backs have a Colts Tip and a Crime Stoppers Tip. The Indiana Law Enforcement, Louis Rich and WTHR logos are printed at the bottom of the card backs.

		MT
Complete Set (8):		6.00
Common Player:		.50
1	Harvey Armstrong	.50
2	Pat Beach	.50
3	Albert Bentley	.75
4	Kevin Call	.50
5	Jeff George	3.00
6	Mike Prior	.50
7	Rohn Stark	.50
8	Clarence Verdin	.50

1991 Colts Police

Measuring 2-5/8" x 4-1/4", the eight-card set showcases a photo on the front, with a photo credit, player's name, Colts' helmet, "Indianapolis Colts" and Indiana Law Enforcement logo beneath it. The card backs feature the player's name, number, position and bio at the top and Colts quiz in the center. An anti-drug message, WTHR and Coke logos are printed at the bottom. The cards are numbered in the lower right corner.

		MT
Complete Set (8):		5.00
Common Player:		.75
1	Jeff George	1.75
2	Jack Trudeau	1.00
3	Jeff Herrod	.75
4	Eric Dickerson	1.50
5	Bill Brooks	1.25
6	Jon Hand	.75
7	Keith Taylor	.75
8	Randy Dixon	.75

1994 Costacos Brothers Poster Cards

Measuring 4-1/4" x 6-1/4", the 12 mini-poster cards were packaged in cello packs. A cardboard sleeve in the packs pictured the set on the front, while the back was numbered of 25,000. The poster was bordered in white on the front, while the backs have the standard postcard look, with the team's logo in the center. The cards are numbered at the bottom center.

		MT
Complete Set (12):		15.00
Common Player:		.50
1	Troy Aikman (Strong Arm of the Law)	2.00
2	Barry Sanders (The Silver Streak)	2.00
3	Steve Young (Run and Gun)	1.00
4	Rick Mirer (Natural Wonder)	.75
5	John Elway (The Rifleman)	1.00
6	Dan Marino (Tropical Storm)	3.00
7	Drew Bledsoe (Patriot Games)	2.00
8	Emmitt Smith (Catch 22)	3.00
9	Warren Moon (Moonshine)	.50
10	Jerry Rice (Elite)	2.00
11	Michael Irvin (Playmaker)	.50
12	Jim Kelly (Machine Gun Kelly)	.50

1992 Courtside Draft Pix Promos

These eight cards were produced to preview Courtside's 1992 Draft Pix set. The cards are similar in design to those in the regular set, but are labeled on the back as being "Promotion - Not For Sale." A card number appears on the back; two #20 cards were made. Some of the cards were given away at card shows and may be stamped on the back in red indicating what show they were given away at.

		MT
Complete Set (8):		15.00
Common Player:		2.00
20A	Tony Brooks	2.00
20B	Amp Lee	3.00
22	Terrell Buckley	2.50
30	Tommy Vardell	2.00
40	Carl Pickens	3.00
44	Quentin Coryatt	2.00
50	Mike Gaddis	2.00
60	Steve Emtman	2.00

1992 Courtside

Courtside's 1992 set had an abundance of insert cards, each of which had a limited print run. The main set's cards are glossy and have a color action photo on the front. A gold stripe at the bottom of the card has the player's name and position inside. The card back has another photo on the top half, with biographical and collegiate statistics under the picture. A card number and the set's logo are also on the back. Special bronze, silver and gold foil versions were also made for each regular card; they were random inserts in limited quantities and command higher prices. There were also autographed cards inserted into the packs; these cards also command premium values, based on the value of the player's regular card. Short printed insert cards were also randomly included in packs. These cards, five each for Award Winners and All-Americans, are numbered using an "AW" or "AA" prefix. In addition, there were 50,000 Steve Emtman foilgram cards randomly inserted in packs.

		MT
Complete Set (140):		6.00
Common Player:		.05
Bronze Cards:		2x
Silver Cards:		2x
Gold Cards:		2x
Common Autograph:		4.00
Autograph Cards:		15x-30x
1	Steve Emtman	.10
2	Quentin Coryatt	.30
3	Ken Swilling	.10
4	Jay Leeuwenburg	.05
5	Mazio Royster	.05
6	Matt Veatch	.05
7	Scott Lockwood	.05
8	Todd Collins	.05
9	Gene McGuire	.05
10	Dale Carter	.10
11	Michael Bankston	.05
12	Jeremy Lincoln	.10
13	Troy Auzenne	.05
14	Rod Smith	.05
15	Andy Kelly	.05
16	Chris Holder	.05
17	Rico Smith	.05
18	Chris Pedersen	.05
19	Brian Treggs	.05
20	Eugene Chung	.05
21	Joel Steed	.05
22	Ricardo McDonald	.05
23	Nate Turner	.05
24	Sean Lumpkin	.05
25	Ty Detmer	.25
26	Matt Darby	.05
27	Michael Warfield	.05
28	Tracy Scroggins	.10
29	Carl Pickens	1.50
30	Chris Mims	.10
31	Mark D'Onofrio	.05
32	Dwight Hollier	.05
33	Siupeli Malamala	.05
34	Mark Barsotti	.05
35	Charles Davenport	.05
36	Brian Bollinger	.05
37	Willie McClendon	.05
38	Calvin Holmes	.05
39	Phillippi Sparks	.05
40	Darryl Williams	.05
41	Greg Skrepenak	.05
42	Larry Webster	.05
43	Dion Lambert	.05
44	Sam Gash	.10
45	Patrick Rowe	.05
46	Scottie Graham	.15
47	Darian Hagan	.05
48	Arthur Marshall	.05
49	Amp Lee	.25
50	Tommy Vardell	.10
51	Robert Porcher	.10
52	Reggie Dwight	.05
53	Torrance Small	.05
54	Ronnie West	.05
55	Tony Brooks	.05
56	Anthony McDowell	.05
57	Chris Haskel	.05
58	Ed Cunningham	.05
59	Ashley Ambrose	.05
60	Alonzo Spellman	.15
61	Harold Heath	.05
62	Ron Lopez	.05
63	Bill Johnson	.05
64	Kent Graham	.05
65	Aaron Pierce	.05
66	Bucky Richardson	.05
67	Todd Kinchen	.10
68	Ken Ealy	.05
69	Carlos Snow	.05
70	Dana Hall	.05
71	Matt Rodgers	.05
72	Howard Dinkins	.05
73	Tim Lester	.05
74	Mark Chmura	.75
75	Johnny Mitchell	.25
76	Mirko Jurkovic	.05
77	Anthony Lynn	.05
78	Roosevelt Collins	.05
79	Tony Sands	.05
80	Kevin Smith	.05
81	Tony Brown	.05
82	Bobby Fuller	.05
83	Darryl Ashmore	.05
84	Tyrone Legette	.05
85	Mike Gaddis	.05
86	Gerald Dixon	.05
87	T.J. Rubley	.05
88	Mark Thomas	.05
89	Corey Widmer	.05
90	Robert Jones	.05
91	Eddie Robinson	.05
92	Rob Tomlinson	.05
93	Russ Campbell	.05
94	Keith Goganious	.05
95	Rod Moore	.05
96	Jerry Ostroski	.05
97	Tyji Armstrong	.10
98	Ronald Humphrey	.05
99	Corey Harris	.05
100	Terrell Buckley	.15
101	Cal Dixon	.05
102	Tyrone Williams	.05
103	Joe Bowden	.05
104	Santana Dotson	.10
105	Jeff Blake	1.50
106	Erick Anderson	.05
107	Steve Israel	.05
108	Chad Roghair	.05
109	Todd Harrison	.05
110	Chester McGlockton	.10
111	Marquez Pope	.10
112	George Rooks	.05
113	Dion Johnson	.05
114	Tim Simpson	.05
115	Chris Walsh	.05
116	Marc Boutte	.05
117	Jamie Gill	.05
118	Willie Clay	.05
119	Tim Paulk	.05
120	Ray Roberts	.05
121	Jeff Thomason	.05
122	Leodis Flowers	.05
123	Robert Brooks	.75
124	Jeff Ellis	.05
125	John Fina	.05
126	Michael Smith	.05
127	Mike Saunders	.05
128	John Brown III	.05
129	Reggie Yarbrough	.05
130	Leon Searcy	.05
131	Marcus Woods	.05
132	Shane Collins	.05
133	Chuck Smith	.05
134	Keith Hamilton	.05
135	Rodney Blackshear	.05
136	Corey Barlow	.05
137	Robert Harris	.05
138	Tony Smith	.05
139	Checklist 1	.05
140	Checklist 2	.05

1992 Courtside Foilgrams

1992 Courtside Draft Pix wrappers offered these foilgram cards as a mail-in offer; collectors could receive one by sending in 10 wrappers. There were 15,000 foilgram cards produced for each card; which is numbered #1 of 5 limited edition foilgram cards.

		MT
Complete Set (5):		5.00
Common Player:		1.00
1	Steve Emtman	1.00
2	Tommy Vardell	1.25
3	Terrell Buckley	1.25
4	Ty Detmer	1.00
5	Amp Lee	1.00

1992 Courtside Inserts

These short-printed foilgram cards, random inserts in 1992 Courtside Draft Pix foil cases, feature glossy color action photos on the front, bordered with a white frame. Five Award Winners and Five All-Americans are featured in the set; the football logo on the card front indicates if the player is an Award Winner or All-American. The card back, which features a color photo on one side and player profile on the other, also distinguishes which type of card it is by using a corresponding "AW" or "AA" prefix for the card number.

		MT
Complete Set (10):		10.00
Common Player:		.50
Award Winners		
1	Outland Trophy (Steve Emtman)	2.00
2	'90 Heisman Trophy (Ty Detmer)	3.00
3	Lombardi Award (Steve Emtman)	2.00
4	Jim Thorpe Award (Terrell Buckley)	2.00
5	Dick Butkus Award (Erick Anderson)	.50
All-America		
1	Carl Pickens	4.00
2	Dale Carter	2.00
3	Tommy Vardell	2.00
4	Amp Lee	2.00
5	Leon Searcy	.50

1993 Courtside Sean Dawkins

Indiana Colts first-round draft pick Sean Dawkins is featured in this five-card insert set. There were 20,000 sets produced; the complete set value below does not include an autographed card. Dawkins signed 5,000 cards, which were randomly inserted within the sets. Each card front has a color action photo against a blurred background. Gold foil stamping is used to incorporate the player's name, a football and "Draft Pix" into the design. A promotional card was also produced, similar to card #3, except it has "Promotional - Not For Sale" and "Authentic Signature" written on the card front.

		MT
Complete Set (5):		10.00
Common Player:		2.00
1	Sean Dawkins (Ball cradles in right arm, running up field)	2.00
2	Sean Dawkins (Hands outstretched to catch ball)	2.00
3	Sean Dawkins (Being handchecked by cornerback)	2.00
4	Sean Dawkins (Kneeling pose)	2.00
5	Sean Dawkins (Dressed in tuxedo)	2.00
----	Sean Dawkins (AU 5000, certified autograph)	15.00

1993 Courtside Russell White

Los Angeles Rams' third-round draft pick Russell White is featured in this five-card insert set. Each card front has a full-bleed color, glossy action photo against a blurred background. Gold foil is used to incorporate the player's name, Draft Pix and football logo into the design of the card. The card back has a color photo of the player, plus either statistics, biographical or player profile information, or highlights. A card number is also included. There were 20,000 sets produced. White autographed 5,000 cards, which were randomly inserted within the set. (The complete set price does not include an autographed card.) Promo cards were also issued for #s 3-5. They can be distinguished from the regular cards by the words "Promotional - Not For Sale,"

which appear on the card front, and the words "Authentic Signature," which also appear on the front.

		MT
Complete Set (5):		10.00
Common White:		2.00
1	Russell White (Running almost straight head)	2.00
2	Russell White (Running toward the right)	2.00
3	Russell White (Running toward defensive player number 78)	2.00
4	Russell White (Running upfield; side view)	2.00
5	Russell White (Dressed in tuxedo)	2.00
----	Russell White (AU/5000, certified autograph)	12.00

1969 Cowboys Team Issue

Measuring 7" x 10", the card fronts showcase color action shots of players. The photos have black rounded-corner borders. The player's name and team are printed below the photo. The unnumbered backs are blank.

		NM
Complete Set (5):		35.00
Common Player:		5.00
1	Walt Garrison	5.00
2	Lee Roy Jordan	7.00
3	Bob Lilly	10.00
4	Dave Manders	5.00
5	Mel Renfro	8.00

1971 Cowboys Team Issue

Measuring 5" x 6-1/2", the 40-card set showcases black-and-white posed shots on the front, bordered in white. The player's name and team are printed below the photo. The cards are unnumbered and have blank backs.

		NM
Complete Set (40):		150.00
Common Player:		2.00
1	Herb Adderley	5.00
2	Lance Alworth	12.00
3	George Andrie	2.00
4	Mike Clark	2.00
5	Larry Cole	2.00
6	Mike Ditka	16.00
7	Dave Edwards	2.00
8	John Fitzgerald	2.00
9	Toni Fritsch	2.00
10	Walt Garrison	2.00
11	Cornell Green	2.00
12	Bill Gregory	2.00
13	Cliff Harris	3.00
14	Bob Hayes	6.00
15	Calvin Hill	5.00
16	Chuck Howley	3.00
17	Lee Roy Jordan	4.00
18	D.D. Lewis	2.00
19	Bob Lilly	10.00
20	Tony Liscio	2.00
21	Dave Manders	2.00
22	Craig Morton	5.00
23	Ralph Neely	2.00
24	John Niland	2.00
25	Jethro Pugh	2.00
26	Dan Reeves	12.00
27	Mel Renfro	8.00
28	Gloster Richardson	2.00
29	Tody Smith	2.00
30	Roger Staubach	30.00
31	Don Talbert	2.00
32	Duane Thomas	2.00
33	Isaac Thomas	2.00
34	Pat Toomay	2.00
35	Billy Truax	2.00
36	Rodney Wallace	2.00
37	Mark Washington	2.00
38	Charlie Waters	3.00
39	Claxton Welch	2.00
40	Ron Widby	2.00

1972 Cowboys Team Issue

Measuring 4-1/4" x 5-1/2", the 13-card set showcases black-and-white photos on the front, bordered in white. The player's name is printed underneath the photo. The cards are unnumbered and have blank backs.

		NM
Complete Set (13):		50.00
Common Player:		2.00
1	Herb Adderley	4.00
2	Mike Ditka	15.00
3	Toni Fritsch	2.00
4	Walt Garrison	2.00
5	Cornell Green	2.00
6	Cliff Harris	3.00
7	Bob Hayes	6.00
8	Calvin Hill	5.00
9	Robert Newhouse	2.00
10	Billy Parks	2.00
11	Mel Renfro	6.00
12	Dan Reeves	10.00
13	Charlie Waters	3.00

1979 Cowboys Police

89 • Billy Joe DuPree
Tight End
DALLAS COWBOYS

Measuring 2-5/8" x 4-1/8", the 15-card set showcases a player photo on the front, with a photo credit, player's name, number, position and team listed below. The Cowboys logo is in the lower left. The card backs have Cowboys Tips in a box, with the Cowboys' helmet at the top. The sponsors are listed at the bottom of the card back. D.D. Lewis replaced Thomas "Hollywood" Henderson during the season, which means lesser amounts were printed of both cards.

		NM
Complete Set (15):		25.00
Common Player:		.50
12	Roger Staubach	6.00
33	Tony Dorsett	4.00
41	Charlie Waters	.75
43	Cliff Harris	.50
44	Robert Newhouse	.50
50	D.D. Lewis (SP)	2.00
53	Bob Breunig	.50
54	Randy White	2.00
56	Thomas Henderson (SP)	2.00
67	Pat Donovan	.50
79	Harvey Martin	.50
80	Tony Hill	.50
88	Drew Pearson	1.00
89	Billy Joe DuPree	.50
NNO	Tom Landry (CO)	2.50

1980 Cowboys Police

Measuring 2-5/8" x 4-1/8", the 14-card set is anchored by a large photo on the front, with the player's name, number, position and team printed under the photo. A photo credit is also listed beneath the photo. The Cowboys' helmet is printed in the lower left, while a Kiwanis logo is located in the lower right. The card backs feature Cowboys Tips inside a box, which features the Cowboys' helmet at the top. The sponsor names are printed at the bottom of the card backs. The cards are numbered by the player's jersey numbers.

		NM
Complete Set (14):		10.00
Common Player:		.50
1	Rafael Septien	1.00
11	Danny White	2.00
25	Aaron Kyle	.50
26	Preston Pearson	1.00
31	Benny Barnes	.75
35	Scott Laidlaw	.50
42	Randy Hughes	.50
62	John Fitzgerald	.75
63	Larry Cole	.50
64	Tom Rafferty	.75

68	Herbert Scott	.50
70	Rayfield Wright	.75
78	John Dutton	.75
87	Jay Saldi	.75

1981 Cowboys Police

Measuring 2-5/8" x 4-1/8", the 14-card set showcases a photo on the front, with a photo credit, player's name, jersey number, position and team printed beneath the photo. The Cowboys' helmet is in the lower left corner, while the Kiwanis' logo is in the lower right. The card backs feature Cowboys Tips inside, a box with the Cowboys helmet at the top. The cards are numbered with the player's jersey number.

		MT
Complete Set (14):		10.00
Common Player:		.50
18	Glenn Carano	.75
20	Ron Springs	1.00
23	James Jones	.50
26	Michael Downs	.75
32	Dennis Thurman	.75
45	Steve Wilson	.50
51	Anthony Dickerson	.50
52	Robert Shaw	.50
58	Mike Hegman	.50
59	Guy Brown	.50
61	Jim Cooper	.50
72	Ed "Too Tall" Jones	2.00
84	Doug Cosbie	1.00
86	Butch Johnson	1.00

1981 Cowboys Thousand Oaks Police

Measuring 2-5/8" x 4-1/8", the 14-card set is anchored by a photo on the front. A photo credit, player's name, jersey number, position and team are printed below the photo. The Cowboys' helmet is in the lower left, while a sponsor's logo is in the lower right. The card backs feature Cowboys Tips inside a box, with the Cowboys' helmet at the top. The sponsors, including the Thousand Oaks Police Dept., are listed at the bottom of the card backs.

		MT
Complete Set (14):		42.00
Common Player:		1.50
11	Danny White	4.00
33	Benny Barnes	1.50
33	Tony Dorsett	8.00
41	Charlie Waters	3.00
42	Randy Hughes	1.50
44	Robert Newhouse	2.00
54	Randy White	6.00
55	D.D. Lewis	1.50
78	John Dutton	1.50
79	Harvey Martin	3.00
80	Tony Hill	3.00
88	Drew Pearson	4.00
89	Billy Joe DuPree	2.00
NNO	Tom Landry (CO)	7.00

1982 Cowboys Carrollton Park

Measuring 3" x 4", the six-card set showcases a large photo on the front, with "Carrollton Park Mall" printed below it inside a white border. The card backs spotlight the card's number at the top inside a circle. The player's name, position and stats are printed below the number. The Cowboys' 1982-83 schedule takes up the bottom 2/3 of the card back. The set is also available in uncut sheets.

		MT
Complete Set (6):		5.00
Common Player:		.50
1	Roger Staubach	2.00
2	Danny White	.75
3	Tony Dorsett	1.00
4	Randy White	.75
5	Charlie Waters	.50
6	Billy Joe DuPree	.50

1983 Cowboys Police

Measuring 2-5/8" x 4-1/8", the 28-card set is anchored by a large photo on the front, with a photo credit, player's name, jersey number, position and team

printed underneath the photo. The Cowboys' helmet is printed in the lower right, while the Kiwanis' logo is in the lower right. The card backs have Cowboys Tips inside a box, with the Cowboys' helmet at the top. The sponsors are listed at the bottom of the card back.

		MT
Complete Set (28):		25.00
Common Player:		.50
1	Rafael Septien	.50
11	Danny White	1.50
20	Ron Springs	.50
24	Everson Walls	.50
26	Michael Downs	.50
32	Timmy Newsome	.50
32	Dennis Thurman	.50
33	Tony Dorsett	3.00
47	Dexter Clinkscale	.50
53	Bob Breunig	.50
54	Randy White	3.00
65	Kurt Petersen	.50
67	Pat Donovan	.50
70	Howard Richards	.50
72	Ed "Too Tall" Jones	2.00
78	John Dutton	.50
79	Harvey Martin	1.00
80	Tony Hill	.75
83	Doug Donley	.50
84	Doug Cosbie	.50
86	Butch Johnson	.50
88	Drew Pearson	1.75
89	Billy Joe DuPree	.50
NNO	Tom Landry (CO)	2.00
NNO	Melinda May (CHEER)	.50
NNO	Dana Presley (CHEER)	.50
NNO	Judy Trammell (CHEER)	.50
NNO	Toni Washington (CHEER)	.50

1985 Cowboys Frito Lay

Measuring 4" x 5-1/2", this 41 card set is anchored on the front by a large black-and-white photo. The player's name, jersey number, position and bio are listed beneath the photo on the front. The Cowboys' helmet is printed in the lower left, with the Frito Lay logo in the lower right. The backs are unnumbered and blank.

		MT
Complete Set (41):		50.00
Common Player:		1.00
1	Vince Albritton	1.00
2	Brian Baldinger	1.00
3	Dexter Clinkscale	1.00
4	Jim Cooper	1.00
5	Fred Cornwell	1.00
6	Doug Crosbie	1.50
7	Steve DeOssie	1.50
8	John Dutton	1.00
9	Ricky Easmon	1.00
10	Ron Fellows	1.00
11	Leon Gonzalez	1.00
12	Gary Hogeboom	1.50
13	Jim Jeffcoat	2.50
14	Ed "Too Tall" Jones	3.00
15	James Jones	1.00
16	Crawford Ker	1.00
17	Robert Lavette	1.00
18	Eugene Lockhart	1.00
19	Timmy Newsome	1.00
20	Drew Pearson (ACO)	2.00
21	Steve Pelluer	1.50
22	Jesse Penn	1.00
23	Kurt Petersen	1.00
24	Karl Powe	1.00
25	Phil Pozderac	1.00
26	Tom Rafferty	1.00
27	Mike Renfro	1.00
28	Howard Richards	1.00
29	Jeff Rohrer	1.00
30	Mike Saxon	1.00
31	Victor Scott	1.00
32	Rafael Septien	1.00
33	Don Smerek	1.00
34	Roger Staubach	10.00
35	Broderick Thompson	1.00
36	Dennis Thurman	1.00
37	Glen Titensor	1.00
38	Mark Tuinei	1.50
39	Everson Walls	1.50
40	John Williams	1.00
41	Team Photo	3.00

1994 Cowboys ProLine Live Kroger Stickers

Each sticker measures 3-5/8 inches and is part of a three-sticker strip which measures 2-1/2" x

12". The sticker fronts showcase the same design as the 1994 Pro Line card series, with the player's name printed in large letters at the bottom of the sticker and his name printed inside a stripe beneath his name. The Classic Pro Line logo is located in the upper right corner. The sticker backs feature $1 off Fuji Film coupons or a team poster sweepstakes form. The strips were sold at Kroger stores for 99 cents for seven weeks. The sticker strips are numbered by their respective weeks.

		MT
Complete Set (7):		5.00
Common Player:		.50
1	Troy Aikman, Darren Woodson, Erik Williams	1.50
2	Emmitt Smith, James Washington, Mark Stepnoski	2.00
3	Michael Irvin, Kenneth Gant, Tony Tolbert	.75
4	Daryl Johnston, Kevin Williams WR, Leon Lett	.50
5	Nate Newton, Shante Carver, Charles Haley	.50
6	Russell Maryland, Mark Tuinei, Kevin Smith	.50
7	Alvin Harper, Willie Jackson, Jay Novacek	.50

1976 Crane Discs

These circular cards measure 3-3/8" in diameter and were produced by Michael Schechter Associates, as noted by the MSA letters on the card back. Each card front has a black- and-white mug shot of a player, along with his team, name and position. The card has a colored border with the word "Crane" at the top, representing Crane Potato Chips, which offered the cards as a mail-in offer. The Crane logo appears on the card back, but there are a few other sponsors which may also appear on the back; these are slightly more valuable than their Crane counterparts. The cards are unnumbered.

		NM
Complete Set (30):		15.00
Common Player:		.10
(1)	Ken Anderson	.50
(2)	Otis Armstrong	.15
(3)	Steve Bartkowski	.35
(4)	Terry Bradshaw	2.00
(5)	John Brockington	.25
(6)	Doug Buffone	.10
(7)	Wally Chambers	.10
(8)	Isaac Curtis	.25
(9)	Chuck Foreman	.20
(10)	Roman Gabriel	.75
(11)	Mel Gray	.15
(12)	Joe Greene	.65
(13)	James Harris	.25
(14)	Jim Hart	.25
(15)	Billy Kilmer	.25
(16)	Greg Landry	.25
(17)	Ed Marinaro	.50
(18)	Lawrence McCutcheon	.25
(19)	Terry Metcalf	.15
(20)	Lydell Mitchell	.25
(21)	Jim Otis	.15
(22)	Alan Page	.35
(23)	Walter Payton	10.00
(24)	Greg Pruitt	.40
(25)	Charlie Sanders	.25
(26)	Ron Shanklin	.25
(27)	Roger Staubach	2.00
(28)	Jan Stenerud	.40
(29)	Charley Taylor	.40
(30)	Roger Wehrli	.25

Values quoted in this guide reflect the retail price of a card — the price a collector can expect to pay when buying a card from a dealer. The wholesale price — that which a collector can expect to receive from a dealer when selling cards — will be significantly lower, depending on desirability and condition.

1992 Crown Pro Dogtags

Measuring 2-1/8" x 3-3/8", the 81 dog tags were manufactured by Chris Martin Enterprises Inc., which later became Crown Pro. Produced of plastic, the tags are similar to credit cards. The tag fronts include a color photo in the center, with the "Dog Tags," NFL logo and tag number inside a white border at the top. The player's name, position and team, along with the team's logo, are printed inside a white border at the bottom. The backs have the player's name, headshot, bio, highlights and a team logo area that could be autographed. The top center of each tag had a hole in it, which allowed collectors to wear the tags on a chain. The team tags were horizontal and featured a photo of the team's stadium on the front. The rookie tags resemble the regular tags, however, they have a gold-foil border at the top. An Emmitt Smith promo tag was also released and it has "promo tag" printed on the back. Chris Martin autographed tags were also produced.

		MT
Complete Set (81):		70.00
Common Player:		.50
1	Atlanta Falcons	.50
2	Buffalo Bills	.50
3	Chicago Bears	.50
4	Cincinnati Bengals	.50
5	Cleveland Browns	.50
6	Dallas Cowboys	.50
7	Denver Broncos	.50
8	Detroit Lions	.50
9	Green Bay Packers	.50
10	Houston Oilers	.50
11	Indianapolis Colts	.50
12	Kansas City Chiefs	.50
13	Los Angeles Raiders	.50
14	Los Angeles Rams	.50
15	Miami Dolphins	.50
16	Minnesota Vikings	.50
17	New England Patriots	.50
18	New Orleans Saints	.50
19	New York Giants	.50
20	New York Jets	.50
21	Philadelphia Eagles	.50
22	Phoenix Cardinals	.50
23	Pittsburgh Steelers	.50
24	San Diego Chargers	.50
25	San Francisco 49ers	.50
26	Seattle Seahawks	.50
27	Tampa Bay Buccaneers	.50
28	Washington Redskins	.50
29A	Chris Martin (Reg.)	1.00
29B	Chris Martin (Gold)	2.00
29AU	Chris Martin (Autograph)	10.00
30	Dan Marino	10.00
31	Chris Miller	.50
32	Deion Sanders	3.00
33	Jim Kelly	1.00
34	Thurman Thomas	1.00
35	Jim Harbaugh	.50
36	Mike Singletary	.50
37	Boomer Esiason	.50
38	Anthony Munoz	.50
39	Bernie Kosar	.50
40	Troy Aikman	5.00
41	Michael Irvin	2.00
42	Emmitt Smith	10.00
43	John Elway	3.00
44	Rodney Peete	.50
45	Sterling Sharpe	1.00
46	Haywood Jeffires	.50
47	Warren Moon	1.00
48	Jeff George	1.00
49	Christian Okoye	.50
50	Derrick Thomas	1.00
51	Howie Long	.50
52	Ronnie Lott	.50
53	Jim Everett	.50
54	Mark Clayton	.50
55	Anthony Carter	.50
56A	Chris Doleman	.50
56B	Chris Doleman (Autograph)	.50
57	Andre Tippett	.50
58A	Pat Swilling	.50
58B	Pat Swilling (Autograph)	.50
59	Jeff Hostetler	.50
60	Lawrence Taylor	1.00
61	Robert Moore	.50
62	Ken O'Brien	.50
63	Keith Byars	.50
64	Randall Cunningham	.50
65	Keith Byars	.50
66	Timm Rosenbach	.50
67	Bubby Brister	.50
68	John Friesz	1.00
69	Jerry Rice	5.00
70	Steve Young	4.00
71	Dan McGwire	.50
72	Broderick Thomas	.50
73	Vinny Testaverde	1.00
74	Gary Clark	.50
75	Mark Rypien	.50

1993 Crown Pro Dogtags

Measuring 2-1/8" x 3-3/8", the tags were produced by Chris Martin Enterprises, which later became Crown Pro. The 138-plastic tag set featured a full-bleed photo on the front with "1993" gold-foil stamped in the upper left and the Dog Tags logo printed in the upper right. The player's name is printed in white inside a stripe in the lower right. The tag backs have the number in the upper left, with the player's headshot, name, number, bio, highlights and stats listed along the right side. An autograph strip is located along the left border. Overall, 50,000 of each tag was produced. Tag Nos. 48 and 138 were not printed for the set. Originally, the tags were sold in packs, however, complete team sets were sold later in the season. Atlanta and the Raiders were not distributed as team sets. In addition, 25,000 Joe Montana bonus tags were available through a mail-in offer. A contest offered collectors the chance to win a 14K gold bead chain or a seven-point diamond tag.

		MT
Complete Set (140):		80.00
Common Player:		.50
1	Atlanta Falcons	.50
2	Buffalo Bills	.50
3	Chicago Bears	.50
4	Cincinnati Bengals	.50
5	Cleveland Browns	.50
6	Dallas Cowboys	.50
7	Denver Broncos	.50
8	Detroit Lions	.50
9	Green Bay Packers	.50
10	Houston Oilers	.50
11	Indianapolis Colts	.50
12	Kansas City Chiefs	.50
13	Los Angeles Raiders	.50
14	Los Angeles Rams	.50
15	Miami Dolphins	.50
16	Minnesota Vikings	.50
17	New England Patriots	.50
18	New Orleans Saints	.50
19	New York Giants	.50
20	New York Jets	.50
21	Philadelphia Eagles	.50
22	Phoenix Cardinals	.50

#	Player	Price
23	Pittsburgh Steelers	.50
24	San Diego Chargers	.50
25	San Francisco 49ers	.50
26	Seattle Seahawks	.50
27	Tampa Bay Buccaneers	.50
28	Washington Redskins	.50
29	Steve Broussard	.50
30	Chris Miller	.50
31	Andre Rison	1.00
32	Deion Sanders	3.00
33	Cornelius Bennett	.50
34	Jim Kelly	1.00
35	Bruce Smith	.50
36	Thurman Thomas	1.00
37	Neal Anderson	.50
38	Mark Carrier	.50
39	Jim Harbaugh	1.00
40	Alonzo Spellman	1.00
41	David Fulcher	.50
42	Harold Green	.50
43	David Klingler	.50
44	Carl Pickens	2.00
45	Bernie Kosar	.50
46	Clay Matthews	.50
47	Eric Metcalf	.50
49	Troy Aikman	4.00
50	Michael Irvin	2.00
51	Russell Maryland	.50
52	Emmitt Smith	8.00
53	Steve Atwater	.50
54	John Elway	3.00
55	Tommy Maddox	.50
56	Shannon Sharpe	1.00
57	Herman Moore	2.00
58	Rodney Peete	.50
59	Barry Sanders	4.00
60	Andre Ware	.50
61	Terrell Buckley	.50
62	Brett Favre	10.00
63	Sterling Sharpe	1.00
64	Reggie White	2.00
65	Ray Childress	.50
66	Haywood Jeffires	.50
67	Warren Moon	1.00
68	Lorenzo White	.50
69	Duane Bickett	.50
70	Quentin Coryatt	.50
71	Steve Emtman	.50
72	Jeff George	.50
73	Dale Carter	.50
74	Neil Smith	.50
75	Derrick Thomas	1.00
76	Harvey Williams	.50
77	Eric Dickerson	.50
78	Howie Long	.50
79	Todd Marinovich	.50
80	Alexander Wright	.50
81A	Flipper Anderson	.50
81B	Flipper Anderson (Autograph)	.50
82A	Jim Everett	.50
82B	Jim Everett (Autograph)	.50
83	Cleveland Gary	.50
84A	Chris Martin	.50
84B	Chris Martin (Autograph)	.50
85	Irving Fryer	.50
86	Keith Jackson	.50
87	Dan Marino	8.00
88	Louis Oliver	.50
89	Terry Allen	2.00
90	Anthony Carter	.50
91	Chris Doleman	.50
92	Rich Gannon	.50
93	Eugene Chung	.50
94	Marv Cook	.50
95	Leonard Russell	.50
96	Andre Tippett	.50
97	Morten Andersen	.50
98	Vaughn Dunbar	.50
99	Rickey Jackson	.50
100	Sam Mills	.50
101	Derek Brown	.50
102	Lawrence Taylor	1.00
103	Rodney Hampton	1.00
104	Phil Simms	.50
105	Johnny Mitchell	.50
106	Rob Moore	.50
107	Blair Thomas	.50
108	Browning Nagle	.50
109	Eric Allen	.50
110	Fred Barnett	.50
111	Randall Cunningham	.50
112	Herschel Walker	.50
113	Chris Chandler	.50
114	Randal Hill	.50
115	Ricky Proehl	.50
116	Eric Swann	.50
117	Barry Foster	.50
118	Eric Green	.50
119	Neil O'Donnell	.50
120	Rod Woodson	.50
121	Marion Butts	.50
122	Stan Humphries	.50
123	Anthony Miller	.50
124	Junior Seau	1.00
125	Amp Lee	.50
126	Jerry Rice	4.00
127	Ricky Watters	2.00
128	Steve Young	3.00
129	Brian Blades	.50
130	Cortez Kennedy	.50
131	Dan McGwire	.50
132	John L. Williams	.50
133	Reggie Cobb	.50
134	Steve Deberg	.50
135	Keith McCants	.50
136	Broderick Thomas	.50
137	Earnest Byner	.50
138	Mark Rypien	.50
140	Ricky Sanders	.50

1994-95 Crown Pro Tags

While the first two sets of these tags were known as Dog Tags, this 168-card issue was called Pro Tags, and was sold in six-card packs. Like Dog Tags, this set was made of plastic and measured 2-1/8" x 3-3/8". Autographed tags were available of Jerome Bettis, J.J. Birden, Dale Carter, Keith Cash, Willie Davis, Sean Gilbert, Chris Martin, Roman Phifer, Todd Lyght and Neil Smith. Pro Tags offered a chance to receive six AFC or six NFC Super Rookie Pro Tags for three proofs of purchase and $10.99 per set, or all 12 for five proofs of purchase and $15.99. The set also exists in a Super Bowl XXIX version, with no premium in price.

#	Player	MT
	Complete Set (168):	70.00
	Common Player:	.50
1	Steve Beuerlein	.50
2	Chuck Cecil	.50
3	Randal Hill	.50
4	Garrison Hearst	.50
5	Ricky Proehl	.50
6	Eric Swann	.50
7	Jeff George	.50
8	Drew Hill	.50
9	Erric Pegram	.50
10	Andre Rison	.50
11	Deion Sanders	1.50
12	Jessie Tuggle	.50
13	Cornelius Bennett	.50
14	Kenneth Davis	.50
15	Jim Kelly	1.00
16	Andre Reed	.50
17	Darryl Talley	.50
18	Steve Tasker	.50
19	Trace Armstrong	.50
20	Curtis Conway	1.00
21	Dante Jones	.50
22	Donnell Woolford	.50
23	Tim Worley	.50
24	Chris Zorich	.50
25	Derrick Fenner	.50
26	Harold Green	.50
27	David Klingler	.50
28	Tony McGee	.50
29	Carl Pickens	1.00
30	Jeff Query	.50
31	Mark Carrier	.50
32	Michael Jackson	.50
33	Eric Metcalf	.50
34	Michael Dean Perry	.50
35	Vinny Testaverde	.50
36	Tommy Vardell	.50
37	Troy Aikman	3.00
38	Alvin Harper	.50
39	Michael Irvin	1.00
40	Russell Maryland	.50
41	Jay Novacek	.50
42	Emmitt Smith	6.00
43	Rod Bernstine	.50
44	Mike Croel	.50
45	John Elway	1.50
46	Glyn Milburn	.50
47	Shannon Sharpe	.50
48	Dennis Smith	.50
49	Jason Hanson	.50
50	Herman Moore	1.00
51	Brett Perriman	.50
52	Barry Sanders	3.00
53	Chris Spielman	.50
54	Pat Swilling	.50
55	Edgar Bennett	.50
56	Terrell Buckley	.50
57	Brett Favre	8.00
58	Chris Jacke	.50
59	Sterling Sharpe	1.00
60	Reggie White	1.00
61	Gary Brown	.50
62	Cody Carlson	.50
63	Ernest Givins	.50
64	Haywood Jeffires	.50
65	Bruce Matthews	.50
66	Webster Slaughter	.50
67	Jason Belser	.50
68	Roosevelt Potts	.50
69	Rodney Culver	.50
70	Jim Harbaugh	1.00
71	Scott Radecic	.50
72	Kerry Cash	.50
73	Marcus Allen	1.00
74	J.J. Birden	.50
75	Dale Carter	.50
76	Keith Cash	.50
77	Willie Davis	.50
78	Neil Smith	.50
79	Eddie Anderson	.50
80	Tim Brown	1.00
81	Jeff Hostetler	.50
82	Raghib Ismail	.50
83	James Jett	.50
84	Terry McDaniel	.50
85	Willie Anderson	.50
86	Jerome Bettis	1.50
87	Todd Drayton	.50
88	Sean Gilbert	.50
89	Todd Lyght	.50
90	Chris Martin	.50
91	Keith Byars	.50
92	Bryan Cox	.50
93	Irving Fryar	.50
94	Terry Kirby	.50
95	Dan Marino	6.00
96	O.J. McDuffie	.50
97	Terry Allen	.50
98	Cris Carter	.50
99	Qadry Ismail	.50
100	Randall McDaniel	.50
101	Warren Moon	1.00
102	Robert Smith	1.00
103	Drew Bledsoe	3.00
104	Vincent Brisby	.50
105	Vincent Brown	.50
106	Marv Cook	.50
107	Leonard Russell	.50
108	Reyna Thompson	.50
109	Morten Andersen	.50
110	Quinn Early	.50
111	Tyrone Hughes	.50
112	Sam Mills	.50
113	William Roaf	.50
114	Renaldo Turnbull	.50
115	Stephen Baker	.50
116	John Elliott	.50
117	Rodney Hampton	.50
118	Mark Jackson	.50
119	David Meggett	.50
120	Kenyon Rasheed	.50
121	Brad Baxter	.50
122	Boomer Esiason	.50
123	Johnny Johnson	.50
124	Ronnie Lott	.50
125	Johnny Mitchell	.50
126	Rob Moore	.50
127	Fred Barnett	.50
128	Mark Bavaro	.50
129	Bubby Brister	.50
130	Randall Cunningham	.50
131	Tim Harris	.50
132	Herschel Walker	.50
133	Gary Anderson	.50
134	Barry Foster	.50
135	Kevin Greene	.50
136	Greg Lloyd	.50
137	Neil O'Donnell	.50
138	Rod Woodson	.50
139	Eric Bieniemy	.50
140	Ronnie Harmon	.50
141	Stan Humphries	.50
142	Natrone Means	1.50
143	Leslie O'Neal	.50
144	Junior Seau	1.00
145	Tim McDonald	.50
146	Jerry Rice	3.00
147	Dana Stubblefield	.50
148	John Taylor	.50
149	Ricky Watters	1.00
150	Steve Young	2.00
151	Brian Blades	.50
152	Cortez Kennedy	.50
153	Rick Mirer	.50
154	Rufus Porter	.50
155	Eugene Robinson	.50
156	Chris Warren	.50
157	Santana Dotson	.50
158	Craig Erickson	.50
159	Hardy Nickerson	.50
160	Dan Stryzinski	.50
161	Charles Wilson	.50
162	Thomas Everett	.50
163	Reggie Brooks	.50
164	Darryl Green	.50
165	Ricky Ervins	.50
166	John Friesz	.50
167	Brian Mitchell	.50
168	Sterling Palmer	.50

1994-95 Crown Pro Mags

This 168-magnet set was sold in five-magnet packs that included a team magnet. It included 140 players and 28 team magnets, which all measure 2-1/8" x 3-3/8". A Warren Moon magnet was also available by mailing in a redemption card and three proofs of purchase along with $6. The magnets display the player's name at the bottom in team colors, with the team name running up the right side. A parallel Super Bowl XXIX set was also issued, but carries no premium in price. The player magnets are numbered on the front, but the team magnets were unnumbered and checklisted in alphabetical order. In addition, a Troy Aikman promo magnet is also listed below.

#	Player	MT
	Complete Set (140):	75.00
	Common Player:	.50
1	Rod Bernstine	.50
2	John Elway	2.00
3	Glyn Milburn	.50
4	Shannon Sharpe	.50
5	Dennis Smith	.50
6	Cody Carlson	.50
7	Ernest Givins	.50
8	Haywood Jeffires	.50
9	Bruce Matthews	.50
10	Webster Slaughter	.50
11	O.J. McDuffie	1.00
12	Keith Byars	.50
13	Bryan Cox	.50
14	Irving Fryar	.50
15	Dan Marino	6.00
16	Barry Foster	.50
17	Kevin Greene	1.00
18	Greg Lloyd	1.00
19	Neil O'Donnell	.50
20	Rod Woodson	.50
21	Steve Beuerlein	.50
22	Chuck Cecil	.50
23	Randal Hill	.50
24	Ricky Proehl	.50
25	Eric Swann	.50
26	Troy Aikman	3.00
27	Emmitt Smith	6.00
28	Michael Irvin	1.00
29	Russell Maryland	.50
30	Jay Novacek	.50
31	Jerome Bettis	2.00
32	Sean Gilbert	.50
33	Todd Lyght	.50
34	Chris Martin	.50
35	Roman Phifer	.50
36	Neal Anderson	.50
37	Quinn Early	.50
38	Rickey Jackson	.50
39	Sam Mills	.50
40	William Roaf	.50
41	Cornelius Bennett	.50
42	Jim Kelly	1.00
43	Kenneth Davis	.50
44	Darryl Tallfy	.50
45	Andre Reed	.50
46	Cris Carter	1.00
47	Warren Moon	1.00
48	Terry Allen	1.00
49	Raghib Ismail	.50
50	Robert Smith	1.00
51	Erric Pegram	.50
52	Andre Rison	.50
53	Deion Sanders	2.00
54	Jessie Tuggle	.50
55	Jeff George	.50
56	Brian Blades	.50
57	Rick Mirer	.50
58	Cortez Kennedy	1.00
59	Chris Warren	1.00
60	Eugene Robinson	.50
61	Reggie Brooks	.50
62	Ricky Ervins	.50
63	Brian Mitchell	.50
64	Ricky Sanders	.50
65	Sterling Palmer	.50
66	Tim Brown	1.00
67	Jeff Hostetler	.50
68	Raghib Ismail	.50
69	Terry McDaniel	.50
70	James Jett	.50
71	Sterling Sharpe	1.00
72	Brett Favre	8.00
73	Reggie White	1.00
74	Terrell Buckley	.50
75	Edgar Bennett	.50
76	Jerry Rice	3.00
77	Steve Young	2.00
78	Ricky Watters	1.00
79	Dana Stubblefield	1.00
80	John Taylor	.50
81	Ronnie Harmon	.50
82	Stan Humphries	.50
83	Natrone Means	1.50
84	Junior Seau	1.00
85	Eric Bieniemy	.50
86	Dean Biasucci	.50
87	Jim Harbaugh	1.00
88	Roosevelt Potts	.50
89	Scott Radecic	.50
90	Rohn Stark	.50
91	Eric Metcalf	.50
92	Michael Dean Perry	.50
93	Vinny Testaverde	.50
94	Mark Carrier	.50
95	Michael Jackson	.50
96	Marcus Allen	1.00
97	Dale Carter	.50
98	Neil Smith	.50
99	J.J. Birden	.50
100	Willie Davis	.50
101	Rodney Hampton	.50
102	Mark Jackson	.50
103	David Meggett	.50
104	John Elliott	.50
105	Kenyon Rasheed	.50
106	Boomer Esiason	.50
107	Johnny Johnson	.50
108	Johnny Mitchell	.50
109	Brad Baxter	.50
110	Ronnie Lott	.50
111	Derrick Fenner	.50
112	David Klingler	.50
113	Bruce Pickens	.50
114	Harold Green	.50
115	Jeff Query	.50
116	Leonard Russell	.50
117	Drew Bledsoe	3.00
118	Marv Cook	.50
119	Vincent Brisby	.50
120	Vincent Brown	.50
121	Trace Armstrong	.50
122	Curtis Conway	1.00
123	Dante Jones	.50
124	Tim Worley	.50
125	Chris Zorich	.50
126	Ron Moore	.50
127	Barry Sanders	3.00
128	Pat Swilling	.50
129	Brett Perriman	.50
130	Chris Spielman	.50
131	Keith Byars	.50
132	Fred Barnett	.50
133	Randall Cunningham	.50
134	Herschel Walker	.50
135	Bubby Brister	.50
136	Craig Erickson	.50
137	Hardy Nickerson	.50
138	Demetrius Dubose	.50
139	Dan Stryzinski	.50
140	Charles Wilson	.50

1995 Crown Pro Magnets

This 150-card set was produced by Chris Martin Enterprises and was sold in five-card packs. The magnets are grouped alphabetically according to team below. There were three insert sets available, called By The Zone, Classics and Die-cuts, as well as a Superhero Jumbos redemption set.

#	Player	MT
	Complete Set (150):	70.00
	Common Player:	.50
1	Larry Centers	.50
2	Garrison Hearst	1.00
3	Seth Joyner	.50
4	Ron Moore	.50
5	Eric Swann	.50
6	Chris Doleman	.50
7	Jeff George	.50
8	Craig Heyward	.50
9	Terrance Mathis	.50
10	Jessie Tuggle	.50
11	Cornelius Bennett	.50
12	Jim Kelly	1.00
13	Andre Reed	.50
14	Bruce Smith	.50
15	Darryl Talley	.50
16	Trace Armstrong	.50
17	Dante Jones	.50
18	Steve Walsh	.50
19	Donnell Woolford	.50
20	Tim Worley	.50
21	Jeff Blake	2.00
22	Harold Green	.50
23	Carl Pickens	1.00
24	Danny Scott	1.00
25	Dan Wilkinson	.50
27	Derrick Alexander	.50
28	Antonio Langham	.50
29	Vinny Testaverde	.50
30	Eric Turner	.50
31	Troy Aikman	2.00
32	Michael Irvin	1.00
33	Darryl Johnston	.50
34	Russell Maryland	.50
35	Emmitt Smith	4.00
36	Rod Bernstine	.50
37	John Elway	1.50
38	Anthony Miller	.50
39	Glyn Milburn	.50
40	Shannon Sharpe	.50
41	Scott Mitchell	1.00
42	Herman Moore	1.00
43	Brett Perriman	.50
44	Barry Sanders	2.00
45	Chris Spielman	.50
46	Edgar Bennett	.50
47	Robert Brooks	.50
48	Brett Favre	6.00
49	Sean Jones	.50
50	Reggie White	1.00
51	Gary Brown	.50
52	Cody Carlson	.50
53	Ernest Givins	.50
54	Haywood Jeffires	.50
55	Bruce Matthews	.50
56	Quentin Coryatt	.50
57	Steve Emtman	.50
58	Marshall Faulk	1.50
59	Jim Harbaugh	1.00
60	Roosevelt Potts	.50
61	Marcus Allen	1.00
62	Steve Bono	.50
63	Willie Davis	.50
64	Lake Dawson	.50
65	Neil Smith	.50
66	Tim Brown	.50
67	Jeff Hostetler	.50
68	Raghib Ismail	.50
69	James Jett	.50
70	Harvey Williams	.50
71	Jerome Bettis	1.00
72	Troy Drayton	.50
73	Wayne Gandy	.50
74	Sean Gilbert	.50
75	Todd Lyght	.50
76	Tim Bowens	.50
77	Bryan Cox	.50
78	Irving Fryar	.50
79	Dan Marino	4.00
80	Bernie Parmalee	.50
81	Terry Allen	1.00
82	Cris Carter	.50
83	Qadry Ismail	.50
84	Warren Moon	1.00
85	John Randle	.50
86	Bruce Armstrong	.50
87	Drew Bledsoe	2.00
88	Vincent Brisby	.50
89	Marion Butts	.50
90	Ben Coates	.50
91	Morten Andersen	.50
92	Quinn Early	.50
93	Jim Everett	.50
94	Tyrone Hughes	.50
95	Renaldo Turnbull	.50
96	Michael Brooks	.50
97	Dave Brown	.50
98	John Elliott	.50
99	Rodney Hampton	.50
100	Mike Sherrard	.50
101	Boomer Esiason	.50
102	Johnny Johnson	.50
103	Nick Lowery	.50
104	Johnny Mitchell	.50
105	Aaron Glenn	.50
106	Fred Barnett	.50
107	Bubby Brister	.50
108	Randall Cunningham	.50
109	Charlie Garner	.50
110	Calvin Williams	.50
111	Byron "Bam" Morris	.50
112	Barry Foster	.50
113	Kevin Greene	.50
114	Neil O'Donnell	.50
115	Rod Woodson	.50
116	Ronnie Harmon	.50
117	Stan Humphries	.50

118	Tony Martin	.50
119	Natrone Means	1.00
120	Junior Seau	1.00
121	William Floyd	1.00
122	Jerry Rice	2.00
123	Deion Sanders	1.50
124	Dana Stubblefield	.50
125	Steve Young	1.50
126	Brian Blades	.50
127	Cortez Kennedy	.50
128	Rick Mirer	.50
129	Eugene Robinson	.50
130	Chris Warren	.50
131	Trent Dilfer	1.00
132	Santana Dotson	.50
133	Craig Erickson	.50
134	Thomas Everett	.50
135	Errict Rhett	1.00
136	Reggie Brooks	.50
137	Ricky Ervins	.50
138	Darryl Green	.50
139	Brian Mitchell	.50
140	Heath Shuler	1.00
141	Frank Ricci	.50
142	Tim McKyer	.50
143	Tyrone Poole	.50
144	Derrick Lassic	.50
145	Bob Christian	.50
146	Steve Beuerlein	.50
147	Cedric Tillman	.50
148	Reggie Cobb	.50
149	Eugene Chung	.50
150	Desmond Howard	.50

1995 Crown Pro Magnets In The Zone

By the Zone as a 12-card magnet insert in 1995 Pro Mags. The magnets feature a borderless color action shot of a player, and were inserted every three packs.

		MT
Complete Set (12):		15.00
Common Player:		.75
1	Troy Aikman	2.00
2	Drew Bledsoe	2.00
3	John Elway	1.50
4	Brett Favre	4.00
5	Jeff Hostetler	.75
6	Stan Humphries	.75
7	Dan Marino	4.00
8	Jim Kelly	.75
9	Warren Moon	.75
10	Neil O'Donnell	.75
11	Rick Mirer	.75
12	Steve Young	1.50

1995 Crown Pro Magnets Magnetic Classics

Classics features 12 players in front of a column background with the team logo. Classics were inserted into every three packs of 1995 Pro Mags.

		MT
Complete Set (12):		15.00
Common Player:		.75
1	Barry Sanders	.75
2	Deion Sanders	1.50
3	Dan Marino	4.00
4	Drew Bledsoe	2.00
5	Marcus Allen	.75
6	Jerome Bettis	1.00
7	John Elway	1.50
8	Jerry Rice	2.00
9	Emmitt Smith	4.00
10	Steve Young	1.50
11	Troy Aikman	2.00
12	Marshall Faulk	1.00

1995 Crown Pro Mags Rookies

This 12-magnet set features players taken in the 1994 NFL Draft. The magnets measure 2-1/8" x 3-3/8" and include a color photo and the player's name printed in gold foil.

		MT
Complete Set (12):		12.00
Common Player:		.75
1	Trent Dilfer	1.50
2	Heath Shuler	1.00
3	John Thierry	.75
4	Wayne Gandy	.75
5	Errict Rhett	1.00
6	David Palmer	1.00
7	Andre Coleman	.75
8	Lake Dawson	1.00
9	Marshall Faulk	1.50
10	Dan Wilkinson	.75
11	Greg Hill	1.00
12	Willie McGinest	1.00

1995 Crown Pro Superhero Jumbos

Chris Martin Enterprises offered this three oversized magnet set through the mail. With details on 1995 Pro Mag packs, collectors received the set for $6. Each card, measuring 3-3/4" x 7", features fantasy art of either Jerome Bettis, John Elway or Warren Moon.

		MT
Complete Set (3):		20.00
Common Player:		6.00
1	Jerome Bettis	7.00
2	John Elway	8.00
3	Warren Moon	6.00

1995 Crown Pro Mags Teams

Each magnet in this set features three top players from an NFL team and the embossed team logo. The unnumbered magnets were originally released as a promo set.

		MT
Complete Set (5):		20.00
Common Player:		3.00
1	Chargers (Junior Seau, Stan Humphries, Natrone Means)	3.00
2	Cowboys (Michael Irvin, Troy Aikman, Emmitt Smith)	6.00
3	Dolphins (Dan Marino, O.J. McDuffie, Bernie Parmalee)	6.00
4	49ers (Ricky Watters, Steve Young, Jerry Rice)	5.00
5	Steelers (Barry Foster, Neil O'Donnell, Rod Woodson)	3.00

1995 Crown Pro Stamps

This 140-stamp set was sold in 12-stamp sheets. The stamps measure 1-1/2" x 2".

		MT
Complete Set (140):		40.00
Common Player:		.25
1	Steve Young DP	.50
2	Jerry Rice	1.00
3	Deion Sanders	.75
4	Dana Stubblefield	.25
5	William Floyd	.40
6	Troy Aikman DP	.75
7	Michael Irvin	.50
8	Emmitt Smith DP	1.50
9	Russell Maryland	.25
10	Daryl Johnston	.40
11	Dan Marino DP	1.50
12	Bernie Parmalee	.25
13	Tim Bowens	.25
14	Irving Fryar	.25
15	Bryan Cox	.25
16	Drew Bledsoe	1.00
17	Bruce Armstrong	.25
18	Vincent Brisby	.25
19	Marion Butts	.25
20	Ben Coates	.25
21	Dave Brown	.25
22	Michael Brooks	.25
23	Jumbo Elliott	.25
24	Rodney Hampton	.25
25	Mike Sherrard	.25
26	Jeff Hostetler	.25
27	Tim Brown	.60
28	Rocket Ismail	.25
29	James Jett	.25
30	Harvey Williams	.25
31	Heath Shuler	.50
32	Reggie Brooks	.25
33	Ricky Ervins	.25
34	Darrell Green UER (Darryl on front)	.25
35	Brian Mitchell	.25
36	Trace Armstrong	.25
37	Dante Jones	.25
38	Steve Walsh	.25
39	Donnell Woolford	.25
40	Tim Worley	.25
41	Boomer Esiason	.25
42	Aaron Glenn	.25
43	Johnny Johnson	.25
44	Nick Lowery	.25
45	Johnny Mitchell	.25
46	Neil O'Donnell	.25
47	Barry Foster	.25
48	Byron "Bam" Morris	.25
49	Rod Woodson	.25
50	Kevin Greene	.25
51	Randall Cunningham	.25
52	Bubby Brister	.25
53	Fred Barnett	.25
54	Charlie Garner	.25
55	Calvin Williams	.25
56	Brett Favre	2.00
57	Reggie White	.60
58	Edgar Bennett	.25
59	Robert Brooks	.25
60	Sean Jones	.25
61	Ronnie Harmon	.25
62	Stan Humphries	.25
63	Natrone Means	.60
64	Tony Martin	.25
65	Junior Seau	.75
66	John Elway	.75
67	Glyn Milburn	.25
68	Rod Bernstine	.25
69	Anthony Miller	.25
70	Shannon Sharpe	.60
71	Barry Sanders	1.00
72	Scott Mitchell	.40
73	Herman Moore	.60
74	Brett Perriman	.40
75	Chris Spielman	.25
76	Marcus Allen	.60
77	Steve Bono	.40
78	Willie Davis	.25
79	Lake Dawson	.25
80	Neil Smith	.25
81	Vinny Testaverde	.60
82	Eric Turner	.25
83	Antonio Langham	.25
84	Leroy Hoard	.25
85	Derrick Alexander WR	.25
86	Jim Kelly	.60
87	Cornelius Bennett	.25
88	Andre Reed	.25
89	Bruce Smith	.25
90	Darryl Talley	.25
91	Warren Moon	.60
92	Qadry Ismail	.25
93	Terry Allen	.60
94	Cris Carter	.60
95	John Randle	.25
96	Jeff George	.60
97	Chris Doleman	.25
98	Craig Heyward	.25
99	Terance Mathis	.25
100	Jessie Tuggle	.25
101	Jerome Bettis	.60
102	Sean Gilbert	.25
103	Troy Drayton	.25
104	Wayne Gandy	.25
105	Todd Lyght	.25
106	Jeff Blake	.75
107	Harold Green	.25
108	Carl Pickens	.60
109	Dan Wilkinson	.25
110	Darnay Scott	.40
111	Cody Carlson	.25
112	Gary Brown	.25
113	Ernest Givins	.25
114	Haywood Jeffires	.25
115	Bruce Matthews	.25
116	Jim Everett	.25
117	Morten Andersen	.25
118	Quinn Early	.25
119	Tyrone Hughes	.25
120	Renaldo Turnbull	.25
121	Larry Centers	.25
122	Garrison Hearst	.60
123	Seth Joyner	.25
124	Ronald Moore	.25
125	Eric Swann	.25
126	Rick Mirer	.60
127	Chris Warren	.40
128	Brian Blades	.25
129	Cortez Kennedy	.25
130	Eugene Robinson	.25
131	Marshall Faulk	.60
132	Quentin Coryatt	.25
133	Jim Harbaugh	.60
134	Roosevelt Potts	.25
135	Steve Emtman	.25
136	Trent Dilfer	.60
137	Santana Dotson	.25
138	Errict Rhett	.60
139	Thomas Everett	.25
140	Craig Erickson	.25

1996 Crown Pro Retail Mags

Not to be confused with the 1996 Pro Magnets, this 12-magnet set was sold in one-magnet cello packs. A cut-out action photo of the player is placed over a team-colored foil background. "Compacted" ghosted images of the action shot are also included in the foil background. The player's name is printed in gold foil along the left side of the magnet. The team logo is in the lower left, while a larger team logo is located in the lower right. The magnet's number is printed in gold foil in the lower right. A 1996 Chris Martin Enterprises copyright tag line is printed at the bottom of the magnet in black. The backs are blank.

		MT
Complete Set (12):		30.00
Common Player:		1.00
1	Tim Brown	1.00
2	John Elway	4.00
3	Marshall Faulk	2.00
4	Dan Marino	6.00
5	Curtis Martin	3.00
6	Rashaan Salaam	1.00
7	Barry Sanders	6.00
8	Emmitt Smith	6.00
9	Neil Smith	1.00
10	Reggie White	2.00
11	Rod Woodson	1.00
12	Steve Young	3.00

1996 Crown Pro Magnets

The 100-card set features a cut-out action photo of a player placed over a team-colored foil background. A marble-type 3-D box is behind the cut-out photo. The player's name is in gold-foil along the left side, with the team's logo in gold-foil near the bottom right. The fronts include the magnet number in the lower left in gold-foil. The team name is printed in all capital letters at the top right of the magnet. The Pro Magnets logo is in the upper left. NFL and NFL Players Inc. logos, along with the Chris Martin Enterprises tag line, are printed at the bottom. The backs are blank.

		MT
Complete Set (100):		70.00
Common Player:		.50
1	Troy Aikman	2.00
2	Michael Irvin	1.00
3	Emmitt Smith	4.00
4	Deion Sanders	1.50
5	Jay Novacek	.50
6	Jerry Rice	2.00
7	Steve Young	1.50
8	J.J. Stokes	.50
9	William Floyd	.50
10	Merton Hanks	.50
11	Greg Lloyd	.50
12	Rod Woodson	.50
13	Kordell Stewart	3.00
14	Yancey Thigpen	.50
15	Charles Johnson	.50
16	Richmond Webb	.50
17	Eric Green	.50
18	Bernie Parmalee	.50
19	Dan Marino	4.00
20	O.J. McDuffie	.50
21	Brett Favre	5.00
22	Reggie White	1.00
23	Robert Brooks	.50
24	Edgar Bennett	.50
25	Marcus Allen	1.00
26	Tamarick Vanover	.50
27	Lake Dawson	.50
28	Neil Smith	.50
29	Steve Bono	.50
30	Harvey Williams	.50
31	Tim Brown	.50
32	Jeff Hostetler	.50
33	Drew Bledsoe	2.00
34	Vincent Brisby	.50
35	Curtis Martin	3.00
36	Rashaan Salaam	.50
37	Erik Kramer	.50
38	Curtis Conway	.50
39	Kerry Collins	2.00
40	Sam Mills	.50
41	Mark Carrier	.50
42	Dave Brown	.50
43	Rodney Hampton	.50
44	Tyrone Wheatley	.50
45	Vinny Testaverde	.50
46	Andre Rison	.50
47	Eric Turner	.50
48	Michael Jackson	.50
49	Mark Brunell	1.50
50	Jeff Lageman	.50
51	Roman Phifer	.50
52	Isaac Bruce	1.00
53	Rodney Peete	.50
54	Ricky Watters	.50
55	Calvin Williams	.50
56	Warren Moon	.50
57	Cris Carter	.50
58	David Palmer	.50
59	Scott Mitchell	.50
60	Barry Sanders	2.00
61	Herman Moore	.50
62	Brett Perriman	.50
63	Jim Kelly	.50
64	Bruce Smith	.50
65	Bryce Paup	.50
66	Junior Seau	1.00
67	Stan Humphries	.50
68	Andre Coleman	.50
69	Tony Martin	.50
70	Terry Allen	.50
71	Heath Shuler	.50
72	John Elway	1.50
73	Terrell Davis	2.00
74	Mike Pritchard	.50
75	Neil O'Donnell	.50
76	Kyle Brady	.50
77	Jim Harbaugh	.50
78	Marshall Faulk	1.00
79	Zack Crockett	.50
80	Quentin Coryatt	.50
81	Jeff George	.50
82	Morten Anderson	.50
83	Eric Metcalf	.50
84	Joey Galloway	1.00
85	Rick Mirer	.50
86	Chris Warren	.50
87	Ray Zellars	.50
88	Alex Allen	.50
89	Jim Everett	.50
90	Jeff Blake	1.00
91	Carl Pickens	.50
92	Ki-Jana Carter	.50
93	Larry Centers	.50
94	Garrison Hearst	.50
95	Trent Dilfer	.50
96	Errict Rhett	1.00
97	Hardy Nickerson	.50
98	Alvin Harper	.50
99	Steve McNair	2.00
100	Haywood Jeffires	.50

1996 Crown Pro Destination All-Pro

This six-magnet set was randomly inserted one per four Pro Magnets packs. The magnets have a cut-out action photo of the player placed over an etched-foil background, which is red and silver for the AFC and blue and silver for the NFC Pro Bowlers. A ghosted image of the player is included in the background at the upper left. The Pro Magnets logo is in the upper right. The AFC or NFC Pro Bowl logo, along with the player's name, are printed in gold foil at the bottom center of the magnet. The magnets are numbered in the lower left with a prefix of "PB". The backs are blank.

		MT
Complete Set (6):		20.00
Common Player:		1.00
1	Jim Harbaugh	1.00
2	Curtis Martin	3.00
3	Yancey Thigpen	1.00
4	Brett Favre	8.00
5	Jerry Rice	4.00
6	Barry Sanders	6.00

1996 Crown Pro Die-Cuts

This 16-magnet set includes a cut-out action shot of the player placed over a die-cut background of the team's logo and player name. The player's first name is printed in gold foil over the top left portion of his last name, which is printed in team colors. "Die-Cut Magnets" is printed in gold foil to the right of the NFL and NFL Players Inc. logos at the bottom. The team's logo is printed in team colors over the upper right portion of the player's last name. A 1996 Chris Martin Enterprises Inc. copyright tag line is printed in black at the bottom center of the magnets. The magnets were sold in one-magnet cello packs.

		MT
Complete Set (16):		50.00
Common Player:		1.00
1	Troy Aikman	4.00
2	Deion Sanders	3.00
3	Emmitt Smith	6.00
4	Jerry Rice	4.00
5	Steve Young	3.00
6	Kordell Stewart	4.00
7	Dan Marino	6.00
8	Brett Favre	8.00
9	Marcus Allen	2.00
10	Drew Bledsoe	4.00
11	Barry Sanders	6.00
12	Marshall Faulk	2.00
13	John Elway	4.00
14	Rashaan Salaam	1.00
15	Jeff Hostetler	1.00
16	Keyshawn Johnson	1.00

1996 Crown Pro Draft Day Future Stars

This six-card chase set included NFL rookies on randomly inserted magnets. The magnets are the same size as the other magnets in the Pro Magnets set.

		MT
Complete Set (6):		15.00
Common Player:		1.00
1	Kevin Hardy	1.00
2	Eddie George	8.00
3	Keyshawn Johnson	5.00
4	Tim Biakabutuka	1.00
5	Lawrence Phillips	3.00
6	Alex Molden	1.00

1996 Crown Pro Stamps

This 144-stamp set is similar to the 1995 series. They are the same size and utilize the same design and many of the same player photos. They were also sold in 12-stamp packs.

		MT
Complete Set (144):		35.00
Common Player:		.25
1	Steve Young	.75
2	Jerry Rice	1.00
3	Merton Hanks	.25
4	J.J. Stokes	.40
5	William Floyd	.25
6	Troy Aikman	1.00
7	Michael Irvin	.50
8	Emmitt Smith	2.00
9	Deion Sanders	.60
10	Daryl Johnston	.25
11	Dan Marino	2.00
12	Bernie Parmalee	.25
13	O.J. McDuffie	.40
14	Richmond Webb	.25
15	Eric Green	.25
16	Drew Bledsoe	1.00
17	Bruce Armstrong	.25
18	Dave Meggett	.25

19	Curtis Martin	1.00
20	Ben Coates	.40
21	Dave Brown	.25
22	Michael Brooks	.25
23	Tyrone Wheatley	.40
24	Rodney Hampton	.40
25	Jeff Hostetler	.25
26	Tim Brown	.50
27	Rocket Ismail	.40
28	James Jett	.25
29	Harvey Williams	.40
30	Heath Shuler	.50
31	Michael Westbrook	.50
32	Terry Allen	.50
33	Darrell Green	.40
34	Brian Mitchell	.25
35	Rashaan Salaam	.25
36	Erik Kramer UER 37	.25
37	Donnell Woolford	.25
38	Alonzo Spellman	.25
39	Kyle Brady	.40
40	Aaron Glenn	.40
41	Adrian Murrell	.40
42	Nick Lowery	.25
43	Charles Johnson	.40
44	Kordell Stewart	1.00
45	Yancey Thigpen	.40
46	Rod Woodson	.40
47	Greg Lloyd	.50
48	Randall Cunningham	.40
49	Rodney Peete	.25
50	Ricky Watters	.50
51	Charlie Garner	.25
52	Calvin Williams	.25
53	Brett Favre	2.50
54	Reggie White	.50
55	Edgar Bennett	.40
56	Robert Brooks	.50
57	Sean Jones	.25
58	Ronnie Harmon	.40
59	Stan Humphries	.40
60	Andre Coleman	.25
61	Tony Martin	.40
62	Junior Seau	.50
63	John Elway	.75
64	Mike Pritchard	.25
65	Terrell Davis	1.00
66	Anthony Miller	.40
67	Shannon Sharpe	.50
68	Barry Sanders	1.25
69	Scott Mitchell	.40
70	Herman Moore	.50
71	Brett Perriman	.40
72	Johnnie Morton	.40
73	Marcus Allen	.50
74	Steve Bono	.40
75	Tamarick Vanover	.25
76	Lake Dawson	.25
77	Neil Smith	.40
78	Vinny Testaverde	.40
79	Eric Turner	.25
80	Michael Jackson	.40
81	Leroy Hoard	.25
82	Andre Rison	.50
83	Jim Kelly	.50
84	Carwell Gardner	.25
85	Andre Reed	.40
86	Bruce Smith	.50
87	Bryce Paup	.40
88	Warren Moon	.50
89	Qadry Ismail	.40
90	Robert Smith	.40
91	Cris Carter	.50
92	David Palmer	.25
93	Jeff George	.50
94	Morten Andersen	.25
95	Craig Heyward	.25
96	Eric Metcalf	.40
97	Jessie Tuggle	.25
98	Roman Phifer	.25
99	Todd Lyght	.25
100	Troy Drayton	.25
101	Isaac Bruce	.50
102	Sean Gilbert	.25
103	Jeff Blake	.60
104	Harold Green	.25
105	Carl Pickens	.40
106	Dan Wilkinson	.25
107	Ki-Jana Carter	.40
108	Steve McNair	.75
109	Gary Brown	.25
110	Haywood Jeffires	.25
111	Bruce Matthews	.25
112	Jim Everett	.25
113	Mario Bates	.25
114	Ray Zellars	.25
115	Tyrone Hughes	.25
116	Eric Allen	.25
117	Larry Centers	.40
118	Garrison Hearst	.50
119	Aeneas Williams	.25
120	Rob Moore	.25
121	Neil O'Donnell	.40
122	Rick Mirer	.25
123	Chris Warren	.25
124	Eric Swann	.25
125	Cortez Kennedy	.25
126	Joey Galloway	.50
127	Marshall Faulk	.50
128	Quentin Coryatt	.25
129	Jim Harbaugh	.50
130	Trev Alberts	.25
131	Zack Crockett	.25
132	Trent Dilfer	.25
133	Hardy Nickerson	.25
134	Errict Rhett	.50
135	Alvin Harper	.25
136	Sam Mills	.25
137	Tyrone Poole	.40
138	Kerry Collins	.75
139	Bob Christian	.25
140	Randy Baldwin	.25
141	Steve Beuerlein	.25
142	Mark Brunell	1.00
143	Tony Boselli	.40
144	Jeff Lageman	.25

D

1986 DairyPak Cartons

These cards were sponsored by various brands of milk across the country in 1986; different colors (purple, green, lavender, aqua, orange, red, light blue, dark blue, black and brown) were used for different sponsors. Each card is perforated and features a black-and-white head shot of the player, plus a facsimilie autograph and card number. Cards which have been cut from the milk carton measure 3-1/4" x 4-7/16", but generally are more valuable if they are left intact as a complete carton. The set was not licensed by the NFL, so no team logos are shown; the NFLPA, however, licensed the set. Below each card was an offer to receive a 24" x 32" poster featuring the 24 cards.

		MT
	Complete Set (24):	65.00
	Common Player:	1.25
1	Joe Montana	10.00
2	Marcus Allen	3.00
3	Art Monk	2.00
4	Mike Quick	1.25
5	John Elway	5.00
6	Eric Hipple	1.25
7	Louis Lipps	1.25
8	Dan Fouts	2.00
9	Phil Simms	2.00
10	Mike Rozier	1.25
11	Greg Bell	1.25
12	Ottis Anderson	1.50
13	Dave Krieg	1.75
14	Anthony Carter	1.25
15	Freeman McNeil	1.25
16	Doug Cosbie	1.25
17	James Lofton	6.00
18	Dan Marino	8.00
19	James Wilder	1.25
20	Cris Collinsworth	1.50
21	Eric Dickerson	4.00
22	Walter Payton	6.00
23	Ozzie Newsome	2.00
24	Chris Hinton	1.25

1971-72 Dell

This 48-player set, which measures 8-1/4" x 10-3/4", from the 1971-72 Dell Pro Football Guide includes a center insert that unfolds to show 48 color photos. The photos, bordered in black and yellow, each measure 1-3/4" x 3". The player's name and team name are located inside a rectangle under the photo. The backs boast action photos, which are bordered in black and white. The football guide includes bios on each of the players offered in the set. The photos are not numbered. A complete set which is still intact in the guides are valued at 25 percent over what is listed here.

		NM
	Complete Set (48):	100.00
	Common Player:	1.00
1	Dan Abramowicz	1.00
2	Herb Adderley	2.00
3	Lem Barney	1.00
4	Bobby Bell	1.00
5	George Blanda	3.00
6	Terry Bradshaw	15.00
7	John Brodie	2.00
8	Larry Brown	1.00
9	Dick Butkus	10.00
10	Fred Carr	1.00
11	Virgil Carter	1.00
12	Mike Curtis	1.00
13	Len Dawson	2.50
14	Carl Eller	1.00
15	Mel Farr	1.00
16	Roman Gabriel	1.50
17	Gary Garrison	1.00
18	Dick Gordon	1.00
19	Bob Griese	5.00
20	Bob Hayes	1.50
21	Rich Jackson	1.00
22	Charlie Johnson	1.00
23	Ron Johnson	1.00
24	Deacon Jones	2.50
25	Sonny Jurgensen	2.50
26	Leroy Kelly	1.50
27	Daryle Lamonica	1.50
28	MacArthur Lane	1.00
29	Willie Lanier	1.50
30	Bob Lilly	3.00
31	Floyd Little	1.00
32	Mike Lucci	1.00
33	Don Maynard	2.50
34	Joe Namath	16.00
35	Tommy Nobis	1.50
36	Merlin Olsen	3.00
37	Alan Page	2.00
38	Gerry Philbin	1.00
39	Jim Plunkett	2.00
40	Tim Rossovich	1.00
41	Gale Sayers	10.00
42	Dennis Shaw	1.00
43	O.J. Simpson	14.00
44	Fran Tarkenton	7.00
45	Johnny Unitas	12.00
46	Paul Warfield	3.00
47	Gene Washington	1.00
48	Larry Wilson	1.50

1933 Diamond Matchbooks Silver

With covers measuring 1-1/2" x 4-1/2" when folded out, the 95-matchbook set has a photo of the player over a pink or green background, bordered in silver. Prices listed here are with the matches removed. The player's name and team are listed at the bottom of the cover fronts. The cover backs showcase the player's name and highlights inside a box. The matchbooks are not numbered. Matchbooks with the matches intact are worth 1-1/2 to 2 times more than what is listed.

		NM
	Complete Set (95):	1100.
	Common Player:	10.00
1	All-American Board of Football Seal	15.00
2	Gene Alford	10.00
3	Marger Apsit	10.00
4	Morris (Red) Badgro	25.00
5	Cliff Battles	35.00
6	Morris (Maury) Bodenger	10.00
7	Jimmy Bowdoin	10.00
8	John Boylan	10.00
9	Hank Bruder	10.00
10	Carl Brumbaugh	15.00
11	Bill Buckler	10.00
12	Jerome Buckley	10.00
13	Dale Burnett	10.00
14	Ernie Caddel	12.00
15	Red Cagle	12.00
16	Glen Campbell	10.00
17	John Cannella	10.00
18	Zuck Carlson	10.00
19	George Christensen	15.00
20	Stu Clancy	10.00
21	Paul (Rip) Collins	10.00
22	John F. Connell	10.00
23	George Corbett	10.00
24	Orien Crow	10.00
25	Ed Danowski	10.00
26	Sylvester (Red) Davis	10.00
27	John Isola	12.00
28	John Doehring	10.00
29	Glen Edwards	20.00
30	Earl Elser	12.00
31	Ox Emerson	15.00
32	Tiny Feather	10.00
33	Ray Flaherty	20.00
34	Ike Frankian	10.00
35	Red Grange	290.00
36	Len Grant	10.00
37	Ace Gutowsky	12.00
38	Mel Hein	20.00
39	Arnie Herber	20.00
40	Bill Hewitt	20.00
41	Herman Hickman	12.00
42	Clarke Hinkle	20.00
43	Cal Hubbard	20.00
44	George Hurley	10.00
45	Herman Hussey	10.00
46	Cecil (Tex) Irvin	12.00
47	Luke Johnson	10.00
48	Bruce Jones	10.00
49	Tom Jones	10.00
50	Thacker Kay	10.00
51	John Kelly	12.00
52	Joe (Doc) Kopcha	12.00

53	Joe Kurth	10.00
54	Milo Lubratevich	10.00
55	Father Lumpkin	12.00
56	Jim MacMurdo	10.00
57	Joe Maniaci	10.00
58	Jack McBride	10.00
59	Ookie Miller	10.00
60	Granville Mitchell	10.00
61	Keith Molesworth	12.00
62	Bob Monnett	10.00
63	Hap Moran	10.00
64	Bill Morgan	10.00
65	Maynard (Doc) Morrison	10.00
66	Mathew Murray	10.00
67	Jim Musick	10.00
68	Bronko Nagurski	290.00
69	Dick Nesbitt	10.00
70	Harry Newman	12.00
71	Steve Owen	15.00
72	Bill (Red) Owen	10.00
73	Andy Pavlicovic	10.00
74	Bert Pearson	10.00
75	William Pendergast	10.00
76	Jerry Pepper	10.00
77	Stan Piawlock	10.00
78	Ernie Pinckert	12.00
79	Glenn Presnell	10.00
80	Jess Quatse	10.00
81	Hank Reese	10.00
82	Dick Richards	10.00
83	Tony Sarausky	10.00
84	Elmer (Dutch) Schaake	10.00
85	John Schneller	10.00
86	Johnny Sisk	10.00
87	Mike Steponovich	10.00
88	Ken Strong	30.00
89	Charles Tackwell	10.00
90	Harry Thayer	15.00
91	Walt Uzdavinis	10.00
92	John Welch	10.00
93	William Whelan	10.00
94	Fay (Mule) Wilson	12.00
95	Frank (Babe) Wright	10.00

1934 Diamond Matchbooks

Measuring 1-1/2" x 4-1/2", each matchbook showcases four different colored borders, including blue, red, tan and green. Many players have each of the four color combinations. Other players have one or two variations of borders. The player's name and team are printed above the photo on the front. The backs spotlight the player's name and highlights. This set features "The Diamond Match Co., N.Y.C" above the striking strip on the matchbook backs. As a note, the 1935 matchbooks resemble this set, but do not have the "Diamond Match" tag line at the bottom. The books are unnumbered. If matches are intact in the book, they are worth 1-1/2 times the values listed.

		NM
	Complete Set (121):	1500.
	Common Player:	10.00
1	Arvo Antilla	10.00
2	Morris (Red) Badgro	20.00
3	Norbert Bartell	10.00
4	Cliff Battles	25.00
5	Chuck Bennis	10.00
6	Jack Beynon	10.00
7	Morris (Maury) Bodenger	10.00
8	John Bond	10.00
9	John Brown	10.00
10	Carl Brumbaugh	10.00
11	Dale Burnett	10.00
12	Ernie Caddel	10.00
13	Red Cagle	10.00
14	Glen Campbell	10.00
15	John Cannella	10.00
16	Joe Carter	10.00
17	Les Caywood	10.00
18	George (Buck) Chapman	10.00
19	Frank Christensen	10.00
20	Stu Clancy	10.00
21	Algy Clark	10.00
22	Paul (Rip) Collins	10.00
23	Jack Connell	10.00
24	Orien Crow	10.00
25	Lone Star Dietz (CO)	10.00
26	John Doehring	10.00
27	Glen Edwards	20.00
28	Ox Emerson	10.00
29	Tiny Feather	10.00
30	Ray Flaherty	20.00
31	Frank Froschauer	10.00
32	Chuck Galbreath	10.00
33	Elbert (Red) Gragg	10.00
34	Red Grange	210.00
35	Cy Grant	10.00
36	Len Grant	10.00

37	Ross Grant	10.00
38	Jack Griffith	10.00
39	Ed Gryboski	10.00
40	Ace Gutowsky	10.00
41	Thomas (Swede) Hanson	10.00
42	Mel Hein	25.00
43	Warren Heller	10.00
44	Bill Hewitt	20.00
45	Cecil (Tex) Irvin	10.00
46	Frank Johnson	10.00
47	Jack Johnson	10.00
48	Bob Jones	10.00
49	Tom Jones	10.00
50	Carl Jorgensen	10.00
51	John Karcis	10.00
52	Eddie Kawal	10.00
53	John Kelly	10.00
54	George Kenneally	10.00
55	Walt Kiesling	20.00
56	Jack Knapper	10.00
57	Frank Knox	10.00
58	Joe (Doc) Kopcha	10.00
59	Joe Kresky	10.00
60	Joe Laws	10.00
61	Russ Lay	10.00
62	Biff Lee	10.00
63	Gil LeFebvre	10.00
64	Jim Leonard	10.00
65	Les Lindberg	10.00
66	John Lipski	10.00
67	Milo Lubratevich	10.00
68	Father Lumpkin	10.00
69	Jim MacMurdo	10.00
70	Ed Matesic	10.00
71	Dave McCollough	10.00
72	John McKnight	10.00
73	Johnny (Blood) McNally	30.00
74	Al Minot	10.00
75	Keith Molesworth	10.00
76	Jim Mooney	10.00
77	Leroy Moorehead	10.00
78	Bill Morgan	10.00
79	Bob Moser	10.00
80	Lee Mulleneaux	10.00
81	George Munday	10.00
82	George Musso	20.00
83	Harry Newman	10.00
84	Al Norgard	10.00
85	John (Cap) Oehler	10.00
86	Charlie Opper	10.00
87	Bill (Red) Owen	10.00
88	Steve Owen	20.00
89	Bert Pearson	10.00
90	Tom Perkinson	10.00
91	Mace Pike	10.00
92	Joe Pilconis	10.00
93	Lew Pope	10.00
94	Crain Portman	10.00
95	Glenn Presnell	10.00
96	Jess Quatse	10.00
97	Clare Randolph	10.00
98	Hank Reese	10.00
99	Paul Riblett	10.00
100	Dick Richards	10.00
101	Jack Roberts	10.00
102	John Rogers	10.00
103	Gene Ronzani	10.00
104	John Schueller	10.00
105	Bob Rowe	10.00
106	Aolph Schwammel	10.00
107	Earl (Red) Seick	10.00
108	Allen Shi	10.00
109	Ben Smith	10.00
110	Ken Strong	30.00
111	Elmer Taber	10.00
112	Charles Tackwell	10.00
113	Ray Tesser	10.00
114	John (Stumpy) Thomason	10.00
115	Charlie Turbyville	10.00
116	Claude Urevig	10.00
117	John (Harp) Vaughan	10.00
118	Henry Wagnon	10.00
119	John West	10.00
120	Lee Woodruff	10.00
121	Jim Zyntell	10.00

1934 Diamond Matchbooks College Rivals

The 12-matchbook set honors a college rivalry with text about the recent history of the games. Bordered in black or tan, matchbooks could be found in either variation. Matchbooks which still have the matches intact are worth 1-1/2 times more than what is listed here.

		NM
	Complete Set (12):	100.00
	Common Player:	10.00
1	Alabama vs. Fordham 1933	10.00
2	Army vs. Navy start to finish	10.00
3	Fordham vs. St. Mary's lose by a 13-6 score	10.00
4	Georgia vs. Georgia Tech Bulldog Alumni and followers	10.00
5	Holy Cross vs. Boston College in atoning for this one defeat	10.00
6	Lafayette vs. Lehigh victory for Lafayette	10.00
7	Michigan vs. Ohio State Champions	10.00
8	Notre Dame vs. Army leader of men, Knute Rockne	12.00
9	Penn vs. Cornell pass	10.00
10	USC vs. Notre Dame year	12.00
11	Yale vs. Harvard Harvard	10.00
12	Yale vs. Princeton scoring 27	10.00

1935 Diamond Matchbooks

In 1935, three different colored borders were used for this set, including tan, green and red. However, this time players were only printed with one color border. Resembling the 1934 set, this set can be identified by the "Made in U.S.A./The Diamond Match Co., N.Y.C" tag line. The unnumbered matchbooks measure 1-1/2" x 4-1/2". The player photo is not bordered and a player position is not listed. Matchbooks with the matches intact are valued at 1-1/2 times the values listed here.

		NM
	Complete Set (96):	1000.
	Common Player:	10.00
1	Alf Anderson	10.00
2	Alec Ashford	10.00
3	Gene Augusterfer	10.00
4	Morris (Red) Badgro	20.00
5	Cliff Battles	25.00
6	Harry Benson	10.00
7	Tony Blazine	10.00
8	John Bond	10.00
9	Maurice (Mule) Bray	10.00
10	Dale Burnett	10.00
11	Charles (Cocky) Bush	10.00
12	Ernie Caddel	10.00
13	Zuck Carlson	10.00
14	Joe Carter	10.00
15	Cy Casper	10.00
16	Paul Causey	10.00
17	Frank Christensen	10.00
18	Stu Clancy	10.00
19	Earl "Dutch" Clark	30.00
20	Paul (Rip) Collins	10.00
21	Dave Cook (Chicago Cardinals)	10.00
22	Fred Crawford	10.00
23	Paul Cuba	10.00
24	Harry Ebding	10.00
25	Glen Edwards	20.00
26	Marvin (Swede) Ellstrom	10.00
27	Beattie Feathers	20.00
28	Ray Flaherty	20.00
29	John Gildea	10.00
30	Tom Graham	10.00
31	Len Grant	10.00
32	Maurice Green	10.00
33	Norman Greeney	10.00
34	Ace Gutowsky	10.00
35	Julius Hall	10.00
36	Thomas (Swede) Hanson	10.00
37	Charles Harold	10.00
38	Tom Haywood	10.00
39	Mel Hein	20.00
40	Bill Hewitt	20.00
41	Cecil (Tex) Irvin	10.00
42	Frank Johnson	10.00
43	Jack Johnson	10.00
44	Luke Johnson	10.00
45	Tom Jones	10.00
46	Carl Jorgensen	10.00
47	George Kenneally	10.00
48	Roger Kirkman	10.00
49	Frank Knox	10.00
50	Joe (Doc) Kopcha	10.00
51	Rick Lackman	10.00
52	Jim Leonard	10.00
53	Joe (Hunk) Malkovich	10.00
54	Ed Manske	10.00
55	Bernie Masterson	10.00
56	James McMillen	10.00
57	Mike Mikulak	10.00
58	Ookie Miller	10.00
59	Milford (Dub) Miller	10.00
60	Al Minot	10.00
61	Buster Mitchell	10.00

62	Bill Morgan	10.00
63	George Musso	20.00
64	Harry Newman	10.00
65	Al Nichelini	10.00
66	Bill (Red) Owen	10.00
67	Steve Owen	20.00
68	Max Padlow	10.00
69	Hal Pangle	10.00
70	Melvin Pittman	10.00
71	William Pollock	10.00
72	Glenn Presnell	10.00
73	George Rado	10.00
74	Clare Randolph	10.00
75	Hank Reese	10.00
76	Ray Richards	10.00
77	Doug Russell	10.00
78	Sandy Sandberg	10.00
79	John Schneller	10.00
80	Michael Sebastian	10.00
81	Allen Shi	10.00
82	Johnny Sisk	10.00
83	Phil Sarboe	10.00
84	James Stacy	10.00
85	Ed Storm	10.00
86	Ken Strong	25.00
87	Art Strutt	10.00
88	Frank Sullivan	10.00
89	Charles Treadaway	10.00
90	John Turley	10.00
91	Claude Urevig	10.00
92	Charles Vaughan	10.00
93	Izzy Weinstock	10.00
94	Henry Wiesenbaugh	10.00
95	Joe Zeller	10.00
96	Vince Zizak	10.00

1935 Diamond Matchbooks College Rivals

With all the variations available, this set goes from 12 matchbooks to 36. Covers include highlights on recent games in the rivalry. The Diamond name is printed in tan with a double-lined company name or the Diamond name is printed on a single line with a tan or black border. Matchbooks with the matches intact are valued at 1-1/2 times more than what is listed here.

		NM
Complete Set (12):		100.00
Common Player:		10.00
1	Alabama vs. Fordham once championship	10.00
2	Army vs. Navy over the Cadets since 1921	10.00
3	Fordham vs. St. Mary's the gamely fighting "Rams"	10.00
4	Georgia vs. Georgia Tech 7-0 defeat	10.00
5	Holy Cross vs. Boston College defeat	10.00
6	Lafayette vs. Lehigh in a 13-7 victory for Lehigh	10.00
7	Michigan vs. Ohio State tory for State	10.00
8	Notre Dame vs. Army Cadets 12-6	12.00
9	Penn vs. Cornell from start to finish	10.00
10	USC vs. Notre Dame carries of Elmer Layden	12.00
11	Yale vs. Harvard set back	10.00
12	Yale vs. Princeton ed still led 7-0	10.00

1936 Diamond Matchbooks

Chicago Bears and Philadelphia Eagles players were featured in this matchbook set. The matchbooks, when folded out, measure 1-1/2" x 4-1/2". The words were printed in black or brown, while borders were in three different colors, tan, red and green. Ray Nolting is the lone exception to the rule, as matchbooks featuring him were printed with black and brown ink. The front of the books include a player picture, his name and team. The backs showcase his name and his highlights. With the different variations available, a complete set totals

96 matchbooks, which are un-numbered. Books with matches intact are worth 1-1/2 times more than what is listed here.

		NM
Complete Set (47):		500.00
Common Player:		10.00
1	Carl Brumbaugh	10.00
2	Zuck Carlson	10.00
3	George Corbett (last line - Sigma Alpha Epsilon.)	10.00
4	John Doehring (last line - is a bachelor.)	10.00
5	Beattie Feathers (first line - ...will be 28 years)	15.00
6	Dan Fortmann (first line - ...April 11, 1916, at)	15.00
7	George Grosvenor	10.00
8	Bill Hewitt	15.00
9	Luke Johnson	10.00
10	William Karr (first line - ...in Ripley,)	10.00
11	Eddie Kawal	10.00
12	Jack Manders (last line - 200, Height 6 ft. 1 in.)	10.00
13	Bernie Masterson (last line - Alpha Epsilon, Single.)	10.00
14	Eddie Michaels	10.00
15	Ookie Miller	10.00
16	Keith Molesworth (last line - 5 ft. 9 1/2 in. Weight 168.)	10.00
17	George Musso (last line - Science degree, Is single.)	20.00
18	Bronko Nagurski	210.00
19	Ray Nolting (first line - ...three years of Cin-)	10.00
20	Vernon Oech	10.00
21	William Pollock	10.00
22	Gene Ronzani (last line - is married.)	10.00
23	Ted Rosequist	10.00
24	Johnny Sisk	10.00
25	Joe Stydahar (last line - is single.)	15.00
26	Frank Sullivan (first line - ...Loyola U.) (New)	10.00
27	Russell Thompson (last line - Sigma Nu fraternity.)	10.00
28	Milt Trost (last line - is single.)	10.00
29	Joe Zeller (last line - and is single, Sigma Nu.)	10.00
30	Bill Brian	10.00
31	Art Buss	10.00
32	Joe Carter	10.00
33	Thomas (Swede) Hanson	10.00
34	Don Jackson	10.00
35	John Kusko	10.00
36	Jim Leonard	10.00
37	Jim MacMurdo	10.00
38	Ed Manske	10.00
39	George McPherson	10.00
40	George Mulligan	10.00
41	Joe Pilconis	10.00
42	Hank Reese	10.00
43	Jim Russell	10.00
44	Dave Smukler	10.00
45	Pete Stevens	10.00
46	John Thomason	10.00
47	Vince Zizak	10.00

1937 Diamond Matchbooks

This time only Chicago Bears players were featured. Measuring 1-1/2" x 4-1/2" when folded out, the matchbooks resemble the 1936 set, however, this 1937 set has a smaller type size. With text printed in gray or black, the 24-matchbook set showcases three different colored borders - red, green and tan. The cover fronts feature a player photo, with his name and team printed above the photo. The backs of the matchbooks have the player's name and highlights inside a box. Matchbooks with the matches intact are valued at 1-1/2 times the prices listed here.

		NM
Complete Set (24):		225.00
Common Player:		7.00
1	Frank Bausch	7.00
2	Delbert Bjork	7.00

3	William Conkright	7.00
4	George Corbett (last line - ion.)	7.00
5	John Doehring (last line - baseball.)	7.00
6	Beattie Feathers (first line - ...turned 29 years)	15.00
7	Dan Fortmann (first line - April 11, 1916, in.)	15.00
8	Harrison Francis	7.00
9	Henry Hammond	7.00
10	William Karr (first line - in Ripley, W.)	7.00
11	Jack Manders (last line - height 6 ft. 1 in.)	12.00
12	Ed Manske	7.00
13	Bernie Masterson (last line - single.)	10.00
14	Keith Molesworth (last line - 9 1/2 in. Weight 168.)	10.00
15	George Musso (last line - married.)	20.00
16	Ray Nolting (first line - ... three years for)	10.00
17	Richard Plasman	7.00
18	Gene Ronzani (last line - married.)	12.00
19	Joe Stydahar (last line - ing. Is single.)	18.00
20	Frank Sullivan (first line - Loyola U. New)	7.00
21	Russell Thompson (last line - year.)	7.00
22	Milt Trost (last line - pounds. Is single.)	7.00
23	George Wilson	12.00
24	Joe Zeller (last line - Nu.)	7.00

1938 Diamond Matchbooks

Showcasing players from the Chicago Bears and Detroit Lions, the 24-matchbook set measures 1-1/2" x 4-1/2" when folded out. They are bordered in silver. The player's highlights feature different colored backgrounds for the two teams - Bears have red backgrounds, while the Lions have blue. No variations are known for this set. The unnumbered matchbooks are listed alphabetically. As always, matchbooks with the matches intact are valued at 1-1/2 times the values listed here.

		NM
Complete Set (24):		225.00
Common Player:		7.00
1	Delbert Bjork	7.00
2	Raymond Buivid	7.00
3	Gary Famiglietti	2.50
4	Dan Fortmann	15.00
5	Bert Johnson	7.00
6	Jack Manders	12.00
7	Joe Maniaci	12.00
8	Lester McDonald	7.00
9	Frank Sullivan	7.00
10	Robert Swisher	7.00
11	Russell Thompson	7.00
12	Gus Zarnas	7.00
13	Ernie Caddel	12.00
14	Lloyd Cardwell	7.00
15	Earl "Dutch" Clark	30.00
16	Jack Johnson	7.00
17	Ed Klewicki	7.00
18	James McDonald	7.00
19	James (Monk) Moscrip	7.00
20	Maurice (Babe) Patt	7.00
21	Bob Reynolds	7.00
22	Kent Ryan	7.00
23	Fred Vanzo	7.00
24	Alex Wojciechowicz	20.00

1967 Dolphins Royal Castle

Measuring 3" x 4-3/8", the 27-card set was released by Royal Castle restaurants in South Florida. The cards showcase a large black-and-white photo, with his facsimile signature under the photo in a white area. The card fronts are bordered in orange. Each card back includes the player's name, position and bio, along with the Royal Castle and Miami Dolphins' logos. A 28th card in the set, featuring George Wilson Jr., may have also been produced.

		NM
Complete Set (27):		2700.
Common Player (1-27):		25.00
Common Player (SP):		100.00
1	Joe Auer (SP)	100.00
2	Tom Beier	25.00
3	Mel Branch	25.00
4	Jon Brittenan	35.00
5	George Chesser	25.00
6	Edward Cooke	25.00
7	Frank Emanuel (SP)	125.00
8	Tom Erlandson (SP)	100.00
9	Norm Evans (SP)	150.00
10	Bob Griese (SP)	800.00
11	Abner Haynes (SP)	175.00
12	Jerry Hopkins (SP)	100.00
13	Frank Jackson	25.00
14	Billy Joe	25.00
15	Wahoo McDaniel	150.00
16	Robert Neff	25.00
17	Billy Neighbors	25.00
18	Rick Norton	25.00
19	Bob Petrich	25.00
20	Jim Riley	25.00
21	John Stofa (SP)	150.00
22	Lavern Torczon	25.00
23	Howard Twilley	80.00
24	Jimmy Warren (SP)	100.00
25	Richard Westmoreland	25.00
26	Maxie Williams (SP)	150.00
27	George Wilson, Sr. (SP) (Head Coach)	150.00

1974 Dolphins All-Pro Graphics

Measuring 8-1/4" x 10-3/4", the 10-photo set showcases color action shots on the front, surrounded by a white border. The player's name, position and team are printed in the top left corner. The unnumbered photos have blank backs.

		NM
Complete Set (10):		100.00
Common Player:		5.00
1	Dick Anderson	8.00
2	Nick Buoniconti	14.00
3	Larry Csonka	18.00
4	Manny Fernandez	6.00
5	Bob Griese	25.00
6	Jim Kiick	8.00
7	Earl Morrall	12.00
8	Mercury Morris	8.00
9	Jake Scott	6.00
10	Garo Yepremian	5.00

1980 Dolphins Police

Measuring 2-5/8" x 4-1/8", the 16-card set features a photo on the front, with the player's name and position under the photo. The Kiwanis logo appears in the lower right. The unnumbered card backs feature Miami Dolphins Tips inside a box, which has the Dolphins' logo at the top. Sponsors are listed at the bottom of the card backs.

		NM
Complete Set (16):		75.00
Common Player:		2.50
5	Uwe Von Schamann	2.50
10	Don Strock	5.00
12	Bob Griese	12.00
22	Tony Nathan	5.00
24	Delvin Williams	5.00
25	Tim Foley	4.00
50	Larry Gordon	2.50
58	Kim Bokamper	2.50
64	Ed Newman	2.50
66	Larry Little (SP)	20.00
67	Bob Kuechenberg	5.00
73	Bob Baumhower	4.00
77	A.J. Duhe	5.00
82	Duriel Harris	4.00
89	Nat Moore	5.00
NNO	Don Shula (CO)	15.00

1981 Dolphins Police

Measuring 2-5/8" x 4-1/8", the 16-card set features a photo, with the player's name, number, position and bio under the photo. The Dolphins and Kiwanis logos appear on the lower left and right, respectively. The card backs, numbered in the upper left corner, have Dolphins Tips in a box, with the Dolphins logo at the top. The sponsors are listed at the bottom of the card backs.

		MT
Complete Set (16):		25.00
Common Player:		1.00
1	Duriel Harris	1.00
2	Bob Kuechenberg	1.00
3	Don Bessillieu	1.00
4	Gerald Small	1.00
5	David Woodley	1.50
6	Don McNeal	1.00
7	Nat Moore	2.00
8	A.J. Duhe	1.75
9	Glenn Blackwood	1.00
10	Don Strock	2.00
11	Doug Betters	1.00
12	George Roberts	1.00
13	Bob Baumhower	1.75
14	Kim Bokamper	1.00
15	Tony Nathan	2.00
16	Don Shula (CO)	6.00

1982 Dolphins Police

Measuring 2-5/8" x 4-1/8", the 16-card set is anchored by a color photo on the front, with the player's name and number in the upper left corner. His position and college are located in a stripe above the photo. The Kiwanis logo is in the lower right. The card fronts are bordered in orange and aqua. The card backs, numbered in the lower right, showcase Dolphins Tips inside a box, with the Dolphins logo in the upper right. The sponsors names are listed in the lower left.

		MT
Complete Set (16):		25.00
Common Player:		1.00
1	Don Shula (CO) (SP)	10.00
2	Uwe Von Schamann (SP)	5.00
3	Jimmy Cefalo	1.50
4	Andra Franklin	1.50
5	Larry Gordon	1.00
6	Nat Moore	1.75
7	Bob Baumhower	1.25
8	A.J. Duhe	1.25
9	Tony Nathan	1.75
10	Glenn Blackwood	1.00
11	Don Strock	2.00
12	David Woodley	1.25
13	Kim Bokamper	1.00
14	Bob Kuechenberg	1.25
15	Duriel Harris	1.25
16	Ed Newman	1.00

1983 Dolphins Police

Measuring 2-5/8" x 4-1/8", the 16-card set is anchored by a photo on the front, with the player's name in the upper left and his position near the bottom of the photo. The cards are bordered in aqua and orange. The card backs, numbered in the lower right, feature Dolphins Tips, with the Dolphins logo in the upper right. The sponsors are listed at the bottom of the card back. The Kiwanis and Burger King logos are printed inside the photo on the front of the cards.

		MT
Complete Set (16):		15.00
Common Player:		.50
1	Earnie Rhone	.50
2	Andra Franklin	.75
3	Eric Laakso	.50
4	Joe Rose	.50
5	David Woodley	1.00
6	Uwe Von Schamann	.50
7	Eddie Hill	.50
8	Bruce Hardy	.50
9	Woody Bennett	.50
10	Fulton Walker	.50
11	Lyle Blackwood	.50
12	A.J. Duhe	.75
13	Bob Baumhower	.75
14	Duriel Harris	.50
15	Bob Brudzinski	.50
16	Don Shula (CO)	3.00

1984 Dolphins Police

Measuring 2-5/8" x 4-1/8", the 17-card set is anchored by a photo on the front, with the player's number and name in the upper left and his position at the

bottom center. Sponsor logos are printed in the two lower corners. The card backs are unnumbered, have a "Dolphins Say" safety tip, with the Dolphins logo in the upper right. The sponsors are listed at the bottom with the Mark Clayton card was added to the set after it was released.

		MT
Complete Set (17):		30.00
Common Player:		.50
1	Bob Baumhower	.75
2	Doug Betters	.50
3	Glenn Blackwood	.50
4	Kim Bokamper	.50
5	Dolfan Denny (Mascot)	.50
6	A.J. Duhe	.75
7	Mark Duper	1.75
8	Jim Jensen	.50
9	Dan Marino	25.00
10	Don McNeal	.50
11	Nat Moore	1.00
12	Tony Nathan	1.00
13	Ed Newman	.50
14	Don Shula (CO)	2.00
15	Dwight Stephenson	.75
16	Fulton Walker	.50
17	Mark Clayton (SP)	4.00

1985 Dolphins Police

Measuring 2-5/8" x 4-1/8", the 16-card set is anchored by a large photo on the front, with the player's name, number and position listed at the bottom center. The Dolphins and Kiwanis logos are in the lower left and right, respectively. The card backs, which are numbered in the lower right, have a "Dolphins Say" safety tip, with the Dolphins logo in the upper right. The sponsors are printed at the bottom of the card backs.

		MT
Complete Set (16):		20.00
Common Player:		.50
1	William Judson	.50
2	Fulton Walker	.50
3	Mark Clayton	1.25
4	Lyle & Glenn Blackwood, Glenn Blackwood (Bruise Brothers)	.50
5	Dan Marino	12.00
6	Reggie Roby	.75
7	Doug Betters	.50
8	Jay Brophy	.50
9	Dolfan Denny (Mascot)	.50
10	Kim Bokamper	.50
11	Mark Duper	1.00
12	Nat Moore	.75
13	Mike Kozlowski	.50
14	Don Shula (CO)	1.50
15	Don McNeal	.50
16	Tony Nathan	.75

1986 Dolphins Police

Measuring 2-5/8" x 4-1/8", the 16-card set is anchored by a large photo on the front, with the player's name printed inside a stripe on the right, his number printed inside a helmet in the lower left and his position located inside a stripe in the lower right. Anon Anew and the Kiwanis logos are printed in the lower right, too. The card backs, which are numbered in the lower right, have a "Dolphins Say" safety tip, along with the sponsors names.

		MT
Complete Set (16):		15.00
Common Player:		.50
1	Dwight Stephenson	.75
2	Bob Baumhower	.75
3	Dolfan Denny (Mascot)	.50
4	Don Shula (CO)	1.50
5	Dan Marino	8.00
6	Tony Nathan	.75
7	Mark Duper	1.00
8	John Offerdahl	.50
9	Fuad Reveiz	.50
10	Hugh Green	.50
11	Lorenzo Hampton	.50
12	Mark Clayton	1.50
13	Nat Moore	.50
14	Bob Brudzinski	.50
15	Reggie Roby	.50
16	T.J. Turner	.50

1987 Dolphins Holsum

The cards in this Miami Dolphins' set were available in Holsum Bread packages. The fronts have a color photo inside a green border and the backs feature basic player information.

		MT
Complete Set (22):		60.00
Common Player:		2.00
1	Bob Baumhower	3.00
2	Mark Brown	2.00
3	Mark Clayton	6.00
4	Mark Duper	4.00
5	Roy Foster	2.00
6	Hugh Green	2.00
7	Lorenzo Hampton	2.00
8	William Judson	2.00
9	George Little	2.00
10	Dan Marino	40.00
11	Nat Moore	3.00
12	Tony Nathan	3.00
13	John Offerdahl	4.00
14	James Pruitt	2.00
15	Fuad Reveiz	2.00
16	Dwight Stephenson	3.00
17	Glenn Blackwood	2.00
18	Bruce Hardy	2.00
19	Reggie Roby	2.00
20	Bob Brudzinski	2.00
21	Ron Jaworski	3.00
22	T.J. Turner	2.00

1987 Dolphins Police

Measuring 2-5/8" x 4-1/8", the 16-card set resembles the 1986 set in design. This time, however, the player's name is printed in a stripe on the left, with his position printed inside a stripe under the photo. The player's number is located inside a helmet in the lower right. The Kiwanis and Fair Oaks Hospital logos appear in the lower left. The card backs, which are numbered in the lower right, have a "Dolphins Say" safety message and the sponsors listed.

		MT
Complete Set (16):		20.00
Common Player:		.50
1	Joe Robbie (OWN)	.50
2	Glenn Blackwood	.50
3	Mark Duper	1.00
4	Fuad Reveiz	.50
5	Dolfan Denny (Mascot)	.50
6	Dwight Stephenson (SP)	5.00
7	Hugh Green	.50
8	Larry Csonka (All-Time Great)	3.00
9	Bud Brown	.50
10	Don Shula (CO)	1.50
11	T.J. Turner	.50
12	Reggie Roby	.50
13	Dan Marino	10.00
14	John Offerdahl	.75
15	Bruce Hardy	.50
16	Lorenzo Hampton	.50

1988 Dolphins Holsum

The standard sized cards in this 12-card set showcase the Holsum logo in the upper left corner, with "1988 Annual Collectors' Edition" printed in the upper right. The player's name and team are printed inside a rectangle at the bottom of the card, beneath the player's photo. The card backs, numbered "of 12," have the player's facsimile autograph at the top and his number, bio and stats printed underneath inside a box. Cards were available in specially marked packages of Holsum Bread.

		MT
Complete Set (12):		30.00
Common Player:		1.50
1	Mark Clayton	3.00
2	Dwight Stephenson	2.00
3	Mark Duper	2.00
4	John Offerdahl	2.00
5	Dan Marino	20.00
6	T.J. Turner	1.50
7	Lorenzo Hampton	1.50
8	Bruce Hardy	1.50
9	Fuad Reveiz	1.50
10	Reggie Roby	1.50

11	William Judson	1.50
12	Bob Brudzinski	1.50

1995 Dolphins Chevron Pin Cards

Each 3" x 5" card in this eight-card set featured a pin at the bottom. The unnumbered cards were part of a Chevron promotion. The card fronts have the player's name and position at the top, with his photo and Dolphins logo underneath. The Chevron logo is next to the pin at the bottom of the card. The card backs have the player's name, number, bio, highlights and a checklist.

		MT
Complete Set (8):		20.00
Common Player:		2.00
1	Miami Dolphins	2.00
2	Dan Marino	10.00
3	Bryan Cox	2.00
4	Troy Vincent	2.00
5	Irving Fryar	2.00
6	Eric Green	2.00
7	Team '95	2.00
8	Hall of Famers	3.00

1996 Dolphins AT&T Set

Fans who attended the Miami Dolphins home season finale were rewarded for their fan appreciation by receiving a photo album card set of the team, sponsored by AT&T. The booklet features Zach Thomas, Dan Marino and the team picture on the cover. The 24-card perforated set, which is standard size, has the player's name vertically along the left side and position along the bottom. The player's number and Dolphins logo appear along the side of the position. The AT&T logo is printed in the top left corner. The backs feature a color profile, as well as personal and career stats. The cards are numbered with the player's jersey numbers.

		MT
Complete Set (24):		15.00
Common Player:		.25
---	Jimmy Johnson	1.00
13	Dan Marino	6.00
17	Jason Kidd	.25
22	Shawn Wooden	.25
25	Louis Oliver	.25
27	Terrell Buckley	.50
33	Karim Abdul-Jabbar	2.00
36	Stanley Pritchett	.25
38	Calvin Jackson	.25
50	Dwight Hollier	.25
55	Zach Thomas	1.00
61	Chris Singleton	.25
62	Tim Ruddy	.25
69	Chris Gray	.25
76	Keith Sims	.25
78	James Brown	.25
80	Richmond Webb	.25
81	Fred Barnett	.50
84	O.J. McDuffie	1.00
92	Troy Drayton	.50
93	Daryl Gardner	.25
95	Trace Armstrong	.25
96	Tim Bowens	.25
	Daniel Stubbs	.25

1996 Dolphins Miami Subs Cards/Coins

The Dolphins and Miami Subs Restaurants produced this 9-card, 9-coin set. The cards front features a color player photo and the backs have the card set checklist. The coins have the player's likeness on one side and the Dolphins logo on the other. The coins are unnumbered. A cardboard holder featuring five Dolphins was produced to hold the set.

		MT
Complete Set (18):		20.00
Complete Card Set (9):		10.00
Complete Coin Set (9):		10.00
Common Card (CA1-CA9):		.75
Common Coin (CO1-CO9):		.75
CA1	(Dan Marino)	6.00

CA2	Larry Csonka	1.50
CA3	Pete Stoyanovich	.75
CA4	Paul Warfield	1.50
CA5	Bernie Kosar	.75
CA6	Mark Clayton	.75
CA7	Fred Barnett	.75
CA8	Nat Moore	1.00
CA9	Super Bowl VII (Don Shula, George Allen)	2.00
CO1	Fred Barnett	.75
CO2	Mark Clayton	.75
CO3	Larry Csonka	1.50
CO4	Bernie Kosar	.75
CO5	Dan Marino	6.00
CO6	Nat Moore	1.00
CO7	Pete Stoyanovich	.75
CO8	Paul Warfield	1.50
CO9	Super Bowl VII Trophy gold coin	1.25
---	Display Holder (Dan Marino, Jimmy Johnson, Bernie Kosar, Mark Clayton, Fred Barnett, Pete	1.50

1991 Domino's Quarterbacks

Upper Deck produced 50-card sets of NFL Quarterback cards in conjunction with a national promotion kicked off during the Aug. 3 NBC telecast of "NFL Quarterback Challenge". The set was sponsored by Domino's, sold in foil packs and feature 32 active quarterbacks, 14 retired quarterbacks and three multi-player cards. Cards were produced especially for this promotion and were distributed through the 5,000 Domino's stores across the country. Each franchise initially received 2,500 packs or two cases of 1,250. Stores could order additional packs in cases of 1,250 or 500. Stores could also order sets.

		MT
Complete Set (50):		6.00
Common Player:		.05
1	Chris Miller	.05
2	Jim Kelly	.20
3	Jim Harbaugh	.10
4	Boomer Esiason	.10
5	Bernie Kosar	.10
6	Troy Aikman	1.00
7	John Elway	.50
8	Rodney Peete	.05
9	Andre Ware	.05
10	Anthony Dilweg	.05
11	Warren Moon	.10
12	Jeff George	.10
13	Jim Everett	.05
14	Jay Schroeder	.05
15	Wade Wilson	.05
16	Dan Marino	1.50
17	Phil Simms	.05
18	Jeff Hostetler	.05
19	Ken O'Brien	.05
20	Timm Rosenbach	.05
21	Bubby Brister	.05
22	Steve DeBerg	.05
23	Randall Cunningham	.10
24	Steve Walsh	.10
25	Billy Joe Tolliver	.05
26	Steve Young	.50
27	Dave Krieg	.05
28	Dan McGwire	.05
29	Vinny Testaverde	.10
30	Stan Humphries	.10
31	Mark Rypien	.05
32	Terry Bradshaw	.75
33	John Brodie	.10
34	Len Dawson	.25
35	Dan Fouts	.25
36	Otto Graham	.50
37	Bob Griese	.25
38	Sonny Jurgensen	.20
39	Daryle Lamonica	.20
40	Archie Manning	.20
41	Jim Plunkett	.10
42	Bart Starr	.40
43	Roger Staubach	.75
44	Joe Theismann	.25
45	Y.A. Tittle	.20
46	Johnny Unitas	.50
47	Cowboy Gunslingers (Troy Aikman, Roger Staubach)	.75
48	Cajun Connection (Bubby Brister, Terry Bradshaw)	.30
49	Dolphin Duo (Dan Marino, Bob Griese)	.75
50	Checklist Card	.05

1995 Donruss Red Zone

Cards for this game were available in both 80-card starter decks and 12-card booster packs. The 336-card set has the game logo in red on the backs of the cards. The cards were unnumbered.

		MT
Complete Set (336):		225.00
Common DP Player:		.05
Common Player:		.30
Common SP Player:		1.50
1	Michael Bankston	.30
2	Larry Centers	.30
3	Ben Coleman (DP)	.05
4	Ed Cunningham (DP)	.05
5	Garrison Hearst	.75
6	Eric Hill	.30
7	Lorenzo Lynch (DP)	.05
8	Clyde Simmons	.05
9	Eric Swann	.30
10	Aeneas Williams (SP)	1.50
11	Chris Doleman	.30
12	Bert Emanuel (DP)	.30
13	Roman Fortin (DP)	.05
14	Jeff George (SP)	2.50
15	Craig Heyward (DP)	.05
16	D.J. Johnson (SP)	1.50
17	Terance Mathis (DP)	2.00
18	Clay Matthews (DP)	.05
19	Kevin Ross (DP)	.05
20	Jessie Tuggle (DP)	.05
21	Bob Whitfield (SP)	1.50
22	Cornelius Bennett (SP)	1.50
23	Russell Copeland (DP)	.05
24	John Fina (SP)	1.50
25	Carwell Gardner (DP)	.05
26	Henry Jones (DP)	.05
27	Jim Kelly (SP)	3.00
28	Mark Maddox (DP)	.05
29	Glenn Parker (DP)	.30
30	Andre Reed (SP)	2.00
31	Bruce Smith (SP)	2.00
32	Thomas Smith (DP)	.05
33	Joe Cain (DP)	.05
34	Mark Carrier	.30
35	Curtis Conway (DP)	.30
36	Al Fontenot (DP)	.05
37	Jeff Graham (DP)	.05
38	Raymont Harris (DP)	.05
39	Andy Heck	.30
40	Erik Kramer (DP)	.10
41	Vinson Smith	.30
42	Lewis Tillman (DP)	.05
43	Steve Walsh	.30
44	James Williams (DP)	.05
45	Donnell Woolford (SP)	1.50
46	Mike Brim (DP)	.05
47	Tony McGee (DP)	.05
48	Carl Pickens	1.00
49	Keith Rucker (DP)	.05
50	Darnay Scott (SP)	3.00
51	Dan Wilkinson (DP)	.10
52	Darryl Williams (DP)	.05
53	Derrick Alexander (WR)	.50
54	Carl Banks (DP)	.05
55	Rob Burnett (SP)	1.50
56	Earnest Byner	.30
57	Steve Everitt (DP)	.05
58	Leroy Hoard (SP)	1.50
59	Michael Jackson (DP)	.10
60	Pepper Johnson	.30
61	Tony Jones	.30
62	Antonio Langham	.30
63	Anthony Pleasant	.05
64	Vinny Testaverde (DP)	.10
65	Eric Turner (SP)	1.50
66	Tommy Vardell	.30
67	Troy Aikman (SP)	12.00
68	Larry Brown	.30

69	Dixon Edwards (DP)	.05
70	Charles Haley (SP)	2.00
71	Michael Irvin (SP)	3.00
72	Daryl Johnston (DP)	.10
73	Leon Lett	.30
74	Nate Newton	.30
75	Jay Novacek (SP)	2.00
76	Darrin Smith	.30
77	Kevin Smith	.30
78	Tony Tolbert (DP)	.05
79	Mark Tuinei (SP)	1.50
80	Kevin Williams (DP)	.10
81	Darren Woodson	.30
82	Elijah Alexander (DP)	.05
83	Steve Atwater	.30
84	Rod Bernstine (SP)	1.50
85	Ray Crockett	.30
86	Shane Dronett (DP)	.05
87	John Elway (SP)	8.00
88	Simon Fletcher	.30
89	Brian Habib (DP)	.05
90	Glyn Milburn	.30
91	Anthony Miller (SP)	3.00
92	Mike Pritchard (DP)	.10
93	Shannon Sharpe	.60
94	Gary Zimmerman (DP)	.05
95	Bennie Blades	.30
96	Lomas Brown (DP)	1.50
97	Mike Johnson (DP)	.05
98	Robert Massey (DP)	.05
99	Scott Mitchell	.10
100	Herman Moore (SP)	5.00
101	Brett Perriman	.60
102	Barry Sanders (SP)	12.00
103	Tracy Scroggins (DP)	.05
104	Chris Spielman	.30
105	Doug Widell (SP)	1.50
106	Edgar Bennett (SP)	3.00
107	LeRoy Butler (DP)	.05
108	Harry Galbreath	.05
109	Sean Jones (SP)	1.50
110	George Koonce (DP)	.05
111	Anthony Morgan (DP)	.05
112	Ken Ruettgers (DP)	.05
113	Fred Strickland (DP)	.05
114	George Teague	.30
115	Reggie White (SP)	4.00
116	Michael Barrow	.30
117	Blaine Bishop (DP)	.05
118	Gary Brown	.30
119	Ray Childress	.30
120	Kenny Davidson (SP)	1.50
121	Cris Dishman (SP)	1.50
122	Brad Hopkins (SP)	1.50
123	Haywood Jeffires (DP)	.05
124	Eddie Robinson (DP)	.05
125	Al Smith (DP)	.05
126	David Williams (SP)	1.50
127	Tony Bennett (SP)	1.50
128	Ray Buchanan (SP)	1.50
129	Quentin Coryatt (DP)	.05
130	Eugene Daniel (DP)	.05
131	Sean Dawkins (DP)	.05
132	Marshall Faulk (SP)	5.00
133	Jim Harbaugh	.60
134	Jeff Herrod (DP)	.05
135	Kirk Lowdermilk (DP)	.05
136	Tony Siragusa (DP)	.05
137	Floyd Turner (DP)	.05
138	Will Wolford (DP)	.05
139	Marcus Allen	.75
140	Kimble Anders (DP)	.05
141	Steve Bono (DP)	.40
142	Dale Carter (DP)	.05
143	Mark Collins (DP)	.05
144	Willie Davis	.30
145	Lake Dawson (DP)	.20
146	Tim Grunhard (DP)	.05
147	Greg Hill (DP)	.10
148	George Jamison (DP)	.05
149	Darren Mickell (DP)	.05
150	Will Shields (DP)	.05
151	Tracy Simien (DP)	.05
152	Neil Smith (SP)	2.00
153	Tim Bowens (DP)	.05
154	J.B. Brown (DP)	.05
155	Keith Byars	.30
156	Bryan Cox	.30
157	Jeff Cross	.30
158	Irving Fryar (SP)	2.00
159	Ron Heller	.30
160	Terry Kirby (SP)	1.50
161	Dan Marino (SP)	24.00
162	O.J. McDuffie (DP)	.05
163	Bernie Parmalee (DP)	.05
164	Chris Singleton (DP)	.05
165	Troy Vincent (SP)	1.50
166	Richmond Webb (SP)	1.50
167	Roy Barker (DP)	.05
168	Cris Carter (DP)	.10
169	Jack Del Rio (SP)	1.50
170	Chris Hinton (DP)	.05
171	Qadry Ismail	.60
172	Amp Lee	.30
173	Ed McDaniel (DP)	.05
174	Randall McDaniel (DP)	.05

175	Warren Moon (SP)	3.00
176	John Randle (SP)	1.50
177	Jake Reed (DP)	.10
178	Robert Smith (DP)	.05
179	Todd Steussie (DP)	.05
180	DeWayne Washington (DP)	.05
181	Bruce Armstrong (DP)	.05
182	Drew Bledsoe	3.00
183	Vincent Brisby (DP)	.05
184	Vincent Brown (DP)	.05
185	Ben Coates (SP)	3.00
186	Sam Gash (DP)	.05
187	Myron Guyton (DP)	.05
188	Maurice Hurst (SP)	1.50
189	Mike Jones (DP)	.05
190	Bob Kratch (DP)	.05
191	Chris Slade (DP)	1.50
192	Derek Brown (DP)	.05
193	Vince Buck (DP)	.05
194	Jim Dombrowski (DP)	.05
195	Quinn Early (DP)	.05
196	Jim Everett	.30
197	Michael Haynes (DP)	.05
198	Wayne Martin (SP)	1.50
199	Lorenzo Neal (DP)	.05
200	William Roaf (SP)	1.50
201	Irv Smith (DP)	.05
202	Jimmy Spencer (DP)	.05
203	Winfred Tubbs (DP)	.05
204	Renaldo Turnbull (DP)	1.50
205	Michael Brooks (DP)	.05
206	Dave Brown (DP)	.05
207	Chris Calloway (DP)	.30
208	Jesse Campbell (DP)	.05
209	John Elliott (DP)	.05
210	Keith Hamilton (DP)	.05
211	Rodney Hampton (DP)	.10
212	Corey Miller (DP)	.05
213	Doug Riesenberg (DP)	.05
214	Mike Sherrard	.30
215	Phillippi Sparks	.30
216	Michael Strahan (DP)	.05
217	Richie Anderson (DP)	.05
218	Brad Baxter (DP)	.05
219	Tony Casillas (DP)	.05
220	Roger Duffy	.30
221	Boomer Esiason (DP)	.10
222	Aaron Glenn (DP)	.05
223	Bobby Houston (DP)	.05
224	Mo Lewis (SP)	1.50
225	Siupeli Malamala (DP)	.05
226	Johnny Mitchell (DP)	.05
227	Eddie Anderson (DP)	.05
228	Jerry Ball (DP)	.05
229	Greg Biekert	.30
230	Tim Brown (SP)	3.00
231	Rob Fredrickson (DP)	.05
232	Nolan Harrison	.30
233	Jeff Hostetler (DP)	.10
234	Rocket Ismail (SP)	2.00
235	Terry McDaniel (SP)	1.50
236	Chester McGlockton (SP)	1.50
237	Don Mosebar	.30
238	Anthony Smith	.30
239	Harvey Williams	.05
240	Steve Wisniewski (DP)	.05
241	Fred Barnett	.30
242	Randall Cunningham	.30
243	William Fuller (SP)	1.50
244	Charlie Garner	.30
245	Vaughn Hebron	.05
246	Lester Holmes	.30
247	Greg Jackson (SP)	1.50
248	Bill Romanowski	.30
249	William Thomas (SP)	1.50
250	Bernard Williams	.30
251	Calvin Williams	.05
252	Michael Zordich (SP)	1.50
253	Chad Brown (SP)	3.00
254	Dermontti Dawson	.05
255	Kevin Greene (SP)	3.00
256	Charles Johnson	.60
257	Carnell Lake	.30
258	Greg Lloyd (SP)	3.00
259	Neil O'Donnell (SP)	3.00
260	Ray Seals (DP)	.05
261	Leon Searcy (SP)	1.50
262	Yancey Thigpen	1.00
263	John L. Williams (DP)	.05

264	Rod Woodson (SP)	3.00
265	Stan Brock	.30
266	Courtney Hall	.30
267	Ronnie Harmon	.30
268	Dwayne Harper (DP)	.05
269	Rodney Harrison (DP)	.05
270	Stan Humphries (DP)	.20
271	Shawn Jefferson	.30
272	Shawn Lee	.30
273	Tony Martin	.75
274	Natrone Means (SP)	5.00
275	Chris Mims (SP)	1.50
276	Leslie O'Neal (SP)	1.50
277	Junior Seau (SP)	3.00
278	Mark Seay (DP)	.10
279	Harry Swayne (DP)	.05
280	Eric Davis	.30
281	William Floyd	.75
282	Merton Hanks (SP)	1.50
283	Brent Jones	.30
284	Tim McDonald (DP)	.05
285	Ken Norton (SP)	1.50
286	Gary Plummer (DP)	.05
287	Jerry Rice (SP)	12.00
288	Dana Stubblefield (SP)	3.00
289	John Taylor (SP)	1.50
290	Bryant Young (DP)	.10
291	Steve Young (SP)	8.00
292	Steve Wallace (SP)	.05
293	Sam Adams (DP)	.05
294	Robert Blackmon (DP)	.05
295	Jeff Blackshear (DP)	.05
296	Brian Blades	.30
297	Howard Ballard (SP)	1.50
298	Cortez Kennedy (DP)	.05
299	Rick Mirer	.75
300	Eugene Robinson (DP)	.05
301	Chris Warren (SP)	3.00
302	Terry Wooden (SP)	1.50
303	Johnny Bailey	.30
304	Isaac Bruce (DP)	.75
305	Shane Conlan (DP)	.05
306	Troy Drayton (DP)	.05
307	Sean Gilbert (DP)	.05
308	Leo Goeas (DP)	.05
309	Jessie Hester	.30
310	Clarence Jones	.30
311	Todd Lyght	.30
312	Chris Miller (DP)	.05
313	Toby Wright (DP)	.05
314	Robert Young (DP)	.05
315	Eric Curry (DP)	.05
316	Trent Dilfer	.75
317	Thomas Everett (DP)	.05
318	Paul Gruber (DP)	.05
319	Jackie Harris (DP)	.05
320	Courtney Hawkins (DP)	.05
321	Lonnie Marts (DP)	.05
322	Tony Mayberry (DP)	.05
323	Martin Mayhew (DP)	.05
324	Hardy Nickerson (DP)	.05
325	Errict Rhett (DP)	.50
326	Reggie Brooks (DP)	.05
327	Tom Carter (DP)	.05
328	Henry Ellard (SP)	1.50
329	Darrell Green (SP)	1.50
330	Ken Harvey (SP)	1.50
331	James Jenkins (DP)	.05
332	Tim Johnson (DP)	.05
333	Jim Lachey	.30
334	Brian Mitchell	.30
335	Heath Shuler	1.00
336	Tony Woods (DP)	.05

1996 Donruss

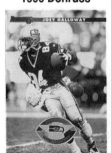

This 250-card set marks the debut of Donruss football cards. The base brand includes 10 Rated Rookies, a subset made popular in the Donruss baseball sets. Each card front has a full-bleed color action photo, with a banner at the top in the team's primary color containing the player's name. The Donruss logo is stamped in silver in the upper left corner. A football, using team colors, is at the bottom of the card, with the position along the top and the team name below. A star in the middle of the football contains a team logo. The horizontal back has the player's position in the upper left corner, with the player's name running in a team-colored banner along the top. Career totals and stats from 1995 are below this information, followed by a brief recap of the player's accomplishments underneath. The background is a team logo. The right side of the card has a number in the upper corner, with a photograph below. Biographical information is in a stripe along the bottom. There were 240 of the cards also produced as a parallel Press Proof set. Each card, numbered 1 of 2,000, has a helmet die-cut in it. The Donruss logo is stamped at the top in gold foil, which is also used for the words "First 2,000 Printed" and "Press Proof" toward the bottom. Insert sets include Hit List, Stop Action, What If?, Will to Win and Silver and Gold Elite cards.

		MT
Complete Set (240):		20.00
Common Player:		.05
Minor Stars:		.10
Wax Box:		20.00
1	Barry Sanders	1.25
2	Flipper Anderson	.05
3	Ben Coates	.05
4	Rob Johnson	.05
5	Rodney Hampton	.05
6	Desmond Howard	.05
7	Craig Heyward	.05
8	Alvin Harper	.05
9	Todd Collins	.05
10	Ken Norton Jr.	.05
11	Stan Humphries	.05
12	Aeneas Williams	.05
13	Jeff Hostetler	.05
14	Frank Sanders	.05
15	J.J. Birden	.05
16	Bryce Paup	.05
17	Bill Brooks	.05
18	Kevin Williams	.05
19	Boomer Esiason	.05
20	O.J. McDuffie	.05
21	Eric Swann	.05
22	Neil Smith	.05
23	Charlie Garner	.05
24	Greg Lloyd	.05
25	Willie Jackson	.05
26	Shawn Jefferson	.05
27	Rodney Peete	.05
28	Michael Westbrook	.50
29	J.J. Stokes	.50
30	Troy Aikman	1.00
31	Sean Dawkins	.05
32	Larry Centers	.05
33	Herschel Walker	.05
34	Stoney Case	.05
35	Kevin Greene	.05
36	Quinn Early	.05
37	Fred Barnett	.05
38	Andre Coleman	.05
39	Mark Chmura	.25
40	Adrian Murrell	.05
41	Roosevelt Potts	.05
42	Jay Novacek	.05
43	Derrick Alexander	.05
44	Ken Dilger	.05
45	Rob Moore	.05
46	Cris Carter	.05
47	Jeff Blake	.50
48	Derek Loville	.05
49	Tyrone Wheatley	.05
50	Terrell Fletcher	.05
51	Sherman Williams	.05
52	Justin Armour	.05
53	Kordell Stewart	1.00
54	Tim Brown	.05
55	Kevin Carter	.05
56	Andre Rison	.05
57	James Stewart	.05
58	Brent Jones	.05
59	Erik Kramer	.05
60	Floyd Turner	.05
61	Ricky Watters	.05
62	Hardy Nickerson	.05
63	Aaron Craver	.05
64	Dave Krieg	.05
65	Warren Moon	.05
66	Wayne Chrebet	.05
67	Napoleon Kaufman	.10
68	Terance Mathis	.05
69	Chad May	.05
70	Andre Reed	.05
71	Reggie White	.10
72	Brett Favre	2.00
73	Chris Zorich	.05
74	Kerry Collins	.30
75	Herman Moore	.05
76	Yancey Thigpen	.50
77	Glenn Foley	.05
78	Quentin Coryatt	.05
79	Terry Kirby	.05
80	Edgar Bennett	.05
81	Mark Brunell	.75
82	Heath Shuler	.05
83	Gus Frerotte	.05
84	Deion Sanders	.50
85	Calvin Williams	.05
86	Junior Seau	.10
87	Jim Kelly	.10
88	Daryl Johnston	.05
89	Irving Fryar	.05
90	Brian Blades	.05
91	Willie Davis	.05
92	Jerome Bettis	.10
93	Marcus Allen	.10
94	Jeff Graham	.05
95	Rick Mirer	.05
96	Harvey Williams	.05
97	Steve Atwater	.05
98	Carl Pickens	.10
99	Darick Holmes	.05
100	Bruce Smith	.05
101	Vinny Testaverde	.05
102	Thurman Thomas	.10
103	Drew Bledsoe	.75
104	Bernie Parmalee	.05
105	Greg Hill	.05
106	Steve McNair	.50
107	Andre Hastings	.05
108	Eric Metcalf	.05
109	Kimble Anders	.05
110	Steve Tasker	.05
111	Mark Carrier	.05
112	Jerry Rice	1.00
113	Joey Galloway	.75
114	Robert Smith	.05
115	Hugh Douglas	.05
116	Willie McGinest	.05
117	Terrell Davis	.75
118	Cortez Kennedy	.05
119	Marshall Faulk	.50
120	Michael Haynes	.05
121	Isaac Bruce	.50
122	Brian Mitchell	.05
123	Bryan Cox	.05
124	Tamarick Vanover	.50
125	William Floyd	.05
126	Chris Chandler	.05
127	Carnell Lake	.05
128	Aaron Bailey	.05
129	Darnay Scott	.20
130	Darren Woodson	.05
131	Ernie Mills	.05
132	Charles Haley	.05
133	Rocket Ismail	.05
134	Bert Emanuel	.05
135	Lake Dawson	.05
136	Jake Reed	.05
137	Dave Brown	.05
138	Steve Bono	.05
139	Terry Allen	.05
140	Errict Rhett	.20
141	Rod Woodson	.05
142	Charles Johnson	.05
143	Emmitt Smith	2.00
144	Ki-Jana Carter	.40
145	Garrison Hearst	.05
146	Rashaan Salaam	.50
147	Tony Boselli	.05
148	Derrick Thomas	.05
149	Mark Seay	.05
150	Derrick Alexander	.05
151	Christian Fauria	.05
152	Aaron Hayden	.05
153	Chris Warren	.10
154	Dave Meggett	.05
155	Jeff George	.10
156	Jackie Harris	.05
157	Michael Irvin	.10
158	Scott Mitchell	.05
159	Trent Dilfer	.05
160	Kyle Brady	.05
161	Dan Marino	2.00
162	Curtis Martin	1.50
163	Mario Bates	.05
164	Erric Pegram	.05
165	Eric Zeier	.05
166	Rodney Thomas	.05
167	Neil O'Donnell	.05
168	Warren Sapp	.05
169	Jim Harbaugh	.10
170	Henry Ellard	.05
171	Anthony Miller	.05
172	Derrick Moore	.05
173	John Elway	.50
174	Vincent Brisby	.05
175	Antonio Freeman	.05
176	Chris Sanders	.30
177	Steve Young	.75
178	Shannon Sharpe	.05
179	Brett Perriman	.05
180	Orlando Thomas	.05
181	Eric Bjornson	.05
182	Natrone Means	.05
183	Jim Everett	.05
184	Curtis Conway	.05
185	Robert Brooks	.10
186	Tony Martin	.05
187	Mark Carrier	.05
188	LeShon Johnson	.05
189	Bernie Kosar	.05
190	Ray Zellars	.05
191	Steve Walsh	.05
192	Craig Erickson	.05
193	Tommy Maddox	.05
194	Leslie O'Neal	.05
195	Harold Green	.05
196	Steve Beuerlein	.05
197	Ron Moore	.05
198	Leslie Shepherd	.05
199	Leroy Hoard	.05
200	Michael Jackson	.05
201	Will Moore	.05
202	Ricky Ervins	.05
203	Keith Jennings	.05
204	Eric Green	.05
205	Mark Rypien	.05
206	Torrance Small	.05
207	Sean Gilbert	.05
208	Mike Alstott	1.50
209	Willie Anderson	.05
210	Alex Molden	.05
211	Jonathan Ogden	.05
212	Stepfret Williams	.05
213	*Jeff Lewis*	.50
214	Regan Upshaw	.05
215	*Daryl Gardener*	.05
216	*Danny Kanell*	.50
217	John Mobley	.05
218	Reggie Brown	.05
219	*Mushin Muhammad*	.75
220	*Kevin Hardy*	.25
221	*Stanley Pritchett*	.40
222	Cedric Jones	.05
223	Marco Battaglia	.05
224	Duane Clemons	.05
225	Jerald Moore	.05
226	*Simeon Rice*	.30
227	Chris Darkins	.10
228	*Bobby Hoying*	.50
229	*Stephen Davis*	3.00
230	*Walt Harris*	.30
231	Jermain Mayberry	.05
232	Tony Brackens	.05
233	*Eric Moulds*	2.00
234	*Alex Van Dyke*	.50
235	*Marvin Harrison*	2.50
236	*Rickey Dudley*	.50
237	*Terrell Owens*	3.50
238	Jerry Rice CL	.25
239	Checklist Dan Marino CL	.30
240	Checklist	.05

1996 Donruss Press Proofs

Press Proofs paralleled the 240-card regular-issue set, and included the words "Press Proof" in gold foil on the front of the card, along with a die-cut. Each Gold Press Proof was numbered 1 of 2,000.

	MT
Complete Set (240):	300.00
Press Proof Cards:	6x-12x

1996 Donruss Elite

Donruss' initial football set continues the legacy of an Elite insert set, which debuted in the company's baseball line in 1991. Ten of the NFL's premiere running backs are featured on two versions of the foil-enhanced card - Silver Elite and Gold Elite. The Silver cards are limited to 10,000 each; the Gold ones are sequentially numbered to 2,000. The card front uses the corresponding color for the foiled borders around the picture, plus the Donruss and Elite logos. The card back uses the appropriate color for the background, which has a scripted Elite "E" and a short player profile on the left side. The right side has a color photo with a team logo underneath. The card number is along the top of the card.

		MT
Complete Set (20):		125.00
Common Player:		1.00
1	Emmitt Smith	15.00
2	Barry Sanders	20.00
3	Marshall Faulk	3.00
4	Curtis Martin	5.00
5	Junior Seau	1.00
6	Troy Aikman	10.00
7	Steve Young	6.00
8	Dan Marino	15.00
9	Brett Favre	20.00
10	John Elway	15.00
11	Kerry Collins	2.00
12	Drew Bledsoe	10.00
13	Jerry Rice	15.00
14	Keyshawn Johnson	6.00
15	Deion Sanders	3.00
16	Isaac Bruce	3.00
17	Rashaan Salaam	1.00
18	Tim Biakabutuka	1.00
19	Lawrence Phillips	2.00
20	Robert Brooks	1.00

1996 Donruss Elite Gold

Donruss Elite Golds run parallel with the Elite Silvers, but are numbered up to 2,000. In this insert, the silver foil is replaced by gold foil.

	MT
Complete Set (20):	250.00
Gold Cards:	2x

1996 Donruss Hit List

These 1996 Donruss insert cards feature the NFL's most physical players on cards which use silver holographic foil and die-cutting for the design. The front has a color photo, with a holographic background. "Hit List" is written at the top of the card; Donruss and the player's team name are below the photo. The sides of the card are die-cut, with foiled rivets in them. The card back has a color photo on it, with most of it, except for the player's face, ghosted as the background. The player's face is in full color, highlighted by a sunburst around it. There's a paragraph below which details a moment when the player survived, or delivered, a devastating hit. A serial number appears in a white rectangle along the bottom. The card number is in the upper right corner.

		MT
Complete Set (20):		100.00
Common Player:		.50
1	Bruce Smith	.50
2	Barry Sanders	12.00
3	Kevin Hardy	.50
4	Greg Lloyd	.50
5	Brett Favre	12.00
6	Emmitt Smith	8.00
7	Kerry Collins	1.00
8	Ken Norton Jr.	.50
9	Steve Atwater	.50
10	Curtis Martin	4.00
11	Chris Warren	.50
12	Steve Young	4.00
13	Marshall Faulk	2.00
14	Junior Seau	.50
15	Lawrence Phillips	6.00
16	Troy Aikman	6.00
17	Jerry Rice	6.00
18	Dan Marino	8.00
19	Reggie White	1.00
20	John Elway	8.00

1996 Donruss Rated Rookies

In a concept first made popular with its baseball line, Donruss has issued this 10-card insert set honoring 10 of the top NFL newcomers.

		MT
Complete Set (10):		40.00
Common Player:		2.00
1	Keyshawn Johnson	5.00
2	Terry Glenn	7.00
3	Tim Biakabutuka	4.00
4	Bobby Engram	2.00
5	Leeland McElroy	2.00
6	Eddie George	8.00
7	Lawrence Phillips	4.00
8	Derrick Mayes	2.00
9	Karim Abdul-Jabbar	5.00
10	Eddie Kennison	4.00

1996 Donruss What If?

These 1996 Donruss inserts go back in time to chronicle the NFL's top talents with a post-dated rookie card. Each card uses rookie photography, with a design that fits the era that the player entered the league. Each card also has a sequential serial number. Cards were in hobby packs only.

		MT
Complete Set (10):		100.00
Common Player:		3.00
1	Troy Aikman	10.00
2	Jerry Rice	10.00
3	Barry Sanders	15.00
4	Drew Bledsoe	8.00
5	Deion Sanders	3.00

6	Brett Favre	15.00
7	Dan Marino	12.00
8	Steve Young	7.00
9	Emmitt Smith	12.00
10	John Elway	10.00

1996 Donruss Stop Action

1996 Donruss football magazine packs have these Stop Action inserts, which feature some of the best action photos in the sport. Each shot is enhanced by holographic foil and die-cutting. Each card is serial numbered to 5,000.

		MT
Complete Set (10):		85.00
Common Player:		2.00
1	Deion Sanders	3.00
2	Troy Aikman	10.00
3	Brett Favre	15.00
4	Steve Young	7.00
5	Joey Galloway	2.00
6	Dan Marino	12.00
7	Jerry Rice	10.00
8	Emmitt Smith	12.00
9	Isaac Bruce	3.00
10	Barry Sanders	15.00

1996 Donruss Will to Win

These inserts are exclusive to 1996 Donruss retail packs only. The cards, having sequential numbering to 5,000, are one of the scarcest inserts in the product. They feature some of the NFL's grittiest competitors.

		MT
Complete Set (10):		85.00
Common Player:		3.00
1	Emmitt Smith	12.00
2	Brett Favre	15.00
3	Curtis Martin	6.00
4	Jerry Rice	10.00
5	Barry Sanders	15.00
6	Errict Rhett	3.00
7	Troy Aikman	10.00
8	Dan Marino	12.00
9	Steve Young	7.00
10	John Elway	12.00

1997 Donruss

The 230-card set features a full-bleed photo on the front. The Donruss logo is in the upper left. The team name is printed vertically in the lower left, while the team logo and player position are in the lower left corner. The player's name is to the right of the team logo. The base set is paralleled with a Press Proofs set, which are numbered "1 of 1,500," and Press Proofs - First 500, which are numbered "1 of 500" and die-cut with gold foil.

		MT
Complete Set (230):		20.00
Common Player:		.05
Minor Stars:		.10
Wax Box:		45.00
1	Dan Marino	1.50
2	Brett Favre	1.75
3	Emmitt Smith	1.50
4	Eddie George	1.25
5	Karim Abdul-Jabbar	.50
6	Terrell Davis	1.00
7	Curtis Martin	1.00
8	Drew Bledsoe	.75
9	Jerry Rice	.75
10	Troy Aikman	.75
11	Barry Sanders	1.25
12	Mark Brunell	.75
13	Kerry Collins	.30
14	Steve Young	.50
15	Kordell Stewart	.75
16	Eddie Kennison	.40
17	Terry Glenn	.75
18	John Elway	.50
19	Joey Galloway	.40
20	Deion Sanders	.40
21	Keyshawn Johnson	.40
22	Lawrence Phillips	.10
23	Ricky Watters	.10
24	Marvin Harrison	.40
25	Bobby Engram	.10
26	Marshall Faulk	.10
27	Carl Pickens	.10
28	Isaac Bruce	.15
29	Herman Moore	.15
30	Jerome Bettis	.10
31	Rashaan Salaam	.10
32	Errict Rhett	.10
33	Tim Biakabutuka	.10
34	Robert Brooks	.10
35	Antonio Freeman	.30
36	Steve McNair	.50
37	Jeff Blake	.10
38	Tony Banks	.30
39	Terrell Owens	.50
40	Eric Moulds	.10
41	Leeland McElroy	.10
42	Chris Sanders	.05
43	Thurman Thomas	.10
44	Bruce Smith	.05
45	Reggie White	.10
46	Chris Warren	.05
47	J.J. Stokes	.05
48	Ben Coates	.05
49	Tim Brown	.05
50	Marcus Allen	.10
51	Michael Irvin	.10
52	William Floyd	.05
53	Ken Dilger	.05
54	Bobby Taylor	.05
55	Keenan McCardell	.05
56	Raymont Harris	.05
57	Keith Byars	.05
58	O.J. McDuffie	.05
59	Robert Smith	.05
60	Bert Emanuel	.05
61	Rick Mirer	.05
62	Vinny Testaverde	.05
63	Kyle Brady	.05
64	Mark Bruener	.05
65	Neil O'Donnell	.05
66	Anthony Johnson	.05
67	Ken Norton	.05
68	Warren Sapp	.05
69	Amani Toomer	.05
70	Simeon Rice	.05
71	Kevin Hardy	.05
72	Junior Seau	.05
73	Neil Smith	.05
74	LeShon Johnson	.05
75	Quinn Early	.05
76	Andre Reed	.05
77	Jake Reed	.05
78	Elvis Grbac	.05
79	Tyrone Wheatley	.05
80	Adrian Murrell	.05
81	Fred Barnett	.05
82	Darrell Green	.05
83	Stan Humphries	.05
84	Troy Drayton	.05
85	Steve Atwater	.05
86	Quentin Coryatt	.05
87	Dan Wilkinson	.05
88	Scott Mitchell	.05
89	Willie McGinest	.05
90	Kevin Smith	.05
91	Gus Frerotte	.05
92	Bam Morris	.05
93	Darick Holmes	.05
94	Zach Thomas	.20
95	Tom Carter	.05
96	Cortez Kennedy	.05
97	Kevin Williams	.05
98	Michael Haynes	.05
99	Lamont Warren	.05
100	Jeff Graham	.05
101	Alex Van Dyke	.05
102	Jim Everett	.05
103	Chris Chandler	.05
104	Qadry Ismail	.05
105	Ray Zellars	.05
106	Chris T. Jones	.05
107	Charlie Garner	.05
108	Bobby Hoying	.05
109	Mark Chmura	.05
110	Cris Carter	.05
111	Darnay Scott	.05
112	Anthony Miller	.05
113	Desmond Howard	.05
114	Terance Mathis	.05
115	Rodney Hampton	.05
116	Napoleon Kaufman	.05
117	Jim Harbaugh	.05
118	Shannon Sharpe	.05
119	Irving Fryar	.05
120	Garrison Hearst	.05
121	Terry Allen	.05
122	Larry Centers	.05
123	Sean Dawkins	.05
124	Jeff George	.05
125	Tony Martin	.05
126	Mike Alstott	.10
127	Rickey Dudley	.05
128	Kevin Carter	.05
129	Derrick Alexander	.05
130	Greg Lloyd	.05
131	Bryce Paup	.05
132	Derrick Thomas	.05
133	Greg Hill	.05
134	Jamal Anderson	.05
135	Curtis Conway	.05
136	Frank Sanders	.05
137	Brett Perriman	.05
138	Edgar Bennett	.05
139	Wayne Chrebet	.05
140	Natrone Means	.05
141	Eric Metcalf	.05
142	Trent Dilfer	.05
143	Terry Kirby	.05
144	Johnnie Morton	.05
145	Dale Carter	.05
146	Michael Westbrook	.05
147	Stanley Pritchett	.05
148	Todd Collins	.05
149	Tamarick Vanover	.05
150	Kevin Greene	.05
151	Lamar Lathon	.05
152	Muhsin Muhammad	.10
153	Dorsey Levens	.05
154	Rod Woodson	.05
155	Brent Jones	.05
156	Michael Jackson	.05
157	Shawn Jefferson	.05
158	Kimble Anders	.05
159	Sean Gilbert	.05
160	Carnell Lake	.05
161	Darren Woodson	.05
162	Dave Meggett	.05
163	Henry Ellard	.05
164	Eric Swann	.05
165	Tony Boselli	.05
166	Daryl Johnston	.05
167	Willie Jackson	.05
168	Wesley Walls	.05
169	Mario Bates	.05
170	Lake Dawson	.05
171	Mike Mamula	.05
172	Ed McCaffrey	.05
173	Tony Brackens	.05
174	Craig Heyward	.05
175	Harvey Williams	.05
176	Dave Brown	.05
177	Aaron Glenn	.05
178	Jeff Hostetler	.05
179	Alvin Harper	.05
180	Ty Detmer	.05
181	James Jett	.05
182	James Stewart	.05
183	Warren Moon	.05
184	Herschel Walker	.05
185	Ki-Jana Carter	.05
186	Leslie O'Neal	.05
187	Danny Kanell	.05
188	Eric Bjornson	.05
189	Alex Molden	.05
190	Bryant Young	.05
191	Merton Hanks	.05
192	Heath Shuler	.05
193	Brian Blades	.05
194	Steve Bono	.05
195	Wayne Simmons	.05
196	*Warrick Dunn*	1.75
197	*Peter Boulware*	.10
198	*David LaFleur*	.50
199	*Shawn Springs*	.40
200	*Reidel Anthony*	1.00
201	*Jim Druckenmiller*	1.00
202	*Orlando Pace*	.40
203	*Yatil Green*	.50
204	*Bryant Westbrook*	.10
205	*Tiki Barber*	1.00
206	*James Farrior*	.10
207	*Rae Carruth*	.25
208	*Danny Wuerffel*	.50
209	*Corey Dillon*	1.50
210	*Ike Hilliard*	1.00
211	*Tony Gonzalez*	1.00
212	*Antowain Smith*	1.25
213	*Pat Barnes*	.50
214	*Troy Davis*	.50
215	*Byron Hanspard*	.50
216	*Joey Kent*	.40
217	*Jake Plummer*	4.00
218	*Kenny Holmes*	.10
219	*Darnell Autry*	.25
220	*Darrell Russell*	.10
221	*Walter Jones*	.10
222	*Dwayne Rudd*	.10
223	*Tom Knight*	.10
224	*Kevin Lockett*	.20
225	*Will Blackwell*	.20
226	Dan Marino CL	.75
227	Brett Favre CL	1.00
228	Emmitt Smith CL	.75
229	Barry Sanders CL	.50
230	Jerry Rice CL	.30

1997 Donruss Press Proof Silvers

Silver Press Proofs were a parallel set to the 230-card Donruss set in 1997. Silver Press Proofs have silver foil added to the front in streaks throughout the card, which originate from the bottom left corner. The words "Press Proof" are printed up the right side in silver foil. Card backs contain a "1 of 1,500" line printed just below the player's name.

	MT
Complete Set (230):	200.00
Silver Cards:	5x-10x

1997 Donruss Press Proof Golds

Gold Press Proofs were a parallel to the 230-card Donruss set in 1997. Gold Press Proofs were die-cut across the top and right side and had rounded corners in the bottom left corner. Fronts featured gold foil streaks across the front that originated in the bottom left corner. The words "Press Proof" are printed in gold up the right side of the card, while the backs are numbered "1 of 500" under the player's name.

	MT
Complete Set (230):	400.00
Gold Cards:	10x-20x

1997 Donruss Elite

The 20-card chase set is featured on Silver and Gold foil cards. The Silver Elite is numbered to 5,000, while the Gold version was produced in an edition of 2,000 sets.

		MT
Complete Set (20):		200.00
Common Player:		5.00
Minor Stars:		10.00
Production 5,000 Sets		
Gold Cards:		2x
Production 2,000 Sets		
1	Emmitt Smith	20.00
2	Dan Marino	20.00
3	Brett Favre	30.00
4	Curtis Martin	10.00
5	Terrell Davis	25.00
6	Barry Sanders	30.00
7	Drew Bledsoe	15.00
8	Mark Brunell	15.00
9	Troy Aikman	15.00
10	Jerry Rice	15.00
11	Steve McNair	10.00
12	Kerry Collins	10.00
13	John Elway	20.00
14	Eddie George	15.00
15	Karim Abdul-Jabbar	15.00
16	Kordell Stewart	15.00
17	Jerome Bettis	5.00
18	Terry Glenn	10.00
19	Errict Rhett	5.00
20	Carl Pickens	5.00

1997 Donruss Legends of the Fall

The 10-card chase set is numbered to 10,000 and features artwork from artist Dan Gardiner. The first 500 of the cards were printed directly on actual canvas.

		MT
Complete Set (10):		125.00
Common Player:		5.00
Canvas Cards:		3x-6x
1	Troy Aikman	16.00
2	Barry Sanders	20.00
3	John Elway	10.00
4	Dan Marino	30.00
5	Emmitt Smith	30.00
6	Jerry Rice	16.00
7	Deion Sanders	10.00
8	Brett Favre	35.00
9	Marcus Allen	5.00
10	Steve Young	10.00

1997 Donruss Passing Grade

The 16-card hobby-exclusive set is styled like a report card. The die-cut insert showcases the talents of the top quarterbacks. It utilizes a card-within-a-card design with red-foil stamping. Each football shaped, die-cut card came in its own envelope. The cards are numbered to 3,000.

		MT
Complete Set (16):		150.00
Common Player:		4.00
Minor Stars:		8.00
Production 3,000 Sets		
1	Steve Young	10.00
2	Drew Bledsoe	15.00
3	Mark Brunell	15.00
4	Kerry Collins	8.00
5	Steve McNair	10.00
6	John Elway	20.00
7	Ty Detmer	4.00
8	Jeff Blake	4.00
9	Dan Marino	20.00
10	Kordell Stewart	12.00
11	Tony Banks	8.00
12	Brett Favre	30.00
13	Gus Frerotte	4.00
14	Troy Aikman	15.00
15	Jeff George	4.00
16	Brad Johnson	8.00

1997 Donruss Rated Rookies

The 10-card chase set features a rookie player, with the Rated Rookies logo in the lower left corner. The set was paralleled by a Medalist micro-etched, all foil set with gold-foil holographic stamping.

		MT
Complete Set (10):		45.00
Common Player:		3.00
Medalist Cards:		5x-10x
1	Ike Hilliard	4.00
2	Warrick Dunn	10.00
3	Yatil Green	3.00
4	Jim Druckenmiller	6.00
5	Rae Carruth	4.00
6	Antowain Smith	8.00
7	Tiki Barber	4.00
8	Byron Hanspard	3.00
9	Reidel Anthony	5.00
10	Jake Plummer	20.00

1997 Donruss Zoning Commission

The 20-card retail-exclusive set is printed on micro-etched, holographic foil card stock, with gold-foil stamping. The cards are numbered to 5,000.

		MT
Complete Set (20):		200.00
Common Player:		5.00
Minor Stars:		10.00
1	Brett Favre	40.00
2	Jerry Rice	20.00
3	Jerome Bettis	10.00
4	Troy Aikman	20.00
5	Drew Bledsoe	20.00
6	Natrone Means	10.00
7	Steve Young	15.00
8	John Elway	15.00
9	Barry Sanders	25.00
10	Emmitt Smith	35.00
11	Curtis Martin	20.00
12	Terry Allen	5.00
13	Dan Marino	35.00
14	Mark Brunell	20.00
15	Terry Glenn	10.00
16	Herman Moore	5.00
17	Ricky Watters	5.00
18	Terrell Davis	20.00
19	Isaac Bruce	10.00
20	Curtis Conway	5.00

1997 Donruss Preferred

The inaugural issue of Donruss Preferred Football contained 150 cards which were divided into four different tiers, with 80 Bronze, 40 Silver, 20 Gold and 10 Platinum cards. The cards are printed on all-foil, micro-etched surfaces and contain an action shot of the player, with his name and team across the bottom and "Donruss Preferred" and the word bronze, silver, gold or platinum across the top. There is also a white star in each corner of the card within the color border. Preferred also had a Cut to the Chase parallel set, as well as Chain Reaction, Staremaster and Precious Metals insert sets. Another interesting facet of this product is that it arrived in collectible tins, of which there were 24 different players featured. The tins were packed into larger Hobby Master Tins for hobby accounts and came in boxes to retail accounts.

	MT
Complete Set (150):	800.00
Complete Bronze (80):	40.00
Common Bronze Player:	.25
Minor Bronze Stars:	.50
Complete Silver (40):	110.00
Common Silver Player:	2.00
Minor Silver Stars:	4.00
Complete Gold (20):	250.00
Common Gold Player:	4.00
Minor Gold Stars:	8.00
Complete Platinum (10):	400.00

#	Player	Price
1	Emmitt Smith P	60.00
2	Steve Young G	15.00
3	Cris Carter S	2.00
4	Tim Biakabutuka S	.25
5	Brett Favre P	70.00
6	Troy Aikman G	20.00
7	Eddie Kennison S	4.00
8	Ben Coates S	.25
9	Dan Marino P	70.00
10	Deion Sanders G	10.00
11	Curtis Conway S	4.00
12	Jeff George S	2.00
13	Barry Sanders P	40.00
14	Kerry Collins G	15.00
15	Marvin Harrison S	4.00
16	Bobby Engram B	.50
17	Jerry Rice P	35.00
18	Kordell Stewart G	20.00
19	Tony Banks S	5.00
20	Jim Harbaugh B	.25
21	Mark Brunell P	35.00
22	Steve McNair G	15.00
23	Terrell Owens S	5.00
24	Raymont Harris B	.25
25	Curtis Martin P	35.00
26	Karim Abdul-Jabbar G	8.00
27	Joey Galloway S	4.00
28	Bobby Hoying B	.25
29	Terrell Davis P	35.00
30	Terry Glenn S	12.00
31	Antonio Freeman S	4.00
32	Brad Johnson B	.50
33	Drew Bledsoe P	35.00
34	John Elway G	20.00
35	Herman Moore G	8.00
36	Robert Brooks S	4.00
37	Rod Smith B	.25
38	Eddie George P	40.00
39	Keyshawn Johnson G	8.00
40	Greg Hill S	2.00
41	Scott Mitchell B	.25
42	Muhsin Muhammad B	.25
43	Isaac Bruce G	8.00
44	Jeff Blake S	4.00
45	Neil O'Donnell B	.25
46	Jimmy Smith B	.25
47	Jerome Bettis G	8.00
48	Terry Allen S	2.00
49	Andre Reed B	.25
50	Frank Sanders B	.25
51	Tim Brown B	4.00
52	Thurman Thomas S	4.00
53	Heath Shuler B	.25
54	Vinny Testaverde B	.25
55	Marcus Allen S	4.00
56	Napoleon Kaufman B	.50
57	Derrick Alexander B	.25
58	Carl Pickens G	4.00
59	Marshall Faulk S	4.00
60	Mike Alstott B	2.00
61	Jamal Anderson B	.50
62	Ricky Watters B	8.00
63	Dorsey Levens S	4.00
64	Todd Collins B	.25
65	Trent Dilfer B	.50
66	Natrone Means B	4.00
67	Gus Frerotte B	.25
68	Irving Fryar B	.25
69	Adrian Murrell S	4.00
70	Rodney Hampton B	.25
71	Garrison Hearst B	.25
72	Reggie White S	4.00
73	Anthony Johnson B	.25
74	Tony Martin B	.25
75	Chris Sanders S	2.00
76	O.J. McDuffie B	.25
77	Leeland McElroy B	.25
78	Ki-Jana Carter S	2.00
79	Anthony Miller B	.25
80	Johnnie Morton B	.25
81	Robert Smith B	2.00
82	Brett Perriman B	.25
83	Errict Rhett B	.25
84	Michael Irvin S	4.00
85	Darnay Scott B	.25
86	Shannon Sharpe B	.25
87	Lawrence Phillips S	2.00
88	Bruce Smith B	.25
89	James Stewart B	.25
90	J.J. Stokes B	.50
91	Chris Warren B	.25
92	Daryl Johnston B	.25
93	Andre Rison B	.25
94	Rashaan Salaam B	.25
95	Amani Toomer B	.25
96	Warrick Dunn B	35.00
97	Tiki Barber S	10.00
98	Peter Boulware B	.50
99	Ike Hilliard S	15.00
100	Antowain Smith B	8.00
101	Yatil Green S	6.00
102	Tony Gonzalez B	2.00
103	Reidel Anthony G	20.00
104	Troy Davis S	6.00
105	Rae Carruth S	6.00
106	David LaFleur S	2.00
107	Jim Druckenmiller G	30.00
108	Joey Kent S	4.00
109	Byron Hanspard S	6.00
110	Darrell Russell B	.50
111	Danny Wuerffel S	8.00
112	Jake Plummer S	12.00
113	Jay Graham B	1.00
114	Corey Dillon S	12.00
115	Orlando Pace B	.50
116	Pat Barnes S	5.00
117	Shawn Springs B	.50
118	Troy Aikman (National Treasures)	2.00
119	Drew Bledsoe B (National Treasures)	2.00
120	Mark Brunell B (National Treasures)	2.00
121	Kerry Collins B (National Treasures)	1.50
122	Terrell Davis B (National Treasures)	2.00
123	Jerome Bettis B (National Treasures)	.25
124	Brett Favre B (National Treasures)	4.00
125	Eddie George B (National Treasures)	3.00
126	Terry Glenn B (National Treasures)	1.00
127	Karim Abdul-Jabbar B (National Treasures)	.50
128	Keyshawn Johnson B (National Treasures)	.25
129	Dan Marino B (National Treasures)	4.00
130	Curtis Martin B (National Treasures)	1.50
131	Natrone Means B (National Treasures)	.25
132	Herman Moore S (National Treasures)	2.00
133	Jerry Rice B (National Treasures)	2.00
134	Barry Sanders B (National Treasures)	2.50
135	Deion Sanders B (National Treasures)	.50
136	Emmitt Smith B (National Treasures)	3.00
137	Kordell Stewart B (National Treasures)	2.00
138	Steve Young B (National Treasures)	1.50
139	Carl Pickens S (National Treasures)	2.00
140	Isaac Bruce S (National Treasures)	2.00
141	Steve McNair S (National Treasures)	5.00
142	John Elway B (National Treasures)	6.00
143	Cris Carter (National Treasures)	.25
144	Tim Brown B (National Treasures)	.25
145	Ricky Watters S (National Treasures)	.25
146	Robert Brooks B (National Treasures)	.25
147	Jeff Blake B (National Treasures)	.25
148	Tiki Barber CL B	.25
149	Jim Druckenmiller CL B	1.00
150	Warrick Dunn CL B	1.50

1997 Donruss Preferred Tins

Each pack of Donruss Preferred arrived for sale in a collectible tin, with 24 different players each featured on their own tin. The 24 tins arrived in five different varieties: smaller blue pack tins were the "base" tins; silver pack tins were in hobby exclusive boxes and numbered to 1,200; gold pack tins were also available in hobby box tins and numbered to 300; blue box tins were hobby exclusive and contained 24 smaller tins - these were numbered to 1,200 and essentially the same as the smaller blue tins except in size; and gold box tins, which were parallel to the larger blue box tins, but printed in gold and numbered to 300. The larger box tins were only available to hobby accounts. Retail accounts received the tins packed in cardboard boxes.

	MT
Complete Blue Pack (24):	20.00

Common Pack:	.25
Complete Silver Pack (24):	200.00
Silver Pack Tins:	5x-10x
Complete Blue Box (24):	150.00
Blue Box Tins:	4x-8x
Complete Gold Pack (24):	400.00
Gold Pack Tins:	10x-20x
Complete Gold Box (24):	300.00
Gold Box Tins:	8x-16x
1 Mark Brunell	1.00
2 Karim Abdul-Jabbar	.50
3 Terry Glenn	.75
4 Brett Favre	2.00
5 Troy Aikman	1.00
6 Eddie George	1.50
7 John Elway	.75
8 Steve Young	.75
9 Terrell Davis	1.00
10 Kordell Stewart	1.00
11 Drew Bledsoe	1.00
12 Kerry Collins	.75
13 Dan Marino	2.00
14 Tim Brown	.25
15 Carl Pickens	.25
16 Warrick Dunn	1.50
17 Herman Moore	.25
18 Curtis Martin	.75
19 Ike Hilliard	.50
20 Barry Sanders	1.25
21 Deion Sanders	.50
22 Emmitt Smith	2.00
23 Keyshawn Johnson	.25
24 Jerry Rice	1.00

1997 Donruss Preferred Chain Reaction

This 24-card insert set captured 12 different offensive teammates on die-cut cards that linked together in order to display them side by side. The insert was printed on thick plastic stock with holographic treatments and sequentially numbered to 3,000.

	MT
Complete Set (24):	350.00
Common Player:	5.00
Minor Stars:	10.00
1a Dan Marino	40.00
1b Karim Abdul-Jabbar	10.00
2a Troy Aikman	20.00
2b Emmitt Smith	40.00
3a Steve McNair	15.00
3b Eddie George	30.00
4a Brett Favre	45.00
4b Robert Brooks	5.00
5a John Elway	15.00
5b Terrell Davis	20.00
6a Terrell Davis	20.00
6b Curtis Martin	15.00
7a Steve Young	15.00
7b Jerry Rice	20.00
8a Mark Brunell	20.00
8b Natrone Means	5.00
9a Barry Sanders	30.00
9b Herman Moore	10.00
10a Kordell Stewart	20.00
10b Jerome Bettis	10.00
11a Jeff Blake	10.00
11b Carl Pickens	5.00
12a Lawrence Phillips	5.00
12b Isaac Bruce	10.00

1997 Donruss Preferred Cut To The Chase

Cut to the Chase paralleled the full 150-card set from Donruss Preferred. The base set was fractured into different colors corresponding to the base set and was also die-cut around the perimeter. Cut to the Chase bronze cards are one per seven packs, silvers are one per 63, golds are one per 189 and platinums are one per 756.

	MT
Complete Set (150):	2500.
Complete Bronze (80):	300.00
Bronze Stars:	4x-8x
Bronze Rookies:	2x-4x
Complete Silver (40):	500.00
Silver Stars:	2x-4x
Silver Rookies:	1x-2x
Complete Gold (20):	600.00
Gold Cards:	1x-2x
Complete Platinum (10):	1100.
Platinum Cards:	2x-3x

1997 Donruss Preferred Precious Metals

Precious Metals was a 15-card partial parallel set that was printed on actual silver, gold or platinum corresponding to which color subset the base card was from. Only 100 individually numbered Precious Metals sets were produced.

	MT
Complete Set (15):	4000.
Common Player:	100.00
1 Drew Bledsoe	250.00
2 Curtis Martin	225.00
3 Troy Aikman	250.00
4 Eddie George	300.00
5 Warrick Dunn	300.00
6 Brett Favre	500.00
7 John Elway	200.00
8 Barry Sanders	350.00
9 Emmitt Smith	400.00
10 Terrell Davis	250.00
11 Mark Brunell	250.00
12 Jerry Rice	250.00
13 Dan Marino	400.00
14 Terry Glenn	125.00
15 Tiki Barber	100.00

1997 Donruss Preferred Staremasters

These horizontal cards were printed on all-foil card stock with holographic foil stamping. Card fronts featured two close-up photos of the player, with one in full color and the other within the foil background. There were 1,500 sequentially numbered sets of Staremaster produced.

	MT
Complete Set (24):	750.00
Common Player:	6.00
Minor Stars:	12.00
1 Tim Brown	6.00
2 Mark Brunell	40.00
3 Kerry Collins	30.00
4 Brett Favre	80.00
5 Eddie George	60.00
6 Terry Glenn	25.00
7 Dan Marino	70.00
8 Curtis Martin	30.00
9 Jerry Rice	40.00
10 Barry Sanders	50.00
11 Deion Sanders	20.00
12 Emmitt Smith	70.00
13 Drew Bledsoe	40.00
14 Troy Aikman	40.00
15 Tiki Barber	12.00
16 Terrell Davis	40.00
17 Karim Abdul-Jabbar	12.00
18 Warrick Dunn	40.00
19 John Elway	30.00
20 Yatil Green	12.00
21 Ike Hilliard	12.00
22 Kordell Stewart	40.00
23 Ricky Watters	6.00
24 Steve Young	30.00

1997 Studio

1997 Studio Football is a special Quarterback Club edition. The 36-card base set features the NFL Quarterback Club stars on 8x10 cards. Each player is captured in full-color portrait photography. The base set features 24 Studio Portraits and 12 Class of Distinction cards. Class of Distinction highlights 12 of the stars in an action shot. The parallel sets include Silver Portrait Proof (individually numbered to 4,000) and Gold Portrait Proof (numbered to 1,000). The insert sets were Red Zone Masterpieces and Stained Glass Stars.

	MT
Complete Set (36):	50.00
Common Player:	.50
Minor Stars:	1.00
Silver Proof Cards:	2x-4x
Gold Proof Cards:	5x-10x
Wax Box:	55.00
1 Troy Aikman	3.00
2 Tony Banks	1.00
3 Jeff Blake	1.00
4 Drew Bledsoe	3.00
5 Mark Brunell	3.00
6 Kerry Collins	1.00
7 Trent Dilfer	1.00
8 John Elway	3.00
9 Brett Favre	6.00
10 Gus Frerotte	.50
11 Jeff George	.50
12 Neil O'Donnell	.50
13 Jim Harbaugh	.50
14 Michael Irvin	1.00
15 Dan Marino	5.00
16 Steve McNair	2.00
17 Rick Mirer	.50
18 Jerry Rice	3.00
19 Barry Sanders	3.00
20 Junior Seau	.50
21 Heath Shuler	.50
22 Emmitt Smith	5.00
23 Kordell Stewart	3.00
24 Steve Young	2.00
25 Troy Aikman (Class of Distinction)	1.50
26 Drew Bledsoe (Class of Distinction)	1.50
27 Mark Brunell (Class of Distinction)	1.50
28 Kerry Collins (Class of Distinction)	1.00
29 John Elway (Class of Distinction)	1.00
30 Brett Favre (Class of Distinction)	3.00
31 Dan Marino (Class of Distinction)	2.50
32 Jerry Rice (Class of Distinction)	1.50
33 Barry Sanders (Class of Distinction)	2.00
34 Emmitt Smith (Class of Distinction)	2.50
35 Kordell Stewart (Class of Distinction)	1.50
36 Steve Young (Class of Distinction)	1.00

1997 Studio Red Zone Masterpiece

Red Zone Masterpieces features the 24 players in the base set on a canvas material card. Each card is individually numbered to 3,500.

	MT
Complete Set (24):	300.00
Common Player:	5.00
Minor Stars:	10.00
1 Troy Aikman	20.00
2 Tony Banks	10.00
3 Jeff Blake	10.00
4 Drew Bledsoe	20.00
5 Mark Brunell	20.00
6 Kerry Collins	15.00
7 Trent Dilfer	10.00
8 John Elway	15.00
9 Brett Favre	40.00
10 Gus Frerotte	5.00
11 Jeff George	5.00
12 Elvis Grbac	5.00
13 Neil O'Donnell	5.00
14 Michael Irvin	10.00
15 Dan Marino	35.00
16 Steve McNair	15.00
17 Rick Mirer	5.00
18 Jerry Rice	20.00
19 Barry Sanders	25.00
20 Warren Moon	5.00
21 Heath Shuler	5.00
22 Emmitt Smith	35.00
23 Kordell Stewart	20.00
24 Steve Young	15.00

1997 Studio Stained Glass Stars

This 24-card insert features the QB Club stars on a die-cut plastic 8x10 card. Multi-color ink is used to give the appearance of stained glass. Stained Glass Stars are numbered to 1,000.

	MT
Complete Set (24):	650.00
Common Player:	10.00
Minor Stars:	20.00
1 Troy Aikman	40.00
2 Tony Banks	20.00
3 Jeff Blake	20.00
4 Drew Bledsoe	40.00
5 Mark Brunell	40.00
6 Kerry Collins	20.00
7 Trent Dilfer	20.00
8 John Elway	25.00
9 Brett Favre	100.00
10 Gus Frerotte	10.00
11 Jeff George	10.00
12 Elvis Grbac	10.00
13 Jim Harbaugh	10.00
14 Michael Irvin	20.00
15 Dan Marino	80.00
16 Steve McNair	30.00
17 Rick Mirer	10.00
18 Jerry Rice	40.00
19 Barry Sanders	60.00
20 Junior Seau	10.00
21 Vinny Testaverde	10.00
22 Emmitt Smith	80.00
23 Kordell Stewart	20.00
24 Steve Young	25.00

1999 Donruss

This was a 200-card set that included 50 different rookie cards that were inserted 1:4 packs. Parallel sets included Career Stat Line and Season Stat Line. Other insert sets included: All-Time Gridiron Kings, All-Time Gridiron Kings Autographs, Elite Inserts, Executive Producers, Fan Club, Gridiron Kings, Private Signings, Rated Rookies, Rookie Gridiron Kings, Zoning Commission and Zoning Commission Red. Packs contained seven cards.

	MT
Complete Set (200):	180.00
Common Player:	.15
Minor Stars:	.30
Common Rookie:	1.50
Inserted 1:4	
Wax Box:	55.00
1 Jake Plummer	.75
2 Rob Moore	.30
3 Adrian Murrell	.15
4 Frank Sanders	.15
5 Jamal Anderson	.50
6 Tim Dwight	.15
7 Terance Mathis	.15
8 Chris Chandler	.30
9 Byron Hanspard	.15
10 Priest Holmes	.50
11 Jermaine Lewis	.15
12 Errict Rhett	.15
13 Doug Flutie	.75
14 Eric Moulds	.50
15 Antowain Smith	.50
16 Thurman Thomas	.30
17 Andre Reed	.30
18 Bruce Smith	.15
19 Tim Biakabutuka	.30
20 Rae Carruth	.15
21 Muhsin Muhammad	.30
22 Curtis Enis	.50
23 Curtis Conway	.30
24 Bobby Engram	.15
25 Corey Dillon	.50
26 Carl Pickens	.30
27 Jeff Blake	.30
28 Darnay Scott	.15
29 Ty Detmer	.15
30 Leslie Shepherd	.15

31	Emmitt Smith	1.50
32	Troy Aikman	1.00
33	Michael Irvin	.30
34	Deion Sanders	.50
35	Raghib Ismail	.15
36	John Elway	1.50
37	Terrell Davis	1.50
38	Ed McCaffrey	.50
39	Shannon Sharpe	.30
40	Rod Smith	.30
41	Bubby Brister	.30
42	Brian Griese	1.00
43	Barry Sanders	2.00
44	Charlie Batch	.75
45	Herman Moore	.50
46	Germane Crowell	.30
47	Johnnie Morton	.15
48	Ron Rivers	.15
49	Brett Favre	2.00
50	Antonio Freeman	.50
51	Dorsey Levens	.50
52	Mark Chmura	.30
53	Corey Bradford	.30
54	Bill Schroeder	.30
55	Peyton Manning	1.50
56	Marvin Harrison	.50
57	E.G. Green	.15
58	Fred Taylor	1.00
59	Mark Brunell	.75
60	Tavian Banks	.30
61	Jimmy Smith	.50
62	Keenan McCardell	.30
63	Warren Moon	.30
64	Derrick Alexander	.15
65	Bam Morris	.15
66	Elvis Grbac	.30
67	Andre Rison	.30
68	Dan Marino	1.50
69	Karim Abdul	.30
70	O.J. McDuffie	.30
71	Tony Martin	.15
72	Randy Moss	2.00
73	Cris Carter	.50
74	Randall Cunningham	.50
75	Robert Smith	.50
76	Jeff George	.30
77	Jake Reed	.30
78	Terry Allen	.30
79	Drew Bledsoe	.75
80	Terry Glenn	.50
81	Ben Coates	.30
82	Tony Simmons	.15
83	Cameron Cleeland	.30
84	Eddie Kennison	.15
85	Kerry Collins	.30
86	Ike Hilliard	.30
87	Gary Brown	.15
88	Joe Jurevicius	.15
89	Kent Graham	.15
90	Wayne Chrebet	.50
91	Keyshawn Johnson	.50
92	Curtis Martin	.50
93	Vinny Testaverde	.30
94	Tim Brown	.30
95	Napoleon Kaufman	.50
96	Charles Woodson	.30
97	Tyrone Wheatley	.30
98	Rich Gannon	.30
99	Charles Johnson	.15
100	Duce Staley	.50
101	Kordell Stewart	.50
102	Jerome Bettis	.50
103	Hines Ward	.30
104	Ryan Leaf	.30
105	Natrone Means	.30
106	Jim Harbaugh	.30
107	Junior Seau	.30
108	Mikhael Ricks	.15
109	Jerry Rice	1.00
110	Steve Young	.75
111	Garrison Hearst	.50
112	Terrell Owens	.75
113	Lawrence Phillips	.30
114	J.J. Stokes	.30
115	Sean Dawkins	.15
116	Derrick Mayes	.30
117	Joey Galloway	.50
118	Jon Kitna	.50
119	Ahman Green	.30
120	Ricky Watters	.30
121	Isaac Bruce	.50
122	Marshall Faulk	.50
123	Az-Zahir Hakim	.30
124	Warrick Dunn	.50
125	Mike Alstott	.50
126	Trent Dilfer	.30
127	Reidel Anthony	.30
128	Jacquez Green	.30
129	Warren Sapp	.15
130	Eddie George	.60
131	Steve McNair	.60
132	Kevin Dyson	.30
133	Yancey Thigpen	.30
134	Frank Wycheck	.15
135	Stephen Davis	.30
136	Brad Johnson	.50
137	Skip Hicks	.30
138	Michael Westbrook	.30
139	Darrell Green	.15
140	Albert Connell	.15
141	*Tim Couch*	15.00
142	*Donovan McNabb*	8.00
143	*Akili Smith*	8.00
144	*Edgerrin James*	25.00
145	*Ricky Williams*	15.00
146	*Torry Holt*	5.00
147	*Champ Bailey*	3.00

148	*David Boston*	5.00
149	*Andy Katzenmoyer*	2.00
150	*Chris McAlister*	2.00
151	*Daunte Culpepper*	8.00
152	*Cade McNown*	8.00
153	*Troy Edwards*	5.00
154	*Kevin Johnson*	5.00
155	*James Johnson*	3.00
156	*Rob Konrad*	2.00
157	*Jim Kleinsasser*	2.00
158	*Kevin Faulk*	3.00
159	*Joe Montgomery*	2.00
160	*Shaun King*	8.00
161	*Peerless Price*	3.50
162	*Michael Cloud*	2.00
163	*Jermaine Fazande*	3.00
164	*D'Wayne Bates*	2.00
165	*Brock Huard*	3.00
166	*Marty Booker*	2.00
167	*Karsten Bailey*	2.00
168	*Shawn Bryson*	1.50
169	*Jeff Paulk*	2.00
170	*Travis McGriff*	2.00
171	*Amos Zereoue*	3.00
172	*Craig Yeast*	1.50
173	*Joe Germaine*	2.00
174	*Dameane Douglas*	1.50
175	*Brandon Stokley*	1.50
176	*Larry Parker*	1.50
177	*Joel Makovicka*	1.50
178	*Wane McGarity*	1.50
179	*Na Brown*	1.50
180	*Cecil Collins*	5.00
181	*Nick Williams*	1.50
182	*Charlie Rogers*	1.50
183	*Darrin Chiaverini*	2.00
184	*Terry Jackson*	2.00
185	*De'Mond Parker*	3.00
186	*Sedrick Irvin*	3.00
187	*Mar Tay Jenkins*	2.00
188	*Kurt Warner*	40.00
189	*Michael Bishop*	3.00
190	*Sean Bennett*	2.00
191	Jamal Anderson CL	.30
192	Eric Moulds CL	.30
193	Terrell Davis CL	.75
194	John Elway CL	.75
195	Barry Sanders CL	1.00
196	Peyton Manning CL	.75
197	Fred Taylor CL	.50
198	Dan Marino CL	.75
199	Randy Moss CL	1.00
200	Terrell Owens CL	.30

1999 Donruss All-Time Gridiron Kings

This insert included five NFL legends. Each card was sequentially numbered to 1,000 and accented with bronze foil. The first 500 of each card was printed on canvas and was autographed.

		MT
Complete Set (5):		70.00
Common Player:		10.00
Production 1,000 Sets		
1	Bart Starr	20.00
2	Johnny Unitas	20.00
3	Earl Campbell	10.00
4	Walter Payton	30.00
5	Jim Brown	25.00

1999 Donruss All-Time Gridiron Kings Autographs

This was a parallel to the All-Time Gridiron Kings insert. Each of these singles was printed on canvas and was autographed. Each single was sequentially numbered to 500.

		MT
Complete Set (5):		600.00
Common Player:		60.00
Production 500 Sets		
1	Bart Starr	125.00
2	Johnny Unitas	125.00
3	Earl Campbell	60.00
4	Walter Payton	250.00
5	Jim Brown	150.00

1999 Donruss Elite Inserts

This 20-card insert set included the NFL's cream of the crop and featured them on foil board with micro-etching and sil-

ver foil stamping. Each card was sequentially numbered to 2,500.

		MT
Complete Set (20):		85.00
Common Player:		2.00
Production 2,500 Sets		
1	Cris Carter	2.00
2	Jerry Rice	6.00
3	Mark Brunell	4.00
4	Brett Favre	10.00
5	Keyshawn Johnson	2.00
6	Eddie George	3.00
7	John Elway	8.00
8	Troy Aikman	6.00
9	Marshall Faulk	2.00
10	Antonio Freeman	2.00
11	Drew Bledsoe	4.00
12	Steve Young	3.00
13	Dan Marino	8.00
14	Emmitt Smith	8.00
15	Fred Taylor	6.00
16	Jake Plummer	4.00
17	Terrell Davis	8.00
18	Peyton Manning	8.00
19	Randy Moss	10.00
20	Barry Sanders	10.00

1999 Donruss Executive Producers

This 45-card insert set included the top producers at quarterback, running back and wide receiver and highlighted each position on a different colored, holographic foil board. Each card was sequentially numbered to the player's specific 1998 stat.

		MT
Complete Set (45):		125.00
Common Player:		2.00
1	Dan Marino 3497	5.00
2	John Elway 2806	7.00
3	Kordell Stewart 2560	2.00
4	Troy Aikman 2330	5.00
5	Steve Young 4170	2.00
6	Doug Flutie 2711	3.00
7	Drew Bledsoe 3633	2.00
8	Jon Kitna 1177	2.00
9	Steve McNair 3228	2.00
10	Mark Brunell 2601	3.00
11	Randall Cunningham 3704	2.00
12	Jake Plummer 3737	3.00
13	Charlie Batch 2178	3.00
14	Peyton Manning 3739	5.00
15	Brett Favre 4212	6.00
16	Terrell Davis 2008	5.00
17	Fred Taylor 1223	5.00
18	Eddie George 1294	2.00
19	Corey Dillon 1130	2.00
20	Jamal Anderson 1846	2.00
21	Curtis Martin 1287	2.00
22	Dorsey Levens 378	3.00
23	Karim Abdul 960	2.00
24	Curtis Enis 497	3.00
25	Mike Alstott 846	2.00
26	Natrone Means 883	2.00
27	Jerome Bettis 1185	2.00
28	Warrick Dunn 1026	2.00
29	Emmitt Smith 1332	6.00
30	Barry Sanders 1491	10.00
31	Jerry Rice 1157	6.00
32	Randy Moss 1313	10.00
33	Keyshawn Johnson 1131	2.00
34	Isaac Bruce 457	3.00
35	Antonio Freeman 1424	2.00
36	Eric Moulds 1368	2.00
37	Tim Dwight 94	12.00
38	Herman Moore 983	2.00
39	Tim Brown 1012	2.00
40	Marshall Faulk 1319	2.00
41	Terry Glenn 792	2.00
42	Joey Galloway 1047	2.00
43	Carl Pickens 1023	2.00
44	Terrell Owens 1097	2.00
45	Cris Carter 1011	2.00

1999 Donruss Fan Club

This 20-card insert set included players who were fan favorites. Each single was sequentially numbered to 5,000.

		MT
Complete Set (20):		60.00
Common Player:		1.00
Minor Stars:		2.00
Production 5,000 Sets		
1	Troy Aikman	5.00
2	Ricky Williams	10.00
3	Jerry Rice	5.00
4	Brett Favre	10.00
5	Terrell Davis	7.00
6	Doug Flutie	3.00
7	John Elway	7.00
8	Steve Young	3.00
9	Steve McNair	2.00
10	Kordell Stewart	2.00
11	Drew Bledsoe	3.00
12	Donovan McNabb	5.00
13	Dan Marino	7.00
14	Cade McNown	5.00
15	Vinny Testaverde	1.00
16	Jake Plummer	3.00
17	Randall Cunningham	2.00
18	Peyton Manning	7.00
19	Keyshawn Johnson	2.00
20	Barry Sanders	10.00

1999 Donruss Gridiron Kings

This 20-card insert set showcased artwork of each player. Singles were sequentially numbered to 5,000. A parallel Canvas version was also made with each of those singles numbered to 500.

		MT
Complete Set (20):		100.00
Common Player:		3.00
Production 5,000 Sets		
1	Randy Moss	12.00
2	Fred Taylor	6.00
3	Doug Flutie	5.00
4	Brett Favre	12.00
5	Mark Brunell	5.00
6	Troy Aikman	6.00
7	John Elway	8.00
8	Jerry Rice	6.00
9	Drew Bledsoe	5.00
10	Eddie George	3.00
11	Randall Cunningham	3.00
12	Emmitt Smith	8.00
13	Dan Marino	8.00
14	Jake Plummer	5.00
15	Jamal Anderson	3.00
16	Terrell Davis	8.00
17	Steve Young	5.00
18	Peyton Manning	8.00
19	Jerome Bettis	3.00
20	Barry Sanders	12.00

A player's name in *italic type* indicates a rookie card.

1999 Donruss Gridiron Kings Canvas

This 20-card insert set was a parallel to the Gridiron Kings insert. Each of these singles was printed on canvas and was sequentially numbered to 500.

	MT
Canvas Cards:	3x
Production 500 Sets	

1999 Donruss Private Signings

This 32-card insert set included autographs from some of the top players in the NFL. More than 10,000 autographs were randomly inserted into packs. The print runs were between 50 and 600, depending on the player.

		MT
Complete Set (32):		1200.
Common Player:		12.50
Minor Stars:		25.00
1	Terrell Davis	75.00
2	Cris Carter	30.00
3	Thurman Thomas	25.00
4	Derrick Thomas	12.50
5	Priest Holmes	12.50
6	Corey Dillon	25.00
7	Antonio Freeman	25.00
8	Duce Staley	12.50
9	Jerome Bettis	12.50
10	Natrone Means	12.50
11	Mike Alstott	30.00
12	Eddie George	45.00
13	Terrell Owens	25.00
14	Curtis Enis	25.00
15	Wesley Walls	12.50
16	Neil Smith	12.50
17	Doug Flutie	45.00
18	Tim Brown	25.00
19	Randy Moss	150.00
20	Ricky Williams	100.00
21	Skip Hicks	12.50
22	Isaac Bruce	30.00
23	Barry Sanders	125.00
24	Fred Taylor	50.00
25	Steve Young	50.00
26	Vinny Testaverde	12.50
27	Randall Cunningham	25.00
28	Jake Plummer	50.00
29	Jerry Rice	100.00
30	Eric Moulds	25.00
31	Kordell Stewart	30.00
32	Brian Griese	35.00

1999 Donruss Rated Rookies

This 20-card insert set included rookies from 1999 and featured them on silver foil board. Each was sequentially numbered to 5,000. A parallel Medalist version was made in

which the first 250 singles were sequentially numbered. Each was printed with gold foil instead of silver.

		MT
Complete Set (20):		75.00
Common Player:		2.00
Production 5,000 Sets		
1	Tim Couch	12.00
2	Peerless Price	4.00
3	Ricky Williams	10.00
4	Torry Holt	5.00
5	Champ Bailey	3.00
6	Rob Konrad	2.00
7	Donovan McNabb	8.00
8	Edgerrin James	20.00
9	David Boston	5.00
10	Akili Smith	8.00
11	Cecil Collins	4.00
12	Troy Edwards	5.00
13	Daunte Culpepper	8.00
14	Kevin Faulk	3.00
15	Kevin Johnson	5.00
16	Cade McNown	8.00
17	Shaun King	8.00
18	Brock Huard	3.00
19	James Johnson	3.00
20	Sedrick Irvin	3.00

1999 Donruss Rated Rookies Medalists

This was a 20-card insert set that paralleled the Rated Rookies set. Each of these singles was sequentially numbered to 250 and had gold foil stamping, rather than the silver foil on the regular cards.

	MT
Medalists Cards:	3x
Production 250 Sets	

1999 Donruss Rookie Gridiron Kings

This 10-card insert set included the top rookies from 1999. Each was sequentially numbered to 5,000 and included gold foil on the front of each card. The first 500 singles were printed on canvas stock.

		MT
Complete Set (10):		65.00
Common Player:		2.50
Production 5,000 Sets		
1	Ricky Williams	10.00
2	Donovan McNabb	8.00
3	Daunte Culpepper	8.00
4	Edgerrin James	18.00
5	David Boston	5.00
6	Champ Bailey	2.50
7	Torry Holt	5.00
8	Cade McNown	8.00
9	Akili Smith	8.00
10	Tim Couch	12.00

1999 Donruss Rookie Gridiron Kings Canvas

This was a 10-card insert set that paralleled the Rookie Gridiron Kings insert. Each of these singles was printed on canvas stock and was sequentially numbered to 500.

	MT
Canvas Cards:	3x
Production 500 Sets	

1999 Donruss Zoning Commission

This 25-card insert set included star players who patrol the end zone. Each die-cut single was sequentially numbered to 1,000. A parallel Red version was made in which each single was sequentially numbered to the player's 1998 touchdown total.

		MT
Complete Set (25):		70.00
Common Player:		2.00
Production 1,000 Sets		
1	Eric Moulds	2.00
2	Steve Young	3.00
3	Brad Johnson	2.00
4	Peyton Manning	7.00
5	Randy Moss	10.00
6	Brett Favre	10.00
7	Emmitt Smith	7.00
8	Mark Brunell	5.00
9	Keyshawn Johnson	2.00
10	Dan Marino	7.00
11	Eddie George	3.00
12	Drew Bledsoe	3.00
13	Terrell Davis	7.00
14	Terrell Owens	2.00
15	Barry Sanders	10.00
16	Curtis Martin	2.00
17	John Elway	7.00
18	Jake Plummer	3.00
19	Jerry Rice	5.00
20	Fred Taylor	5.00
21	Antonio Freeman	2.00
22	Marshall Faulk	2.00
23	Dorsey Levens	2.00
24	Steve McNair	2.00
25	Cris Carter	2.00

1999 Donruss Elite

This is a 200-card base set that includes 40 rookies. Cards #1-100 are printed on 20 point foil board with a foil stamped logo in red and full UV coating on both sides. They were inserted four-per-pack. Cards #101-200 are also printed on 20 point foil board with full UV coating and platinum blue tint on each side. They are found one-per-pack. Inserts include Common Threads, Field of Vision, Passing the Torch, Power Formulas and Primary Colors.

		MT
Complete Set (200):		300.00
Common Player (1-100):		.25
Minor Stars (1-100):		.50
Common Player (101-200):		.50
Minor Stars (101-200):		1.00
Common Rookie (161-200):		3.00
#101-200 Inserted 1:1		
Wax Box:		125.00
1	Warren Moon	.50
2	Terry Allen	.50
3	Jeff George	.50
4	Brett Favre	3.00
5	Rob Moore	.50
6	Bubby Brister	.25
7	John Elway	2.50
8	Troy Aikman	1.50
9	Steve McNair	.75
10	Charlie Batch	1.00
11	Elvis Grbac	.25
12	Trent Dilfer	.50
13	Kerry Collins	.50
14	Neil O'Donnell	.25
15	Tony Simmons	.50
16	Ryan Leaf	1.00
17	Bobby Hoying	.25
18	Marvin Harrison	.50
19	Keyshawn Johnson	.75
20	Cris Carter	.75
21	Deion Sanders	.75
22	Emmitt Smith	2.50
23	Antowain Smith	.75
24	Terry Fair	.25
25	Robert Holcombe	.50
26	Napoleon Kaufman	.75
27	Eddie George	1.00
28	Corey Dillon	.75
29	Adrian Murrell	.25
30	Charles Way	.25
31	Amp Lee	.25
32	Ricky Watters	.50
33	Gary Brown	.25
34	Thurman Thomas	.50
35	Patrick Johnson	.25
36	Jerome Bettis	.75
37	Muhsin Muhammad	.25
38	Kimble Anders	.25
39	Curtis Enis	.75
40	Mike Alstott	.75
41	Charles Johnson	.25
42	Chris Warren	.25
43	Tony Banks	.50
44	Leroy Hoard	.25
45	Chris Fuamatu-Ma'afala	.25
46	Michael Irvin	.75
47	Robert Edwards	.75
48	Hines Ward	.50
49	Trent Green	.50
50	Eric Zeier	.25
51	Sean Dawkins	.25
52	Yancey Thigpen	.50
53	Jacquez Green	.50
54	Zach Thomas	.50
55	Junior Seau	.50
56	Darnay Scott	.25
57	Kent Graham	.25
58	O.J. Santiago	.25
59	Tony Gonzalez	.50
60	Ty Detmer	.25
61	Albert Connell	.25
62	James Jett	.25
63	Bert Emanuel	.25
64	Derrick Alexander	.25
65	Wesley Walls	.25
66	Jake Reed	.25
67	Randall Cunningham	.75
68	Leslie Shepherd	.25
69	Mark Chmura	.25
70	Bobby Engram	.25
71	Rickey Dudley	.25
72	Darick Holmes	.25
73	Andre Reed	.50
74	Az-Zahir Hakim	.50
75	Cameron Cleeland	.25
76	Lamar Thomas	.25
77	Oronde Gadsden	.50
78	Ben Coates	.50
79	Bruce Smith	.25
80	Jerry Rice	1.50
81	Tim Brown	.50
82	Michael Westbrook	.50
83	J.J. Stokes	.50
84	Shannon Sharpe	.50
85	Riedel Anthony	.25
86	Antonio Freeman	.75
87	Keenan McCardell	.50
88	Terry Glenn	.75
89	Andre Rison	.50
90	Neil Smith	.25
91	Terrance Mathis	.25
92	Raghib Ismail	.25
93	Bam Morris	.25
94	Ike Hilliard	.25
95	Eddie Kennison	.25
96	Tavian Banks	.50
97	Yatil Green	.25
98	Frank Wycheck	.25
99	Warren Sapp	.25
100	Germane Crowell	1.00
101	Curtis Martin	2.00
102	John Avery	1.00
103	Eric Moulds	2.00
104	Randy Moss	12.00
105	Terrell Owens	2.00
106	Vinny Testaverde	1.00
107	Doug Flutie	2.50
108	Mark Brunell	3.00
109	Isaac Bruce	1.00
110	Kordell Stewart	2.50
111	Drew Bledsoe	3.00
112	Chris Chandler	.50
113	Dan Marino	6.00
114	Brian Griese	4.00
115	Carl Pickens	.50
116	Jake Plummer	4.00
117	Natrone Means	1.00
118	Peyton Manning	8.00
119	Garrison Hearst	1.00
120	Barry Sanders	8.00
121	Steve Young	3.00
122	Rashaan Shehee	.50
123	Ed McCaffrey	1.50
124	Charles Woodson	2.00
125	Dorsey Levens	1.50
126	Robert Smith	1.50
127	Greg Hill	.50
128	Fred Taylor	5.00
129	Marcus Nash	1.00
130	Terrell Davis	6.00
131	Ahman Green	1.00
132	Jamal Anderson	2.00
133	Karim Abdul	1.00
134	Jermaine Lewis	.50
135	Jerome Pathon	.50
136	Brad Johnson	1.00
137	Herman Moore	1.50
138	Tim Dwight	2.00
139	Johnnie Morton	.50
140	Marshall Faulk	2.00
141	Frank Sanders	1.00
142	Kevin Dyson	1.00
143	Curtis Conway	1.00
144	Derrick Mayes	.50
145	O.J. McDuffie	1.00
146	Joe Jurevicius	.50
147	Jon Kitna	2.00
148	Joey Galloway	1.50
149	Jimmy Smith	1.00
150	Skip Hicks	1.00
151	Rod Smith	1.00
152	Duce Staley	.50
153	James O. Stewart	.50
154	Rob Johnson	.50
155	Mikhael Ricks	.50
156	Wayne Chrebet	1.50
157	Robert Brooks	.50
158	Tim Biakabutuka	.50
159	Priest Holmes	2.00
160	Warrick Dunn	2.00
161	Champ Bailey	10.00
162	D'Wayne Bates	3.00
163	Michael Bishop	8.00
164	David Boston	10.00
165	Na Brown	3.00
166	Chris Claiborne	5.00
167	Joe Montgomery	3.00
168	Mike Cloud	3.00
169	Travis McGriff	3.00
170	Tim Couch	40.00
171	Daunte Culpepper	15.00
172	Autry Denson	5.00
173	Jermaine Fazande	3.00
174	Troy Edwards	10.00
175	Kevin Faulk	10.00
176	Dee Miller	3.00
177	Brock Huard	6.00
178	Torry Holt	10.00
179	Sedrick Irvin	5.00
180	Edgerrin James	45.00
181	Joe Germaine	6.00
182	James Johnson	10.00
183	Kevin Johnson	10.00
184	Andy Katzenmoyer	5.00
185	Jevon Kearse	10.00
186	Shaun King	15.00
187	Rob Konrad	3.00
188	Jim Kleinsasser	3.00
189	Chris McAlister	4.00
190	Donovan McNabb	20.00
191	Cade McNown	15.00
192	De'Mond Parker	3.00
193	Craig Yeast	3.00
194	Shawn Bryson	3.00
195	Peerless Price	8.00
196	Darnell McDonald	3.00
197	Akili Smith	20.00
198	Tai Streets	5.00
199	Ricky Williams	40.00
200	Amos Zereoue	6.00

1999 Donruss Elite Common Threads

Each card is printed on conventional board with foil and game-used jersey swatches. Twelve players are featured with six cards with one player on it and the other six are combo cards. Each is sequentially numbered to 150.

		MT
Complete Set (18):		3000.00
Common Player:		100.00
Production 150 Sets		
1	Randy Moss, Randall Cunningham	400.00
2	Randy Moss	350.00
3	Randall Cunningham	125.00
4	John Elway, Terrell Davis	350.00
5	John Elway	275.00
6	Terrell Davis	225.00
7	Jerry Rice, Steve Young	300.00
8	Jerry Rice	250.00
9	Steve Young	150.00
10	Mark Brunell, Fred Taylor	175.00
11	Mark Brunell	125.00
12	Fred Taylor	150.00
13	Kordell Stewart, Jerome Bettis	150.00
14	Kordell Stewart	125.00
15	Jerome Bettis	100.00
16	Dan Marino, Karim Abdul	300.00
17	Dan Marino	300.00
18	Karim Abdul	100.00

1999 Donruss Elite Field of Vision

Each card is printed on clear plastic with holo-foil stamping. Twelve players are featured on three seperate cards, with each representing a section of the playing field (left-middle-right). Each card is then sequentially numbered to the yards the player gained in that area of the field in 1998.

			MT
Common Player:			5.00
Production #'d to a Season Stat			
1A	Dan Marino	1712	12.00
1B	Dan Marino	834	20.00
1C	Dan Marino	951	20.00
2A	Emmitt Smith	640	20.00
2B	Emmitt Smith	202	35.00
2C	Emmitt Smith	490	20.00
3A	Jake Plummer	1165	10.00
3B	Jake Plummer	624	15.00
3C	Jake Plummer	1948	5.00
4A	Brett Favre	1408	14.00
4B	Brett Favre	983	25.00
4C	Brett Favre	1820	12.00
5A	Fred Taylor	486	10.00
5B	Fred Taylor	400	12.00
5C	Fred Taylor	337	15.00
6A	Drew Bledsoe	1355	5.00
6B	Drew Bledsoe	689	10.00
6C	Drew Bledsoe	1589	5.00
7A	Terrell Davis	1283	12.00
7B	Terrell Davis	306	25.00
7C	Terrell Davis	419	20.00
8A	Jerry Rice	611	10.00
8B	Jerry Rice	234	25.00
8C	Jerry Rice	312	20.00
9A	Randy Moss	639	30.00
9B	Randy Moss	16	350.00
9C	Randy Moss	658	30.00
10A	John Elway	1320	12.00
10B	John Elway	615	25.00
10C	John Elway	871	20.00
11A	Peyton Manning	1141	15.00
11B	Peyton Manning	1020	15.00
11C	Peyton Manning	1578	12.00
12A	Barry Sanders	556	20.00
12B	Barry Sanders	373	30.00
12C	Barry Sanders	562	20.00

1999 Donruss Elite Field of Vision Die Cuts

This is similar to the Field of Vision cards except each card is die-cut and sequentially numbered to the number of attempts, receptions or completions of that particular player.

			MT
Common Player:			25.00
Production #'d to a Season Stat			
1A	Dan Marino	164	45.00
1B	Dan Marino	56	100.00
1C	Dan Marino	90	70.00
2A	Emmitt Smith	158	30.00
2B	Emmitt Smith	64	75.00
2C	Emmitt Smith	97	45.00
3A	Jake Plummer	89	35.00
3B	Jake Plummer	44	60.00
3C	Jake Plummer	191	25.00
4A	Brett Favre	112	60.00
4B	Brett Favre	67	100.00
4C	Brett Favre	168	40.00
5A	Fred Taylor	103	35.00
5B	Fred Taylor	79	45.00
5C	Fred Taylor	82	45.00
6A	Drew Bledsoe	90	30.00
6B	Drew Bledsoe	48	45.00
6C	Drew Bledsoe	125	45.00
7A	Terrell Davis	217	35.00
7B	Terrell Davis	66	70.00
7C	Terrell Davis	109	50.00
8A	Jerry Rice	50	70.00
8B	Jerry Rice	11	325.00
8C	Jerry Rice	21	200.00
9A	Randy Moss	34	225.00
9B	Randy Moss	2	
9C	Randy Moss	33	225.00
10A	John Elway	98	50.00
10B	John Elway	35	150.00
10C	John Elway	75	75.00
11A	Peyton Manning	110	45.00
11B	Peyton Manning	79	60.00
11C	Peyton Manning	137	35.00
12A	Barry Sanders	137	45.00
12B	Barry Sanders	83	85.00
12C	Barry Sanders	123	45.00

1999 Donruss Elite Passing the Torch

Each card is printed with holo-foil board on the front and back with UV coating on both sides and sequentially numbered to 1,500. Twelve players were used with each having an individual card as well as six cards pairing two players together. The first 100 of each card are autographed.

		MT
Complete Set (18):		175.00
Common Player:		5.00
Production 1,500 Sets		
1	Johnny Unitas, Peyton Manning	15.00
2	Johnny Unitas	8.00
3	Peyton Manning	12.00
4	Walter Payton, Barry Sanders	20.00
5	Walter Payton	10.00
6	Barry Sanders	15.00
7	Earl Campbell, Ricky Williams	20.00
8	Earl Campbell	5.00
9	Ricky Williams	25.00
10	Jim Brown, Terrell Davis	15.00
11	Jim Brown	10.00
12	Terrell Davis	15.00
13	Emmitt Smith, Fred Taylor	15.00
14	Emmitt Smith	10.00
15	Fred Taylor	10.00
16	Cris Carter, Randy Moss	20.00
17	Cris Carter	5.00
18	Randy Moss	20.00

1999 Donruss Elite Passing the Torch Autographs

This is the same as the regular Passing the Torch cards except for each one of these are autographed. They are each sequentially numbered to 100.

		MT
Complete Set (18):		5000.00
Common Player:		85.00
Production 100 Sets		
1	Johnny Unitas, Peyton Manning	400.00
2	Johnny Unitas	150.00
3	Peyton Manning	200.00
4	Walter Payton, Barry Sanders	1000.
5	Walter Payton	275.00
6	Barry Sanders	400.00
7	Earl Campbell, Ricky Williams	350.00
8	Earl Campbell	100.00
9	Ricky Williams	250.00
10	Jim Brown, Terrell Davis	400.00
11	Jim Brown	200.00
12	Terrell Davis	250.00
13	Emmitt Smith, Fred Taylor	350.00
14	Emmitt Smith	300.00
15	Fred Taylor	125.00
16	Cris Carter, Randy Moss	325.00
17	Cris Carter	85.00
18	Randy Moss	325.00

1999 Donruss Elite Power Formulas

This 30-card set spotlights the NFL's most powerful players and the statistical formulas behind their greatness. Each is sequentially numbered to 3,500.

		MT
Complete Set (30):		120.00
Common Player:		1.50
Minor Stars:		4.00
Production 3,500 Sets		
1	Randy Moss	15.00
2	Terrell Davis	10.00
3	Brett Favre	12.00
4	Dan Marino	8.00
5	Barry Sanders	12.00
6	Peyton Manning	8.00
7	John Elway	8.00
8	Fred Taylor	6.00
9	Emmitt Smith	8.00
10	Steve Young	5.00
11	Jerry Rice	6.00
12	Jake Plummer	5.00
13	Kordell Stewart	5.00
14	Mark Brunell	5.00
15	Drew Bledsoe	5.00
16	Eddie George	5.00
17	Troy Aikman	6.00
18	Warrick Dunn	4.00
19	Keyshawn Johnson	3.00
20	Jamal Anderson	3.00
21	Randall Cunningham	
22	Doug Flutie	4.00

23 Jerome Bettis 3.00
24 Garrison Hearst 1.50
25 Curtis Martin 3.00
26 Corey Dillon 3.00
27 Antowain Smith 3.00
28 Antonio Freeman 3.00
29 Terrell Owens 3.00
30 Carl Pickens 1.50

1999 Donruss Elite Primary Colors

The 40-card set is printed on holo-foil board and is sequentially numbered to 1,875. This insert has five different parallel sets with a Blue (#'d to 950), Red (#'d to 25), Blue Die-Cut (#'d to 50), Red Die-Cut (#'d to 75) and a Yellow Die-Cut (#'d to 25) version.

	MT
Complete Set (40):	160.00
Common Yellow:	3.00
Production 1,875 Sets	
Blue Cards:	1.5x
Production 950 Sets	
Red Cards:	15x-30x
Red Rookies:	7x-14x
Production 25 Sets	
Blue Die-Cut Cards:	10x-20x
Blue Die-Cut Rookies:	5x-10x
Production 50 Sets	
Red Die-Cut Cards:	7x-14x
Red Die-Cut Rookies:	3x-6x
Production 75 Sets	
Yellow Die-Cut Cards:	15x-30x
Yellow Die-Cut Rookies:	7x-14x
Production 25 Sets	

1 Herman Moore 3.00
2 Marshall Faulk 3.00
3 Dorsey Levens 3.00
4 Napoleon Kaufman 3.00
5 Jamal Anderson 3.00
6 Edgerrin James 10.00
7 Troy Aikman 6.00
8 Cris Carter 3.00
9 Eddie George 4.00
10 Donovan McNabb 10.00
11 Drew Bledsoe 5.00
12 Daunte Culpepper 8.00
13 Mark Brunell 5.00
14 Corey Dillon 3.00
15 Kordell Stewart 3.00
16 Curtis Martin 3.00
17 Jake Plummer 5.00
18 Charlie Batch 4.00
19 Jerry Rice 6.00
20 Antonio Freeman 3.00
21 Steve Young 4.00
22 Steve McNair 3.00
23 Emmitt Smith 8.00
24 Terrell Owens 3.00
25 Fred Taylor 6.00
26 Joey Galloway 3.00
27 John Elway 8.00
28 Ryan Leaf 3.00
29 Barry Sanders 12.00
30 Ricky Williams 20.00
31 Dan Marino 8.00
32 Tim Couch 20.00
33 Brett Favre 12.00
34 Eric Moulds 3.00
35 Peyton Manning 8.00
36 Deion Sanders 3.00
37 Terrell Davis 8.00
38 Tim Brown 3.00
39 Randy Moss 15.00
40 Mike Alstott 3.00

1999 Donruss Preferred QBC

This was a 120-card set that was divided into four levels. The first 45 cards were in Bronze and cards #46-#80 were in Silver and found one-per-pack. Cards #81-#105 were in Gold and inserted 1:4 packs and cards #106-#120 were Platinum singles and found 1:8 packs.

The set featured all 44 members of the Quarterback Club. Insert sets included: Power (parallel), Autographs, Chain Reaction, Hard Hats, Materials, National Treasures, Passing Grade, Precious Metals, Staremasters and X-Ponential Power. SRP was $3.99 for four-card packs.

	MT
Complete Set (120):	250.00
Common Bronze:	.15
Minor Stars Bronze:	.30
Common Silver:	.50
Minor Stars Silver:	1.00
Inserted 1:1	
Common Gold:	1.00
Minor Stars Gold:	2.00
Inserted 1:4	
Common Platinum:	2.50
Inserted 1:8	
Wax Box:	65.00

1 Troy Aikman B 1.50
2 Tony Banks B .30
3 Jeff Blake B .30
4 Drew Bledsoe B 1.00
5 Bubby Brister B .15
6 Chris Chandler B .15
7 Kerry Collins B .30
8 Randall Cunningham B .50
9 Terrell Davis B 2.00
10 Trent Dilfer B .30
11 John Elway B 2.00
12 Boomer Esiason B .30
13 Jim Everett B .15
14 Brett Favre B 3.00
15 Doug Flutie B .75
16 Gus Frerotte B .15
17 Jeff George B .50
18 Elvis Grbac B .15
19 Jim Harbaugh B .30
20 Michael Irvin B .30
21 Brad Johnson B .50
22 Keyshawn Johnson B .50
23 Danny Kanell B .15
24 Jim Kelly B .50
25 Bernie Kosar B .15
26 Erik Kramer B .15
27 Ryan Leaf B .50
28 Peyton Manning B 2.00
29 Dan Marino B 2.00
30 Donovan McNabb B 4.00
31 Steve McNair B .50
32 Cade McNown B 4.00
33 Scott Mitchell B .15
34 Warren Moon B .30
35 Neil O'Donnell B .15
36 Jake Plummer B 1.50
37 Jerry Rice B 1.50
38 Barry Sanders B 3.00
39 Junior Seau B .30
40 Phil Simms B .30
41 Kordell Stewart B .50
42 Vinny Testaverde B .30
43 Ricky Williams B 8.00
44 Steve Young B .75
45 Dan Marino, Brett Favre, John Elway B 2.00
46 Troy Aikman S 2.50
47 Tony Banks S .50
48 Drew Bledsoe S 1.75
49 Bubby Brister S .50
50 Chris Chandler S .50
51 Kerry Collins S 1.00
52 Randall Cunningham S 1.00
53 Terrell Davis S 3.50
54 Trent Dilfer S 1.00
55 John Elway S 3.50
56 Boomer Esiason S 1.00
57 Brett Favre S 5.00
58 Doug Flutie S 1.50
59 Elvis Grbac S .50
60 Jim Harbaugh S .50
61 Michael Irvin S 1.00
62 Brad Johnson S 1.00
63 Keyshawn Johnson S 1.00
64 Jim Kelly S 1.00
65 Ryan Leaf S 1.00
66 Peyton Manning S 3.50
67 Dan Marino S 3.50
68 Donovan McNabb S 6.00
69 Steve McNair S 1.25
70 Cade McNown S 6.00
71 Warren Moon S 1.00
72 Jake Plummer S 2.50
73 Jerry Rice S 2.50
74 Barry Sanders S 5.00
75 Junior Seau S 1.00
76 Phil Simms S 1.00
77 Kordell Stewart S 1.25
78 Vinny Testaverde S 1.00
79 Ricky Williams S 12.00
80 Steve Young S 1.75
81 Troy Aikman G 4.00
82 Drew Bledsoe G 3.00
83 Bubby Brister G 1.00
84 Chris Chandler G 1.00
85 Randall Cunningham G 2.00
86 Terrell Davis G 6.00
87 John Elway G 6.00
88 Brett Favre G 8.00
89 Doug Flutie G 2.50
90 Brad Johnson G 2.00
91 Keyshawn Johnson G 2.00
92 Ryan Leaf G 2.00
93 Peyton Manning G 6.00
94 Dan Marino G 6.00
95 Donovan McNabb G 12.00
96 Steve McNair G 2.00
97 Cade McNown G 12.00
98 Warren Moon G 2.00
99 Jake Plummer G 4.00
100 Jerry Rice G 4.00
101 Barry Sanders G 8.00
102 Kordell Stewart G 2.00
103 Vinny Testaverde G 2.00
104 Ricky Williams G 25.00
105 Steve Young G 2.50
106 Troy Aikman P 8.00
107 Drew Bledsoe P 6.00
108 Terrell Davis P 10.00
109 John Elway P 10.00
110 Brett Favre P 15.00
111 Keyshawn Johnson P 2.50
112 Peyton Manning P 10.00
113 Dan Marino P 10.00
114 Donovan McNabb P 15.00
115 Cade McNown P 15.00
116 Jake Plummer P 8.00
117 Jerry Rice P 8.00
118 Barry Sanders P 15.00
119 Kordell Stewart P 2.50
120 Ricky Williams P 30.00

1999 Donruss Preferred QBC Power Parallel

This was a 120-card parallel to the base set. Each single was printed on holographic-foil board. The Bronze singles were numbered to 500, Silver singles to 300, Gold singles to 150 and Platinum singles to 50.

	MT
Bronze Cards:	3x-6x
Bronze Rookies:	3x
Production 500 Sets	
Silver Cards:	3x-6x
Silver Rookies:	3x
Production 300 Sets	
Gold Cards:	3x-6x
Gold Rookies:	3x
Production 150 Sets	
Platinum Cards:	4x-8x
Platinum Rookies:	4x
Production 50 Sets	

1999 Donruss Preferred QBC Autographs

This was a 15-card insert set that included autographs of the top players in the NFL. Cards were randomly inserted into packs.

	MT
Complete Set (15):	850.00
Common Player:	25.00

1 Steve Young 700 50.00
2 Ricky Williams 700 125.00
3 Jerry Rice 350 100.00
4 Jake Plummer 700 70.00
5 Peyton Manning 650 100.00
6 Michael Irvin 500 35.00
7 Dan Marino 600 125.00
8 Randall Cunningham 700 40.00
9 Troy Aikman 600 85.00
10 Terrell Davis 500 90.00
11 Vinny Testaverde 700 25.00
12 Chris Chandler 600 25.00
13 Bubby Brister 500 25.00
14 Steve McNair 700 50.00
15 Kordell Stewart 700 50.00

1999 Donruss Preferred QBC Chain Reaction

This was a 20-card insert set that included players who know how to move the chains. Each single was sequentially numbered to 5,000 and was printed on prismatic-foil board stock.

	MT
Complete Set (20):	65.00
Common Player:	1.00
Minor Stars:	2.00
Production 5,000 Sets	

1A Terrell Davis 7.00
1B Ricky Williams 10.00
2A Donovan McNabb 5.00
2B Cade McNown 5.00
3A Brett Favre 10.00
3B Barry Sanders 10.00
4A Jerry Rice 5.00
4B Steve Young 3.00
5A John Elway 7.00
5B Chris Chandler 1.00
6A Dan Marino 7.00
6B Drew Bledsoe 4.00
7A Keyshawn Johnson 2.00
7B Vinny Testaverde 2.00
8A Warren Moon 2.00
8B Steve McNair 2.00
9A Jake Plummer 5.00
9B Kordell Stewart 2.00
10A Troy Aikman 5.00
10B Peyton Manning 7.00

1999 Donruss Preferred QBC Hard Hats

This was a 30-card insert set that pictured each player on a helmet-shaped die-cut card. Each single was printed on clear plastic and was sequentially numbered to 3,000.

	MT
Complete Set (30):	125.00
Common Player:	1.50
Minor Stars:	3.00
Production 3,000 Sets	

1 Brett Favre 12.00
2 Keyshawn Johnson 3.00
3 John Elway 8.00
4 Drew Bledsoe 5.00
5 Chris Chandler 1.50
6 Terrell Davis 8.00
7 Ryan Leaf 3.00
8 Ricky Williams 15.00
9 Cade McNown 8.00
10 Barry Sanders 12.00
11 Donovan McNabb 8.00
12 Peyton Manning 8.00
13 Troy Aikman 6.00
14 Steve Young 4.00
15 Vinny Testaverde 1.50
16 Dan Marino 8.00
17 Steve McNair 3.00
18 Kordell Stewart 3.00
19 Michael Irvin 3.00
20 Jake Plummer 6.00
21 Jerry Rice 6.00
22 Brad Johnson 3.00
23 Phil Simms 3.00
24 Jim Kelly 3.00
25 Trent Dilfer 3.00
26 Kerry Collins 1.50
27 Warren Moon 3.00
28 Bubby Brister 1.50
29 Randall Cunningham 3.00
30 Doug Flutie 4.00

1999 Donruss Preferred QBC Materials

This was a 21-card insert set that included either a piece of game-used helmet, jersey or cleats. Jersey and cleat singles were numbered to 300 and helmet singles were numbered to 120. Singles were randomly inserted into packs.

	MT
Common Player:	75.00
#13 never produced	

1 Dan Marino Jersey 300 150.00
2 John Elway Jersey 300 150.00
3 Drew Bledsoe Jersey 300 100.00
4 Jake Plummer Jersey 300 100.00
5A Doug Flutie White Jersey 150 100.00
5B Doug Flutie Blue Jersey 150 100.00
6 Peyton Manning Jersey 300 150.00
7A Jerry Rice White Jersey 150 175.00
7B Jerry Rice Red Jersey 150 175.00
8 Brett Favre Jersey 300 200.00
9 Jim Kelly Jersey 300 75.00
10 Barry Sanders Jersey 300 200.00
11 Keyshawn Johnson Shoes 200 75.00
12 Brett Favre Shoes 100 250.00
14 Troy Aikman Shoes 300 125.00
15 Terrell Davis Shoes 300 125.00
16 Dan Marino Helmets 125 250.00
17 Troy Aikman Helmets 125 200.00
18 Brett Favre Helmets 125 300.00
19 Jerry Rice Helmets 125 200.00
20 Terrell Davis Helmets 125 200.00

1999 Donruss Preferred QBC National Treasures

This 44-card insert set included the top stars in the NFL. Each single was sequentially numbered to 2,000.

	MT
Complete Set (44):	150.00
Common Player:	1.50
Minor Stars:	3.00
Production 2,000 Sets	

1 Jake Plummer 10.00
2 Chris Chandler 1.50
3 Danny Kanell 1.50
4 Tony Banks 1.50
5 Scott Mitchell 1.50
6 Doug Flutie 6.00
7 Jim Kelly 3.00
8 Erik Kramer 1.50
9 Cade McNown 10.00
10 Jeff Blake 3.00
11 Boomer Esiason 3.00
12 Bernie Kosar 1.50
13 Troy Aikman 10.00
14 Michael Irvin 3.00
15 Bubby Brister 3.00
16 Terrell Davis 15.00
17 John Elway 15.00
18 Gus Frerotte 1.50
19 Barry Sanders 20.00
20 Brett Favre 20.00
21 Peyton Manning 15.00
22 Elvis Grbac 1.50
23 Warren Moon 3.00
24 Dan Marino 15.00
25 Randall Cunningham 3.00
26 Jeff George 3.00
27 Drew Bledsoe 8.00
28 Ricky Williams 20.00
29 Kerry Collins 3.00
30 Phil Simms 3.00
31 Keyshawn Johnson 3.00
32 Vinny Testaverde 3.00
33 Donovan McNabb 10.00
34 Kordell Stewart 4.00
35 Jim Harbaugh 3.00
36 Ryan Leaf 3.00
37 Junior Seau 3.00
38 Jerry Rice 10.00
39 Steve Young 6.00
40 Jim Everett 1.50
41 Trent Dilfer 3.00
42 Steve McNair 4.00
43 Brad Johnson 3.00
44 Neil O'Donnell 1.50

1999 Donruss Preferred QBC Passing Grade

This 20-card insert set included the top Quarterbacks in the NFL. Each single was a two-piece card that included a football-shaped die-cut inside a conventional card envelope. Each was sequentially numbered to 1,500.

	MT
Complete Set (20):	150.00
Common Player:	2.00
Minor Stars:	4.00
Production 1,500 Sets	

1 Steve Young 6.00
2 Dan Marino 15.00
3 Kordell Stewart 5.00
4 Trent Dilfer 5.00
5 Doug Flutie 6.00
6 Vinny Testaverde 4.00
7 Donovan McNabb 10.00
8 Brad Johnson 4.00
9 Troy Aikman 10.00
10 Brett Favre 20.00
11 Steve McNair 5.00
12 Peyton Manning 15.00
13 John Elway 15.00
14 Chris Chandler 2.00
15 Randall Cunningham 4.00
16 Cade McNown 10.00
17 Ryan Leaf 4.00
18 Drew Bledsoe 8.00
19 Jake Plummer 10.00
20 Warren Moon 4.00

1999 Donruss Preferred QBC Staremasters

This was a 20-card insert set that included the most intense players in the game today. Each single was sequentially numbered to 1,000.

	MT
Complete Set (20):	230.00
Common Player:	3.00
Minor Stars:	6.00
Production 1,000 Sets	

1 Jake Plummer 15.00
2 Doug Flutie 10.00
3 Cade McNown 15.00
4 Troy Aikman 15.00
5 Michael Irvin 3.00
6 Terrell Davis 20.00
7 John Elway 20.00
8 Barry Sanders 30.00
9 Brett Favre 30.00
10 Peyton Manning 20.00
11 Dan Marino 20.00
12 Randall Cunningham 6.00
13 Drew Bledsoe 12.00
14 Ricky Williams 30.00
15 Keyshawn Johnson 3.00
16 Donovan McNabb 15.00
17 Kordell Stewart 8.00
18 Ryan Leaf 6.00
19 Steve Young 10.00
20 Jerry Rice 15.00

1999 Donruss Preferred QBC X-Ponential Power

This 20-card insert set matched fellow stars from the same position. Each was printed on die-cut plastic with foil highlights and each was numbered to 2,500.

	MT
Complete Set (20):	150.00
Common Player:	5.00
Production 2,500 Sets	

1A Troy Aikman 10.00
1B Cade McNown 10.00
2A Kordell Stewart 5.00
2B Steve McNair 5.00
3A Donovan McNabb 10.00
3B Ricky Williams 20.00
4A Barry Sanders 20.00
4B Terrell Davis 15.00
5A Dan Marino 15.00
5B Peyton Manning 15.00
6A Jerry Rice 10.00
6B Keyshawn Johnson 5.00
7A Doug Flutie 7.00
7B Jim Kelly 5.00
8A Brett Favre 20.00
8B Steve Young 7.00
9A Drew Bledsoe 8.00
9B Ryan Leaf 5.00
10A John Elway 15.00
10B Jake Plummer 10.00

E

1959 Eagles Jay Publishing

Measuring 5" x 7", the 12-card set is anchored by a black-and-white photo on the front, with the player's name and team printed in the white border underneath. The cards are blank-backed and unnumbered. The set was originally sold in 12-card packs for 25 cents.

	NM
Complete Set (12):	75.00
Common Player:	5.00

1 Bill Barnes 5.00
2 Chuck Bednarik 10.00
3 Tom Brookshier 5.00
4 Marion Campbell 5.00
5 Ted Dean 5.00
6 Tommy McDonald 8.00
7 Clarence Peaks 5.00
8 Pete Retzlaff 5.00
9 Jesse Richardson 5.00

10	Norm Van Brocklin	15.00
11	Bobby Walston	5.00
12	Chuck Weber	5.00

1960 Eagles White Border

Measuring 5" x 7", the 11-card set is anchored by a black-and-white photo on the front, with the player's name and team printed in the white border underneath. The cards are blank-backed and unnumbered.

		NM
	Complete Set (11):	50.00
	Common Player:	5.00
1	Maxie Baughan	7.00
2	Chuck Bednarik	10.00
3	Don Burroughs	5.00
4	Jimmy Carr	5.00
5	Howard Keys	5.00
6	Ed Khayat	5.00
7	Jim McCusker	5.00
8	John Nocera	5.00
9	Nick Skorich	5.00
10	J.D. Smith	5.00
11	John Wittenborn	5.00

1961 Eagles Jay Publishing

Measuring 5" x 7", the 12-card set is anchored by a black-and-white photo on the front, with his name and team printed underneath in a white border. The backs are blank and unnumbered. Originally, the set was sold in packs for 25 cents.

		NM
	Complete Set (12):	50.00
	Common Player:	5.00
1	Maxie Baughan	7.00
2	Jim McCusker	5.00
3	Tommy McDonald	7.00
4	Bob Pellegrini	5.00
5	Pete Retzlaff	5.00
6	Jesse Richardson	5.00
7	Joe Robb	5.00
8	Theron Sapp	5.00
9	J.D. Smith	5.00
10	Bobby Walston	5.00
11	Jerry Williams (ACO)	5.00
12	John Wittenborn	5.00

1971 Eagles Team Issue

Measuring 4-1/4" x 5-1/2", the 16-card set showcases a posed black-and-white photo on the front, with the player's name and team printed inside the white border at the bottom of the card. The cards are unnumbered and the backs are blank.

		NM
	Complete Set (16):	45.00
	Common Player:	3.00
1	Gary Ballman	3.00
2	Lee Bouggess	3.00
3	Kent Kramer	3.00
4	Tom McNeill	3.00
5	Mark Nordquist	3.00
6	Ron Porter	3.00
7	Steve Preece	3.00
8	Tim Rossovich (Facing right edge of card)	3.00
9	Tim Rossovich (Facing left edge of card)	3.00
10	Jim Skaggs	3.00
11	Norm Snead	5.00
12	Jim Thrower	3.00
13	Mel Tom	3.00
14	Jim Ward	3.00
15	Adrian Young	3.00
16	Don Zimmerman	3.00

1983 Eagles Frito Lay

Measuring 4-1/4" x 5-1/2", the 37-card set is anchored by an action photo on the front, with the player's facsimile autograph on the photo. The player's name, position and Frito Lay logo are printed inside the white border under the photo. The top white margin features the "Philadelphia Eagles" and their logo on the card front. The set is unnumbered. The backs of Harold Carmichael, Max Runager and Jerry Sisemore's cards are done in a postcard format, while the others are blank.

		MT
	Complete Set (37):	45.00
	Common Player:	1.00
1	Harvey Armstrong	1.00
2	Ron Baker	1.00
3	Greg Brown	1.00
4	Marion Campbell (CO)	1.00
5	Harold Carmichael	3.00
6	Ken Clarke	1.00
7	Dennis DeVaughn	1.00
8	Herman Edwards	1.00
9	Ray Ellis	1.00
10	Major Everett	1.50
11	Anthony Griggs	1.00
12	Michael Haddix	1.50
13	Perry Harrington	1.00
14	Dennis Harrison	1.00
15	Wes Hopkins	1.50
16	Ron Jaworski	4.00
17	Ron Johnson	1.00
18	Vyto Kab	1.00
19	Steve Kenney	1.00
20	Dean Miraldi	1.00
21	Leonard Mitchell	1.00
22	Wilbert Montgomery	4.00
23	Hubie Oliver	1.00
24	Joe Pisarcik	1.50
25	Mike Quick	2.00
26	Jerry Robinson	1.50
27	Max Runager	1.00
28	Buddy Ryan (CO)	4.00
29	Lawrence Sampleton	1.00
30	Jody Schulz	1.00
31	Jerry Sisemore	1.50
32	John Spagnola	1.50
33	Reggie Wilkes	1.00
34	Mike Williams	1.00
35	Tony Woodruff	1.00
36	Glen Young	1.00
37	Roynell Young	1.00

1984 Eagles Police

Measuring 2-5/8" x 4-1/8", this eight-card set is anchored on the front with a photo, with the player's name, number, position, team and Eagles' logo inside a box at the bottom. The backs have the card number, player's name, number, position, bio, safety tip and sponsors.

		MT
	Complete Set (8):	6.00
	Common Player:	.50
1	Mike Quick	1.00
2	Dennis Harrison	.50
3	Jerry Robinson	.75
4	Wilbert Montgomery	1.50
5	Herman Edwards	.50
6	Kenny Jackson	1.00
7	Anthony Griggs	.50
8	Ron Jaworski	1.75

1985 Eagles Police

Measuring 2-5/8" x 4-1/8", the 16-card set is identical on the front to the 1984 set, with the large photo and the player's name, number, position, team and Eagles' logo in a box at the bottom. The backs have the card number, player's name, number, bio, highlights and a safety tip. The sponsors are listed at the bottom of the card back.

		MT
	Complete Set (16):	6.00
	Common Player:	.50
1	Ken Clarke	.50
2	Roynell Young	.50
3	Ray Ellis	.50
4	Ron Baker	.50
5	John Spagnola	.50
6	Reggie Wilkes	.50
7	Ron Jaworski	1.00
8	Steve Kenney	.50
9	Paul McFadden	.50
10	Mike Quick	1.00
11	Hubie Oliver	.50
12	Greg Brown	.50
13	Anthony Griggs	.50
14	Michael Haddix	.50
15	Kenny Jackson	.75
16	Vyto Kab	.50

1985 Eagles Team Issue

Measuring 2-15/16" x 3-7/8", the 53-card set is anchored by a glossy color photo on the front, with the player's name, position and number in the white margin under the photo. The backs have the player's name, position and number at the top, with his career highlights located inside a box. The cards are unnumbered.

		MT
	Complete Set (53):	50.00
	Common Player:	1.00
1	Harvey Armstrong	1.00
2	Ron Baker	1.00
3	Norman Braman (PRES)	1.00
4	Greg Brown	1.00
5	Marion Campbell (CO)	1.00
6	Jeff Christensen	1.00
7	Ken Clarke	1.00
8	Evan Cooper	1.00
9	Byron Darby	1.00
10	Mark Dennard	1.00
11	Herman Edwards	1.00
12	Ray Ellis	1.00
13	Major Everett	1.00
14	Gerry Feehery	1.00
15	Elbert Foules	1.00
16	Gregg Garrity	1.00
17	Anthony Griggs	1.00
18	Michael Haddix	1.00
19	Andre Hardy	1.00
20	Dennis Harrison	1.00
21	Joe Hayes	1.00
22	Melvin Hoover	1.00
23	Wes Hopkins	1.50
24	Mike Horan	1.00
25	Kenny Jackson	1.50
26	Ron Jaworski	4.00
27	Vyto Kab	1.00
28	Steve Kenney	1.00
29	Rich Kraynak	1.00
30	Dean May	1.00
31	Paul McFadden	1.00
32	Dean Miraldi	1.00
33	Leonard Mitchell	1.00
34	Wilbert Montgomery	3.00
35	Hubie Oliver	1.00
36	Mike Quick	2.00
37	Mike Reichenbach	1.00
38	Jerry Robinson	1.00
39	Rusty Russell	1.00
40	Lawrence Sampleton	1.00
41	Jody Schulz	1.00
42	John Spagnola	1.50
43	Tom Strauthers	1.00
44	Andre Waters	2.00
45	Reggie Wilkes	1.00
46	Joel Williams	1.00
47	Michael Williams	1.00
48	Brenard Wilson	1.00
49	Tony Woodruff	1.00
50	Roynell Young	1.00
51	Logo Card (Eagle holding football on both sides)	1.50
52	1985 Schedule Card (Both sides)	1.50
53	Title Card 1985-86 (Eagles' Helmet)	1.50

1986 Eagles Frito Lay

The cards in this set are 4-1/4" x 5-1/2". They can be distinguished from other Eagles Frito Lay sets by the Frito Lay logo in the lower right and the 3/8" borders on the sides. The cards are blank-backed and unnumbered.

		MT
	Complete Set (7):	12.00
	Common Player:	1.00
1	Wes Hopkins	1.50
2	Ron Jaworski	4.00
3	Ron Johnson WR	1.00
4	Mike Quick	2.00
5	Buddy Ryan CO	4.00
6	Tom Strauthers	1.00
7	Andre Waters	1.50

1986 Eagles Police

#12 RANDALL CUNNINGHAM Quarterback
PHILADELPHIA EAGLES

Measuring 2-5/8" x 4-1/8", the 16-card set is anchored by a large photo on the front, with the player's name, number, position, team and Eagles' logo in a box at the bottom. The backs have the card number, player's name, number, bio, position, highlights, safety tip and sponsors. The Eagles' and Frito Lay logos are also shown on the backs.

		MT
	Complete Set (16):	10.00
	Common Player:	.50
1	Greg Brown	.50
2	Reggie White	3.50
3	John Spagnola	.50
4	Mike Quick	.75
5	Ken Clarke	.50
6	Ken Reeves	.50
7	Mike Reichenbach	.50
8	Wes Hopkins	.75
9	Roynell Young	.50
10	Randall Cunningham	3.00
11	Paul McFadden	.50
12	Matt Cavanaugh	.50
13	Ron Jaworski	1.00
14	Byron Darby	.50
15	Andre Waters	.75
16	Buddy Ryan (CO)	1.00

1987 Eagles Police

Measuring 2-3/4" x 4-1/8", the 12-card set includes a photo on the front, along with the player's name, bio and position. The Eagles' helmet is printed in the bottom center. The backs have "Tips from the Eagles" printed at the top, with the New Jersey police force logos printed directly underneath. A safety tip is also included on the unnumbered backs, which feature the sponsor names at the bottom. Overall, 10,000 sets were handed out by New Jersey police officers.

		MT
	Complete Set (12):	60.00
	Common Player:	3.00
1	Ron Baker	3.00
2	Keith Byars	7.00
3	Ken Clarke	3.00
4	Randall Cunningham	12.00
5	Paul McFadden	3.00
6	Mike Quick	5.00
7	Mike Reichenbach	3.00
8	Buddy Ryan (CO)	7.00
9	John Spagnola	3.00
10	Anthony Toney	5.00
11	Andre Waters	3.00
12	Reggie White	16.00

1988 Eagles Police

Measuring 2-3/4" x 4-1/8", the 12-card set is anchored on the front by a large photo. "Philadelphia Eagles" and two Eagles' helmets printed in each corner are at the top of the card fronts. Under the photo are the player's name, number, height, position and weight. The unnumbered backs feature "Tips from the Eagles" at the top, with the New Jersey police logos located directly underneath. The McGruff the Crime Dog logo is printed at the bottom, along with the sponsors.

		MT
	Complete Set (12):	60.00
	Common Player:	3.00
1	Jerome Brown	5.00
2	Keith Byars	5.00
3	Randall Cunningham	8.00
4	Matt Darwin	3.00
5	Keith Jackson	8.00
6	Seth Joyner	5.00
7	Mike Quick	4.00
8	Buddy Ryan (CO)	6.00
9	Clyde Simmons	5.00
10	John Teltschik	3.00
11	Anthony Toney	4.00
12	Reggie White	10.00

1989 Eagles Daily News

Measuring 5-9/16" x 4-1/4", the 24-card set features the Eagles logo in the upper left corner, with "Philadelphia Eagles" on the right side above the photo on the card front. Beneath the photo are the player's name and position, along with McDonald's, KYW radio and the Philadelphia News logos. The unnumbered cards have blank backs.

		MT
	Complete Set (24):	25.00
	Common Player:	1.00
1	Eric Allen	2.00
2	Jerome Brown	2.00
3	Keith Byars	2.00
4	Cris Carter (UER) (Name misspelled Chris on front)	5.00
5	Randall Cunningham	3.00
6	Matt Darwin	1.00
7	Gerry Feehery	1.00
8	Ron Heller	1.00
9A	Terry Hoage (Solid color jersey)	1.00
9B	Terry Hoage (With white collar or undershirt)	1.00
10	Wes Hopkins	1.50
11	Keith Jackson	3.00
12	Seth Joyner	2.00
13	Mike Pitts	1.00
14	Mike Quick	1.50
15	Mike Reichenbach	1.00
16	Clyde Simmons	2.00
17	John Spagnola	1.00
18	Junior Tautalatasi	1.00
19	John Teltschik	1.00
20	Anthony Toney	1.00
21	Andre Waters	1.50
22	Reggie White	6.00
23	Luis Zendejas	1.00

1989 Eagles Police

Measuring 8-1/2" x 11", the nine-card set is anchored by a photo on the front, with the player's name and bio underneath the photo between the New Jersey State Police Crime Prevention Resource Center and Security Savings Bank logos. The unnumbered backs have "Alcohol and Other Drugs: Facts and Myths" and five questions and answers. The team logo and sponsors' logos are on the back. This set was released after the season.

		MT
	Complete Set (9):	50.00
	Common Player:	3.00
1	Cris Carter	15.00
2	Gregg Garrity	3.00
3	Mike Golic	4.00
4	Keith Jackson	7.00
5	Clyde Simmons	6.00
6	John Teltschik	3.00
7	Anthony Toney	3.00
8	Andre Waters	4.00
9	Luis Zendejas	3.00

1989 Eagles Smokey

Measuring 3" x 5", the 49-card set features a full-bleed photo on the front, with the player's name, number and position in the lower right. The unnumbered card backs have the player's name, number, position and bio at the top, with a Smokey the Bear cartoon underneath. The Eagles' and sponsor logos appear at the bottom of the card backs. Some cards were produced with two versions, which can be differentiated by the home and away jerseys.

		MT
	Complete Set (49):	125.00
	Common Player:	1.50
6	Matt Cavanaugh	2.00
9	Luis Zendejas	1.50
9	Don McPherson	2.00
10	John Teltschik	1.50
12A	Randall Cunningham (White jersey)	8.00
12B	Randall Cunningham (Green jersey)	8.00
20	Andre Waters	3.00
21	Eric Allen	3.00
25	Anthony Toney	2.00
33	William Frizzell	1.50
34	Terry Hoage	1.50
41	Keith Byars	3.00
42	Eric Everett	1.50
43	Roynell Young	1.50
46	Izel Jenkins	1.50
48	Wes Hopkins	2.00
50	Dave Rimington	1.50
52	Todd Bell	1.50
53	Mike Reichenbach	1.50
55	Byron Evans	1.50
56	Ty Allert	1.50
59	Seth Joyner	3.00
61	Ben Tamburello	1.50
63	Ron Baker	1.50
66	Ken Reeves	1.50
68	Reggie Singletary	1.50
72	David Alexander	1.50
73	Ron Heller	1.50
74	Mike Pitts	1.50
78	Matt Darwin	1.50
80	Cris Carter	8.00
81	Kenny Jackson	2.00
82A	Mike Quick (White jersey)	2.50
82B	Mike Quick (Green jersey)	2.50
83	Jimmie Giles	1.50
85	Ron Johnson	1.50
86	Gregg Garrity	1.50
88	Keith Jackson	5.00
89	David Little	2.00
90	Mike Golic	2.00
91	Scott Curtis	1.50
92	Reggie White	14.00
96	Clyde Simmons	3.00
97	John Klingel	1.50
99	Jerome Brown	4.00
NNO	Buddy Ryan (CO) (Wearing white cap)	7.00
NNO	Buddy Ryan (CO) (Wearing green cap)	7.00

1990 Eagles Police

Measuring 2-5/8" x 4-1/8", the 12-card set has "Philadelphia Eagles" and two Eagles' helmets at the top of the card fronts above the photo. Beneath the photo are the player's name, position and bio. The unnumbered card backs have "Tips from the Eagles" and sponsor logos at the top, with a tip and McGruff the Crime Dog logo at the bottom.

		MT
	Complete Set (12):	30.00
	Common Player:	2.00
1	David Alexander	2.00
2	Eric Allen	3.00
3	Randall Cunningham	5.00
4	Keith Byars	3.00
5	James Feagles	2.00
6	Mike Golic	3.00
7	Keith Jackson	4.00
8	Rich Kotite (CO)	3.00
9	Roger Ruzek	2.00
10	Mickey Shuler	3.00
11	Clyde Simmons	4.00
12	Reggie White	8.00

1990 Eagles Sealtest

Measuring 2" x 8", the set of six bookmarks showcases the Sealtest logo at the top, with "The Reading Team" inside a scoreboard above the player photo. The Eagles' logo, player name, number, bio and highlights are printed inside a box at the bottom of the card. The backs are unnumbered and contain the sponsor logos and give information on two books that are available to the public library. This set is identical to the 1990 Knudsen 49ers and Chargers sets.

		MT
	Complete Set (6):	15.00
	Common Player:	2.50
1	David Alexander	2.50
2	Eric Allen	3.50
3	Keith Byars	3.50
4	Randall Cunningham	4.00
5	Mike Pitts	2.50
6	Mike Quick	3.50

Post-1980 cards in Near Mint condition will generally sell for about 75% of the quoted Mint value. Excellent-condition cards bring no more than 40%.

1991 Enor Pro Football HOF Promos

The six standard-sized cards were produced to show what the 1991 Enor set would look like. The cards are identical to the regular cards, except for the differences in numbering and color tones. To tell these cards apart from the regular cards, look at the Team NFL logo on the back. If the NFL logo is black and white it is a promo card. If it is red, white and blue, it is a card from the regular series.

		MT
Complete Set (6):		8.00
Common Player:		1.00
1	Pro Football Hall of Fame (Building) (Regular issue card number is also 1)	1.00
2	Earl Campbell (Regular issue card number is 23)	3.50
3	John Hannah (Regular issue card number is 57)	1.00
4	Stan Jones (Regular issue card number is 74)	1.00
5	Jan Stenerud (Regular issue card number is 131)	1.00
6	Tex Schramm ADM (Regular issue card number is 127)	1.00

1991 Enor Pro Football Hall of Fame

Photos from the NFL's files were used for the card fronts for this 160-card set, which features a blend of color and black-and-white photos bordered by black and gold frames. The Pro Football Hall of Fame logo also appears on the card front, in a purple square. The player's name and position are in the lower left corner in a black panel. The card back has a photo of the Hall of Fame on the bottom half, along with a card number. Biographical information, a career summary and the year of induction comprise the rest of the back. Special cards randomly inserted in packs allowed the holder to redeem them for a special Hall of Fame card album and free admission to the museum. Six different promo cards were also produced for the set. The cards, which are numbered on the back, do not match the numbers assigned to their counterparts in the regular set. Also, the cards have a different shade of color and the NFL logo on the back is black-and-white, not in color like those on the regular cards.

		MT
Complete Set (160):		12.00
Common Player:		.10
1	Pro Football Hall of Fame	.15
1A	Free Admission Pro Football Hall of Fame (Canton, OH)	.15
2	Herb Adderley	.15
3	Lance Alworth	.20
4	Doug Atkins	.15
5	Morris (Red) Badgro	.10
6	Cliff Battles	.15
7	Sammy Baugh	.60
8	Chuck Bednarik	.25
9A	Bert Bell (FOUND/OWN) (Factory set version in coat and tie)	.20
9B	Bert Bell (FOUND/OWN) (Wax pack version in Steelers tee shirt)	.20
10	Bobby Bell	.10
11	Raymond Berry	.30
12	Charles W. Bidwill (OWN)	.10
13	Fred Biletnikoff	.25
14	George Blanda	.30
15	Mel Blount	.20
16	Terry Bradshaw	.75
17	Jim Brown	.75
18	Paul Brown (CO/OWN/FOUND)	.20
19	Roosevelt Brown	.10
20	Willie Brown	.15
21	Buck Buchanan	.15
22	Dick Butkus	.50
23	Earl Campbell	.75
24	Tony Canadeo	.10
25	Joe Carr (PRES)	.10
26	Guy Chamberlin	.10
27	Jack Christiansen	.10
28	Earl "Dutch" Clark	.15
29	George Connor	.15
30	Jimmy Conzelman	.10
31	Larry Csonka	.30
32	Willie Davis	.10
33	Len Dawson	.25
34	Mike Ditka	.50
35	Art Donovan	.25
36	John (Paddy) Driscoll	.10
37	Billy Dudley	.15
38	Turk Edwards	.10
39	Weeb Ewbank (CO)	.10
40	Tom Fears	.10
41	Ray Flaherty (CO)	.10
42	Len Ford	.10
43	Dan Fortmann	.10
44	Frank Gatski	.10
45	Bill George	.10
46	Frank Gifford	.50
47	Sid Gillman (CO)	.10
48	Otto Graham	.50
49	Harold (Red) Grange	.50
50	Joe Greene	.20
51	Forrest Gregg	.15
52	Bob Griese	.30
53	Lou Groza	.20
54	Joe Guyon	.10
55	George Halas (CO/OWN/FOUND)	.30
56	Jack Ham	.25
57	John Hannah	.10
58	Franco Harris	.30
59	Ed Healey	.10
60	Mel Hein	.10
61	Ted Hendricks	.10
62	Pete (Fats) Henry	.10
63	Arnie Herber	.10
64	Bill Hewitt	.10
65	Clarke Hinkle	.10
66	Elroy Hirsch	.20
67	Ken Houston	.15
68	Cal Hubbard	.10
69	Sam Huff	.20
70	Lamar Hunt (OWN/FOUND)	.10
71	Don Hutson	.20
72	John Henry Johnson	.15
73	Deacon Jones	.25
74	Stan Jones	.15
75	Sonny Jurgensen	.25
76	Walt Kiesling	.10
77	Frank (Bruiser) Kinard	.10
78	Earl (Curly) Lambeau (CO/FOUND/OWN)	.25
79	Jack Lambert	.30
80	Tom Landry (CO)	.30
81	Dick Lane	.15
82	Jim Langer	.10
83	Willie Lanier	.15
84	Yale Lary	.10
85	Dante Lavelli	.15
86	Bobby Layne	.50
87	Tuffy Leemans	.10
88	Bob Lilly	.25
89	Sid Luckman	.25
90	William Roy Lyman	.10
91	Tim Mara (FOUND/OWN)	.10
92	Gino Marchetti	.20
93	Geo. Preston Marshall (FOUND/OWN)	.10
94	Don Maynard	.20
95	George McAfee	.10
96	Mike McCormack	.10
97	Johnny (Blood) McNally	.10
98	Mike Michalske	.10
99	Wayne Millner	.10
100	Bobby Mitchell	.20
101	Ron Mix	.10
102	Lenny Moore	.20
103	Marion Motley (See also 130)	.20
104	George Musso	.10
105	Bronko Nagurski	.30
106	Earle (Greasy) Neale (CO)	.10
107	Ernie Nevers	.10
108	Ray Nitschke	.25
109	Leo Nomellini	.15
110	Merlin Olsen	.25
111	Jim Otto	.10
112	Steve Owen (CO)	.10
113	Alan Page	.15
114	Clarence (Ace) Parker	.10
115	Jim Parker	.10
116	1958 NFL Championship	.10
117	Pete Pihos	.10
118	Hugh (Shorty) Ray (OFF)	.10
119	Dan Reeves (OWN)	.10
120	Jim Ringo	.15
121	Andy Robustelli	.15
122	Art Rooney (FOUND/ADM)	.15
123	Pete Rozelle (COMM)	.20
124	Bob St. Clair	.15
125	Gale Sayers	.50
126	Joe Schmidt	.15
127	Tex Schramm (ADM)	.15
128	Art Shell	.20
129	Roger Staubach	.75
130	Ernie Stautner (UER) (Numbered as 103)	.20
131	Jan Stenerud	.15
132	Ken Strong	.10
133	Joe Stydahar	.10
134	Fran Tarkenton	.30
135	Charley Taylor	.15
136	Jim Taylor	.15
137	Jim Thorpe	.50
138	Y.A. Tittle	.40
139	George Trafton	.10
140	Charlie Trippi	.10
141	Emlen Tunnell	.10
142	Clyde "Bulldog" Turner	.20
143	Johnny Unitas	.50
144	Gene Upshaw	.15
145	Norm Van Brocklin	.20
146	Steve Van Buren	.20
147	Doak Walker	.20
148	Paul Warfield	.20
149	Bob Waterfield	.20
150	Arnie Weinmeister	.10
151	Bill Willis	.10
152	Larry Wilson	.10
153	Alex Wojciechowicz	.10
154	Willie Wood	.15
155	Enshrinement Day HOF Induction Ceremony	.10
156	Mementoes Exhibit Enshrinee Mementos Room	.10
157	Checklist 1 - The Beginning	.10
158	Checklist 2 - The Early Years	.10
159	Checklist 3 - The Modern Era	.10
160A	Checklist 4 - Evolution of Uniform (includes #133-160)	.10

1994 Enor Pro Football HOF

Having the identical design as the 1991 set, these six cards were inserted into ProGard protective sheet boxes. The cards are unnumbered. They feature each of the players and coach who were inducted into the Hall of Fame in 1994.

		MT
Complete Set (6):		4.00
Common Player:		.40
1	Tony Dorsett	1.25
2	Bud Grant (CO)	.40
3	Jim Johnson	.40
4	Leroy Kelly	.40
5	Jackie Smith	.40
6	Randy White	.75

1995 Enor Pro Football HOF

The company re-released its 1991 Hall of Fame series in a factory set in 1995. This includes the first 159 cards from the 1991 set, in addition to 21 new cards, which feature a 1995 copyright date. The original cards still carry the 1991 copyright. Card No. 160 carries a "B" suffix.

		MT
Complete Set (21):		8.00
Common Player:		.25
160B	Checklist 4 - Evolution of Uniform (includes #133-180)	.25
161	Lem Barney	.25
162	Al Davis	.40
163	John Mackey	.25
164	John Riggins	.50
165	Dan Fouts	.50
166	Larry Little	.25
167	Chuck Noll	.50
168	Bill Walsh	.50
169	Tony Dorsett	1.00
170	Bud Grant	.25
171	Jimmy Johnson	.25
172	Leroy Kelly	.25
173	Jackie Smith	.25
174	Randy White	.50
175	O.J. Simpson	1.00
176	Jim Finks	.25
177	Hank Jordan	.25
178	Steve Largent	.75
179	Lee Roy Selmon	.25
180	Kellen Winslow	.40

1969 Eskimo Pie

These 2-1/2" x 3" panels each feature two mug shot stickers of American Football League players. The panels are in color but are unnumbered. Card 14 (Len Dawson/Jim Otto) has the players' names reversed under their pictures. The bottom half of each panel explains that these cards were also on other Eskimo "take home cartons."

		NM
Complete Set (15):		850.00
Common Player:		50.00
(1)	Lance Alworth, John Charles	95.00
(2)	Al Atkinson, George Goeddeke	50.00
(3)	Marlin Briscoe, Billy Shaw	50.00
(4)	Gino Cappelletti, Dale Livingston	50.00
(5)	Eric Crabtree, Jim Dunaway	50.00
(6)	Ben Davidson, Bob Griese	130.00
(7)	Hewritt Dixon, Pete Beathard	60.00
(8)	Mike Garrett, Bob Hunt	50.00
(9)	Daryle Lamonica, Willie Frazier	60.00
(10)	Jim Lynch, John Hadl	60.00
(11)	Kent McCloughan, Tom Regner	50.00
(12)	Jim Nance, Billy Neighbors	50.00
(13)	Rick Norton, Paul Costa	50.00
(14)	Jim Otto, Len Dawson (Names reversed)	125.00
(15)	Matt Snell, Dick Post	50.00

1948-52 Exhibit W468 Football

The 59-card set, which measures 3-1/4" x 5-3/8", was released by the Exhibit Supply Co. of Chicago in 1948-52. The thick cards were sold in vending machines. The cards, which have blank backs, were originally in black and white. In the following years they were released in sepia, blue, yellow and red. The cards that are colored carry a 3-4 times higher value than the black-and-white and sepia cards. Released in three groups of 32 in 1948, 1950 and 1951, the 1951 set is the easiest to find of the three. The 1951 cards were also reissued in sepia tone in 1952 and possibly 1953. A checklist card was produced in 1950. It was printed in black-and-white and green. It resembles the Bednarik card, however, it lists the 32 players from the 1950 set on the front. In addition, nine-card ad displays were produced, and feature the Bednarik checklist. In 1948, the words "Made in USA" measure 5/8 inch on the card. Also, 11 of the 1948 cards were single prints (Comp, Jacobs, Cifers, Horvath, Mastrangelo, LeForce, Johnson, Pritko, Wedemeyer, Coulter and Schlinkman). In 1950, the single-print cards were Bednarik, Hoerner, Davis, Perry, Ruby and Justice. When the 1950 cards went into a second printing, 11 new cards were issued to replace the original 11 single prints. On the new cards, "Made in USA" measures 7/16 of an inch. The 1951 printing featured only 16 cards, with the six single-print cards from 1950 and 10 cards from 1948 shelved. The 1951 cards feature "Made in USA" in 1/2-inch high letters.

		NM
Complete Set (59):		4000.
Common Player DP:		10.00
Common Player:		40.00
Common Player SP48:		175.00
Common Player SP50:		50.00
1	Frankie Albert (DP) (48/50/51/52)	10.00
2	Dick Barwegan (DP) (51/52)	10.00
3	Sammy Baugh (DP) (48/50/51/52)	45.00
4	Chuck Bednarik (SP50)	125.00
5	Tony Canadeo (DP) (51/52)	15.00
6	Paul Christman (48/50)	40.00
7	Bob Cifers (SP48)	175.00
8	Irv Comp (SP48)	175.00
9	Charley Conerly (DP) (48/50/51/52)	20.00
10	George Connor (DP) (51/52)	15.00
11	Dewitt Coulter (SP50)	175.00
12	Glenn Davis (SP50)	100.00
13	Glenn Dobbs (48/50)	40.00
14	John Dottley (DP) (51/52)	10.00
15	Bill Dudley (48/50)	50.00
16	Tom Fears (DP) (51/52)	15.00
17	Joe Geri (DP) (51/52)	10.00
18	Otto Graham (DP) (48/50/51/52)	50.00
19	Pat Harder (48/50)	40.00
20	Elroy Hirsch (DP) (51/52)	20.00
21	Dick Hoerner (SP50)	60.00
22	Bob Hoernschemeyer (DP) (51/52)	10.00
23	Les Horvath (SP48)	200.00
24	Jack Jacobs (SP48)	175.00
25	Nate Johnson (SP48)	175.00
26	Charlie Justice (SP50)	75.00
27	Bobby Layne (DP) (48/50/51/52)	35.00
28	Clyde LeForce (SP48)	175.00
29	Sid Luckman (48/50)	75.00
30	John Lujack (48/50)	60.00
31	Bill McColl (DP) (51/52)	175.00
32	Ollie Matson (DP) (51/52)	20.00
33	Bill McColl (DP) (51/52)	10.00
34	Fred Morrison (DP) (50/51/52)	10.00
35	Marion Motley (DP) (48/50/51/52)	20.00
36	Chuck Ortmann (DP) (51/52)	10.00
37	Joe Perry (SP50)	100.00
38	Pete Pihos (48/50)	50.00
39	Steve Pritko (SP48)	175.00
40	George Ratterman (48/50)	10.00
41	Jay Rhodemyre (DP) (51/52)	10.00
42	Martin Ruby (SP50)	75.00
43	Julie Rykovich (48/50)	10.00
44	Walt Schlinkman (SP48)	185.00
45	Emil (Red) Sitko (48/50)	10.00
46	Vitamin Smith (DP) (50/51/52)	10.00
47	Norm Standlee (48/50)	40.00
48	George Taliaferro (DP) (50/51/52)	10.00
49	Y.A. Tittle (HOR) (48/50)	75.00
50	Charley Trippi (48/50/51/52)	15.00
51	Frank Tripucka (DP) (48/50/51/52)	12.00
52	Emlen Tunnell (DP) (51/52)	15.00
53	Bulldog Turner (DP) (48/50/51/52)	15.00
54	Steve Van Buren (48/50)	60.00
55	Bob Waterfield (DP) (48/50/51/52)	25.00
56	Herm Wedemeyer (SP48)	500.00
57	Bob Williams (DP) (51/52)	10.00
58	Claude Buddy Young (DP) (passing) (48/50/51/52)	10.00
59	Tank Younger (DP) (50/51/52)	10.00
NNO	Checklist Card SP50 (Chuck Bednarik)	500.00

1990 FACT Pro Set Cincinnati

Produced for 29 schools in the Cincinnati school district, the set was used as an educational tool for grade school students. The promotion ran for 15 straight weeks, with 25-card cello packs handed out to the students. The card fronts are identical to 1990 Pro Set Series I cards, while the backs have math, grammar and science questions. The card backs carry the card numbers in the lower right. The missing numbers from the first series are 338, 376 and 377.

		MT
Complete Set (375):		550.00
Common Player:		1.00
1	Barry Sanders (W1)	25.00
2	Joe Montana (W1)	20.00
3	Coach of the Year (Lindy Infante) (W1) (UER) (missing Coach next to Packers)	1.00
4	Man of the Year (Warren Moon) (W1) (UER) (missing R symbol)	2.00
5	Defensive Player of the Year (Keith Millard) (W1)	1.00
6	Defensive Rookie of the Year (Derrick Thomas) (W1) (UER) (no 1989 on front banner of card)	2.00
7	Comeback Player of the Year (Ottis Anderson) (W1)	1.50
8	Passing Leader (Joe Montana) (W2)	20.00
9	Rushing Leader (Christian Okoye) (W2)	1.00
10	Total Yardage Leader (Thurman Thomas) (W2)	3.00
11	Kick Scoring Leader (Mike Cofer) (W2)	1.00
12	TD Scoring Leader (Dalton Hilliard) (W2) (UER) (O.J. Simpson not listed in stats, but is mentioned in text)	1.00
13	Receiving Leader (Sterling Sharpe) (W2)	3.00
14	Punting Leader (Rich Camarillo) (W3)	1.00
15	Punt Return Leader (Walter Stanley) (W3)	1.00
16	Kickoff Return Leader (Rod Woodson) (W3)	2.00
17	Interception Leader (Felix Wright) (W3)	1.00
18	Sack Leader (Chris Doleman) (W3)	1.00
19	Heisman Trophy (Andre Ware) (W3)	1.00
20	Outland Trophy (Mohammed Elewonibi) (W4)	1.00
21	Lombardi Award (Percy Snow) (W4)	1.00

22	Maxwell Award (Anthony Thompson) (W4)	1.00
23	1990 HOF Selection (Buck Buchanan) (W4) (Sacking Bart Starr)	1.00
24	1990 HOF Selection (Bob Griese) (W4)	1.50
25	1990 HOF Selection (Franco Harris) (W5)	1.50
26	1990 HOF Selection (Ted Hendricks) (W4)	1.00
27	1990 HOF Selection (Jack Lambert) (W5)	1.00
28	1990 HOF Selection (Tom Landry) (W5)	1.50
29	1990 HOF Selection (Bob St. Clair) (W5)	1.00
30	Aundray Bruce (W5) (UER) (Stats say Falcons)	1.00
31	Tony Casillas (W5) (UER) (Stats say Falcons)	1.00
32	Shawn Collins (W5)	1.00
33	Marcus Cotton (W6)	1.00
34	Bill Fralic (W6)	1.00
35	Chris Miller (W6)	1.50
36	Deion Sanders (W6) (UER) (Stats say Falcons)	14.00
37	John Settle (W6)	1.00
38	Jerry Glanville (CO) (W6)	1.00
39	Cornelius Bennett (W7)	1.50
40	Jim Kelly (W7)	3.00
41	Mark Kelso (W7) (UER) (No fumble rec. in '88; mentioned in '89)	1.00
42	Scott Norwood (W7)	1.00
43	Nate Odomes (W7)	1.50
44	Scott Radecic (W7)	1.00
45	Jim Ritcher (W8)	1.00
46	Leonard Smith (W8)	1.00
47	Darryl Talley (W8)	1.00
48	Marv Levy (CO) (W8)	1.00
49	Neal Anderson (W8)	1.00
50	Kevin Butler (W8)	1.00
51	Jim Covert (W9)	1.00
52	Richard Dent (W9)	1.00
53	Jay Hilgenberg (W9)	1.00
54	Steve McMichael (W9)	1.00
55	Ron Morris (W9)	1.00
56	John Roper (W9)	1.00
57	Mike Singletary (W9)	1.50
58	Keith Van Horne (W10)	1.00
59	Mike Ditka (CO) (W10)	3.00
60	Lewis Billups (W10)	1.00
61	Eddie Brown (W10)	1.00
62	Jason Buck (W10)	1.00
63	Rickey Dixon (W10)	1.00
64	Tim McGee (W11)	1.00
65	Eric Thomas (W11)	1.00
66	Ickey Woods (W11)	1.00
67	Carl Zander (W11)	1.00
68	Sam Wyche (CO) (W11)	1.00
69	Paul Farren (W11)	1.00
70	Thane Gash (W12)	1.00
71	David Grayson (W12)	1.00
72	Bernie Kosar (W12)	1.50
73	Reggie Langhorne (W12)	1.00
74	Eric Metcalf (W12)	2.00
75	Ozzie Newsome (W12)	1.50
76	Felix Wright (W12)	1.00
77	Bud Carson (CO) (W13)	1.00
78	Troy Aikman (W13)	25.00
79	Michael Irvin (W13)	4.00
80	Jim Jeffcoat (W13)	1.00
81	Crawford Ker (W13)	1.00
82	Eugene Lockhart (W13)	1.00
83	Kelvin Martin (W13)	1.50
84	Ken Norton Jr. (W13)	1.50
85	Jimmy Johnson (CO) (W14)	2.00
86	Steve Atwater (W14)	1.00

87	Tyrone Braxton (W14)	1.00
88	John Elway (W14)	14.00
89	Simon Fletcher (W15)	1.00
90	Ron Holmes (W15)	1.00
91	Bobby Humphrey (W15)	1.00
92	Vance Johnson (W15)	1.00
93	Ricky Nattiel (W15)	1.00
94	Dan Reeves (CO) (W15)	1.50
95	Jim Arnold (W1)	1.00
96	Jerry Ball (W1)	1.00
97	Bennie Blades (W1)	1.00
98	Lomas Brown (W1)	1.00
99	Michael Cofer (W1)	1.00
100	Richard Johnson (W4)	1.00
101	Eddie Murray (W4)	1.00
102	Barry Sanders (W2)	25.00
103	Chris Spielman (W2)	1.00
104	William White (W2)	1.50
105	Eric Williams (W2)	1.00
106	Wayne Fontes (CO) (W3) (UER) (Says born in MO, actually born in MA)	1.00
107	Brent Fullwood (W3)	1.00
108	Ron Hallstrom (W3)	1.00
109	Tim Harris (W8)	1.00
110	Johnny Holland (W8)	1.00
111	Perry Kemp (W8)	1.00
112	Don Majkowski (W9)	1.00
113	Mark Murphy (W9)	1.00
114	Sterling Sharpe (W9)	4.00
115	Ed West (W9)	1.50
116	Lindy Infante (CO) (W9)	1.00
117	Steve Brown (W9)	1.00
118	Ray Childress (W10)	1.00
119	Ernest Givins (W10)	1.50
120	John Grimsley (W10)	1.00
121	Alonzo Highsmith (W10)	1.00
122	Drew Hill (W10)	1.50
123	Bubba McDowell (W10)	1.50
124	Dean Steinkuhler (W10)	1.00
125	Lorenzo White (W11)	1.00
126	Tony Zendejas (W11)	1.00
127	Jack Pardee (CO) (W11)	1.00
128	Albert Bentley (W11)	1.00
129	Dean Biasucci (W11)	1.00
130	Duane Bickett (W11)	1.00
131	Bill Brooks (W12)	1.50
132	Jon Hand (W12)	1.00
133	Mike Prior (W12)	1.00
134	Andre Rison (W12)	2.00
135	Rohn Stark (W12)	1.00
136	Donnell Thompson (W12)	1.00
137	Clarence Verdin (W13)	1.00
138	Fredd Young (W13)	1.00
139	Ron Meyer (CO) (W14)	1.00
140	Jim Alt (W14)	1.00
141	Steve DeBerg (W14)	1.50
142	Irv Eatman (W1)	1.00
143	Dino Hackett (W2)	1.00
144	Nick Lowery (W2)	1.00
145	Bill Maas (W2)	1.00
146	Stephone Paige (W5)	1.00
147	Neil Smith (W3)	2.00
148	Marty Schottenheimer (CO) (W3)	1.00
149	Steve Beuerlein (W4)	1.00
150	Tim Brown (W4)	3.00
151	Mike Dyal (W4)	1.00
152	Mervyn Fernandez (W4)	1.00
153	Willie Gault (W4)	1.00
154	Bob Golic (W4)	1.00
155	Bo Jackson (W5)	3.00
156	Don Mosebar (W5)	1.00
157	Steve Smith (W5)	1.00
158	Greg Townsend (W5)	1.00
159	Bruce Wilkerson (W6)	1.00
160	Steve Wisniewski (W6) (Blocking for Bo Jackson)	1.00

161	Art Shell (CO) (W6)	2.00
162	Flipper Anderson (W6)	1.00
163	Greg Bell (W6) (UER) (Stats have 5 catches, should be 9)	1.00
164	Henry Ellard (W6)	1.50
165	Jim Everett (W6)	1.50
166	Jerry Gray (W7)	1.00
167	Kevin Greene (W7)	2.00
168	Pete Holohan (W13)	1.00
169	Larry Kelm (W13)	1.00
170	Tom Newberry (W13)	1.00
171	Vince Newsome (W13)	1.00
172	Irv Pankey (W14)	1.00
173	Jackie Slater (W14)	1.00
174	Fred Strickland (W14)	1.00
175	Mike Wilcher (W14) (UER) (Fumble rec. number different from 1989 Pro Set card)	1.00
176	John Robinson (CO) (W7) (UER) (Stats say Rams, should says L.A. Rams)	1.00
177	Mark Clayton (W7)	1.50
178	Roy Foster (W7)	1.00
179	Harry Galbreath (W7)	1.00
180	Jim C. Jensen (W8)	1.00
181	Dan Marino (W15)	35.00
182	Louis Oliver (W15)	1.00
183	Sammie Smith (W15)	1.00
184	Brian Sochia (W15)	1.00
185	Don Shula (CO) (W15)	1.50
186	Joey Browner (W8)	1.00
187	Anthony Carter (W15)	1.50
188	Chris Doleman (W8)	1.00
189	Steve Jordan (W4)	1.00
190	Carl Lee (W4)	1.00
191	Randall McDaniel (W5)	1.00
192	Mike Merriweather (W5)	1.00
193	Keith Millard (W14)	1.00
194	Al Noga (W12)	1.00
195	Scott Studwell (W5)	1.00
196	Henry Thomas (W12)	1.50
197	Herschel Walker (W5)	1.50
198	Wade Wilson (W5)	1.50
199	Gary Zimmerman (W5)	1.00
200	Jerry Burns (CO) (W6)	1.00
201	Vincent Brown (W6)	1.50
202	Hart Lee Dykes (W14)	1.00
203	Sean Farrell (W6)	1.00
204	Fred Marion (W6)	1.00
205	Stanley Morgan (W15) (UER) (Text says he reached 10,000 yards fastest; 3 players did it in 10 seasons)	1.50
206	Eric Sievers (W6)	1.00
207	John Stephens (W15)	1.00
208	Andre Tippett (W15)	1.00
209	Rod Rust (W15)	1.00
210	Morten Andersen (W6)	1.00
211	Brad Edelman (W12)	1.00
212	John Fourcade (W12)	1.00
213	Dalton Hilliard (W13)	1.00
214	Rickey Jackson (W13) (Forcing Jim Kelly fumble)	1.00
215	Vaughan Johnson (W12)	1.00
216	Eric Martin (W13)	1.50
217	Sam Mills (W13)	1.00
218	Pat Swilling (W7) (UER) (Total fumble recoveries listed as 4, should be 5)	1.50
219	Frank Warren (W7)	1.00
220	Jim Wilks (W7)	1.00
221	Jim Mora (CO) (W7)	1.00
222	Raul Allegre (W2)	1.00
223	Carl Banks (W1)	1.00
224	John Elliott (W1)	1.00
225	Erik Howard (W7)	1.00
226	Pepper Johnson (W2)	1.00
227	Leonard Marshall (W7) (UER) (In Super Bowl XXI, George Martin had the safety)	1.00
228	Dave Meggett (W2)	1.50

229	Bart Oates (W3)	1.00
230	Phil Simms (W8)	1.50
231	Lawrence Taylor (W8)	2.00
232	Bill Parcells (CO) (W8)	1.50
233	Troy Benson (W8)	1.00
234	Kyle Clifton (W8) (UER) (Born: Onley, should be Olney)	1.00
235	Johnny Hector (W8)	1.00
236	Jeff Lageman (W9)	1.50
237	Pat Leahy (W9)	1.00
238	Freeman McNeil (W9)	1.00
239	Ken O'Brien (W9)	1.00
240	Al Toon (W9)	1.50
241	Jo Jo Townsell (W9)	1.00
242	Bruce Coslet (CO) (W10)	1.00
243	Eric Allen (W10)	1.00
244	Jerome Brown (W10)	1.50
245	Keith Byars (W10)	1.50
246	Cris Carter (W13)	4.00
247	Randall Cunningham (W13)	2.00
248	Keith Jackson (W14)	1.50
249	Mike Quick (W14)	1.50
250	Clyde Simmons (W14)	1.50
251	Andre Waters (W14)	1.00
252	Reggie White (W15)	2.00
253	Buddy Ryan (CO) (W15)	1.00
254	Rich Camarillo (W15)	1.00
255	Earl Ferrell (W10) (No mention of retirement on card front)	1.00
256	Roy Green (W10)	1.00
257	Ken Harvey (W3)	1.00
258	Ernie Jones (W15)	1.00
259	Tim McDonald (W9)	1.00
260	Timm Rosenbach (W11) (UER) (Born '67, should be '66)	1.50
261	Luis Sharpe (W3)	1.00
262	Vai Sikahema (W3)	1.00
263	J.T. Smith (W1)	1.00
264	Ron Wolfley (W1) (UER) (Born Blaisdell, should be Blasdel)	1.00
265	Joe Bugel (CO) (W11)	1.00
266	Gary Anderson (W11)	1.00
267	Bubby Brister (W1)	1.00
268	Merril Hoge (W11)	1.00
269	Carnell Lake (W2)	1.00
270	Louis Lipps (W11)	1.00
271	David Little (W3)	1.00
272	Greg Lloyd (W3)	2.00
273	Keith Willis (W11)	1.00
274	Tim Worley (W3)	1.00
275	Chuck Noll (CO) (W4)	1.50
276	Marion Butts (W4)	1.00
277	Gill Byrd (W2)	1.00
278	Vencie Glenn (W2) (UER) (Sack total should be 2, not 2.5)	1.00
279	Burt Grossman (W1)	1.00
280	Gary Plummer (W4)	1.00
281	Bill Ray Smith (W2)	1.00
282	Billy Joe Tolliver (W12)	1.00
283	Dan Henning (CO) (W12)	1.00
284	Harris Barton (W1)	1.00
285	Michael Carter (W1)	1.00
286	Mike Cofer (W1)	1.00
287	Roger Craig (W1)	1.50
288	Don Griffin (W1)	1.00
289	Charles Haley (W2)	1.50
290	Pierce Holt (W2)	1.00
291	Ronnie Lott (W2)	1.50
292	Guy McIntyre (W2)	1.00
293	Joe Montana (W2)	20.00
294	Tom Rathman (W2)	1.00
295	Jerry Rice (W3)	20.00
296	Jesse Sapolu (W3)	1.00
297	John Taylor (W3)	1.50
298	Michael Walter (W3)	1.00
299	George Seifert (CO) (W3)	2.00
300	Jeff Bryant (W3)	1.00
301	Jacob Green (W9)	1.00
302	Norm Johnson (UER) (W4) (Card shop not in Garden Grove, should say Fullerton)	1.00
303	Bryan Millard (W4)	1.00
304	Joe Nash (W4)	1.00
305	Eugene Robinson (W4)	1.00
306	John L. Williams (W14)	1.00
307	Dave Wyman (W14) (NFL EXP is in caps, inconsistent with rest of the set)	1.00

308	Chuck Knox (CO) (W14)	1.00
309	Mark Carrier (C14)	1.50
310	Paul Gruber (W14)	1.00
311	Harry Hamilton (W15)	1.00
312	Bruce Hill (W15)	1.00
313	Donald Igwebuike (W15)	1.00
314	Kevin Murphy (W15)	1.00
315	Ervin Randle (W12)	1.00
316	Mark Robinson (W12)	1.00
317	Lars Tate (W12)	1.00
318	Vinny Testaverde (W12)	2.00
319	Ray Perkins (CO) (W12)	1.00
320	Earnest Byner (W12)	1.00
321	Gary Clark (W12) (Randall Cunningham looking on from sidelines)	2.00
322	Darryl Grant (W13)	1.00
323	Darrell Green (W13)	1.00
324	Jim Lachey (W13)	1.00
325	Charles Mann (W13)	1.00
326	Wilber Marshall (W13)	1.00
327	Ralf Mojsiejenko (W13)	1.00
328	Art Monk (W15)	2.00
329	Gerald Riggs (W15)	1.00
330	Mark Rypien (W14)	1.00
331	Ricky Sanders (W14)	1.00
332	Alvin Walton (W4)	1.00
333	Joe Gibbs (CO) (W5)	2.00
334	Aloha Stadium (W5) (Site of Pro Bowl)	1.00
335	Brian Blades (PB) (W5)	1.50
336	James Brooks (PB) (W5)	1.00
337	Shane Conlan (PB) (W5)	1.00
339	Ray Donaldson (PB) (W5)	1.00
340	Ferrell Edmunds (PB) (W5)	1.00
341	Boomer Esiason (PB) (W5)	1.50
342	David Fulcher (PB) (W5)	1.00
343	Chris Hinton (PB) (W5)	1.00
344	Rodney Holman (PB) (W6)	1.00
345	Kent Hull (PB) (W6)	1.00
346	Tunch Ilkin (PB) (W6)	1.00
347	Mike Johnson (PB) (W6)	1.00
348	Greg Kragen (PB) (W7)	1.00
349	Dave Krieg (PB) (W7)	1.00
350	Albert Lewis (PB) (W7)	1.00
351	Howie Long (PB) (W7)	1.50
352	Bruce Matthews (PB) (W8)	1.00
353	Clay Matthews (PB) (W8)	1.00
354	Erik McMillan (PB) (W8)	1.00
355	Karl Mecklenburg (PB) (W8)	1.00
356	Anthony Miller (PB) (W8)	2.00
357	Frank Minnifield (PB) (W8)	1.00
358	Max Montoya (PB) (W8)	1.00
359	Warren Moon (PB) (W10)	2.00
360	Mike Munchak (PB) (W10)	1.00
361	Anthony Munoz (PB) (W10)	1.00
362	John Offerdahl (PB) (W9)	1.00
363	Christian Okoye (PB) (W9)	1.00
364	Leslie O'Neal (PB) (W9)	1.00
365	Rufus Porter (PB) (W9)	1.00
366	Andre Reed (PB)	1.50
367	Johnny Rembert (PB) (W10)	1.00
368	Reggie Roby (PB) (W10)	1.00
369	Kevin Ross (PB) (W10)	1.00
370	Webster Slaughter (PB) (W10)	1.00
371	Bruce Smith (PB) (W11)	1.50
372	Dennis Smith (PB) (W11)	1.00

373	Derrick Thomas (PB) (W11)	2.00
374	Thurman Thomas (PB) (W11)	2.00
375	David Treadwell (PB) (W11)	1.00
376	Lee Williams (PB) (W11)	1.00

1991 FACT Pro Set Mobil

Each of the NFL cities received these cards, sponsored by Mobil Oil and Pro Set, to use as an educational tool for fourth grade students. The cards are identical to the 1990 Pro Set Series I cards, while the backs have questions for the students. Six different sets were issued throughout the program, each with a header card.

		MT
Complete Set (108):		130.00
Common Player:		.75
3	Joe Montana (S1)	10.00
5	Mike Singletary (S2)	1.00
12	Jay Novacek (S3)	1.50
20	Ottis Anderson (S2)	1.00
40	Tim Brown (S1)	1.50
44	Herschel Walker (S1)	1.00
59	Eric Dorsey (S3)	.75
60	John Elliott (S1)	.75
63	Jeff Hostetler (S1)	1.00
69	Eric Moore (S4)	.75
70	Bart Oates (S3)	.75
71	Gary Reasons (S4)	.75
75	Shane Conlan (S3)	.75
78	Jim Kelly (S4)	2.50
84	Darryl Talley (S4)	.75
90	Marv Levy (CO) (S1)	.75
94	Tim Green (S2)	.75
99	Jerry Glanville (CO) (S3)	.75
101	Mark Carrier (S3)	.75
104	Jim Harbaugh (S6)	1.50
105	Brad Muster (S4)	.75
107	Keith Van Horne (S6)	.75
111	Boomer Esiason (S1)	1.00
116	Anthony Munoz (S2)	1.00
117	Sam Wyche (CO) (S4)	.75
118	Paul Farren (S6)	.75
119	Thane Gash (S3)	.75
122	Clay Matthews (S2)	.75
123	Eric Metcalf (S4)	1.25
127	Tommie Agee (S6)	.75
128	Troy Aikman (S6)	12.00
132	Michael Irvin (S6)	3.00
134	Daniel Stubbs (S6)	.75
136	Steve Atwater (S1)	.75
138	John Elway (S2)	8.00
141	Mark Jackson (S6)	.75
142	Karl Mecklenburg (S3)	.75
143	Doug Widell (S2)	.75
153	Wayne Fontes (CO) (S2)	.75
156	Don Majkowski (S1)	.75
157	Tony Mandarich (S6)	.75
158	Mark Murphy (S6)	.75
161	Sterling Sharpe (S4)	2.00
162	Lindy Infante (CO) (S3)	.75
163	Ray Childress (S6)	.75
166	Bruce Matthews (S6)	.75
167	Warren Moon (S6)	2.50
168	Mike Munchak (S4)	.75
169	Al Smith (S6)	.75
174	Bill Brooks (S1)	1.00
179	Clarence Verdin (S3)	.75
182	Steve DeBerg (S1)	1.00
185	Christian Okoye (S3)	.75
189	Marty Schottenheimer (CO) (S1)	.75
191	Howie Long (S2)	1.00
194	Steve Smith (S4)	.75
196	Lionel Washington (S6)	.75
198	Art Shell (CO) (S3)	1.00
203	Buford McGee (S2)	.75
204	Tom Newberry (S4)	.75
205	Frank Stams (S1)	.75
210	Dan Marino (S4)	18.00
212	John Offerdahl (S1)	.75
216	Don Shula (S4)	1.00
217	Darrell Fullington (S6)	.75
218	Tim Irwin (S2)	.75
219	Mike Merriweather (S3)	.75
231	Ed Reynolds (S3)	.75

238	Robert Massey (S4)	.75
246	James Hasty (S1)	.75
247	Erik McMillan (S2)	.75
249	Ken O'Brien (S4)	.75
260	Andre Waters (S2)	.75
270	Joe Bugel (CO) (S2)	.75
271	Gary Anderson (S1)	.75
272	Dermontti Dawson (S4)	.75
275	Tunch Ilkin (S2)	.75
282	Gill Byrd (S4)	.75
290	Michael Carter (S2)	.75
292	Pierce Holt (S3)	.75
297	George Seifert (CO) (S1)	1.25
306	Chuck Knox (CO) (S3)	.75
310	Harry Hamilton (S4)	.75
321	Martin Mayhew (S4)	.75
322	Mark Rypien (S1)	.75
NNO	Title Card - Stay Fit (S1)	.75
NNO	Title Card - Eat Smart (S2)	.75
NNO	Title Card - Stay Off Drugs (S3)	.75
NNO	Title Card - Stay in Tune (S4)	.75
NNO	Title Card - Stay True to Yourself (S5)	.75
NNO	Title Card - Stay in School (S6)	.75
NNO	Title Card - Stay in School (S6)	.75

1992 FACT NFL Properties

The 18-card set was produced by NFL Properties. It showcases a photo of the player, with the NFL shield and "It's A Fact" printed at the top and a slogan at the bottom. The card is bordered in black at the top and bottom. The backs include a quote, with "Think about it..." printed in the lower right. The card number is printed in a black stripe in the lower right.

		MT
Complete Set (18):		35.00
Common Player:		1.00
1	Crack Kills (Warren Moon)	1.50
2	Think Before You Drink (Boomer Esiason)	1.00
3	Play It Straight (Troy Aikman)	8.00
4	Quedate en la Escuela (Anthony Munoz)	1.00
5	Steroids Destroy (Charles Mann)	1.00
6	Never Give Up (Earnest Byner)	1.00
7	Don't Pollute (Joe Jacoby)	1.00
8	Aids Kills (Howie Long)	1.00
9	School's The Ticket (Dan Marino)	12.00
10	Be The Best (Mike Singletary)	1.50
11	Chill (Cornelius Bennett)	1.00
12	Turn It Off (Chris Doleman)	1.00
13	Eat To Win (Jim Harbaugh)	1.50
14	Say It Don't Spray It (Chris Hinton)	1.00
15	Heal The Planet (Nick Lowery)	1.00
16	Respect The Law (Rodney Peete)	1.00
17	Vote (Pat Swilling)	1.00
18	Study (Jim Everett)	1.00

1993 FACT Fleer Shell

Fleer, Shell Oil and Russell Athletic sponsored this 108-card set. The cards were used as educational materials for teachers throughout the country. A set of 18 cards were released each month. The card fronts were identical to the regular 1993 Fleer cards. The backs, however, featured educational questions and player bios.

		MT
Complete Set (108):		50.00
Common Player:		.25
1	Stay in School - Scorecard	
2	Andre Rison	.50
3	Jim Kelly	.50
4	Mark Carrier (DB)	.25
5	David Fulcher	.25
6	Eric Metcalf	.25

7	Emmitt Smith	5.00
8	John Elway	2.00
9	Rodney Peete	.25
10	Brett Favre	5.00
11	Houson Oilers (Warren Moon)	.50
12	Reggie Langhorne	.25
13	Christian Okoye	.25
14	Nick Bell	.25
15	Jim Everett	.25
16	Dan Marino	5.00
17	Chris Doleman	.25
18	Leonard Russell	.25
19	Stay Fit - Scoreboard	.25
20	Sam Mills	.25
21	Rodney Hampton	.50
22	Rob Moore	.25
23	Seth Joyner	.25
24	Chris Chandler	.25
25	Barry Foster	.25
26	Stan Humphries	.25
27	Steve Young	2.00
28	Cortez Kennedy	.25
29	Reggie Cobb	.25
30	Mark Rypien	.25
31	Michael Haynes	.25
32	Thurman Thomas	.50
33	Tom Waddle	.25
34	Harold Green	.25
35	Tommy Vardell	.25
36	Michael Irvin	.50
37	Eat Smart - Scorecard	.25
38	Mike Croel	.25
39	Barry Sanders	3.00
40	Sterling Sharpe	.50
41	Haywood Jeffires	.25
42	Duane Bickett	.25
43	Nick Lowery	.25
44	Greg Townsend	.25
45	Todd Lyght	.25
46	Richmond Webb	.25
47	Cris Carter	.50
48	Marv Cook	.25
49	Vaughan Johnson	.25
50	Pepper Johnson	.25
51	Kyle Clifton	.25
52	Fred Barnett	.25
53	Ken Harvey	.25
54	Rod Woodson	.50
55	Stay In Tune - Scorecard	.25
56	Marion Butts	.25
57	Ricky Watters	.50
58	Brian Blades	.25
59	Broderick Thomas	.25
60	Charles Mann	.25
61	Chris Hinton	.25
62	Cornelius Bennett	.25
63	Jim Harbaugh	.50
64	Tim Krumrie	.25
65	Bernie Kosar	.50
66	Troy Aikman	3.00
67	Shannon Sharpe	.50
68	Chris Spielman	.25
69	Brian Noble	.25
70	Curtis Duncan	.25
71	Quentin Coryatt	.50
72	Derrick Thomas	.25
73	Stay Off Drugs - Scorecard	.25
74	Tim Brown	.50
75	Jackie Slater	.25
76	Keith Jackson	.25
77	Terry Allen	.50
78	Andre Tippett	.25
79	Morten Andersen	.25
80	Phil Simms	.25
81	Jeff Lageman	.25
82	Randall Cunningham	.25
83	Randal Hill	.25
84	Neil O'Donnell	.50
85	Gill Byrd	.25
86	John Taylor	.25
87	Eugene Robinson	.25
88	Paul Gruber	.25
89	Andre Collins	.25
90	Chris Miller	.25
91	Stay True To Yourself - Scorecard	.25
92	Andre Reed	.50
93	Richard Dent	.25
94	David Klingler	.25
95	Jay Novacek	.25
96	Steve Atwater	.25
97	Bennie Blades	.25
98	Terrell Buckley	.25
99	Ray Childress	.25
100	Harvey Williams	.25
101	Howie Long	.50
102	Lawrence Taylor	.50
103	Johnny Mitchell	.25
104	Carnell Lake	.25
105	Junior Seau	.50
106	Kevin Fagan	.25
107	Lawrence Dawsey	.25
108	Art Monk	.50

1994 FACT Fleer Shell

This 108-card set was sponsored by Fleer and Shell

Oil. The educational sets were broken up into six 18-card subsets which showcased 17 player cards and one header card. The fronts feature the same design as the 1994 Fleer set. The card backs include a head shot and an action photo, with questions printed over the top. The card number is printed in the lower left corner, with the player's name and facsimile autograph in the upper left.

		MT
Complete Set (108):		35.00
Common Player:		.10
1	Cover Card - Stay In School	
2	Steve Beuerlein	.10
3	Erric Pegram	.10
4	Darryl Talley	.10
5	Tom Waddle	.10
6	Darryl Williams	.10
7	Tony Jones	.10
8	Jay Novacek	.20
9	Simon Fletcher	.10
10	Jason Hanson	.10
11	Reggie White	.30
12	Ernest Givins	.10
13	Kerry Cash	.10
14	Joe Montana	1.75
15	Anthony Smith	.10
16	Jackie Slater	.10
17	Terry Kirby	.10
18	John Randle	.10
19	Cover Card - Stay Fit	.10
20	Drew Bledsoe	1.75
21	Vaughan Johnson	.10
22	Greg Jackson	.10
23	Rob Moore	.10
24	Byron Evans	.10
25	Rod Woodson	.20
26	Junior Seau	.20
27	Steve Young	1.25
28	Cortez Kennedy	.10
29	Paul Gruber	.10
30	Darrell Green	.10
31	Tyronne Stowe	.10
32	Pierce Holt	.10
33	Steve Tasker	.10
34	Chris Zorich	.10
35	Ricardo McDonald	.10
36	Mark Carrier (WR)	.10
37	Cover Card - Eat Smart	
38	Emmitt Smith	3.50
39	Shannon Sharpe	.20
40	Chris Spielman	.10
41	Ken Ruettgers	.10
42	Bubba McDowell	.10
43	Rohn Stark	.10
44	Derrick Thomas	.20
45	Tim Brown	.20
46	Shane Conlan	.10
47	Marco Coleman	.10
48	Steve Jordan	.10
49	Ben Coates	.20
50	Willie Roaf	.10
51	Carlton Bailey	.10
52	Ronnie Lott	.20
53	Eric Allen	.10
54	Dermontti Dawson	.10
55	Cover Card - Stay In Tune	
56	Ronnie Harmon	.10
57	Dana Stubblefield	.20
58	Rick Mirer	.30
59	Santana Dotson	.10
60	Jim Lachey	.10
61	Ricky Proehl	.10
61	Jessie Tuggle	.10
63	Jim Kelly	.20
64	Mark Carrier (DB)	.10
65	David Klingler	.10
66	Eric Turner	.10
67	Darrin Smith	.10
68	Glyn Milburn	.20
69	Herman Moore	.30
70	Sterling Sharpe	.20
71	Ray Childress	.10
72	Quentin Coryatt	.10
73	Cover Card - Stay Off Drugs	
74	Marcus Allen	.20
75	Jeff Hostetler	.10
76	Jerome Bettis	.40
77	Richmond Webb	.10
78	Randall McDaniel	.10
79	Maurice Hurst	.10
80	Morten Andersen	.10
81	Dave Meggett	.10
82	Brian Washington	.10
83	Randall Cunningham	
84	Kevin Greene	.20
85	Leslie O'Neal	.10
86	Tim McDonald	.10
87	Eugene Robinson	.10
88	Hardy Nickerson	.10
89	Chip Lohmiller	.10
90	Jeff George	.20
91	Cover Card - Stay True To Yourself	
92	Cornelius Bennett	.10
93	Erik Kramer	.10
94	Tommy Vardell	.10

95	Troy Aikman	1.75
96	John Elway	1.25
97	Barry Sanders	1.75
98	Dan Saleaumua	.10
99	Dan Marino	3.50
100	Jack Del Rio	.10
101	Bruce Armstrong	.10
102	Renaldo Turnbull	.10
103	Phil Simms	.10
104	Boomer Esiason	.10
105	Fred Barnett	.10
106	Greg Lloyd	.20
107	John Carney	.10
108	Jerry Rice	1.75

1994 FACT NFL Properties

The 18-card NFL Properties set has the NFL shield and "It's A Fact" printed at the top and a slogan at the bottom. The top and bottom are bordered with a black stripe. The backs include a quote, with "Think About It..." printed in the bottom right. The card number is located in a black stripe in the lower right.

		MT
Complete Set (18):		30.00
Common Player:		.75
1	Play It Straight (Troy Aikman)	4.00
2	Chill (Cornelius Bennett)	.75
3	Aim High (Lesley Visser) (ANN)	.75
4	Eat Smart (Junior Seau)	1.50
5	Clean Up Your Act (Chris Hinton)	.75
6	Plan Ahead (Howie Long)	1.00
7	Heal The Planet (Nick Lowery)	.75
8	Guns Are For Foods (Tony Casillas)	.75
9	School's The Ticket (Dan Marino)	7.00
10	Make A Difference (Warren Moon)	1.25
11	Jim We're - We're the Same Inside (Rod Bernstine)	.75
12	Smoking Is Stupid (Rohn Stark)	.75
13	Respect The Law (Michael Irvin)	1.00
14	Education Works (Steve Young)	3.00
15	Kids Deserve Love (Bart Oates)	.75
16	Be Fit! (Erik George)	.75
17	Don't Quit (Emmitt Smith)	7.00
18	Think (Steve Beuerlein)	.75

1994 FACT NFL Properties Artex

The three-card set carries the same design as the NFL Properties set, except it is numbered 1-3 and the Artex logo is printed on the back. The cards were distributed through K-Mart.

		MT
Complete Set (3):		7.00
Common Player:		1.50
1	Play It Straight (Troy Aikman)	1.50
2	School's The Ticket (Dan Marino)	3.00
3	Don't Quit (Emmitt Smith)	3.00

1995 FACT Fleer Shell

The 108-card set, sponsored by Fleer and Shell Oil, was

used as an educational tool by elementary school teachers. The set was broken up into six subsets of 18 cards each. The card fronts are identical to the 1995 Fleer set, while the backs carry the same design, except for educational questions instead of player stats.

		MT
Complete Set (108):		20.00
Common Player:		.10
1	Cover Card - Stay In School	.10
2	Seth Joyner	.10
3	J.J. Birden	.10
4	Jim Kelly	.20
5	Pete Metzelaars	.10
6	Joe Cain	.10
7	Carl Pickens	.20
8	Leroy Hoard	.10
9	Troy Aikman	1.50
10	Steve Atwater	.10
11	Bennie Blades	.10
12	Brett Favre	3.00
13	Mel Gray	.10
14	Tony Bennett	.10
15	Steve Beuerlein	.10
16	Marcus Allen	.20
17	Tim Brown	.20
18	Tim Bowens	.10
19	Cover Card - Stay Fit	.10
20	Jack Del Rio	.10
21	Drew Bledsoe	1.50
22	Jim Everett	.10
23	Michael Brooks	.10
24	Tony Casillas	.10
25	Fred Barnett	.10
26	Kevin Greene	.10
27	Jerome Bettis	.40
28	John Carney	.10
29	Ken Norton	.10
30	Cortez Kennedy	.10
31	Alvin Harper	.10
32	Henry Ellard	.10
33	Aeneas Williams	.10
34	Jeff George	.20
35	Bryce Paup	.20
36	Sam Mills	.10
37	Cover Card - Eat Smart	
38	Mark Carrier	.10
39	Darnay Scott	.20
40	Pepper Johnson	.10
41	Michael Irvin	.20
42	John Elway	1.00
43	Herman Moore	.30
44	John Jurkovic	.10
45	Al Smith	.10
46	Steve Emtman	.10
47	Darren Carrington	.10
48	Kimble Anders	.10
49	Jeff Hostetler	.10
51	Eric Green	.10
51	Cris Carter	.20
52	Ben Coates	.10
53	Michael Haynes	.10
55	Cover Card - Stay In Tune (Dave Brown)	.10
56	Boomer Esiason	.10
57	Randall Cunningham	
58	Byron "Bam" Morris	.10
59	Sean Gilbert	.10
60	Stan Humphries	.20
61	Jerry Rice	1.50
62	Rick Mirer	.40
63	Hardy Nickerson	.10
64	Ricky Ervins	.10
65	Eric Swann	.10
66	Craig Heyward	.10
67	Andre Reed	.10
68	Frank Reich	.10
69	Steve Walsh	.10
70	Dan Wilkinson	.10
71	Vinny Testaverde	.10
72	Russell Maryland	.10
73	Cover Card - Stay Off Drugs	.10
74	Shannon Sharpe	.10
75	Brett Perriman	.10
76	Reggie White	.25
77	Mark Stepnoski	.10
78	Marshall Faulk	.75
79	Reggie Cobb	.10
80	Lake Dawson	.10
81	Rocket Ismail	.10
82	Dan Marino	3.00
83	Warren Moon	.20
84	Willie McGinest	.10
85	William Roaf	.10
86	Rodney Hampton	.20
87	Marvin Washington	.10
88	Charlie Garner	.10
89	Neil O'Donnell	.20
90	Todd Lyght	.10
91	Cover Card - Stay True To Yourself	.10
92	Natrone Means	.40
93	Deion Sanders	1.00
94	Chris Warren	.20
95	Errict Rhett	1.00
96	Ken Harvey	.10
97	Bruce Smith	.10
98	Chris Zorich	.10
99	Eric Turner	.10
100	Emmitt Smith	3.00

101	Barry Sanders	1.50
102	Neil Smith	.10
103	Chester McGlockton	.10
104	Fuad Reveiz	.10
105	Thomas Lewis	.10
106	Rod Woodson	.10
107	Junior Seau	.20
108	Steve Young	1.00

1995 FACT NFL Properties

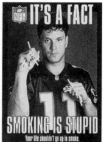

Produced by NFL Properties, the 18-card set had the NFL shield and "It's A Fact" printed at the top on the card fronts. A slogan was printed at the bottom. The card fronts are bordered with black stripes on the top and bottom. The backs have a quote and "Think About It..." printed in the lower right. The card number is printed in a black stripe on the bottom right.

		MT
Complete Set (18):		20.00
Common Player:		.50
1	Troy Aikman	2.50
2	Rocket Ismail, Qadry Ismail	.75
3	Robin Roberts	.50
4	Junior Seau	1.00
5	Chris Hinton	.50
6	Sean Jones	.50
7	Thurman Thomas	1.00
8	Neil Smith	.50
9	Dan Marino	5.00
10	Reggie Williams	.50
11	(Rod Bernstine, Jim Kelly)	1.00
12	Drew Bledsoe	2.50
13	Michael Irvin	1.00
14	Steve Young	1.75
15	Jerry Rice	2.50
16	Herschel Walker	.75
17	Emmitt Smith	5.00
18	Barry Sanders	2.50

1968 Falcons Team Issue

Measuring 7-1/2" x 9-1/2", the fronts feature a black-and-white photo, with the player's name and team printed in the white border at the bottom. The only card not using a posed action photo is Bob Berry's, which features a portrait. The cards are unnumbered and the backs are blank.

		NM
Complete Set (14):		65.00
Common Player:		4.00
1	Bob Berry	4.00
2	Carlton Dabney	4.00
3	Bob Etter	4.00
4	Bill Harris	4.00
5	Ralph Heck	4.00
6	Claude Humphrey	4.00
7	Randy Johnson	4.00
8	George Kunz (White jersey 78)	6.00
9	George Kunz (Dark jersey 75)	6.00
10	Errol Linden	4.00
11	Billy Lothridge	4.00
12	Ken Reaves	4.00
13	Jerry Shay	4.00
14	Tommy Nobis	15.00

1978 Falcons Kinnett Dairies

Measuring 4-1/4" x 6", this six-card set showcases four black-and-white player head shots on the front. The Kinnett logo appears in the middle left, while "Atlanta Player Cards" and the NFLPA logo are printed to the right. The unnumbered cards have blank backs.

	NM
Complete Set (6):	35.00
Common Player:	5.00
1 William Andrews, Jeff Yeates, Wilson Faumuina, Phil McKinnely	5.00
2 Warren Bryant, R.C. Thielemann, Steve Bartkowski, Frank Reed	10.00
3 Wallace Francis, Jim Mitchell, Jeff Van Note, Ray Easterling	5.00
4 Dewey McClain, Billy Ryckman, Paul Ryczek, Bubba Bean	5.00
5 Robert Pennywell, Dave Scott, Jim Bailey, John James	5.00
6 Haskel Stanback, Rick Byas, Mike Esposito, Tom Moriarty	5.00

1980 Falcons Police

Measuring 2-5/8" x 4-1/8", the 30-card set boasts a player photo on the front, with the Falcons' logo in the upper left and the player's name, number, position and bio under the photo on the left. Below the photo on the right is the Falcons' logo. The unnumbered card backs include "Tips from the Falcons" at the top, with the Atlanta Police Athletic League and Atlanta Jaycees logos underneath. A safety tip is printed in the center of the card, with the Coca-Cola logo at the bottom center of the card back.

	NM
Complete Set (30):	30.00
Common Player:	.90
1 William Andrews	3.75
2 Steve Bartkowski	7.50
3 Bubba Bean	2.00
4 Warren Bryant	.90
5 Rick Byas	.90
6 Lynn Cain	2.25
7 Buddy Curry	.90
8 Edgar Fields	.90
9 Wallace Francis	2.75
10 Alfred Jackson	2.25
11 John James	.90
12 Alfred Jenkins	3.00
13 Kenny Johnson	.90
14 Mike Kenn	2.25
15 Fulton Kuykendall	1.50
16 Rolland Lawrence	1.50
17 Tim Mazzetti	.90
18 Dewey McLean	1.50
19 Jeff Merrow	1.50
20 Junior Miller	2.25
21 Tom Pridemore	.90
22 Frank Reed	.90
23 Al Richardson	.90
24 Dave Scott	.90
25 Don Smith	.90
26 Reggie Smith	.90
27 R.C. Thielemann	1.50
28 Jeff Van Note	2.25
29 Joel Williams	.90
30 Jeff Yeates	.90

1981 Falcons Police

Measuring 2-5/8" x 4-1/8", the 30-card set is anchored with a large photo on the front. The Atlanta Police Athletic League logo is printed in the upper left of the card front, while "NFC Western Division Champions 1980" is located in the upper right. Beneath the photo are the player's name, number, position, bio and Falcons' logo. The unnumbered card backs boast a Coca-Cola logo in the upper left and a Chevron logo in the upper right. The player's name and a highlight are printed in the center of the back, with a safety tip located beneath it. Photo and printing credits appear on the bottom of the card backs.

	MT
Complete Set (30):	12.00
Common Player:	.50

6	John James	.50
10	Steve Bartkowski	3.00
16	Reggie Smith	.50
18	Mick Luckhurst	.50
21	Lynn Cain	1.00
23	Bobby Butler	.50
27	Tom Pridemore	.50
30	Scott Woerner	.50
31	William Andrews	1.25
36	Bob Glazebrook	.50
37	Kenny Johnson	.50
50	Buddy Curry	.50
51	Jim Laughlin	.50
54	Fulton Kuykendall	.50
56	Al Richardson	.50
57	Jeff Van Note	.50
58	Joel Williams	.50
65	Don Smith	.50
66	Warren Bryant	.50
68	R.C. Thielemann	.50
70	Dave Scott	.50
74	Wilson Faumuina	.50
75	Jeff Merrow	.50
78	Mike Kenn	.50
79	Jeff Yeates	.50
80	Junior Miller	.50
84	Alfred Jenkins	1.00
85	Alfred Jackson	.50
89	Wallace Francis	1.00
NNO	Leeman Bennett (CO)	.50

1993 FCA Super Bowl

Showcased on the front of these six standard-sized cards is the Fellowship of Christian Athletes' logo in the upper left, with "professional football" located along the left border. The player photo, which is bordered in a screen that goes from light blue to dark blue, is featured on the left side of the card, with the player's name and position printed on the bottom right. The card backs, which are numbered in the upper right, have a player headshot in the upper left, with his name and bio printed along the right. A Christian message from the player is printed in yellow in the center. The FCA's toll-free number is printed at the bottom right.

	MT
Complete Set (6):	8.00
Common Player:	.75
1 Alfred Anderson	.75
2 Bob Lilly	1.50
3 Tom Landry (CO)	2.00
4 Brent Jones	1.00
5 Bruce Matthews	.75
6 Title Card	.75

1992 Finest

Produced in a print run of 3,000 cases, with 20 sets per case, the 44-card set showcases a player photo in foil on the front of the card, with the Topps Football's Finest logo at the top. The player's name and team are listed under the photo in a blue rectangle. "Limited Edition" is printed inside a gold stripe at the bottom. The 33 veteran cards are bordered in blue, gold and black. The 11 rookie cards are bordered in gold and red. The card backs feature "Topps Football's Finest" at the top, with the player's name printed in large letters, overlapping a football helmet on the left. The cards are numbered "of 44" and feature the player's bio and position at the bottom.

	MT
Complete Set (45):	25.00

Common Player:		.25
1	Neal Anderson	.25
2	Cornelius Bennett	.25
3	Marion Butts	.25
4	Anthony Carter	.25
5	Mike Croel	.25
6	John Elway	10.00
7	Jim Everett	.25
8	Ernest Givins	.25
9	Rodney Hampton	.50
10	Alvin Harper	.50
11	Michael Irvin	.75
12	Rickey Jackson	.25
13	Seth Joyner	.25
14	James Lofton	.50
15	Ronnie Lott	.50
16	Eric Metcalf	.25
17	Chris Miller	.25
18	Art Monk	.50
19	Warren Moon	.50
20	Rob Moore	.25
21	Anthony Munoz	.25
22	Christian Okoye	.25
23	Andre Rison	.50
24	Leonard Russell	.50
25	Mark Rypien	.25
26	Barry Sanders	10.00
27	Emmitt Smith	10.00
28	Pat Swilling	.25
29	John Taylor	.25
30	Derrick Thomas	1.00
31	Thurman Thomas	1.00
32	Reggie White	1.00
33	Rod Woodson	.25
34	Edgar Bennett	.50
35	Terrell Buckley	.25
36	Keith Hamilton	.25
37	Amp Lee	.25
38	Ricardo McDonald	.25
39	Chris Mims	.25
40	Robert Porcher	.25
41	Leon Searcy	.25
42	Siran Stacy	.25
43	Tommy Vardell	.25
44	Bob Whitfield	.25
NNO	Checklist	.25

1994 Finest

Topps created its 1994 Finest set using its chromium technology to give the cards a high-tech metallic look. Each front has a full-color player action shot, with a color bar at the bottom that has his name; the Topps Finest logo is at the top of the card. The back is horizontal. One side has a full-color photo bordered by a picture frame. Stats, biographical information and a summary of the player's finest moment in football are on the opposite side. A parallel set featuring refracting foil cards for each regular card was also made. These refractors were randomly inserted into every ninth pack. In addition, super-size versions of 37 specially-designed rookie cards from the main were made in a 4" x 6" format. One of these cards was put into every 24-count box of packs. One in every six of these cards is enhanced with refracting foil.

	MT
Complete Set (220):	80.00
Common Player:	.50
Minor Stars:	1.00
Wax Box:	150.00
1 Emmitt Smith	10.00
2 Calvin Williams	.50
3 Mark Collins	.50
4 Steve McMichael	.50
5 Jim Kelly	1.00
6 Michael Dean Perry	.50
7 Wayne Simmons	.50
8 Raghib Ismail	.50
9 Mark Rypien	.50
10 Brian Blades	.50
11 Barry Word	.50
12 Jerry Rice	8.00
13 Derrick Fenner	.50

14	Karl Mecklenburg	.50
15	Reggie Cobb	.50
16	Eric Swann	.50
17	Neil Smith	.50
18	Barry Foster	.50
19	Willie Roaf	.50
20	Troy Drayton	.50
21	Warren Moon	1.00
22	Richmond Webb	.50
23	Anthony Miller	.50
24	Chris Slade	.50
25	Mel Gray	.50
26	Ronnie Lott	1.00
27	Andre Rison	1.00
28	Jeff George	1.00
29	John Copeland	.50
30	Derrick Thomas	1.00
31	Sterling Sharpe	1.00
32	Chris Doleman	.50
33	Monte Coleman	.50
34	Mark Bavaro	.50
35	Kevin Williams	1.00
36	Eric Metcalf	.50
37	Brent Jones	.50
38	Steve Tasker	.50
39	Dave Meggett	.50
40	Howie Long	1.00
41	Rick Mirer	2.00
42	Jerome Bettis	4.00
43	Marion Butts	.50
44	Barry Sanders	12.00
45	Jason Elam	.50
46	Broderick Thomas	.50
47	Derek Brown	.50
48	Lorenzo White	.50
49	Neil O'Donnell	1.00
50	Chris Burkett	.50
51	John Offerdahl	.50
52	Rohn Stark	.50
53	Neal Anderson	.50
54	Steve Beuerlein	.50
55	Bruce Armstrong	.50
56	Lincoln Kennedy	.50
57	Darrell Green	.50
58	Ricardo McDonald	.50
59	Chris Warren	1.00
60	Mark Jackson	.50
61	Pepper Johnson	.50
62	Chris Spielman	.50
63	Marcus Allen	1.00
64	Jim Everett	.50
65	Greg Townsend	.50
66	Cris Carter	1.00
67	Don Beebe	.50
68	Reggie Langhorne	.50
69	Randall Cunningham	.50
70	Johnny Holland	.50
71	Morten Andersen	.50
72	Leonard Marshall	.50
73	Keith Jackson	.50
74	Leslie O'Neal	.50
75	Hardy Nickerson	.50
76	Dan Williams	.50
77	Steve Young	6.00
78	Deon Figures	.50
79	Michael Irvin	2.00
80	Luis Sharpe	.50
81	Andre Tippett	.50
82	Ricky Sanders	.50
83	Erric Pegram	.50
84	Albert Lewis	.50
85	Anthony Blaylock	.50
86	Pat Swilling	.50
87	Duane Bickett	.50
88	Myron Guyton	.50
89	Clay Matthews	.50
90	Jim McMahon	.50
91	Bruce Smith	.50
92	Reggie White	1.00
93	Shannon Sharpe	.50
94	Rickey Jackson	.50
95	Ronnie Harmon	.50
96	Terry McDaniel	.50
97	Bryan Cox	.50
98	Webster Slaughter	.50
99	Boomer Esiason	.50
100	Tim Krumrie	.50
101	Cortez Kennedy	.50
102	Henry Ellard	.50
103	Clyde Simmons	.50
104	Craig Erickson	.50
105	Eric Green	.50
106	Gary Clark	.50
107	Jay Novacek	.50
108	Dana Stubblefield	.50
109	Mike Johnson	.50
110	Ray Crockett	.50
111	Leonard Russell	.50
112	Robert Smith	3.00
113	Art Monk	1.00
114	Ray Childress	.50
115	O.J. McDuffie	2.00
116	Tim Brown	.50
117	Kevin Ross	.50
118	Richard Dent	.50
119	John Elway	10.00
120	James Hasty	.50
121	Gary Plummer	.50
122	Pierce Holt	.50
123	Eric Martin	.50
124	Brett Favre	12.00
125	Cornelius Bennett	.50
126	Jessie Hester	.50
127	Lewis Tillman	.50
128	Quadry Ismail	.50
129	Jay Schroeder	.50
130	Curtis Conway	3.00

131	Santana Dotson	.50
132	Nick Lowery	.50
133	Lomas Brown	.50
134	Reggie Roby	.50
135	John L. Williams	.50
136	Vinny Testaverde	.50
137	Seth Joyner	.50
138	Ethan Horton	.50
139	Jackie Slater	.50
140	Rod Bernstine	.50
141	Rob Moore	.50
142	Dan Marino	10.00
143	Ken Harvey	.50
144	Ernest Givins	.50
145	Russell Maryland	.50
146	Drew Bledsoe	6.00
147	Kevin Greene	.50
148	Bobby Hebert	.50
149	Junior Seau	1.00
150	Tim McDonald	.50
151	Thurman Thomas	1.00
152	Phil Simms	.50
153	Terrell Buckley	.50
154	Sam Mills	.50
155	Anthony Carter	.50
156	Kelvin Martin	.50
157	Shane Conlan	.50
158	Irving Fryar	.50
159	Demetrius DuBose	.50
160	David Klingler	.50
161	Herman Moore	2.00
162	Jeff Hostetler	1.00
163	Tommy Vardell	.50
164	Craig Heyward	.50
165	Wilber Marshall	.50
166	Quentin Coryatt	.50
167	Glyn Milburn	1.00
168	Fred Barnett	.50
169	Charles Haley	.50
170	Carl Banks	.50
171	Ricky Proehl	.50
172	Joe Montana	8.00
173	Johnny Mitchell	.50
174	Andre Reed	1.00
175	Marco Coleman	.50
176	Vaughan Johnson	.50
177	Carl Pickens	1.00
178	Dwight Stone	.50
179	Ricky Watters	1.00
180	Michael Haynes	.50
181	Roger Craig	.50
182	Cleveland Gary	.50
183	Steve Emtman	.50
184	Patrick Bates	.50
185	Mark Carrier	.50
186	Brad Hopkins	.50
187	Dennis Smith	.50
188	Natrone Means	3.00
189	Michael Jackson	.50
190	Ken Norton	.50
191	Carlton Gray	.50
192	Edgar Bennett	.50
193	Lawrence Taylor	1.00
194	Marv Cook	.50
195	Eric Curry	.50
196	Victor Bailey	.50
197	Ryan McNeil	.50
198	Rod Woodson	1.00
199	Ernest Byner	.50
200	Marvin Jones	.50
201	Thomas Smith	.50
202	Troy Aikman	8.00
203	Audray McMillian	.50
204	Wade Wilson	.50
205	George Teague	.50
206	Deion Sanders	4.00
207	Will Shields	.50
208	John Taylor	.50
209	Jim Harbaugh	.50
210	Michael Barrow	.50
211	Harold Green	.50
212	Steve Everitt	.50
213	Flipper Anderson	.50
214	Rodney Hampton	1.00
215	Steve Atwater	.50
216	James Trapp	.50
217	Terry Kirby	.50
218	Garrison Hearst	4.00
219	Jeff Bryant	.50
220	Roosevelt Potts	.50

1994 Finest Refractors

Refractors paralleled the 220-card regular-issue set with a holographic, rainbow finish on each card. Refractors were inserted every nine packs of Finest.

	MT
Complete Set (220):	1700.
Common Player:	4.00
Minor Stars:	8.00
1 Emmitt Smith	85.00
2 Calvin Williams	4.00
3 Mark Collins	4.00
4 Steve McMichael	4.00
5 Jim Kelly	10.00
6 Michael Dean Perry	4.00
7 Wayne Simmons	4.00
8 Raghib Ismail	4.00
9 Mark Rypien	4.00
10 Brian Blades	4.00
11 Barry Word	4.00
12 Jerry Rice	50.00
13 Derrick Fenner	4.00
14 Karl Mecklenburg	4.00
15 Reggie Cobb	4.00
16 Eric Swann	4.00
17 Neil Smith	4.00
18 Barry Foster	4.00
19 Willie Roaf	4.00
20 Troy Drayton	4.00
21 Warren Moon	8.00
22 Richmond Webb	4.00
23 Anthony Miller	4.00
24 Chris Slade	4.00
25 Mel Gray	4.00
26 Ronnie Lott	8.00
27 Andre Rison	8.00
28 Jeff George	8.00
29 John Copeland	4.00
30 Derrick Thomas	8.00
31 Sterling Sharpe	8.00
32 Chris Doleman	4.00
33 Monte Coleman	4.00
34 Mark Bavaro	4.00
35 Kevin Williams	10.00
36 Eric Metcalf	4.00
37 Brent Jones	4.00
38 Steve Tasker	4.00
39 Dave Meggett	4.00
40 Howie Long	4.00
41 Rick Mirer	8.00
42 Jerome Bettis	25.00
43 Marion Butts	4.00
44 Barry Sanders	100.00
45 Jason Elam	4.00
46 Broderick Thomas	4.00
47 Derek Brown	4.00
48 Lorenzo White	4.00
49 Neil O'Donnell	8.00
50 Chris Burkett	4.00
51 John Offerdahl	4.00
52 Rohn Stark	4.00
53 Neal Anderson	4.00
54 Steve Beuerlein	4.00
55 Bruce Armstrong	4.00
56 Lincoln Kennedy	4.00
57 Darrell Green	4.00
58 Ricardo McDonald	4.00
59 Chris Warren	8.00
60 Mark Jackson	4.00
61 Pepper Johnson	4.00
62 Chris Spielman	4.00
63 Marcus Allen	10.00
64 Jim Everett	4.00
65 Greg Townsend	4.00
66 Cris Carter	8.00
67 Don Beebe	4.00
68 Reggie Langhorne	4.00
69 Randall Cunningham	4.00
70 Johnny Holland	4.00
71 Morten Andersen	4.00
72 Leonard Marshall	4.00
73 Keith Jackson	4.00
74 Leslie O'Neal	4.00
75 Hardy Nickerson	4.00
76 Dan Williams	4.00
77 Steve Young	40.00
78 Deon Figures	4.00
79 Michael Irvin	10.00
80 Luis Sharpe	4.00
81 Andre Tippett	4.00
82 Ricky Sanders	4.00
83 Erric Pegram	4.00
84 Albert Lewis	4.00
85 Anthony Blaylock	4.00
86 Pat Swilling	4.00
87 Duane Bickett	4.00
88 Myron Guyton	4.00
89 Clay Matthews	4.00
90 Jim McMahon	4.00
91 Bruce Smith	4.00
92 Reggie White	10.00
93 Shannon Sharpe	4.00
94 Rickey Jackson	4.00
95 Ronnie Harmon	4.00
96 Terry McDaniel	4.00
97 Bryan Cox	4.00
98 Webster Slaughter	4.00
99 Boomer Esiason	4.00
100 Tim Krumrie	4.00
101 Cortez Kennedy	4.00
102 Henry Ellard	4.00
103 Clyde Simmons	4.00
104 Craig Erickson	4.00
105 Eric Green	4.00
106 Gary Clark	4.00
107 Jay Novacek	4.00
108 Dana Stubblefield	8.00
109 Mike Johnson	4.00

110	Ray Crockett	4.00
111	Leonard Russell	4.00
112	Robert Smith	30.00
113	Art Monk	8.00
114	Ray Childress	4.00
115	O.J. McDuffie	8.00
116	Tim Brown	8.00
117	Kevin Ross	4.00
118	Richard Dent	4.00
119	John Elway	80.00
120	James Hasty	4.00
121	Gary Plummer	4.00
122	Pierce Holt	4.00
123	Eric Martin	4.00
124	Brett Favre	100.00
125	Cornelius Bennett	4.00
126	Jessie Hester	4.00
127	Lewis Tillman	4.00
128	Qadry Ismail	4.00
129	Jay Schroeder	4.00
130	Curtis Conway	30.00
131	Santana Dotson	4.00
132	Nick Lowery	4.00
133	Lomas Brown	4.00
134	Reggie Roby	4.00
135	John L. Williams	4.00
136	Vinny Testaverde	4.00
137	Seth Joyner	4.00
138	Ethan Horton	4.00
139	Jackie Slater	4.00
140	Rob Bernstine	4.00
141	Rob Moore	4.00
142	Dan Marino	85.00
143	Ken Harvey	4.00
144	Ernest Givins	4.00
145	Russell Maryland	4.00
146	Drew Bledsoe	60.00
147	Kevin Greene	4.00
148	Bobby Hebert	4.00
149	Junior Seau	8.00
150	Tim McDonald	4.00
151	Thurman Thomas	10.00
152	Phil Simms	4.00
153	Terrell Buckley	4.00
154	Sam Mills	4.00
155	Anthony Carter	4.00
156	Kelvin Martin	4.00
157	Shane Conlan	4.00
158	Irving Fryar	4.00
159	Demetrius DuBose	4.00
160	David Klingler	4.00
161	Herman Moore	10.00
162	Jeff Hostetler	8.00
163	Tommy Vardell	4.00
164	Craig Heyward	4.00
165	Wilber Marshall	4.00
166	Quentin Coryatt	4.00
167	Glyn Milburn	4.00
168	Fred Barnett	4.00
169	Charles Haley	4.00
170	Carl Banks	4.00
171	Ricky Proehl	4.00
172	Joe Montana	100.00
173	Johnny Mitchell	4.00
174	Andre Reed	8.00
175	Marco Coleman	4.00
176	Vaughan Johnson	4.00
177	Carl Pickens	10.00
178	Dwight Stone	4.00
179	Ricky Watters	8.00
180	Michael Haynes	4.00
181	Roger Craig	4.00
182	Cleveland Gary	4.00
183	Steve Emtman	4.00
184	Patrick Bates	4.00
185	Mark Carrier	4.00
186	Brad Hopkins	4.00
187	Dennis Smith	4.00
188	Natrone Means	25.00
189	Michael Jackson	4.00
190	Ken Norton	4.00
191	Carlton Gray	4.00
192	Edgar Bennett	4.00
193	Lawrence Taylor	8.00
194	Marv Cook	4.00
195	Eric Curry	4.00
196	Victor Bailey	4.00
197	Ryan McNeil	4.00
198	Rod Woodson	8.00
199	Ernest Byner	4.00
200	Marvin Jones	4.00
201	Thomas Smith	4.00
202	Troy Aikman	50.00
203	Audray McMillian	4.00
204	Wade Wilson	4.00
205	George Teague	4.00
206	Deion Sanders	25.00
207	Will Shields	4.00
208	John Taylor	4.00
209	Jim Harbaugh	8.00
210	Michael Barrow	4.00
211	Harold Green	4.00
212	Steve Everitt	4.00
213	Flipper Anderson	4.00
214	Rodney Hampton	8.00
215	Steve Atwater	4.00
216	James Trapp	4.00
217	Terry Kirby	4.00
218	Garrison Hearst	25.00
219	Jeff Bryant	4.00
220	Roosevelt Potts	4.00

A card number in parentheses ( ) indicates the set is unnumbered.

1994 Finest Rookie Jumbos

The Finest Rookie Jumbos set has 37 rookies with identical cards from the regular set; however, the jumbos measure 4-1/2" x 6". These oversized cards were found at a rate of one per 24-count box.

		MT
Complete Set (37):		180.00
Common Player:		3.00
Minor Stars:		6.00
1:Box		

#	Player	Price
7	Wayne Simmons	3.00
19	Willie Roaf	3.00
20	Troy Drayton	3.00
24	Chris Slade	3.00
29	John Copeland	3.00
35	Kevin Williams	3.00
41	Rick Mirer	6.00
42	Jerome Bettis	12.00
45	Jason Elam	6.00
47	Derek Brown (RB)	3.00
56	Lincoln Kennedy	3.00
78	Deon Figures	3.00
108	Dana Stubblefield	6.00
112	Robert Smith	10.00
115	O.J. McDuffie	8.00
128	Qadry Ismail	3.00
130	Curtis Conway	8.00
146	Drew Bledsoe	30.00
159	Demetrius DuBose	3.00
167	Glyn Milburn	6.00
184	Patrick Bates	3.00
186	Brad Hopkins	3.00
188	Natrone Means	8.00
191	Carlton Gray	3.00
195	Eric Curry	3.00
196	Victor Bailey	3.00
197	Ryan McNeil	3.00
200	Marvin Jones	3.00
201	Thomas Smith	3.00
205	George Teague	3.00
207	Will Shields	3.00
210	Michael Barrow	3.00
212	Steve Everitt	3.00
216	James Trapp	3.00
217	Terry Kirby	6.00
218	Garrison Hearst	10.00
220	Roosevelt Potts	3.00

1995 Finest

The regular issue 1995 Topps Finest set was released in two series - Series I had 165 cards, while Series II had 110. Each card comes with the standard Finest Protector, a peel-off laminate, to assure its Mint condition out of the pack. A 1994 Draft Picks subset was included in Series I; it features a different design from the regular cards. A 275-card parallel set of Finest Refractor cards was also made; cards were seeded one per every 12 packs. Series I inserts, titled Fan Favorites, feature impact players on clear cut cards. Series II inserts were Boosters, numbered B166-B187.

		MT
Complete Set (275):		170.00
Complete Series 1 (165):		70.00
Complete Series 2 (110):		100.00
Common Player:		.50
Minor Stars:		1.00
Series 1 Wax Box:		100.00
Series 2 Wax Box:		125.00

#	Player	Price
1	Natrone Means	1.50
2	David Meggett	.50
3	Tim Bowens	1.00
4	Jay Novacek	.50
5	Michael Jackson	.50
6	Eric Allen	.50
7	Neil Smith	.50
8	Chris Gardocki	.50
9	Jeff Burris	1.00
10	Warren Moon	1.00
11	Gary Anderson	.50
12	Bert Emanuel	1.50
13	Rick Tuten	.50
14	Steve Wallace	.50
15	Marion Butts	.50
16	Johnnie Morton	1.50
17	Art Monk	1.00
18	Wayne Gandy	.50
19	Quentin Coryatt	.50
20	Richmond Webb	.50
21	Errict Rhett	1.00
22	Joe Johnson	.50
23	Gary Brown	.50
24	Jeff Hostetler	.50
25	Larry Centers	.50
26	Tom Carter	.50
27	Steve Atwater	.50
28	Doug Pelfrey	.50
29	Bryce Paup	.50
30	Erik Williams	.50
31	Henry Jones	.50
32	Stanley Richard	.50
33	Marcus Allen	1.00
34	Antonio Langham	1.00
35	Lewis Tillman	.50
36	Thomas Randolph	.50
37	Byron Morris	1.00
38	David Palmer	1.00
39	Ricky Watters	1.00
40	Brett Perriman	.50
41	Will Wolford	.50
42	Burt Grossman	.50
43	Vincent Brisby	.50
44	Ronnie Lott	.50
45	Brian Blades	.50
46	Brent Jones	.50
47	Anthony Newman	.50
48	William Roaf	.50
49	Paul Gruber	.50
50	Jeff George	1.00
51	Jamir Miller	1.00
52	Anthony Miller	.50
53	Darrell Green	.50
54	Steve Wisniewski	.50
55	Dan Wilkinson	1.00
56	Brett Favre	10.00
57	Leslie O'Neal	.50
58	Keith Byars	.50
59	James Washington	.50
60	Andre Reed	.50
61	Ken Norton	.50
62	John Randle	.50
63	Lake Dawson	1.00
64	Greg Montgomery	.50
65	Erric Pegram	.50
66	Steve Everitt	.50
67	Chris Brantley	.50
68	Rod Woodson	1.00
69	Eugene Robinson	.50
70	Dave Brown	.50
71	Ricky Reynolds	.50
72	Rohn Stark	.50
73	Randal Hill	.50
74	Brian Washington	.50
75	Heath Shuler	1.50
76	Darion Conner	.50
77	Terry McDaniel	.50
78	Al Del Greco	.50
79	Allen Aldridge	.50
80	Trace Armstrong	.50
81	Darnay Scott	2.00
82	Charlie Garner	2.00
83	Harold Bishop	.50
84	Reggie White	1.00
85	Shawn Jefferson	.50
86	Irving Spikes	1.00
87	Mel Gray	.50
88	D.J. Johnson	.50
89	Daryl Johnston	.50
90	Joe Montana	7.00
91	Michael Strahan	.50
92	Robert Blackmon	.50
93	Ryan Yarborough	.50
94	Terry Allen	.50
95	Michael Haynes	.50
96	Jim Harbaugh	.50
97	Michael Barrow	.50
98	John Thierry	.50
99	Seth Joyner	.50
100	Deion Sanders	3.00
101	Eric Turner	.50
102	LeShon Johnson	1.00
103	John Copeland	.50
104	Cornelius Bennett	.50
105	Sean Gilbert	.50
106	Herschel Walker	.50
107	Henry Ellard	.50
108	Neil O'Donnell	1.00
109	Charles Wilson	.50
110	Willie McGinest	1.00
111	Tim Brown	1.00
112	Simon Fletcher	.50
113	Broderick Thomas	.50
114	Tom Waddle	.50
115	Jessie Tuggle	.50
116	Maurice Hurst	.50
117	Aubrey Beavers	.50
118	Donnell Bennett	.50
119	Shante Carver	.50
120	Eric Metcalf	.50
121	John Carney	.50
122	Thomas Lewis	.50
123	Johnny Mitchell	.50
124	Trent Dilfer	4.00
125	Marshall Faulk	4.00
126	Ernest Givins	.50
127	Aeneas Williams	.50
128	Bucky Brooks	1.00
129	Todd Steussie	1.00
130	Randall Cunningham	1.00
131	Reggie Brooks	.50
132	Morten Andersen	.50
133	James Jett	.50
134	George Teague	.50
135	John Taylor	.50
136	Charles Johnson	1.50
137	Isaac Bruce	4.00
138	Jason Elam	.50
139	Carl Pickens	1.00
140	Chris Warren	1.00
141	Bruce Armstrong	.50
142	Mark Carrier	.50
143	Irving Fryar	.50
144	Van Malone	.50
145	Charles Haley	.50
146	Chris Calloway	.50
147	J.J. Birden	.50
148	Tony Bennett	.50
149	Lincoln Kennedy	.50
150	Stan Humphries	1.00
151	Hardy Nickerson	.50
152	Randall McDaniel	.50
153	Marcus Robertson	.50
154	Ronald Moore	.50
155	Thurman Thomas	1.00
156	Tommy Vardell	.50
157	Ken Ruettgers	.50
158	Rob Frederickson	.50
159	Johnny Bailey	.50
160	Greg Lloyd	.50
161	David Alexander	.50
162	Kevin Mawae	.50
163	Derek Brown	.50
164	William Floyd	1.50
165	Aaron Glenn	1.00
166	Joey Galloway	15.00
167	Troy Drayton	.50
168	Dermontti Dawson	.50
169	Ronald Moore	.50
170	Dan Marino	8.00
171	Dennis Gibson	.50
172	Raymont Harris	.50
173	Shannon Sharpe	.50
174	Kevin Williams	.50
175	Jim Everett	.50
176	Raghib Ismail	.50
177	Mark Fields	.50
178	George Koonce	.50
179	Chris Hudson	.50
180	Jerry Rice	5.00
181	DeWayne Washington	.50
182	Dale Carter	.50
183	Pete Stoyanovich	.50
184	Blake Brockermeyer	.50
185	Troy Aikman	5.00
186	Jeff Blake	2.00
187	Troy Vincent	.50
188	Lamar Lathon	.50
189	Tony Boselli	1.00
190	Emmitt Smith	8.00
191	Bobby Houston	.50
192	Edgar Bennett	.50
193	Derrick Brooks	.50
194	Ricky Proehl	.50
195	Rodney Hampton	.50
196	Dave Krieg	.50
197	Vinny Testaverde	.50
198	Erik Kramer	.50
199	Ben Coates	.50
200	Steve Young	4.00
201	Glyn Milburn	.50
202	Bryan Cox	.50
203	Luther Elliss	.50
204	Mark McMillian	.50
205	Jerome Bettis	1.50
206	Craig Heyward	.50
207	Ray Buchanan	.50
208	Kimble Anders	.50
209	Kevin Greene	.50
210	Eric Allen	.50
211	Ricardo McDonald	.50
212	Ruben Brown	.50
213	Harvey Williams	.50
214	Broderick Thomas	.50
215	Frank Reich	.50
216	Frank Sanders	5.00
217	Craig Newsome	.50
218	Merton Hanks	.50
219	Chris Miller	.50
220	John Elway	4.00
221	Ernest Givins	.50
222	Boomer Esiason	.50
223	Reggie Roby	.50
224	Qadry Ismail	.50
225	Ki-Jana Carter	2.00
226	Leon Lett	.50
227	Eric Hill	.50
228	Scott Mitchell	.50
229	Craig Erickson	.50
230	Drew Bledsoe	5.00
231	Sean Landeta	.50
232	Barrett Brooks	.50
233	Brian Mitchell	.50
234	Tyrone Poole	.50
235	Desmond Howard	.50
236	Wayne Simmons	.50
237	Michael Westbrook	4.00
238	Quinn Early	.50
239	Willie Davis	.50
240	Rashaan Salaam	2.00
241	Devin Bush	.50
242	Dana Stubblefield	.50
243	Dexter Carter	.50
244	Shane Conlan	.50
245	Keith Elias	.50
246	Robert Brooks	1.50
247	Garrison Hearst	1.50
248	Eric Zeier	3.00
249	Nate Newton	.50
250	Barry Sanders	10.00
251	David Meggett	.50
252	Courtney Hawkins	.50
253	Cortez Kennedy	.50
254	Mario Bates	2.50
255	Junior Seau	1.00
256	Brian Washington	.50
257	Darius Holland	.50
258	Jeff Graham	.50
259	Rob Moore	.50
260	Andre Rison	.50
261	Kerry Collins	4.00
262	Roosevelt Potts	.50
263	Cris Carter	1.00
264	Curtis Martin	15.00
265	Rick Mirer	1.50
266	Mo Lewis	.50
267	Mike Sherrard	.50
268	Herman Moore	2.00
269	Eric Metcalf	.50
270	Ray Childress	.50
271	Chris Slade	.50
272	Michael Irvin	1.00
273	Jim Kelly	1.00
274	Terance Mathis	.50
275	LeRoy Butler	.50

1995 Finest Refractors

These cards were randomly inserted into Series I and II packs of 1995 Topps Finest, one per every 12 packs. The cards, a parallel set to the regular issue, have a shiny, rainbow effect when viewed.

		MT
Complete Set (275):		1800.
Complete Series 1 (165):		800.00
Complete Series 2 (110):		1000.
Common Player:		3.00
Minor Stars:		6.00
Unlisted Stars:		5x-10x

#	Player	Price
1	Natrone Means	15.00
2	David Meggett	3.00
3	Tim Bowens	6.00
4	Jay Novacek	3.00
5	Michael Jackson	3.00
6	Eric Allen	3.00
7	Neil Smith	3.00
8	Chris Gardocki	3.00
9	Jeff Burris	6.00
10	Warren Moon	6.00
11	Gary Anderson	3.00
12	Bert Emanuel	25.00
13	Rick Tuten	3.00
14	Steve Wallace	3.00
15	Marion Butts	3.00
16	Johnnie Morton	10.00
17	Art Monk	6.00
18	Wayne Gandy	3.00
19	Quentin Coryatt	3.00
20	Richmond Webb	3.00
21	Errict Rhett	10.00
22	Joe Johnson	3.00
23	Gary Brown	3.00
24	Jeff Hostetler	3.00
25	Larry Centers	3.00
26	Tom Carter	3.00
27	Steve Atwater	3.00
28	Doug Pelfrey	3.00
29	Bryce Paup	3.00
30	Erik Williams	3.00
31	Henry Jones	3.00
32	Stanley Richard	3.00
33	Marcus Allen	6.00
34	Antonio Langham	6.00
35	Lewis Tillman	3.00
36	Thomas Randolph	3.00
37	Byron Morris	10.00
38	David Palmer	6.00
39	Ricky Watters	6.00
40	Brett Perriman	3.00
41	Will Wolford	3.00
42	Burt Grossman	3.00
43	Vincent Brisby	3.00
44	Ronnie Lott	3.00
45	Brian Blades	3.00
46	Brent Jones	3.00
47	Anthony Newman	3.00
48	William Roaf	3.00
49	Paul Gruber	3.00
50	Jeff George	6.00
51	Jamir Miller	6.00
52	Anthony Miller	3.00
53	Darrell Green	3.00
54	Steve Wisniewski	3.00
55	Dan Wilkinson	6.00
56	Brett Favre	100.00
57	Leslie O'Neal	3.00
58	Keith Byars	3.00
59	James Washington	3.00
60	Andre Reed	3.00
61	Ken Norton	3.00
62	John Randle	3.00
63	Lake Dawson	10.00
64	Greg Montgomery	3.00
65	Erric Pegram	3.00
66	Steve Everitt	3.00
67	Chris Brantley	3.00
68	Rod Woodson	6.00
69	Eugene Robinson	3.00
70	Dave Brown	3.00
71	Ricky Reynolds	3.00
72	Rohn Stark	3.00
73	Randal Hill	3.00
74	Brian Washington	3.00
75	Heath Shuler	15.00
76	Darion Conner	3.00
77	Terry McDaniel	3.00
78	Al Del Greco	3.00
79	Allen Aldridge	3.00
80	Trace Armstrong	3.00
81	Darnay Scott	10.00
82	Charlie Garner	20.00
83	Harold Bishop	3.00
84	Reggie White	6.00
85	Shawn Jefferson	3.00
86	Irving Spikes	6.00
87	Mel Gray	3.00
88	D.J. Johnson	3.00
89	Daryl Johnston	3.00
90	Joe Montana	75.00
91	Michael Strahan	3.00
92	Robert Blackmon	3.00
93	Ryan Yarborough	3.00
94	Terry Allen	3.00
95	Michael Haynes	3.00
96	Jim Harbaugh	3.00
97	Michael Barrow	3.00
98	John Thierry	3.00
99	Seth Joyner	3.00
100	Deion Sanders	40.00
101	Eric Turner	3.00
102	LeShon Johnson	6.00
103	John Copeland	3.00
104	Cornelius Bennett	3.00
105	Sean Gilbert	3.00
106	Herschel Walker	3.00
107	Henry Ellard	3.00
108	Neil O'Donnell	6.00
109	Charles Wilson	3.00
110	Willie McGinest	6.00
111	Tim Brown	6.00
112	Simon Fletcher	3.00
113	Broderick Thomas	3.00
114	Tom Waddle	3.00
115	Jessie Tuggle	3.00
116	Maurice Hurst	3.00
117	Aubrey Beavers	3.00
118	Donnell Bennett	3.00
119	Shante Carver	3.00
120	Eric Metcalf	3.00
121	John Carney	3.00
122	Thomas Lewis	3.00
123	Johnny Mitchell	3.00
124	Trent Dilfer	30.00
125	Marshall Faulk	40.00
126	Ernest Givins	3.00
127	Aeneas Williams	3.00
128	Bucky Brooks	6.00
129	Todd Steussie	6.00
130	Randall Cunningham	6.00
131	Reggie Brooks	3.00
132	Morten Andersen	3.00
133	James Jett	3.00
134	George Teague	3.00
135	John Taylor	3.00
136	Charles Johnson	15.00
137	Isaac Bruce	35.00
138	Jason Elam	3.00
139	Carl Pickens	3.00
140	Chris Warren	6.00
141	Bruce Armstrong	3.00
142	Mark Carrier	3.00
143	Irving Fryar	3.00
144	Van Malone	3.00
145	Charles Haley	3.00
146	Chris Calloway	3.00

147	J.J. Birden	3.00
148	Tony Bennett	3.00
149	Lincoln Kennedy	3.00
150	Stan Humphries	6.00
151	Hardy Nickerson	3.00
152	Randall McDaniel	3.00
153	Marcus Robertson	3.00
154	Ronald Moore	3.00
155	Thurman Thomas	6.00
156	Tommy Vardell	3.00
157	Ken Ruettgers	3.00
158	Rob Frederickson	3.00
159	Johnny Bailey	3.00
160	Greg Lloyd	3.00
161	David Alexander	3.00
162	Kevin Mawae	3.00
163	Derek Brown	3.00
164	William Floyd	8.00
165	Aaron Glenn	6.00
166	Joey Galloway	75.00
167	Troy Drayton	3.00
168	Dermontti Dawson	3.00
169	Ronald Moore	3.00
170	Dan Marino	85.00
171	Dennis Gibson	3.00
172	Raymont Harris	3.00
173	Shannon Sharpe	3.00
174	Kevin Williams	3.00
175	Jim Everett	3.00
176	Raghib Ismail	3.00
177	Mark Fields	3.00
178	George Koonce	3.00
179	Chris Hudson	3.00
180	Jerry Rice	60.00
181	DeWayne Washington	3.00
182	Dale Carter	3.00
183	Pete Stoyanovich	3.00
184	Blake Brockermeyer	3.00
185	Troy Aikman	60.00
186	Jeff Blake	8.00
187	Troy Vincent	3.00
188	Lamar Lathon	3.00
189	Tony Boselli	6.00
190	Emmitt Smith	85.00
191	Bobby Houston	3.00
192	Edgar Bennett	3.00
193	Derrick Brooks	3.00
194	Ricky Proehl	3.00
195	Rodney Hampton	3.00
196	Dave Krieg	3.00
197	Vinny Testaverde	3.00
198	Erik Kramer	3.00
199	Ben Coates	3.00
200	Steve Young	45.00
201	Glyn Milburn	3.00
202	Bryan Cox	3.00
203	Luther Elliss	3.00
204	Mark McMillian	3.00
205	Jerome Bettis	25.00
206	Craig Heyward	3.00
207	Ray Buchanan	3.00
208	Kimble Anders	3.00
209	Kevin Greene	3.00
210	Eric Allen	3.00
211	Ricardo McDonald	3.00
212	Ruben Brown	3.00
213	Harvey Williams	3.00
214	Broderick Thomas	3.00
215	Frank Reich	3.00
216	Frank Sanders	25.00
217	Craig Newsome	3.00
218	Merton Hanks	3.00
219	Chris Miller	3.00
220	John Elway	60.00
221	Ernest Givins	3.00
222	Boomer Esiason	3.00
223	Reggie Roby	3.00
224	Qadry Ismail	3.00
225	Ki-Jana Carter	20.00
226	Leon Lett	3.00
227	Eric Hill	3.00
228	Scott Mitchell	3.00
229	Craig Erickson	3.00
230	Drew Bledsoe	60.00
231	Sean Landeta	3.00
232	Barrett Brooks	3.00
233	Brian Mitchell	3.00
234	Tyrone Poole	3.00
235	Desmond Howard	3.00
236	Wayne Simmons	3.00
237	Michael Westbrook	20.00
238	Quinn Early	3.00
239	Willie Davis	3.00
240	Rashaan Salaam	15.00
241	Devin Bush	3.00
242	Dana Stubblefield	3.00
243	Dexter Carter	3.00
244	Shane Conlan	3.00
245	Keith Elias	3.00
246	Robert Brooks	8.00
247	Garrison Hearst	15.00
248	Eric Zeier	20.00
249	Nate Newton	3.00
250	Barry Sanders	100.00
251	David Meggett	3.00
252	Courtney Hawkins	3.00
253	Cortez Kennedy	3.00
254	Mario Bates	8.00
255	Junior Seau	6.00
256	Brian Washington	3.00
257	Darius Holland	3.00
258	Jeff Graham	3.00
259	Rob Moore	3.00
260	Andre Rison	3.00
261	Kerry Collins	30.00
262	Roosevelt Potts	3.00
263	Cris Carter	3.00

264	Curtis Martin	100.00
265	Rick Mirer	10.00
266	Mo Lewis	3.00
267	Mike Sherrard	3.00
268	Herman Moore	15.00
269	Eric Metcalf	3.00
270	Ray Childress	3.00
271	Chris Slade	3.00
272	Michael Irvin	15.00
273	Jim Kelly	6.00
274	Terance Mathis	3.00
275	LeRoy Butler	3.00

1995 Finest Fan Favorite

Steve Young

These cards, random inserts in 1995 Topps Finest football packs, feature impact players on clear cut cards. The back, numbered using an "FF" prefix, has biographical information and a list of where the player played in college and in the NFL. Cards were included in every 12th pack.

		MT
Complete Set (25):		160.00
Common Player:		1.00
Minor Stars:		2.00
1	Drew Bledsoe	10.00
2	Jerome Bettis	6.00
3	Rick Mirer	6.00
4	Andre Rison	1.00
5	Troy Aikman	10.00
6	Cortez Kennedy	1.00
7	Emmitt Smith	15.00
8	Sterling Sharpe	4.00
9	Junior Seau	6.00
10	Michael Irvin	6.00
11	Jim Kelly	6.00
12	Steve Young	7.00
13	John Elway	10.00
14	Jerry Rice	10.00
15	Barry Sanders	20.00
16	Dan Marino	15.00
17	Dan Wilkinson	1.00
18	Reggie White	4.00
19	Deion Sanders	6.00
20	Willie McGinest	1.00
21	Stan Humphries	1.00
22	Heath Shuler	6.00
23	Natrone Means	6.00
24	Warren Moon	6.00
25	Marshall Faulk	3.00

1995 Topps Finest Landmark

This four-card set was available only through Topps direct mailers ($99 plus shipping), and utilizes Finest technology on metal cards overlaid on a four-ounce ingot of solid bronze.

		MT
Complete Set (4):		170.00
Common Player:		25.00
1	Troy Aikman	40.00
2	Jerry Rice	40.00
3	Emmitt Smith	70.00
4	Steve Young	25.00

1995-96 Topps Finest Pro Bowl Jumbos

This 22-card set was distributed at the 1996 NFL Experience Pro Bowl show in Hawaii, and is almost identical to the 1995 Finest cards, except for its 4" x 5-5/8" measurement. The only difference is in addition to the cards' original number, each also carries a new 1-22 card number. A larger, poster-sized Steve Young card was also pro-

duced for promotional purposes and for distribution at the Pro Bowl show. Parallel Refractor versions are also available, but with a reduced print run.

		MT
Complete Set (22):		70.00
Common Player:		1.00
1	Troy Aikman	7.00
2	Tim Brown	2.00
3	Cris Carter	2.00
4	Marshall Faulk	5.00
5	Brett Favre	14.00
6	Merton Hanks	1.00
7	Michael Irvin	2.00
8	Greg Lloyd	1.00
9	Dan Marino	14.00
10	Curtis Martin	10.00
11	Herman Moore	4.00
12	Terry McDaniel	1.00
13	Ken Norton	1.00
14	Bryce Paup	1.00
15	John Randle	1.00
16	Jerry Rice	7.00
17	Barry Sanders	7.00
18	Junior Seau	3.00
19	Steve Young	5.00
20	Reggie White	3.00
21	Chris Warren	2.00
22	Emmitt Smith	14.00
P1	Steve Young (20" by 14" poster Promo)	45.00

1995-96 Topps Finest Pro Bowl Jumbos Refractors

Refractor versions of the Pro Bowl Jumbo Refractors were also available at the 1996 NFL Experience Show in Hawaii. Odds for the Refractor versions are not known.

		MT
Complete Set (22):		1400.
Common Player:		20.00
1	Troy Aikman	140.00
2	Tim Brown	40.00
3	Cris Carter	40.00
4	Marshall Faulk	100.00
5	Brett Favre	275.00
6	Merton Hanks	20.00
7	Michael Irvin	40.00
8	Greg Lloyd	20.00
9	Dan Marino	275.00
10	Curtis Martin	200.00
11	Herman Moore	60.00
12	Terry McDaniel	20.00
13	Ken Norton	20.00
14	Bryce Paup	20.00
15	John Randle	20.00
16	Jerry Rice	140.00
17	Barry Sanders	140.00
18	Junior Seau	60.00
19	Steve Young	100.00
20	Reggie White	60.00
21	Chris Warren	40.00
22	Emmitt Smith	275.00

1996 Finest

Topps' 1996 Finest football has 359 cards, split into five different subsets - 113 Destroyers, 43 Future, 34 Freshman, 115 Playmakers and 52 Sterling cards. Cards are numbered within the regular issue set from 1-359, and also within the subset, using a "D", "F", "P" or "S" prefix. Within the regular issue set there are three types of cards. There are 220 common cards, 91 uncommon cards (one per every four packs) and 47 rare cards (one per every 24 packs). Commons have a bronze border, uncommons have a silver border, and rares have a gold border. Refractors of every card

were also made. Commons are seeded one per every 12 packs, uncommons are one per every 48, and rares are one every 288. Fewer than 150 Refractor sets were produced.

		MT
Complete Set (359)		1700.
Comp. Bronze Ser.1 (110)		40.00
Comp. Bronze Ser.2 (110)		50.00
Common Bronze Player:		.25
Comp. Silver Ser.1 (55)		200.00
Comp. Silver Ser.2 (36)		150.00
Common Silver Player:		2.00
Comp. Gold Ser.1 (26)		800.00
Comp. Gold Ser.2 (22)		500.00
Common Gold Player:		15.00
Wax Box Series 1		170.00
Wax Box Series 2		90.00
1	Kordell Stewart G	50.00
2	Jay Novacek	.25
3	Ray Buchanan	.25
4	Brett Favre S	25.00
5	Phil Hansen	.25
6	Mike Mamula	.25
7	Kimble Anders G	15.00
8	Merton Hanks G	15.00
9	Bernie Parmalee	.25
10	Herman Moore	1.50
11	Shawn Jefferson	.25
12	Chris Doleman	.25
13	Erik Kramer	.25
14	Chester McGlockton S	2.00
15	Orlando Thomas	.25
16	Terrell Davis	10.00
17	Rick Mirer S	25.00
18	Roman Phifer	.25
19	Trent Dilfer	.50
20	Tyrone Hughes S	2.00
21	Darnay Scott	.50
22	Steve McNair S	3.00
23	Lamar Lathon	.25
24	Ty Law S	2.00
25	Brian Mitchell S	2.00
26	Thomas Randolph	.25
27	Michael Jackson	.25
28	Seth Joyner	.25
29	Jeff Lageman	.25
30	Darryl Williams	.25
31	Darren Woodson S	2.00
32	Erric Pegram	.25
33	Craig Newsome G	15.00
34	Sean Dawkins	.25
35	Brian Mitchell S	2.00
36	Bryce Paup S	15.00
37	Dana Stubblefield S	2.00
38	Dan Saleaumua	.25
39	Henry Thomas	.25
40	Dan Marino G	75.00
41	Kerry Collins S	10.00
42	Andre Coleman G	15.00
43	Pat Swilling	.25
44	Marty Carter	.25
45	Anthony Miller	.25
46	Orlando Thomas S	2.00
47	Kevin Carter G	15.00
48	Chris Warren	.50
49	Derek Brown	.25
50	Jerry Rice S	12.00
51	Blaine Bishop	.25
52	Jake Reed	.25
53	Willie McGinest S	2.00
54	Blake Brockermeyer	2.00
55	Vencie Glenn	.25
56	Michael Westbrook	10.00
57	Garrison Hearst S	4.00
58	Derrick Alexander	.25
59	Kyle Brady S	2.00
60	Mark Brunell G	45.00
61	David Palmer G	15.00
62	Tim Brown S	4.00
63	Jeff Graham S	2.00
64	Jessie Tuggle	.25
65	Terrance Shaw	.25
66	David Sloan	.25
67	Dan Marino S	25.00
68	Brent Jones	.25
69	Tamarick Vanover S	10.00
70	William Thomas	.25
71	Robert Smith	.25
72	Wayne Simmons	.25
73	Jim Harbaugh	.50
74	Daryl Johnston S	2.00
75	Carnell Lake G	15.00
76	Wayne Chrebet	.25
77	Chris Hudson	.25
78	Frank Sanders S	5.00
79	Stevon Moore	.25
80	Chris Calloway	.25
81	Tom Carter	.25
82	David Meggett	.25
83	Sam Mills	.25
84	Darryll Lewis S	2.00
85	Carl Pickens S	4.00
86	Renaldo Turnbull	.25
87	Derrick Brooks	.25
88	Jerome Bettis S	4.00
89	Eugene Robinson	.25
90	Terrell Davis S	25.00
91	Rodney Thomas	2.00
92	Dan Wilkinson	.25
93	Mark Fields	.25
94	Warren Sapp	.25
95	Curtis Martin S	5.00

96	Joey Galloway G	30.00
97	Ray Crockett	.25
98	Ed McDaniel	.25
99	Napoleon Kaufman S	10.00
100	Rashaan Salaam S	10.00
101	Craig Heyward	.25
102	Ellis Johnson	.25
103	Barry Sanders S	25.00
104	O.J. McDuffie	.25
105	J.J. Stokes	2.50
106	Mo Lewis	.25
107	Tony Boselli S	2.00
108	Rob Moore	.25
109	Eric Zeier S	2.00
110	Tyrone Wheatley	.50
111	Ken Harvey	.25
112	Melvin Tuten G	15.00
113	Willie Green	.25
114	Willie Davis	.25
115	Andy Harmon	.25
116	Bruce Smith S	2.00
117	Bryan Cox	.25
118	Zack Crockett S	2.00
119	Bert Emanuel	.25
120	Greg Lloyd	.25
121	Aaron Glenn G	15.00
122	Willie Jackson	.25
123	Lorenzo Lynch	.25
124	Pepper Johnson	.25
125	Joey Galloway S	14.00
126	Heath Shuler S	6.00
127	Curtis Martin S	12.00
128	Tyrone Poole	.25
129	Neil Smith	.25
130	Eddie Robinson	.25
131	Bryce Paup G	15.00
132	Brett Favre G	80.00
133	Ken Dilger G	15.00
134	Troy Aikman	5.00
135	Greg Lloyd S	4.00
136	Chris Sanders	2.00
137	Marshall Faulk S	15.00
138	Jim Everett	.25
139	Frank Sanders	.50
140	Barry Sanders G	80.00
141	Cortez Kennedy	.25
142	Glyn Milburn G	15.00
143	Derrick Alexander	.25
144	Rob Fredrickson	.25
145	Chris Zorich	.25
146	Devin Bush	.25
147	Tyrone Poole S	2.00
148	Brett Perriman G	15.00
149	Troy Vincent	.25
150	J.J. Stokes S	10.00
151	Deion Sanders	4.00
152	James Stewart	.25
153	Drew Bledsoe S	15.00
154	Terry McDaniel S	2.00
155	Terrell Fletcher S	2.00
156	Lawrence Dawsey	.25
157	Robert Brooks	.50
158	Rashaan Salaam	2.50
159	Dave Brown S	2.00
160	Kerry Collins S	35.00
161	Tim Brown	.50
162	Brendan Stai	.25
163	Sean Gilbert	.25
164	Lee Woodall G	15.00
165	Jim Harbaugh S	4.00
166	Larry Brown S	2.00
167	Neil Smith S	2.00
168	Herman Moore S	5.00
169	Calvin Williams	.25
170	Deion Sanders S	10.00
171	Ruben Brown	.25
172	Eric Green	.25
173	Marshall Faulk G	30.00
174	Mark Chmura S	4.00
175	Jerry Rice S	5.00
176	Bruce Smith	.25
177	Mark Bruener	.25
178	Troy Aikman S	50.00
179	Lamont Warren	.25
180	Tamarick Vanover	2.50
181	Chris Warren S	4.00
182	Scott Mitchell	.25
183	Robert Brooks S	4.00
184	Steve McNair S	10.00
185	Kordell Stewart S	15.00
186	Terry Wooden	.25
187	Ken Norton	.25
188	Jeff Herrod	.25
189	Charlie Garner S	2.00
190	Drew Bledsoe G	50.00
191	Checklist	.25
192	Gus Frerotte	.25
193	Michael Irvin G	20.00
194	Brett Maxie	.25
195	Harvey Williams S	2.00
196	Warren Moon G	20.00
197	Jeff George S	2.00
198	Eddie Kennison	4.00
199	Ricky Watters S	4.00
200	Steve Young G	35.00
201	Marcus Jones	.25
202	Terry Allen	.50
203	Leroy Hoard	.25
204	Steve Bono S	2.00
205	Reggie White	.50
206	Larry Centers	.25
207	Alex Van Dyke G	25.00
208	Vincent Brisby	.25
209	Michael Timpson	.25
210	Jeff Blake S	6.00
211	John Mobley	.25
212	Clay Matthews	.25

213	Shannon Sharpe	.25
214	Tony Bennett	.25
215	Phillippi Sparks S	.25
216	Mickey Washington	.25
217	Fred Barnett	.25
218	Michael Haynes	.25
219	Stan Humphries	.25
220	Cris Carter G	15.00
221	Winston Moss	.25
222	Tim Biakabutuka	4.00
223	Leeland McElroy	1.50
224	Vinnie Clark	.25
225	Keyshawn Johnson	10.00
226	William Floyd S	4.00
227	Troy Drayton S	2.00
228	Tony Woods	.25
229	Rodney Hampton S	2.00
230	John Elway G	50.00
231	Anthony Pleasant	.25
232	Jeff George	.25
233	Curtis Conway	.50
234	Charles Haley G	15.00
235	Jeff Lewis	2.50
236	Edgar Bennett	.25
237	Regan Upshaw	.25
238	William Fuller	.25
239	Duane Clemons	2.00
240	Jim Kelly G	20.00
241	Willie Anderson	.25
242	Derrick Thomas	.25
243	Marvin Harrison	15.00
244	Darion Conner	.25
245	Antonio Langham	.25
246	Rodney Peete	.25
247	Tim McDonald	.25
248	Robert Jones	.25
249	Curtis Conway	4.00
250	Rodney Hampton G	15.00
251	Mark Carrier	.25
252	Steve Grant	.25
253	John Mobley S	2.00
254	Jeff Hostetler	.25
255	Darrell Green	.25
256	Errict Rhett S	30.00
257	Alex Molden G	15.00
258	Chris Slade	2.00
259	Derrick Thomas S	2.00
260	Kevin Hardy G	25.00
261	Eric Swann	.25
262	Eric Metcalf S	2.00
263	Irv Smith	.25
264	Tim McKyer	.25
265	Emmitt Smith S	20.00
266	Sean Jones	.25
267	Bryant Young G	15.00
268	Jeff Blake S	30.00
269	Jeff Hostetler S	2.00
270	Keyshawn Johnson G	30.00
271	Yancey Thigpen	1.00
272	Thurman Thomas S	4.00
273	Quentin Coryatt	.25
274	Hardy Nickerson	.25
275	Ricardo McDonald	.25
276	Steve Atwater S	2.00
277	Robert Blackmon	.25
278	Junior Seau G	20.00
279	Alonzo Spellman	.25
280	Isaac Bruce S	8.00
281	Rickey Dudley	3.00
282	Joe Cain	.25
283	Neil O'Donnell S	2.00
284	John Randle	.25
285	Terry Kirby G	15.00
286	Vinny Testaverde	.25
287	Jim Kelly S	4.00
288	Lawrence Phillips S	15.00
289	Henry Jones	.25
290	Simeon Rice	1.50
291	Terance Mathis S	.25
292	Errict Rhett S	6.00
293	Hugh Douglas S	15.00
294	Santo Stephens S	2.00
295	Leslie O'Neal	.25
296	Reggie White S	20.00
297	Greg Hill	.25
298	Elvis Grbac S	15.00
299	Walt Harris S	4.00
300	Emmitt Smith S	75.00
301	Eric Metcalf	.25
302	Jamir Miller S	2.00
303	Jerome Woods	.25
304	Ben Coates S	2.00
305	Marcus Allen S	4.00
306	Anthony Smith	.25
307	Darren Perry	.25
308	Jonathan Ogden S	6.00
309	Ricky Watters S	20.00
310	John Elway S	12.00
311	James Hasty	.25
312	Cris Carter	.50
313	Irving Fryar S	2.00
314	Lawrence Phillips	3.00
315	Junior Seau S	4.00
316	Alex Molden S	1.50
317	Aeneas Williams	.25
318	Eric Hill	.25
319	Kevin Hardy	1.50
320	Steve Young S	10.00
321	Chris Chandler	.25
322	Raghib Ismail	.25
323	Anthony Parker	.25
324	John Thierry	.25
325	Michael Barrow	.25
326	Henry Ford	.25
327	Aaron Hayden	.25
328	Terance Mathis	.25
329	Kirk Pointer	.25

330	*Ray Mickens*	.75
331	Jermaine Mayberry	.25
332	Mario Bates	.25
333	Carlton Gray	.25
334	Derek Loville	.25
335	*Mike Alstott*	6.00
336	Eric Guliford	.25
337	Marvcus Patton	.25
338	*Terrell Owens*	20.00
339	Lance Johnstone	.25
340	Lake Dawson	.25
341	Winslow Oliver	.25
342	Adrian Murrell	.25
343	Jason Belser	.25
344	Brian Dawkins	.25
345	Reggie Brown	.25
346	Shaun Gayle	.25
347	*Tony Brackens*	1.00
348	Thomas Lewis	.25
349	Kelvin Pritchett	.25
350	*Bobby Engram*	3.00
351	Moe Williams	.25
352	Thomas Smith	.25
353	Dexter Carter	.25
354	Qadry Ismail	.25
355	Marco Battaglia	.25
356	Levon Kirkland	.25
357	Eric Allen	.25
358	*Bobby Hoying*	2.50
359	Checklist	.25

1996 Finest Refractors

Each card in Topps' 1996 Finest set has a Refractor card made for it, as labeled on the back. Commons are seeded one per every 12 packs, un-commons are one every 48, and rares are one every 288 packs. Fewer than 150 rare Refractor sets were produced.

	MT
Comp. Bronze Ser.1 (110):	550.00
Comp. Bronze Ser.2 (110):	550.00
Common Bronze Player:	3.00
Comp. Silver Ser.1 (55):	1800.00
Comp. Silver Ser.2 (36):	1000.00
Common Silver Player:	12.00
Comp. Gold Ser.1 (26):	2000.00
Comp. Gold Ser.2 (22):	1000.00
Common Gold Player:	25.00

No.	Player	Price
1	Kordell Stewart S	150.00
2	Jay Novacek	3.00
3	Ray Buchanan	3.00
4	Brett Favre S	175.00
5	Phil Hansen	3.00
6	Mike Mamula	3.00
7	Kimble Anders G	25.00
8	Merton Hanks G	25.00
9	Bernie Parmalee	3.00
10	Herman Moore	6.00
11	Shawn Jefferson	3.00
12	Chris Doleman	3.00
13	Erik Kramer	3.00
14	Chester McGlockton S	12.00
15	Orlando Thomas	3.00
16	Terrell Davis	120.00
17	Rick Mirer G	75.00
18	Roman Phifer	3.00
19	Trent Dilfer	6.00
20	Tyrone Hughes G	12.00
21	Darnay Scott	6.00
22	Steve McNair	40.00
23	Lamar Lathon	3.00
24	Ty Law S	12.00
25	Brian Mitchell	12.00
26	Thomas Randolph	3.00
27	Michael Jackson	3.00
28	Seth Joyner	3.00
29	Jeff Lageman	3.00
30	Darryl Williams	3.00
31	Darren Woodson S	12.00
32	Erric Pegram	3.00
33	Craig Newsome G	25.00
34	Sean Dawkins	3.00
35	Brian Mitchell S	12.00
36	Bryce Paup G	25.00
37	Dana Stubblefield	12.00
38	Dan Saleaumua	3.00
39	Henry Thomas	3.00
40	Dan Marino G	175.00
41	Kerry Collins S	60.00
42	Andre Coleman G	25.00
43	Pat Swilling	3.00
44	Marty Carter	3.00
45	Anthony Miller	3.00
46	Orlando Thomas S	12.00
47	Kevin Carter G	25.00
48	Chris Warren	6.00
49	Derek Brown	3.00
50	Jerry Rice S	80.00
51	Blaine Bishop	3.00
52	Jake Reed	3.00
53	Willie McGinest S	12.00
54	Blake Brockermeyer S	12.00
55	Vencie Glenn	3.00
56	Michael Westbrook	75.00
57	Garrison Hearst S	24.00
58	Derrick Alexander	3.00
59	Kyle Brady S	12.00
60	Mark Brunell G	125.00
61	David Palmer G	25.00
62	Tim Brown S	24.00
63	Jeff Graham S	12.00
64	Jessie Tuggle	3.00
65	Terrance Shaw	3.00
66	David Sloan	3.00
67	Dan Marino S	160.00
68	Brent Jones	3.00
69	Tamarick Vanover S	75.00
70	William Thomas	3.00
71	Robert Smith	3.00
72	Wayne Simmons	3.00
73	Jim Harbaugh	6.00
74	Daryl Johnston S	12.00
75	Carnell Lake G	25.00
76	Wayne Chrebet	3.00
77	Chris Hudson	3.00
78	Frank Sanders	24.00
79	Stevon Moore	3.00
80	Chris Calloway	3.00
81	Tom Carter	3.00
82	David Meggett	3.00
83	Sam Mills	3.00
84	Darryll Lewis S	12.00
85	Carl Pickens S	24.00
86	Renaldo Turnbull	3.00
87	Derrick Brooks	3.00
88	Jerome Bettis S	30.00
89	Eugene Robinson	3.00
90	Terrell Davis S	150.00
91	Rodney Thomas	8.00
92	Dan Wilkinson	3.00
93	Mark Fields	3.00
94	Warren Sapp	3.00
95	Curtis Martin	50.00
96	Joey Galloway G	60.00
97	Ray Crockett	3.00
98	Ed McDaniel	3.00
99	Napoleon Kaufman S	24.00
100	Rashaan Salaam S	60.00
101	Craig Heyward	3.00
102	Ellis Johnson	3.00
103	Barry Sanders S	175.00
104	O.J. McDuffie	3.00
105	J.J. Stokes	20.00
106	Mo Lewis	3.00
107	Tony Boselli S	12.00
108	Rob Moore	3.00
109	Eric Zeier S	12.00
110	Tyrone Wheatley	6.00
111	Ken Harvey	3.00
112	Melvin Tuten G	25.00
113	Willie Green	3.00
114	Willie Davis	3.00
115	Andy Harmon	3.00
116	Bruce Smith S	12.00
117	Bryan Cox	3.00
118	Zack Crockett S	12.00
119	Bert Emanuel	3.00
120	Greg Lloyd	3.00
121	Aaron Glenn S	12.00
122	Willie Jackson	3.00
123	Lorenzo Lynch	3.00
124	Pepper Johnson	3.00
125	Joey Galloway S	80.00
126	Heath Shuler S	24.00
127	Curtis Martin S	60.00
128	Tyrone Poole	3.00
129	Neil Smith	3.00
130	Eddie Robinson	3.00
131	Bryce Paup	3.00
132	Brett Favre G	180.00
133	Ken Dilger S	12.00
134	Troy Aikman	60.00
135	Greg Lloyd S	12.00
136	Chris Sanders	6.00
137	Marshall Faulk S	60.00
138	Jim Everett	3.00
139	Frank Sanders	6.00
140	Barry Sanders S	180.00
141	Cortez Kennedy	3.00
142	Glyn Milburn G	25.00
143	Derrick Alexander G	25.00
144	Rob Fredrickson	3.00
145	Chris Zorich	3.00
146	Devin Bush	3.00
147	Tyrone Poole S	12.00
148	Brett Perriman S	25.00
149	Troy Vincent	3.00
150	J.J. Stokes S	75.00
151	Deion Sanders	30.00
152	James Stewart	3.00
153	Drew Bledsoe	80.00
154	Terry McDaniel S	12.00
155	Terrell Fletcher S	12.00
156	Lawrence Dawsey	3.00
157	Robert Brooks	6.00
158	Rashaan Salaam	30.00
159	Dave Brown S	12.00
160	Kerry Collins G	100.00
161	Tim Brown	6.00
162	Brendan Stai	3.00
163	Sean Gilbert	3.00
164	Lee Woodall G	25.00
165	Jim Harbaugh S	24.00
166	Larry Brown S	12.00
167	Neil Smith S	12.00
168	Herman Moore	30.00
169	Calvin Williams	3.00
170	Deion Sanders S	50.00
171	Ruben Brown	3.00
172	Eric Green	3.00
173	Marshall Faulk G	60.00
174	Mark Chmura S	24.00
175	Jerry Rice	60.00
176	Bruce Smith	3.00
177	Mark Bruener	3.00
178	Troy Aikman S	125.00
179	Lamont Warren	3.00
180	Tamarick Vanover	30.00
181	Chris Warren S	24.00
182	Scott Mitchell	3.00
183	Robert Brooks S	24.00
184	Steve McNair S	60.00
185	Kordell Stewart S	80.00
186	Terry Wooden	3.00
187	Ken Norton	3.00
188	Jeff Herrod	3.00
189	Charlie Garner S	12.00
190	Drew Bledsoe S	125.00
191	Checklist	100.00
192	Gus Frerotte	3.00
193	Michael Irvin S	50.00
194	Brett Maxie	3.00
195	Harvey Williams S	12.00
196	Warren Moon G	50.00
197	Jeff George S	12.00
198	Eddie Kennison	25.00
199	Ricky Watters S	24.00
200	Steve Young S	200.00
201	Marcus Jones	3.00
202	Terry Allen	6.00
203	Leroy Hoard	3.00
204	Steve Bono S	12.00
205	Reggie White	6.00
206	Larry Centers	3.00
207	Alex Van Dyke G	75.00
208	Vincent Brisby	3.00
209	Michael Timpson	3.00
210	Jeff Blake S	50.00
211	John Mobley	3.00
212	Clay Matthews	3.00
213	Shannon Sharpe	3.00
214	Tony Bennett	3.00
215	Phillippi Sparks S	12.00
216	Mickey Washington	3.00
217	Fred Barnett	3.00
218	Michael Haynes	3.00
219	Stan Humphries	3.00
220	Cris Carter S	25.00
221	Winston Moss	3.00
222	Tim Biakabutuka	20.00
223	Leeland McElroy	20.00
224	Vinnie Clark	3.00
225	Keyshawn Johnson	50.00
226	William Floyd S	24.00
227	Troy Drayton S	12.00
228	Tony Woods	3.00
229	Rodney Hampton S	12.00
230	John Elway G	125.00
231	Anthony Pleasant	3.00
232	Jeff George	3.00
233	Curtis Conway	6.00
234	Charles Haley S	12.00
235	Jeff Lewis	3.00
236	Edgar Bennett	3.00
237	Regan Upshaw	3.00
238	William Fuller	3.00
239	Duane Clemons S	12.00
240	Jim Kelly S	80.00
241	Willie Anderson	3.00
242	Derrick Thomas	3.00
243	Marvin Harrison	60.00
244	Darion Conner	3.00
245	Antonio Langham	3.00
246	Rodney Peete	3.00
247	Tim McDonald	3.00
248	Robert Jones	3.00
249	Curtis Conway S	24.00
250	Rodney Hampton G	25.00
251	Mark Carrier	3.00
252	Steve Grant	3.00
253	John Mobley S	12.00
254	Jeff Hostetler	3.00
255	Darrell Green	3.00
256	Errict Rhett S	75.00
257	Alex Molden G	25.00
258	Chris Slade S	12.00
259	Derrick Thomas S	12.00
260	Kevin Hardy G	75.00
261	Eric Swann	3.00
262	Eric Metcalf S	12.00
263	Irv Smith	3.00
264	Tim McKyer	3.00
265	Emmitt Smith S	125.00
266	Sean Jones	3.00
267	Bryant Young G	25.00
268	Jeff Blake G	50.00
269	Jeff Hostetler G	25.00
270	Keyshawn Johnson G	75.00
271	Yancey Thigpen	12.00
272	Thurman Thomas S	24.00
273	Quentin Coryatt	3.00
274	Hardy Nickerson	3.00
275	Ricardo McDonald	3.00
276	Steve Atwater S	12.00
277	Robert Blackmon	3.00
278	Junior Seau G	50.00
279	Alonzo Spellman	3.00
280	Isaac Bruce S	50.00
281	Rickey Dudley	15.00
282	Joe Cain	3.00
283	Neil O'Donnell S	12.00
284	John Randle	3.00
285	Terry Kirby G	25.00
286	Vinny Testaverde	3.00
287	Jim Kelly S	24.00
288	Lawrence Phillips S	70.00
289	Henry Jones	3.00
290	Simeon Rice	3.00
291	Terance Mathis S	12.00
292	Errict Rhett S	60.00
293	Hugh Douglas S	12.00
294	Santo Stephens S	12.00
295	Leslie O'Neal	3.00
296	Reggie White G	80.00
297	Greg Hill	3.00
298	Elvis Grbac G	60.00
299	Walt Harris S	24.00
300	Emmitt Smith G	150.00
301	Eric Metcalf	3.00
302	Jamir Miller S	12.00
303	Jerome Woods	3.00
304	Ben Coates S	12.00
305	Marcus Allen S	24.00
306	Anthony Smith	3.00
307	Darren Perry	3.00
308	Jonathan Ogden S	35.00
309	Ricky Watters G	60.00
310	John Elway S	80.00
311	James Hasty	3.00
312	Cris Carter	3.00
313	Irving Fryar S	12.00
314	Lawrence Phillips	30.00
315	Junior Seau S	24.00
316	Alex Molden S	12.00
317	Aeneas Williams	3.00
318	Eric Hill	3.00
319	Kevin Hardy	12.00
320	Steve Young S	60.00
321	Chris Chandler	3.00
322	Raghib Ismail	3.00
323	Anthony Parker	3.00
324	John Thierry	3.00
325	Michael Barrow	3.00
326	Henry Ford	3.00
327	Aaron Hayden	3.00
328	Terance Mathis	3.00
329	Kirk Pointer	3.00
330	Ray Mickens	7.50
331	Jermaine Mayberry	3.00
332	Mario Bates	3.00
333	Carlton Gray	3.00
334	Derek Loville	3.00
335	Mike Alstott	30.00
336	Eric Guliford	3.00
337	Marvcus Patton	3.00
338	Terrell Owens	90.00
339	Lance Johnstone	3.00
340	Lake Dawson	3.00
341	Winslow Oliver	3.00
342	Adrian Murrell	3.00
343	Jason Belser	3.00
344	Brian Dawkins	3.00
345	Reggie Brown	3.00
346	Shaun Gayle	3.00
347	Tony Brackens	3.00
348	Thomas Lewis	3.00
349	Kelvin Pritchett	3.00
350	Bobby Engram	20.00
351	Moe Williams	3.00
352	Thomas Smith	3.00
353	Dexter Carter	3.00
354	Qadry Ismail	3.00
355	Marco Battaglia	3.00
356	Levon Kirkland	3.00
357	Eric Allen	3.00
358	Bobby Hoying	40.00
359	Checklist	3.00

1997 Finest

The 175-card Series I set has a numbering format that features card No. 1-100 labeled as Common, cards No. 101-150 as Uncommon and No. 151-175 as Rare. Each card also has a different number corresponding to its theme. The Finest themes are Masters, Bulldozers, Hit-men, Dynamos and Field Generals. The numbering box on each card back indicates both sets of numbers, and which type of card it is, either Common, Uncommon or Rare. The card's theme is printed at the top of each card. Uncommon cards were seeded 1:4 packs, while Rare cards were inserted 1:24. Embossed Uncommon cards were seeded 1:16, while Embossed Die-Cut Rare cards were inserted 1:96. Embossed Die-Cut Rare cards were found 1:96. Series II was numbered 176-350. It consisted of 100 commons, 50 uncommons and 25 rares. The themes in Series II were Champions, Dominators, Impact, Masters and Stalwarts. Insertion rates for Series II were identical to Series I.

	MT
Complete Set (350):	1000.
Comp. Bronze Ser.1 (100):	30.00
Comp. Bronze Ser.2 (100):	60.00
Common Bronze Player:	.25
Comp. Silver Ser.1 (50):	150.00
Comp. Silver Ser.2 (50):	150.00
Common Silver Player:	2.00
Embossed Silvers:	2x
Comp. Gold Ser.1 (25):	400.00
Comp. Gold Ser.2 (25):	300.00
Common Gold Player:	7.50
Embossed Die-Cut Golds:	1.5x
Wax Box Series 1:	100.00
Wax Box Series 2:	100.00

No.	Player	Price
1	Mark Brunell	3.00
2	Chris Slade	.25
3	Chris Doleman	.25
4	Chris Hudson	.25
5	Karim Abdul-Jabbar	2.00
6	Darren Perry	.25
7	Daryl Johnston	.25
8	Rob Moore	.25
9	Robert Smith	.25
10	Terry Allen	.25
11	Jason Dunn	.25
12	Henry Thomas	.25
13	Rod Stephens	.25
14	Ray Mickens	.25
15	Ty Detmer	.25
16	Fred Barnett	.25
17	Derrick Alexander	.25
18	Marcus Robertson	.25
19	Robert Blackmon	.25
20	Isaac Bruce	.75
21	Chester McGlockton	.25
22	Stan Humphries	.25
23	Lonnie Marts	.25
24	Jason Sehorn	.25
25	Bobby Engram	.25
26	Brett Perriman	.25
27	Stevon Moore	.25
28	Jamal Anderson	2.00
29	Wayne Martin	.25
30	Michael Irvin	.50
31	Thomas Smith	.25
32	Tony Brackens	.25
33	Eric Davis	.25
34	James Stewart	.25
35	Ki-Jana Carter	.25
36	Ken Norton	.25
37	William Thomas	.25
38	Tim Brown	.50
39	Lawrence Phillips	.50
40	Ricky Watters	.50
41	Tony Bennett	.25
42	Jesse Armstead	.25
43	Trent Dilfer	.25
44	Rodney Hampton	.25
45	Sam Mills	.25
46	Rodney Harrison	.25
47	Rob Fredrickson	.25
48	Eric Hill	.25
49	Bennie Blades	.25
50	Eddie George	4.00
51	Dave Brown	.25
52	Raymont Harris	.25
53	Steve Tovar	.25
54	Thurman Thomas	.50
55	Leeland McElroy	.25
56	Brian Mitchell	.25
57	Eric Allen	.25
58	Vinny Testaverde	.25
59	Marvin Washington	.25
60	Junior Seau	.25
61	Bert Emanuel	.25
62	Kevin Carter	.25
63	Mark Carrier	.25
64	Andre Coleman	.25
65	Chris Warren	.25
66	Aeneas Williams	.25
67	Darren Woodson	.25
68	Anthony Johnson	.25
69	Terry Glenn	2.50
70	Troy Vincent	.25
71	John Copeland	.25
72	Warren Sapp	.25
73	Bobby Hebert	.25
74	Jeff Hostetler	.25
75	Willie Davis	.25
76	Bobby Taylor	.25
77	Mickey Washington	.25
78	Cortez Kennedy	.25
79	Michael Strahan	.25
80	Jerome Bettis	.50
81	Andre Hastings	.25
82	Simeon Rice	.25
83	Cornelius Bennett	.25
84	Napoleon Kaufman	2.00
85	Jim Harbaugh	.25
86	Aaron Hayden	.25
87	Gus Frerotte	.25
88	Jeff Blake	.50
89	Anthony Miller	.25
90	Deion Sanders	1.75
91	Curtis Conway	.25
92	William Floyd	.25
93	Eric Moulds	.25
94	Mel Gray	.25
95	Andre Rison	.25
96	Eugene Daniel	.25
97	Jason Belser	.25
98	Mike Mamula	.25
99	Jim Everett	.25
100	Checklist	.25
101	Drew Bledsoe S	12.00
102	Shannon Sharpe S	2.00
103	Ken Harvey S	2.00
104	Isaac Bruce S	4.00
105	Terry Allen S	2.00
106	Lawyer Milloy S	2.00
107	Ashley Ambrose S	2.00
108	Alfred Williams S	2.00
109	Hugh Douglas S	2.00
110	Junior Seau S	2.00
111	Kordell Stewart S	12.00
112	Adrian Murrell S	2.00
113	Byron Morris S	2.00
114	Terrell Buckley S	2.00
115	Dan Marino S	20.00
116	Willie Clay S	2.00
117	Neil Smith S	2.00
118	Blaine Bishop S	2.00
119	John Mobley S	2.00
120	Herman Moore S	3.00
121	Keyshawn Johnson S	6.00
122	Boomer Esiason S	2.00
123	Marshall Faulk S	3.00
124	Keith Jackson S	2.00
125	Ricky Watters S	3.00
126	Carl Pickens S	3.00
127	Cris Carter S	2.00
128	Mike Alstott S	6.00
129	Simeon Rice S	2.00
130	Troy Aikman S	12.00
131	Tamarick Vanover S	3.00
132	Marquez Pope S	2.00
133	Winslow Oliver S	2.00
134	Edgar Bennett S	2.00
135	David Meggett S	2.00
136	Marcus Allen S	3.00
137	Jerry Rice S	12.00
138	Steve Atwater S	2.00
139	Tim McDonald S	2.00
140	Barry Sanders S	20.00
141	Eddie George S	15.00
142	Wesley Walls S	2.00
143	Jerome Bettis S	3.00
144	Kevin Greene S	2.00
145	Terrell Davis S	15.00
146	Gus Frerotte S	2.00
147	Joey Galloway S	3.00
148	Vinny Testaverde S	2.00
149	Hardy Nickerson S	2.00
150	Brett Favre S	30.00
151	Desmond Howard G	7.50
152	Keyshawn Johnson G	12.00
153	Tony Banks G	15.00
154	Chris Spielman G	7.50
155	Reggie White G	12.00
156	Zach Thomas G	12.00
157	Carl Pickens G	7.50
158	Karim Abdul-Jabbar G	12.00
159	Chad Brown G	7.50
160	Kerry Collins G	15.00
161	Marvin Harrison G	12.00
162	Steve Young G	25.00
163	Trent Dilfer G	12.00
164	Deion Sanders G	20.00
165	Barry Sanders G	50.00
166	Cris Carter G	7.50
167	Keenan McCardell G	7.50
168	Terry Glenn G	12.00
169	Emmitt Smith G	40.00
170	John Elway G	30.00
171	Jerry Rice G	30.00
172	Troy Aikman G	30.00
173	Curtis Martin G	25.00
174	Darrell Green G	7.50
175	Mark Brunell G	30.00
176	*Corey Dillon*	10.00
177	Tyrone Poole	.25
178	Anthony Pleasant	.25
179	Frank Sanders	.25
180	Troy Aikman	4.00
181	Bill Romanowski	.25
182	Ty Law	.25
183	Orlando Thomas	.25
184	Quentin Coryatt	.25
185	Kenny Holmes	.25
186	Bryant Young	.25
187	Michael Sinclair	.25
188	Mike Tomczak	.25
189	Bobby Taylor	.25
190	Brett Favre	7.00
191	Kent Graham	.25
192	Jessie Tuggle	.25

193	Jimmy Smith	.25
194	Greg Hill	.25
195	Yatil Green	2.00
196	Mark Fields	.25
197	Phillippi Sparks	.25
198	Aaron Glenn	.25
199	Pat Swilling	.25
200	Barry Sanders	7.00
201	Mark Chmura	.50
202	Marco Coleman	.25
203	Merton Hanks	.25
204	Brian Blades	.25
205	Errict Rhett	.50
206	Henry Ellard	.25
207	Andre Reed	.25
208	Bryan Cox	.25
209	Darnay Scott	.25
210	John Elway	3.00
211	Glyn Milburn	.25
212	Don Beebe	.25
213	Kevin Lockett	.25
214	Dorsey Levens	.50
215	Kordell Stewart	4.00
216	Larry Centers	.25
217	Cris Carter	.50
218	Willie McGinest	.25
219	Renaldo Wynn	.25
220	Jerry Rice	4.00
221	Reidel Anthony	5.00
222	Mark Carrier	.25
223	Quinn Early	.25
224	Chris Sanders	.25
225	Shawn Springs	.50
226	Kevin Smith	.25
227	Ben Coates	.25
228	Tyrone Wheatley	.25
229	Antonio Freeman	1.50
230	Dan Marino	6.00
231	Dwayne Rudd	.50
232	Leslie O'Neal	.25
233	Brent Jones	.25
234	Jake Plummer	20.00
235	Kerry Collins	2.00
236	Rashaan Salaam	.50
237	Tyrone Braxton	.25
238	Herman Moore	.50
239	Keyshawn Johnson	.50
240	Drew Bledsoe	4.00
241	Rickey Dudley	.25
242	Antowain Smith	6.00
243	Jeff Lageman	.25
244	Chris T. Jones	.25
245	Steve Young	3.00
246	Eddie Robinson	.25
247	Chad Cota	.25
248	Michael Jackson	.25
249	Robert Porcher	.25
250	Reggie White	.50
251	Carnell Lake	.25
252	Chris Calloway	.25
253	Terance Mathis	.25
254	Carl Pickens	.50
255	Curtis Martin	3.00
256	Jeff Graham	.25
257	Regan Upshaw	.25
258	Sean Gilbert	.25
259	Will Blackwell	1.00
260	Emmitt Smith	6.00
261	Reinard Wilson	.50
262	Darrell Russell	.50
263	Wayne Chrebet	.25
264	Kevin Hardy	.25
265	Shannon Sharpe	.25
266	Harvey Williams	.25
267	John Randle	.25
268	Tim Bowens	.25
269	Tony Gonzalez	3.00
270	Warrick Dunn	7.00
271	Sean Dawkins	.25
272	Darryll Lewis	.25
273	Alonzo Spellman	.25
274	Mark Collins	.25
275	Checklist 2	.25
276	Pat Barnes S	4.00
277	Dana Stubblefield S	2.00
278	Dan Wilkinson S	2.00
279	Bryce Paup S	2.00
280	Kerry Collins S	8.00
281	Derrick Brooks S	2.00
282	Walter Jones S	2.00
283	Terry McDaniel S	2.00
284	James Farrior S	2.00
285	Curtis Martin S	10.00
286	O.J. McDuffie S	2.00
287	Natrone Means S	3.00
288	Bryant Westbrook S	3.00
289	Peter Boulware S	3.00
290	Emmitt Smith S	15.00
291	Joey Kent S	4.00
292	Eddie Kennison S	4.00
293	LeRoy Butler S	2.00
294	Dale Carter S	2.00
295	Jim Druckenmiller S	15.00
296	Byron Hanspard S	8.00
297	Jeff Blake S	3.00
298	Levon Kirkland S	2.00
299	Michael Westbrook S	2.00
300	John Elway S	12.00
301	Lamar Lathon S	2.00
302	Ray Lewis S	2.00
303	Steve McNair S	7.00
304	Shawn Springs S	3.00
305	Karim Abdul-Jabbar S	4.00
306	Orlando Pace S	3.00
307	Scott Mitchell S	2.00
308	Walt Harris S	2.00
309	Bruce Smith S	2.00
310	Reggie White S	3.00
311	Eric Swann S	2.00
312	Derrick Thomas S	2.00
313	Tony Martin S	2.00
314	Darrell Russell S	2.00
315	Mark Brunell S	12.00
316	Trent Dilfer S	3.00
317	Irving Fryar S	2.00
318	Amani Toomer S	2.00
319	Jake Reed S	2.00
320	Steve Young S	8.00
321	Troy Davis S	4.00
322	Jim Harbaugh S	2.00
323	Neil O'Donnell S	2.00
324	Terry Glenn S	6.00
325	Deion Sanders S	6.00
326	Gus Frerotte G	7.50
327	Tom Knight G	7.50
328	Peter Boulware G	7.50
329	Jerome Bettis G	12.00
330	Orlando Pace G	12.00
331	Darnell Autry G	15.00
332	Ike Hilliard G	25.00
333	David LaFleur G	25.00
334	Jim Harbaugh G	7.50
335	Eddie George G	45.00
336	Vinny Testaverde G	7.50
337	Terry Allen G	7.50
338	Jim Druckenmiller G	30.00
339	Ricky Watters G	15.00
340	Brett Favre G	60.00
341	Simeon Rice G	7.50
342	Shannon Sharpe G	7.50
343	Kordell Stewart G	30.00
344	Isaac Bruce G	15.00
345	Drew Bledsoe G	30.00
346	Jeff Blake G	12.00
347	Herman Moore G	12.00
348	Junior Seau G	7.50
349	Rae Carruth G	20.00
350	Dan Marino G	50.00

1997 Finest Refractors

Each of the 350 base cards has a parallel Refractor. Refractor Common cards were inserted 1:12 packs, while Refractor Uncommon were seeded 1:48. Refractor Rare could be found 1:288 packs. In addition, Refractors of the Embossed and Embossed Die-Cut cards were also randomly seeded. An Embossed Uncommon Refractor was inserted 1:192 packs, while an Embossed Die-Cut Refractor was seeded 1:1,152 packs.

	MT
Complete Set (350):	7200.
Comp. Bronze Ser.1 (100):	500.00
Comp. Bronze Ser.2 (100):	850.00
Common Bronze Player:	3.00
Comp. Silver Ser.1 (50):	900.00
Comp. Silver Ser.2 (50):	900.00
Common Silver Player:	10.00
Embossed Silver Refractors:	2x
Comp. Gold Ser.1 (25):	2000.
Comp. Gold Ser.2 (25):	2000.
Common Gold Player:	40.00
Embossed DC Gold Refractors:	2x

#	Name	Price
1	Mark Brunell	30.00
2	Chris Slade	3.00
3	Chris Doleman	3.00
4	Chris Hudson	3.00
5	Karim Abdul-Jabbar	10.00
6	Darren Perry	3.00
7	Daryl Johnston	3.00
8	Rob Moore	3.00
9	Robert Smith	3.00
10	Terry Allen	3.00
11	Jason Dunn	3.00
12	Henry Thomas	3.00
13	Rod Stephens	3.00
14	Ray Mickens	3.00
15	Ty Detmer	3.00
16	Fred Barnett	3.00
17	Derrick Alexander	3.00
18	Marcus Robertson	3.00
19	Robert Blackmon	3.00
20	Isaac Bruce	10.00
21	Chester McGlockton	3.00
22	Stan Humphries	3.00
23	Lonnie Marts	3.00
24	Jason Sehorn	3.00
25	Bobby Engram	3.00
26	Brett Perriman	3.00
27	Stevon Moore	3.00
28	Jamal Anderson	20.00
29	Wayne Martin	3.00
30	Michael Irvin	6.00
31	Thomas Smith	3.00
32	Tony Brackens	3.00
33	Eric Davis	3.00
34	James Stewart	3.00
35	Ki-Jana Carter	3.00
36	Ken Norton	3.00
37	William Thomas	3.00
38	Tim Brown	3.00
39	Lawrence Phillips	6.00
40	Ricky Watters	6.00
41	Tony Bennett	3.00
42	Jesse Armstead	3.00
43	Trent Dilfer	3.00
44	Rodney Hampton	3.00
45	Sam Mills	3.00
46	Rodney Harrison	3.00
47	Rob Fredrickson	3.00
48	Eric Hill	3.00
49	Bennie Blades	3.00
50	Eddie George	40.00
51	Dave Brown	3.00
52	Raymont Harris	3.00
53	Steve Tovar	3.00
54	Thurman Thomas	6.00
55	Leeland McElroy	3.00
56	Brian Mitchell	3.00
57	Eric Allen	3.00
58	Vinny Testaverde	3.00
59	Marvin Washington	3.00
60	Junior Seau	3.00
61	Bert Emanuel	3.00
62	Kevin Carter	3.00
63	Mark Carrier	3.00
64	Andre Coleman	3.00
65	Chris Warren	3.00
66	Aeneas Williams	3.00
67	Eugene Robinson	3.00
68	Darren Woodson	3.00
69	Anthony Johnson	3.00
70	Terry Glenn	10.00
71	Troy Vincent	3.00
72	John Copeland	3.00
73	Warren Sapp	3.00
74	Bobby Hebert	3.00
75	Jeff Hostetler	3.00
76	Willie Davis	3.00
77	Mickey Washington	3.00
78	Cortez Kennedy	3.00
79	Michael Strahan	3.00
80	Jerome Bettis	6.00
81	Andre Hastings	3.00
82	Simeon Rice	3.00
83	Cornelius Bennett	3.00
84	Napoleon Kaufman	20.00
85	Jim Harbaugh	3.00
86	Aaron Hayden	3.00
87	Gus Frerotte	3.00
88	Jeff Blake	6.00
89	Anthony Miller	3.00
90	Deion Sanders	15.00
91	Curtis Conway	3.00
92	William Floyd	3.00
93	Eric Moulds	3.00
94	Mel Gray	3.00
95	Andre Rison	3.00
96	Eugene Daniel	3.00
97	Jason Belser	3.00
98	Mike Mamula	3.00
99	Jim Everett	3.00
100	Checklist	3.00
101	Drew Bledsoe S	60.00
102	Shannon Sharpe S	10.00
103	Ken Harvey S	10.00
104	Isaac Bruce S	20.00
105	Terry Allen S	10.00
106	Lawyer Milloy S	10.00
107	Ashley Ambrose S	10.00
108	Alfred Williams S	10.00
109	Hugh Douglas S	10.00
110	Junior Seau S	20.00
111	Kordell Stewart S	60.00
112	Adrian Murrell S	10.00
113	Byron Morris S	10.00
114	Terrell Buckley S	10.00
115	Dan Marino S	100.00
116	Willie Clay S	10.00
117	Neil Smith S	10.00
118	Blaine Bishop S	10.00
119	John Mobley S	10.00
120	Herman Moore S	20.00
121	Keyshawn Johnson S	10.00
122	Boomer Esiason S	10.00
123	Marshall Faulk S	15.00
124	Keith Jackson S	10.00
125	Ricky Watters S	20.00
126	Carl Pickens S	20.00
127	Cris Carter S	10.00
128	Mike Alstott S	20.00
129	Simeon Rice S	10.00
130	Troy Aikman S	60.00
131	Tamarick Vanover S	20.00
132	Marquez Pope S	10.00
133	Winslow Oliver S	10.00
134	Edgar Bennett S	10.00
135	David Meggett S	10.00
136	Marcus Allen S	20.00
137	Jerry Rice S	60.00
138	Steve Atwater S	10.00
139	Tim McDonald S	10.00
140	Barry Sanders S	100.00
141	Eddie George S	70.00
142	Wesley Walls S	10.00
143	Jerome Bettis S	20.00
144	Kevin Greene S	10.00
145	Terrell Davis S	75.00
146	Gus Frerotte S	10.00
147	Joey Galloway S	15.00
148	Vinny Testaverde S	10.00
149	Hardy Nickerson S	10.00
150	Brett Favre S	100.00
151	Desmond Howard G	40.00
152	Keyshawn Johnson G	60.00
153	Tony Banks G	80.00
154	Chris Spielman G	40.00
155	Reggie White G	60.00
156	Zach Thomas G	60.00
157	Carl Pickens G	40.00
158	Karim Abdul-Jabbar G	60.00
159	Chad Brown G	40.00
160	Kerry Collins G	75.00
161	Marvin Harrison G	60.00
162	Steve Young G	125.00
163	Deion Sanders G	100.00
164	Trent Dilfer G	75.00
165	Barry Sanders G	300.00
166	Cris Carter G	40.00
167	Keenan McCardell G	40.00
168	Terry Glenn G	100.00
169	Emmitt Smith G	250.00
170	John Elway G	175.00
171	Jerry Rice G	175.00
172	Troy Aikman G	175.00
173	Curtis Martin G	100.00
174	Darrell Green G	40.00
175	Mark Brunell G	175.00
176	Corey Dillon G	60.00
177	Tyrone Poole	3.00
178	Anthony Pleasant	3.00
179	Frank Sanders	3.00
180	Troy Aikman	30.00
181	Bill Romanowski	3.00
182	Ty Law	3.00
183	Orlando Thomas	3.00
184	Quentin Coryatt	3.00
185	Kenny Holmes	3.00
186	Bryant Young	3.00
187	Michael Sinclair	3.00
188	Mike Tomczak	3.00
189	Bobby Taylor	3.00
190	Brett Favre	60.00
191	Kent Graham	3.00
192	Jessie Tuggle	3.00
193	Jimmy Smith	3.00
194	Greg Hill	3.00
195	Yatil Green	10.00
196	Mark Fields	3.00
197	Phillippi Sparks	3.00
198	Aaron Glenn	3.00
199	Pat Swilling	3.00
200	Barry Sanders	60.00
201	Mark Chmura	3.00
202	Marco Coleman	3.00
203	Merton Hanks	3.00
204	Brian Blades	3.00
205	Errict Rhett	6.00
206	Henry Ellard	3.00
207	Andre Reed	3.00
208	Bryan Cox	3.00
209	Darnay Scott	3.00
210	John Elway	30.00
211	Glyn Milburn	3.00
212	Don Beebe	3.00
213	Kevin Lockett	3.00
214	Dorsey Levens	6.00
215	Kordell Stewart	30.00
216	Larry Centers	3.00
217	Cris Carter	6.00
218	Willie McGinest	3.00
219	Renaldo Wynn	3.00
220	Jerry Rice	20.00
221	Reidel Anthony	225.00
222	Mark Carrier	3.00
223	Quinn Early	3.00
224	Chris Sanders	3.00
225	Shawn Springs	6.00
226	Kevin Smith	3.00
227	Ben Coates	3.00
228	Tyrone Wheatley	3.00
229	Antonio Freeman	20.00
230	Dan Marino	50.00
231	Dwayne Rudd	6.00
232	Leslie O'Neal	3.00
233	Brent Jones	3.00
234	Jake Plummer	75.00
235	Kerry Collins	20.00
236	Rashaan Salaam	6.00
237	Tyrone Braxton	3.00
238	Herman Moore	6.00
239	Keyshawn Johnson	6.00
240	Drew Bledsoe	30.00
241	Rickey Dudley	3.00
242	Antowain Smith	35.00
243	Jeff Lageman	3.00
244	Chris T. Jones	3.00
245	Steve Young	20.00
246	Eddie Robinson	3.00
247	Chad Cota	3.00
248	Michael Jackson	3.00
249	Robert Porcher	3.00
250	Reggie White	6.00
251	Carnell Lake	3.00
252	Chris Calloway	3.00
253	Terance Mathis	3.00
254	Carl Pickens	6.00
255	Curtis Martin	25.00
256	Jeff Graham	3.00
257	Regan Upshaw	3.00
258	Sean Gilbert	3.00
259	Will Blackwell	8.00
260	Emmitt Smith	50.00
261	Reinard Wilson	6.00
262	Darrell Russell	6.00
263	Wayne Chrebet	3.00
264	Kevin Hardy	3.00
265	Shannon Sharpe	3.00
266	Harvey Williams	3.00
267	John Randle	3.00
268	Tim Bowens	3.00
269	Tony Gonzalez	20.00
270	Warrick Dunn	75.00
271	Sean Dawkins	3.00
272	Darryll Lewis	3.00
273	Alonzo Spellman	3.00
274	Mark Collins	3.00
275	Checklist 2	3.00
276	Pat Barnes S	20.00
277	Dana Stubblefield S	10.00
278	Dan Wilkinson S	10.00
279	Bryce Paup S	10.00
280	Kerry Collins S	30.00
281	Derrick Brooks S	10.00
282	Walter Jones S	10.00
283	Terry McDaniel S	10.00
284	James Farrior S	10.00
285	Curtis Martin S	40.00
286	O.J. McDuffie S	10.00
287	Natrone Means S	20.00
288	Bryant Westbrook S	20.00
289	Peter Boulware S	20.00
290	Emmitt Smith S	75.00
291	Joey Kent S	20.00
292	Eddie Kennison S	20.00
293	LeRoy Butler S	10.00
294	Dale Carter S	10.00
295	Jim Druckenmiller S	50.00
296	Byron Hanspard S	35.00
297	Jeff Blake S	10.00
298	Levon Kirkland S	10.00
299	Michael Westbrook S	10.00
300	John Elway S	50.00
301	Lamar Lathon S	10.00
302	Ray Lewis S	10.00
303	Steve McNair S	30.00
304	Shawn Springs S	20.00
305	Karim Abdul-Jabbar S	20.00
306	Orlando Pace S	20.00
307	Scott Mitchell S	10.00
308	Walt Harris S	10.00
309	Bruce Smith S	10.00
310	Reggie White S	20.00
311	Eric Swann S	10.00
312	Derrick Thomas S	10.00
313	Tony Martin S	10.00
314	Darrell Russell S	10.00
315	Mark Brunell S	60.00
316	Trent Dilfer S	20.00
317	Irving Fryar S	10.00
318	Amani Toomer S	10.00
319	Jake Reed S	10.00
320	Steve Young S	40.00
321	Troy Davis S	20.00
322	Jim Harbaugh S	10.00
323	Neil O'Donnell S	10.00
324	Terry Glenn S	25.00
325	Deion Sanders S	30.00
326	Gus Frerotte G	40.00
327	Tom Knight G	40.00
328	Peter Boulware G	40.00
329	Jerome Bettis G	60.00
330	Orlando Pace G	60.00
331	Darnell Autry G	60.00
332	Ike Hilliard G	75.00
333	David LaFleur G	60.00
334	Jim Harbaugh G	40.00
335	Eddie George G	150.00
336	Vinny Testaverde G	40.00
337	Terry Allen G	40.00
338	Jim Druckenmiller G	100.00
339	Ricky Watters G	80.00
340	Brett Favre G	300.00
341	Simeon Rice G	40.00
342	Shannon Sharpe G	40.00
343	Kordell Stewart G	150.00
344	Isaac Bruce G	80.00
345	Drew Bledsoe G	150.00
346	Jeff Blake G	60.00
347	Herman Moore G	60.00
348	Junior Seau G	40.00
349	Rae Carruth G	75.00
350	Dan Marino G	250.00

1998 Finest

Finest was issued in two, 150-card series in 1998, with 150 in Series I and 120 in Series II. Each card was available in a Protector (base cards), No-Protector (1:2 packs), Protector Refractor (1:12) and No-Protector Refractor (1:24) version. An interesting twist to the releases was that the 30 rookies (121-150) were available in Protector and No-Protector Refractor versions in Series I, but the No-Protector and Protector Refractor versions were only issued in Series II packs. Series I inserts were: Double-Sided Mystery Finest, Centurions, Undergrads and Jumbos, while Series II inserts included Mystery Finest, Stadium Stars, Future's Finest, Jumbos (base cards), Jumbo Stadium Stars and Jumbo Mystery.

	MT
Complete Set (270):	170.00
Complete Series 1 (150):	130.00
Complete Series 2 (120):	40.00
Common Player:	.25
Minor Stars:	.50
Common Rookie:	1.50
No-Protector Set (270):	600.00
No-Protector Cards:	2x-4x
No-Protector Rookies:	2x
Inserted 1:2	
NP Refractor Set (270):	2000.
NP Refractor Cards:	10x-20x
NP Refractor Rookies:	3x-6x
Inserted 1:24	
Series 1 Wax Box:	130.00
Series 2 Wax Box:	75.00

#	Name	Price
1	John Elway	3.00
2	Terance Mathis	.25
3	Jermaine Lewis	.25
4	Fred Lane	.50
5	Bryan Cox	.25
6	David Dunn	.25
7	Dexter Coakley	.25
8	Carl Pickens	.50
9	Antonio Freeman	.75
10	Herman Moore	.75
11	Kevin Hardy	.25
12	Tony Gonzalez	.50
13	O.J. McDuffie	.50
14	David Palmer	.25
15	Lawyer Milloy	.25
16	Danny Kanell	.25
17	Randal Hill	.25
18	Keyshawn Johnson	.75
19	Charlie Garner	.25
20	Mark Brunell	2.00
21	Donnell Woolford	.25
22	Freddie Jones	.25
23	Ken Norton	.25
24	Tony Banks	.50
25	Isaac Bruce	.50
26	Willie Davis	.25
27	Cris Dishman	.25
28	Aeneas Williams	.25
29	Michael Booker	.25
30	Cris Carter	.75
31	Michael McCrary	.25
32	Eric Moulds	.50
33	Rae Carruth	.25
34	Bobby Engram	.50
35	Jeff Blake	.50
36	Deion Sanders	1.00
37	Rod Smith	.50
38	Bryant Westbrook	.25
39	Mark Chmura	.50
40	Tim Brown	.50
41	Bobby Taylor	.25
42	James Stewart	.25
43	Kimble Anders	.25
44	Karim Abdul-Jabbar	.75
45	Willie McGinest	.25
46	Jessie Armstead	.25
47	Aaron Glenn	.25
48	Greg Lloyd	.25
49	Stephen Davis	.75
50	Jerome Bettis	.75
51	Warren Sapp	.25
52	Horace Copeland	.25
53	Chad Brown	.25
54	Chris Canty	.25
55	Robert Smith	.50
56	Pete Mitchell	.25
57	Aaron Bailey	.25
58	Robert Porcher	.25
59	John Mobley	.25
60	Tony Martin	.25
61	Michael Irvin	.50
62	Charles Way	.25
63	Raymont Harris	.25
64	Chuck Smith	.25
65	Larry Centers	.25
66	Greg Hill	.25
67	Kenny Holmes	.25
68	John Lynch	.25
69	Michael Sinclair	.25
70	Steve Young	1.50
71	Michael Strahan	.25
72	Levon Kirkland	.25
73	Rickey Dudley	.25
74	Marcus Allen	.50
75	John Randle	.25
76	Erik Kramer	.25
77	Neil Smith	.25
78	Byron Hanspard	.50
79	Quinn Early	.25
80	Warren Moon	.50
81	William Thomas	.25
82	Ben Coates	.25
83	Lake Dawson	.25
84	Steve McNair	1.00
85	Gus Frerotte	.25
86	Rodney Harrison	.25

87	Reggie White	.75
88	Derrick Thomas	.25
89	Dale Carter	.25
90	Warrick Dunn	2.00
91	Will Blackwell	.25
92	Troy Vincent	.25
93	Johnnie Morton	.25
94	David LaFleur	.25
95	Tony McGee	.25
96	Lonnie Johnson	.25
97	Thurman Thomas	.50
98	Chris Chandler	.50
99	Jamal Anderson	1.00
100	Checklist	.25
101	Marshall Faulk	1.00
102	Chris Calloway	.25
103	Chris Spielman	.25
104	Zach Thomas	.50
105	Jeff George	.50
106	Darrell Russell	.25
107	Darryll Lewis	.25
108	Reidel Anthony	.50
109	Terrell Owens	1.00
110	Rob Moore	.50
111	Darrell Green	.25
112	Merton Hanks	.25
113	Shawn Jefferson	.25
114	Chris Sanders	.25
115	Scott Mitchell	.50
116	Vaughn Hebron	.25
117	Ed McCaffrey	.50
118	Bruce Smith	.25
119	Peter Boulware	.25
120	Brett Favre	5.00
121	*Peyton Manning*	25.00
122	*Brian Griese*	10.00
123	*Tavian Banks*	6.00
124	*Duane Starks*	1.50
125	*Robert Holcombe*	5.00
126	*Brian Simmons*	1.50
127	*Skip Hicks*	6.00
128	*Keith Brooking*	1.50
129	*Ahman Green*	6.00
130	*Jerome Pathon*	3.00
131	*Curtis Enis*	8.00
132	*Grant Wistrom*	2.00
133	*Germane Crowell*	6.00
134	*Jacquez Green*	6.00
135	*Randy Moss*	50.00
136	*Jason Peter*	2.00
137	*John Avery*	6.00
138	*Takeo Spikes*	2.00
139	*Patrick Johnson*	2.00
140	*Andre Wadsworth*	3.00
141	*Fred Taylor*	15.00
142	*Charles Woodson*	10.00
143	*Marcus Nash*	6.00
144	*Robert Edwards*	8.00
145	*Kevin Dyson*	6.00
146	*Joe Jurevicius*	3.00
147	*Anthony Simmons*	2.00
148	*Hines Ward*	4.00
149	*Greg Ellis*	2.00
150	*Ryan Leaf*	10.00
151	Jerry Rice	2.50
152	Tony Martin	.25
153	Billy Joe Hobert	.25
154	Rob Johnson	.50
155	Shannon Sharpe	.50
156	Bert Emanuel	.25
157	Eric Metcalf	.25
158	Natrone Means	.75
159	Derrick Alexander	.25
160	Emmitt Smith	3.50
161	Jeff Burris	.25
162	Chris Warren	.25
163	Corey Fuller	.25
164	Courtney Hawkins	.25
165	James McKnight	.25
166	Shawn Springs	.25
167	Wayne Martin	.25
168	Michael Westbrook	.25
169	Michael Jackson	.25
170	Dan Marino	3.50
171	Amp Lee	.25
172	James Jett	.25
173	Ty Law	.25
174	Kerry Collins	.50
175	Robert Brooks	.50
176	Blaine Bishop	.25
177	Stephen Boyd	.25
178	Keyshawn Johnson	.75
179	Deon Figures	.25
180	Allen Aldridge	.25
181	Corey Miller	.25
182	Chad Lewis	.25
183	Derrick Rodgers	.25
184	Troy Drayton	.25
185	Darren Woodson	.25
186	Ken Dilger	.25
187	Elvis Grbac	.50
188	Terrell Fletcher	.25
189	Frank Sanders	.25
190	Curtis Martin	1.00
191	Derrick Brooks	.25
192	Darrien Gordon	.25
193	Andre Reed	.50
194	Darnay Scott	.25
195	Curtis Conway	.50
196	Tim McDonald	.25
197	Sean Dawkins	.25
198	Napoleon Kaufman	1.00
199	Willie Clay	.25
200	Terrell Davis	4.00
201	Wesley Walls	.25

202	Santana Dotson	.25
203	Frank Wycheck	.25
204	Wayne Chrebet	.75
205	Andre Rison	.50
206	Jason Sehorn	.25
207	Jessie Tuggle	.25
208	Kevin Turner	.25
209	Jason Taylor	.25
210	Yancey Thigpen	.25
211	Jake Reed	.50
212	Carnell Lake	.25
213	Joey Galloway	.75
214	Andre Hastings	.25
215	Terry Allen	.50
216	Jim Harbaugh	.50
217	Tony Banks	.50
218	Greg Clark	.25
219	Corey Dillon	1.25
220	Troy Aikman	2.50
221	Antowain Smith	1.00
222	Steve Atwater	.25
223	Trent Dilfer	.75
224	Junior Seau	.50
225	Garrison Hearst	.75
226	Eric Allen	.25
227	Chad Cota	.25
228	Vinny Testaverde	.50
229	Chris T. Jones	.25
230	Drew Bledsoe	2.00
231	Charles Johnson	.25
232	Jake Plummer	2.00
233	Errict Rhett	.25
234	Doug Evans	.25
235	Phillippi Sparks	.25
236	Ashley Ambrose	.25
237	Bryan Cox	.25
238	Kevin Smith	.25
239	Hardy Nickerson	.25
240	Terry Glenn	.75
241	Lee Woodall	.25
242	Andre Coleman	.25
243	Michael Bates	.25
244	Mark Fields	.25
245	Eddie Kennison	.50
246	Dana Stubblefield	.25
247	Bobby Hoying	.50
248	Mo Lewis	.25
249	Derrick Mayes	.25
250	Eddie George	2.00
251	Mike Alstott	1.00
252	J.J. Stokes	.50
253	Adrian Murrell	.50
254	Kevin Greene	.25
255	LeRoy Butler	.25
256	Glenn Foley	.50
257	Jimmy Smith	.50
258	Tiki Barber	.25
259	Irving Fryar	.25
260	Ricky Watters	.50
261	Jeff Graham	.25
262	Kordell Stewart	2.00
263	Rod Woodson	.25
264	Leslie Shepherd	.25
265	Ryan McNeil	.25
266	Ike Hilliard	.50
267	Keenan McCardell	.50
268	Marvin Harrison	.75
269	Dorsey Levens	.75
270	Barry Sanders	5.00

1998 Finest Refractors

Both Protector and No-Protector versions had parallel Refractor versions for all 270 cards. Protector Refractors were inserted one per 12 packs and had only the front of the card with a Refractor finish, while No-Protector Refractors were inserted one per 24 packs and were basically a double-sided Refractor. No-Protector Refractor versions of the 30 rookies (121-150) were inserted into Series I packs, while Protector Refractor versions were only in Series II packs.

	MT
Refractors:	6x-12x

1998 Finest Centurions

This 20-card insert set was found in packs of Series I. Regular versions were numbered to 500, while Refractors were numbered to only 75. Centurions inserts were numbered with a "C" prefix.

		MT
Complete Set (20):		550.00
Common Player:		12.00
Minor Stars:		24.00
Inserted 1:125		
Production 500 Sets		
Refractor Set (20):		1100.
Refractors:		2x
Inserted 1:831		
Production 75 Sets		
C1	Brett Favre	100.00
C2	Eddie George	45.00
C3	Antonio Freeman	24.00
C4	Napoleon Kaufman	24.00
C5	Terrell Davis	60.00
C6	Keyshawn Johnson	24.00
C7	Peter Boulware	12.00
C8	Mike Alstott	24.00
C9	Jake Plummer	50.00
C10	Mark Brunell	45.00
C11	Marvin Harrison	12.00
C12	Antowain Smith	24.00
C13	Dorsey Levens	24.00
C14	Terry Glenn	24.00
C15	Warrick Dunn	40.00
C16	Joey Galloway	24.00
C17	Steve McNair	30.00
C18	Corey Dillon	30.00
C19	Drew Bledsoe	45.00
C20	Kordell Stewart	45.00

1998 Finest Future's Finest

This insert set features 20 players taking America's game into the next century. Singles were sequentially numbered to 500 and inserted 1:83 packs. Each card had a parallel Refractor that was numbered to 75 and found 1:557 packs.

		MT
Complete Set (20):		325.00
Common Player:		7.00
Minor Stars:		14.00
Inserted 1:83		
Production 500 Sets		
Refractors:		2x-3x
Inserted 1:557		
Production 75 Sets		
F1	Peyton Manning	40.00
F2	Napoleon Kaufman	14.00
F3	Jake Plummer	25.00
F4	Terry Glenn	14.00
F5	Ryan Leaf	20.00
F6	Drew Bledsoe	25.00
F7	Dorsey Levens	14.00
F8	Andre Wadsworth	7.00
F9	Joey Galloway	14.00
F10	Curtis Enis	18.00
F11	Warrick Dunn	25.00
F12	Kordell Stewart	25.00
F13	Randy Moss	80.00
F14	Robert Edwards	15.00
F15	Eddie George	25.00
F16	Fred Taylor	25.00
F17	Corey Dillon	14.00
F18	Brett Favre	60.00
F19	Kevin Dyson	14.00
F20	Terrell Davis	45.00

1998 Finest Jumbos 1

Eight different Jumbo Finest cards were inserted as box toppers in both Series I and II. The 16-card set was inserted 1:3 boxes (1:2 hobby collector boxes),

with Refractors every 12 boxes (1:6 hobby collector boxes).

		MT
Complete Set (8):		125.00
Common Player:		5.00
Inserted 1:3 Boxes		
Refractors:		2x
Inserted 1:12 Boxes		
1	John Elway	20.00
2	Peyton Manning	35.00
3	Mark Brunell	15.00
4	Curtis Enis	15.00
5	Jerome Bettis	5.00
6	Ryan Leaf	20.00
7	Warrick Dunn	15.00
8	Brett Favre	30.00

1998 Finest Jumbos 2

Eight different Jumbo Finest cards were inserted as box toppers in both Series I and II. The 16-card set was inserted 1:3 boxes (1:2 hobby collector boxes), with Refractors every 12 boxes (1:6 hobby collector boxes).

		MT
Complete Set (7):		100.00
Common Player:		5.00
Inserted 1:3 Boxes		
Refractors:		2x
Inserted 1:12 Boxes		
151	Jerry Rice	15.00
160	Emmitt Smith	25.00
170	Dan Marino	25.00
213	Joey Galloway	5.00
230	Drew Bledsoe	12.00
250	Eddie George	12.00
270	Barry Sanders	30.00

1998 Finest Mystery Finest 1

Twenty different players were displayed either with one of three other players on the back, or by themselves on both sides in Mystery Finest. Each side has a Finest Opaque protector and is numbered with a "M" prefix. Regular versions are seeded one per 36 packs, while Refractors are found every 144 packs.

		MT
Complete Set (50):		1100.
Common Player:		10.00
Inserted 1:36		
Refractor Set (50):		1650.
Refractors:		1.5x
Inserted 1:144		
M1	Brett Favre, Mark Brunell	45.00
M2	Brett Favre, Jake Plummer	45.00
M3	Brett Favre, Steve Young	45.00
M4	Brett Favre, Brett Favre	50.00
M5	Brett Favre, Mark Brunell	15.00
M6	Mark Brunell, Mark Brunell	15.00
M7	Jake Plummer, Mark Brunell	15.00
M8	Jake Plummer, Jake Plummer	20.00
M9	Steve Young, Jake Plummer	15.00
M10	Steve Young, Steve Young	15.00
M11	John Elway, Drew Bledsoe	25.00
M12	John Elway, Troy Aikman	25.00
M13	John Elway, Dan Marino	40.00
M14	John Elway, John Elway	30.00
M15	Drew Bledsoe, Troy Aikman	25.00
M16	Drew Bledsoe, Drew Bledsoe	20.00
M17	Troy Aikman, Dan Marino	40.00
M18	Troy Aikman, Troy Aikman	20.00
M19	Dan Marino, Drew Bledsoe	40.00
M20	Dan Marino, Dan Marino	45.00
M21	Kordell Stewart, Corey Dillon	15.00
M22	Kordell Stewart, Tim Brown	15.00
M23	Kordell Stewart, Barry Sanders	40.00
M24	Kordell Stewart, Kordell Stewart	18.00
M25	Corey Dillon, Tim Brown	10.00
M26	Corey Dillon, Corey Dillon	10.00
M27	Tim Brown, Barry Sanders	40.00
M28	Tim Brown, Tim Brown	10.00
M29	Barry Sanders, Corey Dillon	40.00
M30	Barry Sanders, Barry Sanders	50.00
M31	Terrell Davis, Emmitt Smith	35.00
M32	Terrell Davis, Jerome Bettis	30.00
M33	Terrell Davis, Eddie George	30.00
M34	Terrell Davis, Terrell Davis	35.00
M35	Emmitt Smith, Eddie George	30.00
M36	Emmitt Smith, Emmitt Smith	35.00
M37	Jerome Bettis, Emmitt Smith	30.00
M38	Jerome Bettis, Jerome Bettis	10.00
M39	Eddie George, Jerome Bettis	15.00
M40	Eddie George, Eddie George	15.00
M41	Herman Moore, Jerry Rice	20.00
M42	Herman Moore, Herman Moore	10.00
M43	Warrick Dunn, Herman Moore	15.00
M44	Warrick Dunn, Jerry Rice	25.00
M45	Warrick Dunn, Dorsey Levens	15.00
M46	Warrick Dunn, Warrick Dunn	20.00
M47	Jerry Rice, Dorsey Levens	20.00
M48	Jerry Rice, Jerry Rice	25.00
M49	Dorsey Levens, Herman Moore	10.00
M50	Dorsey Levens, Dorsey Levens	10.00

1998 Finest Mystery Finest 2

Twenty different players were displayed either with one of three other players on the back, or by themselves on both sides in Mystery Finest. Each side has a Finest Opaque protector and is numbered with an "M" prefix. Regular versions are seeded one per 36 packs, while Refractors are found every 144 packs.

		MT
Complete Set (40):		550.00
Common Player:		7.00
Inserted 1:36		
Refractors:		1.5x
Inserted 1:144		
M1	Brett Favre, Dan Marino	30.00
M2	Brett Favre, Peyton Manning	35.00
M3	Brett Favre, Ryan Leaf	25.00
M4	Dan Marino, Peyton Manning	30.00
M5	Dan Marino, Ryan Leaf	25.00
M6	Peyton Manning, Ryan Leaf	25.00
M7	Barry Sanders, Emmitt Smith	30.00
M8	Barry Sanders, Curtis Enis	20.00
M9	Barry Sanders, Fred Taylor	30.00
M10	Emmitt Smith, Curtis Enis	15.00
M11	Emmitt Smith, Fred Taylor	20.00
M12	Curtis Enis, Fred Taylor	15.00
M13	John Elway, Jerry Rice	20.00
M14	John Elway, Randy Moss	40.00
M15	John Elway, Charles Woodson	20.00
M16	Jerry Rice, Randy Moss	40.00
M17	Jerry Rice, Charles Woodson	15.00
M18	Randy Moss, Charles Woodson	35.00
M19	Terrell Davis, Kordell Stewart	20.00
M20	Terrell Davis, Ricky Watters	15.00
M21	Terrell Davis, Kevin Dyson	15.00
M22	Kordell Stewart, Ricky Watters	12.00
M23	Kordell Stewart, Kevin Dyson	12.00
M24	Ricky Watters, Kevin Dyson	7.00
M25	Warrick Dunn, Eddie George	15.00
M26	Warrick Dunn, Curtis Martin	12.00
M27	Warrick Dunn, Robert Edwards	12.00
M28	Eddie George, Curtis Martin	12.00
M29	Eddie George, Robert Edwards	12.00
M30	Curtis Martin, Robert Edwards	12.00
M31	Peyton Manning, Peyton Manning	25.00
M32	Ryan Leaf, Ryan Leaf	15.00
M33	Curtis Enis, Curtis Enis	12.00
M34	Fred Taylor, Fred Taylor	15.00
M35	Randy Moss, Randy Moss	50.00
M36	Charles Woodson, Charles Woodson	12.00
M37	Ricky Watters, Ricky Watters	7.00
M38	Kevin Dyson, Kevin Dyson	10.00
M39	Curtis Martin, Curtis Martin	10.00
M40	Robert Edwards, Robert Edwards	12.00

1998 Finest Mystery Finest Jumbos 2

These singles measured 3-1/2" x 5", were inserted as box toppers and found 1:4 packs. Refractor versions for each single were also produced and found 1:17 boxes.

		MT
Complete Set (3):		50.00
Common Player:		15.00
Inserted 1:4 Boxes		
Refractors:		2x
Inserted 1:17 Boxes		
M3	Brett Favre, Ryan Leaf	15.00
M8	Barry Sanders, Curtis Enis	15.00
M16	Jerry Rice, Randy Moss	30.00

1998 Finest Stadium Stars

Only 20 of the top players in the game were included in this 1:45 pack insert. Each single has the letter "S" prefixed to the card number.

		MT
Complete Set (20):		160.00
Common Player:		5.00
Inserted 1:45		
S1	Barry Sanders	30.00
S2	Steve Young	10.00
S3	Emmitt Smith	20.00

S4	Mark Brunell	10.00
S5	Curtis Martin	5.00
S6	Kordell Stewart	10.00
S7	Jerry Rice	15.00
S8	Warrick Dunn	10.00
S9	Peyton Manning	20.00
S10	Brett Favre	30.00
S11	Terrell Davis	25.00
S12	Cris Carter	5.00
S13	Herman Moore	5.00
S14	Troy Aikman	15.00
S15	Tim Brown	5.00
S16	Dan Marino	20.00
S17	Drew Bledsoe	10.00
S18	Jerome Bettis	5.00
S19	Ryan Leaf	10.00
S20	John Elway	15.00

1998 Finest Stadium Stars Jumbos

These cards were inserted as box toppers at 1:12 boxes. Each single measures 3-1/2" x 5".

		MT
Complete Set (6):		85.00
Common Player:		5.00
Inserted 1:12 Boxes		
9	Peyton Manning	25.00
10	Brett Favre	30.00
11	Terrell Davis	25.00
18	Jerome Bettis	5.00
19	Ryan Leaf	10.00
20	John Elway	20.00

1998 Finest Undergrads

This 20-card insert showcased top rookies and second-year players. Undergrads were numbered with a "U" prefix and inserted one per 72 packs, with Refractor versions one per 216 packs.

		MT
Complete Set (20):		250.00
Common Player:		8.00
Inserted 1:72		
Refractor Set (20):		375.00
Refractors:		1.5x
Inserted 1:216		
U1	Warrick Dunn	20.00
U2	Tony Gonzalez	8.00
U3	Antowain Smith	12.00
U4	Jake Plummer	25.00
U5	Peter Boulware	8.00
U6	Derrick Rodgers	8.00
U7	Freddie Jones	8.00
U8	Reidel Anthony	10.00
U9	Bryant Westbrook	8.00
U10	Corey Dillon	15.00
U11	Curtis Enis	15.00
U12	Andre Wadsworth	8.00
U13	Fred Taylor	30.00
U14	Greg Ellis	8.00
U15	Ryan Leaf	20.00
U16	Robert Edwards	15.00
U17	Germane Crowell	12.00
U18	Brian Griese	14.00
U19	Kevin Dyson	10.00
U20	Peyton Manning	50.00

1999 Finest

This was a 175-card set that included 51 bonus base cards found 1:1. The bonus cards were divided into three subsets: Rookies, Gems and Sensations. Each base card was printed on 27-point stock. Two parallel sets were issued with Refractors and Gold Refractors. Other inserts included: Double Team, Future's Finest, Leading Indicators, Main Attractions, Prominent Figures, Salute and Team Finest. SRP was $5.00 for six-card packs.

		MT
Complete Set (175):		225.00
Common Player:		.50
Minor Stars:		.50
Common Rookie:		2.00
Inserted 1:1		
Wax Box:		100.00
1	Peyton Manning	3.00
2	Priest Holmes	.75
3	Kordell Stewart	1.00
4	Shannon Sharpe	.50
5	Andre Rison	.50
6	Rickey Dudley	.25
7	Duce Staley	.50
8	Randall Cunningham	.75
9	Warrick Dunn	1.00
10	Dan Marino	3.00
11	Kevin Greene	.25
12	Garrison Hearst	.50
13	Eric Moulds	.75
14	Marvin Harrison	1.00
15	Eddie George	1.00
16	Vinny Testaverde	.50
17	Darrell Green	.25
18	Derrick Thomas	.50
19	Chris Chandler	.50
20	Troy Aikman	2.00
21	Terance Mathis	.25
22	Terrell Owens	.75
23	Junior Seau	.50
24	Cris Carter	.75
25	Fred Taylor	2.00
26	Adrian Murrell	.25
27	Terry Glenn	.75
28	Rod Smith	.50
29	Darnay Scott	.25
30	Brett Favre	4.00
31	Cameron Cleeland	.50
32	Ricky Watters	.50
33	Derrick Alexander	.25
34	Bruce Smith	.25
35	Steve McNair	1.00
36	Wayne Chrebet	.75
37	Herman Moore	.75
38	Bert Emanuel	.25
39	Michael Irvin	.50
40	Steve Young	1.50
41	Napoleon Kaufman	.75
42	Tim Biakabutuka	.25
43	Isaac Bruce	.75
44	J.J. Stokes	.50
45	Antonio Freeman	.75
46	John Randle	.25
47	Frank Sanders	.50
48	O.J. McDuffie	.25
49	Keenan McCardell	.25
50	Randy Moss	4.00
51	Ed McCaffrey	.75
52	Yancey Thigpen	.50
53	Curtis Conway	.50
54	Mike Alstott	.75
55	Deion Sanders	1.00
56	Dorsey Levens	.75
57	Joey Galloway	.75
58	Natrone Means	.50
59	Tim Brown	.50
60	Jerry Rice	2.00
61	Robert Smith	.75
62	Carl Pickens	.50
63	Ben Coates	.50
64	Jerome Bettis	.75
65	Corey Dillon	.75
66	Curtis Martin	.75
67	Jimmy Smith	.75
68	Keyshawn Johnson	.75
69	Charlie Batch	1.25
70	Jamal Anderson	.75
71	Mark Brunell	1.50
72	Antowain Smith	.75
73	Aeneas Williams	.25
74	Wesley Walls	.25
75	Jake Plummer	2.00
76	Oronde Gadsden	.50
77	Gary Brown	.25
78	Peter Boulware	.25
79	Stephen Alexander	.25
80	Barry Sanders	4.00
81	Warren Sapp	.25
82	Michael Sinclair	.25
83	Freddie Jones	.25
84	Ike Hilliard	.25
85	Jake Reed	.25
86	Tim Dwight	.75
87	Johnnie Morton	.25
88	Robert Brooks	.25
89	Frank Wycheck	.25
90	Emmitt Smith	3.00
91	Ricky Proehl	.25
92	James Jett	.25
93	Karim Abdul	.50
94	Mark Chmura	.50
95	Andre Reed	.50
96	Michael Westbrook	.50
97	Michael Strahan	.25
98	Chad Brown	.25
99	Trent Dilfer	.25
100	Terrell Davis	3.00
101	Aaron Glenn	.25
102	Skip Hicks	.50
103	Tony Gonzalez	.50
104	Ty Law	.25
105	Jermaine Lewis	.50
106	Ray Lewis	.50
107	Zach Thomas	.50
108	Reidel Anthony	.25
109	Levon Kirkland	.25
110	Drew Bledsoe	2.00
111	Bobby Engram	.25
112	Jerome Pathon	.25
113	Muhsin Muhammed	.25
114	Vonnie Holliday	.50
115	Bill Romanowski	.25
116	Marshall Faulk	1.00
117	Jessie Armstead	.25
118	Mo Lewis	.25
119	Charles Woodson	1.00
120	Doug Flutie	1.25
121	Jon Kitna	1.00
122	Courtney Hawkins	.25
123	Stephen Boyd	.25
124	John Elway	3.00
125	Gems (Barry Sanders)	4.00
126	Gems (Brett Favre)	4.00
127	Gems (Curtis Martin)	.75
128	Gems (Dan Marino)	3.00
129	Gems (Eddie George)	1.00
130	Gems (Emmitt Smith)	3.00
131	Gems (Jamal Anderson)	.75
132	Gems (Jerry Rice)	2.00
133	Gems (John Elway)	3.00
134	Gems (Terrell Davis)	3.00
135	Gems (Troy Aikman)	2.00
136	Sensations (Skip Hicks)	.75
137	Sensations (Charles Woodson)	.75
138	Sensations (Charlie Batch)	1.25
139	Sensations (Curtis Enis)	.75
140	Sensations (Fred Taylor)	2.00
141	Sensations (Jake Plummer)	2.00
142	Sensations (Peyton Manning)	3.00
143	Sensations (Randy Moss)	4.00
144	Sensations (Corey Dillon)	1.00
145	Sensations (Priest Holmes)	.75
146	Sensations (Warrick Dunn)	.75
147	Jevon Kearse	7.00
148	Chris Claiborne	4.00
149	Akili Smith	12.00
150	Brock Huard	4.00
151	Daunte Culpepper	12.00
152	Edgerrin James	30.00
153	Cecil Collins	15.00
154	Kevin Faulk	6.00
155	Amos Zereoue	6.00
156	James Johnson	6.00
157	Sedrick Irvin	6.00
158	Ricky Williams	25.00
159	Michael Cloud	2.00
160	Chris McAlister	2.00
161	Rob Konrad	4.00
162	Champ Bailey	5.00
163	Ebenezer Ekuban	2.00
164	Tim Couch	25.00
165	Cade McNown	12.00
166	Donovan McNabb	12.00
167	Joe Germaine	5.00
168	Shaun King	10.00
169	Peerless Price	6.00
170	Kevin Johnson	8.00
171	Troy Edwards	8.00
172	Karsten Bailey	2.00
173	David Boston	8.00
174	D'Wayne Bates	4.00
175	Torry Holt	8.00

1999 Finest Refractors

This was a 175-card set that paralleled the base set. Each of these singles used the Refractor technology on the fronts of the cards. Singles were found 1:12 packs.

	MT
Refractor Cards:	5x-10x
Refractor Gems/Sensations:	3x-6x
Refractor Rookies:	2x-4x
Inserted 1:12	

1999 Finest Gold Refractors

This was a 175-card parallel to the base set. Each single was die cut and printed with a gold background. They were found 1:72 packs and were sequentially numbered to 100.

	MT
Refractor Cards:	20x-40x
Refractor Gems/Sensations:	10x-20x
Refractor Rookies:	5x-10x
Inserted 1:72	
Production 100 Sets	

1999 Finest Double Team

This seven-card insert set included a pair of teammates on the same card and pictured each on the fronts of the cards. Singles were inserted 1:50 packs. Partial Refractor versions were also issued with half the card a Refractor and the other half normal. They were also found 1:50 packs. A complete Refractor version was issued and found 1:150 packs.

	MT
Complete Set (7):	25.00
Common Player:	2.50
Inserted 1:50	

	MT
Dual Refractors:	2x
Inserted 1:150	
1 Akili Smith, Carl Pickens	8.00
2 Cade McNown, Curtis Enis	10.00
3 Doug Flutie, Eric Moulds	5.00
4 Mark Brunell, Fred Taylor	5.00
5 Kordell Stewart, Jerome Bettis	2.50
6 Jon Kitna, Joey Galloway	2.50
7 Warrick Dunn, Mike Alstott	2.50

1999 Finest Future's Finest

This 10-card insert set included the top rookies from 1999. Singles were inserted 1:253 packs and sequentially numbered to 500. A parallel Refractor version was also released. Each of those singles was sequentially numbered to 100 and found 1:1,262 packs.

		MT
Complete Set (10):		175.00
Common Player:		10.00
Inserted 1:253		
Production 500 Sets		
Refractors:		3x
Inserted 1:1,264		
Production 100 Sets		
1	Akili Smith	20.00
2	Cade McNown	20.00
3	Champ Bailey	10.00
4	Daunte Culpepper	20.00
5	David Boston	15.00
6	Donovan McNabb	20.00
7	Edgerrin James	40.00
8	Ricky Williams	45.00
9	Tim Couch	45.00
10	Torry Holt	15.00

1999 Finest Leading Indicators

Each of the singles in this 10-card set utilized an innovative, heat-sensitive, thermal ink technology and when each star in this insert set. Collectors touched points of the field behind each player image and the player's statistics appeared. Singles were inserted 1:30 packs.

		MT
Complete Set (10):		40.00
Common Player:		2.00
Minor Stars:		4.00
Inserted 1:30		
1	Jamal Anderson	4.00
2	Doug Flutie	5.00
3	Drew Bledsoe	6.00
4	Eddie George	5.00
5	Emmitt Smith	10.00
6	John Elway	10.00
7	Keyshawn Johnson	4.00
8	Steve Young	5.00
9	Terrell Owens	5.00
10	Vinny Testaverde	2.00

1999 Finest Main Attractions

This seven-card insert set included 14 different players with two per card. Singles were found 1:50 packs. A parallel version with half the card a Refractor and the other a non-Refractor was issued at 1:50 packs. The Refractor version with the whole card as a Refractor was issued 1:150 packs.

		MT
Complete Set (7):		35.00
Common Player:		2.50
Inserted 1:50		
Dual Refractors:		2x
Inserted 1:150		
1	Champ Bailey, Deion Sanders	5.00
2	Daunte Culpepper, Steve McNair	8.00
3	Donovan McNabb, Kordell Stewart	8.00
4	Edgerrin James, Marshall Faulk	12.00
5	Kevin Faulk, Warrick Dunn	5.00
6	Joe Germaine, Troy Aikman	7.00
7	Rob Konrad, Mike Alstott	2.50

1999 Finest Prominent Figures

This 60-card insert set included players who were chasing records and the set was divided into six statistical categories. Each of these singles were sequentially numbered to the all-time single season record. Passing Yards were numbered to 5,084 and inserted 1:25 packs. Touchdown Passes were numbered to 48 and inserted 1:2,634. Rushing Yards were numbered to 2,105 and found 1:60 packs. Rushing Touchdowns were numbered to 25 and inserted 1:5,099. Receiving Yards were numbered to 1,848 and found 1:68 packs. Touchdown Receptions were numbered to 22 and found 1:5,779.

	MT
Common QB (1-10):	1.00
Inserted 1:25	
Production 5,084 Sets	
Common QB (11-20):	25.00
Inserted 1:2,634	
Production 48 Sets	
Common RB (21-30):	50.00
Inserted 1:5,099	
Production 25 Sets	
Common RB (31-40):	5.00
Inserted 1:60	
Production 2,105 Sets	
Common WR (41-50):	50.00
Inserted 1:5,779	

Production 22 Sets
Common WR (51-60): 3.00
Inserted 1:68
Production 1,848 Sets

1	Brett Favre	10.00
2	Dan Marino	7.00
3	Drew Bledsoe	4.00
4	Jake Plummer	5.00
5	Mark Brunell	4.00
6	Peyton Manning	7.00
7	Randall Cunningham	2.00
8	Steve Young	3.00
9	Tim Couch	15.00
10	Vinny Testaverde	1.00
11	Brett Favre	150.00
12	Dan Marino	120.00
13	Drew Bledsoe	50.00
14	Jake Plummer	75.00
15	Mark Brunell	50.00
16	Peyton Manning	120.00
17	Randall Cunningham	35.00
18	Steve Young	50.00
19	Tim Couch	200.00
20	Vinny Testaverde	25.00
21	Barry Sanders	250.00
22	Curtis Martin	50.00
23	Eddie George	75.00
24	Emmitt Smith	175.00
25	Fred Taylor	125.00
26	Garrison Hearst	50.00
27	Jamal Anderson	50.00
28	Marshall Faulk	50.00
29	Ricky Williams	300.00
30	Terrell Davis	175.00
31	Barry Sanders	20.00
32	Curtis Martin	5.00
33	Eddie George	6.00
34	Emmitt Smith	15.00
35	Fred Taylor	10.00
36	Garrison Hearst	5.00
37	Jamal Anderson	5.00
38	Marshall Faulk	5.00
39	Ricky Williams	30.00
40	Terrell Davis	15.00
41	Antonio Freeman	50.00
42	David Boston	75.00
43	Cris Carter	50.00
44	Jerry Rice	125.00
45	Joey Galloway	50.00
46	Keyshawn Johnson	50.00
47	Randy Moss	250.00
48	Terrell Owens	50.00
49	Tim Brown	50.00
50	Torry Holt	75.00
51	Antonio Freeman	4.00
52	David Boston	8.00
53	Eric Moulds	4.00
54	Jerry Rice	10.00
55	Joey Galloway	4.00
56	Keyshawn Johnson	4.00
57	Randy Moss	20.00
58	Terrell Owens	4.00
59	Jimmy Smith	3.00
60	Torry Holt	8.00

1999 Finest Salute

One card was made for this set with two parallel versions. The card included the three 1998 season award winners with the NFL Rookie of the Year Randy Moss, NFL MVP Terrell Davis and Super Bowl XXXIII MVP John Elway. The single was found 1:53 packs. A parallel Refractor was made and inserted 1:1,900 packs. Also, a parallel Gold Refractor was found 1:12,384 packs and was sequentially numbered to 100.

	MT
Complete Set (3):	275.00
Inserted 1:53	
Refractor Inserted 1:1,900	
Gold Ref. Inserted 1:12,384	
Production 100 Sets	
Terrell Davis, John Elway, Randy Moss	10.00
Terrell Davis, John Elway, Randy Moss GR	250.00

Terrell Davis, 75.00
John Elway,
Randy Moss REF

1999 Finest Team Finest

This was a 10-card set that included top NFL stars and pictured them on a prismatic card. The base set was in Blue, inserted 1:84 packs and numbered to 1,500. A Gold parallel was made and inserted 1:57 packs and numbered to 250. A Red version was issued at 1:29 packs and numbered to 500. Each had a parallel Refractor version. The Blue singles were found 1:843 packs and numbered to 150. The Red singles were inserted 1:285 packs and numbered to 50. While the Gold singles were issued 1:573 packs and numbered to 25.

	MT
Complete Set (10):	100.00
Common Player:	5.00
Inserted 1:84	
Production 1,500 Sets	
Blue Refractors:	4x
Inserted 1:843	
Production 150 Sets	
Gold Cards:	3x
Inserted 1:57	
Production 250 Sets	
Gold Refractors:	8x-16x
Inserted 1:573	
Production 25 Sets	
Red Cards:	2x
Inserted 1:29	
Production 500 Sets	
Red Refractors:	4x-8x
Inserted 1:285	
Production 50 Sets	
1	Barry Sanders	15.00
2	Brett Favre	15.00
3	Dan Marino	12.00
4	Drew Bledsoe	7.00
5	Jamal Anderson	5.00
6	John Elway	12.00
7	Peyton Manning	12.00
8	Randy Moss	15.00
9	Terrell Davis	12.00
10	Troy Aikman	8.00

1995 Flair

Each of the regular 220 cards in this set features a player on a horizontal card with a foil-etched background. Two photos appear on each front - one is a mug shot of the player without his helmet on, the other is an action photo. The Flair logo is stamped in gold at the top of the card; the player's name and team are stamped at the bottom. The player's initials are scripted in silver foil at the bottom. The card back has a full-bleed action photo, with the

player's name and team helmet stamped in the center in gold foil. The player's statistics are also listed. Insert sets include Hot Numbers, TD Power and Wave of the Future.

	MT
Complete Set (220):	70.00
Common Player:	.20
Minor Stars:	.40
Wax Box:	80.00
1	Larry Centers	.20
2	Garrison Hearst	.75
3	Seth Joyner	.20
4	Dave Krieg	.20
5	Rob Moore	.20
6	*Frank Sanders*	2.00
7	Eric Swann	.20
8	Devin Bush	.20
9	Chris Coleman	.20
10	Bert Emanuel	.75
11	Jeff George	.40
12	Craig Heyward	.20
13	Terance Mathis	.20
14	Eric Metcalf	.20
15	Cornelius Bennett	.20
16	Jeff Burris	.20
17	*Todd Collins*	.40
18	Russell Copeland	.20
19	Jim Kelly	.40
20	Andre Reed	.20
21	Bruce Smith	.20
22	Don Beebe	.20
23	Mark Carrier	.20
24	*Kerry Collins*	7.00
25	Barry Foster	.20
26	Pete Metzelaars	.20
27	Tyrone Poole	.20
28	Frank Reich	.20
29	Curtis Conway	.20
30	Chris Gedney	.20
31	Jeff Graham	.20
32	Raymont Harris	.20
33	Erik Kramer	.20
34	*Rashaan Salaam*	2.00
35	Lewis Tillman	.20
36	Michael Timpson	.20
37	*Jeff Blake*	2.00
38	*Ki-Jana Carter*	3.00
39	Tony McGee	1.00
40	Carl Pickens	.40
41	Corey Sawyer	.20
42	Darnay Scott	1.00
43	Dan Wilkinson	.20
44	Derrick Alexander	.40
45	Leroy Hoard	.20
46	Michael Jackson	.20
47	Antonio Langham	.20
48	Andre Rison	.20
49	Vinny Testaverde	.20
50	Eric Turner	.20
51	Troy Aikman	2.00
52	Charles Haley	.20
53	Michael Irvin	.40
54	Daryl Johnston	.20
55	Leon Lett	.20
56	Jay Novacek	.20
57	Emmitt Smith	6.00
58	Kevin Williams	.20
59	Steve Atwater	.20
60	Rod Bernstine	.20
61	John Elway	1.00
62	Glyn Milburn	.20
63	Anthony Miller	.20
64	Mike Pritchard	.20
65	Shannon Sharpe	.40
66	Scott Mitchell	.40
67	Herman Moore	1.00
68	Johnnie Morton	.20
69	Brett Perriman	.20
70	Barry Sanders	4.00
71	Chris Spielman	.20
72	Edgar Bennett	.20
73	Robert Brooks	.40
74	Brett Favre	6.00
75	LeShon Johnson	.20
76	Sean Jones	.20
77	George Teague	.20
78	Reggie White	.40
79	Micheal Barrow	.20
80	Gary Brown	.20
81	Mel Gray	.20
82	Haywood Jeffires	.20
83	*Steve McNair*	7.00
84	*Rodney Thomas*	.40
85	Trev Alberts	.20
86	Flipper Anderson	.20
87	Tony Bennett	.20
88	Quentin Coryatt	.20
89	Sean Dawkins	.20
90	Craig Erickson	.20
91	Marshall Faulk	2.00
92	Steve Beuerlein	.20
93	*Tony Boselli*	.40
94	Reggie Cobb	.20
95	Ernest Givens	.20
96	Desmond Howard	.20
97	Jeff Lageman	.20
98	*James Stewart*	2.50
99	Marcus Allen	.40
100	Steve Bono	.40
101	Dale Carter	.20
102	Willie Davis	.40
103	Lake Dawson	.40
104	Greg Hill	.20
105	Neil Smith	.20
106	Tim Bowens	.20

107	Bryan Cox	.20
108	Irving Fryar	.20
109	Eric Green	.20
110	Terry Kirby	.20
111	Dan Marino	6.00
112	O.J. McDuffie	.40
113	Bernie Parmalee	.20
114	Derrick Alexander	.20
115	Cris Carter	.40
116	Qadry Ismail	.20
117	Warren Moon	.40
118	Jake Reed	.20
119	Robert Smith	.40
120	DeWayne Washington	.20
121	Drew Bledsoe	3.00
122	Vincent Brisby	.20
123	Ben Coates	.20
124	*Curtis Martin*	8.00
125	Willie McGinest	.20
126	Dave Meggett	.20
127	Chris Slade	.20
128	Eric Allen	.20
129	Mario Bates	.50
130	Jim Everett	.20
131	Michael Haynes	.20
132	Tyrone Hughes	.20
133	Renaldo Turnbull	.20
134	*Ray Zellars*	.40
135	Michael Brooks	.20
136	Dave Brown	.20
137	Rodney Hampton	.20
138	Thomas Lewis	.20
139	Mike Sherrard	.20
140	Herschel Walker	.20
141	*Tyrone Wheatley*	3.00
142	*Kyle Brady*	.75
143	Boomer Esiason	.20
144	Aaron Glenn	.20
145	Mo Lewis	.20
146	Johnny Mitchell	.20
147	Ronald Moore	.20
148	*Joe Aska*	.40
149	Tim Brown	.40
150	Jeff Hostetler	.20
151	Raghib Ismail	.20
152	*Napoleon Kaufman*	4.00
153	Chester McGlockton	.20
154	Harvey Williams	.20
155	Fred Barnett	.20
156	Randall Cunningham	.20
157	Charlie Garner	.20
158	*Mike Mamula*	.40
159	Kevin Turner	.20
160	Ricky Watters	.40
161	Calvin Williams	.20
162	*Mark Bruener*	.75
163	Kevin Greene	.20
164	Charles Johnson	.40
165	Greg Lloyd	.20
166	Bam Morris	.40
167	Neil O'Donnell	.40
168	*Kordell Stewart*	8.00
169	John L. Williams	.20
170	Rod Woodson	.40
171	Jerome Bettis	.40
172	Isaac Bruce	2.00
173	*Kevin Carter*	.40
174	Troy Drayton	.20
175	Sean Gilbert	.20
176	Carlos Jenkins	.20
177	Todd Lyght	.20
178	Chris Miller	.20
179	Andre Coleman	.20
180	Stan Humphries	.40
181	Shawn Jefferson	.20
182	Natrone Means	.40
183	Leslie O'Neal	.40
184	Junior Seau	.40
185	Mark Seay	.20
186	William Floyd	.40
187	Merton Hanks	.20
188	Brent Jones	.20
189	Ken Norton	.20
190	Jerry Rice	2.50
191	Deion Sanders	1.50
192	*J.J. Stokes*	2.00
193	Steve Stubblefield	.20
194	Steve Young	2.50
195	Sam Adams	.20
196	Brian Blades	.20
197	*Joey Galloway*	6.00
198	Cortez Kennedy	.20
199	Rick Mirer	.40
200	Chris Warren	.40
201	Derrick Brooks	.20
202	Lawrence Dawsey	.20
203	Trent Dilfer	.20
204	Alvin Harper	.20
205	Jackie Harris	.20
206	Courtney Hawkins	.20
207	Hardy Nickerson	.20
208	Errict Rhett	2.00
209	*Warren Sapp*	.40
210	Terry Allen	.20
211	Tom Carter	.20
212	Henry Ellard	.20
213	Darrell Green	.20
214	Brian Mitchell	.20
215	Heath Shuler	2.00
216	*Michael Westbrook*	1.75
217	Tydus Winans	.20
218	Checklist	.20
219	Checklist	.20
220	Checklist	.20

1995 Flair Hot Numbers

These 1995 Fleer Flair inserts feature 10 top statistical leaders for the 1994-95 season. Cards, numbered 1 of 10, etc., were were randomly included one per every six packs. The card front has gold foil stamping for the player's name, position and Flair and insert set logos. The key numbers from the player's season statistics are in the background of the card. The horizontal back has another photo of the player, with a box next to it containing a brief summary of his accomplishments. Gold foil stamping is used for his name, team name and "Hot Numbers," which are at the top of the box.

	MT
Complete Set (10):	40.00
Common Player:	1.00
1	Jeff Blake	2.00
2	Drew Bledsoe	7.00
3	Tim Brown	1.00
4	Ben Coates	1.00
5	Trent Dilfer	2.00
6	Brett Favre	14.00
7	Dan Marino	14.00
8	Bam Morris	1.00
9	Ricky Watters	2.00
10	Steve Young	5.00

1995 Flair TD Power

These horizontally-designed insert cards could be found one per every 12 packs of 1995 Fleer Flair. The cards feature 10 of the top touchdown scorers from the previous season. The TD Power logo appears on the front, along with a player action photo and the Flair logo, which is stamped in gold. The player's name and team name are stamped in gold and are at the bottom of the card. The card back has another photo on one side, with a box containing a brief player profile. The insert set logo is included inside the box, at the top. Cards are numbered 1 of 10, etc.

	MT
Complete Set (10):	40.00
Common Player:	2.00
1	Marshall Faulk	5.00
2	William Floyd	2.00
3	Natrone Means	3.00
4	Bam Morris	2.00
5	Errict Rhett	4.00
6	Jerry Rice	7.00
7	Andre Rison	2.00
8	Barry Sanders	7.00
9	Emmitt Smith	14.00
10	Chris Warren	2.00

A player's name in *italic* type indicates a rookie card.

1995 Flair Wave of the Future

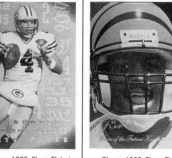

These 1995 Fleer Flair insert cards, randomly included one per every 37 packs, feature nine top rookies. The cards, which use gold foil stamping on the front, offer a unique die-cut that is actually cut around the player's face. The back, numbered 1 of 9, etc., also uses gold foil stamping and includes another action photo. A brief summary of the player's collegiate accomplishments, plus his potential as a pro, is also given.

	MT
Complete Set (9):	175.00
Common Player:	10.00
1	Kyle Brady	10.00
2	Ki-Jana Carter	20.00
3	Kerry Collins	50.00
4	Joey Galloway	30.00
5	Steve McNair	40.00
6	Rashaan Salaam	20.00
7	James Stewart	10.00
8	Michael Westbrook	15.00
9	Tyrone Wheatley	10.00

1997 Flair Showcase

Flair Showcase NFL is a 360-card set featuring 120 players. Each player has three base cards: Style, Grace and Showcase. The fronts feature distinct action and headshots with a holographic foil background on 24 pt card stock. The backs have another photo and complete career statistics. The basic card types have a tiered insertion ratio. Two parallel sets were issued: Legacy, with less than 100 cards per player, and the one-of-a-kind Legacy Masterpiece. Four insert sets were included: Wave of the Future, Hot Hands, Midas Touch and Then & Now.

	MT
Complete Set (360):	1700.
Comp. Style Set (120):	75.00
Common Style (A1-A120):	.25
Comp. Grace Set (120):	150.00
Common Grace (B1-B120):	.50
Comp. Showcase Set (120):	1500.
Common Showcase (C1-C120):	2.00
Wax Box:	140.00
A1	Jerry Rice STY	4.00
A2	Mark Brunell STY	4.00
A3	Eddie Kennison STY	.50
A4	Brett Favre STY	8.00
A5	Karim Abdul-Jabbar STY	.75
A6	*David LaFleur STY*	1.50
A7	John Elway STY	3.00
A8	Troy Aikman STY	4.00
A9	Steve McNair STY	3.00
A10	Kordell Stewart STY	4.00
A11	Drew Bledsoe STY	4.00
A12	Kerry Collins STY	.50

#	Player	Price
A13	Dan Marino STY	6.00
A14	Steve Young STY	3.00
A15	Marvin Harrison STY	1.00
A16	Lawrence Phillips STY	.50
A17	Jeff Blake STY	.50
A18	Yatil Green STY	1.50
A19	Jake Plummer STY	10.00
A20	Barry Sanders STY	4.00
A21	Deion Sanders STY	2.50
A22	Emmitt Smith STY	6.00
A23	Rae Carruth STY	2.00
A24	Chris Warren STY	.25
A25	Terry Glenn STY	1.00
A26	Jim Druckenmiller STY	4.00
A27	Eddie George STY	5.00
A28	Curtis Martin STY	4.00
A29	Warrick Dunn STY	4.00
A30	Terrell Davis STY	4.00
A31	Rashaan Salaam STY	.25
A32	Marcus Allen STY	.50
A33	Jeff George STY	.50
A34	Thurman Thomas STY	.50
A35	Keyshawn Johnson STY	1.00
A36	Jerome Bettis STY	.50
A37	Larry Centers STY	.25
A38	Tony Banks STY	1.00
A39	Marshall Faulk STY	.50
A40	Mike Alstott STY	.50
A41	Elvis Grbac STY	.25
A42	Errict Rhett STY	.50
A43	Edgar Bennett STY	.25
A44	Jim Harbaugh STY	.25
A45	Antonio Freeman STY	1.00
A46	Tiki Barber STY	3.00
A47	Tim Biakabutuka STY	.25
A48	Joey Galloway STY	.50
A49	Tony Gonzalez STY	1.50
A50	Keenan McCardell STY	.25
A51	Darnay Scott STY	.25
A52	Brad Johnson STY	.25
A53	Herman Moore STY	.50
A54	Reidel Anthony STY	3.00
A55	Junior Seau STY	.50
A56	Ricky Watters STY	.25
A57	Amani Toomer STY	.25
A58	Andre Reed STY	.25
A59	Antowain Smith STY	5.00
A60	Ike Hilliard STY	2.50
A61	Byron Hanspard STY	1.50
A62	Robert Smith STY	.25
A63	Gus Frerotte STY	.25
A64	Charles Way STY	.25
A65	Trent Dilfer STY	.25
A66	Adrian Murrell STY	.50
A67	Stan Humphries STY	.25
A68	Robert Brooks STY	.25
A69	Jamal Anderson STY	.50
A70	Natrone Means STY	.50
A71	John Friesz STY	.25
A72	Ki-Jana Carter STY	.25
A73	Marc Edwards STY	.25
A74	Michael Westbrook STY	.25
A75	Neil O'Donnell STY	.25
A76	Scott Mitchell STY	.25
A77	Wesley Walls STY	.25
A78	Bruce Smith STY	.25
A79	Corey Dillon STY	6.00
A80	Wayne Chrebet STY	.25
A81	Tony Martin STY	.25
A82	Jimmy Smith STY	.25
A83	Terry Allen STY	.25
A84	Shannon Sharpe STY	.25
A85	Derrick Alexander STY	.25
A86	Garrison Hearst STY	.25
A87	Tamarick Vanover STY	.25
A88	Michael Irvin STY	.50
A89	Mark Chmura STY	.50
A90	Bert Emanuel STY	.25
A91	Eric Metcalf STY	.25
A92	Reggie White STY	.50
A93	Carl Pickens STY	.25
A94	Chris Sanders STY	.25
A95	Frank Sanders STY	.25
A96	Desmond Howard STY	.25
A97	Michael Jackson STY	.25
A98	Tim Brown STY	.50
A99	O.J. McDuffie STY	.25
A100	Mario Bates STY	.25
A101	Warren Moon STY	.25
A102	Curtis Conway STY	.25
A103	Irving Fryar STY	.25
A104	Isaac Bruce STY	.50
A105	Cris Carter STY	.50
A106	Chris Chandler STY	.25
A107	Charles Johnson STY	.25
A108	Kevin Lockett STY	.25
A109	Rob Moore STY	.25
A110	Napoleon Kaufman STY	.75
A111	Henry Ellard STY	.25
A112	Vinny Testaverde STY	.25
A113	Rick Mirer STY	.25
A114	Ty Detmer STY	.25
A115	Todd Collins STY	.25
A116	Jake Reed STY	.25
A117	Dave Brown STY	.25
A118	Dedric Ward STY	1.50
A119	Heath Shuler STY	.25
A120	Ben Coates STY	.25
B1	Jerry Rice GRA	6.00
B2	Mark Brunell GRA	6.00
B3	Eddie Kennison GRA	1.00
B4	Brett Favre GRA	12.00
B5	Karim Abdul-Jabbar GRA	1.50
B6	David LaFleur GRA	2.00
B7	John Elway GRA	4.50
B8	Troy Aikman GRA	6.00
B9	Steve McNair GRA	4.50
B10	Kordell Stewart GRA	6.00
B11	Drew Bledsoe GRA	6.00
B12	Kerry Collins GRA	1.50
B13	Dan Marino GRA	9.00
B14	Steve Young GRA	4.50
B15	Marvin Harrison GRA	2.00
B16	Lawrence Phillips GRA	.75
B17	Jeff Blake GRA	.75
B18	Yatil Green GRA	2.50
B19	Jake Plummer GRA	15.00
B20	Barry Sanders GRA	6.00
B21	Deion Sanders GRA	4.00
B22	Emmitt Smith GRA	9.00
B23	Rae Carruth GRA	3.00
B24	Chris Warren GRA	.50
B25	Terry Glenn GRA	2.50
B26	Jim Druckenmiller GRA	6.00
B27	Eddie George GRA	7.50
B28	Curtis Martin GRA	6.00
B29	Warrick Dunn GRA	5.00
B30	Terrell Davis GRA	6.00
B31	Rashaan Salaam GRA	.50
B32	Marcus Allen GRA	.75
B33	Jeff George GRA	.75
B34	Thurman Thomas GRA	.75
B35	Keyshawn Johnson GRA	2.00
B36	Jerome Bettis GRA	.75
B37	Larry Centers GRA	.50
B38	Tony Banks GRA	2.00
B39	Marshall Faulk GRA	.75
B40	Mike Alstott GRA	.75
B41	Elvis Grbac GRA	.50
B42	Errict Rhett GRA	.75
B43	Edgar Bennett GRA	.50
B44	Jim Harbaugh GRA	.50
B45	Antonio Freeman GRA	1.50
B46	Tiki Barber GRA	4.50
B47	Tim Biakabutuka GRA	.50
B48	Joey Galloway GRA	.75
B49	Tony Gonzalez GRA	2.00
B50	Keenan McCardell GRA	.50
B51	Darnay Scott GRA	.50
B52	Brad Johnson GRA	.50
B53	Herman Moore GRA	.75
B54	Reidel Anthony GRA	4.50
B55	Junior Seau GRA	.75
B56	Ricky Watters GRA	.75
B57	Amani Toomer GRA	.50
B58	Andre Reed GRA	.50
B59	Antowain Smith GRA	8.00
B60	Ike Hilliard GRA	4.00
B61	Byron Hanspard GRA	1.50
B62	Robert Smith GRA	.50
B63	Gus Frerotte GRA	.50
B64	Charles Way GRA	.50
B65	Trent Dilfer GRA	.50
B66	Adrian Murrell GRA	.75
B67	Stan Humphries GRA	.50
B68	Robert Brooks GRA	.50
B69	Jamal Anderson GRA	.75
B70	Natrone Means GRA	.75
B71	John Friesz GRA	.50
B72	Ki-Jana Carter GRA	.50
B73	Marc Edwards GRA	.50
B74	Michael Westbrook GRA	.50
B75	Neil O'Donnell GRA	.50
B76	Scott Mitchell GRA	.50
B77	Wesley Walls GRA	.50
B78	Bruce Smith GRA	.50
B79	Corey Dillon GRA	8.00
B80	Wayne Chrebet GRA	.50
B81	Tony Martin GRA	.50
B82	Jimmy Smith GRA	.50
B83	Terry Allen GRA	.50
B84	Shannon Sharpe GRA	.50
B85	Derrick Alexander GRA	.50
B86	Garrison Hearst GRA	.50
B87	Tamarick Vanover GRA	.50
B88	Michael Irvin GRA	.75
B89	Mark Chmura GRA	.75
B90	Bert Emanuel GRA	.50
B91	Eric Metcalf GRA	.50
B92	Reggie White GRA	.75
B93	Carl Pickens GRA	.50
B94	Chris Sanders GRA	.50
B95	Frank Sanders GRA	.50
B96	Desmond Howard GRA	.50
B97	Michael Jackson GRA	.50
B98	Tim Brown GRA	.75
B99	O.J. McDuffie GRA	.50
B100	Mario Bates GRA	.50
B101	Warren Moon GRA	.50
B102	Curtis Conway GRA	.50
B103	Irving Fryar GRA	.50
B104	Isaac Bruce GRA	.75
B105	Cris Carter GRA	.75
B106	Chris Chandler GRA	.50
B107	Charles Johnson GRA	.50
B108	Kevin Lockett GRA	.50
B109	Rob Moore GRA	.50
B110	Napoleon Kaufman GRA	1.00
B111	Henry Ellard GRA	.50
B112	Vinny Testaverde GRA	.50
B113	Rick Mirer GRA	.50
B114	Ty Detmer GRA	.50
B115	Todd Collins GRA	.50
B116	Jake Reed GRA	.50
B117	Dave Brown GRA	.50
B118	Dedric Ward GRA	.50
B119	Heath Shuler GRA	.50
B120	Ben Coates GRA	.50
C1	Jerry Rice SHOW	60.00
C2	Mark Brunell SHOW	60.00
C3	Eddie Kennison SHOW	6.00
C4	Brett Favre SHOW	125.00
C5	Karim Abdul-Jabbar SHOW	6.00
C6	David LaFleur SHOW	15.00
C7	John Elway SHOW	50.00
C8	Troy Aikman SHOW	60.00
C9	Steve McNair SHOW	50.00
C10	Kordell Stewart SHOW	60.00
C11	Drew Bledsoe SHOW	60.00
C12	Kerry Collins SHOW	6.00
C13	Dan Marino SHOW	100.00
C14	Steve Young SHOW	50.00
C15	Marvin Harrison SHOW	8.00
C16	Lawrence Phillips SHOW	6.00
C17	Jeff Blake SHOW	4.00
C18	Yatil Green SHOW	6.00
C19	Jake Plummer SHOW	125.00
C20	Barry Sanders SHOW	70.00
C21	Deion Sanders SHOW	40.00
C22	Emmitt Smith SHOW	100.00
C23	Rae Carruth SHOW	25.00
C24	Chris Warren SHOW	2.00
C25	Terry Glenn SHOW	8.00
C26	Jim Druckenmiller SHOW	60.00
C27	Eddie George SHOW	75.00
C28	Curtis Martin SHOW	60.00
C29	Warrick Dunn SHOW	50.00
C30	Terrell Davis SHOW	60.00
C31	Rashaan Salaam SHOW	2.00
C32	Marcus Allen SHOW	6.00
C33	Jeff George SHOW	6.00
C34	Thurman Thomas SHOW	6.00
C35	Keyshawn Johnson SHOW	8.00
C36	Jerome Bettis SHOW	6.00
C37	Larry Centers SHOW	2.00
C38	Tony Banks SHOW	6.00
C39	Marshall Faulk SHOW	6.00
C40	Mike Alstott SHOW	7.50
C41	Elvis Grbac SHOW	2.00
C42	Errict Rhett SHOW	4.00
C43	Edgar Bennett SHOW	2.00
C44	Jim Harbaugh SHOW	2.00
C45	Antonio Freeman SHOW	8.00
C46	Tiki Barber SHOW	25.00
C47	Tim Biakabutuka SHOW	2.00
C48	Joey Galloway SHOW	7.50
C49	Tony Gonzalez SHOW	15.00
C50	Keenan McCardell SHOW	2.00
C51	Darnay Scott SHOW	2.00
C52	Brad Johnson SHOW	2.00
C53	Herman Moore SHOW	7.50
C54	Reidel Anthony SHOW	25.00
C55	Junior Seau SHOW	4.00
C56	Ricky Watters SHOW	4.00
C57	Amani Toomer SHOW	2.00
C58	Andre Reed SHOW	2.00
C59	Antowain Smith SHOW	25.00
C60	Ike Hilliard SHOW	25.00
C61	Byron Hanspard SHOW	6.00
C62	Robert Smith SHOW	2.00
C63	Gus Frerotte SHOW	2.00
C64	Charles Way SHOW	2.00
C65	Trent Dilfer SHOW	6.00
C66	Adrian Murrell SHOW	4.00
C67	Stan Humphries SHOW	2.00
C68	Robert Brooks SHOW	2.00
C69	Jamal Anderson SHOW	7.50
C70	Natrone Means SHOW	6.00
C71	John Friesz SHOW	2.00
C72	Ki-Jana Carter SHOW	2.00
C73	Marc Edwards SHOW	2.00
C74	Michael Westbrook SHOW	2.00
C75	Neil O'Donnell SHOW	2.00
C76	Scott Mitchell SHOW	2.00
C77	Wesley Walls SHOW	2.00
C78	Bruce Smith SHOW	2.00
C79	Corey Dillon SHOW	30.00
C80	Wayne Chrebet SHOW	2.00
C81	Tony Martin SHOW	2.00
C82	Jimmy Smith SHOW	2.00
C83	Terry Allen SHOW	2.00
C84	Shannon Sharpe SHOW	2.00
C85	Derrick Alexander SHOW	2.00
C86	Garrison Hearst SHOW	2.00
C87	Tamarick Vanover SHOW	2.00
C88	Michael Irvin SHOW	5.00
C89	Mark Chmura SHOW	4.00
C90	Bert Emanuel SHOW	2.00
C91	Eric Metcalf SHOW	2.00
C92	Reggie White SHOW	5.00
C93	Carl Pickens SHOW	2.00
C94	Chris Sanders SHOW	2.00
C95	Frank Sanders SHOW	2.00
C96	Desmond Howard SHOW	2.00
C97	Michael Jackson SHOW	2.00
C98	Tim Brown SHOW	4.00
C99	O.J. McDuffie SHOW	2.00
C100	Mario Bates SHOW	2.00
C101	Warren Moon SHOW	2.00
C102	Curtis Conway SHOW	2.00
C103	Irving Fryar SHOW	2.00
C104	Isaac Bruce SHOW	4.00
C105	Cris Carter SHOW	2.00
C106	Chris Chandler SHOW	2.00
C107	Charles Johnson SHOW	2.00
C108	Kevin Lockett SHOW	2.00
C109	Rob Moore SHOW	2.00
C110	Napoleon Kaufman SHOW	6.00
C111	Henry Ellard SHOW	2.00
C112	Vinny Testaverde SHOW	2.00
C113	Rick Mirer SHOW	2.00
C114	Ty Detmer SHOW	2.00
C115	Todd Collins SHOW	2.00
C116	Jake Reed SHOW	2.00
C117	Dave Brown SHOW	2.00
C118	Dedric Ward SHOW	2.00
C119	Heath Shuler SHOW	2.00
C120	Ben Coates SHOW	2.00

Post-1980 cards in Near Mint condition will generally sell for about 75% of the quoted Mint value. Excellent-condition cards bring no more than 40%.

1997 Flair Showcase Legacy

Legacy parallels the 360-base cards in Flair Showcase. The cards feature blue-foil stamping and are sequentially numbered to 100. The backs are done in matte finish. The Legacy Masterpiece versions are a one-of-one parallel of each base card. The cards are stamped to signify their distinctness.

		MT
Common Player:		10.00
Minor Stars:		20.00
Production 100 Sets		
1	Jerry Rice	75.00
2	Mark Brunell	75.00
3	Eddie Kennison	10.00
4	Brett Favre	150.00
5	Karim Abdul-Jabbar	20.00
6	David LaFleur	20.00
7	John Elway	120.00
8	Troy Aikman	75.00
9	Steve McNair	45.00
10	Kordell Stewart	60.00
11	Drew Bledsoe	75.00
12	Kerry Collins	20.00
13	Dan Marino	120.00
14	Steve Young	45.00
15	Marvin Harrison	25.00
16	Lawrence Phillips	20.00
17	Jeff Blake	20.00
18	Yatil Green	10.00
19	Jake Plummer	150.00
20	Barry Sanders	150.00
21	Deion Sanders	20.00
22	Emmitt Smith	120.00
23	Rae Carruth	10.00
24	Chris Warren	10.00
25	Terry Glenn	20.00
26	Jim Druckenmiller	75.00
27	Eddie George	75.00
28	Curtis Martin	45.00
29	Warrick Dunn	60.00
30	Terrell Davis	120.00
31	Rashaan Salaam	10.00
32	Marcus Allen	20.00
33	Jeff George	20.00
34	Thurman Thomas	20.00
35	Keyshawn Johnson	25.00
36	Jerome Bettis	20.00
37	Larry Centers	10.00
38	Tony Banks	20.00
39	Marshall Faulk	25.00
40	Mike Alstott	25.00
41	Elvis Grbac	10.00
42	Errict Rhett	20.00
43	Edgar Bennett	10.00
44	Jim Harbaugh	10.00
45	Antonio Freeman	40.00
46	Tiki Barber	35.00
47	Tim Biakabutuka	20.00
48	Joey Galloway	25.00
49	Tony Gonzalez	35.00
50	Keenan McCardell	10.00
51	Darnay Scott	20.00
52	Brad Johnson	30.00
53	Herman Moore	20.00
54	Reidel Anthony	35.00
55	Junior Seau	20.00
56	Ricky Watters	20.00
57	Amani Toomer	10.00
58	Andre Reed	10.00
59	Antowain Smith	75.00
60	Ike Hilliard	35.00
61	Byron Hanspard	50.00
62	Robert Smith	20.00
63	Gus Frerotte	10.00
64	Charles Way	10.00
65	Trent Dilfer	20.00
66	Adrian Murrell	20.00
67	Stan Humphries	10.00
68	Robert Brooks	10.00
69	Jamal Anderson	40.00
70	Natrone Means	20.00
71	John Friesz	10.00
72	Ki-Jana Carter	10.00
73	Marc Edwards	10.00
74	Michael Westbrook	20.00
75	Neil O'Donnell	10.00
76	Scott Mitchell	10.00
77	Wesley Walls	10.00
78	Bruce Smith	10.00
79	Corey Dillon	85.00
80	Wayne Chrebet	20.00
81	Tony Martin	10.00
82	Jimmy Smith	20.00
83	Terry Allen	20.00
84	Shannon Sharpe	10.00
85	Derrick Alexander	10.00
86	Garrison Hearst	20.00
87	Tamarick Vanover	20.00
88	Michael Irvin	20.00
89	Mark Chmura	20.00
90	Bert Emanuel	10.00
91	Eric Metcalf	10.00
92	Reggie White	20.00
93	Carl Pickens	20.00
94	Chris Sanders	10.00
95	Frank Sanders	10.00
96	Desmond Howard	10.00
97	Michael Jackson	10.00
98	Tim Brown	20.00
99	O.J. McDuffie	10.00
100	Mario Bates	10.00
101	Warren Moon	20.00
102	Curtis Conway	20.00
103	Irving Fryar	10.00
104	Isaac Bruce	20.00
105	Cris Carter	25.00
106	Chris Chandler	10.00
107	Charles Johnson	10.00
108	Kevin Lockett	10.00
109	Rob Moore	20.00
110	Napoleon Kaufman	20.00
111	Henry Ellard	20.00
112	Vinny Testaverde	20.00
113	Rick Mirer	20.00
114	Ty Detmer	10.00
115	Todd Collins	10.00
116	Jake Reed	10.00
117	Dave Brown	20.00
118	Dedric Ward	20.00
119	Heath Shuler	10.00
120	Ben Coates	20.00

1997 Flair Showcase Hot Hands

Hot Hands is a 12-card insert featuring some of the top players in the NFL. The cards are die-cut in the shape of flames and have a fiery background. They are inserted once in every 90 packs. The cards are numbered with the "HH" prefix.

		MT
Complete Set (12):		700.00
Common Player:		10.00
1	Kerry Collins	50.00
2	Emmitt Smith	100.00
3	Terrell Davis	60.00
4	Brett Favre	125.00
5	Eddie George	80.00
6	Marvin Harrison	10.00
7	Mark Brunell	60.00
8	Dan Marino	100.00
9	Curtis Martin	60.00
10	Terry Glenn	45.00
11	Keyshawn Johnson	10.00
12	Jerry Rice	60.00

1997 Flair Showcase Midas Touch

Midas Touch is a 12-card insert featuring superstars with

a "golden touch." The cards have a gold-colored background and were inserted once in every 20 packs. The cards are numbered with the "MT" prefix.

		MT
Complete Set (12):		150.00
Common Player:		3.00
Minor Stars:		6.00
1	Troy Aikman	25.00
2	John Elway	20.00
3	Barry Sanders	25.00
4	Marshall Faulk	6.00
5	Karim Abdul-Jabbar	15.00
6	Drew Bledsoe	25.00
7	Ricky Watters	6.00
8	Kordell Stewart	25.00
9	Tony Martin	3.00
10	Steve Young	20.00
11	Joey Galloway	3.00
12	Isaac Bruce	6.00

1997 Flair Showcase Now & Then

A four-card insert set, Then & Now features 12 NFL players as they looked when they entered the league. Each card highlights a particular draft year and three of the top players who were picked. The cards were inserted once in every 288 packs. The cards are numbered with the "NT" prefix.

		MT
Complete Set (4):		800.00
Common Player:		175.00
1	Marino, Elway, D. Green (1983)	225.00
2	Aikman, B. Sanders, D. Sanders (1989)	175.00
3	E. Smith, C. Warren, J. Seau (1990)	225.00
4	Favre, H. Moore, R. Watters (1991)	275.00

1997 Flair Showcase Wave of the Future

Wave of the Future showcases 25 top rookies entering the 1997 season. The fronts and backs feature a tidal wave design. Inserted once in every four packs. The cards are numbered with the "WF" prefix.

		MT
Complete Set (25):		30.00
Common Player:		1.00
Minor Stars:		2.00
1	Mike Adams	1.00
2	John Allred	1.00
3	Pat Barnes	2.00
4	Kenny Bynum	1.00
5	Will Blackwell	2.00
6	Peter Boulware	2.00
7	Greg Clark	2.00
8	Troy Davis	2.00
9	Albert Connell	2.00
10	Jay Graham	2.00
11	Leon Johnson	1.00
12	Damon Jones	2.00
13	Freddie Jones	3.00
14	George Jones	2.00
15	Chad Levitt	1.00
16	Joey Kent	2.00
17	Danny Wuerffel	2.00
18	Orlando Pace	2.00
19	Darnell Autry	1.00
20	Sedrick Shaw	2.00
21	Shawn Springs	2.00
22	Duce Staley	4.00
23	Darrell Russell	2.00
24	Bryant Westbrook	2.00
25	Antowuan Wyatt	1.00

1998 Flair Showcase Row 3

Row 3 is made up of 80 base cards with four different tiers. Cards 1-20 were inserted 1:0.9 packs, cards 21-40 at 1:1.1, cards 41-60 at 1:1.4 and cards 61-80 at 1:1.8.

		MT
Complete Set (80):		75.00
Common Player:		.25
Minor Stars:		.50
Common Rookie:		1.00
1-20 Inserted 1:0.9		
21-40 Inserted 1:1.1		
41-60 Inserted 1:1.4		
61-80 Inserted 1:1.8		
Wax Box:		100.00
1	Brett Favre	3.00
2	Emmitt Smith	2.00
3	Peyton Manning	12.00
4	Mark Brunell	1.00
5	Randy Moss	20.00
6	Jerry Rice	1.50
7	John Elway	1.50
8	Troy Aikman	1.50
9	Warrick Dunn	1.00
10	Kordell Stewart	1.00
11	Drew Bledsoe	1.00
12	Eddie George	1.00
13	Dan Marino	2.00
14	Antowain Smith	.75
15	Curtis Enis	4.00
16	Jake Plummer	1.00
17	Steve Young	1.00
18	Ryan Leaf	6.00
19	Terrell Davis	2.00
20	Barry Sanders	3.00
21	Corey Dillon	1.00
22	Fred Taylor	6.00
23	Herman Moore	.50
24	Marshall Faulk	.75
25	John Avery	2.50
26	Terry Glenn	.50
27	Keyshawn Johnson	.50
28	Charles Woodson	3.00
29	Garrison Hearst	.50
30	Steve McNair	.75
31	Deion Sanders	.75
32	Robert Holcombe	2.50
33	Jerome Bettis	.50
34	Robert Edwards	3.00
35	Skip Hicks	2.50
36	Marcus Nash	2.50
37	Fred Lane	.25
38	Kevin Dyson	2.50
39	Dorsey Levens	.50
40	Jacquez Green	2.50
41	Shannon Sharpe	.50
42	Michael Irvin	.75
43	Jim Harbaugh	.50
44	Curtis Martin	.75
45	Bobby Hoying	.25
46	Trent Dilfer	.50
47	Yancey Thigpen	.25
48	Warren Moon	.50
49	Danny Kanell	.25
50	Rob Johnson	.50
51	Carl Pickens	.50
52	Scott Mitchell	.50
53	Tim Brown	.50
54	Tony Banks	.50
55	Jamal Anderson	1.00
56	Kerry Collins	.50
57	Elvis Grbac	.25
58	Mike Alstott	.75
59	Glenn Foley	.25
60	Brad Johnson	.75
61	Robert Brooks	.25
62	Irving Fryar	.25
63	Natrone Means	1.00
64	Rae Carruth	.25
65	Isaac Bruce	.75
66	Andre Rison	.50
67	Jeff George	.50
68	Charles Way	.25
69	Derrick Alexander	.25
70	Michael Jackson	.25
71	Rob Moore	.50
72	Ricky Watters	.50
73	Curtis Conway	.50
74	Antonio Freeman	1.25
75	Jimmy Smith	.75
76	Troy Davis	.25
77	Robert Smith	1.25
78	Terry Allen	.50
79	Joey Galloway	1.25
80	Charles Johnson	.25

1998 Flair Showcase Row 2

Row 2 is set up the same way that Row 3 is with 80 base cards and four tiers. It has different insert odds with cards 1-20 found 1:3 packs, cards 21-40 at 1:2.5 packs, cards 41-60 at 1:4 packs and cards 61-80 at 1:3.4 packs.

		MT
Complete Set (80):		150.00
Common Player:		.50
Minor Stars:		1.00
Common Rookie:		1.50
1-20 Inserted 1:3		
21-40 Inserted 1:2.5		
41-60 Inserted 1:4		
61-80 Inserted 1:3.4		
1	Brett Favre	6.00
2	Emmitt Smith	4.00
3	Peyton Manning	18.00
4	Mark Brunell	2.00
5	Randy Moss	35.00
6	Jerry Rice	3.00
7	John Elway	3.00
8	Troy Aikman	3.00
9	Warrick Dunn	2.00
10	Kordell Stewart	2.00
11	Drew Bledsoe	2.00
12	Eddie George	2.00
13	Dan Marino	4.00
14	Antowain Smith	1.50
15	Curtis Enis	6.00
16	Jake Plummer	2.00
17	Steve Young	2.00
18	Ryan Leaf	10.00
19	Terrell Davis	4.00
20	Barry Sanders	6.00
21	Corey Dillon	2.00
22	Fred Taylor	10.00
23	Herman Moore	1.00
24	Marshall Faulk	1.50
25	John Avery	4.00
26	Terry Glenn	1.00
27	Keyshawn Johnson	1.00
28	Charles Woodson	5.00
29	Garrison Hearst	1.00
30	Steve McNair	1.50
31	Deion Sanders	1.50
32	Robert Holcombe	4.00
33	Jerome Bettis	1.00
34	Robert Edwards	4.00
35	Skip Hicks	4.00
36	Marcus Nash	4.00
37	Fred Lane	.50
38	Kevin Dyson	4.00
39	Dorsey Levens	1.00
40	Jacquez Green	4.00
41	Shannon Sharpe	1.00
42	Michael Irvin	1.50
43	Jim Harbaugh	.50
44	Curtis Martin	1.50
45	Bobby Hoying	.50
46	Trent Dilfer	1.00
47	Yancey Thigpen	.50
48	Warren Moon	1.00
49	Danny Kanell	.50
50	Rob Johnson	1.00
51	Carl Pickens	1.00
52	Scott Mitchell	.50
53	Tim Brown	1.00
54	Tony Banks	1.00
55	Jamal Anderson	2.00
56	Kerry Collins	1.00
57	Elvis Grbac	.50
58	Mike Alstott	1.50
59	Glenn Foley	1.00
60	Brad Johnson	1.50
61	Robert Brooks	.50
62	Irving Fryar	.50
63	Natrone Means	1.50
64	Rae Carruth	.50
65	Isaac Bruce	1.25
66	Andre Rison	1.00
67	Jeff George	1.00
68	Charles Way	.50
69	Derrick Alexander	.50
70	Michael Jackson	.50
71	Rob Moore	1.00
72	Ricky Watters	1.00
73	Curtis Conway	.50
74	Antonio Freeman	2.50
75	Jimmy Smith	1.50
76	Troy Davis	.50
77	Robert Smith	2.50
78	Terry Allen	1.00
79	Joey Galloway	2.50
80	Charles Johnson	.50

1998 Flair Showcase Row 1

Row 1 singles are much tougher to find than the previous Row 3 and 2 because of tougher insert odds. Same set-up with 80 cards and four tiers. Cards 1-20 are inserted 1:16 packs, cards 21-40 at 1:24, cards 41-60 at 1:6 and the last tier of cards 61-80 at 1:9.6.

		MT
Complete Set (80):		600.00
Common Player:		1.50
Minor Stars:		3.00
Common Rookie:		4.00
1-20 Inserted 1:16		
21-40 Inserted 1:24		
41-60 Inserted 1:6		
61-80 Inserted 1:9.6		
1	Brett Favre	25.00
2	Emmitt Smith	16.00
3	Peyton Manning	45.00
4	Mark Brunell	8.00
5	Randy Moss	100.00
6	Jerry Rice	12.00
7	John Elway	12.00
8	Troy Aikman	12.00
9	Warrick Dunn	8.00
10	Kordell Stewart	8.00
11	Drew Bledsoe	8.00
12	Eddie George	8.00
13	Dan Marino	16.00
14	Antowain Smith	6.00
15	Curtis Enis	15.00
16	Jake Plummer	8.00
17	Steve Young	8.00
18	Ryan Leaf	25.00
19	Terrell Davis	16.00
20	Barry Sanders	25.00
21	Corey Dillon	8.00
22	Fred Taylor	25.00
23	Herman Moore	3.00
24	Marshall Faulk	6.00
25	John Avery	10.00
26	Terry Glenn	3.00
27	Keyshawn Johnson	3.00
28	Charles Woodson	12.00
29	Garrison Hearst	3.00
30	Steve McNair	6.00
31	Deion Sanders	6.00
32	Robert Holcombe	10.00
33	Jerome Bettis	3.00
34	Robert Edwards	12.00
35	Skip Hicks	10.00
36	Marcus Nash	10.00
37	Fred Lane	1.50
38	Kevin Dyson	4.00
39	Dorsey Levens	3.00
40	Jacquez Green	10.00
41	Shannon Sharpe	3.00
42	Michael Irvin	3.00
43	Jim Harbaugh	1.50
44	Curtis Martin	4.00
45	Bobby Hoying	1.50
46	Trent Dilfer	3.00
47	Yancey Thigpen	1.50
48	Warren Moon	3.00
49	Danny Kanell	1.50
50	Rob Johnson	3.00
51	Carl Pickens	3.00
52	Scott Mitchell	1.50
53	Tim Brown	3.00
54	Tony Banks	3.00
55	Jamal Anderson	5.00
56	Kerry Collins	3.00
57	Elvis Grbac	1.50
58	Mike Alstott	3.00
59	Glenn Foley	1.50
60	Brad Johnson	3.00
61	Robert Brooks	1.50
62	Irving Fryar	1.50
63	Natrone Means	4.00
64	Rae Carruth	1.50
65	Isaac Bruce	3.00
66	Andre Rison	3.00
67	Jeff George	3.00
68	Charles Way	1.50
69	Derrick Alexander	1.50
70	Michael Jackson	1.50
71	Rob Moore	3.00
72	Ricky Watters	3.00
73	Curtis Conway	1.50
74	Antonio Freeman	5.00
75	Jimmy Smith	3.00
76	Troy Davis	1.50
77	Robert Smith	5.00
78	Terry Allen	1.50
79	Joey Galloway	5.00
80	Charles Johnson	1.50

1998 Flair Showcase Row 0

The Row 0 set is made up of 80 cards and is tiered at four different levels. The first level includes cards 1-20 and each is sequentially numbered to 250. The next level includes cards 21-40 and is numbered to 500. Cards 41-60 are numbered to 1,000 and the last level of cards 61-80 are numbered to 2,000.

		MT
Complete Set (80):		3500.00
Common Player (1-20):		7.00
Production 250 Sets		
Common Player (21-40):		5.00
Production 500 Sets		
Common Player (41-60):		3.00
Production 1000 Sets		
Common Player (61-80):		2.00
Production 2000 Sets		
1	Brett Favre	100.00
2	Emmitt Smith	70.00
3	Peyton Manning	120.00
4	Mark Brunell	35.00
5	Randy Moss	250.00
6	Jerry Rice	50.00
7	John Elway	50.00
8	Troy Aikman	50.00
9	Warrick Dunn	35.00
10	Kordell Stewart	35.00
11	Drew Bledsoe	35.00
12	Eddie George	35.00
13	Dan Marino	70.00
14	Antowain Smith	20.00
15	Curtis Enis	40.00
16	Jake Plummer	35.00
17	Steve Young	35.00
18	Ryan Leaf	60.00
19	Terrell Davis	70.00
20	Barry Sanders	100.00
21	Corey Dillon	20.00
22	Fred Taylor	50.00
23	Herman Moore	10.00
24	Marshall Faulk	15.00
25	John Avery	20.00
26	Terry Glenn	10.00
27	Keyshawn Johnson	10.00
28	Charles Woodson	25.00
29	Garrison Hearst	10.00
30	Steve McNair	15.00
31	Deion Sanders	15.00
32	Robert Holcombe	20.00
33	Jerome Bettis	10.00
34	Robert Edwards	20.00
35	Skip Hicks	20.00
36	Marcus Nash	20.00
37	Fred Lane	5.00
38	Kevin Dyson	10.00
39	Dorsey Levens	10.00
40	Jacquez Green	20.00
41	Shannon Sharpe	6.00
42	Michael Irvin	6.00
43	Jim Harbaugh	3.00
44	Curtis Martin	8.00
45	Bobby Hoying	3.00
46	Trent Dilfer	6.00
47	Yancey Thigpen	3.00
48	Warren Moon	6.00
49	Danny Kanell	3.00
50	Rob Johnson	6.00
51	Carl Pickens	6.00
52	Scott Mitchell	3.00
53	Tim Brown	6.00
54	Tony Banks	6.00
55	Jamal Anderson	15.00
56	Kerry Collins	6.00
57	Elvis Grbac	3.00
58	Mike Alstott	8.00
59	Glenn Foley	3.00
60	Brad Johnson	8.00
61	Robert Brooks	2.00
62	Irving Fryar	2.00
63	Natrone Means	10.00
64	Rae Carruth	2.00
65	Isaac Bruce	7.50
66	Andre Rison	4.00
67	Jeff George	4.00
68	Charles Way	2.00
69	Derrick Alexander	2.00
70	Michael Jackson	2.00
71	Rob Moore	4.00
72	Ricky Watters	4.00
73	Curtis Conway	4.00
74	Antonio Freeman	12.50
75	Jimmy Smith	7.50
76	Troy Davis	2.00
77	Robert Smith	12.50
78	Terry Allen	2.00
79	Joey Galloway	12.50
80	Charles Johnson	2.00

1998 Flair Showcase Legacy

Each of the 320 cards in this set has a parallel Legacy card. Each card has a foil front and is sequentially numbered to 100.

		MT
Common Player:		15.00
Minor Stars:		30.00
Production 100 Sets		
Each Player Has Four Different Cards		
1	Brett Favre	200.00
2	Emmitt Smith	150.00
3	Peyton Manning	175.00
4	Mark Brunell	85.00
5	Randy Moss	325.00
6	Jerry Rice	100.00
7	John Elway	100.00
8	Troy Aikman	100.00
9	Warrick Dunn	85.00
10	Kordell Stewart	85.00
11	Drew Bledsoe	85.00
12	Eddie George	85.00
13	Dan Marino	150.00
14	Antowain Smith	50.00
15	Curtis Enis	50.00
16	Jake Plummer	85.00
17	Steve Young	75.00
18	Ryan Leaf	90.00
19	Terrell Davis	150.00
20	Barry Sanders	200.00
21	Corey Dillon	60.00
22	Fred Taylor	100.00
23	Herman Moore	30.00
24	Marshall Faulk	40.00
25	John Avery	40.00
26	Terry Glenn	30.00
27	Keyshawn Johnson	30.00
28	Charles Woodson	50.00
29	Garrison Hearst	30.00
30	Steve McNair	40.00
31	Deion Sanders	40.00
32	Robert Holcombe	40.00
33	Jerome Bettis	30.00
34	Robert Edwards	50.00
35	Skip Hicks	45.00
36	Marcus Nash	45.00
37	Fred Lane	15.00
38	Kevin Dyson	40.00
39	Dorsey Levens	30.00
40	Jacquez Green	45.00
41	Shannon Sharpe	30.00
42	Michael Irvin	40.00
43	Jim Harbaugh	15.00
44	Curtis Martin	40.00
45	Bobby Hoying	15.00
46	Trent Dilfer	30.00
47	Yancey Thigpen	15.00
48	Warren Moon	30.00
49	Danny Kanell	15.00
50	Rob Johnson	30.00
51	Carl Pickens	30.00
52	Scott Mitchell	15.00
53	Tim Brown	30.00
54	Tony Banks	30.00
55	Jamal Anderson	40.00
56	Kerry Collins	30.00
57	Elvis Grbac	15.00
58	Mike Alstott	40.00
59	Glenn Foley	15.00
60	Brad Johnson	30.00
61	Robert Brooks	15.00
62	Irving Fryar	15.00
63	Natrone Means	30.00
64	Rae Carruth	15.00
66	Isaac Bruce	30.00
67	Jeff George	30.00
68	Charles Way	15.00
69	Derrick Alexander	15.00
70	Michael Jackson	15.00
71	Rob Moore	30.00
72	Ricky Watters	15.00
73	Curtis Conway	15.00
74	Antonio Freeman	40.00
75	Jimmy Smith	15.00
76	Troy Davis	15.00
77	Robert Smith	30.00
78	Terry Allen	30.00
79	Joey Galloway	30.00
80	Charles Johnson	15.00

1998 Flair Showcase Feature Film

Each card in this set has an actual slide from the Showcase set mounted on it. Singles were inserted 1:60 packs.

		MT
Complete Set (10):		230.00
Common Player:		10.00
Inserted 1:60		
1	Terrell Davis	35.00
2	Brett Favre	50.00
3	Antowain Smith	10.00
4	Emmitt Smith	35.00
5	Dan Marino	35.00
6	Kordell Stewart	20.00
7	Warrick Dunn	15.00
8	Barry Sanders	50.00
9	Peyton Manning	40.00
10	Ryan Leaf	20.00

1999 Flair Showcase

This was a 192-card set that included three levels of scarcity. The Power subset included 32 veterans, the Passion subset was made up of 64 veterans and the Showcase subset included the last 96 cards with 21 of them being rookies and 11 of them being veterans, sequentially numbered to 1,999. Two parallel sets were issued with the Legacy Collection and Masterpieces. Other inserts included: Class of '99, Feel the Game, First Rounders and Shrine Time. SRP was $4.99 for five-card packs.

		MT
Complete Set (192):		850.00
Common Player:		.25
Minor Stars:		.50
Common Rookie:		10.00
Production 1,999 Sets		
Wax Box:		125.00
1	Troy Aikman	2.00
2	Jamal Anderson	.75
3	Charlie Batch	1.25
4	Jerome Bettis	.75
5	Drew Bledsoe	1.50
6	Mark Brunell	1.50
7	Randall Cunningham	.75
8	Terrell Davis	3.00
9	Corey Dillon	.75
10	Warrick Dunn	.75
11	Curtis Enis	.75
12	Marshall Faulk	.75
13	Brett Favre	4.00
14	Doug Flutie	1.25
15	Eddie George	1.00
16	Brian Griese	1.50
17	Keyshawn Johnson	.75
18	Peyton Manning	3.00
19	Dan Marino	3.00
20	Curtis Martin	.75
21	Steve McNair	1.00
22	Randy Moss	4.00
23	Terrell Owens	.75
24	Jake Plummer	1.50
25	Jerry Rice	2.00
26	Barry Sanders	4.00
27	Antowain Smith	.75
28	Emmitt Smith	3.00
29	Kordell Stewart	.75
30	J.J. Stokes	.50
31	Fred Taylor	2.00
32	Steve Young	1.25
33	Troy Aikman	2.00
34	Mike Alstott	.75
35	Jamal Anderson	.75
36	Charlie Batch	1.25
37	Jerome Bettis	.75
38	Drew Bledsoe	1.50
39	Mark Brunell	1.50
40	Cris Carter	.75
41	Mark Chmura	.50
42	Wayne Chrebet	.75
43	Kerry Collins	.50
44	Randall Cunningham	.75
45	Terrell Davis	3.00
46	Trent Dilfer	.50
47	Corey Dillon	.75
48	Warrick Dunn	.75
49	Kevin Dyson	.25
50	Curtis Enis	.75
51	Marshall Faulk	.75
52	Brett Favre	4.00
53	Doug Flutie	1.25
54	Antonio Freeman	.75
55	Eddie George	1.00
56	Terry Glenn	.75
57	Tony Gonzalez	.50
58	Elvis Grbac	.50
59	Jacquez Green	.50
60	Brian Griese	1.50
61	Marvin Harrison	.75
62	Garrison Hearst	.50
63	Skip Hicks	.50
64	Priest Holmes	.75
65	Michael Irvin	.50
66	Brad Johnson	.75
67	Keyshawn Johnson	.75
68	Napoleon Kaufman	.75
69	Dorsey Levens	.75
70	Peyton Manning	3.00
71	Dan Marino	3.00
72	Curtis Martin	.75
73	Ed McCaffrey	.75
74	Keenan McCardell	.50
75	O.J. McDuffie	.25
76	Steve McNair	1.00
77	Scott Mitchell	.25
78	Randy Moss	4.00
79	Eric Moulds	.75
80	Terrell Owens	.75
81	Lawrence Phillips	.25
82	Jake Plummer	1.50
83	Jerry Rice	2.00
84	Andre Rison	.50
85	Barry Sanders	4.00
86	Shannon Sharpe	.75
87	Antowain Smith	.75
88	Emmitt Smith	3.00
89	Rod Smith	.75
90	Duce Staley	.75
91	Kordell Stewart	.75
92	J.J. Stokes	.50
93	Fred Taylor	3.00
94	Vinny Testaverde	.50
95	Ricky Watters	.75
96	Steve Young	1.25
97	Mike Alstott	.75
98	Jamal Anderson	.75
99	Charlie Batch	1.25
100	Jerome Bettis	.75
101	Tim Biakabutuka	.50
102	Drew Bledsoe	1.50
103	Tim Brown	.50
104	Mark Brunell	1.25
105	Cris Carter	.75
106	Chris Chandler	.50
107	Mark Chmura	.50
108	Wayne Chrebet	.75
109	Ben Coates	.50
110	Kerry Collins	.50
111	Randall Cunningham	.75
112	Trent Dilfer	.50
113	Corey Dillon	.75
114	Warrick Dunn	.75
115	Kevin Dyson	.25
116	Curtis Enis	.75
117	Marshall Faulk	.75
118	Doug Flutie	1.25
119	Antonio Freeman	.75
120	Joey Galloway	.75
121	Rich Gannon	.50
122	Eddie George	1.00
123	Terry Glenn	.75
124	Tony Gonzalez	.50
125	Elvis Grbac	.50
126	Jacquez Green	.50
127	Brian Griese	1.50
128	Marvin Harrison	.75
129	Garrison Hearst	.50
130	Skip Hicks	.50
131	Priest Holmes	.75
132	Michael Irvin	.50
133	Brad Johnson	.75
134	Napoleon Kaufman	.75
135	Terry Kirby	.25
136	Dorsey Levens	.75
137	Curtis Martin	.75
138	Ed McCaffrey	.25
139	Keenan McCardell	.50
140	O.J. McDuffie	.25
141	Steve McNair	1.00
142	Natrone Means	.50
143	Scott Mitchell	.25
144	Herman Moore	.75
145	Eric Moulds	.75
146	Terrell Owens	.75
147	Lawrence Phillips	.25
148	Jerry Rice	2.00
149	Andre Rison	.50
150	Deion Sanders	.50
151	Shannon Sharpe	.50
152	Antowain Smith	.75
153	Rod Smith	.75
154	Duce Staley	.75
155	Kordell Stewart	.75
156	J.J. Stokes	.50
157	Vinny Testaverde	.50
158	Yancey Thigpen	.25
159	Ricky Watters	.50
160	Steve Young	1.25
161	Troy Aikman SP	10.00
162	Champ Bailey	20.00
163	Karsten Bailey	10.00
164	D'Wayne Bates	10.00
165	David Boston	30.00
166	Michael Cloud	15.00
167	Cecil Collins	30.00
168	Tim Couch	150.00
169	Daunte Culpepper	50.00
170	Terrell Davis SP	15.00
171	Troy Edwards	30.00
172	Kevin Faulk	20.00
173	Brett Favre SP	30.00
174	Torry Holt	30.00
175	Sedrick Irvin	20.00
176	Edgerrin James	200.00
177	J.J. Johnson	20.00
178	Kevin Johnson	30.00
179	Keyshawn Johnson SP	5.00
180	Peyton Manning SP	15.00
181	Dan Marino SP	15.00
182	Donovan McNabb	50.00
183	Cade McNown	50.00
184	Joe Montgomery	15.00
185	Randy Moss SP	20.00
186	Jake Plummer SP	10.00
187	Peerless Price	20.00
188	Barry Sanders SP	20.00
189	Akili Smith	50.00
190	Emmitt Smith SP	15.00
191	Fred Taylor SP	15.00
192	Ricky Williams	150.00

1999 Flair Showcase Legacy Collection

This was a 192-card parallel to the base set. Each single was sequentially numbered to 99.

	MT
Legacy Cards:	15x-30x
Legacy Rookies:	1.5x
Production 99 Sets	

1999 Flair Showcase Class of '99

This 15-card insert set included the top rookies from 1999. Each was sequentially numbered to 500.

		MT
Complete Set (15):		275.00
Common Player:		10.00
Production 500 Sets		
1	Tim Couch	50.00
2	Donovan McNabb	25.00
3	Akili Smith	25.00
4	Cade McNown	25.00
5	Daunte Culpepper	25.00
6	Ricky Williams	50.00
7	Edgerrin James	70.00
8	Kevin Faulk	12.00
9	Torry Holt	15.00
10	David Boston	15.00
11	Sedrick Irvin	10.00
12	Peerless Price	12.00
13	Joe Germaine	10.00
14	Brock Huard	10.00
15	Shaun King	15.00

1999 Flair Showcase Feel The Game

This 10-card insert set contained pieces of game-used gloves, shorts, jerseys or shoes. Each single was hand-numbered and inserted 1:168 packs.

	MT
Complete Set (10):	800.00
Common Player:	25.00
Cecil Collins shoes	60.00
Sean Dawkins shoes	25.00
Marshall Faulk jersey	75.00
Brett Favre jersey	150.00
Torry Holt shoes	50.00
Edgerrin James gloves	175.00
Peyton Manning jersey	150.00
Dan Marino jersey	125.00
Jake Plummer shoes	75.00
Antowain Smith shorts	50.00

1999 Flair Showcase First Rounders

This 10-card set included the top skilled position players selected in the 1999 NFL Draft. Singles were inserted 1:10 packs.

		MT
Complete Set (10):		45.00
Common Player:		2.50
Inserted 1:10		
1	Tim Couch	10.00
2	Donovan McNabb	5.00
3	Akili Smith	5.00
4	Cade McNown	5.00
5	Daunte Culpepper	5.00
6	David Boston	2.50
7	Torry Holt	2.50
8	Ricky Williams	10.00
9	Edgerrin James	12.00
10	Troy Edwards	2.50

1999 Flair Showcase Shrine Time

This 15-card insert set included players who could be on their way to the Hall of Fame. Each single was sequentially numbered to 1,500.

		MT
Complete Set (15):		100.00
Common Player:		3.00
Production 1,500 Sets		
1	Peyton Manning	12.00
2	Fred Taylor	8.00
3	Terrell Owens	3.00
4	Charlie Batch	5.00
5	Jerry Rice	8.00
6	Randy Moss	15.00
7	Warrick Dunn	3.00
8	Mark Brunell	6.00
9	Emmitt Smith	12.00
10	Eddie George	5.00
11	Barry Sanders	15.00
12	Terrell Davis	12.00
13	Dan Marino	12.00
14	Troy Aikman	8.00
15	Brett Favre	15.00

1960 Fleer

Fleer's first venture into football depicted cards of players from the newly-formed American Football League. Outside of George Blanda, Sammy Baugh and several rookie cards detailed below, the set basically features a lot of no-names, many of whom appeared on their only card with this issue. It's not surprising that this set includes the most rookie cards of any other set issued since football cards were issued. (Not coincidentally, Topps' 1984 USFL set ranks second because of the amount of rookies who played in that league.) Rookie cards in this set include Sid Gillman (as a coach - this was his only card), Lou Saban (only card), Hank Stram (only card until Pro Set announcer cards), Abner Haynes, and Ron Mix. The card that carries the set is Jack Kemp's rookie card.

		NM
Complete Set (132):		750.00
Common Player:		3.00
1	Harvey White	20.00
2	Tom "Corky" Tharp	3.00
3	Dan McGrew	3.00
4	Bob White	3.25
5	Dick Jamieson	3.00
6	Sam Salerno	3.00
7	Sid Gillman	15.00
8	Ben Preston	3.00
9	George Blanch	3.00
10	Bob Stransky	3.00
11	Fran Curci	3.00
12	George Shirkey	3.00
13	Paul Larson	3.00
14	John Stolte	3.00
15	Serafino Frazio	3.50
16	Tom Dimitroff	3.00
17	Elbert Dubenion	7.50
18	Hogan Wharton	3.00
19	Tom O'Connell	3.00
20	Sammy Baugh	40.00
21	Tony Sardisco	3.00
22	Alan Cann	3.00
23	Mike Hudock	3.00
24	Bill Atkins	3.00
25	Charlie Jackson	3.00
26	Frank Tripucka	4.00
27	Tony Teresa	3.00
28	Joe Amstutz	3.00
29	Bob Fee	3.00
30	Jim Baldwin	3.00
31	Jim Yates	3.00
32	Don Flynn	3.00
33	Ken Adamson	3.00
34	Ron Drzewiecki	3.00
35	J.W. Slack	3.00
36	Bob Yates	3.00
37	Gary Cobb	3.00
38	Jacky Lee	4.00
39	Jack Spikes	3.50
40	Jim Padgett	3.00
41	Jack Larsheid	3.00
42	Bob Reifsnyder	3.00
43	Fran Rogel	3.00
44	Ray Moss	3.00
45	Tony Banfield	3.25
46	George Herring	3.00
47	Willie Smith	3.00
48	Buddy Allen	3.00
49	Bill Brown	3.00
50	Ken Ford	3.00
51	Billy Kinard	3.00
52	Buddy Mayfield	3.00
53	Bill Krisher	3.25
54	Frank Bernardi	3.00
55	Lou Saban	3.50
56	Gene Cockrell	3.00
57	Sam Sanders	3.00
58	George Blanda	40.00
59	Sherrill Headrick	5.50
60	Carl Larpenter	3.00
61	Gene Prebola	3.00
62	Dick Chorovich	3.00
63	Bob McNamara	3.00
64	Tom Saidock	3.00
65	Willie Evans	3.00
66	Billy Cannon	16.00
67	Sam McCord	3.00
68	Mike Simmons	3.00
69	Jim Swink	3.50
70	Don Hitt	3.00
71	Gerhard Schwedes	3.00
72	Thurlow Cooper	3.00
73	Abner Haynes	16.00
74	Billy Shoemaker	3.00
75	Marv Lasater	3.00
76	Paul Lowe	15.00
77	Bruce Hartman	3.00
78	Blanche Martin	3.00
79	Gene Grabosky	3.00
80	Lou Rymkus	3.00
81	Chris Burford	5.50
82	Don Allen	3.00
83	Bob Nelson	3.00
84	Jim Woodard	3.00
85	Tom Rychlec	3.00
86	Bob Cox	3.00
87	Jerry Cornelison	3.00
88	Jack Work	3.00
89	Sam DeLuca	3.00
90	Rommie Loudd	3.00
91	Teddy Edmondson	3.00
92	Buster Ramsey	3.00
93	Doug Asad	3.00
94	Jimmy Harris	3.00
95	Lary Cundiff	3.00
96	Richie Lucas	3.50
97	Don Norwood	3.00
98	Larry Grantham	4.00
99	Bill Mathis	4.00
100	Mel Branch	4.00
101	Marvin Terrell	3.00
102	Charlie Flowers	3.25
103	John McMullan	3.00
104	Charlie Kaaihue	3.00
105	Joe Schaffer	3.00
106	Al Day	3.00
107	Johnny Carson	3.00
108	Alan Goldstein	3.00
109	Doug Cline	3.00
110	Al Carmichael	3.00
111	Bob Dee	3.00
112	John Bredice	3.00
113	Don Floyd	3.00
114	Ronnie Cain	3.00
115	Stan Flowers	3.00
116	Hank Stram	45.00
117	Bob Dougherty	3.00
118	Ron Mix	35.00
120	Elvin Caldwell	3.00
121	Bill Kimber	3.00
122	Jim Matheny	3.00
123	Curley Johnson	3.00
124	Jack Kemp	350.00
125	Ed Denk	3.00
126	Jerry McFarland	3.00
127	Dan Lamphear	3.00
128	Paul Maguire	16.00
129	Ray Collins	3.00
130	Ron Burton	5.00
131	Eddie Erdelatz	3.00
132	Ron Beagle	16.00

1960 Fleer Decals

This group of eight American Football League inserts was inserted in wax packs of Fleer football. The decals, which measure about 1-1/2" x 3-1/2", depict the logo of each AFL team. The decals were unnumbered.

		NM
Complete Set (8):		50.00
Common Team:		
1	Boston Patriots	4.00
2	Buffalo Bills	5.00
3	Dallas Texans	5.00
4	Denver Broncos	5.00
5	Houston Oilers	5.00
6	Los Angeles Chargers	4.00
7	New York Titans	5.00
8	Oakland Raiders	5.00

1960 Fleer College Pennant Decals

This 19-decal set was also

inserted into packs of 1960 Fleer Football along with the AFL Team Decals. These decals measured approximately 2-1/4" x 3" and included two colleges per card.

		NM
Complete Set (19):		180.00
Common Player:		8.00
1	Alabama/Yale	10.00
2	Army/Mississippi	8.00
3	California/Indiana	8.00
4	Duke/Notre Dame	18.00
5	Florida St./Kentucky	10.00
6	Georgia/Oklahoma	10.00
7	Houston/Iowa	8.00
8	Idaho St./Penn.	8.00
9	Iowa St./Penn State	14.00
10	Kansas/UCLA	12.00
11	Marquette/New Mexico	8.00
12	Maryland/Missouri	8.00
13	Miss.South./N.Carolina	8.00
14	Navy/Stanford	10.00
15	Nebraska/Purdue	12.00
16	Pittsburgh/Utah	8.00
17	SMU/West Virginia	8.00
18	So.Carolina/USC	10.00
19	WakeForest/Wisconsin	10.00

1961 Fleer

This 220-card set by Fleer - its biggest of the four it produced was the last to include NFL players (future sets would include only AFL players). Cards 1-132 showcase NFL players; 133-up depict AFLers. Cards are again grouped alphabetically by city name. A number of cards in this set are short-printed, and are indicated by (SP) in the following checklist. Rookies in the '61 Fleer issue include Don Meredith, Tom Flores, Don Maynard, and Jim Otto. Second-year cards include Night Train Lane (his rookie card was in '57), Forrest Gregg, Jerry Kramer, Jack Kemp and Ron Mix. (Key: SP meads short-printed).

		NM
Complete Set (220):		1600.
Common Player (1-132):		8.00
Common Player (133-220):		5.50
1	Ed Brown	12.00
2	Rick Casares	3.50
3	Willie Galimore	5.50
4	Jim Dooley	3.50
5	Harlon Hill	3.50
6	Stan Jones	5.00
7	J.C. Caroline	3.50
8	Joe Fortunato	3.50
9	Doug Atkins	6.25
10	Milt Plum	3.50
11	Jim Brown	130.00
12	Bobby Mitchell	8.00
13	Ray Renfro	3.50
14	Gern Nagler	3.50
15	Jim Shofner	3.50
16	Vince Costello	3.50
17	Galen Fiss	3.50
18	Walt Michaels	3.50
19	Bob Gain	3.50
20	Mal Hammack	3.50
21	Frank Mestnick	3.50
22	Bobby Joe Conrad	3.50
23	John David Crow	4.00
24	Sonny Randle	4.00
25	Don Gillis	3.50
26	Jerry Norton	3.50
27	Bill Stacy	3.50
28	Leo Sugar	3.50
29	Frank Fuller	3.50
30	John Unitas	70.00
31	Alan Ameche	8.00
32	Lenny Moore	12.00
33	Raymond Berry	12.00
34	Jim Mutscheller	3.50
35	Jim Parker	6.50
36	Bill Pellington	3.50
37	Gino Marchetti	6.00
38	Gene Lipscomb	5.50
39	Art Donovan	12.00
40	Eddie LeBaron	5.50
41	Don Meredith	140.00
42	Don McIlhenny	3.50
43	L.G. Dupre	3.50
44	Fred Dugan	3.50
45	Bill Howton	3.50
46	Duane Putnam	3.50
47	Gene Cronin	3.50
48	Jerry Tubbs	3.50
49	Clarence Peaks	3.50
50	Ted Dean	4.00
51	Tommy McDonald	3.50
52	Bill Barnes	3.50
53	Pete Retzlaff	3.50
54	Bobby Walston	3.50
55	Chuck Bednarik	12.00
56	Maxie Baughan	5.50
57	Bob Pellegrini	3.50
58	Jesse Richardson	3.50
59	John Brodie	50.00
60	J.D. Smith	3.50
61	Ray Norton	3.50
62	Monty Stickles	3.50
63	Bob St. Clair	5.00
64	Dave Baker	3.50
65	Abe Woodson	3.50
66	Matt Hazeltine	3.50
67	Leo Nomellini	7.00
68	Charley Conerly	13.00
69	Kyle Rote	5.50
70	Jack Stroud	5.00
71	Roosevelt Brown	5.00
72	Jim Patton	3.50
73	Erich Barnes	3.50
74	Sam Huff	12.00
75	Andy Robustelli	3.50
76	Dick Modzelewski	3.50
77	Roosevelt Grier	4.00
78	Earl Morrall	4.50
79	Jim Ninowski	3.50
80	Nick Pietrosante	3.50
81	Howard Cassady	3.50
82	Jim Gibbons	3.50
83	Gail Cogdill	3.50
84	Dick Lane	6.00
85	Yale Lary	6.00
86	Joe Schmidt	6.50
87	Darris McCord	3.50
88	Bart Starr	50.00
89	Jim Taylor	30.00
90	Paul Hornung	45.00
91	Tom Moore	5.00
92	Boyd Dowler	8.00
93	Max McGee	3.50
94	Forrest Gregg	8.50
95	Jerry Kramer	7.50
96	Jim Ringo	6.50
97	Bill Forester	3.50
98	Frank Ryan	3.50
99	Ollie Matson	9.50
100	Jon Arnett	3.50
101	Dick Bass	4.00
102	Jim Phillips	3.50
103	Del Shofner	3.50
104	Art Hunter	3.50
105	Lindon Crow	3.50
106	Les Richter	4.00
107	Lou Michaels	3.50
108	Ralph Guglielmi	4.00
109	Don Bosseler	3.50
110	John Olszewski	3.50
111	Bill Anderson	3.50
112	Joe Walton	4.00
113	Jim Schrader	3.50
114	Gary Glick	3.50
115	Ralph Felton	3.50
116	Bob Toneff	3.50
117	Bobby Layne	25.00
118	John Henry Johnson	8.00
119	Tom Tracy	3.50
120	Jimmy Orr	6.50
121	John Nisby	3.50
122	Dean Derby	3.50
123	John Reger	3.50
124	George Tarsovic	3.50
125	Ernie Stautner	6.00
126	George Shaw	3.50
127	Hugh McElhenny	9.00
128	Dick Haley	3.50
129	Dave Middleton	3.50
130	Perry Richards	3.50
131	Gene Johnson	3.50
132	Don Joyce	3.50
133	John "Chuck" Green	5.50
134	Wray Carlton	5.50
135	Richie Lucas	5.50
136	Elbert Dubenion	5.50
137	Tom Rychlec (SP)	5.50
138	Mark Yoho (SP)	5.50
139	Phil Blazer (SP)	5.50
140	Dan McGrew (SP)	5.50
141	Bill Atkins	5.50
142	Archie Matsos	5.50
143	Gene Grabosky	5.50
144	Frank Tripucka	6.00
145	Al Carmichael (SP)	6.00
146	Bob McNamara (SP)	6.00
147	Lionel Taylor (SP)	12.00
148	Eldon Danenhauer (SP)	
149	Willie Smith	5.50
150	Carl Larpenter	5.50
151	Ken Adamson	5.50
152	Goose Gonsoulin	5.50
153	Joe Young (SP)	4.00
154	Gordy Molz (SP)	4.00
155	Jack Kemp (SP)	230.00
156	Charlie Flowers (SP)	6.00
157	Paul Lowe	7.00
158	Don Norton	5.50
159	Howard Clark	5.50
160	Paul Maguire	15.00
161	Ernie Wright (SP)	6.00
162	Ron Mix (SP)	16.00
163	Fred Cole (SP)	6.00
164	Jim Sears (SP)	6.00
165	Volney Peters	5.50
166	George Blanda	45.00
167	Jacky Lee	5.50
168	Bob White	5.50
169	Doug Cline (SP)	6.00
170	Dave Smith (SP)	6.00
171	Billy Cannon (SP)	8.00
172	Bill Groman (SP)	6.00
173	Al Jamison	5.50
174	Jim Norton	5.50
175	Dennit Morris	5.50
176	Don Floyd	5.50
177	Butch Songin (SP)	6.00
178	Billy Lott (SP)	6.00
179	Ron Burton (SP)	6.00
180	Jim Colchough (SP)	6.00
181	Charley Leo	5.50
182	Walt Cudzik	5.50
183	Fred Bruney	5.50
184	Ross O'Hanley	5.50
185	Tony Sardisco (SP)	6.00
186	Harry Jacobs (SP)	6.00
187	Bob Dee (SP)	6.00
188	Tom Flores (SP)	35.00
189	Jack Larsheid	5.50
190	Dick Christy	5.50
191	Alan Miller	5.50
192	Jim Smith	5.50
193	Gerald Burch (SP)	6.00
194	Gene Prebola (SP)	6.00
195	Alan Goldstein (SP)	6.00
196	Don Manoukian	6.00
197	Jim Otto	60.00
198	Wayne Crow	5.50
199	Cotton Davidson	5.50
200	Randy Duncan	5.50
201	Jack Spikes (SP)	6.00
202	Johnny Robinson	12.00
203	Abner Haynes (SP)	6.00
204	Chris Burford (SP)	6.00
205	Bill Krisher	5.50
206	Marvin Terrell	5.50
207	Jimmy Harris	5.50
208	Mel Branch (SP)	6.00
209	Paul Miller (SP)	6.00
210	Al Dorow (SP)	6.00
211	Dick Jamieson (SP)	6.00
212	Pete Hart	5.50
213	Bill Shockley	5.50
214	Dewey Bohling	5.50
215	Don Maynard	90.00
216	Bob Mischak	5.50
217	Mike Hudock (SP)	6.00
218	Bob Reifsnyder (SP)	6.00
219	Tom Saidock (SP)	6.00
220	Sid Youngelman (SP)	22.00

1961 Fleer Magic Message Blue Inserts

These 40 cards, which pose a trivia question on the front, instruct collectors to turn and wet the card to determine the answer. A line drawing also appears on the front, as does a card number, which is located in the lower right corner. Along the bottom of the card is a tag line which indicates the cards were printed by Business Service of Long Island, N.Y. The blank-backed cards, measuring 3" x 2-1/8", were inserts in 1961 Fleer football packs.

		NM
Complete Set (40):		125.00
Common Player:		4.00
1	First Sugar Bowl game	4.00
2	Point-A-Minute team	4.00
3	Gloomy Gil	4.00
4	College record for years coached	4.00
5	Two Platoon System	4.00
6	The only Sudden Death playoff	4.00
7	Sudden Death playoff	4.00
8	Longest field goal	4.00
9	Colorado All-American	5.00
10	Michigan All-American sportscaster	5.00
11	First North-South game	4.00
12	First Army-Navy game	4.00
13	Outfielder/All-American back	5.00
14	All-American Mr. Inside & Mr. Outside	5.00
15	The Thundering Herd	4.00
16	First NFL Championship playoff	4.00
17	Record for field goals dropkicked	4.00
18	Longest college winning streak	4.00
19	First collegian drafted	4.00
20	First team to use the huddle	4.00
21	The first Intercollegiate Champion	4.00
22	The first broadcast	4.00
23	The longest field goal	4.00
24	The tackling dummy	4.00
25	Greatest player in teh half-century	5.00
26	The most touchdowns in a game	4.00
27	Who ran the wrong way?	4.00
28	The first college field goal	4.00
29	The first All-American team	4.00
30	The forward pass	4.00
31	The first college to use numbers	4.00
32	The first professional football game	4.00
33	Where is the Football Hall of Fame?	4.00
34	The Four Horsemen	5.00
35	The first Rose Bowl	5.00
36	Record for forward passes in a prof gam	4.00
37	Galloping Ghost	5.00
38	Rose Bowl in California	4.00
39	Seven Blocks of Granite	4.00
40	First game in the U.S.	4.00

1962 Fleer

Fleer's third of four early '60s sets included only AFL players this time around. Cards are again grouped by team, alphabetically by city. The only rookie card of note in this set is Gino Cappelletti; second-year cards in this issue are Don Maynard, Tom Flores and Jim Otto.

		NM
Complete Set (88):		800.00
Common Player:		6.00
1	Billy Lott	15.00
2	Ron Burton	7.00
3	Gino Cappelletti	17.00
4	Babe Parilli	6.00
5	Jim Colclough	6.00
6	Tony Sardisco	6.00
7	Walt Cudzik	6.00
8	Bob Dee	6.00
9	Tommy Addison	6.50
10	Harry Jacobs	6.00
11	Ross O'Hanley	6.00
12	Art Baker	6.00
13	John "Chuck" Green	6.00
14	Elbert Dubenion	3.00
15	Tom Rychlec	3.00
16	Billy Shaw	8.50
17	Ken Rice	6.00
18	Bill Atkins	6.00
19	Richie Lucas	6.00
20	Archie Matsos	6.00
21	Lavern Torczon	6.00
22	Warren Rabb	6.00
23	Jack Spikes	6.00
24	Cotton Davidson	6.00
25	Abner Haynes	9.00
26	Jimmy Saxton	6.00
27	Chris Burford	6.00
28	Bill Miller	6.00
29	Sherrill Headrick	6.00
30	E.J. Holub	9.50
31	Jerry Mays	9.00
32	Mel Branch	6.00
33	Paul Rochester	6.00
34	Frank Tripucka	6.00
35	Gene Mingo	6.00
36	Lionel Taylor	9.50
37	Ken Adamson	6.00
38	Eldon Danenhauer	6.00
39	Goose Gonsoulin	6.00
40	Gordy Holz	6.00
41	Bud McFadin	6.00
42	Jim Stinnette	6.00
43	Bob Hudson	6.00
44	George Herring	6.00
45	Charley Tolar	7.50
46	George Blanda	34.00
47	Billy Cannon	10.00
48	Charlie Hennigan	16.00
49	Bill Groman	6.00
50	Al Jamison	6.00
51	Tony Banfield	6.00
52	Jim Norton	6.00
53	Dennit Morris	6.00
54	Don Floyd	6.00
55	Ed Husmann	6.00
56	Robert Brooks	6.00
57	Al Dorow	6.00
58	Dick Christy	6.00
59	Don Maynard	35.00
60	Art Powell	10.00
61	Mike Hudock	6.00
62	Bill Mathis	6.00
63	Butch Songin	6.00
64	Larry Grantham	6.50
65	Nick Mumley	6.00
66	Tom Saidock	6.00
67	Alan Miller	6.00
68	Tom Flores	10.00
69	Bob Coolbaugh	6.00
70	George Fleming	6.00
71	Wayne Hawkins	6.00
72	Jim Otto	25.00
73	Wayne Crow	6.00
74	Fred Williamson	20.00
75	Tom Lauderback	6.00
76	Volney Peters	6.00
77	Charley Powell	6.00
78	Don Norton	6.00
79	Jack Kemp	250.00
80	Paul Lowe	9.00
81	Dave Kocourek	6.00
82	Ron Mix	13.00
83	Ernie Wright	6.00
84	Dick Harris	6.00
85	Bill Hudson	6.00
86	Ernie Ladd	30.00
87	Earl Faison	7.00
88	Ron Nery	15.00

1963 Fleer

After a four-year run, this 89-card set (88 player cards plus an unnumbered checklist) was the company's football farewell. (Fleer printed football "Teams in Action" sets in the '70s and '80s that featured NFL offenses and defenses, but apparently was unable to obtain a contract allowing the production of individual player cards. The 1963 Fleer football set showcases three of the most sought-after and rarest cards of the '60s - the checklist card (almost impossible to find in Mint condition), and cards #6 (Charles Long) and #64 (Bob Dougherty). The latter two cards were short-printed; it's believed both were pulled to make room for the checklist. The set includes AFL players only. Rookies featured in the set are Nick Buoniconti, Cookie Gilchrist, Keith Lincoln, Len Dawson and Lance Alworth. Gino Cappelletti's second-year card is in the set as well. (Key: SP means short-printed.)

		NM
Complete Set (88):		1900.
Common Player:		8.00
Checklist:		350.00
1	Larry Garron	17.00
2	Babe Parilli	9.00
3	Ron Burton	8.00
4	Jim Colclough	8.00
5	Gino Cappelletti	11.00
6	Charles Long (SP)	180.00
7	Bill Neighbors	8.00
8	Dick Felt	8.00
9	Tommy Addison	8.00
10	Nick Buoniconti	75.00
11	Larry Eisenhauer	10.00
12	Bill Mathis	8.00
13	Lee Grosscup	10.00
14	Dick Christy	8.00
15	Don Maynard	45.00
16	Alex Kroll	8.00
17	Bob Mischak	8.00
18	Dainard Paulson	8.00
19	Lee Riley	8.00
20	Larry Grantham	8.00
21	Hubert Bobo	8.00
22	Nick Mumley	8.00
23	Cookie Gilchrist	40.00
24	Jack Kemp	250.00
25	Wray Carlton	8.00
26	Elbert Dubenion	8.00
27	Ernie Warlick	8.00
28	Billy Shaw	8.00
29	Ken Rice	8.00
30	Booker Edgerson	8.00
31	Ray Abbruzzese	8.00
32	Mike Stratton	9.00
33	Tom Sestak	10.00
34	Charlie Tolar	8.00
35	Dave Smith	8.00
36	George Blanda	55.00
37	Billy Cannon	9.00
38	Charlie Hennegan	13.00
39	Bob Talamini	10.00
40	Jim Norton	8.00
41	Tony Banfield	8.00
42	Doug Cline	8.00
43	Don Floyd	8.00
44	Ed Husmann	8.00
45	Curtis McClinton	12.00
46	Jack Spikes	8.00
47	Len Dawson	250.00
48	Abner Haynes	10.00
49	Chris Burford	8.00
50	Fred Arbanas	12.00
51	Johnny Robinson	9.00
52	E.J. Holub	8.00
53	Sherrill Headrick	8.00
54	Mel Branch	8.00
55	Jerry Mays	8.00
56	Cotton Davidson	15.00
57	Clem Daniels	15.00
58	Bo Roberson	8.00
59	Art Powell	10.00
60	Bob Coolbaugh	8.00
61	Wayne Hawkins	8.00
62	Jim Otto	30.00
63	Fred Williamson	9.00
64	Bob Dougherty (SP)	230.00
65	Dalva Allen	8.00
66	Chuck McMutry	8.00
67	Gerry McDougall	8.00
68	Tobin Rote	9.00
69	Paul Lowe	10.00
70	Keith Lincoln	25.00
71	Dave Kocourek	8.00
72	Lance Alworth	250.00
73	Ron Mix	22.00
74	Charles McNeil	10.00
75	Emil Karas	8.00
76	Ernie Ladd	15.00
77	Earl Faison	8.00
78	Jim Stinnette	8.00
79	Frank Tripucka	9.50
80	Don Stone	8.00
81	Bob Scarpitto	8.00
82	Lionel Taylor	10.50
83	Jerry Tarr	8.00
84	Eldon Danehauer	8.00
85	Goose Gonsoulin	8.00
86	Jim Fraser	8.00
87	Chuck Gavin	10.00
88	Bud McFadin	16.00

1972 Fleer Quiz

This 28-card set was issued at a rate of one per pack with Fleer cloth team patches. Cards measure 2-1/2" x 4" and feature three questions about players and events, with answers upside down. Each card has the words "Official Football Quiz" across the top, a card number in the lower right hand corner and a blank back.

	NM
Complete Set (28):	45.00
Common Player:	2.50

1	Questions 1-3	2.50
2	Questions 4-6	2.50
3	Questions 7-9	2.50
4	Questions 10-12	2.50
5	Questions 13-15	2.50
6	Questions 16-18	2.50
7	Questions 19-21	2.50
8	Questions 22-24	2.50
9	Questions 25-27	2.50
10	Questions 28-30	2.50
11	Questions 31-33	2.50
12	Questions 34-36	2.50
13	Questions 37-39	2.50
14	Questions 40-42	2.50
15	Questions 43-45	2.50
16	Questions 46-48	2.50
17	Questions 49-51	2.50
18	Questions 52-54	2.50
19	Questions 55-57	2.50
20	Questions 58-60	2.50
21	Questions 61-63	2.50
22	Questions 64-66	2.50
23	Questions 67-69	2.50
24	Questions 70-72	2.50
25	Questions 73-75	2.50
26	Questions 76-78	2.50
27	Questions 79-81	2.50
28	Questions 82-84	2.50

1973 Fleer Pro Bowl Scouting Report

The 14-card, blank backed set explains the ideal responsibilities and assignments of each player on an NFL team. These unnumbered cards were found at a rate of one per pack with two cloth football logos from 1972.

		NM
Complete Set (14):		35.00
Common Player:		3.00
1	Center	3.00
2	Cornerback	3.00
3	Defensive End	3.00
4	Defensive Tackle	3.00
5	Guard	3.00
6	Kicker	3.00
7	Linebacker	3.00
8	Offensive Tackle	3.00
9	Punter	3.00
10	Quarterback	3.00
11	Running Back	3.00
12	Safety	3.00
13	Tight End	3.00
14	Wide Receiver	3.00

1974 Fleer Big Signs

The 1974 version of Big Signs is generally considered a Series II issue, but is credited to 1968 in roman numerals on the back. The cards measure 7-3/4" x 11-1/2" and have blank backs that are unnumbered. The 1974 set was issued in a brown box, while the fronts contain generic, faceless color drawings. Two 26-card Big Signs sets were produced by Fleer that carry a 1968 copyright on them, but one released in 1970 with this series releasing in 1974. The former version was issued in a green box and contains the team name in small letters across the top, while the 1974 version has the team name in bold letters across the card bottom.

		NM
Complete Set (26):		45.00
Common Player:		2.50
1	Atlanta Falcons	2.50
2	Baltimore Colts	2.50
3	Buffalo Bills	2.50
4	Chicago Bears	4.00
5	Cincinnati Bengals	2.50
6	Cleveland Browns	2.50
7	Dallas Cowboys	4.00
8	Denver Broncos	2.50
9	Detroit Lions	2.50
10	Green Bay Packers	4.00
11	Houston Oilers	2.50
12	Kansas City Chiefs	2.50
13	Los Angeles Rams	2.50
14	Miami Dolphins	4.00
15	Minnesota Vikings	2.50
16	New England Patriots	2.50
17	New Orleans Saints	2.50
18	New York Giants	2.50
19	New York Jets	2.50
20	Oakland Raiders	4.00
21	Philadelphia Eagles	2.50
22	Pittsburgh Steelers	4.00
23	St. Louis Cardinals	2.50
24	San Diego Chargers	2.50
25	San Francisco 49ers	4.00
26	Washington Redskins	4.00

1974 Fleer Hall of Fame

These cards were issued one per pack, along with two cloth stickers featuring team logos. Each card front has a black- and-white player action photo, with a set logo and "The Immortal Role" at the bottom of the card. The cards, which are unnumbered, are listed below alphabetically and feature 50 players who have been enshrined in the Pro Football Hall of Fame in Canton, Ohio. The Hall of Fame logo appears on the back of the card, along with biographical information about the player. Each card measures 2-1/2" x 4".

		NM
Complete Set (50):		50.00
Common Player:		1.00
(1)	Cliff Battles	1.00
(2)	Sammy Baugh	1.50
(3)	Chuck Bednarik	1.00
(4)	Bert Bell	1.00
(5)	Paul Brown	1.00
(6)	Joe Carr	1.00
(7)	Guy Chamberlin	1.00
(8)	Earl "Dutch" Clark	1.00
(9)	Jimmy Conzelman	1.00
(10)	Art Donovan	1.00
(11)	John (Paddy) Driscoll	1.00
(12)	Billy Dudley	1.00
(13)	Dan Fortmann	1.00
(14)	Otto Graham	1.00
(15)	Red Grange	2.00
(16)	George Halas	1.00
(17)	Mel Hein	1.00
(18)	Fats Henry	1.25
(19)	Bill Hewitt	1.00
(20)	Clarke Hinkle	1.25
(21)	Elroy (Crazylegs) Hirsch	1.00
(22)	Robert (Cal) Hubbard	1.00
(23)	Lamar Hunt	1.00
(24)	Don Hutson	1.00
(25)	Earl (Curly) Lambeau	1.25
(26)	Bobby Layne	1.00
(27)	Vince Lombardi	2.00
(28)	Sid Luckman	1.00
(29)	Gino Marchetti	1.25
(30)	Ollie Matson	1.00
(31)	George McAfee	1.00
(32)	Hugh McElhenny	1.00
(33)	Johnny (Blood) McNally	1.00
(34)	Marion Motley	1.00
(35)	Bronko Nagurski	1.50
(36)	Ernie Nevers	1.00
(37)	Leo Nomellini	1.25
(38)	Steve Owen	1.00
(39)	Joe Perry	1.00
(40)	Pete Pihos	1.25
(41)	Andy Robustelli	1.00
(42)	Ken Strong	1.00
(43)	Jim Thorpe	2.00
(44)	Y.A. Tittle	1.00
(45)	Charlie Trippi	1.00
(46)	Emlen Tunnell	1.25
(47)	Clyde "Bulldog" Turner	1.00
(48)	Norm Van Brocklin	1.00
(49)	Steve Van Buren	1.00
(50)	Bob Waterfield	1.25

1975 Fleer Hall of Fame

These 84 cards, which feature players who have been inducted into the Football Hall of Fame, can be distinguished from the 1974 cards by the card numbers which appear on the card backs. Fifty of the cards in the set are similar to the 1974 cards, except the fronts have brown borders, not white ones like the 1974 cards have. Each card measures 2-1/2" x 4". They were issued in wax packs along with cloth team logo stickers.

		NM
Complete Set (84):		30.00
Common Player:		.35
1	Jim Thorpe	1.00
2	Cliff Battles	.35
3	Bronko Nagurski	.75
4	Harold Grange	1.00
5	Guy Chamberlin	.35
6	Joe Carr	.35
7	George Halas	.50
8	Jimmy Conzelman	.35
9	George McAfee	.35
10	Clarke Hinkle	.35
11	John Driscoll	.35
12	Mel Hein	.35
13	Johnny McNally	.35
14	Earl Clark	.35
15	Steve Owen	.35
16	Bill Hewitt	.35
17	Robert Hubbard	.35
18	Don Hutson	.50
19	Ernie Nevers	.50
20	Dan Fortmann	.35
21	Ken Strong	.35
22	Chuck Bednarik	.50
23	Bert Bell	.35
24	Paul Brown	.50
25	Art Donovan	.50
26	Bill Dudley	.35
27	Otto Graham	1.00
28	Fats Henry	.35
29	Elroy Hirsch	.50
30	Lamar Hunt	.50
31	Earl Lambeau	.75
32	Vince Lombardi	.75
33	Sid Luckman	.75
34	Gino Marchetti	.50
35	Ollie Matson	.50
36	Hugh McElhenny	.50
37	Marion Motley	.50
38	Leo Nomellini	.35
39	Joe Perry	.50
40	Andy Robustelli	.35
41	Pete Pihos	.35
42	Y.A. Tittle	.50
43	Charlie Trippi	.35
44	Emlen Tunnell	.35
45	Clyde Turner	.35
46	Norm Van Brocklin	.50
47	Steve Van Buren	.50
48	Bob Waterfield	.75
49	Bobby Layne	.50
50	Sammy Baugh	1.00
51	Joe Guyon	.35
52	William Roy Lyman	.35
53	George Trafton	.35
54	Albert G. Edwards	.35
55	Ed Healey	.35
56	Mike Michalske	.35
57	Alex Wojciechowicz	.35
58	Dante Lavelli	.35
59	George Connor	.35
60	Wayne Millner	.35
61	Jack Christiansen	.35
62	Roosevelt Brown	.35
63	Joe Stydahar	.35
64	Ernie Stautner	.50
65	Jim Parker	.50
66	Raymond Berry	.50
67	George Preston Marshall	.35
68	Clarence Parker	.50
69	Earle Neale	.35
70	Tim Mara	.35
71	Hugh Ray	.35
72	Tom Fears	.50
73	Arnie Herber	.35
74	Walt Kiesling	.35
75	Frank Kinard	.35
76	Tony Canadeo	.35
77	Bill George	.35
78	Art Rooney	.50
79	Joe Schmidt	.50
80	Dan Reeves	.50
81	Lou Groza	.50
82	Charles W. Bidwill	.35
83	Lenny Moore	.50
84	Dick Lane	.50

1976 Fleer Team Action

Beginning in 1976, and continuing through 1988, Fleer produced a series of "Team Action" cards showing football action shots but not identifying the individual players. All cards measure the standard 2-1/2" x 3-1/2". Because the sets did not contain individual player cards they have held little interest for collectors, and very few cards have any premium value. Generally, only the cards priced above common price are those with recognizable superstars prominently displayed in the action scene. The various years of issue can be determined by the border color on the front and the copyright date on the back. Sets from 1976 through 1984 and 1987 and 1988 feature an odd-numbered offensive card and an even-numbered defensive card for each NFL team. The backs list statistics from the previous year. In 1985 and 1986 each team had a third "In Action" card added - the backs of which show team schedules for the upcoming season. All sets (except 1988) are essentially numbered to correspond to team-city alphabetical order.

The 1976 set is actually comprised of 66 stickercards and is quite scarce. For each subsequent year (up through 1980) the number of cards in the set was increased by one, adding a card for the most recent Super Bowl. Beginning in 1981, all sets were enlarged to 88 cards. Fleer's initial set in 1976 has two cards per team, plus 10 Super Bowl cards. The cards were issued in four-card wax packs, without inserts. It includes a Jack Lambert "rookie", a Joe Namath (not found in Topps) and the only team action card of O.J. Simpson.

		NM
Complete Set (66):		375.00
Common Card:		5.00
Common SB Card:		7.50
1	Baltimore Colts (High Scorers)	5.25
2	Baltimore Colts (Effective Tackle)	5.00
3	Buffalo Bills (Perfect Blocking)	5.00
4	Buffalo Bills (The Sack)	5.00
5	Cincinnati Bengals (Being Hit Behind The Runner)	5.00
6	Cincinnati Bengals (Franco Harris) (A Little Help)	9.00
7	Cleveland Browns (Blocking Tight End)	5.00
8	Cleveland Browns (Stopping the Double Threat)	5.00
9	Denver Broncos (The Swing Pass)	5.00
10	Denver Broncos (The Gang Tackle)	5.00
11	Houston Oilers (Dan Pastorini) (Short Zone Flooded)	6.00
12	Houston Oilers (Franco Harris) (Run Stoppers)	9.00
13	Kansas City Chiefs (Off On the Ball)	5.00
14	Kansas City Chiefs (Forcing the Scramble)	5.00
15	Miami Dolphins (Bob Griese) (Pass Protection)	10.00
16	Miami Dolphins (Natural Turf)	6.00
17	New England Patriots (Quicker Than the Eye)	5.00
18	New England Patriots (The Rugby Touch)	5.00
19	New York Jets (John Riggins, Joe Namath) (They Run, Too)	16.50
20	New York Jets (O.J. Simpson) (The Buck Stops Here)	15.00
21	Oakland Raiders (A Strong Offense)	6.00
22	Oakland Raiders (High and Low)	6.00
23	Pittsburgh Steelers (Terry Bradshaw, Franco Harris, Rocky Bleier) (The Pitch-Out)	14.00
24	Pittsburgh Steelers (Jack Lambert) (The Takeaway)	15.00
25	San Diego Chargers (Run to Daylight)	5.00
26	San Diego Chargers (The Swarm)	5.00
27	Tampa Bay Buccaneers (Stadium)	5.00
28	Tampa Bay Buccaneers (Buccaneers Uniform)	5.00
29	Atlanta Falcons (A Key Block)	5.00
30	Atlanta Falcons (Robert Newhouse) (Breakthrough)	5.00
31	Chicago Bears (An Inside Look)	5.00
32	Chicago Bears (Defensive Emphasis)	5.00
33	Dallas Cowboys (Robert Newhouse) (Eight-Yard Burst)	6.00
34	Dallas Cowboys (The Big Return)	6.00
35	Detroit Lions (Power Sweep)	5.00
36	Detroit Lions (A Tough Defense)	5.00
37	Green Bay Packers (Tearaway Gain)	5.00
38	Green Bay Packers (Good Support)	5.00
39	Los Angeles Rams	5.00
40	Los Angeles Rams (Low-Point Defense)	5.00
41	Minnesota Vikings (Fran Tarkenton, Chuck Foreman) (The Running Guards)	10.00
42	Minnesota Vikings (A Stingy Defense)	5.00
43	New York Giants (The Quick Opener)	5.00
44	New York Giants (Defending a Tradition)	5.00
45	New Orleans Saints (Archie Manning) (Head for the Hole)	6.00
46	New Orleans Saints (The Contain Man)	5.00
47	Philadelphia Eagles (Line Signals)	5.00
48	Philadelphia Eagles (Don't Take Sides)	5.00
49	San Francisco 49ers (The Clues)	5.00
50	San Francisco 49ers (Goal-Line Stand)	5.00
51	St. Louis Cardinals (Jim Hart) (Nonstdard Handoff)	5.00
52	St. Louis Cardinals (Strong Pursuit)	5.00
53	Seattle Seahawks (Stadium)	5.25
54	Seattle Seahawks (Uniform)	5.25
55	Washington Redskins (Billy Kilmer) (A Fancy Passing)	6.00
56	Washington Redskins (Chris Hanburger) (Let's Go Defense)	5.00
57	Super Bowl I (Jim Taylor) (Green Bay vs. Kansas City)	7.50
58	Super Bowl II (Ben Davidson) (Green Bay vs. Oakland)	7.50
59	Super Bowl III (New York vs. Baltimore)	7.50
60	Super Bowl IV (Kansas City vs. Minnesota)	7.50
61	Super Bowl V (Baltimore vs. Dallas)	7.50
62	Super Bowl VI (Roger Staubach, Walt Garrison) (Dallas vs. Miami)	16.00
63	Super Bowl VII (Larry Csonka) (Miami vs. Washington)	9.50
64	Super Bowl VIII (Larry Csonka) (Miami vs. Minnesota)	9.50
65	Super Bowl IX (Pittsburgh vs. Minnesota)	7.50
66	Super Bowl X (Terry Bradshaw, Franco Harris) (Pittsburgh vs. Dallas)	19.00

1977 Fleer Team Action

The 1977 set Fleer set has white borders and is complete at 67 cards, two for each NFL team and one for each Super Bowl. Odd-numbered cards picture offensive teams; defensive squads are on even-numbered cards. The set features Joe Namath (not found in 1977 Topps) and two different first-year Fleer Walter Payton cards. The packs had four cards and four team logo stickers.

		NM
Complete Set (67):		80.00
Common Card:		1.00
Common SB Card:		1.50
1	Baltimore Colts (Bert Jones) (The Easy Chair)	1.75
2	Baltimore Colts (A Handy Solution)	1.00
3	Buffalo Bills (Blocking Tight End)	1.00
4	Buffalo Bills (Search and Destroy)	1.00
5	Cincinnati Bengals (Ken Anderson) (Cutting on a Rug)	1.50
6	Cincinnati Bengals (Strength in the Middle)	1.00
7	Cleveland Browns (Brian Sipe) (Snap, Drop, Set)	1.25
8	Cleveland Browns (High and Low)	1.00
9	Denver Broncos (Green Light)	1.25
10	Denver Broncos (Help From Behind)	1.25
11	Houston Oilers (Room to Move)	1.00
12	Houston Oilers (For The Defense)	1.00
13	Kansas City Chiefs (Chance to Motor)	1.00
14	Kansas City Chiefs (From the Ground Up)	1.00
15	Miami Dolphins (Eye of the Storm)	1.25
16	Miami Dolphins (When Man Takes Flight)	1.25
17	New England Patriots (Turning the Corner)	1.00
18	New England Patriots (A Matter of Inches)	1.00
19	New York Jets (Joe Namath) (Keeping Him Clean)	7.25
20	New York Jets (Plugging the Leaks)	1.00
21	Oakland Raiders (On Solid Ground)	1.25
22	Oakland Raiders (3-4 and Shut the Door)	1.25
23	Pittsburgh Steelers (Rocky Bleier) (Daylight Saving Time)	1.25
24	Pittsburgh Steelers (A Controlled Swarm)	1.25
25	San Diego Chargers (Dan Fouts) (Youth on the Move)	3.75
26	San Diego Chargers (A Rude Housewarming)	1.00
27	Seattle Seahawks (Jim Zorn) (Play Action Pass)	2.00
28	Seattle Seahawks (Birds of Prey)	1.25
29	Atlanta Falcons (Ad-Libbing on Defense)	1.25
30	Atlanta Falcons (A Futile Chase)	1.00
31	Chicago Bears (Walter Payton) (Follow Me)	6.75
32	Chicago Bears (A Nose for the Ball)	1.00
33	Dallas Cowboys (The Plunge)	1.25
34	Dallas Cowboys (Ed "Too Tall" Jones) (Unassisted Sack)	3.00
35	Detroit Lions (Motor City Might)	1.00
36	Detroit Lions (Block Party)	1.00
37	Green Bay Packers (Another Era)	1.00
38	Green Bay Packers (Walter Payton) (Face-to-Face)	6.50
39	Los Angeles Rams (Personal Escort)	1.00
40	Los Angeles Rams (A Closed Case)	1.00
41	Minnesota Vikings (Nothing Fancy)	1.00
42	Minnesota Vikings (Lending a Hand)	1.00

43 New Orleans Saints (Ample Protection) 1.00
44 New Orleans Saints (Well-Timed Contact) 1.00
45 New York Giants (Quick Pitch) 1.00
46 New York Giants (In a Pinch) 1.00
47 Philadelphia Eagles (When to Fly) 1.00
48 Philadelphia Eagles (Swooping Defense) 1.00
49 St. Louis Cardinals (Jim Hart) (Speed Outside) 1.25
50 St. Louis Cardinals (The Circle Tightens) 1.00
51 San Francisco 49ers (Gene Washington) (Sideline Route) 1.25
52 San Francisco 49ers (The Gold Rush) 1.00
53 Tampa Bay Buccaneers (A Rare Occasion) 1.00
54 Tampa Bay Buccaneers (Expansion Blues) 1.00
55 Washington Redskins (Joe Theismann) (Splitting the Seam) 2.75
56 Washington Redskins (The Hands of Time) 1.00
57 Super Bowl I (Green Bay vs. Kansas City) 1.50
58 Super Bowl II (Green Bay vs. Oakland) 1.50
59 Super Bowl III (Tom Matte) (New York vs. Baltimore) 1.50
60 Super Bowl IV (Kansas City vs. Minnesota) 1.50
61 Super Bowl V (Baltimore vs. Dallas) 1.50
62 Super Bowl VI (Walt Garrison, Roger Staubach) (Dallas vs. Miami) 4.25
63 Super Bowl VII (Larry Csonka) (Miami vs. Washington) 2.25
64 Super Bowl VIII (Larry Csonka) (Miami vs. Minnesota) 2.25
65 Super Bowl IX (Pittsburgh vs. Minnesota) 1.50
66 Super Bowl X (Terry Bradshaw, Franco Harris) (Pittsburgh vs. Dallas) 3.75
67 Super Bowl XI (Ken Stabler) (Oakland vs. Minnesota) 3.75

1978 Fleer Team Action

The 1978 Fleer set contains 68 cards, two for each team and for each Super Bowl. The borders are yellow. Fleer continued with its odd-for-offense and even-for-defense numbering scheme. The set is highlighted by a Tony Dorsett "rookie" card. Seven cards and four team logo stickers were in each pack.

	NM
Complete Set (68):	50.00
Common Card:	.55
Common SB Card:	.70

1 Atlanta Falcons (Sticking to Basics) .60
2 Atlanta Falcons (In Pursuit) .55
3 New England Colts (Foward Plunge) .55
4 New England Colts (Stacking It Up) .55
5 Buffalo Bills (Daylight Breakers) .55
6 Buffalo Bills (Swarming Defense) .55
7 Chicago Bears (Walter Payton) (Up the Middle) 6.75
8 Chicago Bears (Rejuvenated Defense) .55
9 Cincinnati Bengals (Ken Anderson) (Poise and Execution) 1.25
10 Cincinnati Bengals (Down-to-Earth) .55
11 Cleveland Browns (Greg Pruitt) (Breakaway) .80
12 Cleveland Browns (Ken Anderson) (Red Dogs) 1.00
13 Dallas Cowboys (Dorsett) (Up and Over) 7.50
14 Dallas Cowboys (Doomsday II) .75
15 Denver Broncos (Mile-Hile Offense) .75
16 Denver Broncos (Walter Payton) (Orange Crush) 5.25
17 Detroit Lions (End-Around) .55
18 Detroit Lions (Special Teams) .55
19 Green Bay Packers (Running Strong) .55
20 Green Bay Packers (Tearin' em Down) .55
21 Houston Oilers (Goal-Line Drive) .55
22 Houston Oilers (Interception) .55
23 Kansas City Chiefs (Ed Podolak) (Running Wide) .60
24 Kansas City Chiefs (Armed Defense) .55
25 Los Angeles Rams (Rushing Power) .55
26 Los Angeles Rams (Backing the Line) .55
27 Miami Dolphins (Bob Griese) (Protective Pocket) 2.50
28 Miami Dolphins (Life in the Pit) .75
29 Minnesota Vikings (Chuck Foreman) (Storm Breakers) .80
30 Minnesota Vikings (Blocking the Kick) .55
31 New England Patriots (Clearing the Way) .55
32 New England Patriots (One-on-One) .55
33 New Orleans Saints (Extra Yardage) .55
34 New Orleans Saints (Drag-Down Defense) .55
35 New York Giants (Ready, Aim, Fire) .55
36 New York Giants (Meeting of Minds) .55
37 New York Jets (Take-Off) .55
38 New York Jets (Ambush) .55
39 Oakland Raiders (Power 31 Left) .75
40 Oakland Raiders (Welcoming Committee) .75
41 Philadelphia Eagles (Taking Flight) .55
42 Philadelphia Eagles (Soaring High) .55
43 Pittsburgh Steelers (Ironclad Offense) .75
44 Pittsburgh Steelers (Jack Lambert) (Curtain Closes) 2.00
45 St. Louis Cardinals (A Good Bet) .55
46 St. Louis Cardinals (Gang Tackle) .55
47 San Diego Chargers (Circus Catch) .55
48 San Diego Chargers (Charge) .55
49 San Francisco 49ers (Follow the Block) .55
50 San Francisco 49ers (Goal-Line Stand) .55

51 Seattle Seahawks (Finding Daylight) .60
52 Seattle Seahawks (Rushing the Pass) .60
53 Tampa Bay Buccaneers (Play Action) .55
54 Tampa Bay Buccaneers (Youth on the Move) .55
55 Washington Redskins (Renegade Runners) .55
56 Washington Redskins (Dual Action) .55
57 Super Bowl I (Bart Starr) (Green Bay vs. Kansas City) 2.25
58 Super Bowl II (Green Bay vs. Oakland) .70
59 Super Bowl III (New York vs. Baltimore) .70
60 Super Bowl IV (Kansas City vs. Minnesota) .70
61 Super Bowl V (Baltimore vs. Dallas) .70
62 Super Bowl VI (Dallas vs. Miami) .70
63 Super Bowl VII (Miami vs. Washington) .70
64 Super Bowl VIII (Larry Csonka) (Miami vs. Minnesota) 1.75
65 Super Bowl IX (Terry Bradshaw, Franco Harris) (Pittsburgh vs. Minnesota) 3.00
66 Super Bowl X (Pittsburgh vs. Dallas) .70
67 Super Bowl XI (Ken Stabler) (Oakland vs. Minnesota) 2.00
68 Super Bowl XII (Roger Staubach, Tony Dorsett) (Dallas vs. Denver) 5.75

1979 Fleer Team Action

The 1979 white-bordered set contains 69 cards, two for each team plus one for each Super Bowl. The cards are numbered to correspond to team-city alphabetical order, followed by a chronological series of all 13 Super Bowls. An odd-offensive and even-defensive numbering format is used again. Earl Campbell's rookie card is the set's most significant. Packs were distributed with seven cards and three logo stickers.

	NM
Complete Set (69):	40.00
Common Card:	.50
Common SB Card:	.60

1 Atlanta Falcons (What's Up Front Counts) .80
2 Atlanta Falcons (Following the Bouncing Ball) .50
3 Baltimore Colts (Big Enough to Drive a Truck Through) .50
4 Baltimore Colts (When the Defense Becomes the Offense) .50
5 Buffalo Bills (Full Steam Ahead) .50
6 Buffalo Bills (Three's a Crowd) .50

7 Chicago Bears (Moving Out as One) .50
8 Chicago Bears (Stack' Em Up) .50
9 Cincinnati Bengals (Out in the Open Field) .50
10 Cincinnati Bengals (Sandwiched) .50
11 Cleveland Browns (Protective Pocket) .50
12 Cleveland Browns (Shake Rattle and Roll) .50
13 Dallas Cowboys (Tony Dorsett) (Paving the Way) 3.75
14 Dallas Cowboys (The Right Place at the Right Time) .65
15 Denver Broncos (A Stable of Runners) .65
16 Denver Broncos (Orange Crush) .65
17 Detroit Lions (Through the Line) .50
18 Detroit Lions (Tracked Down) .50
19 Green Bay Packers (Power Play) .50
20 Green Bay Packers (Four-To-One Odds) .50
21 Houston Oilers (Earl Campbell) (Offensive Gusher) 7.00
22 Houston Oilers (Gotcha) .50
23 Kansas City Chiefs (Get Wings) .50
24 Kansas City Chiefs (Ambushed) .50
25 Los Angeles Rams (Men in the Middle) .50
26 Los Angeles Rams (Nowhere To Go But Down) .50
27 Miami Dolphins (Escort Service) .65
28 Miami Dolphins (All For One) .65
29 Minnesota Vikings (Up and Over) .50
30 Minnesota Vikings (The Purple Gang) .50
31 New England Patriots (Prepare For Takeoff) .50
32 New England Patriots (Dept. of Defense) .50
33 New Orleans Saints (Archie Manning) (Bombs Away) .85
34 New Orleans Saints (Duel in the Dome) .50
35 New York Giants (Battle of the Line of Scrimmage) .50
36 New York Giants (Piled Up) .50
37 New York Jets (Hitting the Hole) .50
38 New York Jets (Making Sure) .50
39 Oakland Raiders (Ken Stabler) (Left-Handed Strength) 2.00
40 Oakland Raiders (Black Sunday) .85
41 Philadelphia Eagles (Ready Aim Fire) .50
42 Philadelphia Eagles (Closing In) .50
43 Pittsburgh Steelers (Anchor Man) .65
44 Pittsburgh Steelers (The Steel Curtain) .85
45 St. Louis Cardinals (Jim Hart) (High Altitude Bomber) .85
46 St. Louis Cardinals (Three On One) .50
47 San Diego Chargers (Charge) .50
48 San Diego Chargers (Special Teams Shot) .50
49 San Francisco 49ers (In For the Score) .50
50 San Francisco 49ers (Nothing But Red Shirts) .50
51 Seattle Seahawks (North-South Runner) .65
52 Seattle Seahawks (The Sting) .65
53 Tampa Bay Buccaneers (Hitting Paydirt) .50
54 Tmpa Bay Buccaneers (Making' Em Pay the Price) .50
55 Washington Redskins (On the Warpath) .50

56 Washington Redskins (Drawing a Crowd) .50
57 Super Bowl I (Jim Taylor) (Green Bay vs. Kansas City) .85
58 Super Bowl II (Bart Starr) (Green Bay vs. Oakland) 2.00
59 Super Bowl III (New York vs. Baltimore) .65
60 Super Bowl IV (Kansas City vs. Minnesota) .65
61 Super Bowl V (Baltimore vs. Dallas) .65
62 Super Bowl VI (Bob Griese, Bob Lilly) (Dallas vs. Miami) 2.00
63 Super Bowl VII (Miami vs. Washington) .65
64 Super Bowl VIII (Bob Griese, Larry Csonka) (Miami vs. Minnesota) 2.00
65 Super Bowl IX (Terry Bradshaw, Franco Harris) (Pittsburgh vs. Minnesota) 3.00
66 Super Bowl X (Pittsburgh vs. Dallas) .65
67 Super Bowl XI (Oakland vs. Minnesota) .65
68 Super Bowl XII (Dallas vs. Denver) .65
69 Super Bowl XIII (Pittsburgh vs Dallas) 1.25

1980 Fleer Team Action

The 1980 Fleer set has white borders and is complete at 70 cards, two for each NFL team and one for each Super Bowl. The cards are numbered to correspond to team-city alphabetical order. Odds are offensive cards, evens are defensive plays. The last 14 picture Super Bowl action. A key card in the set is the Phil Simms "rookie" card. Seven cards and three logo stickers were in each pack.

	NM
Complete Set (70):	38.00
Common Card:	.40
Common SB Card:	.50

1 Atlanta Falcons (Getting the Extra Yards) .70
2 Atlanta Falcons (Falcons Get Their Prey) .40
3 Baltimore Colts (Looking for Daylight) .45
4 Baltimore Colts (Ready If Needed) .40
5 Buffalo Bills (You Block For Me, I'll Block For You) .40
6 Buffalo Bills (Stand 'Em Up and Push 'Em Back) .40
7 Chicago Bears (Walter Payton) (Coming Through) 4.00
8 Chicago Bears (Four On One) .40
9 Cincinnati Bengals (Power Running) .40
10 Cincinnati Bengals (Out Of Running Room) .40
11 Cleveland Browns (Ozzie Newsome) (End Around) 2.00

12 Cleveland Browns (Rubber Band Defense) .40
13 Dallas Cowboys (Tony Dorsett) (Point of Attack) 3.00
14 Dallas Cowboys (Bob Breunig) (Man in the Middle) .60
15 Denver Broncos (Strong and Steady) .45
16 Denver Broncos (Orange Power) .45
17 Detroit Lions (On the March) .40
18 Detroit Lions (The Silver Rush) .40
19 Green Bay Packers (Getting Underway) .40
20 Green Bay Packers (The Best Offense is a Good Defense) .40
21 Houston Oilers (Airborne) .40
22 Houston Oilers (Search and Destroy) .40
23 Kansas City Chiefs (Blazing the Trail) .40
24 Kansas City Chiefs (Making Sure) .40
25 Los Angeles Rams (One Good Turn Deserves Another) .40
26 Los Angeles Rams (Shedding the Block) .40
27 Miami Dolphins (Sweeping the Flanks) .50
28 Miami Dolphins (Keep 'Em Busy) .50
29 Minnesota Vikings (One Man To Beat) .40
30 Minnesota Vikings (Purple People Eaters II) .40
31 New England Patriots (Hitting the Hole) .40
32 New England Patriots (Getting to the Ball) .40
33 New Orleans Saints (Splitting the Defenders) .40
34 New Orleans Saints (Joe Theismann) (Don't Let Him Get Outside) 1.00
35 New York Giants (Phil Simms) (Audible) 4.00
36 New York Giants (Wrong Side Up) .40
37 New York Jets (Make Him Miss) .40
38 New York Jets (Mark Gastineau) (The Only Way To Play) .45
39 Oakland Raiders (Pulling Out All the Stops) .60
40 Oakland Raiders (Right On) .60
41 Philadelphia Eagles (Not Pretty, But Still Points) .40
42 Philadelphia Eagles (Applying the Clamps) .40
43 Pittsburgh Steelers (Franco Harris) (All Systems Go) 1.75
44 Pittsburgh Steelers (Still the Steel Curtain) .70
45 St. Louis Cardinals (Ottis Anderson) (On the Move) 2.00
46 St. Louis Cardinals (Long Gone) .40
47 San Diego Chargers (Short-Range Success) .40
48 San Diego Chargers (Pursuit) .40
49 San Francisco 49ers (Getting Field Position) .40
50 San Francisco 49ers (Finding a Nugget) .40
51 Seattle Seahawks (They'll Try Anything Once) .45
52 Seattle Seahawks (Paying the Price) .45
53 Tampa Bay Buccaneers (Coming of Age) .40
54 Tampa Bay Buccaneers (Walter Payton) (3-4 Shut the Door) 3.00
55 Washington Redskins (Wide Open) .40

56	Washington Redskins (Rude Reception)	.40
57	Super Bowl I (Green Bay vs. Kansas City)	.50
58	Super Bowl II (Bart Starr) (Green Bay vs. Oakland)	1.75
59	Super Bowl III (Joe Namath) (New York vs. Baltimore)	3.75
60	Super Bowl IV (Kansas City vs. Minnesota)	.50
61	Super Bowl V (Baltimore vs. Dallas)	.50
62	Super Bowl VI (Roger Staubach) (Dallas vs. Miami)	3.00
63	Super Bowl VII (Miami vs. Washington)	.50
64	Super Bowl VIII (Miami vs. Minnesota)	.50
65	Super Bowl IX (Terry Bradshaw, Rocky Bleier) (Pittsburgh vs. Minnesota)	1.75
66	Super Bowl X (Jack Lambert) (Pittsburgh vs. Dallas)	.70
67	Super Bowl XI (Chuck Foreman) (Oakland vs. Minnesota)	.60
68	Super Bowl XII (Dallas vs. Denver)	.50
69	Super Bowl XIII (Terry Bradshaw) (Pittsburgh vs. Dallas)	2.00
70	Super Bowl XIV (Franco Harris) (Pittsburgh vs. Los Angeles)	2.00

1981 Fleer Team Action

The 1981 Fleer football set is complete at 88 cards, including two cards for each team, one for each Super Bowl, plus a series of extra cards at the end to round out the set. The front borders are white, while the backs are designed around a red, white and blue color scheme. Once again, Fleer used its alphabetical, offense/defense numbering scheme. Packs were marketed with eight cards and three logo stickers.

		MT
Complete Set (88):		26.50
Common Card:		.30
Common SB Card:		.35
1	Atlanta Falcons (Out In the Open)	.60
2	Atlanta Falcons (Grits Blitz)	.30
3	Baltimore Colts (Sprung Through the Line)	.30
4	Baltimore Colts (Human Pyramid)	.30
5	Buffalo Bills (Buffalo Bills' Wild West Show)	.30
6	Buffalo Bills (Buffaloed)	.30
7	Chicago Bears (Walter Payton) (About to Hit Paydirt)	3.00
8	Chicago Bears (Bear Trap)	.30
9	Cincinnati Bengals (Pete Johnson) (Behind the Wall)	.35
10	Cincinnati Bengals (Black Cloud)	.30
11	Cleveland Browns (Mike Pruitt) (Point of Attack)	.45
12	Cleveland Browns (Rocky Bleier) (The Only Way to Go is Down)	.50
13	Dallas Cowboys (Ron Springs) (Big O in Big D)	.45
14	Dallas Cowboys (Headed Off at the Pass)	.45
15	Dallas Cowboys (Craig Morton) (Man Versus Elements)	.35
16	Denver Broncos (The Old High-Low Treatment)	.35
17	Detroit Lions (Billy Sims) (Play Action)	1.00
18	Detroit Lions (Into the Lions' Den)	.30
19	Green Bay Packers (A Packer Packs the Pigskin)	.30
20	Green Bay Packers (Sandwiched)	.30
21	Houston Oilers (Wait A Minute)	.30
22	Houston Oilers (3-4 Shut the Door)	.30
23	Kansas City Chiefs (On the Ball)	.30
24	Kansas City Chiefs (Seeing Red)	.30
25	Los Angeles Rams (The Point of Attack)	.30
26	Los Angeles Rams (Get Your Hands Up)	.30
27	Miami Dolphins (David Woodley) (Plenty of Time)	.45
28	Miami Dolphins (Pursuit)	.35
29	Minnesota Vikings (Tough Yardage)	.30
30	Minnesota Vikings (Pete Johnson) (Purple Avalanche)	.35
31	New England Patriots (In High Gear)	.30
32	New England Patriots (Ken Stabler) (Keep 'Em Covered)	1.50
33	New Orleans Saints (Archie Manning) (Setting Up)	.45
34	New Orleans Saints (Air Ball)	.30
35	New York Giants (Off Tackle)	.30
36	New York Giants (In the Land of the Giants)	.30
37	New York Jets (Richard Todd) (Cleared for Launching)	.35
38	New York Jets (Airborne)	.30
39	Oakland Raiders (Off and Running)	.45
40	Oakland Raiders (Block that Kick)	.45
41	Philadelphia Eagles (About to Take Flight)	.30
42	Philadelphia Eagles (Robert Newhouse) (Birds of Prey)	.45
43	Pittsburgh Steelers (Franco Harris) (Here Comes the Infantry)	1.25
44	Pittsburgh Steelers (Like a Steel Trap)	.35
45	St. Louis Cardinals (Run to Daylight)	.30
46	St. Louis Cardinals (Stacked Up and Up)	.30
47	San Diego Chargers (Straight-Ahead Power)	.30
48	San Diego Chargers (Stonewalled)	.30
49	San Francisco 49ers (Follow the Leader)	.30
50	San Francisco 49ers (Search and Destroy)	.30
51	Seattle Seahawks (Short-Range Success)	.30
52	Seattle Seahawks (Take Down)	.30
53	Tampa Bay Buccaneers (Jerry Eckwood) (Orange Blossom Special)	.35
54	Tampa Bay Buccaneers (Tropical Storm Buc)	.30
55	Washington Redskins (Alone for a Moment)	.30
56	Washington Redskins (Ambushed)	.30
57	Super Bowl I (Jim Taylor) (Green Bay vs. Kansas City)	.50
58	Super Bowl II (Green Bay vs. Oakland)	.30
59	Super Bowl III (New York vs. Baltimore)	.30
60	Super Bowl IV (Kansas City vs. Minnesota)	.30
61	Super Bowl V (Baltimore vs. Dallas)	.30
62	Super Bowl VI (Dallas vs. Miami)	.30
63	Super Bowl VII (Miami vs. Washington)	.30
64	Super Bowl VIII (Larry Csonka) (Miami vs. Minnesota)	1.00
65	Super Bowl IX (Franco Harris) (Pittsburgh vs. Minnesota)	1.00
66	Super Bowl X (Franco Harris) (Pittsburgh vs. Dallas)	.35
67	Super Bowl XI (Kenny Stabler) (Oakland vs. Minnesota)	1.50
68	Super Bowl XII (Roger Staubach, Tony Dorsett) (Dallas vs. Denver)	2.25
69	Super Bowl XIII (Roger Staubach, Tony Dorsett) (Pittsburgh vs. Dallas)	2.25
70	Super Bowl XIV (Franco Harris) (Pittsburgh vs. Los Angeles)	1.00
71	Super Bowl XV (Jim Plunkett) (Oakland vs. Philadelphia)	.50
72	Steeler Training Camp (Chuck Noll)	.50
73	Practice Makes Perfect	.30
74	Airborn Carrier	.30
75	The National Anthem Chargers	.30
76	Filling Up	.30
77	Terry Bradshaw (Away in Time)	2.00
78	Flat Out	.30
79	Halftime (Band playing)	.30
80	Warm Ups Patriots	.30
81	Getting to the Bottom of It	.30
82	Souvenir (Crowd)	.30
83	A Game of Inches (Officials measuring)	.30
84	The Overview	.30
85	The Dropback	.30
86	Pregame Huddle (Washington Redskins)	.30
87	Every Way But Loose	.30
88	Mudders	.50

1982 Fleer Team Action

The 1982 Fleer set is again complete at 88 cards, but is slightly more valuable than other Fleer sets from this period, because it contains a couple of cards featuring Joe Montana. The same numbering scheme is used, but 16 NFL Team Highlight cards are included and added at the end. Seven cards and three logo stickers were in each pack.

		MT
Complete Set (88):		45.00
Common Card:		.25
Common SB Card:		.30
1	Atlanta Falcons (Running to Daylight)	.50
2	Atlanta Falcons (Airborne Falcons)	.25
3	Baltimore Colts (Mark Gastineau, Bert Jones) (Plenty of Time to Throw)	.45
4	Baltimore Colts (Lassoing the Opponent)	.25
5	Buffalo Bills (Joe Ferguson) (Point of Attack)	.45
6	Buffalo Bills (Capturing the Enemy)	.25
7	Chicago Bears (Walter Payton) (Three on One)	2.50
8	Chicago Bears (Stretched Out)	.25
9	Cincinnati Bengals (Pete Johnson) (About to Hit Paydirt)	.30
10	Cincinnati Bengals (Tiger-Striped Attack)	.25
11	Cleveland Browns (Brian Sipe) (Reading the Field)	.45
12	Cleveland Browns (Covered From All Angles)	.25
13	Dallas Cowboys (Tony Dorsett) (Blocking Convoy)	1.50
14	Dallas Cowboys (Encircled)	.45
15	Denver Broncos (Craig Morton) (Springing into Action)	.45
16	Denver Broncos (High and Low)	.30
17	Detroit Lions (Setting Up the Screen Pass)	.25
18	Detroit Lions (Doug Williams) (Poised and Ready to Attack)	.30
19	Green Bay Packers (Flying Through the Air)	.25
20	Green Bay Packers (Hitting the Pack)	.25
21	Houston Oilers (Earl Campbell) (Waiting for the Hole to Open)	3.25
22	Houston Oilers (Biting the Dust)	.25
23	Kansas City Chiefs (Going in Untouched)	.25
24	Kansas City Chiefs (No Place to Go)	.25
25	Los Angeles Rams (Wendell Tyler) (Getting to the Outside)	.30
26	Los Angeles Rams (John Riggins) (Double Team, Double Trouble)	.70
27	Miami Dolphins (Tony Nathan) (Cutting Back Against the Grain)	.45
28	Miami Dolphins (Taking Two Down)	.30
29	Minnesota Vikings (Running Inside for Tough Yardage)	.25
30	Minnesota Vikings (Bowling Over the Opponent)	.25
31	New England Patriots (Leaping for the First Down)	.25
32	New England Patriots (Gang Tackling)	.25
33	New Orleans Saints (Breaking Into the Clear)	.45
34	New Orleans Saints (Double Jeopardy)	.25
35	New York Giants (Getting Ready to Hit the Opening)	.25
36	New York Giants (Tony Dorsett) (Negative Yardage)	1.25
37	New York Jets (Freeman McNeil) (Off to the Races)	1.00
38	New York Jets (Sandwiched)	.25
39	Oakland Raiders (Marc Wilson) (Throwing the Down and Out)	.45
40	Oakland Raiders (The Second Wave is on the Way)	.45
41	Philadelphia Eagles (Ron Jaworski) (Blasting Up the Middle)	.45
42	Philadelphia Eagles (Carl Hairston, John Riggins) (Triple Teaming)	.70
43	Pittsburgh Steelers (Stretching for the Score)	.30
44	Pittsburgh Steelers (Rising Above the Crowd)	.30
45	St. Louis Cardinals (Jim Hart) (Sweeping to the Right)	.45
46	St. Louis Cardinals (No Place to go but Down)	.25
47	San Diego Chargers (Looking for Someone to Block)	.25
48	San Diego Chargers (Being in the Right Place)	.25
49	San Francisco 49ers (Joe Montana) (Giving Second Effort)	17.50
50	San Francisco 49ers (Steve Bartkowski) (In Your Face)	.50
51	Seattle Seahawks (Jack Lambert) (Nothing But Open Space)	.70
52	Seattle Seahawks (Brian Sipe) (Attacking From the Blind Side)	.45
53	Tampa Bay Buccaneers (Doug Williams) (Everyone in Motion)	.30
54	Tampa Bay Buccaneers (Ring Around the Running Back)	.25
55	Washington Redskins (Joe Theismann) (Knocking Them Down One-By-One)	.70
56	Washington Redskins (Coming From All Directions)	.25
57	Super Bowl I (Jim Taylor) (Green Bay vs. Kansas City)	.50
58	Super Bowl II (Green Bay vs. Oakland)	.25
59	Super Bowl III (New York vs. Baltimore)	.25
60	Super Bowl IV (Kansas City vs. Minnesota)	.25
61	Super Bowl V (Baltimore vs. Dallas)	.25
62	Super Bowl VI (Bob Griese, Bob Lilly) (Dallas vs. Miami)	.80
63	Super Bowl VII (Larry Csonka) (Miami vs. Washington)	.70
64	Super Bowl VIII (Larry Csonka, Paul Warfield) (Miami vs. Minnesota)	1.00
65	Super Bowl IX (Pittsburgh vs. Minnesota)	.25
66	Super Bowl X (Roger Staubach) (Pittsburgh vs. Dallas)	2.00
67	Super Bowl XI (Mark Van Eeghen) (Oakland vs. Minnesota)	.30
68	Super Bowl XII (Roger Staubach) (Dallas vs. Denver)	2.00
69	Super Bowl XIII (Lynn Swann) (Pittsburgh vs. Dallas)	1.00
70	Super Bowl XIV (Pittsburgh vs. Los Angeles)	.25
71	Super Bowl XV (Jim Plunkett) (Oakland vs. Philadelphia)	.45
72	Super Bowl XVI (Dwight Clark) (San Francisco vs. Cincinnati)	.85
73	NFL Team Highlights (Joe Montana) (Pro Bowl)	12.00
74	NFL Team Highlights (Ken Anderson, Anthony Munoz) (Pro Bowl)	2.50
75	NFL Team Highlights (Aloha Stadium)	.75
76	NFL Team Highlights (On the Field Meeting)	.25
77	NFL Team Highlights (Joe Theismann) (First Down)	.70
78	NFL Team Highlights (Jerry Markbright) (The Man in Charge)	.25
79	NFL Team Highlights (Coming Onto the Field)	.25
80	NFL Team Highlights (In the Huddle)	.30
81	NFL Team Highlights (Lying In Wait)	.25
82	NFL Team Highlights (Celebration)	.25
83	NFL Team Highlights (Men in Motion)	.25
84	NFL Team Highlights (Shotgun Formation)	.25
85	NFL Team Highlights (Training Camp)	.25
86	NFL Team Highlights (Bill Walsh) (Halftime Instructions)	.75
87	NFL Team Highlights (Rolf Bernirschke) (Field Goal Attempt)	.30
88	NFL Team Highlights (Free Kick)	.50

1983 Fleer Team Action

The 1983 Fleer football set is again complete at 88 cards, including two cards for each team, one for each Super Bowl, plus a series of "Highlights" cards at the end of the set. There is a numbering error in the set that was not corrected. The card depicting Super Bowl X, which should have been card number "66," was erroneously numbered "67," meaning there are two cards numbered "67" in the set and no card numbered "66." Collectors should be aware that the premium value attached to the Super Bowl X card is because it pictures Terry Bradshaw, and not because of the numbering error. The set follows all of Fleer's usual numbering formats. A Jim McMahon "rookie" card highlights the set. Packs had seven cards and three logo stickers.

		MT
Complete Set (88):		26.00
Common Card:		.25
Common SB Card:		.30
1	Atlanta Falcons (Ronnie Lott) (Breaking Away to Daylight)	2.50
2	Atlanta Falcons (Piles Up)	.25
3	Baltimore Colts (Cutting Back to Daylight)	.25
4	Baltimore Colts (Joe Ferguson) (Pressuring the QB)	.30

#	Card	Price
5	Buffalo Bills (Moving to the Outside)	.30
6	Buffalo Bills (Buffalo Stampede)	.25
7	Chicago Bears (Jim McMahon, Walter Payton) (Ready to Let it Fly)	2.25
8	Chicago Bears (Jump Ball)	.25
9	Cincinnati Bengals (Hurdling Into Open)	.25
10	Cincinnati Bengals (Hands Up)	.25
11	Cleveland Browns (Mike Pruitt) (An Open Field Ahead)	.30
12	Cleveland Browns (Reacting to the Ball Carrier)	.25
13	Dallas Cowboys (Tony Dorsett) (Mid-Air Ballet)	1.50
14	Dallas Cowboys (3, 2, 1 Takeoff)	.30
15	Denver Broncos (Clear Sailing)	.30
16	Denver Broncos (Stacking Up Offense)	.30
17	Detroit Lions (Hitting the Wall)	.25
18	Detroit Lions (Snapping into Action)	.25
19	Green Bay Packers (Ed "Too Tall" Jones) (Fingertip Control)	.60
20	Green Bay Packers (QB Sack)	.25
21	Houston Oilers (Sweeping to Outside)	.25
22	Houston Oilers (Freeman McNeil) (Halting Forward Progress)	.45
23	Kansas City Chiefs (Waiting for the Key Block)	.25
24	Kansas City Chiefs (John Hannah) (Going Head to Head)	.50
25	Los Angeles Raiders (Jim Plunkett) (Bowms Away)	.45
26	Los Angeles Raiders (Caged Bengal)	.45
27	Los Angeles Rams (Clearing Out Middle)	.25
28	Los Angeles Rams (One on One Tackle)	.25
29	Miami Dolphins (Skating Through Hole)	.30
30	Miami Dolphins (Follow the Bouncing Ball)	.30
31	Minnesota Vikings (Tommy Kramer) (Dropping into Pocket)	.30
32	Minnesota Vikings (Attacking from All Angles)	.25
33	New England Patriots (Touchdown)	.25
34	New England Patriots (Walter Payton) (Pouncing Patriots)	2.00
35	New Orleans Saints (Only One Man to Beat)	.25
36	New Orleans Saints (Tony Dorsett) (Closing In)	1.25
37	New York Giants (Setting Up to Pass)	.25
38	New York Giants (In Pursuit)	.25
39	New York Jets (Just Enough Room)	.25
40	New York Jets (Warpping Up Runner)	.25
41	Philadelphia Eagles (Ron Jarowski, Harry Carson) (Play Action Fakers)	.30
42	Philadelphia Eagles (Archie Manning) (Step Away From Sack)	.45
43	Pittsburgh Steelers (Franco Harris, Terry Bradshaw) (Exploding Through a Hole)	1.50
44	Pittsburgh Steelers (Jack Lambert) (Outnumbered)	.60
45	St. Louis Cardinals (Keeping His Balance)	.25
46	St. Louis Cardinals (Waiting for the Reinforcements)	.25
47	San Diego Chargers (Supercharged Charger)	.25
48	San Diego Chargers (Triple Team Tackle)	.25
49	San Francisco 49ers (There's No Stopping Him Now)	.25
50	San Francisco 49ers (Heading 'Em Off at the Pass)	.30
51	Seattle Seahawks (Jim Zorn) (Calling the Signals)	.45
52	Seattle Seahawks (The Hands Have it)	.30
53	Tampa Bay Buccaneers (Off to the Races)	.25
54	Tampa Bay Buccaneers (Buccaneer Sandwich)	.25
55	Washington Redskins (Looking for Daylight)	.25
56	Washington Redskins (Smothering the Ball Carrier)	.25
57	Super Bowl I (Jim Taylor) (Green Bay vs. Kansas City)	.60
58	Super Bowl II (Green Bay vs. Oakland)	.30
59	Super Bowl III (New York vs. Baltimore)	.30
60	Super Bowl IV (Kansas City vs. Minnesota)	.30
61	Super Bowl V (Johnny Unitas) (Baltimore vs. Dallas)	1.50
62	Super Bowl VI (Bob Griese, Bob Lilly) (Dallas vs. Miami)	.75
63	Super Bowl VII (Manny Fernandez) (Miami vs. Washington)	.30
64	Super Bowl VIII (Larry Csonka) (Miami vs. Minnesota)	.60
65	Super Bowl IX (Franco Harris) (Pittsburgh vs. Minnesota)	1.00
66	Super Bowl X (Terry Bradshaw) (Pittsburgh vs. Dallas)	1.75
67	Super Bowl XI (Oakland vs. Minnesota)	.45
68	Super Bowl XII (Dallas vs. Denver)	.30
69	Super Bowl XIII (Terry Bradshaw) (Pittsburgh vs. Dallas)	1.50
70	Super Bowl XIV (Vince Ferragamo) (Pittsburgh vs. Los Angeles)	.30
71	Super Bowl XV (Oakland vs. Philadelphia)	.30
72	Super Bowl XVI (San Francisco vs. Cincinnati)	.30
73	Super Bowl XVII (John Riggins) (Washington vs. Miami)	.60
74	NFL Team Highlights (Dan Fouts) (Pro Bowl)	1.00
75	NFL Team Highlights (Super Bowl XVII Spectacular)	.30
76	NFL Team Highlights (Tampa Stadium: Super Bowl XVIII)	.30
77	NFL Team Highlights (Up, Up, and Away)	.30
78	NFL Team Highlights (Steve Bartkowski) (Sideline Conference)	.30
79	NFL Team Highlights (Mike Lansford) (Barefoot Follow-Through)	.30
80	NFL Team Highlights (Fourth and Long)	.30
81	NFL Team Highlights (Blocked Punt)	.30
82	NFL Team Highlights (Fumble)	.30
83	NFL Team Highlights (National Anthem)	.30
84	NFL Team Highlights (Tony Franklin) (Concentrating on the Ball)	.30
85	NFL Team Highlights (Splashing Around)	.30
86	NFL Team Highlights (Loading in Shotgun)	.30
87	NFL Team Highlights (Taking the Snap)	.30
88	NFL Team Highlights (Line of Scrimmage)	.45

1984 Fleer Team Action

The 1984 Fleer football set is again complete at 88 cards, using Fleer's typical numbering arrangement. However, the newly-relocated Indianapolis Colts are placed in Baltimore's usual position. A series of 18 Super Bowl and 14 NFL Team Highlight cards are included. The most signigicant cards are two of Earl Campbell, which are not found in the 1984 Topps set, a first-year Marcus Allen, and a Howie Long "rookie." Seven cards and three logo stickers were in each pack. Cards green borders.

		MT
Complete Set (88):		23.50
Common Card:		.25
1	Atlanta Falcons	.50
2	Atlanta Falcons (Gang Tackle)	.25
3	Indianapolis Colts (About to Break Free)	.25
4	Indianapolis Colts (Cutting Off All the Angles)	.25
5	Buffalo Bills (Cracking the First Line of Defense)	.25
6	Buffalo Bills (Getting Help from a Friend)	.25
7	Chicago Bears (Jim McMahon, Walter Payton) (Over the Top)	1.75
8	Chicago Bears (You Grab Him High I'll Grab Him Low)	.25
9	Cincinnati Bengals (Skipping Through an Opening)	.25
10	Cincinnati Bengals (Joe Ferguson) (Saying Hello to a QB)	.40
11	Cleveland Browns (Greg Pruitt) (Free Sailing into the End Zone)	.40
12	Cleveland Browns (Making Sure of the Tackle)	.25
13	Dallas Cowboys (Danny White)	.50
14	Dallas Cowboys (Ed "Too Tall" Jones) (Cowboy's Corral)	.60
15	Denver Broncos (Sprinting into the Open)	.40
16	Denver Broncos (Curt Warner) (Ready to Pounce)	.50
17	Detroit Lions (Billy Sims) (Lion on the Prowl)	.50
18	Detroit Lions (John Riggins) (Stacking Up the Ball Carrier)	.60
19	Green Bay Packers (Waiting for the Hole to Open)	.25
20	Green Bay Packers (Packing Up Your Opponent)	.25
21	Houston Oilers (Earl Campbell) (Nothing but Open Spaces Ahead)	2.50
22	Houston Oilers (Meeting Him Head On)	.25
23	Kansas City Chiefs (Going Outside for Extra Yardage)	.25
24	Kansas City Chiefs (A Running Back in Trouble)	.25
25	Los Angeles Raiders (Marcus Allen) (No Defenders in Sight)	2.75
26	Los Angeles Raiders (Howie Long, John Riggins) (Rampaging Raiders)	2.25
27	Los Angeles Rams (Making the Cut)	.25
28	Los Angeles Rams (Caught From Behind)	.25
29	Miami Dolphins (Sliding Down the Line)	.40
30	Miami Dolphins (Making Sure)	.40
31	Minnesota Vikings (Stretching For Touchdown)	.25
32	Minnesota Vikings (Hitting the Wall)	.25
33	New England Patriots (Steve Grogan) (Straight Up the Middle)	.50
34	New England Patriots (Earl Campbell) (Come Here an Give Me a Hug)	2.00
35	New Orleans Saints (One Defender to Beat)	.25
36	New Orleans Saints (Saints Sandwich)	.25
37	New York Giants (A Six Point Landing)	.25
38	New York Giants (Leaping to the Aid of a Teammate)	.25
39	New York Jets (Galloping Through Untouched)	.25
40	New York Jets (Capturing the Enemy)	.25
41	Philadelphia Eagles (One More Block and He's Gone)	.25
42	Philadelphoa Eagles (Meeting an Opponent With Open Arms)	.25
43	Pittsburgh Steelers (The Play Begins to Develop)	.40
44	Pittsburgh Steelers (Rally Around the Ball Carrier)	.40
45	St. Louis Cardinals (Sprinting Around the Corner)	.25
46	St. Louis Cardinals (Overmatched)	.25
47	San Diego Chargers (Up, Up and Away)	.25
48	San Diego Chargers (Engulfing the Opponent)	.25
49	San Francisco 49ers (Wendell Tyler) (Tunneling Up the Middle)	.40
50	San Francisco 49ers (John Riggins) (Nowhere to Go but Down)	.60
51	Seattle Seahawks (Jim Zorn) (Letting the Ball Fly)	.50
52	Seattle Seahawks (Handing Out Some Punishment)	.40
53	Tampa Bay Buccaneers (When He Hits the Ground He's Gone)	.25
54	Tampa Bay Buccaneers (One Leg Takedown)	.25
55	Washington Redskins (John Riggins) (Plenty of Room to Run)	.60
56	Washington Redskins (Squashing the Oppenent)	.25
57	Super Bowl I (Jim Taylor) (Green Bay vs. Kansas City)	.60
58	Super Bowl II (Bart Starr) (Green Bay vs. Oakland)	.80
59	Super Bowl III (New York vs. Baltimore)	.25
60	Super Bowl IV (Kansas City vs. Minnesota)	.25
61	Super Bowl V (Earl Morrall) (Baltimore vs. Dallas)	.75
62	Super Bowl VI (Roger Staubach) (Dallas vs. Miami)	1.50
63	Super Bowl VII (Jim Kiick, Bob Griese) (Miami vs. Washington)	.50
64	Super Bowl VIII (Larry Csonka) (Miami vs. Minnesota)	.75
65	Super Bowl IX (Terry Bradshaw) (Pittsburgh vs. Minnesota)	1.25
66	Super Bowl X (Franco Harris) (Pittsburgh vs. Dallas)	.75
67	Super Bowl XI (Oakland vs. Minnesota)	.75
68	Super Bowl XII (Tony Dorsett) (Dallas vs. Denver)	1.00
69	Super Bowl XIII (Franco Harris) (Pittsburgh vs. Dallas)	.75
70	Super Bowl XIV (Franco Harris) (Pittsburgh vs. Los Angeles)	.75
71	Super Bowl XV (Jim Plunkett) (Oakland vs. Philadelphia)	.40
72	Super Bowl XVI (San Francisco vs. Cincinnati)	.25
73	Super Bowl XVII (Washington vs. Miami)	.25
74	Super Bowl XVIII (Howie Long) (Los Angeles vs. Washington)	1.75
75	NFL Team Highlights (Official's Conference)	.25
76	NFL Team Highlights (Leaping for the Ball Carrier)	.25
77	NFL Team Highlights (Jim Plunkett) (Setting Up in the Passing Pocket)	.40
78	NFL Team Highlights (Field Goal Block)	.25
79	NFL Team Highlights (Steve Grogan) (Stopped for No Gain)	.40
80	NFL Team Highlights (Double Team Block)	.25
81	NFL Team Highlights (Kickoff)	.25
82	NFL Team Highlights (Punt Block)	.25
83	NFL Team Highlights (Coaches Signals)	.25
84	NFL Team Highlights (Training Camp)	.25
85	NFL Team Highlights (Dwight Stephenson) (Fumble)	.50
86	NFL Team Highlights (1984 AFC-NFC Pro Bowl)	.25
87	NFL Team Highlights (Cheerleaders)	.50
88	NFL Team Highlights (Joe Theismann) (In the Huddle)	.80

A card number in parentheses ( ) indicates the set is unnumbered.

1985 Fleer Team Action

SAN FRANCISCO 49ers FINDING A NUGGET

Fleer changed its format slightly for its 1985 set. The set is still complete at 88 cards, but there are three cards for each team this year and fewer Super Bowl cards. The "In Action" cards for each team have a team schedule. Three cards for Super Bowl XIX and a 1985 Pro Bowl card are also included. A first-year Fleer Dan Marino card and a Warren Moon "rookie" card highlight the set. Packs had 15 cards and one logo sticker.

		MT
Complete Set (88):		30.00
Common Card:		.25
1	Atlanta Falcons (Nothing But Open Spaces Ahead)	.50
2	Atlanta Falcons (Leveling Ball Carrier)	.25
3	Atlanta Falcons (Joe Theismann, John Riggins) (Flying Falcon)	.60
4	Buffalo Bills (Ducking Under the Pressure)	.25
5	Buffalo Bills (Swallowing Up the Oppenent)	.25
6	Buffalo Bills (Avoiding Late Hits)	.25
7	Chicago Bears (Walter Payton) (Picking His Spot)	1.50
8	Chicago Bears (C'Mon Guys, Give Me Some Room to Breathe)	.25
9	Chicago Bears (Richard Dent) (Just Hanging Around in Case They're Needed)	2.25
10	Cincinnati Bengals (Struggling for Every Extra Yard)	.25
11	Cincinnati Bengals (Making Opponent Pay)	.25
12	Cincinnati Bengals (Just Out of the Reach of the Defender)	.25
13	Cleveland Browns (Plenty of Time to Fire the Ball)	.25
14	Cleveland Browns (Hitting the Wall)	.25
15	Cleveland Browns (Look What We Found)	.25
16	Dallas Cowboys (Tony Dorsett, Wilbur Marshall) (Waiting for the Right Moment to Burst Upfield)	1.25
17	Dallas Cowboys (Walter Payton, Ed "Too Tall" Jones) (Sorry Buddy, This is the End of the Line)	1.50
18	Dallas Cowboys (Ed "Too Tall" Jones) (Following Through for Three Points)	.60
19	Denver Broncos (Blasting Up the Middle)	.40
20	Denver Broncos (Finishing Off the Tackle)	.40
21	Denver Broncos (About to Hit Paydirt)	.40

22 Detroit Lions .40 (Dexter Manley) (Waiting to Throw Until the Last Second)
23 Detroit Lions .25 (Double Trouble on the Tackle)
24 Detroit Lions .25 (Quick Pitch)
25 Green Bay Packers .90 (Steve McMichael) (Unleashing the Long Bomb)
26 Green Bay Packers 1.50 (Marcus Allen) (Encircling the Ball Carrier)
27 Green Bay Packers .25 (Piggy-Back Ride)
28 Houston Oilers 5.75 (Warren Moon, Earl Campbell) (Retreating into the Pocket)
29 Houston Oilers .25 (Punishing the Enemy)
30 Houston Oilers (No .25 Chance to Block This One)
31 Indianapolis Colts .25 (Getting Ready to Let It Fly)
32 Indianapolis Colts .25 (Pushing the Ball Carrier Backward)
33 Indianapolis Colts .25 (Nowhere to Go)
34 Kansas City Chiefs .25 (Cutting Back for Extra Yardage)
35 Kansas City Chiefs .25 (Reaching for the Deflection)
36 Kansas City Chiefs .25 (Rising to the Occasion)
37 Los Angeles .40 Raiders (Howie Long) (Hurdling into the Open Field)
38 Los Angeles .25 Raiders (No Place to Go)
39 Los Angeles .25 Raiders (Standing Tall in the Pocket)
40 Los Angeles Rams 1.50 (Eric Dickerson) (One More Barrier and He's Off to the Races)
41 Los Angeles Rams .25 (Driving a Shoulder into the Opponent)
42 Los Angeles Rams .25 (The Kickoff)
43 Miami Dolphins .50 (Tony Nathan) (Sidestepping Trouble)
44 Miami Dolphins .40 (Hold On, We're Coming)
45 Miami Dolphins 7.25 (Dan Marino) (The Release Point)
46 Minnesota Vikings .40 (Tommy Kramer) (Putting as Much as He Has into the Pass)
47 Minnesota Vikings .25 (Gang Tackling)
48 Minnesota Vikings .25 (You're Not Getting Away From Me This Time)
49 New England .40 Patriots (Tony Eason) (Throwing on the Run)
50 New England .25 Patriots (The Only Place to Go is Down)
51 New England .25 Patriots (Standing the Ball Carrier Up)
52 New Orleans Saints .25 (Going Up the Middle)
53 New Orleans Saints .25 (Putting Everything They've Got into the Tackle)
54 New Orleans Saints .25 (Getting Off the Ground to Block the Kick)
55 New York Giants .25 (Over the Top)
56 New York Giants .25 (Rallying Around the Opposition)
57 New York Giants .60 (Phil Simms) (The Huddle)

58 New York Jets .25 (Following His Blockers)
59 New York Jets .25 (This is as Far as You Go)
60 New York Jets .25 (Looking Over the Defense)
61 Philadelphia Eagles .25 (Going Through the Opening Untouched)
62 Philadelphia Eagles .25 (Squashing the Enemy)
63 Philadelphia Eagles .25 (There's No Room Here, So Let's Go Outside)
64 Pittsburgh Steelers .40 (Sprinting Around the End)
65 Pittsburgh Steelers .40 (Mismatch)
66 Pittsburgh Steelers .40 (About to Be Thrown Back)
67 St. Louis Cardinals .25 (In for Six)
68 St. Louis Cardinals .25 (Piling Ip the Ball Carrier)
69 St. Louis Cardinals .75 (Joe Theismann) (Causing the Fumble)
70 San Diego .25 Chargers (Plenty of Open Space Ahead)
71 San Diego .25 Chargers (Ready to Be Swallowed Up)
72 San Diego .25 Chargers (A Quarterback in Serious Trouble)
73 San Francisco .25 49ers (Reading the Hole and Exploding Through)
74 San Francisco .25 49ers (Burying the Opponent)
75 San Francisco 49ers 4.25 (Joe Montana, Russ Francis) (Waiting to Throw Until His Receiver Breaks Free)
76 Seattle Seahawks .50 (Dave Krieg) (Getting Just Enough Time to Pass)
77 Seattle Seahawks .50 (Craig James) (Capturing the Enemy)
78 Seattle Seahawks .40 (It's Going to be a Fottrace Now)
79 Tampa Bay .25 Buccaneers (Heading Outside Away From Trouble)
80 Tampa Bay .25 Buccaneers (One-On-One Tackle)
81 Tampa Bay 1.25 Buccaneers (Eric Dickerson) (A Buccaneers Sandwich)
82 Washington .60 Redskins (John Riggins) (Just Enough Room to Get Through)
83 Washington .25 Redskins (Wrapping Up the Opponent)
84 Washington .40 Redskins (Mark Moseley) (Field-Goal Attempt)
85 Super Bowl XIX .90 (Roger Craig) (San Francisco vs. Miami)
86 Super Bowl XIX 3.75 (Joe Montana) (San Francisco vs. Miami)
87 Super Bowl XIX .40 (Tony Nathan) (San Francisco vs. Miami)
88 1985 Pro Bowl .50

1986 Fleer Team Action

The 1986 Fleer football set is again complete at 88 cards and is organized in an identical fashion to the previous year's set. These cards, which have a light blue border, include three for Super Bowl XX and a 1986 Pro Bowl card. Other highlights include a first-year Fleer John Elway, a Bernie Kosar "rookie" and a pre-Topps Keith Byars "rookie." Packs had seven cards and three logo stickers.

	MT
Complete Set (88):	23.00
Common Card:	.25

1 Atlanta Falcons .50 (Preparing to Make Cut)
2 Atlanta Falcons .25 (Everybody Gets Into the Act)
3 Atlanta Falcons .25 (Where Do You Think You're Going)
4 Buffalo Bills .25 (Turning On the After-Burners)
5 Buffalo Bills .25 (Running Into a Wall of Blue)
6 Buffalo Bills (Up .25 and Over)
7 Chicago Bears 1.25 (Jim McMahon, Walter Payton) (Pocket Forms Around Passer)
8 Chicago Bears 1.00 (Richard Dent, Dan Hampton) (Monsters of the Midway II)
9 Chicago Bears .85 (Mike Singletary) (Blitz in a Blizzard)
10 Cincinnati Bengals .60 (Dave Rimington, Anthony Munoz) (Plowing Trough Defense)
11 Cincinnati Bengals .25 (Zeroing in for the Hit)
12 Cincinnati Bengals 1.25 (Marcus Allen) (Oh, No You Don't)
13 Cleveland Browns 2.25 (Bernie Kosar, Kevin Mack) (Looking for a Hole to Develop)
14 Cleveland Browns .25 (Buried by the Browns)
15 Cleveland Browns .25 (Another Runner Pounded Into the Turf)
16 Dallas Cowboys .85 (Tony Dorsett) (Hole You Could Drive Truck Through)
17 Dallas Cowboys .50 (We've Got You Surrounded)
18 Dallas Cowboys .75 (Randy White) (Giving the Referee Some Help)
19 Denver Broncos 3.75 (John Elway) (The Blockers Spring into Action)
20 Denver Broncos .50 (The Orange Crush Shows Its Stuff)
21 Denver Broncos (A .40 Stampede to Block the Kick)
22 Detroit Lions (A .25 Runner's Eye View of the Situation)
23 Detroit Lions .25 (Leveling the Ball Carrier)
24 Detroit Lions (Going .25 All Out to Get the Quarterback)
25 Green Bay Packers .25 (Sweeping Around the Corner)
26 Green Bay Packers .25 (Not Afraid to Go Head to Head)
27 Green Bay Packers .25 (Taking the Snap)
28 Houston Oilers .25 (Plunging for That Extra Yard)
29 Houston Oilers .25 (Tightening the Vise)
30 Houston Oilers .25 (Launching a Field Goal)
31 Indianapolis Colts .25 (Galloping Out of an Arm-Tackle)

32 Indianpolis Colts .25 (Ball is Knocked Loose)
33 Indianapolis Colts .25 (Busting Out of the Backfield)
34 Kansas City Chiefs .25 (About to Head Upfield)
35 Kansas City Chiefs .25 (One the Warpath)
36 Kansas City Chiefs .25 (Getting the Point Across)
37 Los Angeles .40 Raiders (Looks Like Clear Sailing Ahead)
38 Los Angeles Raiders .40 (Surrounded by Unfriendly Faces)
39 Los Angeles .40 Raiders (Vaulting for Six Points)
40 Los Angeles Rams .85 (Eric Dickerson) (Breaking into an Open Field)
41 Los Angeles Rams .25 (Swept Away by a Wave of Rams)
42 Los Angeles Rams .25 (Alertly Scooping Up a Fumble)
43 Miami Dolphins .40 (Clearing a Path for the Running Bacj)
44 Miami Dolphins .40 (Teaching a Painful Lesson)
45 Miami Dolphins .40 (Trying for a Piece of the Ball)
46 Minnesota Vikings .50 (Tommy Kramer) (All Day to Throw)
47 Minnesota Vikings 1.00 (Walter Payton) (The Moment Before Impact)
48 Minnesota Vikings .25 (Leaving the Competition Behind)
49 New England .25 Patriots (Solid Line of Blockers)
50 New England .25 Patriots (Surprise Attack From the Rear)
51 New England .25 Patriots (Getting a Grip on the Opponent)
52 New Orleans Saints .25 (Look Out, I'm Coming Through)
53 New Orleans Saints .25 (A Furious Assault)
54 New Orleans Saints .25 (Line of Scrimmage)
55 New York Giants .75 (Phil Simms, Joe Morris) (Pass Play Develops)
56 New York Giants .25 (Putting Squeeze on Offense)
57 New York Giants .25 (Using a Great Block to Turn Corner)
58 New York Jets (The .25 Runner Spots Lane)
59 New York Jets .25 (About to Deliver a Headache)
60 New York Jets .25 (Flying Formation)
61 Philadelphia Eagles 1.50 (Keith Byars) (Slipping a Tackle)
62 Philadelphia Ealges .25 (Airborne Eagles Break Up Pass)
63 Philadelphia Eagles .50 (Ron Jaworski) (Connecting On Toss Over Middle)
64 Pittsburgh Steelers .25 (Letting Big Guy Lead the Way)
65 Pittsburgh Steelers .25 (Converging From Every Direction)
66 Pittsburgh Steelers .40 (Gary Anderson) (All Eyes are on the Football)
67 St. Louis Cardinals .40 (Neil Lomax, Jim Burt) (Calmly Dropping Back to Pass)
68 St. Louis Cardinals .25 (Applying Some Bruises)

69 St. Louis Cardinals .25 (Looking for Yardage on Interception Return)
70 San Diego Chargers .50 (Human Cannonball)
71 San Diego .50 Chargers (Dave Krieg) (Another One Bites the Dust)
72 San Diego .25 Chargers (A Clean Steel by the Defense)
73 San Francisco — 4.00 49ers (Joe Montana) (Looking for Safe Passage)
74 San Francisco .25 49ers (An Uplifting Experience)
75 San Francisco .50 49ers (Danny White) (In Hot Pursuit)
76 Seattle Seahawks .40 (Perparing for Collision)
77 Seattle Seahawks .40 (A Group Effort)
78 Seattle Seahawks .75 (Dan Fouts) (Forcing a Hurried Throw)
79 Tamps Bay .25 Buccaneers (Protecting Quarterback at All Costs)
80 Tampa Bay .25 Buccaneers (Dishing Out Some Punishment)
81 Tampa Bay .25 Buccaneers (No Trespassing)
82 Washington .25 Redskins (Squaring Off in the Trenches)
83 Washington .50 Redskins (Danny White) (Pouncing on the Passer)
84 Washington .25 Redskins (Two Hits Are Better Than One)
85 Super Bowl XX 1.25 (Walter Payton) (Chicago vs. New England)
86 Super Bowl XX .75 (Jim McMahon) (Chicago vs. New England)
87 Super Bowl XX .40 (Chicago vs. New England)
88 Pro Bowl 1986 1.50 (Marcus Allen)

1987 Fleer Team Action

Again complete at 88 cards, the 1987 Fleer football set contains two cards for each team, one card representing each Super Bowl and eight cards depicting the previous season's playoff games. The cards have a yellow and black border. The set features a first-year Fleer Steve Young and two pre-Topps Bo Jackson "rookies." Each pack had seven cards and three logo stickers.

	MT
Complete Set (88):	21.50
Common Card:	.20

1 Atlanta Falcons .45 (A Clear View Downfield)
2 Atlanta Falcons .45 (Roger Craig) (Pouncing on a Runner)

3 Buffalo Bills .20 (Buffalo Stampede)
4 Buffalo Bills .20 (Double Bill)
5 Chicago Bears 1.00 (Walter Payton) (Stay Out of Our Way)
6 Chicago Bears .45 (Dan Hampton) (Quarterback's Nightmare)
7 Cincinnati Bengals .45 (Eddie Brown) (Irresistible Force)
8 Cincinnati Bengals .20 (Bengals on the Prowl)
9 Cleveland Browns .20 (Following the Lead Blocker)
10 Cleveland Browns .20 (Block That Kick)
11 Dallas Cowboys .30 (Next Stop...End Zone)
12 Dallas Cowboys .30 (Ride 'Em Cowboys)
13 Denver Broncos 2.25 (John Elway) (Pitchout in Progress)
14 Denver Broncos .30 (Broncos' Busters)
15 Detroit Lions .20 (Off to the Races)
16 Detroit Lions .20 (Entering the Lions' Den)
17 Green Bay Packers .20 (Setting the Wheels in Motion)
18 Green Bay Packers .20 (Stack of Packers)
19 Houston Oilers .20 (Making a Cut at the Line of Scrimmage)
20 Houston Oilers (Hit .20 Parade)
21 Indianapolis Colts .20 (The Horses Up Front)
22 Indianapolis Colts .20 (Stopping the Runner in His Tracks)
23 Kansas City Chiefs .20 (It's A Snap)
24 Kansas City Chiefs 1.50 (Bo Jackson) (Nowhere to Hide)
25 Los Angeles 2.00 Raiders (Bo Jackson) (Looking For Daylight)
26 Los Angeles .30 Raiders (Wrapped Up by Raiders)
27 Los Angeles Rams 2.00 (Jim Everett) (Movers and Shakers)
28 Los Angeles Rams .20 (In the Quarterback's Face)
29 Miami Dolphins .30 (Full Speed Ahead)
30 Miami Dolphins .30 (Acrobatic Interception)
31 Minnesota Vikings .20 (Tommy Kramer) (Solid Line of Protection)
32 Minnesota Vikings .20 (Bearing a Heavy Load)
33 New England .45 Patriots (Craig James) (The Blockers Fan Out)
34 New England .20 Patriots (Converging Linebackers)
35 New Orleans Saints .45 (Dalton Hilliard, Jim Burt) (Saints Go Diving In)
36 New Orleans Saints .20 (Crash Course)
37 New York Giants .45 (Phil Simms) (Armed and Dangerous)
38 New York Giants .75 (Lawrence Taylor) (A Giant-sized Hit)
39 New York Jets .30 (Ken O'Brien) (Jets Prepare for Takeoff)
40 New York Jets .20 (Showing No Mercy)
41 Philadelphia Eagles .20 (Taking It Straight Up the Middle)

42 Philadelphia Eagles 1.25 (Reggie White) (The Strong Arm of the Defense)
43 Pittsburgh Steelers .20 (Double-Team Trouble)
44 Pittsburgh Steelers .20 (Caught in a Steel Trap)
45 St. Louis Cardinals .20 (The Kick is Up and...It's Good)
46 St. Louis Cardinals .20 (Seeing Red)
47 San Diego Chargers .20 (Blast Off)
48 San Diego Chargers .45 (Todd Christensen) (Lightning Strikes)
49 San Francisco 49ers .75 (The Rush Is On)
50 San Francisco 49ers .20 (Shoulder to Shoulder)
51 Seattle Seahawks .30 (Curt Warner) (Not a Defender in Sight)
52 Seattle Seahawks .20 (Hard Knocks)
53 Tampa Bay Bucaneers 3.75 (Steve Young) (Rolling Out Against the Grain)
54 Tampa Bay Buccaneers .20 (Crunch Time)
55 Washington Redskins .45 (Jay Schroeder) (Getting the Drop on the Defense)
56 Washington Redskins .20 (The Blitz Claims Another Victim)
57 AFC Championship Game .20 (Denver vs. Cleveland)
58 AFC Divisional Playoff .20 (Cleveland vs. New York Jets)
59 AFC Divisional Playoff .30 (Andre Tippett) (Denver vs. New England)
60 AFC Wild Card Game .20 (New York Jets vs. Kansas City)
61 NFC Championship .60 (Lawrence Taylor) (New York Giants vs. Washington)
62 NFC Divisional Playoff .30 (William Perry) (Chicago vs. Washington)
63 NFC Divisional Playoff .30 (Joe Morris) (New York Giants vs. San Francisco)
64 NFC Wild Card Game .65 (Eric Dickerson) (Washington vs. Los Angeles Rams)
65 Super Bowl I .30 (Green Bay vs. Kansas City)
66 Super Bowl II (Bart .50 Starr) (Green Bay vs. Oakland)
67 Super Bowl III .30 (Matt Snell) (New York vs. Baltimore)
68 Super Bowl IV .20 (Kansas City vs. Minnesota)
69 Super Bowl V .45 (Duane Thomas) (Baltimore vs. Dallas)
70 Super Bowl VI .85 (Roger Staubach) (Dallas vs. Miami)
71 Super Bowl VII .60 (Bob Griese, Jim Kiick) (Miami vs. Washington)
72 Super Bowl VIII .60 (Larry Csonka) (Miami vs. Minnesota)
73 Super Bowl IX .75 (Fran Tarkenton) (Pittsburgh vs. Minnesota)
74 Super Bowl X .75 (Franco Harris) (Pittsburgh vs. Dallas)
75 Super Bowl XI .30 (Chuck Foreman) (Oakland vs. Minnesota)

76 Super Bowl XII .60 (Tony Dorsett) (Dallas vs. Denver)
77 Super Bowl XIII 1.00 (Terry Bradshaw) (Pittsburgh vs. Dallas)
78 Super Bowl XIV .30 (Cullen Bryant) (Pittsburgh vs. Los Angeles)
79 Super Bowl XV .30 (Jim Plunkett) (Oakland vs. Philadelphia)
80 Super Bowl XVI .20 (San Francisco vs. Cincinnati)
81 Super Bowl XVII .20 (Washington vs. Miami)
82 Super Bowl XVIII .20 (Los Angeles vs. Washington)
83 Super Bowl XIX (R. 2.50 Craig, Joe Montana) (San Francisco vs. Miami)
84 Super Bowl XX .45 (Wilber Marshall, Richard Dent) (Chicago vs. New England)
85 Super Bowl XXI .70 (Lawrence Taylor) (New York vs. Denver)
86 Super Bowl XXI .45 (Phil Simms) (New York vs. Denver)
87 Super Bowl XXI .50 (Lawrence Taylor, Carl Banks) (Giants erupt in 3rd, Score 17 Points)
88 Super Bowl XXI .50 (Giants Outrun Broncos by only 27 yards)

1988 Fleer Team Action

The final Fleer Team Action set contained 88 cards, including two for each team, 11 Super Bowl cards, special playoff cards and a few league-leader cards at the end of the set. The set was basically structured alphabetically by team nicknames within each conference. There are three subsets: Super Bowls of the Decade (#s 57-67); Playoff Games (#s 68-75) and "League Leading Teams" (#s 76-88). Other highlights are two cards each for Dan Marino, Joe Montana, John Elway and Bo Jackson. Cards were sold in packs of seven, plus three logo stickers.

	MT
Complete Set (88):	18.50
Common Card:	.18

1 Cincinnati Bengals .80 (Boomer Esiason) (A Great Wall)
2 Cincinnati Bengals .18 (Stacking the Odds)
3 Buffalo Bills (Jim 1.25 Kelly) (Play-Action)
4 Buffalo Bills .18 (Buffalo Soldiers)
5 Denver Broncos 1.25 (John Elway) (Sneak Attack)
6 Denver Broncos .18 (Crushing the Opposition)
7 Cleveland Browns .50 (Bernie Kosar, Kevin Mack) (On the Run)
8 Cleveland Browns .65 (Eric Dickerson) (Dogs' Day)
9 San Diego Chargers .25 (Gary Anderson) (A Bolt of Blue)
10 San Diego Chargers .18 (That's a Wrap)
11 Kansas City Chiefs .18 (Last Line of Offense)
12 Kansas City Chiefs .18 (Hard-Hitting in the Heartland)
13 Indianapolis Colts .18 (An Eye to the End Zone)
14 Indianapolis Colts .18 (Free Ball)

15 Miami Dolphins 2.00 (Dan Marino) (Miami Scoring Machine)
16 Miami Dolphins .25 (No Mercy)
17 New York Jets (Ken .25 O'Brien) (On a Roll)
18 New York Jets .18 (Jets Win a Dogfight)
19 Houston Oilers .85 (Warren Moon) (Well-Oiled Machine)
20 Houston Oilers .18 (Hard Shoulder)
21 New England Patriots .25 (Craig James) (A Clean Sweep)
22 New England Patriots 1.00 (Bo Jackson) (A Fall in New England)
23 Los Angeles Raiders 1.50 (Bo Jackson) (Rush Hour in Los Angeles)
24 Los Angeles Raiders .30 (Howie Long) (Cut Me Some Slack)
25 Seattle Seahawks .25 (Curt Warner) (Follow the Leader)
26 Seattle Seahawks .30 (Brian Bosworth) (Pain, But No Gain)
27 Pittsburgh Steelers .18 (Life in the Fast Lane)
28 Pittsburgh Steelers .18 (No Exit)
29 Chicago Bears .18 (Bearly Audible)
30 Chicago Bears .18 (Here, Kitty, Kitty)
31 Tampa Bay Buccaneers 1.00 (Vinny Testaverde) (Letting Loose)
32 Tampa Bay Buccaneers .18 (In the Grasp)
33 St. Louis Cardinals .25 (Neil Lomax) (You've Gotta Hand it to Him)
34 St. Louis Cardinals .35 (Roger Craig) (Stack of Cards)
35 Dallas Cowboys .50 (Herschel Walker) (Take it Away)
36 Dallas Cowboys .40 (Randy White) (Howdy, Partner)
37 Philadelphia Eagles 1.25 (Randall Cunningham) (Eagle in Flight)
38 Philadelphia Eagles .75 (Reggie White) (Buffalo Sandwich)
39 Atlanta Falcons .18 (Rumbling Runner)
40 Atlanta Falcons .18 (The Brink of Disaster)
41 San Francisco 49ers .40 (Roger Craig) (Move Aside)
42 San Francisco 49ers .50 (Ronnie Lott) (Bullies By the Bay)
43 New York Giants .40 (Phil Simms) (Firing a Fastball)
44 New York Giants (A .18 Giant Headache)
45 Detroit Lions .18 (Charge Up the Middle)
46 Detroit Lions .18 (Rocking and Rolling in Motown)
47 Green Bay Packers .18 (Carl Lee) (Gaining Attitude)
48 Green Bay Packers .18 (This Play is a Hit)
49 Los Angeles Rams .40 (Jim Everett) (Rams Lock Horns)
50 Los Angeles Rams .18 (Greetings from L.A.)
51 Washington Redskins .18 (Capital Gains)
52 Washington Redskins .18 (No More Mr. Nice Guy)
53 New Orleans Saints .18 (Roamin' in the Dome)

54 New Orleans Saints .18 (He'll Feel This One Tomorrow)
55 Minnesota Vikings .45 (Wade Wilson) (Passing Fancy)
56 Minnesota Vikings .18 (A Vikings' Siege)
57 Super Bowl XXII .25 (Timmy Smith) (Washington vs. Denver)
58 Super Bowl Checklist .25 (Timmy Smith)
59 Super Bowl Checklist 1.00 (John Elway)
60 Super Bowl XXI .75 (Lawrence Taylor, Carl Banks) (New York vs. Denver)
61 Super Bowl XX .75 (Walter Payton) (Chicago vs. New England)
62 Super Bowl XIX .30 (Roger Craig) (San Francisco vs. Miami)
63 Super Bowl XVIII .50 (Marcus Allen) (Los Angeles Raiders vs. Washington)
64 Super Bowl XVII .18 (Washington vs. Miami)
65 Super Bowl XVI 1.75 (Joe Montana) (San Francisco vs. Cincinnati)
66 Super Bowl XV .25 (Jim Plunkett) (Oakland vs. Philadelphia)
67 Super Bowl XIV .18 (Pittsburgh vs. Los Angeles Rams)
68 NFC Championship .18 (Washington vs. Minnesota)
69 AFC Championship 1.00 (John Elway) (Denver vs. Cleveland)
70 NFC Playoff Game 1.75 (Joe Montana) (Minnesota vs. San Francisco)
71 NFC Playoff Game .18 (Washington vs. Chicago)
72 AFC Playoff Game .30 (Ozzie Newsome, Kevin Mack) (Cleveland vs. Indianapolis)
73 AFC Playoff Game .18 (Denver vs. Houston)
74 NFC Wild Card Game .18 (Minnesota vs. New Orleans)
75 AFC Wild Card Game .18 (Houston vs. Seattle)
76 League Leading Team Rushing .25 (Roger Craig) (San Francisco 49ers)
77 League Leading Team Passing 1.50 (Dan Marino) (Miami Dolphins)
78 League Leading Team Interceptions .18 (New Orleans Saints)
79 League Leading Team Fumble Recovery .18 (Philadelphia Eagles)
80 League Leading Team Sacks .40 (Richard Dent) (Chicago Bears)
81 League Leading Team Defense Against Kickoff Reurns .18 (Buffalo Bills)
82 League Leading Team Defense Against Punt Returns .18 (New York Jets)
83 League Leading Teams Punt Returns .18 (St. Louis Cardinals)
84 League Leading Team Kickoff Returns .18 (Atlanta Falcons)
85 League Leading Team Fewest Fumbles .18 (Pittsburgh Steelers)

86 League Leading Team Fewest Interceptions .50 (Bernie Kosar) (Cleveland Browns)
87 League Leading Team Fewest Points Allowed .18 (Indianapolis Colts)
88 League Leading Team TD's on Returns .40 (Henry Ellard) (Los Angeles Rams)

1990 Fleer

The 1990 "Premier Edition" football card series, Fleer's first player card issue since 1963, was issued in mid-June. Cards were available in 15- and 43-count packs and 45-count three-pack strips. The cards carry full-color printing on the fronts and backs. Card fronts show full-figure action photography, while backs highlight a head shot, stats and text. The 25 cards in the All-Pro subset are different than the other Premier Edition cards. The All-Pro cards contain two photos on each card front - a large facial close-up and a smaller full-figure shot against a silver background. Special metallic links offer for graphic design effect. Jeff George, Andre Ware, Blair Thomas and Percy Snow are featured within the set as first-round draft choices by their respective teams. With the introduction of this football card set, Fleer was the only manufacturer offering a full line of football, baseball and basketball cards.

	MT
Complete Set (400):	7.00
Common Player:	.03
Wax Box:	6.00

1 Harris Barton .03
2 Chet Brooks .03
3 Michael Carter .03
4 Mike Cofer .03
5 Roger Craig .03
6 *Kevin Fagan* .06
7 Charles Haley .03
8 *Pierce Holt* .15
9 Ronnie Lott .03
10 Joe Montana (stats 1.00 reversed on back)
11 Bubba Paris .03
12 Tom Rathman .03
13 Jerry Rice .75
14 John Taylor .20
15 Keena Turner .03
16 Mike Walter .03
17 Steve Young .75
18 Steve Atwater .03
19 Tyrone Braxton .03
20 *Michael Brooks* .15
21 John Elway .50
22 Simon Fletcher .03
23 Bobby Humphrey .03
24 Mark Jackson .03
25 Vance Johnson .03
26 Greg Kragen .03
27 Ken Lanier .03
28 Karl Mecklenburg .03
29 Orson Mobley .03
30 Steve Sewell .03
31 Dennis Smith .03
32 David Treadwell .03
33 Willie Anderson .03
34 Greg Bell .03
35 Henry Ellard .03
36 Jim Everett .03
37 Jerry Gray .03
38 Kevin Greene .03
39 Pete Holohan .03
40 LeRoy Irvin .03
41 Mike Lansford .03
42 *Buford McGee* .08

43 Tom Newberry .03
44 Vince Newsome .03
45 Jackie Slater .03
46 Mike Wilcher .03
47 Matt Bahr .03
48 Brian Brennan .03
49 Thane Gash .03
50 Mike Johnson .03
51 Bernie Kosar .03
52 Reggie Langhorne .03
53 Tim Manoa .03
54 Clay Matthews .03
55 Eric Metcalf .08
56 Frank Minnifield .03
57 Gregg Rakoczy .03
58 Webster Slaughter .03
59 Bryan Wagner .03
60 Felix Wright .03
61 Raul Allegre .03
62 Ottis Anderson .03
63 Carl Banks .03
64 Mark Bavaro .03
65 Maurice Carthon .03
66 Mark Collins .03
67 *Jeff Hostetler* .50
68 Erik Howard .03
69 Pepper Johnson .03
70 Sean Landeta .03
71 Lionel Manuel .03
72 Leonard Marshall .03
73 Dave Meggett .08
74 Bart Oates .03
75 Doug Riesenberg .03
76 Phil Simms .10
77 Lawrence Taylor .10
79 Jerome Brown .03
80 Keith Byars .03
81 Cris Carter .30
82 Randall Cunningham, Byron Evans (error) .20
83 Ron Heller, Byron Evans (error) .10
84 Ron Heller .03
85 Terry Hoage .03
86 Keith Jackson .20
87 Seth Joyner .03
88 Mike Quick .03
89 Mike Schad .03
90 Clyde Simmons .03
91 John Teltschik .03
92 Anthony Toney .03
93 Reggie White .15
94 Ray Berry .03
95 Joey Browner .03
96 Anthony Carter .03
97 Chris Doleman .03
98 Rick Fenney .03
99 *Rich Gannon* .20
100 Hassan Jones .03
101 Steve Jordan .03
102 Rich Karlis .03
103 *Andre Ware* .20
104 Kirk Lowdermilk .03
105 Keith Millard .03
106 Scott Studwell .03
107 Herschel Walker .03
108 Wade Wilson .03
109 Gary Zimmerman .03
110 Don Beebe .10
111 Cornelius Bennett .03
112 Shane Conlan .03
113 Jim Kelly .20
114 Scott Norwood .03
115 Mark Kelso .03
116 Larry Kinnebrew .03
117 Pete Metzelaars .03
118 Scott Radecic .03
119 Andre Reed .20
120 Jim Richter .03
121 Bruce Smith .03
122 Leonard Smith .03
123 Art Still .03
124 Thurman Thomas .50
125 Steve Brown .03
126 Ray Childress .03
127 Ernest Givins .03
128 John Grimsley .03
129 Alonzo Highsmith .03
130 Drew Hill .03
131 Bruce Matthews .03
132 Johnny Meads .03
133 Warren Moon .20
134 Mike Munchak .03
135 Mike Rozier .03
136 Dean Steinkuhler .03
137 Lorenzo White .15
138 Tony Zendejas .03
139 Gary Anderson .03
140 Bubby Brister .08
141 Thomas Everett .03
142 Derek Hill .03
143 Merril Hoge .03
144 Tim Johnson .03
145 Louis Lipps .03
146 David Little .03
147 Greg Lloyd .03
148 Mike Mularkey .03
149 John Rienstra .03
150 Gerald Williams .08
151 Keith Willis .03
152 Rod Woodson .10
153 Tim Worley .03
154 Gary Clark .10
155 Darryl Grant .03
156 Darrell Green .03
157 Joe Jacoby .03

#	Player	MT	#	Player	MT	#	Player	MT
158	Jim Lachey	.03	276	Jerry Ball	.03	390	Jim Jeffcoat	.03
159	Chip Lohmiller	.03	277	Bennie Blades	.03	391	Eugene Lockhart	.03
160	Charles Mann	.03	278	Lomas Brown	.03	392	*Kelvin Martin*	.15
161	Wilber Marshall	.03	279	Mike Cofer	.03	393	Nate Newton	.03
162	Mark May	.03	280	Bob Gagliano	.03	394	Mike Saxon	.03
163	Ralf Mojsiejenko	.03	281	Richard Johnson	.03	395	Derrick Shepard	.03
164	Art Monk	.06	282	Eddie Murray	.03	396	Steve Walsh	.03
165	Gerald Riggs	.03	283	Rodney Peete	.10	397	Joe Montana,	.70
166	Mark Rypien	.15	284	Barry Sanders	1.25		Jerry Rice	
167	Ricky Sanders	.03	285	Eric Sanders	.03	398	Checklist	.03
168	Don Warren	.03	286	Chris Spielman	.03	399	Checklist	.03
169	Robert Brown	.03	287	*Eric Williams*	.10	400	Checklist	.03
170	Blair Bush	.03	288	Neal Anderson	.08			
171	Brent Fullwood	.03	289	Kevin Butler	.08			
172	Tim Harris	.03		(placekicker/PK				
173	Chris Jacke	.03		placekicker/P				
174	Perry Kemp	.03		punter/P punter/PK)				
175	Don Majkowski	.03	290	Jim Covert	.03			
176	Tony Mandarich	.03	291	Richard Dent	.03			
177	Mark Murphy	.03	292	Dennis Gentry	.03			
178	Brian Noble	.03	293	Jim Harbaugh	.15			
179	Ken Ruettgers	.03	294	Jay Hilgenberg	.03			
180	Sterling Sharpe	.20	295	Vestee Jackson	.03			
181	Ed West	.03	296	Steve McMichael	.03			
182	Keith Woodside	.03	297	Ron Morris	.03			
183	Morten Andersen	.03	298	Brad Muster	.03			
184	Stan Brock	.03	299	Mike Singletary	.03			
185	*Jim Dombrowski*	.10	300	James Thornton	.03			
186	John Fourcade	.03	301	Mike Tomczak	.03			
187	Bobby Hebert	.10	302	Keith Van Horne	.03			
188	Craig Heyward	.03	303	Chris Bahr	.03			
189	Dalton Hilliard	.03	304	*Martin Bayless*	.10			
190	Rickey Jackson	.03	305	Marion Butts	.10			
191	Buford Jordan	.03	306	Gill Byrd	.03			
192	Eric Martin	.03	307	Arthur Cox	.03			
193	Robert Massey	.03	308	Burt Grossman	.03			
194	Sam Mills	.03	309	Jamie Holland	.03			
195	Pat Swilling	.03	310	Jim McMahon	.03			
196	Jim Wilks	.03	311	Anthony Miller	.30			
197	*John Alt*	.10	312	Leslie O'Neal	.03			
198	Walker Lee Ashley	.03	313	Billy Ray Smith	.03			
199	Steve DeBerg	.03	314	Tim Spencer	.03			
200	Leonard Griffin	.03	315	*Broderick*	.10			
201	Albert Lewis	.03		*Thompson*				
202	Nick Lowery	.03	316	Lee Williams	.03			
203	Bill Maas	.03	317	Bruce Armstrong	.03			
204	Pete Mandley	.03	318	Tim Goad	.03			
205	*Chris Martin*	.10	319	Steve Grogan	.03			
206	Christian Okoye	.03	320	Roland James	.03			
207	Stephone Paige	.03	321	Cedric Jones	.03			
208	*Kevin Porter*	.10	322	Fred Marion	.03			
209	Derrick Thomas	.20	323	Stanley Morgan	.03			
210	Lewis Billups	.03	324	Robert Perryman	.03			
211	James Brooks	.03	325	Johnny Rembert	.03			
212	Jason Buck	.03	326	Ed Reynolds	.03			
213	*Rickey Dixon*	.10	327	Kenneth Sims	.03			
214	Boomer Esiason	.10	328	John Stephens	.03			
215	David Fulcher	.03	329	*Danny Villa*	.06			
216	Rodney Holman	.03	330	Robert Awalt	.03			
217	Lee Johnson	.03	331	Anthony Bell	.03			
218	Tim Krumrie	.03	332	Rich Camarillo	.03			
219	Tim McGee	.03	333	Earl Ferrell	.03			
220	Anthony Munoz	.03	334	Roy Green	.03			
221	Bruce Reimers	.03	335	Gary Hogeboom	.03			
222	Leon White	.03	336	Cedric Mack	.03			
223	Ickey Woods	.03	337	Freddie Joe Nunn	.03			
224	Harvey Armstrong	.03	338	Luis Sharpe	.03			
225	Michael Ball	.03	339	Vai Sikahema	.03			
226	Chip Banks	.03	340	J.T. Smith	.03			
227	Pat Beach	.03	341	*Tom Tupa*	.08			
228	Duane Bickett	.03	342	Percy Snow	.10			
229	Bill Brooks	.03	343	Mark Carrier (TB)	.03			
230	Jon Hand	.03	344	Randy Grimes	.03			
231	Andre Rison	.25	345	Paul Gruber	.03			
232	Rohn Stark	.03	346	Ron Hall	.03			
233	Donnell Thompson	.03	347	*Jeff George*	1.25			
234	Jack Trudeau	.03	348	Bruce Hill	.03			
235	Clarence Verdin	.03	349	William Howard	.03			
236	Mark Clayton	.03	350	Donald Igwebuike	.03			
237	Jeff Cross	.03	351	*Chris Mohr*	.08			
238	*Jeff Dellenbach*	.10	352	Winston Moss	.08			
239	Mark Duper	.03	353	Ricky Reynolds	.03			
240	Ferrell Edmunds	.03	354	Mark Robinson	.03			
241	Hugh Green	.03	355	Lars Tate	.03			
242	E.J. Junior	.03	356	Vinny Testaverde	.10			
243	Marc Logan	.03	357	Broderick Thomas	.03			
244	Dan Marino	1.00	358	Troy Benson	.03			
245	John Offerdahl	.03	359	*Jeff Criswell*	.10			
246	Reggie Roby	.03	360	Tony Eason	.03			
247	Sammie Smith	.03	361	James Hasty	.03			
248	Pete Stoyanovich	.03	362	Johnny Hector	.03			
249	Marcus Allen	.08	363	Bobby Humphery	.03			
250	*Eddie Anderson*	.10	364	Pat Leahy	.03			
251	Steve Beuerlein	.15	365	Erik McMillan	.03			
252	Mike Dyal	.03	366	Freeman McNeil	.03			
253	Mervyn Fernandez	.03	367	Ken O'Brien	.03			
254	Bob Golic	.03	368	Ron Stallworth	.03			
255	Mike Harden	.03	369	Al Toon	.03			
256	Bo Jackson	.40	370	*Blair Thomas*	.15			
257	Howie Long	.03	371	Aundray Bruce	.03			
258	Don Mosebar	.03	372	Tony Casillas	.03			
259	Jay Schroeder	.03	373	Shawn Collins	.03			
260	Steve Smith	.03	374	Evan Cooper	.03			
261	Greg Townsend	.03	375	Bill Fralic	.03			
262	Lionel Washington	.03	376	Scott Fulhage	.03			
263	Brian Blades	.10	377	Mike Gann	.03			
264	Jeff Bryant	.03	378	Ron Heller	.03			
265	Grant Feasel	.03	379	Keith Jones	.03			
266	Jacob Green	.03	380	Mike Kenn	.03			
267	James Jefferson	.03	381	Chris Miller	.10			
268	Norm Johnson	.03	382	Deion Sanders	.35			
269	Dave Krieg	.03	383	John Settle	.03			
270	Travis McNeal	.03	384	Troy Aikman	.75			
271	Joe Nash	.03	385	Bill Bates	.03			
272	Rufus Porter	.03	386	Willie Broughton	.03			
273	Kelly Stouffer	.03	387	Steve Folsom	.03			
274	John L. Williams	.03	388	Ray Horton	.03			
275	Jim Arnold	.03	389	Michael Irvin	.25			

1990 Fleer All-Pro

These silver cards were distributed randomly in Fleer wax and cello packs. Cards were prone to damage, since the silver coating easily suffered scratches and dings. Cards were issued approximately one to every six to 10 packs.

		MT
Complete Set (25):		7.50
Common Player:		.25
1	Joe Montana	3.00
2	Jerry Rice	2.00
3	Keith Jackson	.50
4	Barry Sanders	3.00
5	Christian Okoye	.25
6	Tom Newberry	.25
7	Jim Covert	.25
8	Anthony Munoz	.25
9	Mike Munchak	.25
10	Jay Hilgenberg	.25
11	Chris Doleman	.25
12	Keith Millard	.25
13	Derrick Thomas	1.00
14	Lawrence Taylor	.75
15	Karl Mecklenburg	.25
16	Reggie White	.60
17	Tim Harris	.25
18	David Fulcher	.25
19	Ronnie Lott	.50
20	Eric Allen	.25
21	Steve Atwater	.25
22	Rich Camarillo	.25
23	Morten Andersen	.25
24	Andre Reed	1.00
25	Rod Woodson	.50

1990 Fleer Stars 'n Stripes

John Offerdahl Linebacker

Issued in eight-card boxes by the Asher Candy Co., a subsidiary of Fleer, these cards were considered by the parent company to be little more than a test set. Collation was bad, and the set was riddled with basic errors. The first edition of Stars 'N Stripes features 80 players from the 1990 Pro Bowl plus 10 college stars selected in the first round of the 1990 NFL draft. All 90 cards carry full-color printing on both sides, with action photography on the front and a head shot of the player on the back. Pro Bowlers are shown in their all-conference uniforms while first-round picks are shown in collegiate action. Front borders have red, white and blue striping. Each package is shrink-wrapped. A full checklist is on the back of each pack.

		MT
Complete Set (90):		25.00
Common Player:		.05
1	Warren Moon	.35
2	Reggie Roby	.05
3	David Treadwell	.05
4	Dave Krieg	.05
5	James Brooks	.20
6	Erik McMillan	.05
7	Rod Woodson	.10
8	Albert Lewis	.05
9	Kevin Ross	.05
10	Frank Minnifield	.05
11	David Fulcher	.07
12	Thurman Thomas	.25
13	Christian Okoye	.05
14	Dennis Smith	.05
15	Johnny Rembert	.05
16	Ray Donaldson	.05
17	John Offerdahl	.15
18	Clay Matthews	.05
19	Shane Conlan	.05
20	Derrick Thomas	.30
21	Tunch Ilken	.05
22	Mike Munchak	.07
23	Max Montoya	.05
24	Kent Hull	.07
25	Greg Kragen	.05
26	Bruce Matthews	.70
27	Howie Long	.10
28	Chris Hinton	.10
29	Anthony Munoz	.10
30	Bruce Smith	.20
31	Ferrell Edmunds	.05
32	Rodney Holman	.05
33	John Elliott	.05
34	Webster Slaughter	.05
35	Anthony Miller	.20
36	Brian Blades	.10
37	Leslie O'Neal	.10
38	Rufus Porter	.10
39	Lee Williams	.05
40	Ed Murray	.05
41	Mark Rypien	.20
42	Randall	.35
	Cunningham	
43	Rich Camarillo	.05
44	Barry Sanders	2.50
45	Dalton Hilliard	.10
46	Eric Allen	.05
47	Brent Fullwood	.05
48	Ron Wolfley	.05
49	Jerry Gray	.05
50	Dave Meggett	.50
51	Roger Craig	.35
52	Carl Lee	.10
53	Ronnie Lott	.20
54	Tim McDonald	.05
55	Joey Browner	.10
56	Mike Singletary	.20
57	Vaughan Johnson	.05
58	Chris Spielman	.05
59	Doug Smith	.05
60	Lawrence Taylor	.50
61	Chris Doleman	.10
62	Guy McIntyre	.05
63	Jay Hilgenberg	.07
64	Randall McDaniel	.05
65	Gary Zimmerman	.05
66	Luis Sharpe	.05
67	Charles Mann	.05
68	Keith Millard	.10
69	Jackie Slater	.05
70	Bill Fralic	.05
71	Henry Ellard	.10
72	Jerry Rice	.65
73	Steve Jordan	.05
74	Sterling Sharpe	.50
75	Keith Jackson	.25
76	Mark Carrier (TB)	.05
77	Kevin Greene	.10
78	Reggie White	.20
79	Jerry Ball	.10
80	Tim Harris	.10
81	Jeff George	2.50
82	Blair Thomas	3.00
83	Cortez Kennedy	.75
84	Junior Seau	.75
85	Mark Carrier	1.25
86	Andre Ware	1.25
87	Chris Singleton	.50
88	Percy Snow	.75
89	Steve Broussard	.90
90	Rodney Hampton	1.75

Values quoted in this guide reflect the retail price of a card — the price a collector can expect to pay when buying a card from a dealer. The wholesale price — that which a collector can expect to receive when selling cards — will be significantly lower, depending on desirability and condition.

1990 Fleer Update

Stan Humphries Quarterback

Fleer's 1990 update football set of 120 cards was sold to hobby shops in boxed form. Cards are arranged alphabetically by teams and are the same style as 1990 Fleer football.

		MT
Complete Set (120):		30.00
Common Player:		.10
Minor Stars:		.20
1	Albert Bentley	.10
2	Dean Biasucci	.10
3	Ray Donaldson	.10
4	Jeff George	2.00
5	*Ray Agnew*	.10
6	*Greg McMurtry*	.10
7	*Chris Singleton*	.10
8	*James Francis*	.10
9	*Harold Green*	.20
10	John Elliott	.10
11	*Rodney Hampton*	.75
12	Gary Reasons	.10
13	Lewis Tillman	.10
14	Everson Walls	.10
15	David Alexander	.10
16	Jim McMahon	.10
17	*Ben Smith*	.10
18	Andre Waters	.10
19	Calvin Williams	.20
20	Earnest Byner	.10
21	*Andre Collins*	.10
22	Russ Grimm	.10
23	*Stan Humphries*	.50
24	Martin Mayhew	.10
25	*Barry Foster*	.30
26	Eric Green	.30
27	Tunch Ilkin	.10
28	Hardy Nickerson	.10
29	Jerrol Williams	.10
30	Mike Baab	.10
31	*Leroy Hoard*	1.50
32	Eddie Johnson	.10
33	William Fuller	.10
34	*Haywood Jeffires*	.30
35	*Don Maggs*	.10
36	Robert Awalt	.10
37	Robert Awalt	.10
38	Dennis McKinnon	.10
39	Ken Norton Jr.	.30
40	Emmitt Smith	25.00
41	*Alexander Wright*	.10
42	Eric Hill	.10
43	*Johnny Johnson*	.20
44	Timm Rosenbach	.10
45	*Anthony*	.20
	Thompson	
46	*Dexter Carter*	.20
47	Eric Davis	.10
48	Keith DeLong	.10
49	*Brent Jones*	.30
50	*Darryl Pollard*	.10
51	*Steve Wallace*	.10
52	Bern Brostek	.10
53	Aaron Cox	.10
54	Cleveland Gary	.10
55	Fred Strickland	.20
56	Pat Terrell	.10
57	Steve Broussard	.10
58	Scott Case	.10
59	*Brian Jordan*	.30
60	Andre Rison	.30
61	Kevin Haverdink	.10
62	Reuben Mayes	.10
63	Steve Walsh	.20
64	Greg Bell	.10
65	Tim Brown	.30
66	Willie Gault	.10
67	*Vance Mueller*	.10
68	Bill Pickel	.10
69	Aaron Wallace	.10
70	Glenn Parker	.10
71	Frank Reich	.20
72	Leon Seals	.10
73	Darryl Talley	.10
74	*Brad Baxter*	.10
75	Jeff Causwell	.10
76	Jeff Lageman	.10
77	*Rob Moore*	3.00
78	Blair Thomas	.20
79	Louis Oliver	.10
80	Tony Paige	.10
81	*Richmond Webb*	.20
82	*Robert Blackmon*	.10
83	*Derrick Fenner*	.20
84	Andy Heck	.10
85	Cortez Kennedy	.30
86	*Terry Wooden*	.10
87	Jeff Donaldson	.10
88	*Tim Grunhard*	.10
89	Emile Harry	.10
90	*Dan Saleaumua*	.20
91	Percy Snow	.10
92	Andre Ware	.20
93	*Darrell Fullington*	.10
94	Mike Merriweather	.10
95	Henry Thomas	.10
96	Robert Brown	.10
97	*Leroy Butler*	.10
98	Anthony Dilweg	.10
99	*Darrel Thompson*	.10
100	Keith Woodside	.10
101	Gary Plummer	.10
102	*Junior Seau*	3.00
103	Billy Joe Tolliver	.20
104	Mark Vlasic	.10
105	Gary Anderson	.10
106	*Ian Beckles*	.10
107	*Reggie Cobb*	.20
108	*Keith McCants*	.20
109	*Mark Bortz*	.10
110	Maury Buford	.10
111	*Mark Carrier*	.10
112	Dan Hampton	.10
113	William Perry	.10
114	Ron Rivera	.10
115	*Lemuel Stinson*	.10
116	*Melvin Bratton*	.10
117	*Gary Kubiak*	.10
118	*Alton Montgomery*	.10
119	*Ricky Nattiel*	.10
120	Checklist	.10

1991 Fleer

Deion Sanders Falcons DB

Fleer's second football set expanded by 32 cards. The issues again included randomly-packed all-star cards. New features included a league leaders subset, a hitters subset, and Pro Visions and All-Pros randomly-packed insert sets.

		MT
Complete Set (432):		6.00
Common Player:		.03
Wax Box:		3.50
1	Shane Conlan	.07
2	John Davis	.03
3	Kent Hull	.05
4	James Lofton	.10
5	Keith McKeller	.07
6	Scott Norwood	.03
7	Nate Odomes	.03
8	Andre Reed	.20
9	Jim Ritcher	.03
10	Leon Seals	.03
11	Bruce Smith	.15
12	Leonard Smith	.03
13	Steve Tasker	.05
14	Thurman Thomas	.40
15	Lewis Billups	.03
16	James Brooks	.15
17	Eddie Brown	.07
18	Carl Carter	.03
19	Boomer Esiason	.10
20	James Francis	.07
21	David Fulcher	.03
22	Harold Green	.15
23	Rodney Holman	.07
24	Bruce Kozerski	.03
25	Tim McGee	.07
26	Anthony Munoz	.07
27	Bruce Reimers	.03
28	Ickey Woods	.10
29	Carl Zander	.03
30	Mike Baab	.03
31	Brian Brennan	.05
32	Rob Burnett	.05
33	Paul Farren	.03
34	Thane Gash	.03
35	David Grayson	.03
36	Mike Johnson	.03
37	Reggie Langhorne	.05
38	Kevin Mack	.07
39	Eric Metcalf	.07
40	Frank Minnifield	.03
41	Gregg Rakoczy	.03
42	Felix Wright	.03
43	Steve Atwater	.07
44	Michael Brooks	.03
45	John Elway	.35
46	Simon Fletcher	.03

#	Player	MT
47	Bobby Humphrey	.20
48	Mark Jackson	.05
49	Keith Kartz	.03
50	Clarence Kay	.03
51	Greg Kragen	.03
52	Karl Mecklenburg	.10
53	Warren Powers	.03
54	Dennis Smith	.05
55	Jim Szymanski	.03
56	David Treadwell	.03
57	Michael Young	.03
58	Ray Childress	.05
59	Curtis Duncan	.05
60	William Fuller	.03
61	Ernest Givins	.07
62	Drew Hill	.10
63	Haywood Jeffires	.15
64	Richard Johnson	.03
65	Sean Jones	.03
66	Don Maggs	.03
67	Bruce Matthews	.05
68	Johnny Meads	.03
69	Greg Montgomery	.03
70	Warren Moon	.20
71	Mike Munchak	.05
72	Allen Pinkett	.05
73	Lorenzo White	.07
74	Pat Beach	.03
75	Albert Bentley	.05
76	Dean Biasucci	.03
77	Duane Bickett	.05
78	Bill Brooks	.05
79	Sam Clancy	.03
80	Ray Donaldson	.03
81	Jeff George	.30
82	Alan Grant	.03
83	Jessie Hester	.03
84	Jeff Herrod	.03
85	Rohn Stark	.03
86	Jack Trudeau	.05
87	Clarence Verdin	.05
88	John Alt	.03
89	Steve DeBerg	.15
90	Tim Grunhard	.03
91	Dino Hackett	.03
92	Jonathan Hayes	.03
93	Albert Lewis	.07
94	Nick Lowery	.03
95	Bill Maas	.03
96	Christian Okoye	.15
97	Stephone Paige	.07
98	Kevin Porter	.03
99	David Szott	.03
100	Derrick Thomas	.25
101	Barry Word	.20
102	Marcus Allen	.15
103	Tom Benson	.03
104	Tim Brown	.07
105	Riki Ellison	.03
106	Mervyn Fernandez	.07
107	Willie Gault	.07
108	Bob Golic	.03
109	Ethan Horton	.03
110	Bo Jackson	.35
111	Howie Long	.10
112	Don Mosebar	.03
113	Jerry Robinson	.03
114	Jay Schroeder	.10
115	Steve Smith	.05
116	Greg Townsend	.05
117	Steve Wisniewski	.05
118	Mark Clayton	.07
119	Mark Duper	.07
120	Ferrell Edmunds	.03
121	Hugh Green	.03
122	David Griggs	.03
123	Jim Jensen	.03
124	Dan Marino	.75
125	Tim McKyer	.03
126	John Offerdahl	.07
127	Louis Oliver	.05
128	Tony Paige	.03
129	Reggie Roby	.03
130	Keith Sims	.03
131	Sammie Smith	.10
132	Pete Stoyanovich	.03
133	Richmond Webb	.07
134	Bruce Armstrong	.05
135	Vincent Brown	.03
136	Hart Lee Dykes	.05
137	Irving Fryar	.05
138	Tim Goad	.03
139	Tom Hodson	.10
140	Maurice Hurst	.03
141	Ronnie Lippett	.03
142	Greg McMurtry	.03
143	Ed Reynold	.03
144	John Stephens	.10
145	Andre Tippett	.05
146	Danny Villa	.03
147	Brad Baxter	.15
148	Kyle Clifton	.03
149	Jeff Criswell	.03
150	James Hasty	.03
151	Jeff Lageman	.03
152	Pat Leahy	.03
153	Rob Moore	.20
154	Al Toon	.10
155	Gary Anderson	.03
156	Bubby Brister	.15
157	Chris Calloway	.03
158	Donald Evans	.03
159	Eric Green	.15
160	Bryan Hinkle	.03
161	Merril Hoge	.07
162	Tunch Ilkin	.03
163	Louis Lipps	.05
164	David Little	.05
165	Mike Mularkey	.03
166	Gerald Williams	.03
167	Warren Williams	.03
168	Rod Woodson	.10
169	Tim Worley	.07
170	Martin Bayless	.03
171	Marion Butts	.07
172	Gill Byrd	.03
173	Frank Cornish	.03
174	Arthur Cox	.03
175	Burt Grossman	.07
176	Anthony Miller	.15
177	Leslie O'Neal	.07
178	Gary Plummer	.03
179	Junior Seau	.25
180	Billy Joe Tolliver	.07
181	Derrick Walker	.03
182	Lee Williams	.07
183	Robert Blackmon	.03
184	Brian Blades	.10
185	Grant Feasel	.03
186	Derrick Fenner	.25
187	Andy Heck	.03
188	Norm Johnson	.03
189	Tommy Kane	.10
190	Cortez Kennedy	.20
191	Dave Krieg	.10
192	Travis McNeal	.03
193	Eugene Robinson	.03
194	Chris Warren	.50
195	John L. Williams	.10
196	Steve Broussard	.10
197	Scott Case	.03
198	Shawn Collins	.05
199	Darion Conner	.03
200	Tory Epps	.03
201	Bill Fralic	.05
202	Michael Haynes	.25
203	Chris Hinton	.05
204	Keith Jones	.03
205	Brian Jordan	.03
206	Mike Kenn	.03
207	Chris Miller	.15
208	Andre Rison	.25
209	Mike Rozier	.07
210	Deion Sanders	.25
211	Gary Wilkins	.03
212	Neal Anderson	.20
213	Trace Armstrong	.05
214	Mark Bortz	.05
215	Kevin Butler	.03
216	Mark Carrier	.10
217	Wendell Davis	.07
218	Richard Dent	.07
219	Dennis Gentry	.03
220	Jim Harbaugh	.15
221	Jay Hilgenberg	.05
222	Steve McMichael	.05
223	Ron Morris	.03
224	Brad Muster	.05
225	Mike Singletary	.07
226	James Thornton	.03
227	Tommie Agee	.07
228	Troy Aikman	1.50
229	Jack Del Rio	.03
230	Issiac Holt	.03
231	Ray Horton	.03
232	Jim Jeffcoat	.03
233	Eugene Lockhart	.03
234	Kelvin Martin	.07
235	Nate Newton	.03
236	Mike Saxon	.03
237	Emmitt Smith	2.00
238	Danny Stubbs	.03
239	Jim Arnold	.03
240	Jerry Ball	.05
241	Benny Blades	.03
242	Lomas Brown	.03
243	Robert Clark	.05
244	Mike Cofer	.03
245	Mel Gray	.03
246	Rodney Peete	.05
247	Barry Sanders	1.25
248	Andre Ware	.15
249	*Matt Brock*	.03
250	Robert Brown	.03
251	Anthony Dilweg	.07
252	Johnny Holland	.03
253	Tim Harris	.03
254	Chris Jacke	.03
255	Perry Kemp	.03
256	Don Majkowski	.15
257	Tony Mandarich	.05
258	Mark Murphy	.03
259	Brian Noble	.03
260	Jeff Query	.05
261	Sterling Sharpe	.10
262	Ed West	.03
263	Keith Woodside	.03
264	Willie Anderson	.10
265	Aaron Cox	.05
266	Henry Ellard	.07
267	Jim Everett	.15
268	Cleveland Gary	.07
269	Kevin Greene	.07
270	Pete Holohan	.03
271	Mike Lansford	.03
272	Duval Love	.03
273	Buford McGee	.05
274	Tom Newberry	.05
275	Jackie Slater	.05
276	Frank Stams	.05
277	Alfred Anderson	.05
278	Joey Browner	.07
279	Anthony Carter	.07
280	Chris Doleman	.10
281	Rick Fenney	.05
282	Rich Gannon	.07
283	Hassan Jones	.05
284	Steve Jordan	.05
285	Carl Lee	.05
286	Randall McDaniel	.05
287	Keith Millard	.10
288	Herschel Walker	.05
289	Wade Wilson	.05
290	Gary Zimmerman	.03
291	Morten Andersen	.05
292	Jim Dombrowski	.03
293	Gill Fenerty	.07
294	Craig Heyward	.07
295	Dalton Hilliard	.10
296	Rickey Jackson	.05
297	Vaughan Johnson	.05
298	Eric Martin	.05
299	Robert Massey	.05
300	Rueben Mayes	.05
301	Sam Mills	.05
302	Brett Perriman	.05
303	Pat Swilling	.05
304	Steve Walsh	.10
305	Ottis Anderson	.03
306	Matt Bahr	.03
307	Mark Bavaro	.03
308	Maurice Carthon	.03
309	Mark Collins	.03
310	John Elliott	.03
311	Rodney Hampton	.60
312	Jeff Hostetler	.10
313	Erik Howard	.03
314	Pepper Johnson	.03
315	Sean Landeta	.03
316	Dave Meggett	.03
317	Bart Oates	.03
318	Phil Simms	.08
319	Lawrence Taylor	.10
320	Reyna Thompson	.03
321	Everson Walls	.03
322	Eric Allen	.03
323	Fred Barnett	.15
324	Jerome Brown	.03
325	Keith Byars	.03
326	Randall Cunningham	.10
327	Byran Evans	.03
328	Ron Heller	.03
329	Keith Jackson	.06
330	Seth Joyner	.03
331	Heath Sherman	.03
332	Clyde Simmons	.03
333	Ben Smith	.03
334	Anthony Toney	.03
335	Andre Waters	.03
336	Reggie White	.15
337	Calvin Williams	.20
338	Anthony Bell	.03
339	Rich Camarillo	.03
340	Roy Green	.03
341	Tim Jorden	.03
342	Cedric Mack	.03
343	Dexter Manley	.03
344	Freddie Joe Nunn	.03
345	Ricky Proehl	.03
346	Tootie Robbins	.03
347	Timm Rosenbach	.10
348	Luis Sharpe	.03
349	Vai Sikahema	.03
350	Anthony Thompson	.03
351	Lonnie Young	.03
352	Dexter Carter	.03
353	Mike Cofer	.03
354	Kevin Fagan	.03
355	Don Griffin	.03
356	Charles Haley	.03
357	Pierce Holt	.03
358	Brent Jones	.03
359	Guy McIntyre	.03
360	Joe Montana	1.00
361	Darryl Pollard	.03
362	Tom Rathman	.03
363	Jerry Rice	.75
364	Bill Romanowski	.03
365	John Taylor	.10
366	Steve Wallace	.03
367	Steve Young	.40
368	Gary Anderson	.03
369	Ian Beckles	.03
370	Mark Carrier (TB)	.07
371	Reggie Cobb	.25
372	Reuben Davis	.03
373	Randy Grimes	.03
374	Wayne Haddix	.03
375	Ron Hall	.03
376	Harry Hamilton	.03
377	Bruce Hill	.03
378	Keith McCants	.03
379	Bruce Perkins	.03
380	Vinny Testaverde	.10
381	Broderick Thomas	.04
382	Jeff Bostic	.03
383	Earnest Byner	.05
384	Gary Clark	.06
385	Darryl Grant	.03
386	Darrell Green	.05
387	Stan Humphries	.35
388	Jim Lachey	.03
389	Charles Mann	.03
390	Wilber Marshall	.03
391	Art Monk	.06
392	Gerald Riggs	.03
393	Mark Rypien	.15
394	Ricky Sanders	.03
395	Don Warren	.03
396	Bruce Smith (H)	.05
397	Reggie White (H)	.08
398	Lawrence Taylor (H)	.08
399	David Fulcher (H)	.03
400	Derrick Thomas (H)	.08
401	Mark Carrier (H)	.05
402	Mike Singletary (H)	.05
403	Charles Haley (H)	.04
404	Leslie O'Neal (H)	.03
405	Tim Harris (H)	.03
407	Steve Atwater (H)	.03
408	Joe Montana (LL)	.50
409	Randall Cunningham (LL)	.08
410	Warren Moon (LL)	.08
411	Andre Rison (LL)	.08
412	Haywood Jeffires (LL)	.06
413	Stephone Paige (LL)	.03
414	Phil Simms (LL)	.08
415	Barry Sanders (LL)	.50
416	Bo Jackson (LL)	.20
417	Thurman Thomas (LL)	.20
418	Emmitt Smith (LL)	1.00
419	John L. Williams (LL)	.03
420	*Nick Bell (R)*	.10
422	*Eric Bienemy*	.10
423	*Russell Maryland*	.45
424	*Derek Russel*	.10
425	*Chris Smith*	.08
426	*Michael Stonebreaker*	.08
427	Patrick Tyrance	.04
428	Kenny Walker	.08
429	Checklist 1	.03
430	Checklist 2	.03
431	Checklist 3	.03
432	Checklist 4	.03

1991 Fleer Pro Visions

These 1991 Fleer inserts feature artwork from artist Terry Smith. The cards are similar to Fleer's baseball Pro Vision counterparts. The card front has a drawing of the player and his name at the bottom. The back, numbered 1 of 10, etc., has a career summary.

		MT
Complete Set (10):		5.00
Common Player:		.25
1	Joe Montana	1.00
2	Barry Sanders	1.50
3	Lawrence Taylor	.40
4	Mike Singletary	.25
5	Dan Marino	2.00
6	Bo Jackson	.50
7	Randall Cunningham	.40
8	Bruce Smith	.25
9	Derrick Thomas	.50
10	Howie Long	.25

1991 Fleer All-Pro

These standard-size cards were random inserts in 1991 Fleer football packs. The card front has a full-color portrait and a smaller picture of the player in action. Card backs contain the card number and a career summary.

		MT
Complete Set (26):		5.00
Common Player:		.10
1	Andre Reed	.35
2	Bobby Humphrey	.10
3	Kent Hull	.10
4	Mark Bortz	.10
5	Bruce Smith	.10
6	Greg Townsend	.10
7	Ray Childress	.10
8	Andre Rison	.40
9	Barry Sanders	1.50
10	Bo Jackson	.50
11	Neal Anderson	.10
12	Keith Jackson	.30
13	Derrick Thomas	.40
14	John Offerdahl	.10
15	Lawrence Taylor	.40
16	Darrell Green	.10
17	Mark Carrier	.10
18	David Fulcher	.10
19	Joe Montana	1.00
20	Jerry Rice	1.50
21	Charles Haley	.10
22	Mike Singletary	.10
23	Nick Lowery	.10
24	Jim Lachey	.10
25	Anthony Munoz	.10
26	Thurman Thomas	1.00

Values quoted in this guide reflect the retail price of a card — the price a collector can expect to pay when buying a card from a dealer. The wholesale price — that which a collector can expect to receive when selling cards — will be significantly lower, depending on desirability and condition.

1991 Fleer Stars 'n Stripes

This 140-card set was produced by Fleer in conjunction with Asher Candy, which sold the set with cherry-flavored candy sticks. Each card front has a color action photo, with the set logo in the upper left corner. The card back has biographical information, statistics and a card number, plus a circle which contains a player mug shot.

		MT
Complete Set (140):		14.00
Common Player:		.10
1	Shane Conlan	.15
2	Kent Hull	.10
3	Andre Reed	.35
4	Bruce Smith	.30
5	Thurman Thomas	.75
6	James Brooks	.15
7	Boomer Esiason	.35
8	David Fulcher	.10
9	Rodney Holman	.10
10	Anthony Munoz	.15
11	Reggie Langhorne	.10
12	Clay Matthews	.10
13	Eric Metcalf	.20
14	Gregg Rakoczy	.10
15	Steve Atwater	.15
16	John Elway	.50
17	Bobby Humphrey	.15
18	Karl Mecklenburg	.15
19	Dennis Smith	.10
20	Ray Childress	.15
21	Ernest Givins	.20
22	Haywood Jeffires	.25
23	Warren Moon	.60
24	Mike Munchak	.10
25	Albert Bentley	.10
26	Jeff George	.25
27	Rohn Stark	.10
28	Clarence Verdin	.10
29	Albert Lewis	.10
30	Nick Lowery	.10
31	Christian Okoye	.10
32	Stephone Paige	.10
33	Derrick Thomas	.25
34	Barry Word	.10
35	Albert Lewis	.50
36	Howie Long	.15
37	Greg Townsend	.10
38	Steve Wisniewski	.10
39	Mark Clayton	.10
40	Dan Marino	1.50
41	John Offerdahl	.10
42	Richmond Webb	.10
43	Irving Fryar	.15
44	Ed Reynolds	.10
45	John Stephens	.10
46	Rob Moore	.25
47	Ken O'Brien	.15
48	Al Toon	.20
49	Bubby Brister	.20
50	Eric Green	.15
51	Merril Hoge	.10
52	David Little	.10
53	Rod Woodson	.20
54	Marion Butts	.15
55	Leslie O'Neal	.10
56	Junior Seau	.25
57	Billy Joe Tolliver	.15
58	Cortez Kennedy	.20
59	Dave Krieg	.15
60	John L. Williams	.10
61	Steve Broussard	.10
62	Bill Fralic	.15
63	Andre Rison	.35
64	Neal Anderson	.15
65	Mark Carrier	.15
66	Richard Dent	.15
67	Jim Harbaugh	.15
68	Mike Singletary	.15
69	Troy Aikman	2.00
70	Emmitt Smith	3.00
71	Mel Gray	.10
72	Rodney Peete	.20
73	Barry Sanders	2.00
74	Tim Harris	.15
75	Perry Kemp	.10
76	Sterling Sharpe	.40
77	Henry Ellard	.15
78	Jim Everett	.20
79	Kevin Greene	.15
80	Jackie Slater	.15
81	Joey Browner	.15
82	Chris Doleman	.15
83	Steve Jordan	.10
84	Carl Lee	.10
85	Herschel Walker	.25
86	Morten Andersen	.15
87	Dalton Hilliard	.10
88	Vaughan Johnson	.10
89	Steve Walsh	.15
90	Ottis Anderson	.15
91	John Elliott	.10
92	Rodney Hampton	.50
93	Sean Landeta	.10
94	Dave Meggett	.15
95	Phil Simms	.25
96	Lawrence Taylor	.35
97	Randall Cunningham	.25
98	Keith Jackson	.20
99	Seth Joyner	.15
100	Reggie White	.35
101	Roy Green	.15
102	Johnny Johnson	.20
103	Ricky Proehl	.15
104	Tootie Robbins	.10
105	Kevin Fagan	.10
106	Charles Haley	.15
107	Guy McIntyre	.10
108	Joe Montana	3.00
109	Tom Rathman	.10
110	Jerry Rice	1.50
111	John Taylor	.20
112	Wayne Haddix	.10
113	Vinny Testaverde	.15
114	Earnest Byner	.15
115	Gary Clark	.20
116	Darrell Green	.15
117	Jim Lachey	.10
118	Art Monk	.25
119	Mark Rypien	.20
120	Nick Bell	.15
121	Eric Bienemy	.10
122	Jarrod Bunch	.15
123	Aaron Craver	.10
124	Lawrence Dawsey	.25
125	Mike Dumas	.10
126	Jeff Graham	.15
127	Paul Justin	.10
128	Darryll Lewis	.15
129	Todd Marinovich	.15
130	Russell Maryland	.20
131	Kanavis McGhee	.10
132	Ernie Mills	.10
133	Herman Moore	.20
134	Godfrey Myles	.10
135	Browning Nagle	.15
136	Esera Tuaolo	.10
137	Mark Vander Poel	.10
138	Harvey Williams	.15
139	Chris Zorich	.15
140	Checklist Card	.10

1992 Fleer Prototypes

These standard-size cards were distributed as two- and three-card panels to promote Fleer's 1992 cards. Each card back clearly identifies it as a prototype card; "1992 Pre-Production Sample" is written on the card back. Otherwise, the cards are identical in design to the regular 1992 Fleer cards.

		MT
Complete Set (6):		10.00
Common Player:		1.00
93	Mike Croel	1.00
191	Tim Brown	1.50
428	Mark Rypien	1.50
435	Terrell Buckley	1.00
457	Barry Sanders (LL)	3.00
475	Emmitt Smith (PV)	4.00

1992 Fleer

Fleer increased its 1992 set to 480 cards and this time used a glossy format. The player's name, position and team logo are at the bottom, along with "Fleer 92". The back has a close-up shot, with career stats and a biography. The cards are numbered alphabetically by team, beginning with Atlanta and ending with Washington. Subsets include Prospects (#s 432-451), League Leaders (#s 452-470), Pro-Visions (#s 471-476) and checklists (#s 477-480). Insert sets include All-Pro (24 cards, in wax packs), Mark Rypien (12, in wax, rack and cellos), Rookie Sensations (20, in cello packs) and Team Leaders (24, in rack packs).

		MT
Complete Set (480):		8.00
Common Player:		.03
Wax Box:		9.00

No	Player	Price
1	Steve Broussard	.03
2	Rick Bryan	.03
3	Scott Case	.03
4	Tony Epps	.03
5	Bill Fralic	.03
6	Moe Gardner	.03
7	Michael Haynes	.25
8	Chris Hinton	.03
9	Brian Jordan	.03
10	Mike Kenn	.03
11	Tim McKyer	.03
12	Chris Miller	.03
13	Erric Pegram	.20
14	Mike Pritchard	.20
15	Andre Rison	.25
16	Jessie Tuggle	.03
17	Carlton Bailey	.03
18	Howard Ballard	.03
19	Don Beebe	.03
20	Cornelius Bennett	.03
21	Shane Conlan	.03
22	Kent Hull	.03
23	Mark Kelso	.03
24	James Lofton	.03
25	Keith McKeller	.03
26	Scott Norwood	.03
27	Nate Odomes	.03
28	Frank Reich	.03
29	Jim Ritcher	.03
30	Leon Seals	.03
31	Darryl Talley	.03
32	Steve Tasker	.03
33	Thurman Thomas	.50
34	Will Wolford	.03
35	Neal Anderson	.10
36	Trace Armstrong	.03
37	Mark Carrier	.03
38	Richard Dent	.03
39	Shaun Gayle	.03
40	Jim Harbaugh	.03
41	Jay Hilgenberg	.03
42	Darren Lewis	.03
43	Steve McMichael	.03
44	Brad Muster	.03
45	William Perry	.03
46	John Roper	.03
47	Lemuel Stinson	.03
48	Stan Thomas	.03
49	Keith Van Horne	.03
50	Tom Waddle	.10
51	Donnell Woolford	.03
52	Chris Zorich	.03
53	Eddie Brown	.03
54	James Francis	.03
55	David Fulcher	.03
56	David Grant	.03
57	Harold Green	.03
58	Rodney Holman	.03
59	Lee Johnson	.03
60	Tim Krumrie	.03
61	Anthony Munoz	.03
62	*Joe Walter*	.10
63	Mike Baab	.03
64	Stephen Braggs	.04
65	*Rodney Brown*	.10
66	Dan Fike	.03
67	*Scott Galbraith*	.10
68	*Randy Hilliard*	.03
69	Michael Jackson	.15
70	Tony Jones	.03
71	Ed King	.03
72	Kevin Mack	.03
73	Clay Matthews	.03
74	Eric Metcalf	.03
75	Vince Newsome	.03
76	John Rienstra	.03
77	Steve Beuerlein	.15
78	Larry Brown	.03
79	Tony Casillas	.03
80	Alvin Harper	.10
81	Issiac Holt	.03
82	Ray Horton	.03
83	Michael Irvin	.40
84	Daryl Johnston	.08
85	Kelvin Martin	.03
86	Nate Newton	.03
87	Ken Norton	.03
88	Jay Novacek	.15
89	Emmitt Smith	2.00
90	Vinson Smith	.03
91	Mark Stepnoski	.03
92	Steve Atwater	.03
93	Mike Croel	.03
94	John Elway	.50
95	Simon Fletcher	.03
96	Gaston Green	.03
97	Mark Jackson	.03
98	Keith Kartz	.03
99	Greg Kragen	.03
100	Greg Lewis	.03
101	Karl Mecklenburg	.03
102	Derek Russell	.15
103	Steve Sewell	.03
104	Dennis Smith	.03
105	David Treadwell	.03
106	Kenny Walker	.03
107	Doug Widell	.03
108	Michael Young	.03
109	Jerry Ball	.03
110	Bennie Blades	.03
111	Lomas Brown	.03
112	*Scott Conover*	.10
113	Ray Crockett	.03
114	Mike Farr	.03
115	Mel Gray	.03
116	Willie Green	.15
117	*Tracy Hayworth*	.15
118	Erik Kramer	.15
119	Herman Moore	.50
120	Dan Owens	.03
121	Rodney Peete	.03
122	Brett Perriman	.03
123	Barry Sanders	1.25
124	Chris Spielman	.03
125	Marc Spindler	.03
126	Tony Bennett	.03
127	Matt Brock	.03
128	LeRoy Butler	.06
129	Johnny Holland	.03
130	Perry Kemp	.03
131	Don Majkowski	.03
132	Mark Murphy	.03
133	Brian Noble	.03
134	Bryce Paup	.03
135	Sterling Sharpe	.10
136	Scott Stephen	.03
137	Darrell Thompson	.03
138	Mike Tomczak	.03
139	Esera Tuaolo	.03
140	Keith Woodside	.03
141	Ray Childress	.03
142	Cris Dishman	.03
143	Curtis Duncan	.03
144	John Flannery	.03
145	William Fuller	.03
146	Ernest Givins	.03
147	Haywood Jeffires	.15
148	Sean Jones	.03
149	Lamar Lathon	.03
150	Bruce Matthews	.03
151	Bubba McDowell	.03
152	Johnny Meads	.03
153	Warren Moon	.20
154	Mike Munchak	.03
155	Al Smith	.03
156	Doug Smith	.03
157	Lorenzo White	.03
158	Michael Ball	.03
159	Chip Banks	.03
160	Duane Bickett	.03
161	Bill Brooks	.03
162	Ken Clark	.03
163	Jon Hand	.03
164	Jeff Herrod	.03
165	Jessie Hester	.03
166	Scott Radecic	.03
167	Rohn Stark	.03
168	Clarence Verdin	.03
169	John Alt	.03
170	Tim Barnett	.03
171	Tim Grunhard	.03
172	Dino Hackett	.03
173	Jonathan Hayes	.03
174	Bill Maas	.03
175	Chris Martin	.03
176	Christian Okoye	.10
177	Stephone Paige	.03
178	*Jayice Pearson*	.10
179	Kevin Porter	.03
180	Kevin Ross	.03
181	Dan Saleaumua	.03
182	*Tracy Simien*	.10
183	Neil Smith	.03
184	Derrick Thomas	.15
185	Robb Thomas	.03
186	Mark Vlasic	.03
187	Barry Word	.15
188	Marcus Allen	.08
189	Eddie Anderson	.03
190	Nick Bell	.10
191	Tim Brown	.10
192	Scott Davis	.03
193	Riki Ellison	.03
194	Mervyn Fernandez	.03
195	Willie Gault	.03
196	Jeff Gossett	.03
197	Ethan Horton	.03
198	Jeff Jaeger	.03
199	Howie Long	.03
200	Ronnie Lott	.10
201	Todd Marinovich	.10
202	Don Mosebar	.03
203	Jay Schroeder	.03
204	Greg Townsend	.03
205	Lionel Washington	.03
206	Steve Wisniewski	.03
207	Flipper Anderson	.03
208	Bern Brostek	.03
209	Robert Delpino	.03
210	Henry Ellard	.03
211	Jim Everett	.03
212	Cleveland Gary	.03
213	Kevin Greene	.03
214	Darryl Henely	.03
215	Damone Johnson	.03
216	Larry Kelm	.03
217	Todd Lyght	.03
218	Jackie Slater	.03
219	Michael Stewart	.03
220	Pat Terrell	.03
221	Robert Young	.03
222	Mark Clayton	.03
223	Bryan Cox	.03
224	Aaron Craver	.03
225	Jeff Cross	.03
226	Mark Duper	.03
227	Harry Galbreath	.03
228	David Griggs	.03
229	Mark Higgs	.15
230	Vestee Jackson	.03
231	John Offerdahl	.03
232	Louis Oliver	.03
233	Tony Paige	.03
234	Reggie Roby	.03
235	Sammie Smith	.03
236	Pete Stoyanovich	.03
237	Richmond Webb	.03
238	Terry Allen	.20
239	Ray Berry	.03
240	Joey Browner	.03
241	Anthony Carter	.03
242	Cris Carter	.03
243	Chris Doleman	.03
244	Rich Gannon	.10
245	Tim Irwin	.03
246	Steve Jordan	.03
247	Carl Lee	.03
248	Randall Cunningham	.03
249	Mike Merriweather	.03
250	Harry Newsome	.03
251	John Randle	.03
252	Henry Thomas	.03
253	Herschel Walker	.03
254	Ray Agnew	.03
255	Bruce Armstrong	.03
256	Vincent Brown	.03
257	Marv Cook	.03
258	Irving Fryar	.03
259	Pat Harlow	.03
260	Tommy Hodson	.03
261	Maurice Hurst	.03
262	Ronnie Lippett	.03
263	Eugene Lockhart	.03
264	Greg McMurty	.03
265	Hugh Millen	.03
266	Leonard Russell	.25
267	Andre Tippett	.03
268	Brent Williams	.03
269	Morten Andersen	.03
270	Gene Atkins	.03
271	Wesley Carroll	.03
272	Jim Dombrowski	.03
273	Quinn Early	.03
274	Gill Fenerty	.03
275	Bobby Hebert	.03
276	Joel Hilgenberg	.03
277	Rickey Jackson	.03
278	Vaughan Johnson	.03
279	Eric Martin	.03
280	Brett Maxie	.03
281	*Fred McAfee*	.10
282	Sam Mills	.03
283	Pat Swilling	.03
284	Floyd Turner	.03
285	Steve Walsh	.03
286	Frank Warren	.03
287	Stephen Baker	.03
288	Maurice Carthon	.03
289	Mark Collins	.03
290	John Elliott	.03
291	Myron Guyton	.03
292	Rodney Hampton	.10
293	Jeff Hostetler	.10
294	Mark Ingram	.03
295	Pepper Johnson	.03
296	Sean Landeta	.03
297	Leonard Marshall	.03
298	Dave Meggett	.03
299	Bart Oates	.03
300	Phil Simms	.10
301	Reyna Thompson	.03
302	Lewis Tillman	.03
303	Brad Baxter	.03
304	Kyle Clifton	.03
305	James Hasty	.03
306	Joe Kelly	.03
307	Jeff Lageman	.03
308	Mo Lewis	.03
309	Erik McMillan	.03
310	Rob Moore	.10
311	Tony Stargell	.03
312	Jim Sweeney	.03
313	Marvin Washington	.03
314	Lonnie Young	.03
315	Eric Allen	.03
316	Fred Barnett	.10
317	Jerome Brown	.03
318	Keith Byars	.03
319	Wes Hopkins	.03
320	Keith Jackson	.10
321	James Joseph	.03
322	Seth Joyner	.03
323	Jeff Kemp	.03
324	Roger Ruzek	.03
325	Clyde Simmons	.03
326	William Thomas	.03
327	Reggie White	.15
328	Calvin Williams	.15
329	Rich Camarillo	.03
330	Ken Harvey	.03
331	Eric Hill	.03
332	Johnny Johnson	.15
333	Ernie Jones	.03
334	Tim Jorden	.03
335	Tim McDonald	.03
336	Freddie Joe Nunn	.03
337	Luis Sharpe	.03
338	Eric Swann	.03
339	Aeneas Williams	.03
340	Gary Anderson	.03
341	Bubby Brsiter	.03
342	Adrian Cooper	.03
343	Barry Foster	.10
344	Eric Green	.03
345	Bryan Hinkle	.03
346	Tunch Ilkin	.03
347	Carnell Lake	.03
348	Louis Lipps	.03
349	David Little	.03
350	Greg Lloyd	.03
351	Neil O'Donnell	.25
352	Dwight Stone	.03
353	Rod Woodson	.03
354	Rod Bernstine	.03
355	Eric Bieniemy	.03
356	Marion Butts	.03
357	Gill Byrd	.03
358	John Friesz	.03
359	Burt Grossman	.03
360	Courtney Hall	.03
361	Ronnie Harmon	.03
362	Shawn Jefferson	.03
363	Nate Lewis	.03
364	*Craig McEwen*	.10
365	Eric Moten	.03
366	Joe Phillips	.03
367	Gary Plummer	.03
368	Henry Rolling	.03
369	Broderick Thompson	.03
370	Harris Barton	.03
371	*Steve Bono*	1.00
372	Todd Bowles	.03
373	Dexter Carter	.03
374	Michael Carter	.03
375	Mike Cofer	.03
376	Keith DeLong	.03
377	Charles Haley	.03
378	Menton Hanks	.03
379	Tim Harris	.03
380	Brent Jones	.03
381	Guy McIntyre	.03
382	Tom Rathman	.03
383	Bill Romanowski	.03
384	Jesse Sapolu	.03
385	John Taylor	.03
386	Steve Young	1.00
387	Robert Blackmon	.03
388	Brian Blades	.03
389	Jacob Green	.03
390	Dwayne Harper	.03
391	Andy Heck	.03
392	Tommy Kane	.03
393	John Kasay	.03
394	Cortez Kennedy	.15
395	Bryan Millard	.03
396	Rufus Porter	.03
397	Eugene Robinson	.03
398	John L. Williams	.03
399	Terry Wooden	.03
400	Gary Anderson	.03
401	Ian Beckles	.03
402	Mark Carrier	.03
403	Reggie Cobb	.03
404	Lawrence Dawsey	.03
405	Ron Hall	.03
406	Keith McCants	.03
407	Charles McRae	.03
408	Tim Newton	.03
409	Jesse Solomon	.03
410	Vinny Testaverde	.03
411	Broderick Thomas	.03
412	Robert Wilson	.03
413	Jeff Bostic	.03
414	Earnest Byner	.03
415	Gary Clark	.03
416	Andre Collins	.03
417	Brad Edwards	.03
418	Kurt Gouveia	.03
419	Darrell Green	.03
420	Joe Jacoby	.03
421	Jim Lachey	.03
422	Chip Lohmiller	.03
423	Charles Mann	.03
424	Wilber Marshall	.03
425	*Ron Middleton*	.10
426	Brian Mitchell	.03
427	Art Monk	.03
428	Mark Rypien	.10
429	Ricky Sanders	.03
430	*Mark Schlereth*	.10
431	Fred Stokes	.03
432	*Edgar Bennett*	.75
433	*Brian Bollinger*	.08
434	*Joe Bowden*	.08
435	*Terrell Buckley*	.35
436	*Willie Clay*	.10
437	Steve Gordon	.10
438	Keith Hamilton	.10
439	Carlos Huerta	.03
440	Matt LaBounty	.03
441	*Amp Lee*	.40
442	Ricardo McDonald	.10
443	Chris Mims	.20
444	*Michael Mooney*	.10
445	*Patrick Rowe*	.10
446	*Leon Searcy*	.10
447	*Siran Stacy*	.10
448	*Kevin Turner*	.15
449	*Tommy Vardell*	.30
450	*Bob Whitfield*	.10
451	*Darryl Williams*	.10
452	Thurman Thomas (LL)	.25
453	Emmitt Smith (LL)	1.00
454	Haywood Jeffires (LL)	.08
455	Michael Irvin (LL)	.20
456	Mark Clayton (LL)	.03
457	Barry Sanders (LL)	.50
458	Pete Stoyanovich (LL)	.03
459	Chip Lohmiller (LL)	.03
460	William Fuller (LL)	.03
461	Pat Swilling (LL)	.03
462	Ronnie Lott (LL)	.03
463	Ray Crockett (LL)	.03
464	Tim McKyer (LL)	.03
465	Aeneas Williams (LL)	.03
466	Rod Woodson (LL)	.03
467	Mel Gray (LL)	.03
468	Nate Lewis (LL)	.03
469	Steve Young (LL)	.03
470	Reggie Roby (LL)	.03
471	John Friesz (PV)	.10
472	Ronnie Lott (PV)	.03
473	Art Monk (PV)	.03
474	Warren Moon (PV)	.10
475	Emmitt Smith (PV)	1.00
476	Thurman Thomas (PV)	.20
477	Checklist Card	.03
478	Checklist Card	.03
479	Checklist Card	.03
480	Checklist Card	.03

1992 Fleer All-Pro

These 24 inserts were randomly included in 1992 Fleer wax packs. The card front has a red-white-and-blue NFL emblem with a cutout player photo superimposed on it. The card background is blue. The player's name and position are also given in gold foil letters. The back has a pink background with a career summary and color portrait. Cards are numbered 1 of 24, etc.

		MT
Complete Set (24):		7.00
Common Player:		.25

No	Player	Price
1	Marv Cook	.25
2	Mike Kenn	.25
3	Steve Wisniewski	.25
4	Jim Ritcher	.25
5	Jim Lachey	.25
6	Michael Irvin	.75
7	Andre Rison	.50
8	Thurman Thomas	.75
9	Barry Sanders	3.00
10	Bruce Matthews	.25
11	Mark Rypien	.25
12	Jeff Jaeger	.25
13	Reggie White	.75
14	Clyde Simmons	.25
15	Pat Swilling	.25
16	Sam Mills	.25
17	Ray Childress	.25
18	Jerry Ball	.25
19	Derrick Thomas	.50
20	Darrell Green	.25
21	Ronnie Lott	.50
22	Steve Atwater	.25
23	Mark Carrier	.25
24	Jeff Gossett	.25

1992 Fleer Rookie Sensations

These 20 cards, featuring some of the NFL's top rookies in 1991, were random inserts in Fleer cello packs. Each card front is designed like a football field, containing a player photo which slants to the left with shadow borders on the left and bottom. "Rookie Sensations" appears at the top of the card, highlighted by gold foil stripes simulating the flight of a football. The player's name is in gold foil at the bottom. The back, which is designed similar to the front, has a career summary and card number.

		MT
Complete Set (20):		25.00
Common Player:		1.00
Minor Stars:		2.00

No	Player	Price
1	Moe Gardner	1.00
2	Mike Pritchard	2.00
3	Stan Thomas	1.00
4	Larry Brown	2.00
5	Todd Lyght	2.00
6	James Joseph	1.00
7	Aeneas Williams	3.00
8	Michael Jackson	4.00
9	Ed King	1.00
10	Mike Croel	1.00
11	Kenny Walker	1.00
12	Tim Barnett	1.00
13	Nick Bell	1.00
14	Todd Marinovich	1.00
15	Leonard Russell	2.00
16	Pat Harlow	1.00
17	Mo Lewis	1.00
18	John Kasay	1.00
19	Lawrence Dawsey	1.00
20	Charles McRae	1.00

1992 Fleer Mark Rypien

Mark Rypien is featured in this 15-card "Performance Highlight" insert set. Cards were randomly included in 1992 Fleer Football packs. Each card front has a dark blue background with a player action photo outlined in the team's colors. Rypien's name and "Performance Highlights" are in gold-foil lettering at the top. Each back has a summary of a different stage of Rypien's career. Cards are numbered on the back.

Rypien, the MVP of Super Bowl XXVI, autographed more than 2,000 cards, which were then randomly inserted. Collectors could also get three extra Rypien cards by mailing in 10 Fleer pack proofs of purchase. These cards are numbered 13-15.

	MT
Complete Set (12):	4.00
Common Rypien:	.40
1 A Matter of Faith (Mark Rypien)	.40
2 Mr. Everything (Mark Rypien)	.40
3 Great Expectations (Mark Rypien)	.40
4 Hill and Valleys (Mark Rypien)	.40
5 Breakout Season (Mark Rypien)	.40
6 The End of the Beginning (Mark Rypien)	.40
7 Bowled Over (Mark Rypien)	.40
8 Watching and Waiting (Mark Rypien)	.40
9 QB Controversy (Mark Rypien)	.40
10 Redemption (Mark Rypien)	.40
11 Pain and Pressure (Mark Rypien)	.40
12 Jubilation (Mark Rypien)	.40

1992 Fleer Team Leaders

These 24 inserts were randomly included in 1992 Fleer rack packs. Each color photo on the front has a black border. The player's name, position, team and "Team Leader" logo are at the bottom of the card in green foil lettering. Each back has a player portrait in an oval frame in the upper left corner, plus a career summary. The background is grayish-blue. A card number is also included on the card back.

	MT
Complete Set (24):	50.00
Common Player:	1.50
Minor Stars:	3.00
1 Chris Miller	1.50
2 Neal Anderson	1.50
3 Emmitt Smith	20.00
4 Chris Spielman	1.50
5 Brian Noble	1.50
6 Jim Everett	3.00
7 Joey Browner	1.50
8 Sam Mills	1.50
9 Rodney Hampton	3.00
10 Reggie White	4.00
11 Tim McDonald	1.50
12 Charles Haley	3.00
13 Mark Rypien	1.50
14 Cornelius Bennett	1.50
15 Clay Matthews	1.50
16 John Elway	15.00
17 Warren Moon	3.00
18 Derrick Thomas	3.00
19 Greg Townsend	1.50
20 Bruce Armstrong	1.50
21 Brad Baxter	1.50
22 Rod Woodson	1.50
23 Marion Butts	1.50
24 Rufus Porter	1.50

1992 Fleer GameDay Draft Day Promos

These 2-1/2" x 4-11/16" cards feature six players who were projected to be top selections in the 1992 NFL draft. Some

of the players have more than one card, to cover various draft day scenarios. The card front has a full-color action photo with a white border. The player's name, team name and GameDay logo are at the bottom of the card. The back has a mug shot of the player, plus a summary of his collegiate accomplishments. Each card has an NFL Draft logo, and the same card number, #1. NFL Properties produced the set. An ad in a May 1992 issue of USA Today offered the 13-card set for $50. Proceeds went to NFL Charities. Dealers and members of the hobby press also received promo sets.

	MT
Complete Set (13):	30.00
Common Player:	2.00
1 Quentin Coryatt (Los Angeles Rams)	4.00
2 Vaughn Dunbar (Atlanta Falcons)	2.00
3 Vaughn Dunbar (San Francisco 49ers)	2.00
4 Vaughn Dunbar (Seattle Seahawks)	2.00
5 Steve Emtman (Indianapolis Colts)	3.00
6 Steve Emtman (Los Angeles Rams)	3.00
7 Desmond Howard (Indianapolis Colts)	4.00
8 Desmond Howard (Washington Redskins)	4.00
9 David Klingler (Kansas City Chiefs)	3.00
10 David Klingler (New York Giants)	3.00
11 Troy Vincent (Cincinnati Bengals)	2.00
12 Troy Vincent (Indianapolis Colts)	2.00
13 Troy Vincent (Green Bay Packers)	2.00

1992 Fleer GameDay

GameDay's debut set features 500 cards with color action photos against a black-and-white background. Each card is bordered with the player's corresponding team color, and team colors are used for the player's name and GameDay, which are printed at the bottom. Card backs are printed horizontally, and contain a close-up photo, biography, statistics and career highlights. The numbered card backs feature the player's name, team name, position and team logo in his team's colors. What distinguishes these cards from other sets is the size - they are 2-1/2" x 4-11/16", which makes them the same size as Topps' 1965 football issue.

	MT
Complete Set (500):	25.00
Common Player:	.10
Wax Box:	20.00
1 Jim Kelly	.75
2 Mark Ingram	.12
3 Travis McNeal	.10
4 Ricky Ervins	.20
5 Joe Montana	3.50
6 Broderick Thompson	.10
7 Darion Conner	.10
8 Jim Harbaugh	.15

9	Harvey Williams	.35
10	Chip Banks	.10
11	Henry Thomas	.10
12	Derek Brown	.20
13	James Joseph	.15
14	Kevin Fagan	.10
15	Chuck Klingbell	.20
16	Harlon Barnett	.10
17	Jim Price	.10
18	Terrell Buckley	.40
19	Paul McJulien	.15
20	James Hasty	.10
21	James Francis	.12
22	Andre Tippett	.12
23	John Elway	1.00
24	Eric Dickerson	.40
25	James Jefferson	.10
26	Danny Noonan	.10
27	Warren Moon	.40
28	Gene Atkins	.10
29	Jessie Hester	.10
30	Mike Mooney, Kevin Smith, Ron Humphrey, Tracy Boyd	.25
31	Toby Caston	.15
32	Howard Dinkins	.15
33	James Patton	.15
34	Walter Reeves	.12
35	Johnny Mitchell	1.25
36	Michael Brim	.20
37	Irving Fryar	.12
38	Lewis Billups	.10
39	Alonzo Spellman	.50
40	John Friesz	.12
41	Patrick Hunter	.10
42	Reuben Davis	.10
43	Tom Myslinski, Shawn Harper, Mark Thomas, Mike Frier	.15
44	Siran Stacy	.15
45	Stephone Paige	.12
46	Eddie Robinson	.15
47	Tracy Scroggins	.35
48	David Klingler	.50
49a	Deion Sanders	.75
49b	Deion Sanders (Last line of card says plays outfield)	.40
50	Tom Waddle	.20
51	Gary Anderson	.12
52	Kevin Butler	.10
53	Bruce Smith	.12
54	Steve Sewell	.10
55	Wesley Walls	.10
56	Lawrence Taylor	.20
57	Mike Merriweather	.12
58	Roman Phifer	.10
59	Shaun Gayle	.10
60	Marc Boutte	.15
61	Tony Mayberry	.15
62	Antone Davis (Card has 9th pick in 91 draft, was 8th)	.10
63	Rod Bernstine	.12
64	Shane Collins	.25
65	Martin Bayless	.10
66	Corey Harris	.15
67	Jason Hanson	.25
68	John Fina	.15
69	Cornelius Bennett	.12
70	Mark Bortz	.10
71	Gary Anderson	.10
72	Paul Siever	.10
73	Flipper Anderson	.12
74	Shane Dronett	.30
75	Brian Noble	.10
76	Tim Green	.10
77	Percy Snow	.10
78	Greg McMurty	.10
79	Dana Hall	.30
80	Tyji Armstrong	.20
81	Gary Clark	.25
82	Steve Emtman	.30
83	Eric Moore	.10
84	Brent Jones	.12
85	Ray Seals	.20
86	James Jones	.10
87	Jeff Hostetler	.25
88	Keith Jackson	.15
89	Gary Plummer	.10
90	Robert Blackmon	.10
91	Larry Tharpe, Mike Brandon, Anthony Hamlet, Mike Pawlawski	.15
92	Greg Skrepenak	.20
93	Kevin Call	.10
94	Clarence Kay	.10
95	William Fuller	.10
96	Troy Auzenne	.15
97	Carl Pickens	3.50
98	Lorenzo White	.25
99	Doug Smith	.10
100	Dale Carter	.40
101	Fred McAfee	.20
102	Jack Del Rio	.10
103	Vaugn Dunbar	.20
104	J.J. Birden	.10
105	Harris Barton	.10
106	Ray Ethridge	.10
107	John Gesek	.10
108	Mike Singletary	.15
109	Mark Rypien	.15
110	Robb Thomas	.10
111	Joe Kelly	.10
112	Ben Smith	.10

113	Neil O'Donnell	.50
114	John L. Williams	.12
115	Mike Sherrard	.12
116	Chad Hennings	.15
117	Henry Ellard	.12
118	Jay Hilgenberg	.10
119	Charles Dimry	.10
120	Chuck Smith	.15
121	Brian Mitchell	.12
122	Eric Allen	.12
123	Nate Lewis	.20
124	Kevin Ross	.12
125	Jimmy Smith	3.50
126	Kevin Smith	.60
127	Larry Webster	.25
128	Marv Cook	.12
129	Calvin Williams	.10
130	Harry Swayne	.15
131	Jimmie Jones	.10
132	Ethan Horton	.10
133	Chris Mims	.20
134	Derrick Thomas	.20
135	Gerald Dixon	.25
136	Gary Zimmerman	.10
137	Robert Jones	.20
138	Steve Broussard	.12
139	David Wyman	.10
140	Ian Beckles	.10
141	Steve Bono	2.00
142	Cris Carter	.10
143	Anthony Cater	.12
144	Greg Townsend	.10
145	Al Smith	.10
146	Troy Vincent	.25
147	Jessie Tuggle	.10
148	David Fulcher	.10
149	Johnny Rembert	.10
150	Ernie Jones	.10
151	Mark Royals	.10
152	Jeff Bryant	.10
153	Vai Sikahema	.12
154	Tony Woods	.10
155	Joe Bowden, Doug Rigby, Marcus Dowdell, Ostell Miles	.15
156	Mark Carrier	.12
157	Joe Nash	.10
158	Keith Van Horne	.10
159	Kelvin Martin	.12
160	Peter Tom Willis	.12
161	Richard Johnson	.10
162	Louis Oliver	.10
163	Nick Lowery	.12
164	Ricky Proehl	.12
165	Terance Mathis	.10
166	Keith Sims	.10
167	E.J. Junior	.10
168	Scott Mersereau	.10
169	Tom Rathman	.12
170	Robert Harris	.15
171	Ashley Ambrose	.15
172	David Treadwell	.10
173	Mark Green	.10
174	Clayton Holmes	.15
175	Tony Sacca	.25
176	Wes Hopkins	.10
177	Mark Wheeler	.15
178	Robert Clark	.10
179	Eugene Daniel	.10
180	Rob Burnett	.10
181	Al Edwards	.10
182	Clarence Verdin	.10
183	Tom Newberry	.10
184	Mike Jones	.10
185	Roy Foster	.10
186	Leslie O'Neal	.12
187	Izel Jenkins	.10
188	Willie Clay, Ty Detmer, Mike Evans, Ed McDaniel	1.00
189	Mike Tomczak	.12
190	Leonard Wheeler	.15
191	Gaston Green	.10
192	Maury Buford	.10
193	Jeremy Lincoln	.15
194	Todd Collins	.15
195	Billy Ray Smith	.10
196	Renaldo Turnbull	.10
197	Michael Carter	.10
198	Rod Milstead, Hesham Ismail, Reggie E. White	.15
199	Shawn Collins	.10
200	Issiac Holt	.10
201	Irv Eatman	.10
202	Anthony Thompson	.12
203	Chester McGlockton	.25
204	Greg Biggs, Chris Crooms, Ephesians Bartley, Curtis Whitley	
205	James Brown	.15
206	Marvin Washington	.10
207	Richard Cooper	.15
208	Jim C. Jensen	.10
209	Sam Seale	.10
210	Andre Reed	.15
211	Thane Gash	.10
212	Randall Hill	.20
213	Brad Baxter	.12
214	Michael Cofer	.10
215	Ray Crockett	.10
216	Tony Mandarich	.10

217	Warren Williams	.10
218	Erik Kramer	.25
219	Bubby Brister	.12
220	Steve Young	1.50
221	Jeff George	.35
222	James Washington	.10
223	Bruce Alexander	.15
224	Broderick Thomas	.12
225	Bern Brostek	.10
226	Brian Blades	.12
227	Troy Aikman	4.00
228	Aaron Wallace	.10
229	Tommy Jeter	.15
230	Russell Maryland	.30
231	Charles Haley	.12
232	James Lofton	.20
233	William White	.10
234	Tim McGee	.10
235	Haywood Jeffires	.15
236	Charles Mann	.12
237	Robert Lyles	.10
238	Rohn Stark	.10
239	Jim Morrissey	.10
240	Mel Gray	.12
241	Barry Word	.20
242	Dave Widell	.15
243	Sean Gilbert	.40
244	Tommy Maddox	.50
245	Bernie Kosar	.15
246	John Roper	.10
247	Mark Higgs	.20
248	Rob Moore	.20
249	Dan Fike	.10
250	Dan Saleaumua	.10
251	Tim Krumrie	.10
252	Tony Casillas	.10
253	Jayice Pearson	.10
254	Dan Marino	4.00
255	Tony Marty	.10
256	Mike Fox	.10
257	Courtney Hawkins	.75
258	Leonard Marshall	.12
259	Willie Gault	.12
260	Al Toon	.12
261	Browning Nagle	.20
262	Ronnie Lott	.20
263	Sean Jones	.10
264	Ernest Givens	.20
265	Ray Donaldson	.10
266	Vaughan Johnson	.12
267	Tom Hodson	.12
268	Chris Doleman	.12
269	Pat Swilling	.10
270	Merril Hoge	.12
271	Bill Maas	.10
272	Sterling Sharpe	1.00
273	Mitchell Price	.10
274	Richard Brown	.15
275	Randall Cunningham	.25
276	Chris Martin	.10
277	Courtney Hall	.10
278	Michael Walter	.10
279	Ricardo McDonald, David Wilson, Sean Lumpkin, Tony Brooks	.10
280	Bill Brooks	.12
281	Jay Schroeder	.12
282	John Stephens	.12
283	William Perry	.12
284	Floyd Turner	.10
285	Carnell Lake	.10
286	Joel Steed	.15
287	Vinnie Clark	.10
288	Ken Norton	.12
289	Eric Thomas	.10
290	Derrick Fenner	.12
291	Tony Smith	.20
292	Eric Metcalf	.12
293	Roger Craig	.12
294	Leon Searcy	.15
295	Tyrone Legette	.15
296	Rob Taylor	.10
297	Eric Williams	.10
298	David Little	.10
299	Wayne Martin	.10
300	Eric Martin	.12
301	Jim Everett	.20
302	Michael Dean Perry	.20
303	Dwayne White	.12
304	Greg Lloyd	.10
305	Ricky Reynolds	.10
306	Anthony Smith	.10
307	Robert Delpino	.10
308	Ken Clark	.10
309	Chris Jacke	.10
310	Reggie Dwight, Anthony McCoy, Craig Thompson, Klaus Wilmsmeyer	.15
311	Doug Widell	.10
312	Sammie Smith	.12
313	Ken O'Brien	.12
314	Timm Rosenbach	.10
315	Jesse Sapolu	.10
316	Ronnie Harmon	.10
317	Bill Pickel	.10
318	Lonnie Young	.10
319	Chris Burkett	.10
320	Ervin Randle	.10
321	Ed West	.10
322	Tom Thayer	.10
323	Keith McKeller	.10
324	Webster Slaughter	.12
325	Duane Bickett	.10
326	Howie Long	.12
327	Sam Mills	.12

328	Mike Golic	.10
329	Bruce Armstrong	.10
330	Pat Terrell	.10
331	Mike Pritchard	.45
332	Audray McMillian	.10
333	Marquez Pope	.12
334	Pierce Holt	.10
335	Erik Howard	.10
336	Jerry Rice	2.25
337	Vinny Testaverde	.12
338	Bart Oates	.10
339	Nolan Harrison	.10
340	Chris Goode	.10
341	Ken Ruettgers	.10
342	Brad Muster	.12
343	Paul Farren	.10
344	Corey Miller	.20
345	Brian Washington	.10
346	Jim Sweeney	.10
347	Keith McCants	.10
348	Louis Lipps	.12
349	Keith Byars	.12
350	Steve Walsh	.10
351	Jeff Jaeger	.10
352	Christian Okoye	.12
353	Cris Dishman	.10
354	Keith Kartz	.10
355	Harold Green	.15
356	Richard Shelton	.15
357	Jacob Green	.10
358	Al Noga	.10
359	Dean Biasucci	.10
360	Jeff Herrod	.10
361	Bennie Blades	.10
362	Mark Vlasic	.12
363	Chris Miller	.15
364	Bubba McDowell	.10
365	Tyrone Stowe	.15
366	Jon Vaughn	.15
367	Winston Moss	.10
368	Levon Kirkland	.15
369	Ted Washington	.10
370	Cortez Kennedy	.25
371	Jeff Feagles	.10
372	Aundray Bruce	.10
373	Michael Irvin	.30
374	Lemuel Stinson	.10
375	Billy Joe Tolliver	.12
376	Anthony Munoz	.12
377	Nate Newton	.10
378	Steve Smith	.12
379	Eugene Chung	.15
380	Bryan Hinkle	.10
381	Dan McGwire	.30
382	Jeff Cross	.10
383	Ferrell Edmunds	.10
384	Craig Heyward	.12
385	Shannon Sharpe	.50
386	Anthony Miller	.12
387	Eugene Lockhart	.10
388	Darryl Henley	.10
389	LeRoy Butler	.10
390	Scott Fulhage	.10
391	Andre Ware	.35
392	Lionel Washington	.10
393	Rick Fenney	.10
394	John Taylor	.20
395	Chris Singleton	.10
396	Monte Coleman	.10
397	Brett Perriman	.12
398	Hugh Millen	.35
399	Dennis Gentry	.10
400	Eddie Anderson	.10
401	Lance Olberding, Eddie Miller, Dwayne Sabb, Corey Widmer	.15
402	Brent Williams	.10
403	Tony Zendejas	.10
404	Donnell Woolford	.10
405	Boomer Esiason	.20
406	Gill Fenerty	.12
407	Kurt Barber	.12
408	William Thomas	.10
409	Keith Henderson	.10
410	Paul Gruber	.12
411	Alfred Oglesby	.10
412	Wendell Davis	.20
413	Robert Brooks	2.00
414	Ken Willis	.10
415	Aaron Cox	.10
416	Thurman Thomas	.50
417	Alton Montgomery	.10
418	Mike Prior	.10
419	Albert Bentley	.10
420	John Randle	.10
421	Dermontti Dawson	.10
422	Phillippi Sparks	.15
423	Michael Jackson	.30
424	Carl Banks	.12
425	Chris Zorich	.10
426	Dwight Stone	.10
427	Bryan Millard	.10
428	Neal Anderson	.20
429	Michael Haynes	.15
430	Michael Young	.10
431	Dennis Byrd	.12
432	Fred Barnett	.15
433	Junior Seau	.50
434	Mark Clayton	.12
435	Marco Coleman	.50
436	Lee Williams	.12
437	Stan Thomas	.10
438	Lawrence Dawsey	.12
439	Tommy Vardell	.60
440	Steve Israel	.20
441	Ray Childress	.12
442	Darren Woodson	.20

443	Lamar Lathon	.10
444	Reggie Roby	.10
445	Eric Green	.12
446	Mark Carrier	.12
447	Kevin Walker	.10
448	Vince Workman	.20
449	Leonard Griffin	.10
450	Robert Porcher	.40
451	Hart Lee Dykes	.10
452	*Thomas McLemore*	.15
453	*Jamie Dukes*	.15
454	Bill Romanowski	.10
455	Deron Cherry	.10
456	Burt Grossman	.10
457	Lance Smith	.10
458	Jay Novacek	.15
459	Erric Pegram	.20
460	Reggie Rutland	.10
461	Rickey Jackson	.12
462	Dennis Brown	.10
463	Neil Smith	.12
464	Rich Gannon	.15
465	Herman Moore	1.00
466	Rodney Peete	.25
467	Alvin Harper	.50
468	Andre Rison	.50
469	Rufus Porter	.10
470	Robert Wilson	.10
471	Phil Simms	.15
472	Art Monk	.15
473	Mike Tice	.10
474	*Quentin Coryatt*	.60
475	Chris Hinton	.10
476	Vance Johnson	.12
477	Kyle Clifton	.10
478	Garth Jax	.10
479	Ray Agnew	.10
480	*Patrick Rowe*	.15
481	Joe Jacoby	.10
482	Bruce Pickens	.10
483	Keith DeLong	.10
484	Eric Swann	.12
485	Steve McMichael	.12
486	Leroy Hoard	.12
487	Rickey Dixon	.10
488	Robert Perryman	.10
489	*Darryl Williams*	.30
490	Emmitt Smith	6.00
491	Dino Hackett	.10
492	Earnest Byner	.12
493	Bucky Richardson, Bernard Dafney, Anthony Davis, Tony Brown	.50
494	*Bill Johnson*	.20
495	*Darryl Ashmore, Joe Campbell, Kelvin Harris, Tim Lester*	.15
496	Nick Bell	.20
497	Jerry Ball	.12
498	*Edgar Bennett, Mark Chmura, Chris Holder, Mazio Royster*	4.00
499	Steve Christie	.10
500	Kenneth Davis	.12

1992 Fleer GameDay Box Tops

Display boxes from 1992 GameDay featured four different box tops, all of which have blank backs and are unnumbered. Although most photos are different than the player's card in the regular-issue set, Randall Cunningham is on all four tops.

		MT
	Complete Set (4):	2.00
	Common Player:	.50
1	Randall Cunningham, Anthony Munoz, Earnest Byner, Jim Everett	.50
2	Haywood Jeffires, Randall Cunningham, Mark Carrier, Vinny Testaverde	.50
3	Howie Long, Thurman Thomas, Randall Cunningham, Jerry Rice	.75
4	Christian Okoye, Pat Swilling, Steve Emtman, Randall Cunningham	.50

1992 Fleer GameDay National

Persons attending the 13th National Sports Card Convention in Atlanta, Ga., were given this 46-card set, which was contained in a black vinyl binder. The convention logo is printed on the card back,

thereby distinguishing the card from GameDay's regular cards. The card front has a color action photo against a black-and-white background. The back has a card number, biographical information, stats and a mug shot. Each card measures 2-1/2" x 4-11/16".

		MT
	Complete Set (46):	40.00
	Common Player:	1.00
1	Deion Sanders	2.50
2	Jim Kelly	2.00
3	Jim Harbaugh	1.25
4	Boomer Esiason	1.50
5	Bernie Kosar	1.50
6	Troy Aikman	7.00
7	John Elway	3.00
8	Rodney Peete	1.00
9	Sterling Sharpe	2.50
10	Warren Moon	2.00
11	Jeff George	2.00
12	Derrick Thomas	2.00
13	Howie Long	1.25
14	Jim Everett	1.50
15	Dan Marino	5.00
16	Chris Doleman	1.00
17	Irving Fryar	1.25
18	Pat Swilling	1.25
19	Lawrence Taylor	2.00
20	Ken O'Brien	1.00
21	Randall Cunningham	2.00
22	Timm Rosenbach	1.00
23	Bubby Brister	1.25
24	John Friesz	2.00
25	Joe Montana	6.00
26	Dan McGwire	1.00
27	Vinny Testaverde	1.25
28	Mark Rypien	1.25
29	Ronnie Lott	2.00
30	Marco Coleman	1.50
31	Rob Moore	2.00
32	Bill Pickel	1.00
33	Brad Baxter	1.25
34	Steve Broussard	1.00
35	Darion Conner	1.00
36	Chris Hinton	1.00
37	Erric Pegram	1.25
38	Jessie Tuggle	1.00
39	Billy Joe Tolliver	1.00
40	David Klingler	2.00
41	Michael Irvin	3.00
42	Emmitt Smith	8.00
43	Quentin Coryatt	1.50
44	Steve Emtman	1.25
45	Deron Cherry	1.00
46	Ricky Ervins	1.00

1992-93 Fleer GameDay Gamebreakers

This 14-card set previewed the 1993 GameDay design and was available at the Super Bowl show. According to the checklist card, there are 5,000 sets produced.

		MT
	Complete Set (14):	7.00
	Common Player:	.20
1	Marco Coleman	.20
2	Bill Cowher (CO)	.20
3	John Elway	1.50
4	Barry Foster	.20
5	Cortez Kennedy	.20
6	James Lofton	.30
7	Art Monk	.30
8	Jerry Rice	2.00
9	Sterling Sharpe	.40
10	Emmitt Smith	4.00
11	Thurman Thomas	.50
12	Gino Torretta	.20
13	Steve Young	1.75
14	Checklist Card	.20

1992-93 Fleer GameDay SB Program

This six-card set was available through 1993 Super Bowl programs (one card per program). The cards are unnumbered and preview the 1993 GameDay set.

		MT
	Complete Set (6):	10.00
	Common Player:	1.00
1	Troy Aikman	5.00
2	Terry Allen	1.75
3	Ray Childress	1.00
4	Marco Coleman	1.00
5	Barry Foster	1.00
6	Sterling Sharpe	1.50

1993 Fleer

This 500-card set features color action photos and UV coating. The card front has a silver metallic border. The player's name is at the bottom in an embossed, transparent lettering. His team and position are at the lower right. The back has a color-coded panel which includes a close-up photo, stats, profile, biography and team logo. Subsets include Award Winners (#s 236-240, 253-257), League Leaders (#s 241-243, 258-262) and Pro Visions (#s 246-248, 263-264). Insert sets include NFL Prospects (30 cards, randomly in foil packs), All-Pro (25, in foil), Rookie Sensations (20, in jumbo packs), Team Leaders (5, in foil) and Steve Young (10, in foil). A nine-card promo sheet was also produced. It measures 7-1/2" x 10-1/2" and previews the 1993 Fleer card design. The nine players are: Steve Young, Kenny Walker, Chip Lohmiller, Kevin Greene, Craig Heyward, Ernie Jones, Emmitt Smith, Keith Byars and a promotional Fleer card.

		MT
	Complete Set (500):	25.00
	Common Player:	.05
	Minor Stars:	.10
	Wax Box:	24.00
1	Dan Saleaumua	.05
2	Bryan Cox	.05
3	Dermontti Dawson	.05
4	Michael Jackson	.05
5	Calvin Williams	.05
6	Terry McDaniel	.05
7	Jack Del Rio	.05
8	Ernie Jones	.05
9	Brad Muster	.05
10	Harold Green	.05
11	Eric Bieniemy	.05
12	Eric Dorsey	.05
13	Fred Barnett	.05
14	Cleveland Gary	.05
15	Darion Conner	.05
16	Jerry Ball	.05
17	Tony Casillas	.05
18	Brian Blades	.05
19	Tony Bennett	.05
20	Reggie Cobb	.05
21	Kurt Gouveia	.05
22	Greg McMurty	.05
23	Kyle Clifton	.05
24	Trace Armstrong	.05
25	Terry Allen	.50
26	Steve Bono	.50
27	Barry Word	.05
28	Mark Duper	.05
29	Nate Newton	.05
30	Will Wolford	.05
31	Curtis Duncan	.05
32	Nick Bell	.05
33	Don Beebe	.05
34	Rich Camarillo	.05
35	Wade Wilson	.05
36	John Taylor	.05
37	Marion Butts	.05
38	Rodney Hampton	.10
39	Seth Joyner	.05
40	Wilber Marshall	.05
41	Bobby Hebert	.05
42	Bennie Blades	.05
43	Thomas Everett	.05
44	Ricky Sanders	.05
45	Matt Brock	.05
46	Lawrence Dawsey	.05
47	Brad Edwards	.05
48	Vincent Brown	.05
49	Jeff Lageman	.05
50	Mark Carrier	.05
51	Cris Carter	.50
52	Brent Jones	.05
53	Barry Foster	.05
54	Derrick Thomas	.10
55	Scott Zolak	.05
56	Mark Stepnoski	.05
57	Eric Metcalf	.05
58	Al Smith	.05

61	Ronnie Harmon	.05
62	Cornelius Bennett	.05
63	Chris Chandler	.05
64	Toi Cook	.05
65	Tim Krumrie	.05
66	Gill Byrd	.05
67	Mark Jackson	.05
68	Tim Harris	.05
69	Shane Conlan	.05
70	Moe Gardner	.05
71	Lomas Brown	.05
72	Charles Haley	.05
73	Mark Rypien	.05
74	LeRoy Butler	.05
75	Steve DeBerg	.05
76	Darrell Green	.05
77	Marv Cook	.05
78	Chris Burkett	.05
79	Richard Dent	.05
80	Roger Craig	.05
81	Amp Lee	.05
82	Eric Green	.05
83	Willie Davis	.05
84	Mark Higgs	.05
85	Carlton Haselrig	.05
86	Tommy Vardell	.05
87	Haywood Jeffires	.05
88	Tim Brown	.10
89	Randall McDaniel	.05
90	John Elway	1.00
91	Ken Harvey	.05
92	Joel Hilgenberg	.05
93	Steve Wallace	.05
94	Stan Humphries	.10
95	Greg Jackson	.05
96	Clyde Simmons	.05
97	Jim Everett	.05
98	Michael Hayes	.05
99	Mel Gray	.05
100	Alvin Harper	.10
101	Art Monk	.10
102	Brett Favre	2.00
103	Keith McCants	.05
104	Charles Mann	.05
105	Leonard Russell	.05
106	Mo Lewis	.05
107	Shaun Gayle	.05
108	Chris Doleman	.05
109	Tim McDonald	.05
110	Louis Oliver	.05
111	Greg Lloyd	.10
112	Chip Banks	.05
113	Sean Jones	.05
114	Ethan Horton	.05
115	Kenneth Davis	.05
116	Johnny Johnson	.05
117	Vaughan Johnson	.05
118	Scott Fenner	.05
119	Nate Lewis	.05
120	Pepper Johnson	.05
121	Heath Sherman	.05
122	Darryl Henley	.05
123	Pierce Holt	.05
124	Herman Moore	.50
125	Tommy Kane	.05
126	Jackie Harris	.05
127	Michael Irvin	.30
128	Hardy Nickerson	.05
129	Chip Lohmiller	.05
130	Andre Tippett	.05
131	Leonard Marshall	.05
132	Craig Heyward	.05
133	Anthony Carter	.05
134	Tom Rathman	.05
135	Lorenzo White	.05
136	Nick Lowery	.05
137	John Offerdahl	.05
138	Neil O'Donnell	.10
139	Clarence Verdin	.05
140	Ernest Givins	.05
141	Todd Marinovich	.05
142	Jeff Wright	.05
143	Freddie Joe Nunn	.05
144	William Perry	.05
145	Daniel Stubbs	.05
146	Morten Anderson	.05
147	David Meggett	.05
148	Andre Waters	.05
149	Todd Lyght	.05
150	Chris Miller	.05
151	Rodney Peete	.05
152	Jim Jeffcoat	.05
153	Cortez Kennedy	.05
154	Johnny Holland	.05
155	Ricky Reynolds	.05
156	Kevin Greene	.05
157	Jeff Herrod	.05
158	Bruce Matthews	.05
159	Anthony Smith	.05
160	Henry Jones	.05
161	Rob Burnett	.05
162	Eric Swann	.05
163	Tom Waddle	.05
164	Alfred Williams	.05
165	*Darren Carrington*	.05
166	Mike Sherrard	.05
167	Frank Reich	.05
168	*Anthony Newman*	.05
169	Mike Pritchard	.05
170	Andre Ware	.05
171	Daryl Johnston	.05
172	Rufus Porter	.05
173	Reggie White	.05
174	*Charles Mincy*	.05
175	Pete Stoyanovich	.05
176	Rod Woodson	.05
177	Anthony Johnson	.05
178	Rod Woodson	.05

(Note: entries for 59, 60, 179, 180 partially visible)

59	Mark Stepnoski	.05
60	Al Smith	.05
179	Anthony Johnson	.05
180		.05

181	Cody Carlson	.05
182	Gaston Green	.05
183	Audray McMillian	.05
184	Mike Johnson	.05
185	Aeneas Williams	.05
186	Jarrod Bunch	.05
188	Quinn Early	.05
189	James Hasty	.05
190	Darryl Talley	.05
191	Jon Vaughn	.05
192	Andre Rison	.10
193	Kelvin Pritchett	.05
194	Ken Norton	.05
195	Chris Warren	.25
196	Sterling Sharpe	.10
197	Christian Okoye	.05
198	Richmond Webb	.05
199	James Francis	.05
200	Reggie Langhorne	.05
201	J.J. Birden	.05
202	Aaron Wallace	.05
203	Henry Thomas	.05
204	Clay Matthews	.05
205	Robert Massey	.05
206	Donnell Woolford	.05
207	Ricky Watters	.20
208	Wayne Martin	.05
209	Rob Moore	.05
210	Steve Tasker	.05
211	Jackie Slater	.05
212	Steve Young	1.00
213	Barry Sanders	1.25
214	Jay Novacek	.05
215	Eugene Robinson	.05
216	Duane Bickett	.05
217	Broderick Thomas	.05
218	David Fulcher	.05
219	Rohn Stark	.05
220	Warren Moon	.10
221	Steve Wisniewski	.05
222	Nate Odomes	.05
224	Byron Evans	.05
225	Mark Collins	.05
227	Sam Mills	.05
228	Marvin Washington	.05
229	Thurman Thomas	.15
230	Brent Williams	.05
231	Jesse Tuggle	.05
232	Chris Spielman	.05
233	Emmitt Smith	2.00
234	John L. Williams	.05
235	Jeff Cross	.05
236	Chris Doleman	.05
237	John Elway (AW)	.20
238	Barry Foster (AW)	.05
239	Cortez Kennedy (AW)	.05
240	Steve Young (AW)	.50
241	Barry Foster (LL)	.05
242	Warren Moon (LL)	.05
243	Sterling Sharpe (LL)	.05
244	Emmitt Smith (LL)	1.00
245	Thurman Thomas (LL)	.10
246	Michael Irvin (PV)	.15
247	Steve Young (PV)	.05
248	Barry Foster (PV)	.05
249	Checklist	.05
250	Checklist	.05
251	Checklist	.05
252	Checklist	.05
253	Troy Aikman (AW)	.40
254	Jason Hanson (AW)	.05
255	Carl Pickens (AW)	.20
256	Santana Dotson	.05
257	Dale Carter	.05
258	Clyde Simmons	.05
259	Audray McMillian	.05
260	Henry Jones	.05
261	Deion Sanders	.20
262	Haywood Foster	.05
263	Deion Sanders	.20
264	Andre Reed	.05
265	Vince Workman	.05
266	Robert Brown	.05
267	Ray Agnew	.05
268	Ronnie Lott	.05
269	Wesley Carroll	.05
270	John Randle	.05
271	Rodney Culver	.05
272	David Alexander	.05
273	Troy Aikman	1.00
274	Bernie Kosar	.05
275	Scott Case	.05
276	Dan McGwire	.05
277	John Alt	.05
278	Dan Marino	2.00
279	Santana Dotson	.05
280	Johnny Mitchell	.05
281	Alonzo Spellman	.05
282	Adrian Cooper	.05
283	Gary Clark	.05
285	Eric Martin	.05
286	Jesse Solomon	.05
287	Carl Banks	.05
288	Harris Barton	.05
289	Jim Harbaugh	.10
290	Bubba McDowell	.05
291	*Anthony McDowell*	.05
292	Terrell Buckley	.05
293	Bruce Armstrong	.05
294	Kurt Barber	.05
295	Reginald Jones	.05
296	Steve Jordan	.05
297	Kerry Cash	.05
298	Ray Crockett	.05
299	Keith Byars	.05

300	Russell Maryland	.05
301	Johnny Bailey	.05
302	Vinnie Clark	.05
303	Terry Wooden	.05
304	Harvey Williams	.05
305	Marco Coleman	.05
306	Mark Wheeler	.05
307	Greg Townsend	.05
308	Tim McGee	.05
309	Donald Evans	.05
310	Randal Hill	.05
312	Dalton Hilliard	.05
313	Howard Ballard	.05
314	Phil Simms	.05
315	Jerry Rice	1.00
316	Courtney Hall	.05
317	Darren Lewis	.05
318	Greg Montgomery	.05
319	Paul Gruber	.05
320	*George Koonce*	.05
321	Eugene Chung	.05
322	Mike Brim	.05
323	Patrick Hunter	.05
324	Todd Scott	.05
325	Steve Emtman	.05
326	*Andy Harmon*	.05
327	Larry Brown	.05
328	Chuck Cecil	.05
329	Tim McKyer	.05
330	Jeff Bryant	.05
331	Tim Barnett	.05
332	Irving Fryar	.05
333	Tyji Armstrong	.05
334	Brad Baxter	.05
335	Shane Collins	.05
336	Jeff Graham	.05
337	Ricky Proehl	.05
338	Tommy Maddox	.05
339	Jim Dombrowski	.05
340	Bill Brooks	.05
341	*Dave Brown*	.30
342	Eric Davis	.05
345	Mike Munchak	.05
346	Ron Hall	.05
347	Brian Noble	.05
348	Chris Singleton	.05
349	Boomer Esiason	.05
350	Ray Roberts	.05
351	Gary Zimmerman	.05
352	Quentin Coryatt	.05
353	Willie Green	.05
354	Randall Cunningham	.05
355	Kevin Smith	.05
356	Michael Dean Perry	.05
357	Tim Green	.05
358	Dwayne Harper	.05
359	Dale Carter	.05
360	Keith Jackson	.05
361	Martin Mayhew	.05
362	Brian Washington	.05
363	Earnest Byner	.05
364	David Johnson	.05
365	Timm Rosenbach	.05
367	Vaughn Dunbar	.05
368	Phil Hansen	.05
369	Mike Fox	.05
370	Dana Hall	.05
371	Junior Seau	.10
373	Eddie Robinson	.05
374	*Milton Mack*	.05
375	Mike Prior	.05
376	Jerome Henderson	.05
377	Scott Mersereau	.05
378	Neal Anderson	.05
379	Harry Newsome	.05
380	John Baylor	.05
381	Bill Fralic	.05
382	Mark Bavaro	.05
383	Robert Jones	.05
384	Tyronne Stowe	.05
385	Deion Sanders	.50
386	Robert Blackman	.05
387	Neil Smith	.05
388	Mark Ingram	.05
389	Mark Carrier	.05
390	Browning Nagle	.05
391	Ricky Evans	.05
392	Carnell Lake	.05
393	Luis Sharpe	.05
395	Tommy Barnhardt	.05
396	Mark Kelso	.05
397	*Kent Graham*	.10
398	Bill Romanowski	.05
399	Anthony Miller	.05
400	John Roper	.05
401	Lamar Rogers	.05
402	Troy Auzenne	.05
403	Webster Slaughter	.05
404	David Brandon	.05
405	Chris Hinton	.05
406	Andy Heck	.05
407	Tracy Simien	.05
408	Troy Vincent	.05
409	Jason Hanson	.05
410	*Rod Jones*	.05
411	Al Noga	.05
412	Ernie Mills	.05
413	Willie Gault	.05
414	Henry Ellard	.05
415	Rickey Jackson	.05
416	Bruce Smith	.05
417	Derek Brown	.05
418	Kevin Fagan	.05
419	Gary Plummer	.05
420	Wendell Davis	.05
421	Craig Thompson	.05
422	Wes Hopkins	.05

423	Ray Childress	.05
424	Pat Harlow	.05
425	Howie Long	.05
427	Sean Salisbury	.05
428	*Dwight Hollier*	.05
429	Brett Perriman	.10
430	Donald Hollas	.05
431	Jim Lachey	.05
432	Darren Perry	.05
433	Lionel Washington	.05
434	Sean Gilbert	.05
435	Gene Atkins	.05
436	Jim Kelly	.15
437	Ed McCaffrey	.05
438	Don Griffin	.05
439	Jerrol Williams	.05
440	Bryce Paup	.10
441	Darryl Williams	.05
442	Vai Sikahema	.05
443	Cris Dishman	.05
444	Kevin Mack	.05
445	Winston Moss	.05
447	Mike Merriweather	.05
448	Tony Paige	.05
449	Robert Porcher	.05
450	Ricardo McDonald	.05
451	Danny Copeland	.05
452	Tony Tolbert	.05
453	Eric Dickerson	.05
454	Willie Anderson	.05
455	Dave Krieg	.05
456	*Brad Lamb*	.05
457	Bart Oates	.05
458	Guy McIntyre	.05
459	Stanley Richard	.05
460	Edgar Bennett	.05
461	Pat Carter	.05
462	Eric Allen	.05
463	William Fuller	.05
464	James Jones	.05
465	Chester McGlockton	.05
467	Tim Grunhard	.05
468	Jarvis Williams	.05
469	Tracy Scroggins	.05
470	David Klingler	.05
471	Andre Collins	.05
472	Erik Williams	.05
473	Eddie Anderson	.05
474	Marc Boutte	.05
475	Joe Montana	1.00
476	Andre Reed	.10
477	Lawrence Taylor	.10
478	Jeff George	.15
479	Chris Mims	.05
480	Ken Ruettgers	.05
481	Roman Phifer	.05
482	William Thomas	.05
483	Lamar Lathon	.05
484	Vinny Testaverde	.05
485	Mike Kenn	.05
487	Chris Martin	.05
488	Maurice Hurst	.05
489	Pat Swilling	.05
490	Carl Pickens	.75
491	Tony Smith	.05
492	James Washington	.05
493	Jeff Hostetler	.10
494	Jeff Chadwick	.05
495	Kevin Ross	.05
496	Jim Ritcher	.05
497	Jessie Hester	.05
498	Burt Grossman	.05
499	Keith Van Horne	.05
500	Gerald Robinson	.05

1993 Fleer All-Pros

Twenty-five of the NFL's best are featured on these cards, which were randomly inserted into 1993 Fleer foil packs. Each card front is horizontal with white borders and features a color photo of the player superimposed against a black-and-white action photo. The "All-Pro" logo and player's name are in gold foil at the bottom. Each card back is numbered and includes a career summary on a background of team color-coded panels.

	MT
Complete Set (25):	40.00

	Common Player:	1.00
	Minor Stars:	2.00
1	Steve Atwater	1.00
2	Rich Camarillo	1.00
3	Ray Childress	1.00
4	Chris Doleman	1.00
5	Barry Foster	1.00
6	Henry Jones	1.00
7	Cortez Kennedy	1.00
8	Nick Lowery	1.00
9	Wilber Marshall	1.00
10	Bruce Matthews	1.00
11	Randall McDaniel	1.00
12	Audray McMillian	1.00
13	Sam Mills	1.00
14	Jay Novacek	1.00
15	Jerry Rice	8.00
16	Junior Seau	2.00
17	Sterling Sharpe	3.00
18	Clyde Simmons	1.00
19	Emmitt Smith	20.00
20	Derrick Thomas	2.00
21	Steve Wallace	1.00
22	Richmond Webb	1.00
23	Steve Wisniewski	1.00
24	Rod Woodson	1.00
25	Steve Young	8.00

1993 Fleer Prospects

Thirty players from the 1993 NFL draft are featured on these cards, which were randomly inserted in 1993 Fleer foil packs. Each card front has a color cut-out photo of the player on a gold background with blue borders. The "1993 NFL Prospect" logo, player's name, round he was drafted in and team name are in gold foil on the front, too. The back has a close-up shot and a career summary, plus a card number.

	MT
Complete Set (30):	70.00
Common Player:	1.50

1	Drew Bledsoe	25.00
2	Garrison Hearst	10.00
3	John Copeland	1.50
4	Eric Curry	1.50
5	Curtis Conway	7.00
6	Lincoln Kennedy	1.50
7	Jerome Bettis	10.00
8	Patrick Bates	1.50
9	Brad Hopkins	1.50
10	Tom Carter	1.50
11	Irv Smith	1.50
12	Robert Smith	7.00
13	Deon Figures	1.50
14	Leonard Renfro	1.50
15	O.J. McDuffie	5.00
16	Dana Stubblefield	3.00
17	Todd Kelly	1.50
18	George Teague	1.50
19	Demetrius DeBose	1.50
20	Coleman Rudolph	1.50
21	Carlton Gray	1.50
22	Troy Drayton	1.50
23	Natrone Means	8.00
24	Qadry Ismail	4.00
25	Gino Torretta	1.50
26	Carl Simpson	1.50
27	Glyn Milburn	3.00
28	Chad Brown	3.00
29	Reggie Brooks	1.50
30	Billy Joe Hobert	1.50

1993 Fleer Rookie Sensations

These cards feature 20 of the NFL's top players beginning their NFL careers. The cards have the player's name and "Rookie Sensations" logo in gold foil on the front. The backs have a player profile and card number, 1 of 20, etc. Cards were random inserts in 1993 Fleer football jumbo packs.

	MT
Complete Set (20):	100.00
Common Player:	5.00

1	Dale Carter	5.00
2	Eugene Chung	5.00
3	Marco Coleman	5.00
4	Quentin Coryatt	7.00
5	Santana Dotson	7.00
6	Vaughn Dunbar	5.00
7	Steve Emtman	5.00
8	Sean Gilbert	7.00
9	Dana Hall	5.00
10	Jason Hanson	5.00
11	Robert Jones	5.00
12	David Klingler	5.00
13	Amp Lee	7.00
14	Troy Auzenne	5.00
15	Ricardo McDonald	5.00
16	Chris Mims	5.00
17	Johnny Mitchell	7.00
18	Carl Pickens	20.00
19	Darren Perry	5.00
20	Troy Vincent	5.00

1993 Fleer Team Leaders

Five premiere players in the NFL are featured in this insert set; cards were randomly inserted into 1993 Fleer foil packs. The card front features a player action photo against a blue background with lightning streaks. "Team Leader" and the player's name are in gold foil at the bottom. The backs have a blue background with gold border and contain another color photo and career summary, plus a card number (1 of 5 etc.).

	MT
Complete Set (5):	35.00
Common Player:	3.00

1	Brett Favre	15.00
2	Derrick Thomas	3.00
3	Steve Young	7.00
4	John Elway	10.00
5	Cortez Kennedy	3.00

1993 Fleer Steve Young

The NFL's 1992 MVP, Steve Young, is featured in this "Performance Highlights" issue from Fleer. Each card front has an action photo with a white border, plus the set and player's name stamped in gold foil. The back has a close-up shot and player profile against a red background with white borders. The cards are numbered on the backs. Cards 11-13 were available through Fleer through a mail-in offer only, for 10 wrappers and $1. Young also signed more than 2,000 cards, which were randomly inserted.

	MT
Complete Set (10):	10.00
Common Young:	1.00
Autograph:	120.00
Mail-In Young (11-13):	2.00

1993 Fleer Fruit of the Loom

Specially-marked packages of Fruit of the Loom underwear contained six of these cards, which were produced by Fleer. The cards are similar in design to Fleer's regular 1993 set, except a Fruit of the Loom logo appears on the card front. The photos are the same, but the card number, which is on the back, indicates the card is x of 50, etc.

	MT
Complete Set (50):	100.00
Common Player:	1.50

1	Andre Rison	4.00
2	Deion Sanders	6.00
3	Neal Anderson	2.00
4	Jim Harbaugh	2.00
5	Bernie Kosar	2.50
6	Eric Metcalf	3.00
7	John Elway	7.00
8	Karl Mecklenburg	1.50
9	Sterling Sharpe	5.00
10	Reggie White (Traded to Green Bay Packers)	4.00
11	Steve Emtman	2.00
12	Jeff George	3.00
13	Willie Gault	2.00
14	Jim Kelly	5.00
15	Thurman Thomas	5.00
16	Harold Green	2.00
17	Carl Pickens	1.50
18	Troy Aikman	17.00
19	Emmitt Smith	20.00
20	Barry Sanders	10.00
21	Pat Swilling (Traded to Detroit Lions)	2.00
22	Haywood Jeffires	2.50
23	Warren Moon	3.00
24	Derrick Thomas	3.00
25	Christian Okoye	2.00
26	Flipper Anderson	1.50
27	Jim Everett	2.50
28	Keith Jackson	2.50
29	Dan Marino	15.00
30	Andre Tippett	1.50
31	Lawrence Taylor	2.50
32	Randall Cunningham	2.50
33	Barry Foster	4.00
34	Rod Woodson	3.00
35	Jerry Rice	8.00
36	Steve Young	6.00
37	Reggie Cobb	1.50
38	Roger Craig	2.00
39	Chris Doleman	1.50
40	Morten Andersen	1.50
41	Dalton Hilliard	1.50
42	Ronnie Lott (Traded to New York Jets)	2.50
43	Chris Chandler	1.50
44	Stan Humphries	3.00
45	Junior Seau	4.00
46	Brian Blades	2.00
47	Cortez Kennedy	2.00
48	Wilber Marshall	1.50
49	Art Monk	2.50
50	Checklist Card	1.50

1993 Fleer GameDay

GameDay used the same format as its 1992 debut set - oversized cards which measure 2-1/2" x 4-11/16" - but cut back the number of cards by 20. However, the 1993 set included three insert sets - "GameBreakers" (20 cards of impact players), "Rookie Standouts" (16 of the top 1993 NFL draft picks), and "Second-Year Stars" (16 of the game's top sophomores). All three types were randomly inserted in packs.

	MT
Complete Set (480):	50.00
Common Player:	.10
Minor Stars:	.20
Wax Box:	35.00

1	Troy Aikman	2.00
2	Terry Allen	.10
3	Ray Childress	.10
4	Marco Coleman	.10
5	Barry Foster	.20
6	Sterling Sharpe	.30
7	Steve McMichael	.10
8	Steve Young	2.00
9	Derrick Thomas	.20
10	John Elway	1.00
11	*Drew Bledsoe*	7.00
12	Jim Kelly	.30
13	Dan Marino	3.00
14	Mo Lewis	.10
15	David Klingler	.20
16	Darrell Green	.10
17	James Francis	.10
18	*John Copeland*	.30
19	Terry McDaniel	.10
20	Barry Sanders	2.00
21	Deion Sanders	1.00
22	Emmitt Smith	4.00
23	Marion Butts	.10
24	Darryl Talley	.10
25	Randall Cunningham	.20
26	Rod Woodson	.20
27	Terrell Buckley	.10
28	Michael Haynes	.10
29	Tony Jones	.10
30	Santana Dotson	.10
31	Lomas Brown	.10
32	Eric Metcalf	.10
33	Morten Andersen	.10
34	Reggie Cobb	.10
35	Ferrell Edmunds	.10
36	Joe Montana	3.00
37	Ken Harvey	.10
38	Rodney Hampton	.30
39	Kurt Gouveia	.10
40	Ken Norton	.10
41	Frank Reich	.10
42	Kevin Greene	.10
43	Cleveland Gary	.10
44	Maurice Hurst	.10
45	Troy Vincent	.10
46	*Eric Curry*	.30
47	*Curtis Conway*	1.25
48	Christian Okoye	.10
49	Tunch Ilkin	.10
50	Michael Irvin	.50
51	Bart Oates	.10
52	Pepper Johnson	.10
53	Vaughan Johnson	.10
54	Lawrence Taylor	.20
55	Junior Seau	.40
56	Michael Brooks	.10
57	Neal Anderson	.10
58	D.J. Johnson	.10
59	Seth Joyner	.10
60	Marvin Washington	.10
61	Ernest Givins	.10
62	*Jaime Feilds*	.10
63	Vincent Brown	.10
64	Randall McDaniel	.10
65	Tommy Maddox	.10
66	*Steve Everitt*	.30
67	Brian Noble	.10
68	Bryce Paup	.10
69	Brad Baxter	.10
70	*Demetrius DuBose*	.20
71	Duane Bickett	.10
72	Mark Rypien	.10
73	Harris Barton	.10
74	Bruce Matthews	.10
75	Irving Fryar	.10
76	Steve Wisniewski	.10
77	*Will Shields*	.10
78	*Tom Carter*	.40
79	Steve Emtman	.10
80	Jerry Rice	2.00
81	Art Monk	.20
82	Tony Tolbert	.10
83	Johnny Mitchell	.10
84	*Deon Figures*	.30
85	Marv Cook	.10
86	Darion Conner	.10
87	Ricky Proehl	.10
88	Tony Bennett	.10
89	Jay Schroeder	.10
90	Neil Smith	.10
91	Jarvis Williams	.10
92	James Hasty	.10
93	Anthony Miller	.20
94	*Thomas Smith*	.20
95	Richard Dent	.10
96	Henry Jones	.10
97	Renaldo Turnbull	.10
98	Jason Hanson	.10
99	Cortez Kennedy	.20
100	Brett Favre	3.00
101	Anthony Carter	.10
102	Cris Carter	.20
103	*Dana Stubblefield*	1.00
104	Nick Bell	.10
105	Marcus Allen	.20
106	Neil O'Donnell	.40
107	Steve DeBerg	.10
108	Leonard Russell	.10
109	Ethan Horton	.10
110	William Perry	.10
111	Don Griffin	.10
112	Clarence Verdin	.10
113	Amp Lee	.10
114	Earnest Byner	.10
115	Ricky Reynolds	.10
116	Tom Waddle	.10
117	Robert Jones	.10
118	Willie Davis	.10
119	Chris Miller	.10
120	Drew Hill	.10
121	Warren Moon	.30
122	Willie Anderson	.10
123	*George Teague*	.30
124	John L. Williams	.10
125	Ed McCaffrey	.10
126	Eric Green	.10
127	Scott Mersereau	.10
128	Charles Mann	.10
129	Todd Lyght	.10
130	Rodney Culver	.10
131	Richmond Webb	.10
132	*John Parrella*	.10
133	*Reggie Brooks*	.50
134	*Lincoln Kennedy*	.10
135	Tim Johnson	.10
136	Robert Massey	.10
137	Keith Jackson	.20
138	Alfred Williams	.10
139	Leroy Hoard	.10
140	Jessie Tuggle	.10
141	Chris Mims	.10
142	Herschel Walker	.10
143	Clyde Simmons	.10
144	Dana Hall	.10
145	Nate Newton	.10
146	Dennis Smith	.10
147	Rich Camarillo	.10
148	Chris Spielman	.10
149	Jim Dombrowski	.10
150	Steve Beuerlein	.10
151	Mark Clayton	.10
152	Lee Williams	.10
153	*Robert Smith*	1.50
154	Greg Jackson	.10
155	Jay Hilgenberg	.10
156	Howard Ballard	.10
157	*Mike Compton*	.10
158	Brent Williams	.10
159	Tommy Kane	.10
160	Barry Word	.10
161	Darren Lewis	.10
162	Steve Atwater	.10
163	Gary Clark	.10
164	Donnell Woolford	.10
165	Henry Thomas	.10
166	Tim Brown	.25
167	Andre Ware	.10
168	Jackie Harris	.20
169	Browning Nagle	.10
170	Chris Singleton	.10
171	Ronnie Lott	.10
172	Leonard Marshall	.10
173	Dale Carter	.10
174	Bruce Armstrong	.10
175	Tommy Vardell	.10
176	Bubba McDowell	.10
177	*Patrick Bates*	.20
178	Tyji Armstrong	.10
179	Keith Sims	.10
180	Boomer Esiason	.20
181	Ricky Watters	.40
182	Keith Sims	.10
183	Burt Grossman	.10
184	Richard Cooper	.10
185	Marc Boutte	.10
186	Shane Conlan	.10
187	Luis Sharpe	.10
188	*O.J. McDuffie*	2.00
189	Harvey Williams	.10
190	Blair Thomas	.10
191	Charles Haley	.10
192	Chip Lohmiller	.10
193	Vinny Testaverde	.20
194	Desmond Howard	.20
195	Johnny Johnson	.10
196	Bennie Blades	.10
197	Jeff Wright	.10
198	Cody Carlson	.10
199	*Michael Barrow*	.10
200	Pat Swilling	.10
201	*Willie Roaf*	.25
202	Mike Walter	.10
203	Kevin Fagan	.10
204	Nate Odomes	.10
205	Michael Dean Perry	.10
206	Bruce Pickens	.10
207	Mel Gray	.10
208	Jack Trudeau	.10
209	Ricky Sanders	.10
210	Bobby Hebert	.10
211	Craig Heyward	.10
212	Eric Bieniemy	.10
213	Andre Rison	.20
214	Bernie Kosar	.10
215	Lester Holmes	.10
216	*Marcus Buckley*	.20
217	Tony Casillas	.10
218	Cornelius Bennett	.10
219	Kyle Clifton	.10
220	Kirk Lowdermilk	.10
221	Leon Searcy	.10
222	Gary Anderson	.10
223	Tim Barnett	.10
224	Gene Atkins	.10
225	Jeff Cross	.10
226	*Darrin Smith*	.25
227	Rohn Stark	.10
228	Chris Warren	.50
229	Eric Allen	.10
230	*Wayne Simmons*	.10
231	Al Smith	.10
232	*Reggie Rivers*	.10
233	Kevin Smith	.10
234	Vince Workman	.10
235	Thurman Thomas	.30
236	*Kevin Williams*	1.50
237	Dan McGwire	.10
238	Greg Lloyd	.10
239	*Ray Buchanan*	.25
240	Shannon Sharpe	.20
241	Ricardo McDonald	.10

242	Aaron Wallace	.10
243	Chris Hinton	.10
244	Bill Romanowski	.10
245	Randal Hill	.10
246	Ray Agnew	.10
247	Todd Kelly	.10
248	John Stephens	.10
249	Sean Sailsbury	.10
250	Roger Craig	.10
251	Dave Krieg	.10
252	Brian Blades	.10
253	Jerrod Bunch	.10
254	Phil Simms	.10
255	Keith Van Horne	.10
256	Jim Price	.10
257	Garrison Hearst	3.00
258	Derrick Walker	.10
259	Mike Pritchard	.10
260	Leonard Renfro	.10
261	Rodney Peete	.10
262	Jeff Bryant	.10
263	Dermontti Dawson	.10
264	Greg McMurty	.10
265	Wendell Davis	.10
266	Kerry Cash	.10
267	Jackie Slater	.10
268	Sam Mills	.10
269	Carlton Bailey	.10
270	Mark Wheeler	.10
271	Darren Perry	.10
272	Todd Scott	.10
273	John Holland	.10
274	Mike Croel	.10
275	Shane Dronett	.10
276	Andre Collins	.10
277	Eric Swann	.10
278	Jessie Hester	.10
279	Bryan Cox	.10
280	Mark Jackson	.10
281	Thomas Everett	.10
282	James Lofton	.10
283	Carl Pickens	1.00
284	Mark Carrier (Cleve.)	.10
285	Heath Sherman	.10
286	Chris Burkett	.10
287	Coleman Rudolph	.10
288	Todd Marinovich	.10
289	Nate Lewis	.10
290	Fred Barnett	.10
291	Jim Lachey	.10
292	Jerry Ball	.10
293	Jeff George	.50
294	William Fuller	.10
295	Courtney Hawkins	.10
296	Kelvin Martin	.10
297	Trace Armstrong	.10
298	Carl Banks	.10
299	Terry Kirby	.75
301	John Offerdahl	.10
302	Wilber Marshall	.10
303	Guy McIntyre	.10
304	Steve Wallace	.10
305	Chris Slade	.50
306	Anthony Newman	.10
307	Chip Banks	.10
308	Carlton Gray	.10
309	Wayne Martin	.10
310	Tom Rathman	.10
311	Shaun Gayle	.10
312	Billy Joe Hobert	.50
313	Matt Brock	.10
314	Arthur Marshall	.25
315	Wade Wilson	.10
316	Michael Jackson	.10
317	Bruce Kozerski	.10
318	Reggie Langhorne	.10
319	Jerrol Williams	.10
320	Aeneas Williams	.10
321	Tony McGee	.50
322	Carl Simpson	.10
323	Russell Maryland	.10
324	Nick Lowery	.10
325	Steve Tasker	.10
326	Alvin Harper	.40
327	Haywood Jeffires	.10
328	Hardy Nickerson	.10
329	Alonzo Spellman	.10
330	Eric Dickerson	.10
331	Scott Zolak	.10
332	Darryl Henley	.10
333	Daniel Stubbs	.10
334	Andy Heck	.10
335	Mark May	.10
336	Roosevelt Potts	.25
337	Erik Howard	.10
338	Sean Gilbert	.10
339	Jerome Bettis	3.00
340	Darren Carrington	.20
341	Gill Byrd	.10
342	John Friesz	.10
343	Roger Harper	.10
344	Fred Stokes	.10
345	Stanley Richard	.10
346	Johnny Bailey	.10
347	David Wyman	.10
348	Merril Hoge	.10
349	Brett Perriman	.10
350	Kelvin Pritchett	.10
351	Rod Bernstine	.10
352	Jim Ritcher	.10
353	Mark Stepnoski	.10
354	Jeff Lageman	.10
355	Darrin Gordon	.50
356	Don Mosebar	.10
357	Simon Fletcher	.10
358	Charles Mincy	.20
359	Ron Hall	.10
360	Brent Jones	.10
361	Byron Evans	.10
362	Dan Footman	.20
363	Mark Higgs	.10
364	Brian Washington	.10
365	Brad Hopkins	.10
366	Tracy Simien	.10
367	Derrick Fenner	.10
368	Lorenzo White	.10
369	Marvin Jones	.25
370	Chris Doleman	.10
371	Jeff Harrod	.10
372	Jim Harbaugh	.10
373	Jim Jeffcoat	.10
374	Michael Strahan	.10
375	Ricky Ervins	.10
376	Joel Hilgenberg	.10
377	Curtis Duncan	.10
378	Glyn Milburn	.75
379	Jack Del Rio	.10
380	Eric Martin	.10
381	David Meggett	.10
382	Jeff Hostetler	.20
383	Greg Townsend	.10
384	Brad Muster	.10
385	Irv Smith	.50
386	Chris Jacke	.10
387	Ernest Dye	.20
388	Henry Ellard	.10
389	John Taylor	.10
390	Chris Chandler	.10
391	Larry Centers	.50
392	Henry Rolling	.10
393	Dan Saleaumua	.10
394	Moe Gardner	.10
395	Darryl Williams	.10
396	Paul Gruber	.10
397	Dwayne Harper	.10
398	Pat Harlow	.10
399	Rickey Jackson	.10
400	Quentin Coryatt	.10
401	Steve Jordan	.10
402	Rick Mirer	.75
403	Howard Cross	.10
404	Mike Johnson	.10
405	Broderick Thomas	.10
406	Stan Humphries	.40
407	Ronnie Harmon	.10
408	Andy Harmon	.10
409	Troy Drayton	.75
410	Dan Williams	.10
411	Mark Bavaro	.10
412	Bruce Smith	.10
413	Elbert Shelley	.20
414	Tim McGee	.10
415	Tim Harris	.10
416	Rob Moore	.10
417	Rob Burnett	.10
418	Howie Long	.10
419	Chuck Cecil	.10
420	Carl Lee	.10
421	Anthony Smith	.10
422	Jeff Graham	.20
423	Clay Matthews	.10
424	Jay Novacek	.10
425	Phil Hansen	.10
426	Andre Hastings	.75
427	Toi Cook	.10
428	Rufus Porter	.10
429	Mike Pitts	.10
430	Eddie Robinson	.10
431	Herman Moore	1.00
432	Erik Kramer	.10
433	Mark Carrier (Chi.)	.10
434	Natrone Means	3.00
435	Carnell Lake	.10
436	Carlton Haselrig	.10
437	John Randle	.10
438	Louis Oliver	.10
439	Ray Roberts	.10
440	Leslie O'Neal	.10
441	Reggie White	.25
442	Dalton Hilliard	.10
443	Tim Krumrie	.10
444	Leroy Butler	.10
445	Greg Kragen	.10
446	Anthony Johnson	.10
447	Aydrey McMillian	.10
448	Lawrence Dawsey	.10
449	Pierce Holt	.10
450	Brad Edwards	.10
451	J.J. Birden	.10
452	Mike Munchak	.10
453	Tracy Scroggins	.10
454	Mike Tomczak	.10
455	Harold Green	.10
456	Vaughn Dunbar	.10
457	Calvin Williams	.10
458	Pete Stoyanovich	.10
459	Willie Gault	.10
460	Ken Ruettgers	.10
461	Eugene Robinson	.10
462	Larry Brown	.10
463	Antonio London	.10
464	Andre Reed	.10
465	Daryl Johnston	.10
466	Karl Mecklenburg	.10
467	David Lang	.10
468	Bill Brooks	.10
469	Jim Everett	.10
470	Qadry Ismail	1.00
471	Vai Sikahema	.10
472	Andre Tippett	.10
473	Eugene Chung	.10
474	Cris Dishman	.10
475	Tim McDonald	.10
476	Freddie Joe Nunn	.10
477	Checklist #1	.10
478	Checklist #2	.10
479	Checklist #3	.10
480	Checklist #4	.10

1993 Fleer GameDay Game Breakers

SEATTLE SEAHAWKS CORTEZ KENNEDY — GameDay

These 2-1/2" x 4-3/4" cards were randomly inserted in 1993 GameDay packs. Twenty top offensive players are represented. The card front has a color action photo against a black-and-white game action photo, with a black border. The player's and set's name are stamped in gold foil at the bottom. Each back has a close-up picture of the player, his name, his jersey number and a recap of his 1992 season. The backs are borderless and are numbered 1 of 20, etc.

		MT
Complete Set (20):		30.00
Common Player:		.50
Minor Stars:		1.00
1	Troy Aikman	4.00
2	Brett Favre	4.00
3	Steve Young	4.00
4	Dan Marino	6.00
5	Joe Montana	4.00
6	Jim Kelly	1.00
7	Emmitt Smith	7.00
8	Ricky Watters	1.00
9	Barry Foster	.50
10	Barry Sanders	4.00
11	Michael Irvin	1.50
12	Thurman Thomas	1.00
13	Sterling Sharpe	1.00
14	Jerry Rice	4.00
15	Andre Rison	.50
16	Deion Sanders	2.00
17	Harold Green	.50
18	Lorenzo White	.50
19	Terry Allen	.50
20	Haywood Jeffires	.50

1993 Fleer GameDay Rookie Standouts

ERIC CURRY — GameDay '93 THE OFFICIAL NFL CARD

These cards are devoted to the top 16 players chosen in the 1993 NFL Draft. Cards, which measure 2-1/2" x 4-3/4", were random inserts in 1993 GameDay packs. Each card front is dark blue and features a color action photo against a black-and-white action background. The player's and set's name is stamped in gold foil at the bottom. The card back, numbered 1 of 16, etc., is white and includes the player's name and uniform number, plus a color photo and recap of his 1992 season.

		MT
Complete Set (16)		25.00
Common Player:		.50
Minor Stars:		1.00
1	Drew Bledsoe	7.00
2	Rick Mirer	3.00
3	Garrison Hearst	3.00
4	Jerome Bettis	4.00
5	Marvin Jones	.50
6	Reggie Brooks	.50
7	O.J. McDuffie	2.00
8	Qadry Ismail	1.00
9	Glyn Milburn	1.00
10	Andre Hastings	.50
11	Curtis Conway	2.00
12	Eric Curry	.50
13	John Copeland	.50
14	Kevin Williams	2.00
15	Patrick Bates	.50
16	Lincoln Kennedy	.50

1993 Fleer GameDay Second-Year Stars

Sixteen top rookies from the 1992 NFL season are featured on these cards, which were random inserts in 1993 GameDay packs. Each card is 2-1/2" x 4-3/4" and has a green-bordered front which includes a color action photo against a black-and-white action background. The set's and player's name are stamped in gold foil at the bottom. The back has a shot of the player, his name and jersey number and a recap of his 1992 season. Each is numbered 1 of 16, etc.

		MT
Complete Set (16):		10.00
Common Player:		.25
Minor Stars:		2.00
1	Carl Pickens	2.00
2	David Klingler	.50
3	Santana Dotson	.25
4	Chris Mims	.25
5	Steve Emtman	.25
6	Marco Coleman	.25
7	Robert Jones	.25
8	Dale Carter	.25
9	Troy Vincent	.25
10	Tracy Scroggins	.25
11	Vaughn Dunbar	.25
12	Quentin Coryatt	.25
13	Dana Hall	.25
14	Terrell Buckley	.25
15	Tommy Vardell	.25
16	Johnny Mitchell	.25

1994 Fleer

Fleer's 1994 set includes 474 player cards and six checklist cards. There are also 137 different insert cards produced; one was randomly included in every pack. The regular cards have a color-enhanced photo and gold-foil stamped player signature on the front, plus his team logo, position and name. Card backs have two large photos with a screened-back action shot and a closeup player portrait. Insert cards have full-bleed photos; the regular cards have a white frame around the photo on the card front.

		MT
Complete Set (480):		20.00
Common Player:		.05
Minor Stars:		.10
Wax Box:		45.00
1	Michael Bankston	.05
2	Steve Beuerlein	.05
3	John Booty	.05
4	Rich Camarillo	.05
5	Chuck Cecil	.05
6	Larry Centers	.05
7	Gary Clark	.05
8	Garrison Hearst	.50
9	Eric Hill	.05
10	Randal Hill	.05
11	Ron Moore	.10
12	Ricky Proehl	.05
13	Luis Sharpe	.05
14	Clyde Simmons	.05
15	Tyrone Stow	.05
16	Eric Swann	.05
17	Aeneas Williams	.05
18	Darion Conner	.05
19	Moe Gardner	.05
20	Jumpy Geathers	.05
21	Jeff George	.05
22	Roger Harper	.05
23	Bobby Hebert	.10
24	Pierce Holt	.05
25	David Johnson	.05
26	Mike Kenn	.05
27	Lincoln Kennedy	.05
28	Erric Pegram	.05
29	Mike Pritchard	.10
30	Andre Rison	.15
31	Deion Sanders	.40
32	Tony Smith	.05
33	Jesse Solomon	.05
34	Jessie Tuggle	.05
35	Don Beebe	.05
36	Cornelius Bennett	.05
37	Bill Brooks	.05
38	Kenneth Davis	.05
39	John Fina	.05
40	Phil Hansen	.05
41	Kent Hull	.05
42	Henry Jones	.05
43	Jim Kelly	.15
44	Pete Metzelaars	.05
45	Marvcus Patton	.05
46	Andre Reed	.10
47	Frank Reich	.05
48	Bruce Smith	.05
49	Thomas Smith	.05
50	Darryl Talley	.05
51	Steve Tasker	.05
52	Thurman Thomas	.20
53	Jeff Wright	.05
54	Neal Anderson	.05
55	Trace Armstrong	.05
56	Troy Auzenne	.05
57	Joe Cain	.15
58	Mark Carrier	.05
59	Curtis Conway	.10
60	Richard Dent	.05
61	Shaun Gayle	.05
62	Andy Heck	.05
63	Dante Jones	.05
64	Erik Kramer	.05
65	Steve McMichael	.05
66	Terry Obee	.05
67	Vinson Smith	.05
68	Alonzo Spellman	.05
69	Tom Waddle	.05
70	Donnell Woolford	.05
71	Tim Worley	.05
72	Chris Zorich	.05
73	Mike Brim	.05
74	John Copeland	.05
75	Derrick Fenner	.05
76	James Francis	.05
77	Harold Green	.05
78	Rod Jones	.05
79	David Klingler	.10
80	Bruce Kozerski	.05
81	Tim Krumrie	.05
82	Ricardo McDonald	.05
83	Tim McGee	.05
84	Tony McGee	.05
85	Louis Oliver	.05
86	Carl Pickens	.30
87	Jeff Query	.05
88	Daniel Stubbs	.05
89	Steve Tovar	.05
90	Alfred Williams	.05
91	Darryl Williams	.05
92	Rob Burnett	.05
93	Mark Carrier	.05
94	Leroy Hoard	.05
95	Michael Jackson	.05
96	Mike Johnson	.05
97	Pepper Johnson	.05
98	Tony Jones	.05
99	Clay Matthews	.05
100	Eric Metcalf	.05
101	Stevon Moore	.05
102	Michael Dean Perry	.05
103	Anthony Pleasant	.05
104	Vinny Testaverde	.10
105	Eric Turner	.05
106	Tommy Vardell	.05
107	Troy Aikman	.75
108	Larry Brown	.05
109	Dixon Edwards	.05
110	Charles Haley	.05
111	Alvin Harper	.15
112	Michael Irvin	.20
113	Jim Jeffcoat	.05
114	Daryl Johnston	.05
115	Leon Lett	.05
116	Russell Maryland	.05
117	Nate Newton	.05
118	Ken Norton Jr.	.05
119	Jay Novacek	.05
120	Darrin Smith	.05
121	Emmitt Smith	2.00
122	Kevin Smith	.05
123	Mark Stepnoski	.05
124	Tony Tolbert	.05
125	Erik Williams	.05
126	Kevin Williams	.40
127	Darren Woodson	.05
128	Steve Atwater	.05
129	Rod Bernstine	.05
130	Ray Crockett	.05
131	Mike Croel	.05
132	Robert Delpino	.05
133	Shane Dronett	.05
134	Jason Elam	.05
135	John Elway	.40
136	Simon Fletcher	.05
137	Greg Kragen	.05
138	Karl Mecklenburg	.05
139	Glyn Milburn	.10
140	Anthony Miller	.10
141	Derek Russell	.05
142	Shannon Sharpe	.10
143	Dennis Smith	.05
144	Dan Williams	.05
145	Gary Zimmerman	.05
146	Bennie Blades	.05
147	Lomas Brown	.05
148	Bill Fralic	.05
149	Mel Gray	.05
150	Willie Green	.05
151	Jason Hanson	.05
152	Robert Massey	.05
153	Ryn McNeil	.05
154	Scott Mitchell	.15
155	Derrick Moore	.05
156	Herman Moore	.30
157	Brett Perriman	.05
158	Robert Porcher	.05
159	Kelvin Pritchett	.05
160	Barry Sanders	1.25
161	Tracy Scroggins	.05
162	Chris Spielman	.05
163	Pat Swilling	.05
164	Edgar Bennett	.05
165	Robert Brooks	.05
166	Terrell Buckley	.05
167	LeRoy Butler	.05
168	Brett Favre	2.00
169	Harry Galbreath	.05
170	Jackie Harris	.05
171	Johnny Holland	.05
172	Chris Jacke	.05
173	George Koonce	.05
174	Bryce Paup	.05
175	Ken Ruettgers	.05
176	Sterling Sharpe	.15
177	Wayne Simmons	.05
178	George Teague	.05
179	Darrell Thompson	.05
180	Reggie White	.15
181	Gary Brown	.05
182	Cody Carlson	.10
183	Ray Childress	.05
184	Cris Dishman	.05
185	Ernest Givins	.05
186	Haywood Jeffires	.05
187	Sean Jones	.05
188	Lamar Lathon	.05
189	Bruce Matthews	.05
190	Bubba McDowell	.05
191	Glenn Montgomery	.05
192	Greg Montgomery	.05
193	Warren Moon	.15
194	Bo Orlando	.05
195	Marcus Robertson	.05
196	Eddie Robinson	.05
197	Webster Slaughter	.05
198	Lorenzo White	.05
199	John Baylor	.05
200	Jason Belser	.05
201	Tony Bennett	.05
202	Dean Biasucci	.05
203	Ray Buchanan	.05
204	Kerry Cash	.05
205	Quentin Coryatt	.05
206	Eugene Daniel	.05
207	Steve Emtman	.05
208	Jon Hand	.05
209	Jim Harbaugh	.05
210	Jeff Herrod	.05
211	Anthony Johnson	.05
212	Roosevelt Potts	.05
213	Rohn Stark	.05
214	Will Wolford	.05
215	Marcus Allen	.10
216	John Alt	.05
217	Kimble Anders	.05
218	J.J. Birden	.05
219	Dale Carter	.05
220	Keith Cash	.05
221	Tony Casillas	.05
222	Willie Davis	.05
223	Tim Grunhard	.05
224	Nick Lowery	.05
225	Charles Mincy	.05
226	Joe Montana	1.50
227	Dan Saleaumua	.05
228	Travy Simien	.05
229	Neil Smith	.05
230	Derrick Thomas	.10
231	Eddie Anderson	.05
232	Tim Brown	.05
233	Nolan Harrison	.05
234	Jeff Hostetler	.05
235	Raghib Ismail	.05
236	Jeff Jaeger	.05
237	James Jett	.05
238	Joe Kelly	.05
239	Albert Lewis	.05
240	Terry McDaniel	.05
241	Chester McGlockton	.05
242	Winston Moss	.05

243	Gerald Perry	.05
244	Greg Robinson	.05
245	Anthony Smith	.05
246	Steve Smith	.05
247	Greg Townsend	.05
248	Lionel Washington	.05
249	Steve Wisniewski	.05
250	Alexander Wright	.05
251	Willie Anderson	.05
252	Jerome Bettis	.50
253	Marc Boutte	.05
254	Shane Conlan	.05
255	Troy Drayton	.20
256	Henry Ellard	.05
257	Sean Gilbert	.10
258	Nate Lewis	.05
259	Todd Lyght	.05
260	Chris Miller	.10
261	Anthony Newman	.05
262	Roman Phifer	.05
263	Henry Rolling	.05
264	T.J. Rubley	.05
265	Jackie Slater	.05
266	Fred Stokes	.05
267	Robert Young	.05
268	Gene Atkins	.05
269	J.B. Brown	.05
270	Keith Byars	.05
271	Marco Coleman	.05
272	Bryan Cox	.05
273	Jeff Cross	.05
274	Irving Fryar	.05
275	Mark Higgs	.05
276	Dwight Hollier	.05
277	Mark Ingram	.05
278	Keith Jackson	.05
279	Terry Kirby	.10
280	Bernie Kosar	.05
281	Dan Marino	2.00
282	O.J. McDuffie	.20
283	Keith Sims	.05
284	Pete Stoyanovich	.05
285	Troy Vincent	.05
286	Richmond Webb	.05
287	Terry Allen	.05
288	Anthony Carter	.05
289	Cris Carter	.10
290	Jack Del Rio	.05
291	Chris Doleman	.05
292	Vencie Glenn	.05
293	Scottie Graham	.20
294	Chris Hinton	.05
295	Qadry Ismail	.10
296	Carlos Jenkins	.05
297	Steve Jordan	.05
298	Carl Lee	.05
299	Randall McDaniel	.05
300	John Randle	.05
301	Todd Scott	.05
302	Robert Smith	.15
303	Fred Strickland	.05
304	Henry Thomas	.05
305	Bruce Armstrong	.05
306	Harlon Barnett	.05
307	Drew Bledsoe	1.25
308	Vincent Brown	.05
309	Ben Coates	.20
310	Todd Collins	.05
311	Myron Guyton	.05
312	Pat Harlow	.05
313	Maurice Hurst	.05
314	Leonard Russell	.05
315	Chris Slade	.10
316	Michael Thompson	.05
317	Andre Tippett	.05
318	Morten Andersen	.05
319	Derek Brown	.05
320	Vince Buck	.05
321	Toi Cook	.05
322	Quinn Early	.05
323	Jim Everett	.10
324	Michael Haynes	.05
325	Tyrone Hughes	.05
326	Rickey Jackson	.05
327	Vaughan Johnson	.05
328	Eric Martin	.05
329	Wayne Martin	.05
330	Sam Mills	.05
331	William Roaf	.05
332	Irv Smith	.05
333	Keith Taylor	.05
334	Renaldo Turnbull	.05
335	Carlton Bailey	.05
336	Michael Brooks	.05
337	Jarrod Bunch	.05
338	Chris Calloway	.05
339	Mark Collins	.05
340	Howard Cross	.05
341	Stacey Dillard	.05
342	John Elliot	.05
343	Rodney Hampton	.10
344	Greg Jackson	.05
345	Mark Jackson	.05
346	David Meggett	.05
347	Corey Miller	.05
348	Mike Sherrard	.05
349	Phil Simms	.05
350	Lewis Tillman	.05
351	Brad Baxter	.05
352	Kyle Clifton	.05
353	Boomer Esiason	.10
354	James Hasty	.05
355	Bobby Houston	.05
356	Johnny Johnson	.05
357	Jeff Lageman	.05
358	Mo Lewis	.05
359	Ronnie Lott	.05
360	Leonard Marshall	.05

361	Johnny Mitchell	.05
362	Rob Moore	.05
363	Eric Thomas	.05
364	Brian Washington	.05
365	Marvin Washington	.05
366	Eric Allen	.05
367	Fred Barnett	.05
368	Bubby Brister	.05
369	Randall Cunningham	.15
370	Byron Evans	.05
371	William Fuller	.05
372	Andy Harmon	.05
373	Seth Joyner	.05
374	William Perry	.05
375	Leonard Renfro	.05
376	Heath Sherman	.05
377	Ben Smith	.05
378	William Thomas	.05
379	Herschel Walker	.05
380	Calvin Williams	.05
381	Chad Brown	.10
382	Dermontti Dawson	.05
383	Deon Figures	.05
384	Barry Foster	.10
385	Jeff Graham	.05
386	Eric Green	.05
387	Kevin Greene	.05
388	Carlton Haselrig	.05
389	Levon Kirkland	.05
390	Carnell Lake	.05
391	Greg Lloyd	.05
392	Neil O'Donnell	.10
393	Darren Perry	.05
394	Dwight Stone	.05
395	Leroy Thompson	.05
396	Rod Woodson	.10
397	Marion Butts	.05
398	John Carney	.05
399	Darren Carrington	.05
400	Burt Grossman	.05
401	Courtney Hall	.05
402	Ronnie Harmon	.05
403	Stan Humphries	.20
404	Shawn Jefferson	.05
405	Vance Johnson	.05
406	Chris Mims	.05
407	Leslie O'Neal	.05
408	Stanley Richard	.05
409	Junior Seau	.15
410	Harris Barton	.05
411	Dennis Brown	.05
412	Eric Davis	.05
413	Merton Hanks	.05
414	John Johnson	.05
415	Brent Jones	.05
416	Marc Logan	.05
417	Tim McDonald	.05
418	Gary Plummer	.05
419	Tom Rathman	.05
420	Jerry Rice	1.00
421	Bill Romanowski	.05
422	Jesse Sapolu	.05
423	Dana Stubblefield	.10
424	John Taylor	.05
425	Steve Wallace	.05
426	Ted Washington	.05
427	Ricky Watters	.10
428	Troy Wilson	.05
429	Steve Young	1.00
430	Howard Ballard	.05
431	Michael Bates	.05
432	Robert Blackmon	.05
433	Brian Blades	.05
434	Ferrell Edmunds	.05
435	Carlton Gray	.05
436	Patrick Hunter	.05
437	Cortez Kennedy	.10
438	Kelvin Martin	.05
439	Rick Mirer	.10
440	Nate Odomes	.05
441	Ray Roberts	.05
442	Eugene Robinson	.05
443	Rod Stephens	.05
444	Chris Warren	.10
445	John L. Williams	.05
446	Terry Wooden	.05
447	Marty Carter	.05
448	Reggie Cobb	.05
449	Lawrence Dawsey	.05
450	Santana Dotson	.05
451	Craig Erickson	.05
452	Thomas Everett	.05
453	Paul Gruber	.05
454	Courtney Hawkins	.05
455	Martin Mayhew	.05
456	Hardy Nickerson	.05
457	Ricky Reynolds	.05
458	Vince Workman	.05
459	Reggie Brooks	.10
460	Earnest Byner	.05
461	Andre Collins	.05
462	Brad Edwards	.05
463	Kurt Gouveia	.05
464	Darrell Green	.05
465	Ken Harvey	.05
466	Ethan Horton	.05
467	A.J. Johnson	.05
468	Tim Johnson	.05
469	Jim Lachey	.05
470	Chip Lohmiller	.05
471	Art Monk	.10
472	Sterling Palmer	.05
473	Mark Rypien	.05
474	Ricky Sanders	.05
475	Checklist	.05
476	Checklist	.05
477	Checklist	.05

478	Checklist	.05
479	Checklist	.05
480	Checklist	.05

1994 Fleer All-Pros

Fleer selected the top players from each conference for this 24-card insert set. Cards, which were randomly inserted in packs, feature borderless color or action photos on the front, with ghosted images behind the main picture. The player's name is in gold foil running vertical on the left side of the card. The back is borderless and includes a career summary and a photo of the player with a glowing aura about him. Cards are numbered 1 of 24, etc.

		MT
Complete Set (24):		25.00
Common Player:		.25
Minor Stars:		.50
1	Troy Aikman	3.00
2	Eric Allen	.25
3	Jerome Bettis	1.00
4	Barry Foster	.50
5	Michael Irvin	.50
6	Cortez Kennedy	.50
7	Joe Montana	4.00
8	Hardy Nickerson	.25
9	Jerry Rice	3.00
10	Andre Rison	.50
11	Barry Sanders	4.00
12	Deion Sanders	2.00
13	Junior Seau	.50
14	Shannon Sharpe	.50
15	Sterling Sharpe	.50
16	Bruce Smith	.25
17	Emmitt Smith	5.00
18	Neil Smith	.25
19	Derrick Thomas	.50
20	Thurman Thomas	.50
21	Renaldo Turnbull	.25
22	Reggie White	.50
23	Rod Woodson	.50
24	Steve Young	3.00

1994 Fleer Award Winners

Five award-winning performers from the 1993 season are featured on these insert cards randomly available in 1994 packs. Each card front has a smaller cutout photo of the player against a larger black-and-white closeup photo. The player's name is in gold foil in the lower left corner; the set logo is to the right. The backs have a background which fades from black to white and features a color action photo. A color-screened box contains a summary of the player's career. The cards are numbered 1 of 5, etc. The Super Bowl MVP, AFC and NFC Offensive Rookies of the Year, the NFL Defensive Player of the Year, and the NFL Rookie of the Year are represented in the set.

		MT
Complete Set (5):		4.00
Common Player:		.25
1	Jerome Bettis	1.00
2	Rick Mirer	.50
3	Deion Sanders	1.00
4	Emmitt Smith	2.00
5	Dana Stubblefield	.25

1994 Fleer Jerome Bettis

This 12-card set is devoted to former Notre Dame and Los Angeles Rams running back Jerome Bettis, a Rookie of the Year. Each card has a color action photo on the front against an abstract background. A player head shot and Bettis' name are stamped in gold foil at the bottom. The horizontal back includes a color photo, career highlights and a card number. Three cards in the set could be obtained only through the mail for ten 1994 Fleer Football wrappers and $1.50.

	MT
Complete Set (12):	6.00
Common Bettis:	.50
Mail-In Bettis (13-15):	1.00

1994 Fleer League Leaders

The top quarterbacks, running backs and receivers from 1993 are featured in this 10-card insert set devoted to statistical leaders. The card front has a color photo of the player emerging from a blurred background. The "League Leader" logo and player's name are on the front, while the back has a small color photo and a summary of the player's 1993 accomplishments. Cards were randomly inserted in Fleer packs.

		MT
Complete Set (10):		10.00
Common Player:		.50
1	Marcus Allen	.50
2	Tim Brown	.50
3	John Elway	1.50
4	Tyrone Huges	.50
5	Jerry Rice	2.50
6	Sterling Sharpe	.50
7	Emmitt Smith	4.00
8	Neil Smith	.50
9	Thurman Thomas	.50
10	Steve Young	2.00

A player's name in *italic* type indicates a rookie card.

1994 Fleer Living Legends

Six legendary active players are featured in this insert set; cards were randomly inserted in 1994 packs. The horizontally-arranged card front uses a metallic design for the photo, while the player's and set's name are stamped in foil. The card back is numbered 1 of 6, etc., and has a color photo and career highlights.

		MT
Complete Set (6):		75.00
Common Player:		5.00
1	Marcus Allen	5.00
2	John Elway	10.00
3	Joe Montana	15.00
4	Jerry Rice	15.00
5	Emmitt Smith	30.00
6	Reggie White	5.00

1994 Fleer Pro-Vision

This set continues Fleer's tradition of using artwork on the card fronts. The player is featured against a background with a landmark from his team's city. The backs, numbered 1 of 9, etc., have a career summary. Cards were standard size (2-1/2" x 3-1/2") and were random inserts in Fleer packs, but jumbo versions were also made for each card. One nine-card jumbo set was included in every hobby case. Jumbo cards are generally worth two to four times more than the standard-size cards.

		MT
Complete Set (9):		5.00
Common Player:		.25
Minor Stars:		.50
1	Rodney Hampton	.25
2	Ricky Watters	.50
3	Rick Mirer	.50
4	Brett Favre	3.00
5	Troy Aikman	1.25
6	Jerome Bettis	.50
7	Joe Montana	2.00
8	Cornelius Bennett	.25
9	Rod Woodson	.25

1994 Fleer Prospects

This insert set features 25 top collegiate prospects who have a chance to shine in the NFL. The card front shows the player in his collegiate uniform, superimposed against a background of a steel mill. The backs have a card number (1 of 25, etc.), a photo and a summary of the player's collegiate achievements.

		MT
Complete Set (25):		30.00
Common Player:		.50
Minor Stars:		1.00
1	Sam Adams	.50
2	Trev Alberts	.50
3	Derrick Alexander	2.00
4	Mario Bates	1.00
5	Jeff Buris	.50
6	Shante Carver	.50
7	Marshall Faulk	6.00
8	William Floyd	3.00
9	Rob Fredrickson	.50
10	Wayne Gandy	.50
11	Charlie Garner	1.00
12	Aaron Glenn	.50
13	Charles Johnson	2.00
14	Joe Johnson	.50
15	Tre Johnson	.50
16	Antonio Langham	1.00
17	Chuck Levy	1.00
18	Willie McGinest	1.00
19	David Palmer	1.00
20	Errict Rhett	4.00
21	Jason Sehorn	.50
22	Heath Shuler	1.00
23	Charlie Ward	1.00
24	DeWayne Washington	.50
25	Bryant Young	1.00

1994 Fleer Rookie Exchange

This 12-card Rookie Exchange set featured the same design as the 1994 Fleer set and was available by sending in a Rookie Exchange card found in packs.

		MT
Complete Set (12):		16.00
Common Player:		.50
1	Derrick Alexander	1.00
2	Trent Dilfer	2.00
3	Marshall Faulk	5.00
4	Charlie Garner	.50
5	Greg Hill	1.50
6	Charles Johnson	1.00
7	Antonio Langham	.50
8	Willie McGinest	.50
9	Heath Shuler	3.50
10	DeWayne Washington	.50
11	Dan Wilkinson	1.00
12	Bryant Young	1.50
NNO	Rookie Exchange Exp.	.50

1994 Fleer Rookie Sensations

These cards were randomly inserted in 1994 21-card jumbo packs. Players who were rookies during the 1993 NFL season are featured. The card front shows a picture of the player against a wavy background design that is primarily in his team's dominant color. The back also features his team's colors, with a smaller photo and biography. The set name is stamped in foil on the card front; the back has the card number, 1 of 20, etc.

		MT
Complete Set (20):		175.00
Common Player:		4.50
1	Jerome Bettis	20.00
2	Drew Bledsoe	65.00
3	Reggie Brooks	7.00
4	Tom Carter	7.00
5	John Copeland	7.00
6	Jason Elam	7.00
7	Garrison Hearst	20.00
8	Tyrone Hughes	7.00
9	James Jett	7.00
10	Lincoln Kennedy	7.00
11	Terry Kirby	7.00
12	Glyn Milburn	7.00
13	Rick Mirer	10.00
14	Ron Moore	7.00
15	William Roaf	7.00
16	Wayne Simmons	7.00
17	Chris Slade	7.00
18	Darrin Smith	4.50
19	Dana Stubblefield	7.00
20	George Teague	4.50

1994 Fleer Scoring Machines

These cards, inserted only in 15-card 1994 Fleer packs, feature some of the leading point producers in the NFL who play running back, quarterback and receiver. Card fronts have three photos of the player, plus his name and set logo stamped in foil. The back has a color photo and career summary, plus a card number (1of 10, etc.).

		MT
Complete Set (20):		250.00
Common Player:		5.00
1	Marcus Allen	5.00
2	Natrone Means	10.00
3	Jerome Bettis	10.00
4	Tim Brown	5.00
5	Barry Foster	5.00
6	Rodney Hampton	5.00
7	Michael Irvin	5.00
8	Nick Lowery	5.00
9	Dan Marino	40.00
10	Joe Montana	25.00
11	Warren Moon	5.00
12	Andre Rison	5.00
13	Jerry Rice	25.00
14	Andre Rison	5.00
15	Barry Sanders	25.00
16	Shannon Sharpe	5.00
17	Sterling Sharpe	5.00
18	Emmitt Smith	40.00
19	Thurman Thomas	5.00
20	Ricky Watters	5.00

Values quoted in this guide reflect the retail price of a card — the price a collector can expect to pay when buying a card from a dealer. The wholesale price — that which a collector can expect to receive when selling cards — will be significantly lower, depending on desirability and condition.

1994 Fleer GameDay

NFL GameDay from Fleer feature an all-new design in a supersized format. The cards are 35 percent larger than a normal card, measuring 4-11/16" x 2-1/2". UV coating and team color-coding are used on the cards, which feature "up-close-and-personal" photos on the fronts. Card backs have another player photo, with statistics and a player profile. Four insert sets were also made: GameBreakers, 2nd Year Stars, Rookie Standouts, and Flashing Stars.

		MT
Complete Set (420):		42.00
Common Player:		.10
Wax Box:		40.00
1	Michael Bankston	.10
2	Steve Beuerlein	.10
3	Gary Clark	.10
4	Garrison Hearst	1.00
5	Eric Hill	.10
6	Randal Hill	.10
7	Seth Joyner	.10
8	Jim McMahon	.10
9	Jamir Miller	.40
10	Ron Moore	.45
11	Ricky Proehl	.10
12	Luis Sharpe	.10
13	Clyde Simmons	.10
14	Eric Swann	.10
15	Aeneas Williams	.10
16	Chris Doleman	.10
17	Bert Emanuel	1.50
18	Moe Gardner	.10
19	Jeff George	.10
20	Roger Harper	.10
21	Pierce Holt	.10
22	Lincoln Kennedy	.12
23	Erric Pegram	.20
24	Andre Rison	.20
25	Deion Sanders	1.00
26	Tony Smith	.10
27	Jessie Tuggle	.10
28	Don Beebe	.10
29	Cornelius Bennett	.10
30	Bill Brooks	.10
31	Bucky Brooks	.50
32	Jeff Burris	.75
33	Kenneth Davis	.10
34	Phil Hansen	.10
35	Kent Hull	.10
36	Henry Jones	.10
37	Jim Kelly	.30
38	Pete Metzelaars	.10
39	Marvcus Patton	.10
40	Andre Reed	.10
41	Bruce Smith	.10
42	Thomas Smith	.10
43	Darryl Talley	.10
44	Steve Tasker	.10
45	Thurman Thomas	.45
46	Jeff Wright	.10
47	Trace Armstrong	.10
48	Joe Cain	.10
49	Mark Carrier	.10
50	Curtis Conway	.25
51	Shaun Gayle	.10
52	Dante Jones	.10
53	Erik Kramer	.10
54	Terry Obee	.10
55	Vinson Smith	.10
56	Alonzo Spellman	.10
57	John Thierry	.35
58	Tom Waddle	.10
59	Donnell Woolford	.10
60	Tim Worley	.10
61	Chris Zorich	.10
62	Mike Brim	.10
63	John Copeland	.10
64	Derrick Fenner	.10
65	James Francis	.10
66	Harold Green	.10
67	David Klingler	.10
68	Ricardo McDonald	.10
69	Tony McGee	.10
70	Carl Pickens	.10
71	Jeff Query	.10
72	Darnay Scott	2.25
73	Steve Tovar	.10
74	Dan Wilkinson	.60
75	Alfred Williams	.10
76	Darryl Williams	.10
77	Derrick Alexander	.50
78	Rob Burnett	.10
79	Steve Everitt	.10
80	Michael Jackson	.10
81	Pepper Johnson	.10
82	Tony Jones	.10
83	Antonio Langham	.60
84	Eric Metcalf	.10
85	Stevon Moore	.10
86	Michael Dean Perry	.10
87	Anthony Pleasant	.10
88	Vinny Testaverde	.12
89	Eric Turner	.12
90	Tommy Vardell	.10
91	Troy Aikman	2.75
92	Larry Brown	.10
93	Shante Carver	.25
94	Charles Haley	.10
95	Alvin Harper	.10
96	Michael Irvin	.50
97	Daryl Johnston	.10
98	Leon Lett	.10
99	Russell Maryland	.10
100	Nate Newton	.10
101	Jay Novacek	.10
102	Darrin Smith	.10
103	Emmitt Smith	3.00
104	Kevin Smith	.10
105	Mark Stepnoski	.10
106	Tony Tolbert	.10
107	Erik Williams	.10
108	Kevin Williams	.25
109	Darren Woodson	.10
110	Allen Aldridge	.25
111	Steve Atwater	.10
112	Rod Bernstine	.10
113	Ray Crockett	.10
114	Mike Croel	.10
115	Robert Delpino	.10
116	Shane Dronett	.10
117	Jason Elam	.10
118	John Elway	1.00
119	Simon Fletcher	.10
120	Glyn Milburn	.30
121	Anthony Miller	.10
122	Mike Pritchard	.10
123	Shannon Sharpe	.10
124	Dan Williams	.10
125	Bennie Blades	.10
126	Lomas Brown	.10
127	Anthony Carter	.10
128	Mel Gray	.10
129	Jason Hanson	.10
130	Robert Massey	.10
131	Ryan McNeil	.10
132	Scott Mitchell	.15
133	Herman Moore	1.00
134	Johnnie Morton	.90
135	Brett Perriman	.10
136	Robert Porcher	.10
137	Barry Sanders	1.50
138	Tracy Scroggins	.10
139	Chris Spielman	.10
140	Pat Swilling	.10
141	Edgar Bennett	.10
142	Robert Brooks	.10
143	Terrell Buckley	.10
144	LeRoy Butler	.10
145	Reggie Cobb	.10
146	Curtis Duncan	.10
147	Brett Favre	2.00
148	Sean Jones	.10
149	George Koonce	.10
150	Ken Ruettgers	.10
151	Sterling Sharpe	.50
152	Wayne Simmons	.10
153	Aaron Taylor	.25
154	George Teague	.10
155	Reggie White	.10
156	Michael Barrow	.10
157	Gary Brown	.10
158	Rich Camarillo	.10
159	Cody Carlson	.10
160	Ray Childress	.10
161	Cris Dishman	.10
162	Henry Ford	.30
163	Ernest Givins	.10
164	Steve Jackson	.10
165	Haywood Jeffires	.10
166	Bruce Matthews	.10
167	Bubba McDowell	.10
168	Marcus Robertson	.10
169	Eddie Robinson	.10
170	Webster Slaughter	.10
171	Trev Alberts	.50
172	Tony Bennett	.10
173	Ray Buchanan	.10
174	Kerry Cash	.10
175	Quentin Coryatt	.10
176	Eugene Daniel	.10
177	Sean Dawkins	1.00
178	Steve Emtman	.10
179	Marshall Faulk	6.00
180	John Hand	.10
181	Jim Harbaugh	.10
182	Jeff Herrod	.10
183	Roosevelt Potts	.20
184	Rohn Stark	.10
185	Marcus Allen	.10
186	Donnell Bennett	.45
187	J.J. Birden	.10
188	Dale Carter	.10
189	Mark Collins	.10
190	Willie Davis	.10
191	Lake Dawson	1.50
192	Tim Grunhard	.10
193	Greg Hill	.50
194	Joe Montana	2.50
195	Tracy Simion	.10
196	Neil Smith	.10
197	Derrick Thomas	.15
198	Tim Brown	.12
199	James Folston	.25
200	Rob Fredrickson	.25
201	Nolan Harrison	.10
202	Jeff Hostetler	.10
203	Raghib Ismail	.25
204	Jeff Jaeger	.10
205	James Jett	.20
206	Terry McDaniel	.10
207	Chester McGlockton	.10
208	Winston Moss	.10
209	Tom Rathman	.10
210	Anthony Smith	.10
211	Harvey Williams	.10
212	Steve Wisniewski	.10
213	Alexander Wright	.10
214	Willie Anderson	.10
215	Jerome Bettis	1.00
216	Isaac Bruce	4.00
217	Troy Drayton	.20
218	Wayne Gandy	.20
219	Sean Gilbert	.15
220	Nate Lewis	.10
221	Todd Lyght	.10
222	Chris Miller	.10
223	Anthony Newman	.10
224	Roman Phifer	.10
225	Henry Rolling	.10
226	Jackie Slater	.10
227	Fred Stokes	.10
228	Gene Atkins	.10
229	Aubrey Beavers	.30
230	Tim Bowens	.30
231	J.B. Brown	.10
232	Keith Byars	.10
233	Marco Coleman	.10
234	Bryan Cox	.10
235	Jeff Cross	.10
236	Irving Fryar	.10
237	Mark Ingram	.10
238	Keith Jackson	.10
239	Terry Kirby	.25
240	Dan Marino	1.25
241	Michael Stewart	.10
242	Troy Vincent	.10
243	Richmond Webb	.10
244	Terry Allen	.12
245	Cris Carter	.12
246	Jack Del Rio	.10
247	Vencie Glenn	.10
248	Chris Hinton	.10
249	Qadry Ismail	.25
250	Carlos Jenkins	.10
251	Randall McDaniel	.10
252	Warren Moon	.10
253	David Palmer	.50
254	John Randle	.10
255	Jake Reed	.10
256	Todd Scott	.10
257	Todd Steussie	.25
258	Henry Thomas	.10
259	DeWayne Washington	.25
260	Bruce Armstrong	.10
261	Drew Bledsoe	2.00
262	Vincent Brisby	.20
263	Vincent Brown	.10
264	Marion Butts	.10
265	Ben Coates	.10
266	Pat Harlow	.10
267	Maurice Hurst	.10
268	Willie McGinest	.75
269	Chris Slade	.10
270	Michael Timpson	.10
271	Morten Andersen	.10
272	Mario Bates	2.00
273	Derek Brown	.25
274	Quinn Early	.10
275	Jim Everett	.10
276	Michael Haynes	.10
277	Tyrone Hughes	.10
278	Joe Johnson	.25
279	Eric Martin	.10
280	Wayne Martin	.10
281	Sam Mills	.10
282	William Roaf	.15
283	Irv Smith	.10
284	Renaldo Turnbull	.10
285	Carlton Bailey	.10
286	Michael Brooks	.10
287	Dave Brown	.30
288	Jarrod Bunch	.10
289	Howard Cross	.10
290	John Elliott	.10
291	Keith Hamilton	.10
292	Rodney Hampton	.40
293	Mark Jackson	.10
294	Thomas Lewis	.80
295	David Meggett	.10
296	Corey Miller	.10
297	Mike Sherrard	.10
298	Brad Baxter	.10
299	Kyle Clifton	.10
300	Boomer Esiason	.10
301	Aaron Glenn	.25
302	James Hasty	.10
303	Johnny Johnson	.10
304	Jeff Lageman	.10
305	Mo Lewis	.10
306	Ronnie Lott	.10
307	Johnny Mitchell	.10
308	Art Monk	.10
309	Rob Moore	.10
310	Brian Washington	.10
311	Marvin Washington	.10
312	Ryan Yarborough	.45
313	Eric Allen	.10
314	Victor Bailey	.10
315	Fred Barnett	.10
316	Mark Bavaro	.10
317	Randall Cunningham	.20
318	Byron Evans	.10
319	William Fuller	.10
320	Charlie Garner	1.50
321	Andy Harmon	.10
322	Vaughn Hebron	.10
323	Mark McMillan	.10
324	Bill Romanowski	.10
325	William Thomas	.10
326	Greg Townsend	.10
327	Herschel Walker	.10
328	Bernard Williams	.25
329	Calvin Williams	.10
330	Dermontti Dawson	.10
331	Deon Figures	.10
332	Barry Foster	.25
333	Eric Green	.10
334	Kevin Greene	.10
335	Carlton Haselrig	.10
336	Charles Johnson	1.00
337	Levon Kirkland	.10
338	Carnell Lake	.10
339	Greg Lloyd	.10
340	Neil O'Donnell	.10
341	Darren Perry	.10
342	Dwight Stone	.10
343	John L. Williams	.10
344	Rod Woodson	.10
345	John Carney	.10
346	Darren Carrington	.10
347	Isaac Davis	.25
348	Courtney Hall	.10
349	Ronnie Harmon	.10
350	Dwayne Harper	.10
351	Stan Humphries	.10
352	Shawn Jefferson	.10
353	Vance Johnson	.10
354	Natrone Means	.75
355	Chris Mims	.10
356	Leslie O'Neal	.10
357	Stanley Richard	.10
358	Junior Seau	.12
359	Harris Barton	.10
360	Eric Davis	.10
361	Richard Dent	.10
362	William Floyd	2.00
363	Merton Hanks	.10
364	Brent Jones	.10
365	Marc Logan	.10
366	Tim McDonald	.10
367	Ken Norton	.10
368	Jerry Rice	1.00
369	Jesse Sapolu	.10
370	Dana Stubblefield	.15
371	John Taylor	.10
372	Ricky Watters	.10
373	Bryant Young	.50
374	Steve Young	1.50
375	Sam Adams	.35
376	Michael Bates	.10
377	Robert Blackmon	.10
378	Brian Blades	.10
379	Ferrell Edmunds	.10
380	John Kasay	.10
381	Cortez Kennedy	.10
382	Kelvin Martin	.10
383	Rick Mirer	.75
384	Rufus Porter	.10
385	Eugene Robinson	.10
386	Rod Stephens	.10
387	Chris Warren	.10
388	Marty Carter	.10
389	Horace Copeland	.10
390	Eric Curry	.10
391	Lawrence Dawsey	.10
392	Trent Dilfer	1.00
393	Santana Dotson	.10
394	Craig Erickson	.10
395	Thomas Everett	.10
396	Paul Gruber	.10
397	Jackie Harris	.10
398	Courtney Hawkins	.10
399	Martin Mayhew	.10
400	Hardy Nickerson	.10
401	Errict Rhett	4.00
402	Vince Workman	.10
403	Reggie Brooks	.75
404	Tom Carter	.10
405	Andre Collins	.10
406	Henry Ellard	.10
407	Kurt Gouveia	.10
408	Darrell Green	.10
409	Ken Harvey	.10
410	Ethan Horton	.15
411	Desmond Howard	.10
412	Jim Lachey	.10
413	Sterling Palmer	.10
414	Heath Shuler	3.00
415	Tyronne Stowe	.10
416	Tony Woods	.10
417	Checklist	.10
418	Checklist	.10
419	Checklist	.10
420	Checklist	.10

1994 Fleer GameDay Flashing Stars

These cards, the scarcest of all inserts in the 1994 Fleer GameDay set, were randomly included in 1994 packs. The set features four of the NFL's outstanding younger players on 100 percent etched foil. Card backs, numbered 1 of 4, etc., include information about the player and a color photo of the player. Each card measures 4-11/16" x 2-1/2."

		MT
Complete Set (4):		60.00
Common Player:		10.00
1	Jerome Bettis	10.00
2	Rick Mirer	10.00
3	Jerry Rice	20.00
4	Emmitt Smith	40.00

1994 Fleer GameDay Game Breakers

Top running backs, quarterbacks and receivers who can break the game wide open are featured in this 1994 GameDay insert set. The cards, which measure 4-11/16" x 2-1/2" inches, were random inserts in GameDay packs. The card front has a large sepia-toned photo, along with a smaller, color photo of the same picture. The player's name and GameDay logo are stamped in gold foil; "Gamebreaker" is written across the card front in different type sizes and styles. The card back has a color photo against a sepia background, with a card number, too (1 of 16, etc.). A summary of the player's career is also given.

		MT
Complete Set (16):		30.00
Common Player:		.50
1	Troy Aikman	4.00
2	Marcus Allen	.50
3	Tim Brown	.50
4	John Elway	1.50
5	Michael Irvin	.75
6	Dan Marino	6.00
7	Joe Montana	4.00
8	Jerry Rice	4.00
9	Andre Rison	.50
10	Barry Sanders	4.00
11	Deion Sanders	2.00

12	Sterling Sharpe	.75
13	Emmitt Smith	6.00
14	Thurman Thomas	.75
15	Rod Woodson	.50
16	Steve Young	3.00

1994 Fleer GameDay Rookie Standouts

Sixteen "can't-miss" rookies are featured on these cards, which were randomly inserted in 1994 Fleer GameDay packs. The card front shows a color action photo of the player on a 3-D embossed design. Unlike the other inserts in this set, the "Rookie Standouts" insert set does not use any foil stamping. The card back has a player mug shot and provides a scouting report on the player as he enters his first year in the NFL. Cards are numbered 1 of 16, etc., and measure 4-11/16" x 2-1/2."

		MT
Complete Set (16):		25.00
Common Player:		.65
1	Sam Adams	.65
2	Trev Alberts	1.00
3	Lake Dawson	2.00
4	Trent Dilfer	3.00
5	Marshall Faulk	6.00
6	Aaron Glenn	1.00
7	Charles Johnson	3.00
8	Willie McGinest	1.25
9	Jamir Miller	.65
10	Johnnie Morton	2.00
11	David Palmer	4.00
12	Errict Rhett	3.00
13	Heath Shuler	3.00
14	John Thierry	.65
15	Dan Wilkinson	1.50
16	Bryant Young	1.00

1994 Fleer GameDay Second-Year Stars

These cards, randomly inserted in 1994 Fleer GameDay packs, feature 16 of the top rookies in 1993 who are beginning their second year in the NFL in 1994. The "GameDay," the set name and player name are stamped in gold foil on the card front. A small action shot appears against a larger, full-bleed profile shot, which has a swirl effect to it. The card back also has a swirl effect, which is used to present information about the player's first NFL season. Cards, numbered 1

of 16, etc., have an action photo on the back. Cards are 35 percent larger than a standard size card; they measure 4-11/16" x 2-1/2".

	MT
Complete Set (16):	18.00
Common Player:	.50

1	Jerome Bettis	2.00
2	Drew Bledsoe	5.00
3	Reggie Brooks	1.00
4	Tom Carter	.60
5	Eric Curry	.60
6	Steve Everitt	.60
7	Tyrone Hughes	.50
8	James Jett	1.50
9	Terry Kirby	1.00
10	Natrone Means	4.00
11	Rick Mirer	4.00
12	Ron Moore	1.00
13	William Roaf	.50
14	Chris Slade	.50
15	Darrin Smith	.60
16	Dana Stubblefield	1.00

1995 Fleer

Fleer's 1995 set includes 400 cards, using the "Different by Design" concept it has used for baseball issues; different styles are used for different divisions. Several insert sets were randomly included in packs: Pro-Visions (1 in 6 packs); Rookie Sensations (1 in 3 17-card packs); Aerial Attack (1 in 37); Gridiron Leaders (1 in 4); TD Sensations (1 in 3 11- card packs); NFL Prospects (1 in 6); and Flair Preview (1 in each pack). Fleer products were sold in 11-card and 17-card packs. The cards are numbered alphabetically by team names, with the players numbered alphabetically within the team subsets.

		MT
Complete Set (400):		20.00
Common Player:		.05
Minor Stars:		.10
Wax Box:		25.00
1	Michael Bankston	.05
2	Larry Centers	.05
3	Gary Clark	.05
4	Eric Hill	.05
5	Seth Joyner	.05
6	Dave Krieg	.05
7	Lorenzo Lynch	.05
8	Jamir Miller	.05
9	Ron Moore	.05
10	Ricky Proehl	.05
11	Clyde Simmons	.05
12	Eric Swann	.05
13	Aeneas Williams	.05
14	J.J. Birden	.05
15	Chris Doleman	.05
16	Bert Emanuel	.20
17	Jumpy Geathers	.05
18	Jeff George	.10
19	Roger Harper	.05
20	Craig Heyward	.05
21	Pierce Holt	.05
22	D.J. Johnson	.05
23	Terance Mathis	.05
24	Clay Mathews	.05
25	Andre Rison	.10
26	Chuck Smith	.05
27	Jessie Tuggle	.05
28	Cornelius Bennett	.05
29	Bucky Brooks	.05
30	Jeff Burris	.05
31	Russell Copeland	.05
32	Matt Darby	.05
33	Phil Hansen	.05
34	Henry Jones	.05
35	Jim Kelly	.10
36	Mark Maddox	.10
37	Bryce Paup	.05
38	Andre Reed	.10
39	Bruce Smith	.05
40	Darryl Talley	.05
41	Dewell Brewer	.10
42	Mike Fox	.05
43	Eric Guliford	.05

44	Lamar Lathon	.05
45	Pete Metzelaars	.05
46	Sam Mills	.05
47	Frank Reich	.05
48	Rod Smith	.05
49	Jack Trudeau	.05
50	Trace Armstrong	.05
51	Joe Cain	.05
52	Mark Carrier	.05
53	Curtis Conway	.05
54	Shaun Gayle	.05
55	Jeff Graham	.05
56	Raymont Harris	.15
57	Erik Kramer	.05
58	Lewis Tillman	.05
59	Tom Waddle	.05
60	Steve Walsh	.05
61	Donnell Woolford	.05
62	Chris Zorich	.05
63	*Jeff Blake*	.50
64	Mike Brim	.05
65	Steve Broussard	.05
66	James Francis	.05
67	Ricardo McDonald	.05
68	Tony McGee	.05
69	Carl Pickens	.05
70	Darnay Scott	.40
71	Steve Tovar	.05
72	Dan Wilkinson	.05
73	Alfred Williams	.05
74	Darryl Williams	.05
75	Derrick Alexander	.20
76	Randy Baldwin	.05
77	Carl Banks	.05
78	Rob Burnett	.05
79	Steve Everitt	.05
80	Leroy Hoard	.05
81	Michael Jackson	.05
82	Pepper Johnson	.05
83	Tony Jones	.05
84	Antonio Langham	.05
85	Eric Metcalf	.05
86	Stevon Moore	.05
87	Anthony Pleasant	.05
88	Vinny Testaverde	.05
89	Eric Turner	.05
90	Troy Aikman	.60
91	Charles Haley	.05
92	Michael Irvin	.20
93	Daryl Johnston	.05
94	Robert Jones	.05
95	Leon Lett	.05
96	Russell Maryland	.05
97	Nate Newton	.05
98	Jay Novacek	.05
99	Darrin Smith	.05
100	Emmitt Smith	1.50
101	Kevin Smith	.05
102	Erik Williams	.05
103	Kevin Williams	.05
104	Darren Woodson	.05
105	Elijah Alexander	.05
106	Steve Atwater	.05
107	Ray Crockett	.05
108	Shane Dronett	.05
109	Jason Elam	.05
110	John Elway	.25
111	Simon Fletcher	.05
112	Glyn Milburn	.05
113	Anthony Miller	.05
114	Michael Dean Perry	.05
115	Mike Pritchard	.05
116	Derek Russell	.05
117	Leonard Russell	.05
118	Shannon Sharpe	.05
119	Gary Zimmerman	.05
120	Bennie Blades	.05
121	Lomas Brown	.05
122	Willie Clay	.05
123	Mike Johnson	.05
124	Robert Massey	.05
125	Scott Mitchell	.05
126	Herman Moore	.05
127	Brett Perriman	.05
128	Robert Porcher	.05
129	Barry Sanders	1.25
130	Chris Spielman	.05
131	Henry Thomas	.05
132	Edgar Bennett	.05
133	Robert Brooks	.05
134	LeRoy Butler	.05
135	Brett Favre	1.50
136	Sean Jones	.05
137	John Jurkovic	.05
138	George Koonce	.05
139	Wayne Simmons	.05
140	George Teague	.05
141	Reggie White	.10
142	Michael Barrow	.05
143	Gary Brown	.05
144	Cody Carlson	.05
145	Ray Childress	.05
146	Cris Dishman	.05
147	Ernest Givins	.05
148	Mel Gray	.05
149	Darryl Lewis	.05
150	Bruce Matthews	.05
151	Marcus Robertson	.05
152	Webster Slaughter	.05
153	Al Smith	.05
154	Mark Stepnoski	.05
155	Trev Alberts	.05
156	Willie Anderson	.05
157	Jason Belser	.05
158	Tony Bennett	.05
159	Ray Buchanan	.05
160	Quentin Coryatt	.05
161	Sean Dawkins	.15

162	Steve Emtman	.05
163	Marshall Faulk	1.00
164	Steve Grant	.05
165	Jim Harbaugh	.05
166	Jeff Herrod	.05
167	Tony Siragusa	.05
168	Steve Beuerlein	.05
169	Darren Carrington	.05
170	Reggie Cobb	.05
171	Kelvin Martin	.05
172	Kelvin Pritchett	.05
173	Joel Smeenge	.05
174	James Williams	.05
175	Marcus Allen	.10
176	Kimble Anders	.05
177	Dale Carter	.05
178	Mark Collins	.05
179	Willie Davis	.05
180	Lake Dawson	.20
181	Greg Hill	.20
182	Darren Mickell	.05
183	Joe Montana	1.00
184	Tracy Simien	.05
185	Neil Smith	.05
186	William White	.05
187	Greg Biekert	.05
188	Tim Brown	.10
189	Rob Fredrickson	.05
190	*Andrew Glover*	.10
191	Nolan Harrison	.05
192	Jeff Hostetler	.05
193	Raghib Ismail	.05
194	Terry McDaniel	.05
195	Chester McGlockton	.05
196	Winston Moss	.05
197	Anthony Smith	.05
198	Harvey Williams	.05
199	Steve Wisniewski	.05
200	Johnny Bailey	.05
201	Jerome Bettis	.25
202	Isaac Bruce	.50
203	Shane Conlan	.05
204	Troy Drayton	.05
205	Sean Gilbert	.05
206	Jessie Hester	.05
207	Jimmie Jones	.05
208	Todd Lyght	.05
209	Chris Miller	.05
210	Roman Phifer	.05
211	Marquez Pope	.05
212	Robert Young	.05
213	Gene Atkins	.05
214	Aubrey Beavers	.05
215	Tim Bowens	.05
216	Bryan Cox	.05
217	Jeff Cross	.05
218	Irving Fryar	.05
219	Eric Green	.05
220	Mark Ingram	.05
221	Terry Kirby	.05
222	Dan Marino	1.50
223	O.J. McDuffie	.05
224	Bernie Parmalee	.25
225	Keith Sims	.05
226	Irving Spikes	.10
227	Michael Stewart	.05
228	Troy Vincent	.05
229	Richmond Webb	.05
230	Terry Allen	.05
231	Cris Carter	.10
232	Jack Del Rio	.05
233	Vencie Glenn	.05
234	Quadry Ismail	.05
235	Carlos Jenkins	.05
236	Ed Macdaniel	.05
237	Randall McDaniel	.05
238	Warren Moon	.10
239	Anthony Parker	.05
240	John Randle	.05
241	Jake Reed	.05
242	Fuad Reveiz	.05
243	Broderick Thomas	.05
244	DeWayne Washington	.05
245	Bruce Armstrong	.05
246	Drew Bledsoe	1.00
247	Vincent Brisby	.05
248	Vincent Brown	.05
249	Marion Butts	.05
250	Ben Coates	.05
251	Tim Goad	.05
252	Myron Guyton	.05
253	Maurice Hurst	.05
254	Mike Jones	.05
255	Willie McGinest	.05
256	David Meggett	.05
257	Ricky Reynolds	.05
258	Chris Slade	.05
259	Michael Timpson	.05
260	Mario Bates	.20
261	Darion Connor	.05
262	Quinn Early	.05
263	Jim Everett	.05
264	Michael Haynes	.05
265	Tyrone Hughes	.05
266	Joe Johnson	.05
267	Wayne Martin	.05
268	William Roaf	.05
269	Irv Smith	.05
270	Jimmy Spencer	.05
271	Winfred Tubbs	.05
272	Renaldo Turnbull	.05
273	Michael Brooks	.05
274	Dave Brown	.05
275	Chris Calloway	.05
276	Jesse Campbell	.05
277	Howard Cross	.05
278		

279	John Elliott	.05
280	Keith Hamilton	.05
281	Rodney Hampton	.05
282	Thomas Lewis	.05
283	Thomas Randolph	.05
284	Mike Sherrard	.05
285	Michael Strahan	.05
286	Brad Baxter	.05
287	Tony Casillas	.05
288	Kyle Clifton	.05
289	Boomer Esiason	.05
290	Aaron Glenn	.05
291	Bobby Houston	.05
292	Johnny Johnson	.05
293	Jeff Lageman	.05
294	Mo Lewis	.05
295	Johnny Mitchell	.05
296	Rob Moore	.05
297	Marcus Turner	.05
298	Marvin Washington	.05
299	Eric Allen	.05
300	Fred Barnett	.05
301	Randall Cunningham	.10
302	Byron Evans	.05
303	William Fuller	.05
304	Charlie Garner	.10
305	Andy Harmon	.05
306	Greg Jackson	.05
307	Bill Romanowski	.05
308	William Thomas	.05
309	Herschel Walker	.10
310	Calvin Williams	.05
311	Michael Zordich	.05
312	Chad Brown	.05
313	Dermontti Dawson	.05
314	Barry Foster	.10
315	Kevin Greene	.05
316	Charles Johnson	.20
317	Levon Kirkland	.05
318	Carnell Lake	.05
319	Greg Lloyd	.05
320	Bam Morris	.40
321	Neil O'Donnell	.10
322	Darren Perry	.05
323	Ray Seals	.05
324	John L. Williams	.05
325	Rod Woodson	.05
326	John Carney	.05
327	Andre Coleman	.05
328	Courtney Hall	.05
329	Ronnie Harmon	.05
330	Dwayne Harper	.05
331	Stan Humphries	.10
332	Shawn Jefferson	.05
333	Tony Martin	.05
334	Natrone Means	.40
335	Chris Mims	.05
336	Leslie O'Neal	.05
337	Alfred Pupunu	.15
338	Junior Seau	.10
339	Mark Seay	.05
340	Eric Davis	.05
341	William Floyd	.25
342	Merton Hanks	.05
343	Rickey Jackson	.05
344	Brent Jones	.05
345	Tim McDonald	.05
346	Ken Norton	.05
347	Gary Plummer	.05
348	Jerry Rice	.50
349	Deion Sanders	.50
350	Jesse Sapolu	.05
351	Dana Stubblefield	.05
352	John Taylor	.05
353	Steve Wallace	.05
354	Ricky Watters	.10
355	Lee Woodall	.05
356	Bryant Young	.05
357	Steve Young	.40
358	Sam Adams	.05
359	Howard Ballard	.05
360	Robert Blackmon	.05
361	Brian Blades	.05
362	Carlton Gray	.05
363	Cortez Kennedy	.05
364	Rick Mirer	.35
365	Eugene Robinson	.05
366	Chris Warren	.05
367	Terry Wooden	.05
368	Brad Culpepper	.05
369	Lawrence Dawsey	.05
370	Trent Dilfer	.40
371	Santana Dotson	.05
372	Craig Erickson	.05
373	Thomas Everett	.05
374	Paul Gruber	.05
375	Alvin Harper	.05
376	Jackie Harris	.05
377	Courtney Hawkins	.05
378	Martin Mayhew	.05
379	Hardy Nickerson	.05
380	Errict Rhett	.50
381	Charles Wilson	.05
382	Reggie Brooks	.05
383	Tom Carter	.05
384	Andre Collins	.05
385	Henry Ellard	.05
386	Ricky Ervins	.05
387	Darrell Green	.05
388	Ken Harvey	.05
389	Brian Mitchell	.05
390	Stanley Richard	.05
391	Heath Shuler	.50
392	Rod Stephens	.05
393	Tyronne Stowe	.05
394	Tydus Winans	.05
395	Tony Woods	.05

396	Checklist	.05
397	Checklist	.05
398	Checklist	.05
399	Checklist	.05
400	Checklist	.05

1995 Fleer Aerial Attack

This 6-card insert set features two top NFL quarterbacks and four top wide receivers. Cards, which were included one per every 37 packs, use 100 percent foil-etched designs, with an "Aerial Attack" football logo on the front. An action photo is also featured, against a background of footballs. The card back is numbered 1 of 6, etc.

		MT
Complete Set (6):		40.00
Common Player:		3.00
1	Tim Brown	3.00
2	Dan Marino	20.00
3	Joe Montana	10.00
4	Jerry Rice	10.00
5	Andre Rison	3.00
6	Sterling Sharpe	3.00

1995 Fleer Flair Preview

Every pack of 1995 Fleer football included one of these 1995 Fleer Flair preview cards, showcasing the company's 100 percent etched-foil Flair product. The card front uses a horizontal format, with a player mug shot and an action shot. The player's initials are stamped in silver in a scripted typeface. The card back, numbered 1 of 30, etc., has a brief summary of the player's 1994 season. It also indicates the card backs of the regular Flair set will feature statistics and a player photo on them. Cards are glossy poly-laminated and are double in thickness.

		MT
Complete Set (30):		20.00
Common Player:		.25
Minor Stars:		.50
1	Aeneas Williams	.25
2	Jeff George	.50
3	Andre Reed	.25
4	Kerry Collins	.50
5	Mark Carrier	.25
6	Jeff Blake	.50
7	Leroy Hoard	.25
8	Emmitt Smith	3.00
9	Shannon Sharpe	.25
10	Barry Sanders	2.50
11	Reggie White	.50
12	Bruce Matthews	.25
13	Marshall Faulk	2.00
14	Tony Boselli	.75
15	Joe Montana	2.00
16	Tim Brown	.25
17	Jerome Bettis	.75

18	Dan Marino	3.00
19	Cris Carter	.50
20	Drew Bledsoe	2.00
21	William Roaf	.25
22	Rodney Hampton	.25
23	Rob Moore	.25
24	Fred Barnett	.25
25	Rod Woodson	.25
26	Natrone Means	1.50
27	Jerry Rice	1.75
28	Chris Warren	.50
29	Errict Rhett	.75
30	Henry Ellard	.25

1995 Fleer Gridiron Leaders

Ten of the NFL's top statistical leaders from 1994 are shown on these 1995 Fleer insert cards. Cards were randomly included one per every four packs. The card front has the player photo against a grid-like background, with "Gridiron Leader" running along the left side. The back has another color photo and a summary of the player's 1994 accomplishments, plus the categories he led the league in. Cards are numbered 1 of 10, etc.

		MT
Complete Set (10):		8.00
Common Player:		.25
Minor Stars:		.50
1	Cris Carter	.50
2	Ben Coates	.25
3	Marshall Faulk	.50
4	Jerry Rice	1.00
5	Barry Sanders	1.50
6	Deion Sanders	.75
7	Emmitt Smith	2.00
8	Eric Turner	.25
9	Chris Warren	.25
10	Steve Young	1.00

1995 Fleer Prospects

Twenty of the top 1995 NFL draft picks with promising futures are featured on these 1995 insert cards. Cards, numbered on the back 1 of 20, etc., feature a color action photo of the player on the front; he is wearing his collegiate uniform. The background is a metallic-like burst. The player's name and the "NFL Prospects" logo are in gold. The card back has another photo of the player, plus a summary of the player's collegiate achievements.

		MT
Complete Set (20):		30.00
Common Player:		.50
Minor Stars:		1.00
1	Tony Boselli	.75
2	Kyle Brady	1.00
3	Ruben Brown	.50
4	Kevin Carter	1.00

5	Ki-Jana Carter	1.00
6	Kerry Collins	2.00
7	Luther Elliss	.50
8	Jimmy Hitchcock	.50
9	Jack Jackson	.50
10	Ellis Johnson	.50
11	Rob Johnson	2.00
12	Steve McNair	5.00
13	Rashaan Salaam	1.00
14	Warren Sapp	1.00
15	J.J. Stokes	2.00
16	Bobby Taylor	.50
17	John Walsh	.50
18	Michael Westbrook	1.50
19	Tyrone Wheatley	1.00
20	Sherman Williams	1.00

1995 Fleer Pro-Visions

These six 1995 Fleer insert cards feature the usual artwork design which has been used for previous Pro Visions sets. Cards were randomly included one per every six packs. The fronts of the six cards combine to form an interlocking design. Card backs, numbered 1 of 6, etc., have a summary of the player's career, but no photo or artwork.

		MT
Complete Set (6):		5.00
Common Player:		.25
1	Natrone Means	.50
2	Sterling Sharpe	.25
3	Ken Norton	.25
4	Drew Bledsoe	1.00
5	Marshall Faulk	1.00
6	Tim Brown	.50

1995 Fleer Rookie Sensations

Twenty top rookies from 1994 are featured on these insert cards, included one per every three 17-card packs. The card front has a color action photo, with the player's name and "Rookie Sensations" running down the side of the card. Card backs are numbered 1 of 20, etc.

		MT
Complete Set (20):		70.00
Common Player:		2.00
Minor Stars:		4.00
1	Derrick Alexander	3.00
2	Mario Bates	4.00
3	Tim Bowens	2.00
4	Lake Dawson	4.00
5	Bert Emanuel	4.00
6	Marshall Faulk	10.00
7	William Floyd	5.00
8	Rob Fredrickson	2.00
9	Greg Hill	4.00
10	Charles Johnson	4.00
11	Antonio Langham	2.00
12	Willie McGinest	2.00
13	Bam Morris	4.00
14	Errict Rhett	4.00
15	Darnay Scott	5.00

16	Heath Shuler	5.00
17	DeWayne Washington	2.00
18	Dan Wilkinson	2.00
19	Lee Woodall	2.00
20	Bryant Young	2.00

1995 Fleer TD Sensations

Ten top NFL scorers are featured on these 1995 Fleer insert cards, issued one per every three 11-card packs. Card fronts have a color action photo, with the "TD Sensation" logo stamped in green and gold. The player's name is also in gold. The card back has another color photo, plus a brief player profile running down one side of the card. Cards are numbered 1 of 10, etc..

		MT
Complete Set (10):		8.00
Common Player:		.25
Minor Stars:		
1	Marshall Faulk	1.00
2	Dan Marino	2.00
3	Natrone Means	.50
4	Herman Moore	.25
5	Jerry Rice	1.00
6	Sterling Sharpe	.25
7	Emmitt Smith	2.00
8	Chris Warren	.25
9	Ricky Watters	.50
10	Steve Young	1.00

1995 Fleer Bettis/Mirer Sheet

These sheets feature 10 cards of Jerome Bettis on one side and 10 cards of Rick Mirer on the other and were distributed at the Super Bowl show in Miami. The sheets could be purchased for five wrappers and $1. There were also 400 sheets signed by one of the players that were sold for $25.

		MT
Complete Set (1):		2.50
1	Jerome Bettis, Rick Mirer	2.50

1995 Fleer Shell

This 10-card set was produced by Fleer and issued by Shell in its "Drive for the Super Bowl XXX" sweepstakes. The cards are standard sized and were originally attached to a rub-off tab card of equal size and divided by a perforated line.

	MT
Complete Set (10):	10.00
Common Player:	1.00

1	Super Bowl XXIII (Joe Montana's drive)	1.50
2	1967 NFL Championship (Bart Starr's TD)	1.00
3	1986 AFC Championship (The Drive, Mark Jackson)	1.00
4	Super Bowl XIII (Steeler's drive, Terry Bradshaw)	1.00
5	1975 NFC Divisional Playoffs (Cowboy's drive, Doug Dennison featured)	1.00
6	1968 AFL Championship (Jet's drive)	1.00
7	1981 NFC Championship (49ers team shot)	1.00
8	1983 NFC Championship (Redskin's drive, John Riggins' TD)	1.00
9	1969 AFL Divisional Playoffs (Len Dawson in huddle)	1.00
10	Super Bowl V (Colts' field goal, Bob Lilly and Mel Renfro pictured)	1.00

1996 Fleer

Fleer's 1996 football card set contains 200 cards, many of which are from subsets in the main set. The best players from the 1996 draft are featured on 40 cards, while the top 20 from 1995 have their own subset. Key match-ups for 1996's biggest games, as selected by Pro Football Weekly, are spotlighted on 17 other subset cards. Pro Football Weekly writers have also written ten the card backs. Each basic card design includes a "Greatest Game" note on the front, plus career statistics, basic statistics and the player's "Triangle Numbers" - his height, weight and time in the 40-yard dash. Six insert sets were created - Rookie Sensations, Breakthrough, RAC Pack, Statistically Speaking, Rookie Write Up and Signature Series. The Signature Series cards are autographed cards by Eddie George, Leeland McElroy and Tim Biakabutuka. Fleer also offered Rookie Sensation Hot Packs, which contained specially-marked versions of all 11 cards from that insert set. These packs were seeded one per every 960 packs.

		MT
Complete Set (200):		20.00
Common Player:		.05
Minor Stars:		.10
Wax Box:		32.00
1	Garrison Hearst	.10
2	Rob Moore	.05
3	Frank Sanders	.05
4	Eric Swann	.05
5	Aeneas Williams	.05
6	Jeff George	.10
7	Craig Heyward	.05
8	Terance Mathis	.05
9	Eric Metcalf	.05
10	Michael Jackson	.05
11	Andre Rison	.05
12	Vinny Testaverde	.05
13	Eric Turner	.05
14	Darick Holmes	.05
15	Jim Kelly	.10

16	Bryce Paup	.05
17	Bruce Smith	.05
18	Thurman Thomas	.10
19	Kerry Collins	.30
20	Lamar Lathon	.05
21	Derrick Moore	.05
22	Tyrone Poole	.05
23	Curtis Conway	.05
24	Bryan Cox	.05
25	Erik Kramer	.05
26	Rashaan Salaam	.60
27	Jeff Blake	.60
28	Ki-Jana Carter	.25
29	Carl Pickens	.10
30	Darnay Scott	.05
31	Troy Aikman	1.00
32	Charles Haley	.05
33	Michael Irvin	.10
34	Daryl Johnston	.05
35	Jay Novacek	.05
36	Deion Sanders	.60
37	Emmitt Smith	2.00
38	Steve Atwater	.05
39	Terrell Davis	.60
40	John Elway	.50
41	Anthony Miller	.05
42	Shannon Sharpe	.05
43	Scott Mitchell	.05
44	Herman Moore	.30
45	Johnnie Morton	.05
46	Brett Perriman	.05
47	Barry Sanders	1.00
48	Edgar Bennett	.05
49	Robert Brooks	.05
50	Mark Chmura	.30
51	Brett Favre	2.00
52	Reggie White	.10
53	Mel Gray	.05
54	Steve McNair	.60
55	Chris Sanders	.30
56	Rodney Thomas	.05
57	Quentin Coryatt	.05
58	Sean Dawkins	.05
59	Ken Dilger	.05
60	Marshall Faulk	.75
61	Jim Harbaugh	.05
62	Tony Boselli	.05
63	Mark Brunell	.50
64	Natrone Means	.10
65	James Stewart	.05
66	Marcus Allen	.05
67	Steve Bono	.05
68	Neil Smith	.05
69	Derrick Thomas	.05
70	Tamarick Vanover	.60
71	Fred Barnett	.05
72	Eric Green	.05
73	Dan Marino	2.00
74	O.J. McDuffie	.05
75	Bernie Parmalee	.05
76	Cris Carter	.05
77	Qadry Ismail	.05
78	Warren Moon	.05
79	Jake Reed	.05
80	Robert Smith	.05
81	Drew Bledsoe	.75
82	Vincent Brisby	.05
83	Ben Coates	.05
84	Curtis Martin	1.50
85	David Meggett	.05
86	Mario Bates	.05
87	Jim Everett	.05
88	Michael Haynes	.05
89	Renaldo Turnbull	.05
90	Dave Brown	.05
91	Rodney Hampton	.05
92	Thomas Lewis	.05
93	Tyrone Wheatley	.05
94	Kyle Brady	.05
95	Hugh Douglas	.05
96	Aaron Glenn	.05
97	Jeff Graham	.05
98	Adrian Murrell	.05
99	Neil O'Donnell	.05
100	Tim Brown	.05
101	Jeff Hostetler	.05
102	Napoleon Kaufman	.30
103	Chester McGlockton	.05
104	Harvey Williams	.05
105	William Fuller	.05
106	Charlie Garner	.05
107	Ricky Watters	.05
108	Calvin Williams	.05
109	Jerome Bettis	.05
110	Greg Lloyd	.05
111	Bam Morris	.05
112	Kordell Stewart	1.00
113	Yancey Thigpen	.40
114	Rod Woodson	.05
115	Isaac Bruce	.50
116	Troy Drayton	.05
117	Leslie O'Neal	.05
118	Steve Walsh	.05
119	Marco Coleman	.05
120	Aaron Hayden	.05
121	Stan Humphries	.05
122	Junior Seau	.10
123	Junior Seau	.05
124	Brent Jones	.05
125	Ken Norton	.05
126	Jerry Rice	1.00
127	J.J. Stokes	.10
128	Steve Young	.75
129	Brian Blades	.05
130	Joey Galloway	.60
131	Rick Mirer	.05

132	Chris Warren	.10
133	Trent Dilfer	.05
134	Alvin Harper	.05
135	Hardy Nickerson	.05
136	Errict Rhett	.50
137	Terry Allen	.05
138	Henry Ellard	.05
139	Heath Shuler	.30
140	Michael Westbrook	.10
141	Karim Abdul-Jabbar	.50
142	Mike Alstott	1.00
143	Marco Battaglia	.05
144	Tim Biakabutuka	.75
145	Tony Brackens	.05
146	Duane Clemons	.05
147	Ernie Conwell	.05
148	Chris Darkins	.25
149	Stephen Davis	3.00
150	Brian Dawkins	.05
151	Rickey Dudley	.50
152	Jason Dunn	.05
153	Bobby Engram	.50
154	Daryl Gardener	.05
155	Eddie George	3.00
156	Terry Glenn	1.50
157	Kevin Hardy	.40
158	Walt Harris	.05
159	Marvin Harrison	2.00
160	Bobby Hoying	.05
161	Keyshawn Johnson	2.00
162	Cedric Jones	.05
163	Marcus Jones	.05
164	Eddie Kennison	.30
165	Ray Lewis	.05
166	Derrick Mayes	.75
167	Leeland McElroy	.20
168	Johnny McWilliams	.05
169	John Mobley	.05
170	Alex Molden	.05
171	Eric Moulds	1.50
172	Muhsin Muhammad	.75
173	Jonathan Ogden	.05
174	Lawrence Phillips	.50
175	Stanley Pritchett	.25
176	Simeon Rice	.30
177	Bryan Still	.05
178	Amani Toomer	.50
179	Regan Upshaw	.05
180	Alex Van Dyke	.25
181	Minnesota/Detroit (PFW Weekly Matchups)	.05
182	Oakland/Kansas City (PFW Weekly Matchups)	.05
183	Buffalo/Pittsburgh (PFW Weekly Matchups)	.05
184	Atlanta/San Francisco (PFW Weekly Matchups)	.05
185	Carolina/Jacksonville (PFW Weekly Matchups)	.05
186	Philadelphia/Dallas (PFW Weekly Matchups)	.05
187	Green Bay/Chicago (PFW Weekly Matchups)	.05
188	Pittsburgh/Kansas City (PFW Weekly Matchups)	.05
189	Cincinnati/Pittsburgh (PFW Weekly Matchups)	.05
190	Dallas/Miami (PFW Weekly Matchups)	.05
191	Denver/Oakland (PFW Weekly Matchups)	.05
192	Kansas City/Minnesota (PFW Weekly Matchups)	.05
193	San Diego/Indianapolis (PFW Weekly Matchups)	.05
194	Dallas/San Francisco (PFW Weekly Matchups)	.05
195	Miami/Oakland (PFW Weekly Matchups)	.05
196	San Francisco/Pittsburgh (PFW Weekly Matchups)	.05
197	Kansas City/Buffalo (PFW Weekly Matchups)	.05
198	Checklist	.05
199	Checklist	.05
200	Checklist	.05

Post-1980 cards in Near Mint condition will generally sell for about 75% of the quoted Mint value. Excellent-condition cards bring no more than 40%.

1996 Fleer Rookie Sensations

Eleven of the NFL's top rookies entering the 1996 season are featured on these 1996 Fleer football plastic card inserts. The cards were seeded one per every 72 packs. Each front has an action photo on it, with the player's name and a team logo in the upper right corner. The Fleer logo is at the bottom of the card, with the Rookie Sensations logo in the bottom left corner. The card back has a card number (1 of 11, etc.) in the upper right corner; the set's logo is also at the top. A brief career write-up is in the middle, with a Pro Football Weekly logo and the player's name and position underneath. Special Rookie Sensation Hot Packs were also created; these packs contained all 11 cards, each with a special Hot Packs logo on it. Hot Packs were seeded one per every 960 packs.

		MT
Complete Set (11):		125.00
Common Player:		6.00
1	Karim Abdul-Jabbar	15.00
2	Tim Biakabutuka	8.00
3	Rickey Dudley	6.00
4	Eddie George	40.00
5	Terry Glenn	15.00
6	Kevin Hardy	6.00
7	Marvin Harrison	12.00
8	Keyshawn Johnson	20.00
9	Jon Ogden	6.00
10	Lawrence Phillips	15.00
11	Simeon Rice	6.00

1996 Fleer Rookie Sensations Hot Packs

This 11-card insert parallels the Rookie Sensations insert, but was found as a complete set in every 960 packs of Fleer Football. The cards are exactly like regular Rookie Sensations, except for a red foil Hot Packs logo on the front.

	MT
Complete Set (11):	75.00
Hot Pack Cards:	50%

1996 Fleer Rookie Signatures

Three top rookie running backs have autographed cards for this 1996 Fleer insert set. The cards were seeded one per every 288 hobby packs only.

		MT
Complete Set (3):		150.00
A1	Tim Biakabutuka	40.00
A2	Eddie George	100.00
A3	Leeland McElroy	30.00

1996 Fleer Breakthroughs

These players were chosen by Pro Football Weekly to have career seasons in 1996, including rookies who are predicted to have breakthrough campaigns in their first NFL season. The cards, seeded one per every three packs of 1996 Fleer football product, feature a 100% etched foil design for the card front. The Fleer logo and player's name and "Breakthrough" are stamped in gold foil. The horizontal back has the card number in a circle in the upper left corner next to a Pro Football Weekly logo. The player's name, team name, position and a team logo are underneath, followed by a brief write-up about the player's career accomplishments. A photo is on the right half of the card.

		MT
Complete Set (24):		25.00
Common Player:		.50
1	Tim Bowens	.50
2	Kyle Brady	.50
3	Devin Bush	.50
4	Kevin Carter	.50
5	Ki-Jana Carter	.50
6	Kerry Collins	3.00
7	Trent Dilfer	.50
8	Ken Dilger	.50
9	Joey Galloway	2.00
10	Aaron Hayden	.50
11	Napoleon Kaufman	.50
12	Craig Newsome	.50
13	Tyrone Poole	.50
14	Jake Reed	.50
15	Rashaan Salaam	.50
16	Chris Sanders	.50
17	Frank Sanders	.50
18	Kordell Stewart	5.00
19	J.J. Stokes	.50
20	Bobby Taylor	.50
21	Orlando Thomas	.50
22	Michael Timpson	.50
23	Tamarick Vanover	.50
24	Michael Westbrook	.50

1996 Fleer RAC Pack

These 10 cards showcase receivers who rack up yards after the catch (Run After Catch yards). The cards, seeded one every 18th pack of 1996 Fleer product, feature an etched foil and color-foil stamped design for the card front's background (a football field design) and set/brand logos and player's name. The horizontal back has a bull's-eye in the upper left corner, with a player photo against it. The player's name, Pro Football Weekly logo and an ex-planation of the player's run-after-catch skills are on the opposite side.

		MT
Complete Set (10):		25.00
Common Player:		1.00
1	Robert Brooks	1.00
2	Tim Brown	1.00
3	Isaac Bruce	6.00
4	Cris Carter	1.00
5	Curtis Conway	1.00
6	Michael Irvin	2.00
7	Eric Metcalf	1.00
8	Herman Moore	3.00
9	Carl Pickens	2.00
10	Jerry Rice	10.00

1996 Fleer Statistically Speaking

The NFL's statistical standouts are featured on these plastic cards using hot colors. These 1996 Fleer inserts are some of the tougher to find; they are seeded one per every 37 packs. Each card front has an action photo against a box filled with stats. The set's logo and player's name are along the bottom of the card. The background is a ghosted action scene. The horizontal back has a photo of the player on one side, against a ghosted action background which also contains a stat box. The card number (1 of 20, etc.) is in the upper left corner. The right side has a colored panel which has his name, position, team logo, Pro Football Weekly logo and a write-up of his accomplishments.

		MT
Complete Set (20):		100.00
Common Player:		1.50
1	Troy Aikman	10.00
2	Larry Centers	1.50
3	Ben Coates	1.50
4	Brett Favre	20.00
5	Joey Galloway	8.00
6	Rodney Hampton	1.50
7	Dan Marino	20.00
8	Curtis Martin	15.00
9	Anthony Miller	1.50
10	Brian Mitchell	1.50
11	Herman Moore	1.50
12	Errict Rhett	1.50
13	Rashaan Salaam	1.50
14	Barry Sanders	10.00
15	Deion Sanders	6.00
16	Emmitt Smith	20.00
17	Kordell Stewart	10.00
18	Chris Warren	1.50
19	Ricky Watters	1.50
20	Steve Young	8.00

1996 Fleer Rookie Write-Ups

These 10 cards showcase receivers who rack up yards after the catch (Run After Catch yards). These hobby-exclusive insert cards feature 10 rookies en-tering the 1996 NFL season with scouting reports similar to those of previous rookies. Cards were inserted at a ratio of one per every 12 packs of 1996 Fleer hobby packs. The card front has a black band at the top with the player's name stamped in gold foil. His position and the set/brand logos are also stamped in gold. The middle of the card has an action shot of the player, against a written scouting report. The back has the player's name at the top, along with a card number (1 of 10, etc.). The background is white, with a brief write-up of the player and a colored/ghosted photo on it the front. The Pro Football Weekly Logo is also on the back.

		MT
Complete Set (10):		40.00
Common Player:		1.50
1	Tim Biakabutuka	1.50
2	Rickey Dudley	1.50
3	Eddie George	8.00
4	Terry Glenn	7.00
5	Kevin Hardy	1.50
6	Marvin Harrison	4.00
7	Keyshawn Johnson	5.00
8	Leeland McElroy	1.50
9	Lawrence Phillips	1.50
10	Simeon Rice	1.50

1997 Fleer

The 450-card set includes 415 player cards, five checklists and 30 Something Special subset cards. The matte-finish cards have full-bleed photos on the front, with his last name in large block letters at the bottom. His first name is printed in small letters above, while his team and position appear directly below the player's last name. The backs have the name in the upper left, with the card number in the upper right. Rounding out the backs are a player head shot, team name and logo, highlights, bio and career stats. Two parallels are randomly seeded in hobby packs. Crystal Collection cards were seeded 1:2, while Tiffany Collection cards were 1:20.

		MT
Complete Set (450):		40.00
Common Player:		.05
Minor Stars:		.10
Wax Box:		45.00
1	Mark Brunell	1.00
2	Andre Reed	.05
3	Darrell Green	.05
4	Mario Bates	.05
5	Eddie George	1.50
6	Cris Carter	.05
7	Terrell Owens	1.00
8	Bill Romanowski	.05
9	Isaac Bruce	.20
10	Eric Curry	.05
11	Danny Kanell	.05
12	Ki-Jana Carter	.10
13	Antonio Freeman	.30
14	Ricky Watters	.10
15	Ty Law	.05
16	Alonzo Spellman	.05
17	Kordell Stewart	.75
18	Jerry Rice	1.00
19	Derrick Alexander	.05
20	Barry Sanders	2.00
21	Keyshawn Johnson	.75
22	Emmitt Smith	2.00
23	Ricky Proehl	.05
24	Daryl Gardner	.05
25	Dan Saleaumua	.05
26	Kevin Greene	.05
27	Junior Seau	.10
28	Randall McDaniel	.05
29	Marshall Faulk	.25
30	Lorenzo Lynch	.05
31	Terance Mathis	.05
32	Warren Sapp	.05
33	Chris Sanders	.05
34	Tom Carter	.05
35	Aeneas Williams	.05
36	Lawrence Phillips	.10
37	John Elway	.75
38	Stanley Richard	.05
39	Darryl Williams	.05
40	Phillippi Sparks	.05
41	Tedy Bruschi	.05
42	Merton Hanks	.05
43	Ray Lewis	.05
44	Erik Williams	.05
45	Jason Gildon	.05
46	George Koonce	.05
47	Louis Oliver	.05
48	Muhsin Muhammad	.30
49	Daryl Hobbs	.05
50	Terry Glenn	1.25
51	Marvin Harrison	.75
52	Brian Dawkins	.05
53	Dale Carter	.05
54	Alex Molden	.05
55	Raymont Harris	.05
56	Jeff Burris	.05
57	Don Beebe	.05
58	Jamir Miller	.05
59	Carl Pickens	.10
60	Antonio London	.05
61	Courtney Hall	.05
62	Derrick Brooks	.05
63	Chris Boniol	.05
64	Jeff Lageman	.05
65	Roy Barker	.05
66	Devin Bush	.05
67	Aaron Glenn	.05
68	Wayne Simmons	.05
69	Steve Atwater	.05
70	Jimmie Jones	.05
71	Mark Carrier	.05
72	Chris Chandler	.05
73	Andy Harmon	.05
74	John Friesz	.05
75	Karim Abdul-Jabbar	1.00
76	Levon Kirkland	.05
77	Torrance Small	.05
78	Harvey Williams	.05
79	Chris Calloway	.05
80	Vinny Testaverde	.05
81	Bryant Young	.05
82	Ray Buchanan	.05
83	Robert Smith	.05
84	Robert Brooks	.10
85	Ray Crockett	.05
86	Bennie Blades	.05
87	Mark Carrier	.05
88	Mike Tomczak	.05
89	Darick Holmes	.05
90	Drew Bledsoe	1.00
91	Darren Woodson	.05
92	Dan Wilkinson	.05
93	Charles Way	.05
94	Ray Farmer	.05
95	Marcus Allen	.10
96	Marco Coleman	.05
97	Zach Thomas	.30
98	Wesley Walls	.05
99	Frank Wycheck	.05
100	Troy Aikman	1.00
101	Clyde Simmons	.05
102	Courtney Hawkins	.05
103	Chuck Smith	.05
104	Neil O'Donnell	.05
105	Kevin Carter	.05
106	Chris Slade	.05
107	Jessie Armstead	.05
108	Sean Dawkins	.05
109	Robert Blackmon	.05
110	Kevin Smith	.05
111	Lonnie Johnson	.05
112	Craig Newsome	.05
113	Jonathan Ogden	.05
114	Chris Zorich	.05
115	Tim Brown	.05
116	Fred Barnett	.05
117	Michael Haynes	.05
118	Eric Hill	.05
119	Ronnie Harmon	.05
120	Sean Gilbert	.05
121	Derrick Alexander	.05
122	Derrick Thomas	.10
123	Tyrone Wheatley	.10
124	Cortez Kennedy	.05
125	Jeff George	.05
126	Chad Cota	.05
127	Gary Zimmerman	.05
128	Johnnie Morton	.05
129	Chad Brown	.05
130	Marvcus Patton	.05
131	James Stewart	.05
132	Terry Kirby	.05
133	Chris Mims	.05
134	William Thomas	.05
135	Steve Tasker	.05
136	Jason Belser	.05
137	Bryan Cox	.05
138	Jessie Tuggle	.05
139	Ashley Ambrose	.05
140	Mark Chmura	.05
141	Jeff Hostetler	.05
142	Rich Owens	.05
143	Willie Davis	.05
144	Hardy Nickerson	.05
145	Curtis Martin	1.25
146	Ken Norton	.05
147	Victor Green	.05
148	Anthony Miller	.05
149	John Kasay	.05
150	O.J. McDuffie	.05
151	Darren Perry	.05
152	Luther Elliss	.05
153	Greg Hill	.05
154	John Randle	.05
155	Stephen Grant	.05
156	Leon Lett	.05
157	Darrien Gordon	.05
158	Ray Zellars	.05
159	Michael Jackson	.05
160	Leslie O'Neal	.05
161	Bruce Smith	.05
162	Santana Dotson	.05
163	Bobby Hebert	.05
164	Keith Hamilton	.05
165	Tony Boselli	.05
166	Alfred Williams	.05
167	Ty Detmer	.05
168	Chester McGlockton	.05
169	William Floyd	.05
170	Bruce Matthews	.05
171	Simeon Rice	.05
172	Scott Mitchell	.05
173	Ricardo McDonald	.05
174	Tyrone Poole	.05
175	Greg Lloyd	.05
176	Bruce Armstrong	.05
177	Erik Kramer	.05
178	Kimble Anders	.05
179	Lamar Smith	.05
180	Tony Tolbert	.05
181	Joe Aska	.05
182	Eric Allen	.05
183	Eric Turner	.05
184	Brad Johnson	.05
185	Tony Martin	.05
186	Mike Mamula	.05
187	Irving Spikes	.05
188	Keith Jackson	.05
189	Carlton Bailey	.05
190	Tyrone Braxton	.05
191	Chad Bratzke	.05
192	Adrian Murrell	.05
193	Roman Phifer	.05
194	Todd Collins	.05
195	Chris Warren	.05
196	Kevin Hardy	.05
197	Rick Mirer	.10
198	Cornelius Bennett	.05
199	Jimmy Hitchcock	.05
200	Michael Irvin	.10
201	Quentin Coryatt	.05
202	Reggie White	.10
203	Larry Centers	.05
204	Rodney Thomas	.05
205	Dana Stubblefield	.05
206	Rod Woodson	.05
207	Rhett Hall	.05
208	Steve Tovar	.05
209	Michael Westbrook	.10
210	Steve Wisniewski	.05
211	Carlester Crumpler	.05
212	Elvis Grbac	.10
213	Tim Bowens	.05
214	Kevin Porcher	.05
215	John Carney	.05
216	Anthony Newman	.05
217	Ernest Byner	.05
218	DeWayne Washington	.05
219	Willie Green	.05
220	Terry Allen	.10
221	William Fuller	.05
222	Al Del Greco	.05
223	Trent Dilfer	.10
224	Michael Dean Perry	.05
225	Larry Allen	.05
226	Mark Bruener	.05
227	Clay Matthews	.05
228	Ruben Brown	.05
229	Edgar Bennett	.05
230	Neil Smith	.05
231	Ken Harvey	.05
232	Kyle Brady	.05
233	Corey Miller	.05
234	Tony Siragusa	.05
235	Todd Sauerbrun	.05
236	Daniel Stubbs	.05
237	Robb Thomas	.05
238	Jimmy Smith	.05
239	Marquez Pope	.05
240	Tim Biakabutuka	.10
241	Jamie Asher	.05
242	Steve McNair	.75
243	Harold Green	.05
244	Frank Sanders	.05
245	Joe Johnson	.05
246	Eric Bieniemy	.05
247	Kevin Turner	.05
248	Rickey Dudley	.10
249	Orlando Thomas	.05
250	Dan Marino	2.00
251	Deion Sanders	.50
252	Dan Williams	.05
253	Sam Gash	.05
254	Lonnie Marts	.05
255	Mo Lewis	.05
256	Charles Johnson	.05
257	Chris Jacke	.05
258	Keenan McCardell	.05
259	Donnell Woolford	.05
260	Terrance Shaw	.05
261	Jason Dunn	.05
262	Willie McGinest	.05
263	Ken Dilger	.05
264	Keith Lyle	.05
265	Antonio Langham	.05
266	Carlton Gray	.05

267 LeShon Johnson .05
268 Thurman Thomas .10
269 Jesse Campbell .05
270 Carnell Lake .05
271 Cris Dishman .05
272 Kevin Williams .05
273 Troy Brown .05
274 William Roaf .05
275 Terrell Davis 1.25
276 Herman Moore .20
277 Walt Harris .05
278 Mark Collins .05
279 Bert Emanuel .05
280 Qadry Ismail .05
281 Phil Hansen .05
282 Steve Young .75
283 Michael Sinclair .05
284 Jeff Graham .05
285 Sam Mills .05
286 Terry McDaniel .05
287 Eugene Robinson .05
288 Tony Bennett .05
289 Daryl Johnston .05
290 Eric Swann .05
291 Bam Morris .05
292 Thomas Lewis .05
293 Terrell Fletcher .05
294 Gus Frerotte .05
295 Stanley Pritchett .05
296 Mike Alstott .10
297 Will Shields .05
298 Errict Rhett .10
299 Garrison Hearst .05
300 Kerry Collins .25
301 Darryll Lewis .05
302 Chris T. Jones .05
303 Yancey Thigpen .05
304 Jackie Harris .05
305 Steve Christie .05
306 Gilbert Brown .05
307 Terry Wooden .05
308 Pete Mitchell .05
309 Tim McDonald .05
310 Jake Reed .05
311 Ed McCaffrey .05
312 Chris Doleman .05
313 Eric Metcalf .05
314 Ricky Reynolds .05
315 David Sloan .05
316 Marvin Washington .05
317 Herschel Walker .05
318 Michael Timpson .05
319 Blaine Bishop .05
320 Irv Smith .05
321 Seth Joyner .05
322 Terrell Buckley .05
323 Michael Strahan .05
324 Sam Adams .05
325 Leslie Shepherd .05
326 James Jett .05
327 Anthony Pleasant .05
328 Lee Woodall .05
329 Shannon Sharpe .05
330 Jamal Anderson .20
331 Andre Hastings .05
332 Troy Vincent .05
333 Sean LaChapelle .05
334 Winslow Oliver .05
335 Sean Jones .05
336 Darnay Scott .05
337 Todd Lyght .05
338 Leonard Russell .05
339 Nate Newton .05
340 Zack Crockett .05
341 Amp Lee .05
342 Bobby Engram .05
343 Mike Hollis .05
344 Rodney Hampton .05
345 Mel Gray .05
346 Van Malone .05
347 Aaron Craver .05
348 Jim Everett .05
349 Trace Armstrong .05
350 Pat Swilling .05
351 Brent Jones .05
352 Chris Spielman .05
353 Brett Perriman .05
354 Brian Kinchen .05
355 Joey Galloway .30
356 Henry Ellard .05
357 Ben Coates .05
358 Dorsey Levens .20
359 Charlie Garner .05
360 Erric Pegram .05
361 Anthony Johnson .05
362 Rashaan Salaam .10
363 Jeff Blake .20
364 Kent Graham .05
365 Broderick Thomas .05
366 Richmond Webb .05
367 Alfred Pupunu .05
368 Mark Stepnoski .05
369 David Dunn .05
370 Bobby Houston .05
371 Anthony Parker .05
372 Quinn Early .05
373 LeRoy Butler .05
374 Kurt Gouveia .05
375 Greg Biekert .05
376 Jim Harbaugh .05
377 Eric Bjornson .05
378 Craig Heyward .05
379 Steve Bono .05
380 Tony Banks .30
381 John Mobley .05
382 Irving Fryar .05
383 Dermontti Dawson .05
384 Eric Davis .05

385 Natrone Means .10
386 Jason Sehorn .05
387 Michael McCrary .05
388 Corwin Brown .05
389 Kevin Glover .05
390 Jerris McPhail .05
391 Bobby Taylor .05
392 Tony McGee .05
393 Curtis Conway .05
394 Napoleon Kaufman .05
395 Brian Blades .05
396 Richard Dent .05
397 Dave Brown .05
398 Stan Humphries .05
399 Stevon Moore .05
400 Brett Favre 2.00
401 Jerome Bettis .10
402 Darrin Smith .05
403 Chris Penn .05
404 Rob Moore .05
405 Michael Barrow .05
406 Tony Brackens .05
407 Wayne Martin .05
408 Warren Moon .05
409 Jason Elam .05
410 J.J. Birden .05
411 Hugh Douglas .05
412 Lamar Lathon .05
413 John Kidd .05
414 Bryce Paup .05
415 Shawn Jefferson .05
416 Leeland McElroy .10
417 Elbert Shelley .05
418 Jermaine Lewis .05
419 Eric Moulds .10
420 Michael Bates .05
421 John Mangum .05
422 Corey Sawyer .05
423 Jim Schwantz .05
424 Rod Smith .05
425 Glyn Milburn .05
426 Desmond Howard .10
427 John Henry Mills .05
428 Cary Blanchard .05
429 Chris Hudson .05
430 Tamarick Vanover .10
431 Kirby Dar Dar .05
432 David Palmer .05
433 Dave Meggett .05
434 Tyrone Hughes .05
435 Amani Toomer .10
436 Wayne Chrebet .05
437 Carl Kidd .05
438 Derrick Witherspoon .05
439 Jahine Arnold .05
440 Andre Coleman .05
441 Jeff Wilkins .05
442 Jay Bellamy .05
443 Eddie Kennison .50
444 Nilo Silvan .05
445 Brian Mitchell .05
446 Checklist .05
447 Checklist .05
448 Checklist .05
449 Checklist .05
450 Checklist .05

1997 Fleer Crystal Silver

This set paralleled the 445 cards included in Fleer Football (minus five checklist cards) and was seeded one per pack. Each card was distinguished by a "Traditions Crystal" logo on one of the upper corners. This parallel also contained a glossy silver finish, whereas the base cards had a matte finish, and silver foil instead of the gold foil used on the base cards.

	MT
Complete Set (445):	160.00
Crystal Silver Cards:	2x-4x

Post-1980 cards in Near Mint condition will generally sell for about 75% of the quoted Mint value. Excellent-condition cards bring no more than 40%.

1997 Fleer Tiffany Blue

This parallel reprinted 445 cards from Fleer Football and was seeded one per 20 packs. The fronts featured a glossy silver finish versus the matte finish on the base cards, and featured blue foil stamping on the front versus gold foil on the base cards. Card fronts also had a "Traditions Tiffany" logo in either top corner.

	MT
Complete Set (445):	1200.
Tiffany Blue Cards:	15x-30x

1997 Fleer All-Pro

This 24-card set was inserted 1:36 retail packs. All-Pros from the previous season were commemorated.

	MT
Complete Set (24):	160.00
Common Player:	2.00
Minor Stars:	4.00
1 Troy Aikman	15.00
2 Larry Allen	2.00
3 Drew Bledsoe	15.00
4 Terrell Davis	18.00
5 Dermontti Dawson	2.00
6 John Elway	12.00
7 Brett Favre	30.00
8 Herman Moore	4.00
9 Jerry Rice	15.00
10 Barry Sanders	25.00
11 Shannon Sharpe	2.00
12 Erik Williams	2.00
13 Ashley Ambrose	2.00
14 Chad Brown	2.00
15 LeRoy Butler	2.00
16 Kevin Greene	2.00
17 Sam Mills	2.00
18 John Randle	2.00
19 Deion Sanders	8.00
20 Junior Seau	4.00
21 Bruce Smith	2.00
22 Alfred Williams	2.00
23 Darren Woodson	2.00
24 Bryant Young	2.00

1997 Fleer Decade of Excellence

Inserted 1:36 hobby packs, this 12-card set featured photography from 10 years prior. Ten percent of the cards were printed with holographic foil and were inserted 1:360 hobby packs.

	MT
Complete Set (12):	60.00
Common Player:	1.50
1 Marcus Allen	3.00
2 Cris Carter	3.00
3 John Elway	12.00
4 Irving Fryar	1.50
5 Darrell Green	1.50
6 Dan Marino	12.00
7 Jerry Rice	8.00
8 Bruce Smith	1.50
9 Herschel Walker	1.50
10 Reggie White	3.00
11 Rod Woodson	1.50
12 Steve Young	6.00

1997 Fleer Game Breakers

Inserted 1:2 retail packs, this 20-card set showcased players who have the ability to break a game open. A Game Breakers Supreme parallel was inserted 1:18 of all pack types.

	MT
Complete Set (20):	20.00
Common Player:	.30
Minor Stars:	.60
Supreme Cards:	2x-4x
1 Troy Aikman	2.50
2 Jerome Bettis	.60
3 Drew Bledsoe	2.50
4 Isaac Bruce	.75
5 Mark Brunell	2.50
6 Kerry Collins	2.00
7 Terrell Davis	2.50
8 Marshall Faulk	.30
9 Antonio Freeman	.60
10 Joey Galloway	1.00
11 Terry Glenn	.75
12 Desmond Howard	.30
13 Keyshawn Johnson	1.00
14 Eddie Kennison	1.00
15 Curtis Martin	2.50
16 Herman Moore	.30
17 Lawrence Phillips	.60
18 Barry Sanders	3.00
19 Shannon Sharpe	.30
20 Emmitt Smith	5.00

1997 Fleer Million Dollar Moments

The 50-card set was part of a season-long multi-sport promotion which was available in all 1997 packs of Fleer, Fleer Ultra and Flair Showcase football products released after June, 1997. Each pack contained one of 50 different Million Dollar Moments cards. The fronts of the cards had the Million Dollar Moments logo in the upper left. The player's name, date of his highlight and highlight are included at the bottom front. The backs provide the contest details. Cards numbered 1-45 are common, while 46-50 are difficult to find. Those who collected cards 1-45 plus any one of 46-49 won up to a $1,000 shopping spree. The grand prize of $1 million was awarded to the collector of all 50 cards. To reward collectors who complete the "common" 45-card set, Fleer offered the opportunity to redeem the 45-card set (with $5.99 for shipping) for a complete parallel 50-card set.

	MT
Complete Set (45):	5.00
Common Player:	.05
Minor Stars:	.10
1 Checklist	.05
2 Troy Aikman	.50
3 Sid Luckman	.10
4 Barry Sanders	.50
5 Tom Fears	.05
6 Reggie White	.10
7 Lou Groza	.05
8 John Elway	.35
9 Raymond Berry	.05
10 Marcus Allen	.10
11 Paul Hornung	.10
12 Herschel Walker	.05
13 Norm Van Brocklin	.05
14 Bruce Smith	.05
15 Billy Wade	.05
16 Andre Reed	.05
17 Gale Sayers	.10
18 Terrell Davis	.50
19 Jim Bakken	.05
20 Marshall Faulk	.10
21 Tom Dempsey	.05
22 Dan Marino	1.00
23 Garo Yepremian	.05
24 Jerry Rice	.50
25 Herman Edwards	.05
26 Derrick Thomas	.05
27 Kellen Winslow	.05
28 Steve Young	.35
29 Tony Dorsett	.10
30 Desmond Howard	.05
31 Roger Craig	.05
32 Drew Bledsoe	.50
33 Doug Williams	.05
34 Jerome Bettis	.10
35 Bobby Layne	.05
36 Junior Seau	.10
37 Roman Gabriel	.05
38 Cris Carter	.10
39 Drew Pearson	.05
40 Warren Moon	.05
41 Wesley Walker	.05
42 Ricky Watters	.10
43 Carl Eller	.05
44 Kordell Stewart	.50
45 John Mackey	.05
46 Thurman Thomas	.05
47 Ken Stabler	.05
48 Emmitt Smith	.05
49 Jim Brown	.05
50 Eddie George	.05

1997 Fleer Prospects

The 10-card set was inserted 1:6 packs. It featured the top prospects from the 1997 NFL Draft.

	MT
Complete Set (10):	20.00
Common Player:	.75
1 Peter Boulware	.75
2 Rae Carruth	3.00
3 Jim Druckenmiller	5.00
4 Warrick Dunn	7.00
5 Tony Gonzalez	1.50
6 Yatil Green	4.00
7 Ike Hilliard	4.00
8 Orlando Pace	1.50
9 Darrell Russell	.75
10 Shawn Springs	1.50

1997 Fleer Rookie Sensations

Inserted 1:4 packs, the 20-card set focused on rookies who had positive impacts on their team in 1996.

	MT
Complete Set (20):	25.00
Common Player:	.50
Minor Stars:	1.00
1 Karim Abdul-Jabbar	3.00
2 Mike Alstott	1.00
3 Tony Banks	2.00
4 Tony Brackens	.50
5 Rickey Dudley	.50
6 Bobby Engram	.50
7 Eddie George	7.00
8 Terry Glenn	4.00
9 Kevin Hardy	.50
10 Marvin Harrison	2.00
11 Keyshawn Johnson	2.00
12 Eddie Kennison	2.00
13 Jermaine Lewis	.50
14 Ray Lewis	.50
15 John Mobley	.50
16 Eric Moulds	.50
17 Jonathan Ogden	.50
18 Lawrence Phillips	1.00
19 Simeon Rice	.50
20 Zach Thomas	1.50

1997 Fleer Thrill Seekers

Inserted 1:288 packs, the 12-card set looks at players known for making the big play.

	MT
Complete Set (12):	500.00
Common Player:	15.00
1 Karim Abdul-Jabbar	40.00
2 Jerome Bettis	15.00
3 Terrell Davis	50.00
4 John Elway	35.00
5 Brett Favre	90.00
6 Eddie George	65.00
7 Terry Glenn	20.00
8 Keyshawn Johnson	30.00
9 Dan Marino	80.00
10 Curtis Martin	50.00
11 Deion Sanders	20.00
12 Emmitt Smith	80.00

1997 Fleer Goudey

Goudey included 150 cards that adopted the old-time look of the Goudey brand from the 1930s. The cards measure 2-3/8" x 2-7/8", with player pictures appearing as illustrations. Backs include a player synopsis "old-time" text. Also included in the regular-issue set were cards of Chuck Bednarik and Y.A. Tittle, as well as two checklists and a History of Goudey card. Insert sets found in Goudey were Gridiron Greats (parallel set), Heads Up, Concrete Chuck Bednarik Says, Y.A.Tittle Says and Pigskin 2000.

	MT
Complete Set (150):	18.00
Common Player:	.05
Minor Stars:	.10
Wax Box:	50.00
1 Michael Jackson	.05
2 Ray Lewis	.05
3 Vinny Testaverde	.05
4 Eric Turner	.05
5 Jim Kelly	.10
6 Bryce Paup	.05
7 Andre Reed	.05
8 Bruce Smith	.05
9 Thurman Thomas	.10
10 Jeff Blake	.10
11 Ki-Jana Carter	.10
12 Carl Pickens	.05
13 Darnay Scott	.05
14 Terrell Davis	1.25
15 John Elway	.75
16 Anthony Miller	.05
17 John Mobley	.05
18 Shannon Sharpe	.05
19 Chris Chandler	.05
20 Eddie George	1.50
21 Steve McNair	.50
22 Chris Sanders	.05
23 Quentin Coryatt	.05
24 Sean Dawkins	.05
25 Ken Dilger	.05
26 Marshall Faulk	.30
27 Jim Harbaugh	.05
28 Marvin Harrison	.75
29 Tony Brackens	.05
30 Mark Brunell	1.00
31 Kevin Hardy	.10
32 Keenan McCardell	.05
33 James Stewart	.05
34 Marcus Allen	.10
35 Steve Bono	.05
36 Dale Carter	.05
37 Neil Smith	.05
38 Derrick Thomas	.05
39 Tamarick Vanover	.05
40 Karim Abdul-Jabbar	.25
41 Dan Marino	2.00
42 O.J. McDuffie	.05
43 Stanley Pritchett	.05
44 Zach Thomas	.50
45 Drew Bledsoe	1.00
46 Ben Coates	.05
47 Terry Glenn	.25
48 Shawn Jefferson	.05
49 Curtis Martin	1.50
50 David Meggett	.05
51 Hugh Douglas	.05

52	Keyshawn Johnson	.75
53	Adrian Murrell	.05
54	Tim Brown	.05
55	Rickey Dudley	.10
56	Jeff Hostetler	.05
57	Napoleon Kaufman	.05
58	Chester McGlockton	.05
59	Jerome Bettis	.10
60	Andre Hastings	.05
61	Greg Lloyd	.05
62	Kordell Stewart	1.00
63	Yancey Thigpen	.05
64	Rod Woodson	.05
65	Andre Coleman	.05
66	Stan Humphries	.05
67	Tony Martin	.05
68	Leonard Russell	.05
69	Junior Seau	.05
70	Brian Blades	.05
71	Joey Galloway	.50
72	Chris Warren	.05
73	Larry Centers	.05
74	Leeland McElroy	.10
75	Simeon Rice	.10
76	Frank Sanders	.05
77	Eric Swann	.05
78	Jamal Anderson	.40
79	Bert Emanuel	.05
80	Terance Mathis	.05
81	Eric Metcalf	.05
82	Tim Biakabutuka	.40
83	Kerry Collins	.25
84	Kevin Greene	.05
85	Muhsin Muhammad	.10
86	Wesley Walls	.05
87	Curtis Conway	.05
88	Bryan Cox	.05
89	Walt Harris	.05
90	Erik Kramer	.05
91	Rashaan Salaam	.10
92	Troy Aikman	1.00
93	Michael Irvin	.10
94	Daryl Johnston	.05
95	Leon Lett	.05
96	Deion Sanders	.50
97	Emmitt Smith	2.00
98	Scott Mitchell	.05
99	Herman Moore	.10
100	Johnnie Morton	.05
101	Brett Perriman	.05
102	Barry Sanders	1.25
103	Edgar Bennett	.05
104	Robert Brooks	.05
105	Brett Favre	2.00
106	Antonio Freeman	.05
107	Keith Jackson	.05
108	Reggie White	.10
109	Cris Carter	.05
110	Warren Moon	.10
111	John Randle	.05
112	Jake Reed	.05
113	Robert Smith	.05
114	Jim Everett	.05
115	Michael Haynes	.05
116	Alex Molden	.05
117	Ray Zellars	.05
118	Chris Calloway	.05
119	Rodney Hampton	.05
120	Phillippi Sparks	.05
121	Amani Toomer	.10
122	Ty Detmer	.05
123	Jason Dunn	.05
124	Irving Fryar	.05
125	Chris T. Jones	.05
126	Ricky Watters	.10
127	Tony Banks	.25
128	Isaac Bruce	.25
129	Eddie Kennison	.20
130	Lawrence Phillips	.10
131	Merton Hanks	.05
132	Terry Kirby	.05
133	Ken Norton	.05
134	Jerry Rice	1.00
135	J.J. Stokes	.10
136	Steve Young	.75
137	Alvin Harper	.05
138	Jackie Harris	.05
139	Hardy Nickerson	.05
140	Errict Rhett	.20
141	Terry Allen	.05
142	Henry Ellard	.05
143	Gus Frerotte	.05
144	Brian Mitchell	.05
145	Michael Westbrook	.10
146	Chuck Bednarik	.05
147	Y.A. Tittle	.10
148	Checklist	.05
149	Checklist	.05
150	Checklist	.05

Values quoted in this guide reflect the retail price of a card — the price a collector can expect to pay when buying a card from a dealer. The wholesale price — that which a collector can expect to receive from a dealer when selling cards — will be significantly lower, depending on desirability and condition.

1997 Fleer Goudey Gridiron Greats

Gridiron Greats was a 147-card parallel set (150 minus the two checklists and one History of Goudey card) that was found at a rate of one per three packs in Goudey Football. Each card contains a solid black strip across the bottom with the player's name in red foil. Unlike the regular-issue cards, these are actual photos instead of illustrations.

		MT
Complete Set (147):		100.00
Gridiron Greats Cards:		3x-6x

1997 Fleer Goudey Heads Up

Heads Up contained 20 players in a cartoon format, with the player's head larger and in color, compared to the small black and white body. The player's last name runs up the left side in white letters. Heads Up cards were found in every 30 hobby packs and every 36 retail packs.

		MT
Complete Set (20):		150.00
Common Player:		3.00
1	Troy Aikman	15.00
2	Marcus Allen	3.00
3	Tim Biakabutuka	6.00
4	Robert Brooks	3.00
5	Isaac Bruce	6.00
6	Kerry Collins	6.00
7	Terrell Davis	18.00
8	Brett Favre	30.00
9	Terry Glenn	6.00
10	Rodney Hampton	3.00
11	Michael Irvin	6.00
12	Chris T. Jones	3.00
13	Carl Pickens	3.00
14	Barry Sanders	18.00
15	Kordell Stewart	15.00
16	Thurman Thomas	3.00
17	Tamarick Vanover	8.00
18	Chris Warren	3.00
19	Ricky Watters	3.00
20	Steve Young	10.00

1997 Fleer Goudey Pigskin 2000

Pigskin 2000 was a 15-card foil-etched insert that highlighted some of the NFL's elite. The insert name and player's name are included in gold foil

along the left side, with the Fleer Goudey logo in the top left corner. Pigskin 2000 cards are found every 360 hobby packs.

		MT
Complete Set (15):		400.00
Common Player:		10.00
1	Karim Abdul-Jabbar	40.00
2	Jeff Blake	10.00
3	Drew Bledsoe	40.00
4	Robert Brooks	10.00
5	Terrell Davis	40.00
6	Marshall Faulk	20.00
7	Joey Galloway	10.00
8	Eddie George	40.00
9	Terry Glenn	20.00
10	Keyshawn Johnson	20.00
11	Chris T. Jones	10.00
12	Curtis Martin	40.00
13	Steve McNair	25.00
14	Lawrence Phillips	10.00
15	Kordell Stewart	30.00

1997 Fleer Goudey Tittle Says

Y.A. Tittle Says shows 20 of the top offensive stars, with Tittle providing insight on each card back. Each card has a color photo of the player over a color background with the insert's name scattered across it. They were found every 72 hobby and every 85 retail packs.

		MT
Complete Set (20):		225.00
Common Player:		5.00
1	Karim Abdul-Jabbar	8.00
2	Jerome Bettis	5.00
3	Tim Brown	5.00
4	Isaac Bruce	8.00
5	Cris Carter	5.00
6	Curtis Conway	5.00
7	John Elway	12.00
8	Marshall Faulk	10.00
9	Brett Favre	30.00
10	Joey Galloway	5.00
11	Eddie George	25.00
12	Keyshawn Johnson	12.00
13	Dan Marino	30.00
14	Curtis Martin	25.00
15	Herman Moore	5.00
16	Jerry Rice	15.00
17	Barry Sanders	15.00
18	Emmitt Smith	30.00
19	Thurman Thomas	5.00
20	Ricky Watters	5.00

1997 Fleer Goudey Bednarik Says

This insert highlighted 15 of the top defensive players in the league, with Bednarik's assessment of each player on the card back. Cards in this insert are identified by a large solid block pattern in the back featuring the team's colors, with a black strip near the bottom with the words "Concrete Chuck Bednarik" in it. These inserts were found every 60 hobby packs and every 72 retail packs.

		MT
Complete Set (15):		100.00
Common Player:		3.00
1	Kevin Greene	3.00

2	Ray Lewis	3.00
3	Greg Lloyd	3.00
4	Chester McGlockton	3.00
5	Hardy Nickerson	3.00
6	Bryce Paup	3.00
7	Simeon Rice	3.00
8	Deion Sanders	14.00
9	Junior Seau	3.00
10	Bruce Smith	3.00
11	Derrick Thomas	3.00
12	Zach Thomas	12.00
13	Eric Turner	3.00
14	Reggie White	10.00
15	Rod Woodson	3.00

1997 Fleer Goudey II

Goudey Series II is a 150-card set. It contians 145 player cards, all of which feature "Gale Sayers Says" on the backs. There are also two checklist cards and a three card Gale Sayers subset (1:9). The parallel sets are Gridiron Greats (1:3) and Goudey Greats (numbered to 150). Sayers has autographed 40 of each subset card and each card #40 of the Goudey Greats parallel set. The insert sets included Rookie Classics, Glory Days, Vintage Goudey, Big Time Backs and Million Dollar Moments.

		MT
Complete Set (150):		25.00
Common Player:		.05
Minor Stars:		.10
Gridiron Greats:		2x-4x
Goudey Greats Cards:		20x-40x
Goudey Greats Rookies:		10x-20x
Wax Box:		45.00
1	Gale Sayers	1.25
2	Vinny Testaverde	.05
3	Jeff George	.10
4	Brett Favre	2.25
5	Eddie Kennison	.50
6	Ken Norton	.05
7	John Elway	.75
8	Troy Aikman	1.00
9	Steve McNair	.75
10	Kordell Stewart	1.00
11	Drew Bledsoe	1.00
12	Kerry Collins	.25
13	Dan Marino	2.00
14	Brad Johnson	.05
15	Todd Collins	.05
16	Ki-Jana Carter	.10
17	Pat Barnes	.50
18	Aeneas Williams	.05
19	Keyshawn Johnson	.20
20	Barry Sanders	1.25
21	Tiki Barber	1.00
22	Emmitt Smith	2.00
23	Kevin Hardy	.05
24	Mario Bates	.05
25	Ricky Watters	.10
26	Chris Canty	.05
27	Eddie George	1.50
28	Curtis Martin	1.00
29	Adrian Murrell	.10
30	Terrell Davis	1.00
31	Rashaan Salaam	.10
32	Marcus Allen	.25
33	Karim Abdul-Jabbar	.50
34	Thurman Thomas	.10
35	Marvin Harrison	.30
36	Jerome Bettis	.10
37	Larry Centers	.05
38	Stan Humphries	.05
39	Lawrence Phillips	.05
40	Gale Sayers	1.25
41	Henry Ellard	.05
42	Chris Warren	.05
43	Robert Brooks	.10
44	Sedrick Shaw	.05
45	Muhsin Muhammad	.05
46	Napoleon Kaufman	.20
47	Reidel Anthony	1.00
48	Jamal Anderson	.10
49	Scott Mitchell	.05
50	Mark Brunell	1.00
51	William Thomas	.05
52	Bryan Cox	.05
53	Carl Pickens	.05
54	Chris Spielman	.05
55	Junior Seau	.05
56	Hardy Nickerson	.05
57	Dwayne Rudd	.10
58	Peter Boulware	.10
59	Jim Druckenmiller	2.00

60	Michael Westbrook	.05
61	Shawn Springs	.25
62	Zach Thomas	.10
63	David LaFleur	.50
64	Darrell Russell	.10
65	Jake Plummer	1.50
66	Tim Biakabutuka	.10
67	Tyrone Wheatley	.05
68	Elvis Grbac	.05
69	Antonio Freeman	.30
70	Wayne Chrebet	.05
71	Walter Jones	.10
72	Marshall Faulk	.10
73	Jason Dunn	.05
74	Darnay Scott	.05
75	Errict Rhett	.10
76	Orlando Pace	.25
77	Natrone Means	.10
78	Bruce Smith	.05
79	Jamie Sharper	.05
80	Jerry Rice	1.00
81	Tim Brown	.10
82	Brian Mitchell	.05
83	Andre Reed	.05
84	Herman Moore	.10
85	Rob Moore	.05
86	Rae Carruth	.75
87	Bert Emanuel	.05
88	Michael Irvin	.05
89	Mark Chmura	.10
90	Tony Brackens	.05
91	Kevin Greene	.05
92	Reggie White	.05
93	Derrick Thomas	.05
94	Troy Davis	.25
95	Greg Lloyd	.05
96	Cortez Kennedy	.05
97	Simeon Rice	.05
98	Terrell Owens	.50
99	Hugh Douglas	.05
100	Terry Glenn	.25
101	Jim Harbaugh	.05
102	Shannon Sharpe	.05
103	Joey Kent	.30
104	Jeff Blake	.05
105	Terry Allen	.05
106	Cris Carter	.05
107	Amani Toomer	.05
108	Derrick Alexander	.05
109	Darnell Autry	.50
110	Irving Fryar	.05
111	Bryant Westbrook	.10
112	Tony Banks	.50
113	Michael Booker	.05
114	Yatil Green	.40
115	James Farrior	.10
116	Warrick Dunn	1.75
117	Greg Hill	.05
118	Tony Martin	.05
119	Chris Sanders	.05
120	Charles Johnson	.05
121	John Mobley	.05
122	Keenan McCardell	.05
123	Willie McGinest	.05
124	O.J. McDuffie	.05
125	Deion Sanders	.50
126	Curtis Conway	.05
127	Desmond Howard	.05
128	Johnnie Morton	.05
129	Ike Hilliard	1.00
130	Gus Frerotte	.05
131	Tom Knight	.10
132	Sean Dawkins	.10
133	Isaac Bruce	.10
134	Wesley Walls	.05
135	Danny Wuerffel	1.00
136	Tony Gonzalez	.50
137	Ben Coates	.05
138	Joey Galloway	.10
139	Michael Jackson	.05
140	Steve Young	.50
141	Corey Dillon	2.00
142	Jake Reed	.05
143	Edgar Bennett	.05
144	Ty Detmer	.05
145	Darrell Green	.05
146	Antowain Smith	1.50
147	Mike Alstott	.10
148	Checklist	.05
149	Checklist	.05
150	Gale Sayers (Commemorative Card)	1.25

1997 Fleer Goudey II Big Time Backs

This 10-card insert features top quarterbacks and running backs on a die-cut, embossed

card designed as a clipboard. The cards were inserted 1:72.

		MT
Complete Set (10):		150.00
Common Player:		3.00
1	Karim Abdul-Jabbar	10.00
2	Marcus Allen	3.00
3	Jerome Bettis	3.00
4	Terrell Davis	15.00
5	Brett Favre	30.00
6	Eddie George	20.00
7	Dan Marino	25.00
8	Curtis Martin	15.00
9	Barry Sanders	30.00
10	Emmitt Smith	25.00

1997 Fleer Goudey II Glory Days

This 18-card insert features top players on an embossed card. Glory Days was inserted once per 18 retail packs.

		MT
Complete Set (15):		70.00
Common Player:		2.00
1	Troy Aikman	8.00
2	Isaac Bruce	2.00
3	Mark Brunell	8.00
4	Cris Carter	2.00
5	Joey Galloway	4.00
6	Terry Glenn	6.00
7	Marvin Harrison	4.00
8	Dan Marino	15.00
9	Deion Sanders	4.00
10	Shannon Sharpe	2.00
11	Emmitt Smith	15.00
12	Bruce Smith	2.00
13	Kordell Stewart	8.00
14	Ricky Watters	2.00
15	Reggie White	2.00

1997 Fleer Goudey II Rookie Classics

This 20-card insert features top 1997 rookies on a die-cut card. The first down marker is die-cut on the right side of the card. This set was inserted 1:3.

		MT
Complete Set (20):		18.00
Common Player:		.25
1	Reidel Anthony	1.50
2	Pat Barnes	.50
3	Peter Boulware	.25
4	Rae Carruth	.75
5	Troy Davis	.50
6	Corey Dillon	2.50
7	Jim Druckenmiller	2.00
8	Warrick Dunn	3.00
9	Tony Gonzalez	.75
10	Yatil Green	.50
11	Ike Hilliard	1.00
12	Walter Jones	.25
13	David LaFleur	.75
14	Orlando Pace	.25
15	Jake Plummer	5.00
16	Darrell Russell	.25
17	Antowain Smith	2.00
18	Shawn Springs	.25
19	Bryant Westbrook	.25
20	Danny Wuerffel	1.00

A card number in parentheses ( ) indicates the set is unnumbered.

1997 Fleer Goudey II Vintage Goudey

This 15-card insert features players who are throwbacks to old-time football. The players are featured on cards die-cut into a football shape. This set also contained redemption cards for an original 1933 Sport Kings Football card of Red Grange, Jim Thorpe and Knute Rockne. This set was inserted 1:36 in hobby packs.

		MT
Complete Set (15):		120.00
Common Player:		4.00
1	Karim Abdul-Jabbar	8.00
2	Kerry Collins	8.00
3	Terrell Davis	12.00
4	John Elway	8.00
5	Brett Favre	25.00
6	Eddie George	18.00
7	Terry Glenn	8.00
8	Keyshawn Johnson	4.00
9	Curtis Martin	12.00
10	Herman Moore	4.00
11	Jerry Rice	12.00
12	Barry Sanders	20.00
13	Deion Sanders	6.00
14	Zach Thomas	4.00
15	Steve Young	8.00

1998 Fleer

Fleer scrapped its matte finish and produced Tradtion in 1998. The 250-card set, including 247 player cards and three checklists, is printed on a borderless design with the player's name, position and team printed across the bottom in gold foil. Tradition arrived with a parallel set called Heritage, which was numbered to 125 sets, and four different inserts, including Big Numbers, Rookie Sensations, Red Zone Rockers and Playmakers Theatre.

		MT
Complete Set (250):		45.00
Common Player:		.15
Minor Stars:		.30
Wax Box:		50.00
1	Brett Favre	3.00
2	Barry Sanders	2.50
3	John Elway	1.50
4	Emmitt Smith	2.50
5	Dan Marino	2.50
6	Eddie George	1.50
7	Jerry Rice	1.50
8	Jake Plummer	1.50
9	Joey Galloway	.30
10	Mike Alstott	.50
11	Brian Mitchell	.15
12	Keyshawn Johnson	.30
13	Jerald Moore	.15
14	Randal Hill	.15
15	Byron Hanspard	.15
16	Jeff George	.30
17	Terry Glenn	.30
18	Jerome Bettis	.30
19	Curtis Conway	.30
20	Fred Lane	.30
21	Isaac Bruce	.30
22	Tiki Barber	.30
23	Bobby Hoying	.15
24	Marcus Allen	.30
25	Dana Stubblefield	.15
26	Peter Boulware	.15
27	John Randle	.15
28	Jason Sehorn	.15
29	Rod Smith	.30
30	Michael Sinclair	.15
31	Marshall Faulk	.30
32	Karl Williams	.15
33	Kordell Stewart	1.50
34	Corey Dillon	1.00
35	Bryant Young	.15
36	Charlie Garner	.15
37	Andre Reed	.15
38	Ray Buchanan	.15
39	Brett Perriman	.15
40	Leon Lett	.15
41	Keenan McCardell	.15
42	Eric Swann	.15
43	Leslie Shepherd	.15
44	Curtis Martin	1.00
45	Andre Rison	.30
46	Keith Lyle	.15
47	Rae Carruth	.15
48	William Henderson	.15
49	Sean Dawkins	.15
50	Terrell Davis	1.50
51	Tim Brown	.30
52	Willie McGinest	.15
53	Jermaine Lewis	.30
54	Ricky Watters	.30
55	Freddie Jones	.15
56	Robert Smith	.30
57	Reidel Anthony	.15
58	James Stewart	.15
59	Earl Holmes	.15
60	Dale Carter	.15
61	Michael Irvin	.30
62	Jason Taylor	.15
63	Eric Metcalf	.15
64	LeRoy Butler	.15
65	Jamal Anderson	.30
66	Jamie Asher	.15
67	Chris Sanders	.15
68	Warren Sapp	.15
69	Ray Zellars	.15
70	Carl Pickens	.30
71	Garrison Hearst	.30
72	Eddie Kennison	.30
73	John Mobley	.15
74	Rob Johnson	.30
75	William Thomas	.15
76	Drew Bledsoe	1.50
77	Michael Barrow	.15
78	Jim Harbaugh	.30
79	Terry McDaniel	.15
80	Johnnie Morton	.15
81	Danny Kanell	.15
82	Larry Centers	.15
83	Courtney Hawkins	.15
84	Tony Brackens	.15
85	Tony Gonzalez	.30
86	Aaron Glenn	.15
87	Cris Carter	.30
88	Chuck Smith	.15
89	Tamarick Vanover	.15
90	Karim Abdul-Jabbar	.30
91	Bryant Westbrook	.15
92	Mike Pritchard	.15
93	Darren Woodson	.15
94	Wesley Walls	.15
95	Tony Banks	.30
96	Michael Westbrook	.15
97	Shannon Sharpe	.30
98	Jeff Blake	.30
99	Terrell Owens	.30
100	Warrick Dunn	1.50
101	Levon Kirkland	.15
102	Frank Wycheck	.15
103	Gus Frerotte	.15
104	Simeon Rice	.15
105	Shawn Jefferson	.15
106	Irving Fryar	.15
107	Michael McCrary	.15
108	Robert Brooks	.15
109	Chris Chandler	.15
110	Junior Seau	.30
111	O.J. McDuffie	.15
112	Glenn Foley	.15
113	Darryl Williams	.15
114	Elvis Grbac	.15
115	Napoleon Kaufman	.50
116	Anthony Miller	.15
117	Troy Davis	.15
118	Charles Way	.15
119	Scott Mitchell	.15
120	Ken Harvey	.15
121	Tyrone Hughes	.15
122	Mark Brunell	1.25
123	David Palmer	.15
124	Rob Moore	.15
125	Kerry Collins	.75
126	Will Blackwell	.15
127	Ray Crockett	.15
128	Leslie O'Neal	.15
129	Antowain Smith	.75
130	Carlester Crumpler	.15
131	Michael Jackson	.15
132	Trent Dilfer	.30
133	Dan Williams	.15
134	Dorsey Levens	.30
135	Ty Law	.15
136	Rickey Dudley	.15
137	Jessie Tuggle	.15
138	Darrien Gordon	.15
139	Kevin Turner	.15
140	Willie Davis	.15
141	Zach Thomas	.15
142	Tony McGee	.15
143	Dexter Coakley	.15
144	Troy Brown	.15
145	Leeland McElroy	.15
146	Michael Strahan	.15
147	Ken Dilger	.15
148	Bryce Paup	.15
149	Herman Moore	.30
150	Reggie White	.30
151	DeWayne Washington	.15
152	Natrone Means	.30
153	Ben Coates	.15
154	Bert Emanuel	.15
155	Steve Young	1.00
156	Jimmy Smith	.15
157	Darrell Green	.15
158	Troy Aikman	1.50
159	Greg Hill	.15
160	Raymont Harris	.15
161	Troy Drayton	.15
162	Stevon Moore	.15
163	Warren Moon	.30
164	Wayne Martin	.15
165	Jason Gildon	.15
166	Chris Calloway	.15
167	Aeneas Williams	.15
168	Michael Bates	.15
169	Hugh Douglas	.15
170	Brad Johnson	.30
171	Bruce Smith	.15
172	Neil Smith	.15
173	James McKnight	.15
174	Robert Porcher	.15
175	Merton Hanks	.15
176	Ki-Jana Carter	.15
177	Mo Lewis	.15
178	Chester McGlockton	.15
179	Zack Crockett	.15
180	Derrick Thomas	.15
181	J.J. Stokes	.15
182	Derrick Rodgers	.15
183	Daryl Johnston	.15
184	Chris Penn	.15
185	Steve Atwater	.15
186	Amp Lee	.15
187	Frank Sanders	.15
188	Chris Slade	.15
189	Mark Chmura	.15
190	Kimble Anders	.15
191	Charles Johnson	.15
192	William Floyd	.15
193	Jay Graham	.15
194	Hardy Nickerson	.15
195	Terry Allen	.15
196	James Jett	.15
197	Jessie Armstead	.15
198	Yancey Thigpen	.15
199	Terance Mathis	.15
200	Steve McNair	.75
201	Wayne Chrebet	.15
202	Jamir Miller	.15
203	Duce Staley	.15
204	Deion Sanders	.75
205	Carnell Lake	.15
206	Ed McCaffrey	.15
207	Shawn Springs	.15
208	Tony Martin	.15
209	Jerris McPhail	.15
210	Darnay Scott	.15
211	Jake Reed	.15
212	Adrian Murrell	.30
213	Quinn Early	.15
214	Marvin Harrison	.30
215	Ryan McNeil	.15
216	Derrick Alexander	.15
217	Ray Lewis	.15
218	Antonio Freeman	.30
219	Dwayne Rudd	.15
220	Muhsin Muhammad	.15
221	Kevin Hardy	.15
222	Andre Hastings	.15
223	*John Avery*	2.00
224	*Keith Brooking*	1.00
225	*Kevin Dyson*	1.50
226	*Robert Edwards*	2.50
227	*Greg Ellis*	.15
228	*Curtis Enis*	3.00
229	*Terry Fair*	1.00
230	*Ahman Green*	2.00
231	*Jacquez Green*	2.00
232	*Brian Griese*	3.00
233	*Skip Hicks*	2.00
234	*Ryan Leaf*	4.00
235	*Peyton Manning*	8.00
236	*R.W. McQuarters*	.15
237	*Randy Moss*	12.00
238	*Marcus Nash*	2.00
239	*Anthony Simmons*	.50
240	*Brian Simmons*	1.00
241	*Takeo Spikes*	1.00
242	*Duane Starks*	1.00
243	*Fred Taylor*	4.00
244	*Andre Wadsworth*	1.00
245	*Shaun Williams*	1.00
246	*Grant Wistrom*	1.00
247	*Charles Woodson*	2.50
248	Checklist	.15
249	Checklist	.15
250	Checklist	.15

1998 Fleer Heritage

This parallel set was exclusive to hobby packs and was sequentially numbered to 125 sets. Heritage cards added a special foil treatment on the front and sequential numbering on the back.

	MT
Heritage Cards:	30x-60x
Heritage Rookies:	10x-20x

1998 Fleer Big Numbers

Big Numbers was a nine-card interactive set featuring top players at each skill position, with nine total players each featured on 11 different versions (0-9 and a wild card). The goal was to collect four cards, whereby the overprinted numbers, when combined, make out the players total yards through all games of Dec. 1, 1998. Winners were eligible to enter a contest for a chance to win a trip to the 2000 Pro Bowl. Big Numbers inserts were seeded one per four packs.

		MT
Common Player:		.25
BN1	Tim Brown	.25
BN2	Cris Carter	.25
BN3	Terrell Davis	1.00
BN4	John Elway	1.00
BN5	Brett Favre	2.00
BN6	Eddie George	1.00
BN7	Dorsey Levens	.50
BN8	Herman Moore	.50
BN9	Steve Young	.75

1998 Fleer Playmakers Theatre

This 15-card insert set included the game's elite players on silver holofoil and sculpture embossing. Playmakers Theatre cards were sequentially numbered to 100 sets.

		MT
Complete Set (15):		1000.
Common Player:		30.00
Production 100 Sets		
PT1	Terrell Davis	100.00
PT2	Corey Dillon	60.00
PT3	Warrick Dunn	85.00
PT4	John Elway	100.00
PT5	Brett Favre	200.00
PT6	Antonio Freeman	30.00
PT7	Joey Galloway	30.00
PT8	Eddie George	85.00
PT9	Terry Glenn	30.00
PT10	Dan Marino	175.00
PT11	Curtis Martin	60.00
PT12	Jake Plummer	85.00
PT13	Barry Sanders	200.00
PT14	Deion Sanders	50.00
PT15	Kordell Stewart	85.00

A player's name in *italic* type indicates a rookie card.

1998 Fleer Red Zone Rockers

Red Zone Rockers were printed on a horizontal red laser holofoil and inserted one per 32 packs. The insert included 10 players who are best in the clutch.

		MT
Complete Set (10):		70.00
Common Player:		2.00
RZ1	Jerome Bettis	2.00
RZ2	Drew Bledsoe	10.00
RZ3	Mark Brunell	8.00
RZ4	Corey Dillon	6.00
RZ5	Joey Galloway	2.00
RZ6	Keyshawn Johnson	2.00
RZ7	Dorsey Levens	2.00
RZ8	Dan Marino	15.00
RZ9	Barry Sanders	20.00
RZ10	Emmitt Smith	15.00

1998 Fleer Rookie Sensations

This 15-card insert displayed the top rookies in 1998. Cards were embossed with spot UV coating and inserted one per 16 packs.

		MT
Complete Set (15):		60.00
Common Player:		2.00
RS1	John Avery	4.00
RS2	Keith Brooking	4.00
RS3	Kevin Dyson	4.00
RS4	Robert Edwards	5.00
RS5	Greg Ellis	2.00
RS6	Curtis Enis	7.00
RS7	Terry Fair	2.00
RS8	Ryan Leaf	7.00
RS9	Peyton Manning	15.00
RS10	Randy Moss	20.00
RS11	Marcus Nash	4.00
RS12	Fred Taylor	7.00
RS13	Andre Wadsworth	2.00
RS14	Grant Wistrom	2.00
RS15	Charles Woodson	5.00

1998 Fleer Brilliants

This was the premier issue of Brilliants by Fleer. The 150-card set is made up of 100 veterans and 50 rookies (inserted 1:2 packs). The product also included three parallel sets. The easiest being the Brilliant Blues with veterans found 1:3 packs and the rookies 1:6. Each single from this series has a blue background with the letter "B" prefix on the card number. The Brilliant Golds have a sparkling gold background on super bright mirror foil and the letter "G" prefix on the card number. Each single is sequentially numbered to 99. The rarest parallel is the 24-Karat Gold set. Each single has a sparkling gold background on rainbow holographic reflective mirror foil with an actual 24-kt. gold logo. Each single is sequentially numbered to 24.

		MT
Complete Set (150):		250.00
Common Player:		.15
Minor Stars:		.30
Common Rookie:		3.00
Inserted 1:2		
Blue Veterans:		2x-3x
Inserted 1:3		
Blue Rookies:		1.2x
Inserted 1:6		
Brilliant Gold Cards:		20x-40x
Brilliant Gold Rookies:		3x-5x
Production 99 Sets		
24-Karat Gold Cards:		40x-80x
24-Karat Gold Rookies:		5x-10x
Production 24 Sets		
Wax Box:		120.00
1	John Elway	3.00
2	Curtis Conway	.30
3	Danny Wuerffel	.15
4	Emmitt Smith	4.50
5	Marvin Harrison	.30
6	Antowain Smith	.75
7	James Stewart	.15
8	Junior Seau	.30
9	Herman Moore	.50
10	Drew Bledsoe	2.00
11	Rae Carruth	.15
12	Trent Dilfer	.30
13	Derrick Alexander	.15
14	Ike Hilliard	.15
15	Bruce Smith	.15
16	Warren Moon	.30
17	Jermaine Lewis	.15
18	Mike Alstott	.50
19	Robert Brooks	.15
20	Jerome Bettis	.50
21	Brett Favre	6.00
22	Garrison Hearst	.50
23	Neil O'Donnell	.15
24	Joey Galloway	.50
25	Barry Sanders	6.00
26	Donnell Bennett	.15
27	Jamal Anderson	.75
28	Isaac Bruce	.30
29	Chris Chandler	.30
30	Kordell Stewart	1.75
31	Corey Dillon	1.75
32	Troy Aikman	3.00
33	Frank Sanders	.15
34	Cris Carter	.50
35	Greg Hill	.15
36	Tony Martin	.15
37	Shannon Sharpe	.30
38	Wayne Chrebet	.30
39	Trent Green	.30
40	Warrick Dunn	2.00
41	Michael Irvin	.30
42	Eddie George	2.00
43	Carl Pickens	.30
44	Wesley Walls	.15
45	Steve McNair	.75
46	Bert Emanuel	.15
47	Terry Glenn	.30
48	Elvis Grbac	.15
49	Charles Way	.15
50	Steve Young	1.75
51	Deion Sanders	.75
52	Keyshawn Johnson	.50
53	Kerry Collins	.30
54	O.J. McDuffie	.15
55	Ricky Watters	.30
56	Scott Mitchell	.15
57	Antonio Freeman	.50
58	Jake Plummer	2.00
59	Andre Reed	.15
60	Jerry Rice	3.00
61	Dorsey Levens	.50
62	Eddie Kennison	.50
63	Marshall Faulk	.50
64	Michael Jackson	.15
65	Karim Abdul-Jabbar	.30
66	Andre Rison	.30
67	Glenn Foley	.30
68	Jake Reed	.15
69	Tony Banks	.30
70	Dan Marino	4.50
71	Bryan Still	.15
72	Tim Brown	.30
73	Charles Johnson	.15
74	Jeff George	.30
75	Jimmy Smith	.30
76	Ben Coates	.15
77	Rob Moore	.15

78	Johnnie Morton	.15
79	Peter Boulware	.15
80	Curtis Martin	.75
81	James McKnight	.15
82	Danny Kanell	.15
83	Brad Johnson	.30
84	Amani Toomer	.15
85	Terry Allen	.30
86	Rod Smith	.30
87	Keenan McCardell	.30
88	Leslie Shepherd	.15
89	Irving Fryar	.15
90	Terrell Davis	4.50
91	Robert Smith	.50
92	Duce Staley	.15
93	Rickey Dudley	.15
94	Bobby Hoying	.15
95	Terrell Owens	.75
96	Fred Lane	.30
97	Natrone Means	.15
98	Yancey Thigpen	.15
99	Reggie White	.50
100	Mark Brunell	2.00
101	Ahman Green	6.00
102	Skip Hicks	5.00
103	Hines Ward	5.00
104	Marcus Nash	6.00
105	Terry Hardy	3.00
106	Patrick Johnson	4.00
107	Tremayne Stephens	3.00
108	Joe Jurevicius	4.00
109	Moses Moreno	4.00
110	Charles Woodson	10.00
111	Kevin Dyson	6.00
112	Alvis Whitted	3.00
113	Michael Pittman	3.00
114	Stephen Alexander	4.00
115	Tavian Banks	6.00
116	John Avery	6.00
117	Keith Brooking	3.00
118	Jerome Pathon	5.00
119	Terry Fair	4.00
120	Peyton Manning	30.00
121	R.W. McQuarters	4.00
122	Charlie Batch	20.00
123	Jonathan Quinn	5.00
124	Chris Fuamatu-Ma'afala	5.00
125	Jacquez Green	8.00
126	Germane Crowell	6.00
127	Oronde Gadsden	5.00
128	Koy Detmer	4.00
129	Robert Holcombe	8.00
130	Curtis Enis	10.00
131	Brian Griese	15.00
132	Tony Simmons	5.00
133	Vonnie Holliday	4.00
134	Alonzo Mayes	3.00
135	Jon Ritchie	4.00
136	Robert Edwards	12.00
137	Mike Vanderjagt	3.00
138	Jonathon Linton	3.00
139	Fred Taylor	20.00
140	Randy Moss	50.00
141	Rod Rutledge	3.00
142	Andre Wadsworth	4.00
143	Rashaan Shehee	4.00
144	Shaun Williams	3.00
145	Mikhael Ricks	5.00
146	Wade Richey	3.00
147	Carlos King	3.00
148	Tim Dwight	6.00
149	Scott Frost	4.00
150	Ryan Leaf	15.00

1998 Fleer Brilliants Illuminators

Each card in this 15-card set has the players team color in super bright mirror foil on the front. Singles can be found 1:10 packs.

		MT
Complete Set (15):		70.00
Common Player:		1.50
Minor Stars:		3.00
Inserted 1:10		
1	Robert Edwards	6.00
2	Fred Taylor	10.00
3	Kordell Stewart	10.00
4	Troy Aikman	15.00
5	Curtis Enis	6.00
6	Drew Bledsoe	10.00
7	Curtis Martin	4.00
8	Joey Galloway	3.00
9	Jerome Bettis	3.00
10	Glenn Foley	1.50
11	Karim Abdul-Jabbar	3.00
12	Jake Plummer	8.00
13	Jerry Rice	15.00
14	Charlie Batch	12.00
15	Jacquez Green	4.00

1998 Fleer Brilliants Shining Stars

Singles in this insert are two-sided with super bright mirror foil and includes the top 15 players from the NFL. Singles were inserted in 1:20 packs. A parallel version called Pulsars can also be found 1:400 packs.

		MT
Complete Set (15):		120.00
Common Player:		2.00
Inserted 1:20		
Pulsar Cards:		5x-10x
Inserted 1:400		
1	Terrell Davis	15.00
2	Emmitt Smith	15.00
3	Barry Sanders	20.00
4	Mark Brunell	8.00
5	Brett Favre	20.00
6	Ryan Leaf	10.00
7	Randy Moss	30.00
8	Warrick Dunn	8.00
9	Peyton Manning	20.00
10	Corey Dillon	4.00
11	Dan Marino	15.00
12	Keyshawn Johnson	2.00
13	John Elway	10.00
14	Eddie George	8.00
15	Antowain Smith	5.00

1999 Fleer

The 300-card set includes 50 unseeded rookies. The card fronts include the player's name and conference logo in blue foil for the NFC and red for the AFC. Inserts include: Trophy Case, Aerial Assault, Rookie Sensations, Under Pressure and Unsung Heroes.

		MT
Complete Set (300):		50.00
Common Player:		.10
Minor Stars:		.20
Common Rookie:		.40
Wax Box:		60.00
1	Randy Moss	2.00
2	Peyton Manning	1.50
3	Barry Sanders	2.00
4	Terrell Davis	1.50
5	Brett Favre	2.00
6	Fred Taylor	1.00
7	Jake Plummer	1.00
8	John Elway	1.50
9	Emmitt Smith	1.50
10	Kerry Collins	.20
11	Peter Boulware	.10
12	Jamal Anderson	.50
13	Doug Flutie	.75
14	Michael Bates	.10
15	Corey Dillon	.50
16	Curtis Conway	.20
17	Ty Detmer	.20
18	Robert Brooks	.10
19	Dale Carter	.10
20	Charlie Batch	.75
21	Ken Dilger	.10
22	Troy Aikman	1.00
23	Tavian Banks	.10
24	Cris Carter	.50
25	Derrick Alexander	.10
26	Chris Bordano	.10
27	Karim Abdul	.30
28	Jessie Armstead	.10
29	Drew Bledsoe	.75
30	Brian Dawkins	.10
31	Wayne Chrebet	.50
32	Garrison Hearst	.30
33	Eric Allen	.10
34	Tony Banks	.20
35	Jerome Bettis	.50
36	Stephen Alexander	.10
37	Rodney Harrison	.10
38	Mike Alstott	.50
39	Chad Brown	.10
40	Johnny McWilliams	.10
41	Kevin Dyson	.20
42	Keith Brooking	.20
43	Jim Harbaugh	.20
44	Bobby Engram	.10
45	John Holecek	.10
46	Steve Beuerlein	.10
47	Tony McGee	.10
48	Greg Ellis	.10
49	Corey Fuller	.10
50	Stephen Boyd	.10
51	Marshall Faulk	.50
52	Leroy Butler	.10
53	Reggie Barlow	.10
54	Randall Cunningham	.50
55	Aeneas Williams	.10
56	Kimble Anders	.10
57	Cameron Cleeland	.20
58	John Avery	.20
59	Gary Brown	.10
60	Ben Coates	.10
61	Koy Detmer	.10
62	Bryan Cox	.10
63	Edgar Bennett	.10
64	Tim Brown	.20
65	Isaac Bruce	.30
66	Eddie George	.75
67	Reidel Anthony	.10
68	Charlie Jones	.10
69	Terry Allen	.20
70	Joey Galloway	.50
71	Jamir Miller	.10
72	Will Blackwell	.10
73	Ray Buchanan	.10
74	Priest Holmes	.50
75	Michael Irvin	.20
76	Jonathon Linton	.10
77	Curtis Enis	.50
78	Neil O'Donnell	.20
79	Tim Biakabutuka	.10
80	Terry Kirby	.10
81	Germane Crowell	.20
82	Jason Elam	.10
83	Mark Chmura	.10
84	Marvin Harrison	.30
85	Jimmy Hitchcock	.10
86	Tony Brackens	.10
87	Sean Dawkins	.10
88	Tony Gonzalez	.20
89	Kent Graham	.10
90	Oronde Gadsden	.20
91	Hugh Douglas	.10
92	Robert Edwards	.30
93	R.W. McQuarters	.10
94	Aaron Glenn	.10
95	Kevin Carter	.10
96	Rickey Dudley	.10
97	Derrick Brooks	.10
98	Mark Bruener	.10
99	Darrell Green	.10
100	Jessie Tuggle	.10
101	Freddie Jones	.10
102	Rob Moore	.20
103	Ahman Green	.20
104	Chris Chandler	.20
105	Steve McNair	.50
106	Kevin Greene	.10
107	Jermaine Lewis	.20
108	Erik Kramer	.10
109	Eric Moulds	.50
110	Terry Fair	.10
111	Carl Pickens	.20
112	La'Roi Glover	.10
113	Chris Spielman	.10
114	Leroy Hoard	.10
115	Mark Brunell	.75
116	Patrick Jeffers	2.50
117	Elvis Grbac	.10
118	Ike Hilliard	.20
119	Sam Madison	.10
120	Terrell Owens	.50
121	Rich Gannon	.10
122	Skip Hicks	.50
123	Eric Green	.10
124	Trent Dilfer	.50
125	Terry Glenn	.30
126	Trent Green	.50
127	Charles Johnson	.10
128	Adrian Murrell	.20
129	Jason Gildon	.10
130	Tim Dwight	.50
131	Ryan Leaf	.50
132	Raghib Ismail	.10
133	Jon Kitna	.50
134	Alonzo Mayes	.10
135	Yancey Thigpen	.10
136	David LaFleur	.10
137	Ray Lewis	.10
138	Herman Moore	.50
139	Brian Griese	.30
140	Antonio Freeman	.50
141	Darnay Scott	.10
142	Ed McDaniel	.10
143	Andre Reed	.10
144	Andre Hastings	.10
145	Chris Warren	.10
146	Kevin Hardy	.10
147	Joe Jurevicius	.10
148	Jerome Pathon	.10
149	Duce Staley	.20
150	Dan Marino	1.50
151	Jerry Rice	1.00
152	Bam Morris	.10
153	Az-Zahir Hakim	.20
154	Ty Law	.10
155	Warrick Dunn	.50
156	Keyshawn Johnson	.50
157	Brian Mitchell	.10
158	James Jett	.10
159	Fred Lane	.10
160	Courtney Hawkins	.10
161	Andre Wadsworth	.20
162	Natrone Means	.10
163	Andrew Glover	.10
164	Anthony Simmons	.10
165	Leon Lett	.10
166	Frank Wycheck	.10
167	Barry Minter	.10
168	Michael McCrary	.10
169	Johnnie Morton	.10
170	Jay Riemersma	.10
171	Vonnie Holliday	.20
172	Brian Simmons	.10
173	Joe Johnson	.10
174	Ed McCaffrey	.30
175	Jason Sehorn	.10
176	Keenan McCardell	.10
177	Bobby Taylor	.10
178	Andre Rison	.20
179	Greg Hill	.10
180	O.J. McDuffie	.20
181	Darren Woodson	.10
182	Willie McGinest	.10
183	J.J. Stokes	.20
184	Leon Johnson	.10
185	Bert Emanuel	.10
186	Napoleon Kaufman	.50
187	Leslie Shepherd	.10
188	Levon Kirkland	.10
189	Simeon Rice	.10
190	Mikhael Ricks	.10
191	Robert Smith	.50
192	Michael Sinclair	.10
193	Muhsin Muhammad	.10
194	Duane Starks	.10
195	Terance Mathis	.10
196	Antowain Smith	.50
197	Tony Parrish	.10
198	Takeo Spikes	.10
199	Ernie Mills	.10
200	John Mobley	.10
201	Robert Porcher	.10
202	Pete Mitchell	.10
203	Darick Holmes	.10
204	Derrick Thomas	.20
205	David Palmer	.10
206	Jason Taylor	.10
207	Sammy Knight	.10
208	Dwayne Rudd	.10
209	Lawyer Milloy	.10
210	Michael Strahan	.10
211	Mo Lewis	.10
212	William Thomas	.10
213	Darrell Russell	.10
214	Brad Johnson	.30
215	Kordell Stewart	.50
216	Robert Holcombe	.20
217	Junior Seau	.20
218	Jacquez Green	.20
219	Shawn Springs	.10
220	Michael Westbrook	.20
221	Rod Woodson	.10
222	Frank Sanders	.10
223	Bruce Smith	.10
224	Eugene Robinson	.10
225	Bill Romanowski	.10
226	Wesley Walls	.10
227	Jimmy Smith	.20
228	Deion Sanders	.50
229	Lamar Thomas	.10
230	Dorsey Levens	.50
231	Tony Simmons	.10
232	John Randle	.10
233	Curtis Martin	.50
234	Bryant Young	.10
235	Charles Woodson	.50
236	Charles Way	.10
237	Zack Thomas	.20
238	Ricky Proehl	.10
239	Ricky Watters	.20
240	Hardy Nickerson	.10
241	Shannon Sharpe	.20
242	O.J. Santiago	.10
243	Vinny Testaverde	.20
244	Preston Roell	.10
245	James Stewart	.10
246	Jake Reed	.10
247	Steve Young	.75
248	Shaun Williams	.10
249	Rod Smith	.20
250	Warren Sapp	.20
251	Champ Bailey	1.50
252	Karsten Bailey	.40
253	D'Wayne Bates	.75
254	Michael Bishop	1.50
255	David Boston	3.00
256	Na Brown	.40
257	Fernando Bryant	.40
258	Shawn Bryson	.40
259	Darrin Chiaverini	.40
260	Chris Claiborne	1.00
261	Mike Cloud	.40
262	Cecil Collins	2.50
263	Tim Couch	8.00
264	Scott Covington	.40
265	Daunte Culpepper	4.00
266	Antwan Edwards	.40
267	Troy Edwards	2.50
268	Ebenezer Ekuban	.75
269	Kevin Faulk	3.00
270	Jermaine Fazande	.40
271	Joe Germaine	1.25
272	Martin Gramatica	.40
273	Torry Holt	2.50
274	Brock Huard	1.50
275	Sedrick Irvin	1.50
276	Sheldon Jackson	.40
277	Edgerrin James	8.00
278	James Johnson	1.50
279	Kevin Johnson	1.50
280	Malcolm Johnson	.40
281	Andy Katzenmoyer	1.00
282	Jevon Kearse	2.00
283	Patrick Kerney	.40
284	Shaun King	3.00
285	Jim Kleinsasser	.40
286	Rob Konrad	.75
287	Chris McAlister	.75
288	Donovan McNabb	4.00
289	Cade McNown	4.00
290	Dee Miller	.40
291	Joe Montgomery	1.00
292	De'Mond Parker	.40
293	Peerless Price	2.00
294	Akili Smith	4.00
295	Justin Swift	.40
296	Jerame Tuman	.40
297	Ricky Williams	8.00
298	Antoine Winfield	.75
299	Craig Yeast	.40
300	Amos Zereoue	2.00

1999 Fleer Aerial Assault

Each card is printed on plastic with silver holofoil featuring the NFL's top throwers and their targets. The 15 different singles were inserted 1:24 packs.

		MT
Complete Set (15):		85.00
Common Player:		2.00
Minor Stars:		4.00
Inserted 1:24		
1	Troy Aikman	8.00
2	Jamal Anderson	2.00
3	Charlie Batch	4.00
4	Mark Brunell	6.00
5	Terrell Davis	10.00
6	John Elway	10.00
7	Brett Favre	15.00
8	Keyshawn Johnson	4.00
9	Jon Kitna	5.00
10	Peyton Manning	10.00
11	Dan Marino	10.00
12	Randy Moss	15.00
13	Eric Moulds	4.00
14	Jake Plummer	8.00
15	Jerry Rice	8.00

Post-1980 cards in Near Mint condition will generally sell for about 75% of the quoted Mint value. Excellent-condition cards bring no more than 40%.

1999 Fleer Rookie Sensations

Rookies from the 1999 season are featured against team color backgrounds and glistening on silver foil fronts. The 20 different singles can be found 1:6 packs.

		MT
Complete Set (20):		50.00
Common Player:		1.00
Inserted 1:6		
1	Champ Bailey	2.00
2	Michael Bishop	2.50
3	David Boston	3.00
4	Chris Claiborne	1.00
5	Tim Couch	10.00
6	Daunte Culpepper	4.00
7	Troy Edwards	3.00
8	Kevin Faulk	3.00
9	Torry Holt	3.00
10	Brock Huard	2.00
11	Edgerrin James	6.00
12	Kevin Johnson	2.00
13	Shaun King	2.00
14	Rob Konrad	1.00
15	Chris McAlister	1.00
16	Donovan McNabb	4.00
17	Cade McNown	4.00
18	Peerless Price	2.50
19	Akili Smith	4.00
20	Ricky Williams	10.00

1999 Fleer Under Pressure

This 15-card set spotlights a sculpture embossed player image on patterned holofoil. Each is die-cut and found 1:96 packs.

		MT
Complete Set (15):		250.00
Common Player:		8.00
Inserted 1:96		
1	Charlie Batch	12.00
2	Terrell Davis	30.00
3	Warrick Dunn	12.00
4	John Elway	30.00
5	Brett Favre	40.00
6	Keyshawn Johnson	8.00
7	Peyton Manning	30.00
8	Dan Marino	30.00
9	Curtis Martin	12.00
10	Randy Moss	40.00
11	Jake Plummer	20.00
12	Barry Sanders	40.00
13	Emmitt Smith	30.00
14	Fred Taylor	20.00
15	Charles Woodson	8.00

Values quoted in this guide reflect the retail price of a card — the price a collector can expect to pay when buying a card from a dealer. The wholesale price — that which a collector can expect to receive from a dealer when selling cards — will be significantly lower, depending on desirability and condition.

1999 Fleer Unsung Heroes

This 30-card set picks one under-recognized star from each team and highlights him on cardboard. Singles were inserted 1:3 packs.

		MT
Complete Set (30):		7.00
Common Player:		.25
Minor Stars:		.50
Inserted 1:3		
1	Tommy Bennett	.25
2	Lester Archambeau	.25
3	James Jones	.25
4	Phil Hansen	.25
5	Anthony Johnson	.25
6	Bobby Engram	.25
7	Eric Bienemy	.25
8	Daryl Johnston	.25
9	Maa Tanuvasa	.25
10	Stephen Boyd	.25
11	Adam Timmerman	.25
12	Ken Dilger	.25
13	Bryan Barker	.25
14	Rich Gannon	.25
15	O.J. Brigance	.25
16	Jeff Christy	.25
17	Shawn Jefferson	.25
18	Aaron Craver	.25
19	Chris Calloway	.25
20	Pepper Johnson	.25
21	Greg Biekert	.25
22	Duce Staley	.50
23	Courtney Hawkins	.25
24	Rodney Harrison	.25
25	Ray Brown	.25
26	Jon Kitna	1.50
27	D'Marco Farr	.25
28	Brad Culpepper	.25
29	Steve Jackson	.25
30	Brian Mitchell	.25

1999 Fleer Focus

This 175-card set included 75 rookie cards found at four different levels. The 10 defensive rookies were found 1:4 packs. The 25 wide receiver rookies were sequentially numbered to 3,850. The 25 running backs were numbered to 2,500 and the 15 quarterbacks were numbered to 2,250. The Stealth insert was a parallel to the base and each was sequentially numbered to 300. Other inserts include: Feel the Game, Fresh Ink, Glimmer Men, Reflexions, Sparklers and Wondrous. SRP was $2.99 for five-card packs.

	MT
Complete Set (175):	425.00
Common Player:	.20
Minor Stars:	.40
Common Rookie (101-110):	1.00
Inserted 1:4	
Common Rookie (111-135):	3.00
Production 3,850 Sets	
Common Rookie (136-160):	4.00
Production 2,500 Sets	
Common Rookie (161-175):	6.00

		MT
Production 2,250 Sets		
Wax Box:		100.00
1	Randy Moss	4.00
2	Andre Rison	.40
3	Ed McCaffrey	.50
4	Jerry Rice	2.00
5	Tim Biakabutuka	.40
6	Wayne Chrebet	.75
7	Deion Sanders	.75
8	Ricky Watters	.50
9	Skip Hicks	.40
10	Charlie Batch	1.25
11	Joey Galloway	.75
12	Stephen Alexander	.20
13	Curtis Conway	.40
14	Garrison Hearst	.40
15	Kerry Collins	.40
16	Cris Carter	.75
17	Eddie George	1.00
18	Eric Moulds	.75
19	Vinny Testaverde	.75
20	Curtis Enis	.75
21	Gary Brown	.20
22	Junior Seau	.40
23	Kevin Dyson	.40
24	Jeff Blake	.40
25	Herman Moore	.75
26	Natrone Means	.50
27	Terry Glenn	.75
28	Fred Taylor	2.00
29	Ben Coates	.40
30	Corey Dillon	.75
31	Eddie Kennison	.20
32	Bam Morris	.20
33	Doug Pederson	.20
34	Jamal Anderson	.75
35	Michael Westbrook	.40
36	Peyton Manning	3.00
37	Carl Pickens	.40
38	Drew Bledsoe	1.50
39	Jim Harbaugh	.40
40	Kurt Warner	20.00
41	Mark Chmura	.40
42	Hines Ward	.40
43	Terry Kirby	.20
44	Brett Favre	3.00
45	Kordell Stewart	.75
46	Leslie Shepherd	.20
47	Marshall Faulk	.75
48	Troy Aikman	2.00
49	Isaac Bruce	.75
50	Michael Irvin	.40
51	Robert Smith	.75
52	Dorsey Levens	.75
53	Duce Staley	.50
54	Jake Plummer	1.50
55	Adrian Murrell	.40
56	Antonio Freeman	.75
57	Jerome Bettis	.75
58	Elvis Grbac	.40
59	Keyshawn Johnson	.75
60	Steve Beuerlein	.40
61	Yancey Thigpen	.20
62	Doug Flutie	1.25
63	Jacquez Green	.40
64	Jimmy Smith	.75
65	Tim Brown	.75
66	Jason Sehorn	.20
67	Muhsin Muhammad	.40
68	Shannon Sharpe	.40
69	Terrell Owens	.75
70	Keenan McCardell	.40
71	Rich Gannon	.40
72	Scott Mitchell	.20
73	Warrick Dunn	.75
74	Brad Johnson	.75
75	Charles Johnson	.20
76	Chris Chandler	.40
77	Marcus Pollard	.20
78	Mike Alstott	.75
79	Bubby Brister	.40
80	Jon Kitna	1.00
81	Randall Cunningham	.75
82	Antowain Smith	.75
83	Curtis Martin	.75
84	Steve McNair	1.00
85	Tony Gonzalez	.40
86	O.J. McDuffie	.40
87	Steve Young	1.25
88	Terrell Davis	3.00
89	Mark Brunell	1.50
90	Napoleon Kaufman	.75
91	Priest Holmes	.75
92	Trent Dilfer	.50
93	Brian Griese	1.50
94	J.J. Stokes	.40
95	Karim Abdul	.40
96	Barry Sanders	4.00
97	Dan Marino	3.00
98	Emmitt Smith	3.00
99	Marvin Harrison	.75
100	Rod Smith	.50
101	*Champ Bailey*	4.00
102	*Fernando Bryant*	2.00
103	*Chris Claiborne*	2.00
104	*Antwan Edwards*	2.00
105	*Martin Gramatica*	1.00
106	*Andy Katzenmoyer*	2.50
107	*Jevon Kearse*	5.00
108	*Chris McAlister*	2.00
109	*Al Wilson*	2.00
110	*Antoine Winfield*	2.00
111	*Karsten Bailey*	4.00
112	*D'Wayne Bates*	4.00
113	*Marty Booker*	4.00
114	*David Boston*	10.00
115	*Na Brown*	3.00
116	*Desmond Clark*	3.00
117	*Dameane Douglas*	3.00

		MT
118	*Donald Driver*	3.00
119	*Troy Edwards*	10.00
120	*Torry Holt*	10.00
121	*Kevin Johnson*	10.00
122	*Reggie Kelly*	3.00
123	*Jim Kleinsasser*	4.00
124	*Jeremy McDaniel*	3.00
125	*Darnell McDonald*	3.00
126	*Travis McGriff*	3.00
127	*Billy Miller*	3.00
128	*Dee Miller*	3.00
129	*Peerless Price*	8.00
130	*Troy Smith*	3.00
131	*Brandon Stokley*	3.00
132	*Wane McGarity*	3.00
133	*Mark Campbell*	3.00
134	*Jerame Tuman*	3.00
135	*Craig Yeast*	3.00
136	*Jerry Azumah*	5.00
137	*Marlon Barnes*	4.00
138	*Michael Basnight*	5.00
139	*Shawn Bryson*	5.00
140	*Michael Cloud*	7.00
141	*Cecil Collins*	12.00
142	*Autry Denson*	7.00
143	*Kevin Faulk*	10.00
144	*Jermaine Fazande*	7.00
145	*Jim Finn*	4.00
146	*Madre Hill*	5.00
147	*Sedrick Irvin*	10.00
148	*Terry Jackson*	6.00
149	*Edgerrin James*	85.00
150	*J.J. Johnson*	10.00
151	*Rob Konrad*	8.00
152	*Joel Makovicka*	7.00
153	*Cecil Martin*	5.00
154	*Joe Montgomery*	8.00
155	*Demonn Parker*	10.00
156	*Sirr Parker*	5.00
157	*Jeff Paulk*	6.00
158	*Nick Williams*	5.00
159	*Ricky Williams*	45.00
160	*Amos Zereoue*	8.00
161	*Michael Bishop*	10.00
162	*Aaron Brooks*	8.00
163	*Tim Couch*	45.00
164	*Scott Covington*	8.00
165	*Daunte Culpepper*	25.00
166	*Kevin Daft*	7.00
167	*Joe Germaine*	8.00
168	*Chris Greisen*	8.00
169	*Brock Huard*	10.00
170	*Shaun King*	25.00
171	*Cory Sauter*	5.00
172	*Donovan McNabb*	25.00
173	*Cade McNown*	25.00
174	*Chad Plummer*	6.00
175	*Akili Smith*	25.00

1999 Fleer Focus Stealth

This was a 175-card parallel to the base set. Each single was sequentially numbered to 300.

	MT
Complete Set (175):	1000.
Stealth Cards:	5x-10x
Stealth Rookies:	2x
#40 Kurt Warner	100.00
Production 300 Sets	

1999 Fleer Focus Feel the Game

This 10-card insert set included pieces of game-used jer-

seys except for the Brett Favre single which included a piece of game-worn shoes. Singles were inserted 1:192 packs.

		MT
Complete Set (10):		600.00
Common Player:		40.00
Inserted 1:192		
1	Vinny Testaverde	40.00
2	Mark Brunell	60.00
3	Brett Favre Shoes	125.00
4	Fred Taylor	70.00
5	Jeff Blake	40.00
6	Emmitt Smith	100.00
7	Joe Germaine	40.00
8	Cecil Collins	50.00
9	Charles Woodson	50.00
10	Kurt Warner	200.00

1999 Fleer Focus Fresh Ink

This 37-card insert set included autographs of both veterans and rookies. Each single was hand-numbered and found 1:48 packs.

		MT
Complete Set (37):		1250.
Common Player:		10.00
Minor Stars:		20.00
Inserted 1:48		
	Reidel Anthony	10.00
	Charlie Batch	30.00
	Jeff Blake	10.00
	Darrin Chiaverini	20.00
	Wayne Chrebet	20.00
	Daunte Culpepper	45.00
	Terrell Davis	120.00
	Koy Detmer	10.00
	Corey Dillon	30.00
	Troy Edwards	30.00
	Doug Flutie	40.00
	Eddie George	30.00
	Trent Green	10.00
	Marvin Harrison	25.00
	Torry Holt	30.00
	Sedrick Irvin	20.00
	Edgerrin James	200.00
	Brad Johnson	20.00
	Charles Johnson	10.00
	Jon Kitna	30.00
	Jim Kleinsasser	10.00
	Peyton Manning	120.00
	O.J. McDuffie	10.00
	Travis McGriff	10.00
	Donovan McNabb	45.00
	Cade McNown	45.00
	Joe Montgomery	20.00
	Randy Moss	125.00
	Jake Plummer	50.00
	Akili Smith	45.00
	Antowain Smith	20.00
	Duce Staley	20.00
	Brandon Stokley	10.00
	Fred Taylor	50.00
	Vinny Testaverde	20.00
	Ricky Williams	150.00
	Steve Young	50.00

1999 Fleer Focus Glimmer Men

This 10-card insert set included stars from the NFL and were printed with silver and

gold foil. Singles were inserted 1:20 packs.

		MT
Complete Set (10):		45.00
Common Player:		4.00
Inserted 1:20		
1	Tim Couch	8.00
2	Barry Sanders	8.00
3	Terrell Davis	8.00
4	Dan Marino	6.00
5	Troy Aikman	5.00
6	Brett Favre	8.00
7	Randy Moss	8.00
8	Emmitt Smith	6.00
9	Edgerrin James	10.00
10	Fred Taylor	4.00

1999 Fleer Focus Reflexions

This 10-card insert set was a parallel to the Glimmer Men insert. Each single was sequentially numbered to 100.

	MT
Complete Set (10):	350.00
Common Player:	20.00
Production 100 Sets	
1 Tim Couch	75.00
2 Barry Sanders	50.00
3 Terrell Davis	35.00
4 Dan Marino	35.00
5 Troy Aikman	25.00
6 Brett Favre	50.00
7 Randy Moss	50.00
8 Emmitt Smith	35.00
9 Edgerrin James	125.00
10 Fred Taylor	20.00

1999 Fleer Focus Sparklers

This 15-card insert set highlighted the top rookies from 1999. Singles were found 1:10 packs.

		MT
Complete Set (15):		30.00
Common Player:		1.50
Inserted 1:10		
1	Tim Couch	7.00
2	Donovan McNabb	4.00
3	Akili Smith	4.00
4	Cade McNown	4.00
5	Daunte Culpepper	4.00
6	Ricky Williams	7.00
7	Edgerrin James	10.00
8	Kevin Faulk	1.50
9	Torry Holt	3.00
10	David Boston	3.00
11	Sedrick Irvin	1.50
12	Peerless Price	2.00
13	Troy Edwards	3.00
14	Brock Huard	1.50
15	Shaun King	4.00

1999 Fleer Focus Wondrous

This was a 20-card insert set that pictured each star on

silver holo foil with gold foil stamping. Singles were found 1:20 packs.

		MT
Complete Set (20):		65.00
Common Player:		2.00
Inserted 1:20		
1	Peyton Manning	6.00
2	Fred Taylor	4.00
3	Tim Couch	8.00
4	Charlie Batch	3.00
5	Jerry Rice	4.00
6	Randy Moss	8.00
7	Warrick Dunn	2.00
8	Mark Brunell	3.00
9	Emmitt Smith	6.00
10	Eddie George	2.00
11	Brian Griese	3.00
12	Terrell Davis	6.00
13	Dan Marino	6.00
14	Ricky Williams	8.00
15	Brett Favre	8.00
16	Jake Plummer	3.00
17	Troy Aikman	4.00
18	Drew Bledsoe	3.00
19	Edgerrin James	12.00
20	Cade McNown	5.00

1999 Fleer Mystique

The 160-card set included 50 short-printed rookie cards that were sequentially numbered to 2,999 and 10 veteran stars numbered to 2,500. Parallel sets of Gold and Masterpieces were made for the first 100 cards in the base set. Other insert sets included: Feel the Game, Fresh Ink, NFL 2000, Protential and Star Power. SRP was $4.99 for four-card packs.

	MT
Complete Set (160):	650.00
Common Player:	.25
Minor Stars:	.50
Common SP (1-100):	1.50
Common Rookie:	5.00
Production 2,999 Sets	
Common Rookie (151-160):	5.00
Production 2,500 Sets	
Wax Box:	120.00
1 Terrell Davis SP	4.00
2 Jerome Bettis SP	1.50
3 J.J. Stokes	.50
4 Frank Wycheck	.25
5 O.J. McDuffie	.25
6 Johnnie Morton	.25
7 Marshall Faulk SP	1.50
8 Ryan Leaf	.75
9 Sean Dawkins	.25
10 Brett Favre SP	6.00
11 Steve Young SP	2.50
12 Jimmy Smith	.75
13 Isaac Bruce	.75
14 Trent Dilfer	.50
15 Brian Mitchell	.25
16 Kordell Stewart SP	1.50
17 Herman Moore	.75
18 Troy Aikman SP	3.00
19 Cris Carter	.75
20 Barry Sanders SP	6.00
21 Tony Gonzalez	.50
22 Skip Hicks	.50
23 Steve McNair SP	1.50
24 Brad Johnson	.75
25 Mark Chmura	.50
26 Randall Cunningham SP	1.50
27 Jerry Rice SP	3.00
28 Jamie Asher	.25
29 Brian Griese SP	2.50
30 Peyton Manning SP	4.00
31 Keith Poole	.25
32 Wayne Chrebet	.75
33 Rich Gannon	.50
34 Michael Irvin	.50
35 Yancey Thigpen	.50
36 Corey Dillon	.75
37 Steve Beurlein	.50
38 Terry Kirby	.25
39 Jacquez Green	.50
40 Mark Brunell SP	2.50
41 Rickey Dudley	.50
42 Shannon Sharpe	.75

43	Andre Rison	.50
44	Chris Chandler	.50
45	Fred Taylor SP	3.00
46	Kerry Collins	.50
47	Antowain Smith SP	1.50
48	Wesley Walls	.50
49	Rob Moore	.50
50	Dan Marino SP	4.00
51	Robert Smith	.75
52	Keenan McCardell	.50
53	Joey Galloway	.75
54	Fred Lane	.50
55	Napoleon Kaufman	.75
56	Curtis Martin	.75
57	Rod Smith	.75
58	Curtis Conway	.50
59	Kevin Dyson	.50
60	Warrick Dunn SP	1.50
61	Ahman Green	.50
62	Duce Staley	.75
63	Emmitt Smith SP	4.00
64	Adrian Murrell	.25
65	Dorsey Levens	.75
66	Drew Bledsoe SP	2.50
67	Ed McCaffrey	.75
68	Natrone Means	.50
69	Deion Sanders	.50
70	Keyshawn Johnson SP	1.50
71	Antonio Freeman	.75
72	James Stewart	.50
73	Ben Coates	.50
74	Priest Holmes	.75
75	Jake Reed	.50
76	Mike Alstott	.75
77	Vinny Testaverde	.50
78	Ricky Watters	.50
79	Garrison Hearst	.50
80	Junior Seau	.50
81	Tim Brown	.50
82	Jamal Anderson	.75
83	Robert Brooks	.25
84	Marc Edwards	.25
85	Curtis Enis	.75
86	Doug Flutie	1.25
87	Terry Glenn	.75
88	Charlie Batch SP	2.00
89	Marvin Harrison	.75
90	Jake Plummer SP	3.00
91	Terrell Owens	.75
92	Scott Mitchell	.25
93	Tim Dwight	.75
94	Eddie George SP	1.50
95	Ike Hilliard	.50
96	Robert Holcombe	.25
97	Charles Johnson	.25
98	Eric Moulds	.75
99	Michael Westbrook	.75
100	Randy Moss SP	6.00
101	Tim Couch	50.00
102	Donovan McNabb	25.00
103	Akili Smith	25.00
104	Cade McNown	25.00
105	Daunte Culpepper	25.00
106	Ricky Williams	50.00
107	Edgerrin James	75.00
108	Kevin Faulk	12.00
109	Torry Holt	15.00
110	David Boston	15.00
111	Chris Claiborne	7.00
112	Mike Cloud	8.00
113	Joe Germaine	8.00
114	Cecil Collins	15.00
115	Tim Alexander	5.00
116	Brandon Stokley	5.00
117	Lamarr Glenn	5.00
118	Shawn Bryson	5.00
119	Jeff Paulk	5.00
120	Kevin Johnson	15.00
121	Charlie Rogers	10.00
122	Joe Montgomery	10.00
123	Travis McGriff	7.00
124	Dee Miller	7.00
125	Rob Konrad	8.00
126	Peerless Price	10.00
127	D'Wayne Bates	7.00
128	Craig Yeast	7.00
129	Malcolm Johnson	5.00
130	Brock Huard	10.00
131	Sedrick Irvin	10.00
132	Troy Smith	5.00
133	Troy Edwards	15.00
134	Al Wilson	5.00
135	Terry Jackson	7.00
136	Dameane Douglas	5.00
137	Amos Zereoue	8.00
138	Shaun King	15.00
139	James Johnson	10.00
140	Jermaine Fazande	7.00
141	Autry Denson	7.00
142	Darren Hall	5.00
143	Na Brown	5.00
144	Mike Lucky	5.00
145	Karsten Bailey	6.00
146	Kevin Daft	5.00
147	Sean Bennett	8.00
148	Madre Hill	5.00
149	Michael Bishop	12.00
150	Scott Covington	7.00
151	Randy Moss STAR	20.00
152	Fred Taylor STAR	10.00
153	Brett Favre STAR	20.00
154	Dan Marino STAR	15.00
155	Terrell Davis STAR	15.00
156	Barry Sanders STAR	20.00
157	Emmitt Smith STAR	15.00
158	Jake Plummer STAR	8.00
159	Warrick Dunn STAR	5.00
160	Troy Aikman STAR	10.00

1999 Fleer Mystique Gold

This was a parallel to the first 100 cards in the set. The name is in gold foil rather than silver in the base set. Singles were randomly inserted.

	MT
Complete Set (100):	300.00
Gold Cards:	3x-6x

1999 Fleer Mystique Feel The Game

This 10-card insert set featured a piece of game-used memorabilia. Each single was hand-numbered and randomly inserted.

		MT
Complete Set (10):		550.00
Common Player:		25.00
1	Terrell Davis jersey 510	100.00
2	Charles Johnson shoes 325	25.00
3	Jon Kitna shorts 640	50.00
4	Dorsey Levens jersey 515	50.00
5	Dan Marino socks 220	150.00
6	Curtis Martin jersey 690	50.00
7	Johnnie Morton jersey 580	25.00
8	Randy Moss jersey 510	175.00
9	Brandon Stokley gloves 85	50.00
10	Steve Young jersey 580	85.00

1999 Fleer Mystique Fresh Ink

This 30-card insert set ncluded autographs of both veterans and rookies. Each single was hand-numbered and randomly inserted.

		MT
Complete Set (30):		1850.
Common Player:		10.00
Minor Stars:		20.00
1	Charlie Batch 250	50.00
2	Mark Brunell 45	125.00
3	Shawn Bryson 650	10.00
4	Cecil Collins 725	35.00
5	Daunte Culpepper 300	60.00
6	Randall Cunningham 200	35.00
7	Terrell Davis 50	200.00
8	Sean Dawkins 700	10.00
9	Corey Dillon 250	30.00
10	Dameane Douglas 750	10.00
11	Tim Dwight 725	10.00
12	Troy Edwards 200	50.00
13	Doug Flutie 250	50.00
14	Eddie George 250	35.00
15	Joe Germaine 575	20.00
16	Trent Green 350	20.00
17	Torry Holt 350	40.00
18	Brock Huard 700	20.00
19	Edgerrin James 150	300.00
20	Brad Johnson 300	25.00
21	Jon Kitna 350	40.00
22	Peyton Manning 150 250	150.00
23	Randy Moss 750	200.00
24	Doug Peterson 750	10.00
25	Jake Plummer 300	40.00
26	Peerless Price 675	20.00
27	Akili Smith 100	120.00
28	Antowain Smith 150	45.00
29	Emmitt Smith 125	200.00

| 30 | Ricky Williams 150 | 250.00 |

1999 Fleer Mystique NFL 2000

This 10-card insert set included players who are ready for super-stardom. Each single was sequentially numbered to 999.

		MT
Complete Set (10):		45.00
Common Player:		3.00
Production 999 Sets		
1	Peyton Manning	15.00
2	Ryan Leaf	5.00
3	Charlie Batch	7.00
4	Fred Taylor	10.00
5	Keyshawn Johnson	5.00
6	J.J. Stokes	3.00
7	Jake Plummer	8.00
8	Brian Griese	8.00
9	Antowain Smith	5.00
10	Jamal Anderson	5.00

1999 Fleer Mystique Pro-Tential

This 10-card insert set included the top rookies from 1999. Each of these singles was sequentially numbered to 1,999.

		MT
Complete Set (10):		65.00
Common Player:		5.00
Production 1,999 Sets		
1	Tim Couch	20.00
2	Donovan McNabb	10.00
3	Akili Smith	10.00
4	Cade McNown	10.00
5	Daunte Culpepper	10.00
6	Ricky Williams	20.00
7	Edgerrin James	25.00
8	Kevin Faulk	5.00
9	Torry Holt	7.00
10	David Boston	7.00

1999 Fleer Mystique Star Power

This 10-card insert set included the superstars from the NFL and featured them on a plastic card with a full silver-metallic holofoil background. Each single was sequentially numbered to 100.

		MT
Complete Set (10):		350.00
Common Player:		15.00
Production 100 Sets		
1	Randy Moss	70.00
2	Warrick Dunn	15.00
3	Mark Brunell	30.00
4	Emmitt Smith	50.00
5	Eddie George	15.00
6	Barry Sanders	70.00
7	Terrell Davis	50.00
8	Dan Marino	50.00
9	Troy Aikman	35.00
10	Brett Favre	70.00

1995 Flickball NFL Helmets

Flickball debuted in 1995 and featured team helmets and Super Bowl logos. They arrived in six-card packs and featured two expansion team helmets, cards 61 and 62, that were found every 48 packs.

		MT
Complete Set (60):		12.00
Common Player:		.25
1	Dallas Cowboys	.50
2	New York Giants	.25

3	Arizona Cardinals	.25
4	Philadelphia Eagles	.25
5	Washington Redskins	.35
6	Minnesota Vikings	.25
7	Chicago Bears	.35
8	Green Bay Packers	.50
9	Detroit Lions	.25
10	Tampa Bay Buccaneers	.25
11	San Francisco 49ers	.50
12	New Orleans Saints	.25
13	Atlanta Falcons	.25
14	Carolina Panthers	.35
15	St. Louis Rams	.25
16	New England Patriots	.25
17	Miami Dolphins	.35
18	Buffalo Bills	.25
19	Indianapolis Colts	.25
20	New York Jets	.25
21	Pittsburgh Steelers	.35
22	Cleveland Browns	.25
23	Cincinnati Bengals	.25
24	Jacksonville Jaguars	.35
25	Houston Oilers	.25
26	San Diego Chargers	.25
27	Oakland Raiders	.35
28	Kansas City Chiefs	.25
29	Denver Broncos	.25
30	Seattle Seahawks	.25
31	Super Bowl I	.25
32	Super Bowl II	.25
33	Super Bowl III	.25
34	Super Bowl IV	.25
35	Super Bowl V	.25
36	Super Bowl VI	.25
37	Super Bowl VII	.25
38	Super Bowl VIII	.25
39	Super Bowl IX	.25
40	Super Bowl X	.25
41	Super Bowl XI	.25
42	Super Bowl XII	.25
43	Super Bowl XIII	.25
44	Super Bowl XIV	.25
45	Super Bowl XV	.25
46	Super Bowl XVI	.25
47	Super Bowl XVII	.25
48	Super Bowl XVIII	.25
49	Super Bowl XIX	.25
50	Super Bowl XX	.25
51	Super Bowl XXI	.25
52	Super Bowl XXII	.25
53	Super Bowl XXIII	.25
54	Super Bowl XXIV	.25
55	Super Bowl XXV	.25
56	Super Bowl XXVI	.25
57	Super Bowl XXVII	.25
58	Super Bowl XXVIII	.25
59	Super Bowl XXIX	.25
60	Super Bowl XXX Logo	.25
61	Carolina Panthers Inaugural Season	1.25
62	Jacksonville Jaguars Inaugural Season	1.25

1995 Flickball Prototypes

This unnumbered 10-card set was a prelude to the 1996 Flickball release. Each card arrived in the shape of a football and featured a finger-sized cutout space used to flick the card as part of a game. Card No. 7 included a different player on each side and was called a "Double Flick". Each card in this prototype set contained the words "Pre-Production" on its back.

		MT
Complete Set (10):		5.00
Common Player:		.25
1	Bill Bates	.25
2	Jeff Blake	.50
3	Drew Bledsoe	1.00
4	Brett Favre	2.00
5	Kevin Greene	.25
6	Daryl Johnston	.25
7	Steve McNair, Kerry Collins	1.00
8	Jerry Rice	1.00
9	Tamarick Vanover	.50
10	Chris Warren	.25

Post-1980 cards in Near Mint condition will generally sell for about 75% of the quoted Mint value. Excellent-condition cards bring no more than 40%.

1996 Flickball

The first Flickball set to feature players contained 100 top stars and arrived in seven-card packs. Inserts included in the release were: Commemoratives, DoubleFlicks, Hawaiian Flicks, PreviewFlick Cowboys and Rookies.

		MT
Complete Set (100):		20.00
Common Player:		.10
1	Troy Aikman	1.00
2	Emmitt Smith	2.00
3	Neil O'Donnell (UER, name spelled Niel)	.10
4	Deion Sanders	.50
5	Bill Bates	.10
6	Rodney Peete	.10
7	Ricky Watters	.20
8	Fred Barnett	.10
9	Dave Krieg	.10
10	Larry Centers	.10
11	Garrison Hearst	.20
12	Dave Brown	.10
13	Rodney Hampton	.20
14	Mike Sherrard	.10
15	Gus Frerotte	.20
16	Henry Ellard	.10
17	Darrell Green	.10
18	Scott Mitchell	.20
19	Barry Sanders	1.00
20	Herman Moore	.30
21	Erik Kramer	.10
22	Curtis Conway	.25
23	Jeff Graham	.10
24	Brett Favre	2.00
25	Edgar Bennett	.20
26	Robert Brooks	.30
27	Reggie White	.25
28	Warren Moon	.20
29	Robert Smith	.20
30	Cris Carter	.20
31	Trent Dilfer	.30
32	Errict Rhett	.75
33	Santana Dotson	.10
34	Steve Young	.75
35	Jerry Rice	1.00
36	Merton Hanks	.10
37	Ken Norton	.10
38	Jesse Sapolu	.10
39	Jim Everett	.10
40	Willie Roaf	.10
41	Tyrone Hughes	.10
42	Chris Miller	.10
43	Isaac Bruce	.75
44	Shane Conlan	.10
45	Jeff George	.20
46	Eric Metcalf	.10
47	Craig Heyward	.10
48	Sam Mills	.10
49	Mark Carrier (WR)	.10
50	Brett Maxie	.10
51	Jim Kelly	.20
52	Andre Reed	.10
53	Bruce Smith	.20
54	Bryce Paup	.10
55	Jim Harbaugh	.20
56	Marshall Faulk	.75
57	Sean Dawkins	.10
58	Dan Marino	2.00
59	Terry Kirby	.10
60	O.J. McDuffie	.20
61	Bernie Parmalee	.10
62	Wayne Chrebet	.20
63	Adrian Murrell	.20
64	Ron Moore	.10
65	Drew Bledsoe	1.00
66	Vincent Brisby	.20
67	Vincent Brown	.10
68	Neil O'Donnell	.20
69	Erric Pegram	.10
70	Rohn Stark	.10
71	Kevin Greene	.20
72	Greg Lloyd	.20
73	Todd McNair	.10
74	Mark Stepnoski	.10
75	Bruce Matthews	.10
76	Jeff Blake	.20
77	Carl Pickens	.20
78	John Copeland	.10
79	Vinny Testaverde	.10

80	Andre Rison	.10
81	Leroy Hoard	.10
82	Mark Brunell	1.00
83	Cedric Tillman	.10
84	Desmond Howard	.20
85	Stan Humphries	.20
86	Natrone Means	.30
87	Junior Seau	.20
88	Steve Bono	.20
89	Marcus Allen	.20
90	Derrick Thomas	.20
91	Neil Smith	.10
92	Rick Mirer	.30
93	Chris Warren	.20
94	Cortez Kennedy	.10
95	Jeff Hostetler	.10
96	Tim Brown	.20
97	Terry McDaniel	.10
98	John Elway	.75
99	Shannon Sharpe	.20
100	Steve Atwater	.10

1996 Flickball Commemoratives

This four-card Flickball insert was inserted every 357 packs, with each card being hand-numbered to 700.

		MT
Complete Set (4):		75.00
Common Player:		15.00
C1	Emmitt Smith (25 Touchdowns)	20.00
C2	Dan Marino (Most passing yards)	20.00
C3	Brett Favre (MVP)	20.00
C4	Curtis Martin (Rookie of the Year)	15.00

1996 Flickball DoubleFlicks

This 12-card, double-sided insert was inserted in every three packs. Cards feature a player on each side from the same position. The cards are numbered with the "DF" prefix.

		MT
Complete Set (12):		18.00
Common Player:		.75
1	Dan Marino, Drew Bledsoe	5.00
2	Troy Aikman, Steve Young	2.50
3	Kerry Collins, Steve McNair	2.50
4	Eric Zeier, Kordell Stewart	2.50
5	Emmitt Smith, Marshall Faulk	5.00
6	Barry Sanders, Errict Rhett	2.50
7	Curtis Martin, Terrell Davis	3.50
8	Rashaan Salaam, Napoleon Kaufman	1.50
9	Michael Irvin, Jerry Rice	2.50
10	Tim Brown, Cris Carter	.75
11	Joey Galloway, J.J. Stokes	1.50
12	Frank Sanders, Michael Westbrook	1.25

1996 Flickball Hawaiian Flicks

Four different players that are native to Hawaii are featured in Hawaiian Flicks. These were found every eight packs.

		MT
Complete Set (4):		4.00
Common Player:		1.00
H1	Mark Tuinei	1.00
H2	Jesse Sapolu	1.00
H3	Jason Elam	1.00
H4	Junior Seau	1.50

1996 Flickball PreviewFlick Cowboys

PreviewFlick Cowboys were included in every four packs. The set includes eight Cowboys, with cards carrying a "P" prefix on the card number.

	MT
Complete Set (8):	6.00
Common Player:	.50

1	Daryl Johnston	1.00
2	Jay Novacek	1.00
3	Kevin Williams (WR)	1.50
4	Charles Haley	1.00
5	Darren Woodson	.50
6	Leon Lett	.75
7	Chad Hennings	.50
8	Mark Tuinei	.50

1996 Flickball Rookies

This 20-card insert captured the top rookies from the 1995 season, and was inserted every two packs.

		MT
	Complete Set (20):	18.00
	Common Player:	.25
R1	Sherman Williams	.25
R2	Mike Mamula	.25
R3	Frank Sanders	.50
R4	Steve Stentsrom	.25
R5	Michael Westbrook	1.00
R6	Warren Sapp	.50
R7	Rashaan Salaam	1.50
R8	J.J. Stokes	1.00
R9	Kevin Carter	.25
R10	Kerry Collins	2.50
R11	Curtis Martin	3.00
R12	Kordell Stewart	2.50
R13	Steve McNair	2.00
R14	Rodney Thomas	.25
R15	Eric Zeier	.25
R16	Tony Boselli	.25
R17	Tamarick Vanover	1.00
R18	Joey Galloway	1.75
R19	Napoleon Kaufman	.75
R20	Terrell Davis	3.00

1996 FlickBall Team Sets

These three team sets were regionally distributed. Each set consisted of five player cards and one team helmet card.

		MT
	Complete Set (18):	17.00
	Comp. Cowboys Set (6):	7.00
	Comp. Vikings Set (6):	3.50
	Comp. Packers Set (6):	7.00
	Common Player:	.50
DC1	Troy Aikman	2.00
DC2	Deion Sanders	1.25
DC3	Emmitt Smith	4.00
DC4	Daryl Johnston	.75
DC5	Cowboys Helmet	.50
DC6	Darren Woodson	.50
MV1	Warren Moon	.75
MV2	Cris Carter	.75
MV3	Robert Smith	.75
MV4	Qadry Ismail	.50
MV5	Vikings Helmet	.50
MV6	David Palmer	.50
GBP1	Brett Favre	5.00
GBP2	Edgar Bennett	.75
GBP3	Reggie White	1.00
GBP4	Robert Brooks	1.00
GBP5	Packers Helmet	.50
GBP6	George Teague	.50

1988 Football Heroes Sticker Book

This 20-page booklet served as an introduction to American football, with a discussion of how the game is played and a glossary. The sticker book measures 9-1/4" x 12-1/2", while the stickers measure three inches in height. Stickers were issued on two sheets of 15 and were to be stuck in a glossy Football Heroes poster.

		MT
	Complete Set (30):	30.00
	Common Player:	.20
1	Marcus Allen	.50
2	Gary Anderson	.20
3	Brian Bosworth	.20
4	Anthony Carter	.20
5	Deron Cherry	.20
6	Eric Dickerson	.50
7	John Elway	2.00
8	Bo Jackson	1.00
9	Rich Karlis	.20
10	Bernie Kosar	.20
11	Steve Largent	.50
12	Mick Luckhurst	.20
13	Dexter Manley	.20
14	Dan Marino	6.00
15	Jim McMahon	.40
16	Joe Montana	3.00
17	Joe Morris	.20
18	Anthony Munoz	.20
19	Ozzie Newsome	.20
20	Walter Payton	4.00
21	William Perry	.40
22	Jerry Rice	3.00
23	Ricky Sanders	.20
24	Phil Simms	.40
25	Mike Singletary	.40
26	Dwight Stephenson	.20
27	Lawrence Taylor	.40
28	Herschel Walker	.40
29	Doug Williams	.40
30	Kellen Winslow	.40

1985-87 Football Immortals

JOHN (Blood) McNALLY
Charter Enshrinee, 1963

Although this set was produced in both 1985 and 1987, they are similar enough to group together. The 1985 set had 135 cards, while the 1987 set featured 142 Hall of Famers, with their induction year on the front and back of each card. The first 45 cards feature a red border, while cards 46-90 feature a blue border, 91-135 have a green border and 136-142 have a yellow border.

		MT
	Complete Set (147):	75.00
	Common Player:	.35
1	Pete Rozelle	.70
2	Joe Namath	1.50
3	Frank Gatski	.35
4	O.J. Simpson	1.50
5	Roger Staubach	1.25
6	Herb Adderley	.50
7	Lance Alworth	.70
8	Doug Atkins	.50
9	Morris (Red) Badgro	.35
10	Cliff Battles	.35
11	Sammy Baugh	1.00
12	Raymond Berry	.70
13	Charles W. Bidwill	.35
14	Chuck Bednarik	.70
15	Bert Bell	.35
16	Bobby Bell	.50
17	George Blanda	.70
18	Jim Brown	1.25
19	Paul Brown	.75
20	Roosevelt Brown	.50
21	Ray Flaherty	.35
22	Len Ford	.35
23	Dan Fortmann	.35
24	Bill George	.50
25	Art Donovan	.75
26	John (Paddy) Driscoll	.35
27	Jimmy Conzelman	.35
28	Willie Davis	.50
29	Earl "Dutch" Clark	.50
30	George Connor	.50
31	Guy Chamberlin	.50
32	Jack Christiansen	.50
33	Tony Canadeo	.50
34	Joe Carr	.35
35	Willie Brown	.50
36	Dick Butkus	1.25
37	Bill Dudley	.50
38	Glen Edwards	.35
39	Weeb Ewbank	.35
40	Tom Fears	.50
41	Otto Graham	1.25
42	Red Grange	1.25
43	Frank Gifford	1.25
44	Sid Gillman	.35
45	Forrest Gregg	.50
46	Lou Groza	.75
47	Joe Guyon	.35
48	George Halas	1.00
49	Ed Healy	.35
50	Mel Hein	.50
51	Fats Henry	.35
52	Arnie Herber	.35
53	Bill Hewitt	.35
54	Clarke Hinkle	.35
55	Elroy Hirsch	.60
56	Robert (Cal) Hubbard	.35
57	Sam Huff	.50
58	Lamar Hunt	.50
59	Don Hutson	.50
60	Deacon Jones	.50
61	Sonny Jurgensen	.50
62	Walt Kiesling	.35
63	Frank (Bruiser) Kinard	.35
64	Earl (Curly) Lambeau	.35
65	Dick (Night Train) Lane	.50
66	Yale Lary	.50
67	Dante Lavelli	.50
68	Bobby Layne	1.00
69	Tuffy Leemans	.35
70	Bob Lilly	.50
71	Vince Lombardi	1.00
72	Sid Luckman	1.00
73	Link Lyman	.35
74	Tim Mara	.35
75	Gino Marchetti	.50
76	Geo. Preston Marshall	.35
77	Ollie Matson	.60
78	George McAfee	.50
79	Mike McCormack	.50
80	Hugh McElhenny	.60
81	Johnny (Blood) McNally	.35
82	Mike Michalske	.35
83	Wayne Millner	.35
84	Bobby Mitchell	.50
85	Ron Mix	.50
86	Lenny Moore	.60
87	Marion Motley	.60
88	George Musso	.35
89	Bronko Nagurski	.75
90	Earl (Greasy) Neale	.35
91	Ernie Nevers	.50
92	Ray Nitschke	.50
93	Leo Nomellini	.50
94	Merlin Olsen	.75
95	Jim Otto	.50
96	Steve Owen	.35
97	Clarence (Ace) Parker	.35
98	Jim Parker	.50
99	Joe Perry	.60
100	Pete Pihos	.50
101	Hugh (Shorty) Ray	.35
102	Dan Reeves (OWN)	.35
103	Jim Ringo	.50
104	Andy Robustelli	.50
105	Art Rooney	.35
106	Gale Sayers	1.25
107	Joe Schmidt	.50
108	Bart Starr	1.25
109	Ernie Stautner	.50
110	Ken Strong	.50
111	Joe Stydahar	.35
112	Charley Taylor	.50
113	Jim Taylor	.60
114	Jim Thorpe	1.25
115	Y.A. Tittle	1.25
116	George Trafton	.35
117	Charley Trippi	.50
118	Emlen Tunnell	.50
119	Clyde "Bulldog" Turner	.50
120	Johnny Unitas	1.50
121	Norm Van Brocklin	.75
122	Steve Van Buren	.60
123	Paul Warfield	.50
124	Bob Waterfield	.75
125	Arnie Weinmeister	.35
126	Bill Willis	.35
127	Larry Wilson	.50
128	Alex Wojciechowicz	.35
129	Pro Football Hall of Fame (Entrance pictured)	.35
130A	Jim Thorpe Statue	1.00
130B	Doak Walker	3.00
131A	Enshrinement Galleries	.75
131B	Willie Lanier	1.75
132	Pro Football HOF on Enshrinement Day (Aerial shot of crowd)	.35
133A	Eric Dickerson (Display)	1.00
133B	Paul Hornung	5.00
134A	Walter Payton (Display)	1.50
134B	Ken Houston	1.75
135A	Super Bowl Display	1.00
135B	Fran Tarkenton	5.00
136	Don Maynard	2.50
137	Larry Csonka	5.00
138	Joe Greene	5.00
139	Len Dawson	4.00
140	Gene Upshaw	2.00
141	Jim Langer	1.25
142	John Henry Johnson	1.50

1955 49ers White Border

This 38-card set was available direct from the team as part of a package to fans. Cards are unnumbered and very similar to other issues, except for the text on the back. The fronts feature a black and white posed photo, with the player's signature across the bottom.

		NM
	Complete Set (38):	185.00
	Common Player:	3.00
1	Frankie Albert (CO One of Red)	3.00
2	Joe Arenas (The All-Time)	3.00
3	Harry Babcock	3.00
4	Ed Beatty (After searching)	3.00
5	Phil Bengtson (An All-America)	3.00
6	Rex Berry (One of the)	3.00
7	Hardy Brown	7.00
8	Marion Campbell	5.00
9	Al Carapella	3.00
10	Paul Carr (Drafted by)	3.00
11	Maury Duncan	3.00
12	Bob Hantla	3.00
13	Carroll Hardy	3.00
14	Matt Hazeltine (Won All-America)	4.00
15	Red Hickey (CO After 14 years)	4.00
16	Doug Hogland	3.00
17	Bill Johnson (Here's one..with ten lines of text)	3.00
18	John Henry Johnson	18.00
19	Eldred Kraemer	3.00
20	Bud Laughlin	3.00
21	Bobby Luna	3.00
22	George Maderos (The greatest..)	3.00
23	Clay Matthews	4.00
24	Hugh McElhenny (NFL Commissioner)	18.00
25	Dick Moegle (25 text lines)	4.00
26	Leo Nomellini (Leo was..)	14.00
27	Lou Palatella (Like Eldred)	3.00
28	Joe Perry (First man)	18.00
29	Charley Powell (Charley..)	4.00
30	Gordy Soltau (One of the..)	3.00
31	Bob St. Clair (In two years)	14.00
32	Tom Stolhandske	3.00
33	Roy Storey (ANN Bob Fouts ANN and Red Strader Co)	3.00
34	Red Strader (CO)	3.00
35	Y.A. Tittle (Jinxed by..)	20.00
36	Bob Toneff (Rated the..)	3.00
37	Billy Wilson (Named the..)	5.00
38	Sid Youngelman	3.00

1956 49ers White Border

This 29-card set was available direct from the team as part of a package for fans. Many of the cards are similar to other early issues, and are only distinguishable by the text on the back. Cards are black and white posed photos with the player's signature across the bottom.

		NM
	Complete Set (29):	125.00
	Common Player:	3.00
1	Frankie Albert (Frank Culling Albert, who..)	3.00
2	Ed Beatty (Traded by..)	3.00
3	Phil Bengtson (Phil is known..)	3.00
4	Rex Berry (Unanimously..)	3.00
5	Bruce Bosley (Bosley was..)	4.00
6	Fred Bruney	3.00
7	Paul Carr (A redshirt..)	3.00
8	Clyde Conner (One of the..)	3.00
9	Paul Goad	3.00
10	Matt Hazeltine (Matt reported..)	3.00
11	Ed Henke (After attending)	3.00
12	Bill Herchman (Bill was..)	3.00
13	Red Hickey (Red Hickey..)	3.00
14	Bill Jessup (Bill is one..)	3.00
15	Bill Johnson (Here's one..with nine lines of text)	3.00
16	George Maderos (A 21st..)	3.00
17	Dick Moegle (San..with 11 lines of text)	4.00
18	George Morris	3.00
19	Leo Nomellini (A 49er standby..)	14.00
20	Lou Palatella (Most..same as 1957)	3.00
21	Joe Perry (Joe is..)	18.00
22	Charley Powell (Equipped..)	4.00
23	Leo Rucka	3.00
24	Ed Sharkey	3.00
25	Charles Smith	3.00
26	Gordy Soltau (No all-time)	3.00
27	Bob St. Clair (Tallest man)	10.00
28	Bob Toneff (Another..)	3.00
29	Billy Wilson (Billy is..)	4.00

1957 49ers White Border

As with many other early 49ers issues, this 43-card set is very similar to previous issues, except for the text on the card backs. For the players that were included in the 1956 set, the photos are the same. This issue features the first John Brodie card, which predates his Topps and Fleer rookies by four years.

		NM
	Complete Set (43):	180.00
	Common Player:	3.00
1	Frankie Albert (CO Frank Culling Albert played..same as 1958)	3.00
2	Joe Arenas (Again in 1956..)	3.00
3	Gene Babb (Drafted 19th..)	3.00
4	Larry Barnes	3.00
5	Phil Bengtson (CO Beginning his eighth..)	3.00
6	Bruce Bosley (After a same as 1958)	3.00
7	John Brodie (According to..)	30.00
8	Paul Carr (Versatile on..)	3.00
9	Clyde Conner (Football)	3.00
10	Ted Connolly (The 49er..)	3.00
11	Bob Cross	3.00
12	Mark Duncan (CO Mark..same as 1958)	3.00
13	Bob Fouts (ANN Lon Simmons ANN and Frankie Albert CO same as 1958)	3.00
14	John Gonzaga (One of the)	3.00
15	Tom Harmon (Kids' ages are 11, 8 and 5)	5.00
16	Matt Hazeltine (An All-American)	3.00
17	Ed Henke (Studious-looking)	3.00
18	Bill Herchman (The 49ers)	3.00
19	Red Hickey (CO After 14 campaigns same as 1958)	3.00
20	Bobby Holladay	3.00
21	Bill Jessup (One of the)	3.00
22	Bill Johnson (CO No all-time same as 1958)	3.00
23	Marv Matuszak (Traded to)	3.00
24	Hugh McElhenny (Sidelined)	14.00
25	Dick Moegle (An with 11 lines of text)	3.00
26	Frank Morze (The 49ers, used)	3.00
27	Leo Nomellini (He was)	10.00
28	R.C. Owens (If the)	5.00
29	Lou Palatella (Most.. same as 1956)	3.00
30	Joe Perry (The greatest)	14.00
31	Charley Powell (Name almost)	3.00
32	Jim Ridlon (Teaming with)	3.00
33	Karl Rubke (The 16th)	3.00
34	J.D. Smith (J.D.'s football)	3.00
35	Gordy Soltau (Already listed)	3.00
36	Bob St. Clair (A born leader)	8.00
37	Bill Stits (An All-American)	3.00
38	Y.A. Tittle (For sheer)	18.00
39	Bob Toneff (After a)	3.00
40	Lynn Waldorf (Director of Personnel Vertical text, same as 1958)	3.00
41	Val Walker	3.00
42	Billy Wilson (Born on)	4.00
43	49ers Coaches (Bill Johnson, Phil Bengtson, Frankie Albert, Mark Duncan, Red Hickey) (Blank back, same as	3.00

1958 49ers White Border

This 44-card set is very similar to other issues and is only distinguishable by the text on the card backs. The cards are in black and white, with posed photos and a signature across the bottom.

		NM
	Complete Set (44):	185.00
	Common Player:	3.00
1	Frankie Albert (Frank culling Albert played same as 1957)	3.00
2	Bill Atkins (Alabama)	3.00
3	Gene Babb (A great)	3.00
4	Phil Bengtson (CO Beginning 9th..)	3.00
5	Bruce Bosley (After a same as 1957)	3.00
6	John Brodie (With John)	18.00
7	Clyde Conner (In signing running pose)	3.00
8	Ted Connolly (When Santa Clara)	3.00
9	Fred Dugan (Butch Dugan)	3.00
10	Mark Duncan (CO Mark same as 1957)	3.00
11	Bob Fouts (Lon Simmons ANN and Frankie Albert CO same as 1957)	3.00
12	John Gonzaga (Recommended)	3.00
13	Tom Harmon (ANN Kids' ages are 12, 9 and 6)	4.00
14	Matt Hazeltine (Improved)	4.00
15	Ed Henke (The Frank Buck)	3.00
16	Bill Herchman (A lineman's)	3.00
17	Red Hickey (CO After 14 campaigns same as 1957)	3.00
18	Bill Jessup (Hard luck)	3.00
19	Bill Johnson (No all-time same as 1957)	3.00
20	Marv Matuszak (The best)	4.00
21	Hugh McElhenny (More people)	14.00
22	Jerry Mertens (A 20th draft selection, Jerry)	3.00
23	Dick Moegle (13 text lines)	3.00
24	Dennit Morris	3.00
25	Frank Morze (The 49ers drafted)	3.00
26	Leo Nomellini (Defensive)	10.00
27	R.C. Owens (There's always)	5.00
28	Jim Pace	3.00
29	Lou Palatella (When)	3.00
30	Joe Perry (The all-time)	12.00
31	Jim Ridlon (After a)	3.00
32	Karl Rubke (Desperately)	3.00
33	J.D. Smith (Used mainly)	3.00
34	Gordy Soltau (In the eight)	3.00
35	Bob St. Clair (The only)	8.00
36	Bill Stits (When the)	3.00
37	John Thomas (This is)	3.00

38	Y.A. Tittle (His real)	18.00
39	Bob Toneff (A chronic)	3.00
40	Lynn Waldorf (Director of Personnel Vertical text same as 1957)	3.00
41	Billy Wilson (Em Tunnell, great)	3.00
42	John Wittenborn (John)	3.00
43	Abe Woodson (The 49ers)	5.00
44	49ers Coaches (Bill Johnson, Phil Bengtson, Frankie Albert, Mark Duncan, Red Hickey) (Blank back, same as	3.00

1959 49ers White Border

This 45-card set is very similar to other team issues around this time and can only be distinguished by the text on the back. Sets were available as part of a package available to fans. Fronts feature a black and white posed photo with a signature across the bottom.

		NM
Complete Set (45):		185.00
Common Player:		3.00
1	Bill Atkins (Played defensive)	3.00
2	Dave Baker	3.00
3	Bruce Bosley (Starred as)	3.00
4	John Brodie (Led NFL)	18.00
5	Jack Christiansen (CO)	8.00
6	Monte Clark	4.00
7	Clyde Conner (Standing pose, uniform number 88)	3.00
8	Ted Connolly (Realized his)	3.00
9	Tommy Davis	4.00
10	Eddie Dove	3.00
11	Fred Dugan (Made)	3.00
12	Mark Duncan (CO A versatile)	3.00
13	Bob Fouts (ANN)	3.00
14	John Gonzaga (One of few)	3.00
15	Bob Harrison	3.00
16	Matt Hazeltine (One of the)	3.00
17	Ed Henke (Suffered a)	3.00
18	Bill Herchman (Starting)	3.00
19	Red Hickey (Baseball)	3.00
20	Russ Hodges (ANN)	4.00
21	Bill Johnson (CO Bill Johnson)	3.00
22	Charlie Krueger	3.00
23	Lenny Lyles	3.00
24	Hugh McElhenny (One of the)	14.00
25	Jerry Mertens (A 20th draft selection last)	3.00
26	Dick Moegle (7 text lines)	4.00
27	Frank Morze (Transferred)	3.00
28	Leo Nomellini (Has never)	10.00
29	Clancy Osborne	3.00
30	R.C. Owens (Have football)	5.00
31	Joe Perry (Football's)	14.00
32	Jim Ridlon (Showed)	3.00
33	Karl Rubke (Started his)	3.00
34	Bob St. Clair (Tallest player)	8.00
35	Henry Schmidt	3.00
36	Bob Shaw (CO)	3.00
37	Lon Simmons (ANN)	3.00
38	J.D. Smith (One of the)	3.00
39	John Thomas (Didn't make)	3.00
40	Y.A. Tittle (In 11 years)	18.00
41	Jerry Tubbs	4.00
42	Lynn Waldorf (Director of Personnel Horizontal text)	3.00
43	Billy Wilson (Emlen Tunnell, 12-year)	4.00
44	John Wittenborn (Handy)	3.00
45	Abe Woodson (Received)	4.00

1960 49ers White Border

This 44-card set was available through a package offered to fans and is similar to other issues in that time span and can be distinguished by the text on the back. Players are featured in black and white posed photos, with a facsimile signature across the photo.

		NM
Complete Set (44):		185.00
Common Player:		3.00
1	Dave Baker (David Lee Baker)	3.00
2	Bruce Bosley (Born in Fresno)	3.00
3	John Brodie (This could be)	14.00
4	Jack Christiansen (ACO)	8.00
5	Monte Clark (A special chapter)	5.00
6	Dan Colchico (Big Dan)	3.00
7	Clyde Conner (Clyde Raymond)	3.00
8	Ted Connolly (When Theodore)	3.00
9	Tommy Davis (San Francisco)	4.00
10	Eddie Dove (Edward Everett)	3.00
11	Mark Duncan (ACO A versatile)	3.00
12	Bob Fouts (ANN)	3.00
13	Bob Harrison (There is no more)	3.00
14	Matt Hazeltine (Matthew Hazeltine)	3.00
15	Ed Henke (Desire and)	3.00
16	Red Hickey (CO Baseball)	3.00
17	Russ Hodges (ANN)	3.00
18	Bill Johnson (CO Bill Johnson)	3.00
19	Gordon Kelley (This Southern)	3.00
20	Charlie Krueger (The 49ers)	4.00
21	Lenny Lyles (Leonard Lyles)	3.00
22	Hugh McElhenny (San Francisco's)	14.00
23	Mike Magac (Mike was)	3.00
24	Jerry Mertens (Jerome William)	3.00
25	Frank Morze (Anyone with)	3.00
26	Leo Nomellini (Leo Joseph)	10.00
27	Clancy Osborne (Desire)	4.00
28	R.C. Owens (Few players)	5.00
29	Jim Ridlon (James Ridlon)	3.00
30	C.R. Roberts (After trials)	3.00
31	Len Rohde (Len, a three)	3.00
32	Karl Rubke (Only 20 years)	3.00
33	Bob St. Clair (Robert Bruce)	8.00
34	Henry Schmidt (After two years)	3.00
35	Lon Simmons (ANN)	3.00
36	J.D. Smith (In J.D. Smith)	4.00
37	Gordy Soltau (ANN)	3.00
38	Monty Stickles (The football)	3.00
39	John Thomas (Noted more)	3.00
40	Y.A. Tittle (When Yelberton)	18.00
41	Lynn Waldorf (Director of Personnel)	3.00
42	Bobby Waters (A smart)	5.00
43	Billy Wilson (Only Don Hutson)	4.00
44	Abe Woodson (A Big 10)	4.00

1968 49ers White Border

This 35-card oversized set measures 8-1/2" x 11" and displays different 49ers players in posed, black and white photos. Card backs are blank, with no card numbers listed either. In addition, Steve Spurrier's card

in this set predates his rookie by four years.

		NM
Complete Set (35):		125.00
Common Player:		2.50
1	Kermit Alexander	2.50
2	Cas Banaszek	2.50
3	Ed Beard	2.50
4	Forrest Blue	4.00
5	Bruce Bosley	2.50
6	John Brodie	10.00
7	Elmer Collett	2.50
8	Doug Cunningham	2.50
9	Tommy Davis	4.00
10	Kevin Hardy	2.50
11	Matt Hazeltine	4.00
12	Stan Hindman	2.50
13	Tom Holzer	2.50
14	Jim Johnson	8.00
15	Charlie Krueger	4.00
16	Roland Lakes	2.50
17	Gary Lewis	2.50
18	Kay McFarland	2.50
19	Clifton McNeil	4.00
20	George Mira	5.00
21	Howard Mudd	2.50
22	Dick Nolan (CO)	4.00
23	Frank Nunley	2.50
24	Don Parker	2.50
25	Mel Phillips	2.50
26	Al Randolph	2.50
27	Len Rohde	2.50
28	Steve Spurrier	28.00
29	John Thomas	2.50
30	Bill Tucker	2.50
31	Dave Wilcox	4.00
32	Ken Willard	4.00
33	Bob Windsor	4.00
34	Dick Witcher	4.00
35	Team Photo	10.00

1972 49ers Redwood City Tribune

This six-card set measures 3" x 5-1/2" and contains a head shot of the featured player in black and white with white borders. There is a large white space below the photo that contains a facsimile autograph. Cards are unnumbered and listed below in alphabetical order.

		NM
Complete Set (6):		50.00
Common Player:		8.00
1	Frank Edwards	8.00
2	Frank Nunley	8.00
3	Len Rohde	8.00
4	Larry Schreiber	8.00
5	Steve Spurrier	30.00
6	Gene Washington	12.00

1982 49ers Team Issue

This 5" x 8" set has 44 cards in black and white with white borders. The backs of the cards are blank and unnumbered.

		MT
Complete Set (44):		55.00
Common Player:		1.00
1	Dan Audick	1.00
2	John Ayers	1.00
3	Guy Benjamin	1.00
4	Dwaine Board	1.00
5	Ken Bungarda	1.00
6	Dan Bunz	1.00
7	Dwight Clark	4.00
8	Ricky Churchman	1.00
9	Earl Cooper	1.00
10	Randy Cross	1.50
11	Johnny Davis	1.00
12	Fred Dean	1.00
13	Walt Downing	1.00
14	Walt Easley	1.00
15	Lenvil Elliott	1.00
16	Keith Fahnhorst	1.00
17	Rick Gervais	1.00
18	Willie Harper	1.00
19	John Harty	1.00
20	Pete Kugler	1.00
21	Amos Lawrence	1.00
22	Bobby Leopold	1.00
23	Saladin Martin	1.00
24	Milt McColl	1.00
25	Jim Miller	1.00
26	Joe Montana	22.00
27	Ricky Patton	1.00
28	Lawrence Pillers	1.00
29	Craig Puki	1.00
30	Fred Quillan	1.00
31	Eason Ramson	1.00
32	Archie Reese	1.00
33	Jack Reynolds	1.00
34	Mike Shumann	1.00
35	Freddie Solomon	1.50
36	Scott Stauch	1.00

37	Jim Stuckey	1.00
38	Lynn Thomas	1.00
39	Keena Turner	1.25
40	Ray Wersching	1.00
41	Carlton Williamson	1.00
42	Mike Wilson	1.00
43	Eric Wright	1.00
44	Charlie Young	1.00

1984 49ers Police

This 12-card set was issued in three panels of four cards each and measures 2-1/2" x 4". The set is unnumbered and sponsored by 7-Eleven, Dr. Pepper and KCB's.

		MT
Complete Set (12):		25.00
Common Player:		1.00
1	Dwaine Board	1.00
2	Roger Craig	3.50
3	Riki Ellison	1.00
4	Keith Fahnhorst	1.00
5	Joe Montana, Dwight Clark	10.00
6	Jack Reynolds	1.00
7	Freddie Solomon	1.00
8	Keena Turner	1.00
9	Wendall Tyler	1.00
10	Bill Walsh (CO)	3.00
11	Ray Wersching	1.00
12	Eric Wright	1.00

1985 49ers Police

This 16-card set was issued in four panels of four cards each, and is very similar to the 1984 set except its sponsored only by Dr. Pepper and 7-Eleven. The cards are unnumbered and measure 2-1/2" x 4".

		MT
Complete Set (16):		18.00
Common Player:		.50
1	John Ayers	.50
2	Roger Craig	2.00
3	Fred Dean	.75
4	Riki Ellison	.50
5	Keith Fahnhorst	.50
6	Russ Francis	.75
7	Dwight Hicks	.50
8	Ronnie Lott	1.75
9	Dana McLemore	.50
10	Joe Montana	10.00
11	Todd Shell	.50
12	Freddie Solomon	.75
13	Keena Turner	.50
14	Bill Walsh (CO)	1.50
15	Ray Wersching	.50
16	Eric Wright	.50

1985 49ers Smokey

This seven-card oversized set measures approximately 3" x 4-3/8". It was issued by the 49ers and Smokey Bear, and features a cartoon fire safety tip and a facsimile signature on the back.

		MT
Complete Set (7):		30.00
Common Player:		2.00
1	Group Picture with (Smokey Player list on back of card)	6.00
2	Joe Montana	18.00
3	Jack Reynolds	3.00
4	Eric Wright	2.00
5	Dwight Hicks	2.00
6	Dwight Clark	4.00
7	Keena Turner	2.00

1988 49ers Police

This 20-card set included 19 players and one coach card and was sponsored by 7-Eleven and Oscar Mayer. The fronts are almost full-bleed photos with a thin white border. Backs have a football tip and a McGruff crime tip.

		MT
Complete Set (20):		20.00
Common Player:		.50
1	Harris Barton	.75
2	Dwaine Board	.50
3	Michael Carter	.75
4	Roger Craig	1.50
5	Randy Cross	.75
6	Riki Ellison	.50
7	John Frank	.50
8	Jeff Fuller	.50
9	Pete Kugler	.50
10	Ronnie Lott	1.50

11	Joe Montana	8.00
12	Tom Rathman	1.75
13	Jerry Rice	8.00
14	Jeff Stover	.50
15	Keena Turner	.75
16	Bill Walsh (CO)	1.50
17	Michael Walter	.50
18	Mike Wilson	.50
19	Eric Wright	.75
20	Steve Young	8.00

1988 49ers Smokey

This 35-card set was printed on a 5" x 8" format and is unnumbered, except for the uniform number. Fronts feature a full-bleed shot with a thin white border around the inside of the card. Backs have a fire safety cartoon usually featuring Smokey the Bear.

		MT
Complete Set (35):		100.00
Common Player:		1.00
1	Harris Barton	1.50
2	Dwaine Board (SP)	8.00
3	Michael Carter	1.50
4	Bruce Collie	1.00
5	Roger Craig	3.50
6	Randy Cross	1.75
7	Eddie DeBartolo (Jr Owner, President)	2.50
8	Riki Ellison	1.00
9	Kevin Fagan	1.00
10	Jim Fahnhorst	1.00
11	John Frank	1.00
12	Jeff Fuller	1.00
13	Don Griffin	1.50
14	Charles Haley	3.00
15	Ron Heller	1.00
16	Tom Holmoe	1.00
17	Pete Kugler	1.00
18	Ronnie Lott	4.00
19	Tim McKyer	1.50
20	Joe Montana	20.00
21	Tory Nixon	1.00
22	Bubba Paris	1.00
23	John Paye	1.00
24	Tom Rathman	3.00
25	Jerry Rice	20.00
26	Jeff Stover	1.00
27	Harry Sydney	1.00
28	John Taylor	4.00
29	Keena Turner	1.50
30	Steve Wallace	1.50
31	Bill Walsh (CO)	3.00
32	Michael Walter	1.00
33	Mike Wilson	1.00
34	Eric Wright	1.50
35	Steve Young	20.00

1990-91 49ers SF Examiner

This 16-card set was issued on two unperforated sheets measuring 14" x 11", and was issued by the San Francisco Examiner. Eight-card panels included a newspaper headline across the top reading "San Francisco Examiner Salutes the 49ers' Finest." Card fronts are in color with a thin orange border on the red-face card. Backs are horizontal and black and white with a head shot and stats.

		MT
Complete Set (16):		10.00
Common Player:		.50
1	Harris Barton	.75
2	Michael Carter	.50
3	Mike Cofer	.50
4	Roger Craig	1.00
5	Kevin Fagan	.50
6	Don Griffin	.50
7	Charles Haley	1.25
8	Pierce Holt	.50
9	Brent Jones	1.25
10	Ronnie Lott	1.25
11	Guy McIntyre	.50
12	Matt Millen	.75
13	Joe Montana	4.00
14	Tom Rathman	1.00
15	Jerry Rice	4.00
16	John Taylor	1.50

1992 49ers FBI

This 40-card set was available in different packs for free with 49ers' edition of GameDay Magazine at regular-season home games each week at Candlestick Park. The set was sponsored by the 49ers and the FBI and contains a public ser-

vice message on the back in the form of a player quote.

		MT
Complete Set (40):		45.00
Common Player:		.50
1	Michael Carter	.50
2	Kevin Fagan	.50
3	Charles Haley	1.00
4	Guy McIntyre	.50
5	George Seifert (CO)	1.00
6	Harry Sydney	.50
7	John Taylor	1.00
8	Mike Walter	.50
9	Steve Young	10.00
10	Mike Cofer	.50
11	Keith DeLong	.50
12	Don Griffin	.50
13	Pierce Holt	.50
14	Mike Sherrard	.75
15	Larry Roberts	.50
16	Bill Romanowski	.50
17	Tom Rathman	1.00
18	Jesse Sapolu	.75
19	Brent Jones	1.25
20	Brian Bollinger	.50
21	Eric Davis	.50
22	Antonio Goss	.50
23	Alan Grant	.50
24	Harris Barton	.75
25	Ricky Watters	4.00
26	Darin Jordan	.50
27	Odessa Turner	.50
28	David Wilkins	.50
29	Merton Hanks	1.00
30	David Whitmore	.50
31	Joe Montana	10.00
32	Klaus Wilmsmeyer	.50
33	Tim Harris	.75
34	Roy Foster	.50
35	Bill Musgrave	.75
36	Dana Hall	.75
37	Steve Wallace	.75
38	Steve Bono	4.00
39	Jerry Rice	10.00
NNO	Title Card	1.00

1994 49ers Pro Mags/Pro Tags

49ers Pro Mags and Pro Tags were each a six-card set issued in a black cardboard box and numbered out of 750. Each card is borderless and contains a gold-foil Super Bowl XXIX logo printed in the lower right corner. The tags feature Roman numerals XXIX in back of a superimposed shot of the player. Magnet backs are black and blank, Tags backs have a color close-up photo, an autograph strip and a player profile. The magnets are listed 1-6, while the tags are 7-12.

		MT
Complete Set (12):		20.00
Common Player:		1.00
1	Ken Norton	1.00
2	Jerry Rice	4.00
3	Deion Sanders	2.50
4	John Taylor	1.00
5	Ricky Watters	1.50
6	Steve Young	3.00
7	Ken Norton	1.00
8	Jerry Rice	4.00
9	Deion Sanders	2.50
10	John Taylor	1.00
11	Ricky Watters	1.50
12	Steve Young	3.00

1996 49ers Save Mart

This nine-card set celebrates the 49ers' star Super Bowl players. Each full-bleed card front includes an action shot of the player, with his last name and San Francisco logo appearing along the right border. Each card back includes the 50-year anniversary and 49ers' logos along with the checklist. The Save Mart and UPI Marketing Inc. logos appear at the bottom, with the card number located in the lower right. One card and one coin were sold in each cello pack. The coins feature the player's likeness, name, team, years with the team and his jersey number on the front. The reverse side of the coin boasts the 49ers' 50-year logo. A coin holder was also given away.

	MT
Complete Set (9):	12.00

Common Player:		.50
1	Steve Young	3.00
2	Roger Craig	1.00
3	Jerry Rice	4.00
4	Ronnie Lott	1.00
5	Ken Norton Jr.	.50
6	Dwight Clark	.50
7	Brent Jones	.50
8	Joe Montana	5.00
9	Super Bowl	1.00

1989 Franchise Game

The 1989 Franchise Game is modeled after Monopoly, with players beginning with a sum of money and traveling around the board acquiring different players to fill out a 23-man roster. There are 304 players depicted and 28 different NFL teams. Fronts have the player's name, team, point value and salary. Backs contain the player's position written at the top, as well as a large acronym for the position in the middle of the player's city. Franchise was produced by Rohrwood Enterprises.

		MT
Complete Set (332):		200.00
Common Player:		.60
1	Neal Anderson	.60
2	Kevin Butler	.60
3	Jimbo Covert	.60
4	Dave Duerson	.60
5	Dan Hampton	1.00
6	Jay Hilgenberg	.60
7	Mike Richardson	.60
8	Ron Rivera	.60
9	Mike Singletary	1.00
10	Mike Tomczak	1.00
11	Keith Van Horne	.60
12	Lewis Billups	.60
13	Jim Breech	.60
14	James Brooks	.75
15	Eddie Brown	.60
16	Ross Browner	.60
17	Jason Buck	.60
18	Cris Collinsworth	.75
19	Eddie Edwards	.60
20	Boomer Esiason	.75
21	David Fulcher	.60
22	Ray Horton	.60
23	Tim Krumrie	.60
24	Max Montoya	.60
25	Anthony Munoz	1.50
26	Jim Skow	.60
27	Reggie Williams	.60
28	Ickey Woods	.60
29	Cornelius Bennett	1.00
30	Shane Conlan	1.00
31	Joe Devlin	.60
32	Nate Odomes	.60
33	Scott Norwood	.60
34	Andre Reed	1.50
35	Jim Ritcher	.60
36	Fred Smerlas	.60
37	Bruce Smith	1.50
38	Art Still	.60
39	Keith Bishop	.60
40	Bill Bryan	.60
41	Tony Dorsett	3.00
42	Simon Fletcher	.60
43	Mike Harden	.60
44	Mark Haynes	.60
45	Mike Horan	.60
46	Vance Johnson	.75
47	Rulon Jones	.60
48	Rich Karlis	.60
49	Karl Mecklenburg	1.00
50	Dennis Smith	.60
51	Dave Studdard	.60
52	Andre Townsend	.60
53	Steve Watson	.60
54	Sammy Winder	.60
55	Matt Bahr	.60
56	Rickey Bolden	.60
57	Earnest Byner	.75
58	Sam Clancy	.60
59	Hanford Dixon	.60
60	Bob Golic	.60
61	Carl Hairston	.60
62	Eddie Johnson	.60
63	Kevin Mack	.60
64	Clay Matthews	.75
65	Frank Minnifield	.60
66	Ozzie Newsome	1.00
67	Cody Risien	.60
68	John Cannon	.60
69	Ron Holmes	.60
70	Winston Moss	.60
71	Rob Taylor	.60
72	Joe Bostic	.60
73	Roy Green	.75
74	Ricky Hunley	.60
75	E.J. Junior	.60
76	Neil Lomax	.60
77	Tim McDonald	.60
78	Cedric Mack	.60
79	Freddie Joe Nunn	.60
80	Gary Anderson	.75
81	Keith Baldwin	.60
82	Gill Byrd	.60
83	Elvis Patterson	.60
84	Gary Plummer	.60
85	Billy Ray Smith	.60
86	Lee Williams	.60
87	Mike Bell	.60
88	Lloyd Burruss	.60
89	Carlos Carson	.60
90	Deron Cherry	.60
91	Jack Del Rio	.60
92	Irv Eatman	.60
93	Dino Hackett	.60
94	Bill Kenney	.60
95	Albert Lewis	.60
96	David Lutz	.60
97	Bill Maas	.60
98	Stephone Paige	.75
99	Neil Smith	1.50
100	Dean Biasucci	.60
101	Duane Bickett	.60
102	Chris Chandler	1.50
103	Eugene Daniel	.60
104	Ray Donaldson	.60
105	Jon Hand	.60
106	Chris Hinton	.60
107	Joe Klecko	.60
108	Cliff Odom	.60
109	Rohn Stark	.60
110	Donnell Thompson	.60
111	Willie Tullis	.60
112	Freddie Young	.60
113	Michael Downs	.60
114	Michael Irvin	3.00
115	Jim Jeffcoat	.60
116	Ed "Too Tall" Jones	1.00
117	Tom Rafferty	.60
118	Herschel Walker	1.25
119	Everson Walls	.60
120	Danny White	.75
121	Randy White	1.50
122	Bob Brudzinski	.60
123	Mark Clayton	.75
124	Mark Duper	1.00
125	Ron Jaworski	1.00
126	Paul Lankford	.60
127	John Offerdahl	.60
128	John Offerdahl	.60
129	Reggie Roby	.60
130	Dwight Stephenson	.60
131	Randall Cunningham	.75
132	Ron Heller	.60
133	Mike Quick	.75
134	Ken Reeves	.60
135	Dave Rimington	.60
136	Reggie Singletary	.60
137	Andre Waters	.60
138	Reggie White	2.00
139	Roynell Young	.60
140	Aundray Bruce	.60
141	Bobby Butler	.60
142	Bill Fralic	.60
143	Mike Kenn	.60
144	Chris Miller	.60
145	John Settle	.60
146	George Yarno	.60
147	Michael Carter	.60
148	Wes Chandler	1.00
149	Roger Craig	1.50
150	Randy Cross	.60
151	Riki Ellison	.60
152	Jim Fahnhorst	.60
153	Charles Haley	1.50
154	Barry Helton	.60
155	Guy McIntyre	.75
156	Tim McKyer	.60
157	Joe Montana	10.00
158	Jerry Rice	10.00
159	Keena Turner	.60
160	Eric Wright	.60
161	Steve Young	10.00
162	Raul Allegre	.60
163	Ottis Anderson	.75
164	Billy Ard	.60
165	Carl Banks	.60
166	Mark Bavaro	.60
167	Jim Burt	.60
168	Harry Carson	.75
169	John Elliott	.60
170	Terry Kinard	.60
171	Sean Landeta	.60
172	Lionel Manuel	.60
173	Joe Morris	.60
174	Bart Oates	.60
175	Phil Simms	1.00
176	Pat Leahy	.60
177	Marty Lyons	.60
178	Erik McMillan	.60
179	Freeman McNeil	1.00
180	Scott Mersereau	.60
181	Ken O'Brien	.60
182	Jim Sweeney	.60
183	Al Toon	.75
184	Wesley Walker	.75
185	Jim Arnold	.60
186	Bennie Blades	.60
187	Mike Cofer	.60
188	Keith Ferguson	.60
189	Steve Mott	.60
190	Eddie Murray	.60
191	Harvey Salem	.60
192	Bobby Watkins	.60
192	Keith Bostic	.60
193	Richard Byrd	.60
194	Ray Childress	.75
195	Ernest Givins	.75
196	Kenny Johnson	.60
197	Sean Jones	.75
198	Robert Lyles	.60
199	Robert Lyles	.60
200	Bruce Matthews	.75
201	Johnny Meads	.60
202	Warren Moon	2.00
203	Mike Munchak	.75
204	Mike Rozier	.60
205	Dean Steinkuhler	.60
206	Tony Zendejas	.60
207	Mark Cannon	.60
208	Alphonso Carreker	.60
209	Phillip Epps	.60
210	Tim Harris	.75
211	Brian Noble	.60
212	Raymond Clayborn	.60
213	Steve Grogan	.75
214	Roland James	.60
215	Fred Marion	.60
216	Stanley Morgan	.75
217	Kenneth Sims	.60
218	Andre Tippett	.75
219	Marcus Allen	2.00
220	Chris Bahr	.60
221	Steve Beuerlein	.75
222	Tim Brown	4.00
223	Todd Christensen	.75
224	Ron Fellows	.60
225	Willie Gault	.60
226	Mike Haynes	.60
227	Bo Jackson	2.00
228	James Lofton	1.50
229	Howie Long	1.50
230	Vann McElroy	.60
231	Rod Martin	.60
232	Matt Millen	.75
233	Bill Pickel	.60
234	Jay Schroeder	.75
235	Stacey Toran	.60
236	Greg Townsend	.60
237	Greg Bell	.60
238	Henry Ellard	1.25
239	Jerry Gray	.60
240	Leroy Irvin	.60
241	Gary Jeter	.60
242	Johnnie Johnson	.60
243	Larry Kelm	.60
244	Mike Lansford	.60
245	Shawn Miller	.60
246	Mel Owens	.60
247	Jackie Slater	.60
248	Charles White	.60
249	Jeff Bostic	.60
250	Kelvin Bryant	.60
251	Dave Butz	.60
252	Gary Clark	1.50
253	Steve Cox	.60
254	Darryl Grant	.60
255	Darrell Green	.75
256	Joe Jacoby	.60
257	Mel Kaufman	.60
258	Jim Lachey	.60
259	Dexter Manley	.60
260	Charles Mann	.60
261	Mark May	.60
262	Art Monk	1.50
263	Ricky Sanders	.60
264	Alvin Walton	.60
265	Doug Williams	.75
266	Morten Andersen	.60
267	Bruce Clark	.60
268	Jim Dombrowski	.60
269	Mel Gray	.75
270	Bobby Hebert	.60
271	Rickey Jackson	.60
272	Van Jakes	.60
273	Steve Korte	.60
274	Rueben Mayes	.60
275	Sam Mills	.75
276	Dave Waymer	.60
277	Jeff Bryant	.60
278	Blair Bush	.60
279	Jacob Green	.60
280	Melvin Jenkins	.60
281	Norm Johnson	.60
282	Dave Krieg	.75
283	Bryan Millard	.60
284	Ruben Rodriguez	.60
285	Terry Taylor	.60
286	Curt Warner	1.00
287	Tony Woods	.60
288	Gary Anderson	.60
289	Tunch Ilkin	.60
290	Earnest Jackson	.60
291	Louis Lipps	.60
292	Mike Webster	.75
293	Rod Woodson	3.00
294	Joey Browner	.60
295	Anthony Carter	1.25
296	Chris Doleman	.75
297	Tim Irwin	.60
298	Tommy Kramer	.75
299	Carl Lee	.60
300	Kirk Lowdermilk	.60
301	Keith Millard	.60
302	Scott Studwell	.60
303	Wade Wilson	.75
304	Gary Zimmerman	.60
T1	Atlanta Falcons Team Helmet	.60
T2	Buffalo Bills	.60
T3	Chicago Bears	.60
T4	Cincinnati Bengals	.60
T5	Cleveland Browns	.60
T6	Dallas Cowboys	.75
T7	Denver Broncos	.60
T8	Detroit Lions	.60
T9	Green Bay Packers	.60
T10	Houston Oilers	.60
T11	Indianapolis Colts	.60
T12	Kansas City Chiefs	.60
T13	Los Angeles Raiders	.75
T14	Los Angeles Rams	.60
T15	Miami Dolphins	.75
T16	Minnesota Vikings	.60
T17	New England Patriots	.60
T18	New Orleans Saints	.60
T19	New York Giants	.60
T20	New York Jets	.60
T21	Philadelphia Eagles	.60
T22	Phoenix Cardinals	.60
T23	Pittsburgh Steelers	.60
T24	San Diego Chargers	.60
T25	San Francisco 49ers	.60
T26	Seattle Seahawks	.60
T27	Tampa Bay Buccaneers	.60
T28	Washington Redskins	.60

1993 Front Row Gold Collection

The 10-card, standard-size set features "Gold Collection" in gold foil on the card front over the color action photo. The card backs have another borderless color photo with a brief player summary (odd-numbered) and bio and stat information (even-numbered). Each of the 5,000 sets produced came with a certificate of authenticity.

		MT
Complete Set (10):		5.00
Common Player:		.50
1	Eric Curry	.75
2	Eric Curry	.75
3	Lincoln Kennedy	.50
4	Lincoln Kennedy	.50
5	O.J. McDuffie	1.00
6	O.J. McDuffie	1.00
7	Qadry Ismail	1.00
8	Qadry Ismail	1.00
9	Andre Hastings	1.00
10	Andre Hastings	1.00

G

1956 Giants Team Issue

This 36-card, black and white set contains posed player shots on the front surrounded by a white border and a facsimile signature. Backs are unnumbered, while each card measures approximately 5" x 7".

		NM
Complete Set (36):		200.00
Common Player:		4.00
1	Bill Austin	4.00
2	Ray Beck	4.00
3	Roosevelt Brown	10.00
4	Hank Burnine	4.00
5	Don Chandler	4.00
6	Bobby Clatterbuck	4.00
7	Charley Conerly	20.00
8	Frank Gifford	30.00
9	Roosevelt Grier	10.00
10	Don Heinrich	5.00
11	John Hermann	4.00
12	Jim Lee Howell (CO)	5.00
13	Sam Huff	16.00
14	Ed Hughes	4.00
15	Gerald Huth	4.00
16	Jim Katcavage	6.00
17	Gene Kirby (ANN)	4.00
18	Ken MacAfee	4.00
19	Dick Modzelewski (Misspelled Modelewski on the reverse)	5.00
20	Henry Moore	4.00
21	Dick Nolan	5.00
22	Jimmy Patton	5.00
23	Andy Robustelli	10.00
24	Kyle Rote	10.00
25	Chris Schenkel (ANN)	5.00
26	Bob Schnelker	4.00
27	Jack Stroud	4.00
28	Harland Svare	4.00
29	Bill Svoboda	4.00
30	Bob Topp	4.00
31	Mel Triplett	5.00
32	Emlen Tunnell	10.00
33	Alex Webster	5.00
34	Ray Wietecha	4.00
35	Dick Yelvington	4.00
36	Walt Yowarsky	4.00

1957 Giants Team Issue

This 1957 Giants team set measures approximately 5" x 7", with black and white photos and a glossy finish. The set contains 40 unnumbered cards that are listed below in alphabetical order.

		NM
Complete Set (40):		250.00
Common Player:		4.00
1	Ben Agajanian	4.00
2	Bill Austin	4.00
3	Ray Beck	4.00
4	John Bookman	4.00
5	Roosevelt Brown	8.00
6	Don Chandler	5.00
7	Bobby Clatterbuck	4.00
8	Charley Conerly	15.00
9	John Dell Isola (CO)	4.00
10	Gene Filipski	5.00
11	Frank Gifford	25.00
12	Don Heinrich	5.00
13	Jim Lee Howell (CO)	5.00
14	Sam Huff	16.00
15	Ed Hughes	4.00
16	Gerald Huth	4.00
17	Jim Katcavage	5.00
18	Ken Kavanaugh (CO)	5.00
19	Les Keiter (ANN)	4.00
20	Tom Landry (CO)	45.00
21	Cliff Livingston	4.00
22	Vince Lombardi (CO)	50.00
23	Ken MacAfee	5.00
24	Dennis Mendyk	4.00
25	Dick Modzelewski	5.00
26	Dick Nolan	5.00
27	Jim Patton	5.00
28	Andy Robustelli	10.00
29	Kyle Rote	10.00
30	Chris Schenkel (ANN)	5.00
31	Jack Spinks	4.00
32	Jack Stroud	4.00
33	Harland Svare	4.00
34	Bill Svoboda	4.00
35	Mel Triplett	5.00
36	Emlen Tunnell	8.00
37	Alex Webster	5.00
38	Ray Wietecha	4.00
39	Dick Yelvington	4.00
40	Walt Yowarsky	4.00

1960 Giants Jay Publishing

This 12-card set shows players in black and white on 5" x 7" cards. Cards were sold in 12-card packs and have blank, unnumbered backs.

		NM
Complete Set (12):		85.00
Common Player:		4.00
1	Roosevelt Brown	8.00
2	Don Chandler	4.00
3	Charley Conerly	8.00
4	Frank Gifford	20.00
5	Roosevelt Grier	8.00
6	Sam Huff	10.00
7	Phil King	4.00
8	Andy Robustelli	6.00
9	Kyle Rote	6.00
10	Bob Schnelker	4.00
11	Pat Summerall	6.00
12	Alex Webster	5.00

1960 Giants Shell/Riger Posters

This set features 10 black and white posters by Robert Siger and distributed by Shell Oil in 1960. Each poster measures approximately 11-3/4" x 13-3/4".

		NM
Complete Set (10):		150.00
Common Player:		10.00
1	Charley Connerly	25.00
2	Frank Gifford	45.00
3	Sam Huff	20.00
4	Dick Modzelewski	10.00
5	Jim Patton	10.00
6	Andy Robustelli	16.00
7	Kyle Rote	16.00
8	Bob Schnelker	10.00
9	Pat Summerall	20.00
10	Alex Webster, Roosevelt Brown	16.00

1961 Giants Jay Publishing

Similar to the 1960 issue, this 12-card set is composed of black and white, 5" x 7" photos. It features traditional players and was available in 12-card packs.

		NM
Complete Set (12):		65.00
Common Player:		4.00
1	Roosevelt Brown	10.00
2	Don Chandler	4.00
3	Charley Conerly	10.00
4	Roosevelt Grier	8.00
5	Sam Huff	10.00
6	Dick Modzelewski	4.00
7	Jimmy Patton	5.00
8	Jim Podoley	4.00
9	Andy Robustelli	5.00
10	Allie Sherman (CO)	4.00
11	Del Shofner	5.00
12	Y.A. Tittle	15.00

1973 Giants Color Litho

Measuring 8-1/2" x 11", the eight-card set showcased color lithographs on the front. A facsimile player signature is printed at the bottom right inside a white triangle. The unnumbered cards are not bordered and have blank backs.

		NM
Complete Set (8):		50.00
Common Player:		5.00
1	Jim Files	5.00
2	Jack Gregory	5.00
3	Ron Johnson	7.50
4	Greg Larson	5.00
5	Spider Lockhart	7.50
6	Norm Snead	12.00
7	Bob Tucker	7.50
8	Brad Van Pelt	7.50

1987 Giants Police

Measuring 2-3/4" x 4-1/8", the 12-card set is anchored by a large photo on the front, with "New York Giants" printed at the top. Beneath the photo are the player's name and position printed between Giants' helmets. The card backs, which are unnumbered, have "Tips from the Giants" at the top, with two New Jersey law enforcement logos printed below. A safety tip and a McGruff the Crime Dog logo round out the backs. Overall, 10,000 sets were printed.

		MT
Complete Set (12):		75.00
Common Player:		3.00
1	Carl Banks	5.00
2	Mark Bavaro	5.00
3	Brad Benson	3.00
4	Jim Burt	3.00
5	Harry Carson	5.00
6	Maurice Carthon	3.00
7	Sean Landeta	3.00
8	Leonard Marshall	5.00
9	George Martin	3.00
10	Joe Morris	6.00
11	Bill Parcells (CO)	8.00
12	Phil Simms	25.00

1988 Giants Police

Measuring 2-3/4" x 4-1/8", the card fronts are anchored by a large photo. A Giants' helmet is printed in both corners at the top, with "New York Giants" located at the top center. Beneath the photo are the player's name, number, position and bio. The unnumbered backs have "Tips from the Giants" at the top, with two New Jersey law enforcement logos located underneath. A safety tip and a McGruff the Crime Dog logo round out the card backs.

		MT
Complete Set (12):		55.00
Common Player:		3.00
1	Billy Ard	3.00
2	Jim Burt	3.00
3	Harry Carson	5.00
4	Maurice Carthon	3.00
5	Leonard Marshall	5.00
6	George Martin	3.00
7	Phil McConkey	3.00
8	Joe Morris	6.00
9	Karl Nelson	3.00
10	Bart Oates	5.00
11	Bill Parcells (CO)	8.00
12	Phil Simms	16.00

1990 Giants Police

Measuring 2-3/4" x 4-1/8", the 12-card set is anchored by a large photo on the front, with a Giants' helmet in each of the top corners, with "New York Giants" printed at the top center. The player's name, position and bio are printed under the photo. The card backs, which are unnumbered, have "Tips from the Giants" at the top, with two New Jersey law enforcement logos beneath it. A safety tip and a McGruff the Crime Dog logo round out the card backs.

		MT
Complete Set (12):		45.00
Common Player:		2.50
1	Ottis Anderson	5.00
2	Matt Bahr	2.50
3	Eric Dorsey	2.50
4	John Elliott	2.50
5	Ray Handley (CO)	2.50
6	Jeff Hostetler	7.00
7	Erik Howard	2.50
8	Pepper Johnson	4.00
9	Leonard Marshall	4.00
10	Bart Oates	4.00
11	Gary Reasons	2.50
12	Phil Simms	8.00

1992 Giants Police

Measuring 2-3/4" x 4-1/8", the 12-card set is anchored on the front by a large photo and the player's name and bio beneath the photo. "New York Giants" is printed above the photo. The unnumbered card backs have "Tips from the Giants" at the top, a safety tip and a McGruff the Crime Dog logo at the bottom.

		MT
Complete Set (12):		20.00
Common Player:		1.00
1	Ottis Anderson	2.00
2	Matt Bahr	1.00
3	Eric Dorsey	1.00
4	John Elliott	1.00
5	Ray Handley (CO)	1.00
6	Jeff Hostetler	3.00
7	Erik Howard	1.00
8	Pepper Johnson	1.50
9	Leonard Marshall	1.50
10	Bart Oates	1.50
11	Gary Reasons	1.00
12	Phil Simms	5.00

1969 Glendale Stamps

These unnumbered stamps, which measure 1-13/16" x 3-15/16", feature a color player photo on the front; the back has his name, team and instructions on how to apply the stamp to the corresponding album which was produced. "Dampen strip and affix in ablum" is on the back. The album measures 9" x 12" and is arranged alphabetically by team city.

		NM
Complete Set (312):		200.00
Common Player:		.25
(1)	Bob Berry	.40
(2)	Clark Miller	.25
(3)	Jim Butler	.25
(4)	Junior Coffey	.25
(5)	Paul Flatley	.40

(6)	Randy Johnson	.45
(7)	Charlie Bryant	.25
(8)	Billy Lothridge	.25
(9)	Tommy Nobis	2.00
(10)	Claude Humphrey	.40
(11)	Ken Reaves	.25
(12)	Jerry Simmons	.40
(13)	Mike Curtis	.75
(14)	Dennis Gaubatz	.25
(15)	Jerry Logan	.25
(16)	Lenny Lyles	.25
(17)	John Mackey	2.00
(18)	Tom Matte	.50
(19)	Lou Michaels	.35
(20)	Jimmy Orr	.50
(21)	Willie Richardson	.35
(22)	Don Shinnick	.25
(23)	Dan Sullivan	.25
(24)	Johnny Unitas	15.00
(25)	Houston Antwine	.25
(26)	John Bramlett	.25
(27)	Aaron Marsh	.25
(28)	R.C. Gamble	.25
(29)	Gino Cappelletti	.75
(30)	John Charles	.25
(31)	Larry Eisenhauer	.25
(32)	Jon Morris	.25
(33)	Jim Nance	.50
(34)	Len St. Jean	.25
(35)	Mike Taliaferro	.25
(36)	Jim Whalen	.25
(37)	Stew Barber	.35
(38)	Al Bemiller	.25
(39)	George (Butch) Byrd	.35
(40)	Booker Edgerson	.25
(41)	Harry Jacobs	.35
(42)	Jack Kemp	18.00
(43)	Ron McDole	.35
(44)	Joe O'Donnell	.25
(45)	John Pitts	.35
(46)	George Saimes	.35
(47)	Mike Stratton	.25
(48)	O.J. Simpson	35.00
(49)	Ronnie Bull	.35
(50)	Dick Butkus	8.00
(51)	Jim Cadile	.25
(52)	Jack Concannon	.35
(53)	Dick Evey	.25
(54)	Bennie McRae	.25
(55)	Ed O'Bradovich	.25
(56)	Brian Piccolo	10.00
(57)	Mike Pyle	.25
(58)	Gale Sayers	10.00
(59)	Dick Gordon	.35
(60)	Roosevelt Taylor	.35
(61)	Al Beauchamp	.25
(62)	Dave Middendorf	.25
(63)	Harry Gunner	.25
(64)	Bobby Hunt	.25
(65)	Bob Johnson	.40
(66)	Charley King	.25
(67)	Andy Rice	.25
(68)	Paul Robinson	.35
(69)	Bill Staley	.25
(70)	Pat Matson	.25
(71)	Bob Trumpy	2.00
(72)	Sam Wyche	5.00
(73)	Erich Barnes	.35
(74)	Gary Collins	.35
(75)	Ben Davis	.25
(76)	John Demarie	.25
(77)	Gene Hickerson	.35
(78)	Jim Houston	.35
(79)	Ernie Kellerman	.25
(80)	Leroy Kelly	3.00
(81)	Dale Lindsey	.25
(82)	Bill Nelsen	.75
(83)	Jim Kanicki	.25
(84)	Dick Schafrath	.35
(85)	George Andrie	.75
(86)	Mike Clark	.25
(87)	Cornell Green	.50
(88)	Bob Hayes	1.50
(89)	Chuck Howley	.75
(90)	Lee Roy Jordan	1.25
(91)	Bob Lilly	3.00
(92)	Craig Morton	1.00
(93)	John Niland	.25
(94)	Dan Reeves	5.00
(95)	Mel Renfro	1.00
(96)	Lance Rentzel	.50
(97)	Tom Beer	.25
(98)	Billy Van Heusen	.25
(99)	Mike Current	.25
(100)	Al Denson	.25
(101)	Pete Duranko	.25
(102)	George Goeddeke	.25
(103)	John Huard	.25
(104)	Richard Jackson	.25
(105)	Pete Jaquess	.35
(106)	Fran Lynch	.25
(107)	Floyd Little	2.00
(108)	Steve Tensi	.50
(109)	Lem Barney	3.00
(110)	Nick Eddy	.50
(111)	Mel Farr	.75
(112)	Ed Flanagan	.25
(113)	Larry Hand	.25
(114)	Alex Karras	2.50
(115)	Dick LeBeau	.35
(116)	Mike Lucci	.35
(117)	Earl McCulloch	.35
(118)	Bill Munson	.40
(119)	Jerry Rush	.25
(120)	Wayne Walker	.35
(121)	Herb Adderley	2.00
(122)	Donny Anderson	.50

(123)	Lee Roy Caffey	.25
(124)	Carroll Dale	.35
(125)	Willie Davis	1.50
(126)	Boyd Dowler	.35
(127)	Marv Fleming	.50
(128)	Bob Jeter	.35
(129)	Henry Jordan	.35
(130)	Dave Robinson	.35
(131)	Bart Starr	10.00
(132)	Willie Wood	1.50
(133)	Pete Beathard	.75
(134)	Jim Beirne	.25
(135)	Garland Boyette	.25
(136)	Woody Campbell	.25
(137)	Miller Farr	.25
(138)	Hoyle Granger	.25
(139)	Mac Haik	.25
(140)	Ken Houston	3.00
(141)	Bobby Maples	.35
(142)	Alvin Reed	.25
(143)	Don Trull	.35
(144)	George Webster	.50
(145)	Bobby Bell	2.00
(146)	Aaron Brown	.25
(147)	Buck Buchanan	2.00
(148)	Len Dawson	5.00
(149)	Mike Garrett	.50
(150)	Robert Holmes	.35
(151)	Willie Lanier	3.00
(152)	Frank Pitts	.25
(153)	Johnny Robinson	.75
(154)	Jan Stenerud	3.00
(155)	Otis Taylor	.75
(156)	Jim Tyrer	.50
(157)	Dick Bass	.35
(158)	Maxie Baughan	.50
(159)	Rich Petitbon	.50
(160)	Roger Brown	.35
(161)	Roman Gabriel	1.50
(162)	Bruce Gossett	.25
(163)	David (Deacon) Jones	1.50
(164)	Tom Mack	1.25
(165)	Tommy Mason	.50
(166)	Ed Meador	.35
(167)	Merlin Olsen	3.00
(168)	Pat Studstill	.35
(169)	Jack Clancy	.25
(170)	Maxie Williams	.25
(171)	Larry Csonka	10.00
(172)	Jimmy Warren	.25
(173)	Norm Evans	.25
(174)	Rick Norton	.25
(175)	Bob Griese	7.50
(176)	Howard Twilley	.35
(177)	Billy Neighbors	.35
(178)	Nick Buoniconti	1.25
(179)	Tom Goode	.25
(180)	Dick Westmoreland	.25
(181)	Grady Alderman	.25
(182)	Bill Brown	.75
(183)	Fred Cox	.35
(184)	Clint Jones	.35
(185)	Joe Kapp	1.00
(186)	Paul Krause	1.00
(187)	Gary Larsen	.25
(188)	Jim Marshall	1.50
(189)	Dave Osborn	.25
(190)	Alan Page	4.00
(191)	Mike Tingelhoff	.75
(192)	Roy Winston	.25
(193)	Dan Abramowicz	.50
(194)	Doug Atkins	1.50
(195)	Bo Burris	.25
(196)	John Douglas	.25
(197)	Don Shy	.25
(198)	Bill Kilmer	.75
(199)	Tony Lorick	.25
(200)	David Parks	.50
(201)	Dave Rowe	.25
(202)	Monty Stickles	.25
(203)	Steve Stonebreaker	.35
(204)	Del Williams	.25
(205)	Pete Case	.25
(206)	Tommy Crutcher	.25
(207)	Scott Eaton	.25
(208)	Tucker Frederickson	.75
(209)	Peter Gogolak	.35
(210)	Homer Jones	.35
(211)	Ernie Koy	.35
(212)	Carl (Spider) Lockhart	.35
(213)	Bruce Maher	.25
(214)	Aaron Thomas	.35
(215)	Fran Tarkenton	12.00
(216)	Jim Katcavage	.35
(217)	Al Atkinson	.25
(218)	Emerson Boozer	.35
(219)	John Elliott	.25
(220)	Dave Herman	.35
(221)	Winston Hill	.35
(222)	Jim Hudson	.35
(223)	Pete Lammons	.35
(224)	Gerry Philbin	.35
(225)	George Sauer	.50
(226)	Joe Namath	20.00
(227)	Matt Snell	.50
(228)	Jim Turner	.35
(229)	Fred Biletnikoff	3.00
(230)	Willie Brown	1.50
(231)	Billy Cannon	.35
(232)	Dan Conners	.25
(233)	Ben Davidson	.75
(234)	Hewritt Dixon	.35
(235)	Daryle Lamonica	1.00
(236)	Ike Lassiter	.25
(237)	Ken McCloughan	.25
(238)	Jim Otto	1.50

(239)	Harry Schuh	.25
(240)	Gene Upshaw	3.00
(241)	Gary Ballman	.35
(242)	Joe Carollo	.25
(243)	Dave Lloyd	.25
(244)	Fred Hill	.25
(245)	Al Nelson	.25
(246)	Joe Scarpati	.25
(247)	Sam Baker	.35
(248)	Fred Brown	.25
(249)	Floyd Peters	.50
(250)	Nate Ramsey	.25
(251)	Norman Snead	.50
(252)	Tom Woodeshick	.25
(253)	John Hilton	.25
(254)	Kent Nix	.25
(255)	Paul Martha	.50
(256)	Ben McGee	.25
(257)	Andy Russell	.50
(258)	Dick Shiner	.25
(259)	J.R. Wilburn	.25
(260)	Marv Woodson	.25
(261)	Earl Gros	.25
(262)	Dick Hoak	.50
(263)	Roy Jefferson	.35
(264)	Larry Gagner	.25
(265)	Johnny Roland	.75
(266)	Jackie Smith	3.00
(267)	Jim Bakken	.50
(268)	Don Brumm	.25
(269)	Bob DeMarco	.35
(270)	Irv Goode	.25
(271)	Ken Gray	.35
(272)	Charlie Johnson	1.00
(273)	Ernie McMillan	.35
(274)	Larry Stallings	.35
(275)	Jerry Stovall	.50
(276)	Larry Wilson	1.50
(277)	Chuck Allen	.25
(278)	Lance Alworth	3.00
(279)	Kenny Graham	.25
(280)	Steve DeLong	.35
(281)	Willie Frazier	.35
(282)	Gary Garrison	.25
(283)	Sam Gruniesen	.25
(284)	John Hadl	.75
(285)	Brad Hubbert	.25
(286)	Ron Mix	2.00
(287)	Dick Post	.35
(288)	Walt Sweeney	.35
(289)	Kermit Alexander	.50
(290)	Ed Beard	.25
(291)	Bruce Bosley	.35
(292)	John Brodie	3.00
(293)	Stan Hindman	.25
(294)	Jim Johnson	1.50
(295)	Charlie Krueger	.35
(296)	Clifton McNeil	.35
(297)	Gary Lewis	.25
(298)	Howard Mudd	.25
(299)	Dave Wilcox	.50
(300)	Ken Willard	.50
(301)	Charlie Gogolak	.50
(302)	Len Hauss	.50
(303)	Sonny Jurgensen	3.50
(304)	Carl Kammerer	.25
(305)	Walt Rock	.25
(306)	Ray Schoenke	.25
(307)	Chris Hanburger	.75
(308)	Tom Brown	.50
(309)	Sam Huff	2.00
(310)	Bob Long	.25
(311)	Vince Promuto	.25
(312)	Pat Richter	.50

1989 Goal Line Hall of Fame

These postcard-size cards (4" x 6") feature full-color action paintings of inductees into the Pro Football Hall of Fame. The cards were part of an art series done by artist Gary Thomas and were offered by subscription. Each set was packaged in a custom box and was given a serial number (Set No. x of 5,000), which appears on each card, too. The back of the card is white and uses black ink. The player's name, college, position, biographical information, years he played, teams he played with and the year he was inducted are all listed, as well as a set and card number. A Football Hall of Fame logo is also given. Each of the first five series contains 30 cards; series 6 has 25. However, a card for Johnny Unitas (#174) was never issued. Series I was issued in 1989; a new series has followed each year since then. The cards are numbered alphabetically within each series.

		MT
Complete Set (175):		400.00
Common Player:		2.00
1	Lance Alworth	6.00
2	Morris (Red) Badgro	2.50
3	Cliff Battles	2.50
4	Mel Blount	2.50
5	Terry Bradshaw	10.00
6	Jim Brown	12.00
7	George Connor	2.50
8	Turk Edwards	2.50
9	Tom Fears	2.50
10	Frank Gifford	10.00
11	Otto Graham	6.00
12	Red Grange	5.00
13	George Halas	4.00
14	Clarke Hinkle	2.50
15	Robert (Cal) Hubbard	2.50
16	Sam Huff	2.50
17	Frank (Bruiser) Kinard	2.50
18	Dick (Night Train) Lane	2.50
19	Sid Luckman	6.00
20	Bobby Mitchell	2.50
21	Merlin Olsen	4.00
22	Jim Parker	2.50
23	Joe Perry	3.00
24	Pete Rozelle	2.50
25	Art Shell	3.00
26	Fran Tarkenton	9.00
27	Jim Thorpe	6.00
28	Paul Warfield	3.00
29	Larry Wilson	2.50
30	Willie Wood	2.50
31	Doug Atkins	2.50
32	Bobby Bell	2.00
33	Raymond Berry	2.00
34	Paul Brown	2.00
35	Guy Chamberlin	2.00
36	Earl "Dutch" Clark	2.00
37	Jimmy Conzelman	2.00
38	Len Dawson	2.00
39	Mike Ditka	8.00
40	Dan Fortmann	2.00
41	Frank Gatski	2.00
42	Bill George	2.00
43	Elroy Hirsch	3.00
44	Paul Hornung	4.00
45	John Henry Johnson	2.00
46	Walt Kiesling	2.00
47	Yale Lary	2.00
48	Bobby Layne	3.00
49	Tuffy Leemans	2.00
50	Geo. Preston Marshall	2.00
51	George McAfee	2.00
52	Wayne Millner	2.00
53	Bronko Nagurski	3.00
54	Joe Namath	12.00
55	Ray Nitschke	3.00
56	Jim Ringo	2.00
57	Art Rooney	2.00
58	Joe Stydahar	2.00
59	Charley Taylor	2.00
60	Charlie Trippi	2.00
61	Fred Biletnikoff	2.00
62	Buck Buchanan	2.00
63	Dick Butkus	3.00
64	Earl Campbell	8.00
65	Tony Canadeo	2.00
66	Art Donovan	3.00
67	Ray Flaherty	2.00
68	Forrest Gregg	2.50
69	Lou Groza	3.00
70	John Hannah	2.00
71	Don Hutson	2.50
72	David (Deacon) Jones	2.00
73	Stan Jones	2.00
74	Sonny Jurgensen	3.00
75	Vince Lombardi	3.00
76	Tim Mara	2.00
77	Ollie Matson	2.00
78	Mike McCormack	2.00
79	John (Blood) McNally	2.00
80	Marion Motley	2.00
81	George Musso	2.00
82	Earle (Greasy) Neale	2.00
83	Clarence (Ace) Parker	2.00
84	Pete Pihos	2.00
85	Tex Schramm	2.00
86	Roger Staubach	12.00
87	Jan Stenerud	2.00
88	Y.A. Tittle	3.00
89	Clyde "Bulldog" Turner	2.00
90	Steve Van Buren	2.00
91	Herb Adderley	2.00
92	Lem Barney	2.00
93	Sammy Baugh	5.00
94	Chuck Bednarik	3.00
95	Charles W. Bidwill	2.00
96	Willie Brown	2.00
97	Al Davis	4.00
98	Bill Dudley	2.00
99	Weeb Ewbank	2.00
100	Len Ford	2.00
101	Sid Gillman	2.00
102	Jack Ham	2.00
103	Mel Hein	2.00
104	Bill Hewitt	2.00
105	Dante Lavelli	2.00
106	Bob Lilly	3.00
107	John Mackey	2.00
108	Hugh McElhenny	3.00
109	Mike Michalske	2.00
110	Ron Mix	2.00
111	Leo Nomenllini	2.00
112	Steve Owen	2.00
113	Alan Page	2.50
114	Dan Reeves	2.00
115	John Riggins	3.00
116	Gale Sayers	6.00
117	Ken Strong	2.00
118	Gene Upshaw	3.00
119	Norm Van Brocklin	4.00
120	Alex Wojciechowicz	2.00
121	Bert Bell	2.00
122	George Blanda	4.00
123	Joe Carr	2.00
124	Larry Csonka	4.00
125	John (Paddy) Driscoll	2.00
126	Dan Fouts	3.00
127	Bob Griese	4.00
128	Ed Healy	2.00
129	Wilbur (Fats) Henry	2.00
130	Ken Houston	2.00
131	Lamar Hunt	2.00
132	Jack Lambert	2.50
133	Tom Landry	4.00
134	Willie Lanier	2.00
135	Larry Little	2.00
136	Don Maynard	3.00
137	Lenny Moore	3.00
138	Chuck Noll	2.00
139	Jim Otto	2.00
140	Walter Payton	10.00
141	Hugh (Shorty) Ray	2.00
142	Andy Robustelli	2.00
143	Bob St. Clair	2.00
144	Joe Schmidt	3.00
145	Jim Taylor	3.00
146	Doak Walker	3.00
147	Bill Walsh	3.00
148	Bob Waterfield	3.00
149	Arnie Weinmeister	2.00
150	Bill Willis	2.00
151	Roosevelt Brown	2.00
152	Jack Christiansen	2.00
153	Willie Davis	3.00
154	Tony Dorsett	6.00
155	Bud Grant	2.00
156	Joe Greene	5.00
157	Joe Guyon	2.00
158	Franco Harris	4.00
159	Ted Hendricks	2.00
160	Arnie Herber	2.00
161	Jimmy Johnson	2.00
162	Leroy Kelly	2.00
163	Curly Lambeau	2.00
164	Jim Langer	2.00
165	Link Lyman	2.00
166	Gino Marchetti	3.00
167	Ernie Nevers	2.00
168	O.J. Simpson	12.00
169	Jackie Smith	2.00
170	Bart Starr	6.00
171	Ernie Stautner	2.50
172	George Trafton	2.00
173	Emlen Tunnell	2.00
174	Johnny Unitas (not issued)	
175	Randy White	2.00
176	Jim Finks	2.00
177	Henry Jordan	2.00
178	Steve Largent	4.00
179	Lee Roy Selmon	2.00
180	Kellen Winslow	2.00

1939 Gridiron Greats Blotters

The 12-card, 3-7/8" x 9" blotter set was sponsored by Louis F. Dow Company. The blotter set fronts feature a headshot on the left side, superimposed over a football, with the collegiate player's school letter appearing in a pennant below. The right side of the card blotters feature a player profile and a monthly calendar, as each of the 12 blotter cards have a different month. The backs are blank. The cards are numbered with the "B" prefix.

	NM
Complete Set (12):	3500.
Common Player:	150.00
3941 Jim Thorpe	700.00
3942 Walter Eckersall	150.00
3943 Edward Mahan	150.00
3944 Sammy Baugh	550.00
3945 Thomas Shevlin	150.00
3946 Red Grange	600.00
3947 Ernie Nevers	325.00
3948 George Gipp	525.00
3949 Pudge Heffelfinger	150.00
3950 Bronko Nagurski	600.00
3951 Willie Heston	150.00
3952 Jay Berwanger	150.00

1992 Gridiron Promos

The four-card, standard-size promo set was issued to show the design of the 1992 regular set. The cards are similar in design to the base set and each card has a "P" prefix.

	MT
Complete Set (4):	5.00
Common Player:	.50
1 Siran Stacy	.50
2 Casey Weldon	.75
3 Mike Saunders	.50
4 Jeff Blake	5.00

1992 Gridiron

The 110-card, standard-size set, produced by Lafayette Sportscard Corporation, features the top players and coaches from the top 25 college teams. Three players and one coach represent each team. Production was limited to 50,000 sets. The card fronts feature a glossy color action shot while the back contains bio and stat information.

	MT
Complete Set (110):	25.00
Common Player:	.10
1 Robert Perez	.20
2 Jason Jones	.10
3 Jason Christ	.10
4 Fisher DeBerry (CO)	.20
5 Danny Woodson	.10
6 Siran Stacy	.20
7 Robert Stewart	.10
8 Gene Stallings (CO)	.75
9 Santana Dotson	.50
10 Curtis Hafford	.10
11 John Turnpaugh	.10
12 Grant Teaff (CO)	.30
13B Desmond Howard	.50
14 Brian Treggs	.10
15 Troy Auzenne	.20
16 Bruce Snyder (CO)	.10
17 DeChane Cameron	.10
18 Levon Kirkland	.35
19 Ed McDaniel	.20
20 Ken Hatfield (CO)	.25
21 Darian Hagan	.20
22 Rico Smith	.20
23 Joel Steed	.20
24 Bill McCartney (CO)	.75
25 Jeff Blake	4.00
26 David Daniels	.10
27 Robert Jones	.20
28 Bill Lewis (CO)	.20
29 Tim Paulk	.10
30 Arden Czyzewski	.10
31 Cal Dixon	.10
32 Steve Spurrier (CO)	2.00
33B Desmond Howard	.50
34 Casey Weldon	.35
35 Kirk Carruthers	.10
36 Bobby Bowden (CO)	2.00
37 Mark Barsotti	.10
38 Kelvin Means	.10
39 Marquez Pope	.20
40 Jim Sweeney (CO)	.25

41 Kameno Bell	.10
42 Elbert Turner	.10
43 Marlin Primous	.10
44 John Mackovic (CO)	.50
45 Matt Rodgers	.20
46 Mike Saunders	.10
47 John Derby	.10
48 Hayden Fry (CO)	.75
49 Carlos Huerta	.20
50 Leon Searcy	.20
51 Claude Jones	.10
52 Dennis Erickson (CO)	.75
53 Erick Anderson	.10
54 J.D. Carlson	.10
55 Greg Skrepenak	.35
56 Gary Moeller	.20
57 Keithen McCant	.20
58 Nate Turner	.10
59 Pat Englebert	.10
60 Tom Osborne (CO)	2.00
61 Charles Davenport	.10
62 Mark Thomas	.10
63 Clyde Hawley	.10
64 Dick Sheridan (CO)	.20
65 Derek Brown (TE)	.20
66 Rodney Culver	.20
67 Tony Smith	.20
68 Lou Holtz (CO)	2.00
69 Kent Graham	.35
70 Scottie Graham	1.25
71 John Kacherski	.10
72 John Cooper (CO)	.50
73 Mike Gaddis	.20
74 Joe Bowden	.20
75 Mike McKinley	.10
76 Gary Gibbs (CO)	.20
77 Sam Gash	.20
78 Keith Goganious	.20
79 Darren Perry	.35
80 Joe Paterno (CO)	3.00
81 Steve Israel	.20
82 Eric Seaman	.10
83 Glen Deveaux	.10
84 Paul Hackett (CO)	.35
85 Tommy Vardell	.35
86 Chris Walsh	.10
87 Jason Palumbis	.10
88 Dennis Green (CO)	.75
89 Andy Kelly	.10
90 Dale Carter	.75
91 Shon Walker	.10
92 Johnny Majors	.50
93 Bucky Richardson	.20
94 Quentin Coryatt	1.25
95 Kevin Smith	.75
96 R.C. Slocum (CO)	.75
97 Ed Cunningham	.20
98 Mario Bailey	.20
99 Donald Jones	.10
100 Don James (CO)	.75
101 Vaughn Dunbar	.35
102 Ray Yarbrough	.10
103 Matt Blundin	.35
104 Tony Sands	.10
105B Desmond Howard	.50
106 Ty Detmer	.50
107B Desmond Howard	.50
NNO Mario Bates CL, Jeff Blake	1.00
NNO Mike Gaddis CL, Tommy Vardell	.20
NNO Title Card	.10

1991 GTE Super Bowl Theme Art

The 25-card, 4-5/8" x 6" set was distributed by GTE in correlation with the 25th anniversary of the Super Bowl. The card fronts feature the Super Bowl program art while the backs contain game summaries and a GTE Telefact.

	MT
Complete Set (25):	5.00
Common Player:	.30
1 Super Bowl I	.50
2 Super Bowl II	.30
3 Super Bowl III	.30
4 Super Bowl IV	.30
5 Super Bowl V	.30
6 Super Bowl VI	.30
7 Super Bowl VII	.30
8 Super Bowl VIII	.30
9 Super Bowl IX	.30
10 Super Bowl X	.30
11 Super Bowl XI	.30
12 Super Bowl XII	.30
13 Super Bowl XIII	.30
14 Super Bowl XIV	.30
15 Suepr Bowl XV	.30
16 Super Bowl XVI	.30
17 Super Bowl XVII	.30
18 Super Bowl XVIII	.30
19 Super Bowl XIX	.30
20 Super Bowl XX	.30
21 Super Bowl XXI	.30
22 Super Bowl XXII	.30
23 Super Bowl XXIII	.30
24 Super Bowl XXIV	.30
25 Super Bowl XXV	.30

H

1990 Hall of Fame Stickers

These 80 stickers feature members of the Pro Football Hall of Fame. Each sticker measures 1-7/8" x 2-1/8" and was created for inclusion in a book titled "The Official Pro Football Hall of Fame Fun and Fact Sticker Book." Artist Mark Rucker did the original artwork which appears on each sticker. The player's name, position and sticker number are given on the front.

	MT
Complete Set (80):	12.00
Common Player:	.15
1 Wilbur Henry	.20
2 George Trafton	.15
3 Mike Michalske	.15
4 Turk Edwards	.15
5 Bill Hewitt	.20
6 Mel Hein	.15
7 Joe Stydahar	.15
8 Dan Fortmann	.15
9 Alex Wojciechowicz	.15
10 George Connor	.20
11 Jim Thorpe	.75
12 Ernie Nevers	.35
13 John McNally	.25
14 Ken Strong	.15
15 Bronko Nagurski	.50
16 Clarke Hinkle	.15
17 Ace Parker	.15
18 Billy Dudley	.20
19 Don Hutson	.30
20 Dante Lavelli	.15
21 Elroy Hirsch	.25
22 Raymond Berry	.25
23 Bobby Mitchell	.25
24 Don Maynard	.25
25 Mike Ditka	.50
26 Lance Alworth	.25
27 Charley Taylor	.25
28 Paul Warfield	.30
29 Lou Groza	.35
30 Art Donovan	.15
31 Leo Nomellini	.15
32 Andy Robustelli	.15
33 Gino Marchetti	.15
34 Forrest Gregg	.15
35 Jim Otto	.20
36 Ron Mix	.15
37 Deacon Jones	.25
38 Bob Lilly	.25
39 Merlin Olsen	.25
40 Alan Page	.20
41 Joe Greene	.25
42 Art Shell	.25
43 Sammy Baugh	.35
44 Sid Luckman	.25
45 Bob Waterfield	.40
46 Bobby Layne	.25
47 Norm Van Brocklin	.25
48 Y.A. Tittle	.25
49 Johnny Unitas	.50
50 Bart Starr	.35
51 Sonny Jurgensen	.25
52 Joe Namath	.75
53 Roger Staubach	.75
54 Terry Bradshaw	.50
55 Steve Van Buren	.25
56 Marion Motley	.25
57 Joe Perry	.25
58 Hugh McElhenny	.25
59 Frank Gifford	.50
60 Jim Brown	1.00
61 Jim Taylor	.25
62 Gale Sayers	.35
63 Larry Csonka	.25
64 Emlen Tunnell	.15
65 Jack Christiansen	.15
66 Dick (Night Train) Lane	.15
67 Sam Huff	.25
68 Ray Nitschke	.25
69 Larry Wilson	.15
70 Willie Wood	.20
71 Bobby Bell	.15
72 Willie Brown	.20
73 Dick Butkus	.35
74 Jack Ham	.25
75 George Halas	.25
76 Steve Owen	.15
77 Art Rooney	.20
78 Bert Bell	.15
79 Paul Brown	.25
80 Pete Rozelle	.20

1993 Heads and Tails SB XXVII

The 25-card, regular-sized set, produced by Heads and Tails Inc., honored players from Super Bowl XXVII (Dallas vs. Buffalo), as well as past Super Bowl stars and current Pro Bowl players. The card fronts feature the player's name printed down one side with a silver foil "Rose Bowl" emblem along the bottom border. The card backs feature a filled Rose Bowl with Cowboys and Bills airbrushed end zones and player highlights. Gold-foil versions were randomly inserted (10,000) in the entire run (200,000).

	MT
Complete Set (25):	10.00
Common Player:	.25
1 Title Card CL	.25
2 Lawrence Taylor, Mike Singletary	.50
3 Dennis Byrd	.25
4 Junior Seau	.50
5 Steve Young	1.00
6 Sterling Sharpe	.50
7 Cortez Kennedy	.25
8 Terry Bradshaw	.75
9 Fred Biletnikoff	.25
10 John Riggins	.25
11 Phil Simms	.25
12 Cornelius Bennett	.50
13 Jim Kelly	.50
14 Bruce Smith	.50
15 Andre Reed	.50
16 Keith McKeller	.25
17 James Lofton	.25
18 Thurman Thomas	.75
19 Emmitt Smith	3.00
20 Kelvin Martin	.25
21 Troy Aikman	1.50
22 Charles Haley	.25
23 Alvin Harper	.25
24 Michael Irvin	.50
25 Jay Novacek	.25

1991 Heisman Collection I

CHARLES WHITE

The 20-card, regular-sized set, produced by College Classics in association with The Downtown Athletic Club of New York, features 20 Heisman winners in skip-numbered order (based on chronological order). The card fronts feature a color posed shot of the player with a Heisman trophy in the lower right corner. The card back informs collectors of the year the player won the award, player summary and a larger Heisman Trophy image. The production total was 100,000 sets and each case (1,000 sets) contained two player autograph cards. The set also had a serially numbered header card and a sample Bo Jackson card was also distributed.

	MT
Complete Set (21):	5.00
Common Player:	.15
1 Jay Berwanger	.15
7 Tom Harmon	.25
9 Angelo Bertelli	.15
11 Doc Blanchard	.25
13 John Lujack	.25
15 Leon Hart	.15
16 Vic Janowicz	.25
19 John Lattner	.25
23 John David Crow	.15
26 Joe Bellino	.15
30 John Huarte	.15
32 Steve Spurrier	1.00
36 Jim Plunkett	.40
37 Archie Griffin	.25
42 Tony Dorsett	1.00
43 Earl Campbell	1.00
44 Charles White	.15
48 Herschel Walker	1.00
51 Bo Jackson	1.00
53 Tim Brown	.40
NNO Title Card	.15
SAM Bo Jackson (Sample Promo)	3.00

1992 Heisman Collection II

The 20-card, standard-size set is a continuation of the 1991 Hesiman Collection set, as the set is skip-numbered in chronological order. The card fronts and backs are identical in design with the 1991 set. As with the previous set, 100,000 sets were produced by College Classics and each set comes with a serially numbered header card. Sample cards of Barry Sanders and Roger Staubach were also available in 3-1/2" x 7-1/2" strips.

	MT
Complete Set (21):	10.00
Common Player:	.50
2 Larry Kelley	.50
3 Clint Frank	.50
5 Niles Kinnick	.75
8 Bruce Smith	.50
10 Les Horvath	.50
14 Doak Walker	.75
17 Dick Kazmaier	.50
20 Alan Ameche	.50
21 Howard Cassady	.50
25 Billy Cannon	.75
27 Ernie Davis	1.75
29 Roger Staubach	2.00
31 Mike Garrett	.50
35 Steve Owens	.50
38 Johnny Rodgers	.75
39 John Cappelletti	.50
44 Billy Sims	.75
50 Doug Flutie	1.50
52 Vinny Testaverde	.50
54 Barry Sanders	2.50
NNO Title Card	.50
SAM Barry Sanders (Sample Promo)	10.00
SAM Roger Staubach (Sample Promo)	12.00

1970 Hi-C Posters

These posters were featured on the insides of Hi-C drink can labels. The featured players were statistical leaders at their positions during the 1969 season. Each poster measures 6-5/8" x 13-3/4" and is numbered below the player photo.

	NM
Complete Set (10):	700.00
Common Player:	75.00
(1) Greg Cook	80.00
(2) Fred Cox	75.00
(3) Sonny Jurgensen	125.00
(4) David Lee	75.00
(5) Dennis Partee	75.00
(6) Dick Post	75.00
(7) Mel Renfro	90.00
(8) Gale Sayers	175.00
(9) Emmitt Thomas	80.00
(10) Jim Turner	75.00

1991 Homers

In 1991, boxes of QB's Cookies contained one of six different cards featuring Hall of Fame football players. Each standard-size card has a sepia-toned photograph on the front, with a bronze frame. The player's name is in a bronze panel in the lower left. The numbered back has a checklist for the set, plus information about the player's accomplishments, biographical information and the year he was inducted into the Hall of Fame. The set was sponsored by Legend Food Products.

	MT
Complete Set (6):	10.00
Common Player:	1.00
1 Vince Lombardi	2.00
2 Hugh McElhenny	2.00
3 Elroy Hirsch	2.00
4 Jim Thorpe	4.00
5 Dick Lane	1.00
6 Bart Starr	3.00

I

1992-93 Intimidator Bio Sheets

The 36-card, 8-1/2" x 11" set features color action shots

on the glossy card fronts with the player's name printed in gold foil down the right side, along wih his team name and uniform number. The card backs contain college and pro summaries, as well as biographical information.

	MT
Complete Set (36):	65.00
Common Player:	1.00
1 Troy Aikman	8.00
2 Jerry Ball	1.00
3 Cornelius Bennett	1.00
4 Earnest Byner	1.00
5 Randall Cunningham	1.00
6 Chris Doleman	1.00
7 John Elway	5.00
8 Jim Everett	1.00
9 Michael Irvin	2.50
10 Jim Kelly	2.50
11 James Lofton	1.00
12 Howie Long	1.50
13 Ronnie Lott	1.50
14 Nick Lowery	1.00
15 Charles Mann	1.00
16 Dan Marino	12.00
17 Art Monk	1.50
18 Joe Montana	8.00
19 Warren Moon	2.50
20 Christian Okoye	1.00
21 Leslie O'Neal	1.00
22 Andre Reed	2.50
23 Jerry Rice	8.00
24 Andre Rison	2.50
25 Deion Sanders	5.00
26 Junior Seau	2.50
27 Mike Singletary	1.50
28 Bruce Smith	2.50
29 Emmitt Smith	12.00
30 Neil Smith	2.50
31 Pat Swilling	1.00
32 Lawrence Taylor	2.50
33 Broderick Thomas	1.00
34 Derrick Thomas	2.50
35 Thurman Thomas	2.50
36 Lorenzo White	1.00

1984 Invaders Smokey

The five-card, 5" x 7" set featured four players and Smokey The Bear in a forestry promotion set. The card fronts feature a posed player shot with Smokey, as well as the player's signature. The card backs contain bio information. Notable in the set is future NFL linebacker Gary Plummer, who went on to play with San Diego and San Francisco.

	MT
Complete Set (5):	65.00
Common Player:	10.00
1 Dupre Marshall	10.00
2 Gary Plummer	20.00
3 David Shaw	10.00
4 Kevin Shea	10.00
5 Smokey Bear (With players above)	10.00

J

1986 Jeno's Pizza

Two players from each of the 28 NFL teams were selected for this 58-card set offered by Jeno's Pizza. Specially-marked Jeno's Pizza boxes each contained one card inside, sealed in plastic. Current and former stars are represented in the set. Each card back has a number which corresponds to the location in a Terry Bradshaw Action Play Book which was created to display the cards. The Play Book was available through a mail-in coupon. Each card back also has a summary of the player's career accomplishments.

	MT
Complete Set (56):	25.00
Common Player:	.40
1 Duane Thomas	.75
2 Butch Johnson	.40
3 Andy Headen	.40
4 Joe Morris	.60
5 Wilbert Montgomery	.50
6 Harold Carmichael	.75

7	Ottis Anderson	.60
8	Roy Green	.50
9	Mark Murphy	.40
10	Joe Theismann	1.50
11	Jim McMahon	1.00
12	Walter Payton	3.00
13	Billy Sims	.75
14	James Jones	.40
15	Willie Davis	.75
16	Eddie Lee Ivery	.40
17	Fran Tarkenton	2.00
18	Alan Page	.75
19	Ricky Bell	.60
20	Cecil Johnson	.40
21	Bubba Bean	.40
22	Gerald Riggs	.50
23	Eric Dickerson, Barry Redden	1.00
24	Jack Reynolds	.50
25	Archie Manning	1.00
26	Wayne Wilson	.60
27	Dan Bunz, Pete Johnson	.40
28	Roger Craig	1.00
29	O.J. Simpson	6.00
30	Joe Cribbs	.50
31	Rick Volk, Leroy Kelly	.60
32	Earl Morrall	.75
33	Jim Klick	.50
34	Dan Marino	5.00
35	Craig James	1.00
36	Julius Adams	.40
37	Joe Namath	4.00
38	Freeman McNeil	.60
39	Pete Johnson	.40
40	Larry Kinnebrew	.40
41	Brian Sipe	.50
42	Kevin Mack, Earnest Byner	.60
43	Dan Pastorini	.60
44	Elvin Bethea, Carter Hartwig	.40
45	Fran Tarkenton, Jack Lambert	1.00
46	Terry Bradshaw	3.00
47	Randy Gradishar, Steve Foley	.50
48	Sammy Winder	.40
49	Robert Holmes	.40
50	Buck Buchanan	.75
51	Willie Jones, Cedrick Hardman	.40
52	Marcus Allen	1.50
53	Dan Fouts, Don Macek	.75
54	Dan Fouts	1.50
55	Blair Bush	.40
56	Steve Largent	2.50
----	Play Book (Terry Bradshaw)	3.00

1966 Jets Team Issue

The nine-card, 5" x 7" set features black and white player photos on the fronts with blank backs.

		NM
Complete Set (9):		80.00
Common Player:		4.00
1	Ralph Baker	4.00
2	Larry Grantham	5.00
3	Bill Mathis	4.00
4	Don Maynard	15.00
5	Joe Namath	40.00
6	Gerry Philbin	5.00
7	Mark Smolinski	4.00
8	Matt Snell	8.00
9	Bake Turner	4.00

1969 Jets Tasco Prints

The six-card, 11" x 16" set, produced by Tasco Associates, features an artist's depiction of the players with blank backs.

		NM
Complete Set (6):		100.00
Common Player:		10.00
1	Winston Hill	10.00
2	Joe Namath	50.00
3	Gerry Philbin	15.00
4	Johnny Sample	10.00
5	Matt Snell	18.00
6	Jim Turner	10.00

1981 Jets Police

The 10-card, 2-5/8" x 4-1/8" set have green-bordered fronts and were sponsored by Frito-Lay, Kiwanis, local law enforcement and the Jets. The card backs contain a safety tip in red print. Apparently, four of

the cards were short-printed and thus are more scarce.

		MT
Complete Set (10):		20.00
Common Player:		1.00
14	Richard Todd (SP)	4.00
42	Bruce Harper	1.00
51	Greg Buttle	1.00
73	Joe Klecko	2.50
79	Marvin Powell	2.00
80	Johnny Lam Jones (SP)	3.50
85	Wesley Walker (SP)	5.00
93	Marty Lyons	2.50
99	Mark Gastineau	2.50
xx0	Team Effort (SP)	2.50

1997 John Elway Convenience Store News

This 7" x 10" Elway card was rubber cemented inside the April 7, 1997 issue of Convenience Store News. The front features Elway in a posed shot of him passing the ball, with the words "Trading Cards" in bold white letters across the top, with the NFL logo in the middle. The back is split, with half containing facts and the other half featuring a comic.

	MT
Complete Set (1):	8.00
Common Player:	8.00
John Elway	8.00

K

1959 Kahn's

Kahn's Wieners produced this set, which features members of the Cleveland Indians and Pittsburgh Steelers. The card front contains the Kahn's slogan (The Wiener the World Awaited), plus a black-and-white photograph and a facsimile autograph. Each back has biographical and statistical information. Each unnumbered card measures 3-1/4" x 3-15/16".

		NM
Complete Set (31):		1250.
Common Player:		30.00
(1)	Dick Alban	30.00
(2)	Jim Brown	375.00
(3)	Jack Butler	30.00
(4)	Lew Carpenter	35.00
(5)	Preston Carpenter	30.00
(6)	Vince Costello	30.00
(7)	Dale Dodrill	30.00
(8)	Bob Gain	30.00
(9)	Gary Glick	30.00
(10)	Lou Groza	75.00
(11)	Gene Hickerson	30.00
(12)	Billy Howton	35.00
(13)	Art Hunter	30.00
(14)	Joe Kruppa	30.00
(15)	Bobby Layne	65.00
(16)	Joe Lewis	30.00
(17)	Jack McClairen	30.00
(18)	Mike McCormack	45.00
(19)	Walt Michaels	40.00
(20)	Bobby Mitchell	75.00
(21)	Jim Ninowski	35.00
(22)	Chuck Noll	110.00
(23)	Jimmy Orr	35.00
(24)	Milt Plum	35.00
(25)	Ray Renfro	35.00
(26)	Mike Sandusky	30.00
(27)	Billy Ray Smith	30.00
(28)	Jim Ray Smith	30.00
(29)	Ernie Stautner	50.00
(30)	Tom Tracy	30.00
(31)	Frank Varrichione	30.00

1960 Kahn's

Kahn's once again featured members of the Pittsburgh Steelers and Cleveland Browns in this 38-card set. The 3-1/4" x 3-15/16" cards had black-and-white photos on the front, along with the Kahn's slogan. The back has statistical and biographical information, plus an offer for col-

lectors to send in for a free album and instructional booklet. The cards are not numbered and are listed alphabetically.

		NM
Complete Set (38):		1200.
Common Player:		25.00
(1)	Sam Baker	25.00
(2)	Jim Brown	230.00
(3)	Ray Campbell	25.00
(4)	Preston Carpenter	25.00
(5)	Vince Costello	25.00
(6)	Willie Davis	65.00
(7)	Galen Fiss	25.00
(8)	Bob Gain	30.00
(9)	Lou Groza	50.00
(10)	Gene Hickerson	25.00
(11)	John Henry Johnson	55.00
(12)	Rich Kreitling	25.00
(13)	Joe Krupa	25.00
(14)	Bobby Layne	50.00
(15)	Jack McClairen	25.00
(16)	Mike McCormack	35.00
(17)	Walt Michaels	25.00
(18)	Bobby Mitchell	40.00
(19)	Dicky Moegle	25.00
(20)	John Morrow	25.00
(21)	Gern Nagler	25.00
(22)	John Nisby	25.00
(23)	Jimmy Orr	30.00
(24)	Bernie Parrish	25.00
(25)	Milt Plum	30.00
(26)	John Reger	25.00
(27)	Ray Renfro	30.00
(28)	Will Renfro	25.00
(29)	Mike Sandusky	30.00
(30)	Dick Schafrath	25.00
(31)	Jim Ray Smith	25.00
(32)	Billy Ray Smith	25.00
(33)	Ernie Stautner	40.00
(34)	George Tarasovic	25.00
(35)	Tom Tracy	30.00
(36)	Frank Varrichione	25.00
(37)	John Wooten	25.00
(38)	Lowe W. Wren	25.00

1961 Kahn's

In addition to featuring Cleveland Browns and Pittsburgh Steelers, as Kahn's sets from the two years before did, the 1961 set included players from the Baltimore Colts, Los Angeles Rams and Philadelphia Eagles. The cards are slightly larger than previous years' issues, measuring 3-1/4" x 4-1/16". The backs are similar to the 1961 backs, except the offer for the album and instructional booklet is slightly different. (The 1960 cards required two labels to be sent in for the album; the 1961 cards only required one.) The fronts are black-and-white and have a facsimile autograph and the Kahn's slogan. Once again, the cards are unnumbered.

		NM
Complete Set (36):		1000.
Common Player:		20.00
(1)	Sam Baker	20.00
(2)	Jim Brown	225.00
(3)	Preston Carpenter	20.00
(4)	Vince Costello	20.00
(5)	Buddy Dial	20.00
(6)	Dean Derby	25.00
(7)	Don Fleming	25.00
(8)	Bob Gain	20.00
(9)	Bobby Joe Green	20.00
(10)	Gene Hickerson	25.00
(11)	Jim Houston	25.00
(12)	Dan James	20.00
(13)	John Henry Johnson	40.00
(14)	Rich Kreitling	20.00
(15)	Joe Krupa	20.00
(16)	Larry Krutko (photo actually Tom Tracy)	20.00
(17)	Bobby Layne	60.00
(18)	Joe Lewis	20.00
(19)	Gene Lipscomb	40.00
(20)	Mike McCormack	30.00
(21)	Bobby Mitchell	45.00
(22)	John Morrow	20.00
(23)	John Nisby	20.00
(24)	Jimmy Orr	25.00
(25)	Milt Plum	25.00
(26)	John Reger	20.00
(27)	Ray Renfro	30.00
(28)	Will Renfro	20.00
(29)	Mike Sandusky	20.00
(30)	Dick Schafrath	20.00
(31)	Jim Ray Smith	20.00
(32)	Ernie Stautner	45.00
(33)	George Tarasovic	20.00
(34)	Tom Tracy (photo actually Larry Krutko)	20.00
(35)	Frank Varrichione	20.00
(36)	John Wooten	20.00

1962 Kahn's

This Kahn's set adds three new teams to the mix - the Chicago Bears, Detroit Lions and Minnesota Vikings. The unnumbered cards are 3-1/4" x 4-3/16" and can be identified from previous issues by the player's name on the back, which is in bold. The stats on the back are also double-spaced. Basically, the card design is similar to previous issues.

		NM
Complete Set (38):		1000.
Common Player:		20.00
(1)	Maxie Baughan	22.00
(2)	Charley Britt	20.00
(3)	Jim Brown	185.00
(4)	Preston Carpenter	20.00
(5)	Pete Case	22.00
(6)	Howard Cassady	25.00
(7)	Vince Costello	20.00
(8)	Buddy Dial	22.00
(9)	Gene Hickerson	20.00
(10)	Jim Houston	22.00
(11)	Dan James	20.00
(12)	Rich Kreitling	20.00
(13)	Joe Krupa	20.00
(14)	Bobby Layne	50.00
(15)	Ray Lemek	20.00
(16)	Gene Lipscomb	30.00
(17)	David Lloyd	20.00
(18)	Lou Michaels	22.00
(19)	Larry Morris	20.00
(20)	John Morrow	20.00
(21)	Jim Ninowski	22.00
(22)	Buzz Nutter	20.00
(23)	Jimmy Orr	25.00
(24)	Bernie Parrish	20.00
(25)	Milt Plum	22.00
(26)	Myron Pottios	20.00
(27)	John Reger	20.00
(28)	Ray Renfro	22.00
(29)	Frank Ryan	25.00
(30)	John Sample	22.00
(31)	Mike Sandusky	20.00
(32)	Dick Schafrath	20.00
(33)	Jim Shofner	22.00
(34)	Jim Ray Smith	20.00
(35)	Ernie Stautner	35.00
(36)	Fran Tarkenton	250.00
(37)	Paul Wiggin	22.00
(38)	John Wooten	20.00

1963 Kahn's

Kahn's included players from all 14 NFL teams this year, by adding players from the Dallas Cowboys, Green Bay Packers, New York Giants, St. Louis Cardinals, San Francisco 49ers and Washington Redskins to its 1963 lineup of eight teams. Although the backs are generally similar to those from previous sets, these cards can be distinguished from prior sets by the card front, which for the first time, uses a white border around the black-and-white photo. Once again, the cards are unnumbered and measure 3-1/4" x 4-3/16".

		NM
Complete Set (92):		2300.
Common Player:		18.00
(1)	Bill Barnes	18.00
(2)	Erich Barnes	18.00
(3)	Dick Bass	20.00
(4)	Don Bosseler	18.00
(5)	Jim Brown	200.00
(6)	Roger Brown	20.00
(7)	Roosevelt Brown	25.00
(8)	Ron Bull	20.00
(9)	Preston Carpenter	18.00
(10)	Frank Clarke	18.00
(11)	Gail Cogdill	18.00
(12)	Bobby Joe Conrad	18.00
(13)	John David Crow	30.00
(14)	Dan Currie	18.00
(15)	Buddy Dial	20.00
(16)	Mike Ditka	70.00
(17)	Fred Dugan	18.00
(18)	Galen Fiss	18.00
(19)	Bill Forester	18.00
(20)	Bob Gain	18.00
(21)	Willie Gailmore	18.00
(22)	Bill George	25.00
(23)	Frank Gifford	125.00
(24)	Bill Glass	22.00
(25)	Forrest Gregg	35.00
(26)	Fred Hageman	18.00
(27)	Jimmy Hill	18.00
(28)	Sam Huff	30.00
(29)	Dan James	18.00
(30)	John Henry Johnson	25.00
(31)	Sonny Jurgensen	35.00
(32)	Jim Katcavage	20.00
(33)	Ron Kostelnik	18.00
(34)	Jerry Kramer	25.00
(35)	Ron Kramer	22.00
(36)	Dick Lane	25.00
(37)	Yale Lary	25.00
(38)	Eddie LeBaron	25.00
(39)	Dick Lynch	18.00
(40)	Tommy Mason	20.00
(41)	Tommy McDonald	20.00
(42)	Lou Michaels	18.00
(43)	Bobby Mitchell	30.00
(44)	Dick Modzelewski	18.00
(45)	Lenny Moore	30.00
(46)	John Morrow	18.00
(47)	John Nisby	18.00
(48)	Ray Nitschke	40.00
(49)	Leo Nomellini	25.00
(50)	Jimmy Orr	20.00
(51)	John Paluck	18.00
(52)	Jim Parker	25.00
(53)	Bernie Parrish	18.00
(54)	Jim Patton	18.00
(55)	Don Perkins	20.00
(56)	Richie Petitbon	18.00
(57)	Jim Phillips	18.00
(58)	Nick Pietrosante	20.00
(59)	Milt Plum	20.00
(60)	Myron Pottios	18.00
(61)	Sonny Randle	18.00
(62)	John Reger	18.00
(63)	Ray Renfro	22.00
(64)	Pete Retzlaff	20.00
(65)	Pat Richter	22.00
(66)	Jim Ringo	25.00
(67)	Andy Robustelli	25.00
(68)	Joe Rutgens	18.00
(69)	Bob St. Clair	25.00
(70)	John Sample	18.00
(71)	Lonnie Sanders	18.00
(72)	Dick Schafrath	18.00
(73)	Joe Schmidt	30.00
(74)	Del Shofner	20.00
(75)	J.D. Smith	18.00
(76)	Norm Snead	20.00
(77)	Billy Stacy	18.00
(78)	Bart Starr	60.00
(79)	Ernie Stautner	30.00
(80)	Jim Steffen	18.00
(81)	Andy Stynchula	18.00
(82)	Fran Tarkenton	110.00
(83)	Jim Taylor	40.00
(84)	Clendon Thomas	18.00
(85)	Fred (Fuzzy) Thurston	25.00
(86)	Y.A. Tittle	50.00
(87)	Bob Toneff	18.00
(88)	Jerry Tubbs	18.00
(89)	John Unitas	130.00
(90)	Billy Wade	18.00
(91)	Willie Wood	25.00
(92)	Abe Woodson	18.00

1964 Kahn's

Kahn's introduced color to its 1964 set, making it distinctively different from its prior black-and-white efforts. The Kahn's slogan has also been removed from the card fronts; it has been placed on the card back instead. The card backs are generally the same as those in previous issues. The unnumbered cards measure 3" x 3-5/8".

		NM
Complete Set (53):		1400.
Common Player:		15.00
(1)	Doug Atkins	25.00
(2)	Terry Barr	15.00
(3)	Dick Bass	20.00
(4)	Ordell Braase	15.00
(5)	Ed Brown	20.00
(6)	Jimmy Brown	160.00
(7)	Gary Collins	20.00
(8)	Bobby Joe Conrad	20.00
(9)	Mike Ditka	45.00
(10)	Galen Fiss	15.00
(11)	Paul Flatley	22.00
(12)	Joe Fortunato	18.00
(13)	Bill George	25.00
(14)	Bill Glass	18.00
(15)	Ernie Green	18.00
(16)	Dick Hoak	18.00
(17)	Paul Hornung	45.00
(18)	Sam Huff	35.00
(19)	Charlie Johnson	20.00
(20)	John Henry Johnson	30.00
(21)	Alex Karras	35.00
(22)	Jim Katcavage	18.00
(23)	Joe Krupa	15.00
(24)	Dick Lane	25.00
(25)	Tommy Mason	18.00
(26)	Don Meredith	60.00
(27)	Bobby Mitchell	30.00
(28)	Larry Morris	15.00
(29)	Jimmy Orr	18.00
(30)	Jim Parker	25.00
(31)	Bernie Parrish	15.00
(32)	Don Perkins	18.00
(33)	Jim Phillips	15.00
(34)	Sonny Randle	
(35)	Pete Retzlaff	18.00
(36)	Jim Ringo	25.00
(37)	Frank Ryan	20.00
(38)	Dick Schafrath	18.00
(39)	Joe Schmidt	25.00
(40)	Del Shofner	18.00
(41)	J.D. Smith	15.00
(42)	Norm Snead	18.00
(43)	Bart Starr	60.00
(44)	Fran Tarkenton	75.00
(45)	Jim Taylor	30.00
(46)	Clendon Thomas	15.00
(47)	Y.A. Tittle	50.00
(48)	Jerry Tubbs	18.00
(49)	John Unitas	80.00
(50)	Billy Wade	18.00
(51)	Paul Warfield	65.00
(52)	Alex Webster	18.00
(53)	Abe Woodson	15.00

1970 Kellogg's

Kellogg's cereal entered the football card market in 1970 with a set of 60 cards featuring the 3D effect utilized for many of its baseball card issues from the same period. The cards, which measure approximately 2-1/4" x 3-1/2", could be obtained from cereal boxes or through a mail-in offer. Because of the process used to make the 3D effect, the cards are susceptible to cracking and curling, making perfect condition somewhat difficult.

		NM
Complete Set (60):		50.00
Common Player:		.40
1	Carl Eller	1.25
2	Jim Otto	1.25
3	Tom Matte	.60
4	Bill Nelson	.50
5	Travis Williams	.40
6	Len Dawson	2.00
7	Gene Washington	.60
8	Jim Nance	.50
9	Norm Snead	.60
10	Dick Butkus	4.00
11	George Sauer	.50
12	Billy Kilmer	.75
13	Alex Karras	3.00
14	Larry Wilson	1.25
15	Dave Robinson	.50
16	Bill Brown	.50
17	Bob Griese	4.00
18	Al Denson	.40
19	Dick Post	.40
20	Jan Stenerud	.60
21	Paul Warfield	1.50
22	Mel Farr	.50
23	Mel Renfro	.60
24	Roy Jefferson	.40
25	Mike Garrett	.40
26	Harry Jacobs	.40
27	Carl Garrett	.40
28	Dave Wilcox	.50
29	Matt Snell	.60
30	Tom Woodeshick	.40
31	Leroy Kelly	.75
32	Floyd Little	.75
33	Ken Willard	.60
34	John Mackey	1.25
35	Merlin Olsen	3.50
36	David Grayson	.40
37	Lem Barney	2.00
38	Deacon Jones	1.25
39	Bob Hayes	.75
40	Lance Alworth	2.00
41	Larry Csonka	3.00
42	Bobby Bell	1.25
43	George Webster	.50
44	John Roland	.50
45	Dick Shiner	.40
46	Charles (Bubba) Smith	2.00
47	Daryle Lamonica	.75
48	O.J. Simpson	20.00
49	Calvin Hill	1.00
50	Fred Biletnikoff	1.50
51	Gale Sayers	5.00
52	Homer Jones	.50
53	Sonny Jurgensen	2.50
54	Bob Lilly	2.00
55	Johnny Unitas	6.00
56	Tommy Nobis	.75
57	Ed Meador	.50
58	Carl Lockhart	.40
59	Don Maynard	1.25
60	Greg Cook	.50

1971 Kellogg's

The 1971 Kellogg's football set was again complete at 60 cards and featured the 3D effect. The cards measure approximately 2-1/4" x 3-1/2", and again, because of the process used to achieve the 3D effect, are susceptible to cracking and curling. Cards from the 1971 set were available only in boxes of cereal. Because sets were not available through a mail-in offer, the '71 Kellogg's set is considerably scarcer and more valuable than the '70 set.

		NM
Complete Set (60):		360.00
Common Player:		4.50
1	Tom Barrington	4.50
2	Chris Hanburger	5.00
3	Frank Nunley	4.50
4	Houston Antwine	4.50
5	Ron Johnson	5.00
6	Craig Morton	6.50
7	Jack Snow	4.50
8	Mel Renfro	5.00
9	Les Josephson	4.50
10	Gary Garrison	4.50
11	Dave Herman	4.50
12	Fred Dryer	6.50
13	Larry Brown	5.00
14	Gene Washington	4.50
15	Joe Greene	25.00
16	Marlin Briscoe	4.50
17	Bob Grant	4.50
18	Dan Conners	4.50
19	Mike Curtis	5.00
20	Harry Schuh	4.50
21	Rich Jackson	4.50
22	Clint Jones	4.50
23	Hewritt Dixon	4.50
24	Jess Phillips	4.50
25	Gary Cuozzo	4.50
26	Bo Scott	4.50
27	Glen Ray Hines	4.50
28	Johnny Unitas	27.00
29	John Gilliam	4.50
30	Harmon Wages	4.50
31	Walt Sweeney	4.50
32	Bruce Taylor	5.00
33	George Blanda	17.00
34	Ken Bowman	4.50
35	Johnny Robinson	5.00
36	Ed Podolak	4.50
37	Curley Culp	4.50
38	Jim Hart	6.50
39	Dick Butkus	20.00
40	Floyd Little	6.50
41	Nick Buoniconti	6.50
42	Larry Smith	4.50
43	Wayne Walker	4.50
44	MacArthur Lane	5.00
45	John Brodie	15.00
46	Dick LeBeau	4.50
47	Claude Humphrey	4.50
48	Jerry LeVias	4.50
49	Erich Barnes	4.50
50	Andy Russell	5.00
51	Donny Anderson	5.00
52	Mike Reid	7.50
53	Al Atkinson	4.50
54	Tom Dempsey	5.00
55	Bob Griese	18.00
56	Dick Gordon	4.50
57	Charlie Sanders	4.50
58	Doug Cunningham	4.50
59	Cyril Pinder	4.50
60	Dave Osborn	5.00

1978 Kellogg's Stickers

Measuring 2-1/2" x 2-5/8", the sticker fronts showcase the team's name beneath the team helmets. Spotlighted on the back are a brief history on each team and a referee's signals quiz. Each sticker is numbered on the back.

		NM
Complete Set (28):		30.00
Common Player:		1.00
1	Atlanta Falcons	1.00
2	Baltimore Colts	1.00
3	Buffalo Bills	1.00
4	Chicago Bears	1.00
5	Cincinnati Bengals	1.00
6	Cleveland Browns	1.00
7	Dallas Cowboys	2.00
8	Denver Broncos	1.00
9	Detroit Lions	1.00
10	Green Bay Packers	1.50
11	Houston Oilers	1.00
12	Kansas City Chiefs	1.00
13	Los Angeles Rams	1.00
14	Miami Dolphins	2.00
15	Minnesota Vikings	1.00
16	New England Patriots	1.00
17	New Orleans Saints	1.00
18	New York Giants	1.00
19	New York Jets	1.00
20	Oakland Raiders	2.00
21	Philadelphia Eagles	1.00
22	Pittsburgh Steelers	2.00
23	St. Louis Cardinals	1.00
24	San Diego Chargers	1.00
25	San Francisco 49ers	2.00
26	Seattle Seahawks	1.00
27	Tampa Bay Buccaneers	1.00
28	Washington Redskins	2.00

1982 Kellogg's

After a hiatus of more than a decade, Kellogg's returned in 1982 with a small (24-card) set that appeared in three-card panels on the backs of Raisin Bran boxes. The individual cards measure the standard 2-1/2" x 3-1/2", but the set is usually collected in panel-form, so it has little value if cut into individual cards. The prices below, therefore, are for complete panels. The cards are unnumbered and are checklisted here in alphabetical order based on the last name of the first player on each panel. Each panel measures approximately 4-1/8" x 7-1/2". Card fronts have the player's name, position and team on the bottom left, with the Kellogg's logo inside a football on the bottom right. Card backs feature the player's name and bio in the middle. His honors received are printed at the bottom, along with the team helmet and NFLPA and NFL logos. Billy Joe DuPree's photo is mistakenly labeled Harvey Martin, while Martin's is labeled DuPree.

		MT
Complete Set (8):		5.00
Common Panel:		.60
1	Ken Anderson, Frank Lewis, Gifford Nielsen	.75
2	Ottis Anderson, Chris Collinsworth, Franco Harris	1.75
3	William Andrews, Brian Sipe, Fred Smerlas	.60
4	Steve Bartkowski, Robert Brazile, Jack Rudnay	.60
5	Tony Dorsett, Eric Hipple, Pat McInally	1.25
6	Billy Joe DuPree, David Hill, John Stallworth	.75
7	Harvey Martin, Mike Pruitt, Joe Senser	.60
8	Art Still, Mel Gray, Tommy Kramer	.60

1982 Kellogg's Teams

Inserted into specially marked boxes of Kellogg's Raisin Bran cereal, this 28-poster set measures 8" x 10-1/2". Inside a black border, color artwork of generic players is featured, with a smaller color painting inset on one side. The team name, helmet and NFL shield are located inside an oval at the bottom. The backs include the official rules and an entry form for the "Raisin Bran Super Bowl Sweepstakes." If the team won the 1983 Super Bowl, the collector had to fill out the form and mail the poster to Kellogg's to win various prizes.

		MT
Complete Set (28):		100.00
Common Player:		5.00
1	Atlanta Falcons	5.00
2	Buffalo Bills	5.00
3	Chicago Bears	5.00
4	Cincinnati Bengals	5.00
5	Cleveland Browns	5.00
6	Dallas Cowboys	8.00
7	Denver Broncos	5.00
8	Detroit Lions	5.00
9	Green Bay Packers	8.00
10	Houston Oilers	5.00
11	Indianapolis Colts	5.00
12	Kansas City Chiefs	5.00
13	Los Angeles Raiders	8.00
14	Los Angeles Rams	5.00
15	Miami Dolphins	8.00
16	Minnesota Vikings	5.00
17	New England Patriots	5.00
18	New Orleans Saints	5.00
19	New York Giants	5.00
20	New York Jets	5.00
21	Philadelphia Eagles	5.00
22	Pittsburgh Steelers	5.00
23	St. Louis Cardinals	5.00
24	San Diego Chargers	5.00
25	San francisco 49ers	8.00
26	Seattle Seahawks	5.00
27	Tampa Bay Buccaneers	5.00
28	Washington Redskins	8.00

1989 King B Discs

These red-bordered discs, which feature 24 NFL stars, were included in specially-marked cans of King B beef jerky, one per can. The front has a color head shot of the player, along with the King B logo. "1st Annual Collectors Edition" is also written on the front. The back includes the King B and NFLPA logos, plus biographical information and 1988 and career statistics. A ring of stars runs along the border. The cards, produced by Michael Schechter Associates, are numbered on the back.

		MT
Complete Set (24):		50.00
Common Player:		1.00
1	Chris Miller	2.50
2	Shane Conlan	1.25
3	Richard Dent	1.75
4	Boomer Esiason	1.75
5	Frank Minnifield	1.00
6	Herschel Walker	2.00
7	Karl Mecklenburg	1.50
8	Mike Cofer	1.00
9	Warren Moon	3.00
10	Chris Chandler	1.50
11	Deron Cherry	1.00
12	Bo Jackson	2.00
13	Jim Everett	1.50
14	Dan Marino	12.00
15	Anthony Carter	1.25
16	Andre Tippett	1.50
17	Bobby Hebert	1.50
18	Phil Simms	1.75
19	Al Toon	1.50
20	Gary Anderson	1.00
21	Joe Montana	14.00
22	Dave Krieg	1.50
23	Randall Cunningham	2.50
24	Bubby Brister	1.00

1990 King B Discs

Once again, these discs were available in specially-marked cans of King B beef jerky, one per can. The front has a color mug shot of the player, surrounded by a red border with a yellow background. The year 1990 appears at the bottom of the card in green; the King B logo is underneath the year. Each card back is numbered and has a border of stars around it. Biographical information and a comment about the player's accomplishments are also given on the back, along with the King B and NFLPA logos.

		MT
Complete Set (24):		45.00
Common Player:		1.00
1	Jim Everett	2.00
2	Marcus Allen	2.00
3	Brian Blades	1.50
4	Bubby Brister	1.00
5	Mark Carrier	1.50
6	Steve Jordan	1.00
7	Barry Sanders	7.00
8	Ronnie Lott	2.00
9	Howie Long	2.00
10	Steve Atwater	1.50
11	Dan Marino	8.00
12	Boomer Esiason	2.00
13	Dalton Hilliard	1.00
14	Phil Simms	2.50
15	Jim Kelly	3.00
16	Mike Singletary	1.50
17	John Stephens	1.50
18	Christian Okoye	1.50
19	Art Monk	2.00
20	Chris Miller	2.50
21	Roger Craig	2.00
22	Duane Bickett	1.00
23	Don Majkowski	1.00
24	Eric Metcalf	2.50

1991 King B Discs

Specially-marked cans of King B beef jerky each contained a disc featuring one of 24 NFL stars. The front has a color mug shot of the player surrounded by a purple border. His name, team and position are printed in gold. The King B logo and 1991 are printed at the bottom of the disc. The back is numbered and includes 1990 and career statistics, plus brief biographical information, all in red ink. A ring of stars comprises the border. An NFLPA and King B logo are also included on the back. The discs were produced by Michael Schechter Associates.

		MT
Complete Set (24):		35.00
Common Player:		1.00
1	Mark Rypien	1.25
2	Art Monk	2.00
3	Sean Jones	1.00
4	Bubby Brister	1.00
5	Warren Moon	3.00
6	Andre Rison	2.00
7	Emmitt Smith	9.00
8	Mervyn Fernandez	1.00
9	Rickey Jackson	1.00
10	Bruce Armstrong	1.00
11	Neal Anderson	1.25
12	Christian Okoye	1.00
13	Thurman Thomas	3.00
14	Bruce Smith	1.25
15	Jeff Hostetler	1.50
16	Barry Sanders	6.00
17	Andre Reed	1.25
18	Derrick Thomas	2.50
19	Jim Everett	1.25
20	Boomer Esiason	1.50
21	Merril Hoge	1.00
22	Steve Atwater	1.25
23	Dan Marino	8.00
24	Mark Collins	1.00

1992 King B Discs

This fourth annual collectors' edition features 24 NFL stars on discs available in specially-marked cans of King B beef jerky. The front of each disc, which is black with a yellow border, has a color mug shot of the player. His name, team and position are written in white at the top of the card. A yellow King B logo and the year, 1992, are at the bottom. The back is numbered and includes 1991 and career statistics, plus brief biographical information. King B and NFLPA logos also appear. An alternating ring of white and black stars runs along the border of the back. Michael Schechter Associates again produced the set.

		MT
Complete Set (24):		30.00
Common Player:		1.00
1	Derrick Thomas	2.00
2	Wilber Marshall	1.50
3	Andre Rison	2.00
4	Thurman Thomas	2.50
5	Emmitt Smith	8.00
6	Charles Mann	1.00
7	Michael Irvin	3.00
8	Jim Everett	1.50
9	Gary Anderson	1.00
10	Trace Armstrong	1.00
11	John Elway	3.50
12	Chip Lohmiller	1.00
13	Bobby Hebert	1.00
14	Cornelius Bennett	1.25
15	Chris Miller	1.50
16	Warren Moon	2.00
17	Charles Haley	1.50
18	Mark Rypien	1.00
19	Darrell Green	1.25
20	Barry Sanders	5.00
21	Rodney Hampton	2.50
22	Shane Conlan	1.00
23	Jerry Ball	1.00
24	Morten Andersen	1.50

1993 King B Discs

These 2-3/8" discs were included one per specially-marked can of King B beef jerky. Twenty-four NFL stars are featured. The front of the card uses a green football field motif and features a color mug shot of the player. A black panel at the top includes the player's name, team and position, written in orange and white letters. A blue King B logo and the year appear at the bottom of the disc. The back is numbered and uses black ink to present brief biographical information, plus a brief career summary. King B and NFLPA logos are also included on the back, which has black and white stars along the rim. Each disc, produced by Michael Schechter Associates, measures 2-3/8". An uncut sheet, measuring 17-1/4" x 12-3/4", was also issued.

		MT
Complete Set (24):		30.00
Common Player:		1.00
1	Luis Sharpe	1.00
2	Erik McMillan	1.00
3	Chris Doleman	1.25
4	Cortez Kennedy	1.50
5	Howie Long	1.25
6	Bill Romanowski	1.00
7	Andre Tippett	1.00
8	Simon Fletcher	1.50
9	Derrick Thomas	2.00
10	Rodney Peete	1.00
11	Ronnie Lott	1.50
12	Duane Bickett	1.00
13	Steve Walsh	1.25
14	Stan Humphries	1.50
15	Jeff George	2.75
16	Jay Novacek	2.00
17	Andre Reed	2.00
18	Andre Rison	2.00
19	Emmitt Smith	8.00
20	Neal Anderson	1.00
21	Ricky Sanders	1.25
22	Thurman Thomas	2.50
23	Lorenzo White	1.00
24	Barry Foster	1.00

1994 King B Discs

The sixth edition of this set, issued by Michael Schechter Associates, was inserted one disc per specially marked can of King B beef jerky. Each disc measures 2-3/8" in diameter. Color headshots of the player are showcased over a green background. The player's name, position and team name are included in a yellow rectangle at the bottom of the photo. The white backs have the player's name with his team, position and bio listed at the top, along with the NFLPA logo. His stats are listed in the center. All print on the backs is in green. The back is bordered with stars.

		MT
Complete Set (24):		25.00
Common Player:		.75
1	Marcus Allen	1.50
2	Jerome Bettis	2.00
3	Terrell Buckley	.75
4	Craig Erickson	.75
5	Brett Favre	6.00
6	Barry Foster	.75
7	Irving Fryar	.75
8	Gary Brown	.75
9	Rodney Hampton	.75
10	Qadry Ismail	.75
11	Jim Jeffcoat	.75
12	Jim Lachey	.75
13	Natrone Means	2.00
14	Tony Meola	.75
15	Pete Metzelaars	.75
16	Scott Mitchell	1.00
17	Ronald Moore	1.00
18	Andre Rison	.75
19	Jay Schroeder	.75
20	Junior Seau	1.25
21	Shannon Sharpe	1.00
22	Sterling Sharpe	1.00
23	Tim Brown	1.00
24	Chris Warren	1.00

1995 King B Discs

Labeled on the disc front as the "7th Annual Collectors Edition," these discs measure 2-5/8". A color headshot of the player is featured, with a background drawing of a running back chased by two defensive players. A brown and gold vertical striped background borders the left side of the disc. The King B logo is also printed at the left. The player's name and position are located at the bottom. The disc backs feature the player's name, team and bio at the top. His stats are in the middle, with the King B logo and the disc number at the bottom. Text is housed inside a circle of alternating stars and footballs. The discs were available either one disc per shredded beef jerky can or as a 17-1/4" x 12-1/2" collector sheet.

		MT
Complete Set (24):		18.00
Common Player:		.50
1	Errict Rhett	1.00
2	Andre Reed	.50
3	Rodney Hampton	.75
4	Kevin Greene	.50
5	Merton Hanks	.50
6	Jerome Bettis	1.50
7	Johnny Johnson	.50
8	Ricky Watters	1.00
9	Harvey Williams	.50
10	Mel Gray	.50
11	Craig Erickson	.50
12	Stan Humphries	.50
13	Natrone Means	1.50
14	Terance Mathis	.50
15	Ken Harvey	.50
16	Brian Mitchell	.50
17	Cris Carter	.50
18	Tim Brown	1.00
19	Marshall Faulk	2.00
20	Eric Turner	.50
21	Terry Allen	.50
22	Chris Warren	1.00
23	Randy Baldwin	.50
24	Ben Coates	.50

1996 All King B Sack Attack Team

Measuring 2-3/8" in diameter, the 24-disc set focused on defensive players. The front of the disc includes a headshot of the player, his name at the top and a "Sack-It-To-'Em" logo at the bottom. A drawing of a defensive player is included along the left border. The disc backs feature the player's career sacks. One disc was included in each specially marked King B beef jerky canister.

	MT
Complete Set (24):	15.00
Common Player:	.50
1 Reggie White	2.00
2 Rickey Jackson	.50
3 Kevin Greene	1.00
4 Tony Bennett	.50
5 Bryce Paup	1.00
6 John Copeland	.50
7 Pat Swilling	.50
8 Willie McGinest	.50
9 Charles Haley	.50
10 Chris Doleman	.50
11 Clyde Simmons	.50
12 Hugh Douglas	.50
13 Henry Thomas	.50
14 John Randle	1.00
15 Phil Hansen	.50
16 Bruce Smith	1.00
17 Jim Flanigan	1.00
18 D'Marco Farr	.50
19 Ray Seals	.50
20 Neil Smith	1.00
21 Andy Harmon	.50
22 William Fuller	.50
23 Tracy Scoggins	.50
24 Leslie O'Neal	.50

1997 King B Discs

This 24-disc set includes only rookies from the 1997 season and were distributed one per specially marked package of the beef jerky snack. The discs contain the player's portrait over a purple background which features diagrammed plays. The King B logo is in the lower left portion of the photo, while "Rookies Collector Edition" and the player's name and position are included inside a purple area at the bottom of the disc front.

	MT
Complete Set (24):	20.00
Common Player:	.50
1 Orlando Pace	1.00
2 Darrell Russell	.50
3 Shawn Springs	1.00
4 Peter Boulware	.50
5 Bryant Westbrook	.50
6 Walter Jones	.50
7 Ike Hilliard	1.50
8 James Farrior	.50
9 Tom Knight	.50
10 Chris Naeole	.50
11 Warrick Dunn	3.00
12 Tony Gonzalez	1.25
13 Reinard Wilson	.50
14 Yatil Green	.50
15 Reidel Anthony	1.50
16 Dwayne Rudd	1.50
17 Renaldo Wynn	.50
18 David LaFleur	1.00
19 Antowain Smith	2.00
20 Chad Scott	.50
21 Jim Druckenmiller	2.00
22 Rae Carruth	1.50
23 Jake Plummer	3.00
24 Ronnie McAda	.50

1989 Knudsen Raiders

Measuring 2" x 8", this bookmark set of 12 was introduced by Knudsen's Dairy of California. The bookmarks were available to children who checked out books from the Los Angeles Public Library during the 1989 season. The fronts featured a photo of a Raiders player, with "Knudsen presents Raiders Readers" at the top. The Raiders' logo, the player's name, position and bio, along with his highlights are listed below the photo. The unnumbered backs have reading tips, the player's name, L.A. Public Library, MCLS, Knudsen and Raiders' logos. The Mike Shanahan card is a tough one to locate, as it was not distributed or pulled after he left the Raiders for a position with another NFL team.

	MT
Complete Set (14):	30.00
Common Player:	1.50
6 Jeff Gossett	1.50
13 Jay Schroeder	2.00
26 Vann McElroy	1.50
35 Steve Smith	2.00
36 Terry McDaniel	1.50
70 Scott Davis	1.50
72 Don Mosebar	1.50
75 Howie Long	2.50
76 Steve Wisniewski	1.50
81 Tim Brown	6.00
83 Willie Gault	2.00
NNO Mike Shanahan (SP) (CO)	16.00
NNO Raiders/Super Bowl	1.50
NNO Raiderettes (SP)	2.00

1990 Knudsen Chargers

Measuring 2" x 8", the Chargers bookmarks were available at San Diego libraries. The fronts showcase the Knudsen logo at the top, with "The Reading Team" below it. The player photo is shown in the middle, with the Chargers' logo, player's name, uniform number and bio in a box under the photo. The unnumbered backs contain the Knudsen, American Library Association and San Diego libraries' logos.

	MT
Complete Set (6):	10.00
Common Player:	1.50
1 Marion Butts	2.50
2 Anthony Miller	3.50
3 Leslie O'Neal	2.50
4 Gary Plummer	1.50
5 Billy Ray Smith	1.50
6 Billy Joe Tolliver	2.00

1990 Knudsen Rams

Measuring 2" x 8", the six-bookmark set promoted reading to children under 15 years of age in the Los Angeles area. The front design is the same as the Chargers, 49ers and Patriots sets of 1990.

	MT
Complete Set (6):	25.00
Common Player:	4.00
1 Henry Ellard	8.00
2 Jim Everett	6.00
3 Jerry Gray	4.00
4 Pete Holohan	4.00
5 Mike Lansford	4.00
6 Irv Pankey	4.00

1991 Knudsen

Measuring 2" x 8", this six-card bookmark set was given to children under 15 years of age at libraries in the San Francisco metro area. The design is basically the same as the Chargers set, with the Knudsen logo at the top and "The Reading Team" below it. The player's photo is in the center, above a box which contains the 49ers' logo and the player's name, uniform number and bio. The unnumbered backs have the Knudsen logo at the top and the San Francisco Public Library logo at the bottom. Two books are listed on the back of each bookmark.

	MT
Complete Set (6):	25.00
Common Player:	1.50
1 Roger Craig	2.50
2 Ronnie Lott	4.00
3 Joe Montana	12.00
4 Jerry Rice	12.00
5 George Siefert (CO)	3.00
6 Michael Walter	1.50

1990 Knudsen/Sealtest Patriots

Measuring 2" x 8", this six-card bookmark set was sponsored by Knudsen's and Sealtest. Those children under 15 years of age in the New England area received the bookmarks at their local libraries. The Knudsen or Sealtest logos were located at the top of the front, with "The Reading Team" below it. The player's photo is showcased above a box which contains the Patriots' logo, player's name, uniform number and bio. The backs have the sponsor logos and information on two books.

	MT
Complete Set (6):	25.00
Common Player:	4.00
1 Steve Grogan	6.00
2 Ronnie Lippett	4.00
3 Eric Sievers	4.00
4 Mosi Tatupu	4.00
5 Andre Tippett	6.00
6 Garin Veris	4.00

L

1983 Latrobe Police

The black-and-white or sepia-toned standard sized cards were issued in Latrobe, Pa. Titled "Birthplace of Pro Football," the 30-card set featured a photo of the player in an oval, with his name and position in a box at the bottom of the card. The card backs, which came in two versions, have the 1895 "Birthplace of Pro Football" logo in the upper left, with the player's name and position at the right. A write-up of his career highlights also is included on the horizontal card backs. The cards were produced by Chess Promotions Inc. of Latrobe, Pa. The variation backs include safety tips.

	MT
Complete Set (30):	8.00
Common Player:	.30
1 John Brallier	1.00
2 John K. Brallier	.50
3 Latrobe YMCA Team 1895	.50
4 Brallier and Team at W and J 1895	.50
5 Latrobe A.A. Team 1896	.50
6 Latrobe A.A. 1897	.50
7 1st All Pro Team 1897	.50
8 David Berry (Mgr.)	.30
9 Harry Ryan (RT)	.30
10 Walter Okeson (LE)	.30
11 Edward Wood (RE)	.30
12 E. Hammer (C)	.30
13 Marcus Saxman (LH)	.30
14 Charles Shumaker (SUB)	.30
15 Charles McDyre (LE)	.30
16 Edward Abbatticchio (FB)	.30
17 George Flickinger (C/LT)	.30
18 Walter Howard (RH)	.30
19 Thomas Trenchard	.50
20 John Kinport Brallier (QB)	.75
21 Jack Gass (LH)	.30
22 Dave Campbell (LT)	.30
23 Edward Blair (RH)	.30
24 John Johnston (RG)	.30
25 Sam Johnston (LG)	.30
26 Alex Laird (SUB)	.30
27 Latrobe A.A. 1897 Team	.50
28 Pro Football Memorial Plaque	.30
29 Commemorative Medallion	.30
30 Birth of Pro Football Checklist Card	.50

1975 Laughlin Flaky Football

Artist R.G. Laughlin created this 26-card set in 1975 as a parody to the NFL. Measuring 2-1/2" x 3-3/8", the card fronts have the city name and a parody NFL nickname, such as the Green Bay Porkers, with artwork relating to the nickname. "Flaky Football" is printed at the top of the cards, with the card number in a white circle in one of the corners of the horizontal fronts. The backs of the cards are blank.

	NM
Complete Set (27):	125.00
Common Player:	4.50
1 Pittsburgh Stealers	8.00
2 Minnesota Spikings	6.00
3 Cincinnati Bungles	6.00
4 Chicago Bares	6.00
5 Miami Dullfins	8.00
6 Philadelphia Eggles	4.50
7 Cleveland Brawns	4.50
8 New York Gianuts	4.50
9 Buffalo Bulls	4.50
10 Dallas Plowboys	8.00
11 New England Pastry Nuts	4.50
12 Green Bay Porkers	8.00
13 Denver Bongos	4.50
14 St. Louis Cigardinals	4.50
15 New York Jests	4.50
16 Washington Redshins	8.00
17 Oakland Waders	8.00
18 Los Angeles Yams	4.50
19 Baltimore Kilts	4.50
20 New Orleans Scents	4.50
21 San Diego Charges	4.50
22 Detroit Loins	4.50
23 Kansas City Chefs	4.50
24 Atlanta Fakin's	4.50
25 Houston Owlers	4.50
26 San Francisco 40 Miners	8.00
NNO Title Card Flaky Football	8.00

1948 Leaf

This 98-card set, the first of two Leaf sets to be issued in the late 1940s, features players posed in front of solid backgrounds (player hands and faces are in black and white). Cards measure 2-3/8" x 2-7/8", and the final 49 cards are more difficult to find than the first 49. Rookies in this set include Sid Luckman, Bulldog Turner, Doak Walker, Bobby Layne, Pete Pihos, George McAfee, Steve Van Buren, Bob Waterfield, Charlie Trippi, Sammy Baugh, Bill Dudley, George Connor, Frank Tripucka, Leo Nomellini, Charley Conerly, Chuck Bednarik, and Jackie Jensen.

	NM
Complete Set (98):	5800.
Common Player (1-49):	20.00
Common Player (50-98):	100.00
1 Sid Luckman	300.00
2 Steve Suhey	20.00
3 Bulldog Turner	90.00
4 Doak Walker	125.00
5 Levi Jackson	20.00
6 Bobby Layne	300.00
7 Bill Fischer	20.00
8 Vice Banonis	20.00
9 Tommy Thompson	40.00
10 Perry Moss	20.00
11 Terry Brennan	20.00
12 William Swiacki	25.00
13 Johnny Lujack	125.00
14 Mal Kutner	20.00
15 Charlie Justice	60.00
16 Pete Pihos	95.00
17 Kenny Washington	55.00
18 Harry Gilmer	30.00
19 George McAfee	100.00
20 George Taliaferro	25.00
21 Paul Christman	40.00
22 Steve Van Buren	140.00
23 Ken Kavanaugh	25.00
24 Jim Martin	25.00
25 Bud Angsman	20.00
26 Bob Waterfield	200.00
27 Fred Davis	20.00
28 Whitey Wistert	20.00
29 Charlie Trippi	100.00
30 Paul Governali	20.00
31 Tom McWilliams	20.00
32 Larry Zimmerman	20.00
33 Pat Harder	40.00
34 Sammy Baugh	425.00
35 Ted Fritsch Sr.	20.00
36 Bill Dudley	85.00
37 George Connor	65.00
38 Frank Dancewicz	20.00
39 Billy Dewell	20.00
40 John Nolan	20.00
41 Harry Szulborski	20.00
42 Tex Coulter	20.00
43 Robert Nussbaumer	20.00
44 Bob Mann	20.00
45 Jim White	20.00
46 Jack Jacobs	20.00
47 John Clement	20.00
48 Frank Reagan	20.00
49 Frank Tripucka	30.00
50 John Rauch	100.00
51 Mike Dimitrio	100.00
52 Leo Nomellini	250.00
53 Charlie Conerly	250.00
54 Chuck Bednarik	400.00
55 Chick Jagade	100.00
56 Bob Folsom	100.00
57 Eugene Rossides	100.00
58 Art Weiner	100.00
59 Alex Sarkisian	100.00
60 Dick Harris	100.00
61 Len Younce	100.00
62 Gene Derricotte	100.00
63 Roy Steiner	100.00
64 Frank Seno	100.00
65 Bob Hendreen	100.00
66 Jack Cloud	100.00
67 Harrell Collins	100.00
68 Clyde LeForce	100.00
69 Larry Joe	100.00
70 Phil O'Reilly	100.00
71 Paul Campbell	100.00
72 Ray Evans	100.00
73 Jackie Jensen	300.00
74 Russ Steger	100.00
75 Tony Minisi	100.00
76 Clayton Tonnemaker	100.00
77 George Savitsky	100.00
78 Clarence Self	100.00
79 Rod Franz	100.00
80 Jim Youle	100.00
81 Billy Bye	100.00
82 Fred Enke	100.00
83 Fred Folger	100.00
84 Jug Girard	100.00
85 Joe Scott	100.00
86 Bob Demoss	100.00
87 Dave Templeton	100.00
88 Herb Siegert	100.00
89 Bucky O'Conner	100.00
90 Joe Whisler	100.00
91 Leon Hart	175.00
92 Earl Banks	100.00
93 Frank Aschenbrenner	100.00
94 John Goldsberry	100.00
95 Porter Payne	100.00
96 Pete Perini	100.00
97 Jay Rhodemyre	100.00
98 Al DiMarco	175.00

1949 Leaf

The 1949 Leaf issue is quite possibly the stupidest of what is considered the "major" football issues. There are but 49 cards in the set, but numerically the set jumps around until it reaches a 150 count. There are several gaps in the numbering sequence. Even less appealing is the fact that there is exactly one rookie card in the set - that of #1, Bob Hendren. Cards, which measure 2-3/8" x 2-7/8", bear close resemblance to the 1948 Leaf football set, as well as to the Leaf baseball sets of the era. The second-year cards in the set include those of Hall of Famers Sid Luckman, Charley Trippi, Bill Dudley, Sammy Baugh, Pete Pihos, George Connor, Ken McAfee (last card), Bobby Layne, Steve Van Buren, Bob Waterfield, Chuck Bednarik, and Bulldog Turner. Other sophomore cards include Charley Conerly, Johnny Lujack, and Frank Tripucka.

	NM
Complete Set (49):	2000.
Common Player:	25.00
1 Bob Hendren	75.00
2 Joe Scott	25.00
3 Frank Reagan	25.00
4 John Rauch	25.00

7	Bill Fischer	25.00
9	Bud Angsman	25.00
10	Billy Dewell	25.00
13	Tommy Thompson	25.00
15	Sid Luckman	100.00
16	Charlie Trippi	45.00
17	Bob Mann	25.00
19	Paul Christman	25.00
22	Bill Dudley	45.00
23	Clyde LeForce	25.00
26	Sammy Baugh	250.00
28	Pete Pihos	45.00
31	Tex Coulter	25.00
32	Mal Kutner	25.00
35	Whitey Wistert	25.00
37	Ted Fritsch Sr.	25.00
38	Vince Banonis	25.00
39	Jim White	25.00
40	George Connor	45.00
41	George McAfee	45.00
43	Frank Tripucka	25.00
47	Fred Enke	25.00
49	Charlie Conerly	80.00
51	Ken Kavanaugh	25.00
56	John Lujack	80.00
57	Jim Youle	25.00
62	Harry Gilmer	25.00
65	Robert Nussbaumer	25.00
67	Bobby Layne	140.00
70	Herb Siegert	25.00
74	Tony Minisi	25.00
79	Steve Van Buren	80.00
81	Perry Moss	25.00
89	Bob Waterfield	90.00
90	Jack Jacobs	25.00
95	Kenny Washington	30.00
101	Pat Harder	25.00
110	William Swiacki	25.00
118	Fred Davis	25.00
126	Jay Rhodemyre	25.00
134	Chuck Bednarik	100.00
144	George Savitsky	25.00
150	Bulldog Turner	125.00

1996 Leaf

Leaf Football contained 190 cards in the regular-issue set, plus 10 Gold Leaf Rookies that were numbered like inserts, but considered part of the regular-issue set. Leaf arrived for the first time since 1949, and was packaged in 10-card packs. The 190 players from the base set were also available in factory sets receiving special foil treatment and limited to 1,996 sets. The factory sets also included one of 25 different autographed future stars. Inserts found in Leaf Football included: 190-card Press Proof parallel set, Statistical Standouts, Grass Roots, Gold Leaf Stars, American All-Stars and Shirt Off My Back. Cards from regular packs had the bottom strip of the card in the player's team colors, with no foil, while pre- priced packs featured red foil and Collector's Edition cards had gold foil.

		MT
Complete Set (190):		20.00
Common Player:		.10
Minor Stars:		.20
Wax Box:		30.00
1	Troy Aikman	1.50
2	Ricky Watters	.20
3	Robert Brooks	.10
4	Ki-Jana Carter	.20
5	Drew Bledsoe	1.25
6	Eric Swann	.10
7	Hardy Nickerson	.10
8	Tony Martin	.10
9	Garrison Hearst	.10
10	Bernie Parmalee	.10
11	Neil Smith	.10
12	Aaron Craver	.10
13	Rashaan Salaam	.20
14	Greg Hill	.10
15	Charlie Garner	.10
16	Kimble Anders	.10
17	Steve McNair	1.00
18	Neil O'Donnell	.10

19	Greg Lloyd	.10
20	Warren Moon	.10
21	Bernie Kosar	.10
22	Derrick Thomas	.10
23	Andre Hastings	.10
24	Wayne Chrebet	.10
25	Mark Seay	.10
26	Eric Metcalf	.10
27	Shawn Jefferson	.10
28	Napoleon Kaufman	.10
29	Steve Walsh	.10
30	Derrick Alexander	.10
31	Rodney Peete	.10
32	Terance Mathis	.10
33	Michael Westbrook	.20
34	Kevin Carter	.10
35	Aaron Hayden	.10
36	J.J. Stokes	.20
37	Andre Reed	.10
38	Chris Warren	.20
39	Jerry Rice	1.50
40	Ben Coates	.10
41	Reggie White	.25
42	Joey Galloway	1.25
43	Sean Dawkins	.10
44	Brett Favre	3.00
45	Jeff George	.10
46	Robert Smith	.10
47	Ken Dilger	.10
48	Larry Centers	.10
49	Jackie Harris	.10
50	Hugh Douglas	.10
51	Herschel Walker	.10
52	Kerry Collins	.30
53	Michael Irvin	.20
54	Willie McGinest	.10
55	Herman Moore	.20
56	Leroy Hoard	.10
57	Scott Mitchell	.10
58	Terrell Davis	1.50
59	Kevin Greene	.10
60	Yancey Thigpen	.20
61	Kevin Smith	.10
62	Trent Dilfer	.10
63	Cortez Kennedy	.10
64	Carnell Lake	.10
65	Quinn Early	.10
66	Kyle Brady	.10
67	Marshall Faulk	.30
68	Fred Barnett	.10
69	Quentin Coryatt	.10
70	Dan Marino	3.00
71	Junior Seau	.10
72	Andre Coleman	.10
73	Terry Kirby	.10
74	Curtis Martin	2.00
75	Isaac Bruce	.75
76	Mark Chmura	.10
77	Edgar Bennett	.10
78	Mario Bates	.10
79	Eric Zeier	.10
80	Adrian Murrell	.10
81	Mark Brunell	1.00
82	Mark Rypien	.10
83	Erric Pegram	.10
84	Bryan Cox	.10
85	Heath Shuler	.10
86	Lake Dawson	.10
87	O.J. McDuffie	.10
88	Emmitt Smith	3.00
89	Jim Harbaugh	.10
90	Aaron Bailey	.10
91	Jim Kelly	.20
92	Rodney Hampton	.10
93	Cris Carter	.10
94	Henry Ellard	.10
95	Darnay Scott	.20
96	Daryl Johnston	.10
97	Tamarick Vanover	.20
98	Jeff Blake	.75
99	Anthony Miller	.10
100	Darren Woodson	.10
101	Irving Fryar	.10
102	Craig Heyward	.10
103	Derek Loville	.10
104	Ernie Mills	.10
105	Brian Blades	.10
106	Gus Frerotte	.10
107	Alvin Harper	.10
108	Tyrone Wheatley	.10
109	John Elway	1.00
110	Charles Haley	.10
111	Terrell Fletcher	.10
112	Vincent Brisby	.10
113	Jerome Bettis	.20
114	Barry Sanders	1.50
115	Ken Norton Jr.	.10
116	Sherman Williams	.10
117	Antonio Freeman	.10
118	Bert Emanuel	.10
119	Marcus Allen	.20
120	Stan Humphries	.10
121	Chris Sanders	.10
122	Jeff Graham	.10
123	Jay Novacek	.10
124	Aeneas Williams	.10
125	Kordell Stewart	1.25
126	Steve Young	1.00
127	Jake Reed	.10
128	Rick Mirer	.10
129	Jeff Hostetler	.10
130	Tim Brown	.20
131	Shannon Sharpe	.10
132	Dave Brown	.10
133	Harvey Williams	.10
134	Rodney Thomas	.10
135	Frank Sanders	.10
136	Brett Perriman	.10

137	Steve Bono	.10
138	Steve Atwater	.10
139	Andre Rison	.10
140	Orlando Thomas	.10
141	Terry Allen	.10
142	Carl Pickens	.20
143	William Floyd	.10
144	Bryce Paup	.10
145	James Stewart	.10
146	Eric Bjornson	.10
147	Errict Rhett	.20
148	Darick Holmes	.10
149	Bill Brooks	.10
150	Brent Jones	.10
151	Natrone Means	.10
152	Rod Woodson	.10
153	Bruce Smith	.10
154	Deion Sanders	.75
155	Kevin Williams	.10
156	Erik Kramer	.10
157	Jim Everett	.10
158	Vinny Testaverde	.10
159	Boomer Esiason	.10
160	Floyd Turner	.10
161	Curtis Conway	.20
162	Thurman Thomas	.20
163	Tony Brackens	.10
164	Stepfret Williams	.10
165	Alex Van Dyke	.75
166	Cedric Jones	.10
167	Stanley Pritchett	.10
168	Willie Anderson	.10
169	Regan Upshaw	.10
170	Daryl Gardener	.10
171	Alex Molden	.10
172	John Mobley	.10
173	Danny Kanell	.50
174	Marco Battaglia	.10
175	Simeon Rice	.10
176	Tony Banks	.75
177	Stephen Davis	3.00
178	Walt Harris	.30
179	Amani Toomer	.30
180	Derrick Mayes	1.00
181	Jeff Lewis	.50
182	Chris Darkins	.10
183	Rickey Dudley	.75
184	Jonathan Ogden	.10
185	Mike Alstott	1.75
186	Eric Moulds	2.00
187	Karim Abdul-Jabbar	.75
188	Checklist	.10
189	Checklist	.10
190	Checklist	.10

1996 Leaf Press Proofs

The first 190 cards in 1996 Leaf Football were die-cut and printed in gold foil to form this Press Proof parallel set. Each Press Proof insert carried a 1 of 2,000 produced number.

	MT
Complete Set (190):	600.00
Press Proof Cards:	15x-30x

1996 Leaf Gold Leaf Rookies

Gold Leaf Rookies were numbered as an insert set, but are actually considered part of the base set. It features 10 rookies on a distinctly different design than base cards.

		MT
Complete Set (10):		40.00
Common Player:		3.00
1	Leeland McElroy	3.00
2	Marvin Harrison	6.00
3	Lawrence Phillips	4.00
4	Bobby Engram	3.00
5	Kevin Hardy	3.00
6	Keyshawn Johnson	5.00
7	Tim Biakabutuka	4.00
8	Eddie George	12.00
9	Terry Glenn	8.00

1996 Leaf American All-Stars

American All-Stars showcased 20 NFL players who were All-America selections in college. The cards were printed on a simulated sailcloth card stock that attempts to have the look and feel of an American flag. American All-Stars arrived in regular and Gold Team versions, with 5,000 regular sets and 1,000 Gold Team sets.

		MT
Complete Set (20):		300.00
Common Player:		4.00
1	Emmitt Smith	40.00
2	Drew Bledsoe	15.00
3	Jerry Rice	20.00
4	Kerry Collins	20.00
5	Eddie George	25.00
6	Keyshawn Johnson	15.00
7	Lawrence Phillips	4.00
8	Rashaan Salaam	4.00
9	Deion Sanders	15.00
10	Marshall Faulk	15.00
11	Steve Young	15.00
12	Ki-Jana Carter	4.00
13	Curtis Martin	30.00
14	Joey Galloway	18.00
15	Troy Aikman	20.00
16	Barry Sanders	30.00
17	Dan Marino	40.00
18	John Elway	15.00
19	Steve McNair	4.00
20	Tim Biakabutuka	4.00

1996 Leaf American All-Stars Gold

American All-Stars Gold featured the same 20 cards found in the All-Stars Silver set, but with upgraded cloth stock and gold enhancements. Gold versions are sequentially numbered up to 1,000.

	MT
Complete Set (20):	900.00
Gold Cards:	2x-3x

1996 Leaf Gold Leaf Stars

Fifteen of the top players in the NFL were included in Gold Leaf Stars. These were found in retail packs only and contain a 22kt. gold logo.

		MT
Complete Set (15):		550.00
Common Player:		10.00
1	Drew Bledsoe	30.00
2	Jerry Rice	40.00
3	Emmitt Smith	80.00
4	Dan Marino	80.00
5	Isaac Bruce	20.00
6	Kerry Collins	30.00
7	Barry Sanders	40.00
8	Keyshawn Johnson	30.00
9	Errict Rhett	10.00
10	Joey Galloway	20.00
11	Brett Favre	80.00
12	Curtis Martin	60.00
13	Steve Young	30.00
14	Troy Aikman	40.00
15	John Elway	20.00

1996 Leaf Grass Roots

Printed on a card stock that simulates artificial turf, Grass Roots highlighted 20 running backs that perform the best on artificial turf. This insert was limited to 5,000 sets produced.

		MT
Complete Set (20):		250.00
Common Player:		4.00
Minor Stars:		8.00
1	Thurman Thomas	8.00
2	Eddie George	25.00
3	Rodney Hampton	4.00
4	Rashaan Salaam	8.00
5	Natrone Means	4.00
6	Errict Rhett	8.00
7	Leeland McElroy	8.00
8	Emmitt Smith	40.00
9	Marshall Faulk	8.00
10	Ricky Watters	4.00
11	Chris Warren	4.00
12	Tim Biakabutuka	8.00
13	Barry Sanders	20.00
14	Karim Abdul-Jabbar	20.00
15	Darick Holmes	4.00
16	Terrell Davis	20.00
17	Lawrence Phillips	8.00
18	Ki-Jana Carter	8.00
19	Curtis Martin	30.00
20	Kordell Stewart	20.00

1996 Leaf Shirt Off My Back

Shirt Off My Back inserts were found only in special pre-priced retail packs. The cards were printed on stock that simulates jersey material and includes 10 of the top quarterbacks. Shirt Off My Back was limited to 2,500 sets.

		MT
Complete Set (10):		170.00
Common Player:		5.00
1	Steve Young	10.00
2	Jeff Blake	5.00
3	Drew Bledsoe	15.00
4	Kordell Stewart	10.00
5	Troy Aikman	15.00
6	Steve McNair	10.00
7	John Elway	25.00
8	Dan Marino	25.00
9	Kerry Collins	5.00
10	Brett Favre	30.00

1996 Leaf Statisical Standouts

Printed on simulated leather and inserted only in hobby packs, Statistical Standouts includes 15 top players. These cards have the feel of leather and are individually numbered to 2,500.

		MT
Complete Set (15):		425.00
Common Player:		10.00
1	John Elway	30.00
2	Jerry Rice	40.00
3	Reggie White	10.00
4	Drew Bledsoe	30.00
5	Chris Warren	10.00
6	Bruce Smith	10.00
7	Barry Sanders	40.00
8	Greg Lloyd	10.00
9	Emmitt Smith	80.00
10	Dan Marino	80.00
11	Steve Young	30.00
12	Steve Atwater	10.00
13	Isaac Bruce	20.00
14	Deion Sanders	20.00
15	Brett Favre	80.00

1996 Leaf Collector's Edition Autographs

This 12-card autographed set was found one per Collector's Edition factory sets from Leaf. The autographed cards all carry the words "Authentic Signature" on the front. Autographs of Leeland McElroy, Marvin Harrison, Lawrence Phillips, Bobby Engram and Eddie Kennison were printed on Gold Leaf Rookies inserts. Autographs of Tony Banks and Karim Abdul-Jabbar were on rookie subset cards, while the remaining autographs were found on regular-issue cards.

	MT
Complete Set (12):	200.00
Common Player:	10.00
Karim Abdul-Jabbar	15.00
Tony Banks	15.00
Isaac Bruce	20.00
Terrell Davis	75.00
Bobby Engram	10.00
Joey Galloway	20.00
Marvin Harrison	35.00
Eddie Kennison	10.00
Leeland McElroy	10.00
Lawrence Phillips	15.00
Rashaan Salaam	10.00
Tamarick Vanover	10.00

Post-1980 cards in Near Mint condition will generally sell for about 75% of the quoted Mint value. Excellent-condition cards bring no more than 40%.

1997 Leaf

Leaf Football is a 200-card set featuring a player action shot on the front and a close-up on the back. The backs also include the past season's statistics. The Fractal Matrix chase set makes its Leaf Football debut. This base set parallel features three different color schemes and three different die-cuts. The breakdown of die-cuts and colors is 100 X-Axis (5 gold/20 silver/75 bronze), 60 Y-Axis (10 gold/30 silver/20 bronze) and 40 Z-Axis (25 gold/10 silver/5 bronze). Inserts in this set include 1948 Leaf Reproductions, Lettermen, Run & Gun and Hardwear.

		MT
Complete Set (200):		35.00
Common Player:		.15
Minor Stars:		.30
Signature Proof Cards:		20x-40x
Signature Proof Rookies:		10x-20x
Production 200 Sets		
Wax Box:		60.00
1	Steve Young	1.00
2	Brett Favre	3.00
3	Barry Sanders	3.00
4	Drew Bledsoe	1.50
5	Troy Aikman	1.50
6	Kerry Collins	.30
7	Dan Marino	2.00
8	Jerry Rice	1.50
9	John Elway	1.50
10	Emmitt Smith	2.00
11	Tony Banks	.30
12	Gus Frerotte	.15
13	Elvis Grbac	.15
14	Neil O'Donnell	.15
15	Michael Irvin	.30
16	Marshall Faulk	.50
17	Todd Collins	.15
18	Scott Mitchell	.15
19	Trent Dilfer	.30
20	Rick Mirer	.15
21	Frank Sanders	.15
22	Larry Centers	.15
23	Brad Johnson	.30
24	Garrison Hearst	.30
25	Steve McNair	.75
26	Dorsey Levens	.30
27	Eric Metcalf	.15
28	Jeff George	.30
29	Rodney Hampton	.15
30	Michael Westbrook	.15
31	Cris Carter	.50
32	Heath Shuler	.15
33	Warren Moon	.30
34	Rod Woodson	.15
35	Ken Dilger	.15
36	Ben Coates	.15
37	Andre Reed	.15
38	Terrell Owens	.75
39	Jeff Blake	.30
40	Vinny Testaverde	.15
41	Robert Brooks	.15
42	Shannon Sharpe	.30
43	Terry Allen	.30
44	Terance Mathis	.15
45	Bobby Engram	.15
46	Rickey Dudley	.15
47	Alex Molden	.15
48	Lawrence Phillips	.15
49	Curtis Martin	.75
50	Jim Harbaugh	.30
51	Wayne Chrebet	.30
52	Quentin Coryatt	.15
53	Eddie George	1.50
54	Michael Jackson	.15
55	Greg Lloyd	.15
56	Natrone Means	.30
57	Marcus Allen	.30
58	Desmond Howard	.15
59	Stan Humphries	.30
60	Reggie White	.30
61	Brett Perriman	.15
62	Warren Sapp	.15
63	Adrian Murrell	.30
64	Mark Brunell	1.50
65	Carl Pickens	.30
66	Kordell Stewart	1.50
67	Ricky Watters	.30
68	Tyrone Wheatley	.15

#	Player	Price
69	Stanley Pritchett	.15
70	Kevin Greene	.15
71	Karim Abdul-Jabbar	.30
72	Ki-Jana Carter	.15
73	Rashaan Salaam	.15
74	Simeon Rice	.15
75	Napoleon Kaufman	.75
76	Muhsin Muhammad	.15
77	Bruce Smith	.15
78	Eric Moulds	.50
79	O.J. McDuffie	.15
80	Danny Kanell	.15
81	Harvey Williams	.15
82	Greg Hill	.15
83	Terrell Davis	2.00
84	Dan Wilkinson	.15
85	Yancey Thigpen	.15
86	Darrell Green	.15
87	Tamarick Vanover	.15
88	Mike Alstott	.50
89	Johnnie Morton	.15
90	Dale Carter	.15
91	Jerome Bettis	.30
92	James Stewart	.15
93	Irving Fryar	.15
94	Junior Seau	.30
95	Sean Dawkins	.15
96	J.J. Stokes	.30
97	Tim Biakabutuka	.30
98	Bert Emanuel	.15
99	Eddie Kennison	.30
100	Ray Zellars	.15
101	Dave Brown	.15
102	Leeland McElroy	.15
103	Chris Warren	.15
104	Bam Morris	.15
105	Thurman Thomas	.30
106	Kyle Brady	.15
107	Anthony Miller	.15
108	Derrick Thomas	.15
109	Mark Chmura	.30
110	Deion Sanders	.50
111	Eric Swann	.15
112	Amani Toomer	.15
113	Raymont Harris	.15
114	Jake Reed	.15
115	Bryant Young	.15
116	Keenan McCardell	.30
117	Herman Moore	.30
118	Errict Rhett	.15
119	Henry Ellard	.15
120	Bobby Hoying	.15
121	Robert Smith	.30
122	Keyshawn Johnson	.50
123	Zach Thomas	.30
124	Charlie Garner	.15
125	Terry Kirby	.15
126	Darren Woodson	.15
127	Darnay Scott	.15
128	Chris Sanders	.15
129	Charles Johnson	.15
130	Joey Galloway	.50
131	Curtis Conway	.30
132	Isaac Bruce	.30
133	Bobby Taylor	.15
134	Jamal Anderson	.75
135	Ken Norton	.15
136	Darick Holmes	.30
137	Tony Brackens	.15
138	Tony Martin	.15
139	Antonio Freeman	.75
140	Neil Smith	.15
141	Terry Glenn	.30
142	Marvin Harrison	.30
143	Daryl Johnston	.15
144	Tim Brown	.30
145	Kimble Anders	.15
146	Derrick Alexander	.15
147	LeShon Johnson	.15
148	Anthony Johnson	.15
149	Leslie Shepherd	.15
150	Chris T. Jones	.15
151	Edgar Bennett	.15
152	Ty Detmer	.15
153	*Ike Hilliard*	1.00
154	*Jim Druckenmiller*	1.50
155	*Warrick Dunn*	2.00
156	*Yatil Green*	.30
157	*Reidel Anthony*	1.50
158	*Antowain Smith*	1.50
159	*Rae Carruth*	.75
160	*Tiki Barber*	1.00
161	*Byron Hanspard*	.50
162	*Jake Plummer*	4.00
163	*Joey Kent*	.30
164	*Corey Dillon*	2.50
165	*Kevin Lockett*	.15
166	*Will Blackwell*	.30
167	*Troy Davis*	.30
168	*James Farrior*	.15
169	*Danny Wuerffel*	.75
170	*Pat Barnes*	.50
171	*Darnell Autry*	.30
172	*Tom Knight*	.15
173	*David LaFleur*	.30
174	*Tony Gonzalez*	.75
175	*Kenny Holmes*	.15
176	*Reinard Wilson*	.15
177	*Renaldo Wynn*	.15
178	*Bryant Westbrook*	.30
179	*Darrell Russell*	.30
180	*Orlando Pace*	.30
181	*Shawn Springs*	.30
182	*Peter Boulware*	.30
183	Dan Marino (Legacy)	1.00
184	Brett Favre (Legacy)	1.50
185	Emmitt Smith (Legacy)	1.00
186	Eddie George (Legacy)	.75
187	Curtis Martin (Legacy)	.50
188	Tim Brown (Legacy)	.15
189	Mark Brunell (Legacy)	.75
190	Isaac Bruce (Legacy)	.15
191	Deion Sanders (Legacy)	.30
192	John Elway (Legacy)	.75
193	Jerry Rice (Legacy)	.75
194	Barry Sanders (Legacy)	1.50
195	Herman Moore (Legacy)	.15
196	Carl Pickens (Legacy)	.15
197	Karim Abdul-Jabbar (Legacy)	.15
198	Drew Bledsoe CL	.75
199	Troy Aikman CL	.75
200	Terrell Davis CL	.75

1997 Leaf Fractal Matrix

This 200-card parallel features multi-fractured technology. Each card is done in one of three colors: bronze (100 cards), silver (60 cards) or gold (40 cards).

#	Player	MT
	Common Bronze X:	2.00
	Common Bronze Y:	1.50
	Common Bronze Z:	1.50
	Common Silver X:	6.00
	Common Silver Y:	5.00
	Common Silver Z:	4.00
1	Steve Young GZ	70.00
2	Brett Favre GX	500.00
3	Barry Sanders GZ	100.00
4	Drew Bledsoe GZ	100.00
5	Troy Aikman GZ	100.00
6	Kerry Collins GZ	85.00
7	Dan Marino GX	450.00
8	Jerry Rice GZ	100.00
9	John Elway GZ	70.00
10	Emmitt Smith GX	450.00
11	Tony Banks GY	50.00
12	Gus Frerotte SX	6.00
13	Elvis Grbac SX	6.00
14	Neil O'Donnell BX	2.00
15	Michael Irvin SY	7.00
16	Marshall Faulk SY	7.00
17	Todd Collins SX	6.00
18	Scott Mitchell BX	2.00
19	Trent Dilfer SY	5.00
20	Rick Mirer SX	6.00
21	Frank Sanders SX	6.00
22	Larry Centers BX	2.00
23	Brad Johnson SX	2.00
24	Garrison Hearst SY	5.00
25	Steve McNair GZ	85.00
26	Dorsey Levens BX	4.00
27	Eric Metcalf BX	2.00
28	Jeff George SX	6.00
29	Rodney Hampton BX	2.00
30	Michael Westbrook SY	5.00
31	Cris Carter SY	5.00
32	Heath Shuler SX	6.00
33	Warren Moon SX	2.00
34	Rod Woodson SX	6.00
35	Ken Dilger BX	2.00
36	Ben Coates BX	2.00
37	Andre Reed BX	2.00
38	Terrell Owens SZ	25.00
39	Jeff Blake SY	5.00
40	Vinny Testaverde BX	2.00
41	Robert Brooks SY	5.00
42	Shannon Sharpe SX	6.00
43	Terry Allen SY	5.00
44	Terance Mathis BX	2.00
45	Bobby Engram BZ	3.00
46	Rickey Dudley BX	2.00
47	Alex Molden BX	2.00
48	Lawrence Phillips SY	5.00
49	Curtis Martin GZ	100.00
50	Jim Harbaugh BX	2.00
51	Wayne Chrebet BX	2.00
52	Quentin Coryatt BX	2.00
53	Eddie George GX	325.00
54	Michael Jackson BX	2.00
55	Greg Lloyd BX	2.00
56	Natrone Means SZ	7.00
57	Marcus Allen GY	30.00
58	Desmond Howard BX	2.00
59	Stan Humphries BX	2.00
60	Reggie White GY	30.00
61	Brett Perriman SY	5.00
62	Warren Sapp BX	4.00
63	Adrian Murrell SZ	4.00
64	Mark Brunell BZ	100.00
65	Carl Pickens GY	5.00
66	Kordell Stewart GZ	100.00
67	Ricky Watters GY	30.00
68	Tyrone Wheatley BX	2.00
69	Stanley Pritchett BX	2.00
70	Kevin Greene BX	2.00
71	Karim Abdul-Jabbar GZ	85.00
72	Ki-Jana Carter SY	5.00
73	Rashaan Salaam SY	5.00
74	Simeon Rice BX	2.00
75	Napoleon Kaufman SY	5.00
76	Muhsin Muhammad SZ	4.00
77	Bruce Smith GY	5.00
78	Eric Moulds SX	6.00
79	O.J. McDuffie BX	2.00
80	Danny Kanell SY	1.50
81	Harvey Williams BX	1.50
82	Greg Hill SY	5.00
83	Terrell Davis GZ	100.00
84	Dan Wilkinson BX	2.00
85	Yancey Thigpen SY	5.00
86	Darrell Green BX	6.00
87	Tamarick Vanover SX	6.00
88	Mike Alstott BX	2.00
89	Johnnie Morton SX	6.00
90	Dale Carter BX	2.00
91	Jerome Bettis SZ	30.00
92	James Stewart BX	2.00
93	Irving Fryar SX	6.00
94	Junior Seau SY	5.00
95	Sean Dawkins BX	2.00
96	J.J. Stokes SZ	1.50
97	Tim Biakabutuka SY	2.00
98	Bert Emanuel BX	2.00
99	Eddie Kennison GY	50.00
100	Ray Zellars BX	2.00
101	Dave Brown BX	2.00
102	Leeland McElroy SY	5.00
103	Chris Warren SY	5.00
104	Bam Morris BX	2.00
105	Thurman Thomas GY	30.00
106	Kyle Brady BX	2.00
107	Anthony Miller GY	10.00
108	Derrick Thomas SY	5.00
109	Mark Chmura SY	5.00
110	Deion Sanders GZ	50.00
111	Eric Swann BX	2.00
112	Amani Toomer SY	6.00
113	Raymont Harris BX	2.00
114	Jake Reed BX	2.00
115	Bryant Young BX	2.00
116	Keenan McCardell SX	2.00
117	Herman Moore SY	20.00
118	Errict Rhett SZ	4.00
119	Henry Ellard BX	2.00
120	Bobby Hoying SX	6.00
121	Robert Smith BX	4.00
122	Keyshawn Johnson GZ	50.00
123	Zach Thomas BX	10.00
124	Charlie Garner BX	2.00
125	Terry Kirby BX	2.00
126	Darren Woodson BX	2.00
127	Darnay Scott SX	6.00
128	Chris Sanders SX	6.00
129	Charles Johnson SX	6.00
130	Joey Galloway SZ	8.00
131	Curtis Conway SY	8.00
132	Isaac Bruce GZ	20.00
133	Bobby Taylor SY	5.00
134	Jamal Anderson SY	5.00
135	Ken Norton BX	2.00
136	Darick Holmes BX	2.00
137	Tony Brackens BX	2.00
138	Tony Martin BX	2.00
139	Antonio Freeman SZ	15.00
140	Neil Smith BX	2.00
141	Terry Glenn SY	85.00
142	Marvin Harrison SY	25.00
143	Daryl Johnston SY	5.00
144	Tim Brown GY	10.00
145	Kimble Anders BX	2.00
146	Derrick Alexander SY	6.00
147	LeShon Johnson BX	2.00
148	Anthony Johnson BX	2.00
149	Leslie Shepherd BX	2.00
150	Chris T. Jones BX	2.00
151	Edgar Bennett BX	2.00
152	Ty Detmer BX	2.00
153	*Ike Hilliard GX*	100.00
154	*Jim Druckenmiller SZ*	30.00
155	*Warrick Dunn GZ*	100.00
156	*Yatil Green GZ*	20.00
157	*Reidel Anthony GZ*	30.00
158	*Antowain Smith GZ*	15.00
159	*Rae Carruth SY*	5.00
160	*Tiki Barber GZ*	30.00
161	*Byron Hanspard SZ*	10.00
162	*Jake Plummer SY*	15.00
163	*Joey Kent SZ*	10.00
164	*Corey Dillon SY*	25.00
165	*Kevin Lockett BZ*	3.00
166	*Will Blackwell BY*	6.00
167	*Troy Davis GZ*	25.00
168	*James Farrior BX*	4.00
169	*Danny Wuerffel SY*	15.00
170	*Pat Barnes SY*	10.00
171	*Darnell Autry SY*	10.00
172	*Tom Knight BY*	4.00
173	*David LaFleur BY*	10.00
174	*Tony Gonzalez SY*	10.00
175	*Kenny Holmes BX*	4.00
176	*Reinard Wilson BX*	4.00
177	*Renaldo Wynn BX*	4.00
178	*Bryant Westbrook BX*	4.00
179	*Darrell Russell BX*	4.00
180	*Orlando Pace BX*	6.00
181	*Shawn Springs BX*	4.00
182	*Peter Boulware BX*	4.00
183	Dan Marino BY (Legacy)	20.00
184	Brett Favre BY (Legacy)	25.00
185	Emmitt Smith BY (Legacy)	20.00
186	Eddie George BY (Legacy)	18.00
187	Curtis Martin BY (Legacy)	15.00
188	Tim Brown BZ (Legacy)	3.00
189	Mark Brunell BY (Legacy)	15.00
190	Isaac Bruce BY (Legacy)	3.00
191	Deion Sanders BY (Legacy)	6.00
192	John Elway BY (Legacy)	10.00
193	Jerry Rice BY (Legacy)	15.00
194	Barry Sanders BY (Legacy)	20.00
195	Herman Moore BY (Legacy)	3.00
196	Carl Pickens BY (Legacy)	3.00
197	Karim Abdul-Jabbar BY (Legacy)	10.00
198	Checklist (Drew Bledsoe BY)	15.00
199	Checklist (Troy Aikman BY)	15.00
200	Checklist (Terrell Davis BY)	15.00

1997 Leaf Fractal Matrix Die-Cuts

This insert adds die-cutting to the Fractal Matrix parallel. The breakdown of cards is 100 X-Axis (5 gold/20 silver/75 bronze), 60 Y-Axis (10 gold/30 silver/20 bronze) and 40 Z-Axis (25 gold/10 silver/5 bronze).

#	Player	MT
	Common X-Axis:	5.00
	Common Y-Axis:	8.00
	Common Z-Axis:	12.00
1	Steve Young GZ	100.00
2	Brett Favre GX	120.00
3	Barry Sanders GZ	150.00
4	Drew Bledsoe GZ	150.00
5	Troy Aikman GZ	150.00
6	Kerry Collins GZ	125.00
7	Dan Marino GX	100.00
8	Jerry Rice GZ	150.00
9	John Elway GZ	100.00
10	Emmitt Smith GX	100.00
11	Tony Banks GY	60.00
12	Gus Frerotte SX	5.00
13	Elvis Grbac SX	5.00
14	Neil O'Donnell BX	5.00
15	Michael Irvin SY	15.00
16	Marshall Faulk SY	15.00
17	Todd Collins SX	5.00
18	Scott Mitchell SX	5.00
19	Trent Dilfer SY	8.00
20	Rick Mirer SX	5.00
21	Frank Sanders SX	5.00
22	Larry Centers BX	5.00
23	Brad Johnson SX	5.00
24	Garrison Hearst SY	8.00
25	Steve McNair GZ	125.00
26	Dorsey Levens BX	5.00
27	Eric Metcalf BX	5.00
28	Jeff George SX	5.00
29	Rodney Hampton BX	5.00
30	Michael Westbrook SY	8.00
31	Cris Carter SY	8.00
32	Heath Shuler SX	5.00
33	Warren Moon SX	5.00
34	Rod Woodson SX	5.00
35	Ken Dilger BX	5.00
36	Ben Coates BX	5.00
37	Andre Reed BX	5.00
38	Terrell Owens SZ	75.00
39	Jeff Blake SY	15.00
40	Vinny Testaverde BX	5.00
41	Robert Brooks SY	10.00
42	Shannon Sharpe SX	5.00
43	Terry Allen SY	8.00
44	Terance Mathis BX	5.00
45	Bobby Engram BZ	25.00
46	Rickey Dudley BX	5.00
47	Alex Molden BX	5.00
48	Lawrence Phillips SY	8.00
49	Curtis Martin GZ	150.00
50	Jim Harbaugh BX	5.00
51	Wayne Chrebet BX	5.00
52	Quentin Coryatt BX	5.00
53	Eddie George GZ	75.00
54	Michael Jackson BX	5.00
55	Greg Lloyd BX	5.00
56	Natrone Means SZ	25.00
57	Marcus Allen GY	15.00
58	Desmond Howard BX	5.00
59	Stan Humphries BX	5.00
60	Reggie White GY	15.00
61	Brett Perriman SY	8.00
62	Warren Sapp BX	5.00
63	Adrian Murrell SZ	12.00
64	Mark Brunell GZ	150.00
65	Carl Pickens GY	15.00
66	Kordell Stewart GZ	150.00
67	Ricky Watters GY	15.00
68	Tyrone Wheatley BX	5.00
69	Stanley Pritchett BX	5.00
70	Kevin Greene BX	5.00
71	Karim Abdul-Jabbar GZ	100.00
72	Ki-Jana Carter SY	8.00
73	Rashaan Salaam SY	8.00
74	Simeon Rice BX	5.00
75	Napoleon Kaufman SY	15.00
76	Muhsin Muhammad SZ	12.00
77	Bruce Smith GY	8.00
78	Eric Moulds SX	5.00
79	O.J. McDuffie BX	5.00
80	Danny Kanell BZ	12.00
81	Harvey Williams BX	5.00
82	Greg Hill SY	8.00
83	Terrell Davis GZ	150.00
84	Dan Wilkinson BX	5.00
85	Yancey Thigpen SY	8.00
86	Darrell Green BX	5.00
87	Tamarick Vanover SX	5.00
88	Mike Alstott BX	5.00
89	Johnnie Morton SX	5.00
90	Dale Carter BX	5.00
91	Jerome Bettis GY	15.00
92	James Stewart BX	5.00
93	Irving Fryar SX	5.00
94	Junior Seau SY	5.00
95	Sean Dawkins BX	5.00
96	J.J. Stokes SZ	12.00
97	Tim Biakabutuka SY	5.00
98	Bert Emanuel BX	5.00
99	Eddie Kennison GY	60.00
100	Ray Zellars BX	5.00
101	Dave Brown BX	5.00
102	Leeland McElroy SY	8.00
103	Chris Warren SY	8.00
104	Bam Morris BX	5.00
105	Thurman Thomas GY	15.00
106	Kyle Brady BX	5.00
107	Anthony Miller GY	8.00
108	Derrick Thomas SY	5.00
109	Mark Chmura SY	5.00
110	Deion Sanders GZ	75.00
111	Eric Swann BX	5.00
112	Amani Toomer SX	5.00
113	Raymont Harris BX	5.00
114	Jake Reed BX	5.00
115	Bryant Young BX	5.00
116	Keenan McCardell SX	5.00
117	Herman Moore GZ	25.00
118	Errict Rhett SZ	25.00
119	Henry Ellard BX	5.00
120	Bobby Hoying SX	5.00
121	Robert Smith BX	5.00
122	Keyshawn Johnson GZ	75.00
123	Zach Thomas BX	20.00
124	Charlie Garner BX	5.00
125	Terry Kirby BX	5.00
126	Darren Woodson BX	5.00
127	Darnay Scott SY	5.00
128	Chris Sanders SY	8.00
129	Charles Johnson SX	5.00
130	Joey Galloway SY	25.00
131	Curtis Conway SY	8.00
132	Isaac Bruce GZ	25.00
133	Bobby Taylor BX	5.00
134	Jamal Anderson SY	8.00
135	Ken Norton BX	5.00
136	Darick Holmes BX	5.00
137	Tony Brackens BX	5.00
138	Tony Martin BX	5.00
139	Antonio Freeman SZ	60.00
140	Neil Smith BX	5.00
141	Terry Glenn GZ	130.00
142	Marvin Harrison SY	60.00
143	Daryl Johnston BX	5.00
144	Tim Brown SY	8.00
145	Kimble Anders BX	5.00
146	Derrick Alexander SX	5.00
147	LeShon Johnson BX	5.00
148	Anthony Johnson BX	5.00
149	Leslie Shepherd BX	5.00
150	Chris T. Jones BX	5.00
151	Edgar Bennett BX	5.00
152	Ty Detmer BX	5.00
153	*Ike Hilliard GX*	20.00
154	*Jim Druckenmiller SZ*	100.00
155	*Warrick Dunn GZ*	150.00
156	*Yatil Green GZ*	40.00
157	*Reidel Anthony GZ*	60.00
158	*Antowain Smith GZ*	70.00
159	*Rae Carruth SY*	30.00
160	*Tiki Barber GZ*	40.00
161	*Byron Hanspard SZ*	20.00
162	*Jake Plummer SY*	30.00
163	*Joey Kent SZ*	15.00
164	*Corey Dillon SY*	45.00
165	*Kevin Lockett BZ*	12.00
166	*Will Blackwell BY*	15.00
167	*Troy Davis SY*	40.00
168	*James Farrior BX*	5.00
169	*Danny Wuerffel SY*	60.00
170	*Pat Barnes SY*	20.00
171	*Darnell Autry SY*	15.00
172	*Tom Knight BX*	5.00
173	*David LaFleur BY*	20.00
174	*Tony Gonzalez BY*	20.00
175	*Kenny Holmes BX*	5.00
176	*Reinard Wilson BX*	5.00
177	*Renaldo Wynn BX*	5.00
178	*Bryant Westbrook BX*	5.00
179	*Darrell Russell BX*	5.00
180	*Orlando Pace BX*	10.00
181	*Shawn Springs BX*	5.00
182	*Peter Boulware BX*	5.00
183	Dan Marino BY (Legacy)	100.00
184	Brett Favre BY (Legacy)	100.00
185	Emmitt Smith BY (Legacy)	100.00
186	Eddie George BY (Legacy)	75.00
187	Curtis Martin BY (Legacy)	50.00
188	Tim Brown BZ (Legacy)	12.00
189	Mark Brunell BY (Legacy)	50.00
190	Isaac Bruce BY (Legacy)	15.00
191	Deion Sanders BY (Legacy)	25.00
192	John Elway BY (Legacy)	35.00
193	Jerry Rice BY (Legacy)	50.00
194	Barry Sanders BY (Legacy)	50.00
195	Herman Moore BY (Legacy)	8.00
196	Carl Pickens BY (Legacy)	8.00
197	Karim Abdul-Jabbar BY (Legacy)	40.00
198	Checklist (Drew Bledsoe BY)	50.00
199	Checklist (Troy Aikman BY)	50.00
200	Checklist (Terrell Davis BY)	50.00

Post-1980 cards in Near Mint condition will generally sell for about 75% of the quoted Mint value. Excellent-condition cards bring no more than 40%.

1997 Leaf Hardwear

Hardwear is a 20-card insert featuring top players on a plastic card. The cards are die-cut into a helmet-shaped design and sequentially numbered to 3,500.

		MT
Complete Set (20):		250.00
Common Player:		4.00
Minor Stars:		8.00
Production 3,500 Sets		
1	Dan Marino	25.00
2	Brett Favre	30.00
3	Emmitt Smith	25.00
4	Jerry Rice	15.00
5	Barry Sanders	30.00
6	Deion Sanders	8.00
7	Reggie White	8.00
8	Tim Brown	4.00
9	Steve McNair	8.00
10	Steve Young	12.00
11	Mark Brunell	15.00
12	Ricky Watters	4.00
13	Eddie Kennison	4.00
14	Kordell Stewart	12.00
15	Kerry Collins	4.00
16	Joey Galloway	8.00
17	Terrell Owens	10.00
18	Terry Glenn	8.00
19	Keyshawn Johnson	8.00
20	Eddie George	15.00

1997 Leaf Letterman

The cards in this 15-card insert look and feel like a college letter. The cards are also embossed and foil stamped. Each card is sequentially numbered to 1,000.

		MT
Complete Set (15):		500.00
Common Player:		15.00
Production 1,000 Sets		
1	Brett Favre	60.00
2	Emmitt Smith	45.00
3	Dan Marino	45.00
4	Jerry Rice	30.00
5	Mark Brunell	30.00
6	Barry Sanders	60.00
7	John Elway	30.00
8	Eddie George	30.00
9	Troy Aikman	30.00
10	Curtis Martin	20.00
11	Karim Abdul-Jabbar	15.00
12	Terrell Davis	45.00
13	Ike Hilliard	15.00
14	Yatil Green	15.00
15	Drew Bledsoe	30.00

1997 Leaf Run & Gun

This 18-card insert features a top quarterback/running back combo from the same team, one on each side of the card. One side features holographic foil stock and the other is foil stamped. The cards are numbered to 3,500.

		MT
Complete Set (18):		250.00
Common Player:		5.00
Minor Stars:		10.00
Production 3,500 Sets		
1	Dan Marino, Karim Abdul-Jabbar	25.00
2	Troy Aikman, Emmitt Smith	25.00
3	John Elway, Terrell Davis	40.00
4	Drew Bledsoe, Curtis Martin	20.00
5	Kordell Stewart, Jerome Bettis	20.00
6	Mark Brunell, Natrone Means	15.00
7	Kerry Collins, Tim Biakabutuka	10.00
8	Rick Mirer, Rashaan Salaam	5.00
9	Scott Mitchell, Barry Sanders	30.00
10	Steve McNair, Eddie George	15.00
11	Trent Dilfer, Warrick Dunn	15.00
12	Jeff Blake, Ki-Jana Carter	5.00
13	Tony Banks, Lawrence Phillips	10.00
14	Steve Young, Garrison Hearst	15.00
15	Jim Harbaugh, Marshall Faulk	10.00
16	Elvis Grbac, Marcus Allen	5.00
17	Neil O'Donnell, Adrian Murrell	5.00
18	Gus Frerotte, Terry Allen	5.00

1997 Leaf Reproductions

Twelve current and 12 former NFL stars are featured in this 24-card set. The cards are a reproduction of Leaf's 1948 set design. The first 500 cards of each former great are autographed. Each insert card is numbered to 1,948.

		MT
Complete Set (24):		375.00
Common Player:		7.00
Minor Stars:		14.00
Production 1,948 Sets		
Complete Autograph Set (11):		300.00
Common Autograph (13-24):		20.00
Minor Autograph Stars:		40.00
Production 500 Sets		
1	Emmitt Smith	30.00
2	Brett Favre	40.00
3	Dan Marino	30.00
4	Barry Sanders	40.00
5	Jerry Rice	20.00
6	Terrell Davis	30.00
7	Curtis Martin	14.00
8	Troy Aikman	20.00
9	Drew Bledsoe	20.00
10	Herman Moore	7.00
11	Isaac Bruce	7.00
12	Carl Pickens	7.00
13	Len Dawson	14.00
14	Dan Fouts	14.00
15	Jim Plunkett	7.00
16	Ken Stabler	14.00
17	Joe Theismann	14.00
18	Billy Kilmer	14.00
19	Danny White	14.00
20	Archie Manning	7.00
21	Ron Jaworski	7.00
22	Y.A. Tittle	14.00
23	Sid Luckman	14.00
23a	Sid Luckman AUTO	180.00

1997 Leaf Signature

Leaf Signature Football consisted of 118 8" x 10" cards that featured top established players and rookies. The card fronts feature a large color shot of the player, with a large off-color oval taking up the bottom portion. The player's name is stamped in silver foil above this oval, with a Leaf '97 Football logo in silver and black above that. The backs are horizontal and unnumbered and contain a large close-up shot of the player on the left side with a brief biography on the right. Most of the players also arrive in an autographed version, which have "Authentic Signature" printed in black across the bottom. Also included in packs were Old School Draft Autographs, which featured 11 retired quarterbacks.

		MT
Complete Set (118):		150.00
Common Player:		.50
Minor Stars:		1.00
Wax Box:		100.00
1	Karim Abdul-Jabbar	2.00
2	Troy Aikman	5.00
3	Derrick Alexander	.50
4	Terry Allen	1.00
5	Mike Alstott	2.00
6	Jamal Anderson	3.00
7	Reidel Anthony	2.50
8	Darnell Autry	1.00
9	Tony Banks	1.00
10	Tiki Barber	1.00
11	Pat Barnes	1.00
12	Jerome Bettis	1.00
13	Tim Biakabutuka	1.00
14	Will Blackwell	1.00
15	Jeff Blake	1.00
16	Drew Bledsoe	5.00
17	Peter Boulware	.50
18	Robert Brooks	.50
19	Dave Brown	.50
20	Tim Brown	1.00
21	Isaac Bruce	1.00
22	Mark Brunell	5.00
23	Rae Carruth	2.00
24	Cris Carter	2.00
25	Ki-Jana Carter	.50
26	Larry Centers	.50
27	Ben Coates	1.00
28	Kerry Collins	1.00
29	Todd Collins	.50
30	Albert Connell	.50
31	Curtis Conway	1.00
32	Terrell Davis	8.00
33	Troy Davis	1.00
34	Trent Dilfer	2.00
35	Corey Dillon	6.00
36	Jim Druckenmiller	5.00
37	Warrick Dunn	10.00
38	John Elway	5.00
39	Bert Emmanuel	.50
40	Bobby Engram	.50
41	Boomer Esiason	.50
42	Jim Everett	.50
43	Marshall Faulk	2.00
44	Brett Favre	10.00
45	Antonio Freeman	2.00
46	Gus Frerotte	.50
47	Irving Fryar	.50
48	Joey Galloway	2.00
49	Eddie George	6.00
50	Jeff George	1.00
51	Tony Gonzalez	2.00
52	Jay Graham	1.00
53	Elvis Grbac	1.00
54	Darrell Green	.50
55	Yatil Green	1.00
56	Rodney Hampton	.50
57	Byron Hanspard	2.00
58	Jim Harbaugh	1.00
59	Marvin Harrison	1.00
60	Garrison Hearst	2.00
61	Greg Hill	.50
62	Ike Hilliard	2.00
63	Jeff Hostetler	.50
64	Brad Johnson	2.00
65	Keyshawn Johnson	2.00
66	Darryl Johnston	.50
67	Napoleon Kaufman	3.00
68	Jim Kelly	1.00
69	Eddie Kennison	1.00
70	Joey Kent	1.00
71	Bernie Kosar	.50
72	Eric Kramer	.50
73	Dorsey Levens	1.00
74	Kevin Lockett	.50
75	Dan Marino	8.00
76	Curtis Martin	4.00
77	Tony Martin	.50
78	Leeland McElroy	.50
79	Steve McNair	4.00
80	Natrone Means	1.00
81	Eric Metcalf	.50
82	Anthony Miller	.50
83	Rick Mirer	.50
84	Scott Mitchell	.50
85	Warren Moon	1.00
86	Herman Moore	1.00
87	Muhsin Muhammad	.50
88	Adrian Murrell	1.00
89	Neil O'Donnell	.50
90	Terrell Owens	3.00
91	Brett Perrimon	.50
92	Lawrence Phillips	.50
93	Jake Plummer	10.00
94	Andre Reed	.50
95	Jerry Rice	5.00
96	Darrell Russell	.50
97	Rashaan Salaam	.50
98	Barry Sanders	10.00
99	Deion Sanders	2.00
100	Frank Sanders	.50
101	Chris Sanders	.50
102	Junior Seau	.50
103	Darnay Scott	.50
104	Shannon Sharpe	1.00
105	Sedrick Shaw	.50
106	Heath Shuler	.50
107	Antowain Smith	5.00
108	Bruce Smith	.50
109	Emmitt Smith	8.00
110	Kordell Stewart	5.00
111	J.J. Stokes	1.00
112	Vinny Testaverde	1.00
113	Thurman Thomas	1.00
114	Tamarick Vanover	.50
115	Herschel Walker	.50
116	Michael Westbrook	.50
117	Danny Wuerffel	2.00
118	Steve Young	3.50

1997 Leaf Signature Autographs

All but 11 of the players included in Leaf Signature Series Football signed cards for the product. Signature cards are identified by the player's autograph, usually found in the large, off-color oval part of the card and the words "Authentic Signature" in black letters across the bottom. Signature cards were inserted at a rate of one per pack. Included below with the player listing is the number of cards that was reported that each player signed.

		MT
Common Player:		10.00
Minor Stars:		20.00
First Down Markers:		2x
Karim Abdul-Jabbar 2500		30.00
Derrick Alexander 4000		10.00
Terry Allen 3000		20.00
Mike Alstott 4000		30.00
Jamal Anderson 4000		20.00
Reidel Anthony 2000		30.00
Darnell Autry 4000		20.00
Tony Banks 500		45.00
Tiki Barber 4000		30.00
Pat Barnes 4000		20.00
Jerome Bettis 500		60.00
Tim Biakabutuka 3000		20.00
Will Blackwell 2500		20.00
Jeff Blake 500		45.00
Drew Bledsoe 500		150.00
Peter Boulware 4000		10.00
Robert Brooks 1000		30.00
Dave Brown 500		40.00
Tim Brown 2500		30.00
Isaac Bruce 2500		30.00
Mark Brunell 500		150.00
Rae Carruth 5000		20.00
Cris Carter 2500		20.00
Larry Centers 4000		10.00
Ben Coates 4000		10.00
Todd Collins 4000		10.00
Albert Connell 4000		10.00
Curtis Conway 3000		20.00
Terrell Davis 2500		100.00
Troy Davis 4000		20.00
Trent Dilfer 500		60.00
Corey Dillon 4000		60.00
Jim Druckenmiller 5000		50.00
Warrick Dunn 2000		120.00
John Elway 500		150.00
Bert Emmanuel 4000		10.00
Bobby Engram 3000		10.00
Boomer Esiason 500		50.00
Jim Everett 500		40.00
Marshall Faulk 3000		
Antonio Freeman 2000		30.00
Gus Frerotte 500		40.00
Irving Fryar 3000		10.00
Joey Galloway 3000		30.00
Eddie George 300		180.00
Jeff George 300		40.00
Tony Gonzalez 3500		20.00
Jay Graham 1000		30.00
Elvis Grbac 500		40.00
Darrell Green 2500		10.00

		MT
Yatil Green 5000		30.00
Rodney Hampton 4000		10.00
Byron Hanspard 4000		20.00
Jim Harbaugh 500		40.00
Marvin Harrison 3000		30.00
Garrison Hearst 4000		10.00
Greg Hill 4000		10.00
Ike Hilliard 2000		20.00
Jeff Hostetler 500		20.00
Brad Johnson 2000		20.00
Keyshawn Johnson 900		45.00
Darryl Johnston 10.00		
Jim Kelly 500		75.00
Eddie Kennison 3000		20.00
Joey Kent 4000		10.00
Bernie Kosar 500		40.00
Eric Kramer 500		40.00
Dorsey Levens 3000		30.00
Kevin Lockett 4000		10.00
Tony Martin 4000		10.00
Leeland McElroy 4000		10.00
Natrone Means 4000		20.00
Eric Metcalf 4000		10.00
Anthony Miller 3000		10.00
Rick Mirer 4000		10.00
Scott Mitchell 500		40.00
Warren Moon 500		50.00
Herman Moore 2500		20.00
Muhsin Muhammad 3000		10.00
Adrian Murrell 3000		20.00
Neil O'Donnell 500		40.00
Terrell Owens 3000		30.00
Brett Perriman 700		40.00
Lawrence Phillips 750		40.00
Jake Plummer 5000		60.00
Andre Reed 3000		10.00
Darrell Russell 2000		20.00
Rashaan Salaam 3000		10.00
Frank Sanders 3000		10.00
Chris Sanders 3000		10.00
Junior Seau 500		40.00
Darnay Scott 2000		30.00
Shannon Sharpe 1000		
Sedrick Shaw 4000		20.00
Heath Shuler 500		40.00
Antowain Smith 5000		50.00
Kordell Stewart 500		150.00
J.J. Stokes 3000		10.00
Vinny Testaverde 250		80.00
Thurman Thomas 2500		20.00
Tamarick Vanover 4000		10.00
Herschel Walker 3000		10.00
Michael Westbrook 3000		10.00
Danny Wuerffel 3000		20.00
Steve Young 500		150.00

1997 Leaf Signature Old School Drafts Autographs

Old School Drafts Autographs included 11 former quarterbacks on 8" x 10" cards. The cards feature the insert name in large bold letters across the top and are individually numbered to 1,000. Card No. 10 is not available.

		MT
Complete Set (11):		500.00
Common Player:		25.00

Card #10 not included		
1	Joe Theismann	50.00
2	Archie Manning	50.00
3	Len Dawson	50.00
4	Sammy Baugh	120.00
5	Dan Fouts	75.00
6	Danny White	50.00
7	Ron Jaworski	25.00
8	Jim Plunkett	25.00
9	Y.A. Tittle	85.00
10	N/A	
11	Ken Stabler	85.00
12	Billy Kilmer	25.00

1998 Leaf Rookies & Stars

This is the first Leaf product released under Playoff. The 300-card set includes short-printed cards of 70 rookies and 30 Power Tools inserted 1:2 packs. Two parallel sets with the True Blue singles sequentially numbered to 500 and the Longevity parallel numbered to 50. The product also includes 13 other sequentially numbered inserts.

		MT
Complete Set (300):		450.00
Common Player:		.15
Minor Stars:		.30
Common Rookie (171-240):		2.00
Common Power Tool (241-270):		2.00
Inserted 1:2		
Longevity Cards:		50x-100x
Longevity Rookies:		2x
Longevity PT Cards:		10x-20x
Longevity PT Rookies:		2x-4x
Production 50 Sets		
True Blue Cards:		7x-14x
True Blue Rookies:		1x
True Blue PT:		2x
Production 500 Sets		
Wax Box:		100.00
1	Keyshawn Johnson	.50
2	Marvin Harrison	.30
3	Eddie Kennison	.15
4	Bryant Young	.15
5	Darren Woodson	.15
6	Tyrone Wheatley	.15
7	Michael Westbrook	.15
8	Charles Way	.15
9	Ricky Watters	.30
10	Chris Warren	.15
11	Wesley Walls	.15
12	Tamarick Vanover	.15
13	Zach Thomas	.30
14	Derrick Thomas	.15
15	Yancey Thigpen	.15
16	Vinny Testaverde	.30
17	Dana Stubblefield	.15
18	J.J. Stokes	.30
19	James Stewart	.15
20	Jeff George	.30
21	John Randle	.15
22	Gary Brown	.15
23	Ed McCaffrey	.30
24	James Jett	.15
25	Rob Johnson	.30
26	Daryl Johnston	.15
27	Jermaine Lewis	.15
28	Tony Martin	.15
29	Derrick Mayes	.15
30	Keenan McCardell	.30
31	O.J. McDuffie	.30
32	Chris Chandler	.30
33	Doug Flutie	.75
34	Scott Mitchell	.30
35	Warren Moon	.30
36	Rob Moore	.30
37	Johnnie Morton	.15
38	Neil O'Donnell	.15
39	Rich Gannon	.15
40	Andre Reed	.15
41	Jake Reed	.15
42	Errict Rhett	.15
43	Simeon Rice	.15
44	Andre Rison	.30
45	Eric Moulds	.30
46	Frank Sanders	.15
47	Darnay Scott	.15
48	Junior Seau	.30
49	Shannon Sharpe	.30

50	Bruce Smith	.15
51	Jimmy Smith	.30
52	Robert Smith	.30
53	Derrick Alexander	.15
54	Kimble Anders	.15
55	Jamal Anderson	.75
56	Mario Bates	.15
57	Edgar Bennett	.15
58	Tim Biakabutuka	.15
59	Ki-Jana Carter	.15
60	Larry Centers	.15
61	Mark Chmura	.30
62	Wayne Chrebet	.30
63	Ben Coates	.30
64	Curtis Conway	.30
65	Randall Cunningham	.75
66	Rickey Dudley	.15
67	Bert Emanuel	.15
68	Bobby Engram	.15
69	William Floyd	.15
70	Irving Fryar	.15
71	Elvis Grbac	.15
72	Kevin Greene	.15
73	Jim Harbaugh	.30
74	Raymont Harris	.15
75	Garrison Hearst	.50
76	Greg Hill	.15
77	Desmond Howard	.15
78	Bobby Hoying	.30
79	Michael Jackson	.15
80	Terry Allen	.30
81	Jerome Bettis	.30
82	Jeff Blake	.30
83	Robert Brooks	.30
84	Tim Brown	.30
85	Isaac Bruce	.30
86	Cris Carter	.50
87	Ty Detmer	.30
88	Trent Dilfer	.30
89	Marshall Faulk	.50
90	Antonio Freeman	.75
91	Gus Frerotte	.30
92	Joey Galloway	.50
93	Michael Irvin	.50
94	Brad Johnson	.50
95	Danny Kanell	.15
96	Napoleon Kaufman	.50
97	Dorsey Levens	.50
98	Natrone Means	.50
99	Herman Moore	.50
100	Adrian Murrell	.30
101	Carl Pickens	.30
102	Rod Smith	.30
103	Thurman Thomas	.30
104	Reggie White	.50
105	Jim Druckenmiller	.30
106	Antowain Smith	.50
107	Reidel Anthony	.30
108	Ike Hilliard	.15
109	Rae Carruth	.15
110	Troy Davis	.15
111	Terrance Mathis	.15
112	Brett Favre	3.00
113	Dan Marino	2.00
114	Emmitt Smith	2.00
115	Barry Sanders	3.00
116	Eddie George	1.25
117	Drew Bledsoe	1.25
118	Troy Aikman	1.50
119	Terrell Davis	2.50
120	John Elway	1.75
121	Mark Brunell	1.25
122	Jerry Rice	1.50
123	Kordell Stewart	1.25
124	Steve McNair	.75
125	Curtis Martin	.75
126	Steve Young	1.00
127	Kerry Collins	.50
128	Terry Glenn	.50
129	Deion Sanders	.50
130	Mike Alstott	.50
131	Tony Banks	.50
132	Karim Abdul-Jabbar	.50
133	Terrell Owens	.75
134	Yatil Green	.30
135	Tony Gonzalez	.30
136	Byron Hanspard	.30
137	David LaFleur	.30
138	Danny Wuerffel	.30
139	Tiki Barber	.30
140	Peter Boulware	.15
141	Will Blackwell	.15
142	Warrick Dunn	1.00
143	Corey Dillon	.75
144	Jake Plummer	1.25
145	Neil Smith	.15
146	Charles Johnson	.30
147	Fred Lane	.30
148	Dan Wilkinson	.15
149	Ken Norton Jr.	.15
150	Stephen Davis	.15
151	Gilbert Brown	.15
152	Kenny Bynum	.15
153	Derrick Cullors	.15
154	Charlie Garner	.15
155	Jeff Graham	.15
156	Warren Sapp	.15
157	Jerald Moore	.15
158	Sean Dawkins	.15
159	Charlie Jones	.15
160	Kevin Lockett	.15
161	James McKnight	.15
162	Chris Penn	.15
163	Leslie Shepherd	.15
164	Karl Williams	.15
165	Mark Bruener	.15
166	Ernie Conwell	.15
167	Ken Dilger	.15
168	Troy Drayton	.15
169	Freddie Jones	.15
170	Dale Carter	.15
171	Charles Woodson	20.00
172	Alonzo Mayes	2.00
173	Andre Wadsworth	6.00
174	Grant Winstrom	4.00
175	Greg Ellis	6.00
176	Chris Howard	2.00
177	Keith Brooking	4.00
178	Takeo Spikes	6.00
179	Anthony Simmons	4.00
180	Brian Simmons	4.00
181	Sam Cowart	2.00
182	Ken Oxendine	4.00
183	Vonnie Holliday	6.00
184	Terry Fair	4.00
185	Shaun Williams	4.00
186	Tremayne Stephens	2.00
187	Duane Starks	6.00
188	Jason Peter	4.00
189	Tebucky Jones	2.00
190	Donovin Darius	2.00
191	R.W. McQuarters	4.00
192	Corey Chavous	4.00
193	Cameron Cleeland	8.00
194	Stephen Alexander	6.00
195	Rod Rutledge	2.00
196	Scott Frost	2.00
197	Fred Beasley	2.00
198	Dorian Boose	2.00
199	Randy Moss	80.00
200	Jacquez Green	15.00
201	Marcus Nash	15.00
202	Hines Ward	8.00
203	Kevin Dyson	15.00
204	E.G. Green	10.00
205	Germane Crowell	8.00
206	Joe Jurevicius	8.00
207	Tony Simmons	15.00
208	Tim Dwight	15.00
209	Az-Zahir Hakim	12.00
210	Jerome Pathon	8.00
211	Patrick Johnson	8.00
212	Mikhael Ricks	8.00
213	Donald Hayes	4.00
214	Jammi German	4.00
215	Larry Shannon	2.00
216	Brian Alford	4.00
217	Curtis Enis	15.00
218	Fred Taylor	40.00
219	Robert Edwards	15.00
220	Ahman Green	12.00
221	Tavian Banks	8.00
222	Skip Hicks	12.00
223	Robert Holcombe	8.00
224	John Avery	8.00
225	Chris Fuamatu-Ma'afala	8.00
226	Michael Pittman	6.00
227	Rashaan Shehee	6.00
228	Jonathon Linton	8.00
229	Jon Ritchie	4.00
230	Chris Floyd	2.00
231	Wilmont Perry	2.00
232	Raymond Priester	2.00
233	Peyton Manning	80.00
234	Ryan Leaf	15.00
235	Brian Griese	25.00
236	Jeff Ogden	4.00
237	Charlie Batch	30.00
238	Moses Moreno	4.00
239	Jonathan Quinn	6.00
240	Flozell Adams	2.00
241	Brett Favre PT	14.00
242	Dan Marino PT	10.00
243	Emmitt Smith PT	10.00
244	Barry Sanders PT	14.00
245	Eddie George PT	8.00
246	Drew Bledsoe PT	6.00
247	Troy Aikman PT	7.00
248	Terrell Davis PT	12.00
249	John Elway PT	8.00
250	Carl Pickens PT	2.00
251	Jerry Rice PT	7.00
252	Kordell Stewart PT	6.00
253	Steve McNair PT	4.00
254	Curtis Martin PT	5.00
255	Steve Young PT	5.00
256	Herman Moore PT	2.00
257	Dorsey Levens PT	2.00
258	Deion Sanders PT	3.00
259	Napoleon Kaufman PT	2.00
260	Warrick Dunn PT	5.00
261	Corey Dillon PT	4.00
262	Jerome Bettis PT	2.00
263	Tim Brown PT	2.00
264	Cris Carter PT	3.00
265	Antonio Freeman PT	3.00
266	Randy Moss PT	45.00
267	Curtis Enis PT	7.00
268	Fred Taylor PT	20.00
269	Robert Edwards PT	8.00
270	Peyton Manning PT	25.00
271	Barry Sanders TL	1.50
272	Eddie George TL	.50
273	Troy Aikman TL	.75
274	Mark Brunell TL	.50
275	Kordell Stewart TL	.50
276	Kerry Collins TL	.15
277	Terry Glenn TL	.30
278	Mike Alstott TL	.30
279	Tony Banks TL	.15
280	Karim Abdul TL	.30
281	Terrell Owens TL	.40
282	Byron Hanspard TL	.15
283	Jake Plummer TL	.50
284	Terry Allen TL	.15
285	Jeff Blake TL	.15
286	Brad Johnson TL	.30
287	Danny Kanell TL	.15
288	Natrone Means TL	.30
289	Rod Smith TL	.15
290	Thurman Thomas TL	.15
291	Reggie White TL	.30
292	Troy Davis TL	.15
293	Curtis Conway TL	.15
294	Irving Fryar TL	.15
295	Jim Harbaugh TL	.15
296	Andre Rison TL	.15
297	Ricky Watters TL	.15
298	Keyshawn Johnson TL	.30
299	Jeff George TL	.15
300	Marshall Faulk TL	.30

A card number in parentheses ( ) indicates the set is unnumbered.

1998 Leaf Rookies & Stars Extreme Measures

This 10-card set takes the top players in the game and highlights an outstanding but extreme statistic for each. These cards are each printed on foil board and sequentially numbered to 1,000.

		MT
	Complete Set (10):	135.00
	Common Player:	5.00
1	Barry Sanders/918	30.00
2	Mark Brunell/941	10.00
3	Barry Sanders/930	5.00
4	John Elway/419	35.00
5	Jerry Rice/929	15.00
6	Kordell Stewart/972	10.00
7	Steve McNair/191	30.00
8	Deion Sanders/888	20.00
9	Jake Plummer/615	25.00
10	Steve Young/965	30.00

1998 Leaf Rookies & Stars Crosstraining

Each card in this 10-card set highlights the same player on front and back, demonstrating the different skills that make them great. All cards are printed on foil board and are sequentially numbered to 1,000.

		MT
	Complete Set (10):	85.00
	Common Player:	6.00
	Production 1,000 Sets	
1	Brett Favre	30.00
2	Mark Brunell	12.00
3	Barry Sanders	30.00
4	John Elway	20.00
5	Jerry Rice	15.00
6	Kordell Stewart	12.00
7	Steve McNair	6.00
8	Deion Sanders	6.00
9	Jake Plummer	12.00
10	Steve Young	10.00

1998 Leaf Rookies & Stars Crusade

The 30-card set includes both stars and rookies from '98. Each of the Green singles are sequentially numbered to 250. A parallel Purple set is numbered to 100 and a parallel Red set is numbered to 25.

		MT
	Complete Set (30):	650.00
	Common Player:	10.00
	Production 250 Sets	
	Purple Cards:	2x
	Production 100 Sets	
	Red Cards:	2x-4x
	Production 25 Sets	
1	Brett Favre	60.00
2	Dan Marino	45.00
3	Emmitt Smith	45.00
4	Barry Sanders	60.00
5	Eddie George	25.00
6	Drew Bledsoe	25.00
7	Troy Aikman	30.00
8	Terrell Davis	50.00
9	John Elway	40.00
10	Mark Brunell	25.00
11	Jerry Rice	30.00
12	Kordell Stewart	25.00
13	Steve McNair	10.00
14	Curtis Martin	10.00
16	Steve Young	20.00
18	Deion Sanders	10.00
22	Terrell Owens	10.00
23	Jamal Anderson	10.00
25	Jerome Bettis	10.00
30	Cris Carter	10.00
32	Marshall Faulk	10.00
40	Antonio Freeman	10.00
40	Dorsey Levens	10.00
49	Garrison Hearst	10.00
57	Warrick Dunn	20.00
59	Jake Plummer	25.00
66	Peyton Manning	50.00
69	Randy Moss	100.00
77	Fred Taylor	45.00
78	Robert Edwards	20.00

1998 Leaf Rookies & Stars Extreme Measures Die Cuts

Each single in this set is sequentially numbered to a stat that was picked by the manufacturer. Each player in this set has a different amount of cards printed. Cards are identical to their Extreme Measures card except for being die cut in this set.

		MT
	Complete Set (10):	725.00
	Common Player:	15.00
1	Barry Sanders/82	150.00
2	Warrick Dunn/59	60.00
3	Curtis Martin/70	35.00
4	Terrell Davis/581	25.00
5	Troy Aikman/71	75.00
6	Drew Bledsoe/28	175.00
7	Eddie George/809	15.00
8	Emmitt Smith/112	100.00
9	Dan Marino/385	50.00
10	Brett Favre/35	300.00

1998 Leaf Rookies & Stars Freshman Orientation

This 20-card set not only features the future stars of the game, but also highlights which round and overall number each player was selected in the NFL draft. Each card is sequentially numbered to 2,500 and printed on holographic foil.

	MT
Complete Set (20):	100.00

1998 Leaf Rookies & Stars Game Plan

Each card in this inside the game set is printed on foil board and sequentially numbered to 5,000. The first 500 of each card is treated with a "Master Game Plan" logo and unique color coating.

		MT
	Complete Set (20):	45.00
	Common Player:	1.50
	Minor Stars:	3.00
	Production 5,000 Sets	
	Master Cards:	3x
	Production First 500 Sets	
1	Ryan Leaf	5.00
2	Peyton Manning	12.00
3	Brett Favre	8.00
4	Mark Brunell	4.00
5	Isaac Bruce	3.00
6	Dan Marino	6.00
7	Jerry Rice	4.00
8	Cris Carter	3.00
9	Emmitt Smith	6.00
10	Kordell Stewart	4.00
11	Corey Dillon	3.00
12	Barry Sanders	8.00
13	Curtis Martin	3.00
14	Carl Pickens	1.50
15	Eddie George	4.00
16	Warrick Dunn	3.00
17	Jake Plummer	4.00
18	Curtis Enis	4.00
19	Drew Bledsoe	4.00
20	Terrell Davis	6.00

1998 Leaf Rookies & Stars Great American Heroes

The theme to this insert is players that have helped make the great American game of football. Each card in this set is stamped with holographic foil and sequentially numbered to 2,500.

		MT
	Complete Set (20):	85.00
	Common Player:	2.00
	Minor Stars:	4.00
	Production 2,500 Sets	
1	Brett Favre	12.00
2	Dan Marino	8.00
3	Emmitt Smith	8.00
4	Barry Sanders	12.00
5	Eddie George	5.00
6	Drew Bledsoe	5.00
7	Troy Aikman	6.00
8	Terrell Davis	10.00
9	John Elway	7.00
10	Mark Brunell	5.00
11	Jerry Rice	6.00
12	Kordell Stewart	5.00
13	Steve McNair	4.00
14	Curtis Martin	4.00
15	Steve Young	4.00
16	Dorsey Levens	2.00
17	Herman Moore	2.00
18	Deion Sanders	2.00
19	Thurman Thomas	2.00
20	Peyton Manning	18.00

1998 Leaf Rookies & Stars Greatest Hits

The top 20 players in the NFL are included in this insert and each card is sequentially numbered to 2,500.

		MT
	Complete Set (20):	85.00
	Common Player:	2.00
	Minor Stars:	4.00
	Production 2,500 Sets	
1	Brett Favre	12.00
2	Eddie George	5.00
3	John Elway	7.00
4	Steve Young	4.00
5	Napoleon Kaufman	2.00
6	Dan Marino	8.00
7	Drew Bledsoe	5.00
8	Mark Brunell	5.00
9	Warrick Dunn	4.00
10	Dorsey Levens	2.00
11	Emmitt Smith	8.00
12	Troy Aikman	6.00
13	Jerry Rice	6.00
14	Jake Plummer	5.00
15	Herman Moore	2.00
16	Barry Sanders	12.00
17	Terrell Davis	10.00
18	Kordell Stewart	5.00
19	Jerome Bettis	2.00
20	Isaac Bruce	2.00

1998 Leaf Rookies & Stars MVP Contenders

The set is made up of 20 of the league's top players who will contend for the MVP award. Each card is accented with holographic foil stamping and sequentially numbered to 2,500.

		MT
Complete Set (20):		85.00
Common Player:		2.00
Minor Stars:		4.00
Production 2,500 Sets		
1	Tim Brown	2.00
2	Herman Moore	2.00
3	Jake Plummer	5.00
4	Warrick Dunn	4.00
5	Dorsey Levens	2.00
6	Steve McNair	4.00
7	John Elway	7.00
8	Troy Aikman	6.00
9	Steve Young	5.00
10	Curtis Martin	4.00
11	Kordell Stewart	5.00
12	Jerry Rice	6.00
13	Mark Brunell	5.00
14	Terrell Davis	10.00
15	Drew Bledsoe	5.00
16	Eddie George	5.00
17	Barry Sanders	12.00
18	Emmitt Smith	8.00
19	Dan Marino	8.00
20	Brett Favre	12.00

1998 Leaf Rookies & Stars Standing Ovation

This 10-card set is printed with holographic foil stamping and sequentially numbered to 5,000. It features players who truly deserve a standing ovation for their accomplishments.

		MT
Complete Set (10):		40.00
Common Player:		1.50
Minor Stars:		3.00
Production 5,000 Sets		
1	Brett Favre	8.00
2	Dan Marino	6.00
3	Emmitt Smith	6.00
4	Barry Sanders	8.00
5	Terrell Davis	7.00
6	Jerry Rice	4.00
7	Steve Young	3.00
8	Reggie White	1.50
9	John Elway	5.00
10	Eddie George	3.00

1998 Leaf Rookies & Stars Ticket Masters

This double-sided 20-card set is printed on foil board and features players from the same team, like Terrell Davis and John Elway, that fill the seats for their franchise. Each card is sequentially numbered to 2,500 with the first 500 die-cut like a ticket.

		MT
Complete Set (20):		120.00
Common Player:		2.00
Minor Stars:		4.00
Production 2,500 Sets		
Die-Cut Cards:		3x
Production First 500 Sets		
1	Brett Favre, Dorsey Levens	12.00
2	Dan Marino, Karim Abdul	8.00
3	Troy Aikman, Deion Sanders	6.00
4	Barry Sanders, Herman Moore	12.00
5	Steve McNair, Eddie George	5.00
6	Drew Bledsoe, Robert Edwards	5.00
7	Terrell Davis, John Elway	10.00
8	Jerry Rice, Steve Young	6.00
9	Kordell Stewart, Jerome Bettis	5.00
10	Curtis Martin, Keyshawn Johnson	4.00

11	Warrick Dunn, Trent Dilfer	5.00
12	Corey Dillon, Carl Pickens	4.00
13	Tim Brown, Napoleon Kaufman	2.00
14	Jake Plummer, Frank Sanders	5.00
15	Ryan Leaf, Natrone Means	8.00
16	Peyton Manning, Marshall Faulk	15.00
17	Mark Brunell, Fred Taylor	10.00
18	Curtis Enis, Curtis Conway	5.00
19	Cris Carter, Randy Moss	30.00
20	Isaac Bruce, Tony Banks	2.00

1998 Leaf Rookies & Stars Touchdown Club

The 20 players showcased in this insert set are known for their ability to get into the end zone. Whether it's through the air, on the ground or both, these NFL stars get the job done. Each card is printed on foil board and sequentially numbered to 5,000.

		MT
Complete Set (20):		50.00
Common Player:		1.50
Minor Stars:		3.00
Production 5,000 Sets		
1	Brett Favre	8.00
2	Dan Marino	6.00
3	Emmitt Smith	6.00
4	Barry Sanders	8.00
5	Eddie George	3.00
6	Drew Bledsoe	4.00
7	Terrell Davis	7.00
8	Mark Brunell	4.00
9	Jerry Rice	5.00
10	Kordell Stewart	4.00
11	Curtis Martin	1.50
12	Karim Abdul	1.50
13	Warrick Dunn	3.00
14	Corey Dillon	3.00
15	Jerome Bettis	1.50
16	Antonio Freeman	1.50
17	Keyshawn Johnson	1.50
18	John Elway	5.00
19	Steve Young	3.00
20	Jake Plummer	4.00

1999 Leaf Certified

This was a 225-card set that was divided into four tiers. The first 100 cards contained one star and were found four to a pack. Two-star cards included #101-150 and they were inserted one-per-pack. Three-star cards included #151-175 and they were inserted 1:3 packs. The four-star singles were cards #176-225 and they were found 1:5 packs. Parallel sets included Mirror Red and Mirror Gold. Other inserts included: Certified Skills, Fabric of the Game, Gold Future, Gold Team and Gridiron Gear. SRP was $3.99 for five-card packs.

		MT
Complete Set (225):		850.00
Common Player (1-100):		.20
Minor Stars (1-100):		.40
Inserted 4:1		
Common Player (101-150):		.50
Minor Stars (101-150):		1.00
Inserted 1:1		
Common Player (151-175):		1.00
Minor Stars (151-175):		2.00
Inserted 1:3		
Common Player (176-225):		5.00
Inserted 1:5		
Wax Box:		150.00
1	Simeon Rice	.20
2	Frank Sanders	.40
3	Andre Wadsworth	.20
4	Larry Centers	.20
5	Terance Mathis	.20
6	O.J. Santiago	.20
7	Chris Calloway	.20
8	Michael Jackson	.20
9	Rod Woodson	.20
10	Pat Johnson	.20
11	Rob Johnson	.20
12	Andre Reed	.20
13	Tim Biakabutuka	.20
14	Rae Carruth	.20
15	Fred Lane	.20
16	Muhsin Muhammad	.40
17	Wesley Walls	.20
18	Edgar Bennett	.20
19	Curtis Conway	.20
20	Bobby Engram	.20
21	Jeff Blake	.20
22	Darnay Scott	.20
23	Ty Detmer	.20
24	Sedrick Shaw	.20
25	Leslie Shepherd	.20
26	Keith Byars	.20
27	Chris Warren	.20
28	Raghib Ismail	.20
29	Marcus Nash	.20
30	Neil Smith	.20
31	Bubby Brister	.20
32	Brian Griese	1.50
33	Germane Crowell	.40
34	Johnnie Morton	.20
35	Gus Frerotte	.20
36	Robert Brooks	.40
37	Mark Chmura	.40
38	Derrick Mayes	.40
39	Jerome Pathon	.20
40	Jimmy Smith	.40
41	James Stewart	.20
42	Tavian Banks	.20
43	Derrick Alexander	.20
44	Kimble Anders	.20
45	Elvis Grbac	.20
46	Derrick Thomas	.20
47	Bam Morris	.20
48	Tony Gonzalez	.40
49	John Avery	.20
50	Tyrone Wheatley	.20
51	Zach Thomas	.40
52	Lamar Thomas	.20
53	Jeff George	.40
54	John Randle	.20
55	Jake Reed	.20
56	Leroy Hoard	.20
57	Robert Edwards	.40
58	Ben Coates	.40
59	Tony Simmons	.20
60	Shawn Jefferson	.20
61	Eddie Kennison	.20
62	Lamar Smith	.20
63	Tiki Barber	.20
64	Kerry Collins	.40
65	Ike Hilliard	.20
66	Gary Brown	.20
67	Joe Jurevicius	.20
68	Kent Graham	.20
69	Dedric Ward	.20
70	Terry Allen	.20
71	Neil O'Donnell	.40
72	Desmond Howard	.20
73	James Jett	.20
74	Jon Ritchie	.20
75	Rickey Dudley	.20
76	Charles Johnson	.20
77	Chris Fuamatu-Ma'afala	.20
78	Hines Ward	.40
79	Ryan Leaf	.50
80	Jim Harbaugh	.20
81	Junior Seau	.40
82	Mikhael Ricks	.20
83	J.J. Stokes	.40
84	Ahman Green	.20
85	Tony Banks	.20
86	Robert Holcombe	.20
87	Az-Zahir Hakim	.20
88	Greg Hill	.20
89	Trent Green	.20
90	Eric Zeier	.20
91	Riedel Anthony	.20
92	Bert Emmanuel	.20
93	Warren Sapp	.20
94	Kevin Dyson	.40
95	Yancey Thigpen	.20

97	Frank Wycheck	.20
98	Michael Westbrook	.40
99	Albert Connell	.20
100	Darrell Green	.20
101	Rob Moore	.50
102	Adrian Murrell	.20
103	Jake Plummer	3.00
104	Chris Chandler	1.00
105	Jamal Anderson	1.50
106	Tim Dwight	1.50
107	Jermaine Lewis	.50
108	Priest Holmes	1.50
109	Bruce Smith	.50
110	Eric Moulds	1.50
111	Antowain Smith	1.00
112	Curtis Enis	1.50
113	Corey Dillon	1.00
114	Michael Irvin	1.00
115	Ed McCaffrey	1.00
116	Shannon Sharpe	1.00
117	Terrell Davis	5.00
118	Charlie Batch	2.00
119	Antonio Freeman	1.50
120	Dorsey Levens	1.00
121	Marvin Harrison	1.50
122	Peyton Manning	5.00
123	Keenan McCardell	1.00
124	Fred Taylor	3.00
125	Andre Rison	.50
126	O.J. McDuffie	.50
127	Karim Abdul	1.00
128	Randy Moss	7.00
129	Terry Glenn	1.50
130	Vinny Testaverde	1.00
131	Keyshawn Johnson	1.50
132	Curtis Martin	1.50
133	Wayne Chrebet	1.00
134	Napoleon Kaufman	1.00
135	Charles Woodson	1.50
136	Duce Staley	1.00
137	Kordell Stewart	1.75
138	Terrell Owens	1.50
139	Ricky Watters	1.00
140	Joey Galloway	1.50
141	Jon Kitna	1.75
142	Isaac Bruce	1.00
143	Jacquez Green	.50
144	Warrick Dunn	1.50
145	Mike Alstott	1.50
146	Trent Dilfer	1.00
147	Steve McNair	1.50
148	Eddie George	1.50
149	Skip Hicks	1.00
150	Brad Johnson	1.50
151	Doug Flutie	3.00
152	Thurman Thomas	2.00
153	Carl Pickens	2.00
154	Emmitt Smith	7.00
155	Troy Aikman	5.00
156	Deion Sanders	3.00
157	John Elway	7.00
158	Rod Smith	1.00
159	Barry Sanders	10.00
160	Herman Moore	2.00
161	Brett Favre	10.00
162	Mark Brunell	4.00
163	Warren Moon	2.00
164	Dan Marino	7.00
165	Randall Cunningham	2.00
166	Robert Smith	2.00
167	Cris Carter	2.00
168	Drew Bledsoe	4.00
169	Tim Brown	2.00
170	Jerome Bettis	2.00
171	Natrone Means	1.00
172	Jerry Rice	5.00
173	Steve Young	3.00
174	Garrison Hearst	2.00
175	Marshall Faulk	2.00
176	David Boston	25.00
177	Jeff Paulk	10.00
178	Reginald Kelly	5.00
179	Brandon Stokely	10.00
180	Chris McAlister	10.00
181	Shawn Bryson	5.00
182	Peerless Price	20.00
183	Cade McNown	40.00
184	Jerry Azumah	10.00
185	D'Wayne Bates	10.00
186	Marty Booker	10.00
187	Akili Smith	40.00
188	Craig Yeast	10.00
189	Tim Couch	80.00
190	Kevin Johnson	25.00
191	Wane McGarity	10.00
192	Olandis Gary	25.00
193	Travis McGriff	10.00
194	Sedrick Irvin	15.00
195	Chris Claiborne	10.00
196	De'Mond Parker	10.00
197	Dee Miller	10.00
198	Edgerrin James	80.00
199	Michael Cloud	10.00
200	Larry Parker	10.00
201	Cecil Collins	50.00
202	James Johnson	20.00
203	Rob Konrad	10.00
204	Daunte Culpepper	40.00
205	Jim Kleinsasser	10.00
206	Kevin Faulk	20.00
207	Andy Katzenmoyer	10.00
208	Ricky Williams	80.00
209	Joe Montgomery	15.00
210	Sean Bennett	10.00
211	Dameane Douglas	10.00
212	Donovan McNabb	40.00
213	Na Brown	10.00

214	Amos Zereoue	20.00
215	Troy Edwards	25.00
216	Jermaine Fazande	10.00
217	Tai Streets	10.00
218	Brock Huard	15.00
219	Charlie Rogers	10.00
220	Karsten Bailey	10.00
221	Joe Germaine	15.00
222	Torry Holt	25.00
223	Shaun King	30.00
224	Jevon Kearse	18.00
225	Champ Bailey	15.00

1999 Leaf Certified Mirror Gold

This was a 225-card parallel to the base set found at four different tiers. Each single was printed on holographic stock with gold tint. The first 100 cards were sequentially numbered to 45. Cards 101-150 were numbered to 35. Cards 151-175 were numbered to 25 and cards 176-225 were numbered to 30.

	MT
Common Player (1-100):	10.00
1-Star Cards:	35x-70x
Production 45 Sets	
Common Player (101-150):	20.00
2-Star Cards:	25x-50x
Production 35 Sets	
Common Player (151-175):	35.00
3-Star Cards:	20x-40x
Production 25 Sets	
Common Player (176-225):	25.00
4-Star Cards:	2x-4x
Production 30 Sets	

1999 Leaf Certified Mirror Red

This was a 225-card parallel to the base set found at four different tiers. Each single was printed on holographic stock with red tint. The first 100 cards were found 1:17 packs. Cards 101-150 were inserted 1:53 packs. Cards 151-175 were found 1:125 and cards 176-225 were inserted 1:89 packs.

	MT
Common Player (1-100):	3.00
1-Star Cards:	10x-20x
Inserted 1:17	
Common Player (101-150):	
2-Star Cards:	4x-8x
Inserted 1:53	
Common Player (151-175):	
3-Star Cards:	5x-10x
Inserted 1:125	
Common Player (176-225):	10.00
4-Star Cards:	1.5x
Inserted 1:89	

1999 Leaf Certified Fabric of the Game

This was a 75-card insert set with the singles found at three levels. The three technologies used were nylon, leather and plastic. A total of 25 players were showcased according to Pro Bowl appearances, career TDs and career yards. Each level had five categories with different sequential numbering ranging from 100 to 1,000.

		MT
Complete Set (75):		1650.00
Common Player:		5.00
1	John Elway 100	120.00
2	Barry Sanders 100	120.00
3	Jerry Rice 100	60.00
4	Brett Favre 250	70.00
5	Steve Young 250	25.00
6	Troy Aikman 250	40.00
7	Deion Sanders 250	15.00
8	Terrell Davis 500	30.00
9	Mark Brunell 500	15.00
10	Drew Bledsoe 500	15.00
11	Randall Cunningham 500	10.00
12	Eddie George 500	12.00
13	Jamal Anderson 750	8.00
14	Doug Flutie 750	12.00
15	Robert Smith 750	8.00
16	Garrison Hearst 750	8.00
17	Keyshawn Johnson 750	8.00
18	Randy Moss 750	40.00
19	Eric Moulds 1000	8.00
20	Curtis Enis 1000	8.00
21	Ricky Williams 1000	50.00
22	Peyton Manning 1000	30.00
23	Tim Couch 1000	50.00
24	Cade McNown 1000	20.00
25	Akili Smith 1000	20.00
26	Dan Marino 100	100.00
27	Jerry Rice 100	60.00
28	Emmitt Smith 100	100.00
29	Cris Carter 250	15.00
30	Steve Young 250	25.00
31	Herman Moore 250	15.00
32	Tim Brown 250	15.00
33	Jerome Bettis 500	10.00
34	Natrone Means 500	5.00
35	Antonio Freeman 500	10.00
36	Terrell Davis 500	30.00
37	Carl Pickens 500	5.00
38	Karim Abdul 750	5.00
39	Mike Alstott 750	8.00
40	Jake Plummer 750	15.00
41	Steve McNair 750	8.00
42	Terrell Owens 750	8.00
43	Kordell Stewart 750	10.00
44	Randy Moss 1000	35.00
45	Fred Taylor 1000	20.00
46	Peyton Manning 1000	30.00
47	Tim Couch 1000	50.00
48	Akili Smith 1000	20.00
49	Torry Holt 1000	12.00
50	Donovan McNabb 1000	20.00
51	Barry Sanders 100	120.00
52	Dan Marino 100	100.00
53	Jerry Rice 100	60.00
54	John Elway 250	50.00
55	Brett Favre 250	70.00
56	Emmitt Smith 250	50.00
57	Mark Brunell 250	30.00
58	Jake Plummer 500	20.00
59	Ricky Watters 500	10.00
60	Dorsey Levens 500	10.00
61	Curtis Martin 500	10.00
62	Marshall Faulk 500	10.00
63	Eddie George 750	10.00
64	Corey Dillon 750	8.00
65	Warrick Dunn 750	10.00
66	Antowain Smith 750	8.00
67	Napoleon Kaufman 750	8.00

68	Joey Galloway 750	8.00
69	Fred Taylor 1000	20.00
70	Charlie Batch 1000	10.00
71	Ricky Williams 1000	50.00
72	Edgerrin James 1000	50.00
73	Jon Kitna 1000	10.00
74	Daunte Culpepper 1000	20.00
75	Skip Hicks 1000	5.00

1999 Leaf Certified Gold Future

This 30-card insert set included the top rookies from the 1999 NFL Draft. Each single was printed on mirror Mylar with foil and micro-etching. Singles were found 1:17 packs. A parallel Mirror Black version was also made with each of those singles sequentially numbered to 25.

		MT
Complete Set (30):		185.00
Common Player:		3.00
Inserted 1:17		
Mirror Black Cards:		6x-12x
Production 25 Sets		
1	Travis McGriff	4.00
2	Jermaine Fazande	3.00
3	Kevin Faulk	6.00
4	Edgerrin James	25.00
5	Ricky Williams	25.00
6	Tim Couch	25.00
7	Torry Holt	8.00
8	Kevin Johnson	8.00
9	Amos Zereoue	6.00
10	Joe Germaine	4.00
11	Shawn Bryson	3.00
12	D'Wayne Bates	3.00
13	Akili Smith	12.00
14	Shaun King	5.00
15	Joe Montgomery	4.00
16	Troy Edwards	8.00
17	Rob Konrad	4.00
18	David Boston	8.00
19	Reginald Kelly	3.00
20	Donovan McNabb	12.00
21	Champ Bailey	5.00
22	Craig Yeast	3.00
23	Daunte Culpepper	12.00
24	Peerless Price	6.00
25	Cecil Collins	15.00
26	Cade McNown	12.00
27	Karsten Bailey	3.00
28	James Johnson	5.00
29	Brock Huard	5.00
30	Michael Cloud	4.00

1999 Leaf Certified Gold Team

This 30-card insert set included the top veterans and pictured them on mirror Mylar board with foil. Singles were inserted 1:17. A parallel Mirror Black version was also produced with each of those singles sequentially numbered to 25.

		MT
Complete Set (30):		200.00
Common Player:		3.00
Inserted 1:17		
Mirror Black Cards:		6x-12x
Production 25 Sets		
1	Randy Moss	25.00
2	Terrell Davis	18.00
3	Peyton Manning	18.00
4	Fred Taylor	12.00
5	Jake Plummer	12.00
6	Drew Bledsoe	8.00
7	John Elway	18.00
8	Mark Brunell	8.00
9	Joey Galloway	3.00
10	Troy Aikman	12.00
11	Jerome Bettis	3.00
12	Tim Brown	3.00
13	Dan Marino	18.00
14	Antonio Freeman	3.00
15	Steve Young	7.00
16	Jamal Anderson	3.00
17	Brett Favre	25.00
18	Jerry Rice	12.00
19	Corey Dillon	3.00
20	Barry Sanders	25.00
21	Doug Flutie	7.00
22	Emmitt Smith	18.00
23	Curtis Martin	3.00
24	Dorsey Levens	3.00
25	Kordell Stewart	6.00
26	Eddie George	6.00
27	Terrell Owens	3.00
28	Keyshawn Johnson	3.00
29	Steve McNair	6.00
30	Cris Carter	3.00

1999 Leaf Certified Gridiron Gear

This 72-card insert set included pieces of game-used jerseys from the top veterans in the NFL. Each of the singles was sequentially numbered to 300.

		MT
Common Player:		50.00
Multi-Colored Swatches:		1.5x
Production 300 Sets		
KA33	Karim Abdul	50.00
TA8	Troy Aikman	150.00
JA32	Jamal Anderson	75.00
JB36	Jerome Bettis	75.00
DB11	Drew Bledsoe	125.00
TB71	Tony Boselli	50.00
RB87	Robert Brooks	50.00
TB81	Tim Brown	50.00
IB80	Isaac Bruce	75.00
MB8A	Mark Brunell White	100.00
MB8H	Mark Brunell Teal	100.00
MC89	Mark Chmura	50.00
BC87	Ben Coates	50.00
CC80	Curtis Conway	50.00
RC7	Randall Cunningham	75.00
TD30A	Terrell Davis White	150.00
TD30H	Terrell Davis Blue	150.00
TD12	Trent Dilfer	50.00
WD28	Warrick Dunn	75.00
JE7H	John Elway Blue	175.00
JE7HC	John Elway Orange	175.00
BF4A	Brett Favre White	200.00
BF4H	Brett Favre Green	200.00
DF7A	Doug Flutie White	100.00
DF7H	Doug Flutie Blue	100.00
AF86	Antonio Freeman	75.00
EG27	Eddie George	75.00
DG28	Darrell Green	50.00
MH88	Marvin Harrison	50.00
DH80	Desmond Howard	50.00
MI88	Michael Irvin	50.00
JJ82	James Jett	50.00
KJ19	Keyshawn Johnson	75.00
NK26A	Napoleon Kaufman White	
NK26H	Napoleon Kaufman Black	50.00
JK12	Jim Kelly	75.00
RL16	Ryan Leaf	50.00
DL25A	Dorsey Levens White	75.00
DL25H	Dorsey Levens Green	75.00
PM18	Peyton Manning	175.00
DM13A	Dan Marino White	175.00
DM13H	Dan Marino Teal	175.00
CM28	Curtis Martin	75.00
KM87	Keenan McCardell	50.00
OM81	O.J. McDuffie	50.00
SM9	Steve McNair	75.00
NM20	Natrone Means	50.00
JM19	Joe Montana	200.00
WM1	Warren Moon	50.00
HMB4	Herman Moore	75.00
RM84A	Randy Moss White	250.00
RM84H	Randy Moss Purple	250.00
JP16	Jake Plummer	100.00
JR80A	Jerry Rice White	150.00
JR80H	Jerry Rice Red	150.00
BS20	Barry Sanders	200.00
CS81	Chris Sanders	50.00
DS21	Deion Sanders	75.00
WS99	Warren Sapp	50.00
JS55	Junior Seau	50.00
PH12	Phil Simms	50.00
ES22	Emmitt Smith	175.00
NS90	Neil Smith	50.00
JS82	Jimmy Smith	50.00
JS33	James Stewart	50.00
KS10	Kordell Stewart	75.00
VT12	Vinny Testaverde	50.00
DT58	Derrick Thomas	50.00
TT34	Thurman Thomas	50.00
ZT54	Zach Thomas	50.00
CW24	Charles Woodson	75.00
SY8	Steve Young	100.00

1999 Leaf Certified Skills

This 20-card insert set featured 20 pairs of NFL superstars back-to-back on dual-sided mirror Mylar board. Singles were inserted 1:35 packs. A parallel Mirror Black version was also produced and each of those singles was sequentially numbered to 25.

		MT
Complete Set (20):		225.00
Common Player:		7.00
Inserted 1:35		
Mirror Black Cards:		5x-10x
Production 25 Sets		
1	Deion Sanders, Champ Bailey	7.00
2	John Elway, Cade McNown	25.00
3	Cris Carter, David Boston	7.00
4	Marshall Faulk, Edgerrin James	25.00
5	Jerry Rice, Randy Moss	30.00
6	Antonio Freeman, Terrell Owens	7.00
7	Terrell Davis, Ricky Williams	30.00
8	Drew Bledsoe, Doug Flutie	12.00
9	Eddie George, Jamal Anderson	10.00
10	Troy Aikman, Peyton Manning	25.00
11	Barry Sanders, Warrick Dunn	30.00
12	Randall Cunningham, Daunte Culpepper	12.00
13	Dan Marino, Tim Couch	30.00
14	Emmitt Smith, Fred Taylor	20.00
15	Keyshawn Johnson, Eric Moulds	7.00
16	Steve Young, Mark Brunell	12.00
17	Donovan McNabb, Akili Smith	10.00
18	Brett Favre, Jake Plummer	30.00
19	Kordell Stewart, Steve McNair	7.00
20	Torry Holt, Troy Edwards	7.00

1999 Leaf Rookies & Stars

MARCUS ROBINSON

This was a 300-card base set that included 100 rookie cards found 1:2 packs. The Longevity insert was a parallel to the base set with each card sequentially numbered. The first 200 cards were numbered to 50 and the 100 were numbered to 30. Other inserts included: Cross Training, Dress for Success, John Elway Collection, Freshman Orientation, Game Plan, Great American Heroes, Greatest Hits, Prime Cuts, Signature Series, Slide Show, Statistical Standouts, Ticket Masters and Touchdown Club. SRP was $2.99 for 9-card packs.

		MT
Complete Set (300):		400.00
Common Player:		.15
Minor Stars:		.30
Common Rookie:		2.00
Inserted 1:2		
Wax Box:		110.00
1	Frank Sanders	.15
2	Adrian Murrell	.15
3	Rob Moore	.30
4	Simeon Rice	.15
5	Michael Pittman	.30
6	Jake Plummer	.75
7	Chris Chandler	.30
8	Tim Dwight	.50
9	Chris Calloway	.15
10	Terance Mathis	.15
11	Jamal Anderson	.50
12	Byron Hanspard	.30
13	O.J. Santiago	.15
14	Ken Oxendine	.30
15	Priest Holmes	.50
16	Scott Mitchell	.15
17	Tony Banks	.30
18	Patrick Johnson	.15
19	Rod Woodson	.30
20	Jermaine Lewis	.15
21	Errict Rhett	.30
22	Stoney Case	.30
23	Andre Reed	.30
24	Eric Moulds	.50
25	Rob Johnson	.30
26	Doug Flutie	.75
27	Bruce Smith	.15
28	Jay Riemersma	.15
29	Antowain Smith	.50
30	Thurman Thomas	.30
31	Jonathon Linton	.30
32	Muhsin Muhammad	.30
33	Rae Carruth	.15
34	Wesley Walls	.30
35	Fred Lane	.30
36	Kevin Greene	.15
37	Tim Biakabutuka	.30
38	Curtis Enis	.50
39	Shane Matthews	.30
40	Bobby Engram	.15
41	Curtis Conway	.30
42	Marcus Robinson	1.00
43	Darnay Scott	.30
44	Carl Pickens	.30
45	Corey Dillon	.50
46	Jeff Blake	.30
47	Terry Kirby	.15
48	Ty Detmer	.15
49	Leslie Shepherd	.15
50	Karim Abdul	.30
51	Emmitt Smith	1.50
52	Deion Sanders	.50
53	Michael Irvin	.30
54	Raghib Ismail	.15
55	David LaFleur	.15
56	Troy Aikman	1.00
57	Ed McCaffrey	.50
58	Rod Smith	.50
59	Shannon Sharpe	.30
60	Brian Griese	1.00
61	John Elway	1.50
62	Bubby Brister	.30
63	Neil Smith	.15
64	Terrell Davis	1.50
65	John Avery	.30
66	Derek Loville	.15
67	Ron Rivers	.15
68	Herman Moore	.50
69	Johnnie Morton	.15
70	Charlie Batch	.75
71	Barry Sanders	2.00
72	Germane Crowell	.30
73	Greg Hill	.15
74	Gus Frerotte	.30
75	Corey Bradford	.30
76	Dorsey Levens	.50
77	Antonio Freeman	.50
78	Mark Chmura	.30
79	Brett Favre	2.00
80	Bill Schroeder	.30
81	Matt Hasselbeck	.50
82	E.G. Green	.30
83	Ken Dilger	.15
84	Jerome Pathon	.15
85	Marvin Harrison	.50
86	Peyton Manning	1.50
87	Tavian Banks	.30
88	Keenan McCardell	.30
89	Mark Brunell	.75
90	Fred Taylor	1.00
91	Jimmy Smith	.75
92	James Stewart	.50
93	Kyle Brady	.15
94	Derrick Thomas	.30
95	Rashaan Shehee	.15
96	Derrick Alexander	.15
97	Bam Morris	.15
98	Andre Rison	.30
99	Elvis Grbac	.30
100	Tony Gonzalez	.30
101	Donnell Bennett	.15
102	Warren Moon	.30
103	Zach Thomas	.30
104	Oronde Gadsden	.30
105	Dan Marino	1.50
106	O.J. McDuffie	.30
107	Tony Martin	.15
108	Randy Moss	2.00
109	Cris Carter	.50
110	Robert Smith	.50
111	Randall Cunningham	.50
112	Jake Reed	.30
113	John Randle	.15
114	Leroy Hoard	.15
115	Jeff George	.50
116	Ty Law	.15
117	Shawn Jefferson	.15
118	Troy Brown	.15
119	Robert Edwards	.30
120	Tony Simmons	.30
121	Terry Glenn	.50
122	Ben Coates	.30
123	Drew Bledsoe	.75
124	Terry Allen	.30
125	Cameron Cleeland	.30
126	Eddie Kennison	.15
127	Amani Toomer	.15
128	Kerry Collins	.30
129	Joe Jurevicius	.30
130	Tiki Barber	.15
131	Ike Hilliard	.30
132	Michael Strahan	.15
133	Gary Brown	.15
134	Jason Sehorn	.15
135	Curtis Martin	.50
136	Vinny Testaverde	.30
137	Dedric Ward	.30
138	Keyshawn Johnson	.50
139	Wayne Chrebet	.50
140	Tyrone Wheatley	.30
141	Napoleon Kaufman	.50
142	Tim Brown	.30
143	Rickey Dudley	.30
144	Jon Ritchie	.15
145	James Jett	.15
146	Rich Gannon	.30
147	Charles Woodson	.30
148	Charles Johnson	.15
149	Duce Staley	.30
150	Will Blackwell	.15
151	Kordell Stewart	.50
152	Jerome Bettis	.50
153	Hines Ward	.30
154	Richard Huntley	.30
155	Natrone Means	.30
156	Mikhael Ricks	.15
157	Junior Seau	.30
158	Jim Harbaugh	.30
159	Ryan Leaf	.50
160	Erik Kramer	.15
161	Terrell Owens	.50
162	J.J. Stokes	.30
163	Lawrence Phillips	.30
164	Charlie Garner	.30
165	Jerry Rice	1.00
166	Garrison Hearst	.50
167	Steve Young	.75
168	Derrick Mayes	.30
169	Ahman Green	.30
170	Joey Galloway	.50
171	Ricky Watters	.30
172	Jon Kitna	.50
173	Sean Dawkins	.15
174	Az-Zahir Hakim	.15
175	Robert Holcombe	.30
176	Isaac Bruce	.50
177	Amp Lee	.15
178	Marshall Faulk	.50
179	Trent Green	.30
180	Eric Zeier	.15
181	Bert Emanuel	.15
182	Jacquez Green	.30
183	Reidel Anthony	.30
184	Warren Sapp	.30
185	Mike Alstott	.50
186	Warrick Dunn	.50
187	Trent Dilfer	.30
188	Neil O'Donnell	.30
189	Eddie George	.60
190	Yancey Thigpen	.30
191	Steve McNair	.60
192	Kevin Dyson	.30
193	Frank Wycheck	.30
194	Stephen Davis	.50
195	Stephen Alexander	.30
196	Darrell Green	.15
197	Skip Hicks	.30
198	Brad Johnson	.50
199	Michael Westbrook	.30
200	Albert Connell	.15
201	*David Boston*	*10.00*
202	*Joel Makovicka*	*4.00*
203	*Chris Greisen*	*3.00*
204	*Jeff Paulk*	*2.00*
205	*Reginald Kelly*	*2.00*
206	*Chris McAlister*	*3.00*
207	*Brandon Stokley*	*2.00*
208	*Antoine Winfield*	*3.00*
209	*Bobby Collins*	*3.00*
210	*Peerless Price*	*7.00*
211	*Shawn Bryson*	*2.00*
212	*Sheldon Jackson*	*2.00*
213	*Kamil Loud*	*2.00*
214	*D'Wayne Bates*	*3.00*
215	*Jerry Azumah*	*3.00*
216	*Marty Booker*	*3.00*
217	*Cade McNown*	*25.00*
218	*James Allen*	*3.00*
219	*Nick Williams*	*2.00*
220	*Akili Smith*	*20.00*
221	*Craig Yeast*	*2.00*
222	*Damon Griffin*	*3.00*
223	*Scott Covington*	*2.00*
224	*Michael Basnight*	*2.00*
225	*Ronnie Powell*	*2.00*
226	*Rahim Abdullah*	*2.00*
227	*Tim Couch*	*50.00*
228	*Kevin Johnson*	*10.00*
229	*Darrin Chiaverini*	*4.00*
230	*Mark Campbell*	*2.00*
231	*Mike Lucky*	*2.00*
232	*Robert Thomas*	*2.00*
233	*Ebenezer Ekuban*	*3.00*
234	*Dat Nguyen*	*3.00*
235	*Wane McGarity*	*3.00*
236	*Jason Tucker*	*10.00*
237	*Olandis Gary*	*20.00*
238	*Al Wilson*	*3.00*
239	*Travis McGriff*	*3.00*
240	*Desmond Clark*	*2.00*
241	*Andre Cooper*	*2.00*
242	*Chris Watson*	*3.00*
243	*Sedrick Irvin*	*6.00*
244	*Chris Claiborne*	*3.00*
245	*Cory Sauter*	*2.00*
246	*Brock Olivo*	*2.00*
247	*De'Mond Parker*	*6.00*
248	*Aaron Brooks*	*3.00*
249	*Antwan Edwards*	*3.00*
250	*Basil Mitchell*	*2.00*
251	*Terrence Wilkins*	*10.00*
252	*Edgerrin James*	*85.00*
253	*Fernando Bryant*	*2.00*
254	*Michael Cloud*	*3.00*
255	*Larry Parker*	*2.00*
256	*Rob Konrad*	*3.00*
257	*Cecil Collins*	*8.00*
258	*James Johnson*	*6.00*
259	*Jim Kleinsasser*	*3.00*
260	*Daunte Culpepper*	*20.00*
261	*Michael Bishop*	*6.00*
262	*Andy Katzenmoyer*	*4.00*
263	*Kevin Faulk*	*6.00*
264	*Brett Bech*	*2.00*
265	*Ricky Williams*	*50.00*
266	*Sean Bennett*	*3.00*
267	*Joe Montgomery*	*4.00*
268	*Dan Campbell*	*2.00*
269	*Ray Lucas*	*20.00*
270	*Scott Dreisbach*	*3.00*
271	*Jed Weaver*	*2.00*
272	*Dameane Douglas*	*3.00*
273	*Cecil Martin*	*2.00*
274	*Donovan McNabb*	*20.00*
275	*Na Brown*	*3.00*
276	*Jerame Tuman*	*2.00*
277	*Amos Zereoue*	*4.00*
278	*Troy Edwards*	*10.00*
279	*Jermaine Fazande*	*4.00*
280	*Steve Heiden*	*2.00*
281	*Jeff Garcia*	*10.00*
282	*Terry Jackson*	*3.00*
283	*Charlie Rogers*	*3.00*
284	*Brock Huard*	*6.00*
285	*Karsten Bailey*	*3.00*
286	*Lamar King*	*2.00*
287	*Justin Watson*	*3.00*
288	*Kurt Warner*	*100.00*
289	*Torry Holt*	*10.00*
290	*Joe Germaine*	*4.00*
291	*Dre' Bly*	*3.00*
292	*Martin Gramatica*	*2.00*
293	*Rabih Abdullah*	*2.00*
294	*Shaun King*	*20.00*
295	*Anthony McFarland*	*3.00*
296	*Darnell McDonald*	*4.00*
297	*Kevin Daft*	*2.00*
298	*Jevon Kearse*	*10.00*
299	*Mike Sellers*	*2.00*
300	*Champ Bailey*	*6.00*

1999 Leaf Rookies & Stars Longevity

DARNELL McDONALD

This was a 300-card parallel to the base set. Each single was printed on foil board with holographic foil stamping. The first 200 cards were sequentially numbered to 50 and the 100 rookies were numbered to 30.

	MT
Longevity Cards:	40x-80x
Production 50 Sets	
Longevity Rookies:	3x-6x
Production 30 Sets	

1999 Leaf Rookies & Stars Cross Training

This 25-card insert set included the most versatile players in the NFL. Each card highlighted the player's different skills, one on each side of the card. Each card in the set was sequentially numbered to 1,250.

		MT
Complete Set (25):		125.00
Common Player:		3.00
Production 1,250 Sets		
1	Champ Bailey	3.00
2	Mark Brunell	6.00
3	Daunte Culpepper	10.00
4	Randall Cunningham	3.00
5	Terrell Davis	10.00
6	Charlie Batch	5.00
7	Dorsey Levens	3.00
8	John Elway	10.00
9	Marshall Faulk	3.00
10	Brett Favre	15.00
11	Doug Flutie	6.00
12	Edgerrin James	30.00
13	Curtis Martin	5.00
14	Donovan McNabb	10.00
15	Steve McNair	4.00
16	Cade McNown	10.00
17	Randy Moss	15.00
18	Jake Plummer	6.00
19	Barry Sanders	15.00
20	Deion Sanders	3.00
21	Akili Smith	10.00
22	Kordell Stewart	3.00
23	Ricky Williams	15.00
24	Charles Woodson	3.00
25	Steve Young	6.00

1999 Leaf Rookies & Stars Dress for Success

This 30-card insert set included 20 of the top players in the NFL. Each single included a piece of a game-worn jersey by that player. Ten of the cards included two players on the front of the cards. Single-jersey cards were numbered to 200 and dual-jersey cards were numbered to 100.

	MT
Complete Set (30):	3250.
Common Player:	50.00
Single Jersey 200 Sets	

		MT
Dual Jersey 100 Sets		
1	Barry Sanders	150.00
2	Emmitt Smith	125.00
3	Barry Sanders, Emmitt Smith	300.00
4	Eddie George	50.00
5	Terrell Davis	125.00
6	Eddie George, Terrell Davis	200.00
7	Tim Couch	150.00
8	Dan Marino	125.00
9	Tim Couch, Dan Marino	300.00
10	Brett Favre	150.00
11	Troy Aikman	100.00
12	Brett Favre, Troy Aikman	300.00
13	Drew Bledsoe	75.00
14	Mark Brunell	75.00
15	Drew Bledsoe, Mark Brunell	150.00
16	Randy Moss	150.00
17	Jerry Rice	120.00
18	Randy Moss, Jerry Rice	275.00
19	Antonio Freeman	50.00
20	Terry Glenn	50.00
21	Antonio Freeman, Terry Glenn	75.00
22	Steve Young	75.00
23	Kordell Stewart	50.00
24	Steve Young, Kordell Stewart	125.00
25	Fred Taylor	100.00
26	Dorsey Levens	50.00
27	Fred Taylor, Dorsey Levens	150.00
28	Keyshawn Johnson	50.00
29	Herman Moore	50.00
30	Keyshawn Johnson, Herman Moore	85.00

1999 Leaf Rookies & Stars John Elway Collection

This 5-card insert set included pieces of authentic game-worn jerseys, shoes and helmets. The helmet and shoe singles were sequentially numbered to 125 and the jersey singles were numbered to 300.

		MT
Complete Set (5):		850.00
Common Player:		125.00
Helmet/Shoes 125 Sets		
Jersey 300 Sets		
1	John Elway Home Jer.	125.00
2	John Elway Away Jer.	125.00
3	John Elway Shoe	200.00
4	John Elway Blue Hel.	250.00
5	John Elway Orange Hel.	250.00

1999 Leaf Rookies & Stars Freshman Orientation

This 25-card insert set included the best rookies from the 1999 NFL Draft. Each card was printed on silver foil board and was sequentially numbered to 2,500.

		MT
Complete Set (25):		75.00
Common Player:		2.00
Production 2,500 Sets		
1	Champ Bailey	3.00
2	D'Wayne Bates	2.00
3	David Boston	4.00
4	Kurt Warner	25.00
5	Cecil Collins	4.00
6	Tim Couch	12.00
7	Daunte Culpepper	6.00
8	Troy Edwards	4.00
9	Kevin Faulk	3.00
10	Joe Germaine	3.00
11	Torry Holt	4.00
12	Brock Huard	3.00
13	Sedrick Irvin	3.00
14	Edgerrin James	20.00
15	Kevin Johnson	4.00
16	Shaun King	6.00
17	Rob Konrad	3.00
18	Sean Bennett	2.00
19	Donovan McNabb	6.00
20	Cade McNown	6.00
21	Peerless Price	3.00
22	Akili Smith	6.00
23	Ricky Williams	10.00
24	James Johnson	3.00
25	Olandis Gary	7.00

1999 Leaf Rookies & Stars Game Plan

This 25-card insert set included a mix of veterans and rookies. Each card was printed on foil board and was sequentially numbered to 2,500. A Masters parallel was also produced on holographic foil board and each of those was numbered to 50.

		MT
Complete Set (25):		75.00
Common Player:		2.00
Production 2,500 Sets		
1	Jamal Anderson	2.00
2	Jerome Bettis	2.00
3	Drew Bledsoe	4.00
4	Tim Brown	2.00
5	Mark Brunell	4.00
6	Tim Couch	10.00
7	Terrell Davis	8.00
8	Corey Dillon	2.00
9	Warrick Dunn	2.00
10	Brad Johnson	2.00
11	Brett Favre	10.00
12	Doug Flutie	4.00
13	Joey Galloway	2.00
14	Eddie George	2.00
15	Keyshawn Johnson	2.00
16	Peyton Manning	8.00
17	Dan Marino	8.00
18	Donovan McNabb	6.00
19	Cade McNown	6.00
20	Randy Moss	10.00
21	Jake Plummer	8.00
22	Barry Sanders	10.00
23	Emmitt Smith	8.00
24	Ricky Williams	10.00
25	Steve Young	4.00

1999 Leaf Rookies & Stars Game Plan Masters

This was a 25-card parallel to the Game Plan insert. Each of these singles was printed on holographic foil board and was sequentially numbered to 50.

	MT
Masters Cards:	5x-10x
Production 50 Sets	

Values quoted in this guide reflect the retail price of a card — the price a collector can expect to pay when buying a card from a dealer. The wholesale price — that which a collector can expect to receive from a dealer when selling cards — will be significantly lower, depending on desirability and condition.

1999 Leaf Rookies & Stars Great American Heroes

This 25-card insert set included mostly veterans. Singles were sequentially numbered to 2,500.

		MT
Complete Set (25):		75.00
Common Player:		2.00
Production 2,500 Sets		
1	Troy Aikman	6.00
2	Jamal Anderson	2.00
3	Drew Bledsoe	4.00
4	Mark Brunell	4.00
5	Cris Carter	2.00
6	Randall Cunningham	2.00
7	Terrell Davis	8.00
8	John Elway	8.00
9	Brett Favre	10.00
10	Doug Flutie	4.00
11	Antonio Freeman	2.00
12	Eddie George	3.00
13	Peyton Manning	8.00
14	Dan Marino	8.00
15	Curtis Martin	2.00
16	Warren Moon	2.00
17	Randy Moss	10.00
18	Jake Plummer	4.00
19	Jerry Rice	6.00
20	Barry Sanders	10.00
21	Deion Sanders	2.00
22	Emmitt Smith	8.00
23	Fred Taylor	6.00
24	Ricky Williams	10.00
25	Steve Young	4.00

1999 Leaf Rookies & Stars Greatest Hits

This 25-card insert set included the hottest superstars from the NFL. Singles were sequentially numbered to 2,500.

		MT
Complete Set (25):		70.00
Common Player:		2.00
Production 2,500 Sets		
1	Troy Aikman	6.00
2	Terry Glenn	2.00
3	Jamal Anderson	2.00
4	Drew Bledsoe	4.00
5	Cris Carter	2.00
6	Terrell Davis	8.00
7	John Elway	8.00
8	Brett Favre	10.00
9	Antonio Freeman	2.00
10	Eddie George	3.00
11	Priest Holmes	2.00
12	Keyshawn Johnson	2.00
13	Dorsey Levens	2.00
14	Dan Marino	8.00
15	Curtis Martin	2.00
16	Randy Moss	10.00
17	Eric Moulds	2.00
18	Terrell Owens	2.00
19	Carl Pickens	2.00
20	Jake Plummer	4.00
21	Jerry Rice	6.00
22	Barry Sanders	10.00
23	Marvin Harrison	2.00
24	Robert Smith	2.00
25	Fred Taylor	6.00

1999 Leaf Rookies & Stars Prime Cuts

This 15-card insert set included prime cuts from game-worn jerseys and incorporated them in this insert. Singles were randomly inserted.

		MT
Complete Set (15):		2500.
Common Player:		100.00
1	Tim Couch	300.00
2	Fred Taylor	150.00
3	Terry Glenn	100.00
4	Drew Bledsoe	125.00
5	Dan Marino	250.00
6	Jerry Rice	200.00
7	Barry Sanders	300.00
8	Mark Brunell	125.00
9	Brett Favre	300.00
10	Steve Young	125.00
11	Keyshawn Johnson	100.00
12	Antonio Freeman	100.00
13	Randy Moss	300.00
14	Troy Aikman	200.00
15	Emmitt Smith	250.00

1999 Leaf Rookies & Stars Signature Series

This 30-card insert set included signatures of the top veteran and rookies in the NFL. Single signed cards were sequentially numbered to 150 and dual signature cards were numbered to 50.

		MT
Common Player:		50.00
Singles 150 Sets		
Duals 50 Sets		
1	Terrell Davis	120.00
2	Edgerrin James	275.00
3	Terrell Davis, Edgerrin James	600.00
4	Eddie George	50.00
5	Ricky Williams	200.00
6	Eddie George, Ricky Williams	325.00
7	Jake Plummer	75.00
8	Donovan McNabb	125.00
9	Jake Plummer, Donovan McNabb	200.00
10	Randall Cunningham	50.00
11	Daunte Culpepper	125.00
12	Randall Cunningham, Daunte Culpepper	175.00
13	Fred Taylor	85.00
14	Cecil Collins	50.00
15	Fred Taylor, Cecil Collins	125.00
16	Randy Moss	150.00
17	Torry Holt	75.00
18	Randy Moss, Torry Holt	300.00
19	Steve Young	75.00
20	Cade McNown	125.00
21	Steve Young, Cade McNown	200.00
22	Jerry Rice	120.00
23	David Boston	75.00
24	Jerry Rice, David Boston	225.00
25	Doug Flutie	75.00
26	Akili Smith	120.00
27	Doug Flutie, Akili Smith	150.00
28	Dan Marino	150.00
29	Tim Couch	200.00
30	Dan Marino, Tim Couch	300.00

1999 Leaf Rookies & Stars Slide Show

This 25-card insert set included mostly veterans and a few rookies. Each single was printed on red foil board and was sequentially numbered to 100. A parallel Green set was made with each of those singles numbered to 50. The parallel Blue set was numbered to 25 and the parallel Studios only had one card of each.

		MT
Complete Set (25):		500.00
Common Player:		10.00
Production 100 Sets		
Green Cards:		2x
Production 50 Sets		
Blue Cards:		3x
Production 25 Sets		
Studio Cards:		
Production 1 Set		
1	Troy Aikman	30.00
2	Drew Bledsoe	20.00
3	Mark Brunell	20.00
4	Tim Couch	50.00
5	Terrell Davis	40.00
6	John Elway	40.00
7	Brett Favre	50.00
8	Antonio Freeman	10.00
9	Eddie George	10.00
10	Torry Holt	20.00
11	Edgerrin James	85.00
12	Keyshawn Johnson	10.00
13	Jon Kitna	10.00
14	Dorsey Levens	10.00
15	Peyton Manning	40.00
16	Dan Marino	40.00
17	Randy Moss	50.00
18	Jake Plummer	20.00
19	Jerry Rice	30.00
20	Barry Sanders	50.00
21	Marvin Harrison	10.00
22	Emmitt Smith	40.00
23	Fred Taylor	30.00
24	Ricky Williams	50.00
25	Steve Young	20.00

1999 Leaf Rookies & Stars Statistical Standouts

This 25-card insert set included the top producers in receiving, rushing and passing, and highlighted them on simulated leather with white foil. Each single was sequentially numbered to 1,250. A parallel Die Cut version was also produced with each of those singles numbered to a 1998 stat.

		MT
Complete Set (25):		100.00
Common Player:		2.00
Minor Stars:		4.00
Production 1,250 Sets		
1	Jamal Anderson	4.00
2	Jerome Bettis	4.00
3	Drew Bledsoe	6.00
4	Cris Carter	4.00
5	Randall Cunningham	4.00
6	Terrell Davis	10.00
7	John Elway	10.00
8	Marshall Faulk	4.00
9	Brett Favre	15.00
10	Antonio Freeman	4.00
11	Joey Galloway	4.00
12	Eddie George	4.00
13	Garrison Hearst	2.00
14	Keyshawn Johnson	4.00
15	Peyton Manning	10.00
16	Steve McNair	4.00
17	Randy Moss	15.00
18	Eric Moulds	4.00
19	Terrell Owens	4.00
20	Jake Plummer	6.00
21	Barry Sanders	15.00
22	Emmitt Smith	10.00
23	Fred Taylor	8.00
24	Vinny Testaverde	2.00
25	Steve Young	5.00

1999 Leaf Rookies & Stars Ticket Masters

This 25-card insert set included the top NFL stars. Each

single was sequentially numbered to 2,500. A parallel Executive Ticket Master set was also produced with each of those singles die cut and numbered to 50.

		MT
Complete Set (25):		100.00
Common Player:		2.00
Production 2,500 Sets		
1	Randy Moss,	12.00
	Cris Carter	
2	Brett Favre,	12.00
	Antonio Freeman	
3	Cecil Collins,	10.00
	Dan Marino	
4	Brian Griese,	8.00
	Terrell Davis	
5	Edgerrin James,	25.00
	Peyton Manning	
6	Emmitt Smith,	10.00
	Troy Aikman	
7	Jerry Rice,	8.00
	Steve Young	
8	Mark Brunell,	7.00
	Fred Taylor	
9	David Boston,	5.00
	Jake Plummer	
10	Terry Glenn,	5.00
	Drew Bledsoe	
11	Charlie Batch,	5.00
	Herman Moore	
12	Mike Alstott,	2.00
	Warrick Dunn	
13	Eddie George,	3.00
	Steve McNair	
14	Kordell Stewart,	2.00
	Jerome Bettis	
15	Chris Chandler,	2.00
	Jamal Anderson	
16	Akili Smith,	4.00
	Corey Dillon	
17	Curtis Enis,	8.00
	Cade McNown	
18	Isaac Bruce,	3.00
	Marshall Faulk	
19	Eric Moulds,	5.00
	Doug Flutie	
20	Joey Galloway,	2.00
	Ricky Watters	
21	Michael	2.00
	Westbrook,	
	Brad Johnson	
22	Curtis Martin,	3.00
	Keyshawn Johnson	
23	Napoleon	2.00
	Kaufman,	
	Tim Brown	
24	Kevin Johnson,	15.00
	Tim Couch	
25	Duce Staley,	10.00
	Donovan McNabb	

1999 Leaf Rookies & Stars Ticket Masters Executives

This was a parallel to the Ticket Master insert. Each of these singles was die cut and numbered to 50.

	MT
Executive Cards:	5x-10x
Production 50 Sets	

1999 Leaf Rookies & Stars Touchdown Club

This 20-card insert set included the players who see the end zone the most. Each of these singles was sequentially numbered to 1,000. A parallel Die Cut version was also produced with each of those singles numbered to 60.

		MT
Complete Set (20):		150.00
Common Player:		4.00
Production 1,000 Sets		
1	Randy Moss	20.00
2	Brett Favre	20.00
3	Dan Marino	15.00
4	Barry Sanders	20.00
5	John Elway	15.00
6	Terrell Davis	15.00
7	Peyton Manning	15.00
8	Emmitt Smith	15.00
9	Jerry Rice	12.00
10	Fred Taylor	12.00
11	Drew Bledsoe	8.00
12	Steve Young	8.00
13	Eddie George	5.00
14	Cris Carter	4.00
15	Antonio Freeman	4.00
16	Marvin Harrison	4.00
17	Kurt Warner	30.00

18	Stephen Davis	4.00
19	Terry Glenn	4.00
20	Brad Johnson	4.00

1999 Leaf Rookies & Stars Touchdown Club Die Cuts

This was a parallel to the Touchdown Club insert. Each of these singles was sequentially numbered to 60 and was die cut.

	MT
Die-Cut Cards:	3x-6x
Production 60 Sets	

1961 Lions Jay Publishing

Measuring approximately 5" x 7", the 12-card set showcases black-and-white photos of players in the vintage football card poses. The blank-backed cards were sold in 12-card packs for 25 cents. The cards were unnumbered.

		NM
Complete Set (12):		65.00
Common Player:		5.00
1	Carl Brettschneider	5.00
2	Howard Cassady	6.00
3	Gail Cogdill	5.00
4	Jim Gibbons	6.00
5	Alex Karras	12.00
6	Yale Lary	10.00
7	Jim Martin	5.00
8	Earl Morrall	8.00
9	Jim Ninowski	6.00
10	Nick Pietrosante	6.00
11	Joe Schmidt	10.00
12	George Wilson	5.00

1964 Lions White Border

Measuring 7-3/8" x 9-3/8", the 24-card set includes black-and-white photos that are bordered in white. The player's name and position, along with the Detroit Lions, are printed under the photo. The unnumbered cards could have been released in many series, as later cards have a date stamped on the otherwise blank backs.

		NM
Complete Set (24):		90.00
Common Player:		4.00
1	Dick Compton	4.00
2	Larry Ferguson	4.00
3	Dennis Gaubatz	4.00
4	Jim Gibbons	5.00
5	John Gonzaga	4.00
6	John Gordy	5.00
7	Tom Hall	4.00
8	Roger LaLonde	4.00
9	Dan LaRose	4.00
10	Yale Lary	10.00
11	Dan Lewis	5.00
12	Gary Lowe	4.00
13	Bruce Maher	5.00
14	Hugh McInnis	4.00
15	Max Messner	4.00
16	Floyd Peters	6.00
17	Daryl Sanders	4.00
18	Joe Schmidt	12.00
19	Bob Scholtz	4.00
20	James Simon	4.00
21	J.D. Smith	5.00
22	Bill Quinlan	4.00
23	Bob Whitlow	4.00
24	Sam Williams	4.00

1966 Lions Marathon Oil

The 5" x 7" photos showcase black-and-white photos on the front, surrounded by white borders. The player's name, position and Detroit Lions are printed under the photo. The backs are unnumbered and blank.

		NM
Complete Set (7):		42.00
Common Player:		5.00
1	Gail Cogdill	5.00
2	John Gordy	5.00
3	Alex Karras	15.00
4	Ron Kramer	6.00

5	Milt Plum	8.00
6	Wayne Rasmussen	5.00
7	Daryl Sanders	5.00

1986 Lions Police

Measuring 2-5/8" x 4-1/8", this 14-card police set is sponsored by Oscar Mayer, WJR/WHYT, Detroit Lions, Claussen, Pontiac Police Athletic League and the Detroit Crime Prevention Section. Card fronts have the player's name, uniform number and position in a box at the bottom center, while the Lions' logo is at the top center. A white border surrounds the photo. The card backs have the player's name, bio and highlights in a box on the left of the horizontal backed cards. A safety tip is located on the right.

		MT
Complete Set (14):		5.00
Common Player:		.50
1	William Gay	.50
2	Pontiac Silverdome	.60
3	Leonard Thompson	.60
4	Eddie Murray	1.00
5	Eric Hipple	1.00
6	James Jones	.75
7	Darryl Rogers (CO)	.75
8	Chuck Long	.75
9	Garry James	.60
10	Michael Cofer	.60
11	Jeff Chadwick	.60
12	Jimmy Williams	.50
13	Keith Dorney	.50
14	Bobby Watkins	.50

1987 Lions Police

Measuring 2-5/8" x 4-1/8", the 14-card set is sponsored by Oscar Mayer, WJR/WHYT, Claussen, Detroit Lions, Pontiac Police Athletic League and the Detroit Crime Prevention Section. The card fronts have the Lions and NFL logos at the top, with the photo in the center. The player's name, uniform number and position are printed inside a box at the bottom center. The Oscar Mayer and Claussen logos are in the lower corners of the card front. The card backs include a cartoon in the upper left, with the player's highlights. The upper left has a safety tip.

		MT
Complete Set (14):		5.00
Common Player:		.40
1	Michael Cofer,	.50
	Vernon Maxwell,	
	William Gay	
2	Rich Strenger	.40
3	Keith Ferguson	.40
4	James Jones	.50
5	Jeff Chadwick	.40
6	Devon Mitchell	.40
7	Eddie Murray	.75
8	Reggie Rogers	.50
9	Chuck Long	.60
10	Jimmie Giles	.50
11	Eric Williams	.40
12	Lomas Brown	.50
13	Jimmy Williams	.40
14	Garry James	.50

1988 Lions Police

Measuring 2-5/8" x 4-1/8", the 14-card set boasts 13 single-player cards which feature veterans. The remaining card has three of the Lions' top three 1988 draft picks. The card fronts have the Lions logo under the photo, which is opposite the 1987 Lions Police set. The card backs have the standard career highlights and safety tips.

		MT
Complete Set (14):		5.00
Common Player:		.50
1	Rob Rubick	.50
2	Paul Butcher	.50
3	Pete Mandley	.60
4	Jimmy Williams	.50
5	Harvey Salem	.50
6	Chuck Long	.60
7	Pat Carter, Bennie	1.00
	Blades, Chris	
	Spielman	
8	Jerry Ball	.75

9	Lomas Brown	.60
10	Dennis Gibson	.50
11	Jim Arnold	.50
12	Michael Cofer	.50
13	James Jones	.60
14	Steve Mott	.50

1989 Lions Police

Measuring 2-5/8" x 4-1/8", the 12-card set has the Lions logo and NFL shields at the top. The player's name, uniform number and position are printed in a box at the bottom, sandwiched between Oscar Mayer and Claussen logos. The backs feature a cartoon in the upper left, with a highlight directly under it. The horizontal backs also include a safety tip in the upper right. A WWJ logo is printed on the bottom left, with the card number located at bottom center. The cards are printed on thin paper stock. These cards were distributed in Michigan and Ontario.

		MT
Complete Set (12):		14.00
Common Player:		.35
1	George Jamison	.35
2	Wayne Fontes (CO)	.75
3	Kevin Glover	.35
4	Chris Spielman	1.00
5	Eddie Murray	.75
6	Bennie Blades	.75
7	Joe Milinichik	.35
8	Michael Cofer	.35
9	Jerry Ball	.50
10	Dennis Gibson	.35
11	Barry Sanders	10.00
12	Jim Arnold	.35

1990 Lions Police

Measuring 2-5/8" x 4-1/8", the 12-card set includes the player's name and position at the bottom center, with his uniform number printed in much larger type. The Oscar Mayer and Claussen logos are in the lower left and right corners, respectively. The card backs have the player's name at the top, with a drawing of him and highlight directly under. A "Little Oscar" safety tip is included in the lower left. The card number is in the lower right, along with the WWJ Radio logo.

		MT
Complete Set (12):		5.00
Common Player:		.35
1	William White	.35
2	Chris Spielman	.75
3	Rodney Peete	.75
4	Jimmy Williams	.35
5	Bennie Blades	.50
6	Barry Sanders	3.00
7	Jerry Ball	.50
8	Richard Johnson	.50
9	Michael Cofer	.35
10	Lomas Brown	.50
11	Joe Schmidt,	.50
	Andre Ware,	
	Wayne Fontes	
12	Eddie Murray	.50

1991 Lions Police

Measuring 2-5/8" x 4-1/8", the 12-card set was available through Michigan police officers. The yellow-bordered cards feature a color action photo, with the Oscar Mayer logo in the low-

er left, the player's name in the lower center and Lions helmet in the lower right. Above and below the player's name are blue horizontal lines. Card backs include a player photo at the top, with his position and name below it. A Little Oscar safety tip is in the lower left. The cards are numbered and are located in the lower right. The WWJ Radio logo is in the lower right.

		MT
Complete Set (12):		5.00
Common Player:		.35
1	Mel Gray	.50
2	Ken Dallafior	.35
3	Chris Spielman	.50
4	Bennie Blades	.50
5	Robert Clark	.50
6	Eric Andolsek	.50
7	Rodney Peete	.75
8	William White	.35
9	Lomas Brown	.50
10	Jerry Ball	.50
11	Michael Cofer	.35
12	Barry Sanders	3.00

1993 Lions 60th Season Commemorative

After years of odd-sized cards, the Lions finally introduced a standard-sized set. The 16-card set features full-bleed photos on the front, with the Lions' 60th anniversary logo in one of the upper corners. The player's name or, in some cases, the card's caption are printed in a rectangle at the bottom. The horizontal card backs feature the player's name and the years he played with the team in the upper left. His career highlights are printed along the left side, with a black-and-white headshot of the player in the upper right. The Lions' 60th anniversary logo is in the lower right, along with the card number. The cards were housed in a 6" x 8" black binder.

		MT
Complete Set (16):		10.00
Common Player:		.50
1	Barry Sanders	5.00
2	Joe Schmidt	1.00
3	The Fearsome	.75
	Foursome	
	(Sam Williams,	
	Roger Brown,	
	Alex Karras,	
	Darris McCord)	
4	Chris Spielman	.75
5	Billy Sims	.75
6	'40s Phenoms	.75
	(Alex	
	Wojciechowicz,	
	Byron White)	
7	Thunder and	.50
	Lightning	
	(Bennie Blades,	
	Mel Gray)	
8	Bobby Layne	1.50
9	Dutch Clark	.75
10	Great Games,	.50
	Thanksgiving 1962	
11	Charlie Sanders	.75
12	Lomas Brown	.50
13	Doug English	.75
14	Doak Walker	1.50
15	Roaring 20's	2.00
	(Lem Barney,	
	Billy Sims,	
	Barry Sanders)	
16	Anniversary Card	.50

1990 Little Big Leaguers

Boyhood photos and the highlights of the player's early athletic career are included in this 45-card set. The book, published by Simon and Schuster, included five 8-1/2" x 11" sheets, which included nine perforated cards. The card fronts included a black-and-white photo of the athlete as a child. A white border surrounds the card, with the player's name printed in a blue band at the top and "Little Football Big Leaguers" printed in a blue band at the bottom. The backs include the player's name,

position, team, bio and write-up. The cards are unnumbered.

		MT
Complete Set (45):		40.00
Common Player:		.50
1	Troy Aikman	10.00
2	Morten Andersen	.50
3	Jerry Ball	.50
4	Carl Banks	.75
5	Bennie Blades	.50
6	Brian Blades	.75
7	Joey Browner	.50
8	Keith Byars	.75
9	Anthony Carter	.75
10	Deron Cherry	.50
11	Roger Craig	.75
12	John Elway	7.00
13	Doug Flutie	1.00
14	Tim Goad	.50
15	Bob Golic	.50
16	Dino Hackett	.50
17	Dan Hampton	.75
18	Bobby Hebert	.75
19	Darryl Henley	.50
20	Wes Hopkins	.50
21	Hank Ilesic	.50
22	Tunch Ilkin	.50
23	Perry Kemp	.50
24	Bernie Kosar	.75
25	Mike Lansford	.50
26	Shawn Lee	.50
27	Charles Mann	.75
28	Dan Marino	14.00
29	Bruce Matthews	.75
30	Clay Matthews	.75
31	Freeman McNeil	.75
32	Warren Moon	2.00
33	Anthony Munoz	.75
34	Andre Reed	1.00
35	Andre Rison	.75
36	Phil Simms	.75
37	Mike Singletary	.75
38	Rohn Stark	.50
39	Kelly Stouffer	.50
40	Vinny Testaverde	.75
41	Doug Williams	.50
42	Marc Wilson	.50
43	Craig Wolfley	.50
44	Ron Wolfley	.50
45	Steve Young	7.00

M

1977 Marketcom Test

With posters measuring approximately 5-1/2" x 8-1/2", the set boasts only two confirmed mini-posters. The unnumbered posters each have folds in them. The posters are blank-backed, except for a Marketcom 1977 copyright tag line at the bottom.

		NM
Complete Set (2):		100.00
Common Player:		50.00
1	Greg Pruitt	50.00
2	Jack Youngblood	50.00

1978 Marketcom Test

These unnumbered posters, featuring 32 NFL stars, measure 5-1/2" x 8-1/2". The fronts feature full-color photos, along with the player's name in the upper left corner. Marketcom, which produced the set, is listed in the lower right corner. The backs are blank.

		NM
Complete Set (32):		225.00
Common Player:		4.00
(1)	Otis Armstrong	6.00
(2)	Steve Bartkowski	9.00
(3)	Terry Bradshaw	25.00
(4)	Earl Campbell	25.00
(5)	Dave Casper	7.00
(6)	Dan Dierdorf	10.00
(7)	Dan Fouts	15.00
(8)	Tony Galbreath	4.00
(9)	Randy Gradishar	7.00
(10)	Bob Griese	12.00
(11)	Steve Grogan	5.00
(12)	Ray Guy	6.00
(13)	Pat Haden	8.00
(14)	Jack Ham	7.00
(15)	Cliff Harris	7.00
(16)	Franco Harris	8.00
(17)	Jim Hart	5.00
(18)	Ron Jaworski	5.00

(19)	Bert Jones	10.00
(20)	Jack Lambert	10.00
(21)	Reggie McKenzie	4.00
(22)	Karl Mecklenberg	7.00
(23)	Craig Morton	5.00
(24)	Dan Pastorini	4.00
(25)	Walter Payton	25.00
(26)	Lee Roy Selmon	5.00
(27)	Roger Staubach	25.00
(28)	Joe Theismann (misspelled Theisman)	9.00
(29)	Wesley Walker	7.00
(30)	Randy White	7.00
(31)	Jack Youngblood	12.00
(32)	Jim Zorn	5.00

1980 Marketcom

These white-bordered posters, measuring 5-1/2" x 8-1/2", feature 50 NFL stars. The player's name appears at the top of the card; Marketcom, the set's producer, is credited in the bottom lower right corner. A white facsimile autograph also appears on the card front. The back has the player's name at the top, and a card number on the bottom (Mini-Poster 1 of 50, etc.). Marketcom, of St. Louis, sold the posters in packs of five.

		NM
Complete Set (50):		25.00
Common Player:		.50
1	Ottis Anderson	1.00
2	Brian Sipe	.60
3	Lawrence McCutcheon	.60
4	Ken Anderson	1.25
5	Roland Harper	.50
6	Chuck Foreman	.75
7	Gary Danielson	.50
8	Wallace Francis	.50
9	John Jefferson	.75
10	Charlie Waters	.75
11	Jack Ham	1.00
12	Jack Lambert	1.25
13	Walter Payton	5.00
14	Bert Jones	1.00
15	Harvey Martin	.75
16	Jim Hart	.60
17	Craig Morton	.75
18	Reggie McKenzie	.50
19	Keith Wortman	.50
20	Otis Armstrong	.75
21	Steve Grogan	.75
22	Jim Zorn	.75
23	Bob Griese	2.00
24	Tony Dorsett	2.00
25	Wesley Walker	.75
26	Dan Fouts	2.00
27	Dan Dierdorf	1.00
28	Steve Bartkowski	.75
29	Archie Manning	1.00
30	Randy Gradishar	.75
31	Randy White	1.25
32	Joe Theismann	2.00
33	Tony Galbreath	.50
34	Cliff Harris	.75
35	Ray Guy	1.00
36	Dave Casper	.75
37	Ron Jaworski	.75
38	Greg Pruitt	.75
39	Ken Burrough	.60
40	Robert Brazile	.60
41	Pat Haden	1.00
42	Dan Pastorini	.60
43	Lee Roy Selmon	.75
44	Franco Harris	2.00
45	Jack Youngblood	1.25
46	Terry Bradshaw	5.00
47	Roger Staubach	6.00
48	Earl Campbell	5.00
49	Phil Simms	3.00
50	Delvin Williams	.50

Post-1980 cards in Near Mint condition will generally sell for about 75% of the quoted Mint value. Excellent-condition cards bring no more than 40%.

1981 Marketcom

John Jefferson

The 1981 Marketcom posters are the first set to include detailed information on the back of the poster. Along with biographical and statistical information for 1980 and for the player's career, a comprehensive summary of the player's accomplishments is provided. A poster number is also given. Each poster, measuring 5-1/2" x 8-1/2", has a full-color action photo of the player on the front, along with his facsimile signature. His name is listed in the upper left corner.

		MT
Complete Set (50):		32.00
Common Player:		.50
1	Ottis Anderson	.75
2	Brian Sipe	.60
3	Rocky Bleier	.75
4	Ken Anderson	1.00
5	Roland Harper	.50
6	Steve Furness	.50
7	Gary Danielson	.50
8	Wallace Francis	.60
9	John Jefferson	.60
10	Charlie Waters	.75
11	Jack Ham	.75
12	Jack Lambert	1.25
13	Walter Payton	5.00
14	Bert Jones	1.00
15	Harvey Martin	.75
16	Jim Hart	.75
17	Craig Morton	.75
18	Reggie McKenzie	.50
19	Keith Wortman	.50
20	Joe Greene	1.50
21	Steve Grogan	.75
22	Jim Zorn	.75
23	Bob Griese	2.00
24	Tony Dorsett	2.50
25	Wesley Walker	.75
26	Dan Fouts	2.00
27	Dan Dierdorf	1.00
28	Steve Bartkowski	.75
29	Archie Manning	1.00
30	Randy Gradishar	.75
31	Randy White	1.25
32	Joe Theismann	2.00
33	Tony Galbreath	.50
34	Cliff Harris	.75
35	Ray Guy	1.00
36	Joe Ferguson	.75
37	Ron Jaworski	.75
38	Greg Pruitt	.75
39	Ken Burrough	.60
40	Robert Brazile	.50
41	Pat Haden	1.00
42	Ken Stabler	2.00
43	Lee Roy Selmon	.75
44	Franco Harris	2.00
45	Jack Youngblood	1.25
46	Terry Bradshaw	6.00
47	Roger Staubach	6.00
48	Earl Campbell	4.00
49	Phil Simms	1.50
50	Delvin Williams	.50

1982 Marketcom

These 50 mini-posters from Marketcom are similar in design to the previous year's issue. Each poster is 5-1/2" x 8-1/2" and has a full-color action photo on the front, along with a facsimile signature in white letters. The backs are similar to the backs of the 1981 posters - they have a detailed career summary and biographical information, plus statistics for the player's career and 1981 season. In addition to a number, the back also says "St. Louis - Marketcom - Series C".

	MT
Complete Set (48):	175.00

1982 Marketcom Cowboys

Measuring 5-1/2" x 8-1/2", these nine NFL mini-posters feature the player at the top left, with a color photo dominating the white-bordered fronts. The player's facsimile autograph also appears on the photo. The unnumbered card backs showcase the player's name at the top, with his bio directly underneath. His career highlights are also included. "St. Louis Marketcom" is printed in the lower right of the back. Some experts say a 10th card may exist.

		MT
Complete Set (9):		50.00
Common Player:		5.00
1	Bob Breunig	5.00
2	Pat Donovan	5.00
3	Michael Downes	5.00
4	Butch Johnson	6.00
5	Harvey Martin	6.00
6	Timmy Newsome	5.00
7	Drew Pearson	6.00
8	Danny White	8.00
9	Randy White	10.00

1971 Mattel Mini-Records

Measuring approximately 2-1/2" in diameter, each of the 17 discs in the set were to be played on a specially made Mattel mini-record player. Some discs were packaged four to a pack, like Olsen, Hayes, Sayers and Brodie or Mackey, Lamonica, Simpson and Butkus. Other packs showcased eight discs and a Joe Namath or Bart Starr booklet. The discs have color artwork on one side and the recording on the reverse. The recording side has the player's name and "Instant Replay."

		NM
Complete Set (17):		200.00
Common Player:		4.00
1	Donny Anderson	4.00
2	Lem Barney	6.00
3	John Brodie (DP)	6.00
4	Dick Butkus (DP)	15.00
5	Bob Hayes (DP)	6.00
6	Sonny Jurgensen	10.00
7	Alex Karras	10.00
8	Leroy Kelly	9.00
9	Daryle Lamonica (DP)	4.00
10	John Mackey (DP)	6.00
11	Earl Morrall	4.00
12	Joe Namath	50.00
13	Merlin Olsen (DP)	6.00
14	Alan Page	9.00
15	Gale Sayers (DP)	9.00
16	O.J. Simpson (DP)	25.00
17	Bart Starr	30.00
NNO	Record Player	100.00

1894 Mayo

Thirty-five Ivy League college football players are included in this 35-card set. The card fronts include a sepia-toned photo and a black border. The player's name, college and Mayo Cut Plug advertisement are printed at the bottom. The un-numbered cards measure 1-5/8" x 2-7/8".

		NM
Complete Set (35):		32500.
Common Player:		750.00
1	R Acton (Harvard)	750.00
2	George Adee (Yale AA94)	1500.
3	R. Armstrong (Yale)	1000.
4	H.W. Barnett (Princeton)	1200.
5	A.M. Beale (Harvard)	825.00
6	Anson Beard (Yale)	1600.
7	Charles Brewer (Harvard AA92/93/95)	750.00
8	Brown (Princeton)	1200.
9	Burt (Princeton)	1000.
10	Frank Butterworth (Yale AA93/94)	750.00
11	Eddie Crowdis (Princeton)	900.00
12	Robert Emmons (Harvard)	1000.
13	M.G. Gonterman (UER Harvard) (Misspelled Gouterman)	1000.
14	G.A. Grey (Harvard)	750.00
15	John Greenway (Yale)	900.00
16	William Hickok (Yale AA93/94)	1000.
17	Frank Hinkey (Yale AA91/92/93/94)	4500.
18	Augustus Holly (Princeton)	1000.
19	Langdon Lea (Princeton AA93/94/95)	900.00
20	W.C. Mackie (Harvard)	1000.
21	T.J. Manahan (Harvard)	1000.
22	Jim McCrea (Yale)	1000.
23	Frank Morse (Princeton AA93)	750.00
24	Fred Murphy (Yale AA95/96)	1000.
25	Poe (Princeton thought to be Neilson or Arthur)	3500.
26	Dudley Riggs (Princeton AA95)	1200.
27	Phillip Stillman (Yale AA94)	1200.
28	Knox Taylor (Princeton)	1500.
29	Brinck Thorne (Yale AA95)	800.00
30	Thomas Trenchard (Princeton AA93)	750.00
31	William Ward (Princeton)	800.00
32	Bert Waters (Harvard AA92/94)	1000.
33	Arthur Wheeler (Princeton AA92/93/94)	1000.
34	Edgar Wrightington (Harvard AA96)	1000.
35	Anonymous (reportedly John Dunlop-Harvard)	3000.

1975 McDonald's Quarterbacks

Measuring 2-1/2" x 3-7/16", this four-card set was a McDonald's promotion. The yellow-bordered card fronts showcase the player's name and team at the top, with a photo in the center. Printed below the photo is "Get a quarter back..." The McDonald's logo is in the lower right. The backs of each card have different colors. The unnumbered card backs have the player's name, position and team at the top, with his stats below. The perforated coupon below explains the promotion. Each card was good for one week. Prices are for cards which have the coupons intact.

		NM
Complete Set (4):		10.00
Common Player:		.50
1	Terry Bradshaw	6.00
2	Joe Ferguson	1.00
3	Ken Stabler	4.00
4	Al Woodall	.50

1985 McDonald's Bears

This 32-card set picturing only Chicago Bears was issued by McDonald's in the Chicago area, apparently to test the concept of using football cards as a promotion. The full-color cards have three different tab colors (blue, orange, yellow), each referring to a specific week in the playoffs or Super Bowl. The cards measure approximately 4-1/2" x 5-7/8" with the tab intact. The prices below are for cards with the tab intact. Cards without the tabs have little collector value and are worth considerably less. Because of space limitations, only players with a significant value over common price are listed individually. Players not listed are worth approximately the common price (or perhaps slightly above for minor stars). The individual values listed are for the least expensive color tabs (yellow or orange). Cards with blue tabs are worth about twice as much as values listed. Card numbers refer to a player's uniform number.

		MT
Complete Set (Blue):		45.00
Complete Set (Orange):		25.00
Complete Set (Yellow):		20.00
Common Player:		.50
4	Steve Fuller	.75
6	Kevin Butler	1.00
8	Maury Buford	.50
9	Jim McMahon	2.50
21	Leslie Frazier	.50
22	Dave Duerson	.50
26	Matt Suhey	.75
27	Mike Richardson	.50
29	Dennis Gentry	.50
33	Calvin Thomas	.50
34	Walter Payton	7.00
45	Gary Fencik	.75
50	Mike Singletary	2.50
55	Otis Wilson	.50
58	Wilber Marshall	1.00
62	Mark Bortz	.50
63	Jay Hilgenberg	.75
72	William Perry	1.25
73	Mike Hartenstine	.50
74	Jim Covert	.75
76	Stefan Humphries	.50
76	Steve McMichael	1.00
78	Keith Van Horne	.50
80	Tim Wrightman	.50
82	Ken Margerum	.50
83	Willie Gault	1.00
85	Dennis McKinnon	.75
87	Emery Moorehead	.50
95	Richard Dent	2.00
99	Dan Hampton	2.00
	Mike Ditka (CO)	2.50
	Buddy Ryan (ACO)	1.50

1986 McDonald's All-Stars

Measuring 3-1/16" x 4-11/16" with the tab intact or 3-1/16" x 3-5/8" without, this 30-

card set was for participating McDonald's outside of an NFL market. Released over four weeks, the set featured different colored tabs -- with blue (first week), black or gray (second week), gold or orange (third week) and green (fourth week). The backs feature McDonald's All-Star Team printed at the top. Also included on the backs are the player's name, jersey number, career and 1985 highlights and a 1986 copyright date.

		MT
Complete Set (Blue):		6.00
Complete Set (Black):		6.00
Complete Set (Gold):		6.00
Complete Set (Green):		6.00
Common Player:		.15
9	Jim McMahon	.35
11	Phil Simms	.35
13	Dan Marino	2.50
14	Dan Fouts	.35
16	Joe Montana	2.00
20A	Deron Cherry	.15
20B	Joe Morris	.15
32	Marcus Allen	.35
33	Roger Craig	.25
34A	Kevin Mack	.25
35B	Walter Payton	1.75
42	Gerald Riggs	.15
45	Kenny Easley	.15
47A	Joey Browner	.15
47B	LeRoy Irvin	.15
52	Mike Webster	.25
54A	E.J. Junior	.15
54B	Randy White	.25
56	Lawrence Taylor	.35
63	Mike Munchak	.15
66	Joe Jacoby	.15
73	John Hannah	.25
75A	Chris Hinton	.15
75B	Rulon Jones	.15
75C	Howie Long	.25
78	Anthony Munoz	.25
81	Art Monk	.35
82A	Ozzie Newsome	.35
82B	Mike Quick	.15
99	Mark Gastineau	.15

1986 McDonald's Chicago Bears

Released in the Chicago area, the 24-card set was released over four weeks at participating McDonald's. The tab colors were as follows: blue (first week), black or gray (second), gold or orange (third) and green (fourth). With the tab intact, the cards measure 3-1/16" x 4-11/16" and 3-1/16" x 3-5/8" without. The card fronts have the McDonald's logo in the upper left, Bears helmet in the upper right, NFL shield in the lower left and the NFLPA logo in the lower right. The card backs have "Super Bowl Collectors Edition" at the top. The player's name, uniform number, bio and 1986 and career highlights are also listed on the backs.

		MT
Complete Set (Blue):		15.00
Complete Set (Black):		7.50
Complete Set (Gold):		7.50
Complete Set (Green):		7.50
Common Player:		.30
6	Kevin Butler (DP)	.40
8	Maury Buford	.30
9	Jim McMahon (DP)	1.25
22	Dave Duerson	.30
26	Matt Suhey	.40
27	Mike Richardson	.30
34	Walter Payton (DP)	1.75
45	Gary Fencik	.40
50	Mike Singletary (DP)	1.25
55	Otis Wilson	.30
57	Tom Thayer	.30

58	Wilber Marshall	.50
62	Mark Bortz (DP)	.30
63	Jay Hilgenberg	.40
72	William Perry (DP)	.50
74	Jim Covert	.40
76	Steve McMichael	.50
78	Keith Van Horne	.30
80	Tim Wrightman	.30
82	Ken Margerum	.30
83	Willie Gault	.50
87	Emery Moorehead	.30
95	Richard Dent	1.00
99	Dan Hampton	1.00

1986 McDonald's Cincinnati Bengals

The Cincinnati area received the benefits of this 24-card set, which was part of the McDonald's promotion of 1986. The card fronts showcase the McDonald's logo in the upper left, with the Cincinnati helmet in the upper right. The NFL shield and NFLPA logos appear in the bottom left and right, respectively, of the color action photo. Card backs feature the player's number, name, bio, stats and highlights. The cards measure 3-1/16" x 4-11/16" with the tab and 3-1/16" x 3-5/8" without. Released over four weeks, the first week's cards had blue tabs, second week had black or gray, third had gold or orange and the fourth week tabs were green.

		MT
Complete Set (Blue):		25.00
Complete Set (Black):		12.50
Complete Set (Gold):		12.50
Complete Set (Green):		12.50
Common Player:		.50
7	Boomer Esiason	2.50
14	Ken Anderson (DP)	1.00
20	Ray Horton	.60
21	James Brooks (DP)	1.00
22	James Griffin	.50
28	Larry Kinnebrew	.60
34	Louis Breeden (DP)	.50
37	Robert Jackson	.50
40	Charles Alexander (DP)	.50
52	Dave Rimington	.60
57	Reggie Williams	.75
65	Max Montoya	.60
69	Tim Krumrie	.75
73	Eddie Edwards	.60
74	Brian Blados (DP)	.50
77	Mike Wilson	.50
78	Anthony Munoz	1.25
79	Ross Browner	.60
80	Cris Collinsworth	1.00
81	Eddie Brown (DP)	.75
82	Rodney Holman	.60
83	M.L. Harris	.50
90	Emanuel King	.50
91	Carl Zander	.50

1986 McDonald's Buffalo Bills

Measuring 3-1/16" x 4-11/16" with the tab and 3-1/16" x 3-5/8" without, the 24-card set was distributed over four weeks of the 1986 season in the Buffalo area. In the top corners of the color action photo on the card front were the McDonald's logo and Bills helmet. At the bottom corners of the photo were the NFL shield and NFLPA logo. The player's name, number and position appear under the photo. The card backs have the player's name, jersey number and highlights. Each week

---

featured a different colored tab: blue (first), black or gray (second), gold or orange (third) and green (fourth).

		MT
Complete Set (Blue):		150.00
Complete Set (Black):		30.00
Complete Set (Gold):		15.00
Complete Set (Green):		15.00
Common Player:		.75
4	John Kidd	.75
7	Bruce Mathison	.75
11	Scott Norwood	1.00
22	Steve Freeman	.75
26	Charles Romes	.75
28	Greg Bell (DP)	1.00
29	Derrick Burroughs (DP)	.75
43	Martin Bayless (DP)	.75
51	Jim Ritcher	1.00
54	Eugene Marve	.75
55	Jim Haslett	.75
57	Lucius Sanford	.75
63	Justin Cross	.75
65	Tim Vogler	.75
70	Joe Devlin	.75
72	Ken Jones	.75
76	Fred Smerlas	1.00
77	Ben Williams	1.00
78	Bruce Smith	5.00
80	Jerry Butler (DP)	1.00
83	Andre Reed	5.00
85	Chris Burkett (DP)	1.00
87	Eason Ramson	.75
95	Sean McNanie	.75

1986 McDonald's Denver Broncos

Released over four weeks in the Denver area during the 1986 season, this 24-card set measured 3-1/16" x 4-11/16" with the tab and 3-1/16" x 3-5/8" without. The card fronts and backs followed the same format as the other McDonald's sets of that season. Each week's cards featured a different colored tab: blue (first), black or gray (second), gold or orange (third) and green (fourth).

		MT
Complete Set (Blue):		25.00
Complete Set (Black):		8.00
Complete Set (Gold):		8.00
Complete Set (Green):		8.00
Common Player:		.30
3	Rich Karlis	.30
7	John Elway	3.50
20	Louis Wright	.40
22	Tony Lilly	.30
23	Sammy Winder	.40
30	Steve Sewell	.40
31	Mike Harden	.40
43	Steve Foley	.40
47	Gerald Wilhite	.40
49	Dennis Smith	.50
54	Jim Ryan	.30
54	Keith Bishop (DP)	.30
57	Rick Dennison (DP)	.30
57	Tom Jackson	1.25
60	Paul Howard	.30
64	Bill Bryan (DP)	.30
68	Rubin Carter (DP)	.30
70	Dave Studdard	.30
75	Rulon Jones	.40
77	Karl Mecklenburg	.60
79	Barney Chavous (DP)	.30
81	Steve Watson	.40
82	Vance Johnson	.60
84	Clint Sampson	.30

1986 McDonald's Cleveland Browns

Issued over four weeks of the 1986 season in the Cleveland area, the 24-card set measure 3-

---

1/16" x 4-11/16" with the tab and 3-1/16" x 3-5/8" without. The card fronts feature a color photo, with the McDonald's logo in the upper left and Browns helmet in the upper right. The NFL shields and NFLPA logo are on the bottom corners, left and right respectively. The card backs have the player's name, jersey number, bio and highlights. Each week's cards featured different colored tabs: blue (first), black or gray (second), gold or orange (third) and green (fourth).

		MT
Complete Set (Blue):		10.00
Complete Set (Black):		6.00
Complete Set (Gold):		6.00
Complete Set (Green):		6.00
Common Player:		.25
9	Matt Bahr (DP)	.25
18	Gary Danielson	.25
19	Bernie Kosar (DP)	1.75
27	Al Gross	.25
29	Hanford Dixon	.35
31	Frank Minnifield	.35
34	Kevin Mack	.50
37	Chris Rockins	.25
44	Earnest Byner	.75
57	Eddie Johnson	.25
55	Curtis Weathers	.25
56	Chip Banks (DP)	.35
57	Clay Matthews	.50
60	Tom Cousineau	.25
61	Mike Baab (DP)	.25
63	Cody Risien	.35
77	Rickey Bolden (DP)	.25
78	Carl Hairston	.25
79	Bob Golic	.35
82	Ozzie Newsome	1.00
84	Glen Young	.25
85	Clarence Weathers	.25
88	Brian Brennan (DP)	.35
96	Reggie Camp	.25

1986 McDonald's Tampa Bay Buccaneers

Issued over four weeks in the Tampa area during the 1986 season, the 24-card set measures 3-1/16" x 4-11/16" with the tab and 3-1/16" x 3-5/8" without. The card fronts have a color photo, with the McDonald's logo in the upper left and Tampa Bay helmet in the upper right. The NFL shield and NFLPA logo are in the bottom corners, left and right respectively. The card backs have the player's name, jersey number, bio and highlights. Each week's cards had different colored tabs: blue (first), black or gray (second), gold or orange (third) and green (fourth).

		MT
Complete Set (Blue):		15.00
Complete Set (Black):		15.00
Complete Set (Gold):		15.00
Complete Set (Green):		15.00
Common Player:		.30
1	Donald Igwebuike	.30
8	Steve Young	8.00
17	Steve DeBerg	.75
21	John Holt	.30
23	Jeremiah Castille (DP)	.30
30	David Greenwood	.30
43	James Wilder	.50
44	Ivory Sully	.30
51	Chris Washington	.30
54	Scot Brantley	.30
54	Ervin Randle	.30
58	Jeff Davis (DP)	.30
60	Randy Grimes	.30
62	Sean Farrell	.40
66	George Yarno	.30
73	Ron Heller	.30
76	David Logan	.30

78	John Cannon (DP)	.30
82	Jerry Bell (DP)	.30
86	Calvin Magee	.30
87	Gerald Carter	.30
88	Jimmie Giles	.50
89	Kevin House	.50
90	Ron Holmes	.30

1986 McDonald's St. Louis Cardinals

Released over four weeks in the St. Louis area during the 1986 season, the 24-card set measures 3-1/16" x 4-11/16" with the tabs and 3-1/16" x 3-5/8" without. The card fronts showcase a color photo, with the McDonald's logo in the upper left and the Cardinals' helmet in the upper right. The NFL shield and NFLPA logo appear at the bottom, left and right respectively. The player's name, jersey number and position are printed under the photo. The card backs showcase the player's name, jersey number, bio and highlights. Each week's card had a different colored tab: blue (first), black or gray (second), gold or orange (third) and green (fourth).

		MT
Complete Set (Blue):		10.00
Complete Set (Black):		6.00
Complete Set (Gold):		6.00
Complete Set (Green):		6.00
Common Player:		.25
9	Matt Bahr (DP)	.25
18	Gary Danielson	.25
19	Bernie Kosar (DP)	1.75
27	Al Gross	.25
29	Hanford Dixon	.35
31	Frank Minnifield	.35
34	Kevin Mack	.50
37	Chris Rockins	.25
44	Earnest Byner	.75
55	Curtis Weathers	.25
56	Chip Banks (DP)	.35
57	Clay Matthews	.50
60	Tom Cousineau	.25
61	Mike Baab (DP)	.25
63	Cody Risien	.35
77	Rickey Bolden (DP)	.25
78	Carl Hairston	.25
79	Bob Golic	.35
82	Ozzie Newsome	1.00
84	Glen Young	.25
85	Clarence Weathers	.25
88	Brian Brennan (DP)	.35
96	Reggie Camp	.25

1986 McDonald's Kansas City Chiefs

Released over a four-week time span at Kansas City area McDonald's, the 24-card set measures 3-1/16" x 4-11/16" with the tab and 3-1/16" x 3-5/8" without. Anchored with a color photo on the card front, the McDonald's logo is in the upper left and Chiefs' helmet in the upper right. The NFL shield and NFLPA logo are in the bottom corners, left and right respectively. The player's name, jersey number and position are located under the photo. The card backs have the player's name, jersey number, position, bio and career highlights. Each week's cards had different colored tabs: blue (first), black or gray (second), gold or orange (third) and green (fourth).

		MT
Complete Set (Blue):		20.00
Complete Set (Black):		40.00
Complete Set (Gold):		20.00
Complete Set (Green):		20.00
Common Player:		.75
6	Jim Arnold (DP)	.75
8	Nick Lowery	1.00
9	Bill Kenney	.75
14	Todd Blackledge (DP)	1.00
20	Deron Cherry (DP)	1.25
29	Albert Lewis	1.50
31	Kevin Ross	1.25
34	Lloyd Burruss (DP)	.75
41	Garcia Lane	.75
42	Jeff Smith	.75
43	Mike Pruitt	1.00
44	Herman Heard	.75
50	Calvin Daniels	.75

Released over four weeks in the San Diego area, the 24-card set measures 3-1/16" x 4-11/16"

---

with the tab and 3-1/16" x 3-5/8" without. The card fronts showcase a color photo, with the McDonald's logo in the upper right, Chargers' helmet in the upper right and NFLPA logo in the lower right. The player's name, jersey number and position are printed under the photo. The card backs include the player's name, number, position, bio and highlights. Each week's cards had a different colored tab: blue (first), black or gray (second), gold or orange (third) and green (fourth).

		MT
Complete Set (Blue):		20.00
Complete Set (Black):		15.00
Complete Set (Gold):		10.00
Complete Set (Green):		10.00
Common Player:		.40
9	Mark Herrmann	.40
14	Dan Fouts	1.50
18	Charlie Joiner	1.25
21	Buford McGee	.40
22	Gill Byrd (DP)	.50
26	Lionel James	.50
29	John Hendy	.40
37	Jeff Dale (DP)	.40
40	Gary Anderson (RB) (DP)	.75
43	Tim Spencer	.40
51	Woodrow Lowe	.40
54	Bill Ray Smith	.50
62	Dennis McKnight	.40
62	Don Macek	.40
63	Ed White	.50
74	Jim Lachey	.50
78	Chuck Ehin (DP)	.40
80	Kellen Winslow	1.50
83	Trumaine Johnson	.40
85	Eric Sievers	.40
88	Pete Holohan	.50
89	Wes Chandler (DP)	.50
93	Earl Wilson	.40
99	Lee Williams	.50

1986 McDonald's San Diego Chargers

Released over four weeks in the San Diego area, the 24-card set measures 3-1/16" x 4-11/16"

59	Gary Spani	.75
63	Bill Maas	.75
65	Bob Olderman	.75
66	Brad Budde (DP)	.75
67	Art Still	.75
72	David Lutz	.75
83	Stephone Paige	1.25
85	Jonathan Hayes	1.00
88	Carlos Carson (DP)	1.00
89	Henry Marshall	.75
97	Scott Radecic	.75

1986 McDonald's Indianapolis Colts

Released during a four-week time span at Indianapolis McDonald's, the 24-card set measures 3-1/16" x 4-11/16" with the tab and 3-1/16" x 3-5/8" without. Anchored with a color photo, the card fronts have a McDonald's logo in the upper left and a Colts' helmet in the upper right. The NFL shield and NFLPA logo are in the bottom corners, left and right respectively. The player's name, number and position are printed below the photo. The card backs showcase the player's name, number, bio and highlights. Each week's cards featured different colored tabs: blue (first), black or gray (second), gold or orange (third) and green (fourth).

		MT
Complete Set (Blue):		100.00
Complete Set (Black):		20.00
Complete Set (Gold):		15.00
Complete Set (Green):		20.00
Common Player:		.60
2	Raul Allegre (DP)	.60
3	Rohn Stark	.75
25	Nesby Glasgow	.60
27	Preston Davis	.60
32	Randy McMillian	.75
34	George Wonsley	.60
38	Eugene Daniel	.75
44	Owen Gill	.60
47	Leonard Coleman	.60
50	Duane Bickett (DP)	1.00
53	Ray Donaldson	.75
55	Barry Krauss	.60
64	Ben Utt	.60
66	Ron Solt	.60
72	Karl Baldischwiler (DP)	.60
75	Chris Hinton	.75
81	Pat Beach (DP)	.60
85	Matt Bouza (DP)	.60
87	Wayne Capers (DP)	.60
88	Robbie Martin	.60
92	Brad White	.60
93	Cliff Odom	.60
96	Blaise Winter	.60
98	Johnie Cooks	.60

1986 McDonald's Dallas Cowboys

Issued over four weeks at Dallas-area McDonald's, the 25-

card set measures 3-1/16" x 4-11/16" with the tab and 3-1/16" x 3-5/8" without. The card fronts boast a color photo, with the McDonald's logo in the upper left and Dallas helmet in the upper right. The NFL shield and NFLPA logo are located in the lower corners, left and right respectively. The player's name, number and position are printed under the photo. The card backs feature the player's name, number, bio and highlights. Each week's cards featured a different colored tab: blue (first), black or gray (second), gold or orange (third) and green (fourth).

		MT
Complete Set (Blue):		10.00
Complete Set (Black):		10.00
Complete Set (Gold):		10.00
Complete Set (Green):		10.00
Common Player:		.25
1	Rafael Septien	.25
11	Danny White	.50
24	Everson Walls	.35
26	Michael Downs (DP)	.25
27	Ron Fellows	.25
30	Timmy Newsome	.25
33	Tony Dorsett (DP)	1.50
34	Herschel Walker	2.00
40	Bill Bates (DP)	.50
47	Dexter Clinkscale	.25
50	Jeff Rohrer	.25
54	Randy White	.75
56	Eugene Lockhart	.35
58	Mike Hegman	.25
61	Jim Cooper (DP)	.25
63	Glen Titensor	.25
64	Tom Rafferty	.25
65	Kurt Peterson	.25
72	Ed "Too Tall" Jones	.75
75	Phil Pozderac	.25
77	Jim Jeffcoat	.50
78	John Dutton	.35
80	Tony Hill	.35
82	Mike Renfro	.25
84	Doug Cosbie (DP)	.25

1986 McDonald's Miami Dolphins

Issued over four weeks at Miami-area McDonald's, the 25-card set measure 3-1/16" x 4-11/16" with the tab and 3-1/16" x 3-5/8" without. Each card front is anchored with a color photo, with the McDonald's logo in the upper left and Miami helmet in the upper right. The NFL shield and NFLPA logo are in the bottom corners, left and right respectively. Below the photo are the player's name, number and position. The card backs showcase the player's name, number, position and highlights. Each week's cards featured a different colored tab: blue (first), black or gray (second), gold or orange (third) and green (fourth).

		MT
Complete Set (Blue):		40.00
Complete Set (Black):		20.00
Complete Set (Gold):		20.00
Complete Set (Green):		20.00
Common Player:		.50
4	Reggie Roby	.75
7	Fuad Reveiz	.75
10	Don Strock	.75
13	Dan Marino	10.00
22	Tony Nathan	.75
23A	Joe Carter (ERR) (Photo actually Tony Nathan 22)	.75
23B	Joe Carter (COR)	.50
27	Lorenzo Hampton	.50
30	Ron Davenport	.50
43	Bud Brown (DP)	.50
47	Glenn Blackwood (DP)	.50
49	William Judson	.50
55	Hugh Green	.75
57	Dwight Stephenson	.75
58	Kim Bokamper (DP)	.50
59	Bob Brudzinski (DP)	.50
61	Roy Foster	.50
71	Mike Charles	.50
75	Doug Betters (DP)	.50
79	Jon Giesler	.50
83	Mark Clayton	2.00
84	Bruce Hardy	.50
85	Mark Duper	1.00
89	Nat Moore	.75
91	Mack Moore	.50

A player's name in *italic type* indicates a rookie card.

1986 McDonald's Philadelphia Eagles

Issued over a four-week time span at Philadelphia-area McDonald's, the 24-card set measures 3-1/16" x 4-11/16" with the tab and 3-1/16" x 3-5/8" without. A color photo anchors the card front, with the McDonald's logo in the upper left and the Eagles' helmet in the upper right. The NFL shield and NFLPA logos are in the bottom corners, left and right respectively. The player's name, number and position are printed under the photo. The card backs have the player's name, number, bio and highlights. Each week's cards featured a different colored tab: blue (first), black or gray (second), gold or orange (third) and green (fourth).

		MT
Complete Set (Blue):		60.00
Complete Set (Black):		20.00
Complete Set (Gold):		10.00
Complete Set (Green):		10.00
Common Player:		.25
7	Ron Jaworski	.50
8	Paul McFadden	.25
12	Randall Cunningham (DP)	2.00
22	Brenard Wilson	.25
24	Ray Ellis	.25
29	Elbert Foules	.25
36	Herman Hunter	.35
41	Earnest Jackson	.35
43	Roynell Young	.25
48	Wes Hopkins	.25
50	Garry Cobb (DP)	.25
63	Ron Baker (DP)	.25
66	Ken Reeves	.25
71	Ken Clarke (DP)	.25
73	Steve Kenney	.25
74	Leonard Mitchell	.25
81	Kenny Jackson	.35
82	Mike Quick	.35
85	Ron Johnson	.25
88	John Spagnola	.25
91	Reggie White	4.00
93	Thomas Strauthers	.25
94	Byron Darby (DP)	.25
98	Greg Brown (DP)	.25

1986 McDonald's Atlanta Falcons

Released over a four-week time span at Atlanta-area McDonald's, the 24-card set measures 3-1/16" x 4-11/16" with the tab and 3-1/16" x 3-5/8" without. The card fronts are anchored with a color photo, with the McDonald's logo in the upper left and Falcons' helmet in the upper right. The NFL shield and NFLPA logo are located at the

bottom, left and right respectively. The player's name, number and position are printed below the photo. The card backs include the player's name, number, position, bio and highlights. Each week's cards featured a different colored tab: blue (first), black or gray (second), gold or orange (third) and green (fourth). The values listed are for cards with the tabs intact.

		MT
Complete Set (Blue):		60.00
Complete Set (Black):		200.00
Complete Set (Gold):		40.00
Complete Set (Green):		15.00
Common Player:		.60
3	Rick Donnelly	.60
16	Dave Archer (DP)	1.00
18	Mick Luckhurst	.60
23	Bobby Butler	.60
26	James Britt (DP)	.60
37	Kenny Johnson	.60
39	Cliff Austin	.60
42	Gerald Riggs	.75
50	Buddy Curry	.60
56	Al Richardson	.60
57	Jeff Van Note	.75
58	David Frye	.60
61	John Scully	.60
62	Brett Miller	.60
74	Mike Pitts	.60
76	Mike Gann	.60
77	Rick Bryan	.60
78	Mike Kenn	.75
79	Bill Fralic	1.00
81	Billy Johnson	.75
82	Stacey Bailey (DP)	.60
87	Cliff Benson (DP)	.60
88	Arthur Cox	.60
89	Charlie Brown (DP)	.75

1986 McDonald's San Francisco 49ers

Released over a four-week time span at San Francisco-area McDonald's, the 24-card set measures 3-1/16" x 4-11/16" with the tab and 3-1/16" x 3-5/8" without. The card fronts are anchored with a color photo, with the McDonald's logo in the upper left and 49ers' helmet in the upper right. The NFL shield and NFLPA logo are located at the bottom, left and right respectively. The player's name, number and position are printed below the photo. The card backs include the player's name, number, bio and highlights. Each week featured a different colored tab: blue (first), black or gray (second), gold or orange (third) and green (fourth). The values listed are for the tabs intact.

		MT
Complete Set (Blue):		50.00
Complete Set (Black):		25.00
Complete Set (Gold):		25.00
Complete Set (Green):		25.00
Common Player:		.75
16	Joe Montana	12.00
21	Eric Wright	1.00
26	Wendell Tyler	1.00
27	Carlton Williamson	.75
33	Roger Craig (DP)	1.25
42	Ronnie Lott	2.00
49	Jeff Fuller	.75
50	Riki Ellison	.75
51	Randy Cross (DP)	1.00
56	Fred Quillan	.75
58	Keena Turner	.75
62	Guy McIntyre	.75
68	John Ayers (DP)	.75
71	Keith Fahnhorst	.75
77	Jeff Stover	.75
76	Dwaine Board (DP)	.75
67	Bubba Paris	.75
78	Manu Tuiasosopo	.75
80	Jerry Rice	12.00
81	Russ Francis	1.00
86	John Frank	.75
87	Dwight Clark (DP)	1.00
90	Todd Shell	.75
95	Michael Carter (DP)	1.00

1986 McDonald's New York Giants

Released over a four-week time span at New York-area McDonald's, the 24-card set measures 3-1/16" x 4-11/16" with

the tab and 3-1/16" x 3-5/8" without. The card fronts are anchored with a color photo, with the McDonald's logo in the upper left and Giants' helmet in the upper right. The NFL shield and NFLPA logo are located at the bottom, left and right respectively. The player's name, number and position are printed below the photo. The card backs include the player's name, number, bio and highlights. Each week featured a different colored tab: blue (first), black or gray (second), gold or orange (third) and green (fourth). The values listed are for cards with the tabs intact.

		MT
Complete Set (Blue):		12.00
Complete Set (Black):		10.00
Complete Set (Gold):		6.00
Complete Set (Green):		6.00
Common Player:		.25
5	Sean Landeta	.35
11	Phil Simms	1.00
20	Joe Morris	.50
24	Perry Williams	.25
26	Rob Carpenter (DP)	.25
33	George Adams (DP)	.35
48	Elvis Patterson	.35
43	Terry Kinard	.25
47	Maurice Carthon	.25
48	Kenny Hill	.25
53	Harry Carson	.35
54	Andy Headen	.25
56	Lawrence Taylor	1.50
57	Brad Benson (DP)	.25
63	Karl Nelson	.25
64	Jim Burt (DP)	.35
67	Billy Ard (DP)	.25
70	Leonard Marshall	.35
75	George Martin	.25
80	Phil McConkey	.35
84	Zeke Mowatt	.25
85	Don Hasselbeck	.25
86	Lionel Manuel	.35
89	Mark Bavaro (DP)	.35

1986 McDonald's New York Jets

Released over a four-week time span at New York-area McDonald's, the 24-card set measures 3-1/16" x 4-11/16" with the tab and 3-1/16" x 3-5/8" without. The card fronts are anchored with a color photo, with the McDonald's logo in the upper left and Jets' helmet in the upper right. The NFL shield and NFLPA logo are located at the bottom, left and right respectively. The player's name, number and position are printed below the photo. The card backs include the player's name, number, bio and highlights. Each week featured a different colored tab: blue (first), black or gray (second), gold or orange (third) and green (fourth). The values listed are for cards with the tabs intact.

		MT
Complete Set (Blue):		150.00
Complete Set (Black):		150.00
Complete Set (Gold):		25.00
Complete Set (Green):		25.00
Common Player:		1.00
5	Pat Leahy	1.00
7	Ken O'Brien	1.50
21	Kirk Springs	1.00
24	Freeman McNeil	2.00
27	Russell Carter (DP)	1.00
29	Johnny Lynn	1.00
34	Johnny Hector	1.00
39	Harry Hamilton	1.00
49	Tony Paige	1.00
53	Jim Sweeney	1.00
55	Lance Mehl	1.00
59	Kyle Clifton (DP)	1.00
65	Dan Alexander (DP)	1.00
65	Joe Fields (DP)	1.00
73	Joe Klecko	1.25
68	Barry Bennett (DP)	1.00
80	Johnny Lam Jones	1.00
82	Mickey Shuler	1.00
85	Wesley Walker	1.25
87	Kurt Sohn	1.00
88	Al Toon	2.00
89	Rocky Klever	1.00
93	Marty Lyons	1.00
99	Mark Gastineau	1.50

A card number in parentheses ( ) indicates the set is unnumbered.

1986 McDonald's Detroit Lions

Released over a four-week time span at Detroit-area McDonald's, the 24-card set measures 3-1/16" x 4-11/16" with the tab and 3-1/16" x 3-5/8" without. The card fronts are anchored with a color photo, with the McDonald's logo in the upper left and Lions' helmet in the upper right. The NFL shield and NFLPA logo are located at the bottom, left and right respectively. The player's name, number and position are printed below the photo. The card backs include the player's name, number, bio and highlights. Each week featured a different colored tab: blue (first), black or gray (second), gold or orange (third) and green (fourth). The values listed are for cards which have the tabs intact.

		MT
Complete Set (Blue):		12.00
Complete Set (Black):		10.00
Complete Set (Gold):		6.00
Complete Set (Green):		6.00
Common Player:		.25
3	Eddie Murray	.35
11	Michael Black (DP)	.25
17	Eric Hipple	.35
20	Billy Sims	.50
21	Demetrious Johnson	.25
29	Bobby Watkins	.25
29	Bruce McNorton	.25
30	James Jones	.35
33	William Graham	.25
35	Alvin Hall	.25
48	Leonard Thompson	.35
50	August Curley (DP)	.25
54	Steve Mott	.25
55	Mike Cofer (DP)	.35
59	Jimmy Williams	.25
70	Keith Dorney (DP)	.25
71	Rich Strenger	.25
72	Lomas Brown (DP)	.35
76	Eric Williams	.25
79	William Gay	.25
82	Pete Mandley	.25
86	Mark Nichols	.25
87	David Lewis	.25
89	Jeff Chadwick (DP)	.25

1986 McDonald's Houston Oilers

Released over a four-week time span at Houston-area McDonald's, the 24-card set measures 3-1/16" x 4-11/16" with the tab and 3-1/16" x 3-5/8" without. The card fronts are anchored with a color photo, with the McDonald's logo in the upper left and Oilers' helmet in the upper right. The NFL shield and NFLPA logo are located at the bottom, left and right respectively. The player's name, number and position are printed below the photo. The card backs include the player's name, number, bio and highlights. Each week featured a different colored tab: blue (first), black or gray (second), gold or orange (third) and green (fourth). The values listed are for cards which have the tabs intact.

		MT
Complete Set (Blue):		12.00
Complete Set (Black):		8.00
Complete Set (Gold):		8.00
Complete Set (Green):		8.00
Common Player:		.30
1	Warren Moon	4.00
7	Tony Zendejas	.30
10	Oliver Luck	.40
21	Bo Eason	.30
23	Richard Johnson	.30
24	Steve Brown (DP)	.30
25	Keith Bostic (DP)	.30
29	Patrick Allen (DP)	.30
33	Mike Rozier	.50
40	Butch Woolfolk	.30
53	Avon Riley	.30
56	Robert Abraham (DP)	.30
63	Mike Munchak	.40
67	Mike Stensrud	.30
70	Dean Steinkuhler	.40
71	Richard Byrd (DP)	.30
73	Harvey Salem	.30
74	Bruce Matthews	.75
79	Ray Childress	.75
83	Tim Smith	.30
85	Drew Hill	.75
87	Jamie Williams	.30
93	Johnny Meads	.30
94	Frank Bush	.30

1986 McDonald's Green Bay Packers

Released over a four-week time span at Green Bay-area McDonald's, the 24-card set measures 3-1/16" x 4-11/16" with the tab and 3-1/16" x 3-5/8" without. The card fronts are anchored with a color photo, with the McDonald's logo in the upper left and Packers' helmet in the upper right. The NFL shield and NFLPA logo are located at the bottom, left and right respectively. The player's name, number and position are printed below the photo. The card backs include the player's name, number, position, bio and highlights. Each week featured a different colored tab: blue (first), black or gray (second), gold or orange (third) and green (fourth). The values listed are for cards which have the tabs intact.

		MT
Complete Set (Blue):		6.00
Complete Set (Black):		6.00
Complete Set (Gold):		6.00
Complete Set (Green):		6.00
Common Player:		.25
10	Al Del Greco (DP)	.25
12	Lynn Dickey	.35
16	Randy Wright	.35
18	Jim Zorn	.35
26	Mark Lee	.25
31	Gerry Ellis	.25
33	Jessie Clark (DP)	.25
37	Mark Murphy	.35
41	Tom Flynn	.25
42	Gary Ellerson	.25
53	Mike Douglass	.25
55	Randy Scott	.25
59	John Anderson (DP)	.25
67	Karl Swanke	.25
75	Ken Ruettgers	.25
76	Alphonso Carreker (DP)	.25
77	Mike Butler (DP)	.25
79	Donnie Humphrey	.25
82	Paul Coffman (DP)	.25
85	Phillip Epps	.35
90	Ezra Johnson	.25
91	Brian Noble	.35
94	Charles Martin	.25

Post-1980 cards in Near Mint condition will generally sell for about 75% of the quoted Mint value. Excellent-condition cards bring no more than 40%.

1986 McDonald's New England Patriots

		MT
Complete Set (Blue):		20.00
Complete Set (Black):		10.00
Complete Set (Gold):		6.00
Complete Set (Green):		6.00
Common Player:		.25
1	Marc Wilson	.35
8	Ray Guy (DP)	.50
10	Chris Bahr (DP)	.25
16	Jim Plunkett	.50
22	Mike Haynes	.35
26	Vann McElroy	.25
27	Frank Hawkins	.25
32	Marcus Allen (DP)	1.50
36	Mike Davis (DP)	.25
37	Lester Hayes	.35
46	Todd Christenson (DP)	.50
53	Rod Martin	.35
54	Reggie McKenzie	.25
55	Matt Millen	.35
70	Henry Lawrence	.25
71	Bill Pickel	.25
72	Don Mosebar	.35
73	Charley Hannah	.25
75	Howie Long	1.00
79	Bruce Davis (DP)	.25
84	Jessie Hester	.50
85	Dokie Williams	.25
91	Brad Van Pelt	.25
99	Sean Jones	.50

Released over a four-week time span at New England-area McDonald's, the 24-card set measures 3-1/16" x 4-11/16" with the tab and 3-1/16" x 3-5/8" without. The card fronts are anchored with a color photo, with the McDonald's logo in the upper left and Patriots' helmet in the upper right. The NFL shield and NFLPA logo are located at the bottom, left and right respectively. The player's name, number and position are printed below the photo. The card backs include the player's name, number, position, and highlights. Each week featured a different colored tab: blue (first), black or gray (second), gold or orange (third) and green (fourth). The values listed are for cards which have the tabs intact.

1986 McDonald's Los Angeles Rams

		MT
Complete Set (Blue):		6.00
Complete Set (Black):		6.00
Complete Set (Gold):		6.00
Complete Set (Green):		6.00
Common Player:		.25
3	Rich Camarillo (DP)	.25
11	Tony Eason (DP)	.35
14	Steve Grogan	.50
24	Robert Weathers	.25
26	Raymond Clayborn (DP)	.25
30	Mosi Tatupu	.25
31	Fred Marion	.25
32	Craig James	.50
33	Tony Collins (DP)	.35
38	Roland James	.25
42	Ronnie Lippett	.25
50	Larry McGrew	.25
55	Don Blackmon (DP)	.25
56	Andre Tippett	.50
57	Steve Nelson	.25
58	Pete Brock (DP)	.25
60	Garin Veris	.25
61	Ron Wooten	.25
73	John Hannah	.50
77	Kenneth Sims	.25
80	Irving Fryar	1.00
81	Stephen Starring	.25
83	Cedric Jones	.25
86	Stanley Morgan	.50

1986 McDonald's Los Angeles Raiders

Released over a four-week time span at Los Angeles-area McDonald's, the 24-card set measures 3-1/16" x 4-11/16" with the tab and 3-1/16" x 3-5/8" without. The card fronts are anchored with a color photo, with the McDonald's logo in the upper left and Raiders' helmet in the upper right. The NFL shield and NFLPA logo are located at the bottom, left and right respectively. The player's name, number and position are printed below the photo. The card backs include the player's name, number, position, bio and highlights. Each week featured a different colored tab: blue (first), black or gray (second), gold or orange (third) and green (fourth). The values listed are for cards which have the tabs intact.

1986 McDonald's Washington Redskins

		MT
Complete Set (Blue):		150.00
Complete Set (Black):		30.00
Complete Set (Gold):		20.00
Complete Set (Green):		25.00
Common Player:		.75
3	Bobby Hebert	2.00
7	Morten Andersen (DP)	1.00
10	Brian Hansen	.75
18	Dave Wilson	.75
20	Russell Gary	.75
23	Johnnie Poe	.75
30	Wayne Wilson	.75
44	Dave Waymer	.75
46	Hokie Gajan	.75
49	Frank Wattelett	.75
50	Jack Del Rio (DP)	1.00
57	Rickey Jackson	1.00
60	Steve Korte	.75
61	Joel Hilgenberg	.75
63	Brad Edelman (DP)	.75
64	Dave Lafary	.75
67	Stan Brock (DP)	.75
73	Frank Warren	.75
75	Bruce Clark (DP)	.75
84	Eric Martin	1.50
85	Hoby Brenner (DP)	.75
88	Eugene Goodlow	.75
89	Tyrone Young	.75
99	Tony Elliott	.75

1986 McDonald's Seattle Seahawks

		MT
Complete Set (Blue):		6.00
Complete Set (Black):		6.00
Complete Set (Gold):		6.00
Complete Set (Green):		6.00
Common Player:		.25
3	Mark Moseley	.25
10	Jay Schroeder	.50
22	Curtis Jordan	.25
28	Darrell Green	.50
32	Vernon Dean	.25
35	Keith Griffin	.25
37	Raphel Cherry (DP)	.25
38	George Rogers	.35
51	Monte Coleman (DP)	.35
52	Neal Olkewicz	.25
53	Jeff Bostic (DP)	.25
55	Mel Kaufman	.25
57	Rich Milot	.25
65	Dave Butz (DP)	.35
68	Joe Jacoby	.35
71	Russ Grimm	.50
72	Charles Mann	.50
72	Dexter Manley	.35
73	Mark May	.35
77	Darryl Grant	.25
81	Art Monk	1.00
84	Gary Clark (DP)	1.00
85	Don Warren	.35
86	Clint Didier	.25

1986 McDonald's New Orleans Saints

		MT
Complete Set (Blue):		9.00
Complete Set (Black):		6.00
Complete Set (Gold):		6.00
Complete Set (Green):		6.00
Common Player:		.25
1	Mike Lansford	.25
3	Dale Hatcher	.25
5	Dieter Brock (DP)	.25
20	Johnnie Johnson	.25
21	Nolan Cromwell (DP)	.35
22	Vince Newsome	.25
29	Gary Green	.25
29	Eric Dickerson (DP)	1.00
44	Mike Guman	.25
47	LeRoy Irvin	.35
50	Jim Collins (DP)	.25
54	Mike Wilcher	.25
55	Carl Ekern	.25
56	Doug Smith	.25
58	Mel Owens	.25
71	Dennis Harrah	.25
71	Reggie Doss (DP)	.25
72	Kent Hill	.25
75	Irv Pankey	.25
78	Jackie Slater	.50
80	Henry Ellard	.75
81	David Hill	.25
87	Tony Hunter	.25
89	Ron Brown (DP)	.35

Released over a four-week time span at New Orleans-area McDonald's, the 24-card set measures 3-1/16" x 4-11/16" with the tab and 3-1/16" x 3-5/8" without. The card fronts are anchored with a color photo, with the McDonald's logo in the upper left and Saints' helmet in the upper right. The NFL shield and NFLPA logo are located at the bottom, left and right respectively. The player's name, number and position are printed below the photo. The card backs include the player's name, number, position, bio and highlights. Each week featured a different colored tab: blue (first), black or gray (second), gold or orange (third) and green (fourth). The values listed are for cards which have the tabs intact.

		MT
65	Edwin Bailey (DP)	.25
72	Joe Nash	.25
77	Jeff Bryant (DP)	.25
78	Bob Cryder (DP)	.25
79	Jacob Green	.35
80	Steve Largent	2.00
81	Daryl Turner	.25
82	Paul Skansi	.25

1986 McDonald's Pittsburgh Steelers

		MT
Complete Set (Blue):		50.00
Complete Set (Black):		25.00
Complete Set (Gold):		10.00
Complete Set (Green):		10.00
Common Player:		.40
1	Gary Anderson (K) (DP)	.50
16	Mark Malone	.50
21	Eric Williams	.40
24	Rich Erenberg (DP)	.40
30	Frank Pollard	.40
31	Donnie Shell	.50
34	Walter Abercrombie (DP)	.40
49	Dwayne Woodruff (DP)	.40
50	David Little	.40
52	Mike Webster	.50
53	Bryan Hinkle	.50
56	Robin Cole (DP)	.40
57	Mike Merriweather	.50
62	Tunch Ilkin	.40
65	Ray Pinney	.40
67	Gary Dunn (DP)	.40
73	Craig Wolfley	.40
74	Terry Long	.40
80	John Stallworth	.75
83	Louis Lipps	.75
87	Weegie Thompson	.40
92	Keith Gary (DP)	.40
93	Keith Willis	.40
99	Darryl Sims	.40

Released over a four-week time span at Pittsburgh-area McDonald's, the 24-card set measures 3-1/16" x 4-11/16" with the tab and 3-1/16" x 3-5/8" without. The card fronts are anchored with a color photo, with the McDonald's logo in the upper left and Steelers' helmet in the upper right. The NFL shield and NFLPA logo are located at the bottom, left and right respectively. The player's name, number and position are printed below the photo. The card backs include the player's name, number, position, bio and highlights. Each week featured a different colored tab: blue (first), black or gray (second), gold or orange (third) and green (fourth). The values listed are for cards which have the tabs intact.

1986 McDonald's Minnesota Vikings

		MT
Complete Set (Blue):		10.00
Complete Set (Black):		7.00
Complete Set (Gold):		7.00
Complete Set (Green):		7.00
Common Player:		.25
9	Norm Johnson	.35
17	Dave Krieg	.50
20	Terry Taylor	.25
22	Dave Brown (DP)	.25
28	Curt Warner (DP)	.50
33	Dan Doornink	.25
44	John Harris	.25
45	Kenny Easley	.35
46	David Hughes	.25
50	Fredd Young	.25
53	Keith Butler (DP)	.25
56	Michael Jackson	.25
58	Bruce Scholtz	.25
59	Blair Bush (DP)	.25
61	Robert Pratt	.25
64	Ron Essink	.25

Released over a four-week

Released over a four-week time span at Minneapolis-area McDonald's, the 24-card set measures 3-1/16" x 4-11/16" with the tab and 3-1/16" x 3-5/8" without. The card fronts are anchored with a color photo, with the McDonald's logo in the upper left and Vikings' helmet in the upper right. The NFL shield and NFLPA logo are located at the bottom, left and right respectively. The player's name, number and position are printed below the photo. The card backs include the player's name, number, position, bio and highlights. Each week featured a different colored tab: blue (first), black or gray (second), gold or orange (third) and green (fourth). The values listed are for cards which have the tabs intact.

		MT
Complete Set (Blue):		45.00
Complete Set (Black):		30.00
Complete Set (Gold):		15.00
Complete Set (Green):		15.00
Common Player:		.60
8	Greg Coleman (DP)	.60
9	Tommy Kramer	.75
11	Wade Wilson	.75
20	Darrin Nelson	.60
23	Ted Brown (DP)	.60
37	Willie Teal	.60
39	Carl Lee	.75
46	Alfred Anderson (DP)	.60
47	Joey Browner (DP)	.75
55	Scott Studwell	.60
56	Chris Doleman	.75
59	Matt Blair (DP)	.75
68	Dennis Swilley	.60
68	Curtis Rouse	.60
75	Keith Millard	.75
76	Tim Irwin	.60
77	Mark Mullaney	.60
79	Doug Martin	.60
81	Anthony Carter (DP)	1.25
83	Steve Jordan	.75
87	Leo Lewis	.75
89	Mike Jones	.60
96	Tim Newton	.60
99	David Howard	.60

1993 McDonald's GameDay

These cards were issued as part of the McDonald's/NFL Kickoff Playoff promotion. With a certain food combination purchase, customers received a game piece which offered prizes ranging from a trip to the Super Bowl to food. Or, the game piece had a point value on it - 6 (touchdown), 3 (field goal) or 1 (extra point). For 10 points, a collector could obtain a six-card panel featuring players from the NFL team in that participating McDonald's market. A different six-player sheet was given away in each of three weeks, making a complete set three panels, or 18 cards. The cards are identical in size to the regular issues (2-1/2" x 4-3/4"), but have a McDonald's logo on each side. Cards are also numbered using a McD prefix. Some restaurants also offered three sheets featuring 18 different All-Stars.

	MT
Complete Set:	35.00
Common Player:	1.50

1 All-Stars A 1.50 (Deion Sanders, Thurman Thomas, Troy Aikman, John Elway, Barry Sanders, Sterling
2 All-Stars B (Derrick 1.50 Thomas, Howie Long, Dan Marino, Chris Doleman, Vaughan Johnson, Phil Simms)
3 All-Stars C (Randall 1.00 Cunningham, Barry Foster, Jerry Rice, Junior Seau, Cortez Kennedy, Mark
4 Atlanta Falcons A 1.50 (Deion Sanders, Moe Gardner, Tim Green, Michael Haynes, Chris Hinton, Tim McKyer)
5 Atlanta Falcons B 1.00 (Chris Miller, Bruce Pickens, Mike Pritchard, Andre Rison, Chris Miller, Bruce ,(Darion Conner, Jessie Tuggle)
6 Atlanta Falcons C .75 (Drew Hill, Pierce Holt, Elbert Shelley, Jesse Solomon, Bobby Hebert, Lincoln
7 Buffalo Bills A 1.00 (Howard Ballard, Don Beebe, Cornelius Bennett, Phil Hansen, Henry Jones, Jim Kelly)
8 Buffalo Bills B .75 (Nate Odomes, Andre Reed, Frank Reich, Bruce Smith, Darryl Talley, Steve Tasker)
9 Buffalo Bills C 1.25 (Bill Brooks, Jim Ritcher, Thurman Thomas, Kenneth Davis, Jeff Wright, Thomas
10 Chicago Bears A .75 (Neal Anderson, Trace Armstrong, Mark Carrier DB, Wendell Davis, Richard Dent, Shaun
11 Chicago Bears B .75 (Jim Harbaugh, Darren Lewis, Jim Morrissey, William Perry, Alonzo Spellman, Tom
12 Chicago Bears C 1.00 (Steve McMichael, Craig Heyward, Lemuel Stinson, Keith Van Horne, Donnell Woolford,
13 Cincinnati Bengals A .75 (Derrick Fenner, James Francis, David Fulcher, Harold Green, Rod Jones CB, David
14 Cincinnati Bengals B .75 (Bruce Kozerski, Tim Krumrie, Ricardo McDonald, Carl Pickens, Reggie Rembert, Daniel
15 Cincinnati Bengals C .75 (Eddie Brown, Gary Reasons, Lamar Rogers, Alfred Williams, Darryl Williams, John
16 Cleveland Browns A 1.00 (Rob Burnett, Jay Hilgenberg, Leroy Hoard, Michael Jackson, Mike Johnson, Bernie
17 Cleveland Browns B 1.00 (Eric Metcalf, Michael Dean Perry, Clay Matthews, Lawyer Tillman, Eric Turner, Tommy
18 Cleveland Browns C .75 (David Brandon, Tony Jones T,

Scott Galbraith, James Jones DT, Vinny Testaverde, Steve
19 Dallas Cowboys A 1.75 (Troy Aikman, Tony Casillas, Thomas Everett, Charles Haley, Alvin Harper, Michael
20 Dallas Cowboys B 1.00 (Jim Jeffcoat, Daryl Johnston, Robert Jones, Nate Newton, Ken Norton Jr., Jay
21 Dallas Cowboys C 2.00 (Russell Maryland, Emmitt Smith, Kevin Smith, Mark Stepnoski, Tony Tolbert, Larry Brown
22 Denver Broncos A 1.50 (Steve Atwater, Mike Croel, Shane Dronett, John Elway, Simon Fletcher, Reggie
23 Denver Broncos B .75 (Vance Johnson, Greg Lewis, Tommy Maddox, Arthur Marshall, Shannon Sharpe, Dennis
24 Denver Broncos C .75 (Rod Bernstine, Michael Brooks, Wymon Henderson, Greg Kragen, Karl Mecklenburg, Dan
25 Detroit Lions A .75 (Bennie Blades, Michael Cofer, Ray Crockett, Mel Gray, Willie Green, Jason Hanson)
26 Detroit Lions B 1.50 (Herman Moore, Rodney Peete, Brett Perriman, Kelvin Pritchett, Barry Sanders, Tracy
27 Detroit Lions C 1.00 (Pat Swilling, Lomas Brown, Erik Kramer, Chris Spielman, Andre Ware, William
28 Green Bay Packers A 2.00 (Tony Bennett, Matt Brock, Terrell Buckley, LeRoy Butler, Chris Jacke, Brett
29 Green Bay Packers B 1.00 (Jackie Harris, Brian Noble, Bryce Paup, Sterling Sharpe, Ed West, Johnny
30 Green Bay Packers C 1.50 (Tunch Ilkin, George Teague, Reggie White, Ken O'Brien, John Stephens, Wayne
31 Houston Oilers A .75 (Cody Carlson, Ray Childress, Curtis Duncan, William Fuller, Haywood Jeffires, Lamar
32 Houston Oilers B 1.00 (Bruce Matthews, Bubba McDowell, Warren Moon, Mike Munchak, Eddie Robinson, Webster
33 Houston Oilers C .75 (Ernest Givins, Cris Dishman, Al Smith, Lorenzo White, Lee Williams, Brad
34 Indianapolis Colts A .75 (Chip Banks, Kerry Cash, Quentin Coryatt, Rodney Culver, Steve Emtman, Reggie
35 Indianapolis Colts B 1.00 (Jeff Herrod, Anthony Johnson, Jeff George, Rohn Stark, Jack Trudeau, Clarence
36 Indianapolis Colts C .75 (Duane Bickett,

Eugene Daniel, Jessie Hester, Chris Goode, Kirk Lowderdirk, Sean
37 Kansas City Chiefs A (Dale Carter, .75 Willie Davis, Dave Krieg, Albert Lewis, Nick Lowery, J.J.
38 Kansas City Chiefs B (Charles Mincy, .75 Christian Okoye, Kevin Ross, Dan Saleaumua, Tracy Simien, Harvey
39 Kansas City Chiefs C (Todd McNair, 1.50 Neil Smith, Derrick Thomas, Leonard Griffin, Barry Word, Joe
40 Los Angeles Raiders A .75 (Eddie Anderson, Jeff Gossett, Ethan Horton, Jeff Jaeger, Howie Long, Todd
41 Los Angeles Raiders B .75 (Terry McDaniel, Don Mosebar, Anthony Smith, Greg Townsend, Aaron Wallace, Steve
42 Los Angeles Raiders C 1.00 (Nick Bell, Tim Brown, Eric Dickerson, James Lofton, Jeff Hostetler, Patrick
43 Los Angeles Rams A (Flipper .75 Anderson, Marc Boutte, Henry Ellard, Bill Hawkins, Cleveland Gary, David
44 Los Angeles Rams B (Jim Everett, 1.00 Darryl Henley, Todd Lyght, Anthony Newman, Roman Phifer, Jim
45 Los Angeles Rams C (Shane Conlan, 1.25 Henry Rolling, Larry Kelm, Jackie Slater, Fred Stokes, Jerome
46 Miami Dolphins A .75 (Marco Coleman, Bryan Cox, Jeff Cross, Mark Duper, Keith Sims, Mark Higgs)
47 Miami Dolphins B 2.00 (Keith Jackson, Dan Marino, John Offerdahl, Louis Oliver, Tony Paige, Pete
48 Miami Dolphins C 1.00 (Tony Martin, Irving Fryar, Troy Vincent, Richmond Webb, Jarvis Williams, O.J.
49 Minnesota Vikings A 1.00 (Terry Allen, Anthony Carter, Cris Carter, Jack Del Rio, Chris Doleman, Rich
50 Minnesota Vikings B (Steve Jordan, .75 Carl Lee, Randall McDaniel, John Randle, Sean Salisbury, Todd
51 Minnesota Vikings C (Jim McMahon, .75 Audray McMillian, Mike Merriweather, Henry Thomas, Gary Zimmerman, Brad
52 New England Patriots A .75 (Ray Agnew, Bruce Armstrong, Vincent Brown, Eugene Chung, Marv Cook, Maurice
53 New England Patriots B 1.00 (Pat Harlow, Eugene Lockhart, Greg McMurtry, Scott Zolak, Leonard Russell, Andre

54 New England Patriots C 1.50 (David Howard, Johnny Rembert, Jon Vaughn, Brent Williams, Scott Secules, Drew
55 New Orleans Saints A (Morten .75 Andersen, Gene Atkins, Toi Cook, Richard Cooper, Jim Dombrowski, Vaughn
56 New Orleans Saints B (Joel Hilgenberg, .75 Rickey Jackson, Vaughan Johnson, Wayne Martin, Renaldo Turnbull,
57 New Orleans Saints C (Irv Smith, .75 Brad Muster, Dalton Hilliard, Eric Martin, Sam Mills, Willie
58 New York Giants A 1.00 (Jarrod Bunch, Mark Collins, Howard Cross, Rodney Hampton, Erik Howard, Greg
59 New York Giants B 1.00 (Pepper Johnson, Sean Landeta, Ed McCaffrey, Dave Meggett, Bart Oates, Phil
60 New York Giants C 1.00 (Carlton Bailey, Carl Banks, John Elliott, Eric Dorsey, Lawrence Taylor, Mike
61 New York Jets A .75 (Brad Baxter, Scott Mersereau, Chris Burkett, Kyle Clifton, Jeff Lageman, Mo
62 New York Jets B .75 (Johnny Mitchell, Rob Moore, Browning Nagle, Blair Thomas, Brian Washington, Marvin
63 New York Jets C 1.00 (Boomer Esiason, James Hasty, Ronnie Lott, Leonard Marshall, Terance Mathis, Marvin
64 Philadelphia Eagles A 1.00 (Eric Allen, Fred Barnett, Randall Cunningham, Byron Evans, Andy Harmon, Seth
65 Philadelphia Eagles B 1.00 (Heath Sherman, Vai Sikahema, Clyde Simmons, Herschel Walker, Andre Waters, Calvin
66 Philadelphia Eagles C .75 (Keith Byars, Mike Golic, Leonard Renfro, William Thomas, Antone Davis, Lester
67 Phoenix Cardinals A .75 (Johnny Bailey, Rich Camarillo, Larry Centers, Chris Chandler, Ken Harvey, Randal
68 Phoenix Cardinals B 1.00 (Mark May, Robert Massey, Freddie Joe Nunn, Ricky Proehl, Eric Hill, Eric
69 Phoenix Cardinals C 1.00 (Gary Clark, John Booty, Chuck Cecil, Steve Beuerlein, Ernest Dye, Garrison
70 Pittsburgh Steelers A 1.00 (Dermontti Dawson, Barry Foster, Jeff Graham, Eric Green, Carlton Haselrig, Bryan
71 Pittsburgh Steelers B 1.00 (Merril Hoge, D.J. Johnson, Carnell Lake, David Little, Neil O'Donnell, Darren
72 Pittsburgh Steelers C 1.00 (Bubby Brister, Kevin Greene,

Greg Lloyd, Leon Searcy, Rod Woodson, Deon
73 San Diego 1.00 Chargers A (Eric Bieniemy, Marion Butts, Burt Grossman, Ronnie Harmon, Stan Humphries, Nate
74 San Diego 1.00 Chargers B (Chris Mims, Leslie O'Neal, Stanley Richard, Junior Seau, Harry Swayne, Derrick
75 San Diego 1.00 Chargers C (Jerrol Williams, Gill Byrd, John Friesz, Anthony Miller, Gary Plummer, Darrien
76 San Francisco 1.00 49ers A (Ricky Watters, Michael Carter, Don Griffin, Dana Hall, Brent Jones, Harris
77 San Francisco 49ers 1.50 B (Tom Rathman, Jerry Rice, Bill Romanowski, John Taylor, Steve Wallace, Mike
78 San Francisco 1.50 49ers C (Kevin Fagan, Todd Kelly, Guy McIntyre, Tim McDonald, Steve Young, Dana
79 Seattle Seahawks A .75 (Robert Blackmon, Brian Blades, Jeff Bryant, Dwayne Harper, Andy Heck, Tommy
80 Seattle Seahawks B 1.00 (Cortez Kennedy, Dan McGwire, Rufus Porter, Ray Roberts, Eugene Robinson, Chris
81 Seattle Seahawks C 1.25 (Ferrell Edmunds, Kelvin Martin, John L. Williams, Tony Woods, David Wyman, Rick
82 Tampa Bay .75 Buccaneers A (Gary Anderson RB, Tyji Armstrong, Reggie Cobb, Lawrence Dawsey, Steve DeBerg
83 Tampa Bay .75 Buccaneers B (Ron Hall, Courtney Hawkins, Keith McCants, Charles McRae, Ricky Reynolds,
84 Tampa Bay .75 Buccaneers C (Vince Workman, Paul Gruber, Hardy Nickerson, Marty Carter, Mark Wheeler, Eric
85 Washington 1.00 Redskins A (Earnest Byner, Andre Collins, Brad Edwards, Ricky Ervins, Darrell Green, Desmond
86 Washington 1.00 Redskins B (Tim Johnson, Jim Lachey, Chip Lohmiller, Mark Rypien, Ricky Sanders, Mark
87 Washington 1.00 Redskins C (Al Noga, Kurt Gouveia, Charles Mann, Wilber Marshall, Art Monk, Tom Carter)

1996 McDonald's Looney Tunes Cups

These four cups were available at McDonalds during the 1996 NFL season. Each cup featured a player and a Looney Tunes character.

	MT
Complete Set (4):	6.00
Common Cup:	1.00
1 Wile E. Coyote (Drew Bledsoe)	1.00
2 Daffy Duck (Dan Marino)	2.00
3 Tazmanian Devil (Barry Sanders)	1.50
4 Bugs Bunny (Emmitt Smith)	2.00

1995 Metal

Fleer's 1995 Metal features the set's computer-generated metallic, hand foil-etched fronts with a color action photo. The player's name is written in a foil panel at the bottom of the card, next to the brand logo. The cards have a triangle in the lower left which has the card number; cards are numbered as subsets by team, alphabetically by city name and then by player name. An action photo comprises the top part of the card, with a bar graph depicting 1994 and career totals. Biographical information is also included. The team name is written along the right side of the card. Three insert sets were created: Silver Flashers, Gold Blasters and Platinum Portraits. As an added bonus, a Super Bowl XXX instant win card was randomly included in a pack; the finder was entitled to a trip to Super Bowl XXX in Phoenix.

	MT
Complete Set (200):	50.00
Common Player:	.10
Minor Stars:	.20
Wax Box:	40.00
1 Garrison Hearst	.25
2 Seth Joyner	.10
3 Dave Krieg	.10
4 Lorenzo Lynch	.10
5 Rob Moore	.10
6 Eric Swann	.10
7 Aeneas Williams	.10
8 Chris Doleman	.10
9 Bert Emanuel	.50
10 Jeff George	.25
11 Craig Heyward	.10
12 Terance Mathis	.10
13 Eric Metcalf	.10
14 Cornelius Bennett	.10
15 Bucky Brooks	.10
16 Jeff Burris	.10
17 Jim Kelly	.20
18 Andre Reed	.20
19 Bruce Smith	.10
20 Don Beebe	.10
21 Kerry Collins	1.50
22 Barry Foster	.20
23 Lamar Lathon	.10
24 Sam Mills	.10
25 Tyrone Poole	.20
26 Frank Reich	.10
27 Joe Cain	.10
28 Curtis Conway	.10
29 Jeff Graham	.10
30 Erik Kramer	.10
31 Rashaan Salaam	.50
32 Lewis Tillman	.10
33 Chris Zorich	.10
34 Jeff Blake	.75
35 Ki-Jana Carter	.50
36 Carl Pickens	.50
37 Corey Sawyer	.10
38 Darnay Scott	.75
39 Dan Wilkinson	.10
40 Darryl Williams	.10
41 Derrick Alexander	.30
42 Leroy Hoard	.10
43 Michael Jackson	.10
44 Antonio Langham	.10
45 Andre Rison	.20

46	Vinny Testaverde	.10
47	Eric Turner	.10
48	Troy Aikman	1.50
49	Charles Haley	.10
50	Michael Irvin	.50
51	Daryl Johnston	.10
52	Jay Novacek	.10
53	Emmitt Smith	3.00
54	Kevin Williams	.10
55	Steve Atwater	.10
56	Rod Bernstine	.10
57	John Elway	.75
58	Glyn Milburn	.10
59	Anthony Miller	.10
60	Mike Pritchard	.10
61	Shannon Sharpe	.10
62	Mike Johnson	.10
63	Scott Mitchell	.10
64	Herman Moore	1.00
65	Brett Perriman	.10
66	Barry Sanders	2.50
67	Chris Spielman	.10
68	Edgar Bennett	.10
69	Robert Brooks	.10
70	Brett Favre	3.00
71	LeShon Johnson	.10
72	George Koonce	.10
73	Reggie White	.20
74	Gary Brown	.10
75	Cris Dishman	.10
76	Mel Gray	.10
77	*Steve McNair*	4.50
78	Webster Slaughter	.10
79	*Rodney Thomas*	.20
80	Trev Alberts	.10
81	Quentin Coryatt	.10
82	Sean Dawkins	.10
83	Craig Erickson	.10
84	Marshall Faulk	2.00
85	Stephen Grant	.20
86	Steve Beuerlein	.10
87	*Tony Boselli*	.50
88	Desmond Howard	.10
89	*James Stewart*	1.50
90	Marcus Allen	.20
91	Kimble Anders	.10
92	Steve Bono	.30
93	Lake Dawson	.40
94	Greg Hill	.40
95	Neil Smith	.20
96	Derrick Thomas	.20
97	Tim Bowens	.10
98	Brian Cox	.10
99	Irving Fryar	.10
100	Eric Green	.10
101	Dan Marino	3.00
102	O.J. McDuffie	.10
103	Bernie Parmalee	.40
104	Cris Carter	.20
105	Jack Del Rio	.10
106	Quadry Ismail	.10
107	Warren Moon	.20
108	Jake Reed	.10
109	DeWayne Washington	.10
110	Bruce Armstrong	.10
111	Drew Bledsoe	2.00
112	Vincent Brisby	.10
113	Ben Coates	.10
114	Willie McGinnest	.10
115	David Meggett	.10
116	Chris Slade	.10
117	Mario Bates	.50
118	Quinn Early	.10
119	Jim Everett	.20
120	Michael Haynes	.10
121	Tyrone Hughes	.10
122	Renaldo Turnbull	.10
123	*Ray Zellers*	.50
124	Dave Brown	.10
125	Chris Calloway	.10
126	Rodney Hampton	.20
127	Thomas Lewis	.10
128	Phillippi Sparks	.10
129	*Tyrone Wheatley*	.50
130	*Kyle Brady*	.75
131	Boomer Esiason	.10
132	Aaron Glenn	.10
133	Bobby Houston	.10
134	Mo Lewis	.10
135	Johnny Mitchell	.10
136	Ron Moore	.10
137	Greg Biekert	.10
138	Tim Brown	.20
139	Jeff Hostetler	.20
140	Raghib Ismail	.10
141	*Napoleon Kaufman*	4.00
142	Chester McGlockton	.10
143	Harvey Williams	.10
144	Fred Barnett	.10
145	Randall Cunningham	.10
146	William Fuller	.10
147	Charlie Garner	.10
148	Andy Harmon	.10
149	Ricky Watters	.20
150	Calvin Williams	.10
151	Kevin Greene	.10
152	Charles Johnson	.40
153	Greg Lloyd	.10
154	Bam Morris	.75
155	Neil O'Donnell	.10
156	Darren Perry	.10
157	Rod Woodson	.10
158	Jerome Bettis	.50
159	Isaac Bruce	.50
160	Troy Drayton	.10
161	Sean Gilbert	.10
162	Todd Lyght	.10
163	Chris Miller	.10
164	Andre Coleman	.10
165	Stan Humphries	.20
166	Shawn Jefferson	.10
167	Natrone Means	1.25
168	Leslie O'Neal	.10
169	Junior Seau	.30
170	Mark Seay	.10
171	William Floyd	.60
172	Merton Hanks	.10
173	Brent Jones	.10
174	Jerry Rice	2.00
175	Deion Sanders	1.25
176	*J.J. Stokes*	2.00
177	Lee Woodall	.10
178	Bryant Young	.10
179	Steve Young	1.50
180	Brian Blades	.10
181	*Joey Galloway*	4.00
182	Cortez Kennedy	.10
183	Kevin Mawae	.10
184	Rick Mirer	.50
185	Chris Warren	.20
186	Lawrence Dawsey	.10
187	Trent Dilfer	.75
188	Paul Gruber	.10
189	Hardy Nickerson	.10
190	Errict Rhett	.20
191	*Warren Sapp*	.50
192	Tom Carter	.10
193	Henry Ellard	.10
194	Darrell Green	.10
195	Brian Mitchell	.10
196	Heath Shuler	.30
197	*Michael Westbrook*	1.50
198	Checklist	.10
199	Checklist	.10
200	Checklist	.10

1995 Metal Platinum Portraits

Twelve of the NFL's elite players are featured on these 1995 Fleer Metal insert football cards. Cards, numbered on the back "number x of 12!", were random inserts, one in every ninth pack. The horizontal card front has a color closeup of the player on the left, with ghosted images of his team logo and him in action on the right. The metallic background features his team's primary uniform color. Along the upper top of the card are several player icons, with the player's name and brand logo just below in the right corner. The back has a player profile written towards the top, with small and large icons from the front incorporated into the design.

		MT
Complete Set (12):		60.00
Common Player:		3.00
1	Drew Bledsoe	7.00
2	Ki-Jana Carter	3.00
3	Marshall Faulk	7.00
4	Natrone Means	5.00
5	Bam Morris	3.00
6	Jerry Rice	7.00
7	Andre Rison	3.00
8	Barry Sanders	8.00
9	Deion Sanders	6.00
10	Emmitt Smith	15.00
11	J.J. Stokes	8.00
12	Ricky Watters	3.00

1995 Metal Gold Blasters

This 1995 Fleer Metal set highlights 18 of the players who have had a major impact on the NFL. Cards were randomly inserted into every fifth pack of 1995 Fleer Metal football. The card front has color action photo against a swirled, gold metallic background. The player's name is in a bar at the bottom of the card, next to the brand logo. The card back, numbered 1 of 18, etc., at the bottom, has the insert set icon in the lower left corner. A player profile is in the upper right corner.

		MT
Complete Set (18):		70.00
Common Player:		2.00
1	Troy Aikman	7.00
2	Jerome Bettis	3.00
3	Tim Brown	2.00
4	Ben Coates	2.00
5	John Elway	5.00
6	Brett Favre	12.00
7	William Floyd	2.00
8	Joey Galloway	5.00
9	Rodney Hampton	2.00
10	Dan Marino	12.00
11	Steve McNair	6.00
12	Herman Moore	2.00
13	Errict Rhett	2.00
14	Rashaan Salaam	2.00
15	Chris Warren	2.00
16	Michael Westbrook	3.00
17	Rod Woodson	2.00
18	Steve Young	7.00

Values quoted in this guide reflect the retail price of a card — the price a collector can expect to pay when buying a card from a dealer. The wholesale price — that which a collector can expect to receive from a dealer when selling cards — will be significantly lower, depending on desirability and condition.

1995 Metal Silver Flashers

This 50-card set features some of the NFL's flashiest performers. Cards were random inserts, one every two packs of 1995 Fleer Metal football. The card front has a silver metallic background, with a color action photo superimposed in the forefront. The player's name is in a silver foil panel at the bottom, next to the brand logo in the lower right corner. The back's design has the brand logo incorporated into its design at the top, with a written player profile also included. A card number is in a triangle in the lower left corner.

		MT
Complete Set (50):		70.00
Common Player:		.50
Minor Stars:		1.00
1	Troy Aikman	4.00
2	Marcus Allen	.50
3	Jerome Bettis	1.00
4	Drew Bledsoe	4.00
5	Tim Brown	.50
6	Cris Carter	.50
7	Ki-Jana Carter	1.00
8	Ben Coates	.50
9	Kerry Collins	1.50
10	Randall Cunningham	1.00
11	Lake Dawson	.50
12	Trent Dilfer	1.00
13	John Elway	2.00
14	Jim Everett	.50
15	Marshall Faulk	2.00
16	Brett Favre	8.00
17	William Floyd	1.00
18	Jeff George	.50
19	Rodney Hampton	.50
20	Jeff Hostetler	.50
21	Stan Humphries	.50
22	Michael Irvin	1.00
23	Cortez Kennedy	.50
24	Dan Marino	8.00
25	Terance Mathis	.50
26	Willie McGinnest	.50
27	Natrone Means	1.25
28	Rick Mirer	1.00
29	Warren Moon	.50
30	Herman Moore	.50
31	Bam Morris	1.00
32	Carl Pickens	1.00
33	Errict Rhett	1.50
34	Jerry Rice	4.00
35	Andre Rison	.50
36	Rashaan Salaam	2.00
37	Barry Sanders	5.00
38	Deion Sanders	2.50
39	Junior Seau	.50
40	Shannon Sharpe	.50
41	Heath Shuler	1.00
42	Emmitt Smith	8.00
43	J.J. Stokes	4.00
44	Chris Warren	2.00
45	Ricky Watters	.50
46	Michael Westbrook	1.50
47	Tyrone Wheatley	1.00
48	Reggie White	.50
49	Rod Woodson	.50
50	Steve Young	2.00

1996 Metal

Fleer's 1996 Metal set has an all-new look for 1996 - metalized foil engraved by hand on each card front, meaning no two player cards are alike. The basic set contains 123 regular cards, 25 rookies and two checklists. The card front has a full-bleed color photograph, with the player's name "tearing through" the lower right-hand corner of the card. The back has another photo, a close-cropped headshot bursting through the card, 1995 and career statistics, and biographical information. An extra-rare parallel set - Precious Metal - was also produced. These cards, seeded one per box, feature an all-silver front and were limited to less than 550 each. They are numbered on the back using a PM prefix. There were five other insert sets included in packs - Goldfingers, Goldflingers, Platinum Portraits, Molten Metal and Freshly Forged.

		MT
Complete Set (150):		30.00
Common Player:		.10
Minor Stars:		.20
Wax Box:		50.00
1	Garrison Hearst	.10
2	Rob Moore	.10
3	Frank Sanders	.10
4	Eric Swann	.10
5	Jeff George	.20
6	Craig Heyward	.10
7	Terance Mathis	.10
8	Eric Metcalf	.10
9	Derrick Alexander	.10
10	Andre Rison	.10
11	Vinny Testaverde	.10
12	Eric Turner	.10
13	Jim Kelly	.10
14	Bryce Paup	.10
15	Bruce Smith	.10
16	Thurman Thomas	.20
17	Bob Christian	.10
18	Kerry Collins	.40
19	Lamar Lathon	.10
20	Tyrone Poole	.10
21	Curtis Conway	.10
22	Bryan Cox	.10
23	Erik Kramer	.10
24	Rashaan Salaam	.50
25	Jeff Blake	.20
26	Ki-Jana Carter	.50
27	Carl Pickens	.20
28	Darnay Scott	.30
29	Troy Aikman	1.50
30	Michael Irvin	.20
31	Daryl Johnston	.10
32	Deion Sanders	.75
33	Emmitt Smith	3.00
34	Terrell Davis	1.25
35	John Elway	.75
36	Anthony Miller	.10
37	Shannon Sharpe	.10
38	Scott Mitchell	.10
39	Herman Moore	.75
40	Brett Perriman	.10
41	Barry Sanders	2.00
42	Edgar Bennett	.10
43	Robert Brooks	.20
44	Mark Chmura	.30
45	Brett Favre	3.00
46	Reggie White	.20
47	Mel Gray	.10
48	Steve McNair	1.00
49	Chris Sanders	.30
50	Rodney Thomas	.10
51	Quentin Coryatt	.10
52	Sean Dawkins	.10
53	Ken Dilger	.10
54	Marshall Faulk	.75
55	Jim Harbaugh	.20
56	Tony Boselli	.10
57	Mark Brunell	1.00
58	Natrone Means	.20
59	James Stewart	.10
60	Marcus Allen	.20
61	Steve Bono	.20
62	Neil Smith	.10
63	Tamarick Vanover	.20
64	Eric Green	.10
65	Terry Kirby	.10
66	Dan Marino	3.00
67	O.J. McDuffie	.10
68	Cris Carter	.10
69	Qadry Ismail	.10
70	Warren Moon	.10
71	Jake Reed	.10
72	Drew Bledsoe	1.25
73	Ben Coates	.10
74	Curtis Martin	2.50
75	David Meggett	.10
76	Mario Bates	.10
77	Jim Everett	.10
78	Michael Haynes	.10
79	Tyrone Hughes	.10
80	Dave Brown	.10
81	Rodney Hampton	.10
82	Thomas Lewis	.10
83	Tyrone Wheatley	.10
84	Kyle Brady	.10
85	Hugh Douglas	.10
86	Adrian Murrell	.10
87	Neil O'Donnell	.10
88	Tim Brown	.10
89	Jeff Hostetler	.10
90	Napoleon Kaufman	.30
91	Harvey Williams	.10
92	Charlie Garner	.10
93	Rodney Peete	.10
94	Ricky Watters	.10
95	Calvin Williams	.10
96	Jerome Bettis	.20
97	Greg Lloyd	.10
98	Kordell Stewart	1.00
99	Yancey Thigpen	.30
100	Rod Woodson	.10
101	Isaac Bruce	.30
102	Kevin Carter	.10
103	Steve Walsh	.10
104	Aaron Hayden	.10
105	Stan Humphries	.10
106	Junior Seau	.10
107	William Floyd	.10
108	Brent Jones	.10
109	Jerry Rice	1.50
110	J.J. Stokes	.20
111	Steve Young	1.00
112	Brian Blades	.10
113	Joey Galloway	1.00
114	Rick Mirer	.10
115	Chris Warren	.20
116	Trent Dilfer	.10
117	Alvin Harper	.10
118	Hardy Nickerson	.10
119	Errict Rhett	.30
120	Terry Allen	.10
121	Brian Mitchell	.10
122	Heath Shuler	.10
123	Michael Westbrook	.20
124	*Karim Abdul-Jabbar*	.75
125	*Tim Biakabutuka*	1.00
126	*Duane Clemons*	.10
127	*Stephen Davis*	4.00
128	*Rickey Dudley*	.75
129	*Bobby Engram*	.50
130	*Daryl Gardener*	.10
131	*Eddie George*	4.00
132	*Terry Glenn*	2.00
133	*Kevin Hardy*	.20
134	*Walt Harris*	.10
135	*Marvin Harrison*	3.00
136	*Keyshawn Johnson*	2.50
137	*Cedric Jones*	.10
138	*Eddie Kennison*	.30
139	*Sam Manuel, Sean Manuel*	
140	*Leeland McElroy*	.30
141	*Ray Mickens*	.10
142	*Jonathan Ogden*	.10
143	*Lawrence Phillips*	.75
144	*Kavika Pittman*	.10
145	*Simeon Rice*	.20
146	*Regan Upshaw*	.10
147	*Alex Van Dyke*	.20
148	*Stepfret Williams*	.10
149	Checklist	.10
150	Checklist	.10

1996 Metal Precious Metal

One Precious Metals parallel card was found in each box of Metal Football in 1996. The set included each card in the regular-issue set (minus the two checklists), but featured all-silver fronts and the letters "PM" preceding the card number on the back.

	MT
Complete Set (148):	800.00
Precious Metal Cards:	15x-30x

1996 Metal Goldfingers

These 24-karat etched gold foil-stamped inserts feature some of the NFL's top-flight receivers. Each card front has a color action photo against a metallic background with an image of a gold hand. The Fleer logo is in the upper left corner. The player's name and "Goldfingers" are in gold foil in an arch at the bottom. The card back, numbered 1 of 10, etc., has a color photo on one side, with the player's name in the upper left corner. A brief player profile is below. Cards were seeded one per every eight packs.

		MT
Complete Set (12):		40.00
Common Player:		2.00
1	Isaac Bruce	5.00
2	Joey Galloway	7.00
3	Michael Irvin	3.00
4	Herman Moore	4.00
5	Carl Pickens	2.00
6	Jerry Rice	10.00
7	Chris Sanders	3.00
8	Frank Sanders	2.00
9	J.J. Stokes	4.00
10	Yancey Thigpen	4.00
11	Tamarick Vanover	2.00
12	Michael Westbrook	4.00

1996 Metal Goldflingers

Twelve of the top quarterbacks in football were included in the Goldflingers insert, not to be confused with Goldfingers, which were both out of Metal. Goldflingers was a retail exclusive insert found every 12 packs.

		MT
Complete Set (12):		50.00
Common Player:		2.00
1	Troy Aikman	7.00
2	Steve Bono	2.00
3	Kerry Collins	4.00
4	Trent Dilfer	2.00
5	Brett Favre	14.00
6	Gus Frerotte	2.00
7	Stan Humphries	2.00
8	Dan Marino	14.00
9	Steve McNair	5.00
10	Scott Mitchell	2.00
11	Steve Young	5.00
12	Eric Zeier	2.00

1996 Metal Platinum Portraits

This 1996 Fleer Metal set uses the serillusion process to profile 10 NFL stars. The front shows a closeup head shot of the player, using a silvery embossed effect to create depth. The Fleer Metal logo is in the upper left corner; "Platinum Portraits" is written along the right side of the card. The player's name is along the bottom. The horizontal card back shows an image of the photo from the front as a background, with a brief writeup over it. One side of the card has a color action photo on it. The card number, 1 of 12, etc., is in the upper left corner, with the player's name next to it.

		MT
Complete Set (10):		100.00
Common Player:		5.00
1	Isaac Bruce	5.00
2	Terrell Davis	16.00
3	John Elway	12.00
4	Joey Galloway	16.00
5	Steve McNair	15.00
6	Errict Rhett	10.00
7	Rashaan Salaam	10.00
8	Barry Sanders	25.00
9	Chris Warren	5.00
10	Steve Young	18.00

Post-1980 cards in Near Mint condition will generally sell for about 75% of the quoted Mint value. Excellent-condition cards bring no more than 40%.

1996 Metal Molten Metal

Featuring 10 red-hot superstars, these 1996 Fleer inserts use foil embossing on the front. The Fleer Metal logo is in an upper corner; Molten Metal, in gold foil, is in the lower left corner. The player's name is in gold foil, too, along the right side of the card. The card back, numbered 1 of 10, etc., has a photo on one side. The other side has a white rectangle which includes a brief player profile. The player's name is above the box. These cards are the scarcest of the Fleer Metal inserts; they were seeded one per every 120 packs.

		MT
Complete Set (10):		250.00
Common Player:		10.00
1	Troy Aikman	25.00
2	Ki-Jana Carter	10.00
3	Kerry Collins	15.00
4	Terrell Davis	35.00
5	Marshall Faulk	15.00
6	Brett Favre	50.00
7	Keyshawn Johnson	15.00
8	Curtis Martin	35.00
9	Deion Sanders	15.00
10	Emmitt Smith	50.00

1996 Metal Freshly Forged

These 1996 Fleer Metal inserts highlight second-year NFL standouts and flashy rookies. The cards, seeded one per every 30 hobby packs only, are acrylic. The card front has a color action photo on it, with an NFL logo and line drawing of the photo as the background. The Fleer Metal logo is in an upper corner. The player's name and "Freshly Forged" are stamped in gold foil along the bottom. The card back shows the entire NFL logo, with a description of the player's skills inside. A card number, 1 of 10, etc., is also on the back.

		MT
Complete Set (10):		125.00
Common Player:		4.00
1	Tim Biakabutuka	4.00
2	Jeff Blake	10.00
3	Ki-Jana Carter	4.00
4	Eddie George	25.00
5	Terry Glenn	20.00
6	Keyshawn Johnson	12.00
7	Curtis Martin	20.00
8	Leeland McElroy	8.00
9	Lawrence Phillips	12.00
10	Kordell Stewart	18.00

1997 Metal

The 200-card set contains 173 player cards, two checklists and 25 rookies. Each card features all etched foil. The players are presented in original Marvel comic illustrations on full-bleed backgrounds, with the player's name, team, position and Metal Universe logo located near the bottom of the card. Card backs contain another player photo and stats.

		MT
Complete Set (200):		30.00
Common Player:		.10
Minor Stars:		.20
Wax Box:		40.00
1	Terry Glenn	.30
2	Terry Kirby	.10
3	Thomas Lewis	.10
4	Tim Biakabutuka	.20
5	Tim Brown	.10
6	Todd Collins	.10
7	Tony Banks	.40
8	Tony Brackens	.10
9	Tony Martin	.10
10	Trent Dilfer	.20
11	Troy Aikman	1.00
12	Ty Detmer	.10
13	Tyrone Wheatley	.10
14	Vinny Testaverde	.10
15	Wayne Chrebet	.10
16	Wesley Walls	.10
17	William Floyd	.10
18	Willie McGinest	.10
19	Yancey Thigpen	.10
20	Zach Thomas	.30
21	Terry Allen	.10
22	Terrell Owens	.50
23	Terrell Davis	1.25
24	Terance Mathis	.10
25	Ted Johnson	.10
26	Tamarick Vanover	.20
27	Steve Young	.75
28	Steve McNair	.75
29	Stan Humphries	.10
30	Simeon Rice	.10
31	Shannon Sharpe	.10
32	Sean Jones	.10
33	Scott Mitchell	.10
34	Sam Mills	.10
35	Rodney Hampton	.10
36	Rod Woodson	.10
37	Robert Smith	.10
38	Rob Moore	.10
39	Ricky Watters	.20
40	Rickey Dudley	.10
41	Rick Mirer	.10
42	Reggie White	.20
43	Ray Zellars	.10
44	Ray Lewis	.10
45	Rashaan Salaam	.20
46	Quentin Coryatt	.10
47	Qadry Ismail	.10
48	O.J. McDuffie	.10
49	Nilo Silvan	.10
50	Neil Smith	.10
51	Neil O'Donnell	.10
52	Natrone Means	.20
53	Napoleon Kaufman	.10
54	Mike Tomczak	.10
55	Mike Alstott	.20
56	Michael Westbrook	.10
57	Michael Jackson	.10
58	Michael Irvin	.20
59	Michael Haynes	.10
60	Michael Bates	.10
61	Mel Gray	.10
62	Marvin Harrison	.50
63	Marshall Faulk	.30
64	Mark Brunell	1.00
65	Mario Bates	.10
66	Marcus Allen	.20
67	Lorenzo Neal	.10
68	Levon Kirkland	.10
69	Leonard Russell	.10
70	Leeland McElroy	.10
71	Lawyer Milloy	.10
72	Lawrence Phillips	.20
73	Larry Centers	.10
74	Lamar Lathon	.10
75	Kordell Stewart	.75
76	Kimble Anders	.10
77	Ki-Jana Carter	.10
78	Keyshawn Johnson	.50
79	Kevin Turner	.10
80	Jermaine Lewis	.10
81	Jerome Bettis	.20
82	Jerris McPhail	.10
83	Joey Galloway	.40
84	Jerry Rice	1.00
85	Jim Everett	.10
86	Jimmy Smith	.10
87	Jim Harbaugh	.10
88	John Elway	.75
89	John Friez	.10
90	John Mobley	.10
91	Johnnie Morton	.10
92	Junior Seau	.10
93	Karim Abdul-Jabbar	.30
94	Keenan McCardell	.10
95	Ken Dilger	.10
96	Ken Norton	.10
97	Kent Graham	.10
98	Kerry Collins	.30
99	Kevin Greene	.10
100	Kevin Hardy	.10
101	Jeff Lewis	.10
102	Jeff George	.10
103	Jeff Graham	.10
104	Jeff Blake	.30
105	Jason Sehorn	.10
106	Jason Dunn	.10
107	Jamie Asher	.10
108	Jamal Anderson	.30
109	Jake Reed	.10
110	Isaac Bruce	.30
111	Irving Fryar	.10
112	Iheanyi Uwaezuoke	.10
113	Hugh Douglas	.10
114	Herman Moore	.20
115	Harvey Williams	.10
116	Hardy Nickerson	.10
117	Gus Frerotte	.10
118	Greg Hill	.10
119	Glyn Milburn	.10
120	Frank Wycheck	.10
121	Frank Sanders	.10
122	Errict Rhett	.20
123	Erik Kramer	.10
124	Eric Moulds	.10
125	Eric Metcalf	.10
126	Emmitt Smith	2.00
127	Edgar Bennett	.10
128	Eddie Kennison	.50
129	Eddie George	1.50
130	Drew Bledsoe	1.00
131	Dorsey Levens	.20
132	Desmond Howard	.10
133	Derrick Thomas	.10
134	Derrick Alexander	.10
135	Deion Sanders	.50
136	Dave Brown	.10
137	Daryl Johnston	.10
138	Darnay Scott	.10
139	Darick Holmes	.10
140	Dan Marino	2.00
141	Curtis Martin	1.25
142	Curtis Conway	.10
143	Cris Carter	.10
144	Chris Warren	.10
145	Chris T. Jones	.10
146	Chris Slade	.10
147	Chris Sanders	.10
148	Chester McGlockton	.10
149	Charlie Jones	.10
150	Charles Way	.10
151	Carl Pickens	.10
152	Bryan Still	.10
153	Bruce Smith	.10
154	Brian Mitchell	.10
155	Brett Perriman	.10
156	Brett Favre	2.50
157	Brad Johnson	.10
158	Thurman Thomas	.20
159	Bobby Engram	.10
160	Bert Emanuel	.10
161	Ben Coates	.10
162	Barry Sanders	1.50
163	Bam Morris	.10
164	Ashley Ambrose	.10
165	Antonio Freeman	.30
166	Anthony Miller	.10
167	Anthony Johnson	.10
168	Andre Rison	.10
169	Andre Reed	.10
170	Alex Molden	.10
171	Aeneas Williams	.10
172	Adrian Murrell	.10
173	Aaron Hayden	.10
174	*Darnell Autry*	.20
175	*Orlando Pace*	.30
176	*Darrell Russell*	.10
177	*Peter Boulware*	.10
178	*Shawn Springs*	.30
179	*Bryant Westbrook*	.10
180	*Dwayne Rudd*	.10
181	*Rae Carruth*	.25
182	*Troy Davis*	.50
183	*Antowain Smith*	2.50
184	*James Farrior*	.10
185	*Walter Jones*	.10
186	*Sam Madison*	.10
187	*Tom Knight*	.10
188	*Reidel Anthony*	2.00
189	*Warrick Dunn*	3.00
190	*Reinard Wilson*	.10
191	*Tyrus McCloud*	.10
192	*Michael Booker*	.10
193	*Tony Gonzalez*	1.25
194	*Pat Barnes*	.30
195	*Tiki Barber*	1.00
196	*Sedrick Shaw*	.50
197	*Corey Dillon*	3.00
198	*Danny Wuerffel*	1.00
199	Checklist	.10
200	Checklist	.10

1997 Metal Precious Metal Gems

The 198-card parallel of the base set, not including the two checklists, was randomly seeded in packs. SkyBox produced 150 serial numbered sets. The first 15 cards of the print run were printed with green foil.

	MT
Precious Metal Stars:	40x-80x
Precious Metal Rookies:	20x-40x

1997 Metal Autographics Previews

Inserted 1:500 packs, autographed cards of 10 of the 75 NFL players appearing in the debut of the Autographics program are found here.

		MT
Complete Set (12):		800.00
Common Player:		25.00
	Karim Abdul-Jabbar	100.00
	Mike Alstott	50.00
	Darnell Autry	40.00
	Rae Carruth	60.00
	Ty Detmer	25.00
	Eddie Kennison	75.00
	Brian Manning	25.00
	Ed McCaffrey	25.00
	Jerry Rice	350.00
	Shannon Sharpe	40.00
	Mike Vrabel	25.00
	Chris Warren	25.00

1997 Metal Body Shop

Inserted 1:96 packs, the 15-card set mixes photography and technology. Drew Bledsoe's arm and Jamal Anderson's legs turn bionic on these cards. The cards are numbered with a "BS" prefix.

		MT
Complete Set (15):		220.00
Common Player:		10.00
Minor Stars:		20.00
1	Zach Thomas	20.00
2	Steve Young	25.00
3	Steve McNair	35.00
4	Simeon Rice	10.00
5	Shannon Sharpe	10.00
6	Napoleon Kaufman	10.00
7	Mike Alstott	20.00
8	Michael Westbrook	10.00
9	Kordell Stewart	35.00
10	Kevin Hardy	10.00
11	Kerry Collins	20.00
12	Junior Seau	10.00
13	Jamal Anderson	10.00
14	Drew Bledsoe	35.00
15	Deion Sanders	25.00

Values quoted in this guide reflect the retail price of a card — the price a collector can expect to pay when buying a card from a dealer. The wholesale price — that which a collector can expect to receive from a dealer when selling cards — will be significantly lower, depending on desirability and condition.

1997 Metal Gold Universe

The 10-card set was inserted 1:120 retail packs. The players are illustrated in space on the card fronts. The cards are numbered with a "GU" prefix.

		MT
Complete Set (10):		200.00
Common Player:		10.00
1	Dan Marino	75.00
2	Deion Sanders	25.00
3	Drew Bledsoe	40.00
4	Isaac Bruce	15.00
5	Joey Galloway	15.00
6	Karim Abdul-Jabbar	25.00
7	Lawrence Phillips	15.00
8	Marshall Faulk	15.00
9	Marvin Harrison	15.00
10	Steve Young	25.00

1997 Metal Iron Rookies

Inserted 1:24 packs, the 15-card set features the top players who were chosen in the 1997 NFL Draft. The cards are numbered with an "IC" prefix.

		MT
Complete Set (15):		70.00
Common Player:		2.50
Minor Stars:		5.00
1	Darnell Autry	6.00
2	Orlando Pace	5.00
3	Peter Boulware	2.50
4	Shawn Springs	5.00
5	Bryant Westbrook	2.50
6	Rae Carruth	8.00
7	Troy Davis	12.00
8	Antowain Smith	10.00
9	James Farrior	2.50
10	Dwayne Rudd	2.50
11	Darrell Russell	2.50
12	Warrick Dunn	20.00
13	Sedrick Shaw	5.00
14	Danny Wuerffel	5.00
15	Sam Madison	2.50

1997 Metal Marvel Metal

Inserted 1:6 packs, the 20-card set compares the players

with Marvel Superheroes. For example, Isaac Bruce is pictured with Spider-Man. The cards are numbered with the "MM" prefix.

		MT
Complete Set (20):		40.00
Common Player:		1.00
Minor Stars:		2.00
1	Barry Sanders	7.00
2	Bruce Smith	1.00
3	Desmond Howard	1.00
4	Eddie George	6.00
5	Eddie Kennison	2.50
6	Jerry Rice	5.00
7	Joey Galloway	2.00
8	John Elway	3.00
9	Karim Abdul-Jabbar	2.00
10	Kerry Collins	2.00
11	Kevin Hardy	1.00
12	Kordell Stewart	4.00
13	Mark Brunell	5.00
14	Marshall Faulk	2.00
15	Michael Westbrook	1.00
16	Simeon Rice	1.00
17	Steve McNair	4.00
18	Terry Glenn	2.00
19	Tony Brackens	1.00
20	Tony Martin	1.00

1997 Metal Platinum Portraits

Inserted 1:288 packs, the 10-card set features the players on the card fronts with an etched-foil look. This was the third year for the chase set. The cards are numbered with a "PP" prefix.

		MT
Complete Set (10):		450.00
Common Player:		20.00
1	Troy Aikman	45.00
2	Terrell Davis	45.00
3	Marvin Harrison	20.00
4	Keyshawn Johnson	20.00
5	Jerry Rice	45.00
6	Emmitt Smith	80.00
7	Dan Marino	80.00
8	Curtis Martin	45.00
9	Brett Favre	90.00
10	Barry Sanders	75.00

1997 Metal Titanium

Inserted 1:72 hobby packs, the 20-card set featured a titanium background on die-cut cards. The cards are numbered with a "TT" prefix.

		MT
Complete Set (20):		400.00
Common Player:		7.00
Minor Stars:		14.00
1	Barry Sanders	45.00
2	Brett Favre	60.00
3	Curtis Martin	30.00
4	Eddie George	35.00
5	Eddie Kennison	7.00
6	Emmitt Smith	50.00
7	Herman Moore	7.00
8	Isaac Bruce	7.00
9	Jerry Rice	30.00
10	John Elway	25.00
11	Keyshawn Johnson	14.00
12	Lawrence Phillips	7.00
13	Mark Brunell	30.00
14	Mike Alstott	7.00
15	Steve McNair	25.00
16	Steve Young	25.00
17	Terrell Davis	30.00
18	Terry Glenn	14.00
19	Tony Banks	7.00
20	Troy Aikman	30.00

Post-1980 cards in Near Mint condition will generally sell for about 75% of the quoted Mint value. Excellent-condition cards bring no more than 40%.

1998 Metal Universe

BRETT FAVRE

Metal Universe was released in a single series, 200-card set for 1998. The cards featured foil-etched designs in the background pertaining to the player or the city they play in. The set was paralleled in a Precious Metal Gems set. Inserts in Metal Universe include: Decided Edge, E-X2001 Previews, Planet Football, Quasars and Titanium.

		MT
Complete Set (200):		35.00
Common Player:		.10
Minor Stars:		.20
Wax Box:		60.00
1	Jerry Rice	1.00
2	Muhsin Muhammad	.10
3	Ed McCaffrey	.10
4	Brett Favre	2.50
5	Troy Brown	.10
6	Brad Johnson	.20
7	John Elway	1.00
8	Herman Moore	.20
9	O.J. McDuffie	.10
10	Tim Brown	.20
11	Byron Hanspard	.10
12	Rae Carruth	.10
13	Rod Smith	.10
14	John Randle	.10
15	Karim Abdul-Jabbar	.20
16	Bobby Hoying	.10
17	Steve Young	.50
18	Andre Hastings	.10
19	Chidi Ahanotu	.10
20	Barry Sanders	2.00
21	Bruce Smith	.10
22	Kimble Anders	.10
23	Troy Davis	.10
24	Jamal Anderson	.10
25	Curtis Conway	.20
26	Mark Chmura	.20
27	Reggie White	.20
28	Jake Reed	.10
29	Willie McGinest	.10
30	Terrell Davis	1.00
31	Joey Galloway	.20
32	Leslie Shepherd	.10
33	Peter Boulware	.10
34	Chad Lewis	.10
35	Marcus Allen	.20
36	Randal Hill	.10
37	Jerome Bettis	.20
38	William Floyd	.10
39	Warren Moon	.20
40	Mike Alstott	.40
41	Jay Graham	.10
42	Emmitt Smith	2.00
43	James Stewart	.10
44	Charlie Garner	.10
45	Merton Hanks	.10
46	Shawn Springs	.10
47	Chris Calloway	.10
48	Larry Centers	.10
49	Michael Jackson	.10
50	Deion Sanders	.50
51	Jimmy Smith	.10
52	Jason Sehorn	.10
53	Charles Johnson	.10
54	Garrison Hearst	.10
55	Chris Warren	.10
56	Warren Sapp	.10
57	Corey Dillon	.75
58	Marvin Harrison	.20
59	Chris Sanders	.10
60	Jamie Asher	.10
61	Yancey Thigpen	.10
62	Freddie Jones	.10
63	Rob Moore	.10
64	Jermaine Lewis	.10
65	Michael Irvin	.20
66	Natrone Means	.20
67	Charles Way	.10
68	Terry Kirby	.10
69	Tony Banks	.10
70	Steve McNair	.50
71	Vinny Testaverde	.10
72	Dexter Coakley	.10
73	Keenan McCardell	.10
74	Glenn Foley	.10
75	Isaac Bruce	.20
76	Terry Allen	.10
77	Todd Collins	.10
78	Troy Aikman	1.00
79	Damon Jones	.10
80	Leon Johnson	.10
81	James Jett	.10
82	Frank Wycheck	.10
83	Andre Reed	.10
84	Derrick Alexander	.10
85	Jason Taylor	.10
86	Wayne Chrebet	.10
87	Napoleon Kaufman	.50
88	Eddie George	1.00
89	Ernie Conwell	.10
90	Antowain Smith	.50
91	Johnnie Morton	.10
92	Jerris McPhail	.10
93	Cris Carter	.20
94	Danny Kanell	.10
95	Stan Humphries	.10
96	Terrell Owens	.20
97	Willie Davis	.10
98	David Dunn	.10
99	Tony Brackens	.10
100	Kordell Stewart	1.00
101	Rodney Thomas	.10
102	Keyshawn Johnson	.20
103	Carl Pickens	.10
104	Mark Brunell	.75
105	Jeff George	.20
106	Bert Emanuel	.10
107	Wesley Walls	.10
108	Bryant Westbrook	.10
109	Dorsey Levens	.20
110	Drew Bledsoe	1.00
111	Adrian Murrell	.10
112	Aeneas Williams	.10
113	Raymont Harris	.10
114	Tony Gonzalez	.20
115	Sean Dawkins	.10
116	Billy Joe Hobert	.10
117	James McKnight	.10
118	Reidel Anthony	.10
119	Terance Mathis	.10
120	Darrien Gordon	.10
121	Dale Carter	.10
122	Duce Staley	.10
123	Jerald Moore	.10
124	Eric Swann	.10
125	Antonio Freeman	.20
126	Chris Penn	.10
127	Ken Dilger	.10
128	Robert Smith	.20
129	Tiki Barber	.30
130	Mark Bruener	.10
131	Junior Seau	.20
132	Trent Dilfer	.20
133	Gus Frerotte	.10
134	Jake Plummer	1.00
135	Jeff Blake	.20
136	Jim Harbaugh	.20
137	Michael Strahan	.10
138	Gary Brown	.10
139	Tony Martin	.10
140	Stephen Davis	.10
141	Thurman Thomas	.20
142	Scott Mitchell	.10
143	Dan Marino	2.00
144	David Palmer	.10
145	J.J. Stokes	.10
146	Chris Chandler	.10
147	Darnell Autry	.20
148	Robert Brooks	.10
149	Derrick Mayes	.10
150	Curtis Martin	.75
151	Steve Broussard	.10
152	Eddie Kennison	.20
153	Kerry Collins	.30
154	Shannon Sharpe	.20
155	Andre Rison	.20
156	Dwayne Rudd	.10
157	Orlando Pace	.10
158	Terry Glenn	.20
159	Frank Sanders	.10
160	Ricky Proehl	.10
161	Marshall Faulk	.20
162	Irving Fryar	.10
163	Courtney Hawkins	.10
164	Eric Metcalf	.10
165	Warrick Dunn	1.00
166	Cris Dishman	.10
167	Fred Lane	.10
168	John Mobley	.10
169	Elvis Grbac	.10
170	Ben Coates	.10
171	Rickey Dudley	.10
172	Ricky Watters	.20
173	*Alonzo Mayes*	.30
174	*Andre Wadsworth*	.50
175	*Brian Simmons*	1.00
176	*Charles Woodson*	3.00
177	*Curtis Enis*	3.00
178	*Fred Taylor*	5.00
179	*Germane Crowell*	2.00
180	*Greg Ellis*	.30
181	*Jacquez Green*	2.00
182	*Jason Peter*	.30
183	*John Dutton*	.10
184	*Kevin Dyson*	2.00
185	*Kivuusama Mays*	.10
186	*Marcus Nash*	.75
187	*Michael Myers*	.10
188	*Ahman Green*	1.00
189	*Peyton Manning*	10.00
190	*Randy Moss*	10.00
191	*Robert Edwards*	1.00
192	*Robert Holcombe*	1.00
193	*Ryan Leaf*	2.00
194	*Takeo Spikes*	.50
195	*Tavian Banks*	1.00
196	*Tim Dwight*	2.00
197	*Vonnie Holliday*	.50
198	Dorsey Levens	.10
199	Jerry Rice	.50
200	Dan Marino	1.00

1998 Metal Universe Precious Metal Gems

Precious Metal Gems was a 200-card parallel set found only in hobby packs. Cards were sequentially numbered to 50 sets on the back.

	MT
Metal Gem Cards:	100x-200x
Metal Gem Rookies:	15x-30x

1998 Metal Universe Decided Edge

Decided Edge was a 10-card insert that was seeded one per 288 packs. The outside of these cards was silver foil with the player's image etched into it, while the inside could be pulled out to reveal another card of the player. Three circles were cut into the outside of the front, and one circle was on the back - each allowed you to see the inner card. When lined up the player's face could be seen through each of the circles. Decided Edge inserts were numbered with a "CE" prefix on the inside card.

		MT
Complete Set (10):		450.00
Common Player:		20.00
1	Terrell Davis	45.00
2	Brett Favre	90.00
3	John Elway	45.00
4	Barry Sanders	80.00
5	Eddie George	45.00
6	Jerry Rice	45.00
7	Emmitt Smith	75.00
8	Dan Marino	75.00
9	Troy Aikman	45.00
10	Marcus Allen	20.00

1998 Metal Universe E-X2001 Previews

Terrell Davis

This 15-card insert previewed the upcoming E-X2001 set. Cards featured the two layered, plastic design, but added the word "Preview" in gold foil under the E-X2001 logo. The Metal Universe logo does not appear anywhere on the card. Preview inserts were seeded one per 144 packs. Cards are numbered with an "EX" prefix.

1998 Metal Universe Planet Football

Barry Sanders

Planet Football was a 15-card insert that was seeded one per eight packs. The player's color image was shown over a foil etched background that contained a large football in space. Cards are numbered with a "PF" prefix.

		MT
Complete Set (15):		50.00
Common Player:		1.00
1	Barry Sanders	8.00
2	Corey Dillon	3.00
3	Warrick Dunn	5.00
4	Jake Plummer	5.00
5	John Elway	5.00
6	Kordell Stewart	3.00
7	Curtis Martin	3.00
8	Mark Brunell	4.00
9	Dorsey Levens	1.00
10	Troy Aikman	5.00
11	Terry Glenn	1.00
12	Eddie George	5.00
13	Keyshawn Johnson	1.00
14	Steve McNair	3.00
15	Jerry Rice	5.00

1998 Metal Universe Quasars

QUASARS

JACQUEZ GREEN

This 15-card set showcased the top rookies from the 1998 NFL Draft. Cards had a color shot of the player in his college uniform over a etched foil background. These were inserted one per 20 packs. Cards are numbered with a "QS" prefix.

		MT
Complete Set (15):		100.00
Common Player:		2.00
1	Peyton Manning	20.00
2	Ryan Leaf	14.00
3	Charles Woodson	10.00
4	Randy Moss	30.00
5	Curtis Enis	10.00
6	Tavian Banks	6.00
7	Germane Crowell	2.00
8	Kevin Dyson	6.00
9	Robert Edwards	8.00
10	Jacquez Green	8.00
11	Alonzo Mayes	3.00
12	Brian Simmons	2.50
13	Takeo Spikes	2.00
14	Andre Wadsworth	3.00
15	Ahman Green	8.00

1998 Metal Universe Titanium

STEVE McNAIR

Titanium was a 10-card insert printed on a silver holofoil background. The insert name runs up the left side with the letters in circles. These were inserted one per 96 packs. Cards are numbered with a "TM" prefix.

		MT
Complete Set (10):		140.00
Common Player:		8.00
1	Corey Dillon	8.00
2	Emmitt Smith	30.00
3	Terrell Davis	30.00
4	Brett Favre	40.00
5	Mark Brunell	15.00
6	Dan Marino	30.00
7	Curtis Martin	12.00
8	Kordell Stewart	15.00
9	Warrick Dunn	15.00
10	Steve McNair	8.00

1999 Metal Universe

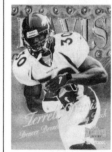

The 250-card base set features each player's name stamped in a steel-look foil across the top and stats laid into another steel motif on the card backs. The 182 player cards are joined by the 25 all-rookie "N.F.L.P.D." subset. The base set also includes forty non-seeded rookies and three checklists. Top inserts include: Precious Metal, Gem Masters, Autographics, Linchpins, Planet Metal, Quasars and Starchild.

		MT
Complete Set (250):		50.00
Common Player:		.10
Minor Stars:		.20
Common Rookie:		.50
Wax Box:		50.00
1	Eric Moulds	.50
2	David Palmer	.10
3	Ricky Watters	.20
4	Antonio Freeman	.50
5	Hugh Douglas	.10
6	Johnnie Morton	.10
7	Corey Fuller	.10
8	J.J. Stokes	.20
9	Keith Poole	.10
10	Steve Beuerlein	.10
11	Keenan McCardell	.10
12	Carl Pickens	.20
13	Mark Bruener	.10
14	Warren Sapp	.10
15	Rich Gannon	.10
16	Bruce Smith	.10
17	Mark Chmura	.20
18	Drew Bledsoe	.75
19	Charles Woodson	.50
20	Ahman Green	.20
21	Ricky Proehl	.10
22	Corey Dillon	.50
23	Terry Fair	.10

1999 Metal Universe

		MT
Complete Set (15):		300.00
Common Player:		6.00
Minor Stars:		12.00
1	Barry Sanders	50.00
2	Brett Favre	60.00
3	Corey Dillon	15.00
4	John Elway	30.00
5	Drew Bledsoe	30.00
6	Eddie George	30.00
7	Emmitt Smith	50.00
8	Joey Galloway	6.00
9	Karim Abdul-Jabbar	12.00
10	Kordell Stewart	20.00
11	Mark Brunell	20.00
12	Mike Alstott	15.00
13	Warrick Dunn	30.00
14	Antonio Freeman	6.00
15	Terrell Davis	30.00

#	Player	MT
24	Mark Brunell	.75
25	Leroy Hoard	.10
26	La'Roi Glover	.10
27	Tim Brown	.20
28	Kevin Turner	.10
29	Terrell Owens	.50
30	Mike Alstott	.50
31	Rob Moore	.10
32	Troy Aikman	1.00
33	Derrick Alexander	.10
34	Chris Calloway	.10
35	Kordell Stewart	.75
36	Reidel Anthony	.20
37	Michael Westbrook	.20
38	Ray Lewis	.10
39	Alonzo Mayes	.10
40	Rod Smith	.20
41	Reggie Barlow	.10
42	Sean Dawkins	.10
43	Duce Staley	.50
44	R.W. McQuarters	.10
45	Robert Holcombe	.10
46	Priest Holmes	.50
47	Erik Kramer	.10
48	Shannon Sharpe	.20
49	Mike Vanderjagt	.10
50	Cris Carter	.50
51	Billy Joe Tolliver	.10
52	Vinny Testaverde	.20
53	Antonio Langham	.10
54	Damon Gibson	.10
55	Garrison Hearst	.30
56	Brad Johnson	.50
57	Randall Cunningham	.50
58	Jim Harbaugh	.20
59	Curtis Enis	.50
60	Bill Romanowski	.10
61	Marcus Pollard	.10
62	Zach Thomas	.20
63	Cameron Cleeland	.20
64	Curtis Martin	.50
65	Charlie Garner	.10
66	Jerris McPhail	.10
67	Jon Kitna	.75
68	Chris Chandler	.20
69	Emmitt Smith	1.50
70	Andre Rison	.20
71	Wayne Chrebet	.50
72	Mikhael Ricks	.10
73	Yancey Thigpen	.20
74	Peter Boulware	.10
75	Bobby Engram	.10
76	John Mobley	.10
77	Peyton Manning	1.50
78	O.J. McDuffie	.20
79	Tony Simmons	.10
80	Mo Lewis	.10
81	Bryan Still	.10
82	Eugene Robinson	.10
83	Curtis Conway	.20
84	Ed McCaffrey	.30
85	Marvin Harrison	.30
86	Dan Marino	1.50
87	Ty Law	.10
88	Leon Johnson	.10
89	Junior Seau	.20
90	Terance Mathis	.10
91	Wesley Walls	.10
92	John Elway	1.50
93	Marshall Faulk	.50
94	Oronde Gadsden	.20
95	Keyshawn Johnson	.50
96	Muhsin Muhammad	.10
97	Dorsey Levens	.50
98	Shawn Jefferson	.10
99	Rocket Ismail	.10
100	Vonnie Holliday	.20
101	Terry Glenn	.30
102	Shawn Springs	.10
103	Tim Dwight	.50
104	Terrell Davis	1.50
105	Karim Abdul	.30
106	Bryan Cox	.10
107	Steve McNair	.75
108	Tony Martin	.10
109	Jason Elam	.10
110	John Avery	.20
111	Aaron Glenn	.10
112	Eddie George	.75
113	Larry Centers	.10
114	Darnay Scott	.10
115	Jimmy Smith	.20
116	Tiki Barber	.10
117	Charles Johnson	.10
118	Mike Archie	.10
119	Adrian Murrell	.10
120	Dexter Coakley	.10
121	Dale Carter	.10
122	Kent Graham	.10
123	Hines Ward	.20
124	Greg Hill	.10
125	Skip Hicks	.50
126	Doug Flutie	.75
127	Leslie Shepherd	.10
128	Neil O'Donnell	.20
129	Herman Moore	.50
130	Kevin Hardy	.10
131	Randy Moss	2.00
132	Andre Hastings	.10
133	Rickey Dudley	.10
134	Jerome Bettis	.50
135	Jerry Rice	1.00
136	Jake Plummer	1.00
137	Billy Davis	.10
138	Tony Gonzalez	.20
139	Ike Hilliard	.20
140	Freddie Jones	.10
141	Isaac Bruce	.30

#	Player	MT
142	Darrell Green	.10
143	Trent Green	.50
144	Jamal Anderson	.50
145	Deion Sanders	.50
146	Bam Morris	.10
147	Charles Way	.10
148	Natrone Means	.30
149	Frank Wycheck	.10
150	Brett Favre	2.00
151	Michael Bates	.10
152	Ben Coates	.20
153	Koy Detmer	.10
154	Eddie Kennison	.10
155	Eric Metcalf	.10
156	Takeo Spikes	.10
157	Fred Taylor	1.00
158	Gary Brown	.10
159	Levon Kirkland	.10
160	Trent Dilfer	.30
161	Antowain Smith	.50
162	Robert Brooks	.10
163	Robert Smith	.50
164	Napoleon Kaufman	.50
165	Chad Brown	.10
166	Warrick Dunn	.75
167	Joey Galloway	.50
168	Frank Sanders	.20
169	Michael Irvin	.20
170	Elvis Grbac	.20
171	Michael Strahan	.10
172	Ryan Leaf	.50
173	Stephen Alexander	.10
174	Andre Reed	.10
175	Barry Sanders	2.00
176	Jake Reed	.10
177	James Jett	.10
178	Steve Young	.75
179	Jermaine Lewis	.20
180	Charlie Batch	.75
181	Jacquez Green	.20
182	Kevin Dyson	.20
183	Roell Preston	.10
184	Randall Cunningham	.20
185	Charlie Batch	.20
186	Kordell Stewart	.20
187	Bennie Thompson	.10
188	Deion Sanders	.20
189	Jake Plummer	.50
190	Eric Moulds	.20
191	Derrick Brooks	.10
192	Steve McNair	.20
193	Ryan Leaf	.20
194	Keyshawn Johnson	.20
195	Eddie George	.20
196	Warrick Dunn	.20
197	Jessie Tuggle	.10
198	Rodney Harrison	.10
199	Vinny Testaverde	.10
200	Marshall Faulk	.20
201	Ray Buchanan	.10
202	Garrison Hearst	.10
203	John Randle	.10
204	Drew Bledsoe	.50
205	Sam Gash	.10
206	Troy Aikman	.50
207	Michael McCrary	.10
208	*Chris Claiborne*	1.00
209	*Ricky Williams*	7.00
210	*Tim Couch*	7.00
211	*Champ Bailey*	1.50
212	*Torry Holt*	3.00
213	*Donovan McNabb*	4.00
214	*David Boston*	3.00
215	*Chris McAlister*	.75
216	*Aaron Gibson*	.50
217	*Daunte Culpepper*	4.00
218	*Matt Stinchcomb*	.50
219	*Edgerrin James*	10.00
220	*Jevon Kearse*	4.00
221	*Ebenezer Ekuban*	.50
222	*Kris Farris*	.50
223	*Chris Terry*	.50
224	*Cecil Collins*	1.00
225	*Akili Smith*	4.00
226	*Shaun King*	4.00
227	*Rahim Abdullah*	.50
228	*Peerless Price*	1.50
229	*Antoine Winfield*	.50
230	*Antuan Edwards*	.50
231	*Rob Konrad*	.75
232	*Troy Edwards*	2.00
233	*John Thornton*	.50
234	*Fred Vinson*	.50
235	*Gary Stills*	.50
236	*Desmond Clark*	.50
237	*Jared DeVries*	.50
238	*Jared DeVries*	.50
239	*Martin Gramatica*	.50
240	*Montae Reagor*	.50
241	*Andy Katzenmoyer*	1.00
242	*Rufus French*	.50
243	*D'Wayne Bates*	.75
244	*Amos Zereoue*	1.00
245	*Dre' Bly*	.75
246	*Kevin Johnson*	3.00
247	*Cade McNown*	4.00
248	Kordell Stewart	.20
249	Deion Sanders	.20
250	Vinny Testaverde	.10

1999 Metal Universe Precious Metal Gem

This is a 250-card parallel to the base that is sequentially numbered to 50.

1999 Metal Universe Linchpins

This 10-card set spotlights a laser die-cut design and highlights key players who hold their teams together on the field and in the clubhouse. Singles were found 1:360 packs.

		MT
Complete Set (10):		400.00
Common Player:		25.00
Inserted 1:360		
1	Emmitt Smith	60.00
2	Charlie Batch	25.00
3	Fred Taylor	60.00
4	Jake Plummer	40.00
5	Brett Favre	80.00
6	Barry Sanders	80.00
7	Mark Brunell	35.00
8	Peyton Manning	60.00
9	Randy Moss	80.00
10	Terrell Davis	60.00

1999 Metal Universe Planet Metal

Each player in this 15-card set is printed on a die-cut card that features a metallic view of the planet. Singles were inserted 1:36 packs.

		MT
Complete Set (15):		135.00
Common Player:		4.00
Inserted 1:36		
1	Terrell Davis	15.00
2	Troy Aikman	10.00
3	Peyton Manning	15.00
4	Mark Brunell	8.00
5	John Elway	15.00
6	Doug Flutie	8.00
7	Dan Marino	15.00
8	Brett Favre	20.00
9	Barry Sanders	20.00
10	Emmitt Smith	15.00
11	Fred Taylor	10.00
12	Jerry Rice	10.00
13	Jamal Anderson	4.00
14	Randall Cunningham	4.00
15	Randy Moss	20.00

Values quoted in this guide reflect the retail price of a card — the price a collector can expect to pay when buying a card from a dealer. The wholesale price — that which a collector can expect to receive for a card — will be significantly lower, depending on desirability and condition.

1999 Metal Universe Quasars

This 15-card set features the top rookies from 1999 and puts them on a silver rainbow holofoil card. They were inserted 1:18 packs.

		MT
Complete Set (15):		85.00
Common Player:		2.00
Inserted 1:18		
1	Ricky Williams	25.00
2	Tim Couch	25.00
3	Shaun King	3.00
4	Champ Bailey	3.00
5	Torry Holt	5.00
6	Donovan McNabb	8.00
7	David Boston	6.00
8	Andy Katzenmoyer	4.00
9	Daunte Culpepper	8.00
10	Edgerrin James	15.00
11	Cade McNown	8.00
12	Troy Edwards	4.00
13	Akili Smith	8.00
14	Peerless Price	4.00
15	Amos Zereoue	4.00

1999 Metal Universe Starchild

This 20-card insert has a young star theme to it and prints each player on a silver rainbow holofoil background. Singles were found 1:6 packs.

		MT
Complete Set (20):		30.00
Common Player:		1.00
Minor Stars:		2.00
Inserted 1:6		
1	Skip Hicks	2.00
2	Mike Alstott	2.00
3	Joey Galloway	2.00
4	Tony Simmons	1.00
5	Jamal Anderson	2.00
6	John Avery	1.00
7	Charles Woodson	2.00
8	Jon Kitna	3.00
9	Marshall Faulk	2.00
10	Eric Moulds	2.00
11	Keyshawn Johnson	3.00
12	Ryan Leaf	2.00
13	Curtis Enis	2.00
14	Steve McNair	2.00
15	Corey Dillon	2.00
16	Tim Dwight	2.00
17	Brian Griese	4.00
18	Drew Bledsoe	5.00
19	Eddie George	4.00
20	Terrell Owens	3.00

1992 Metallic Images Tins

These collector's tins were used to package two decks of playing cards. Two active quarterbacks and two Hall of Famers were selected for the tins. The Marino and Moon tins have play-

ing cards which incorporate the Quarterback Club logo into the design; the other two use a Quarterback Legends emblem on the card front. The unnumbered tins were produced by Metallic Images Inc. and were sold in 7-Eleven stores to benefit the Children's Miracle Network.

		MT
Complete Set (4):		15.00
Common Player:		3.00
1	Dan Marino	10.00
2	Warren Moon	4.00
3	Y.A. Tittle	3.00
4	Johnny Unitas	5.00

1993 Metallic Images QB Legends

These metal cards, honoring 20 star NFL quarterbacks, each measures 2-9/16" x 3-9/16" and was included inside a special collectors tin. Metallic Images produced the cards; each has a color action shot against a team color-coded background with gold stripes running through it. The player's team logo, uniform number and mug shot are also featured on the front. The back is numbered and gives a career summary of the player, framed by a team color-coded border. There were 49,000 numbered sets produced; each includes a certificate of authenticity.

		MT
Complete Set (20):		35.00
Common Player:		1.50
1	Steve Bartkowski	1.50
2	John Brodie	2.50
3	Charley Conerly	2.50
4	Lynn Dickey	1.50
5	Tom Flores	2.00
6	Roman Gabriel	2.00
7	Bob Griese	5.00
8	Steve Grogan	1.50
9	James Harris	1.50
10	Jim Hart	1.50
11	Sonny Jurgensen	3.00
12	Billy Kilmer	2.00
13	Daryle Lamonica	2.50
14	Archie Manning	3.00
15	Craig Morton	1.50
16	Dan Pastorini	1.50
17	Jim Plunkett	2.50
18	Y.A. Tittle	5.00
19	Johnny Unitas	7.50
20	Danny White	2.00

1985 Miller Lite Beer

Measuring 4-3/4" x 7", the eight-card set is anchored on the front with a large player photo. The player's name, position, team helmet, player bio and NFL/Lite logo are beneath the photo. The card backs, which are unnumbered, have the Lite logo in the upper left, with the player's name and position on the upper right. The player's highlights on the field and off the field are printed at the bottom of the card.

		MT
Complete Set (6):		150.00
Common Player:		15.00
1	Larry Csonka	35.00
2	John Hadl (CO)	15.00
3	Freeman McNeil (NFL Man of the Year)	15.00
4	Jack Reynolds (Lite Beer All-Stars)	15.00
5	Steve Young (USFL Man of the Year)	80.00
6	1985 LA Express (Cheerleaders)	15.00

1988 Monte Gum

Monte Gum, in Europe, produced these 100 cards along with an album to hold them. The cards, 1-15/16" x 2-3/4", feature a generic team action photo and caption describing the play on the front. A card number is also included on the front, which has a yellow border around the photo. The backs are blank.

		MT
Complete Set (100):		85.00
Common Player:		1.00
1	Atlanta Falcons	1.75
2	Atlanta Falcons	1.00
3	Atlanta Falcons	1.00
4	Buffalo Bills	1.25
5	Chicago Bears	1.25
6	Chicago Bears	1.00
7	Cincinnati Bengals	1.00
8	Cincinnati Bengals	1.00
9	Cincinnato Bengals	5.00
10	Cincinnati Bengals	1.00
11	Cincinnati Bengals	1.50
12	Cleveland Browns	1.00
13	Cleveland Browns	2.50
14	Cleveland Browns	1.00
15	Cleveland Browns	1.00
16	Dallas Cowboys	1.00
17	Dallas Cowboys	1.25
18	Dallas Cowboys	1.25
19	Denver Broncos	1.00
20	Denver Broncos	1.00
21	Denver Broncos	2.00
22	Detroit Lions	1.00
23	Green Bay Packers	1.00
24	Green Bay Packers	1.00
25	Houston Oilers	1.00
26	Houston Oilers	1.00
27	Indianapolis Colts	1.00
28	Kansas City Chiefs	1.00
29	Kansas City Chiefs	1.00
30	Kansas City Chiefs	1.25
31	Los Angeles Raiders	1.00
32	Los Angeles Raiders	1.00
33	Los Angeles Raiders	1.00
34	Los Angeles Raiders	2.00
35	Los Angeles Rams	1.00
36	Los Angeles Rams	2.00
37	Los Angeles Rams	1.00
38	Miami Dolphins	1.25
39	Miami Dolphins	1.25
40	Minnesota Vikings	1.00
41	Minnesota Vikings	1.00
42	New England Patriots	1.00
43	New England Patriots	1.25
44	New England Patriots	3.00
45	New Orleans Saints	1.50
46	New Orleans Saints (photo actually shows Washington and Michigan in '81 Rose Bowl game)	1.25
47	New York Giants	1.25
48	New York Giants	1.00
49	New York Jets	1.00
50	New York Jets	1.00
51	Philadelphia Eagles	1.00
52	Philadelphia Eagles	1.00
53	Philadelphia Eagles	1.00
54	Philadelphia Eagles	1.00
55	Pittsburgh Steelers	1.00
56	Pittsburgh Steelers	1.50
57	Pittsburgh Steelers	1.00
58	St. Louis Cardinals	1.00
59	St. Louis Cardinals	1.00
60	St. Louis Cardinals	1.00
61	St. Louis Cardinals	1.00
62	San Diego Chargers	1.00
63	San Diego Chargers	1.00
64	San Diego Chargers	1.25
65	San Diego Chargers	1.00
66	San Francisco 49ers	1.00
67	San Francisco 49ers	1.00
68	San Francisco 49ers	10.00
69	San Francisco 49ers	1.25
70	Seattle Seahawks	1.00
71	Seattle Seahawks	1.00
72	Tampa Bay Buccaneers	1.00
73	Tampa Bay Buccaneers	1.00
74	Tampa Bay Buccaneers	1.00
75	Tampa Bay Buccaneers	1.00
76	Washington Redskins	1.00
77	Washington Redskins	1.00
78	Washington Redskins	1.00
79	Washington Redskins	1.00

MT
Precious Metal Cards: 75x-150x
Precious Metal Rookies: 15x-30x
Production 50 Sets

80	Official NFL Football	1.00
81	Helmets: Falcons/Bills	1.00
82	Helmets: Bears/Bengals	1.00
83	Helmets: Browns/Cowboys	1.00
84	Helmets: Broncos/Lions	1.00
85	Helmets: Packers/Oilers	1.00
86	Helmets: Colts/Chiefs	1.00
87	Helmets: Raiders/Rams	1.00
88	Helmets: Dolphins/Vikings	1.00
89	Helmets: Patriots/Saints	1.00
90	Helmets: Giants/Jets	1.00
91	Philadelphia Eagles Helmet	1.00
92	Pittsburgh Steelers Helmet	1.00
93	St. Louis Cardinals Helmet	1.00
94	San Diego Chargers Helmet	1.00
95	San Francisco 49ers Helmet	1.00
96	Seattle Seahawks Helmet	1.00
97	Tampa Bay Buccaneers Helmet	1.00
98	Washington Redskins Helmet	1.00
99	National Football League Logo	1.00
100	American Football Fans	1.50

1996 Motion Vision

Motion Vision debuted in 1996 with two, 12-card series. The first was called Motion Vision, the second carried a 2.0 suffix. This product arrived in one card "packs" that actually resembled a compact disk case, with the cards inside a poly-sleeve. Motion Vision used Kodak technology to simulate actual game footage with tremendous clarity. The cards carried a Movi Motion Vision logo in the upper left-hand corner and the card number in the upper right-hand corner. The bottom of the card has the player's name, with nothing on the back. The card is best viewed by holding the plastic card up to light and rotating it to see game action. Motion Vision also had a 10-card Limited Digital Replay insert that was differentiated by having 25,000 produced.

		MT
Complete Set (24):		150.00
Comp. Series 1 (12):		75.00
Comp. Series 2 (12):		75.00
Common Player:		4.00
Series 1 Wax Box:		200.00
Series 2 Wax Box:		160.00
1	Troy Aikman	10.00
2	Dan Marino	15.00
3	Steve Young	7.00
4	Emmitt Smith	15.00
5	Drew Bledsoe	10.00
6	Kordell Stewart	10.00
7	Jerry Rice	10.00
8	Warren Moon	4.00
9	Junior Seau	4.00
10	Barry Sanders	12.00
11	Jim Harbaugh	4.00
12	John Elway	10.00
13	Brett Favre	17.00
14	Brett Favre	17.00
15	Troy Aikman	10.00
16	Emmitt Smith	15.00
17	Dan Marino	15.00
18	Kordell Stewart	10.00
19	John Elway	10.00
20	Kerry Collins	6.00
21	Jim Kelly	4.00

22	Drew Bledsoe	10.00
23	Mark Brunell	10.00
24	Jerry Rice	10.00

1996 Motion Vision Limited Digital Replays

Limited Digital Replays were the only insert set in 1996 Motion Vision. The first six cards were inserted every 25 packs of Series I, with only 2,500 sets produced, while the last four were found in Series 2.0 at a rate of one per 22 packs, with 3,500 sets produced. LDRs are distinguished by having a card back that features another shot of the player and statistics (regular-issue cards have no backs). LDR fronts also carry no logos on the front and instead of a phrase at the bottom describing the play, LDRs have only the player's name. Cards are numbered LDR1-LDR10.

		MT
Complete Set (10):		400.00
Comp. Series 1 (6):		200.00
Comp. Series 2 (4):		200.00
Autographs of Aikman,Bledsoe, Stewart and Young: 10x		
1	Troy Aikman	30.00
2	Dan Marino	60.00
3	Steve Young	25.00
4	Emmitt Smith	60.00
5	Drew Bledsoe	30.00
6	Kordell Stewart	25.00
7	Brett Favre	60.00
8	Brett Favre	60.00
9	Emmitt Smith	60.00
10	Kerry Collins	20.00

1996 Motion Vision LDR Autographs

Limted Digital Replays Autographs consisted of four players who signed their LDR insert in 1996 Motion Vision. Drew Bledsoe, Kordell Stewart and Steve Young were inserted in Series I, while Troy Aikman and the remaining Steve Young cards were in Series 2.0. Fronts of these were the same, with the autograph on the back along with a seal to prove its autheticity.

		MT
Complete Set (4):		1000.
Common Player:		250.00
1	Troy Aikman AUTO	300.00
3	Steve Young AUTO	250.00
5	Drew Bledsoe AUTO	300.00
6	Kordell Stewart AUTO	275.00

1997 Motion Vision

Motion Vision second year in football cards produced 28

cards, with 20 cards in Series I and eight in Series II. Packs consisted of compact disc-like cases that could be opened to expose the card, which is more like a video shown on thick plastic. The card is best viewed when held up to light and moved slightly with the hand. Each series had four insert cards, which were inserted one per 25, with Series I containing LDR1-4 and a Terrell Davis autograph version, while Series II had LDR5-6 and two redemption cards.

		MT
Complete Set (28):		150.00
Complete Series 1 (20):		90.00
Complete Series 2 (8):		60.00
Common Player:		3.00
Series 1 Wax Box:		45.00
Series 2 Wax Box:		45.00
1	Terrell Davis	10.00
2	Curtis Martin	7.00
3	Joey Galloway	3.00
4	Eddie George	10.00
5	Isaac Bruce	3.00
6	Antonio Freeman	3.00
7	Terry Glenn	4.00
8	Deion Sanders	5.00
9	Jerome Bettis	3.00
10	Reggie White	3.00
11	Brett Favre	15.00
12	Dan Marino	12.00
13	Emmitt Smith	12.00
14	Mark Brunell	8.00
15	John Elway	8.00
16	Drew Bledsoe	8.00
17	Barry Sanders	10.00
18	Jeff Blake	3.00
19	Kerry Collins	3.00
20	Jerry Rice	8.00
21	Dan Marino	12.00
22	Troy Aikman	8.00
23	Brett Favre	15.00
24	Emmitt Smith	12.00
25	Kordell Stewart	8.00
26	Terrell Davis	8.00
27	Eddie George	8.00
28	Drew Bledsoe	8.00

1997 Motion Vision Box Toppers

Five different box toppers were offered with boxes of Motion Vision Series II Football. The cards measure 4" x 6" and were included at a rate of one per box.

		MT
Complete Set (4):		50.00
Common Player:		7.00
1	John Elway	10.00
2	Brett Favre	20.00
3	Dan Marino	15.00
4	Steve Young	7.00

1997 Motion Vision Limited Digital Replays

Each series of Motion Vision included four inserts at a rate of one per 25 packs. The Limited Digital Replays are numbered LDR1-6, with numbers 5 and 6 being trade cards for Warrick Dunn and Antoine Smith. Also included are Dunn and Smith XVRR inserts. In addition, an autographed version of Terrell Davis' LDR was available.

		MT
Complete Set (8):		140.00
Complete Series 1 (4):		100.00
Complete Series 2 (4):		40.00
Common Player:		10.00
1	Terrell Davis	30.00
1A	Terrell Davis AUTO	200.00
2	Curtis Martin	25.00
3	Brett Favre	45.00
4	Barry Sanders	30.00
5	Warrick Dunn	10.00

1997 Motion Vision Super Bowl XXXI

This four-card set was available through a redemption offer in 1996 MotionVision Series Two packs. The cards commemorate the Conference Championships

and Super Bowl XXXI. The fourth card is jumbo format (5-5/8" x 3-3/4"). Each card is numbered one of 5,000.

		MT
Complete Set (4):		75.00
Common Player:		15.00
1	AFC Championship Game (Drew Bledsoe)	15.00
2	NFC Championship Game (Brett Favre)	20.00
3	Super Bowl XXXI (Brett Favre)	20.00
4	Super Bowl XXXI (Brett Favre Jumbo)	20.00

1981 Michael Schechter Associates Test Discs

These discs, produced by Michael Schecter Associates, were included in specially-marked packages of bread. The front shows a head shot of the player, but team logos have been airbrushed off the helmets. An NFLPA logo appears on the card front, along with the player's name, team, position and biographical information. Four stars appear at the top of the card. The unnumbered cards have blank backs. Holsum and Gardner's are among the brands of bread which included the cards inside packages. These two companies also made different posters which were intended to be used to display the discs.

		MT
Complete Set (32):		175.00
Common Player:		2.50
(1)	Ken Anderson	4.00
(2)	Ottis Anderson	6.00
(3)	Steve Bartkowski	3.00
(4)	Ricky Bell	3.00
(5)	Terry Bradshaw	17.50
(6)	Harold Carmichael	3.00
(7)	Joe Cribbs	2.50
(8)	Gary Danielson	2.50
(9)	Lynn Dickey	2.50
(10)	Dan Doornink	2.50
(11)	Vince Evans	3.00
(12)	Joe Ferguson	3.00
(13)	Vagas Ferguson	2.50
(14)	Dan Fouts	8.00
(15)	Steve Fuller	2.50
(16)	Archie Griffin	3.00
(17)	Steve Grogan	3.00
(18)	Bruce Harper	2.50
(19)	Jim Hart	3.00
(20)	Jim Jensen	2.50
(21)	Bert Jones	3.00
(22)	Archie Manning	4.00
(23)	Ted McKnight	2.50
(24)	Joe Montana	85.00
(25)	Craig Morton	3.00
(26)	Robert Newhouse	3.00
(27)	Phil Simms	9.00
(28)	Billy Taylor	2.50
(29)	Joe Theismann	5.00
(30)	Mark Van Eeghen	2.50
(31)	Delvin Williams	2.50
(32)	Tim Wilson	2.50

1990 Michael Schechter Associates Superstars

These unnumbered cards, produced by Michael Schechter Associates, were included two per box of Ralston Purina's Staff and Food Club Frosted Flakes cereal. Each card front has a color closeup shot of the player, with "Superstars" written at the top, and the player's name and team at the bottom. Three footballs are in different corners; an NFLPA logo is in the fourth corner. The card back also has the NFLPA

logo, plus biographical information and statistics.

		MT
Complete Set (12):		15.00
Common Player:		.75
(1)	Carl Banks	.75
(2)	Cornelius Bennett	.75
(3)	Roger Craig	1.50
(4)	Jim Everett	1.00
(5)	Bo Jackson	2.00
(6)	Ronnie Lott	1.50
(7)	Don Majkowski	.75
(8)	Dan Marino	8.00
(9)	Karl Mecklenburg	.75
(10)	Christian Okoye	.75
(11)	Mike Singletary	1.00
(12)	Herschel Walker	1.00

N

1994 Nabisco A.1. "Masters of the Grill"

A.1. Masters of the Grill features 28 of the larger NFL stars, one from each team, equipped with all the necessary grill utensils and A.1. clothing, from chef hats to aprons. All the cards present grill recipes on the back; each recipe has A.1. as a key ingredient. The cards are surrounded by a black border and have an A.1. Masters of the Grill logo.

		MT
Complete Set (28):		7.00
Common Player:		.25
(1)	Harris Barton	.25
(2)	Jerome Bettis	1.50
(3)	Ray Childress	.25
(4)	Eugene Chung	.25
(5)	Jamie Dukes	.25
(6)	Steve Emtman	.25
(7)	Burt Grossman	.25
(8)	Courney Hall	.25
(9)	Ken Harvey	.35
(10)	Chris Hinton	.35
(11)	Kent Hull	.25
(12)	Keith Jackson	.50
(13)	Rickey Jackson	.30
(14)	Cortez Kennedy	.35
(15)	Tim Krumrie	.25
(16)	Jeff Lageman	.25
(17)	Greg Lloyd	.35
(18)	Howie Long	.35
(19)	Hardy Nickerson	.30
(20)	Bart Oates	.25
(21)	Ken Ruettgers	.25
(22)	Dan Saleaumua	.25
(23)	Alonzo Spellman	.30
(24)	Eric Swann	.25
(25)	Pat Swilling	.25
(26)	Tommy Vardell	.25
(27)	Erik Williams	.25
(28)	Gary Zimmerman	.25

1935 National Chicle

The granddaddy of all football card sets, the 36-card National Chicle set was the first to be circulated nationally and the first set to feature only football players (all were pro football players except for Notre Dame coach Knute Rockne). Cards measure 2-3/8" x 2-7/8". The first 24 cards are easier to obtain than the final 12. Rookie cards in this set include Hall of Famers Earl "Dutch" Clark, Cliff Battles, Ken Strong, Turk Edwards, Clarke Hinkle and Bronko Nagurski. Nagurski's card is

the most valuable football card in existence.

		NM
Complete Set (36):		17500.
Common Player (1-24):		110.00
Common Player (25-36):		375.00
1	Earl "Dutch" Clark	950.00
2	Bo Molenda	110.00
3	George Kenneally	110.00
4	Ed Matesic	110.00
5	Glenn Presnell	110.00
6	Pug Rentner	110.00
7	Ken Strong	225.00
8	Jim Zyntell	110.00
9	Knute Rockne	3000.
10	Cliff Battles	220.00
11	Turk Edwards	220.00
12	Tom Hupke	110.00
13	Homer Griffiths	110.00
14	Phil Sorboe	110.00
15	Ben Ciccone	110.00
16	Ben Smith	110.00
17	Tom Jones	110.00
18	Mike Mikulak	110.00
19	Ralph Kercheval	110.00
20	Warren Heller	110.00
21	Cliff Montgomery	110.00
22	Shipwreck Kelley	110.00
23	Beattie Feathers	220.00
24	Clarke Hinkle	200.00
25	Dale Burnett	375.00
26	John Isola	375.00
27	Bill Tosi	375.00
28	Stan Kosta	375.00
29	Jim MacMurdo	375.00
30	Ernie Caddel	375.00
31	Nic Niccola	375.00
32	Swede Johnston	375.00
33	Ernie Smith	375.00
34	Bronko Nagurski	6500.
35	Luke Johnson	375.00
36	Bernie Masterson	1300.

1992 NewSport

NewSport was issued exclusively in France, with four cards being distributed each month from November 1991 to June 1992. The 32-card glossy set was either issued in individual cards or in four-card strips. Each card measures 4" x 6", with card backs written in French.

		MT
Complete Set (32):		200.00
Common Player:		6.00
1	Bubby Brister	6.00
2	James Brooks	6.00
3	Joey Browner	6.00
4	Gill Byrd	6.00
5	Eric Dickerson	8.00
6	Henry Ellard	6.00
7	John Elway	20.00
8	Mervyn Fernandez	6.00
9	David Fulcher	6.00
10	Ernest Givins	6.00
11	Jay Hilgenberg	6.00
12	Michael Irvin	10.00
13	Dave Krieg	6.00
14	Albert Lewis	6.00
15	James Lofton	6.00
16	Dan Marino	45.00
17	Wilber Marshall	6.00
18	Freeman McNeil	6.00
19	Karl Mecklenberg	6.00
20	Joe Montana	35.00
21	Christian Okoye	6.00
22	Michael Dean Perry	6.00
23	Tom Rathman	6.00
24	Mark Rypien	6.00
25	Barry Sanders	30.00
26	Deion Sanders	20.00
27	Sterling Sharpe	8.00
28	Pat Swilling	6.00
29	Lawrence Taylor	10.00
30	Vinny Testaverde	6.00
31	Andre Tippett	6.00
32	Reggie White	10.00

1991 NFL Experience

These oversized cards feature artwork highlights from the first 25 Super Bowls. The black-bordered cards, which measure 2-1/2" x 4-3/4", were produced by the NFL, so each has an NFL Experience logo on the front. The back is in a horizontal format, with a pink bar at the top which has "The NFL Experience" written in it, plus the card number. A pink bar at the bottom carries a description of the action on the front. Sandwiched between the two bars is a brief comment about life in the NFL, plus a sponsor logo.

		MT
Complete Set (28):		4.00
Common Player:		.20
1	NFL Experience Theme Art	.20
2	Super Bowl I (Max McGee)	.20
3	Super Bowl II (Vince Lombardi, Bart Starr)	.50
4	Super Bowl III (Don Shula, Joe Namath)	.75
5	Super Bowl IV	.20
6	Super Bowl V - Colts vs. Cowboys	.20
7	Super Bowl VI (Duane Thomas, Bob Lily, Roger Staubach, Tom Landry, Tex Schramm)	.60
8	Super Bowl VII	.20
9	Super Bowl VIII (Larry Csonka)	.30
10	Super Bowl IX	.20
11	Super Bowl X (Lynn Swann, Jack Lambert)	.30
12	Super Bowl XI - Raiders vs. Vikings (John Madden)	.30
13	Super Bowl XII (Randy White, Harvey Martin, Craig Morton)	.30
14	Super Bowl XIII - Steelers vs. Cowboys	.20
15	Super Bowl XIV (Terry Bradshaw)	.60
16	Super Bowl XV - Raiders vs. Eagles	.20
17	Super Bowl XVI - 49ers vs. Bengals	.20
18	Super Bowl XVII (John Riggins)	.30
19	Super Bowl XVIII (Marcus Allen)	.30
20	Super Bowl XIX - 49ers vs. Dolphins	.20
21	Super Bowl XX (Richard Dent)	.30
22	Super Bowl XXI	.20
23	Super Bowl XXII (John Elway, Doug Williams)	.30
24	Super Bowl XXIII - 49ers vs. Bengals	.20
25	Super Bowl XXIV (Joe Montana)	1.00
26	Super Bowl XXV Collage of 25 Super Bowls	.20
27	Super Bowl XXVI - Lombardi Trophy	.20
28	Joe Theismann	.30

1993 NFL Properties Santa Claus

This 12-card set was available through a mail-in offer of any 30 1993 NFL trading card wrappers and $1.50 for postage and handling. In addition, sets were sent out to dealers with a season's greeting card. All 12 NFL trading card licensees produced a Santa Claus card, and there was a checklist card issued by NFL Properties included.

		MT
Complete Set (13):		15.00
Common Player:		1.50
1	Santa Claus Action Packed (Action Packed)	1.50
2	Santa Claus Classic	1.50
3	Santa Claus Collector's Edge	1.50
4	Santa Claus Fleer	1.50
5	Santa Claus Pacific	1.50

6	Santa Claus Pinnacle	1.50
7	Santa Claus Playoff	1.50
8	Santa Claus Pro Set	1.50
9	Santa Claus SkyBox	1.50
10	Santa Claus Topps	1.50
11	Santa Claus Upper Deck	1.50
12	Santa Claus Wild Card	1.50
13	Checklist Card NFL Properties	1.50

1993-95 NFL Properties Show Redemption Cards

This NFL Properties product was handed out to attendees at card shows over a three-year span, with a banner at the top of each card showing the city and dates that the show was held. The first card was issued at Chicago and is the only unnumbered card (others have roman numerals on the back). Card No. 2 was given out at a Labor Day Weekend Show in San Francisco and is the only card in the set to show the team's schedule on the back (others have text about players on the front). Card No. 4B was limited to 3,000 total cards, and replaced card No. 4A, which was done to commemorate the St. Louis Stallions NFL franchise that never materalized so it was not issued. Card No. 6A was issued at the Cocktail Reception sponsored by NFL Properties at the 15th National Sports Collectors Convention, with the three players autographing the card in blue ink. Card No. 6B was issued as part of the Back-to-School promotion, with collectors redeeming two proof of purchases for the oversized Elway NFL FACT card.

		MT
Complete Set (9):		750.00
Common Player:		10.00
1	Chicago Bears Saluting Hall of Famers (Dick Butkus, Mike Ditka, Gale Sayers) (7/24/93) (200) (Signed in silver	100.00
2	San Francisco 49ers Labor Day Weekend (NFL Kickoff '93, Ricky Watters, Steve Young, Keith DeLong, Jerry (9/93) (1,000) (1993 49er schedule on card back)	20.00
3	San Francisco 49ers Labor Day Weekend (Y.A. Tittle, Ken Stabler) (9/93, 1,000) Saluting Bay Area Legends, (Career	15.00
3AU	San Francisco 49ers AUTO Labor Day Weekend (Y.A. Tittle, Ken Stabler) (9/93) (1,000) Saluting Bay Area Legends	180.00
4B	St. Louis Cardinals Saluting Three Decades of Gateway City QBs (Jim Hart, Charlie Johnson, Neil	10.00
5	Dallas Cowboys Saluting the Super Bowl Champions (Michael Irvin, Troy Aikman, Emmitt Smith, Jay Novacek, (11/19-21/93) 3000)	15.00
6A	Houston Oilers Saluting a Trio of Oilers Legends (Earl Campbell, Dan Pastorini, Ken Stabler) (Autographed)	180.00
6B	1995 Spokesman NFL Trading Cards (John Elway) (Autographed) (300)	100.00

7	Joe Namath, John Elway (Autographed) (300)	180.00

1994 NFL Back-to-School

This 11-card set had one card by each of the 11 NFL licensees and was available to collectors who sent in 20 wrappers from NFL licensed products by the deadline of Nov. 30, 1994. Cards are unnumbered on the backs, except Action Packed (BS1) and Upper Deck (19) and are standard sized. At one point Pro Set had planned to do a Brett Favre card, however it went out of business before the card could be issued.

		MT
Complete Set (11):		15.00
Common Player:		.50
1	NFL Quarterback Club (Action Packed)	1.50
2	Emmitt Smith (Classic)	4.00
3	John Elway (Collector's Edge)	1.25
4	Jerome Bettis (Fleer)	1.00
5	Sterling Sharpe (Pacific)	.75
6	Drew Bledsoe (Pinnacle)	2.00
7	Dana Stubblefield (Playoff)	.75
8	Jim Kelly (SkyBox)	.75
9	Jerry Rice (Topps)	2.00
10	Joe Montana (Upper Deck)	2.50
11	Checklist NFL Properties	.50

1994 NFL Properties Santa Claus

Each of the NFL's 10 card licensees printed a Santa card for the set, which was available through the mail in exchange for 20 NFL-licensed card wrappers and $1.50 postage. There is no consistent design throughout the set, as each company was allowed to create their own design. Some cards are numbered and others are not. The fronts each include Santa artwork, while the backs have holiday greetings.

		MT
Complete Set (10):		10.00
Common Player:		1.25
1	Santa Claus Action Packed	1.25
2	Santa Claus Classic	1.25
3	Santa Claus Collector's Edge	1.25
4	Santa Claus Fleer	1.25
5	Santa Claus Pacific	1.25

6	Santa Claus Pinnacle	1.25
7	Santa Claus Playoff	1.25
8	Santa Claus SkyBox	1.25
9	Santa Claus Upper Deck	1.25
10	Checklist Card, NFL Properties	1.25

1995 NFL Properties Santa Claus

Eight of the NFL's card licensees produced cards for this nine-card set. The fronts and backs do not have a consistent design. The set was available for 20 wrappers and $1.50 shipping.

		MT
Complete Set (9):		10.00
Common Player:		1.00
1	Title Card (Santa and friend)	1.00
2	Santa Claus Classic ProLine (Emmitt Smith, Drew Bledsoe)	2.00
3	Santa Claus Collector's Edge	1.00
4	Santa Claus Pacific	1.00
5	Santa Claus Pinnacle (Dan Marino, Emmitt Smith, Steve Young)	4.00
6	Santa Claus Playoff	1.00
7	Santa Claus SkyBox	1.00
8	Santa Claus Topps	1.00
9	Santa Claus Upper Deck	1.00

1996 NFL Properties 7-11

Fleer/SkyBox, Pinnacle, Topps and Upper Deck, along with NFL Properties, combined to produce this nine-card set. Each card front and back is designed identically to the companies' sets from 1996. The cards are numbered 1-9 on the backs. To receive the cards, collectors needed to send in two wrappers from any 1996 NFL trading card product, a 7-11 store receipt with the trading card purchase circled, completed entry form or 3 x 5 card and $1 for shipping had to be sent to a redemption house in Minnesota.

		MT
Complete Set (9):		20.00
Common Player:		1.00
1	John Elway	3.00
2	Jerry Rice	3.00
3	Dan Marino	4.00
4	Barry Sanders	5.00
5	Kordell Stewart	3.00
6	Steve Young	3.00
7	Joe Namath	3.00
8	Brett Favre	6.00
9	Trent Dilfer	1.00

1996 NFL Properties Back-to-School

One of each of the NFL's card licensees, along with NFL Properties, joined forces to produce this nine-card set. To receive the set, collectors needed to send in 20 wrappers from any 1996 NFL-licensed trading cards and $1.50 for shipping to a redemption house in Minnesota. The offer expired Nov. 30, 1996.

		MT
Complete Set (9):		10.00
Common Player:		.50
1	Pacific (Chris Warren)	.50
2	Pinnacle (Dan Marino, Steve Young)	2.00
3	NFLP (John Elway)	1.50
4	Topps (Steve Young)	1.00
5	Fleer (Brett Favre)	3.00
6	Collector's Edge (Steve Bono)	.50
7	Upper Deck (Dan Marino)	2.00
8	Classic (Emmitt Smith)	2.00

9	Playoff (Deion Sanders)	1.00

1996 NFL Properties Santa Claus

This nine-card set consists of cards produced by the eight NFL trading card licensees. All the cards feature Santa Claus and some have NFL players as well. The cards could be obtained via redemption of 20 wrappers of any participating manufacturers football products.

		MT
Complete Set (9):		8.00
Common Player:		1.00
1	Title Card - Santa Claus	1.00
2	Santa Claus (Collector's Edge with Jeff Blake and Steve Bono)	1.00
3	Santa Claus (Fleer/Skybox with Brett Favre on back)	1.00
4	Santa Claus (Pacific)	1.00
5	Santa Claus (Pinnacle with Drew Bledsoe and Jim Harbaugh)	1.00
6	Santa Claus (Playoff)	1.00
7	Santa Claus (Score Board with Troy Aikman)	1.00
8	Santa Claus (Topps)	1.00
9	Santa Claus (Upper Deck)	1.00

1972 NFLPA Wonderful World Stamps

These numbered stamps, which each measure 1-15/16" x 2-7/8", feature stars from each team in the NFL. The front of each stamp has a color photo of the player; the back has player's name, a stamp number and a place for it to be glued so it can be put into an accompanying album. The 30-page 9-1/2" x 13-1/4" album traces the history of pro football in the United States and provides short biographies of the players who are featured on the stamps. The NFLPA sponsored the album, which is titled "The Wonderful World of Pro Football USA." Stamps which are listed in the checklist with an A were issued in 1971.

		NM
Complete Set (390):		275.00
Common Player:		.35
1	Bob Berry	.50
2	Greg Brezina	.35
3	Ken Burrow	.35
4	Jim Butler	.40
5	Wes Chesson	.35
6	Claude Humphrey	.35
7	George Kunz	1.00
8	Tom McCauley	.35
9	Jim Mitchell	.50
10	Tommy Nobis	3.00
11	Ken Reaves	.35
12	Bill Sandeman	.35
13	John Small	.35
14	Harmon Wages	.35
15	John Zook	.50
16	Norm Bulaich	.60
17	Bill Curry	.75
18	Mike Curtis	.50
19	Ted Hendricks	3.00
20	Roy Hilton	.35
21	Eddie Hinton	.35

22	David Lee	.35
23	Jerry Logan	.35
24	John Mackey	2.00
25	Tom Matte	.75
26	Jim O'Brien	.50
27	Glenn Ressler	.35
28	Johnny Unitas	15.00
29	Bob Vogel	.50
30	Rick Volk	.50
31	Paul Costa	.35
32	Jim Dunaway	.50
33	Paul Guidry	.35
34	Jim Harris	.35
35	Robert James	.35
36	Mike McBath	.35
37	Haven Moses	1.00
38	Wayne Patrick	.35
39	John Pitts	.35
40	Jim Reilly	.35
41	Pete Richardson	.35
42	Dennis Shaw	.50
43	O.J. Simpson	25.00
44	Mike Stratton	.50
45	Bob Tatarek	.35
46	Dick Butkus	8.00
47	Jim Cadile	.35
48	Jack Concannon	.50
49	Bobby Douglass	.75
50	George Farmer	.35
51	Dick Gordon	.50
52	Bob Green	.35
53	Ed O'Bradovich	.35
54	Bob Hyland	.35
54A	Mac Percival	.35
55A	Ed O'Bradovich	.50
55	Gale Sayers	9.00
56A	Mac Percival	.35
56B	George Seals	.35
57	Jim Seymour	.35
58A	George Seals	.35
58B	Ron Smith	.50
59	Bill Staley	.35
60	Cecil Turner	.40
61	Al Beauchamp	.45
62	Virgil Carter	.50
63	Vernon Holland	.35
64	Bob Johnson	.50
65	Ron Lamb	.35
66	Dave Lewis	.35
67	Rufus Mayes	.50
68	Horst Muhlmann	.35
69	Lemar Parrish	.75
70	Jess Phillips	.35
71	Mike Reid	2.00
72	Ken Riley	1.00
73	Paul Robinson	.50
74	Bob Trumpy	2.25
75	Fred Willis	.35
76	Don Cockroft	.50
77	Gary Collins	.50
78	Gene Hickerson	.50
79	Fair Hooker	.75
80	Jim Houston	.50
81	Walter Johnson	.50
82	Joe Jones	.35
83	Leroy Kelly	3.00
84	Milt Morin	.50
85	Reece Morrison	.35
86	Bill Nelsen	.50
87	Mike Phipps	.75
88	Bo Scott	.50
89	Jerry Sherk	.50
90	Ron Snidow	.35
91	Herb Adderley	3.00
92	George Andrie	.75
93	Mike Clark	.35
94	Dave Edwards	.50
95	Walt Garrison	1.50
96	Cornell Green	.75
97	Bob Hayes	2.00
98	Calvin Hill	2.00
99	Chuck Howley	.75
100	Lee Roy Jordan	2.50
101	Dave Manders	.50
102	Craig Morton	1.25
103	Ralph Neely	.50
104	Mel Renfro	1.00
105	Roger Staubach	30.00
106	Bobby Anderson	.75
107	Sam Brunelli	.35
108	Dave Costa	.35
109	Mike Current	.35
110	Pete Duranko	.35
111	George Goeddeke	.35
112	Cornell Gordon	.35
113	Don Horn	.50
114	Rich Jackson	.50
115	Larry Kaminski	.35
116	Floyd Little	1.50
117	Marv Montgomery	.35
118	Steve Ramsey	.50
119	Paul Smith	.50
120	Billy Thompson	.75
121	Lem Barney	3.00
122	Nick Eddy	.50
123	Mel Farr	.75
124	Ed Flanagan	.35
125	Larry Hand	.35
126	Greg Landry	.75
127	Dick LeBeau	.50
128	Mike Lucci	.50
129	Earl McCulloch	.50
130	Bill Munson	.75
131	Wayne Rasmussen	.35
132	Joe Robb	.35
133	Jerry Rush	.35
134	Altie Taylor	.50
135	Wayne Walker	.50

136	Ken Bowman	.35
137	John Brockington	.75
138	Fred Carr	.50
139	Carroll Dale	.50
140	Ken Ellis	.35
141	Gale Gillingham	.50
142	Dave Hampton	.50
143	Doug Hart	.35
144A	John Hilton	.35
144B	MacArthur Lane	.35
145	Mike McCoy	.50
146	Ray Nitschke	2.50
147	Frank Patrick	.35
148	Francis Peay	.35
149	Dave Robinson	.75
150	Bart Starr	9.00
151	Bob Atkins	.35
152	Elvin Bethea	.75
153	Garland Boyette	.35
154	ken Burrough	.75
155	Woody Campbell	.35
156	John Charles	.35
157	Lynn Dickey	.75
158	Elbert Drungo	.35
159	Gene Ferguson	.35
160	Charlie Johnson	.75
161	Charlie Joyner	3.00
162	Dan Pastorini	.75
163	Ron Pritchard	.35
164	Walt Suggs	.35
165	Mike Tilleman	.35
166	Bobby Bell	3.00
167	Aaron Brown	.50
168	Buck Buchanan	2.00
169	Ed Buddle	.75
170	Curley Culp	1.00
171	Len Dawson	6.00
172	Willie Lanier	2.50
173	Jim Lynch	.50
174	Jim Marsalis	.50
175	Mo Moorman	.35
176	Ed Podolak	.50
177	Johnny Robinson	.75
178	Jan Stenerud	2.00
179	Otis Taylor	1.50
180	Jim Tyrer	.75
181	Kermit Alexander	.50
182	Coy Bacon	.35
183	Dick Buzin	.35
184	Roman Gabriel	1.00
185	Gene Howard	.35
186	Ken Iman	.35
187	Les Josephson	.50
188	Marlin McKeever	.50
189	Merlin Olsen	4.00
190A	Richie Petitbon	.75
190B	Phil Olsen	.35
191	David Ray	.35
192	Lance Rentzel	.75
193	Isiah Robertson	.50
194	Larry Smith	.35
195	Jack Snow	.75
196	Nick Buoniconti	2.00
197	Doug Crusan	.35
198	Larry Csonka	8.00
199	Bob DeMarco	.50
200	Marv Fleming	.50
201	Bob Griese	10.00
202	Jim Klick	1.00
203	Bob Kuechenberg	1.00
204	Mercury Morris	1.25
205A	Jim Riley	.35
205B	John Richardson	.35
206	Jim Riley	.35
207	Jake Scott	.75
208	Howard Twilley	.75
209	Paul Warfield	5.00
210	Garo Yepremian	.75
211	Grady Alderman	.50
212	John Beasley	.35
213	John Henderson	.35
214	Wally Hilgenberg	.50
215	Clinton Jones	.50
216	Karl Kassulke	.35
217	Paul Krause	1.25
218	Dave Osborn	.50
219	Alan Page	2.00
220	Ed Sharockman	.35
221	Fran Tarkenton	10.00
222	Mick Tingelhoff	.75
223	Charlie West	.35
224	Lonnie Warwick	.35
225	Gene Washington	.75
226	Hank Barton	.35
227A	Larry Carwell	.35
227B	Ron Berger	.35
228	Larry Carwell	.35
229A	Carl Garrett	.50
229B	Jim Cheyunski	.50
230A	Jim Hunt	.35
230B	Carl Garrett	.50
231	Rickie Harris	.35
232	Daryl Johnson	.35
233	Steve Kiner	.35
234	Jon Morris	.35
235	Jim Nance	.75
236	Tom Neville	.35
237	Jim Plunkett	4.00
238	Ron Sellers	.50
239	Len St. Jean	.35
240A	Gerald Warren	.35
240B	Don Webb	.35
241	Dan Abramowicz	.75
242A	Tony Baker	.35
242B	Dick Absher	.35
243	Leo Carroll	.35
244	Jim Duncan	.35
245	Al Dodd	.35

246	Jim Flanigan	.35
247	Hoyle Granger	.35
248	Edd Hargett	.75
249	Glen Ray Hines	.35
250	Hugo Hollas	.35
251	Jake Kupp	.35
252	Dave Long	.35
253	Mike Morgan	.35
254	Tom Roussel	.35
255	Del Williams	.35
256	Otto Brown	.35
257	Bobby Duhon	.50
258	Scott Eaton	.35
259	Jim Flies	.35
260	Tucker Fredrickson	.35
261A	Don Herrmann	.35
261B	Pete Gogolak	.50
262	Bob Grim	.50
263	Don Herrmann	.35
264A	Ernie Koy	.75
264B	Ron Johnson	1.00
265A	Spider Lockhart	.35
265B	Jim Kanicki	.35
266	Spider Lockhart	.50
267	Joe Morrison	.75
268	Bob Tucker	2.00
269	Willie Williams	.35
270	Willie Young	.35
271	Al Atkinson	.35
272	Ralph Baker	.35
273	Emerson Boozer	.75
274	John Elliott	.35
275	Dave Herman	.35
276A	Dave Herman	.35
276B	Winston Hill	.50
277	Gus Hollomon	.35
278	Bob Howfield	.35
279	Pete Lammons	.50
280	Joe Namath (numbered 281)	22.00
281	Gerry Philbin	.50
282	Matt Snell	.75
283	Steve Tannen	.35
284	Earlie Thomas	.35
285	Al Woodall	.35
286	Fred Biletnikoff	4.00
287	George Blanda	6.00
288	Willie Brown	3.00
289	Ray Chester	1.00
290	Tony Cline	.35
291	Dan Conners	.35
292	Ben Davidson	1.50
293	Hewritt Dixon	.50
294	Tom Keating	.50
295	Daryle Lamonica	1.50
296	Gus Otto	.35
297	Jim Otto	3.00
298	Rod Sherman	.35
299	Bubba Smith	.50
300A	Warren Wells	.50
300B	Gene Upshaw	3.00
301	Rick Arrington	.35
302	Gary Ballman	.50
303	Lee Bouggess	.35
304	Bill Bradley	.75
305A	Richard Harris	.35
305B	Happy Feller	.75
306A	Ben Hawkins	.50
306B	Richard Harris	.35
307	Ben Hawkins	.50
308	Harold Jackson	1.50
309	Pete Liske	.75
310	Al Nelson	.35
311	Gary Pettigrew	.35
312	Tim Rossovich	.75
313	Tom Woodeshick	.50
314	Adrian Young	.50
315	Steve Zabel	.35
316	Chuck Allen	.35
317	Warren Bankston	.35
318	Chuck Beatty	.35
319	Terry Bradshaw	20.00
320	John Fuqua	.50
321	Terry Hanratty	1.00
322	Ray Mansfield	.35
323	Ben McGee	.35
324	John Rowser	.35
325	Andy Russell	1.00
326	Ron Shanklin	.50
327	Dave Smith	.35
328	Bruce Van Dyke	.35
329	Lloyd Voss	.35
330	Bobby Walden	.35
331	Donny Anderson	.75
332	Jim Bakken	.75
333	Pete Beathard	.75
334A	Mel Gray	2.00
334B	Miller Farr	.50
335A	Jim Hart	1.00
335B	Mel Gray	1.00
336	Jim Hart	1.00
337A	Chuck Latourette	.35
337B	Rol Krueger	.35
338	Chuck Latourette	.35
339A	Bob Reynolds	.35
339B	Ernie McMillan	.50
340	Bob Reynolds	.35
341	Jackie Smith	3.50
342	Larry Stallings	.50
343	Chuck Walker	.35
344	Roger Wehrli	.75
345	Larry Wilson	2.00
346	Bob Babich	.35
347	Pete Barnes	.35
348A	Marty Domres	.35
348B	Steve DeLong	.50
349	Marty Domres	.50
350	Gary Garrison	.50

351A	Walker Gillette	.35
351B	John Hadl	1.25
352	Kevin Hardy	.35
353	Bob Howard	.35
354A	Jim Hill	.35
354B	Deacon Jones	1.75
355	Terry Owens	.75
356	Dennis Partee	.35
357A	Dennis Partee	.35
357B	Jeff Queen	.35
358	Jim Tolbert	.35
359	Russ Washington	.35
360	Doug Wilkerson	.35
361	John Brodie	3.50
362	Doug Cunningham	.35
363	Bruce Gossett	.35
364	Stan Hindman	.35
365	John Isenbarger	.35
366	Charlie Krueger	.50
367	Frank Nunley	.35
368	Woody Peoples	.35
369	Len Rohde	.35
370	Steve Spurrier	6.50
371	Gene Washington	1.00
372	Dave Wilcox	.75
373	Ken Willard	1.00
374	Bob Windsor	.50
375	Dick Witcher	.50
376	Verlon Biggs	.75
377	Larry Brown	3.00
378	Speedy Duncan	.50
379	Chris Hanburger	1.00
380	Charlie Harraway	.50
381	Sonny Jurgensen	5.00
382	Bill Kilmer	1.50
383	Tommy Mason	.50
384	Ron McDole	.50
385	Brig Owens	.35
386	Jack Pardee	2.00
387	Myron Pottios	1.00
388	Jerry Smith	.50
389	Diron Talbert	.50
390	Charley Taylor	4.00

1972 NFLPA Vinyl Stickers

These stickers feature 20 of the NFL's stars and were sold through vending machines. Each sticker is 2-3/4" x 4-3/4" and is copyrighted on the front by the NFLPA. Each player's head appears on a caricature drawing of him in a football uniform; the outline of his body is what can actually be used as a sticker. Consequently, the backs are blank. The stickers are unnumbered.

		NM
Complete Set (20):		95.00
Common Player:		2.00
(1)	Donny Anderson	2.00
(2)	George Blanda	5.00
(3)	Terry Bradshaw	17.00
(4)	John Brockington	2.00
(5)	John Brodie	4.00
(6)	Dick Butkus	8.00
(7)	Dick Gordon	2.00
(8)	Joe Greene	5.00
(9)	John Hadl	2.00
(10)	Bob Hayes	3.00
(11)	Ron Johnson	9.00
(12)	Floyd Little	3.00
(13)	Joe Namath	25.00
(14)	Tommy Nobis	3.00
(15)	Alan Page	15.00
(16)	Jim Plunkett	5.00
(17)	Gale Sayers	10.00
(18)	Roger Staubach	22.00
(19)	Johnny Unitas	18.00
(20)	Paul Warfield	4.00

1972 NFLPA Iron Ons

These 35 cards were created as cloth patches to be ironed onto clothes. Hence, the backs are blank. The front of the card has a full color head shot of the player, with his name and 1972 NFLPA copyright at the bottom. The player's name is above the photo, which is framed by a black border. The cards, which were sold through vending machines, measure 2-1/4" x 3-1/2" and are unnumbered.

		NM
Complete Set (35):		175.00
Common Player:		2.00
(1)	Donny Anderson	2.00
(2)	George Blanda	7.50
(3)	Terry Bradshaw	20.00
(4)	John Brockington	2.00
(5)	John Brodie	5.00
(6)	Dick Butkus	10.00
(7)	Larry Csonka	10.00
(8)	Mike Curtis	2.00
(9)	Len Dawson	6.00
(10)	Carl Eller	3.00
(11)	Mike Garrett	2.00
(12)	Joe Greene	8.00
(13)	Bob Griese	9.00
(14)	Dick Gordon	2.00
(15)	John Hadl	2.00
(16)	Bob Hayes	3.00
(17)	Ron Johnson	2.00
(18)	Deacon Jones	3.00
(19)	Sonny Jurgensen	6.00
(20)	Leroy Kelly	3.00
(21)	Jim Kiick	2.50
(22)	Greg Landry	2.00
(23)	Floyd Little	3.00
(24)	Mike Lucci	2.00
(25)	Archie Manning	5.00
(26)	Joe Namath	35.00
(27)	Tommy Nobis	3.00
(28)	Alan Page	3.00
(29)	Jim Plunkett	4.00
(30)	Gale Sayers	10.00
(31)	O.J. Simpson	35.00
(32)	Roger Staubach	30.00
(33)	Duane Thomas	2.00
(34)	Johnny Unitas	25.00
(35)	Paul Warfield	5.00

1979 NFLPA Pennant Stickers

Each of these 50 stickers, sponsored by the NFLPA, is shaped like a pennant and features a black-and-white head shot of a player inside a circle. The NFLPA football logo is also on the front of the sticker. Different colors are used for the backgrounds of the stickers; some stickers can be found with various colors for a background, too. The stickers measure 2-1/2" x 5" and have the player's name, position and team on the front.

		NM
Complete Set (50):		425.00
Common Player:		2.50
(1)	Lyle Alzado	5.00
(2)	Ken Anderson	7.50
(3)	Steve Bartkowski	10.00
(4)	Ricky Bell	4.00
(5)	Elvin Bethea	2.50
(6)	Tom Blanchard	2.50
(7)	Terry Bradshaw	25.00
(8)	Bob Breunig	4.00
(9)	Greg Brezina	5.00
(10)	Doug Buffone	9.00
(11)	Earl Campbell	50.00
(12)	John Cappelletti	3.00
(13)	Harold Carmichael	4.00
(14)	Chuck Crist	15.00
(15)	Sam Cunningham	4.00
(16)	Joe DeLamielleure	2.50
(17)	Tom Dempsey	4.00
(18)	Tony Dorsett	15.00
(19)	Dan Fouts	20.00
(20)	Roy Gerela	4.00
(21)	Bob Griese (misspelled Greise)	12.00
(22)	Franco Harris	15.00
(23)	Jim Hart	12.00
(24)	Charlie Joiner	6.00
(25)	Paul Krause	4.00
(26)	Bob Kuechenberg	4.00
(27)	Greg Landry	2.50
(28)	Archie Manning	6.00
(29)	Chester Marcol	2.50
(30)	Harvey Martin	4.00
(31)	Lawrence McCutcheon	12.00
(32)	Craig Morton	4.00
(33)	Haven Moses	2.50
(34)	Steve Odom	3.00
(35)	Morris Owens	2.50
(36)	Dan Pastorini	9.00
(37)	Walter Payton	35.00
(38)	Greg Pruitt	14.00
(39)	John Riggins	9.00
(40)	Jake Scott	3.00
(41)	Ken Stabler	20.00
(42)	Roger Staubach	30.00
(43)	Jan Stenerud	6.00
(44)	Art Still	9.00
(45)	Mick Tingelhoff	4.00
(46)	Richard Todd	2.50
(47)	Phil Villapiano	9.00
(48)	Wesley Walker	9.00
(49)	Roger Werhli	9.00
(50)	Jim Zorn	12.00

1995 NFLPA Super Bowl Party Giveaways

Produced as a premium for the NFLPA Super Bowl XXIX party, each NFL card licensee designed one card for the 10-card set. Overall, 500 of each card were printed. The cards are unnumbered. The NFL Players logo is included on the front of each card.

		MT
Complete Set (10):		200.00
Common Player:		10.00
1	Marcus Allen (Pinnacle)	12.00
2	Jerome Bettis (Fleer)	12.00
3	Tim Brown (Collector's Edge)	10.00
4	Trent Dilfer (SkyBox)	12.00
5	Marshall Faulk (Pacific)	30.00
6	Ronnie Lott (Classic)	10.00
7	Dan Marino (Upper Deck)	80.00
8	Junior Seau (Stadium Club)	12.00
9	Sterling Sharpe (Action Packed)	10.00
10	Heath Shuler (Playoff)	20.00

1996 NFLPA Super Bowl Party Giveaways

Produced as a premium for the NFLPA Sega Sports Super Bowl XXX party, each NFL card licensee created one card for the 12-card set. The NFL Players' logo appears on the front and backs of the unnumbered cards.

		MT
Complete Set (12):		15.00
Common Player:		.75
1	Marcus Allen, Ronnie Lott (Collector's Edge)	1.00
2	Steve Beuerlein (Topps)	.75
3	Jeff Blake (Pacific)	1.50
4	Tim Brown (Action Packed)	1.00
5	Kerry Collins (Classic)	3.00
6	Kevin Greene (Playoff)	.75
7	Garrison Hearst (Fleer Metal)	1.00
8	Daryl Johnston (SkyBox Impact)	.75
9	Joe Montana (Upper Deck)	3.00
10	Deion Sanders (Donruss Red Zone)	1.50
11	Herschel Walker (Pinnacle)	.75
12	Logo Card (Checklist back)	.75

1997 NFLPA Super Bowl Player's Party

This 11-card set was distributed at the NFLPA Super Bowl XXXI player's party. Cards were contributed by each NFL trading card licensee. The cards are unnumbered.

		MT
Complete Set (11):		12.00
Common Player:		.75
1	SkyBox (Morten Andersen)	.75
2	Collector's Edge (Steve Bono)	.75
3	Pacific (Robert Brooks)	.75
4	Topps (Tony Dorsett)	1.50
5	Donruss (Gus Frerotte)	.75
6	Pinnacle (Kevin Hardy)	.75
7	Score Board (Tyrone Hughes)	.75
8	Upper Deck (Dan Marino)	3.00
9	SkyBox (Curtis Martin)	2.00
10	Playoff (Deion Sanders)	1.50
11	Checklist Card - Upper Deck	.75

1961 Oilers Jay Publishing

Measuring 5" x 7", the 24-card set is anchored by a black-and-white player photo on the front. The player's name and team appear in the white border beneath the photo. The player's facsimile signature is printed on the photo. The cards are unnumbered and have blank backs. Originally, the cards were sold in 12-card packs for 25 cents.

		NM
Complete Set (24):		125.00
Common Player:		5.00
1	Dalva Allen	5.00
2	Tony Banfield	5.00
3	George Blanda	12.00
4	Billy Cannon	6.00
5	Doug Cline	5.00
6	Willard Dewveall	5.00
7	Mike Dukes	5.00
8	Don Floyd	6.00
9	Freddy Glick	6.00
10	Bill Groman	6.00
11	Charlie Hennigan	6.00
12	Ed Husmann	5.00
13	Al Jamison	5.00
14	Mark Johnston	5.00
15	Jacky Lee	6.00
16	Bob McLeod	5.00
17	Rich Michael	5.00
18	Dennit Morris	5.00
19	Jim Norton	6.00
20	Bob Schmidt	5.00
21	Dave Smith	5.00
22	Bob Talamini	6.00
23	Charles Tolar	6.00
24	Hogan Wharton	5.00

1964-65 Oilers Color Team Issue

Measuring 7-3/4" x 9-3/4", the 16-photo set is anchored by a color photo on the front, bordered in white. A facsimile signature is printed over the photo. The photos are unnumbered and have blank backs. The photos were sold in eight-photo packs for 50 cents.

		NM
Complete Set (16):		80.00
Common Player:		5.00
1	Scott Appleton	6.00
2	Tony Banfield	6.00
3	Sonny Bishop	6.00
4	George Blanda	12.00
5	Sid Blanks	6.00
6	Danny Brabham	6.00

7	Ode Burrell	6.00
8	Doug Cline	5.00
9	Don Floyd	6.00
10	Freddy Glick	6.00
11	Charlie Hennigan	6.00
12	Ed Husmann	5.00
13	Walt Suggs	6.00
14	Don Talamini	5.00
15	Charley Tolar	6.00
16	Don Trull	6.00

1967 Oilers Team Issue

Measuring 5-1/8" x 7", the 14-card set is anchored on the front with a black-and-white photo. The cards, which are unnumbered, have blank backs.

		NM
Complete Set (14):		45.00
Common Player:		4.00
1	Pete Barnes	4.00
2	Sonny Bishop	5.00
3	Ode Burrell	5.00
4	Ronnie Caveness	4.00
5	Joe Childress (CO)	4.00
6	Glen Ray Hines	5.00
7	Pat Holmes	4.00
8	Bobby Jancik	5.00
9	Pete Johns	4.00
10	Jim Norton	5.00
11	Willie Parker	4.00
12	Bob Poole	4.00
13	Alvin Reed	4.00
14	Olen Underwood	4.00

1969 Oilers Team Issue

Measuring 8" x 10", the 39-photo set is anchored by a large black-and-white photo on the front, bordered in white. The player's name, team and position are located beneath the photo. The unnumbered photos have blank backs.

		NM
Complete Set (39):		125.00
Common Player:		3.00
1	Jim Beirne (Wide receiver)	4.00
2	Jim Beirne (Split end)	4.00
3	Elvin Bethea	5.00
4	Sonny Bishop	4.00
5	Garland Boyette	4.00
6	Ode Burrell	4.00
7	Ed Carrington	3.00
8	Joe Childress (CO)	3.00
9	Bob Davis	3.00
10	Hugh Devore (CO)	3.00
11	Tom Domres	3.00
12	F.A. Dry	3.00
13	Miller Farr	4.00
14	Mac Haik (Action shot)	3.00
15	Mac Haik (Portrait)	3.00
16	W.K. Hicks	3.00
17	Glen Ray Hines	4.00
18	Pat Holmes	3.00
19	Roy Hopkins	3.00
20	Charlie Joiner	18.00
21	Jim LeMoine	3.00
22	Bobby Maples	4.00
23	Richard Marshall	3.00
24	Zeke Moore	4.00
25	Willie Parker	3.00
26	Johnny Peacock	3.00
27	Ron Pritchard (Back peddling)	3.00
28	Ron Pritchard (Cutting left)	3.00
29	Ron Pritchard (Preparing to fend off blocker)	3.00
30	Tom Regner	3.00
31	George Rice	3.00
32	George Rice	3.00
33	Bob Robertson	3.00
34	Walt Suggs	3.00
35	Don Trull	4.00
36	Olen Underwood	3.00
37	Loyd Wainscott	3.00
38	Wayne Walker	4.00
39	Glenn Woods	3.00

1971 Oilers Team Issue

Measuring 4" x 5-1/2", the 23-card set showcases a black-and-white photo on the front, with an Oilers' helmet in the upper left, "Houston Oilers" at the top center and the NFL shield in the upper right. The player's name and position are printed beneath the photo. The blank-backed cards are unnumbered.

		NM
Complete Set (23):		50.00
Common Player:		2.00
1	Willie Alexander	2.50
2	Jim Beirne	2.50
3	Elvin Bethea	3.00
4	Ron Billingsley	2.00
5	Garland Boyette	2.50
6	Leo Brooks	2.00
7	Ken Burrough	4.00
8	Woody Campbell	2.00
9	Lynn Dickey	4.00
10	Elbert Drungo	2.00
11	Pat Holmes	2.00
12	Robert Holmes	2.50
13	Ken Houston	10.00
14	Charlie Johnson	4.00
15	Charlie Joiner	12.00
16	Zeke Moore	2.50
17	Mark Moseley	4.00
18	Dan Pastorini	5.00
19	Alvin Reed	2.00
20	Tom Regner	2.00
21	Floyd Rice	2.00
22	Mike Tilleman	2.00
23	George Webster	3.00

1972 Oilers Team Issue

Measuring 5" x 7", the 11-card set showcases full-bleed black-and-white photos on the front. The unnumbered backs are blank.

		NM
Complete Set (11):		25.00
Common Player:		2.00
1	Ron Billingsley	2.00
2	Garland Boyette	2.00
3	Levert Carr	2.00
4	Walter Highsmith	2.00
5	Albert Johnson	2.00
6	Benny Johnson	2.00
7	Guy Murdock	2.00
8	Ron Saul	3.00
9	Mike Tilleman	2.00
10	Ward Walsh	2.00
11	George Webster	4.00

1973 Oilers McDonald's

Measuring 8" x 10", the three-photo card set is anchored by a color photo on the front, with the player's name and team beneath it. The fronts are bordered in white. The backs, which are unnumbered, have the player's name, bio, highlights and schedule, along with the 1973 Oilers' schedule. The McDonald's logo is printed in the lower right.

		NM
Complete Set (3):		25.00
Common Player:		6.00
1	John Matuszak	12.00
2	Zeke Moore	6.00
3	Dan Pastorini	12.00

1973 Oilers Team Issue

Measuring 5" x 8", the 17-card set is anchored by a large black-and-white photo on the front of the white-bordered cards. The blank-backed cards are unnumbered.

		NM
Complete Set (17):		35.00
Common Player:		2.00
1	Mack Alston	2.00
2	Bob Atkins	2.00
3	Skip Butler	2.00
4	Al Cowlings	3.00
5	Lynn Dickey	3.00
6	Mike Fanucci	2.00
7	Edd Hargett	2.50
8	Lewis Jolley	2.00
9	Clifton McNeil	2.50
10	Ralph Miller	2.00
11	Zeke Moore	2.50
12	Dave Parks	2.50
13	Willie Rodgers	2.00
14	Greg Sampson	2.00
15	Finn Seemann	2.00
16	Jeff Severson	2.00
17	Fred Willis	2.50

1980 Oilers Police

The 14-card, 2-5/8" x 4-1/8" set, sponsored by Kiwanis, local law enforcement and the Oilers,

features front color action photos with "Oilers Tips" appearing on the backs.

		NM
Complete Set (14):		12.00
Common Player:		.75
1	Gregg Bingham	1.00
2	Robert Brazile	.75
3	Ken Burrough	1.50
4	Rob Carpenter	1.00
5	Ronnie Coleman	1.00
6	Curley Culp	1.00
7	Carter Hartwig	.75
8	Billy Johnson	1.50
9	Carl Mauck	.75
10	Gifford Nielsen	1.00
11	Cliff Parsley	.75
12	Bum Phillips (CO)	1.00
13	Mike Renfro	1.00
14	Ken Stabler	4.00

1984 Pacific Legends

The 30-card, regular-size set features well-known athletes from the Pac 10 football conference, including John Wayne, Pop Warner, Jackie Robinson, Frank Gifford and Lynn Swann.

		MT
Complete Set (30):		20.00
Common Player:		.30
1	O.J. Simpson	5.00
2	Mike Garrett	.50
3	Pop Warner	.50
4	Bob Schloredt	.30
5	Pat Haden	.60
6	Ernie Nevers	.50
7	Jackie Robinson	2.50
8	Arnie Weinmeister	.50
9	Gary Beban	.50
10	Jim Plunkett	.60
11	Bobby Grayson	.30
12	Craig Morton	.50
13	Ben Davidson	.60
14	Jim Hardy	.30
15	Vern Burke	.30
16	Hugh McElhenny	.75
17	John Wayne	4.00
18	Ricky Bell (UER) (Name spelled Rickey on both sides)	.50
19	George Wildcat Wilson	.30
20	Bob Waterfield	.75
21	Charlie Mitchell	.30
22	Donn Moomaw	.30
23	Don Heinrich	.30
24	Terry Baker	.50
25	Jack Thompson	.50
26	Charles White	.50
27	Frank Gifford	1.50
28	Lynn Swann	1.75
29	Brick Muller	.30
30	Ron Yary	.50

1989 Pacific Steve Largent

This 110-card set is devoted to Hall of Fame wide receiver Steve Largent and commemorates his career with the Seattle Seahawks. Each card front, with a silver border, captures an event in Largent's career. The horizontally-designed backs describe the action on the front and have light blue borders. There were 85 cards in the set

which were numbered; the remaining 25 cards form a 12-1/2" x 17-1/2" poster of Largent. The entire set was available as a factory set or wax packs of 10 cards each. Pacific Trading Cards produced them.

		MT
Complete Set (110):		25.00
Common Player (1-85):		.25
1	Title Card (Steve Largent) (Checklist 1-42 On Back)	1.00
2	Santa, Can You Please (Steve Largent)	.25
3	Age 9 (Steve Largent)	.25
4	Junior High 1968 (Steve Largent)	.25
5	High School 1971 (Steve Largent)	.25
6	Baseball or Football (Steve Largent)	.25
7	Tulsa, Senior Bowl (Steve Largent)	.25
8	Led Nation in TD's (Steve Largent)	.25
9	Coach Patera, Coach Jerry Rhome	.40
10	Rookie 1976 (Steve Largent)	.50
11	First NFL TD (Steve Largent)	.25
12	Seahawk's First Win (Steve Largent)	.25
13	First Team All-Rookie (Steve Largent)	.40
14	Beats Buffalo 56-7 (Steve Largent)	.25
15	The Huddle (Steve Largent)	.25
16	Captains (Steve Largent, Norm Evans)	.40
17	First Win Against Raiders (Steve Largent)	.25
18	3000 Yards Receiving (Steve Largent)	.25
19	Jerry Rhome, Steve Largent	.50
20	Great Hands (Steve Largent)	.25
21	Climbs Mt. Rainier (Steve Largent)	.25
22	Zorn Connection (Steve Largent)	.40
23	Steve Largent, Jim Zorn	.40
24	First Team All-AFC (Steve Largent)	.25
25	Seahawks MVP 1981 (Steve Largent)	.40
26	Strike Season 1982 (Steve Largent)	.25
27	Training Camp 1983 (Steve Largent)	.25
28	Head Coach (Chuck Knox)	.40
29	50 Career TD's (Steve Largent)	.25
30	7000 Yards Receiving (Steve Largent)	.25
31	Tilley and Largent	.50
32	Cold Day in Cincy (Steve Largent)	.25
33	Catches 3 TD Passes (Steve Largent)	.25
34	Seahawks 12-4 in 1984 (Steve Largent)	.25
35	Defeated in AFC Championships (Steve Largent)	.25
36	Preparing for 1985 (Steve Largent)	.25
37	Career High 79 Catches (Steve Largent)	.25
38	Career High 1287 Yards (Steve Largent)	.25
39	10000 Yards Receiving (Steve Largent)	.25
40	Throws a Pass (Steve Largent)	.25
41	Game Day 1985 (Steve Largent)	.25
42	Seattle Sports Star of the Year (Steve Largent)	.40
43	A Very Sore Elbow (Steve Largent)	.25
44	The Concentration (Steve Largent)	.25
45	Steve Largent, Eugene Robinson	.40
46	Breaks Carmichael's Record (Steve Largent)	.35

47	Seahawks 37, Raiders 0 (Steve Largent)	.25
48	11000 Yards Receiving (Steve Largent)	.25
49	Rough Game (Steve Largent)	.25
50	Streak Continues (Steve Largent)	.25
51	Captains Lane, Brown and Largent	.40
52	Steve & Kyle Catch a Big One (Steve Largent)	.25
53	Krieg Connection (Steve Largent)	.40
54	Seahawk Camp (Steve Largent)	.25
55	NFL All-Time Leading Receiver (Steve Largent)	.40
56	Hall of Fame Bowl (Steve Largent)	.25
57	Steve Largent, Coach Knox	.40
58	1987 Seahawks MVP (Steve Largent)	.40
59	Largent at Quarterback (Steve Largent)	.50
60	NFL All-Time Great (Steve Largent)	.40
61	Travelers' NFL Man of the Year 1988 (Steve Largent)	.40
62	Steve Largent, Terry Largent	.25
63	Holding for Norm Johnson (Steve Largent)	.40
64	Great Moves (Steve Largent)	.25
65	Great Hands (Steve Largent)	.25
66	Seven-Time Pro Bowl Selection (Steve Largent)	.25
67	Agee, Steve Largent, Paul Skansi	.40
68	Signing for Fans (Steve Largent)	.25
69	Miller, Joe Nash, Steve Largent, Bryan Millard	.25
70	Pro Bowl Greats (Steve Largent, John Elway)	1.50
71	Hanging onto the Ball (Steve Largent)	.25
72	1618 Career Yards vs. Denver (Steve Largent)	.25
73	17 Pro Bowl Receptions (Steve Largent)	.25
74	Jim Zorn, Steve Largent	.40
75	Mr. Seahawk (Steve Largent)	.40
76	Sets NFL Career Yardage Record (Steve Largent)	.40
77	Two of the Greatest (Steve Largent)	.50
78	Steve Largent, Jerry Rhome, Charlie Joiner	.50
79	NFL All-Time Leader in Receptions (Steve Largent)	.40
80	Leader in Consecutive Game Receptions (Steve Largent)	.40
81	All-Time Leader 12686 Receiving Yards (Steve Largent)	.25
82	NFL All-Time Leader 1000 Yard Seasons (Steve Largent)	.40
83	First Recipient of the Bart Starr Trophy (Steve Largent)	.50
84	Steve Largent (Steve Largent)	.40
85	Future Hall of Famer (Steve Largent)	.75

1991 Pacific Prototypes

These cards were produced by Pacific Trading Cards to promote its 1991 set, its debut set. The cards, which are numbered on the back, use different numbers than their counterparts in the regular set, and can also be identified from the regulars by the statistics line on the card back. The prototype

cards use zeroes to fill in the stats on the back. Approximately 5,000 sets were made and distributed to dealers.

		MT
Complete Set (5):		200.00
Common Player:		25.00
1	Joe Montana	75.00
2	Barry Sanders	50.00
3	Bo Jackson	25.00
4	Eric Metcalf	25.00
5	Troy Aikman	75.00

1991 Pacific

Pacific's inaugural issue features full-color fronts with ultraviolet coating and full-color backs. Cards began shipping in late June and were numbered alphabetically by city name and player name. Pacific's border colors echo the player's team colors.

		MT
Complete Set (660):		20.00
Complete Series 1 (550):		10.00
Complete Series 2 (110):		10.00
Common Player:		.04
Series 1 Wax Box:		5.00
Series 2 Wax Box:		8.00
1	Deion Sanders	.25
2	Steve Broussard	.04
3	Aundray Bruce	.04
4	Rick Bryant	.04
5	John Rade	.04
6	Scott Case	.04
7	Tony Casillas	.04
8	Shawn Collins	.04
9	Darion Conner	.04
10	Tory Epps	.04
11	Bill Fralic	.04
12	Mike Gann	.04
13	Tim Green	.04
14	Chris Hinton	.04
15	Houston Hoover	.04
16	Chris Miller	.04
17	Andre Rison	.25
18	Mike Rozier	.04
19	Jessie Tuggle	.04
20	Don Beebe	.04
21	Ray Bentley	.04
22	Shane Conlan	.04
23	Kent Hull	.04
24	Mark Kelso	.04
25	James Lofton	.04
26	Scott Norwood	.04
27	Andre Reed	.20
28	Leonard Smith	.04
29	Bruce Smith	.04
30	Leon Seals	.04
31	Darryl Talley	.04
32	Steve Tasker	.04
33	Thurman Thomas	.50
34	James Williams	.04
35	Will Wolford	.04
36	Frank Reich	.04
37	*Jeff Wright*	.12
38	Neal Anderson	.10
39	Trace Armstrong	.04
40	Johnny Bailey	.04
41	Mark Bortz	.04
42	Cap Boso	.04
43	Kevin Butler	.04
44	Mark Carrier	.04
45	Jim Covert	.04
46	Wendell Davis	.10
47	Richard Dent	.10
48	Shaun Gayle	.04
49	Jim Harbaugh	.10
50	Jay Hilgenberg	.04
51	Brad Muster	.04
52	William Perry	.04
53	Mike Singletary	.10
54	Peter Tom Willis	.04
55	Donnell Woolford	.04
56	Steve McMichael	.04
57	Eric Ball	.04
58	Lewis Billups	.04
59	Jim Breech	.04
60	James Brooks	.04
61	Eddie Brown	.04
62	Rickey Dixon	.04
63	Boomer Esiason	.15
64	James Francis	.04
65	David Fulcher	.04

66	David Grant	.04
67	Harold Green	.15
68	Rodney Holman	.04
69	Stanford Jennings	.04
70	Tim Krumrie	.04
71	Tim McGee	.04
72	Anthony Munoz	.04
73	Mitchell Price	.04
74	Eric Thomas	.04
75	Ickey Woods	.04
76	Mike Baab	.04
77	Thane Gash	.04
78	David Grayson	.04
79	Mike Johnson	.04
80	Reggie Langhorne	.04
81	Kevin Mack	.04
82	Clay Matthews	.04
83	Eric Metcalf	.04
84	Frank Minnifield	.04
85	Mike Oliphant	.04
86	Mike Pagel	.04
87	John Talley	.04
88	Lawyer Tillman	.04
89	Felix Wright	.04
90	Bryan Wagner	.04
91	*Bob Burnett*	.10
92	Tommie Agee	.04
93	Troy Aikman	1.00
94	Bill Bates	.04
95	Jack Del Rio	.04
96	Issiac Holt	.04
97	Michael Irvin	.50
98	Jim Jeffcoat	.04
99	Jimmy Jones	.04
100	Kelvin Martin	.04
101	Nate Newton	.04
102	Danny Noonan	.04
103	Ken Norton	.04
104	Jay Novacek	.15
105	Mike Saxon	.04
106	Derrick Sheppard	.04
107	Emmitt Smith	2.00
108	Daniel Stubbs	.04
109	Tony Tolbert	.04
110	Alexander Wright	.09
111	Steve Atwater	.04
112	Melvin Bratton	.04
113	Tyrone Braxton	.04
114	Alphonso Carreker	.04
115	John Elway	.35
116	Simon Fletcher	.04
117	Bobby Humphrey	.04
118	Mark Jackson	.04
119	Vance Johnson	.04
120	Greg Kragen	.04
121	Karl Mecklenburg	.04
122	Orson Mobley	.04
123	Alton Montgomery	.04
124	Rickey Nattiel	.04
125	Steve Sewell	.04
126	Shannon Sharpe	.50
127	Dennis Smith	.04
128	Andre Townsend	.50
129	Mike Horan	.04
130	Jerry Ball	.04
131	Bennie Blades	.04
132	Lomas Brown	.04
133	Jeff Campbell	.04
134	Robert Clark	.04
135	Michael Cofer	.04
136	Dennis Gibson	.04
137	Mel Gray	.04
138	LeRoy Irvin	.04
139	*George Jamison*	.12
140	Richard Johnson	.04
141	Eddie Murray	.04
142	Dan Owens	.04
143	Rodney Peete	.04
144	Barry Sanders	1.25
145	Chris Spielman	.04
146	Mark Spindler	.04
147	Andre Ware	.12
148	William White	.04
149	Tony Bennett	.04
150	Robert Brown	.04
151	LeRoy Butler	.04
152	Anthony Dilweg	.04
153	Michael Haddix	.04
154	Ron Hallstrom	.04
155	Tim Harris	.04
156	Johnny Holland	.04
157	Chris Jacke	.04
158	Perry Kemp	.04
159	Mark Lee	.04
160	Don Majkowski	.04
161	Tony Mandarich	.04
162	Mark Murphy	.04
163	Brian Noble	.04
164	Shawn Patterson	.04
165	Jeff Query	.04
166	Sterling Sharpe	.60
167	Darrell Thompson	.12
168	Ed West	.04
169	Ray Childress	.04
170	*Chris Dishman*	.35
171	Curtis Duncan	.04
172	William Fuller	.04
173	Ernest Givins	.04
174	Drew Hill	.04
175	Haywood Jeffires	.20
176	Sean Jones	.04
177	Lamar Lathon	.04
178	Bruce Matthews	.04
179	Bubba McDowell	.04
180	Johnny Meads	.04
181	Warren Moon	.15
182	Mike Munchak	.04
183	Allen Pinkett	.04
184	Dean Steinkuhler	.04
185	Lorenzo White	.25
186	John Grimsby	.04
187	Pat Beach	.04
188	Albert Bentley	.04
189	Dean Biasucci	.04
190	Duane Bickett	.04
191	Bill Brooks	.04
192	Eugene Daniel	.04
193	Jeff George	.30
194	Jon Hand	.04
195	Jeff Herrod	.04
196	Jesse Hester	.04
197	Mike Prior	.04
198	Stacey Simmons	.04
199	Rohn Stark	.04
200	Pat Tomberlin	.04
201	Clarence Verdin	.04
202	Keith Taylor	.04
203	Jack Trudeau	.04
204	Chip Banks	.04
205	John Alt	.04
206	Deron Cherry	.04
207	Steve DeBerg	.04
208	Tim Grunhard	.04
209	Albert Lewis	.04
210	Nick Lowery	.04
211	Bill Maas	.04
212	Chris Martin	.04
213	Todd McNair	.04
214	Christian Okoye	.04
215	Stephone Paige	.04
216	Steve Pelluer	.04
217	Kevin Porter	.04
218	Kevin Ross	.04
219	Dan Sealeaumua	.04
220	Neil Smith	.04
221	David Szott	.04
222	Derrick Thomas	.25
223	Barry Word	.12
224	Percy Snow	.04
225	Marcus Allen	.04
226	Eddie Anderson	.04
227	Steve Beuerlein	.25
228	Tim Brown	.20
229	Scott Davis	.04
230	Mike Dyal	.04
231	Mervyn Fernandez	.04
232	Willie Gault	.04
233	Ethan Horton	.04
234	Bo Jackson	.50
235	Howie Long	.04
236	Terry McDaniel	.04
237	Max Montoya	.04
238	Don Mosebar	.04
239	Jay Schroeder	.04
240	Steve Smith	.04
241	Greg Townsend	.04
242	Aaron Wallace	.04
243	Lionel Washington	.04
244	Steve Wisniewski	1.00
245	Willie Anderson	.04
246	Latin Berry	.04
247	Robert Delpino	.04
248	Marcus Dupree	.04
249	Henry Ellard	.04
250	Jim Everett	.04
251	Cleveland Gary	.04
252	Jerry Gray	.04
253	Kevin Greene	.04
254	Pete Holohan	.04
255	Buford McGee	.04
256	Tom Newberry	.04
257	Irv Pankey	.04
258	Jackie Slater	.04
259	Doug Smith	.04
260	Frank Stams	.04
261	Michael Stewart	.04
262	Fred Strickland	.04
263	J.D. Brown	.04
264	Mark Clayton	.04
265	Jeff Cross	.04
266	Mark Dennis	.04
267	Mark Duper	.04
268	Ferrell Edmunds	.04
269	Dan Marino	2.00
270	John Offerdahl	.04
271	Louis Oliver	.04
272	Tony Paige	.04
273	Reggie Roby	.04
274	Sammie Smith	.04
275	Keith Sims	.04
276	Brian Sochia	.04
277	Pete Stoyanovich	.04
278	Richmond Webb	.04
279	Jarvis Williams	.04
280	Tim McKyer	.04
281	Jim Jensen	.04
282	*Scott Secules*	.12
283	Ray Berry	.04
284	Anthony Carter	.04
285	Anthony Carter	.04
286	Cris Carter	.25
287	Chris Doleman	.04
288	Mark Dusbabek	.04
289	Hassan Jones	.04
290	Steve Jordan	.04
291	Carl Lee	.04
292	Kirk Lowdermilk	.04
293	Randall McDaniel	.04
294	Mike Merriweather	.04
295	Keith Millard	.04
296	Al Noga	.04
297	Scott Studwell	.04
298	Henry Thomas	.04
299	Herschel Walker	.04
300	Gary Zimmerman	.04
301	Rich Gannon	.10
302	Wade Wilson	.04
303	Vincent Brown	.04
304	Marv Cook	.04
305	Hart Lee Dykes	.04
306	Irving Fryar	.04
307	Tom Hodson	.04
308	Maurice Hurst	.04
309	Ronnie Lippett	.04
310	Fred Marion	.04
311	Greg McMurtry	.04
312	Johnny Rembert	.04
313	Chris Singleton	.04
314	Ed Reynolds	.04
315	Andre Tippett	.04
316	Garin Veris	.04
317	Brent Williams	.04
318	John Stephens	.75
319	Sammy Martin	.04
320	Bruce Armstrong	.04
321	Morten Andersen	.10
322	Gene Atkins	.04
323	Vince Buck	.04
324	John Fourcade	.04
325	Kevin Haverdink	.04
326	Bobby Hebert	.04
327	Craig Heyward	.04
328	Dalton Hilliard	.04
329	Rickey Jackson	.04
330	Vaughan Johnson	.04
331	Eric Martin	.04
332	Wayne Martin	.04
333	Rueben Mayes	.04
334	Sam Mills	.04
335	Brett Perriman	.04
336	Pat Swilling	.04
337	Renaldo Turnbull	.04
338	Lonzell Hill	.04
339	Steve Walsh	.04
340	Carl Banks	.04
341	Mark Bavaro	.04
342	Maurice Carthon	.04
343	*Pat Harlow*	.08
344	Eric Dorsey	.04
345	John Elliott	.04
346	Rodney Hampton	.50
347	Jeff Hostetler	.20
348	Erik Howard	.04
349	Pepper Johnson	.04
350	Sean Landeta	.04
351	Leonard Marshall	.04
352	David Meggett	.04
353	Bart Oates	.04
354	Gary Reasons	.04
355	Phil Simms	.10
356	Lawrence Taylor	.10
357	Reyna Thompson	.04
358	Brian Williams	.04
359	Matt Boyer	.04
360	Mark Ingram	.04
361	Brad Baxter	.15
362	Mark Boyer	.04
363	Dennis Byrd	.04
364	Dave Cadigan	.04
365	Kyle Clifton	.04
366	James Hasty	.04
367	Joe Kelly	.04
368	Jeff Lageman	.04
369	Pat Leahy	.04
370	Terance Mathis	.10
371	Erik McMillan	.04
372	Rob Moore	.25
373	Ken O'Brien	.04
374	Tony Stargell	.04
375	Jim Sweeney	.04
376	Al Toon	.04
377	Johnny Hector	.04
378	Jeff Criswell	.04
379	Mike Haight	.04
380	Troy Benson	.04
381	Eric Allen	.04
382	Fred Barnett	.15
383	Jerome Brown	.04
384	Keith Byars	.04
385	Randall Cunningham	.20
386	Byron Evans	.04
387	Wes Hopkins	.04
388	Keith Jackson	.20
389	Seth Joyner	.04
390	*Bobby Wilson*	.10
391	Heath Sherman	.04
392	Clyde Simmons	.04
393	Ben Smith	.04
394	Andre Waters	.04
395	Reggie White	.20
396	Calvin Williams	.15
397	Al Harris	.04
398	Anthony Toney	.04
399	Mike Quick	.04
400	Anthony Bell	.04
401	Rich Camarillo	.04
402	Roy Green	.04
403	Ken Harvey	.04
404	Eric Hill	.04
405	*Garth Jax*	.07
406	Ernie Jones	.04
407	Cedric Mack	.04
408	Dexter Manley	.04
409	Tim McDonald	.04
410	Freddie Joe Nunn	.04
411	Rickey Proehl	.10
412	*Moe Gardner*	.12
413	Timm Rosenbach	.04
414	Luis Sharpe	.04
415	Vai Sikahema	.04
416	Anthony Thompson	.04
417	Ron Wolfley	.04
418	Lonnie Young	.04
419	Gary Anderson	.04
420	Bubby Brister	.04
421	Thomas Everett	.04
422	Eric Green	.10
423	Delton Hall	.04
424	Bryan Hinkle	.04
425	Merril Hoge	.04
426	Carnell Lake	.04
427	Louis Lipps	.04
428	David Little	.04
429	Greg Lloyd	.04
430	Mike Mularkey	.04
431	Keith Willis	.04
432	Dwayne Woodruff	.04
433	Rod Woodson	.04
434	Tim Worley	.04
435	Warren Williams	.04
436	Terry Long	.04
437	Martin Bayless	.04
438	*Jarrod Bunch*	.15
439	Marion Butts	.04
440	Gill Byrd	.04
441	Arthur Cox	.04
442	John Friesz	.04
443	Leo Goeas	.04
444	Burt Grossman	.04
445	Courtney Hall	.04
446	Ronnie Harmon	.04
447	*Nate Lewis*	.25
448	Anthony Miller	.04
449	Leslie O'Neal	.04
450	Gary Plummer	.04
451	Junior Seau	.30
452	Billy Ray Smith	.04
453	Billy Joe Tolliver	.04
454	Broderick Thompson	.04
455	Lee Williams	.04
456	Michael Carter	.04
457	Mike Cofer	.04
458	Kevin Fagan	.04
459	Charles Haley	.04
460	Pierce Holt	.04
461	Johnny Jackson	.04
462	Brent Jones	.04
463	Guy McIntyre	.04
464	Joe Montana	1.00
465	Bubba Paris	.04
466	Tom Rathman	.04
467	Jerry Rice	1.00
468	Mike Sherrard	.04
469	John Taylor	.15
470	Steve Young	.75
471	Dennis Brown	.04
472	Dexter Carter	.04
473	Bill Romanowski	.04
474	Dave Waymer	.04
475	Robert Blackmon	.04
476	Derrick Fenner	.10
477	Nesby Glasgow	.04
478	Jacob Green	.04
479	Andy Heck	.04
480	Norm Johnson	.04
481	Tommy Kane	.04
482	Cortez Kennedy	.30
483	Dave Krieg	.04
484	Bryan Millard	.04
485	Joe Nash	.04
486	Rufus Porter	.04
487	Eugene Robinson	.04
488	*Mike Tice*	.10
489	Chris Warren	.50
490	John L. Williams	.04
491	Terry Wooden	.04
492	Tony Woods	.04
493	Brian Blades	.04
494	Paul Skansi	.04
495	Gary Anderson	.04
496	Mark Carrier	.04
497	Chris Chandler	.04
498	Steve Christie	.04
499	Reggie Cobb	.25
500	Reuben Davis	.04
501	Willie Drewery	.04
502	Randy Grimes	.04
503	Paul Gruber	.04
504	Wayne Haddix	.04
505	Ron Hall	.04
506	Harry Hamilton	.04
507	Bruce Hill	.04
508	Eugene Marve	.04
509	Keith McCants	.04
510	Winston Moss	.04
511	Kevin Murphy	.04
512	Mark Robinson	.04
513	Vinny Testaverde	.04
514	Broderick Thomas	.04
515	Jeff Bostic	.04
516	Todd Bowles	.04
517	Earnest Byner	.04
518	Gary Clark	.20
519	*Craig Erickson*	.50
520	Darryl Green	.04
521	Darrell Green	.04
522	Russ Grimm	.04
523	Stan Humphries	.30
524	Joe Jacoby	.04
525	Jim Lachey	.04
526	Chip Lohmiller	.04
527	Charles Mann	.04
528	Wilber Marshall	.04
529	Art Monk	.04
530	Tracy Rocker	.04
531	Mark Rypien	.12
532	Ricky Sanders	.04
533	Alvin Walton	.04
534	*Todd Marinovich*	.15
535	Mike Dumas	.04
536	Russell Maryland	.50
537	Eric Turner	.20
538	Ernie Mills	.20
539	*Ed King*	.10
540	Michael Stonebreaker	.04
541	*Chris Zorich*	.25
542	Mike Croel	.35
543	Eric Moten	.10
544	Dan McGwire	.15
545	*Keith Cash*	.04
546	Kenny Walker	.12
547	Leroy Hoard	.08
548	Luis Chrisobol	.04
549	Stacy Danley	.04
550	*Todd Lyght*	.10
551	Brett Favre	3.00
552	*Mike Pritchard*	.50
553	Moe Gardner	.05
554	Tim McKyer	.05
555	*Erric Pegram*	.50
556	Norm Johnson	.05
557	*Bruce Pickens*	.10
558	*Henry Jones*	.35
559	*Phil Hansen*	.20
560	Cornelius Bennett	.05
561	Stan Thomas	.05
562	Chris Zorich	.10
563	*Anthony Morgan*	.15
564	*Darren Lewis*	.30
565	Mike Stonebreaker	.05
566	*Alfred Williams*	.15
567	Lamar Rogers	.05
568	*Erik Wilhelm*	.30
569	Ed King	.05
570	*Michael Jackson*	.75
571	*James Jones*	.15
572	Russell Maryland	.15
573	*Dixon Edwards*	.10
574	Derrick Brownlow	.05
575	*Larry Brown*	.50
576	Mike Croel	.20
577	*Keith Traylor*	.08
578	Kenny Walker	.05
579	*Reggie Johnson*	.12
580	*Herman Moore*	3.50
581	*Kelvin Pritchett*	.10
582	*Kevin Scott*	.10
583	*Vinnie Clark*	.10
584	*Esera Tuaolo*	.10
585	Don Davey	.05
586	*Blair Kiel*	.12
587	Mike Dumas	.05
588	*Darryll Lewis*	.10
589	*John Flannery*	.10
590	*Kevin Donnally*	.05
591	Shane Curry	.05
592	*Mark Vander Poel*	.08
593	*Dave McCloughan*	.05
594	*Mel Agee*	.10
595	*Kerry Cash*	.12
596	*Harvey Williams*	.50
597	*Joe Valerio*	.05
598	*Tim Barnett*	.30
599	*Todd Marinovich*	.05
600	*Nick Bell*	.20
601	*Roger Craig*	.05
602	*Ronnie Lott*	.10
603	*Mike Jones*	.10
604	*Todd Lyght*	.10
605	*Roman Phifer*	.05
606	*David Lang*	.15
607	*Aaron Craver*	.10
608	*Mark Higgs*	.75
609	Chris Green	.05
610	*Randy Baldwin*	.10
611	Pat Harlow	.05
612	Leonard Russell	.20
613	*Jerome Henderson*	.10
614	*Scott Zolak*	.20
615	*Jon Vaughn*	.15
616	*Harry Colon*	.12
617	*Wesley Carroll*	.15
618	*Quinn Early*	.05
619	*Reggie Jones*	.15
620	Jarrod Bunch	.10
621	*Kanavis McGhee*	.15
622	*Ed McCaffrey*	2.00
623	*Browning Nagle*	.35
624	*Mo Lewis*	.10
625	*Blair Thomas*	.10
626	Antone Davis	.10
627	Jim McMahon	.05
628	*Scott Kowalkowski*	.10
629	*Brad Goebel*	.10
630	*William Thomas*	.10
631	*Eric Swann*	.20
632	*Mike Jones*	.10
633	*Aeneas Williams*	.12
634	Dexter Davis	.05
635	Tom Tupa	.05
636	Johnny Johnson	.20
637	Randal Hill	.30
638	*Jeff Graham*	.75
639	Ernie Mills	.10
640	*Adrian Cooper*	.15
641	*Stanley Richard*	.35
642	Eric Bieniemy	.15
643	Eric Moten	.05
644	*Shawn Jefferson*	.35
645	*Ted Washington*	.10
646	*John Johnson*	.10
647	Dan McGwire	.05
648	*Doug Thomas*	.05
649	David Daniels	.05
650	*John Kasay*	.12
651	Jeff Kemp	.05
652	*Charles McRae*	.08
653	*Lawrence Dawsey*	.20
654	Robert Wilson	.05
655	Dexter Manley	.05
656	Chuck Weatherspoon	.05
657	Tim Ryan	.05
658	Bobby Wilson	.05
659	*Ricky Ervins*	.35
660	Matt Millen	.05

1991 Pacific Checklists

These checklists were issued for Pacific's first series of 1991 football cards and were randomly included in late-issue foil and wax packs. Pacific stated it only produced 10,000 checklist sets. Cards were numbered on the back.

		MT
Complete Set (5):		10.00
Common Player:		2.50
1	Checklist 1	2.50
2	Checklist 2	2.50
3	Checklist 3	2.50
4	Checklist 4	2.50
5	Checklist 5	2.50

1991 Pacific Picks The Pros

Pacific produced a 25-card insert set, including its choice as the best player at each position offensively and defensively plus a card of 1991 #1 draft choice Russell Maryland. Cards were either bordered in silver or gold, with 10,000 of each type produced and randomly inserted (gold in foil packs, silver in cello).

		MT
Complete Set (25):		60.00
Common Player:		2.00
1	Russell Maryland	3.00
2	Andre Reed	3.00
3	Jerry Rice	12.00
4	Keith Jackson	3.00
5	Jim Lachey	2.00
6	Anthony Munoz	2.00
7	Randall McDaniel	2.00
8	Bruce Matthews	2.00
9	Kent Hull	2.00
10	Joe Montana	10.00
11	Barry Sanders	15.00
12	Thurman Thomas	8.00
13	Morten Anderson	3.00
14	Jerry Ball	3.00
15	Jerome Brown	3.00
16	Reggie White	6.00
17	Bruce Smith	7.50
18	Derrick Thomas	4.00
19	Lawrence Taylor	3.00
20	Charles Haley	3.00
21	Albert Lewis	3.00
22	Rod Woodson	3.00
23	David Fulcher	3.00
24	Joey Browner	3.00
25	Sean Landeta	3.00

1991 Pacific Flash Cards

These mathematical flash cards contain a problem on the front which, when worked out correctly, equals the uniform number of the player pictured on the card back. The back of the card has a glossy picture of the player and either a career summary or highlights from the previous season. A card number also appears on the back. The cards are standard size.

	MT
Complete Set (110):	8.00

1992 Pacific Prototypes

These 1992 prototypes feature Pacific's new design for 1992. A full-color glossy photo is on the card front, framed by a white border. A color stripe, containing the player's name and team helmet, runs along the left side of the card. The back is numbered and includes a mug shot and career summary. Approximately 5,000 sets were produced; most were given away at the Super Bowl Card Show in Minneapolis.

		MT
Complete Set (6):		40.00
Common Player:		6.00
1	Warren Moon	10.00
2	Pat Swilling	6.00
3	Michael Irvin	12.00
4	Haywood Jeffires	8.00
5	Thurman Thomas	12.00
6	Leonard Russell	8.00

1992 Pacific

Pacific issued this set of 660 standard-sized cards in two series of 330 cards each. The glossy fronts feature color action shots framed by white borders. The player's name and team helmet run in a stripe down the left side. The backs are done in a horizontal format and also feature a color photo, plus statistics and a player profile. Cards are numbered alphabetically by player, by team, beginning with Atlanta and ending with Washington. Draft Picks are featured in a subset. Insert sets include Checklists (8 cards randomly inserted in packs); Bob Griese and Steve Largent (9 Legends of the Game cards for each, plus 1,000 autographed cards each; all were random inserts); Prisms (10 cards featuring top running backs, randomly inserted); Statistical Leaders (30 cards featuring the 28 statistical leaders from the 28 NFL teams, plus two cards devoted to the AFC and NFC rushing leaders; all were randomly inserted); and Pacific Picks the Pros (25 cards, Pacific's selection of the top players at each position). The Picks the Pros cards come in two versions - with gold foil or silver foil borders, and corresponding lettering.

		MT
Complete Set (660):		20.00
Complete Series 1 (330):		10.00
Complete Series 2 (330):		10.00
Complete Factory Set (690):		25.00
Common Player:		.05
Wax Box:		7.00

Common Player: .05

#	Player	Price
1	Steve Young	.40
2	Hart Lee Dykes	.05
3	Timm Rosenbach	.05
4	Andre Collins	.05
5	Johnny Johnson	.20
6	Nick Lowery	.05
7	John Stephens	.05
8	Jim Arnold	.05
9	Steve DeBerg	.15
10	Christian Okoye	.05
11	Eric Swann	.10
12	Jerry Robinson	.05
13	Steve Wisniewski	.05
14	Jim Harbaugh	.10
15	Steve Broussard	.05
16	Mike Singletary	.15
17	Tim Green	.05
18	Roger Craig	.15
19	Maury Buford	.05
20	Marcus Allen	.25
21	Deion Sanders	.40
22	Chris Miller	.20
23	Joey Browner	.10
24	Bubby Brister	.10
25	Buford McGee	.05
26	Ed West	.05
27	Mark Murphy	.05
28	Tim Worley	.10
29	Keith Willis	.05
30	Rich Gannon	.05
31	Jim Everett	.15
32	Duval Love	.05
33	Bob Nelson	.05
34	Anthony Munoz	.15
35	Boomer Esiason	.20
36	Kenny Walker	.05
37	Mike Horan	.05
38	Gary Kubiak	.05
39	David Treadwell	.05
40	Robert Wilson	.05
41	Lewis Billups	.05
42	Kevin Mack	.05
43	John Elway	.50
44	Lee Johnson	.05
45	Ken Willis	.05
46	Herman Moore	.40
47	Eddie Murray	.05
48	Mike Saxon	.05
49	John L. Williams	.10
50	Barry Sanders	1.00
51	Andre Ware	.15
52	Dave Krieg	.10
53	Cortez Kennedy	.25
54	Bo Jackson	.50
55	Derrick Fenner	.05
56	Steve Walsh	.10
57	Brett Maxie	.05
58	Stan Brock	.05
59	DeMond Winston	.05
60	Sam Mills	.10
61	Eric Martin	.10
62	Michael Carter	.10
63	Steve Wallace	.05
64	Jesse Sapolu	.05
65	Bill Romanowski	.05
66	Joe Montana	2.00
67	Sean Landeta	.05
68	Doug Riesenberg	.05
69	Myron Guyton	.05
70	Andre Reed	.15
71	John Elliott	.05
72	Jeff Hostetler	.15
73	Rohn Stark	.05
74	Jeff George	.20
75	Duane Bickett	.05
76	Emmitt Smith	2.00
77	Michael Irvin	.50
78	Tony Stargell	.05
79	Kyle Clifton	.05
80	John Booty	.05
81	Fred Barnett	.20
82	Blair Thomas	.10
83	Erik McMillan	.05
84	Broderick Thomas	.10
85	Jim Skow	.05
86	Gary Anderson	.10
87	Mark Robinson	.05
88	Steve Christie	.05
89	Cody Carlson	.15
90	Warren Moon	.35
91	Lorenzo White	.10
92	Reggie Roby	.05
93	Jim C. Jensen	.05
94	Mark Clayton	.10
95	Willie Gault	.10
96	Don Mosebar	.05
97	Gary Plummer	.05
98	Leslie O'Neal	.10
99	Neal Anderson	.15
100	Derrick Thomas	.25
101	Luis Sharpe	.05
102	D.J. Dozier	.05
103	Jarrod Bunch	.05
104	Mark Ingram	.05
105	James Lofton	.15
106	Jay Schroeder	.10
107	Ronnie Lott	.15
108	Todd Marinovich	.10
109	Chris Zorich	.15
110	Charles McRae	.05
1	Steve Broussard	.05
2	Darion Conner	.05
3	Tory Epps	.05
4	Michael Haynes	.30
5	Chris Hinton	.05
6	Mike Kenn	.05
7	Tim McKyer	.05
8	Chris Miller	.05
9	Erric Pegram	.20
10	Mike Pritchard	.20
11	Moe Gardner	.05
12	Tim Green	.05
13	Norm Johnson	.05
14	Don Beebe	.05
15	Cornelius Bennett	.05
16	Al Edwards	.05
17	Mark Kelso	.05
18	James Lofton	.15
19	Frank Reich	.05
20	Leon Seals	.05
21	Darryl Talley	.05
22	Kent Hall	.05
23	Jeff Wright	.05
24	Nate Odomes	.05
25	Thurman Thomas	.40
26	Carwell Gardner	.05
27	Neal Anderson	.10
28	Mark Carrier	.05
29	Johnny Bailey	.05
30	Jim Harbaugh	.05
31	Jay Hilgenberg	.05
32	William Perry	.05
33	Wendell Davis	.05
34	Donnell Woolford	.05
35	Keith Van Horne	.05
36	Shaun Gayle	.05
37	Tom Waddle	.12
38	Chris Zorich	.05
39	Tom Thayer	.05
40	Rickey Dixon	.05
41	James Francis	.05
42	David Fulcher	.05
43	Reggie Rembert	.05
44	Anthony Munoz	.05
45	Harold Green	.05
46	Mitchell Price	.05
47	Rodney Holman	.05
48	Bruce Kozerski	.05
49	Bruce Reimers	.05
50	Erik Wilhelm	.05
51	Harlon Barnett	.05
52	Mike Johnson	.05
53	Brian Brennan	.05
54	Ed King	.05
55	Reggie Langhorne	.05
56	James Jones	.05
57	Mike Baab	.05
58	Dan Fike	.05
59	Frank Minnifield	.05
60	Clay Matthews	.05
61	Kevin Mack	.05
62	Tony Casillas	.05
63	Jay Novacek	.15
64	Larry Brown	.05
65	Michael Irvin	.25
66	Jack Del Rio	.05
67	Ken Willis	.05
68	Emmitt Smith	2.25
69	Alan Veingrad	.05
70	John Gesek	.05
71	Steve Beuerlein	.20
72	*Vinson Smith*	.08
73	Steve Atwater	.05
74	Mike Croel	.05
75	John Elway	.35
76	Gaston Green	.05
77	Mike Horan	.05
78	Vance Johnson	.05
79	Karl Mecklenburg	.05
80	Shannon Sharpe	.05
81	David Treadwell	.05
82	Kenny Walker	.05
83	Greg Lewis	.05
84	Shawn Moore	.05
85	Alton Montgomery	.05
86	Michael Young	.05
87	Jerry Ball	.05
88	Bennie Blades	.05
89	Mel Gray	.05
90	Herman Moore	.50
91	Erik Kramer	.05
92	Willie Green	.12
93	George Jamison	.05
94	Chris Spielman	.05
95	Kelvin Pritchett	.05
96	William White	.05
97	Mike Utley	.12
98	Tony Bennett	.05
99	LeRoy Butler	.05
100	Vinnie Clark	.05
101	Ron Hallstrom	.05
102	Chris Jacke	.05
103	Tony Mandarich	.05
104	Sterling Sharpe	.45
105	Don Maikowski	.05
106	Johnny Holland	.05
107	Esera Tuaolo	.05
108	Darrell Thompson	.05
109	Bubba McDowell	.05
110	Curtis Duncan	.05
111	Lamar Lathon	.05
112	Drew Hill	.05
113	Bruce Matthews	.05
114	*Bo Orlando*	.15
115	Don Maggs	.05
116	Lorenzo White	.05
117	Ernest Givins	.05
118	Tony Jones	.05
119	Dean Steinkuhler	.05
120	Dean Biasucci	.05
121	Duane Bickett	.05
122	Bill Brooks	.05
123	Ken Clark	.05
124	Jessie Hester	.05
125	Anthony Johnson	.05
126	Chip Banks	.05
127	Mike Prior	.05
128	Rohn Stark	.05
129	Jeff Herrod	.05
130	Clarence Verdin	.05
131	Tim Manoa	.05
132	*Brian Baldinger*	.05
133	Tim Barnett	.05
134	J.J. Birden	.05
135	Deron Cherry	.05
136	Steve DeBerg	.05
137	Nick Lowery	.05
138	Todd McNair	.05
139	Christian Okoye	.05
140	Mark Vlasic	.05
141	Dan Saleaumua	.05
142	Neil Smith	.05
143	Robb Thomas	.05
144	Eddie Anderson	.05
145	Nick Bell	.12
146	Tim Brown	.30
147	Roger Craig	.05
148	Jeff Gossett	.05
149	Ethan Horton	.05
150	Jamie Holland	.05
151	Jeff Jaeger	.05
152	Todd Marinovich	.05
153	Marcus Allen	.05
154	Steve Smith	.05
155	Flipper Anderson	.05
156	Robert Delpino	.05
157	Cleveland Gary	.05
158	Kevin Greene	.05
159	Dale Hatcher	.05
160	Duval Love	.05
161	Ron Brown	.05
162	Jackie Slater	.05
163	Doug Smith	.05
164	Aaron Cox	.05
165	Larry Kelm	.05
166	Mark Clayton	.05
167	Louis Oliver	.05
168	Mark Higgs	.15
169	Aaron Craver	.05
170	Sammie Smith	.05
171	Tony Paige	.05
172	Jeff Cross	.05
173	David Griggs	.05
174	Richmond Webb	.05
175	Vestee Jackson	.05
176	Jim C. Jensen	.05
177	Anthony Carter	.05
178	Cris Carter	.05
179	Chris Doleman	.05
180	Rich Gannon	.10
181	Al Noga	.05
182	Randall McDaniel	.05
183	Todd Scott	.05
184	Henry Thomas	.05
185	Felix Wright	.05
186	Gary Zimmerman	.05
187	Herschel Walker	.05
188	Vincent Brown	.05
189	Harry Colon	.05
190	Irving Fryar	.05
191	Marv Cook	.05
192	Leonard Russell	.25
193	Hugh Millen	.05
194	Pat Harlow	.05
195	Jon Vaughn	.12
196	*Ben Coates*	2.00
197	Johnny Rembert	.05
198	Greg McMurtry	.05
199	Morten Andersen	.05
200	Tommy Barnhardt	.05
201	Bobby Hebert	.05
202	Dalton Hilliard	.05
203	Sam Mills	.05
204	Pat Swilling	.05
205	Rickey Jackson	.05
206	Stan Brock	.05
207	Reggie Jones	.05
208	Gill Fenerty	.05
209	Eric Martin	.05
210	Matt Bahr	.05
211	Rodney Hampton	.40
212	Jeff Hostetler	.15
213	Pepper Johnson	.05
214	Leonard Marshall	.05
215	Doug Riesenberg	.05
216	Stephen Baker	.05
217	Mike Fox	.05
218	Bart Oates	.05
219	Everson Walls	.05
220	Gary Reasons	.05
221	Jeff Lageman	.05
222	Joe Kelly	.05
223	Mo Lewis	.05
224	Tony Stargell	.05
225	Jim Sweeney	.05
226	Freeman McNeil	.05
227	Brian Washington	.05
228	Johnny Hector	.05
229	Terance Mathis	.05
230	Rob Moore	.20
231	Brad Baxter	.05
232	Eric Allen	.05
233	Fred Barnett	.20
234	Jerome Brown	.05
235	Keith Byars	.05
236	William Thomas	.05
237	Jessie Small	.05
238	Robert Drummond	.05
239	Reggie White	.15
240	James Joseph	.05
241	Brad Goebel	.08
242	Clyde Simmons	.05
243	Rich Camarillo	.05
244	Ken Harvey	.05
245	Garth Jax	.05
246	Johnny Johnson	.15
247	Mike Jones	.05
248	Ernie Jones	.05
249	Tom Tupa	.05
250	Ron Wolfley	.05
251	Luis Sharpe	.05
252	Eric Swann	.05
253	Anthony Thompson	.05
254	Gary Anderson	.05
255	Dermontti Dawson	.05
256	Jeff Graham	.12
257	Eric Green	.05
258	Louis Lipps	.05
259	Neil O'Donnell	.25
260	Rod Woodson	.05
261	Dwight Stone	.05
262	Aaron Jones	.05
263	Keith Willis	.05
264	Ernie Mills	.05
265	Martin Bayless	.05
266	Rod Bernstine	.05
267	John Carney	.05
268	John Friesz	.05
269	Nate Lewis	.05
270	Shawn Jefferson	.05
271	Burt Grossman	.05
272	Eric Moten	.05
273	Gary Plummer	.05
274	Henry Rolling	.05
275	*Steve Hendrickson*	.10
276	Michael Carter	.05
277	*Steve Bono*	1.00
278	Dexter Carter	.05
279	Mike Cofer	.05
280	Charles Haley	.05
281	Tom Rathman	.05
282	Guy McIntyre	.05
283	John Taylor	.05
284	Dave Waymer	.05
285	Steve Wallace	.05
286	Jamie Williams	.05
287	Brian Blades	.05
288	Jeff Bryant	.05
289	Grant Feasel	.05
290	Jacob Green	.05
291	Andy Heck	.05
292	Kelly Stouffer	.05
293	John Kasay	.05
294	Cortez Kennedy	.15
295	Bryan Millard	.05
296	Eugene Robinson	.05
297	Tony Woods	.05
298	Jesse Anderson	.05
299	Gary Anderson	.05
300	Mark Carrier	.05
301	Reggie Cobb	.12
302	Robert Wilson	.05
303	Jesse Solomon	.05
304	Broderick Thomas	.05
305	Lawrence Dawsey	.05
306	Charles McRae	.05
307	Paul Gruber	.05
308	Vinny Testaverde	.05
309	Mark Mitchell	.05
310	Darrell Green	.05
311	Art Monk	.05
312	Russ Grimm	.05
313	Mark Rypien	.20
314	Bobby Wilson	.05
315	Wilber Marshall	.05
316	Gerald Riggs	.05
317	Chip Lohmiller	.05
318	Joe Jacoby	.05
319	Martin Mayhew	.05
320	*Amp Lee*	.35
321	*Terrell Buckley*	.30
322	*Tommy Vardell*	.25
323	*Ricardo McDonald*	.10
324	*Joe Bowden*	.08
325	*Darryl Williams*	.20
326	Carlos Huerta	.05
327	Patrick Rowe	.10
328	*Siran Stacy*	.15
329	*Dexter McNabb*	.08
330	*Willie Clay*	.05
331	Oliver Barnett	.05
332	Aundray Bruce	.05
333	*Ken Tippins*	.10
334	Jessie Tuggle	.05
335	Brian Jordan	.06
336	Andre Rison	.30
337	Houston Hoover	.05
338	Bill Fralic	.05
339	*Pat Chaffey*	.15
340	Keith Jones	.05
341	*Jamie Dukes*	.05
342	Chris Mohr	.05
343	John Davis	.05
344	Ray Bentley	.05
345	Scott Norwood	.05
346	Shane Conlan	.06
347	Steve Tasker	.06
348	Will Wolford	.05
349	*Gary Baldinger*	.10
350	Kirby Jackson	.05
351	Jamie Mueller	.05
352	Pete Metzelaars	.05
353	Darrell Dent	.05
354	Ron Rivera	.05
355	Jim Morrissey	.05
356	John Roper	.05
357	Steve McMichael	.05
358	Ron Morris	.05
359	Darren Lewis	.15
360	Anthony Morgan	.10
361	Stan Thomas	.05
362	James Thornton	.05
363	Brad Muster	.05
364	Tim Krumrie	.05
365	Lee Johnson	.05
366	Eric Ball	.05
367	Alonzo Mitz	.05
368	David Grant	.05
369	Lynn James	.05
370	Lewis Billups	.05
371	Jim Breech	.05
372	Alfred Williams	.05
373	Wayne Haddix	.05
374	Tim McGee	.05
375	Michael Jackson	.10
376	Leroy Hoard	.05
377	Tony Jones	.05
378	Vince Newsome	.05
379	*Todd Philcox*	.15
380	Eric Metcalf	.05
381	John Rienstra	.05
382	Matt Stover	.05
383	Brian Hansen	.05
384	Joe Morris	.05
385	Anthony Pleasant	.05
386	Mark Stepnoski	.05
387	Erik Williams	.05
388	Jimmie Jones	.05
389	Kevin Gogan	.05
390	Manny Hendrix	.10
391	Issiac Holt	.05
392	Ken Norton	.05
393	Tommie Agee	.05
394	Alvin Harper	.10
395	Alexander Wright	.05
396	Mike Saxon	.05
397	Michael Brooks	.05
398	Bobby Humphrey	.05
399	Ken Lanier	.05
400	Steve Sewell	.05
401	Robert Perryman	.05
402	Wymon Henderson	.05
403	Keith Kartz	.05
404	Clarence Kay	.05
405	Keith Traylor	.05
406	Doug Widell	.05
407	Dennis Smith	.05
408	Marc Spindler	.05
409	Lomas Brown	.05
410	Robert Clark	.05
411	Eric Andolsek	.05
412	Mike Farr	.05
413	Ray Crockett	.05
414	Jeff Campbell	.05
415	Dan Owens	.05
416	Jim Arnold	.05
417	Barry Sanders	1.25
418	Eddie Murray	.05
419	Vince Workman	.10
420	Ed West	.05
421	Charles Wilson	.05
422	Perry Kemp	.05
423	Chuck Cecil	.05
424	James Campen	.05
425	Robert Brown	.05
426	Brian Noble	.05
427	Rich Moran	.05
428	Vai Sikahema	.05
429	Allen Rice	.05
430	Haywood Jeffires	.15
431	Warren Moon	.20
432	Greg Montgomery	.05
433	Sean Jones	.05
434	Richard Johnson	.05
435	Al Smith	.05
436	Johnny Meads	.05
437	William Fuller	.05
438	Mike Munchak	.05
439	Ray Childress	.05
440	Cody Carlson	.05
441	Scott Radecic	.10
442	*Quintus McDonald*	.10
443	Eugene Daniel	.05
444	Mark Herrmann	.15
445	*John Baylor*	.12
446	Dave McCloughan	.05
447	Mark Vander Poel	.05
448	Randy Dixon	.05
449	Keith Taylor	.05
450	Alan Grant	.05
451	Tony Siragusa	.05
452	Rich Baldinger	.05
453	Derrick Thomas	.20
454	Bill Jones	.05
455	Troy Stradford	.05
456	Barry Word	.15
457	Tim Grunhard	.05
458	Chris Martin	.05
459	*Jayice Pearson*	.10
460	Dino Hackett	.05
461	David Lutz	.05
462	Albert Lewis	.06
463	*Fred Jones*	.12
464	Winston Moss	.05
465	*Sam Grady*	.20
466	Steve Wisniewski	.05
467	Jay Schroeder	.05
468	Ronnie Loft	.05
469	Willie Gault	.05
470	Greg Townsend	.05
471	Max Montoya	.05
472	Howie Long	.05
473	Lionel Washington	.05
474	Riki Ellison	.05
475	Tom Newberry	.05
476	Damone Johnson	.05
477	Pat Terrell	.05
478	Marcus Dupree	.05
479	Todd Lyght	.10
480	Buford McGee	.05
481	Bern Brostek	.05
482	Jim Price	.05
483	Robert Young	.05
484	Tony Zendejas	.05
485	*Robert Bailey*	.05
486	Alvin Wright	.05
487	Pat Carter	.05
488	Pete Stoyanovich	.05
489	Reggie Roby	.05
490	Harry Galbreath	.05
491	*Michael McGruder*	.10
492	J.B. Brown	.05
493	E.J. Junior	.05
494	Ferrell Edmunds	.05
495	Scott Secules	.05

496	Greg Baty	.15
497	Mike Iaquaniello	.05
498	Keith Sims	.05
499	John Randle	.05
500	Joey Browner	.05
501	Steve Jordan	.08
502	Darrin Nelson	.05
503	Audray McMillian	.05
504	Harry Newsome	.05
505	Hassan Jones	.05
506	Ray Berry	.05
507	Mike Merriweather	.05
508	Leo Lewis	.05
509	Tim Irwin	.05
510	Kirk Lowdermilk	.05
511	Alfred Anderson	.05
512	Michael Timpson	.75
513	Jerome Henderson	.05
514	Andre Tippett	.05
515	Chris Singleton	.05
516	John Stephens	.05
517	Ronnie Lippett	.05
518	Bruce Armstrong	.05
519	Marion Hobby	.10
520	Tim Goad	.05
521	Mickey Washington	.08
522	Fred Smerlas	.05
523	Wayne Martin	.05
524	Frank Warren	.05
525	Floyd Turner	.05
526	Wesley Carroll	.05
527	Gene Atkins	.05
528	Vaughan Johnson	.05
529	Hoby Brenner	.05
530	Renaldo Turnbull	.05
531	Joel Hilgenberg	.05
532	Craig Heyward	.05
533	Vince Buck	.05
534	Jim Dombrowski	.05
535	Fred McAfee	.12
536	Phil Simms	.10
537	Lewis Tillman	.05
538	John Elliott	.05
539	Dave Meggett	.05
540	Mark Collins	.05
541	Ottis Anderson	.05
542	Bobby Abrams	.10
543	Sean Landeta	.05
544	Brian Williams	.05
545	Erik Howard	.05
546	Mark Ingram	.05
547	Kanavis McGhee	.05
548	Kyle Clifton	.05
549	Marvin Washington	.05
550	Jeff Criswell	.05
551	Dave Cadigan	.05
552	Chris Burkett	.05
553	Erik McMillan	.05
554	James Hasty	.05
555	Louie Aguiar	.10
556	Troy Johnson	.10
557	Troy Taylor	.10
558	Pat Kelly	.08
559	Heath Sherman	.05
560	Roger Ruzek	.05
561	Andre Waters	.05
562	Izel Jenkins	.05
563	Keith Jackson	.15
564	Byron Evans	.05
565	Wes Hopkins	.05
566	Rich Miano	.05
567	Seth Joyner	.05
568	Thomas Sanders	.05
569	David Alexander	.05
570	Jeff Kemp	.05
571	Jock Jones	.10
572	Craig Patterson	.10
573	Robert Massey	.05
574	Bill Lewis	.05
575	Freddie Joe Nunn	.05
576	Aeneas Williams	.05
577	John Jackson	.05
578	Tim McDonald	.05
579	Michael Zordich	.10
580	Eric Hill	.05
581	Lorenzo Lynch	.05
582	Vernice Smith	.10
583	Greg Lloyd	.05
584	Carnell Lake	.05
585	Hardy Nickerson	.05
586	Delton Hall	.05
587	Gerald Williams	.05
588	Bryan Hinkle	.05
589	Barry Foster	.45
590	Bubby Brister	.05
591	Rick Strom	.15
592	David Little	.05
593	Leroy Thompson	.40
594	Eric Bieniemy	.05
595	Courtney Hall	.05
596	George Thornton	.05
597	Donnie Elder	.05
598	Billy Ray Smith	.05
599	Gill Byrd	.05
600	Marion Butts	.10
601	Ronnie Harmon	.05
602	Anthony Shelton	.05
603	Mark May	.05
604	Craig McEwen	.10
605	Steve Young	1.00
606	Keith Henderson	.05
607	Pierce Holt	.05
608	Roy Foster	.05
609	Don Griffin	.05
610	Harry Sydney	.05
611	Todd Bowles	.05
612	Ted Washington	.05

613	Johnny Jackson	.05
614	Jesse Sapolu	.05
615	Brent Jones	.05
616	Travis McNeal	.05
617	Darrick Brilz	.10
618	Terry Wooden	.05
619	Tommy Kane	.05
620	Nesby Glasgow	.05
621	Dwayne Harper	.05
622	Rick Tuten	.05
623	Chris Warren	.30
624	John L. Williams	.05
625	Rufus Porter	.05
626	David Daniels	.05
627	Keith McCants	.05
628	Reuben Davis	.05
629	Mark Royals	.05
630	Marty Carter	.15
631	Ian Beckles	.05
632	Ron Hall	.05
633	Eugene Marve	.05
634	Willie Drewrey	.05
635	Tom McHale	.10
636	Kevin Murphy	.05
637	Robert Hardy	.10
638	Ricky Sanders	.05
639	Gary Clark	.10
640	Andre Collins	.05
641	Brad Edwards	.05
642	Monte Coleman	.05
643	Clarence Vaughn	.10
644	Fred Stokes	.05
645	Charles Mann	.05
646	Earnest Byner	.05
647	Jim Lachey	.05
648	Jeff Bostic	.05
649	Chris Mims	.30
650	George Williams	.10
651	Ed Cunningham	.08
652	Tony Smith	.10
653	Will Furrer	.15
654	Mike Mooney	.08
655	Eddie Blake	.10
656	Leon Searcy	.12
657	Kevin Turner	.20
658	Keith Hamilton	.15
659	Alan Haller	.10

1992 Pacific Checklists

These inserts were released in 1992 Pacific foil, jumbo and 25-cent packs. Each card is numbered on the back 1 of 8, etc. Cards 1-4 were in Series I packs; cards 5-8 were in Series II packs.

		MT
Complete Set (8):		3.00
Common Player:		.50
1	Checklist 1 - (1-110)	.50
2	Checklist 2 - (111-220)	.50
3	Checklist 3 - (221-330)	.50
4	Checklist 4 (Highlight Cards)	.50
5	Checklist 5 - (1-110)	.50
6	Checklist 6 - (111-220)	.50
7	Checklist 7 - (221-330)	.50
8	Checklist 8 (Highlight Cards)	.50

1992 Pacific Legends of the Game Bob Griese

Miami Dolphins Hall of Fame quarterback Bob Griese is featured on this nine-card insert set. The cards, subtitled "Legends of the Game," were random inserts in 1992 Pacific Series II foil and jumbo packs. Each white-bordered card front has a color action shot, along with a caption and Griese's name in a colorful stripe at the bottom next to the Pacific logo. The back is in a horizontal format and features another photo of the player, plus a career summary. The cards are a continuation of the "Legends of the Game" series, so they start at 10, where the 1992 Steve Largent set ended. The Griese cards are also randomly inserted in triple folder card packs and five-card change-maker packs. Griese also autographed 1,000 cards.

	MT
Complete Set (9):	5.00
Common Griese:	.50

10	Purdue Star (Bob Griese)	.50
11	AFL Star (Bob Griese)	.50
12	Super Bowl Star (Bob Griese)	.50
13	Thinking Man's QB (Bob Griese)	.50
14	349 Yards (Bob Griese)	.50
15	All Star (Bob Griese)	.50
16	The 25,000 Yard Club (Bob Griese)	.50
17	Number 12 Retired (Bob Griese)	.50
18	Hall of Fame (Bob Griese)	.50

1992 Pacific Legends of the Game Steve Largent

Seattle Seahawks Hall of Fame wide receiver Steve Largent is featured in this nine-card insert set. Cards were randomly inserted in Series I and jumbo packs. Fronts feature color action photos with white borders. The card title and Largent's name are in a colored panel at the bottom. The backs have a photo, career summary and card number, 1 of 9, etc. They are in a horizontal format. Largent autographed 1,000 cards.

		MT
Complete Set (9):		5.00
Common Player:		.50
1	Great Rookie Start	.50
2	Largent Leads NFL	.50
3	Hi-Steppin'	.50
4	NFL Leader	.50
5	Team Captain	.50
6	Pro Bowl	.50
7	Man of the Year	.50
8	The Final Season	.50
9	Retirement Celebration	.50

1992 Pacific Picks The Pros

Pacific selected the best player at each position for this 25-card insert set. Gold foil versions of the cards, which say "Pacific Picks The Pros" in gold foil down the left side, were randomly inserted in Series I foil packs. Silver versions were also made and were random inserts in Series I jumbo packs. The backs present a career summary in a diagonal format with a red and yellow background. A card number is also included. The cards have the same value for both versions.

		MT
Complete Set (25):		40.00
Common Player:		1.00
1	Mark Rypien	1.00
2	Marv Cook	1.00
3	Jim Lachey	1.00
4	Darrell Green	1.00
5	Derrick Thomas	3.00
6	Thurman Thomas	6.00
7	Kent Hull	1.00
8	Tim McDonald	1.00
9	Mike Croel	1.00
10	Anthony Munoz	1.00
11	Jerome Brown	1.00
12	Reggie White	3.00
13	Gill Byrd	1.00
14	Jessie Tuggle	1.00
15	Randall McDaniel	1.00
16	Sam Mills	1.00
17	Pat Swilling	1.00
18	Eugene Robinson	1.00
19	Michael Irvin	6.00
20	Emmitt Smith	15.00
21	Jeff Gossett	1.00
22	Jeff Jaeger	1.00
23	William Fuller	1.00
24	Mike Munchak	1.00
25	Andre Rison	4.00

1992 Pacific Prism Inserts

The top 10 running backs in the NFL are featured in this set. Pacific stated it produced only 10,000 of each card and randomly inserted them in 1992 Pacific Series II foil packs and triple folder card packs. The front of each card features a player photo superimposed against a prism-patterned background. A color streak at the bottom contains the player's name. Each back has a green football field for a background and uses team-color bar graphics to give the back's rushing totals for each game in 1991. Backs are numbered 1 of 10, etc.

		MT
Complete Set (10):		25.00
Common Player:		1.50
1	Thurman Thomas	2.00
2	Gaston Green	1.50
3	Christian Okoye	2.75
4	Leonard Russell	2.50
5	Mark Higgs	2.50
6	Emmitt Smith	8.00
7	Barry Sanders	6.00
8	Rodney Hampton	2.00
9	Earnest Byner	2.50
10	Herschel Walker	1.50

1992 Pacific Statistical Leaders

These cards, which feature statistical leaders from each NFL team, were random inserts in Series I foil packs. The front of the card has a glossy action photo bordered by a white frame. The player's name and

category he lead are at the bottom in a multi-colored stripe. Three other team leaders are featured on each back, plus small photos of the player in action. The cards are also numbered on the back. Additional cards were made for the AFC and NFC rushing leaders.

		MT
Complete Set (30):		9.00
Common Player:		.25
1	Chris Miller	.25
2	Thurman Thomas	1.25
3	Jim Harbaugh	.25
4	Jim Breech	.25
5	Kevin Mack	.25
6	Emmitt Smith	4.00
7	Gaston Green	.25
8	Barry Sanders	2.50
9	Tony Bennett	.25
10	Warren Moon	.50
11	Bill Brooks	.25
12	Christian Okoye	.25
13	Jay Schroeder	.30
14	Robert Delpino	.25
15	Mark Higgs	.25
16	John Randle	.25
17	Leonard Russell	.25
18	Pat Swilling	.30
19	Rodney Hampton	.50
20	Terance Mathis	.40
21	Fred Barnett	.25
22	Aeneas Williams	.25
23	Neil O'Donnell	.35
24	Marion Butts	.25
25	Steve Young	1.25
26	John L. Williams	.25
27	Reggie Cobb	.25
28	Mark Rypien	.35
29	Thurman Thomas	.50
30	Emmitt Smith	1.50

1992 Pacific Triple Folders

One player from each NFL team was selected for this 28-card Pacific Trading Cards set. Each card front has two panels which, when closed, form a 3-1/2" x 5" glossy color action photo. The player's name and team helmet are on one side, while his position is on the other side. When opened up, the inside of the card reveals three smaller photos of the featured player. The cards use team color-coding for the background and have a player profile on the back, along with a card number. Each Triple Folder pack also included one card as an insert from the following sets: Steve Largent, Bob Griese, Statistical Leaders, Gold/Foil Prisms, Rushing Leaders Prisms, or checklists.

		MT
Complete Set (28):		17.00
Common Player:		.50
1	Chris Miller	1.00
2	Thurman Thomas	1.50
3	Neal Anderson	.50
4	Tim McGee	.50
5	Kevin Mack	.50
6	Emmitt Smith	5.00
7	John Elway	2.00
8	Barry Sanders	3.00
9	Sterling Sharpe	2.00
10	Warren Moon	1.25
11	Bill Brooks	.50
12	Christian Okoye	.50
13	Nick Bell	.50
14	Robert Delpino	.50
15	Mark Higgs	.75
16	Rich Gannon	.50
17	Leonard Russell	1.00
18	Pat Swilling	.75
19	Rodney Hampton	1.25
20	Rob Moore	1.25
21	Reggie White	1.50
22	Johnny Johnson	1.00

23	Neil O'Donnell	1.50
24	Marion Butts	1.00
25	Steve Young	3.00
26	John L. Williams	.50
27	Reggie Cobb	.50
28	Mark Rypien	1.00

1993 Pacific Protypes

The five-card, standard-size set was issued at the 1993 National Convention in Chicago as samples, with a production total of 5,000 sets.

		MT
Complete Set (5):		20.00
Common Player:		1.50
1	Emmitt Smith	10.00
2	Barry Sanders	5.00
3	Derrick Thomas	1.50
4	Jim Everett	1.50
5	Steve Young	4.00

1993 Pacific

Pacific's 1993 set features glossy cards with team color-coded marble backgrounds. The 440-card set has two subsets - "NFL Stars" (#s 393-417) and "Rookies" (#s 418-440). Random inserts include Prism (20 cards) and Pacific Picks the Pros (25) cards. The five prototype cards are similar to the regular set, except they say "1993 Prototypes" on the back. Approximately 5,000 sets were made; many were given away at the 1993 National Sports Collectors Convention in Chicago in July.

		MT
Complete Set (440):		18.00
Common Player:		.05
Minor Stars:		.10
Checklist Set (4):		4.00
Wax Box:		20.00
1	Emmitt Smith	1.50
2	Troy Aikman	.75
3	Larry Brown	.05
4	Tony Castilla	.05
5	Thomas Everett	.05
6	Alvin Harper	.10
7	Michael Irvin	.30
8	Charles Haley	.05
9	Leon Lett	.30
10	Kevin Smith	.05
11	Robert Jones	.05
12	Jimmy Smith	.25
13	Derrick Gainer	.05
14	Lin Elliott	.05
15	William Thomas	.05
16	Clyde Simmons	.05
17	Seth Joyner	.05
18	Randall Cunningham	.10
19	Byron Evans	.05
20	Fred Barnett	.05
21	Calvin Williams	.05
22	James Joseph	.05
23	Heath Sherman	.05
24	Siran Stacy	.05
25	Andy Harmon	.05

#	Player	
26	Eric Allen	.05
27	Herschel Walker	.05
28	Vai Sikahema	.05
29	Ernest Byner	.05
30	Jeff Bostic	.05
31	Monte Coleman	.05
32	Ricky Ervins	.05
33	Darrell Green	.05
34	Mark Schlereth	.05
35	Mark Rypien	.05
36	Art Monk	.10
37	Brian Mitchell	.05
38	Chip Lohmiller	.05
39	Charles Mann	.05
40	Shane Collins	.05
41	Jim Lachey	.05
42	Joe Jacoby	.05
43	Rodney Hampton	.10
44	*Dave Brown*	.60
45	Mark Collins	.05
46	Jerrod Bunch	.05
47	William Roberts	.05
48	Sean Landetta	.05
49	Lawrence Taylor	.10
50	Ed McCaffrey	.05
51	Bart Oates	.05
52	Pepper Johnson	.05
53	Eric Dorsey	.05
54	Erik Howard	.05
55	Phil Simms	.10
56	Derek Brown	.05
57	Johnny Bailey	.05
58	Rich Camarillo	.05
59	*Larry Centers*	.50
60	Chris Chandler	.05
61	Randal Hill	.05
62	Rickey Proehl	.05
63	Freddie Joe Nunn	.05
64	Robert Massey	.05
65	Aeneas Williams	.05
66	Luis Sharpe	.05
67	Eric Swann	.05
68	Timm Rosenbach	.05
69	*Anthony Edwards*	.10
70	Greg Davis	.05
71	Terry Allen	.10
72	Anthony Carter	.05
73	Cris Carter	.10
74	Roger Craig	.05
75	Jack Del Rio	.05
76	Chris Doleman	.05
77	Rich Gannon	.05
78	Hassan Jones	.05
79	Steve Jordan	.05
80	Randall McDaniel	.05
81	Sean Salisbury	.05
82	Harry Newsome	.05
83	Carlos Jenkins	.05
84	Jake Reed	.05
85	Edgar Bennett	.10
86	Tony Bennett	.05
87	Terrell Buckley	.05
88	Ty Detmer	.05
89	Brett Favre	1.50
90	Chris Jackie (Jackie)	.05
91	Sterling Sharpe	.10
92	James Campen	.05
93	Brian Noble	.05
94	*Lester Archambeau*	.05
95	Harry Sydney	.05
96	Corey Harris	.05
97	Don Majkowski	.05
98	Ken Ruettgers	.05
99	Lomas Brown	.05
100	Jason Hanson	.05
101	Robert Porcher	.05
102	Chris Spielman	.05
103	Erik Kramer	.05
104	Tracy Scroggins	.05
105	Rodney Peete	.05
106	Barry Sanders	1.25
107	Herman Moore	.30
108	Brett Perriman	.05
109	Mel Gray	.05
110	Dennis Gibson	.05
111	Bennie Blades	.05
112	Andre Ware	.05
113	Gary Anderson	.05
114	Tyji Armstrong	.05
115	Reggie Cobb	.05
116	Marty Carter	.05
117	Lawrence Dawsey	.05
118	Steve DeBerg	.05
119	Ron Hall	.05
120	Courtney Hawkins	.05
121	Broderick Thomas	.05
122	Keith McCants	.05
123	Bruce Reimers	.05
124	Darrick Brownlow	.05
125	Mark Wheeler	.05
126	Ricky Reynolds	.05
127	Neal Anderson	.05
128	Trace Armstrong	.05
129	Mark Carrier	.05
130	Richard Dent	.05
131	Wendall Davis	.05
132	Darren Lewis	.05
133	Tom Waddle	.05
134	Jim Harbaugh	.05
135	Steve McMichael	.05
136	William Perry	.05
137	Alonzo Spellman	.05
138	John Roper	.05
139	Peter Tom Willis	.05
140	Dante Jones	.05
141	Harris Barton	.05
142	Michael Carter	.05
143	Eric Davis	.05
144	Dana Hall	.05
145	Amp Lee	.05
146	Don Griffin	.05
147	Jerry Rice	.75
148	Ricky Watters	.20
149	Steve Young	.75
150	Bill Romanowski	.05
151	Klaus Wilmsmeyer	.05
152	Steve Bono	.30
153	Tom Rathman	.05
154	Odessa Turner	.05
155	Morten Andersen	.05
156	Richard Cooper	.05
157	Toi Cook	.05
158	Quinn Early	.05
159	Vaughn Dunbar	.05
160	Rickey Jackson	.05
161	Wayne Martin	.05
162	Hoby Brenner	.05
163	Joel Hilgenberg	.05
164	Mike Buck	.05
165	Torrance Small	.05
166	Eric Martin	.05
167	Vaughan Johnson	.05
168	Sam Mills	.05
169	Steve Broussard	.05
170	Darion Conner	.05
171	Drew Hill	.05
172	Chris Hinton	.05
173	Chris Miller	.05
174	Tim McKyer	.05
175	Norm Johnson	.05
176	Mike Pritchard	.05
177	Andre Rison	.10
178	Deion Sanders	.40
179	Tony Smith	.05
180	Bruce Pickens	.05
181	Michael Haynes	.05
182	Jessie Tuggle	.05
183	Makr Boutte	.05
184	Don Bracken	.05
185	Bern Brostek	.05
186	Henry Ellard	.05
187	Jim Everett	.10
188	Sean Gilbert	.05
189	Cleveland Gary	.05
190	Todd Kinchen	.10
191	Pat Terrell	.05
192	Jackie Slater	.05
193	David Lang	.05
194	Willie Anderson	.05
195	Tony Zendejas	.05
196	Roman Phifer	.05
197	Steve Christie	.05
198	Cornelius Bennett	.05
199	Phil Hansen	.05
200	Don Beebe	.05
201	Mark Kelso	.05
202	Bruce Smith	.05
203	Darryl Talley	.05
204	Andre Reed	.05
205	Mike Lodish	.05
206	Jim Kelly	.20
207	Thurman Thomas	.20
208	Kenneth Davis	.05
209	Frank Reich	.05
210	Kent Hall	.05
211	Marco Coleman	.05
212	Bryan Cox	.05
213	Jeff Cross	.05
214	Mark Higgs	.05
215	Keith Jackson	.05
216	Scott Miller	.05
217	John Offerdahl	.05
218	Dan Marino	1.50
219	Keith Sims	.05
220	Chuck Klingbell	.05
221	Troy Vincent	.05
222	*Mike Williams*	.05
223	Pete Stoyanovich	.05
224	J.B. Brown	.05
225	Ashley Ambrose	.05
226	*Jason Belser*	.05
227	Jeff George	.10
228	Quentin Coryatt	.05
229	Duane Bickett	.05
230	Steve Emtmann	.05
231	Anthony Johnson	.05
232	Rohn Stark	.05
233	Jessie Hester	.05
234	Reggie Langhorne	.05
235	Clarence Verdin	.05
236	Dean Biasucci	.05
237	Jack Trudeau	.05
238	Tony Siragusa	.05
239	Chris Burkett	.05
240	Brad Baxter	.05
241	Rob Moore	.05
242	Browning Nagle	.05
243	Jim Sweeney	.05
244	Kent Barber	.05
245	Siupeli Malamala	.05
246	Mike Brim	.05
247	Mo Lewis	.05
248	Johnny Mitchell	.05
249	*Ken Whisenhunt*	.05
250	James Hasty	.05
251	Kyle Clifton	.05
252	Terance Mathis	.05
253	Ray Agnew	.05
254	Eugene Chung	.05
255	Marv Cook	.05
256	Johnny Rembert	.05
257	Maurice Hurst	.05
258	John Vaughn	.05
259	Leonard Russell	.05
260	Pat Harlow	.05
261	Andre Tippet	.05
262	Michael Timpson	.05
263	Greg McCarthy	.05
264	Chris Singleton	.05
265	*Reggie Redding*	.05
266	Walter Stanley	.05
267	Gary Anderson	.05
268	Merril Hoge	.05
269	Barry Foster	.10
270	Charles Davenport	.05
271	Jeff Graham	.05
272	Adrian Cooper	.05
273	David Little	.05
274	Neil O'Donnell	.10
275	Rod Woodson	.05
276	Ernie Mills	.05
277	Dwight Stone	.05
278	Darren Perry	.05
279	Dermontti Dawson	.05
280	Carlton Haselrig	.05
281	Pat Coleman	.05
282	Ernest Givins	.05
283	Warren Moon	.10
284	Haywood Jeffires	.05
285	Cody Carlson	.05
286	Ray Childress	.05
287	Bruce Matthews	.05
288	Webster Slaughter	.05
289	Bo Orlando	.05
290	Lorenzo White	.05
291	Eddie Robinson	.05
292	Bubba McDowell	.05
293	Bucky Richardson	.10
294	Sean Jones	.05
295	David Brandon	.05
296	Shawn Collins	.05
297	Lawyer Tillman	.05
298	Bob Dahl	.05
299	Kevin Mack	.05
300	Bernie Kosar	.05
301	Tommy Vardell	.05
302	Jay Hilgenberg	.05
303	Michael Dean Perry	.05
304	Michael Jackson	.05
305	Eric Metcalf	.05
306	*Rico Smith*	.05
307	*Stevon Moore*	.05
308	Leroy Hoard	.05
309	Eric Ball	.05
310	Derrick Fenner	.05
311	James Francis	.05
312	Ricardo McDonald	.05
313	Tim Krumrie	.05
314	Carl Pickens	.50
315	David Klingler	.10
316	Donald Hollas	.05
317	Harold Green	.05
318	Daniel Stubbs	.05
319	Alfred Williams	.05
320	Darryl Williams	.05
321	*Mike Arthur*	.05
322	Leonard Wheeler	.05
323	Gil Byrd	.05
324	Eric Bieniemy	.05
325	Marion Butts	.05
326	John Carney	.05
327	Stan Humphries	.10
328	Ronnie Harmon	.05
329	Junior Seau	.10
330	Nate Lewis	.05
331	Harry Swayne	.05
332	Leslie O'Neal	.05
333	Eric Moten	.05
334	*Blaise Winter*	.05
335	Anthony Miller	.05
336	Gary Plummer	.05
337	Willie Davis	.05
338	J.T. Birden	.05
339	Tim Barnett	.05
340	Dave Krieg	.05
341	Barry Word	.05
342	Tracy Simien	.05
343	Christian Okoye	.05
344	Todd McNair	.05
345	Dan Salesaumua	.05
346	Derrick Thomas	.10
347	Harvey Williams	.05
348	*Kimble Anders*	.10
349	Tim Grunhard	.05
350	*Tony Hargain*	.05
351	Simon Fletcher	.05
352	John Elway	.30
353	Mike Croel	.05
354	Steve Atwater	.05
355	Tommy Maddox	.05
356	Karl Mecklenberg	.05
357	Shane Dronett	.05
358	Kenny Walker	.05
359	*Reggie Rivers*	.05
360	*Cedric Tilman*	.05
361	*Arthur Marshall*	.10
362	Greg Lewis	.05
363	Shannon Sharpe	.10
364	Doug Widell	.05
365	Todd Marinovich	.05
366	Nick Bell	.05
367	Eric Dickerson	.05
368	Max Montoya	.05
369	Winston Moss	.05
370	Howie Long	.05
371	Willie Gault	.05
372	Tim Brown	.10
373	Steve Smith	.05
374	Steve Wisniewski	.05
375	Alexander Wright	.05
376	Ethan Horton	.05
377	Napoleon McCallum	.05
378	Terry McDaniel	.05
379	Patrick Hunter	.05
380	Robert Blackmon	.05
381	John Kasay	.05
382	Cortez Kennedy	.10
383	Andy Heck	.05
384	*Bill Hitchcock*	.05
385	*Rick Mirer*	.30
386	Jeff Bryant	.05
387	Eugene Robinson	.05
388	John L. Williams	.05
389	Chris Warren	.20
390	Rufus Porter	.05
391	*Joe Tofflemire*	.05
392	Dan McGwire	.05
393	Boomer Esiason	.10
394	Brad Muster	.05
395	James Lofton	.05
396	Tim McGee	.05
397	Steve Beurlein	.10
398	Gaston Green	.05
399	Bill Brooks	.05
400	Ronnie Lott	.05
401	Jay Schroeder	.05
402	Marcus Allen	.10
403	Kevin Green	.05
404	Kirk Lowdermilk	.05
405	Hugh Millen	.05
406	Pat Swilling	.05
407	Bobby Herbert	.05
408	Carl Banks	.05
409	Jeff Hostetler	.10
410	Leonard Marshall	.05
411	Ken O'Brien	.05
412	Joe Montana	1.00
413	Reggie White	.10
414	Gary Clark	.05
415	Johnny Johnson	.05
416	Tim McDonald	.05
417	Pierce Holt	.05
418	*Joe Torretta*	.10
419	*Glyn Milburn*	.30
420	*O.J. McDuffie*	.60
421	*Coleman Rudolph*	.10
422	*Reggie Brooks*	.10
423	*Garrison Hearst*	1.50
424	*Leonard Renfro*	.10
425	*Kevin Williams*	.30
426	*Demetrius DuBose*	.10
427	*Elvis Grbac*	1.00
428	*Lincoln Kennedy*	.10
429	*Carlton Gray*	.10
430	*Michael Barrow*	.10
431	*George Teague*	.25
432	*Curtis Conway*	1.00
433	*Natrone Means*	1.00
434	*Jerome Bettis*	1.00
435	*Drew Bledsoe*	3.00
436	*Robert Smith*	1.00
437	*Deon Figures*	.20
438	*Qadry Ismail*	.50
439	*Chris Slade*	.30
440	*Dana Stubblefield*	.50

1993 Pacific Picks the Pros Gold

Pacific's top picks at each position are featured in this 25-card insert set. Cards were randomly included in packs and have a color action photo on the front with a gold-foil border. The player's name and position are at the bottom in a gold-foil panel. The back is in a horizontal format and includes the player's name, position, team name and season recap in black letters on a blue and gray background. A card number is also given. A silver version was also made for these cards; these cards were randomly included in 1993 Pacific Triple Folders.

		MT
Complete Set (25):		75.00
Common Player:		2.00
Minor Stars:		4.00
1	Jerry Rice	15.00
2	Sterling Sharpe	4.00
3	Richmond Webb	2.00
4	Harris Barton	2.00
5	Randall McDaniel	2.00
6	Steve Wisniewski	2.00
7	Mark Stepnoski	2.00
8	Steve Young	15.00
9	Emmitt Smith	20.00
10	Barry Foster	4.00
11	Nick Lowery	2.00
12	Reggie White	6.00
13	Leslie O'Neal	2.00
14	Cortez Kennedy	4.00
15	Ray Childress	2.00
16	Vaughan Johnson	2.00
17	Wilber Marshall	2.00
18	Junior Seau	6.00
19	Sam Mills	2.00
20	Rod Woodson	4.00
21	Ricky Reynolds	2.00
22	Steve Atwater	2.00
23	Chuck Cecil	2.00
24	Rich Camarillo	2.00
25	Dale Carter	2.00

1993 Pacific Silver Prism Inserts

Pacific produced three versions of its 1993 Prism inserts. The first version, the regular prism inserts, have triangular prisms for a background. There were 8,000 of each of these cards made; they were randomly included in 1993 Pacific packs and 1993 Pacific Triple Folder packs. A circular version background was also made; these cards were randomly included in retail packs and were easier to find than the triangular versions. The third type of prism insert was limited to 1,000 per card and features a gold triangular prism background. They were randomly included in 1993 Pacific Triple Folder packs. Each card design is basically the same for all three versions. The front has a color action photo against the prism background; the player's name is at the bottom in block letters in team colors. The back has the same photo used for the front, except the entire background of the photo is also used. The player's name and position are given in scripted white letters. A card number is also given (1 of 20, etc.).

		MT
Complete Set (20):		100.00
Common Player:		2.00
Minor Stars:		2.00
Comp. Gold Set (20):		300.00
Gold Cards:		1.5x-3x
1	Troy Aikman	7.00
2	Jerome Bettis	10.00
3	Drew Bledsoe	10.00
4	Reggie Brooks	4.00
5	Brett Favre	15.00
6	Barry Foster	4.00
7	Garrison Hearst	4.00
8	Michael Irvin	4.00
9	Cortez Kennedy	2.00
10	David Klingler	2.00
11	Dan Marino	15.00
12	Rick Mirer	4.00
13	Joe Montana	10.00
14	Jay Novacek	2.00
15	Jerry Rice	8.00
16	Barry Sanders	10.00
17	Sterling Sharpe	4.00
18	Emmitt Smith	15.00
19	Thurman Thomas	4.00
20	Steve Young	8.00

Post-1980 cards in Near Mint condition will generally sell for about 75% of the quoted Mint value. Excellent-condition cards bring no more than 40%.

1993 Pacific Prisms

Approximately 17,000 of each card in this 108-card set were produced. Each card front has a player action photo against a prism-like foil background. The player's name is in team colors and appears at the bottom of the card. The back is numbered and includes a player profile, two photos, a team helmet and the Pacific logo. The card back is in a horizontal format and uses a gray background. There were also two promotional cards made for the set - (22) Emmitt Smith and (61) Drew Bledsoe. The cards, which were given away at the 1993 National Card Collectors Convention in Chicago, are similar in design to the regular set.

		MT
Complete Set (108):		130.00
Common Player:		.50
Minor Stars:		1.00
Checklist (NNO):		.25
Wax Box:		70.00
1	Chris Miller	.50
2	Mike Pritchard	.50
3	Andre Rison	1.00
4	Deion Sanders	3.00
5	Tony Smith	.50
6	Jim Kelly	2.00
7	Andre Reed	1.00
8	Thurman Thomas	2.00
9	Neal Anderson	.50
10	Jim Harbaugh	.50
11	Donnell Woolford	.50
12	David Klingler	.50
13	Carl Pickens	3.00
14	Alfred Williams	.50
15	Michael Jackson	.50
16	Bernie Kosar	1.00
17	Tommy Vardell	.50
18	Troy Aikman	8.00
19	Alvin Harper	2.00
20	Michael Irvin	2.00
21	Russell Maryland	.50
22	Emmitt Smith	12.00
23	John Elway	5.00
24	Tommy Maddox	.50
25	Shannon Sharpe	.50
26	Herman Moore	3.00
27	Rodney Peete	.50
28	Barry Sanders	10.00
29	Pat Swilling	.50
30	Terrell Buckley	.50
31	Brett Favre	12.00
32	Sterling Sharpe	2.00
33	Reggie White	1.00
34	Ernest Givins	.50
35	Haywood Jeffires	.50
36	Warren Moon	2.00
37	Lorenzo White	.50
38	Steve Emtman	.50
39	Jeff George	2.00
40	Reggie Langhorne	.50
41	Dale Carter	.50
42	Joe Montana	10.00
43	Derrick Thomas	1.00
44	Barry Word	.50
45	Nick Bell	.50
46	Eric Dickerson	1.00
47	Jeff Jaeger	.50
48	Jerome Bettis	5.00
49	Henry Ellard	.50
50	Jim Everett	1.00
51	Cleveland Gary	.50
52	Marco Coleman	.50
53	Mark Higgs	.50
54	Keith Jackson	.50
55	Dan Marino	15.00
56	Troy Vincent	.50
57	Terry Allen	.50
58	Jack Del Rio	.50
59	Sean Salisbury	.50
60	Robert Smith	5.00
61	Drew Bledsoe	16.00
62	Marv Cook	.50
63	Irving Fryar	.50
64	Leonard Russell	.50
65	Andre Tippett	.50
66	Morten Andersen	.50
67	Vaughn Dunbar	.50

68 Eric Martin .50
69 David Brown 2.00
70 Rodney Hampton 2.00
71 Phil Simms .50
72 Lawrence Taylor 1.00
73 Ronnie Lott .50
74 Johnny Mitchell .50
75 Rob Moore .50
76 Browning Nagle .50
77 Fred Barnett .50
78 Randall Cunningham 1.00
79 Herschel Walker .50
80 Gary Clark .50
81 Ken Harvey .50
82 Garrison Hearst 6.00
83 Ricky Proehl .50
84 Barry Foster 1.00
85 Ernie Mills .50
86 Neil O'Donnell 1.50
87 Stan Humphries 1.50
88 Leslie O'Neil .50
89 Junior Seau 2.00
90 Amp Lee .50
91 Jerry Rice 7.00
92 Ricky Watters 2.00
93 Steve Young 7.00
94 Cortez Kennedy .50
95 Rick Mirer 1.00
96 Eugene Robinson .50
97 Chris Warren 1.00
98 John L. Williams .50
99 Reggie Cobb .50
100 Lawrence Dawsey .50
101 Santana Dotson .50
102 Courtney Hawkins .50
103 Reggie Brooks 2.00
104 Ricky Ervins .50
105 Desmond Howard 1.00
106 Art Monk 1.00
107 Mark Rypien .50
108 Ricky Sanders .50

1993 Pacific Triple Folders

These cards feature two panels on the front which, when closed, form a color action photo of an NFL star player. The player's name and team helmet are on one panel; his position is printed on the other side. When opened up, the inside of the card panels reveal additional player photos. The card back is numbered and has 1992 statistics, a career summary, the player's name and team helmet, and position, all against a team color-coded marble-like background. Approximately 2,500 cases were produced.

MT
Complete Set (30): 18.00
Common Player: .45
1 Thurman Thomas 1.25
2 Carl Pickens .75
3 Glyn Milburn .75
4 Lorenzo White .45
5 Anthony Johnson .45
6 Joe Montana 3.50
7 Nick Bell .45
8 Dan Marino 2.50
9 Anthony Carter .45
10 Drew Bledsoe 3.00
11 Rob Moore .75
12 Barry Foster 1.00
13 Stan Humphries .75
14 Cortez Kennedy .75
15 Rick Mirer 2.25
16 Deion Sanders 1.50
17 Curtis Conway 1.00
18 Tommy Vardell .75
19 Emmitt Smith 4.50
20 Barry Sanders 2.50
21 Brett Favre 1.50
22 Cleveland Gary .45
23 Morten Andersen .45
24 Marcus Buckley .45
25 Rodney Hampton 1.00
26 Herschel Walker .75
27 Garrison Hearst 1.00
28 Jerry Rice 2.00
29 Lawrence Dawsey .45

30 Desmond Howard 1.00

1993 Pacific Triple Folder Superstars

Drew Bledsoe

These 20 cards were randomly inserted into 1993 Pacific Triple Folder packs. Each card front has a borderless, full-color action photo, with the player's name in white letters at the bottom of the card. His position is also given. The back is numbered and has a player profile, along with the player's name, position and team helmet. The background uses the player's team colors. Some of the players featured in the set were rookies.

MT
Complete Set (20): 20.00
Common Player: .35
1 Troy Aikman 3.50
2 *Victor Bailey* .50
3 *Jerome Bettis* 3.50
4 *Drew Bledsoe* 3.50
5 *Reggie Brooks* 1.25
6 *Derek Brown* 1.00
7 *Marcus Buckley* .35
8 *Curtis Conway* .75
9 Brett Favre 2.00
10 Barry Foster .75
11 *Garrison Hearst* .75
12 Cortez Kennedy .50
13 Rick Mirer .50
14 Joe Montana 4.00
15 Jerry Rice 2.50
16 Barry Sanders 2.50
17 Sterling Sharpe 1.50
18 Emmitt Smith 5.00
19 *Robert Smith* .50
20 Thurman Thomas 1.00

1994 Pacific

Crown Collection 1994 Football from Pacific Trading Cards contained 450 cards in the primary set, with three insert sets called Gems of the Crown, Crown Collection Crystalline and Knights of the Gridiron. There were only 7,000 of each insert set produced and a card from one of the three was inserted into each 12-card pack.

MT
Complete Set (450): 28.00
Common Player: .05
Wax Box: 40.00
1 Troy Aikman 1.00
2 Charles Haley .05
3 Alvin Harper .05
4 Michael Irvin .10
5 Jim Jeffcoat .05
6 Daryl Johnston .05
7 Robert Jones .05
8 *Brock Marion* .05
9 Russell Maryland .05
10 Ken Norton .05
11 Jay Novacek .05
12 Emmitt Smith 2.00
13 Kevin Smith .05
14 Tony Tolbert .05
15 Kevin Williams .40
16 Don Beebe .05
17 Cornelius Bennett .05
18 Bill Brooks .05
19 Steve Christie .05
20 Russell Copeland .05
21 Kenneth Davis .05
22 Kent Hull .05
23 Jim Kelly .10
24 Pete Metzelaars .05
25 Andre Reed .05
26 Frank Reich .05
27 Bruce Smith .05
28 Darryl Talley .05
29 Steve Tasker .05
30 Thurman Thomas .10
31 Steve Bono .20
32 Dexter Carter .05
33 Kevin Fagan .05
34 Dana Hall .05
35 Brent Jones .05
36 Amp Lee .05
37 Marc Logan .05
38 Tim McDonald .05
39 Guy McIntyre .05
40 Tom Rathman .05
41 Jerry Rice 1.00
42 Dana Stubblefield .05
43 Steve Wallace .05
44 Ricky Watters .10
45 Steve Young 1.00
46 Marcus Allen .10
47 Kimble Anders .05
48 Tim Barnett .05
49 J.J. Birden .05
50 Dale Carter .05
51 Jonathan Hayes .05
52 Dave Krieg .05
53 Albert Lewis .05
54 Nick Lowery .05
55 Joe Montana 1.00
56 Neil Smith .05
57 John Stephens .05
58 Derrick Thomas .10
59 Harvey Williams .05
60 Michael Barrow .05
61 Gary Brown .05
62 Cody Carlson .05
63 Ray Childress .05
64 Curtis Duncan .05
65 Ernest Givins .05
66 Haywood Jeffires .05
67 Wilber Marshall .05
68 Bubba McDowell .05
69 Warren Moon .05
70 Mike Munchak .05
71 Marcus Robertson .05
72 Webster Slaughter .05
73 *Gary Wellman* .05
74 Lorenzo White .05
75 Ray Crockett .05
76 Jason Hanson .05
77 Rodney Holman .05
78 George Jamison .05
79 Erik Kramer .05
80 Ryan McNeil .05
81 Derrick Moore .05
82 Herman Moore .50
83 Rodney Peete .05
84 Brett Perriman .05
85 Barry Sanders 1.25
86 Chris Spielman .05
87 Pat Swilling .05
88 Vernon Turner .05
89 Andre Ware .05
90 Michael Brooks .05
91 Dave Brown .05
92 Derek Brown .05
93 Jarrod Bunch .05
94 Chris Calloway .05
95 Kent Graham .05
96 Rodney Hampton .10
97 Mark Jackson .05
98 Ed McCaffrey .05
99 Dave Meggett .05
100 Aaron Pierce .05
101 Mike Sherrard .05
102 Phil Simms .05
103 Lewis Tillman .05
104 Eddie Anderson .05
105 Patrick Bates .05
106 Nick Bell .05
107 Tim Brown .10
108 Willie Gault .05
109 Jeff Gossett .05
110 Ethan Horton .05
111 Jeff Hostetler .05
112 Rocket Ismail .05
113 Chester McGlockton .05
114 Anthony Smith .05
115 Steve Smith .05
116 Greg Townsend .05
117 Steve Wisniewski .05
118 Alexander Wright .05
119 Steve Atwater .05
120 Rod Bernstine .05
121 Mike Croel .05
122 Shane Dronett .05
123 Jason Elam .05
124 John Elway .30
125 Brian Habib .05
126 Rondell Jones .05
127 Tommy Maddox .05
128 Karl Mecklenburg .05
129 Glyn Milburn .05
130 Derek Russell .05
131 Shannon Sharpe .05
132 Dennis Smith .05
133 Edgar Bennett .05
134 Tony Bennett .05
135 Robert Brooks .20
136 Terrell Buckley .05
137 LeRoy Butler .05
138 Mark Clayton .05
139 Ty Detmer .05
140 Brett Favre 2.00
141 *John Jurkovic* .10
142 Bryce Paup .05
143 Sterling Sharpe .10
144 George Teague .05
145 Darrell Thompson .05
146 Ed West .05
147 Reggie White .10
148 Terry Allen .05
149 Anthony Carter .05
150 Cris Carter .05
151 Roger Craig .05
152 Jack Del Rio .05
153 Chris Doleman .05
154 *Scottie Graham* .10
155 Eric Guliford .05
156 Qadry Ismail .10
157 Steve Jordan .05
158 Randall McDaniel .05
159 Jim McMahon .05
160 Audray McMillian .05
161 Sean Salisbury .05
162 Robert Smith .25
163 Henry Thomas .05
164 Gary Anderson .05
165 Deon Figures .05
166 Barry Foster .05
167 Jeff Graham .05
168 Kevin Greene .05
169 *Dave Hoffman* .05
170 Merril Hoge .05
171 Gary Jones .05
172 Greg Lloyd .05
173 Ernie Mills .05
174 Neil O'Donnell .10
175 Darren Perry .05
176 Leon Searcy .05
177 Leroy Thompson .05
178 *Willie Williams* .05
179 Rod Woodson .05
180 Keith Byars .05
181 Marco Coleman .05
182 Bryan Cox .05
183 Irving Fryar .05
184 John Grimsley .05
185 Mark Higgs .05
186 Mark Ingram .05
187 Keith Jackson .05
188 Terry Kirby .10
189 Dan Marino 2.00
190 O.J. McDuffie .25
191 Scott Mitchell .10
192 Pete Stoyanovich .05
193 Troy Vincent .05
194 Richmond Webb .05
195 Brad Baxter .05
196 Chris Burkett .05
197 Rob Carpenter .05
198 Boomer Esiason .05
199 Johnny Johnson .05
200 Jeff Lageman .05
201 Mo Lewis .05
202 Ronnie Lott .05
203 Leonard Marshall .05
204 Terance Mathis .05
205 Johnny Mitchell .05
206 Rob Moore .05
207 Anthony Prior .05
208 Blair Thomas .05
209 Brian Washington .05
210 Eric Bieniemy .05
211 Marion Butts .05
212 Gill Byrd .05
213 John Carney .05
214 Darren Carrington .05
215 John Friesz .05
216 Ronnie Harmon .05
217 Stan Humphries .05
218 Nate Lewis .05
219 Natrone Means .25
220 Anthony Miller .05
221 Chris Mims .05
222 Eric Moten .05
223 Leslie O'Neal .05
224 Junior Seau .10
225 Morten Andersen .05
226 Gene Atkins .05
227 Derek Brown .05
228 Toi Cook .05
229 Vaughn Dunbar .05
230 Quinn Early .05
231 Reggie Freeman .05
232 Tyrone Hughes .05
233 Rickey Jackson .05
234 Eric Martin .05
235 Sam Mills .05
236 Brad Muster .05
237 Torrance Small .05
238 Irv Smith .05
239 Wade Wilson .05
240 Eric Allen .05
241 Victor Bailey .05
242 Fred Barnett .05
243 Mark Bavaro .05
244 Bubby Brister .05
245 Randall Cunningham .05
246 Antone Davis .05
247 *Britt Hager* .05
248 Vaughn Hebron .05
249 James Joseph .05
250 Seth Joyner .05
251 Rich Maino .05
252 Heath Sherman .05
253 Clyde Simmons .05
254 Herschel Walker .05
255 Calvin Williams .05
256 Jerry Ball .05
257 Mark Carrier .05
258 Michael Jackson .05
259 Mike Johnson .05
260 James Jones .05
261 Brian Kinchen .05
262 Clay Matthews .05
263 Eric Metcalf .05
264 Stevon Moore .05
265 Michael Dean Perry .05
266 Todd Philcox .05
267 Anthony Pleasant .05
268 Vinny Testaverde .05
269 Eric Turner .05
270 Tommy Vardell .05
271 Neal Anderson .05
272 Trace Armstrong .05
273 Mark Carrier .05
274 Bob Christian .05
275 Curtis Conway .30
276 Richard Dent .05
277 Robert Green .05
278 Jim Harbaugh .05
279 Craig Heyward .05
280 Terry Obee .05
281 Alonzo Spellman .05
282 Tom Waddle .05
283 Peter Tom Willis .05
284 Donnell Woolford .05
285 Tim Worley .05
286 Chris Zorich .05
287 Steve Broussard .05
288 Darion Conner .05
289 James Geathers .05
290 Michael Haynes .05
291 Bobby Hebert .05
292 Lincoln Kennedy .05
293 Chris Miller .05
294 *David Mims* .05
295 Erric Pegram .05
296 Mike Pritchard .05
297 Andre Rison .10
298 Deion Sanders .50
299 Chuck Smith .05
300 Tony Smith .05
301 Johnny Bailey .05
302 Steve Beuerlein .05
303 Chuck Cecil .05
304 Chris Chandler .05
305 Gary Clark .05
306 *Rick Cunningham* .05
307 Ken Harvey .05
308 Garrison Hearst .50
309 Randal Hill .05
310 Robert Massey .05
311 Ron Moore .05
312 Ricky Proehl .05
313 Eric Swann .05
314 Aeneas Williams .05
315 Michael Bates .05
316 Brian Blades .05
317 Carlton Gray .05
318 *Paul Green* .05
319 Patrick Hunter .05
320 John Kasay .05
321 Cortez Kennedy .05
322 Kelvin Martin .05
323 Dan McGwire .05
324 Rick Mirer .30
325 Eugene Robinson .05
326 Rick Tuten .05
327 Chris Warren .15
328 John L. Williams .05
329 Reggie Cobb .05
330 Horace Copeland .05
331 Lawrence Dawsey .05
332 Santana Dotson .05
333 Craig Erickson .05
334 Ron Hall .05
335 Courtney Hawkins .05
336 Keith McCants .05
337 Hardy Nickerson .05
338 *Mazio Royster* .05
339 Broderick Thomas .05
340 *Casey Weldon* .10
341 Mark Wheeler .05
342 Vince Workman .05
343 Willie Anderson .05
344 Jerome Bettis .30
345 *Richard Buchanan* .05
346 Shane Conlan .05
347 Troy Drayton .05
348 Henry Ellard .05
349 Jim Everett .05
350 Cleveland Gary .05
351 Sean Gilbert .05
352 David Lang .05
353 Todd Lyght .05
354 *T.J. Rubley* .05
355 Jackie Slater .05
356 Russell White .05
357 Bruce Armstrong .05
358 Drew Bledsoe 1.00
359 Vincent Brisby .05
360 Vincent Brown .05
361 Ben Coates .10
362 Marv Cook .05
363 *Ray Crittenden* .10
364 *Corey Croom* .05
365 Pat Harlow .05
366 Dion Lambert .05
367 Greg McMurtry .05
368 Leonard Russell .05
369 Scott Secules .05
370 Chris Slade .05
371 Michael Timpson .05
372 Kevin Turner .05
373 Ashley Ambrose .05
374 Dean Biasucci .05
375 Duane Bickett .05
376 Quentin Coryatt .05
377 Rodney Culver .05
378 *Sean Dawkins* .25
379 Jeff George .10
380 Jeff Herrod .05
381 Jessie Hester .05
382 Anthony Johnson .05
383 Reggie Langhorne .05
384 Roosevelt Potts .05
385 *William Schultz* .05
386 Rohn Stark .05
387 Clarence Verdin .05
388 Carl Banks .05
389 Reggie Brooks .10
390 Earnest Byner .05
391 Tom Carter .05
392 Cary Conklin .05
393 *Pat Ellers* .05
394 Ricky Ervins .05
395 Rich Gannon .05
396 Darrell Green .05
397 Desmond Howard .05
398 Chip Lohmiller .05
399 *Sterling Palmer* .05
400 Mark Rypien .05
401 Ricky Sanders .05
402 *Johnny Thomas* .05
403 John Copeland .05
404 Derrick Fenner .05
405 Alex Gordon .05
406 Harold Green .05
407 Lance Gunn .05
408 David Klingler .05
409 Ricardo McDonald .05
410 Tim McGee .05
411 Reggie Rembert .05
412 Patrick Robinson .05
413 Jay Schroeder .05
414 Erik Wilhelm .05
415 Alfred Williams .05
416 Darryl Williams .05
417 *Sam Adams* .10
418 *Mario Bates* .10
419 *James Bostic* .10
420 *Bucky Brooks* .10
421 *Jeff Burris* .10
422 *Shante Carver* .10
423 Jeff Cothran .05
424 *Lake Dawson* .10
425 *Trent Dilfer* 2.00
426 *Marshall Faulk* 4.00
427 *Cory Fleming* .10
428 *William Floyd* .50
429 *Glenn Foley* .75
430 *Rob Fredrickson* .10
431 *Charles Garner* .50
432 *Greg Hill* .50
433 *Charles Johnson* .50
434 *Calvin Jones* .10
435 *Jimmy Klingler* .05
436 *Antonio Langham* .10
437 *Kevin Lee* .10
438 *Chuck Levy* .10
439 *Willie McGinest* .25
440 *Jamir Miller* .10
441 *Johnnie Morton* .30
442 *David Palmer* .25
443 *Errict Rhett* .75
444 *Cory Sawyer* .10
445 *Darnay Scott* 1.00
446 *Heath Shuler* .25
447 *Lamar Smith* .10
448 *Dan Wilkinson* .10
449 *Bernard Williams* .10
450 *Bryant Young* .30

1994 Pacific Crystalline

Crown Collection Crystalline features an action shot of one of the top 20 running backs in the NFL. These cards are made of plastic and have a multi-color pattern on the left half of the card and clear plastic on the right half. The player's name is in the top-left corner, with his position under it and the Pacific Crown Collection logo under it. The player is postioned mostly on the clear side with a small portion of his body located over the pattern. The back features a close-up and stats on the pattern side and the reverse-angle player on the clear.

		MT
Complete Set (20):		80.00
Common Player:		2.00
1	Emmitt Smith	35.00
2	Jerome Bettis	7.00
3	Thurman Thomas	10.00
4	Erric Pegram	2.00
5	Barry Sanders	20.00
6	Leonard Russell	2.00
7	Rodney Hampton	6.00
8	Chris Warren	2.00
9	Reggie Brooks	3.00
10	Ron Moore	2.00
11	Gary Brown	2.00
12	Ricky Watters	6.00
13	Johnny Johnson	2.00
14	Rod Bernstine	2.00
15	Marcus Allen	2.00
16	Leroy Thompson	2.00
17	Marion Butts	2.00
18	Herschel Walker	2.00
19	Barry Foster	6.00
20	Roosevelt Potts	2.00

1994 Pacific Gems of the Crown

Gems of the Crown present a top offensive player on a card with an etched gold foil border. The Pacific logo appears in the bottom-left corner of this 20-card set, with the player name at the bottom in etched gold foil. The back contains a player close-up and a brief statistics, along with "Gems of the Crown" written across the top-right corner and card numbers in the opposite corner.

		MT
Complete Set (36):		140.00
Common Player:		2.00
Minor Stars:		4.00
1	Troy Aikman	10.00
2	Marcus Allen	4.00
3	Jerome Bettis	6.00
4	Drew Bledsoe	10.00
5	Reggie Brooks	2.00
6	Gary Brown	2.00
7	Tim Brown	4.00
8	Cody Carlson	2.00
9	John Elway	8.00
10	Boomer Esiason	2.00
11	Brett Favre	20.00
12	Rodney Hampton	4.00
13	Alvin Harper	2.00
14	Jeff Hostetler	2.00
15	Jim Kelly	4.00
16	Dan Marino	20.00
17	Eric Martin	2.00
18	O.J. McDuffie	2.00
19	Natrone Means	10.00
20	Rick Mirer	4.00
21	Joe Montana	15.00
22	Herman Moore	6.00
23	Ron Moore	2.00
24	Neil O'Donnell	4.00
25	Erric Pegram	2.00
26	Roosevelt Potts	2.00
27	Jerry Rice	10.00
28	Barry Sanders	2.00
29	Shannon Sharpe	2.00
30	Sterling Sharpe	4.00
31	Emmitt Smith	20.00
32	Thurman Thomas	4.00
33	Herschel Walker	2.00
34	Chris Warren	4.00
35	Ricky Watters	4.00
36	Steve Young	10.00

1994 Pacific Knights of the Gridiron

Knights of the Gridiron is a 20-card prism insert that showcases the top rookies and draft picks. Cards show an action-shot of the player with his name at the bottom. His first name is in a color box, depending on his team colors, and his last name is in gold prism and shadowed in a team color. The Pacific logo appears in the top left corner of this shiny gold prism card. The backs show a picture of the player with a large Pacific Crown Collection logo and Knight of the Gridiron, player name and team above the logo.

		MT
Complete Set (20):		130.00
Common Player:		3.00
Minor Stars:		6.00
1	Mario Bates	6.00
2	Jerome Bettis	6.00
3	Drew Bledsoe	16.00
4	Vincent Brisby	3.00
5	Reggie Brooks	3.00
6	Derek Brown	3.00
7	Jeff Burris	3.00
8	Trent Dilfer	6.00
9	Troy Drayton	3.00
10	Marshall Faulk	15.00
11	William Floyd	6.00
12	Rocket Ismail	3.00
13	Terry Kirby	3.00
14	Thomas Lewis	3.00
15	Natrone Means	6.00
16	Rick Mirer	6.00
17	David Palmer	6.00
18	Errict Rhett	6.00
19	Darnay Scott	6.00
20	Heath Shuler	3.00

1994 Pacific Marquee Prisms

These 36 cards, produced in both silver and gold versions, feature several veteran and younger stars of the NFL. Each card front has a player photo superimposed over either a gold or silver foil background. The Crown Collection logo is in the upper left corner; the player's name and position are at the bottom in a marquee banner. The card back has a player photo on the left and a marquee billboard on the right which says "Now Appearing," followed by the player's name, position and team, plus a card number. A gold or silver card was issued in every pack of 1994 Pacific marquee prism, but gold cards were found at a ratio of only two per every box.

		MT
Complete Set (36):		35.00
Common Player:		.50
Minor Stars:		1.00
Complete Gold Set (36):		250.00
Gold Cards:		4x-8x
1	Troy Aikman	3.00
2	Marcus Allen	1.00
3	Jerome Bettis	1.00
4	Drew Bledsoe	3.00
5	Reggie Brooks	.50
6	Dave Brown	.50
7	Ben Coates	.50
8	Reggie Cobb	.50
9	Curtis Conway	1.00
10	John Elway	2.00
11	Marshall Faulk	3.00
12	Brett Favre	5.00
13	Barry Foster	.50
14	Rodney Hampton	1.00
15	Michael Irvin	1.00
16	Terry Kirby	.50
17	Dan Marino	5.00
18	Natrone Means	2.00
19	Rick Mirer	1.00
20	Joe Montana	3.00
21	Warren Moon	1.00
22	Ron Moore	.50
23	David Palmer	.50
24	Errict Rhett	2.00
25	Jerry Rice	3.00
26	Bucky Richardson	.50
27	Barry Sanders	3.00
28	Shannon Sharpe	.50
29	Sterling Sharpe	1.00
30	Heath Shuler	1.00
31	Emmitt Smith	5.00
32	Irving Spikes	.50
33	Thurman Thomas	1.00
34	Chris Warren	1.00
35	Ricky Watters	1.00
36	Steve Young	2.00

1994 Pacific Prisms

This set offers Pacific's splashy design and technology. The cards have full-color fronts and backs and are printed on a heavier card stock. Production is limited to a maximum of 2,999 individually-numbered 20-box cases. Four or five players from each team are represented in the set, which also includes top draft picks. The cards were done in silver versions (only 16,000 of each card were made) and gold versions (1,138 of each card). The borderless card front has an action photo superimposed over a prism-like background. The card back has the same cutout photo as the front, but the background is blurred. Gold versions are generally worth 4 to 7 times the value of the listed prices.

		MT
Complete Set (126):		160.00
Common Player:		.50
Wax Box:		70.00
1	Troy Aikman	10.00
2	Marcus Allen	1.00
3	Morten Andersen	.50
4	Fred Barnett	.50
5	Mario Bates	1.00
6	Edgar Bennett	.50
7	Rod Bernstine	.50
8	Jerome Bettis	3.00
9	Steve Beuerlein	.50
10	Brian Blades	.50
11	Drew Bledsoe	10.00
12	Vincent Brisby	1.00
13	Reggie Brooks	.50
14	Derek Brown	.50
15	Gary Brown	.50
16	Tim Brown	1.00
17	Marion Butts	.50
18	Keith Byars	.50
19	Cody Carlson	.50
20	Anthony Carter	.50
21	Tom Carter	.50
22	Gary Clark	.50
23	Ben Coates	1.00
24	Reggie Cobb	.50
25	Curtis Conway	1.50
26	John Copeland	.50
27	Randall Cunningham	.50
28	Willie Davis	.50
29	Sean Dawkins	1.50
30	Lawrence Dawsey	.50
31	Richard Dent	.50
32	Trent Dilfer	5.00
33	Troy Drayton	.50
34	Vaughn Dunbar	.50
35	Henry Ellard	.50
36	John Elway	5.00
37	Craig Erickson	.50
38	Boomer Esiason	.50
39	Marshall Faulk	10.00
40	Brett Favre	16.00
41	William Floyd	1.50
42	Glenn Foley	1.00
43	Barry Foster	.50
44	Irving Fryar	.50
45	Jeff George	1.00
46	Scottie Graham	1.50
47	Rodney Hampton	.50
48	Jim Harbaugh	.50
49	Alvin Harper	.50
50	Courtney Hawkins	.50
51	Garrison Hearst	3.00
52	Vaughn Hebron	.50
53	Greg Hill	1.50
54	Jeff Hostetler	1.00
55	Michael Irvin	1.50
56	Qadry Ismail	.50
57	Rocket Ismail	.50
58	Anthony Johnson	.50
59	Charles Johnson	1.50
60	Johnny Johnson	.50
61	Brent Jones	.50
62	Kyle Clifton	.50
63	Jim Kelly	1.50
64	Cortez Kennedy	.50
65	Terry Kirby	1.00
66	David Klingler	.50
67	Erik Kramer	.50
68	Reggie Langhorne	.50
69	Chuck Levy	1.00
70	Dan Marino	16.00
71	O.J. McDuffie	1.50
72	Natrone Means	2.00
73	Eric Metcalf	.50
74	Glyn Milburn	.50
75	Anthony Miller	.50
76	Rick Mirer	2.00
77	Johnny Mitchell	.50
78	Scott Mitchell	1.00
79	Joe Montana	10.00
80	Warren Moon	1.00
81	Derrick Moore	.50
82	Herman Moore	4.00
83	Rob Moore	.50
84	Ron Moore	.50
85	Johnnie Morton	3.00
86	Neil O'Donnell	.50
87	David Palmer	1.00
88	Erric Pegram	.50
89	Carl Pickens	2.00
90	Anthony Pleasant	.50
91	Roosevelt Potts	.50
92	Mike Pritchard	.50
93	Andre Reed	1.00
94	Errict Rhett	2.00
95	Jerry Rice	10.00
96	Andre Rison	1.00
97	Greg Robinson	.50
98	T.J. Rubley	.50
99	Leonard Russell	.50
100	Deion Sanders	10.00
101	Deion Sanders	4.00
102	Ricky Sanders	.50
103	Junior Seau	2.00
104	Shannon Sharpe	1.50
105	Sterling Sharpe	1.50
106	Heath Shuler	1.00
107	Phil Simms	.50
108	Webster Slaughter	.50
109	Bruce Smith	.50
110	Emmitt Smith	16.00
111	Irv Smith	.50
112	Robert Smith	2.00
113	Vinny Testaverde	1.00
114	Derrick Thomas	1.00
115	Thurman Thomas	2.00
116	Leroy Thompson	.50
117	Lewis Tillman	.50
118	Michael Timpson	.50
119	Herschel Walker	.50
120	Chris Warren	1.50
121	Ricky Watters	2.00
122	Lorenzo White	.50
123	Reggie White	2.00
124	Dan Wilkinson	1.50
125	Kevin Williams	1.00
126	Steve Young	5.00

1994 Pacific Prisms Gold

The 126-card, regular-sized cards are a parallel to the base prism issue. Only 10 percent of the total print run were produced in gold foil.

	MT
Complete Set (126):	900.00

1994 Pacific Prisms Team Helmets

Each of these prism cards features the helmet of an NFL team on the card front, along with a team history and ghosted helmet on the back. The cards, which are numbered on the back (1 of 30, etc.) were random inserts in 1994 Pacific Prisms foil packs. The card front has a borderless prism-like background.

		MT
Complete Set (30):		2.50
Common Player:		.10
1	Arizona Cardinals	.10
2	Atlanta Falcons	.10
3	Buffalo Bills	.10
4	Carolina Panthers	.10
5	Chicago Bears	.10
6	Cincinnati Bengals	.10
7	Cleveland Browns	.10
8	Dallas Cowboys	.10
9	Denver Broncos	.10
10	Detroit Lions	.10
11	Green Bay Packers	.10
12	Houston Oilers	.10
13	Indianapolis Colts	.10
14	Jacksonville Jaguars	.10
15	Kansas City Chiefs	.10
16	Los Angeles Raiders	.10
17	Los Angeles Rams	.10
18	Miami Dolphins	.10
19	Minnesota Vikings	.10
20	New England Patriots	.10
21	New Orleans Saints	.10
22	New York Giants	.10
23	New York Jets	.10
24	Philadelphia Eagles	.10
25	Pittsburgh Steelers	.10
26	San Diego Chargers	.10
27	San Francisco 49ers	.10
28	Seattle Seahawks	.10
29	Tampa Bay Buccaneers	.10
30	Washington Redskins	.10

1994 Pacific Triple Folders

Each card in the 33-card set measures 3-1/2" x 5" when folded, features color photos on all panels. The front panels can be closed and merged into a single action photo. The set, arranged into alphabetical order by teams, was limited to a production run of less than 3,000.

		MT
Complete Set (33):		20.00
Common Player:		.50
1	Ron Moore	.50
2	Erric Pegram	.50
3	Jim Kelly	.75
4	Thurman Thomas	.75
5	Curtis Conway	1.00
6	Vinny Testaverde	.50
7	Troy Aikman	1.75
8	Emmitt Smith	3.00
9	John Elway	1.00
10	Shannon Sharpe	.50
11	Barry Sanders	1.75
12	Brett Favre	3.00
13	Sterling Sharpe	.75
14	Gary Brown	.50
15	Marshall Faulk	1.50
16	Joe Montana	2.00
17	Rocket Ismail	.75
18	Jerome Bettis	1.00
19	Dan Marino	3.00
20	David Palmer	.50
21	Drew Bledsoe	2.00
22	Ben Coates	.75
23	Derrick Ned	.50
24	Rodney Hampton	.75
25	Boomer Esiason	.50
26	Barry Foster	.50
27	Charles Johnson	.50
28	Natrone Means	1.00
29	Steve Young	1.50
30	Rick Mirer	.75
31	Chris Warren	.75
32	Trent Dilfer	1.00
33	Heath Shuler	1.50

1994 Pacific Triple Folders Rookies/Stars

The 40-card, regular-sized set was randomly inserted in Triple Folder packs. The fronts feature color action shots with the player's name and position in gold-foil on the card bottom.

		MT
Complete Set (40):		20.00
Common Player:		.30
1	Ronald Moore	.30
2	Jeff George	.50
3	Jim Kelly	.50
4	Thurman Thomas	.75
5	Curtis Conway	.75
6	Darnay Scott	.60
7	Vinny Testaverde	.30
8	Troy Aikman	1.50
9	Emmitt Smith	3.00
10	John Elway	1.00
11	Shannon Sharpe	.30
12	Barry Sanders	1.50
13	LeShon Johnson	.30
14	Sterling Sharpe	.50
15	Gary Brown	.30
16	Marshall Faulk	1.50
17	Lake Dawson	.30
18	Greg Hill	.60
19	Joe Montana	2.00
20	Tim Brown	.50
21	Jerome Bettis	.60
22	Dan Marino	3.00
23	Terry Allen	.30
24	David Palmer	.30
25	Drew Bledsoe	1.75
26	Ben Coates	.50
27	Michael Haynes	.30
28	Rodney Hampton	.50
29	Thomas Lewis	.30
30	Aaron Glenn	.30
31	Charlie Garner	.30
32	Charles Johnson	.30
33	Byron "Bam" Morris	.50
34	Natrone Means	.75
35	Ricky Watters	.50
36	Steve Young	1.25
37	Rick Mirer	.60
38	Trent Dilfer	1.00
39	Errict Rhett	2.00
40	Heath Shuler	1.50

1995 Pacific

Pacific's 1995 Crown Collection set includes 450 cards, each using double-etched foil technology and etched gold foil. A 40-card subset features the season's top rookie draft picks. Two parallel sets were also created - a hobby only Royal Platinum Pt and a retail only Techn-Chrome Cr (both sets' cards were randomly included nine per every 37 packs). The regular card design has a gold-foiled panel which includes the player's name and position outlined in his team's colors. A full-bleed color photo is on the right, with the Pacific Crown Collection in the upper right. The card back has the player's name at the top, along with a mug shot, position, biographical information and a brief profile. Complete yearly statistics are also included on the back, which incorporates a team logo and the team's colors into the background. Seven insert sets were produced: Gems of the Crown; Gold Die-Cut Crown; Rookies 95; Young Warriors; G-Force; Hometown Heroes; and Cramer's Choice Awards.

		MT
Complete Set (450):		25.00
Common Player:		.05
Minor Stars:		.10
Wax Box:		50.00
1	Randy Baldwin	.05
2	Tommy Barnhardt	.05
3	Tim McKyer	.05
4	Sam Mills	.05
5	Brian O'Neal	.05
6	Frank Reich	.05
7	Jack Trudeau	.05
8	Vernon Turner	.05
9	*Kerry Collins*	1.00
10	Shawn King	.10
11	Steve Beuerlein	.05
12	Derek Brown	.05
13	Reggie Clark	.10
14	Reggie Cobb	.05
15	Desmond Howard	.05
16	Jeff Lageman	.05
17	Kelvin Pritchett	.05
18	Cedric Tillman	.05
19	*Tony Boselli*	.20
20	*James Stewart*	1.50
21	Eric Davis	.05
22	William Floyd	.30
23	Elvis Grbac	.05
24	Brent Jones	.05
25	Ken Norton Jr.	.05
26	Bart Oates	.05
27	Jerry Rice	.75
28	Deion Sanders	.40
29	John Taylor	.05
30	*Adam Walker*	.10
31	Steve Wallace	.05
32	Ricky Watters	.15
33	Lee Woodall	.05
34	Bryant Young	.05
35	Steve Young	.75
36	J.J. Stokes	1.00
37	Troy Aikman	.50
38	Larry Allen	.05
39	Chris Boniol	.05
40	Lincoln Coleman	.05
41	Charles Haley	.05
42	Alvin Harper	.10
43	Chad Hennings	.05
44	Michael Irvin	.20
45	Daryl Johnston	.05
46	Leon Lett	.05
47	Nate Newton	.05
48	Jay Novacek	.05
49	Emmitt Smith	2.00
50	James Washington	.05
51	Kevin Williams	.05
52	*Sherman Williams*	.30
53	Barry Foster	.05
54	Eric Green	.05
55	Kevin Greene	.05
56	Andre Hastings	.05
57	Charles Johnson	.20
58	Greg Lloyd	.05
59	Ernie Mills	.05
60	Byron "Bam" Morris	.10
61	Neil O'Donnell	.10
62	Darren Perry	.05
63	*Yancey Thigpen*	.50
64	Mike Tomczak	.05
65	John L. Williams	.05
66	Rod Woodson	.05
67	*Mark Bruener*	.50
68	Kordell Stewart	4.00
69	Jeff Brohm	.10
70	Andre Coleman	.05
71	Rueben Davis	.05
72	Dennis Gibson	.05
73	Darrien Gordon	.05
74	Stan Humphries	.15
75	Shawn Jefferson	.05
76	Tony Martin	.05
77	Natrone Means	.40
78	Shannon Mitchell	.10
79	Leslie O'Neal	.05
80	Alfred Pupunu	.05
81	Stanley Richard	.05
82	Junior Seau	.10
83	Mark Seay	.05
84	Derrick Alexander	.05
85	Carl Banks	.05
86	Issac Booth	.10
87	Rob Burnett	.05
88	Earnest Byner	.05
89	Steve Everitt	.05
90	Leroy Hoard	.05
91	Pepper Johnson	.05
92	Antonio Langham	.05
93	Eric Metcalf	.05
94	Anthony Pleasant	.05
95	Frank Stams	.05
96	Vinny Testaverde	.05
97	Eric Turner	.05
98	Mike Miller	.10
99	Craig Powell	.05
100	Gene Atkins	.05
101	Aubrey Beavers	.05
102	Tim Bowens	.05
103	Keith Byars	.05
104	Bryan Cox	.05
105	Aaron Craver	.05
106	Jeff Cross	.05
107	Irving Fryar	.05
108	Dan Marino	2.00
109	O.J. McDuffie	.05
110	Bernie Parmalee	.20
111	James Saxon	.05
112	Keith Sims	.05
113	Irving Spikes	.05
114	Pete Mitchell	.10
115	Terry Allen	.05
116	Cris Carter	.10
117	Adrian Cooper	.05
118	Bernard Dafney	.05
119	Jack Del Rio	.05
120	Vencie Glenn	.05
121	Qadry Ismail	.05
122	Carlos Jenkins	.05
123	Andrew Jordan	.05
124	Ed McDaniel	.05
125	Warren Moon	.10
126	David Palmer	.05
127	John Randle	.05
128	Jake Reed	.05
129	Derrick Alexander	.15
130	*Chad May*	.30
131	Korey Stringer	.10
132	Bruce Armstrong	.05
133	Drew Bledsoe	1.00
134	Vincent Brisby	.05
135	Troy Brown	.10
136	Vincent Brown	.05
137	Marion Butts	.05
138	Ben Coates	.05
139	Ray Crittenden	.05
140	Maurice Hurst	.05
141	Aaron Jones	.05
142	Willie McGinest	.05
143	Marty Moore	.10
144	Mike Pitts	.05
145	Leroy Thompson	.05
146	Michael Timpson	.05
147	Bennie Blades	.05
148	Jocelyn Borgella	.05
149	Anthony Carter	.05
150	Willie Clay	.05
151	Mel Gray	.05
152	Mike Johnson	.05
153	Dave Kreig	.05
154	Robert Massey	.05
155	Scott Mitchell	.10
156	Herman Moore	.10
157	Johnnie Morton	.05
158	Barry Sanders	1.25
159	Chris Spielman	.05
160	Broderick Thomas	.05
161	Cory Schlesinger	.05
162	Marcus Allen	.10
163	Donnell Bennett	.05
164	J.J. Birden	.05
165	Matt Blundin	.05
166	Steve Bono	.15
167	Dale Carter	.05
168	Lake Dawson	.20
169	Ron Dickerson	.05
170	Lin Elliott	.05
171	Jaime Fields	.05
172	Greg Hill	.20
173	Danan Hughes	.05
174	Neil Smith	.05
175	*Steve Stenstrom*	.20
176	Edgar Bennett	.05
177	Robert Brooks	.05
178	Mark Brunell	.75
179	Doug Evans	.05
180	Brett Favre	2.00
181	Corey Harris	.05
182	LeShon Johnson	.05
183	Sean Jones	.05
184	Lenny McGill	.10
185	Terry Mickens	.05
186	Sterling Sharpe	.10
187	Joe Sims	.05
188	Darrell Thompson	.05
189	Reggie White	.10
190	Craig Newsome	.15
191	Tim Brown	.10
192	Vince Evans	.05
193	Rob Fredrickson	.05
194	*Andrew Glover*	.10
195	Jeff Hostetler	.05
196	Raghib Ismail	.05
197	Jeff Jaeger	.05
198	James Jett	.05
199	Chester McGlockton	.05
200	Don Mosebar	.05
201	Tom Rathman	.05
202	Harvey Williams	.05
203	Steve Wisniewski	.05
204	Alexander Wright	.05
205	*Napoleon Kaufman*	2.00
206	Trace Armstrong	.05
207	Curtis Conway	.05
208	Raymont Harris	.05
209	Erik Kramer	.05
210	Nate Lewis	.05
211	*Shane Matthews*	2.00
212	John Thierry	.05
213	Lewis Tillman	.05
214	Tom Waddle	.05
215	Steve Walsh	.05
216	James Williams	.05
217	Donnell Woolford	.05
218	Chris Zorich	.05
219	*Rashaan Salaam*	.50
220	John Booty	.05
221	Michael Brooks	.05
222	Dave Brown	.05
223	Chris Calloway	.05
224	Gary Downs	.10
225	Kent Graham	.05
226	Keith Hamilton	.05
227	Rodney Hampton	.05
228	Brian Kozlowski	.15
229	Thomas Lewis	.05
230	Dave Meggett	.05
231	Aaron Pierce	.05
232	Mike Sherrard	.05
233	Phillippi Sparks	.05
234	*Tyrone Wheatley*	.40
235	Trev Alberts	.05
236	Aaron Bailey	.05
237	Jason Belser	.05
238	Tony Bennett	.05
239	Kerry Cash	.05
240	Marshall Faulk	1.00
241	Stephen Grant	.10
242	Jeff Herrod	.05
243	Ronald Humphrey	.10
244	Kirk Lowdermilk	.05
245	Don Majkowski	.05
246	Tony McCoy	.05
247	Floyd Turner	.05
248	Lamont Warren	.05
249	Zack Crockett	.05
250	Michael Bankston	.05
251	Larry Centers	.05
252	Gary Clark	.05
253	Ed Cunningham	.05
254	Garrison Hearst	.05
255	Eric Hill	.05
256	Terry Irving	.05
257	Lorenzo Lynch	.05
258	Jamir Miller	.05
259	Ron Moore	.05
260	Terry Samuels	.10
261	Jay Schroeder	.05
262	Eric Swann	.05
263	Aeneas Williams	.05
264	*Frank Sanders*	.75
265	Morten Andersen	.20
266	Mario Bates	.20
267	Derek Brown	.05
268	Darion Conner	.05
269	Quinn Early	.05
270	Jim Everett	.05
271	Michael Haynes	.05
272	Wayne Martin	.05
273	Derrell Mitchell	.05
274	Lorenzo Neal	.05
275	Jimmy Spencer	.05
276	Winfred Tubbs	.05
277	Renaldo Turnbull	.05
278	Jeff Uhlenhake	.05
279	Steve Atwater	.05
280	Keith Burns	.05
281	Butler By'not'e	.15
282	Jeff Campbell	.05
283	Derrick Clark	.10
284	Shane Dronett	.05
285	Jason Elam	.05
286	John Elway	.30
287	Jerry Evans	.10
288	Karl Mecklenburg	.05
289	Glyn Milburn	.05
290	Anthony Miller	.05
291	Tom Rouen	.05
292	Leonard Russell	.05
293	Shannon Sharpe	.05
294	Steve Russ	.10
295	Mel Agee	.05
296	Lester Archambeau	.05
297	Bert Emanuel	.20
298	Jeff George	.10
299	Craig Heyward	.05
300	Bobby Hebert	.05
301	D.J. Johnson	.05
302	Mike Kenn	.05
303	Terance Mathis	.05
304	Clay Matthews	.05
305	Erric Pegram	.05
306	Andre Rison	.05
307	Chuck Smith	.05
308	Jessie Tuggle	.05
309	Lorenzo Styles	.05
310	Cornelius Bennett	.05
311	Bill Brooks	.05
312	Jeff Burris	.05
313	Carwell Gardner	.05
314	Kent Hull	.05
315	Yonel Jourdain	.15
316	Jim Kelly	.05
317	Vince Marrow	.05
318	Pete Metzelaars	.05
319	Andre Reed	.05
320	Kurt Schulz	.05
321	Bruce Smith	.05
322	Darryl Talley	.05
323	Matt Darby	.05
324	Justin Armour	.10
325	*Todd Collins*	.30
326	David Alexander	.05
327	Eric Allen	.05
328	Fred Barnett	.05
329	Randall Cunningham	.05
330	William Fuller	.05
331	Charlie Garner	.05
332	Vaughn Hebron	.05
333	James Joseph	.05
334	Bill Romanowski	.05
335	Ken Rose	.05
336	Jeff Snyder	.05
337	William Thomas	.05
338	Herschel Walker	.05
339	Calvin Williams	.05
340	*Dave Barr*	.25
341	Chidi Ahanotu	.05
342	Barney Bussey	.05
343	Horace Copeland	.05
344	Trent Dilfer	.40
345	Craig Erickson	.05
346	Paul Gruber	.05
347	Courtney Hawkins	.05
348	Lonnie Marts	.05
349	Martin Mayhew	.05
350	Hardy Nickerson	.05
351	Errict Rhett	.50
352	Lamar Thomas	.05
353	Charles Wilson	.05
354	Vince Workman	.05
355	Derrick Brooks	.20
356	*Warren Sapp*	.30
357	Sam Adams	.05
358	Michael Bates	.05
359	Brian Blades	.05
360	Carlton Gray	.05
361	Bill Hitchcock	.05
362	Cortez Kennedy	.05
363	Rick Mirer	.30
364	Eugene Robinson	.05
365	Michael Sinclair	.05
366	Steve Smith	.05
367	Bob Spitulski	.05
368	Rick Tuten	.05
369	Chris Warren	.10
370	Terrence Warren	.05
371	*Christian Fauria*	.10
372	*Joey Galloway*	2.00
373	Boomer Esiason	.05
374	Aaron Glenn	.05
375	Victor Green	.10
376	Johnny Johnson	.05
377	Mo Lewis	.05
378	Ronnie Lott	.05
379	Nick Lowery	.05
380	Johnny Mitchell	.05
381	Rob Moore	.05
382	Adrian Murrell	.05
383	Anthony Prior	.05
384	Brian Washington	.05
385	Matt Willig	.05
386	*Kyle Brady*	.25
387	Willie Anderson	.05
388	Johnny Bailey	.05
389	Jerome Bettis	.25
390	Isaac Bruce	.30
391	Shane Conlan	.05
392	Troy Drayton	.05
393	D'Marco Farr	.05
394	Jessie Hester	.05
395	Todd Kinchen	.05
396	Ron Middleton	.05
397	Chris Miller	.05
398	Marquez Pope	.05
399	Robert Young	.05
400	Tony Zendejas	.05
401	*Kevin Carter*	.20
402	Reggie Brooks	.05
403	Tom Carter	.05
404	Andre Collins	.05
405	Pat Eilers	.05
406	Henry Ellard	.05
407	Ricky Ervins	.05
408	Gus Frerotte	.25
409	Ken Harvey	.05
410	Jim Lachey	.05
411	Brian Mitchell	.05
412	Reggie Roby	.05
413	Heath Shuler	.50
414	Tyrone Stowe	.05
415	Tydus Winans	.05
416	Cory Raymer	.05
417	*Michael Westbrook*	1.00
418	*Jeff Blake*	.50
419	Steve Broussard	.05
420	Dave Cadigan	.05
421	Jeff Cothran	.05
422	Derrick Fenner	.05
423	James Francis	.05
424	Lee Johnson	.05
425	Louis Oliver	.05
426	Carl Pickens	.20
427	Jeff Query	.05
428	Corey Sawyer	.05
429	Darnay Scott	.30
430	Dan Wilkinson	.05
431	Alfred Williams	.05
432	*Ki-Jana Carter*	.50
433	David Dunn	.15
434	*John Walsh*	.25
435	Gary Brown	.05
436	Pat Carter	.05
437	Ray Childress	.05
438	Ernest Givins	.05
439	Haywood Jeffires	.05
440	Lamar Lathon	.05
441	Bruce Matthews	.05
442	Marcus Robertson	.05
443	Eddie Robinson	.05
444	*Malcolm Seabron*	.10
445	Webster Slaughter	.05
446	Al Smith	.05
447	Billy Joe Tolliver	.05
448	Lorenzo White	.05
449	*Steve McNair*	3.00
450	*Rodney Thomas*	.20

1995 Pacific Blue/Platinum

The two, 450-card card parallel sets were inserted every 37 packs (blue in retail, platinum in hobby).

	MT
Complete Set (45):	225.00
Common Player:	.30
Veteran Stars:	3x-6x
Young Stars:	2x-4x
RCs:	1.5x-3x

1995 Pacific Cramer's Choice

These 1995 Pacific Crown Collection inserts feature six top NFL players in six different categories, as selected by Pacific President and CEO Michael Cramer. The die-cut cards, done in a trophy design, were seeded one per every 720 packs. The front has a marble-like base which includes the Crown logo and designation of the award, plus who won it. The player photo appears in the middle of the metallic silver pyramid design, with another Crown Collection logo at the top of the point. The card back is marble-like, with an extensive quote from Cramer about the player. A small closeup shot is also provided, as is a card number, which uses a "CC" prefix.

		MT
Complete Set (6):		750.00
Common Player:		50.00
1	Ki-Jana Carter	50.00
2	Emmitt Smith	200.00
3	Marshall Faulk	75.00
4	Jerry Rice	125.00
5	Deion Sanders	75.00
6	Steve Young	125.00

1995 Pacific Gems of the Crown

These 36 insert cards feature a color photo on the front, etched by a gold frame. The Pacific Crown Collection logo is in the upper right corner; the player's name is in the bottom right corner, with gold foil outlining the letters. The horizontal back has a closeup shot of the player on the left, with his name, position and team name underneath. On the right is a paragraph summarizing the player's career, plus an insert set logo and a card number (using a GC prefix). Cards were random inserts, two per every 37 packs of 1995 Pacific Crown Collection football.

		MT
Complete Set (36):		180.00
Common Player:		3.00
1	Jim Kelly	5.00
2	Kerry Collins	6.00
3	Darnay Scott	3.00
4	Jeff Blake	6.00
5	Terry Allen	3.00
6	Emmitt Smith	16.00
7	Michael Irvin	5.00
8	Troy Aikman	10.00
9	John Elway	7.00
10	Dave Krieg	3.00
11	Barry Sanders	15.00
12	Brett Favre	16.00
13	Marshall Faulk	8.00
14	Marcus Allen	5.00
15	Tim Brown	3.00
16	Bernie Parmalee	3.00
17	Dan Marino	16.00
18	Cris Carter	5.00
19	Drew Bledsoe	10.00
20	Mario Bates	3.00
21	Rodney Hampton	3.00
22	Ben Coates	3.00
23	Charles Johnson	5.00
24	Byron "Bam" Morris	5.00
25	Stan Humphries	3.00
26	Deion Sanders	6.00
27	Jerry Rice	10.00
28	Ricky Watters	5.00
29	Steve Young	10.00
30	Natrone Means	6.00
31	William Floyd	5.00
32	Chris Warren	5.00
33	Rick Mirer	5.00
34	Jerome Bettis	5.00
35	Errict Rhett	3.00
36	Heath Shuler	5.00

1995 Pacific G-Force

Ten of the NFL's top running backs are featured on these insert cards, randomly included one per every 37 packs of Pacific's 1995 Crown Collection football. The card front has a color photo of the player against a black background which includes several starbursts, plus the number of yards he gained rushing in 1994. "G-Force" is written at the top of the card; the player's name is at the bottom. The card back has a similar design for the background, with a closeup shot of the player in the upper right corner. His name, team and card number, using a "GF" prefix, are to the left of the photo. A paragraph recapping the player's 1994 accomplishments is featured in the middle of the card.

	MT
Complete Set (10):	45.00
Common Player:	2.00
1 Marcus Allen	3.00
2 Terry Allen	2.00
3 Emmitt Smith	12.00
4 Barry Sanders	10.00
5 Marshall Faulk	6.00
6 Rodney Hampton	2.00
7 Natrone Means	3.00
8 Chris Warren	3.00
9 Jerome Bettis	3.00
10 Errict Rhett	2.00

1995 Pacific Gold Crown Die-Cuts

These 36 insert cards could be randomly found two per every 37 packs of 1995 Pacific Crown Collection football. The cards, numbered on the back using a "DC" prefix, feature a full-bleed color action photo on the front, with a die-cut foiled crown at the top. The player's name is at the bottom in foil.

	MT
Complete Set (20):	375.00
Common Player:	7.00
Comp. Flat Gold Set (20):	700.00
Flat Gold Cards:	1x-2x
1 Ki-Jana Carter	7.00
2 Michael Irvin	7.00
3 Emmitt Smith	50.00
4 Troy Aikman	25.00
5 John Elway	15.00
6 Barry Sanders	35.00
7 Marshall Faulk	25.00
8 Dan Marino	50.00
9 Ben Coates	7.00
10 Drew Bledsoe	25.00
11 Byron "Bam" Morris	7.00
12 Jerry Rice	25.00
13 William Floyd	7.00
14 Steve Young	25.00
15 Natrone Means	10.00
16 Deion Sanders	16.00
17 Rick Mirer	7.00
18 Chris Warren	7.00
19 Jerome Bettis	7.00
20 Errict Rhett	7.00

1995 Pacific Hometown Heroes

These insert cards feature 10 top NFL stars and pay tribute to the players' hometown. Each

card front has a color photo of the player, with his hometown's state flag flying on the left side. His name and "Hometown Hereos" are written in foil at the bottom of the card. The horizontal card back has two photos - one a close-up, the other an action photo of the player framed by the borders of his state. A star is used to pinpoint his city's location on the map. A banner at the top of the card includes the insert set's name, with a recap of where the player started his football career. Cards, randomly included one per every 37 packs of Pacific Crown Collection football, are numbered with an "HH" prefix.

	MT
Complete Set (10):	50.00
Common Player:	3.00
1 Emmitt Smith	12.00
2 Troy Aikman	6.00
3 Barry Sanders	6.00
4 Marshall Faulk	3.00
5 Dan Marino	12.00
6 Drew Bledsoe	6.00
7 Natrone Means	3.00
8 Steve Young	6.00
9 Jerry Rice	6.00
10 Errict Rhett	3.00

1995 Pacific Rookies

Inserted into 1995 Pacific Crown Collection football packs at a rate of two per every 37 packs, these 20 cards feature top rookies of 1995. The card front has a color photo of the player in his college uniform, with his name in silver foil running down the left side. "Rookies '95" is also written along the side. A football helmet of the team which drafted the player is in the lower right corner. The card back has another photo of the player in the upper left, with his pro team's helmet on the right. The player's name runs across the center of the card, just above a paragraph which summarizes his skills.

	MT
Complete Set (20):	50.00
Common Player:	2.00
1 Dave Barr	2.00
2 Kyle Brady	2.00
3 Mark Bruener	2.00
4 Ki-Jana Carter	2.00
5 Kerry Collins	5.00
6 Todd Collins	2.00
7 Christian Fauria	2.00
8 Joey Galloway	3.00
9 Chris Jones	2.00
10 Napoleon Kaufman	5.00
11 Chad May	2.00
12 Steve McNair	6.00
13 Rashaan Salaam	2.00
14 Warren Sapp	3.00
15 James Stewart	3.00
16 Kordell Stewart	8.00
17 J.J. Stokes	2.00
18 Michael Westbrook	2.00
19 Tyrone Wheatley	2.00
20 Sherman Williams	2.00

Values quoted in this guide reflect the retail price of a card — the price a collector can expect to pay when buying a card from a dealer. The wholesale price — that which a collector can expect to receive from a dealer when selling cards — will be significantly lower, depending on desirability and condition.

1995 Pacific Young Warriors

Twenty of the NFL's top second-year stars are featured on these 1995 Pacific Crown Collection inserts. The card front is full gold foil, with "Young Warrior" written down the right side of the card. The Pacific logo is in the upper left corner; the player's name is at the bottom in his team's colors. The back has two pillars, with the insert set name and the player's team name inside at the top. His name is at the very top of the card. Between the two pillars is an image of the player in action. A brief 1994 recap is also given, below the image.

	MT
Complete Set (20):	35.00
Common Player:	2.00
Minor Stars:	3.00
1 Bert Emanuel	3.00
2 Darnay Scott	3.00
3 Dan Wilkinson	2.00
4 Derrick Alexander	2.00
5 Willie McGinest	2.00
6 Marshall Faulk	10.00
7 Lake Dawson	3.00
8 Greg Hill	3.00
9 Tim Bowens	2.00
10 David Palmer	2.00
11 Aaron Glenn	2.00
12 Mario Bates	3.00
13 Charles Johnson	3.00
14 Byron "Bam" Morris	3.00
15 William Floyd	2.00
16 Adam Walker	2.00
17 Bryant Young	3.00
18 Trent Dilfer	3.00
19 Errict Rhett	3.00
20 Heath Shuler	6.00

1995 Pacific Crown Royale

Pacific's 1995 Crown Collection II Crown Royale football set features a hobby first - all cards are die-cut. The horizontal card front has a die-cut crown at the top in gold foil, which is also used for the player's name and position at the bottom. A team helmet also appears at the bottom in the lower right corner. The card back has another color photo of the player, along with a recap of his 1994 season. Hobby and retail versions of Crown Royale were produced. Two distinct parallel sets exist, with distinguishing foils for both hobby and retail versions, and are seeded four per every 25 packs. Three insert sets were created - Pro Bowl Die-Cut, Pride of the NFL and Cramer's Choice Awards.

	MT
Complete Set (144):	150.00

Common Player:	.50
Minor Stars:	1.00
Wax Box:	125.00
1 Lake Dawson	1.00
2 Steve Beuerlein	.50
3 Jake Reed	.50
4 Jim Everett	.50
5 Sean Dawkins	.50
6 Jeff Hostetler	.50
7 Marshall Faulk	4.00
8 *Jeff Blake*	3.00
9 Dave Brown	.50
10 Frank Reich	.50
11 Raghib Ismail	.50
12 Jerry Jones	4.00
13 Dan Marino	10.00
14 Ricky Watters	1.00
15 Herman Moore	1.50
16 Daryl Johnston	.50
17 Craig Erickson	.50
18 Alexander Wright	.50
19 Reggie White	1.00
20 Andre Rison	.50
21 Fred Barnett	.50
22 *Tyrone Wheatley*	2.00
23 Charles Johnson	1.00
24 *Rashaan Salaam*	3.00
25 Mark Brunell	5.00
26 Derek Loville	.50
27 Garrison Hearst	1.00
28 Ken Norton Jr.	.50
29 Kerry Collins	5.00
30 Isaac Bruce	2.00
31 Andre Reed	.50
32 Leon Lett	.50
33 Deion Sanders	4.00
34 Terance Mathis	.50
35 Tim Bowens	.50
36 Shannon Sharpe	.50
37 Quinn Early	.50
38 Jerry Rice	5.00
39 Bruce Smith	.50
40 Drew Bledsoe	5.00
41 Alvin Harper	.50
42 Jim Kelly	.50
43 *Napoleon Kaufman*	10.00
44 Errict Rhett	1.00
45 Henry Ellard	.50
46 Barry Sanders	7.00
47 Vincent Brisby	.50
48 Chris Zorich	.50
49 Zack Crockett	.50
50 Haywood Jeffires	.50
51 Byron "Bam" Morris	1.00
52 John Kasay	.50
53 Scott Mitchell	.50
54 Boomer Esiason	.50
55 Eric Metcalf	.50
56 Kevin Greene	.50
57 Courtney Hawkins	.50
58 Adrian Murrell	.50
59 Larry Centers	.50
60 Leroy Hoard	.50
61 Lorenzo White	.50
62 Chris Spielman	.50
63 Carl Pickens	1.50
64 Steve Young	5.00
65 Trent Dilfer	1.00
66 Eric Kramer	.50
67 Cortez Kennedy	.50
68 Ray Childress	.50
69 Rick Mirer	1.00
70 Kevin Williams	.50
71 *Joey Galloway*	10.00
72 Dan Wilkinson	.50
73 *Antonio Freeman*	15.00
74 Curtis Conway	1.00
75 Troy Aikman	5.00
76 Natrone Means	1.00
77 Jeff George	1.00
78 *Curtis Martin*	12.00
79 William Floyd	1.00
80 Anthony Miller	.50
81 Greg Hill	1.00
82 Craig Heyward	.50
83 Brian Mitchell	.50
84 Anthony Carter	.50
85 Jerome Bettis	1.00
86 Jim Harbaugh	.50
87 Harvey Williams	.50
88 Tony Martin	.50
89 Rob Moore	.50
90 Neil O'Donnell	.50
91 Cris Carter	.50
92 *Warren Sapp*	1.00
93 Terry Allen	1.00
94 Michael Irvin	1.00
95 Heath Shuler	2.00
96 Cornelius Bennett	.50
97 Randy Baldwin	.50
98 Vince Workman	.50
99 Irving Fryar	.50
100 Randall Cunningham	.50
101 *James Stewart*	6.00
102 Stan Humphries	.50
103 Mario Bates	1.50
104 Ben Coates	.50
105 Charlie Garner	.50
106 *Todd Collins*	1.00
107 Tim Brown	1.00
108 Edgar Bennett	.50
109 *J.J. Stokes*	3.00
110 Michael Timpson	.50
111 Junior Seau	.50
112 Bernie Parmalee	1.00
113 Willie McGinest	.50
114 David Dunn	.50
115 *Kyle Brady*	1.50
116 Vinny Testaverde	.50
117 Ernest Givins	.50
118 *Eric Zeier*	2.00
119 Michael Jackson	.50
120 *Chad May*	1.00
121 Dave Krieg	.50
122 Rodney Hampton	.50
123 Darnay Scott	2.00
124 Chris Miller	.50
125 Emmitt Smith	8.00
126 *Steve McNair*	12.00
127 Warren Moon	.50
128 Robert Brooks	1.50
129 Bert Emanuel	1.50
130 John Elway	2.00
131 Chris Warren	1.00
132 Herschel Walker	.50
133 Terry Kirby	.50
134 *Michael Westbrook*	4.00
135 *Kordell Stewart*	15.00
136 *Terrell Davis*	25.00
137 Desmond Howard	.50
138 *Rodney Thomas*	1.00
139 Brett Favre	10.00
140 *Ray Zellars*	1.00
141 Marcus Allen	1.00
142 Gus Frerotte	2.00
143 Steve Bono	1.00
144 Aaron Craver	.50

1995 Pacific Crown Royale Blue Holofoil

The 144-card, regular-size set was inserted into retail packs with the fronts having blue holographic background rather than gold-foil backgrounds.

	MT
Complete Set (144):	850.00
Common Player:	3.00
Veteran Stars:	3.5x-7x
Young Stars:	2.5x-5x
RCs:	2x-4x

1995 Pacific Crown Royale Copper

The 144-card, regular-sized parallel set was randomly inserted in hobby packs and features copper foil instead of gold foil on the die-cut crown.

	MT
Complete Set (144):	700.00
Common Player:	2.00
Veteran Stars:	2.5x-5x
Young Stars:	2x-4x
RCs:	1.5x-3x

1995 Pacific Crown Royale Cramer's Choice Jumbos

These six cards are similar to their 1995 Pacific counterparts, except they are oversized, in a new foil format. One player is also different; Rashaan Salaam replaces Ki-Jana Carter in the set. The cards are included one per every 16 boxes of Crown Royale football product and represent Mike Cramer's top picks in offensive and defensive categories. Cramer is Pacific's CEO and president. The cards are numbered and have a "CC" prefix.

	MT
Complete Set (6):	550.00

Common Player:	50.00
1 Rashaan Salaam	50.00
2 Emmitt Smith	140.00
3 Marshall Faulk	80.00
4 Jerry Rice	90.00
5 Deion Sanders	50.00
6 Steve Young	80.00

1995 Pacific Crown Royale Pride of the NFL

This set represents 36 of the NFL's top players, using a new foil wave design on the card front. The card back is numbered using a "PN" prefix. Cards were random inserts in three of every 25 packs.

	MT
Complete Set (36):	325.00
Common Player:	5.00
1 Jim Kelly	5.00
2 Kerry Collins	18.00
3 Darnay Scott	5.00
4 Jeff Blake	15.00
5 Terry Allen	5.00
6 Emmitt Smith	35.00
7 Michael Irvin	5.00
8 Troy Aikman	20.00
9 John Elway	15.00
10 Napoleon Kaufman	10.00
11 Barry Sanders	20.00
12 Brett Favre	35.00
13 Michael Westbrook	5.00
14 Marcus Allen	5.00
15 Tim Brown	5.00
16 Bernie Parmalee	5.00
17 Dan Marino	35.00
18 Cris Carter	5.00
19 Drew Bledsoe	17.00
20 Mario Bates	5.00
21 Rodney Hampton	5.00
22 Ben Coates	5.00
23 Charles Johnson	5.00
24 Bam Morris	5.00
25 Stan Humphries	5.00
26 Rashaan Salaam	5.00
27 Jerry Rice	17.00
28 Ricky Watters	5.00
29 Steve Young	17.00
30 Natrone Means	5.00
31 William Floyd	5.00
32 Chris Warren	5.00
33 Rick Mirer	5.00
34 Jerome Bettis	8.00
35 Errict Rhett	5.00
36 Heath Shuler	10.00

1995 Pacific Crown Royale Pro Bowl Die Cuts

These 1995 Pacific Crown Royale die-cut cards feature 20 players who participated in the 1995 Pro Bowl game, played in Honolulu, Hawaii. Thus, a palm tree foiled die-cut design is used, and the Pro Bowl logo is displayed on each card. Cards were random inserts, one per every 25 packs. The cards are numbered with the "PB" prefix.

		MT
Complete Set (20):		700.00
Common Player:		15.00
1	Drew Bledsoe	50.00
2	Ben Coates	15.00
3	John Elway	40.00
4	Marshall Faulk	50.00
5	Dan Marino	120.00
6	Natrone Means	20.00
7	Junior Seau	15.00
8	Chris Warren	15.00
9	Rod Woodson	15.00
10	Tim Brown	15.00
11	Troy Aikman	50.00
12	Jerome Bettis	15.00
13	Michael Irvin	15.00
14	Jerry Rice	50.00
15	Barry Sanders	90.00
16	Deion Sanders	40.00
17	Emmitt Smith	120.00
18	Steve Young	40.00
19	Reggie White	15.00
20	Cris Carter	15.00

1995 Pacific Gridiron

These 3-1/2" x 5" oversized cards capture the NFL's toughest players in their most aggressive and powerful moments on the field. The card front features a full-bleed color photo. The card back details the play on the front in a newspaper-style article and includes a closeup shot of the player. Only 1,500 cases of Pacific's Gridiron were produced. There were 750 hobby cases produced, with each card stamped with blue foil for the player's name on the front. There were also 750 retail cases produced; these cards are stamped with red foil. Each of these sets will also have a "Presidential Series" parallel set, too. The hobby parallel set will be stamped in platinum foil and represent 10 percent of the sets produced. The retail parallel set is stamped in copper foil and represents 10 percent of the sets produced.

		MT
Complete Set (100):		110.00
Common Player:		1.00
Wax Box:		50.00
1	Natrone Means	3.00
2	Dave Meggett	1.00
3	Curtis Conway	1.00
4	Sam Adams	1.00
5	Quadry Ismail	1.00
6	Steve Young	4.00
7	Errict Rhett	5.00
8	Nate Lewis	1.00
9	Barry Sanders	4.00
10	Sterling Sharpe	1.00
11	Steve Beuerlein	1.00
12	Irving Spikes	1.00
13	Byron "Bam" Morris	1.00
14	Eric Metcalf	1.00
15	Michael Irvin	2.00
16	Dan Marino	8.00
17	Stan Humphries	1.00
18	Leroy Hoard	1.00
19	Marcus Allen	1.00
20	Barry Foster	1.00
21	Rob Moore	1.00
22	Rodney Hampton	1.00
23	Ben Coates	1.00
24	Vernon Turner	1.00
25	Shannon Sharpe	1.00
26	Larry Centers	1.00
27	Mack Strong	1.00
28	Reggie White	1.00
29	Harvey Williams	1.00
30	Darnay Scott	2.00
31	Drew Bledsoe	4.00
32	Marshall Faulk	4.00
33	Troy Aikman	4.00
34	Boomer Esiason	1.00
35	Bobby Hebert	1.00
36	Brian Mitchell	1.00
37	Andre Rison	1.00
38	Brett Favre	8.00
39	Don Majkowski	1.00
40	Johnny Johnson	1.00
41	Mark Carrier	1.00
42	James Joseph	1.00
43	Mario Bates	2.00
44	Craig Heyward	1.00
45	Henry Ellard	1.00
46	Thurman Thomas	2.00
47	Jerome Bettis	2.00
48	Dave Brown	1.00
49	Lorenzo White	1.00
50	Joe Montana	5.00
51	Vinny Testaverde	1.00
52	Lake Dawson	2.00
53	Michael Timpson	1.00
54	Ricky Ervins	1.00
55	Cris Carter	1.00
56	Raymont Harris	2.00
57	Andre Coleman	1.00
58	Craig Erickson	1.00
59	Jeff Hostetler	1.00
60	Deion Sanders	2.00
61	Eric Turner	1.00
62	Darryl Johnston	1.00
63	Bernie Parmalee	1.00
64	Ricky Watters	1.00
65	David Palmer	1.00
66	Aaron Glenn	1.00
67	Todd Kinchen	1.00
68	Edgar Bennett	1.00
69	Mel Gray	1.00
70	Randall Cunningham	1.00
71	Michael Haynes	1.00
72	Chris Miller	1.00
73	Glyn Milburn	1.00
74	Steve McNair	7.00
75	Lewis Tillman	1.00
76	Chuck Levy	1.00
77	Carl Pickens	1.00
78	Michael Bates	1.00
79	Jeff Blake	2.00
80	O.J. McDuffie	1.00
81	Tim Brown	1.00
82	Haywood Jeffires	1.00
83	Jeff Burris	1.00
84	John Elway	4.00
85	Charles Johnson	2.00
86	Emmitt Smith	8.00
87	William Floyd	2.00
88	Herschel Walker	1.00
89	Rick Mirer	3.00
90	Roosevelt Potts	1.00
91	Rod Woodson	2.00
92	Greg Hill	1.00
93	Junior Seau	1.00
94	Dave Krieg	1.00
95	Jim Kelly	1.00
96	Warren Moon	1.00
97	Leroy Thompson	1.00
98	Ki-Jana Carter	5.00
99	Herman Moore	2.00
100	Jerry Rice	4.00

1995 Pacific Gridiron Copper/Platinum

The 100-card, regular-size parallel set featured copper/platinum foil rather than the blue foil. Only 10 percent of the sets produced were copper/platinum.

	MT
Complete Set (100):	800.00
Common Player:	4.00
Veteran Stars:	4x-8x
Young Stars:	3x-6x
RCs:	2x-4x

1995 Pacific Gridiron Gold

The 100-card, regular-sized parallel set features gold foil on the card front instead of red foil. Of the sets produced, only 10 percent were gold foil.

	MT
Common Player (100):	50.00
Semistars:	100.00
Veteran Stars:	75x-130x
Young Stars/RCs:	50x-90x

> Post-1980 cards in Near Mint condition will generally sell for about 75% of the quoted Mint value. Excellent-condition cards bring no more than 40%.

1995 Pacific Prisms

Pacific released its 1995 set in two 108-card series, with each of the 216 cards reprinted in a parallel Gold Prism set (one every 30 Series I packs, two every 37 Series II packs). Each card front has an action photo on the left, along with the player's name in silver foil. A closeup shot appears on the right side of the horizontally-designed card. The back has another action photo of the player against a backdrop with a photo of his team's helmet. A few career accomplishment tidbits are also included on the back. The player's name runs down the right side. Production was limted to 1,500 hobby and 1,500 retail cases for each series. Series I inserts include Red Hot Super Stars, Red Hot Rookies and two Expansion Extra inserts, a Barry Foster card for Carolina and a Steve Beuerlein card for Jacksonville. Series II inserts include Royal Connections, and Kings of the NFL.

		MT
Complete Set (216):		250.00
Complete Series 1 Set (108):		125.00
Complete Series 2 Set (108):		125.00
Common Player:		1.00
Minor Stars:		2.00
Series 1 or 2 Wax Box:		55.00
1	Chuck Levy	1.00
2	Ron Moore	1.00
3	Jay Schroeder	1.00
4	Bert Emanuel	1.00
5	Terance Mathis	1.00
6	Andre Rison	2.00
7	Bucky Brooks	1.00
8	Jeff Burris	1.00
9	Jim Kelly	2.00
10	Lewis Tillman	1.00
11	Steve Walsh	1.00
12	Chris Zorich	1.00
13	Jeff Blake	3.00
14	Steve Broussard	1.00
15	Jeff Cothran	1.00
16	Ernest Byner	1.00
17	Leroy Hoard	1.00
18	Vinny Testaverde	2.00
19	Troy Aikman	7.00
20	Alvin Harper	1.00
21	Leon Lett	1.00
22	Jay Novacek	1.00
23	John Elway	5.00
24	Karl Mecklenburg	1.00
25	Leonard Russell	1.00
26	Mel Gray	1.00
27	Barry Sanders	8.00
28	Dave Krieg	1.00
29	Chris Spielman	1.00
30	Robert Brooks	2.00
31	LeShon Johnson	1.00
32	Sterling Sharpe	2.00
33	Ernest Givins	1.00
34	Billy Joe Tolliver	1.00
35	Lorenzo White	1.00
36	Charles Arbuckle	1.00
37	Sean Dawkins	2.00
38	Marshall Faulk	7.00
39	Marcus Allen	2.00
40	Donnell Bennett	1.00
41	Matt Blundin	1.00
42	Greg Hill	2.00
43	Tim Brown	2.00
44	Billy Joe Hobert	1.00
45	Raghib Ismail	1.00
46	James Jett	1.00
47	Tim Bowens	1.00
48	Irving Fryar	1.00
49	O.J. McDuffie	2.00
50	Irving Spikes	1.00
51	Terry Allen	1.00
52	Cris Carter	2.00
53	Amp Lee	1.00
54	Drew Bledsoe	7.00
55	Willie McGinest	1.00
56	Leroy Thompson	1.00
57	Michael Timpson	1.00
58	Michael Haynes	1.00
59	Derrell Mitchell	1.00
60	Dave Brown	1.00
61	Thomas Lewis	1.00
62	Dave Meggett	1.00
63	Boomer Esiason	1.00
64	Aaron Glenn	1.00
65	Ronnie Lott	1.00
66	Randall Cunningham	2.00
67	Charlie Garner	1.00
68	Herschel Walker	1.00
69	Barry Foster	1.00
70	Charles Johnson	2.00
71	Jim Miller	2.00
72	Rod Woodson	2.00
73	Andre Coleman	1.00
74	Natrone Means	3.00
75	Shannon Mitchell	1.00
76	Junior Seau	1.00
77	Elvis Grbac	2.00
78	Deion Sanders	3.00
79	Adam Walker	1.00
80	Ricky Watters	2.00
81	Michael Bates	1.00
82	Brian Blades	1.00
83	Eugene Robinson	1.00
84	Chris Warren	2.00
85	Jerome Bettis	2.00
86	Troy Drayton	1.00
87	Chris Miller	1.00
88	Trent Dilfer	2.00
89	Hardy Nickerson	1.00
90	Errict Rhett	2.00
91	Henry Ellard	1.00
92	Gus Frerotte	2.00
93	Ricky Irvins	1.00
94	Dave Barr	1.00
95	Kyle Brady	1.00
96	Mark Bruener	2.00
97	Ki-Jana Carter	3.00
98	Kerry Collins	5.00
99	Joey Galloway	8.00
100	Napoleon Kaufman	10.00
101	Steve McNair	12.00
102	Craig Newsome	1.00
103	Rashaan Salaam	3.00
104	Kordell Stewart	14.00
105	J.J. Stokes	3.00
106	Rodney Thomas	3.00
107	Michael Westbrook	3.00
108	Tyrone Wheatley	3.00
109	Larry Centers	1.00
110	Garrison Hearst	2.00
111	Jamir Miller	1.00
112	Jeff George	2.00
113	Craig Heyward	1.00
114	Cornelius Bennett	1.00
115	Andre Reed	2.00
116	Randy Baldwin	1.00
117	Tommy Barnhardt	1.00
118	Sam Mills	1.00
119	Brian O'Neal	1.00
120	Frank Reich	1.00
121	Tony Smith	1.00
122	Lawyer Tillman	1.00
123	Jack Trudeau	1.00
124	Vernon Turner	1.00
125	Curtis Conway	2.00
126	Erik Kramer	1.00
127	Nate Lewis	1.00
128	Carl Pickens	2.00
129	Darnay Scott	2.00
130	Dan Wilkinson	1.00
131	Derrick Alexander	1.00
132	Carl Banks	1.00
133	Michael Irvin	2.00
134	Emmitt Smith	12.00
135	Kevin Williams	1.00
136	Glyn Milburn	1.00
137	Anthony Miller	1.00
138	Shannon Sharpe	2.00
139	Scott Mitchell	1.00
140	Herman Moore	3.00
141	Edgar Bennett	1.00
142	Brett Favre	12.00
143	Reggie White	2.00
144	Gary Brown	1.00
145	Haywood Jeffires	1.00
146	Webster Slaughter	1.00
147	Craig Erickson	1.00
148	Paul Justin	1.00
149	Lamont Warren	1.00
150	Steve Beuerlein	1.00
151	Derek Brown	1.00
152	Mark Brunell	6.00
153	Reggie Cobb	1.00
154	Desmond Howard	1.00
155	Kelvin Pritchett	1.00
156	James Stewart	5.00
157	Cedric Tillman	1.00
158	Kimble Anders	1.00
159	Lake Dawson	1.00
160	Keith Byars	1.00
161	Dan Marino	12.00
162	Bernie Parmalee	1.00
163	Qadry Ismail	1.00
164	Warren Moon	1.00
165	Jake Reed	1.00
166	Marion Butts	1.00
167	Ben Coates	1.00
168	Mario Bates	1.00
169	Quinn Early	1.00
170	Jim Everett	1.00
171	Rodney Hampton	1.00
172	Mike Horan	1.00
173	Mike Sherrard	1.00
174	Johnny Johnson	1.00
175	Adrian Murrell	2.00
176	Andrew Glover	1.00
177	Jeff Hostetler	1.00
178	Harvey Williams	1.00
179	Fred Barnett	1.00
180	Vaughn Hebron	1.00
181	Jeff Sydner	1.00
182	Kevin Greene	1.00
183	Byron "Bam" Morris	1.00
184	Neil O'Donnell	1.00
185	Stan Humphries	2.00
186	Tony Martin	2.00
187	Mark Seay	1.00
188	William Floyd	2.00
189	Rickey Jackson	1.00
190	Jerry Rice	7.00
191	Steve Young	5.00
192	Cortez Kennedy	1.00
193	Rick Mirer	3.00
194	Jessie Hester	1.00
195	Curtis Martin	15.00
196	Horace Copeland	1.00
197	Charles Wilson	1.00
198	Reggie Brooks	1.00
199	Brian Mitchell	1.00
200	Heath Shuler	2.00
201	Justin Armour	1.00
202	Jay Barker	1.00
203	Zack Crockett	1.00
204	Christian Fauria	1.00
205	Antonio Freeman	8.00
206	Chad May	1.00
207	Frank Sanders	3.00
208	Steve Stenstrom	1.00
209	Lorenzo Styles	1.00
210	Sherman Williams	1.00
211	Ray Zellars	1.00
212	Eric Zeier	1.00
213	Joey Galloway	4.00
214	Napoleon Kaufman	1.00
215	Rashaan Salaam	2.00
216	J.J. Stokes	2.00
NNO	Barry Foster (Carolina)	5.00
NNO	Steve Beuerlein (Jacksonville)	5.00

1995 Pacific Prisms Gold

The 216-card, standard-sized parallel set was inserted every 37 packs. The cards feature gold backgrounds instead of silver.

	MT
Complete Set (216):	1600.00
Common Player:	3.00
Veteran Stars:	2.5x-5x
Young Stars:	2x-4x
RCs:	1.75x-3.5x

1995 Pacific Prisms Connections

These 1995 Pacific Prism Series II inserts feature 10 top quarterback/receiver combinations; there are 20 cards in the set. Hobby cases feature the receiver halves; retail packs have the 10 quarterback cards. Both appear in one per every 73 of their respective packs. The cards are fitted together to form a particular team's qb/receiver tandem. The quarterback cards, numbered 1-10 using an (A) suffix, have the city name along the top; receiver cards (B) have the team nickname. The players' names run along the bottom of the cards. The foiled background includes team logos, plus half of the Royal Connections logo, which fits with its counterpart to form a circle. The quarterback cards have a throwing quarterback symbol as part of its de-sign; receiver cards have a symbol of a player making a catch. Card backs also have the Royal Connections symbol, a player mug shot and a career summary. In addition to (A) and (B) suffixes, cards are numbered using an "RC" prefix.

		MT
Complete Green Set (20):		350.00
Common Green Player:		10.00
Complete Blue Set (20):		1000.
Common Blue Player:		20.00
Blue Cards:		2x-4x
1A	Steve Young	40.00
1B	Jerry Rice	40.00
2A	Dan Marino	80.00
2B	Irving Fryar	10.00
3A	Drew Bledsoe	40.00
3B	Ben Coates	10.00
4A	John Elway	25.00
4B	Shannon Sharpe	10.00
5A	Jeff Hostetler	10.00
5B	Tim Brown	10.00
6A	Warren Moon	10.00
6B	Cris Carter	10.00
7A	Neil O'Donnell	10.00
7B	Charles Johnson	10.00
8A	Troy Aikman	40.00
8B	Michael Irvin	10.00
9A	Stan Humphries	10.00
9B	Shawn Jefferson	10.00
10A	Jim Kelly	10.00
10B	Andre Reed	10.00

1995 Pacific Prisms Kings of the NFL

These 10 1995 Pacific Prism Series II football inserts feature statistical leaders from the 1994 season. Cards were inserted one per every 361 packs. The card front has a color action photo of the player, forming the body of a gold foil hourglass which has the category he led the league in listed at the top, along with the statistical number he reached. The bottom of the hourglass has the Pacific Collection Crown icon and the player's name. The card back has a square with a color mug shot inside, with the number he reached adjacent to it, at the top, but below the category heading he led in. His name runs across the middle of the card, followed by a player profile and a few specific examples of when he had productive weeks in his particular category.

		MT
Complete Set (10):		750.00
Common Player:		40.00
1	Emmitt Smith	110.00
2	Steve Young	60.00
3	Jerry Rice	75.00
4	Deion Sanders	40.00
5	Emmitt Smith	110.00
6	Dan Marino	110.00
7	Drew Bledsoe	75.00
8	Barry Sanders	90.00
9	Marshall Faulk	40.00
10	Marshall Faulk, Natrone Means	40.00

> Values quoted in this guide reflect the retail price of a card — the price a collector can expect to pay when buying a card from a dealer. The wholesale price — that which a collector can expect to receive from a dealer when selling cards — will be significantly lower, depending on desirability and condition.

1995 Pacific Prisms Red Hot Rookies

These nine insert cards could be found in 1995 Pacific Prism Series I packs, one per every 73 hobby packs. The cards have a color action photo of the player in his collegiate uniform against a red foil background which has his pro team's nickname printed several times within it. His name runs along the left side of the card. The back, numbered using 1, 2, 3, etc., is horizontal and includes a closeup shot of the player on the left side. A photo of his new pro team appears on the right side. His name, position and pro team are superimposed over the helmet, as is a summary of when the player was selected in the 1995 draft.

		MT
Complete Set (9):		140.00
Common Player:		5.00
Inserted 1:73		
1	Ki-Jana Carter	5.00
2	Joey Galloway	30.00
3	Steve McNair	30.00
4	Tyrone Wheatley	5.00
5	Kerry Collins	15.00
6	Rashaan Salaam	5.00
7	Michael Westbrook	10.00
8	J.J. Stokes	15.00
9	Napoleon Kaufman	30.00

1995 Pacific Prisms Red Hot Stars

These 1995 Pacific Prism Series I inserts feature nine of the NFL's top stars. The cards were included one per every 73 retail packs. The card front has a color action photo of the player against a red foil spiderweb pattern. The player's name appears at the bottom of the card. The card back, numbered 1, 2, 3, etc., is horizontal and has a closeup shot of the player on the left side. The other side has his name, position, team name and 1994 season recap all superimposed against a football background.

		MT
Complete Set (9):		375.00
Common Player:		30.00
1	Barry Sanders	50.00
2	Steve Young	45.00
3	Emmitt Smith	80.00
4	Drew Bledsoe	45.00
5	Natrone Means	30.00
6	Dan Marino	80.00
7	Marshall Faulk	30.00
8	Jerry Rice	45.00
9	Errict Rhett	30.00

> A card number in parentheses ( ) indicates the set is unnumbered.

1995 Pacific Prisms Super Bowl Logos

This 30-card insert features the game-specific Super Bowl logo on the front and details of the game on the back. The cards are unnumbered.

		MT
Complete Set (30):		4.00
Common Player:		.15
1	Super Bowl I	.15
2	Super Bowl II	.15
3	Super Bowl III	.15
4	Super Bowl IV	.15
5	Super Bowl V	.15
6	Super Bowl VI	.15
7	Super Bowl VII	.15
8	Super Bowl VIII	.15
9	Super Bowl IX	.15
10	Super Bowl X	.15
11	Super Bowl XI	.15
12	Super Bowl XII	.15
13	Super Bowl XIII	.15
14	Super Bowl XIV	.15
15	Super Bowl XV	.15
16	Super Bowl XVI	.15
17	Super Bowl XVII	.15
18	Super Bowl XVIII	.15
19	Super Bowl XIX	.15
20	Super Bowl XX	.15
21	Super Bowl XXI	.15
22	Super Bowl XXII	.15
23	Super Bowl XXIII	.15
24	Super Bowl XXIV	.15
25	Super Bowl XXV	.15
26	Super Bowl XXVI	.15
27	Super Bowl XXVII	.15
28	Super Bowl XXVIII	.15
29	Super Bowl XXIX	.15
30	Super Bowl XXX	.15

1995 Pacific Prisms Team Helmets

This 30-card insert includes one card for each NFL team. The fronts feature the team helmet and the backs have team history.

		MT
Complete Set (30):		4.00
Common Player:		.15
1	Arizona Cardinals	.15
2	Atlanta Falcons	.15
3	Buffalo Bills	.15
4	Carolina Panthers	.15
5	Chicago Bears	.15
6	Cincinnati Bengals	.15
7	Cleveland Browns	.15
8	Dallas Cowboys	.25
9	Denver Broncos	.15
10	Detroit Lions	.15
11	Green Bay Packers	.25
12	Detroit Lions	.15
13	Indianapolis Colts	.15
14	Jacksonville Jaguars	.15
15	Kansas City Chiefs	.15
16	Los Angeles Raiders	.25
17	Miami Dolphins	.25
18	Minnesota Vikings	.15
19	New England Patriots	.15
20	New Orleans Saints	.15
21	New York Giants	.15
22	New York Jets	.15
23	Philadelphia Eagles	.15
24	Pittsburgh Steelers	.25
25	San Diego Chargers	.15
26	San Francisco 49ers	.25
27	Seattle Seahawks	.15
28	St. Louis Rams	.15
29	Tampa Bay Buccaneers	.15
30	Washington Redskins	.25

1995 Pacific Prisms Team Uniforms

This 30-card insert includes one card per NFL team. The cards feature a horizontal layout with the team uniform on the front and team history on the back.

		MT
Complete Set (30):		4.00
Common Player:		.15
1	Arizona Cardinals	.15
2	Atlanta Falcons	.15
3	Buffalo Bills	.15
4	Carolina Panthers	.15
5	Chicago Bears	.15
6	Cincinnati Bengals	.15
7	Cleveland Browns	.15
8	Dallas Cowboys	.25
9	Denver Broncos	.15
10	Detroit Lions	.15
11	Green Bay Packers	.25
12	Detroit Lions	.15
13	Indianapolis Colts	.15
14	Jacksonville Jaguars	.15
15	Kansas City Chiefs	.15
16	Los Angeles Raiders	.25
17	Miami Dolphins	.25
18	Minnesota Vikings	.15
19	New England Patriots	.15
20	New Orleans Saints	.15
21	New York Giants	.15
22	New York Jets	.15
23	Philadelphia Eagles	.15
24	Pittsburgh Steelers	.25
25	San Diego Chargers	.15
26	San Francisco 49ers	.25
27	Seattle Seahawks	.15
28	St. Louis Rams	.15
29	Tampa Bay Buccaneers	.15
30	Washington Redskins	.25

1995 Pacific Triple Folders

These cards feature two panels on the front which, when closed, form a color action photo of an NFL star player. The format is the same as previous editions, but the 1995 cards have been reduced in size to standard-sized cards. The player's name and the Pacific Crown Collection are on one panel on the front; a team helmet is on the other. When opened up, the inside of the card panels reveal three more photos, with the player's team name in the center. The card back, a green football field, contains a closeup photo of the player, a card number and a brief recap of the 1994 season. Insert sets include: Rookies and Stars (which have different color foil versions for hobby and retail versions, plus another parallel set, with yet another different color foil for each); Team Triple Folders; Crystalline; Big Guns; and Careers.

		MT
Complete Set (48):		18.00
Common Player:		.25
Minor Stars:		.50
Wax Box:		55.00
1	Garrison Hearst	.50
2	*Kerry Collins*	1.50
3	Jeff George	.25
4	Herschel Walker	.25
5	Lake Dawson	.25
6	Cris Carter	.25
7	Byron "Bam" Morris	.25
8	Jim Kelly	.25
9	*Rashaan Salaam*	1.00
10	Eric Zeier	.75
11	*Curtis Martin*	3.00
12	Jerry Rice	1.50
13	Chris Warren	.50
14	Trent Dilfer	.25
15	Terry Allen	.25
16	*Jeff Blake*	1.25
17	Drew Bledsoe	1.50
18	Tim Brown	.25
19	Wayne Chrebet	.25
20	Bernie Parmalee	.25
21	Stan Humphries	.25
22	Jerome Bettis	.25
23	*Michael Westbrook*	1.00
24	Charlie Garner	.25
25	Mario Bates	.50
26	Marcus Allen	.25
27	James Stewart	.25
28	Ben Coates	.25
29	Tyrone Wheatley	1.50
30	Steve Young	1.50
31	Natrone Means	.50
32	*Terrell Davis*	1.50
33	*Napoleon Kaufman*	.75
34	Charles Johnson	.25
35	Barry Sanders	1.50
36	John Elway	1.00
37	*Joey Galloway*	1.50
38	Brett Favre	1.50
39	Errict Rhett	1.50
40	Gary Brown	.25
41	Reggie White	.25
42	Steve Bono	.25
43	Marshall Faulk	1.50
44	Dan Marino	3.50
45	Emmitt Smith	3.50
46	Troy Aikman	1.50
47	Ricky Watters	.25
48	Michael Irvin	.75

1995 Pacific Triple Folder Big Guns

Twelve of the NFL's top quarterbacks are featured on these 1995 Pacific Triple Folder inserts, seeded two per every 37 packs. The card front has a color photo of the player against a prism background which has several geometric shapes cut into it. The player's name is in gold foil in the lower left corner; the insert set logo is in the bottom right corner. The horizontal card back has a football as the background, with a mug shot, brief career summary and cannon firing a football superimposed over it. Three opponents' helmets, representing games in which the quarterback had big numbers, are also shown on the back, along with the statistics from those games.

		MT
Complete Set (12):		75.00
Common Player:		3.00
1	Drew Bledsoe	10.00
2	Dan Marino	20.00
3	Warren Moon	3.00
4	John Elway	7.00
5	Jeff Blake	10.00
6	Brett Favre	10.00
7	Steve Young	10.00
8	Boomer Esiason	3.00
9	Jim Everett	3.00
10	Jim Kelly	3.00
11	Jeff George	3.00
12	Dave Kreig	3.00

> Post-1980 cards in Near Mint condition will generally sell for about 75% of the quoted Mint value. Excellent-condition cards bring no more than 40%.

1995 Pacific Triple Folder Careers

Eight of the NFL's top stars are featured on these 1995 Pacific Triple Folder inserts, seeded one every 181 packs. The metallic card front has a color photo of the player, with his name in the upper left corner, adjacent to the Pacific logo. "Careers" runs down the right side of the card front, which includes several of the player's career numbers scattered throughout the card background. The back, numbered using a "C" prefix, has a closeup shot of the player, plus a recap of some of the key numbers from his career statistics.

		MT
Complete Set (8):		350.00
Common Player:		12.00
1	Troy Aikman	45.00
2	Marcus Allen	12.00
3	John Elway	30.00
4	Dan Marino	80.00
5	Jerry Rice	45.00
6	Barry Sanders	45.00
7	Emmitt Smith	80.00
8	Steve Young	45.00

1995 Pacific Triple Folder Crystaline

These 1995 Pacific Triple Folder inserts were seeded four per every 37 packs. Each is a plastic card with clear area above the player photo and his team's primary color and gold foil at the bottom for his name, team nickname and Pacific logo. The card back, numbered using a "Cr" prefix, contains the player's name, position, team and biographical information against the shadow of the card front photo. A team helmet, mug shot and brief career summary are also included on the back.

		MT
Complete Set (20):		125.00
Common Player:		2.00
Minor Stars:		4.00
1	Troy Aikman	8.00
2	Jeff Blake	6.00
3	Drew Bledsoe	8.00
4	Kerry Collins	10.00
5	John Elway	6.00
6	Marshall Faulk	8.00
7	Gus Frerotte	4.00
8	Joey Galloway	10.00
9	Garrison Hearst	4.00
10	Jeff Hostetler	2.00
11	Dan Marino	18.00
12	Natrone Means	4.00
13	Errict Rhett	8.00
14	Rashaan Salaam	6.00

15	Barry Sanders	8.00
16	Deion Sanders	5.00
17	Emmitt Smith	18.00
18	J.J. Stokes	6.00
19	Steve Young	8.00
20	Eric Zeier	4.00

1995 Pacific Triple Folder Rookies and Stars

This set features a mix of 36 stars and rookies, featured on different color foiled cards for the retail and hobby versions, plus a third parallel set which uses yet another color for the foil. The hobby and retail inserts were each seeded three per every four of their respective packs, while the parallel cards are seeded three per every 37 packs. The card front features a full-bleed color photo, with foil for the insert set logo and at the bottom for the player's name. The card back, numbered using an "RS" prefix, has a mug shot of the player, plus a brief recap of the player's previous season.

		MT
Complete Gold Set (36):		30.00
Common Gold Player:		.50
Blue Cards:		2x-4x
Raspberry Cards:		2x-4x
1	Garrison Hearst	.50
2	Darrick Holmes	1.00
3	Kerry Collins	2.00
4	Rashaan Salaam	1.50
5	Jeff Blake	1.50
6	Eric Zeier	1.00
7	Troy Aikman	1.50
8	Eric Bjorson	.50
9	Deion Sanders	1.00
10	Emmitt Smith	3.00
11	Sherman Williams	.50
12	Terrell Davis	2.00
13	John Elway	1.00
14	Barry Sanders	1.50
15	Steve McNair	1.50
16	Marshall Faulk	1.50
17	James Stewart	.50
18	Steve Bono	.50
19	Tamarick Vanover	1.50
20	Dan Marino	3.00
21	Drew Bledsoe	1.50
22	Curtis Martin	3.00
23	Tyrone Wheatley	1.00
24	Tim Brown	.50
25	Napoleon Kaufman	1.00
26	Ricky Watters	.50
27	Natrone Means	1.00
28	Jerry Rice	1.50
29	J.J. Stokes	1.00
30	Steve Young	1.50
31	Joey Galloway	1.50
32	Chris Warren	1.00
33	Jerome Bettis	.50
34	Errict Rhett	1.50
35	Terry Allen	.50
36	Michael Westbrook	1.50

> Values quoted in this guide reflect the retail price of a card — the price a collector can expect to pay when buying a card from a dealer. The wholesale price — that which a collector can expect to receive from a dealer when selling cards — will be significantly lower, depending on desirability and condition.

1995 Pacific Triple Folder Teams

These 1995 Pacific Triple Folders feature three players from a team. The two flaps feature one player; the inside features another player, while the back features a third teammate and a card number. The inside of the card uses gold foil stamping for that player's name and the Pacific Crown Collection logo, plus a circle which surrounds the players' team helmet, which is at the bottom of the card. These inserts were randomly included one per every 37 packs.

		MT
Complete Set (30):		40.00
Common Player:		.50
Minor Stars:		1.00
1	Garrison Hearst, Dave Kreig, Rob Moore	.50
2	Jeff George, Terance Mathis, Eric Metcalf	.50
3	Darick Holmes, Jim Kelly, Andre Reed	1.00
4	Edgar Bennett, Brett Favre, Reggie White	2.00
5	Haywood Jeffires, Chris Chandler, Steve McNair	2.00
6	Marshall Faulk, Jim Harbaugh, Sean Dawkins	2.00
7	Bob Christian, Tim McKyer, Kerry Collins	2.00
8	Rashaan Salaam, Erik Kramer, Michael Timpson	1.50
9	Carl Pickens, Jeff Blake, Darnay Scott	1.50
10	Leroy Hoard, Andre Rison, Vinny Testaverde	.50
11	Troy Aikman, Michael Irvin, Emmitt Smith	5.00
12	John Elway, Terrell Davis, Shannon Sharpe	2.00
13	Scott Mitchell, Herman Moore, Barry Sanders	2.00
14	James Stewart, Mark Brunell, Desmond Howard	1.00
15	Marcus Allen, Steve Bono, Greg Hill	.50
16	Bernie Parmalee, Dan Marino, Irving Fryar	4.00
17	Robert Smith, Warren Moon, Cris Carter	.50
18	Chris Martin, Drew Bledsoe, Ben Coates	4.00
19	Mario Bates, Jim Everett, Michael Haynes	.50
20	Rodney Hampton, Dave Brown, Herschel Walker	.50
21	Wayne Chrebet, Kyle Brady, Adrian Murrell	.50
22	Napoleon Kaufman, Jeff Hostetler, Tim Brown	.50
23	Ricky Watters, Charlie Garner, Mike Malmua	.50
24	Bam Morris, Mike Tomczak, Charles Johnson	.50
25	Natrone Means, Stan Humphries, Tony Martin	1.00
26	Jerry Rice, Steve Young, J.J. Stokes	3.00
27	Chris Warren, Rick Mirer, Joey Galloway	2.00
28	Jerome Bettis, Kelvin Carter, Isaac Bruce	1.00
29	Errict Rhett, Trent Dilfer, Alvin Harper	1.50
30	Terry Allen, Gus Frerotte, Michael Westbrook	1.50

1996 Pacific Super Bowl Bronze/Gold

The six-card, standard-size set was produced with both bronze and gold. The bronze set was available to collectors through a special wrapper redemption program at the 1996 Super Bowl Card Show in Phoenix. The gold set was available through a wrapper redemption program with 1995 Triple Folders. The gold cards are parallel to the bronze set, except with a Super Bowl XXX logo on the card fronts.

		MT
Complete Set (6):		14.00
Common Player:		1.00
1	Chris Warren	1.00
2	Kordell Stewart	3.00
3	Curtis Martin	5.00
4	Errict Rhett	2.00
5	Neil O'Donnell	1.00
6	Barry Sanders	4.00

1996 Pacific

Pacific's 1996 Crown Collection set includes 450 cards (no subsets), each of which has gold-foiled etching along the bottom for the player's name, team helmet and a gridiron. The Pacific logo is also stamped in gold on the front, which features a full-bleed color action photo. The horizontal back has a color closeup shot on one side, with the player's name and position in team colors on the opposite side in the top corner. Underneath is biographical information and a career recap. The card number and a Pacific logo are in the lower right corner. Two parallel versions of the regular set were also made - Scorching Red Foil (nine in every 37 retail packs) and Electric Blue Foil (nine in every 37 hob-

by packs). There are six insert sets - Card-Supials, Cramer's Choice Awards, Bomb Squad, Gold Crown Die-Cuts, Gems of the Crown and The Zone.

		MT
Complete Set (450):		40.00
Common Player:		.05
Minor Stars:		.10
Wax Box:		40.00
1	Jeff Feagles	.05
2	Rob Moore	.05
3	Clyde Simmons	.05
4	Mike Buck	.05
5	Aeneas Williams	.05
6	Simeon Rice	.25
7	Garrison Hearst	.10
8	Eric Swann	.05
9	Dave Krieg	.05
10	Leeland McElroy	.75
11	Oscar McBride	.05
12	Frank Sanders	.05
13	Larry Centers	.05
14	Seth Joyner	.05
15	Stevie Anderson	.05
16	Craig Heyward	.05
17	Devin Bush	.05
18	Eric Metcalf	.05
19	Jeff George	.10
20	Richard Huntley	.05
21	Jamal Anderson	8.00
22	Bert Emanuel	.05
23	Terance Mathis	.05
24	Roman Fortin	.05
25	Jessie Tuggle	.05
26	Morten Andersen	.05
27	Chris Doleman	.05
28	D.J. Johnson	.05
29	Kevin Ross	.05
30	Michael Jackson	.05
31	Eric Zeier	.05
32	Jonathan Ogden	.05
33	Eric Turner	.05
34	Andre Rison	.05
35	Lorenzo White	.05
36	Earnest Byner	.05
37	Derrick Alexander	.05
38	Brian Kinchen	.05
39	Anthony Pleasant	.05
40	Vinny Testaverde	.05
41	Pepper Johnson	.05
42	Frank Hartley	.05
43	Craig Powell	.05
44	Leroy Hoard	.05
45	Kent Hull	.05
46	Bryce Paup	.05
47	Andre Reed	.05
48	Darick Holmes	.05
49	Russell Copeland	.05
50	Jerry Ostroski	.05
51	Chris Green	.05
52	Eric Moulds	2.00
53	Justin Armour	.05
54	Jim Kelly	.10
55	Cornelius Bennett	.05
56	Steve Tasker	.05
57	Thurman Thomas	.10
58	Bruce Smith	.05
59	Todd Collins	.05
60	Shawn King	.05
61	Don Beebe	.05
62	John Kasay	.05
63	Tim McKyer	.05
64	Darion Conner	.05
65	Pete Metzelaars	.05
66	Derrick Moore	.05
67	Blake Brockermeyer	.05
68	Tim Biakabutuka	1.00
69	Sam Mills	.05
70	Vince Workman	.05
71	Kerry Collins	.75
72	Carlton Bailey	.05
73	Mark Carrier	.05
74	Donnell Woolford	.05
75	Walt Harris	.25
76	John Thierry	.05
77	Al Fontenot	.05
78	Lewis Tillman	.05
79	Curtis Conway	.10
80	Chris Zorich	.05
81	Mark Carrier	.05
82	Bobby Engram	.75
83	Alonzo Spellman	.05
84	Rashaan Salaam	.50
85	Michael Timpson	.05
86	Nate Lewis	.05
87	James Williams	.05
88	Jeff Graham	.05
89	Erik Kramer	.05
90	Willie Anderson	.05
91	Tony McGee	.05
92	Marco Battaglia	.05
93	Dan Wilkinson	.05
94	John Walsh	.05
95	Eric Bieniemy	.05
96	Ricardo McDonald	.05
97	Carl Pickens	.10
98	Kevin Sargent	.05
99	David Dunn	.05
100	Jeff Blake	.50
101	Harold Green	.05
102	James Francis	.05
103	John Copeland	.05
104	Darnay Scott	.05
105	Darren Woodson	.05
106	Jay Novacek	.05
107	Charles Haley	.05
108	Mark Tuinei	.05
109	Michael Irvin	.10
110	Troy Aikman	.75
111	Chris Boniol	.05
112	Sherman Williams	.05
113	Deion Sanders	.50
114	Emmitt Smith	2.00
115	Eric Bjornson	.05
116	Nate Newton	.05
117	Larry Allen	.05
118	Kevin Williams	.05
119	Leon Lett	.05
120	John Mobley	.05
121	Anthony Miller	.05
122	Brian Habib	.05
123	Aaron Craver	.05
124	Glyn Milburn	.05
125	Shannon Sharpe	.05
126	Steve Atwater	.05
127	Jason Elam	.05
128	John Elway	.35
129	Reggie Rivers	.05
130	Mike Pritchard	.05
131	Vance Johnson	.05
132	Terrell Davis	1.25
133	Tyrone Braxton	.05
134	Ed McCaffrey	.05
135	Chris Spielman	.05
136	Luther Elliss	.05
137	Johnnie Morton	.05
138	Zefross Moss	.05
139	Barry Sanders	1.25
140	Lomas Brown	.05
141	Cory Schlesinger	.05
142	Jason Hanson	.05
143	Kevin Glover	.05
144	Ron Rivers	.50
145	Aubrey Matthews	.05
146	Reggie Brown	.05
147	Herman Moore	.30
148	Scott Mitchell	.05
149	Brett Favre	2.00
150	Sean Jones	.05
151	Leroy Butler	.05
152	Mark Chmura	.20
153	Mark Ingram	.05
154	Derrick Mayes	1.00
155	Antonio Freeman	.05
156	Chris Darkins	.25
157	Robert Brooks	.10
158	William Henderson	.05
159	George Koonce	.05
160	Craig Newsome	.05
161	Darius Holland	.05
162	George Teague	.05
163	Edgar Bennett	.05
164	Reggie White	.10
165	Michael Barrow	.05
166	Mel Gray	.05
167	Anthony Dorsett Jr.	.05
168	Roderick Lewis	.05
169	Henry Ford	.05
170	Mark Stepnoski	.05
171	Chris Sanders	.05
172	Anthony Cook	.05
173	Eddie Robinson	.05
174	Steve McNair	.50
175	Haywood Jeffires	.05
176	Eddie George	3.50
177	Marion Butts	.05
178	Malcolm Seabron	.05
179	Rodney Thomas	.05
180	Ken Dilger	.05
181	Zack Crockett	.05
182	Tony Bennett	.05
183	Quentin Coryatt	.05
184	Marshall Faulk	.50
185	Sean James	.05
186	Jim Harbaugh	.05
187	Eugene Daniel	.05
188	Roosevelt Potts	.05
189	Lamont Warren	.05
190	Will Wolford	.05
191	Tony Siragusa	.05
192	Aaron Bailey	.05
193	Trev Alberts	.05
194	Kevin Hardy	.10
195	Greg Spann	.05
196	Steve Beuerlein	.05
197	Steve Taneyhill	.05
198	Vaughn Dunbar	.05
199	Mark Brunell	.75
200	Bernard Carter	.05
201	James Stewart	.05
202	Tony Boselli	.05
203	Chris Doering	.05
204	Jack Willson	.05
205	Tony Brackens	.30
206	Ernest Givins	.05
207	Le'Shai Maston	.05
208	Pete Mitchell	.05
209	Desmond Howard	.05
210	Vinnie Clark	.05
211	Jeff Lageman	.05
212	Derrick Walker	.05
213	Dan Saleaumua	.05
214	Derrick Thomas	.05
215	Neil Smith	.05
216	Willie Davis	.05
217	Mark Collins	.05
218	Lake Dawson	.05
219	Greg Hill	.05
220	Anthony Davis	.05
221	Kimble Anders	.05
222	Webster Slaughter	.05
223	Tamarick Vanover	.50
224	Marcus Allen	.10
225	Steve Bono	.10
226	Will Shields	.05
227	Karim Abdul-Jabbar	.75
228	Tim Bowens	.05
229	Keith Sims	.05
230	Terry Kirby	.05
231	Gene Atkins	.05
232	Dan Marino	2.00
233	Richmond Webb	.05
234	Gary Clark	.05
235	O.J. McDuffie	.05
236	Marco Coleman	.05
237	Bernie Parmalee	.05
238	Randal Hill	.05
239	Bryan Cox	.05
240	Irving Fryar	.05
241	Derrick Alexander	.05
242	Qadry Ismail	.05
243	Warren Moon	.05
244	Cris Carter	.05
245	Chad May	.05
246	Robert Smith	.05
247	Fuad Reveiz	.05
248	Orlando Thomas	.05
249	Chris Hinton	.05
250	Jack Del Rio	.05
251	Moe Williams	.05
252	Roy Barker	.05
253	Jake Reed	.05
254	Adrian Cooper	.05
255	Curtis Martin	1.50
256	Ben Coates	.05
257	Drew Bledsoe	.75
258	Maurice Hurst	.05
259	Troy Brown	.05
260	Bruce Armstrong	.05
261	Myron Guyton	.05
262	Dave Meggett	.05
263	Terry Glenn	1.75
264	Chris Slade	.05
265	Vincent Brisby	.05
266	Willie McGinest	.05
267	Vincent Brown	.05
268	Will Moore	.05
269	Jay Barker	.05
270	Ray Zellars	.05
271	Derek Brown	.05
272	William Roaf	.05
273	Quinn Early	.05
274	Michael Haynes	.05
275	Rufus Porter	.05
276	Renaldo Turnbull	.05
277	Wayne Martin	.05
278	Tyrone Hughes	.05
279	Irv Smith	.05
280	Eric Allen	.05
281	Mark Fields	.05
282	Mario Bates	.05
283	Jim Everett	.05
284	Vince Buck	.05
285	Alex Molden	.05
286	Tyrone Wheatley	.05
287	Chris Calloway	.05
288	Jessie Armstead	.05
289	Arthur Marshall	.05
290	Aaron Pierce	.05
291	Dave Brown	.05
292	Rodney Hampton	.05
293	John Elliott	.05
294	Mike Sherrard	.05
295	Howard Cross	.05
296	Michael Brooks	.05
297	Herschel Walker	.05
298	Danny Kanell	.75
299	Keith Elias	.05
300	Bobby Houston	.05
301	Dexter Carter	.05
302	Tony Casillas	.05
303	Kyle Brady	.05
304	Glenn Foley	.05
305	Ron Moore	.05
306	Ryan Yarborough	.05
307	Aaron Glenn	.05
308	Adrian Murrell	.05
309	Boomer Esiason	.05
310	Kyle Clifton	.05
311	Wayne Chrebet	.05
312	Erik Howard	.05
313	Keyshawn Johnson	2.50
314	Marvin Washington	.05
315	Johnny Mitchell	.05
316	Alex Van Dyke	.50
317	Billy Joe Hobert	.05
318	Andrew Glover	.05
319	Vince Evans	.05
320	Chester McGlockton	.05
321	Pat Swilling	.05
322	Raghib Ismail	.05
323	Eddie Anderson	.05
324	Rickey Dudley	.75
325	Steve Wisniewski	.05
326	Harvey Williams	.05
327	Napoleon Kaufman	.05
328	Tim Brown	.10
329	Jeff Hostetler	.05
330	Anthony Smith	.05
331	Terry McDaniel	.05
332	Charlie Garner	.05
333	Ricky Watters	.05
334	Brian Dawkins	.05
335	Randall Cunningham	.05
336	Gary Anderson	.05
337	Calvin Williams	.05
338	Chris T. Jones	.05
339	Bobby Hoying	.75
340	William Fuller	.05
341	William Thomas	.05
342	Mike Mamula	.05
343	Fred Barnett	.05
344	Rodney Peete	.05
345	Mark McMillian	.05
346	Bobby Taylor	.05
347	Yancey Thigpen	.35
348	Neil O'Donnell	.05
349	Rod Woodson	.05
350	Kordell Stewart	.75
351	Dermontti Dawson	.05
352	Norm Johnson	.05
353	Ernie Mills	.05
354	Bam Morris	.05
355	Mark Bruener	.05
356	Kevin Greene	.05
357	Greg Lloyd	.05
358	Andre Hastings	.05
359	Erric Pegram	.05
360	Carnell Lake	.05
361	Dwayne Harper	.05
362	Ronnie Harmon	.05
363	Leslie O'Neal	.05
364	John Carney	.05
365	Stan Humphries	.05
366	Brian Roche	.05
367	Terrell Fletcher	.05
368	Shaun Gayle	.05
369	Alfred Pupunu	.05
370	Shawn Jefferson	.05
371	Junior Seau	.05
372	Mark Seay	.05
373	Aaron Hayden	.05
374	Tony Martin	.05
375	Steve Young	.75
376	J.J. Stokes	.50
377	Jerry Rice	.75
378	Derek Loville	.05
379	Lee Woodall	.05
380	Terrell Owens	3.50
381	Elvis Grbac	.05
382	Ricky Ervins	.05
383	Eric Davis	.05
384	Dana Stubblefield	.05
385	Gary Plummer	.05
386	Tim McDonald	.05
387	William Floyd	.05
388	Ken Norton Jr.	.05
389	Merton Hanks	.05
390	Bart Oates	.05
391	Brent Jones	.05
392	Steve Broussard	.05
393	Robert Blackmon	.05
394	Rick Tuten	.05
395	Pete Kendall	.05
396	John Friesz	.05
397	Terry Wooden	.05
398	Rick Mirer	.05
399	Chris Warren	.10
400	Joey Galloway	.50
401	Howard Ballard	.05
402	Jason Kyle	.05
403	Kevin Mawae	.05
404	Mack Strong	.05
405	Reggie Brown	.05
406	Cortez Kennedy	.05
407	Sean Gilbert	.05
408	J.T. Thomas	.05
409	Shane Conlan	.05
410	Johnny Bailey	.05
411	Mark Rypien	.05
412	Leonard Russell	.05
413	Troy Drayton	.05
414	Jerome Bettis	.05
415	Jessie Hester	.05
416	Isaac Bruce	.50
417	Roman Phifer	.05
418	Todd Kinchen	.05
419	Alexander Wright	.05
420	Marcus Jones	.05
421	Horace Copeland	.05
422	Eric Curry	.05
423	Courtney Hawkins	.05
424	Alvin Harper	.05
425	Derrick Brooks	.05
426	Errict Rhett	.25
427	Trent Dilfer	.05
428	Hardy Nickerson	.05
429	Brad Culpepper	.05
430	Warren Sapp	.05
431	Reggie Roby	.05
432	Santana Dotson	.05
433	Jerry Ellison	.05
434	Lawrence Dawsey	.05
435	Heath Shuler	.05
436	Stanley Richard	.05
437	Rod Stephens	.05
438	Stephen Davis	3.50
439	Terry Allen	.05
440	Michael Westbrook	.40
441	Ken Harvey	.05
442	Coleman Bell	.05
443	Marvcus Patton	.05
444	Gus Frerotte	.05
445	Leslie Shepherd	.05
446	Tom Carter	.05
447	Brian Mitchell	.05
448	Darrell Green	.05
449	Tony Woods	.05
450		.05

1996 Pacific Blue/Red/Silver

Pacific Crown Collection Football was offered in three different parallel versions - blue, red and silver. Electric Blue versions of the 450-card set were available in hobby packs, with Scorching Red versions in retail, both seeded nine per 37 packs. There was also a Silver version available in special retail packs, with roughly the same production as the Red and Blue set. The only differences in these cards from the base cards is the color of the foil stamping.

	MT
Complete Blue Set (450):	300.00
Blue Cards:	4x-8x
Complete Red Set (450):	300.00
Red Cards:	4x-8x
Complete Silver Set (450):	300.00
Silver Cards:	4x-8x

1996 Pacific Bomb Squad

The NFL's finest quarterback/receiver combinations are spotlighted on these 1996 Pacific inserts. The cards, seeded one per every 73 packs, feature a player on each side against a background of team-colored swirls. The Pacific logo is in the upper left corner; the player's name and position run down the right side of the card. One side has a card number, which uses a "BS" prefix.

		MT
Complete Set (10):		200.00
Common Player:		10.00
1	Jeff Blake, Carl Pickens	10.00
2	John Elway, Anthony Miller	16.00
3	Scott Mitchell, Herman Moore	10.00
4	Troy Aikman, Jay Novacek	25.00
5	Brett Favre, Robert Brooks	45.00
6	Steve McNair, Chris Sanders	15.00
7	Dan Marino, Irving Fryar	45.00
8	Drew Bledsoe, Terry Glenn	35.00
9	Kordell Stewart, Kordell Stewart	20.00
10	Steve Young, Jerry Rice	25.00

1996 Pacific Card-Supials

This 36-card Pacific insert set features cards with flashy gold embossing on the front for the Pacific logo, player's name and outline of the letters in the player's position and team name. The back has a little cut in the card, creating a pouch for another mini (1-1/4" x 1-3/4") card of the player - a marsupial. Hence, the name Card-Supials. The card back of the regular card is black-and-white; the mini card, when placed in the pouch, fills in the area with color. The bottom of the card has a brief paragraph about the player, plus a card number (1 of 36, etc.). The mini card's back has the player's name and position along the side. A closeup shot and player profile complete the back. The card is numbered 1a of 36, etc. Cards were seeded one per every 37 packs, but the minis were not always matched up with the larger card.

		MT
Complete Set (72):		500.00
Comp. Large Set (36):		300.00
Comp. Small Set (36):		200.00
Common Large:		4.00
Small Cards: Half Price		
1	Garrison Hearst	4.00
2	Jeff George	4.00
3	Eric Zeier	4.00
4	Jim Kelly	4.00
5	Kerry Collins	8.00
6	Rashaan Salaam	6.00
7	Jeff Blake	6.00
8	Troy Aikman	20.00
9	Emmitt Smith	40.00
10	Terrell Davis	20.00
11	John Elway	10.00
12	Deion Sanders	12.00
13	Barry Sanders	20.00
14	Brett Favre	40.00
15	Steve McNair	10.00
16	Marshall Faulk	6.00
17	Mark Brunell	15.00
18	Tamarick Vanover	6.00
19	Dan Marino	40.00
20	Cris Carter	4.00
21	Keyshawn Johnson	6.00
22	Rodney Hampton	4.00
23	Curtis Martin	25.00
24	Drew Bledsoe	20.00
25	Mario Bates	4.00
26	Napoleon Kaufman	4.00
27	Ricky Watters	4.00
28	Kordell Stewart	20.00
29	Junior Seau	4.00
30	Steve Young	18.00
31	Jerry Rice	20.00
32	Isaac Bruce	8.00
33	Joey Galloway	15.00
34	Chris Warren	4.00
35	Errict Rhett	6.00
36	Michael Westbrook	6.00

1996 Pacific Cramer's Choice Awards

Cramer's Choice Awards return as an insert for Pacific's 1996 football line. The die-cut cards, which showcase some of the NFL's most amazing athletes, have a silver background for the card, which is shaped like a trophy. The cards are the rarest in this product line; they are seeded one per every 721 packs. The back has comments about the player by Michael Cramer, CEO and president of Pacific, who made the selections.

		MT
Complete Set (10):		900.00
Common Player:		40.00
1	Emmitt Smith	100.00
2	John Elway	100.00
3	Barry Sanders	125.00
4	Brett Favre	125.00
5	Reggie White	40.00
6	Dan Marino	100.00
7	Curtis Martin	50.00
8	Keyshawn Johnson	60.00
9	Kordell Stewart	80.00
10	Jerry Rice	80.00

Values quoted in this guide reflect the retail price of a card — the price a collector can expect to pay when buying a card from a dealer. The wholesale price — that which a collector can expect to receive when selling cards — will be significantly lower, depending on desirability and condition.

1996 Pacific The Zone

Only the NFL's most productive players who found the end zone on a regular basis in 1995 are featured on these die-cut inserts. The cards were seeded one per every 145 packs. Each card front has a die-cut goal post, with the player photo between the posts. The player's name is in gold foil on the cross bar. His team's name is on the post. Pacific and the logo are in gold foil on the bottom of the card, which has a grassy background. The card back has a closeup shot of the player, his name and a team logo between the posts. His position and city name are on the cross bar. The bottom of the card has a grassy background with a recap of some of the player's accomplishments. The card number is also at the bottom, using a "Z" prefix.

		MT
Complete Set (20):		700.00
Common Player:		10.00
1	Jim Kelly	20.00
2	Rashaan Salaam	10.00
3	Carl Pickens	10.00
4	Jeff Blake	20.00
5	Kerry Collins	20.00
6	Emmitt Smith	70.00
7	Troy Aikman	40.00
8	John Elway	40.00
9	Barry Sanders	50.00
10	Herman Moore	10.00
11	Scott Mitchell	10.00
12	Brett Favre	80.00
13	Robert Brooks	10.00
14	Marshall Faulk	20.00
15	Dan Marino	80.00
16	Drew Bledsoe	40.00
17	Curtis Martin	40.00
18	Steve Young	30.00
19	Jerry Rice	40.00
20	Chris Warren	10.00

1996 Pacific Gold Crown Die-Cuts

These 1996 Pacific inserts were seeded one per every 37 packs. Each card features a full-bleed color action photo on the front, with a die-cut gold foiled crown at the top. The player's name is at the bottom in foil, too, next to a team helmet. The card back has the crown image at the top. The player's name runs across the middle, with a closeup shot of the player in a diamond on one side and brief player profile on the other. A card number, using a "GC" prefix, is in the lower left corner.

	MT
Complete Set (20):	350.00

		MT
Common Player:		5.00
1	Emmitt Smith	30.00
2	Troy Aikman	20.00
3	Barry Sanders	40.00
4	Kerry Collins	8.00
5	Jeff Blake	5.00
6	John Elway	20.00
7	Terrell Davis	30.00
8	Deion Sanders	15.00
9	Brett Favre	40.00
10	Dan Marino	30.00
11	Eddie George	25.00
12	Curtis Martin	15.00
13	Drew Bledsoe	20.00
14	Keyshawn Johnson	10.00
15	Napoleon Kaufman	10.00
16	Kordell Stewart	20.00
17	Steve Young	15.00
18	Jerry Rice	20.00
19	Joey Galloway	10.00
20	Chris Warren	5.00

1996 Pacific Gems of the Crown

These 1996 Pacific inserts, numbered 19-36, were seeded one per every 37 packs. (Cards 1-18 were inserts in 1996 Dynagon Prism packs.) The horizontal card front has a color photo in the middle, with an outline around it. The team name is stamped in gold along the left side; the player's last name is stamped in gold along the right. A gold-foiled panel along the top has the Pacific logo and the player's first name in the upper right corner.

		MT
Complete Set (18):		130.00
Common Player:		3.00
19	Garrison Hearst	3.00
20	Jeff Blake	8.00
21	Troy Aikman	12.00
22	Deion Sanders	10.00
23	Brett Favre	20.00
24	Robert Smith	3.00
25	Mario Bates	3.00
26	Napoleon Kaufman	3.00
27	Kordell Stewart	12.00
28	Jim Kelly	3.00
29	Jim Harbaugh	3.00
30	Tamarick Vanover	3.00
31	Dan Marino	20.00
32	Warren Moon	3.00
33	Curtis Martin	18.00
34	Rodney Hampton	3.00
35	Ricky Watters	3.00
36	Joey Galloway	10.00

1996 Pacific Power Corps

Power Corps was a 20-card insert that was only available in special retail packs on Pacific Crown Collection in 1996. The cards contained the words "Power Corps" running down the left side, with the player's name running down the right side. The cards were numbered PC1-PC20. There were also foil parallel versions of card numbers 1, 11, 14, 17 and 19.

		MT
Complete Set (20):		80.00
Common Player:		2.50
1	Troy Aikman	6.00
2	Jeff Blake	2.50
3	Drew Bledsoe	6.00
4	Kerry Collins	6.00
5	Terrell Davis	8.00
6	John Elway	4.00
7	Marshall Faulk	3.00
8	Brett Favre	12.00
9	Joey Galloway	2.50
10	Garrison Hearst	2.50
11	Dan Marino	12.00
12	Curtis Martin	8.00
13	Steve McNair	6.00
14	Jerry Rice	6.00
15	Rashaan Salaam	4.00
16	Barry Sanders	6.00
17	Emmitt Smith	12.00
18	Kordell Stewart	6.00
19	Chris Warren	2.50
20	Steve Young	4.00

1996 Pacific Crown Royale

Pacific's 1996 Crown Royale release features 144 regular-size cards that are highlighted by etched, die-cut cards. Each horizontal card is topped with a die-cut gold crown and the front has the player's name, position and team logo. Two parallel versions are available: Royale Blue (hobby) and Royale Silver (retail). Also, five insert sets were inserted: Cramer's Choice Awards, Field Force Etch-Tech, Pro Bowl Die-Cut, Triple Crown Die-Cut and NFL Regime. The 144-card base set was sold in five-card packs and each regular card back was listed by the "CR" prefix.

		MT
Complete Set (144):		150.00
Common Player:		.50
Minor Stars:		1.00
Wax Box:		110.00
1	Dan Marino	10.00
2	Frank Sanders	.50
3	Bobby Engram	2.00
4	Cornelius Bennett	.50
5	Steve Bono	.50
6	Aaron Hayden	.50
7	Leroy Hoard	.50
8	Brett Perriman	.50
9	Irv Smith	.50
10	Jim Kelly	1.00
11	Rodney Thomas	.50
12	Eric Bieniemy	.50
13	Darnay Scott	1.00
14	Ki-Jana Carter	2.00
15	Kerry Collins	1.50
16	Shannon Sharpe	.50
17	Michael Westbrook	1.00
18	Steve McNair	6.00
19	Tony Banks	4.00
20	Rashaan Salaam	1.00
21	Terrell Fletcher	.50
22	Michael Timpson	.50
23	Bobby Hoying	4.00
24	Quinn Early	.50
25	Warren Moon	1.00
26	Tommy Vardell	.50
27	Marvin Harrison	12.00
28	Lake Dawson	.50
29	Karim Abdul-Jabbar	4.00
30	Chris Warren	2.00
31	Heath Shuler	1.00
32	Bert Emanuel	.50
33	Howard Griffith	.50
34	Alex Van Dyke	2.00
35	Isaac Bruce	1.00
36	Mark Brunell	5.00
37	Winslow Oliver	.50
38	O.J. McDuffie	.50
39	Terrell Owens	20.00
40	Jerry Rice	5.00
41	Henry Ellard	.50
42	Chris Sanders	.50
43	Craig Heyward	.50
44	Eddie Kennison	2.50
45	Terrell Davis	8.00
46	Rodney Hampton	.50
47	Bryan Still	.50
48	Tim Brown	.50
49	Keyshawn Johnson	10.00
50	Barry Sanders	12.00
51	Terry Allen	1.00
52	Sean Dawkins	.50
53	Bryce Paup	.50
54	Brett Favre	12.00
55	Deion Sanders	3.00
56	Kevin Hardy	2.00
57	Kevin Williams	.50
58	Jeff George	.50
59	Tim Biakabutuka	5.00
60	Drew Bledsoe	5.00
61	Michael Jackson	.50
62	James Stewart	.50
63	Mario Bates	.50
64	Daryl Johnston	.50
65	Herman Moore	2.00
66	Ben Coates	.50
67	Terry Glenn	7.00
68	Robert Smith	.50
69	Irving Fryar	.50
70	Napoleon Kaufman	.50
71	Rickey Dudley	3.00
72	Bernie Parmalee	.50
73	Kyle Brady	.50
74	Neil O'Donnell	.50
75	Lawrence Phillips	4.00
76	Hardy Nickerson	.50
77	John Elway	4.00
78	Pete Mitchell	.50
79	Jason Dunn	.50
80	Reggie White	1.00
81	J.J. Stokes	2.00
82	Jake Reed	.50
83	Yancey Thigpen	.50
84	Jonathan Ogden	.50
85	Larry Centers	.50
86	Scott Mitchell	.50
87	Eric Zeier	.50
88	Anthony Miller	.50
89	Brian Blades	.50
90	Cris Carter	.50
91	Kordell Stewart	8.00
92	Charles Way	.50
93	Jeff Hostetler	.50
94	Brad Johnson	5.00
95	Marcus Allen	1.00
96	Errict Rhett	2.00
97	Stan Humphries	.50
98	Michael Haynes	.50
99	Curtis Martin	8.00
100	Troy Aikman	5.00
101	Earnest Byner	.50
102	Vincent Brisby	.50
103	Zack Crockett	.50
104	Haywood Jeffires	.50
105	Joey Galloway	4.00
106	Carl Pickens	1.00
107	Leeland McElroy	1.50
108	Adrian Murrell	.50
109	Joe Horn	.50
110	Steve Young	4.00
111	Andre Rison	.50
112	Jim Everett	.50
113	Jamie Asher	2.00
114	Steve Walsh	.50
115	Robert Brooks	1.00
116	Eric Moulds	8.00
117	Edgar Bennett	.50
118	Greg Lloyd	.50
119	Jerris McPhail	.50
120	Marshall Faulk	3.00
121	Dave Brown	.50
122	Harvey Williams	.50
123	Trent Dilfer	1.00
124	Eddie George	15.00
125	Jeff Blake	2.00
126	Mark Chmura	.50
127	Boomer Esiason	.50
128	Jim Harbaugh	.50
129	Bryan Cox	.50
130	Ricky Watters	1.00
131	Amani Toomer	.50
132	Jim Miller	.50
133	Cortez Kennedy	.50
134	Courtney Hawkins	.50
135	Junior Seau	.50
136	Tamarick Vanover	2.00
137	Jerome Bettis	1.00
138	Chris Calloway	.50
139	Rick Mirer	.50
140	Thurman Thomas	1.00
141	Sheddrick Wilson	.50
142	Charlie Garner	.50
143	Erik Kramer	.50
144	Emmitt Smith	10.00

Post-1980 cards in Near Mint condition will generally sell for about 75% of the quoted Mint value. Excellent-condition cards bring no more than 40%.

1996 Pacific Crown Royale Blue/Silver

Each card in the 144-card 1996 Crown Royale set were re-printed in two different versions. Hobby packs had Royale Blue parallels, while retail packs had Royale Silver parallels, with both seeded four per 25 packs. These parallel sets are distinguished only by the color of the foil stamping.

	MT
Complete Blue Set (144):	700.00
Blue Cards:	2x-4x
Complete Silver Set (144):	1000.
Silver Cards:	3x-6x

1996 Pacific Crown Royale Cramer's Choice Awards

The large-sized set (5-1/2" x 4") was offered as part of a redemption offer in the Crown Royale set. Redemption cards, inserted every 385 packs, enabled collectors to obtain the 10-card, die-cut set. The cards are cut into the shape of a pyramid and the players honored were chosen by Pacific President and CEO Michael Cramer. The card backs are each listed with the "CC" prefix.

		MT
Complete Set (10):		800.00
Common Player:		50.00
1	John Elway	80.00
2	Brett Favre	125.00
3	Keyshawn Johnson	50.00
4	Dan Marino	125.00
5	Curtis Martin	100.00
6	Jerry Rice	85.00
7	Barry Sanders	100.00
8	Emmitt Smith	125.00
9	Kordell Stewart	75.00
10	Reggie White	50.00

Values quoted in this guide reflect the retail price of a card — the price a collector can expect to pay when buying a card from a dealer. The wholesale price — that which a collector can expect to receive when selling cards — will be significantly lower, depending on desirability and condition.

1996 Pacific Crown Royale Triple Crown Die-Cut

The 10-card, regular-sized, die-cut set honors 10 players who led the league in at least three different categories. Inserted every 73 packs in 1996 Crown Royale, the cards feature a similar die-cut crown design with gold foil as the base cards in Crown Royale. The card backs are labeled with the "TC" prefix and are individually numbered.

		MT
Complete Set (10):		600.00
Common Player:		20.00
1	Troy Aikman	60.00
2	John Elway	40.00
3	Brett Favre	90.00
4	Keyshawn Johnson	20.00
5	Dan Marino	90.00
6	Curtis Martin	80.00
7	Jerry Rice	60.00
8	Barry Sanders	60.00
9	Emmitt Smith	90.00
10	Steve Young	40.00

1996 Pacific Crown Royale Field Force

The 20-card, regular-sized set was inserted in 1996 packs of Crown Royale. Inserted every 49 packs, the horizontal cards employ etch-tech design and feature the player's name written on the side margins in foil etching of the player's team colors. The card backs contain a headshot of the player and are numbered with the "FF" prefix.

		MT
Complete Set (20):		900.00
Common Player:		15.00
1	Troy Aikman	60.00
2	Karim Abdul-Jabbar	45.00
3	Jeff Blake	25.00
4	Drew Bledsoe	60.00
5	Lawrence Phillips	35.00
6	Kerry Collins	25.00
7	Terrell Davis	65.00
8	John Elway	40.00
9	Brett Favre	100.00
10	Eddie George	60.00
11	Dan Marino	100.00
12	Curtis Martin	80.00
13	Jerry Rice	65.00
14	Rashaan Salaam	15.00
15	Barry Sanders	60.00
16	Deion Sanders	50.00
17	Emmitt Smith	100.00
18	Kordell Stewart	65.00
19	Chris Warren	15.00
20	Steve Young	50.00

1996 Pacific Crown Royale Pro Bowl Die-Cut

The 20-card, regular-sized, die-cut cards were inserted every 25 packs of Crown Royale. Each player is pictured in his Pro Bowl jersey and is backdropped with a die-cut palm tree and pineapple. The card backs feature an exploding volcano and a headshot of the player and are numbered with the "PB" prefix.

		MT
Complete Set (20):		550.00
Common Player:		10.00
1	Jeff Blake	12.00
2	Mark Chmura	10.00
3	Marshall Faulk	12.00
4	Brett Favre	100.00
5	Charles Haley	10.00
6	Merton Hanks	10.00
7	Greg Lloyd	10.00
8	Dan Marino	100.00
9	Curtis Martin	70.00
10	Anthony Miller	10.00
11	Herman Moore	12.00
12	Bryce Paup	10.00
13	Jerry Rice	50.00
14	Barry Sanders	50.00
15	Junior Seau	10.00
16	Emmitt Smith	100.00
17	Yancey Thigpen	10.00
18	Chris Warren	10.00
19	Ricky Watters	10.00
20	Steve Young	35.00

1996 Pacific Crown Royale NFL Regime

The 110-card, regular-sized set was included in each of the 1996 Crown Royale five-card packs. The card fronts feature a gray border with the player's name on top in red lettering and a white globe centered on a red ribbon which reads "NFL Regime." The card backs contain a headshot of the player and the prefix "NR."

		MT
Complete Set (110):		25.00
Common Player:		.20
Minor Stars:		.40
1	Steve Young	1.00
2	Jamir Miller	.20
3	Tyrone Brown	.20
4	Chris Shelling	.20
5	Warren Moon	.20
6	Shane Bonham	.20
7	Gary Brown	.20
8	Chris Chandler	.20
9	Bradford Banta	.20
10	John Elway	.75
11	Tom McManus	.20
12	Alfred Jackson	.20
13	Jay Barker	.20

Values quoted in this guide reflect the retail price of a card — the price a collector can expect to pay when buying a card from a dealer. The wholesale price — that which a collector can expect to receive when selling cards — will be significantly lower, depending on desirability and condition.

14	Kirk Botkin	.20
15	Jim Kelly	.20
16	Lou Benfatti	.20
17	Billy Joe Hobert	.20
18	John Jackson	.20
19	Torin Dorn	.20
20	Drew Bledsoe	1.00
21	Gale Gilbert	.20
22	James Atkins	.20
23	John Lynch	.20
24	James Jenkins	.20
25	Kerry Collins	.50
26	Eric Swann	.20
27	Dan Stryzinski	.20
28	Mike Groh	.20
29	Tim Tindale	.20
30	Kordell Stewart	1.25
31	Frank Garcia	.20
32	Mill Coleman	.20
33	Bracey Walker	.20
34	Ryan McNeil	.20
35	Rodney Hampton	.20
36	John Mobley	.20
37	Derek Russell	.20
38	Jeff George	.20
39	Steve Morrison	.20
40	Rashaan Salaam	.40
41	Ryan Christopherson	.20
42	Darren Anderson	.20
43	Ronnie Williams	.20
44	Scottie Graham	.20
45	Thurman Thomas	.40
46	Corwin Brown	.20
47	Lee DeRamus	.20
48	Ray Agnew	.20
49	Erik Howard	.20
50	Emmitt Smith	2.50
51	Dan Land	.20
52	Vinny Testaverde	.20
53	Myron Bell	.20
54	Keith Lyle	.20
55	Aaron Hayden	.20
56	Jeff Brohm	.20
57	Ronnie Harris	.20
58	Trent Dilfer	.20
59	Browning Nagle	.20
60	Jeff Blake	.75
61	Rich Owens	.20
62	Anthony Edwards	.20
63	Orlando Brown	.20
64	Matthew Campbell	.20
65	Ricky Watters	.40
66	Travis Hannah	.20
67	Melvin Tuten	.20
68	Aaron Taylor	.20
69	Dale Hellestrae	.20
70	Marshall Faulk	1.00
71	Gary Anderson	.20
72	David Williams	.20
73	Jim Harbaugh	.20
74	Ray Hall	.20
75	Dan Marino	2.50
76	Chris Mims	.20
77	Matt Blundin	.20
78	Roy Barker	.20
79	John Burke	.20
80	Troy Aikman	1.25
81	Ed King	.20
82	Stan White	.20
83	Vance Joseph	.20
84	David Klingler	.20
85	Terrell Davis	1.00
86	Bobby Hoying	.20
87	Lethon Flowers	.20
88	Dwayne White	.20
89	Vaughn Parker	.20
90	Jerry Rice	1.25
91	Casey Weldon	.20
92	Rick Mirer	.20
93	Jim Pyne	.20
94	Matt Turk	.20
95	Marcus Allen	.20
96	Rob Moore	.20
97	Ruben Brown	.20
98	Zach Thomas	.20
99	Carwell Gardner	.20
100	Barry Sanders	1.75
101	Ben Coleman	.20
102	Steve Rhem	.20
103	Everett McIver	.20
104	Cole Ford	.20
105	Dave Krieg	.20
106	Anthony Parker	.20
107	Michael Brandon	.20
108	Michael McCrary	.20
109	Chad Fann	.20
110	Brett Favre	2.50

1996 Pacific Dynagon

Pacific's 1996 Dynagon Prism set has 144 regular-issue cards and five insert sets. It is sold as a retail and hobby product, with inserts exclusive to both. The regular card front has a gold-foiled football stamped on the left, with a player photo in the middle. The player's name is written along the right side. The card uses the team's primary colors in the design. The horizontal back has a player profile shot on one side, flanked by his name, position and team name, card number and brief career summary. The five insert sets are Dynamic Duos, Gems of the Crown, Kings of the NFL, Tandems and Best Kept Secrets.

		MT
Complete Set (144):		150.00
Common Player:		.75
Minor Stars:		1.50
Wax Box:		65.00
1	Larry Centers	.75
2	Garrison Hearst	1.50
3	Dave Krieg	.75
4	Frank Sanders	1.50
5	Jeff George	1.50
6	Craig Heyward	.75
7	Terance Mathis	.75
8	Eric Metcalf	.75
9	Todd Collins	.75
10	Darick Holmes	.75
11	Jim Kelly	1.50
12	*Eric Moulds*	5.00
13	Bryce Paup	.75
14	Thurman Thomas	1.50
15	*Tim Biakabutuka*	2.50
16	Blake Brockermeyer	.75
17	Mark Carrier	.75
18	Kerry Collins	2.00
19	Derrick Moore	.75
20	*Bobby Engram*	2.00
21	Jeff Graham	.75
22	Erik Kramer	.75
23	Rashaan Salaam	1.50
24	Steve Stenstrom	.75
25	Chris Zorich	.75
26	Jeff Blake	2.00
27	David Dunn	.75
28	Carl Pickens	1.50
29	Darnay Scott	.75
30	Earnest Byner	.75
31	Leroy Hoard	.75
32	Keenan McCardell	.75
33	Eric Zeier	.75
34	Troy Aikman	5.00
35	Chris Boniol	.75
36	Michael Irvin	1.50
37	Daryl Johnston	.75
38	Deion Sanders	3.00
39	Emmitt Smith	10.00
40	*Stepfret Williams*	1.50
41	John Elway	5.00
42	Terrell Davis	10.00
43	Anthony Miller	.75
44	Shannon Sharpe	.75
45	Scott Mitchell	.75
46	Herman Moore	1.50
47	Brett Perriman	.75
48	Barry Sanders	10.00
49	Cory Schlesinger	.75
50	Edgar Bennett	.75
51	Robert Brooks	.75
52	Mark Chmura	1.50
53	Brett Favre	10.00
54	Reggie White	1.50
55	*Eddie George*	10.00
56	Steve McNair	4.00
57	Chris Sanders	1.50
58	Rodney Thomas	1.50
59	Ben Bronsen	.75
60	Zack Crockett	.75
61	Marshall Faulk	2.50
62	Jim Harbaugh	.75
63	Mark Brunell	4.00
64	*Kevin Hardy*	1.50
65	Willie Jackson	.75
66	Pete Mitchell	.75
67	James Stewart	.75
68	Marcus Allen	1.50
69	Steve Bono	1.50
70	Lake Dawson	.75
71	Neil Smith	.75
72	Tamarick Vanover	1.50
73	Irving Fryar	.75
74	Terry Kirby	.75
75	Dan Marino	10.00
76	O.J. McDuffie	.75
77	Bernie Parmalee	.75
78	*Stanley Pritchett*	.75
79	Cris Carter	.75
80	Qadry Ismail	.75
81	Chad May	.75
82	Warren Moon	.75
83	Robert Smith	.75
84	Drew Bledsoe	5.00
85	Ben Coates	.75
86	*Terry Glenn*	4.00
87	Curtis Martin	6.00
88	Willie McGinest	.75
89	Mario Bates	.75
90	Jim Everett	.75
91	Wayne Martin	.75
92	Shane Pahukoa	.75
93	Ray Zellars	.75
94	Dave Brown	.75
95	Chris Calloway	.75
96	Rodney Hampton	.75
97	Tyrone Wheatley	.75
98	Wayne Chrebet	.75
99	Glenn Foley	.75
100	*Keyshawn Johnson*	6.00
101	Adrian Murrell	.75
102	*Alex Van Dyke*	1.50
103	Tim Brown	.75
104	Harvey Williams	.75
105	Billy Joe Hobert	.75
106	Raghib Ismail	.75
107	Napoleon Kaufman	1.50
108	Charlie Garner	.75
109	Rodney Peete	.75
110	Ricky Watters	.75
111	Calvin Williams	.75
112	Mark Bruener	.75
113	Kevin Greene	.75
114	Ernie Mills	.75
115	Kordell Stewart	6.00
116	Yancey Thigpen	1.50
117	Dave Barr	.75
118	Jerome Bettis	.75
119	Isaac Bruce	1.50
120	*Lawrence Phillips*	2.00
121	J.T. Thomas	.75
122	Ronnie Harmon	.75
123	Aaron Hayden	1.50
124	Stan Humphries	.75
125	Junior Seau	1.50
126	William Floyd	.75
127	Elvis Grbac	.75
128	Jerry Rice	5.00
129	J.J. Stokes	1.50
130	Steve Young	5.00
131	Joey Galloway	2.00
132	Cortez Kennedy	.75
133	Kevin Mawae	.75
134	Rick Mirer	.75
135	Chris Warren	1.50
136	Trent Dilfer	.75
137	Jerry Ellison	.75
138	Alvin Harper	.75
139	Errict Rhett	1.50
140	Terry Allen	.75
141	Brian Mitchell	.75
142	Gus Frerotte	.75
143	Michael Westbrook	1.50
144	Heath Shuler	1.50

1996 Pacific Dynagon Dynamic Duos

This 24-card 1996 Pacific Dynagon insert set showcases football's best one-two combinations on 12 teams. Cards 1-12 are found in hobby cases, while 13-24 can be found in retail cases; they are seeded in every 37th pack. Each card front has a color action photo against a metallic background which has one half of the team's helmet on it; the two cards can be placed next to each other to complete the helmet and showcase the duo. The back has a closeup shot of the player, with his name, team name and card number (using a "DD" prefix) at the top. His career accomplishments are also summarized.

		MT
Complete Set (24):		275.00
Common Player:		4.00
Minor Stars:		8.00
1	Troy Aikman	20.00
2	Jerry Rice	20.00
3	Brett Favre	40.00
4	Marshall Faulk	8.00
5	Carl Pickens	4.00
6	Terrell Davis	20.00
7	Curtis Martin	20.00
8	Dan Marino	35.00
9	Herman Moore	4.00
10	Kordell Stewart	20.00
11	Emmitt Smith	35.00
12	Trent Dilfer	4.00
13	Deion Sanders	12.00
14	Steve Young	15.00
15	Robert Brooks	4.00
16	Jim Harbaugh	4.00
17	Jeff Blake	8.00
18	John Elway	15.00
19	Drew Bledsoe	20.00
20	Bernie Parmalee	4.00
21	Barry Sanders	25.00
22	Kevin Greene	4.00
23	Sherman Williams	4.00
24	Errict Rhett	8.00

1996 Pacific Dynagon Gems of the Crown

These 36 Pacific insert cards are distributed in two base brands; cards 1-18 are seeded two per every 37 packs of Dynamic Prism, while 19-36 are seeded in Crown Collection Football packs. The horizontal card front has a color action photo in the center. The top has a gold-foiled panel which has the Pacific logo in the upper left corner; the player's last name is in the upper right corner, with his last name stamped in gold down the side. The player's team logo is in gold along the left side, on a panel using team colors. The horizontal back has a color closeup shot on one side, with the player's position and team name below. The opposite side has the player's name in the upper corner, with a brief career summary underneath. The card is numbered using a "GC" prefix.

		MT
Complete Set (18):		80.00
Common Player:		2.00
1	Kerry Collins	5.00
2	Rashaan Salaam	4.00
3	Steve Young	8.00
4	Rodney Thomas	2.00
5	Michael Westbrook	4.00
6	Cris Carter	2.00
7	Jerry Rice	8.00
8	Drew Bledsoe	8.00
9	Steve McNair	6.00
10	Terrell Davis	12.00
11	Barry Sanders	12.00
12	Robert Brooks	2.00
13	Chris Warren	2.00
14	Marshall Faulk	8.00
15	John Elway	5.00
16	Isaac Bruce	4.00
17	Emmitt Smith	15.00
18	Thurman Thomas	2.00

A player's name in *italic type* indicates a rookie card.

1996 Pacific Dynagon Kings of the NFL

Ten of the NFL's biggest stars are featured on these 1996 Pacific Dynagon inserts. The cards, numbered using a "K" prefix, were seeded one per every 361 packs. The card front is covered with etched foil at the top around the player's name, and at the bottom is a crown with a significant achievement inside it. A color action photo dominates the center of the card. The back has the player's name and team name at the top, with a career summary along the left side. A color action photo is on the right side. The accomplishment highlighted on the front is indicated at the bottom of the card.

		MT
Complete Set (10):		350.00
Common Player:		15.00
1	Emmitt Smith	40.00
2	Dan Marino	40.00
3	Barry Sanders	50.00
4	Curtis Martin	15.00
5	Brett Favre	40.00
6	Kordell Stewart	15.00
7	Emmitt Smith	40.00
8	Jerry Rice	25.00
9	John Elway	40.00
10	Dan Marino	40.00

1996 Pacific Dynagon Gold Tandems

This 72-card parallel set pairs the fronts of two cards from Pacific's main 1996 Dynagon set. The cards were seeded one per every 37 packs.

		MT
Complete Set (72):		1400.
Common Player:		8.00
1	Dan Marino, Troy Aikman	160.00
2	Emmitt Smith, Rashaan Salaam	150.00
3	Jim Kelly, John Elway	50.00
4	Steve Young, Brett Favre	150.00
5	Curtis Martin, Terrell Davis	85.00
6	Kordell Stewart, Napoleon Kaufman	60.00
7	Barry Sanders, Jerry Rice	100.00
8	Joey Galloway, J.J. Stokes	50.00
9	Kerry Collins, Jeff Blake	20.00
10	Deion Sanders, Reggie White	40.00
11	Herman Moore, Mark Chmura	20.00
12	Eric Zeier, Tyrone Wheatley	15.00
13	Errict Rhett, Robert Brooks	25.00
14	Trent Dilfer, Steve McNair	40.00
15	Marshall Faulk, Drew Bledsoe	50.00
16	Tamarick Vanover, Michael Westbrook	25.00
17	Heath Shuler, Jerome Bettis	20.00
18	Isaac Bruce, Tim Brown	25.00
19	Terry Allen, Chris Warren	12.00
20	Brian Mitchell, Alex Van Dyke	12.00
21	Jerry Ellison, Kevin Mawae	8.00
22	Alvin Harper, Stanley Pritchett	8.00
23	Rick Mirer, Elvis Grbac	8.00
24	Cortez Kennedy, Junior Seau	8.00
25	William Floyd, Aaron Hayden	12.00
26	Stan Humphries, Dave Barr	8.00
27	J.T. Thomas, Stepfret Williams	12.00
28	Ronnie Harmon, Yancey Thigpen	12.00
29	Ernie Mills, Calvin Williams	8.00
30	Mark Bruener, Eddie George	50.00
31	Kevin Greene, Eric Moulds	12.00
32	Ricky Watters, Harvey Williams	8.00
33	Rodney Peete, Keyshawn Johnson	35.00
34	Charlie Garner, Adrian Murrell	8.00
35	Raghib Ismail, Wayne Chrebet	8.00
36	Billy Jo Hobert, Glenn Foley	8.00
37	Rodney Hampton, Ben Coates	8.00
38	Chris Calloway, Qadry Ismail	8.00
39	Dave Brown, Warren Moon	8.00
40	Ray Zellars, Robert Smith	8.00
41	Shane Pahukoa, Bernie Parmalee	8.00
42	Wayne Martin, Neil Smith	8.00
43	Jim Everett, Steve Bono	8.00
44	Mario Bates, Terry Kirby	8.00
45	Willie McGinest, Lawrence Phillips	15.00
46	Chad May, Mark Brunell	30.00
47	Cris Carter, O.J. McDuffie	8.00
48	Irving Fryar, Lake Dawson	8.00
49	Marcus Allen, James Stewart	8.00
50	Willie Jackson, Terry Glenn	50.00
51	Pete Mitchell, Kevin Hardy	15.00
52	Jim Harbaugh, Scott Mitchell	8.00
53	Zack Crockett, Rodney Thomas	15.00
54	Ben Bronson, Chris Sanders	8.00
55	Edgar Bennett, Tim Biakabutuka	8.00
56	Brett Perriman, Anthony Miller	8.00
57	Cory Schlesinger, Daryl Johnston	8.00
58	Shannon Sharpe, Michael Irvin	8.00
59	Chris Boniol, Thurman Thomas	8.00
60	Keenan McCardell, Darnay Scott	8.00
61	Leroy Hoard, Chris Zorich	8.00
62	Earnest Byner, Jeff Graham	8.00
63	Carl Pickens, Darick Holmes	8.00
64	David Dunn, Mark Carrier	8.00
65	Steve Stenstrom, Todd Collins	8.00
66	Eric Kramer, Derrick Moore	8.00
67	Larry Centers, Bobby Engram	25.00
68	Garrison Hearst, Jeff George	15.00
69	Dave Krieg, Craig Heyward	8.00
70	Frank Sanders, Terance Mathis	8.00
71	Gus Frerotte, Eric Metcalf	8.00
72	Bryce Paup, Blake Brockermeyer	8.00

1996 Pacific Gridiron

The only oversized football card set on the market returned for a second year in 1996 under the Pacific Pure Gridiron brand. A total of 1,500 cases of the product were produced, meaning the various inserts are rather limited in availability. Each card front uses gold foil stamping for the player's name and Crown Collection logo at the bottom. The photo on the front is a full-bleed color action shot. The back recaps the game from which the photo was taken, and another photo. Five parallel sets were made - Electric Blue (hobby), Scorching Red (retail), Presidential Copper (hobby, four per 37 packs), Presidential Platinum (retail, four per 37) and Presidential Gold (two per 721 packs of both retail and hobby; only 30 of these sets exist). Insert sets include Gold Crown die-cuts, Driving Force, Gridiron Performers and Gridiron Gems.

		MT
Complete Set (125):		90.00
Common Player:		.50
Wax Box:		60.00
1	Larry Centers	.50
2	Garrison Hearst	.50
3	Dave Krieg	.50
4	*Frank Sanders*	.50
5	*Jamal Anderson*	5.00
6	J.J. Birden	.50
7	Eric Metcalf	.50
8	Jeff George	1.00
9	Cornelius Bennett	.50
10	Todd Collins	.50
11	Darick Holmes	1.00
12	Jim Kelly	1.00
13	Bryce Paup	.50
14	Bob Christian	.50
15	Kerry Collins	4.50
16	Pete Metzelaars	.50
17	Derrick Moore	.50
18	Curtis Conway	.50
19	Jim Flanigan	.50
20	Erik Kramer	.50
21	Rashaan Salaam	2.00
22	Eric Bieniemy	.50
23	Jeff Blake	2.00
24	Tony McGee	.50
25	Darnay Scott	.50
26	Vashone Adams	.50
27	Leroy Hoard	.50
28	Andre Rison	.50
29	Tommy Vardell	.50
30	Troy Aikman	4.00
31	Michael Irvin	1.00
32	Daryl Johnston	.50
33	Deion Sanders	2.00
34	Emmitt Smith	8.00
35	Terrell Davis	5.00
36	John Elway	2.00
37	Ed McCaffrey	.50
38	Anthony Miller	.50
39	Scott Mitchell	.50
40	Brett Perriman	.50
41	Barry Sanders	4.00
42	Chris Spielman	.50
43	Edgar Bennett	.50
44	Robert Brooks	.50
45	Brett Favre	8.00
46	Antonio Freeman	.50
47	Reggie White	.50
48	Haywood Jeffires	.50
49	Steve McNair	3.00
50	Rodney Thomas	1.50
51	Frank Wycheck	.50
52	Ashley Ambrose	.50
53	Mark Brunell	4.00
54	Ken Dilger	.50
55	Marshall Faulk	2.00
56	Jim Harbaugh	.50
57	Tony Boselli	.50
58	Pete Mitchell	.50
59	James Stewart	.50
60	Marcus Allen	.50
61	Steve Bono	.50
62	Lake Dawson	.50
63	Tamarick Vanover	2.00
64	Bryan Cox	.50
65	Dan Marino	8.00
66	O.J. McDuffie	.50
67	Bernie Parmalee	.50
68	Cris Carter	.50
69	Qadry Ismail	.50
70	Warren Moon	.50
71	Robert Smith	.50
72	Drew Bledsoe	4.00
73	Vincent Brisby	.50
74	Ben Coates	.50
75	Curtis Martin	6.00
76	Mario Bates	.50
77	Derek Brown	.50
78	Jim Everett	.50
79	Dave Brown	.50
80	Chris Calloway	.50
81	Rodney Hampton	.50
82	Tyrone Wheatley	.50
83	Kyle Brady	.50
84	Wayne Chrebet	.50
85	Adrian Murrell	.50
86	Tim Brown	.50
87	Rob Carpenter	.50
88	Charlie Garner	.50
89	Daryl Hobbs	.50
90	Napoleon Kaufman	1.50
91	Rodney Peete	.50
92	Ricky Watters	.50
93	Calvin Williams	.50
94	Kevin Greene	.50
95	Greg Lloyd	.50
96	Neil O'Donnell	.50
97	Erric Pegram	.50
98	Kordell Stewart	4.50
99	Yancey Thigpen	2.00
100	Rod Woodson	.50
101	Isaac Bruce	2.00
102	Jerome Bettis	.50
103	J.T. Thomas	.50
104	Ronnie Harmon	.50
105	*Aaron Hayden*	1.50
106	Stan Humphries	.50
107	Alfred Pupunu	.50
108	William Floyd	.50
109	Brent Jones	.50
110	Jerry Rice	4.00
111	J.J. Stokes	2.00
112	John Taylor	.50
113	Steve Young	4.00
114	Harvey Williams	.50
115	John Friesz	.50
116	Joey Galloway	3.00
117	Cortez Kennedy	.50
118	Rick Mirer	.50
119	Chris Warren	1.00
120	Trent Dilfer	.50
121	Alvin Harper	.50
122	Errict Rhett	3.00
123	Terry Allen	.50
124	Gus Frerotte	.50
125	Michael Westbrook	2.50

1996 Pacific Gridiron Copper/Platinum

The 125-card, regular-size parallel set to the Gridiron issue, these sets can be distinguished by the foil on the card fronts. Both Copper and platinum were inserted four times every 37 packs.

	MT
Complete Set (125):	600.00
Common Player:	4.00
Semistars:	7.00
Cop./Plat.:	3x-6x

1996 Pacific Gridiron Gold

The 125-card, regular-sized set paralleled the Gridiron issue. The cards were inserted twice every 721 packs, with just 30 sets produced.

	MT
Common Player (1-125):	50.00
Semistars:	100.00

1996 Pacific Gridiron Driving Force

The top 10 running backs in the NFL are highlighted in this 1996 Pacific Pure Gridiron insert set. Cards were seeded one per every 73 packs. The card front has a color action photo, with a team color-coordinated hourglass with gold foil highlights behind the player. Gold foil is also used for the card's background, set name and player's name, which is highlighted in his team's color. The Crown logo is in the upper left corner. The back also uses the player's primary team color for the background, and has a color action photo in the center, with the set name above the photo and the player's name below. A brief recap of the player's 1995 season accomplishments is below the photo. A card number, using a "DF" prefix, is in the lower right corner.

		MT
Complete Set (10):		175.00
Common Player:		10.00
1	Chris Warren	10.00
2	Emmitt Smith	50.00
3	Barry Sanders	25.00
4	Rashaan Salaam	15.00
5	Errict Rhett	25.00
6	Curtis Martin	40.00
7	Garrison Hearst	10.00
8	Marshall Faulk	25.00
9	Terrell Davis	25.00
10	Edgar Bennett	10.00

1996 Pacific Gridiron Gems

These 1996 Pacific Pure Gridiron inserts feature 50 top NFL stars. Cards, numbered on the back using a GG prefix, were randomly inserted three per every four packs. The front has a color action photo in the center, with the Crown logo in the upper left corner. A puzzle-like border is used to frame three sides; a gridiron, with the player's name and brand logo, is stamped along the bottom of the card in green foil. The horizontal back repeats the puzzle pattern and has a color photo on one side and a recap of the player's 1995 achievements on the other.

		MT
Complete Set (50):		45.00
Common Player:		.50
1	J.J. Birden	.50
2	Garrison Hearst	.50
3	Bryce Paup	.50
4	Kerry Collins	3.00
5	Alonzo Spellman	.50

6	Chris Zorich	.50
7	Harold Green	.50
8	Lee Johnson	.50
9	Eric Zeier	.50
10	Troy Aikman	3.00
11	Deion Sanders	1.50
12	Emmitt Smith	6.00
13	John Elway	1.50
14	Mike Pritchard	.50
15	Shane Bonham	.50
16	Barry Sanders	3.00
17	Edgar Bennett	.50
18	Brett Favre	6.00
19	Reggie White	.50
20	Eddie Robinson	.50
21	Marshall Faulk	3.00
22	Brian Stablein	.50
23	Don Davey	.50
24	Neil Smith	.50
25	Derrick Thomas	.50
26	Eric Green	.50
27	Jake Reed	.50
28	Troy Brown	.50
29	Will Moore	.50
30	Wesley Walls	.50
31	Herschel Walker	.50
32	Keyshawn Johnson	3.00
33	Billy Joe Hobert	.50
34	Ricky Watters	.50
35	Ernie Mills	.50
36	Kordell Stewart	3.00
37	Terrell Fletcher	.50
38	Junior Seau	.50
39	Elvis Grbac	.50
40	Gary Plummer	.50
41	Jerry Rice	3.00
42	Steve Young	3.00
43	Carlester Crumpler	.50
44	Joey Galloway	3.00
45	Cortez Kennedy	.50
46	Chris Warren	1.00
47	Greg Robinson	.50
48	Errict Rhett	3.00
49	Terry Allen	.50
50	Stanley Richard	.50

1996 Pacific Gridiron Gold Crown Die-Cut

These cards could be obtained by sending in a redemption card bearing the player's name and card number. The cards were seeded one per every 37 packs of 1996 Pacific Pure Gridiron product. The front is a die-cut crown, with gold foil used to complete the crown. Gold foil is also used for the player's name, which is at the bottom adjacent to a team helmet. A full-bleed color action photo is in the center of the card. The back, numbered using a "GC" prefix, has a crown at the top, with a player photo in the center and his name below. Career, 1995 and most prolific games are recapped in brief summaries below.

		MT
Complete Set (20):		400.00
Common Player:		10.00
1	Barry Sanders	30.00
2	Ricky Watters	10.00
3	Troy Aikman	30.00
4	Deion Sanders	20.00
5	Kerry Collins	30.00
6	Dan Marino	50.00
7	Steve Young	30.00
8	Drew Bledsoe	30.00
9	Jerry Rice	30.00
10	Steve McNair	30.00
11	Joey Galloway	25.00
12	John Elway	15.00
13	Terrell Davis	25.00
14	Rashaan Salaam	15.00
15	Kordell Stewart	30.00
16	Emmitt Smith	50.00
17	Curtis Martin	45.00
18	Marshall Faulk	30.00
19	Brett Favre	50.00
20	Chris Warren	10.00

1996 Pacific Gridiron Rock Solid Rookies

Six of the NFL's top rookies from the 1995 season are featured on these 1996 Pacific Pure Gridiron inserts. The cards, seeded one per every 121 packs, are numbered on the back using an "RP" prefix. The front has a color action photo in the center, with a granite rock background and gold-foil borders. The player's team helmet is at the bottom in gold, too. "Rock Solid Rookie" is written in rock-like letters at the bottom. The Pacific Crown logo is in the upper left corner. The back has the player's name and set name running along opposite sides. A color photo is in a square at the top of the card, while a recap of the player's rookie season is underneath. The background is a gray marble.

		MT
Complete Set (6):		150.00
Common Player:		15.00
1	Joey Galloway	30.00
2	Napoleon Kaufman	15.00
3	Michael Westbrook	20.00
4	Kerry Collins	40.00
5	Aaron Hayden	15.00
6	Kordell Stewart	40.00

1996 Pacific Invincible

Pacific's 1996 Invincible Football (Prism II) has 150 cards in the set. Each is paralleled in four different versions. The regular card front has a color action photo in the middle, with a gold-foiled sunburst design as a background pattern. The Pacific logo is in the upper left corner; the player's team logo is in a team color-coordinated banner at the bottom. The lower left corner has a small oval with a plastic piece inside featuring the player's mug shot. His name is in gold foil above the photo; his position is below. The back side has a rectangle at the top, with a color photo to inside it. The Pacific logo is in the upper left corner. The player's name is below the photo, with a recap of his career comprising most of the back side. The plastic mug shot is reversed on the front and is in the lower left corner. The card number (using an "I" prefix) is at the bottom of the card. The regular cards have four parallel versions. Hobby packs have a bronze parallel (four per 25 packs), while retail packs have a silver parallel (four per 25 packs).

Then a platinum (one per 25) and a gold parallel set are found in both hobby and retail packs. There are also four insert sets - Kick-Starters Die-Cuts, Pro Bowl Stars, Smash Mouth, and a 10-card Chris Warren set.

		MT
Complete Set (150):		150.00
Common Player:		1.00
Minor Stars:		2.00
Wax Box:		60.00
1	Larry Centers	1.00
2	Garrison Hearst	1.00
3	Seth Joyner	1.00
4	*Simeon Rice*	2.00
5	Eric Swann	1.00
6	Bert Emanuel	1.00
7	Jeff George	1.00
8	Craig Heyward	1.00
9	Terance Mathis	1.00
10	Eric Metcalf	1.00
11	Derrick Alexander	1.00
12	Leroy Hoard	1.00
13	Andre Rison	1.00
14	Tommy Vardell	1.00
15	Eric Zeier	1.00
16	Jim Kelly	2.00
17	*Eric Moulds*	7.00
18	Bryce Paup	1.00
19	Bruce Smith	1.00
20	Thurman Thomas	2.00
21	*Tim Biakabutuka*	4.00
22	Blake Brockermeyer	1.00
23	Kerry Collins	3.00
24	Howard Griffith	1.00
25	Lamar Lathon	1.00
26	Mark Carrier	1.00
27	Curtis Conway	1.00
28	Erik Kramer	1.00
29	Rashaan Salaam	2.00
30	Alonzo Spellman	1.00
31	Jeff Blake BR	4.00
32	Harold Green	1.00
33	Carl Pickens	2.00
34	Darnay Scott	2.00
35	Dan Wilkinson	1.00
36	Troy Aikman	6.00
37	Jay Novacek	1.00
38	Deion Sanders	5.00
39	Emmitt Smith	12.00
40	Kevin Williams	1.00
41	Terrell Davis	12.00
42	John Elway	4.00
43	Anthony Miller	1.00
44	Michael Dean Perry	1.00
45	Shannon Sharpe	1.00
46	Scott Mitchell	1.00
47	Herman Moore	2.00
48	Brett Perriman	1.00
49	Barry Sanders	8.00
50	Chris Spielman	1.00
51	Edgar Bennett	1.00
52	Robert Brooks	1.00
53	Brett Favre	12.00
54	*Derrick Mayes*	3.00
55	Reggie White	2.00
56	*Eddie George*	12.00
57	Haywood Jeffires	1.00
58	Steve McNair	5.00
59	Chris Sanders	2.00
60	Rodney Thomas	2.00
61	Tony Bennett	1.00
62	Quentin Coryatt	1.00
63	Ken Dilger	1.00
64	Marshall Faulk	4.00
65	Jim Harbaugh	1.00
66	Tony Boselli	1.00
67	Mark Brunell	5.00
68	Kevin Hardy	1.00
69	Desmond Howard	1.00
70	James Stewart	1.00
71	Marcus Allen	2.00
72	Steve Bono	1.00
73	Neil Smith	1.00
74	Derrick Thomas	1.00
75	Tamarick Vanover	1.00
76	*Karim Abdul-Jabbar*	3.00
77	Irving Fryar	1.00
78	Eric Green	1.00
79	Dan Marino	12.00
80	Bernie Parmalee	1.00
81	Cris Carter	1.00
82	Warren Moon	1.00
83	Jake Reed	1.00
84	Robert Smith	1.00
85	Moe Williams	1.00
86	Drew Bledsoe	6.00
87	Ben Coates	1.00
88	*Terry Glenn*	6.00
89	Curtis Martin	5.00
90	Dave Meggett	1.00
91	Mario Bates	1.00
92	Jim Everett	1.00
93	Michael Haynes	1.00
94	Torrance Small	1.00
95	Ray Zellars	1.00
96	Kyle Brady	1.00
97	Wayne Chrebet	1.00
98	*Keyshawn Johnson*	8.00
99	Adrian Murrell	1.00
100	*Alex Van Dyke*	2.00
101	Michael Brooks	1.00
102	Dave Brown	1.00
103	Chris Calloway	1.00
104	Rodney Hampton	1.00
105	*Amani Toomer*	2.00
106	Tyrone Wheatley	1.00
107	Tim Brown	1.00
108	*Rickey Dudley*	3.00
109	Billy Joe Hobert	1.00
110	Raghib Ismail	1.00
111	Napoleon Kaufman	1.00
112	Harvey Williams	1.00
113	Charlie Garner	1.00
114	*Bobby Hoying*	2.50
115	Rodney Peete	1.00
116	Ricky Watters	2.00
117	Greg Lloyd	1.00
118	Erric Pegram	1.00
119	Kordell Stewart	7.00
120	Yancey Thigpen	2.00
121	Jon Witman	1.00
122	Aaron Hayden	1.00
123	Stan Humphries	1.00
124	Tony Martin	1.00
125	Leslie O'Neal	1.00
126	Junior Seau	1.00
127	Jerome Bettis	2.00
128	Isaac Bruce	2.00
129	Ernie Conwell	1.00
130	*Lawrence Phillips*	3.00
131	William Floyd	1.00
132	*Terrell Owens*	12.00
133	Jerry Rice	7.00
134	J.J. Stokes	2.00
135	Steve Young	6.00
136	Brian Blades	1.00
137	Christian Fauria	1.00
138	Joey Galloway	6.00
139	Rick Mirer	1.00
140	Chris Warren	2.00
141	Horace Copeland	1.00
142	Trent Dilfer	1.00
143	Alvin Harper	1.00
144	Dave Moore	1.00
145	Errict Rhett	2.00
146	Terry Allen	1.00
147	Gus Frerotte	1.00
148	Brian Mitchell	1.00
149	Heath Shuler	1.00
150	Michael Westbrook	2.00

1996 Pacific Invincible Bronze/Silver/Platinum

Pacific's 150-card Invincible set was paralleled in a total of four different versions. Hobby packs contained Bronze parallels, while retail packs had Silver versions of the base set, with both seeded four per 25 packs. In addition, Invincible Platinums (1:25) and Golds were available in both types of packs at a reduced rate. Each version is distinguished by the color foil used.

	MT
Complete Bronze Set (149):	1000.
Bronze Cards:	3x-6x
Complete Silver Set (149):	1000.
Silver Cards:	3x-6x
Complete Platinum Set (149):	2000.
Platinum Cards:	6x-12x

1996 Pacific Invincible Chris Warren

This 10-card set is entirely devoted to Seattle Seahawks running back Chris Warren. Each card features a different action shot of Warren, with cards found every 10 packs.

		MT
Complete Set (10):		10.00
Common Warren:		1.00
1	Chris Warren	1.00
2	Chris Warren	1.00
3	Chris Warren	1.00
4	Chris Warren	1.00
5	Chris Warren	1.00
6	Chris Warren	1.00
7	Chris Warren	1.00
8	Chris Warren	1.00
9	Chris Warren	1.00
10	Chris Warren	1.00

1996 Pacific Invincible Kick-Starters

These 1996 Pacific Invincible inserts are the most limited; they are seeded one per every 49 packs. The cards are die-cut into a gold-foiled football with a color action photo on it. The player's name is written along the left side of the card against a grassy background. The Pacific logo is in the upper left corner. The card back has a color action photo on the football part of the card; the right side has the player's name and a recap of a time when the player jump-started his team. The card is numbered using a "KS" prefix.

		MT
Complete Set (20):		500.00
Common Player:		15.00
1	Jeff Blake	18.00
2	Tim Brown	15.00
3	Kerry Collins	20.00
4	John Elway	30.00
5	Marshall Faulk	18.00
6	Brett Favre	75.00
7	Keyshawn Johnson	25.00
8	Dan Marino	75.00
9	Curtis Martin	50.00
10	Steve McNair	25.00
11	Errict Rhett	18.00
12	Jerry Rice	40.00
13	Rashaan Salaam	15.00
14	Barry Sanders	40.00
15	Deion Sanders	30.00
16	Emmitt Smith	75.00
17	Kordell Stewart	30.00
18	Tamarick Vanover	18.00
19	Chris Warren	15.00
20	Ricky Watters	15.00

1996 Pacific Invincible Pro Bowl

Every 25th pack of 1996 Pacific Invincible has one of these insert cards devoted to participants in the previous Pro Bowl game. Each card front shows the player in his Pro Bowl uniform against a colorful metallic background which incorporates the Pacific logo into the pattern. The player's name is written along the bottom. The horizontal back, numbered using a "PB" prefix, has a close-up shot of the player in his uniform, along with a Pro Bowl logo

and a recap of some of his accomplishments as a Pro Bowler.

		MT
Complete Set (20):		175.00
Common Player:		4.00
1	Jeff Blake	6.00
2	Steve Bono	4.00
3	Tim Brown	4.00
4	Cris Carter	4.00
5	Ben Coates	4.00
6	Brett Favre	30.00
7	Jim Harbaugh	4.00
8	Curtis Martin	25.00
9	Warren Moon	4.00
10	Herman Moore	8.00
11	Carl Pickens	4.00
12	Jerry Rice	18.00
13	Barry Sanders	25.00
14	Shannon Sharpe	4.00
15	Emmitt Smith	30.00
16	Yancey Thigpen	7.00
17	Chris Warren	4.00
18	Ricky Watters	4.00
19	Reggie White	4.00
20	Steve Young	14.00

1996 Pacific Invincible Smash-Mouth

Some of the NFL's most intense players and hardest hitters are featured on these 1996 Pacific Invincible inserts. The cards, numbered on the back using an "SM" prefix, were seeded two per pack. Each card front shows a player busting through a hole against a football field background. The Pacific logo is in the upper right corner; the player's name is along the bottom. The back has a square in the upper right corner which has a mug shot inside. A summary of some of his accomplishments is given below the photo. The player's name, team name and position are written along the left side of the card, below the Pacific logo.

		MT
Complete Set (180):		30.00
Common Player:		.20
Minor Stars:		.40
1	Marcus Dowdell	.20
2	Karl Dunbar	.20
3	Eric England	.20
4	Garrison Hearst	.20
5	Bryan Reeves	.20
6	Simeon Rice	.20
7	Jeff George	.20
8	Bobby Hebert	.20
9	Craig Heyward	.20
10	Dave Richard	.20
11	Elbert Shelley	.20
12	Lonnie Johnson	.20
13	Jim Kelly	.20
14	Corbin Lacina	.20
15	Bryce Paup	.20
16	Sam Rogers	.20
17	Bruce Smith	.20
18	Thurman Thomas	.40
19	Carl Banks	.20
20	Dan Footman	.20
21	Louis Riddick	.20
22	Matt Stover	.20
23	Tommy Barnhardt	.20
24	Kerry Collins	.75
25	Mark Dennis	.20
26	Matt Elliott	.20
27	Eric Guliford	.20
28	Lamar Lathon	.20
29	Joe Cain	.20
30	Marty Carter	.20
31	Robert Green	.20
32	Erik Kramer	.20
33	Todd Perry	.20
34	Rashaan Salaam	.40
35	Alonzo Spellman	.20
36	Jeff Blake	.75
37	Andre Collins	.20
38	Todd Kelly	.20

#	Player	Price
39	Carl Pickens	.20
40	Kevin Sargent	.20
41	Troy Aikman	1.25
42	Charles Haley	.20
43	Daryl Johnston	.20
44	Nate Newton	.20
45	Deion Sanders	.75
46	Emmitt Smith	3.00
47	Steve Atwater	.20
48	Terrell Davis	1.00
49	John Elway	.75
50	Michael Dean Perry	.20
51	Shannon Sharpe	.20
52	Dave Wyman	.20
53	Bennie Blades	.20
54	Kevin Glover	.20
55	Herman Moore	.50
56	Robert Porcher	.20
57	Barry Sanders	1.25
58	Henry Thomas	.20
59	Edgar Bennett	.20
60	Robert Brooks	.20
61	Brett Favre	3.00
62	Harry Galbreath	.20
63	Sean Jones	.20
64	Reggie White	.40
65	Blaine Bishop	.20
66	Chuck Cecil	.20
67	Cris Dishman	.20
68	Steve McNair	.75
69	Rodney Thomas	.20
70	Jason Belser	.20
71	Ray Buchanan	.20
72	Quentin Coryatt	.20
73	Marshall Faulk	1.00
74	Jim Harbaugh	.20
75	Devon McDonald	.20
76	Tony Boselli	.20
77	Tony Brackens	.20
78	Mark Brunell	.75
79	Don Davey	.20
80	Rich Gottfried	.20
81	Kevin Hardy	.20
82	Mickey Washington	.20
83	Louis Aguiar	.20
84	Dan Saleaumua	.20
85	Will Shields	.20
86	Neil Smith	.20
87	Derrick Thomas	.20
88	Tamarick Vanover	.75
89	Gene Atkins	.20
90	Bryan Cox	.20
91	Steve Emtman	.20
92	Chris Gray	.20
93	Dan Marino	3.00
94	Derrick Alexander	.20
95	Cris Carter	.20
96	Jeff Christy	.20
97	Robert Smith	.20
98	Korey Stringer	.20
99	Orlando Thomas	.20
100	Esera Tuaolo	.20
101	Drew Bledsoe	1.00
102	Eddie Cade	.20
103	Mike Jones	.20
104	Curtis Martin	2.00
105	Willie McGinest	.20
106	Chris Slade	.20
107	Eric Allen	.20
108	Mario Bates	.20
109	Jim Dombrowski	.20
110	Wayne Martin	.20
111	William Roaf	.20
112	Irv Smith	.20
113	Michael Brooks	.20
114	Stacey Dillard	.20
115	Rodney Hampton	.20
116	Doug Riesenberg	.20
117	Coleman Rudolph	.20
118	Tyrone Wheatley	.20
119	Kyle Brady	.20
120	Roger Duffy	.20
121	Keyshawn Johnson	1.00
122	Gary Jones	.20
123	Eddie Anderson	.20
124	Rickey Dudley	.40
125	Napoleon Kaufman	.20
126	Greg Skrepenak	.20
127	Pat Swilling	.20
128	Steve Wisniewski	.20
129	William Fuller	.20
130	Kurt Gouveia	.20
131	Andy Harmon	.20
132	Mike Mamula	.20
133	Guy McIntyre	.20
134	Ricky Watters	.20
135	Kevin Greene	.20
136	Bill Johnson	.20
137	Carnell Lake	.20
138	Greg Lloyd	.20
139	Erric Pegram	.20
140	Leon Searcy	.20
141	Shane Conlan	.20
142	Troy Drayton	.20
143	Wayne Gandy	.20
144	Sean Gilbert	.20
145	Carlos Jenkins	.20
146	Lawrence Phillips	.75
147	Aaron Hayden	.20
148	Stan Humphries	.20
149	Leslie O'Neal	.20
150	Bo Orlando	.20
151	Junior Seau	.20
152	Harry Swayne	.20
153	Harris Barton	.20
154	Merton Hanks	.20
155	Rod Milstead	.20
156	Ken Norton Jr.	.20
157	Gary Plummer	.20
158	Jerry Rice	1.50
159	Steve Wallace	.20
160	Steve Young	1.00
161	James Atkins	.20
162	Brian Blades	.20
163	Matt Joyce	.20
164	Cortez Kennedy	.20
165	Kevin Mawae	.20
166	Winston Moss	.20
167	Chris Warren	.40
168	Derrick Brooks	.20
169	Trent Dilfer	.20
170	Santana Dotson	.20
171	Alvin Harper	.20
172	Hardy Nickerson	.20
173	Errict Rhett	.40
174	Warren Sapp	.20
175	Terry Allen	.20
176	John Gesek	.20
177	Ken Harvey	.20
178	Tre Johnson	.20
179	Rod Stephens	.20
180	Michael Westbrook	.40

1996 Pacific Litho-Cel

The 100-card, regular-sized set actually is two 100-card sets, with Cel and Litho versions. The Cel cards feature a clear oval center with a blue color image. The Litho cards are the same card fronts, but with a red color, non-clear oval center image. When the Cel card is placed over the Litho card, a 3-D effect makes the center oval image appear in full color. The card backs of the Cel cards are numbered with the "Cel" prefix while the Litho cards feature the same corresponding number with a "Litho" prefix. Litho-Cel came in three-card packs and included Moments In Time, Feature Performers, Game Time, Litho-Proof and Certified Litho-Proof inserts, as well as parallel silver foil (3:25) and Blue-Platinum (retail 3:25) versions. Pacific Litho-Cel was available in three-card packs which contained one Cel card, one Litho card and one Game Time card or other insert card.

		MT
Complete Set (100):		75.00
Common Player:		.25
Minor Stars:		.50
Wax Box:		

Prices are for both Litho and Cel cards together.

#	Player	Price
1	Kent Graham	.25
2	LeShon Johnson	.25
3	Leeland McElroy	.75
4	Frank Sanders	.25
5	Jamal Anderson	10.00
6	Cornelius Bennett	.25
7	Bobby Hebert	.25
8	Earnest Byner	.25
9	Michael Jackson	.25
10	Vinny Testaverde	.50
11	Jim Kelly	1.00
12	Andre Reed	.50
13	Bruce Smith	.25
14	Thurman Thomas	1.00
15	Kerry Collins	1.00
16	Lamar Lathon	.25
17	Kevin Greene	.25
18	Bobby Engram	.75
19	Erik Kramer	.25
20	Rashaan Salaam	.50
21	Jeff Blake	1.00
22	Garrison Hearst	1.00
23	Carl Pickens	.50
24	Darnay Scott	.25
25	Troy Aikman	3.00
26	Eric Bjornson	.25
27	Deion Sanders	1.00
28	Emmitt Smith	5.00
29	Terrell Davis	10.00
30	John Elway	5.00
31	Anthony Miller	.25
32	John Mobley	.25
33	Scott Mitchell	.25
34	Herman Moore	1.00
35	Brett Perriman	.25
36	Barry Sanders	6.00
37	Edgar Bennett	.25
38	Robert Brooks	.25
39	Brett Favre	6.00
40	Reggie White	1.00
41	Chris Chandler	.75
42	Eddie George	10.00
43	Steve McNair	3.00
44	Chris Sanders	.25
45	Ken Dilger	.25
46	Marshall Faulk	1.00
47	Jim Harbaugh	.50
48	Mark Brunell	.50
49	Keenan McCardell	.50
50	James Stewart	1.00
51	Marcus Allen	1.00
52	Steve Bono	.50
53	Greg Hill	.50
54	Tamarick Vanover	.50
55	Karim Abdul-Jabbar	3.00
56	Dan Marino	5.00
57	Zach Thomas	1.50
58	Cris Carter	1.00
59	Warren Moon	.50
60	Robert Smith	1.00
61	Drew Bledsoe	3.00
62	Terry Glenn	4.00
63	Curtis Martin	2.00
64	Mario Bates	.25
65	Jim Everett	.50
66	Haywood Jeffires	.25
67	Dave Brown	.25
68	Rodney Hampton	.25
69	Amani Toomer	1.00
70	Adrian Murrell	.50
71	Neil O'Donnell	.50
72	Alex Van Dyke	.50
73	Tim Brown	.50
74	Jeff Hostetler	.25
75	Napoleon Kaufman	.75
76	Irving Fryar	.25
77	Chris T. Jones	.25
78	Ricky Watters	1.00
79	Jerome Bettis	1.00
80	Kordell Stewart	2.50
81	Tony Banks	2.00
82	Eddie Kennison	.75
83	Lawrence Phillips	2.00
84	Stan Humphries	.25
85	Tony Martin	.25
86	Leonard Russell	.25
87	Junior Seau	.50
88	Jerry Rice	3.00
89	J.J. Stokes	.50
90	Tommy Vardell	.25
91	Steve Young	2.00
92	Joey Galloway	1.00
93	Rick Mirer	.50
94	Chris Warren	.25
95	Mike Alstott	3.00
96	Trent Dilfer	.75
97	Nilo Silvan	.25
98	Terry Allen	.50
99	Gus Frerotte	.50
100	Michael Westbrook	.75

1996 Pacific Litho-Cel Bronze/Silver

Each card in the 100-card Litho-Cel set was reprinted in two different foil versions. Silver foil parallels were found in three per 25 hobby packs, while bronze versions were found in three per 25 retail packs. The only difference between these parallels and the regular-issue cards is the color or of the foil stamping.

	MT
Complete Bronze Set (100):	700.00
Bronze Cards:	2x-4x
Complete Silver Set (100):	700.00
Silver Cards:	2x-4x

1996 Pacific Litho-Cel Feature Performers

The 20-card, regular-sized inserts were included in every 25 packs of Litho-Cel cards. The card fronts feature the player over gold foil with his respective team helmet outline on the bottom half of the card. The player's name is written in the player's team color down the right side while the backs are numbered with the "FP" prefix.

		MT
Complete Set (20):		300.00
Common Player:		7.00
1	Jim Kelly	7.00
2	Troy Aikman	20.00
3	Deion Sanders	15.00
4	Emmitt Smith	30.00
5	Terrell Davis	30.00
6	John Elway	20.00
7	Herman Moore	10.00
8	Barry Sanders	25.00
9	Robert Brooks	15.00
10	Brett Favre	40.00
11	Eddie George	25.00
12	Jim Harbaugh	7.00
13	Marcus Allen	7.00
14	Karim Abdul-Jabbar	15.00
15	Dan Marino	40.00
16	Joey Galloway	15.00
17	Curtis Martin	30.00
18	Jerome Bettis	10.00
19	Jerry Rice	20.00
20	Steve Young	15.00

1996 Pacific Litho-Cel Litho-Proof

The 36-card, regular-sized set was inserted in every 97 packs of 1996 Litho-Cel cards. The card fronts feature the same color photo and design as the basic Litho-Cel set, without the clear blue cel imaging. Also differentiating between the two sets is a gray seal in the lower left section of the card front which reads, "1996 Pacific Litho Cards - Litho-Proof." The cards are sequentially numbered as "x of 360" and are listed with a "Litho-Proof" prefix. A parallel version, Certified Litho-Proof, features a second seal "Pacific Collection" and is inserted every 481 packs.

		MT
Complete Set (36):		1600.
Common Player:		15.00
1	Jim Kelly	15.00
2	Kerry Collins	30.00
3	Rashaan Salaam	30.00
4	Jeff Blake	30.00
5	Carl Pickens	15.00
6	Troy Aikman	80.00
7	Deion Sanders	70.00
8	Emmitt Smith	160.00
9	Terrell Davis	100.00
10	John Elway	70.00
11	Herman Moore	30.00
12	Barry Sanders	120.00
13	Robert Brooks	15.00
14	Brett Favre	160.00
15	Reggie White	15.00
16	Eddie George	90.00
17	Marshall Faulk	50.00
18	Jim Harbaugh	15.00
19	Mark Brunell	70.00
20	Marcus Allen	15.00
21	Steve Bono	15.00
22	Karim Abdul-Jabbar	70.00
23	Dan Marino	160.00
24	Warren Moon	15.00
25	Drew Bledsoe	80.00
26	Curtis Martin	100.00
27	Amani Toomer	15.00
28	Tim Brown	15.00
29	Napoleon Kaufman	15.00
30	Ricky Watters	15.00
31	Jerome Bettis	15.00
32	Kordell Stewart	80.00
33	Jerry Rice	80.00
34	Steve Young	70.00
35	Joey Galloway	70.00
36	Terry Allen	15.00

Values quoted in this guide reflect the retail price of a card — the price a collector can expect to pay when buying a card from a dealer. The wholesale price — that which a collector can expect to receive from a dealer when selling cards — will be significantly lower, depending on desirability and condition.

1996 Pacific Litho-Cel Certified Litho-Proofs

Certified Litho-Proofs are similar to the regular Litho-Proof inserts, but contain a large Pacific Crown Collection logo over top of the Litho-Proof logo in the bottom left corner. Certified Litho-Proofs were inserted at a rate of one per 481 packs.

	MT
Complete Set (36):	6000.
Certified Litho-Proofs:	2x-4x

1996 Pacific Litho-Cel Game Time

The 96-card, regular-sized set was inserted in each pack of Litho-Cel cards. The card fronts feature the player centered in an array of statistical cut-out boxes and the player's name is written in a curved pattern over the position on the bottom. The card backs feature headshots of the players in the lower lefthand corner, framed in a stop watch. The cards are numbered with the "GT" prefix.

		MT
Complete Set (96):		25.00
Common Player:		.20
Minor Stars:		.40
1	Eddie George	2.00
2	Larry Bowie	.20
3	Jarius Hayes	.20
4	Jamal Anderson	2.00
5	Earnest Hunter	.20
6	Darick Holmes	.20
7	Kerry Collins	.50
8	Raymont Harris	.20
9	Jeff Blake	.50
10	Troy Aikman	1.50
11	Terrell Davis	2.00
12	Kevin Glover	.20
13	Brett Favre	3.00
14	Al Del Greco	.20
15	Marshall Faulk	.75
16	Bryan Barker	.20
17	Rich Gannon	.20
18	Dwight Hollier	.20
19	Dixon Edwards	.20
20	Drew Bledsoe	1.00
21	Paul Green	.20
22	Lawrence Dawsey	.20
23	Ron Carpenter	.20
24	Joe Aska	.20
25	Joe Panos	.20
26	Norm Johnson	.20
27	Tony Banks	.50
28	Darren Bennett	.20
29	Steve Israel	.20
30	Mike Barber	.20
31	Dexter Nottage	.20
32	Kwamie Lassiter	.20
33	Travis Hall	.20
34	Greg Montgomery	.20
35	Jim Kelly	.20
36	Matt Elliott	.20
37	Jack Jackson	.20
38	Ki-Jana Carter	.40
39	Deion Sanders	.50
40	Jason Elam	.20
41	Johnnie Morton	.20
42	Darius Holland	.20
43	Sheddrick Wilson	.20
44	Derrick Frazier	.20
45	Travis Davis	.20
46	Pellom McDaniels	.20
47	Dan Marino	3.00
48	Ben Hanks	.20
49	Tedy Bruschi	.20
50	Tom Hodson	.20
51	Amani Toomer	.50
52	Brian Hansen	.20
53	Paul Butcher	.20
54	Kevin Turner	.20
55	Darren Perry	.20
56	Mike Gruttadauria	.20
57	Charlie Jones	.20
58	Iheanyi Uwaezuoke	.20
59	Glenn Montgomery	.20
60	Mike Alstott	.75
61	Joe Patton	.20
62	Leeland McElroy	.75
63	Robbie Tobeck	.20
64	Vinny Testaverde	.20
65	Chris Spielman	.20
66	Anthony Johnson	.20
67	Todd Sauerbrun	.20
68	Jeff Hill	.20
69	Emmitt Smith	3.00
70	John Elway	1.00
71	Barry Sanders	3.00
72	Brian Williams	.20
73	Chris Gardocki	.20
74	Jimmy Smith	.20
75	Ricky Siglar	.20
76	Tim Ruddy	.20
77	Moe Williams	.20
78	Willie Clay	.20
79	Henry Lusk	.20
80	Brian Williams	.20
81	Ronald Moore	.20
82	Trey Junkin	.20
83	James Willis	.20
84	Joel Steed	.20
85	Jamie Martin	.20
86	Shawn Lee	.20
87	Steve Young	1.00
88	Barrett Robbins	.20
89	Charles Dimry	.20
90	Darryl Pounds	.20
91	Herschel Walker	.20
92	Bill Romanowski	.20
93	David Tate	.20
94	Marrio Grier	.20
95	Rodney Young	.20
96	Lamar Smith	.20

1996 Pacific Litho-Cel Moments in Time

The 20-card, regular-sized, die-cut set was inserted every 49 packs of Litho-Cel cards. The horizontal cards are die-cut in the shape of a scoreboard and feature red-foil printing. The score of a particular game, along with the player's statistics for that game are included on the card front in scoreboard script, while the card back describes the player's performance with a highlight. The cards are numbered with the "MT" prefix.

		MT
Complete Set (20):		500.00
Common Player:		8.00
1	Jim Kelly	8.00
2	Kerry Collins	16.00
3	Rashann Salaam	8.00
4	Troy Aikman	50.00
5	Deion Sanders	30.00
6	Emmitt Smith	100.00
7	Terrell Davis	50.00
8	John Elway	30.00
9	Barry Sanders	50.00
10	Robert Brooks	8.00

11	Brett Favre	100.00
12	Marshall Faulk	20.00
13	Jim Harbaugh	8.00
14	Steve Bono	8.00
15	Dan Marino	100.00
16	Drew Bledsoe	50.00
17	Curtis Martin	60.00
18	Jerry Rice	50.00
19	Steve Young	40.00
20	Terry Allen	8.00

1997 Pacific

The 450-card set showcases a full-bleed photo on the front, with the Pacific Crown Collection logo in the upper left. The team's helmet is in color in the lower left and reproduced in gold foil towards the bottom center. The player's name is printed in capital gold-foil letters in the lower right of the front. A Copper parallel was inserted 1:1 hobby packs, while a Silver parallel was seeded 1:1 retail packs. A Platinum Blue hobby and retail parallel was included in 1:73 packs. Red-foil parallels were found one per Treat Entertainment U.S. retail pack.

		MT
Complete Set (450):		40.00
Common Player:		.05
Minor Stars:		.10
Copper/Silver Cards:		3x-6x
Blue Cards:		50x-100x
Wax Box:		50.00

1	Lomas Brown	.05
2	Pat Carter	.05
3	Larry Centers	.05
4	Matt Darby	.05
5	Marcus Dowdell	.05
6	Aaron Graham	.05
7	Kent Graham	.10
8	LeShon Johnson	.05
9	Seth Joyner	.05
10	Leeland McElroy	.10
11	Rob Moore	.05
12	Simeon Rice	.05
13	Eric Swann	.05
14	Aeneas Williams	.05
15	Morten Andersen	.05
16	Jamal Anderson	.20
17	Lester Archambeau	.05
18	Cornelius Bennett	.05
19	J.J. Birden	.05
20	Antone Davis	.05
21	Bert Emanuel	.05
22	Travis Hall	.05
23	Bobby Hebert	.05
24	Craig Heyward	.05
25	Terance Mathis	.05
26	Tim McKyer	.05
27	Eric Metcalf	.05
28	Jessie Tuggle	.05
29	Derrick Alexander	.05
30	Orlando Brown	.05
31	Rob Burnett	.05
32	Earnest Byner	.05
33	Ray Ethridge	.05
34	Steve Everitt	.05
35	Carwell Gardner	.05
36	Michael Jackson	.05
37	Jamal Lewis	.05
38	Stevon Moore	.05
39	Bam Morris	.05
40	Jonathan Ogden	.05
41	Vinny Testaverde	.10
42	Todd Collins	.10
43	Russell Copeland	.05
44	Quinn Early	.05
45	John Fina	.05
46	Phil Hansen	.05
47	Eric Moulds	.15
48	Bryce Paup	.05
49	Andre Reed	.05
50	Kurt Schulz	.05
51	Bruce Smith	.05
52	Chris Spielman	.05
53	Steve Tasker	.05
54	Thurman Thomas	.05
55	Carlton Bailey	.05
56	Michael Bates	.05
57	Blake Brockermeyer	.05
58	Mark Carrier	.05
59	Kerry Collins	.25
60	Eric Davis	.05
61	Kevin Greene	.05
62	Raghib Ismail	.05
63	Anthony Johnson	.05
64	Shawn King	.05
65	Greg Kragen	.05
66	Sam Mills	.05
67	Tyrone Poole	.05
68	Wesley Walls	.05
69	Mark Carrier	.05
70	Curtis Conway	.10
71	Bobby Engram	.10
72	Jim Flanigan	.05
73	Al Fontenot	.05
74	Raymont Harris	.05
75	Walt Harris	.05
76	Andy Heck	.05
77	Dave Krieg	.05
78	Rashaan Salaam	.10
79	Vinson Smith	.05
80	Alonzo Spellman	.05
81	Michael Timpson	.05
82	James Williams	.05
83	Ashley Ambrose	.05
84	Eric Bieniemy	.05
85	Jeff Blake	.15
86	Ki-Jana Carter	.05
87	John Copeland	.05
88	David Dunn	.05
89	Jeff Hill	.05
90	Ricardo McDonald	.05
91	Tony McGee	.05
92	Greg Myers	.05
93	Carl Pickens	.10
94	Corey Sawyer	.05
95	Darnay Scott	.05
96	Dan Wilkinson	.05
97	Troy Aikman	1.00
98	Larry Allen	.05
99	Eric Bjornson	.05
100	Ray Donaldson	.05
101	Michael Irvin	.10
102	Daryl Johnston	.05
103	Nate Newton	.05
104	Deion Sanders	.40
105	Jim Schwantz	.05
106	Emmitt Smith	1.75
107	Broderick Thomas	.05
108	Tony Tolbert	.05
109	Erik Williams	.05
110	Sherman Williams	.05
111	Darren Woodson	.05
112	Steve Atwater	.05
113	Aaron Craver	.05
114	Ray Crockett	.05
115	Terrell Davis	1.25
116	Jason Elam	.05
117	John Elway	.60
118	Todd Kinchen	.05
119	Ed McCaffrey	.05
120	Anthony Miller	.05
121	John Mobley	.05
122	Michael Dean Perry	.05
123	Reggie Rivers	.05
124	Shannon Sharpe	.05
125	Alfred Williams	.05
126	Reggie Brown	.05
127	Luther Elliss	.05
128	Kevin Glover	.05
129	Jason Hanson	.05
130	Pepper Johnson	.05
131	Glyn Milburn	.05
132	Scott Mitchell	.05
133	Herman Moore	.15
134	Johnnie Morton	.05
135	Brett Perriman	.05
136	Robert Porcher	.05
137	Ron Rivers	.05
138	Barry Sanders	1.25
139	Henry Thomas	.05
140	Don Beebe	.05
141	Edgar Bennett	.05
142	Robert Brooks	.05
143	LeRoy Butler	.05
144	Mark Chmura	.05
145	Brett Favre	2.00
146	Antonio Freeman	.25
147	Chris Jacke	.05
148	Travis Jervey	.05
149	Sean Jones	.05
150	Dorsey Levens	.10
151	John Michels	.05
152	Craig Newsome	.05
153	Eugene Robinson	.05
154	Reggie White	.10
155	Michael Barrow	.05
156	Blaine Bishop	.05
157	Chris Chandler	.05
158	Anthony Cook	.05
159	Malcolm Floyd	.05
160	Eddie George	1.25
161	Roderick Lewis	.05
162	Steve McNair	.75
163	John Henry Mills	.05
164	Derek Russell	.05
165	Chris Sanders	.05
166	Mark Stepnoski	.05
167	Frank Wycheck	.05
168	Robert Young	.05
169	Trev Alberts	.05
170	Aaron Bailey	.05
171	Tony Bennett	.05
172	Ray Buchanan	.05
173	Quentin Coryatt	.05
174	Eugene Daniel	.05
175	Sean Dawkins	.05
176	Ken Dilger	.05
177	Marshall Faulk	.10
178	Jim Harbaugh	.05
179	Marvin Harrison	.40
180	Paul Justin	.05
181	Lamont Warren	.05
182	Bernard Whittingham	.05
183	Tony Bosselli	.05
184	Tony Brackens	.05
185	Mark Brunell	.75
186	Brian DeMarco	.05
187	Rich Griffith	.05
188	Kevin Hardy	.05
189	Willie Jackson	.05
190	Jeff Lageman	.05
191	Keenan McCardell	.10
192	Natrone Means	.05
193	Pete Mitchell	.05
194	Joel Smeenge	.05
195	Jimmy Smith	.10
196	James Stewart	.05
197	Marcus Allen	.10
198	John Art	.05
199	Kimble Anders	.05
200	Steve Bono	.10
201	Vaughn Booker	.05
202	Dale Carter	.05
203	Mark Collins	.05
204	Greg Hill	.05
205	Joe Horn	.05
206	Dan Saleaumua	.05
207	Will Shields	.05
208	Neil Smith	.05
209	Derrick Thomas	.10
210	Tamarick Vanover	.10
211	Karim Abdul-Jabbar	.25
212	Fred Barnett	.05
213	Tim Bowens	.05
214	Kirby Dar Dar	.05
215	Troy Drayton	.05
216	Craig Erickson	.05
217	Daryl Gardener	.05
218	Randal Hill	.05
219	Dan Marino	1.75
220	O.J. McDuffie	.05
221	Bernie Parmalee	.05
222	Stanley Pritchett	.05
223	Daniel Stubbs	.05
224	Zach Thomas	.20
225	Derrick Alexander	.05
226	Cris Carter	.10
227	Jeff Christy	.05
228	Qadry Ismail	.05
229	Brad Johnson	.05
230	Andrew Jordan	.05
231	Randall McDaniel	.05
232	David Palmer	.05
233	John Randle	.05
234	Jake Reed	.05
235	Scott Sisson	.05
236	Korey Stringer	.05
237	Darryl Talley	.05
238	Orlando Thomas	.05
239	Bruce Armstrong	.05
240	Drew Bledsoe	1.00
241	Willie Clay	.05
242	Ben Coates	.05
243	Frank Collins	.05
244	Terry Glenn	.25
245	Jerome Henderson	.05
246	Shawn Jefferson	.05
247	Dietrich Jells	.05
248	Ty Law	.05
249	Curtis Martin	1.25
250	Willie McGinest	.05
251	David Meggett	.05
252	Lawyer Milloy	.05
253	Chris Slade	.05
254	Je'Rod Cherry	.05
255	Jim Everett	.05
256	Mark Fields	.05
257	Michael Haynes	.05
258	Tyrone Hughes	.05
259	Haywood Jeffires	.05
260	Wayne Martin	.05
261	Mark McMillian	.05
262	Rufus Porter	.05
263	William Roaf	.05
264	Torrance Small	.05
265	Renaldo Turnbull	.05
266	Ray Zellars	.05
267	Jessie Armstead	.05
268	Chad Bratzke	.05
269	Dave Brown	.05
270	Chris Calloway	.05
271	Howard Cross	.05
272	Lawrence Dawsey	.05
273	Rodney Hampton	.05
274	Danny Kanell	.05
275	Arthur Marshall	.05
276	Aaron Pierce	.05
277	Phillippi Sparks	.05
278	Amani Toomer	.05
279	Charles Way	.05
280	Richie Anderson	.05
281	Fred Baxter	.05
282	Wayne Chrebet	.05
283	Kyle Clifton	.05
284	John Elliott	.05
285	Aaron Glenn	.05
286	Jeff Graham	.05
287	Bobby Hamilton	.05
288	Keyshawn Johnson	.40
289	Adrian Murrell	.05
290	Neil O'Donnell	.05
291	Webster Slaughter	.05
292	Alex Van Dyke	.05
293	Marvin Washington	.05
294	Joe Aska	.05
295	Jerry Ball	.05
296	Tim Brown	.10
297	Rickey Dudley	.10
298	Pat Harlow	.05
299	Nolan Harrison	.05
300	Billy Joe Hobert	.05
301	James Jett	.05
302	Napoleon Kaufman	.10
303	Lincoln Kennedy	.05
304	Albert Lewis	.05
305	Chester McGlockton	.05
306	Pat Swilling	.05
307	Steve Wisniewski	.05
308	Darion Conner	.05
309	Ty Detmer	.05
310	Jason Dunn	.05
311	Irving Fryar	.05
312	Jeff Fuller	.05
313	William Fuller	.05
314	Charlie Garner	.05
315	Bobby Hoying	.05
316	Tom Hutton	.05
317	Chris T. Jones	.05
318	Mike Mamula	.05
319	Mark Seay	.05
320	Bobby Taylor	.05
321	Ricky Watters	.10
322	Jahine Arnold	.05
323	Jerome Bettis	.10
324	Chad Brown	.05
325	Mark Bruener	.05
326	Andre Hastings	.05
327	Norm Johnson	.05
328	Levon Kirkland	.05
329	Carnell Lake	.05
330	Greg Lloyd	.05
331	Ernie Mills	.05
332	Orpheus Roye	.05
333	Kordell Stewart	.75
334	Yancey Thigpen	.05
335	Mike Tomczak	.05
336	Rod Woodson	.05
337	Tony Banks	.25
338	Bern Brostek	.05
339	Isaac Bruce	.15
340	Ernie Conwell	.05
341	Keith Crawford	.05
342	Wayne Gandy	.05
343	Harold Green	.05
344	Carlos Jenkins	.05
345	Jimmie Jones	.05
346	Eddie Kennison	.40
347	Todd Lyght	.05
348	Leslie O'Neal	.05
349	Lawrence Phillips	.10
350	Greg Robinson	.05
351	Darren Bennett	.05
352	Lewis Bush	.05
353	Eric Castle	.05
354	Terrell Fletcher	.05
355	Darrien Gordon	.05
356	Kurt Gouveia	.05
357	Aaron Hayden	.05
358	Stan Humphries	.05
359	Tony Martin	.05
360	Vaughn Parker	.05
361	Brian Roche	.05
362	Leonard Russell	.05
363	Junior Seau	.10
364	Roy Barker	.05
365	Harris Barton	.05
366	Dexter Carter	.05
367	Chris Doleman	.05
368	Tyrone Drakeford	.05
369	Elvis Grbac	.05
370	Derek Loville	.05
371	Tim McDonald	.05
372	Ken Norton	.05
373	Terrell Owens	.50
374	Gary Plummer	.05
375	Jerry Rice	1.00
376	Dana Stubblefield	.05
377	Lee Woodall	.05
378	Steve Young	.60
379	Robert Blackmon	.05
380	Brian Blades	.05
381	Carlester Crumpler	.05
382	Christian Fauria	.05
383	John Friesz	.05
384	Joey Galloway	.25
385	Derrick Graham	.05
386	Cortez Kennedy	.05
387	Warren Moon	.10
388	Winston Moss	.05
389	Mike Pritchard	.05
390	Michael Sinclair	.05
391	Lamar Smith	.05
392	Chris Warren	.05
393	Chidi Ahanotu	.05
394	Mike Alstott	.15
395	Reggie Brooks	.05
396	Trent Dilfer	.10
397	Jerry Ellison	.05
398	Paul Gruber	.05
399	Alvin Harper	.05
400	Courtney Hawkins	.05
401	Dave Moore	.05
402	Errict Rhett	.10
403	Warren Sapp	.05
404	Nilo Silvan	.05
405	Regan Upshaw	.05
406	Casey Weldon	.05
407	Terry Allen	.05
408	Jamie Asher	.05
409	Bill Brooks	.05
410	Tom Carter	.05
411	Henry Ellard	.05
412	Gus Frerotte	.05
413	Darrell Green	.05
414	Ken Harvey	.05
415	Tre' Johnson	.05
416	Brian Mitchell	.05
417	Rich Owens	.05
418	Heath Shuler	.05
419	Michael Westbrook	.05
420	Tony Woods	.05
421	Reidel Anthony	1.50
422	Darnell Autry	.50
423	Tiki Barber	1.00
424	Pat Barnes	.30
425	Terry Battle	.10
426	Will Blackwell	.30
427	Peter Boulware	.10
428	Rae Carruth	1.00
429	Troy Davis	.50
430	Jim Druckenmiller	2.00
431	Warrick Dunn	1.75
432	Marc Edwards	.10
433	James Farrior	.10
434	Yatil Green	.50
435	Byron Hanspard	.50
436	Ike Hilliard	1.50
437	David LaFleur	.50
438	Kevin Lockett	.25
439	Sam Madison	.10
440	Brian Manning	.10
441	Orlando Pace	.50
442	Jake Plummer	4.00
443	Chad Scott	.10
444	Sedrick Shaw	.30
445	Antowain Smith	1.25
446	Shawn Springs	.30
447	Ross Verba	.20
448	Bryant Webster	.10
449	Renaldo Wynn	.10
450	Jimmy Johnson	.30

1997 Pacific Card Supials

Inserted 1:37 packs, the 36-card set features a player photo superimposed on the front, with a gold-foil version of the same photo printed along the right side of the front. The Crown logo is in the upper left, while the player's first name is in the upper right. His last name is printed vertically along the left edge of the front. The backs include a slot where a miniature die-cut card of the player can be inserted. The mini card includes a photo inside a die-cut football, which is sitting on a tee. The team's logo is in the lower right of the mini-card front.

		MT
Complete Set (72):		500.00
Complete Large Set (36):		300.00
Complete Small Set (36):		200.00
Common Large Player:		2.00
Minor Large Stars:		4.00
Small Cards:		70%
Inserted 1:37		
1	Todd Collins	2.00
2	Kerry Collins	4.00
3	Wesley Walls	2.00
4	Jeff Blake	4.00
5	Troy Aikman	15.00
6	Emmitt Smith	25.00
7	Terrell Davis	25.00
8	John Elway	20.00
9	Herman Moore	4.00
10	Barry Sanders	30.00
11	Brett Favre	30.00
12	Dorsey Levens	4.00
13	Eddie George	15.00
14	Steve McNair	10.00
15	Marshall Faulk	6.00
16	Mark Brunell	15.00
17	Natrone Means	4.00
18	Marcus Allen	4.00
19	Karim Abdul-Jabbar	4.00
20	Dan Marino	25.00
21	Brad Johnson	4.00
22	Drew Bledsoe	15.00
23	Terry Glenn	6.00
24	Curtis Martin	10.00
25	Napoleon Kaufman	8.00
26	Ricky Watters	4.00
27	Jerome Bettis	4.00
28	Kordell Stewart	15.00
29	Tony Banks	4.00
30	Isaac Bruce	4.00
31	Eddie Kennison	4.00
32	Jerry Rice	15.00
33	Steve Young	10.00
34	Joey Galloway	6.00
35	Chris Warren	2.00
36	Gus Frerotte	2.00

1997 Pacific Big Number Die-Cuts

Inserted 1:37 packs, the 20-card die-cut set features the player's last name and jersey number on the front of the card. The backs feature the player's name at the top, with the Pacific Crown logo in the upper right. A player photo is in the center, with his highlights located inside a box near the bottom.

		MT
Complete Set (20):		285.00
Common Player:		4.00
Minor Stars:		8.00
Inserted 1:37		
1	Jamal Anderson	15.00
2	Kerry Collins	8.00
3	Troy Aikman	20.00
4	Emmitt Smith	30.00
5	Terrell Davis	35.00
6	John Elway	30.00
7	Barry Sanders	40.00
8	Brett Favre	40.00
9	Eddie George	20.00
11	Mark Brunell	20.00
12	Karim Abdul-Jabbar	8.00
13	Dan Marino	30.00
14	Drew Bledsoe	20.00
15	Curtis Martin	15.00
16	Napoleon Kaufman	10.00
17	Jerome Bettis	8.00
18	Eddie Kennison	4.00
19	Jerry Rice	20.00
20	Steve Young	15.00

1997 Pacific Cramer's Choice Awards

Inserted 1:721 packs, the 10-card set showcases a player photo superimposed over a pyra-

mid die-cut background. "1997 Cramer's Choice Awards" and the Crown logo are printed at the top of the award, while the gold base of the award includes the Crown logo, player's name and position.

		MT
Complete Set (10):		750.00
Common Player:		25.00
Inserted 1:721		
1	Kevin Greene	25.00
2	Emmitt Smith	125.00
3	Terrell Davis	150.00
4	John Elway	125.00
5	Barry Sanders	150.00
6	Brett Favre	150.00
7	Eddie George	75.00
8	Mark Brunell	75.00
9	Terry Glenn	40.00
10	Jerry Rice	75.00

1997 Pacific Gold Crown Die-Cuts

The 36-card set was inserted 1:37 packs. The top of the cards feature a die-cut gold crown at the top. The player's photo is superimposed over the crown. The bottom of the card front has three gold-foil stripes, with the player's name printed in the center of the middle stripe. A circle at the bottom center feature the team logo inside a shield. Eight sun rays are printed diagonally at the bottom of the front.

		MT
Complete Set (36):		575.00
Common Player:		4.00
Minor Stars:		8.00
Inserted 1:37		
1	Larry Centers	4.00
2	Vinny Testaverde	8.00
3	Kerry Collins	8.00
4	Kevin Green	4.00
5	Anthony Johnson	4.00
6	Jeff Blake	8.00
7	Troy Aikman	25.00
8	Emmitt Smith	40.00
9	Terrell Davis	45.00
10	John Elway	40.00
11	Barry Sanders	50.00
12	Brett Favre	50.00
13	Antonio Freeman	12.00
14	Eddie George	25.00
15	Marshall Faulk	12.00
16	Mark Brunell	20.00
17	Jimmy Smith	8.00
18	Marcus Allen	8.00
19	Karim Abdul-Jabbar	8.00
20	Dan Marino	40.00
21	Brad Johnson	12.00
22	Drew Bledsoe	20.00
23	Terry Glenn	12.00
24	Curtis Martin	15.00
25	Adrian Murrell	4.00
26	Tim Brown	4.00
27	Jerome Bettis	12.00
28	Kordell Stewart	20.00
29	Tony Banks	8.00
30	Terrell Owens	25.00
31	Jerry Rice	25.00
32	Steve Young	15.00
33	Chris Warren	4.00
34	Terry Allen	8.00
35	Gus Frerotte	4.00
36	Jim Druckenmiller	8.00

1997 Pacific Mark Brunell

The four-card set was split between Crown Collection and Invincible. Card Nos. 1-2 were seeded 1:72 packs of Crown, while Nos. 3-4 were inserted 1:72 in Invincible packs.

	MT
Complete Set (4):	40.00
Common Player:	10.00

1997 Pacific Team Checklists

The 30-card set is inserted 1:37 packs. The fronts feature an action shot of a player on the left side, with his name printed in gold across his body, while the team's two other stars have each of their head shot printed on football-shaped acetate pieces on the right. Their names appear above the top football and below the bottom football. The team's name and the word "checklist" are repeated many times beginning on the left border and continuing to a thin area on the right side.

		MT
Complete Set (30):		375.00
Common Player:		6.00
Minor Stars:		12.00
Inserted 1:37		
1	Arizona Cardinals	6.00
2	Atlanta Falcons	6.00
3	Baltimore Ravens	6.00
4	Buffalo Bills	12.00
5	Carolina Panthers	12.00
6	Chicago Bears	6.00
7	Cincinnati Bengals	12.00
8	Dallas Cowboys	40.00
9	Denver Broncos	30.00
10	Detroit Lions	50.00
11	Green Bay Packers	50.00
12	Houston Oilers	30.00
13	Indianapolis Colts	6.00
14	Jacksonville Jaguars	20.00
15	Kansas City Chiefs	6.00
16	Miami Dolphins	40.00
17	Minnesota Vikings	12.00
18	New England Patriots	30.00
19	New Orleans Saints	6.00
20	New York Giants	6.00
21	New York Jets	6.00
22	Oakland Raiders	6.00
23	Philadelphia Eagles	6.00
24	Pittsburgh Steelers	15.00
25	St. Louis Rams	12.00
26	San Diego Chargers	6.00
27	San Francisco 49ers	30.00
28	Seattle Seahawks	6.00
29	Tampa Bay Buccaneers	6.00
30	Washington Redskins	6.00

1997 Pacific The Zone

Inserted 1:73 packs, the 20-card set is die-cut in the shape of a goal post. The front has a photo of the player inside the uprights, while his name and position are printed at the base of the goal post.

		MT
Complete Set (20):		475.00
Common Player:		6.00
Minor Stars:		12.00
Inserted 1:73		
1	Kerry Collins	12.00
2	Jeff Blake	12.00

		MT
3	Emmitt Smith	40.00
4	Terrell Davis	40.00
5	John Elway	30.00
6	Barry Sanders	50.00
7	Brett Favre	50.00
8	Mark Brunell	25.00
9	Karim Abdul-Jabbar	12.00
10	Dan Marino	40.00
11	Drew Bledsoe	25.00
12	Terry Glenn	12.00
13	Curtis Martin	20.00
14	Napoleon Kaufman	15.00
15	Jerome Bettis	12.00
16	Eddie Kennison	6.00
17	Tony Martin	6.00
18	Jerry Rice	25.00
19	Steve Young	20.00
20	Terry Allen	12.00

1997 Pacific Crown Royale

Crown Royale is a 144-card, all die-cut set. The base cards feature a player shot on a crown-shaped die-cut card. The two parallel sets are silver and holographic gold foil (4:25) and silver and holographic blue foil (1:25). Insert sets include NFL Cel-Fusions, Chalk Talk Laser Cuts, Pro Bowl Die-Cuts, Firestone on Football and Premium-sized Cramer's Choice Awards.

		MT
Complete Set (144):		150.00
Common Player:		.50
Minor Stars:		1.00
Gold/Silver Cards:		2x-4x
Gold/Silver Rookies:		2x
Blue Cards:		6x-12x
Blue Rookies:		3x-6x
Wax Box:		100.00
1	Larry Centers	.50
2	Kent Graham	1.00
3	LeShon Johnson	.50
4	Leeland McElroy	.50
5	*Jake Plummer*	20.00
6	Jamal Anderson	1.00
7	Chris Chandler	.50
8	*Byron Hanspard*	1.50
9	Michael Haynes	.50
10	Derrick Alexander	.50
11	*Jay Graham*	1.50
12	Michael Jackson	.50
13	Vinny Testaverde	.50
14	Todd Collins	1.00
15	Jay Riemersma	.50
16	*Antowain Smith*	6.00
17	Steve Tasker	.50
18	Thurman Thomas	1.00
19	*Rae Carruth*	4.00
20	Kerry Collins	1.00
21	Anthony Johnson	.50
22	*Fred Lane*	3.00
23	Muhsin Muhammad	.50
24	Wesley Walls	.50
25	*Darnell Autry*	1.00
26	Raymont Harris	1.00
27	Erik Kramer	.50
28	Rick Mirer	.50
29	Rashaan Salaam	.50
30	Jeff Blake	1.00
31	Ki-Jana Carter	.50
32	*Corey Dillon*	8.00
33	Carl Pickens	1.00
34	Troy Aikman	6.00
35	Michael Irvin	1.00
36	Daryl Johnston	.50
37	*David LaFleur*	2.00
38	Deion Sanders	3.00
39	Emmitt Smith	10.00
40	Terrell Davis	6.00
41	John Elway	4.00
42	Ed McCaffrey	.50
43	Shannon Sharpe	.50
44	Neil Smith	.50
45	Scott Mitchell	.50
46	Herman Moore	1.00
47	Johnnie Morton	.50
48	Barry Sanders	7.00
49	Robert Brooks	.50
50	Mark Chmura	.50
51	Brett Favre	12.00
52	Antonio Freeman	1.00
53	Dorsey Levens	1.00
54	Reggie White	1.00

		MT
55	Ken Dilger	.50
56	Marshall Faulk	1.00
57	Jim Harbaugh	.50
58	Marvin Harrison	2.00
59	Mark Brunell	6.00
60	Rob Johnson	.50
61	Keenan McCardell	.50
62	Natrone Means	1.00
63	Jimmy Smith	.50
64	Marcus Allen	1.00
65	Tony Gonzalez	6.00
66	Elvis Grbac	.50
67	Greg Hill	.50
68	Tamarick Vanover	.50
69	Karim Abdul-Jabbar	1.50
70	Fred Barnett	.50
71	Dan Marino	10.00
72	O.J. McDuffie	.50
73	Jerris McPhail	.50
74	Cris Carter	.50
75	Randall Cunningham	.50
76	Brad Johnson	1.00
77	Jake Reed	.50
78	Robert Smith	1.00
79	Drew Bledsoe	6.00
80	Ben Coates	.50
81	Terry Glenn	1.50
82	Curtis Martin	6.00
83	*Troy Davis*	1.50
84	Heath Shuler	.50
85	Irv Smith	.50
86	*Danny Wuerffel*	6.00
87	*Tiki Barber*	6.00
88	Dave Brown	.50
89	Rodney Hampton	.50
90	*Ike Hilliard*	1.50
91	Amani Toomer	.50
92	Wayne Chrebet	.50
93	Keyshawn Johnson	2.00
94	Adrian Murrell	1.00
95	Neil O'Donnell	.50
96	Dedric Ward	.50
97	Tim Brown	1.00
98	Jeff George	1.00
99	Desmond Howard	.50
100	Napoleon Kaufman	2.00
101	Ty Detmer	.50
102	Irving Fryar	.50
103	Bobby Hoying	.50
104	Ricky Watters	1.00
105	Jerome Bettis	1.00
106	*Will Blackwell*	2.00
107	Charles Johnson	.50
108	*George Jones*	1.00
109	Kordell Stewart	6.00
110	Tony Banks	2.00
111	Isaac Bruce	1.00
112	Eddie Kennison	2.00
113	Lawrence Phillips	1.00
114	Jim Everett	.50
115	Stan Humphries	.50
116	*Freddie Jones*	1.50
117	Tony Martin	.50
118	Junior Seau	1.00
119	*Jim Druckenmiller*	8.00
120	Garrison Hearst	.50
121	Brent Jones	.50
122	Terrell Owens	5.00
123	Jerry Rice	6.00
124	Steve Young	4.00
125	Chad Brown	.50
126	Joey Galloway	1.00
127	*Jon Kitna*	40.00
128	Warren Moon	.50
129	Chris Warren	.50
130	Mike Alstott	3.00
131	*Reidel Anthony*	6.00
132	Trent Dilfer	1.00
133	*Warrick Dunn*	8.00
134	Karl Williams	.50
135	Willie Davis	.50
136	Eddie George	8.00
137	*Joey Kent*	1.50
138	Steve McNair	4.00
139	Chris Sanders	.50
140	Terry Allen	.50
141	Jamie Asher	.50
142	Stephen Davis	.50
143	Henry Ellard	.50
144	Gus Frerotte	.50

1997 Pacific Crown Royale Cel-Fusions

This 20-card insert consists of a die-cut cel football

fused to a trading card. The cards were inserted 1:49.

		MT
Complete Set (20):		700.00
Common Player:		12.00
1	Antowain Smith	30.00
2	Troy Aikman	50.00
3	Emmitt Smith	100.00
4	Terrell Davis	50.00
5	John Elway	35.00
6	Barry Sanders	50.00
7	Brett Favre	100.00
8	Mark Brunell	50.00
9	Elvis Grbac	12.00
10	Karim Abdul-Jabbar	20.00
11	Dan Marino	100.00
12	Drew Bledsoe	50.00
13	Curtis Martin	50.00
14	Danny Wuerffel	30.00
15	Tiki Barber	20.00
16	Jeff George	12.00
17	Kordell Stewart	50.00
18	Tony Banks	12.00
19	Jerry Rice	50.00
20	Steve Young	35.00

1997 Pacific Crown Royale Chalk Talk

This 20-card insert features a player action shot with a laser cut diagram of one of their signature plays. This set was inserted 1:73.

		MT
Complete Set (20):		900.00
Common Player:		25.00
1	Kerry Collins	30.00
2	Troy Aikman	60.00
3	Emmitt Smith	125.00
4	Terrell Davis	60.00
5	John Elway	40.00
6	Barry Sanders	80.00
7	Brett Favre	150.00
8	Mark Brunell	60.00
9	Marcus Allen	25.00
10	Dan Marino	125.00
11	Drew Bledsoe	60.00
12	Curtis Martin	60.00
13	Troy Davis	25.00
14	Napoleon Kaufman	25.00
15	Jerome Bettis	25.00
16	Jim Druckenmiller	45.00
17	Jerry Rice	60.00
18	Steve Young	40.00
19	Warrick Dunn	70.00
20	Eddie George	85.00

1997 Pacific Crown Royale Cramer's Choice Jumbos

Cramer's Choice is a jumbo-sized insert featuring 10 players on cards die-cut to look like trophies. This insert was found one card per box.

		MT
Complete Set (10):		85.00
Common Player:		4.00
1	Deion Sanders	4.00
2	Emmitt Smith	20.00
3	Terrell Davis	10.00
4	John Elway	7.00
5	Barry Sanders	15.00
6	Brett Favre	25.00
7	Mark Brunell	10.00
8	Drew Bledsoe	10.00
9	Jim Druckenmiller	12.00
10	Eddie George	15.00

A card number in parentheses ( ) indicates the set is unnumbered.

1997 Pacific Crown Royale Firestone on Football

These 20 cards feature players on an etched-foil design. The backs have comments from Roy Firestone. A #21 card was made featuring Firestone with comments from a future Hall of Fame QB on the back. This set was inserted 1:25.

		MT
Complete Set (21):		600.00
Common Player:		7.00
1	Kerry Collins	14.00
2	Troy Aikman	30.00
3	Deion Sanders	18.00
4	Emmitt Smith	60.00
5	Terrell Davis	30.00
6	John Elway	25.00
7	Barry Sanders	40.00
8	Brett Favre	70.00
9	Reggie White	7.00
10	Mark Brunell	30.00
11	Marcus Allen	7.00
12	Dan Marino	60.00
13	Drew Bledsoe	30.00
14	Terry Glenn	14.00
15	Curtis Martin	30.00
16	Jerome Bettis	7.00
17	Jerry Rice	30.00
18	Steve Young	25.00
19	Eddie George	45.00
20	Gus Frerotte	7.00
21	Roy Firestone	7.00

1997 Pacific Crown Royale Pro Bowl Die-Cuts

These die-cut cards feature Pro Bowl players against an ocean background. The 20 cards were inserted 1:25.

		MT
Complete Set (20):		500.00
Common Player:		10.00
1	Kerry Collins	20.00
2	Troy Aikman	50.00
3	Deion Sanders	25.00
4	Terrell Davis	50.00
5	John Elway	30.00
6	Shannon Sharpe	10.00
7	Barry Sanders	50.00
8	Brett Favre	100.00
9	Reggie White	10.00
10	Mark Brunell	50.00
11	Derrick Thomas	10.00
12	Drew Bledsoe	50.00
13	Ben Coates	10.00
14	Curtis Martin	50.00
15	Jerome Bettis	10.00
16	Isaac Bruce	10.00
17	Jerry Rice	50.00
18	Steve Young	30.00
19	Terry Allen	10.00
20	Gus Frerotte	10.00

1997 Pacific Dynagon

The 1997 Pacific Dynagon prism set consists of 144 regular-sized cards. The card fronts feature a gold-foil helmet background with the player's image outlined on top. The background also has the player's team colors with the player's name printed down the right side. The card backs include a head shot in the upper right-hand corner and a brief career highlight. Included with Dynagon Prism football are Tandems, Careers, Player Of The Week, Royal Connections and Best Kept Secrets insert sets. Each pack of Dynagon Prism contains three cards: one base card, one Best Kept Secrets card and one other insert card. A Silver parallel was available in retail packs (2:37), while a Copper parallel was included in 2:37 hobby packs. Red-foil parallels were found in 4:21 Treat Entertainment U.S. retail packs.

		MT
Complete Set (144):		120.00
Common Player:		.50
Minor Stars:		1.00
Wax Box:		60.00
1	Larry Centers	.50
2	Kent Graham	.50
3	Leeland McElroy	1.00
4	Frank Sanders	.50
5	Jamal Anderson	1.00
6	Bert Emanuel	.50
7	Bobby Hebert	.50
8	Terance Mathis	.50
9	Eric Metcalf	.50
10	Derrick Alexander	.50
11	Earnest Byner	.50
12	Michael Jackson	.50
13	Vinny Testaverde	.50
14	Quinn Early	.50
15	Jim Kelly	.50
16	Eric Moulds	2.00
17	Andre Reed	.50
18	Bruce Smith	.50
19	Thurman Thomas	1.00
20	Tshimanga Biakabutuka	1.00
21	Mark Carrier	.50
22	Kerry Collins	1.00
23	Kevin Greene	.50
24	Anthony Johnson	.50
25	Wesley Walls	.50
26	Curtis Conway	.50
27	Bobby Engram	1.00
28	Raymont Harris	.50
29	Dave Krieg	.50
30	Rashaan Salaam	1.00
31	Jeff Blake	1.00
32	Ki-Jana Carter	.50
33	Garrison Hearst	.50
34	Carl Pickens	.50
35	Darnay Scott	.50
36	Troy Aikman	5.00
37	Chris Boniol	.50
38	Michael Irvin	1.00
39	Deion Sanders	3.00
40	Emmitt Smith	10.00
41	Herschel Walker	.50
42	Terrell Davis	7.00
43	John Elway	4.00
44	Ed McCaffrey	.50
45	Shannon Sharpe	.50
46	Alfred Williams	.50
47	Scott Mitchell	.50
48	Herman Moore	1.00
49	Brett Perriman	.50
50	Barry Sanders	7.00
51	Edgar Bennett	.50
52	Robert Brooks	.50
53	Mark Chmura	.50
54	Brett Favre	10.00
55	Antonio Freeman	1.50
56	Desmond Howard	.50
57	Reggie White	1.00
58	Chris Chandler	.50
59	Eddie George	7.00
60	James McKeehan	.50
61	Steve McNair	3.50
62	Chris Sanders	.50
63	Sean Dawkins	.50
64	Ken Dilger	.50
65	Marshall Faulk	2.00
66	Jim Harbaugh	.50
67	Marvin Harrison	2.50
68	Tony Boselli	.50
69	Mark Brunell	5.00
70	Keenan McCardell	.50
71	Natrone Means	1.00
72	Jimmy Smith	.50
73	Marcus Allen	1.00
74	Kimble Anders	.50
75	Dale Carter	.50
76	Greg Hill	.50
77	Derrick Thomas	.50
78	Tamarick Vanover	1.00
79	Karim Abdul-Jabbar	1.00
80	Dan Marino	10.00
81	O.J. McDuffie	.50
82	Jerris McPhail	.50
83	Zach Thomas	1.50
84	Cris Carter	.50
85	Brad Johnson	.50
86	Jake Reed	.50
87	Robert Smith	.50
88	Drew Bledsoe	5.00
89	Ben Coates	.50
90	Terry Glenn	1.00
91	Curtis Martin	8.00
92	Willie McGinest	.50
93	Jim Everett	.50
94	Michael Haynes	.50
95	Haywood Jeffires	.50
96	Ray Zellars	.50
97	Dave Brown	.50
98	Rodney Hampton	.50
99	Danny Kanell	.50
100	Thomas Lewis	.50
101	Wayne Chrebet	.50
102	Keyshawn Johnson	2.50
103	Adrian Murrell	.50
104	Neil O'Donnell	.50
105	Tim Brown	.50
106	Rickey Dudley	1.00
107	Jeff Hostetler	.50
108	Napoleon Kaufman	.50
109	Ty Detmer	.50
110	Jason Dunn	.50
111	Irving Fryar	.50
112	Chris T. Jones	.50
113	Ricky Watters	.50
114	Jerome Bettis	1.00
115	Chad Brown	.50
116	Kordell Stewart	4.00
117	Mike Tomczak	.50
118	Rod Woodson	.50
119	Tony Banks	1.50
120	Isaac Bruce	1.50
121	Eddie Kennison	1.00
122	Lawrence Phillips	.50
123	Terrell Fletcher	.50
124	Stan Humphries	.50
125	Tony Martin	.50
126	Junior Seau	.50
127	Elvis Grbac	.50
128	Terrell Owens	3.00
129	Ted Popson	.50
130	Jerry Rice	5.00
131	Steve Young	4.00
132	John Friesz	.50
133	Joey Galloway	2.00
134	Michael McCrary	.50
135	Lamar Smith	.50
136	Chris Warren	.50
137	Mike Alstott	1.00
138	Trent Dilfer	.50
139	Courtney Hawkins	.50
140	Errict Rhett	1.00
141	Terry Allen	.50
142	Henry Ellard	.50
143	Gus Frerotte	.50
144	Leslie Shepherd	.50

1997 Pacific Dynagon Careers

The 10-card, regular-sized cards were inserted every 360 packs in Dynagon Prism. The card fronts feature gold foil in an outline of a football. The player's name is printed down the right side in blue and the player's image is outlined over a crescent-shaped swirl of the player's sta-

tistics. The card backs feature a circular photo of the player with several career highlights and are numbered 1-10.

		MT
Complete Set (10):		450.00
Common Player:		30.00
1	Jim Kelly	30.00
2	Emmitt Smith	100.00
3	John Elway	40.00
4	Barry Sanders	90.00
5	Brett Favre	100.00
6	Reggie White	30.00
7	Dan Marino	100.00
8	Drew Bledsoe	50.00
9	Jerry Rice	50.00
10	Steve Young	40.00

1997 Pacific Dynagon Player of the Week

The 20-card, regular-sized set was inserted every 37 packs of Dynagon Prism. The card fronts feature an action shot centered in a diamond. The player's first name is printed on the upper right section of the diamond while the last name appears on the lower left section. The player's team helmet is located in the upper right part of the horizontal card front, centered in a diamond. The card backs feature another shot of the player, again centered in a diamond. The card number corresponds with the week the player excelled during the 1996 season and was voted by visitors to Pacific's website as the Player Of The Week.

		MT
Complete Set (20):		250.00
Common Player:		5.00
1	Karim Abdul-Jabbar	7.00
2	Eddie George	15.00
3	Curtis Martin	20.00
4	Mark Brunell	15.00
5	John Elway	10.00
6	Drew Bledsoe	15.00
7	Emmitt Smith	30.00
8	Terrell Davis	20.00
9	Troy Aikman	15.00
10	Jerry Rice	15.00
11	Dan Marino	30.00
12	Barry Sanders	25.00
13	Brett Favre	30.00
14	Steve Young	10.00
15	Kerry Collins	5.00
16	Eddie Kennison	5.00
17	Terry Allen	5.00
18	Brett Favre	30.00
19	Desmond Howard	5.00
20	Mark Brunell	15.00

1997 Pacific Dynagon Royal Connections

Royal Connections, inserted every 73 packs of 1997 Dynagon

Prism, is actually a 30-card, regular-sized, die-cut set that can be fitted with its counterpart to form 15 3-1/2" x 4-1/4" cards. The cards are numbered to 15 with "A" and "B" versions. The A versions feature quarterbacks and the right edge of the card is die-cut in the shape of a football with laces. The "B" versions highlight a wide receiver from a corresponding team and the left side is die-cut to allow the "A" version to fit with it to form a single card.

		MT
Complete Set (30):		425.00
Common Player:		8.00
Minor Stars:		16.00
Inserted 1:73		
1A	Kent Graham	8.00
1B	Larry Centers	8.00
2A	Jim Kelly	16.00
2B	Andre Reed	8.00
3A	Kerry Collins	16.00
3B	Wesley Walls	8.00
4A	Jeff Blake	16.00
4B	Carl Pickens	8.00
5A	Troy Aikman	30.00
5B	Michael Irvin	16.00
6A	John Elway	40.00
6B	Shannon Sharpe	16.00
7A	Brett Favre	60.00
7B	Antonio Freeman	20.00
8A	Mark Brunell	30.00
8B	Keenan McCardell	8.00
9A	Dan Marino	45.00
9B	O.J. McDuffie	8.00
10A	Brad Johnson	16.00
10B	Jake Reed	8.00
11A	Drew Bledsoe	30.00
11B	Terry Glenn	16.00
12A	Ty Detmer	8.00
12B	Irving Fryar	8.00
13A	Kordell Stewart	30.00
13B	Charles Johnson	8.00
14A	Tony Banks	16.00
14B	Isaac Bruce	16.00
15A	Steve Young	25.00
15B	Jerry Rice	30.00

1997 Pacific Dynagon Tandems

Inserted 1:37 packs, the 72 double-fronted cards feature the same 144 players from the base set, with one player on each side. Foiled in emerald, the cards have the numbers printed in the upper right.

		MT
Complete Set (72):		1300.
Common Player:		10.00
Minor Stars:		20.00
Inserted 1:37		
1	Jerome Bettis, Eddie George	50.00
2	Jamal Anderson, Eric Moulds	50.00
3	Kerry Collins, Kordell Stewart	50.00
4	Jeff Blake, Ty Detmer	20.00
5	Michael Irvin, Tim Brown	20.00
6	Deion Sanders, Ray Zellars	20.00
7	Emmitt Smith, Steve Young	85.00
8	Terrell Davis, Barry Sanders	150.00
9	John Elway, Dan Marino	100.00
10	Robert Brooks, Eddie Kennison	10.00
11	Mark Chmura, Shannon Sharpe	20.00
12	Brett Favre, Mark Brunell	85.00
13	Antonio Freeman, Isaac Bruce	30.00
14	Desmond Howard, Natrone Means	20.00

1997 Pacific Invincible

The 150-card set features a player action photo superimposed over a multicolored and gold-foiled background. At the bottom center of the card front is a player head shot printed on acetate. The player's name is printed in gold foil inside a black banner beneath the shield. The Pacific Invincible logo is located in the upper left. The base set is paralleled in Copper foil in hobby packs (2:37), Silver parallel in retail (2:37) and Platinum Blue (1:73). Red-foil parallel was seeded 4:37 in Treat Entertainment U.S. retail packs.

		MT
Complete Set (150):		150.00
Common Player:		.75
Minor Stars:		1.50
Copper Cards:		4x-8x
Silver Cards:		4x-8x
Blue Cards:		10x-20x
Wax Box:		80.00
1	Larry Centers	.75
2	Kent Graham	.75
3	LeShon Johnson	.75
4	Leeland McElroy	1.50
5	Jake Plummer	7.00
6	Frank Sanders	.75
7	Morten Andersen	.75
8	Jamal Anderson	1.50
9	Bert Emanuel	.75
10	Bobby Hebert	.75
11	Roell Preston	.75
12	Derrick Alexander	.75
13	Michael Jackson	.75
14	Bam Morris	.75
15	Vinny Testaverde	.75
16	Todd Collins	1.50
17	Andre Reed	.75
18	Antowain Smith	5.00
19	Steve Tasker	.75
20	Thurman Thomas	1.50
21	Tim Biakabutuka	1.50
22	Rae Carruth	4.00
23	Kerry Collins	2.00
24	Kevin Greene	.75
25	Anthony Johnson	.75
26	Wesley Walls	.75
27	Darnell Autry	1.50
28	Curtis Conway	.75
29	Raymont Harris	.75
30	Rashaan Salaam	1.50
31	Jeff Blake	1.50
32	Ki-Jana Carter	1.50
33	David Dunn	.75
34	Carl Pickens	.75
35	Darnay Scott	.75
36	Troy Aikman	5.00
37	Michael Irvin	1.50
38	Deion Sanders	3.00
39	Emmitt Smith	10.00
40	Herschel Walker	.75
41	Kevin Williams	.75
42	Steve Atwater	.75
43	Terrell Davis	5.00
44	John Elway	4.00
45	Ed McCaffrey	.75
46	Shannon Sharpe	.75
47	Scott Mitchell	.75
48	Herman Moore	1.50
49	Brett Perriman	.75
50	Barry Sanders	8.00
51	Edgar Bennett	.75
52	Robert Brooks	.75
53	Brett Favre	12.00
54	Antonio Freeman	2.00
55	Dorsey Levens	.75
56	Reggie White	1.50
57	Eddie George	7.00
58	Steve McNair	4.00
59	Chris Sanders	.75
60	Sean Dawkins	.75
61	Marshall Faulk	1.50
62	Jim Harbaugh	.75
63	Marvin Harrison	2.50
64	Brian Stablein	.75
65	Mark Brunell	4.00
66	Keenan McCardell	.75
67	Natrone Means	1.50
68	Pete Mitchell	.75

15	Reggie White, Keyshawn Johnson	20.00
16	Edgar Bennett, Chris Sanders	10.00
17	Terry Glenn, Jerry Rice	60.00
18	Steve McNair, Karim Abdul-Jabbar	30.00
19	Marshall Faulk, Tamarick Vanover	20.00
20	Gus Frerotte, Brad Johnson	20.00
21	Jim Kelly, Tim Biakabutuka	20.00
22	Lawrence Phillips, Ben Coates	20.00
23	Napoleon Kaufman, Terrell Owens	40.00
24	Elvis Grbac, Junior Seau	10.00
25	Drew Bledsoe, Tony Banks	45.00
26	Curtis Martin, Troy Aikman	60.00
27	Curtis Conway, Brett Perriman	10.00
28	Bobby Engram, Larry Centers	10.00
29	Raymont Harris, Eric Metcalf	10.00
30	Dave Krieg, Derrick Alexander	10.00
31	Rashaan Salaam, Leeland McElroy	10.00
32	Ki-Jana Carter, Herman Moore	20.00
33	Garrison Hearst, Earnest Byner	10.00
34	Carl Pickens, Frank Sanders	10.00
35	Darnay Scott, Michael Jackson	10.00
36	Chris Boniol, Kent Graham	10.00
37	Herschel Walker, Thurman Thomas	10.00
38	Ed McCaffrey, Quinn Early	20.00
39	Alfred Williams, Mike Alstott	10.00
40	Scott Mitchell, Mark Carrier	10.00
41	Bert Emanuel, Henry Ellard	10.00
42	Bobby Hebert, Trent Dilfer	20.00
43	Terance Mathis, Andre Reed	10.00
44	Vinny Testaverde, Chris Warren	10.00
45	Bruce Smith, Kevin Greene	10.00
46	Anthony Johnson, Terry Allen	10.00
47	Wesley Walls, Errict Rhett	10.00
48	John Friesz, Jeff Hostetler	10.00
49	Joey Galloway, Leslie Shepherd	20.00
50	Michael McCrary, Chris T. Jones	10.00
51	Lamar Smith, Courtney Hawkins	10.00
52	Rickey Dudley, Jason Dunn	10.00
53	Irving Fryar, Tony Martin	10.00
54	Ted Popson, Ricky Watters	10.00
55	Chad Brown, Zach Thomas	20.00
56	Mike Tomczak, Stan Humphries	10.00
57	Rod Woodson, Willie McGinnest	10.00
58	Terrell Fletcher, Jerris McPhail	10.00
59	O.J. McDuffie, Cris Carter	20.00
60	Jake Reed, Marcus Allen	20.00
61	Robert Smith, Greg Hill	10.00
62	Jim Everett, Dave Brown	10.00
63	Michael Haynes, James McKeehan	10.00
64	Haywood Jeffires, Sean Dawkins	10.00
65	Rodney Hampton, Adrian Murrell	10.00
66	Danny Kanell, Marvin Harrison	20.00
67	Thomas Lewis, Dale Carter	10.00
68	Wayne Chrebet, Ken Dilger	20.00
69	Neil O'Donnell, Chris Chandler	10.00
70	Jim Harbaugh, Jimmy Smith	10.00
71	Derrick Thomas, Tony Boselli	10.00
72	Keenan McCardell, Kimble Anders	10.00

69	Jimmy Smith	.75
70	Marcus Allen	1.50
71	Kimble Anders	.75
72	Greg Hill	.75
73	Kevin Lockett	.75
74	Derrick Thomas	.75
75	Tamarick Vanover	.75
76	Karim Abdul-Jabbar	2.00
77	*Yatil Green*	2.00
78	Randal Hill	.75
79	Dan Marino	10.00
80	Stanley Pritchett	.75
81	Irving Spikes	.75
82	Cris Carter	.75
83	Brad Johnson	.75
84	Robert Smith	.75
85	Darryl Talley	.75
86	Drew Bledsoe	5.00
87	Ben Coates	.75
88	Terry Glenn	2.00
89	Curtis Martin	5.00
90	*Sedrick Shaw*	1.50
91	Mario Bates	.75
92	*Troy Davis*	2.00
93	Jim Everett	.75
94	Michael Haynes	.75
95	*Tiki Barber*	5.00
96	Dave Brown	.75
97	Rodney Hampton	.75
98	*Ike Hilliard*	4.00
99	Danny Kanell	.75
100	Wayne Chrebet	.75
101	Keyshawn Johnson	2.50
102	Adrian Murrell	.75
103	Neil O'Donnell	.75
104	Alex Van Dyke	.75
105	Joe Aska	.75
106	Tim Brown	.75
107	Rickey Dudley	.75
108	Napoleon Kaufman	1.50
109	Carl Kidd	.75
110	Ty Detmer	.75
111	Jason Dunn	.75
112	Irving Fryar	.75
113	Bobby Hoying	.75
114	Ricky Watters	1.50
115	Jerome Bettis	1.50
116	Charles Johnson	.75
117	Greg Lloyd	.75
118	Kordell Stewart	4.00
119	Rod Woodson	.75
120	Tony Banks	2.50
121	Isaac Bruce	1.50
122	Eddie Kennison	1.50
123	Lawrence Phillips	1.50
124	Stan Humphries	.75
125	Tony Martin	.75
126	*Corey Dillon*	7.00
127	Leonard Russell	.75
128	Junior Seau	1.50
129	*Jim Druckenmiller*	6.00
130	Marc Edwards	.75
131	Ken Norton Jr.	.75
132	Terrell Owens	3.50
133	Jerry Rice	5.00
134	Iheanyi Uwaezuoke	.75
135	Steve Young	4.00
136	John Friesz	.75
137	Joey Galloway	2.00
138	Warren Moon	.75
139	Todd Peterson	.75
140	Chris Warren	.75
141	Mike Alstott	5.00
142	*Reidel Anthony*	5.00
143	Trent Dilfer	1.50
144	*Warrick Dunn*	7.00
145	Errict Rhett	1.50
146	Terry Allen	.75
147	Henry Ellard	.75
148	Gus Frerotte	.75
149	Brian Mitchell	.75
150	Leslie Shepherd	.75

1997 Pacific Invincible Canton, Ohio

The 10-card Canton, Ohio, chase set was inserted 1:361 packs. The player's photo is superimposed over a crown and multicolored background. The player is standing on an oval, while his name is printed directly beneath it. The chase set's name is printed at the top, with the Invincible logo at the top center.

		MT
Complete Set (10):		500.00
Common Player:		30.00
1	Troy Aikman	50.00
2	Emmitt Smith	100.00
3	John Elway	40.00
4	Barry Sanders	90.00
5	Brett Favre	100.00
6	Reggie White	30.00
7	Marcus Allen	30.00
8	Dan Marino	100.00
9	Jerry Rice	50.00
10	Steve Young	40.00

1997 Pacific Invincible Moments in Time

The 20-card Moments in Time was inserted 1:73 packs. The die-cut cards have a scoreboard-like front, with a player photo on the left. His name is printed beneath his team's and opponent's helmets. The date of the game, his yards and stats, along with the score of the game are printed on the front.

		MT
Complete Set (20):		800.00
Common Player:		20.00
1	Kerry Collins	30.00
2	Troy Aikman	50.00
3	Emmitt Smith	100.00
4	Terrell Davis	50.00
5	John Elway	35.00
6	Barry Sanders	50.00
7	Brett Favre	100.00
8	Reggie White	20.00
9	Eddie George	50.00
10	Mark Brunell	50.00
11	Marcus Allen	20.00
12	Karim Abdul-Jabbar	30.00
13	Dan Marino	100.00
14	Drew Bledsoe	50.00
15	Kevin Greene	30.00
16	Curtis Martin	50.00
17	Jerome Bettis	20.00
18	Eddie Kennison	20.00
19	Jerry Rice	50.00
20	Steve Young	35.00

1997 Pacific Invincible Pop Cards

The 10-card set was inserted 2:37 packs. The front of the card included a player photo, which was surrounded by gold-foil squares. The player's name and position are printed at the bottom center. The Pop Card redemption program worked like this: Remove the Pop Card piece from the card back to reveal a player photo and create a new card. If a collector collected all four pieces of a given player's card, the pieces could be sent to Pacific to receive a limited edition gold-foil card of that same player. Details are provided on the backs of each card.

		MT
Complete Set (10):		50.00
Common Player:		3.00
1	Kerry Collins	3.00
2	Troy Aikman	6.00
3	Emmitt Smith	12.00
4	John Elway	3.00
5	Barry Sanders	10.00
6	Brett Favre	12.00
7	Mark Brunell	6.00
8	Dan Marino	12.00
9	Drew Bledsoe	6.00
10	Jerry Rice	6.00

1997 Pacific Invincible Smash Mouth

This 220-card bonus set was inserted one or two per pack. The cards feature a player photo on the front inside an oval, surrounded by a metal-diamond-type border. The team's logo is in the lower left, while the player's position is in the lower right. The player's name runs along the bottom of the front. In addition, a Smash Mouth X-tra 59-card set was also inserted one or two cards per pack. The card fronts include a large photo on the left, with the player's name printed in a stencil font vertically along the right border. The backs include a photo in the upper right corner.

		MT
Complete Set (220):		20.00
Common Player:		.10
Minor Stars:		.20
1	Don Majkowski	.10
2	Leo Araguz	.10
3	John Carney	.10
4	Brett Favre	2.25
5	Cole Ford	.10
6	Marty Carter	.10
7	John Elway	.75
8	Mark Brunell	1.00
9	Rodney Peete	.10
10	Jeff Feagles	.10
11	Drew Bledsoe	1.00
12	Kerry Collins	.75
13	Dan Marino	2.00
14	Torrian Gray	.10
15	Reidel Anthony	.75
16	Jim Druckenmiller	1.00
17	Jim Everett	.10
18	Pat Barnes	.20
19	Ike Hilliard	.50
20	Barry Sanders	1.25
21	Terry Allen	.20
22	Emmitt Smith	2.00
23	Antowain Smith	.75
24	Robert Griffith	.10
25	Mickey Washington	.10
26	Napoleon Kaufman	.30
27	Eddie George	1.50
28	Curtis Martin	1.00
29	Anthony Lynn	.10
30	Terrell Davis	1.00
31	Steve Broussard	.10
32	Ricky Watters	.20
33	Karim Abdul-Jabbar	.50
34	Thurman Thomas	.20
35	Ross Verba	.10
36	Jerome Bettis	.20
37	Chad Cota	.10
38	Antonio Langham	.10
39	Brett Maxie	.10
40	James Hasty	.10
41	Conrad Hamilton	.10
42	Chris Warren	.10
43	George Jones	.10
44	Byron Hanspard	.50
45	Henri Crockett	.10
46	Brent Alexander	.10
47	John Lynch	.10
48	Renaldo Wynn	.10
49	Jared Tomich	.10
50	James Francis	.10
51	Brian Williams	.10
52	Kevin Mawae	.10
53	Marvcus Patton	.10
54	Mike Barber	.10
55	Robert Jones	.10
56	Ernest Dixon	.10
57	Mo Lewis	.10
58	Peter Boulware	.10
59	Wayne Simmons	.10
60	Anthony Redmon	.10
61	Tim Ruddy	.10
62	Victor Green	.10
63	Kirk Lowdermilk	.10
64	John Jurkovic	.10
65	John Jackson	.10
66	Kevin Gogan	.10
67	Adam Schrieber	.10
68	Mike Morris	.10
69	Albert Connell	.10
70	Tony Mayberry	.10
71	Mark Tuinei	.10
72	Harry Swayne	.10
73	Todd Steussie	.10
74	Glenn Parker	.10
75	(D'Marco Farr)	.10
76	Ed Simmons	.10
77	Tarik Glenn	.10
78	Rick Hamilton	.10
79	Dave Szott	.10
80	Jerry Rice	1.00
81	Tim Brown	.20
82	Charlie Jones	.10
83	Jerry Wunsch	.10
84	Lonnie Johnson	.10
85	Reggie Johnson	.10
86	Willie Davis	.10
87	Greg Clark	.10
88	Deems May	.10
89	J.J. Birden	.10
90	Chuck Smith	.10
91	Coleman Rudolph	.10
92	Leon Johnson	.10
93	Trace Armstrong	.10
94	John Thierry	.10
95	Dean Wells	.10
96	Mike Jones	.10
97	Mike Lodish	.10
98	Tony Siragusa	.10
99	Daved Benefield	.10
100	Michael Bankston	.10
101	Jamal Anderson	.20
102	Greg Montgomery	.10
103	Mark Maddox	.10
104	Matt Elliott	.10
105	Joe Cain	.10
106	Jeff Blake	.20
107	Troy Aikman	1.00
108	Brian Habib	.10
109	Pete Chryplewicz	.10
110	Earl Dotson	.10
111	Joe Bowden	.10
112	Marshall Faulk	.20
113	Reggie Barlow	.10
114	Marcus Allen	.20
115	Jeff Buckey	.10
116	Mitch Berger	.10
117	Corwin Brown	.10
118	Troy Davis	.50
119	Rodney Hampton	.10
120	Tom Knight	.10
121	Michael Booker	.10
122	Matt Stover	.10
123	Mark Pike	.10
124	Rohn Stark	.10
125	Todd Sauerbrun	.10
126	Corey Dillon	.50
127	Tyji Armstrong	.10
128	Vaughn Hebron	.10
129	Antonio London	.10
130	Santana Dotson	.10
131	Cris Dishman	.10
132	Stephen Grant	.10
133	Mike Hollis	.10
134	Martin Bayless	.10
135	Sam Madison	.10
136	Esera Tuaolo	.10
137	Hason Graham	.10
138	Jim Dombrowski	.10
139	Bernard Holsey	.10
140	Kyle Brady	.10
141	David Klingler	.10
142	Don Griffin	.10
143	Bernard Dafney	.10
144	Derrick Harris	.10
145	Charles Johnson	.10
146	Dedrick Dodge	.10
147	Antonio Edwards	.10
148	Jorge Diaz	.10
149	Marc Logan	.10
150	Lou D'Agostino	.10
151	Lance Johnstone	.10
152	Ray Farmer	.10
153	Brenston Buckner	.10
154	Tony Banks	.50
155	'OMar Ellison	.10
156	Derrick Deese	.10
157	Howard Ballard	.10
158	Ronde Barber	.10
159	Gus Frerotte	.10
160	Leeland McElroy	.10
161	Devin Bush	.10
162	Eddie Sutter	.10
163	Sam Rogers	.10
164	Carl Simpson	.10
165	Lee Johnson	.10
166	Tony Casillas	.10
167	Randy Hilliard	.10
168	Ryan McNeil	.10
169	William Henderson	.10
170	Irv Eatman	.10
171	Derwin Gray	.10
172	Rob Johnson	.10
173	Derrick Walker	.10
174	Chris Singleton	.10
175	Chris Walsh	.10
176	Marty Moore	.10
177	Paul Green	.10
178	Brian Williams	.10
179	Robert Farmer	.10
180	Derrick Witherspoon	.10
181	Jim Miller	.10
182	James Harris	.10
183	Shannon Mitchell	.10
184	Steve Young	.75
185	Ronnie Harris	.10
186	Trent Dilfer	.25
187	Joe Patton	.10
188	Jake Plummer	.30
189	Ron George	.10
190	Vinny Testaverde	.10
191	Ryan Wetnight	.10
192	Steve Tovar	.10
193	Godfrey Myles	.10
194	Rod Smith	.10
195	Zefross Moss	.10
196	Jerald Sowell	.10
197	Jason Layman	.10
198	Ray McElroy	.10
199	Tom McManus	.10
200	Shawn Wooden	.10
201	Tony Johnson	.10
202	James Farrior	.10
203	Marc Woodard	.10
204	Chad Scott	.10
205	Dwayne White	.10
206	Warrick Dunn	2.00
207	Joe Wolf	.10
208	Dedric Ward	.10
209	Bennie Thompson	.10
210	Bracey Walker	.10
211	Tracy Scroggins	.10
212	Derrick Mason	.10
213	Ed King	.10
214	Harry Galbreath	.10
215	Joel Steed	.10
216	Jackie Harris	.10
217	Craig Sauer	.10
218	Reinard Wilson	.10
219	Barron Wortham	.10
220	Errict Rhett	.10

1997 Pacific Invincible Smash Mouth X-tra

This 59-card set was randomly inserted into packs of Invincible. The card features the player's name running up the right side in team colors, and is numbered in the bottom right corner on the back where the insert name is also indicated.

		MT
Complete Set (59):		15.00
Common Player:		.10
Minor Stars:		.20
1	Steve Young	.75
2	Jeff Blake	.20
3	Troy Aikman	1.00
4	Brett Favre	2.25
5	Gus Frerotte	.10
6	Tony Banks	.20
7	John Elway	.75
8	Mark Brunell	1.00
9	Rodney Peete	.10
10	Trent Dilfer	.30
11	Drew Bledsoe	1.00
12	Kerry Collins	.75
13	Dan Marino	2.00
14	Vinny Testaverde	.10
15	Reidel Anthony	.75
16	Jim Druckenmiller	1.00
17	Jim Everett	.10
18	Pat Barnes	.30
19	Ike Hilliard	.50
20	Barry Sanders	1.25
21	Terry Allen	.20
22	Emmitt Smith	2.00
23	Antowain Smith	.75
24	Jake Plummer	.30
25	Vaughn Hebron	.10
26	Napoleon Kaufman	.25
27	Eddie George	1.50
28	Curtis Martin	1.00
29	Rodney Hampton	.10
30	Terrell Davis	1.00
31	Marshall Faulk	.20
32	Ricky Watters	.20
33	Karim Abdul-Jabbar	.50
34	Thurman Thomas	.20
35	Troy Davis	.50
36	Jerome Bettis	.20
37	Warrick Dunn	2.00
38	Leeland McElroy	.10
39	William Henderson	.10
40	Jamal Anderson	.20
41	Errict Rhett	.10
42	Chris Warren	.10
43	George Jones	.10
44	Byron Hanspard	.50
45	Jerald Sowell	.10
46	Marcus Allen	.20
47	Kirk Lowdermilk	.10
48	Brian Habib	.10
49	Derrick Mason	.10
50	Jerry Rice	1.00
51	Albert Connell	.10
52	Kyle Brady	.10
53	Tim Brown	.20
54	Charles Johnson	.10
55	Jackie Harris	.10
56	Lonnie Johnson	.10
57	Deems May	.10
58	Peter Boulware	.10
59	Wayne Simmons	.10

1997 Pacific Philadelphia

The 330-card set features a white border on the front of the cards, surrounding the player photo. The Philadelphia logo is in the upper left. The bottom left of the photo includes the player's name, team and position. The team's logo is printed in the lower right. The backs included the player's name inside a stripe at the top left, with the card number inside a circle in the upper right. The player's bio, highlights and stats round out the back. Two football player images are printed in the background of the highlights and stats. Red-foil parallels were included one per Treat Entertainment U.S. retail pack.

		MT
Complete Set (330):		30.00
Common Player:		.05
Minor Stars:		.10
Wax Box:		45.00
1	Kevin Butler	.05
2	Larry Centers	.05
3	Kent Graham	.05
4	Leeland McElroy	.10
5	Ronald McKinnon	.05
6	Johnny McWilliams	.05
7	Brad Ottis	.05
8	Frank Sanders	.05
9	Rob Selby	.05
10	Cedric Smith	.05
11	Joe Staysniak	.05
12	Cornelius Bennett	.05
13	David Brandon	.05
14	Tyrone Brown	.05
15	John Burrough	.05
16	Browning Nagle	.05
17	Dan Owens	.05
18	Anthony Phillips	.05
19	Roell Preston	.05
20	Darnell Walker	.05
21	Bob Whitfield	.05
22	Mike Zandofsky	.05
23	Vashone Adams	.05
24	Derrick Alexander	.05
25	Harold Bishop	.05
26	Jeff Blackshear	.05
27	Donny Brady	.05
28	Mike Frederick	.05
29	Tim Goad	.05

No	Player	Value
30	DeRon Jenkins	.05
31	Ray Lewis	.05
32	Rick Lyle	.05
33	Bam Morris	.05
34	Chris Brantley	.05
35	Jeff Burris	.05
36	Todd Collins	.10
37	Rob Coons	.05
38	Corbin Lacina	.05
39	Emanuel Martin	.05
40	Marlo Perry	.05
41	Sahwn Price	.05
42	Thomas Smith	.05
43	Matt Stevens	.05
44	Thurman Thomas	.15
45	Jay Barker	.05
46	Tshimanga Biakabutuka	.10
47	Kerry Collins	1.50
48	Matt Elliott	.05
49	Howard Griffith	.05
50	Anthony Johnson	.05
51	John Kasay	.05
52	Muhsin Muhammad	.40
53	Winslow Oliver	.05
54	Walter Rasby	.05
55	Gerald Williams	.05
56	Mark Butterfield	.05
57	Bryan Cox	.05
58	Mike Faulkerson	.05
59	Paul Grasmanis	.05
60	Robert Green	.05
61	Jack Jackson	.05
62	Bob Neely	.05
63	Todd Perry	.05
64	Evan Pilgrim	.05
65	Octus Polk	.05
66	Rashaan Salaam	.10
67	Willie Anderson	.05
68	Jeff Blake	.20
69	Scott Brumfield	.05
70	Jeff Cothran	.05
71	Gerald Dixon	.05
72	Garrison Hearst	.05
73	James Hundon	.05
74	Brian Milne	.05
75	Troy Sadowski	.05
76	Tom Tumulty	.05
77	Kimo Von Oelhoffen	.05
78	Troy Aikman	1.50
79	Dale Hellestrae	.05
80	Roger Harper	.05
81	Michael Irvin	.10
82	John Jett	.05
83	Kelvin Martin	.05
84	Deion Sanders	.75
85	Darrin Smith	.05
86	Emmitt Smith	3.00
87	Herschel Walker	.05
88	Charlie Williams	.05
89	Glenn Cadrez	.05
90	Dwayne Carswell	.05
91	Terrell Davis	1.75
92	David Diaz-Infante	.05
93	John Elway	1.00
94	Harold Hasselbach	.05
95	Tory James	.05
96	Bill Musgrave	.05
97	Ralph Tamm	.05
98	Maa Tunavasa	.05
99	Gary Zimmerman	.05
100	Shane Bonham	.05
101	Stephen Boyd	.05
102	Jeff Hartings	.05
103	Hessley Hempstead	.05
104	Scott Kowalkowski	.05
105	Herman Moore	.20
106	Barry Sanders	1.50
107	Tony Semple	.05
108	Ryan Stewart	.05
109	Mike Wells	.05
110	Richard Woodley	.05
111	Brett Favre	3.00
112	Bernardo Harris	.05
113	Keith McKenzie	.05
114	Terry Mickens	.05
115	Doug Pederson	.05
116	Jeff Thomason	.05
117	Adam Timmerman	.05
118	Reggie White	.20
119	Bruce Wilkerson	.05
120	Gabe Wilkens	.05
121	Tyrone Williams	.05
122	Al Del Greco	.05
123	Anthony Dorsett	.05
124	Josh Evans	.05
125	Eddie George	2.00
126	Lemanski Hall	.05
127	Ronnie Harmon	.05
128	Steve McNair	1.00
129	Michael Roan	.05
130	Marcus Robertson	.05
131	Jon Runyan	.05
132	Chris Sanders	.05
133	Kerwin Bell	.05
134	Marshall Faulk	.30
135	Clif Groce	.05
136	Jim Harbaugh	.05
137	Marvin Harrison	1.00
138	Eric Mahlum	.05
139	Tony Mandarich	.05
140	Dedric Mathis	.05
141	Marcus Pollard	.05
142	Scott Slutzker	.05
143	Mark Stock	.05
144	Bucky Brooks	.05
145	Mark Brunell	1.50
146	Kendricke Bullard	.05
147	Randy Jordan	.05
148	Jeff Kopp	.05
149	Le'Shai Maston	.05
150	Keenan McCardell	.05
151	Clyde Simmons	.05
152	Jimmy Smith	.05
153	Rich Tylski	.05
154	Dave Widell	.05
155	Marcus Allen	.10
156	Keith Cash	.05
157	Donnie Edwards	.05
158	Trezelle Jenkins	.05
159	Sean LaChapelle	.05
160	Greg Manusky	.05
161	Steve Matthews	.05
162	Pellom McDaniels	.05
163	Chris Penn	.05
164	Danny Villa	.05
165	Jerome Woods	.05
166	Karim Abdul-Jabbar	1.25
167	John Bock	.05
168	O.J. Brigance	.05
169	Norman Hand	.05
170	Anthony Harris	.05
171	Larry Izzo	.05
172	Charles Jordan	.05
173	Dan Marino	3.00
174	Everett McIver	.05
175	Joe Nedney	.05
176	Robert Wilson	.05
177	David Dixon	.05
178	Charlie Evans	.05
179	Hunter Goodwin	.05
180	Ben Hanks	.05
181	Warren Moon	.10
182	Harold Morrow	.05
183	Fernando Smith	.05
184	Robert Smith	.10
185	Sean Vanhorse	.05
186	Jay Walker	.05
187	DeWayne Washington	.05
188	Moe Williams	.05
189	Mike Bartrum	.05
190	Drew Bledsoe	1.50
191	Troy Brown	.05
192	Chad Eaton	.05
193	Sam Gash	.05
194	Mike Gisler	.05
195	Curtis Martin	1.75
196	Dave Richards	.05
197	Todd Rucci	.05
198	Chris Sullivan	.05
199	Adam Vinatieri	.05
200	Doug Brien	.05
201	Derek Brown	.05
202	Lee DeRamus	.05
203	Jim Everett	.05
204	Mercury Hayes	.05
205	Joe Johnson	.05
206	Henry Lusk	.05
207	Andy McCollum	.05
208	Alex Molden	.05
209	Ray Zellars	.05
210	Marcus Buckley	.05
211	Doug Coleman	.05
212	Percy Ellsworth	.05
213	Rodney Hampton	.05
214	Brian Saxton	.05
215	Jason Sehorn	.05
216	Stan White	.05
217	Corey Widmer	.05
218	Rodney Young	.05
219	Rob Zatechka	.05
220	Henry Bailey	.05
221	Chad Cascadden	.05
222	Wayne Chrebet	.05
223	Tyrone Davis	.05
224	Kwame Ellis	.05
225	Glenn Foley	.05
226	Erik Howard	.05
227	Gary Jones	.05
228	Adrian Murrell	.05
229	Marc Spindler	.05
230	Lonnie Young	.05
231	Eric Zomalt	.05
232	Tim Brown	.10
233	Aundray Bruce	.05
234	Darren Carrington	.05
235	Rick Cunningham	.05
236	Rob Homberg	.05
237	Jeff Hostetler	.05
238	Lorenzo Lynch	.05
239	Barrett Robbins	.05
240	Dan Turk	.05
241	Harvey Williams	.05
242	Brian Dawkins	.05
243	Ty Detmer	.05
244	Troy Drake	.05
245	Rhett Hall	.05
246	Joe Panos	.05
247	Johnny Thomas	.05
248	Kevin Turner	.05
249	Ricky Watters	.10
250	Derrick Witherspoon	.05
251	Sylvester Wright	.05
252	Jerome Bettis	.20
253	Carlos Emmons	.05
254	Jason Gildon	.05
255	Jonathan Hayes	.05
256	Kevin Henry	.05
257	Jerry Olsavsky	.05
258	Erric Pegram	.05
259	Brenden Stai	.05
260	Justin Strzelczyk	.05
261	Mike Tomczak	.05
262	Tony Banks	.50
263	Hayward Clay	.05
264	Percell Gaskins	.05
265	Eddie Kennison	.05
266	Aaron Laing	.05
267	Keith Lyle	.05
268	Jamie Martin	.05
269	Lawrence Phillips	.10
270	Zach Wiegert	.05
271	Toby Wright	.05
272	Darren Bennett	.05
273	Tony Berti	.05
274	Freddie Bradley	.05
275	Joe Cocozzo	.05
276	Andre Coleman	.05
277	Marco Coleman	.05
278	Rodney Harrison	.05
279	David Hendrix	.05
280	Leonard Russell	.05
281	Sean Salisbury	.05
282	Dennis Brown	.05
283	Chris Dalman	.05
284	Brent Jones	.05
285	Sean Manuel	.05
286	Marquez Pope	.05
287	Jerry Rice	1.50
288	Kirk Scrafford	.05
289	Iheanyi Uwaezuoke	.05
290	Tommy Vardell	.05
291	Steve Young	1.00
292	James Atkins	.05
293	T.J. Cunningham	.05
294	Stan Gelbaugh	.05
295	James Logan	.05
296	James McKnight	.05
297	Rick Mirer	.10
298	Todd Peterson	.05
299	Fred Thomas	.05
300	Rick Tuten	.05
301	Chris Warren	.05
302	Donnie Abraham	.05
303	Trent Dilfer	.10
304	Kenneth Gant	.05
305	Jeff Gooch	.05
306	Courtney Hawkins	.05
307	Tyoka Jackson	.05
308	Melvin Johnson	.05
309	Lonnie Marts	.05
310	Hardy Nickerson	.05
311	Errict Rhett	.20
312	Terry Allen	.10
313	Flipper Anderson	.05
314	William Bell	.05
315	Scott Blanton	.05
316	Leomont Evans	.05
317	Gus Frerotte	.05
318	Darryl Morrison	.05
319	Matt Turk	.05
320	Jeff Uhlenhake	.05
321	Bryan Walker	.05
322	Mark Brunell (1996 Statistical Leaders)	.75
323	Barry Sanders (1996 Statistical Leaders)	.75
324	Isaac Bruce (1996 Statistical Leaders)	.05
325	Terry Allen (1996 Statistical Leaders)	.05
326	Steve Young (1996 Statistical Leaders)	.50
327	Jerry Rice (1996 Statistical Leaders)	.75
328	Ricky Watters (1996 Statistical Leaders)	.05
329	Kevin Greene (1996 Statistical Leaders)	.05
330	Brett Favre (1996 Statistical Leaders)	1.50

1997 Pacific Philadelphia Gold

The 200-card set was a bonus in packs of the product. Each pack contained two Philadelphia Gold cards and either one insert card or an additional Philadelphia Gold card per pack. The card fronts showcased a full-bleed photo, with the Philadelphia logo in the upper left. The player's name is printed in gold foil over a gold-foil "spiral background" at the bottom left of the card. The team's logo is printed inside a banner over a football in the lower right. The backs have the player's name, position and highlights along the left, with a photo on the right. The card number is printed inside a circle in the lower right. A Hobby parallel version was printed with copper foil and inserted 2:37 packs. A Retail parallel version was produced with silver foil and inserted 2:37 packs.

	MT
Complete Set (200):	40.00
Common Player:	.15
Minor Stars:	.30
Copper Cards:	2x-4x
Silver Cards:	3x-6x

No	Player	Value
1	Ryan Christopherson	.15
2	James Dexter	.15
3	Boomer Esiason	.15
4	Jarius Hayes	.15
5	Eric Hill	.15
6	Trey Junkin	.15
7	Kwamie Lassiter	.15
8	Patrick Bates	.15
9	Brad Edwards	.15
10	Roman Fortin	.15
11	Harper LeBel	.15
12	Lorenzo Styles	.15
13	Robbie Tobeck	.15
14	Mike Caldwell	.15
15	Eric Green	.15
16	Brian Kinchen	.15
17	Eric Turner	.15
18	Jerrol Williams	.15
19	Eric Zeier	.15
20	Darick Holmes	.30
21	Ken Irvin	.15
22	Jerry Ostroski	.15
23	Andre Reed	.15
24	Steve Tasker	.15
25	Thurman Thomas	.30
26	Steve Beuerlein	.15
27	Kerry Collins	2.00
28	Eric Davis	.15
29	Norberto Garrido	.15
30	Lamar Lathon	.15
31	Andre Royal	.15
32	Tony Carter	.15
33	Jerry Fontenot	.15
34	Raymont Harris	.30
35	Anthony Marshall	.15
36	Barry Minter	.15
37	Steve Stenstrom	.15
38	Donnell Woolford	.15
39	Ken Blackman	.15
40	Jeff Blake	.50
41	Carl Pickens	.30
42	Artie Smith	.15
43	Ramondo Stallings	.15
44	Melvin Tuten	.15
45	Joe Walter	.15
46	Troy Aikman	2.00
47	Billy Davis	.15
48	Chad Hennings	.15
49	Emmitt Smith	4.00
50	George Teague	.15
51	Kevin Williams	.15
52	Terrell Davis	2.50
53	John Elway	1.25
54	Tom Nalen	.15
55	Bill Romanowski	.15
56	Rod Smith	.15
57	Dan Williams	.15
58	Mike Compton	.15
59	Eric Lynch	.15
60	Aubrey Matthews	.15
61	Pete Metzelaars	.15
62	Herman Moore	.30
63	Barry Sanders	2.00
64	Keith Washington	.15
65	Edgar Bennett	.15
66	Brett Favre	4.00
67	Lamont Hollinquest	.15
68	Keith Jackson	.15
69	Derrick Mayes	.15
70	Andre Rison	.15
71	Eddie George	2.50
72	Mel Gray	.15
73	Darryll Lewis	.15
74	John Henry Mills	.15
75	Rodney Thomas	.15
76	Gary Walker	.15
77	Troy Auzenne	.15
78	Sammie Burroughs	.15
79	Jim Harbaugh	.15
80	Tony McCoy	.15
81	Brian Stablein	.15
82	Kipp Vickers	.15
83	Aaron Beasley	.15
84	Mark Brunell	2.00
85	Don Davey	.15
86	Chris Hudson	.15
87	Greg Huntington	.15
88	Ernie Logan	.15
89	Donnell Bennett	.15
90	Anthony Davis	.15
91	Tim Grunhard	.15
92	Danan Hughes	.15
93	Tony Richardson	.15
94	Tracy Simien	.15
95	Karim Abdul-Jabbar	1.50
96	Dwight Hollier	.15
97	John Kidd	.15
98	Dan Marino	4.00
99	Jerris McPhail	.15
100	Irving Spikes	.15
101	Richmond Webb	.15
102	Jeff Brady	.15
103	Richard Brown	.15
104	Corey Fuller	.15
105	John Gerak	.15
106	Scottie Graham	.15
107	Amp Lee	.15
108	Drew Bledsoe	2.00
109	Tedy Bruschi	.15
110	Todd Collins	.15
111	Bob Kratch	.15
112	Curtis Martin	2.50
113	David Meggett	.15
114	Tom Tupa	.15
115	Eric Allen	.15
116	Mario Bates	.15
117	Clarence Jones	.15
118	Sean Lumpkin	.15
119	Doug Nussmeier	.15
120	Irv Smith	.15
121	Winfred Tubbs	.15
122	Willie Beamon	.15
123	Greg Bishop	.15
124	Dave Brown	.15
125	Gary Downs	.15
126	Thomas Lewis	.15
127	Michael Strahan	.15
128	Tyrone Wheatley	.15
129	Matt Brock	.15
130	Mike Chalenski	.15
131	Roger Duffy	.15
132	John Hudson	.15
133	Frank Reich	.15
134	David Williams	.15
135	Greg Biekert	.15
136	Mike Jones	.15
137	Napoleon Kaufman	.15
138	Carl Kidd	.15
139	Terry McDaniel	.15
140	Mike Morton	.15
141	Orlanda Truitt	.15
142	Gary Anderson	.15
143	Richard Cooper	.15
144	Jimmie Johnson	.15
145	Joe Kelly	.15
146	William Thomas	.15
147	Ricky Watters	.30
148	Ed West	.15
149	Michael Zordich	.15
150	Jerome Bettis	.50
151	Dermontti Dawson	.15
152	Lethon Flowers	.15
153	Charles Johnson	.15
154	Darren Perry	.15
155	Kordell Stewart	2.00
156	Will Wolford	.15
157	Isaac Bruce	.75
158	Kevin Carter	.15
159	Torin Dorn	.15
160	Leo Goeas	.15
161	Gerald McBurrows	.15
162	Chuck Osborne	.15
163	J.T. Thomas	.15
164	Dwayne Gordon	.15
165	Stan Humphries	.15
166	Shawn Lee	.15
167	Chris Mims	.15
168	John Parrella	.15
169	Junior Seau	.15
170	Bryan Still	.15
171	Curtis Buckley	.15
172	William Floyd	.15
173	Merton Hanks	.15
174	Terry Kirby	.15
175	Jerry Rice	2.00
176	J.J. Stokes	.15
177	Jeff Wilkins	.15
178	Bryant Young	.15
179	Sam Adams	.15
180	John Friesz	.15
181	Joey Galloway	.75
182	Pete Kendall	.15
183	Jason Kyle	.15
184	Darryl Jackson	.15
185	Ronnie Williams	.15
186	Mike Alstott	.30
187	Trent Dilfer	.30
188	Tyrone Legette	.15
189	Martin Mayhew	.15
190	Jason Odom	.15
191	Warren Sapp	.15
192	Karl Williams	.15
193	Terry Allen	.15
194	Romeo Bandison	.15
195	Alcides Catanho	.15
196	Gus Frerotte	.15
197	William Gaines	.15
198	Ken Harvey	.15
199	Trevor Matich	.15
200	Scott Turner	.15

Post-1980 cards in Near Mint condition will generally sell for about 75% of the quoted Mint value. Excellent-condition cards bring no more than 40%.

1997 Pacific Philadelphia Heart of the Game

The 20-card set was inserted 1:73 packs. The fronts showcased a full-bleed photo, with the Philadelphia logo in the upper left corner. The player's name is printed in large gold-foil letters at the bottom of the front. In the bottom center of the name is an oval globe. A red heartbeat runs from the lower left to the lower right, with the date of a key game printed in red in the center.

	MT
Complete Set (20):	275.00
Common Player:	6.00
Minor Stars:	12.00

No	Player	Value
1	Thurman Thomas	6.00
2	Kerry Collins	20.00
3	Troy Aikman	20.00
4	Emmitt Smith	40.00
5	Terrell Davis	20.00
6	John Elway	15.00
7	Barry Sanders	25.00
8	Brett Favre	45.00
9	Antonio Freeman	12.00
10	Marshall Faulk	12.00
11	Mark Brunell	20.00
12	Marcus Allen	6.00
13	Dan Marino	40.00
14	Drew Bledsoe	20.00
15	Curtis Martin	20.00
16	Napoleon Kaufman	6.00
17	Jerome Bettis	12.00
18	Isaac Bruce	12.00
19	Jerry Rice	20.00
20	Steve Young	15.00

1997 Pacific Philadelphia Milestones

The 20-card set was inserted 1:37 packs. The fronts feature a red-orange border, with a player photo superimposed over a helmet and gold-foil Milestones banner that runs from the upper right to the lower left. The player's milestone is printed in the center of the banner, with his name in the lower left of the banner. The Philadelphia logo is located in the lower right.

	MT
Complete Set (20):	200.00
Common Player:	4.00
Minor Stars:	8.00

No	Player	Value
1	Simeon Rice	4.00
2	Thurman Thomas	4.00
3	Troy Aikman	15.00
4	Emmitt Smith	30.00
5	Terrell Davis	15.00
6	John Elway	12.00
7	Brett Favre	35.00
8	Desmond Howard	4.00
9	Reggie White	8.00
10	Mark Brunell	15.00

11	Marcus Allen	4.00
12	Karim Abdul-Jabbar	12.00
13	Dan Marino	30.00
14	Drew Bledsoe	15.00
15	Terry Glenn	15.00
16	Curtis Martin	15.00
17	Tony Banks	8.00
18	Jerry Rice	15.00
19	Steve Young	12.00
20	Terry Allen	4.00

1997 Pacific Philadelphia Photoengravings

Inserted 2:37 packs, the 36-card set has the look and feel of playing cards. The rounded-bordered cards have a player photo in the center of the card surrounded by a brown border and background. The player's name is printed in black at the bottom center. The Philadelphia logo is located in the upper left of the card front.

		MT
Complete Set (36):		225.00
Common Player:		3.00
Minor Stars:		6.00
1	Thurman Thomas	6.00
2	Kerry Collins	12.00
3	Jeff Blake	6.00
4	Troy Aikman	12.00
5	Deion Sanders	7.00
6	Emmitt Smith	25.00
7	Terrell Davis	15.00
8	John Elway	10.00
9	Herman Moore	6.00
10	Barry Sanders	15.00
11	Brett Favre	30.00
12	Desmond Howard	3.00
13	Dorsey Levens	3.00
14	Eddie George	15.00
15	Marshall Faulk	6.00
16	Jim Harbaugh	3.00
17	Marvin Harrison	6.00
18	Mark Brunell	12.00
19	Keenan McCardell	3.00
20	Karim Abdul-Jabbar	10.00
21	Dan Marino	25.00
22	Brad Johnson	3.00
23	Drew Bledsoe	12.00
24	Terry Glenn	12.00
25	Curtis Martin	12.00
26	Keyshawn Johnson	6.00
27	Tim Brown	3.00
28	Napoleon Kaufman	3.00
29	Ricky Watters	3.00
30	Jerome Bettis	6.00
31	Kordell Stewart	12.00
32	Eddie Kennison	6.00
33	Jerry Rice	12.00
34	Steve Young	10.00
35	Chris Warren	3.00
36	Terry Allen	3.00

1997 Pacific Revolution

Revolution is a 150-card set. The base cards all feature holographic foil, etching and emboss-

ing. Three parallel sets were created: Silver & Holographic Gold (retail, 2:25), Copper & Holographic Silver (hobby, 2:25) and Platinum Blue & Holographic Gold (1:49). The inserts included Proteges, Air Mail Die-Cuts, Silks and Ring Bearer Laser-Cuts.

		MT
Complete Set (150):		120.00
Common Player:		.50
Minor Stars:		1.00
Copper/Red Cards:		4x-8x
Copper/Red Rookies:		2x-4x
Silver Cards:		4x-8x
Silver Rookies:		2x-4x
Blue Cards:		10x-20x
Blue Rookies:		5x-10x
Wax Box:		80.00
1	Larry Centers	.50
2	Kent Graham	.50
3	Leeland McElroy	.50
4	Rob Moore	.50
5	*Jake Plummer*	12.00
6	Jamal Anderson	1.00
7	Bert Emanuel	.50
8	*Byron Hanspard*	1.50
9	Terance Mathis	.50
10	O.J. Santiago	.50
11	Derrick Alexander	.50
12	Peter Boulware	.50
13	*Jay Graham*	1.00
14	Michael Jackson	.50
15	Vinny Testaverde	.50
16	Todd Collins	1.00
17	Andre Reed	.50
18	Jay Riemersma	.50
19	*Antowain Smith*	5.00
20	Bruce Smith	.50
21	Thurman Thomas	1.00
22	*Rae Carruth*	2.00
23	Kerry Collins	1.00
24	Anthony Johnson	.50
25	Muhsin Muhammad	.50
26	Wesley Walls	.50
27	Curtis Conway	1.00
28	Bobby Engram	.50
29	Raymont Harris	.50
30	Rick Mirer	.50
31	Rashaan Salaam	.50
32	Jeff Blake	1.00
33	*Corey Dillon*	7.00
34	Carl Pickens	.50
35	Darnay Scott	.50
36	Troy Aikman	4.00
37	Michael Irvin	1.00
38	Daryl Johnston	.50
39	Deion Sanders	2.00
40	Emmitt Smith	8.00
41	Terrell Davis	4.00
42	John Elway	3.00
43	Ed McCaffrey	.50
44	Shannon Sharpe	.50
45	Neil Smith	.50
46	Scott Mitchell	.50
47	Herman Moore	1.00
48	Johnnie Morton	.50
49	Barry Sanders	7.00
50	Robert Brooks	.50
51	LeRoy Butler	.50
52	Brett Favre	10.00
53	Antonio Freeman	1.00
54	Dorsey Levens	1.00
55	Reggie White	1.00
56	Sean Dawkins	.50
57	Ken Dilger	.50
58	Marshall Faulk	1.00
59	Jim Harbaugh	.50
60	Marvin Harrison	2.00
61	Mark Brunell	4.00
62	Keenan McCardell	.50
63	Natrone Means	1.00
64	Jimmy Smith	.50
65	James Stewart	.50
66	Marcus Allen	1.00
67	*Tony Gonzalez*	2.00
68	Elvis Grbac	.50
69	Greg Hill	.50
70	Andre Rison	.50
71	Karim Abdul-Jabbar	2.00
72	Fred Barnett	.50
73	Dan Marino	8.00
74	O.J. McDuffie	.50
75	Irving Spikes	.50
76	Cris Carter	.50
77	Matthew Hatchette	.50
78	Brad Johnson	1.00
79	Jake Reed	.50
80	Robert Smith	1.00
81	Drew Bledsoe	4.00
82	Ben Coates	.50
83	Terry Glenn	1.50
84	Curtis Martin	4.00
85	Dave Meggett	.50
86	*Troy Davis*	1.50
87	Andre Hastings	.50
88	Heath Shuler	.50
89	Irv Smith	.50
90	*Danny Wuerffel*	4.00
91	Ray Zellars	.50
92	*Tiki Barber*	4.00
93	Dave Brown	.50
94	Chris Calloway	.50
95	Rodney Hampton	.50
96	Amani Toomer	.50
97	Wayne Chrebet	.50
98	Keyshawn Johnson	2.00
99	Adrian Murrell	1.00
100	Neil O'Donnell	.50
101	Dedric Ward	.50
102	Tim Brown	1.00
103	Rickey Dudley	.50
104	Jeff George	.50
105	Desmond Howard	.50
106	Napoleon Kaufman	1.00
107	Ty Detmer	.50
108	Jason Dunn	.50
109	Irving Fryar	.50
110	Rodney Peete	.50
111	Ricky Watters	1.00
112	Jerome Bettis	1.00
113	*Will Blackwell*	1.00
114	Charles Johnson	.50
115	Kordell Stewart	4.00
116	Tony Banks	2.00
117	Isaac Bruce	1.00
118	Ernie Conwell	.50
119	Eddie Kennison	1.00
120	Lawrence Phillips	.50
121	Stan Humphries	.50
122	Tony Martin	.50
123	Eric Metcalf	.50
124	Junior Seau	1.00
125	*Jim Druckenmiller*	5.00
126	Kevin Greene	.50
127	Garrison Hearst	.50
128	Terrell Owens	4.00
129	Jerry Rice	4.00
130	J.J. Stokes	.50
131	Rod Woodson	.50
132	Steve Young	3.00
133	Joey Galloway	1.00
134	Cortez Kennedy	.50
135	*Jon Kitna*	35.00
136	Warren Moon	.50
137	Chris Warren	.50
138	Mike Alstott	2.00
139	*Reidel Anthony*	5.00
140	Trent Dilfer	1.00
141	*Warrick Dunn*	7.00
142	Willie Davis	.50
143	Eddie George	6.00
144	Steve McNair	3.00
145	Chris Sanders	.50
146	Terry Allen	.50
147	Jamie Asher	.50
148	Henry Ellard	.50
149	Gus Frerotte	.50
150	Leslie Shepherd	.50

1997 Pacific Revolution Air Mail

The cards in this 36-card insert are die-cut to look like stamps. They were inserted once in every 25 packs.

		MT
Complete Set (36):		500.00
Common Player:		5.00
Minor Stars:		10.00
1	Vinny Testaverde	5.00
2	Andre Reed	5.00
3	Kerry Collins	10.00
4	Jeff Blake	10.00
5	Troy Aikman	25.00
6	Deion Sanders	15.00
7	Emmitt Smith	50.00
8	Michael Irvin	10.00
9	Terrell Davis	25.00
10	John Elway	18.00
11	Barry Sanders	45.00
12	Brett Favre	60.00
13	Antonio Freeman	10.00
14	Mark Brunell	25.00
15	Marcus Allen	10.00
16	Elvis Grbac	5.00
17	Dan Marino	50.00
18	Brad Johnson	10.00
19	Drew Bledsoe	25.00
20	Terry Glenn	10.00
21	Curtis Martin	25.00
22	Danny Wuerffel	10.00
23	Jeff George	5.00
24	Napoleon Kaufman	10.00
25	Kordell Stewart	25.00
26	Tony Banks	10.00
27	Isaac Bruce	10.00
28	Jim Druckenmiller	30.00
29	Jerry Rice	25.00
30	Steve Young	18.00
31	Warren Moon	5.00
32	Trent Dilfer	10.00
33	Warrick Dunn	40.00
34	Eddie George	40.00
35	Steve McNair	20.00
36	Gus Frerotte	5.00

1997 Pacific Revolution Proteges

These 20 insert cards feature a proven veteran alongside their young understudy. The foiled cards were inserted 2:25.

		MT
Complete Set (20):		200.00
Common Player:		3.00
1	Kent Graham, Jake Plummer	8.00
2	Jamal Anderson, Byron Hanspard	3.00
3	Thurman Thomas, Antowain Smith	8.00
4	Troy Aikman, Jason Garrett	15.00
5	Emmitt Smith, Sherman Williams	25.00
6	John Elway, Jeff Lewis	12.00
7	Barry Sanders, Ron Rivers	20.00
8	Brett Favre, Doug Pederson	30.00
9	Mark Brunell, Rob Johnson	15.00
10	Marcus Allen, Greg Hill	3.00
11	Dan Marino, Damon Huard	30.00
12	Curtis Martin, Marrio Grier	15.00
13	Heath Shuler, Danny Wuerffel	6.00
14	Rodney Hampton, Tiki Barber	8.00
15	Jerome Bettis, George Jones	3.00
16	Jerry Rice, Terrell Owens	15.00
17	Steve Young, Jim Druckenmiller	12.00
18	Warren Moon, Jon Kitna	3.00
19	Errict Rhett, Warrick Dunn	15.00
20	Terry Allen, Stephen Davis	3.00

1997 Pacific Revolution Ring Bearers

These 10 fully foiled and embossed cards are die-cut and laser-cut to look like a championship ring. The cards feature 10 of the NFL's best and were inserted 1:121.

		MT
Complete Set (12):		500.00
Common Player:		25.00
Inserted 1:121		
1	Emmitt Smith	75.00
2	John Elway	60.00
3	Barry Sanders	100.00
4	Brett Favre	100.00
5	Mark Brunell	50.00
6	Dan Marino	75.00
7	Drew Bledsoe	50.00
8	Steve Young	25.00
9	Warrick Dunn	25.00
10	Eddie George	50.00

1997 Pacific Revolution Silks

This 18-card, oversized insert features top NFL players on a silk-like material. The cards were inserted 1:49.

		MT
Complete Set (18):		400.00
Common Player:		8.00
1	Kerry Collins	10.00
2	Troy Aikman	25.00
3	Deion Sanders	15.00
4	Emmitt Smith	50.00
5	Terrell Davis	25.00
6	John Elway	18.00
7	Barry Sanders	40.00
8	Brett Favre	60.00
9	Mark Brunell	25.00
10	Marcus Allen	8.00
11	Dan Marino	50.00
12	Drew Bledsoe	25.00
13	Curtis Martin	25.00
14	Jerome Bettis	8.00
15	Jim Druckenmiller	30.00
16	Jerry Rice	25.00
17	Warrick Dunn	40.00
18	Eddie George	40.00

1998 Pacific

The 450-card silver-foiled main set captures the NFL's pinpoint passes, touchdown runs and goal-line stands with the sharpest action photography. The set is designed with the die-hard football fan in mind, this set delivers outstanding player selection, including the strong crop of rookies from 1998. Each card back includes full year-by-year career stats. A parallel Red version can be found one per special retail pack and the Platinum Blue parallel singles can be found 1:73 packs.

		MT
Complete Set (450):		70.00
Common Player:		.10
Minor Stars:		.20
Common Rookie:		1.00
Platinum Blue Cards:		60x-120x
Platinum Blue Rookies:		10x-20x
Inserted 1:73		
Wax Box:		60.00
1	Mario Bates	.10
2	Lomas Brown	.10
3	Larry Centers	.10
4	Chris Gedney	.10
5	Terry Irving	.10
6	Tom Knight	.10
7	Eric Metcalf	.10
8	Jamir Miller	.10
9	Rob Moore	.20
10	Joe Nedney	.10
11	Jake Plummer	1.00
12	Simeon Rice	.10
13	Frank Sanders	.10
14	Eric Swann	.10
15	Aeneas Williams	.10
16	Morten Andersen	.10
17	Jamal Anderson	.50
18	Michael Booker	.10
19	Keith Brooking	.10
20	Ray Buchanan	.10
21	Devin Bush	.10
22	Chris Chandler	.20
23	Tony Graziani	.10
24	Harold Green	.10
25	Byron Hanspard	.10
26	Todd Kinchen	.10
27	Tony Martin	.10
28	Terance Mathis	.10
29	Eugene Robinson	.10
30	O.J. Santiago	.10
31	Chuck Smith	.10
32	Jessie Tuggle	.10
33	Bob Whitfield	.10
34	Peter Boulware	.10
35	Jay Graham	.10
36	Eric Green	.10
37	Jim Harbaugh	.20
38	Michael Jackson	.10
39	Jermaine Lewis	.10
40	Ray Lewis	.10
41	Michael McCrary	.10
42	Stevon Moore	.10
43	Jonathan Ogden	.10
44	Errict Rhett	.10
45	Matt Stover	.10
46	Rod Woodson	.10
47	Eric Zeier	.10
48	Ruben Brown	.10
49	Steve Christie	.10
50	Quinn Early	.10
51	John Fina	.10
52	Doug Flutie	.75
53	Phil Hansen	.10
54	Lonnie Johnson	.10
55	Rob Johnson	.20
56	Henry Jones	.10
57	Eric Moulds	.10
58	Andre Reed	.10
59	Antowain Smith	.50
60	Bruce Smith	.10
61	Thurman Thomas	.20
62	Ted Washington	.10
63	Michael Bates	.10
64	Tim Biakabutuka	.10
65	Blake Brockermeyer	.10
66	Mark Carrier	.10
67	Rae Carruth	.10
68	Kerry Collins	.20
69	Doug Evans	.10
70	William Floyd	.10
71	Sean Gilbert	.10
72	Raghib Ismail	.10
73	John Kasay	.10
74	Fred Lane	.20
75	Lamar Lathon	.10
76	Muhsin Muhammad	.10
77	Wesley Walls	.10
78	Edgar Bennett	.10
79	Tom Carter	.10
80	Curtis Conway	.20
81	Bobby Engram	.10
82	*Curtis Enis*	3.00
83	Jim Flanigan	.10
84	Walt Harris	.10
85	Jeff Jaeger	.10
86	Erik Kramer	.10
87	John Mangum	.10
88	Glyn Milburn	.10
89	Barry Minter	.10
90	Chris Penn	.10
91	Todd Sauerbrun	.10
92	James Williams	.10
93	Ashley Ambrose	.10
94	Willie Anderson	.10
95	Eric Bieniemy	.10
96	Jeff Blake	.10
97	Ki-Jana Carter	.10
98	John Copeland	.10
99	Corey Dillon	.75
100	Tony McGee	.10
101	Neil O'Donnell	.20
102	Carl Pickens	.20
103	Kevin Sargent	.10
104	Darnay Scott	.20
105	*Takeo Spikes*	1.00
106	Troy Aikman	1.50
107	Larry Allen	.10
108	Eric Bjornson	.10
109	Billy Davis	.10
110	Jason Garrett	.10
111	Michael Irvin	.20
112	Daryl Johnston	.10
113	David LaFleur	.10
114	Everett McIver	.10
115	Ernie Mills	.10
116	Nate Newton	.10
117	Deion Sanders	.50
118	Emmitt Smith	2.00
119	Kevin Smith	.10
120	Erik Williams	.10
121	Steve Atwater	.10
122	Tyrone Braxton	.10
123	Ray Crockett	.10
124	Terrell Davis	2.00
125	Jason Elam	.10
126	John Elway	1.50
127	Willie Green	.10

No.	Player	MT
128	*Brian Griese*	4.00
129	Tony Jones	.10
130	Ed McCaffrey	.20
131	John Mobley	.10
132	Tom Nalen	.10
133	*Marcus Nash*	2.00
134	Bill Romanowski	.10
135	Shannon Sharpe	.20
136	Neil Smith	.10
137	Rod Smith	.20
138	Keith Traylor	.10
139	Stephen Boyd	.10
140	Mark Carrier	.10
141	*Charlie Batch*	5.00
142	Jason Hanson	.10
143	Scott Mitchell	.20
144	Herman Moore	.50
145	Johnnie Morton	.10
146	Robert Porcher	.10
147	Ron Rivers	.10
148	Barry Sanders	3.00
149	Tracy Scroggins	.10
150	David Sloan	.10
151	Tommy Vardell	.10
152	Kerwin Waldroup	.10
153	Bryant Westbrook	.10
154	Robert Brooks	.10
155	Gilbert Brown	.10
156	LeRoy Butler	.10
157	Mark Chmura	.20
158	Earl Dotson	.10
159	Santana Dotson	.10
160	Brett Favre	3.00
161	Antonio Freeman	.50
162	Raymont Harris	.10
163	William Henderson	.10
164	*Vonnie Holliday*	1.50
165	George Koonce	.10
166	Dorsey Levens	.20
167	Derrick Mayes	.10
168	Craig Newsome	.10
169	Ross Verba	.10
170	Reggie White	.50
171	Elijah Alexander	.10
172	Aaron Bailey	.10
173	Jason Belser	.10
174	Robert Blackmon	.10
175	Zack Crockett	.10
176	Ken Dilger	.10
177	Marshall Faulk	.50
178	Tarik Glenn	.10
179	Marvin Harrison	.20
180	Tony Mandarich	.10
181	*Peyton Manning*	10.00
182	Marcus Pollard	.10
183	Lamont Warren	.10
184	*Tavian Banks*	2.00
185	Reggie Barlow	.10
186	Tony Boselli	.10
187	Tony Brackens	.10
188	Mark Brunell	1.00
189	Kevin Hardy	.10
190	Mike Hollis	.10
191	Jeff Lageman	.10
192	Keenan McCardell	.20
193	Pete Mitchell	.10
194	Bryce Paup	.10
195	Leon Searcy	.10
196	Jimmy Smith	.20
197	James Stewart	.10
198	*Fred Taylor*	5.00
199	Renaldo Wynn	.10
200	Derrick Alexander	.10
201	Kimble Anders	.10
202	Donnell Bennett	.10
203	Dale Carter	.10
204	Anthony Davis	.10
205	Rich Gannon	.10
206	Tony Gonzalez	.20
207	Elvis Grbac	.20
208	James Hasty	.10
209	Leslie O'Neal	.10
210	Andre Rison	.10
211	*Rashaan Shehee*	1.50
212	Will Shields	.10
213	Pete Stoyanovich	.10
214	Derrick Thomas	.20
215	Tamarick Vanover	.10
216	Karim Abdul-Jabbar	.10
217	Trace Armstrong	.10
218	*John Avery*	2.00
219	Tim Bowens	.10
220	Terrell Buckley	.10
221	Troy Drayton	.10
222	Daryl Gardener	.10
223	*Damon Huard*	7.00
224	Charles Jordan	.10
225	Dan Marino	2.00
226	O.J. McDuffie	.10
227	Bernie Parmalee	.10
228	Stanley Pritchett	.10
229	Derrick Rodgers	.10
230	Lamar Thomas	.10
231	Zach Thomas	.20
232	Richmond Webb	.10
233	Derrick Alexander	.10
234	Jerry Ball	.10
235	Cris Carter	.50
236	Randall Cunningham	.50
237	Charles Evans	.10
238	Corey Fuller	.10
239	Andrew Glover	.10
240	Leroy Hoard	.10
241	Brad Johnson	.50
242	Ed McDaniel	.10
243	Randall McDaniel	.10
244	*Randy Moss*	15.00
245	John Randle	.10
246	Jake Reed	.10
247	Dwayne Rudd	.10
248	Robert Smith	.20
249	Bruce Armstrong	.10
250	Drew Bledsoe	1.00
251	Vincent Brisby	.10
252	Tedy Bruschi	.10
253	Ben Coates	.20
254	Derrick Cullors	.10
255	Terry Glenn	.10
256	Shawn Jefferson	.10
257	Ted Johnson	.10
258	Ty Law	.10
259	Willie McGinest	.10
260	Lawyer Milloy	.10
261	Sedrick Shaw	.10
262	Chris Slade	.10
263	Troy Davis	.10
264	Mark Fields	.10
265	Andre Hastings	.10
266	Billy Joe Hobert	.10
267	Qadry Ismail	.10
268	Tony Johnson	.10
269	Sammy Knight	.10
270	Wayne Martin	.10
271	Chris Naeole	.10
272	Keith Poole	.10
273	William Roaf	.10
274	Pio Sagapolutele	.10
275	Danny Wuerffel	.20
276	Ray Zellars	.10
277	Jessie Armstead	.10
278	Tiki Barber	.20
279	Chris Calloway	.10
280	Percy Ellsworth	.10
281	Sam Garnes	.10
282	Kent Graham	.10
283	Ike Hilliard	.10
284	Danny Kanell	.10
285	Corey Miller	.10
286	Phillippi Sparks	.10
287	Michael Strahan	.10
288	Amani Toomer	.10
289	Charles Way	.10
290	Tyrone Wheatley	.10
291	Tito Wooten	.10
292	Kyle Brady	.10
293	Keith Byars	.10
294	Wayne Chrebet	.20
295	John Elliott	.10
296	Glenn Foley	.10
297	Aaron Glenn	.10
298	Keyshawn Johnson	.50
299	Curtis Martin	.50
300	Otis Smith	.10
301	Vinny Testaverde	.20
302	Alex Van Dyke	.10
303	Dedric Ward	.10
304	Greg Biekert	.10
305	Tim Brown	.20
306	Rickey Dudley	.10
307	Jeff George	.20
308	Pat Harlow	.10
309	Desmond Howard	.10
310	James Jett	.10
311	Napoleon Kaufman	.50
312	Lincoln Kennedy	.10
313	Russell Maryland	.10
314	Darrell Russell	.10
315	Eric Turner	.10
316	Steve Wisniewski	.10
317	*Charles Woodson*	4.00
318	James Darling	.10
319	Jason Dunn	.10
320	Irving Fryar	.10
321	Charlie Garner	.20
322	Jeff Graham	.10
323	Bobby Hoying	.20
324	Chad Lewis	.10
325	Rodney Peete	.10
326	Freddie Solomon	.10
327	Duce Staley	.10
328	Bobby Taylor	.10
329	William Thomas	.10
330	Kevin Turner	.10
331	Troy Vincent	.10
332	Jerome Bettis	.50
333	Will Blackwell	.10
334	Mark Bruener	.10
335	Andre Coleman	.10
336	Dermontti Dawson	.10
337	Jason Gildon	.10
338	Courtney Hawkins	.10
339	Charles Johnson	.10
340	Levon Kirkland	.10
341	Carnell Lake	.10
342	Tim Lester	.10
343	Joel Steed	.10
344	Kordell Stewart	1.00
345	Will Wolford	.10
346	Tony Banks	.20
347	Isaac Bruce	.20
348	Ernie Conwell	.10
349	D'Marco Farr	.10
350	Wayne Gandy	.10
351	*Robert Holcombe*	2.00
352	Eddie Kennison	.10
353	Amp Lee	.10
354	Keith Lyle	.10
355	Ryan McNeil	.10
356	Jerald Moore	.20
357	Orlando Pace	.10
358	Roman Phifer	.10
359	David Thompson	.10
360	Darren Bennett	.10
361	John Carney	.10
362	Marco Coleman	.10
363	Terrell Fletcher	.10
364	William Fuller	.10
365	Charlie Jones	.10
366	Freddie Jones	.10
367	*Ryan Leaf*	4.00
368	Natrone Means	.50
369	Junior Seau	.20
370	Terrance Shaw	.10
371	Tremayne Stephens	.10
372	Bryan Still	.10
373	Aaron Taylor	.10
374	Greg Clark	.10
375	Ty Detmer	.10
376	Jim Druckenmiller	.10
377	Marc Edwards	.10
378	Merton Hanks	.10
379	Garrison Hearst	.20
380	Chuck Levy	.10
381	Ken Norton	.10
382	Terrell Owens	.75
383	Marquez Pope	.10
384	Jerry Rice	1.50
385	Irv Smith	.10
386	J.J. Stokes	.20
387	Iheanyi Uwaezuoke	.10
388	Bryant Young	.10
389	Steve Young	.75
390	Sam Adams	.10
391	Chad Brown	.10
392	Christian Fauria	.10
393	Joey Galloway	.50
394	*Ahman Green*	2.50
395	Walter Jones	.10
396	Cortez Kennedy	.10
397	Jon Kitna	.50
398	James McKnight	.10
399	Warren Moon	.20
400	Mike Pritchard	.10
401	Michael Sinclair	.10
402	Shawn Springs	.10
403	Ricky Watters	.20
404	Darryl Williams	.10
405	Mike Alstott	.50
406	Reidel Anthony	.10
407	Derrick Brooks	.10
408	Brad Culpepper	.10
409	Trent Dilfer	.50
410	Warrick Dunn	1.00
411	Bert Emanuel	.10
412	*Jacquez Green*	2.50
413	Paul Gruber	.10
414	Patrick Hape	.10
415	Dave Moore	.10
416	Hardy Nickerson	.10
417	Warren Sapp	.10
418	Robb Thomas	.10
419	Regan Upshaw	.10
420	Karl Williams	.10
421	Blaine Bishop	.10
422	Anthony Cook	.10
423	Willie Davis	.10
424	Al Del Greco	.10
425	*Kevin Dyson*	2.00
426	Henry Ford	.10
427	Eddie George	1.00
428	Jackie Harris	.10
429	Steve McNair	.75
430	Chris Sanders	.10
431	Mark Stepnoski	.10
432	Yancey Thigpen	.10
433	Barron Wortham	.10
434	Frank Wycheck	.10
435	Stephen Alexander	.10
436	Terry Allen	.10
437	Jamie Asher	.10
438	Bob Dahl	.10
439	Stephen Davis	.10
440	Cris Dishman	.10
441	Gus Frerotte	.10
442	Darrell Green	.10
443	Trent Green	.10
444	Ken Harvey	.10
445	*Skip Hicks*	2.00
446	Jeff Hostetler	.10
447	Brian Mitchell	.10
448	Leslie Shepherd	.10
449	Michael Westbrook	.20
450	Dan Wilkinson	.10

1998 Pacific Cramer's Choice Awards

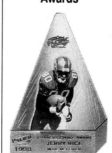

Pacific President/CEO Michael Cramer selected and wrote about the 10 players that are on these die-cut awards. Each card is in the shape of a triangle and were inserted 1:721 packs.

	MT
Complete Set (10):	850.00
Common Player:	50.00
Inserted 1:721	
1 Terrell Davis	125.00
2 John Elway	100.00
3 Barry Sanders	150.00
4 Brett Favre	150.00
5 Peyton Manning	125.00
6 Mark Brunell	70.00
7 Dan Marino	125.00
8 Ryan Leaf	60.00
9 Jerry Rice	85.00
10 Warrick Dunn	50.00

1998 Pacific Dynagon Turf

This sparkling insert features action photography and a mirror-patterned full-foil background. Singles from this 20-card set were inserted 4:37 packs. A parallel Titanium Turf set was added for hobby-only packs. Each single is sequentially numbered to 99.

	MT
Complete Set (20):	100.00
Common Player:	2.00
Inserted 4:37	
Titanium Cards:	7x-14x
Production 99 Sets	
1 Corey Dillon	3.00
2 Troy Aikman	6.00
3 Emmitt Smith	10.00
4 Terrell Davis	10.00
5 John Elway	6.00
6 Barry Sanders	12.00
7 Brett Favre	12.00
8 Peyton Manning	12.00
9 Mark Brunell	5.00
10 Dan Marino	10.00
11 Drew Bledsoe	5.00
12 Curtis Martin	3.00
13 Napoleon Kaufman	2.00
14 Jerome Bettis	2.00
15 Kordell Stewart	5.00
16 Ryan Leaf	6.00
17 Jerry Rice	6.00
18 Steve Young	4.00
19 Warrick Dunn	4.00
20 Eddie George	4.00

1998 Pacific Gold Crown Die-Cuts

This die-cut dual-foiled insert honors 36 of football's elite players. These singles were created with Pacific's cutting-edge technology and feature super-thick 24-point stock. Singles were inserted 1:37 packs.

	MT
Complete Set (36):	425.00
Common Player:	5.00
Minor Stars:	10.00
Inserted 1:37	
1 Jake Plummer	15.00
2 Antowain Smith	10.00
3 Curtis Enis	12.00
4 Corey Dillon	10.00
5 Troy Aikman	20.00
6 Deion Sanders	10.00
7 Emmitt Smith	30.00
8 Terrell Davis	30.00
9 John Elway	20.00
10 Barry Sanders	40.00
11 Brett Favre	40.00
12 Dorsey Levens	5.00
13 Marshall Faulk	10.00
14 Peyton Manning	40.00
15 Mark Brunell	15.00
16 Fred Taylor	20.00
17 Derrick Thomas	5.00
18 Dan Marino	30.00
19 Brad Johnson	10.00
20 Robert Smith	10.00
21 Drew Bledsoe	15.00
22 Glenn Foley	5.00
23 Curtis Martin	10.00
24 Napoleon Kaufman	10.00
25 Charles Woodson	15.00
26 Jerome Bettis	10.00
27 Kordell Stewart	15.00
28 Ryan Leaf	20.00
29 Garrison Hearst	5.00
30 Jerry Rice	20.00
31 J.J. Stokes	5.00
32 Steve Young	12.00
33 Joey Galloway	10.00
34 Ricky Watters	5.00
35 Warrick Dunn	15.00
36 Eddie George	15.00

1998 Pacific Team Checklists

This uniquely-designed insert highlights a team leader side-by-side with the holographic silver-foiled NFL logo of his respective team. On the back you'll find another photo of that player and a complete team checklist. Singles were inserted 2:37 packs.

	MT
Complete Set (30):	150.00
Common Player:	2.00
Minor Stars:	4.00
Inserted 2:37	
1 Jake Plummer	7.00
2 Jamal Anderson	4.00
3 Eric Zeier	2.00
4 Rob Johnson	2.00
5 Fred Lane	2.00
6 Curtis Enis	8.00
7 Corey Dillon	4.00
8 Troy Aikman	10.00
9 John Elway	10.00
10 Barry Sanders	20.00
11 Brett Favre	20.00
12 Peyton Manning	20.00
13 Mark Brunell	8.00
14 Elvis Grbac	2.00
15 Dan Marino	15.00
16 Robert Smith	4.00
17 Drew Bledsoe	8.00
18 Danny Wuerffel	2.00
19 Tiki Barber	2.00
20 Curtis Martin	4.00
21 Napoleon Kaufman	4.00
22 Duce Staley	2.00
23 Kordell Stewart	8.00
24 Tony Banks	4.00
25 Ryan Leaf	10.00
26 Jerry Rice	10.00
27 Warren Moon	4.00
28 Warrick Dunn	7.00
29 Eddie George	7.00
30 Terry Allen	2.00

1998 Pacific Timelines

Timelines features 20 superstars, giving a chronological history of each player complete with photos from early in their careers. These singles could be found in hobby-only packs at a ratio of 1:181.

	MT
Complete Set (20):	750.00
Common Player:	10.00
Minor Stars:	20.00
Inserted 1:181 Hobby	
1 Troy Aikman	50.00
2 Deion Sanders	20.00
3 Emmitt Smith	75.00
4 Terrell Davis	75.00
5 John Elway	50.00
6 Barry Sanders	100.00
7 Brett Favre	100.00
8 Peyton Manning	100.00
9 Mark Brunell	35.00
10 Dan Marino	75.00
11 Drew Bledsoe	40.00
12 Curtis Martin	20.00
13 Jerome Bettis	10.00
14 Kordell Stewart	40.00
15 Ryan Leaf	50.00
16 Jerry Rice	50.00
17 Steve Young	30.00
18 Ricky Watters	10.00
19 Warrick Dunn	40.00
20 Eddie George	40.00

1998 Pacific Aurora

The Aurora main set shines its light on 200 of football's most exciting players, each featured on their own 24-point stock card. Each card back gives you the latest in-depth player information and statistics along with a trivia question.

	MT
Complete Set (200):	75.00
Common Player:	.20
Minor Stars:	.40
Wax Box:	85.00
1 Rob Moore	.20
2 Jake Plummer	1.50
3 Frank Sanders	.20
4 Eric Swann	.20
5 Jamal Anderson	.75
6 Chris Chandler	.20
7 Byron Hanspard	.20
8 Terance Mathis	.20
9 O.J. Santiago	.20
10 Chuck Smith	.20
11 Jessie Tuggle	.20
12 Jay Graham	.20
13 Jim Harbaugh	.20
14 Michael Jackson	.20
15 *Patrick Johnson*	.40
16 Jermaine Lewis	.20
17 Errict Rhett	.20
18 Rod Woodson	.20
19 Quinn Early	.20
20 Andre Reed	.20
21 Antowain Smith	1.00
22 Bruce Smith	.20
23 Thurman Thomas	.40
24 Ted Washington	.20
25 Michael Bates	.20
26 Rae Carruth	.20
27 Kerry Collins	.40
28 Fred Lane	.40
29 Wesley Walls	.20
30 Edgar Bennett	.20
31 Curtis Conway	.40
32 *Curtis Enis*	5.00
33 Walt Harris	.20
34 Erik Kramer	.20
35 Barry Minter	.20
36 Jeff Blake	.40
37 Corey Dillon	1.25
38 Carl Pickens	.20
39 Darnay Scott	.20
40 Troy Aikman	2.00
41 Michael Irvin	.40
42 Deion Sanders	.75
43 Emmitt Smith	3.00
44 Chris Warren	.20
45 Terrell Davis	3.00
46 John Elway	2.00
47 *Brian Griese*	4.00
48 Ed McCaffrey	.20
49 John Mobley	.20
50 Shannon Sharpe	.40
51 Neil Smith	.20
52 Rod Smith	.20

53	Stephen Boyd	.20
54	Scott Mitchell	.20
55	Herman Moore	.75
56	Johnnie Morton	.20
57	Robert Porcher	.20
58	Barry Sanders	4.00
59	Robert Brooks	.20
60	Mark Chmura	.40
61	Brett Favre	4.00
62	Antonio Freeman	.75
63	Vonnie Holliday	1.00
64	Dorsey Levens	.40
65	Ross Verba	.20
66	Reggie White	.40
67	Elijah Alexander	.20
68	Ken Dilger	.20
69	Marshall Faulk	.75
70	Marvin Harrison	.40
71	Peyton Manning	12.00
72	Bryan Barker	.20
73	Mark Brunell	1.50
74	Keenan McCardell	.20
75	Jimmy Smith	.20
76	James Stewart	.20
77	Derrick Alexander	.20
78	Kimble Anders	.20
79	Donnell Bennett	.20
80	Elvis Grbac	.20
81	Andre Rison	.20
82	Rashaan Shehee	.75
83	Derrick Thomas	.20
84	Karim Abdul-Jabbar	.40
85	Trace Armstrong	.20
86	Charles Jordan	.20
87	Dan Marino	3.00
88	O.J. McDuffie	.20
89	Zach Thomas	.40
90	Cris Carter	.40
91	Charles Evans	.20
92	Andrew Glover	.20
93	Brad Johnson	.40
94	Randy Moss	15.00
95	John Randle	.20
96	Jake Reed	.20
97	Robert Smith	.40
98	Bruce Armstrong	.20
99	Drew Bledsoe	1.50
100	Ben Coates	.20
101	Robert Edwards	4.00
102	Terry Glenn	.40
103	Willie McGinest	.20
104	Sedrick Shaw	.20
105	Tony Simmons	2.00
106	Chris Slade	.20
107	Billy Joe Hobert	.20
108	Qadry Ismail	.20
109	Heath Shuler	.20
110	Lamar Smith	.20
111	Ray Zellars	.20
112	Tiki Barber	.40
113	Chris Calloway	.20
114	Ike Hilliard	.20
115	Joe Jurevicius	1.00
116	Danny Kanell	.20
117	Amani Toomer	.20
118	Charles Way	.20
119	Tyrone Wheatley	.20
120	Wayne Chrebet	.20
121	John Elliott	.20
122	Glenn Foley	.20
123	Scott Frost	.40
124	Aaron Glenn	.20
125	Keyshawn Johnson	.40
126	Curtis Martin	1.00
127	Vinny Testaverde	.20
128	Tim Brown	.40
129	Rickey Dudley	.20
130	Jeff George	.40
131	James Jett	.20
132	Napoleon Kaufman	.75
133	Darrell Russell	.20
134	Charles Woodson	5.00
135	James Darling	.20
136	Koy Detmer	.20
137	Irving Fryar	.20
138	Charlie Garner	.20
139	Bobby Hoying	.20
140	Chad Lewis	.20
141	Duce Staley	.20
142	Kevin Turner	.20
143	Jerome Bettis	.40
144	Will Blackwell	.20
145	Mark Bruener	.20
146	Dermontti Dawson	.20
147	Charles Johnson	.20
148	Levon Kirkland	.20
149	Tim Lester	.20
150	Kordell Stewart	1.50
151	Tony Banks	.75
152	Isaac Bruce	.40
153	Robert Holcombe	5.00
154	Eddie Kennison	.40
155	Amp Lee	.20
156	Jerald Moore	.20
157	Charlie Jones	.20
158	Freddie Jones	.20
159	Ryan Leaf	6.00
160	Natrone Means	.40
161	Junior Seau	.40
162	Bryan Still	.20
163	Marc Edwards	.20
164	Merton Hanks	.20
165	Garrison Hearst	.40
166	Terrell Owens	.40
167	Jerry Rice	2.00
168	J.J. Stokes	.20
169	Bryant Young	.20
170	Steve Young	1.00
171	Chad Brown	.20
172	Joey Galloway	.75
173	Walter Jones	.20
174	Cortez Kennedy	.20
175	Jon Kitna	.20
176	James McKnight	.20
177	Warren Moon	.40
178	Michael Sinclair	.20
179	Mike Alstott	.40
180	Reidel Anthony	.20
181	Derrick Brooks	.20
182	Trent Dilfer	.40
183	Warrick Dunn	1.50
184	Hardy Nickerson	.20
185	Warren Sapp	.20
186	Willie Davis	.20
187	Eddie George	1.25
188	Steve McNair	.75
189	Jon Runyan	.20
190	Chris Sanders	.20
191	Frank Wycheck	.20
192	Stephen Alexander	.20
193	Terry Allen	.20
194	Stephen Davis	.20
195	Cris Dishman	.20
196	Gus Frerotte	.20
197	Darrell Green	.20
198	Skip Hicks	1.50
199	Dana Stubblefield	.20
200	Michael Westbrook	.20

1998 Pacific Aurora Championship Fever

Each of the singles in this 50-card set are printed on gold foil and etched. Singles were inserted one-per-pack. This insert also has three parallel sets. The easiest being the Silvers that are found in retail packs and are sequentially numbered to 250. The Platinum Blues are numbered to 100 and can be found in both hobby and retail packs. The Copper cards are limited to 20 and are found in hobby packs.

	MT
Complete Set (50):	50.00
Common Player:	.30
Minor Stars:	.60
Inserted 1:1	
Silver Cards:	15x-30x
Production 250 Sets	
Platinum Blue Cards:	25x-50x
Production 100 Sets	
Copper Cards:	75x-150x
Production 20 Sets	

#	Player	Price
1	Jake Plummer	2.00
2	Antowain Smith	1.00
3	Bruce Smith	.30
4	Kerry Collins	.60
5	Kevin Greene	.30
6	Jeff Blake	.30
7	Corey Dillon	1.50
8	Carl Pickens	.30
9	Troy Aikman	3.00
10	Michael Irvin	.60
11	Deion Sanders	.75
12	Emmitt Smith	4.00
13	Terrell Davis	4.00
14	John Elway	3.00
15	Shannon Sharpe	.30
16	Herman Moore	.60
17	Barry Sanders	6.00
18	Brett Favre	6.00
19	Antonio Freeman	.75
20	Dorsey Levens	.60
21	Marshall Faulk	.75
22	Peyton Manning	6.00
23	Mark Brunell	2.00
24	Elvis Grbac	.30
25	Andre Rison	.30
26	Rashaan Shehee	.60
27	Derrick Thomas	.30
28	Dan Marino	4.00
29	Cris Carter	.30
30	Robert Smith	.60
31	Drew Bledsoe	2.00
32	Robert Edwards	3.00
33	Terry Glenn	.60
34	Danny Kanell	.30
35	Keyshawn Johnson	.60
36	Tim Brown	.60
37	Napoleon Kaufman	.75
38	Bobby Hoying	.30
39	Jerome Bettis	.60
40	Kordell Stewart	2.00
41	Ryan Leaf	3.00
42	Jerry Rice	3.00
43	Steve Young	1.50
44	Joey Galloway	.75
45	Mike Alstott	.60
46	Trent Dilfer	.60
47	Warrick Dunn	2.00
48	Eddie George	2.00
49	Steve McNair	.75
50	Gus Frerotte	.30

1998 Pacific Aurora Cubes

The Cubes insert could only be found in hobby boxes and were inserted one per box. Only 20 of the top players from the NFL were included in this insert.

	MT
Complete Set (20):	170.00
Common Player:	4.00
One Per Box	

#	Player	Price
1	Corey Dillon	6.00
2	Troy Aikman	10.00
3	Emmitt Smith	15.00
4	Terrell Davis	15.00
5	John Elway	10.00
6	Barry Sanders	20.00
7	Brett Favre	20.00
8	Dorsey Levens	4.00
9	Peyton Manning	15.00
10	Mark Brunell	8.00
11	Dan Marino	15.00
12	Drew Bledsoe	8.00
13	Napoleon Kaufman	4.00
14	Jerome Bettis	4.00
15	Kordell Stewart	8.00
16	Ryan Leaf	8.00
17	Jerry Rice	10.00
18	Steve Young	6.00
19	Warrick Dunn	8.00
20	Eddie George	8.00

1998 Pacific Aurora Face Mask Cel-Fusions

Each player in this 20-card foiled and etched set is profiled against a die-cut helmet that is fused to a cel-portion face mask. Singles were inserted 1:73 packs.

	MT
Complete Set (20):	550.00
Common Player:	10.00
Inserted 1:73	

#	Player	Price
1	Corey Dillon	15.00
2	Troy Aikman	35.00
3	Emmitt Smith	50.00
4	Terrell Davis	50.00
5	John Elway	35.00
6	Barry Sanders	70.00
7	Brett Favre	70.00
8	Antonio Freeman	10.00
9	Peyton Manning	60.00
10	Mark Brunell	25.00
11	Dan Marino	50.00
12	Drew Bledsoe	25.00
13	Napoleon Kaufman	10.00
14	Jerome Bettis	10.00
15	Kordell Stewart	25.00
16	Ryan Leaf	25.00
17	Jerry Rice	35.00
18	Steve Young	15.00
19	Warrick Dunn	20.00
20	Eddie George	20.00

1998 Pacific Aurora Gridiron Laser-Cuts

Each single in this 20-card set is laser cut and was inserted 4:37 packs. They could only be found in hobby packs.

	MT
Complete Set (20):	125.00
Common Player:	3.00
Inserted 4:37 Hobby	

#	Player	Price
1	Jake Plummer	6.00
2	Corey Dillon	5.00
3	Troy Aikman	8.00
4	Emmitt Smith	10.00
5	Terrell Davis	10.00
6	John Elway	8.00
7	Barry Sanders	15.00
8	Brett Favre	15.00
9	Peyton Manning	10.00
10	Mark Brunell	6.00
11	Dan Marino	10.00
12	Drew Bledsoe	6.00
13	Jerome Bettis	3.00
14	Kordell Stewart	6.00
15	Ryan Leaf	7.00
16	Jerry Rice	8.00
17	Steve Young	5.00
18	Warrick Dunn	6.00
19	Eddie George	6.00
20	Steve McNair	4.00

1998 Pacific Aurora NFL Command

This insert salutes 10 NFL stars with this coveted fully-foiled and etched insert. Singles were inserted 1:361 packs.

	MT
Complete Set (10):	650.00
Common Player:	50.00
Inserted 1:361	

#	Player	Price
1	Terrell Davis	100.00
2	John Elway	100.00
3	Barry Sanders	125.00
4	Brett Favre	125.00
5	Peyton Manning	100.00
6	Mark Brunell	50.00
7	Dan Marino	100.00
8	Drew Bledsoe	50.00
9	Ryan Leaf	50.00
10	Warrick Dunn	50.00

1998 Pacific Crown Royale

This 144-card base set features football's brightest stars and top rookies on the Crown Royale double-foiled, double-etched, all-die-cut format. The parallel Limited Series cards are printed on 24-point stock and are sequentially numbered to 99.

	MT
Complete Set (144):	180.00
Common Player:	.50
Minor Stars:	1.00
Common Rookie:	1.00
Limited Series Cards:	15x-30x
Limited Series Rookies:	3x-6x
Production 99 Sets	
Wax Box:	120.00

#	Player	Price
1	Larry Centers	.50
2	Rob Moore	.50
3	Adrian Murrell	.50
4	Jake Plummer	3.00
5	Jamal Anderson	1.50
6	Chris Chandler	.50
7	Tim Dwight	3.00
8	Tony Martin	.50
9	Jay Graham	.50
10	Patrick Johnson	2.00
11	Jermaine Lewis	.50
12	Eric Zeier	.50
13	Rob Johnson	1.00
14	Eric Moulds	1.50
15	Antowain Smith	1.50
16	Bruce Smith	.50
17	Steve Beuerlein	.50
18	Anthony Johnson	.50
19	Fred Lane	1.00
20	Muhsin Muhammad	.50
21	Curtis Conway	1.00
22	Curtis Enis	6.00
23	Erik Kramer	.50
24	Tony Parrish	1.00
25	Corey Dillon	2.00
26	Neil O'Donnell	.50
27	Carl Pickens	1.00
28	Takeo Spikes	2.00
29	Troy Aikman	4.00
30	Michael Irvin	1.00
31	Deion Sanders	1.50
32	Emmitt Smith	6.00
33	Chris Warren	.50
34	Terrell Davis	6.00
35	John Elway	4.00
36	Brian Griese	10.00
37	Ed McCaffrey	1.00
38	Shannon Sharpe	1.00
39	Rod Smith	1.00
40	Charlie Batch	15.00
41	Herman Moore	1.00
42	Johnnie Morton	.50
43	Barry Sanders	8.00
44	Bryant Westbrook	.50
45	Robert Brooks	.50
46	Brett Favre	8.00
47	Antonio Freeman	1.50
48	Raymont Harris	.50
49	Vonnie Holliday	3.00
50	Reggie White	1.00
51	Marshall Faulk	1.50
52	E.G. Green	3.00
53	Marvin Harrison	1.00
54	Peyton Manning	20.00
55	Jerome Pathon	3.00
56	Tavian Banks	4.00
57	Mark Brunell	4.00
58	Keenan McCardell	.50
59	Jimmy Smith	1.00
60	Fred Taylor	15.00
61	Derrick Alexander	.50
62	Tony Gonzalez	.50
63	Elvis Grbac	.50
64	Andre Rison	.50
65	Rashaan Shehee	2.00
66	Derrick Thomas	.50
67	Karim Abdul-Jabbar	1.00
68	John Avery	4.00
69	Oronde Gadsden	3.00
70	Dan Marino	6.00
71	O.J. McDuffie	.50
72	Cris Carter	1.50
73	Randall Cunningham	1.50
74	Brad Johnson	1.00
75	Randy Moss	30.00
76	John Randle	.50
77	Jake Reed	.50
78	Robert Smith	1.00
79	Drew Bledsoe	3.00
80	Robert Edwards	7.00
81	Terry Glenn	1.00
82	Tebucky Jones	1.00
83	Tony Simmons	3.00
84	Mark Fields	1.00
85	Andre Hastings	.50
86	Danny Wuerffel	1.00
87	Ray Zellars	.50
88	Tiki Barber	1.00
89	Ike Hilliard	1.00
90	Joe Jurevicius	2.00
91	Danny Kanell	.50
92	Wayne Chrebet	1.00
93	Glenn Foley	1.00
94	Keyshawn Johnson	1.50
95	Leon Johnson	.50
96	Curtis Martin	1.50
97	Tim Brown	1.00
98	Jeff George	1.00
99	Napoleon Kaufman	1.50
100	Jon Ritchie	1.50
101	Charles Woodson	7.00
102	Irving Fryar	.50
103	Bobby Hoying	1.00
104	Allen Rossum	1.00
105	Duce Staley	.50
106	Jerome Bettis	1.00
107	Chris Fuamatu-Ma'afala	3.00
108	Charles Johnson	1.00
109	Levon Kirkland	.50
110	Kordell Stewart	3.00
111	Hines Ward	3.00
112	Tony Banks	1.00
113	Tony Horne	1.00
114	Eddie Kennison	1.00
115	Amp Lee	.50
116	Freddie Jones	.50
117	Ryan Leaf	7.00
118	Natrone Means	1.00
119	Mikhael Ricks	3.00
120	Bryan Still	.50
121	Marc Edwards	.50
122	Garrison Hearst	1.00
123	Terrell Owens	1.50
124	Jerry Rice	4.00
125	J.J. Stokes	1.00
126	Steve Young	2.50
127	Joey Galloway	1.50
128	Ahman Green	5.00
129	Warren Moon	1.00
130	Ricky Watters	1.00
131	Mike Alstott	1.50
132	Trent Dilfer	1.00
133	Warrick Dunn	3.00
134	Jacquez Green	6.00
135	Warren Sapp	.50
136	Kevin Dyson	5.00
137	Eddie George	3.00
138	Steve McNair	2.00
139	Yancey Thigpen	1.00
140	Stephen Alexander	1.00
141	Terry Allen	1.00
142	Trent Green	1.00
143	Skip Hicks	4.00
144	Michael Westbrook	1.00

1998 Pacific Crown Royale Cramer's Choice Awards Jumbos

These singles are identical to the Cramer's Choice awards found in Pacific except for the size. Singles from this set are larger and found on top of boxes at one per. The twist to this insert is the six different parallels with varying foil colors and number of sets produced. The Dark Blues are numbered to 35, Greens are numbered to 30, Reds to 25, Light Blues to 20, Golds to 10 and only one Purple set.

	MT
Complete Set (10):	150.00
Common Player:	10.00
One Per Box	
Dark Blue Cards:	10x-20x
Production 35 Sets	
Green Cards:	10x-20x
Production 30 Sets	
Red Cards:	10x-20x
Production 25 Sets	
Light Blue Cards:	10x-20x
Production 20 Sets	
Gold Cards:	15x-30x
Production 10 Sets	

#	Player	Price
1	Terrell Davis	15.00
2	John Elway	12.00
3	Barry Sanders	20.00
4	Brett Favre	20.00
5	Peyton Manning	20.00
6	Mark Brunell	10.00
7	Dan Marino	15.00
8	Randy Moss	35.00
9	Jerry Rice	12.00
10	Warrick Dunn	10.00

1998 Pacific Crown Royale Living Legends

The players selected for this insert were based on the dozens of records, awards and championships that each player has earned. Each card in this insert is sequentially numbered to 375.

	MT
Complete Set (10):	300.00
Common Player:	20.00
Production 375 Sets	

#	Player	Price
1	Troy Aikman	30.00
2	Emmitt Smith	45.00
3	Terrell Davis	45.00
4	John Elway	30.00
5	Barry Sanders	60.00
6	Brett Favre	60.00
7	Mark Brunell	20.00
8	Dan Marino	45.00
9	Drew Bledsoe	25.00
10	Jerry Rice	30.00

1998 Pacific Crown Royale Master Performers

Master Performers includes the top 20 players from the NFL and was inserted 2:25 hobby packs.

	MT
Complete Set (20):	120.00
Common Player:	2.00
Minor Stars:	4.00
Inserted 2:25 Hobby	

#	Player	Price
1	Corey Dillon	2.00
2	Troy Aikman	7.00
3	Emmitt Smith	10.00
4	Terrell Davis	10.00
5	John Elway	7.00
6	Charlie Batch	8.00
7	Barry Sanders	14.00
8	Brett Favre	14.00
9	Peyton Manning	14.00
10	Mark Brunell	5.00
11	Fred Taylor	6.00

12	Dan Marino	10.00
13	Randy Moss	25.00
14	Drew Bledsoe	5.00
15	Curtis Martin	4.00
16	Kordell Stewart	5.00
17	Ryan Leaf	6.00
18	Jerry Rice	7.00
19	Steve Young	5.00
20	Warrick Dunn	5.00

1998 Pacific Crown Royale Pillars of the Game

These holographic gold foil cards served as the bottom card in every pack and featured a strong mix of NFL mainstays and rising stars. These could only be found in hobby packs.

		MT
Complete Set (25):		45.00
Common Player:		.50
Minor Stars:		1.00
Inserted 1:1 Hobby		
1	Antowain Smith	.50
2	Corey Dillon	1.00
3	Troy Aikman	1.50
4	Emmitt Smith	2.00
5	Terrell Davis	2.00
6	John Elway	1.50
7	Charlie Batch	4.00
8	Barry Sanders	3.00
9	Brett Favre	3.00
10	Antonio Freeman	1.00
11	Peyton Manning	6.00
12	Mark Brunell	1.25
13	Dan Marino	2.00
14	Randy Moss	14.00
15	Drew Bledsoe	1.25
16	Curtis Martin	1.00
17	Napoleon Kaufman	1.00
18	Jerome Bettis	1.00
19	Kordell Stewart	1.25
20	Ryan Leaf	4.00
21	Jerry Rice	1.50
22	Steve Young	1.00
23	Ricky Watters	.50
24	Eddie George	1.25
25	Warrick Dunn	1.25

1998 Pacific Crown Royale Pivotal Players

This 25-card holographic silver foil insert featured some of football's most dynamic superstars along with several top rookies from 1998. Singles were found one-per-pack in hobby packs only.

		MT
Complete Set (25):		30.00
Common Player:		.50
Inserted 1:1 Hobby		
1	Jake Plummer	1.00
2	Antowain Smith	.50
3	Corey Dillon	.75
4	Troy Aikman	1.50
5	Deion Sanders	.50
6	Emmitt Smith	2.00
7	Terrell Davis	2.00
8	John Elway	1.50
9	Charlie Batch	4.00
10	Barry Sanders	3.00
11	Brett Favre	3.00
12	Peyton Manning	6.00
13	Mark Brunell	1.00
14	Fred Taylor	3.00
15	Dan Marino	2.00
16	Randy Moss	14.00
17	Drew Bledsoe	1.25
18	Curtis Martin	.75
19	Napoleon Kaufman	.50
20	Jerome Bettis	.50
21	Kordell Stewart	1.25
22	Ryan Leaf	4.00
23	Jerry Rice	1.50
24	Eddie George	1.25
25	Warrick Dunn	1.00

1998 Pacific Crown Royale Rookie Paydirt

The fully foiled and etched Rookie Paydirt set gave collectors an early look at the top 20 rookies from 1998. Singles were inserted into hobby packs at a ratio of 1:25.

		MT
Complete Set (20):		175.00
Common Player:		3.00

Inserted 1:25 Hobby		
1	Curtis Enis	8.00
2	Marcus Nash	6.00
3	Charlie Batch	15.00
4	Vonnie Holliday	4.00
5	E.G. Green	3.00
6	Peyton Manning	30.00
7	Jerome Pathon	3.00
8	Tavian Banks	6.00
9	Fred Taylor	15.00
10	Rashaan Shehee	3.00
11	John Avery	6.00
12	Randy Moss	60.00
13	Robert Edwards	10.00
14	Charles Woodson	8.00
15	Hines Ward	5.00
16	Ryan Leaf	12.00
17	Mikhael Ricks	4.00
18	Ahman Green	6.00
19	Jacquez Green	8.00
20	Kevin Dyson	8.00

1998 Pacific Omega

Omega football consists of a 250-card base set and five inserts. The base cards have a horizontal layout. The fronts feature three photos separated by a football stitching pattern. The color center photo is duplicated in silver foil on the right. Another color photo is on the left.

		MT
Complete Set (250):		50.00
Common Player:		.10
Minor Stars:		.20
Wax Box:		50.00
1	Larry Centers	.10
2	Rob Moore	.10
3	Michael Pittman	.10
4	Jake Plummer	2.00
5	Simeon Rice	.10
6	Frank Sanders	.10
7	Eric Swann	.10
8	Morten Anderson	.10
9	Jamal Anderson	.20
10	Chris Chandler	.10
11	Harold Green	.10
12	Byron Hanspard	.10
13	Terance Mathis	.10
14	O.J. Santiago	.10
15	Peter Boulware	.10
16	Jay Graham	.10
17	Eric Green	.10
18	Michael Jackson	.10
19	Jermaine Lewis	.10
20	Ray Lewis	.10
21	Jonathan Ogden	.10
22	Eric Zeier	.10
23	Steve Christie	.10
24	Todd Collins	.10
25	Quinn Early	.10
26	Eric Moulds	.20
27	Andre Reed	.10
28	Antowain Smith	1.00
29	Bruce Smith	.10
30	Thurman Thomas	.20
31	Ted Washington	.10
32	Michael Bates	.10
33	Tim Biakabutuka	.10
34	Mark Carrier	.10
35	Rae Carruth	.20
36	Kerry Collins	.30
37	Kevin Greene	.10
38	Fred Lane	.20
39	Muhsin Muhammad	.10
40	Wesley Walls	.10
41	Curtis Conway	.20
42	Bobby Engram	.10
43	*Curtis Enis*	5.00
44	Raymont Harris	.10
45	Erik Kramer	.10
46	Chris Penn	.10
47	Ryan Wetnight	.10
48	Jeff Blake	.10
49	Ki-Jana Carter	.10
50	John Copeland	.10
51	Corey Dillon	1.00
52	Tony McGee	.10
53	Carl Pickens	.20
54	Darnay Scott	.10
55	Takeo Spikes	.10
56	Troy Aikman	1.50
57	Eric Bjornson	.10
58	*Greg Ellis*	.20

59	Michael Irwin	.20
60	Daryl Johnston	.10
61	David LaFleur	.10
62	Deion Sanders	.50
63	Emmitt Smith	2.50
64	Jason Garrett	.10
65	Nicky Sualua	.10
66	Steve Atwater	.10
67	Terrell Davis	1.50
68	John Elway	1.50
69	*Brian Griese*	4.00
70	Ed McCaffrey	.10
71	John Mobley	.10
72	*Marcus Nash*	2.00
73	Shannon Sharpe	.20
74	Neil Smith	.10
75	Rod Smith	.20
76	*Charlie Batch*	6.00
77	*Germane Crowell*	1.50
78	Jason Hanson	.10
79	Scott Mitchell	.10
80	Herman Moore	.20
81	Johnnie Morton	.10
82	Barry Sanders	3.00
83	Tommy Vardell	.10
84	Robert Brooks	.10
85	Gilbert Brown	.10
86	Leroy Butler	.10
87	Mark Chmura	.10
88	Brett Favre	3.00
89	Antonio Freeman	.20
90	William Henderson	.10
91	*Vonnie Holliday*	.20
92	Dorsey Levens	.20
93	Reggie White	.20
94	Aaron Bailey	.10
95	Quentin Coryatt	.10
96	Zack Crockett	.10
97	Ken Dilger	.10
98	Marshall Faulk	.20
99	*E.G. Green*	.20
100	Marvin Harrison	.20
101	*Peyton Manning*	10.00
102	Jerome Pathon	.10
103	*Tavian Banks*	3.00
104	Tony Boselli	.10
105	Tony Brackens	.10
106	Mark Brunell	1.25
107	Kevin Hardy	.10
108	Keenan McCardell	.10
109	Pete Mitchell	.10
110	Jimmy Smith	.20
111	James Stewart	.20
112	*Fred Taylor*	4.00
113	Kimble Anders	.10
114	Dale Carter	.10
115	Tony Gonzalez	.20
116	Elvis Grbac	.10
117	Donnell Bennett	.10
118	Andre Rison	.10
119	Rashaan Shehee	.50
120	Derrick Thomas	.20
121	Tamarick Vanover	.10
122	Karim Abdul-Jabbar	.30
123	*John Avery*	2.50
124	Troy Drayton	.10
125	John Dutton	.10
126	Craig Erickson	.10
127	Dan Marino	2.50
128	O.J. McDuffie	.10
129	Jerris McPhail	.10
130	Stanley Pritchett	.10
131	Larry Shannon	.10
132	Zach Thomas	.20
133	Cris Carter	.20
134	Randall Cunningham	.20
135	Andrew Glover	.10
136	Brad Johnson	.10
137	Randall McDaniel	.10
138	David Palmer	.10
139	John Randle	.10
140	Jake Reed	.10
141	Robert Smith	.20
142	Drew Bledsoe	1.25
143	Ben Coates	.10
144	*Robert Edwards*	3.00
145	Terry Glenn	.30
146	Shawn Jefferson	.10
147	Willie McGinest	.10
148	Tony Simmons	.10
149	Chris Slade	.10
150	Troy Davis	.10
151	Mark Fields	.10
152	Andre Hastings	.10
153	Billy Joe Hobert	.10
154	William Roaf	.10
155	Heath Shuler	.10
156	Danny Wuerffel	.10
157	Ray Zellars	.10
158	Jessie Armstead	.10
159	Tiki Barber	.20
160	Chris Calloway	.10
161	Mike Cherry	.10
162	Danny Kanell	.10
163	Amani Toomer	.10
164	Charles Way	.10
165	Tyrone Wheatley	.10
166	Kyle Brady	.10
167	Wayne Chrebet	.20
168	Glenn Foley	.10
169	*Scott Frost*	.20
170	Keyshawn Johnson	.20
171	Leon Johnson	.10
172	Alex Van Dyke	.10
173	Dedric Ward	.10
174	Tim Brown	.20
175	Rickey Dudley	.10

176	Jeff George	.20
177	Desmond Howard	.10
178	James Jett	.10
179	Napoleon Kaufman	.50
180	Darrell Russell	.10
181	*Charles Woodson*	4.00
182	Jason Dunn	.10
183	Irving Fryar	.10
184	Charlie Garner	.20
185	Bobby Hoying	.10
186	Chris T. Jones	.10
187	Michael Timpson	.10
188	Kevin Turner	.10
189	Jerome Bettis	.20
190	Will Blackwell	.10
191	Mark Bruener	.10
192	Charles Johnson	.10
193	George Jones	.10
194	Levon Kirkland	.10
195	Kordell Stewart	1.25
196	*Hines Ward*	2.00
197	Tony Banks	.20
198	Isaac Bruce	.20
199	Ernie Conwell	.10
200	*Robert Holcombe*	3.00
201	Eddie Kennison	.20
202	Amp Lee	.10
203	Orlando Pace	.10
204	Charlie Jones	.10
205	Freddie Jones	.10
206	*Ryan Leaf*	5.00
207	Natrone Means	.20
208	Junior Seau	.20
209	Bryan Still	.10
210	Greg Clark	.10
211	Jim Druckenmiller	.20
212	Marc Edwards	.10
213	Garrison Hearst	.20
214	Terrell Owens	.20
215	Jerry Rice	1.50
216	J.J. Stokes	.10
217	Bryant Young	.10
218	Steve Young	1.00
219	Chad Brown	.10
220	Joey Galloway	.30
221	Cortez Kennedy	.10
222	Jon Kitna	.10
223	James McKnight	.10
224	Warren Moon	.20
225	Michael Sinclair	.10
226	Ricky Watters	.20
227	Mike Alstott	.30
228	Reidel Anthony	.20
229	Derrick Brooks	.10
230	Trent Dilfer	.20
231	Warrick Dunn	2.00
232	Dave Moore	.10
233	Hardy Nickerson	.10
234	Warren Sapp	.10
235	Karl Williams	.10
236	Willie Davis	.10
237	*Kevin Dyson*	2.00
238	Eddie George	1.25
239	Derrick Mason	.10
240	Steve McNair	.75
241	Chris Sanders	.10
242	Frank Wycheck	.10
243	Terry Allen	.10
244	Jamie Asher	.10
245	Gus Frerotte	.10
246	Darrell Green	.10
247	*Skip Hicks*	1.50
248	Brian Mitchell	.10
249	Leslie Shepherd	.10
250	Michael Westbrook	.10

1998 Pacific Omega EO Portraits

EO Portraits is a 20-card insert seeded 1:73. The cards feature a color player photo with a closeup photo of the player's face laser-cut into the card. A hoobby-only parallel version is numbered to one.

		MT
Complete Set (20):		350.00
Common Player:		10.00
Inserted 1:73		
1	Jake Plummer	25.00
2	Corey Dillon	15.00
3	Troy Aikman	25.00
4	Emmitt Smith	40.00
5	Terrell Davis	25.00
6	John Elway	25.00

1998 Pacific Omega Face To Face

Face To Face is a 10-card insert seeded 1:145. The cards have a horizontal layout and feature two NFL stars on the front.

		MT
Complete Set (10):		300.00
Common Player:		20.00
Inserted 1:145		
1	Peyton Manning, Ryan Leaf	40.00
2	Barry Sanders, Warrick Dunn	50.00
3	Dan Marino, John Elway	40.00
4	Jerry Rice, Antonio Freeman	25.00
5	Jake Plummer, Drew Bledsoe	25.00
6	Corey Dillon, Eddie George	20.00
7	Emmitt Smith, Terrell Davis	40.00
8	Steve Young, Mark Brunell	25.00
9	Kordell Stewart, Steve McNair	25.00
10	Troy Aikman, Brett Favre	50.00

1998 Pacific Omega Online

Online is a 36-card insert seeded 4:37. The card is designed to resemble a computer, with the color player photo on the monitor. The player's name, position, team logo and team web page appear on the keyboard at the bottom.

		MT
Complete Set (36):		200.00
Common Player:		2.00
Inserted 4:37		
1	Jake Plummer	10.00
2	Antowain Smith	5.00
3	Curtis Enis	10.00
4	Corey Dillon	6.00
5	Troy Aikman	10.00
6	Emmitt Smith	15.00
7	Terrell Davis	10.00
8	John Elway	10.00
9	Shannon Sharpe	2.00
10	Herman Moore	2.00
11	Barry Sanders	20.00
12	Brett Favre	20.00
13	Antonio Freeman	2.00
14	Dorsey Levens	2.00
15	Peyton Manning	20.00
16	Marshall Faulk	2.00
17	Mark Brunell	8.00
18	Fred Taylor	6.00
19	Dan Marino	15.00
20	Robert Smith	2.00
21	Drew Bledsoe	8.00
22	Tiki Barber	2.00
23	Danny Kanell	2.00
24	Tim Brown	2.00
25	Napoleon Kaufman	2.00
26	Charles Woodson	10.00
27	Jerome Bettis	2.00
28	Kordell Stewart	8.00
29	Ryan Leaf	7.00
30	Jerry Rice	10.00
31	Steve Young	6.00
32	Joey Galloway	2.00
33	Trent Dilfer	2.00
34	Warrick Dunn	10.00
35	Eddie George	8.00
36	Steve McNair	5.00

1998 Pacific Omega Prisms

Prism is a 20-card insert seeded one per 37 packs. The cards have a horizontal layout on prismatic foil. A color player photo is on the left with a pyramid and team logo on the right.

		MT
Complete Set (20):		200.00
Common Player:		1.50
Inserted 1:37		
1	Jake Plummer	12.00
2	Corey Dillon	8.00
3	Troy Aikman	12.00
4	Emmitt Smith	20.00
5	Terrell Davis	12.00
6	John Elway	12.00
7	Barry Sanders	25.00
8	Brett Favre	25.00
9	Peyton Manning	25.00
10	Mark Brunell	10.00
11	Dan Marino	20.00
12	Drew Bledsoe	10.00
13	Napoleon Kaufman	6.00
14	Jerome Bettis	1.50
15	Kordell Stewart	10.00
16	Ryan Leaf	10.00
17	Jerry Rice	12.00
18	Steve Young	8.00
19	Warrick Dunn	12.00
20	Eddie George	10.00

1998 Pacific Omega Rising Stars

Rising Stars is a 30-card insert seeded 4:37. The set features NFL rookies from 1998. The insert is paralleled five times, each with a different foil color. The blue foil parallel is numbered to 100, red to 75, green to 50, purple to 25 and gold to one.

		MT
Complete Set (30):		90.00

Common Player: 2.00
Inserted 4:37 Hobby
1 Michael Pittman 2.00
2 Keith Brooking 2.00
3 Duane Starks 2.00
4 Curtis Enis 10.00
5 Marcus Nash 5.00
6 Brian Griese 6.00
7 Terry Fair 2.00
8 Germane Crowell 5.00
9 Charlie Batch 5.00
10 E.G. Green 2.00
11 Peyton Manning 20.00
12 Jerome Pathon 2.00
13 Fred Taylor 8.00
14 Tavian Banks 6.00
15 Rashaan Shehee 4.00
16 John Avery 5.00
17 John Dutton 2.00
18 Robert Edwards 5.00
19 Tony Simmons 4.00
20 Joe Jurevicius 4.00
21 Scott Frost 2.00
22 Charles Woodson 8.00
23 Hines Ward 5.00
24 Robert Holcombe 6.00
25 Az-Zahir Hakim 2.00
26 Ryan Leaf 6.00
27 Ahman Green 6.00
28 Kevin Dyson 5.00
29 Stephen Alexander 2.00
30 Skip Hicks 5.00

1998 Pacific Paramount

Paramount Football consists of a 250-card base set with three parallels and four inserts. The base cards feature full-bleed photos with the player's name, position and team logo at the bottom. The regular cards have Copper, Silver and Platinum Blue parallels. Inserts include Pro Bowl Die-Cuts, Super Bowl XXXII Highlights, Personal Bests and Kings of the NFL.

MT
Complete Set (250): 25.00
Common Player: .10
Minor Stars: .20
Wax Box: 45.00
1 Larry Centers .10
2 Chris Gedney .10
3 Rob Moore .10
4 Jake Plummer 1.00
5 Simeon Rice .10
6 Frank Sanders .10
7 Mark Smith .10
8 Eric Swann .10
9 Jamal Anderson .20
10 Chris Chandler .10
11 Bert Emanuel .10
12 Tony Graziani .10
13 Byron Hanspard .20
14 Terance Mathis .10
15 O.J. Santiago .10
16 Chuck Smith .10
17 Derrick Alexander .10
18 Peter Boulware .10
19 Jay Graham .10
20 *Priest Holmes* 10.00
21 Michael Jackson .10
22 Bam Morris .10
23 Vinny Testaverde .20
24 Eric Zeier .10
25 Todd Collins .10
26 Quinn Early .10
27 Bryce Paup .10
28 Andre Reed .10
29 Jay Riemersma .10
30 Antowain Smith .50
31 Bruce Smith .10
32 Thurman Thomas .20
33 Michael Bates .10
34 Mark Carrier .10
35 Rae Carruth .20
36 Kerry Collins .30
37 Fred Lane .10
38 Lamar Lathon .10
39 Muhsin Muhammad .10
40 Wesley Walls .10
41 Darnell Autry .20
42 Curtis Conway .20
43 Raymont Harris .20
44 Tyrone Hughes .10

45 Chris Penn .10
46 Ricky Proehl .10
47 Steve Stenstrom .10
48 Ryan Wetnight .10
49 Jeff Blake .20
50 Ki-Jana Carter .10
51 Corey Dillon .75
52 David Dunn .10
53 Boomer Esiason .10
54 Brian Milne .10
55 Carl Pickens .20
56 Darnay Scott .10
57 Troy Aikman 1.00
58 Eric Bjornson .10
59 Michael Irvin .20
60 Daryl Johnston .10
61 Anthony Miller .10
62 Deion Sanders .40
63 Emmitt Smith 1.50
64 Omar Stoutmire .10
65 Sherman Williams .10
66 Terrell Davis 1.25
67 John Elway 1.00
68 Darrien Gordon .10
69 Ed McCaffrey .10
70 Bill Romanowski .10
71 Shannon Sharpe .10
72 Neil Smith .10
73 Rod Smith .10
74 Maa Tanuvasa .10
75 Tommie Boyd .10
76 Glyn Milburn .10
77 Scott Mitchell .10
78 Herman Moore .10
79 Johnnie Morton .10
80 Robert Porcher .10
81 Barry Sanders 1.50
82 Bryant Westbrook .10
83 Robert Brooks .10
84 LeRoy Butler .10
85 Mark Chmura .10
86 Brett Favre 2.00
87 Antonio Freeman .20
88 Dorsey Levens .20
89 Eugene Robinson .10
90 *Bill Schroeder* 4.00
91 Reggie White .20
92 Aaron Bailey .10
93 Quentin Coryatt .10
94 Zack Crockett .10
95 Sean Dawkins .10
96 Ken Dilger .10
97 Marshall Faulk .20
98 Jim Harbaugh .10
99 Marvin Harrison .20
100 Bryan Barker .10
101 Tony Boselli .10
102 Tony Brackens .10
103 Mark Brunell 1.00
104 Mike Hollis .10
105 Keenan McCardell .10
106 Natrone Means .20
107 Jimmy Smith .10
108 James Stewart .10
109 Marcus Allen .20
110 Kimble Anders .10
111 Dale Carter .10
112 Tony Gonzalez .20
113 Elvis Grbac .20
114 Greg Hill .10
115 Andre Rison .10
116 Will Shields .10
117 Derrick Thomas .10
118 Karim Abdul-Jabbar .30
119 Trace Armstrong .10
120 *Damon Huard* 7.00
121 Charles Jordan .10
122 Dan Marino 1.50
123 O.J. McDuffie .10
124 Irving Spikes .10
125 Zach Thomas .10
126 Cris Carter .10
127 *Charles Woodson* 3.00
128 Brad Johnson .20
129 Randall McDaniel .10
130 John Randle .10
131 Jake Reed .10
132 Robert Smith .10
133 Todd Steussie .10
134 Bruce Armstrong .10
135 Drew Bledsoe 1.00
136 Ben Coates .10
137 Derrick Cullors .10
138 Terry Glenn .30
139 Shawn Jefferson .10
140 Curtis Martin .75
141 Chris Slade .10
142 Larry Whigham .10
143 Troy Davis .20
144 Andre Hastings .10
145 Randal Hill .10
146 Sammy Knight .10
147 William Roaf .10
148 Heath Shuler .10
149 Danny Wuerffel .20
150 Ray Zellars .10
151 Jessie Armstead .10
152 Tiki Barber .40
153 Chris Calloway .10
154 Danny Kanell .10
155 David Patten .10
156 Michael Strahan .10
157 Charles Way .10
158 Tyrone Wheatley .10
159 Kyle Brady .10
160 Wayne Chrebet .10
161 Glenn Foley .10
162 Aaron Glenn .10
163 Leon Johnson .10
164 Adrian Murrell .10

165 Neil O'Donnell .10
166 Dedric Ward .10
167 Tim Brown .20
168 Rickey Dudley .10
169 Jeff George .20
170 Desmond Howard .10
171 James Jett .10
172 Napoleon Kaufman .20
173 Chester McGlockton .10
174 Darrell Russell .10
175 Ty Detmer .10
176 Irving Fryar .10
177 Charlie Garner .10
178 Bobby Hoying .10
179 Chad Lewis .10
180 Duce Staley .10
181 Kevin Turner .10
182 Ricky Watters .20
183 Jerome Bettis .20
184 Will Blackwell .10
185 Charles Johnson .10
186 George Jones .10
187 Levon Kirkland .10
188 Carnell Lake .10
189 Kordell Stewart 1.00
190 Yancey Thigpen .10
191 Tony Banks .30
192 Isaac Bruce .20
193 Ernie Conwell .10
194 Craig Heyward .10
195 Eddie Kennison .20
196 Amp Lee .10
197 Orlando Pace .10
198 Torrance Small .10
199 Gary Brown .10
200 Kenny Bynum .10
201 Freddie Jones .10
202 Tony Martin .10
203 Eric Metcalf .10
204 Junior Seau .20
205 Craig Whelihan .10
206 William Floyd .10
207 Merton Hanks .10
208 Garrison Hearst .10
209 Brent Jones .10
210 Terrell Owens .20
211 Jerry Rice 1.00
212 J.J. Stokes .10
213 Rod Woodson .10
214 Steve Young .50
215 Steve Broussard .10
216 Joey Galloway .20
217 Cortez Kennedy .10
218 Jon Kitna .10
219 James McKnight .10
220 Warren Moon .20
221 Michael Sinclair .10
222 *Ryan Leaf* 3.00
223 Darryl Williams .10
224 Mike Alstott .30
225 Reidel Anthony .20
226 Derrick Brooks .10
227 Horace Copeland .10
228 Trent Dilfer .10
229 Warrick Dunn 1.00
230 Hardy Nickerson .10
231 Warren Sapp .10
232 Karl Williams .10
233 Blaine Bishop .10
234 Willie Davis .10
235 Eddie George 1.25
236 Derrick Mason .10
237 Bruce Matthews .10
238 Steve McNair .75
239 Chris Sanders .10
240 Rodney Thomas .10
241 Frank Wycheck .10
242 Terry Allen .10
243 Jamie Asher .10
244 Larry Bowie .10
245 Albert Connell .10
246 Stephen Davis .10
247 Gus Frerotte .10
248 Ken Harvey .10
249 Leslie Shepherd .10
250 Michael Westbrook .10

1998 Pacific Paramount Copper/Silver

The 250-card base set is paralleled in the Copper hobby-only and Silver retail-only sets (1:1).

MT
Copper/Silver Cards: 2x-4x

1998 Pacific Paramount Platinum Blue

Platinum Blue is a full parallel of the Paramount base set, seeded one per 73 packs.

MT
Platinum Blue Cards: 40x-80x

1998 Pacific Paramount Kings of the NFL

Kings of the NFL is a fully-foiled 20-card insert seeded one per 73 packs. The cards have a color photo with the player's name, position and team logo at the bottom.

MT
Complete Set (20): 450.00
Common Player: 7.00
1 Antowain Smith 15.00
2 Corey Dillon 20.00
3 Troy Aikman 30.00
4 Emmitt Smith 50.00
5 Terrell Davis 30.00
6 John Elway 30.00
7 Barry Sanders 50.00
8 Brett Favre 60.00
9 Dorsey Levens 7.00
10 Reggie White 7.00
11 Mark Brunell 30.00
12 Dan Marino 50.00
13 Curtis Martin 20.00
14 Drew Bledsoe 30.00
15 Jerome Bettis 7.00
16 Kordell Stewart 30.00
17 Jerry Rice 30.00
18 Steve Young 20.00
19 Warrick Dunn 30.00
20 Eddie George 30.00

1998 Pacific Paramount Personal Bests

Personal Bests is a 36-card insert seeded 4:37. The cards have a color player photo on holographic silver foil. The player's name is printed vertically on the left.

MT
Complete Set (36): 100.00
Common Player: 1.50
1 Jake Plummer 8.00
2 Antowain Smith 5.00
3 Kerry Collins 4.00
4 Raymont Harris 1.50
5 Corey Dillon 6.00
6 Troy Aikman 8.00
7 Deion Sanders 4.00
8 Emmitt Smith 10.00
9 Terrell Davis 8.00
10 John Elway 8.00
11 Shannon Sharpe 1.50
12 Herman Moore 1.50
13 Barry Sanders 12.00
14 Brett Favre 16.00
15 Antonio Freeman 1.50
16 Dorsey Levens 1.50
17 Marshall Faulk 1.50
18 Mark Brunell 8.00
19 Dan Marino 10.00
20 Robert Smith 1.50
21 Curtis Martin 6.00
22 Drew Bledsoe 8.00
23 Danny Kanell 1.50
24 Adrian Murrell 1.50
25 Napoleon Kaufman 4.00
26 Jerome Bettis 1.50
27 Kordell Stewart 8.00
28 Terrell Owens 1.50
29 Jerry Rice 8.00
30 Steve Young 5.00
31 Warren Moon 1.50
32 Mike Alstott 4.00
33 Trent Dilfer 1.50
34 Warrick Dunn 8.00
35 Eddie George 8.00
36 Steve McNair 6.00

1998 Pacific Paramount Pro Bowl Die-Cuts

Pro Bowl Die-Cuts is a 20-card insert featuring players in their uniforms from the 1998 Pro Bowl. The background has a Hawaiian theme and the left side of the card features a die-cut outrigger. This set was inserted 1:37.

MT
Complete Set (20): 200.00
Common Player: 4.00
1 Terrell Davis 20.00
2 John Elway 20.00
3 Shannon Sharpe 4.00
4 Herman Moore 4.00
5 Barry Sanders 30.00
6 Mark Chmura 4.00
7 Brett Favre 40.00
8 Dorsey Levens 4.00
9 Mark Brunell 20.00
10 Andre Rison 4.00
11 Cris Carter 4.00
12 Drew Bledsoe 20.00
13 Ben Coates 4.00
14 Jerome Bettis 4.00
15 Steve Young 10.00
16 Warren Moon 4.00
17 Mike Alstott 10.00
18 Trent Dilfer 4.00
19 Warrick Dunn 20.00
20 Eddie George 20.00

1998 Pacific Paramount Super Bowl XXXII Highlights

Super Bowl XXXII Highlights is a 10-card insert seeded two per 37 packs. The cards feature photography from the Super Bowl.

MT
Complete Set (10): 40.00
Common Player: 2.00
1 Terrell Davis 8.00
2 John Elway 8.00
3 John Elway 8.00
4 Brett Favre 12.00
5 Antonio Freeman 4.00
6 Dorsey Levens 4.00
7 Ed McCaffrey 2.00
8 Eugene Robinson 2.00
9 Bill Romanowski 2.00
10 Darren Sharper 2.00

1998 Pacific Revolution

Pacific Revolution Football consists of a 150-card base set with one parallel and five inserts. The base cards feature a color player photo with a swirled foil background. The cards are etched and embossed. The player's name and his team helmet are featured on a black bar on the bottom. The base set is paralleled by Shadow Series. The inserts include Icons, Prime Time Performers, Rookies & Stars, Showstoppers and Touchdown Laser-Cuts.

MT
Complete Set (150): 140.00
Common Player: .25
Minor Stars: .50
Wax Box: 80.00
1 Larry Centers .25
2 Leeland McElroy .25
3 Rob Moore .25
4 Jake Plummer 5.00
5 Frank Sanders .25
6 Jamal Anderson .25
7 Chris Chandler .25
8 Byron Hanspard .25
9 Jay Graham .25
10 Michael Jackson .25
11 Vinny Testaverde .25
12 Eric Zeier .25
13 Todd Collins .25
14 Quinn Early .25
15 Andre Reed .25
16 Antowain Smith 2.00
17 Bruce Smith .25
18 Thurman Thomas .50
19 Rae Carruth .50
20 Kerry Collins .50
21 Wesley Walls .25
22 Darnell Autry .50
23 Curtis Conway .50
24 Bobby Engram .25
25 *Curtis Enis* 8.00
26 Raymont Harris .25
27 Jeff Blake .50
28 Corey Dillon 3.00
29 Carl Pickens .25
30 Darnay Scott .25
31 Troy Aikman 5.00
32 Michael Irvin .50
33 Deion Sanders 2.00
34 Emmitt Smith 8.00
35 Steve Atwater .25
36 Terrell Davis 5.00
37 John Elway 4.00
38 *Brian Griese* 8.00
39 Ed McCaffrey .25
40 *Marcus Nash* 3.00
41 Shannon Sharpe .25
42 Neil Smith .25
43 Rod Smith .25
44 *Charlie Batch* 10.00
45 *Germane Crowell* .25
46 Scott Mitchell .25
47 Herman Moore .50
48 Barry Sanders 7.00
49 Robert Brooks .25
50 Mark Chmura .25
51 Brett Favre 10.00
52 Antonio Freeman .50
53 Dorsey Levens .50
54 Sean Dawkins .25

55	Ken Dilger	.25
56	Marshall Faulk	.50
57	Marvin Harrison	.50
58	*Peyton Manning*	16.00
59	*Tavian Banks*	5.00
60	Tony Brackens	.25
61	Mark Brunell	4.00
62	Keenan McCardell	.25
63	Natrone Means	.50
64	Jimmy Smith	.25
65	James Stewart	.25
66	*Fred Taylor*	10.00
67	Tony Gonzalez	.50
68	Elvis Grbac	.25
69	Greg Hill	.25
70	Andre Rison	.25
71	Derrick Thomas	.25
72	Karim Abdul-Jabbar	.50
73	*John Avery*	4.00
74	Troy Drayton	.25
75	Dan Marino	8.00
76	O.J. McDuffie	.25
77	Cris Carter	.25
78	Brad Johnson	.50
79	John Randle	.25
80	Jake Reed	.25
81	Robert Smith	.50
82	Drew Bledsoe	5.00
83	Ben Coates	.25
84	*Robert Edwards*	6.00
85	Terry Glenn	.50
86	*Tony Simmons*	.25
87	Troy Davis	.50
88	Heath Shuler	.25
89	Danny Wuerffel	.25
90	Ray Zellars	.25
91	Tiki Barber	1.00
92	*Joe Jurevicius*	1.50
93	Danny Kanell	.25
94	Charles Way	.25
95	Tyrone Wheatley	.25
96	Wayne Chrebet	.25
97	Glenn Foley	.25
98	Keyshawn Johnson	.50
99	Curtis Martin	3.00
100	Tim Brown	.50
101	Rickey Dudley	.25
102	Jeff George	.50
103	Desmond Howard	.25
104	Napoleon Kaufman	1.50
105	*Charles Woodson*	7.00
106	Jason Dunn	.25
107	Irving Fryar	.25
108	Charlie Garner	.25
109	Bobby Hoying	.25
110	Jerome Bettis	.50
111	Mark Bruener	.25
112	Charles Johnson	.25
113	Levon Kirkland	.25
114	Kordell Stewart	5.00
115	*Hines Ward*	3.00
116	Tony Banks	.50
117	Isaac Bruce	.50
118	*Robert Holcombe*	5.00
119	Eddie Kennison	.50
120	Freddie Jones	.25
121	*Ryan Leaf*	8.00
122	Tony Martin	.25
123	Junior Seau	.50
124	Jim Druckenmiller	.50
125	Garrison Hearst	.25
126	Terrell Owens	.50
127	Jerry Rice	5.00
128	J.J. Stokes	.25
129	Steve Young	2.00
130	Joey Galloway	.50
131	*Ahman Green*	6.00
132	Cortez Kennedy	.25
133	Jon Kitna	.25
134	James McKnight	.25
135	Warren Moon	.50
136	Mike Alstott	2.00
137	Reidel Anthony	.50
138	Trent Dilfer	.50
139	Warrick Dunn	5.00
140	Warren Sapp	.25
141	*Kevin Dyson*	3.00
142	Eddie George	5.00
143	Steve McNair	2.00
144	Chris Sanders	.25
145	Frank Wycheck	.25
146	Stephen Alexander	.25
147	Terry Allen	.25
148	Gus Frerotte	.25
149	*Skip Hicks*	3.00
150	Michael Westbrook	.25

1998 Pacific Revolution Shadows

Shadows are a full parallel of the Revolution base set. The parallel cards are numbered to 99.

	MT
Shadow Cards:	10x-20x
Shadow Rookies:	5x-10x

Post-1980 cards in Near Mint condition will generally sell for about 75% of the quoted Mint value. Excellent-condition cards bring no more than 40%.

1998 Pacific Revolution Icons

Icons is a 10-card insert seeded one per 121 packs. The cards have a die-cut design resembling the NFL's shield logo.

		MT
Complete Set (10):		500.00
Common Player:		30.00
1	Emmitt Smith	85.00
2	Terrell Davis	50.00
3	John Elway	40.00
4	Barry Sanders	80.00
5	Brett Favre	100.00
6	Mark Brunell	30.00
7	Dan Marino	85.00
8	Jerry Rice	50.00
9	Warrick Dunn	50.00
10	Eddie George	50.00

1998 Pacific Revolution Prime Time Performers

Prime Time Performers is a 20-card insert seeded 1:25. The cards feature a small player photo on the left and a football with the team's logo laser-cut on the right. The cards have a horizontal layout.

		MT
Complete Set (20):		275.00
Common Player:		7.00
1	Jake Plummer	16.00
2	Corey Dillon	12.00
3	Troy Aikman	16.00
4	Deion Sanders	10.00
5	Emmitt Smith	25.00
6	Terrell Davis	16.00
7	John Elway	16.00
8	Barry Sanders	30.00
9	Brett Favre	30.00
10	Peyton Manning	25.00
11	Mark Brunell	16.00
12	Dan Marino	30.00
13	Drew Bledsoe	16.00
14	Jerome Bettis	7.00
15	Kordell Stewart	16.00
16	Jerry Rice	16.00
17	Steve Young	10.00
18	Warrick Dunn	16.00
19	Eddie George	16.00
20	Steve McNair	10.00

Values quoted in this guide reflect the retail price of a card — the price a collector can expect to pay when buying a card from a dealer. The wholesale price — that which a collector can expect to receive when selling cards — will be significantly lower, depending on desirability and condition.

1998 Pacific Revolution Rookies and Stars

Rookies & Stars is a 30-card hobby-only insert. Seeded 4:25, the set features 20 rookies and 10 established stars. A gold parallel version was also produced. The parallel cards are numbered to 50.

		MT
Complete Set (30):		150.00
Common Player:		1.50
Minor Stars:		3.00
Inserted 4:25 Hobby		
Gold Cards:		8x-16x
Production 50 Sets		
1	Michael Pittman	1.50
2	Curtis Enis	5.00
3	Takeo Spikes	1.50
4	Greg Ellis	3.00
5	Emmitt Smith	10.00
6	Terrell Davis	8.00
7	John Elway	8.00
8	Brian Griese	4.00
9	Marcus Nash	3.00
10	Charlie Batch	6.00
11	Barry Sanders	15.00
12	Brett Favre	15.00
13	Vonnie Holliday	3.00
14	E.G. Green	1.50
15	Peyton Manning	12.00
16	Fred Taylor	6.00
17	John Avery	3.00
18	Dan Marino	10.00
19	Drew Bledsoe	6.00
20	Robert Edwards	6.00
21	Joe Jurevicius	1.50
22	Charles Woodson	6.00
23	Kordell Stewart	6.00
24	Robert Holcombe	4.00
25	Ryan Leaf	6.00
26	Warrick Dunn	6.00
27	Jacquez Green	4.00
28	Kevin Dyson	3.00
29	Eddie George	6.00
30	Stephen Alexander	1.50

1998 Pacific Revolution Showstoppers

Showstoppers is a 36-card insert seeded two per 25 packs. The background features the player's name and team name printed in holographic silver foil.

		MT
Complete Set (36):		250.00
Common Player:		2.00
Minor Stars:		4.00
1	Jake Plummer	15.00
2	Antowain Smith	7.00
3	Kerry Collins	4.00
4	Corey Dillon	10.00
5	Troy Aikman	15.00
6	Deion Sanders	7.00
7	Emmitt Smith	30.00
8	Terrell Davis	15.00
9	John Elway	12.00
10	Shannon Sharpe	2.00
11	Herman Moore	4.00
12	Barry Sanders	25.00
13	Brett Favre	35.00
14	Antonio Freeman	4.00
15	Dorsey Levens	4.00
16	Peyton Manning	15.00
17	Mark Brunell	12.00
18	Dan Marino	30.00
19	Robert Smith	2.00
20	Drew Bledsoe	15.00
21	Danny Kanell	2.00
22	Curtis Martin	12.00
23	Tim Brown	2.00
24	Napoleon Kaufman	6.00
25	Jerome Bettis	4.00
26	Kordell Stewart	15.00
27	Ryan Leaf	10.00
28	Terrell Owens	2.00
29	Jerry Rice	15.00
30	Steve Young	10.00
31	Ricky Watters	2.00
32	Mike Alstott	6.00
33	Trent Dilfer	2.00
34	Warrick Dunn	15.00
35	Eddie George	15.00
36	Steve McNair	8.00

1998 Pacific Revolution Touchdown

Touchdown Laser-Cuts is a 20-card insert seeded one per 49 packs. The cards have a color player photo in the foreground with a set of goal posts in the background. The netting behind the goal posts is laser-cut.

		MT
Complete Set (20):		250.00
Common Player:		7.00
1	Jake Plummer	15.00
2	Corey Dillon	10.00
3	Troy Aikman	15.00
4	Emmitt Smith	25.00
5	Terrell Davis	15.00
6	John Elway	12.50
7	Barry Sanders	25.00
8	Brett Favre	30.00
9	Dorsey Levens	7.00
10	Peyton Manning	25.00
11	Mark Brunell	12.50
12	Marcus Allen	7.00
13	Dan Marino	25.00
14	Drew Bledsoe	15.00
15	Jerome Bettis	7.00
16	Kordell Stewart	15.00
17	Jerry Rice	15.00
18	Steve Young	10.00
19	Warrick Dunn	15.00
20	Eddie George	15.00

1999 Pacific

Pacific Football is a 450-card set that includes more than 30 unseeded rookie cards. Copper, Gold, Opening Day and Platinum Blue are the four different parallel sets. Other inserts include: Cramer's Choice, Dynagon Turf, Gold Crown Die Cuts, Pro Bowl Die Cuts, Record Breakers and Team Checklists.

		MT
Complete Set (450):		100.00
Common Player:		.15
Minor Stars:		.30
Common Rookie:		.50
Wax Box:		60.00
1	Mario Bates	.15
2	Larry Centers	.15
3	Chris Gedney	.15
4	Kwamie Lassiter	.15
5	Johnny McWilliams	.15
6	Eric Metcalf	.15
7	Rob Moore	.30
8	Adrian Murrell	.15
9	Jake Plummer	1.00
10	Simeon Rice	.15
11	Frank Sanders	.30
12	Andre Wadsworth	.30
13	Aeneas Williams	.15
14	Michael Pittman, Ronnie Anderson	.15
15	Morten Andersen	.15
16	Jamal Anderson	.50
17	Lester Archambeau	.15
18	Chris Chandler	.15
19	Bob Christian	.15
20	Steve DeBerg	.15
21	Tim Dwight	.50
22	Tony Martin	.15
23	Terance Mathis	.15
24	Eugene Robinson	.15
25	O.J. Santiago	.15
26	Chuck Smith	.15
27	Jessie Tuggle	.15
28	Jammi German, Ken Oxendine	.15
29	Peter Boulware	.15
30	Jay Graham	.15
31	Jim Harbaugh	.30
32	Priest Holmes	.75
33	Michael Jackson	.15
34	Jermaine Lewis	.15
35	Ray Lewis	.15
36	Michael McCrary	.15
37	Jonathan Ogden	.15
38	Errict Rhett	.15
39	James Roe	.15
40	Floyd Turner	.15
41	Rod Woodson	.15
42	Eric Zeier	.15
43	Wally Richardson, Patrick Johnson	.15
44	Ruben Brown	.15
45	Quinn Early	.15
46	Doug Flutie	.50
47	Sam Gash	.15
48	Phil Hansen	.15
49	Lonnie Johnson	.15
50	Rob Johnson	.30
51	Eric Moulds	.50
52	Andre Reed	.15
53	Jay Riemersma	.15
54	Antowain Smith	.30
55	Bruce Smith	.15
56	Thurman Thomas	.30
57	Ted Washington	.15
58	Jonathon Linton, Kamil Loud	.15
59	Michael Bates	.15
60	Steve Beuerlein	.15
61	Tshimanga Biakabutuka	.15
62	Mark Carrier	.15
63	Eric Davis	.15
64	William Floyd	.15
65	Sean Gilbert	.15
66	Kevin Greene	.15
67	Raghib Ismail	.15
68	Anthony Johnson	.15
69	Fred Lane	.15
70	Muhsin Muhammad	.15
71	Winslow Oliver	.15
72	Wesley Walls	.15
73	Dameyune Craig, Shane Matthews	.15
74	Edgar Bennett	.15
75	Curtis Conway	.30
76	Bobby Engram	.15
77	Curtis Enis	.50
78	Ty Hallock	.15
79	Walt Harris	.15
80	Jeff Jaeger	.15
81	Erik Kramer	.15
82	Glyn Milburn	.15
83	Chris Penn	.15
84	Steve Stenstrom	.15
85	Ryan Wetnight	.15
86	Moses Moreno, James Allen	.15
87	Ashley Ambrose	.15
88	Brandon Bennett	.15
89	Eric Bieniemy	.15
90	Jeff Blake	.30
91	Corey Dillon	.50
92	Paul Justin	.15
93	Eric Kresser	.15
94	Tremain Mack	.15
95	Tony McGee	.15
96	Neil O'Donnell	.15
97	Carl Pickens	.15
98	Darnay Scott	.15
99	Takeo Spikes	.15
100	Ty Detmer	.15
101	Chris Gardocki	.15
102	Damon Gibson	.15
103	Antonio Langham	.15
104	Jerris McPhail	.15
105	Irv Smith	.15
106	Freddie Solomon	.15
107	Scott Milanovich, Fred Brock	.15
108	Troy Aikman	1.25
109	Larry Allen	.15
110	Eric Bjornson	.15
111	Billy Davis	.15
112	Michael Irvin	.30
113	David LaFleur	.15
114	Ernie Mills	.15
115	Nate Newton	.15
116	Deion Sanders	.50
117	Emmitt Smith	1.75
118	Chris Warren	.15
119	Bubby Brister	.15
120	Terrell Davis	2.00
121	Jason Elam	.15
122	John Elway	2.00
123	Willie Green	.15
124	Howard Griffith	.15
125	Vaughn Hebron	.15
126	Ed McCaffrey	.30
127	John Mobley	.15
128	Bill Romanowski	.15
129	Shannon Sharpe	.30
130	Neil Smith	.15
131	Rod Smith	.30
132	Brian Griese, Marcus Nash	.50
133	Charlie Batch	1.00
134	Stephen Boyd	.15
135	Mark Carrier	.15
136	Germane Crowell	.30
137	Terry Fair	.15
138	Jason Hanson	.15
139	Greg Jeffries	.15
140	Herman Moore	.30
141	Johnnie Morton	.15
142	Robert Porcher	.15
143	Ron Rivers	.15
144	Barry Sanders	2.50
145	Tommy Vardell	.15
146	Bryant Westbrook	.15
147	Robert Brooks	.15
148	LeRoy Butler	.15
149	Mark Chmura	.15
150	Tyrone Davis	.15
151	Brett Favre	2.50
152	Antonio Freeman	.50
153	Raymont Harris	.15
154	Vonnie Holliday	.30
155	Darick Holmes	.15
156	Dorsey Levens	.30
157	Brian Manning	.15
158	Derrick Mayes	.15
159	Roell Preston	.15
160	Jeff Thomason	.15
161	Tyrone Williams	.15
162	Corey Bradford, Michael Blair	.15
163	Aaron Bailey	.15
164	Ken Dilger	.15
165	Marshall Faulk	.50
166	E.G. Green	.30
167	Marvin Harrison	.30
168	Craig Heyward	.15
169	Peyton Manning	2.50
170	Jerome Pathon	.30
171	Marcus Pollard	.15
172	Torrance Small	.15
173	Mike Vanderjagt	.15
174	Lamont Warren	.15
175	Tavian Banks	.30
176	Reggie Barlow	.15
177	Tony Boselli	.15
178	Tony Brackens	.15
179	Mark Brunell	1.00
180	Kevin Hardy	.15
181	Damon Jones	.15
182	Jamie Martin	.15
183	Keenan McCardell	.15
184	Pete Mitchell	.15
185	Bryce Paup	.15
186	Jimmy Smith	.15
187	Fred Taylor	1.50
188	Alvis Whitted, Chris Howard	.15
189	Derrick Alexander	.15
190	Kimble Anders	.15
191	Donnell Bennett	.15
192	Dale Carter	.15
193	Rich Gannon	.15
194	Tony Gonzalez	.15
195	Elvis Grbac	.15
196	Joe Horn	.15
197	Kevin Lockett	.15
198	Bam Morris	.15
199	Andre Rison	.30
200	Derrick Thomas	.15
201	Tamarick Vanover	.15
202	Gregory Favors, Rashaan Shehee	.15
203	Karim Abdul	.30
204	Trace Armstrong	.15
205	John Avery	.30
206	Lorenzo Bromell	.15
207	Terrell Buckley	.15
208	Oronde Gadsden	.30
209	Sam Madison	.15
210	Dan Marino	1.75
211	O.J. McDuffie	.15
212	Ed Perry	.15
213	Jason Taylor	.15
214	Lamar Thomas	.15
215	Zach Thomas	.30
216	Henry Lusk, Nate Jacquet	.15

217	Damon Huard, Todd Doxton	.15
218	Gary Anderson	.15
219	Cris Carter	.50
220	Randall Cunningham	.50
221	Andrew Glover	.15
222	Matthew Hatchette	.15
223	Brad Johnson	.50
224	Ed McDaniel	.15
225	Randall McDaniel	.15
226	Randy Moss	4.00
227	David Palmer	.15
228	John Randle	.15
229	Jake Reed	.15
230	Robert Smith	.30
231	Todd Steussie	.15
232	Stalin Colinet, Kivuusama Mays	.15
233	Jay Fiedler, Todd Bouman	.15
234	Drew Bledsoe	1.00
235	Troy Brown	.15
236	Ben Coates	.30
237	Derrick Cullors	.15
238	Robert Edwards	.30
239	Terry Glenn	.30
240	Shawn Jefferson	.15
241	Ty Law	.15
242	Lawyer Milloy	.15
243	Lovett Purnell	.15
244	Sedrick Shaw	.15
245	Tony Simmons	.30
246	Chris Slade	.15
247	Rod Rutledge, Anthony Ladd	.15
248	Chris Floyd, Harold Shaw	.15
249	Ink Aleaga	.15
250	Cameron Cleeland	.30
251	Kerry Collins	.30
252	Troy Davis	.15
253	Sean Dawkins	.15
254	Mark Fields	.15
255	Andre Hastings	.15
256	Sammy Knight	.15
257	Keith Poole	.15
258	William Roaf	.15
259	Lamar Smith	.15
260	Danny Wuerffel	.15
261	Josh Wilcox, Brett Bech	.15
262	Chris Bordeleau, Wilmont Perry	.15
263	Jessie Armstead	.15
264	Tiki Barber	.15
265	Chad Bratzke	.15
266	Gary Brown	.15
267	Chris Calloway	.15
268	Howard Cross	.15
269	Kent Graham	.15
270	Ike Hilliard	.15
271	Danny Kanell	.15
272	Michael Strahan	.15
273	Amani Toomer	.15
274	Charles Way	.15
275	Mike Cherry, Greg Comella	.15
276	Kyle Brady	.15
277	Keith Byars	.15
278	Chad Cascadden	.15
279	Wayne Chrebet	.30
280	Bryan Cox	.15
281	Glenn Foley	.30
282	Aaron Glenn	.15
283	Keyshawn Johnson	.50
284	Leon Johnson	.15
285	Mo Lewis	.15
286	Curtis Martin	.50
287	Otis Smith	.15
288	Vinny Testaverde	.30
289	Dedric Ward	.15
290	Tim Brown	.30
291	Rickey Dudley	.15
292	Jeff George	.30
293	Desmond Howard	.15
294	James Jett	.15
295	Lance Johnstone	.15
296	Randy Jordan	.15
297	Napoleon Kaufman	.50
298	Lincoln Kennedy	.15
299	Terry Mickens	.15
300	Darrell Russell	.15
301	Harvey Williams	.15
302	Jon Ritchie, Charles Woodson	.30
303	Rodney Williams, Jermaine Williams	.15
304	Koy Detmer	.15
305	Hugh Douglas	.15
306	Jason Dunn	.15
307	Irving Fryar	.15
308	Charlie Garner	.15
309	Jeff Graham	.15
310	Bobby Hoying	.15
311	Rodney Peete	.15
312	Allen Rossum	.15
313	Duce Staley	.15
314	William Thomas	.15
315	Kevin Turner	.15
316	Kaseem Sinceno, Corey Walker	.15
317	Jahine Arnold	.15
318	Jerome Bettis	.30
319	Will Blackwell	.15
320	Mark Bruener	.15
321	Dermontti Dawson	.15
322	Chris Fuamatu-Ma'afala	.15

323	Courtney Hawkins	.15
324	Richard Huntley	.15
325	Charles Johnson	.15
326	Levon Kirkland	.15
327	Kordell Stewart	.75
328	Hines Ward	.30
329	DeWayne Washington	.15
330	Tony Banks	.30
331	Steve Bono	.15
332	Isaac Bruce	.30
333	June Henley	.15
334	Robert Holcombe	.30
335	Mike Jones	.15
336	Eddie Kennison	.15
337	Amp Lee	.15
338	Jerald Moore	.15
339	Ricky Proehl	.15
340	J.T. Thomas	.15
341	Derrick Harris, Az-Zahir Hakim	.15
342	Roland Williams, Grant Wistrom	.15
343	Kurt Warner, Tony Horne	45.00
344	Terrell Fletcher	.15
345	Greg Jackson	.15
346	Charlie Jones	.15
347	Freddie Jones	.15
348	Ryan Leaf	1.00
349	Natrone Means	.30
350	Mikhael Ricks	.15
351	Junior Seau	.30
352	Bryan Still	.15
353	Tremayne Stephens, Ryan Thelwell	.15
354	Greg Clark	.15
355	Marc Edwards	.15
356	Merton Hanks	.15
357	Garrison Hearst	.30
358	R.W. McQuarters	.15
359	Ken Norton Jr.	.15
360	Terrell Owens	.50
361	Jerry Rice	1.25
362	J.J. Stokes	.30
363	Bryant Young	.15
364	Steve Young	1.00
365	Chad Brown	.15
366	Christian Fauria	.15
367	Joey Galloway	.50
368	Ahman Green	.30
369	Cortez Kennedy	.15
370	Jon Kitna	.75
371	James McKnight	.15
372	Mike Pritchard	.15
373	Michael Sinclair	.15
374	Shawn Springs	.15
375	Ricky Watters	.30
376	Darryl Williams	.15
377	Robert Wilson, Kerry Joseph	.15
378	Mike Alstott	.30
379	Reidel Anthony	.15
380	Derrick Brooks	.15
381	Trent Dilfer	.30
382	Warrick Dunn	.75
383	Bert Emanuel	.15
384	Jacquez Green	.30
385	Patrick Hape	.15
386	John Lynch	.15
387	Dave Moore	.15
388	Hardy Nickerson	.15
389	Warren Sapp	.15
390	Karl Williams	.15
391	Blaine Bishop	.15
392	Joe Bowden	.15
393	Isaac Byrd	.15
394	Willie Davis	.15
395	Al Del Greco	.15
396	Kevin Dyson	.30
397	Eddie George	.75
398	Jackie Harris	.15
399	Dave Krieg	.15
400	Steve McNair	.50
401	Michael Roan	.15
402	Yancey Thigpen	.15
403	Frank Wycheck	.15
404	Derrick Mason, Stephen Matthews	.15
405	Stephen Alexander	.15
406	Terry Allen	.30
407	Jamie Asher	.15
408	Stephen Davis	.15
409	Darrell Green	.15
410	Trent Green	.30
411	Skip Hicks	.30
412	Brian Mitchell	.15
413	Leslie Shepherd	.15
414	Michael Westbrook	.15
415	Terry Hardy, Rabih Abdullah	.15
416	Corey Thomas, Mike Quinn	.15
417	Jonathan Quinn, Kelly Holcomb	.15
418	Brian Alford, Blake Spence	.15
419	Andy Haase, Carlos King	.15
420	Karl Hankton, James Thrash	.15
421	Fred Beasley, Itula Mili	.15
422	Champ Bailey	2.50
423	D'Wayne Bates	1.00
424	Michael Bishop	3.00
425	David Boston	3.00

426	Shawn Bryson	.50
427	Tim Couch	10.00
428	Scott Covington	1.00
429	Daunte Culpepper	4.00
430	Autry Denson	1.00
431	Troy Edwards	3.00
432	Kevin Faulk	3.00
433	Joe Germaine	2.00
434	Torry Holt	3.00
435	Brock Huard	2.00
436	Sedrick Irvin	1.50
437	Edgerrin James	10.00
438	Andy Katzenmoyer	1.00
439	Shaun King	4.00
440	Rob Konrad	.50
441	Donovan McNabb	5.00
442	Cade McNown	5.00
443	Billy Miller	1.00
444	Dee Miller	1.00
445	Sirr Parker	1.00
446	Peerless Price	3.00
447	Akili Smith	5.00
448	Tai Streets	1.00
449	Ricky Williams	10.00
450	Amos Zereoue	2.00

1999 Pacific Copper

This 450-card parallel was a hobby-only release and was sequentially numbered to 99.

	MT
Copper Cards:	30x-60x
Copper Rookies:	5x-10x
Production 99 Sets	

1999 Pacific Gold

This 450-card set is a parallel to the base and was hobby only and is sequentially numbered to 199.

	MT
Gold Cards:	15x-30x
Gold Rookies:	3x-6x
Production 199 Sets	

1999 Pacific Opening Day

This 450-card set is a parallel to the base and each card is sequentially numbered to 45.

	MT
Opening Day Cards:	50x-100x
Opening Day Rookies:	10x-20x
Production 45 Sets	

1999 Pacific Platinum Blue

This is a 450-card set that is a parallel to the base with each single sequentially numbered to 75.

	MT
Platinum Blue Cards:	40x-80x
Platinum Blue Rookies:	8x-16x
Production 75 Sets	

1999 Pacific Cramer's Choice Awards

This insert includes the top ten players in the NFL and captures them on a dual-foiled trophy card. Each is die cut in the shape of a pyramid and is sequentially numbered to 299.

	MT
Complete Set (10):	950.00
Common Player:	40.00

1	Jamal Anderson	40.00
2	Terrell Davis	125.00
3	John Elway	125.00
4	Barry Sanders	150.00
5	Brett Favre	150.00
6	Peyton Manning	100.00
7	Fred Taylor	85.00
8	Dan Marino	125.00
9	Randall Cunningham	40.00
10	Randy Moss	175.00

1999 Pacific Dynagon Turf

Each card in this 20-card set is printed on a silver-foil card and is horizontal. Singles were inserted 2:25 packs. A parallel Titanium Turf was made and is sequentially numbered to 99.

	MT
Complete Set (20):	85.00
Common Player:	.75
Minor Stars:	1.50
Inserted 2:25	
Titanium Turf Singles:	6x-12x
Production 99 Sets	

1	Jake Plummer	6.00
2	Jamal Anderson	1.50
3	Doug Flutie	1.50
4	Emmitt Smith	10.00
5	Terrell Davis	10.00
6	John Elway	10.00
7	Barry Sanders	12.00
8	Brett Favre	12.00
9	Peyton Manning	8.00
10	Mark Brunell	4.00
11	Fred Taylor	6.00
12	Dan Marino	10.00
13	Randall Cunningham	1.50
14	Randy Moss	15.00
15	Drew Bledsoe	4.00
16	Curtis Martin	1.50
17	Jerome Bettis	.75
18	Jerry Rice	6.00
19	Jon Kitna	1.50
20	Eddie George	3.00

1999 Pacific Gold Crown Die-Cuts

Each card in this 36-card set is printed on dual-foil board and is die cut in the shape of a gold crown. Singles were inserted 1:25 packs.

	MT
Complete Set (36):	300.00
Common Player:	3.00
Minor Stars:	6.00
Inserted 1:25	

1	Jake Plummer	12.00
2	Jamal Anderson	6.00
3	Priest Holmes	6.00
4	Doug Flutie	6.00
5	Antowain Smith	3.00
6	Corey Dillon	6.00
7	Troy Aikman	15.00
8	Emmitt Smith	20.00
9	Terrell Davis	20.00
10	John Elway	20.00

11	Brian Griese	8.00
12	Charlie Batch	12.00
13	Barry Sanders	30.00
14	Brett Favre	30.00
15	Antonio Freeman	6.00
16	Marshall Faulk	6.00
17	Peyton Manning	20.00
18	Mark Brunell	12.00
19	Fred Taylor	18.00
20	Dan Marino	20.00
21	Randall Cunningham	6.00
22	Randy Moss	35.00
23	Drew Bledsoe	12.00
24	Keyshawn Johnson	6.00
25	Curtis Martin	6.00
26	Napoleon Kaufman	6.00
27	Jerome Bettis	6.00
28	Kordell Stewart	10.00
29	Terrell Owens	8.00
30	Jerry Rice	15.00
31	Steve Young	10.00
32	Joey Galloway	6.00
33	Jon Kitna	6.00
34	Trent Dilfer	3.00
35	Warrick Dunn	8.00
36	Eddie George	8.00

1999 Pacific Pro Bowl Die-Cuts

The 20 players in this set are printed on a die-cut card with an erupting volcano in the background. Singles were inserted 1:49 packs.

	MT
Complete Set (20):	150.00
Common Player:	4.00
Inserted 1:49	

1	Jamal Anderson	6.00
2	Chris Chandler	4.00
3	Doug Flutie	6.00
4	Deion Sanders	6.00
5	Emmitt Smith	20.00
6	Terrell Davis	20.00
7	John Elway	20.00
8	Barry Sanders	30.00
9	Antonio Freeman	6.00
10	Marshall Faulk	6.00
11	Randall Cunningham	6.00
12	Randy Moss	35.00
13	Robert Smith	4.00
14	Ty Law	4.00
15	Keyshawn Johnson	6.00
16	Curtis Martin	6.00
17	Jerry Rice	15.00
18	Steve Young	10.00
19	Mike Alstott	6.00
20	Eddie George	8.00

1999 Pacific Record Breakers

This was a hobby only insert that included record-breaking achievements from 1998. Singles from this 20-card insert were sequentially numbered to 199.

	MT
Complete Set (20):	1250.
Common Player:	40.00
Production 199 Sets	

1	Jake Plummer	75.00
2	Jamal Anderson	40.00
3	Doug Flutie	40.00
4	Troy Aikman	75.00
5	Emmitt Smith	125.00
6	Terrell Davis	125.00
7	John Elway	125.00
8	Barry Sanders	150.00
9	Brett Favre	150.00
10	Marshall Faulk	40.00
11	Peyton Manning	100.00
12	Mark Brunell	60.00
13	Fred Taylor	85.00
14	Dan Marino	125.00
15	Randall Cunningham	40.00
16	Randy Moss	175.00
17	Drew Bledsoe	60.00
18	Curtis Martin	40.00
19	Jerry Rice	75.00
20	Steve Young	50.00

1999 Pacific Team Checklists

Each card in this 31-card set includes each team with a star player from that team on the fronts of the horizontal card. The backs include the team checklist for each player in the base set. Singles were inserted 2:25 packs.

	MT
Complete Set (31):	100.00
Common Player:	1.25
Minor Stars:	2.50
Inserted 2:25	

1	Jake Plummer	8.00
2	Jamal Anderson	2.50
3	Priest Holmes	2.50
4	Doug Flutie	2.50
5	Muhsin Muhammad	1.25
6	Curtis Enis	2.50
7	Corey Dillon	2.50
8	Ty Detmer	1.25
9	Emmitt Smith	12.00
10	John Elway	12.00
11	Barry Sanders	16.00
12	Brett Favre	16.00
13	Peyton Manning	10.00
14	Fred Taylor	8.00
15	Andre Rison	1.25
16	Dan Marino	12.00
17	Randy Moss	20.00
18	Drew Bledsoe	6.00
19	Cameron Cleeland	1.25
20	Ike Hilliard	1.25
21	Curtis Martin	2.50
22	Napoleon Kaufman	2.50
23	Duce Staley	1.25
24	Jerome Bettis	2.50
25	Isaac Bruce	2.50
26	Ryan Leaf	4.00
27	Steve Young	4.00
28	Joey Galloway	2.50
29	Warrick Dunn	4.00
30	Eddie George	4.00
31	Michael Westbrook	1.25

1999 Pacific Aurora

Each card in this 200-card set has a large posed photo and a smaller action photo in a vintage looking sepia color. A total of 150 cards were used with 50 star players and rookies duplicated with a pinstripe background and posed photo on front. Inserts include: Premiere Date, Canvas Creations, Championship Fever, Complete Players, Leather Bound and Styrotechs.

	MT
Complete Set (200):	85.00
Common Player:	.15
Minor Stars:	.30
Wax Box:	75.00

1	David Boston	3.00
2	Larry Centers	.15
3	Rob Moore	.30
4	Adrian Murrell	.15
5C	Jake Plummer	1.00
5D	Jake Plummer	1.00

6C	Jamal Anderson	.50
6D	Jamal Anderson	.50
7	Chris Chandler	.30
8	Tim Dwight	.50
9	Terance Mathis	.15
10	O.J. Santiago	.15
11C	Priest Holmes	.50
11D	Priest Holmes	.50
12	Michael Jackson	.15
13	Jermaine Lewis	.30
14	Ray Lewis	.15
15	Michael McCrary	.15
16C	Doug Flutie	.75
16D	Doug Flutie	.75
17C	Eric Moulds	.50
17D	Eric Moulds	.50
18	*Peerless Price*	2.50
19	Antowain Smith	.50
20	Bruce Smith	.15
21	Steve Beuerlein	.15
22	Tshimanga Biakabutuka	.15
23	Kevin Greene	.15
24	Muhsin Muhammad	.15
25	Wesley Walls	.15
26	Curtis Conway	.30
27	Bobby Engram	.15
28	Curtis Enis	.30
29	Erik Kramer	.15
30C	*Cade McNown*	5.00
30D	*Cade McNown*	5.00
31	Jeff Blake	.30
32C	Corey Dillon	.50
32D	Corey Dillon	.50
33	Carl Pickens	.30
34	Darnay Scott	.15
35C	*Akili Smith*	4.00
35D	*Akili Smith*	4.00
36C	*Tim Couch*	10.00
36D	*Tim Couch*	10.00
37	Ty Detmer	.15
38	*Kevin Johnson*	3.00
39	Terry Kirby	.15
40C	Troy Aikman	1.00
40D	Troy Aikman	1.00
41	Michael Irvin	.30
42	Raghib Ismail	.15
43C	Deion Sanders	.50
43D	Deion Sanders	.50
44C	Emmitt Smith	1.50
44D	Emmitt Smith	1.50
45	Bubby Brister	.30
46C	Terrell Davis	1.50
46D	Terrell Davis	1.50
47	Brian Griese	1.00
48	Ed McCaffrey	.30
49C	Shannon Sharpe	.30
49D	Shannon Sharpe	.30
50	Rod Smith	.30
51C	Charlie Batch	.75
51D	Charlie Batch	.75
52	*Sedrick Irvin*	2.00
53C	Herman Moore	.50
53D	Herman Moore	.50
54	Johnnie Morton	.15
55C	Barry Sanders	2.00
55D	Barry Sanders	2.00
56	Robert Brooks	.15
57C	Brett Favre	2.00
57D	Brett Favre	2.00
58C	Antonio Freeman	.50
58D	Antonio Freeman	.50
59	Dorsey Levens	.50
60	Derrick Mayes	.30
61	Marvin Harrison	.50
62C	*Edgerrin James*	10.00
62D	*Edgerrin James*	10.00
63C	Peyton Manning	1.50
63D	Peyton Manning	1.50
64	Jerome Pathon	.15
65	Tavian Banks	.30
66C	Mark Brunell	.75
66D	Mark Brunell	.75
67	Keenan McCardell	.15
68	Jimmy Smith	.30
69C	Fred Taylor	1.00
69D	Fred Taylor	1.00
70	Derrick Alexander	.15
71	Kimble Anders	.15
72	Michael Cloud	1.50
73	Elvis Grbac	.30
74	Andre Rison	.30
75	Karim Abdul	.30
76	*James Johnson*	2.00
77C	Dan Marino	1.50
77D	Dan Marino	1.50
78	O.J. McDuffie	.30
79	Lamar Thomas	.15
80C	Cris Carter	.50
80D	Cris Carter	.50
81	*Daunte Culpepper*	5.00
82C	Randall Cunningham	.50
82D	Randall Cunningham	.50
83C	Randy Moss	2.50
83D	Randy Moss	2.50
84	John Randle	.15
85C	Robert Smith	.50
85D	Robert Smith	.50
86C	Drew Bledsoe	.75
86D	Drew Bledsoe	.75
87	Ben Coates	.15
88	*Kevin Faulk*	3.00
89C	Terry Glenn	.50
89D	Terry Glenn	.50
90	Ty Law	.15
91	Cameron Cleeland	.30
92	Andre Hastings	.15
93	Billy Joe Hobert	.15

94C	*Ricky Williams*	10.00
94D	*Ricky Williams*	10.00
95	Tiki Barber	.15
96	Kent Graham	.15
97	Ike Hilliard	.15
98	Charles Way	.15
99	Wayne Chrebet	.50
100C	Keyshawn Johnson	.50
100D	Keyshawn Johnson	.50
101C	Curtis Martin	.50
101D	Curtis Martin	.50
102C	Vinny Testaverde	.30
102D	Vinny Testaverde	.30
103	Dedric Ward	.15
104C	Tim Brown	.30
104D	Tim Brown	.30
105	Rickey Dudley	.15
106	James Jett	.15
107	Napoleon Kaufman	.50
108	Charles Woodson	.50
109	Jeff Graham	.15
110	Charles Johnson	.15
111C	*Donovan McNabb*	5.00
111D	*Donovan McNabb*	5.00
112	Duce Staley	.30
113C	Jerome Bettis	.50
113D	Jerome Bettis	.50
114	*Troy Edwards*	3.00
115	Courtney Hawkins	.15
116C	Kordell Stewart	.50
116D	Kordell Stewart	.50
117	*Amos Zereoue*	2.50
118	Isaac Bruce	.30
119C	Marshall Faulk	.50
119D	Marshall Faulk	.50
120	*Joe Germaine*	2.00
121C	*Torry Holt*	3.00
121D	*Torry Holt*	3.00
122	Amp Lee	.15
123	Charlie Jones	.15
124	Ryan Leaf	.30
125	Natrone Means	.30
126	Junior Seau	.50
127	Garrison Hearst	.50
128C	Terrell Owens	.50
128D	Terrell Owens	.50
129C	Jerry Rice	1.00
129D	Jerry Rice	1.00
130	J.J. Stokes	.30
131C	Steve Young	.75
131D	Steve Young	.75
132	Chad Brown	.15
133C	Joey Galloway	.50
133D	Joey Galloway	.50
134	*Brock Huard*	2.00
135C	Jon Kitna	.50
135D	Jon Kitna	.50
136C	Ricky Watters	.30
136D	Ricky Watters	.30
137C	Mike Alstott	.50
137D	Mike Alstott	.50
138	Reidel Anthony	.30
139	Trent Dilfer	.30
140C	Warrick Dunn	.50
140D	Warrick Dunn	.50
141	Jacquez Green	.30
142	*Shaun King*	4.00
143C	Eddie George	.50
143D	Eddie George	.50
144C	Steve McNair	.50
144D	Steve McNair	.50
145	Yancey Thigpen	.30
146	Frank Wycheck	.15
147	*Champ Bailey*	2.00
148	Skip Hicks	.30
149	Brad Johnson	.50
150	Michael Westbrook	.30

1999 Pacific Aurora Premiere Date

This 200-card set is a parallel to the base and is sequentially numbered to 77. Singles were only found in hobby product and were inserted 1:25 packs.

	MT
Premiere Date Cards:	30x-60x
Premiere Date Rookies:	8x-16x
Production 77 Sets	

1999 Pacific Aurora Canvas Creations

Each player in this 10-card set was printed on real canvas.

Singles were inserted 1:193 packs.

	MT
Complete Set (10):	275.00
Common Player:	15.00
Inserted 1:193	
1 Troy Aikman	30.00
2 Terrell Davis	45.00
3 Barry Sanders	60.00
4 Brett Favre	60.00
5 Peyton Manning	45.00
6 Dan Marino	45.00
7 Randy Moss	60.00
8 Drew Bledsoe	25.00
9 Steve Young	20.00
10 Jon Kitna	15.00

1999 Pacific Aurora Championship Fever

This 20-card set was issued at 4:25 packs. Each card has a parallel Copper issue that was only found in hobby product and are sequentially numbered to 20. A Platinum Blue parallel was also made and are numbered to 100. The retail only Silver parallel are numbered to 250.

	MT
Complete Set (20):	35.00
Common Player:	1.00
Inserted 4:25	
Copper Cards:	25x-50x
Production 20 Sets	
Platinum Blue Cards:	8x-16x
Production 100 Sets	
1 Jake Plummer	2.50
2 Jamal Anderson	1.00
3 Tim Couch	6.00
4 Troy Aikman	2.50
5 Emmitt Smith	3.50
6 Terrell Davis	3.50
7 Barry Sanders	5.00
8 Brett Favre	5.00
9 Peyton Manning	3.50
10 Fred Taylor	2.50
11 Dan Marino	3.50
12 Randy Moss	5.00
13 Drew Bledsoe	2.00
14 Ricky Williams	6.00
15 Keyshawn Johnson	1.00
16 Terrell Owens	1.00
17 Jerry Rice	2.50
18 Steve Young	1.50
19 Jon Kitna	1.00
20 Eddie George	1.25

1999 Pacific Aurora Complete Players

Ten players were used in this insert with two different cards. One in hobby product and the other in retail. Each product has a 10-card set with each single sequentially numbered to 299. Each card is printed on 10-point double laminated stock with full foil on both sides. A parallel Hologold set was made and inserted into both products and are sequentially numbered to 25.

	MT
Complete Set (10):	125.00
Common Player:	10.00
Production 299 Sets	
Hologold Cards:	4x-8x
Production 25 Sets	
1 Troy Aikman	15.00
2 Terrell Davis	20.00
3 Barry Sanders	30.00
4 Brett Favre	30.00
5 Peyton Manning	20.00
6 Randy Moss	30.00
7 Drew Bledsoe	10.00
8 Jerry Rice	15.00
9 Steve Young	10.00

1999 Pacific Aurora Leather Bound

This hobby-only insert features 20 players on a laminated leather football card with white foil embossed laces. They were found 2:25 packs.

	MT
Complete Set (20):	85.00
Common Player:	2.00
Inserted 2:25	
1 Jake Plummer	5.00
2 Jamal Anderson	2.00
3 Tim Couch	12.00
4 Troy Aikman	5.00
5 Emmitt Smith	7.00
6 Terrell Davis	7.00
7 Barry Sanders	10.00
8 Brett Favre	10.00
9 Peyton Manning	7.00
10 Fred Taylor	5.00
11 Dan Marino	7.00
12 Randy Moss	10.00
13 Drew Bledsoe	4.00
14 Ricky Williams	12.00
15 Curtis Martin	2.00
16 Jerome Bettis	2.00
17 Jerry Rice	5.00
18 Steve Young	4.00
19 Jon Kitna	3.00
20 Eddie George	3.00

1999 Pacific Aurora Terrell Owens Autograph

Owens signed a total of 197 cards for Aurora Football. Each card is full foil and hand sequentially numbered.

	MT
Production 197 Sets	
AU1 Terrell Owens Auto	85.00

1999 Pacific Aurora Styrotechs

Each card in this 20-card set is horizontal with two photos of the player. One in color and the other a smaller photo of the player in black and white. Singles are printed on styrene and were inserted 1:25.

	MT
Complete Set (20):	125.00
Common Player:	3.00
Inserted 1:25	
1 Jake Plummer	8.00
2 Jamal Anderson	3.00
3 Tim Couch	16.00
4 Troy Aikman	8.00
5 Emmitt Smith	12.00
6 Terrell Davis	12.00
7 Barry Sanders	16.00
8 Brett Favre	16.00
9 Peyton Manning	12.00
10 Fred Taylor	8.00
11 Dan Marino	12.00
12 Randy Moss	16.00
13 Drew Bledsoe	5.00
14 Ricky Williams	16.00
15 Curtis Martin	3.00
16 Jerry Rice	8.00
17 Steve Young	5.00
18 Joey Galloway	3.00
19 Jon Kitna	4.00
20 Eddie George	4.00

1999 Pacific Crown Royale

This was a 144-card base set that featured each single die-cut, double-etched and on a double-foiled format. Each veteran card had a gold foil crown while the rookies were printed on a silver foil crown. Parallel sets included Limited Series and Premiere Date. Other inserts included: Card Supials, Century 21, Cramer's Choice Jumbos, Franchise Glory, Gold Crown Die Cuts, Rookie Gold and Test of Time. SRP was $5.99 for six-card packs.

	MT
Complete Set (144):	185.00
Common Player:	.30
Minor Stars:	.60
Common Rookie:	2.00
Wax Box:	125.00
1 *David Boston*	6.00
2 *Chris Greisen*	2.00
3 Rob Moore	.60
4 Jake Plummer	3.00
5 Frank Sanders	.60
6 Jamal Anderson	1.50
7 Chris Chandler	.60
8 Tim Dwight	1.50
9 Byron Hanspard	.60
10 Stoney Case	.30
11 Priest Holmes	1.50
12 Jermaine Lewis	.60
13 *Chris McCalister*	3.00
14 *Brandon Stokley*	2.00
15 Doug Flutie	1.50
16 Eric Moulds	1.50
17 *Peerless Price*	3.00
18 Antowain Smith	1.50
19 Steve Beuerlein	.60
20 Tshimanga Biakabutuka	.60
21 Muhsin Muhammad	1.00
22 Curtis Conway	.60
23 Curtis Enis	1.50
24 Shane Matthews	1.50
25 *Cade McNown*	12.00
26 Marcus Robinson	3.00
27 Jeff Blake	1.00
28 Scott Covington	2.00
29 Corey Dillon	1.50
30 Damon Griffin	1.50
31 Carl Pickens	1.00
32 *Akili Smith*	12.00
33 *Tim Couch*	20.00
34 *Kevin Johnson*	6.00
35 Terry Kirby	.30
36 Leslie Shepherd	.30
37 Troy Aikman	4.00
38 Raghib Ismail	.30
39 *Wane McGarity*	3.00
40 Deion Sanders	1.50
41 Emmitt Smith	4.00
42 Terrell Davis	4.00
43 Brian Griese	3.00
44 Ed McCaffrey	1.50
45 Shannon Sharpe	.75
46 Rod Smith	1.50
47 Charlie Batch	2.00
48 Germane Crowell	.75
49 *Sedrick Irvin*	4.00
50 Herman Moore	1.50
51 Barry Sanders	6.00
52 Brett Favre	6.00
53 Antonio Freeman	1.50
54 Matt Hasselbeck	1.50
55 Dorsey Levens	1.50
56 *Basil Mitchell*	3.00
57 E.G. Green	1.50
58 Marvin Harrison	1.50
59 *Edgerrin James*	30.00
60 Peyton Manning	4.00
61 *Terrence Wilkins*	10.00
62 Mark Brunell	2.00

63	Keenan McCardell	.60
64	Jimmy Smith	1.50
65	Fred Taylor	3.00
66	Derrick Alexander	.30
67	Elvis Grbac	.60
68	Warren Moon	.60
69	*Larry Parker*	2.00
70	Andre Rison	.60
71	Cecil Collins	6.00
72	Damon Huard	2.00
73	James Johnson	4.00
74	Rob Konrad	3.00
75	Dan Marino	4.00
76	O.J. McDuffie	.60
77	Cris Carter	1.50
78	*Daunte Culpepper*	12.00
79	Randall Cunningham	1.50
80	Randy Moss	6.00
81	Robert Smith	1.50
82	*Michael Bishop*	3.00
83	Drew Bledsoe	2.00
84	Ben Coates	.60
85	*Kevin Faulk*	4.00
86	Terry Glenn	1.50
87	Billy Joe Hobert	.30
88	Eddie Kennison	.60
89	Keith Poole	.30
90	*Ricky Williams*	20.00
91	Sean Bennett	3.00
92	Kerry Collins	.60
93	Pete Mitchell	.30
94	Amani Toomer	.60
95	Wayne Chrebet	1.50
96	Keyshawn Johnson	1.50
97	Curtis Martin	1.50
98	Tim Brown	1.00
99	Scott Dreisbach	2.00
100	Rich Gannon	.60
101	Napoleon Kaufman	1.50
102	Tyrone Wheatley	.60
103	Charles Johnson	.30
104	*Donovan McNabb*	12.00
105	Torrance Small	.30
106	Duce Staley	1.50
107	*Jed Weaver*	2.00
108	Jerome Bettis	1.50
109	*Troy Edwards*	6.00
110	Kordell Stewart	1.50
111	*Amos Zereoue*	4.00
112	Isaac Bruce	1.50
113	Marshall Faulk	1.50
114	*Joe Germaine*	3.00
115	*Torry Holt*	6.00
116	Kurt Warner	40.00
117	Jim Harbaugh	.60
118	Erik Kramer	.30
119	Natrone Means	.75
120	Junior Seau	.75
121	*Jeff Garcia*	10.00
122	Terrell Owens	1.50
123	Jerry Rice	3.00
124	J.J. Stokes	.60
125	Steve Young	2.00
126	Sean Dawkins	.30
127	*Brock Huard*	4.00
128	Jon Kitna	2.00
129	Derrick Mayes	.75
130	*Charlie Rogers*	2.00
131	Ricky Watters	1.00
132	Mike Alstott	1.50
133	Trent Dilfer	1.00
134	Warrick Dunn	1.50
135	Eric Zeier	.30
136	*Kevin Daft*	2.00
137	Kevin Dyson	.60
138	Eddie George	1.75
139	Steve McNair	1.75
140	Neil O'Donnell	.60
141	*Champ Bailey*	4.00
142	Albert Connell	.30
143	Stephen Davis	1.50
144	Brad Johnson	1.50

1999 Pacific Crown Royale Limited Series

This was a 144-card parallel to the base set. Each single was sequentially numbered to 99.

	MT
Limited Ser. Cards:	8x-16x
Limited Ser. Rookies:	2x-4x
Production 99 Sets	

1999 Pacific Crown Royale Premiere Date

This was a 144-card parallel to the base set. Singles were sequentially numbered to 68 and found 1:25 packs.

	MT
Premiere Date Cards:	10x-20x
Premiere Date Rookies:	3x-6x
Inserted 1:25	
Production 68 Sets	

1999 Pacific Crown Royale Card Supials

This 20-card insert set included a full-size card with a "Card-Supial" inserted into a special die-cut pouch on the back of the full-size card. The mini (1/4 the full card size) card is inserted into a different player's full-size card. Singles were inserted 2:25 packs.

		MT
Complete Set (20):		100.00
Common Player:		2.00
Small Cards:		.7x
Inserted 2:25		
1	Cade McNown	6.00
2	Tim Couch	10.00
3	Troy Aikman	6.00
4	Emmitt Smith	8.00
5	Barry Sanders	10.00
6	Brett Favre	10.00
7	Edgerrin James	15.00
8	Peyton Manning	8.00
9	Mark Brunell	5.00
10	Fred Taylor	5.00
11	Damon Huard	4.00
12	Dan Marino	8.00
13	Randy Moss	10.00
14	Drew Bledsoe	4.00
15	Ricky Williams	10.00
16	Jerome Bettis	2.00
17	Kurt Warner	15.00
18	Terrell Owens	2.00
19	Jerry Rice	6.00
20	Jon Kitna	3.00

1999 Pacific Crown Royale Century 21

This 10-card insert set included football's most dominating players. Each of the singles were sequentially numbered to 375.

		MT
Complete Set (10):		100.00
Common Player:		7.00
Production 375 Sets		
1	Jake Plummer	10.00
2	Tim Couch	15.00
3	Terrell Davis	15.00
4	Peyton Manning	15.00
5	Mark Brunell	7.00
6	Fred Taylor	10.00
7	Randy Moss	15.00
8	Drew Bledsoe	7.00
9	Ricky Williams	15.00
10	Kurt Warner	30.00

1999 Pacific Crown Royale Cramer's Choice Jumbos

This 10-card insert set included both veterans and a few

---

of the hot rookies from 1999. Singles were inserted one per box. Six different parallel sets were also issued and they include: Dark Blue (#'d to 35), Green (#'d to 30), Red (#'d to 25), Light Blue (#'d to 20), Gold (#'d to 10) and Purple (#'d to 1).

	MT
Complete Set (10):	85.00
Common Player:	5.00
1:Box	
Dark Blue Cards:	6x-12x
Production 35 Sets	
Gold Cards:	15x-30x
Production 10 Sets	
Green Cards:	6x-12x
Production 30 Sets	
Light Blue Cards:	10x-20x
Production 20 Sets	
Purple Cards:	
Production 1 Set	
Red Cards:	10x-20x
Production 25 Sets	

1	Cade McNown	8.00
2	Tim Couch	12.00
3	Emmitt Smith	12.00
4	Edgerrin James	20.00
5	Mark Brunell	8.00
6	Fred Taylor	10.00
7	Randy Moss	15.00
8	Kurt Warner	20.00
9	Jon Kitna	10.00
10	Eddie George	5.00

1999 Pacific Crown Royale Franchise Glory

This 25-card insert set included NFL team leaders, veterans and rising stars. Each is printed with the American flag and fireworks in the background. They were found one-per-pack.

		MT
Complete Set (25):		45.00
Common Player:		1.00
Inserted 1:1		
1	Doug Flutie	2.00
2	Corey Dillon	1.00
3	Troy Aikman	3.00
4	Emmitt Smith	4.00
5	Terrell Davis	4.00
6	Herman Moore	1.00
7	Barry Sanders	5.00
8	Brett Favre	5.00
9	Antonio Freeman	1.00
10	Peyton Manning	4.00
11	Mark Brunell	2.00
12	Fred Taylor	3.00
13	Dan Marino	4.00
14	Randy Moss	5.00
15	Drew Bledsoe	2.00
16	Keyshawn Johnson	1.00
17	Jerome Bettis	1.00
18	Marshall Faulk	1.00
19	Kurt Warner	15.00
20	Terrell Owens	1.00
21	Jerry Rice	3.00
22	Steve Young	2.00
23	Warrick Dunn	1.00
24	Eddie George	1.00
25	Brad Johnson	1.00

1999 Pacific Crown Royale Gold Crown Die Cuts

Singles from this six-card insert set were over-sized and sequentially numbered to 976.

		MT
Complete Set (6):		60.00
Common Player:		5.00
Production 976 Sets		
1	Tim Couch	15.00
2	Troy Aikman	10.00

3	Emmitt Smith	10.00
4	Damond Huard	5.00
5	Randy Moss	15.00
6	Kurt Warner	25.00

1999 Pacific Crown Royale Rookie Gold

This 25-card insert set included the top rookies from 1999. Singles were found one-per-pack. A parallel die-cut version was also made and each of those singles was sequentially numbered to 10.

		MT
Complete Set (25):		50.00
Common Player:		1.00
Inserted 1:1		
1	David Boston	3.00
2	Brandon Stokley	1.00
3	Cade McNown	4.00
4	Akili Smith	4.00
5	Tim Couch	6.00
6	Kevin Johnson	3.00
7	Wane McGarity	1.00
8	Edgerrin James	10.00
9	Terrence Wilkins	4.00
10	Cecil Collins	2.00
11	Rob Konrad	1.00
12	James Johnson	4.00
13	Daunte Culpepper	4.00
14	Michael Bishop	1.50
15	Kevin Faulk	1.50
16	Ricky Williams	6.00
17	Scott Dreisbach	1.00
18	Donovan McNabb	4.00
19	Troy Edwards	3.00
20	Amos Zereoue	1.00
21	Joe Germaine	1.00
22	Torry Holt	3.00
23	Brock Huard	1.50
24	Charlie Rogers	1.00
25	Champ Bailey	1.50

1999 Pacific Crown Royale Test of Time

This 10-card insert set included seasoned veterans along with a few rookies. Each player was pictured on a die-cut single with a clock-shaped design. Singles were inserted 1:25 packs.

		MT
Complete Set (10):		65.00
Common Player:		3.00
Inserted 1:25		
1	Tim Couch	12.00
2	Emmitt Smith	10.00
3	Terrell Davis	10.00
4	Barry Sanders	12.00
5	Brett Favre	12.00
6	Antonio Freeman	3.00
7	Edgerrin James	20.00
8	Mark Brunell	5.00
9	Dan Marino	10.00
10	Jerry Rice	8.00

1999 Pacific Omega

This was a 250-card set that included 48 unseeded rookie cards. Each single was horizontal and used silver foil. Four parallel sets were issued and they include: Copper, Gold, Platinum Blue and Premiere Date. Other inserts include: 5-Star Attack, Draft Class, EO Portraits, Gridiron Masters and TD 99. SRP was $1.99 for six-card packs.

		MT
Complete Set (250):		60.00
Common Player:		.15
Minor Stars:		.30
Common Rookie:		.50
Wax Box:		55.00
1	Mario Bates	.15
2	David Boston	2.50
3	Rob Moore	.30
4	Adrian Murrell	.15
5	Jake Plummer	1.00
6	Frank Sanders	.15
7	Aeneas Williams	.15
8	Joel Makovicka, L.J. Shelton	1.00
9	Jamal Anderson	.50
10	Ray Buchanan	.15
11	Chris Chandler	.30
12	Tim Dwight	.50
13	Byron Hanspard	.15
14	Terance Mathis	.15
15	O.J. Santiago	.15
16	Danny Kanell, Chris Calloway	.15
17	Peter Boulware	.15
18	Priest Holmes	.50
19	Patrick Johnson	.15
20	Jermaine Lewis	.15
21	Ray Lewis	.15
22	Michael McCrary	.15
23	Jonathan Ogden	.15
24	Tony Banks, Scott Mitchell	.15
25	Doug Flutie	.75
26	Rob Johnson	.15
27	Eric Moulds	.50
28	Andre Reed	.15
29	Antowain Smith	.30
30	Bruce Smith	.15
31	Kevin Williams	.15
32	Shawn Bryson, Peerless Price	1.75
33	Steve Beuerlein	.15
34	Tshimanga Biakabutuka	.30
35	Rae Carruth	.15
36	Dameyune Craig	1.50
37	William Floyd	.15
38	Kevin Greene	.15
39	Muhsin Muhammad	.30
40	Wesley Walls	.15
41	Edgar Bennett	.15
42	Robert Chancey	1.00
43	Curtis Conway	.30
44	Bobby Engram	.15
45	Curtis Enis	.50
46	Cade McNown	4.00
47	Ryan Wetnight	.15
48	D'Wayne Bates, Marty Booker	1.50
49	Jeff Blake	.30
50	Scott Covington	1.00
51	Corey Dillon	.50
52	James Hundon	.15
53	Carl Pickens	.30
54	Darnay Scott	.30
55	Akili Smith	4.00
56	Craig Yeast	1.00
57	Tim Couch	8.00
58	Ty Detmer	.15
59	Marc Edwards	.15
60	Kevin Johnson	2.50
61	Terry Kirby	.15
62	Sedrick Shaw	.15
63	Leslie Shepherd	.15
64	Rahim Abdullah, Daylon McCutcheon	.50
65	Troy Aikman	1.00
66	Michael Irvin	.30
67	David LaFleur	.15
68	Wane McGarity	1.00

69	Ernie Mills	.15
70	Deion Sanders	.50
71	Emmitt Smith	1.50
72	Raghib Ismail, James McKnight	.15
73	Bubby Brister	.30
74	Byron Chamberlain	1.25
75	Terrell Davis	1.50
76	Olandis Gary	4.00
77	Brian Griese	1.00
78	Ed McCaffrey	.50
79	Shannon Sharpe	.30
80	Rod Smith	.30
81	Travis McGriff, Al Wilson	1.00
82	Charlie Batch	.75
83	Chris Claiborne	1.00
84	Germane Crowell	.30
85	Terry Fair	.15
86	Sedrick Irvin	1.50
87	Herman Moore	.50
88	Johnnie Morton	.15
89	Barry Sanders	2.00
90	Mark Chmura	.30
91	Brett Favre	2.00
92	Antonio Freeman	.50
93	Desmond Howard	.15
94	Dorsey Levens	.50
95	Derrick Mayes	.30
96	Bill Schroeder	.30
97	Aaron Brooks, Dee Miller	1.25
98	Ken Dilger	.15
99	E.G. Green	.15
100	Marvin Harrison	.50
101	Edgerrin James	8.00
102	Peyton Manning	1.50
103	Jerome Pathon	.15
104	Marcus Pollard	.15
105	Alexander	.15
106	Reggie Barlow	.15
107	Tony Boselli	.15
108	Mark Brunell	.75
109	George Jones	.15
110	Keenan McCardell	.30
111	Jimmy Smith	.30
112	James Stewart	.30
113	Fred Taylor	1.00
114	Kimble Anders	.15
115	Michael Cloud	1.00
116	Tony Gonzalez	.30
117	Elvis Grbac	.30
118	Bam Morris	.15
119	Andre Rison	.30
120	Derrick Thomas	.30
121	Karim Abdul	.30
122	Oronde Gadsden	.30
123	James Johnson	1.75
124	Rob Konrad	1.00
125	Dan Marino	1.50
126	O.J. McDuffie	.30
127	Lamar Thomas	.15
128	Zach Thomas	.30
129	Cris Carter	.50
130	Daunte Culpepper	4.00
131	Randall Cunningham	.50
132	Matthew Hatchette	.15
133	Leroy Hoard	.15
134	David Palmer	.15
135	John Randle	.15
136	Randy Moss	2.00
137	Robert Smith	.30
138	Drew Bledsoe	.75
139	Ben Coates	.30
140	Kevin Faulk	2.00
141	Terry Glenn	.50
142	Shawn Jefferson	.15
143	Ty Law	.15
144	Tony Simmons	.15
145	Michael Bishop, Andy Katzenmoyer	1.75
146	Cameron Cleeland	.30
147	Andre Hastings	.15
148	Billy Joe Hobert	.15
149	Joe Johnson	.15
150	Keith Poole	.15
151	William Roaf	.15
152	Billy Joe Tolliver	.15
153	Ricky Williams	8.00
154	Tiki Barber	.30
155	Gary Brown	.15
156	Kent Graham	.15
157	Ike Hilliard	.30
158	David Patten	.15
159	Jason Sehorn	.15
160	Amani Toomer	.15
161	Joe Montgomery, Luke Petitgout	1.25
162	Wayne Chrebet	.30
163	Bryan Cox	.15
164	Aaron Glenn	.15
165	Keyshawn Johnson	.50
166	Leon Johnson	.15
167	Curtis Martin	.50
168	Vinny Testaverde	.30
169	Dedric Ward	.15
170	Tim Brown	.30
171	Rickey Dudley	.30
172	James Jett	.15
173	Napoleon Kaufman	.50
174	Jon Ritchie	.15
175	Darrell Russell	.15
176	Charles Woodson	.50
177	Rich Gannon, Heath Shuler	.15
178	Hugh Douglas	.15

179	Donovan McNabb	4.00
180	Allen Rossum	.15
181	Duce Staley	.30
182	Kevin Turner	.15
183	Charles Johnson, Doug Pederson	.15
184	Barry Gardner, Cecil Martin	.50
185	Jerome Bettis	.50
186	Mark Bruener	.15
187	Troy Edwards	2.50
188	Courtney Hawkins	.15
189	Levon Kirkland	.15
190	Kordell Stewart	.50
191	Hines Ward	.15
192	Malcolm Johnson, Amos Zereoue	1.75
193	Greg Clark	.15
194	Terrell Fletcher	.15
195	Charlie Jones	.15
196	Cecil Collins	4.00
197	Natrone Means	.30
198	Mikhael Ricks	.15
199	Junior Seau	.30
200	Bryan Still	.15
201	Ryan Thelwell	.15
202	Garrison Hearst	.30
203	Terry Jackson	.50
204	R.W. McQuarters	.15
205	Terrell Owens	.50
206	Jerry Rice	1.00
207	J.J. Stokes	.30
208	Tommy Vardell	.15
209	Steve Young	.75
210	Karsten Bailey	1.00
211	Chad Brown	.15
212	Christian Fauria	.15
213	Joey Galloway	.50
214	Ahman Green	.30
215	Brock Huard	1.50
216	Cortez Kennedy	.15
217	Jon Kitna	.75
218	Ricky Watters	.50
219	Isaac Bruce	.50
220	Az-Zahir Hakim	.30
221	June Henley	.15
222	Greg Hill	.15
223	Torry Holt	2.50
224	Amp Lee	.15
225	Ricky Proehl	.15
226	Marshall Faulk, Trent Green	.50
227	Mike Alstott	.50
228	Reidel Anthony	.30
229	Trent Dilfer	.30
230	Warrick Dunn	.50
231	Bert Emanuel	.15
232	Jacquez Green	.30
233	Warren Sapp	.15
234	Shaun King, Anthony McFarland	3.00
235	Mike Archie	.50
236	Kevin Dyson	.30
237	Eddie George	.75
238	Derrick Mason	.15
239	Steve McNair	.75
240	Yancey Thigpen	.30
241	Frank Wycheck	.15
242	Darran Hall, Jevon Kearse	2.00
243	Stephen Alexander	.15
244	Champ Bailey	1.50
245	Stephen Davis	.50
246	Skip Hicks	.30
247	James Thrash	.15
248	Michael Westbrook	.30
249	Dan Wilkinson	.15
250	Brad Johnson, Larry Centers	.15

1999 Pacific Omega Copper

This was a 250-card parallel to the base set. Each of the singles used copper foil rather than silver foil on the base cards. These were only found in hobby packs and each was sequentially numbered to 99.

	MT
Copper Cards:	15x-30x
Copper Rookies:	5x-10x
Production 99 Sets	

1999 Pacific Omega Gold

This was a 250-card parallel to the base set. Each of these singles used gold foil rather than silver foil on the base cards. These were only found in retail packs and each was sequentially numbered to 299.

MT
Gold Cards: 8x-16x
Gold Rookies: 2x-4x
Production 299 Sets

1999 Pacific Omega Platinum Blue

This was a 250-card parallel to the base set. Each of these singles used blue foil rather than silver foil on the base cards. These were found in both hobby and retail packs and each was sequentially numbered to 75.

MT
Platinum Blue Cards: 20x-40x
Platinum Blue Rookies: 6x-12x
Production 75 Sets

1999 Pacific Omega Premiere Date

This was a 250-card parallel to the base set. Each of these singles used red foil rather than silver foil on the base cards. Each of these singles was sequentially numbered to 60.

MT
Premiere Date Cards: 20x-40x
Premiere Date Rookies: 6x-12x
Production 60 Sets

1999 Pacific Omega 5-Star Attack

This was a 30-card insert that included the NFL's top stars and premier rookies. Singles were inserted 4:37 packs and could only be found in hobby packs. Five parallel sets were issued and include: Blue (#'d to 100), Red (#'d to 75), Green (#'d to 50), Purple (#'d to 25) and Gold (#'d to 1).

MT
Complete Set (30): 50.00
Common Player: .50
Minor Stars: 1.00
Inserted 4:37
Blue Cards: 5x-10x
Production 100 Sets
Gold Cards:
Production 1 Set
Green Cards: 8x-16x
Production 50 Sets
Purple Cards: 10x-20x
Production 25 Sets
Red Cards: 7x-14x
Production 75 Sets
1 Chris Chandler .50
2 Tim Couch 6.00
3 Peyton Manning 4.00
4 Dan Marino 4.00
5 Drew Bledsoe 2.00
6 Vinny Testaverde .50
7 Randall Cunningham 1.00
8 Doug Flutie 1.50
9 Charlie Batch 1.50
10 Mark Brunell 2.00
11 Steve Young 1.75
12 Jon Kitna 1.50
13 Jamal Anderson 1.00
14 Priest Holmes 1.00
15 Emmitt Smith 4.00
16 Fred Taylor 3.00
17 Curtis Martin 1.00
18 Eddie George 1.50
19 Ed McCaffrey .50
20 Antonio Freeman 1.00
21 Randy Moss 6.00
22 Keyshawn Johnson 1.00
23 Terrell Owens 1.00
24 Joey Galloway 1.00
25 Cade McNown 3.00
26 Akili Smith 3.00
27 Edgerrin James 6.00
28 Daunte Culpepper 3.00
29 Ricky Williams 6.00
30 Donovan McNabb 3.00

1999 Pacific Omega Draft Class

This 10-card insert included two players from the same draft year and pictured them on the front of each card. Singles were inserted 1:145 packs.

MT
Complete Set (10): 125.00
Common Player: 10.00
Inserted 1:145
1 1983 (Darrell Green, Dan Marino) 20.00
2 1985 (Jerry Rice, Bruce Smith) 15.00
3 1989 (Troy Aikman, Barry Sanders) 30.00
4 1990 (Shannon Sharpe, Emmitt Smith) 20.00
5 1991 (Brett Favre, Herman Moore) 30.00
6 1993 (Drew Bledsoe, Mark Brunell) 10.00
7 1995 (Terrell Davis, Curtis Martin) 20.00
8 1997 (Warrick Dunn, Jake Plummer) 10.00
9 1998 (Peyton Manning, Randy Moss) 30.00
10 1999 (Tim Couch, Ricky Williams) 25.00

1999 Pacific Omega EO Portraits

This 20-card insert included mostly veterans and a few rookies. Each single used electro-optical technology and each had the player's portrait laser cut into the card. Singles were inserted 1:73 packs.

MT
Complete Set (20): 150.00
Common Player: 5.00
Inserted 1:73
1 Jake Plummer 10.00
2 Jamal Anderson 5.00
3 Akili Smith 10.00
4 Tim Couch 20.00
5 Troy Aikman 10.00
6 Emmitt Smith 15.00
7 Terrell Davis 15.00
8 Barry Sanders 20.00
9 Brett Favre 20.00
10 Peyton Manning 15.00
11 Mark Brunell 8.00
12 Fred Taylor 8.00
13 Dan Marino 15.00
14 Randy Moss 20.00
15 Ricky Williams 20.00
16 Curtis Martin 5.00
17 Jerry Rice 10.00
18 Jon Kitna 8.00
19 Warrick Dunn 5.00
20 Eddie George 8.00

1999 Pacific Omega Gridiron Masters

This 36-card insert included both veterans and rookies. Singles were inserted 4:37 packs.

MT
Complete Set (36): 40.00
Common Player: .50
Minor Stars: 1.00
Inserted 4:37
1 David Boston 1.75
2 Jake Plummer 2.50
3 Jamal Anderson .50
4 Chris Chandler .50
5 Priest Holmes 1.00
6 Doug Flutie 1.75
7 Akili Smith 2.50
8 Cade McNown 2.50
9 Tim Couch 5.00
10 Deion Sanders 1.00
11 Emmitt Smith 3.50
12 Rod Smith .50
13 Charlie Batch 1.75
14 Herman Moore 1.00
15 Barry Sanders 5.00
16 Antonio Freeman 1.00
17 Edgerrin James 5.00
18 Mark Brunell 1.75
19 Fred Taylor 2.50
20 Randall Cunningham 1.00
21 Randy Moss 5.00
22 Terry Glenn 1.00
23 Keyshawn Johnson 1.00
24 Curtis Martin 1.00
25 Vinny Testaverde .50
26 Donovan McNabb 2.50
27 Jerome Bettis 1.00
28 Terrell Owens 1.00
29 Jerry Rice 2.50
30 Steve Young 1.75
31 Joey Galloway 1.50
32 Jon Kitna 1.50
33 Warrick Dunn 1.00
34 Shaun King 1.50
35 Eddie George 1.25
36 Steve McNair 1.25

1999 Pacific Omega TD '99

This 20-card insert included the NFL's most renown TD leaders. Each was printed on a prism-style holographic foil board. Singles were inserted 1:37 packs.

MT
Complete Set (20): 50.00
Common Player: 1.50
Inserted 1:37
1 Jamal Anderson 1.50
2 Priest Holmes 1.50
3 Doug Flutie 3.00
4 Tim Couch 10.00
5 Troy Aikman 5.00
6 Emmitt Smith 7.00
7 Terrell Davis 7.00
8 Herman Moore 1.50
9 Brett Favre 10.00
10 Antonio Freeman 2.00
11 Mark Brunell 4.00
12 Fred Taylor 5.00
13 Randall Cunningham 2.00
14 Randy Moss 10.00
15 Drew Bledsoe 4.00
16 Terrell Owens 2.00
17 Steve Young 3.00
18 Jon Kitna 3.00
19 Warrick Dunn 3.00
20 Eddie George 3.00

1999 Pacific Paramount

Pacific Paramount Football is a 250-card set that includes all of the top rookies from 1999. The base has six different parallel sets with Copper, Gold, Premiere Date, HoloGold, HoloSilver and Platinum Blue. Other inserts include: Canton Bound, End Zone Net-Fusions, Personal Bests and Team Checklists.

MT
Complete Set (250): 60.00
Common Player: .10
Minor Stars: .20
Common Rookie: .50
Wax Box: 50.00
1 *David Boston* 3.00
2 Larry Centers .10
3 *Joel Makovicka* 1.00
4 Eric Metcalf .10
5 Rob Moore .20
6 Adrian Murrell .20
7 Jake Plummer 1.00
8 Frank Sanders .20
9 Aeneas Williams .10
10 Morten Andersen .10
11 Jamal Anderson .50
12 Chris Chandler .20
13 Tim Dwight .50
14 Terance Mathis .10
15 *Jeff Paulk* 1.00
16 O.J. Santiago .10
17 Chuck Smith .10
18 Peter Boulware .10
19 Priest Holmes .50
20 Michael Jackson .10
21 Jermaine Lewis .20
22 Ray Lewis .10
23 Michael McCrary .10
24 Bennie Thompson .10
25 Rod Woodson .20
26 *Shawn Bryson* .50
27 Doug Flutie .75
28 Eric Moulds .50
29 *Peerless Price* 1.50
30 Andre Reed .10
31 Jay Riemersma .10
32 Antowain Smith .50
33 Bruce Smith .10
34 Michael Bates .10
35 Steve Beuerlein .10
36 Tshimanga Biakabutuka .10
37 Kevin Greene .10
38 Anthony Johnson .10
39 Fred Lane .10
40 Muhsin Muhammad .10
41 Wesley Walls .10
42 *D'Wayne Bates* .75
43 Edgar Bennett .10
44 Marty Booker .50
45 Curtis Conway .20
46 Bobby Engram .10
47 Curtis Enis .50
48 Erik Kramer .10
49 *Cade McNown* 4.00

MT
50 Jeff Blake .20
51 *Scott Covington* 1.00
52 Corey Dillon .50
53 *Quincy Jackson* .50
54 Carl Pickens .20
55 Darnay Scott .10
56 *Akili Smith* 4.00
57 *Craig Yeast* .50
58 Jerry Ball .10
59 *Darrin Chiaverini* .50
60 *Tim Couch* 10.00
61 Ty Detmer .10
62 *Kevin Johnson* 1.25
63 Terry Kirby .10
64 *Daylon McCutcheon* .50
65 Irv Smith .10
66 Troy Aikman 1.00
67 *Ebenezer Ekuban* .50
68 Michael Irvin .20
69 Daryl Johnston .10
70 *Wayne McGarity* .75
71 *Dat Nguyen* 1.00
72 Deion Sanders .50
73 Emmitt Smith 1.50
74 Bubby Brister .30
75 Terrell Davis 1.50
76 Jason Elam .10
77 *Olandis Gary* 4.00
78 Brian Griese .75
79 Ed McCaffrey .30
80 *Travis McGriff* 1.00
81 Shannon Sharpe .20
82 Rod Smith .20
83 Charlie Batch .75
84 *Chris Claiborne* 1.00
85 Germane Crowell .20
86 *Sedrick Irvin* 1.50
87 Herman Moore .50
88 Johnnie Morton .10
89 Barry Sanders 2.00
90 Robert Brooks .10
91 *Aaron Brooks* 1.50
92 Mark Chmura .10
93 Brett Favre 2.00
94 Antonio Freeman .50
95 Vonnie Holliday .20
96 Dorsey Levens .20
97 *De'Mond Parker* .75
98 Ken Dilger .10
99 Marvin Harrison .30
100 *Edgerrin James* 10.00
101 Peyton Manning 1.50
102 Jerome Pathon .10
103 *Mike Peterson* .50
104 Marcus Pollard .10
105 Tavian Banks .20
106 Reggie Barlow .10
107 Tony Boselli .10
108 Mark Brunell .75
109 Keenan McCardell .10
110 Bryce Paup .10
111 Jimmy Smith .20
112 Fred Taylor 1.00
113 Dave Thomas .10
114 Kimble Anders .10
115 Donnell Bennett .10
116 *Mike Cloud* 1.00
117 Tony Gonzalez .20
118 Elvis Grbac .20
119 *Larry Parker* .50
120 Andre Rison .20
121 *Brian Shay* .50
122 Karim Abdul .30
123 Oronde Gadsden .20
124 *James Johnson* 1.50
125 *Rob Konrad* 1.00
126 Dan Marino 1.50
127 O.J. McDuffie .20
128 Zach Thomas .20
129 Cris Carter .20
130 *Daunte Culpepper* 4.00
131 Randall Cunningham .10
132 Matthew Hatchette .10
133 Leroy Hoard .10
134 Randy Moss 2.00
135 John Randle .10
136 Jake Reed .10
137 Robert Smith .50
138 *Michael Bishop* 2.00
139 Drew Bledsoe .75
140 Ben Coates .10
141 *Kevin Faulk* 2.50
142 Terry Glenn .30
143 Shawn Jefferson .10
144 *Andy Katzenmoyer* 1.00
145 Tony Simmons .20
146 *Cuncho Brown* .50
147 Cameron Cleeland .20
148 Mark Fields .10
149 La'Roi Glover .10
150 Andre Hastings .10
151 Billy Joe Hobert .10
152 William Roaf .10
153 Billy Joe Tolliver .10
154 Ricky Williams 10.00
155 Jessie Armstead .10
156 Tiki Barber .20
157 Gary Brown .10
158 Kent Graham .10
159 Ike Hilliard .20
160 *Joe Montgomery* 1.25
161 Amani Toomer .10
162 Charles Way .10
163 Wayne Chrebet .50
164 Bryan Cox .10
165 Aaron Glenn .10
166 Keyshawn Johnson .50
167 Leon Johnson .10
168 Curtis Martin .50
169 Vinny Testaverde .20
170 Dedric Ward .10
171 Tim Brown .20
172 *Dameane Douglas* .75
173 Rickey Dudley .20
174 James Jett .10
175 Napoleon Kaufman .50
176 Darrell Russell .10
177 Harvey Williams .10
178 Charles Woodson .50
179 *Na Brown* .10
180 Hugh Douglas .10
181 Cecil Martin .50
182 *Donovan McNabb* 4.00
183 Duce Staley .10
184 Kevin Turner .10
185 Jerome Bettis .50
186 *Troy Edwards* 2.00
187 Jason Gildon .10
188 Courtney Hawkins .10
189 *Malcolm Johnson* .50
190 Kordell Stewart .75
191 *Jerame Tuman* .50
192 *Amos Zereoue* 2.00
193 Isaac Bruce .30
194 Kevin Carter .10
195 *Jermaine Copeland* .50
196 *Joe Germaine* 1.75
197 Az-Zahir Hakim .20
198 *Torry Holt* 2.50
199 Amp Lee .10
200 Ricky Proehl .10
201 Charlie Jones .10
202 Freddie Jones .10
203 Ryan Leaf .50
204 Natrone Means .30
205 Mikhael Ricks .10
206 Junior Seau .20
207 Bryan Still .10
208 Garrison Hearst .30
209 Terry Jackson .50
210 R.W. McQuarters .10
211 Ken Norton Jr. .10
212 Terrell Owens .50
213 Jerry Rice 1.00
214 J.J. Stokes .20
215 *Tai Streets* 1.00
216 Steve Young .75
217 *Karsten Bailey* 1.00
218 Chad Brown .10
219 Joey Galloway .50
220 Ahman Green .20
221 *Brock Huard* 1.50
222 Cortez Kennedy .10
223 Jon Kitna .75
224 Shawn Springs .10
225 Ricky Watters .20
226 Mike Alstott .50
227 Reidel Anthony .20
228 Trent Dilfer .30
229 Warrick Dunn .75
230 Bert Emanuel .10
231 *Martin Gramatica* .20
232 Jacquez Green .20
233 *Shaun King* 3.00
234 *Anthony McFarland* 1.00
235 Warren Sapp .10
236 Willie Davis .10
237 Kevin Dyson .20
238 Eddie George .75
239 *Darran Hall* .50
240 Jackie Harris .10
241 Steve McNair .50
242 Yancey Thigpen .20
243 Frank Wycheck .10
244 Stephen Alexander .10
245 *Champ Bailey* 1.50
246 Stephen Davis .10
247 Darrell Green .10
248 Skip Hicks .50
249 Brian Mitchell .10
250 Michael Westbrook .20

1999 Pacific Paramount Copper

This is a parallel to the base and could only be found in hobby by product at one-per-pack.

MT
Complete Set (250): 135.00
Copper Cards: 3x
Copper Rookies: 1.5x
Inserted 1:1

1999 Pacific Paramount HoloGold

This is a parallel to the base set and was only found in retail product. Each card was sequentially numbered to 199.

MT
HoloGold Cards: 20x-40x
HoloGold Rookies: 5x-10x
Production 199 Sets

1999 Pacific Paramount Holographic Silver

This is a parallel to the base and was inserted into hobby product. Each card was sequentially numbered to 99.

	MT
Silver Cards:	40x-80x
Silver Rookies:	7x-14x
Production 99 Sets	

1999 Pacific Paramount Platinum Blue

This is a parallel to the base and was inserted in both hobby and retail product. Cards were found 1:73 packs.

	MT
Blue Cards:	40x-80x
Blue Rookies:	7x-14x
Inserted 1:73	

1999 Pacific Paramount Premiere Date

This is a parallel to the base that was found 1:37 hobby packs and each is sequentially numbered to 62.

	MT
Premiere Date Cards:	50x-100x
Premiere Date Rookies:	9x-18x
Inserted 1:37	

1999 Pacific Paramount Canton Bound

Each card is fully foiled and etched with just ten of the top players heading to Canton. Each card is horizontal and were inserted 1:361 packs. A parallel Proof set was also issued with each card sequentially numbered to 20.

	MT
Complete Set (10):	550.00
Common Player:	40.00
Inserted 1:361	
Proofs:	4x
Production 20 Sets	
1 Troy Aikman	60.00
2 Emmitt Smith	80.00
3 Terrell Davis	80.00
4 Barry Sanders	100.00
5 Brett Favre	100.00
6 Dan Marino	80.00
7 Randy Moss	100.00
8 Drew Bledsoe	50.00
9 Jerry Rice	60.00
10 Steve Young	40.00

1999 Pacific Paramount End Zone Net-Fusions

Each card in this 20-card set has a die-cut design that includes actual netting from behind the goal posts. Singles were inserted 1:73 packs.

	MT
Complete Set (20):	325.00
Common Player:	10.00
Inserted 1:73	
1 Jake Plummer	20.00
2 Jamal Anderson	10.00
3 Doug Flutie	15.00

4	Tim Couch	40.00
5	Troy Aikman	20.00
6	Emmitt Smith	30.00
7	Terrell Davis	30.00
8	Barry Sanders	40.00
9	Brett Favre	40.00
10	Peyton Manning	30.00
11	Mark Brunell	15.00
12	Fred Taylor	15.00
13	Dan Marino	30.00
14	Randy Moss	40.00
15	Drew Bledsoe	15.00
16	Ricky Williams	40.00
17	Jerry Rice	20.00
18	Steve Young	15.00
19	Jon Kitna	10.00
20	Eddie George	12.00

1999 Pacific Paramount Personal Bests

Thirty-six of the NFL's top players are featured on these holographic patterned foil cards. Singles were inserted 1:37 packs.

		MT
Complete Set (36):		225.00
Common Player:		4.00
Inserted 1:37		
1	Jake Plummer	10.00
2	Jamal Anderson	4.00
3	Priest Holmes	6.00
4	Doug Flutie	8.00
5	Antowain Smith	4.00
6	Corey Dillon	4.00
7	Akili Smith	10.00
8	Tim Couch	25.00
9	Troy Aikman	10.00
10	Emmitt Smith	15.00
11	Terrell Davis	15.00
12	Barry Sanders	20.00
13	Brett Favre	20.00
14	Antonio Freeman	4.00
15	Edgerrin James	15.00
16	Peyton Manning	15.00
17	Mark Brunell	8.00
18	Fred Taylor	10.00
19	Dan Marino	15.00
20	Randall Cunningham	4.00
21	Randy Moss	20.00
22	Drew Bledsoe	8.00
23	Kevin Faulk	6.00
24	Ricky Williams	25.00
25	Curtis Martin	4.00
26	Napoleon Kaufman	4.00
27	Donovan McNabb	10.00
28	Jerome Bettis	4.00
29	Kordell Stewart	6.00
30	Terrell Owens	6.00
31	Jerry Rice	10.00
32	Steve Young	8.00
33	Jon Kitna	6.00
34	Warrick Dunn	6.00
35	Eddie George	6.00
36	Steve McNair	4.00

1999 Pacific Paramount Team Checklists

Each card in this 31-card set highlights one player from

each team and uses his photo on the front with his name in gold foil. The back has a smaller photo with a checklist of players from that team. Singles were inserted 2:37 packs.

		MT
Complete Set (31):		125.00
Common Player:		1.50
Minor Stars:		3.00
Inserted 2:37		
1	Jake Plummer	6.00
2	Jamal Anderson	3.00
3	Priest Holmes	3.00
4	Doug Flutie	5.00
5	Muhsin Muhammad	1.50
6	Cade McNown	6.00
7	Corey Dillon	3.00
8	Tim Couch	15.00
9	Troy Aikman	6.00
10	Terrell Davis	8.00
11	Barry Sanders	12.00
12	Brett Favre	12.00
13	Peyton Manning	8.00
14	Fred Taylor	6.00
15	Elvis Grbac	1.50
16	Dan Marino	8.00
17	Randy Moss	12.00
18	Drew Bledsoe	5.00
19	Ricky Williams	15.00
20	Ike Hilliard	1.50
21	Curtis Martin	3.00
22	Napoleon Kaufman	3.00
23	Donovan McNabb	6.00
24	Jerome Bettis	3.00
25	Torry Holt	4.00
26	Natrone Means	1.50
27	Jerry Rice	6.00
28	Jon Kitna	4.00
29	Warrick Dunn	4.00
30	Eddie George	4.00
31	Skip Hicks	3.00

1999 Pacific Prisms

This 150-card base set pictured players on a holographic prismatic background. A total of five parallel sets were issued and they include: Holographic Blue, Holographic Gold, Holographic Mirror, Holographic Purple and Premiere Date. Other inserts include: Dial-a-Stats, Ornaments, Prospects and Sunday's Best. SRP was $4.99 for five-card packs.

		MT
Complete Set (150):		90.00
Common Player:		.20
Minor Stars:		.40
Common Rookie:		1.00
Wax Box:		75.00
1	David Boston	3.00
2	Rob Moore	.40
3	Adrian Murrell	.20
4	Jake Plummer	1.50
5	Frank Sanders	.40
6	Jamal Anderson	.75
7	Chris Chandler	.40
8	Tim Dwight	.75
9	Terance Mathis	.20
10	Peter Boulware	.20
11	Priest Holmes	.75
12	Patrick Johnson	.40
13	Jermaine Lewis	.20
14	Doug Flutie	1.25
15	Eric Moulds	.75
16	Peerless Price	2.00
17	Antowain Smith	.75
18	Bruce Smith	.20
19	Steve Beuerlein	.40
20	Tim Biakabutuka	.40
21	Muhsin Muhammad	.75
22	Wesley Walls	.20
23	Edgar Bennett	.20
24	Curtis Conway	.40
25	Bobby Engram	.20
26	Curtis Enis	.75
27	Cade McNown	6.00
28	Jeff Blake	.40
29	Scott Covington	1.00
30	Corey Dillon	.75
31	Carl Pickens	.40

32	Akili Smith	6.00
33	Craig Yeast	1.00
34	Tim Couch	10.00
35	Ty Detmer	.20
36	Kevin Johnson	3.00
37	Terry Kirby	.20
38	Leslie Shepherd	.20
39	Troy Aikman	1.50
40	Michael Irvin	.40
41	Deion Sanders	.75
42	Emmitt Smith	2.00
43	Bubby Brister	.40
44	Terrell Davis	2.00
45	Brian Griese	1.50
46	Ed McCaffrey	.75
47	Shannon Sharpe	.40
48	Rod Smith	.40
49	Charlie Batch	1.25
50	Germane Crowell	.75
51	Sedrick Irvin	2.00
52	Herman Moore	.75
53	Johnnie Morton	.40
54	Barry Sanders	3.00
55	Mark Chmura	.40
56	Brett Favre	3.00
57	Antonio Freeman	.75
58	Dorsey Levens	.75
59	Ken Dilger	.20
60	Marvin Harrison	.75
61	Edgerrin James	15.00
62	Peyton Manning	2.00
63	Jerome Pathon	.40
64	Mark Brunell	1.25
65	Keenan McCardell	.40
66	Jimmy Smith	.75
67	Fred Taylor	1.50
68	Derrick Alexander	.20
69	Michael Cloud	1.00
70	Tony Gonzalez	.40
71	Elvis Grbac	.40
72	Andre Rison	.40
73	Cecil Collins	3.00
74	Oronde Gadsden	.40
75	James Johnson	2.00
76	Dan Marino	2.00
77	O.J. McDuffie	.40
78	Lamar Thomas	.20
79	Cris Carter	.75
80	Daunte Culpepper	6.00
81	Randall Cunningham	.75
82	Matthew Hatchette	.40
83	Randy Moss	3.00
84	John Randle	.20
85	Robert Smith	.75
86	Drew Bledsoe	1.25
87	Ben Coates	.40
88	Kevin Faulk	2.00
89	Terry Glenn	.75
90	Shawn Jefferson	.20
91	Cameron Cleeland	.40
92	Billy Joe Hobert	.20
93	Keith Poole	.20
94	Ricky Williams	10.00
95	Gary Brown	.20
96	Kent Graham	.20
97	Ike Hilliard	.40
98	Amani Toomer	.40
99	Wayne Chrebet	.75
100	Keyshawn Johnson	.75
101	Curtis Martin	.75
102	Vinny Testaverde	.40
103	Tim Brown	.75
104	James Jett	.20
105	Napoleon Kaufman	.75
106	Charles Woodson	.75
107	Koy Detmer	.20
108	Donovan McNabb	6.00
109	Duce Staley	.75
110	Kevin Turner	.20
111	Jerome Bettis	.75
112	Mark Bruener	.20
113	Troy Edwards	3.00
114	Levon Kirkland	.20
115	Kordell Stewart	.75
116	Amos Zereoue	1.50
117	Ryan Leaf	.75
118	Natrone Means	.40
119	Mikhael Ricks	.40
120	Junior Seau	.40
121	Garrison Hearst	.40
122	Terrell Owens	.75
123	Jerry Rice	1.50
124	J.J. Stokes	.40
125	Steve Young	1.25
126	Chad Brown	.20
127	Joey Galloway	.75
128	Brock Huard	2.00
129	Jon Kitna	1.00
130	Ricky Watters	.40
131	Isaac Bruce	.75
132	Joe Germaine	1.50
133	Marshall Faulk	.75
134	Torry Holt	3.00
135	Trent Green	.40
136	Mike Alstott	.75
137	Reidel Anthony	.40
138	Trent Dilfer	.40
139	Warrick Dunn	.75
140	Jacquez Green	.40
141	Shaun King	5.00
142	Darnell McDonald	1.50
143	Eddie George	1.00
144	Steve McNair	1.00
145	Yancey Thigpen	.40
146	Frank Wycheck	.20
147	Champ Bailey	2.00
148	Albert Connell	.40

149	Skip Hicks	.40
150	Michael Westbrook	.40

1999 Pacific Prisms Holographic Blue

This was a 150-card parallel to the base set. Each of these singles was printed with blue foil on the background. Singles were found in both hobby and retail packs. Each was sequentially numbered on the front to 80.

	MT
Blue Cards:	12x-24x
Blue Rookies:	4x-8x
Production 80 Sets	

1999 Pacific Prisms Holographic Gold

This was a 150-card parallel to the base set. Each of these singles was printed with gold foil on the background. Singles were found in both hobby and retail packs. Each was sequentially numbered on the front to 480.

	MT
Gold Cards:	3x-6x
Gold Rookies:	2x
Production 480 Sets	

1999 Pacific Prisms Holographic Mirror

This was a 150-card parallel to the base set. Each of these singles was printed with a mirror foil background. Singles were found in both hobby and retail packs. Each was sequentially numbered on the front to 160.

	MT
Mirror Cards:	10x-20x
Mirror Rookies:	3x-6x
Production 160 Sets	

1999 Pacific Prisms Holographic Purple

This was a 150-card parallel to the base set. Each of these singles was printed with purple foil on the background. Singles were found only in hobby packs. Each was sequentially numbered on the front to 320.

	MT
Purple Cards:	5x-10x
Purple Rookies:	3x
Production 320 Sets	

1999 Pacific Prisms Premiere Date

This was a 150-card parallel to the base set. Each of these singles was printed with red foil on the background. Singles were found one-per-box and each was sequentially numbered to 61.

	MT
Premiere Date Cards:	15x-30x
Premiere Date Rookies:	5x-10x
Production 61 Sets	

1999 Pacific Prisms Dial-a-Stats

This 10-card insert included a spinning wheel on the card that allowed collectors to dial up a player's top performances. Singles were inserted 1:193 packs.

		MT
Complete Set (10):		185.00
Common Player:		10.00
Inserted 1:193		
1	Tim Couch	40.00
2	Emmitt Smith	30.00
3	Terrell Davis	30.00
4	Barry Sanders	40.00
5	Brett Favre	40.00
6	Mark Brunell	15.00
7	Dan Marino	30.00
8	Ricky Williams	40.00
9	Curtis Martin	10.00
10	Terrell Owens	10.00

1999 Pacific Prisms Ornaments

This 20-card insert had a Christmas theme to each single. Five different die cuts could be found in the shapes of Christmas trees, stockings, balls, etc. Each came with a string attached so collectors could hang these on their Christmas trees. Cards were found 1:25 packs.

		MT
Complete Set (20):		150.00
Common Player:		5.00
Inserted 1:25		
1	Jake Plummer	10.00
2	Jamal Anderson	5.00
3	Cade McNown	10.00
4	Tim Couch	15.00
5	Troy Aikman	10.00
6	Deion Sanders	5.00
7	Emmitt Smith	10.00
8	Terrell Davis	15.00
9	Barry Sanders	20.00
10	Brett Favre	20.00
11	Peyton Manning	15.00
12	Mark Brunell	8.00
13	Fred Taylor	10.00
14	Dan Marino	15.00
15	Randy Moss	20.00
16	Drew Bledsoe	8.00

17	Terrell Owens	5.00
18	Jerry Rice	10.00
19	Steve Young	8.00
20	Jon Kitna	5.00

1999 Pacific Prisms Prospects

This 10-card insert included rookies from the 1999 NFL Draft. Singles were only found in hobby product and inserted 1:97 packs.

		MT
Complete Set (10):		75.00
Common Player:		5.00
Inserted 1:97		
1	David Boston	5.00
2	Cade McNown	10.00
3	Akili Smith	10.00
4	Tim Couch	15.00
5	Edgerrin James	20.00
6	Cecil Collins	5.00
7	Daunte Culpepper	10.00
8	Ricky Williams	15.00
9	Donovan McNabb	10.00
10	Torry Holt	5.00

1999 Pacific Prisms Sunday's Best

This 20-card insert included a mix of veterans and rookies. Singles were inserted 2:25 packs.

		MT
Complete Set (20):		80.00
Common Player:		2.00
Inserted 2:25		
1	Jake Plummer	5.00
2	Akili Smith	5.00
3	Tim Couch	10.00
4	Emmitt Smith	8.00
5	Terrell Davis	8.00
6	Barry Sanders	10.00
7	Brett Favre	10.00
8	Peyton Manning	8.00
9	Mark Brunell	4.00
10	Fred Taylor	5.00
11	Dan Marino	8.00
12	Randy Moss	10.00
13	Drew Bledsoe	4.00
14	Ricky Williams	10.00
15	Curtis Martin	2.00
16	Terrell Owens	2.00
17	Jerry Rice	5.00
18	Steve Young	3.00
19	Jon Kitna	3.00
20	Eddie George	3.00

Values quoted in this guide reflect the retail price of a card — the price a collector can expect to pay when buying a card from a dealer. The wholesale price — that which a collector can expect to receive when selling cards — will be naturally lower, depending on desirability and condition.

1999 Pacific Revolution

Pacific Revolution is a 175-card set that includes 50 seeded rookies at 1:4 packs. Each card includes dual foiling, etching and embossing. Opening Day, Shadow and Red are three parallel sets. Other inserts include: Chalk Talk, Icons, Showstoppers and Thorn in the Side.

		MT
Complete Set (175):		75.00
Common Player:		.25
Minor Stars:		.50
Common Rookie:		1.00
Inserted 1:4		
Wax Box:		80.00
1	David Boston	5.00
2	Joel Makovicka	2.00
3	Rob Moore	.50
4	Adrian Murrell	.25
5	Jake Plummer	2.00
6	Frank Sanders	.25
7	Jamal Anderson	1.00
8	Chris Chandler	.50
9	Tim Dwight	.75
10	Terance Mathis	.25
11	Jeff Paulk	2.00
12	O.J. Santiago	.25
13	Peter Boulware	.25
14	Priest Holmes	1.00
15	Michael Jackson	.25
16	Jermaine Lewis	.25
17	Doug Flutie	1.50
18	Eric Moulds	1.00
19	Peerless Price	4.00
20	Andre Reed	.50
21	Antowain Smith	1.00
22	Bruce Smith	.25
23	Steve Beuerlein	.25
24	Kevin Greene	.25
25	Fred Lane	.25
26	Muhsin Muhammad	.25
27	Wesley Walls	.25
28	Marty Booker	1.00
29	Curtis Conway	.50
30	Bobby Engram	.25
31	Curtis Enis	1.00
32	Erik Kramer	.25
33	Cade McNown	8.00
34	Scott Covington	2.00
35	Corey Dillon	1.25
36	Carl Pickens	.50
37	Darnay Scott	.25
38	Akili Smith	7.00
39	Craig Yeast	2.00
40	Darrin Chiaverini	2.00
41	Tim Couch	15.00
42	Ty Detmer	.25
43	Kevin Johnson	3.00
44	Terry Kirby	.25
45	Daylon McCutcheon	1.00
46	Irv Smith	.25
47	Troy Aikman	2.00
48	Michael Irvin	.75
49	Wayne McGarity	2.00
50	Deion Sanders	1.00
51	Emmitt Smith	3.00
52	Terrell Davis	3.00
53	John Elway	3.00
54	Brian Griese	1.50
55	Ed McCaffrey	.75
56	Travis McGriff	2.00
57	Shannon Sharpe	.50
58	Rod Smith	.50
59	Charlie Batch	1.50
60	Chris Claiborne	3.00
61	Sedrick Irvin	3.00
62	Herman Moore	1.00
63	Johnnie Morton	.25
64	Barry Sanders	4.00
65	Aaron Brooks	2.00
66	Mark Chmura	.50
67	Brett Favre	4.00
68	Antonio Freeman	1.00
69	Dorsey Levens	.75
70	De'Mond Parker	1.00
71	Marvin Harrison	.50
72	Edgerrin James	15.00
73	Peyton Manning	3.00
74	Jerome Pathon	.25
75	Mike Peterson	2.00

77	Reggie Barlow	.25
78	Mark Brunell	1.50
79	Keenan McCardell	.50
80	Jimmy Smith	.75
81	Fred Taylor	2.00
82	Mike Cloud	2.00
83	Tony Gonzalez	.50
84	Elvis Grbac	.25
85	Larry Parker	1.00
86	Andre Rison	.50
87	Brian Shay	1.00
88	Karim Abdul	.75
89	Oronde Gadsden	.50
90	James Johnson	3.00
91	Rob Konrad	2.00
92	Dan Marino	3.00
93	O.J. McDuffie	.50
94	Cris Carter	1.00
95	Daunte Culpepper	8.00
96	Randall Cunningham	1.00
97	Jim Kleinsasser	2.00
98	Randy Moss	5.00
99	Jake Reed	.25
100	Robert Smith	.75
101	Drew Bledsoe	1.50
102	Ben Coates	.50
103	Kevin Faulk	5.00
104	Terry Glenn	.75
105	Shawn Jefferson	.25
106	Andy Katzenmoyer	3.00
107	Cameron Cleeland	.50
108	Andre Hastings	.25
109	Billy Joe Tolliver	.25
110	Ricky Williams	15.00
111	Gary Brown	.25
112	Kent Graham	.25
113	Ike Hilliard	.25
114	Joe Montgomery	2.00
115	Amani Toomer	.25
116	Wayne Chrebet	.75
117	Keyshawn Johnson	1.00
118	Leon Johnson	.25
119	Curtis Martin	1.00
120	Vinny Testaverde	.50
121	Dedric Ward	.25
122	Tim Brown	.75
123	Dameane Douglas	2.00
124	Rickey Dudley	.50
125	James Jett	.25
126	Napoleon Kaufman	1.00
127	Charles Woodson	1.00
128	Na Brown	2.00
129	Cecil Martin	2.00
130	Donovan McNabb	8.00
131	Duce Staley	.25
132	Kevin Turner	.25
133	Jerome Bettis	.75
134	Troy Edwards	4.00
135	Courtney Hawkins	.25
136	Malcolm Johnson	2.00
137	Kordell Stewart	1.00
138	Jerame Tuman	1.00
139	Amos Zereoue	4.00
140	Isaac Bruce	1.00
141	Joe Germaine	4.00
142	Torry Holt	5.00
143	Amp Lee	.25
144	Ricky Proehl	.25
145	Freddie Jones	.25
146	Ryan Leaf	1.50
147	Natrone Means	1.00
148	Mikhael Ricks	.25
149	Garrison Hearst	.75
150	Terry Jackson	2.00
151	Terrell Owens	1.00
152	Jerry Rice	2.00
153	J.J. Stokes	.50
154	Steve Young	1.50
155	Karsten Bailey	2.00
156	Joey Galloway	1.00
157	Ahman Green	.50
158	Brock Huard	3.00
159	Jon Kitna	1.00
160	Ricky Watters	.75
161	Mike Alstott	1.00
162	Reidel Anthony	.50
163	Trent Dilfer	.75
164	Warrick Dunn	1.25
165	Shaun King	6.00
166	Anthony McFarland	2.00
167	Kevin Dyson	.50
168	Eddie George	1.25
169	Darran Hall	2.00
170	Steve McNair	1.00
171	Frank Wycheck	.25
172	Stephen Alexander	.25
173	Champ Bailey	2.50
174	Skip Hicks	.50
175	Michael Westbrook	.25

1999 Pacific Revolution Opening Day

This is a parallel to the base set and each single is sequentially numbered to 68.

		MT
Opening Day Cards:		20x-40x
Opening Day Rookies:		5x-10x
Production 68 Sets		

1999 Pacific Revolution Red

This is a parallel to the base set and each single is sequentially numbered to 299.

		MT
Red Cards:		3x-6x
Red Rookies:		2x
Production 299 Sets		

1999 Pacific Revolution Shadow

This is a parallel to the base set and each single is sequentially numbered to 99.

		MT
Shadow Cards:		15x-30x
Shadow Rookies:		4x-8x
Production 99 Sets		

1999 Pacific Revolution Chalk Talk

Each card in this 20-card set has the player pictured on a chalk board with a diagram of an offensive play. Singles were inserted 1:49 packs.

		MT
Complete Set (20):		200.00
Common Player:		5.00
Inserted 1:49		
1	Jake Plummer	10.00
2	Jamal Anderson	5.00
3	Doug Flutie	7.00
4	Tim Couch	25.00
5	Troy Aikman	10.00
6	Emmitt Smith	15.00
7	Terrell Davis	15.00
8	John Elway	15.00
9	Barry Sanders	20.00
10	Brett Favre	20.00
11	Peyton Manning	15.00
12	Mark Brunell	8.00
13	Fred Taylor	10.00
14	Dan Marino	15.00
15	Randy Moss	25.00
16	Drew Bledsoe	8.00
17	Ricky Williams	25.00
18	Jerry Rice	10.00
19	Jon Kitna	5.00
20	Eddie George	7.00

1999 Pacific Revolution Icons

Each card is silver foiled, etched and die-cut. The 10 players in the set were found 1:121 packs.

		MT
Complete Set (10):		275.00
Common Player:		15.00
Inserted 1:121		
1	Emmitt Smith	35.00
2	Terrell Davis	35.00

3	John Elway	35.00
4	Barry Sanders	50.00
5	Brett Favre	50.00
6	Peyton Manning	35.00
7	Dan Marino	35.00
8	Randy Moss	60.00
9	Jerry Rice	25.00
10	Jon Kitna	15.00

1999 Pacific Revolution Showstoppers

The top 36 players in the NFL are in this insert that is etched and includes silver foil on the fronts. Singles were inserted 2:25 packs.

		MT
Complete Set (36):		160.00
Common Player:		2.50
Minor Stars:		5.00
Inserted 2:25		
1	Jake Plummer	7.50
2	Jamal Anderson	2.50
3	Priest Holmes	5.00
4	Doug Flutie	6.00
5	Antowain Smith	5.00
6	Cade McNown	7.00
7	Tim Couch	20.00
8	Corey Dillon	5.00
9	Akili Smith	7.00
10	Troy Aikman	7.50
11	Emmitt Smith	10.00
12	Terrell Davis	10.00
13	John Elway	10.00
14	Charlie Batch	6.00
15	Barry Sanders	15.00
16	Brett Favre	15.00
17	Antonio Freeman	2.50
18	Edgerrin James	10.00
19	Peyton Manning	10.00
20	Mark Brunell	6.00
21	Fred Taylor	7.50
22	Dan Marino	10.00
23	Randall Cunningham	1.50
24	Randy Moss	15.00
25	Drew Bledsoe	6.00
26	Ricky Williams	20.00
27	Curtis Martin	5.00
28	Napoleon Kaufman	5.00
29	Donovan McNabb	7.00
30	Kordell Stewart	5.00
31	Terrell Owens	5.00
32	Jerry Rice	7.50
33	Steve Young	6.00
34	Jon Kitna	5.00
35	Warrick Dunn	6.00
36	Eddie George	6.00

1999 Pacific Revolution Thorn in the Side

Each card is die cut and on the back includes an analysis of how that player has hurt an opposing team. A total of 20 players were used for this insert and were found 1:25 packs.

		MT
Complete Set (20):		125.00
Common Player:		2.50
Minor Stars:		5.00
Inserted 1:25		
1	Jake Plummer	7.50
2	Jamal Anderson	2.50
3	Doug Flutie	6.00
4	Tim Couch	20.00
5	Troy Aikman	7.50
6	Emmitt Smith	10.00
7	Terrell Davis	10.00
8	John Elway	10.00
9	Barry Sanders	15.00
10	Brett Favre	15.00
11	Peyton Manning	10.00
12	Fred Taylor	7.50
13	Dan Marino	10.00
14	Randy Moss	15.00
15	Drew Bledsoe	6.00
16	Ricky Williams	20.00
17	Curtis Martin	5.00
18	Jerome Bettis	2.50
19	Jerry Rice	7.50
20	Jon Kitna	5.00

1961 Packers Lake to Lake

The 36-card, 2-1/2" x 3-1/4" set was issued by Lake to Lake out of Sheboygan, Wis. The card fronts feature a player shot with the card number and the player's number, height, weight and college attended. The card backs give offers for premium upgrades, such as a football or a ceramic figurine. Cards 1-8 and 17-24 are much more difficult to obtain.

		NM
Complete Set (36):		625.00
Common Player (1-8/17-24):		25.00
Common Player (9-16/25-32):		2.50
Common Player (33-36):		5.00
Common SP:		25.00
1	Jerry Kramer (SP)	45.00
2	Norm Masters (SP)	25.00
3	Willie Davis (SP)	50.00
4	Bill Quinlan (SP)	25.00
5	Jim Temp (SP)	25.00
6	Emlen Tunnell (SP)	45.00
7	Gary Knafelc (SP)	25.00
8	Hank Jordan (SP)	45.00
9	Bill Forester	25.00
10	Paul Hornung	15.00
11	Jesse Whittenton	2.50
12	Andy Cverko	2.50
13	Jim Taylor	10.00
14	Hank Gremminger	2.50
15	Tom Moore	3.00
16	John Symank	2.50
17	Max McGee (SP)	40.00
18	Bart Starr (SP)	85.00
19	Ray Nitschke (SP)	65.00
20	Dave Hanner (SP)	30.00
21	Tom Bettis (SP)	25.00
22	Fuzzy Thurston (SP)	30.00
23	Lew Carpenter (SP)	25.00
24	Boyd Dowler (SP)	30.00
25	Ken Iman	2.50
26	Bob Skoronski	2.50
27	Forrest Gregg	7.50
28	Jim Ringo	7.50
29	Ron Kramer	3.00
30	Herb Adderley	12.00
31	Dan Currie	2.50
32	John Roach	2.50
33	Dale Hackbart	5.00
34	Larry Hickman	5.00
35	Nelson Toburen	5.00
36	Willie Wood	12.00

1966 Packers Mobil Posters

The eight-poster, 11" x 14" set features color action art with blank backs. The posters were available with envelopes which gave the art's title and number.

		NM
Complete Set (8):		80.00
Common Player:		10.00
1	The Pass (Bart Starr back to pass)	25.00
2	The Block (Jerry Kramer blocking for Elijah Pitts)	12.00
3	The Punt (Don Chandler punting)	10.00
4	The Sweep (Jim Taylor following blocking)	15.00
5	The Catch (Boyd Dowler)	12.00
6	The Tackle	10.00
7	The Touchdown (Tom Moore scoring)	12.00

8	The Extra Point (Don Chandler with Bart Starr holding)	12.00

1969 Packers Drenks Potato Chip Pins

The 20-pin, 1-1/8" in diameter set were issued by Drenks Potato Chips. The pins have a black and white headshot with green and white backgrounds. "Green Bay Packers" appears on the top edge while the bottom edge has the player's name and position.

		NM
Complete Set (20):		80.00
Common Player:		2.00
1	Herb Adderley	8.00
2	Lionel Aldridge	2.00
3	Donny Anderson	3.00
4	Ken Bowman	2.00
5	Carroll Dale	2.00
6	Willie Davis	8.00
7	Boyd Dowler	3.00
8	Marv Fleming	3.00
9	Gale Gillingham	2.00
10	Jim Grabowski	3.00
11	Forrest Gregg	8.00
12	Don Horn	2.00
13	Bob Jeter	2.00
14	Hank Jordan	8.00
15	Ray Nitschke	10.00
16	Elijah Pitts	3.00
17	Dave Robinson	3.00
18	Bart Starr	16.00
19	Travis Williams	3.00
20	Willie Wood	8.00

1969 Packers Tasco Prints

The seven-piece, 11" x 16" print set features artwork of the player with his name and position, with the backs blank.

		NM
Complete Set (7):		50.00
Common Player:		10.00
1	Donny Anderson	10.00
2	Boyd Dowler	10.00
3	Jim Grabowski	10.00
4	Hank Jordan	15.00
5	Ray Nitschke	25.00
6	Bart Starr	30.00
7	Willie Wood	15.00

1972 Packers Team Issue

The 45-card, 8" x 10" set was printed on glossy paper and featured posed player shots. The card front bottoms have the player's name and position while the backs are blank.

		NM
Complete Set (45):		50.00
Common Player:		2.00
1	Ken Bowman	2.00
2	John Brockington	4.00
3	Bob Brown (DT)	2.00
4	Willie Buchanon	3.00
5	Fred Carr	2.00
6	Jim Carter	2.00
7	Carroll Dale	3.00
8	Carroll Dale (Action pose)	3.00
9	Dan Devine (CO/GM)	3.00
10	Ken Ellis	2.00
11	Len Garrett	2.00
12	Gale Gillingham	2.00
13	Leland Glass	2.00
14	Charlie Hall	2.00
15	Jim Hill	2.00
16	Dick Himes	2.00
17	Bob Hudson (Head shot)	2.00
18	Bob Hudson (Kneeling pose)	2.00
19	Kevin Hunt	2.00
20	Scott Hunter	3.00
21	Dave Kopay	2.00
22	Bob Kroll	2.00
23	Pete Lammons	2.00
24	MacArthur Lane	4.00
25	Bill Lueck	2.00
26	Al Matthews	2.00
27	Mike McCoy	2.00
28	Rich McGeorge	2.00
29	Charlie Napper	2.00
30	Ray Nitschke	10.00
31	Charles Pittman	3.00
32	Malcolm Snider (action pose, Falcons Uniform)	2.00

33	Malcolm Snider (Kneeling pose)	2.00
34	Jon Staggers	3.00
35	Bart Starr	12.00
36	Jerry Tagge	3.00
37	Isaac Thomas (Action pose)	2.00
38	Isaac Thomas (Kneeling pose)	2.00
39	Vern Vanoy	2.00
40	Ron Widby (Action pose, Cowboys uniform)	2.00
41	Ron Widby (Kneeling pose)	2.00
42	Clarence Williams	2.00
43	Perry Williams	2.00
44	Keith Wortman	2.00
45	Coaching Staff (Bart Starr, Hank Kuhlmann, Dave Hanner, Burt Gustafson, John Polonchek, Don Doll, Red, (Rollie Dotsch)	12.00

1974 Packers Team Issue

The 14-card, 6" x 9" set featured the players in posed shots with facsimile autographs and blank backs.

		NM
Complete Set (14):		25.00
Common Player:		3.00
1	John Brockington	5.00
2	Willie Buchanon	4.00
3	Fred Carr	4.00
4	Jim Carter	4.00
5	Jack Concannon	4.00
6	Bill Curry	5.00
7	John Hadl	5.00
8	Bill Lueck	3.00
9	Chester Marcol	4.00
10	Rich McGeorge	4.00
11	Alden Roche	3.00
12	Barry Smith	3.00
13	Barty Smith	3.00
14	Clarence Williams	3.00

1983 Packers Police

The 19-card, 2-5/8" x 4-1/8" set featured action shots on white card stock with three different card backs: First Wisconsin Bank, Waukesha Police and without First Wisconsin Bank, with the latter one being the most rare set. "Packer Tips" are given on the back.

		MT
Complete Set (19):		20.00
Common Player:		1.00
10	Jan Stenerud	2.00
12	Lynn Dickey	1.50
24	Johnnie Gray	1.00
29	Mike McCoy	1.25
31	Gerry Ellis	1.00
40	Eddie Lee Ivery	1.50
52	George Cumby	1.00
53	Mike Douglass	1.25
54	Larry McCarren	1.00
59	John Anderson	1.25
63	Terry Jones	1.00
64	Sid Kitson	1.00
68	Greg Koch	1.00
80	James Lofton	4.00
82	Paul Coffman	1.50
83	John Jefferson	2.00
85	Phillip Epps	1.50
90	Ezra Johnson	1.00
	Bart Starr (CO)	4.00

1984 Packers Police

83 • John Jefferson

The 25-card, 2-5/8" x 4" set was sponsored by First Wisconsin Bank, local law enforce-

ment and the Packers. The card backs contain "Packer Tips."

		MT
Complete Set (25):		10.00
Common Player:		.40
1	John Jefferson	.60
2	Forrest Gregg (CO)	2.00
3	John Anderson	.50
4	Eddie Garcia	.40
5	Tim Lewis	.40
6	Jessie Clark	.40
7	Karl Swanke	.40
8	Lynn Dickey	1.00
9	Eddie Lee Ivery	.60
10	Dick Modzelewski (CO) (Defensive Coord.)	.40
11	Mark Murphy	.40
12	Dave Drechsler	.40
13	Mike Douglass	.40
14	James Lotton	2.50
15	Bucky Scribner	.40
16	Randy Scott	.40
17	Mark Lee	.50
18	Gerry Ellis	.40
19	Terry Jones	.40
20	Bob Schnelker (CO) (Offensive Coord.)	.40
21	George Cumby	.40
22	George Cumby	.40
23	Larry McCarren	.40
24	Sid Kitson	.40
25	Paul Coffman	.50

1985 Packers Police

80 • James Lofton
6'3" Wide Receiver
197 lbs. Stanford

The 25-card, 2-3/4" x 4" set, as with the previous year's, was issued by First Wisconsin Bank, local law enforcement and Green Bay and contains "Packer Tips" on the card backs.

		MT
Complete Set (25):		8.00
Common Player:		.40
1	Forrest Gregg (CO)	1.75
2	Paul Coffman	.60
3	Terry Jones	.40
4	Ron Hallstrom	.40
5	Eddie Lee Ivery	.60
6	John Anderson	.40
7	Tim Lewis	.40
8	Bob Schnelker (CO) (Offensive Corrd.)	.40
9	Al Del Greco	.40
10	Mark Murphy	.40
11	Tim Huffman	.40
12	Del Rodgers	.40
13	Mark Lee	.40
14	Tom Flynn	.40
15	Dick Modzelewski (CO) (Defensive Corrd.)	.40
16	Randy Scott	.40
17	Bucky Scribner	.40
18	George Cumby	.40
19	James Lotton	2.50
20	Mike Douglass	.50
21	Alphonso Carreker	.40
22	Greg Koch	.40
23	Gerry Ellis	.40
24	Ezra Johnson	.40
25	Lynn Dickey	.75

1986 Packers Police

The 25-card, 2-3/4" x 4" set was sponsored by local law enforcement, First Wisconsin Bank and the Packers. The card backs feature player bios and stats, as well as a safety tip.

		MT
Complete Set (25):		8.00
Common Player:		.35
10	Al Del Greco	.35
12	Lynn Dickey	.60
16	Randy Wright	.60
26	Tim Lewis	.35
31	Gerry Ellis	.35
33	Jessie Clark	.35

37	Mark Murphy	.50
40	Eddie Lee Ivery	.50
41	Tom Flynn	.35
42	Gary Ellerson	.35
55	Randy Scott	.35
58	Mark Cannon	.35
59	John Anderson	.50
65	Ron Hallstrom	.35
67	Karl Swanke	.35
76	Alphonso Carreker	.35
80	James Lofton	1.50
82	Paul Coffman	.50
85	Phillip Epps	.50
90	Ezra Johnson	.35
91	Brian Noble	.50
93	Robert Brown	.35
94	Charles Martin	.35
99	John Dorsey	.35
	Forrest Gregg (CO)	1.25

1987 Packers Police

Measuring 2-3/4" x 4", the 22-card set showcased "1987 Packers" at the top, with a photo in the center and the Packers' helmet, player's jersey number and name under the photo. The card backs, printed in green on white paper stock, has the player's name and jersey number at the top, his bio and highlights follow. A safety tip is also included on the back. The cards were sponsored by local law enforcement agencies, the Packers, Employers Health Insurance Co. and Arson Task Force. Approximately 35,000 sets were handed out. Card Nos. 5, 6 and 20 were never distributed as they featured players who were waived or traded before the set was released.

		MT
Complete Set (22):		8.00
Common Player:		.35
1	Forrest Gregg (CO)	1.00
2	George Greene	.35
3	Ron Hallstrom	.35
4	Ezra Johnson	.35
7	Robert Brown	.35
8	Tom Neville	.35
9	Rich Moran	.35
10	Ken Ruettgers	.50
11	Alan Veingrad	.35
12	Mark Lee	.50
13	John Dorsey	.35
14	Paul Ott Carruth	.35
15	Randy Wright	.50
16	Phillip Epps	.50
17	Al Del Greco	.35
18	Tim Harris	1.00
21	Kenneth Davis	1.00
22	John Anderson	.50
23	Mark Murphy	.50
24	Brian Noble	.50
25	Mark Cannon	.35

1988 Packers Police

Measuring 2-3/4" x 4", the 25-card set was anchored by a large photo on the front, with the player's name, number, height, weight and position listed at the bottom. The Packers' helmet appears in the lower right. The card backs included a Packers' helmet at the top, with a "Packers Tips" boxed in section underneath. The set was sponsored by Copps, Brown County Arson Task Force, local law enforcement agencies and the Packers.

		MT
Complete Set (25):		10.00
Common Player:		.40
1	John Anderson	.50
2	Jerry Boyarsky	.40
3	Don Bracken	.40
4	Dave Brown	.40
5	Mark Cannon	.40
6	Alphonso Carreker	.40
7	Paul Ott Carruth	.40
8	Kenneth Davis	.75
9	John Dorsey	.40
10	Brent Fullwood	.40
11	Tiger Greene	.40
12	Ron Hallstrom	.40
13	Tim Harris	.75
14	Johnny Holland	.50
15	Lindy Infante (CO)	.50
16	Mark Lee	.50
17	Don Majkowski	.75
18	Rich Moran	.40
19	Mark Murphy	.40
20	Ken Ruettgers	.50
21	Walter Stanley	.60
22	Keith Uecker	.40

23	Ed West	.50
24	Randy Wright	.40
25	Max Zendejas	.40

1989 Packers Police

Measuring 2-3/4" x 4", the 15-card set showcases a photo on the card front, with the player's name, jersey number, position and year in the league listed below. The Packers' helmet is at the bottom center. The backs have a Packers Tip boxed in the center, with the Packers' logo at the top. The card number is listed at the bottom center of the text box. The front photo is bordered in yellow, with the card printed on white stock.

		MT
Complete Set (15):		5.00
Common Player:		.35
1	Lindy Infante (CO)	.50
2	Don Majkowski	.60
3	Brent Fullwood	.35
4	Mark Lee	.50
5	Dave Brown	.35
6	Mark Murphy	.35
7	Johnny Holland	.50
8	John Anderson	.50
9	Ken Ruettgers	.50
10	Sterling Sharpe	2.00
11	Ed West	.35
12	Walter Stanley	.50
13	Brian Noble	.50
14	Shawn Patterson	.35
15	Tim Harris	.50

1990 Packers Police

Measuring 2-3/4" x 4", the 20-card set is anchored by a large photo on the front. "Packers '90" is printed at the top, with the player's name, number, position and year in the league listed under the photo. The Packers' helmet is located in the lower left.

		MT
Complete Set (20):		5.00
Common Player:		.25
1	Lindy Infante (CO)	.35
2	Keith Woodside	.25
3	Chris Jacke	.35
4	Chuck Cecil	.35
5	Tony Mandarich	.25
6	Brent Fullwood	.25
7	Robert Brown	.25
8	Scott Stephen	.25
9	Anthony Dilweg	.25
10	Mark Murphy	.25
11	Johnny Holland	.35
12	Sterling Sharpe	1.00
13	Tim Harris	.35
14	Ed West	.25
15	Jeff Query	.25
16	Mark Lee	.25
17	Rich Moran	.35
18	Perry Kemp	.25
19	Brian Noble	.35
20	Don Majkowski	.50

1990 Packers 25th Anniversary

Pacific Trading Cards produced this 45-card standard sized set, while Champion Cards released it. The card fronts feature a 25th Anniversary pennant in the upper left, either a color or sepia-toned photo and the player's name and position. The Packers' helmet is pictured in the lower right corner. The backs feature the player's name, position and number at the top. His bio and career highlights are also listed. The card's number is printed in the lower right.

		MT
Complete Set (25):		10.00
Common Player:		.25
1	Introduction Card	.50
2	Bart Starr	2.00
3	Herb Adderley	.75
4	Bob Skoronski	.25
5	Tom Brown	.35
6	Lee Roy Caffey	.35
7	Ray Nitschke	1.00
8	Carroll Dale	.35
9	Jim Taylor	1.25
10	Ken Bowman	.25
11	Gale Gillingham	.25
12	Jim Grabowski	.50
13	Dave Robinson	.50

14	Donny Anderson	.50
15	Willie Wood	.75
16	Zeke Bratkowski	.50
17	Doug Hart	.25
18	Jerry Kramer	.75
19	Marv Fleming	.35
20	Lionel Aldridge	.35
21	Red Mack (UER) (Text reads returned to football before the following season should be retired)	.25
22	Ron Kostelnik	.25
23	Boyd Dowler	.50
24	Vince Lombardi (CO)	1.25
25	Forrest Gregg	.75
26	Max McGee (Superstar)	.35
27	Fuzzy Thurston	.50
28	Bob Brown (DT)	.35
29	Willie Davis	.75
30	Elijah Pitts	.50
31	Hank Jordan	.75
32	Bart Starr	2.00
33	Super Bowl I (Jim Taylor)	.75
34	1996 Packers	.50
35	Max McGee	.50
36	Jim Weatherwax	.25
37	Bob Long	.25
38	Don Chandler	.35
39	Bill Anderson	.35
40	Tommy Crutcher	.35
41	Dave Hathcock	.25
42	Steve Wright	.25
43	Phil Vandersea	.25
44	Bill Curry	.50
45	Bob Jeter	.35

1991 Packers Police

The green-bordered, 20-card set features a yellow banner in the upper left corner of the card front which includes "1991 Packers". The photo is surrounded by a green and yellow border. The player's name and position are printed in the upper right, while his year in the league and his college are printed inside a yellow band at the bottom of the card. The Packers' logo is printed in the lower right of the photo. Numbered "of 20," the card backs feature "1991 Packer Tips". The sponsors' logos appear at the bottom of the standard-sized card backs. Each card back is vertical, except for the Lambeau Field card which is horizontal.

		MT
Complete Set (20):		5.00
Common Player:		.30
1	Lambeau Field	.30
2	Sterling Sharpe	1.00
3	James Campen	.40
4	Chuck Cecil	.40
5	Lindy Infante (CO)	.40
6	Keith Woodside	.30
7	Perry Kemp	.30
8	Johnny Holland	.40
9	Don Majkowski	.40
10	Tony Bennett	.50
11	Leroy Butler	.40
12	Tony Mandarich	.30
13	Darrell Thompson	.40
14	Matt Brock	.30
15	Charles Wilson	.50
16	Brian Noble	.30
17	Ed West	.30
18	Chris Jacke	.30
19	Blair Kiel	.40
20	Mark Murphy	.30

1991 Packers Super Bowl II

The 25th anniversary of the Packers' Super Bowl II victory is honored on this standard-sized 50-card set. The card fronts include a photo which is surrounded by a dark green border. The player's name, Packers' logo and Super Bowl II are located inside a yellow band at the bottom of the card. The card backs feature the player's name, bio and highlights, along with his stats. A photo credit and "Copyright Champion Cards" appear at the bottom left. The card number is printed at the bottom center inside a football.

	MT
Complete Set (50):	10.00
Common Player:	.25
1 Intro Card Super Bowl Trophy	.50
2 Steve Wright	.25
3 Jim Flanigan	.25
4 Tom Brown	.35
5 Tommy Joe Crutcher	.35
6 Doug Hart	.35
7 Bob Hyland	.25
8 John Rowser	.25
9 Bob Skoronski	.25
10 Jim Weatherwax	.25
11 Ben Wilson	.25
12 Don Horn	.35
13 Allen Brown	.25
14 Dick Capp	.25
15 Super Bowl II Action (Donny Anderson)	.50
16 Ice Bowl: The Play (Bart Starr)	1.00
17 Chuck Mercein	.35
18 Herb Adderley	.75
19 Ken Bowman	.25
20 Lee Roy Caffey	.35
21 Carroll Dale	.35
22 Marv Fleming	.35
23 Jim Grabowski	.50
24 Bob Jeter	.35
25 Jerry Kramer	.75
26 Max McGee	.50
27 Elijah Pitts	.50
28 Bart Starr	1.50
29 Fuzzy Thurston	.50
30 Willie Wood	.75
31 Lionel Aldridge	.35
32 Donny Anderson	.50
33 Zeke Bratkowski	.50
34 Bob Brown (DT)	.35
35 Don Chandler	.35
36 Willie Davis	.75
37 Boyd Dowler	.50
38 Gale Gillingham	.35
39 Hank Jordan	.75
40 Ron Kostelnik	.25
41 Vince Lombardi (CO)	1.25
42 Bob Long	.25
43 Ray Nitschke	1.00
44 Dave Robinson	.50
45 Bart Starr (MVP)	1.25
46 Travis Williams	.35
47 1967 Packers Team	.50
48 Ice Bowl Game Summary	.25
49 Ice Bowl	.25
50 NNO Packer Pro Shop	.25

1992 Packers Hall of Fame

This 110-card set, available only at the Packer Hall of Fame Gift Shop, honors 106 members of the Packer Hall of Fame. The card fronts are anchored by a photo inside an oval. The Packers Hall of Fame logo appears in the upper left, with an old Packers' logo in the upper right. The player's name, position and jersey number are included inside a gold rectangle at the bottom of the card, which is bordered in green. Card backs have the player's name in green inside a gold banner at the top. His bio and highlights appear at the center of the horizontal card back. The card number is printed at the bottom center inside a helmet. Card No. 1 does not exist, but two No. 45 cards were printed.

	MT
Complete Set (110):	20.00
Common Player:	.25
2 Red Dunn	.20
3 Mike Michalske	.50
4 Cal Hubbard	.50
5 Johnny (Blood) McNally	.50
6 Verne Lewellen	.10
7 Cub Buck	.10
8 Whitey Woodin	.10
9 Jug Earp	.10
10 Charlie Mathys	.10
11 Andrew Turnbull (PRES)	.10
12 Curly Lambeau (Founder/Coach)	.50
13 George Calhoun (PUB)	.10
14 Boob Darling	.10
15 Eddie Jankowski	.10
16 Swede Johnston	.10
17 George Svendsen	.10
18 Bob Monnett	.10
19 Joe Laws	.10
20 Tiny Engebretsen	.10
21 Milt Gantenbein	.10
22 Hank Bruder	.10
23 Clarke Hinkle	.50
24 Lon Evans	.10
25 Buckets Goldenberg	.10
26 Nate Barrager	.10
27 Arnie Herber	.30
28 Lee Joannes (PRES)	.10
29 Jerry Clifford (VP)	.10
30 Pete Tinsley	.10
31 Buford Ray	.10
32 Andy Uram	.10
33 Larry Craig	.10
34 Charlie Brock	.10
35 Ted Fritsch	.20
36 Lou Brock	.10
37 Carl Mulleneaux	.10
38 Harry Jacunski	.10
39 Cecil Isbell	.30
40 Bud Svendsen	.10
41 Russ Letlow	.10
42 Don Hutson	.75
43 Irv Comp	.10
44 John Martinkovic	.10
45A Bobby Dillon	.20
45B Lavern Dilweg (UER) (Back is that of card 45 card, Bobby Dillon)	.10
46 Wilner Burke (Band Director)	.10
47 Dick Wildung	.10
48 Billy Howton	.30
49 Tobin Rote	.30
50 Jim Ringo	.10
51 Deral Teteak	.10
52 Bob Forte	.50
53 Tony Canadeo	.10
54 Al Carmichael	.10
55 Bob Mann	.10
56 Jack Vainisi (Scout)	.10
57 Ken Bowman	.10
58 Bob Skoronski	.10
59 Dave Hanner	.10
60 Bill Forester	.20
61 Fred Cone	.10
62 Lionel Aldridge	.20
63 Carroll Dale	.20
64 Howard Ferguson	.10
65 Gary Knafelc	.10
66 Ron Kramer	.20
67 Forrest Gregg	.50
68 Phil Bengtson (CO)	.10
69 Dan Currie	.10
70 Al Schneider (Contributor)	.10
71 Bob Jeter	.20
72 Jesse Whittenton	.10
73 Hank Gremminger	.10
74 Ron Kostelnik	.10
75 Gale Gillingham	.20
76 Lee Roy Caffey	.20
77 Hank Jordan	.50
78 Boyd Dowler	.30
79 Fred Carr	.10
80 Bud Jorgensen (TR)	.10
81 Eugene Brusky (Team Physician)	.10
82 Fred Trowbridge (Executive Committee)	.10
83 Jan Stenerud	.50
84 Jerry Atkinson (Contributor)	.10
85 Larry McCarren	.10
86 Fred Leicht (Executive Committee)	.10
87 Max McGee	.30
88 Zeke Bratkowski	.30
89 Dave Robinson	.30
90 Herb Adderley	.50
91 Dominic Olejniczak (President)	.20
92 Jerry Kramer	.50
93 Super Bowl I	.10
94 Don Chandler	.10
95 John Brockington	.30
96 Lynn Dickey	.20
97 Bart Starr	1.00
98 Willie Wood	.50
99 Packer Hall of Fame	.20
100 Donny Anderson	.20
101 Chester Marcol	.20
102 Fuzzy Thurston	.20
103 Paul Hornung	.75
104 Jim Taylor	.75
105 Vince Lombardi (CO)	
106 Willie Davis	.50
107 Ray Nitschke	.50
108 Elijah Pitts	.50
109 NNO Honor Roll (Checklist Card)	.20
110 NNO Packer Hall of Fame (Catalog Order Form)	.20

1992 Packers Police

This unnumbered 20-card set is anchored by a color photo on the front. The backs of the cards have text printed in green on a white background. The logos of the various sponsors also appear. This set has one of the first cards to feature Brett Favre as a Packer.

	MT
Complete Set (20):	10.00
Common Player:	.25
1 Tony Bennett	.50
2 Matt Brock	.25
3 Leroy Butler	.25
4 Vinnie Clark	.35
5 Brett Favre	6.00
6 Jackie Harris	.50
7 Johnny Holland	.25
8 Mike Holmgren (CO)	1.50
9 Chris Jacke	.25
10 Sherman Lewis (CO)	.25
11 Don Majkowski	.35
12 Tony Mandrich	.25
13 Paul McJulien	.25
14 Brian Noble	.35
15 Bryce Paup	2.00
16 Ray Rhodes (CO)	1.00
17 Tootie Robbins	.25
18 Sterling Sharpe	.75
19 Darrell Thompson	.25
20 Ron Wolf (GM)	.35

1993 Packers Archives Postcards

Curly Lambeau • 1919

Measuring 3-1/2" x 5-1/2", this 40-postcard set features Packer players from the team's 75-year history. A photo dominates the card fronts, which are bordered in white. Card fronts also include the Packers' 75th anniversary logo and the player's name and year the photo was taken. The horizontal card backs are divided in half, with the player's name, bio and highlights printed on the left side. The right side of the card back includes the Champion Cards' logo printed over the Vince Lombardi Trophy. The card number is printed inside a football at the bottom center.

	MT
Complete Set (40):	10.00
Common Player:	.50
1 The First Team 1919	.75
2 The 1920s	.50
3 The 1930s	.50
4 The 1940s	.50
5 The 1950s	.50
6 The 1960s	.50
7 The 1970s	.50
8 The 1980s	.50
9 The 1990s	.50
10 Curly Lambeau (1919)	.75
11 Jim Ringo (1953)	.75
12 Ice Bowl 1967	.75
13 Jerry Kramer (1958)	.75
14 Ray Nitschke (1958)	1.00
15 Fuzzy Thurston (1959)	.75
16 James Lofton (1978-86)	.75
17 Super Bowl I Action	.75
18 Don Hutson (1935-45)	1.00
19 Tony Canadeo (1941-43, 46-52)	.75
20 Bobby Dillon (1952-59)	.50
21 The Quarterback	.75
22 Willie Wood (1960-71)	.75
23 Dave Beverly (1975-80)	.50
24 James Lofton (1978)	.75
25 Tim Harris (1986-90)	.75
26 1929 Championship Team	.50
27 1930 Championship Team	.50
28 1931 Championship Team	.50
29 1936 Championship Team	.50
30 1939 Championship Team	.50
31 1944 Championship Team	.50
32 1961 Championship Team	.75
33 1962 Championship Team	.75
34 1965 Championship Team	.75
35 1966 Championship Team	.75
36 1967 Championship Team	.75
37 Old City Stadium	.50
38 New City Stadium	.50
39 Lambeau Field-1992	.50
40 NNO Title Card (3-3/4" x 5-3/4")	.75

1993 Packers Police

CELEBRATING 75 SEASONS OF PRO FOOTBALL 1919-1993

The 20-card set is bordered in white on the front, with a color photo anchoring it. The Packers' 75th anniversary logo appears inside the photo in the upper left. "Celebrating 75 seasons of Pro Football 1919-1993" is printed under the photo. The vertical card backs have the Packers' helmet in the upper left, with the player's name, position, year in the league and college listed to the right. Elementary students' saftey tips are printed in the center of the card. The card number "of 20" is located under the tip. Various sponsor logos appear at the bottom of the card backs.

	MT
Complete Set (20):	8.00
Common Player:	.25
1 Ron Wolf (GM)	.25
2 Wayne Simmons	.35
3 James Campen	.25
4 Matt Brock	.25
5 Mike Holmgren (CO)	1.00
6 Brian Noble	.35
7 Ken O'Brien	.35
8 George Teague	.35
9 Brett Favre	4.00
10 LeRoy Butler	.35
11 Harry Galbreath	.25
12 Chris Jacke	.35
13 Sterling Sharpe	.75
14 Terrell Buckley	.35
15 Ken Ruettgers	.35
16 Johnny Holland	.35
17 Edgar Bennett	1.50
18 Jackie Harris	.50
19 Tony Bennett	.50
20 Reggie White	1.50

1994 Packers Police

The 20-card set includes a color photo on the front, with "1994 Green Bay Packers" printed at the top. The player's name and jersey number are printed inside a green band under the photo. Numbered "of 20," has the Packers' logo in the upper left, with the player's number, name, position, year in the league and college listed to the right. A student tip is printed in the center of the card back. Logos from the various sponsors are printed at the bottom.

	MT
Complete Set (20):	8.00
Common Player:	.30
1 Sherman Lewis	.30
2 Sterling Sharpe	.75
3 Ken Ruettgers	.40
4 Reggie White	1.00
5 Edgar Bennett	1.00
6 Fritz Shurmur (CO)	.40
7 Brett Favre	3.00
8 John Jurkovic	.50
9 Robert Brooks	2.00
10 Reggie Cobb	.30
11 Bryce Paup	.75
12 Harry Galbreath	.30
13 Mike Holmgren (CO)	.50
14 Ed West	.30
15 Sean Jones	.50
16 Ron Wolf (GM)	.30
17 Chris Jacke	.40
18 Wayne Simmons	.40
19 LeRoy Butler	.30
20 George Teague	.40

1995 Packers Safety Fritsch

Produced by Larry Fritsch Cards, the 20-card set showcases a color photo on the front, with "Packers" printed vertically along the left side inside a ghosted area. A 1995 diamond logo is located at the upper left. The player's name and number are printed inside a yellow stripe at the bottom. The cards are bordered in green on the front. Card backs feature the player's name, number, position, year in the league and college at the top, with a student tip printed below it. The card number "of 20" is printed in the lower center, above the various sponsors' names.

	MT
Complete Set (20):	8.00
Common Player:	.30
1 Mike Holmgren (CO)	.40
2 Ron Wolf (VP/GM)	.30
3 Brett Favre	3.00
4 Ty Detmer	1.00
5 Chris Jacke	.50
6 Craig Hentrich	.30
7 Craig Newsome	.30
8 George Teague	.50
9 Edgar Bennett	1.00
10 LeRoy Butler	.50
11 George Koonce	.30
12 John Jurkovic	.50
13 Aaron Taylor	.30
14 Ken Ruettgers	.30
15 Robert Brooks	1.50
16 Mark Chmura	1.50
17 Reggie White	1.00
18 Doug Evans	.30
19 Sean Jones	.50
20 Wayne Simmons	.50

1996 Packers Police

The 20-card standard-sized set features a photo of the player placed over a two-toned green background. "Packers 1996" is featured at the top, while "1995 Central Division Champions" is printed in yellow along the right side of the card. The player's name is printed in yellow in the lower left. The card backs, numbered "of 20," has the player's name position, jersey number and university at the top. A student tip is located in the center, with the card number underneath it. The various sponsors are listed at the bottom.

	MT
Complete Set (20):	8.00
Common Player:	.30
1 Edgar Bennett	.30
2 Robert Brooks	.50
3 Gilbert Brown	.75
4 LeRoy Butler	.30
5 Mark Chmura	.50
6 Santana Dotson	.30
7 Doug Evans	.30
8 Brett Favre	3.00
9 Antonio Freeman	.75
10 Craig Hendricks	.30
11 Chris Jacke	.30
12 Wayne Simmons	.30
13 George Koonce	.30
14 Craig Newsome	.30
15 Ron Wolf	.50
16 Ken Ruettgers	.20
17 Keith Jackson	.30
18 Aaron Taylor	.30
19 Reggie White	1.00
20 Mike Holmgren	.50

1997 Packers Playoff

This 50-card set commemorates the Packers' Super Bowl XXXI victory. The card fronts contain a color action shot and the Super Bowl logo. The backs have player information and the final score of the Super Bowl with the Superdome as the background.

	MT
Complete Set (50):	30.00
Common Player:	.40
1 Super Bowl XXXI Champions (Scoreboard Photo)	.50
2 Brett Favre MVP	3.00
3 Minister of Defense (Reggie White)	1.50
4 Desmond Howard MVP	.50
5 NFC Championship Trophy Presentation	.40
6 Mike Holmgren CO	.50
7 Brett Favre	5.00
8 Chris Jacke	.40
9 Craig Hentrich	.40
10 Craig Newsome	.50
11 Dorsey Levens	2.00
12 Doug Evans	.40
13 Edgar Bennett	.50
14 Leroy Butler	.50
15 Eugene Robinson	.40
16 Brian Williams	.40
17 Frank Winters	.40
18 Ron Cox	.40
19 Wayne Simmons	.50
20 Adam Timmerman	.40
21 Bruce Wilkerson	.40
22 Santana Dotson	.40
23 Earl Dotson	.40
24 Aaron Taylor	.40
25 Desmond Howard	.50
26 Don Beebe	.50
27 Andre Rison	.50
28 Antonio Freeman	2.00
29 Terry Mickens	.40
30 Keith Jackson	.50
31 Mark Chmura	1.00
32 Reggie White	1.50
33 Gilbert Brown	.50
34 Sean Jones	.50
35 Robert Brooks, George Koonce	.75
36 Derrick Mayes, Gary Brown	.50
37 Jim McMahon	.50
38 William Henderson	.40
39 Travis Jervey, Roderick Mullen	.50
40 Tyrone Williams	.40
41 John Michels	.50
42 Mike Prior	.40
43 Calvin Jones, Jeff Thomason	.40
44 Brett Favre	3.00
45 Jeff Dellenbach	.40
46 Bernardo Harris	.40
47 Darius Holland	.40
48 Lamont Hollinquest	.40
49 Lindsay Knapp	.40
50 Gabe Wilkins	.40

A player's name in *italic type* indicates a rookie card.

1997 Packers Police

This 20-card Packers set boasts the Vince Lombardi Trophy in the lower right and the words "96 Super Bowl Champs" down the right side. Fronts capture a color photo of the player cut out over a purple background, with the player's name down the left side in a vertical gold strip. Card backs are numbered "of 20" and have the player's name, number, position, college and various sponsors. Included in the background is a photo of the Packers' three Super Bowl trophies.

		MT
Complete Set (20):		8.00
Common Player:		.30
1	Super Bowl XXXI Trophy	.50
2	Mike Holmgren	.50
3	Ron Wolf	.50
4	Brett Favre	3.00
5	Reggie White	1.00
6	LeRoy Butler	.30
7	Frank Winters	.30
8	Aaron Taylor	.30
9	Robert Brooks	.50
10	Gilbert Brown	.75
11	Mark Chmura	.50
12	Earl Dotson	.30
13	Santana Dotson	.30
14	Doug Evans	.30
15	Antonio Freeman	.75
16	William Henderson	.30
17	Craig Hentrich	.30
18	Dorsey Levens	1.00
19	Craig Newsome	.30
20	Edgar Bennett	.30

1988 Panini Stickers

These stickers, which each measure 2-1/8" x 2-3/4", were made to be stored in a special collector's album which was produced. John Elway is featured on the cover of the album, which has the stickers arranged on pages according to the way they are numbered. The sticker number appears on both sides of the sticker. The front of the sticker has a close-up shot of the player, between two team color-coded bars. His team's name is above the photo; his name is below the photo. The stickers were sold in packs which also included one of three types of foil stickers - team name stickers, team helmet stickers, and team uniform stickers. Each team name sticker was produced with a player sticker, listed in parenthesis. Backs for the team name stickers had a referee signal, while helmet foils had a stadium shot and uniform foils had a mascot cartoon on the back.

		MT
Complete Set (447):		35.00
Common Player:		.05
1	Super Bowl XXII Program Cover	.15
2	Bills Helmet	.05
3	Bills Action	.05
4	Cornelius Bennett	.50
5	Chris Burkett	.05
6	Derrick Burroughs	.05
7	Shane Conlan	.25
8	Ronnie Harmon	.25
9	Jim Kelly	.80
10	Buffalo Bills	.05
11	Mark Kelso	.05
12	Nate Odomes	.05
13	Andre Reed	.25
14	Fred Smerlas	.10
15	Bruce Smith	.25
16	Uniform	.05
17	Bengals Helmet	.05
18	Bengals Action	.05
19	Jim Breech	.05
20	James Brooks	.10
21	Eddie Brown	.10
22	Cris Collinsworth	.10
23	Boomer Esiason	.20
24	Rodney Holman	.10
25	Bengals	.05
26	Larry Kinnebrew	.05
27	Tim Krumrie	.05
28	Anthony Munoz	.15
29	Reggie Williams	.10
30	Carl Zander	.05
31	Uniform	.05
32	Browns Helmet	.05
33	Browns Action	.15
34	Earnest Byner	.10
35	Hanford Dixon	.05
36	Bob Golic	.10
37	Mike Johnson	.05
38	Bernie Kosar	.30
39	Kevin Mack	.10
40	Browns	.05
41	Clay Matthews	.15
42	Gerald McNeil	.05
43	Frank Minnifield	.05
44	Ozzie Newsome	.15
45	Cody Risien	.05
46	Uniform	.05
47	Broncos Helmet	.05
48	Broncos Action	.05
49	Keith Bishop	.05
50	Tony Dorsett	.35
51	John Elway	1.25
52	Simon Fletcher	.25
53	Mark Jackson	.10
54	Vance Johnson	.10
55	Broncos	.05
56	Rulon Jones	.05
57	Rick Karlis	.05
58	Karl Mecklenburg	.10
59	Ricky Nattiel	.10
60	Sammy Winder	.05
61	Uniform	.05
62	Oilers Helmet	.05
63	Oilers Action	.25
64	Keith Bostic	.05
65	Steve Brown	.05
66	Ray Childress	.15
67	Jeff Donaldson	.05
68	John Grimsley	.05
69	Robert Lyles	.05
70	Oilers	.05
71	Drew Hill	.10
72	Warren Moon	.85
73	Mike Munchak	.15
74	Mike Rozier	.10
75	Johnny Meads	.05
76	Uniform	.05
77	Colts Helmet	.05
78	Colts Action	.15
79	Albert Bentley	.10
80	Dean Biasucci	.05
81	Duane Bickett	.15
82	Bill Brooks	.15
83	Johnny Cooks	.05
84	Eric Dickerson	.40
85	Colts	.05
86	Ray Donaldson	.05
87	Chris Hinton	.10
88	Cliff Odom	.05
89	Barry Krauss	.10
90	Jack Trudeau	.15
91	Uniform	.05
92	Chiefs Helmet	.05
93	Chiefs Action	.05
94	Carlos Carson	.05
95	Deron Cherry	.10
96	Dino Hackett	.05
97	Bill Kenney	.05
98	Albert Lewis	.10
99	Nick Lowery	.10
100	Chiefs	.05
101	Bill Maas	.05
102	Christian Okoye	.15
103	Stephone Paige	.10
104	Paul Palmer	.05
105	Kevin Ross	.10
106	Uniform	.05
107	Raiders Helmet	.05
108	Raiders Action	.25
109	Marcus Allen	.35
110	Todd Christensen	.15
111	Mike Haynes	.15
112	Bo Jackson	.60
113	James Lofton	.20
114	Howie Long	.15
115	Raiders	.05
116	Rod Martin	.05
117	Vann McElroy	.05
118	Bill Pickel	.05
119	Don Mosebar	.05
120	Stacey Toran	.05
121	Uniform	.05
122	Dolphins Helmet	.05
123	Dolphins Action	.05
124	John Bosa	.05
125	Mark Clayton	.15
126	Mark Duper	.05
127	Lorenzo Hampton	.05
128	William Judson	.05
129	Dan Marino	2.50
130	Dolphins	.05
131	John Offerdahl	.05
132	Reggie Roby	.05
133	Jackie Shipp	.05
134	Dwight Stephenson	.10
135	Troy Stradford	.10
136	Uniform	.05
137	Patriots Helmet	.05
138	Patriots Action	.05
139	Bruce Armstrong	.05
140	Raymond Clayborn	.05
141	Reggie Dupard	.05
142	Steve Grogan	.10
143	Craig James	.25
144	Ronnie Lippett	.05
145	Patriots	.05
146	Fred Marion	.05
147	Stanley Morgan	.15
148	Mosi Tatupu	.05
149	Andre Tippett	.10
150	Garin Veris	.05
151	Uniform	.05
152	Jets Helmet	.05
153	Jets Action	.05
154	Bob Crable	.05
155	Mark Gastineau	.10
156	Pat Leahy	.05
157	Johnny Hector	.10
158	Marty Lyons	.10
159	Freeman McNeil	.15
160	Jets	.05
161	Ken O'Brien	.10
162	Mickey Shuler	.05
163	Al Toon	.10
164	Roger Vick	.05
165	Wesley Walker	.10
166	Uniform	.05
167	Steelers Helmet	.05
168	Steelers Action	.05
169	Walter Abercrombie	.05
170	Gary Anderson	.05
171	Todd Blackledge	.05
172	Thomas Everett	.15
173	Delton Hall	.05
174	Bryan Hinkle	.05
175	Steelers	.05
176	Earnest Jackson	.10
177	Louis Lipps	.10
178	David Little	.05
179	Mike Merriweather	.10
180	Mike Webster	.15
181	Uniform	.05
182	Chargers Helmet	.05
183	Chargers Action	.05
184	Gary Anderson	.15
185	Chip Banks	.10
186	Martin Bayless	.05
187	Chuck Ehin	.05
188	Venice Glenn	.05
189	Lionel James	.05
190	Chargers	.05
191	Mark Malone	.05
192	Ralf Mojsiejenko	.05
193	Billy Ray Smith	.10
194	Lee Williams	.15
195	Kellen Winslow	.15
196	Uniform	.05
197	Seahawks Helmet	.05
198	Seahawks Action	.10
199	Eugene Robinson	.05
200	Jeff Bryant	.05
201	Ray Butler	.05
202	Jacob Green	.10
203	Norm Johnson	.10
204	Dave Krieg	.10
205	Seahawks	.05
206	Steve Largent	.75
207	Joe Nash	.05
208	Curt Warner	.10
209	Bobby Joe Edmonds	.10
210	Daryl Turner	.05
211	Uniform	.05
212	AFC Logo	.05
213	Bernie Kosar	.35
214	Curt Warner	.10
215	Jerry Rice, Steve Largent	1.25
216	Mark Bavaro, Anthony Munoz	.15
217	Gary Zimmerman, Bill Fralic	.10
218	Dwight Stephenson, Mike Munchak	.10
219	Joe Montana, Charles White, Eric Dickerson	3.00
220	Charles White, Eric Dickerson	.40
221	Morten Andersen, Vai Sikahema	.10
222	Bruce Smith, Reggie White	.30
223	Michael Carter, Steve McMichael	.10
224	Jim Arnold	.05
225	Carl Banks, Andre Tippett	.10
226	Barry Wilburn, Mike Singletary	.10
227	Hanford Dixon, Frank Minnifield	.05
228	Ronnie Lott, Joey Browner	.15
229	NFC Logo	.05
230	Gary Clark	.15
231	Richard Dent	.15
232	Falcons Helmet	.05
233	Falcons Action	.05
234	Rick Bryan	.10
235	Bobby Butler	.05
236	Tony Casillas	.15
237	Floyd Dixon	.05
238	Rick Donnelly	.05
239	Bill Fralic	.10
240	Falcons	.05
241	Mike Gann	.05
242	Chris Miller	.40
243	Robert Moore	.05
244	John Rade	.05
245	Gerald Riggs	.10
246	Uniform	.05
247	Bears Helmet	.05
248	Bears Action	.15
249	Neal Anderson	.30
250	Jim Covert	.10
251	Richard Dent	.15
252	Dave Duerson	.05
253	Dennis Gentry	.05
254	Jay Hilgenberg	.10
255	Bears	.05
256	Jim McMahon	.20
257	Steve McMichael	.10
258	Matt Suhey	.05
259	Mike Singletary	.20
260	Otis Wilson	.10
261	Uniform	.05
262	Cowboys Helmet	.05
263	Cowboys Action	.15
264	Bill Bates	.10
265	Doug Crosbie	.05
266	Ron Francis	.05
267	Jim Jeffcoat	.05
268	Ed "Too Tall" Jones	.20
269	Eugene Lockhart	.05
270	Cowboys	.05
271	Danny Noonan	.05
272	Steve Pelleur	.10
273	Herschel Walker	.10
274	Everson Walls	.20
275	Randy White	.05
276	Uniform	.05
277	Lions Helmet	.05
278	Lions Action	.05
279	Jim Arnold	.10
280	Jerry Ball	.05
281	Michael Cofer	.05
282	Keith Ferguson	.05
283	Dennis Gibson	.05
284	James Griffin	.05
285	Lions	.05
286	James Jones	.10
287	Chuck Long	.10
288	Pete Mandley	.05
289	Eddie Murray	.05
290	Garry James	.05
291	Uniform	.05
292	Packers Helmet	.05
293	Packers Action	.05
294	John Anderson	.05
295	Dave Brown	.10
296	Alphonso Carreker	.05
297	Kenneth Davis	.20
298	Phillip Epps	.05
299	Brent Fullwood	.05
300	Packers	.05
301	Tim Harris	.15
302	Johnny Holland	.10
303	Mark Murphy	.05
304	Brian Noble	.05
305	Walter Stanley	.10
306	Uniform	.05
307	Rams Helmet	.05
308	Rams Action	.05
309	Jim Collins	.05
310	Henry Ellard	.15
311	Jim Everett	.30
312	Jerry Gray	.05
313	LeRoy Irvin	.05
314	Mike Lansford	.05
315	Los Angeles Rams	.05
316	Mel Owens	.05
317	Jackie Slater	.10
318	Doug Smith	.05
319	Charles White	.10
320	Mike Wilcher	.05
321	Uniform	.05
322	Vikings Helmet	.05
323	Vikings Action	.05
324	Joey Browner	.10
325	Anthony Carter	.15
326	Chris Doleman	.15
327	D.J. Dozier	.10
328	Steve Jordan	.10
329	Tommy Kramer	.10
330	Vikings	.05
331	Darrin Nelson	.10
332	Jesse Solomon	.10
333	Scott Studwell	.10
334	Wade Wilson	.35
335	Gary Zimmerman	.10
336	Uniform	.05
337	Saints Helmet	.05
338	Saints Action	.15
339	Morten Andersen	.15
340	Bruce Clark	.05
341	Brad Edelman	.05
342	Bobby Hebert	.15
343	Dalton Hilliard	.10
344	Rickey Jackson	.15
345	Saints	.05
346	Vaughan Johnson	.10
347	Rueben Mayes	.10
348	Sam Mills	.10
349	Lionel Manuel	.35
350	Dave Waymer	.05
351	Uniform	.05
352	Giants Helmet	.05
353	Giants Action	.05
354	Carl Banks	.15
355	Mark Bavaro	.15
356	Jim Burt	.10
357	Harry Carson	.10
358	Terry Kinard	.05
359	Lionel Manuel	.05
360	Giants	.05
361	Leonard Marshall	.10
362	George Martin	.05
363	Joe Morris	.10
364	Phil Simms	.50
365	George Adams	.05
366	Uniform	.05
367	Eagles Helmet	.05
368	Eagles Action	.25
369	Jerome Brown	.30
370	Keith Byars	.15
371	Randall Cunningham	.40
372	Terry Hoage	.05
373	Seth Joyner	.20
374	Mike Quick	.15
375	Eagles	.05
376	Clyde Simmons	.20
377	Anthony Toney	.05
378	Andre Waters	.10
379	Reggie White	.35
380	Roynell Young	.05
381	Uniform	.05
382	Cardinals Helmet	.05
383	Cardinals Action	.05
384	Robert Awalt	.05
385	Roy Green	.15
386	Neil Lomax	.10
387	Stump Mitchell	.05
388	Niko Noga	.06
389	Freddie Joe Nunn	.05
390	Cardinals	.05
391	Luis Sharpe	.10
392	Vai Sikahema	.10
393	J.T. Smith	.10
394	Leonard Smith	.05
395	Lonnie Young	.05
396	Uniform	.05
397	49ers Helmet	.05
398	49ers Action	1.50
399	Dwaine Board	.05
400	Michael Carter	.10
401	Roger Craig	.25
402	Jeff Fuller	.05
403	Don Griffin	.05
404	Ronnie Lott	.20
405	49ers	.05
406	Joe Montana	3.00
407	Tom Rathman	.25
408	Jerry Rice	1.50
409	Keena Turner	.05
410	Michael Walter	.05
411	Uniform	.05
412	Bucs Helmet	.05
413	Bucs Action	.05
414	Mark Carrier	.25
415	Gerald Carter	.05
416	Ron Holmes	.10
417	Rod Jones	.05
418	Calvin Magee	.05
419	Ervin Randle	.05
420	Buccaneers	.05
421	Donald Igwebuike	.05
422	Vinny Testaverde	.25
423	Jackie Walker	.05
424	Chris Washington	.05
425	James Wilder	.10
426	Uniform	.05
427	Redskins Helmet	.05
428	Redskins Action	.10
429	Gary Clark	.15
430	Monte Coleman	.05
431	Darrell Green	.15
432	Charles Mann	.10
433	Kelvin Bryant	.10
434	Art Monk	.25
435	Redskins	.05
436	Ricky Sanders	.15
437	Jay Schroeder	.15
438	Alvin Walton	.05
439	Barry Wilburn	.05
440	Doug Williams	.10
441	Uniform	.05
442	Super Bowl Action	.05
443	Super Bowl Action	.05
444	Doug Williams (Super Bowl MVP)	.15
445	Super Bowl Action	.05
446	Super Bowl Action	.05
447	Super Bowl Action	.05
----	Panini Album (John Elway on cover)	2.00

1989 Panini Stickers

LLOYD BURRUSS

These 1989 stickers from Panini are slightly larger than those issued in 1988, measuring 1-15/16" x 3."

		MT
Complete Set (416):		30.00
Common Player:		.05
1	SB XXIII Program	.10
2	SB XXIII Program	.05
3	Floyd Dixon	.05
4	Tony Casillas	.10
5	Bill Fralic	.10
6	Aundray Bruce	.05
7	Scott Case	.05
8	Rick Donnelly	.05
9	Atlanta logo	.05
10	Helmet	.05
11	Marcus Cotton	.05
12	Chris Miller	.25
13	Robert Moore	.05
14	Bobby Butler	.05
15	Rick Bryan	.05
16	John Settle	.10
17	Jim McMahon	.15
18	Neal Anderson	.15
19	Dave Duerson	.05
20	Steve McMichael	.05
21	Jay Hilgenberg	.05
22	Dennis McKinnon	.05
23	Chicago logo	.05
24	Helmet	.05
25	Richard Dent	.15
26	Dennis Gentry	.05
27	Mike Singletary	.15
28	Vestee Jackson	.05
29	Mike Tomczak	.15
30	Dan Hampton	.15
31	Michael Irvin	1.75
32	Eugene Lockhart	.10
33	Herschel Walker	.30
34	Kelvin Martin	.15
35	Jim Jeffcoat	.10
36	Everson Walls	.10
37	Dallas logo	.05
38	Helmet	.05
39	Danny Noonan	.05
40	Ray Alexander	.05
41	Garry Cobb	.05
42	Ed "Too Tall" Jones	.15
43	Kevin Brooks	.05
44	Bill Bates	.10
45	Detroit logo	.05
46	Chuck Long	.10
47	Jim Arnold	.05
48	Michael Cofer	.05
49	Eddie Murray	.05
50	Keith Ferguson	.05
51	Pete Mandley	.05
52	Helmet	.05
53	Jerry Ball	.05
54	Bennie Blades	.15
55	Dennis Gibson	.05
56	Chris Spielman	.15
57	Eric Williams	.05
58	Lomas Brown	.05
59	Johnny Holland	.05
60	Tim Harris	.05
61	Mark Murphy	.05
62	Walter Stanley	.05
63	Brent Fullwood	.05
64	Ken Ruettgers	.10
65	Green Bay logo	.05
66	Helmet	.05
67	John Anderson	.05
68	Brian Noble	.05
69	Sterling Sharpe	1.50
70	Keith Woodside	.10
71	Mark Lee	.05
72	Don Majkowski	.15
73	Aaron Cox	.05
74	LeRoy Irvin	.05
75	Jim Everett	.15
76	Mike Lansford	.05
77	Mike Wilcher	.05
78	Henry Ellard	.10
79	Rams helmet	.05
80	Jerry Gray	.05
81	Doug Smith	.05
82	Tom Newberry	.10
83	Jackie Slater	.05
84	Greg Bell	.10
85	Kevin Greene	.10
86	Chris Doleman	.10
87	Steve Jordan	.10
88	Jesse Solomon	.05
89	Randall McDaniel	.05
90	Hassan Jones	.05
91	Joey Browner	.10
92	Vikings logo	.05
93	Helmet	.05
94	Anthony Carter	.10
95	Gary Zimmerman	.05
96	Wade Wilson	.15
97	Scott Studwell	.05
98	Keith Millard	.10
99	Carl Lee	.05
100	Morten Andersen	.10
101	Bobby Hebert	.15
102	Rueben Mayes	.10
103	Sam Mills	.10
104	Vaughan Johnson	.10
105	Pat Swilling	.15
106	Saints logo	.05
107	Helmet	.05
108	Brad Edelman	.05
109	Craig Heyward	.15
110	Eric Martin	.10
111	Dalton Hilliard	.05
112	Lonzell Hill	.05
113	Rickey Jackson	.10
114	Erik Howard	.05
115	Phil Simms	.35

#	Player	Price
116	Leonard Marshall	.10
117	Joe Morris	.10
118	Bart Oates	.10
119	Mark Bavaro	.10
120	Giants logo	.05
121	Helmet	.05
122	Terry Kinard	.05
123	Carl Banks	.10
124	Lionel Manuel	.05
125	Stephen Baker	.15
126	Pepper Johnson	.10
127	Jim Burt	.05
128	Cris Carter	.35
129	Mike Quick	.10
130	Terry Hoage	.05
131	Keith Jackson	.80
132	Clyde Simmons	.15
133	Eric Allen	.05
134	Eagles logo	.05
135	Helmet	.05
136	Randall Cunningham	.40
137	Mike Pitts	.05
138	Keith Byars	.10
139	Seth Joyner	.15
140	Jerome Brown	.15
141	Reggie White	.30
142	Jay Novacek	.30
143	Neil Lomax	.10
144	Ken Harvey	.10
145	Freddie Joe Nunn	.05
146	Robert Awalt	.05
147	Niko Noga	.05
148	Phoenix logo	.05
149	Helmet	.05
150	Tim McDonald	.25
151	Roy Green	.10
152	Stump Mitchell	.10
153	J.T. Smith	.10
154	Luis Sharpe	.05
155	Vai Sikahema	.10
156	Jeff Fuller	.05
157	Joe Montana	3.00
158	Harris Barton	.05
159	Michael Carter	.10
160	Jeff Fuller	.05
161	Jerry Rice	2.00
162	49ers logo	.05
163	Helmet	.05
164	Tom Rathman	.15
165	Roger Craig	.20
166	Ronnie Lott	.30
167	Charles Haley	.15
168	John Taylor	.50
169	Michael Walter	.05
170	Ron Hall	.05
171	Ervin Randle	.05
172	James Wilder	.10
173	Ron Holmes	.05
174	Mark Carrier	.15
175	William Howard	.05
176	Tampa Bay logo	.05
177	Helmet	.05
178	Lars Tate	.05
179	Vinny Testaverde	.20
180	Paul Gruber	.15
181	Bruce Hill	.10
182	Reuben Davis	.05
183	Ricky Reynolds	.05
184	Ricky Sanders	.15
185	Gary Clark	.15
186	Mark May	.05
187	Darrell Green	.10
188	Jim Lachey	.10
189	Doug Williams	.10
190	Helmet	.05
191	Redskins logo	.05
192	Kelvin Bryant	.05
193	Charles Mann	.05
194	Alvin Walton	.05
195	Art Monk	.20
196	Barry Wilburn	.05
197	Mark Rypien	.25
198	NFC logo	.05
199	Scott Case	.05
200	Herschel Walker	.30
201	Herschel Walker, Roger Craig	.25
202	Henry Ellard, Jerry Rice	.65
203	Bruce Matthews, Tom Newberry	.05
204	Gary Zimmerman, Anthony Munoz	.10
205	Boomer Esiason	.15
206	Jay Hilgenberg	.10
207	Keith Jackson	.25
208	Reggie White, Bruce Smith	.25
209	Keith Millard, Tim Krumrie	.10
210	Carl Lee, Frank Minnifield	.05
211	Joey Browner, Deron Cherry	.10
212	Shane Conlan	.10
213	Mike Singletary	.15
214	Cornelius Bennett	.10
215	AFC logo	.05
216	Boomer Esiason	.25
217	Erik McMillan	.05
218	Jim Kelly	.60
219	Cornelius Bennett	.15
220	Fred Smerlas	.10
221	Shane Conlan	.05
222	Scott Norwood	.05
223	Mark Kelso	.05
224	Bills logo	.05

#	Player	Price
225	Helmet	.05
226	Thurman Thomas	1.50
227	Pete Metzelaars	.05
228	Bruce Smith	.25
229	Art Still	.10
230	Kent Hull	.10
231	Andre Reed	.25
232	Tim Krumrie	.05
233	Boomer Esiason	.25
234	Ickey Woods	.10
235	Eric Thomas	.05
236	Rodney Holman	.10
237	Jim Skow	.05
238	Bengals helmet	.05
239	James Brooks	.10
240	David Fulcher	.10
241	Carl Zander	.05
242	Eddie Brown	.10
243	Max Montoya	.05
244	Anthony Munoz	.15
245	Felix Wright	.05
246	Clay Matthews	.15
247	Hanford Dixon	.05
248	Ozzie Newsome	.15
249	Bernie Kosar	.25
250	Kevin Mack	.10
251	Bengals Helmet	.05
252	Brian Brennan	.05
253	Reggie Langhorne	.05
254	Cody Risien	.05
255	Webster Slaughter	.15
256	Mike Johnson	.05
257	Frank Minnifield	.05
258	Mike Horan	.05
259	Dennis Smith	.10
260	Ricky Nattiel	.05
261	Karl Mecklenburg	.10
262	Keith Bishop	.05
263	John Elway	1.50
264	Broncos helmet	.05
265	Broncos logo	.05
266	Simon Fletcher	.15
267	Vance Johnson	.10
268	Tony Dorsett	.35
269	Greg Kragen	.10
270	Mike Harden	.05
271	Mark Jackson	.05
272	Warren Moon	.75
273	Mike Rozier	.10
274	Houston logo	.05
275	Allen Pinkett	.10
276	Tony Zendejas	.05
277	Alonzo Highsmith	.05
278	Johnny Meads	.05
279	Helmet	.05
280	Mike Munchak	.10
281	John Grimsley	.05
282	Ernest Givins	.15
283	Drew Hill	.10
284	Bruce Matthews	.05
285	Ray Childress	.10
286	Colts logo	.05
287	Chris Hinton	.10
288	Clarence Verdin	.10
289	Jon Hand	.05
290	Chris Chandler	.15
291	Eugene Daniel	.05
292	Dean Biasucci	.05
293	Helmet	.05
294	Duane Bickett	.10
295	Rohn Stark	.05
296	Albert Bentley	.10
297	Bill Brooks	.10
298	O'Brien Alston	.05
299	Ray Donaldson	.05
300	Carlos Carson	.05
301	Lloyd Burruss	.05
302	Steve DeBerg	.15
303	Irv Eatman	.05
304	Dino Hackett	.05
305	Albert Lewis	.05
306	Chiefs helmet	.05
307	Chiefs logo	.05
308	Deron Cherry	.10
309	Paul Palmer	.05
310	Neil Smith	.40
311	Christian Okoye	.10
312	Stephone Paige	.10
313	Bill Maas	.05
314	Marcus Allen	.40
315	Vann McElroy	.05
316	Mervyn Fernandez	.10
317	Bill Pickel	.05
318	Greg Townsend	.05
319	Tim Brown	1.25
320	Raiders logo	.05
321	Helmet	.05
322	James Lofton	.15
323	Willie Gault	.10
324	Jay Schroeder	.10
325	Matt Millen	.05
326	Howie Long	.10
327	Bo Jackson	.50
328	Lorenzo Hampton	.05
329	Jarvis Williams	.05
330	Jim C. Jensen	.05
331	Dan Marino	2.50
332	John Offerdahl	.10
333	Brian Sochia	.05
334	Miami logo	.05
335	Helmet	.05
336	Ferrell Edmunds	.05
337	Mark Brown	.05
338	Mark Duper	.10
339	Troy Stradford	.05
340	T.J. Turner	.05
341	Mark Clayton	.15
342	Patriots logo	.05

#	Player	Price
343	Johnny Rembert	.05
344	Garin Veris	.05
345	Stanley Morgan	.10
346	John Stephens	.15
347	Fred Marion	.05
348	Irving Fryar	.15
349	Helmet	.05
350	Andre Tippett	.10
351	Roland James	.05
352	Brent Williams	.05
353	Raymond Clayborn	.05
354	Tony Eason	.10
355	Bruce Armstrong	.05
356	Jets logo	.05
357	Marty Lyons	.10
358	Bobby Humphrey	.05
359	Pat Leahy	.05
360	Mickey Shuler	.05
361	James Hasty	.05
362	Ken O'Brien	.10
363	Helmet	.05
364	Alex Gordon	.05
365	Al Toon	.10
366	Erik McMillan	.10
367	Johnny Hector	.05
368	Wesley Walker	.10
369	Freeman McNeil	.10
370	Steelers logo	.05
371	Gary Anderson	.05
372	Rodney Carter	.05
373	Merril Hoge	.10
374	David Little	.05
375	Bubby Brister	.15
376	Thomas Everett	.05
377	Helmet	.05
378	Rod Woodson	.40
379	Bryan Hinkle	.05
380	Tunch Ilkin	.05
381	Aaron Jones	.05
382	Louis Lipps	.10
383	Warren Williams	.05
384	Anthony Miller	.75
385	Gary Anderson	.15
386	Lee Williams	.10
387	Lionel James	.10
388	Gary Plummer	.05
389	Gill Byrd	.10
390	Chargers helmet	.05
391	Ralf Mojsiejenko	.05
392	Rod Bernstine	.25
393	Keith Browner	.05
394	Billy Ray Smith	.10
395	Leslie O'Neal	.15
396	Jamie Holland	.05
397	Tony Woods	.10
398	Bruce Scholtz	.05
399	Joe Nash	.05
400	Curt Warner	.10
401	John L. Williams	.10
402	Bryan Millard	.05
403	Seahawks logo	.05
404	Helmet	.05
405	Steve Largent	.30
406	Norm Johnson	.10
407	Jacob Green	.05
408	Dave Krieg	.10
409	Paul Moyer	.05
410	Brian Blades	.50
411	Helmet	.05
412	Jerry Rice	1.50
413	SB XXIII	.10
414	SB XXIII	.10
415	SB XXIII	.10
416	SB XXIII	.10
----	Panini Album (Joe Montana on conver)	4.00

1990 Panini Stickers

These stickers were intended to be stored in an album titled "The Hitters." Ronnie Lott, Mike Singletary and Lawrence Taylor are featured on the album cover. The stickers measure 1-7/8" x 2-15/16" and have a color action photo on the front, using a design distinctly different from those used the two years before.

	MT
Complete Set (396):	20.00
Common Player:	.05

#	Player	Price
1	Super Bowl XXIV Program Cover (top)	.15
2	Super Bowl XXIV Program Cover (bottom)	.10
3	Bills Crest	.05
4	Thurman Thomas	.50
5	Nate Odomes	.05
6	Jim Kelly	.45
7	Cornelius Bennett	.20
8	Scott Norwood	.05
9	Mark Kelso	.05
10	Kent Hull	.05
11	Jim Ritcher	.05
12	Darryl Talley	.10
13	Bruce Smith	.15
14	Shane Conlan	.10
15	Andre Reed	.15
16	Jason Buck	.05
17	David Fulcher	.05
18	Jim Skow	.05
19	Anthony Munoz	.15
20	Eric Thomas	.05
21	Eric Ball	.05
22	Tim Krumrie	.05
23	James Brooks	.10
24	Bengals Crest	.05
25	Rodney Holman	.05
26	Boomer Esiason	.25
27	Eddie Brown	.10
28	Tim McGee	.10
29	Browns Crest	.05
30	Mike Johnson	.05
31	David Grayson	.05
32	Thane Gash	.05
33	Robert Banks	.05
34	Eric Metcalf	.20
35	Kevin Mack	.10
36	Reggie Langhorne	.05
37	Webster Slaughter	.10
38	Felix Wright	.05
39	Bernie Kosar	.25
40	Frank Minnifield	.05
41	Clay Matthews	.15
42	Vance Johnson	.10
43	Ron Holmes	.05
44	Melvin Bratton	.10
45	Greg Kragen	.05
46	Karl Mecklenburg	.10
47	Dennis Smith	.05
48	Bobby Humphrey	.05
49	Simon Fletcher	.05
50	Broncos Crest	.05
51	Michael Brooks	.05
52	Steve Atwater	.15
53	John Elway	.80
54	David Treadwell	.05
55	Oilers Crest	.05
56	Bubba McDowell	.05
57	Ray Childress	.10
58	Bruce Matthews	.05
59	Allen Pinkett	.05
60	Warren Moon	.55
61	John Grimsley	.05
62	Alonzo Highsmith	.05
63	Mike Munchak	.05
64	Ernest Givins	.10
65	Johnny Meads	.05
66	Drew Hill	.10
67	William Fuller	.05
68	Duane Bickett	.05
69	Jack Trudeau	.10
70	Jon Hand	.05
71	Chris Hinton	.10
72	Bill Brooks	.10
73	Donnell Thompson	.05
74	Jeff Herrod	.05
75	Andre Rison	.25
76	Colts Crest	.05
77	Chris Chandler	.05
78	Ray Donaldson	.05
79	Albert Bentley	.05
80	Keith Taylor	.05
81	Chiefs Crest	.05
82	Leonard Griffin	.05
83	Dino Hackett	.05
84	Christian Okoye	.10
85	Chris Martin	.05
86	John Alt	.05
87	Kevin Ross	.05
88	Steve DeBerg	.10
89	Albert Lewis	.05
90	Stephone Paige	.10
91	Derrick Thomas	.40
92	Neil Smith	.15
93	Pete Mandley	.05
94	Howie Long	.10
95	Greg Townsend	.05
96	Mervyn Fernandez	.05
97	Scott Davis	.05
98	Steve Beuerlein	.40
99	Mike Dyal	.05
100	Willie Gault	.05
101	Eddie Anderson	.05
102	Raiders Crest	.05
103	Trey McDaniel	.05
104	Bo Jackson	.30
105	Steve Wisniewski	.05
106	Steve Smith	.10
107	Dolphins Crest	.05
108	Mark Clayton	.05
109	Louis Oliver	.05
110	Jarvis Williams	.05
111	Ferrell Edmunds	.05
112	Jeff Cross	.05
113	John Offerdahl	.10
114	Brian Sochia	.05

#	Player	Price
115	Dan Marino	2.00
116	Jim C. Jensen	.05
117	Sammie Smith	.05
118	Reggie Roby	.05
119	Roy Foster	.05
120	Bruce Armstrong	.05
121	Steve Grogan	.10
122	Hart Lee Dykes	.05
123	Andre Tippett	.10
124	Johnny Rembert	.05
125	Ed Reynolds	.05
126	Cedric Jones	.05
127	Vincent Brown	.05
128	Patriots Crest	.05
129	Brent Williams	.05
130	John Stephens	.10
131	Eric Sievers	.05
132	Maurice Hurst	.05
133	Jets Crest	.05
134	Johnny Hector	.10
135	Eric McMillan	.05
136	Jeff Lageman	.05
137	Al Toon	.10
138	James Hasty	.05
139	Kyle Clifton	.05
140	Ken O'Brien	.10
141	Jim Sweeney	.05
142	JoJo Townsell	.10
143	Dennis Byrd	.20
144	Mickey Shuler	.10
146	Alex Gordon	.05
147	Keith Willis	.05
148	Louis Lipps	.10
149	David Little	.05
150	Greg Lloyd	.10
151	Carnell Lake	.05
152	Tim Worley	.10
153	Dwayne Woodruff	.05
154	Gerald Williams	.05
155	Steelers Crest	.05
156	Bubby Brister	.10
158	Merril Hoge	.10
159	Rod Woodson	.15
160	Charger Crest	.05
161	Leslie O'Neal	.10
162	Billy Ray Smith	.05
163	Marion Butts	.15
164	Lee Williams	.10
165	Gill Byrd	.10
166	Jim McMahon	.15
167	Courtney Hall	.05
168	Burt Grossman	.15
169	Gary Plummer	.05
170	Anthony Miller	.40
171	Billy Joe Tolliver	.15
172	Venice Glenn	.05
173	Andy Heck	.05
174	Brian Blades	.15
175	Bryan Millard	.05
176	Tony Woods	.05
177	Rufus Porter	.05
178	Dave Wyman	.05
179	John L. Williams	.10
180	Jacob Green	.05
181	Seahawks Crest	.05
182	Eugene Robinson	.05
183	Jeff Bryant	.05
184	Dave Krieg	.10
185	Joe Nash	.05
186	Christian Okoye	.05
187	Felix Wright	.05
188	Rod Woodson	.10
189	Barry Sanders, Christian Okoye	.75
190	Jerry Rice, Sterling Sharpe	1.00
191	Bruce Matthews	.05
192	Jay Hilgenberg	.05
193	Tom Newbury	.05
194	Anthony Munoz	.10
195	Jim Lachey	.05
196	Keith Jackson	.15
197	Joe Montana	1.50
	David Fulcher, Ronnie Lott	.10
198	Albert Lewis, Eric Allen	.05
199	Reggie White	.20
200	Keith Millard	.05
201	Chris Doleman	.05
202	Mike Singletary	.15
203	Tim Harris	.05
204	Lawrence Taylor	.20
205	Rich Camarillo	.05
206	Sterling Sharpe	.25
207	Chris Doleman	.05
208	Barry Sanders	.55
209	Falcons Crest	.05
210	Michael Haynes	.30
211	Scott Case	.05
212	Marcus Cotton	.05
213	Chris Miller	.15
214	Keith Jones	.05
215	Tim Green	.05
216	Deion Sanders	.50
217	Shawn Collins	.05
218	John Settle	.05
219	Bill Fralic	.05
220	Aundray Bruce	.05
221	Jessie Tuggle	.05
222	James Thornton	.05
223	Dennis Gentry	.05
224	Richard Dent	.15
225	Jay Hilgenberg	.05
226	Steve McMichael	.05
227	Brad Muster	.10
228	Donnell Woodford	.05

#	Player	Price
229	Mike Singletary	.15
230	Bears Crest	.05
231	Mark Bortz	.05
232	Kevin Butler	.05
233	Neal Anderson	.10
234	Trace Armstrong	.05
235	Cowboys Crest	.05
236	Mark Tuinei	.10
237	Tony Tolbert	.05
238	Eugene Lockhart	.05
239	Daryl Johnston	.25
240	Troy Aikman	3.00
241	Jim Jeffcoat	.10
242	James Dixon	.05
243	Jesse Solomon	.05
244	Ken Norton	.25
245	Kelvin Martin	.05
246	Danny Noonan	.05
247	Michael Irvin	.50
248	Eric Williams	.05
249	Richard Johnson	.05
250	Michael Cofer	.05
251	Chris Spielman	.10
252	Rodney Peete	.20
253	Bennie Blades	.10
254	Jerry Ball	.05
255	Eddie Murray	.08
256	Lions Crest	.05
257	Barry Sanders	1.75
258	Jerry Holmes	.05
259	Dennis Gibson	.05
260	Lomas Brown	.05
261	Packers Crest	.05
262	Dave Brown	.05
263	Mark Murphy	.05
264	Perry Kemp	.05
265	Don Majkowski	.10
266	Chris Jacke	.05
267	Keith Woodside	.10
268	Tony Mandarich	.05
269	Robert Brown	.05
270	Sterling Sharpe	.75
271	Tim Harris	.10
272	Brent Fullwood	.05
273	Brian Noble	.05
274	Alvin Wright	.05
275	Flipper Anderson	.10
276	Jackie Slater	.10
277	Kevin Greene	.10
278	Pete Holohan	.05
279	Tom Newberry	.05
280	Jerry Gray	.05
281	Henry Ellard	.10
282	Rams Crest	.05
283	LeRoy Irvin	.05
284	Jim Everett	.15
285	Greg Bell	.10
286	Doug Smith	.05
287	Vikings Crest	.05
288	Joey Browner	.10
289	Wade Wilson	.15
290	Chris Doleman	.10
291	Al Noga	.05
292	Herschel Walker	.20
293	Henry Thomas	.10
294	Steve Jordan	.10
295	Anthony Carter	.10
296	Keith Millard	.10
297	Carl Lee	.05
298	Randall McDaniel	.05
299	Gary Zimmerman	.05
300	Morten Andersen	.05
301	Rickey Jackson	.05
302	Sam Mills	.05
303	Hoby Brenner	.05
304	Dalton Hilliard	.05
305	Robert Massey	.05
306	John Fourcade	.10
307	Lonzell Hill	.05
308	Saints Crest	.05
309	Jim Dombrowski	.05
310	Pat Swilling	.15
311	Vaughan Johnson	.05
312	Eric Martin	.10
313	Giants Crest	.05
314	Ottis Anderson	.10
315	Myron Guyton	.05
316	Terry Kinard	.05
317	Mark Bavaro	.10
318	Phil Simms	.25
319	Lawrence Taylor	.30
320	Odessa Turner	.05
321	Erik Howard	.05
322	Mark Collins	.05
323	Dave Meggett	.15
324	Leonard Marshall	.05
325	Carl Banks	.10
326	Anthony Toney	.05
327	Seth Joyner	.15
328	Cris Carter	.20
329	Eric Allen	.05
330	Keith Jackson	.20
331	Clyde Simmons	.10
332	Byron Evans	.05
333	Keith Byars	.10
334	Eagles Crest	.05
335	Reggie White	.25
336	Izel Jenkins	.05
337	Jerome Brown	.15
338	David Alexander	.05
339	Cardinals Crest	.05
340	Rich Camarillo	.05
341	Ken Harvey	.05
342	Luis Sharpe	.05
343	Timm Rosenbach	.05
344	Tim McDonald	.15
345	Vai Sikahema	.05
346	Freddie Joe Nunn	.05

		MT
347	Ernie Jones	.05
348	J.T. Smith	.10
349	Eric Hill	.05
350	Roy Green	.10
351	Anthony Bell	.05
352	Kevin Fagan	.05
353	Roger Craig	.15
354	Ronnie Lott	.20
355	Mike Cofer	.05
356	John Taylor	.20
357	Joe Montana	3.00
358	Charles Haley	.10
359	Guy McIntyre	.05
360	49ers Crest	.05
361	Pierce Holt	.15
362	Tom Rathman	.15
363	Jerry Rice	1.50
364	Michael Carter	.10
365	Buccaneers Crest	.05
366	Lars Tate	.05
367	Paul Gruber	.10
368	Winston Moss	.05
369	Reuben Davis	.05
370	Mark Robinson	.05
371	Bruce Hill	.05
372	Kevin Murphy	.05
373	Ricky Reynolds	.05
374	Harry Hamilton	.05
375	Vinny Testaverde	.15
376	Mark Carrier	.15
377	Ervin Randle	.05
378	Ricky Sanders	.10
379	Charles Mann	.10
380	Jim Lachey	.10
381	Wilber Marshall	.10
382	A.J. Johnson	.05
383	Darrell Green	.10
384	Mark Rypien	.15
385	Gerald Riggs	.10
386	Redskins Crest	.05
387	Alvin Walton	.05
388	Art Monk	.15
389	Gary Clark	.15
390	Earnest Byner	.10
391	SB XXIV Action (Jerry Rice)	.75
392	SB XXIV Action (49er Offensive Line)	.15
393	SB XXIV Action (Tom Rathman)	.25
394	SB XXIV Action (Chet Brooks)	.10
395	SB XXIV Action (John Elway)	1.00
396	SB XXIV Action (Joe Montana)	3.00
----	Panini Album	2.00

1995 Panthers SkyBox

The Panthers' inaugural season is commemorated on this 21-card set. The card fronts feature a full-bleed photo, with the player's name and position listed on a team-colored band near the bottom. The Panther logo is featured next to the name. The backs include a photo on the right, with the player's name, bio and highlights inside a box on the left. The card number is printed inside a circle in the upper right. Stats are located in the lower right.

		MT
Complete Set (21):		15.00
Common Player:		.75
1	John Kasay	.75
2	Kerry Collins	4.00
3	Frank Reich	1.25
4	Rod Smith	.75
5	Tim McKyer	.75
6	Randy Baldwin	.75
7	Bubba McDowell	.75
8	Tyrone Poole	1.00
9	Sam Mills	1.00
10	Carlton Bailey	.75
11	Darion Conner	.75
12	Lamar Lathon	.75
13	Blake Brockermeyer	1.00
14	Mike Fox	.75
15	Don Beebe	1.00
16	Mark Carrier	1.00
17	Pete Metzelaars	.75
18	Shawn King	.75
19	Howard Griffith	.75
20	Bob Christian	1.00
NNO	Cover Card (checklist back)	.75

1996 Panthers Fleer/SkyBox Impact Promo Sheet

This six-card promo sheet was distributed by Fleer/SkyBox at the NFL Experience Card Show in Charlotte in 1996. It features six players from the Carolina Panthers.

		MT
Complete Sheet (1):		5.00
Common Sheet:		5.00
1	Promo Sheet (Tim Biakabutuka, Lamar Lathon, Muhsin Muhammad, Kerry Collins, Tyrone Poole, Mark Carrier)	5.00

1974 Parker Brothers Pro Draft

These 50 cards were included inside a Parker Brothers board game called Pro Draft. The cards, featuring only offensive players, were produced by Topps and use the identical design as the 1974 Topps set. However, some differences can be noted on certain cards. Some of the game cards have 1972 statistics on the card backs, and others have different player poses on the front (#s 23, 49, 116, 124, 126 and 127). Players with an * have 1972 statistics. Card numbers in this set are identical to the card numbers the players have in the regular 1974 Topps set.

		NM
Complete Set (50):		75.00
Common Player:		1.25
4	Ken Bowman	1.25
6	Jerry Smith	3.00
7	Ed Podolak	2.50
8	Pat Matson	1.25
11	Frank Pitts	2.00
15	Winston Hill	1.25
18	Rich Coady	2.00
19	Ken Willard	3.75
21	Ben Hawkins	2.00
23	Norm Snead (vertical pose)	10.00
24	Jim Yarborough	2.00
28	Bob Hayes	5.00
32	Dan Dierdorf	8.00
35	Essex Johnson	2.00
39	Mike Siani	1.25
42	Del Williams	1.25
43	Don McCauley	2.00
44	Randy Jackson	2.00
46	Gene Washington	3.50
49	Bob Windsor (vertical pose)	6.00
50	John Hadl	4.00
52	Steve Owens	4.00
54	Rayfield Wright	2.00
57	Milt Sunde	2.00
58	Bill Kilmer	5.50
61	Rufus Mayes	2.00
63	Gene Washington	2.50
65	Eugene Upshaw	4.50
75	Fred Willis	2.00
77	Tom Neville	1.25
78	Ted Kwalick	3.00
80	John Niland	2.00
81	Ted Fritsch Jr.	1.25
83	Jack Snow	3.00
87	Mike Phipps	3.00
90	MacArthur Lane	3.00
95	Calvin Hill	3.50
98	Len Rohde	1.25
101	Gary Garrison	2.50
103	Len St. Jean	1.25
107	Jim Mitchell	2.00
109	Harry Schuh	1.25
110	Greg Pruitt	5.00
111	Ed Flanagan	1.25
113	Chuck Foreman	6.00
116	Charlie Johnson (vertical pose)	8.00
119	Roy Jefferson	4.00
124	Forrest Blue (not All-Pro on card)	6.00
126	Tom Mack (not All-Pro on card)	8.00
127	Bob Tucker (not All-Pro on card)	6.00

1989 Parker Brothers Talking Football

Licensed by the NFL Players Association, the 34-card set features a "Superstar Lineup Talking Football" logo in the upper left. Up to three player photos can appear on the front of the card. The NFLPA logo also appears on the front of the card.

The backs of the cards, which are unnumbered, include the name of player (s), bio and highlights. The bottom right of the card back carries a Parker Brothers copyright.

		MT
Complete Set (34):		90.00
Common Player:		2.00
1	AFC Team Roster	2.00
2	Marcus Allen	5.00
3	Cornelius Bennett, John Offerdahl	3.00
4	Keith Bishop, Mike Munchak	2.00
5	Keith Bostic, Deron Cherry, Hanford Dixon	2.00
6	Carlos Carson, Stanley Morgan	2.00
7	Todd Christensen, Mickey Shuler	2.50
8	Eric Dickerson	4.00
9	Ray Donaldson, Irving Fryar	2.00
10	Jacob Green, Bruce Smith	2.00
11	Mark Haynes, Frank Minnifield, Dennis Smith	2.00
12	Chris Hinton, Anthony Munoz	2.50
13	Steve Largent, Al Toon	5.00
14	Howie Long, Bill Maas	3.00
15	Nick Lowery, Reggie Roby	2.00
16	Dan Marino	25.00
17	Karl Mecklenburg, Andre Tippett	2.50
18	NFC Team Roster	2.00
19	Morten Andersen, Jim Arnold	2.00
20	Carl Banks, Mike Singletary	3.00
21	Mark Bavaro, Doug Cosbie	2.50
22	Joey Browner, Darrell Green, Leonard Smith	2.00
23	Anthony Carter, Jerry Rice	12.00
24	Gary Clark, Mike Quick	4.00
25	Richard Dent, Chris Doleman	3.00
26	Brad Edelman, Bill Fralic	2.00
27	Carl Ekern, Rickey Jackson	2.00
28	Jerry Gray, LeRoy Irvin, Ronnie Lott	2.50
29	Mel Gray, Jay Hilgenberg	3.00
30	Dexter Manley, Reggie White	2.50
31	Rueben Mayes	2.00
32	Joe Montana	20.00
33	Jackie Slater, Gary Zimmerman	2.00
34	Herschel Walker	3.00

1988 Patriots Holsum

Available only in specially marked packages of Holsum Bread, the 12 standard-sized cards feature the Holsum logo in the upper left, with "1988 Annual Collectors' Edition" printed in the upper right. The player photo dominates the front, while the player's name and team are located inside a box beneath the photo. The card backs include the player's facsimile autograph, jersey number, bio and card number "of 12" printed at the top. The remainder of the card back is filled with stats and various logos.

		MT
Complete Set (12):		40.00
Common Player:		4.00
1	Andre Tippett	4.00
2	Stanley Morgan	6.00
3	Steve Grogan	6.00
4	Ronnie Lippett	4.00
5	Kenneth Sims	4.00
6	Pete Brock	4.00
7	Sean Farrell	4.00
8	Garin Veris	4.00
9	Mosi Tatupu	4.00
10	Raymond Clayborn	5.00
11	Tony Franklin	4.00
12	Reggie Dupard	4.00

A player's name in *italic* type indicates a rookie card.

1988 Walter Payton Commemorative

Chicagoland Processing Corp. produced 16,726 of these sets to commemorate the total rushing yards Hall of Fame running back Walter Payton gained during his career with the Chicago Bears. The 132-card set chronicles his illustrious career; each card recaptures a significant moment. The standard-size cards were packaged in a blue plastic box and were issued in conjunction with a soft-cover book titled "Sweetness." Each card front has a dark blue border around an action photo. The Bears' logo and NFL logo are also on the front. The cards are numbered on the back and have a title and text which ties to the photo on the front. The cards are listed by the title used on the back.

		MT
Complete Set (132):		50.00
Common Player:		.50
1	Leading Scorer in NCAA History	2.00
2	1975 Game-by-Game	.50
3	Vs. New York Jets	.50
4	Vs. Miami Dolphins	.50
5	Vs. Baltimore/Indianapolis Colts	.50
6	Vs. Buffalo Bills	.50
7	Vs. New England Patriots	.50
8	Vs. Houston Oilers	.50
9	Vs. Pittsburgh Steelers	.50
10	Vs. Cincinnati Bengals	.50
11	Vs. Cleveland Browns	.50
12	Vs. Kansas City Chiefs	.50
13	Vs. Oakland/Los Angeles Raiders	.50
14	Vs. San Diego Chargers	.50
15	Vs. Denver Broncos	.50
16	Vs. Seattle Seahawks	.50
17	Vs. Washington Redskins	.50
18	Vs. New York Giants	.50
19	Vs. Dallas Cowboys	.50
20	Vs. St. Louis Cardinals	.50
21	Vs. Philadelphia Eagles	.50
22	Vs. New Orleans Saints	.50
23	Vs. Atlanta Falcons	.50
24	Vs. Los Angeles Rams	.50
25	Vs. San Francisco 49ers	.50
26	Vs. Detroit Lions	.50
27	Vs. Minnesota Vikings	.50
28	Vs. Tampa Bay Buccaneers	.50
29	Vs. Green Bay Packers	.50
30	1976 Game-by-Game	.50
31	Appears in Nine Pro Bowls	.50
32	Post-Season Stats	.50
33	Owns 23 Bear Records	.50
34	Season-by-Season Statistics	.50
35	1977 Game-by-Game	.50
36	Most Yards Gained, Rushing	.50
37	Most Combined Yards, Career	.50
38	Most Rushing Touchdowns	.50
39	Most Games, 100 Yards Rushing, Career	.50
40	Consecutive Combined 2000-Yard Seasons	.50
41	Most Yards Gained, Rushing, Game	.50
42	Most Rushing Attempts, Career	.50
43	Most Combined Attempts, Career	.50
44	Most Seasons, 1000 Yards Rushing	.50
45	1978 Game-by-Game	.50
46	Top 10 Average Per Carry Days 1	.50
47	Top 10 Average Per Carry Days 2	.50
48	Top 10 Average Per Carry Days 3	.50
49	Top 10 Average Per Carry Days 4	.50
50	Top 10 Average Per Carry Days 5	.50
51	Top 10 Average Per Carry Days 6	.50
52	Top 10 Average Per Carry Days 7	.50
53	Top 10 Average Per Carry Days 8	.50
54	Top 10 Average Per Carry Days 9	.50
55	Top 10 Average Per Carry Days 10	.50
56	1979 Game-by-Game	.50
57	In Training Didn't Play Until 11th Grad	.50
58	In Training Running the Hill	.50
59	In Training Jumping Rope	.50
60	In Training	.50
61	Personal Life Interests Include...	.50
62	Personal Life Corporate Spokesman	.50
63	Personal Life Family Man	.50
64	Personal Life Realtives in NFL	.50
65	"Sweetness" autobiography written, 1978	.50
66	National Committee, Child Abuse Preven.	.50
67	Chicago 1986 Sports Father of the Year	.50
68	Active in Many Charities	.50
69	Personal Life Parade Grand Marshall	.50
70	1980 Game-by-Game	.50
71	1976 TSN MFC Player of the Year	.50
72	1976 Chicago Red Cloud Athlete of the Year	.50
73	1977 UPI Atlete of the Year	.50
74	1977 PFWA NFL MVP	.50
75	1977 UPI and TSN NFC Player of the Year	.50
76	1977 All Pro Pick AP, UPI, and NEA	.50
77	1977 PFWA,NEA,Mut.Radio,AP,FB Dig., POT	.50
78	TSN NFC All-Star 1976-79	.50
79	TSN NFL All-Star 1980,1984, and 1985	.50
80	1981 Game-by-Game	.50
81	As Quarterback	.50
82	Kickoff Return	.50
83	Complete Player	.50
84	Toouchdown	.50
85	1982 Game-by-Game	.50
86	Most Consecutive Games, Career	.50
87	Five Longest Runs	.50
88	Pass Receiving	.50
89	Ditka on Payton	.50
90	1983 Game-by-Game	.50
91	Breaks Career Rushing Record	.50
92	Breaks Career Rushing	.50
93	Breaks Career Rushing	.50
94	Breaks Career Rushing	.50
95	1984 Game-by-Game	.50
96	Bears Win 1985 NFC Champ. over Rams	.50
97	Super Bowl XX	.50
98	Super Bowl XX	.50
99	Super Bowl XX	.50
100	Super Bowl XX	.50
101	1985 Game-by-Game	.50
102	Sweetness	.50
103	Sweetness Choice to Pro Bowl Squad 1977	.50
104	Sweetness	.50
105	Sweetness 1979 Pro Bowl Starter, AP NFC	.50
106	Sweetness	.50
107	Sweetness	.50
108	Sweetness	.50
109	Sweetness	.50
110	1986 Game-by-Game	.50
111	Final Season Goodbye to Green Bay	.50
112	Final Season	.50
113	Last Regular Season Home Game	.50
114	Last Reg.Season Home Game,Number Retire	.50
115	Last Home Game,Presented with Portrait	.50
116	Last Regular Season Home Game	.50
117	Soldier Field,Known As Payton's Place	.50
118	Last Regular Season Home Game	.50
119	Last Regular Season Game vs. Raiders	.50
120	Last Regular Season Game	.50
121	Last Reg. Season Game, Catches 2 Passes	.50
122	Last Regular Season Game	.50
123	Last Regular Season Game	.50
124	Plays 190th Game, Bears All-Time Record	.50
125	Last Regular Season Game	.50
126	Ends Career with 21,803 Combined Yards	.50
127	Finishes w/4542 Career Receiving Yards	.50
128	16,726 Career Rushing Yards	.50
129	1987 Game-by-Game	.50
130	The End of an Era	.50
131	Thanks for the Memories	.50
132	Last Few Moments	2.00

1976 Pepsi Discs

This set was regionally produced in the Cincinnati area; hence the majority of the discs feature members of the Cincinnati Bengals (#s 21-40). The remaining discs feature top NFL stars. The cards are valued with the tab intact; this is how they are commonly found. The tab was used to hang the disc from a bottle included in six packs of Pepsi products. Each disc is 3-1/2" in diameter and features a player photo, biographical information and 1975 statistics on the front. Discs 1, 5, 7, 8 and 14 are reportedly scarcer than the others because they were short-printed. A free, personalized T-shirt was also offered to those who sent in 200 capliners which read "Pepsi Players." The shirt would picture either Ken Anderson or Archie Griffin, with the collector's first name. It would say "To my buddy xxxx, Best Wishes, Ken Anderson."

#	NM	
Complete Set (40):	90.00	
Common Player:	.50	
1	Steve Bartkowski	22.00
2	Lydell Mitchell	1.50
3	Wally Chambers	.50
4	Doug Buffone	.50
5	Jerry Sherk	22.00
6	Drew Pearson	1.00
7	Otis Armstrong	22.00
8	Charlie Sanders	20.00
9	John Brockington	.75
10	Curley Culp	.75
11	Jan Stenerud	1.50
12	Lawrence McCutcheon	.75
13	Chuck Foreman	1.00
14	Bob Pollard	20.00
15	Ed Marinaro	12.00
16	Jack Lambert	5.00
17	Terry Metcalf	.75
18	Mel Gray	.75
19	Russ Washington	.50
20	Charley Taylor	2.50
21	Ken Anderson	2.50
22	Bob Brown	.50
23	Ron Carpenter	.50
24	Tom Casanova	1.25
25	Boobie Clark	1.00
26	Isaac Curtis	1.00
27	Lenvil Elliott	.50
28	Stan Fritts	.50
29	Vernon Holland	.50
30	Bob Johnson	1.00
31	Ken Johnson	.50
32	Bill Kollar	.50
33	Jim LeClair	.75
34	Chip Myers	.50
35	Lemar Parrish	.75
36	Rob Pritchard	.50
37	Bob Trumpy	1.50
38	Sherman White	.50
39	Archie Griffin	1.50
40	John Shinners	.50

1964 Philadelphia

MERLIN OLSEN
LOS ANGELES RAMS
TACKLE

This was Philly's first of four straight 198-card sets, and Philly covered the NFL players while Topps, possibly unable to reach an agreement with the NFL, showcased only American Football League players. For the first time, a card with a team play and a black-and-white photo of the coach was included in a football card set. As would be the case throughout the Philly run, cards are numbered alphabetically by player's last name and by city name. Two checklists appear at the end of each of the four Philly sets. Rookies in this set include John Mackey, Tom Matte, Jack Pardee, Mick Tingelhoff, Irv Cross, and Hall of Famers Herb Adderly, Willie Davis and Merlin Olsen. Making their debut on cards on coaches' issues were Don Shula, Vince Lombardi and Allie Sherman. Second-year cards in the set include Bob Lilly and Jim Marshall. This set held the final regular-issue cards of Gino Marchetti, Night Train Lane, Joe Schmidt, Jerry Kramer, Frank Gifford, Y.A. Tittle, and Bob St. Clair. One error does exist in the set -- card #169 does not picture Garland Boyette as advertised, it's unclear who the player actually is.

#	NM	
Complete Set (198):	875.00	
Common Player:	1.75	
1	Raymond Berry	20.00
2	Tom Gilburg	1.75
3	John Mackey	25.00
4	Gino Marchetti	4.00
5	Jim Martin	1.75
6	Tom Matte	6.00
7	Jimmy Orr	1.75
8	Jim Parker	3.00
9	Bill Pellington	1.75
10	Alex Sandusky	1.75
11	Dick Szymanski	1.75
12	Johnny Unitas	40.00
13	Baltimore Colts Team	1.75
14	Don Shula	25.00
15	Doug Atkins	2.50
16	Ron Bull	1.75
17	Mike Ditka	32.00
18	Joe Fortunato	1.75
19	Willie Galimore	1.75
20	Joe Marconi	1.75
21	Bennie McRae	2.00
22	Johnny Morris	1.75
23	Richie Petitbon	2.50
24	Mike Pyle	1.75
25	Roosevelt Taylor	4.00
26	Bill Wade	1.75
27	Chicago Bears Team	1.75
28	George Halas	10.00
29	Johnny Brewer	1.75
30	Jim Brown	65.00
31	Gary Collins	6.00
32	Vince Costello	1.75
33	Galen Fiss	1.75
34	Bill Glass	1.75
35	Ernie Green	4.00
36	Rich Kreitling	1.75
37	John Morrow	1.75
38	Frank Ryan	3.00
39	Charlie Scales	3.00
40	Dick Schafrath	2.00
41	Cleveland Browns Team	1.75
42	Cleveland Browns Play of the Year (Blanton Collier)	1.75
43	Don Bishop	1.75
44	Frank Clarke	3.00
45	Mike Connelly	1.75
46	Lee Folkins	1.75
47	Cornell Green	5.00
48	Bob Lilly	40.00
49	Amos Marsh	1.75
50	Tommy McDonald	1.75
51	Don Meredith	35.00
52	Pettis Norman	2.00
53	Don Perkins	2.00
54	Guy Reese	1.75
55	Dallas Cowboys Team	1.75
56	Tom Landry	12.00
57	Terry Barr	1.75
58	Roger Brown	1.75
59	Gail Cogdill	1.75
60	John Gordy	1.75
61	Dick Lane	4.00
62	Yale Lary	4.00
63	Dan Lewis	1.75
64	Darris McCord	1.75
65	Earl Morrall	5.00
66	Joe Schmidt	4.00
67	Pat Studstill	4.00
68	Wayne Walker	4.00
69	Detroit Lions Team	1.75
70	Detroit Lions Player of the Year (George Wilson)	1.75
71	Herb Adderley	30.00
72	Willie Davis	30.00
73	Forrest Gregg	4.00
74	Paul Hornung	25.00
75	Henry Jordan	1.75
76	Jerry Kramer	5.00
77	Tom Moore	1.75
78	Jim Ringo	4.00
79	Bart Starr	40.00
80	Jim Taylor	15.00
81	Jess Whittenton	2.50
82	Willie Wood	8.00
83	Green Bay Packers Team	1.75
84	Vince Lombardi	24.00
85	Jon Arnett	1.75
86	Pervis Atkins	2.00
87	Dick Bass	1.75
88	Carroll Dale	1.75
89	Roman Gabriel	6.00
90	Ed Meador	1.75
91	Merlin Olsen	50.00
92	Jack Pardee	7.00
93	Jim Phillips	1.75
94	Carver Shannon	1.75
95	Frank Varrichione	1.75
96	Danny Villanueva	1.75
97	Los Angeles Rams team	1.75
98	Los Angeles Rams Play of the Year (Harland Svare)	1.75
99	Grady Alderman	2.00
100	Larry Bowie	1.75
101	Bill Brown	5.00
102	Paul Flatley	2.00
103	Rip Hawkins	1.75
104	Jim Marshall	8.00
105	Tommy Mason	1.75
106	Jim Prestel	1.75
107	Jerry Reichow	1.75
108	Ed Sharockman	1.75
109	Fran Tarkenton	30.00
110	Mick Tingelhoff	8.00
111	Minnesota Vikings Team	1.75
112	Norm Van Brocklin	4.00
113	Erich Barnes	1.75
114	Roosevelt Brown	3.00
115	Don Chandler	1.75
116	Darrell Dess	1.75
117	Frank Gifford	45.00
118	Dick James	1.75
119	Jim Katcavage	1.75
120	John Lovetere	1.75
121	Dick Lynch	2.00
122	Jim Patton	1.75
123	Del Shofner	1.75
124	Y.A. Tittle	20.00
125	New York Giants Team	1.75
126	Player of the year (Allie Sherman)	1.75
127	Sam Baker	1.75
128	Maxie Baughan	1.75
129	Timmy Brown	1.75
130	Mike Clark	1.75
131	Irv Cross	6.00
132	Ted Dean	1.75
133	Ron Goodwin	1.75
134	King Hill	1.75
135	Clarence Peaks	1.75
136	Pete Retzlaff	1.75
137	Jim Schrader	1.75
138	Norm Snead	3.00
139	Philadelphia Eagles Team	1.75
140	Philadelphia Eagles Play of the Year (Joe Kuharich)	1.75
141	Gary Ballman	3.00
142	Charley Bradshaw	1.75
143	Ed Brown	1.75
144	John Henry Johnson	5.00
145	Joe Krupa	1.75
146	Bill Mack	1.75
147	Lou Michaels	1.75
148	Buzz Nutter	1.75
149	Myron Pottios	1.75
150	John Reger	1.75
151	Mike Sandusky	1.75
152	Clendon Thomas	1.75
153	Pittsburgh Steelers Team	1.75
154	Pittsburgh Steelers Play of the Year (Buddy Parker)	1.75
155	Kermit Alexander	3.00
156	Bernie Casey	1.75
157	Dan Colchico	1.75
158	Clyde Conner	1.75
159	Tommy Davis	1.75
160	Matt Hazeltine	1.75
161	Jim Johnson	15.00
162	Don Lisbon	2.00
163	Lamar McHan	1.75
164	Bob St. Clair	4.00
165	J.D. Smith	1.75
166	Abe Woodson	1.75
167	San Francisco 49ers Team	1.75
168	San Francisco 49ers Play of the Year (Red Hickey)	1.75
169	Garland Boyette	1.75
170	Bobby Joe Conrad	1.75
171	Bob DeMarco	3.00
172	Ken Gray	3.00
173	Jimmy Hill	1.75
174	Charlie Johnson	3.00
175	Ernie McMillan	1.75
176	Dale Meinert	1.75
177	Luke Owens	1.75
178	Sonny Randle	1.75
179	Joe Robb	1.75
180	Bill Stacy	1.75
181	St. Louis Cardinals Team	1.75
182	St. Louis Cardinals Play of the Year (Wally Lem)	1.75
183	Bill Barnes	1.75
184	Don Bosseler	1.75
185	Sam Huff	6.00
186	Sonny Jurgensen	18.00
187	Ed Khayat	1.75
188	Riley Mattson	1.75
189	Bobby Mitchell	6.00
190	John Nisby	1.75
191	Vince Promuto	1.75
192	Joe Rutgens	1.75
193	Lonnie Sanders	1.75
194	Jim Steffen	1.75
195	Washington Redskins Team	1.75
196	Washington Redskins Play of the Year (Bill McPeak)	1.75
197	Checklist 1	1.75
198	Checklist 2	1.75

1965 Philadelphia

This Philly set was the second one of NFLers issued in its four-year run during the mid-60s. The standard-size 198-card set lists players alphabetically by last name, and alphabetically by city name. Card fronts show the player name in a black box below the photo, with the NFL logo to the right. Card backs had a rub-off game below the statistics. Play of the year cards displayed a diagrammed play the team had used; accompanying it on the front of the card is a small black-and-white picture of the coach. Team cards were once again issued, as were set checklists. One error in the set has Merlin Olsen spelled "Olson" on the checklist card. Rookies in this set include Hall of Famers Paul Warfield and Charley Taylor; all-time interception leader Paul Krause; future NFL head coach Floyd Peters; Carl Eller; Fred Cox; Jack Concannon; Jim Bakken and Pat Fischer. Second-year cards in the set depict Hall of Famers Herb Adderly, Willie Davis, Ray Nitschke (his first Philly card), Vince Lombardi, Deacon Jones, and Merlin Olsen. Others include Mick Tingelhoff, Allie Sherman and Irv Cross. The final regular-issue cards of these players are also in the set: Hall of Famers Yale Lary, Norm Van Brocklin (on a play of the year card), John Henry Johnson, and Sam Huff. This set also had the last regular-issue card of Roosevelt Grier.

#	NM	
Complete Set (198):	775.00	
Common Player:	1.50	
1	Baltimore Colts Team	11.00
2	Raymond Berry	6.00
3	Bob Boyd	1.50
4	Wendell Harris	1.50
5	Jerry Logan	1.50
6	Tony Lorick	1.50
7	Lou Michaels	1.50
8	Lenny Moore	6.00
9	Jimmy Orr	1.50
10	Jim Parker	3.00
11	Dick Szymanski	1.50
12	Johnny Unitas	35.00
13	Bob Vogel	1.50
14	Don Shula	14.00
15	Chicago Bears Team	1.50
16	Jon Arnett	1.50
17	Doug Atkins	3.00
18	Rudy Bukich	3.00
19	Mike Ditka	25.00
20	Dick Evey	1.50
21	Joe Fortunato	1.50
22	Bobby Joe Green	1.50
23	Johnny Morris	1.50
24	Mike Pyle	1.50
25	Roosevelt Taylor	1.50
26	Bill Wade	1.50
27	Bob Wetoska	1.50
28	George Halas	6.00
29	Cleveland Browns Team	1.50
30	Walter Beach	1.50
31	Jim Brown	60.00
32	Gary Collins	1.50
33	Bill Glass	1.50
34	Ernie Green	1.50
35	Jim Houston	3.00
36	Dick Modzelewski	1.50
37	Bernie Parrish	1.50
38	Walter Roberts	1.50
39	Frank Ryan	1.50
40	Dick Schafrath	1.50
41	Paul Warfield	75.00
42	Cleveland Browns Play of the Year (Blanton Collier)	1.50
43	Dallas Cowboys Team	1.50
44	Frank Clarke	1.50
45	Mike Connelly	1.50
46	Buddy Dial	1.50
47	Bob Lilly	20.00
48	Tony Liscio	1.75
49	Tommy McDonald	1.50
50	Don Meredith	25.00
51	Pettis Norman	1.50
52	Don Perkins	2.00
53	Mel Renfro	30.00
54	Jim Ridlon	1.50
55	Jerry Tubbs	1.50
56	Tom Landry	7.00
57	Detroit Lions Team	1.50
58	Terry Barr	1.50
59	Roger Brown	1.50
60	Gail Cogdill	1.50
61	Jim Gibbons	1.50
62	John Gordy	1.50
63	Yale Lary	3.00
64	Dick LeBeau	4.00
65	Earl Morrall	4.00
66	Nick Pietrosante	1.50
67	Pat Studstill	1.50
68	Wayne Walker	1.50
69	Tom Watkins	1.50
70	Detroit Lions Play of the Year (George Wilson)	1.50
71	Green Bay Packers Team	1.50
72	Herb Adderley	8.00
73	Willie Davis	8.00
74	Boyd Dowler	1.50
75	Forrest Gregg	4.00
76	Paul Hornung	25.00
77	Henry Jordan	1.50
78	Tom Moore	1.50
79	Ray Nitschke	15.00
80	Elijah Pitts	5.00
81	Bart Starr	25.00
82	Jim Taylor	14.00
83	Willie Wood	8.00
84	Vince Lombardi	12.00
85	Los Angeles Rams Team	1.50
86	Dick Bass	1.50
87	Roman Gabriel	5.00
88	Roosevelt Grier	3.00
89	Deacon Jones	8.00
90	Lamar Lundy	3.00
91	Marlin McKeever	1.50
92	Ed Meador	1.50
93	Bill Munson	3.00
94	Merlin Olsen	17.00
95	Bobby Smith	1.50
96	Frank Varrichione	1.50
97	Ben Wilson	1.50
98	Los Angeles Rams Play of the Year (Harland Svare)	1.50
99	Minnesota Vikings Team	1.50
100	Grady Alderman	1.50
101	Hal Bedsole	1.50
102	Bill Brown	1.50
103	Bill Butler	1.50
104	Fred Cox	4.00
105	Carl Eller	26.00
106	Paul Flatley	1.50
107	Jim Marshall	6.00
108	Tommy Mason	1.50
109	George Rose	1.50
110	Fran Tarkenton	30.00
111	Mick Tingelhoff	2.00
112	Norm Van Brocklin	3.00
113	New York Giants Team	1.50
114	Erich Barnes	1.50
115	Roosevelt Brown	4.00
116	Clarence Childs	1.50
117	Jerry Hillebrand	1.50
118	Greg Larson	1.50
119	Dick Lynch	1.50
120	Joe Morrison	4.00
121	Lou Slaby	1.50
122	Aaron Thomas	2.50
123	Steve Thurlow	1.50
124	Ernie Wheelwright	1.50
125	Gary Wood	1.50
126	New York Giants Play of the Year (Allie Sherman)	1.50
127	Philadelphia Eagles Team	1.50
128	Sam Baker	1.50
129	Maxie Baughan	1.50
130	Timmy Brown	1.50
131	Jack Concannon	1.50
132	Irv Cross	2.50
133	Earl Gros	1.50
134	Dave Lloyd	1.50
135	Floyd Peters	4.00
136	Nate Ramsey	1.50
137	Pete Retzlaff	1.50
138	Jim Ringo	4.00
139	Norm Snead	2.00
140	Philadelphia Eagles Play of the Year (Joe Kuharich)	1.50
141	Pittsburgh Steelers Team	1.50
142	John Baker	1.50
143	Gary Ballman	1.50
144	Charley Bradshaw	1.50
145	Ed Brown	1.50
146	Dick Haley	1.50
147	John Henry Johnson	4.50
148	Brady Keys	1.50
149	Ray Lemek	1.50
150	Ben McGee	1.50
151	Clarence Peaks	1.50
152	Myron Pottios	1.50
153	Clendon Thomas	1.50
154	Pittsburgh Steelers Play of the Year (Buddy Parker)	1.50
155	St. Louis Cardinals Team	1.50
156	Jim Bakken	4.50
157	Joe Childress	1.50
158	Bobby Joe Conrad	1.50
159	Bob DeMarco	1.50
160	Pat Fischer	4.50
161	Irv Goode	1.50
162	Ken Gray	1.50
163	Charlie Johnson	1.50
164	Bill Koman	1.50
165	Dale Meinert	1.50
166	Jerry Stovall	2.50
167	Abe Woodson	1.50
168	St. Louis Cardinals Play of the Year (Wally Lemon)	1.50
169	San Francisco 49ers Team	1.50
170	Kermit Alexander	1.50
171	John Brodie	12.00
172	Bernie Casey	1.50
173	John David Crow	1.50
174	Tommy Davis	1.50
175	Matt Hazeltine	1.50
176	Jim Johnson	1.50
177	Charlie Krueger	1.50
178	Roland Lakes	1.50
179	George Mira	5.00
180	Dave Parks	4.00
181	John Thomas	1.50
182	Jack Christiansen	2.00
183	Washington Redskins Team	1.50
184	Pervis Atkins	1.50
185	Preston Carpenter	1.50
186	Angelo Coia	1.50
187	Sam Huff	6.00
188	Sonny Jurgensen	15.00
189	Paul Krause	16.00
190	Jim Martin	1.50
191	Bobby Mitchell	6.00
192	John Nisby	1.50
193	John Paluck	1.50
194	Vince Promuto	1.50
195	Charley Taylor	60.00
196	Bill McPeak	1.50
197	Checklist 1	20.00
198	Checklist 2	35.00

1966 Philadelphia

BOB HAYES
DALLAS COWBOYS END

This 198-card set of NFL players is best known for the inclusion of rookie cards of Gale Sayers and Dick Butkus (the other significant rookie card is that of Bob Hayes). This was the final year regular-issue cards were produced of players including Hall of Famers Lenny Moore, Jim Parker, Jim Brown, Roosevelt Brown, and Jim Ringo. The 198-card set lists players in alphabetical order according to city. The play card for each team features a color action photo on the front, with a description of the play on the back.

#	NM	
Complete Set (198):	875.00	
Common Player:	1.50	
1	Falcons Logo	8.00
2	Larry Benz	1.50
3	Dennis Claridge	1.50
4	Perry Lee Dunn	1.50
5	Dan Grimm	1.50
6	Alex Hawkins	1.50
7	Ralph Heck	1.50
8	Frank Lasky	1.50
9	Guy Reese	1.50
10	Bob Richards	1.50
11	Ron Smith	1.50
12	Ernie Wheelwright	1.50
13	Atlanta Falcons Roster	1.50
14	Baltimore Colts Team Card	1.50
15	Raymond Berry	7.00
16	Bob Boyd	1.50
17	Jerry Logan	1.50
18	John Mackey	6.00
19	Tom Matte	1.50
20	Lou Michaels	1.50
21	Lenny Moore	6.00
22	Jimmy Orr	1.50
23	Jim Parker	3.00
24	Johnny Unitas	30.00
25	Bob Vogel	1.50
26	Baltimore Colts Play Card	1.50
27	Chicago Bears Team Card	1.50
28	Doug Atkins	1.50
29	Rudy Bukich	1.50
30	Ron Bull	1.50
31	Dick Butkus	185.00
32	Mike Ditka	25.00
33	Joe Fortuanto	1.50
34	Bobby Joe Green	1.50
35	Roger LeClerc	1.50
36	Johnny Morris	1.50
37	Mike Pyle	1.50
38	Gale Sayers	210.00

#	Player	Price
39	Gale Sayers (Bears)	25.00
40	Cleveland Browns Team Card	1.50
41	Jim Brown	55.00
42	Gary Collins	1.50
43	Ross Fichtner	1.50
44	Ernie Green	1.50
45	Gene Hickerson	2.00
46	Jim Houston	1.50
47	John Morrow	1.50
48	Walter Roberts	1.50
49	Frank Ryan	1.50
50	Dick Schafrath	1.50
51	*Paul Wiggin*	2.00
52	Cleveland Browns Play Card	1.50
53	Dallas Cowboys Team Card	1.50
54	*George Andrie*	2.00
55	Frank Ryan	1.50
56	Mike Connelly	1.50
57	Cornell Green	1.50
58	*Bob Hayes*	25.00
59	Chuck Howley	10.00
60	Bob Lilly	15.00
61	Don Meredith	25.00
62	Don Perkins	1.50
63	Mel Renfro	8.00
64	Danny Villanueva	1.50
65	Dallas Cowboys Play Card	1.50
66	Detroit Lions Team Card	1.50
67	Roger Brown	1.50
68	John Gordy	1.50
69	Alex Karras	10.00
70	Dick LeBeau	1.50
71	Amos Marsh	1.50
72	Milt Plum	1.50
73	Bobby Smith	1.50
74	Wayne Rasmussen	1.50
75	Pat Studstill	1.50
76	Wayne Walker	1.50
77	Tom Watkins	1.50
78	Detroit Lions Play Card	1.50
79	Green Bay Packers Team Card	1.50
80	Herb Adderley	5.00
81	*Lee Roy Caffey*	2.00
82	Don Chandler	1.50
83	Willie Davis	5.00
84	Boyd Dowler	1.50
85	Forrest Gregg	4.00
86	Tom Moore	1.50
87	Ray Nitschke	10.00
88	Bart Starr	25.00
89	Jim Taylor	13.00
90	Willie Wood	4.50
91	Green Bay Packers Play Card	1.50
92	Los Angeles Rams Team Card	1.50
93	Willie Brown	1.50
94	Dick Bass, Roman Gabriel	2.50
95	Bruce Gossett	2.50
96	Deacon Jones	6.00
97	Tommy McDonald	1.50
98	Marlin McKeever	1.50
99	Aaron Martin	1.50
100	Ed Meador	1.50
101	Bill Munson	2.00
102	Merlin Olsen	9.00
103	Jim Stiger	1.50
104	Los Angeles Rams Play Card	1.50
105	Minnesota Vikings Team Card	1.50
106	Grady Alderman	1.50
107	Bill Brown	1.50
108	Fred Cox	1.50
109	Paul Flatley	1.50
110	Rip Hawkins	1.50
111	Tommy Mason	1.50
112	Ed Sharockman	1.50
113	Gordon Smith	1.50
114	Fran Tarkenton	20.00
115	Mick Tingelhoff	2.00
116	*Bobby Walden*	1.50
117	Minnesota Vikings Play Card	1.50
118	New York Giants Team Card	1.50
119	Roosevelt Brown	4.00
120	*Henry Carr*	2.00
121	Clarence Childs	1.50
122	*Tucker Frederickson*	2.00
123	Jerry Hillebrand	1.50
124	Greg Larson	1.50
125	*Spider Lockhart*	3.00
126	Dick Lynch	1.50
127	Earl Morrall, Bob Scholtz	1.50
128	Joe Morrison	1.50
129	Steve Thurlow	1.50
130	New York Giants Play Card	1.50
131	Philadelphia Eagles Team Card	1.50
132	Sam Baker	1.50
133	Maxie Baughan	1.50
134	*Bob Brown*	6.00
135	Timmy Brown	1.50
136	Irv Cross	2.00
137	Earl Gros	1.50
138	Ray Poage	1.50
139	Nate Ramsey	1.50
140	Pete Retzlaff	1.50
141	Jim Ringo	3.50
142	Norm Snead	2.00
143	Philadelphia Eagles Play Card	1.50
144	Pittsburgh Steelers Team Card	1.50
145	Gary Ballman	1.50
146	Charley Bradshaw	1.50
147	Jim Butler	1.50
148	Mike Clark	1.50
149	*Dick Hoak*	2.00
150	*Roy Jefferson*	2.00
151	Frank Lambert	1.50
152	Mike Lind	1.50
153	*Bill Nelsen*	4.00
154	Clarence Peaks	1.50
155	Clendon Thomas	1.50
156	Pittsburgh Steelers Play Card	1.50
157	St. Louis Cardinals Team Card	1.50
158	Jim Bakken	1.50
159	Bobby Joe Conrad	1.50
160	*Willis Crenshaw*	2.00
161	Bob DeMarco	1.50
162	Pat Fischer	2.00
163	Charlie Johnson	2.00
164	Dale Meinert	1.50
165	Sonny Randle	1.50
166	*Sam Silas*	2.00
167	Bill Triplett	1.50
168	Larry Wilson	4.00
169	St. Louis Cardinals Play Card	1.50
170	San Francisco 49ers Team Card	1.50
171	Kermit Alexander	1.50
172	Bruce Bosley	1.50
173	John Brodie	9.00
174	Bernie Casey	1.50
175	John David Crow	1.50
176	Tommy Davis	1.50
177	Jim Johnson	1.50
178	Gary Lewis	1.50
179	Dave Parks	1.50
180	Walter Rock	1.50
181	*Ken Willard*	4.00
182	San Francisco 49ers Play Card	1.50
183	Washington Redskins Team Card	1.50
184	Rickie Harris	1.50
185	Sonny Jurgensen	9.00
186	Paul Krause	5.00
187	Bobby Mitchell	5.00
188	Vince Promuto	1.50
189	*Pat Richter*	3.00
190	Joe Rutgens	1.50
191	John Sample	1.50
192	Lonnie Sanders	1.50
193	Jim Steffen	1.50
194	Charley Taylor	18.00
195	Washington Redskins Play Card	1.50
196	Referee signals	5.00
197	Checklist 1	15.00
198	Checklist 2	40.00

1967 Philadelphia

This was the last time until 1989 that Topps would face a direct challenge in the football card market, as the Philadelphia Chewing Gum Corp. ceased production of football cards after this issue. (The company returned with sets of NFL Hall of Famers in 1988 and 1989). The 198-card set has yellow borders on the front, and backs were printed on white or brown card stock. As usual, teams were grouped alphabetically by city name, players were grouped alphabetically by last name. Team logo cards rounded out the grouping of each team. There is an error in the set: on card #14, Raymond Berry, the picture actually shows Bob Boyd. Also, the roster for the New Orleans Saints team card (#121) was included on the back of the logo card (#132), the set includes team picture cards and team logo cards for all other teams except the expansion Saints (The front of the card reads, "On the back of this card are names of New Orleans players and the teams from which they were picked" while the back simply has a capsule on the Saints' New Orleans impact). Another error, on card #26 reads "Bukich" on the front and "Buckich" on the back. Rookies in this set include Tommy Nobis, Leroy Kelly, Lee Roy Jordan, and Chris Hanburger. Second-year cards include Dick Butkus, Gale Sayers, Bob Brown, Roy Jefferson, Jim Bakken and Ken Willard. This was the last year for regular-issue cards of Hall of Famers Forrest Gregg and Paul Hornung. The first members of the New Orleans Saints made their debut in the '67 Philly set.

#	Player	NM
	Complete Set (198):	650.00
	Common Player:	1.50
1	Falcons Team	5.00
2	*Junior Coffey*	1.50
3	Alex Hawkins	1.50
4	*Randy Johnson*	3.00
5	Lou Kirouac	1.50
6	Billy Martin	1.50
7	*Tommy Nobis*	16.00
8	*Jerry Richardson*	6.00
9	Marion Rushing	1.50
10	Ron Smith	1.50
11	Ernie Wheelwright	1.50
12	Atlanta Falcons Insignia	1.50
13	Baltimore Colts	1.50
14	Raymond Berry	5.00
15	Bob Boyd	1.50
16	Ordell Braase	1.50
17	Alvin Haymond	1.50
18	Tony Lorick	1.50
19	Lenny Lyles	1.50
20	John Mackey	5.00
21	Tom Matte	1.50
22	Lou Michaels	1.50
23	Johnny Unitas	30.00
24	Baltimore Colts Insignia	1.50
25	Chicago Bears Team	1.50
26	Rudy Bukich	1.50
27	Ron Bull	1.50
28	Dick Butkus	60.00
29	Mike Ditka	25.00
30	*Dick Gordon*	1.50
31	Roger LeClerc	1.50
32	Bennie McRae	1.50
33	Richie Petibon	2.50
34	Mike Pyle	1.50
35	Gale Sayers	75.00
36	Chicago Bears Insignia	1.50
37	Cleveland Browns Team	1.50
38	Johnny Brewer	1.50
39	Gary Collins	1.50
40	Ross Fichtner	1.50
41	Ernie Green	1.50
42	Gene Hickerson	1.50
43	Leroy Kelly	30.00
44	Frank Ryan	1.50
45	Dick Schafrath	1.50
46	Paul Warfield	20.00
47	John Wooten	1.50
48	Cleveland Browns Insignia	1.50
49	Dallas Cowboys Team	1.50
50	George Andrie	1.50
51	Cornell Green	1.50
52	Bob Hayes	10.00
53	Chuck Howley	1.50
54	*Lee Roy Jordan*	22.00
55	Bob Lilly	12.00
56	*Dave Manders*	2.00
57	Don Meredith	20.00
58	*Dan Reeves*	33.00
59	Mel Renfro	2.50
60	Dallas Cowboys Insignia	1.50
61	Detroit Lions Team	1.50
62	Roger Brown	1.50
63	Gail Cogdill	1.50
64	John Gordy	1.50
65	Ron Kramer	1.50
66	Dick LeBeau	1.50
67	*Mike Lucci*	6.00
68	Amos Marsh	1.50
69	Tom Nowatzke	1.50
70	Pat Studstill	1.50
71	Karl Sweetan	1.50
72	Detroit Lions Insignia	1.50
73	Green Bay Packers Team	1.50
74	Herb Adderley	4.50
75	Lee Roy Caffey	1.50
76	Willie Davis	4.50
77	Forrest Gregg	4.00
78	Henry Jordan	1.50
79	Ray Nitschke	6.00
80	*Dave Robinson*	5.00
81	Bob Skoronski	1.50
82	Bart Starr	20.00
83	Willie Wood	3.00
84	Green Bay Packers Insignia	1.50
85	Los Angeles Rams Team	1.50
86	Dick Bass	1.50
87	Maxie Baughan	1.50
88	Roman Gabriel	4.00
89	Bruce Gossett	1.50
90	Deacon Jones	5.00
91	Tommy McDonald	1.50
92	Marlin McKeever	1.50
93	Tom Moore	1.50
94	Merlin Olsen	7.00
95	Clancy Williams	1.50
96	Los Angeles Rams Insignia	1.50
97	Minnesota Vikings Team	1.50
98	Grady Alderman	1.50
99	Bill Brown	1.50
100	Fred Cox	1.50
101	Paul Flatley	1.50
102	Dale Hackbart	1.50
103	Jim Marshall	3.00
104	Tommy Mason	1.50
105	Milt Sunde	1.50
106	Fran Tarkenton	20.00
107	Mick Tingelhoff	2.00
108	Minnesota Vikings Insignia	1.50
109	New York Giants Team	1.50
110	Henry Carr	1.50
111	Clarence Childs	1.50
112	Allen Jacobs	1.50
113	*Homer Jones*	2.00
114	Tom Kennedy	1.50
115	Spider Lockhart	1.50
116	Joe Morrison	1.50
117	Francis Peay	1.50
118	Jeff Smith	1.50
119	Aaron Thomas	1.50
120	New York Giants Insignia	1.50
121	New Orleans Saints Team	2.00
122	Charley Bradshaw	1.50
123	Paul Hornung	18.00
124	Elbert Kimbrough	1.50
125	Earl Leggett	1.50
126	Obert Logan	1.50
127	Riley Mattson	1.50
128	John Morrow	1.50
129	Bob Scholtz	1.50
130	*Dave Whitsell*	2.00
131	Gary Wood	1.50
132	New Orleans Saints Insignia	1.50
133	Philadelphia Eagles Team	1.50
134	Sam Baker	1.50
135	Bob Brown	2.00
136	Jim Brown	1.50
137	Earl Gros	1.50
138	Dave Lloyd	1.50
139	Floyd Peters	1.50
140	Pete Retzlaff	1.50
141	Joe Scarpati	1.50
142	Norm Snead	2.00
143	Jim Skaggs	1.50
144	Philadelphia Eagles Insignia	1.50
145	Pittsburgh Steelers Team	1.50
146	Bill Asbury	1.50
147	John Baker	1.50
148	Gary Ballman	1.50
149	Mike Clark	1.50
150	Riley Gunnels	1.50
151	John Hilton	1.50
152	Roy Jefferson	1.50
153	Brady Keys	1.50
154	Ben McGee	1.50
155	Bill Nelsen	2.00
156	Pittsburgh Steelers Insignia	1.50
157	St. Louis Cardinals Team	1.50
158	Jim Bakken	1.50
159	Bobby Joe Conrad	1.50
160	Ken Gray	1.50
161	Charlie Johnson	2.00
162	Joe Robb	1.50
163	*Johnny Roland*	4.00
164	Roy Shivers	1.50
165	*Jackie Smith*	15.00
166	Jerry Stovall	1.50
167	Larry Wilson	4.00
168	St. Louis Cardinals Insignia	1.50
169	San Francisco 49ers Team	1.50
170	Kermit Alexander	1.50
171	Bruce Bosley	1.50
172	John Brodie	7.50
173	Bernie Casey	1.50
174	Tommy Davis	1.50
175	Howard Mudd	1.50
176	Dave Parks	1.50
177	John Thomas	1.50
178	*Dave Wilcox*	5.00
179	Ken Willard	4.00
180	San Francisco 49ers Insignia	1.50
181	Washington Redskins Team	1.50
182	*Charlie Gogolak*	2.00
183	*Chris Hanburger*	8.00
184	*Len Hauss*	3.00
185	Sonny Jurgensen	8.00
186	Bobby Mitchell	5.00
187	Bris Owens	1.50
188	Jim Shorter	1.50
189	*Jerry Smith*	2.00
190	Charley Taylor	7.50
191	A.D. Whitfield	1.50
192	Washington Redskins Insignia	1.50
193	Cleveland Browns	5.00
194	New York Giants Play Card (Joe Morrison)	1.50
195	Atlanta Falcons Play Card (Ernie Wheelright)	1.50
196	Referee Signals	2.00
197	Checklist 1	18.00
198	Checklist 2	35.00

1991 Pinnacle Promo Panels

The 18-card, 5" x 7" panel set each features four preview cards from Pinnacle's 1991 football debut and were issued at the Super Bowl XXVI Card Show. The four-card panels have the same design as the regular-issue set.

#	Players	MT
	Complete Set (18):	100.00
	Common Player:	3.00
1	John Alt, Eric Green, Don Mosebar, Greg Townsend	3.00
2	Bruce Armstrong, Joe Montana, Jim Lachey, Bruce Matthews	8.00
3	Don Beebe, Irving Fryar, Ricky Proehl, Vinny Testaverde	4.00
4	Duane Bickett, Tony Bennett, John Friesz, Rob Burnett	3.00
5	Mark Bortz, Warren Moon, Jim Breech, Eric Metcalf	4.00
6	Roger Craig, Issiac Holt, Kevin Mack, Shane Conlan	4.00
7	Wendell Davis, Gaston Green, Tony Mandarich, Merril Hoge	3.00
8	Dermontti Dawson, Jerry Gray, Nick Lowery, Scott Case	3.00
9	Chris Doleman, Troy Aikman, Sterling Sharpe, Sean Landeta	8.00
10	Darryl Henley, Karl Mecklenberg, Sam Mills, Rod Woodson	4.00
11	Mark Higgs, Jay Schroeder, Mark Carrier, Jim Everett	4.00
12	Jay Hilgenberg, Dan Marino, Anthony Carter, Howie Long	15.00
13	Louis Lipps, John Offerdahl, Herschel Walker, Jeff George	4.00
14	Greg McMurtry, Henry Ellard, Brian Mitchell, Mark Clayton	4.00
15	Nate Odomes, Allen Pinkett, Don Majkowski, Dave Meggett	3.00
16	Andre Rison, Jeff Hostetler, Hugh Millen, Jack Del Rio	4.00
17	Emmitt Smith, Dennis Smith, Bill Brooks, Bobby Hebert	18.00
18	Reyna Thompson, Louis Oliver, Steve Broussard, Andre Reed	4.00

1991 Pinnacle

Score's first effort at a premium edition is its 415-card 1991 Pinnacle set. Each card front features an action shot and a mug shot against a black background with white borders. The back has an action photo superimposed against a black background, plus statistics, a profile and a biography. An anti-counterfeit band appears on the back of each card. Subsets include Head-to-Head, Technicians, Game Winners, Idols and Sidelines. There are also 58 rookies featured in the set; their cards have green backgrounds on the front, and a mug shot on the back. A standard-size Emmitt Smith promotional card was also created. It is identical in design to its regular set's counterpart, except the text on the back of the promo card mentions Smith's holdout before the season. Twelve four-card panels (5" x 7" each) were also made and use the same design as the regular 1991 cards. Each card in the panel has the same number as its counterpart in the regular set, but the panel is unnumbered.

#	Player	MT
	Complete Set (415):	35.00
	Common Player:	.10
	Minor Stars:	.20
	Wax Box:	20.00
1	Warren Moon	.30
2	Morten Andersen	.10
3	Rohn Stark	.10
4	Mark Bortz	.10
5	*Mark Higgs*	.10
6	Troy Aikman	4.00
7	John Elway	1.50
8	Neal Anderson	.10
9	Chris Doleman	.10
10	Jay Schroeder	.10
11	Sterling Sharpe	.40
12	Steve DeBerg	.10
13	Ronnie Lott	.10
14	Sea Landeta	.10
15	Jim Everett	.10
16	Jim Breech	.10
17	Barry Foster	.10
18	Mike Merriweather	.10
19	Eric Metcalf	.40
20	Mark Carrier	.10
21	James Brooks	.10
22	Nate Odomes	.10
23	Rodney Hampton	.50
24	Chris Miller	.10
25	Roger Craig	.10
26	Louis Oliver	.10
27	Allen Pinkett	.10
28	Bubby Brister	.10
29	Reyna Thompson	.10
30	Issiac Holt	.10
31	Steve Broussard	.10
32	Christian Okoye	.10
33	Dave Meggett	.10
34	Andre Reed	.20
35	Shane Conlan	.10
36	Eric Ball	.10
37	Johnny Bailey	.10
38	Don Majkowski	.10
39	Gerald Williams	.10
40	Kevin Mack	.10
41	Jeff Herrod	.10
42	Emmitt Smith	6.00
43	Wendell Davis	.10
44	Lorenzo White	.10
45	Andre Rison	.20
46	Jerry Gray	.10
47	Dennis Smith	.10
48	Gaston Green	.10
49	Dermontti Dawson	.10
50	Jeff Hostetler	.30
51	Nick Lowery	.10
52	Merril Hoge	.10
53	Bobby Hebert	.10
54	Scott Case	.10
55	Jack Del Rio	.10
56	Cornelius Bennett	.10
57	Tony Mandarich	.10
58	Bill Brooks	.10
59	Jessie Tuggle	.10
60	*Hugh Millen*	.10
61	Tony Bennett	.10
62	*Chris Dishman*	.10
63	*Darryl Henley*	.10
64	Duane Bickett	.10
65	Jay Hilgenberg	.10
66	Joe Montana	3.50
67	Bill Fralic	.10
68	Sam Mills	.10
69	Bruce Armstrong	.10
70	Dan Marino	5.00
71	Jim Lachey	.10
72	Rod Woodson	.10
73	Simon Fletcher	.10
74	Bruce Matthews	.10
75	Howie Long	.10
76	John Friesz	.10
77	Karl Mecklenburg	.10
78	John L. Williams	.10
79	*Rob Burnett*	.10
80	Anthony Carter	.10
81	Henry Ellard	.10
82	Don Beebe	.10
83	Louis Lipps	.10
84	Greg McMurty	.10
85	Will Wolford	.10
86	Eric Green	.20
87	Irving Fryar	.10
88	John Offerdahl	.10
89	John Alt	.10
90	Tom Tupa	.10
91	Don Mosebar	.10

#	Player	MT
92	Jeff George	1.00
93	Vinny Testaverde	.20
94	Greg Townsend	.10
95	Derrick Fenner	.10
96	Brian Mitchell	.10
97	Herschel Walker	.10
98	Ricky Proehl	.10
99	Mark Clayton	.10
100	Derrick Thomas	.20
101	Jim Harbaugh	.50
102	Barry Word	.10
103	Jerry Rice	4.00
104	Keith Byars	.10
105	Marion Butts	.10
106	Rich Moran	.10
107	Thurman Thomas	.75
108	Stephone Paige	.10
109	David Johnson	.10
110	William Perry	.10
111	Haywood Jeffires	.10
112	Rodney Peete	.10
113	Andy Heck	.10
114	Kevin Ross	.10
115	Michael Carter	.10
116	Tim McKyer	.10
117	Heath Davis	.10
118	Richmond Webb	.10
119	Rich Camarillo	.10
120	James Francis	.10
121	Craig Heyward	.10
122	Hardy Nickerson	.10
123	Michael Brooks	.10
124	Fred Barnett	.30
125	Cris Carter	.40
126	Brian Jordan	.10
127	Pat Leahy	.10
128	Kevin Greene	.10
129	Trace Armstrong	.10
130	Eugene Lockhart	.10
131	Albert Lewis	.10
132	Ernie Jones	.10
133	Eric Martin	.10
134	Anthony Thompson	.10
135	Tim Krumrie	.10
136	James Lofton	.10
137	John Taylor	.10
138	Jeff Cross	.10
139	Tommy Kane	.10
140	Robb Thomas	.10
141	Gary Anderson	.10
142	Mark Murphy	.10
143	Rickey Jackson	.10
144	Ken O'Brien	.10
145	Ernest Givins	.10
146	Jessie Hester	.10
147	Deion Sanders	1.75
148	*Keith Henderson*	.10
149	Chris Singleton	.10
150	Rod Bernstine	.10
151	Quinn Early	.10
152	Boomer Esiason	.10
153	Mike Gann	.10
154	Dino Hackett	.10
155	Perry Kemp	.10
156	Mark Ingram	.10
157	Daryl Johnston	.75
158	Eugene Daniel	.10
159	Dalton Hilliard	.10
160	Rufus Porter	.10
161	Tunch Ilkin	.10
162	James Hasty	.10
163	Keith McKeller	.10
164	Heath Sherman	.10
165	Vai Sikahema	.10
166	Pat Terrell	.10
167	Anthony Munoz	.10
168	*Brad Edwards*	.10
169	Tom Rathman	.10
170	Steve McMichael	.10
171	Vaughan Johnson	.10
172	*Nate Lewis*	.10
173	Mark Rypien	.10
174	Rob Moore	.10
175	Tim Green	.10
176	Tony Casillas	.10
177	Jon Hand	.10
178	Todd McNair	.10
179	*Toi Cook*	.10
180	Eddie Brown	.10
181	Mark Jackson	.10
182	Pete Stoyanovich	.10
183	*Bryce Paup*	2.00
184	Anthony Miller	.20
185	Dan Saleaumua	.10
186	Guy McIntyre	.10
187	Broderick Thomas	.10
188	Frank Warren	.10
189	Drew Hill	.10
190	Reggie White	.40
191	Chris Hinton	.10
192	David Little	.10
193	David Fulcher	.10
194	Clarence Verdin	.10
195	Junior Seau	1.00
196	Blair Thomas	.10
197	Stan Brock	.10
198	Gary Clark	.10
199	Michael Irvin	.75
200	Ronnie Harmon	.10
201	Steve Young	3.00
202	Brian Noble	.10
203	Dan Stryzinski	.10
204	Darryl Talley	.10
205	David Alexander	.10
206	Pat Swilling	.10
207	Gary Plummer	.10
208	Robert Delpino	.10
209	Norm Johnson	.10
210	Mike Singletary	.10
211	Anthony Johnson	.10
212	Eric Allen	.10
213	Gill Fenerty	.10
214	Neil Smith	.10
215	Joe Phillips	.10
216	Ottis Anderson	.10
217	LeRoy Butler	.10
218	Ray Childress	.10
219	Rodney Holman	.10
220	Kevin Fagan	.10
221	Bruce Smith	.10
222	Brad Muster	.10
223	Mike Horan	.10
224	Steve Atwater	.10
225	Rich Gannon	.10
226	Anthony Pleasant	.10
227	Steve Jordan	.10
228	Lomas Brown	.10
229	Jackie Slater	.10
230	Brad Baxter	.10
231	Joe Morris	.10
232	Marcus Allen	.20
233	Chris Warren	1.00
234	Johnny Johnson	.10
235	Phil Simms	.10
236	Dave Krieg	.10
237	Jim McMahon	.10
238	Richard Dent	.10
239	*John Washington*	.10
240	Sammie Smith	.10
241	Brian Brennan	.10
242	Cortez Kennedy	.20
243	Tim McDonald	.10
244	Charles Haley	.10
245	Joey Browner	.10
246	Eddie Murray	.10
247	Bob Golic	.10
248	Myron Guyton	.10
249	Dennis Byrd	.10
250	Barry Sanders	4.00
251	Clay Matthews	.10
252	Pepper Johnson	.10
253	*Eric Swann*	1.00
254	Lamar Lathon	.10
255	Andre Tippett	.10
256	Tom Newberry	.10
257	Kyle Clifton	.10
258	Leslie O'Neal	.10
259	Bubba McDowell	.10
260	Scott Davis	.10
261	Wilber Marshall	.10
262	Marv Cook	.10
263	Jeff Lageman	.10
264	Mike Young	.10
265	Gary Zimmerman	.10
266	Mike Munchak	.10
267	David Treadwell	.10
268	Steve Wisniewski	.10
269	Mark Duper	.10
270	Chris Spielman	.10
271	Brett Perriman	.50
272	Lionel Washington	.10
273	Lawrence Taylor	.20
274	Mark Collins	.10
275	Mark Carrier	.10
276	Paul Gruber	.10
277	Earnest Byner	.10
278	Andre Collins	.10
279	Reggie Cobb	.10
280	Art Monk	.20
281	*Henry Jones*	.20
282	*Mike Pritchard*	.75
283	*Moe Gardner*	.20
284	*Chris Zorich*	.50
285	*Keith Traylor*	.20
286	*Mike Dumas*	.20
287	*Ed King*	.20
288	*Russell Maryland*	.20
289	*Alfred Williams*	.20
290	*Derek Russell*	.20
291	*Vinnie Clark*	.20
292	*Mike Croel*	.20
293	*Todd Marinovich*	.20
294	*Phil Hansen*	.20
295	*Aaron Craver*	.20
296	*Nick Bell*	.20
297	*Kenny Walker*	.20
298	*Roman Phifer*	.20
299	*Kanavis McGhee*	.20
300	*Ricky Ervins*	.20
301	*Jim Price*	.20
302	*John Johnson*	.20
303	*George Thornton*	.10
304	*Huey Richardson*	.20
305	*Harry Colon*	.20
306	*Antone Davis*	.20
307	*Todd Lyght*	.30
308	*Bryan Cox*	1.00
309	*Brad Goebel*	.20
310	*Eric Moten*	.20
311	*John Kasay*	.30
312	*Esera Tuaolo*	.20
313	*Bobby Wilson*	.20
314	*Mo Lewis*	.20
315	*Harvey Williams*	1.00
316	*Mike Stonebreaker*	.10
317	*Charles McRae*	.20
318	*John Flannery*	.20
319	*Ted Washington*	.20
320	*Stanley Richard*	.20
321	*Browning Nagle*	.20
322	*Ed McCaffery*	3.50
323	*Jeff Graham*	2.00
324	*Stan Thomas*	.10
325	*Lawrence Dawsey*	.20
326	*Eric Bieniemy*	.30
327	*Tim Barnett*	.20
328	*Erric Pegram*	1.50
329	Lamar Rogers	.10
330	Ernie Mills	.20
331	*Pat Harlow*	.20
332	Greg Lewis	.20
333	*Jarrod Bunch*	.20
334	*Dan McGwire*	.20
335	*Randal Hill*	.50
336	*Leonard Russell*	.50
337	Carnell Lake	.10
338	Brian Blades	.10
339	Darrell Green	.10
340	Bobby Humphrey	.10
341	Mervyn Fernandez	.10
342	Ricky Sanders	.10
343	Keith Jackson	.20
344	Carl Banks	.10
345	Gill Byrd	.10
346	Al Toon	.10
347	Stephen Baker	.10
348	Randall Cunningham	.10
349	Flipper Anderson	.10
350	Jay Novacek	.10
351	Young/Smith (HH)	.40
352	Sanders/Browner (HH)	.75
353	Montana/Carrier (HH)	.50
354	Thomas/Taylor (HH)	.20
355	Rice/Green (HH)	.50
356	Warren Moon	.20
357	Anthony Munoz (TECH)	.10
358	Barry Sanders (TECH)	1.50
359	Jerry Rice (TECH)	1.00
360	Joey Browner (TECH)	.10
361	Morten Andersen (TECH)	.10
362	Sean Landeta (TECH)	.10
363	Thurman Thomas (GW)	.20
364	Emmitt Smith (GW)	3.00
365	Gaston Green (GW)	.10
366	Barry Sanders (GW)	2.00
367	Christian Okoye (GW)	.10
368	Earnest Byner (GW)	.10
369	Neal Anderson (GW)	.10
370	Herschel Walker (GW)	.10
371	Rodney Hampton (GW)	.20
372	Darryl Talley (IDOL)	.10
373	Mark Carrier (IDOL)	.10
374	Jim Breech (IDOL)	.10
375	Rodney Hampton (IDOL)	.20
376	Kevin Mack (IDOL)	.10
377	Steve Jordan (IDOL)	.10
378	Boomer Esiason (IDOL)	.10
379	Steve DeBerg (IDOL)	.10
380	Al Toon (IDOL)	.10
381	Ronnie Lott (IDOL)	.10
382	Henry Ellard (IDOL)	.10
383	Troy Aikman (IDOL)	1.25
384	Thurman Thomas (IDOL)	.50
385	Dan Marino (IDOL)	1.75
386	Howie Long (IDOL)	.10
387	Immaculate Reception (Franco Harris)	.10
388	Esera Tuaolo	.10
389	Super Bowl XXVI (Super Bowl Records)	.10
390	Charles Mann	.10
391	Kenny Walker	.10
392	Reggie Roby	.10
393	*Bruce Pickens*	.20
394	Ray Childress (SL)	.10
395	Karl Mecklenburg (SL)	.10
396	Dean Biasucci (SL)	.10
397	John Alt (SL)	.10
398	Marcus Allen (SL)	.10
399	John Offerdahl (SL)	.10
400	Richard Tardits (SL)	.10
401	Al Toon (SL)	.10
402	Joey Browner (SL)	.10
403	Spencer Tillman (SL)	.10
404	Jay Novacek (SL)	.10
405	Stephen Braggs (SL)	.10
406	Mike Tice (SL)	.10
407	Kevin Greene (SL)	.10
408	Reggie White (SL)	.10
409	Brian Noble (SL)	.10
410	Bart Oates (SL)	.10
411	Art Monk (SL)	.10
412	Ron Wolfley (SL)	.10
413	Louis Lipps (SL)	.10
414	*Dante Jones* (SL)	.10
415	Kenneth Davis (SL)	.10

A card number in parentheses ( ) indicates the set is unnumbered.

1992 Pinnacle Samples

The six-card, standard-size set features six cards from the 1992 Pinnacle football set with the same design, as well as the same card numbers on the backs as their regular-issue counterparts.

		MT
Complete Set (6):		5.00
Common Player:		1.00
1	Reggie White	2.00
5	Pepper Johnson	1.00
19	Chris Spielman	1.00
59	Mike Croel	1.00
100	Bobby Hebert	1.00
102	Rodney Hampton	1.50

1992 Pinnacle

Score decreased its second Pinnacle set to 360 cards. The fronts have action shots with a white frame and black border. Parts of the photos extend over the background, giving them a cut-out look. The player's name is at the bottom of the card in a team color-coded bar. The horizontal backs have black backgrounds with white borders and a purple band that contains the player's name. Also included on the backs are a profile, biography, statistics and a mug shot. Subsets include Rookies, Sidelines, Game Winners, Hall of Famers and Idols. Insert sets include Team Pinnacle cards (13) and Team 2000 (30 cards). A six-card promotional set was also produced to preview the regular set. The cards have a similar design to the regular set, but each card back is marked as a "SAMPLE."

		MT
Complete Set (360):		20.00
Common Player:		.05
Minor Stars:		.10
Wax Box:		25.00
1	Reggie White	.10
2	Eric Green	.05
3	Craig Heyward	.05
4	Phil Simms	.05
5	Pepper Johnson	.05
6	Sean Landeta	.05
7	Dino Hackett	.05
8	Andre Ware	.05
9	Ricky Nattiel	.05
10	Jim Price	.05
11	Jim Ritcher	.05
12	Kelly Stouffer	.05
13	Ray Crockett	.05
14	Steve Tasker	.05
15	Barry Sanders	3.50
16	Pat Swilling	.05
17	Moe Gardner	.05
18	Steve Young	2.50
19	Chris Spielman	.05
20	Richard Dent	.05
21	Anthony Munoz	.05
22	Thurman Thomas	.50
23	Ricky Sanders	.05
24	Steve Atwater	.05
25	Tony Tolbert	.05
26	Haywood Jeffires	.05
27	Duane Bickett	.05
28	Tim McDonald	.05
29	Cris Carter	.10
30	Derrick Thomas	.10
31	Hugh Millen	.05
32	Bart Oates	.05
33	Darryl Talley	.05
34	Marion Butts	.05
35	Pete Stoyanovich	.05
36	Ronnie Lott	.05
37	Simon Fletcher	.05
38	Morten Andersen	.05
39	Clyde Simmons	.05
40	Mark Rypien	.05
41	Henry Ellard	.05
42	Michael Irvin	.50
43	Louis Lipps	.05
44	John L. Williams	.05
45	Broderick Thomas	.05
46	Don Majkowski	.05
47	William Perry	.05
48	David Fulcher	.05
49	Tony Bennett	.05
50	Clay Matthews	.05
51	Warren Moon	.10
52	Bruce Armstrong	.05
53	Bill Brooks	.05
54	Greg Townsend	.05
55	Steve Broussard	.05
56	Mel Gray	.05
57	Kevin Mack	.05
58	Emmitt Smith	5.00
59	Mike Croel	.05
60	Brian Mitchell	.05
61	Bennie Blades	.05
62	Carnell Lake	.05
63	Cornelius Bennett	.05
64	Darrell Thompson	.05
65	Jessie Hester	.05
66	Marv Cook	.05
67	Tim Brown	.10
68	Mark Duper	.05
69	Robert Delpino	.05
70	Eric Martin	.05
71	Wendell Davis	.05
72	Vaughan Johnson	.05
73	Brian Blades	.05
74	Ed King	.05
75	Gaston Green	.05
76	Christian Okoye	.05
77	Rohn Stark	.05
78	Kevin Greene	.05
79	Jay Novacek	.10
80	Chip Lohmiller	.05
81	Cris Dishman	.05
82	Ethan Horton	.05
83	Pat Harlow	.05
84	Mark Ingram	.05
85	Mark Carrier	.05
86	Sam Mills	.05
87	Mark Higgs	.05
88	Keith Jackson	.10
89	Gary Anderson	.05
90	Ken Harvey	.05
91	Anthony Carter	.05
92	Randall McDaniel	.05
93	Johnny Johnson	.10
94	Shane Conlan	.05
95	Sterling Sharpe	.10
96	Guy McIntyre	.05
97	Albert Lewis	.05
98	Chris Doleman	.05
99	Andre Rison	.10
100	Bobby Hebert	.05
101	Dan Owens	.05
102	Rodney Hampton	.10
103	Ernie Jones	.05
104	Reggie Cobb	.05
105	Wilber Marshall	.05
106	Mike Munchak	.05
107	Cortez Kennedy	.05
108	Todd Lyght	.05
109	Burt Grossman	.05
110	Ferrell Edmunds	.05
111	Jim Everett	.05
112	Hardy Nickerson	.05
113	Andre Tippett	.05
114	Ronnie Harmon	.05
115	Andre Waters	.05
116	Ernest Givins	.05
117	Eric Hill	.05
118	Eric Pegram	.10
119	Jarrod Bunch	.05
120	Marcus Allen	.10
121	Barry Foster	.25
122	Kent Hull	.05
123	Neal Anderson	.05
124	Stephen Braggs	.05
125	Nick Lowery	.05
126	Jeff Hostetler	.10
127	Michael Carter	.05
128	Don Warren	.05
129	Brad Baxter	.05
130	John Taylor	.05
131	Harold Green	.05
132	Mike Merriweather	.05
133	Gary Clark	.05
134	Vince Buck	.05
135	Dan Saleaumua	.05
136	Gary Zimmerman	.05
137	Richmond Webb	.05
138	Art Monk	.05
139	Mervyn Fernandez	.05
140	Mark Jackson	.05
141	Freddie Joe Nunn	.05
142	Jeff Lageman	.05
143	Kenny Walker	.05
144	Mark Carrier	.05
145	Jon Vaughn	.05
146	Greg Davis	.05
147	Bubby Brister	.05
148	Mo Lewis	.05
149	Howie Long	.05
150	Rod Bernstine	.05
151	Nick Bell	.05
152	Terry Allen	.50
153	William Fuller	.05
154	Dexter Carter	.05
155	Gene Atkins	.05
156	Don Beebe	.05
157	Mark Collins	.05
158	Jerry Ball	.05
159	Fred Barnett	.05
160	Rodney Holman	.05
161	Stephen Baker	.05
162	Jeff Graham	.10
163	Leonard Russell	.10
164	Jeff Gossett	.05
165	Vinny Testaverde	.05
166	Maurice Hurst	.05
167	Louis Oliver	.05
168	Jim Morrissey	.05
169	Greg Kragen	.05
170	Andre Collins	.05
171	Dave Meggett	.05
172	Keith Henderson	.05
173	Vince Newsome	.05
174	Chris Hinton	.05
175	James Hasty, Steve Sewell	.05
176	John Offerdahl	.05
177	Lomas Brown	.05
178	Neil O'Donnell	.10
179	Leonard Marshall	.05
180	Bubba McDowell	.05
181	Herman Moore	2.00
182	Rob Moore	.05
183	Earnest Byner	.05
184	Keith McCants	.05
185	Floyd Turner	.05
186	Steve Jordan	.05
187	Nate Odomes	.05
188	Jeff Herrod	.05
189	Jim Harbaugh	.10
190	Jessie Tuggle	.05
191	Al Smith	.05
192	Lawrence Dawsey	.05
193	*Steve Bono*	1.00
194	Greg Lloyd	.05
195	Steve Wisniewski	.05
196	Larry Kelm	.05
197	Tommy Kane	.05
198	*Mark Schlereth*	.05
199	Ray Childress	.05
200	Vincent Brown	.05
201	Rodney Peete	.10
202	Dennis Smith	.05
203	Bruce Matthews	.05
204	Rickey Jackson	.05
205	Eric Allen	.05
206	Rich Camarillo	.05
207	Jim Lachey	.05
208	Kevin Ross	.05
209	Irving Fryar	.05
210	Mark Clayton	.05
211	Keith Byars	.05
212	John Elway	.75
213	Harris Barton	.05
214	Aeneas Williams	.05
215	Rich Gannon	.05
216	Toi Cook	.05
217	Rod Woodson	.10
218	Gary Anderson	.05
219	Reggie Roby	.05
220	Karl Mecklenburg	.05
221	Rufus Porter	.05
222	Jon Hand	.05
223	Tim Barnett	.05
224	Eric Swann	.10
225	Eugene Robinson	.05
226	Mike Young	.05
227	Frank Warren	.05
228	Mike Kenn	.05
229	Tim Green	.05
230	Barry Word	.05
231	Mike Pritchard	.05
232	John Kasay	.05
233	Derek Russell	.05
234	Jim Breech	.05
235	Pierce Holt	.05
236	Tim Krumrie	.05
237	William Roberts	.05
238	Erik Kramer	.10
239	Brett Perriman	.05
240	Reyna Thompson	.05
241	Chris Miller	.05
242	Drew Hill	.05
243	Curtis Duncan	.05
244	Seth Joyner	.05
245	Calvin Williams	.05
246	Ken Norton	.05
247	James Joseph	.05
248	*Bennie Thompson*	.05
249	Tunch Ilkin	.05
250	Brad Edward	.05
251	Jeff Jaeger	.05
252	Gill Byrd	.05
253	Jeff Feagles	.05
254	*Jamie Dukes*	.05
255	Greg McMurtry	.05

256	Anthony Johnson	.05
257	Lamar Lathon	.05
258	John Roper	.05
259	Lorenzo White	.05
260	Brian Noble	.05
261	Chris Singleton	.05
262	Todd Marinovich	.05
263	Jay Hilgenberg	.05
264	Kyle Clifton	.05
265	Tony Casillas	.05
266	James Francis	.05
267	Eddie Anderson	.05
268	Tim Harris	.05
269	James Lofton	.05
270	Jay Schroeder	.05
271	Ed West	.05
272	Don Mosebar	.05
273	Jackie Slater	.05
274	*Fred McAfee*	.05
276	Charles Mann	.05
277	Ron Hall	.05
278	Darrell Green	.05
279	Jeff Cross	.05
280	Jeff Wright	.05
281	Issiac Holt	.05
282	Dermontti Dawson	.05
283	Michael Haynes	.05
284	Tony Mandarich	.05
285	Leroy Hoard	.05
286	Darryl Henley	.05
287	Tim McGee	.05
288	Willie Gault	.05
289	Dalton Hilliard	.05
290	Tim McKyer	.05
291	Tom Waddle	.05
292	Eric Thomas	.05
293	Herschel Walker	.05
294	Donnell Woolford	.05
295	James Brooks	.05
296	Brad Muster	.05
297	Brent Jones	.05
298	Erik Howard	.05
299	Alvin Harper	.10
300	Joey Browner	.05
301	Jack Del Rio	.05
302	Cleveland Gary	.05
303	Brett Favre	5.00
304	Freeman McNeil	.05
305	Willie Green	.05
306	Percy Snow	.05
307	Neil Smith	.05
308	Eric Bieniemy	.05
309	Keith Traylor	.05
310	Ernie Mills	.05
311	Will Wolford	.05
312	Robert Young	.05
313	Anthony Smith	.05
314	*Robert Porcher*	.50
315	*Leon Searcy*	.05
316	*Amp Lee*	.20
317	*Siran Stacy*	.05
318	*Patrick Rowe*	.05
319	*Chris Mims*	.05
320	*Matt Elliott*	.05
321	*Ricardo McDonald*	
322	Keith Hamilton	.05
323	*Edgar Bennett*	1.00
324	*Chris Hakel*	.05
325	*Dexter McNabb*	.05
326	*Roderick Milstead*	.05
327	*Joe Bowden*	.05
328	*Brian Bollinger*	.05
329	*Darryl Williams*	.05
330	*Tommy Vardell*	.15
331	Glenn Parker	.05
332	Herschel Walker	.05
333	Mike Cofer	.05
334	Mark Rypien	.05
335	Andre Rison	.10
336	Henry Ellard	.05
337	Rob Moore	.05
338	Fred Barnett	.05
339	Mark Clayton	.05
340	Eric Martin	.05
341	Irving Fryar	.05
342	Tim Brown	.10
343	Sterling Sharpe	.10
344	Gary Clark	.05
345	John Mackey	.05
346	Lem Barney	.05
347	John Riggins	.05
348	Marion Butts	.05
349	Jeff Lageman	.05
350	Eric Green	.05
351	Reggie White	.10
352	Marv Cook	.05
353	John Elway, Roger Staubach	.50
354	Steve Tasker	.05
355	Nick Lowery	.05
356	Mark Clayton	.05
357	Warren Moon	.10
358	Eric Metcalf	.05
359	Charles Haley	.05
360	*Terrell Buckley*	.05

rate of one per every 36 packs. The cards have a gold foil stripe at the bottom with the player's name and position. A black stripe beneath this gold stripe has a card number (1 of 13, etc.), but this number only appears on one side of the card. An offensive player is featured on one side, while a standout defensive counterpart is on the other. The cards feature the artwork of Christopher Greco.

		MT
Complete Set (13):		80.00
Common Player:		5.00
Minor Stars:		10.00
1	Mark Rypien, Ronnie Lott	5.00
2	Barry Sanders, Derrick Thomas	20.00
3	Thurman Thomas, Pat Swilling	10.00
4	Eric Green, Steve Atwater	5.00
5	Haywood Jeffires, Darrell Green	5.00
6	Michael Irvin, Eric Allen	10.00
7	Bruce Matthews, Jerry Ball	5.00
8	Steve Wisniewski, Pepper Johnson	5.00
9	William Roberts, Karl Mecklenburg	5.00
10	Jim Lachey, William Fuller	5.00
11	Anthony Munoz, Reggie White	10.00
12	Mel Gray, Steve Tasker	5.00
13	Jeff Jaeger, Jeff Gossett	5.00

1992 Pinnacle Team 2000

BRETT FAVRE

The NFL's projected stars of the year 2000 are featured on these inserts, available randomly two per 27-card jumbo pack of 1992 Score Pinnacle football. The card is framed on the left and bottom by a black border. "Team 2000" is written in gold foil along the left side of the card; the player's name is in gold foil at the bottom. A team helmet logo intersects the two borders. The card back has a career summary and player photo against a black background. The horizontally-designed back also has a card number (1 of 30, etc.).

		MT
Complete Set (30):		15.00
Common Player:		.25
Minor Stars:		.50
1	Todd Marinovich	.25
2	Rodney Hampton	.50
3	Mike Croel	.25
4	Leonard Russell	.50
5	Herman Moore	.75
6	Rob Moore	.50
7	Jon Vaughn	.25
8	Lamar Lathon	.25
9	Ed King	.25
10	Moe Gardner	.25
11	Barry Foster	.25
12	Eric Green	.25
13	Kenny Walker	.25
14	Tim Barnett	.25
15	Derrick Thomas	.50
16	Steve Atwater	.25
17	Nick Bell	.25
18	John Friesz	.50
19	Emmitt Smith	3.00
20	Eric Swann	.25
21	Barry Sanders	4.00
22	Mark Carrier	.25
23	Brett Favre	4.00
24	James Francis	.25
25	Lawrence Dawsey	.25

1992 Pinnacle Team Pinnacle

Each of these 13 insert cards features two players on it, one on each side. Score randomly included the cards in 1992 Score Pinnacle packs at a

26	Keith McCants	.25
27	Broderick Thomas	.25
28	Mike Pritchard	.25
29	Bruce Pickens	.25
30	Todd Lyght	.25

1993 Pinnacle Samples

The six-card, standard size set gave collectors a preview of the 1993 base set by issuing the first six cards of the regular-issue set. The cards were distributed in 7-1/2" x 7" panels with two rows of three cards.

		MT
Complete Set (6):		8.00
Common Player:		1.00
1	Brett Favre	6.00
2	Tommy Vardell	1.00
3	Jarrod Bunch	1.00
4	Mike Croel	1.00
5	Morten Andersen	1.00
6	Barry Foster	1.00

1993 Pinnacle

Score's 1993 Pinnacle set has 360 cards and includes two subsets - Hall of Famers and Hometown Heroes. The cards have black backgrounds, with the player's team name at the top and his name at the bottom of the card. Backs have a mug shot, one-year and career statistics, a profile and biographical information. Insert sets include Men of Autumn (55 cards), Rookies (25), Super Bowl XXVII (10), Team 2001 (30) and Team Pinnacle (13 cards). Six sample cards on a 7-1/2" x 7" panel was also produced as previews of the regular set. The cards are similar in design to the regular set, including numbers, but the sample cards are labeled as such on the backs under the anti-counterfeit band.

		MT
Complete Set (360):		25.00
Common Player:		.10
Minor Stars:		.20
Autograph F. Harris:		25.00
Wax Box:		60.00
1	Brett Favre	4.00
2	Tommy Vardell	.10
3	Jarrod Bunch	.10
4	Mike Croel	.10
5	Morten Andersen	.10
6	Barry Foster	.30
7	Chris Spielman	.10
8	Jim Jeffcoat	.10
9	Ken Ruettgers	.10
10	Cris Dishman	.10
11	Ricky Watters	.30
12	Alfred Williams	.10
13	Mark Kelso	.10
14	Moe Gardner	.10
15	Terry Allen	.10
16	Willie Gault	.10
17	Bubba McDowell	.10
18	Brian Mitchell	.10
19	Karl Mecklenburg	.10
20	Jim Everett	.20
21	Bobby Humphrey	.10
22	Tim Krumrie	.10
23	Ken Norton	.10
24	Wendell Davis	.10
25	Brad Baxter	.10
26	Mel Gray	.10
27	Jon Vaughn	.10
28	James Hasty	.10
29	Chris Warren	.50
30	Tim Harris	.10
31	Eric Metcalf	1.00
32	Rob Moore	.10
33	Charles Haley	.10
34	Leonard Marshall	.10
35	Jeff Graham	.10
36	Eugene Robinson	.10
37	Darryl Talley	.10
38	Brent Jones	.10
39	Reggie Roby	.10
40	Bruce Armstrong	.10
41	Audray McMillian	.10
42	Bern Brostek	.10
43	Tony Bennett	.10
44	Albert Lewis	.10
45	Derrick Thomas	.25
46	Cris Carter	.20
47	Richmond Webb	.10
48	Sean Landeta	.10
49	Cleveland Gary	.10
50	Mark Carrier	.10
51	Lawrence Dawsey	.10
52	Lamar Lathon	.10
53	Nick Bell	.10
54	Curtis Duncan	.10
55	Irving Fryar	.10
56	Seth Joyner	.10
57	Jay Novacek	.10
58	John L. Williams	.10
59	Amp Lee	.10
60	Marion Butts	.10
61	Clyde Simmons	.10
62	Rich Gannon	.10
63	Anthony Johnson	.10
64	Dave Meggett	.10
65	James Francis	.10
66	Trace Armstrong	.10
67	Mo Lewis	.10
68	Cornelius Bennett	.10
69	Mark Duper	.10
70	Frank Reich	.10
71	Eric Green	.10
72	Bruce Matthews	.10
73	Steve Broussard	.10
74	Anthony Carter	.10
75	Sterling Sharpe	.30
76	Mike Kenn	.10
77	Andre Rison	.30
78	Todd Marinovich	.10
79	Vincent Brown	.10
80	Harold Green	.10
81	Art Monk	.10
82	Reggie Cobb	.10
83	Johnny Johnson	.10
84	Tommy Kane	.10
85	Rohn Stark	.10
86	Steve Tasker	.10
87	Ronnie Harmon	.10
88	Pepper Johnson	.10
89	Hardy Nickerson	.10
90	Alvin Harper	.20
91	Louis Oliver	.10
92	Rod Woodson	.25
93	Sam Mills	.10
94	Randall McDaniel	.10
95	Johnny Holland	.10
96	Jackie Slater	.10
97	Don Mosebar	.10
98	Andre Ware	.10
99	Kelvin Martin	.10
100	Emmitt Smith	4.00
101	Michael Brooks	.10
102	Dan Saleaumua	.10
103	John Elway	1.00
104	Henry Jones	.10
105	William Perry	.10
106	James Lofton	.10
107	Carnell Lake	.10
108	Chip Lohmiller	.10
109	Andre Tippett	.10
110	Barry Word	.10
111	Haywood Jeffires	.10
112	Kenny Walker	.10
113	John Randle	.10
114	Donnell Woolford	.10
115	Johnny Bailey	.10
116	Marcus Allen	.25
117	Mark Jackson	.10
118	Ray Agnew	.10
119	Gill Byrd	.10
120	Kyle Clifton	.10
121	Marv Cook	.10
122	Jerry Ball	.10
123	Steve Jordan	.10
124	Shannon Sharpe	.25
125	Brian Blades	.10
126	Rodney Hampton	.30
127	Bobby Hebert	.10
128	Jessie Tuggle	.10
129	Tom Newberry	.10
130	Keith McCants	.10
131	Richard Dent	.10
132	Herman Moore	1.00
133	Michael Irvin	.50
134	Ernest Givins	.10
135	Mark Rypien	.10
136	Leonard Russell	.10
137	Reggie White	.25
138	Thurman Thomas	.50
139	Nick Lowery	.10
140	Al Smith	.10
141	Jackie Harris	.10
142	Duane Bickett	.10
143	Lawyer Tillman	.10
144	Steve Wisniewski	.10
145	Derrick Fenner	.10
146	Harris Barton	.10
147	Rich Camarillo	.10
148	John Offerdahl	.10
149	Mike Johnson	.10
150	Ricky Reynolds	.10
151	Fred Barnett	.10
152	Nate Newton	.10
153	Chris Doleman	.10
154	Todd Scott	.10
155	Tim McKyer	.10
156	Ken Harvey	.10
157	Jeff Feagles	.10
158	Vince Workman	.10
159	Bart Oates	.10
160	Chris Miller	.10
161	Pete Stoyanovich	.10
162	Steve Wallace	.10
163	Dermontti Dawson	.10
164	Kenneth Davis	.10
165	Mike Munchak	.10
166	George Jamison	.10
167	Christian Okoye	.10
168	Chris Hinton	.10
169	Vaughan Johnson	.10
170	Gaston Green	.10
171	Kevin Greene	.10
172	Rob Burnett	.10
173	Norm Johnson	.10
174	Eric Hill	.10
175	Lomas Brown	.10
176	Chip Banks	.10
177	Greg Townsend	.10
178	David Fulcher	.10
179	Gary Anderson	.10
180	Brian Washington	.10
181	Brett Perriman	.10
182	Chris Chandler	.10
183	Phil Hansen	.10
184	Mark Clayton	.10
185	Frank Warren	.10
186	Tim Brown	.30
187	Mark Stepnoski	.10
188	Bryan Cox	.10
189	Gary Zimmerman	.10
190	Neil O'Donnell	.30
191	Anthony Smith	.10
192	Craig Heyward	.10
193	Keith Byars	.10
194	Sean Salisbury	.10
195	Todd Lyght	.10
196	Jessie Hester	.10
197	Rufus Porter	.10
198	Steve Christie	.10
199	Nate Lewis	.10
200	Barry Sanders	3.00
201	Michael Haynes	.10
202	John Taylor	.10
203	John Friesz	.10
204	William Fuller	.10
205	Dennis Smith	.10
206	Adrian Cooper	.10
207	Henry Thomas	.10
208	Gerald Williams	.10
209	Chris Burkett	.10
210	Broderick Thomas	.10
211	Marvin Washington	.10
212	Bennie Blades	.10
213	Tony Casillas	.10
214	Bubby Brister	.10
215	Don Griffin	.10
216	Jeff Cross	.10
217	Derrick Walker	.10
218	Lorenzo White	.10
219	Ricky Sanders	.10
220	Rickey Jackson	.10
221	Simon Fletcher	.10
222	Troy Vincent	.10
223	Gary Clark	.10
224	Stanley Richard	.10
225	Dave Krieg	.10
226	Warren Moon	.25
227	Reggie Langhorne	.10
228	Kent Hull	.10
229	Ferrell Edmunds	.10
230	Cortez Kennedy	.20
231	Hugh Millen	.10
232	Eugene Chung	.10
233	Rodney Peete	.10
234	Tom Waddle	.10
235	David Klingler	.10
236	Mark Carrier	.10
237	Jay Schroeder	.10
238	James Jones	.10
239	Phil Simms	.10
240	Steve Atwater	.10
241	Jeff Herrod	.10
242	Dale Carter	.10
243	*Glenn Cadrez*	.10
244	Wayne Martin	.10
245	Willie Davis	.10
246	Lawrence Taylor	.20
247	Stan Humphries	.50
248	Byron Evans	.10
249	Wilber Marshall	.10
250	*Michael Bankston*	.10
251	Steve McMichael	.10
252	Brad Edwards	.10
253	Will Wolford	.10
254	Paul Gruber	.10
255	Steve Young	2.00
256	Chuck Cecil	.10
257	Pierce Holt	.10
258	Anthony Miller	.10
259	Carl Banks	.10
260	Brad Muster	.10
261	Clay Matthews	.10
262	Rod Bernstine	.10
263	Tim Barnett	.10
264	Greg Lloyd	.10
265	Sean Jones	.10
266	J.J. Birden	.10
267	Tim McDonald	.10
268	Charles Mann	.10
269	Bruce Smith	.10
270	Sean Gilbert	.10
271	Ricardo McDonald	.10
272	Jeff Hostetler	.10
273	Russell Maryland	.10
274	*Dave Brown*	1.00
275	Ronnie Lott	.10
276	Jim Kelly	.25
277	Joe Montana	3.00
278	Eric Allen	.10
279	Browning Nagle	.10
280	Neal Anderson	.10
281	Troy Aikman	2.00
282	Ed McCaffrey	.10
283	Robert Jones	.10
284	Dalton Hilliard	.10
285	Johnny Mitchell	.10
286	Jay Hilgenberg	.10
287	Eric Martin	.10
288	Steve Emtman	.10
289	Vaughn Dunbar	.10
290	Mark Wheeler	.10
291	Leslie O'Neal	.10
292	Jerry Rice	2.00
293	Neil Smith	.10
294	Kerry Cash	.10
295	Dan McGwire	.10
296	Carl Pickens	1.00
297	Terrell Buckley	.10
298	Randall Cunningham	.25
299	Santana Dotson	.10
300	Keith Jackson	.10
301	Jim Lachey	.10
302	Dan Marino	3.50
303	Lee Williams	.10
304	Burt Grossman	.10
305	Kevin Mack	.10
306	Pat Swilling	.10
307	*Arthur Marshall*	.20
308	Jim Harbaugh	.10
309	Kurt Barber	.10
310	Harvey Williams	.10
311	Ricky Ervins	.10
312	Willie Anderson	.10
313	Bernie Kosar	.20
314	Boomer Esiason	.20
315	Deion Sanders	1.00
316	Ray Childress	.10
317	Howie Long	.10
318	Henry Ellard	.10
319	Marco Coleman	.10
320	Chris Mims	.10
321	Quentin Coryatt	.10
322	Jason Hanson	.10
323	Ricky Proehl	.10
324	Randal Hill	.10
325	Vinny Testaverde	.10
326	Jeff George	.20
327	Junior Seau	.40
328	Earnest Byner	.10
329	Andre Reed	.20
330	Phillippi Sparks	.10
331	Kevin Ross	.10
332	Clarence Verdin	.10
333	Darryl Henley	.10
334	Dana Hall	.10
335	Greg McMurtry	.10
336	Ron Hall	.10
337	Darrell Green	.10
338	Carlton Bailey	.10
339	Irv Eatman	.10
340	Greg Kragen	.10
341	Wade Wilson	.10
342	Klaus Wilmsmeyer	.10
343	Derek Brown	.10
344	Erik Williams	.10
345	Jim McMahon	.10
346	Mike Sherrard	.10
347	Mark Bavaro	.10
348	Anthony Munoz	.10
349	Eric Dickerson	.10
350	Steve Beuerlein	.10
351	Tim McGee	.10
352	Terry McDaniel	.10
353	Dan Fouts (Hall of Fame)	.20
354	Chuck Noll (Hall of Fame)	
355	Bill Walsh (Hall of Fame)	
356	Larry Little (Hall of Fame)	.10
357	Todd Marinovich (Hometown Hero)	.10
358	Jeff George (Hometown Hero)	.20
359	Bernie Kosar (Hometown Hero)	.10
360	Rob Moore (Hometown Hero)	.10

1993 Pinnacle Men of Autumn

ERIC METCALF

These 55 cards were randomly inserted into 1993 Score football 16-card foil packs. The cards feature a glossy black laminate with a color action photo with a red frame. The set's logo is at the bottom, along with the player's name and position, which are in gold foil. Each back is horizontal and numbered and has a closeup shot of the player, plus a brief career summary.

	MT
Complete Set (55):	15.00
Common Player:	.25
Minor Stars:	.50
1 Andre Rison	.50
2 Thurman Thomas	.50
3 Wendell Davis	.25
4 Harold Green	.25
5 Eric Metcalf	.25
6 Michael Irvin	.50
7 John Elway	1.50
8 Barry Sanders	3.00
9 Sterling Sharpe	.50
10 Warren Moon	.50
11 Rohn Stark	.25
12 Derrick Thomas	.50
13 Terry McDaniel	.25
14 Cleveland Gary	.25
15 Dan Marino	3.00
16 Terry Allen	.25
17 Marv Cook	.25
18 Bobby Hebert	.25
19 Rodney Hampton	.50
20 Brad Baxter	.25
21 Reggie White	.50
22 Ricky Proehl	.25
23 Barry Foster	.50
24 Junior Seau	.50
25 Steve Young	2.00
26 Cortez Kennedy	.25
27 Reggie Cobb	.25
28 Mark Rypien	.25
29 Deion Sanders	1.00
30 Bruce Smith	.25
31 Richard Dent	.25
32 Alfred Williams	.25
33 Clay Matthews	.25
34 Emmitt Smith	4.00
35 Simon Fletcher	.25
36 Chris Spielman	.25
37 Brett Favre	4.00
38 Bruce Matthews	.25
39 Jeff Herrod	.25
40 Nick Lowery	.25
41 Steve Wisniewski	.25
42 Jim Everett	.25
43 Keith Jackson	.25
44 Chris Doleman	.25
45 Irving Fryar	.25
46 Rickey Jackson	.25
47 Pepper Johnson	.25
48 Randall Cunningham	.50
49 Rich Camarillo	.25
50 Rod Woodson	.50
51 Ronnie Harmon	.25
52 Ricky Watters	.50
53 Chris Warren	.50
54 Lawrence Dawsey	.50
55 Wilber Marshall	.25

1993 Pinnacle Rookies

These inserts cards have a black front with a color action photo emerging from a diamond-shaped metallic design in the middle. The set's name and Pinnacle logo are foil stamped in copper on the card, too. A metallic bar in team colors contains the player's name and team. The back is black and has a copper panel which includes career information. The player's name is in copper at the top of the card, which is also numbered 1 of 25, etc. Cards were reportedly randomly inserted one per every 36 1993 Pinnacle foil packs and feature several of the NFL's top rookies in 1993.

	MT
Complete Set (25):	400.00
Common Player:	7.00
1 Drew Bledsoe	175.00
2 Garrison Hearst	30.00
3 John Copeland	7.00
4 Eric Curry	7.00
5 Curtis Conway	25.00
6 Lincoln Kennedy	7.00
7 Jerome Bettis	50.00
8 Dan Williams	7.00
9 Patrick Bates	7.00
10 Brad Hopkins	7.00
11 Wayne Simmons	7.00
12 Rick Mirer	10.00
13 Tom Carter	7.00
14 Irv Smith	7.00
15 Marvin Jones	7.00
16 Deon Figures	7.00
17 Leonard Renfro	7.00
18 O.J. McDuffie	20.00
19 Dana Stubblefield	14.00
20 Carlton Gray	7.00
21 Demetrius DuBose	7.00
22 Troy Drayton	7.00
23 Natrone Means	30.00
24 Reggie Brooks	7.00
25 Glyn Milburn	14.00

1993 Pinnacle Super Bowl XXVII

The 1993 Super Bowl Champion Dallas Cowboys are featured on this 10-card insert set. Cards were randomly inserted in foil packs, one per hobby box of 1993 Pinnacle. Horizontal fronts feature a borderless color photo, plus a blue stripe that has the set name in blue foil. The backs are horizontal, too, and has the player's name, game highlights, Buffalo Bills and Cowboys helmets and the Super Bowl logo. Each card is numbered 1 of 10, etc.

	MT
Complete Set (10):	125.00
Common Player:	10.00
1 Rose Bowl	10.00
2 Dominant "D"	10.00
3 Emmitt Smith	50.00
4 Ken Norton Jr.	10.00
5 Michael Irvin	20.00
6 Jay Novacek	10.00
7 Charles Haley	10.00
8 Leon Lett	10.00
9 Alvin Harper	10.00
10 Sweet Victory	10.00

1993 Pinnacle Team Pinnacle

Each of these cards features two player paintings on it - one per side. An AFC player is featured with his NFC counterpart at that position. The paintings are framed by a thin white border and a larger black one. The player's name, position and conference are given in a stripe at the bottom. Both sides are numbered 1 of 13, etc. Cards were random inserts in 1993 Pinnacle foil packs, at least one per every 90 packs.

	MT
Complete Set (13):	250.00
Common Player:	10.00
1 Troy Aikman, Joe Montana	120.00
2 Thurman Thomas, Emmitt Smith	75.00
3 Rodney Hampton, Barry Foster	10.00
4 Sterling Sharpe, Anthony Miller	15.00
5 Haywood Jeffires, Michael Irvin	15.00
6 Jay Novacek, Keith Jackson	10.00
7 Richmond Webb, Steve Wallace	10.00
8 Reggie White, Leslie O'Neal	10.00
9 Cortez Kennedy, Sean Gilbert	10.00
10 Derrick Thomas, Wilber Marshall	10.00
11 Sam Mills, Junior Seau	15.00
12 Rod Woodson, Deion Sanders	20.00
13 Steve Atwater, Tim McDonald	10.00

1993 Pinnacle Team 2001

Promising young NFL players who might become stars by the year 2001 are featured in this 30-card insert set. A wide black stripe along the left and bottom of the card front borders a color action photo of the player. The set's and player's name are stamped in gold foil at the bottom, too, near a team logo. The back is done in a horizontal format and has a player mug shot and a black panel with a 1992 recap, team name and position, plus the player's name in gold foil. Cards, numbered 1 of 27, etc., were randomly inserted in 1993 Pinnacle 27-card super packs, one per pack.

	MT
Complete Set (30):	15.00
Common Player:	.50
Minor Stars:	1.00
1 Junior Seau	1.00
2 Cortez Kennedy	.50
3 Carl Pickens	3.00
4 David Klingler	.50
5 Santana Dotson	.50
6 Sean Gilbert	.50
7 Brett Favre	8.00
8 Steve Emtman	.50
9 Rodney Hampton	1.00
10 Browning Nagle	.50
11 Amp Lee	.50
12 Vaughn Dunbar	.50
13 Quentin Coryatt	.50
14 Marco Coleman	.50
15 Johnny Mitchell	.50
16 Arthur Marshall	.50
17 Dale Carter	.50
18 Henry Jones	.50
19 Terrell Buckley	.50
20 Tommy Vardell	.50
21 Tommy Maddox	.50
22 Barry Foster	1.00
23 Herman Moore	3.00
24 Ricky Watters	1.00
25 Mike Croel	.50
26 Russell Maryland	.50
27 Terry Allen	.50
28 Jon Vaughn	.50
29 Todd Marinovich	.50
30 Jeff Graham	.50

1994 Pinnacle Samples

The 10-card, regular-size set was issued as a preview for the 1994 regular-issue set. The cards have the same design as the cards in the base set, complete with same card-back numbers, but with a hole punched in a corner.

	MT
Complete Set (10):	10.00
Common Player:	.75
1 Deion Sanders (last line of text reads "es for a 17.7-yard...")	1.50
3 Trophy Collection (Barry Sanders) (name in brown ink on back)	2.50
24 Sean Gilbert (last line of text reads "mage to earn...")	.75
30 Alvin Harper (last line of text reads "tions and scored...")	.75
32 Derrick Thomas (last line of text reads "bles last season")	.75
85 James Jett (hometown/drafted line 1-3/16" long instead of 1-5/16")	.75
214 Chuck Levy (card number in white letters)	.75
DP8 William Floyd (last line of text reads "over would-be tacklers.")	1.25
NNO Ad Card	.75
NNO Pick Pinnacle Redemp. Card. (no player name on front)	.75

1994 Pinnacle

Pinnacle football 1994 contained full-bleed action shots with a gold foil football appearing on top of a large, textured, gold foil pyramid. Each player's name also appears in gold foil. The backs contain a close-up of the player and statistics on a football background. There were six insert sets in Pinnacle football: Trophy Collection, Team Pinnacle, Pick Pinnacle, Draft Pinnacle, Pinnacle Passer and Performers. Trophy is a 270-card parallel set that utilizes the Dufex printing process on regular-issue cards. Cards from the set are inserted at a rate of one-per-four packs. These cards feature the same shot as in the regular set, but have a Dufex background (shiny with silver highlights). Card backs are the same, except for a Trophy Collection logo in the bottom-right corner. Three insert sets were also made: Draft Picks, Performers and Team Pinnacle.

	MT
Complete Set (270):	25.00
Common Player:	.10
Minor Stars:	.20
Retail Wax Box:	75.00
Hobby Wax Box:	80.00
1 Deion Sanders	.75
2 Eric Metcalf	.10
3 Barry Sanders	2.50
4 Ernest Givins	.10
5 Phil Simms	.10
6 Rod Woodson	.20
7 Michael Irvin	.20
8 Cortez Kennedy	.20
9 Eric Martin	.10
10 Jeff Hostetler	.20
11 Sterling Sharpe	.30
12 John Elway	1.00
13 Neal Anderson	.10
14 Terry Kirby	.20
15 Jim Everett	.10
16 Lawrence Dawsey	.10
17 Kelvin Martin	.10
18 Tim McGee	.10
19 Cris Carter	.20
20 Ronnie Harmon	.10
21 Jim Kelly	.30
22 Steve Young	1.50
23 Johnny Johnson	.10
24 Sean Gilbert	.10
25 Brian Mitchell	.10
26 Carl Pickens	.10
27 Tim Brown	.20
28 Reggie Langhorne	.10
29 Webster Slaughter	.10
30 Alvin Harper	.20
31 Andre Rison	.20
32 Derrick Thomas	.20
33 Irving Fryar	.10
34 Vinny Testaverde	.10
35 Steve Beuerlein	.10
36 Brett Favre	3.00
37 Barry Foster	.20
38 Vaughan Johnson	.10
39 Carlton Bailey	.10
40 Steve Emtman	.10
41 Anthony Miller	.10
42 Jeff Cross	.10
43 Trace Armstrong	.10
44 Derek Russell	.10
45 Vincent Brisby	.30
46 Mark Jackson	.10
47 Eugene Robinson	.10
48 John Friesz	.10
49 Scott Mitchell	.20
50 Steve Atwater	.10
51 Ken Norton	.10
52 Vincent Brown	.10
53 Morten Andersen	.10
54 Gary Anderson	.10
55 Eric Curry	.10
56 Henry Jones	.10
57 Willie Anderson	.10
58 Pat Swilling	.10
59 Erric Pegram	.10
60 Bruce Matthews	.10
61 Willie Davis	.10
62 O.J. McDuffie	.20
63 Qadry Ismail	.20
64 Anthony Smith	.10
65 Eric Allen	.10
66 Marion Butts	.10
67 Chris Miller	.10
68 Terrell Buckley	.10
69 Thurman Thomas	.30
70 Roosevelt Potts	.10
71 Tony McGee	.10
72 Jason Hanson	.10
73 Victor Bailey	.10
74 Albert Lewis	.10
75 Nate Odomes	.10
76 Ben Coates	.20
77 Warren Moon	.20
78 Derek Brown	.10
79 David Klingler	.10
80 Cleveland Gary	.10
81 Emmitt Smith	3.00
82 Jay Novacek	.10
83 Dana Stubblefield	.20
84 Michael Brooks	.10
85 James Jett	.20
86 J.J. Birden	.10
87 William Fuller	.10
88 Glyn Milburn	.10
89 Tim Worley	.10
90 Brett Perriman	.10
91 Randall Cunningham	.20
92 Drew Bledsoe	2.00
93 Jerome Bettis	1.00
94 Boomer Esiason	.10
95 Garrison Hearst	.20
96 Bruce Smith	.10
97 Jackie Harris	.10
98 Jeff George	.20
99 Tom Waddle	.10
100 John Copeland	.10
101 Bobby Hebert	.10
102 Joe Montana	2.00
103 Herman Moore	.75
104 Rick Mirer	.20
105 Ricky Watters	.20
106 Neil O'Donnell	.20
107 Herschel Walker	.10
108 Rob Moore	.10
109 Reggie Brooks	.10
110 Tommy Vardell	.10
111 Eric Green	.10
112 Stan Humphries	.20
113 Greg Robinson	.10
114 Eric Swann	.10
115 Courtney Hawkins	.10
116 Andre Reed	.20
117 Steve McMichael	.10
118 Gary Brown	.10
119 Terry Allen	.10
120 Dan Marino	3.00
121 Gary Clark	.10
122 Chris Warren	.20
123 Pierce Holt	.10
124 Anthony Carter	.10
125 Quentin Coryatt	.10
126 Harold Green	.10
127 Leonard Russell	.10
128 Tim McDonald	.10
129 Chris Spielman	.10
130 Cody Carlson	.10
131 Ron Moore	.10
132 Renaldo Turnbull	.10
133 Ronnie Lott	.20
134 Natrone Means	.75
135 Keith Byars	.10
136 Henry Ellard	.10
137 Steve Jordan	.10
138 Calvin Williams	.10
139 Brian Blades	.10
140 Michael Jackson	.10
141 Charles Haley	.10
142 Curtis Conway	.10
143 Nick Lowery	.10
144 Bill Brooks	.10
145 Michael Haynes	.10
146 Willie Green	.10
147 Duane Bickett	.10
148 Shannon Sharpe	.20
149 Ricky Proehl	.10
150 Troy Aikman	1.50
151 Mike Sherrard	.10
152 Reggie Cobb	.10
153 Norm Johnson	.10
154 Neil Smith	.10
155 James Francis	.10
156 Greg McMurtry	.10
157 Greg Townsend	.10
158 Mel Gray	.10
159 Rocket Ismail	.10
160 Leslie O'Neal	.10
161 Johnny Mitchell	.10
162 Brent Jones	.10
163 Chris Doleman	.10
164 Seth Joyner	.10
165 Marco Coleman	.10
166 Mark Higgs	.10
167 John L. Williams	.10
168 Darrell Green	.10
169 Mark Carrier	.10
170 Reggie White	.20
171 Darryl Talley	.10
172 Russell Maryland	.10
173 Mark Collins	.10
174 Chris Jacke	.10
175 Richard Dent	.10
176 John Taylor	.10
177 Rodney Hampton	.20
178 Dwight Stone	.10
179 Cornelius Bennett	.10
180 Cris Dishman	.10
181 Jerry Rice	1.50
182 Rod Bernstine	.10
183 Keith Hamilton	.10
184 Keith Jackson	.10
185 Craig Erickson	.10
186 Marcus Allen	.20
187 Marcus Robertson	.10
188 Junior Seau	.20
189 LeShon Johnson	.40
190 Perry Klein	.30
191 Bryant Young	.50
192 Byron Morris	.20
193 Jeff Cothran	.20
194 Lamar Smith	.20
195 Calvin Jones	.40
196 James Bostic	.20
197 Dan Wilkinson	.40
198 Marshall Faulk	5.00
199 Heath Shuler	.50
200 Willie McGinest	.40
201 Trev Alberts	.30
202 Trent Dilfer	3.00
203 Sam Adams	.30
204 Charles Johnson	1.00
205 Johnnie Morton	.75
206 Thomas Lewis	.20
207 Greg Hill	.50
208 William Floyd	1.00
209 Derrick Alexander	.50
210 Darnay Scott	1.50
211 Lake Dawson	.30
212 Errict Rhett	1.00
213 Kevin Lee	.30
214 Chuck Levy	.30
215 David Palmer	.50
216 Ryan Yarborough	.30
217 Charlie Garner	2.00
218 Mario Bates	.30
219 Jamir Miller	.30
220 Bucky Brooks	.30
221 Donnell Bennett	.30
222 Kevin Greene	.10
223 LeRoy Butler	.10
224 Anthony Pleasant	.10
225 Steve Christie	.10
226 Bill Romanowski	.10
227 Darren Carrington	.10
228 Chester McGlockton	.10
229 Jack Del Rio	.10
230 Kevin Smith	.10
231 Chris Zorich	.10
232 Donnell Woolford	.10
233 Tony Casillas	.10
234 Terry McDaniel	.10
235 Ray Childress	.10
236 Clyde Simmons	.10
237 Dante Jones	.10
238 Karl Mecklenburg	.10
239 Daryl Johnston	.10
240 Hardy Nickerson	.10
241 Jeff Lageman	.10
242 Lewis Tillman	.10
243 Jim McMahon	.10
244 Mike Pritchard	.10
245 Harvey Williams	.10
246 Sean Jones	.10
247 Stevon Moore	.10
248 Pete Metzelaars	.10
249 Mike Johnson	.10
250 Chris Slade	.20
251 Chris Slade	.20
252 Jessie Hester	.10

253	Louis Oliver	.10
254	Ken Harvey	.10
255	Bryan Cox	.10
256	Erik Kramer	.10
257	Andy Harmon	.10
258	Rickey Jackson	.10
259	Mark Carrier	.10
260	Greg Lloyd	.10
261	Robert Brooks	.10
262	Dave Brown	.20
263	Dennis Smith	.10
264	Michael Dean Perry	.10
265	Dan Saleaumua	.10
266	Mo Lewis	.10
267	Checklist	.10
268	Checklist	.10
269	Checklist	.10
270	Checklist	.10
271SP	Jerry Rice TD King	7.00
NNO	Drew Bledsoe Pin. Pass.	70.00

1994 Pinnacle Trophy Collection

The 270-card, regular-size set was a parallel Dufex version of the base card set, inserted every four packs.

	MT
Complete Set (270):	600.00
Common Player:	1.50
Veteran Stars:	8x-16x
Young Stars:	7x-14x
RCs:	5x-10x

1994 Pinnacle Draft Pinnacle

Draft Pinnacle displays the NFL's top 10 picks in their NFL uniforms. The bottom of the card shows a football texture background with "Draft" printed in gold, along with the Pinnacle logo, while "Pinnacle '94" is printed in white. The rest of the front pictures the draft pick. The back is made of half football texture with a brief biography and the other half contains a picture of the player. Cards are numbered DP 1 through DP 10.

		MT
Complete Set (10):		40.00
Common Player:		.50
Minor Stars:		1.00
Dufex Cards:		1x
1	Dan Wilkinson	1.00
2	Marshall Faulk	15.00
3	Heath Shuler	15.00
4	Trent Dilfer	15.00
5	Charles Johnson	1.00
6	Johnnie Morton	5.00
7	Darnay Scott	7.00
8	William Floyd	7.00
9	Errict Rhett	7.00
10	Chuck Levy	.50

A player's name in *italic type* indicates a rookie card.

1994 Pinnacle Performers

Pinnacle Performers was an 18-card insert set featuring some of the top talent in the NFL. These were inserted exclusively into jumbo packs at a rate of one every four packs.

		MT
Complete Set (18):		55.00
Common Player:		.50
Minor Stars:		1.00
Inserted 1:4 Jumbo		
1	Troy Aikman	5.00
2	Emmitt Smith	8.00
3	Sterling Sharpe	1.00
4	Barry Sanders	10.00
5	Jerry Rice	5.00
6	Steve Young	4.00
7	John Elway	8.00
8	Michael Irvin	1.00
9	Jerome Bettis	1.00
10	Tim Brown	1.00
11	Joe Montana	6.00
12	Reggie Brooks	.50
13	Brett Favre	10.00
14	Drew Bledsoe	5.00
15	Ricky Watters	1.00
16	Garrison Hearst	1.00
17	Rodney Hampton	.50
18	Dan Marino	8.00

1994 Pinnacle Team Pinnacle

Team Pinnacle is a double-fronted, 10-card insert set that was found one in every 90 packs. Cards feature two top performers at a variety of different positions.

		MT
Complete Set (10):		275.00
Common Player:		10.00
1	Troy Aikman, Joe Montana	90.00
2	Brett Favre, Rick Mirer	60.00
3	Thurman Thomas, Emmitt Smith	60.00
4	Barry Sanders, Barry Foster	40.00
5	Jerome Bettis, Natrone Means	20.00
6	Tim Brown, Sterling Sharpe	10.00
7	Anthony Miller, Jerry Rice	40.00
8	Michael Irvin, James Jett	10.00
9	Reggie White, Bruce Smith	10.00
10	Cortez Kennedy, Sean Gilbert	10.00

Post-1980 cards in Near Mint condition will generally sell for about 75% of the quoted Mint value. Excellent-condition cards bring no more than 40%.

1994 Pinnacle Canton Bound

The Canton Bound NFL boxed set was released by Pinnacle containing 25 cards. It featured the game's most accomplished veterans and the brightest young stars. Pinnacle produced 100,000 numbered sets, each came with a factory seal and serial number. The cards showcase a full-bleed design with the player's name and Pinnacle logo in gold-foil. At the bottom of the card is the "Canton Bound" neon logo. The back of the card includes two photos, the player's bio, highlights, 1993 and career stats.

		MT
Complete Set (25):		10.00
Common Player:		.25
1	Troy Aikman	1.50
2	Emmitt Smith	3.00
3	Barry Sanders	1.50
4	Jerry Rice	1.50
5	Sterling Sharpe	.35
6	Ronnie Lott	.35
7	John Elway	1.00
8	Joe Montana	1.50
9	Reggie White	.35
10	Thurman Thomas	.50
11	Bruce Smith	.35
12	Cortez Kennedy	.35
13	Dan Marino	3.00
14	James Lofton	.35
15	Art Monk	.35
16	Warren Moon	.35
17	Barry Foster	.25
18	Steve Young	1.00
19	Phil Simms	.35
20	Richard Dent	.25
21	Marcus Allen	.35
22	Junior Seau	.50
23	Michael Irvin	.50
24	Deion Sanders	.75
25	Jerome Bettis	.50
26	Ronnie Lott Sample	1.50

1994 Sportflics Samples

The seven-card, regular-sized set was issued as a preview for the 1994 Sportflics base set. The upper right corners of the cards are cut off indicating it as a sample. The set is virtually identical in design to the regular-issue set.

		MT
Complete Set (7):		8.00
Common Player:		.50
3	Flipper Anderson (yellow "Anderson" name on back missing shadow)	.50
50	Reggie Brooks (yellow "Brooks" name on back missing shadow)	.50
70	Herman Moore (name on front 1/4" away from year logo)	1.50
145	Chuck Levy (back photo black and white)	.50
180	Jerome Bettis ("TM" by Starflics logo on front)	2.00
HH1	Barry Jones (Head-to-Head production number box on back missing)	2.50
NNO	Sportflics Ad Card (corners intact)	.50

1994 Sportflics

Pinnacle revealed its premier edition of Sportflics 2000 Football in a 184-card set. Each card contains two different shots of the player on the same card. One shot is visible instantly, the second is apparent with a slight turn. Sportflics contained five insert sets. Random cards from Sack Attack, Head to Head, Artist's Proof, Find the Football and Rookie Rivalry were inserted in the five-card packs. Within the primary set itself, there were two subsets, entitled Starflics and The Rookies.

		MT
Complete Set (184):		40.00
Common Player:		.15
Minor Stars:		.30
Wax Box:		65.00
1	Deion Sanders	1.25
2	Leslie O'Neal	.15
3	Willie Anderson	.15
4	Anthony Carter	.15
5	Thurman Thomas, Vincent Brisby	.15
6	Johnny Mitchell	.15
7	Jeff Hostetler	.15
8	Renaldo Turnbull	.15
9	Chris Warren	.40
10	Darrell Green	.15
11	Randall Cunningham	.15
12	Barry Sanders	2.00
13	Jeff Cross	.15
14	Glyn Milburn	.15
15	Willie Davis	.15
16	Tony McGee	.15
17	Gary Clark	.15
18	Michael Jackson	.15
19	Alvin Harper	.15
20	Tim Worley	.15
21	Quentin Coryatt	.15
22	Michael Brooks	.15
23	Boomer Esiason	.15
24	Ricky Watters	.30
25	Craig Erickson	.15
26	Willie Green	.15
27	Brett Favre	3.00
28	John Elway	1.00
29	Steve Beuerlein	.15
30	Emmitt Smith	4.00
31	Troy Aikman	2.00
32	Cody Carlson	.15
33	Brian Mitchell	.15
34	Herschel Walker	.15
35	Bruce Smith	.15
36	Harold Green	.15
37	Erric Pegram	.15
38	Ronnie Harmon	.15
39	Brian Blades	.15
40	Sterling Sharpe	.30
41	Leonard Russell	.15
42	Cleveland Gary	.15
43	Tom Waddle, Lamar Smith	.15
44	Lawrence Dawsey	.15
45	Jerry Rice	2.00
46	Terry Allen	.15
47	Reggie Langhorne	.15
48	Derek Brown	.15
49	Terry Kirby, Lake Dawson	.15
50	Reggie Brooks	.15
51	Calvin Williams	.15
52	Cornelius Bennett	.15
53	Russell Maryland	.15
54	Rob Moore	.15
55	Dana Stubblefield	.15
56	Rod Woodson	.15
57	Rodney Hampton	.30
58	Neil Smith	.15
59	Anthony Smith	.15
60	Neal Anderson	.15
61	Drew Bledsoe	2.00
62	John Copeland	.15
63	David Klingler	.15
64	Phil Simms	.15
65	Vincent Brisby	.15
66	Richard Dent	.15
67	Eric Metcalf	.15
68	Eric Curry	.15
69	Victor Bailey	.15
70	Herman Moore	1.00
71	Steve Jordan	.15
72	Jerome Bettis	.50
73	Natrone Means	.75
74	Webster Slaughter	.15
75	Jackie Harris	.15
76	Michael Irvin	.30
77	Steve Emtman	.15
78	Eugene Robinson	.15
79	Tim Brown	.30
80	Derrick Thomas	.15
81	Vinny Testaverde	.15
82	Mark Jackson	.15
83	Ricky Proehl	.15
84	Stan Humphries	.15
85	Garrison Hearst	1.00
86	Jim Kelly	.30
87	Brent Jones	.15
88	Eric Martin	.15
89	Wilber Marshall	.15
90	Chris Spielman	.15
91	Eric Green	.15
92	Andre Rison	.15
93	Andre Reed	.15
94	Carl Pickens	.75
95	Junior Seau	.30
96	Dwight Stone	.15
97	Mike Sherrard	.15
98	Vincent Brown	.15
99	Cris Carter	.15
100	Mark Higgs	.15
101	Steve Young	2.00
102	Mark Carrier	.15
103	Barry Foster	.15
104	Tommy Vardell	.15
105	Shannon Sharpe	.30
106	Reggie White	.30
107	Ernest Givins	.15
108	Marcus Allen	.30
109	James Jett	.15
110	Keith Jackson	.15
111	Irving Fryar	.15
112	Ronnie Lott	.15
113	Cortez Kennedy	.15
114	Ron Moore	.15
115	Rick Mirer	.75
116	Neil O'Donnell	.30
117	Courtney Hawkins	.15
118	Johnny Johnson	.15
119	Ben Coates	.30
120	Dan Marino	4.00
121	Sean Gilbert	.15
122	Rocket Ismail	.15
123	Joe Montana	2.00
124	Roosevelt Potts	.15
125	Gary Brown	.15
126	Reggie Cobb	.15
127	Marion Butts	.15
128	Scott Mitchell	.15
129	John L. Williams	.15
130	Jeff George	.30
131	Bobby Hebert	.15
132	John Friesz	.15
133	Michael Miller	.15
134	Jim Harbaugh	.15
135	Eric Kramer	.15
136	Jim Everett	.15
137	Michael Haynes	.15
138	Rod Bernstine	.15
139	Chris Miller	.15
140	Henry Ellard	.15
141	William Fuller	.15
142	Warren Moon	.30
143	*Lamar Smith*	.15
144	*Charlie Garner*	1.50
145	*Chuck Levy*	.15
146	*Dan Wilkinson*	.30
147	*Perry Klein*	.15
148	*William Floyd*	1.00
149	*Lake Dawson*	1.00
150	*David Palmer*	.50
151	*James Bostic*	.15
152	*Marshall Faulk*	6.00
153	*Greg Hill*	1.00
154	*Heath Shuler*	3.00
155	*Errict Rhett*	4.00
156	*Sam Adams*	.15
157	*Charles Johnson*	.15
158	*Ryan Yarborough*	.15
159	*Thomas Lewis*	.15
160	*Willie McGinest*	.50
161	*Jamir Miller*	.15
162	*Calvin Jones*	.15
163	*Donnell Bennett*	.15
164	*Trev Alberts*	.15
165	*LeShon Johnson*	.15
166	*Johnnie Morton*	.30
167	*Derrick Alexander*	.50
168	*Jeff Cothran*	.15
169	*Bucky Brooks*	.30
170	*Bert Emanuel*	2.00
171	*Darnay Scott*	3.00
172	*Kevin Lee*	.15
173	*Mario Bates*	2.00
174	*Bryant Young*	.75
175	*Trent Dilfer*	2.00
176	Joe Montana	1.00
177	Emmitt Smith	2.00
178	Troy Aikman	1.00
179	Steve Young	1.00
180	Jerome Bettis	.40
181	John Elway	.50
182	Dan Marino	1.00
183	Brett Favre	1.00
184	Barry Sanders	1.00

1994 Sportflics Artist's Proofs

The 184-card, standard-size set was issued as a parallel version to the base set. "Artist's Proof" is printed on the card fronts.

	MT
Complete Set (184):	900.00
Common Player:	2.00
Artist's Proof Cards:	8x-16x

1994 Sportflics Head-To-Head

Head-to-Head captured some of the game's fiercest rivalries. Cards show a close-up shot of both players with their helmets on, on opposing sides of the card. The second shot captures the player in action, with three photos to give the illusion of movement. The Sportflics logo is between the helmets on the one shot and, on the second shot it turns into a large Head to Head logo with both players' names. The back shows a close shot of the two, with their name and team name next to them.

		MT
Complete Set (10):		220.00
Common Player:		7.00
1	Barry Sanders, Dante Jones	25.00
2	Emmitt Smith, Carlton Bailey	50.00
3	Rod Woodson, Dan Marino	50.00
4	Jerry Rice, Deion Sanders	25.00
5	Vaughan Johnson, Jerome Bettis	7.00
6	Reggie White, Troy Aikman	25.00
7	Steve Young, Renaldo Turnbull	25.00
8	Sterling Sharpe, Eric Allen	7.00
9	Joe Montana, Anthony Smith	25.00
10	John Elway, Neil Smith	10.00

1994 Sportflics Pride of Texas

The four-card, standard-size set was given away at the National Convention in Houston by Pinnacle. One Dallas Cowboys (Harper), one Houston Oilers (Brown) and two Dallas Stars (Modano, Hatcher). Production was limited to 2,500 of each card. Each card has an "N" prefix.

		MT
Complete Set (4):		15.00
Common Player:		3.00
1	Alvin Harper	3.00
2	Gary Brown	3.00
3	Mike Modano	6.00
4	Derian Hatcher	3.00

Post-1980 cards in Near Mint condition will generally sell for about 75% of the quoted Mint value. Excellent-condition cards bring no more than 40%.

1994 Sportflics Rookie Rivalry

Rookie Rivalry pits two of the league's top prospects against each other. This 12-card insert had an insertion ratio of one per 24 packs and was in hobby packs only.

		MT
Complete Set (10):		65.00
Common Player:		3.00
Minor Stars:		6.00
1	William Floyd, Marshall Faulk	17.00
2	Dan Wilkinson, Sam Adams	3.00
3	Trent Dilfer, Heath Shuler	8.00
4	Jamir Miller, Trev Alberts	3.00
5	Johnnie Morton, Charles Johnson	6.00
6	Chuck Levy, Charles Garner	6.00
7	Thomas Lewis, Derrick Alexander	3.00
8	Darnay Scott, Isaac Bruce	15.00
9	David Palmer, Ryan Yarborough	3.00
10	LeShon Johnson, Donnell Bennett	3.00

1994 Pinnacle/Sportflics Super Bowl

This seven-card set was distributed at the 1994 Super Bowl Show in Atlanta, and was available by exchanging five Pinnacle Brands wrappers for one card. These Magic Motion cards were produced in the following quantities: Gary Brown and Emmitt Smith (3,000); Sterling Sharpe and Jerome Bettis/Reggie Brooks and Drew Bledsoe/Rick Mirer (2,000); and Jerry Rice and Deion Sanders (1,000).

		MT
Complete Set (7):		250.00
Common Player:		15.00
1	Gary Brown	15.00
2	Emmitt Smith	60.00
3	Sterling Sharpe	25.00
4	Jerome Bettis, Reggie Brooks	30.00
5	Drew Bledsoe, Rick Mirer	40.00
6	Jerry Rice	50.00
7	Deion Sanders	50.00

1995 Pinnacle Promos

This four-card set was used to promote the 1995 Pinnacle set. It included two regular-issue cards, one Showcase insert and a header card.

		MT
Complete Set (4):		7.00
Common Player:		.50
1	Showcase Card (Dan Marino)	4.00
39	Barry Sanders	2.00
62	Steve Young	1.25
NNO	Ad Card	.50

1995 Pinnacle

Pinnacle's 1995 football set has 250 cards plus two Dufex parallel sets. Each regular card front has a full-bleed color action photo on the front, with a Pinnacle logo in an upper corner. The player's name and position are stamped in gold foil at the bottom of the card, along with the seams of a football. The card back has a color photo, player profile, biographical information and 1994 and career statistics. There are four subsets within the main set - Draft Picks, Pinnacle Passers, Checklists and a "Judge" card, which pays tribute to Steve Young for passing the bar exam. Parallel sets are Trophy Collection, which reprints all 250 cards on a dufex design, and Artist's Proofs, which parallels the Trophy Collection, but has an Artist's Proof stamp on each card. Five insert sets were made: Showcase, Black 'n Blue, Team Pinnacle, Clear Shots and Gamebreakers.

		MT
Complete Set (250):		30.00
Common Player:		.10
Minor Stars:		.20
Hobby Wax Box:		60.00
Retail Wax Box:		75.00
1	Reggie White	.20
2	Troy Aikman	1.00
3	Willie Davis	.10
4	Jerry Rice	1.00
5	Bruce Smith	.10
6	Keith Byars	.10
7	Chris Warren	.20
8	Erik Kramer	.10
9	Leon Lett	.10
10	Greg Lloyd	.10
11	Jackie Harris	.10
12	Irving Fryar	.10
13	Rodney Hampton	.10
14	Michael Irvin	.30
15	Michael Haynes	.10
16	Irving Spikes	.10
17	Calvin Williams	.10
18	Ken Norton Jr.	.10
19	Herman Moore	.20
20	Lewis Tillman	.10
21	Cortez Kennedy	.10
22	Dan Marino	2.50
23	Erric Pegram	.10
24	Tim Brown	.20
25	Jeff Blake	.50
26	Brett Favre	2.50
27	Garrison Hearst	.20
28	Ronnie Harmon	.10
29	Qadry Ismail	.10
30	Ben Coates	.10
31	Deion Sanders	.60
32	John Elway	.50
33	Natrone Means	.60
34	Derrick Alexander	.30
35	Craig Heyward	.10
36	Jake Reed	.10
37	Steve Walsh	.10
38	John Randle	.10
39	Barry Sanders	2.00
40	Tydus Winans	.10
41	Thomas Lewis	.10
42	Jim Kelly	.30
43	Gus Frerotte	.40
44	Cris Carter	.20
45	Kevin Williams	.10
46	Dave Meggett	.10
47	Pat Swilling	.10
48	Neil O'Donnell	.20
49	Terance Mathis	.10
50	Desmond Howard	.10
51	Bryant Young	.10
52	Stan Humphries	.20
53	Alvin Harper	.10
54	Henry Ellard	.10
55	Jessie Hester	.10
56	Lorenzo White	.10
57	John Friesz	.10
58	Anthony Smith	.10
59	Bert Emanuel	.40
60	Gary Clark	.10
61	Bill Brooks	.10
62	Steve Young	1.00
63	Jerome Bettis	.30
64	John Taylor	.10
65	Ricky Proehl	.10
66	Junior Seau	.20
67	Bubby Brister	.10
68	Neil Smith	.10
69	Dan McGwire	.10
70	Brett Perriman	.10
71	Chris Spielman	.10
72	Jeff George	.20
73	Emmitt Smith	2.50
74	Chris Penn	.10
75	Derrick Fenner	.10
76	Reggie Brooks	.10
77	Chris Chandler	.10
78	Rod Woodson	.10
79	Isaac Bruce	.30
80	Reggie Cobb	.10
81	Bryce Paup	.10
82	Warren Moon	.20
83	Bryan Reeves	.10
84	Lake Dawson	.30
85	Larry Centers	.10
86	Marshall Faulk	1.00
87	Jim Harbaugh	.10
88	Ray Childress	.10
89	Eric Metcalf	.10
90	Ernie Mills	.10
91	Lamar Lathon	.10
92	Errict Rhett	.20
93	David Klingler	.10
94	Vincent Brown	.10
95	Andre Rison	.10
96	Brian Mitchell	.10
97	Mark Rypien	.10
98	Eugene Robinson	.10
99	Eric Green	.10
100	Rocket Ismail	.10
101	Flipper Anderson	.10
102	Randall Cunningham	.10
103	Ricky Watters	.20
104	Amp Lee	.10
105	Ernest Givins	.10
106	Daryl Johnston	.10
107	Dave Krieg	.10
108	Dana Stubblefield	.10
109	Torrance Small	.10
110	Yancey Thigpen	.50
111	Chester McGlockton	.10
112	Craig Erickson	.10
113	Herschel Walker	.10
114	Mike Sherrard	.10
115	Tony McGee	.10
116	Adrian Murrell	.10
117	Frank Reich	.10
118	Hardy Nickerson	.10
119	Andre Reed	.10
120	Leonard Russell	.10
121	Eric Allen	.10
122	Jeff Hostetler	.10
123	Barry Foster	.10
124	Anthony Miller	.10
125	Shawn Jefferson	.10
126	Richie Anderson	.10
127	Steve Bono	.20
128	Seth Joyner	.10
129	Darnay Scott	.60
130	Johnny Mitchell	.10
131	Eric Swann	.10
132	Drew Bledsoe	1.50
133	Marcus Allen	.20
134	Carl Pickens	.20
135	Michael Brooks	.10
136	John L. Williams	.10
137	Steve Beuerlein	.10
138	Robert Smith	.10
139	O.J. McDuffie	.10
140	Haywood Jeffires	.10
141	Aeneas Williams	.10
142	Rick Mirer	.40
143	William Floyd	.50
144	Fred Barnett	.10
145	Leroy Hoard	.10
146	Terry Kirby	.10
147	Boomer Esiason	.10
148	Ken Harvey	.10
149	Cleveland Gary	.10
150	Brian Blades	.10
151	Eric Turner	.10
152	Vinny Testaverde	.10
153	Ron Moore	.10
154	Curtis Conway	.10
155	Johnnie Morton	.10
156	Kenneth Davis	.10
157	Scott Mitchell	.10
158	Sean Gilbert	.10
159	Shannon Sharpe	.10
160	Mark Seay	.10
161	Cornelius Bennett	.10
162	Heath Shuler	.75
163	Bam Morris	.50
164	Robert Brooks	.10
165	Glyn Milburn	.10
166	Gary Brown	.10
167	Jim Everett	.10
168	Steve Atwater	.10
169	Darren Woodson	.10
170	Mark Ingram	.10
171	Donnell Woolford	.10
172	Trent Dilfer	.50
173	Charlie Garner	.10
174	Charles Johnson	.40
175	Mike Pritchard	.10
176	Derek Brown	.10
177	Chris Miller	.10
178	Charles Haley	.10
179	J.J. Birden	.10
180	Jeff Graham	.10
181	Bernie Parmalee	.30
182	Mark Brunell	1.00
183	Greg Hill	.40
184	Michael Timpson	.10
185	Terry Allen	.10
186	Ricky Ervins	.10
187	Dave Brown	.10
188	Dan Wilkinson	.10
189	Jay Novacek	.10
190	Harvey Williams	.10
191	Mario Bates	.30
192	Steve Young	.50
193	Joe Montana	2.00
194	Steve Young	.50
195	Troy Aikman	.40
196	Drew Bledsoe	.75
197	Dan Marino	1.00
198	John Elway	.20
199	Brett Favre	.75
200	Heath Shuler	.40
201	Warren Moon	.20
202	Jim Kelly	.20
203	Jeff Hostetler	.20
204	Rick Mirer	.20
205	Dave Brown	.10
206	Randall Cunningham	.10
207	Neil O'Donnell	.10
208	Jim Everett	.10
209	Ki-Jana Carter	.30
210	Steve McNair	4.00
211	Michael Westbrook	1.50
212	Kerry Collins	2.00
213	Joey Galloway	3.00
214	Kyle Brady	.20
215	J.J. Stokes	1.50
216	Tyrone Wheatley	.50
217	Rashaan Salaam	.30
218	Napoleon Kaufman	1.50
219	Frank Sanders	.30
220	Stoney Case	.20
221	Todd Collins	.30
222	Warren Sapp	.20
223	Sherman Williams	.20
224	Rob Johnson	1.50
225	Mark Bruener	.20
226	Derrick Brooks	.20
227	Chad May	.20
228	James Stewart	.20
229	Ray Zellars	.20
230	Dave Barr	.20
231	Kordell Stewart	3.00
232	Jimmy Oliver	.20
233	Tony Boselli	.30
234	James Stewart	1.75
235	Derrick Alexander	.20
236	Lovell Pinkney	.20
237	John Walsh	.20
238	Tyrone Davis	.20
239	Joe Aska	.20
240	Korey Stringer	.20
241	Hugh Douglas	.20
242	Christian Fauria	.20
243	Terrell Fletcher	.20
244	Dan Marino CL	.40
245	Drew Bledsoe CL	.20
246	John Elway CL	.20
247	Emmitt Smith CL	.40
248	Steve Young CL	.25
249	Barry Sanders CL	.50
250	Jerry Rice CL	.25

card. This 249-card set features the same all-foil dufex printing as the Trophy Collection parallel, but is identified by a round seal that includes the Artist's Proof logo. This parallel set was seeded every 48 packs.

	MT
Complete Set (249):	2600.
Common Player:	7.00
Semistars	10.00
193 Montana AP Not Issued	
AP Veteran Stars:	35x-65x
AP Young Stars:	25x-45x
AP RCs:	15x-30x

1995 Pinnacle Trophy Collection

CURTIS CONWAY
WIDE RECEIVER

This 250-card parallel set was included in every four packs of Pinnacle Football and is printed in all-foil dufex. The cards have the same photo on the front as regular-issue cards, but have the words Trophy Collection written in large letters on the back.

	MT
Complete Set (250):	600.00
Common Player:	1.25
Veteran Stars:	6x-12x
Young Stars:	4x-8x
RCs:	2.5x-5x

1995 Pinnacle Black 'N Blue

D. WILKINS

BLACK 'N BLUE

These 1995 Pinnacle football cards picture some of the NFL's toughest players. The cards, featuring a micro-etched foil design for the front, were seeded one per every 18 jumbo packs.

		MT
Complete Set (30):		250.00
Common Player:		7.00
1	Junior Seau	7.00
2	Bam Morris	7.00
3	Craig Heyward	7.00
4	Drew Bledsoe	25.00
5	Barry Sanders	25.00
6	Jerome Bettis	7.00
7	William Floyd	7.00
8	Greg Lloyd	7.00
9	John Elway	15.00
10	Jerry Rice	25.00
11	Kevin Greene	7.00
12	Errict Rhett	7.00
13	Steve Young	25.00
14	Bruce Smith	7.00
15	Steve Atwater	7.00
16	Natrone Means	7.00
17	Ben Coates	7.00
18	Reggie White	7.00
19	Ken Harvey	7.00
20	Dan Marino	50.00
21	Marshall Faulk	7.00
22	Seth Joyner	7.00
23	Rod Woodson	7.00
24	Hardy Nickerson	7.00
25	Brett Favre	50.00
26	Bryan Cox	7.00
27	Rodney Hampton	7.00
28	Jeff Hostetler	7.00
29	Brent Jones	7.00
30	Emmitt Smith	50.00

1995 Pinnacle Clear Shots

HAMMIN AIKMAN

These 1995 Pinnacle football inserts are one of the most exclusive ones in the base brand; they are seeded one per every 60 packs. The cards display 10 of the league's best veterans on a clear plastic card stock overprinted with rainbow holographic foil. The process is called Spectraview.

		MT
Complete Set (10):		125.00
Common Player:		5.00
1	Jerry Rice	15.00
2	Dan Marino	30.00
3	Steve Young	15.00
4	Drew Bledsoe	15.00
5	Emmitt Smith	30.00
6	Barry Sanders	18.00
7	Marshall Faulk	5.00
8	Troy Aikman	15.00
9	Ki-Jana Carter	5.00
10	Steve McNair	15.00

1995 Pinnacle Gamebreakers

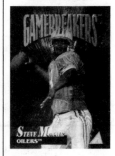

GAMEBREAKERS

STEVE McNAIR
OILERS

These 15 insert cards were exclusive to 1995 Pinnacle hobby packs, one per every 24 hobby packs. The card front has a metallic shine to it, with the insert set name featured at the top of the card. The player's name and team name are in the lower left corner, opposite the Pinnacle base brand logo.

		MT
Complete Set (15):		150.00
Common Player:		4.00
1	Marshall Faulk	4.00
2	Emmitt Smith	20.00
3	Steve Young	10.00
4	Ki-Jana Carter	4.00
5	Drew Bledsoe	10.00
6	Troy Aikman	10.00
7	Rashaan Salaam	4.00
8	Tyrone Wheatley	4.00
9	Dan Marino	20.00
10	Natrone Means	4.00
11	Barry Sanders	12.00
12	Jerry Rice	10.00
13	Bam Morris	4.00
14	Steve McNair	10.00
15	Kerry Collins	6.00

1995 Pinnacle Artist's Proof

JOEY GALLOWAY
1995 ROOKIE

Artist's Proofs were a parallel set of the 1995 Pinnacle set, minus Joe Montana, who didn't have an Artist's Proof

1995 Pinnacle Showcase

This 1995 Pinnacle insert set features 21 top NFL stars,

using black-and-white portraits for the card fronts. The front design also uses silver foil stamping for the player's name and brand name. A silver bar outlines the letters in the word "Showcase." The card back, numbered 1 of 21, etc., has another black-and-white photo, but this one is an action shot, unlike the front one, which shows the player without his helmet on. The insert set icon and a facsimile autograph are also included on the card back. Cards were seeded one per every 18 packs.

		MT
Complete Set (21):		80.00
Common Player:		3.00
1	Drew Bledsoe	7.00
2	Joey Galloway	7.00
3	Steve Young	7.00
4	Joe Aska	3.00
5	Barry Sanders	7.00
6	Troy Aikman	7.00
7	Dan Marino	14.00
8	Randall Cunningham	3.00
9	John Elway	5.00
10	Brett Favre	14.00
11	Jim Kelly	3.00
12	Warren Moon	3.00
13	Dave Brown	3.00
14	Jeff Hostetler	3.00
15	Rick Mirer	4.00
16	Ki-Jana Carter	3.00
17	Kerry Collins	5.00
18	J.J. Stokes	3.00
19	Kordell Stewart	10.00
20	Michael Westbrook	3.00
21	Todd Collins	3.00

1995 Pinnacle Team Pinnacle

These cards are the rarest of all 1995 Pinnacle football inserts, seeded one per every 90 packs. The 10 cards feature some of the hottest AFC and NFC players at their positions, back-to-back. The set has 20 variations, because each card exists with just one side printed with Pinnacle's exclusive textured-foil process. The player is pictured against a background which shows his team's logo.

		MT
Complete Set (10):		275.00
Common Player:		14.00
1	Steve Young, Drew Bledsoe	30.00
2	Emmitt Smith, Marshall Faulk	40.00
3	Barry Sanders, Natrone Means	30.00
4	Troy Aikman, Dan Marino	50.00
5	Jerry Rice, Tim Brown	30.00
6	Errict Rhett, Bam Morris	14.00
7	Brett Favre, John Elway	50.00
8	Ki-Jana Carter, Rashaan Salaam	14.00
9	Steve McNair, Kerry Collins	25.00
10	Michael Westbrook, Joey Galloway	14.00

1995 Pinnacle Super Bowl Card Show

The four-card, standard-size set was available at the 1995 NFL Experience in ex-change for five Pinnacle-brand wrappers. Gold Zone (2,000) and Platinum (1,000) cards were also randomly issued.

		MT
Complete Set (4):		25.00
Common Player:		3.50
1	Jeff Blake	6.00
2	Drew Bledsoe	12.00
3	Marshall Faulk	8.00
4	Natrone Means	3.50

1995 Pinnacle Club Collection Promos

The four-card, standard-size set, issued in a cello pack, previewed the 1995 Pinnacle Club Collection series. The set contained two base cards, one Arms Race card and an advertisement card. The card backs are identified with a "Promo" stamp.

		MT
Complete Set (4):		8.00
Common Player:		.50
1	Steve Young	2.00
11	Dan Marino	4.00
AR11	Arm's Race (Drew Bledsoe)	2.00
NNO	Pinnacle Ad Card	.50

1995 Pinnacle Club Collection

This set, in conjunction with Pinnacle's sponsorship of the NFL Quarterback Club, features 20 members of the NFL's Quarterback Club. Each player in the 261-card set has at least four cards - a regular one and three subset cards. The subset cards are: Xs and Os, which feature the players with an Xs and Os graphic design of their favorite plays; Rookie Replay, which shows the players from their rookie season; and Defining Moment, which highlights top performances for each player. A pin redemption card was also produced; it was seeded one per every 24 packs and entitles the finder to one of 20 Quarterback Club pins if the card is mailed in. There were three insert sets made: Arms Race and Aerial Assault, both of which are dedicated to the quarterbacks, and Spotlight, which focuses on non-quarterbacks. An interactive game that goes along with the Arms Race insert was also designed; as each featured quarterback accumulates statistics, collectors earned chances at winning prizes.

		MT
Complete Set (261):		25.00
Common Player:		.05
Minor Stars:		.10
Each player has nine cards.		
Wax Box:		35.00
1	Steve Young (R)	.50
2	Steve Young	.50
3	Steve Young	.50
4	Steve Young	.50
5	Steve Young	.50
6	Steve Young	.50
7	Steve Young (XO)	.50
8	Steve Young (RR)	.50
9	Steve Young (DM)	.50
10	Dan Marino (R)	1.00
11	Dan Marino	1.00
12	Dan Marino	1.00
13	Dan Marino	1.00
14	Dan Marino	1.00
15	Dan Marino	1.00
16	Dan Marino (XO)	1.00
17	Dan Marino (RR)	1.00
18	Dan Marino (DM)	1.00
19	Troy Aikman (R)	.40
20	Troy Aikman	.40
21	Troy Aikman	.40
22	Troy Aikman	.40
23	Troy Aikman	.40
24	Troy Aikman	.40
25	Troy Aikman (XO)	.40
26	Troy Aikman (RR)	.40
27	Troy Aikman (DM)	.40
28	Drew Bledsoe (R)	.50
29	Drew Bledsoe	.50
30	Drew Bledsoe	.50
31	Drew Bledsoe	.50
32	Drew Bledsoe	.50
33	Drew Bledsoe	.50
34	Drew Bledsoe (XO)	.50
35	Drew Bledsoe (RR)	.50
36	Drew Bledsoe (DM)	.50
37	Bubby Brister (R)	.05
38	Bubby Brister	.05
39	Bubby Brister	.05
40	Bubby Brister	.05
41	Bubby Brister	.05
42	Bubby Brister	.05
43	Bubby Brister (XO)	.05
44	Bubby Brister (RR)	.05
45	Bubby Brister (DM)	.05
46	Dave Brown (R)	.05
47	Dave Brown	.05
48	Dave Brown	.05
49	Dave Brown	.05
50	Dave Brown	.05
51	Dave Brown	.05
52	Dave Brown (XO)	.05
53	Dave Brown (RR)	.05
54	Dave Brown (DM)	.05
55	Randall Cunningham (R)	.10
56	Randall Cunningham	.10
57	Randall Cunningham	.10
58	Randall Cunningham	.10
59	Randall Cunningham	.10
60	Randall Cunningham	.10
61	Randall Cunningham (XO)	.10
62	Randall Cunningham (RR)	.10
63	Randall Cunningham (DM)	.10
64	John Elway (R)	.30
65	John Elway	.30
66	John Elway	.30
67	John Elway	.30
68	John Elway	.30
69	John Elway	.30
70	John Elway (XO)	.30
71	John Elway (RR)	.30
72	John Elway (DM)	.30
73	Boomer Esiason (R)	.05
74	Boomer Esiason	.05
75	Boomer Esiason	.05
76	Boomer Esiason	.05
77	Boomer Esiason	.05
78	Boomer Esiason	.05
79	Boomer Esiason (XO)	.05
80	Boomer Esiason (RR)	.05
81	Boomer Esiason (DM)	.05
82	Jim Everett (R)	.05
83	Jim Everett	.05
84	Jim Everett	.05
85	Jim Everett	.05
86	Jim Everett	.05
87	Jim Everett	.05
88	Jim Everett (XO)	.05
89	Jim Everett (RR)	.05
90	Jim Everett (DM)	.05
91	Brett Favre	.50
92	Brett Favre	.50
93	Brett Favre	.50
94	Brett Favre	.50
95	Brett Favre	.50
96	Brett Favre	.50
97	Brett Favre (XO)	.50
98	Brett Favre (RR)	.50
99	Brett Favre (DM)	.50
100	Jim Harbaugh (R)	.05
101	Jim Harbaugh	.05
102	Jim Harbaugh	.05
103	Jim Harbaugh	.05
104	Jim Harbaugh	.05
105	Jim Harbaugh	.05
106	Jim Harbaugh (XO)	.05
107	Jim Harbaugh (RR)	.05
108	Jim Harbaugh (DM)	.05
109	Jeff Hostetler (R)	.05
110	Jeff Hostetler	.05
111	Jeff Hostetler	.05
112	Jeff Hostetler	.05
113	Jeff Hostetler	.05
114	Jeff Hostetler	.05
115	Jeff Hostetler (XO)	.05
116	Jeff Hostetler (RR)	.05
117	Jeff Hostetler (DM)	.05
118	Michael Irvin (R)	.25
119	Michael Irvin	.25
120	Michael Irvin	.25
121	Michael Irvin	.25
122	Michael Irvin	.25
123	Michael Irvin	.25
124	Michael Irvin (XO)	.25
125	Michael Irvin (RR)	.25
126	Michael Irvin (DM)	.25
127	Jim Kelly (R)	.20
128	Jim Kelly	.20
129	Jim Kelly	.20
130	Jim Kelly	.20
131	Jim Kelly	.20
132	Jim Kelly	.20
133	Jim Kelly (XO)	.20
134	Jim Kelly (RR)	.20
135	Jim Kelly (DM)	.20
136	David Klingler (R)	.05
137	David Klingler	.05
138	David Klingler	.05
139	David Klingler	.05
140	David Klingler	.05
141	David Klingler	.05
142	David Klingler (XO)	.05
143	David Klingler (RR)	.05
144	David Klingler (DM)	.05
145	Bernie Kosar (R)	.05
146	Bernie Kosar	.05
147	Bernie Kosar	.05
148	Bernie Kosar	.05
149	Bernie Kosar	.05
150	Bernie Kosar	.05
151	Bernie Kosar (XO)	.05
152	Bernie Kosar (RR)	.05
153	Bernie Kosar (DM)	.05
154	Chris Miller (R)	.05
155	Chris Miller	.05
156	Chris Miller	.05
157	Chris Miller	.05
158	Chris Miller	.05
159	Chris Miller	.05
160	Chris Miller (XO)	.05
161	Chris Miller (RR)	.05
162	Chris Miller (DM)	.05
163	Rick Mirer (R)	.25
164	Rick Mirer	.25
165	Rick Mirer	.25
166	Rick Mirer	.25
167	Rick Mirer	.25
168	Rick Mirer	.25
169	Rick Mirer (XO)	.25
170	Rick Mirer (RR)	.25
171	Rick Mirer (DM)	.25
172	Warren Moon (R)	.10
173	Warren Moon	.10
174	Warren Moon	.10
175	Warren Moon	.10
176	Warren Moon	.10
177	Warren Moon	.10
178	Warren Moon (XO)	.10
179	Warren Moon (RR)	.10
180	Warren Moon (DM)	.10
181	Neil O'Donnell (R)	.05
182	Neil O'Donnell	.05
183	Neil O'Donnell	.05
184	Neil O'Donnell	.05
185	Neil O'Donnell	.05
186	Neil O'Donnell	.05
187	Neil O'Donnell (XO)	.05
188	Neil O'Donnell (RR)	.05
189	Neil O'Donnell (DM)	.05
190	Jerry Rice (R)	.50
191	Jerry Rice	.50
192	Jerry Rice	.50
193	Jerry Rice	.50
194	Jerry Rice	.50
195	Jerry Rice	.50
196	Jerry Rice (XO)	.50
197	Jerry Rice (RR)	.50
198	Jerry Rice (DM)	.50
199	Mark Rypien (R)	.05
200	Mark Rypien	.05
201	Mark Rypien	.05
202	Mark Rypien	.05
203	Mark Rypien	.05
204	Mark Rypien	.05
205	Mark Rypien (XO)	.05
206	Mark Rypien (RR)	.05
207	Mark Rypien (DM)	.05
208	Barry Sanders (R)	.50
209	Barry Sanders	.50
210	Barry Sanders	.50
211	Barry Sanders	.50
212	Barry Sanders	.50
213	Barry Sanders	.50
214	Barry Sanders (XO)	.50
215	Barry Sanders (RR)	.50
216	Barry Sanders (DM)	.50
217	Junior Seau (R)	.10
218	Junior Seau	.10
219	Junior Seau	.10
220	Junior Seau	.10
221	Junior Seau	.10
222	Junior Seau	.10
223	Junior Seau (XO)	.10
224	Junior Seau (RR)	.10
225	Junior Seau (DM)	.10
226	Emmitt Smith (R)	1.00
227	Emmitt Smith	1.00
228	Emmitt Smith	1.00
229	Emmitt Smith	1.00
230	Emmitt Smith	1.00
231	Emmitt Smith	1.00
232	Emmitt Smith (XO)	1.00
233	Emmitt Smith (RR)	1.00
234	Emmitt Smith (DM)	1.00
235	Phil Simms (R)	.05
236	Phil Simms	.05
237	Phil Simms	.05
238	Phil Simms	.05
239	Phil Simms	.05
240	Phil Simms	.05
241	Phil Simms (XO)	.05
242	Phil Simms (RR)	.05
243	Phil Simms (DM)	.05
244	Heath Shuler (R)	.30
245	Heath Shuler	.30
246	Heath Shuler	.30
247	Heath Shuler	.30
248	Heath Shuler	.30
249	Heath Shuler	.30
250	Heath Shuler (XO)	.30
251	Heath Shuler (RR)	.30
252	Heath Shuler (DM)	.30
253	Frank Reich (R)	.05
254	Frank Reich	.05
255	Frank Reich	.05
256	Frank Reich	.05
257	Frank Reich	.05
258	Frank Reich (XO)	.05
259	Frank Reich (RR)	.05
260	Frank Reich (DM)	.05
261	Frank Reich	.05

1995 Pinnacle Club Collection Aerial Assault

These 18 cards have all-foil printing on one side, and Pinnacle's exclusive Dufex textured-foil printing on the other. Both sides say "Aerial Assault," but only the all-foil side has a card number, which uses an "AA" prefix. This side also has a brief recap of the player's accomplishments. Cards were random inserts, one per every 36 packs of 1995 Pinnacle Club Collection football.

		MT
Complete Set (18):		125.00
Common Player:		3.00
1	Troy Aikman	20.00
2	Dave Brown	3.00
3	Drew Bledsoe	20.00
4	Randall Cunningham	3.00
5	Jim Everett	3.00
6	Jeff Hostetler	3.00
7	David Klingler	3.00
8	Dan Marino	45.00
9	Rick Mirer	3.00
10	Neil O'Donnell	3.00
11	Brett Favre	20.00
12	Boomer Esiason	3.00
13	Jim Harbaugh	3.00
14	John Elway	10.00
15	Steve Young	20.00
16	Warren Moon	3.00
17	Jim Kelly	5.00
18	Heath Shuler	15.00

Post-1980 cards in Near Mint condition will generally sell for about 75% of the quoted Mint value. Excellent-condition cards bring no more than 40%.

1995 Pinnacle Club Collection Arms Race

These cards, featuring double-sided Gold Rush technology that puts all-foil printing on both sides of the card, were from an interactive game-card insert set comprised of 18 members of the Quarterback Club. As each quarterback gained points for TD passes, victories and in six statistical categories, the card holder would move closer toward winning prizes. Collectors who had the card of the highest point total finisher at the end of the season had chances at the prizes. Cards were seeded one per every 18 packs. The front of the card had a gold-foiled scope as a background, with the color action photo in the foreground. Arms Race and the player's team name are along the left side of the card. The player's last name is in the lower left corner. The card back, numbered 1 of 18, etc., has a close-up shot of the player on the top half, with a scope as a background. The bottom half has contest rules for the game sweepstakes, plus the set logo.

		MT
Complete Set (18):		60.00
Common Player:		3.00
1	Steve Young	10.00
2	Troy Aikman	10.00
3	John Elway	7.00
4	Dan Marino	18.00
5	Brett Favre	10.00
6	Heath Shuler	8.00
7	Jim Kelly	5.00
8	Randall Cunningham	3.00
9	Dave Brown	3.00
10	Jim Everett	3.00
11	Drew Bledsoe	10.00
12	Rick Mirer	3.00
13	Jeff Hostetler	3.00
14	Neil O'Donnell	3.00
15	Warren Moon	5.00
16	Boomer Esiason	3.00
17	Chris Miller	3.00
18	David Klingler	3.00

1995 Pinnacle Club Collection Spotlight

These five cards pay a special tribute to superstars who are not quarterbacks. The cards use a micro-etching process that puts fine textured lines into a holographic foil, creating a flashy effect for the front. Cards were random inserts, one per every 90 packs of 1995 Pinnacle Club Collection.

	MT
Complete Set (5):	60.00
Common Player:	5.00
1 Emmitt Smith	35.00
2 Barry Sanders	20.00
3 Jerry Rice	20.00
4 Michael Irvin	5.00
5 Junior Seau	5.00

1995 Sportflix

This set marked Pinnacle's debut for Sportflix Football cards. The 175-card set includes more than 30 top rookies, plus a 20-card Game Winners subset. Cards were issued in packs of five, which could also contain one of five different insert cards - Artist's Proof (175-card parallel set, one per every 36 packs), Rolling Thunder, Rookie Lightning, ProMotion and Man 2 Man, which could be found in jumbo packs only. The regular cards feature two different pictures on the front, each visible through the concept of "magic motion" when the card is tilted. The player's name appears along the right side, with the letters increasing in size as the card is tilted. His position and the Sportflix logo are also along the side. The horizontal card back has a photo of the player on one side, flanked by key career statistical totals in the middle and a brief career summary on the opposite side. The player's name is in the upper left corner; the Sportflix logo is in the lower right corner.

	MT
Complete Set (175):	30.00
Common Player:	.10
Minor Stars:	.20
Inserted 1:36 Hobby	
Wax Box:	45.00
1 Troy Aikman	1.00
2 Rodney Hampton	.10
3 Jerry Rice	1.00
4 Reggie White	.30
5 Mark Ingram	.10
6 Chris Spielman	.10
7 Curtis Conway	.20
8 Erik Kramer	.20
9 Emmitt Smith	1.50
10 Alvin Harper	.10
11 Junior Seau	.20
12 Mike Pritchard	.10
13 Ricky Ervins	.10
14 Jim Harbaugh	.20
15 Dan Marino	1.50
16 Marshall Faulk	.50
17 Lorenzo White	.10
18 Cortez Kennedy	.10
19 Rocket Ismail	.10
20 Eric Metcalf	.10
21 Chris Chandler	.20
22 John Elway	1.00
23 Boomer Esiason	.20
24 Herman Moore	.20
25 Deion Sanders	.50
26 Charles Johnson	.20
27 Daryl Johnston	.10
28 Dave Krieg	.10
29 Jim Kelly	.20
30 Warren Moon	.20
31 Lewis Tillman	.10
32 Bruce Smith	.10
33 Jake Reed	.20
34 Craig Heyward	.10
35 Frank Reich	.10
36 Stan Humphries	.10
37 Charles Haley	.10
38 Andre Rison	.20
39 James Jett	.10
40 Jay Novacek	.10
41 Gary Brown	.10
42 Steve Bono	.20
43 Cris Carter	.30
44 Steve Atwater	.10

45 Andre Reed	.20
46 Greg Lloyd	.10
47 Mark Seay	.10
48 Dave Meggett	.10
49 Steve Beuerlein	.10
50 Jeff Graham	.10
51 Barry Sanders	2.00
52 Willie Davis	.10
53 Robert Smith	.30
54 Steve Walsh	.10
55 Michael Irvin	.20
56 Natrone Means	.30
57 Chris Warren	.20
58 Tim Brown	.20
59 Steve Young	.75
60 Jerome Bettis	.30
61 Shannon Sharpe	.20
62 Errict Rhett	.20
63 Scott Mitchell	.20
64 Leroy Hoard	.20
65 Garrison Hearst	.30
66 Terance Mathis	.20
67 Sean Gilbert	.10
68 Fred Barnett	.10
69 Hardy Nickerson	.10
70 Jim Everett	.10
71 Randall Cunningham	.30
72 Carl Pickens	.20
73 Jeff Hostetler	.10
74 Marcus Allen	.30
75 Jeff George	.20
76 Brett Favre	2.00
77 Chris Miller	.10
78 Craig Erickson	.10
79 Herschel Walker	.10
80 Bert Emanuel	.10
81 Leonard Russell	.10
82 Ricky Watters	.20
83 Robert Brooks	.20
84 Dave Brown	.20
85 Henry Ellard	.10
86 Barry Foster	.10
87 Johnny Mitchell	.10
88 Eric Allen	.10
89 Darnay Scott	.10
90 Harvey Williams	.10
91 Neil O'Donnell	.20
92 Drew Bledsoe	1.00
93 Ken Harvey	.10
94 Irving Fryar	.10
95 Rod Woodson	.10
96 Anthony Miller	.10
97 Mario Bates	.20
98 *Jeff Blake*	.50
99 Rick Mirer	.20
100 William Floyd	.20
101 Michael Haynes	.10
102 Flipper Anderson	.10
103 Greg Hill	.20
104 Mark Brunell	1.00
105 Vinny Testaverde	.30
106 Heath Shuler	.20
107 Ron Moore	.20
108 Ernest Givins	.10
109 Mike Sherrard	.10
110 Charlie Garner	.20
111 Trent Dilfer	.30
112 Bam Morris	.20
113 Lake Dawson	.10
114 Brian Blades	.10
115 Brent Jones	.10
116 Ronnie Harmon	.10
117 Eric Green	.10
118 Ben Coates	.20
119 *Ki-Jana Carter*	.30
120 *Steve McNair*	3.00
121 *Michael Westbrook*	1.25
122 *Kerry Collins*	1.50
123 *Joey Galloway*	2.50
124 *Kyle Brady*	.30
125 *J.J. Stokes*	1.50
126 *Tyrone Wheatley*	.30
127 *Rashaan Salaam*	.30
128 *Napoleon Kaufman*	2.50
129 *Frank Sanders*	1.00
130 *Stoney Case*	.20
131 *Todd Collins*	.20
132 *Lovell Pinkney*	.10
133 *Sherman Williams*	.20
134 *Rob Johnson*	2.00
135 *Mark Bruener*	.30
136 *Lee DeRamus*	.10
137 *Chad May*	.20
138 *James Stewart*	.30
139 *Ray Zellars*	.20
140 *Dave Barr*	.20
141 *Kordell Stewart*	5.00
142 *Jimmy Oliver*	.10
143 *Terrell Fletcher*	.30
144 *James Stewart*	2.50
145 *Terrell Davis*	12.00
146 *Joe Aska*	.10
147 *John Walsh*	.20
148 *Tyrone Davis*	.10
149 *Emmitt Smith*	.75
150 Barry Sanders	1.00
151 Jerry Rice	.50
152 Steve Young	.40
153 Dan Marino	.75
154 Troy Aikman	.50
155 Drew Bledsoe	.50
156 John Elway	.50
157 Brett Favre	1.00
158 Michael Irvin	.10
159 Heath Shuler	.10

160 Warren Moon	.10
161 Jim Kelly	.10
162 Randall Cunningham	.15
163 Jeff Hostetler	.10
164 Dave Brown	.10
165 Neil O'Donnell	.10
166 Rick Mirer	.10
167 Jim Everett	.10
168 Boomer Esiason	.10
169 Dan Marino	.75
170 Drew Bledsoe	.50
171 John Elway	.50
172 Emmitt Smith	.75
173 Steve Young	.40
174 Barry Sanders	1.00
175 Jerry Rice	.50

1995 Sportflix Artist's Proofs

The 175-card, standard-size set was a parallel version of the base set and was inserted every 36 packs. The Artist's Proof logo in gold and black appears on the card front.

	MT
Complete Set (175):	1400.
Common Player:	2.50
Artist's Proof Cards:	15x-30x
Artist's Proof Rookies:	6x-12x

1995 Sportflix Man 2 Man

These 1995 Pinnacle Sportflix cards were randomly included one per every eight jumbo packs of the base product. Each card front features two players, so 24 are represented in the 12-card set. The cards do not use the "magic motion" concept, but do feature the players superimposed against a football game scene. The player's names are on the front, along with the Sportflix and insert set logos. The card back is numbered 1 of 12, etc., and includes a color photo of each player superimposed against a black-and-white photo of the same shot. Two small paragraphs between the photos offer brief descriptions of the players' skills.

	MT
Complete Set (12):	100.00
Common Player:	5.00
1 Troy Aikman, Dan Marino	20.00
2 Emmitt Smith, Marshall Faulk	20.00
3 Kerry Collins, Drew Bledsoe	14.00
4 Steve Young, Steve McNair	12.00
5 Barry Sanders, Ki-Jana Carter	12.00
6 Heath Shuler, John Elway	8.00
7 Rashaan Salaam, Bam Morris	8.00
8 Ricky Watters, Natrone Means	5.00
9 Jerry Rice, J.J. Stokes	12.00
10 Kordell Stewart, Warren Moon	12.00
11 Brett Favre, Jeff Blake	15.00
12 Michael Westbrook, Joey Galloway	5.00

> A card number in parentheses ( ) indicates the set is unnumbered.

1995 Sportflix ProMotion

These 1995 Pinnacle Sportflix insert cards showcase the company's unique morphing technology, in which a player turns into, or morphs into, his team logo through 36 frames of action. The Sportflix logo is in the upper right corner; the player's last name appears above a football, which says "Pro" inside and is located alongside the word "Motion." The horizontal card back uses this same design at the bottom; a player photo and brief player profile are included on the back. Cards are numberd using a "PM" prefix. Cards were randomly included one per every 48 packs.

	MT
Complete Set (12):	180.00
Common Player:	5.00
1 Steve Young	20.00
2 Troy Aikman	18.00
3 Dan Marino	35.00
4 Drew Bledsoe	25.00
5 John Elway	10.00
6 Jim Kelly	5.00
7 Jerry Rice	20.00
8 Michael Irvin	8.00
9 Emmitt Smith	35.00
10 Marshall Faulk	25.00
11 Natrone Means	10.00
12 Ki-Jana Carter	18.00

1995 Sportflix Rolling Thunder

These Rolling Thunder insert cards feature 12 running backs each against a spinning pinwheel background on the front. "Rolling Thunder" is written along the left side of the card; the player's name, which increases in size as the card is tilted, is in the lower left corner. A Sportflix logo is in the upper right corner. The card back, numbered 1 of 12, etc., has a full color photo of the player in the upper portion of the card; the bottom portion contains the bottom half of the photo in a ghosted format, with the insert set name and a brief player profile superimposed over it. A team helmet is also in the upper right corner. Cards were random inserts, one every 12 packs of 1995 Pinnacle Sportflix.

	MT
Complete Set (12):	75.00
Common Player:	3.00
1 Emmitt Smith	18.00
2 Barry Sanders	10.00
3 Marshall Faulk	8.00
4 Ki-Jana Carter	8.00

5 Rashaan Salaam	8.00
6 Tyrone Wheatley	6.00
7 Natrone Means	5.00
8 Jerome Bettis	3.00
9 Errict Rhett	8.00
10 Bam Morris	3.00
11 William Floyd	5.00
12 Mario Bates	3.00

1995 Sportflix Rookie Lightning

These insert cards feature 12 of the top rookies entering the NFL in 1995. Cards were random inserts, one per every 36 packs of 1995 Pinnacle Sportflix. The card front uses the "magic motion" concept to create two different photos when the card is tilted. "Rookie" and "Lightning" alternate along the right side when the card is tilted, while the player's name at the bottom increases in size. The Sportflix logo and the player's position are in the upper left corner. The card back has the set logo and number (1 of 12, etc.) in the upper right corner. The outline of one of the photos from the front is also on the back.

	MT
Complete Set (11):	120.00
Common Player:	7.00
1 Ki-Jana Carter	15.00
2 Steve McNair	20.00
3 Michael Westbrook	10.00
4 Kerry Collins	25.00
5 Joey Galloway	20.00
6 J.J. Stokes	20.00
7 Tyrone Wheatley	7.00
8 Rashaan Salaam	20.00
9 Napoleon Kaufman	12.00
10 Kordell Stewart	25.00
11 James Stewart	7.00

1995 Pinnacle Dial Corporation

The 30-card, regular-sized cards were issued as part of a promotion sponsored by Dial soap and Purex laundry products. UPC labels from these products could be sent in, with $2.50, for the set. As part of the promotion, 90-card sheets were awarded with Bruce Smith signatures. The cards are numbered with the "DC" prefix.

	MT
Complete Set (30):	15.00
Common Player:	.30
1 Troy Aikman	1.50
2 Frank Reich	.30
3 Drew Bledsoe	1.50
4 Bubby Brister	.30
5 Dave Brown	.30
6 Randall Cunningham	.30
7 John Elway	1.00
8 Boomer Esiason	.30
9 Jim Everett	.30
10 Bruce Smith	.40
11 Brett Favre	3.00
12 Jim Harbaugh	.40
13 Jeff Hostetler	.30
14 Michael Irvin	.60
15 Jim Kelly	.40
16 David Klingler	.30
17 Bernie Kosar	.30
18 Dan Marino	3.00
19 Chris Miller	.30
20 Rick Mirer	.60
21 Warren Moon	.40
22 Neil O'Donnell	.40
23 Jerry Rice	1.50
24 Mark Rypien	.30
25 Barry Sanders	1.50
26 Junior Seau	.60

27 Heath Shuler	.40
28 Phil Simms	.30
29 Emmitt Smith	3.00
30 Steve Young	1.00
P1 Uncut Sheet Prize	45.00

1996 Pinnacle Super Bowl Card Show

The 15-card, standard-size set features color action shots over a metallic Dufex background. The card fronts feature a Super Bowl XXX Card Show logo while the horizontal backs have a player shot with a highlight. Pinnacle distributed the set in three-card packs in exchange for two Pinnacle wrappers.

	MT
Complete Set (15):	25.00
Common Player:	1.00
1 Steve Young	2.50
2 Dan Marino	5.00
3 Troy Aikman	3.00
4 Drew Bledsoe	3.00
5 John Elway	1.75
6 Brett Favre	5.00
7 Jim Harbaugh	1.00
8 Jeff Hostetler	1.00
9 Michael Irvin	1.25
10 Jim Kelly	1.25
11 Warren Moon	1.25
12 Jerry Rice	3.00
13 Barry Sanders	3.00
14 Junior Seau	1.25
15 Emmitt Smith	5.00

1996 Pinnacle

Pinnacle's 1996 football set includes 200 cards in the regular set, including 30 Rookies, six Bid For Six subset cards, five checklists and a Brett Favre Cheesehead card. The set is paralleled twice in normal packs - Trophy Collection (one in five packs, these cards use all-foil Dufex) and Artist's Proof (one in 47 packs, these have a holographic gold foil stamp). These parallel cards are labeled accordingly on them. Each regular card has a full-bleed color action photo on the front, with a Pinnacle logo in an upper corner. The player's name is in a gold-foil triangle at the bottom. The card back has logo in an upper corner, with the card number in white in a black square. The upper half of the card has a photo; the lower half has a brief profile, stats, biographical information, the player's name and team logo, and his position. Insert sets include Black 'N Blue, Double Disguise, On the Line, Team Pinnacle and 321 Die-Cut Jersey cards. Pinnacle also offers hobby-exclusive packs called premium stock, which contain 25 cards and carry a suggested retail price of $6.99. In these packs each common card in the set is printed on a super-premium, 24-point card stock featuring silver foil stamping. Premium stock packs also have five inserts - Trophy Collection, Artist's Proofs, Team Pinnacle, Double Disguise and an exclusive rainbow holographic foil version of 321.

	MT
Complete Set (200):	25.00
Common Player:	.10
Minor Stars:	.20
Wax Box:	30.00
1 Emmitt Smith	2.50
2 Robert Brooks	.20
3 Joey Galloway	.75

4	Dan Marino	2.50
5	Frank Sanders	.20
6	Cris Carter	.10
7	Jeff Blake	.75
8	Steve McNair	.75
9	Tamarick Vanover	.75
10	Andre Reed	.10
11	Junior Seau	.10
12	Alvin Harper	.10
13	Trent Dilfer	.10
14	Kordell Stewart	1.00
15	Kyle Brady	.10
16	Charles Haley	.10
17	Greg Lloyd	.10
18	Mario Bates	.10
19	Shannon Sharpe	.10
20	Scott Mitchell	.10
21	Craig Heyward	.10
22	Marcus Allen	.10
23	Curtis Martin	1.75
24	Drew Bledsoe	1.00
25	Jerry Rice	1.00
26	Charlie Garner	.10
27	Michael Irvin	.10
28	Curtis Conway	.10
29	Terrell Davis	1.25
30	Jeff Hostetler	.10
31	Neil O'Donnell	.10
32	Errict Rhett	.50
33	Stan Humphries	.10
34	Jeff Graham	.10
35	Floyd Turner	.10
36	Vincent Brisby	.10
37	Steve Young	1.00
38	Carl Pickens	.10
39	Terance Mathis	.10
40	Brett Favre	2.50
41	Ki-Jana Carter	.40
42	Jim Everett	.10
43	Marshall Faulk	.75
44	William Floyd	.10
45	Deion Sanders	.50
46	Garrison Hearst	.10
47	Chris Sanders	.10
48	Isaac Bruce	.75
49	Natrone Means	.10
50	Troy Aikman	1.25
51	Ben Coates	.10
52	Tony Martin	.10
53	Rod Woodson	.10
54	Edgar Bennett	.10
55	Eric Zeier	.10
56	Steve Bono	.10
57	Tim Brown	.10
58	Kevin Williams	.10
59	Erik Kramer	.10
60	Jim Kelly	.10
61	Larry Centers	.10
62	Terrell Fletcher	.10
63	Michael Westbrook	.20
64	Kerry Collins	.50
65	Jay Novacek	.10
66	J.J. Stokes	.20
67	John Elway	.50
68	Jim Harbaugh	.10
69	Aeneas Williams	.10
70	Tyrone Wheatley	.10
71	Chris Warren	.20
72	Rodney Thomas	.10
73	Jeff George	.10
74	Rick Mirer	.10
75	Yancey Thigpen	.10
76	Herman Moore	.50
77	Gus Frerotte	.10
78	Anthony Miller	.10
79	Ricky Watters	.10
80	Sherman Williams	.10
81	Hardy Nickerson	.10
82	Henry Ellard	.10
83	Aaron Craver	.10
84	Rodney Peete	.10
85	Eric Metcalf	.10
86	Brian Blades	.10
87	Rob Moore	.10
88	Kimble Anders	.10
89	Harvey Williams	.10
90	Thurman Thomas	.20
91	Dave Brown	.10
92	Terry Allen	.10
93	Ken Norton	.10
94	Reggie White	.20
95	Mark Chmura	.20
96	Bert Emanuel	.10
97	Brett Perriman	.10
98	Antonio Freeman	.10
99	Brian Mitchell	.10
100	Orlando Thomas	.10
101	Aaron Hayden	.10
102	Quinn Early	.10
103	Lovell Pinkney	.10
104	Napoleon Kaufman	.20
105	Daryl Johnston	.10
106	Steve Tasker	.10
107	Brent Jones	.10
108	Mark Brunell	.75
109	Leslie O'Neal	.10
110	Irving Fryar	.10
111	Jim Miller	.10
112	Sean Dawkins	.10
113	Boomer Esiason	.10
114	Heath Shuler	.10
115	Bruce Smith	.10
116	Russell Maryland	.10
117	Jake Reed	.10
118	O.J. McDuffie	.10
119	Erik Williams	.10
120	Willie McGinest	.10
121	Terry Kirby	.10
122	Fred Barnett	.10
123	Andre Hastings	.10

124	Dale Hellestrae	.10
125	Darren Woodson	.10
126	Steve Atwater	.10
127	Quentin Coryatt	.10
128	Derrick Thomas	.10
129	Nate Newton	.10
130	Kevin Greene	.10
131	Barry Sanders	1.25
132	Warren Moon	.10
133	Rashaan Salaam	.50
134	Rodney Hampton	.10
135	James Stewart	.10
136	Erric Pegram	.10
137	Bryan Cox	.10
138	Adrian Murrell	.10
139	Robert Smith	.10
140	Bernie Parmalee	.10
141	Bryce Paup	.10
142	Darick Holmes	.10
143	Hugh Douglas	.10
144	Ken Dilger	.10
145	Derek Loville	.10
146	Horace Copeland	.10
147	Wayne Chrebet	.10
148	Andre Coleman	.10
149	Greg Hill	.10
150	Eric Swann	.10
151	Tyrone Hughes	.10
152	Ernie Mills	.10
153	Terry Glenn	2.00
154	Cedric Jones	.10
155	Leeland McElroy	.30
156	Bobby Engram	.50
157	Willie Anderson	.10
158	Mike Alstott	1.75
159	Alex Van Dyke	.20
160	Jeff Lewis	.50
161	Keyshawn Johnson	3.00
162	Regan Upshaw	.10
163	Eric Moulds	2.50
164	Tim Biakabutuka	1.00
165	Kevin Hardy	.20
166	Marvin Harrison	3.00
167	Karim Abdul-Jabbar	1.00
168	Tony Brackens	.30
169	Stepfret Williams	.10
170	Eddie George	4.00
171	Lawrence Phillips	.75
172	Danny Kanell	.50
173	Derrick Mayes	1.00
174	Daryl Gardener	.10
175	Jonathan Ogden	.10
176	Alex Molden	.10
177	Chris Darkins	.20
178	Stephen Davis	4.00
179	Rickey Dudley	.30
180	Eddie Kennison	.50
181	Simeon Rice	.40
182	Bobby Hoying	.75
183	Troy Aikman	.50
184	Emmitt Smith	1.00
185	Michael Irvin	.10
186	Deion Sanders	.25
187	Daryl Johnston	.10
188	Jay Novacek	.10
189	Steve Young	.40
190	Jerry Rice	.50
191	J.J. Stokes	.10
192	Ken Norton	.10
193	William Floyd	.10
194	Brent Jones	.10
195	Dan Marino CL	.40
196	Brett Favre CL	.30
197	Emmitt Smith CL	.40
198	Barry Sanders CL	.30
199	Checklist (Emmitt Smith, Dan Marino, Brett Favre, Barry Sanders CL)	.30
200	Brett Favre Cheese	2.50

1996 Pinnacle Foils

AARON HAYDEN

	MT
Complete Set (200):	35.00
Foil Cards:	1.5x

Pinnacle Foils were available only in All-Foil packs, which were available in retail locations. These Foils were the "regular-issue" cards of All-Foil packs that also included Black and Blue inserts.

1996 Pinnacle Artist's Proofs

DAN MARINO

This 200-card parallel set features each card in 1996 Pinnacle Football, but includes a holographic Artist's Proof logo on the front, as well as a logo on the back. Artist's Proofs were included in every 48 hobby and retail packs. Regular Artist's Proofs contained gold foil at the bottom of the card in contrast to Premium Stock Artist's Proofs that included silver foil and are included in a separate entry.

	MT
Complete Set (200):	1500.
Artist's Proof Cards:	25x-50x

1996 Pinnacle Premium Stock

Pinnacle Premium Stock was issued as a hobby exclusive product that was offered in addition to regular Pinnacle Football. The base cards were different in that they had silver foil at the bottom instead of gold foil. Packs of Premium Stock contained 25 cards, and included Artist's Proofs, Trophy Collection, Team Pinnacle, Die-Cut Jerseys and Double Disguise inserts. Only the Artist's Proofs and Die-Cut Jerseys are different than regular-issue inserts.

	MT
Complete Set (200):	50.00
Premium Stock Cards:	2x

1996 Pinnacle Trophy Collection

MARCUS ALLEN

Trophy Collection features all 200 cards from 1996 Pinnacle, reprinted in Dufex foil fronts and a stamp on the back that reads "Trophy Collection." Regular packs had Trophy Collection cards every five packs, while Premium Stock packs contained them every two packs. There is no difference between regular and Premium Stock cards in Trophy Collection.

1996 Pinnacle Premium Stock Artist's Proofs

Each card in the 200-card Premium Stock set was featured in the parallel Artist's Proof insert. This means that the Premium Stock Artist's Proofs feature silver foil on the

fronts instead of gold foil on the regular-issue Artist's Proofs. Premium Stock Artist's Proofs were inserted every 12 packs.

	MT
Complete Set (200):	1500.
PS Artist's Proofs:	25x-50x

1996 Pinnacle Die-Cut Jerseys

The best and youngest players in the NFL - those with three or less years of experience - are featured on these die-cut Pinnacle insert cards. The cards are hobby-exclusive; they were seeded one per every 23 hobby packs. The card front has a color or action shot against a die-cut version of his jersey. "3-2-1" is included as a tag in the jersey's collar. The Pinnacle logo and player's name are stamped in gold foil along the bottom of the card. The back of the card uses the back of the player's jersey as a background. A second photo appears, along with a team logo, a brief summary of his accomplishments, and a card number (1 of 20, etc.).

		MT
Complete Set (20):		160.00
Common Player:		4.00
Comp. Holofoil (20):		320.00
Holofoil Cards:		2x
1	Errict Rhett	6.00
2	Marshall Faulk	8.00
3	Isaac Bruce	8.00
4	William Floyd	4.00
5	Heath Shuler	4.00
6	Kerry Collins	8.00
7	Kordell Stewart	14.00
8	Rashaan Salaam	6.00
9	Terrell Davis	18.00
10	Rodney Thomas	4.00
11	Curtis Martin	20.00
12	Steve McNair	10.00
13	J.J. Stokes	10.00
14	Joey Galloway	10.00
15	Michael Westbrook	6.00
16	Keyshawn Johnson	10.00
17	Lawrence Phillips	8.00
18	Terry Glenn	18.00
19	Tim Biakabutuka	8.00
20	Eddie George	20.00

1996 Pinnacle Premium Stock Die-Cut Jerseys

Premium Stock packs included a unique version of the Die-cut Jerseys that featured the fronts in prismatic foil. These versions of Die-Cut Jerseys were inserted every six packs and only included in Premium Stock.

	MT
Complete Set (20):	320.00
PS Die-Cut Jerseys:	2x

1996 Pinnacle Double Disguise

These 1996 Pinnacle inserts showcase five players in 20 different combinations. The cards are printed on plastic and are covered with an opaque plastic protector which is meant to be peeled off. Each side features combinations of Emmitt Smith, Dan Marino, Brett Favre, Kerry Collins and Steve Young matched up. The card's background shows the length of a football field as seen through a fisheye lens. The front side uses gold-foil stamping for the Pinnacle logo, player's name and set name. These are not in foil on the opposite side, which has a card number (1 of 20, etc.). The cards were seeded one per every 18 packs.

		MT
Complete Set (20):		150.00
Common Player:		4.00
1	Emmitt Smith, Emmitt Smith	15.00
2	Emmitt Smith, Dan Marino	15.00
3	Emmitt Smith, Brett Favre	12.00
4	Emmitt Smith, Steve Young	10.00
5	Dan Marino, Dan Marino	12.00
6	Dan Marino, Emmitt Smith	15.00
7	Dan Marino, Kerry Collins	10.00
8	Dan Marino, Steve Young	10.00
9	Kerry Collins, Kerry Collins	4.00
10	Kerry Collins, Dan Marino	10.00
11	Kerry Collins, Brett Favre	10.00
12	Kerry Collins, Steve Young	4.00
13	Brett Favre, Brett Favre	10.00
14	Brett Favre, Kerry Collins	10.00
15	Brett Favre, Dan Marino	10.00
16	Brett Favre, Emmitt Smith	12.00
17	Steve Young, Steve Young	4.00
18	Steve Young, Brett Favre	8.00
19	Steve Young, Emmitt Smith	10.00
20	Steve Young, Kerry Collins	4.00

1996 Pinnacle Black 'N Blue

STEVE YOUNG

Twenty-five of the NFL's most rugged players show the hard-nosed, aggressive play

which has earned them a spot in this set. The cards were seeded one per every 33 magazine packs. Each card front has two photos on it.

		MT
Complete Set (25):		275.00
Common Player:		5.00
1	Steve Young	15.00
2	Troy Aikman	20.00
3	Dan Marino	40.00
4	Michael Irvin	5.00
5	Jerry Rice	20.00
6	Emmitt Smith	40.00
7	Brett Favre	40.00
8	Drew Bledsoe	20.00
9	John Elway	15.00
10	Barry Sanders	25.00
11	Cris Carter	5.00
12	Jeff Blake	5.00
13	Chris Warren	5.00
14	Kerry Collins	8.00
15	Natrone Means	5.00
16	Herman Moore	5.00
17	Steve McNair	10.00
18	Ricky Watters	5.00
19	Tamarick Vanover	10.00
20	Deion Sanders	15.00
21	Terrell Davis	20.00
22	Rodney Thomas	5.00
23	Rashaan Salaam	8.00
24	Darick Holmes	5.00
25	Eric Zeier	5.00

1996 Pinnacle Team Pinnacle

These 1996 Pinnacle inserts feature the best AFC player at each position on a card that is complemented by the top NFC position player on the flip side. The cards were seeded one per every 90 packs for both hobby and retail packs. The design shows a pinstripe-framed color action photo against a football background. The player's name, position and Team Pinnacle are written in a rectangle at the bottom. The card is numbered 1 of 20, etc.

		MT
Complete Set (10):		150.00
Common Player:		8.00
Inserted 1:90		
1	Troy Aikman, Drew Bledsoe	15.00
2	Steve Young, Jeff Blake	12.00
3	Brett Favre, John Elway	40.00
4	Kerry Collins, Dan Marino	30.00
5	Emmitt Smith, Curtis Martin	30.00
6	Barry Sanders, Chris Warren	35.00
7	Errict Rhett, Marshall Faulk	8.00
8	Jerry Rice, Carl Pickens	15.00
9	Michael Irvin, Joey Galloway	8.00
10	Isaac Bruce, Kordell Stewart	12.00

Complete Trophy Set (200): 500.00
Trophy Cards: 10x-20x

1996 Pinnacle On the Line

The NFL's top pass catchers are featured on these 1996 Pinnacle inserts. The cards, seeded one per every 23 retail packs, use Dufex for the design. The card front has a full-bleed color action photo on it, with the player's name at the bottom near a grid which says "On the Line." The Pinnacle logo is in an upper corner.

		MT
Complete Set (15):		80.00
Common Player:		3.00
1	Michael Irvin	3.00
2	Robert Brooks	3.00
3	Herman Moore	6.00
4	Cris Carter	3.00
5	Chris Sanders	3.00
6	Jerry Rice	20.00
7	Michael Westbrook	3.00
8	Carl Pickens	3.00
9	Bobby Engram	6.00
10	Alex Van Dyke	3.00
11	Keyshawn Johnson	12.00
12	Terry Glenn	18.00
13	Eric Moulds	8.00
14	Marvin Harrison	13.00
15	Eddie Kennison	6.00

1996 Laser View

Each of these 1996 Pinnacle Laserview cards features nearly four seconds of taped replay action from NFL Films in the form of a hologram. Each regular card has the hologram on one side, with a small action photo, the player's name and the LaserView logo on the opposite. The background of the horizontal card front is black. The card back has a ghosted image for the background, with a small action photo, biographical information, a card number, team logo and brief writeup toward the top of the card. Two team-colored stripes separate this information from the player's name, position and 1995 and career statistics at the bottom. Laserview Gold parallel gold-foiled cards were seeded every 12th pack. Other inserts include Eye on the Prize and Inscriptions. Every box also comes with a Pinnacle authenticator lens that allows collectors to prove the authenticity of the printing. A small box on the back of each card has a multi-colored pattern of lines that can only be read by the lens; the message "PBI 96" appears when this is done. If the lens is turned another way, a rainbow pattern appears. Pinnacle claims no counterfeit techniques would be able to duplicate this printing because the pattern of lines is so thin.

		MT
Complete Set (40):		50.00
Common Player:		.50
Minor Stars:		1.00
Wax Box:		90.00
1	Jim Kelly	1.00
2	Troy Aikman	5.00
3	Michael Irvin	1.00
4	Emmitt Smith	10.00
5	John Elway	4.00
6	Barry Sanders	5.00
7	Brett Favre	10.00
8	Jim Harbaugh	.50
9	Dan Marino	10.00
10	Warren Moon	.50
11	Drew Bledsoe	5.00
12	Jim Everett	.50
13	Jeff Hostetler	.50
14	Neil O'Donnell	.50
15	Junior Seau	.50
16	Jerry Rice	5.00
17	Steve Young	4.00
18	Rick Mirer	1.00
19	Boomer Esiason	.50
20	Bernie Kosar	.50
21	Heath Shuler	1.00
22	Dave Brown	.50
23	Jeff Blake	1.00
24	Kerry Collins	1.50
25	Kordell Stewart	5.00
26	Scott Mitchell	.50
27	Kerry Collins PE	3.00
28	Troy Aikman PE	3.00
29	Kordell Stewart PE	3.00
30	Michael Irvin PE	5.00
31	Emmitt Smith PE	5.00
32	John Elway PE	1.00
33	Barry Sanders PE	3.00
34	Brett Favre PE	5.00
35	Dan Marino PE	5.00
36	Drew Bledsoe PE	3.00
37	Neil O'Donnell PE	.50
38	Jerry Rice PE	5.00
39	Steve Young PE	2.00
40	Jeff Blake PE	2.00

1996 Laser View Golds

This 40-card parallel set used all 40 cards in the regular-issue LaserView set in a gold version. Gold parallels were found every 12 packs.

	MT
Complete Set (40):	150.00
Golds:	2x-3x

1996 Laser View Eye on the Prize

This 1996 Pinnacle Laserview insert spotlights 12 of the NFL's elite superstars as they compete for the coveted Lombardi Trophy as winners of the Super Bowl. The cards put a different holographic angle on the players by picturing the player with a holographic background. The cards were seeded one per every 24 packs.

		MT
Complete Set (12):		100.00
Common Player:		3.00
1	Troy Aikman	10.00

2	Emmitt Smith	20.00
3	Michael Irvin	3.00
4	Steve Young	8.00
5	Jerry Rice	10.00
6	Dan Marino	20.00
7	John Elway	8.00
8	Junior Seau	3.00
9	Neil O'Donnell	3.00
10	Jeff Hostetler	3.00
11	Jim Kelly	3.00
12	Kordell Stewart	10.00

1996 Laser View Inscriptions

This 1996 Pinnacle Laserview insert set features 25 of the top members of the NFL Quarterback Club who each signed a serial-numbered card. The cards, seeded one per every 24 packs, are printed on clear plastic stock which gives collectors a backwards-forwards look at the signature. The front has a color panel at the top which includes the brand and set names, with a color mug shot underneath framed in yellow. The closeup shot is flanked by a black-and-white action scene. The player's signature is below his photo, followed by another colored band at the bottom which has the player's name and team name inside. The back, which shows reverse images of the front, includes the serial number in a white rectangle at the top.

		MT
Complete Set (25):		1450.
Jeff Blake 3125		40.00
Drew Bledsoe 2775		100.00
Dave Brown 3100		25.00
Mark Brunell 3200		90.00
Kerry Collins 3000		50.00
John Elway 3100		100.00
Boomer Esiason 1500		160.00
Jim Everett 3100		20.00
Brett Favre 4850		125.00
Jeff George 2900		20.00
Jim Harbaugh 3500		25.00
Jeff Hostetler 3750		25.00
Michael Irvin 3050		25.00
Jim Kelly 3100		40.00
Bernie Kosar 3200		20.00
Erik Kramer 3150		20.00
Rick Mirer 3150		30.00
Scott Mitchell 4900		20.00
Warren Moon 2800		25.00
Neil O'Donnell 1600		50.00
Jerry Rice 900		350.00
Barry Sanders 2900		150.00
Junior Seau 3000		25.00
Heath Shuler 3100		25.00
Steve Young 1950		110.00

1996 Pinnacle Mint Cards

This 1996 Pinnacle Laserview insert spotlights 12 of the NFL's elite superstars as they

The 30-card, regular-sized set comes in three-card packs and contains two coin cards and one regular-issue card. The die-cut coin cards feature a closeup

player shot and an action shot on the front with the same action shot in black and white on the back. The cards have a circular cutout in the upper right quadrant where the included brass, nickel- silver or gold coins fit. The regular-issue cards feature a foil team emblem (where the hole is on the coin cards) in brass (common), silver (1:20) or gold (1:48). Each of the 30 players represented in the set are members of the Quarterback Club.

		MT
Complete Die-Cut (30):		18.00
Common Player:		.20
Minor Stars:		.40
Bronze Cards:		2x
Silver Cards:		4x-8x
Gold Cards:		10x-20x
Wax Box:		30.00
1	Troy Aikman	1.50
2	John Elway	.75
3	Jim Kelly	.40
4	Dan Marino	3.00
5	Warren Moon	.20
6	Steve Young	1.50
7	Jerry Rice	1.50
8	Boomer Esiason	.20
9	Jim Everett	.20
11	Brett Favre	3.00
11	Jim Harbaugh	.40
12	Jeff Hostetler	.20
13	Neil O'Donnell	.20
14	Drew Bledsoe	1.50
15	Rick Mirer	.20
16	Emmitt Smith	3.00
17	Barry Sanders	1.50
18	Junior Seau	.20
19	Dave Brown	.20
20	Heath Shuler	.20
21	Jeff Blake	.40
22	Kerry Collins	.75
23	Scott Mitchell	.20
24	Kordell Stewart	1.50
25	Jeff George	.20
26	Mark Brunell	1.00
27	Erik Kramer	.20
28	Bernie Kosar	.20
29	Frank Reich	.20
30	Randall Cunningham	.20

1996 Pinnacle Mint Coins

The 30-piece set was included twice in every three-pack of Pinnacle Mint Collection football. Two variations of the common brass coin were available: nickel-silver (1:20) and 24 kt. gold (1:48). Solid silver coins were also inserted every 2,300 packs and one redemption card was available for an all-gold coin with the odds being one in 47,200. The coin face has the image of the player's face with his name, team and uniform number. The coin backs feature the Quarterback Club logo, as each of the 30 players represented in the set are members.

		MT
Complete Brass (30):		50.00
Common Brass Coin:		.75
Minor Brass Stars:		1.50
Nickel Coins:		2x-4x
Gold Plated Coins:		4x-8x
1	Troy Aikman	4.00
2	John Elway	3.00
3	Jim Kelly	1.50
4	Dan Marino	8.00
5	Warren Moon	.75
6	Steve Young	3.00
7	Jerry Rice	4.00
8	Boomer Esiason	.75
9	Jim Everett	.75
10	Brett Favre	8.00
11	Jim Harbaugh	.75
12	Jeff Hostetler	.75
13	Neil O'Donnell	.75
14	Drew Bledsoe	4.00
15	Rick Mirer	.75
16	Emmitt Smith	8.00
17	Barry Sanders	4.00
18	Junior Seau	1.50
19	Dave Brown	.75
20	Heath Shuler	.75
21	Jeff Blake	1.50
22	Kerry Collins	1.50
23	Scott Mitchell	.75
24	Kordell Stewart	4.00
25	Jeff George	.75
26	Mark Brunell	3.00
27	Erik Kramer	.75
28	Bernie Kosar	.75
29	Frank Reich	.75
30	Randall Cunningham	.75

1996 Pinnacle Bimbo Bread

These magic motion cards were distributed in Mexico through Bimbo Bakery products. The 30 cards measure 1-1/2" x 2-1/2" and feature a magic motion photo and the Bimbo logo on the front. The backs have another player photo and biographical information.

		MT
Complete Set (30):		300.00
Common Player:		4.00
1	Troy Aikman	30.00
2	Michael Irvin	8.00
3	Emmitt Smith	60.00
4	Jim Kelly	8.00
5	John Elway	25.00
6	Barry Sanders	35.00
7	Brett Favre	70.00
8	Jim Harbaugh	4.00
9	Dan Marino	60.00
10	Warren Moon	4.00
11	Drew Bledsoe	30.00
12	Jim Everett	4.00
13	Jeff Hostetler	4.00
14	Neil O'Donnell	4.00
15	Junior Seau	6.00
16	Jerry Rice	30.00
17	Steve Young	20.00
18	Rick Mirer	4.00
19	Jeff Blake	8.00
20	David Klingler	4.00
21	Boomer Esiason	4.00
22	Heath Shuler	4.00
23	Dave Brown	4.00
24	Bernie Kosar	4.00
25	Kordell Stewart	30.00
26	Mark Brunell	30.00
27	Kerry Collins	25.00
28	Scott Mitchell	4.00
29	Erik Kramer	4.00
30	Jeff George	6.00

1997 Pinnacle

Pinnacle Football has a 200-card base set. Both sides feature a player action photo. Pinnacle Football also has two partial base set parallels (Artist's Proof and Trophy Collection) and three inserts. Trophy Collection utilizes Dufex technology. Artist's Proof parallels Trophy Collection by adding the Artist's Proof stamp. The parallel sets are re-numbered. The inserts include Epix (24 cards, 1:19), Scoring Core (24 cards, 1:89) and Team Pinnacle (10 cards, 1:240).

		MT
Complete Set (200):		25.00
Common Player:		.10
Minor Stars:		.20
Wax Box:		45.00
1	Brett Favre	2.50
2	Dan Marino	2.00
3	Emmitt Smith	2.00

4	Steve Young	.75
5	Drew Bledsoe	1.00
6	Eddie George	1.50
7	Barry Sanders	1.25
8	Jerry Rice	1.00
9	John Elway	.75
10	Troy Aikman	1.00
11	Kerry Collins	.25
12	Rick Mirer	.10
13	Jim Harbaugh	.10
14	Elvis Grbac	.10
15	Gus Frerotte	.10
16	Neil O'Donnell	.10
17	Jeff George	.10
18	Kordell Stewart	1.00
19	Junior Seau	.20
20	Vinny Testaverde	.10
21	Terry Glenn	.30
22	Anthony Johnson	.10
23	Boomer Esiason	.10
24	Terrell Owens	.50
25	Natrone Means	.20
26	Marcus Allen	.20
27	James Jett	.10
28	Chris T. Jones	.10
29	Stan Humphries	.10
30	Keith Byars	.10
31	John Friesz	.10
32	Mike Alstott	.20
33	Eddie Kennison	.40
34	Eric Moulds	.10
35	Frank Sanders	.10
36	Daryl Johnston	.10
37	Cris Carter	.20
38	Errict Rhett	.10
39	Ben Coates	.10
40	Shannon Sharpe	.10
41	Jamal Anderson	.10
42	Tim Biakabutuka	.10
43	Jeff Blake	.20
44	Michael Irvin	.20
45	Terrell Davis	1.00
46	Bam Morris	.10
47	Rashaan Salaam	.10
48	Adrian Murrell	.20
49	Ty Detmer	.10
50	Terry Allen	.10
51	Mark Brunell	1.00
52	O.J. McDuffie	.10
53	Willie McGinest	.10
54	Chris Warren	.10
55	Trent Dilfer	.20
56	Jerome Bettis	.20
57	Tamarick Vanover	.10
58	Ki-Jana Carter	.10
59	Ray Zellars	.10
60	J.J. Stokes	.10
61	Cornelius Bennett	.10
62	Scott Mitchell	.10
63	Tyrone Wheatley	.10
64	Steve McNair	.75
65	Tony Banks	.40
66	James Stewart	.10
67	Robert Smith	.10
68	Thurman Thomas	.20
69	Mark Chmura	.10
70	Napoleon Kaufman	.20
71	Ken Norton	.10
72	Herschel Walker	.10
73	Joey Galloway	.20
74	Neil Smith	.10
75	Simeon Rice	.10
76	Michael Jackson	.10
77	Muhsin Muhammad	.10
78	Kevin Hardy	.10
79	Irving Fryar	.10
80	Eric Swann	.10
81	Yancey Thigpen	.10
82	Jim Everett	.10
83	Karim Abdul-Jabbar	.30
84	Garrison Hearst	.10
85	Lawrence Phillips	.20
86	Bryan Cox	.10
87	Larry Centers	.10
88	Wesley Walls	.10
89	Curtis Conway	.10
90	Darnay Scott	.10
91	Anthony Miller	.10
92	Edgar Bennett	.10
93	Willie Green	.10
94	Kent Graham	.10
95	Dave Brown	.10
96	Wayne Chrebet	.10
97	Ricky Watters	.20
98	Tony Martin	.10
99	Warren Moon	.10
100	Curtis Martin	1.00
101	Dorsey Levens	.30
102	Jim Pyne	.10
103	Antonio Freeman	.30
104	Leeland McElroy	.10
105	Isaac Bruce	.20
106	Chris Sanders	.10
107	Tim Brown	.10
108	Greg Lloyd	.10
109	Terrell Buckley	.10
110	Deion Sanders	.40
111	Carl Pickens	.10
112	Bobby Engram	.10
113	Andre Reed	.10
114	Terance Mathis	.10
115	Herman Moore	.20
116	Robert Brooks	.10
117	Ken Dilger	.10
118	Keenan McCardell	.10
119	Andre Hastings	.10
120	Willie Davis	.10

121	Bruce Smith	.10
122	Rob Moore	.10
123	Johnnie Morton	.10
124	Sean Dawkins	.10
125	Mario Bates	.10
126	Henry Ellard	.10
127	Derrick Alexander	.10
128	Kevin Green	.10
129	Derrick Thomas	.10
130	Rod Woodson	.10
131	Rodney Hampton	.10
132	Marshall Faulk	.20
133	Michael Westbrook	.10
134	Erik Kramer	.10
135	Todd Collins	.10
136	Bill Romanowski	.10
137	Jake Reed	.10
138	Heath Shuler	.10
139	Keyshawn Johnson	.40
140	Marvin Harrison	.40
141	Andre Rison	.10
142	Zach Thomas	.20
143	Eric Metcalf	.10
144	Amani Toomer	.10
145	Desmond Howard	.10
146	Jimmy Smith	.10
147	Brad Johnson	.10
148	Troy Vincent	.10
149	Bryce Paup	.10
150	Reggie White	.20
151	*Jake Plummer*	4.00
152	*Darnell Autry*	.25
153	*Tiki Barber*	.75
154	*Pat Barnes*	.30
155	*Orlando Pace*	.20
156	*Peter Boulware*	.10
157	*Shawn Springs*	.20
158	*Troy Davis*	.30
159	*Ike Hilliard*	.75
160	*Jim Druckenmiller*	1.50
161	*Warrick Dunn*	1.75
162	*James Farrior*	.10
163	*Tony Gonzalez*	.75
164	*Darrell Russell*	.10
165	*Byron Hanspard*	.50
166	*Corey Dillon*	2.00
167	*Kenny Holmes*	.10
168	*Walter Jones*	.10
169	*Danny Wuerffel*	.75
170	*Tom Knight*	.10
171	*David LaFleur*	.40
172	*Kevin Lockett*	.10
173	*Will Blackwell*	.20
174	*Reidel Anthony*	1.00
175	*Dwayne Rudd*	.10
176	*Yatil Green*	.30
177	*Antowain Smith*	1.25
178	*Rae Carruth*	.75
179	*Bryant Westbrook*	.75
180	*Reinard Wilson*	.10
181	*Joey Kent*	.30
182	*Renaldo Wynn*	.10
183	Brett Favre	1.25
184	Emmitt Smith	1.00
185	Dan Marino	1.00
186	Troy Aikman	.50
187	Jerry Rice	.50
188	Drew Bledsoe	.50
189	Eddie George	.75
190	Terry Glenn	.10
191	John Elway	.30
192	Steve Young	.30
193	Mark Brunell	.50
194	Barry Sanders	.50
195	Kerry Collins	.30
196	Curtis Martin	.50
197	Terrell Davis	.50
198	Checklist	.10
199	Checklist	.10
200	Checklist	.10

1997 Pinnacle Trophy Collection

Trophy Collection is a 100-card partial parallel of the base set. The cards were re-numbered and feature Dufex technology. They were inserted one per nine packs.

		MT
Complete Set (100):		250.00
Common Player:		1.00
Minor Stars:		2.00
P1	Brett Favre	25.00
P2	Dan Marino	20.00
P3	Emmitt Smith	20.00
P4	Steve Young	8.00
P5	Drew Bledsoe	12.00
P6	Eddie George	16.00
P7	Barry Sanders	12.00
P8	Jerry Rice	12.00
P9	John Elway	10.00
P10	Troy Aikman	12.00
P11	Kerry Collins	3.00
P12	Rick Mirer	1.00
P13	Jim Harbaugh	1.00
P14	Elvis Grbac	1.00
P15	Gus Frerotte	1.00
P16	Neil O'Donnell	1.00
P17	Jeff George	1.00
P18	Kordell Stewart	12.00
P19	Junior Seau	1.00
P20	Vinny Testaverde	1.00
P21	Terry Glenn	10.00
P22	Natrone Means	2.00
P23	Marcus Allen	2.00
P24	Stan Humphries	1.00
P25	John Friesz	1.00
P26	Cris Carter	1.00
P27	Shannon Sharpe	1.00
P28	Tim Biakabutuka	2.00
P29	Jeff Blake	2.00
P30	Michael Irvin	2.00
P31	Terrell Davis	12.00
P32	Rashaan Salaam	1.00
P33	Adrian Murrell	2.00
P34	Ty Detmer	1.00
P35	Mark Brunell	12.00
P36	Chris Warren	1.00
P37	Trent Dilfer	2.00
P38	Jerome Bettis	2.00
P39	Scott Mitchell	1.00
P40	Steve McNair	10.00
P41	Tony Banks	3.00
P42	Joey Galloway	3.00
P43	Karim Abdul-Jabbar	8.00
P44	Lawrence Phillips	2.00
P45	Dave Brown	1.00
P46	Warren Moon	1.00
P47	Curtis Martin	12.00
P48	Dorsey Levens	1.00
P49	Deion Sanders	5.00
P50	Herman Moore	2.00
P51	Bruce Smith	1.00
P52	Keyshawn Johnson	2.00
P53	Reggie White	1.00
P54	Jake Plummer	10.00
P55	Darnell Autry	4.00
P56	Tiki Barber	8.00
P57	Pat Barnes	4.00
P58	Orlando Pace	2.00
P59	Peter Boulware	1.00
P60	Shawn Springs	2.00
P61	Troy Davis	3.00
P62	Ike Hilliard	6.00
P63	Jim Druckenmiller	12.00
P64	Warrick Dunn	20.00
P65	James Farrior	1.00
P66	Tony Gonzalez	5.00
P67	Darrell Russell	1.00
P68	Byron Hanspard	3.00
P69	Corey Dillon	12.00
P70	Kenny Holmes	1.00
P71	Walter Jones	1.00
P72	Danny Wuerffel	10.00
P73	Tom Knight	1.00
P74	David LaFleur	5.00
P75	Kevin Lockett	1.00
P76	Will Blackwell	2.00
P77	Reidel Anthony	8.00
P78	Dwayne Rudd	1.00
P79	Yatil Green	2.00
P80	Antowain Smith	12.00
P81	Rae Carruth	6.00
P82	Bryant Westbrook	2.00
P83	Reinard Wilson	1.00
P84	Joey Kent	2.00
P85	Renaldo Wynn	1.00
P86	Brett Favre	12.00
P87	Emmitt Smith	10.00
P88	Dan Marino	10.00
P89	Troy Aikman	6.00
P90	Jerry Rice	6.00
P91	Drew Bledsoe	6.00
P92	Eddie George	8.00
P93	Terry Glenn	4.00
P94	John Elway	4.00
P95	Steve Young	4.00
P96	Mark Brunell	6.00
P97	Barry Sanders	6.00
P98	Kerry Collins	2.00
P99	Curtis Martin	6.00
P100	Terrell Davis	6.00

1997 Pinnacle Artist's Proof

Artist's Proof is a 100-card partial parallel of Pinnacle Football. The cards feature Dufex technology and the Artist's Proof stamp. The cards are re-numbered from one to 100.

		MT
Complete Set (100):		850.00
Common Player:		3.00
Minor Stars:		6.00
P1	Brett Favre	75.00
P2	Dan Marino	60.00
P3	Emmitt Smith	60.00
P4	Steve Young	20.00
P5	Drew Bledsoe	40.00
P6	Eddie George	50.00
P7	Barry Sanders	40.00
P8	Jerry Rice	40.00
P9	John Elway	30.00
P10	Troy Aikman	40.00
P11	Kerry Collins	8.00
P12	Rick Mirer	3.00
P13	Jim Harbaugh	3.00
P14	Elvis Grbac	3.00
P15	Gus Frerotte	3.00
P16	Neil O'Donnell	3.00
P17	Jeff George	3.00
P18	Kordell Stewart	3.00
P19	Junior Seau	3.00
P20	Vinny Testaverde	3.00
P21	Terry Glenn	30.00
P22	Natrone Means	6.00
P23	Marcus Allen	6.00
P24	Stan Humphries	3.00
P25	John Friesz	3.00
P26	Cris Carter	3.00
P27	Shannon Sharpe	3.00
P28	Tim Biakabutuka	6.00
P29	Jeff Blake	6.00
P30	Michael Irvin	6.00
P31	Terrell Davis	40.00
P32	Rashaan Salaam	6.00
P33	Adrian Murrell	6.00
P34	Ty Detmer	3.00
P35	Mark Brunell	40.00
P36	Chris Warren	3.00
P37	Trent Dilfer	6.00
P38	Jerome Bettis	6.00
P39	Scott Mitchell	3.00
P40	Steve McNair	30.00
P41	Tony Banks	8.00
P42	Joey Galloway	6.00
P43	Karim Abdul-Jabbar	20.00
P44	Lawrence Phillips	6.00
P45	Dave Brown	3.00
P46	Warren Moon	6.00
P47	Curtis Martin	40.00
P48	Dorsey Levens	3.00
P49	Deion Sanders	20.00
P50	Herman Moore	6.00
P51	Bruce Smith	3.00
P52	Keyshawn Johnson	6.00
P53	Reggie White	6.00
P54	Jake Plummer	25.00
P55	Darnell Autry	12.00
P56	Tiki Barber	20.00
P57	Pat Barnes	10.00
P58	Orlando Pace	6.00
P59	Peter Boulware	3.00
P60	Shawn Springs	3.00
P61	Troy Davis	6.00
P62	Ike Hilliard	15.00
P63	Jim Druckenmiller	30.00
P64	Warrick Dunn	50.00
P65	James Farrior	3.00
P66	Tony Gonzalez	12.00
P67	Darrell Russell	3.00
P68	Byron Hanspard	8.00
P69	Corey Dillon	30.00
P70	Kenny Holmes	3.00
P71	Walter Jones	3.00
P72	Danny Wuerffel	25.00
P73	Tom Knight	3.00
P74	David LaFleur	12.00
P75	Kevin Lockett	3.00
P76	Will Blackwell	6.00
P77	Reidel Anthony	20.00
P78	Dwayne Rudd	3.00
P79	Yatil Green	6.00
P80	Antowain Smith	25.00
P81	Rae Carruth	15.00
P82	Bryant Westbrook	6.00
P83	Reinard Wilson	3.00
P84	Joey Kent	6.00
P85	Renaldo Wynn	3.00
P86	Brett Favre	40.00
P87	Emmitt Smith	30.00
P88	Dan Marino	30.00
P89	Troy Aikman	20.00
P90	Jerry Rice	20.00
P91	Drew Bledsoe	20.00
P92	Eddie George	25.00
P93	Terry Glenn	15.00
P94	John Elway	15.00
P95	Steve Young	15.00
P96	Mark Brunell	20.00
P97	Barry Sanders	20.00
P98	Kerry Collins	8.00
P99	Curtis Martin	20.00
P100	Terrell Davis	20.00

1997 Pinnacle Epix

Epix is a 24-card insert which features holographic ef-fects. The set consists of Game, Moment and Season cards which highlight each player's top performances. Orange, Pur-ple and Emerald versions of each card were produced. The overall insertion rate for Epix was 1:19.

		MT
Complete Set (24):		400.00
Common Game (E1-E8):		4.00
Common Moment (E9-E16):		12.00
Common Season (E17-E24):		8.00
Purple Cards:		2x
Emerald Cards:		3x
1	Emmitt Smith	25.00
2	Troy Aikman	15.00
3	Terrell Davis	15.00
4	Drew Bledsoe	15.00
5	Jeff George	4.00
6	Kerry Collins	10.00
7	Antonio Freeman	4.00
8	Herman Moore	4.00
9	Barry Sanders	50.00
10	Brett Favre	80.00
11	Michael Irvin	12.00
12	Steve Young	30.00
13	Mark Brunell	40.00
14	Jerome Bettis	12.00
15	Deion Sanders	25.00
16	Jeff Blake	12.00
17	Dan Marino	50.00
18	Eddie George	35.00
19	Jerry Rice	25.00
20	John Elway	20.00
21	Curtis Martin	20.00
22	Kordell Stewart	25.00
23	Junior Seau	8.00
24	Reggie White	8.00

1997 Pinnacle Scoring Core

Scoring Core is a 24-card insert seeded 1:89 packs. Each card is specially die-cut and fea-tures foil-etching.

		MT
Complete Set (24):		375.00
Common Player:		4.00
Minor Stars:		8.00
1	Emmitt Smith	50.00
2	Troy Aikman	30.00
3	Michael Irvin	8.00
4	Robert Brooks	8.00
5	Brett Favre	60.00
6	Antonio Freeman	8.00
7	Curtis Martin	30.00
8	Drew Bledsoe	30.00
9	Terry Glenn	8.00
10	Tim Biakabutuka	4.00
11	Kerry Collins	8.00
12	Muhsin Muhammad	4.00
13	Karim Abdul-Jabbar	15.00
14	Dan Marino	50.00
15	O.J. McDuffie	4.00
16	Terrell Davis	30.00
17	John Elway	20.00
18	Shannon Sharpe	4.00
19	Garrison Hearst	4.00
20	Steve Young	20.00
21	Jerry Rice	30.00
22	Natrone Means	8.00
23	Mark Brunell	30.00
24	Keenan McCardell	4.00

1997 Pinnacle Team Pinnacle

Team Pinnacle is a 10-card insert consisting of double-sid-ed foil cards. The cards feature two players from the same posi-tion, one from each conference. Team Pinnacle cards were in-serted 1:240.

		MT
Complete Set (10):		400.00
Common Player:		25.00
1	Dan Marino, Troy Aikman	80.00

2	Drew Bledsoe, Brett Favre	100.00
3	Mark Brunell, Kerry Collins	50.00
4	John Elway, Steve Young	40.00
5	Terrell Davis, Emmitt Smith	80.00
6	Curtis Martin, Barry Sanders	50.00
7	Eddie George, Tim Biakabutuka	60.00
8	Karim Abdul-Jabbar, Lawrence Phillips	25.00
9	Terry Glenn, Jerry Rice	50.00
10	Joey Galloway, Michael Irvin	25.00

1997 Pinnacle Inscriptions

Inscriptions consists of a 50-card base set, two parallel sets and two inserts. The base set features a color player photo with a black and white back-ground. The parallel sets are Challenge Collection (1:7) and Artist's Proof (1:35). Artist's Proof features Dufex technolo-gy and the Artist's Proof seal. The inserts are Autographs (30 cards, 1:23) and V2 (18 cards, 1:11). Each pack contained three cards and was packaged in a collectable box.

		MT
Complete Set (50):		75.00
Common Player:		.50
Minor Stars:		1.00
Artist Proof Cards:		8x-16x
Chall. Collection Cards:		2x-4x
Wax Box:		150.00
1	Mark Brunell	4.00
2	Steve Young	3.00
3	Rick Mirer	.50
4	Brett Favre	10.00
5	Tony Banks	1.00
6	Elvis Grbac	.50
7	John Elway	3.00
8	Troy Aikman	4.00
9	Neil O'Donnell	.50
10	Kordell Stewart	4.00
11	Drew Bledsoe	4.00
12	Kerry Collins	1.00
13	Dan Marino	8.00
14	Jeff George	1.00
15	Scott Mitchell	.50
16	Jim Harbaugh	.50
17	Dave Brown	.50
18	Jeff Blake	1.00
19	Trent Dilfer	1.00
20	Barry Sanders	5.00
21	Jerry Rice	4.00
22	Emmitt Smith	8.00
23	Vinny Testaverde	.50
24	Warren Moon	.50
25	Junior Seau	.50
26	Gus Frerotte	.50
27	Heath Shuler	.50
28	Erik Kramer	.50
29	Boomer Esiason	.50
30	Jim Kelly	1.00
31	Mark Brunell	2.00
32	Steve Young	1.50
33	Brett Favre	5.00
34	Tony Banks	1.00
35	John Elway	1.50
36	Troy Aikman	2.00
37	Kordell Stewart	2.00
38	Drew Bledsoe	2.00
39	Kerry Collins	1.00
40	Dan Marino	4.00
41	Jim Harbaugh	.50
42	Jeff Blake	.50
43	Barry Sanders	2.50
44	Jerry Rice	2.00
45	Emmitt Smith	4.00
46	Rick Mirer	.50
47	Jeff George	.50
48	Neil O'Donnell	.50
49	Elvis Grbac	.50
50	Scott Mitchell	.50

1997 Pinnacle Inscriptions Autographs

Autographs is a 30-card in-sert which was seeded one per 23 packs. The cards are plastic, signed by the player and hand-numbered. Each player signed a different number of cards.

		MT
Common Player:		25.00
Minor Stars:		50.00
	Tony Banks 1925	50.00
	Jeff Blake 1470	50.00
	Drew Bledsoe 1970	150.00
	Dave Brown 1970	25.00
	Mark Brunell 2000	150.00
	Kerry Collins 1300	100.00
	Trent Dilfer 1950	25.00
	John Elway 1975	150.00
	Jim Everett 2000	25.00
	Brett Favre 215	700.00
	Gus Frerotte 1975	25.00
	Jeff George 1935	25.00
	Elvis Grbac 1985	25.00
	Jim Harbaugh 1975	25.00
	Jeff Hostetler 2000	25.00
	Jim Kelly 1925	50.00
	Bernie Kosar 1975	25.00
	Eric Kramer 2000	25.00
	Dan Marino 440	500.00
	Rick Mirer 2000	25.00
	Scott Mitchell 1995	25.00
	Warren Moon 1975	25.00
	Neil O'Donnell 1990	25.00
	Jerry Rice 950	300.00
	Junior Seau 1900	25.00
	Heath Shuler 1865	25.00
	Emmitt Smith 220	600.00
	Kordell Stewart 1495	150.00
	Vinny Testaverde 1975	25.00
	Steve Young 1900	125.00

1997 Pinnacle Inscriptions V2

V2 is an 18-card insert con-sisting of plastic motion cards. Inserted 1:11, the cards came with a clear-coat protector.

		MT
Complete Set (18):		200.00
Common Player:		4.00
Minor Stars:		8.00
1	Mark Brunell	15.00
2	Steve Young	10.00
3	Brett Favre	35.00
4	Tony Banks	8.00
5	John Elway	10.00
6	Troy Aikman	15.00
7	Kordell Stewart	15.00
8	Drew Bledsoe	15.00
9	Kerry Collins	8.00
10	Dan Marino	30.00
11	Barry Sanders	20.00
12	Jerry Rice	15.00
13	Emmitt Smith	30.00
14	Neil O'Donnell	4.00
15	Scott Mitchell	4.00
16	Jim Harbaugh	4.00
17	Jeff Blake	8.00
18	Trent Dilfer	8.00

1997 Pinnacle Inside

Pinnacle Inside featured a 150-card base set and 28 collectible cans. The base cards include three different player shots. Silver Lining (1:7) and Gridiron Gold (1:63) were the parallel sets. The inserts are Fourth & Goal and Autographed Cards.

	MT
Complete Set (150):	40.00
Common Player:	.20
Minor Stars:	.40
Silver Cards:	6x-12x
Silver Rookies:	3x-6x
Inserted 1:7	
Gridiron Gold Cards:	20x-40x
Gridiron Gold Rookies:	10x-20x
Inserted 1:63	
1 Troy Aikman	1.50
2 Dan Marino	3.00
3 Barry Sanders	1.50
4 Drew Bledsoe	1.50
5 Kerry Collins	.50
6 Emmitt Smith	3.00
7 Brett Favre	3.00
8 John Elway	1.00
9 Jerry Rice	1.50
10 Mark Brunell	1.50
11 Elvis Grbac	.20
12 Junior Seau	.20
13 Eddie George	1.75
14 Steve Young	1.00
15 Terrell Davis	1.50
16 Thurman Thomas	.40
17 Deion Sanders	.75
18 Terrell Owens	.75
19 Neil O'Donnell	.20
20 Carl Pickens	.20
21 Marcus Allen	.40
22 Ricky Watters	.40
23 Vinny Testaverde	.20
24 Kordell Stewart	1.25
25 Tony Banks	.75
26 Terry Glenn	.50
27 Todd Collins	.20
28 Robert Brooks	.40
29 Heath Shuler	.20
30 Shannon Sharpe	.20
31 Michael Westbrook	.20
32 Reggie White	.40
33 Brad Johnson	.20
34 Tamarick Vanover	.20
35 Larry Centers	.20
36 Terance Mathis	.20
37 Hardy Nickerson	.20
38 Jamal Anderson	.40
39 Kevin Hardy	.20
40 Stan Humphries	.20
41 Chris Warren	.20
42 Tim Brown	.20
43 Joey Galloway	.60
44 Boomer Esiason	.20
45 Jake Reed	.20
46 Kent Graham	.20
47 Marshall Faulk	.40
48 Sean Dawkins	.20
49 Dave Brown	.20
50 Willie Green	.20
51 Andre Hastings	.20
52 Erik Kramer	.20
53 Michael Irvin	.40
54 Gus Frerotte	.20
55 Winslow Oliver	.20
56 Jimmy Smith	.20
57 Derrick Alexander	.20
58 Adrian Murrell	.20
59 Ki-Jana Carter	.20
60 Garrison Hearst	.20
61 Chris Sanders	.20
62 Johnnie Morton	.20
63 Lawrence Phillips	.40
64 Bobby Engram	.20
65 Tim Biakabutuka	.40
66 Anthony Johnson	.20
67 Keyshawn Johnson	.60
68 Jeff George	.20
69 Errict Rhett	.20
70 Cris Carter	.40
71 Chris T. Jones	.20
72 Eric Moulds	.20
73 Rick Mirer	.20
74 Keenan McCardell	.20
75 Simeon Rice	.20
76 Eddie Kennison	.75
77 Herman Moore	.40
78 Jim Harbaugh	.20
79 Robert Smith	.20
80 Bruce Smith	.20
81 John Friesz	.20
82 Irving Fryar	.20
83 Edgar Bennett	.20
84 Ty Detmer	.20
85 Curtis Conway	.20
86 Napoleon Kaufman	.20
87 Tony Martin	.20
88 Amani Toomer	.20
89 Willie McGinest	.20
90 Daryl Johnston	.20
91 Stanley Pritchett	.20
92 Chris Chandler	.20
93 Natrone Means	.20
94 Kimble Anders	.20
95 Steve McNair	1.00
96 Curtis Martin	1.50
97 O.J. McDuffie	.20
98 Ben Coates	.20
99 Jerome Bettis	.40
100 Andre Reed	.20
101 Jeff Blake	.40
102 Wesley Walls	.20
103 Warren Moon	.40
104 Isaac Bruce	.40
105 Terry Allen	.20
106 Rodney Hampton	.20
107 Karim Abdul-Jabbar	.50
108 Marvin Harrison	.75
109 Dorsey Levens	.20
110 Rashaan Salaam	.40
111 Scott Mitchell	.20
112 Darnay Scott	.20
113 Aeneas Williams	.20
114 Trent Dilfer	.20
115 Antonio Freeman	.40
116 Jim Everett	.20
117 Muhsin Muhammad	.20
118 Rickey Dudley	.20
119 Mike Alstott	.20
120 *Jim Druckenmiller*	2.50
121 *Tiki Barber*	1.50
122 *Ike Hilliard*	1.25
123 *Orlando Pace*	.50
124 *Jake Plummer*	2.00
125 *Yatil Green*	.75
126 *Byron Hanspard*	.75
127 *James Farrior*	.20
128 *Corey Dillon*	2.50
129 *Pat Barnes*	.50
130 *Kenny Holmes*	.20
131 *Rae Carruth*	1.25
132 *Danny Wuerffel*	1.50
133 *Darnell Autry*	.75
134 *Reidel Anthony*	2.00
135 *Darrell Russell*	.20
136 *Will Blackwell*	.50
137 *Peter Boulware*	.20
138 *Shawn Springs*	.50
139 *Joey Kent*	.75
140 *Troy Davis*	.75
141 *Antowain Smith*	1.50
142 *Walter Jones*	.20
143 *Tony Gonzalez*	.75
144 *David LaFleur*	.75
145 *Warrick Dunn*	2.50
146 *Bryant Westbrook*	.20
147 *Dwayne Rudd*	.20
148 *Tom Knight*	.20
149 *Kevin Lockett*	.20
150 Checklist	.20

1997 Pinnacle Inside Cans

Inside cards were available in 28 different cans. The first 25 cans featured a single player with the image of their Inside card on the outside of the can. Three special cans - Brett Favre MVP, Dan Marino passing record and Ice Bowl commemorative - were also issued. A Gold Can parallel set was also created. Gold Cans were found once per 47 cans.

	MT
Complete Set (28):	30.00
Common Can:	.50
Common Sealed Can:	3.00
Sealed Cans:	1x-2x
Gold Cans:	4x-8x
Gold Sealed Cans:	8x-16x
1 Brett Favre	3.00
2 Dan Marino	2.50
3 Emmitt Smith	2.50
4 Troy Aikman	1.50
5 Barry Sanders	1.50
6 Kerry Collins	1.00
7 Mark Brunell	1.50
8 John Elway	1.00
9 Steve Young	1.00
10 Jerry Rice	1.50
11 Terrell Davis	1.50
12 Curtis Martin	1.50
13 Terry Glenn	1.00
14 Eddie George	2.00
15 Jeff Blake	.50
16 Kordell Stewart	1.50
17 Rick Mirer	.50
18 Karim Abdul-Jabbar	1.00
19 Jeff George	.50
20 Keyshawn Johnson	.50
21 Jim Harbaugh	.50
22 Drew Bledsoe	1.50
23 Deion Sanders	1.00
24 Tony Banks	1.00
25 Jerome Bettis	.50
26 Brett Favre (MVP)	3.00
27 Dan Marino (Passing)	2.50
28 Ice Bowl	2.50

1997 Pinnacle Inside Fourth & Goal

This 20-card insert features clutch players on a foil card. These cards were inserted 1:23.

	MT
Complete Set (20):	500.00
Common Player:	10.00
1 Brett Favre	60.00
2 Drew Bledsoe	30.00
3 Troy Aikman	30.00
4 Mark Brunell	30.00
5 Steve Young	25.00
6 Vinny Testaverde	10.00
7 Dan Marino	50.00
8 Kerry Collins	15.00
9 John Elway	25.00
10 Emmitt Smith	50.00
11 Barry Sanders	30.00
12 Eddie George	40.00
13 Terrell Davis	30.00
14 Curtis Martin	30.00
15 Terry Glenn	15.00
16 Jerry Rice	30.00
17 Herman Moore	10.00
18 Jeff Blake	10.00
19 Warrick Dunn	35.00
20 Antowain Smith	20.00

1997 Pinnacle Mint Cards

This 30-card base set features a player photo and a foil stamped bronze medallion on the front. A die-cut parallel was created to hold the set's coins. The other parallels are Silver Team Pinnacle (silver foil printing, 1:15) and Gold Team Pinna-cle (gold Dufex etched foil, 1:47). Inserts include Commemorative Collection, a six-card set capturing the top moments of 1996 with silver foil and inserted 1:31. Pinnacle Mint also includes Solid Gold Redemption Cards. The solid gold cards are a parallel of the regular set. One redemption card per player was issued and they were inserted 1:47,000.

	MT
Complete Die-Cut (30):	20.00
Common Player:	.20
Minor Stars:	.40
Bronze Cards:	1x-2x
Silver Cards:	6x-12x
Gold Cards:	12x-24x
Wax Box:	60.00
1 Brett Favre	2.50
2 Drew Bledsoe	1.25
3 Mark Brunell	1.25
4 Kerry Collins	.50
5 Troy Aikman	1.25
6 Steve Young	1.00
7 Dan Marino	2.00
8 Barry Sanders	1.25
9 John Elway	1.00
10 Emmitt Smith	2.00
11 Rick Mirer	.20
12 Kordell Stewart	1.25
13 Tony Banks	.75
14 Jeff George	.20
15 Jerry Rice	1.25
16 Jeff Blake	.40
17 Jim Harbaugh	.20
18 Heath Shuler	.20
19 Scott Mitchell	.20
20 Neil O'Donnell	.20
21 Brett Favre (Minted Highlights)	1.25
22 Drew Bledsoe (Minted Highlights)	.75
23 Mark Brunell (Minted Highlights)	.75
24 Kerry Collins (Minted Highlights)	.40
25 Troy Aikman (Minted Highlights)	.50
26 Dan Marino (Minted Highlights)	1.00
27 Barry Sanders (Minted Highlights)	.75
28 Emmitt Smith (Minted Highlights)	1.00
29 Tony Banks (Minted Highlights)	.20
30 John Elway (Minted Highlights)	.50

1997 Pinnacle Mint Coins

The 30-base coins feature each players face and match up with one of the base cards. Six parallels of the base coins were made. Nickel-Silver (1:20), Gold Plated (1:47), Brass Proof (numbered to 500), Silver Proof (numbered to 250), Gold Proof (numbered to 100) and Solid Silver (1:288) versions were all added to Pinnacle Mint. The only insert is Commemorative Collection.

	MT
Complete Brass (30):	60.00
Common Brass Coin:	.75
Minor Brass Stars:	1.50
Nickel Coins:	2.5x-5x
Gold Plated Coins:	6x-12x
1 Brett Favre	8.00
2 Drew Bledsoe	4.00
3 Mark Brunell	4.00
4 Kerry Collins	2.00
5 Troy Aikman	4.00
6 Steve Young	3.00
7 Dan Marino	6.00
8 Barry Sanders	4.00
9 John Elway	3.00
10 Emmitt Smith	6.00
11 Rick Mirer	.75
12 Kordell Stewart	4.00
13 Tony Banks	1.50
14 Jeff George	.75
15 Jerry Rice	4.00
16 Jeff Blake	1.50
17 Jim Harbaugh	.75

1997 Pinnacle Mint Commemorative Cards

This six-card insert highlights six top moments of 1996. The cards feature silver foil and were inserted 1:31.

	MT
Complete Set (6):	60.00
Common Player:	8.00
1 Barry Sanders	25.00
2 Brett Favre	18.00
3 Mark Brunell	8.00
4 Emmitt Smith	16.00
5 Dan Marino	16.00
6 Jerry Rice	8.00

1997 Pinnacle Mint Commemorative Coins

These six coins are double-sized brass and match up with the Commemorative Collection cards. They also highlight top events of 1996 and were inserted 1:31.

	MT
Complete Set (6):	120.00
Common Player:	16.00
1 Barry Sanders	25.00
2 Brett Favre	35.00
3 Mark Brunell	16.00
4 Emmitt Smith	35.00
5 Dan Marino	35.00
6 Jerry Rice	16.00

1997 Pinnacle X-Press

This 150-base card set features a 22-card Rookie subset, a 10-card Peak Performers subset and three checklist cards. The base cards are laid-out horizontally with two player photos on the front. The inserts included the Pursuit of Paydirt interactive game, Metal Works, Bombs Away and Divide & Conquer. Autumn Warriors is a base set parallel. The silver foil cards were inserted 1:7.

	MT
Complete Set (150):	25.00
Common Player:	.05
Minor Stars:	.10
Aut. Warrior Cards:	6x-12x
Aut. Warrior Rookies:	3x-6x
Wax Box:	60.00
1 Drew Bledsoe	1.00
2 Steve Young	.75
3 Brett Favre	2.25
4 John Elway	.75
5 Dan Marino	2.00
6 Jerry Rice	1.00
7 Tony Banks	.40
8 Kerry Collins	.25
9 Mark Brunell	1.00
10 Troy Aikman	1.00
11 Barry Sanders	1.25
12 Elvis Grbac	.05
13 Eddie George	1.50
14 Terry Glenn	.25
15 Kordell Stewart	.10
16 Junior Seau	.10
17 Herman Moore	.05
18 Gus Frerotte	.05
19 Warren Moon	.05
20 Emmitt Smith	2.00
21 Chris Chandler	.05
22 Rashaan Salaam	.05
23 Sean Dawkins	.05
24 Tyrone Wheatley	.05
25 Lawrence Phillips	.05
26 Ty Detmer	.05
27 Vinny Testaverde	.05
28 Dorsey Levens	.10
29 Ricky Watters	.05
30 Natrone Means	.05
31 Curtis Conway	.05
32 Larry Centers	.05
33 Johnnie Morton	.05
34 Desmond Howard	.05
35 Marcus Allen	.10
36 Cris Carter	.05
37 James Stewart	.05
38 Frank Sanders	.05
39 Bruce Smith	.05
40 Carl Pickens	.05
41 Neil O'Donnell	.05
42 Trent Dilfer	.10
43 Rodney Peete	.05
44 Terance Mathis	.05
45 Muhsin Muhammad	.05
46 Jake Reed	.05
47 Jim Harbaugh	.05
48 Todd Collins	.05
49 Ki-Jana Carter	.05
50 Scott Mitchell	.05
51 Kevin Hardy	.05
52 Stanley Pritchett	.05
53 Dave Brown	.05
54 Jeff George	.05
55 Stan Humphries	.05
56 Isaac Bruce	.10
57 Eric Moulds	.10
58 Robert Brooks	.05
59 Steve McNair	.75
60 Adrian Murrell	.10
61 Mike Alstott	.10
62 Michael Jackson	.05
63 Tamarick Vanover	.05
64 Edgar Bennett	.05
65 Andre Hastings	.05
66 Robert Smith	.05
67 Thurman Thomas	.10
68 Tim Biakabutuka	.05
69 Rick Mirer	.05
70 Deion Sanders	.50
71 Curtis Martin	1.00
72 Garrison Hearst	.05
73 Kent Graham	.05
74 Anthony Johnson	.05
75 Antonio Freeman	.10
76 Marshall Faulk	.10
77 O.J. McDuffie	.05
78 Heath Shuler	.05
79 Napoleon Kaufman	.05
80 Aeneas Williams	.05
81 Hardy Nickerson	.05
82 Keenan McCardell	.05
83 Erik Kramer	.05
84 Ben Coates	.05
85 Shannon Sharpe	.05
86 Tony Martin	.05
87 Chris Sanders	.05
88 Jamal Anderson	.05
89 Karim Abdul-Jabbar	.50
90 Keyshawn Johnson	.40
91 Terrell Owens	.10
92 Michael Irvin	.10
93 John Friesz	.05
94 Chris Warren	.05
95 Errict Rhett	.05
96 Terry Allen	.10
97 Michael Westbrook	.05
98 Simeon Rice	.05
99 Willie Green	.05
100 Jerome Bettis	.10
101 Reggie White	.10
102 Bert Emanuel	.05
103 Zach Thomas	.05
104 Tim Brown	.10
105 Darnay Scott	.05
106 Terrell Davis	1.00
107 Andre Reed	.05
108 Amani Toomer	.05
109 Irving Fryar	.05
110 Joey Galloway	.10
111 Marvin Harrison	.40
112 Derrick Alexander	.05
113 Jeff Blake	.05
114 Brad Johnson	.05
115 Eddie Kennison	.40
116 *Rae Carruth*	.75
117 *Tony Gonzalez*	.50
118 *Joey Kent*	.50
119 *Peter Boulware*	.10
120 *Orlando Pace*	.50
121 *David LaFleur*	.50
122 *Darnell Autry*	.50
123 *Tiki Barber*	1.00
124 *Troy Davis*	.50
125 *Jim Druckenmiller*	1.50
126 *Corey Dillon*	1.50
127 *Ike Hilliard*	.75

128	Reidel Anthony	1.00
129	Byron Hanspard	.50
130	Antowain Smith	1.00
131	Jake Plummer	1.25
132	Warrick Dunn	1.50
133	Bryant Westbrook	.10
134	Darrell Russell	.10
135	Yatil Green	.50
136	Shawn Springs	.10
137	Danny Wuerffel	.75
138	Brett Favre (Peak Performer)	1.00
139	Emmitt Smith (Peak Performer)	1.00
140	Barry Sanders (Peak Performer)	.50
141	Troy Aikman (Peak Performer)	.50
142	Drew Bledsoe (Peak Performer)	.50
143	Jerry Rice (Peak Performer)	.50
144	Dan Marino (Peak Performer)	1.00
145	John Elway (Peak Performer)	.30
146	Kerry Collins (Peak Performer)	.30
147	Mark Brunell (Peak Performer)	.30
148	Checklist (Brett Favre)	.50
149	Checklist (Dan Marino)	.50
150	Checklist (Troy Aikman)	.25

1997 Pinnacle X-Press Bombs Away

This 18-card insert features top quarterbacks on a full foil, micro-etched card. Bombs Away was inserted 1:19.

		MT
Complete Set (18):		100.00
Common Player:		2.00
Minor Stars:		4.00
1	Brett Favre	20.00
2	Dan Marino	18.00
3	Troy Aikman	10.00
4	Drew Bledsoe	10.00
5	Kerry Collins	5.00
6	Mark Brunell	10.00
7	John Elway	8.00
8	Steve Young	8.00
9	Jeff Blake	4.00
10	Kordell Stewart	10.00
11	Jeff George	2.00
12	Rick Mirer	2.00
13	Neil O'Donnell	2.00
14	Scott Mitchell	2.00
15	Jim Harbaugh	2.00
16	Warren Moon	2.00
17	Trent Dilfer	4.00
18	Jim Druckenmiller	8.00

1997 Pinnacle X-Press Divide & Conquer

Divide & Conquer is a 20-card insert on full foil, micro-etched card stock. The cards fea-

ture a player action shot and heliogram print technology. They are numbered to 500.

		MT
Complete Set (20):		750.00
Common Player:		7.00
1	Tim Biakabutuka	7.00
2	Karim Abdul-Jabbar	30.00
3	Jerome Bettis	14.00
4	Eddie George	80.00
5	Terrell Davis	60.00
6	Barry Sanders	60.00
7	Emmitt Smith	100.00
8	Brett Favre	120.00
9	Dan Marino	100.00
10	Troy Aikman	60.00
11	Jerry Rice	60.00
12	Drew Bledsoe	60.00
13	Kerry Collins	15.00
14	Mark Brunell	60.00
15	John Elway	45.00
16	Steve Young	45.00
17	Warrick Dunn	90.00
18	Byron Hanspard	25.00
19	Troy Davis	40.00
20	Jeff Blake	14.00

1997 Pinnacle X-Press Pursuit of Paydirt- Quarterbacks

The Pursuit of Paydirt insert was an interactive game which ran during the 1997 season. This 30-card insert (found 1:2) featured quarterbacks and gave collectors the chance to win if they found the QB who led the league in touchdowns during the season.

		MT
Complete Set (30):		25.00
Common Player:		.25
Minor Stars:		.50
1	Drew Bledsoe	2.00
2	Steve Young	1.50
3	Brett Favre	4.50
4	John Elway	1.50
5	Dan Marino	4.00
6	Tony Banks	1.00
7	Kerry Collins	.75
8	Mark Brunell	2.00
9	Troy Aikman	2.00
10	Elvis Grbac	.25
11	Kordell Stewart	2.00
12	Gus Frerotte	.25
13	Warren Moon	.25
14	Chris Chandler	.25
15	Rick Mirer	.25
16	Vinny Testaverde	.25
17	Neil O'Donnell	.25
18	Trent Dilfer	.50
19	Rodney Peete	.25
20	Jim Harbaugh	.25
21	Todd Collins	.25
22	Scott Mitchell	.25
23	Dave Brown	.25
24	Jeff George	.25
25	Stan Humphries	.25
26	Steve McNair	1.50
27	Heath Shuler	.25
28	Jeff Blake	.50
29	Brad Johnson	.25
30	Jim Druckenmiller	2.00

1997 Pinnacle X-Press Pursuit of Paydirt- Running Backs

This 30-card insert featured running backs and gave collectors the chance to win prizes if they could match the leading TD scorer with the number of TDs he made. This insert was found 1:2.

		MT
Complete Set (30):		25.00
Common Player:		.25
Minor Stars:		.50
1	Errict Rhett	.25
2	Terry Allen	.50
3	Jerome Bettis	.50
4	Terrell Davis	2.00
5	Tiki Barber	1.50
6	Troy Davis	1.25
7	Byron Hanspard	1.25
8	Greg Hill	.25
9	Barry Sanders	2.00
10	Eddie George	3.00
11	Emmitt Smith	4.00
12	Rashaan Salaam	.25
13	Tyrone Wheatley	.25
14	Lawrence Phillips	.25
15	Ricky Watters	.50
16	Natrone Means	.50
17	Marcus Allen	.50
18	James Stewart	.25
19	Ki-Jana Carter	.25
20	Dorsey Levens	.50
21	Robert Smith	.50
22	Thurman Thomas	.50
23	Tim Biakabutuka	.50
24	Curtis Martin	2.00
25	Garrison Hearst	.25
26	Marshall Faulk	.50
27	Napoleon Kaufman	1.00
28	Jamal Anderson	.25
29	Karim Abdul-Jabbar	1.50
30	Chris Warren	.25

1997 Pinnacle Rembrandt

This nine-card set was inserted one per box of Rembrandt's Ultra-PRO plastic sheets. The cards feature an action shot and a bronze-colored foil section. Silver and gold foil parallel sets were also created. Collectors who assembled an entire bronze, silver or gold set could redeem them for prizes from Rembrandt.

		MT
Complete Set (9):		20.00
Common Player:		1.50
*Gold Cards:		6x-12x
*Silver Cards:		3x-6x
1	Brett Favre	5.00
2	Troy Aikman	2.00
3	John Elway	1.50
4	Dan Marino	4.00
5	Drew Bledsoe	2.00
6	Emmitt Smith	4.00
7	Jerry Rice	2.00
8	Barry Sanders	2.50
9	Mark Brunell	2.00

1992 Playoff Promos

This seven-card promo-

tional set gave collectors a glimpse of what Playoff's 1992 set would look like. These cards were printed on 22-point stock. The player's names were printed in silver inside a black box at the bottom of the card. The card backs, numbered "of 6 promo," feature a full-bleed photo, with the player's name located along the left margin of the card. A write-up about the player was included in the lower left of the card back.

		MT
Complete Set (7):		15.00
Common Player:		1.00
1	Calvin Williams	1.25
2	John Elway	4.00
3	Dalton Hilliard	1.00
4	Steve Young	4.00
5	Emmitt Smith	8.00
6	Mike Golic	1.00
NNO	Header/Intro Card	1.00

1992 Playoff

This 150-card set features standard-size cards printed on stock which is thicker than usual. The card front has a full-bleed color photo, plus the player's name in a black bar at the bottom. Most of the backgrounds are black-and-white and, using a metallic-like process, give the cards depth. The card back has a close-up shot of the player, plus his team's name in a team color-coded bar. Information contained in a black box details the player's performance from a key game during the previous season. There were also seven promotional cards made as previews of the regular 1992 set.

		MT
Complete Set (150):		45.00
Common Player:		.25
Minor Stars:		.50
Wax Box:		45.00
1	Emmitt Smith	10.00
2	Steve Young	5.00
3	Jack Del Rio	.25
4	Bobby Hebert	.25
5	Shannon Sharpe	.50
6	Gary Clark	.25
7	Christian Okoye	.25
8	Ernest Givins	.25
9	Mike Horan	.25
10	Dennis Gentry	.25
11	Michael Irvin	1.00
12	Eric Floyd	.25
13	Brent Jones	.25
14	Anthony Carter	.25
15	Tony Martin	.75
16	Greg Lewis ("Returning" should be "returned" on back)	.25
17	Todd McNair	.25
18	Earnest Byner	.25
19	Steve Beuerlein	.25
20	Roger Craig	.25
21	Mark Higgs	.25
22	Guy McIntyre	.25
23	Don Warren	.25
24	Alvin Harper	.50
25	Mark Jackson	.25
26	Chris Doleman	.25
27	Jesse Sapolu	.25
28	Tony Talbert	.25
29	Wendell Davis	.25
30	Dan Saleaumua	.25
31	Jeff Bostic	.25
32	Jay Novacek	.25
33	Cris Carter	.50
34	Tony Paige	.25
35	Greg Kragen	.25
36	Jeff Dellenbach	.25
37	Keith DeLong	.25
38	Todd Scott	.25
39	Jeff Feagles	.25
40	Mike Saxon	.25
41	Martin Mayhew	.25
42	Steve Bono	1.00
43	Willie Davis	.50
44	Mark Stepnoski	.25
45	Harry Newsome	.25
46	Thane Gash	.25
47	Gaston Green	.25
48	James Washington	.25
49	Kenny Walker	.25
50	Jeff Davidson	.25
51	Shane Conlan	.25
52	Richard Dent	.25
53	Haywood Jeffires	.25
54	Harry Galbreath	.25
55	Terry Allen	1.00
56	Tommy Barnhardt	.25
57	Mike Golic	.25
58	Dalton Hilliard	.25
59	Danny Copeland	.25
60	Jerry Fontenot	.25
61	Kelvin Martin	.25
62	Mark Kelso	.25
63	Wymon Henderson	.25
64	Mark Rypien	.25
65	Bobby Humphrey	.25
66	Rich Gannon (Tarkington misspelled, Minneapolis instead of Minnesota on back)	.25
67	Darren Lewis	.25
68	Barry Foster	.25
69	Ken Norton	.25
70	James Lofton	.25
71	Trace Armstrong	.25
72	Vestee Jackson	.25
73	Clyde Simmons	.25
74	Brad Muster	.25
75	Cornelius Bennett	.25
76	Mike Merriweather	.25
77	John Elway	2.00
78	Herschel Walker	.25
79	Hassan Jones (Minneapolis instead of Minnesota on back)	.25
80	Jim Harbaugh	.50
81	Issiac Holt	.25
82	David Alexander	.25
83	Brian Mitchell	.25
84	Mark Tuinei	.25
85	Tom Rathman	.25
86	Reggie White	.50
87	William Perry	.25
88	Jeff Wright	.25
89	Keith Kartz	.25
90	Andre Waters	.25
91	Darryl Talley	.25
92	Morten Andersen	.25
93	Tom Waddle	.25
94	Felix Wright (Minneapolis instead of Minnesota on back)	.25
95	Keith Jackson	.25
96	Art Monk	.50
97	Seth Joyner	.25
98	Steve McMichael	.25
99	Thurman Thomas	1.00
100	Warren Moon	.75
101	Tony Casillas	.25
102	Vance Johnson	.25
103	Doug Dawson	.25
104	Bill Maas	.25
105	Mark Clayton	.25
106	Hoby Brenner	.25
107	Gary Anderson	.25
108	Marc Logan	.25
109	Ricky Sanders	.25
110	Vai Sikahema	.25
111	Neil Smith	.25
112	Cody Carlson	.25
113	Jimmie Jones	.25
114	Pat Swilling	.25
115	Neil O'Donnell	1.00
116	Chip Lohmiller	.25
117	Mike Croel	.25
118	Pete Metzelaars	.25
119	Ray Childress	.25
120	Fred Banks	.25
121	Derek Kennard	.25
122	Daryl Johnston	.25
123	Lorenzo White (Minneapolis instead of Minnesota on back)	.25
124	Hardy Nickerson	.25
125	Derrick Thomas	.50
126	Steve Walsh	.25
127	Doug Widell	.25
128	Calvin Williams	.25
129	Tim Harris	.25
130	Rod Woodson	.50
131	Craig Heyward	.25
132	Barry Word	.25
133	Mark Duper	.25
134	Tim Johnson	.25
135	John Gesek	.25
136	Steve Jackson	.25
137	Dave Krieg	.25
138	Barry Sanders	7.00
139	Michael Haynes	.25
140	Eric Metcalf	.25
141	Stan Humphries	1.00
142	Sterling Sharpe	.50
143	Todd Marinovich	.25
144	Rodney Hampton	1.00
145	Rodney Peete	.50
146	Darryl Williams	.25
147	Darren Perry	.25
148	Terrell Buckley	.25
149	Amp Lee	.75
150	Ricky Watters	1.50

1993 Playoff Promos

This six-card promotional set gave collectors a glimpse of what the 1993 Playoff set would look like. The card fronts feature the Playoff logo at the top and the player's name, printed in silver inside a black box, near the bottom of the card. The card backs have a full-bleed photo, with the player's name inside a box on the upper left corner. A write-up about the player is included in the lower right. The cards, printed on 22-point stock, are numbered "of 6 promo."

		MT
Complete Set (6):		12.00
Common Player:		1.00
1	Emmitt Smith	6.00
2	Barry Foster	1.00
3	Quinn Early	1.00
4	Tim Brown	1.50
5	Steve Young	3.00
6	Sterling Sharpe	1.50

1993 Playoff

Playoff increased its 1993 set to 315 cards. Subsets within the regular set include "The Backs" (#s 277-282, featuring top running backs), "Connections" (#s 283-292, featuring top quarterback/wide receiver combinations), and "Rookies" (#s 293-315). Redemption cards were randomly inserted in packs for "Headliner" (six cards) and "Rookie Roundup" (10 cards) sets. Other insert sets included Checklists (eight cards), Playoff Club (seven cards), and Brett Favre and Ricky Watters (five cards each). Six promotional cards, which have the same design as the regular cards, were also made.

		MT
Complete Set (315):		60.00
Common Player:		.15
Minor Stars:		.25
Hobby Wax Box:		45.00
Retail Wax Box:		40.00
1	Troy Aikman	3.00
2	Jerry Rice	3.00
3	Keith Jackson	.15
4	Sean Gilbert	.15
5	Jim Kelly	.25
6	Junior Seau	.25
7	Deion Sanders	2.00
8	Joe Montana	4.00
9	Terrell Buckley	.15
10	Emmitt Smith	5.00
11	Pete Stoyanovich	.15

No.	Player	MT
12	Randall Cunningham	.25
13	Boomer Esiason	.25
14	Mike Saxon	.15
15	Chuck Cecil	.15
16	Vinny Testaverde	.25
17	Jeff Hostetler	.25
18	Mark Clayton	.15
19	Nick Bell	.15
20	Frank Reich	.15
21	Henry Ellard	.15
22	Andre Reed	.25
23	Mark Ingram	.15
24	Mike Brim	.15
25	Bernie Kosar	.25
26	Jeff George	.25
27	Tommy Maddox	.15
28	*Kent Graham*	.75
29	David Klingler	.15
30	Robert Delpino	.15
31	Kevin Fagan	.15
32	Mark Bavaro	.15
33	Harold Green	.15
34	Shawn McCarthy	.15
35	Ricky Proehl	.15
36	Eugene Robinson	.15
37	Phil Simms	.15
38	David Lang	.15
39	Santana Dotson	.15
40	Brett Perriman	.15
41	Jim Harbaugh	.15
42	Keith Byars	.15
43	Quentin Coryatt	.15
44	Louis Oliver	.15
45	Howie Long	.15
46	Mike Sherrard	.15
47	Earnest Byner	.15
48	Neil Smith	.15
49	Audray McMillan	.15
50	Vaughn Dunbar	.15
51	Ronnie Lott	.15
52	Clyde Simmons	.15
53	Kevin Scott	.15
54	Bubby Brister	.15
55	Randal Hill	.15
56	Pat Swilling	.15
57	Steve Beuerlein	.15
58	Gary Clark	.15
59	Brian Noble	.15
60	Leslie O'Neal	.15
61	Vincent Brown	.15
62	Edgar Bennett	.25
63	Anthony Carter	.15
64	Glenn Cadez	.15
65	Dalton Hilliard	.15
66	James Lofton	.15
67	Walter Stanley	.15
68	Tim Harris	.15
69	Carl Banks	.15
70	Andre Ware	.15
71	Karl Mecklenburg	.15
72	Russell Maryland	.15
73	LeRoy Thompson	.15
74	Tommy Kane	.15
75	Dan Marino	5.00
76	Darrell Fullington	.15
77	Jessie Tuggle	.15
78	Bruce Smith	.15
79	Neal Anderson	.15
80	Kevin Mack	.15
81	Shane Dronett	.15
82	Nick Lowery	.15
83	Sheldon White	.15
84	Willie (Flipper) Anderson	.15
85	Jeff Herrod	.15
86	Dwight Stone	.15
87	Dave Krieg	.15
88	Bryan Cox	.15
89	Greg McMurty	.15
90	Rickey Jackson	.15
91	Ernie Mills	.15
92	Browning Nagle	.15
93	John Taylor	.15
94	Eric Dickerson	.15
95	Johnny Holland	.15
96	Anthony Miller	.15
97	Fred Barnett	.15
98	Ricky Ervins	.15
99	Leonard Russell	.15
100	Lawrence Taylor	.25
101	Tony Casillas	.15
102	John Elway	1.50
103	Bennie Blades	.15
104	Harry Sydney	.15
105	Bubba McDowell	.15
106	Todd McNair	.15
107	Steve Smith	.15
108	Jim Everett	.25
109	Bobby Humphrey	.15
110	Rich Gannon	.15
111	Marv Cook	.15
112	Wayne Martin	.15
113	Sean Landeta	.15
114	Brad Baxter	.15
115	Reggie White	.25
116	Johnny Johnson	.15
117	Jeff Graham	.15
118	*Darren Carrington*	.25
119	Ricky Watters	.25
120	Art Monk	.25
121	Cornelius Bennett	.15
122	Wade Wilson	.15
123	Daniel Stubbs	.15
124	Brad Muster	.15
125	Mike Tomczak	.15
126	Jay Novacek	.25
127	Shannon Sharpe	.25
128	Rodney Peete	.15
129	Daryl Johnston	.15
130	Warren Moon	.25
131	Willie Gault	.15
132	Tony Martin	.15
133	Terry Allen	.15
134	Hugh Millen	.15
135	Rob Moore	.15
136	*Andy Harmon*	.15
137	Kelvin Martin	.15
138	Rod Woodson	.25
139	Nate Lewis	.15
140	Darryl Talley	.15
141	Guy McIntyre	.15
142	John L. Williams	.15
143	Brad Edwards	.15
144	Trace Armstrong	.15
145	Kenneth Davis	.15
146	Clay Matthews	.15
147	Gaston Green	.15
148	Chris Spielman	.15
149	Cody Carlson	.15
150	Derrick Thomas	.25
151	Terry McDaniel	.15
152	Kevin Greene	.15
153	Roger Craig	.15
154	Craig Heyward	.15
155	Rodney Hampton	.25
156	Heath Sherman	.15
157	Mark Stepnoski	.15
158	Chris Chandler	.15
159	Rob Berstine	.15
160	Pierce Holt	.15
161	Wilber Marshall	.15
162	Reggie Cobb	.15
163	Tom Rathman	.15
164	Michael Haynes	.15
165	Nate Odomes	.15
166	Tom Waddle	.15
167	Eric Ball	.15
168	Brett Favre	5.00
169	Michael Jackson	.15
170	Lorenzo White	.15
171	Cleveland Gary	.15
172	Jay Schroeder	.15
173	Tony Paige	.15
174	Jack Del Rio	.15
175	Jon Vaughn	.15
176	Morten Andersen	.15
177	Chris Burkett	.15
178	Vai Sikahema	.15
179	Ronnie Harmon	.15
180	Amp Lee	.15
181	Chip Lohmiller	.15
182	Steve Broussard	.15
183	Don Beebe	.15
184	Tommy Vardell	.15
185	Keith Jennings	.15
186	Simon Fletcher	.15
187	Mel Gray	.15
188	Vince Workman	.15
189	Haywood Jeffires	.15
190	Barry Word	.15
191	Ethan Horton	.15
192	Mark Higgs	.15
193	Irving Fryar	.15
194	Charles Haley	.15
195	Steve Bono	1.00
196	Mike Golic	.15
197	Gary Anderson	.15
198	Sterling Sharpe	.25
199	Andre Tippett	.15
200	Thurman Thomas	1.00
201	Chris Miller	.15
202	Henry Jones	.15
203	Mo Lewis	.15
204	Marion Butts	.15
205	Mike Johnson	.15
206	Alvin Harper	.25
207	Ray Childress	.15
208	Anthony Newman	.15
209	Tony Bennett	.15
210	*Antony Newman*	.15
211	Christian Okoye	.15
212	Marcus Allen	.25
213	Jackie Harris	.15
214	Mark Duper	.15
215	Cris Carter	.25
216	John Stephens	.15
217	Barry Sanders	3.50
218	Herman Moore	2.00
219	Marvin Washington	.15
220	Calvin Williams	.15
221	John Randle	.15
222	Marco Coleman	.15
223	Eric Martin	.15
224	David Meggett	.15
225	Brian Washington	.15
226	Barry Foster	.25
227	Michael Zordich	.15
228	Stan Humphries	.15
229	Mike Cofer	.15
230	Chris Warren	1.00
231	Keith McCants	.15
232	Mark Rypien	.15
233	James Francis	.15
234	Andre Rison	.25
235	William Perry	.15
236	Chip Banks	.15
237	Willie Davis	.15
238	Chris Doleman	.15
239	Tim Brown	.25
240	Darren Perry	.15
241	Johnny Bailey	.15
242	Ernest Givins	.15
243	John Carney	.15
244	Cortez Kennedy	.25
245	Lawrence Dawsey	.15
246	Martin Mayhew	.15
247	Shane Conlan	.15
248	J.J. Birden	.15
249	Quinn Early	.15
250	Michael Irvin	.25
251	Neil O'Donnell	.25
252	Stan Gelbaugh	.15
253	Drew Hill	.15
254	Wendell Davis	.15
255	Tim Johnson	.15
256	Seth Joyner	.15
257	Derrick Fenner	.15
258	Steve Young	3.00
259	Jackie Slater	.15
260	Eric Metcalf	.15
261	Rufus Porter	.15
262	Ken Norton	.15
263	Tim McDonald	.15
264	Mark Jackson	.15
265	Hardy Nickerson	.15
266	Anthony Munoz	.15
267	Mark Carrier	.15
268	Mike Pritchard	.15
269	Steve Emtman	.15
270	Ricky Sanders	.15
271	Robert Massey	.15
272	Pete Metzelaars	.15
273	Reggie Langhorne	.15
274	Tim McGee	.15
275	*Reggie Rivers*	.15
276	Jimmie Jones	.15
277	Lorenzo White	.15
278	Emmitt Smith	3.00
279	Thurman Thomas	.25
280	Barry Sanders	2.00
281	Rodney Hampton	.25
282	Barry Foster	.25
283	Troy Aikman	1.50
284	Michael Irvin	.25
285	Brett Favre	2.00
286	Sterling Sharpe	.25
287	Steve Young	2.00
288	Jerry Rice	2.00
289	Stan Humphries	.25
290	Anthony Miller	.15
291	Dan Marino	3.00
292	Keith Jackson	.15
293	*Patrick Bates*	.15
294	*Jerome Bettis*	3.00
295	*Drew Bledsoe*	8.00
296	*Tom Carter*	.25
297	*Curtis Conway*	2.00
298	*John Copeland*	.25
299	*Eric Curry*	.25
300	*Reggie Brooks*	.25
301	*Steve Everitt*	.25
302	*Deon Figures*	.25
303	*Garrison Hearst*	3.00
304	*Qadry Ismail*	1.00
305	*Marvin Jones*	.25
306	*Lincoln Kennedy*	.25
307	*O.J. McDuffie*	3.00
308	*Rick Mirer*	.50
309	*Wayne Simmons*	.25
310	*Irv Smith*	.25
311	*Robert Smith*	3.00
312	*Dana Stubblefield*	1.50
313	*George Teague*	.25
314	*Dan Williams*	.25
315	*Kevin Williams*	.50

No.	Player	
2	Barry Sanders	1.00
3	Deion Sanders	1.00
4	Ron Woodson	1.00
5	Junior Seau	1.00
6	Mark Rypien	.75
7	Derrick Thomas	1.00
8	Dallas Players (Daryl Johnston, Alvin Harper, Michael Irvin) (UER) (Stan Humphries listed as 299; should be	.75

1993 Playoff Club

These insert cards feature a gold Playoff Club logo on the card front which distinguishes it as an insert card from the regular Playoff cards. A color player closeup shot, surrounded by a black-and-white background, is also included on the card front. The player has also signed his signature in gold ink. The back, numbered using a "PC" prefix, gives a summary of the player's career against a grey Playoff Club logo which is ghosted in the background. These were inserted into retail and hobby boxes.

		MT
Complete Set (7):		25.00
Common Player:		2.00
1	Joe Montana	15.00
2	Art Monk	2.00
3	Lawrence Taylor	4.00
4	Ronnie Lott	2.00
5	Reggie White	4.00
6	Anthony Munoz	2.00
7	Jackie Slater	2.00

1993 Playoff Brett Favre

Green Bay Packer quarterback Brett Favre is featured in this five-card insert set. The fronts have a metallic shine to them and feature a full-bleed color photo. A black box at the bottom contains Favre's name. The card back has a ghosted image of Favre throwing a pass, plus season highlights against a green background. Cards, numbered 1 of 5, etc., were randomly inserted in hobby display boxes.

		MT
Complete Set (5):		100.00
Common Player:		20.00
1	The Early Years (Brett Favre)	20.00
2	The College Years (Brett Favre)	20.00
3	Turning Pro (Brett Favre)	20.00
4	Green Bay Star (Brett Favre)	20.00
5	1992: The Storybook Season (Brett Favre)	20.00

1993 Playoff Checklists

Randomly seeded in packs, this eight-card set showcases an action shot of a player. A silver box, featuring highlights about the player, is included at the bottom of the card. The box is bordered on the left side by a black box which has "Check It Out" inside it. The card back features a portion of the checklist printed inside a white area in the center of the card. The top of the card has a red stripe, while the bottom of the card has a black stripe.

		MT
Complete Set (8):		7.00
Common Player:		.75
1A	Warren Moon (UER) (Kosar misspelled Kozar)	1.00
1B	Warren Moon (COR)	1.00

1993 Playoff Headliners Redemption

Randomly seeded in retail foil packs, the redemption card could be redeemed for this six-card set. Overall, 48,475 redemption cards were inserted into packs. The card front features a gray background with silver type. A color photo of the player is featured, with the player's name located inside a black box at the top of the card front. The Headliners' logo is printed to the right of the player's name. The card backs showcase the player's name and highlights printed inside a black box at the top, with the card number in the upper right. A headshot of the player is located in the center of the card back. The cards are numbered with an "H" prefix.

		MT
Complete Set (6):		25.00
Common Player:		1.00
1	Brett Favre	14.00
2	Sterling Sharpe	2.00
3	Emmitt Smith	14.00
4	Jerry Rice	7.00
5	Thurman Thomas	2.00
6	David Klingler	1.00
NNO	Headliner Redemption	1.00

1993 Playoff Promo Inserts

Each 1993 Playoff special retail pack included one promo insert (or Playoff Ricky Watters card). The full-bleed photo on the card front includes the Playoff logo at the top and the player's name in silver inside a black rectangle, located at the bottom left. The player is highlighted in color, with the background in black-and-white. Showcased on the card back are highlights from the player's career. With the card number in the upper right (labeled "Promo X of 6"), the player's name appears in white inside a black band in the upper left corner.

		MT
Complete Set (6):		10.00
Common Player:		1.50
1	Michael Irvin	1.50
2	Barry Foster	1.50
3	Quinn Early	1.50
4	Tim Brown	1.50
5	Reggie White	2.00
6	Sterling Sharpe	2.00

1993 Playoff Rookie Roundup Redemption

A 10-card set would be given to collectors in exchange for a 1993 Playoff Rookie Roundup Redemption card, which was found in hobby foil packs. The mail-in offer expired on July 3, 1994. Silver type over a gray background served as the backdrop to the color photo of the player. The Rookie Roundup and the Playoff logos also appear on the card front. The player's name is printed in the lower right corner. The card back has a color photo of the player in the center, over a white background with gray team logos in the background. A black box at the bottom of the card back houses the player's name and 1993 highlights. Overall, 15,683 exchange cards were printed. Cards are prefixed with "R."

		MT
Complete Set (10):		40.00
Common Player:		2.00
1	Jerome Bettis	10.00
2	Drew Bledsoe	15.00
3	Reggie Brooks	3.00
4	Derek Brown (RB)	3.00
5	Garrison Hearst	6.00
6	Terry Kirby	3.00
7	Glyn Milburn	3.00
8	Rick Mirer	6.00
9	Roosevelt Potts	2.00
10	Dana Stubblefield	3.00
NNO	Rookie Roundup Redemption Card	.50

1993 Playoff Ricky Watters

This five-card set features San Francisco 49er running back Ricky Watters. The front has a full-bleed color photo against a metallic background. Watters' name is at the bottom of the card in a black box. The Playoff logo is also on the front. The back has a ghosted image of Watters running the ball, plus career highlights against a tan background. Cards, which are numbered 1 of 5, etc., were randomly inserted in retail display boxes.

		MT
Complete Set (5):		20.00
Common Watters:		4.00
1	The Early Years (Ricky Watters)	4.00
2	Irish Eyes Were Smiling (Ricky Watters)	4.00
3	The Bay Watters (Ricky Watters)	4.00
4	A Second-Year Rookie (Ricky Watters)	4.00
5	Rookie of the Year (Ricky Watters)	4.00

1993 Playoff Contenders Promos

This six-card promotional set gave collectors a glimpse of what the 1993 Contenders set would look like. The borderless fronts showcase the Playoff logo and player's name inside of a silver box at the bottom of the card. A color photo of the player is located on the left of the horizontal card back. The right side is a team-colored area which includes the player's team helmet, his name and his season highlight. In the upper right is the card number, which is indicated with a Roman numeral.

		MT
Complete Set (6):		12.00
Common Player:		.75
1	Drew Bledsoe	3.00
2	Neil Smith	.75
3	Rick Mirer	1.00
4	Rodney Hampton	.75
5	Barry Sanders	2.50
6	Emmitt Smith	4.00

1993 Playoff Contenders

This 150-card Playoff Contenders set uses a unique ink-on-foil printing process called Tekchrome. The cards are printed on a heavy card stock, making them among the thickest and sturdiest in the hobby. Cards include photos and game information from the 1993 season; the set is primarily composed of players from teams that were most likely to make the NFL playoffs, plus 49 top rookies and free agents from the season. The set also includes two insert sets - "Rookie Contenders" (10 of the top first-year players) and a five-card set tracing the collegiate and professional career of Seattle Seahawk rookie quarterback Rick Mirer. The regular cards have the player's name and Playoff logo in a silver box on the card front.

		MT
Complete Set (150):		35.00
Common Player:		.15
Minor Stars:		.25
Wax Box:		40.00
1	Brett Favre	4.00
2	Thurman Thomas	.25
3	Barry Word	.15
4	Herman Moore	1.00
5	Reggie Langhorne	.15
6	Wilber Marshall	.15
7	Ricky Watters	.25
8	Marcus Allen	.25
9	Jeff Hostetler	.25
10	Steve Young	2.00
11	Bobby Hebert	.15
12	David Klingler	.15
13	Craig Heyward	.15
14	Andre Reed	.25
15	Tommy Vardell	.15
16	Anthony Carter	.15
17	Mel Gray	.15
18	Dan Marino	4.00
19	Haywood Jeffires	.15
20	Joe Montana	3.00
21	Tim Brown	.25
22	Jim McMahon	.15
23	Scott Mitchell	.25
24	Rickey Jackson	.15
25	Troy Aikman	2.00
26	Rodney Hampton	.25
27	Fred Barnett	.15
28	Gary Clark	.15
29	Barry Foster	.25
30	Brian Blades	.15
31	Tim McDonald	.15
32	Kelvin Martin	.15
33	Henry Jones	.15
34	Erric Pegram	.15
35	Don Beebe	.15
36	Eric Metcalf	.15
37	Charles Haley	.15
38	Robert Delpino	.15
39	Leonard Russell	.15
40	Jackie Harris	.15
41	Ernest Givins	.15
42	Willie Davis	.15
43	Alexander Wright	.15
44	Keith Byars	.15
45	David Meggett	.15
46	Johnny Johnson	.15
47	Mark Bavaro	.15
48	Seth Joyner	.15
49	Junior Seau	.25
50	Emmitt Smith	4.00
51	Shannon Sharpe	.25
52	Rodney Peete	.15
53	Andre Rison	.25
54	Cornelius Bennett	.15
55	Mark Carrier	.15
56	Mark Clayton	.15
57	Warren Moon	.25
58	J.J. Birden	.15
59	Howie Long	.15
60	Irving Fryar	.15
61	Mark Jackson	.15
62	Eric Martin	.15
63	Herschel Walker	.15
64	Cortez Kennedy	.25
65	Steve Beuerlein	.25
66	Jim Kelly	.25
67	Bernie Kosar	.25
68	Pat Swilling	.15
69	Michael Irvin	.25
70	Harvey Williams	.15
71	Steve Smith	.15
72	Wade Wilson	.15
73	Phil Simms	.15
74	Vinny Testaverde	.25
75	Barry Sanders	2.50
76	Ken Norton	.15
77	Rod Woodson	.25
78	Webster Slaughter	.15
79	Derrick Thomas	.25
80	Mike Sherrard	.15
81	Calvin Williams	.15
82	Jay Novacek	.15
83	Michael Brooks	.15
84	Randall Cunningham	.25
85	Chris Warren	.50
86	Johnny Mitchell	.15
87	Jim Harbaugh	.15
88	Rod Bernstine	.15
89	John Elway	1.00
90	Jerry Rice	2.00
91	Brent Jones	.15
92	Cris Carter	.25
93	Alvin Harper	.25
94	Horace Copeland	.50
95	Raghib Ismail	.25
96	Darrin Smith	.25
97	Reggie Brooks	.25
98	Demetrius DuBose	.25
99	Eric Curry	.25
100	Rick Mirer	.75
101	Carlton Gray	.15
102	Dana Stubblefield	1.00
103	Todd Kelly	.15
104	Natrone Means	2.00
105	Darrien Gordon	.50
106	Deon Figures	.30
107	Garrison Hearst	3.00
108	Ron Moore	.50
109	Leonard Renfro	.15
110	Lester Holmes	.15
111	Vaughn Hebron	.25
112	Marvin Jones	.25
113	Irv Smith	.25
114	Willie Roaf	.25
115	Derek Brown	.25
116	Vincent Brisby	1.00
117	Drew Bledsoe	7.00
118	Gino Torretta	.25
119	Robert Smith	1.00
120	Qadry Ismail	1.00
121	O.J. McDuffie	1.75
122	Terry Kirby	.75
123	Troy Drayton	1.00
124	Jerome Bettis	3.00
125	Patrick Bates	.25
126	Rosevelt Potts	.25
127	Tom Carter	.40
128	Patrick Robinson	.25
129	Brad Hopkins	.15
130	George Teague	.40
131	Wayne Simmons	.15
132	Mark Brunell	7.00
133	Ryan McNeil	.15
134	Dan Williams	.15
135	Glyn Milburn	.50
136	Kevin Williams	1.50
137	Derrick Lassic	.25
138	Steve Everitt	.25
139	Lance Gunn	.25
140	John Copeland	.25
141	Curtis Conway	2.00
142	Thomas Smith	.25
143	Russell Copeland	1.00
144	Lincoln Kennedy	.25
145	Boomer Esiason	.15
146	Neil Smith	.15
147	Jack Del Rio	.15
148	Morten Andersen	.15
149	Sterling Sharpe (CL)	.15
150	Reggie White	.25

1993 Playoff Contenders Rookie Contenders

These 10 inserts cards, randomly included in 1993 Playoff Contenders packs, feature 10 of the top rookies in 1993. Each card front has a borderless color action photo, with a metallic shine and blurred background. The player's name and set logo appear in the lower left corner in a gold box. Each card is white and has the player's name at the top; the set name is given in white in two black bands, one on top and the other on the bottom. The backs are numbered and include a summary of the player's collegiate accomplishments.

		MT
Complete Set (10):		120.00
Common Player:		5.00
1	Jerome Bettis	20.00
2	Drew Bledsoe	45.00
3	Reggie Brooks	5.00
4	Derek Brown	5.00
5	Garrison Hearst	20.00
6	Vaughn Hebron	5.00
7	Qadry Ismail	10.00
8	Derrick Lassic	5.00
9	Glyn Milburn	5.00
10	Dana Stubblefield	7.00

1994 Playoff Prototypes

This six-card set gave collectors a glimpse of what the 1994 Playoff set would look like. A full-bleed color photo dominates the front, with the Playoff logo near the bottom, located inside an oval that also housed the player's name. The card back also had a full-bleed shot of the player, with his name in a black box next to his helmet. Below the name on the unnumbered card back is the player's career highlights.

		MT
Complete Set (6):		8.00
Common Player:		1.00
1	Marcus Allen	1.00
2	Rick Mirer	1.25
3	Barry Sanders	2.00
4	Junior Seau	1.25
5	Sterling Sharpe	1.25
6	Emmitt Smith	3.00

A card number in parentheses ( ) indicates the set is unnumbered.

1993 Playoff Contenders Rick Mirer

These five cards, devoted to Seattle Seahawks first-round draft pick Rick Mirer, were randomly inserted in 1993 Playoff Contenders packs. The fronts have a borderless color action shot with a metallic shine. Mirer's name is at the bottom in a black box. Mirer's photo from the front of card 3 is used as a ghosted image for all five card backs. Career highlights and a card number, 1 of 5, etc., are also given on the backs.

		MT
Complete Set (5):		40.00
Common Mirer:		8.00
1	This Kid Can Play (Rick Mirer)	8.00
2	Notre Dame All-American (Rick Mirer)	8.00
3	First-Round Draft Pick (Rick Mirer)	8.00
4	Seattle in the Hunt (Rick Mirer)	8.00
5	A Tough Guy (Rick Mirer)	8.00

Values quoted in this guide reflect the retail price of a card — the price a collector can expect to pay when buying a card from a dealer. The wholesale price — that which a collector can expect to receive when selling cards from a dealer — will be significantly lower, depending on desirability and condition.

1994 Playoff

These Playoff cards use the company's Tekchrome II ink-on-foil process for the full-color card fronts. The photo is full-bleed and has the set's logo in the upper right corner. The card back has another photo of the player, along with his name and team helmet. A brief player profile is also included. Subsets within the main set include Sack Pack, Ground Attack, Summerall's Best and Rookies. Insert sets include the Silver Playoff Club, which features Gale Sayers (some of them are autographed); the Jerome Bettis Collection; the Jerry Rice Collection; the Playoff Club; the Barry Sanders Collection; and the Headliners. Six prototype cards were also produced, previewing the regular cards.

		MT
Complete Set (336):		45.00
Common Player:		.15
Wax Box:		45.00
1	Joe Montana	2.00
2	Derrick Thomas	.35
3	Dan Marino	4.00
4	Cris Carter	.25
5	Boomer Esiason	.30
6	Bruce Smith	.25
7	Andre Rison	.40
8	Curtis Conway	.40
9	Michael Irvin	.50
10	Shannon Sharpe	.35
11	Pat Swilling	.25
12	John Parrella	.15
13	Mel Gray	.15
14	Ray Childress	.15
15	Willie Davis	.15
16	Raghib Ismail	.45
17	Jim Everett	.20
18	Mark Higgs	.15
19	Trace Armstrong	.15
20	Jim Kelly	.60
21	Rob Burnett	.15
22	Jay Novacek	.35
23	Robert Delpino	.15
24	Brett Perriman	.15
25	Troy Aikman	2.00
26	Reggie White	.30
27	Lorenzo White	.15
28	Bubba McDowell	.15
29	Steve Emtman	.15
30	Brett Favre	4.00
31	Derek Russell	.15
32	Jeff Hostetler	.20
33	Henry Ellard	.15
34	Jack Del Rio	.15
35	Mike Saxon	.15
36	Rickey Jackson	.15
37	Phil Simms	.25
38	Quinn Early	.15
39	Russell Copeland	.15
40	Carl Pickens	.25
41	Lance Gunn	.15
42	Bernie Kosar	.25
43	John Elway	1.00
44	George Teague	.30
45	Nick Lowery	.25
46	Haywood Jeffires	.25
47	Will Shields	.15
48	Daryl Johnson	.20
49	Pete Metzelaars	.15
50	Warren Moon	.25
51	Cornelius Bennett	.20
52	Vinny Testaverde	.20
53	John Mangun	.15
54	Tommy Vardell	.25
55	Lincoln Coleman	.60
56	Karl Mecklenburg	.15
57	Jackie Harris	.20
58	Curtis Duncan	.15
59	Quentin Coryatt	.25
60	Tim Brown	.35
61	Irving Fryar	.30
62	Sean Gilbert	.20
63	Qadry Ismail	.25
64	Irv Smith	.25
65	Mark Jackson	.15
66	Ronnie Lott	.20
67	Henry Jones	.15
68	Horace Copeland	.25
69	John Copeland	.15
70	Mark Carrier	.15
71	Michael Jackson	.25
72	Jason Elam	.20
73	Rod Bernstine	.20
74	Wayne Simmons	.15
75	Cody Carlson	.15
76	Alexander Wright	.15
77	Shane Conlan	.15
78	Keith Jackson	.25
79	Sean Salisbury	.15
80	Vaughan Johnson	.15
81	Rob Moore	.15
82	Andre Reed	.30
83	David Klingler	.35
84	Jim Harbaugh	.15
85	John Jett	.30
86	Sterling Sharpe	.25
87	Webster Slaughter	.20
88	J.J. Birden	.15
89	O.J. McDuffie	.60
90	Andre Tippett	.15
91	Don Beebe	.15
92	Mark Stepnoski	.15
93	Neil Smith	.20
94	Terry Kirby	.85
95	Wade Wilson	.15
96	Darryl Talley	.15
97	Anthony Smith	.15
98	Willie Roaf	.25
99	Mo Lewis	.15
100	James Washington	.15
101	Nate Odomes	.15
102	Chris Gedney	.15
103	Joe Walter	.15
104	Alvin Harper	.20
105	Simon Fletcher	.25
106	Rodney Peete	.15
107	Terrell Buckley	.15
108	Jeff George	.30
109	James Jett	.50
110	Tony Casillas	.15
111	Marco Coleman	.15
112	Anthony Carter	.15
113	Lincoln Kennedy	.20
114	Chris Calloway	.15
115	Randall Cunningham	.20
116	Steve Beuerlein	.25
117	Neil O'Donnell	.30
118	Stan Humphries	.15
119	John Taylor	.20
120	Cortez Kennedy	.20
121	Santana Dotson	.15
122	Thomas Smith	.15
123	Kevin Williams	.30
124	Andre Ware	.15
125	Ethan Horton	.15
126	Mike Sherrard	.15
127	Fred Barnett	.15
128	Rickey Proehl	.15
129	Kevin Greene	.15
130	John Carney	.15
131	Tim McDonald	.25
132	Rick Mirer	1.00
133	Blair Thomas	.15
134	Hardy Nickerson	.15
135	Heath Sherman	.15
136	Andre Hastings	.15
137	Randal Hill	.15
138	Mike Cofer	.15
139	Brian Blades	.15
140	Earnest Byner	.15
141	Bill Bates	.15
142	Junior Seau	.20
143	Johnny Bailey	.15
144	Dwight Stone	.15
145	Todd Kelly	.15
146	Tyrone Montgomery	.15
147	Herschel Walker	.15
148	Gary Clark	.15
149	Eric Green	.20
150	Steve Young	2.00
151	Anthony Miller	.25
152	Dana Stubblefield	.50
153	Dean Wells	.15
154	Vincent Brisby	.60
155	Chris Chandler	.15
156	Clyde Simmons	.15
157	Rod Woodson	.20
158	Nate Lewis	.15
159	Martin Harrison	.15
160	Kelvin Martin	.15
161	Craig Erickson	.25
162	Johnny Mitchell	.20
163	Calvin Williams	.15
164	Deon Figures	.30
165	Tom Rathman	.15
166	Rick Hamilton	.15
167	John L. Williams	.15
168	Demetrius Dubose	.15
169	Michael Brooks	.15
170	Marion Butts	.30
171	Brent Jones	.20
172	Bobby Hebert	.20
173	Brad Edwards	.15
174	Dave Wyman	.15
175	Herman Moore	1.00
176	Leroy Butler	.20
177	Reggie Langhorne	.15
178	Dave Krieg	.15
179	Patrick Bates	.15
180	Erik Kramer	.15
181	Troy Drayton	.30
182	David Meggett	.15
183	Eric Allen	.30
184	Mark Bavaro	.15
185	Leslie O'Neal	.25
186	Jerry Rice	2.00
187	Desmond Howard	.25
188	Deion Sanders	1.00
189	Bill Maas	.15
190	Frank Wycheck	.15
191	Ernest Givins	.15
192	Terry McDaniel	.15
193	Bryan Cox	.20
194	Guy McIntyre	.15
195	Pierce Holt	.15
196	Fred Stokes	.15
197	Mike Pritchard	.25
198	Terry Obee	.15
199	Mark Collins	.15
200	Drew Bledsoe	3.00
201	Barry Wood	.15
202	Derrick Lassic	.35
203	Chris Spielman	.15
204	John Jurkovic	.25
205	Ken Norton Jr.	.15
206	Dale Carter	.20
207	Chris Doleman	.15
208	Keith Hamilton	.15
209	Andy Harmon	.15
210	John Friesz	.20
211	Steve Bono	.20
212	Mark Rypien	.15
213	Ricky Sanders	.15
214	Michael Haynes	.35
215	Todd McNair	.15
216	Leon Lett	.15
217	Scott Mitchell	.50
218	Mike Morris	.15
219	Darrin Smith	.15
220	Jim McMahon	.15
221	Garrison Hearst	1.50
222	Leroy Thompson	.15
223	Darren Carrington	.15
224	Pete Stoyanovich	.15
225	Chris Miller	.20
226	Bruce Smith	.30
227	Simon Fletcher	.30
228	Reggie White	.20
229	Neil Smith	.20
230	Chris Doleman	.20
231	Keith Hamilton	.15
232	Dana Stubblefield	.20
233	Erric Pegram	.40
234	Thurman Thomas	.50
235	Lewis Tillman	.15
236	Harold Green	.15
237	Eric Metcalf	.15
238	Emmitt Smith	4.00
239	Glyn Milburn	.20
240	Barry Sanders	3.00
241	Edgar Bennett	.20
242	Gary Brown	.20
243	Rossevelt Potts	.15
244	Marcus Allen	.15
245	Greg Robinson	.15
246	Jerome Bettis	.75
247	Keith Byars	.15
248	Robert Smith	.50
249	Leonard Russell	.20
250	Derek Brown	.55
251	Rodney Hampton	.55
252	Johnny Johnson	.15
253	Vaughn Hebron	.15
254	Ron Moore	.40
255	Barry Foster	.50
256	Natrone Means	.75
257	Ricky Watters	.30
258	Chris Warren	.15
259	Vince Workman	.15
260	Reggie Brooks	.30
261	Carolina Panthers	.20
262	Jacksonville Jaguars	.20
263	Troy Aikman	1.75
264	Barry Sanders	1.50
265	Emmitt Smith	2.00
266	Michael Irvin	.40
267	Jerry Rice	1.00
268	Shannon Sharpe	.25
269	Bob Kratch	.15
270	Howard Ballard	.15
271	Erik Williams	.15
272	Guy McIntyre	.15
273	Kelvin Williams	.25
274	Mel Gray	.15
275	Eddie Murray	.15
276	Mark Stepnoski	.15
277	Tommy Barnhardt	.15
278	Derrick Thomas	.20
279	Ken Norton Jr.	.20
280	Chris Spielman	.15
281	Deion Sanders	.15
282	Mark Collins	.15
283	Bruce Smith	.20
284	Reggie White	.20
285	Sean Gilbert	.20
286	Cortez Kennedy	.20
287	Steve Atwater	.15
288	Tim McDonald	.15
289	Jerome Bettis	.75
290	Dana Stubblefield	.20
291	Bert Emanuel	1.00
292	Jeff Burris	.30
293	Bucky Brooks	.65
294	Dan Wilkinson	.85
295	Darnay Scott	2.00
296	Derrick Alexander	.75
297	Antonio Langham	.50
298	Shante Carver	.40
299	Shelby Hill	.25
300	Larry Allen	.30

301	Johnnie Morton	.75
302	Van Malone	.25
303	Aaron Taylor	.35
304	Marshall Faulk	8.00
305	Eric Mahlum	.25
306	Trev Alberts	.90
307	Greg Hill	.50
308	Donnell Bennett	.30
309	Rob Fredrickson	.25
310	James Folston	.25
311	Isaac Bruce	5.00
312	Tim Ruddy	.25
313	Aubrey Beavers	.25
314	David Palmer	.50
315	DeWayne Washington	.45
316	Willie McGinest	.50
317	Mario Bates	.30
318	Kevin Lee	.50
319	Jason Sehorn	.15
320	Thomas Randolph	.35
321	Ryan Yarborough	.40
322	Bernard Williams	.25
323	Chuck Levy	.75
324	Jamir Miller	.50
325	Charles Johnson	1.00
326	Bryant Young	.35
327	William Floyd	.50
328	Kevin Mitchell	.25
329	Sam Adams	.50
330	Kevin Mawae	.15
331	Errict Rhett	1.00
332	Trent Dilfer	1.00
333	Heath Shuler	.50
334	Aaron Glenn	.40
335	Todd Steussie	.30
336	Toby Wright	.15

1994 Playoff Jerome Bettis

1993 NFL Rookie of the Year Jerome Bettis is featured in this five-card insert set. Cards devoted to the Los Angeles Rams running back were random inserts in 1994 Playoff hobby packs. Each card front has a color action photo against a silver foil background which has Bettis' name written on it in several different typefaces. The "1994 Playoff Collection" logo is also on the front, in the lower right corner. The yellow backs have biographical information about Bettis, and the card title, plus a card number.

		MT
Complete Set (5):		50.00
Common Bettis:		10.00
1	Jerome Bettis	10.00
2	Jerome Bettis	10.00
3	Jerome Bettis	10.00
4	Jerome Bettis	10.00
5	Jerome Bettis	10.00

1994 Playoff Checklists

Full-bleed metallic color photos dominate the front, with the featured player's highlights printed inside a silver box at the bottom center. The card backs, numbered "of 10," highlight a portion of the set's checklists. The cards were randomly seeded.

	MT
Complete Set (10):	5.00
Common Player:	.50
1 Keith Cash	.50
2 Kerry Cash	.50
3 Qadry Ismail	.75
4 Rocket Ismail	.75
5 Bruce Matthews	.50
6 Clay Matthews	.50
7 Shannon Sharpe	1.00
8 Sterling Sharpe	1.00
9 John Taylor	.50
10 Keith Taylor	.50

1994 Playoff Club

These inserts, randomly included in 1994 Playoff packs, feature six future Hall of Famers. Each card has a borderless front with a metallic action photo. The set logo appears at the bottom of the card, along with a facsimile autograph. The card back is white and has the player's name and a career summary. Backs are numbered with a "PC" prefix.

		MT
Complete Set (6):		35.00
Commom Player:		2.75
8	Jerry Rice	20.00
9	Marcus Allen	5.00
10	Howie Long	5.00
11	Clay Matthews	2.75
12	Richard Dent	2.75
13	Morten Andersen	2.75

1994 Playoff Headliners Redemption

In exchange for a redemption card, a collector would receive this six-card set. Card fronts have a prism effect, with the player's name and Headliners' logo printed at the bottom. Showcased on the horizontal card back is a headshot of the player, his name and an explanation of his 1994 milestone.

		MT
Complete Set (6):		18.00
Common Player:		2.00
1	Tim Brown	3.00
2	Bernie Parmalee	2.00
3	Sterling Sharpe	3.00
4	Natrone Means	4.00
5	Alvin Harper	2.00
6	Deion Sanders	6.00
NNO	Headliners Redemption	.50

1994 Playoff Jerry Rice

San Francisco 49er wide receiver Jerry Rice is featured in this five-card insert set. Cards were randomly included in 1994 Playoff retail display packs. The card front has a color action photo against a foil background, plus a "1994 Playoff Collection" logo. The card back has another photo and career summary, plus a card number.

		MT
Complete Set (5):		120.00
Common Rice:		25.00
1	Born to Run (Jerry Rice)	25.00
2	All American (Jerry Rice)	25.00
3	The 49ers Start the Dynasty (Jerry Rice)	25.00
4	The Offensive Player of the Year (Again, Jerry Rice)	25.00
5	Breaking Jim Brown's Record (Jerry Rice)	25.00

1994 Playoff Rookie Roundup Redemption

A mail-in offer allowed collectors to exchange the redemption card for this nine-card set. The exchange card was randomly seeded in packs. Card fronts have a photo of the player, with a team-colored border on either side of the card. Located on the horizontal backs are a full-bleed photo, with his name and biographical information printed inside boxes. This offer expired Dec. 31, 1995.

		MT
Complete Set (9):		30.00
Common Player:		3.00
1	Heath Shuler	6.00
2	David Palmer	3.00
3	Dan Wilkinson	3.00
4	Marshall Faulk	10.00
5	Charlie Garner	4.00
6	Errict Rhett	8.00
7	Trent Dilfer	5.00
8	Antonio Langham	3.00
9	Gus Frerotte	6.00
NNO	Redemption Card	.50

1994 Playoff Barry Sanders

Detroit Lions running back Barry Sanders is highlighted in this five-card insert set. Cards were randomly included in Playoff's Four Star Edition of the set. These sets were distributed to selected hobby stores, Wal-Mart, Books-A-Million, Walden Books and other retail stores.

		MT
Complete Set (5):		120.00
Common Sanders:		25.00
1	Barry Sanders	25.00
2	Barry Sanders	25.00
3	Barry Sanders	25.00
4	Barry Sanders	25.00
5	Barry Sanders	25.00

Values quoted in this guide reflect the retail price of a card — the price a collector can expect to pay when buying a card from a dealer. The wholesale price — that which a collector can expect to receive from a dealer when selling cards — will be significantly lower, depending on desirability and condition.

1994 Playoff Super Bowl Redemption

This six-card set, which featured Dallas players, was traded to collectors in exchange for a redemption card through a mail-in offer. The redemption card was randomly seeded in packs. A Super Bowl Playoff logo, along with the player's name, are printed at the top of the full-bleed card fronts. The horizontal card backs have the Super Bowl Playoff logo, Cowboys and Bills helmets and the player's Super Bowl accomplishments.

		MT
Complete Set (6):		30.00
Common Player:		2.50
1	Troy Aikman	10.00
2	Emmitt Smith	20.00
3	Leon Lett	2.50
4	Michael Irvin	3.00
5	James Washington	2.50
6	Darrin Smith	2.50
NNO	Super Bowl Redemption	1.00

1994 Playoff Julie Bell Art Redemption

Fantasy artist Julie Bell used her talents to create this six-card set, featuring players in superhuman poses. The fronts are borderless, with a Playoff logo. The backs have a repeat of a portion of the artwork, along with a quote from Bell. "Julie Bell's Fantasy Football" is printed at the top. The set was available as a mail-in offer with a redemption found randomly inserted in packs.

		MT
Complete Set (6):		20.00
Common Player:		2.00
1	Emmitt Smith	10.00
2	Marcus Allen	2.00
3	Junior Seau	3.00
4	Barry Sanders	5.00
5	Rick Mirer	2.00
6	Sterling Sharpe	2.00

1994 Playoff Super Bowl Promos

To commemorate Super Bowl XXVIII, Playoff produced this six-card set. The full-bleed fronts have the player's name and the Playoff logo printed in an oval at the bottom of the card. The white card backs, numbered "of 6 promo," show-case the Super Bowl XXVIII logo in the center.

		MT
Complete Set (6):		16.00
Common Player:		1.50
1	Jerry Rice	6.00
2	Daryl Johnston	1.50
3	Herschel Walker	1.50
4	Reggie White	2.50
5	Scott Mitchell	2.00
6	Thurman Thomas	2.50

1994 Playoff Contenders Promos

This seven-card set gave collectors a glimpse of what the 1994 Playoff Contenders set would look like. The city name of the player's team was printed at the top of the card fronts, with the player's name in silver foil on a green border at the bottom. The Playoff Contenders' logo is also included at the bottom. The unnumbered card backs have a headshot of the player, with his highlights printed below. The NFL's 75th anniversary logo is located above the write-up.

		MT
Complete Set (7):		10.00
Common Player:		1.00
1	Qadry Ismail	2.50
2	Daryl Johnston	1.50
3	John Jurkovic	1.00
4	Eric Metcalf	2.00
5	Andre Reed	1.50
6	Calvin Williams	1.00
7	Title Card	1.00

1994 Playoff Contenders

This 120-card set uses Playoff's patented, ink-on-foil Tekchrome printing process. Fronts capture the player in an intense game action photo. A grass strip at the bottom contains the player's name; his team's name is at the top of the card. A set logo appears in the lower right corner. The card back has a close-up shot of the player, which takes up two-thirds of the card. A blue strip at the bottom of the card contains some biographical information. The entire background is grey marble. A 27-card Draft Pick subset is contained within the main set. There were also four insert sets produced - 75th anniversary Throwbacks, Rookie Contenders, Sophomore Contenders and Back-To-Backs.

	MT
Complete Set (120):	40.00

Common Player:		.15
Minor Stars:		.30
Wax Box:		160.00
1	Drew Bledsoe	3.00
2	Barry Sanders	3.00
3	Jerry Rice	3.00
4	Rod Woodson	.30
5	Irving Fryar	.15
6	Charles Haley	.15
7	Chris Warren	.30
8	Craig Erickson	.15
9	Eric Metcalf	.15
10	Marcus Allen	.30
11	Chris Miller, Charles Johnson	.15
12	Andre Rison	.30
13	Art Monk	.30
14	Calvin Williams	.15
15	Shannon Sharpe, Bryant Young	.15
16	Rodney Hampton	.30
17	Marion Butts	.15
18	John Jurkovic	.50
19	Jim Kelly	.30
20	Emmitt Smith	5.00
21	Jeff Hostetler	.30
22	Barry Foster	.30
23	Boomer Esiason	.30
24	Jim Harbaugh	.15
25	Joe Montana	3.00
26	Jeff George	.50
27	Warren Moon	.30
28	Steve Young	3.00
29	Randall Cunningham	.30
30	Shawn Jefferson	.15
31	Cortez Kennedy	.30
32	Reggie Brooks	.15
33	Alvin Harper	.30
34	Brent Jones	.15
35	O.J. McDuffie	.40
36	Jerome Bettis	1.00
37	Daryl Johnston	.15
38	Herman Moore	1.00
39	Dave Meggett	.15
40	Reggie White	.30
41	Junior Seau	.50
42	Dan Marino	5.00
43	Scott Mitchell	.15
44	John Elway	4.00
45	Troy Aikman	3.00
46	Terry Allen	.15
47	David Klingler	.15
48	Stan Humphries	.40
49	Rick Mirer	.30
50	Neil O'Donnell	.30
51	Keith Jackson	.15
52	Ricky Watters	.30
53	Dave Brown	.30
54	Neil Smith	.15
55	Johnny Mitchell	.15
56	Jackie Harris	.15
57	Terry Kirby	.15
58	Willie Davis	.15
59	Rob Moore	.15
60	Nate Newton	.15
61	Deion Sanders	2.00
62	John Taylor	.15
63	Sterling Sharpe	.30
64	Natrone Means	1.00
65	Steve Beuerlein	.15
66	Erik Kramer	.15
67	Qadry Ismail	.15
68	Johnny Johnson	.15
69	Herschel Walker	.15
70	Mark Stepnoski	.15
71	Brett Favre	5.00
72	Dana Stubblefield	.15
73	Bruce Smith	.30
74	Leroy Hoard	.15
75	Steve Walsh	.15
76	Jay Novacek	.15
77	Derrick Thomas	.30
78	Keith Byars	.15
79	Ben Coates	.40
80	Lorenzo Neal	.15
81	Ronnie Lott	.15
82	Tim Brown	.30
83	Michael Irvin	.50
84	Ron Moore	.15
85	Andre Reed	.30
86	James Jett	.15
87	Curtis Conway	.30
88	Bernie Parmalee	.30
89	Keith Cash	.15
90	Russell Copeland	.15
91	Kevin Williams	.50
92	Gary Brown	.15
93	Thurman Thomas	.50
94	Jamir Miller	.30
95	Bert Emanuel	2.00
96	Buck Brooks	.50
97	Jeff Burris	.50
98	Antonio Langham	.50
99	Derrick Alexander	.50
100	Dan Wilkinson	.50
101	Shante Carver	.40
102	Johnnie Morton	.75
103	LeShon Johnson	.50
104	Marshall Faulk	5.00
105	Greg Hill	.50
106	Lake Dawson	.50
107	Irving Spikes	.50
108	David Palmer	.50
109	Willie McGinest	.50
110	Joe Johnson	.30
111	Aaron Glenn	.30
112	Charlie Garner	2.50

113	Charles Johnson		.50
114	Byron Bam Morris		.50
115	Bryant Young		.75
116	William Floyd		.50
117	Trent Dilfer		3.00
118	Errict Rhett		1.00
119	Heath Shuler		.50
120	Gus Frerotte		1.00

1994 Playoff Contenders Back-to-Back

Each card in this 60-card insert set shows two card fronts from the 120 regular cards. The card fronts are matched up so that two key players from the same position appear on the card. Team names and Playoff Contenders logos are foil stamped on the cards, and the photos are embossed, meaning they are raised up off the card.

		MT
Complete Set (60):		1250.
Common Player:		12.50
Minor Stars:		25.00
Inserted 1:24		
1	Joe Montana, Dan Marino	150.00
2	Drew Bledsoe, John Elway	100.00
3	Jerry Rice, Sterling Sharpe	75.00
4	Barry Sanders, Emmitt Smith	150.00
5	Troy Aikman, Steve Young	75.00
6	Erik Kramer, Steve Walsh	12.50
7	Nate Newton, Bruce Smith	12.50
8	Johnny Mitchell, Aaron Glenn	12.50
9	Neil O'Donnell, Charles Johnson	12.50
10	Herman Moore, Calvin Williams	25.00
11	Alvin Harper, Michael Irvin	25.00
12	Jim Harbaugh, Curtis Conway	25.00
13	Brett Favre, LeShon Johnson	125.00
14	Marshall Faulk, Eric Metcalf	35.00
15	Qadry Ismail, David Palmer	12.50
16	Deion Sanders, Andre Rison	35.00
17	Jackie Harris, Errict Rhett	12.50
18	Keith Jackson, Keith Byars	12.50
19	Dave Meggett, Jeff Burris	12.50
20	Dana Stubblefield, William Floyd	12.50
21	Randall Cunningham, Reggie White	25.00
22	Shannon Sharpe, Keith Cash	25.00
23	Marcus Allen, Greg Hill	25.00
24	Irving Fryar, Russell Copeland	12.50
25	Johnny Johnson, Willie McGinest	12.50
26	John Taylor, Brent Jones	12.50
27	Terry Kirby, Bernie Parmalee	12.50
28	Ricky Watters, Ronnie Lott	25.00
29	Scott Mitchell, Johnnie Morton	12.50
30	O.J. McDuffie, Irving Spikes	12.50
31	Shawn Jefferson, Andre Reed	12.50
32	Rodney Hampton, Lorenzo Neal	12.50

33	Chris Miller, Joe Johnson	12.50
34	Charles Haley, Thurman Thomas	25.00
35	Herschel Walker, Charlie Garner	12.50
36	Natrone Means, Stan Humphries	25.00
37	Willie Davis, Lake Dawson	12.50
38	Dave Brown, Gary Brown	12.50
39	Jerome Bettis, Terry Allen	35.00
40	Cortez Kennedy, Junior Seau	12.50
41	David Klingler, Derrick Alexander	12.50
42	Chris Warren, Bucky Brooks	12.50
43	Mark Stepnoski, Kevin Williams	12.50
44	Steve Beuerlein, Ron Moore	12.50
45	Rob Moore, James Jett	12.50
46	Neil Smith, Derrick Thomas	12.50
47	Rick Mirer, Bryant Young	12.50
48	Daryl Johnston, Jay Novacek	12.50
49	Reggie Brooks, Gus Frerotte	12.50
50	Barry Foster, Byron "Bam" Morris	12.50
51	Art Monk, Heath Shuler	12.50
52	Craig Erickson, Trent Dilfer	25.00
53	Jeff George, Bert Emanuel	12.50
54	Rod Woodson, Antonio Langham	12.50
55	Marion Butts, Ben Coates	12.50
56	John Jurkovic, Dan Wilkinson	12.50
57	Jim Kelly, Shante Carver	25.00
58	Jeff Hostetler, Tim Brown	12.50
59	Boomer Esiason, Jamir Miller	12.50
60	Warren Moon, Terry Allen	25.00

1994 Playoff Contenders Rookie Contenders

Six first-year standouts are showcased in this 1994 Playoff Contenders insert set, which combines three different foil effects. Each card has a split background, with the left side having a glittery silver foil and the right side having a purple foil. The player's name is written in silver foil within the purple foil. Above his name is a Rookie Contender logo stamped in foil. Below his name is a Playoff logo. These cards are inserted one per 48 packs.

		MT
Complete Set (6):		125.00
Common Player:		10.00
Minor Stars:		15.00
1	Marshall Faulk	45.00
2	Charles Garner	15.00
3	Trent Dilfer	15.00
4	Heath Shuler	10.00
5	Dan Wilkinson	10.00
6	David Palmer	10.00

A card number in parentheses ( ) indicates the set is unnumbered.

1994 Playoff Contenders Sophomore Contenders

Six of the top second-year NFL players are featured on these insert cards, available at a rate of one per 48 packs. These cards feature a foil-etched burst-pattern design. The top one third of the card has a purple prism design. It has the player's name on the left and a Sophomore Contenders logo on the right, both in silver foil. The bottom two-thirds has the player on a silver burst-patterned background.

		MT
Complete Set (6):		100.00
Common Player:		5.00
1	Drew Bledsoe	50.00
2	Jerome Bettis	10.00
3	Natrone Means	12.00
4	Rick Mirer	7.00
5	Reggie Brooks	5.00
6	O.J. McDuffie	5.00

1994 Playoff Contenders Throwbacks

This 30-card insert set shows at least one star from each NFL team in his "Throwback" uniform. The front shows the player in a foil-enhanced background. A strip across the bottom contains the player's name in silver foil, with an NFL Throwback Week logo centered on this strip. These cards were randomly included in Playoff Contender packs at a ratio of one per 12 packs.

		MT
Complete Set (30):		200.00
Common Player:		5.00
1	Larry Centers	5.00
2	Andre Rison	5.00
3	Jim Kelly	8.00
4	Curtis Conway	5.00
5	David Klingler	5.00
6	Vinny Testaverde	5.00
7	Troy Aikman	15.00
8	Emmitt Smith	30.00
9	John Elway	12.00
10	Barry Sanders	20.00
11	Sterling Sharpe	8.00
12	Gary Brown	5.00
13	Jim Harbaugh	5.00
14	Joe Montana	15.00
15	Tim Brown	8.00
16	Chris Miller	5.00
17	Dan Marino	30.00
18	Terry Allen	5.00
19	Marion Butts	5.00
20	Jim Everett	5.00
21	Dave Brown	5.00
22	Johnny Johnson	5.00
23	Randall Cunningham	5.00

24	Barry Foster	5.00
25	Stan Humphries	8.00
26	Jerry Rice	15.00
27	Steve Young	12.00
28	Chris Warren	8.00
29	Errict Rhett	5.00
30	John Freisz	5.00

1995 Playoff Absolute-Prime

Playoff's 1995 200-card football set was released in two different designs - a hobby version (Absolute) and a totally different retail version (Prime). The hobby-only Absolute features a Pigskins Preview insert set devoted to six NFC players, a Quad Series parallel set (four players per card), and Die-Cut Helmets. Common to both Absolute and Prime packs are Unsung Heroes and First Draft Picks for the two new expansion teams - Jacksonville and Carolina. Playoff Prime has the remaining six Pigskin Preview cards, which are devoted to AFC players. Draft Picks cards are a subset of the regular set.

		MT
Complete Absolute Set (200):		35.00
Common Absolute Player:		.15
Minor Absolute Stars:		.30
Complete Prime Set (200):		17.00
Prime Cards: Half Price		
Absolute Box:		50.00
Prime Box:		25.00
1	John Elway	.50
2	Reggie White	.30
3	Errict Rhett	.30
4	Deion Sanders	.75
5	Raghib Ismail	.15
6	Jerome Bettis	.30
7	Randall Cunningham	.15
8	Mario Bates	.50
9	Dave Brown	.15
10	Stan Humphries	.30
11	Drew Bledsoe	1.50
12	Neil O'Donnell	.30
13	Dan Marino	3.00
14	Larry Centers	.15
15	Craig Heyward	.15
16	Bruce Smith	.15
17	Erik Kramer	.15
18	Jeff Blake	.50
19	Vinny Testaverde	.15
20	Barry Sanders	2.00
21	Boomer Esiason	.15
22	Emmitt Smith	3.00
23	Warren Moon	.30
24	Junior Seau	.30
25	Heath Shuler	1.25
26	Jackie Harris	.15
27	Terance Mathis	.15
28	Raymont Harris	.15
29	Jim Kelly	.30
30	Dan Wilkinson	.15
31	Herman Moore	.50
32	Shannon Sharpe	.15
33	Antonio Langham	.15
34	Charles Haley	.15
35	Brett Favre	3.00
36	Marshall Faulk	.30
37	Neil Smith	.15
38	Harvey Williams	.15
39	Johnny Bailey	.15
40	O.J. McDuffie	.15
41	David Palmer	.15
42	Willie McGinest	.15
43	Quinn Early	.15
44	Johnny Johnson	.15
45	Derek Brown	.15
46	Charlie Garner	.15
47	Bam Morris	.30
48	Natrone Means	.30
49	Ken Norton	.15
50	Troy Aikman	1.25
51	Reggie Brooks	.15
52	Trent Dilfer	.50
53	Cortez Kennedy	.15

54	Chuck Levy	.15
55	Jeff George	.30
56	Steve Young	1.25
57	Lewis Tillman	.15
58	Carl Pickens	.30
59	Brett Perriman	.15
60	Jay Novacek	.15
61	Greg Hill	.30
62	James Jett	.15
63	Terry Kirby	.15
64	Qadry Ismail	.15
65	Ben Coates	.15
66	Kevin Greene	.15
67	Bryant Young	.15
68	Brian Mitchell	.15
69	Steve Walsh	.15
70	Darnay Scott	.75
71	Daryl Johnston	.15
72	Glyn Milburn	.15
73	Tim Brown	.30
74	Isaac Bruce	.50
75	Bernie Parmalee	.30
76	Terry Allen	.15
77	Jim Everett	.15
78	Thomas Lewis	.15
79	Vaughn Hebron	.15
80	Rod Woodson	.15
81	Rick Mirer	.40
82	Dana Stubblefield	.15
83	Bert Emanuel	.50
84	Andre Reed	.15
85	Jeff Graham	.15
86	Johnnie Morton	.15
87	LeShon Johnson	.15
88	Michael Irvin	.40
89	Derrick Alexander	.15
90	Lake Dawson	.50
91	Cody Carlson	.15
92	Chris Warren	.30
93	William Floyd	.50
94	Charles Johnson	.30
95	Roosevelt Potts	.15
96	Cris Carter	.30
97	Aaron Glenn	.15
98	Curtis Conway	.30
99	Kevin Williams	.15
100	Jerry Rice	1.25
101	Frank Reich	.15
102	Harold Green	.15
103	Russell Copeland	.15
104	Rob Moore	.15
105	Edgar Bennett	.15
106	Darren Carrington	.15
107	Tommy Maddox	.15
108	Dave Meggett	.15
109	Fred Barnett	.15
110	Mark Seay	.15
111	Gus Frerotte	.50
112	Brent Jones	.15
113	Chris Miller	.15
114	Cedric Tillman	.15
115	Mark Ingram	.15
116	Eric Turner	.15
117	Mark Carrier	.15
118	Garrison Hearst	.30
119	Craig Erickson	.15
120	Derek Russell	.15
121	Mike Sherrard	.15
122	Horace Copeland	.15
123	Jack Trudeau	.15
124	Leroy Hoard	.15
125	Gary Brown	.15
126	Mel Gray	.15
127	Steve Beuerlein	.15
128	Marcus Allen	.30
129	Irving Fryar	.15
130	Marion Butts	.15
131	Ricky Watters	.30
132	Tony Martin	.15
133	Lawrence Dawsey	.15
134	Ronnie Harmon	.15
135	Herschel Walker	.15
136	Michael Haynes	.15
137	Eric Green	.15
138	Steve Bono	.40
139	Jamir Miller	.15
140	Rod Smith	.15
141	Andre Rison	.30
142	Eric Metcalf	.15
143	Michael Timpson	.15
144	Cornelius Bennett	.15
145	Sean Dawkins	.30
146	Scott Mitchell	.15
147	Ray Childress	.15
148	Jim Harbaugh	.30
149	Reggie Cobb	.15
150	Willie Roaf	.15
151	Stevie Anderson	.15
152	Barry Foster	.15
153	Joe Montana	2.00
154	David Klingler	.15
155	Chris Chandler	.15
156	Carnell Lake	.15
157	Calvin Williams	.15
158	Kenneth Davis	.15
159	Tydus Winans	.15
160	Sam Adams	.15
161	Ron Moore	.15
162	Vincent Brisby	.15
163	Alvin Harper	.15
164	Jake Reed	.15
165	Jeff Hostetler	.15
166	Mark Brunell	1.50
167	Leonard Russell	.15
168	Greg Lloyd	.15
169	Pete Metzelaars	.15
170	Dave Krieg	.15
171	Lorenzo White	.15

172	Robert Brooks	.30
173	Willie Davis	.15
174	Irving Spikes	.15
175	Rodney Hampton	.15
176	Erric Pegram	.15
177	Brian Blades	.15
178	Shawn Jefferson	.15
179	Tyrone Poole	.15
180	Rob Johnson	5.00
181	Ki-Jana Carter	1.00
182	Steve McNair	5.00
183	Michael Westbrook	1.00
184	Kerry Collins	2.00
185	Kevin Carter	.30
186	Tony Boselli	.30
187	Joey Galloway	4.00
188	Kyle Brady	.50
189	J.J. Stokes	1.00
190	Warren Sapp	.50
191	Tyrone Wheatley	.75
192	Napoleon Kaufman	4.00
193	James Stewart	2.00
194	Rashaan Salaam	1.00
195	Ray Zellars	.75
196	Todd Collins	.75
197	Sherman Williams	.50
198	Frank Sanders	.50
199	Terrell Fletcher	.50
200	Chad May	.50
DP1	Tony Boselli Draft	3.00
DP2	Kerry Collins Draft	10.00

1995 Playoff Unsung Heroes

These 28 cards were inserted in both 1995 Playoff Absolute and Prime packs, one per 13 packs. The card front has a color photo of the player against a football field pattern. "Unsung Heroes" and the Playoff logo are stamped in gold in the upper corners. The player's name is in the lower left corner. The card back has goal posts which have a brief recap of the player's 1994 season between them.

		MT
Complete Set (28):		25.00
Common Player:		1.00
Minor Stars:		2.00
1	Garth Jax	1.00
2	Craig Heyward	1.00
3	Steve Tasker	1.00
4	Raymont Harris	2.00
5	Jeff Blake	7.00
6	Bob Dahl	1.00
7	Jason Garrett	1.00
8	Gary Zimmerman	1.00
9	Tom Beer	1.00
10	John Jurkovic	2.00
11	Spencer Tillman	1.00
12	Devon McDonald	1.00
13	John Alt	1.00
14	Steve Wisniewski	1.00
15	Tim Bowens	1.00
16	Amp Lee	2.00
17	Todd Rucci	1.00
18	Tyrone Hughes	1.00
19	Michael Strahan	1.00
20	Brad Baxter	1.00
21	Mark Bavaro	1.00
22	Yancy Thigpen	5.00
23	Courtney Hall	1.00
24	Eric Davis	1.00
25	Rufus Porter	1.00
26	Jackie Slater	1.00
27	Courtney Hawkins	1.00
28	Gus Frerotte	3.00

1995 Playoff Absolute Die Cut Helmets

These die-cut cards feature all 30 teams with a star player from each club on a clear plastic card. The front has a color photo of the player against a background of his team's helmet. His name appears in the lower right corner. The back of the card, numbered using an "HDC" prefix, has a white outline of the helmet and photo depicted on the front. These inserts were randomly included in hobby-only 1995 Playoff Absolute Packs, one per 25.

		MT
Complete Set (30):		600.00
Common Player:		6.00
Minor Stars:		12.00
1	Garrison Hearst	12.00
2	Jim Kelly	12.00
3	Jeff Blake	12.00
4	Emmitt Smith	70.00
5	John Elway	30.00
6	Brett Favre	70.00
7	Marshall Faulk	25.00
8	Marcus Allen	12.00
9	Jerome Bettis	12.00
10	Dan Marino	70.00
11	Cris Carter	12.00
12	Drew Bledsoe	45.00
13	Jim Everett	6.00
14	Rodney Hampton	6.00
15	Natrone Means	12.00
16	Steve Young	30.00
17	Rick Mirer	12.00
18	Errict Rhett	30.00
19	Heath Shuler	25.00
20	Lewis Tillman	6.00
21	Barry Sanders	45.00
22	Leroy Hoard	6.00
23	Rod Woodson	12.00
24	Gary Brown	6.00
25	Terance Mathis	6.00
26	Frank Reich	6.00
27	Steve Beuerlein	6.00
28	Raghib Ismail	6.00
29	Johnny Johnson	6.00
30	Charlie Garner	6.00

1995 Playoff Absolute Pigskin Previews

These hobby-only 1995 Playoff Absolute inserts feature six NFC stars. Cards were randomly included one per 145 packs. The front has a color photo superimposed over a leather football. Gold foil stamping is used at the bottom for the player's name and insert set logo. The card back has a color photo of the player against his team's city skyline. A brief recap of the player's 1994 accomplishments is given at the top of the card; his 1994 and career stats are listed in a panel at the bottom.

	MT
Complete Set (6):	400.00
Common Player:	20.00
1 Emmitt Smith	150.00
2 Steve Young	80.00
3 Barry Sanders	80.00
4 Deion Sanders	65.00
5 Cris Carter	20.00
6 Errict Rhett	20.00

1995 Playoff Absolute Quad Series

These 50 cards are a creative variation as a parallel set to Playoff's 1995 Absolute set. Each card features four players on it, two per side. Their names and the set and insert set logos are stamped in gold foil down the middle of the card. The backgrounds for each player are a pattern of metallic swirls. One side has a card number, using a "Q" prefix.

		MT
Complete Set (50):		1600.
Common Player:		10.00
Minor Stars:		16.00
1	Joe Montana,	225.00
	Steve Young,	
	Dan Marino,	
	John Elway	
2	Troy Aikman,	225.00
	Drew Bledsoe,	
	Brett Favre,	
	Rick Mirer	
3	Trent Dilfer,	60.00
	Heath Shuler,	
	Mark Brunell,	
	Jeff Blake	
4	Randall	16.00
	Cunningham,	
	Warren Moon,	
	Jim Kelly,	
	Boomer Esiason	
5	Dave Brown,	16.00
	Jeff George,	
	Stan Humphries,	
	Jim Everett	
6	Barry Sanders,	175.00
	Emmitt Smith,	
	Marshall Faulk,	
	Errict Rhett	
7	Marcus Allen,	25.00
	Ricky Watters,	
	William Floyd,	
	Natrone Means	
8	Garrison Hearst,	25.00
	Jerome Bettis,	
	Lewis Tillman,	
	Gary Brown	
9	Michael Irvin,	90.00
	Jerry Rice,	
	Tim Brown,	
	Cris Carter	
10	Pete Metzelaars,	16.00
	Bam Morris,	
	Ben Coates,	
	Andre Rison	
11	Reggie White,	35.00
	Bruce Smith,	
	Junior Seau,	
	Deion Sanders	
12	Rob Moore,	10.00
	Larry Centers,	
	Jamir Miller,	
	Chuck Levy	
13	Craig Haywood,	10.00
	Terance Mathis,	
	Bert Emanuel,	
	Eric Metcalf	
14	Kenneth Davis,	10.00
	Andre Reed,	
	Russell Copeland,	
	Cornelius Bennett	
15	Frank Reich,	10.00
	Jack Trudeau,	
	Mark Carrier,	
	Tyrone Poole	
16	Jeff Graham,	16.00
	Curtis Conway,	
	Erik Kramer,	
	Steve Walsh	
17	Carl Pickens,	16.00
	Darnay Scott,	
	Harold Green,	
	David Klinger	
18	Vinny Testaverde,	10.00
	Derrick Alexander,	
	Leroy Hoard,	
	Lorenzo White	
19	Charles Haley,	10.00
	Kevin Williams,	
	Daryl Johnston,	
	Jay Novacek	
20	Glyn Milburn,	10.00
	Leonard Russell,	
	Derek Russell,	
	Shannon Sharpe	
21	Scott Mitchell,	16.00
	Brett Perriman,	
	Herman Moore,	
	Johnnie Morton	
22	Edgar Bennett,	10.00
	LeShon Johnson,	
	Robert Brooks,	
	Mark Ingram	
23	Cody Carlson,	10.00
	Mel Gray,	
	Chris Chandler,	
	Ray Childress	
24	Jim Harbaugh,	10.00
	Craig Erickson,	
	Roosevelt Potts,	
	Sean Dawkins	
25	Steve Beuerlein,	10.00
	Rob Johnson,	
	Cedric Tillman,	
	Reggie Cobb	
26	Greg Hill,	16.00
	Willie Davis,	
	Lake Dawson,	
	Steve Bono	
27	Jeff Hostetler,	10.00
	Harvey Williams,	
	James Jett,	
	Raghib Ismail	
28	Bernie Parmalee,	10.00
	Irving Spikes,	
	Terry Kirby,	
	Irving Fryar	
29	Terry Allen,	10.00
	David Palmer,	
	Qadry Ismail,	
	Jake Reed	
30	Marion Butts,	10.00
	Vincent Brisby,	
	Dave Meggett,	
	Willie McGinest	
31	Willie Roaf,	10.00
	Mario Bates,	
	Quinn Early,	
	Michael Haynes	
32	Herschel Walker,	10.00
	Mike Sherrard,	
	Derek Brown,	
	Thomas Lewis	
33	Stevie Anderson,	10.00
	Aaron Glenn,	
	Johnny Johnson,	
	Ron Moore	
34	Calvin Williams,	10.00
	Fred Barnett,	
	Vaughn Hebron,	
	Charlie Garner	
35	Neil O'Donnell,	16.00
	Charles Johnson,	
	Rod Woodson,	
	Erric Pegram	
36	Ronnie Harmon,	10.00
	Shawn Jefferson,	
	Tony Martin,	
	Mark Seay	
37	Brent Jones,	10.00
	Dana Stubblefield,	
	Bryant Young,	
	Ken Norton	
38	Chris Warren,	10.00
	Cortez Kennedy,	
	Sam Adams,	
	Brian Blades	
39	Tommy Maddox,	50.00
	Chris Miller,	
	Johnny Bailey,	
	Isaac Bruce	
40	Lawrence Dawsey,	10.00
	Alvin Harper,	
	Jackie Harris,	
	Horace Copeland	
41	Gus Frerotte,	25.00
	Brian Mitchell,	
	Reggie Brooks,	
	Tydus Winans	
42	Steve McNair,	100.00
	Kerry Collins,	
	Todd Collins,	
	Chad May	
43	Ki-Jana Carter,	40.00
	Tyrone Wheatley,	
	Napoleon Kaufman,	
	Rashaan Salaam	
44	Terrell Fletcher,	16.00
	Sherman Williams,	
	Ray Zellars,	
	James Stewart	
45	Michael Westbrook,	40.00
	Joseph Galloway,	
	J.J. Stokes,	
	Frank Sanders	
46	Kevin Carter,	16.00
	Tony Boselli,	
	Warren Sapp,	
	Kyle Brady	
47	Greg Truitt,	10.00
	Dan Wilkinson,	
	Eric Turner,	
	Antonio Langham	
48	Carnell Lake,	10.00
	Neil Smith,	
	Rod Smith,	
	Kevin Greene	
49	O.J. McDuffie,	10.00
	Darren Carrington,	
	Michael Timpson,	
	Raymont Harris	
50	Rodney Hampton,	10.00
	Dave Krieg,	
	Barry Foster,	
	Kevin Greene	

1995 Playoff Prime Fantasy Team

These inserts, available in 1995 Playoff Prime retail packs, were seeded at a ratio of one per 25 packs. Each clear plastic card features a star player against an exciting multi-color holographic foil background. If the card is moved to change the angle of the light, the phrase "Playoff Fantasy Team" flashes in three different dimensions.

		MT
Complete Set (20):		220.00
Common Player:		3.00
Minor Stars:		6.00
1	Jerome Bettis	6.00
2	Shannon Sharpe	3.00
3	Fuad Reveiz	3.00
4	John Carney	3.00
5	Steve Young	20.00
6	Brett Favre	40.00
7	Tim Brown	6.00
8	Ben Coates	3.00
9	Marshall Faulk	15.00
10	Stan Humphries	3.00
11	Dan Marino	40.00
12	Jerry Rice	25.00
13	Errict Rhett	12.00
14	Chris Warren	6.00
15	Barry Sanders	25.00
16	Cris Carter	6.00
17	Michael Irvin	6.00
18	Emmitt Smith	40.00
19	Terance Mathis	3.00
20	Herman Moore	6.00

1995 Playoff Prime Minis

These 1995 Playoff Prime Mini insert cards were seeded one per every seven retail packs. The cards are a miniature version of the 200-card base set; each measures 2-1/4" x 3-1/8" and isolates the corresponding base set player photo against a holographic foil background. Blue foil is used for the player's name along the right side of the card, and the set icon, printed in the lower left corner. The card back has a clo-

seup shot of the player toward the top, along with the card number. Below the photo is a brief player profile.

		MT
Complete Set (200):		700.00
Common Player:		2.00
Minor Stars:		4.00
1	John Elway	14.00
2	Reggie White	4.00
3	Errict Rhett	20.00
4	Deion Sanders	18.00
5	Raghib Ismail	2.00
6	Jerome Bettis	6.00
7	Randall Cunningham	4.00
8	Mario Bates	8.00
9	Dave Brown	2.00
10	Stan Humphries	4.00
11	Drew Bledsoe	30.00
12	Neil O'Donnell	2.00
13	Dan Marino	50.00
14	Larry Centers	2.00
15	Craig Heyward	2.00
16	Bruce Smith	2.00
17	Erik Kramer	4.00
18	Jeff Blake	20.00
19	Vinny Testaverde	4.00
20	Barry Sanders	40.00
21	Boomer Esiason	2.00
22	Emmitt Smith	50.00
23	Warren Moon	4.00
24	Junior Seau	4.00
25	Heath Shuler	15.00
26	Jackie Harris	2.00
27	Terance Mathis	2.00
28	Raymont Harris	4.00
29	Jim Kelly	6.00
30	Dan Wilkinson	2.00
31	Herman Moore	12.00
32	Shannon Sharpe	4.00
33	Antonio Langham	2.00
34	Charles Haley	2.00
35	Brett Favre	50.00
36	Marshall Faulk	30.00
37	Neil Smith	2.00
38	Harvey Williams	2.00
39	Johnny Bailey	2.00
40	O.J. McDuffie	2.00
41	David Palmer	2.00
42	Willie McGinest	2.00
43	Quinn Early	2.00
44	Johnny Johnson	2.00
45	Derek Brown	2.00
46	Charlie Garner	2.00
47	Bam Morris	10.00
48	Natrone Means	10.00
49	Ken Norton	2.00
50	Troy Aikman	30.00
51	Reggie Brooks	2.00
52	Trent Dilfer	14.00
53	Cortez Kennedy	2.00
54	Chuck Levy	2.00
55	Jeff George	6.00
56	Steve Young	30.00
57	Lewis Tillman	2.00
58	Carl Pickens	6.00
59	Brett Perriman	4.00
60	Jay Novacek	2.00
61	Greg Hill	8.00
62	James Jett	2.00
63	Terry Kirby	2.00
64	Qadry Ismail	2.00
65	Ben Coates	2.00
66	Kevin Greene	2.00
67	Bryant Young	2.00
68	Brian Mitchell	2.00
69	Steve Walsh	2.00
70	Darnay Scott	14.00
71	Daryl Johnston	2.00
72	Glyn Milburn	2.00
73	Tim Brown	4.00
74	Isaac Bruce	25.00
75	Bernie Parmalee	2.00
76	Terry Allen	2.00
77	Jim Everett	2.00
78	Thomas Lewis	2.00
79	Vaughn Hebron	2.00
80	Rod Woodson	4.00
81	Rick Mirer	10.00
82	Dana Stubblefield	4.00
83	Bert Emanuel	4.00
84	Andre Reed	4.00
85	Jeff Graham	2.00
86	Johnnie Morton	2.00
87	LeShon Johnson	2.00
88	Michael Irvin	12.00
89	Derrick Alexander	2.00
90	Lake Dawson	8.00
91	Cody Carlson	2.00
92	Chris Warren	6.00
93	William Floyd	12.00
94	Charles Johnson	6.00
95	Roosevelt Potts	2.00
96	Cris Carter	4.00
97	Aaron Glenn	2.00
98	Curtis Conway	4.00
99	Kevin Williams	4.00
100	Jerry Rice	30.00
101	Frank Reich	2.00
102	Harold Green	2.00
103	Russell Copeland	2.00
104	Rob Moore	2.00
105	Edgar Bennett	2.00
106	Darren Carrington	2.00
107	Tommy Maddox	2.00
108	Dave Meggett	2.00
109	Fred Barnett	2.00
110	Mark Seay	2.00
111	Gus Frerotte	12.00
112	Brent Jones	2.00
113	Chris Miller	2.00
114	Cedric Tillman	2.00
115	Mark Ingram	2.00
116	Eric Turner	2.00
117	Mark Carrier	2.00
118	Garrison Hearst	6.00
119	Craig Erickson	2.00
120	Derek Russell	2.00
121	Mike Sherrard	2.00
122	Horace Copeland	2.00
123	Jack Trudeau	2.00
124	Leroy Hoard	2.00
125	Gary Brown	2.00
126	Mel Gray	2.00
127	Steve Beuerlein	2.00
128	Marcus Allen	6.00
129	Irving Fryar	2.00
130	Marion Butts	2.00
131	Ricky Watters	6.00
132	Tony Martin	2.00
133	Lawrence Dawsey	2.00
134	Ronnie Harmon	2.00
135	Herschel Walker	2.00
136	Michael Haynes	2.00
137	Eric Green	2.00
138	Steve Bono	6.00
139	Jamir Miller	2.00
140	Rod Smith	2.00
141	Andre Rison	4.00
142	Eric Metcalf	2.00
143	Michael Timpson	2.00
144	Cornelius Bennett	2.00
145	Sean Dawkins	4.00
146	Scott Mitchell	4.00
147	Ray Childress	2.00
148	Jim Harbaugh	4.00
149	Reggie Cobb	2.00
150	Willie Roaf	2.00
151	Stevie Anderson	2.00
152	Barry Foster	2.00
153	Joe Montana	30.00
154	David Klingler	2.00
155	Chris Chandler	2.00
156	Carnell Lake	2.00
157	Calvin Williams	2.00
158	Kenneth Davis	2.00
159	Tydus Winans	2.00
160	Sam Adams	2.00
161	Ron Moore	2.00
162	Vincent Brisby	2.00
163	Alvin Harper	4.00
164	Jake Reed	2.00
165	Jeff Hostetler	4.00
166	Mark Brunell	20.00
167	Leonard Russell	2.00
168	Greg Truitt	2.00
169	Pete Metzelaars	2.00
170	Dave Krieg	2.00
171	Lorenzo White	2.00
172	Robert Brooks	4.00
173	Willie Davis	2.00
174	Irving Spikes	2.00
175	Rodney Hampton	2.00
176	Erric Pegram	2.00
177	Brian Blades	2.00
178	Shawn Jefferson	2.00
179	Tyrone Poole	2.00
180	Rob Johnson	6.00
181	Ki-Jana Carter	4.00
182	Steve McNair	25.00
183	Michael Westbrook	30.00
184	Kerry Collins	30.00
185	Kevin Carter	6.00
186	Tony Boselli	6.00
187	Joseph Galloway	25.00
188	Kyle Brady	6.00
189	J.J. Stokes	10.00
190	Warren Sapp	6.00
191	Tyrone Wheatley	7.00
192	Napoleon Kaufman	12.00
193	James Stewart	10.00
194	Rashaan Salaam	10.00
195	Ray Zellars	6.00
196	Todd Collins	6.00
197	Sherman Williams	6.00
198	Frank Sanders	10.00
199	Terrell Fletcher	6.00
200	Chad May	6.00

1995 Playoff Prime Pigskin Previews

These retail-only 1995 Playoff Prime inserts feature six AFC stars. Cards were randomly included one per 145 packs. The front has a color photo superimposed over a leather football. Gold foil stamping is used for the player's name and insert set logo. The card back has a color photo of the player against his team's city skyline. A brief recap of the player's 1994 accomplishments is given at the top of the card; his 1994 and career stats are listed in a panel at the bottom.

	MT
Complete Set (6):	350.00
Common Player:	20.00
7 Dan Marino	125.00
8 Marshall Faulk	40.00
9 Natrone Means	30.00
10 Tim Brown	20.00
11 Drew Bledsoe	70.00
12 Marcus Allen	20.00

1995 Playoff Night of the Stars

Playoff produced this six-card set to hand out to those attending the 1995 National Sports Collectors Convention Trade Show in St. Louis. The set was also available at the Playoff booth during the National by exchanging 10 wrappers for one of the six cards. The borderless fronts featured the "Night of the Stars," the player's name, Playoff logo and team helmet at the bottom. The backs include the player's name and an endorsement for the 1995 National.

	MT
Complete Set (6):	20.00
Common Player:	2.00
1 Jerome Bettis	4.00
2 Ben Coates	2.00
3 Deion Sanders	5.00
4 Ki-Jana Carter	3.00
5 Steve McNair	8.00
6 Errict Rhett	3.00

1995 Playoff Super Bowl Card Show

To commemorate the Super Bowl XXIX Card Show, Playoff produced this eight-card set. Overall, 3,000 of each card was issued. A color photo of the player is printed over a red, silver and gold-foil background. In the upper left is the player's name in silver foil. The card backs have the player's name, highlights and the Super Bowl XXIX logo. The card number is printed in the upper right of the card back, which sports a black background.

	MT
Complete Set (8):	25.00
Common Player:	2.00
1 Marshall Faulk	6.00
2 Heath Shuler	4.00
3 David Palmer	2.00
4 Errict Rhett	6.00
5 Charlie Garner	3.00
6 Irving Spikes	3.00
7 Shante Carver	2.00
8 Greg Hill	3.00

1995 Playoff Contenders

As with previous editions, Playoff's 1995 Contenders set emphasizes players whose teams are in contention for post-season play. The 150-card set includes a 30-card Rookies subset and three insert sets. The regular card uses a metallic process which gives the card a depth to it. The band at the top and the player's name use a team-related color, as does the back, which includes a closeup shot of the player and a brief recap of a game in which he had a key role. Insert sets include Hog Heaven Pigskins, Rookie Kickoff and Back-to-Backs, a 75-card parallel set which includes two players per card.

	MT
Complete Set (150):	35.00
Common Player:	.20
Minor Stars:	.40
Wax Box:	75.00
1 Steve Young	1.50
2 Jeff Blake	1.00
3 Rick Mirer	.40
4 Brett Favre	4.00
5 Heath Shuler	1.00
6 Steve Bono	.40
7 John Elway	.50
8 Troy Aikman	2.00
9 Rodney Peete	.20
10 Gus Frerotte	.50
11 Drew Bledsoe	1.50
12 Jim Kelly	.40
13 Dan Marino	4.00
14 Errict Rhett	1.00
15 Jeff Hostetler	.20
16 Erik Kramer	.20
17 Jim Everett	.20
18 Elvis Grbac	.20
19 Scott Mitchell	.20
20 Barry Sanders	1.50
21 Deion Sanders	1.00
22 Emmitt Smith	4.00
23 Garrison Hearst	.40
24 Mario Bates	.40
25 Mark Brunell	1.00
26 Robert Smith	.20
27 Rodney Hampton	.20
28 Marshall Faulk	.40
29 Greg Hill	.40
30 Bernie Parmalee	.20
31 Natrone Means	.40
32 Marcus Allen	.40
33 Bam Morris	.40
34 Edgar Bennett	.20
35 Vincent Brisby	.20
36 Jerome Bettis	.40
37 Craig Heyward	.20
38 Anthony Miller	.20
39 Curtis Conway	.20
40 William Floyd	.40
41 Chris Warren	.40
42 Terry Kirby	.20
43 Herschel Walker	.40
44 Eric Metcalf	.20
45 Darnay Scott	.40
46 Jackie Harris	.20
47 Dana Stubblefield	.20
48 Daryl Johnston	.20
49 Dave Meggett	.20
50 Ricky Watters	.40
51 Ken Norton	.20
52 Boomer Esiason	.20
53 Lake Dawson	.40
54 Eric Green	.20
55 Junior Seau	.40
56 Yancey Thigpen	1.00
57 James Jett	.20
58 Leonard Russell	.20
59 Brent Jones	.20
60 Trent Dilfer	.40
61 Terance Mathis	.20
62 Jeff George	.20
63 Alvin Harper	.20
64 Terry Allen	.20
65 Stan Humphries	.20
66 Robert Green	.20
67 Bryce Paup	.40
68 Tamarick Vanover	.75
69 Desmond Howard	.20
70 Derek Loville	.20
71 Dave Brown	.20
72 Carl Pickens	.40
73 Gary Clark	.20
74 Gary Brown	.20
75 Brett Perriman	.20
76 Charlie Garner	.20
77 Ben Coates	.20
78 Bruce Smith	.20
79 Erric Pegram	.20
80 Jerry Rice	1.50
81 Tim Brown	.20
82 John Taylor	.20
83 Will Moore	.20
84 Jay Novacek	.20
85 Kevin Williams	.20
86 Raghib Ismail	.20
87 Robert Brooks	.40
88 Michael Irvin	.40
89 Mark Chmura	.75
90 Shannon Sharpe	.20
91 Henry Ellard	.20
92 Reggie White	.40
93 Isaac Bruce	.50
94 Charles Haley	.20
95 Jake Reed	.20
96 Pete Metzelaars	.20
97 Dave Krieg	.20
98 Tony Martin	.20
99 Charles Jordan	.20
100 Bert Emanuel	.50
101 Andre Rison	.20
102 Jeff Graham	.20
103 O.J. McDuffie	.20
104 Randall Cunningham	.20
105 Harvey Williams	.20
106 Cris Carter	.20
107 Irving Fryar	.20
108 Jim Harbaugh	.20
109 Bernie Kosar	.20
110 Charles Johnson	.40
111 Warren Moon	.40
112 Neil O'Donnell	.40
113 Fred Barnett	.20
114 Herman Moore	.75
115 Chris Miller	.20
116 Vinny Testaverde	.20
117 Craig Erickson	.20
118 Qadry Ismail	.20
119 Willie Davis	.20
120 Michael Jackson	.20
121 Stoney Case	.40
122 Frank Sanders	.50
123 Todd Collins	.40
124 Kerry Collins	2.00
125 Sherman Williams	.40
126 Terrell Davis	12.00
127 Luther Elliss	.40
128 Steve McNair	4.00
129 Chris Sanders	1.00
130 Ki-Jana Carter	1.00
131 Rodney Thomas	.50
132 Tony Boselli	.40
133 Rob Johnson	3.00
134 James Stewart	1.50
135 Chad May	.40
136 Eric Bjorson	.40
137 Tyrone Wheatley	.50
138 Kyle Brady	.40
139 Curtis Martin	4.00
140 Eric Zeier	.50
141 Ray Zellars	.40
142 Napoleon Kaufman	3.00
143 Mike Mamula	.40
144 Mark Bruener	.40
145 Kordell Stewart	.40
146 J.J. Stokes	1.00
147 Joey Galloway	2.50
148 Warren Sapp	.40
149 Michael Westbrook	1.00
150 Rashaan Salaam	1.00

1995 Playoff Contenders Back-to-Back

This 1995 Playoff Contenders insert set is a 75-card parallel set which features two players per card, one on each side. The cards use foil stamping for the player's name and set logo, which appear at the bottom and top, respectively. The cards have a glossier finish than their regular counterparts. These inserts are seeded one per 19 packs.

	MT
Complete Set (75):	1000.
Common Player:	5.00
Minor Stars:	10.00
Inserted 1:19	
1 Troy Aikman, Dan Marino	50.00
2 Emmitt Smith, Marshall Faulk	40.00
3 Brett Favre, John Elway	60.00
4 Steve Young, Drew Bledsoe	25.00
5 Barry Sanders, Errict Rhett	50.00
6 Deion Sanders, Jerry Rice	25.00
7 Jeff Blake, Rick Mirer	5.00
8 Michael Irvin, Tim Brown	10.00
9 Chris Warren, Ricky Watters	5.00
10 Herman Moore, Vincent Brisby	10.00
11 James Jett, Eric Metcalf	5.00
12 Henry Ellard, Terance Mathis	5.00
13 Curtis Conway, Isaac Bruce	10.00
14 Steve Bono, Jeff Hostetler	5.00
15 Greg Hill, Harvey Williams	5.00
16 Garrison Hearst, Jerome Bettis	10.00
17 Jay Novacek, Brent Jones	5.00
18 Reggie White, Bruce Smith	10.00
19 Eric Green, Shannon Sharpe	10.00
20 Gus Frerotte, Jeff George	10.00
21 Erik Kramer, Brian Mitchell	5.00
22 Warren Moon, Jim Kelly	10.00
23 Mark Chmura, Ben Coates	5.00
24 Trent Dilfer, Heath Shuler	10.00
25 Craig Heyward, Edgar Bennett	5.00
26 Jim Everett, Dave Brown	5.00
27 Bert Emanuel, Andre Rison	5.00
28 Robert Brooks, Alvin Harper	5.00
29 Desmond Howard, Tony Martin	5.00
30 Rodney Peete, Fred Barnett	5.00
31 Natrone Means, William Floyd	10.00
32 Brett Perriman, Raghib Ismail	5.00
33 Cris Carter, Irving Fryar	10.00
34 Tamarick Vanover, Darnay Scott	5.00
35 Charles Haley, Dana Stubblefield	5.00
36 Bryce Paup, Ken Norton	5.00
37 Marcus Allen, Herschel Walker	10.00
38 Leonard Russell, Terry Allen	5.00
39 Junior Seau, Derrick Loville	5.00
40 Lake Dawson, Charles Johnson	5.00
41 Kevin Williams, Charles Jordan	5.00
42 Jeff Graham, Carl Pickens	5.00
43 Anthony Miller, O.J. McDuffie	5.00
44 Elvis Grbac, Jim Harbaugh	5.00
45 Dave Meggett, Terry Kirby	5.00
46 Dave Krieg, Stan Humphries	5.00
47 Mark Brunell, Boomer Esiason	20.00
48 Craig Erickson, Vinny Testaverde	5.00
49 Randall Cunningham, Bernie Kosar	10.00
50 Erric Pegram, Charlie Garner	5.00
51 Will Moore, Gary Clark	5.00
52 Qadry Ismail, Willie Davis	5.00
53 Neil O'Donnell, Chris Miller	5.00
54 Mario Bates, Robert Smith	5.00
55 Rodney Hampton, Bernie Parmalee	5.00
56 Bam Morris, Daryl Johnston	5.00
57 Jackie Harris, Jake Reed	5.00
58 John Taylor, Pete Metzelaars	5.00
59 Yancey Thigpen, Michael Jackson	5.00
60 Gary Brown, Robert Green	5.00
61 Rashaan Salaam, Napoleon Kaufman	15.00
62 Mark Bruener, Kyle Brady	5.00
63 Ki-Jana Carter, Rodney Thomas	5.00
64 Chad May, Steve McNair	15.00
65 Frank Sanders, J.J. Stokes	10.00
66 Mike Mamula, Warren Sapp	5.00
67 Stoney Case, Kordell Stewart	30.00
68 Terrell Davis, Curtis Martin	50.00
69 Sherman Williams, Chris Sanders	5.00
70 James Stewart, Eric Bjornson	5.00
71 Tyrone Wheatley, Ray Zellars	5.00
72 Tony Boselli, Luther Elliss	5.00
73 Rob Johnson, Todd Collins	15.00
74 Kerry Collins, Eric Zeier	10.00
75 Joey Galloway, Michael Westbrook	15.00

1995 Playoff Contenders Hog Heaven

Hog Heaven Pigskins cards were randomly inserted one per 48 packs of 1995 Playoff Contenders football packs. The thick cards, which showcase 30 players, feature a photo among cloud formations, next to a leather football. The set logo is in the upper left corner; the player's name is in gold foil in the lower right hand corner of the horizontally-designed card. The card back is all leather and features a caricature of the player, plus his name, position and team name. The card number uses an "HH" prefix.

	MT
Complete Set (30):	425.00
Common Player:	5.00
Minor Stars:	10.00
Inserted 1:48	
1 Troy Aikman	30.00
2 Marcus Allen	10.00
3 Jeff Blake	10.00
4 Drew Bledsoe	30.00
5 Steve Bono	5.00
6 Isaac Bruce	10.00
7 Trent Dilfer	10.00
8 John Elway	45.00
9 Marshall Faulk	15.00
10 Brett Favre	60.00
11 Gus Frerotte	5.00
12 Irving Fryar	5.00
13 Jeff George	10.00
14 Rodney Hampton	5.00
15 Garrison Hearst	10.00
16 Michael Irvin	10.00
17 Erik Kramer	5.00
18 Dan Marino	45.00
19 Natrone Means	10.00
20 Errict Rhett	5.00
21 Jerry Rice	30.00
22 Barry Sanders	60.00
23 Deion Sanders	15.00
24 Shannon Sharpe	5.00
25 Emmitt Smith	45.00
26 Robert Smith	10.00
27 Chris Warren	5.00
28 Reggie White	10.00
29 Harvey Williams	5.00
30 Steve Young	25.00

1995 Playoff Contenders Rookie Kick Off

These 1995 Playoff Absolute inserts were seeded one per 24 packs. Thirty rookies appear on a plastic die-cut card shaped like a football waiting to be kicked off. The player's name and set logo are in gold foil at the bottom. The card back is blank.

	MT
Complete Set (30):	400.00
Common Player:	3.00
1 Eric Bjornson	7.00
2 Tony Boselli	7.00
3 Kyle Brady	7.00
4 Mark Bruener	6.00
5 Ki-Jana Carter	6.00
6 Stoney Case	6.00
7 Kerry Collins	12.00
8 Todd Collins	6.00
9 Terrell Davis	75.00
10 Luther Elliss	7.00
11 Joey Galloway	15.00
12 Rob Johnson	7.00
13 Napoleon Kaufman	25.00
14 Mike Mamula	7.00
15 Curtis Martin	50.00
16 Chad May	7.00
17 Steve McNair	35.00
18 Rashaan Salaam	10.00
19 Chris Sanders	10.00
20 Frank Sanders	10.00
21 Warren Sapp	7.00
22 James Stewart	7.00
23 Kordell Stewart	50.00
24 J.J. Stokes	10.00
25 Rodney Thomas	3.00
26 Michael Westbrook	10.00
27 Tyrone Wheatley	7.00
28 Sherman Williams	7.00
29 Eric Zeier	7.00
30 Ray Zellars	7.00

1996 Playoff National Promos

Handed out at the 1996 National Sports Collectors Convention in Anaheim, this seven-card set was available through a wrapper redemption program at the show. Three wrappers from a Playoff product could be exchanged for one card. A foil box of wrappers was good for the complete set. The card fronts featured a photo of the player over a background of a California scene. The "17th National Sports Collectors Convention" is printed along one side of the acetate card. The card backs are the reverse of the fronts, with the player's bio written in the shadow of the player. The cards are numbered "x/7." Kordell Stewart's card was only available through the foil box complete set redemption offer.

	MT
Complete Set (7):	35.00
Common Player:	3.00
1 Kordell Stewart	8.00
2 Curtis Martin	10.00
3 Tyrone Wheatley	3.00
4 Joey Galloway	5.00
5 Steve McNair	6.00
6 Kerry Collins	8.00
7 Napoleon Kaufman	4.00

1996 Playoff Super Bowl Card Show

As a redemption offer at the Super Bowl XXX Card Show, Playoff issued this six-card set. Player photos are showcased over Arizona desert scenery. The player's name is printed along one side of the card, with the Playoff logo in one of the lower corners. The Super Bowl Card Show logo is located in one of the upper corners. The card back features the Super

Bowl Card Show logo at the top, with the player's highlights printed in a box at the bottom. The cards are numbered "X/6." A collector could exchange a Playoff wrapper for a different card each day of the show, which was held in Tempe, Ariz. A collector could receive the entire set in exchange for 10 wrappers. The cards have a 1995 copyright date on the card back.

	MT
Complete Set (6):	17.00
Common Player:	2.00
1 Deion Sanders	4.00
2 Rashaan Salaam	3.00
3 Garrison Hearst	2.00
4 Robert Brooks	2.00
5 Barry Sanders	5.00
6 Errict Rhett	3.00

1996 Playoff Absolute Promos

This six-card promo set gave collectors and dealers a sneak peak at the designs for 1996 Playoff Absolute. The same six players are featured in Prime Promos, but the photos and logos are different.

	MT
Complete Set (6):	20.00
Common Player:	1.50
Terrell Davis	7.00
Tamarick Vanover	3.00
Rashaan Salaam	3.00
J.J. Stokes	3.00
Antonio Freeman	3.00
Zack Crockett	1.50

1996 Playoff Absolute

Playoff's 1996 Absolute football cards feature a full-color player action photo on the front, set against a colorful snapshot of the player's stadium with a game in progress. Each card back has a head-and-shoulder shot of the player, complete career and 1995 NFL statistics and an intriguing or unusual fact about the player. A 20-card subset of the top 1996 draft choices is included within the main set. Four insert sets were also produced: Metal X (also in Prime), Xtreme Team, Quad Series and Unsung Heroes (also in Prime). In an innovative pack-within-a-pack concept, three types of color-coded packs are available within 1996 Playoff Absolute boxes. Each box of 1996 Playoff Absolute contains 24 Red packs, each containing five cards, and either a White or Blue inner pack. Each Red pack contains five

base cards from the #1-100 low level series, plus one White or Blue inner pack, and a potential random insert card. Each White inner pack contains one base card from the #101-150 mid level series, or a random insert card. Each box includes approximately 18 White inner packs. Each Blue inner pack has one base card from the #150-200 high level series, or a random insert card. Each box includes approximately six Blue inner packs.

	MT
Complete Set (200):	150.00
Complete Red Set (100):	15.00
Complete White Set (50):	45.00
Complete Blue Set (50):	90.00
Common Red (1-100):	.10
Common White (101-150):	.40
Common Blue (151-200):	1.00
Wax Box:	70.00
1 Jim Kelly	.20
2 Michael Irvin	.20
3 Jim Harbaugh	.10
4 Warren Moon	.20
5 Rick Mirer	.10
6 Drew Bledsoe	1.25
7 Steve Young	1.50
8 Junior Seau	.20
9 Sherman Williams	.10
10 Jay Novacek	.10
11 Bill Brooks	.10
12 Steve Bono	.20
13 Leroy Hoard	.10
14 Willie Jackson	.10
15 Irving Fryer	.10
16 Tony McGee	.10
17 Neil O'Donnell	.20
18 Fred Barnett	.10
19 Eric Pegram	.10
20 Derrick Moore	.10
21 Johnnie Morton	.10
22 James Jett	.10
23 Tim Brown	.20
24 Kevin Miniefield	.10
25 Jim McMahon	.10
26 Brian Blades	.10
27 Henry Ellard	.10
28 Calvin Williams	.10
29 Chris Chandler	.10
30 Rod Woodson	.10
31 Ronnie Harmon	.10
32 Brent Jones	.10
33 Qadry Ismail	.10
34 Steve Tasker	.10
35 Eric Green	.10
36 Brian Mitchell	.10
37 Herschel Walker	.10
38 Sean Dawkins	.10
39 Bryce Paup	.10
40 Dorsey Levens	.25
41 Andre Rison	.10
42 Lamont Warren	.10
43 Earnest Byner	.10
44 *Bobby Engram*	1.00
45 *Simeon Rice*	.25
46 Michael Jackson	.10
47 *Marvin Harrison*	3.00
48 Thurman Thomas	.20
49 Charles Haley	.10
50 Rob Moore	.10
51 Bryan Cox	.10
52 Horace Copeland	.10
53 Rodney Peete	.10
54 Jeff Graham	.10
55 Charles Johnson	.10
56 Natrone Means	.20
57 Terrell Fletcher	.10
58 Eric Bieniemy	.10
59 Karim Abdul-Jabbar	1.00
60 Quinn Early	.10
61 Mark Bruener	.10
62 Shawn Jefferson	.10
63 Vinny Testaverde	.10
64 *Derrick Mayes*	1.25
65 Mario Bates	.10
66 J.J. Birden	.10
67 *Eddie Kennison*	.75
68 Steve Walsh	.10
69 Mark Chmura	.30
70 Mike Sherrard	.10
71 Boomer Esiason	.10
72 *Alex Van Dyke*	.75
73 Jake Reed	.10
74 Jackie Harris	.10
75 Mark Rypien	.10
76 Chris Calloway	.10
77 *Amani Toomer*	.50
78 Terrell Davis	8.00
79 Raghib Ismail	.10
80 Derek Loville	.10
81 Ben Coates	.10
82 Kyle Brady	.10
83 Willie Green	.10
84 Randall Cunningham	
85 Amp Lee	.10
86 Bert Emanuel	.10
87 *Jason Dunn*	.25
88 Michael Haynes	.10
89 Robert Green	.10
90 Willie Davis	.10
91 O.J. McDuffie	.10
92 Harold Green	.10
93 Ken Dilger	.10
94 Brett Perriman	.10
95 Eric Zeier	.10
96 Jerome Bettis	.10
97 *Rickey Dudley*	.75
98 Darnay Scott	.10
99 Mark Brunell	1.00
100 Christian Fauria	.10
101 Jeff Blake	.75
102 Troy Aikman	5.00
103 John Elway	3.00
104 Barry Sanders	7.00
105 Curtis Conway	.75
106 Wayne Chrebet	.40
107 Lake Dawson	.40
108 Jerry Rice	5.00
109 Kevin Williams	.40
110 Zack Crockett	.40
111 Vincent Brisby	.40
112 Rodney Thomas	.75
113 Rodney Hampton	.40
114 Adrian Murrell	.40
115 Bruce Smith	.40
116 Napoleon Kaufman	.75
117 Bam Morris	.40
118 Anthony Miller	.40
119 *Aaron Hayden*	1.00
120 Joey Galloway	4.00
121 Trent Dilfer	.75
122 Stoney Case	.40
123 Tamarick Vanover	.75
124 Eric Metcalf	.40
125 Marcus Allen	.40
126 James Stewart	.40
127 Charlie Garner	.40
128 Yancey Thigpen	1.25
129 William Floyd	.40
130 Terry Allen	.40
131 Robert Smith	.40
132 Todd Kinchen	.40
133 Gus Frerotte	.40
134 Frank Sanders	.75
135 Scott Mitchell	.40
136 Greg Hill	.40
137 Edgar Bennett	.40
138 Alvin Harper	.40
139 Reggie White	.40
140 Craig Heyward	.40
141 Todd Collins	.40
142 Ernie Mills	.40
143 *Keyshawn Johnson*	6.00
144 Mark Carrier	.40
145 Robert Brooks	.40
146 Bernie Parmalee	.40
147 Carl Pickens	.75
148 *Kevin Hardy*	.75
149 *Jonathan Ogden*	.75
150 *Lawrence Phillips*	2.50
151 Emmitt Smith	25.00
152 Brett Favre	25.00
153 Dan Marino	25.00
154 Jim Everett	1.00
155 Dave Brown	1.00
156 Jeff Hostetler	1.00
157 Heath Shuler	1.00
158 Daryl Johnston	1.00
159 Terance Mathis	1.00
160 Curtis Martin	16.00
161 Ray Zellars	1.00
162 Ricky Watters	1.00
163 Chris Warren	1.00
164 Larry Centers	1.00
165 Steve McNair	10.00
166 Terry Kirby	1.00
167 Rob Johnson	1.00
168 Dave Meggett	1.00
169 Antonio Freeman	1.00
170 Marshall Faulk	5.00
171 Andre Hastings	1.00
172 Stan Humphries	1.00
173 Errict Rhett	1.00
174 Michael Westbrook	1.50
175 Deion Sanders	7.00
176 Jeff George	2.00
177 Cris Carter	1.50
178 Chris Sanders	1.50
179 Ki-Jana Carter	1.50
180 Kordell Stewart	12.00
181 Isaac Bruce	2.00
182 *Terry Glenn*	6.00
183 Garrison Hearst	1.00
184 Erik Kramer	1.00
185 *Leeland McElroy*	2.00
186 Rashaan Salaam	2.00
187 Kimble Anders	1.00
188 Chad May	1.00
189 Tony Martin	1.00
190 J.J. Stokes	7.00
191 Darick Holmes	1.00
192 *Eric Moulds*	10.00
193 Shannon Sharpe	1.00
194 *Tim Biakabutuka*	5.00
195 *Eddie George*	15.00
196 *Mike Alstott*	7.00
197 Kerry Collins	3.00
198 Harvey Williams	1.00
199 Herman Moore	2.00
200 Tyrone Wheatley	1.00

1996 Playoff Absolute/Prime Metal XL

These cards were available in both 1996 Playoff Absolute (#s 1-18) and 1996 Playoff Prime (#s 19-36). The cards introduce the first-ever concept of a collector coin and card in one. A metal coin commemorating each player's team is imbedded in each card. Cards were available only in Blue inner packs, one in 96 packs.

	MT
Complete Set (36):	800.00
Comp. Absolute Set (18):	500.00
Comp. Prime Set (18):	300.00
Common Player:	10.00
1 Troy Aikman	40.00
2 Emmitt Smith	80.00
3 Barry Sanders	40.00
4 Brett Favre	80.00
5 Dan Marino	80.00
6 Jerry Rice	40.00
7 Marshall Faulk	25.00
8 Curtis Martin	60.00
9 Rashaan Salaam	20.00
10 Harvey Williams	10.00
11 Ricky Watters	10.00
12 Yancey Thigpen	10.00
13 Chris Warren	10.00
14 Errict Rhett	20.00
15 Terry Allen	10.00
16 Robert Brooks	10.00
17 Anthony Miller	10.00
18 Erik Kramer	10.00
19 Michael Irvin	10.00
20 John Elway	35.00
21 Jim Harbaugh	10.00
22 Steve Young	35.00
23 Deion Sanders	35.00
24 Terrell Davis	50.00
25 Reggie White	10.00
26 Herman Moore	20.00
27 Rodney Hampton	10.00
28 Cris Carter	10.00
29 Isaac Bruce	25.00
30 Kordell Stewart	40.00
31 Brett Perriman	10.00
32 Joey Galloway	35.00
33 Drew Bledsoe	40.00
34 J.J. Stokes	15.00
35 Napoleon Kaufman	10.00
36 Tim Brown	10.00

1996 Playoff Absolute Quad Series

These 35 insert cards were avaiable only in Playoff's 1996 Absolute Red packs, one in 24. Each card features four players on it. There were also five rookies-only Quad cards produced. The background is foiled, with a silver-stamped insert set logo with the player's team name around it. The player's names are stamped in copper foil on each side of the card. Copper is also used for a card number, which appears on one side only.

	MT
Complete Set (35):	700.00
Common Player:	7.50
Minor Stars:	15.00
1 Stoney Case, Garrison Hearst, Rob Moore, Frank Sanders	7.50
2 J.J. Birden, Bert Emanuel, Jeff George, Craig Heyward	7.50
3 Todd Collins, Bill Brooks, Jim Kelly, Bryce Paup	7.50
4 Mark Carrier, Kerry Collins, Willie Green, Derrick Moore	50.00
5 Curtis Conway, Robert Green, Erik Kramer, Kevin Miniefield	7.50
6 Eric Bieniemy, Jeff Blake, Harold Green, Tony McGee	7.50
7 Earnest Byner, Michael Jackson, Andre Rison, Eric Zeier	7.50
8 Michael Irvin, Jay Novacek, Deion Sanders, Kevin Williams	30.00
9 Terrell Davis, John Elway, Anthony Miller, Shannon Sharpe	40.00
10 Scott Mitchell, Herman Moore, Johnnie Morton, Brett Perriman	15.00
11 Edgar Bennett, Mark Chmura, Antonio Freeman, Reggie White	15.00
12 Chris Chandler, Steve McNair, Chris Sanders, Rodney Thomas	30.00
13 Zack Crockett, Sean Dawkins, Ken Dilger, Jim Harbaugh	7.50
14 Mark Brunell, Willie Jackson, Rob Johnson, James Stewart	25.00
15 Marcus Allen, Kimble Anders, Lake Dawson, Tamarick Vanover	15.00
16 Eric Green, Terry Kirby, O.J. McDuffie, Bernie Parmalee	7.50
17 Cris Carter, Warren Moon, Robert Smith, Chad May	15.00
18 Drew Bledsoe, Vincent Brisby, Ben Coates, Dave Meggett	40.00
19 Mario Bates, Jim Everett, Michael Haynes, Ray Zellars	7.50
20 Dave Brown, Chris Calloway, Rodney Hampton, Tyrone Wheatley	15.00
21 Kyle Brady, Wayne Chrebet, Adrian Murrell, Neil O'Donnell	7.50
22 Tim Brown, Jeff Hostetler, Raghib Ismail, Napoleon Kaufman	15.00
23 Charlie Garner, Rodney Peete, Ricky Watters, Calvin Williams	7.50
24 Andre Hastings, Ernie Mills, Kordell Stewart, Rod Woodson	45.00
25 Terrell Fletcher, Ronnie Harmon, Aaron Hayden, Junior Seau	15.00
26 William Floyd, Derek Loville, J.J. Stokes, Steve Young	40.00
27 Brian Blades, Christian Fauria, Joey Galloway, Rick Mirer	35.00
28 Mark Rypien, Isaac Bruce, Todd Kinchen, Steve Walsh	20.00
29 Horace Copeland, Trent Dilfer, Alvin Harper, Jackie Harris	15.00
30 Henry Ellard, Gus Frerotte, Heath Shuler, Michael Westbrook	15.00
31 Keyshawn Johnson, Kevin Hardy, Simeon Rice, Jonathan Ogden	70.00
32 Lawrence Phillips, Tim Biakabutuka, Terry Glenn, Rickey Dudley	60.00
33 Eddie George, Marvin Harrison, Eric Moulds, Eddie Kennison	60.00
34 Derrick Mayes, Karim Abdul-Jabbar, Alex Van Dyke, Bobby Engram	50.00
35 Leeland McElroy, Jason Dunn, Mike Alstott, Amani Toomer	30.00

1996 Playoff Absolute/Prime Unsung Heroes

These cards were available in 1996 Playoff Absolute (#s 1-15, NFC players) and 1996 Playoff Prime (#s 16-30, AFC players). The cards, which utilize a brand-new Tekchrome design, honor players long on desire and grit, but short on headlines. The players were chosen by fans in nationwide voting and were honored at the 23rd Annual NFLPA Banquet in March 1996 to benefit the Washington D.C. chapter of the Special Olympics. The cards were only available in Red packs, one in 24 packs. Fronts have a color action photo, with the brand/insert set logos and player's name toward the bottom.

	MT
Complete Set (30):	30.00
Complete Absolute Set (15):	13.00
Complete Prime Set (15):	17.00
Common Player:	.50
Minor Stars:	1.00
1 Bill Bates	.50
2 Jeff Brady	.50
3 Ray Brown	.50
4 Isaac Bruce	4.00
5 Larry Centers	1.00
6 Mark Chmura	2.00
7 Keith Elias	.50
8 Robert Green	.50
9 Andy Harmon	.50
10 Rodney Holman	.50
11 Derek Loville	1.00
12 J.J. McCleskey	.50
13 Sam Mills	.50
14 Hardy Nickerson	.50
15 Jessie Tuggle	.50
16 Eric Bieniemy	.50
17 Blaine Bishop	.50
18 Mark Brunell	5.00
19 Wayne Chrebet	.50
20 Vince Evans	.50
21 Sam Gash	.50
22 Tim Grunhard	.50
23 Jim Harbaugh	2.00
24 Dwayne Harper	.50
25 Bernie Parmalee	.50
26 Reggie Rivers	.50
27 Eugene Robinson	.50
28 Kordell Stewart	8.00
29 Steve Tasker	.50
30 Bennie Thompson	.50

1996 Playoff Absolute Xtreme Team

Thirty of the game's most coveted players appear to jump out at you on these 1996 Playoff Absolute cards. Each card is clear plastic, foil-enhanced, and available only in White inner packs (one in 24 packs). Fronts have a color action photo on one side against a clear background that has the player's name (along the left side) and a team logo showing through. The player's name is stamped in gold foil along the left side. The right side has a color panel with a gold-foil stamped brand logo. Gold foil is also used for part of the X in the insert set logo. The card back (numbered XT01, etc.) has a reverse angle of the photo from the front, plus a brief recap of the player's accomplishments.

		MT
Complete Set (30):		300.00
Common Player:		5.00
Minor Stars:		10.00
1	Troy Aikman	20.00
2	Emmitt Smith	40.00
3	Jerry Rice	20.00
4	Dan Marino	40.00
5	Brett Favre	40.00
6	Barry Sanders	25.00
7	Michael Irvin	10.00
8	John Elway	15.00
9	Joey Galloway	15.00
10	Steve Young	15.00
11	Deion Sanders	15.00
12	Terrell Davis	25.00
13	Herman Moore	10.00
14	Reggie White	5.00
15	Cris Carter	5.00
16	Rodney Hampton	5.00
17	Isaac Bruce	10.00
18	Brett Perriman	5.00
19	Curtis Conway	5.00
20	Scott Mitchell	5.00
21	Rashaan Salaam	10.00
22	Robert Brooks	5.00
23	Marshall Faulk	12.00
24	Curtis Martin	30.00
25	Harvey Williams	5.00
26	Yancey Thigpen	5.00
27	Chris Warren	10.00
28	Errict Rhett	10.00
29	Terry Allen	5.00
30	Carl Pickens	10.00

1996 Playoff Prime Promos

This six-card promo set gave collectors and dealers a sneak peak at the designs for 1996 Playoff Prime. The same six players were featured in 1996 Absolute Promos, but the photos and logos are different.

	MT
Complete Set (6):	20.00
Common Player:	1.50
Terrell Davis	7.00
Tamarick Vanover	3.00
Rashaan Salaam	3.00
J.J. Stokes	3.00
Antonio Freeman	3.00
Zack Crockett	1.50

1996 Playoff Prime

Playoff's 1996 Prime set is its 200-card retail version. The checklist order and card design are different than Prime's Absolute hobby version. Four insert sets are available; Prime Boss Hog is exclusive to Prime retail packs, while Metal XL and Unsung Heroes are in hobby and retail packs, with the retail versions picking up the numbering where the hobby versions ended. 1996 Playoff Prime also continues the pack-within-a-pack concept explained in the 1996 Playoff Absolute set introduction in this book.

		MT
Complete Set (200):		200.00
Comp. Bronze Set (100):		10.00
Comp. Silver Set (50):		60.00
Comp. Gold Set (50):		130.00
Common Bronze:		.10
Common Silver:		.40
Common Gold:		1.00
Wax Box:		50.00
1	Brett Favre	4.00
2	Jerry Rice	1.50
3	Troy Aikman	1.50
4	Bruce Smith	.10
5	Marshall Faulk	1.25
6	Erik Kramer	.10
7	Carl Pickens	.20
8	Anthony Miller	.10
9	Cris Carter	.10
10	Todd Kinchen	.10
11	Stoney Case	.10
12	Chris Calloway	.10
13	Andre Rison	.10
14	Bill Brooks	.10
15	Shawn Jefferson	.10
16	Eric Zeier	.10
17	Yancey Thigpen	.30
18	Edgar Bennett	.10
19	Garrison Hearst	.20
20	Daryl Johnston	.10
21	Tyrone Wheatley	.10
22	Darick Holmes	.10
23	Dave Brown	.10
24	*Leeland McElroy*	.30
25	Craig Heyward	.10
26	*Kevin Hardy*	.30
27	Scott Mitchell	.10
28	Willie Green	.10
29	Vincent Brisby	.10
30	Mike Tomczak	.10
31	Luther Ellis	.10
32	Mike Pritchard	.10
33	Robert Green	.10
34	Jeff Graham	.10
35	Tamarick Vanover	.30
36	William Floyd	.10
37	Alvin Harper	.10
38	Stan Humphries	.10
39	Herman Moore	.40
40	Tony Martin	.10
41	Jonathan Ogden	.10
42	Randall Cunningham	.10
43	Chris Warren	.20
44	Bobby Hobert	.10
45	Jerome Bettis	.10
46	Joey Galloway	1.25
47	Ernie Mills	.10
48	Steve McNair	1.00
49	*Karim Abdul-Jabbar*	1.00
50	Chad May	.10
51	Jim Everett	.10
52	Robert Smith	.10
53	Tony Boselli	.10
54	William Henderson	.10
55	*Terry Glenn*	2.50
56	Neil O'Donnell	.10
57	Chris Chandler	.10
58	Michael Jackson	.10
59	*Jason Dunn*	.30
60	James Stewart	.10
61	Greg Hill	.10
62	Mark Carrier	.10
63	Bernie Parmalee	.10
64	Chris Sanders	.30
65	Jeff Hostetler	.10
66	*Eric Moulds*	4.00
67	James Jett	.10
68	Henry Ellard	.10
69	Mario Bates	.10
70	Natrone Means	.20
71	*Bobby Engram*	1.25
72	Christian Fauria	.10
73	Gus Frerotte	.10
74	Aaron Hayden	.30
75	Reggie White	.20
76	Dave Meggett	.10
77	Harvey Williams	.10
78	Terance Mathis	.10
79	Bam Morris	.10
80	Trent Dilfer	.10
81	Irving Fryar	.10
82	Quinn Early	.10
83	Lake Dawson	.10
84	Todd Collins	.10
85	Eric Metcalf	.10
86	*Tim Biakabutuka*	1.25
87	Rob Johnson	.10
88	Charlie Garner	.10
89	Mike Mamula	.10
90	Steve Walsh	.10
91	Charles Haley	.10
92	*Mike Alstott*	2.00
93	Wayne Chrebet	.10
94	Vinny Testaverde	.10
95	Fred Barnett	.10
96	Boomer Esiason	.10
97	Zack Crockett	.10
98	Kevin Williams	.10
99	Eric Bieniemy	.10
100	Bryan Cox	.10
101	Larry Centers	.40
102	Jeff George	.75
103	Bryce Paup	.40
104	Kerry Collins	1.00
105	Derrick Moore	.40
106	Adrian Murrell	.40
107	Harold Green	.40
108	Ki-Jana Carter	.75
109	Sherman Williams	.40
110	Deion Sanders	2.50
111	Emmitt Smith	12.00
112	Shannon Sharpe	.40
113	Johnnie Morton	.40
114	*Eddie Kennison*	1.50
115	*Marvin Harrison*	8.00
116	*Amani Toomer*	1.00
117	*Rickey Dudley*	1.00
118	*Alex Van Dyke*	1.00
119	Dorsey Levens	2.00
120	Antonio Freeman	.40
121	Willie Davis	.40
122	Lamont Warren	.40
123	Sean Dawkins	.40
124	Willie Jackson	.40
125	Kimble Anders	.40
126	Dan Marino	12.00
127	Terry Kirby	.40
128	Amp Lee	.40
129	Jake Reed	.40
130	Curtis Martin	8.00
131	Ray Zellars	.40
132	Herschel Walker	.40
133	Mike Sherrard	.40
134	Kyle Brady	.40
135	Raghib Ismail	.40
136	Ricky Watters	.40
137	Kordell Stewart	5.00
138	Andre Hastings	.40
139	Ronnie Harmon	.40
140	Terrell Fletcher	.40
141	J.J. Stokes	3.00
142	Brent Jones	.40
143	Tony McGee	.40
144	Brian Blades	.40
145	Isaac Bruce	.75
146	Errict Rhett	.75
147	Warren Sapp	.40
148	Horace Copeland	.40
149	Heath Shuler	.75
150	Michael Westbrook	.75
151	Frank Sanders	1.00
152	Rob Moore	1.00
153	Bert Emanuel	1.00
154	J.J. Birden	1.00
155	Thurman Thomas	2.00
156	Jim Kelly	2.00
157	Curtis Conway	2.00
158	Darnay Scott	2.00
159	Jeff Blake	2.00
160	Jay Novacek	1.00
161	Michael Irvin	2.00
162	John Elway	15.00
163	Terrell Davis	20.00
164	Barry Sanders	15.00
165	Brett Perriman	1.00
166	Keyshawn Johnson	15.00
167	*Eddie George*	14.00
168	*Derrick Mayes*	3.50
169	*Simeon Rice*	1.00
170	*Lawrence Phillips*	5.00
171	Robert Brooks	2.00
172	Mark Chmura	1.50
173	Rodney Thomas	1.00
174	Jim Harbaugh	1.00
175	Ken Dilger	1.00
176	Mark Brunell	10.00
177	Steve Bono	2.00
178	Marcus Allen	2.00
179	O.J. McDuffie	1.00
180	Eric Green	1.00
181	Warren Moon	2.00
182	Drew Bledsoe	12.00
183	Ben Coates	1.00
184	Michael Haynes	1.00
185	Rodney Hampton	1.00
186	Rashaan Salaam	2.00
187	Napoleon Kaufman	1.00
188	Tim Brown	1.00
189	Rodney Peete	1.00
190	Calvin Williams	1.00
191	Erric Pegram	1.00
192	Mark Bruener	1.00
193	Junior Seau	2.00
194	Steve Young	10.00
195	Derek Loville	1.00
196	Rick Mirer	2.00
197	Mark Rypien	1.00
198	Jackie Harris	1.00
199	Tracy Allen	1.00
200	Brian Mitchell	1.00

1996 Playoff Prime Boss Hogs

These cards were exclusive inserts in 1996 Playoff Prime retail packs.

		MT
Complete Set (18):		675.00
Common Player:		15.00
1	Curtis Martin	75.00
2	Chris Warren	15.00
3	Emmitt Smith	100.00
4	Barry Sanders	60.00
5	Rashaan Salaam	30.00
6	Marshall Faulk	40.00
7	Errict Rhett	35.00
8	Thurman Thomas	15.00
9	Kerry Collins	30.00
10	Dan Marino	100.00
11	Jerry Rice	60.00
12	Troy Aikman	60.00
13	Jeff George	15.00
14	Brett Favre	100.00
15	Robert Brooks	15.00
16	John Elway	25.00
17	Deion Sanders	30.00
18	Kordell Stewart	50.00

1996 Playoff Prime X's and O's

X's & O's is a 200-card parallel set of Prime, and was inserted one per 7.2 packs. It is considered a parallel set since it has an identical checklist to the base set, but X's & O's were printed on a die-cut plastic surface, with the player's team helmet in the background. There is a holographic strip on the bottom that includes the player's name, position and an X's & O's logo.

		MT
Complete Set (200):		850.00
Common Player:		2.00
Minor Stars:		4.00
1	Brett Favre	50.00
2	Jerry Rice	30.00
3	Troy Aikman	25.00
4	Bruce Smith	2.00
5	Marshall Faulk	25.00
6	Erik Kramer	2.00
7	Carl Pickens	4.00
8	Anthony Miller	2.00
9	Cris Carter	4.00
10	Todd Kinchen	2.00
11	Stoney Case	2.00
12	Chris Calloway	2.00
13	Andre Rison	2.00
14	Bill Brooks	2.00
15	Shawn Jefferson	2.00
16	Eric Zeier	2.00
17	Yancey Thigpen	15.00
18	Edgar Bennett	2.00
19	Garrison Hearst	4.00
20	Daryl Johnston	2.00
21	Tyrone Wheatley	2.00
22	Darick Holmes	4.00
23	Dave Brown	2.00
24	Leeland McElroy	10.00
25	Craig Heyward	2.00
26	Kevin Hardy	4.00
27	Scott Mitchell	2.00
28	Willie Green	2.00
29	Vincent Brisby	2.00
30	Mike Tomczak	2.00
31	Luther Ellis	2.00
32	Mike Pritchard	2.00
33	Robert Green	2.00
34	Jeff Graham	2.00
35	Tamarick Vanover	15.00
36	William Floyd	4.00
37	Alvin Harper	2.00
38	Stan Humphries	2.00
39	Herman Moore	15.00
40	Tony Martin	2.00
41	Jonathan Ogden	2.00
42	Randall Cunningham	
43	Chris Warren	4.00
44	Bobby Hobert	2.00
45	Jerome Bettis	4.00
46	Joey Galloway	20.00
47	Ernie Mills	2.00
48	Steve McNair	20.00
49	Karim Abdul-Jabbar	25.00
50	Chad May	2.00
51	Jim Everett	2.00
52	Robert Smith	4.00
53	Tony Boselli	2.00
54	William Henderson	2.00
55	Terry Glenn	30.00
56	Neil O'Donnell	4.00
57	Chris Chandler	2.00
58	Michael Jackson	2.00
59	Jason Dunn	4.00
60	James Stewart	2.00
61	Greg Hill	2.00
62	Mark Carrier	2.00
63	Bernie Parmalee	2.00
64	Chris Sanders	2.00
65	Jeff Hostetler	2.00
66	Eric Moulds	12.00
67	James Jett	2.00
68	Henry Ellard	2.00
69	Mario Bates	2.00
70	Natrone Means	4.00
71	Bobby Engram	12.00
72	Christian Fauria	2.00
73	Gus Frerotte	4.00
74	Aaron Hayden	4.00
75	Reggie White	4.00
76	Dave Meggett	2.00
77	Harvey Williams	2.00
78	Terance Mathis	2.00
79	Bam Morris	2.00
80	Trent Dilfer	2.00
81	Irving Fryar	2.00
82	Quinn Early	2.00
83	Lake Dawson	2.00
84	Todd Collins	2.00
85	Eric Metcalf	2.00
86	Tim Biakabutuka	20.00
87	Rob Johnson	6.00
88	Charlie Garner	2.00
89	Mike Mamula	2.00
90	Steve Walsh	2.00
91	Charles Haley	2.00
92	Mike Alstott	20.00
93	Wayne Chrebet	2.00
94	Vinny Testaverde	2.00
95	Fred Barnett	2.00
96	Boomer Esiason	2.00
97	Zack Crockett	2.00
98	Kevin Williams	2.00
99	Eric Bieniemy	2.00
100	Bryan Cox	2.00
101	Larry Centers	2.00
102	Jeff George	6.00
103	Bryce Paup	2.00
104	Kerry Collins	6.00
105	Derrick Moore	2.00
106	Adrian Murrell	2.00
107	Harold Green	2.00
108	Ki-Jana Carter	6.00
109	Sherman Williams	2.00
110	Deion Sanders	15.00
111	Emmitt Smith	50.00
112	Shannon Sharpe	2.00
113	Johnnie Morton	2.00
114	Eddie Kennison	15.00
115	Marvin Harrison	20.00
116	Amani Toomer	6.00
117	Rickey Dudley	10.00
118	Alex Van Dyke	8.00
119	Dorsey Levens	6.00
120	Antonio Freeman	4.00
121	Willie Davis	2.00
122	Lamont Warren	2.00
123	Sean Dawkins	2.00
124	Willie Jackson	2.00
125	Kimble Anders	2.00
126	Dan Marino	50.00
127	Terry Kirby	2.00
128	Amp Lee	2.00
129	Jake Reed	2.00
130	Curtis Martin	40.00
131	Ray Zellars	2.00
132	Herschel Walker	2.00
133	Mike Sherrard	2.00
134	Kyle Brady	2.00
135	Raghib Ismail	2.00
136	Ricky Watters	4.00
137	Kordell Stewart	25.00
138	Andre Hastings	2.00
139	Ronnie Harmon	2.00
140	Terrell Fletcher	2.00
141	J.J. Stokes	15.00
142	Brent Jones	2.00
143	Tony McGee	2.00
144	Brian Blades	2.00
145	Isaac Bruce	15.00
146	Errict Rhett	15.00
147	Warren Sapp	2.00
148	Horace Copeland	2.00
149	Heath Shuler	4.00
150	Michael Westbrook	15.00
151	Frank Sanders	2.00
152	Rob Moore	2.00
153	Bert Emanuel	2.00
154	J.J. Birden	2.00
155	Thurman Thomas	4.00
156	Jim Kelly	4.00
157	Curtis Conway	4.00
158	Darnay Scott	4.00
159	Jeff Blake	15.00
160	Jay Novacek	2.00
161	Michael Irvin	6.00
162	John Elway	35.00
163	Terrell Davis	60.00
164	Barry Sanders	50.00
165	Brett Perriman	2.00
166	Keyshawn Johnson	20.00
167	Eddie George	40.00
168	Derrick Mayes	10.00
169	Simeon Rice	4.00
170	Lawrence Phillips	6.00
171	Robert Brooks	4.00
172	Mark Chmura	4.00
173	Rodney Thomas	4.00
174	Jim Harbaugh	4.00
175	Ken Dilger	2.00
176	Mark Brunell	25.00
177	Steve Bono	4.00
178	Marcus Allen	4.00
179	O.J. McDuffie	2.00
180	Eric Green	2.00
181	Warren Moon	4.00
182	Drew Bledsoe	30.00
183	Ben Coates	2.00
184	Michael Haynes	2.00
185	Rodney Hampton	2.00
186	Rashaan Salaam	10.00
187	Napoleon Kaufman	6.00
188	Tim Brown	2.00
189	Rodney Peete	2.00
190	Calvin Williams	2.00
191	Erric Pegram	2.00
192	Mark Bruener	2.00
193	Junior Seau	4.00
194	Steve Young	25.00
195	Derek Loville	2.00
196	Rick Mirer	4.00
197	Mark Rypien	2.00
198	Jackie Harris	2.00
199	Terry Allen	2.00
200	Brian Mitchell	2.00

1996 Playoff Prime Surprise

This 14-card set was inserted in Prime at a rate of one in 288 packs.

		MT
Complete Set (14):		375.00
Common Player:		10.00
Minor Stars:		20.00
Inserted 1:288		
1	Dan Marino	50.00
2	Brett Favre	60.00
3	Emmitt Smith	50.00
4	Kordell Stewart	30.00
5	Jerry Rice	30.00
6	Troy Aikman	30.00
7	Barry Sanders	60.00
8	Curtis Martin	25.00
9	Marshall Faulk	20.00
10	Joey Galloway	20.00
11	Robert Brooks	10.00
12	Deion Sanders	25.00
13	Reggie White	10.00
14	Marcus Allen	10.00

A player's name in *italic* type indicates a rookie card.

1996 Playoff Prime Playoff Honors

This 1996 Playoff Prime set features three of the NFL's brightest stars - Brett Favre, Emmitt Smith and Curtis Martin. The leather cards are seeded one per 7,200 packs.

	MT
Complete Set (3):	500.00
Common Player:	100.00
Inserted 1:7,200	
1 Emmitt Smith	175.00
2 Curtis Martin	100.00
3 Brett Favre	250.00

1996 Playoff Unsung Heroes Banquet

To honor the NFL's Unsung Heroes, Playoff produced this 30-card set which was handed out at the March 8, 1996 NFL Players Award Banquet in Washington, D.C. The card fronts have a color photo of the player over a purple striped background. At the bottom of the front, are "1996," and the Playoff and Unsung Heroes' logos. The card backs have a color photo of the player, his name and why he was named an Unsung Hero. The date of the banquet is also featured at the top of the horizontal card backs.

	MT
Complete Set (30):	20.00
Common Player:	.50
1 Bill Bates	.50
2 Jeff Brady	.50
3 Ray Brown	.50
4 Isaac Bruce	3.00
5 Larry Centers	.75
6 Mark Chmura	1.75
7 Keith Elias	.50
8 Robert Green	.50
9 Andy Harmon	.50
10 Rodney Holman	.50
11 Derek Loville	.75
12 J.J. McCleskey	.50
13 Sam Mills	.50
14 Hardy Nickerson	.75
15 Jessie Tuggle	.50
16 Eric Bienamy	.50
17 Blaine Bishop	.50
18 Mark Brunell	4.00
19 Wayne Chrebet	2.00
20 Vince Evans	.50
21 Sam Gash	.50
22 Tim Grunhard	.50
23 Jim Harbaugh	.75
24 Dwayne Harper	.50
25 Bernie Parmalee	.50
26 Reggie Rivers	.50
27 Eugene Robinson	.50
28 Kordell Stewart	6.00
29 Steve Tasker	.50
30 Bennie Thompson	.50

1996 Playoff Contenders Leather

This 100-card base set lives up to its name, with a leather card front. The player's name, which can be printed in green, purple or red, is printed inside a black oval along the left side of the card. The Playoff Contenders' and Genuine Leather logos appear on the front. If the player's name is printed in green foil, it is a "Scarce" card, which was most frequently inserted. Purple foil is a "Rare" card, seeded one per 11 packs. Red foil is "Ultra Rare," and seeded one per 22 packs. The card backs include a full-bleed photo of the player. The card number is printed in the upper right.

	MT
Complete Set (100):	1200.
Common Player:	.75
Wax Box:	80.00
1 Brett Favre R	100.00
2 Steve Young R	20.00
3 Herman Moore P	5.00
4 Jim Harbaugh P	3.00
5 Curtis Martin R	60.00
6 Junior Seau	.75
7 John Elway R	45.00
8 Troy Aikman R	50.00
9 Terry Allen	.75
10 Kordell Stewart R	50.00
11 Drew Bledsoe R	50.00
12 Jim Kelly R	10.00
13 Dan Marino R	100.00
14 Andre Rison	.75
15 Jeff Hostetler	.75
16 Scott Mitchell	.75
17 Carl Pickens	.75
18 Larry Centers R	5.00
19 Craig Heyward	.75
20 Barry Sanders R	60.00
21 Deion Sanders P	15.00
22 Emmitt Smith R	100.00
23 Rashaan Salaam P	9.00
24 Mario Bates	.75
25 Lawrence Phillips R	10.00
26 Napoleon Kaufman P	7.00
27 Rodney Hampton	.75
28 Marshall Faulk R	20.00
29 Trent Dilfer	.75
30 Leeland McElroy	3.00
31 Marcus Allen	2.00
32 Ricky Watters R	10.00
33 Karim Abdul-Jabbar R	40.00
34 Herschel Walker	.75
35 Thurman Thomas	2.00
36 Jerome Bettis	2.00
37 Gus Frerotte P	3.00
38 Neil O'Donnell P	3.00
39 Rick Mirer	.75
40 Mike Alstott P	15.00
41 Vinny Testaverde P	3.00
42 Derek Loville	.75
43 Ben Coates	.75
44 Steve McNair R	6.00
45 Bobby Engram	2.00
46 Yancey Thigpen	.75
47 Lake Dawson	.75
48 Terrell Davis	10.00
49 Kerry Collins R	6.00
50 Eric Metcalf	.75
51 Stanley Pritchett P	3.00
52 Robert Brooks	.75
53 Isaac Bruce R	10.00
54 Tim Brown	.75
55 Edgar Bennett	.75
56 Warren Moon	.75
57 Jerry Rice R	50.00
58 Michael Westbrook	.75
59 Keyshawn Johnson R	30.00
60 Steve Bono	.75
61 Derrick Mayes	2.00
62 Erik Kramer	.75
63 Rodney Peete	.75
64 Eddie Kennison P	6.00
65 Derrick Thomas	.75
66 Joey Galloway P	15.00
67 Amani Toomer	2.00
68 Reggie White P	7.00
69 Heath Shuler R	7.00
70 Dave Brown R	7.00
71 Tony Banks	6.00
72 Chris Warren R	7.00
73 J.J. Stokes R	8.00
74 Rickey Dudley	3.00
75 Stan Humphries	.75
76 Jason Dunn	.75
77 Tyrone Wheatley P	3.00
78 Jim Everett P	7.00
79 Cris Carter P	3.00
80 Alex Van Dyke	2.00
81 O.J. McDuffie	.75
82 Mark Chmura	.75
83 Terry Glenn	10.00
84 Boomer Esiason	.75
85 Bruce Smith	.75
86 Curtis Conway	3.00
87 Ki-Jana Carter	2.00
88 Tamarick Vanover	2.00
89 Michael Jackson	.75
90 Mark Brunell P	20.00
91 Tim Biakabutuka P	12.00
92 Anthony Miller P	3.00
93 Marvin Harrison R	15.00
94 Jeff George R	7.00
95 Jeff Blake P	6.00
96 Eddie George R	50.00
97 Eric Moulds	2.00
98 Mike Tomczak P	3.00
99 Chris Sanders P	3.00
100 Chris Chandler	.75

1996 Playoff Contenders Pennants

This 100-card pennant-shaped base set includes a photo of the player, with the Playoff Pennants 1996 logo at the top. The player's name is printed in silver foil, also at the top. The felt-like material is coordinated with the player's team color. Three levels of this base set exist. If the "Pennants" logo is green it is a "Scarce" card, which was the most frequently inserted card. If it is purple, it is a "Rare" and inserted one per eight packs. If it is red, it is "Ultra Rare" and inserted one per 16 packs. Card backs also have the felt-like surface, with the player's name in a colored bar in the middle.

	MT
Complete Set (100):	800.00
Common Player:	1.00
1 Brett Favre R	90.00
2 Steve Young R	40.00
3 Herman Moore R	10.00
4 Jim Harbaugh R	2.00
5 Curtis Martin R	40.00
6 Junior Seau	1.00
7 John Elway R	35.00
8 Troy Aikman P	20.00
9 Terry Allen	1.00
10 Kordell Stewart R	40.00
11 Drew Bledsoe	10.00
12 Jim Kelly P	6.00
13 Dan Marino R	40.00
14 Andre Rison	1.00
15 Jeff Hostetler	1.00
16 Scott Mitchell	1.00
17 Carl Pickens R	6.00
18 Larry Centers R	3.00
19 Craig Heyward	1.00
20 Barry Sanders R	20.00
21 Deion Sanders R	20.00
22 Emmitt Smith R	90.00
23 Rashaan Salaam R	10.00
24 Mario Bates	1.00
25 Lawrence Phillips	5.00
26 Napoleon Kaufman	1.00
27 Rodney Hampton	1.00
28 Marshall Faulk P	10.00
29 Trent Dilfer	1.00
30 Leeland McElroy P	5.00
31 Marcus Allen P	6.00
32 Ricky Watters	2.00
33 Karim Abdul-Jabbar	4.00
34 Herschel Walker P	3.00
35 Thurman Thomas R	10.00
36 Jerome Bettis P	6.00
37 Gus Frerotte	1.00
38 Neil O'Donnell	1.00
39 Rick Mirer	1.00
40 Mike Alstott R	20.00
41 Vinny Testaverde R	6.00
42 Derek Loville	1.00
43 Ben Coates	1.00
44 Steve McNair R	25.00
45 Bobby Engram P	6.00
46 Yancey Thigpen	1.00
47 Lake Dawson	1.00
48 Terrell Davis R	40.00
49 Kerry Collins R	10.00
50 Eric Metcalf	1.00
51 Stanley Pritchett R	6.00
52 Robert Brooks R	6.00
53 Isaac Bruce	3.00
54 Tim Brown	1.00
55 Edgar Bennett P	3.00
56 Warren Moon	1.00
57 Jerry Rice R	40.00
58 Michael Westbrook	2.00
59 Keyshawn Johnson	5.00
60 Steve Bono R	6.00
61 Derrick Mayes R	6.00
62 Erik Kramer P	3.00
63 Rodney Peete	1.00
64 Eddie Kennison	6.00
65 Derrick Thomas	1.00
66 Joey Galloway R	15.00
67 Amani Toomer P	6.00
68 Reggie White P	2.00
69 Heath Shuler	1.00
70 Dave Brown	1.00
71 Tony Banks P	8.00
72 Chris Warren	1.00
73 J.J. Stokes	2.00
74 Rickey Dudley P	7.00
75 Stan Humphries	1.00
76 Jason Dunn P	3.00
77 Tyrone Wheatley	1.00
78 Jim Everett	1.00
79 Cris Carter P	3.00
80 Alex Van Dyke P	6.00
81 O.J. McDuffie	1.00
82 Mark Chmura P	3.00
83 Terry Glenn P	20.00
84 Boomer Esiason R	6.00
85 Bruce Smith	1.00
86 Curtis Conway	1.00
87 Ki-Jana Carter	2.00
88 Tamarick Vanover	2.00
89 Michael Jackson	1.00
90 Mark Brunell	10.00
91 Tim Biakabutuka R	25.00
92 Anthony Miller	1.00
93 Marvin Harrison	20.00
94 Jeff George P	3.00
95 Jeff Blake R	10.00
96 Eddie George	12.00
97 Eric Moulds P	10.00
98 Mike Tomczak	1.00
99 Chris Sanders	1.00
100 Chris Chandler	1.00

1996 Playoff Contenders Open Field

These mini-cards, which measure 3-1/8" x 2-1/4", were part of the Contenders base set. A color photo of the player is showcased, with a holographic background of a football field. The Open Field logo also is included in the hologram. Three levels of this base set exist. The "Scarce" cards, which have the player's name in a green oval, are the most frequently inserted. The "Rare" cards have the oval in purple and were inserted one per five packs. The "Ultra Rare" cards have the oval in red and are seeded one per nine packs. Card backs have a photo on the left, with a "Playoff The Wall Fact" on the right.

	MT
Complete Set (100):	400.00
Common Player:	.75
1 Brett Favre P	20.00
2 Steve Young R	15.00
3 Herman Moore P	4.00
4 Jim Harbaugh	.75
5 Curtis Martin R	15.00
6 Junior Seau P	2.00
7 John Elway P	10.00
8 Troy Aikman R	18.00
9 Terry Allen	.75
10 Kordell Stewart P	12.00
11 Drew Bledsoe	6.00
12 Jim Kelly	2.00
13 Dan Marino R	35.00
14 Andre Rison	2.00
15 Jeff Hostetler	.75
16 Scott Mitchell R	3.00
17 Carl Pickens	.75
18 Larry Centers	.75
19 Craig Heyward R	3.00
20 Barry Sanders R	20.00
21 Deion Sanders R	8.00
22 Emmitt Smith P	20.00
23 Rashaan Salaam R	6.00
24 Mario Bates P	3.00
25 Lawrence Phillips P	3.00
26 Napoleon Kaufman	.75
27 Rodney Hampton	.75
28 Marshall Faulk R	10.00
29 Trent Dilfer	.75
30 Leeland McElroy R	6.00
31 Marcus Allen	2.00
32 Ricky Watters R	4.00
33 Karim Abdul-Jabbar P	15.00
34 Herschel Walker	3.00
35 Thurman Thomas	2.00
36 Jerome Bettis	2.00
37 Gus Frerotte R	3.00
38 Neil O'Donnell	.75
39 Rick Mirer	.75
40 Mike Alstott	3.00
41 Vinny Testaverde	.75
42 Derek Loville	.75
43 Ben Coates	.75
44 Steve McNair	3.00
45 Bobby Engram R	6.00
46 Yancey Thigpen	.75
47 Lake Dawson P	2.00
48 Terrell Davis P	8.00
49 Kerry Collins P	4.00
50 Eric Metcalf	.75
51 Stanley Pritchett	.75
52 Robert Brooks P	2.00
53 Isaac Bruce P	3.00
54 Tim Brown P	2.00
55 Edgar Bennett	.75
56 Warren Moon P	2.00
57 Jerry Rice R	15.00
58 Michael Westbrook	2.00
59 Keyshawn Johnson P	8.00
60 Steve Bono	.75
61 Derrick Mayes R	6.00
62 Erik Kramer	.75
63 Rodney Peete	.75
64 Eddie Kennison	4.00
65 Derrick Thomas	.75
66 Joey Galloway R	10.00
67 Amani Toomer R	6.00
68 Reggie White R	6.00
69 Heath Shuler P	2.00
70 Dave Brown	.75
71 Tony Banks R	6.00
72 Chris Warren	.75
73 J.J. Stokes	2.00
74 Rickey Dudley R	6.00
75 Stan Humphries	.75
76 Jason Dunn R	3.00
77 Tyrone Wheatley	.75
78 Jim Everett	.75
79 Cris Carter	.75
80 Alex Van Dyke R	6.00
81 O.J. McDuffie P	2.00
82 Mark Chmura	.75
83 Terry Glenn R	25.00
84 Boomer Esiason	.75
85 Bruce Smith	.75
86 Curtis Conway	.75
87 Ki-Jana Carter R	6.00
88 Tamarick Vanover R	4.00
89 Michael Jackson R	3.00
90 Mark Brunell	6.00
91 Tim Biakabutuka	4.00
92 Anthony Miller	.75
93 Marvin Harrison	4.00
94 Jeff George	.75
95 Jeff Blake	4.00
96 Eddie George P	20.00
97 Eric Moulds R	12.00
98 Mike Tomczak R	3.00
99 Chris Sanders	.75
100 Chris Chandler	.75

1996 Playoff Contenders Leather Accents

The difference between Genuine Leather and Genuine Leather Accents parallel set is Accents has the Genuine Leather and Playoff Contenders' logo and name oval in teal foil. Different scarcities also exist with the green, purple and red foils on the player's names. The card backs have a full-bleed photo, with the card number in the upper right. "Accent" is printed in teal foil in the lower center on the card back. One card was seeded per 216 packs.

	MT
Common Player:	10.00
Minor Stars:	20.00
1 Brett Favre	125.00
2 Steve Young	50.00
3 Herman Moore	20.00
4 Jim Harbaugh	10.00
5 Curtis Martin	40.00
6 Junior Seau	20.00
7 John Elway	100.00
8 Troy Aikman	60.00
9 Terry Allen	10.00
10 Kordell Stewart	50.00
11 Drew Bledsoe	60.00
12 Jim Kelly	20.00
13 Dan Marino	100.00
14 Andre Rison	10.00
15 Jeff Hostetler	10.00
16 Scott Mitchell	10.00
17 Carl Pickens	20.00
18 Larry Centers	10.00
19 Craig Heyward	10.00
20 Barry Sanders	125.00
21 Deion Sanders	40.00
22 Emmitt Smith	100.00
23 Rashaan Salaam	20.00
24 Mario Bates	10.00
25 Lawrence Phillips	20.00
26 Napoleon Kaufman	20.00
27 Rodney Hampton	10.00
28 Marshall Faulk	30.00
29 Trent Dilfer	20.00
30 Leeland McElroy	10.00
31 Marcus Allen	20.00
32 Ricky Watters	20.00
33 Karim Abdul-Jabbar	20.00
34 Herschel Walker	10.00
35 Thurman Thomas	20.00
36 Jerome Bettis	20.00
37 Gus Frerotte	10.00
38 Neil O'Donnell	10.00
39 Rick Mirer	10.00
40 Mike Alstott	25.00
41 Vinny Testaverde	20.00
42 Derek Loville	10.00
43 Ben Coates	20.00
44 Steve McNair	40.00
45 Bobby Engram	10.00
46 Yancey Thigpen	10.00
47 Lake Dawson	10.00
48 Terrell Davis	100.00
49 Kerry Collins	20.00
50 Eric Metcalf	10.00
51 Stanley Pritchett	10.00
52 Robert Brooks	10.00
53 Isaac Bruce	25.00
54 Tim Brown	20.00
55 Edgar Bennett	10.00
56 Warren Moon	20.00
57 Jerry Rice	60.00
58 Michael Westbrook	20.00
59 Keyshawn Johnson	40.00
60 Steve Bono	10.00
61 Derrick Mayes	20.00
62 Erik Kramer	10.00
63 Rodney Peete	10.00
64 Eddie Kennison	10.00
65 Derrick Thomas	10.00
66 Joey Galloway	30.00
67 Amani Toomer	10.00
68 Reggie White	20.00
69 Heath Shuler	10.00
70 Dave Brown	10.00
71 Tony Banks	20.00
72 Chris Warren	10.00

73	J.J. Stokes	20.00
74	Rickey Dudley	10.00
75	Stan Humphries	10.00
76	Jason Dunn	10.00
77	Tyrone Wheatley	20.00
78	Jim Everett	10.00
79	Cris Carter	20.00
80	Alex Van Dyke	10.00
81	O.J. McDuffie	10.00
82	Mark Chmura	10.00
83	Terry Glenn	25.00
84	Boomer Esiason	10.00
85	Bruce Smith	10.00
86	Curtis Conway	10.00
87	Ki-Jana Carter	10.00
88	Tamarick Vanover	10.00
89	Michael Jackson	10.00
90	Mark Brunell	60.00
91	Tim Biakabutuka	10.00
92	Anthony Miller	10.00
93	Marvin Harrison	40.00
94	Jeff George	20.00
95	Jeff Blake	10.00
96	Eddie George	50.00
97	Eric Moulds	20.00
98	Mike Tomczak	10.00
99	Chris Sanders	10.00
100	Chris Chandler	10.00

1996 Playoff Contenders Ground Hogs

This insert set, which was seeded one per 44 packs, featured a leather front. A rainbow foil "swoosh" follows behind the player. The Ground Hogs logo appears in one of the lower corners. The player's name is in gold foil at the top of the card. The card back has the Playoff Contenders' logo in the upper left and the card number, prefixed by "GH," in the upper right. A color photo of the player is featured on the back, with the running back in focus and the background blurry.

		MT
Complete Set (8):		160.00
Common Player:		15.00
1	Emmitt Smith	30.00
2	Barry Sanders	40.00
3	Marshall Faulk	20.00
4	Curtis Martin	20.00
5	Chris Warren	15.00
6	Ricky Watters	15.00
7	Thurman Thomas	15.00
8	Terrell Davis	30.00

1996 Playoff Contenders Pennant Flyers

This pennant-shaped insert set includes a felt-like surface on the right, with the player's last name embossed on the left in a gold-foil bar along the left border. The Playoff Pennant Flyer logo is pictured on the front, with

"1996" embossed in a gold-foil oval. The player's team's main color is used for the felt on the front and back. The card backs include the player's full name embossed in the gold-foil band, team logo inside a circle and a gold-foil embossed Playoff Contenders' logo. These were seeded one per 48 packs. The card numbers are prefixed with "PF."

		MT
Complete Set (8):		125.00
Common Player:		10.00
1	Jerry Rice	45.00
2	Joey Galloway	15.00
3	Isaac Bruce	15.00
4	Herman Moore	15.00
5	Carl Pickens	10.00
6	Yancey Thigpen	10.00
7	Deion Sanders	20.00
8	Robert Brooks	10.00

1996 Playoff Contenders Air Command

This insert set features a photograph of the player showcased over a hologram background comprised of jets and clouds. The Playoff Air Command '96 logo appears in the upper left. The player's name is printed in gold foil in the lower left. The card back has a silver and blue etched-foil background and a color photo of the player. The Playoff Contenders logo is in the upper left, with the card number, prefixed by "AC," in the upper right. Each card measures 3-1/8" x 2-1/4". The cards are inserted one per 96 packs.

		MT
Complete Set (8):		125.00
Common Player:		10.00
1	Dan Marino	25.00
2	Brett Favre	35.00
3	Troy Aikman	20.00
4	Mike Tomczak	10.00
5	John Elway	25.00
6	Jeff George	15.00
7	Chris Chandler	10.00
8	Steve Bono	10.00

1996 Playoff Contenders Honors

A continuation from Prime, this insert set had a new design that featured the Playoff Honors' logo and player's name in teal foil on the front of the card. The holographic background includes the various achievements of the player. The card back has a full-bleed photo of the player. The card numbers, prefixed by a "PH," are

in the upper right. One card was seeded per 7,200 packs.

		MT
Complete Set (3):		300.00
Common Player:		50.00
4	Dan Marino	200.00
5	Deion Sanders	50.00
6	Marcus Allen	50.00

1996 Playoff Illusions

The 120-card set's base cards are printed in different color schemes and graphics. The set features six different designs, each representing the six NFL divisions, as well as two levels of insertions. Cards #s 1-63 appeared approximately 3.5 cards per pack, while card #s 64-120 were found approximately one card per pack.

		MT
Complete Set (120):		125.00
Common Player (1-63):		.25
Common Player (64-120):		.50
Wax Box:		60.00
1	Troy Aikman	2.00
2	Larry Centers	.25
3	Terance Mathis	.25
4	Calvin Williams	.25
5	Jim Kelly	.25
6	Tim Biakabutuka	1.50
7	Rashaan Salaam	.75
8	Ki-Jana Carter	.50
9	Anthony Miller	.25
10	Deion Sanders	1.25
11	Scott Mitchell	.25
12	Robert Brooks	.25
13	Willie Davis	.25
14	Zack Crockett	.25
15	James Stewart	.25
16	Tamarick Vanover	.75
17	Stanley Pritchett	.25
18	Warren Moon	.25
19	Shawn Jefferson	.25
20	Shannon Sharpe	.25
21	Jim Everett	.25
22	Dave Brown	.25
23	Adrian Murrell	.25
24	Rickey Dudley	.75
25	Chris T. Jones	.25
26	Andre Hastings	.25
27	Stan Humphries	.25
28	Steve Young	1.50
29	Joey Galloway	1.50
30	Jim Harbaugh	.25
31	Eddie Kennison	1.00
32	Mike Alstott	2.50
33	Michael Westbrook	.50
34	Leeland McElroy	.75
35	Erik Kramer	.25
36	Mark Chmura	.25
37	Cris Carter	.25
38	Ben Coates	.25
39	Wayne Chrebet	.25
40	Jerome Bettis	.50
41	Tim Brown	.25
42	Jason Dunn	.25
43	William Henderson	.25
44	Rick Mirer	.25
45	J.J. Stokes	.50
46	Rodney Peete	.25
47	Neil O'Donnell	.25
48	Tyrone Wheatley	.25
49	Terry Glenn	2.50
50	Junior Seau	.25
51	Jake Reed	.25
52	O.J. McDuffie	.25
53	Steve Bono	.25
54	Steve McNair	2.00
55	Antonio Freeman	.50
56	Johnnie Morton	.25
57	Eric Metcalf	.25
58	Andre Reed	.25
59	Bobby Engram	1.00
60	Gus Frerotte	.25
61	Jeff Blake	.75
62	Erric Pegram	.25
63	Jeff Hostetler	.25
64	Edgar Bennett	.50
65	Eddie George	10.00
66	Marvin Harrison	7.00
67	LeShon Johnson	.50

68	Jamal Anderson	15.00
69	Thurman Thomas	1.00
70	Barry Sanders	5.00
71	Muhsin Muhammad	4.00
72	Robert Green	.50
73	Garrison Hearst	.50
74	John Elway	4.00
75	Herman Moore	1.00
76	Chris Chandler	.50
77	Marshall Faulk	1.50
78	Mark Brunell	4.00
79	Tony Banks	3.00
80	Terrell Davis	8.00
81	Marcus Allen	1.00
82	Dan Marino	10.00
83	Robert Smith	.50
84	Curtis Martin	7.00
85	Amani Toomer	1.00
86	Napoleon Kaufman	.50
87	Ricky Watters	1.00
88	Kordell Stewart	5.00
89	Keyshawn Johnson	6.00
90	Emmitt Smith	10.00
91	Chris Warren	.50
92	Isaac Bruce	1.50
93	Terry Allen	.50
94	Trent Dilfer	.50
95	Vinny Testaverde	.50
96	Bruce Smith	.50
97	Kerry Collins	2.00
98	Curtis Conway	.50
99	Karim Abdul-Jabbar	2.00
100	Brett Favre	10.00
101	Carl Pickens	.50
102	Brett Perriman	.50
103	Keith Jackson	.50
104	Drew Bledsoe	5.00
105	Rodney Hampton	.50
106	Ray Zellars	.50
107	Jeff Graham	.50
108	Irving Fryar	.50
109	Lawrence Phillips	2.00
110	Jerry Rice	5.00
111	Mike Tomczak	.50
112	Tony Martin	.50
113	Brian Blades	.50
114	Bill Brooks	.50
115	Rob Moore	.50
116	Quinn Early	.50
117	Darnay Scott	.50
118	Ken Dilger	.50
119	Derek Loville	.50
120	Reggie White	1.00

1996 Playoff Illusions Spectralusion Elite

This 120-card parallel set utilizes IIllusion printing technology and silver holographic foil background. It is one of four different parallel sets associated with the Illusion product, and is the easiest to get with a one per five packs insertion rate.

		MT
Complete Set (120):		300.00
Common Player:		1.00
1	Troy Aikman	10.00
2	Larry Centers	1.00
3	Terance Mathis	1.00
4	Calvin Williams	1.00
5	Jim Kelly	2.00
6	Tim Biakabutuka	4.00
7	Rashaan Salaam	2.00
8	Ki-Jana Carter	2.00
9	Anthony Miller	1.00
10	Deion Sanders	7.00
11	Scott Mitchell	1.00
12	Robert Brooks	1.00
13	Willie Davis	1.00
14	Zack Crockett	1.00
15	James Stewart	1.00
16	Tamarick Vanover	5.00
17	Stanley Pritchett	1.00
18	Warren Moon	1.00
19	Shawn Jefferson	1.00
20	Shannon Sharpe	1.00
21	Jim Everett	1.00
22	Dave Brown	1.00
23	Adrian Murrell	1.00
24	Rickey Dudley	4.00

25	Chris T. Jones	1.00
26	Andre Hastings	1.00
27	Stan Humphries	1.00
28	Steve Young	8.00
29	Joey Galloway	7.00
30	Jim Harbaugh	1.00
31	Eddie Kennison	6.00
32	Mike Alstott	8.00
33	Michael Westbrook	2.00
34	Leeland McElroy	2.00
35	Erik Kramer	1.00
36	Mark Chmura	1.00
37	Cris Carter	1.00
38	Ben Coates	1.00
39	Wayne Chrebet	1.00
40	Jerome Bettis	2.00
41	Tim Brown	1.00
42	Jason Dunn	1.00
43	William Henderson	1.00
44	Rick Mirer	1.00
45	J.J. Stokes	2.00
46	Rodney Peete	1.00
47	Neil O'Donnell	1.00
48	Tyrone Wheatley	1.00
49	Terry Glenn	12.00
50	Junior Seau	1.00
51	Jake Reed	1.00
52	O.J. McDuffie	1.00
53	Steve Bono	1.00
54	Steve McNair	5.00
55	Antonio Freeman	1.00
56	Johnnie Morton	1.00
57	Eric Metcalf	1.00
58	Andre Reed	1.00
59	Bobby Engram	4.00
60	Gus Frerotte	1.00
61	Jeff Blake	4.00
62	Erric Pegram	1.00
63	Jeff Hostetler	1.00
64	Edgar Bennett	1.00
65	Eddie George	12.00
66	Marvin Harrison	8.00
67	LeShon Johnson	1.00
68	Jamal Anderson	20.00
69	Thurman Thomas	2.00
70	Barry Sanders	12.00
71	Muhsin Muhammad	2.00
72	Robert Green	1.00
73	Garrison Hearst	1.00
74	John Elway	7.00
75	Herman Moore	3.00
76	Chris Chandler	1.00
77	Marshall Faulk	4.00
78	Mark Brunell	6.00
79	Tony Banks	5.00
80	Terrell Davis	20.00
81	Marcus Allen	2.00
82	Dan Marino	20.00
83	Robert Smith	1.00
84	Curtis Martin	12.00
85	Amani Toomer	2.00
86	Napoleon Kaufman	8.00
87	Ricky Watters	2.00
88	Kordell Stewart	10.00
89	Keyshawn Johnson	8.00
90	Emmitt Smith	20.00
91	Chris Warren	1.00
92	Isaac Bruce	5.00
93	Terry Allen	1.00
94	Trent Dilfer	1.00
95	Vinny Testaverde	1.00
96	Bruce Smith	1.00
97	Kerry Collins	3.00
98	Curtis Conway	1.00
99	Karim Abdul-Jabbar	10.00
100	Brett Favre	20.00
101	Carl Pickens	1.00
102	Brett Perriman	1.00
103	Keith Jackson	1.00
104	Drew Bledsoe	10.00
105	Rodney Hampton	1.00
106	Ray Zellars	1.00
107	Jeff Graham	1.00
108	Irving Fryar	1.00
109	Lawrence Phillips	2.00
110	Jerry Rice	10.00
111	Mike Tomczak	1.00
112	Tony Martin	1.00
113	Brian Blades	1.00
114	Bill Brooks	1.00
115	Rob Moore	1.00
116	Quinn Early	1.00
117	Darnay Scott	1.00
118	Ken Dilger	1.00
119	Derek Loville	1.00
120	Reggie White	2.00

1996 Playoff Illusions Spectralusion Dominion

Spectralusion Dominion was a 120-card parallel set that utilized Illusion printing technology and a gold holographic foil background. These parallel cards were inserted every 192 packs.

	MT
Spec. Dominion Cards:	10x-20x

1996 Playoff Illusions XXXI

XXXI reprints all 120 cards in the base set in a die-cut, parallel that features the Roman numerals XXXI across the top of the card. This parallel set is inserted at a rate of one per 12 packs. These cards are also featured in a more difficult gold holographic parallel called Spectralusion Dominion.

	MT
Complete XXXI Set (120):	600.00
XXXI Cards:	2x

1996 Playoff Illusions XXXI Spectralusion Dominion

XXXI Spectralusion Dominion reprints the die-cut XXXI cards and adds a gold holographic background. These parallel cards are found in every 96 packs.

	MT
XXXI Spec. Dominion:	6x-12x

1996 Playoff Illusions Optical Illusions

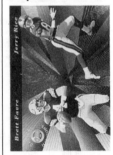

This 18-card chase set, found one per 96 packs, featured Troy Aikman handing off to Barry Sanders and Brett Favre passing to Jerry Rice.

		MT
Complete Set (18):		800.00
Common Player:		15.00
1	Brett Favre, Jerry Rice	150.00
2	Troy Aikman, Barry Sanders	120.00
3	Dan Marino, Emmitt Smith	175.00
4	Warren Moon, Carl Pickens	15.00
5	John Elway, Herman Moore	60.00
6	Steve Young, Anthony Miller	60.00
7	Jim Harbaugh, Terrell Davis	60.00
8	Kordell Stewart, Kordell Stewart	70.00
9	Deion Sanders, Deion Sanders	50.00
10	Kerry Collins, Curtis Martin	90.00
11	Scott Mitchell, Robert Brooks	15.00
12	Jeff Blake, Tony Martin	25.00
13	Mark Brunell, Marshall Faulk	50.00

14	Drew Bledsoe,	70.00
	Jerome Bettis	
15	Gus Frerotte,	40.00
	Karim Abdul-Jabbar	
16	Steve Bono,	15.00
	Ricky Watters	
17	Chris Chandler,	15.00
	Terry Allen	
18	Tony Banks,	40.00
	Keyshawn Johnson	

1996 Playoff Trophy Contenders

Playoff Trophy Contenders' regular 1996 football set puts a cap on the 1995 NFL season by highlighting members of the two teams in the Super Bowl - the Pittsburgh Steelers and Dallas Cowboys. Each regular card front has the player's name in a bar at the top. An action photo is in the center of the card; the Playoff and insert set logos are toward the bottom. The back has a color photo of the player, with the player's name and team at the top. A brief player profile and 1995 statistics are also included. The Steelers and Cowboys are featured in a 60-card mini parallel set called Back-to-Back. The first 11 cards in the set have an opposing player from each team on different card sides. Rookie Stallions and Playoff Zone cards are also included as inserts in packs, as are special cards redeemable for Wilson commemorative Super Bowl XXX footballs.

		MT
Complete Set (120):		26.00
Common Player:		.10
Minor Stars:		.20
Wax Box:		50.00
1	Brett Favre	3.00
2	Troy Aikman	1.50
3	Dan Marino	3.00
4	Emmitt Smith	3.00
5	Marshall Faulk	1.50
6	Jeff Blake	1.00
7	John Elway	1.00
8	Steve Young	1.50
9	Curtis Martin	4.00
10	Kordell Stewart	2.50
11	Drew Bledsoe	1.50
12	Jim Kelly	.20
13	Steve Bono	.20
14	Neil O'Donnell	.20
15	Jeff Hostetler	.10
16	Jim Harbaugh	.10
17	Jim Everett	.10
18	Erric Pegram	.10
19	Tyrone Wheatley	.20
20	Barry Sanders	1.50
21	Deion Sanders	1.00
22	Harvey Williams	.10
23	Garrison Hearst	.20
24	Aaron Hayden	1.00
25	Dorsey Levens	.30
26	Napoleon Kaufman	.50
27	Rodney Hampton	.10
28	Scott Mitchell	.10
29	Greg Hill	.10
30	Charlie Garner	.10
31	Rashaan Salaam	1.00
32	Errict Rhett	1.00
33	Bam Morris	.20
34	Edgar Bennett	.10
35	Jeff George	.10
36	Rodney Peete	.10
37	Stan Humphries	.10
38	Kimble Anders	.10
39	Natrone Means	.25
40	Sherman Williams	.10
41	Eric Metcalf	.10
42	Chris Warren	.10
43	Marcus Allen	.10
44	Bill Brooks	.10
45	Wayne Chrebet	.10
46	Irving Fryar	.10
47	Tony Martin	.10
48	Daryl Johnston	.10
49	O.J. McDuffie	.10
50	Frank Sanders	.50
51	Ken Norton	.10
52	Jake Reed	.10
53	Bert Emanuel	.10
54	Floyd Turner	.10
55	Junior Seau	.10
56	Ernie Mills	.10
57	Mark Pike	.10
58	Warren Moon	.10
59	Mike Mamula	.10
60	Kerry Collins	.50
61	Nate Newton	.10
62	Terry Allen	.10
63	Bernie Parmalee	.10
64	James Stewart	.10
65	Isaac Bruce	1.00
66	Lake Dawson	.10
67	Terance Mathis	.10
68	Chris Sanders	.50
69	Anthony Miller	.10
70	Jay Novacek	.10
71	Sean Dawkins	.10
72	J.J. Birden	.10
73	Calvin Williams	.10
74	Rick Mirer	.10
75	Steve McNair	1.50
76	Lamont Warren	.10
77	Rod Woodson	.10
78	Larry Brown	.10
79	Zack Crockett	.10
80	Jerry Rice	1.50
81	Tim Brown	.10
82	Yancey Thigpen	.75
83	J.J. Stokes	1.00
84	Herman Moore	.50
85	Kevin Williams	.10
86	Gus Frerotte	.10
87	Robert Brooks	.10
88	Michael Irvin	.50
89	Steve Tasker	.10
90	Joey Galloway	1.50
91	Kevin Greene	.10
92	Reggie White	.10
93	Cris Carter	.10
94	Charles Haley	.10
95	Bryce Paup	.10
96	Heath Shuler	.10
97	Eric Zeier	.20
98	Antonio Freeman	.10
99	Erik Kramer	.10
100	Derek Loville	.10
101	Rodney Thomas	.50
102	Terrell Davis	2.00
103	Ricky Watters	.10
104	Craig Heyward	.10
105	Terry Kirby	.10
106	Bruce Smith	.10
107	Curtis Conway	.10
108	Charles Johnson	.10
109	Brett Perriman	.10
110	Carl Pickens	.20
111	Michael Westbrook	1.00
112	Brent Jones	.10
113	Ken Dilger	.10
114	Fred Barnett	.10
115	Mark Bruener	.10
116	Tamarick Vanover	.20
117	Quinn Early	.10
118	Mark Chmura	.10
119	Andre Hastings	.10
120	Craig Newsome	.10

1996 Playoff Trophy Contenders Mini Back-to-Backs

Eleven members from the Super Bowl participants, the Dallas Cowboys and Pittsburgh Steelers, are highlighted on the first 11 cards in this 1996 Playoff Trophy Contenders insert set. The mini cards form a 60-card parallel set to the main set, putting those 120 cards in a back-to-back format. These cards are seeded one per 17 packs.

		MT
Complete Set (60):		900.00
Common Player:		10.00
Minor Stars:		20.00
1	Troy Aikman,	50.00
	Neil O'Donnell	
2	Sherman Williams,	45.00
	Kordell Stewart	
3	Deion Sanders,	35.00
	Andre Hastings	
4	Emmitt Smith,	90.00
	Bam Morris	
5	Daryl Johnston,	10.00
	Erric Pegram	
6	Nate Newton,	10.00
	Kevin Greene	
7	Larry Brown,	10.00
	Charles Johnson	
8	Jay Novacek,	10.00
	Mark Bruener	
9	Kevin Williams,	25.00
	Yancey Thigpen	
10	Michael Irvin,	25.00
	Ernie Mills	
11	Charles Haley,	10.00
	Rod Woodson	
12	Brett Favre,	90.00
	Steve Young	
13	Edgar Bennett,	10.00
	Derek Loville	
14	Reggie White,	10.00
	Ken Norton	
15	Robert Brooks,	60.00
	Jerry Rice	
16	Dorsey Levens,	20.00
	J.J. Stokes	
17	Mark Chmura,	10.00
	Brent Jones	
18	Craig Newsome,	20.00
	Antonio Freeman	
19	Dan Marino,	90.00
	Jim Kelly	
20	Bernie Parmalee,	10.00
	Bruce Smith	
21	Irving Fryar,	10.00
	Bill Brooks	
22	O.J. McDuffie,	10.00
	Steve Tasker	
23	Terry Kirby,	10.00
	Bryce Paup	
24	Jim Harbaugh,	20.00
	Steve Bono	
25	Marshall Faulk,	20.00
	Greg Hill	
26	Lamont Warren,	10.00
	Marcus Allen	
27	Floyd Turner,	10.00
	Kimble Anders	
28	Sean Dawkins,	10.00
	Lake Dawson	
29	Zack Crockett,	20.00
	Tamarick Vanover	
30	Scott Mitchell,	10.00
	Rodney Peete	
31	Barry Sanders,	60.00
	Ricky Watters	
32	Brett Perriman,	10.00
	Calvin Williams	
33	Herman Moore,	25.00
	Fred Barnett	
34	Stan Humphries,	20.00
	Jeff George	
35	Natrone Means,	20.00
	Craig Heyward	
36	Aaron Hayden,	10.00
	Terance Mathis	
37	Junior Seau,	10.00
	Bert Emanuel	
38	Tony Martin,	10.00
	J.J. Birden	
39	Jeff Blake,	20.00
	Carl Pickens	
40	Erik Kramer,	10.00
	Curtis Conway	
41	Garrison Hearst,	25.00
	Frank Sanders	
42	John Elway,	30.00
	Anthony Miller	
43	Steve McNair,	45.00
	Chris Sanders	
44	Warren Moon,	20.00
	Cris Carter	
45	Drew Bledsoe,	90.00
	Curtis Martin	
46	Jim Everett,	10.00
	Quinn Early	
47	Rodney Hampton,	10.00
	Tyrone Wheatley	
48	Jeff Hostetler,	10.00
	Tim Brown	
49	Rick Mirer,	25.00
	Joey Galloway	
50	Gus Frerotte,	20.00
	Michael Westbrook	
51	Heath Shuler,	20.00
	Terry Allen	
52	Charlie Garner,	10.00
	Mike Mamula	
53	Harvey Williams,	25.00
	Napoleon Kaufman	
54	Errict Rhett,	20.00
	Rashaan Salaam	
55	Mark Pike,	25.00
	Kerry Collins	
56	Ken Dilger,	25.00
	Eric Zeier	
57	Chris Warren,	50.00
	Terrell Davis	
58	Isaac Bruce,	25.00
	Jake Reed	
59	Eric Metcalf,	10.00
	Wayne Chrebet	
60	James Stewart,	25.00
	Rodney Thomas	

1996 Playoff Trophy Contenders Playoff Zone

This 36-card insert set captures some of the top NFL players on gold and silver foil backgrounds. The player's name is written in the foil along the right side, while his team's name and position are in the upper left corner. The Playoff Zone logo, showing a referee signaling a touchdown, is in the lower left corner. Cards were seeded one per 24 packs of 1996 Playoff Trophy Contenders.

		MT
Complete Set (36):		350.00
Common Player:		5.00
Minor Stars:		10.00
1	Troy Aikman	30.00
2	Jeff Blake	10.00
3	John Elway	15.00
4	Brett Favre	50.00
5	Jeff George	5.00
6	Jim Harbaugh	5.00
7	Erik Kramer	5.00
8	Dan Marino	50.00
9	Scott Mitchell	5.00
10	Warren Moon	5.00
11	Neil O'Donnell	10.00
12	Steve Young	30.00
13	Marcus Allen	5.00
14	Terry Allen	5.00
15	Edgar Bennett	5.00
16	Marshall Faulk	30.00
17	Rodney Hampton	5.00
18	Craig Heyward	5.00
19	Errict Rhett	10.00
20	Barry Sanders	30.00
21	Emmitt Smith	50.00
22	Chris Warren	10.00
23	Ricky Watters	10.00
24	Harvey Williams	10.00
25	Robert Brooks	10.00
26	Isaac Bruce	10.00
27	Cris Carter	5.00
28	Curtis Conway	5.00
29	Michael Irvin	10.00
30	Anthony Miller	5.00
31	Herman Moore	10.00
32	Brett Perriman	5.00
33	Carl Pickens	5.00
34	Jerry Rice	30.00
35	Deion Sanders	20.00
36	Yancey Thigpen	10.00

1996 Playoff Trophy Contenders Rookie Stallions

The top 20 rookies from the 1995 season are featured on these 1996 Playoff Trophy Contenders insert cards. Cards, seeded one per 24 packs, are gold-foil etched, with "Stallions" etched into the background.

	MT
Complete Set (20):	300.00
Common Player:	5.00
Minor Stars:	10.00
1 Mark Bruener	5.00
2 Wayne Chrebet	5.00
3 Kerry Collins	15.00
4 Zack Crockett	5.00
5 Terrell Davis	30.00
6 Antonio Freeman	5.00
7 Joey Galloway	20.00
8 Napoleon Kaufman	10.00
9 Curtis Martin	40.00
10 Steve McNair	25.00
11 Rashaan Salaam	20.00
12 Chris Sanders	10.00
13 Frank Sanders	10.00
14 Kordell Stewart	30.00
15 J.J. Stokes	20.00
16 Rodney Thomas	10.00
17 Tamarick Vanover	20.00
18 Michael Westbrook	20.00
19 Tyrone Wheatley	10.00
20 Eric Zeier	10.00

1997 Playoff Absolute

The 200-card set showcases an action shot of the player with a map of his hometown serving as the background on the card front. Named "Absolute Beginnings," the backs include the player's bio at the top left and the card number in the upper right inside a shape of an NFL shield. A headshot of the player is featured in the left center, while his name, number, position and team, along with interesting facts regarding the player's hometown and his pre-collegiate years are included to the right of the photo. His 1996 and total stats are printed along the bottom. The base set has three levels of color coded insertion ratios: Green (card #s 1-100, 3.5 per pack), Blue (#s 101-150, 1 per pack) and Red (#s 151-200, 1 per every 2 packs). The backs for each colored card are identical. The cards are standard size.

	MT
Complete Set (200):	170.00
Comp. Green Set (100):	20.00
Comp. Blue Set (50):	40.00
Comp. Red Set (50):	110.00
Common Green (1-100):	.10
Minor Green Stars:	.20
Common Blue (101-150):	.40
Minor Blue Stars:	.75
Common Red (151-200):	1.00
Minor Red Stars:	2.00
Wax Box:	80.00
1 Marcus Allen	.20
2 Eric Bieniemy	.10
3 Jason Dunn	.10
4 Jim Harbaugh	.20
5 Michael Westbrook	.20
6 *Tiki Barber*	2.00
7 Frank Reich	.10
8 Irving Fryar	.10
9 Courtney Hawkins	.10
10 Eric Zeier	.10
11 Kent Graham	.10
12 Trent Dilfer	.20
13 Neil O'Donnell	.10
14 *Reidel Anthony*	2.00
15 Jeff Hostetler	.10
16 Lawrence Phillips	.20
17 Dave Brown	.10
18 Mike Tomczak	.10
19 Jake Reed	.10
20 Anthony Miller	.10
21 Eric Metcalf	.10
22 *Sedrick Shaw*	.50
23 Anthony Johnson	.10
24 Mario Bates	.10
25 Dorsey Levens	.30
26 Stan Humphries	.10
27 Ben Coates	.10
28 Tyrone Wheatley	.10
29 Adrian Murrell	.10
30 William Henderson	.10
31 *Warrick Dunn*	3.00
32 LeShon Johnson	.10
33 James Stewart	.10
34 Edgar Bennett	.10
35 Raymont Harris	.10
36 Leroy Butler	.10
37 Darren Woodson	.10
38 *Darnell Autry*	.40
39 Johnnie Morton	.10
40 William Floyd	.10
41 Terrell Fletcher	.10
42 Leonard Russell	.10
43 Henry Ellard	.10
44 Terrell Owens	.75
45 John Friesz	.10
46 *Antowain Smith*	2.00
47 Charles Johnson	.10
48 Rickey Dudley	.10
49 Lake Dawson	.10
50 Bert Emanuel	.10
51 Zach Thomas	.30
52 Ernest Byner	.10
53 *Yatil Green*	.75
54 Chris Spielman	.10
55 Muhsin Muhammad	.30
56 Bobby Engram	.20
57 Eric Bjornson	.10
58 Willie Green	.10
59 Derrick Mayes	.10
60 Chris Sanders	.10
61 Jimmy Smith	.10
62 *Tony Gonzalez*	.75
63 Rich Gannon	.10
64 Stanley Pritchett	.10
65 Brad Johnson	.10
66 Rodney Peete	.10
67 Sam Gash	.10
68 Chris Calloway	.10
69 Chris T. Jones	.10
70 *Will Blackwell*	.50
71 Mark Bruener	.10
72 Terry Kirby	.10
73 Brian Blades	.10
74 Craig Heyward	.10
75 Jamie Asher	.10
76 Terance Mathis	.10
77 *Troy Davis*	.50
78 Bruce Smith	.10
79 Simeon Rice	.10
80 Fred Barnett	.10
81 Tim Brown	.20
82 James Jett	.10
83 Mark Carrier	.10
84 Shawn Jefferson	.10
85 Ken Dilger	.10
86 *Rae Carruth*	1.00
87 Keenan McCardell	.10
88 Michael Irvin	.20
89 Mark Chmura	.20
90 Derrick Alexander	.10
91 Andre Reed	.10
92 Ed McCaffrey	.10
93 Erik Kramer	.10
94 Albert Connell	.10
95 Frank Wycheck	.10
96 Zach Crockett	.10
97 Jim Everett	.10
98 Michael Haynes	.10
99 Jeff Graham	.10
100 Brent Jones	.10
101 Troy Aikman	3.50
102 *Byron Hanspard*	.50
103 Robert Brooks	.50
104 Karim Abdul-Jabbar	2.50
105 Drew Bledsoe	3.50
106 Napoleon Kaufman	.40
107 Steve Young	2.50
108 Leeland McElroy	.40
109 Jamal Anderson	1.50
110 *David LaFleur*	1.75
111 Vinny Testaverde	.40
112 Eric Moulds	.75
113 Tim Biakabutuka	.75
114 Rick Mirer	.75
115 Jeff Blake	.75
116 Jim Schwantz	.40
117 Herman Moore	1.00
118 *Ike Hilliard*	4.00
119 Reggie White	.75
120 Steve McNair	2.00
121 Marshall Faulk	1.25
122 Natrone Means	.75
123 Greg Hill	.40
124 O.J. McDuffie	.40
125 Robert Smith	.40
126 *Bryant Westbrook*	1.25
127 Ray Zellars	.40
128 Rodney Hampton	.40
129 Wayne Chrebet	.40
130 Desmond Howard	.75
131 Ty Detmer	.75
132 Erric Pegram	.40
133 Yancey Thigpen	.40
134 *Danny Wuerffel*	4.00
135 Charlie Jones	.40
136 Chris Warren	.75
137 Isaac Bruce	1.25
138 Errict Rhett	1.00
139 Gus Frerotte	.40
140 Frank Sanders	.40
141 Todd Collins	.40
142 *Jake Plummer*	10.00
143 Darnay Scott	.75
144 Rashaan Salaam	.75
145 Terrell Davis	4.00
146 Scott Mitchell	.40
147 Junior Seau	.75
148 Warren Moon	.40

149	Wesley Walls	.40
150	Daryl Johnston	.40
151	Brett Favre	14.00
152	Emmitt Smith	12.00
153	Dan Marino	12.00
154	Larry Centers	1.00
155	Michael Jackson	1.00
156	Kerry Collins	2.00
157	Curtis Conway	2.00
158	Peter Boulware	1.00
159	Carl Pickens	2.00
160	Shannon Sharpe	2.00
161	Brett Perriman	1.00
162	Eddie George	8.00
163	Mark Brunell	6.00
164	Tamarick Vanover	2.00
165	Cris Carter	1.00
166	*Corey Dillon*	10.00
167	Curtis Martin	7.00
168	Amani Toomer	1.00
169	Jeff George	1.00
170	Kordell Stewart	6.00
171	Garrison Hearst	1.00
172	Tony Banks	3.00
173	Mike Alstott	2.00
174	*Jim Druckenmiller*	10.00
175	Chris Chandler	1.00
176	Bam Morris	1.00
177	Billy Joe Hobert	1.00
178	Ernie Mills	1.00
179	Ki-Jana Carter	1.00
180	Deion Sanders	4.00
181	Ricky Watters	2.00
182	*Shawn Springs*	3.00
183	Barry Sanders	10.00
184	Antonio Freeman	3.00
185	Marvin Harrison	3.00
186	Elvis Grbac	1.00
187	Terry Glenn	5.00
188	Willie Roaf	1.00
189	Keyshawn Johnson	3.00
190	*Orlando Pace*	3.00
191	Jerome Bettis	2.00
192	Tony Martin	1.00
193	Jerry Rice	6.00
194	Joey Galloway	2.00
195	Terry Allen	2.00
196	Eddie Kennison	3.00
197	Thurman Thomas	2.00
198	Darrell Russell	1.00
199	Rob Moore	1.00
200	John Elway	5.00

1997 Playoff Absolute Autographed Pennants

Measuring 3-1/2" x 5", one of the eight signed pennants were randomly inserted in boxes of Playoff Absolute. The cards are numbered with an "A" prefix.

		MT
Complete Set (8):		600.00
Common Player:		40.00
1	Kordell Stewart	125.00
2	Eddie George	175.00
3	Karim Abdul-Jabbar	75.00
4	Mike Alstott	40.00
5	Terry Glenn	80.00
6	Napoleon Kaufman	40.00
7	Terry Allen	40.00
8	Tim Brown	40.00

1997 Playoff Absolute Chip Shots

Inserted one per pack, the Chip Shots resembled poker chips. The chips, which measure approximately 1-1/2" in diameter, were available in assorted colors. The plastic tokens were a 200-player parallel of the base set.

		MT
Complete Set (200):		220.00
Common Player:		.40
Minor Stars:		.75
1	Marcus Allen	.75
2	Eric Bieniemy	.40
3	Jason Dunn	.40
4	Jim Harbaugh	.40
5	Michael Westbrook	.40
6	Tiki Barber	4.00
7	Frank Reich	.40
8	Irving Fryar	.40
9	Courtney Hawkins	.40
10	Eric Zeier	.40
11	Kent Graham	.40
12	Trent Dilfer	.75
13	Neil O'Donnell	.40
14	Reidel Anthony	4.00
15	Jeff Hostetler	.40
16	Lawrence Phillips	.75
17	Dave Brown	.40
18	Mike Tomczak	.40
19	Jake Reed	.40
20	Anthony Miller	.40

21	Eric Metcalf	.40
22	Sedrick Shaw	1.00
23	Anthony Johnson	.40
24	Mario Bates	.40
25	Dorsey Levens	1.00
26	Stan Humphries	.40
27	Ben Coates	.40
28	Tyrone Wheatley	.40
29	Adrian Murrell	.40
30	William Henderson	.40
31	Warrick Dunn	10.00
32	LeShon Johnson	.40
33	James Stewart	.40
34	Edgar Bennett	.40
35	Raymont Harris	.40
36	Leroy Butler	.40
37	Darren Woodson	.40
38	Darnell Autry	2.00
39	Johnnie Morton	.40
40	William Floyd	.40
41	Terrell Fletcher	.40
42	Leonard Russell	.40
43	Henry Ellard	.40
44	Terrell Owens	4.00
45	John Friesz	.40
46	Antowain Smith	5.00
47	Charles Johnson	.40
48	Rickey Dudley	.40
49	Lake Dawson	.40
50	Bert Emanuel	.40
51	Zach Thomas	1.00
52	Ernest Byner	.40
53	Yatil Green	3.00
54	Chris Spielman	.40
55	Muhsin Muhammad	.75
56	Bobby Engram	.75
57	Eric Bjornson	.40
58	Willie Green	.40
59	Derrick Mayes	.40
60	Chris Sanders	.40
61	Jimmy Smith	.40
62	Tony Gonzalez	1.00
63	Rich Gannon	.40
64	Stanley Pritchett	.40
65	Brad Johnson	.75
66	Rodney Peete	.40
67	Sam Gash	.40
68	Chris Calloway	.40
69	Chris T. Jones	.40
70	Will Blackwell	.75
71	Mark Bruener	.40
72	Terry Kirby	.40
73	Brian Blades	.40
74	Craig Heyward	.40
75	Jamie Asher	.40
76	Terance Mathis	.40
77	Troy Davis	3.00
78	Bruce Smith	.40
79	Simeon Rice	.40
80	Fred Barnett	.40
81	Tim Brown	.40
82	James Jett	.40
83	Mark Carrier	.40
84	Shawn Jefferson	.40
85	Ken Dilger	.40
86	Rae Carruth	2.00
87	Keenan McCardell	.75
88	Michael Irvin	.75
89	Mark Chmura	.40
90	Derrick Alexander	.40
91	Andre Reed	.40
92	Ed McCaffrey	.40
93	Erik Kramer	.40
94	Albert Connell	.40
95	Frank Wycheck	.40
96	Zach Crockett	.40
97	Jim Everett	.40
98	Michael Haynes	.40
99	Jeff Graham	.40
100	Brent Jones	.40
101	Troy Aikman	7.00
102	Byron Hanspard	2.00
103	Robert Brooks	.75
104	Karim Abdul-Jabbar	4.00
105	Drew Bledsoe	7.00
106	Napoleon Kaufman	.75
107	Steve Young	4.00
108	Leeland McElroy	.40
109	Jamal Anderson	1.00
110	David LaFleur	1.50
111	Vinny Testaverde	.40
112	Eric Moulds	.75
113	Tim Biakabutuka	.75
114	Rick Mirer	.40
115	Jeff Blake	1.00
116	Jim Schwantz	.40
117	Herman Moore	1.00
118	Ike Hilliard	4.00
119	Reggie White	.75
120	Steve McNair	4.00
121	Marshall Faulk	1.00
122	Natrone Means	.75
123	Greg Hill	.40
124	O.J. McDuffie	.40
125	Robert Smith	.40
126	Bryant Westbrook	1.00
127	Ray Zellars	.40
128	Rodney Hampton	.40
129	Wayne Chrebet	.40
130	Desmond Howard	.40
131	Ty Detmer	.40
132	Erric Pegram	.40
133	Yancey Thigpen	.40
134	Danny Wuerffel	4.00
135	Charlie Jones	.40
136	Chris Warren	.40
137	Isaac Bruce	1.00
138	Errict Rhett	.75

139	Gus Frerotte	.40
140	Frank Sanders	.40
141	Todd Collins	.40
142	Jake Plummer	6.00
143	Darnay Scott	.40
144	Rashaan Salaam	.75
145	Terrell Davis	8.00
146	Scott Mitchell	.40
147	Junior Seau	.75
148	Warren Moon	.40
149	Wesley Walls	.40
150	Daryl Johnston	.40
151	Brett Favre	14.00
152	Emmitt Smith	12.00
153	Dan Marino	12.00
154	Larry Centers	.40
155	Michael Jackson	.40
156	Kerry Collins	1.00
157	Curtis Conway	.75
158	Peter Boulware	.75
159	Carl Pickens	.40
160	Shannon Sharpe	.40
161	Brett Perriman	.40
162	Eddie George	10.00
163	Mark Brunell	7.00
164	Tamarick Vanover	.75
165	Cris Carter	.40
166	Corey Dillon	6.00
167	Curtis Martin	8.00
168	Amani Toomer	.40
169	Jeff George	.40
170	Kordell Stewart	7.00
171	Garrison Hearst	.40
172	Tony Banks	3.00
173	Mike Alstott	3.00
174	Jim Druckenmiller	7.00
175	Chris Chandler	.40
176	Bam Morris	.40
177	Billy Joe Hobert	.40
178	Ernie Mills	.40
179	Ki-Jana Carter	.40
180	Deion Sanders	3.00
181	Ricky Watters	.75
182	Shawn Springs	1.00
183	Barry Sanders	10.00
184	Antonio Freeman	1.00
185	Marvin Harrison	3.00
186	Elvis Grbac	.40
187	Terry Glenn	6.00
188	Willie Roaf	.40
189	Keyshawn Johnson	3.00
190	Orlando Pace	2.00
191	Jerome Bettis	.75
192	Tony Martin	.40
193	Jerry Rice	7.00
194	Joey Galloway	1.00
195	Terry Allen	.40
196	Eddie Kennison	3.00
197	Thurman Thomas	.75
198	Darrell Russell	.75
199	Rob Moore	.75
200	John Elway	4.00

1997 Playoff Absolute Leather Quads

The 18-card set, which was produced on leather, was inserted 1:144 packs. Each card included four players, with two appearing on each side. The player photos were superimposed over the leather background. The players' names are printed vertically in green along the left and right borders. "Leather Quad" is printed in white over a black stripe which runs diagonally between the two players' photos. The Playoff logo and "1997" are printed in green at the bottom center on both sides of the cards. The card numbers appear in the top center inside a green oval on both sides of the cards with a "LQ" prefix.

		MT
Complete Set (18):		1200.
Common Player:		20.00
Minor Stars:		40.00
1	Brett Favre, Jerry Rice, Dan Marino, Emmitt Smith	300.00
2	Barry Sanders, Terrell Davis, Eddie George, Curtis Martin	180.00
3	Kordell Stewart, Herman Moore, Elvis Grbac, Chris Warren	75.00
4	Troy Aikman, Leeland McElroy, Cris Carter, Zach Thomas	75.00
5	Drew Bledsoe, Jamal Anderson, Michael Jackson, Jim Harbaugh	75.00
6	John Elway, Reggie White, Warren Moon, Terrell Owens	60.00
7	Kerry Collins, Rashaan Salaam, Shannon Sharpe, Ricky Watters	75.00
8	Mark Brunell, Eric Moulds, Mario Bates, Larry Centers	75.00
9	Karim Abdul-Jabbar, Robert Brooks, Jerome Bettis, Carl Pickens	60.00
10	Steve Young, Tim Biakabutuka, Jeff George, Tony Martin	50.00
11	Terry Glenn, Jeff Blake, Mike Alstott, Curtis Conway	50.00
12	Joey Galloway, Antonio Freeman, Anthony Johnson, Rick Mirer	40.00
13	Steve McNair, Marshall Faulk, Jimmy Smith, Isaac Bruce	50.00
14	Deion Sanders, Tony Banks, Vinny Testaverde, Rodney Hampton	40.00
15	Marvin Harrison, Lawrence Phillips, Thurman Thomas, Chris Chandler	20.00
16	Keyshawn Johnson, Napoleon Kaufman, Gus Frerotte, Greg Hill	20.00
17	Eddie Kennison, Terry Allen, Scott Mitchell, Errict Rhett	20.00
18	Warrick Dunn, Orlando Pace, Jim Druckenmiller, Darrell Russell	80.00

1997 Playoff Absolute Pennants

Inserted one per box, the pennants measure 3-1/2" x 5". Each of the 192 pennants in the set have a felt-like feel to them. The pennant fronts have the player's name printed inside a rectangle in the upper left, while a cutout color action photo of the player is included in the center of the pennant. The Playoff Pennants 1997 logo is on the right of the front. The vertical backs have the player's name, appropriate logos and pennant number in a stripe at the top. The player's headshot is included inside a circle in the center of the back, which also has a felt-like feel to it. The Playoff Pennants' logo is on the bottom of the back.

		MT
Common Player:		5.00
Minor Stars:		10.00
1	Marcus Allen	10.00
2	Eric Bieniemy	5.00
3	Jason Dunn	5.00
4	Jim Harbaugh (QBC)	5.00
5	Michael Westbrook	5.00
6	Tiki Barber	5.00
7	Frank Reich (QBC)	5.00
8	Irving Fryar	5.00
9	Courtney Hawkins	5.00
10	Eric Zeier	5.00
11	Kent Graham	5.00
12	Trent Dilfer (QBC)	10.00
13	Neil O'Donnell (QBC)	5.00
14	Reidel Anthony	30.00
15	Jeff Hostetler (QBC)	5.00
16	Lawrence Phillips	10.00
17	Dave Brown (QBC)	5.00
18	Mike Tomczak	5.00
19	Jake Reed	5.00
20	Anthony Miller	5.00
21	Eric Metcalf	5.00
22	Sedrick Shaw	20.00
23	Anthony Johnson	5.00
24	Mario Bates	5.00
25	Dorsey Levens	10.00
26	Stan Humphries	5.00
27	Ben Coates	5.00
28	Tyrone Wheatley	5.00
29	Adrian Murrell	5.00
30	William Henderson	5.00
31	Warrick Dunn	65.00
32	LeShon Johnson	5.00
33	James Stewart	5.00
34	Edgar Bennett	5.00
35	Raymont Harris	5.00
36	Leroy Butler	5.00
37	Darren Woodson	5.00
38	Darnell Autry	20.00
39	Johnnie Morton	5.00
40	William Floyd	10.00
41	Terrell Fletcher	5.00
42	Leonard Russell	5.00
43	Henry Ellard	5.00
44	Terrell Owens	40.00
45	John Friesz	5.00
46	Antowain Smith	25.00
47	Charles Johnson	5.00
48	Rickey Dudley	5.00
49	Lake Dawson	5.00
50	Bert Emanuel	5.00
51	Zach Thomas	15.00
52	Earnest Byner	5.00
53	Yatil Green	25.00
54	Chris Spielman	5.00
55	Muhsin Muhammad	5.00
56	Bobby Engram	5.00
57	Eric Bjornson	5.00
58	Willie Green	5.00
59	Derrick Mayes	5.00
60	Chris Sanders	5.00
61	Jimmy Smith	5.00
62	Tony Gonzalez	20.00
63	Rich Gannon	5.00
64	Stanley Pritchett	5.00
65	Brad Johnson	10.00
66	Rodney Peete (QBC)	5.00
67	Sam Gash	5.00
68	Chris Galloway	5.00
69	Chris T. Jones	5.00
70	Will Blackwell	10.00
71	Mark Bruener	5.00
72	Terry Kirby	5.00
73	Brian Blades	5.00
74	Craig Heyward	5.00
75	Jamie Asher	5.00
76	Terance Mathis	5.00
77	Troy Davis	10.00
78	Bruce Smith	5.00
79	Simeon Rice	5.00
80	Fred Barnett	5.00
81	Jerry Rice	75.00
82	James Jett	5.00
83	Mark Carrier	5.00
84	Shawn Jefferson	5.00
85	Ken Dilger	5.00
86	Rae Carruth	25.00
87	Keenan McCardell	10.00
88	Michael Irvin (QBC)	10.00
89	Mark Chmura	10.00
90	Derrick Alexander	5.00
91	Andre Reed	5.00
92	Ed McCaffrey	5.00
93	Erik Kramer (QBC)	5.00
94	Albert Connell	5.00
95	Frank Wycheck	5.00
96	Zach Crockett	5.00
97	Jim Everett (QBC)	5.00
98	Michael Haynes	5.00
99	Jeff Graham	5.00
100	Brent Jones	5.00
101	Troy Aikman (QBC)	75.00
102	Byron Hanspard	25.00
103	Robert Brooks	10.00
104	Joey Galloway	15.00
105	Drew Bledsoe (QBC)	75.00
106	Eddie Kennison	10.00
107	Steve Young (QBC)	50.00
108	Leeland McElroy	5.00
109	Jamal Anderson	15.00
110	David LaFleur	20.00
111	Vinny Testaverde	5.00
112	Eric Moulds	5.00

113	Tim Biakabutuka	10.00
114	Rick Mirer (QBC)	5.00
115	Jeff Blake (QBC)	15.00
116	Jim Schwantz	5.00
117	Herman Moore	25.00
118	Ike Hilliard	25.00
119	Reggie White	10.00
120	Steve McNair (QBC)	65.00
121	Marshall Faulk	10.00
122	Natrone Means	10.00
123	Greg Hill	5.00
124	O.J. McDuffie	5.00
125	Robert Smith	5.00
126	Bryant Westbrook	10.00
127	Ray Zellars	5.00
128	Rodney Hampton	5.00
129	Wayne Chrebet	5.00
130	Desmond Howard	5.00
131	Ty Detmer	5.00
132	Erric Pegram	5.00
133	Yancey Thigpen	5.00
134	Danny Wuerffel	25.00
135	Charlie Jones	5.00
136	Chris Warren	5.00
137	Isaac Bruce	15.00
138	Errict Rhett	10.00
139	Gus Frerotte (QBC)	5.00
140	Frank Sanders	5.00
141	Todd Collins	10.00
142	Jake Plummer	30.00
143	Darnay Scott	5.00
144	Rashaan Salaam	10.00
145	Terrell Davis	75.00
146	Scott Mitchell (QBC)	5.00
147	Junior Seau (QBC)	10.00
148	Warren Moon (QBC)	5.00
149	Wesley Walls	5.00
150	Daryl Johnston	5.00
151	Brett Favre (QBC)	130.00
152	Emmitt Smith	100.00
153	Dan Marino (QBC)	100.00
154	Larry Centers	5.00
155	Michael Jackson	5.00
156	Kerry Collins (QBC)	10.00
157	Curtis Conway	10.00
158	Peter Boulware	5.00
159	Carl Pickens	10.00
160	Shannon Sharpe	5.00
161	Brett Perriman	5.00
162	Thurman Thomas	10.00
163	Mark Brunell (QBC)	75.00
164	Tamarick Vanover	10.00
165	Cris Carter	10.00
166	Corey Dillon	40.00
167	Curtis Martin	60.00
168	Amani Toomer	5.00
169	Jeff George (QBC)	5.00
170	Darrell Russell	5.00
171	Garrison Hearst	5.00
172	Tony Banks (QBC)	10.00
173	Rob Moore	5.00
174	Jim Druckenmiller	45.00
175	Chris Chandler	5.00
176	Bam Morris	5.00
177	Billy Joe Hobert	5.00
178	Ernie Mills	5.00
179	Ki-Jana Carter	10.00
180	Deion Sanders	35.00
181	Ricky Watters	10.00
182	Shawn Springs	20.00
183	Barry Sanders (QBC)	85.00
184	Antonio Freeman	15.00
185	Marvin Harrison	35.00
186	Elvis Grbac (QBC)	5.00
187	John Elway (QBC)	50.00
188	Willie Roaf	5.00
189	Keyshawn Johnson	35.00
190	Orlando Pace	15.00
191	Jerome Bettis	10.00
192	Tony Martin	5.00

1997 Playoff Absolute Playoff Honors

This three-card set, which was inserted 1:7,200 packs, was a continuation from the 1996 Playoff Prime and Contenders sets. The felt-like cards feature a player photo superimposed over a checkered background on the front. The Playoff Honors' logo appears in one of the upper corners of the card, with the player's name printed in a lower corner. The cards carry a prefix of "PF."

		MT
Complete Set (3):		350.00
Common Player:		50.00
7	Jerry Rice	125.00
8	Reggie White	50.00
9	John Elway	200.00

1997 Playoff Absolute Reflex

The 200-card set is a parallel of the base set printed on mirror board. The card fronts have "Reflex" printed at the top, with the player's photo superimposed over a silver mirror background. "Playoff '97" is printed vertically along the left border, while his name is printed vertically along the right border. The cards were inserted 1:288 packs.

		MT
	Common Player:	30.00
	Minor Stars:	60.00
1	Brett Favre	750.00
2	Dorsey Levens	60.00
3	Antonio Freeman	60.00
4	Robert Brooks	30.00
5	Mark Chmura	60.00
6	Reggie White	60.00
7	Drew Bledsoe	350.00
8	Curtis Martin	275.00
9	Ben Coates	30.00
10	Terry Glenn	100.00
11	Kerry Collins	75.00
12	Tim Biakabutuka	30.00
13	Anthony Johnson	30.00
14	Wesley Walls	30.00
15	Muhsin Muhammad	30.00
16	Mark Brunell	350.00
17	Natrone Means	60.00
18	Jimmy Smith	30.00
19	John Elway	400.00
20	Terrell Davis	400.00
21	Anthony Miller	30.00
22	Shannon Sharpe	30.00
23	Steve Young	300.00
24	Garrison Hearst	30.00
25	Jerry Rice	350.00
26	Troy Aikman	350.00
27	Deion Sanders	200.00
28	Emmitt Smith	600.00
29	Michael Irvin	60.00
30	Kordell Stewart	350.00
31	Jerome Bettis	60.00
32	Charles Johnson	30.00
33	Ty Detmer	30.00
34	Ricky Watters	60.00
35	Irving Fryar	30.00
36	Todd Collins	30.00
37	Thurman Thomas	60.00
38	Bruce Smith	30.00
39	Eric Moulds	30.00
40	Brad Johnson	60.00
41	Robert Smith	60.00
42	Cris Carter	60.00
43	Elvis Grbac	30.00
44	Greg Hill	30.00
45	Marcus Allen	60.00
46	Gus Frerotte	30.00
47	Terry Allen	60.00
48	Michael Westbrook	30.00
49	Jim Harbaugh	60.00
50	Marshall Faulk	60.00
51	Marvin Harrison	100.00
52	Jeff Blake	60.00
53	Ki-Jana Carter	30.00
54	Carl Pickens	30.00
55	Junior Seau	60.00
56	Tony Martin	30.00
57	Dan Marino	600.00
58	Karim Abdul-Jabbar	100.00
59	Stanley Pritchett	30.00
60	Zach Thomas	30.00
61	Steve McNair	250.00
62	Eddie George	350.00
63	Chris Sanders	30.00
64	Rick Mirer	30.00
65	Rashaan Salaam	60.00
66	Curtis Conway	30.00
67	Bobby Engram	30.00
68	Kent Graham	30.00
69	Leeland McElroy	30.00
70	Larry Centers	30.00
71	Frank Sanders	30.00
72	Jeff George	60.00
73	Napoleon Kaufman	200.00
74	Desmond Howard	30.00
75	Tim Brown	60.00
76	John Friesz	30.00
77	Chris Warren	30.00
78	Joey Galloway	100.00
79	Tony Banks	100.00
80	Lawrence Phillips	60.00
81	Isaac Bruce	100.00
82	Eddie Kennison	100.00
83	Errict Rhett	60.00
84	Mike Alstott	125.00
85	Rodney Hampton	30.00
86	Amani Toomer	30.00
87	Scott Mitchell	30.00
88	Barry Sanders	525.00
89	Herman Moore	60.00
90	Vinny Testaverde	30.00
91	Bam Morris	30.00
92	Michael Jackson	30.00
93	Chris Chandler	30.00
94	Eric Metcalf	30.00
95	Jamal Anderson	60.00
96	Jim Everett	30.00
97	Mario Bates	30.00
98	Wayne Chrebet	30.00
99	Adrian Murrell	60.00
100	Keyshawn Johnson	60.00
101	William Henderson	30.00
102	Edgar Bennett	30.00
103	LeRoy Butler	30.00
104	Derrick Mayes	30.00
105	Sedrick Shaw	60.00
106	Sam Gash	30.00
107	Shawn Jefferson	30.00
108	Mark Carrier	30.00
109	Rae Carruth	100.00
110	Ernie Mills	30.00
111	James Stewart	30.00
112	Keenan McCardell	30.00
113	Willie Green	30.00
114	Ed McCaffrey	30.00
115	William Floyd	30.00
116	Terrell Owens	100.00
117	Terry Kirby	30.00
118	Brent Jones	30.00
119	Jim Schwantz	30.00
120	Jim Druckenmiller	150.00
121	Darren Woodson	30.00
122	Eric Bjornson	30.00
123	David LaFleur	60.00
124	Daryl Johnston	30.00
125	Mike Tomczak	30.00
126	Will Blackwell	30.00
127	Mark Bruener	30.00
128	Erric Pegram	30.00
129	Yancey Thigpen	30.00
130	Jason Dunn	30.00
131	Chris T. Jones	30.00
132	Rodney Peete	30.00
133	Antowain Smith	150.00
134	Chris Spielman	30.00
135	Andre Reed	30.00
136	Billy Joe Hobert	30.00
137	Jake Reed	30.00
138	Tamarick Vanover	30.00
139	Lake Dawson	30.00
140	Tony Gonzalez	60.00
141	Rich Gannon	30.00
142	Henry Ellard	30.00
143	Jamie Asher	30.00
144	Albert Connell	30.00
145	Ken Dilger	30.00
146	Zack Crockett	30.00
147	Eric Bieniemy	30.00
148	Darnay Scott	30.00
149	Corey Dillon	175.00
150	Stan Humphries	30.00
151	Terrell Fletcher	30.00
152	Leonard Russell	30.00
153	Charlie Jones	30.00
154	Yatil Green	100.00
155	Fred Barnett	30.00
156	O.J. McDuffie	30.00
157	Frank Wycheck	30.00
158	Raymont Harris	30.00
159	Darnell Autry	60.00
160	Erik Kramer	30.00
161	LeShon Johnson	30.00
162	Simeon Rice	30.00
163	Jake Plummer	200.00
164	Rob Moore	30.00
165	Jeff Hostetler	30.00
166	Rickey Dudley	30.00
167	James Jett	30.00
168	Darrell Russell	30.00
169	Brian Blades	30.00
170	Warren Moon	60.00
171	Shawn Springs	30.00
172	Craig Heyward	30.00
173	Orlando Pace	60.00
174	Courtney Hawkins	30.00
175	Trent Dilfer	60.00
176	Reidel Anthony	100.00
177	Warrick Dunn	200.00
178	Tiki Barber	100.00
179	Dave Brown	30.00
180	Tyrone Wheatley	30.00
181	Chris Calloway	30.00
182	Ike Hilliard	100.00
183	Frank Reich	30.00
184	Johnnie Morton	30.00
185	Bryant Westbrook	30.00
186	Brett Perriman	30.00
187	Eric Zeier	30.00
188	Earnest Byner	30.00
189	Derrick Alexander	30.00
190	Peter Boulware	30.00
191	Bert Emanuel	30.00
192	Terance Mathis	30.00
193	Byron Hanspard	75.00
194	Troy Davis	75.00
195	Michael Haynes	30.00
196	Ray Zellars	30.00
197	Danny Wuerffel	75.00
198	Willie Roaf	30.00
199	Neil O'Donnell	30.00
200	Jeff Graham	30.00

> Values quoted in this guide reflect the retail price of a card — the price a collector can expect to pay when buying a card from a dealer. The wholesale price — that which a collector can expect to receive from a dealer when selling cards — will be significantly lower, depending on desirability and condition.

1997 Playoff Absolute Unsung Heroes

The 30-card set honors the players selected as the 1996 Playoff/Players Inc. Unsung Heroes, which were voted on by the fans and players. In its third year, the set includes a color photo of the player superimposed over a silver background on the right side of the front. His name is printed in the upper right. A black-and-white close-up photo, which is an enlarged version of the color photo, is printed on the left side of the card, with "1997" printed over the top of it. The Unsung Heroes logo is printed at the bottom. The backs are numbered in a red box in the upper left. The player's name, bio and write-up are printed on the left side over a green background. Along the right side of the back is a color headshot of the player. The cards were inserted 1:12 packs.

		MT
	Complete Set (30):	20.00
	Common Player:	.50
	Minor Stars:	1.00
1	Larry Centers	.50
2	Jessie Tuggle	.50
3	Stevon Moore	.50
4	Mark Pike	.50
5	Anthony Johnson	1.00
6	Anthony Carter	.50
7	Eric Bieniemy	.50
8	Jim Schwantz	.50
9	Tyrone Braxton	.50
10	Bennie Blades	.50
11	Don Beebe	.50
12	Barron Wortham	.50
13	Jason Belser	.50
14	Mickey Washington	.50
15	Dave Szott	.50
16	Zach Thomas	4.00
17	Chris Walsh	.50
18	Sam Gash	.50
19	Willie Roaf	.50
20	Charles Way	.50
21	Wayne Chrebet	1.00
22	Russell Maryland	.50
23	Michael Zordich	.50
24	Tim Lester	.50
25	Harold Green	.50
26	Rodney Harrison	.50
27	Gary Plummer	.50
28	Winston Moss	.50
29	Robb Thomas	.50
30	Darrick Brownlow	.50

1997 Playoff Contenders

Playoff Contenders includes a 150-card base set. Printed on 30 pt. stock, these cards feature player shots on each side, with foil etching and holographic technology. The player's name is added in silver on each side. A Blue Level parallel version was included in 1:4 packs, while a Red Level version was sequentially numbered to 25. Inserts include Playoff Clash, Leather Die-Cut Helmets, Playoff Plaques, Playoff Pennants and Playoff Rookie Wave Pennants.

		MT
	Complete Set (150):	140.00
	Common Player:	.50
	Minor Stars:	1.00
	Blue Cards:	2x-4x
	Blue Rookies:	2x
	Inserted 1:4	
	Red Cards:	40x-80x
	Red Rookies:	20x-40x
	Production 25 Sets	
	Wax Box:	85.00
1	Kent Graham	.50
2	Leeland McElroy	.50
3	Rob Moore	.50
4	Frank Sanders	.50
5	*Jake Plummer*	15.00
6	Chris Chandler	.50
7	Bert Emanuel	.50
8	O.J. Santiago	.50
9	*Byron Hanspard*	3.00
10	Vinny Testaverde	.50
11	Michael Jackson	.50
12	Ernest Byner	.50
13	Jermaine Lewis	.50
14	Derrick Alexander	.50
15	*Jay Graham*	1.00
16	Todd Collins	1.00
17	Thurman Thomas	1.00
18	Bruce Smith	.50
19	Andre Reed	.50
20	Quinn Early	.50
21	*Antowain Smith*	6.00
22	Kerry Collins	1.50
23	Tim Biakabutuka	.50
24	Anthony Johnson	.50
25	Wesley Johnson	.50
26	*Fred Lane*	3.00
27	Rae Carruth	4.00
28	Raymont Harris	.50
29	Rick Mirer	.50
30	*Darnell Autry*	3.00
31	Jeff Blake	1.00
32	Ki-Jana Carter	1.00
33	Carl Pickens	.50
34	Darnay Scott	.50
35	*Corey Dillon*	6.00
36	Troy Aikman	6.00
37	Emmitt Smith	10.00
38	Michael Irvin	1.00
39	Deion Sanders	3.00
40	Anthony Miller	.50
41	Eric Bjornson	.50
42	*David LaFleur*	3.00
43	John Elway	6.00
44	Terrell Davis	6.00
45	Shannon Sharpe	.50
46	Ed McCaffrey	.50
47	Rod Smith	.50
48	Scott Mitchell	.50
49	Barry Sanders	7.00
50	Herman Moore	2.00
51	Brett Favre	12.00
52	Dorsey Levens	1.00
53	William Henderson	.50
54	Derrick Mayes	.50
55	Antonio Freeman	1.00
56	Robert Brooks	.50
57	Mark Chmura	.50
58	Reggie White	1.00
59	Darren Sharper	.50
60	Jim Harbaugh	.50
61	Marshall Faulk	1.00
62	Marvin Harrison	2.00
63	Mark Brunell	6.00
64	Natrone Means	1.00
65	Jimmy Smith	.50
66	Keenan McCardell	.50
67	Elvis Grbac	.50
68	Greg Hill	.50
69	Marcus Allen	1.00
70	Andre Rison	.50
71	Kimble Anders	.50
72	*Tony Gonzalez*	6.00
73	*Pat Barnes*	2.00
74	Dan Marino	10.00
75	Karim Abdul-Jabbar	3.00
76	Zach Thomas	1.00
77	O.J. McDuffie	.50
78	*Brian Manning*	1.00
79	Brad Johnson	1.00
80	Cris Carter	1.00
81	Jake Reed	.50
82	Robert Smith	1.00
83	Drew Bledsoe	6.00
84	Curtis Martin	6.00
85	Ben Coates	.50
86	Terry Glenn	3.00
87	Shawn Jefferson	.50
88	Heath Shuler	.50
89	Andre Hastings	.50
90	*Troy Davis*	4.00
91	Ray Zellars	.50
92	*Danny Wuerffel*	4.00
93	Dave Brown	.50
94	Chris Calloway	.50
95	*Tiki Barber*	6.00
96	Mike Cherry	.50
97	Neil O'Donnell	1.00
98	Keyshawn Johnson	2.00
99	Adrian Murrell	1.00
100	Wayne Chrebet	.50
101	Dedric Ward	.50
102	Leon Johnson	.50
103	Jeff George	1.00
104	Napoleon Kaufman	2.00
105	Tim Brown	1.00
106	James Jett	.50
107	Ty Detmer	.50
108	Ricky Watters	1.00
109	Irving Fryar	.50
110	Michael Timpson	.50
111	Chad Lewis	.50
112	Kordell Stewart	6.00
113	Jerome Bettis	1.00
114	Charles Johnson	.50
115	*George Jones*	1.00
116	*Will Blackwell*	1.00
117	Stan Humphries	.50
118	Junior Seau	1.00
119	*Freddie Jones*	1.00
120	Steve Young	4.00
121	Jerry Rice	6.00
122	Garrison Hearst	.50
123	William Floyd	.50
124	Terrell Owens	3.00
125	J.J. Stokes	.50
126	Marc Edwards	.50
127	*Jim Druckenmiller*	8.00
128	Warren Moon	.50
129	Chris Warren	.50
130	Joey Galloway	1.00
131	*Shawn Springs*	1.00
132	Tony Banks	3.00
133	Lawrence Phillips	1.00
134	Isaac Bruce	1.00
135	Eddie Kennison	2.00
136	*Orlando Pace*	1.00
137	Trent Dilfer	1.00
138	Mike Alstott	3.00
139	Horace Copeland	.50
140	Jackie Harris	.50
141	*Warrick Dunn*	8.00
142	*Reidel Anthony*	6.00
143	Steve McNair	5.00
144	Eddie George	8.00
145	Chris Sanders	.50
146	Gus Frerotte	.50
147	Terry Allen	.50
148	Henry Ellard	.50
149	Leslie Shepherd	.50
150	Michael Westbrook	.50

1997 Playoff Contenders Clash

Clash is a 12-card insert highlighting some of the NFL's top match-ups. The cards feature two players with their team helmets die-cut in the background. Silver Level cards were inserted 1:48 and Blue Level cards were found 1:192.

		MT
	Complete Set (12):	500.00
	Common Player:	20.00
	Blue Cards:	3x
1	Brett Favre, Troy Aikman	100.00
2	Barry Sanders, Brad Johnson	75.00
3	Curtis Martin, Warrick Dunn	50.00
4	Steve Young, John Elway	40.00
5	Jerry Rice, Marcus Allen	50.00
6	Dan Marino, Drew Bledsoe	85.00
7	Terrell Davis, Napoleon Kaufman	50.00
8	Eddie George, Emmitt Smith	85.00
9	Mark Brunell, Tim Brown	40.00
10	Kerry Collins, Reggie White	25.00
11	Deion Sanders, Carl Pickens	20.00
12	Mike Alstott, Keyshawn Johnson	20.00

1997 Playoff Contenders Leather Helmets

This 18-card insert features a die-cut leather helmet. The Silver Level was found 1:24, Blue Level 1:216 and the Red Parallel was numbered to 25.

		MT
	Complete Set (18):	425.00
	Common Player:	6.00
	Minor Stars:	12.00
	Inserted 1:24	
	Blue Cards:	2x-4x
	Inserted 1:216	
	Red Cards:	5x-10x
	Production 25 Sets	
1	Dan Marino	40.00
2	Troy Aikman	25.00
3	Brett Favre	50.00
4	Barry Sanders	50.00
5	Drew Bledsoe	25.00
6	Deion Sanders	12.00
7	Curtis Martin	15.00
8	Warrick Dunn	20.00
9	Napoleon Kaufman	6.00
10	Eddie George	20.00
11	Antowain Smith	12.00
12	Emmitt Smith	40.00
13	John Elway	30.00
14	Steve Young	15.00
15	Mark Brunell	25.00
16	Terrell Davis	40.00
17	Terry Glenn	6.00
18	Terrell Owens	12.00

1997 Playoff Contenders Pennants

Pennants features player shots on a fuzzy pennant. The 36 cards came in Silver Level (1:12) and Blue Parallel (1:72) versions.

		MT
	Complete Set (36):	600.00
	Common Player:	4.00
	Minor Stars:	8.00
	Blue Cards:	4x
1	Dan Marino	40.00
2	Kordell Stewart	25.00
3	Drew Bledsoe	25.00
4	Kerry Collins	10.00
5	John Elway	20.00
6	Trent Dilfer	8.00
7	Jerry Rice	25.00
8	Emmitt Smith	40.00
9	Jeff George	4.00
10	Eddie George	30.00
11	Terrell Davis	25.00
12	Mike Alstott	10.00
13	Jim Druckenmiller	20.00
14	Antowain Smith	15.00
15	Marcus Allen	8.00
16	Jerome Bettis	8.00
17	Terrell Owens	8.00
18	Gus Frerotte	4.00
19	Troy Aikman	25.00
20	Andre Rison	4.00
21	Mark Brunell	25.00
22	Antonio Freeman	8.00
23	Brett Favre	50.00
24	Steve McNair	20.00
25	Barry Sanders	40.00
26	Steve Young	20.00
27	Curtis Martin	25.00
28	Napoleon Kaufman	8.00
29	Deion Sanders	12.00
30	Terry Glenn	18.00
31	Warrick Dunn	25.00
32	Danny Wuerffel	10.00
33	Elvis Grbac	4.00
34	Cris Carter	4.00
35	Joey Galloway	8.00
36	Corey Dillon	20.00

1997 Playoff Contenders Plaques

These 45 die-cut cards feature a player shot on a card designed to resemble a plaque. Plaques were made in Silver Level (1:12) and Blue Parallel (1:36) versions.

		MT
Complete Set (45):		600.00
Common Player:		4.00
Minor Stars:		8.00
Blue Cards:		3x
1	Jim Druckenmiller	20.00
2	Danny Wuerffel	10.00
3	Antowain Smith	15.00
4	Warrick Dunn	30.00
5	Terrell Owens	8.00
6	Elvis Grbac	4.00
7	Andre Rison	4.00
8	Tim Brown	4.00
9	Trent Dilfer	8.00
10	Brad Johnson	4.00
11	Deion Sanders	12.00
12	Dan Marino	50.00
13	Kerry Collins	10.00
14	Steve McNair	20.00
15	Eddie George	30.00
16	Ricky Watters	8.00
17	Jerome Bettis	8.00
18	Robert Brooks	4.00
19	Keyshawn Johnson	8.00
20	Antonio Freeman	8.00
21	Eddie Kennison	8.00
22	Mike Alstott	10.00
23	Brett Favre	60.00
24	Troy Aikman	25.00
25	Emmitt Smith	50.00
26	Terrell Davis	25.00
27	John Elway	20.00
28	Barry Sanders	35.00
29	Steve Young	20.00
30	Curtis Martin	25.00
31	Cris Carter	4.00
32	Drew Bledsoe	25.00
33	Mark Brunell	25.00
34	Kordell Stewart	25.00
35	Tony Banks	8.00
36	Napoleon Kaufman	8.00
37	Marcus Allen	8.00
38	Terry Glenn	10.00
39	Herman Moore	8.00
40	Michael Irvin	8.00
41	Joey Galloway	8.00
42	Karim Abdul-Jabbar	10.00
43	Reggie White	8.00
44	Jerry Rice	25.00
45	Gus Frerotte	4.00

1997 Playoff Contenders Rookie Wave

Similar to the Pennants, except with a wavy design, this 27-card insert was only available in Silver Level (1:6).

		MT
Complete Set (27):		150.00
Common Player:		1.50
Minor Stars:		3.00
1	Jim Druckenmiller	10.00
2	Antowain Smith	12.00
3	Will Blackwell	3.00
4	Tiki Barber	3.00
5	Rae Carruth	6.00
6	Jay Graham	3.00
7	Darnell Autry	4.00
8	David LaFleur	4.00
9	Tony Gonzalez	4.00
10	Chad Lewis	1.50
11	Freddie Jones	3.00
12	Shawn Springs	3.00
13	Danny Wuerffel	5.00
14	Warrick Dunn	15.00
15	Troy Davis	5.00
16	Reidel Anthony	8.00
17	Jake Plummer	25.00
18	Byron Hanspard	5.00
19	Fred Lane	4.00
20	Corey Dillon	12.00
21	Darren Sharper	3.00
22	Pat Barnes	5.00
23	Mike Cherry	1.50
24	Leon Johnson	1.50
25	George Jones	3.00
26	Marc Edwards	1.50
27	Orlando Pace	3.00

1997 Playoff Zone

Playoff Zone consists of a 150-card base set done on 24 pt. Techchrome and 14 insert sets. The inserts include Prime Target, Prime Target Parallel, Sharp Shooters, Sharp Shooters Parallel, Rookies, Close-Ups, Frenzy and Treasures as well as a "1 of 5" parallel set of each insert. The parallels are limited to five each and are sequentially numbered.

		MT
Complete Set (150):		40.00
Common Player:		.10
Minor Stars:		.20
Wax Box:		40.00
1	Brett Favre	3.00
2	Dorsey Levens	.20
3	William Henderson	.10
4	Derrick Mayes	.10
5	Antonio Freeman	.20
6	Robert Brooks	.10
7	Mark Chmura	.10
8	Reggie White	.20
9	Randall Cunningham	.10
10	Brad Johnson	.20
11	Robert Smith	.10
12	Cris Carter	.10
13	Jake Reed	.10
14	Trent Dilfer	.20
15	Errict Rhett	.10
16	Mike Alstott	.20
17	Scott Mitchell	.10
18	Barry Sanders	2.00
19	Herman Moore	.20
20	Erik Kramer	.10
21	Rick Mirer	.10
22	Rashaan Salaam	.10
23	Troy Aikman	1.50
24	Deion Sanders	.75
25	Emmitt Smith	2.50
26	Daryl Johnston	.10
27	Anthony Miller	.10
28	Eric Bjornson	.10
29	Michael Irvin	.20
30	Chris Jones	.10
31	Ty Detmer	.10
32	Ricky Watters	.20
33	Irving Fryar	.10
34	Rodney Peete	.10
35	Jeff Hostetler	.10
36	Terry Allen	.20
37	Michael Westbrook	.10
38	Gus Frerotte	.10
39	Frank Sanders	.10
40	Larry Centers	.10
41	Kent Graham	.10
42	Dave Brown	.10
43	Rodney Hampton	.10
44	Tyrone Wheatley	.10
45	Chris Calloway	.10
46	Ernie Mills	.10
47	Tim Biakabutuka	.10
48	Anthony Johnson	.10
49	Wesley Walls	.10
50	Muhsin Muhammad	.10
51	Kerry Collins	.30
52	Terrell Owens	1.00
53	Garrison Hearst	.10
54	Jerry Rice	1.50
55	Steve Young	1.00
56	Lawrence Phillips	.10
57	Isaac Bruce	.20
58	Eddie Kennison	.50
59	Tony Banks	.75
60	Heath Shuler	.10
61	Andre Hastings	.10
62	Mario Bates	.10
63	Chris Chandler	.10
64	Jamal Anderson	.10
65	Bert Emanuel	.10
66	Drew Bledsoe	1.50
67	Curtis Martin	1.50
68	Ben Coates	.10
69	Terry Glenn	.40
70	Dan Marino	2.50
71	Karim Abdul-Jabbar	.40
72	Fred Barnett	.10
73	O.J. McDuffie	.10
74	Jim Harbaugh	.10
75	Marshall Faulk	.20
76	Zack Crockett	.10
77	Ken Dilger	.10
78	Marvin Harrison	.50
79	Keyshawn Johnson	.50
80	Neil O'Donnell	.10
81	Adrian Murrell	.20
82	Wayne Chrebet	.10
83	Todd Collins	.10
84	Thurman Thomas	.20
85	Bruce Smith	.10
86	Eric Moulds	.10
87	Rob Johnson	.10
88	Mark Brunell	1.50
89	Natrone Means	.20
90	Jimmy Smith	.10
91	Keenan McCardell	.10
92	Kordell Stewart	1.50
93	Jerome Bettis	.20
94	Charles Johnson	.10
95	Courtney Hawkins	.10
96	Greg Lloyd	.10
97	Ki-Jana Carter	.10
98	Carl Pickens	.10
99	Jeff Blake	.20
100	Steve McNair	1.00
101	Chris Sanders	.10
102	Eddie George	2.00
103	Vinny Testaverde	.10
104	Michael Jackson	.10
105	Derrick Alexander	.10
106	Willie Green	.10
107	Shannon Sharpe	.10
108	Rod Smith	.10
109	Terrell Davis	1.50
110	John Elway	1.00
111	Elvis Grbac	.10
112	Greg Hill	.10
113	Marcus Allen	.20
114	Derrick Thomas	.20
115	Brett Perriman	.10
116	Andre Rison	.10
117	Rickey Dudley	.10
118	Tim Brown	.10
119	Desmond Howard	.10
120	Napoleon Kaufman	.30
121	Jeff George	.20
122	Warren Moon	.10
123	John Friesz	.10
124	Chris Warren	.10
125	Joey Galloway	.20
126	Stan Humphries	.10
127	Tony Martin	.10
128	Eric Metcalf	.10
129	Jim Everett	.10
130	*Warrick Dunn*	3.00
131	*Reidel Anthony*	2.50
132	*Derrick Mason*	.10
133	*Joey Kent*	.20
134	*Will Blackwell*	.20
135	*Jim Druckenmiller*	3.00
136	*Byron Hanspard*	.50
137	*John Allred*	.10
138	*David LaFleur*	1.00
139	*Danny Wuerffel*	2.00
140	*Tiki Barber*	2.00
141	*Ike Hilliard*	1.50
142	*Troy Davis*	.30
143	*Sedrick Shaw*	.10
144	*Tony Gonzalez*	1.00
145	*Jake Plummer*	6.00
146	*Antowain Smith*	2.00
147	*Rae Carruth*	1.75
148	*Darnell Autry*	1.00
149	*Corey Dillon*	3.00
150	*Orlando Pace*	.20

1997 Playoff Zone Close-Up

This 32-card insert features helmetless close-ups of top NFL players. The cards were inserted 1:6.

		MT
Complete Set (32):		100.00
Common Player:		.75
Minor Stars:		1.50
1	Brett Favre	12.00
2	Mark Brunell	5.00
3	Dan Marino	10.00
4	Kerry Collins	2.00
5	Troy Aikman	5.00
6	Drew Bledsoe	5.00
7	John Elway	4.00
8	Kordell Stewart	5.00
9	Steve Young	4.00
10	Steve McNair	4.00
11	Tony Banks	3.00

1997 Playoff Zone Frenzy

This 26-card insert set was done on etched foil cards and inserted 1:12.

		MT
Complete Set (26):		175.00
Common Player:		1.00
Minor Stars:		2.00
1	Brett Favre	25.00
2	Dan Marino	20.00
3	Troy Aikman	10.00
4	Drew Bledsoe	10.00
5	John Elway	10.00
6	Kordell Stewart	10.00
7	Steve Young	6.00
8	Steve McNair	6.00
9	Tony Banks	4.00
10	Emmitt Smith	20.00
11	Barry Sanders	15.00
12	Deion Sanders	4.00
13	Terrell Davis	10.00
14	Curtis Martin	8.00
15	Karim Abdul-Jabbar	4.00
16	Terry Glenn	2.00
17	Eddie George	10.00
18	Keyshawn Johnson	2.00
19	Marvin Harrison	2.00
20	Joey Galloway	2.00
21	Antonio Freeman	2.00
22	Jeff Blake	2.00
23	Michael Irvin	2.00
24	Eddie Kennison	2.00
25	Reggie White	2.00
26	Robert Brooks	1.00

1997 Playoff Zone Prime Target

This 20-card insert features the NFL's top pass catchers backed by a blue and silver die-cut target design. This set had an insert rate of 1:24.

		MT
Complete Set (20):		170.00
Common Player:		4.00
Minor Stars:		8.00
Red Cards:		3x

		MT
Complete Set (24):		100.00
Common Player:		1.00
Minor Stars:		2.00
1	Emmitt Smith	25.00
2	Barry Sanders	20.00
3	Jerry Rice	15.00
4	Terrell Davis	15.00
5	Curtis Martin	15.00
6	Karim Abdul-Jabbar	10.00
7	Terry Glenn	12.00
8	Eddie George	20.00
9	Keyshawn Johnson	8.00
10	Joey Galloway	8.00
11	Antonio Freeman	8.00
12	Herman Moore	8.00
13	Tim Brown	4.00
14	Michael Irvin	8.00
15	Isaac Bruce	8.00
16	Eddie Kennison	8.00
17	Shannon Sharpe	4.00
18	Cris Carter	4.00
19	Napoleon Kaufman	8.00
20	Carl Pickens	4.00

1997 Playoff Zone Rookies

This insert features 24 rookies on etched foil cards. The cards were inserted 1:8.

		MT
Complete Set (24):		100.00
Common Player:		1.00
Minor Stars:		2.00
1	Jake Plummer	20.00
2	George Jones	1.00
3	Pat Barnes	4.00
4	Brian Manning	1.00
5	O.J. Santiago	1.00
6	Byron Hanspard	4.00
7	Antowain Smith	8.00
8	Rae Carruth	6.00
9	Darnell Autry	4.00
10	Corey Dillon	10.00
11	David LaFleur	4.00
12	Tony Gonzalez	4.00
13	Sedrick Shaw	4.00
14	Danny Wuerffel	6.00
15	Troy Davis	6.00
16	Ike Hilliard	6.00
17	Tiki Barber	6.00
18	Will Blackwell	1.00
19	Jim Druckenmiller	8.00
20	Orlando Pace	2.00
21	Warrick Dunn	12.00
22	Reidel Anthony	7.00
23	Derrick Mason	1.00
24	Joey Kent	2.00

1997 Playoff Zone Sharpshooters

The top NFL QBs are highlighted in this 18-card set with flaming graphics in the background. The cards were inserted 1:72.

		MT
Complete Set (18):		160.00
Common Player:		3.00
Minor Stars:		6.00
Red Cards:		2x
1	Brett Favre	35.00
2	Dan Marino	30.00
3	John Elway	12.00
4	Troy Aikman	15.00
5	Drew Bledsoe	15.00

6	Todd Collins	3.00
7	Brad Johnson	6.00
8	Stan Humphries	3.00
9	John Friesz	3.00
10	Tony Banks	8.00
11	Ty Detmer	3.00
12	Steve McNair	12.00
13	Rob Johnson	3.00
14	Kordell Stewart	15.00
15	Danny Wuerffel	12.00
16	Jim Druckenmiller	12.00
17	Jake Plummer	10.00
18	Kerry Collins	6.00

1997 Playoff Zone Treasures

This 12-card insert features the top collectible NFL players. The cards were inserted 1:196.

		MT
Complete Set (12):		700.00
Common Players:		25.00
1	Brett Favre	120.00
2	Dan Marino	100.00
3	Troy Aikman	50.00
4	Drew Bledsoe	50.00
5	Emmitt Smith	100.00
6	Barry Sanders	75.00
7	Warrick Dunn	60.00
8	Deion Sanders	25.00
9	Terrell Davis	50.00
10	Curtis Martin	40.00
11	Tiki Barber	25.00
12	Eddie George	50.00

1997 Playoff 1st & 10

The 250-card set features a color photo of a player superimposed over a purple "1st and 10" background on the front. The player's name is printed in light purple in the upper center and right, while "Nineteen Ninety Seven" appears vertically along the lower left border. The "1st and 10" logo appears in the lower right. The backs have the card number in the upper right, while the player's number, position, name, highlights, bio and stats all are printed along the left side over a purple "1st and 10" background. The player's head shot is printed on the right. In addition, a Kickoff parallel 250-card set was inserted 1:9 packs. The card fronts are identical to the base cards except they are printed on translucent lucite and a gold-foil Kickoff logo is stamped in the upper left. The only printing on the backs are the Players Inc., Play Football and the Playoff 1997 copyright tag line.

		MT
Complete Set (250):		30.00
Common Player:		.10
Minor Stars:		.20
Kickoff Cards:		10x-20x
Kickoff Rookies:		5x-10x
Inserted 1:9		
Wax Box:		55.00
1	Marcus Allen	.20
2	Eric Bieniemy	.10
3	Jason Dunn	.10
4	Jim Harbaugh	.10
5	Michael Westbrook	.10
6	*Tiki Barber*	1.00
7	Frank Reich	.10
8	Irving Fryar	.10
9	Courtney Hawkins	.10
10	Eric Zeier	.10
11	Kent Graham	.10
12	Trent Dilfer	.10
13	Neil O'Donnell	.10
14	*Reidel Anthony*	1.00
15	Jeff Hostetler	.10

#	Player	Price
16	Lawrence Phillips	.20
17	Dave Brown	.10
18	Mike Tomczak	.10
19	Jake Reed	.10
20	Anthony Miller	.10
21	Eric Metcalf	.10
22	*Sedrick Shaw*	.50
23	Anthony Johnson	.10
24	Mario Bates	.10
25	Dorsey Levens	.25
26	Stan Humphries	.10
27	Ben Coates	.10
28	Tyrone Wheatley	.10
29	Adrian Murrell	.10
30	William Henderson	.10
31	*Warrick Dunn*	1.50
32	LeShon Johnson	.10
33	James Stewart	.10
34	Edgar Bennett	.10
35	Raymont Harris	.10
36	Leroy Butler	.10
37	Darren Woodson	.10
38	*Darnell Autry*	.75
39	Johnnie Morton	.10
40	William Floyd	.10
41	Terrell Fletcher	.10
42	Leonard Russell	.10
43	Henry Ellard	.10
44	Terrell Owens	.50
45	John Friesz	.10
46	*Antowain Smith*	1.25
47	Charles Johnson	.10
48	Rickey Dudley	.10
49	Lake Dawson	.10
50	Bert Emanuel	.10
51	Zach Thomas	.10
52	Earnest Byner	.10
53	*Yatil Green*	.75
54	Chris Spielman	.10
55	Muhsin Muhammad	.10
56	Bobby Engram	.10
57	Eric Bjornson	.10
58	Willie Green	.10
59	Derrick Mayes	.10
60	Chris Sanders	.10
61	Jimmy Smith	.10
62	*Tony Gonzalez*	.50
63	Rich Gannon	.10
64	Stanley Pritchett	.10
65	Brad Johnson	.10
66	Rodney Peete	.10
67	Sam Gash	.10
68	Chris Calloway	.10
69	Chris T. Jones	.10
70	*Will Blackwell*	.20
71	Mark Bruener	.10
72	Terry Kirby	.10
73	Brian Blades	.10
74	Craig Heyward	.10
75	Jamie Asher	.10
76	Terance Mathis	.10
77	*Troy Davis*	.30
78	Bruce Smith	.10
79	Simeon Rice	.10
80	Fred Barnett	.10
81	Tim Brown	.10
82	James Jett	.10
83	Mark Carrier	.10
84	Shawn Jefferson	.10
85	Ken Dilger	.10
86	*Rae Carruth*	.75
87	Keenan McCardell	.10
88	Michael Irvin	.20
89	Mark Chmura	.10
90	Derrick Alexander	.10
91	Andre Reed	.10
92	Ed McCaffrey	.10
93	Erik Kramer	.10
94	Albert Connell	.10
95	Frank Wycheck	.10
96	Zack Crockett	.10
97	Jim Everett	.10
98	Michael Haynes	.10
99	Jeff Graham	.10
100	Brent Jones	.10
101	Troy Aikman	1.00
102	*Byron Hanspard*	.75
103	Robert Brooks	.10
104	Karim Abdul-Jabbar	.25
105	Drew Bledsoe	1.00
106	Napoleon Kaufman	.10
107	Steve Young	.50
108	Leeland McElroy	.10
109	Jamal Anderson	.10
110	*David LaFleur*	.50
111	Vinny Testaverde	.10
112	Eric Moulds	.20
113	Tim Biakabutuka	.20
114	Rick Mirer	.10
115	Jeff Blake	.20
116	Jim Schwantz	.10
117	Herman Moore	.20
118	*Ike Hilliard*	1.00
119	Reggie White	.20
120	Steve McNair	.50
121	Marshall Faulk	.20
122	Natrone Means	.20
123	Greg Hill	.10
124	O.J. McDuffie	.10
125	Robert Smith	.10
126	*Bryant Westbrook*	.20
127	Ray Zellars	.10
128	Rodney Hampton	.10
129	Wayne Chrebet	.10
130	Desmond Howard	.10
131	Ty Detmer	.10
132	Erric Pegram	.10
133	Yancey Thigpen	.10
134	*Danny Wuerffel*	.75
135	Charlie Jones	.10
136	Chris Warren	.10
137	Isaac Bruce	.25
138	Errict Rhett	.20
139	Gus Frerotte	.10
140	Frank Sanders	.10
141	Todd Collins	.10
142	*Jake Plummer*	3.00
143	Darnay Scott	.10
144	Rashaan Salaam	.20
145	Terrell Davis	1.50
146	Scott Mitchell	.10
147	Junior Seau	.20
148	Warren Moon	.10
149	Wesley Walls	.10
150	Daryl Johnston	.10
151	Brett Favre	2.25
152	Emmitt Smith	2.00
153	Dan Marino	2.00
154	Larry Centers	.10
155	Michael Jackson	.10
156	Kerry Collins	.30
157	Curtis Conway	.20
158	*Peter Boulware*	.20
159	Carl Pickens	.10
160	Shannon Sharpe	.10
161	Brett Perriman	.10
162	Eddie George	1.50
163	Mark Brunell	1.00
164	Tamarick Vanover	.20
165	Cris Carter	.10
166	*Corey Dillon*	1.50
167	Curtis Martin	1.25
168	Amani Toomer	.10
169	Jeff George	.10
170	Kordell Stewart	.75
171	Garrison Hearst	.10
172	Tony Banks	.50
173	Mike Alstott	.20
174	*Jim Druckenmiller*	.75
175	Chris Chandler	.10
176	Bam Morris	.10
177	Billy Joe Hobert	.10
178	Ernie Mills	.10
179	Ki-Jana Carter	.10
180	Deion Sanders	.50
181	Ricky Watters	.20
182	*Shawn Springs*	.10
183	Barry Sanders	1.25
184	Antonio Freeman	.30
185	Marvin Harrison	.50
186	Elvis Grbac	.10
187	Terry Glenn	1.00
188	Willie Roaf	.10
189	Keyshawn Johnson	.50
190	*Orlando Pace*	.30
191	Jerome Bettis	.20
192	Tony Martin	.10
193	Jerry Rice	1.00
194	Joey Galloway	.30
195	Terry Allen	.10
196	Eddie Kennison	.50
197	Thurman Thomas	.20
198	*Darrell Russell*	.20
199	Rob Moore	.10
200	John Elway	.50
201	Quinn Early	.10
202	Kevin Greene	.10
203	Robert Green	.10
204	Tony Carter	.10
205	Michael Timpson	.10
206	Kevin Smith	.10
207	Herschel Walker	.10
208	Steve Atwater	.10
209	Tyrone Braxton	.10
210	Willie Davis	.10
211	Lamont Warren	.10
212	Sean Dawkins	.10
213	Dale Carter	.10
214	Kimble Anders	.10
215	Derrick Thomas	.10
216	Chris Penn	.10
217	Irving Spikes	.10
218	Amp Lee	.10
219	Qadry Ismail	.10
220	Dave Meggett	.10
221	Tyrone Hughes	.10
222	Haywood Jeffries	.10
223	Torrance Small	.10
224	Danny Kanell	.10
225	Thomas Lewis	.10
226	Kyle Brady	.10
227	Harvey Williams	.10
228	Bobby Hoying	.10
229	Charlie Garner	.10
230	Andre Hastings	.10
231	Heath Shuler	.10
232	J.J. Stokes	.10
233	Ken Norton	.10
234	Steve Walsh	.10
235	Harold Green	.10
236	Reggie Brooks	.10
237	Robb Thomas	.10
238	Brian Mitchell	.10
239	Bill Brooks	.10
240	Leslie Shepherd	.10
241	Jay Graham	.10
242	*Kevin Lockett*	.20
243	Derrick Mason	.10
244	*Marc Edwards*	.20
245	*Joey Kent*	.40
246	*Pat Barnes*	.50
247	Sherman Williams	.10
248	Ray Brown	.10
249	Stephen Davis	.10
250	Lamar Smith	.10

1997 Playoff 1st & 10 Chip Shots

Similar to a poker chip, the 250 plastic Chip Shot tokens were inserted one per pack. The fronts have the player's name at the top, while his photo is in the center. The Playoff logo and team name are printed at the bottom, with the token number appearing on the left and right sides of the front. The backs have "Chip Shot" printed at the top, with the player's name in the center. "'97" is printed on the left and right of the token. "NFL" appears at the bottom.

		MT
Complete Set (250):		200.00
Common Player:		.25
Minor Stars:		.50
1	Marcus Allen	.50
2	Eric Bieniemy	.25
3	Jason Dunn	.25
4	Jim Harbaugh	.25
5	Michael Westbrook	.25
6	Tiki Barber	3.00
7	Frank Reich	.25
8	Irving Fryar	.25
9	Courtney Hawkins	.25
10	Eric Zeier	.25
11	Kent Graham	.25
12	Trent Dilfer	.25
13	Neil O'Donnell	.25
14	Riedel Anthony	3.00
15	Jeff Hostetler	.25
16	Lawrence Phillips	.50
17	Dave Brown	.25
18	Mike Tomczak	.25
19	Jake Reed	.25
20	Anthony Miller	.25
21	Eric Metcalf	.25
22	Sedrick Shaw	.75
23	Anthony Johnson	.25
24	Mario Bates	.25
25	Dorsey Levens	.25
26	Stan Humphries	.25
27	Ben Coates	.25
28	Tyrone Wheatley	.25
29	Adrian Murrell	.25
30	William Henderson	.25
31	Warrick Dunn	8.00
32	LeShon Johnson	.25
33	James Stewart	.25
34	Edgar Bennett	.25
35	Raymont Harris	.25
36	Leroy Butler	.25
37	Darren Woodson	.25
38	Darnell Autry	1.50
39	Johnnie Morton	.25
40	William Floyd	.25
41	Terrell Fletcher	.25
42	Leonard Russell	.25
43	Henry Ellard	.25
44	Terrell Owens	3.00
45	John Friesz	.25
46	Antowain Smith	4.00
47	Charles Johnson	.25
48	Rickey Dudley	.25
49	Lake Dawson	.25
50	Bert Emanuel	.25
51	Zach Thomas	.75
52	Earnest Byner	.25
53	Yatil Green	1.00
54	Chris Spielman	.25
55	Muhsin Muhammad	.25
56	Bobby Engram	.25
57	Eric Bjornson	.25
58	Willie Green	.25
59	Derrick Mayes	.25
60	Chris Sanders	.25
61	Jimmy Smith	.25
62	Tony Gonzalez	.75
63	Rich Gannon	.25
64	Stanley Pritchett	.25
65	Brad Johnson	.25
66	Rodney Peete	.25
67	Sam Gash	.25
68	Chris Calloway	.25
69	Chris T. Jones	.25
70	Will Blackwell	.50
71	Mark Bruener	.25
72	Terry Kirby	.25
73	Brian Blades	.25
74	Craig Heyward	.25
75	Jamie Asher	.25
76	Terance Mathis	.25
77	Troy Davis	1.00
78	Bruce Smith	.25
79	Simeon Rice	.25
80	Fred Barnett	.25
81	Tim Brown	.25
82	James Jett	.25
83	Mark Carrier	.25
84	Shawn Jefferson	.25
85	Ken Dilger	.25
86	Rae Carruth	2.50
87	Keenan McCardell	.25
88	Michael Irvin	.50
89	Mark Chmura	.25
90	Derrick Alexander	.25
91	Andre Reed	.25
92	Ed McCaffrey	.25
93	Erik Kramer	.25
94	Albert Connell	.25
95	Frank Wycheck	.25
96	Zack Crockett	.25
97	Jim Everett	.25
98	Michael Haynes	.25
99	Jeff Graham	.25
100	Brent Jones	.25
101	Troy Aikman	5.00
102	Byron Hanspard	2.00
103	Robert Brooks	.25
104	Karim Abdul-Jabbar	1.00
105	Drew Bledsoe	5.00
106	Napoleon Kaufman	.25
107	Steve Young	3.00
108	Leeland McElroy	.25
109	Jamal Anderson	.50
110	David LaFleur	.75
111	Vinny Testaverde	.25
112	Eric Moulds	.50
113	Tim Biakabutuka	.50
114	Rick Mirer	.25
115	Jeff Blake	.50
116	Jim Schwantz	.25
117	Herman Moore	.50
118	Ike Hilliard	3.00
119	Reggie White	.50
120	Steve McNair	4.00
121	Marshall Faulk	.50
122	Natrone Means	.50
123	Greg Hill	.25
124	O.J. McDuffie	.25
125	Robert Smith	.25
126	Bryant Westbrook	.50
127	Ray Zellars	.25
128	Rodney Hampton	.25
129	Wayne Chrebet	.25
130	Desmond Howard	.25
131	Ty Detmer	.25
132	Erric Pegram	.25
133	Yancey Thigpen	.25
134	Danny Wuerffel	3.00
135	Charlie Jones	.25
136	Chris Warren	.25
137	Isaac Bruce	.75
138	Errict Rhett	.50
139	Gus Frerotte	.25
140	Frank Sanders	.25
141	Todd Collins	.25
142	Jake Plummer	4.00
143	Darnay Scott	.25
144	Rashaan Salaam	.50
145	Terrell Davis	6.00
146	Scott Mitchell	.25
147	Junior Seau	.25
148	Warren Moon	.25
149	Wesley Walls	.25
150	Daryl Johnston	.25
151	Brett Favre	10.00
152	Emmitt Smith	8.00
153	Dan Marino	8.00
154	Larry Centers	.25
155	Michael Jackson	.25
156	Kerry Collins	1.00
157	Curtis Conway	.50
158	Peter Boulware	.50
159	Carl Pickens	.25
160	Shannon Sharpe	.25
161	Brett Perriman	.25
162	Eddie George	6.00
163	Mark Brunell	5.00
164	Tamarick Vanover	.50
165	Cris Carter	.25
166	Corey Dillon	5.00
167	Curtis Martin	6.00
168	Amani Toomer	.25
169	Jeff George	.25
170	Kordell Stewart	5.00
171	Garrison Hearst	.25
172	Tony Banks	2.00
173	Mike Alstott	2.00
174	Jim Druckenmiller	5.00
175	Chris Chandler	.25
176	Bam Morris	.25
177	Billy Joe Hobert	.25
178	Ernie Mills	.25
179	Ki-Jana Carter	.25
180	Deion Sanders	2.50
181	Ricky Watters	.50
182	Shawn Springs	.50
183	Barry Sanders	8.00
184	Antonio Freeman	1.50
185	Marvin Harrison	2.50
186	Elvis Grbac	.25
187	Terry Glenn	1.00
188	Willie Roaf	.25
189	Keyshawn Johnson	2.50
190	Orlando Pace	.50
191	Jerome Bettis	.50
192	Tony Martin	.25
193	Jerry Rice	5.00
194	Joey Galloway	1.00
195	Terry Allen	.25
196	Eddie Kennison	2.50
197	Thurman Thomas	.50
198	Darrell Russell	.25
199	Rob Moore	.25
200	John Elway	3.00
201	Quinn Early	.25
202	Kevin Greene	.25
203	Robert Green	.25
204	Tony Carter	.25
205	Michael Timpson	.25
206	Kevin Smith	.25
207	Herschel Walker	.25
208	Steve Atwater	.25
209	Tyrone Braxton	.25
210	Willie Davis	.25
211	Lamont Warren	.25
212	Sean Dawkins	.25
213	Dale Carter	.25
214	Kimble Anders	.25
215	Derrick Thomas	.25
216	Chris Penn	.25
217	Irving Spikes	.25
218	Amp Lee	.25
219	Qadry Ismail	.25
220	Dave Meggett	.25
221	Tyrone Hughes	.25
222	Haywood Jeffries	.25
223	Torrance Small	.25
224	Danny Kanell	.25
225	Thomas Lewis	.25
226	Kyle Brady	.25
227	Harvey Williams	.25
228	Bobby Hoying	.25
229	Charlie Garner	.25
230	Andre Hastings	.25
231	Heath Shuler	.25
232	J.J. Stokes	.25
233	Ken Norton	.25
234	Steve Walsh	.25
235	Harold Green	.25
236	Reggie Brooks	.25
237	Robb Thomas	.25
238	Brian Mitchell	.25
239	Bill Brooks	.25
240	Leslie Shepherd	.25
241	Jay Graham	.25
242	Kevin Lockett	.50
243	Derrick Mason	.50
244	Marc Edwards	.50
245	Joey Kent	.75
246	Pat Barnes	.75
247	Sherman Williams	.25
248	Ray Brown	.25
249	Stephen Davis	.25
250	Lamar Smith	.25

1997 Playoff 1st & 10 Extra Point Autograph

Inserted 1:444 packs, the autographed cards are signed by either Tony Banks or Terrell Davis. The cards have a gold-foil stripe at the top front with "Authentic Autograph" embossed on it. The Extra Point logo appears in the upper left. Black felt surrounds the photo of the respective player. The autograph is signed on the felt and into the photo. The player's name is listed inside a white stripe on the right border of the front. The backs, which are numbered with an "XPA" prefix, have a photo bordered in black. The number appears in an oval in the upper right.

		MT
Complete Set (2):		200.00
Common Player:		50.00
1	Tony Banks	50.00
2	Terrell Davis	150.00

1997 Playoff 1st & 10 Hot Pursuit

Inserted 1:180 packs, the 100-card set has the player photo superimposed on an orange background on the front. The Hot Pursuit logo is in the top center, while "Playoff '97" is printed vertically along the left border and the player's name is printed vertically along the right border. The card fronts did not include a Playoff peelable protective coating. The backs featured a full-bleed photo of the player, with the card number in the upper right.

		MT
Complete Set (100):		1250.00
Common Player:		5.00
Minor Stars:		10.00
1	Brett Favre	100.00
2	Dorsey Levens	20.00
3	Antonio Freeman	5.00
4	Robert Brooks	5.00
5	Mark Chmura	5.00
6	Reggie White	10.00
7	Drew Bledsoe	50.00
8	Curtis Martin	25.00
9	Ben Coates	5.00
10	Terry Glenn	20.00
11	Kerry Collins	10.00
12	Tim Biakabutuka	5.00
13	Anthony Johnson	5.00
14	Wesley Walls	10.00
15	Muhsin Muhammad	10.00
16	Mark Brunell	50.00
17	Natrone Means	10.00
18	Jimmy Smith	20.00
19	John Elway	100.00
20	Terrell Davis	100.00
21	Anthony Miller	5.00
22	Shannon Sharpe	10.00
23	Steve Young	30.00
24	Garrison Hearst	20.00
25	Jerry Rice	50.00
26	Troy Aikman	50.00
27	Deion Sanders	20.00
28	Emmitt Smith	80.00
29	Michael Irvin	20.00
30	Kordell Stewart	25.00
31	Jerome Bettis	20.00
32	Charles Johnson	5.00
33	Ty Detmer	5.00
34	Ricky Watters	10.00
35	Irving Fryar	5.00
36	Todd Collins	5.00
37	Thurman Thomas	10.00
38	Bruce Smith	10.00
39	Eric Moulds	20.00
40	Brad Johnson	20.00
41	Robert Smith	20.00
42	Cris Carter	20.00
43	Elvis Grbac	10.00
44	Greg Hill	5.00
45	Marcus Allen	20.00
46	Gus Frerotte	5.00
47	Terry Allen	10.00
48	Michael Westbrook	20.00
49	Jim Harbaugh	10.00
50	Marshall Faulk	25.00
51	Marvin Harrison	25.00
52	Jeff Blake	10.00
53	Ki-Jana Carter	10.00
54	Carl Pickens	10.00
55	Junior Seau	10.00
56	Tony Martin	5.00
57	Dan Marino	100.00
58	Karim Abdul-Jabbar	10.00
59	Stanley Pritchett	5.00
60	Zach Thomas	10.00
61	Steve McNair	25.00
62	Eddie George	50.00
63	Chris Sanders	5.00
64	Rick Mirer	5.00
65	Rashaan Salaam	5.00
66	Curtis Conway	10.00
67	Bobby Engram	5.00
68	Kent Graham	5.00
69	Leeland McElroy	5.00
70	Larry Centers	5.00
71	Frank Sanders	10.00
72	Jeff George	10.00
73	Napoleon Kaufman	10.00
74	Desmond Howard	10.00
75	Tim Brown	20.00
76	John Friesz	10.00
77	Chris Warren	20.00
78	Joey Galloway	20.00
79	Tony Banks	20.00
80	Lawrence Phillips	10.00
81	Isaac Bruce	25.00
82	Eddie Kennison	10.00
83	Errict Rhett	10.00
84	Mike Alstott	25.00
85	Rodney Hampton	5.00
86	Amani Toomer	10.00
87	Scott Mitchell	5.00
88	Barry Sanders	100.00
89	Herman Moore	20.00
90	Vinny Testaverde	20.00
91	Bam Morris	5.00
92	Michael Jackson	5.00
93	Chris Chandler	5.00
94	Eric Metcalf	5.00
95	Jamal Anderson	20.00
96	Jim Everett	5.00
97	Mario Bates	5.00
98	Wayne Chrebet	10.00

99	Adrian Murrell	5.00
100	Keyshawn Johnson	20.00

1997 Playoff 1st & 10 Xtra Point

KARIM ABDUL-JABBAR

The 10-card set was inserted 1:432 packs. The card fronts featured the Extra Point logo in the upper left, and a player photo in the center. Both were surrounded by felt. The player's name is printed inside a white stripe along the right border. The card backs, which featured a prefix of "XP," have the player photo surrounded by felt. The card's number is printed inside an oval in the upper right.

		MT
Complete Set (10):		275.00
Common Player:		10.00
Inserted 1:432		
1	Kordell Stewart	20.00
2	Dan Marino	45.00
3	Brett Favre	60.00
4	Emmitt Smith	45.00
5	John Elway	45.00
6	Eddie George	30.00
7	Karim Abdul-Jabbar	10.00
8	Terry Glenn	12.00
9	Curtis Martin	15.00
10	Joey Galloway	15.00

1997 Playoff Sports Cards Picks

Playoff produced this six-card set which was distributed to collectors who purchased a subscription to Sports Cards magazine at the 1997 National.

		MT
Complete Set (6):		8.00
Common Player:		1.00
1	Brett Favre	3.00
2	Barry Sanders	2.00
3	Terrell Davis	1.50
4	Jerry Rice	1.50
5	Deion Sanders	1.00
6	Kordell Stewart	1.50

1997 Playoff Super Bowl Card Show

This set was available through wrapper redemption at the 1997 Super Bowl Card Show. Each card was available in exchange for three Playoff wrappers opened at the Playoff booth. The only exception is the Terrell Davis card, which could only be obtained by redeeming an entire box of wrappers for a complete seven-card set. The cards are not numbered.

		MT
Complete Set (7):		20.00
Common Player:		2.00
1	Terry Allen	2.00
2	Jerome Bettis	3.00
3	Terrell Davis	5.00
4	Marshall Faulk	3.00
5	Eddie George	8.00
6	Deion Sanders	3.50
7	Reggie White	3.00

1998 Playoff Absolute Hobby

Absolute SSD was made for the hobby-only and contained 200 cards on super-thick 24-point stock. The horizontal cards featured brushed silver foil with a celluloid player image laminated between the front and back. Playoff also produced a retail version, called Absolute, which included all 200 cards, but on a thinner stock with a different twist to some of the inserts. The set was paralleled twice, in a Silver foil version and a Gold foil version numbered to 25 sets. Inserts include: Checklists, Draft Picks, Honors, Marino Milestones, Platinum Quads, Shields, Red Zone and Statistically Speaking.

		MT
Complete Set (200):		275.00
Common Player:		.50
Minor Stars:		1.00
Wax Box:		100.00
1	John Elway	6.00
2	Marcus Nash	8.00
3	Brian Griese	15.00
4	Terrell Davis	8.00
5	Rod Smith	1.00
6	Shannon Sharpe	1.00
7	Ed McCaffrey	.50
8	Brett Favre	12.00
9	Dorsey Levens	1.00
10	Derrick Mayes	.50
11	Antonio Freeman	1.00
12	Robert Brooks	.50
13	Mark Chmura	1.00
14	Reggie White	1.00
15	Kordell Stewart	5.00
16	Hines Ward	8.00
17	Jerome Bettis	1.00
18	Charles Johnson	.50
19	Courtney Hawkins	.50
20	Will Blackwell	.50
21	Mark Bruener	.50
22	Steve Young	4.00
23	Jim Druckenmiller	1.00
24	Garrison Hearst	1.00
25	R.W. McQuarters	2.00
26	Marc Edwards	.50
27	Irv Smith	.50
28	Jerry Rice	6.00
29	Terrell Owens	1.00
30	J.J. Stokes	1.00
31	Elvis Grbac	1.00
32	Rashaan Shehee	2.00
33	Donnell Bennett	.50
34	Kimble Anders	.50
35	Ted Popson	.50
36	Derrick Alexander	.50
37	Tony Gonzalez	1.00
38	Andre Rison	1.00
39	Brad Johnson	1.00
40	Randy Moss	60.00
41	Robert Smith	1.00
42	Leroy Hoard	.50
43	Cris Carter	1.00
44	Jake Reed	.50
45	Drew Bledsoe	6.00
46	Tony Simmons	1.00
47	Chris Floyd	1.00
48	Robert Edwards	12.00
49	Shawn Jefferson	.50
50	Ben Coates	.50
51	Terry Glenn	1.00
52	Trent Dilfer	1.00
53	Jacquez Green	12.00
54	Warrick Dunn	6.00
55	Mike Alstott	1.00
56	Reidel Anthony	1.00
57	Bert Emanuel	.50
58	Warren Sapp	.50
59	Charlie Batch	20.00
60	Germane Crowell	8.00
61	Scott Mitchell	.50
62	Barry Sanders	12.00
63	Tommy Vardell	.50
64	Herman Moore	1.00
65	Johnnie Morton	.50
66	Mark Brunell	5.00
67	Jonathan Quinn	1.00
68	Fred Taylor	20.00
69	James Stewart	.50
70	Jimmy Smith	1.00
71	Damon Jones	.50
72	Keenan McCardell	.50
73	Dan Marino	10.00
74	Larry Shannon	1.00
75	John Avery	8.00
76	Troy Drayton	.50
77	Stanley Pritchett	.50
78	Karim Abdul-Jabbar	1.00
79	O.J. McDuffie	1.00
80	Yatil Green	1.00
81	Danny Kanell	.50
82	Tiki Barber	1.00
83	Tyrone Wheatley	.50
84	Charles Way	.50
85	Gary Brown	.50
86	Brian Alford	1.00
87	Joe Jurevicius	2.00
88	Ike Hilliard	1.00
89	Troy Aikman	6.00
90	Deion Sanders	3.00
91	Emmitt Smith	10.00
92	Chris Warren	.50
93	Daryl Johnston	.50
94	Michael Irvin	1.00
95	David LaFleur	.50
96	Kevin Dyson	8.00
97	Steve McNair	5.00
98	Eddie George	5.00
99	Yancey Thigpen	.50
100	Frank Wycheck	.50
101	Glenn Foley	1.00
102	Vinny Testaverde	1.00
103	Keyshawn Johnson	1.00
104	Curtis Martin	3.00
105	Keith Byars	.50
106	Scott Frost	1.00
107	Wayne Chrebet	1.00
108	Warren Moon	1.00
109	Ahman Green	10.00
110	Steve Broussard	.50
111	Ricky Watters	1.00
112	Joey Galloway	1.00
113	Mike Pritchard	.50
114	Brian Blades	.50
115	Gus Frerotte	.50
116	Skip Hicks	6.00
117	Terry Allen	.50
118	Michael Westbrook	1.00
119	Jamie Asher	.50
120	Leslie Shepherd	.50
121	Jeff Blake	1.00
122	Corey Dillon	4.00
123	Carl Pickens	1.00
124	Tony McGee	.50
125	Darnay Scott	.50
126	Kerry Collins	1.00
127	Fred Lane	1.00
128	William Floyd	.50
129	Rae Carruth	.50
130	Wesley Walls	.50
131	Muhsin Muhammad	.50
132	Jake Plummer	6.00
133	Adrian Murrell	1.00
134	Michael Pittman	.50
135	Larry Centers	.50
136	Frank Sanders	.50
137	Rob Moore	.50
138	Andre Wadsworth	3.00
139	Mario Bates	.50
140	Chris Chandler	.50
141	Byron Hanspard	1.00
142	Jamal Anderson	1.00
143	Terance Mathis	.50
144	O.J. Santiago	.50
145	Tony Martin	.50
146	Jammi German	1.00
147	Jim Harbaugh	1.00
148	Errict Rhett	.50
149	Michael Jackson	.50
150	Patrick Johnson	1.00
151	Eric Green	.50
152	Doug Flutie	4.00
153	Rob Johnson	1.00
154	Antowain Smith	3.00
155	Bruce Smith	.50
156	Eric Moulds	.50
157	Andre Reed	.50
158	Erik Kramer	.50
159	Darnell Autry	.50
160	Edgar Bennett	.50
161	Curtis Enis	12.00
162	Curtis Conway	.50
163	E.G. Green	1.00
164	Jerome Pathon	2.00
165	Peyton Manning	35.00
166	Marshall Faulk	1.00
167	Zack Crockett	.50
168	Ken Dilger	.50
169	Marvin Harrison	1.00
170	Danny Wuerffel	.50
171	Lamar Smith	.50
172	Ray Zellars	.50
173	Qadry Ismail	.50
174	Sean Dawkins	.50
175	Andre Hastings	.50
176	Jeff George	1.00
177	Charles Woodson	15.00
178	Napoleon Kaufman	3.00
179	Jon Ritchie	1.00
180	Desmond Howard	.50
181	Tim Brown	.50
182	James Jett	.50
183	Rickey Dudley	.50
184	Bobby Hoying	.50
185	Rodney Peete	.50
186	Charlie Garner	.50
187	Irving Fryar	.50
188	Chris T. Jones	.50
189	Jason Dunn	.50
190	Tony Banks	1.00
191	Robert Holcombe	12.00
192	Craig Heyward	.50
193	Isaac Bruce	1.00
194	Az-Zahir Hakim	1.00
195	Eddie Kennison	1.00
196	Mikhael Ricks	1.00
197	Ryan Leaf	15.00
198	Natrone Means	1.00
199	Junior Seau	1.00
200	Freddie Jones	.50

1998 Playoff Absolute Hobby Silver/Gold

Two parallel versions of the 200-card Absolute SSD set exist. Silver foil versions were printed on a silver foil versus the team colored foil used on base cards. These were inserted one per three packs. Gold versions were printed on gold foil and sequentially numbered to 25 on the back.

	MT
Silver Cards:	3x
Silver Rookies:	2x
Gold Cards:	50x-100x
Gold Rookies:	7x-14x

1998 Playoff Absolute Hobby Checklist

This 30-card insert featured a horizontal shot of a key player from one of the NFL teams, with that team's home stadium in the background. On the back, each player card from that team is listed. Checklists were inserted one per 19 packs.

		MT
Complete Set (30):		300.00
Common Player:		5.00
Inserted 1:19		
1	Jake Plummer	15.00
2	Jamal Anderson	5.00
3	Jim Harbaugh	5.00
4	Rob Johnson	5.00
5	Fred Lane	5.00
6	Curtis Enis	15.00
7	Corey Dillon	12.00
8	Troy Aikman	20.00
9	Terrell Davis	20.00
10	Barry Sanders	30.00
11	Brett Favre	30.00

1998 Playoff Absolute Hobby Draft Picks

CURTIS ENIS

This 36-card insert set featured top players from the 1998 NFL Draft over a foil background. These were inserted one per 10 packs. In addition, Bronze versions of each card were available only through special three-card packs that contained only these Bronze versions. Those packs were inserted one per four boxes.

		MT
Complete Set (36):		300.00
Common Player:		4.00
Inserted 1:10		
1	Peyton Manning	30.00
2	Ryan Leaf	15.00
3	Andre Wadsworth	6.00
4	Charles Woodson	15.00
5	Curtis Enis	12.00
6	Fred Taylor	20.00
7	Kevin Dyson	10.00
8	Robert Edwards	10.00
9	Randy Moss	40.00
10	R.W. McQuarters	4.00
11	John Avery	10.00
12	Marcus Nash	10.00
13	Jerome Pathon	4.00
14	Jacquez Green	12.00
15	Robert Holcombe	10.00
16	Patrick Johnson	4.00
17	Germane Crowell	8.00
18	Tony Simmons	4.00
19	Joe Jurevicius	6.00
20	Mikhael Ricks	4.00
21	Charlie Batch	20.00
22	Jon Ritchie	4.00
23	Scott Frost	4.00
24	Skip Hicks	6.00
25	Brian Alford	4.00
26	E.G. Green	4.00
27	Jammi German	4.00
28	Ahman Green	12.00
29	Chris Floyd	4.00
30	Larry Shannon	4.00
31	Jonathan Quinn	4.00
32	Rashaan Shehee	6.00
33	Brian Griese	12.00
34	Hines Ward	8.00
35	Michael Pittman	4.00
36	Az-Zahir Hakim	4.00

1998 Playoff Absolute Hobby Marino Milestones

Playoff continued its 15-card Marino Milestones insert, with cards 6-10 inserted one per 397 packs of Absolute. Cards 1-5 were found in Prestige SSD and 11-15 were inserted into Momentum SSD. All versions were signed and featured a different record of Dan Marino's.

		MT
Complete Set (5):		600.00
Common Player:		125.00

Inserted 1:397

6	Dan Marino (7,452)	125.00
7	Dan Marino (56/9)	125.00
8	Dan Marino (5,084)	125.00
9	Dan Marino (9)	125.00
10	Dan Marino (96.0)	125.00

1998 Playoff Absolute Hobby Platinum Quads

Platinum Quads was an 18-card insert that captured four players on a single card, with two per side. Cards were printed horizontally with the player's image appearing over foil with a "sunburst" etch. These were inserted one per 73 packs of Absolute SSD.

		MT
Complete Set (18):		1100.
Common Player:		30.00
Inserted 1:73		
1	Brett Favre, John Elway, Barry Sanders, Warrick Dunn	150.00
2	Dan Marino, Terrell Davis, Napoleon Kaufman, Jerome Bettis	125.00
3	Jerry Rice, Brad Johnson, Marshall Faulk, Jimmy Smith	80.00
4	Troy Aikman, Herman Moore, Mark Chmura, Gus Frerotte	80.00
5	Steve Young, Mike Alstott, Tiki Barber, Keyshawn Johnson	50.00
6	Kordell Stewart, Robert Brooks, Karim Abdul-Jabbar, Shannon Sharpe	60.00
7	Mark Brunell, Dorsey Levens, Carl Pickens, Rob Moore	60.00
8	Drew Bledsoe, Joey Galloway, Tim Brown, Fred Lane	60.00
9	Eddie George, Rob Johnson, Irving Fryar, Andre Rison	50.00
10	Jake Plummer, Antonio Freeman, Steve McNair, Warren Moon	50.00
11	Emmitt Smith, Cris Carter, Junior Seau, Danny Kanell	125.00
12	Corey Dillon, Jake Reed, Curtis Martin, Bobby Hoying	50.00
13	Deion Sanders, Jim Druckenmiller, Reidel Anthony, Terry Allen	30.00
14	Antowain Smith, Wesley Walls, Isaac Bruce, Terry Glenn	30.00
15	Charlie Batch, Scott Frost, Jonathan Quinn, Brian Griese	50.00
16	Kevin Dyson, Randy Moss, Marcus Nash, Jerome Pathon	125.00
17	Curtis Enis, Fred Taylor, Robert Edwards, John Avery	65.00
18	Peyton Manning, Ryan Leaf, Andre Wadsworth, Charles Woodson	100.00

1998 Playoff Absolute Hobby Playoff Honors

This three-card insert continued Playoff's Honors insert through all of its products, and was numbered PH13-PH15. These die-cut cards showed the player's image over a large black Playoff logo with white letters. Honors were inserted one per 3,970 packs of Absolute SSD.

		MT
Complete Set (3):		400.00
Common Player:		75.00
Inserted 1:3,970		
13	John Elway	250.00
14	Jerome Bettis	75.00
15	Steve Young	100.00

1998 Playoff Absolute Hobby Red Zone

Red Zone featured 26 different players on a horizontal card with a mock-football field across the background. The insert name was printed in large letters in red foil, with his photo off to the right side. These were inserted one per 19 packs.

		MT
Complete Set (26):		250.00
Common Player:		4.00
Inserted 1:19		
1	Terrell Davis	20.00
2	Jerome Bettis	4.00
3	Mike Alstott	4.00
4	Brett Favre	35.00
5	Mark Brunell	15.00
6	Jeff George	4.00
7	John Elway	20.00
8	Troy Aikman	20.00
9	Steve Young	15.00
10	Kordell Stewart	15.00
11	Drew Bledsoe	20.00
12	James Jett	4.00
13	Dan Marino	25.00
14	Brad Johnson	4.00
15	Jake Plummer	15.00
16	Karim Abdul-Jabbar	4.00
17	Eddie George	15.00
18	Warrick Dunn	15.00
19	Cris Carter	4.00
20	Barry Sanders	35.00
21	Corey Dillon	10.00
22	Steve McNair	10.00
23	Herman Moore	4.00
24	Antonio Freeman	4.00
25	Dorsey Levens	4.00
26	James Stewart	4.00

1998 Playoff Absolute Hobby Shields

Shields was a 20-card insert that featured the player over

a die-cut football with the Playoff logo cut across the top. These were inserted one per 37 packs.

		MT
Complete Set (20):		350.00
Common Player:		10.00
Inserted 1:37		
1	Terrell Davis	25.00
2	Corey Dillon	15.00
3	Dorsey Levens	10.00
4	Brett Favre	50.00
5	Warrick Dunn	20.00
6	Jerome Bettis	10.00
7	John Elway	25.00
8	Troy Aikman	25.00
9	Mark Brunell	20.00
10	Kordell Stewart	20.00
11	Eddie George	20.00
12	Jerry Rice	25.00
13	Dan Marino	40.00
14	Emmitt Smith	40.00
15	Napoleon Kaufman	10.00
16	Ryan Leaf	20.00
17	Curtis Martin	15.00
18	Peyton Manning	40.00
19	Cris Carter	10.00
20	Barry Sanders	50.00

1998 Playoff Absolute Hobby Statistically Speaking

Statistically Speaking features 18 cards, with the player shown over a brushed foil background that highlights individual numbers of the featured player. These were inserted one per 55 packs.

		MT
Complete Set (18):		350.00
Common Player:		7.00
Inserted 1:55		
1	Jerry Rice	25.00
2	Barry Sanders	50.00
3	Deion Sanders	12.00
4	Brett Favre	50.00
5	Curtis Martin	12.00
6	Warrick Dunn	20.00
7	John Elway	25.00
8	Steve Young	15.00
9	Cris Carter	7.00
10	Kordell Stewart	20.00
11	Terrell Davis	25.00
12	Irving Fryar	7.00
13	Dan Marino	40.00
14	Tim Brown	7.00
15	Jerome Bettis	7.00
16	Troy Aikman	25.00
17	Napoleon Kaufman	15.00
18	Emmitt Smith	40.00

1998 Playoff Contenders Leather

Leather cards are one of three base sets found in Contenders. Each Leather card is printed on actual leather with three different foil stamps and are found one-per-pack. The

100-card set includes 70 veterans and 30 rookies from 1998. The parallel Red set has the players last name in red foil. Singles from this insert were found 1:9 hobby packs.

		MT
Complete Set (100):		225.00
Common Player:		.50
Minor Stars:		1.00
Common Rookie:		1.00
Inserted 1:1		
Red Cards:		3x
Red Rookies:		2x
Inserted 1:9		
Wax Box:		100.00
1	Adrian Murrell	.50
2	Michael Pittman	2.00
3	Jake Plummer	5.00
4	Andre Wadsworth	3.00
5	Jamal Anderson	2.00
6	Chris Chandler	1.00
7	Tim Dwight	6.00
8	Patrick Johnson	3.00
9	Jermaine Lewis	.50
10	Doug Flutie	3.00
11	Antowain Smith	2.00
12	Muhsin Muhammad	.50
13	Bobby Engram	.50
14	Curtis Enis	7.00
15	Alonzo Mayes	1.00
16	Corey Dillon	3.00
17	Carl Pickens	1.00
18	Troy Aikman	5.00
19	Michael Irvin	2.00
20	Deion Sanders	2.00
21	Emmitt Smith	7.00
22	Terrell Davis	8.00
23	John Elway	6.00
24	Brian Griese	8.00
25	Rod Smith	1.00
26	Charlie Batch	12.00
27	Germane Crowell	4.00
28	Terry Fair	3.00
29	Herman Moore	1.00
30	Barry Sanders	10.00
31	Brett Favre	10.00
32	Antonio Freeman	1.50
33	Vonnie Holliday	3.00
34	Reggie White	1.50
35	Marshall Faulk	1.50
36	Marvin Harrison	1.00
37	Peyton Manning	20.00
38	Jerome Pathon	3.00
39	Tavian Banks	3.00
40	Mark Brunell	4.00
41	Keenan McCardell	1.00
42	Fred Taylor	18.00
43	Elvis Grbac	.50
44	Andre Rison	1.00
45	Rashaan Shehee	2.00
46	Karim Abdul-Jabbar	1.00
47	John Avery	4.00
48	Dan Marino	7.00
49	O.J. McDuffie	1.00
50	Cris Carter	1.50
51	Brad Johnson	1.50
52	Randy Moss	40.00
53	Robert Smith	1.50
54	Drew Bledsoe	4.00
55	Ben Coates	1.00
56	Robert Edwards	7.00
57	Chris Floyd	2.00
58	Terry Glenn	1.50
59	Cameron Cleeland	4.00
60	Kerry Collins	1.00
61	Danny Kanell	.50
62	Charles Way	.50
63	Glenn Foley	1.00
64	Keyshawn Johnson	1.50
65	Curtis Martin	1.50
66	Tim Brown	1.00
67	Jeff George	1.00
68	Napoleon Kaufman	1.50
69	Charles Woodson	7.00
70	Irving Fryar	.50
71	Bobby Hoying	1.00
72	Jerome Bettis	1.00
73	Kordell Stewart	4.00
74	Hines Ward	3.00
75	Ryan Leaf	10.00
76	Natrone Means	1.00
77	Mikhael Ricks	3.00
78	Junior Seau	1.00
79	Garrison Hearst	1.00
80	Terrell Owens	1.50
81	Jerry Rice	5.00
82	Steve Young	3.00
83	Joey Galloway	1.50
84	Ahman Green	3.00
85	Warren Moon	1.00
86	Ricky Watters	1.50
87	Tony Banks	1.00
88	Isaac Bruce	1.00
89	Robert Holcombe	3.00
90	Mike Alstott	1.50
91	Trent Dilfer	1.00
92	Warrick Dunn	2.00
93	Jacquez Green	4.00
94	Kevin Dyson	4.00
95	Eddie George	4.00
96	Steve McNair	2.00
97	Yancey Thigpen	.50
98	Terry Allen	1.00
99	Skip Hicks	4.00
100	Michael Westbrook	.50

1998 Playoff Contenders Leather Gold

This insert parallel's the Leather set but each single is sequentially numbered to a player's featured stat. The cards look identical to the base Leather card except for the player's last name is in gold foil and the numbering is stamped on the back.

		MT
Common Player:		10.00
Minor Stars:		20.00
1	Adrian Murrell/27	30.00
2	Michael Pittman/32	30.00
3	Jake Plummer/53	100.00
4	Andre Wadsworth/29	50.00
5	Jamal Anderson/29	75.00
6	Chris Chandler/94	20.00
7	Tim Dwight/39	75.00
8	Patrick Johnson/55	20.00
9	Jermaine Lewis/42	20.00
10	Doug Flutie/48	75.00
11	Antowain Smith/28	75.00
12	Muhsin Muhammad/52	20.00
13	Bobby Engram/78	10.00
14	Curtis Enis/36	75.00
15	Alonzo Mayes/47	10.00
16	Corey Dillon/27	100.00
17	Carl Pickens/52	25.00
18	Troy Aikman/62	100.00
19	Michael Irvin/61	30.00
20	Deion Sanders/36	50.00
21	Emmitt Smith/40	200.00
22	Terrell Davis/35	275.00
23	John Elway/27	250.00
24	Brian Griese/33	125.00
25	Rod Smith/70	20.00
26	Charlie Batch/23	150.00
27	Germane Crowell/53	35.00
28	Terry Fair/42	30.00
29	Herman Moore/52	30.00
30	Barry Sanders/33	300.00
31	Brett Favre/35	300.00
32	Antonio Freeman/58	50.00
33	Vonnie Holliday/64	30.00
34	Reggie White/36	75.00
35	Marshall Faulk/47	50.00
36	Marvin Harrison/73	20.00
37	Peyton Manning/26	250.00
38	Jerome Pathon/69	20.00
39	Tavian Banks/33	45.00
40	Mark Brunell/52	85.00
41	Keenan McCardell/85	10.00
42	Fred Taylor/31	225.00
43	Elvis Grbac/29	35.00
44	Andre Rison/72	10.00
45	Rashaan Shehee/72	20.00
46	Karim Abdul-Jabbar/44	60.00
47	John Avery/26	60.00
48	Dan Marino/16	500.00
49	O.J. McDuffie/35	30.00
50	Cris Carter/89	20.00
51	Brad Johnson/37	50.00
52	Randy Moss/25	650.00
53	Robert Smith/90	20.00
54	Drew Bledsoe/28	175.00
55	Ben Coates/42	30.00
56	Robert Edwards/27	100.00
57	Chris Floyd/63	10.00
58	Terry Glenn/50	40.00
59	Cameron Cleeland/50	30.00
60	Kerry Collins/39	30.00
61	Danny Kanell/53	20.00
62	Charles Way/76	10.00
63	Glenn Foley/56	20.00
64	Keyshawn Johnson/70	25.00
65	Curtis Martin/41	40.00
66	Tim Brown/60	30.00
67	Jeff George/29	40.00
68	Napoleon Kaufman/40	50.00
69	Charles Woodson/27	120.00
70	Irving Fryar/75	10.00
71	Bobby Hoying/53	20.00
72	Jerome Bettis/31	65.00
73	Kordell Stewart/22	150.00
74	Hines Ward/55	30.00
75	Ryan Leaf/33	125.00
76	Natrone Means/78	20.00
77	Mikhael Ricks/47	25.00
78	Junior Seau/33	40.00
79	Garrison Hearst/74	20.00
80	Terrell Owens/60	35.00
81	Jerry Rice/16	325.00
82	Steve Young/19	175.00
83	Joey Galloway/72	25.00
84	Ahman Green/42	40.00
85	Warren Moon/25	85.00
86	Ricky Watters/56	25.00
87	Tony Banks/51	20.00
88	Isaac Bruce/30	30.00
89	Robert Holcombe/35	45.00
90	Mike Alstott/88	25.00
91	Trent Dilfer/38	45.00
92	Warrick Dunn/39	75.00
93	Jacquez Green/61	30.00
94	Kevin Dyson/60	30.00
95	Eddie George/30	150.00
96	Steve McNair/52	45.00
97	Yancey Thigpen/79	10.00
98	Terry Allen/58	30.00
99	Skip Hicks/48	45.00
100	Michael Westbrook/45	20.00

1998 Playoff Contenders Pennant

Pennant singles are printed on conventional stock with felt-like flocking and foil stamping. The 100-card set includes 70 veterans and 30 rookies from 1998. Pennant cards are found one-per-pack. Each player in the set has six different cards with each having a different color felt. The parallel Red singles are the same as the base except for the foil on the card is red. Singles are found 1:9 packs. The parallel Gold cards are in gold foil and are sequentially numbered to 98.

		MT
Complete Set (100):		225.00
Common Player:		.50
Minor Stars:		1.00
Common Rookie:		1.00
Each Card Issued In Six Colors		
Inserted 1:1		
Red Cards:		3x
Red Rookies:		2x
Inserted 1:9		
Gold Cards:		6x-12x
Gold Rookies:		4x-8x
Production 98 Sets		
1	Jake Plummer	5.00
2	Frank Sanders	.50
3	Jamal Anderson	2.00
4	Tim Dwight	6.00
5	Jammi German	2.00
6	Tony Martin	1.00
7	Jim Harbaugh	1.00
8	Rod Woodson	.50
9	Rob Johnson	1.00
10	Eric Moulds	1.50
11	Antowain Smith	1.50
12	Steve Beuerlein	.50
13	Fred Lane	1.00
14	Curtis Enis	5.00
15	Corey Dillon	3.00
16	Neil O'Donnell	.50
17	Carl Pickens	1.00
18	Darnay Scott	.50
19	Takeo Spikes	2.00
20	Troy Aikman	5.00
21	Michael Irvin	1.00
22	Deion Sanders	1.50
23	Emmitt Smith	7.00
24	Chris Warren	.50
25	Terrell Davis	8.00
26	John Elway	6.00
27	Brian Griese	6.00
28	Ed McCaffrey	1.00
29	Marcus Nash	3.00
30	Shannon Sharpe	1.00
31	Rod Smith	1.00
32	Charlie Batch	10.00
33	Germane Crowell	3.00
34	Herman Moore	1.00
35	Barry Sanders	10.00
36	Mark Chmura	1.00
37	Brett Favre	10.00
38	Antonio Freeman	1.50
39	Reggie White	1.00
40	Marshall Faulk	1.50
41	E.G. Green	2.50
42	Peyton Manning	15.00
43	Jerome Pathon	2.00
44	Mark Brunell	4.00
45	Jonathan Quinn	2.00
46	Fred Taylor	12.00
47	Tony Gonzalez	.50
48	Andre Rison	1.00
49	Karim Abdul-Jabbar	1.00
50	John Avery	3.00
51	Dan Marino	7.00
52	Cris Carter	1.50
53	Randall Cunningham	1.50
54	Brad Johnson	1.50
55	Randy Moss	30.00
56	Robert Smith	1.00
57	Drew Bledsoe	4.00
58	Robert Edwards	5.00
59	Terry Glenn	1.50
60	Tony Simmons	2.50
61	Tiki Barber	1.00
62	Joe Jurevicius	2.00
63	Danny Kanell	.50
64	Keyshawn Johnson	1.50
65	Curtis Martin	1.50
66	Vinny Testaverde	1.00
67	Tim Brown	1.00
68	Jeff George	1.00
69	Napoleon Kaufman	1.50
70	Jon Ritchie	2.00
71	Charles Woodson	5.00
72	Irving Fryar	.50
73	Duce Staley	1.00
74	Jerome Bettis	1.50
75	Chris Fuamatu-Ma'afala	2.00
76	Kordell Stewart	4.00
77	Hines Ward	2.50
79	Ryan Leaf	8.00
80	Natrone Means	1.50
81	Mikhael Ricks	2.00
82	Garrison Hearst	1.50
82	R.W. McQuarters	2.00
83	Jerry Rice	5.00
84	J.J. Stokes	1.00
85	Steve Young	3.00
86	Joey Galloway	1.50
87	Ahman Green	3.00
88	Warren Moon	1.00
89	Ricky Watters	1.00
90	Isaac Bruce	1.00
91	Robert Holcombe	2.50
92	Mike Alstott	1.50
93	Trent Dilfer	1.00
94	Warrick Dunn	3.00
95	Jacquez Green	3.00
96	Kevin Dyson	3.00
97	Eddie George	4.00
98	Steve McNair	2.00
99	Terry Allen	1.00
100	Skip Hicks	3.00

1998 Playoff Contenders Ticket

The 99-card Ticket set is made up of 80 veterans and 19 rookies and was inserted one-per-pack. Each Ticket card was printed on conventional stock with foil stamping and has a ticket design to it. All of the rookie cards in this set are autographed. The quantities vary from player to player depending on how many they signed. A parallel Red and Gold insert was also produced. Red's were found 1:9 hobby packs and the Gold's were sequentially numbered to 25. The name on the fronts will either be in red or gold depending on which single you have.

		MT
Complete Set (99):		900.00
Common Player:		.50
Minor Stars:		1.00
Common Rookie Autograph:		25.00
Inserted 1:1		
Red Cards:		3x
Red Rookies:		.2x
Inserted 1:9		
Gold Cards:		35x-70x
Gold Rookies:		.2x
Production 25 Sets		

1	Rob Moore	1.00
2	Jake Plummer	4.00
3	Jamal Anderson	1.50
4	Terance Mathis	.50
5	Priest Holmes	6.00
6	Michael Jackson	.50
7	Eric Zeier	.50
8	Andre Reed	.50
9	Antowain Smith	1.50
10	Bruce Smith	.50
11	Thurman Thomas	1.00
12	Raghib Ismail	.50
13	Wesley Walls	.50
14	Curtis Conway	1.00
15	Jeff Blake	1.00
16	Corey Dillon	2.00
17	Carl Pickens	1.00
18	Troy Aikman	5.00
19	Michael Irvin	1.00
20	Ernie Mills	.50
21	Deion Sanders	1.50
22	Emmitt Smith	7.00
23	Terrell Davis	8.00
24	John Elway	6.00
25	Neil Smith	.50
26	Rod Smith	1.00
27	Herman Moore	1.00
28	Johnnie Morton	.50
29	Barry Sanders	10.00
30	Robert Brooks	.50
31	Brett Favre	10.00
32	Antonio Freeman	1.50
33	Dorsey Levens	1.00
34	Reggie White	1.00
35	Marshall Faulk	1.50
36	Mark Brunell	4.00
37	Jimmy Smith	1.00
38	James Stewart	.50
39	Donnell Bennett	.50
40	Andre Rison	1.00
41	Derrick Thomas	1.00
42	Karim Abdul-Jabbar	1.00
43	Dan Marino	7.00
44	Cris Carter	1.50
45	Brad Johnson	1.50
46	Robert Smith	1.00
47	Drew Bledsoe	4.00
48	Terry Glenn	1.50
49	Lamar Smith	.50
50	Ike Hilliard	.50
51	Danny Kanell	.50
52	Wayne Chrebet	1.50
53	Keyshawn Johnson	1.50
54	Curtis Martin	1.50
55	Tim Brown	1.00
56	Rickey Dudley	.50
57	Jeff George	1.00
58	Napoleon Kaufman	1.50
59	Irving Fryar	.50
60	Jerome Bettis	1.50
61	Charles Johnson	.50
62	Kordell Stewart	4.00
63	Natrone Means	1.00
64	Bryan Still	.50
65	Garrison Hearst	1.50
66	Jerry Rice	5.00
67	Steve Young	3.00
68	Joey Galloway	1.50
69	Warren Moon	1.00
70	Ricky Watters	1.00
71	Isaac Bruce	1.00
72	Mike Alstott	1.50
73	Reidel Anthony	1.00
74	Trent Dilfer	1.00
75	Warrick Dunn	3.00
76	Warren Sapp	.50
77	Eddie George	4.00
78	Steve McNair	2.00
79	Terry Allen	1.00
80	Gus Frerotte	.50
81	Andre Wadsworth AUTO	25.00
82	Tim Dwight AUTO	50.00
83	Curtis Enis AUTO	50.00
85	Charlie Batch AUTO	85.00
86	Germane Crowell AUTO	40.00
87	Peyton Manning AUTO	200.00
88	Jerome Pathon AUTO	25.00
89	Fred Taylor AUTO	150.00
90	Tavian Banks AUTO	30.00
92	Randy Moss AUTO	300.00
93	Robert Edwards AUTO	35.00
94	Hines Ward AUTO	30.00
95	Ryan Leaf AUTO	50.00
96	Mikhael Ricks AUTO	25.00
97	Ahman Green AUTO	30.00
98	Jacquez Green AUTO	35.00
99	Kevin Dyson AUTO	45.00
100	Skip Hicks AUTO	35.00
103	Chris Fuamatu-Ma'afala AUTO	25.00

1998 Playoff Contenders Checklist

Each card in this 30-card set displays the top star from each club on the front and a checklist of each player from that team featured in our three base sets on the back. Each card measures 3" x 5" and was found one-per-box.

		MT
Complete Set (30):		150.00
Common Player:		2.50
Minor Stars:		5.00
Inserted 1:Box		
1	Jake Plummer	8.00
2	Jamal Anderson	5.00
3	Jermaine Lewis	2.50
4	Antowain Smith	5.00
5	Muhsin Muhammad	2.50
6	Curtis Enis	5.00
7	Corey Dillon	6.00
8	Deion Sanders	5.00
9	Terrell Davis	18.00
10	Barry Sanders	20.00
11	Brett Favre	20.00
12	Peyton Manning	15.00
13	Mark Brunell	8.00
14	Andre Rison	2.50
15	Dan Marino	15.00
16	Randy Moss	30.00
17	Drew Bledsoe	8.00
18	Kerry Collins	5.00
19	Danny Kanell	2.50
20	Curtis Martin	5.00
21	Tim Brown	2.50
22	Irving Fryar	2.50
23	Kordell Stewart	8.00
24	Natrone Means	5.00
25	Steve Young	6.00
26	Isaac Bruce	5.00
27	Warren Moon	5.00
28	Warrick Dunn	8.00
29	Eddie George	8.00
30	Terry Allen	5.00

1998 Playoff Contenders Honors

This is an insert that began with 1996 Playoff Prime and has continued throughout Playoff products over the past three years. Cards 19-21 can be found in this insert and are found 1:3,241 hobby packs.

		MT
Complete Set (3):		300.00
Common Player:		75.00
Inserted 1:3,241 Hobby		
19	Dan Marino	150.00
20	Jerry Rice	100.00
21	Mark Brunell	75.00

1998 Playoff Contenders MVP Contenders

This set showcases the players who are in contention for the league MVP. Each card is printed on holographic stock with an MVP graphic stamped in gold foil. Singles were inserted 1:19 hobby packs.

		MT
Complete Set (36):		160.00
Common Player:		4.00
Inserted 1:19		
1	Terrell Davis	18.00
2	Jerry Rice	10.00
3	Jerome Bettis	4.00
4	Brett Favre	20.00
5	Natrone Means	4.00
6	Steve Young	6.00
7	John Elway	12.00
8	Troy Aikman	10.00
9	Steve McNair	4.00
10	Kordell Stewart	8.00
11	Drew Bledsoe	8.00
12	Tim Brown	4.00
13	Dan Marino	15.00
14	Mark Brunell	8.00
15	Marshall Faulk	4.00
16	Jake Plummer	8.00
17	Corey Dillon	6.00
18	Carl Pickens	4.00
19	Keyshawn Johnson	4.00
20	Barry Sanders	20.00
21	Deion Sanders	4.00
22	Emmitt Smith	15.00
23	Antowain Smith	4.00
24	Curtis Martin	4.00
25	Cris Carter	4.00
26	Napoleon Kaufman	4.00
27	Eddie George	8.00
28	Warrick Dunn	8.00
29	Antonio Freeman	4.00
30	Joey Galloway	4.00
31	Herman Moore	4.00
32	Jamal Anderson	6.00
33	Terry Glenn	4.00
34	Garrison Hearst	4.00
35	Robert Smith	4.00
36	Mike Alstott	4.00

1998 Playoff Contenders Rookie of the Year

Playoff included the top 12 rookies from '98 who were battling for the rookie of the year award. Each card is printed on a wood-grain finish with two types of foil stamping. Singles were inserted 1:55 hobby packs.

		MT
Complete Set (12):		160.00
Common Player:		7.00
Inserted 1:55		
1	Tim Dwight	10.00
2	Curtis Enis	10.00
3	Charlie Batch	20.00
4	Peyton Manning	30.00
5	Fred Taylor	25.00
6	John Avery	7.00
7	Randy Moss	60.00
8	Robert Edwards	10.00
9	Charles Woodson	10.00
10	Ryan Leaf	12.00
11	Jacquez Green	7.00
12	Kevin Dyson	7.00

1998 Playoff Contenders Rookie Stallions

Only the top NFL draftees were featured in this 18-card set. Each card was printed on all micro-etched foil stock with silver foil stamping. Singles were inserted 1:19 hobby packs.

		MT
Complete Set (18):		100.00
Common Player:		2.50
Minor Stars:		5.00
Inserted 1:19		
1	Tim Dwight	6.00
2	Curtis Enis	6.00
3	Brian Griese	8.00
4	Charlie Batch	12.00
5	Germane Crowell	5.00
6	Peyton Manning	20.00
7	Tavian Banks	5.00
8	Fred Taylor	18.00
9	Rashaan Shehee	2.50
10	John Avery	5.00
11	Randy Moss	40.00
12	Robert Edwards	6.00
13	Charles Woodson	7.00
14	Ryan Leaf	10.00
15	Ahman Green	5.00
16	Jacquez Green	5.00
17	Kevin Dyson	5.00
18	Skip Hicks	5.00

1998 Playoff Contenders Super Bowl Leather

Each card in this set highlights a piece of an actual game-used football from Super Bowl XXXII. Each card back features a replica of the letter from the NFL verifying the authenticity of the ball. Cards are printed on conventional stock with foil stamping and were inserted 1:2,401 hobby packs.

		MT
Complete Set (6):		1000.
Common Player:		75.00
Inserted 1:2,401		
1	Brett Favre	350.00
2	John Elway	275.00
3	Robert Brooks	75.00
4	Rod Smith	100.00
5	Antonio Freeman	125.00
6	Terrell Davis	300.00

1998 Playoff Contenders Touchdown Tandems

Two teammates from over 20 NFL franchises were paired on the front of each card in this debut insert set. These cards, printed on holographic foil stock with foil stamping, show the players known for carrying the scoring load for their respective clubs. Singles were found 1:19 hobby packs.

		MT
Complete Set (24):		150.00
Common Player:		4.00
Inserted 1:19		
1	Brett Favre, Antonio Freeman	20.00
2	Dan Marino, Karim Abdul-Jabbar	15.00
3	Emmitt Smith, Troy Aikman	15.00
4	Barry Sanders, Herman Moore	20.00
5	Eddie George, Steve McNair	8.00
6	Robert Edwards, Drew Bledsoe	8.00
7	Terrell Davis, Rod Smith	15.00
8	Mark Brunell, Fred Taylor	12.00
9	Jerry Rice, Steve Young	10.00
10	Jerome Bettis, Kordell Stewart	8.00
11	Curtis Martin, Keyshawn Johnson	4.00
12	Mike Alstott, Warrick Dunn	6.00
13	Isaac Bruce, Tony Banks	4.00
14	Adrian Murrell, Jake Plummer	8.00
15	Tim Brown, Napoleon Kaufman	4.00
16	Cris Carter, Randy Moss	30.00
17	Joey Galloway, Ricky Watters	4.00
18	Peyton Manning, Marshall Faulk	15.00
19	Ryan Leaf, Natrone Means	8.00
20	Carl Pickens, Corey Dillon	4.00
21	Doug Flutie, Antowain Smith	6.00
22	Randall Cunningham, Robert Smith	4.00
23	Chris Chandler, Jamal Anderson	5.00
24	John Elway, Ed McCaffrey	12.00

1998 Playoff Momentum Hobby

Each card in this 250-card set was printed on premium doublesided metalized mylar with double micro-etching on both sides. The shortprinted Rookie subset included 48 rising NFL stars and were inserted 1:6 packs. Each card also has a Red and Gold parallel version. The Reds were inserted 1:4 hobby packs while the Golds were sequentially numbered to 25.

		MT
Complete Set (250):		750.00
Common Player:		.30
Minor Stars:		.60
Common Rookie:		4.00
Inserted 1:6		
Red Cards:		2x-4x
Red Rookies:		1.2x
Inserted 1:4		
Gold Cards:		50x-100x
Gold Rookies:		3x-6x
Production 25 Sets		
Wax Box:		85.00
1	Jake Plummer	3.00
2	Eric Metcalf	.30
3	Adrian Murrell	.30
4	Larry Centers	.30
5	Frank Sanders	.30
6	Rob Moore	.60
7	*Andre Wadsworth*	8.00
8	Chris Chandler	.60
9	Jamal Anderson	1.00
10	Terry Martin	.30
11	Terrance Mathis	.30
12	*Tim Dwight*	15.00
13	*Jammi German*	8.00
14	O.J. Santiago	.30
15	Jim Harbaugh	.60
16	Eric Zeier	.30
17	*Duane Starks*	8.00
18	Rod Woodson	.30
19	Errict Rhett	.30
20	Jay Graham	.30
21	Ray Lewis	.30
22	Michael Jackson	.30
23	Jermaine Lewis	.30
24	*Patrick Johnson*	4.00
25	Eric Green	.30
26	Doug Flutie	3.00
27	Rob Johnson	.60
28	Antowain Smith	2.00
29	Thurman Thomas	.60
30	*Jonathon Linton*	4.00
31	Bruce Smith	.30
32	Eric Moulds	.60
33	Kevin Williams	.30
34	Andre Reed	.30
35	Steve Beurlein	.30
36	Kerry Collins	.60
37	Anthony Johnson	.30

38	Fred Lane	.60
39	William Floyd	.30
40	Raghib Ismail	.30
41	Wesley Walls	.30
42	Muhsin Muhammad	.30
43	Rae Carruth	.30
44	Kevin Greene	.30
45	Greg Lloyd	.30
46	Moses Moreno	8.00
47	Erik Kramer	.30
48	Edgar Bennett	.30
49	*Curtis Enis*	30.00
50	Curtis Conway	.60
51	Bobby Engram	.30
52	Alonzo Mayes	4.00
53	Jeff Blake	.60
54	Neil O'Donnell	.30
55	Corey Dillon	3.00
56	*Takeo Spikes*	4.00
57	Carl Pickens	.60
58	Tony McGee	.30
59	Darnay Scott	.30
60	Troy Aikman	4.00
61	Deion Sanders	1.00
62	Emmitt Smith	6.00
63	Darren Woodson	.30
64	Chris Warren	.30
65	Daryl Johnston	.30
66	Ernie Mills	.30
67	Billy Davis	.30
68	Michael Irvin	.60
69	David LaFleur	.30
70	John Elway	4.00
71	*Brian Griese*	30.00
72	Steve Atwater	.30
73	Terrell Davis	6.00
74	Rod Smith	.60
75	*Marcus Nash*	25.00
76	Shannon Sharpe	.60
77	Ed McCaffrey	.60
78	Neil Smith	.30
79	*Charlie Batch*	60.00
80	*Germane Crowell*	25.00
81	Scott Mitchell	.60
82	Barry Sanders	8.00
83	*Terry Fair*	8.00
84	Herman Moore	1.00
85	Johnnie Morton	.30
86	Brett Favre	8.00
87	Rick Mirer	.30
88	Dorsey Levens	.60
89	William Henderson	.30
90	Derrick Mayes	.30
91	Antonio Freeman	1.00
92	Robert Brooks	.30
93	Mark Chmura	.30
94	*Vonnie Holliday*	8.00
95	Reggie White	1.00
96	*E.G. Green*	8.00
97	*Jerome Pathon*	8.00
98	*Peyton Manning*	70.00
99	Marshall Faulk	1.00
100	Zack Crockett	.30
101	Ken Dilger	.30
102	Marvin Harrison	.60
103	Mark Brunell	3.00
104	*Jonathon Quinn*	8.00
105	*Tavian Banks*	20.00
106	*Fred Taylor*	60.00
107	James Stewart	.30
108	Jimmy Smith	.60
109	Keenan McCardell	.30
110	Elvis Grbac	.30
111	Rich Gannon	.30
112	*Rashaan Shehee*	8.00
113	Donnell Bennett	.30
114	Kimble Anders	.30
115	Derrick Thomas	.30
116	Kevin Lockett	.30
117	Derrick Alexander	.30
118	Tony Gonzalez	.60
119	Andre Rison	.30
120	Craig Erickson	.30
121	Dan Marino	6.00
122	*John Avery*	25.00
123	Karim Abdul-Jabbar	.60
124	Zach Thomas	.60
125	O.J. McDuffie	.30
126	Troy Drayton	.30
127	Randall Cunningham	1.00
128	Brad Johnson	.60
129	Robert Smith	.60
130	Cris Carter	1.00
131	Randy Moss	100.00
132	Jake Reed	.30
133	John Randle	.30
134	Drew Bledsoe	3.00
135	*Tony Simmons*	15.00
136	Sedrick Shaw	.30
137	*Chris Floyd*	4.00
138	*Robert Edwards*	25.00
139	*Rod Rutledge*	4.00
140	Shawn Jefferson	.30
141	Ben Coates	.60
142	Terry Glenn	.60
143	Heath Shuler	.30
144	Danny Wuerffel	.30
145	Troy Davis	.30
146	Qadry Ismail	.30
147	Ray Zellars	.30
148	Lamar Smith	.30
149	*Cameron Cleeland*	12.00
150	Sean Dawkins	.30
151	Andre Hastings	.30
152	Danny Kanell	.30
153	Tiki Barber	.60

154	Tyrone Wheatley	.30
155	Charles Way	.30
156	Gary Brown	.30
157	*Shaun Williams*	4.00
158	Chris Calloway	.30
159	Amani Toomer	.30
160	Brian Alford	4.00
161	*Joe Jurevicius*	8.00
162	Ike Hilliard	.30
163	Michael Strahan	.30
164	Glenn Foley	.60
165	Vinny Testaverde	.60
166	Keyshawn Johnson	.60
167	Curtis Martin	1.00
168	Leon Johnson	.30
169	Keith Byars	.30
170	Wayne Chrebet	.60
171	Kyle Brady	.30
172	Dedric Ward	.30
173	Jeff George	.60
174	*Charles Woodson*	30.00
175	Napoleon Kaufman	1.00
176	*Jon Ritchie*	4.00
177	Tim Brown	.60
178	James Jett	.30
179	Rickey Dudley	.30
180	Bobby Hoying	.30
181	Duce Staley	.30
182	Charlie Garner	.30
183	Irvin Fryar	.30
184	Jeff Graham	.30
185	Jason Dunn	.30
186	Kordell Stewart	3.00
187	Jerome Bettis	1.00
188	Andre Coleman	.30
189	*Chris Fuamatu-Ma'afala*	10.00
190	Charles Johnson	.30
191	Hines Ward	20.00
192	Mark Bruener	.30
193	Courtney Hawkins	.30
194	Will Blackwell	.30
195	Levon Kirkland	.30
196	Mikhail Ricks	15.00
197	*Ryan Leaf*	35.00
198	Natrone Means	.60
199	Junior Seau	.60
200	Bryan Still	.30
201	Freddie Jones	.30
202	Steve Young	2.00
203	Jim Druckenmiller	1.00
204	Garrison Hearst	.60
205	*R.W. McQuarters*	8.00
206	Merton Hanks	.30
207	Marc Edwards	.30
208	Jerry Rice	4.00
209	Terrell Owens	1.50
210	J.J. Stokes	.30
211	Tony Banks	.60
212	*Robert Holcombe*	20.00
213	Greg Hill	.30
214	Amp Lee	.30
215	Jerald Moore	.30
216	Isaac Bruce	.60
217	*Az-Zahir Hakim*	12.00
218	Eddie Kennison	.30
219	*Grant Wistrom*	4.00
220	Warren Moon	.60
221	*Ahman Green*	20.00
222	Steve Broussard	.30
223	Ricky Watters	.60
224	James McKnight	.30
225	Joey Galloway	1.00
226	Mike Pritchard	.30
227	Trent Dilfer	.60
228	Warrick Dunn	3.00
229	Mike Alstott	1.00
230	John Lynch	.30
231	*Jacquez Green*	25.00
232	Reidel Anthony	.60
233	Bert Emanuel	.30
234	Warren Sapp	.30
235	Steve McNair	1.50
236	Eddie George	3.00
237	Chris Sanders	.30
238	Yancey Thigpen	.30
239	Willie Davis	.30
240	*Kevin Dyson*	25.00
241	Frank Wycheck	.30
242	Trent Green	.60
243	Gus Frerotte	.30
244	*Skip Hicks*	25.00
245	Terry Allen	.30
246	Stephen Davis	.30
247	*Stephen Alexander*	4.00
248	Michael Westbrook	.60
249	Dana Stubblefield	.30
250	Dan Wilkinson	.30

Values quoted in this guide reflect the retail price of a card — the price a collector can expect to pay when buying a card from a dealer. The wholesale price — that which a collector can expect to receive from a dealer when selling cards — will be significantly lower, depending on desirability and condition.

1998 Playoff Momentum Hobby Class Reunion Quads

Each card in this set includes stars from every draft class since the famous one in 1983. Four players drafted in the same year appear on each card (two on the front, two on the back). Cards are printed on doublesided mirror foil stock with micro-etching on each side as well as gold foil stamping. Singles were inserted 1:81 hobby packs.

		MT
Complete Set (16):		700.00
Common Player:		20.00
Inserted 1:81		
1	1983 (Dan Marino, John Elway, Bruce Matthews, Darrell Green)	75.00
2	1984 (Steve Young, Irving Fryar, Reggie White, Jeff Hostetler)	35.00
3	1985 (Jerry Rice, Bruce Smith, Andre Reed, Doug Flutie)	50.00
4	1986 (Keith Byars, Leslie O'Neal, Seth Joyner, Ray Brown)	20.00
5	1987 (Cris Carter, Vinny Testaverde, Jim Harbaugh, Rod Woodson)	20.00
6	1988 (Tim Brown, Chris Chandler, Michael Irvin, Neil Smith)	20.00
7	1989 (Troy Aikman, Barry Sanders, Deion Sanders, Andre Rison)	100.00
8	1990 (Emmitt Smith, Jeff George, Neil O'Donnell, Shannon Sharpe)	75.00
9	1991 (Brett Favre, Herman Moore, Yancey Thigpen, Ricky Watters)	100.00
10	1992 (Mark Chmura, Brad Johnson, Carl Pickens, Robert Brooks)	20.00
11	1993 (Drew Bledsoe, Jerome Bettis, Mark Brunell, Garrison Hearst)	40.00
12	1994 (Trent Dilfer, Dorsey Levens, Marshall Faulk, Isaac Bruce)	25.00
13	1995 (Terrell Davis, Kordell Stewart, Napoleon Kaufman, Curtis Martin)	75.00
14	1996 (Eddie George, Keyshawn Johnson, Karim Abdul-Jabbar, Terry Glenn)	40.00
15	1997 (Warrick Dunn, Corey Dillon, Jake Plummer, Antowain Smith)	40.00
16	1998 (Peyton Manning, Ryan Leaf, Curtis Enis, Randy Moss)	125.00

1998 Playoff Momentum Hobby EndZone Xpress

This 29-card set spotlights the NFL's best who have a knack for getting into the end zone. Each card is printed on die-cut clear plastic with holographic foil stamping. Singles were found 1:9 hobby packs.

		MT
Complete Set (29):		250.00
Common Player:		2.00
Minor Stars:		4.00
Inserted 1:9		
1	Jake Plummer	10.00
2	Herman Moore	2.00
3	Terrell Davis	18.00
4	Antowain Smith	5.00
5	Curtis Enis	10.00
6	Corey Dillon	7.00
7	Troy Aikman	12.00
8	John Elway	12.00
9	Barry Sanders	25.00
10	Brett Favre	25.00
11	Peyton Manning	25.00
12	Mark Brunell	10.00
13	Andre Rison	2.00
14	Dan Marino	18.00
15	Randy Moss	35.00
16	Drew Bledsoe	10.00
17	Jerome Bettis	4.00
18	Tim Brown	2.00
19	Antonio Freeman	4.00
20	Napoleon Kaufman	4.00
21	Emmitt Smith	18.00
22	Kordell Stewart	10.00
23	Curtis Martin	6.00
24	Ryan Leaf	12.00
25	Jerry Rice	12.00
26	Joey Galloway	4.00
27	Warrick Dunn	10.00
28	Eddie George	10.00
29	Steve McNair	7.00

1998 Playoff Momentum Hobby Headliners

These cards cover the events and milestones that made these players great. Each is printed on holographic stock with foil stamping. Singles were inserted 1:49 hobby packs.

		MT
Complete Set (23):		650.00
Common Player:		15.00
Inserted 1:49		
1	Brett Favre	80.00
2	Jerry Rice	40.00
3	Barry Sanders	80.00
4	Troy Aikman	40.00
5	Warrick Dunn	30.00
6	Dan Marino	60.00
7	John Elway	40.00
8	Drew Bledsoe	30.00
9	Kordell Stewart	30.00
10	Mark Brunell	30.00
11	Eddie George	30.00
12	Terrell Davis	60.00
13	Emmitt Smith	60.00

14	Steve McNair	20.00
15	Mike Alstott	15.00
16	Peyton Manning	80.00
17	Antonio Freeman	30.00
18	Curtis Martin	20.00
19	Terry Glenn	15.00
20	Brad Johnson	15.00
21	Karim Abdul-Jabbar	15.00
22	Ryan Leaf	40.00
23	Jerome Bettis	15.00

1998 Playoff Momentum Hobby Playoff Honors

This insert has appeared in most Playoff products since it debuted in 1996 Prime. These singles (#16-18) were inserted 1:3,841 hobby packs.

	MT
Complete Set (3):	400.00
Common Player:	100.00
Inserted 1:3,841	
PH16 Brett Favre	225.00
PH17 Kordell Stewart	100.00
PH18 Troy Aikman	125.00

1998 Playoff Momentum Hobby Marino Milestones

The final five cards (#11-15) of this chase set were inserted into Momentum packs at a ratio of 1:385. All cards are printed on premium card stock with film laminates and foil stamping designed to showcase the soon to be "Hall of Fame" autograph of Dan found on each.

	MT
Complete Set (11-15):	600.00
Common Player:	125.00
Inserted 1:385	

1998 Playoff Momentum Hobby NFL Rivals

Top NFL stars and rookie rivals were paired together on the front of these tough inserts. Each card in this 22-card set is printed on premium mirror foil board stock with gold foil stamping. Each was inserted 1:49 packs.

		MT
Complete Set (22):		650.00
Common Player:		15.00
Inserted 1:49		
1	Mark Brunell, John Elway	40.00
2	Jerome Bettis, Eddie George	30.00
3	Barry Sanders, Emmitt Smith	80.00
4	Dan Marino, Drew Bledsoe	60.00
5	Troy Aikman, Jake Plummer	40.00
6	Terrell Davis, Napoleon Kaufman	60.00
7	Cris Carter, Herman Moore	15.00
8	Warrick Dunn, Dorsey Levens	30.00
9	Kordell Stewart, Steve McNair	30.00
10	Curtis Martin, Antowain Smith	20.00
11	Jerry Rice, Michael Irvin	40.00
12	Steve Young, Brett Favre	80.00

1998 Playoff Momentum Hobby Rookie Double Feature

Each card in this set was printed on doublesided foil board with three patterned micro-etches on each side. Two rookies with similar styles of play are matched in this 20-card chase set. One on the front and one on the back. Singles were inserted 1:17 hobby packs.

		MT
Complete Set (20):		200.00
Common Player:		4.00
Inserted 1:17		
1	Peyton Manning, Brian Griese	30.00
2	Ryan Leaf, Charlie Batch	25.00
3	Charles Woodson, Terry Fair	12.00
4	Curtis Enis, Tavian Banks	12.00
5	Fred Taylor, John Avery	20.00
6	Kevin Dyson, E.G. Green	10.00
7	Robert Edwards, Chris Fuamatu-Ma'afala	12.00
8	Randy Moss, Tim Dwight	40.00
9	Marcus Nash, Joe Jurevicius	10.00
10	Jerome Pathon, Az-Zahir Hakim	6.00
11	Jacquez Green, Tony Simmons	10.00
12	Robert Holcombe, Jon Ritchie	8.00
13	Cameron Cleeland, Alonzo Mayes	6.00
14	Patrick Johnson, Mikhail Ricks	4.00
15	Germane Crowell, Hines Ward	10.00
16	Skip Hicks, Chris Floyd	8.00
17	Brian Alford, Jammi German	4.00
18	Ahman Green, Rashaan Shehee	8.00
19	Jonathan Quinn, Moses Moreno	4.00
20	R.W. McQuarters, Duane Starks	4.00

Post-1980 cards in Near Mint condition will generally sell for about 75% of the quoted Mint value. Excellent-condition cards bring no more than 40%.

1998 Playoff Momentum Hobby Team Threads

Each card in this 20-card set showcased authentic team jerseys that the pros use. All the Home jerseys were in color while the parallel Away jerseys were in white. Home jerseys could be found 1:33 hobby packs while the Away singles were tougher at 1:65.

		MT
Complete Set (20):		350.00
Common Player:		7.00
Inserted 1:33		
Away Cards:		2x
Inserted 1:65		
1	Jerry Rice	20.00
2	Terrell Davis	30.00
3	Warrick Dunn	15.00
4	Brett Favre	40.00
5	Napoleon Kaufman	10.00
6	Corey Dillon	10.00
7	John Elway	20.00
8	Troy Aikman	20.00
9	Mark Brunell	15.00
10	Kordell Stewart	15.00
11	Drew Bledsoe	15.00
12	Curtis Martin	10.00
13	Dan Marino	30.00
14	Jerome Bettis	7.00
15	Eddie George	15.00
16	Ryan Leaf	20.00
17	Jake Plummer	15.00
18	Peyton Manning	40.00
19	Steve Young	12.00
20	Barry Sanders	40.00

1998 Playoff Momentum Retail

Each of the base cards in this set have a pigskin embossed style to them. Rookie cards are seeded at 1:3 retail packs. Each card has a parallel Red version with singles found 1:4 retail packs.

		MT
Complete Set (250):		150.00
Common Player:		.15
Minor Stars:		.30
Common Rookie:		1.00
Inserted 1:3		
Red Cards:		3x
Red Rookies:		1.5x
Inserted 1:4		
Wax Box:		60.00
1	Karim Abdul	.50
2	Troy Aikman	1.50
3	Derrick Alexander	.30
4	*Stephen Alexander*	3.00
5	*Brian Alford*	2.00
6	Terry Allen	.30
7	Mike Alstott	.50
8	Kimble Anders	.15
9	Jamal Anderson	.75
10	Reidel Anthony	.30
11	Steve Atwater	.15

12	John Avery	4.00
13	Tavian Banks	3.50
14	Tony Banks	.30
15	Tiki Barber	.15
16	Charlie Batch	15.00
17	Donnell Bennett	.15
18	Edgar Bennett	.15
19	Jerome Bettis	.50
20	Steve Beuerlein	.15
21	Will Blackwell	.15
22	Jeff Blake	.30
23	Drew Bledsoe	1.25
24	Kyle Brady	.15
25	Robert Brooks	.30
26	Steve Broussard	.15
27	Gary Brown	.15
28	Tim Brown	.30
29	Isaac Bruce	.30
30	Mark Bruener	.15
31	Mark Brunell	1.25
32	Keith Byars	.15
33	Chris Calloway	.15
34	Rae Carruth	.15
35	Cris Carter	.50
36	Larry Centers	.15
37	Chris Chandler	.50
38	Mark Chmura	.30
39	Wayne Chrebet	.50
40	Cameron Cleeland	3.00
41	Ben Coates	.30
42	Kerry Collins	.30
43	Andre Coleman	.15
44	Curtis Conway	.30
45	Zack Crockett	.15
46	Germane Crowell	4.00
47	Randall Cunningham	1.00
48	Billy Davis	.15
49	Stephen Davis	.15
50	Terrell Davis	2.50
51	Troy Davis	.15
52	Willie Davis	.15
53	Sean Dawkins	.15
54	Trent Dilfer	.30
55	Ken Dilger	.15
56	Corey Dillon	1.00
57	Troy Drayton	.15
58	Jim Druckenmiller	.30
59	Rickey Dudley	.15
60	Jason Dunn	.15
61	Warrick Dunn	1.25
62	Tim Dwight	4.00
63	Kevin Dyson	4.00
64	Marc Edwards	.15
65	Robert Edwards	7.00
66	John Elway	1.75
67	Bert Emanuel	.15
68	Bobby Engram	.15
69	Curtis Enis	6.00
70	Craig Erickson	.15
71	Terry Fair	3.00
72	Marshall Faulk	.75
73	Brett Favre	3.00
74	Chris Floyd	1.00
75	William Floyd	.15
76	Doug Flutie	1.00
77	Glenn Foley	.30
78	Antonio Freeman	.50
79	Gus Frerotte	.30
80	Irving Fryar	.15
81	Chris Fuamatu-Ma'afala	2.00
82	Joey Galloway	.50
83	Rich Gannon	.15
84	Charlie Garner	.15
85	Eddie George	1.25
86	Jeff George	.30
87	Jammi German	3.00
88	Terry Glenn	.50
89	Tony Gonzalez	.30
90	Jay Graham	.15
91	Jeff Graham	.15
92	Elvis Grbac	.30
93	Ahman Green	3.00
94	E.G. Green	3.00
95	Eric Green	.15
96	Jacquez Green	4.00
97	Trent Green	.50
98	Kevin Greene	.15
99	Brian Griese	10.00
100	Az-Zahir Hakim	3.00
101	Merton Hanks	.15
102	Jim Harbaugh	.30
103	Marvin Harrison	.30
104	Andre Hastings	.15
105	Courtney Hawkins	.15
106	Garrison Hearst	.50
107	William Henderson	.15
108	Skip Hicks	5.00
109	Greg Hill	.15
110	Ike Hilliard	.15
111	Robert Holcombe	3.00
112	Vonnie Holliday	3.00
113	Bobby Hoying	.30
114	Michael Irvin	.30
115	Qadry Ismail	.15
116	Raghib Ismail	.15
117	Michael Jackson	.15
118	Shawn Jefferson	.15
119	James Jett	.15
120	Anthony Johnson	.15
121	Brad Johnson	.50
122	Charles Johnson	.15
123	Keyshawn Johnson	.50
124	Leon Johnson	.15
125	Patrick Johnson	3.00
126	Rob Johnson	.50
127	Daryl Johnston	.15

128	Freddie Jones	.15
129	Joe Jurevicius	3.00
130	Danny Kanell	.15
131	Napoleon Kaufman	.50
132	Eddie Kennison	.30
133	Levon Kirkland	.15
134	Erik Kramer	.15
135	David LaFleur	.15
136	Fred Lane	.30
137	Ryan Leaf	8.00
138	Amp Lee	.15
139	Dorsey Levens	.50
140	Jermaine Lewis	.30
141	Ray Lewis	.15
142	Jonathon Linton	2.00
143	Greg Lloyd	.15
144	Kevin Lockett	.15
145	John Lynch	.15
146	Peyton Manning	25.00
147	Dan Marino	2.00
148	Curtis Martin	.50
149	Tony Martin	.30
150	Terance Mathis	.15
151	Alonzo Mayes	1.00
152	Derrick Mayes	.15
153	Ed McCaffrey	.30
154	Keenan McCardell	.30
155	O.J. McDuffie	.30
156	Tony McGee	.15
157	James McKnight	.15
158	Steve McNair	.75
159	R.W. McQuarters	2.00
160	Natrone Means	.50
161	Eric Metcalf	.15
162	Ernie Mills	.15
163	Rick Mirer	.15
164	Scott Mitchell	.30
165	Warren Moon	.30
166	Herman Moore	.50
167	Jerald Moore	.15
168	Rob Moore	.30
169	Moses Moreno	2.00
170	Johnnie Morton	.15
171	Randy Moss	40.00
172	Eric Moulds	.75
173	Muhsin Muhammad	.15
174	Adrian Murrell	.30
175	Marcus Nash	4.00
176	Neil O'Donnell	.15
177	Terrell Owens	.75
178	Jerome Pathon	3.00
179	Carl Pickens	.50
180	Jake Plummer	1.25
181	Mike Pritchard	.15
182	Jonathan Quinn	3.00
183	John Randle	.15
184	Andre Reed	.30
185	Jake Reed	.30
186	Errict Rhett	.15
187	Jerry Rice	1.50
188	Mikhael Ricks	3.00
189	Andre Rison	.30
190	John Ritchie	2.00
191	Rod Rutledge	1.00
192	Barry Sanders	3.00
193	Chris Sanders	.15
194	Deion Sanders	.50
195	Frank Sanders	.15
196	O.J. Santiago	.30
197	Warren Sapp	.15
198	Darnay Scott	.15
199	Junior Seau	.30
200	Shannon Sharpe	.30
201	Sedrick Shaw	.15
202	Rashaan Shehee	2.00
203	Heath Shuler	.15
204	Tony Simmons	4.00
205	Antowain Smith	.50
206	Bruce Smith	.15
207	Emmitt Smith	2.00
208	Jimmy Smith	.50
209	Lamar Smith	.15
210	Neil Smith	.15
211	Robert Smith	.30
212	Rod Smith	.30
213	Takeo Spikes	2.00
214	Duce Staley	.30
215	Duane Starks	2.00
216	James Stewart	.15
217	Kordell Stewart	1.25
218	Bryan Still	.15
219	J.J. Stokes	.30
220	Michael Strahan	.15
221	Dana Stubblefield	.15
222	Fred Taylor	15.00
223	Vinny Testaverde	.30
224	Yancey Thigpen	.15
225	Derrick Thomas	.15
226	Thurman Thomas	.30
227	Zach Thomas	.30
228	Amani Toomer	.15
229	Andre Wadsworth	4.00
230	Wesley Walls	.15
231	Dedric Ward	.15
232	Hines Ward	3.00
233	Chris Warren	.30
234	Ricky Watters	.50
235	Charles Way	.15
236	Michael Westbrook	.15
237	Tyrone Wheatley	.15
238	Reggie White	.50
239	Dan Wilkinson	.15
240	Kevin Williams	.15
241	Shaun Williams	1.00
242	Grant Wistrom	2.00
243	Charles Woodson	7.00
244	Darren Woodson	.15
245	Rod Woodson	.15

246	Danny Wuerffel	.15
247	Frank Wycheck	.15
248	Steve Young	1.00
249	Eric Zeier	.15
250	Ray Zellars	.15

1998 Playoff Momentum Retail Class Reunion Tandems

The idea behind this insert was to pick two of the top players drafted from a specific season and picture one on the front and the other on the back. The set starts with the year 1983 and ends with 1998. Singles were inserted 1:121 retail packs.

		MT
Complete Set (16):		500.00
Common Player:		12.00
Minor Stars:		24.00
Inserted 1:121		
1	Dan Marino, John Elway	70.00
2	Steve Young, Reggie White	30.00
3	Jerry Rice, Bruce Smith	40.00
4	Keith Byars, Leslie O'Neal	12.00
5	Cris Carter, Vinny Testaverde	24.00
6	Tim Brown, Michael Irvin	24.00
7	Troy Aikman, Barry Sanders	80.00
8	Emmitt Smith, Jeff George	60.00
9	Brett Favre, Herman Moore	80.00
10	Brad Johnson, Carl Pickens	24.00
11	Drew Bledsoe, Mark Brunell	40.00
12	Dorsey Levens, Isaac Bruce	24.00
13	Terrell Davis, Kordell Stewart	70.00
14	Eddie George, Keyshawn Johnson	35.00
15	Warrick Dunn, Jake Plummer	35.00
16	Peyton Manning, Ryan Leaf	50.00

1998 Playoff Momentum Retail EndZone X-press

Each card in this set is similar to the hobby version except these singles aren't die cut. They are printed on plastic with gold foil and were inserted 1:13 retail packs.

		MT
Complete Set (29):		100.00
Common Player:		1.00
Minor Stars:		2.00

Inserted 1:13		
1	Jake Plummer	5.00
2	Herman Moore	2.00
3	Terrell Davis	8.00
4	Antowain Smith	2.00
5	Curtis Enis	3.00
6	Corey Dillon	3.00
7	Troy Aikman	6.00
8	John Elway	6.00
9	Barry Sanders	10.00
10	Brett Favre	10.00
11	Peyton Manning	10.00
12	Mark Brunell	6.00
13	Andre Rison	1.00
14	Dan Marino	8.00
15	Randy Moss	20.00
16	Drew Bledsoe	6.00
17	Jerome Bettis	2.00
18	Tim Brown	1.00
19	Antonio Freeman	2.00
20	Napoleon Kaufman	2.00
21	Emmitt Smith	8.00
22	Kordell Stewart	6.00
23	Curtis Martin	4.00
24	Ryan Leaf	5.00
25	Jerry Rice	6.00
26	Joey Galloway	2.00
27	Warrick Dunn	5.00
28	Eddie George	5.00
29	Steve McNair	3.00

1998 Playoff Momentum Retail Headliners

These red foil front cards highlight a record that the player had set in the past. Singles were found 1:73 retail packs.

		MT
Complete Set (23):		275.00
Common Player:		7.00
Inserted 1:73		
1	Brett Favre	40.00
2	Jerry Rice	20.00
3	Barry Sanders	40.00
4	Troy Aikman	20.00
5	Warrick Dunn	15.00
6	Dan Marino	30.00
7	John Elway	25.00
8	Drew Bledsoe	15.00
9	Kordell Stewart	15.00
10	Mark Brunell	15.00
11	Eddie George	15.00
12	Terrell Davis	35.00
13	Emmitt Smith	30.00
14	Steve McNair	10.00
15	Mike Alstott	7.00
16	Peyton Manning	30.00
17	Antonio Freeman	10.00
18	Curtis Martin	10.00
19	Terry Glenn	7.00
20	Brad Johnson	7.00
21	Karim Abdul	7.00
22	Ryan Leaf	15.00
23	Jerome Bettis	7.00

1998 Playoff Momentum Retail NFL Rivals

This set is identical to the hobby version except for the

"R" prefix on these retail singles. Each card pictures two players who compete at the same position. Singles are found 1:73 retail packs.

		MT
Complete Set (22):		280.00
Common Player:		10.00
Inserted 1:73		
1	Mark Brunell, John Elway	20.00
2	Jerome Bettis, Eddie George	15.00
3	Barry Sanders, Emmitt Smith	40.00
4	Dan Marino, Drew Bledsoe	30.00
5	Troy Aikman, Jake Plummer	20.00
6	Terrell Davis, Napoleon Kaufman	30.00
7	Cris Carter, Herman Moore	10.00
8	Warrick Dunn, Dorsey Levens	15.00
9	Kordell Stewart, Steve McNair	15.00
10	Curtis Martin, Antowain Smith	10.00
11	Jerry Rice, Michael Irvin	20.00
12	Steve Young, Brett Favre	40.00
13	Corey Dillon, Fred Taylor	20.00
14	Tim Brown, Andre Rison	10.00
15	Mike Alstott, Robert Smith	10.00
16	Brad Johnson, Scott Mitchell	10.00
17	Robert Edwards, John Avery	15.00
18	Deion Sanders, Rob Moore	10.00
19	Antonio Freeman, Randy Moss	50.00
20	Peyton Manning, Ryan Leaf	35.00
21	Curtis Enis, Jacquez Green	15.00
22	Keyshawn Johnson, Terry Glenn	10.00

1998 Playoff Momentum Retail Rookie Double Feature

The hobby version of this set features two players on one card, where this set has the players on their own card. Each card also has the "R" prefix before the card number and were found 1:25 retail packs.

		MT
Complete Set (40):		220.00
Common Player:		2.00
Minor Stars:		4.00
Inserted 1:25		
1	Peyton Manning	30.00
2	Ryan Leaf	10.00
3	Charles Woodson	10.00
4	Curtis Enis	8.00
5	Fred Taylor	15.00
6	Kevin Dyson	8.00
7	Robert Edwards	8.00
8	Randy Moss	60.00
9	Marcus Nash	6.00
10	Jerome Pathon	4.00
11	Jacquez Green	6.00
12	Robert Holcombe	5.00
13	Cameron Cleeland	5.00
14	Patrick Johnson	4.00
15	Germane Crowell	6.00
16	Skip Hicks	6.00
17	Brian Alford	2.00
18	Ahman Green	5.00
19	Jonathan Quinn	4.00
20	R.W. McQuarters	4.00
21	Brian Griese	10.00
22	Charlie Batch	18.00
23	Terry Fair	4.00
24	Tavian Banks	5.00
25	John Avery	6.00
26	E.G. Green	4.00
27	Chris Fuamatu-Ma'afala	4.00
28	Tim Dwight	6.00
29	Joe Jurevicius	4.00
30	Az-Zahir Hakim	4.00
31	Tony Simmons	5.00
32	Jon Ritchie	4.00
33	Alonzo Mayes	2.00
34	Mikhael Ricks	4.00
35	Hines Ward	4.00
36	Chris Floyd	2.00
37	Jammi German	4.00
38	Rashaan Shehee	4.00
39	Moses Moreno	2.00
40	Duane Starks	4.00

1998 Playoff Momentum Retail Team Jerseys

Team Jersey cards feature a photo of the player on the front and a piece of an authentic jersey on the back. It isn't an actual game worn but a jersey that the pros use. The Home versions carry a colored swatch and were inserted 1:49 retail packs. The parallel Away versions feature the white jerseys and were inserted 1:97 packs.

		MT
Complete Set (20):		600.00
Common Player:		15.00
Inserted 1:49		
Away Cards:		1.5x
Inserted 1:97		
1	Jerry Rice	30.00
2	Terrell Davis	50.00
3	Warrick Dunn	25.00
4	Brett Favre	60.00
5	Napoleon Kaufman	15.00
6	Corey Dillon	15.00
7	John Elway	30.00
8	Troy Aikman	30.00
9	Mark Brunell	25.00
10	Kordell Stewart	25.00
11	Drew Bledsoe	25.00
12	Curtis Martin	15.00
13	Dan Marino	30.00
14	Jerome Bettis	15.00
15	Eddie George	25.00
16	Ryan Leaf	25.00
17	Jake Plummer	30.00
18	Peyton Manning	50.00
19	Steve Young	20.00
20	Barry Sanders	60.00

1998 Playoff Prestige

Prestige was a 200-card set that arrived with two different looks - one in hobby and one in retail. Prestige SSD cards are printed on 30-point etched silver foil stock. Retail versions are printed on thinner stock, with a foil strip across the bottom. While hobby cards are paralled in red and gold versions, retail cards are paralleled in red and green foil versus the silver foil used on base cards. Inserts include: Alma Mater (both retail and hobby), Award Winning Performers (both), Best of the NFL (both), Checklists (both), Draft Picks (both), Honors (hobby), Inside the Numbers (both) and Marino Milestones (hobby).

	MT
Complete Set (200):	170.00
Common Player:	.30
Minor Stars:	.60
Common Rookie (165-200):	1.50
Wax Box:	100.00
1 John Elway	4.00
2 Steve Atwater	.30
3 Terrell Davis	5.00
4 Bill Romanowski	.30
5 Rod Smith	.30
6 Shannon Sharpe	.30
7 Ed McCaffrey	.30
8 Neil Smith	.30
9 Brett Favre	8.00
10 Dorsey Levens	.60
11 LeRoy Butler	.30
12 Antonio Freeman	.60
13 Robert Brooks	.60
14 Mark Chmura	.60
15 Gilbert Brown	.30
16 Kordell Stewart	3.00
17 Jerome Bettis	.60
18 Carnell Lake	.30
19 Dermontti Dawson	.30
20 Charles Johnson	.30
21 Greg Lloyd	.30
22 Levon Kirkland	.30
23 Steve Young	4.00
24 Jim Druckenmiller	.60
25 Garrison Hearst	.30
26 Merton Hanks	.30
27 Ken Norton	.30
28 Jerry Rice	5.00
29 Terrell Owens	.60
30 J.J. Stokes	.30
31 Trent Dilfer	.60
32 Warrick Dunn	4.00
33 Mike Alstott	.75
34 Reidel Anthony	.60
35 Warren Sapp	.60
36 Elvis Grbac	.30
37 Kimble Anders	.30
38 Ted Popson	.30
39 Derrick Thomas	.60
40 Tony Gonzalez	.60
41 Andre Rison	.30
42 Derrick Alexander	.30
43 Brad Johnson	.60
44 Robert Smith	.60
45 Randall McDaniel	.30
46 Cris Carter	.60
47 Jake Reed	.30
48 John Randle	.30
49 Drew Bledsoe	4.00
50 Willie Clay	.30
51 Chris Slade	.30
52 Willie McGinest	.30
53 Shawn Jefferson	.30
54 Ben Coates	.30
55 Terry Glenn	.60
56 Jason Hanson	.30
57 Scott Mitchell	.30
58 Barry Sanders	10.00
59 Herman Moore	.60
60 Johnnie Morton	.30
61 Mark Brunell	4.00
62 James Stewart	.30
63 Tony Boselli	.30
64 Jimmy Smith	.30
65 Keenan McCardell	.30
66 Dan Marino	8.00
67 Troy Drayton	.30
68 Bernie Parmalee	.30
69 Karim Abdul-Jabbar	.75
70 Zach Thomas	.30
71 O.J. McDuffie	.30
72 Tim Bowens	.30
73 Danny Kanell	.30
74 Tiki Barber	.60
75 Tyrone Wheatley	.30
76 Charles Way	.30
77 Jason Sehorn	.30
78 Ike Hilliard	.60
79 Michael Strahan	.30
80 Troy Aikman	4.00
81 Deion Sanders	2.00
82 Emmitt Smith	7.00
83 Darren Woodson	.30
84 Daryl Johnston	.30
85 Michael Irvin	.60
86 David LaFleur	.60
87 Glenn Foley	.30
88 Neil O'Donnell	.30
89 Keyshawn Johnson	.60
90 Aaron Glenn	.30
91 Wayne Chrebet	.30
92 Curtis Martin	2.00
93 Steve McNair	2.00
94 Eddie George	3.00
95 Bruce Matthews	.30
96 Frank Wycheck	.30
97 Yancey Thigpen	.30
98 Gus Frerotte	.30
99 Terry Allen	.30

100 Michael Westbrook	.30
101 Jamie Asher	.30
102 Marshall Faulk	.60
103 Zack Crockett	.30
104 Ken Dilger	.30
105 Marvin Harrison	.60
106 Chris Chandler	.30
107 Byron Hanspard	.60
108 Jamal Anderson	.60
109 Terance Mathis	.30
110 Peter Boulware	.30
111 Michael Jackson	.30
112 Jim Harbaugh	.60
113 Errict Rhett	.30
114 Antowain Smith	3.00
115 Thurman Thomas	.60
116 Bruce Smith	.30
117 Doug Flutie	3.00
118 Rob Johnson	.60
119 Kerry Collins	.75
120 Fred Lane	.30
121 Wesley Walls	.30
122 William Floyd	.30
123 Kevin Greene	.30
124 Erik Kramer	.30
125 Darnell Autry	.60
126 Curtis Conway	.30
127 Edgar Bennett	.30
128 Jeff Blake	.60
129 Corey Dillon	4.00
130 Carl Pickens	.30
131 Darnay Scott	.30
132 Jake Plummer	4.00
133 Larry Centers	.30
134 Frank Sanders	.30
135 Rob Moore	.30
136 Adrian Murrell	.60
137 Troy Davis	.30
138 Ray Zellars	.30
139 Willie Roaf	.30
140 Andre Hastings	.30
141 Jeff George	.60
142 Napoleon Kaufman	.75
143 Desmond Howard	.30
144 Tim Brown	.30
145 James Jett	.30
146 Rickey Dudley	.30
147 Bobby Hoying	.30
148 Duce Staley	.30
149 Charlie Garner	.30
150 Irving Fryar	.30
151 Chris T. Jones	.30
152 Tony Banks	.60
153 Craig Heyward	.30
154 Isaac Bruce	.60
155 Eddie Kennison	.60
156 Junior Seau	.30
157 Tony Martin	.30
158 Freddie Jones	.30
159 Natrone Means	.30
160 Warren Moon	.60
161 Steve Broussard	.30
162 Joey Galloway	.60
163 Brian Blades	.30
164 Ricky Watters	.60
165 *Peyton Manning*	20.00
166 *Ryan Leaf*	12.00
167 *Andre Wadsworth*	3.00
168 *Charles Woodson*	8.00
169 *Curtis Enis*	7.00
170 *Fred Taylor*	15.00
171 *Kevin Dyson*	5.00
172 *Robert Edwards*	8.00
173 *Randy Moss*	30.00
174 *R.W. McQuarters*	1.50
175 *John Avery*	5.00
176 *Marcus Nash*	5.00
177 *Jerome Pathon*	3.00
178 *Jacquez Green*	6.00
179 *Robert Holcombe*	6.00
180 *Patrick Johnson*	1.50
181 *Germane Crowell*	4.00
182 *Tony Simmons*	3.00
183 *Joe Jurevicius*	3.00
184 *Mikhael Ricks*	1.50
185 *Charlie Batch*	15.00
186 *Jon Ritchie*	1.50
187 *Scott Frost*	1.50
188 *Skip Hicks*	5.00
189 *Brian Alford*	1.50
190 *E.G. Green*	3.00
191 *Jammi German*	1.50
192 *Ahman Green*	7.00
193 *Chris Floyd*	1.50
194 *Larry Shannon*	1.50
195 *Jonathan Quinn*	2.00
196 *Rashaan Shehee*	3.00
197 *Brian Griese*	10.00
198 *Hines Ward*	5.00
199 *Michael Pittman*	1.50
200 *Az-Zahir Hakim*	1.50

> Values quoted in this guide reflect the retail price of a card — the price a collector can expect to pay when buying a card from a dealer. The wholesale price — that which a collector can expect to receive from a dealer when selling cards — will be significantly lower, depending on desirability and condition.

1998 Playoff Prestige Red Hobby

All 200 cards in Prestige SSD were paralleled in this red foil version. Red parallels were seeded one per three packs.

	MT
Red Cards:	3x
Red Rookies:	2x

1998 Playoff Prestige Gold

All 200 cards in Prestige were available in a gold foil parallel version. These were sequentially numbered to 25 on the card back.

	MT
Gold Cards:	50x-100x
Gold Rookies:	12x-25x

1998 Playoff Prestige Alma Maters

This 28-card set featured three players from the same college on the silver foilboard. The back showed the same three players are gave a "Did you Know?" statistic about each. Silver versions were seeded one per 17 hobby packs, while Blue versions were seeded one per 25 retail packs.

	MT
Complete Set (28):	375.00
Common Player:	6.00
1 Favre, Jackson, P. Carter	45.00
2 Irvin, Maryland, Testaverde	6.00
3 Dunn, Wadsworth, Boulware	20.00
4 D. Sanders, Bennett, B. Johnson	12.00
5 E. Smith, F. Taylor, Anthony	30.00
6 A. Smith, Anders, Lathon	12.00
7 Barry Sanders, R.J. McQuarters, Thurman Thomas	40.00
8 Leaf, Bledsoe, Hansen	25.00
9 Brunell, Moon, Shehee	20.00
10 Kaufman, Dillon, Pathon	15.00
11 Manning, Pickens, R. White	40.00
12 K. Stewart, Carruth, Westbrook	20.00
13 Enis, Collins, McDuffie	20.00
14 George, Hoying, Dudley	20.00
15 C. Carter, Glenn, Galloway	6.00

	MT
16 Grbac, Harbaugh, Woodson	15.00
17 Elway, McCaffrey, Milburn	20.00
18 T. Davis, Hearst, Edwards	25.00
19 Walker, Hastings, Ward	6.00
20 Marino, C. Martin, Heyward	40.00
21 Aikman, Stokes, Hicks	25.00
22 Seau, K. Johnson, Morton	6.00
23 Bettis, T. Brown, Watters	6.00
24 Faulk, Scott, Hakim	6.00
25 B. Smith, Druckenmiller, Freeman	6.00
26 Plummer, Woodson, Bates	20.00
27 H. Moore, Barber, Way	6.00
28 Avery, Walls, Bowens	6.00

1998 Playoff Prestige Award Winning Performers

This 22-card insert showcased top players on a large trophy, with the record they achieved and the Playoff logo near the top of the trophy. Hobby versions of this inserted were printed on silver foil, die-cut around the trophy and inserted one per 65 packs, while retail versions were printed on blue foil, not die-cut and inserted one per 97 packs.

	MT
Complete Set (22):	750.00
Common Player:	15.00
1 Terrell Davis	60.00
2 Troy Aikman	50.00
3 Brett Favre	90.00
4 Barry Sanders	90.00
5 Warrick Dunn	45.00
6 John Elway	50.00
7 Jerome Bettis	15.00
8 Jake Plummer	45.00
9 Corey Dillon	25.00
10 Jerry Rice	50.00
11 Steve Young	30.00
12 Mark Brunell	35.00
13 Drew Bledsoe	45.00
14 Dan Marino	75.00
15 Kordell Stewart	45.00
16 Emmitt Smith	75.00
17 Deion Sanders	20.00
18 Mike Alstott	15.00
19 Herman Moore	15.00
20 Cris Carter	15.00
21 Eddie George	35.00
22 Dorsey Levens	15.00

1998 Playoff Prestige Best of the NFL

Best in the NFL features 24 top players over a large NFL logo.

Hobby versions of this insert were die-cut around the top of the NFL shield and inserted one per 33 hobby packs, while retail versions were not die-cut and inserted one per 49 retail packs.

	MT
Complete Set (24):	400.00
Common Player:	6.00
1 Terrell Davis	25.00
2 Troy Aikman	25.00
3 Brett Favre	50.00
4 Barry Sanders	40.00
5 Warrick Dunn	20.00
6 John Elway	25.00
7 Jerome Bettis	6.00
8 Jake Plummer	20.00
9 Corey Dillon	15.00
10 Jerry Rice	25.00
11 Steve Young	15.00
12 Mark Brunell	20.00
13 Drew Bledsoe	25.00
14 Dan Marino	40.00
15 Kordell Stewart	25.00
16 Emmitt Smith	40.00
17 Deion Sanders	15.00
18 Mike Alstott	6.00
19 Herman Moore	6.00
20 Cris Carter	6.00
21 Eddie George	25.00
22 Dorsey Levens	6.00
23 Peyton Manning	35.00
24 Ryan Leaf	25.00

1998 Playoff Prestige Checklist

This 30-card insert arrived in both retail and hobby packs, and contained a star player from each NFL team on the front and shots of each player on that team's cards on the back. Silver hobby versions were seeded one per 17 hobby packs, while gold retail versions were seeded one per 17 retail packs.

	MT
Complete Set (30):	350.00
Common Player:	4.00
1 Jake Plummer	20.00
2 Byron Hanspard	4.00
3 Michael Jackson	4.00
4 Antowain Smith	10.00
5 Wesley Walls	4.00
6 Erik Kramer	4.00
7 Corey Dillon	15.00
8 Troy Aikman	35.00
9 John Elway	20.00
10 Barry Sanders	35.00
11 Brett Favre	40.00
12 Peyton Manning	35.00
13 Mark Brunell	35.00
14 Andre Rison	4.00
15 Dan Marino	35.00
16 Cris Carter	4.00
17 Drew Bledsoe	25.00
18 Troy Davis	4.00
19 Danny Kanell	4.00
20 Glenn Foley	4.00
21 Napoleon Kaufman	6.00
22 Bobby Hoying	4.00
23 Kordell Stewart	25.00
24 Isaac Bruce	6.00
25 Ryan Leaf	25.00
26 Jerry Rice	25.00
27 Joey Galloway	6.00
28 Warrick Dunn	20.00
29 Eddie George	25.00
30 Gus Frerotte	4.00

> Post-1980 cards in Near Mint condition will generally sell for about 75% of the quoted Mint value. Excellent-condition cards bring no more than 40%.

1998 Playoff Prestige Draft Picks

This 30-card insert featured the top draft picks from 1998. Silver versions were seeded one per nine hobby packs, while Silver Jumbos were inserted one per hobby box. Bronze standard sized cards were seeded one per nine retail packs, while Bronze Jumbos were inserted one per retail box. Green standard sized cards and Green Jumbos were also available, but only in special retail boxes, and both seeded one per box.

	MT
Complete Set (33):	250.00
Common Player:	3.00
Jumbos:	1x
1 Peyton Manning	30.00
2 Ryan Leaf	15.00
3 Andre Wadsworth	6.00
4 Charles Woodson	12.00
5 Curtis Enis	12.00
6 Fred Taylor	15.00
7 Kevin Dyson	10.00
8 Robert Edwards	12.00
9 Randy Moss	40.00
10 R.W. McQuarters	3.00
11 John Avery	10.00
12 Marcus Nash	10.00
13 Jerome Pathon	3.00
14 Jacquez Green	10.00
15 Robert Holcombe	10.00
16 Patrick Johnson	3.00
17 Germane Crowell	3.00
18 Tony Simmons	6.00
19 Joe Jurevicius	6.00
20 Mikhael Ricks	3.00
21 Charlie Batch	12.00
22 Jon Ritchie	3.00
23 Scott Frost	3.00
24 Skip Hicks	10.00
25 Brian Alford	3.00
26 E.G. Green	3.00
27 Jammi German	3.00
28 Ahman Green	12.00
29 Chris Floyd	3.00
30 Larry Shannon	3.00
31 Jonathan Quinn	3.00
32 Rashaan Shehee	6.00
33 Brian Griese	12.00

1998 Playoff Prestige Playoff Honors

This three-card insert was found only in hobby packs of Pretige. The cards were unnumbered and are listed alphabetically. The were inserted one per 3,200 packs.

	MT
Complete Set (3):	400.00
Common Player:	75.00
PH10 Terrell Davis	150.00
PH11 Barry Sanders	200.00
PH12 Warrick Dunn	75.00

> A player's name in *italic* type indicates a rookie card.

1998 Playoff Prestige Inside the Numbers

This 18-card insert set featured a player over some statistic that he has achieved. Hobby versions were die-cut and inserted one per 49 hobby packs, while retail not die-cut and inserted one per 72 retail packs.

		MT
Complete Set (18):		450.00
Common Player:		10.00
1	Barry Sanders	75.00
2	Terrell Davis	45.00
3	Jerry Rice	30.00
4	Kordell Stewart	30.00
5	Dan Marino	60.00
6	Warrick Dunn	30.00
7	Corey Dillon	20.00
8	Drew Bledsoe	30.00
9	Herman Moore	10.00
10	Troy Aikman	30.00
11	Brett Favre	75.00
12	Mark Brunell	25.00
13	Tim Brown	10.00
14	Jerome Bettis	10.00
15	Eddie George	30.00
16	Dorsey Levens	10.00
17	Napoleon Kaufman	10.00
18	John Elway	40.00

1998 Playoff Prestige Marino Milestones

The first five Marino Milestones cards were inserted into Prestige SSD at a rate of one per 321 packs. Each card highlighted a different record held by Marino, and no unautographed versions were available. Cards 6-10 were inserted into Absolute SSD and 11-15 were in Momentum SSD.

		MT
Complete Set (5):		600.00
Common Player:		125.00
1	55.416 (Dan Marino)	125.00
2	13/4 (Dan Marino)	125.00
3	6 (Dan Marino)	125.00
4	48 (Dan Marino)	125.00
5	2.03 (Dan Marino)	125.00

1998 Playoff Prestige Retail

Prestige Retail contained the same 200-card checklist that the hobby version had, but was printed on a thinner card stock and featured silver strip across the bottom with the player's name embossed in it. This set was paralleled in both a red (retail) and green (special retail jumbos) foil set.

	MT
Complete Set (200):	75.00
Common Player:	.20

	MT
Minor Stars:	.40
Retail Cards:	.5x Hobby
Wax Box:	55.00

1998 Playoff Prestige Red/Green Retail

Each card in the Prestige retail set was paralleled in both red and green foil versions. The 200-card set contained either red foil (retail) or green foil (special retail) across the bottom instead of the silver used on base cards. Red foil versions were seeded one per three packs, while green foil versions were seeded one per Jumbo retail pack.

	MT
Red/Green Cards:	1.5x
Red/Green Rookies:	1x

1998 Playoff Super Bowl Show

This seven-card set was available exclusively at the NFL Experience Show in conjunction with Super Bowl XXXII. The cards are horizontal with the player's image superimposed over Qualcomm Stadium and the player's last name running up the right side. The backs capture a superimposed shot of the player over San Diego scenery with the card number in the upper right.

		MT
Complete Set (7):		18.00
Common Player:		1.00
1	Trent Dilfer	2.00
2	Tony Martin	1.00
3	Terrell Davis	7.00
4	Antonio Freeman	2.00
5	Herschel Walker	1.00
6	Kordell Stewart	5.00
7	Drew Bledsoe	4.00

1999 Playoff Absolute EXP

This was a 200-card set that included 40 unseeded

---

rookie cards. Each single was printed on 20-point stock with foil stamping. Inserts included: Tools of the Trade (parallel), Absolute Heroes, Absolute Rookies, Extreme Team, Terrell Davis Salute, Rookie Reflex, Barry Sanders Commemorative and Team Jersey Tandems. SRP was $2.99 for eight-card packs.

		MT
Complete Set (200):		70.00
Common Player:		.15
Minor Stars:		.30
Common Rookie:		.50
Wax Box:		55.00
1	Tim Couch	8.00
2	Donovan McNabb	4.00
3	Akili Smith	4.00
4	Edgerrin James	8.00
5	Ricky Williams	8.00
6	Torry Holt	3.00
7	Champ Bailey	1.50
8	David Boston	3.00
9	Chris Claiborne	1.00
10	Chris McAlister	1.00
11	Daunte Culpepper	4.00
12	Cade McNown	4.00
13	Troy Edwards	3.00
14	Kevin Johnson	3.00
15	James Johnson	2.50
16	Rob Konrad	1.00
17	Jim Kleinsasser	1.00
18	Kevin Faulk	2.00
19	Joe Montgomery	1.50
20	Shaun King	3.00
21	Peerless Price	2.50
22	Mike Cloud	1.00
23	Jermaine Fazande	1.00
24	D'Wayne Bates	1.00
25	Brock Huard	1.50
26	Marty Booker	1.50
27	Karsten Bailey	1.00
28	Shawn Bryson	.50
29	Jeff Paulk	1.00
30	Sedrick Irvin	1.75
31	Craig Yeast	1.50
32	Joe Germaine	1.50
33	Dameane Douglas	.50
34	Brandon Stokley	.50
35	Larry Parker	.50
36	Wane McGarity	1.00
37	Na Brown	.50
38	Cecil Collins	4.00
39	Darrin Chiaverini	.50
40	Madre Hill	.50
41	Adrian Murrell	.30
42	Jake Plummer	1.50
43	Frank Sanders	.30
44	Rob Moore	.30
45	Andre Wadsworth	.30
46	Simeon Rice	.15
47	Eric Swann	.15
48	Terance Mathis	.15
49	Tim Dwight	.50
50	Jamal Anderson	.50
51	Chris Chandler	.30
52	Chris Calloway	.15
53	O.J. Santiago	.15
54	Jermaine Lewis	.30
55	Priest Holmes	.50
56	Scott Mitchell	.15
57	Tony Banks	.30
58	Rod Woodson	.15
59	Andre Reed	.15
60	Thurman Thomas	.30
61	Bruce Smith	.15
62	Rob Johnson	.30
63	Eric Moulds	.50
64	Doug Flutie	1.00
65	Antowain Smith	.50
66	Tim Biakabutuka	.30
67	Muhsin Muhammad	.30
68	Steve Beuerlein	.30
69	Bobby Engram	.15
70	Curtis Conway	.30
71	Curtis Enis	.50
72	Edgar Bennett	.15
73	Jeff Blake	.30
74	Darnay Scott	.30
75	Carl Pickens	.30
76	Corey Dillon	.50
77	Ty Detmer	.15
78	Leslie Shepherd	.15
79	Sedrick Shaw	.15
80	Raghib Ismail	.15
81	Emmitt Smith	2.00
82	Michael Irvin	.30
83	Troy Aikman	1.50
84	Deion Sanders	.50
85	Darren Woodson	.15
86	Chris Warren	.15
87	John Elway	2.00
88	Brian Griese	1.25
89	Shannon Sharpe	.30
90	Terrell Davis	2.00
91	Bubby Brister	.30
92	Ed McCaffrey	.30
93	Rod Smith	.30
94	Germane Crowell	.30
95	Johnnie Morton	.15
96	Barry Sanders	3.00
97	Herman Moore	.50
98	Charlie Batch	1.00
99	Mark Chmura	.30
100	Derrick Mayes	.30
101	Dorsey Levens	.50

102	Brett Favre	3.00
103	Antonio Freeman	.50
104	Robert Brooks	.15
105	Desmond Howard	.15
106	Jerome Pathon	.15
107	Marvin Harrison	.50
108	Peyton Manning	2.00
109	E.G. Green	.15
110	Tavian Banks	.30
111	Keenan McCardell	.30
112	Jimmy Smith	.50
113	Mark Brunell	1.25
114	Fred Taylor	1.50
115	Bam Morris	.15
116	Andre Rison	.30
117	Elvis Grbac	.30
118	Warren Moon	.30
119	Tony Gonzalez	.30
120	Derrick Alexander	.15
121	Rashaan Shehee	.15
122	Zach Thomas	.30
123	Oronde Gadsden	.30
124	Dan Marino	2.00
125	Karim Abdul	.30
126	O.J. McDuffie	.30
127	Jake Reed	.30
128	John Randle	.15
129	Randy Moss	2.00
130	Cris Carter	.50
131	Randall Cunningham	.50
132	Robert Smith	.50
133	Terry Glenn	.50
134	Ben Coates	.30
135	Drew Bledsoe	1.25
136	Ty Law	.15
137	Tony Simmons	.30
138	Eddie Kennison	.15
139	Cam Cleeland	.30
140	Ike Hilliard	.15
141	Joe Jurevicius	.15
142	Gary Brown	.15
143	Kerry Collins	.30
144	Tiki Barber	.30
145	Jason Sehorn	.15
146	Dedric Ward	.15
147	Vinny Testaverde	.30
148	Wayne Chrebet	.50
149	Curtis Martin	.50
150	Keyshawn Johnson	.50
151	James Jett	.15
152	Napoleon Kaufman	.50
153	Tim Brown	.30
154	Charles Woodson	.30
155	Rickey Dudley	.30
156	Charles Johnson	.15
157	Duce Staley	.30
158	Chris Fuamatu-Ma'afala	.15
159	Jerome Bettis	.50
160	Kordell Stewart	.50
161	Levon Kirkland	.15
162	Hines Ward	.30
163	Mikhael Ricks	.15
164	Natrone Means	.30
165	Ryan Leaf	.30
166	Jim Harbaugh	.30
167	Junior Seau	.30
168	Steve Young	1.00
169	J.J. Stokes	.30
170	Terrell Owens	.50
171	Jerry Rice	1.50
172	Garrison Hearst	.30
173	Ricky Watters	.30
174	Jon Kitna	.75
175	Joey Galloway	.50
176	Ahman Green	.30
177	Isaac Bruce	.50
178	Marshall Faulk	.50
179	Trent Green	.50
180	Amp Lee	.15
181	Greg Hill	.15
182	Warren Sapp	.15
183	Hardy Nickerson	.15
184	Trent Dilfer	.30
185	Reidel Anthony	.30
186	Jacquez Green	.30
187	Warrick Dunn	.50
188	Mike Alstott	.50
189	Kevin Dyson	.30
190	Eddie George	.75
191	Yancey Thigpen	.30
192	Steve McNair	.75
193	Willie Davis	.15
194	Frank Wycheck	.15
195	Darrell Green	.15
196	Stephen Alexander	.15
197	Albert Connell	.15
198	Michael Westbrook	.30
199	Brad Johnson	.50
200	Skip Hicks	.30

1999 Playoff Absolute EXP Tools of the Trade

Charlie Batch

This was a 200-card parallel to the base set. Each single was printed on foil board with holographic foil stamping. Defensive players were sequentially numbered to 1,000, wide receivers to 750, running backs to 500 and quarterbacks to 250.

	MT
Defensive Cards:	3x-6x
Defensive Rookies:	2x
Production 1,000 Sets	
Receiver Cards:	3x-6x
Receiver Rookies:	3x
Production 750 Sets	
Running Back Cards:	5x-10x
Running Back Rookies:	4x
Production 500 Sets	
Quarterback Cards:	7x-14x
Quarterback Rookies:	6x
Production 250 Sets	

1999 Playoff Absolute EXP Absolute Heroes

This 24-card insert included superstars and highlighted them on mirror board with red foil stamping and silver borders. Singles were inserted 1:25 packs.

		MT
Complete Set (24):		65.00
Common Player:		2.00
Inserted 1:25		
1	Terrell Owens	2.00
2	Troy Aikman	5.00
3	Cris Carter	2.00
4	Brett Favre	10.00
5	Jamal Anderson	2.00
6	Doug Flutie	3.00
7	John Elway	7.00
8	Steve Young	3.00
9	Jerome Bettis	2.00
10	Emmitt Smith	7.00
11	Drew Bledsoe	4.00
12	Fred Taylor	5.00
13	Dan Marino	7.00
14	Antonio Freeman	2.00
15	Mark Brunell	4.00
16	Jake Plummer	5.00
17	Warrick Dunn	2.00
18	Peyton Manning	7.00
19	Randy Moss	10.00
20	Barry Sanders	10.00
21	Keyshawn Johnson	2.00
22	Eddie George	2.00
23	Terrell Davis	7.00
24	Jerry Rice	5.00

1999 Playoff Absolute EXP Absolute Rookies

This 36-card insert included the hottest rookies from the '99 NFL Draft and pictured them on holographic board with bronze foil stamping. Each single had green borders. Cards were found 1:13 packs.

		MT
Complete Set (36):		60.00
Common Player:		.75
Inserted 1:13		
1	Champ Bailey	1.50
2	Karsten Bailey	.75
3	D'Wayne Bates	.75
4	Marty Booker	.75
5	David Boston	3.00
6	Shawn Bryson	.75
7	Chris Claiborne	.75
8	Mike Cloud	.75
9	Cecil Collins	5.00
10	Tim Couch	10.00
11	Daunte Culpepper	5.00
12	Demeane Douglas	.75
13	Troy Edwards	3.00
14	Kevin Faulk	2.00
15	Jermaine Fazande	.75
16	Joe Germaine	1.50
17	Torry Holt	3.00
18	Brock Huard	1.50
19	Edgerrin James	10.00
20	James Johnson	3.00
21	Kevin Johnson	3.00
22	Shaun King	3.00
23	Jim Kleinsasser	.75
24	Rob Konrad	.75
25	Chris McAlister	.75
26	Travis McGriff	.75
27	Donovan McNabb	5.00
28	Cade McNown	5.00
29	Joe Montgomery	1.50
30	Larry Parker	.75
31	Jeff Paulk	.75
32	Peerless Price	2.00
33	Akili Smith	5.00
34	Brandon Stokley	.75
35	Ricky Williams	10.00
36	Craig Yeast	.75

1999 Playoff Absolute EXP Extreme Team

Steve McNair

This was a 36-card insert that highlighted the leaders of their team. Each was featured with holographic foil with foil stamping. Singles were inserted 1:25 packs.

		MT
Complete Set (36):		150.00
Common Player:		2.50
Inserted 1:25		
1	Steve Young	4.00
2	Fred Taylor	6.00
3	Kordell Stewart	3.00
4	Emmitt Smith	8.00
5	Barry Sanders	12.00
6	Jerry Rice	6.00
7	Jake Plummer	6.00

		MT
8	Eric Moulds	2.50
9	Randy Moss	12.00
10	Steve McNair	3.00
11	Curtis Martin	2.50
12	Dan Marino	8.00
13	Peyton Manning	8.00
14	Jon Kitna	2.50
15	Napoleon Kaufman	2.50
16	Eddie George	3.00
17	Brett Favre	12.00
18	Marshall Faulk	2.50
19	John Elway	8.00
20	Corey Dillon	2.50
21	Terrell Davis	8.00
22	Randall Cunningham	3.00
23	Mark Brunell	5.00
24	Tim Brown	2.50
25	Drew Bledsoe	5.00
26	Jerome Bettis	2.50
27	Charlie Batch	3.50
28	Jamal Anderson	2.50
29	Mike Alstott	2.50
30	Troy Aikman	6.00
31	Dorsey Levens	3.00
32	Joey Galloway	2.50
33	Skip Hicks	2.50
34	Terrell Owens	2.50
35	Keyshawn Johnson	2.50
36	Doug Flutie	4.00

1999 Playoff Absolute EXP Terrell Davis Salute

This was a 5-card set that highlighted Davis' 1998 season. Singles were inserted 1:289 packs. The first 150 of each single was autographed and sequentially numbered.

		MT
Complete Set (5):		60.00
Common Player:		12.00
Inserted 1:289		
Autographed Cards:		8x
Production 150 Sets		
1	Terrell Davis	12.00
2	Terrell Davis	12.00
3	Terrell Davis	12.00
4	Terrell Davis	12.00
5	Terrell Davis	12.00

1999 Playoff Absolute EXP Rookie Reflex

This was an 18-card set that highlighted the top rookies from 1999. Each single was printed on holographic foil board with micro-etching. Singles were found 1:49 packs.

		MT
Complete Set (18):		120.00
Common Player:		3.00
Inserted 1:49		
1	Peerless Price	6.00
2	Daunte Culpepper	12.00
3	Joe Montgomery	4.00
4	David Boston	8.00
5	Shaun King	8.00
6	Champ Bailey	4.00
7	Rob Konrad	3.00
8	Torry Holt	8.00
9	Kevin Faulk	6.00
10	Ricky Williams	25.00
11	James Johnson	6.00
12	Edgerrin James	25.00
13	Kevin Johnson	8.00
14	Akili Smith	12.00
15	Troy Edwards	8.00
16	Donovan McNabb	12.00
17	Cade McNown	12.00
18	Tim Couch	25.00

1999 Playoff Absolute EXP Barry Sanders Commemorative

This was a 5-card insert that commemorated the career of Barry Sanders. Singles were found 1:289 packs.

		MT
Complete Set (5):		75.00
Common Player:		15.00
Inserted 1:289		
2	Barry Sanders	15.00
3	Barry Sanders	15.00
4	Barry Sanders	15.00
5	Barry Sanders	15.00
6	Barry Sanders	15.00

1999 Playoff Absolute EXP Team Jersey Tandems

This was a 31-card insert that pictured a tandem with a swatch of a home and away authentic team jersey. One player was pictured on each side and singles were inserted 1:97 packs.

		MT
Complete Set (31):		1300.
Common Player:		25.00
Inserted 1:97		
1	Jake Plummer, David Boston	50.00
2	Troy Aikman, Emmitt Smith	85.00
3	Skip Hicks, Brad Johnson	35.00
4	Joe Montgomery, Ike Hilliard	25.00
5	Charles Johnson, Donovan McNabb	50.00
6	Randy Moss, Cris Carter	100.00
7	Warrick Dunn, Mike Alstott	25.00
8	Barry Sanders, Charlie Batch	100.00
9	Antonio Freeman, Brett Favre	100.00
10	Curtis Enis, Cade McNown	50.00
11	Tim Biakabutuka, Muhsin Muhammad	25.00
12	Eddie Kennison, Ricky Williams	100.00
13	Steve Young, Jerry Rice	50.00
14	Marshall Faulk, Torry Holt	40.00
15	Jamal Anderson, Chris Chandler	25.00
16	Dan Marino, O.J. McDuffie	85.00
17	Drew Bledsoe, Terry Glenn	50.00
18	Eric Moulds, Doug Flutie	50.00
19	Peyton Manning, Edgerrin James	100.00
20	Keyshawn Johnson, Wayne Chrebet	35.00
21	Kordell Stewart, Jerome Bettis	35.00
22	Mark Brunell, Fred Taylor	50.00
23	Tim Couch, Kevin Johnson	100.00
24	Carl Pickens, Akili Smith	50.00
25	Jermaine Lewis, Tony Banks	25.00
26	Eddie George, Steve McNair	40.00
27	Napoleon Kaufman, Tim Brown	25.00
28	John Elway, Terrell Davis	85.00
29	Jon Kitna, Joey Galloway	35.00
30	Andre Rison, Elvis Grbac	25.00
31	Natrone Means, Mikhael Ricks	25.00

1999 Playoff Absolute SSD

Brad Johnson

This was a 200-card set that included 50 short printed singles. The 31 Checklist cards were found 1:9 packs and the 19 Canton Absolute cards were found 1:17. Each of the regular 150 base cards were found in five different colors. Blue, Green, Purple and Red were all found at equal ratios. The Orange singles were in shorter quanities and valued higher. Each base card featured the player in a cell window with foil stamping and wood grain embossing. Parallel sets included: Coaches Collection Gold and Coaches Collection Silver. Partial parallel sets included: Honor Red, Honor Gold and Honor Silver. Other insert sets included: Boss Hogs Autographs, Force, Heroes, Rookie Roundup, Rookies and Team Jersey Quads.

		MT
Complete Set (200):		250.00
Common Player:		.30
Minor Stars:		.60
Common Canton:		4.00
Inserted 1:17		
Common CL:		2.50
Inserted 1:9		
Common Rookie:		1.00
Blue,Green,Purple,Red:		1x
Orange Cards:		5x-10x
Orange Canton:		3x
Orange CL:		3x
Orange Rookies:		3x
Wax Box:		60.00
1	Rob Moore	.60
2	Frank Sanders	.30
3	Jake Plummer	2.50
4	Adrian Murrell	.30
5	Chris Chandler	.60
6	Jamal Anderson	1.00
7	Tim Dwight	1.00
8	Terance Mathis	.30
9	Priest Holmes	1.00
10	Jermaine Lewis	.30
11	Antowain Smith	.60
12	Doug Flutie	2.00
13	Eric Moulds	1.00
14	Muhsin Muhammad	.60
15	Tim Biakabutuka	.60
16	Curtis Enis	1.00
17	Curtis Conway	.60
18	Bobby Engram	.30
19	Corey Dillon	1.00
20	Carl Pickens	.60
21	Darnay Scott	.60
22	Sedrick Shaw	.30
23	Leslie Shepherd	.30
24	Ty Detmer	.30
25	Deion Sanders	1.00
26	Troy Aikman	3.00
27	Michael Irvin	.60
28	Emmitt Smith	4.50
29	Raghib Ismail	.30
30	Rod Smith	.60
31	Ed McCaffrey	.60
32	Bubby Brister	.60
33	Terrell Davis	4.50
34	Shannon Sharpe	.60
35	Brian Griese	3.00
36	John Elway	4.50
37	Charlie Batch	2.00
38	Herman Moore	1.00
39	Barry Sanders	6.00
40	Johnnie Morton	.30
41	Antonio Freeman	1.00
42	Brett Favre	6.00
43	Dorsey Levens	1.00
44	Derrick Mayes	.60
45	Mark Chmura	.60
46	Peyton Manning	4.50
47	Marvin Harrison	1.00
48	Jerome Pathon	.30
49	Fred Taylor	3.00
50	Mark Brunell	2.50
51	Jimmy Smith	1.00
52	Keenan McCardell	.60
53	Elvis Grbac	.60
54	Andre Rison	.60
55	Bam Morris	.30
56	O.J. McDuffie	.60
57	Karim Abdul	.60
58	Dan Marino	4.50
59	Oronde Gadsden	.60
60	Robert Smith	1.00
61	Randall Cunningham	1.00
62	Cris Carter	1.00
63	Randy Moss	6.00
64	Drew Bledsoe	2.50
65	Ben Coates	.60
66	Terry Glenn	1.00
67	Cameron Cleeland	.60
68	Eddie Kennison	.30
69	Kerry Collins	.60
70	Gary Brown	.30
71	Joe Jurevicius	.30
72	Ike Hilliard	.60
73	Keyshawn Johnson	1.00
74	Curtis Martin	1.00
75	Wayne Chrebet	1.00
76	Tim Brown	.60
77	Napoleon Kaufman	.60
78	James Jett	.30
79	Duce Staley	1.00
80	Charles Johnson	.30
81	Kordell Stewart	1.00
82	Jerome Bettis	1.00
83	Chris Fuamatu-Ma'afala	.30
84	Jim Harbaugh	.60
85	Ryan Leaf	1.00
86	Natrone Means	.60
87	Mikhael Ricks	.30
88	Garrison Hearst	.75
89	Jerry Rice	3.00
90	Terrell Owens	1.00
91	J.J. Stokes	.60
92	Steve Young	2.00
93	Joey Galloway	1.00
94	Jon Kitna	.60
95	Ricky Watters	.60
96	Trent Green	.60
97	Marshall Faulk	1.00
98	Isaac Bruce	.60
99	Mike Alstott	1.00
100	Warrick Dunn	1.00
101	Jacquez Green	.60
102	Reidel Anthony	.60
103	Trent Dilfer	.60
104	Steve McNair	1.25
105	Yancey Thigpen	.60
106	Eddie George	1.25
107	Kevin Dyson	.60
108	Skip Hicks	.60
109	Brad Johnson	1.00
110	Michael Westbrook	.60
111	Thurman Thomas CA	4.00
112	Andre Reed CA	4.00
113	Emmitt Smith CA	12.00
114	Troy Aikman CA	10.00
115	Deion Sanders CA	4.00
116	John Elway CA	12.00
117	Terrell Davis CA	12.00
118	Barry Sanders CA	15.00
119	Brett Favre CA	15.00
120	Warren Moon CA	4.00
121	Dan Marino CA	12.00
122	Cris Carter CA	6.00
123	Vinny Testaverde CA	4.00
124	Tim Brown CA	4.00
125	Jerome Bettis CA	4.00
126	Junior Seau CA	4.00
127	Jerry Rice CA	10.00
128	Steve Young CA	8.00
129	Eddie George CA	6.00
130	Dan Marino CA	8.00
131	Vinny Testaverde CL	2.50
132	Drew Bledsoe CL	5.00
133	Peyton Manning CL	8.00
134	Doug Flutie CL	5.00
135	Akili Smith CL	5.00
136	Tim Couch CL	8.00
137	Kordell Stewart CL	5.00
138	Fred Taylor CL	6.00
139	Steve McNair CL	5.00
140	Priest Holmes CL	2.50
141	Terrell Davis CL	8.00
142	Jon Kitna CL	5.00
143	Tim Brown CL	2.50
144	Natrone Means CL	2.50
145	Andre Rison CL	2.50
146	Troy Aikman CL	7.00
147	Kerry Collins CL	2.50
148	Jake Plummer CL	6.00
149	Brad Johnson CL	5.00
150	Donovan McNabb CL	5.00
151	Barry Sanders CL	10.00
152	Brett Favre CL	10.00
153	Cade McNown CL	5.00
154	Mike Alstott CL	5.00
155	Randy Moss CL	10.00
156	Ricky Williams CL	8.00
157	Muhsin Muhammad CL	2.50
158	Marshall Faulk CL	2.50
159	Jamal Anderson CL	2.50
160	Jerry Rice CL	6.00
161	*Tim Couch*	12.00
162	*Donovan McNabb*	7.00
163	*Akili Smith*	7.00
164	*Edgerrin James*	15.00
165	*Ricky Williams*	10.00
166	*Torry Holt*	5.00
167	*Champ Bailey*	3.00
168	*David Boston*	5.00
169	*Chris Claiborne*	2.00
170	*Chris McAlister*	2.00
171	*Daunte Culpepper*	7.00
172	*Cade McNown*	7.00
173	*Troy Edwards*	5.00
174	*Kevin Johnson*	5.00
175	*James Johnson*	3.00
176	*Rob Konrad*	5.00
177	*Jim Kleinsasser*	2.00
178	*Kevin Faulk*	5.00
179	*Joe Montgomery*	2.00
180	*Shaun King*	7.00
181	*Peerless Price*	4.00
182	*Mike Cloud*	4.00
183	*Jermaine Fazande*	2.00
184	*D'Wayne Bates*	1.00
185	*Brock Huard*	3.00
186	*Marty Booker*	1.00
187	*Karsten Bailey*	1.00
188	*Shawn Bryson*	1.00
189	*Jeff Paulk*	1.00
190	*Sedrick Irvin*	3.00
191	*Craig Yeast*	1.00
192	*Joe Germaine*	2.00
193	*Demeane Douglas*	1.00
194	*Brandon Stokley*	1.00
195	*Larry Parker*	1.00
196	*Wane McGarity*	1.00
197	*Na Brown*	1.00
198	*Cecil Collins*	4.00
199	*Darrin Chiaverini*	2.00
200	*Madre Hill*	1.00

1999 Playoff Absolute SSD Coaches Collection Gold

This was a 200-card parallel to the base set. Each single was sequentially numbered to 25.

	MT
Gold Cards:	25x-50x
Gold Canton:	8x-16x
Gold CL:	5x-10x
Gold Rookies:	8x-16x
Production 25 Sets	

1999 Playoff Absolute SSD Coaches Collection Silver

Jerry Rice

This was a 200-card parallel to the base set. Each of these singles was sequentially numbered to 500.

	MT
Silver Cards:	2x-4x
Silver Canton:	2x
Silver CL:	2x
Silver Rookies:	2x
Production 500 Sets	

1999 Playoff Absolute SSD Honors Red

This was a 150-card partial parallel to the base set. Each single had the Playoff logo in the background. Each card was sequentially numbered to 200.

	MT
Red Cards:	5x-10x
Red Rookies:	3x
Production 200 Sets	
Gold Cards:	25x-50x
Gold Rookies:	8x-16x
Production 25 Sets	
Silver Cards:	8x-16x
Silver Rookies:	3x-6x
Production 100 Sets	

1999 Playoff Absolute SSD Boss Hogs Autographs

This 10-card insert set included autographs of the top playmakers and each signed on real football leather. Each single was sequentially numbered to 400.

		MT
Complete Set (10):		550.00
Common Player:		25.00
Production 400 Sets		
1	Ricky Williams	125.00
2	Terrell Davis	75.00
3	Mike Alstott	25.00
4	Jake Plummer	50.00
5	Vinny Testaverde	25.00
6	Cris Carter	25.00
7	Peyton Manning	125.00
8	Natrone Means	25.00
9	Eddie George	35.00
10	Barry Sanders	150.00

1999 Playoff Absolute SSD Force

This 36-card insert included the hobby's hottest stars and featured them on a mirror board with gold foil stamping. Singles were found 1:19 packs.

		MT
Complete Set (36):		150.00
Common Player:		4.00
Inserted 1:19		
1	Steve Young	6.00
2	Fred Taylor	8.00
3	Kordell Stewart	4.00
4	Emmitt Smith	10.00
5	Barry Sanders	15.00
6	Jerry Rice	8.00
7	Jake Plummer	7.00
8	Eric Moulds	4.00
9	Randy Moss	15.00
10	Steve McNair	4.00
11	Curtis Martin	4.00
12	Dan Marino	10.00
13	Peyton Manning	10.00
14	Jon Kitna	4.00
15	Napoleon Kaufman	4.00
16	Keyshawn Johnson	4.00
17	Eddie George	5.00
18	Antonio Freeman	6.00
19	Doug Flutie	6.00
20	Brett Favre	15.00
21	Marshall Faulk	4.00
22	John Elway	10.00
23	Warrick Dunn	4.00
24	Corey Dillon	4.00
25	Terrell Davis	10.00
26	Randall Cunningham	4.00
27	Cris Carter	4.00
28	Mark Brunell	6.00
29	Tim Brown	4.00
30	Drew Bledsoe	6.00
31	Jerome Bettis	4.00
32	Charlie Batch	5.00
33	Jamal Anderson	4.00
34	Mike Alstott	4.00
35	Troy Aikman	8.00
36	Terrell Owens	4.00

1999 Playoff Absolute SSD Heroes

This 24-card insert included the top NFL superstars and highlighted them on a die-cut mirror board with red foil stamping and micro-etching. Singles were found 1:19 packs. A parallel Red (#'d to 100) and Jumbo (one per hobby box) version was also issued.

		MT
Complete Set (24):		125.00
Common Player:		3.00
Inserted 1:19		
Jumbo Cards:		1x
1:Box		
Red Cards:		4x-8x
Production 100 Sets		
1	Terrell Owens	3.00
2	Troy Aikman	6.00
3	Cris Carter	3.00
4	Brett Favre	12.00
5	Jamal Anderson	3.00
6	Doug Flutie	4.00
7	John Elway	8.00
8	Steve Young	4.00
9	Jerome Bettis	3.00
10	Emmitt Smith	8.00
11	Drew Bledsoe	5.00
12	Fred Taylor	6.00
13	Dan Marino	8.00
14	Antonio Freeman	3.00
15	Mark Brunell	5.00
16	Jake Plummer	5.00
17	Warrick Dunn	3.00
18	Peyton Manning	8.00
19	Randy Moss	12.00
20	Barry Sanders	12.00
21	Keyshawn Johnson	3.00
22	Eddie George	4.00
23	Terrell Davis	8.00
24	Jerry Rice	6.00

1999 Playoff Absolute SSD Rookie Roundup

This 18-card insert included both first and second round picks from the 1999 NFL Draft. First round pick cards were inserted 1:46 packs and second round picks were inserted 1:69. Each single was printed on mirror board with foil stamping.

		MT
Complete Set (18):		125.00
Common Player:		5.00
1st Rounders Inserted 1:46		
2nd Rounders Inserted 1:69		
1	Peerless Price	8.00
2	Daunte Culpepper	12.00
3	Joe Montgomery	5.00
4	David Boston	8.00
5	Shaun King	15.00
6	Champ Bailey	5.00
7	Rob Konrad	5.00
8	Torry Holt	8.00
9	Kevin Faulk	7.00
10	Ricky Williams	20.00
11	James Johnson	5.00
12	Edgerrin James	30.00
13	Kevin Johnson	10.00
14	Akili Smith	12.00
15	Troy Edwards	8.00
16	Donovan McNabb	12.00
17	Cade McNown	12.00
18	Tim Couch	20.00

Post-1980 cards in Near Mint condition will generally sell for about 75% of the quoted Mint value. Excellent-condition cards bring no more than 40%.

1999 Playoff Absolute SSD Rookies

This 36-card insert included the hottest rookies from the '99 NFL Draft. Each was printed on holographic foil board with blue foil stamping. Singles were inserted 1:10 packs. A parallel Red version was also made and each of those singles were sequentially numbered to 100.

		MT
Complete Set (36):		75.00
Common Player:		1.00
Minor Stars:		2.00
Inserted 1:10		
Red Cards:		5x-10x
Production 100 Sets		
1	Champ Bailey	2.50
2	Karsten Bailey	1.00
3	D'Wayne Bates	1.00
4	Marty Booker	1.00
5	David Boston	4.00
6	Shawn Bryson	1.00
7	Chris Claiborne	2.00
8	Mike Cloud	2.00
9	Cecil Collins	4.00
10	Tim Couch	10.00
11	Daunte Culpepper	6.00
12	Demeane Douglas	1.00
13	Troy Edwards	4.00
14	Kevin Faulk	3.00
15	Jermaine Fazande	2.00
16	Joe Germaine	2.00
17	Torry Holt	4.00
18	Brock Huard	2.50
19	Edgerrin James	15.00
20	James Johnson	2.50
21	Kevin Johnson	4.00
22	Shaun King	6.00
23	Jim Kleinsasser	2.00
24	Rob Konrad	2.00
25	Chris McAlister	2.00
26	Travis McGriff	1.00
27	Donovan McNabb	6.00
28	Cade McNown	6.00
29	Joe Montgomery	2.00
30	Larry Parker	1.00
31	Jeff Paulk	1.00
32	Peerless Price	3.00
33	Akili Smith	6.00
34	Brandon Stokley	1.00
35	Ricky Williams	10.00
36	Craig Yeast	1.00

1999 Playoff Absolute SSD Team Jersey Quads

This 31-card insert showcased an authentic team jersey and four superstars from each NFL team. Each was printed on a foil board with micro etching. Singles were inserted 1:73 packs.

	MT
Complete Set (31):	1600.
Common Player:	20.00
Minor Stars:	40.00
Inserted 1:73	

1	David Boston, Adrian Murrell, Jake Plummer, Frank Sanders	60.00
2	Troy Aikman, Michael Irvin, Deion Sanders, Emmitt Smith	85.00
3	Champ Bailey, Skip Hicks, Brad Johnson, Michael Westbrook	40.00
4	Gary Brown, Kerry Collins, Ike Hilliard, Joe Montgomery	20.00
5	Na Brown, Charles Johnson, Donovan McNabb, Duce Staley	60.00
6	Cris Carter, Randall Cunningham, Randy Moss, Robert Smith	100.00
7	Mike Alstott, Reidel Anthony, Trent Dilfer, Warrick Dunn	40.00
8	Charlie Batch, Herman Moore, Johnnie Morton, Barry Sanders	100.00
9	Mark Chmura, Brett Favre, Antonio Freeman, Dorsey Levens	100.00
10	Curtis Conway, Bobby Engram, Curtis Enis, Cade McNown	60.00
11	Steve Beuerlein, Tim Biakabutuka, Muhsin Muhammad, Wesley Walls	20.00
12	Cam Cleeland, Eddie Kennison, Willie Roaf, Ricky Williams	75.00
13	Garrison Hearst, Terrell Owens, Jerry Rice, Steve Young	85.00
14	Isaac Bruce, Marshall Faulk, Trent Green, Torry Holt	40.00
15	Jamal Anderson, Chris Chandler, Tim Dwight, Terrance Mathis	20.00
16	Karim Abdul, Cecil Collins, Dan Marino, O.J. McDuffie	100.00
17	Drew Bledsoe, Ben Coates, Kevin Faulk, Terry Glenn	60.00
18	Doug Flutie, Eric Moulds, Peerless Price, Antowain Smith	60.00
19	Marvin Harrison, Edgerrin James, Peyton Manning, Jerome Pathon	125.00
20	Wayne Chrebet, Keyshawn Johnson, Curtis Martin, Vinny Testaverde	40.00
21	Jerome Bettis, Troy Edwards, Kordell Stewart, Hines Ward	50.00
22	Mark Brunell, Keenan McCardell, Jimmy Smith, Fred Taylor	60.00
23	Tim Couch, Kevin Johnson, Sedrick Shaw, Leslie Shepherd	85.00
24	Corey Dillon, Carl Pickens, Darnay Scott, Akili Smith	50.00
25	Tony Banks, Priest Holmes, Jermaine Lewis, Chris McAllister	20.00
26	Kevin Dyson, Eddie George, Steve McNair, Yancey Thigpen	40.00
27	Tim Brown, James Jett, Napoleon Kaufman, Charles Woodson	40.00
28	Terrell Davis, John Elway, Ed McCaffrey, Rod Smith	100.00
29	Joey Galloway, Ahman Green, Jon Kitna, Ricky Watters	40.00
30	Mike Cloud, Elvis Grbac, Bam Morris, Andre Rison	20.00
31	Ryan Leaf, Natrone Means, Mikhael Ricks, Junior Seau	20.00

1999 Playoff Contenders SSD

This was a 200-card base set that had 44 Rookie Tickets and 15 short-printed Playoff Tickets (1:7). Each card was printed on 30-point embossed holographic foil stock with foil stamping. Each of the Rookie Tickets were autographed by that player. Parallel sets included: Finesse Gold, Power Blue and Speed Red. Other inserts included: Game Day Souvenirs, MVP Contenders, Quads, Round Numbers Autographs, ROY Contenders, ROY Contenders Autographs, Touchdown Tandems and Triple Threat. SRP was $7.99 for four-card packs.

		MT
Complete Set (200):		1400.
Common Player:		.30
Minor Stars:		.60
Common Rookie Auto:		12.00
Common PT:		2.00
Inserted 1:7		
Wax Box:		135.00
1	Randy Moss	8.00
2	Randall Cunningham	1.00
3	Cris Carter	1.00
4	Robert Smith	1.00
5	Jake Reed	.60
6	Albert Connell	.60
7	Jeff George	1.00
8	Brett Favre	8.00
9	Antonio Freeman	1.00
10	Dorsey Levens	1.00
11	Mark Chmura	.60
12	Mike Alstott	1.00
13	Warrick Dunn	.60
14	Trent Dilfer	.60
15	Jacquez Green	.60
16	Reidel Anthony	.60
17	Warren Sapp	.60
18	Amani Toomer	.30
19	Curtis Enis	1.00
20	Curtis Conway	.60
21	Bobby Engram	.30
22	Barry Sanders	8.00
23	Charlie Batch	2.50
24	Herman Moore	1.00
25	Johnnie Morton	.30
26	Greg Hill	.30
27	Germane Crowell	.60
28	Kerry Collins	.60
29	Ike Hilliard	.60
30	Joe Jurevicius	.30
31	Stephen Davis	1.00
32	Brad Johnson	1.00
33	Skip Hicks	.60
34	Michael Westbrook	.60
35	Jake Plummer	3.00
36	Adrian Murrell	.30
37	Frank Sanders	.60
38	Rob Moore	.60
39	Gary Brown	.30
40	Duce Staley	1.00
41	Charles Johnson	.30
42	Emmitt Smith	6.00
43	Troy Aikman	4.00
44	Michael Irvin	.60
45	Deion Sanders	1.00
46	Raghib Ismail	.30
47	Jerry Rice	4.00
48	Terrell Owens	1.00
49	Steve Young	2.50
50	Garrison Hearst	.60
51	J.J. Stokes	.60
52	Lawrence Phillips	.60
53	Jamal Anderson	1.00
54	Chris Chandler	.60
55	Terance Mathis	.30
56	Tim Dwight	1.00
57	Charlie Garner	.60
58	Chris Calloway	.30
59	Eddie Kennison	.30
60	Billy Joe Hobert	.30
61	Tim Biakabutuka	.60
62	Muhsin Muhammad	.60
63	Olandis Gary	50.00
64	Wesley Walls	.60
65	Isaac Bruce	1.00
66	Marshall Faulk	1.00
67	Kordell Stewart	1.00
68	Jerome Bettis	1.00
69	Hines Ward	.60
70	Corey Dillon	1.00
71	Carl Pickens	.60
72	Darnay Scott	.60
73	Steve McNair	1.75
74	Eddie George	1.75
75	Yancey Thigpen	.60
76	Kevin Dyson	.60
77	Fred Taylor	4.00
78	Mark Brunell	3.00
79	Jimmy Smith	1.00
80	Keenan McCardell	.60
81	James Stewart	.60
82	Jermaine Lewis	.30
83	Priest Holmes	1.00
84	Stoney Case	.30
85	Errict Rhett	.60
86	Bill Schroeder	.60
87	Terry Kirby	.30
88	Leslie Shepherd	.30
89	Terrence Wilkins	70.00
90	Dan Marino	6.00
91	O.J. McDuffie	.60
92	Karim Abdul	.60
93	Zach Thomas	.60
94	Terry Allen	.60
95	Tony Martin	.30
96	Drew Bledsoe	3.00
97	Terry Glenn	1.00
98	Ben Coates	.60
99	Tony Simmons	.60
100	Curtis Martin	1.00
101	Keyshawn Johnson	1.00
102	Vinny Testaverde	.60
103	Wayne Chrebet	1.00
104	Peyton Manning	6.00
105	Marvin Harrison	1.00
106	E.G. Green	.30
107	Doug Flutie	2.50
108	Thurman Thomas	.60
109	Andre Reed	.60
110	Eric Moulds	1.00
111	Antowain Smith	1.00
112	Bruce Smith	.60
113	Terrell Davis	6.00
114	John Elway	6.00
115	Ed McCaffrey	.75
116	Rod Smith	.75
117	Shannon Sharpe	.60
118	Jeff Garcia	175.00
119	Brian Griese	3.00
120	Justin Watson	125.00
121	Bubby Brister	.60
122	Ryan Leaf	1.00
123	Natrone Means	.75
124	Mikhael Ricks	.30
125	Junior Seau	.60
126	Jim Harbaugh	.60
127	Andre Rison	.60
128	Elvis Grbac	.60
129	Bam Morris	.60
130	Rashaan Shehee	.30
131	Warren Moon	.60
132	Tony Gonzalez	.60
133	Derrick Alexander	.30
134	Jon Kitna	1.50
135	Ricky Watters	.60
136	Joey Galloway	1.00
137	Ahman Green	.60
138	Derrick Mayes	.60
139	Tyrone Wheatley	.60
140	Napoleon Kaufman	1.00
141	Tim Brown	.60
142	Charles Woodson	1.00
143	Rich Gannon	.60
144	Rickey Dudley	.60
145	Az-Zahir Hakim	.60
146	Kurt Warner	225.00
147	Sean Bennett	15.00
148	Brandon Stokley	12.00
149	Amos Zereoue	20.00
150	Brock Huard	25.00
151	Tim Couch	100.00
152	Ricky Williams	100.00
153	Donovan McNabb	65.00
154	Edgerrin James	250.00
155	Torry Holt	45.00
156	Daunte Culpepper	80.00
157	Akili Smith	60.00
158	Champ Bailey	20.00
159	Chris Claiborne	12.00
160	Chris McAlister	12.00
161	Troy Edwards	45.00
162	Jevon Kearse	120.00
163	Darnell McDonald	12.00
164	David Boston	45.00
165	Peerless Price	30.00
166	Cecil Collins	25.00
167	Rob Konrad	15.00
168	Cade McNown	65.00
169	Shawn Bryson	12.00
170	Kevin Faulk	25.00
171	Corby Jones	12.00
172	James Johnson	25.00
173	Autry Denson	20.00
174	Sedrick Irvin	20.00
175	Michael Bishop	20.00
176	Joe Germaine	20.00
177	De'Mond Parker	20.00
178	Shaun King	65.00
179	D'Wayne Bates	12.00
180	Tai Streets	15.00
181	Na Brown	12.00
182	Desmond Clark	12.00
183	Jim Kleinsasser	15.00
184	Kevin Johnson	45.00
185	Joe Montgomery	20.00
186	John Elway PT	8.00
187	Dan Marino PT	8.00
188	Jerry Rice PT	6.00
189	Barry Sanders PT	12.00
190	Steve Young PT	4.00
191	Doug Flutie PT	4.00
192	Troy Aikman PT	6.00
193	Drew Bledsoe PT	5.00
194	Brett Favre PT	12.00
195	Randall Cunningham PT	2.00
196	Terrell Davis PT	8.00
197	Kordell Stewart PT	2.00
198	Keyshawn Johnson PT	2.00
199	Jake Plummer PT	5.00
200	Peyton Manning PT	8.00

1999 Playoff Contenders SSD Finesse Gold

This was a 200-card parallel insert that showcased each single with a gold background. Singles were sequentially numbered to 25.

	MT
Gold Cards:	20x-40x
Gold Rookies:	3x
Gold PT Cards:	10x-20x
Production 25 Sets	

1999 Playoff Contenders SSD Power Blue

This was a 200-card parallel insert that had each single printed with a blue background. Each card was sequentially numbered to 50.

	MT
Blue Cards:	10x-20x
Blue Rookies:	1.5x
Blue PT Cards:	5x-10x
Production 50 Sets	

1999 Playoff Contenders SSD Speed Red

This was a 200-card parallel insert to the base set. Each of these singles were printed with a red background and were sequentially numbered to 100.

	MT
Red Cards:	5x-10x
Red Rookies:	1.2x
Red PT Cards:	3x-6x
Production 100 Sets	

1999 Playoff Contenders SSD Game Day Souvenirs

This 15-card insert included swatches of game-dated, game-used footballs from the 1998-99 season. Singles were found 1:308 packs.

		MT
Complete Set (15):		1250.
Common Player:		50.00
Inserted 1:308		
1	Terrell Owens	50.00
2	Jerry Rice	100.00
3	Steve Young	75.00
4	Akili Smith	50.00
5	Tim Couch	125.00
6	Mark Brunell	75.00
7	Eddie George	60.00
8	Dorsey Levens	50.00
9	Brett Favre	150.00
10	Antonio Freeman	50.00
11	Ricky Williams	125.00
12	Steve McNair	60.00
13	Kurt Warner	250.00
14	John Elway	125.00
15	Terrell Davis	125.00

1999 Playoff Contenders SSD MVP Contenders

This 20-card insert included candidates for the NFL's MVP award. Each single was printed with actual leather in the background. Singles were inserted 1:43 packs.

		MT
Complete Set (20):		160.00
Common Player:		5.00
Inserted 1:43		
1	Jamal Anderson	5.00
2	Eddie George	7.00
3	Emmitt Smith	20.00
4	Jerry Rice	15.00
5	Barry Sanders	30.00
6	Keyshawn Johnson	5.00
7	Brett Favre	30.00
8	Randy Moss	30.00
9	Mark Brunell	10.00
10	Fred Taylor	15.00
11	Dan Marino	20.00
12	Peyton Manning	20.00
13	Drew Bledsoe	10.00
14	Antonio Freeman	5.00
15	Steve Young	10.00
16	Terrell Davis	20.00
17	Terrell Owens	5.00
18	Troy Aikman	15.00
19	Steve McNair	7.00
20	Jake Plummer	10.00

1999 Playoff Contenders SSD Quads

This 12-card insert featured two powerful, potential playoff opponents on each side of the card. Each card was printed on holographic board with micro-etching. Singles were found 1:57 packs.

		MT
Complete Set (12):		225.00
Common Player:		10.00
Inserted 1:57		
1	Jake Plummer, David Boston, Emmitt Smith, Troy Aikman	25.00
2	Jerry Rice, Steve Young, Jamal Anderson, Chris Chandler	20.00
3	Randy Moss, Cris Carter, Brett Favre, Antonio Freeman	35.00
4	Warrick Dunn, Mike Alstott, Stephen Davis, Brad Johnson	10.00
5	Cade McNown, Curtis Enis, Barry Sanders, Charlie Batch	30.00
6	Ricky Williams, Eddie Kennison, Marshall Faulk, Torry Holt	25.00
7	Kordell Stewart, Jerome Bettis, Eddie George, Steve McNair	15.00
8	Doug Flutie, Eric Moulds, Drew Bledsoe, Terry Glenn	15.00
9	Dan Marino, Cecil Collins, Keyshawn Johnson, Curtis Martin	25.00
10	Terrell Davis, Brian Griese, Mark Brunell, Fred Taylor	20.00
11	Jon Kitna, Joey Galloway, Napoleon Kaufman, Tim Brown	10.00
12	Peyton Manning, Edgerrin James, Tim Couch, Kevin Johnson	70.00

1999 Playoff Contenders SSD Round Numbers Autographs

This 10-card insert included autographs from one of ten pairs of rookies drafted from the same round. Both the player's

image and autograph appeared on the front of the cards. Singles were inserted 1:109 packs.

		MT
Complete Set (10):		650.00
Common Player:		30.00
Inserted 1:109		
1	Kevin Johnson, Peerless Price	50.00
2	Ricky Williams, Edgerrin James	275.00
3	Donovan McNabb, Akili Smith	75.00
4	Sean Bennett, Brandon Stokley	30.00
5	Tim Couch, Cade McNown	150.00
6	David Boston, Troy Edwards	50.00
7	Daunte Culpepper, Torry Holt	75.00
8	Kevin Faulk, James Johnson	40.00
9	Joe Montgomery, Rob Konrad	30.00
10	Cecil Collins, De'Mond Parker	40.00

1999 Playoff Contenders SSD ROY Contenders

This 12-card insert included rookies who would challenge for the Rookie of the Year Award. Each single was printed on actual wood and inserted 1:29 packs. A parallel autographed version was also issued with each of those singles sequentially numbered to 100.

		MT
Complete Set (12):		100.00
Common Player:		5.00
Inserted 1:29		
1	Tim Couch	20.00
2	Donovan McNabb	12.00
3	Akili Smith	10.00
4	Daunte Culpepper	12.00
5	Cade McNown	12.00
6	Edgerrin James	25.00
7	Ricky Williams	20.00
8	Cecil Collins	5.00
9	Torry Holt	8.00
10	David Boston	8.00
11	Troy Edwards	8.00
12	Champ Bailey	5.00

1999 Playoff Contenders SSD ROY Contenders Autographs

This was a 12-card parallel to the ROY Contenders insert. Each of these singles were printed on actual wood and sequentially numbered to 100.

		MT
Complete Set (12):		1000.
Common Player:		25.00
Production 100 Sets		
1	Tim Couch	180.00
2	Donovan McNabb	100.00
3	Akili Smith	80.00
4	Daunte Culpepper	100.00
5	Cade McNown	100.00
6	Edgerrin James	250.00
7	Ricky Williams	180.00
8	Cecil Collins	25.00
9	Torry Holt	60.00
10	David Boston	50.00
11	Troy Edwards	50.00
12	Champ Bailey	25.00

A card number in parentheses ( ) indicates the set is unnumbered.

1999 Playoff Contenders SSD Touchdown Tandems

This was a 24-card insert that matched up two touchdown-scoring teammates and each was printed on dual-sided holographic foil board. Singles were inserted 1:15 packs. A parallel die-cut version was also issued with each of those singles sequentially numbered to the player's 1998 TD total.

		MT
Complete Set (24):		100.00
Common Player:		2.00
Minor Stars:		4.00
Inserted 1:15		
1	Keyshawn Johnson, Curtis Martin	2.00
2	Dan Marino, Tony Martin	10.00
3	Drew Bledsoe, Terry Glenn	5.00
4	Peyton Manning, Marvin Harrison	10.00
5	Doug Flutie, Thurman Thomas	4.00
6	Steve McNair, Eddie George	4.00
7	Kordell Stewart, Jerome Bettis	4.00
8	Akili Smith, Carl Pickens	5.00
9	Mark Brunell, Jimmy Smith	5.00
10	Jon Kitna, Joey Galloway	4.00
11	John Elway, Terrell Davis	10.00
12	Napoleon Kaufman, Tim Brown	2.00
13	Troy Aikman, Emmitt Smith	10.00
14	Jake Plummer, Rob Moore	5.00
15	Donovan McNabb, Charles Johnson	6.00
16	Brad Johnson, Michael Westbrook	2.00
17	Brett Favre, Antonio Freeman	12.00
18	Randall Cunningham, Randy Moss	12.00
19	Mike Alstott, Warrick Dunn	2.00
20	Cade McNown, Curtis Enis	6.00
21	Barry Sanders, Herman Moore	12.00
22	Steve Young, Jerry Rice	8.00
23	Chris Chandler, Jamal Anderson	2.00
24	Marshall Faulk, Isaac Bruce	4.00

1999 Playoff Contenders SSD Touchdown Tandems Die Cuts

This was a 24-card parallel to the Touchdown Tandem insert. Each of these singles were die-cut and sequentially numbered to the player's 1998 TD total.

		MT
Common Player:		15.00
1	Keyshawn Johnson, Curtis Martin 20	45.00
2	Dan Marino, Tony Martin 29	120.00
3	Drew Bledsoe, Terry Glenn 23	50.00

1999 Playoff Contenders SSD Touchdown Tandems

4	Peyton Manning, Marvin Harrison 33	120.00
5	Doug Flutie, Thurman Thomas 24	50.00
6	Steve McNair, Eddie George 25	45.00
7	Kordell Stewart, Jerome Bettis 16	45.00
8	Akili Smith, Carl Pickens 41	25.00
9	Mark Brunell, Jimmy Smith 28	50.00
10	Jon Kitna, Joey Galloway 18	35.00
11	John Elway, Terrell Davis 46	70.00
12	Napoleon Kaufman, Tim Brown 11	35.00
13	Troy Aikman, Emmitt Smith 29	85.00
14	Jake Plummer, Rob Moore 26	50.00
15	Donovan McNabb, Charles Johnson 37	50.00
16	Brad Johnson, Michael Westbrook 13	40.00
17	Brett Favre, Antonio Freeman 46	60.00
18	Randall Cunningham, Randy Moss 52	50.00
19	Mike Alstott, Warrick Dunn 11	45.00
20	Cade McNown, Curtis Enis 28	70.00
21	Barry Sanders, Herman Moore 9	225.00
22	Steve Young, Jerry Rice 51	35.00
23	Chris Chandler, Jamal Anderson 43	15.00
24	Marshall Faulk, Isaac Bruce 11	50.00

1999 Playoff Contenders SSD Triple Threat

This was a 20-card insert that pictured three teammates on a mirror board with foil stamping. Singles were inserted 1:15 packs. A Triple Threat parallel was issued with one of the teammates on the front of each card for a total of 60 cards. Each was sequentially numbered to a player-specific stat.

		MT
Complete Set (20):		70.00
Common Player:		2.50
Inserted 1:15		
1	Jake Plummer, David Boston, Frank Sanders	5.00
2	Deion Sanders, Troy Aikman, Emmitt Smith	7.00
3	Terrell Owens, Jerry Rice, Steve Young	5.00
4	Dan Marino, O.J. McDuffie, Cecil Collins	7.00
5	Keyshawn Johnson, Wayne Chrebet, Curtis Martin	2.50
6	Jamal Anderson, Chris Chandler, Terance Mathis	2.50
7	Brian Griese, Terrell Davis, Shannon Sharpe	7.00
8	Shaun King 36	100.00
	Fred Taylor, Mark Brunell, Keenan McCardell	5.00
9	Randy Moss, Cris Carter, Randall Cunningham	10.00
10	Antonio Freeman, Brett Favre, Dorsey Levens	10.00

1999 Playoff Contenders SSD Triple Threat Parallel

This was a 60-card parallel to the Triple Threat insert. Each single featured one of the teammates on the front. Each was sequentially numbered to the player-specific stat.

		MT
Common Player:		8.00
1	Jake Plummer 17	85.00
2	Deion Sanders 16	45.00
3	Terrell Owens 14	45.00
4	Dan Marino 23	200.00
5	Keyshawn Johnson 10	60.00
6	Jamal Anderson 14	50.00
7	Brian Griese 33	60.00
8	Fred Taylor 14	125.00
9	Randy Moss 17	275.00
10	Antonio Freeman 14	50.00
11	Brad Johnson 48	15.00
12	Barry Sanders 73	80.00
13	Eddie George 37	45.00
14	Kordell Stewart 11	60.00
15	Antowain Smith 8	45.00
16	Terry Glenn 86	12.00
17	Mike Alstott 8	85.00
18	Peyton Manning 26	225.00
19	Corey Dillon 66	15.00
20	Isaac Bruce 80	12.00
21	David Boston 13	100.00
22	Troy Aikman 12	150.00
23	Jerry Rice 75	45.00
24	O.J. McDuffie 90	8.00
25	Wayne Chrebet 63	15.00
26	Chris Chandler 25	30.00
27	Terrell Davis 21	100.00
28	Mark Brunell 20	85.00
29	Cris Carter 12	70.00
30	Brett Favre 31	150.00
31	Skip Hicks 8	50.00
32	Herman Moore 82	8.00
33	Steve McNair 15	75.00
34	Jerome Bettis 4	100.00
35	Eric Moulds 84	12.00
36	Kevin Faulk 12	75.00
37	Warrick Dunn 50	30.00
38	Marvin Harrison 61	20.00
39	Akili Smith 32	75.00
40	Torry Holt 11	120.00
41	Frank Sanders 89	8.00
42	Emmitt Smith 13	175.00
43	Steve Young 36	75.00
44	Cecil Collins 28	50.00
45	Curtis Martin 60	15.00
46	Terance Mathis 11	30.00
47	Shannon Sharpe 10	45.00
48	Keenan McCardell 67	8.00
49	Randall Cunningham 34	40.00
50	Dorsey Levens 25	25.00
51	Champ Bailey 22	50.00
52	Charlie Batch 98	25.00
53	Yancey Thigpen 13	25.00
54	Troy Edwards 27	70.00
55	Doug Flutie 20	85.00
56	Drew Bledsoe 20	85.00
57	Shaun King 36	100.00
58	Edgerrin James 17	500.00
59	Carl Pickens 67	8.00
60	Marshall Faulk 78	25.00

Post-1980 cards in Near Mint condition will generally sell for about 75% of the quoted Mint value. Excellent-condition cards bring no more than 40%.

11	Brad Johnson, Skip Hicks, Champ Bailey	2.50
12	Barry Sanders, Herman Moore, Charlie Batch	10.00
13	Eddie George, Steve McNair, Yancey Thigpen	4.00
14	Kordell Stewart, Jerome Bettis, Troy Edwards	3.00
15	Antowain Smith, Eric Moulds, Doug Flutie	3.00
16	Terry Glenn, Kevin Faulk, Drew Bledsoe	4.00
17	Mike Alstott, Warrick Dunn, Shaun King	6.00
18	Peyton Manning, Marvin Harrison, Edgerrin James	15.00
19	Corey Dillon, Akili Smith, Carl Pickens	3.00
20	Isaac Bruce, Torry Holt, Marshall Faulk	4.00

1999 Playoff Momentum SSD

This was a 200-card base set that was divided into three tiers. Cards #1-100 were printed on foil board with micro-etching and inserted 4:1 packs. Cards #101-150 were printed on clear plastic with dual-sided holographic foil stamping and inserted 1:1. Rookie cards #151-200 were printed on clear plastic with clear holographic foil and micro-etching and inserted 1:5 packs. Parallel sets included O's and X's. Other inserts included: Chart Toppers, Terrell Davis Salute, Gridiron Force, Hog Heaven, Rookie Quads, Rookie Recall, Barry Sanders Commemorate, Star Gazing and Team Thread Checklists. SRP was $4.99 for five-card packs.

		MT
Complete Set (200):		375.00
Common Player:		.15
Minor Stars:		.30
Common Player (101-150):		.25
Minor Stars (101-150):		.50
Inserted 1:1		
Common Rookie:		2.50
Inserted 1:5		
Wax Box:		80.00
1	Rob Moore	.30
2	Adrian Murrell	.15
3	Frank Sanders	.15
4	Andre Wadsworth	.15
5	Tim Dwight	.75
6	Terance Mathis	.15
7	Priest Holmes	.75
8	Jermaine Lewis	.30
9	Scott Mitchell	.15
10	Patrick Johnson	.30
11	Tony Banks	.30
12	Thurman Thomas	.30
13	Andre Reed	.30
14	Bruce Smith	.15
15	Tim Biakabutuka	.30
16	Muhsin Muhammad	.50
17	Wesley Walls	.30
18	Rae Carruth	.15
19	Curtis Conway	.30
20	Bobby Engram	.15
21	Jeff Blake	.30
22	Darnay Scott	.15
23	Ty Detmer	.15
24	Leslie Shepherd	.15
25	Sedrick Shaw	.15
26	Michael Irvin	.30
27	Raghib Ismail	.15
28	Ed McCaffrey	.50
29	Marcus Nash	.30
30	Shannon Sharpe	.30
31	Neil Smith	.15
32	Rod Smith	.50
33	Bubby Brister	.30
34	Germane Crowell	.15
35	Johnnie Morton	.15
36	Bill Schroeder	.15
37	Mark Chmura	.30
38	Marvin Harrison	.75
39	E.G. Green	.15
40	Jerome Pathon	.15
41	Keenan McCardell	.30
42	Jimmy Smith	.75
43	Kyle Brady	.15
44	Tavian Banks	.30
45	Warren Moon	.30
46	Derrick Alexander	.15
47	Elvis Grbac	.30
48	Andre Rison	.30
49	Bam Morris	.15
50	Rashaan Shehee	.30
51	Karim Abdul	.30
52	John Avery	.30
53	Tony Martin	.15
54	O.J. McDuffie	.30
55	Oronde Gadsden	.15
56	Robert Smith	.75
57	Jeff George	.75
58	Jake Reed	.30
59	Leroy Hoard	.15
60	Terry Allen	.30
61	Terry Glenn	.75

62	Ben Coates	.30
63	Tony Simmons	.30
64	Cameron Cleeland	.30
65	Eddie Kennison	.15
66	Billy Joe Hobert	.15
67	Amani Toomer	.30
68	Kerry Collins	.30
69	Ike Hilliard	.30
70	Gary Brown	.15
71	Joe Jurevicius	.15
72	Wayne Chrebet	.75
73	Vinny Testaverde	.30
74	Charles Woodson	.50
75	James Jett	.15
76	Charles Johnson	.15
77	Duce Staley	.50
78	Hines Ward	.30
79	Jim Harbaugh	.30
80	Ryan Leaf	.75
81	Junior Seau	.30
82	Mikhael Ricks	.15
83	Garrison Hearst	.50
84	J.J. Stokes	.30
85	Lawrence Phillips	.30
86	Derrick Mayes	.30
87	Mike Pritchard	.15
88	Ahman Green	.30
89	Ricky Watters	.50
90	Robert Holcombe	.30
91	Isaac Bruce	.75
92	Trent Dilfer	.50
93	Reidel Anthony	.30
94	Jacquez Green	.30
95	Warren Sapp	.30
96	Kevin Dyson	.30
97	Yancey Thigpen	.30
98	Stephen Davis	.75
99	Irving Fryar	.15
100	Michael Westbrook	.50
101	Jake Plummer	2.00
102	Jamal Anderson	1.00
103	Chris Chandler	.50
104	Doug Flutie	1.50
105	Eric Moulds	1.00
106	Antowain Smith	.50
107	Jonathon Linton	.50
108	Curtis Enis	1.00
109	Corey Dillon	1.00
110	Carl Pickens	.50
111	Emmitt Smith	3.00
112	Troy Aikman	2.00
113	Deion Sanders	1.00
114	John Elway	3.00
115	Terrell Davis	3.00
116	Brian Griese	2.00
117	Barry Sanders	4.00
118	Charlie Batch	1.50
119	Herman Moore	1.00
120	Brett Favre	4.00
121	Antonio Freeman	1.00
122	Dorsey Levens	1.00
123	Peyton Manning	3.00
124	Fred Taylor	2.00
125	Mark Brunell	1.50
126	Dan Marino	3.00
127	Randy Moss	4.00
128	Cris Carter	1.00
129	Randall Cunningham	1.00
130	Drew Bledsoe	1.50
131	Keyshawn Johnson	1.00
132	Curtis Martin	1.00
133	Tim Brown	.75
134	Napoleon Kaufman	1.00
135	Kordell Stewart	1.00
136	Jerome Bettis	1.00
137	Natrone Means	.75
138	Jerry Rice	2.00
139	Steve Young	1.50
140	Terrell Owens	1.00
141	Joey Galloway	1.00
142	Jon Kitna	1.00
143	Marshall Faulk	1.00
144	Kurt Warner	50.00
145	Warrick Dunn	1.00
146	Mike Alstott	1.00
147	Eddie George	1.25
148	Steve McNair	1.25
149	Brad Johnson	1.00
150	Skip Hicks	.25
151	Tim Couch	30.00
152	Donovan McNabb	20.00
153	Akili Smith	20.00
154	Edgerrin James	40.00
155	Ricky Williams	30.00
156	Torry Holt	12.00
157	Champ Bailey	8.00
158	David Boston	12.00
159	Chris Claiborne	5.00
160	Chris McAlister	5.00
161	Daunte Culpepper	20.00
162	Cade McNown	20.00
163	Troy Edwards	12.00
164	Jevon Kearse	10.00
165	Kevin Johnson	12.00
166	James Johnson	8.00
167	Reginald Kelly	2.50
168	Rob Konrad	4.00
169	Jim Kleinsasser	4.00
170	Kevin Faulk	8.00
171	Joe Montgomery	5.00
172	Shaun King	20.00
173	Peerless Price	8.00
174	Michael Cloud	5.00
175	Jermaine Fazande	5.00
176	D'Wayne Bates	2.50
177	Brock Huard	8.00
178	Marty Booker	2.50
179	Karsten Bailey	2.50
180	Shawn Bryson	2.50
181	Jeff Paulk	2.50
182	Travis McGriff	2.50
183	Amos Zereoue	4.00
184	Craig Yeast	2.50
185	Joe Germaine	5.00
186	Dameane Douglas	2.50
187	Sedrick Irvin	8.00
188	Brandon Stokley	2.50
189	Larry Parker	2.50
190	Sean Bennett	2.50
191	Wane McGarity	2.50
192	Olandis Gary	25.00
193	Na Brown	2.50
194	Aaron Brooks	5.00
195	Cecil Collins	12.00
196	Darrin Chiaverini	4.00
197	Kevin Daft	2.50
198	Darnell McDonald	4.00
199	Joel Makovicka	4.00
200	Michael Bishop	7.00

1999 Playoff Momentum SSD O's

This was a 200-card parallel to the base set. Each single was printed on holographic foil board with foil stamping. Cards were sequentially numbered to 25.

	MT
O's Cards:	50x-100x
O's Cards (101-150):	35x-70x
O's Rookies (144,151-200):	3x-6x
Production 25 Sets	

1999 Playoff Momentum SSD X's

This was a 200-card parallel to the base set. Each was die cut in the shape of the letter "X" and was printed on holographic foil board with foil stamping. They were sequentially numbered to 300.

	MT
X's Cards:	6x-12x
X's Cards (101-150):	5x-10x
X's Rookies (144,151-200):	1.5x
Production 300 Sets	

1999 Playoff Momentum SSD Chart Toppers

This 24-card insert included some of the top veteran and rookies in the NFL. Each was printed on holographic foil board with holographic foil stamping. Singles were found 1:33 packs.

		MT
Complete Set (24):		150.00
Common Player:		3.00
Inserted 1:33		
1	Donovan McNabb	8.00
2	Randy Moss	15.00
3	Cade McNown	8.00
4	Brett Favre	15.00
5	Edgerrin James	20.00
6	Dan Marino	12.00
7	Jamal Anderson	3.00
8	Barry Sanders	15.00
9	Kordell Stewart	3.00
10	John Elway	12.00
11	Eddie George	4.00
12	Terrell Davis	12.00
13	Ricky Williams	12.00
14	Peyton Manning	12.00
15	Tim Couch	12.00
16	Emmitt Smith	12.00
17	Doug Flutie	6.00
18	Troy Aikman	10.00
19	Steve Young	6.00
20	Jerry Rice	10.00
21	Mark Brunell	6.00
22	Fred Taylor	10.00
23	Jake Plummer	10.00
24	Drew Bledsoe	6.00

1999 Playoff Momentum SSD Terrell Davis Salute

This was a 5-card insert that covered Davis' career. Singles were numbered 11-15 and they were found 1:255 packs. The first 150 of each card were autographed and sequentially numbered.

		MT
Complete Set (5):		60.00
Common Player:		12.00
Inserted 1:255		
Common Autograph:		75.00
Production 150 Sets		
11	Terrell Davis	12.00
12	Terrell Davis	12.00
13	Terrell Davis	12.00
14	Terrell Davis	12.00
15	Terrell Davis	12.00

1999 Playoff Momentum SSD Gridiron Force

This 24-card insert included some of the top players in the NFL. Each was printed on holographic foil board with gold foil stamping. Singles were inserted 1:17 packs.

		MT
Complete Set (24):		85.00
Common Player:		2.00
Inserted 1:17		
1	Cris Carter	2.00
2	Brett Favre	12.00
3	Jamal Anderson	2.00
4	Dan Marino	10.00
5	Deion Sanders	2.00
6	Barry Sanders	12.00
7	Jerome Bettis	2.00
8	John Elway	10.00
9	Eddie George	3.00
10	Peyton Manning	10.00
11	Warrick Dunn	2.00
12	Troy Aikman	6.00
13	Keyshawn Johnson	2.00
14	Jerry Rice	6.00
15	Terrell Owens	2.00
16	Randy Moss	12.00
17	Fred Taylor	6.00
18	Mark Brunell	4.00
19	Steve Young	4.00
20	Drew Bledsoe	4.00
21	Kordell Stewart	2.00
22	Emmitt Smith	10.00
23	Terrell Davis	10.00
24	Jake Plummer	6.00

1999 Playoff Momentum SSD Hog Heaven

This 12-card insert pictured the players on a die-cut card with real football leather and foil stamping. Singles were inserted 1:81 packs.

		MT
Complete Set (12):		200.00
Common Player:		15.00
Inserted 1:81		
1	Ricky Williams	30.00
2	Terrell Davis	20.00
3	Emmitt Smith	20.00
4	Brett Favre	30.00
5	Fred Taylor	15.00
6	Tim Couch	30.00
7	John Elway	20.00
8	Dan Marino	20.00
9	Randy Moss	30.00
10	Barry Sanders	30.00
11	Jerry Rice	20.00
12	Jake Plummer	15.00

1999 Playoff Momentum SSD Rookie Quads

This was a 12-card insert that featured two rookies on each side of the card on a mirror board with micro-etching. Singles were inserted 1:97 packs. A parallel Gold version was also issued and each of those singles included holographic gold foil stamping and were sequentially numbered to 50.

		MT
Complete Set (12):		230.00
Common Player:		10.00
Inserted 1:97		
Gold Cards:		2x
Production 50 Sets		
1	Tim Couch, Aaron Brooks, Shaun King, Michael Bishop	40.00
2	Edgerrin James, Michael Cloud, Jeff Paulk, Joel Makovicka	50.00
3	Torry Holt, Reginald Kelly, Marty Booker, Dameane Douglas	20.00
4	Champ Bailey, Chris Claiborne, Chris McAlister, Anthony McFarland	10.00
5	David Boston, Jim Kleinsasser, Karsten Bailey, Brandon Stokley	15.00
6	Ricky Williams, Amos Zereoue, Cecil Collins, Olandis Gary	50.00
7	Donovan McNabb, Brock Huard, Daunte Culpepper, Scott Covington	30.00
8	James Johnson, Jermaine Fazande, Sedrick Irvin, Sean Bennett	15.00
9	Troy Edwards, Peerless Price, Travis McGriff, Larry Parker	25.00
10	Rob Konrad, Kevin Faulk, Joe Montgomery, Shawn Bryson	10.00
11	Cade McNown, Joe Germaine, Akili Smith, Chris Griesen	30.00
12	Kevin Johnson, D'Wayne Bates, Craig Yeast, Wane McGarity	20.00

1999 Playoff Momentum SSD Rookie Recall

This was a 30-card insert that featured photos of NFL stars on the front with their rookie photos on the back. Singles were found 1:49 packs.

		MT
Complete Set (30):		185.00
Common Player:		5.00
Inserted 1:49		
1	Jerome Bettis	5.00
2	Tim Brown	5.00
3	Cris Carter	5.00
4	Marshall Faulk	5.00
5	Doug Flutie	8.00
6	Randall Cunningham	5.00
7	Brett Favre	20.00
8	Dan Marino	15.00
9	Barry Sanders	20.00
10	John Elway	15.00
11	Emmitt Smith	15.00
12	Troy Aikman	12.00
13	Jerry Rice	12.00
14	Steve Young	8.00
15	Randy Moss	20.00
16	Peyton Manning	15.00
17	Fred Taylor	10.00
18	Jake Plummer	10.00
19	Drew Bledsoe	8.00
20	Mark Brunell	8.00
21	Charlie Batch	7.00
22	Antonio Freeman	5.00
23	Curtis Martin	5.00
24	Eddie George	5.00
25	Kordell Stewart	5.00
26	Jamal Anderson	5.00
27	Curtis Martin	5.00
28	Terrell Davis	15.00
29	Eric Moulds	5.00
30	Terrell Owens	5.00

1999 Playoff Momentum SSD Barry Sanders Commemorate

This was a five-card insert that covered the career of Barry Sanders. Singles were numbered 7 to 11 and found 1:275 packs.

		MT
Complete Set (5):		100.00
Common Player:		20.00
Inserted 1:275		
1	Barry Sanders	20.00
2	Barry Sanders	20.00
3	Barry Sanders	20.00
4	Barry Sanders	20.00
5	Barry Sanders	20.00

1999 Playoff Momentum SSD Star Gazing

This was a 45-card insert that was divided into three levels. The Red singles were the first eight cards in the set, each was autographed and found 1:185 packs. The next 22 cards were Blue and they were inserted 1:17 packs. The last 15 cards were Green and they were issued at 1:65 packs. Each single had a parallel Gold version and each of those singles were sequentially numbered to 50.

		MT
Complete Set (45):		500.00
Common Red Auto. (1-8):		25.00
Inserted 1:185		
Common Blue (9-30):		1.50
Inserted 1:17		
Common Green (31-45):		5.00
Inserted 1:65		
1	Terrell Davis (red)	75.00
2	Dan Marino (red)	100.00
3	Joey Galloway (red)	25.00
4	Steve McNair (red)	25.00
5	Doug Flutie (red)	35.00
6	Kordell Stewart (red)	25.00
7	Fred Taylor (red)	45.00
8	Jamal Anderson (red)	25.00
9	Karim Abdul (blue)	1.50
10	Mike Alstott (blue)	3.00
11	Jerome Bettis (blue)	1.50
12	Carl Pickens (blue)	1.50
13	Cris Carter (blue)	3.00
14	Randall Cunningham (blue)	3.00
15	Corey Dillon (blue)	3.00
16	Tim Dwight (blue)	1.50
17	Cade McNown (blue)	5.00
18	Marshall Faulk (blue)	3.00
19	Napoleon Kaufman (blue)	1.50
20	Antonio Freeman (blue)	1.50
21	Edgerrin James (blue)	15.00
22	Terrell Owens (blue)	3.00
23	Garrison Hearst (blue)	1.50
24	Keyshawn Johnson (blue)	3.00
25	Akili Smith (blue)	5.00
26	Curtis Martin (blue)	3.00
27	Dorsey Levens (blue)	1.50
28	Deion Sanders (blue)	3.00
29	Herman Moore (blue)	1.50
30	Eric Moulds (blue)	1.50
31	Randy Moss (green)	15.00
32	Eddie George (green)	5.00
33	Barry Sanders (green)	15.00
34	John Elway (green)	12.00
35	Peyton Manning (green)	12.00
36	Emmitt Smith (green)	12.00
37	Troy Aikman (green)	10.00
38	Jerry Rice (green)	10.00
39	Mark Brunell (green)	6.00
40	Steve Young (green)	6.00
41	Tim Couch (green)	15.00
42	Ricky Williams (green)	15.00
43	Donovan McNabb (green)	10.00
44	Drew Bledsoe (green)	6.00
45	Brett Favre (green)	15.00

1999 Playoff Momentum SSD Team Threads

This was a 31-card insert that featured swatches of authentic NFL team jerseys on the front and back of each card. Singles were inserted 1:17 packs.

		MT
Complete Set (31):		425.00
Common Player:		5.00
Minor Stars:		10.00
Inserted 1:17		
1	Dan Marino	30.00
2	Drew Bledsoe	15.00
3	Keyshawn Johnson	10.00
4	Eric Moulds	10.00
5	Peyton Manning	30.00
6	Natrone Means	5.00
7	Jon Kitna	5.00
8	Bam Morris	5.00
9	Tim Brown	10.00
10	Terrell Davis	30.00
11	Kordell Stewart	10.00
12	Fred Taylor	20.00
13	Tim Couch	30.00
14	Eddie George	12.00
15	Priest Holmes	10.00

16	Akili Smith	15.00
17	Emmitt Smith	30.00
18	Skip Hicks	5.00
19	Jake Plummer	15.00
20	Donovan McNabb	20.00
21	Ike Hilliard	5.00
22	Barry Sanders	40.00
23	Cade McNown	20.00
24	Randy Moss	40.00
25	Brett Favre	40.00
26	Mike Alstott	5.00
27	Marshall Faulk	15.00
28	Ricky Williams	30.00
29	Jamal Anderson	5.00
30	Jerry Rice	20.00
31	Tim Biakabutuka	5.00

1999 Playoff Prestige EXP

BRIAN GRIESE

This 200-card set was a retail only release that included 40 unseeded rookie cards. It had two parallel sets with Reflections Gold and Reflections Silver. Other inserts include: Alma Maters, Checklists, Crowd Pleasers, Terrell Davis Salute, Draft Picks, Performers and Stars of the NFL.

		MT
Complete Set (200):		70.00
Common Player:		.20
Minor Stars:		.40
Common Rookie:		.50
Wax Box:		60.00
1	Anthony McFarland	1.00
2	Al Wilson	1.00
3	Jevon Kearse	3.00
4	Aaron Brooks	1.50
5	Travis McGriff	1.00
6	Jeff Paulk	1.00
7	Shawn Bryson	.50
8	Karsten Bailey	1.00
9	Mike Cloud	1.00
10	James Johnson	2.00
11	Tai Streets	1.00
12	Jermaine Fazande	1.00
13	Ebenezer Ekuban	.50
14	Joe Montgomery	1.50
15	Craig Yeast	1.00
16	Joe Germaine	2.00
17	Andy Katzenmoyer	1.50
18	Kevin Faulk	1.00
19	Chris McAlister	1.00
20	Sedrick Irvin	2.00
21	Brock Huard	2.00
22	Cade McNown	5.00
23	Shaun King	4.00
24	Amos Zereoue	2.50
25	Dameane Douglas	1.00
26	D'Wayne Bates	1.00
27	Kevin Johnson	3.00
28	Rob Konrad	1.50
29	Troy Edwards	3.00
30	Peerless Price	2.50
31	Daunte Culpepper	5.00
32	Akili Smith	4.00
33	David Boston	3.00
34	Chris Claiborne	1.50
35	Torry Holt	3.00
36	Champ Bailey	2.00
37	Edgerrin James	10.00
38	Donovan McNabb	5.00
39	Ricky Williams	8.00
40	Tim Couch	8.00
41	Charles Woodson (Repeat Performers)	.20
42	Skip Hicks (Repeat Performers)	.20
43	Brian Griese (Repeat Performers)	.75
44	Tim Dwight (Repeat Performers)	.20
45	Ryan Leaf (Repeat Performers)	.50
46	Curtis Enis (Repeat Performers)	.20
47	Charlie Batch (Repeat Performers)	.75
48	Fred Taylor (Repeat Performers)	1.00
49	Peyton Manning (Repeat Performers)	1.50
50	Randy Moss (Repeat Performers)	2.00

51	Jim Harbaugh (Trading Places)	.20
52	Warren Moon (Trading Places)	.75
53	Jeff George (Trading Places)	.20
54	Rich Gannon (Trading Places)	.20
55	Scott Mitchell (Trading Places)	.20
56	Kerry Collins (Trading Places)	.20
57	Brad Johnson (Trading Places)	.75
58	Charles Johnson (Trading Places)	.20
59	Chris Calloway (Trading Places)	.20
60	Tyrone Wheatley (Trading Places)	.20
61	Michael Westbrook	.40
62	Skip Hicks	.75
63	Terry Allen	.20
64	Albert Connell	.20
65	Kevin Dyson	.40
66	Frank Wycheck	.20
67	Yancey Thigpen	.20
68	Steve McNair	.75
69	Eddie George	1.00
70	Eric Zeier	.20
71	Jacquez Green	.40
72	Reidel Anthony	.40
73	Warren Sapp	.20
74	Mike Alstott	.75
75	Warrick Dunn	1.00
76	Trent Dilfer	.40
77	Ahman Green	.40
78	Joey Galloway	.75
79	Ricky Watters	.40
80	Jon Kitna	1.00
81	Amp Lee	.20
82	Isaac Bruce	.40
83	Robert Holcombe	.20
84	Greg Hill	.20
85	Marshall Faulk	.75
86	Trent Green	.75
87	J.J. Stokes	.40
88	Terrell Owens	.75
89	Jerry Rice	2.00
90	Garrison Hearst	.40
91	Steve Young	1.25
92	Junior Seau	.40
93	Mikhael Ricks	.20
94	Natrone Means	.40
95	Ryan Leaf	.75
96	Courtney Hawkins	.20
97	Chris Fuamatu-Ma'afala	.20
98	Jerome Bettis	.75
99	Kordell Stewart	.75
100	Bobby Hoying	.40
101	Charlie Garner	.40
102	Duce Staley	.40
103	Charles Woodson	.75
104	James Jett	.20
105	Rickey Dudley	.20
106	Tim Brown	.50
107	Napoleon Kaufman	.75
108	Wayne Chrebet	.50
109	Keyshawn Johnson	.75
110	Vinny Testaverde	.40
111	Curtis Martin	.75
112	Joe Jurevicius	.20
113	Tiki Barber	.20
114	Ike Hilliard	.20
115	Kent Graham	.20
116	Gary Brown	.20
117	Lamar Smith	.20
118	Eddie Kennison	.20
119	Cameron Cleeland	.20
120	Tony Simmons	.40
121	Ben Coates	.40
122	Darick Holmes	.20
123	Terry Glenn	.75
124	Drew Bledsoe	1.50
125	Leroy Hoard	.20
126	Jake Reed	.20
127	Randy Moss	4.00
128	Cris Carter	.75
129	Robert Smith	.75
130	Randall Cunningham	.75
131	Lamar Thomas	.20
132	John Avery	.40
133	O.J. McDuffie	.40
134	Dan Marino	3.00
135	Karim Abdul	.40
136	Rashaan Shehee	.20
137	Derrick Alexander	.20
138	Bam Morris	.20
139	Andre Rison	.40
140	Elvis Grbac	.40
141	Tavian Banks	.20
142	Keenan McCardell	.40
143	Jimmy Smith	.40
144	Fred Taylor	2.00
145	Mark Brunell	1.50
146	Jerome Pathon	.20
147	Marvin Harrison	.40
148	Peyton Manning	3.00
149	Robert Brooks	.20
150	Mark Chmura	.40
151	Antonio Freeman	.75
152	Dorsey Levens	.75
153	Brett Favre	4.00
154	Johnnie Morton	.20
155	Germane Crowell	.40
156	Barry Sanders	4.00

157	Herman Moore	.75
158	Charlie Batch	1.25
159	Marcus Nash	.20
160	Shannon Sharpe	.40
161	Rod Smith	.40
162	Ed McCaffrey	.40
163	Terrell Davis	3.00
164	John Elway	3.00
165	Ernie Mills	.20
166	Michael Irvin	.40
167	Deion Sanders	.75
168	Emmitt Smith	3.00
169	Troy Aikman	2.00
170	Chris Spielman	.20
171	Terry Kirby	.20
172	Ty Detmer	.20
173	Leslie Shepherd	.20
174	Darnay Scott	.20
175	Jeff Blake	.40
176	Carl Pickens	.40
177	Corey Dillon	.75
178	Bobby Engram	.20
179	Curtis Conway	.40
180	Curtis Enis	.75
181	Muhsin Muhammad	.20
182	Steve Beuerlein	.20
183	Tim Biakabutuka	.20
184	Bruce Smith	.20
185	Andre Reed	.20
186	Thurman Thomas	.40
187	Eric Moulds	.75
188	Antowain Smith	.75
189	Doug Flutie	1.25
190	Jermaine Lewis	.20
191	Priest Holmes	.75
192	O.J. Santiago	.20
193	Tim Dwight	.75
194	Terrance Mathis	.20
195	Chris Chandler	.40
196	Jamal Anderson	.75
197	Rob Moore	.40
198	Frank Sanders	.20
199	Adrian Murrell	.20
200	Jake Plummer	1.50

1999 Playoff Prestige EXP Reflections Gold

JAMAL ANDERSON

This is a parallel to the base set and each single is the same as the base card except for these singles are printed on a gold foil card and are sequentially numbered to 1,000.

	MT
Complete Set (200):	280.00
Gold Cards:	3x-6x
Gold Rookies:	3x
Production 1,000 Sets	

1999 Playoff Prestige EXP Reflections Silver

DAVID BOSTON

This is a parallel to the base set and is identical to the base card except each single is printed on a silver foil card and is sequentially numbered to 3,250.

	MT
Complete Set (200):	140.00
Silver Cards:	2x
Silver Rookies:	1.5x
Production 3,250 Sets	

1999 Playoff Prestige EXP Alma Maters

Each card in this 30-card set pictures two players that went to the same college. Singles were inserted 1:25 packs.

		MT
Complete Set (30):		100.00
Common Player:		2.00
Minor Stars:		4.00
Inserted 1:25		
1	Priest Holmes, Ricky Williams	12.00
2	Tim Couch, Dermonti Dawson	12.00
3	Terrell Davis, Garrison Hearst	8.00
4	Troy Brown, Randy Moss	10.00
5	Barry Sanders, Thurman Thomas	10.00
6	Emmitt Smith, Fred Taylor	8.00
7	Doug Flutie, Bill Romanowski	5.00
8	Brett Favre, Michael Jackson	10.00
9	Charlie Batch, Ron Rice	5.00
10	Mark Brunell, Chris Chandler	5.00
11	Warrick Dunn, Deion Sanders	4.00
12	Cris Carter, Eddie George	4.00
13	Drew Bledsoe, Ryan Leaf	5.00
14	Corey Dillon, Napoleon Kaufman	2.00
15	Jerome Bettis, Tim Brown	2.00
16	Marshall Faulk, Darnay Scott	2.00
17	Tiki Barber, Herman Moore	2.00
18	Jamal Anderson, Chris Fuamatu-Ma'afala	2.00
19	Troy Aikman, Cade McNown	7.00
20	Brian Griese, Charles Woodson	6.00
21	Charles Johnson, Kordell Stewart	4.00
22	Kevin Faulk, Eddie Kennison	4.00
23	Donovan McNabb, Rob Moore	5.00
24	Steve McNair, John Thierry	4.00
25	Michael Irvin, Vinny Testaverde	2.00
26	Randall Cunningham, Keenan McCardell	4.00
27	Keyshawn Johnson, Junior Seau	2.00
28	Karim Abdul, Skip Hicks	2.00
29	Curtis Enis, O.J. McDuffie	2.00
30	Joey Galloway, Robert Smith	2.00

1999 Playoff Prestige EXP Checklists

PEYTON MANNING

This 31-card set includes a

card for each NFL team and highlights one player on the front of these silver foil singles. The backs include photos of each player on that team in the base set and includes their card number. Singles were inserted 1:25 packs.

		MT
Complete Set (31):		85.00
Common Player:		1.50
Minor Stars:		3.00
Inserted 1:25		
1	Jake Plummer	6.00
2	Chris Chandler	1.50
3	Priest Holmes	3.00
4	Doug Flutie	4.00
5	Wesley Walls	1.50
6	Curtis Enis	3.00
7	Corey Dillon	3.00
8	Kevin Johnson	3.00
9	Troy Aikman	6.00
10	Terrell Davis	8.00
11	Barry Sanders	12.00
12	Antonio Freeman	3.00
13	Peyton Manning	8.00
14	Fred Taylor	6.00
15	Andre Rison	1.50
16	Dan Marino	8.00
17	Randy Moss	12.00
18	Kevin Faulk	4.00
19	Ricky Williams	12.00
20	Joe Montgomery	3.00
21	Vinny Testaverde	1.50
22	Tim Brown	3.00
23	Duce Staley	1.50
24	Jerome Bettis	3.00
25	Natrone Means	3.00
26	Terrell Owens	3.00
27	Joey Galloway	3.00
28	Isaac Bruce	3.00
29	Mike Alstott	3.00
30	Eddie George	4.00
31	Skip Hicks	3.00

1999 Playoff Prestige EXP Crowd Pleasers

Each card in this 30-card set highlights the hottest players who fill the stadiums. Singles were inserted 1:49 packs.

		MT
Complete Set (30):		200.00
Common Player:		2.50
Minor Stars:		5.00
Inserted 1:49		
1	Terrell Davis	15.00
2	Fred Taylor	10.00
3	Corey Dillon	5.00
4	Eddie George	6.00
5	Napoleon Kaufman	5.00
6	Jamal Anderson	5.00
7	Tim Couch	20.00
8	Emmitt Smith	15.00
9	Deion Sanders	5.00
10	Garrison Hearst	2.50
11	Peyton Manning	10.00
12	Ricky Williams	20.00
13	Barry Sanders	20.00
14	Jerry Rice	10.00
15	Jake Plummer	8.00
16	Tim Brown	2.50
17	Terrell Owens	5.00
18	Dan Marino	15.00
19	Chris Chandler	2.50
20	Drew Bledsoe	7.00
21	Charlie Batch	6.00
22	Mark Brunell	7.00
23	Troy Aikman	10.00
24	John Elway	15.00
25	Jon Kitna	5.00
26	Jerome Bettis	5.00
27	Brett Favre	20.00
28	Steve Young	6.00
29	Randy Moss	20.00
30	Antonio Freeman	5.00

1999 Playoff Prestige EXP Terrell Davis Salute

This 5-card set highlights 15 milestones in Davis' career.

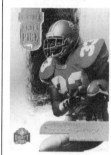

Each single is sequentially numbered to 750 and the first 150 of each single were autographed.

		MT
Complete Set (5):		60.00
Common Player:		12.00
Production 750 Sets		
Common Autographs:		85.00
First 150-cards were signed		
1	Terrell Davis	12.00
2	Terrell Davis	12.00
3	Terrell Davis	12.00
4	Terrell Davis	12.00
5	Terrell Davis	12.00

1999 Playoff Prestige EXP Draft Picks

This insert includes the top 30 players drafted in 1999. It pictures each player in their college uniform on a silver foil card. Singles were inserted 1:13 packs.

		MT
Complete Set (30):		60.00
Common Player:		1.00
Minor Stars:		2.00
Inserted 1:13		
1	Tim Couch	12.00
2	Ricky Williams	12.00
3	Donovan McNabb	5.00
4	Edgerrin James	7.00
5	Champ Bailey	2.50
6	Torry Holt	4.00
7	Chris Claiborne	2.00
8	David Boston	4.00
9	Akili Smith	5.00
10	Daunte Culpepper	5.00
11	Peerless Price	3.00
12	Troy Edwards	4.00
13	Rob Konrad	1.00
14	Kevin Johnson	4.00
15	D'Wayne Bates	2.00
16	Cecil Collins	5.00
17	Amos Zereous	3.00
18	Shaun King	3.00
19	Cade McNown	5.00
20	Brock Huard	2.50
21	Sedrick Irvin	2.50
22	Chris McAlister	1.00
23	Kevin Faulk	3.00
24	Jevon Kearse	2.50
25	Joe Germaine	2.50
26	Andy Katzenmoyer	2.00
27	Joe Montgomery	2.00
28	Al Wilson	1.00
29	Jermaine Fazande	1.00
30	Ebenezer Ekuban	1.00

1999 Playoff Prestige EXP Performers

This 24-card insert includes the top performers from 1998. Singles were inserted 1:97 packs.

		MT
Complete Set (24):		200.00
Common Player:		3.00
Minor Stars:		6.00
Inserted 1:97		
1	Marshall Faulk	6.00
2	Jake Plummer	15.00
3	Antonio Freeman	6.00
4	Brett Favre	30.00
5	Troy Aikman	15.00
6	Randy Moss	30.00
7	John Elway	20.00
8	Mark Brunell	10.00
9	Jamal Anderson	6.00
10	Doug Flutie	8.00
11	Drew Bledsoe	12.00
12	Barry Sanders	30.00
13	Dan Marino	20.00
14	Randall Cunningham	6.00
15	Steve Young	8.00
16	Carl Pickens	3.00
17	Peyton Manning	20.00
18	Herman Moore	6.00

#	Player	Price
19	Eddie George	7.00
20	Fred Taylor	15.00
21	Garrison Hearst	6.00
22	Emmitt Smith	20.00
23	Jerry Rice	15.00
24	Terrell Davis	20.00

1999 Playoff Prestige EXP Barry Sanders Commemorative

This was a special insert found 1:289 packs that was commemorating Sanders run for the record.

		MT
RR1	Barry Sanders	20.00

1999 Playoff Prestige EXP Stars of the NFL

Each card in this 20-card set is printed on clear plastic and is die cut. Singles were inserted 1:73 packs.

		MT
Complete Set (20):		160.00
Common Player:		5.00
Inserted 1:73		
1	Jerry Rice	12.00
2	Steve Young	8.00
3	Drew Bledsoe	10.00
4	Jamal Anderson	6.00
5	Eddie George	5.00
6	Keyshawn Johnson	5.00
7	Kordell Stewart	6.00
8	Barry Sanders	25.00
9	Tim Brown	5.00
10	Mark Brunell	8.00
11	Fred Taylor	12.00
12	Randy Moss	25.00
13	Peyton Manning	18.00
14	Emmitt Smith	18.00
15	Deion Sanders	5.00
16	Troy Aikman	12.00
17	Brett Favre	25.00
18	Dan Marino	18.00
19	Terrell Davis	18.00
20	John Elway	18.00

1999 Playoff Prestige SSD

Prestige SSD was a 200-card set that was a hobby-only product. It had 50 short prints with 40 rookies and 10 Repeat Performers that were inserted 1:2 packs. It has a parallel Spectrum insert in five different colors that include Blue, Gold, Green, Purple and Red. Other inserts include: Alma Maters, Checklists, Checklists Autographs, Draft Picks, For the Record, Gridiron Heritage, Inside the Numbers and Barry Sanders Run for the Record.

		MT
Complete Set (200):		175.00
Common Player:		.25
Minor Stars:		.50
Common RP (151-160):		1.00
Common Rookie:		2.00
Inserted 1:2		
Wax Box:		100.00
1	Jake Plummer	2.50
2	Adrian Murrell	.25
3	Frank Sanders	.50
4	Rob Moore	.50
5	Jamal Anderson	1.00
6	Chris Chandler	.50
7	Terrance Mathis	.25
8	Tim Dwight	1.00
9	O.J. Santiago	.25
10	Priest Holmes	1.50
11	Jermaine Lewis	.50
12	Doug Flutie	1.50
13	Antowain Smith	1.00
14	Eric Moulds	1.00
15	Thurman Thomas	.50
16	Andre Reed	.25

#	Player	Price
17	Bruce Smith	.25
18	Tim Biakabutuka	.50
19	Steve Beuerlein	.25
20	Muhsin Muhammed	.25
21	Curtis Enis	1.00
22	Curtis Conway	.50
23	Bobby Engram	.25
24	Corey Dillon	1.00
25	Carl Pickens	.50
26	Jeff Blake	.50
27	Darnay Scott	.25
28	Leslie Shepherd	.25
29	Ty Detmer	.25
30	Terry Kirby	.25
31	Chris Spielman	.25
32	Troy Aikman	2.50
33	Emmitt Smith	4.00
34	Deion Sanders	1.00
35	Michael Irvin	.50
36	Ernie Mills	.25
37	John Elway	4.00
38	Terrell Davis	4.00
39	Ed McCaffrey	.50
40	Rod Smith	.50
41	Shannon Sharpe	.50
42	Marcus Nash	.50
43	Charlie Batch	2.00
44	Herman Moore	1.00
45	Barry Sanders	5.00
46	Germane Crowell	.50
47	Johnnie Morton	.25
48	Brett Favre	5.00
49	Dorsey Levens	1.00
50	Antonio Freeman	1.00
51	Mark Chmura	.50
52	Robert Brooks	.50
53	Peyton Manning	4.00
54	Marvin Harrison	.50
55	Jerome Pathon	.25
56	Mark Brunell	2.00
57	Fred Taylor	2.50
58	Jimmy Smith	.50
59	Keenan McCardell	.25
60	Tavian Banks	.50
61	Elvis Grbac	.50
62	Andre Rison	.50
63	Bam Morris	.50
64	Derrick Alexander	.25
65	Rashaan Shehee	.25
66	Karim Abdul	.75
67	Dan Marino	4.00
68	O.J. McDuffie	.50
69	John Avery	.50
70	Lamar Thomas	.25
71	Randall Cunningham	1.00
72	Robert Smith	.75
73	Cris Carter	1.00
74	Randy Moss	6.00
75	Jake Reed	.25
76	Leroy Hoard	.25
77	Drew Bledsoe	2.00
78	Terry Glenn	.75
79	Darick Holmes	.25
80	Ben Coates	.50
81	Tony Simmons	.50
82	Cam Cleeland	.50
83	Eddie Kennison	.25
84	Lamar Smith	.25
85	Gary Brown	.25
86	Kent Graham	.25
87	Ike Hilliard	.50
88	Tiki Barber	.25
89	Joe Jurevicius	.25
90	Curtis Martin	1.00
91	Vinny Testaverde	.50
92	Keyshawn Johnson	1.00
93	Wayne Chrebet	1.00
94	Napoleon Kaufman	1.00
95	Tim Brown	.50
96	Rickey Dudley	.25
97	James Jett	.25
98	Charles Woodson	1.00
99	Duce Staley	.25
100	Charlie Garner	.25
101	Bobby Hoying	.25
102	Kordell Stewart	1.50
103	Jerome Bettis	1.00
104	Chris Fuamatu-Ma'afala	.25
105	Courtney Hawkins	.25
106	Ryan Leaf	1.50
107	Natrone Means	.75
108	Mikhael Ricks	.25
109	Junior Seau	.50
110	Steve Young	2.00
111	Garrison Hearst	1.00
112	Jerry Rice	2.50
113	Terrell Owens	1.00
114	J.J. Stokes	.50
115	Trent Green	1.00
116	Marshall Faulk	1.00
117	Greg Hill	.25
118	Robert Holcombe	.50
119	Isaac Bruce	.75
120	Amp Lee	.25
121	Jon Kitna	1.50
122	Ricky Watters	.75
123	Joey Galloway	1.00
124	Ahman Green	.50
125	Trent Dilfer	.50
126	Warrick Dunn	1.50
127	Mike Alstott	1.00
128	Warren Sapp	.25
129	Reidel Anthony	.50
130	Jacquez Green	.50
131	Eric Zeier	.25
132	Eddie George	1.50

#	Player	Price
133	Steve McNair	1.00
134	Yancey Thigpen	.50
135	Frank Wycheck	.25
136	Kevin Dyson	.50
137	Albert Connell	.25
138	Terry Allen	.50
139	Skip Hicks	1.00
140	Michael Westbrook	.50
141	Tyrone Wheatley (Trading Places)	.25
142	Chris Calloway (Trading Places)	.25
143	Charles Johnson (Trading Places)	.25
144	Brad Johnson (Trading Places)	.50
145	Kerry Collins (Trading Places)	.25
146	Scott Mitchell (Trading Places)	.25
147	Rich Gannon (Trading Places)	.25
148	Jeff George (Trading Places)	.25
149	Warren Moon (Trading Places)	.25
150	Jim Harbaugh (Trading Places)	.25
151	Randy Moss (Repeat Performers)	10.00
152	Peyton Manning (Repeat Performers)	8.00
153	Fred Taylor (Repeat Performers)	6.00
154	Charlie Batch (Repeat Performers)	3.00
155	Curtis Enis (Repeat Performers)	1.00
156	Ryan Leaf (Repeat Performers)	2.00
157	Tim Dwight (Repeat Performers)	2.00
158	Brian Griese (Repeat Performers)	3.00
159	Skip Hicks (Repeat Performers)	1.00
160	Charles Woodson (Repeat Performers)	2.00
161	*Tim Couch*	30.00
162	*Ricky Williams*	30.00
163	*Donovan McNabb*	15.00
164	*Edgerrin James*	30.00
165	*Champ Bailey*	6.00
166	*Torry Holt*	10.00
167	*Chris Claiborne*	4.00
168	*David Boston*	10.00
169	*Akili Smith*	15.00
170	*Peerless Price*	8.00
171	*Troy Edwards*	10.00
172	*Rob Konrad*	3.00
173	*Kevin Johnson*	10.00
174	*D'Wayne Bates*	3.00
175	*Daunte Culpepper*	15.00
176	*Dameane Douglas*	2.00
177	*Amos Zereoue*	6.00
178	*Shaun King*	12.00
179	*Cade McNown*	15.00
180	*Brock Huard*	5.00
181	*Sedrick Irvin*	5.00
182	*Chris McAlister*	4.00
183	*Kevin Faulk*	6.00
184	*Andy Katzenmoyer*	4.00
185	*Joe Germaine*	5.00
186	*Craig Yeast*	2.00
187	*Joe Montgomery*	3.00
188	*Ebenezer Ekuban*	3.00
189	*Jermaine Fazande*	2.00
190	*Tai Streets*	2.00
191	*James Johnson*	6.00
192	*Mike Cloud*	2.00
193	*Karsten Bailey*	3.00
194	*Shawn Bryson*	2.00
195	*Jeff Paulk*	2.00
196	*Travis McGriff*	3.00
197	*Aaron Brooks*	3.00
198	*Jevon Kearse*	7.00
199	*Al Wilson*	2.00
200	*Anthony McFarland*	2.00

1999 Playoff Prestige SSD Spectrum Blue

This is a 200-card parallel to the base and is the same except for the background color is in blue and the foil on the fronts are also in blue. Each card is sequentially numbered to 500. There is also a Gold, Green, Purple and Red version that are also numbered to 500 and are only different by the colors on the fronts of the cards.

	MT
Complete Set (200):	600.00
Spectrum Blue Cards:	4x
Spectrum Blue Rookies:	1x
Production 500 Sets	

Prices and production are the same for Gold, Green, Purple and Red.

1999 Playoff Prestige SSD Alma Maters

Each of these horizontal cards picture two players that went to the same college and put them on a foil card. Singles were inserted 1:17 packs. A parallel Jumbo version was also produced and inserted as a box topper.

		MT
Complete Set (30):		185.00
Common Player:		4.00
Inserted 1:17		
Jumbos:		1x
One Per Box		
1	Priest Holmes, Ricky Williams	30.00
2	Tim Couch, Dermontti Dawson	30.00
3	Terrell Davis, Garrison Hearst	15.00
4	Troy Brown, Randy Moss	25.00
5	Barry Sanders, Thurman Thomas	25.00
6	Emmitt Smith, Fred Taylor	15.00
7	Doug Flutie, Bill Romanowski	8.00
8	Brett Favre, Michael Jackson	25.00
9	Charlie Batch, Ron Rice	8.00
10	Mark Brunell, Chris Chandler	8.00
11	Warrick Dunn, Deion Sanders	7.00
12	Cris Carter, Eddie George	7.00
13	Drew Bledsoe, Ryan Leaf	8.00
14	Corey Dillon, Napoleon Kaufman	4.00
15	Jerome Bettis, Tim Brown	4.00
16	Marshall Faulk, Darnay Scott	4.00
17	Tiki Barber, Herman Moore	4.00
18	Jamal Anderson, Chris Fuamatu-Ma'afala	4.00
19	Troy Aikman, Cade McNown	12.00
20	Brian Griese, Charles Woodson	8.00
21	Charles Johnson, Kordell Stewart	6.00
22	Kevin Faulk, Eddie Kennison	7.00
23	Donovan McNabb, Rob Moore	8.00
24	Steve McNair, John Thierry	6.00
25	Michael Irvin, Vinny Testaverde	4.00
26	Randall Cunningham, Keenan McCardell	4.00
27	Keyshawn Johnson, Junior Seau	6.00
28	Karim Abdul, Skip Hicks	4.00
29	Curtis Enis, O.J. McDuffie	4.00
30	Joey Galloway, Robert Smith	4.00

1999 Playoff Prestige SSD Checklist

Each NFL team has a card in this 31-card insert with a player from each team on the fronts of the foil singles. The backs have a small picture from each player on that team with their card number next to it. Singles were found 1:17 packs.

		MT
Complete Set (31):		200.00
Common Player:		2.50
Minor Stars:		5.00
Inserted 1:17		
1	Jake Plummer	12.00
2	Chris Chandler	2.50
3	Priest Holmes	6.00
4	Doug Flutie	8.00
5	Wesley Walls	2.50
6	Curtis Enis	5.00
7	Corey Dillon	5.00
8	Kevin Johnson	5.00
9	Troy Aikman	18.00
10	Terrell Davis	18.00
11	Barry Sanders	25.00
12	Antonio Freeman	5.00
13	Peyton Manning	18.00
14	Fred Taylor	12.00
15	Andre Rison	2.50
16	Dan Marino	18.00
17	Randy Moss	25.00
18	Kevin Faulk	8.00
19	Ricky Williams	25.00
20	Joe Montgomery	5.00
21	Vinny Testaverde	2.50
22	Tim Brown	5.00
23	Duce Staley	2.50
24	Jerome Bettis	5.00
25	Natrone Means	2.50
26	Terrell Owens	5.00
27	Joey Galloway	5.00
28	Isaac Bruce	5.00
29	Mike Alstott	5.00
30	Eddie George	6.00
31	Skip Hicks	5.00

1999 Playoff Prestige SSD Checklist Autographs

These cards are identical to the Checklist insert except for that each of these singles are autographed on the fronts. Each is sequentially numbered to 250.

		MT
Complete Set (31):		2000.
Common Player:		20.00
Minor Stars:		40.00
Production 250 Sets		
1	Jake Plummer	85.00
2	Chris Chandler	20.00
3	Priest Holmes	40.00
4	Doug Flutie	60.00
5	Wesley Walls	20.00
6	Curtis Enis	40.00
7	Corey Dillon	40.00
8	Kevin Johnson	40.00
9	Troy Aikman	120.00
10	Terrell Davis	150.00

#	Player	Price
11	Barry Sanders	250.00
12	Antonio Freeman	40.00
13	Peyton Manning	150.00
14	Fred Taylor	100.00
15	Andre Rison	20.00
16	Dan Marino	200.00
17	Randy Moss	250.00
18	Kevin Faulk	60.00
19	Ricky Williams	250.00
20	Joe Montgomery	40.00
21	Vinny Testaverde	20.00
22	Tim Brown	40.00
23	Duce Staley	20.00
24	Jerome Bettis	40.00
25	Natrone Means	20.00
26	Terrell Owens	50.00
27	Joey Galloway	50.00
28	Isaac Bruce	40.00
29	Mike Alstott	40.00
30	Eddie George	50.00
31	Skip Hicks	40.00

1999 Playoff Prestige SSD Draft Picks

Each card in this 30-card set is printed on a silver-foiled card with a blue foil background. Singles were inserted 1:9 packs.

		MT
Complete Set (30):		135.00
Common Player:		2.00
Minor Stars:		4.00
Inserted 1:9		
1	Tim Couch	30.00
2	Ricky Williams	30.00
3	Donovan McNabb	10.00
4	Edgerrin James	15.00
5	Champ Bailey	5.00
6	Torry Holt	8.00
7	Chris Claiborne	4.00
8	David Boston	8.00
9	Akili Smith	10.00
10	Daunte Culpepper	10.00
11	Peerless Price	5.00
12	Troy Edwards	6.00
13	Rob Konrad	2.00
14	Kevin Johnson	4.00
15	D'Wayne Bates	2.00
16	Cecil Collins	8.00
17	Amos Zereous	6.00
18	Shaun King	5.00
19	Cade McNown	10.00
20	Brock Huard	5.00
21	Sedrick Irvin	4.00
22	Chris McAlister	2.00
23	Kevin Faulk	8.00
24	Jevon Kearse	5.00
25	Joe Germaine	5.00
26	Andy Katzenmoyer	4.00
27	Joe Montgomery	4.00
28	Al Wilson	2.00
29	Jermaine Fazande	2.00
30	Ebenezer Ekuban	2.00

1999 Playoff Prestige SSD For the Record

Each card in this set has a player that broke a record in

1998 or projections for a player in 1999. They were printed on a holographic foil board with the name in gold foil. Singles were found 1:161 packs.

	MT
Complete Set (30):	750.00
Common Player:	15.00
Inserted 1:161	
1 Mark Brunell	30.00
2 Jerry Rice	40.00
3 Peyton Manning	50.00
4 Barry Sanders	70.00
5 Deion Sanders	15.00
6 Eddie George	20.00
7 Corey Dillon	15.00
8 Jerome Bettis	15.00
9 Curtis Martin	15.00
10 Ricky Williams	70.00
11 Jake Plummer	40.00
12 Emmitt Smith	50.00
13 Dan Marino	50.00
14 Terrell Davis	50.00
15 Fred Taylor	40.00
16 Warrick Dunn	20.00
17 Steve McNair	15.00
18 Cris Carter	15.00
19 Mike Alstott	15.00
20 Steve Young	25.00
21 Charlie Batch	25.00
22 Tim Couch	70.00
23 Jamal Anderson	15.00
24 Randy Moss	70.00
25 Brett Favre	70.00
26 Drew Bledsoe	30.00
27 Troy Aikman	40.00
28 John Elway	50.00
29 Kordell Stewart	20.00
30 Keyshawn Johnson	15.00

1999 Playoff Prestige SSD Gridiron Heritage

Each card in this 24-card set tracks the players career from high school to the NFL. Each is printed on actual leather and were inserted 1:33 packs.

	MT
Complete Set (24):	375.00
Common Player:	10.00
Inserted 1:33	
1 Randy Moss	40.00
2 Terrell Davis	30.00
3 Brett Favre	40.00
4 Barry Sanders	30.00
5 Peyton Manning	30.00
6 John Elway	30.00
7 Fred Taylor	20.00
8 Cris Carter	10.00
9 Jamal Anderson	10.00
10 Jake Plummer	20.00
11 Steve Young	15.00
12 Mark Brunell	15.00
13 Dan Marino	30.00
14 Emmitt Smith	30.00
15 Deion Sanders	10.00
16 Troy Aikman	20.00
17 Drew Bledsoe	15.00
18 Jerry Rice	20.00
19 Ricky Williams	40.00
20 Tim Couch	40.00
21 Jerome Bettis	10.00
22 Eddie George	12.00
23 Marshall Faulk	10.00
24 Terrell Owens	12.00

1999 Playoff Prestige SSD Inside the Numbers

Each card in this 20-card set is printed on clear plastic and each is sequentially numbered to a different number. Overall odds for these cards were 1:49 packs.

	MT
Complete Set (20):	300.00
Common Player:	10.00
Inserted 1:49	
1 Tim Brown 1012	10.00
2 Charlie Batch 2178	10.00
3 Deion Sanders 226	15.00
4 Eddie George 1294	15.00
5 Keyshawn Johnson 1131	15.00
6 Jamal Anderson 1846	10.00
7 Steve Young 4170	12.00
8 Tim Couch 4275	30.00
9 Ricky Williams 6279	25.00
10 Jerry Rice 1157	25.00
11 Randy Moss 1313	50.00
12 Edgerrin James 1416	30.00
13 Peyton Manning 3739	20.00
14 John Elway 2803	25.00
15 Terrell Davis 2008	25.00
16 Fred Taylor 1213	25.00
17 Brett Favre 4212	25.00
18 Jake Plummer 3737	12.00
19 Mark Brunell 2601	12.00
20 Barry Sanders 1491	50.00

1999 Playoff Prestige SSD Barry Sanders

This is a 10-card set that celebrates Sanders ten years of pursuit for the rushing record. Singles were found 1:161 packs.

	MT
Complete Set (10):	750.00
Common Player:	75.00
Inserted 1:161	

1985 Police Raiders/Rams

Broken down into two 15-card subsets for each team, the cards are not numbered, except with the player's uniform numerals. It was sponsored by KIIS Radio, the Rams and Raiders and the Los Angeles County Sheriff's Department. Card fronts include a photo of the player, with his name underneath, along with his team's helmet and sponsor logo. Card backs have the player's name, uniform number, position, bio and a safety message printed in black. The cards measure 2-13/16 x 4-1/8".

	MT
Complete Set (30):	20.00
Common Raiders (1-15):	.75
Common Rams (16-30):	.50
1 Marcus Allen	4.00
2 Lyle Alzado	1.50
3 Todd Christensen	1.00
4 Dave Dalby	.75
5 Mike Davis	.75
6 Ray Guy	1.00
7 Frank Hawkins	.75
8 Lester Hayes	1.00
9 Mike Haynes	1.00
10 Howie Long	2.00
11 Rod Martin	.75
12 Mickey Marvin	.75
13 Jim Plunkett	1.25
14 Brad Van Pelt	.75
15 Dokie Williams	.75
16 Bill Bain	.50
17 Mike Barber	.50
18 Dieter Brock	.75
19 Nolan Cromwell	.75
20 Eric Dickerson	3.00
21 Reggie Doss	.50
22 Carl Ekern	.50
23 Kent Hill	.50
24 LeRoy Irvin	.75
25 Johnnie Johnson	.50
26 Jeff Kemp	.50
27 Mike Lansford	.50
28 Mel Owens	.50
29 Barry Redden	.50
30 Mike Wilcher	.50

1986 Police Bears/Patriots

Featuring the two teams from Super Bowl XX, this 17-card set measures 2-5/8" x 4-1/4". The card fronts boast a photo of the player, with his name, uniform number and position at the bottom. The card

backs have "Super Bowl Superstars 1986 presents" at the top, with a safety tip listed at the bottom of the card. The card number is located in the lower right. Chicago players are on card #s 2-9, while New England players are highlighted on #s 10-17.

	MT
Complete Set (17):	15.00
Common Player:	.50
1 Title Card (Checklist on back of card)	.75
2 Richard Dent	2.00
3 Walter Payton	6.00
4 William Perry	1.00
5 Jim McMahon	1.50
6 Dave Duerson	.75
7 Gary Fencik	.75
8 Otis Wilson	.75
9 Willie Gault	1.00
10 Craig James	1.00
11 Fred Marion	.50
12 Ronnie Lippett	.50
13 Stanley Morgan	1.00
14 John Hannah	1.00
15 Andre Tippett	1.00
16 Tony Franklin	.50
17 Tony Eason	1.00

1976 Popsicle Teams

Each NFL team is represented in this 28-card set, which features a color action shot on the front of each card, plus the corresponding team's helmet. The back provides a historical overview of the team. The cards, which are unnumbered, are listed below alphabetically. Each one is 3-3/8" x 2-1/8" and resembles a thin plastic credit card with rounded corners. A title card, which says "Pro Quarterback, Pro Football's Leading Magazine," was also produced.

	NM
Complete Set (30):	40.00
Common Player:	2.50
(1) Atlanta Falcons	2.50
(2) Baltimore Colts	2.50
(3) Buffalo Bills	2.50
(4) Chicago Bears	2.50
(5) Cincinnati Bengals	2.50
(6) Cleveland Browns	2.50
(7) Dallas Cowboys	4.00
(8) Denver Broncos	2.50
(9) Detriot Lions	2.50
(10) Green Bay Packers	2.50
(11) Houston Oilers	2.50
(12) Kansas City Chiefs	2.50
(13) Los Angeles Rams	2.50
(14) Miami Dolphins	4.00
(15) Minnesota Vikings	2.50
(16) New England Patriots	2.50
(17) New Orleans Saints	2.50
(18A) New York Giants (Giants on helmet)	3.50
(18B) New York Giants (New York on helmet)	4.50
(19) New York Jets	2.50
(20) Oakland Raiders	4.00
(21) Philadelphia Eagles	2.50
(22) Pittsburgh Steelers	4.00
(23) St. Louis Cardinals	2.50
(24) San Diego Chargers	2.50
(25) San Francisco 49ers	3.00
(26) Seattle Seahawks	2.50
(27) Tampa Bay Buccaneers	2.50
(28) Washington Redskins	3.50
---- Title Card, Pro Quarterback	30.00

1962 Post Cereal

Post Cereal's only U.S. football issue, the 1962 set is complete at 200 cards. The blank-backed cards were printed on the back panels of various Post cereals and measure the standard 2-1/2" x 3-1/2" when properly cut. Like the Post Cereal baseball issues from the same period, the cards must be very carefully cut from the boxes to be considered in top condition. Players who were pictured on boxes of the less-popular cereals are scarcer

and more valuable, explaining the higher prices on about two dozen of the cards listed below.

	NM
Complete Set (200):	2500.
Common Player:	3.50
1 Dan Currie	3.50
2 Boyd Dowler	3.50
3 Bill Forester	3.50
4 Forrest Gregg	4.00
5 Dave Hanner	3.50
6 Paul Hornung	14.00
7 Henry Jordan	3.50
8 Jerry Kramer	12.00
9 Max McGee	3.50
10 Tom Moore	100.00
11 Jim Ringo	6.00
12 Bart Starr	20.00
13 Jim Taylor	12.00
14 Fred Thurston	3.50
15 Kess Whittenton	3.50
16 Erich Barnes	3.50
17 Roosevelt Grier	5.00
18 Bob Gaiters	3.50
19 Roosevelt Brown	5.00
20 Sam Huff	8.00
21 Jim Katcavage	3.50
22 Cliff Livingston	3.50
23 Dick Lynch	3.50
24 Joe Morrison	20.00
25 Dick Nolan	18.00
26 Andy Robustelli	5.00
27 Kyle Rote	7.00
28 Del Shofner	25.00
29 Y.A. Tittle	60.00
30 Alex Webster	3.50
31 Bill Barnes	3.50
32 Maxie Baughan	3.50
33 Chuck Bednarik	8.00
34 Tom Brookshier	6.00
35 Jimmy Carr	3.50
36 Ted Dean	3.50
37 Sonny Jurgensen	12.00
38 Tommy McDonald	3.50
39 Clarence Peaks	3.50
40 Pete Retzlaff	3.50
41 Jesse Richardson	30.00
42 Leo Sugar	3.50
43 Bobby Walston	40.00
44 Chuck Weber	3.50
45 Ed Khayat	3.50
46 Howard Cassady	3.50
47 Gail Cogdill	3.50
48 Jim Gibbons	3.50
49 Bill Glass	3.50
50 Alex Karras	3.50
51 Dick Lane	3.50
52 Yale Lary	3.50
53 Dan Lewis	3.50
54 Darris McCord	50.00
55 Jim Martin	3.50
56 Earl Morrall	3.50
57 Jim Ninowski	3.50
58 Nick Pietrosante	3.50
59 Joe Schmidt	50.00
60 Harley Sewell	3.50
61 Jim Brown	60.00
62 Galen Fiss	40.00
63 Bob Gain	3.50
64 Jim Houston	3.50
65 Mike McCormack	3.50
66 Gene Hickerson	3.50
67 Bob Mitchell	3.50
68 John Morrow	3.50
69 Bernie Parrish	3.50
70 Milt Plum	3.50
71 Ray Renfro	3.50
72 Dick Schafrath	3.50
73 Jim Ray Smith	3.50
74 Sam Baker	220.00
75 Paul Wiggin	3.50
76 Raymond Berry	3.50
77 Bob Boyd	3.50
78 Ordell Braase	3.50
79 Art Donovan	3.50
80 Dee Mackey	3.50
81 Gino Marchetti	3.50
82 Lenny Moore	3.50
83 Jim Mutscheller	3.50
84 Steve Myhra	3.50
85 Jimmy Orr	3.50
86 Jim Parker	3.50
87 Bill Pellington	3.50
88 Alex Sandusky	3.50
89 Dick Szymanski	3.50
90 Johnny Unitas	25.00
91 Bruce Bosley	3.50
92 John Brodie	12.00
93 Dave Baker	125.00
94 Tommy Davis	3.50
95 Bob Harrison	3.50
96 Matt Hazeltine	3.50
97 Jim Johnson	50.00
98 Bill Kilmer	8.00
99 Jerry Mertens	3.50
100 Frank Morze	3.50
101 R.C. Owens	3.50
102 J.D. Smith	3.50
103 Bob St. Clair	60.00
104 Monty Stickles	3.50
105 Abe Woodson	3.50
106 Doug Atkins	3.50
107 Ed Brown	3.50
108 J.C. Caroline	3.50
109 Rick Casares	3.50
110 Angelo Coia	175.00
111 Mike Ditka	20.00
112 Joe Fortunato	3.50
113 Willie Galimore	3.50
114 Bill George	5.50
115 Stan Jones	3.50
116 Johnny Morris	5.50
117 Larry Morris	40.00
118 Rich Pettibon	3.50
119 Bill Wade	4.00
120 Maury Youmans	3.50
121 Preston Carpenter	3.50
122 Buddy Dial	3.50
123 Bobby Joe Green	3.50
124 Mike Henry	3.50
125 John Henry Johnson	5.50
126 Bobby Layne	15.00
127 Gene Lipscomb	5.50
128 Lou Michaels	3.50
129 John Nisby	3.50
130 John Reger	3.50
131 Mike Sandusky	3.50
132 George Tarasovic	3.50
133 Tom Tracy	40.00
134 Glynn Gregory	3.50
135 Frank Clarke	40.00
136 Mike Connelly	40.00
137 L.G. Dupre	3.50
138 Bob Fry	3.50
139 Allen Green	60.00
140 Bill Howton	3.50
141 Bob Lilly	12.00
142 Don Meredith	16.00
143 Dick Moegle	3.50
144 Don Perkins	5.50
145 Jerry Tubbs	60.00
146 J.W. Lockett	3.50
147 Ed Cook	3.50
148 John David Crow	5.50
149 Sam Etcheverry	5.50
150 Frank Fuller	3.50
151 Prentice Gautt	3.50
152 Jimmy Hill	3.50
153 Bill Koman	3.50
154 Larry Wilson	5.50
155 Dale Meinert	3.50
156 Ed Henke	3.50
157 Sonny Randle	3.50
158 Ralph Guglielmi	40.00
159 Joe Childress	3.50
160 Jon Arnett	5.50
161 Dick Bass	3.50
162 Zeke Bratkowski	5.50
163 Carroll Dale	3.50
164 Art Hunter	3.50
165 John Lovetere	3.50
166 Lamar Lundy	3.50
167 Ollie Matson	8.00
168 Ed Meador	3.50
169 Jack Pardee	60.00
170 Jim Phillips	3.50
171 Les Richter	3.50
172 Frank Ryan	3.50
173 Frank Varrichione	3.50
174 Grady Alderman	3.50
175 Rip Hawkins	3.50
176 Don Joyce	60.00
177 Bill Lapham	3.50
178 Tommy Mason	3.50
179 Hugh McElhenny	3.50
180 Dave Middleton	3.50
181 Dick Pesonen	3.50
182 Karl Rubke	3.50
183 George Shaw	3.50
184 Fran Tarkenton	35.00
185 Mel Triplett	3.50
186 Frank Youso	40.00
187 Bill Bishop	3.50
188 Bill Anderson	40.00
189 Don Bosseler	3.50
190 Fred Hageman	3.50
191 Sam Horner	3.50
192 Jim Kerr	3.50
193 Joe Krakoski	150.00
194 Fred Dugan	3.50
195 John Paluck	3.50
196 Vince Promuto	3.50
197 Joe Rutgens	3.50
198 Norm Snead	5.50
199 Andy Stynchula	3.50
200 Bob Toneff	3.50

1962 Post Booklets

Measuring 5" x 3", each of the four booklets included 15 pages. The booklet covers include a drawing of the player, with his name, position and team, along with the title. The book covers are numbered to a different player, right with a prefix of "book."

	NM
Complete Set (4):	65.00
Common Player:	10.00
1 Football Formations To Watch (Jon Arnett) (Important Rules of the Game)	10.00
2 Fundamentals of Football (Paul Hornung)	25.00
3 How To Play On Offense (Sonny Jurgensen (How To Call Signals And Key Plays)	20.00
4 How To Play Defense (Sam Huff)	15.00

1977 Pottsville Maroons

This 1977 17-card set commemorates the 1925 NFL champion team with photos of the players on the front. The player's name, number and team are printed on the front of the card front. The back include the player's name, number, bio, position and career highlights. At the bottom of the card back is the 1977 copyright line, which attributes the set to the estate of Joseph C. Zacko Sr. and executor Russel F. Zacko.

	NM
Complete Set (17):	25.00
Common Player:	1.50
1 Team History	1.50
2 The Symbolic Shoe	1.50
3 Jack Ernst	1.50
4 Tony Latone	1.50
5 Duke Osborn	1.50
6 Frank Bucher	1.50
7 Frankie Racis	1.50
8 Russ Hathaway	1.50
9 W.H. Flanagan	1.50
10 Charlie Berry	3.00
11 Russ Stein, Herb Stein	1.50
12 Howard Lebengood	1.50
13 Denny Hughes	1.50
14 Barney Wentz	1.50
15 Eddie Doyle (UER) (Bio says American troops landed in Africa 1943; should be 1942)	1.50
16 Walter French	1.50
17 Dick Rauch	3.00

1994 Predators Arena Team Issue

This set was issued by the Orlando Predators of the Arena Football League and sold through their concession stands and gift shop. The cards are unnumbered.

	MT
Complete Set (27):	7.00
Common Player:	.25
1 Ben Bennett	.25
2 Henry Brown	.25
3 Webbie Burnett	.25
4 Jorge Cimadevilla	.25
5 Bernard Clark	.25
6 Wayne Dickson	.25
7 Eric Drakes	.25
8 Chris Ford	.25
9 Victor Hall	.25
10 Paul McGowan	.25
11 Perry Moss CO	.25
12 Jerry Odom	.25
13 Billy Owens	.25
14 Marshall Roberts	.25
15 Durwood Roquemore	.25
16 Rusty Russell DL	.25
17 Tony Scott	.25
18 Ricky Shaw	.25
19 Alex Shell	.25
20 Bill Stewart	.25
21 Duke Tobin	.25
22 Barry Wagner	.25
23 Jackie Walker	.25
24 Herkie Walls	.25
25 Isaac Williams	.25
26 Coaches	.25
27 The Klaw (mascot)	.25

1994 Press Pass SB Photo Board

Measuring 10" x 14", these Photo Boards showcased color photos of both Buffalo and Dallas players on the front, along with the Super Bowl logo in gold foil. Each of the boards are individually numbered of 50,000. The product was sold at the Super Bowl Card Show in Atlanta. The backs include photos and statistic leaders in both conferences.

		MT
Complete Set (1):		10.00
Common Panel:		10.00
1	SB XXVIII Photo Board	10.00
	(John Elway, Rick Mirer, Reggie Langhorne, Neil Smith, Nate Odomes, Thurman, (Sterling Sharpe, Reggie White, Deion Sanders, Emmitt Smith)	

1996 Press Pass

Top rookies slated to make NFL debuts in 1996 are featured in this 55-card 1996 Press Pass Football Draft Picks set, the company's first devoted to football. Each card front has a pair of color action photos on it, along with gold foil stamping which is used for the player's name at the bottom and the brand logo in the upper left corner. The back has the player's name, college and card number at the top, with a box below with information about his college career. In the center is a circle with statistics around the diameter and a color photo in the center. Another box below the photo has biographical information in it. Three parallel sets were also created. First, autographed versions of all 55 cards are available at a rate of one per every 72 packs. Next, Emerald Proofs were limited to only 380 of each card, with an insertion rate of one per every 36 packs. Last, each pack includes a Holofoil version of the set, which features a holographic finish on the front. Insert sets include Crystal Ball, and four different denominations of Prime Time Phone cards of nine different players.

	MT
Complete Set (55):	25.00
Common Player:	.25
1 Keyshawn Johnson	3.00
2 Jonathan Ogden	.25
3 Duane Clemons	.25
4 Kevin Hardy	.25
5 Eddie George	5.00
6 Karim Abdul-Jabbar	1.50
7 Terry Glenn	1.50
8 Leeland McElroy	1.00
9 Simeon Rice	.25
10 Roman Oben	.25
11 Daryl Gardener	.25
12 Marcus Coleman	.25
13 Christian Peter	.25
14 Tim Biakabutuka	1.00
15 Eric Moulds	.75
16 Chris Darkins	.50
17 Andre Johnson	.25
18 Lawyer Milloy	.25
19 Jon Runyan	.25
20 Mike Alstott	.50
21 Jeff Hartings	.25
22 Amani Toomer	.75
23 Danny Kanell	.75
24 Marco Battaglia	.50
25 Stephen Davis	.75
26 Johnny McWilliams	.50
27 Israel Ifeanyi	.25
28 Scott Slutzker	.50
29 Bryant Mix	.25
30 Brian Roche	.25
31 Stanley Pritchett	.25
32 Jerome Woods	.25
33 Tommie Frazier	.25
34 Stepfret Williams	.25
35 Ray Mickens	.25
36 Alex Van Dyke	.50
37 Bobby Hoying	.50
38 Tony Brackens	.25
39 Dietrich Jells	.25
40 Jason Odom	.25
41 Randall Godfrey	.25
42 Willie Anderson	.25
43 Tony Banks	.25
44 Michael Cheever	.25
45 Jerod Cherry	.25
46 Chris Doering	.25
47 Steve Taneyhill	.25
48 Kyle Wachholz	.25
49 Dusty Zeigler	.25
50 Derrick Mayes	.50
51 Orpheus Roye	.25
52 Sedric Clark	.25
53 Richard Huntley	.25
54 Donnie Edwards	.25
55 Zach Thomas	.25

1996 Press Pass Holofoil

The 55-card, standard-size set was issued as a parallel to the base Press Pass set. The cards were inserted in each pack and featured holofoil stock.

	MT
Complete Set (55):	50.00
Common Player:	.30
Stars:	2x

1996 Press Pass Holofoil Emerald Proofs

The 55-card, standard-size set was issued as a parallel to the base set. Inserted every 36 packs, the cards feature holofoil stock with "Emerald Proof" printed on each card front. Production of each card was limited to just 280.

	MT
Complete Set (55):	375.00
Common Player:	1.00
Stars:	8x-16x

1996 Press Pass Autographs

The 12-card, standard-size set, inserted every 72 packs, is similar to the base cards, except with the player's autograph on the card front. The card backs inform the collector that he/she has received a "limited edition" signed card.

	MT
Complete Set (12):	200.00

1996 Press Pass Crystal Ball

These 1996 Press Pass inserts were seeded one per 18 packs. The die-cut cards, numbered using a "CB" prefix, have a crystal ball on the front with a player photo inside. His name is written along the base of the crystal ball. The back has the player's name inside the ball with an analysis of the player's talents. The card number is in a circle in the lower left corner.

	MT
Complete Set (12):	120.00
Common Player:	5.00
1 Lawyer Milloy	5.00
2 Terry Glenn	15.00
3 Duane Clemons	5.00
4 Kevin Hardy	5.00
5 Eddie George	25.00
6 Jonathan Ogden	5.00
7 Karim Abdul-Jabbar	15.00
8 Tim Biakabutuka	12.00
9 Eric Moulds	8.00
10 Danny Kanell	6.00
11 Israel Ifeanyi	5.00
12 Keyshawn Johnson	40.00

1996 Press Pass Prime Time Phone Cards

Four different denominations - $5, $10, $20 and $1,996 - are used for these Prime Time Phone cards, found one every 36 packs of 1996 Press Pass Football Draft Picks product. Nine players are featured on the cards, which have a color action photo on the front, plus the denomination. The back, numbered using a "PT" prefix, has instructions on how to use the card.

	MT
Complete Set (9):	120.00
Common Player:	10.00
Ten Dollar Cards:	2x-4x
Twenty Dollar Cards:	3x-6x
1 Keyshawn Johnson	30.00
2 Jonathan Ogden	10.00
3 Tommie Frazier	12.00
4 Eddie George	20.00
5 Karim Abdul-Jabbar	15.00
6 Terry Glenn	15.00
7 Leeland McElroy	12.00
8 Tim Biakabutuka	18.00
9 Kevin Hardy	10.00

1996 Press Pass Paydirt

The 75-card, standard-size set was issued in five-card packs. The set is the retail version and includes inserts such as: Paydirt Holofoil, Paydirt Red Foil, Paydirt Autographs and Paydirt Eddie George.

	MT
Complete Set (75):	30.00
Common Player:	.10
1 Keyshawn Johnson	4.00
2 Jonathan Ogden	.25
3 Duane Clemons	.40
4 Kevin Hardy	.50
5 Eddie George	3.50
6 Karim Abdul-Jabbar	2.00
7 Terry Glenn	3.00
8 Leeland McElroy	2.00
9 Simeon Rice	.40
10 Roman Oben	.10
11 Daryl Gardener	.40
12 Marcus Coleman	.10
13 Christian Peter	.10
14 Tim Biakabutuka	3.00
15 Eric Moulds	1.25
16 Chris Darkins	1.00
17 Andre Johnson	.10
18 Lawyer Milloy	.25
19 Jon Runyan	.10
20 Mike Alstott	1.50
21 Jeff Hartings	.10
22 Amani Toomer	1.25
23 Danny Kanell	1.25
24 Marco Battaglia	.60
25 Stephen Davis	1.00
26 Johnny McWilliams	.40
27 Israel Ifeanyi	.10
28 Scott Slutzker	.10
29 Bryant Mix	.10
30 Brian Roche	.10
31 Stanley Pritchett	.40
32 Jerome Woods	.10
33 Tommie Frazier	1.50
34 Stepfret Williams	.75
35 Ray Mickens	.10
36 Alex Van Dyke	1.00
37 Bobby Hoying	1.25
38 Tony Brackens	.10
39 Dietrich Jells	.10
40 Jason Odom	.10
41 Randall Godfrey	.25
42 Willie Anderson	.25
43 Tony Banks	.75
44 Michael Cheever	.10
45 Je'Rod Cherry	.25
46 Chris Doering	.25
47 Steve Taneyhill	.40
48 Kyle Wachholz	.40
49 Dusty Zeigler	.10
50 Derrick Mayes	1.25
51 Orpheus Roye	.10
52 Sedric Clark	.10
53 Richard Huntley	.10
54 Donnie Edwards	.10
55 Zach Thomas	.10
56 Alex Molden	.30
57 Jimmy Herndon	.10
58 Mike Alstott	1.50
59 Scott Greene	.40
60 Danny Kanell	1.25
61 Jonathan Ogden	.25
62 Simeon Rice	.40
63 Kevin Hardy	.50
64 Jon Runyan	.10
65 Stephen Davis	1.00
66 Tim Biakabutuka	3.00
67 Terry Glenn	3.00
68 Leeland McElroy	2.00
69 Eric Moulds	1.25
70 Karim Abdul-Jabbar	2.00
71 Lawyer Milloy	.25
72 Derrick Mayes	1.25
73 Tommie Frazier	1.50
74 Bobby Hoying	1.25
75 Kyle Wachholz (CL)	.10

1996 Press Pass Paydirt Holofoil

The 75-card, standard-size set, a parallel to the base set with holofoil paper, was inserted every four packs.

	MT
Complete Set (75):	125.00
Common Player:	.40
Stars:	2x-4x

1996 Press Pass Paydirt Red Foil

The 75-card, regular-size set was inserted in each pack of Paydirt and was also known as Torquers. The foil wrappers incorrectly describe the parallel set as having "blue foil."

	MT
Complete Set (75):	60.00

1996 Press Pass Paydirt Autographs

The 16-card, standard-size set was inserted every 72 packs of Paydirt. The card fronts contain the player's autograph while the backs inform the collectors of his/her pull. The cards are unnumbered.

	MT
Complete Set (16):	250.00
Common Player:	10.00
1 Karim Abdul-Jabbar	35.00
2 Tony Banks	30.00
3 Tim Biakabutuka	20.00
4 Duane Clemons	10.00
5 Stephen Davis	30.00
6 Chris Doering	10.00
7 Bobby Hoying	25.00
8 Keyshawn Johnson	30.00
9 Danny Kanell	15.00
10 Derrick Mayes	15.00
11 Leeland McElroy	20.00
12 Lawyer Milloy	10.00
13 Eric Moulds	15.00
14 Jonathan Ogden	10.00
15 Steve Taneyhill	10.00
16 Alex Van Dyke	15.00

1996 Press Pass Paydirt Eddie George

The four-card, standard-size set features the 1995 Heisman Trophy winner. The cards were inserted into packs at a progressive insertion rate. Card No. 1 was every 36 packs; card No. 2 was every 72; card No. 3 every 216; and card No. 4 every 864 packs. The cards are numbered with the "EG" prefix.

	MT
Complete Set (4):	150.00
Common Player:	7.00
1 Eddie George	7.00
2 Eddie George	14.00
3 Eddie George	40.00
4 Eddie George	125.00

1996 Press Pass Paydirt Game Breakers

The 12-card, standard-size set was inserted every 18 packs and features players who excelled in college. The cards are numbered with the "GB" prefix.

	MT
Complete Set (12):	70.00
Common Player:	4.00
1 Lawyer Milloy	4.00
2 Terry Glenn	15.00
3 Duane Clemons	4.00
4 Kevin Hardy	6.00
5 Eddie George	18.00
6 Jonathan Ogden	4.00
7 Karim Abdul-Jabbar	12.00
8 Tim Biakabutuka	10.00
9 Eric Moulds	8.00
10 Danny Kanell	6.00
11 Leeland McElroy	8.00
12 Keyshawn Johnson	10.00

1997 Press Pass

The 55-card set features full-bleed fronts, with the player's name, position and Press

	MT
Common Player:	.20
Stars:	1x-2x

Pass logo at the bottom in gold foil. The backs have a player photo on the left over a "groovy" multicolored background. The player's name, bio, highlights and stats are printed on the right side. Red Zone is a red-foil parallel that was inserted 1:1 hobby packs. Torquers, which is a blue-foil parallel, was inserted 1:1 mass market packs. In addition, a 50-card all-foil die-cut "set within a set" was inserted 1:1 pack.

	MT
Complete Set (50):	15.00
Common Player:	.10
Minor Stars:	.20
1 Orlando Pace	.75
2 Warrick Dunn	2.00
3 Danny Wuerffel	.50
4 Darnell Autry	.30
5 Troy Davis	.30
6 Jake Plummer	3.00
7 Corey Dillon	2.00
8 Reidel Anthony	1.25
9 Byron Hanspard	.75
10 Tiki Barber	.75
11 Ike Hilliard	1.25
12 Rae Carruth	.30
13 Yatil Green	.30
14 Peter Boulware	.10
15 Jim Druckenmiller	.50
16 Pat Barnes	.20
17 Trevor Pryce	.10
18 Kevin Lockett	.10
19 Koy Detmer	.20
20 Bryant Westbrook	.40
21 Darrell Russell	.20
22 Tony Gonzalez	.75
23 Shawn Springs	.50
24 Chris Canty	.10
25 David LaFleur	.50
26 Dwayne Rudd	.10
27 Bob Sapp	.10
28 Mike Vrabel	.10
29 Antowain Smith	1.00
30 Keith Poole	.10
31 Sedrick Shaw	.10
32 Tremain Mack	.10
33 Matt Russell	.10
34 Reinard Wilson	.10
35 Marc Edwards	.10
36 Greg Jones	.10
37 Michael Booker	.10
38 James Farrior	.10
39 Danny Wuerffel	.75
40 Troy Davis	.50
41 Corey Dillon	1.00
42 Jake Plummer	1.50
43 Peter Boulware, Reinard Wilson	.10
44 Eddie Robinson	.20
45 Bobby Bowden	.75
46 Steve Spurrier	1.00
47 Gary Barnett	.10
48 Checklist (Tom Osborne)	.50
49 Checklist (Jarrett Irons)	.10

1997 Press Pass Combine

Combine was a 50-card parallel set to the Press Pass Draft Picks set that was included one per pack. These die-cut cards were printed on silver foil and include towers up both sides. The word "Combine" and the player's name is printed in red letters across the bottom.

	MT
Combine Cards:	2x

> Post-1980 cards in Near Mint condition will generally sell for about 75% of the quoted Mint value. Excellent-condition cards bring no more than 40%.

1997 Press Pass Red Zone

Red Zone was another parallel set to the 50-card Press Pass Draft Picks. These parallels were identical to base cards except they were printed with red foil on the front instead of the gold foil used on base cards. Red Zone parallels were inserted one per pack.

		MT
Red Zone Cards:		2x

1997 Press Pass Big 12

Inserted 1:12 packs, the 12-card set features a player photo superimposed over an etched foil background. The player's name, chase set name and Press Pass logo are printed at the bottom of the card front. The backs include a player photo over a "sun ray" background. The player's name and highlights are printed inside a box along the right side. The cards are numbered with a prefix of "B".

		MT
Complete Set (12):		45.00
Common Player:		2.00
1	Orlando Pace	5.00
2	Peter Boulware	2.00
3	Shawn Springs	4.00
4	Warrick Dunn	12.00
5	Dwayne Rudd	2.00
6	Rae Carruth	6.00
7	Bryant Westbrook	4.00
8	Darrell Russell	2.00
9	Yatil Green	6.00
10	David LaFleur	4.00
11	Jim Druckenmiller	8.00
12	Reidel Anthony	6.00

1997 Press Pass Can't Miss

The six-card foil set was inserted on a progressive scale.

Card No. 1 was inserted 1:720, while No. 2 was seeded at 1:360. The rest were as follows: No. 3 1:180, No. 4 1:90, No. 5 1:45 and No. 6 1:36. The player's photo is superimposed over a foil background. A football field and X's and O's also appear on the front. The Can't Miss logo and the player's name are printed at the bottom. The backs have a photo of each of the six players. The numbers have a prefix of "CM".

		MT
Complete Set (6):		225.00
Common Player:		10.00
1	Warrick Dunn	100.00
2	Jim Druckenmiller	60.00
3	Yatil Green	45.00
4	Orlando Pace	30.00
5	Rae Carruth	20.00
6	Peter Boulware	10.00

1997 Press Pass Head-Butt

Inserted 1:18 packs, the nine-card set features the player's photo superimposed over the player's college helmet. The Head Butt logo is in gold foil at the bottom, while the player's name is printed inside a gold-foil stripe at the bottom center. The backs have the player's photo printed over his college helmet. The bottom of the card back has the player's name and his highlights. The card numbers carry a prefix of "HB". A die-cut parallel version is randomly seeded 1:36 packs.

		MT
Complete Set (9):		60.00
Common Player:		3.00
Die Cuts:		2x
1	Warrick Dunn	16.00
2	Orlando Pace	8.00
3	Troy Davis	10.00
4	Reidel Anthony	10.00
5	Rae Carruth	10.00
6	Yatil Green	10.00
7	Corey Dillon	3.00
8	Danny Wuerffel	12.00
9	Darnell Autry	8.00

1997 Press Pass Marquee Matchups

Inserted 1:18 packs, the nine-card set features two players on the front, with their names printed at the bottom in prism foil. "Marquee Matchup" is printed in black inside a prism stripe at the bottom of the front. The backs have two player photos, their names and highlights. The card numbers are prefixed by "MM".

		MT
Complete Set (9):		40.00
Common Player:		2.00
1	Jim Druckenmiller, Danny Wuerffel	12.00
2	Warrick Dunn, Corey Dillon	10.00
3	Darnell Autry, Troy Davis	8.00
4	Byron Hanspard, Tiki Barber	6.00
5	Reidel Anthony, Bryant Westbrook	5.00
6	Orlando Pace, Peter Boulware	4.00
7	Rae Carruth, Ike Hilliard	5.00
8	Yatil Green, Shawn Springs	5.00
9	David LaFleur, Tony Gonzalez	2.00

1998 Press Pass

Press Pass Draft Picks Football contained 50 cards in 1998, with 45 players eligible for the 1998 NFL Draft, four coaches and a checklist card featuring Peyton Manning. Cards featured a black strip across the bottom identifying the player, with his position and several logo above over the bottom of the player photograph. The set was paralleled in Paydirt (hobby), Pickoffs (retail), Reflectors and Reflector Solos sets. Inserts include: Fields of Fury, Head Butt, Jerseys, Kick-off, Triple Threat and Trophy Case.

		MT
Complete Set (50):		18.00
Common Player:		.10
Minor Stars:		.20
Wax Box:		60.00
1	Peyton Manning	3.50
2	Ryan Leaf	2.50
3	Charles Woodson	1.50
4	Andre Wadsworth	.75
5	Randy Moss	5.00
6	Curtis Enis	1.50
7	T. Thomas	.10
8	Flozell Adams	.10
9	Jason Peter	.10
10	Brian Simmons	.10
11	Takeo Spikes	.10
12	Michael Myers	.10
13	Kevin Dyson	.75
14	Grant Wistrom	.10
15	Fred Taylor	2.00
16	Germane Crowell	.75
17	Sam Cowart	.10
18	Anthony Simmons	.10
19	Robert Edwards	1.50
20	Shawn Williams	.10
21	Phil Savoy	.10
22	Leonard Little	.10
23	Saladin McCullough	.10
24	Duane Starks	.10
25	John Avery	.75
26	Vonnie Holliday	.10
27	Tim Dwight	.50
28	Donovin Darius	.10
29	Alonzo Mayes	.30
30	Jerome Pathon	.30
31	Brian Kelly	.10
32	Hines Ward	.50
33	Jacquez Green	.75
34	Marcus Nash	.75
35	Ahman Green	.75
36	Joe Jurevicius	.50
37	Tavian Banks	1.00
38	Donald Hayes	.30
39	Robert Holcombe	.75
40	Eric Green	.50
41	John Dutton	.30
42	Skip Hicks	.75
43	Patrick Johnson	.10
44	Keith Brooking	.10
45	Alan Faneca	.10
46	Steve Spurrier	1.00
47	Mike Price	.10
48	Bobby Bowden	.75
49	Tom Osborne	1.00
50	Manning - Checklist	1.50

1998 Press Pass Paydirt

Paydirt included all 50 cards, but were distinguised by red foil stamping versus the gold used on base cards. These were found in hobby packs only and inserted one per pack.

		MT
Paydirt Cards:		2x

1998 Press Pass Pickoff

Pickoff included parallel versions of all 50 cards, but were distinguished by silver foil stamping on the front versus the gold foil used on base cards. These were retail exclusive and inserted one per pack.

		MT
Pickoff Cards:		2x

1998 Press Pass Reflectors

This 50-card parallel set was seeded one per 180 packs and arrived with a protective covering over the card. This covering could be peeled back to reveal a holofoil finish. Reflectors were numbered with a "R" prefix. In addition, Solos versions of Reflectors were also available, with only one existing set. These were distinguised by a "Solos 1 of 1" stamp on the card back.

		MT
Reflector Cards:		25x-50x

1998 Press Pass Autographs

Autographed versions of Press Pass cards were seeded one per 18 hobby packs and one

per 36 retail packs. They were similar to base cards, except for a faded area across the bottom of the photograph that included the player's signature. Backs were green, with the word "Autograph" in large white letters and a paragraph that congratulated the collector and certified the card. Autographs were unnumbered and are listed in alphabetical order.

		MT
Complete Set (38):		300.00
Common Player:		8.00
Minor Stars:		12.00
1	John Avery	12.00
2	Tavian Banks	20.00
3	Bobby Bowden	20.00
4	Germane Crowell	20.00
5	Donovin Darius	8.00
6	Tim Dwight	15.00
7	Kevin Dyson	20.00
8	Robert Edwards	30.00
9	Curtis Enis	30.00
10	Alan Faneca	8.00
11	Ahman Green	20.00
12	Jacquez Green	25.00
13	Donald Hayes	12.00
14	Skip Hicks	15.00
15	Robert Holcombe	12.00
16	Vonnie Holliday	15.00
17	Patrick Johnson	8.00
18	Joe Jurevicius	15.00
19	Brian Kelly	8.00
20	Ryan Leaf	50.00
21	Peyton Manning	100.00
22	Alonzo Mayes	12.00
23	Randy Moss	125.00
24	Michael Myers	8.00
25	Marcus Nash	15.00
26	Tom Osborne	25.00
27	Jason Peter	8.00
28	Mike Price	8.00
29	Phil Savoy	12.00
30	Anthony Simmons	8.00
31	Brian Simmons	8.00
32	Takeo Spikes	12.00
33	Steve Spurrier	25.00
34	Fred Taylor	40.00
35	Andre Wadsworth	15.00
36	Hines Ward	15.00
37	Shaun Williams	8.00
38	Grant Wistrom	8.00

1998 Press Pass Fields of Fury

This horizontal, nine-card set featured the player off to the right side, with a game highlight of him roughly bordered in black across the majority of the card. Fields of Fury were numbered with a "FF" prefix and inserted one per 36 packs.

		MT
Complete Set (9):		90.00
Common Player:		7.00
1	Peyton Manning	30.00
2	Marcus Nash	10.00
3	Ryan Leaf	12.00
4	Randy Moss	40.00
5	Robert Edwards	8.00
6	Curtis Enis	10.00
7	Kevin Dyson	10.00
8	Fred Taylor	12.00
9	Jacquez Green	7.00

Values quoted in this guide reflect the retail price of a card — the price a collector can expect to pay when buying a card from a dealer. The wholesale price — that which a collector can expect to receive when selling cards — will be significantly lower, depending on desirability and condition.

1998 Press Pass Head Butt

Head Butt was a nine-card insert that included a film-like shot of the player over a black background, with his embossed college team helmet at the bottom center. These were numbered with a "HB" prefix and inserted one per 18 packs. Die-cut versions were seeded one per 36 packs.

		MT
Complete Set (9):		50.00
Common Player:		3.00
Die-Cut Cards:		2x
1	Peyton Manning	18.00
2	Charles Woodson	8.00
3	Ryan Leaf	7.00
4	Curtis Enis	8.00
5	Jacquez Green	3.00
6	Ahman Green	3.00
7	Randy Moss	20.00
8	Tavian Banks	6.00
9	Robert Edwards	7.00

1998 Press Pass Jerseys

Jerseys was a four-card insert that featured a swatch of the player's game-used college jersey embedded in the front. These were sequentially numbered to 425 sets, numbered with a "JC" prefix and inserted one per 720 packs.

		MT
Complete Set (4):		500.00
Common Player:		70.00
PM	Peyton Manning	200.00
RL	Ryan Leaf	125.00
KD	Kevin Dyson	70.00
TB	Tavian Banks	70.00

1998 Press Pass Kick-Off

Kick-Off included 36 of the players from the base set on a die-cut, football-shaped card. The player's image and the football were both embossed. These were numbered with a "KO" prefix and inserted one per pack in both hobby and retail.

		MT
Complete Set (36):		30.00
Common Player:		.20
1	Peyton Manning	6.00
2	Ryan Leaf	3.00
3	Charles Woodson	3.00
4	Andre Wadsworth	1.50
5	Randy Moss	8.00
6	Curtis Enis	3.00
7	Donald Hayes	.20
8	Flozell Adams	.20
9	Jason Peter	.20
10	Brian Simmons	.20
11	Takeo Spikes	.20

12	Germane Crowell	.20
13	Donovin Darius	.20
14	Grant Wistrom	.20
15	Alonzo Mayes	.20
16	Kevin Dyson	1.50
17	John Avery	1.50
18	Anthony Simmons	.20
19	Robert Edwards	1.50
20	Shaun Williams	.20
21	Leonard Little	.20
22	Skip Hicks	1.50
23	Phil Savoy	.20
24	Tavian Banks	2.00
25	Robert Holcombe	1.00
26	Eric Green	1.00
27	Tim Dwight	.20
28	Saladin McCullough	.20
29	Fred Taylor	1.50
30	Jerome Pathon	.20
31	Brian Kelly	.20
32	Hines Ward	1.00
33	Jacquez Green	1.00
34	Marcus Nash	1.50
35	Ahman Green	1.50
36	Joe Jurevicius	.20

1998 Press Pass Triple Threat

This nine-card insert featured three different players, with each having three different fit-together cards to form a three-card panel. They were numbered with a "TT" prefix and inserted one per 12 packs.

		MT
Complete Set (9):		40.00
Common Player:		3.00
1	Peyton Manning	8.00
2	Peyton Manning	8.00
3	Peyton Manning	8.00
4	Ryan Leaf	6.00
5	Ryan Leaf	6.00
6	Ryan Leaf	6.00
7	Charles Woodson	3.00
8	Charles Woodson	3.00
9	Charles Woodson	3.00

1998 Press Pass Trophy Case

This 12-card insert was printed on silver foilboard, with the player's name across the top and the insert name across the bottom. Trophy Case cards are numbered with a "TC" prefix and inserted one per nine packs.

		MT
Complete Set (12):		40.00
Common Player:		2.00
1	Peyton Manning	12.00
2	Ryan Leaf	6.00
3	Charles Woodson	6.00
4	Randy Moss	16.00
5	Curtis Enis	6.00
6	Grant Wistrom	4.00
7	Kevin Dyson	4.00
8	Fred Taylor	6.00
9	Tavian Banks	4.00
10	Ahman Green	2.00
11	Skip Hicks	4.00
12	Andre Wadsworth	4.00

1999 Press Pass

This 45-card set includes all of the top draft picks from 1999. Each is pictured in his college uniform and each name is in gold foil. Three parallel sets were made with Paydirt, Torquers and Reflectors. Other inserts include: Autographs, Big Numbers, Game Jerseys, Goldenarm, Hardware and X's and O's.

		MT
Complete Set (45):		20.00
Common Player:		.10
Minor Stars:		.20
Paydirt Cards:		1.5x
Inserted 1:1 Hobby		
Torquer Cards:		1.5x
Inserted 1:1 Mass		
Reflector Cards:		12x-24x
Inserted 1:180		
Wax Box:		45.00
1	Ricky Williams	3.00
2	Tim Couch	3.00
3	Champ Bailey	.50
4	Chris Claiborne	.20
5	Donovan McNabb	2.00
6	Edgerrin James	5.00
7	Akili Smith	2.00
8	John Tait	.10
9	Jevon Kearse	1.00
10	Torry Holt	1.25
11	Troy Edwards	1.25
12	Chris McAlister	.20
13	Daunte Culpepper	2.00
14	Andy Katzenmoyer	.20
15	David Boston	1.25
16	Ebenezer Ekuban	.10
17	Peerless Price	.75
18	Shaun King	2.00
19	Joe Germaine	.30
20	Brock Huard	.50
21	Michael Bishop	.50
22	Amos Zereoue	.30
23	Sedrick Irvin	.50
24	Autry Denson	.20
25	Kevin Faulk	.50
26	James Johnson	.50
27	D'Wayne Bates	.20
28	Kevin Johnson	1.25
29	Tai Streets	.30
30	Craig Yeast	.20
31	Dre Bly	.10
32	Anthony Poindexter	.10
33	Jared DeVries	.10
34	Rob Konrad	.20
35	Dat Nguyen	.10
36	Cade McNown	2.00
37	Scott Covington	.20
38	Jon Jansen	.10
39	Rufus French	.10
40	Mike Rucker	.10
41	Aaron Gibson	.10
42	Kris Farris	.10
43	Anthony McFarland	.10
44	Matt Stinchcomb	.10
45	Checklist (Dee Miller)	.10

1999 Press Pass Autographs

Each autographed card in this set has the same photo as his base card but the name is in smaller type and the autograph is above it. Singles were inserted 1:16 packs.

		MT
Complete Set (50):		750.00
Common Player:		6.00
Minor Stars:		12.00
Inserted 1:16 Hobby		
Inserted 1:36 Retail		
	Champ Bailey	15.00
	D'Wayne Bates	12.00
	Michael Bishop	15.00
	Dre Bly	6.00
	David Boston	25.00
	Chris Claiborne	12.00
	Mike Cloud	12.00
	Tim Couch	75.00
	Scott Covington	12.00
	Daunte Culpepper	35.00
	Autry Denson	12.00
	Jared DeVries	6.00
	Antwan Edwards	12.00
	Troy Edwards	25.00
	Ebenezer Ekuban	6.00
	Kris Farris	6.00
	Kevin Faulk	15.00
	Rufus French	6.00
	Joe Germaine	12.00
	Aaron Gibson	6.00
	Torry Holt	25.00
	Brock Huard	15.00
	Sedrick Irvin	15.00
	Edgerrin James	100.00
	Jon Jansen	6.00
	James Johnson	15.00
	Kevin Johnson	25.00
	Andy Katzenmoyer	12.00
	Jevon Kearse	20.00
	Shaun King	35.00
	Rob Konrad	12.00
	Chris McAlister	12.00
	Darnell McDonald	12.00
	Anthony McFarland	6.00
	Donovan McNabb	35.00
	Cade McNown	35.00
	Dee Miller	6.00
	Dat Nguyen	6.00
	Mike Peterson	6.00
	Anthony Poindexter	6.00
	Peerless Price	20.00
	Mike Rucker	6.00
	Akili Smith	35.00
	Matt Stinchcomb	6.00
	Tai Streets	12.00
	John Tait	6.00
	Jerame Tuman	6.00
	Ricky Williams	75.00
	Craig Yeast	6.00
	Amos Zereoue	12.00

1999 Press Pass Big Numbers

Each card in this 9-card set is printed on foil board with a photo of the player and the number that he was drafted in the background. Singles were inserted 1:16 packs. A parallel Die Cut version was also made with each single the same except for die cut. Those were found 1:32 packs.

		MT
Complete Set (9):		30.00
Common Player:		2.50
Inserted 1:16		
Die-Cut Cards:		2x
Inserted 1:32		
1	Tim Couch	7.00
2	Ricky Williams	7.00
3	Donovan McNabb	5.00
4	Edgerrin James	10.00
5	Peerless Price	3.00
6	Amos Zereoue	2.50
7	Daunte Culpepper	5.00
8	Tai Streets	2.50
9	Akili Smith	5.00

A player's name in *italic type* indicates a rookie card.

1999 Press Pass Goldenarm

Each card in this 9-card set is horizontal and includes the top quarterbacks drafted in 1999. They were printed on foil board and were inserted 1:10 packs.

		MT
Complete Set (9):		25.00
Common Player:		1.50
Inserted 1:10		
1	Tim Couch	7.00
2	Donovan McNabb	4.00
3	Akili Smith	4.00
4	Daunte Culpepper	4.00
5	Cade McNown	4.00
6	Brock Huard	1.50
7	Joe Germaine	1.50
8	Shaun King	4.00
9	Michael Bishop	2.00

1999 Press Pass Hardware

Only the top rookies were included in this 12-card insert that was inserted 1:8 packs.

		MT
Complete Set (12):		30.00
Common Player:		1.50
Inserted 1:8		
1	Cade McNown	3.50
2	Ricky Williams	7.00
3	Torry Holt	2.00
4	Tim Couch	7.00
5	David Boston	2.00
6	Troy Edwards	2.00
7	Michael Bishop	1.50
8	Mike Cloud	1.50
9	Champ Bailey	1.50
10	Kevin Faulk	1.50
11	Autry Denson	1.50
12	Donovan McNabb	3.50

1999 Press Pass Jersey Cards

Each single in this 6-card set features a piece of game-used jersey on the card. Singles were found 1:640 packs.

		MT
Complete Set (6):		425.00
Common Player:		40.00
Inserted 1:640 Hobby		
Inserted 1:720 Mass		
TC	Tim Couch	175.00
DC	Daunte Culpepper	80.00
TH	Torry Holt	60.00
AS	Akili Smith	80.00
CM	Cade McNown	80.00
PP	Peerless Price	40.00

A card number in parentheses ( ) indicates the set is unnumbered.

1999 Press Pass "X's and O's"

The top 36 players from the base set were included in this insert that was found one-per-pack. Each is die cut and embossed on extra thick stock.

		MT
Complete Set (36):		20.00
Common Player:		.25
Minor Stars:		.50
Inserted 1:1		
1	Ricky Williams	4.00
2	Tim Couch	4.00
3	Champ Bailey	.75
4	Donovan McNabb	2.00
5	Edgerrin James	6.00
6	Akili Smith	2.00
7	Torry Holt	1.25
8	Troy Edwards	1.25
9	Daunte Culpepper	2.00
10	Andy Katzenmoyer	.50
11	David Boston	1.25
12	Peerless Price	.75
13	Shaun King	2.00
14	Joe Germaine	.50
15	Brock Huard	.75
16	Michael Bishop	.75
17	Amos Zereoue	.50
18	Sedrick Irvin	.75
19	Autry Denson	.50
20	Kevin Faulk	.75
21	James Johnson	.75
22	D'Wayne Bates	.50
23	Kevin Johnson	1.25
24	Tai Streets	.50
25	Cade McNown	2.00
26	Scott Covington	.50
27	Chris Claiborne	.50
28	Jevon Kearse	1.00
29	Rob Konrad	.25
30	Dat Nguyen	.25
31	Chris McAlister	.25
32	Craig Yeast	.25
33	Anthony Poindexter	.25
34	Dre Bly	.25
35	Mike Rucker	.25
36	Checklist (Tim Couch)	2.00

1993-94 Pro Athletes Outreach

Measuring 7-1/8" x 4-1/8", the 12-card set was made up of triple-fold cards, which showcased a player photo on the right panel. Beneath the photo is the PAO logo, player's name and position. The player's career highlights and his Christian philosophy also are featured on the unnumbered card.

		MT
Complete Set (12):		6.00
Common Player:		.50
1	Mark Boyer	.50
2	Gill Byrd	.50
3	Darren Carrington	.50
4	Paul Coffman	.50
5	Burnell Dent	.50
6	Johnny Holland	.50
7	Jeff Kemp	1.00
8	Steve Largent	3.00
9	John Offerdahl	.50
10	Stephone Paige	.50
11	Doug Smith	.50
12	Rob Taylor	.50

1990 Pro Line Samples

These Pro Line samples can be identified from the regular set's card by several factors, including having the word SAMPLE written on the card back next to a player head shot. The card fronts have photos which are entirely different, or cropped differently, than their regular counterparts. The front also has a silver border; the regular cards are full-bleed. Some backs also have different photos than those used in the regular set and quotes. Card numbers are from 1-37, using all the odd numbers except 15.

		MT
Complete Set (18):		120.00
Common Player:		7.00
1	Charles Mann	7.00
3	Troy Aikman	25.00
5	Boomer Esiason	10.00
7	Warren Moon	12.00
9	Bill Fralic	7.00
11	Lawrence Taylor	10.00
13	George Seifert	7.00
17	Dan Marino	20.00
19	Jim Everett	10.00
21	John Elway	12.00
23	Jeff George	10.00
25	Lindy Infante	7.00
27	Dan Reeves	7.00
29	Steve Largent	12.00
31	Roger Craig	10.00
33	Marty Schottenheimer	7.00
35	Mike Ditka	8.00
37	Sam Wyche	7.00

1991 Pro Line Portraits

This set of high-end cards issued by NFL Properties shows a number of past and present NFL players in posed shots, wearing team apparel without football equipment. These cards were issued in August 1991 in 12-card wax packs. Some 250,000 autographed, embossed and unnumbered were randomly packed. Cards are not licensed by the NFL Players Association, so non-association members such as Eric Dickerson, Michael Dean Perry, Jim Kelly, Bernie Kosar, Webster Slaughter and Cornelius Bennett appear here while they don't appear in any other 1991 sets. A subset, Spirit Collectibles, shows seven player wives. Two other cards, Pro Line Portraits Collectible #1 (Ahmad Rashad and family) and #2 (Payne Stewart), were limited to 10,000 randomly issued cards. Each card in the regular set was also autographed.

		MT
Complete Set (300):		4.50
Common Player:		.03
Wax Box:		9.00
1	Jim Kelly	.20
2	Carl Banks	.03
3	Neal Anderson	.03
4	James Brooks	.03
5	Reggie Langhorne	.03
6	Robert Awalt	.03
7	Greg Kragen	.03
8	Steve Young	.50
9	*Nick Bell*	.10
10	Ray Childress	.03
11	Albert Bentley	.03
12	Albert Lewis	.03
13	Howie Long	.03
14	Willie Anderson	.03
15	Mark Clayton	.03
16	*Jarrod Bunch*	.10
17	Bruce Armstrong	.03
18	*Vinnie Clark*	.10
19	Rob Moore	.10
20	Eric Allen	.03
21	Timm Rosenbach	.03
22	Gary Anderson	.03
23	Martin Bayless	.03
24	Kevin Fagan	.03
25	Brian Blades	.03
26	Gary Anderson	.03
27	Earnest Byner	.03

#	Player	Price
28	O.J. Simpson	1.00
29	Dan Henning	.03
30	Sean Landeta	.03
31	James Lofton	.03
32	Mike Singletary	.03
33	David Fulcher	.03
34	Mark Murphy	.03
35	Issiac Holt	.03
36	Dennis Smith	.03
37	Lomas Brown	.03
38	Ernest Givins	.03
39	Duane Bickett	.03
40	Barry Word	.03
41	Tony Mandarich	.03
42	Cleveland Gary	.03
43	Ferrell Edmunds	.03
44	Randal Hill	.25
45	Irving Fryar	.03
46	Henry Jones	.10
47	Blair Thomas	.03
48	Andre Waters	.03
49	J.T. Smith	.03
50	Thomas Everett	.03
51	Marion Butts	.03
52	Tom Rathman	.03
53	Vann McElroy	.03
54	Mark Carrier (T.B.)	.03
55	Jim Lachey	.03
56	Joe Theismann	.03
57	Jerry Glanville	.03
58	Doug Riesenberg	.03
59	Cornelius Bennett	.03
60	Mark Carrier (Chi.)	.03
61	Rodney Holman	.03
62	Leroy Hoard	.03
63	Michael Irvin	.65
64	Bobby Humphrey	.03
65	Mel Gray	.03
66	Brian Noble	.03
67	Al Smith	.03
68	Eric Dickerson	.10
69	Steve DeBerg	.03
70	Jay Schroeder	.03
71	Irv Pankey	.03
72	Reggie Roby	.03
73	Wade Wilson	.03
74	Reggie Rembert	.03
75	Russell Maryland	.40
76	Al Toon	.03
77	Randall Cunningham	.10
78	Lonnie Young	.03
79	Carnell Lake	.03
80	Brut Grossman	.03
81	Jim Mora	.03
82	Dave Krieg	.03
83	Bruce Hill	.03
84	Ricky Sanders	.03
85	Roger Staubach	.10
86	Richard Williamson	.03
87	Everson Walls	.03
88	Shane Conlan	.03
89	Mike Ditka	.10
90	Mark Bortz	.03
91	Tim McGee	.03
92	Michael Dean Perry	.10
93	Danny Noonan	.03
94	Mark Jackson	.03
95	Chris Miller	.03
96	Ed McCaffrey	.50
97	Lorenzo White	.10
98	Ray Donaldson	.03
99	Nick Lowery	.03
100	Steve Smith	.03
101	Jackie Slater	.03
102	Louis Oliver	.03
103	Kanavis McGhee	.10
104	Ray Agnew	.03
105	Sam Mills	.03
106	Bill Pickel	.03
107	Keith Byars	.03
108	Ricky Proehl	.10
109	Merril Hoge	.03
110	Rod Berstine	.03
111	Andy Heck	.03
112	Broderick Thomas	.03
113	Andre Reed	.03
114	Paul Warfield	.03
115	Bill Belichick	.03
116	Ottis Anderson	.03
117	Andre Reed	.10
118	Andre Rison	.20
119	Dexter Carter	.03
120	Anthony Munoz	.03
121	Bernie Kosar	.03
122	Alonzo Highsmith	.03
123	David Treadwell	.03
124	Rodney Peete	.03
125	Haywood Jeffires	.15
126	Clarence Verdin	.03
127	Christian Okoye	.03
128	Greg Townsend	.03
129	Tom Newberry	.03
130	Keith Sims	.03
131	Myron Guyton	.03
132	Andre Tippett	.03
133	Steve Walsh	.03
134	Erik McMillan	.03
135	Jim McMahon	.03
136	Derek Hill	.03
137	David Johnson	.03
138	Leslie O'Neal	.03
139	Pierce Holt	.03
140	Cortez Kennedy	.20
141	Danny Peebles	.03
142	Alvin Walton	.03
143	Drew Pearson	.03
144	Dick MacPherson	.03
145	Erik Howard	.03
146	Steve Tasker	.03
147	Bill Fralic	.03
148	Don Warren	.03
149	Eric Thomas	.03
150	Jack Pardee	.03
151	Gary Zimmerman	.03
152	Leonard Marshall	.03
153	Chris Spielman	.03
154	Sam Wyche	.03
155	Rohn Stark	.03
156	Stephone Paige	.03
157	Lionel Washington	.03
158	Henry Ellard	.03
159	Dan Marino	.75
160	Lindy Infante	.03
161	Dan McGwire	.10
162	Ken O'Brien	.03
163	Tim McDonald	.03
164	Louis Lipps	.03
165	Billy Joe Tolliver	.03
166	Harris Barton	.03
167	Tony Woods	.03
168	Matt Millen	.03
169	Gale Sayers	.03
170	Ron Meyer	.03
171	William Roberts	.03
172	Thurman Thomas	.25
173	Steve McMichael	.03
174	Ickey Woods	.03
175	Eugene Lockhart	.03
176	George Seifert	.03
177	Keith Jones	.03
178	Jack Trudeau	.03
179	Kevin Porter	.03
180	Ronnie Lott	.10
181	Marty Schottenheimer	.03
182	Morten Andersen	.03
183	Anthony Thompson	.03
184	Tim Worley	.03
185	Billy Ray Smith	.03
186	David Whitmore	.03
187	Jacob Green	.03
188	Browning Nagle	.15
189	Franco Harris	.10
190	Art Shell	.03
191	Bart Oates	.03
192	William Perry	.03
193	Chuck Noll	.03
194	Troy Aikman	1.00
195	Jeff George	.15
196	Derrick Thomas	.15
197	Roger Craig	.03
198	John Fourcade	.03
199	Rod Woodson	.03
200	Anthony Miller	.03
201	Jerry Rice	.75
202	Eugene Robinson	.03
203	Charles Mann	.03
204	Mel Blount	.03
205	Don Shula	.03
206	John Elliott	.03
207	Jay Hilgenberg	.03
208	Deron Cherry	.03
209	Dan Reeves	.03
210	Roman Phifer	.10
211	David Little	.03
212	Lee Williams	.03
213	John Taylor	.10
214	Monte Coleman	.03
215	Walter Payton	.10
216	John Robinson	.03
217	Pepper Johnson	.03
218	Tom Thayer	.03
219	Dan Saleaumua	.03
220	Ernest Spears	.03
221	Bubby Brister	.03
222	Junior Seau	.20
223	Brent Jones	.03
224	Rufus Porter	.03
225	Jack Kemp	.10
226	Wayne Fontes	.03
227	Phil Simms	.10
228	Shaun Gayle	.03
229	Bill Maas	.03
230	Renaldo Turnbull	.03
231	Bryan Hinkle	.03
232	Gary Plummer	.03
233	Jerry Burns	.03
234	Lawrence Taylor	.10
235	Joe Gibbs	.03
236	Neil Smith	.03
237	Rich Kotite	.03
238	Jim Covert	.03
239	Tim Grunhard	.03
240	Joe Bugel	.03
241	Dave Wyman	.03
242	Maruy Buford	.03
243	Kevin Ross	.03
244	Jimmy Johnson	.03
245	Jim Morrissey	.03
246	Jeff Hostetler	.03
247	Andre Ware	.10
248	Steve Largent	.10
249	Chuck Knox	.03
250	Boomer Esiason	.10
251	Kevin Butler	.03
252	Bruce Smith	.03
253	Webster Slaughter	.03
254	Mike Sherrard	.03
255	Steve Broussard	.03
256	Warren Moon	.15
257	John Elway	.25
258	Bob Golic	.03
259	Jim Everett	.03
260	Bruce Coslet	.03
261	James Francis	.03
262	Eric Dorsey	.03
263	Marcus Dupree	.03
264	Hart Lee Dykes	.03
265	Vinny Testaverde	.03
266	Chip Lohmiller	.03
267	John Riggins	.03
268	Mike Schad	.03
269	Kevin Greene	.03
270	Dean Biasucci	.03
271	Mike Pritchard	.40
272	Ted Washington	.10
273	Alfred Williams	.10
274	Chris Zorich	.15
275	Reggie Barrett	.03
276	Chris Hinton	.03
277	Tracy Johnson	.10
278	Jim Harbaugh	.03
279	John Roper	.03
280	Mike Dumas	.03
281	Herman Moore	3.50
282	Eric Turner	.15
283	Steve Atwater	.03
284	Michael Cofer (Det.)	.03
285	Darion Conner	.03
286	Darryl Talley	.03
287	Donnell Woolford	.03
288	Keith McCants	.03
289	Ray Handley	.03
290	Ahmad Rashad	.03
291	Eric Swann	.15
292	Dalton Hilltiard	.03
293	Rickey Jackson	.03
294	Vaughan Johnson	.03
295	Eric Martin	.03
296	Pat Swilling	.03
297	Anthony Carter	.03
298	Guy McIntyre	.03
299	Bennie Blades	.03
300	Paul Farren	.03

1991 Pro Line Portraits Autographs

Each card in the regular set was also autographed. The card is the same as the regular one, except it is not numbered. These cards command premium prices and were random inserts in packs, about one every three boxes.

		MT
	Complete Set (301):	5250.
	Common Player:	6.00
	Minor Stars:	12.00
1A	Jim Kelly (Autopenned)	20.00
1B	Jim Kelly (Real Signature)	250.00
2	Carl Banks	6.00
3	Neal Anderson	6.00
4	James Brooks	6.00
5	Reggie Langhorne	60.00
6	Robert Awalt	6.00
7	Greg Kragen	6.00
8	Steve Young	125.00
9	Nick Bell	6.00
10	Ray Childress	6.00
11	Albert Bentley	6.00
12	Albert Lewis (Most signatures are cut off)	60.00
13	Howie Long	35.00
14	Flipper Anderson	12.00
15	Mark Clayton	12.00
16	Jarrod Bunch	6.00
17	Bruce Armstrong	6.00
18	Vinnie Clark	6.00
19	Rob Moore	20.00
20	Eric Allen	6.00
21	Timm Rosenbach	6.00
22	Gary Anderson (K)	6.00
23	Martin Bayless	6.00
24	Kevin Fagan	6.00
25	Brian Blades	12.00
26	Gary Anderson (RB)	6.00
27	Earnest Byner	6.00
28	O.J. Simpson (RET)	300.00
29	Dan Henning (CO)	6.00
30	Sean Landeta	6.00
31	James Lofton	25.00
32	Mike Singletary	40.00
33	David Fulcher	6.00
34	Mark Murphy	6.00
35	Issiac Holt	6.00
36	Dennis Smith	6.00
37	Lomas Brown	6.00
38	Ernest Givins	12.00
39	Duane Bickett	6.00
40	Barry Word	6.00
41	Tony Mandarich	12.00
42	Cleveland Gary	6.00
43	Ferrell Edmunds	6.00
44	Randal Hill	12.00
45	Irving Fryar	12.00
46	Henry Jones	6.00
47	Blair Thomas	6.00
48	Andre Waters	6.00
49	J.T. Smith	6.00
50	Thomas Everett	6.00
51	Marion Butts	12.00
52	Tom Rathman	12.00
53	Vann McElroy	6.00
54	Mark Carrier (WR)	6.00
55	Jim Lachey	6.00
56	Joe Theismann (RET)	30.00
57	Jerry Glanville (CO)	12.00
58	Doug Riesenberg	6.00
59	Cornelius Bennett	6.00
60	Mark Carrier (DB)	100.00
61	Rodney Holman	225.00
62	Leroy Hoard	12.00
63	Michael Irvin	35.00
64	Bobby Humphrey	6.00
65	Mel Gray	12.00
66	Brian Noble	6.00
67	Al Smith	6.00
68	Eric Dickerson	30.00
69	Steve DeBerg	12.00
70	Jay Schroeder	12.00
71	Irv Pankey	6.00
72	Reggie Roby	12.00
73	Wade Wilson	6.00
74	Johnny Rembert	6.00
75	Russell Maryland	12.00
76	Al Toon	12.00
77	Randall Cunningham	30.00
78	Lonnie Young	6.00
79	Carnell Lake	12.00
80	Brut Grossman	6.00
81	Jim Mora (CO)	6.00
82	Dave Krieg	12.00
83	Bruce Hill	6.00
84	Ricky Sanders	6.00
85	Roger Staubach (RET) (Most signatures are cut off)	150.00
86	Richard Williamson (CO)	6.00
87	Everson Walls	12.00
88	Shane Conlan	6.00
89	Mike Ditka (CO)	40.00
90	Mark Bortz	6.00
91	Tim McGee	6.00
92	Michael Dean Perry	12.00
93	Danny Noonan	6.00
94	Mark Jackson	12.00
95	Chris Miller	12.00
96	Ed McCaffrey	25.00
97	Lorenzo White	12.00
98	Ray Donaldson	6.00
99	Nick Lowery (May be autopenned)	6.00
100	Steve Smith	6.00
101	Jackie Slater	12.00
102	Louis Oliver	6.00
103	Kanavis McGhee	6.00
104	Ray Agnew	6.00
105	Sam Mills	12.00
106	Bill Pickel	6.00
107	Keith Byars	12.00
108	Ricky Proehl	12.00
109	Merril Hoge	6.00
110	Rod Berstine	6.00
111	Andy Heck	6.00
112	Broderick Thomas	6.00
113	Andre Collins	6.00
114	Paul Warfield (RET)	25.00
115	Bill Belichick (CO)	12.00
116	Ottis Anderson	12.00
117	Andre Reed	25.00
118A	Andre Reed (Ball-point pen)	15.00
118B	Andre Rison (Signed in Sharpie)	30.00
119	Dexter Carter	12.00
120	Anthony Munoz	12.00
121	Bernie Kosar	15.00
122	Alonzo Highsmith	60.00
123	David Treadwell	6.00
124	Rodney Peete	12.00
125	Haywood Jeffires	12.00
126	Clarence Verdin	6.00
127	Christian Okoye	12.00
128	Greg Townsend	125.00
129	Tom Newberry	6.00
130	Keith Sims	6.00
131	Myron Guyton	6.00
132	Andre Tippett	6.00
133	Steve Walsh	12.00
134	Erik McMillan	6.00
135	Jim McMahon	280.00
136	Derek Hill	6.00
137	D.J. Johnson	6.00
138	Leslie O'Neal	12.00
139	Pierce Holt	6.00
140	Cortez Kennedy	12.00
141	Danny Peebles	6.00
142	Alvin Walton	6.00
143	Drew Pearson (RET)	12.00
144	Dick MacPherson (CO)	6.00
145	Erik Howard	6.00
146	Steve Tasker	6.00
147	Bill Fralic	6.00
148	Don Warren	6.00
149	Eric Thomas	6.00
150	Jack Pardee (CO)	6.00
151	Gary Zimmerman	6.00
152	Leonard Marshall (Frequently miscut)	12.00
153	Chris Spielman	12.00
154	Sam Wyche (CO)	6.00
155	Rohn Stark	6.00
156	Stephone Paige	6.00
157	Lionel Washington (Most signatures are cut off)	120.00
158	Henry Ellard	12.00
159	Dan Marino	200.00
160	Lindy Infante (CO)	6.00
161	Dan McGwire	6.00
162	Ken O'Brien	12.00
163	Tim McDonald	6.00
164	Louis Lipps	6.00
165	Billy Joe Tolliver	12.00
166	Harris Barton	6.00
167	Tony Woods	6.00
168	Matt Millen	6.00
169	Gale Sayers (RET)	35.00
170	Ron Meyer (CO)	12.00
171	William Roberts	6.00
172	Thurman Thomas	30.00
173	Steve McMichael	6.00
174	Ickey Woods	6.00
175	Eugene Lockhart	6.00
176	George Seifert (CO)	12.00
177	Keith Jones	6.00
178	Jack Trudeau	6.00
179	Kevin Porter	6.00
180	Ronnie Lott	15.00
181	Marty Schottenheimer (CO)	12.00
182	Morten Andersen	12.00
183	Anthony Thompson	6.00
184	Tim Worley	6.00
185	Billy Ray Smith	6.00
186	David Whitmore	6.00
187	Jacob Green	6.00
188	Browning Nagle	6.00
189	Franco Harris (RET) (Most signatures are cut off)	45.00
190	Art Shell (CO)	15.00
191	Bart Oates	6.00
192	William Perry	12.00
193	Chuck Noll (CO)	30.00
194	Troy Aikman	100.00
195	Jeff George	25.00
196	Derrick Thomas	40.00
197	Roger Craig	12.00
198	John Fourcade	6.00
199	Rod Woodson	12.00
200	Anthony Miller	12.00
201	Jerry Rice	150.00
202	Eugene Robinson	6.00
203	Charles Mann	6.00
204	Mel Blount (RET)	12.00
205	Don Shula (CO)	45.00
206	John Elliott	6.00
207	Jay Hilgenberg	6.00
208	Deron Cherry	6.00
209	Dan Reeves (CO)	12.00
210	Roman Phifer	6.00
211	David Little	6.00
212	Lee Williams	6.00
213	John Taylor	12.00
214	Monte Coleman	6.00
215	Walter Payton (RET)	150.00
216	John Robinson (CO)	6.00
217	Pepper Johnson	6.00
218	Tom Thayer	6.00
219	Dan Saleaumua	6.00
220	Ernest Spears	6.00
221	Bubby Brister (Signed Bubby 6)	12.00
222	Junior Seau	20.00
223	Brent Jones	12.00
224	Rufus Porter	6.00
225	Jack Kemp (RET) (Autopenned)	30.00
226	Wayne Fontes (CO)	6.00
227	Phil Simms	30.00
228	Shaun Gayle	6.00
229	Bill Maas	6.00
230	Renaldo Turnbull	6.00
231	Bryan Hinkle	6.00
232	Gary Plummer	6.00
233	Jerry Burns (CO)	6.00
234	Lawrence Taylor	40.00
235	Joe Gibbs (CO)	20.00
236	Neil Smith (Most signatures are cut off)	60.00
237	Rich Kotite (CO)	6.00
238	Jim Covert	6.00
239	Tim Grunhard (Two different signatures known for this card)	6.00
240	Joe Bugel (CO)	6.00
241	Dave Wyman	6.00
242	Maruy Buford	6.00
243	Kevin Ross	6.00
244	Jimmy Johnson (CO)	40.00
245	Jim Morrissey	6.00
246	Jeff Hostetler	12.00
247	Andre Ware	6.00
248	Steve Largent (RET)	40.00
249	Chuck Knox (CO)	12.00
250	Boomer Esiason	12.00
251	Kevin Butler	6.00
252	Bruce Smith	12.00
253	Webster Slaughter	6.00
254	Mike Sherrard	6.00
255	Steve Broussard	6.00
256	Warren Moon	35.00
257	John Elway	100.00
258	Bob Golic	6.00
259	Jim Everett	12.00
260	Bruce Coslet (CO)	6.00
261	James Francis	280.00
262	Eric Dorsey	6.00
263	Marcus Dupree	6.00
264	Hart Lee Dykes	6.00
265	Vinny Testaverde	15.00
266	Chip Lohmiller	6.00
267	John Riggins (RET)	50.00
268	Mike Schad	6.00
269	Kevin Greene	12.00
270	Dean Biasucci	6.00
271	Mike Pritchard	6.00
272	Ted Washington	6.00
273	Alfred Williams	6.00
274	Chris Zorich	6.00
275	Reggie Barrett	6.00
276	Chris Hinton	6.00
277	Tracy Johnson	6.00
278	Jim Harbaugh	12.00
279	John Roper	6.00
280	Mike Dumas	6.00
281	Herman Moore	60.00
282	Eric Turner	6.00
283	Steve Atwater	6.00
284	Michael Cofer	6.00
285	Darion Conner	6.00
286	Darryl Talley	6.00
287	Donnell Woolford	6.00
288	Keith McCants	6.00
289	Ray Handley (CO)	6.00
290	Ahmad Rashad (RET)	175.00
291	Eric Swann	12.00
292	Dalton Hilliard (Signatures usually miscut)	25.00
293	Rickey Jackson	6.00
294	Vaughan Johnson	6.00
295	Eric Martin	6.00
296	Pat Swilling	12.00
297	Anthony Carter (Signatures usually miscut)	25.00
298	Guy McIntyre	75.00
299	Bennie Blades	6.00
300	Paul Farren	6.00
PLC2	Payne Stewart (Golfer)	85.00
NNO	Santa Claus Sendaway (Signed)	30.00
	Santa Claus Sendaway (Signed and numbered)	60.00

1991 Pro Line Portraits Collectibles

These two cards were randomly inserted in 1991 Pro Line foil packs and feature NBC sports commentator Ahmad Rashad and pro golfer Payne Stewart. The Stewart card shows him kissing a trophy and offers a tip on the back on how to approach the game. The card, like the Rashad card, has a number on the back, along with the words "Pro Line Portraits Collectible." The Rashad card pictures him and his family on the front, including his wife, TV actress, Phylicia. The back, in a horizontal format, has a quote from Rashad about the importance of family life.

		MT
	Complete Set (2):	20.00
	Common Player:	10.00
1	Rashad Family (Ahmad Rashad)	10.00
2	Golfer (Payne Stewart)	10.00

1991 Pro Line Portraits Wives

Wives of some of the most popular NFL players are featured in this seven-card "Spirit" set. The cards are numbered on the back and were included in the 1991 Pro Line Portraits set.

		MT
	Common Wife:	.05
1	Jennifer Montana	.25
2	Babette Kosar	.05
3	Janet Elway	.05
4	Michelle Oates	.05
5	Toni Lipps	.05

6	Stacey O'Brien	.05
7	Phylicia Rashad	.20

1991 Pro Line Portraits Wives Autographs

The seven-card, standard-size set featured wives of top NFL players and was inserted in packs of 1991 NFL Pro Line. The Rashad signed card was limited to 15, thus giving it its high value. The cards are identical to the seven wives featured in the base set, except with signatures.

		MT
Complete Set (7):		550.00
Common Player:		15.00
1	Jennifer Montana	75.00
2	Babette Kosar	15.00
3	Janet Elway	15.00
4	Michelle Oates	15.00
5	Toni Lipps	15.00
6	Stacey O'Brien	15.00
7	Phylicia Rashad	450.00

1991 Pro Line Punt, Pass and Kick

Eleven NFL quarterbacks are featured in this 12-card set issued to promote nationwide Punt, Pass and Kick competitions. Each card front has a full bleed posed shot of the player, along with Pro Line Portraits and Punt, Pass and Kick logos. The card back is numbered and includes a player head shot and a quote from him about being a successful NFL quarterback. A checklist card was also produced.

		MT
Complete Set (11):		75.00
Common Player:		5.00
1	Troy Aikman	20.00
2	Bubby Brister	5.00
3	Randall Cunningham	8.00
4	John Elway	8.00
5	Boomer Esiason	7.00
6	Jim Everett	5.00
7	Jim Kelly	10.00
8	Bernie Kosar	7.00
9	Dan Marino	15.00
10	Warren Moon	10.00
11	Phil Simms	7.00

1991 Pro Line Profiles Anthony Munoz

Cincinnati Bengals lineman Anthony Munoz is profiled in this set of cards, which was included inside Super Bowl XXVI programs. The cards chronicle Munoz's career and are listed below according to the topic presented on the card back. Each back is also numbered. A full-color photo appears on the card front, along with the Pro Line Profiles logo. The back has a smaller photo and provides information and quotes from Munoz about his life, community service projects, his family and his NFL career.

		MT
Complete Set (9):		4.00
Common Player:		.50
1	1991 NFL Man of Year	.50
2	Little League player	.50
3	1980 Rose Bowl	.50
4	Community Service	.50
5	Portrait	.50
6	1981 AFC Championship Game	.50
7	1992 Pro Bowl	.50
8	Super Bowl XVI and XXIII	.50
9	Physical Fitness Video	.50

1992 Pro Line Draft Day

The two-card, regular-size set features top pick Steve Emt-

man on one card with NFL coaches on the other. The card back features Emtman on No. 1 with a quote, an ESPN announcer Chris Berman on No. 2, also with a quote.

		MT
Complete Set (2):		4.00
Common Player:		2.00
1	Steve Emtman	2.00
2	Coaches Photo	2.00

1992 Pro Line Mobil

This 72-card set was available in nine-card packs in an eight-week promotion in Southern California. It could be obtained by purchasing eight or more gallons of Mobil Super Unleaded Plus. The first nine cards are from 1991 Portraits, while the final 63 cards are from 1992 Portraits, both of which are produced by NFL Properties. The first pack included a checklist card, a title card and a card for each of the seven players featured, with the dates that their nine-card packs would be available. Card number nine of Eric Dickerson in a Raiders' uniform is an exclusive to the set. Only one player is featured per pack, with cards numbered "X of 9."

		MT
Complete Set (72):		8.00
Common Player:		.10
1	Title Card (October 3-9)	.10
2	Checklist	.10
3	Ronnie Lott	.15
4	Junior Seau	.40
5	Jim Everett	.10
6	Howie Long	.15
7	Jerry Rice	1.00
8	Art Shell (CO)	.15
9	Eric Dickerson	.25
10	Ronnie Lott (October 10-16) (Making Hit)	.15
11	Ronnie Lott (Little Leaguer)	.15
12	Ronnie Lott (Playing for USC)	.15
13	Ronnie Lott (Exultation)	.15
14	Ronnie Lott (Portrait)	.15
15	Ronnie Lott (Behind Bar)	.15
16	Ronnie Lott (With Family)	.15
17	Ronnie Lott (Catching Ball)	.15
18	Ronnie Lott (Tuxedo)	.15
19	Junior Seau (October 17-23) (With Ball)	.25
20	Junior Seau (Young Junior)	.25
21	Junior Seau (Pointing)	.25
22	Junior Seau (Over Fallen Opponent)	.25
23	Junior Seau (Portrait)	.25
24	Junior Seau (With Wife)	.25
25	Junior Seau (Running in Surf)	.25
26	Junior Seau (Weightlifting)	.25
27	Junior Seau (Seaweed Boa)	.25
28	Jim Everett (October 24-30) (Looking for Receiver)	.10
29	Jim Everett (Young Jim)	.10
30	Jim Everett (Playing for Purdue)	.10
31	Jim Everett (With Parents, Sister)	.10
32	Jim Everett (Portrait)	.10
33	Jim Everett (Eluding Rush)	.10
34	Jim Everett (Fishing)	.10
35	Jim Everett (Handing Off)	.10
36	Jim Everett (Studio Photo)	.10
37	Howie Long (October 31-November 6) (Hand Up to Block Pass)	.15
38	Howie Long (High School Footballer)	.15
39	Howie Long (Closing in for Sack)	.15
40	Howie Long (With Family)	.15
41	Howie Long (Portrait)	.15
42	Howie Long (Fundraising for Kids)	.15
43	Howie Long (Hitting the Heavy Bag)	.15
44	Howie Long (Taking Swipe at Ball)	.15
45	Howie Long (Studio Photo)	.15
46	Jerry Rice (November 7-13) (With Trophy)	.50
47	Jerry Rice (Avoiding Block)	.50
48	Jerry Rice (Eluding Steeler)	.50
49	Jerry Rice (With Family)	.50
50	Jerry Rice (Portrait)	.50
51	Jerry Rice (With Toddler)	.50
52	Jerry Rice (Playing Tennis)	.50
53	Jerry Rice (Scoring TD)	.50
54	Jerry Rice (Studio Photo)	.50
55	Art Shell (CO) (November 14-20) (In Front of his Team)	.15
56	Art Shell (CO) (At Maryland State)	.15
57	Art Shell (CO) (Blocking Viking)	.15
58	Art Shell (CO) (Playing Basketball)	.15
59	Art Shell (CO) (Portrait)	.15
60	Art Shell (CO) (Talking to Player)	.15
61	Art Shell (CO) (In Front of TV)	.15
62	Art Shell (CO) (Blocking for Raiders)	.15
63	Art Shell (CO) (With Teddy Bear)	.15
64	Eric Dickerson (November 21-30) (Studio Suit Up)	.15
65	Eric Dickerson (Running for SMU)	.15
66	Eric Dickerson (With Mom)	.15
67	Eric Dickerson (49ers in Pursuit)	.15
68	Eric Dickerson (Portrait)	.15
69	Eric Dickerson (Running for Colts)	.15
70	Eric Dickerson (On Training Ramp)	.15
71	Eric Dickerson (Running Against Rams)	.15
72	Eric Dickerson (Posed With Football)	.15

1992 Pro Line Prototypes

The 13-card, regular-size set was distributed by Pro Line to sample its upcoming releases. Featured in the sample set are Profiles, Spirit and Portraits. The Profiles backs have "Prototype" printed while Portraits backs have "Sample."

	MT
Complete Set (13):	8.00
Common Player:	.50

12	Kathie Lee Gifford	1.00
28	Thurman Thomas (Bills' uniform, action shot)	.75
29	Thurman Thomas (With his mother)	.75
30	Thurman Thomas (OSU Cowboy uniform, action shot)	.75
31	Thurman Thomas (With family)	.75
32	Thurman Thomas (Color portrait)	.75
33	Thurman Thomas (Action shot, Super Bowl XXV)	.75
34	Thurman Thomas (Fishing)	.75
35	Thurman Thomas (Stretching on track)	.75
36	Thurman Thomas (Close-up photo)	.75
379	Jessie Tuggle	.50
386	Neil O'Donnell	.50
NNO	Advertisement Card	.50

1992 Pro Line Portraits

This 1992 Pro Line Portraits set continues numbering where the 1991 set ended, starting at #301. The front has a full-bleed color non-action photo; the back has a mug shot and player information. CO means coach; RET means retired. There were also cards autographed by the players. These command premium prices. They are identical to those in the regular set, except they are unnumbered. Cards 349, 370, 417, 428, 451 and 462 were never signed, however.

		MT
Complete Set (167):		7.00
Common Player:		.04
Wax Box:		9.00
301	*Steve Emtman*	.15
302	Al Edwards	.04
303	Wendell Davis	.05
304	Lewis Billups	.04
305	Brian Brennan	.04
306	John Gesek	.04
307	*Terrell Buckley*	.25
308	*Johnny Mitchell*	.60
309	LeRoy Butler	.04
310	William Fuller	.04
311	Bill Brooks	.06
312	Dino Hackett	.04
313	Willie Gault	.06
314	Aaron Cox	.04
315	Jeff Cross	.04
316	Emmitt Smith	2.00
317	Marv Cook	.06
318	Gill Fenerty	.06
319	*Jeff Carlson*	.20
320	Brad Baxter	.06
321	Fred Barnett	.10
322	Kurt Barber	.10
323	Eric Green	.06
324	Greg Clark	.10
325	Keith DeLong	.04
326	Patrick Hunter	.04
327	*Troy Vincent*	.10
328	Gary Clark	.08
329	Joe Montana	1.75
330	Michael Haynes	.25
331	*Edgar Bennett*	.50
332	Darren Lewis	.15
333	Derrick Fenner	.06
334	Rob Burnett	.04
335	Alvin Harper	.40
336	Vance Johnson	.06
337	William White	.04
338	Sterling Sharpe	.50
339	Sean Jones	.04
340	Jeff Herrod	.04
341	Chris Martin	.04
342	Ethan Horton	.04
343	Robert Delpino	.06
344	Mark Higgs	.15

345	Chris Doleman	.06
346	Tom Hodson	.06
347	Craig Heyward	.06
348	Cary Conklin	.06
349	James Hasty	.04
350	Antone Davis	.04
351	Ernie Jones	.04
352	Greg Lloyd	.04
353	John Friesz	.06
354	Charles Haley	.06
355	*Tracy Scroggins*	.06
356	Paul Gruber	.06
357	Ricky Ervins	.10
358	Brad Muster	.06
359	Deion Sanders	.20
360	*Mitch Frerotte*	.04
361	Stan Thomas	.04
362	Harold Green	.08
363	Eric Metcalf	.06
364	Ken Norton Jr.	.06
365	Dave Widell, Doug Widell	.04
366	Mike Tomczak	.06
367	Bubba McDowell	.04
368	Jessie Hester	.04
369	Ervin Randle	.04
370	Tony Smith	.04
371	Pat Terrell	.04
372	Jim C. Jensen	.04
373	Mike Merriweather	.06
374	Chris Singleton	.04
375	Floyd Turner	.04
376	Jim Sweeney	.04
377	Keith Jackson	.15
378	Walter Reeves	.04
379	Neil O'Donnell	.50
380	Nate Lewis	.12
381	Keith Henderson	.04
382	Kelly Stouffer	.04
383	Ricky Reynolds	.04
384	Joe Jacoby	.04
385	(Fred Biletnikoff) (RET)	.10
386	Jessie Tuggle	.04
387	Tom Waddle	.12
388	Dave Shula (CO)	.10
389	*Van Waiters*	.10
390	Jay Novacek	.12
391	Michael Young	.04
392	Mike Holmgren	.08
393	Doug Smith	.04
394	Mike Prior	.04
395	Harvey Williams	.10
396	Aaron Wallace	.04
397	Tony Zendejas	.04
398	Sammie Smith	.06
399	Henry Thomas	.04
400	Jon Vaughn	.12
401	Brian Washington	.04
402	*Leon Searcy*	.10
403	Lance Smith	.04
404	Warren Williams	.04
405	(Bobby Ross) (CO)	.10
406	Harry Sydney	.04
407	John L. Williams	.06
408	Ken Willis	.04
409	Brian Mitchell	.04
410	(Dick Butkus) (RET)	.10
411	(Chuck Knox) (RET)	.10
412	*Robert Porcher*	.25
413	Calvin Williams	.10
414	(Bill Cowher) (CO)	.10
415	Eric Moore	.04
416	*Derek Brown*	.20
417	(Dennis Greene) (CO)	.10
418	Tom Flores (CO)	.04
419	*Dale Carter*	.30
420	(Tony Dorsett) (RET)	.10
421	*Marco Coleman*	.40
422	(Sam Wyche) (CO)	.10
423	Ray Crockett	.04
424	Dan Fouts (RET)	.10
425	Hugh Millen	.15
426	Quentin Coryatt	.40
427	Brian Jordan	.06
428	(Frank Gifford) (RET)	
429	Toby Caston	.10
430	(Ted Marchibroda) (CO)	.04
431	Cris Carter	.06
432	Tim Krumrie	.04
433	(Otto Graham) (CO)	.10
434	*Vaughn Dunbar*	.25
435	*John Fina*	.04
436	(Sonny Jurgensen) (RET)	.10
437	*Robert Jones*	.15
438	Steve DeOssie	.04
439	(Eddie LeBaron) (RET)	.10
440	*Chester McGlockton*	.15
441	(Ken Stabler) (RET)	.10
442	(Joe DeLamielleure) (RET)	.10
443	(Charley Taylor) (RET)	.10
444	*Greg Skrepenak* (Y.A. Tittle) (RET)	.10
445	*Chuck Smith*	.10
446	(Kellen Winslow) (RET)	.10
447	*Kevin Smith*	.30
448	*Phillippi Sparks*	.12
449	*Alonzo Spellman*	.20
450		

451	Mark Rypien	.10
452	*Darryl Williams*	.15
453	*Tommy Vardell*	.20
454	*Tommy Maddox*	.30
455	*Steve Israel*	.12
456	*Marquez Pope*	.12
457	*Eugene Chung*	.10
458	(Lynn Swann) (RET)	.10
459	*Sean Gilbert*	.40
460	Chris Mims	.30
461	(Al Davis)	.04
462	Richard Todd	.04
463	Mike Fox	.04
464	*David Klingler*	.40
465	*Darren Woodson*	.12
466	*Jason Hanson*	.12
467	(Lem Barney) (RET)	.10
1NNO	Santa Sendaway	5.00
2NNO	Mrs. Claus Sendaway	7.00
1NNO	Santa Sendaway	5.00
2NNO	Mrs. Claus Sendaway	7.00

1992 Pro Line Portraits Checklists

These checklist cards were randomly included in 1992 Pro Line Portraits foil packs. The cards use letters instead of card numbers. The card fronts form a 3x3 puzzle which shows the Pro Line Collection emblem on a screened background with NFL logos. The backs include checklists for the 1991-92 Portraits series, 1992 Profiles series and collectible series.

		MT
Complete Set (9):		1.00
Common Checklists:		.15
A	Introduction Card	.15
B	Checklist 1-75	.15
C	Checklist 76-150	.15
D	Checklist 151-225	.15
E	Checklist 226-300	.15
F	Checklist 301-375	.15
G	Checklist 376-450	.15
H	Checklist 451-467 and inserts	.15
I	Checklist Profiles	.15

1992 Pro Line Portraits Autographs

This 1992 Pro Line Portraits set was autographed by the players. These command premium prices. They are identical to those in the regular set, except they are unnumbered. Cards 349, 370, 417, 428, 451 and 462 were never signed, however.

		MT
Complete Set (161):		1200.
Common Player:		4.00
Minor Stars:		8.00
301	Steve Emtman	4.00
302	Al Edwards	4.00
303	Wendell Davis	4.00
304	Lewis Billups	8.00
305	Brian Brennan	4.00
306	John Gesek	4.00
307	Terrell Buckley	8.00
308	Johnny Mitchell	4.00
309	LeRoy Butler	4.00
310	William Fuller	4.00
311	Bill Brooks	4.00
312	Dino Hackett	4.00
313	Willie Gault	4.00
314	Aaron Cox	4.00
315	Jeff Cross	4.00
316	Emmitt Smith	85.00
317	Marv Cook	4.00
318	Gill Fenerty	4.00
319	Jeff Carlson	4.00
320	Brad Baxter	4.00
321	Fred Barnett	8.00
322	Kurt Barber	4.00
323	Eric Green	4.00
324	Greg Clark	4.00
325	Keith DeLong	4.00
326	Patrick Hunter	4.00
327	Troy Vincent	8.00
328	Gary Clark	4.00
329	Joe Montana	120.00
330	Michael Haynes	8.00
331	Edgar Bennett	8.00
332	Darren Lewis	4.00
333	Derrick Fenner	4.00
334	Rob Burnett	4.00
335	Alvin Harper	8.00
336	Vance Johnson	4.00
337	William White	4.00
338	Sterling Sharpe	20.00
339	Sean Jones	4.00
340	Jeff Herrod	4.00

#	Player	Price
341	Chris Martin	4.00
342	Ethan Horton	4.00
343	Robert Delpino	4.00
344	Mark Higgs	4.00
345	Chris Doleman	4.00
346	Tom Hodson	4.00
347	Craig Heyward	4.00
348	Cary Conklin	4.00
349	James Hasty	4.00
350	Antone Davis	4.00
351	Ernie Jones	4.00
352	Greg Lloyd	8.00
353	John Friesz	8.00
354	Charles Haley	8.00
355	Tracy Scroggins	4.00
356	Paul Gruber	4.00
357	Ricky Ervins	4.00
358	Brad Muster	4.00
359	Deion Sanders (Deion also signed and numbered 200 cards from his personal stock; these are worth double)	40.00
360	Mitch Frerotte	4.00
361	Stan Thomas	4.00
362	Harold Green	4.00
363	Eric Metcalf	8.00
364	Ken Norton Jr.	8.00
365	Dave Widell, Doug Widell	8.00
366	Mike Tomczak	8.00
367	Bubba McDowell	4.00
368	Jessie Hester (Signed in ballpoint pen)	4.00
369	Ervin Randle	4.00
370	Tony Smith	4.00
371	Pat Terrell	4.00
372	Jim C. Jensen	4.00
373	Mike Merriweather	4.00
374	Chris Singleton	4.00
375	Floyd Turner	4.00
376	Jim Sweeney	4.00
377	Keith Jackson	8.00
378	Walter Reeves	4.00
379	Neil O'Donnell	8.00
380	Nate Lewis	4.00
381	Keith Henderson	4.00
382	Kelly Stouffer	4.00
383	Ricky Reynolds	4.00
384	Joe Jacoby	4.00
385	(Fred Biletnikoff) (RET)	180.00
386	Jessie Tuggle	4.00
387	Tom Waddle	4.00
388	Dave Shula (CO)	4.00
389	Van Waiters	4.00
390	Jay Novacek	8.00
391	Michael Young	4.00
392	Mike Holmgren (CO)	25.00
393	Doug Smith	4.00
394	Mike Prior	4.00
395	Harvey Williams	8.00
396	Aaron Wallace	4.00
397	Tony Zendejas	4.00
398	Sammie Smith	4.00
399	Henry Thomas	4.00
400	Jon Vaughn	4.00
401	Brian Washington	4.00
402	Leon Searcy	4.00
403	Lance Smith	4.00
404	Warren Williams	4.00
405	(Bobby Ross) (CO)	4.00
406	Harry Sydney	4.00
407	John L. Williams	4.00
408	Ken Willis	4.00
409	Brian Mitchell	4.00
410	(Dick Butkus) (RET)	25.00
411	(Chuck Knox) (CO)	4.00
412	Robert Porcher	4.00
413	Calvin Williams	4.00
414	(Bill Cowher) (CO)	15.00
415	Eric Moore	4.00
416	Derek Brown (TE)	4.00
417	(Dennis Greene) (CO)	8.00
418	Tom Flores (CO)	4.00
419	Dale Carter	4.00
420	(Tony Dorsett) (RET)	25.00
421	Marco Coleman	4.00
422	(Sam Wyche) (CO)	4.00
423	Ray Crockett	4.00
424	Dan Fouts (RET)	15.00
425	Hugh Millen	4.00
426	Quentin Coryatt	8.00
427	Brian Jordan	8.00
428	(Frank Gifford) (RET)	12.00
429	Toby Caston	4.00
430	(Ted Marchibroda) (CO)	4.00
431	Cris Carter	35.00
432	Tim Krumrie	4.00
433	(Otto Graham) (CO)	25.00
434	Vaughn Dunbar	4.00
435	John Fina	4.00
436	(Sonny Jurgensen) (RET)	20.00
437	Robert Jones	4.00
438	Steve DeOssie	4.00
439	(Eddie LeBaron) (RET)	8.00
440	Chester McGlockton	8.00
441	(Ken Stabler) (RET)	25.00
442	(Joe DeLamielleure) (RET)	4.00
443	(Charley Taylor) (RET)	8.00
444	Greg Skrepenak	4.00
445	(Y.A. Tittle) (RET)	25.00
446	Chuck Smith	4.00
447	(Kellen Winslow) (RET)	8.00
448	Kevin Smith	4.00
449	Phillippi Sparks	4.00
450	Alonzo Spellman	4.00
451	Mark Rypien	4.00
452	Darryl Williams	4.00
453	Tommy Vardell	4.00
454	Tommy Maddox	4.00
455	Steve Israel	4.00
456	Marquez Pope	4.00
457	Eugene Chung	4.00
458	(Lynn Swann) (RET)	75.00
459	Sean Gilbert	8.00
460	Chris Mims	8.00
461	(Al Davis) (OWN)	325.00
462	Richard Todd	4.00
463	Mike Fox	4.00
464	David Klingler	8.00
465	Darren Woodson	8.00
466	Jason Hanson	8.00
467	(Lem Barney) (RET)	8.00
NNO	Santa Claus	8.00
NNO	Mrs. Santa Claus	8.00
1NNO	Santa Sendaway	5.00
2NNO	Mrs. Claus Sendaway	7.00

1992 Pro Line Portraits Collectibles

These cards continue numbering where two prior special insert cards left off the preceding year. Each card front has a full-color photo and the set logo; the back has the card number with a "PLC" suffix and a quote on a silver background. Cards were random inserts in 1992 Pro Line foil packs.

		MT
Complete Set (6):		12.00
Common Player:		2.00
3	Coaches Photo (Chris Berman)	2.00
4	Joe Gibbs CO (Racing)	2.00
5	Gifford Family (Frank, Kathie Lee, Cody)	2.00
6	Dale Jarrett (NASCAR driver)	4.00
7	Paul Tagliabue COM (Autographed)	2.00
8	Don Shula, Dave Shula (CO)	3.00

1992 Pro Line Portraits Collectibles Autographs

Randomly seeded in 1992 Pro Line foil packs, the cards are anchored by a borderless photo on the front, with the Pro Line logo at the bottom. The card backs, which are unnumbered, have a quote from the featured person in a silver-colored area. His autograph is signed over his photo on the bottom of the card back.

		MT
Complete Set (4):		160.00
Common Player:		5.00
3	Coaches Photo (Chris Berman)	25.00
6	Dale Jarrett (NASCAR driver)	40.00
7	Paul Tagliabue (COM) (Autopenned)	5.00
8	Don Shula CO, Dave Shula CO	100.00

1992 Pro Line Portraits QB Gold

These 18 insert cards, randomly included in 1992 Pro Line foil packs, feature some of the top quarterbacks in the NFL. Each card front has a color action photo on it, with gold foil stripes on the left and right borders. The player's name and "Quarterback Gold" are printed in black in the foil stripes. The backs also have gold stripes for borders; they are at the top and bottom. Statistics are given against a white background. The cards are also numbered on the back. Pro Line stated it put an average of three of these insert cards in each box it made. The company also sent a complete set to dealers who ordered a hobby case of the cards.

		MT
Complete Set (18):		10.00
Common Player:		.25
Minor Stars:		.50
1	Troy Aikman	1.50
2	Bubby Brister	.25
3	Randall Cunningham	.25
4	John Elway	1.00
5	Boomer Esiason	.25
6	Jim Everett	.25
7	Jeff George	.50
8	Jim Harbaugh	.25
9	Jeff Hostetler	.25
10	Jim Kelly	.50
11	Bernie Kosar	.25
12	Dan Marino	3.00
13	Chris Miller (Birthdate incorrectly listed as 8-91-65)	.25
14	Joe Montana	1.50
15	Warren Moon	.50
16	Mark Rypien	.25
17	Phil Simms	.25
18	Steve Young	1.50

1992 Pro Line Portraits Rookie Gold

These insert cards, randomly included one per every 1992 Pro Line jumbo pack, feature some of the top rookies in the NFL. Each card front shows a color action photo, with gold foil stripes creating borders on the right and left sides. The player's name and "Rookie Gold" are printed in black in the stripes. The backs have white backgrounds with collegiate statistics in black, plus a card number. Gold foil stripes appear at the top and bottom of the card, too. A complete set of the cards was sent to every dealer for each hobby case they ordered.

		MT
Complete Set (28):		12.00
Common Player:		.30
1	Tony Smith	.50
2	John Fina	.30
3	Alonzo Spellman	.50
4	David Klinger	1.75
5	Tommy Vardell	.60
6	Kevin Smith	.60
7	Tommy Maddox	1.25
8	Robert Porcher	.50
9	Terrell Buckley	.60
10	Eddie Robinson	.30
11	Steve Emtman	.30
12	Quentin Coryatt	.75
13	Dale Carter	.50
14	Chester McGlockton	.30
15	Sean Gilbert	.75
16	Troy Vincent	.50
17	Robert Harris	.30
18	Eugene Chung	.30
19	Vaughn Dunbar	.60
20	Derek Brown	.50
21	Johnny Mitchell	1.50
22	Siran Stacy	.50
23	Tony Sacca	.50
24	Leon Searcy	.30
25	Chris Mims	.60
26	Dana Hall	.50
27	Courtney Hawkins	.75
28	Shane Collins	.30

1992 Pro Line Portraits Team NFL

Celebrities and entertainers from outside the sporting world are featured on these five insert cards. Each card front shows the entertainer/celebrity wearing his favorite team's apparel. The backs, done in a horizontal format, have a silver panel which contains a quote from the person. The back is numbered with a "TNC" prefix and has team color-coded stripes at the top.

		MT
Complete Set (5):		10.00
Common Player:		1.50
1	Muhammad Ali	5.00
2	Milton Berle	2.50
3	Don Mattingly	3.00
4	Martin Mull	1.50
5	Isiah Thomas	2.50

1992 Pro Line Portraits Team NFL Autographs

This five-card set features stars from other sports and celebrities, with each personality pictured on the card front in their favorite team's attire. This unnumbered set marks the debut of Pro Line's Team Collectible cards, and includes a very limited number of signed Muhammad Ali cards, with his birth name Cassius Clay.

		MT
Complete Set (5):		200.00
Common Player:		20.00
1A	Muhammad Ali	150.00
1B	Muhammad Ali	475.00
2	Milton Berle	30.00
3	Don Mattingly	50.00
4	Martin Mull	20.00
5	Isiah Thomas	25.00

1992 Pro Line Portraits Wives

These insert cards, included in 1992 Pro Line Portraits packs, continue with numbers from where a similar set ended in 1991. The cards feature full-bleed photos of wives whose husbands are star coaches or players in the NFL. The card back has a profile shot of the wife, plus a quote from her. A card number is also included on the back. Each of the wives, except Kathie Lee Gifford, autographed her cards, too. They are identical to the regular cards, except they are unnumbered with a "SC" prefix and command premium prices.

		MT
Complete Set (16):		1.00
Common Wives:		.10
8	Ortancis Carter	.10
9	Faith Cherry	.10
10	Kaye Cowher	.10
11	Dainnese Gault	.10
12	Kathie Lee Gifford	.20
13	Carole Hinton	.10
14	Diane Long	.10
15	Karen Lott	.10
16	Felicia Moon	.10
17	Cindy Noble	.10
18	Line Seifert	.10
19	Mitzi Testaverde	.10
20	Robin Swilling	.10
21	Lesley Visser (ANN)	.20
22	Toni Doleman	.10
23	Diana Ditka (with Mike Ditka)	.20

1992 Pro Line Portraits Wives Autographs

These insert cards, included in 1992 Pro Line Portraits packs, continue with numbers from where a similar set ended in 1991. Each of the wives, except Kathie Lee Lee Gifford, autographed her cards. They are identical to the regular cards, except they are unnumbered and command premium prices.

		MT
Complete Set (16):		90.00
Common Wives:		6.00
8	Ortancis Carter	6.00
9	Faith Cherry	6.00
10	Kaye Cowher	6.00
11	Dainnese Gault	6.00
12	Kathie Lee Gifford	6.00
13	Carole Hinton	6.00
14	Diane Long	6.00
15	Karen Lott	6.00
16	Felicia Moon	6.00
17	Cindy Noble	6.00
18	Line Seifert	6.00
19	Mitzi Testaverde	6.00
20	Robin Swilling	6.00
21	Lesley Visser (ANN)	20.00
22	Toni Doleman	6.00
23	Diana Ditka (with Mike Ditka)	6.00

1992 Pro Line Profiles

This set features nine-card sets for 55 pro football players. Each card set traces the player's progress from his collegiate days to his professional career and life off the field. The card front has a full-bleed color action shot; the back has an action shot and a quote from the player. A 10-card Art Monk set was also offered by a mail-in exchange.

		MT
Complete Set (504):		12.00
Common Player:		.04
Wax Box:		5.00
NNO	Art Monk (Collection Bonus Set title card)	1.00
1	Ronnie Lott (Tackling opponent (1-9))	.06
2	Ronnie Lott (As youth, in baseball uniform)	.06
3	Ronnie Lott (Playing for USC)	.06
4	Ronnie Lott (Arms raised in triumph)	.06
5	Ronnie Lott (Portrait by Chris Hopkins)	.06
6	Ronnie Lott (At the Sports City Cafe)	.06
7	Ronnie Lott (With family)	.06
8	Ronnie Lott (Catching)	.06
9	Ronnie Lott (In tuxedo)	.06
10	Rodney Peete (Right arm raised (10-18))	.10
11	Rodney Peete (As youth, in football uniform)	.10
12	Rodney Peete (Playing baseball)	.10
13	Rodney Peete (In sweats with ball)	.10
14	Rodney Peete (Portrait by Merv Corning)	.10
15	Rodney Peete (Looking for receiver)	.10
16	Rodney Peete (Playing pool)	.10
17	Rodney Peete (Passing)	.10
18	Rodney Peete (Injured)	.10
19	Carl Banks (In action on field (19-27))	.04
20	Carl Banks (Playing basketball at Beecher High School)	.04
21	Carl Banks (In Michigan State uniform)	.04
22	Carl Banks (With family)	.04
23	Carl Banks (Portrait by Merv Corning)	.04
24	Carl Banks (Talking, wearing suit)	.04
25	Carl Banks (Tackling opponent)	.04
26	Carl Banks (On the air)	.04
27	Carl Banks (Close-up)	.04
28	Thurman Thomas (Running with ball, blue jersey (28-36))	.40
29	Thurman Thomas (With mother, Terlisha Cockrell)	.25
30	Thurman Thomas (At Oklahoma State)	.25
31	Thurman Thomas (With family)	.25
32	Thurman Thomas (Portrait by Gary Kelley)	.25
33	Thurman Thomas (Running with ball, white jersey)	.25
34	Thurman Thomas (Fishing)	.25
35	Thurman Thomas (Stretching)	.25
36	Thurman Thomas (Close-up)	.25
37	Roger Staubach (With Heisman Trophy (37-45))	.15
38	Roger Staubach (At Naval Academy)	.15
39	Roger Staubach (In Navy dress whites)	.15
40	Roger Staubach (Front view, running with ball)	.15
41	Roger Staubach (Portrait by John Collier)	.15
42	Roger Staubach (Passing, side view)	.15
43	Roger Staubach (With family)	.15
44	Roger Staubach (With young person at Daytop, substance abuse recovery facility)	.15
45	Roger Staubach (Calling the play)	.15
46	Jerry Rice (With MVP trophy (46-54))	.50
47	Jerry Rice (At Mississippi Valley State)	.50
48	Jerry Rice (Running with ball)	.50
49	Jerry Rice (With family)	.50
50	Jerry Rice (Portrait by Gary Kelley)	.50
51	Jerry Rice (With March of Dimes Ambassador, Ashley Johnson)	.50
52	Jerry Rice (Playing tennis)	.50
53	Jerry Rice (Arms raised in triumph)	.50
54	Jerry Rice (Close-up)	.50
55	Vinny Testaverde (Posed with Heisman (55-63))	.04
56	Vinny Testaverde (At Fork Union Military Academy)	.04
57	Vinny Testaverde (Playing for the University of Miami)	.04
58	Vinny Testaverde (Passing)	.04
59	Vinny Testaverde (Portrait by Merv Corning)	.04
60	Vinny Testaverde (Running with ball)	.04
61	Vinny Testaverde (With family)	.04
62	Vinny Testaverde (View from hips up, fist raised in triumph)	.04
63	Vinny Testaverde (With Vince Hanley)	.04

64 Anthony Carter (Manuevering around opponent, with ball 64-72) .06

65 Anthony Carter (In high school football game, black-and-white) .06

66 Anthony Carter (At Michigan, running with ball) .06

67 Anthony Carter (Fishing) .06

68 Anthony Carter (Portrait by John Collier) .06

69 Anthony Carter (Running, looking over shoulder) .06

70 Anthony Carter (With family) .06

71 Anthony Carter (Catching pass) .06

72 Anthony Carter (Close-up) .06

73 Sterling Sharpe (Catching (73-81)) .35

74 Sterling Sharpe (Passing, in high school) .35

75 Sterling Sharpe (Walking on field at South Carolina) .35

76 Sterling Sharpe (With books on SC campus) .35

77 Sterling Sharpe (Portrait by Chris Hopkins) .35

78 Sterling Sharpe (Running with ball against Rams) .35

79 Sterling Sharpe (At the piano) .35

80 Sterling Sharpe (Running with ball against Lions) .35

81 Sterling Sharpe (In brick arch with football) .35

82 Anthony Munoz (With NFL Man of the Year award (82-90)) .04

83 Anthony Munoz (As youth, batting) .04

84 Anthony Munoz (Playing for USC) .04

85 Anthony Munoz (With child at Children's Hospital) .04

86 Anthony Munoz (Portrait by Merv Corning) .04

87 Anthony Munoz (Blocking opponent) .04

88 Anthony Munoz (Holding baby, with fellow players and children) .04

89 Anthony Munoz (In action for Bengals) .04

90 Anthony Munoz (Close-up) .04

91 Bubby Brister (Passing, white jersey (91-99)) .04

92 Bubby Brister (NLU uniform) .04

93 Bubby Brister (Baseball unform) .04

94 Bubby Brister (With kids at Ronald McDonald House) .04

95 Bubby Brister (Portrait by Greg Spalenka) .04

96 Bubby Brister (Wearing western attire) .04

97 Bubby Brister (Running with ball, white jersey) .04

98 Bubby Brister (Passing, black jersey) .04

99 Bubby Brister (Close-up) .04

100 Bernie Kosar (Passing, white jersey (100-108)) .10

101 Bernie Kosar (In high school) .10

102 Bernie Kosar (Playing for Miami) .10

103 Bernie Kosar (Being tackled) .10

104 Bernie Kosar (Portrait by Greg Spalenka) .10

105 Bernie Kosar (With family) .10

106 Bernie Kosar (Playing golf) .10

107 Bernie Kosar (Looking for receiver) .10

108 Bernie Kosar (Close-up) .10

109 Art Shell (On sidelines (109-117)) .06

110 Art Shell (At Maryland State) .06

111 Art Shell (Playing for Raiders) .06

112 Art Shell (Playing basketball with sons) .06

113 Art Shell (Portrait by Chris Hopkins) .06

114 Art Shell (Talking to player on sidelines) .06

115 Art Shell (In front of big screen TV) .06

116 Art Shell (In line of scrimmage) .06

117 Art Shell (With teddy bear) .06

118 Don Shula (With players) .06

119 Don Shula (At John Carroll University) .06

120 Don Shula (Coaching Baltimore Colts) .06

121 Don Shula (With son, Mike) .06

122 Don Shula (Portrait by Merv Corning) .06

123 Don Shula (With daughters) .06

124 Don Shula (With Dan Marino) .06

125 Don Shula (With doctor at the Don Shula Foundation) .06

126 Don Shula (With Super Bowl trophies) .06

127 Joe Gibbs (Writing out play) .06

128 Joe Gibbs (Playing for San Diego State) .06

129 Joe Gibbs (Coaching on sidelines) .06

130 Joe Gibbs (With sons) .06

131 Joe Gibbs (Portrait by John Collier) .06

132 Joe Gibbs (Reading in office) .06

133 Joe Gibbs (With Youth For Tomorrow group) .06

134 Joe Gibbs (In front of race car) .06

135 Joe Gibbs (In front of Church) .06

136 Junior Seau (Holding ball (136-144)) .15

137 Junior Seau (As youth, in football uniform) .15

138 Junior Seau (At USC) .15

139 Junior Seau (Finger pointing up) .15

140 Junior Seau (Portrait by Merv Corning) .15

141 Junior Seau (With wife, Gina) .15

142 Junior Seau (Running on beach) .15

143 Junior Seau (Lifting weights) .15

144 Junior Seau (In swim trunks with seaweed) .15

145 Al Toon (Running with ball, white jersey 145-153) .06

146 Al Toon (During Pee-Wee football days) .06

147 Al Toon (On the field at Wisconsin) .06

148 Al Toon (With family) .06

149 Al Toon (Portrait by Gary Kelley) .06

150 Al Toon (Catching) .06

151 Al Toon (Working out) .06

152 Al Toon (Running with ball, green jersey) .06

153 Al Toon (Close-up) .06

154 Jack Kemp (In office (154-162)) .10

155 Jack Kemp (Portrait from Occidental College) .10

156 Jack Kemp (Playing for Chargers) .10

157 Jack Kemp (With family) .10

158 Jack Kemp (Portrait by Merv Corning) .10

159 Jack Kemp (Playing for Buffalo) .10

160 Jack Kemp (Passing) .10

161 Jack Kemp (With son, Jeff) .10

162 Jack Kemp (In Washington) .10

163 Jim Harbaugh (Passing, blue jersey (163-171)) .10

164 Jim Harbaugh (Playing in high school) .10

165 Jim Harbaugh (Playing for Michigan) .10

166 Jim Harbaugh (Passing, white jersey) .10

167 Jim Harbaugh (Portrait by Gary Kelley) .10

168 Jim Harbaugh (With children in children's home) .10

169 Jim Harbaugh (Working out) .10

170 Jim Harbaugh (Calling play) .10

171 Jim Harbaugh (Close-up) .10

172 Dan McGwire (From waist up (172-180)) .15

173 Dan McGwire (At Purdue) .15

174 Dan McGwire (At San Diego) .15

175 Dan McGwire (From waist down) .15

176 Dan McGwire (Portrait by Chris Hopkins) .15

177 Dan McGwire (Passing, blue jersey) .15

178 Dan McGwire (Passing, white jersey) .15

179 Dan McGwire (Working out) .15

180 Dan McGwire (With wife, Dana) .15

181 Troy Aikman (Passing, wearing blue jersey (181-189)) .75

182 Troy Aikman (As youth) .75

183 Troy Aikman (Passing, at UCLA) .75

184 Troy Aikman (Preparing to pass, with Cowboys) .75

185 Troy Aikman (Portrait by Greg Spalenka) .75

186 Troy Aikman (Golfing) .75

187 Troy Aikman (Looking for opening, front view) .75

188 Troy Aikman (In sweats, passing) .75

189 Troy Aikman (In cowboy hat) .75

190 Keith Byars (With little brother (190-198)) .06

191 Keith Byars (Childhood picture) .06

192 Keith Byars (High School football photo) .06

193 Keith Byars (Ohio State photo, red jersey) .06

194 Keith Byars (Portrait by Chris Hopkins) .06

195 Keith Byars (Working out) .06

196 Keith Byars (Running, green jersey) .06

197 Keith Byars (Running, white jersey) .06

198 Keith Byars (Close-up) .06

199 Timm Rosenbach (Running with ball, red jersey 199-207)) .04

200 Timm Rosenbach (In high school football uniform) .04

201 Timm Rosenbach (At Washington State) .04

202 Timm Rosenbach (With wife, Kerry) .04

203 Timm Rosenbach (Portrait by John Collier) .04

204 Timm Rosenbach (Passing, white jersey) .04

205 Timm Rosenbach (Roping a calf) .04

206 Timm Rosenbach (Working out) .04

207 Timm Rosenbach (Seated on hay, in western attire) .04

208 Gary Clark (In the end zone (208-216)) .12

209 Gary Clark (Playing for James Madison University) .12

210 Gary Clark (Catching ball in end zone) .12

211 Gary Clark (With daughter) .12

212 Gary Clark (Portrait by John Collier) .12

213 Gary Clark (Running, slouched position) .12

214 Gary Clark (Playing basketball) .12

215 Gary Clark (Lifted by teammates) .12

216 Gary Clark (Close-up) .12

217 Chris Doleman (Playing for Vikings, white jersey 217-225)) .04

218 Chris Doleman (In Pittsburgh uniform) .04

219 Chris Doleman (With wife, Toni, and dog) .04

220 Chris Doleman (Playing for Vikings, blue jersey) .04

221 Chris Doleman (Portrait by John Collier) .04

222 Chris Doleman (Working out) .04

223 Chris Doleman (Leaping over opponent) .04

224 Chris Doleman (Playing golf) .04

225 Chris Doleman (Close-up) .04

226 John Elway (Passing, orange jersey (226-234)) .25

227 John Elway (Playing for Stanford) .25

228 John Elway (Passing, white jersey) .25

229 John Elway (With family) .25

230 John Elway (Portrait by Greg Spalenka) .25

231 John Elway (Working out) .25

232 John Elway (Sitting on car) .25

233 John Elway (Running with ball) .25

234 John Elway (Close-up) .25

235 Boomer Esiason (Calling play (235-243)) .15

236 Boomer Esiason (In high school) .15

237 Boomer Esiason (In Terps uniform) .15

238 Boomer Esiason (Passing) .15

239 Boomer Esiason (Portrait by Greg Spalenka) .15

240 Boomer Esiason (With dogs) .15

241 Boomer Esiason (With Kinny McQuade) .15

242 Boomer Esiason (Looking for pass receiver) .15

243 Boomer Esiason (Close-up) .15

244 Jim Everett (Passing, white jersey (244-252)) .10

245 Jim Everett (In high school uniform) .10

246 Jim Everett (Playing for Purdue) .10

247 Jim Everett (With family) .10

248 Jim Everett (Portrait by Greg Spalenka) .10

249 Jim Everett (Running with ball, blue jersey) .10

250 Jim Everett (Fishing) .10

251 Jim Everett (Handing off ball) .10

252 Jim Everett (Close-up) .10

253 Eric Green (Running with ball (253-261)) .04

254 Eric Green (With coach Sam Rutigliano) .04

255 Eric Green (Being blocked by opponent) .04

256 Eric Green (Playing basketball) .04

257 Eric Green (Portrait by Merv Corning) .04

258 Eric Green (In locker room) .04

259 Eric Green (Blocking opponent) .04

260 Eric Green (Catching) .04

261 Eric Green (Close-up) .04

262 Jerry Glanville (On motorcycle (262-270)) .04

263 Jerry Glanville (With Lions coaching staff) .04

264 Jerry Glanville (Coaching, clapping) .04

265 Jerry Glanville (With family) .04

266 Jerry Glanville (Portrait by Gary Kelley) .04

267 Jerry Glanville (Coaching, with players) .04

268 Jerry Glanville (In race car) .04

269 Jerry Glanville (With country music stars) .04

270 Jerry Glanville (In black western attire) .04

271 Jeff Hostetler (Passing, blue jersey (271-279)) .12

272 Jeff Hostetler (Playing for West Virginia) .12

273 Jeff Hostetler (Lifting weights) .12

274 Jeff Hostetler (With family) .12

275 Jeff Hostetler (Portrait by John Collier) .12

276 Jeff Hostetler (Passing, white jersey) .12

277 Jeff Hostetler (At Ronald McDonald house) .12

278 Jeff Hostetler (With father-in-law) .12

279 Jeff Hostetler (Close-up) .12

280 Haywood Jeffires (Catching, Houston uniform (280-288)) .15

281 Haywood Jeffires (Playing for North Carolina) .15

282 Haywood Jeffires (With wife, Robin) .15

283 Haywood Jeffires (Pushing past opponent) .15

284 Haywood Jeffires (Portrait by John Collier) .15

285 Haywood Jeffires (With car) .15

286 Haywood Jeffires (With Boy and Girls Club members) .15

287 Haywood Jeffires (Being tackled) .15

288 Haywood Jeffires (Close-up) .15

289 Michael Irvin (Running with ball (289-297)) .40

290 Michael Irvin (Playing basketball) .40

291 Michael Irvin (In Miami uniform) .40

292 Michael Irvin (With wife, Sandy) .40

293 Michael Irvin (Portrait by Gary Kelley) .40

294 Michael Irvin (Catching) .40

295 Michael Irvin (With student, Nyna Sherte) .40

296 Michael Irvin (Playing in Pro Bowl) .40

297 Michael Irvin (Close-up) .40

298 Steve Largent (Catching, blue jersey (298-306)) .10

299 Steve Largent (Playing for Tulsa) .10

300 Steve Largent (With family) .10

301 Steve Largent (At school for disabled children) .10

302 Steve Largent (Portrait by Chris Hopkins) .10

303 Steve Largent (Catching, white jersey) .10

304 Steve Largent (In dress attire) .10

305 Steve Largent (Running, white jersey) .10

306 Steve Largent (Close-up) .10

307 Ken O'Brien (Passing, side view (307-315)) .04

308 Ken O'Brien (With University of California-Davis) .04

309 Ken O'Brien (With family) .04

310 Ken O'Brien (Passing, front view) .04

311 Ken O'Brien (Portrait by Chris Hopkins) .04

312 Ken O'Brien (Shaking hands with Tony Eason) .04

313 Ken O'Brien (Playing golf) .04

314 Ken O'Brien (Handing off the ball) .04

315 Ken O'Brien (Close-up) .04

316 Christian Okoye (Running with ball, red jersey 316-324) .06

317 Christian Okoye (Close-up at Asuza Pacific Univ.) .06

318 Christian Okoye (Cooking) .06

319 Christian Okoye (Running with ball, white jersey) .06

320 Christian Okoye (Portrait by Chris Hopkins) .06

321 Christian Okoye (In Nigerian attire) .06

322 Christian Okoye (With daughter, Christiana) .06

323 Christian Okoye (Withstanding an opponent) .06

324 Christian Okoye (In casual attire) .06

325 Michael Dean Perry (Blocking opponent, white jersey 325-333) .12

326 Michael Dean Perry (Playing for Clemson) .12

327 Michael Dean Perry (Blocking opponent, brown jersey) .12

328 Michael Dean Perry (With family) .12

329 Michael Dean Perry (Portrait by Merv Corning) .12

330 Michael Dean Perry (At Children's Hospital) .12

331 Michael Dean Perry (Playing basketball) .12

332 Michael Dean Perry (Blocking opponent, horizontal shot) .12

333 Michael Dean Perry (With AFC Player of the Year trophy) .12

334 Chris Miller (Passing, black jersey (334-342)) .10

335 Chris Miller (As youth, fishing) .10

336 Chris Miller (Playing for Oregon) .10

337 Chris Miller (In baseball uniform) .10

338 Chris Miller (Portrait by Greg Spalenka) .10

#	Player	Price
339	Chris Miller (Running with ball)	.10
340	Chris Miller (With wife, Jennifer)	.10
341	Chris Miller (In the Pro Bowl)	.10
342	Chris Miller (Close-up)	.10
343	Phil Simms (Passing, blue jersey (343-351))	.10
344	Phil Simms (Calling the play)	.10
345	Phil Simms (With family)	.10
346	Phil Simms (Playing pool)	.10
347	Phil Simms (Portrait by Greg Spalenka)	.10
348	Phil Simms (Running with ball)	.10
349	Phil Simms (With young man from the Eastern Christian School for handicapped children)	.10
350	Phil Simms (Passing, white jersey)	.10
351	Phil Simms (Close-up)	.10
352	Bruce Smith (Tackling opponent, white jersey 352-360))	.06
353	Bruce Smith (At Virginia Tech)	.06
354	Bruce Smith (Close-up in game)	.06
355	Bruce Smith (With wife, Carmen)	.06
356	Bruce Smith (Portrait by John Collier)	.06
357	Bruce Smith (In Pro Bowl)	.06
358	Bruce Smith (Working out)	.06
359	Bruce Smith (Blocking, blue jersey)	.06
360	Bruce Smith (Close-up)	.06
361	Derrick Thomas (Running, red jersey (361-369))	.15
362	Derrick Thomas (At the University of Alabama)	.15
363	Derrick Thomas (With his father's Air Force momentos)	.15
364	Derrick Thomas (Seated on helmet)	.15
365	Derrick Thomas (Portrait by Merv Corning)	.15
366	Derrick Thomas (With motivational program participants)	.15
367	Derrick Thomas (Posed with Limo)	.15
368	Derrick Thomas (In Pro Bowl)	.15
369	Derrick Thomas (Close-up)	.15
370	Pat Swilling (Relaxed against tree (370-378))	.06
371	Pat Swilling (At Georgia Tech)	.06
372	Pat Swilling (With family)	.06
373	Pat Swilling (Running on field)	.06
374	Pat Swilling (Portrait by John Collier)	.06
375	Pat Swilling (Working out)	.06
376	Pat Swilling (Tackling opponent on icy field)	.06
377	Pat Swilling (With underprivileged children)	.06
378	Pat Swilling (Relaxed at home)	.06
379	Eric Dickerson (Close-up in Rams football gear 379-387))	.10
380	Eric Dickerson (Playing for SMU)	.10
381	Eric Dickerson (With great aunt Viola)	.10
382	Eric Dickerson (Running with ball, Rams uniform)	.10
383	Eric Dickerson (Portrait by Merv Corning)	.10
384	Eric Dickerson (Running with ball, Colts uniform)	.10
385	Eric Dickerson (Working out)	.10
386	Eric Dickerson (Leaping over other players, Colts uniform)	.10
387	Eric Dickerson (Close-up)	.10
388	Howie Long (Being blocked by opponent (388-396))	.06
389	Howie Long (At Villanova)	.06
390	Howie Long (Rushing quarterback)	.06
391	Howie Long (With family)	.06
392	Howie Long (Portrait by Chris Hopkins)	.06
393	Howie Long (On sidelines)	.06
394	Howie Long (Boxing)	.06
395	Howie Long (Blocking pass)	.06
396	Howie Long (Close-up)	.06
397	Mike Singletary (Crouched, ready for play)	.06
398	Mike Singletary (At Baylor)	.06
399	Mike Singletary (With children)	.06
400	Mike Singletary (In the gym)	.06
401	Mike Singletary (Portrait by Gary Kelley)	.06
402	Mike Singletary (Rushing, white jersey)	.06
403	Mike Singletary (With Man of the Year Award)	.06
404	Mike Singletary (Tackling, blue jersey)	.06
405	Mike Singletary (In sweatshirt)	.06
406	John Taylor (Celebrating on the field (406-414))	.10
407	John Taylor (In high school)	.10
408	John Taylor (Playing for Delaware State)	.10
409	John Taylor (Posed with bowling ball and pins)	.10
410	John Taylor (Portrait by John Collier)	.10
411	John Taylor (With family)	.10
412	John Taylor (With kids from Northern Light School)	.10
413	John Taylor (Catching)	.10
414	John Taylor (Close-up)	.10
415	Andre Tippett (Blocking opponent, arms outspread)	.04
416	Andre Tippett (At Iowa State (416-423))	.04
417	Andre Tippett (With daughter, Janea Lynn)	.04
418	Andre Tippett (In Okinawa with karate masters)	.04
419	Andre Tippett (Portrait by Gary Kelley)	.04
420	Andre Tippett (Running on the field)	.04
421	Andre Tippett (Performing karate move)	.04
422	Andre Tippett (In action, from knees up)	.04
423	Andre Tippett (Close-up)	.04
424	Jim Kelly (Passing, white jersey (424-432))	.25
425	Jim Kelly (With Punt, Pass, and Kick trophy)	.25
426	Jim Kelly (Passing for Miami)	.25
427	Jim Kelly (With family)	.25
428	Jim Kelly (Portrait by Greg Spalenka)	.25
429	Jim Kelly (With sports jersey collection)	.25
430	Jim Kelly (With young cancer patients)	.25
431	Jim Kelly (Calling play)	.25
432	Jim Kelly (Close-up)	.25
433	Mark Rypien (Passing, horizontal shot (433-441))	.10
434	Mark Rypien (In high school football uniform)	.10
435	Mark Rypien (At Washington State)	.10
436	Mark Rypien (Playing golf)	.10
437	Mark Rypien (Portrait by Merv Corning)	.10
438	Mark Rypien (With family)	.10
439	Mark Rypien (Passing, vertical shot)	.10
440	Mark Rypien (With young cystic fibrosis patients)	.10
441	Mark Rypien (Close-up)	.10
442	Warren Moon (Passing, white jersey (442-450))	.20
443	Warren Moon (As youth, in football uniform)	.20
444	Warren Moon (Playing for Washington)	.20
445	Warren Moon (With Edmonton Eskimos)	.20
446	Warren Moon (Portrait by Greg Spalenka)	.20
447	Warren Moon (With family)	.20
448	Warren Moon (Calling the play)	.20
449	Warren Moon (In his office)	.20
450	Warren Moon (Posed with football and helmet)	.20
451	Deion Sanders (In position for a play (451-459))	.15
452	Deion Sanders (As youth, in football uniform)	.15
453	Deion Sanders (With Florida State)	.15
454	Deion Sanders (Playing baseball)	.15
455	Deion Sanders (Portrait by Gary Kelley)	.15
456	Deion Sanders (Running with ball)	.15
457	Deion Sanders (With family)	.15
458	Deion Sanders (Walking on field)	.15
459	Deion Sanders (Close-up)	.15
460	Lawrence Taylor (Facing opponent, blue jersey (460-468))	.10
461	Lawrence Taylor (At North Carolina State)	.10
462	Lawrence Taylor (Side view, white jersey)	.10
463	Lawrence Taylor (Playing golf on football field)	.10
464	Lawrence Taylor (Portrait by Chris Hopkins)	.10
465	Lawrence Taylor (In Honolulu)	.10
466	Lawrence Taylor (In front of his restaurant)	.10
467	Lawrence Taylor (Steping over Jets player)	.10
468	Lawrence Taylor (Close-up)	.10
469	Randall Cunningham (Looking for receiver)	.10
470	Randall Cunningham (In Pop Warner team uniform)	.15
471	Randall Cunningham	.15
472	Randall Cunningham (Running with ball)	.15
473	Randall Cunningham (Portrait by Greg Spalenka)	.15
474	Randall Cunningham (Playing golf)	.15
475	Randall Cunningham (Passing)	.15
476	Randall Cunningham (Working out)	.15
477	Randall Cunningham (In dress attire)	.15
478	Earnest Byner (Redskins uniform, running, side view 478-486))	.06
479	Earnest Byner (At East Carolina, black and white)	.06
480	Earnest Byner (Browns, brown jersey)	.06
481	Earnest Byner (With family)	.06
482	Earnest Byner (Portrait by Chris Hopkins)	.06
483	Earnest Byner (Browns, white jersey)	.06
484	Earnest Byner (Fishing)	.06
485	Earnest Byner (Redskins, uniform, running, front view)	.06
486	Earnest Byner (In workout attire)	.06
487	Mike Ditka (On sideline, in shirt and tie 487-495))	.10
488	Mike Ditka (Playing for Bears)	.10
489	Mike Ditka (With family)	.10
490	Mike Ditka (Playing for Cowboys)	.10
491	Mike Ditka (Portrait by Garry Kelley)	.10
492	Mike Ditka (With antique car)	.10
493	Mike Ditka (Playing golf)	.10
494	Mike Ditka (Eating)	.10
495	Mike Ditka (Close-up)	.10
496	Art Monk (Catching, close-up (496-504))	.75
497	Art Monk (Running hurdles in high school)	.75
498	Art Monk (Running with ball, front view)	.75
499	Art Monk (With family)	.75
500	Art Monk (Portrait by Gary Kelley)	.75
501	Art Monk (With youth at his football camp)	.75
502	Art Monk (Running with ball, side view)	.75
503	Art Monk (Working out)	.75
504	Art Monk (Ready to catch ball, hands extended)	.75

1992 Pro Line Profiles Autographs

Profiles Autographs run parallel to the Profiles set and were inserted in Pro Line foil packs at a rate of one per box. The cards were signed in black Sharpies, embossed with an NFL seal and are missing the card number to distinguish them from regular cards. Cards signed by Jack Kemp, Chris Miller and Mark Rypien do not exist, as well as cards 46-49, 56, 58, 356, 376, 383, 457-459 and 504. Art Monk's autographed cards were the first ones sent to wrapper redemption offers and do not have the card numbers removed and are not considered part of the set. Prices below are for the entire set of that player.

	MT
Complete Set (457):	3200.

Troy Aikman (181-189):	45.00
Carl Banks (19-27):	4.00
Bubby Brister (91-99):	4.00
Keith Byars (190-198):	4.00
Earnest Byner (478-486):	4.00
Anthony Carter (64-72):	4.00
Gary Clark (208-216):	4.00
Randall Cunningham (469-477):	20.00
Eric Dickerson (379-387):	10.00
Mike Ditka (487-495):	20.00
Chris Doleman (217-225):	4.00
John Elway (226-234):	45.00
Boomer Esiason (235-243):	8.00
Jim Everett (244-252):	25.00
Joe Gibbs (127-135):	8.00
Jerry Glanville (262-270):	4.00
Eric Green (253-261):	4.00
Jim Harbaugh (163-171):	4.00
Jeff Hostetler (271-279):	4.00
Michael Irvin (289-297):	20.00
Haywood Jeffires (280-288):	4.00
Jim Kelly (424-432):	20.00
Jack Kemp (154-162):	25.00
Bernie Kosar (100-108):	4.00
Steve Largent (298-306):	25.00
Howie Long (388-396):	20.00
Ronnie Lott (1-9):	8.00
Dan McGwire (172-180):	4.00
Art Monk (496-504):	35.00
Warren Moon (442-450):	10.00
Anthony Munoz (82-90):	8.00
Ken O'Brien (307-315):	4.00
Christian Okoye (316-324):	4.00
Rodney Peete (10-18):	4.00
Michael D. Perry (325-333):	4.00
Jerry Rice (46-54):	50.00
Timm Rosenbach (199-207):	4.00
Deion Sanders (451-459):	30.00
Junior Seau (136-144):	8.00
Sterling Sharpe (73-81):	10.00
Art Shell (109-117):	8.00
Don Shula (118-126):	20.00
Phil Simms (343-351):	15.00
Mike Singletary (397-405):	15.00
Bruce Smith (352-360):	8.00
Roger Staubach (37-45):	25.00
Pat Swilling (370-378):	4.00
John Taylor (406-414):	4.00
Lionel Taylor (460-468):	10.00
Vinny Testaverde (55-63):	8.00
Derrick Thomas (361-369):	35.00
Thurman Thomas (28-36):	12.00
Andre Tippett (415-423):	4.00
Al Toon (145-153):	4.00

Post-1980 cards in Near Mint condition will generally sell for about 75% of the quoted Mint value. Excellent-condition cards bring no more than 40%.

1992-93 Pro Line SB Program

Numbered "of 9," the nine-card set chronicles the career of Steve Young from BYU to the L.A. Express to Tampa Bay and San Francisco. Showcased on the front are borderless photos, with his name in a strip at the top and the Pro Line logo at the bottom. The card back includes a photo, along with highpoints of his life and football career. A promo card was included with copies of the 1993 Super Bowl program.

		MT
Complete Set (9):		8.00
Common Player:		1.00
1	Steve Young (Just after release of ball)	1.00
2	Steve Young (Posed beside statue of Brigham Young)	1.00
3	Steve Young (in BYU uniform)	1.00
4	Steve Young (in Los Angeles Express uniform USFL)	1.00
5	Steve Young (Portrait)	1.00
6	Steve Young (in Tampa Bay Buccaneers uniform)	1.00
7	Steve Young (Posed with children for the Children's Miracle Network)	1.00
8	Steve Young (in San Francisco 49ers uniform)	1.00
9	Steve Young (Close-up shot, posed in law library)	1.00

1993 Pro Line Live Draft Day NYC

This 10-card set included cards which featured the four possible top draft picks of the 1993 draft with different teams. The set was housed in a cellophane pack and given to attendees at the NFL Draft in New York. The fronts include a photo, with a colored stripe down the right side which includes the player's name and possible team, along with the NFL Draft logo. The Classic Pro Line Live logo is in the lower left. The card backs have a photo at the top, with a write-up, stats and the card number printed below. To add to the confusion, each card was No. 1. Classic produced 1,000 sets.

		MT
Complete Set (10):		75.00
Common Player:		2.50
1A	Drew Bledsoe	20.00
1B	Drew Bledsoe	20.00
1C	Drew Bledsoe	20.00
1D	Eric Curry	2.50
1E	Eric Curry	2.50
1F	Marvin Jones	2.50
1G	Marvin Jones	2.50
1H	Rick Mirer	7.00
1I	Rick Mirer	7.00
1J	Rick Mirer	7.00

1993 Pro Line Live Draft Day QVC

Resembling the Draft Day New York City set on the front, the backs of the 10-card set included the Classic Pro Line Live logo, draft date and set number "of 9,300" printed over a continuous background of "Draft Day 1993." The cards also featured different versions with the players on different teams. The set was produced for sale on the QVC television network.

		MT
Complete Set (10):		20.00
Common Player:		1.00
1A	Drew Bledsoe	4.00
1B	Drew Bledsoe	4.00
1C	Drew Bledsoe	4.00
1D	Eric Curry	1.00
1E	Eric Curry	1.00
1F	Marvin Jones	1.00
1G	Marvin Jones	1.00
1H	Rick Mirer	2.00
1I	Rick Mirer	2.00
1J	Rick Mirer	2.00

1993 Pro Line Previews

Randomly seeded in 1993 Classic Football Draft Picks foil packs, the five-card set focused on the previous five No. 1 NFL Draft picks. According to Classic, 12,000 of each card was produced. Versions of Pro Line Live, Portraits and Profiles are on the card fronts, while the backs for each card are identical, listing the season and the player's name. The cards carry a "PL" prefix.

		MT
Complete Set (5):		45.00
Common Player:		4.00
1	Troy Aikman (Live)	20.00
2	Jeff George (Profile)	6.00
3	Russell Maryland (Live)	4.00

4 Steve Emtman 4.00
5 Drew Bledsoe 20.00
(Portrait)

1993 Pro Line Live

This premiere edition features 285 Classic Pro Line Live cards, 48 Portraits cards and 13 nine-card Profiles sets. The card front has a full-bleed color action photo with the team and player's name on the right in its corresponding color. The back has an action photo and player information. Randomly inserted autographed cards were also issued, two per case. Players (35) signed between 900-1,050 cards; the autograph and the limited-edition card number appear on the card front. The card front is basically the same design as those in the regular set. The card back indicates the card is a limited-edition autographed card. The players who signed cards are #s 7, 16, 23, 34, 46, 51, 67, 70, 76, 79, 87, 88, 91, 96, 99, 107, 108, 109, 119, 120, 121, 124, 129, 131, 146, 151, 158, 160, 188, 199, 201, 217, 227, 231, and 242. These command premium prices.

	MT
Complete Set (285):	15.00
Common Player:	.05
Minor Stars:	.10
Wax Box:	15.00
1 Michael Haynes	.10
2 Chris Hinton	.05
3 Pierce Holt	.05
4 Chris Miller	.10
5 Mike Pritchard	.05
6 Andre Rison	.20
7 Deion Sanders	.50
8 Jessie Tuggle	.05
9 Lincoln Kennedy	.10
10 Roger Harper	.10
11 Cornelius Bennett	.05
12 Henry Jones	.05
13 Jim Kelly	.20
14 Bill Brooks	.05
15 Nate Odomes	.05
16 Andre Reed	.10
17 Frank Reich	.05
18 Bruce Smith	.05
19 Steve Tasker	.05
20 Thurman Thomas	.20
21 Thomas Smith	.10
22 John Parrella	.10
23 Neal Anderson	.05
24 Mark Carrier	.05
25 Jim Harbaugh	.10
26 Darren Lewis	.05
27 Steve McMichael	.05
28 Alonzo Spellman	.05
29 Tom Waddle	.05
30 Curtis Conway	.50
31 Carl Simpson	.05
32 David Fulcher	.05
33 Harold Green	.05
34 David Klingler	.10
35 Tim Krumrie	.05
36 Carl Pickens	.50
37 Alfred Williams	.05
38 Darryl Williams	.05
39 John Copeland	.10
40 Tony McGee	.10
41 Bernie Kosar	.05
42 Kevin Mack	.05
43 Clay Mathews	.05
44 Eric Metcalf	.05
45 Michael Dean Perry	.05
46 Vinny Testaverde	.05
47 Jerry Ball	.05
48 Tommy Vardell	.05
49 Steve Everitt	.10
50 Dan Footman	.05
51 Troy Aikman	.75
52 Daryl Johnston	.05
53 Tony Casillas	.05
54 Charles Haley	.05
55 Alvin Harper	.10
56 Michael Irvin	.20
57 Robert Jones	.05
58 Russell Maryland	.05
59 Nate Newton	.05
60 Ken Norton	.05
61 Jay Novacek	.05
62 Emmitt Smith	1.50
63 Kevin Smith	.20
64 Kevin Williams	.20
65 Darrin Smith	.10
66 Steve Atwater	.05
67 Rod Bernstine	.05
68 Mike Croel	.05
69 John Elway	1.00
70 Tommy Maddox	.10
71 Karl Mecklenburg	.05
72 Shannon Sharpe	.20
73 Dennis Smith	.05
74 Dan Williams	.10
75 Glyn Milburn	.20
76 Pat Swilling	.05
77 Bernie Blades	.05
78 Herman Moore	.50
79 Rodney Peete	.05
80 Brett Perriman	.05
81 Barry Sanders	2.00
82 Chris Spielman	.05
83 Andre Ware	.05
84 Ryan McNeil	.10
85 Antonio London	.05
86 Tony Bennett	.05
87 Terrell Buckley	.05
88 Brett Favre	2.00
89 Brian Noble	.05
90 Ken O'Brien	.05
91 Sterling Sharpe	.20
92 Reggie White	.20
93 John Stephens	.05
94 Wayne Simmons	.10
95 George Teague	.10
96 Ray Childress	.05
97 Curtis Duncan	.05
98 Ernest Givins	.05
99 Haywood Jeffires	.05
100 Bubba McDowell	.05
101 Warren Moon	.20
102 Al Smith	.05
103 Lorenzo White	.05
104 Brad Hopkins	.05
105 Michael Barrow	.10
106 Duane Bickett	.05
107 Quentin Coryatt	.10
108 Steve Emtman	.05
109 Jeff George	.20
110 Anthony Johnson	.05
111 Reggie Langhorne	.05
112 Jack Trudeau	.05
113 Clarence Verdin	.05
114 Sean Dawkins	.05
115 Roosevelt Potts	.10
116 Dale Carter	.05
117 Dave Krieg	.05
118 Nick Lowery	.05
119 Christian Okoye	.05
120 Neil Smith	.05
121 Derrick Thomas	.20
122 Harvey Williams	.05
123 Barry Word	.05
124 Joe Montana	1.00
125 Marcus Allen	.20
126 James Lofton	.05
127 Nick Bell	.05
128 Tim Brown	.20
129 Eric Dickerson	.10
130 Jeff Hostetler	.05
131 Howie Long	.10
132 Todd Marinovich	.05
133 Greg Townsend	.05
134 Patrick Bates	.05
135 Billy Joe Hobart	.05
136 Willie Anderson	.05
137 Shane Conlan	.05
138 Henry Ellard	.05
139 Jim Everett	.05
140 Cleveland Gary	.05
141 Sean Gilbert	.05
142 Todd Lyght	.05
143 Jerome Bettis	1.50
144 Troy Drayton	.20
145 Louis Oliver	.05
146 Marco Coleman	.05
147 Bryan Cox	.05
148 Mark Duper	.05
149 Irving Fryar	.05
150 Mark Higgs	.05
151 Keith Jackson	.10
152 Dan Marino	1.50
153 Troy Vincent	.10
154 Richmond Webb	.05
155 O.J. McDuffie	.75
156 Terry Kirby	.20
157 Terry Allen	.20
158 Anthony Carter	.05
159 Cris Carter	.50
160 Chris Doleman	.05
161 Randall McDaniel	.05
162 Audray McMillian	.05
163 Henry Thomas	.05
164 Gary Zimmerman	.05
165 Robert Smith	1.00
166 Qadry Ismail	.20
167 Vincent Brown	.05
168 Marv Cook	.05
169 Greg McMurtry	.05
170 Jon Vaughn	.05
171 Leonard Russell	.10
172 Andre Tippett	.05
173 Scott Zolak	.05
174 Drew Bledsoe	3.00
175 Chris Slade	.10
176 Morten Andersen	.05
177 Vaughn Dunbar	.05
178 Rickey Jackson	.05
179 Vaughan Johnson	.05
180 Eric Martin	.05
181 Sam Mills	.05
182 Brad Muster	.05
183 Willie Roaf	.10
184 Irv Smith	.20
185 Reggie Freeman	.10
186 Michael Brooks	.05
187 Dave Brown	.10
188 Rodney Hampton	.05
189 Pepper Johnson	.05
190 Ed McCaffrey	.30
191 David Meggett	.05
192 Bart Oates	.05
193 Phil Simms	.10
194 Lawrence Taylor	.05
195 Michael Strahan	.05
196 Brad Baxter	.05
197 Johnny Johnson	.10
198 Boomer Esiason	.05
199 Ronnie Lott	.10
200 Johnny Mitchell	.05
201 Rob Moore	.20
202 Browning Nagle	.05
203 Blair Thomas	.05
204 Marvin Jones	.10
205 Coleman Rudolph	.05
206 Eric Allen	.05
207 Fred Barnett	.05
208 Tim Harris	.05
209 Randall Cunningham	.20
210 Seth Joyner	.05
211 Clyde Simmons	.05
212 Herschel Walker	.10
213 Calvin Williams	.05
214 Lester Holmes	.10
215 Leonard Renfro	.10
216 Chris Chandler	.20
217 Gary Clark	.05
218 Ken Harvey	.05
219 Randal Hill	.05
220 Steve Beuerlein	.10
221 Ricky Proehl	.05
222 Timm Rosenbach	.05
223 Garrison Hearst	1.00
224 Ernest Dye	.10
225 Bubby Brister	.05
226 Dermontti Dawson	.05
227 Barry Foster	.05
228 Kevin Greene	.05
229 Merril Hoge	.05
230 Greg Lloyd	.05
231 Neil O'Donnell	.20
232 Rod Woodson	.10
233 Deon Figures	.10
234 Chad Brown	.20
235 Marion Butts	.05
236 Gill Byrd	.05
237 Ronnie Harmon	.05
238 Stan Humphries	.10
239 Anthony Miller	.05
240 Leslie O'Neil	.05
241 Stanley Richard	.05
242 Junior Seau	.20
243 Darrien Gordon	.20
244 Natrone Means	1.00
245 Dana Hall	.05
246 Brent Jones	.05
247 Tim McDonald	.05
248 Steve Bono	.05
249 Jerry Rice	1.00
250 John Taylor	.05
251 Ricky Watters	.20
252 Steve Young	.75
253 Dana Stubblefield	.10
254 Todd Kelly	.10
255 Brian Blades	.05
256 Ferrell Edmunds	.05
257 Stan Gelbaugh	.05
258 Cortez Kennedy	.10
259 Dan McGwire	.05
260 Chris Warren	.10
261 John L. Williams	.05
262 David Wyman	.05
263 Rick Mirer	.25
264 Carlton Gray	.05
265 Marty Carter	.05
266 Reggie Cobb	.05
267 Lawrence Dawsey	.05
268 Santana Dotson	.05
269 Craig Erickson	.10
270 Paul Gruber	.05
271 Keith McCants	.05
272 Broderick Thomas	.05
273 Eric Curry	.10
274 Demetrius Duboise	.10
275 Earnest Byner	.05
276 Ricky Ervins	.05
277 Brad Edwards	.05
278 Jim Lachey	.05
279 Charles Mann	.05
280 Carl Banks	.05
281 Art Monk	.10
282 Mark Rypien	.05
284 Tom Carter	.10
285 Reggie Brooks	.20

1993 Pro Line Live Autographs

Randomly seeded two per 10-box case, the card fronts carry the same design as the regular cards, with the autograph signed over the photo. The backs congratulate the winner of the autograph. The Classic, NFL and NFLPA logos appear at the bottom. The cards are unnumbered, but are listed below respective of the player's regular card.

	MT
Complete Set (38):	1200.
Common Player:	10.00
Minor Stars:	20.00
7 Deion Sanders (900)	75.00
16 Andre Reed (1050)	20.00
23 Neal Anderson (1050)	10.00
34 David Klingler (1200)	10.00
46 Vinny Testaverde (900)	30.00
51 Troy Aikman (700)	80.00
67 Rod Bernstine (1000)	10.00
70 Tommy Maddox (1050)	10.00
76 Pat Swilling (950)	10.00
79 Rodney Peete (1000)	10.00
87 Terrell Buckley (1050)	20.00
88 Brett Favre (650)	200.00
91 Sterling Sharpe (1050)	20.00
96 Ray Childress (950)	10.00
99 Haywood Jeffires (950)	10.00
107 Quentin Coryatt (900)	10.00
108 Steve Emtman (800)	10.00
109 Jeff George (1050)	20.00
119 Christian Okoye (900)	10.00
120 Neil Smith (1050)	20.00
121 Derrick Thomas (550)	35.00
124 Joe Montana (600)	200.00
129 Eric Dickerson (900)	20.00
131 Howie Long (950)	20.00
146 Marco Coleman (1000)	10.00
151 Keith Jackson (650)	10.00
158 Anthony Carter (950)	10.00
160 Chris Doleman (1000)	10.00
188 Rodney Hampton (650)	20.00
199 Ronnie Lott (1050)	20.00
201 Rob Moore (950)	30.00
212 Herschel Walker (400)	20.00
217 Gary Clark (1050)	10.00
227 Barry Foster (750)	10.00
231 Neil O'Donnell (1050)	20.00
242 Junior Seau (900)	20.00
275 Earnest Byner (750)	10.00
281 Art Monk (750)	20.00

1993 Pro Line Live Future Stars

The 28-card set was seeded one per Pro Line Live jumbo pack. The fronts are anchored with a photo, with a colored stripe running along the right side of the card. The player's name and team appears in the stripe. The Pro Line Live logo is located in the lower left. The backs have the photo at the top, with his name and position in the upper left. His highlights and stats are printed in a colored rectangle at the bottom of the card. The card fronts also boast a gold-foil stamp of "1 of 22,000" printed to the inside of the stripe on the right side. The cards are numbered with "FS."

	MT
Complete Set (28):	15.00
Common Player:	.25
Minor Stars:	.50
1 Patrick Bates	.25
2 Jerome Bettis	2.00
3 Drew Bledsoe	4.50
4 Tom Carter	.25
5 Curtis Conway	.75
6 Steve Everitt	.25
7 Deon Figures	.25
8 Darrien Gordon	.25
9 Lester Holmes	.25
10 Brad Hopkins	.25
11 Marvin Jones	.50
12 Lincoln Kennedy	.25
13 O.J. McDuffie	1.00
14 Rick Mirer	.50
15 Willie Roaf	.50
16 Will Shields	.25
17 Wayne Simmons	.25
18 Robert Smith	2.00
19 Thomas Smith	.25
20 Michael Strahan	.25
21 Dan Williams	.50
22 Dana Stubblefield	.25
23 Kevin Williams (WR)	.25
24 Garrison Hearst	2.00
25 John Copeland	.25
26 Ryan McNeil	.25
27 Eric Curry	.25
28 Roosevelt Potts	.25

1993 Pro Line Live Illustrated

Artwork was the main feature of this six-card set, created by artist Neal Adams. The fronts showcase artwork on the left, with the player's name and team in a colored stripe on the right side. The Pro Line logo is in the lower left. "One of 10,000" is printed along the inside of the stripe on the right side. The backs carry the same design as the base cards, but are numbered with a prefix of "SP." The cards were seeded three per case. Classic produced 10,000 of each card.

	MT
Complete Set (6):	20.00
Common Player:	2.00
1 Troy Aikman	4.50
2 Jerry Rice	6.00
3 Michael Irvin	2.00
4 Thurman Thomas	2.00
5 Lawrence Taylor	2.00
6 Deion Sanders	3.00

1993 Pro Line Live LPs

Randomly seeded in packs, the 20-card set included a large photo on the front, with the player's name in a colored stripe on the right side. The Pro Line logo is in the lower left corner, while a "one of 40,000" gold-foil seal is on the front corner. The backs, prefixed with an "LP," have the player's name in the upper left of the photo. The player's write-up is included beneath the photo, with the card number in the lower right.

	MT
Complete Set (20):	30.00
Common Player:	.75
Minor Stars:	1.50
1 Chris Webber (Dunking football)	2.00
2 Shaquille O'Neal (Wearing street clothes)	5.00
3 Jamal Mashburn (Wearing ProLine apparel)	1.50
4 Marcus Allen	1.50
5 Neal Anderson	.75
6 Reggie Cobb	.75
7 Rod Bernstine	.75
8 Barry Word	.75
9 Troy Aikman	3.00
10 Brett Favre	6.00
11 Ricky Watters	1.50
12 Terry Allen	1.50
13 Rodney Hampton	.75
14 Garrison Hearst	1.50
15 Jerome Bettis	1.50
16 Barry Foster	.75
17 Harold Green	.75
18 Tommy Vardell	.75
19 Lorenzo White	.75
20 Marion Butts	.75

1993 Pro Line Live Tonx

Randomly seeded in packs, the six-milk cap set previewed the NFL Tonx set. The milk cap, which measures 1-5/8 inches in diameter, could be removed from the standard size card. The front of the disc features a full-bleed photo, while the back has the team's helmet, player name and Tonx logo. The card front announces that Tonx is coming in the fall, while the card back explains the Tonx set. Each card is unnumbered.

	MT
Complete Set (6):	6.00
Common Player:	.50
1 Troy Aikman	2.00
2 Michael Irvin	.50
3 Jerry Rice	1.50
4 Deion Sanders	1.00
5 Lawrence Taylor	.50
6 Thurman Thomas	.50

1993 Pro Line Live Portraits

These cards continue where the numbers from the 1992 Pro Line Portraits left off, at #468. The players are featured in non-game photos on the front, with a small mug shot on the card back. A quote from the player also appears on the back.

	MT
Complete Set (44):	7.50
Common Player:	.05
468 Willie Roaf	.15
469 Terry Allen	.15
470 Jerry Ball	.05
471 Patrick Bates	.15
472 Ray Bentley	.05
473 Jerome Bettis	.50
474 Steve Beuerlein	.10
475 Drew Bledsoe	3.00
476 Dave Brown	.10
477 Gill Byrd	.05
478 Tony Casillas	.05
479 Chuck Cecil	.05
480 Reggie Cobb	.05
481 Pat Harlow	.05
482 John Copeland	.25
483 Bryan Cox	.05
484 Eric Curry	.25
485 Jeff Lageman	.05
486 Brett Favre	.75
487 Barry Foster	.25
488 Gaston Green	.05
489 Rodney Hampton	.25
490 Tim Harris	.05
491 Garrison Hearst	1.00
492 Tony Smith	.05
493 Marvin Jones	.20
494 Lincoln Kennedy	.25
495 Wilber Marshall	.05
496 Terry McDaniel	.05
497 Rick Mirer	.50
498 Art Monk	.08
499 Mike Munchak	.05
500 Frank Reich	.05
501 Barry Sanders	1.00
502 Shannon Sharpe	.05
503 Gino Torretta	.25
504 Ricky Watters	.40
505 Richmond Webb	.05
506 Reggie White	.25
507 Bert Jones	.05
508 Billy Kilmer	.05
509 John Mackey	.05
510 Archie Manning	.05
511 Harvey Martin	.05

1993 Pro Line Portraits Autographs

The 26-card set includes a full-bleed photo on the front, with the Pro Line logo in the bottom center. The card front is autographed. The back has the player's name in the upper left, team in the upper right and a quote in the center of the card. His photo is at the bottom center.

	MT
Complete Set (26):	750.00
Common Player:	20.00
468 Willie Roaf	20.00
471 Patrick Bates	20.00
473 Jerome Bettis	45.00
474 Steve Beuerlein	20.00
478 Tony Casillas	20.00
479 Chuck Cecil	20.00
480 Reggie Cobb	20.00
481 Pat Harlow	20.00
482 John Copeland	20.00
484 Eric Curry	20.00
485 Jeff Lageman	20.00
486 Brett Favre	250.00
488 Gaston Green	20.00
489 Rodney Hampton	25.00
492 Tony Smith	20.00
493 Marvin Jones	20.00
494 Lincoln Kennedy	20.00
496 Terry McDaniel	20.00
499 Mike Munchak	20.00
500 Frank Reich	25.00
502 Shannon Sharpe	35.00
503 Gino Torretta	20.00
507 Bert Jones (TB)	20.00
508 Billy Kilmer (TB)	30.00
510 Archie Manning (TB)	30.00
511 Harvey Martin (TB)	20.00

1993 Pro Line Portraits Wives

This four-card set features wives of NFL players and was inserted into packs of 1993 Pro Line. The cards are numbered SC25-SC28 in a continuation from 1992 Pro Line Wives, however card number SC24 was never produced.

	MT
Complete Set (4):	.50
Common Player:	.15
25 Annette Rypien	.15
26 Ann Stark	.15
27 Cindy Walker	.15
28 Cindy Reed	.15

1993 Pro Line Portraits Wives Autographs

The set features the same design as the Portraits Wives set, except these are autographed. Three of the four wives featured in the basic set signed cards, with the exception of Cindy Walker.

	MT
Complete Set (3):	75.00
Common Player:	25.00
25 Annette Rypien	25.00
26 Ann Stark	25.00
28 Cindy Reed	25.00

1994 Pro Line Live Draft Day Prototypes

The 1994 Draft was previewed by this 13-card set. The fronts are anchored by a borderless photo, with the NFL Draft logo in the upper right and the player's name and possible team at the bottom. The backs showcase a cutout of a portion of a photo, with the rest of the photo grayed out. The cards are

numbered by a prefix of "FD" in the upper right. The backs state, "1994 NFL Draft prototype set April 24, 1994, limited edition 1 of 19,940."

	MT
Complete Set (13):	25.00
Common Player:	1.00
1 Dan Wilkinson	1.00
2 Dan Wilkinson	1.00
3 Marshall Faulk	5.00
4 Marshall Faulk	5.00
5 Marshall Faulk	5.00
6 1989 First Pick (Troy Aikman)	3.00
7 Trent Dilfer	2.00
8 Trent Dilfer	2.00
9 Heath Shuler	3.00
10 Heath Shuler	3.00
11 Aaron Glenn	1.00
12 Aaron Glenn	1.00
13 Dan Wilkinson	1.00

1994 Pro Line Live Previews

This five-card set boasts a full-bleed photo on the front, with the Classic Pro Line logo in the upper left and player's name and team at the bottom. The backs, numbered in the lower left with a prefix of "PL," have the player's name and position in the upper left and his highlights and bio in a stripe along the left side of the card. An action shot and his stats are printed over his photo. The back also has a tagline which says the card is one of 12,000.

	MT
Complete Set (5):	45.00
Common Player:	7.00
1 Troy Aikman	12.00
2 Jerry Rice	12.00
3 Steve Young	10.00
4 Rick Mirer	7.00
5 Drew Bledsoe	12.00

1994 Pro Line Live

Classic Games Inc. produced the 405-card 1994 Pro Line Live set. The set includes 327 NFL veterans and 62 rookies. Each card front has a borderless color action photo on the front, along with the player's name and team and set logo. The back has another color photo of the player, with statistics, biographical information and a brief career summary. More than 150 players also autographed their cards; these cards, issued one per box, command premium values. Two subsets were also made, featuring the league's two new expansion teams — the Jacksonville Jaguars and Carolina Panthers, and the player illustrations of comic book artist Neal Adams (#s 401-405). There were also three insert sets produced. Emmitt Smith is honored with 15,000 sequentially-numbered inserts, while another set honors 45 players who were MVP candidates. Collectors who obtained one of the 2,083 cards of the 1994 NFL MVP could redeem it for a limited, uncut sheet of the 45 cards. The other insert series previews the company's 1994 Basketball Draft Pick series.

	MT
Complete Set (405):	20.00
Common Player:	.05
Minor Stars:	.10
Wax Box:	35.00
1 Emmitt Smith	1.50
2 Andre Rison	.10
3 Deion Sanders	.50
4 Jeff George	.10
5 Cornelius Bennett	.05
6 Jim Kelly	.25
7 Andre Reed	.10
8 Bruce Smith	.05
9 Thurman Thomas	.25
10 Mark Carrier	.05
11 Curtis Conway	.25
12 Donnell Woolford	.05
13 Chris Zorich	.05
14 Erik Kramer	.10
15 John Copeland	.05
16 Harold Green	.05
17 David Klingler	.10
18 Tony McGee	.05
19 Carl Pickens	.25
20 Michael Jackson	.10
21 Eric Metcalf	.05
22 Michael Dean Perry	.10
23 Vinny Testaverde	.25
24 Eric Turner	.05
25 Tommy Vardell	.05
26 Troy Aikman	1.00
27 Charles Haley	.05
28 Michael Irvin	.25
29 Pierce Holt	.05
30 Russell Maryland	.05
31 Erik Williams	.05
32 Thomas Everett	.05
33 Steve Atwater	.10
34 John Elway	1.50
35 Glyn Milburn	.10
36 Shannon Sharpe	.25
37 Anthony Miller	.05
38 Barry Sanders	2.00
39 Chris Spielman	.05
40 Pat Swilling	.05
41 Brett Perriman	.05
42 Herman Moore	.30
43 Scott Mitchell	.10
44 Edgar Bennett	.05
45 Terrell Buckley	.05
46 LeRoy Butler	.05
47 Brett Favre	2.00
48 Jackie Harris	.05
49 Sterling Sharpe	.25
50 Reggie White	.25
51 Gary Brown	.10
52 Cody Carlson	.05
53 Ray Childress	.05
54 Ernest Givins	.05
55 Bruce Matthews	.05
56 Quentin Coryatt	.05
57 Steve Emtman	.05
58 Roosevelt Potts	.05
59 Tony Bennett	.05
60 Marcus Allen	.25
61 Joe Montana	1.00
62 Neil Smith	.05
63 Derrick Thomas	.10
64 Dale Carter	.05
65 Tim Brown	.25
66 Jeff Hostetler	.05
67 Terry McDaniel	.05
68 Chester McGlockton	.05
69 Anthony Smith	.05
70 Albert Lewis	.05
71 Jerome Bettis	.50
72 Shane Conlan	.05
73 Troy Drayton	.05
74 Sean Gilbert	.05
75 Chris Miller	.05
76 Bryan Cox	.05
77 Irving Fryar	.05
78 Keith Jackson	.05
79 Terry Kirby	.10
80 Dan Marino	1.50
81 O.J. McDuffie	.25
82 Terry Allen	.05
83 Cris Carter	.50
84 Chris Doleman	.05
85 Randall McDaniel	.05
86 John Randle	.10
87 Robert Smith	.05
88 Jason Belser	.05
89 Jack Del Rio	.05
90 Vincent Brown	.05
91 Ben Coates	.10
92 Chris Slade	.05
93 Derek Brown	.05
94 Morten Andersen	.05
95 Willie Roaf	.05
96 Irv Smith	.05
97 Tyrone Hughes	.05
98 Michael Haynes	.05
99 Jim Everett	.05
100 Michael Brooks	.05
101 Leroy Thompson	.05
102 Rodney Hampton	.10
103 David Meggett	.05
104 Phil Simms	.10
105 Boomer Esiason	.05
106 Johnny Johnson	.05
107 Gary Anderson	.05
108 Mo Lewis	.05
109 Ronnie Lott	.10
110 Johnny Mitchell	.05
111 Howard Cross	.05
112 Victor Bailey	.05
113 Fred Barnett	.05
114 Randall Cunningham	.25
115 Calvin Williams	.05
116 Steve Beuerlein	.05
117 Gary Clark	.05
118 Ron Moore	.05
119 Ricky Proehl	.05
120 Eric Swann	.05
121 Barry Foster	.05
122 Kevin Greene	.05
123 Greg Lloyd	.05
124 Neil O'Donnell	.10
125 Rod Woodson	.05
126 Ronnie Harmon	.05
127 Mark Higgs	.05
128 Stan Humphries	.10
129 Leslie O'Neal	.05
130 Chris Mims	.05
131 Stanley Richard	.05
132 Junior Seau	.10
133 Brent Jones	.05
134 Tim McDonald	.05
135 Jerry Rice	1.00
136 Dana Stubblefield	.10
137 Ricky Watters	.25
138 Steve Young	.75
139 Cortez Kennedy	.05
140 Rick Mirer	.10
141 Eugene Robinson	.05
142 Chris Warren	.10
143 Nate Odomes	.05
144 Howard Ballard	.05
145 Willie Anderson	.05
146 Chris Jacke	.05
147 Santana Dotson	.05
148 Craig Erickson	.05
149 Hardy Nickerson	.05
150 Lawrence Dawsey	.05
151 Terry Wooden	.05
152 Ethan Horton	.05
153 John Kasay	.05
154 Desmond Howard	.05
155 Ken Harvey	.05
156 William Fuller	.05
157 Clyde Simmons	.05
158 Randal Hill	.05
159 Garrison Hearst	.50
160 Mike Pritchard	.05
161 Jessie Tuggle	.05
162 Erric Pegram	.05
163 Kevin Ross	.05
164 Bill Brooks	.05
165 Darryl Talley	.05
166 Steve Tasker	.05
167 Pete Stoyanovich	.05
168 Dante Jones	.05
169 Vencie Glenn	.05
170 Tom Waddle	.05
171 Harlon Barnett	.05
172 Trace Armstrong	.05
173 Tim Worley	.05
174 Alfred Williams	.05
175 Louis Oliver	.05
176 Darryl Williams	.05
177 Clay Matthews	.05
178 Kyle Clifton	.05
179 Alvin Harper	.05
180 Jay Novacek	.05
181 Ken Norton	.05
182 Kevin Williams	.10
183 Daryl Johnson	.05
184 Rod Bernstine	.05
185 Karl Mecklenburg	.05
186 Dennis Smith	.05
187 Robert Delpino	.05
188 Bennie Blades	.05
189 Jason Hanson	.05
190 Derrick Moore	.05
191 Mark Clayton	.05
192 Webster Slaughter	.05
193 Haywood Jeffires	.05
194 Bubba McDowell	.05
195 Warren Moon	.25
196 Al Smith	.05
197 Bill Romanowski	.05
198 John Carney	.05
199 Kerry Cash	.05
200 Darren Carrington	.05
201 Jeff Lageman	.05
202 Tracy Simien	.05
203 Willie Davis	.05
204 Dan Saleaumua	.05
205 Raghib Ismail	.05
206 James Jett	.10
207 Todd Lyght	.05
208 Roman Phifer	.05
209 Jimmie Jones	.10
210 Jeff Cross	.05
211 Eric Davis	.05
212 Keith Byars	.05
213 Richmond Webb	.05
214 Anthony Carter	.05
215 Henry Thomas	.05
216 Andre Tippett	.05
217 Rickey Jackson	.05
218 Vaughan Johnson	.05
219 Eric Martin	.05
220 Sam Mills	.05
221 Renaldo Turnbull	.05
222 Mark Collins	.05
223 Mike Johnson	.05
224 Rob Moore	.25
225 Seth Joyner	.05
226 Herschel Walker	.05
227 Marion Butts	.05
228 Eric Green	.05
229 John Friesz	.10
230 John Taylor	.05
231 Dexter Carter	.05
232 Brian Blades	.05
233 Reggie Cobb	.05
234 Paul Gruber	.05
235 Ricky Reynolds	.05
236 Vince Workman	.05
237 Darrell Green	.05
238 Jim Lachey	.05
239 James Hasty	.05
240 Howie Long	.10
241 Aeneas Williams	.05
242 Mike Kenn	.05
243 Henry Jones	.05
244 Kenneth Davis	.05
245 Tim Krumrie	.05
246 Derrick Fenner	.05
247 Mark Carrier	.05
248 Robert Porcher	.05
249 Darren Woodson	.05
250 Kevin Smith	.05
251 Mark Stepnoski	.05
252 Simon Fletcher	.05
253 Derek Russell	.05
255 Mike Croel	.05
256 Johnny Holland	.05
257 Bryce Paup	.05
258 Cris Dishman	.05
259 Sean Jones	.05
260 Marcus Robertson	.05
261 Steve Jackson	.05
262 Jeff Herrod	.05
263 John Alt	.05
264 Nick Lowery	.05
265 Greg Robinson	.05
266 Alexander Wright	.05
267 Steve Wisniewski	.05
268 Henry Ellard	.05
269 Tracy Scroggins	.05
270 Jackie Slater	.05
271 Troy Vincent	.05
272 Qadry Ismail	.10
273 Steve Jordan	.05
274 Leonard Russell	.05
275 Maurice Hurst	.05
276 *Scottie Graham*	.10
277 Carlton Bailey	.05
278 John Elliott	.05
279 Corey Miller	.05
280 Brad Baxter	.05
281 Brian Washington	.05
282 Tim Harris	.05
283 Byron Evans	.05
284 Dermontti Dawson	.05
285 Carnell Lake	.05
286 Jeff Graham	.05
287 Merton Hanks	.05
288 Harris Barton	.05
289 Guy McIntyre	.05
290 Kelvin Martin	.05
291 John Williams	.05
292 Courtney Hawkins	.05
293 Vaughn Hebron	.05
294 Brian Mitchell	.05
295 Andre Collins	.05
296 Art Monk	.10
297 Mark Rypien	.10
298 Ricky Sanders	.05
299 Eric Hill	.05
301 Larry Centers	.05
302 Norm Johnson	.05
303 Pete Metzelaars	.05
304 Ricardo McDonald	.05
305 Stevon Moore	.05
306 Mike Sherrard	.05
307 Andy Harmon	.05
308 Anthony Johnson	.05
309 J.J. Birden	.05
310 Neal Anderson	.05
311 Lewis Tillman	.05
312 Richard Dent	.10
313 Nate Newton	.05
314 *Sean Dawkins*	.25
315 Lawrence Taylor	.25
316 Wilber Marshall	.05
317 Tim Carter	.05
318 Reggie Brooks	.10
319 Eric Curry	.05
320 Horace Copeland	.05
321 Natrone Means	.50
322 Eric Allen	.05
323 Marvin Jones	.05
324 Keith Hamilton	.05
325 Vincent Brisby	.10
326 Drew Bledsoe	1.00
327 Tom Rathman	.05
328 Ed McCaffrey	.30
329 Steve Israel	.05
348 Johnnie Morton	.40
349 Rob Fredrickson	.10
350 Shante Carver	.10
351 Thomas Lewis	.50
352 Greg Hill	.50
353 Henry Ford	.10
354 Jeff Burris	.50
355 William Floyd	.50
356 Derrick Alexander	.25
357 Darnay Scott	.75
358 Isaac Bruce	4.00
359 Errict Rhett	.50
360 Kevin Lee	.10
361 Chuck Levy	.25
362 David Palmer	.50
363 Ryan Yarborough	.10
364 Charlie Garner	1.50
365 Isaac Davis	.10
366 Mario Bates	.25
367 Bert Emanuel	.75
368 Thomas Randolph	.10
369 Bucky Brooks	.10
370 Allen Aldridge	.10
371 Charlie Ward	.50
372 Audrey Beavers	.10
373 Donnell Bennett	.50
374 Jason Sehorn	.25
375 Lonnie Johnson	.25
376 Tyrone Drakeford	.10
377 Andre Coleman	.10
378 Lamar Smith	.25
379 Calvin Jones	.25
380 LeShon Johnson	.25
381 Byron Morris	.50
382 Lake Dawson	.25
383 Corey Sawyer	.10
384 Willie Jackson	.10
385 Perry Klein	.10
386 Ronnie Woolfork	.10
387 Doug Nussmeier	.10
388 Rob Waldrop	.10
389 Glenn Foley	.50
390 Aikman, Irvin	.50
391 Young, Rice	.50
392 Favre, Sharpe	1.00
393 Kelly, Reed	.10
394 Elway, Sharpe	.75
395 Carolina Panthers	.05
396 Jacksonville Jaguars	.05
397 Checklist #1	.05
398 Checklist #2	.05
399 Checklist #3	.05
400 Checklist #4	.05
401 Sterling Sharpe	.10
402 Derrick Thomas	.05
403 Joe Montana	.50
404 Emmitt Smith	.75
405 Barry Sanders	1.00

1994 Pro Line Live Autographs

This 132-card autographed set showcases the same design as the base cards, except they are signed and numbered on the front. The card backs congratulate the collector on receiving an autographed card. The Pro Line Live logo is in the center of the unnumbered card back. The cards are numbered below according to the player's base card number.

	MT
Complete Set (132):	2750.
Common Player:	20.00
Minor Stars:	20.00
Inserted 1:36	
1 Emmitt Smith (925)	125.00
4 Jeff George (2140)	20.00
12 Donnell Woolford (1000)	10.00
14 Eric Kramer (1020)	10.00
17 David Klingler (2140)	10.00
20 Michael Jackson (1490)	10.00
24 Eric Turner (1030)	10.00
25 Tommy Vardell (1000)	10.00
26 Troy Aikman (340)	125.00
28 Michael Irvin (450)	25.00
29 Pierce Holt (2020)	10.00
30 Russell Maryland (1945)	10.00

330 Heath Shuler .50
331 Willie McGinest .25
332 Trev Alberts .25
333 Trent Dilfer 2.50
334 Bryant Young .50
335 Sam Adams .25
336 Antonio Langham .25
337 Jamir Miller .25
338 John Thierry .25
339 Aaron Glenn .25
340 Joe Johnson .25
341 Bernard Williams .10
342 Wayne Gandy .10
343 Aaron Taylor .10
344 Charles Johnson .25
345 DeWayne Washington .25
346 Todd Steussie .25
347 Tim Bowens .10

328 Dan Wilkinson .25
329 Marshall Faulk 4.00

33	Steve Atwater (1040)	10.00
34	John Elway (1000)	100.00
35	Glyn Milburn (440)	20.00
36	Shannon Sharpe (1020)	20.00
37	Anthony Miller (2070)	10.00
47	Brett Favre (1130)	100.00
49	Sterling Sharpe (450)	35.00
51	Gary Brown (950)	10.00
53	Ray Childress (2240)	10.00
56	Quentin Coryatt (970)	10.00
57	Steve Emtman (1900)	10.00
61	Joe Montana (920)	150.00
62	Neil Smith (1000)	20.00
63	Derrick Thomas (1087)	50.00
64	Dale Carter (1031)	10.00
65	Tim Brown (1920)	20.00
66	Jeff Hostetler (955)	10.00
67	Terry McDaniel (1980)	10.00
72	Shane Conlan (1110)	10.00
73	Troy Drayton (450)	20.00
77	Irving Fryar (1040)	10.00
78	Keith Jackson (1020)	10.00
93	Derek Brown (RB/449)	10.00
96	Irv Smith (470)	20.00
97	Tyrone Hughes (470)	10.00
99	Jim Everett (1265)	10.00
102	Rodney Hampton (1090)	20.00
105	Boomer Esiason (920)	20.00
109	Ronnie Lott (910)	20.00
112	Victor Bailey (920)	20.00
116	Steve Beuerlein (970)	10.00
119	Ricky Proehl (1020)	10.00
121	Barry Foster (1080)	10.00
127	Mark Higgs (980)	10.00
129	Leslie O'Neal (2050)	10.00
133	Brent Jones (1880)	10.00
134	Tim McDonald (2040)	10.00
138	Steve Young (925)	75.00
149	Hardy Nickerson (1175)	10.00
159	Garrison Hearst (1435)	25.00
162	Erric Pegram (1020)	10.00
164	Bill Brooks (1030)	10.00
177	Clay Matthews (2000)	10.00
184	Rod Bernstine (1010)	10.00
187	Robert Delpino (1030)	10.00
208	Roman Phifer (2140)	10.00
212	Keith Byars (1020)	10.00
213	Richmond Webb (1020)	10.00
214	Anthony Carter (1020)	10.00
216	Andre Tippett (1090)	10.00
220	Sam Mills (1115)	10.00
221	Renaldo Turnbull (945)	10.00
224	Rob Moore (1025)	20.00
228	Marion Butts (2040)	10.00
229	John Friesz (2150)	20.00
230	John Taylor (1030)	10.00
238	Jim Lachey (1850)	10.00
244	Kenneth Davis (1170)	10.00
266	Steve Wisniewski (2150)	10.00
269	Jackie Slater (1110)	10.00
271	Qadry Ismail (450)	20.00
277	John Elliott (2150)	10.00
279	Brad Baxter (1070)	10.00
284	Carnell Lake (1985)	10.00
287	Harris Barton (2120)	10.00
294	Andre Collins (1100)	10.00
315	Tom Carter (460)	10.00
316	Reggie Brooks (460)	20.00
318	Horace Copeland (450)	10.00
319	Natrone Means (445)	40.00
320	Eric Allen (1980)	10.00
324	Drew Bledsoe (1150)	65.00
325	Tom Rathman (2230)	10.00
326	Ed McCaffrey (2030)	25.00
327	Steve Israel (2020)	10.00
328	Dan Wilkinson (1960)	10.00
329	Marshall Faulk (2230)	50.00
330	Heath Shuler (2020)	20.00
331	Willie McGinest (3520)	10.00
333	Trent Dilfer (2680)	20.00
336	Antonio Langham (1240)	10.00
338	John Thierry (1150)	10.00
339	Aaron Glenn (1140)	10.00
342	Wayne Gandy (1040)	10.00
343	Aaron Taylor (950)	10.00
344	Charles Johnson	10.00
345	DeWayne Washington (1040)	10.00
348	Johnnie Morton (2945)	10.00
349	Rob Fredrickson (1160)	10.00
350	Shante Carver (1160)	10.00
351	Thomas Lewis (1140)	10.00
352	Greg Hill (1145)	20.00
353	Henry Ford (1110)	10.00
354	Jeff Burris (1140)	10.00
355	William Floyd (950)	20.00
356	Derrick Alexander (WR/950)	20.00
357	Darnay Scott (1400)	20.00
359	Errict Rhett (1120)	20.00
360	Kevin Lee (1190)	10.00
361	Chuck Levy (950)	10.00
362	David Palmer (950)	20.00
364	Charlie Garner (1130)	20.00
365	Isaac Davis (1150)	10.00
366	Mario Bates (1145)	10.00
368	Thomas Randolph (1100)	10.00
369	Bucky Brooks (1090)	10.00
372	Aubrey Beavers (1150)	10.00
373	Donnell Bennett (1130)	20.00
374	Jason Sehorn (950)	10.00
377	Andre Coleman (1000)	10.00
378	Lamar Smith (1130)	10.00
379	Calvin Jones (960)	10.00
381	Byron "Bam" Morris (1130)	10.00
382	Lake Dawson (1100)	10.00
384	Willie Jackson (1140)	10.00
385	Perry Klein (1000)	10.00
386	Ronnie Woolfork (360)	20.00
387	Doug Nussmeier (1150)	10.00
389	Glenn Foley (890)	20.00
390	Troy Aikman, Michael Irvin (Combo/345)	225.00
391	Steve Young, Jerry Rice (Combo/450)	275.00

1994 Pro Line Live MVP Sweepstakes

This 45-card insert set contains candidates to win the 1994 NFL MVP Award. Collectors who obtain one of the 2,083 cards of the eventual 1994 NFL MVP could redeem the card for a limited-edition uncut sheet of the 45 cards. Each card front has four player photos on it. Card backs are numbered with an "MVP" prefix.

		MT
Complete Set (45):		200.00
Common Player:		2.50
Minor Stars:		5.00
Inserted 1:72		
1	Jeff George	5.00
2	Andre Rison	5.00
3	Jim Kelly	5.00
4	Thurman Thomas	5.00
5	Troy Aikman	15.00
6	Emmitt Smith	20.00
7	Michael Irvin	5.00
8	John Elway	20.00
9	Brett Favre	30.00
10	Sterling Sharpe	5.00
11	Barry Sanders	30.00
12	Scott Mitchell	2.50
13	Gary Brown	2.50
14	Warren Moon	5.00
15	Marcus Allen	5.00
16	Joe Montana	20.00
17	Tim Brown	5.00
18	Jeff Hostetler	2.50
19	Dan Marino	20.00
20	Terry Kirby	2.50
21	Terry Allen	5.00
22	Drew Bledsoe	15.00
23	Chris Miller	2.50
24	Jerome Bettis	5.00
25	Derek Brown	2.50
26	Rodney Hampton	2.50
27	Phil Simms	2.50
28	Randall Cunningham	5.00
29	Barry Foster	2.50
30	Neil O'Donnell	2.50
31	Boomer Esiason	2.50
32	Johnny Johnson	2.50
33	Garrison Hearst	7.00
34	Ron Moore	2.50
35	Natrone Means	7.00
36	Steve Young	10.00
37	Ricky Watters	5.00
38	Jerry Rice	15.00
39	Rick Mirer	5.00
40	Chris Warren	2.50
41	Reggie Brooks	2.50
42	Marshall Faulk	7.00
43	Heath Shuler	5.00
44	Trent Dilfer	10.00
45	Field Card	2.50

1994 Pro Line Live Spotlight

The chromium cards have the player's name and the Spotlight logo inside a border on the left side of the card. The Classic Pro Line logo is in the upper left. The cards were seeded one per 16-card pack. The card backs, numbered in the lower left with a prefix of "PB," have the player's name, position, team and bio inside a stripe on the left side. A photo is anchored on the right side of the card, with his stats printed toward the bottom.

		MT
Complete Set (25):		25.00
Common Player:		.25
Minor Stars:		.50
1	Trent Dilfer	1.00
2	Heath Shuler	.50
3	Marshall Faulk	2.00
4	Troy Aikman	1.50
5	Emmitt Smith	2.00
6	Thurman Thomas	.50
7	Andre Rison	.50
8	Jerry Rice	1.50
9	Sterling Sharpe	.50
10	Brett Favre	3.00
11	Steve Young	1.00
12	Drew Bledsoe	1.50
13	Rick Mirer	.50
14	Barry Sanders	3.00
15	Joe Montana	2.00
16	Jerome Bettis	.50
17	Ricky Watters	.50
18	Rodney Hampton	.25
19	Tim Brown	.50
20	Reggie Brooks	.25
21	Natrone Means	.50
22	Marcus Allen	.50
23	Gary Brown	.25
24	Barry Foster	.25
25	Dan Marino	2.00

1995 Pro Line Previews

These five cards preview the design of Classic's microlined insert cards from its 1995 NFL Pro Line set. The Game Breakers, seeded one per box of 1995 Classic NFL Rookies product, feature players who have the ability to change the course of a game at any moment. The insert set logo is in the lower left corner; the Classic Pro Line brand logo is in the upper left corner. The player's name and position are in a black band at the bottom. The card back is numbered using a "GP" prefix.

		MT
Complete Set (5):		35.00
Common Player:		5.00
1	Dan Marino	15.00
2	Natrone Means	5.00
3	Joe Montana	8.00
4	Barry Sanders	8.00
5	Deion Sanders	7.00

1995 Pro Line Previews Phone Cards $2

These four cards were random inserts in 1995 Classic Basketball Rookies packs, one per two boxes of the product. The cards preview 1995 Classic Pro Line Series II $2 phone cards.

		MT
Complete Set (4):		45.00
Common Player:		8.00
1	Troy Aikman	12.00
2	Drew Bledsoe	18.00
3	Ki-Jana Carter	8.00
4	Marshall Faulk	18.00

1995 Pro Line Previews Phone Cards $5

These four cards were random inserts in 1995 Classic Basketball Rookies packs, seeded one per case of the product. The cards preview the 1995 Classic NFL Pro Line Series II $5 phone cards.

		MT
Complete Set (4):		90.00
Common Player:		16.00
1	Troy Aikman	20.00
2	Drew Bledsoe	35.00
3	Ki-Jana Carter	16.00
4	Marshall Faulk	35.00

1995 Pro Line

Only in Classic's 1995 NFL Pro Line will collectors find cards autographed by some of the NFL's marquee players, including Steve Young, Emmitt Smith and Drew Bledsoe. The complete Pro Line series has 400 cards from all 30 NFL teams, including the expansion Jacksonville Jaguars and Carolina Panthers. Forty rookies, including the first 32 selected in the draft, are also included in the set. Each card, which has 29 percent thicker stock than before, has a full-bleed color action photo on the front. The player's name is in the lower left corner; the player's team is in a bar along the bottom, with his position above the bar. The Pro Line logo is in the upper left corner. The card back has a color photo on one side, with a recap of the previous season, biographical information and stats on the other. The card number is in the upper left corner in a box. As a bonus, more than 100 top NFL players personally signed a maximum of 2,500 cards each. One autographed card was guaranteed to be in every box. Pro Line also continued its Hot Boxes program. Each pack in a Hot Box contains 40 percent inserts. Hot Boxes were randomly inserted one in every 10 cases. Exclusive to Hot Boxes are 10 Team Record Breaker acetate cards sequentially numbered to 350. Other insert sets include Pro Line Impact, MVP Interactive cards, Game Breaker cards, Pro Line Silver cards and Basketball Rookies Preview cards. A parallel insert set of the regular cards printed on silver foil board was also produced; these cards were included one per pack.

		MT
Complete Set (400):		20.00
Common Player:		.05
Minor Stars:		.10
Series 1 Wax Box:		50.00
Series 2 Wax Box:		65.00
1	Garrison Hearst	.10
2	Anthony Miller	.05
3	Brett Favre	1.50
4	Jessie Hester	.05
5	Mike Fox	.05
6	*Jeff Blake*	1.00
7	J.J. Birden	.05
8	Greg Jackson	.05
9	Leon Lett	.05
10	Bruce Matthews	.05
11	Andre Reed	.05
12	Joe Montana	1.00
13	Craig Heyward	.05
14	Henry Ellard	.05
15	Chris Spielman	.05
16	Tony Woods	.05
17	Carl Banks	.05
18	*Eric Zeier*	.75
19	Michael Brooks	.05
20	Kevin Ross	.05
21	Qadry Ismail	.05
22	Mel Gray	.05
23	Ty Law	.15
24	Mark Collins	.05
25	Neil O'Donnell	.10
26	Ellis Johnson	.15
27	Rick Mirer	.40
28	Fred Barnett	.05
29	*Mike Mamula*	.10
30	Jim Jeffcoat	.05
31	Reggie Cobb	.05
32	Mark Carrier	.05
33	Darnay Scott	.40
34	Michael Jackson	.05
35	Terrell Buckley	.05
36	Nolan Harrison	.05
37	Thurman Thomas	.20
38	Anthony Smith	.05
39	Phillippi Sparks	.05
40	Cornelius Bennett	.05
41	Robert Young	.05
42	Pierce Holt	.05
43	Greg Lloyd	.05
44	*Chad May*	.10
45	Darrien Gordon	.05
46	Bryan Cox	.05
47	Junior Seau	.10
48	Al Smith	.05
49	Chris Slade	.05
50	Hardy Nickerson	.05
51	Brad Baxter	.05
52	Darryl Lewis	.05
53	Bryant Young	.05
54	Chris Warren	.05
55	Darion Conner	.05
56	Thomas Everett	.05
57	Charles Haley	.05
58	Chris Mims	.05
59	Sean Jones	.05
60	*Tamarick Vanover*	1.00
61	Daryl Johnston	.05
62	*Rashaan Salaam*	1.00
63	James Hasty	.05
64	Dante Jones	.05
65	Darren Perry	.05
66	Troy Drayton	.05
67	Mark Fields	.10
68	Brian Williams	.10
69	Steve Bono	.15
70	Eric Allen	.05
71	Chris Zorich	.05
72	Dave Brown	.05
73	Ken Norton	.05
74	Wayne Martin	.05
75	Mo Lewis	.05
76	Johnny Mitchell	.05
77	Todd Lyght	.05
78	Erric Pegram	.05
79	Kevin Greene	.05
80	Randal Hill	.05
81	Brett Perriman	.05
82	Mike Sherrard	.05
83	Curtis Conway	.05
84	Mark Tuinei	.05
85	Mark Seay	.05
86	Randy Baldwin	.05
87	Ricky Ervins	.05
88	Chester McGlockton	.05
89	*Tyrone Wheatley*	.50
90	Michael Barrow	.05
91	Kenneth Davis	.05
92	*Napoleon Kaufman*	2.00
93	Webster Slaughter	.05
94	Darren Woodson	.05
95	Pete Stoyanovich	.05
96	Jimmie Jones	.05
97	Craig Erickson	.05
98	*Michael Westbrook*	1.00
99	*Steve McNair*	2.50
100	Errict Rhett	.50
101	Devin Bush	.15
102	Dewayne Washington	.05
103	Bart Oates	.05
104	Aaron Pierce	.05
105	*Warren Sapp*	.25
106	Eric Green	.05
107	Glyn Milburn	.05
108	Johnny Johnson	.05
109	Marshall Faulk	.75
110	William Thomas	.05
111	George Koonce	.05
112	Dana Stubblefield	.05
113	Steve Tovar	.05
114	Steve Israel	.05
115	Brent Williams	.05
116	Shane Conlan	.05
117	Winston Moss	.05
118	Nate Newton	.05
119	Michael Irvin	.20
120	Jeff Lageman	.05
121	*Ki-Jana Carter*	2.00
122	Dan Marino	1.50
123	Tony Casillas	.05
124	*Kevin Carter*	.20
125	Warren Moon	.10
126	Byron Morris	.40
127	Ben Coates	.10
128	Michael Bankston	.05
129	Anthony Parker	.05
130	LeRoy Butler	.05
131	Tony Bennett	.05
132	Alvin Harper	.05
133	Tim Brown	.10
134	Tom Carter	.05
135	Lorenzo White	.05
136	Shane Dronett	.05
137	John Elliott	.05
138	Korey Stringer	.05
139	Jerry Rice	.50
140	*Sherman Williams*	.10
141	Kevin Turner	.05
142	Randall Cunningham	.10
143	Vinny Testaverde	.05
144	Tim Bowens	.05
145	Russell Maryland	.05
146	Chris Miller	.05
147	Vince Buck	.05
148	Willie Clay	.05
149	Jeff Graham	.05
150	Shannon Sharpe	.10
151	Carnell Lake	.05
152	*Mark Bruener*	.30
153	James Washington	.05
154	Pepper Johnson	.05
155	Bert Emanuel	.20
156	Mark Stepnoski	.05
157	Robert Jones	.05
158	Cris Dishman	.05
159	Henry Jones	.05
160	Henry Thomas	.05
161	John L. Williams	.05
162	Joe Cain	.05
163	Mike Johnson	.05
164	Merton Hanks	.05
165	Deion Sanders	.35
166	William Floyd	.25
167	Leroy Thompson	.05
168	Ray Childress	.05
169	Donnell Woolford	.05
170	Tony Siragusa	.05
171	Chad Brown	.05
172	Stanley Richard	.05
173	*Rob Johnson*	2.00
174	Derrick Brooks	.10
175	Drew Bledsoe	.75
176	Maurice Hurst	.05
177	Ricky Watters	.10
178	Myron Guyton	.05
179	Ricky Proehl	.05
180	Haywood Jeffires	.05
181	Michael Strahan	.05
182	Charles Wilson	.05
183	Mark Carrier	.05
184	*James Stewart*	1.25
185	Andy Harmon	.05
186	Ronnie Lott	.05
187	Clay Matthews	.05
188	John Carney	.05
189	Andre Rison	.10
190	Aeneas Williams	.05
191	Alexander Wright	.05
192	Desmond Howard	.05
193	Herman Moore	.10
194	Alfred Williams	.05
195	Tyrone Poole	.10
196	Darren Mickell	.05
197	Steve Young	.50
198	Roman Phifer	.05
199	Darrell Green	.05
200	Terry Wooden	.05
201	Chris Calloway	.05
202	Lewis Tillman	.05
203	Cris Carter	.10
204	Jim Everett	.05
205	Adrian Murrell	.05
206	Barry Sanders	1.25
207	Mario Bates	.05
208	Shawn Lee	.05
209	Charles Mincy	.05
210	*Kerry Collins*	2.00
211	Steve Walsh	.05
212	Chris Chandler	.05
213	Bennie Blades	.05
214	Kevin Williams	.10
215	Jim Kelly	.10
216	Marion Butts	.05
217	Jay Novacek	.05
218	Shawn Jefferson	.05
219	O.J. McDuffie	.05
220	Ray Seals	.05
221	Arthur Marshall	.05
222	Karl Mecklenburg	.05
223	Terance Mathis	.05
224	David Klingler	.05

225	Rod Woodson	.05
226	Quentin Coryatt	.05
227	Leroy Hoard	.05
228	Brian Blades	.05
229	Rob Moore	.05
230	Boomer Esiason	.05
231	Dave Krieg	.05
232	Sterling Sharpe	.10
233	Marcus Allen	.10
234	John Randle	.05
235	Craig Powell	.05
236	John Elway	.25
237	Mark Ingram	.05
238	Cortez Kennedy	.05
239	Brent Jones	.05
240	Ken Harvey	.05
241	Keenan McCardell	.05
242	Dan Wilkinson	.05
243	Don Beebe	.05
244	Jack Del Rio	.05
245	Byron Evans	.05
246	Ron Moore	.05
247	Edgar Bennett	.05
248	William Fuller	.05
249	James Williams	.05
250	Neil Smith	.05
251	Sam Mills	.05
252	Willie McGinest	.05
253	Howard Cross	.05
254	Troy Aikman	.60
255	Herschel Walker	.05
256	Dale Carter	.05
257	Sean Dawkins	.15
258	Greg Hill	.25
259	Stan Humphries	.10
260	Erik Kramer	.05
261	Leslie O'Neal	.05
262	Trezelle Jenkins	.10
263	Antonio Langham	.05
264	Bryce Paup	.05
265	Jake Reed	.05
266	Richmond Webb	.05
267	Eric Davis	.05
268	Mark McMillian	.05
269	*John Walsh*	.25
270	Irving Fryar	.05
271	Raghib Ismail	.05
272	Phil Hansen	.05
273	J.J. Stokes	1.00
274	*Craig Newsome*	.10
275	Leonard Russell	.05
276	Derrick Deese	.05
277	Broderick Thomas	.05
278	Bobby Houston	.05
279	Lamar Lathon	.05
280	Eugene Robinson	.05
281	Dan Saleaumua	.05
282	*Kyle Brady*	.10
283	John Taylor	.05
284	*Tony Boselli*	.10
285	Seth Joyner	.05
286	Steve Beuerlein	.05
287	Sam Adams	.05
288	Frank Reich	.05
289	Patrick Hunter	.05
290	Sean Gilbert	.05
291	Dermontti Dawson	.05
292	Shaun Gayle	.05
293	Vincent Brown	.05
294	Terry Kirby	.05
295	Courtney Hawkins	.05
296	Carl Pickens	.05
297	Luther Elliss	.10
298	Steve Atwater	.05
299	James Francis	.05
300	Rob Burnett	.05
301	Keith Hamilton	.05
302	Rob Fredrickson	.05
303	Jerome Bettis	.30
304	Emmitt Smith	1.50
305	Clyde Simmons	.05
306	Reggie White	.10
307	Rodney Hampton	.05
308	Steve Emtman	.05
309	*Hugh Douglas*	.10
310	Bernie Parmalee	.20
311	Trent Dilfer	.40
312	Willie Anderson	.05
313	Heath Shuler	.75
314	Rod Smith	.05
315	*Ray Zellars*	.10
316	Robert Brooks	.05
317	Lee Woodall	.05
318	Robert Porcher	.05
319	*Todd Collins*	.10
320	Willie Roaf	.05
321	Erik Williams	.05
322	Steve Wisniewski	.05
323	Derrick Alexander	.20
324	Frank Warren	.05
325	Kelvin Pritchett	.05
326	Dennis Gibson	.05
327	Jason Belser	.05
328	Vincent Brisby	.05
329	Calvin Williams	.05
330	Derek Brown	.05
331	Blake Brockermeyer	.05
332	Jeff Herrod	.05
333	Darryl Williams	.05
334	Aaron Glenn	.05
335	Eric Metcalf	.05
336	Billy Milner	.05
337	Terry McDaniel	.05
338	Trace Armstrong	.05
339	*Yancey Thigpen*	1.00
340	Jackie Harris	.05
341	Jeff George	.10
342	Darryl Talley	.05

343	Marcus Robertson	.05
344	Robert Massey	.05
345	Jessie Tuggle	.05
346	Scott Mitchell	.05
347	Harvey Williams	.05
348	*Jack Jackson*	.10
349	Brian Mitchell	.05
350	Lawrence Dawsey	.05
351	Erik Howard	.05
352	Quinn Early	.05
353	Terry Allen	.05
354	Simon Fletcher	.05
355	Eric Turner	.05
356	Natrone Means	.40
357	*Frank Sanders*	.20
358	Michael Timpson	.05
359	Michael Haynes	.05
360	Ruben Brown	.05
361	Troy Vincent	.05
362	Floyd Turner	.05
363	Larry Centers	.05
364	Eric Swann	.05
365	Albert Lewis	.05
366	Barry Foster	.05
367	Michael Dean Perry	.05
368	Jumpy Geathers	.05
369	*Kordell Stewart*	4.00
370	Chuck Smith	.05
371	Lake Dawson	.20
372	Terry Hoage	.05
373	Jeff Cross	.05
374	Tony McGee	.05
375	Eric Curry	.05
376	Harold Green	.05
377	Eric Hill	.05
378	Ray Buchanan	.05
379	Willie Davis	.05
380	*Chris Jones*	.20
381	Martin Mayhew	.05
382	Anthony Pleasant	.05
383	*Joey Galloway*	2.00
384	Anthony Morgan	.05
385	Harlon Barnett	.05
386	Bruce Smith	.05
387	Jeff Hostetler	.05
388	Randall McDaniel	.05
389	David Meggett	.05
390	Bill Romanowski	.05
391	Gary Brown	.05
392	Charles Johnson	.20
393	Chris Doleman	.05
394	Tony Martin	.05
395	Raymont Harris	.15
396	John Copeland	.05
397	Checklist #1 (Emmitt Smith)	.40
398	Checklist #2 (Steve Young)	.25
399	Checklist #3 (Marshall Faulk)	.40
400	Checklist #4 (Ki-Jana Carter)	.40

1995 Pro Line Printer's Proofs

Packaged two per hobby box, this set is a parallel to the base set. "Printer's Proof" is printed near the bottom of the card front. Overall, 400 of each card were printed.

	MT
Complete Set (400):	700.00
Common Player:	1.25
Veteran Stars:	10x-20x
RCs:	5x-10x

1995 Pro Line Printer's Proof Silver

Randomly seeded one per hobby box, this set is a parallel to the 400-card base set. "Printer's Proof" is printed on the front over silver foil. Overall, 175 of each card were produced.

	MT
Complete Set (400):	1300.00
Common Player:	2.50

Semistars		4.00
Veteran Stars:		25x-50x
RCs:		15x-30x

1995 Pro Line Silver

Randomly seeded one per hobby and retail pack, this is a 400-card parallel to the base set. A silver-foil background is the distinguishing feature of this set.

	MT
Complete Set (400):	80.00
Common Player:	.20
Veteran Stars:	2x-4x
RCs:	2x

1995 Pro Line Autographs

Randomly seeded one per box, the 128-card set was signed by NFL players, who signed less than 2,500 cards each. The card fronts have the identical design to the base cards, while the backs offer congratulations to the card holder for picking up an autographed card.

		MT
	Complete Set (128):	2200.
	Common Player:	10.00
1	Garrison Hearst	25.00
2	Anthony Miller (2385)	12.00
5	Mike Fox (1445)	10.00
6	Jeff Blake (1200)	40.00
7	J.J. Birden (775)	12.00
9	Leon Lett (1550)	12.00
11	Andre Reed (1440)	12.00
13A	Craig Heyward (1200)	12.00
13B	Craig Heyward (265AP)	12.00
14	Henry Ellard (1440)	12.00
18	Eric Zeier (500)	30.00
21	Qadry Ismail (1170)	12.00
23	Ty Law (1460)	10.00
24	Mark Collins (1430)	10.00
29	Mike Mamula (1250)	10.00
34	Michael Jackson (1200)	12.00
40A	Cornelius Bennett (1200)	12.00
40B	Cornelius Bennett (255AP)	12.00
42	Pierce Holt (1440)	10.00
44A	Chad May (1180)	12.00
44B	Chad May (2410AP)	12.00
45	Darrien Gordon (2400)	10.00
48	Al Smith (1360)	10.00
49A	Chris Slade (1100)	10.00
49B	Chris Slade (2417AP)	10.00
57	Charles Haley (1420)	12.00
59	Sean Jones (2385)	12.00
60	Tamarick Vanover (1155)	30.00
62	Rashaan Salaam (1320)	30.00
66	Troy Drayton (1375)	10.00
68A	Brian Williams (1175)	10.00
68B	Brian Williams (2670AP)	10.00
68C	Brian Williams (865AP)	10.00
70A	Eric Allen (1225)	10.00
70B	Eric Allen (2398AP)	10.00
70C	Eric Allen (745AP)	10.00
81A	Brett Perriman (1380)	12.00
81B	Brett Perriman (935)	12.00
82	Mike Sherrard (1450)	12.00
83	Curtis Conway (1200)	15.00

86A	Randy Baldwin (1435)	10.00
86B	Randy Baldwin (2405AP)	10.00
86C	Randy Baldwin (760AP)	10.00
88	Chester McGlockton (1280)	12.00
97A	Craig Erickson (630)	12.00
97B	Craig Erickson (890AP)	12.00
99	Steve McNair (3490)	40.00
100	Errict Rhett (1400)	45.00
106	Eric Green (1460)	12.00
109	Marshall Faulk (1030)	75.00
114A	Steve Israel (1200)	12.00
114B	Steve Israel (2413AP)	10.00
114C	Steve Israel (750AP)	10.00
119	Michael Irvin (1490)	15.00
126	Byron "Bam" Morris (1430)	12.00
127	Ben Coates (1175)	15.00
131	Tony Bennett (1475)	12.00
133	Tim Brown (2410)	15.00
137	John Elliott (2380)	10.00
140	Sherman Williams (1460)	12.00
142	Randall Cunningham (470)	30.00
143	Vinny Testaverde (1250)	12.00
145	Russell Maryland (1250)	12.00
149	Jeff Graham (1465)	12.00
155	Bert Emanuel (1445)	15.00
156	Mark Stepnoski (1500)	10.00
160	Henry Thomas (1420)	10.00
168A	Ray Childress (1200)	10.00
168B	Ray Childress (235AP)	10.00
173A	Rob Johnson (2815)	15.00
173B	Rob Johnson (500)	15.00
174	Derrick Brooks (1470)	12.00
175	Drew Bledsoe (515)	125.00
179	Ricky Proehl (1475)	10.00
180	Haywood Jeffires (1470)	12.00
185	Andy Harmon (1200)	10.00
186	Ronnie Lott (1900)	15.00
187	Clay Matthews (2385)	12.00
193	Herman Moore (2070)	20.00
197	Steve Young (500)	100.00
198	Roman Phifer (2395)	10.00
202	Lewis Tillman (1170)	12.00
207	Mario Bates (1480)	15.00
210	Kerry Collins (3300)	45.00
211A	Steve Walsh (1185)	12.00
211B	Steve Walsh (1015AP)	12.00
215	Jim Kelly (470)	40.00
217	Jay Novacek (1195)	12.00
218A	Shawn Jefferson (1165)	10.00
218B	Shawn Jefferson (240AP)	12.00
221A	Arthur Marshall (1165)	10.00
221B	Arthur Marshall (2400AP)	10.00
221C	Arthur Marshall (870AP)	10.00
226	Quentin Coryatt (1400)	12.00
228	Brian Blades (1465)	12.00
230	Boomer Esiason (1700)	12.00
231	Dave Krieg (1470)	12.00
234A	John Randle (1170)	12.00
234B	John Randle (2400AP)	12.00
234C	John Randle (757AP)	12.00
238	Cortez Kennedy (1380)	12.00
241A	Keenan McCardell (1235)	12.00
241B	Keenan McCardell (2403AP)	12.00
243A	Don Beebe (1200)	12.00
243B	Don Beebe (275AP)	12.00
244A	Jack Del Rio (1480)	10.00
244B	Jack Del Rio (930AP)	10.00
247	Edgar Bennett (1475)	12.00

250	Neil Smith (1465)	12.00
251	Sam Mills (1470)	12.00
252A	Willie McGinest (1160)	12.00
252B	Willie McGinest (2407AP)	12.00
252C	Willie McGinest (754AP)	12.00
254	Troy Aikman (500)	125.00
256	Dale Carter (1400)	12.00
258	Greg Hill (1455)	12.00
262	Trezelle Jenkins (1470)	10.00
263A	Antonio Langham (1200)	10.00
263B	Antonio Langham (1200)	10.00
265	Jake Reed (1470)	12.00
268A	Mark McMillian (1175)	10.00
268B	Mark McMillian (2400AP)	10.00
268C	Mark McMillian (1175)	10.00
269	John Walsh (3340)	12.00
270	Irving Fryar (1500)	12.00
273	J.J. Stokes (1435)	35.00
276A	Derrick Deese (1200)	10.00
276B	Derrick Deese (2375AP)	10.00
276C	Derrick Deese (735AP)	10.00
285	Seth Joyner (1480)	10.00
286	Steve Beuerlein (1465)	12.00
289	Patrick Hunter (2375)	10.00
292A	Shaun Gayle (1200)	10.00
292B	Shaun Gayle (265AP)	10.00
294	Terry Kirby (1450)	12.00
295	Courtney Hawkins (1445)	12.00
297	Luther Elliss (1470)	12.00
304	Emmitt Smith (500)	200.00
305	Clyde Simmons (735)	12.00
307	Rodney Hampton (1120)	15.00
308	Steve Emtman (2365)	10.00
311A	Trent Dilfer (2010)	15.00
311B	Trent Dilfer (306AP)	15.00
312	Flipper Anderson (1140)	12.00
313A	Heath Shuler (2000)	25.00
313B	Heath Shuler (366AP)	35.00
320A	Willie Roaf (1200)	12.00
320B	Willie Roaf (245AP)	12.00
329	Calvin Williams (1200)	12.00
331A	Blake Brockermeyer (1445)	12.00
331B	Blake Brockermeyer (2315AP)	12.00
337	Terry McDaniel (2340)	10.00
341	Jeff George (1295)	15.00
345A	Jessie Tuggle (1200)	10.00
345B	Jessie Tuggle (195AP)	12.00
348	Jack Jackson (1475)	12.00
352	Quinn Early (1200)	12.00
356	Natrone Means (1058)	15.00
359	Michael Haynes (1180)	12.00
361	Troy Vincent (1490)	10.00
366	Barry Foster (1455)	12.00
367A	Michael Dean Perry (1200)	12.00
367B	Michael Dean Perry (295AP)	12.00
374	Tony McGee (1385)	12.00
379	Willie Davis (1500)	12.00
383	Joey Galloway (1445)	45.00
390	Bill Romanowski (1450)	10.00

1995 Pro Line Bonus Card Jumbos

This complete set of 14 oversized cards was issued in four series. Cards 1-3 were inserted in 1995 Classic NFL Rookies cases (one per hobby case); cards 4-8 were inserted in 1995 Classic Pro Line cases (one per case); cards 9-11 were inserted in 1995 Classic NFL Pro Line Series II cases (one per case); cards 13-15 were inserted in 1996 Classic NFL Experience (one per case). Cards are sequentially numbered up to 2,500 and measure 4-3/4" x 2-1/2". There was no #12 card made.

		MT
	Complete Set (14):	175.00
	Comp. Series 1 (3):	30.00
	Comp. Series 2 (5):	70.00
	Comp. Series 3 (3):	30.00
	Comp. Series 4 (3):	45.00
	Common Player:	6.00
1	Ki-Jana Carter	6.00
2	Steve McNair	12.00
3	Kerry Collins	15.00
4	Deion Sanders	10.00
5	Steve Young	15.00
6	Emmitt Smith	30.00
7	Natrone Means	8.00
8	Drew Bledsoe	14.00
9	Troy Aikman	14.00
10	Marshall Faulk	6.00
11	J.J. Stokes	6.00
13	Emmitt Smith	30.00
14	Rashaan Salaam	6.00

1995 Pro Line Field Generals

These 10 insert cards were randomly included one per every 60 packs of 1995 Classic NFL Pro Line Series II product. The acetate cards, featuring some of the NFL's leaders on the field, are sequentially numbered to 1,700. Card backs are numbered using a "G" prefix.

		MT
	Complete Set (10):	300.00
	Common Player:	15.00
1	Marshall Faulk	15.00
2	Emmitt Smith	50.00
3	Steve Young	20.00
4	Ki-Jana Carter	15.00
5	Rashaan Salaam	15.00
6	Dan Marino	50.00
7	J.J. Stokes	15.00
8	Drew Bledsoe	30.00
9	Brett Favre	50.00
10	Barry Sanders	30.00

1995 Pro Line Game of the Week

The 60-card interactive game set showcased two teams in a key game from the 1995 season. "H" or "V" prefixes are listed on the back and stand for home or visitor. A set of 30 NFL Pro Line silver-foil winning cards with the final score printed on the card was given to the first 1,000 collectors who redeemed 21-30 different game cards. In addition, 2,500 collectors who redeemed 10-20 winning game cards received a set of 30 Pro Line winning cards with the score stamped on them. Those who redeemed 30 winning cards were entered into a drawing for a Steve Young or Jerry Rice game-used jersey.

		MT
	Complete Set (60):	25.00
	Common Player:	.40
1	Barry Sanders, Reggie White	1.50
2	Jeff Hostetler, John Elway	.75
3	Michael Westbrook, Ricky Watters	.75
4	Jim Kelly, Mo Lewis	.60
5	Marshall Faulk, Jerome Bettis	1.00
6	Natrone Means, Bam Morris	.60
7	Seth Joyner, Michael Irvin	.60
8	Errict Rhett, Heath Shuler	1.00
9	Junior Seau, Randall Cunningham	.60
10	Drew Bledsoe, Steve Young	1.00
11	Dave Krieg, Kerry Collins	1.50
12	Steve Beuerlein, Alvin Harper	.40
13	Ben Coates, Troy Vincent	.60
14	Jerry Rice, Michael Irvin	1.50
15	Rodney Hampton, Cortez Kennedy	.60

16	Ray Childress, Leroy Hoard	.40
17	Thurman Thomas, Irving Fryar	.60
18	Andre Rison, Ki-Jana Carter	.75
19	Dan Marino, Boomer Esiason	2.00
20	Brett Favre, Warren Moon	2.00
21	Anthony Miller, Tim Brown	.40
22	Chris Warren, Steve Bono	.60
23	Shannon Sharpe, Neil Smith	.40
24	John Randle, Dana Stubblefield	.40
25	Jim Everett, Terance Mathis	.40
26	Troy Aikman, Mike Mamula	1.50
27	Trent Dilfer, Cris Carter	.60
28	Steve Walsh, Scott Mitchell	.40
29	Greg Lloyd, Vinny Testaverde	.60
30	Jeff George, Garrison Hearst	.60

1995 Pro Line Game Breakers

These 1995 Classic NFL Pro Line insert cards use an attention-grabbing micro-lined foil-board for the cards. The cards, featuring players who can break a game open at any moment, were randomly seeded one per box of the football product. Cards are numbered using a "GB" prefix. Printer's Proof cards were also made for these inserts.

		MT
Complete Set (30):		130.00
Common Player:		2.00
Minor Stars:		4.00
Comp. Prin. Proof Set (30):		
800.00		
Printer's Proofs:		4x-8x
1	Troy Aikman	10.00
2	Drew Bledsoe	10.00
3	Tim Brown	4.00
4	Cris Carter	4.00
5	Ki-Jana Carter	7.00
6	Kerry Collins	10.00
7	John Elway	8.00
8	Marshall Faulk	4.00
9	Brett Favre	20.00
10	Garrison Hearst	4.00
11	Michael Irvin	6.00
12	Jim Kelly	4.00
13	Dan Marino	20.00
14	Natrone Means	6.00
15	Eric Metcalf	2.00
16	J.J. Stokes	6.00
17	Carl Pickens	2.00
18	Jerry Rice	10.00
19	Andre Rison	4.00
20	Barry Sanders	10.00
21	Deion Sanders	4.00
22	Junior Seau	4.00
23	Emmitt Smith	20.00
24	Thurman Thomas	4.00
25	Ricky Watters	4.00
26	Reggie White	4.00
27	Rod Woodson	2.00
28	Steve Young	10.00
29	Rashaan Salaam	6.00
30	Michael Westbrook	5.00

1995 Pro Line Grand Gainers

The 30-card retail-only set has an action photo, with white mesh in the background on the top half of the card front, while the bottom half of the card has the photo background. The player's name and position are printed in a box in the lower right, with the Grand Gainers' logo in the lower left. The backs include an action photo of the player, his name, position and write-up on the left. The player's yardage is printed inside a stripe on the right side of the card back, which are numbered with a "G" prefix.

		MT
Complete Set (30):		25.00
Common Player:		.40
1	Barry Sanders	4.00
2	Emmitt Smith	4.00
3	Natrone Means	.60
4	Marshall Faulk	1.00
5	Errict Rhett	1.00
6	Jerry Rice	2.00
7	Tim Brown	.60
8	Cris Carter	.60
9	Irving Fryar	.40
10	Ben Coates	.40
11	Fred Barnett	.40
12	Andre Rison	.40
13	Drew Bledsoe	2.00
14	Dan Marino	4.00
15	Warren Moon	.60
16	Steve Young	1.50
17	Brett Favre	4.00
18	John Elway	1.50
19	Randall Cunningham	.40
20	Stan Humphries	.60
21	Jim Kelly	.60
22	Ki-Jana Carter	1.00
23	Rodney Hampton	.60
24	Tyrone Wheatley	.60
25	J.J. Stokes	1.00
26	Michael Irvin	.40
27	Herman Moore	.75
28	Kerry Collins	2.50
29	Steve McNair	2.00
30	Rob Johnson	.60

1995 Pro Line Images Previews

This five-card preview of the 1995 Images series was inserted one per 18 packs of Series Two.

		MT
Complete Set (5):		25.00
Common Player:		3.00
1	Emmitt Smith	10.00
2	Steve Young	4.00
3	Drew Bledsoe	5.00
4	Kerry Collins	7.00
5	Marshall Faulk	3.00

1995 Pro Line Impact

These 30 exclusive cards of Impact NFL superstars are each sequentially numbered to only 4,500. The horizontal cards were seeded at a rate of one per every box of 1995 Classic Pro Line football product. A rarer version, Pro Line Golden Impact was also created. These cards, each sequentially numbered to 1,750, were seeded one per 90 packs.

		MT
Complete Set (30):		140.00
Common Player:		2.00
Minor Stars:		4.00
Comp. Golden Set (30):		375.00
Gold Cards:		2x-4x
1	Jim Kelly	4.00
2	Thurman Thomas	4.00
3	Troy Aikman	10.00
4	Michael Irvin	6.00
5	Emmitt Smith	18.00
6	John Elway	8.00
7	Barry Sanders	10.00
8	Brett Favre	18.00
9	Reggie White	4.00
10	Marshall Faulk	4.00
11	Ki-Jana Carter	4.00
12	Tim Brown	4.00
13	Jeff Hostetler	2.00
14	Dan Marino	18.00
15	Drew Bledsoe	15.00
16	Ben Coates	2.00
17	Rodney Hampton	2.00
18	Randall Cunningham	4.00
19	Ricky Watters	4.00
20	Bam Morris	6.00
21	Natrone Means	6.00
22	Junior Seau	6.00
23	Jerry Rice	10.00
24	Steve Young	10.00
25	William Floyd	6.00
26	Rick Mirer	6.00
27	Chris Warren	2.00
28	Jerome Bettis	6.00
29	Alvin Harper	4.00
30	Heath Shuler	6.00

1995 Pro Line MVP Redemption

These 1995 Classic NFL Pro Line inserts feature foil-board cards of the top 34 candidates for the Associated Press' 1995 Offensive MVP Award, plus one field card. Cards which depicted the MVP winner were winners and were redeemable for one of the following prizes: winner cards stamped 1 of 4,000 were redeemable for a prepaid $50 phone card of the player; winner cards hand-numbered to 200 were redeemable for a $100 phone card of the player; the winner card hand-numbered "1/200" was redeemable for the $100 phone card and a complete 1995 Pro Line autographed set of more than 100 cards. The MVP Interactive cards were seeded an average of one per two boxes.

		MT
Complete Set (35):		200.00
Common Player:		3.00
1	Garrison Hearst	4.00
2	Terance Mathis	3.00
3	Jim Kelly	4.00
4	Thurman Thomas	4.00
5	Kerry Collins	10.00
6	Rashaan Salaam	5.00
7	Ki-Jana Carter	4.00
8	Andre Rison	3.00
9	Troy Aikman	12.00
10	Michael Irvin	3.00
11	Emmitt Smith	25.00
12	John Elway	10.00
13	Barry Sanders	15.00
14	Brett Favre	30.00
15	Marshall Faulk	3.00
16	Marcus Allen	3.00
17	Jeff Hostetler	3.00
18	Dan Marino	25.00
19	Cris Carter	3.00
20	Warren Moon	4.00
21	Drew Bledsoe	15.00
22	Ben Coates	3.00
23	Rodney Hampton	3.00
24	Boomer Esiason	3.00
25	Ricky Watters	4.00
26	Barry Foster	3.00
27	Natrone Means	4.00
28	Rick Mirer	4.00
29	Chris Warren	3.00
30	Jerry Rice	15.00
31	Steve Young	10.00
32	Jerome Bettis	5.00
33	Errict Rhett	6.00
34	Heath Shuler	5.00
35	Field Card	4.00

1995 Pro Line National Attention

Randomly seeded in Pro Line National boxes sold by dealers who had a booth at the National Convention in St. Louis, Mo., the 10-card set is numbered with a prefix of "NA".

		MT
Complete Set (10):		60.00
Common Player:		4.00
1	Jerome Bettis	6.00
2	Sean Gilbert	4.00
3	Chris Miller	4.00
4	Troy Aikman	15.00
5	Kevin Carter	4.00
6	Marshall Faulk	8.00
7	Drew Bledsoe	15.00
8	Shane Conlan	4.00
9	Emmitt Smith	25.00
10	Steve Young	10.00

A player's name in *italic* type indicates a rookie card.

1995 Pro Line Phone Cards $1

Phone cards were randomly inserted into 1995 Classic NFL Series II packs at a ratio of one per pack, and at least three $2 cards and a $5 card per box. Printer's Proof versions were also made of these $1 cards. They are stamped with a printer's proof logo and are numbered 1 of 699. The proof cards were seeded at a ratio of one per 44 packs.

		MT
Complete Set (30):		40.00
Common Player:		1.50
Comp. Art. Proofs Set (30):		75.00
Artist Proofs Cards:		2x-4x
1	Kerry Collins	3.00
2	Barry Foster	1.50
3	Jeff Blake	2.00
4	Troy Aikman	3.00
5	Reggie White	1.50
6	Marshall Faulk	3.00
7	Steve Bono	1.50
8	Drew Bledsoe	3.00
9	Byron Morris	1.50
10	Rodney Hampton	1.50
11	Trent Dilfer	2.00
12	Errict Rhett	3.00
13	Heath Shuler	2.00
14	Mike Mamula	1.50
15	Ricky Watters	1.50
16	Stan Humphries	1.50
17	Natrone Means	2.00
18	William Floyd	2.00
19	Joey Galloway	2.00
20	Ki-Jana Carter	2.00
21	Andre Rison	1.50
22	Steve McNair	2.00
23	Napoleon Kaufman	1.50
24	Kyle Brady	1.50
25	Desmond Howard	1.50
26	Ben Coates	1.50
27	Eric Metcalf	1.50
28	Steve Beurlein	1.50
29	Deion Sanders	2.00
30	J.J. Stokes	2.00

1995 Pro Line Phone Cards $5

Phone cards were randomly inserted into 1995 Classic NFL Pro Line Series II packs at a ratio of one per pack, and at least three $2 cards and a $5 card in every box. Printer's proof versions were also made of these $5 cards. They are stamped with a printer's proof logo and are numbered 1 of 297. The proof cards were seeded at a ratio of one per 210 packs.

		MT
Complete Set (15):		100.00
Common Player:		7.00
1	Marshall Faulk	18.00
2	Troy Aikman	12.00
3	Drew Bledsoe	17.00
4	Deion Sanders	10.00
5	Kerry Collins	14.00
6	Steve McNair	12.00
7	Kyle Brady	7.00
8	J.J. Stokes	10.00
9	Ki-Jana Carter	12.00
10	Emmitt Smith	20.00
11	William Floyd	10.00
12	Ricky Watters	7.00
13	Reggie White	7.00
14	Warren Sapp	7.00
15	Steve Young	12.00

1995 Pro Line Phone Cards $2

Phone cards were randomly inserted into 1995 Classic NFL Pro Line Series II packs at a ratio of one per pack, and at least three $2 cards and one $5 card in every pack. Printer's proof versions were also made of these $2 cards. They are stamped with a printer's proof logo and are numbered 1 of 494. The proof cards are seeded at a ratio of one per 75 packs.

	MT
Complete Set (25):	90.00
Common Player:	2.50

1995 Pro Line Phone Cards $20

Phone cards were randomly inserted into 1995 Classic NFL Pro Line Series II packs at a ratio of one per pack, and at least three $2 cards and a $5 card in every box. The higher denominations were seeded at scarcer rates.

		MT
Complete Set (5):		125.00
Common Player:		30.00
1	Steve Young	30.00
2	Drew Bledsoe	30.00
3	Marshall Faulk	40.00
4	Ki-Jana Carter	30.00
5	Kerry Collins	30.00

1995 Pro Line Phone Cards $100

One phone card is seeded in each pack of 1995 Classic Pro Line Series II packs; at least three $2 cards and a $5 card are in every box. These $100 phone cards, featuring four NFL stars and a promising rookie, were fairly scarce.

		MT
Complete Set (5):		600.00
Common Player:		100.00
1	Emmitt Smith	200.00
2	Steve Young	150.00
3	Drew Bledsoe	100.00
4	Ki-Jana Carter	100.00
5	Troy Aikman	150.00

1995 Pro Line Phone Cards $1,000

Phone cards were randomly inserted into 1995 Classic NFL Pro Line Series II packs, one per every pack, and at least three $2 cards and one $5 card in every box. The higher the denomination, the more exclusive the number made.

		MT
Complete Set (4):		5000.
Common Player:		900.00
1	Steve Young	1250.
2	Drew Bledsoe	900.00
3	Ki-Jana Carter	900.00
4	Troy Aikman	1400.

1995 Pro Line Phone Cards $1,500

Dallas Cowboys' star running back Emmitt Smith is featured on this 1995 Classic NFL Pro Line Series II phone card insert. This card is the scarcest of the phone card inserts.

		MT
Complete Set (1):		2000.
Common Player:		2000.
1	Emmitt Smith	2000.

1995 Pro Line Pogs

The 30-card retail-only set included an action photo on the front, with two Pogs punched out on the card. The backs have the player's name and stats. The cards carry a "C" prefix.

		MT
Complete Set (30):		8.00
Common Player:		.25
1	Steve Walsh, Rashaan Salaam	.35
2	Kerry Collins, Barry Foster	.75
3	Jim Kelly, Thurman Thomas	.35
4	Terance Mathis, Jeff George	.25
5	Garrison Hearst, Seth Joyner	.25
6	Barry Sanders, Herman Moore	.75
7	John Elway, Shannon Sharpe	.50
8	Troy Aikman, Emmitt Smith	1.50
9	Leroy Hoard, Andre Rison	.25
10	Jeff Blake, Ki-Jana Carter	.50
11	Marcus Allen, Steve Bono	.35
12	Tony Boselli, Steve Beuerlein	.25
13	Marshall Faulk, Quentin Coryatt	.35
14	Steve McNair, Gary Brown	.35
15	Brett Favre, Reggie White	1.50
16	Jim Everett, Michael Bates	.35
17	Drew Bledsoe, Ben Coates	.75
18	Warren Moon, Cris Carter	.35
19	Dan Marino, Irving Fryar	1.50
20	Jeff Hostetler, Tim Brown	.35
21	Kevin Greene, Bam Morris	.35
22	Derek Brown, Rodney Hampton	.25
23	Boomer Esiason, Mo Lewis	.25
24	Randall Cunningham, Ricky Watters	.25

		MT
25	Natrone Means, Junior Seau	.25
26	Heath Shuler, Michael Westbrook	.35
27	Trent Dilfer, Errict Rhett	.35
28	Jerome Bettis, Ki-Jana Carter	.35
29	Steve Young, Jerry Rice	1.00
30	Rick Mirer, Chris Warren	.35

1995 Pro Line Precision Cuts

These 20 die-cut cards feature NFL superstars on silver foil board. The cards were exclusive inserts in 1995 Classic Pro Line Series II cases, one per 45 packs. The cards are sequentially numbered up to 1,250.

		MT
Complete Set (20):		375.00
Common Player:		7.00
1	Jim Kelly	9.00
2	John Elway	14.00
3	Kerry Collins	25.00
4	Ki-Jana Carter	7.00
5	Andre Rison	7.00
6	Troy Aikman	25.00
7	Emmitt Smith	50.00
8	Barry Sanders	40.00
9	Warren Moon	9.00
10	Jeff Hostetler	7.00
11	Dan Marino	50.00
12	Drew Bledsoe	35.00
13	Rodney Hampton	7.00
14	Ricky Watters	9.00
15	Byron Morris	7.00
16	Natrone Means	7.00
17	Steve Young	25.00
18	Jerry Rice	25.00
19	J.J. Stokes	18.00
20	Errict Rhett	7.00

1995 Pro Line Pro Bowl

The 30-card set was seeded one per box in $1.99 retail packs. The ticket-shaped die-cut fronts have an action photo of the player on a silver-foil background. Every card showcases the number "250392" on the top and bottom. The card backs, numbered with a "PB" prefix, have another action shot, with the player's name, position and write-up included.

		MT
Complete Set (30):		50.00
Common Player:		1.00
1	Seth Joyner	1.00
2	Andre Reed	1.00
3	Bruce Smith	1.50
4	Michael Irvin	1.50
5	Troy Aikman	3.00
6	Emmitt Smith	6.00
7	Charles Haley	1.00
8	Shannon Sharpe	1.00
9	John Elway	2.00
10	Barry Sanders	3.00
11	Reggie White	1.25
12	Marshall Faulk	2.00
13	Tim Brown	1.25
14	Chester McGlockton	1.00
15	Dan Marino	6.00
16	Cris Carter	1.25
17	Warren Moon	1.25
18	Ben Coates	1.25
19	Drew Bledsoe	2.50
20	Rod Woodson	1.25
21	Natrone Means	1.25
22	Leslie O'Neal	1.00
23	Junior Seau	1.25
24	Jerry Rice	3.00
25	Chris Warren	1.25
26	Brent Jones	1.00
27	Steve Young	2.50
28	Dana Stubblefield	1.00
29	Deion Sanders	2.00
30	Jerome Bettis	1.25

Values quoted in this guide reflect the retail price of a card — the price a collector can expect to pay when buying a card from a dealer. The wholesale price — that which a collector can expect to receive when selling cards to a dealer — will be significantly lower, depending on desirability and condition.

1995 Pro Line Record Breakers

These Record Breaker acetate cards were exclusive inserts in 1995 Classic NFL Pro Line Hot Boxes. Each pack in a Hot Box contains 40 percent inserts. Hot Boxes were randomly inserted one per 10 cases of 1995 Classic NFL Pro Line cases. Cards 1-5 were hobby inserts; 6-10 were retail inserts. They carried a "RB" prefix. Cards were sequentially numbered up to 350.

		MT
Complete Set (10):		500.00
Common Player:		20.00
1	Drew Bledsoe	75.00
2	Cris Carter	20.00
3	Jerry Rice	75.00
4	Steve Young	75.00
5	Marshall Faulk	40.00
6	Emmitt Smith	125.00
7	Barry Sanders	75.00
8	Natrone Means	20.00
9	Ben Coates	20.00
10	Bruce Smith	20.00

1995 Pro Line Series II

Classic's 1995 NFL Pro Line Series II contains 75 cards, including the NFL's top stars, most promising rookies and traded veterans in their new uniforms. The basic format for the cards is similar to the Series I cards, but the cards can be distinguished because they say Series II on the front. Exclusive to hobby cases is a 75-card parallel set of Printer's Proofs cards, which feature holographic foil-stamped logos. These cards are seeded one per 18 packs in hobby cases. Phone cards have a dominant presence in Series II, with denominations of $1, $2, $5, $20, $100 and $1,000. One phone card appears in each pack and at least three $2 cards and one $5 phone card are in a box. Printer's Proof versions of the $1 (one per 44 packs), $2 (one per 75) and $5 (one per 210) also exist. The $1 phone cards are stamped with the printer's proof logo and are numbered 1 of 699. The $2 cards are also stamped with the logo and are numbered 1 of 494, while the $5 cards are stamped and numbered 1 of 297. Other inserts include Precision Cut, NFL Images Preview cards, Field Generals, and a continuation of Classic's oversized bonus cards program. These micro-lined cards are

numbered 9-11 in the bonus series and are sequentially numbered 1,250. One oversized bonus card is packed in every case of 1995 Pro Line Series II product.

		MT
Complete Set (75):		15.00
Common Player:		.05
Minor Stars:		.10
1	Jim Kelly	.10
2	Steve Walsh	.05
3	Jeff Blake	1.00
4	Vinny Testaverde	.05
5	Jeff Hostetler	.05
6	Dan Marino	1.50
7	Cris Carter	.10
8	Drew Bledsoe	1.00
9	Jim Everett	.05
10	Neil O'Donnell	.05
11	Rodney Hampton	.05
12	Troy Aikman	.75
13	John Elway	.50
14	Barry Sanders	1.25
15	Reggie White	.10
16	Marshall Faulk	.50
17	Marcus Allen	.10
18	James Stewart	.10
19	Randall Cunningham	.10
20	Natrone Means	.50
21	Rick Mirer	.40
22	Jerry Rice	.75
23	Errict Rhett	.50
24	Heath Shuler	.50
25	Jerome Bettis	.25
26	Garrison Hearst	.10
27	Jeff George	.05
28	Andre Reed	.05
29	Warren Moon	.10
30	Ben Coates	.05
31	Mario Bates	.20
32	Byron Morris	.40
33	Dave Brown	.05
34	Emmitt Smith	1.50
35	Anthony Miller	.05
36	Herman Moore	.10
37	Brett Favre	1.50
38	Steve Bono	.20
39	Stan Humphries	.05
40	Steve Young	.75
41	Trent Dilfer	.30
42	Chris Miller	.05
43	Herschel Walker	.05
44	Michael Irvin	.20
45	Junior Seau	.10
46	Deion Sanders	.40
47	William Floyd	.30
48	Ki-Jana Carter	.75
49	Kerry Collins	1.00
50	Steve McNair	1.00
51	Tony Boselli	.10
52	Kyle Brady	.10
53	Mike Mamula	.05
54	Warren Sapp	.10
55	J.J. Stokes	.75
56	Joey Galloway	1.00
57	Hugh Douglas	.05
58	Michael Westbrook	.50
59	Napoleon Kaufman	.50
60	Rashaan Salaam	1.00
61	Tyrone Wheatley	.50
62	*Terrell Fletcher*	.50
63	Eric Metcalf	.05
64	Kevin Carter	.05
65	Andre Rison	.05
66	Eric Green	.05
67	Dave Meggett	.05
68	Ricky Watters	.10
69	Steve Beuerlein	.05
70	Craig Erickson	.05
71	Michael Dean Perry	.05
72	Alvin Harper	.05
73	Rob Moore	.05
74	Frank Reich	.05
75	Checklist	.05

1995 Pro Line Series II Printer's Proofs

The 75-card set is a parallel to the Series II cards. Seeded one per 18 packs, the cards have a printer's proof logo on the front.

	MT
Complete Set (75):	300.00
Common Player:	1.50
PP Veteran Stars:	10x-18x
PP RCs:	5x-10x

Post-1980 cards in Near Mint condition will generally sell for about 75% of the quoted Mint value. Excellent-condition cards bring no more than 40%.

1996 Pro Line

Pro Line's 1996 football offers one autographed card in every box and cards of newly-signed free agents and rookies. Each regular card front has a full-bleed color or action photo on it, with the Pro Line logo at the top. The player's name and position are in the lower left corner, opposite his team's logo. The card back has a color photo on the right, flanked by a recap of some of the player's accomplishments. The player's name, position and card number are at the top; a team logo, biographical information and statistics are along the bottom. The autographed cards of players are available in blue and gold foil-stamped versions, with gold ones limited to a maximum of 250 cards. One autographed card is seeded in every 25th pack. Five cards are jointly autographed by a quarterback/wide receiver combination. Other inserts include Cels, Cover Story, Rivalries and Touchdown Performers.

		MT
Complete Set (350):		25.00
Common Player:		.05
Minor Stars:		.10
1	Troy Aikman	1.00
2	Steve Young	1.00
3	John Elway	.50
4	Jim Kelly	.10
5	Dan Marino	1.50
6	Brett Favre	2.00
7	Kerry Collins	1.25
8	Jeff Blake	.50
9	Stan Humphries	.05
10	Steve Bono	.05
11	Jeff George	.10
12	Mark Brunell	.75
13	Scott Mitchell	.05
14	Steve McNair	1.00
15	Jeff Hostetler	.05
16	Jim Everett	.05
17	Rick Mirer	.05
18	Boomer Esiason	.05
19	Neil O'Donnell	.05
20	Dave Brown	.05
21	Erik Kramer	.05
22	Trent Dilfer	.05
23	Jim Harbaugh	.05
24	Vinny Testaverde	.05
25	Thurman Thomas	.10
26	Rodney Peete	.05
27	Gus Frerotte	.05
28	Warren Moon	.05
29	Eric Zeier	.05
30	Randall Cunningham	.05
31	Heath Shuler	.40
32	John Friesz	.05
33	Tommy Maddox	.05
34	Glenn Foley	.05
35	Drew Bledsoe	.75
36	Kordell Stewart	1.25
37	Natrone Means	.15
38	Errict Rhett	.30
39	Rashaan Salaam	.30
40	Emmitt Smith	2.00
41	Larry Centers	.05
42	Terrell Davis	1.00
43	Marshall Faulk	.50
44	Rodney Hampton	.05
45	Byron Morris	.05
46	Chris Warren	.15
47	Curtis Martin	2.00
48	Ricky Watters	.05
49	Marcus Allen	.05
50	Barry Sanders	1.25
51	Edgar Bennett	.05
52	Adrian Murrell	.05
53	James Stewart	.05
54	Leroy Hoard	.05
55	Jerome Bettis	.05
56	Craig Heyward	.05
57	Harvey Williams	.05
58	Bernie Parmalee	.05
59	Garrison Hearst	.05
60	Terry Allen	.05
61	Charlie Garner	.05

		MT
62	Dorsey Levens	.10
63	Derek Loville	.05
64	Greg Hill	.05
65	Derrick Moore	.05
66	Rodney Thomas	.40
67	Daryl Johnston	.05
68	Mario Bates	.05
69	*Aaron Hayden*	.10
70	Napoleon Kaufman	.05
71	Terry Kirby	.05
72	Glyn Milburn	.05
73	Robert Smith	.05
74	Ki-Jana Carter	.40
75	Tyrone Wheatley	.05
76	Erric Pegram	.05
77	Brian Mitchell	.05
78	Vaughn Dunbar	.05
79	Dave Meggett	.05
80	Scottie Graham	.05
81	Darick Holmes	.05
82	Marion Butts	.05
83	Harold Green	.05
84	Zack Crockett	.05
85	Amp Lee	.05
86	Lamont Warren	.05
87	Mark Chmura	.25
88	Irving Fryar	.05
89	Tim Brown	.05
90	Michael Irvin	.05
91	Tony Martin	.05
92	Alvin Harper	.05
93	Darnay Scott	.05
94	Eric Metcalf	.05
95	Michael Timpson	.05
96	Sean Dawkins	.05
97	Qadry Ismail	.05
98	Yancey Thigpen	.50
99	Joey Galloway	1.00
100	Herman Moore	.25
101	J.J. Stokes	.10
102	Wayne Chrebet	.05
103	Ernest Givins	.05
104	Michael Jackson	.05
105	Henry Ellard	.05
106	Thomas Lewis	.05
107	Anthony Miller	.05
108	Terance Mathis	.05
109	Horace Copeland	.05
110	Raghib Ismail	.05
111	Quinn Early	.05
112	Haywood Jeffires	.05
113	Mark Carrier	.05
114	Brent Jones	.05
115	Ben Coates	.05
116	Ken Dilger	.05
117	Irv Smith	.05
118	Jay Novacek	.05
119	Tony McGee	.05
120	Troy Drayton	.05
121	Johnny Mitchell	.05
122	Rob Moore	.05
123	Kevin Williams	.05
124	O.J. McDuffie	.05
125	Carl Pickens	.05
126	Curtis Conway	.05
127	Ed McCaffrey	.05
128	Arthur Marshall	.05
129	Ernie Mills	.05
130	Cris Carter	.05
131	Isaac Bruce	.50
132	Brian Blades	.05
133	Michael Westbrook	.10
134	Andre Reed	.05
135	Andre Rison	.05
136	Brett Perriman	.05
137	Willie Jackson	.05
138	Ryan Yarborough	.05
139	Chris T. Jones	.05
140	Jerry Rice	1.00
141	Lake Dawson	.05
142	Robert Brooks	.05
143	Vincent Brisby	.05
144	Desmond Howard	.05
145	Johnnie Morton	.05
146	Steve Tasker	.05
147	Ty Detmer	.05
148	Todd Kinchen	.05
149	Mike Sherrard	.05
150	Eric Green	.05
151	Mark Bruener	.05
152	Kyle Brady	.05
153	Frank Sanders	.05
154	Willie Green	.05
155	Jeff Graham	.05
156	Bert Emanuel	.05
157	Courtney Hawkins	.05
158	Mark Seay	.05
159	Chris Calloway	.05
160	John Taylor	.05
161	Fred Barnett	.05
162	Tamarick Vanover	.60
163	Keenan McCardell	.05
164	Bill Brooks	.05
165	Alexander Wright	.05
166	Jake Reed	.05
167	Floyd Turner	.05
168	Mike Pritchard	.05
169	Lawrence Dawsey	.05
170	Shawn Jefferson	.05
171	Michael Haynes	.05
172	Shannon Sharpe	.05
173	Jackie Harris	.05
174	Daryl Hobbs	.05
175	Chris Sanders	.25
176	Willie Davis	.05
177	Marco Coleman	.05
178	Pat Swilling	.05
179	Alonzo Spellman	.05

		MT
180	Simon Fletcher	.05
181	Sean Gilbert	.05
182	Tracy Scroggins	.05
183	Hugh Douglas	.05
184	Eric Swann	.05
185	Russell Maryland	.05
186	Warren Sapp	.05
187	Jim Flanigan	.05
188	Cortez Kennedy	.05
189	Andy Harmon	.05
190	Dan Saleaumua	.05
191	Kelvin Pritchett	.05
192	John Randle	.05
193	Dan Wilkinson	.05
194	Chester McGlockton	.05
195	Leon Lett	.05
196	Neil Smith	.05
197	Mike Mamula	.05
198	Mike Jones	.05
199	Reggie White	.05
200	Anthony Pleasant	.05
201	Phil Hansen	.05
202	Ray Seals	.05
203	Tony Bennett	.05
204	Leslie O'Neal	.05
205	Jeff Cross	.05
206	Anthony Cook	.05
207	Clyde Simmons	.05
208	Renaldo Turnbull	.05
209	Charles Haley	.05
210	John Copeland	.05
211	John Thierry	.05
212	Michael Strahan	.05
213	Jeff Lageman	.05
214	William Fuller	.05
215	Rickey Jackson	.05
216	Wayne Martin	.05
217	Steve Emtman	.05
218	Shawn Lee	.05
219	Chris Zorich	.05
220	Henry Thomas	.05
221	Dana Stubblefield	.05
222	D'Marco Farr	.05
223	Pierce Holt	.05
224	Sean Jones	.05
225	Robert Porcher	.05
226	Kevin Carter	.05
227	Chris Doleman	.05
228	Tony Tolbert	.05
229	Bruce Smith	.05
230	Marvin Washington	.05
231	Blaine Bishop	.05
232	Bryant Young	.05
233	Rob Burnett	.05
234	*Lawrence Phillips*	.50
235	Trev Alberts	.05
236	Eric Curry	.05
237	Anthony Smith	.05
238	Sam Mills	.05
239	Seth Joyner	.05
240	Quentin Coryatt	.05
241	Levon Kirkland	.05
242	Cornelius Bennett	.05
243	Chris Spielman	.05
244	Mo Lewis	.05
245	Lee Woodall	.05
246	Derrick Thomas	.05
247	Willie McGinest	.05
248	Terry Wooden	.05
249	Greg Lloyd	.05
250	Jack Del Rio	.05
251	Hardy Nickerson	.05
252	Michael Barrow	.05
253	Lamar Lathon	.05
254	Bryan Cox	.05
255	Randy Kirk	.05
256	Jessie Tuggle	.05
257	Roman Phifer	.05
258	Ken Harvey	.05
259	Junior Seau	.05
260	Pepper Johnson	.05
261	Chris Slade	.05
262	Gary Plummer	.05
263	Wayne Simmons	.05
264	Bryce Paup	.05
265	William Thomas	.05
266	Kevin Greene	.05
267	*Bobby Engram*	1.00
268	Ken Norton	.05
269	Eric Hill	.05
270	Darion Conner	.05
271	Tyrone Poole	.05
272	Cris Dishman	.05
273	Marcus Jones	.05
274	Rod Woodson	.05
275	Mark McMillan	.05
276	Dale Carter	.05
277	Darrell Green	.05
278	Donnell Woolford	.05
279	Troy Vincent	.05
280	Larry Brown	.05
281	Aeneas Williams	.05
282	Eric Allen	.05
283	Ray Buchanan	.05
284	Ty Law	.05
285	Eric Davis	.05
286	Todd Lyght	.05
287	Terry McDaniel	.05
288	Darryl Lewis	.05
289	Deion Sanders	.50
290	Phillippi Sparks	.05
291	Bobby Taylor	.05
292	Mark Collins	.05
293	Steve Atwater	.05
294	Stanley Richard	.05
295	Stevon Moore	.05
296	Bennie Blades	.05
297	Tim McDonald	.05

298	Shaun Gayle	.05
299	Darren Woodson	.05
300	Mark Carrier	.05
301	Carnell Lake	.05
302	James Washington	.05
303	LeRoy Butler	.05
304	Henry Jones	.05
305	Darryl Williams	.05
306	Darren Perry	.05
307	Merton Hanks	.05
308	Orlando Thomas	.05
309	Eric Turner	.05
310	Nate Newton	.05
311	Steve Wisniewski	.05
312	Derrick Deese	.05
313	Larry Allen	.05
314	Aaron Taylor	.05
315	Blake Brockermeyer	.05
316	William Roaf	.05
317	John Elliott	.05
318	*Keyshawn Johnson*	2.00
319	*Karim Abdul-Jabbar*	1.00
320	*Kevin Hardy*	.30
321	Duane Clemons	.05
322	Jevon Langford	.05
323	*Mike Alstott*	1.50
324	Scott Greene	.05
325	*Derrick Mayes*	.75
326	Chris Doering	.05
327	*Amani Toomer*	.05
328	*Eric Moulds*	1.50
329	Alex Molden	.05
330	Lawyer Milloy	.05
331	Daryl Gardener	.05
332	Randall Godfrey	.05
333	Willie Anderson	.05
334	*Tony Banks*	.50
335	*Jeff Lewis*	.50
336	Roman Oben	.05
337	Andre Johnson	.05
338	Brian Roche	.05
339	Johnny McWilliams	.05
340	*Alex Van Dyke*	.10
341	Ray Mickens	.05
342	*Marvin Harrison*	2.00
343	*Terry Glenn*	1.75
344	*Tim Biakabutuka*	1.00
345	*Simeon Rice*	.30
346	Cedric Jones	.05
347	*Eddie George*	3.50
348	Checklist 1	.05
349	Checklist 2	.30
350	Checklist 3	.30

1996 Pro Line National

This 350-card parallel set was inserted 1:1 in 1996 Pro Line National packs. The card fronts feature the 1996 National logo printed in silver foil. Each card is numbered one of 499.

	MT
Complete Set (350):	400.00
Common Player:	.50
National Stars:	4x-8x
National RCs:	2x-4x

1996 Pro Line Printer's Proof

Inserted at a rate of one per 10 packs, this 350-card set parallels the regular-issue set. Printer's Proof cards are distinguished by a large red foil "Printer's Proof" stamp.

	MT
Complete Set (350):	500.00
Printer's Proof Cards:	10x-20x

Post-1980 cards in Near Mint condition will generally sell for about 75% of the quoted Mint value. Excellent-condition cards bring no more than 40%.

1996 Pro Line Autographs

This 73-card insert features authentic player autographs printed in gold foil. The cards were inserted 1:170 in hobby and retail packs and 1:200 in jumbo packs. The cards in this insert are not numbered. Blue foil versions were inserted 1:25 hobby and retail and 1:90 jumbo.

		MT
Complete Set (73):		2700.
Common Gold Foil:		20.00
Comp. Blue Set (68):		650.00
Common Blue Foil:		10.00
Blue Cards:		.5x
1	Troy Aikman, Emmitt Smith (Gold only)	500.00
2	Eric Allen	20.00
3	Mike Alstott	40.00
4	Tony Banks	40.00
5	Blaine Bishop	20.00
6	Drew Bledsoe	150.00
7	Tim Brown	25.00
8	Marion Butts	20.00
9	Sedric Clark	20.00
10	Duane Clemons	20.00
11	Marco Coleman	20.00
12	Eric Davis	20.00
13	Derrick Deese	20.00
14	Jack Del Rio	20.00
15	Ty Detmer	30.00
16	Chris Doering	20.00
17	Jumbo Elliott	20.00
18	Marshall Faulk	60.00
19	Glenn Foley	20.00
20	John Friesz	20.00
21	Daryl Gardener	20.00
22	Randall Godfrey	20.00
23	Scott Greene	20.00
24	Rhett Hall	20.00
25	Merton Hanks	20.00
26	Kevin Hardy	20.00
27	Richard Huntley	20.00
28	Michael Jackson	20.00
29	Ron Jaworski	25.00
30	Andre Johnson	20.00
31	Keyshawn Johnson	100.00
32	Keyshawn Johnson, Neil O'Donnell (Gold only)	175.00
33	Mike Jones	20.00
34	Jim Kick	20.00
35	Jeff Lewis	25.00
36	Tommy Maddox	20.00
37	Arthur Marshall	20.00
38	Russell Maryland	20.00
39	Derrick Mayes	40.00
40	Ed McCaffrey	20.00
41	Keenan McCardell	25.00
42	Terry McDaniel	20.00
43	Tim McDonald	20.00
44	Willie McGinest	20.00
45	Mark McMillian	20.00
46	Johnny McWilliams	20.00
47	Ray Mickens	20.00
48	Anthony Miller	20.00
49	Rick Mirer	20.00
50	Alex Molden	20.00
51	Johnnie Morton	25.00
52	Eric Moulds	30.00
53	Roman Oben	20.00
54	Neil O'Donnell (Gold only)	60.00
55	Leslie O'Neal	20.00
56	Roman Phifer	20.00
57	Gary Plummer	20.00
58	Jim Plunkett	20.00
59	Stanley Pritchett	20.00
60	John Randle	20.00
61	Brian Roche	20.00
62	Orpheus Roye	20.00
63	Mark Seay	20.00
64	Mike Sherrard	20.00
65	Chris Slade	20.00
66	Scott Slutzker	20.00
67	Emmitt Smith (Gold only)	350.00
68	Steve Taneyhill	20.00
69	Robb Thomas	20.00
70	William Thomas	20.00
71	Alex Van Dyke	20.00
72	Randy White	30.00
73	Steve Young (Gold only)	150.00

1996 Pro Line Cels

Each of these 1996 Pinnacle inserts features a top NFL veteran or rookie on an acetate card and contains two foil stamps on it. The cards were seeded exclusively in hobby packs, one per 75 packs. They are numbered with a "C" prefix.

		MT
Complete Set (20):		350.00
Common Player:		6.00
1	Bryce Paup	6.00
2	Kerry Collins	30.00
3	Troy Aikman	35.00
4	Deion Sanders	20.00
5	Emmitt Smith	50.00
6	Steve McNair	20.00
7	Drew Bledsoe	30.00
8	Kordell Stewart	30.00
9	Ricky Watters	6.00
10	Jerry Rice	35.00
11	Steve Young	25.00
12	Errict Rhett	15.00
13	Brett Favre	50.00
14	Jeff Blake	20.00
15	Joey Galloway	25.00
16	Herman Moore	6.00
17	Curtis Martin	30.00
18	Keyshawn Johnson	20.00
19	Eddie George	25.00
20	Simeon Rice	6.00

1996 Pro Line Rivalries

This 30-card 1996 Pro Line insert set provides an in-depth look at some of the NFL's most heated battles. Each card side features an action shot of one of two players along with a decorative foil stamp, used for the player's name. His team logo and highlights from the two team's rivalries are also on each side. The metallic background shows a ghosted image of the player's opponent. A card number, using an "R" prefix, is on one side only. Cards were seeded one per every 10 packs.

		MT
Complete Set (20):		200.00
Common Player:		3.00
1	Drew Bledsoe, Jim Kelly	12.00
2	Dan Marino, Greg Lloyd	20.00
3	Kordell Stewart, Mark Brunell	12.00
4	Tamarick Vanover, Napoleon Kaufman	12.00
5	John Elway, Jeff Blake	8.00
6	Emmitt Smith, Ricky Watters	12.00
7	Troy Aikman, Steve Young	12.00
8	Deion Sanders, Gus Frerotte	8.00
9	Brett Favre, Errict Rhett	20.00
10	Rashaan Salaam, Warren Moon	10.00
11	Kerry Collins, Ken Norton Jr.	12.00
12	Jeff George, Isaac Bruce	8.00
13	Rod Woodson, Rodney Thomas	3.00
14	Herman Moore, Reggie White	8.00
15	Marshall Faulk, Curtis Martin	16.00
16	Keyshawn Johnson, Marvin Harrison	20.00
17	Kevin Hardy, Alex Molden	3.00
18	Terry Glenn, Simeon Rice	12.00
19	Eddie George, Tim Biakabutuka	16.00
20	Karim Abdul-Jabbar, Cedric Jones	8.00

1996 Pro Line Cover Story

This 20-card set was inserted one per 30 periodical packs. The cards feature a newspaper design and carry a "CS" prefix on the card number. The insert is made up of a mix of top 1995 players as well as some of the top rookies from 1996.

		MT
Complete Set (20):		125.00
Common Player:		2.00
1	Bryce Paup	2.00
2	Kerry Collins	12.00
3	Rashaan Salaam	5.00
4	Troy Aikman	12.00
5	Emmitt Smith	25.00
6	Herman Moore	4.00
7	Curtis Martin	18.00
8	Kordell Stewart	12.00
9	Ricky Watters	2.00
10	Carl Pickens	2.00
11	Joey Galloway	8.00
12	Errict Rhett	5.00
13	Deion Sanders	7.00
14	Reggie White	4.00
15	Hugh Douglas	2.00
16	Tamarick Vanover	7.00
17	Derrick Mayes	2.00
18	Marvin Harrison	7.00
19	Tim Biakabutuka	6.00
20	Terry Glenn	12.00

1996 Pro Line Touchdown Performers

Touchdown Performers is a 20-card insert that was found every 75 retail packs. The cards are numbered TD1-TD20.

		MT
Complete Set (20):		250.00
Common Player:		5.00
1	Kerry Collins	20.00
2	Troy Aikman	20.00
3	Deion Sanders	12.00
4	Emmitt Smith	40.00
5	Mark Brunell	15.00
6	Steve McNair	15.00
7	Marshall Faulk	15.00
8	Dan Marino	40.00
9	Cris Carter	5.00
10	Drew Bledsoe	18.00
11	Yancey Thigpen	5.00
12	Jerry Rice	20.00
13	J.J. Stokes	14.00
14	Terrell Davis	25.00
15	Carl Pickens	5.00
16	Joey Galloway	16.00
17	Kordell Stewart	20.00
18	Isaac Bruce	14.00
19	Keyshawn Johnson	20.00
20	Amani Toomer	5.00

1996 Pro Line II Intense

Pro Line II Intense features 100 cards, a parallel set and four

insert sets. Each regular card has a full-bleed color photo on the front, with the Intense logo at the top. The player's name and position are in a bar along the bottom, flanked by a team helmet in the lower left corner. The back has a card number and the player's name at the top, with a photo on one side and statistics on the other. A box with biographical information is in the lower left corner. There were also parallel Double Intensity cards made; they were seeded one per five packs and are stamped in bronze on the front. Three other insert sets were also made - Determined and $3 and $5 Sprint Foncards. There's an average of $11 in phone time in every box.

		MT
Complete Set (100):		20.00
Common Player:		.05
Minor Stars:		.10
Wax Box:		30.00
1	Kerry Collins	1.25
2	Jeff George	.05
3	Mark Brunell	1.00
4	Steve McNair	.75
5	Rick Mirer	.05
6	Dave Brown	.05
7	Rashaan Salaam	.50
8	Marshall Faulk	.50
9	Erric Pegram	.05
10	Cris Carter	.05
11	Eric Allen	.05
12	Jim Kelly	.05
13	Jeff Blake	.50
14	Stan Humphries	.05
15	Scott Mitchell	.05
16	Jeff Hostetler	.05
17	Rodney Peete	.05
18	Warren Moon	.05
19	Errict Rhett	.40
20	Terrell Davis	2.00
21	J.J. Stokes	.10
22	Marco Coleman	.05
23	Heath Shuler	.05
24	Duane Clemons	.05
25	*Amani Toomer*	.10
26	Leslie O'Neal	.05
27	Tamarick Vanover	.50
28	Steve Bono	.05
29	Jim Everett	.05
30	Erik Kramer	.05
31	Trent Dilfer	.10
32	Jim Harbaugh	.05
33	Vinny Testaverde	.05
34	Rodney Hampton	.05
35	Chris Warren	.10
36	Curtis Martin	2.00
37	*Eddie Kennison*	.50
38	Herman Moore	.40
39	Terance Mathis	.05
40	Carl Pickens	.05
41	Isaac Bruce	.50
42	Reggie White	.10
43	Junior Seau	.05
44	Bryce Paup	.05
45	Deion Sanders	.50
46	Thurman Thomas	.10
47	Gus Frerotte	.05
48	Jerome Bettis	.10
49	Michael Irvin	.10
50	Wayne Chrebet	.05
51	*Bobby Engram*	.75
52	Marcus Jones	.05
53	Daryl Gardener	.05
54	*Alex Van Dyke*	.10
55	Cedric Jones	.05
56	Regan Upshaw	.05
57	*Jason Dunn*	.30
58	Mark Chmura	.25
59	Ray Lewis	.05
60	*Rickey Dudley*	.20
61	*Leeland McElroy*	.20
62	Derrick Thomas	.05
63	*Bobby Hoying*	.75
64	Robert Brooks	.05
65	Tim Brown	.05
66	Michael Westbrook	.40
67	Jim Miller	.05
68	Aaron Hayden	.05
69	Marcus Allen	.05
70	Steve Young	1.00
71	Steve Young	.75
72	Neil O'Donnell	.05
73	Drew Bledsoe	.75
74	Emmitt Smith	2.00
75	Ki-Jana Carter	.30
76	Irving Fryar	.05
77	Joey Galloway	.75
78	Russell Maryland	.05
79	Kordell Stewart	1.00
80	Barry Sanders	1.25
81	Bryan Cox	.05
82	*Keyshawn Johnson*	1.50
83	*Karim Abdul-Jabbar*	1.75
84	*Kevin Hardy*	.30
85	Rodney Thomas	.05
86	John Elway	.50
87	Dan Marino	2.00
88	Brett Favre	2.00
89	John Mobley	.05
90	Jonathan Ogden	.05
91	*Eddie George*	2.50
92	*Simeon Rice*	.25
93	*Tim Biakabutuka*	1.00
94	*Terry Glenn*	1.75
95	*Marvin Harrison*	1.00
96	*Lawrence Phillips*	.50
97	Natrone Means	.10
98	Jerry Rice	.75
99	Ricky Watters	.10
100	Checklist	.05

1996 Pro Line II Intense Double Intensity

Pro Line II Intense Double Intensity was a 100-card parallel set that included the words "Double Intensity" on the front in foil. These parallel cards were inserted at a rate of one per five packs.

	MT
Complete Set (100):	160.00
Double Intensity Cards:	4x-8x

1996 Pro Line II Intense Determined

These 1996 Pro Line II inserts offer an in-depth view of the look and determination of 20 of the NFL's fiercest competitors. Each card front has an action photo of the player against a metallic ghosted close-up image of him as the background. The Pro Line II logo is at the top of the card; the player's name and position are in a bar at the bottom, above the word "Determined." The card back, numbered 1 of 20, etc., has a full-bleed color action photo on it, with an oval toward the bottom which recaps some of the player's achievements.

		MT
Complete Set (20):		250.00
Common Player:		4.00
1	Kerry Collins	15.00
2	Troy Aikman	15.00
3	Herman Moore	6.00
4	Mark Brunell	15.00
5	Dan Marino	30.00
6	Kordell Stewart	15.00
7	Junior Seau	4.00
8	Steve Young	12.00
9	John Elway	12.00
10	Emmitt Smith	30.00
11	Steve McNair	10.00
12	Drew Bledsoe	15.00
13	Joey Galloway	12.00
14	Deion Sanders	12.00
15	Kevin Hardy	4.00
16	Keyshawn Johnson	10.00
17	Marvin Harrison	10.00
18	Tim Biakabutuka	4.00
19	Eddie George	25.00
20	Terry Glenn	20.00

1996 Pro Line II Intense $3 Phone Cards

Fifty top players are featured in this 1996 Pro Line II insert set, which is licensed by the NFL and sponsored by Sprint. The cards, randomly inserted one per 18 packs, contain $3 worth of prepaid Sprint long-distance calling. The card front has the brand and Sprint logos at the top; the player's name, position and a team helmet are at the bottom. The card back explains how to use the card and when it expires.

		MT
Complete Set (50):		250.00
Common Player:		3.00
1	Jim Kelly	3.00
2	Kerry Collins	8.00
3	Jeff George	3.00
4	Troy Aikman	8.00
5	John Elway	5.00
6	Herman Moore	4.00
7	Barry Sanders	8.00
8	Brett Favre	12.00
9	Jim Harbaugh	3.00
10	Steve Bono	3.00
11	Dan Marino	16.00
12	Drew Bledsoe	6.00
13	Jim Everett	3.00
14	Neil O'Donnell	3.00
15	Ricky Watters	3.00
16	Junior Seau	3.00
17	Jerry Rice	8.00
18	Errict Rhett	3.00
19	Joey Galloway	6.00
20	Steve Young	6.00
21	Kordell Stewart	8.00
22	Rodney Hampton	3.00
23	Curtis Martin	12.00
24	Mark Brunell	6.00
25	Steve McNair	5.00
26	Deion Sanders	5.00
27	Carl Pickens	3.00
28	Michael Irvin	3.00
29	Tamarick Vanover	5.00
30	Emmitt Smith	15.00
31	Chris Warren	3.00
32	Stan Humphries	3.00
33	J.J. Stokes	5.00
34	Tim Biakabutuka	5.00
35	Keyshawn Johnson	10.00
36	Simeon Rice	3.00
37	Jonathan Ogden	3.00
38	Rashaan Salaam	4.00
39	Bobby Engram	4.00
40	John Mobley	3.00
41	Derrick Mayes	3.00
42	Eddie George	8.00
43	Marvin Harrison	7.00
44	Kevin Hardy	3.00
45	Karim Abdul-Jabbar	8.00
46	Duane Clemons	3.00
47	Terry Glenn	8.00
48	Cedric Jones	3.00
49	Rickey Dudley	3.00
50	Lawrence Phillips	8.00

Values quoted in this guide reflect the retail price of a card — the price a collector can expect to pay when buying a card from a dealer. The wholesale price — that which a collector can expect to receive from a dealer when selling cards — will be significantly lower, depending on desirability and condition.

1996 Pro Line II Intense $5 Phone Cards

Twenty top players are featured in this 1996 Pro Line II insert set, which is licensed by the NFL and sponsored by Sprint. The cards, randomly inserted one per 35 packs, contain $5 worth of prepaid Sprint long-distance calling. The card front has the brand logo at the top; the Sprint logo, denomination and player's name and team are at the bottom. The card back explains how to use the card and when it expires.

		MT
Complete Set (20):		150.00
Common Player:		6.00
1	Kerry Collins	10.00
2	Troy Aikman	10.00
3	Herman Moore	6.00
4	Mark Brunell	10.00
5	Dan Marino	20.00
6	Kordell Stewart	10.00
7	Junior Seau	6.00
8	Steve Young	8.00
9	John Elway	6.00
10	Emmitt Smith	20.00
11	Steve McNair	6.00
12	Drew Bledsoe	8.00
13	Joey Galloway	8.00
14	Deion Sanders	8.00
15	Kevin Hardy	6.00
16	Keyshawn Johnson	12.00
17	Marvin Harrison	10.00
18	Tim Biakabutuka	9.00
19	Eddie George	10.00
20	Terry Glenn	12.00

1996 Pro Line Memorabilia

Pro Line Memorabilia was the third installment of Pro Line Football in 1996. The same 100 players from Intense were used, but with different designs. Memorabilia included one autographed memorabilia redemption card, two autographed cards, with one of a 1996 NFL first-round pick, as well as two inserts - Down the Stretch and Producers.

		MT
Complete Set (100):		25.00
Common Player:		.10
Minor Stars:		.20
Wax Box:		100.00
1	Kerry Collins	1.50
2	Jeff George	.10
3	Mark Brunell	1.50
4	Steve McNair	1.00
5	Rick Mirer	.20
6	Dave Brown	.10
7	Rashaan Salaam	.30
8	Marshall Faulk	.30
9	Erric Pegram	.10
10	Cris Carter	.10
11	Eric Allen	.10

12	Jim Kelly	.20
13	Jeff Blake	.30
14	Stan Humphries	.10
15	Scott Mitchell	.10
16	Jeff Hostetler	.10
17	Rodney Peete	.10
18	Warren Moon	.20
19	Errict Rhett	.30
20	Terrell Davis	1.75
21	J.J. Stokes	.20
22	Marco Coleman	.10
23	Heath Shuler	.20
24	Duane Clemons	.10
25	Amani Toomer	.20
26	Leslie O'Neal	.10
27	Tamarick Vanover	.20
28	Steve Bono	.10
29	Jim Everett	.10
30	Erik Kramer	.10
31	Trent Dilfer	.20
32	Jim Harbaugh	.10
33	Vinny Testaverde	.10
34	Rodney Hampton	.10
35	Chris Warren	.10
36	Curtis Martin	1.75
37	Eddie Kennison	1.50
38	Herman Moore	.30
39	Terance Mathis	.10
40	Carl Pickens	.20
41	Isaac Bruce	.30
42	Reggie White	.20
43	Junior Seau	.20
44	Bryce Paup	.10
45	Deion Sanders	.75
46	Thurman Thomas	.20
47	Gus Frerotte	.10
48	Tony Mandarich	.10
49	Michael Irvin	.10
50	Wayne Chrebet	.10
51	Bobby Engram	1.00
52	Marcus Jones	.10
53	Daryl Gardener	.10
54	Alex Van Dyke	.20
55	Andre Rison	.10
56	Regan Upshaw	.10
57	Jason Dunn	.10
58	Mark Chmura	.20
59	Ray Lewis	.10
60	Rickey Dudley	.30
61	Leeland McElroy	.20
62	Derrick Thomas	.10
63	Bobby Hoying	.20
64	Robert Brooks	.20
65	Tim Brown	.20
66	Michael Westbrook	.10
67	Jim Miller	.10
68	Aaron Hayden	.10
69	Marcus Allen	.20
70	Troy Aikman	1.50
71	Steve Young	1.00
72	Neil O'Donnell	.10
73	Drew Bledsoe	1.50
74	Emmitt Smith	3.00
75	Ki-Jana Carter	.20
76	Irving Fryar	.10
77	Joey Galloway	.50
78	Russell Maryland	.10
79	Kordell Stewart	1.50
80	Barry Sanders	1.50
81	Bryan Cox	.10
82	Keyshawn Johnson	1.50
83	Karim Abdul-Jabbar	.20
84	Kevin Hardy	.20
85	Rodney Thomas	.10
86	John Elway	1.00
87	Dan Marino	3.00
88	Brett Favre	3.00
89	Eric Metcalf	.10
90	Jonathan Ogden	.20
91	Eddie George	3.00
92	Simeon Rice	.20
93	Tim Biakabutuka	.30
94	Terry Glenn	2.50
95	Marvin Harrison	1.50
96	Lawrence Phillips	.30
97	Natrone Means	.20
98	Jerry Rice	1.50
99	Ricky Watters	.20
100	Checklist (Emmitt Smith)	.50

1996 Pro Line Memorabilia Stretch Drive

Stretch Drive featured 30 top players on a foil background, with cards numbered

DS1-DS30. Regular versions were inserted every three packs, while Signature Series versions, which had facsimile signatures, were inserted every 25 packs.

		MT
Complete Set (30):		150.00
Common Player:		2.50
Minor Stars:		5.00
1	Jim Kelly	5.00
2	Kerry Collins	10.00
3	Rashaan Salaam	5.00
4	Jeff Blake	5.00
5	Deion Sanders	6.00
6	Troy Aikman	10.00
7	Emmitt Smith	18.00
8	John Elway	8.00
9	Terrell Davis	12.00
10	Barry Sanders	10.00
11	Herman Moore	5.00
12	Brett Favre	18.00
13	Steve McNair	8.00
14	Eddie George	12.00
15	Marshall Faulk	5.00
16	Marvin Harrison	6.00
17	Dan Marino	18.00
18	Curtis Martin	12.00
19	Drew Bledsoe	10.00
20	Terry Glenn	10.00
21	Neil O'Donnell	2.50
22	Keyshawn Johnson	6.00
23	Ricky Watters	5.00
24	Kordell Stewart	10.00
25	J.J. Stokes	2.50
26	Steve Young	8.00
27	Joey Galloway	6.00
28	Lawrence Phillips	5.00
29	Isaac Bruce	5.00
30	Errict Rhett	5.00

1996 Pro Line Memorabilia Producers

Producers was a 10-card insert found in every six packs of Memorabilia. Cards in this insert were numbered P1-P10. There are also Signature Series Producers, which have facsimile signatures, inserted every 100 packs.

		MT
Complete Set (10):		50.00
Common Player:		1.00
Minor Stars:		2.00
Silver Signatures:		2x-4x
1	Keyshawn Johnson	3.00
2	Barry Sanders	8.00
3	Eddie George	8.00
4	Emmitt Smith	10.00
5	Jerry Rice	5.00
6	Brett Favre	10.00
7	Marshall Faulk	1.00
8	Dan Marino	10.00
9	Deion Sanders	4.00
10	Ricky Watters	1.00

1996 Pro Line Memorabilia Rookie Autographs

This 15-card insert features autographs of NFL rookies from 1996 and was inserted

1:12. Each card is limited to a different production number and sequentially numbered. The cards are not numbered within the insert set.

		MT
Complete Set (15):		900.00
Common Player:		15.00
1	Tim Biakabutuka/210	75.00
2	Tim Biakabutuka/600, Eddie George	200.00
3	Duane Clemons/1255	15.00
4	Daryl Gardener/1390	15.00
5	Eddie George/395	175.00
6	Terry Glenn/600, Keyshawn Johnson	175.00
7	Kevin Hardy/940	20.00
8	Jeff Hartings/1370	15.00
9	Andre Johnson/1370	15.00
10	Keyshawn Johnson/195	125.00
11	Pete Kendall/1495	15.00
12	Alex Molden/1320	15.00
13	Eric Moulds/1010	30.00
14	Jamain Stephens/795	15.00
15	Jerome Woods/1375	15.00

1996 Pro Line DC III

Pro Line III DC, by Classic, follows the hobby trend with all 100 cards printed on a die-cut design. Every card is printed on 24-point stock, die-cut around the top. The back has final statistics from the 1995 season, plus career totals, biographical information, a color action photo, and trivial notes about the player. There were also insert sets created for the set: Road to the Super Bowl and All-Pro/All-Pro Rookies.

		MT
Complete Set (100):		50.00
Common Player:		.20
Minor Stars:		.40
Wax Box:		40.00
1	Emmitt Smith	6.00
2	Larry Centers	.20
3	Jeff George	.40
4	Jim Kelly	.40
5	Kerry Collins	4.00
6	Erik Kramer	.20
7	Jeff Blake	2.00
8	Andre Rison	.20
9	John Elway	1.50
10	Herman Moore	.75
11	Robert Brooks	.50
12	Steve McNair	3.00
13	Jim Harbaugh	.20
14	Mark Brunell	1.00
15	Steve Bono	.40
16	Dan Marino	6.00
17	Warren Moon	.40
18	Drew Bledsoe	3.00
19	Jim Everett	.20
20	Rodney Hampton	.20
21	Kyle Brady	.20
22	Jeff Hostetler	.20
23	Neil O'Donnell	.40
24	Ricky Watters	.20
25	Isaac Bruce	1.50
26	Steve Young	3.00
27	Stan Humphries	.20
28	Joey Galloway	3.00
29	Errict Rhett	2.00
30	Terry Allen	.20
31	Eric Swann	.20
32	Craig Heyward	.20
33	Bryce Paup	.20
34	Sam Mills	.20
35	Jim Flanigan	.20
36	Carl Pickens	.40
37	Pepper Johnson	.20
38	Troy Aikman	3.00
39	Terrell Davis	3.00
40	Scott Mitchell	.20
41	Brett Favre	6.00
42	Chris Sanders	1.00

43	Marshall Faulk	3.00
44	James Stewart	.20
45	Marcus Allen	.20
46	Bernie Parmalee	.20
47	Cris Carter	.20
48	Ben Coates	.20
49	Quinn Early	.20
50	Tyrone Wheatley	.40
51	Adrian Murrell	.20
52	Tim Brown	.20
53	Yancey Thigpen	1.50
54	Andy Harmon	.20
55	Jerome Bettis	.20
56	Jerry Rice	3.00
57	Natrone Means	.50
58	Chris Warren	.40
59	Warren Sapp	.20
60	Michael Westbrook	2.00
61	Aeneas Williams	.20
62	Eric Metcalf	.20
63	Bruce Smith	.20
64	Rashaan Salaam	2.00
65	Michael Irvin	.75
66	Anthony Miller	.20
67	Barry Sanders	3.00
68	Reggie White	.40
69	Rodney Thomas	1.50
70	Zack Crockett	.20
71	Neil Smith	.20
72	Bryan Cox	.20
73	Curtis Martin	5.00
74	Eric Allen	.20
75	Hugh Douglas	.20
76	Napoleon Kaufman	.75
77	Greg Lloyd	.20
78	Charlie Garner	.20
79	Lee Woodall	.20
80	Tony Martin	.20
81	Cortez Kennedy	.20
82	Gus Frerotte	.40
83	Darick Holmes	.50
84	Jay Novacek	.20
85	Brett Perriman	.20
86	Mark Chmura	.40
87	Chester McGlockton	.20
88	Dave Brown	.20
89	William Thomas	.20
90	Ken Norton	.20
91	Junior Seau	.40
92	Deion Sanders	2.00
93	J.J. Stokes	2.00
94	Kordell Stewart	3.00
95	Tamarick Vanover	2.00
96	Ken Harvey	.20
97	John Randle	.20
98	Lamont Warren	.20
99	Dorsey Levens	.40
100	Frank Sanders	1.00

1996 Pro Line DC III All-Pros

These cards, printed on 24-point fabric stock, were inserted one per 100 packs of 1996 Pro Line III DC product. The card back is numbered using an "AP" prefix.

		MT
Complete Set (20):		650.00
Common Player:		8.00
1	Bryce Paup	8.00
2	Kerry Collins	50.00
3	Rashaan Salaam	30.00
4	Emmitt Smith	80.00
5	Terrell Davis	60.00
6	Herman Moore	8.00
7	Barry Sanders	50.00
8	Brett Favre	80.00
9	Marshall Faulk	30.00
10	Dan Marino	80.00
11	Cris Carter	8.00
12	Curtis Martin	70.00
13	Hugh Douglas	8.00
14	Kordell Stewart	45.00
15	Jerry Rice	45.00
16	J.J. Stokes	30.00
17	Joey Galloway	40.00
18	Isaac Bruce	25.00
19	Steve McNair	40.00
20	Tim Brown	8.00

1996 Pro Line DC III Road to the Super Bowl

The key members and moments in the 1995 season are captured in this 30-card Road to the Super Bowl set. The cards, which were inserted one per 15 packs of 1996 Pro Line III DC product, have the player's name at the top, with "Road to the Super Bowl" written along the bottom. The back has statistics or a brief box score of the game being recalled, plus a photo of the player inside a circle. A map of Phoenix is used as a background motif on both sides of the card. The card number is listed as 1 of 30, etc..

	MT
Complete Set (30):	300.00
Common Player:	4.00
Minor Stars:	8.00
1 Larry Centers	4.00
2 Eric Metcalf	4.00
3 Jim Kelly	8.00
4 Bryce Paup	4.00
5 Kerry Collins	20.00
6 Carl Pickens	8.00
7 Emmitt Smith	45.00
8 Michael Irvin	8.00
9 Troy Aikman	25.00
10 Terrell Davis	25.00
11 Barry Sanders	25.00
12 Herman Moore	8.00
13 Brett Favre	45.00
14 Robert Brooks	8.00
15 Jim Harbaugh	4.00
16 Tony Bennett	4.00
17 Steve Bono	8.00
18 Dan Marino	45.00
19 Cris Carter	4.00
20 Curtis Martin	30.00
21 Tim Brown	4.00
22 Ricky Watters	4.00
23 Yancey Thigpen	15.00
24 Neil O'Donnell	4.00
25 Kordell Stewart	25.00
26 Isaac Bruce	15.00
27 Tony Martin	4.00
28 Steve Young	25.00
29 Jerry Rice	25.00
30 Chris Warren	8.00

1997 Pro Line

The 300-card set featured a full-bleed photo with a stripe at the bottom that included the player's name, team and position. The team's logo is included inside a circle at the bottom center. The Pro Line logo is in the upper left.

	MT
Complete Set (300):	30.00
Common Player:	.05
Minor Stars:	.10
Wax Box:	50.00
1 Larry Centers	.05
2 Kent Graham	.05
3 LeShon Johnson	.05
4 Leeland McElroy	.10
5 Rob Moore	.05
6 Simeon Rice	.05
7 Frank Sanders	.05
8 Eric Swann	.05
9 Aeneas Williams	.05
10 Jamal Anderson	.15
11 Cornelius Bennett	.05
12 Ray Buchanan	.05
13 Bert Emanuel	.05
14 Terance Mathis	.05
15 Eric Metcalf	.05
16 Jessie Tuggle	.05
17 Derrick Alexander	.05
18 Earnest Byner	.05
19 Michael Jackson	.05
20 Antonio Langham	.05
21 Ray Lewis	.05
22 Bam Morris	.05
23 Jonathan Ogden	.05
24 Vinny Testaverde	.05
25 Eric Moulds	.10
26 Todd Collins	.05
27 Quinn Early	.05
28 Phil Hansen	.05
29 Darick Holmes	.10
30 Bryce Paup	.05

31 Andre Reed	.05
32 Bruce Smith	.05
33 Chris Spielman	.05
34 Matt Stevens	.05
35 Steve Tasker	.05
36 Thurman Thomas	.10
37 Mark Carrier	.05
38 Kerry Collins	.25
39 Tim Biakabutuka	.25
40 Eric Davis	.05
41 Kevin Greene	.05
42 Anthony Johnson	.05
43 Lamar Lathon	.05
44 Sam Mills	.05
45 Wesley Walls	.05
46 Muhsin Muhammad	.10
47 Mark Carrier	.05
48 Curtis Conway	.10
49 Bryan Cox	.05
50 Bobby Engram	.05
51 Raymont Harris	.05
52 Walt Harris	.05
53 Rick Mirer	.05
54 Rashaan Salaam	.10
55 Alonzo Spellman	.05
56 Ashley Ambrose	.05
57 Jeff Blake	.15
58 Ki-Jana Carter	.10
59 John Copeland	.05
60 James Francis	.05
61 Tony McGee	.05
62 Carl Pickens	.10
63 Darnay Scott	.05
64 Steve Tovar	.05
65 Dan Wilkinson	.05
66 Troy Aikman	1.00
67 Eric Bjornson	.05
68 Michael Irvin	.10
69 Daryl Johnston	.05
70 Nate Newton	.05
71 Deion Sanders	.40
72 Emmitt Smith	2.00
73 Kevin Smith	.05
74 Kevin Williams	.05
75 Darren Woodson	.05
76 Mark Tuinei	.05
77 Steve Atwater	.05
78 Terrell Davis	1.25
79 John Elway	.75
80 Ed McCaffrey	.05
81 Anthony Miller	.05
82 John Mobley	.05
83 Michael Dean Perry	.05
84 Shannon Sharpe	.05
85 Alfred Williams	.05
86 Reggie Brown	.05
87 Luther Elliss	.05
88 Scott Mitchell	.05
89 Herman Moore	.15
90 Johnnie Morton	.05
91 Brett Perriman	.05
92 Robert Porcher	.05
93 Barry Sanders	1.25
94 Henry Thomas	.05
95 Edgar Bennett	.05
96 Robert Brooks	.10
97 Gilbert Brown	.05
98 LeRoy Butler	.05
99 Mark Chmura	.05
100 Brett Favre	2.25
101 Santana Dotson	.05
102 Antonio Freeman	.20
103 Dorsey Levens	.20
104 Wayne Simmons	.05
105 Reggie White	.10
106 Willie Davis	.05
107 Eddie George	1.50
108 Darryll Lewis	.05
109 Steve McNair	.30
110 Marcus Robertson	.05
111 Chris Sanders	.05
112 Al Smith	.05
113 Tony Bennett	.05
114 Quentin Coryatt	.05
115 Ken Dilger	.05
116 Sean Dawkins	.05
117 Marshall Faulk	.20
118 Jim Harbaugh	.05
119 Marvin Harrison	.30
120 Jeff Herrod	.05
121 Tony Boselli	.05
122 Tony Brackens	.05
123 Mark Brunell	1.00
124 Kevin Hardy	.05
125 Jeff Lageman	.05
126 Keenan McCardell	.05
127 Natrone Means	.10
128 Eddie Robinson	.05
129 Jimmy Smith	.05
130 James Stewart	.05
131 Marcus Allen	.10
132 Dale Carter	.05
133 Mark Collins	.05
134 Lake Dawson	.05
135 Greg Hill	.05
136 Sean LaChapelle	.05
137 Chris Penn	.05
138 Derrick Thomas	.05
139 Tamarick Vanover	.05
140 Elvis Grbac	.05
141 Karim Abdul-Jabbar	.30
142 Fred Barnett	.05
143 Terrell Buckley	.05
144 Daryl Gardener	.05
145 Randal Hill	.05
146 Dan Marino	2.00
147 O.J. McDuffie	.05
148 Jerris McPhail	.05

149 Zach Thomas	.20
150 Cris Carter	.05
151 Dixon Edwards	.05
152 Leroy Hoard	.05
153 Qadry Ismail	.05
154 Brad Johnson	.05
155 John Randle	.05
156 Jake Reed	.05
157 Robert Smith	.05
158 Orlando Thomas	.05
159 DeWayne Washington	.05
160 Drew Bledsoe	1.00
161 Tedy Bruschi	.05
162 Willie Clay	.05
163 Ben Coates	.05
164 Terry Glenn	.25
165 Shawn Jefferson	.05
166 Ty Law	.05
167 Curtis Martin	1.25
168 Willie McGinest	.05
169 Chris Slade	.05
170 Eric Allen	.05
171 Mario Bates	.05
172 Jim Everett	.05
173 Michael Haynes	.05
174 Wayne Martin	.05
175 Torrance Small	.05
176 Dave Brown	.05
177 Chris Calloway	.05
178 Rodney Hampton	.05
179 Danny Kanell	.05
180 Thomas Lewis	.05
181 Jason Sehorn	.05
182 Amani Toomer	.05
183 Charles Way	.05
184 Tyrone Wheatley	.05
185 Wayne Chrebet	.05
186 Hugh Douglas	.05
187 Aaron Glenn	.05
188 Jeff Graham	.05
189 Keyshawn Johnson	.30
190 Mo Lewis	.05
191 Adrian Murrell	.05
192 Neil O'Donnell	.05
193 Tim Brown	.05
194 Rickey Dudley	.05
195 Jeff George	.10
196 Napoleon Kaufman	.05
197 Russell Maryland	.05
198 Terry McDaniel	.05
199 Chester McGlockton	.05
200 Desmond Howard	.05
201 Pat Swilling	.05
202 Ty Detmer	.05
203 Jason Dunn	.05
204 Ray Farmer	.05
205 Irving Fryar	.05
206 Chris T. Jones	.05
207 Bobby Taylor	.05
208 William Thomas	.05
209 Hollis Thomas	.05
210 Kevin Turner	.05
211 Ricky Watters	.10
212 Jerome Bettis	.05
213 Andre Hastings	.05
214 Charles Johnson	.05
215 Levon Kirkland	.05
216 Carnell Lake	.05
217 Greg Lloyd	.05
218 Darren Perry	.05
219 Kordell Stewart	.75
220 Rod Woodson	.05
221 Andre Coleman	.05
222 Marco Coleman	.05
223 Leonard Russell	.05
224 Stan Humphries	.05
225 Shawn Lee	.05
226 Tony Martin	.05
227 Chris Mims	.05
228 Junior Seau	.10
229 Chris Doleman	.05
230 William Floyd	.05
231 Merton Hanks	.05
232 Brent Jones	.05
233 Terry Kirby	.05
234 Ken Norton	.05
235 Terrell Owens	.75
236 Jerry Rice	1.00
237 Bryant Young	.05
238 Steve Young	.75
239 Garrison Hearst	.05
240 Brian Blades	.05
241 Chad Brown	.05
242 John Friesz	.05
243 Joey Galloway	.30
244 Cortez Kennedy	.05
245 Chris Warren	.05
246 Darryl Williams	.05
247 Tony Banks	.15
248 Isaac Bruce	.15
249 Kevin Carter	.05
250 Eddie Kennison	.05
251 Todd Lyght	.05
252 Leslie O'Neal	.05
253 Anthony Parker	.05
254 Roman Phifer	.05
255 Lawrence Phillips	.10
256 Mike Alstott	.15
257 Derrick Brooks	.05
258 Trent Dilfer	.10
259 Jackie Harris	.05
260 Hardy Nickerson	.05
261 Errict Rhett	.05
262 Warren Sapp	.05
263 Terry Allen	.05
264 Jamie Asher	.05
265 Henry Ellard	.05

266 Gus Frerotte	.05
267 Sean Gilbert	.05
268 Darrell Green	.05
269 Ken Harvey	.05
270 Brian Mitchell	.05
271 Michael Westbrook	.05
272 Koy Detmer	.30
273 Yatil Green	.40
274 Troy Davis	.30
275 Darrell Russell	.05
276 Warrick Dunn	1.50
277 David LaFleur	.30
278 Tony Gonzalez	.30
279 Jake Plummer	4.00
280 Antowain Smith	1.25
281 Peter Boulware	.05
282 Shawn Springs	.25
283 Bryant Westbrook	.10
284 Rae Carruth	.30
285 Corey Dillon	1.50
286 Byron Hanspard	.30
287 Greg Jones	.05
288 Trevor Pryce	.05
289 Michael Booker	.05
290 Orlando Pace	.40
291 James Farrior	.05
292 Walter Jones	.05
293 Reinard Wilson	.05
294 Ike Hilliard	1.00
295 Kenard Lang	.05
296 Reidel Anthony	1.00
297 Brett Favre CL	.75
298 Kerry Collins CL	.30
299 Drew Bledsoe CL	.30
300 Terrell Davis CL	.50

1997 Pro Line Board Members

This 15-card set was inserted 1:112 packs. It includes an inside look at the NFL Players that Score Board has signed to exclusive spokesman contracts. The cards are numbered with a "B" prefix.

	MT
Complete Set (15):	275.00
Common Player:	7.00
1 Troy Aikman	25.00
2 Kerry Collins	14.00
3 Terrell Davis	25.00
4 Brett Favre	50.00
5 Gus Frerotte	7.00
6 Emmitt Smith	40.00
7 Kordell Stewart	25.00
8 Steve Young	20.00
9 Eddie George	30.00
10 Terry Glenn	14.00
11 Troy Davis	7.00
12 Darrell Russell	7.00
13 Peter Boulware	7.00
14 Warrick Dunn	30.00
15 Rae Carruth	15.00

1997 Pro Line Brett Favre

This 10-card set, which was inserted 1:28 packs, is an interactive insert series that focuses on Brett Favre. All 10 cards could be redeemed for autographed memorabilia. All sets redeemed won either an autographed jersey or a Super Bowl XXXI autographed plaque.

	MT
Complete Set (10):	150.00
Common Player:	10.00
1 Brett Favre	10.00
2 Brett Favre	10.00
3 Brett Favre	10.00
4 Brett Favre	10.00
5 Brett Favre	10.00
6 Brett Favre	10.00
7 Brett Favre	10.00
8 Brett Favre	10.00
9 Brett Favre	10.00
10 Brett Favre	75.00

1997 Pro Line Rivalries

The 20-card set, which is numbered with an "R" prefix, was inserted 1:35 packs. The double-front cards provide insight into the top games of the 1997 campaign.

	MT
Complete Set (20):	275.00
Common Player:	4.00
1 John Elway, Derrick Thomas	15.00
2 Jeff Blake, Vinny Testaverde	4.00
3 Emmitt Smith, Ricky Watters	35.00
4 Jim Harbaugh, Thurman Thomas	4.00
5 Barry Sanders, Reggie White	20.00
6 Desmond Howard, Junior Seau	4.00
7 Dan Marino, Hugh Douglas	35.00
8 Jerome Bettis, Carl Pickens	4.00
9 Mark Brunell, Kordell Stewart	25.00
10 Karim Abdul-Jabbar, Bruce Smith	10.00
11 Rashaan Salaam, Brad Johnson	4.00
12 Steve Young, Kerry Collins	20.00
13 Brett Favre, Troy Aikman	40.00
14 Drew Bledsoe, Marshall Faulk	20.00
15 Steve McNair, Ki-Jana Carter	15.00
16 Jerry Rice, Terrell Davis	25.00
17 Deion Sanders, Dave Brown	15.00
18 Darrell Russell, Orlando Pace	4.00
19 Warrick Dunn, Bryant Westbrook	20.00
20 Yatil Green, Reidel Anthony	6.00

1997 Pro Line Gems

The 100-card base set consists of three subsets. Veterans is a 60-card set on blue foil-stamped cards, Rookies features 30 black foil-stamped cards and Leaders is a 10-card set with black and blue foil-stamping. The insert sets include Gems of the NFL, Championship Ring and Through the Years.

	MT
Complete Set (100):	35.00
Common Player:	.10
Minor Stars:	.20
Wax Box:	35.00
1 Brett Favre	3.50
2 Robert Brooks	.10
3 Reggie White	.20
4 Drew Bledsoe	1.50
5 Curtis Martin	1.50
6 Terry Glenn	.30
7 Kerry Collins	.30
8 Kevin Greene	.10
9 Troy Aikman	1.50
10 Emmitt Smith	3.00
11 Deion Sanders	.75
12 John Elway	1.00
13 Terrell Davis	1.50
14 Kordell Stewart	1.50
15 Jerome Bettis	.20
16 Steve Young	1.00
17 Jerry Rice	1.50
18 Bruce Smith	.10
19 Thurman Thomas	.20
20 Jim Harbaugh	.10
21 Marshall Faulk	.20
22 Marvin Harrison	.50
23 Ricky Watters	.20
24 Seth Joyner	.10
25 Mark Brunell	1.50
26 Natrone Means	.20
27 Dan Marino	3.00
28 Zach Thomas	.50
29 Karim Abdul-Jabbar	.30
30 Isaac Bruce	.20
31 Eddie Kennison	.30
32 Tony Banks	.50
33 Tony Martin	.10
34 Junior Seau	.20
35 Barry Sanders	1.50
36 Herman Moore	.20
37 Leeland McElroy	.10
38 Jamal Anderson	.20
39 Rick Mirer	.10
40 Rashaan Salaam	.20
41 Vinny Testaverde	.10
42 Elvis Grbac	.10
43 Cris Carter	.10
44 Brad Johnson	.20
45 Keyshawn Johnson	.50
46 Adrian Murrell	.10
47 Joey Galloway	.30
48 Trent Dilfer	.20
49 Gus Frerotte	.10
50 Terry Allen	.10
51 Tim Brown	.20
52 Desmond Howard	.10
53 Jeff George	.10
54 Heath Shuler	.10
55 Steve McNair	1.25
56 Eddie George	2.00
57 Jeff Blake	.20
58 Carl Pickens	.10
59 Dave Brown	.10
60 Brett Favre	1.50
61 Antowain Smith	1.50
62 Emmitt Smith	1.25
63 Terry Glenn	.50
64 Herman Moore	.10
65 Barry Sanders	.50
66 Derrick Thomas	.10
67 Brett Favre	1.50
68 Warrick Dunn	2.50
69 Emmitt Smith	1.25
70 Brett Favre	1.50
71 Orlando Pace	.10
72 Darrell Russell	.10
73 Shawn Springs	.10
74 Warrick Dunn	3.00
75 Tiki Barber	.30
76 Tom Knight	.10
77 Peter Boulware	.10
78 David LaFleur	.50
79 Tony Gonzalez	.50
80 Yatil Green	.30
81 Ike Hilliard	.30
82 James Farrior	.10
83 Jim Druckenmiller	2.00
84 Jon Harris	.10
85 Walter Jones	.10
86 Reidel Anthony	1.25
87 Jake Plummer	1.50
88 Reinard Wilson	.10
89 Kevin Lockett	.10
90 Rae Carruth	1.00
91 Byron Hanspard	.50
92 Renaldo Wynn	.10
93 Troy Davis	.75
94 Duce Staley	.75
95 Kenard Lang	.10
96 Freddie Jones	.75
97 Corey Dillon	2.00
98 Antowain Smith	1.50
99 Dwayne Rudd	.10
100 Warrick Dunn	.75

1997 Pro Line Gems Gems of the NFL

This 15-card insert features either a sapphire or emerald gemstone on a 23-karat gold card. These cards were seeded one per box (24 packs per box). The cards are numbered with a "G" prefix.

		MT
Complete Set (15):		400.00
Common Player:		5.00
1	Kerry Collins	10.00
2	Troy Aikman	25.00
3	Emmitt Smith	45.00
4	Terrell Davis	25.00
5	Barry Sanders	60.00
6	Brett Favre	50.00
7	Eddie George	35.00
8	Mark Brunell	25.00
9	Dan Marino	45.00
10	Curtis Martin	25.00
11	Terry Glenn	10.00
12	Jerome Bettis	5.00
13	Steve Young	15.00
14	Jerry Rice	25.00
15	Warrick Dunn	40.00

1997 Pro Line Gems Championship Ring

This card featured Brett Favre and his Super Bowl XXXI championship ring. The card contains a real diamond and was inserted one per case (10 boxes per case, 24 packs per box).

		MT
Complete Set (1):		100.00
Common Player:		100.00
CR1	Brett Favre	100.00

1997 Pro Line Gems Through the Years

This 20-card insert features 10 veterans and 10 rookies. The cards are die-cut to fit one of the rookies' cards with one of the veterans'. The cards were inserted 1:12. The cards are numbered with a "TY" prefix.

		MT
Complete Set (20):		150.00
Common Player:		2.50
Minor Stars:		
1	Emmitt Smith	20.00
2	Brett Favre	25.00
3	Deion Sanders	8.00
4	Dan Marino	20.00
5	Barry Sanders	15.00
6	Herman Moore	5.00
7	Curtis Martin	10.00
8	Jerome Bettis	5.00
9	Mark Brunell	10.00
10	Jerry Rice	10.00
11	Warrick Dunn	15.00
12	Jim Druckenmiller	10.00
13	Shawn Springs	2.50
14	Tony Banks	5.00
15	Byron Hanspard	5.00
16	Ike Hilliard	5.00
17	Antowain Smith	10.00
18	Eddie George	15.00
19	Jake Plummer	15.00
20	Terry Glenn	5.00

Values quoted in this guide reflect the retail price of a card — the price a collector can expect to pay when buying a card from a dealer. The wholesale price — that which a collector can expect to receive from a dealer when selling cards — will be significantly lower, depending on desirability and condition.

1997 Pro Line DC III

The 100-card, regular-sized, die-cut set includes two subsets: Rewind and DC Top Ten. The first 67 cards in the set are die-cut in a circular pattern with a rectangular base. Cards 68-89 are die-cut with wave outlines on the sides (Rewind) while cards 90-100 are horizontal with the top die-cut in the shape of a football. All cards have gold foil.

		MT
Complete Set (100):		50.00
Common Player:		.20
Minor Stars:		.40
Wax Box:		50.00
1	Emmitt Smith	5.00
2	Rod Woodson	.20
3	Eddie George	3.50
4	Ty Detmer	.20
5	Zach Thomas	1.00
6	Kevin Greene	.20
7	Michael Jackson	.20
8	Isaac Bruce	1.00
9	Joey Galloway	1.50
10	Bryant Young	.20
11	Terrell Davis	3.00
12	Mark Brunell	2.00
13	Marvin Harrison	1.50
14	Jake Reed	.20
15	Terry Allen	.20
16	Kordell Stewart	2.00
17	Reggie White	.40
18	Michael Irvin	.40
19	Tony Martin	.20
20	Barry Sanders	2.50
21	Tony Boselli	.20
22	Carl Pickens	.20
23	Simeon Rice	.20
24	Adrian Murrell	.20
25	Lamar Lathon	.20
26	Thurman Thomas	.40
27	Tim Brown	.20
28	Karim Abdul-Jabbar	.75
29	Brad Johnson	.20
30	Keenan McCardell	.20
31	Keyshawn Johnson	1.50
32	Ricky Watters	.40
33	Michael McCrary	.20
34	Brett Favre	5.00
35	Steve McNair	2.00
36	Herman Moore	.40
37	Tony Banks	1.00
38	Deion Sanders	1.75
39	Kerry Collins	.75
40	Shannon Sharpe	.20
41	Drew Bledsoe	2.50
42	Jim Everett	.20
43	Jamal Anderson	.40
44	Irving Fryar	.20
45	Terry Glenn	.75
46	Jerry Rice	2.50
47	Curtis Martin	3.50
48	Curtis Conway	.20
49	Jerome Bettis	.40
50	Vinny Testaverde	.20
51	Mike Alstott	.75
52	Anthony Johnson	.20
53	Dan Marino	5.00
54	Junior Seau	.20
55	Steve Young	1.75
56	Troy Aikman	2.50
57	Jimmy Smith	.20
58	Cris Carter	.20
59	Gus Frerotte	.20
60	Marcus Allen	.40
61	Rodney Hampton	.20
62	Bruce Smith	.20
63	Leroy Butler	.20
64	Jeff Blake	.75
65	Antonio Freeman	.75
66	John Elway	1.75
67	Checklist	.20
68	Barry Sanders	1.50
69	Troy Aikman	1.00
70	Jerome Bettis	.20
71	Mark Brunell	1.00
72	Junior Seau	.20
73	John Elway	.75
74	Chad Brown	.20
75	Irving Fryar	.20
76	Drew Bledsoe	1.00
77	Jerry Rice	1.00
78	Larry Centers	.20
79	Terrell, Davis	1.50
80	Carl Pickens	.20
81	Emmitt Smith	2.00
82	Kerry Collins	1.00
83	Eddie Kennison	.20
84	Kordell Stewart	1.00
85	Natrone Means	.20
86	Curtis Martin	1.50
87	Dorsey Levens	.20
88	Desmond Howard	.20
89	Checklist (Brett Favre MVP)	2.00
90	Brett Favre	2.00
91	Terrell Davis	1.50
92	Kevin Greene	.20
93	Terry Allen	.20
94	Barry Sanders	1.50
95	John Elway	.75
96	Ricky Watters	.20
97	Reggie White	.20
98	Jerome Bettis	.20
99	Jerry Rice	1.00
100	Checklist (Brett Favre CL)	2.00

1997 Pro Line DC III Perennial/Future All-Pros

The 20-card, regular-sized, die-cut set was inserted every 24 packs of Pro Line III DC football. The cards feature the same die-cut design as the Rewind subset in the base set, except the cards in Perennial/Future All-Pros are vertical, making the wave cut design on the card's top and bottom. The cards feature bronze foil on the top and bottom and the backs are numbered as "x of 20." The backs have a color action shot imaged over a white background with a black-and-white closeup behind a brief statistical analysis. The cards are numbered with an "AP" prefix.

		MT
Complete Set (20):		475.00
Common Player:		7.00
1	Emmitt Smith	60.00
2	Brett Favre	60.00
3	Jerry Rice	30.00
4	Steve Young	25.00
5	Barry Sanders	30.00
6	Reggie White	15.00
7	Ricky Watters	7.00
8	Lawrence Phillips	7.00
9	Kerry Collins	14.00
10	Mark Brunell	30.00
11	John Elway	25.00
12	Dan Marino	60.00
13	Drew Bledsoe	30.00
14	Curtis Martin	45.00
15	Terrell Davis	35.00
16	Karim Abdul-Jabbar	14.00
17	Marvin Harrison	15.00
18	Keyshawn Johnson	15.00
19	Terry Glenn	14.00
20	Eddie George	30.00

1997 Pro Line DC III Road to the Super Bowl

The 30-card, regular-sized, die-cut set was inserted every 12 packs of Pro Line III DC. The cards feature the same die-cut design as the DC Top Ten subset in the base set. The cards are numbered with a "SB" prefix.

		MT
Complete Set (30):		400.00
Common Player:		5.00
1	Ricky Watters	10.00
2	Ty Detmer	5.00
3	Emmitt Smith	50.00
4	Troy Aikman	25.00
5	Kerry Collins	10.00
6	Kevin Greene	5.00

1998 Pro Line DC III

Pro Line DC III was a 100-card, all die-cut set that included 20 DC Rewind subset cards and 10 Rookie Uprising subset cards. The primary base cards feature the player in an oval shot with gold foil extended and squared off on all four corners, with the Pro Line DC logo in the upper right corner. Inserts in the product included: Clear Cuts, X-Tra Effort, Decade Draft, SB Team Totals and Choice Cuts. Each card and insert was also included in a Perfect Cut 1 of 1 set that was encapsulated in a PSA container and graded Mint. This included 170 total cards and these were available through redemptions.

		MT
Complete Set (100):		50.00
Common Player:		.30
Minor Stars:		.60
Wax Box:		80.00
1	Drew Bledsoe	2.00
2	Emmitt Smith	3.00
3	Dana Stubblefield	.30
4	Brett Favre	4.00
5	Derrick Alexander	.30
6	Bert Emanuel	.30
7	Joey Galloway	.60
8	Terrell Davis	2.00
9	Mark Brunell	2.00
10	Marshall Faulk	.60
11	Jake Reed	.30
12	Terry Allen	.30
13	Kordell Stewart	2.00
14	Reggie White	.60
15	Michael Irvin	.60
16	Tony Martin	.30
17	Barry Sanders	3.00
18	Carl Pickens	.30
19	Bobby Hoying	.30
20	Adrian Murrell	.60
21	Jeff George	.60
22	Tim Brown	.30
23	Karim Abdul-Jabbar	.60
24	Robert Smith	.30
25	Eddie George	2.50
26	Corey Dillon	1.50
27	Keyshawn Johnson	.60
28	Ricky Watters	.60
29	Robert Brooks	.30
30	Antonio Freeman	.60
31	Danny Kanell	.30
32	Steve McNair	1.50
33	Antowain Smith	1.50
34	Warrick Dunn	3.00
35	Napoleon Kaufman	.60
36	Trent Dilfer	.60
37	Herman Moore	.60
38	Brad Johnson	.60
39	Deion Sanders	1.00
40	Kerry Collins	1.25
41	Shannon Sharpe	.30
42	Irving Fryar	.30
43	Dorsey Levens	.60
44	Jerry Rice	2.00
45	Curtis Martin	2.00
46	Jerome Bettis	.60
47	Raymont Harris	.30
48	Vinny Testaverde	.30
49	Dan Marino	3.00
50	Junior Seau	.30
51	Steve Young	1.50
52	Troy Aikman	2.00
53	Jimmy Smith	.30
54	Ben Coates	.30
55	Gus Frerotte	.30
56	Marcus Allen	.60
57	Bruce Smith	.30
58	Jeff Blake	.30
59	John Elway	1.50
60	Rod Smith	.30
61	Andre Rison	.30
62	Isaac Bruce	.60
63	Cris Carter	.30
64	Danny Wuerffel	1.00
65	Rob Moore	.30
66	Garrison Hearst	.30
67	Warren Moon	.30
68	Checklist (Jerome Bettis)	.30
69	Marcus Allen (DC Rewind)	.30
70	James Stewart (DC Rewind)	.30
71	Karim Abdul-Jabbar (DC Rewind)	.30
72	Joey Galloway (DC Rewind)	.30
73	Corey Dillon (DC Rewind)	1.50
74	Andre Rison (DC Rewind)	.30
75	Napoleon Kaufman (DC Rewind)	.30
76	Dorsey Levens (DC Rewind)	.30
77	Irving Fryar (DC Rewind)	.30
78	Eric Metcalf (DC Rewind)	.30
79	Darrien Gordon (DC Rewind)	.30
80	Neil O'Donnell (DC Rewind)	.30
81	Rod Woodson (DC Rewind)	.30
82	Rob Johnson (DC Rewind)	.30
83	Michael Westbrook (DC Rewind)	.30
84	Jake Plummer (DC Rewind)	1.50
85	Bobby Hoying (DC Rewind)	.30
86	Adrian Murrell (DC Rewind)	.30
87	Jim Druckenmiller (DC Rewind)	1.50
88	Warren Moon (DC Rewind)	.30
89	Checklist (Dorsey Levens) (DC Rewind)	.30
90	Tony Gonzalez (Rookie Uprising)	.30
91	Jim Druckenmiller (Rookie Uprising)	1.50
92	Corey Dillon (Rookie Uprising)	1.50
93	Darrell Russell (Rookie Uprising)	.30
94	Byron Hanspard (Rookie Uprising)	1.00
95	Rae Carruth (Rookie Uprising)	1.00
96	Peter Boulware (Rookie Uprising)	.30
97	Troy Davis (Rookie Uprising)	1.00
98	Reidel Anthony (Rookie Uprising)	1.25
99	Tiki Barber (Rookie Uprising)	1.25
100	Checklist (Jake Plummer) (Rookie Uprising)	.30

1998 Pro Line DC III Choice Cuts

DAN MARINO

Choice Cuts were randomly inserted into packs of Pro

Line DC III. The cards are horizontal and die-cut in design, with the player featured on the left side, and a large blue "C" die-cut out of the right side. The insert name is included in the blue "C" with "Choice" on the top and "Cuts" across the bottom. Choice Cuts are numbered on the back with a "CHC" prefix, with 10 cards in the set.

		MT
Complete Set (10):		75.00
Common Player:		3.00
1	Deion Sanders	6.00
2	Jerome Bettis	3.00
3	Troy Aikman	12.00
4	Jerry Rice	12.00
5	Mark Brunell	12.00
6	Curtis Martin	10.00
7	Cris Carter	3.00
8	Steve Young	8.00
9	Reggie White	3.00
10	Dan Marino	20.00

1998 Pro Line DC III Clear Cuts

This 10-card set was printed on horizontal plastic that was die-cut. Clear Cuts were hobby exclusive, inserted one per 95 packs and sequentially numbered to 500. Cards featured the insert name printed across the top, with a gold foil finish. A color shot of the player was centered on the card, with his name and team logo off to the right. Clear Cuts inserts were numbered on the back with a "CLC" prefix.

		MT
Complete Set (10):		475.00
Common Player:		20.00
1	John Elway	40.00
2	Drew Bledsoe	50.00
3	Terrell Davis	50.00
4	Brett Favre	100.00
5	Cris Carter	20.00
6	Eddie George	75.00
7	Kordell Stewart	50.00
8	Warrick Dunn	75.00
9	Tim Brown	20.00
10	Barry Sanders	85.00

1998 Pro Line DC III Decade Draft

Decade Draft was a 10-card insert that was inserted at a rate of one per 24 packs in Pro Line DC III. The cards are die-cut in the shape of a "D" with foil etched around the edge. An action shot of the player is shown on the right side of the card with a closer shot on the left. Decade Draft inserts are numbered with a "DD" prefix on the back.

1998 Pro Line DC III Team Totals (set header)

		MT
Complete Set (10):		120.00
Common Player:		2.50
1	T. Aikman,	25.00
	B. Sanders	
2	J. George,	20.00
	E. Smith	
3	R. Maryland,	30.00
	B. Favre	
4	S. Emtman,	2.50
	C. Pickens	
5	D. Bledsoe,	12.00
	D. Bledsoe	
6	D. Wilkinson,	5.00
	M. Faulk	
7	K. Carter, T. Davis	20.00
8	K. Johnson, E.	15.00
	George	
9	O. Pace, W. Dunn	15.00
10	1998 Top Draft	8.00
	Pick	

1998 Pro Line DC III Team Totals

Team Totals was a 30-card insert that was found in packs of Pro Line DC III at a rate of one per eight packs. The cards were die-cut in the shape of a crystal ball, with the insert name across the bottom in gold foil and two shots of the player in the ball part - an action shot on the right and a close-up on the left. Team Totals inserts are numbered on the back with a "TT" prefix.

		MT
Complete Set (30):		100.00
Common Player:		2.00
Minor Stars:		4.00
1	Ben Coates,	2.00
	Willie McGinest	
2	Michael Irvin,	6.00
	Deion Sanders	
3	Carl Pickens,	2.00
	Dan Wilkinson	
4	LeRoy Butler,	6.00
	Antonio Freeman	
5	Adrian Murrell,	3.00
	Hugh Douglas	
6	Raymont Harris,	2.00
	Bryan Cox	
7	Ricky Watters,	4.00
	William Thomas	
8	Neil Smith,	3.00
	Shannon Sharpe	
9	Dana Stubblefield,	3.00
	Garrison Hearst	
10	Keenan McCardell,	2.00
	Jeff Lageman	
11	Rae Carruth,	4.00
	Lamar Lathon	
12	Yancey Thigpen,	2.00
	Greg Lloyd	
13	Chris Calloway,	2.00
	Michael Strahan	
14	Troy Davis,	3.00
	Wayne Martin	
15	Warren Moon,	3.00
	Cortez Kennedy	
16	Rob Moore,	3.00
	Simeon Rice	
17	O.J. McDuffie,	3.00
	Zach Thomas	
18	John Randle,	3.00
	Robert Smith	
19	Derrick Thomas,	3.00
	Elvis Grbac	
20	Antowain Smith,	10.00
	Bruce Smith	
21	Jeff George,	2.00
	Darrell Russell	
22	Steve McNair,	10.00
	Darryll Lewis	
23	Isaac Bruce,	4.00
	Leslie O'Neal	
24	Junior Seau,	3.00
	Tony Martin	
25	Warren Sapp,	4.00
	Mike Alstott	
26	Jessie Tuggle,	2.00
	Jamal Anderson	
27	Michael Jackson,	2.00
	Peter Boulware	
28	Quentin Coryatt,	4.00
	Marvin Harrison	
29	Bryant Westbrook,	2.00
	Scott Mitchell	
30	Michael Westbrook,	3.00
	Darrell Green	

1998 Pro Line DC III X-Tra Effort

X-Tra Effort inserts are die-cut in the shape of an "X" on a horizontal format. Card fronts have the player's first name in the top left corner, his last name in the top right corner, a Pro Line DC logo in the bottom left and the insert name in the bottom right corner. The player is centered in the card with lightning bolts coming out on all sides. In addition, the front bears gold foil on all sides of the "X" as if a gold oval was set in back of the card to form a second layer. X-Tra Effort was a 20-card insert that was found one per 24 hobby packs and sequentially numbered to 1,000 sets. Cards carried an "XE" prefix on the back card number.

		MT
Complete Set (20):		325.00
Common Player:		5.00
1	Reggie White	8.00
2	Emmitt Smith	40.00
3	Junior Seau	5.00
4	Brett Favre	50.00
5	Warrick Dunn	30.00
6	Keyshawn Johnson	8.00
7	Dan Marino	40.00
8	Thurman Thomas	5.00
9	Steve Young	15.00
10	Curtis Martin	20.00
11	Karim Abdul-Jabbar	10.00
12	John Elway	20.00
13	Marcus Allen	8.00
14	Napoleon Kaufman	8.00
15	Irving Fryar	5.00
16	Mark Brunell	20.00
17	Andre Rison	5.00
18	Herman Moore	8.00
19	Jerry Rice	20.00
20	Kordell Stewart	20.00

1988 Pro Set Test Designs

Philadelphia Eagles quarterback Randall Cunningham is featured on these five prototype cards, used to preview Pro Set's 1989 debut set. The card numbers are the same on each card, but five different designs were used for the fronts. These are indicated with the corresponding card. Each card back is designed horizontally, with a mug shot, statistics, player profile and biographical information provided.

		MT
Complete Set (5):		160.00
Common Player:		40.00
315A	Randall	40.00
	Cunningham (No	
	team or name	
	listed on card front;	
	borderless; logo is	
	vertical)	
315B	Randall	40.00
	Cunningham (No	
	team or name	
	listed on card front;	
	border is white;	
	logo is vertical)	
315C	Randall	40.00
	Cunningham	
	(Name and team	

are listed on card front; borderless; logo is horizontal)

315D	Randall	40.00
	Cunningham	
	(Team and name	
	listed on card front;	
	border is black;	
	logo is horizontal)	
315E	Randall	40.00
	Cunningham	
	(Team and name	
	listed on card front;	
	border is gray; logo	
	is horizontal)	

1988 Pro Set Test

These promotional cards, used to preview Pro Set's debut set in 1989, can be distinguished from regular cards in several manners. First, each of the card backs is designed in a vertical fashion; the regular cards use a horizontal format. Also, the card number includes a # symbol before it. Plus, all the photos used for the fronts, except for the Jerry Rice photo, are different than those used on the regular cards.

		MT
Complete Set (8):		200.00
Common Player:		10.00
1	Dan Marino	80.00
2	Jerry Rice	65.00
3	Eric Dickerson	25.00
4	Reggie White	25.00
5	Mike Singletary	15.00
6	Frank Minnifield	10.00
7	Phil Simms	25.00
8	Jim Kelly	45.00

1989 Pro Set Promos

These five cards preview Pro Set's 1989 card design. The Santa Claus card was given to dealers, NFL representatives and members of the hobby press in December 1989. The Super Bowl card was given to those who attended the card show at Super Bowl XXIV in New Orleans in January 1990. The three player cards were samples which were mistakenly handed out at card shows in San Francisco and Chicago. The Bush and Lofton cards were intended to be included in Pro Set's Series II cards, but were bumped for Eric Dickerson and Greg Townsend. Sanders was given #446.

		MT
Complete Set (5):		125.00
Common Player:		10.00
445	Thomas Sanders	20.00
455	Blair Bush	20.00
463	James Lofton	25.00
1989	Santa Claus	50.00

1989 Pro Set

Pro Set's premier football issue was released in two series in the summer and fall of 1989. Printed on heavy white cardboard stock, the standard-size cards come in a variety of colors and feature full-color action shots on the front, full-color head shots on the back, and biographical notes and statistics on the back. The 615-card set (541 player/coach cards, 23

Super Bowl cards, 30 announcer cards, 20 Final Update cards, one commissioner card) was not released in factory-issued sets. Pro Set is the only one of the three 1989 football card sets featuring coaches cards. Pro Set released its first series in late July 1989, and its second series in September 1989. The third series, labeled "Final Update" on the boxes only, contained 20 additional cards of traded players, rookies and players not previously included in the set. Along with the re-released Art Shell card, these blue-bordered cards were included with Series I and II cards. Art Shell cards were printed on separate sheets and were inserted into late Series II and all Final Update print runs; the card was usually found on top of the pack.

		MT
Complete Set (561):		30.00
Complete Series 1 (440):		8.00
Complete Series 2 (100):		20.00
Complete Series 3 (21):		2.00
Common Player:		.03
Minor Stars:		.10
Series 1 Wax Box:		10.00
Series 2 Wax Box:		20.00
1	Stacey Bailey	.03
2	Aundray Bruce	.03
3	Rick Bryan	.03
4	Bobby Butler	.03
5	Scott Case	.10
6	Tony Casillas	.03
7	Floyd Dixon	.03
8	Rick Donnelly	.03
9	Bill Fralic	.03
10	Mike Gann	.03
11	Mike Kenn	.03
12	Chris Miller	.25
13	John Rade	.03
14	Gerald Riggs	.03
15	John Settle	.10
16	Marion Campbell	.03
17	Cornelius Bennett	.10
18	Derrick Burroughs	.03
19	Shane Conlan	.03
20	Ronnie Harmon	.03
21	Kent Hull	.10
22	Jim Kelly	.50
23	Mark Kelso	.03
24	Pete Metzelaars	.03
25	Scott Norwood	.03
26	Andre Reed	.10
27	Fred Smerlas	.03
28	Bruce Smith	.10
29	Leonard Smith	.03
30	Art Still	.03
31	Darryl Talley	.03
32	Thurman Thomas	1.50
33	Will Wolford	.03
34	Marv Levy (C)	.03
35	Neal Anderson	.03
36	Kevin Butler	.03
37	Jim Covert	.03
38	Richard Dent	.10
39	Dave Duerson	.03
40	Dennis Gentry	.03
41	Dan Hampton	.03
42	Jay Hilgenberg	.03
43	Dennis McKinnon	.03
44	Jim McMahon	.10
45	Steve McMichael	.03
46	Brad Muster	.03
47	William Perry ERR	3.00
48	Ron Rivera	.03
49	Vestee Jackson	.03
50	Mike Singletary	.10
51	Mike Tomczak	.03
52	Keith Van Horne	.03
53	Mike Ditka (C HOF stripe)	.10
54	Lewis Billups	.03
55	James Brooks	.03
56	Eddie Brown	.03
57	Jason Buck	.03
58	Boomer Esiason	.10
59	David Fulcher	.03
60	Rodney Holman	.10
61	Reggie Williams	.03
62	Joe Kelly	.03
63	Tim Krumrie	.03
64	Tim McGee	.03
65	Max Montoya	.03
66	Anthony Munoz	.10
67	Jim Skow	.03
68	Eric Thomas	.03
69	Leon White	.03
70	Ickey Woods	.03
71	Carl Zander	.03
72	Sam Wyche (C)	.03
73	Brian Brennan	.03
74	Earnest Byner	.10
75	Hanford Dixon	.03
76	Mike Pagel	.03
77	Bernie Kosar	.10
78	Reggie Langhorne	.03
79	Kevin Mack	.03
80	Clay Matthews	.03

81	Gerald McNeil	.03
82	Frank Minnifield	.03
83	Cody Risien	.03
84	Webster Slaughter	.10
85	Felix Wright	.03
86	Bud Carson (C)	.03
87	Bill Bates	.03
88	Kevin Brooks	.03
89	Michael Irvin	1.50
90	Jim Jeffcoat	.03
91	Too Tall Jones	.03
92	Eugene Lockhart	.03
93	Nate Newton	.20
94	Danny Noonan	.03
95	Steve Pelluer	.03
96	Herschel Walker	.10
97	Everson Walls	.03
98	Jimmy Johnson (C)	.10
99	Keith Bishop	.03
100	John Elway DRAFT	4.00
100a	John Elway TRADE	2.00
101	Simon Fletcher	.10
102	Mike Harden	.03
103	Mike Horan	.03
104	Mark Jackson	.03
105	Vance Johnson	.03
106	Rulon Jones	.03
107	Clarence Kay	.03
108	Karl Mecklenburg	.03
109	Ricky Nattiel	.03
110	Steve Sewell	.10
111	Dennis Smith	.03
112	Gerald Willhite	.03
113	Sammy Winder	.03
114	Dan Reeves	.03
115	Jim Arnold	.03
116	Jerry Ball	.10
117	Bennie Blades	.10
118	Lomas Brown	.03
119	Michael Cofer	.03
120	Garry James	.03
121	James Jones	.03
122	Chuck Long	.03
123	Pete Mandley	.03
124	Eddie Murray	.03
125	Chris Spielman	.10
126	Dennis Gibson	.03
127	Wayne Fontes (C)	.03
128	John Anderson	.03
129	Brent Fullwood	.03
130	Mark Cannon	.03
131	Tim Harris	.03
132	Mark Lee	.03
133	Don Majkowski	.10
134	Mark Murphy	.03
135	Brian Noble	.03
136	Ken Ruettgers	.03
137	Johnny Holland	.03
138	Randy Wright	.03
139	Lindy Infante (C)	.03
140	Steve Brown	.03
141	Ray Childress	.03
142	Jeff Donaldson	.03
143	Ernest Givins	.10
144	John Grimsley	.03
145	Alonzo Highsmith	.03
146	Drew Hill	.03
147	Robert Lyles	.03
148	Bruce Matthews	.10
149	Warren Moon	.25
150	Mike Munchak	.03
151	Allen Pinkett	.03
152	Mike Rozier	.03
153	Tony Zendejas	.03
154	Jerry Glanville (C)	.10
155	Albert Bentley	.03
156	Dean Biasucci	.03
157	Duane Bickett	.03
158	Bill Brooks	.03
159	Chris Chandler	2.00
160	Pat Beach	.03
161	Ray Donaldson	.03
162	Jon Hand	.03
163	Chris Hinton	.03
164	Rohn Stark	.03
165	Fredd Young	.03
166	Ron Meyer (C)	.03
167	Lloyd Burruss	.03
168	Carlos Carson	.03
169	Deron Cherry	.03
170	Irv Eatman	.03
171	Dino Hackett	.03
172	Steve DeBerg	.03
173	Albert Lewis	.03
174	Nick Lowery	.03
175	Bill Maas	.03
176	Christian Okoye	.10
177	Stephone Paige	.03
178	Mark Addickes	.03
179	Kevin Ross	.10
180	Neil Smith	.50
181	Marty Schottenheimer (C)	.03
182	Marcus Allen	.25
183	Tim Brown	1.50
184	Willie Gault	.03
185	Bo Jackson	.25
186	Howie Long	.10
187	Vann McElroy	.03
188	Matt Millen	.10
189	Don Mosebar	.03
190	Bill Pickel	.03
191	Jerry Robinson	.03
192	Jay Schroeder	.03
193	Stacey Toran	.10
193a	Stacey Toran (1961-1989)	.50
194	Mike Shanahan (C)	.10

195	Greg Bell	.03
196	Ron Brown	.03
197	Aaron Cox	.03
198	Henry Ellard	.03
199	Jim Everett	.10
200	Jerry Gray	.03
201	Kevin Greene	.10
202	Pete Holohan	.03
203	LeRoy Irvin	.03
204	Mike Lansford	.03
205	Tom Newberry	.10
206	Mel Owens	.03
207	Jackie Slater	.03
208	Doug Smith	.03
209	Mike Wilcher	.03
210	John Robinson (C)	.03
211	John Bosa	.03
212	Mark Brown	.03
213	Mark Clayton	.03
214	Ferrell Edmunds (corrected)	.10
214a	Ferrell Edmonds (error)	.50
215	Roy Foster	.03
216	Lorenzo Hampton	.03
217	Jim Jensen	.03
218	William Judson	.03
219	Eric Kumerow	.03
220	Dan Marino	2.00
221	John Offerdahl	.03
222	Fuad Reveiz	.03
223	Reggie Roby	.03
224	Brian Sochia	.03
225	Don Shula (C)	.20
226	Alfred Anderson	.03
227	Joey Browner	.03
228	Anthony Carter	.03
229	Chris Doleman	.03
230	Hassan Jones	.03
231	Steve Jordan	.03
232	Tommy Kramer	.03
233	Carl Lee	.03
234	Kirk Lowdermilk	.10
235	Randall McDaniel	.10
236	Doug Martin	.03
237	Keith Millard	.03
238	Darrin Nelson	.03
239	Jesse Solomon	.03
240	Scott Studwell	.03
241	Wade Wilson	.03
242	Gary Zimmerman	.03
243	Jerry Burns (C)	.03
244	Bruce Armstrong	.10
245	Raymond Clayburn	.03
246	Reggie Dupard	.03
247	Tony Eason	.03
248	Sean Farrell	.03
249	Doug Flutie	.75
250	Brent Williams	.03
251	Roland James	.03
252	Ronnie Lippett	.03
253	Fred Marion	.03
254	Lawrence McGrew	.03
255	Stanley Morgan	.03
256	Johnny Rembert	.03
257	John Stephens	.10
258	Andre Tippett	.03
259	Garin Veris	.03
260	Ray Berry (C HOF stripe)	.10
261	Morten Andersen	.10
262	Hoby Brenner	.03
263	Stan Brock	.03
264	Brad Edelman	.03
265	James Geathers	.03
266	Bobby Hebert ("touchdown passers")	.50
266a	Bobby Hebert ("touchdown passes")	.10
267	Craig Heyward	.10
268	Lonzell Hill	.03
269	Dalton Hilliard	.03
270	Rickey Jackson	.03
271	Steve Korte	.03
272	Eric Martin	.03
273	Reuben Mayes	.03
274	Sam Mills	.03
275	Brett Perriman	.25
276	Pat Swilling	.10
277	John Tice	.03
278	Jim Mora (C)	.03
279	Eric Moore	.03
280	Carl Banks	.03
281	Mark Bavaro	.03
282	Maurice Carthon	.03
283	Mark Collins	.03
284	Erik Howard	.03
285	Terry Kinard	.03
286	Sean Landeta	.03
287	Lionel Manuel	.03
288	Leonard Marshall	.03
289	Joe Morris	.03
290	Bart Oates	.03
291	Phil Simms	.10
292	Lawrence Taylor	.20
293	Bill Parcells (C)	.15
294	Dave Cadigan	.03
295	Kyle Clifton	.03
296	Alex Gordon	.03
297	James Hasty	.03
298	Johnny Hector	.03
299	Bobby Humphery	.03
300	Pat Leahy	.03
301	Marty Lyons	.03
302	Reggie McElroy	.03
303	Erik McMillan	.10

304 Freeman McNeil	.03
305 Ken O'Brien	.03
306 Pat Ryan	.03
307 Mickey Shuler	.03
308 Al Toon	.03
309 JoJo Townsell	.03
310 Roger Vick	.03
311 Joe Walton (C)	.03
312 Jerome Brown	.03
313 Keith Byars	.03
314 *Cris Carter*	2.50
315 Randall Cunningham	.40
316 Terry Hoage	.03
317 Wes Hopkins	.03
318 *Keith Jackson*	.20
319 Mike Quick	.03
320 Mike Reichenbach	.03
321 Dave Rimington	.03
322 John Teltschik	.03
323 Anthony Toney	.03
324 Andre Waters	.03
325 Reggie White	.25
326 Luis Zendejas	.03
327 Buddy Ryan (C)	.03
328 Robert Awalt	.03
329 *Tim McDonald*	.10
330 Roy Green	.03
331 Neil Lomax	.03
332 Cedric Mack	.03
333 Stump Mitchell	.03
334 Niko Noga	.03
335 *Jay Novacek*	.25
336 Freddie Joe Nunn	.03
337 Luis Sharpe	.03
338 Vai Sikahema	.03
339 J.T. Smith	.03
340 Ron Wolfley	.03
341 Gene Stallings (C)	.03
342 Gary Anderson (Pit.)	.03
343 *Bubby Brister*	.75
344 *Dermontti Dawson*	.10
345 *Thomas Everett*	.10
346 Delton Hall	.03
347 Bryan Hinkle	.10
348 *Merril Hoge*	.10
349 Tunch Ilken	.03
350 Aaron Jones	.10
351 Louis Lipps	.03
352 David Little	.03
353 *Hardy Nickerson*	.20
354 Rod Woodson	.75
355 Chuck Noll ("One of the only three") (C)	.15
355a Chuck Noll ("One of only two") (C)	.15
356 Gary Anderson (S.D.)	.03
357 *Rod Berstine*	.10
358 Gill Byrd	.03
359 Vencie Glenn	.03
360 Dennis McKnight	.03
361 Lionel James	.03
362 Mark Malone	.03
363 *Anthony Miller 14.8*	.40
363a *Anthony Miller 3*	.40
364 Ralf Mojsiejenko	.03
365 Leslie O'Neal	.03
366 Jamie Holland	.03
367 Lee Williams	.03
368 Dan Henning	.03
369 Harris Barton	.10
370 Michael Carter	.03
371 Mike Cofer (S.F.)	.10
372 Roger Craig	.03
373 Riki Ellison	.03
374 Jim Fahnhorst	.03
375 John Frank	.03
376 Jeff Fuller	.03
377 Don Griffin	.03
378 Charles Haley	.10
379 Ronnie Lott	.10
380 Tim McKyer	.03
381 Joe Montana	1.50
382 Tom Rathman	.03
383 Jerry Rice	1.50
384 *John Taylor*	.25
385 Keena Turner	.03
386 Michael Walter	.03
387 Bubba Paris	.03
388 Steve Young	1.00
389 *George Siefert* (C)	.10
390 Brian Blades	.20
391 Brian Bosworth (Seahawks)	.10
391a Brian Bosworth (Seattle)	.10
392 Jeff Bryant	.03
393 Jacob Green	.03
394 Norm Johnson	.03
395 Dave Krieg	.03
396 Steve Largent	.15
397 Bryan Millard	.03
398 Paul Moyer	.03
399 Joe Nash	.03
400 Rufus Porter	.03
401 *Eugene Robinson*	.20
402 Bruce Scholtz	.03
403 *Kelly Stouffer*	.03
404 Curt Warner 1455 (yards 1,455)	1.00
404a Curt Warner (yards 6,074)	.15
405 John L. Williams	.03
406 *Tony Woods*	.10

407 David Wyman	.03
408 Chuck Knox (C)	.03
409 *Mark Carrier*	.50
410 Randy Grimes	.03
411 *Paul Gruber*	.10
412 Harry Hamilton	.03
413 Ron Holmes	.03
414 Donald Igwebuike	.03
415 Dan Turk	.03
416 Ricky Reynolds	.03
417 Bruce Hill	.03
418 Lars Tate	.03
419 Vinny Testaverde	.30
420 James Wilder	.03
421 Ray Perkins (C)	.03
422 Jeff Bostic	.03
423 Kelvin Bryant	.03
424 Gary Clark	.10
425 Monte Coleman	.03
426 Darrell Green	.10
427 Joe Jacoby	.03
428 Jim Lachey	.03
429 Charles Mann	.03
430 Dexter Manley	.03
431 Darryl Grant	.03
432 *Mark May*	.10
433 Art Monk	.15
434 *Mark Rypien*	.20
435 Ricky Sanders	.10
436 *Alvin Walton*	.10
437 Don Warren	.03
438 Jamie Morris	.03
439 Doug Williams	.10
440 Joe Gibbs (C)	.10
441 Marcus Cotton	.03
442 Joel Williams	.03
443 Joe Devlin	.03
444 Robb Riddick	.03
445 William Perry	.10
446 *Thomas Sanders*	.03
447 Brian Blades	
448 Cris Collinsworth	.10
449 Stanford Jennings	.03
450 Barry Krauss	.03
451 Ozzie Newsome	.10
452 Mike Oliphant	.03
453 Tony Dorsett	.15
454 Bruce McNorton	.03
455 Eric Dickerson	.20
456 Keith Bostic	.03
457 Sam Clancy	.03
458 Jack Del Rio	.03
459 Mike Webster	.03
460 Bob Golic	.03
461 Otis Wilson	.03
462 Mike Haynes	.03
463 Greg Townsend	.03
464 Mark Duper	.03
465 E.J. Junior	.03
466 Troy Stradford	.03
467 Mike Merriweather	.03
468 Irving Fryar	.10
469 *Vaughan Johnson*	.10
470 Pepper Johnson	.03
471 Gary Reasons	.03
472 *Perry Williams*	.10
473 Wesley Walker	.03
474 Anthony Bell	.03
475 Earl Ferrell	.03
476 Craig Wolfley	.03
477 Billy Ray Smith	.03
478 Jim McMahon	.10
478a Jim McMahon (traded)	.40
479 Eric Wright	.03
480 Earnest Byner	.10
480a Earnest Byner (traded)	.30
481 Russ Grimm	.03
482 Wilber Marshall	.03
483 Gerald Riggs	.03
484 *Brian Davis*	.03
485 *Shawn Collins*	.10
486 *Deion Sanders*	2.00
487 *Trace Armstrong*	.10
488 *Donnell Woolford*	.20
489 *Eric Metcalf*	.25
490 *Troy Aikman*	3.00
491 *Steve Walsh*	.30
492 *Steve Atwater*	.30
493 Bobby Humphrey	.10
494 *Barry Sanders*	15.00
495 *Tony Mandarich*	.20
496 *David Williams*	.10
497 *Andre Rison*	1.00
498 *Derrick Thomas*	1.00
499 *Cleveland Gary*	.20
500 *Bill Hawkins*	.10
501 *Louis Oliver*	.10
502 *Sammie Smith*	.10
503 *Hart Lee Dykes*	.10
504 *Wayne Martin*	.10
505 *Brian Williams*	.10
506 *Jeff Lageman*	.10
507 *Eric Hill*	.10
508 *Joe Wolf*	.10
509 *Timm Rosenbach*	.10
510 *Tom Ricketts*	.10
511 *Tim Worley*	.10
512 *Burt Grossman*	.10
513 *Keith DeLong*	.10
514 *Andy Heck*	.10
515 *Broderick Thomas*	.10
516 *Don Beebe*	.25
517 *James Thornton*	.10
518 *Eric Kattus*	.10
519 *Bruce Kozerski*	.10
520 *Brian Washington*	.10

521 *Rodney Peete*	.25
522 *Erik Affholter*	.10
523 *Anthony Dilweg*	.10
524 *O'Brien Alston*	.10
525 *Mike Elkins*	.10
526 *Jonathan Hayes*	.03
527 *Terry McDaniel*	.10
528 *Frank Stams*	.10
529 *Darryl Ingram*	.10
530 *Henry Thomas*	.10
531 *Eric Coleman*	.10
532 *Sheldon White*	.10
533 *Eric Allen*	.20
534 *Robert Drummond*	.03
535 Gizmo Williams ("Scouting Photo")	10.00
535a Gizmo Williams (no "Scouting Photo")	.25
535b Gizmo Williams (no "Scouting Photo," "Canadian Football" on back)	.15
536 *Billy Joe Tolliver*	.20
537 *Danny Stubbs*	.10
538 *Wesley Walls*	.40
539 *James Jefferson* (no stripe)	.30
539a *James Jefferson* (Pro Set Prospect stripe)	.10
540 Tracy Rocker	.03
541 Art Shell (C)	.10
542 Lemuel Stinson	.15
543 Tyrone Braxton	.10
543a Tyrone Braxton (back photo actually Ken Bell)	.10
544 *David Treadwell*	.10
545 *Willie Anderson*	.20
546 *Dave Meggett*	.25
547 *Lewis Tillman*	.20
548 *Carnell Lake*	.20
549 *Marion Butts*	.20
550 *Sterling Sharpe*	1.00
551 Ezra Johnson	.03
552 *Clarence Verdin*	.10
553 Mervyn Fernandez	.03
554 Ottis Anderson	.10
555 Gary Hogeboom	.03
556 Paul Palmer	.03
557 Jesse Solomon	.03
558 Chip Banks	.03
559 Steve Pelluer	.03
560 Darrin Nelson	.03
561 Herschel Walker	.10
CC1 Pete Rozelle	.50

1989 Pro Set Super Bowl Inserts

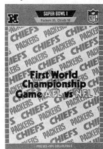

Pro Set included a glossy Super Bowl card (1 through 23) in each wax pack of its 1989 Series I cards. The standard-size cards show the official logo of each Super Bowl surrounded by a bright orange border on the front of the card, with the stylized names of the two participating teams in the background. Card backs include a recap of the game and a line score.

		MT
Complete Set (23):		5.00
Common Player:		.25
1	Super Bowl I	.25
2	Super Bowl II	.25
3	Super Bowl IV	.25
4	Super Bowl IV	.25
5	Super Bowl V	.25
6	Super Bowe VI	.25
7	Super Bowl VII	.25
8	Super Bowl VIII	.25
9	Super Bowl IX	.25
10	Super Bowl X	.25
11	Super Bowl XI	.25
12	Super Bowl XII	.25
13	Super Bowl XIII	.25
14	Super Bowl XIV	.25
15	Super Bowl XV	.25
16	Super Bowl XVI	.25
17	Super Bowl XVII	.25
18	Super Bowl XVIII	.25
19	Super Bowl XIX	.25
20	Super Bowl XX	.25
21	Super Bowl XXI	.25
22	Super Bowl XXII	.25
23	Super Bowl XXIII	.25

1989 Pro Set GTE SB Album

This 40-card set was made available to those who attended the Super Bowl XXIV game in New Orleans in 1990. Players from the participants in the game, the San Francisco 49ers and Denver Broncos, are represented in the set. The card numbers are identical to those in the regular set, but these cards can be distinguished from the regulars by the NFC or AFC Champs designation on the card front, along with the Super Bowl logo. GTE issued the cards in conjunction with Pro Set, and created a card album to hold the set.

1989 Pro Set Announcer Inserts

This set of 30 cards was issued in Pro Set's Series II wax packs, one per pack. Like the Super Bowl inserts, the glossy cards are standard size. They feature color photos (bordered in bright orange) of the announcer on the front and back - if the announcer is a former player, a shot of him in action is shown. If the announcer made it to the Hall of Fame as a player (Terry Bradshaw, O.J. Simpson), a yellow stripe bearing a "Hall of Fame" label in the lower left corner of his action picture. Pro Set had announced the names of the players of its first 20 cards in its premier issue of Pro Set Gazette. Since the initial announcement, Pro Set acquired the rights to NBC announcers and added them shortly before the presses began to roll. Verne Lundquist was apparently substituted for Dan Jiggetts just before the print run began.

		MT
Complete Set (30):		5.00
Common Player:		.08
1	Dan Dierdorf	.25
2	Frank Gifford	.75
3	Al Michaels	.15
4	Pete Axthelm	.08
5	Chris Berman	.25
7	Mike Patrick	.08
8	John Saunders	.08
9	Joe Theismann	.30
10	Steve Sabol	.08
11	Jack Buck	.08
12	Terry Bradshaw	.50
13	James Brown	.08
14	Dan Fouts	.30
15	Dick Butkus	.50
16	Irv Cross	.08
17	Brent Musberger	.15
18	Ken Stabler	.25
19	Dick Stockton	.08
20	Hank Stram	.08
21	Verne Lundquist	.08
22	Will McDonough	.08
23	Bob Costas	.25
24	Dick Enberg	.15
25	Joe Namath	.65
26	Bob Trumpy	.08
27	Merlin Olsen	.25
28	Ahmad Rashad	.30
29	O.J. Simpson	2.00
30	Bill Walsh	.30

did get through to the hob... sued in November 1990, the second series of Pro Set was, unlike the year before, not included in Series I wax boxes. In addition, space was saved in the middle of the set for the mail-in Final Update offer. Five cards were inserted on a rotating basis in every 50th pack: Paul Tagliabue (carried over from Series I), Payne Stewart (same), Santa Claus, Joe Robbie, and Marvel Comics Super Pro. The Final Update was available in late January through a mail-in offer. It included 28 cards, plus three other special cards: card 799, which featured Ronnie Lott in his role as a spokesman for the NFL's "Stay in School" program; the Series I Andre Rison card with a traded stripe; and cards 800, Emmitt Smith and Mark Carrier, the 1990 NFL Pro Set Rookies of the Year in the 1991 Pro Set design. One correction was made very early in the print run. The text on the back of card 772, Dexter Manley, originally read, "Reinstated by Paul Tagliabue 11 weeks into the 1990 season after suspension for violating the league's substance-abuse policy." According to reports, Manley's agent objected to the wording, and it was changed to "After missing the first 10 weeks of the 1990 season, Dexter returned to the NFL." Very few of the original cards were issued.

		MT
Complete Set (40):		30.00
Common Player:		.40
99	Keith Bishop	.40
100	John Elway	6.00
101	Simon Fletcher	.60
103	Mike Horan	.40
104	Mark Jackson	.70
105	Vance Johnson	.60
107	Clarence Kay	.40
108	Karl Mecklenburg	.60
109	Ricky Nattiel	.60
110	Steve Sewell	.50
111	Dennis Smith	.50
113	Sammy Winder	.50
114	Dan Reeves CO	.60
369	Harris Barton	.40
370	Michael Carter	.60
371	Mike Cofer	.40
372	Roger Craig	1.75
374	Jim Fahnhorst	.40
377	Don Griffin	.50
378	Charles Haley	.60
379	Ronnie Lott	2.50
380	Tim McKyer	.50
381	Joe Montana	11.00
382	Tom Rathman	.75
383	Jerry Rice	8.00
384	John Taylor	2.00
385	Keena Turner	.50
386	Michael Walter	.40
387	Bubba Paris	.40
388	Steve Young	4.00
389	George Seifert CO	.50
479	Eric Wright	.60
492	Steve Atwater	1.00
493	Bobby Humphrey	.75
537	Danny Stubbs	.40
543	Tyrone Braxton	.50
544	David Treadwell	.40
----	AFC Logo XXIV Collectible	.60
----	NFC logo XXIV Collectible	.60
----	Superdome XXIV Collectible	.60

1990 Pro Set Draft Day

Each of these cards, numbered 669, was issued by Pro Set on the day of the 1990 NFL draft to present various scenarios for the draft. The card fronts preview Pro Set's 1990 main set design; each back uses a horizontal format and includes a mug shot, biographical information and a player profile.

		MT
Complete Set (3):		25.00
Common Player:		3.00
669A	Jeff George	12.00
669A	Jeff George	12.00
669D	Keith McCants	3.00

1990 Pro Set

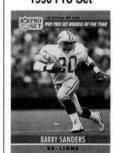

THE OFFICIAL NFL CARD — 1989 PRO SET ROOKIE OF THE YEAR — BARRY SANDERS — RB·LIONS

Pro Set's Series I was issued in late May of 1990. The sophomore set for the Dallas-based company was its first using its own printing press, and that allowed Pro Set to create die-cut borderless cards. Again, several insert cards were included throughout Series I: Paul Tagliabue was randomly included in early Series I wax packs; golfer Payne Stewart was added to the rotation; and Jeff George completed the rotating triumverate in late Series I printings. Because of a squabble over what card companies he wanted to appear with, Eric Dickerson was not to appear in any 1990 card sets. Pro Set already had a card of him created, however, and was forced to pull them by hand from Series I. Some, however,

		MT
Complete Set (801):		15.00
Complete Series 1 (377):		6.00
Complete Series 2 (392):		6.00
Complete Series 3 (32):		3.00
Common Player:		.03
Series 1 or 2 Wax Box:		7.00
1	Barry Sanders (ROY)	.75
2	Joe Montana (SPL, back reads "Kelly-3,521 yards")	.50
2a	Joe Montana (SPL, back corrected to "Kelly: 3,130 yards")	.75
3	Lindy Infante (SPL)	.03
4	Warren Moon (SPL)	.10
5	Keith Millard (SPL)	.10
6	Derrick Thomas (SPL)	.10
7	Ottis Anderson (SPL)	.03
8	Joe Montana (LL)	.50
9	Christian Okoye (SPL)	.03
11	Thurman Thomas	.25
12	Mike Cofer (SPL)	.03
13	Dalton Hilliard (SPL)	.03
14	Sterling Sharpe (LL)	.20
15	Rich Camarillo (LL)	.03
15	Walter Stanley (SPL, #8 on back)	.10
15a	Walter Stanley (SPL, #86 on back)	.10
16	Rod Woodson (LL)	.03
17	Felix Wright (LL)	.03
18	Chris Doleman (SPL, error back)	.10
18a	Chris Doleman (SPL, back corrected to 104.5 sacks for Taylor; "Townsent" corrected to "Townsend")	.10
19	Andre Ware (SPL)	.10
19a	Andre Ware (SPL, drafted stripe added)	.10
20	Mohammed Elewonibi (SPL)	.05
20a	Mohammed Elewonibi (SPL, drafted stripe added)	.05
21	Percy Snow (SPL)	.05
21a	Percy Snow (SPL, drafted stripe added)	.05
22	Anthony Thompson (SPL)	.10
22a	Anthony Thompson (SPL, drafted stripe added)	.10
23	Buck Buchanan (HOF)	.03
24	Bob Griese (HOF)	.03
25	Franco Harris (HOF)	.05
25a	Franco Harris (HOF, corrected birthdate: 3/7/50)	.05
26	Ted Hendricks (HOF)	.03

No.	Player	Price
27	Jack Lambert (HOF)	.08
27a	Jack Lambert (HOF, corrected birthdate 7/8/52)	.08
28	Tom Landry (HOF)	.06
29	Bob St. Clair (HOF)	.03
30	Aundray Bruce	.06
31	Tony Casillas	.03
32	Shawn Collins	.03
33	Marcus Cotton	.03
34	Bill Fralic	.03
35	Chris Miller	.06
36	Deion Sanders	.30
37	John Settle	.03
38	Jerry Glanville	.03
39	Cornelius Bennett	.03
40	Jim Kelly	.35
41	Mark Kelso	.03
42	Scott Norwood	.03
43	Nate Odomes	.30
44	Scott Radecic	.03
45	Jim Ritcher	.03
46	Leonard Smith	.03
47	Darryl Talley	.03
48	Marv Levy (C)	.03
49	Neal Anderson	.03
50	Kevin Butler	.03
51	Jim Covert	.03
52	Richard Dent	.03
53	Jay Hilgenberg	.03
54	Steve McMichael	.03
55	Ron Morris	.03
56	John Roper	.03
57	Mike Singletary	.03
58	Mike Ditka (C)	.03
59	Lewis Billups	.03
60	Eddie Brown	.03
61	Jason Buck	.03
62	Rickey Dixon (no bio notes under photo)	.10
63	Rickey Dixon (with bio notes)	.10
64	Tim McGee	.03
65	Eric Thomas	.03
66	Ickey Woods	.03
67	Carl Zander	.03
68	Sam Wyche (C, no bio notes under photo)	.05
68a	Sam Wyche (C, corrected)	.05
69	Paul Farren	.03
70	Thane Gash	.03
71	David Grayson	.03
72	Bernie Kosar	.03
73	Reggie Langhorne	.03
74	Eric Metcalf	.03
75	Ozzie Newsome	.10
75a	Ozzie Newsome (corrected hometown: Muscle Shoals, AL)	.10
75	Cody Risien (SP)	.10
76	Felix Wright	.03
77	Bud Carson (C)	.03
78	Troy Aikman	1.00
79	Michael Irvin	.30
80	Jim Jeffcoat	.03
81	Crawford Ker	.03
82	Eugene Lockhart	.03
83	Kelvin Martin	.25
84	Ken Norton Jr.	.50
85	Jimmy Johnson (C)	.03
86	Steve Atwater	.03
87	Tyrone Braxton	.03
88	John Elway	.40
89	Simon Fletcher	.03
90	Ron Holmes	.03
91	Bobby Humphrey	.03
92	Vance Johnson	.03
93	Ricky Nattiel	.03
94	Dan Reeves	.03
95	Jim Arnold	.03
96	Jerry Ball	.03
97	Bennie Blades	.03
98	Lomas Brown	.03
99	Michael Cofer	.03
100	Richard Johnson	.03
101	Eddie Murray	.03
102	Barry Sanders	1.25
103	Chris Spielman	.03
104	William White	.08
105	Eric Williams	.08
106	Wayne Fontes (C)	.03
107	Brent Fullwood	.03
108	Ron Hallstrom	.08
109	Tim Harris	.03
110	Johnny Holland (no name, number on back)	1.00
110a	Johnny Holland (corrected)	.15
111	Perry Kemp (Ken Stills photo on back)	.10
111a	Perry Kemp (corrected)	.10
112	Don Majkowski	.03
113	Mark Murphy	.03
114	Sterling Sharpe	.20
114a	Sterling Sharpe (corrected birthplace: Chicago, IL)	.20
115	Ed West	.03
116	Lindy Infante (C)	.03
117	Steve Brown	.03
118	Ray Childress	.03
119	Ernest Givins	.03
120	John Grimsley	.03
121	Alonzo Highsmith	.03
122	Drew Hill	.03
123	Bubba McDowell	.03
124	Dean Steinkuhler	.03
125	Lorenzo White	.10
126	Tony Zendejas	.03
127	Jack Pardee (C)	.03
128	Albert Bentley	.03
129	Dean Biasucci	.03
130	Duane Bickett	.03
131	Bill Brooks	.03
132	John Hand	.03
133	Mike Prior	.03
134	Andre Rison (no stripe)	.25
134a	Andre Rison (with stripe)	.50
135	Rohn Stark	.03
136	Donnell Thompson	.03
137	Clarence Verdin	.03
138	Fredd Young	.03
139	Ron Meyer (C)	.03
140	John Alt	.08
141	Steve DeBerg	.03
142	Irv Eatman	.03
143	Dino Hackett	.03
144	Nick Lowery	.03
145	Bill Maas	.03
146	Stephone Paige	.03
147	Neil Smith	.25
148	Marty Schottenheimer (C)	.03
149	Steve Beuerlein	.25
150	Tim Brown	.35
151	Mike Dyal	.03
152	Mervyn Fernandez	.10
152a	Mervyn Fernandez (status corrected to "Drafted 10th round '83")	.10
153	Willie Gault	.03
154	Bob Golic	.03
155	Bo Jackson	.40
156	Don Mosebar	.03
157	Steve Smith	.03
158	Greg Townsend	.03
159	Bruce Wilkerson	.08
160	Steve Wisniewski	.03
161	Art Shell (C)	.10
161a	Art Shell (C, birthdate corrected to 11/26/46)	.10
162	Willie Anderson	.10
163	Greg Bell	.03
164	Henry Ellard	.03
165	Jim Everett	.03
166	Jerry Gray	.03
167	Kevin Greene	.03
168	Pete Holohan	.03
169	Larry Kelm	.08
170	Tom Newberry	.03
171	Vince Newsome	.03
172	Irv Pankey	.03
173	Jackie Slater	.03
174	Fred Strickland	.08
175	Mike Wilcher	.03
176	John Robinson (C)	.03
177	Mark Clayton	.03
178	Roy Foster	.03
179	Harry Galbreath	.08
180	Jim Jensen	.03
181	Dan Marino	.75
182	Louis Oliver	.03
183	Sammie Smith	.03
184	Brian Sochia	.03
185	Don Shula (C)	.03
186	Joey Browner	.03
187	Anthony Carter	.03
188	Chris Doleman	.03
189	Steve Jordan	.03
190	Carl Lee	.03
191	Randall McDaniel	.03
192	Mike Merriweather	.03
193	Keith Millard	.03
194	Al Noga	.03
195	Scott Studwell	.03
196	Henry Thomas	.03
197	Herschel Walker	.03
198	Wade Wilson	.03
199	Gary Zimmerman	.03
200	Jerry Burns (C)	.03
201	Vincent Brown	.15
202	Hart Lee Dykes	.03
203	Sean Farrell	.03
204	Fred Marion (49er with belt)	.05
204a	Fred Marion (corrected)	.05
205	Stanley Morgan	.03
206	Eric Sievers	.03
207	John Stephens	.03
208	Andre Tippett	.03
209	Rod Rust (C)	.03
210	Morten Andersen (name in white on back)	.03
210a	Morten Andersen (corrected)	.10
211	Brad Edelman	.03
212	John Fourcade	.03
213	Dalton Hilliard	.03
214	Rickey Jackson	.03
215	Vaughan Johnson	.03
216	Eric Martin (name in white on back)	.05
216a	Eric Martin (corrected)	.05
217	Sam Mills	.03
218	Pat Swilling	.03
219	Frank Warren	.08
220	Jim Wilks	.03
221	Jim Mora (C, name in white on back)	.03
221a	Jim Mora (C, corrected)	.03
222	Raul Allegre	.03
223	Carl Banks	.03
224	John Elliot	.03
225	Erik Howard	.03
226	Pepper Johnson	.03
227	Leonard Marshall	.03
228	David Meggett	.10
229	Bart Oates	.03
230	Phil Simms	.10
231	Lawrence Taylor	.10
232	Bill Parcells (C)	.03
233	Troy Benson	.03
234	Kyle Clifton	.03
235	Johnny Hector	.03
236	Jeff Lageman	.03
237	Pat Leahy	.03
238	Freeman McNeil	.03
239	Ken O'Brien	.03
240	Al Toon	.03
241	JoJo Townsell	.03
242	Bruce Coslet (C)	.03
243	Eric Allen	.03
244	Jerome Brown	.03
245	Keith Byars	.03
246	Cris Carter	.35
247	Randall Cunningham	.15
248	Keith Jackson	.25
249	Mike Quick	.03
250	Clyde Simmons	.03
251	Andre Waters	.03
252	Reggie White	.15
253	Buddy Ryan (C)	.03
254	Rich Camarillo	.03
255	Earl Ferrell	.03
256	Roy Green	.03
257	Ken Harvey	.08
258	Ernie Jones	.10
259	Tim McDonald	.03
260	Timm Rosenbach	.03
261	Luis Sharpe	.03
262	Vai Sikahema	.03
263	J.T. Smith	.03
264	Ron Wolfley	.03
265	Joe Bugel (C)	.03
266	Gary Anderson	.03
267	Bubby Brister	.10
268	Merril Hoge	.03
269	Carnell Lake	.03
270	Louis Lipps	.03
271	David Little	.03
272	Greg Lloyd	.03
273	Keith Willie	.03
274	Tim Worley	.03
275	Chuck Noll (C)	.03
276	Marion Butts	.06
277	Gill Byrd	.03
278	Vencie Glenn	.03
279	Burt Grossman	.03
280	Gary Plummer	.03
281	Billy Ray Smith	.03
282	Billy Joe Tolliver	.03
283	Dan Henning (C)	.03
284	Harris Barton	.03
285	Michael Carter	.03
286	Mike Cofer	.03
287	Roger Craig	.03
288	Don Griffin	.03
289	Charles Haley	.05
289a	Charles Haley (stats corrected to 5 total fumble recoveries)	.05
290	Pierce Holt	.10
291	Ronnie Lott	.10
292	Guy McIntyre	.03
293	Joe Montana	1.00
294	Tom Rathman	.03
295	Jerry Rice	.75
296	Jesse Sapolu	.05
297	John Taylor	.20
298	Michael Walter	.03
299	George Seifert (C)	.03
300	Jeff Bryant	.03
301	Jacob Green	.03
302	Norm Johnson	.03
303	Bryan Millard	.03
304	Joe Nash	.03
305	Eugene Robinson	.03
306	John L. Williams	.03
307	Dave Wyman	.03
308	Chuck Knox (C)	.03
309	Mark Carrier	.03
310	Paul Gruber	.03
311	Harry Hamilton	.03
312	Bruce Hill	.03
313	Donald Igwebuike	.03
314	Kevin Murphy	.03
315	Ervin Randle	.03
316	Mark Robinson	.03
317	Lars Tate	.03
318	Vinny Testaverde	.03
319	Ray Perkins (C, no name, number on back)	.05
319a	Ray Perkins (C, corrected)	.05
320	Earnest Byner	.03
321	Gary Clark	.15
322	Darryl Grant	.03
323	Darrell Green	.03
324	Jim Lachey	.03
325	Charles Mann	.03
326	Wilber Marshall	.03
327	Ralf Mojsiejenko	.03
328	Art Monk	.03
329	Gerald Riggs	.03
330	Mark Rypien	.10
331	Ricky Sanders	.03
332	Alvin Walton	.03
333	Joe Gibbs (C)	.03
334	Aloha Stadium - PB	.03
335	Brian Blades (PB)	.03
336	James Brooks (PB)	.03
337	Shane Conlan (PB)	.03
338	Eric Dickerson	4.00
339	Ray Donaldson (PB)	.03
340	Ferrell Edmunds	.03
341	Boomer Esiason (PB)	.06
342	David Fulcher (PB)	.03
343	Chris Hinton (PB, no traded stripe)	.05
343a	Chris Hinton (PB, traded)	.05
344	Rodney Holman (PB)	.06
345	Kent Hull (PB)	.03
346	Tunch Ilkin (PB)	.03
347	Mike Johnson (PB)	.03
348	Greg Kragen (PB)	.03
349	Dave Krieg (PB)	.03
350	Albert Lewis (PB)	.03
351	Howie Long (PB)	.03
352	Bruce Matthews	.03
353	Clay Matthews (PB)	.03
354	Erik McMillan (PB)	.03
355	Karl Mecklenburg (PB)	.03
356	Anthony Miller (PB)	.25
357	Frank Minnifield (PB)	.03
358	Max Montoya (PB)	.03
359	Warren Moon (PB)	.08
360	Mike Munchak (PB)	.03
361	Anthony Munoz (PB)	.03
362	John Offerdahl (PB)	.03
363	Christian Okoye (PB)	.03
364	Leslie O'Neal (PB)	.06
365	Rufus Porter (PB)	.03
366	Andre Reed (PB)	.06
367	Johnny Rembert (PB)	.03
368	Reggie Roby (PB)	.03
369	Kevin Ross (PB)	.03
370	Webster Slaughter (PB)	.03
371	Bruce Smith (PB)	.06
372	Dennis Smith (PB)	.03
373	Derrick Thomas (PB)	.06
374	Thurman Thomas (PB)	.25
375	David Treadwell (PB)	.03
376	Lee Williams (PB)	.03
377	Rod Woodson (PB)	.03
378	Bud Carson (PB)	.03
379	Eric Allen (PB)	.03
380	Neal Anderson (PB)	.03
381	Jerry Ball (PB)	.03
382	Joey Browner (PB)	.03
383	Rich Camarillo (PB)	.03
384	Mark Carrier (PB)	.03
385	Roger Craig (PB)	.03
386	Randall Cunningham (PB)	.10
387	Chris Doleman (PB)	.03
388	Henry Ellard (PB)	.03
389	Bill Fralic (PB)	.03
390	Brent Fullwood (PB)	.03
391	Jerry Gray (PB)	.03
392	Kevin Greene (PB)	.03
393	Tim Harris (PB)	.03
394	Jay Hilgenberg (PB)	.03
395	Dalton Hilliard (PB)	.03
396	Keith Jackson (PB)	.08
397	Vaughan Johnson (PB)	.03
398	Steve Jordan (PB)	.03
399	Carl Lee (PB)	.03
400	Ronnie Lott (PB)	.06
401	Don Majkowski (PB)	.03
402	Charles Mann (PB)	.03
403	Randall McDaniel (PB)	.03
404	Tim McDonald (PB)	.03
405	Guy McIntyre (PB)	.03
406	Dave Meggett (PB)	.03
407	Keith Millard (PB)	.03
408	Joe Montana (PB)	.50
409	Eddie Murray (PB)	.03
410	Tom Newberry (PB)	.03
411	Jerry Rice (PB)	.40
412	Mark Rypien (PB)	.03
413	Barry Sanders (PB)	.75
414	Luis Sharpe (PB)	.03
415	Sterling Sharpe (PB)	.20
416	Mike Singletary (PB)	.03
417	Jackie Slater (PB)	.03
418	Doug Smith (PB)	.03
419	Chris Spielman (PB)	.03
420	Pat Swilling (PB)	.03
421	John Taylor (PB)	.10
422	Lawrence Taylor (PB)	.10
423	Reggie White (PB)	.08
424	Ron Wolfley (PB)	.03
425	Gary Zimmerman (PB)	.03
426	John Robinson (PB)	.03
427	Scott Case	.03
428	Mike Kenn	.03
429	Mike Gann	.03
430	Tim Green	.03
431	Michael Haynes	.30
432	Jessie Tuggle	.20
433	John Rade	.03
434	Andre Rison	.25
435	Don Beebe	.03
436	Ray Bentley	.03
437	Shane Conlan	.03
438	Kent Hull	.03
439	Pete Metzelaars	.03
440	Andre Reed	.15
441	Frank Reich	.15
442	Leon Seals	.08
443	Bruce Smith	.03
444	Thurman Thomas	.40
445	Will Wolford	.03
446	Trace Armstrong	.03
447	Mark Bortz	.10
448	Tom Thayer	.10
449	Dan Hampton (DE back)	.05
449a	Dan Hampton (DT back)	.05
451	Dennis Gentry	.03
452	Jim Harbaugh	.10
453	Vestee Jackson	.03
454	Brad Muster	.03
455	William Perry	.03
456	Ron Rivera	.03
457	James Thornton	.03
458	Mike Tomczak	.03
459	Donnell Woolford	.03
460	Eric Ball	.03
461	James Brooks	.03
462	David Fulcher	.03
463	Boomer Esiason	.10
464	Rodney Holman	.03
465	Bruce Kozerski	.03
466	Tim Krumrie	.03
467	Anthony Munoz	.03
468	Mike Baab	.03
469	Brian Brennan	.03
470	Raymond Clayborn	.03
471	Mike Johnson	.03
472	Kevin Mack	.03
473	Clay Matthews	.03
474	Frank Minnifield	.03
475	Gregg Rakoczy	.03
476	Webster Slaughter	.03
477	Felix Wright	.03
478	James Dixon	.03
479	Robert Awalt	.03
480	Dennis McKinnon	.03
481	Danny Noonan	.03
482	Jesse Solomon	.03
483	Danny Stubbs	.03
484	Steve Walsh	.03
485	Michael Brooks	.25
486	Mark Jackson	.03
487	Greg Kragen	.03
488	Ken Lanier	.08
489	Karl Mecklenburg	.03
490	Steve Sewell	.03
491	Dennis Smith	.03
492	David Treadwell	.03
493	Michael Young	.08
494	Robert Clark	.10
495	Dennis Gibson	.03
496	Kevin Glover (C-G back)	.15
496a	Kevin Glover (G back)	.10
497	Mel Gray	.03
498	Rodney Peete	.10
499	Dave Brown	.03
500	Jerry Holmes	.03
501	Chris Jacke	.03
502	Alan Veingrad	.03
503	Mark Lee	.03
504	Tony Mandarich	.03
505	Brian Noble	.03
506	Jeff Query	.03
507	Ken Ruettgers	.03
508	Patrick Allen	.03
509	Curtis Duncan	.03
510	William Fuller	.03
511	Haywood Jeffires	.50
512	Sean Jones	.03
513	Terry Kinard	.03
514	Bruce Matthews	.03
515	Gerald McNeil	.03
516	Greg Montgomery	.08
517	Warren Moon	.03
518	Mike Munchak	.03
519	Allen Pinkett	.03
520	Pat Beach	.03
521	Eugene Daniel	.03
522	Kevin Call	.03
523	Ray Donaldson	.03
524	Jeff Herrod	.03
525	Keith Taylor	.03
526	Jack Trudeau	.03
527	Deron Cherry	.03
528	Jeff Donaldson	.03
529	Albert Lewis	.03
530	Pete Mandley	.03
531	Chris Martin	.08
532	Christian Okoye	.03
533	Steve Pelluer	.03
534	Kevin Ross	.03
535	Dan Saleaumua	.03
536	Derrick Thomas	.25
537	Mike Webster	.03
538	Marcus Allen	.03
539	Greg Bell	.03
540	Thomas Benson	.03
541	Ron Brown	.03
542	Scott Davis	.03
543	Riki Ellison	.03
544	Jamie Holland	.03
545	Howie Long	.03
546	Terry McDaniel	.03
547	Max Montoya	.03
548	Jay Schroeder	.03
549	Lionel Washington	.03
550	Robert Delpino	.03
551	Bobby Humphery	.03
552	Mike Lansford	.03
553	Michael Stewart	.08
554	Doug Smith	.03
555	Curt Warner	.03
556	Alvin Wright	.03
557	Jeff Cross	.03
558	Jeff Dellenbach	.08
559	Mark Duper	.03
560	Ferrell Edmunds	.03
561	Tim McKyer	.03
562	John Offerdahl	.03
563	Reggie Roby	.03
564	Pete Stoyanovich	.03
565	Alfred Anderson	.03
566	Ray Berry	.03
567	Rick Fenney	.03
568	Rich Gannon	.25
569	Tim Irwin	.03
570	Hassan Jones	.03
571	Cris Carter	.30
572	Kirk Lowdermilk	.03
573	Reggie Rutland	.08
574	Ken Stills	.03
575	Bruce Armstrong	.03
576	Irving Fryar	.03
577	Roland James	.03
578	Robert Perryman	.03
579	Cedric Jones	.03
580	Steve Grogan	.03
581	Johnny Rembert	.03
582	Ed Reynolds	.03
583	Brent Williams	.03
584	Marc Wilson	.03
585	Hoby Brenner	.03
586	Stan Brock	.03
587	Jim Dombrowski	.08
588	Joel Hilgenberg	.10
589	Robert Massey	.03
590	Floyd Turner	.10
591	Ottis Anderson	.03
592	Mark Bavaro	.03
593	Maurice Carthon	.03
594	Eric Dorsey	.10
595	Myron Guyton	.03
596	Jeff Hostetler	.75
597	Sean Landeta	.03
598	Lionel Manuel	.03
599	Odessa Turner	.10
600	Perry Williams	.03
601	James Hasty	.03
602	Erik McMillan	.03
603	Alex Gordon	.03
604	Ron Stallworth	.03
605	Byron Evans	.03
606	Ron Heller	.10
607	Wes Hopkins (black, red fumble/interceptions head)	.10
607a	Wes Hopkins (red fumble/interceptions head)	.10
608	Mickey Shuler	.03
609	Seth Joyner	.03
610	Jim McMahon	.03
611	Mike Pitts	.03
612	Izel Jenkins	.03
613	Anthony Bell	.03
614	David Galloway	.03
615	Eric Hill	.03
616	Cedric Mack	.03
617	Freddie Joe Nunn	.03
618	Tootie Robbins	.03
619	Tom Tupa	.10
620	Joe Wolf	.03
621	Dermontti Dawson	.03
622	Thomas Everett	.03
623	Tunch Ilken	.03
624	Hardy Nickerson	.03
625	Gerald Williams	.08
626	Rod Woodson (black, red fumbles/interceptions head)	.25
626a	Rod Woodson (red fumbles/interceptions head)	.25
627	Rod Bernstine (error TE)	.03
627a	Rod Bernstine (corrected RB)	.15
628	Courtney Hall	.03
629	Ronnie Harmon	.03
630	Anthony Miller (WR back)	.25
630a	Anthony Miller (WR-KR back)	.20
630b	Anthony Miller (WR-KR back, front)	.20

631 Joe Philips .03
632 Leslie O'Neal (LB-DE front) .20
632a Leslie O'Neal (LB front) .15
633 David Richards (G-T back) .05
633a David Richards (G back) .05
634 Mark Vlasic .08
635 Lee Williams .03
636 Chet Brooks .03
637 Keena Turner .03
638 Kevin Fagan .03
639 Brent Jones .70
640 Matt Millen .03
641 Bubba Paris .03
642 Bill Romanowski .10
643 Fred Smerlas .03
644 Dave Waymer .03
645 Steve Young .40
646 Brian Blades .10
647 Andy Heck .03
648 Dave Krieg .03
649 Rufus Porter .03
650 Kelly Stouffer .03
651 Tony Woods .03
652 Gary Anderson .03
653 Reuben Davis .03
654 Randy Grimes .03
655 Ron Hall .03
656 Eugene Marve .03
657 Curt Jarvis (no "Official NFL card") .05
657a Curt Jarvis ("Official NFL card" added) .05
658 Ricky Reynolds .03
659 Broderick Thomas .03
660 Jeff Bostic .03
661 Todd Bowles .10
662 Ravin Caldwell .03
663 Russ Grimm .03
664 Joe Jacoby .03
665 Mark May .03
666 Walter Stanley .03
667 Don Warren .03
668 Stan Humphries .75
669 Jeff George (Illinois) 1.00
670 Blair Thomas (R1) .10
671 Cortez Kennedy .25
672 Keith McCants (R1) .08
673 Junior Seau 1.00
674 Mark Carrier (R1) .25
675 Andre Ware (R1) .10
676 Chris Singleton (R1) .15
677 Richmond Webb (R1) .15
678 Ray Agnew (R1) .10
679 Anthony Smith .30
680 James Francis (R1) .10
681 Percy Snow (R1) .10
682 Renaldo Turnbull (R1) .35
683 Lamar Lathon (R1) .10
684 James Williams (R1) .10
685 Emmitt Smith 3.00
686 Tony Bennett (R1) .25
687 Darrell Thompson .20
688 Steve Broussard (R1) .08
689 Eric Green .25
690 Ben Smith (R1) .08
691 Bern Brostek (R1) .08
692 Rodney Hampton 1.25
693 Dexter Carter (R1) .10
694 Rob Moore 1.50
695 Alexander Wright (R2) .20
696 Darion Conner (R2) .10
697 Reggie Rembert (R2)
698 Terry Wooden (R2, back number 51) .05
698a Terry Wooden (R2, back number 90) .05
699 Reggie Cobb .60
700 Anthony Thompson (R2) .03
701 Fred Washington (R2) .05
701a Fred Washington (R2) (Final Update memorial) .05
702 Ron Cox (R2) .10
703 Robert Blackmon (R2) .10
704 Dan Owens (R2) .10
705 Anthony Johnson (R2) .15
706 Aaron Wallace (R2) .15
707 Harold Green .35
708 Keith Sims (R2) .10
709 Tim Grunhard (R2) .10
710 Jeff Alm (R2) .03
711 Carwell Gardner (R2) .10
712 Ken Davidson (R2) .10
713 Vince Buck (R2) .03
714 Leroy Hoard (R2) .50
715 Andre Collins (R2) .08
716 Dennis Brown (R2) .03
717 Leroy Butler .20
718 Pat Terrell (R2, back number 41) .20

718a Pat Terrell (R2, back number 37) .10
719 Mike Bellamy (R2) .03
720 Mike Fox (R2) .08
721 Alton Montgomery (R2) .08
722 Eric Davis (R2) .08
723 Oliver Barnett (PR, DT front) .30
723a Oliver Barnett (PR, NT front) .10
724 Houston Hoover (PR) .08
725 Howard Ballard (PR) .08
726 Keith McKeller (PR) .08
727 Wendell Davis .10
728 Peter Tom Willis (PR) .10
729 Bernard Clark (PR) .03
730 Doug Widell (PR) .10
731 Eric Andolsek (PR) .03
732 Jeff Campbell (PR) .08
733 Marc Spindler (PR) .08
734 Keith Woodside .03
735 Willis Peguese (PR) .08
736 Frank Stams (PR) .03
737 Jeff Uhlenhake (PR) .03
738 Todd Kalis (PR) .03
739 Tom Hodson (PR) .03
740 Greg McMurtry (PR) .03
741 Mike Buck (PR) .03
742 Kevin Haverdink (PR) .03
743 Johnny Bailey (PR, back number 46) .50
743a Johnny Bailey (PR, back number 22) .25
744 Eric Moore (PR, no prospect stripe) .10
744a Eric Moore (PR, stripe added) .10
745 Tony Stargell (PR) .08
746 Fred Barnett .60
747 Walter Reeves (PR) .03
748 Derek Hill (PR) .03
749 Quinn Early (PR) .35
750 Ronald Lewis (PR) .05
751 Ken Clark (PR) .05
752 Garry Lewis (PR) .03
753 James Lofton .03
754 Jim Morrissey .03
755 Jim Shofner .03
756 Jimmie Jones .10
757 Jay Novacek .40
758 Jessie Hester .20
759 Barry Word .30
760 Eddie Anderson .08
761 Cleveland Gary .08
762 Marcus Dupree .03
763 David Griggs .08
764 Rueben Mayes .08
765 Stephen Baker .03
766 Reyna Thompson .03
767 Everson Walls .03
768 Brad Baxter .25
769 Steve Walsh .03
770 Heath Sherman .20
771 Johnny Johnson .10
772 Dexter Manley .03
773 Rickey Proehl .50
774 Frank Cornish .03
775 Tommy Kane .10
776 Derrick Fenner .10
777 Steve Christie .10
778 Wayne Haddix .08
779 Richard Williamson .03
780 Brian Mitchell .50
781 American Bowl London .03
782 American Bowl Berlin .03
783 American Bowl Tokyo .03
784 American Bowl Montreal .03
785 Paul Tagliabue (NR, "peered through the Berlin Wall") .05
785a Paul Tagliabue (NR, "posed at the Berlin Wall") .05
786 Al Davis (NR) .10
787 Jerry Glanville (NR) .03
788 WLF (NR) .03
789 Overseas (NR) .03
790 Mike Mularkey (PC) .03
791 Gary Reasons (PC) .03
792 Maurice Hurst, Drew Hill (PC) .03
793 Ronnie Lott (PC) .03
794 Barry Sanders, Felix Wright (PC) .75
795 George Seifert (PC) .03
796 Doug Smith (PC) .03
797 Doug Widell (PC) .03
798 Cris Carter, Todd Bowles (PC) .03
799 Ronnie Lott (Stay in School) .03
800 Mark Carrier (ROY), Emmitt Smith (ROY) 1.00

SC3 Joe Robbie Stadium 1.00
CC2 Paul Tagliabue 1.00
NNO Lombardi Trophy (2-9,999) 50.00
SC2 Santa Claus 1.00
SC Super Pro 1.00
NNO Super Bowl XXIVB logo .30
SP1 Payne Stewart 1.00

1990 Pro Set Super Bowl MVPs

These 1990 Pro Set Series II inserts feature the 24 players who were named MVP of a Super Bowl. Each card front has a portrait of the player done by artist Merv Corning. Two silver panels are also on the front, one on top, the other at the bottom. The player's name is in the bottom panel, which is bordered by two stripes featuring the player's team colors. The horizontal card back has a color action photo and summary of the player's Super Bowl achievement. The cards are numbered in a chronological manner, beginning with Super Bowl I.

		MT
Complete Set (24):		4.00
Common Player:		.10
1	Super Bowl I (Bart Starr)	.30
2	Super Bowl II (Bart Starr)	.30
3	Super Bowl III (Joe Namath)	.50
4	Super Bowl IV (Len Dawson)	.20
5	Super Bowl V (Chuck Howley)	.10
6	Super Bowl VI (Roger Staubach)	.50
7	Super Bowl VII (Jake Scott)	.10
8	Super Bowl VIII (Larry Csonka)	.30
9	Super Bowl IX (Franco Harris)	.30
10	Super Bowl X (Lynn Swann)	.20
11	Super Bowl XI (Fred Biletnikoff)	.20
12	Super Bowl XII (Harvey Martin)	.10
13	Super Bowl XIII (Terry Bradshaw)	.20
14	Super Bowl XIV (Terry Bradshaw)	.40
15	Super Bowl XV (Jim Plunkett)	.20
16	Super Bowl XVI (Joe Montana)	.50
17	Super Bowl XVII (John Riggins)	.20
18	Super Bowl XVIII (Marcus Allen)	.10
19	Super Bowl XIX (Joe Montana)	.50
20	Super Bowl XX (Richard Dent)	.10
21	Super Bowl XXI (Phil Simms)	.20
22	Super Bowl XXII (Doug Williams)	.10
23	Super Bowl XXIII (Jerry Rice)	.30
24	Super Bowl XXIV (Joe Montana)	.50

1990 Pro Set Collect-A-Books

These 2-1/2" x 3-1/2" 8-page booklets were issued in three series of 12. Each series came in its own box, and included one player who was a rookie. The front of the booklet has an action photo of the player, along with his name, and set logos. Page two has a color mug shot of the player; pages 3-4 provide a career summary in text form. Pages 6-7 are a double-page action photo of the player; page 8 has statistics and trademark information. Two players who have booklets - Eric Dickerson and Michael Dean Perry - were not included in Pro Set's regular 1990 card set.

		MT
Complete Set (36):		7.50
Common Player:		.15
1	Jim Kelly	.50
2	Andre Ware	.20
3	Phil Simms	.25
4	Bubby Brister	.20
5	Bernie Kosar	.25
6	Eric Dickerson	.25
7	Barry Sanders	.75
8	Jerry Rice	1.00
9	Keith Millard	.15
10	Erik McMillan	.15
11	Ickey Woods	.15
12	Mike Singletary	.25
13	Randall Cunningham	.30
14	Boomer Esiason	.25
15	John Elway	.25
16	Wade Wilson	.20
17	Troy Aikman	1.50
18	Dan Marino	1.50
19	Lawrence Taylor	.35

1990 Pro Set Theme Art

The 25-card set spotlights Super Bowl theme art on the front, which resembles the cover art of Super Bowl programs. The Pro Set logo is in the lower left, with the Super Bowl listed in the lower right, with the site and city name listed beneath. Card backs include a photo of the winning team's championship ring. The Super Bowl number and date, along with the score, are listed at the top, with background text also included. The cards were seeded one per 1990 Pro Set Series 1 pack.

		MT
Complete Set (25):		3.00
Common Player:		.15
1	Super Bowl I	.15
2	Super Bowl II	.15
3	Super Bowl III	.15
4	Super Bowl IV	.15
5	Super Bowl V	.15
6	Super Bowl VI	.15
7	Super Bowl VII	.15
8	Super Bowl VIII	.15
9	Super Bowl IX	.15
10	Super Bowl X	.15
11	Super Bowl XI	.15
12	Super Bowl XII	.15
13	Super Bowl XIII UER (Colgate University 7, sould be Colgate 13)	.15
14	Super Bowl XIV	.15
15	Super Bowl XV	.15
16	Super Bowl XVI	.15
17	Super Bowl XVII	.15
18	Super Bowl XVIII	.15
19	Super Bowl XIX	.15
20	Super Bowl XX	.15
21	Super Bowl XXI	.15
22A	Super Bowl XXII ERR (Jan. 31, 1989 on back)	.50
22B	Super Bowl XXII COR (Jan. 31, 1988 on back)	
23	Super Bowl XXIII	.15
24	Super Bowl XXIV	.15
	Theme Art	

1990 Pro Set Pro Bowl 106

Participants in the annual Pro Bowl game are honored in this 106-card set produced by Pro Set. The set includes a white binder which features the Pro Bowl game logo on the front cover. The cards, except for four, are identical to their corresponding numbered counterparts in the regular set; there is no indication they were in the Pro Bowl set. However, four players who are featured in the Final Update set have "1990 Final Update" on the front (#s 754, 766, 771 and 778). This is not written on the fronts of the regular update cards.

		MT
Complete Set (106):		10.00
Common Player:		.03
20	Roger Craig	.25
21	Merril Hoge	.15
22	Christian Okoye	.15
23	Blair Thomas	.30
24	William Perry	.20
25	Bill Fralic	.15
26	Warren Moon	.30
27	Jim Everett	.20
28	Jeff George	.50
29	Shane Conlan	.15
30	Carl Banks	.15
31	Charles Mann	.15
32	Anthony Munoz	.25
33	Dan Hampton	.15
34	Michael Dean Perry	.15
35	Joey Browner	.15
36	Ken O'Brien	.20
39	Cornelius Bennett	.10
40	Jim Kelly	.25
49	Neal Anderson	.05
52	Richard Dent	.05
53	Jay Hilgenberg	.03
57	Mike Singletary	.08
86	Steve Atwater	.05
91	Bobby Humphrey	.03
96	Jerry Ball	.03
98	Lomas Brown	.03
102	Barry Sanders	1.00
114	Sterling Sharpe	.75
118	Ray Childress	.05
119	Ernest Givins	.05
122	Drew Hill	.05
135	Rohn Stark	.03
137	Clarence Verdin	.03
144	Nick Lowery	.03
155	Bo Jackson	.40
156	Don Mosebar	.05
158	Greg Townsend	.05
160	Steve Wisniewski	.03
173	Jackie Slater	.05
186	Joey Browner	.05
188	Chris Doleman	.05
190	Carl Lee	.03
191	Randall McDaniel	.05
210	Morten Andersen	.05
215	Vaughan Johnson	.03
226	Pat Swilling	.05
229	Pepper Johnson	.03
231	Lawrence Taylor	.15
244	Jerome Brown	.03
247	Randall Cunningham	.15
248	Keith Jackson	.15
252	Reggie White	.25
271	David Little	.03
276	Marion Butts	.10
289	Charles Haley	.05
291	Ronnie Lott	.10
292	Guy McIntyre	.03
293	Joe Montana	1.00
295	Jerry Rice	.75
320	Earnest Byner	.03
321	Gary Clark	.05
323	Darrell Green	.05
324	Jim Lachey	.03
334	Pro Bowl Aloha Stadium	.03
434	Andre Rison	.25
438	Kent Hull	.03
440	Andre Reed	.15
443	Bruce Smith	.10
444	Thurman Thomas	.25
447	Mark Bortz	.03
464	David Fulcher	.03
467	Rodney Holman	.03
477	Anthony Munoz	.10
490	Dennis Smith	.03
497	Mel Gray	.05
517	Bruce Matthews	.03
526	Warren Moon	.25
534	Albert Lewis	.05
553	Kevin Ross	.03
557	Derrick Thomas	.20
560	Jeff Cross	.03
562	Ferrell Edmunds	.03
575	John Offerdahl	.05
587	Bruce Armstrong	.03
597	Sean Landeta	.03
626	Rod Woodson	.20
630	Anthony Miller	.10
632	Leslie O'Neal	.05
677	Richmond Webb	.05
754	Steve Tasker	8.00
766	Reyna Thompson	.08
771	Johnny Johnson	12.00
778	Wayne Haddix	8.00
SB1	Super Bowl I	.15
SB2	Super Bowl II	.15
SB3	Super Bowl III	.15
SB4	Super Bowl IV	.15
SB5	Super Bowl V	.15
SB6	Super Bowl VI	.15
SB7	Super Bowl VII	.15
SB8	Super Bowl VIII	.15
SB9	Super Bowl IX	.15
SB10	Super Bowl X	.15
SB11	Super Bowl XI	.15
SB12	Super Bowl XII	.15
SB13	Super Bowl XIII	.15
SB14	Super Bowl XIV	.15
SB15	Super Bowl XV	.15
SB16	Super Bowl XVI	.15
SB17	Super Bowl XVII	.15
SB18	Super Bowl XVIII	.15
SB19	Super Bowl XIX	.15
SB20	Super Bowl XX	.15
SB21	Super Bowl XXI	.15
SB22	Super Bowl XXII	.15
SB23	Super Bowl XXIII	.15
SB24	Super Bowl XXIV	.15

1990 Pro Set Super Bowl 160

This set was issued in its own commemorative box and traces the history of the Super Bowl in four categories - Super Bowl Tickets, Super Bowl Supermen, Super Bowl Super Moments, and puzzle cards, which make up art for Super Bowl XXV. Cards were also sold in packs of eight and were originally given away at Texas Stadium during the Dallas Cowboys Pro Set Sports Collectors Show.

		MT
Complete Set (160):		5.00
Common Player:		.05
Common Puzzle:		.03
1	SB 1 Ticket	.10
2	SB II Ticket	.05
3	SB III Ticket	.05
4	SB IV Ticket	.05
5	SB V Ticket	.05
6	SB VI Ticket	.05
7	SB VII Ticket	.05
8	SB VIII Ticket	.05
9	SB IX Ticket	.05
10	SB X Ticket	.05
11	SB XI Ticket	.05
12	SB XII Ticket	.05
13	SB XIII Ticket	.05
14	SB XIV Ticket	.05
15	SB XV Ticket	.05
16	SB XVI Ticket	.05
17	SB XVII Ticket	.05
18	SB XVIII Ticket	.05
19	SB XIX Ticket	.05
20	SB XX Ticket	.05
21	SB XXI Ticket	.05
22	SB XXII Ticket	.05
23	SB XXIII Ticket	.05
24	SB XXIV Ticket	.05
25	Tom Flores (CO)	.05
26	Joe Gibbs (CO)	.05
27	Tom Landry (CO)	.15
28	Vince Lombardi (CO)	.15
29	Chuck Noll (CO)	.10
30	Don Shula (CO)	.15
31	Bill Walsh (CO)	.15
32	Terry Bradshaw	.25
33	Joe Montana	.50
34	Joe Namath	.35
35	Jim Plunkett	.20
36	Bart Starr	.20
37	Roger Staubach	.35
38	Marcus Allen	.20
39	Roger Craig	.10

40	Larry Csonka	.10
41	Franco Harris	.10
42	John Riggins	.10
43	Timmy Smith	.05
44	Matt Snell	.05
45	Fred Biletnikoff	.10
46	Cliff Branch	.05
47	Max McGee	.10
48	Jerry Rice	.50
49	Ricky Sanders	.05
50	George Sauer	.05
51	John Stallworth	.10
52	Lynn Swann	.15
53	Dave Casper	.05
54	Marv Fleming	.05
55	Dan Ross	.05
56	Forrest Gregg	.10
57	Winston Hill	.05
58	Joe Jacoby	.05
59	Anthony Munoz	.10
60	Art Shell	.05
61	Rayfield Wright	.05
62	Ron Yary	.05
63	Randy Cross	.05
64	Jerry Kramer	.10
65	Bob Kuechenberg	.05
66	Larry Little	.05
67	Gerry Mullins	.05
68	John Niland	.05
69	Gene Upshaw	.10
70	Dave Dalby	.05
71	Jim Langer	.05
72	Dwight Stephenson	.05
73	Mike Webster	.10
74	Ross Browner	.05
75	Willie Davis	.10
76	Richard Dent	.10
77	L.C. Greenwood	.10
78	Ed "Too Tall" Jones	.10
79	Harvey Martin	.05
80	Dwight White	.05
81	Buck Buchanan	.10
82	Curley Culp	.05
83	Manny Fernandez	.05
84	Joe Greene	.15
85	Bob Lilly	.15
86	Alan Page	.15
87	Randy White	.10
88	Nick Buoniconti	.10
89	Lee Roy Jordan	.05
90	Jack Lambert	.15
91	Willie Lanier	.10
92	Ray Nitschke	.15
93	Mike Singletary	.15
94	Carl Banks	.05
95	Charles Haley	.05
96	Jack Ham	.10
97	Ted Hendricks	.10
98	Chuck Howley	.05
99	Rod Martin	.05
100	Herb Adderley	.10
101	Mel Blount	.10
102	Willie Brown	.10
103	Lester Hayes	.05
104	Mike Haynes	.05
105	Ronnie Lott	.15
106	Mel Renfro	.05
107	Eric Wright	.05
108	Dick Anderson	.05
109	David Fulcher	.05
110	Cliff Harris	.05
111	Johnny Robinson	.05
112	Jake Scott	.05
113	Donnie Shell	.05
114	Mike Wagner	.05
115	Willie Wood	.10
116	Ray Guy	.10
117	Lee Johnson	.05
118	Larry Seiple	.05
119	Jerrel Wilson	.05
120	Kevin Butler	.05
121	Don Chandler	.05
122	Jan Stenerud	.10
123	Jim Turner	.05
124	Ray Wersching	.05
125	Larry Anderson	.05
126	Stanford Jennings	.05
127	Mike Nelms	.05
128	John Taylor	.10
129	Fulton Walker	.05
130	E.J. Holub	.05
131	George Siefert CO	.05
132	Jim Taylor	.10
133	Joe Theismann	.15
134	Johnny Unitas	.25
135	Reggie Williams	.05
136	Two Networks (Paul Christman, Frank Gifford)	.05
137	First Fly-Over (Military jets)	.05
138	Weeb Ewbank (Super Bowl Super Moment)	.05
139	Otis Taylor (Super Bowl Super Moment)	.05
140	Jim O'Brien (Super Bowl Super Moment)	.05
141	Garo Yepremian (Super Bowl Super Moment)	.05
142	(Pete Rozelle, Art Rooney)	.05
143	Percy Howard (Super Bowl Super Moment)	.05
144	Jackie Smith (Super Bowl Super Moment)	.05
145	Record Crowd (Super Bowl Super Moment)	.05
146	Yellow Ribbon UER (Fourth line says more than year, should say more than a year)	.05
147	(Dan Bunz, Charles Alexander) (Super Bowl Super Moment)	.05
148	Smurfs (Redskins) (Super Bowl Super Moment)	.05
149	(William "The Fridge" Perry) (Scores, Super Bowl Super Moment)	.05
150	Phil McConkey (Super Bowl Super Moment)	.05
151	Doug Williams (Super Bowl Super Moment)	.05
152	Top row left	.03
153	Top row middle XXV Theme Art Puzzle	.03
154	Top row left XXV Theme Art Puzzle	.03
155	Center row left XXV Theme Art Puzzle	.03
156	Center row right XXV Theme Art Puzzle	.03
157	Center row right XXV Theme Art Puzzle	.03
158	Bottom row left VVX Theme Art Puzzle	.03
159	Bottom row right XXV Theme Art Puzzle	.03
160	Bottom row right XXV Theme Art Puzzle	.03
	Special Offer Card	.10

1990 Pro Set Super Bowl Binder

This 56-card set, with Buick as its sponsor, was given to those who attended Super Bowl XXV between the New York Giants and Buffalo Bills. Included within the set are a cover card for Buick, a commemorative card for the 2-millionth Super Bowl fan, cards for the NFC and AFC Championship trophies, and a Ronnie Lott Stay in School card from Pro Set's Final Update set. Players from the two participating Super Bowl teams are featured in the set, along with 27 cards featuring fans' choices for the Silver Anniversary Super Bowl Team. Super Bowl participants' cards have the same photos as their counterparts in the regular set, but have NFC or AFC Champions designated on the front. A binder with pages that hold four cards per page was also issued to store the cards in.

		MT
	Complete Set (56):	25.00
	Common Player:	.25
1	Vince Lombardi	.35
2	Joe Montana	4.00
3	Larry Csonka	.50
4	Franco Harris	.50
5	Jerry Rice	3.00
6	Lynn Swann	.50
7	Forrest Gregg	.35
8	Art Shell	.35
9	Jerry Kramer	.25
10	Gene Upshaw	.35
11	Mike Webster	.35
12	Dave Casper	.25
13	Jan Stenerud	.35
14	John Taylor	.35
15	L.C. Greenwood	.25
16	Ed "Too Tall" Jones	.35
17	Joe Greene	.50
18	Randy White	.50
19	Jack Lambert	.50
20	Mike Singletary	.35
21	Jack Ham	.35
22	Ted Hendricks	.35
23	Mel Blount	.35
24	Ronnie Lott	.50
25	Donnie Shell	.25
26	Willie Wood	.35
27	Ray Guy	.35

SC1	2,000,000th Fan	.50
SC2	Buick Checklist Card	.50
SC3	Lamar Hunt Trophy	.50
SC4	George Halas Trophy	.50
799	Ronnie Lott Education	.35
39	Cornelius Bennett	.50
40	Jim Kelly	1.50
47	Darryl Talley	.25
48	Marv Levy (CO)	.25
437	Shane Conlan	.25
438	Kent Hull	.25
440	Andre Reed	1.00
443	Bruce Smith	1.00
444	Thurman Thomas	2.50
725	Howard Ballard	.25
753	James Lofton	.50
754	Steve Tasker	.25
223	Carl Banks	.25
226	Pepper Johnson	.25
228	Dave Meggett	.25
230	Phil Simms	.25
231	Lawrence Taylor	.75
232	Bill Parcells (CO)	.35
591	Ottis Anderson	.50
592	Mark Bavaro	.25
596	Jeff Hostetler	.35
692	Rodney Hampton	1.00
765	Stephen Baker	.25
766	Reyna Thompson	.25

1991 Pro Set Draft Day

These cards, issued in conjunction with the 1991 NFL draft, create different scenarios regarding the first selection in the draft. Each card is numbered 694 and features the player in his collegiate uniform. The card back is in a horizontal format and has another player photo on it, plus biographical information and statistics.

		MT
	Complete Set (8):	250.00
	Common Player:	20.00
694A	Nick Bell	25.00
694B	Mike Croel	25.00
694C	Raghib (Rocket) Ismail (Cowboys)	65.00
694D	Raghib (Rocket) Ismail (Falcons)	50.00
694E	Raghib (Rocket) Ismail (Patriots)	50.00
694F	Todd Lyght	20.00
694G	Russell Maryland	25.00
694H	Dan McGwire	30.00

1991 Pro Set Promos

These six promotional cards were distributed in various manners. Each is unnumbered. The Kids on the Block card was given away during the Super Bowl XXV Football Clinic, which featured NFL stars talking about drug education. The card was sponsored by Pro Set, Sports Illustrated for Kids and The Learning Channel, which broadcast the clinic. The Super Bowl XXV Card Show II card is similiar to the Card Show I issued in 1989, except the front gives the date of the second card show, which occurred Jan. 24-27, 1991. The cards for William Roberts and Michael Dean Perry (there were two versions for the Perry card) were intended to be in the previously issued Pro Bowl set, but were withdrawn. The Emmitt Smith card was a mail-in offer through the Pro Set Gazette, a quarterly publication designed to provide an overview of the hobby to young collectors.

		MT
	Complete Set (6):	150.00
	Common Player:	2.00
NNO	NLF Kids on the Block (Tele-clinic)	2.00
NNO	Super Bowl XXV (Card Show II)	5.00
NNO	Michael Dean Perry Pro Bowl (unnumbered, with Pro Set logo)	75.00
NNO	Michael Dean Perry Pro Bowl (unnumbered, without Pro Set logo)	50.00
NNO	William Roberts Pro Bowl (unnumbered)	50.00
NNO	Emmitt Smith Gazette (Pro Set Gazette)	4.00
----	Pro Bowl Special (Michael Dean Perry)	50.00
----	Pro Bowl Special (Michael Dean Perry) (with Pro Set logo)	75.00
----	Pro Bowl Special (William Roberts)	50.00
----	Gazette (Emmitt Smith) (Given away with pro Set Gazette mail-ou t)	3.00

1991 Pro Set

Released in late April, Pro Set's third annual football set was again divided into two series. Subsets added this year to Series I include Heisman Heroes, Super Bowl XXV Replay, NFL Officials, and Think About It messages. World League of American Football cards made their debut in Series I as well. Again, randomly-packed insert cards were included in Series I: Super Bowl XXV logo, Walter Payton and Team 34, a mini Pro Set Gazette, Red Grange, Russell Maryland 31 Draft Pick (only in Series I), and 1,000 autographed Lawrence Taylor cards. (Key: L - leader, M - milestone, HOF - Hall of Fame, AW - college award winner, HH - Heisman hero, SBR - Super Bowl XXV replay, R - 1990 replay, NR - newsreel, O - official, M - NFL message, NFC - all-NFC team, C - coach).

		MT
	Complete Set (850):	18.00
	Complete Series 1 (405):	7.00
	Complete Series 2 (407):	7.00
	Complete Final (38):	4.00
	Common Player:	.03
	Series 1 Wax Box:	5.00
	Series 2 Wax Box:	8.00
1	Emmitt Smith (LL)	1.00
2	Mark Carrier (LL)	.25
3	Joe Montana (LL)	.50
4	Art Shell (LL)	.03
5	Mike Singletary (LL)	.03
6	Bruce Smith (LL)	.04
7	Barry Word (LL)	.03
8	Jim Kelly (LL, with NFLPA logo)	.25
8a	Jim Kelly (LL, without NFLPA logo)	.20
8b	Jim Kelly (LL, without NFLPA logo, with registered symbol)	6.00
9	Warren Moon (LL)	.08
10	Barry Sanders (LL)	.50
11	Jerry Rice (LL)	.40
12	Jay Novacek (LL)	.05
13	Thurman Thomas (LL)	.20
14	Nick Lowery (LL)	.03
15	Mike Horan (LL)	.03
16	Clarence Verdin (LL)	.03
17	Kevin Clark (LL)	.03
18	Mark Carrier (LL)	.03
19	Derrick Thomas (LL, error: Bills helmet on front)	15.00
19a	Derrick Thomas (LL, corrected: Chiefs helmet on front)	.25
20	Ottis Anderson (M)	.03
21	Roger Craig (M)	.03
22	Art Monk (M)	.05
23	Chuck Noll (M)	.03
24	Randall Cunningham (M)	.08
25	Dan Marino (M)	.40
26	Charles Haley (M)	.03
27	Earl Campbell (HOF)	.10
28	John Hannah (HOF)	.03
29	Stan Jones (HOF)	.03
30	Tex Schramm (HOF)	.03
31	Jan Stenerud (HOF)	.03
32	Russell Maryland (AW)	.40
33	Chris Zorich (AW)	.15
34	Darryl Lewis (AW)	.03
35	Alfred Williams (AW)	.08
36	Raghib Ismail (AW)	1.00
37	Ty Detmer (HH)	1.00
38	Andre Ware (HH)	.05
39	Barry Sanders (HH)	.50
40	Tim Brown (HH)	.05
41	Vinny Testaverde (HH)	.03
42	Bo Jackson (HH)	.15
43	Mike Rozier (HH)	.03
44	Herschel Walker (HH)	.03
45	Marcus Allen (HH)	.04
46	James Lofton (SBR, with NFLPA logo)	.05
46a	James Lofton (SBR, NFLPA logo removed)	.08
47	Bruce Smith (SBR, "Official NFL Card" in white)	.15
47a	Bruce Smith (SBR, "Official NFL Card" in black)	.10
48	Myron Guyton (SBR)	.03
49	Stephen Baker (SBR)	.03
50	Mark Ingram (SBR)	.03
51	O.J. Anderson (SBR)	.03
52	Thurman Thomas (SBR)	.20
53	Matt Bahr (SBR)	.03
54	Scott Norwood (SBR)	.03
55	Stephen Baker	.03
56	Carl Banks	.03
57	Mark Collins	.03
58	Steve DeOssie	.03
59	Eric Dorsey	.03
60	John Elliott	.03
61	Myron Guyton	.03
62	Rodney Hampton	.50
63	Jeff Hostetler	.15
64	Erik Howard	.03
65	Mark Ingram	.03
66	Greg Jackson	.08
67	Leonard Marshall	.03
68	David Meggett	.03
69	Eric Moore	.03
70	Bart Oates	.03
71	Gary Reasons	.03
72	Bill Parcells (C)	.03
73	Howard Ballard	.03
74	Cornelius Bennett (with NFLPA logo)	.25
74a	Cornelius Bennett (NFLPA logo removed)	.10
75	Shane Conlan	.03
76	Kent Hull	.03
77	Kirby Jackson	.03
78	Jim Kelly (w/o logo)	.35
79	Mark Kelso	.03
80	Nate Odomes	.03
81	Andre Reed	.08
82	Jim Ritcher	.03
83	Bruce Smith	.03
84	Darryl Talley	.03
85	Steve Tasker	.03
86	Thurman Thomas	.35
87	James Williams	.03
88	Will Wolford	.03
89	Jeff Wright	.03
90	Marv Levy (C)	.03
91	Steve Broussard	.03
92	Darion Conner (error: "Drafted 1st Round '99")	6.00
92a	Darion Conner (corrected: "Drafted 2nd Round '90")	.15
93	Bill Fralic	.03
94	Tim Green	.03
95	Michael Haynes	.03
96	Chris Hinton	.03
97	Chris Miller	.03
98	Deion Sanders	.20
99	Jerry Glanville (C)	.03
100	Kevin Butler	.03
101	Mark Carrier (Chi.)	.03
102	Jim Covert	.03
103	Richard Dent	.03
104	Jim Harbaugh	.08
105	Brad Muster	.03
106	Lemuel Stinson	.03
107	Keith Van Horne	.03
108	Mike Ditka (C)	.05
109	Lewis Billups	.03
110	James Brooks	.03
111	Boomer Esiason	.10
112	James Francis	.03
113	David Fulcher	.03
114	Rodney Holman	.03
115	Tim McGee	.03
116	Anthony Munoz	.03
117	Sam Wyche (C)	.03
118	Paul Farren	.03
119	Thane Gash	.03
120	Mike Johnson	.03
121	Bernie Kosar (with NFLPA logo)	.05
121a	Bernie Kosar (NFLPA logo removed)	.10
122	Clay Matthews	.03
123	Eric Metcalf	.03
124	Frank Minnifield	.03
125	Webster Slaughter (with NFLPA logo)	.05
125a	Webster Slaughter (NFLPA logo removed)	.05
126	Bill Belichick (C)	.03
127	Tommie Agee	.03
128	Troy Aikman	1.00
129	Jack Del Rio	.03
130	John Gesek	.06
131	Issiac Holt	.03
132	Michael Irvin	.55
133	Ken Norton	.03
134	Daniel Stubbs	.03
135	Jimmy Johnson (C)	.05
136	Steve Atwater (AW)	.03
137	Michael Brooks	.03
138	John Elway	.35
139	Wymon Henderson	.03
140	Bobby Humphrey	.03
141	Mark Jackson	.03
142	Karl Mecklenburg	.03
143	Doug Widell	.03
144	Dan Reeves (C)	.03
145	Eric Andolsek	.03
146	Jerry Ball	.03
147	Bennie Blades	.03
148	Lomas Brown	.03
149	Robert Clark	.03
150	Michael Cofer	.03
151	Dan Owens	.03
152	Rodney Peete	.03
153	Wayne Fontes (C)	.03
154	Tim Harris	.03
155	Johnny Holland	.03
156	Don Majkowski	.03
157	Tony Mandarich	.03
158	Mark Murphy	.03
159	Brian Noble	.03
160	Jeff Query	.03
161	Sterling Sharpe	.20
162	Lindy Infante (C)	.03
163	Ray Childress	.03
164	Ernest Givins	.03
165	Richard Johnson	.03
166	Bruce Matthews	.03
167	Warren Moon	.15
168	Mike Munchak	.03
169	Al Smith	.03
170	Lorenzo White	.08
171	Jack Pardee (C)	.03
172	Albert Bentley	.03
173	Duane Bickett	.03
174	Bill Brooks	.03
175	Eric Dickerson (with NFLPA logo)	.50
175a	Eric Dickerson (NFLPA logo removed, error text: 667)	1.25
175b	Eric Dickerson (NFLPA logo removed, corrected text: 677))	.25
176	Ray Donaldson	.03
177	Jeff George	.20
178	Jeff Herrod	.03
179	Clarence Verdin	.03
180	Ron Meyer (C)	.03
181	John Alt	.03
182	Steve DeBerg	.03
183	Albert Lewis	.03
184	Nick Lowery	.03
185	Christian Okoye	.03
186	Stephone Paige	.03
187	Kevin Porter	.03
188	Derrick Thomas	.15
189	Marty Schottenheimer (C)	.03
190	Willie Gault	.03
191	Howie Long	.03
192	Terry McDaniel	.03
193	Jay Schroeder	.03
194	Steve Smith	.03
195	Greg Townsend	.03
196	Lionel Washington	.03
197	Steve Wisniewski	.03
198	Art Shell (C)	.03
199	Henry Ellard	.03
200	Jim Everett	.03
201	Jerry Gray	.03
202	Kevin Greene	.03
203	Buford McGee	.03
204	Tom Newberry	.03
205	Frank Stams, David Wyman	.03
206	Alvin Wright	.03
207	John Robinson (C)	.03
208	Jeff Gross	.03

No.	Name	Value
209	Mark Duper	.03
210	Dan Marino	.75
211	Tim McKyer	.03
211a	Tim McKyer (traded stripe added)	.05
212	John Offerdahl	.03
213	Sammie Smith	.03
214	Richmond Webb	.03
215	Jarvis Williams	.03
216	Don Shula (C)	.03
217	Darrell Fullington (missing registered symbol by NFLPA logo)	.05
217a	Darrell Fullington (corrected)	.05
218	Tim Irwin	.03
219	Mike Merriweather	.03
220	Keith Millard	.03
221	Al Noga	.03
222	Henry Thomas	.03
223	Wade Wilson	.03
224	Gary Zimmerman	.03
225	Jerry Burns (C)	.03
226	Bruce Armstrong	.03
227	Marv Cook	.03
228	Hart Lee Dykes	.03
229	Tom Hodson	.03
230	Ronnie Lippett	.03
231	Ed Reynolds	.03
232	Chris Singleton	.03
233	John Stephens	.03
234	Dick MacPherson (C)	.03
235	Stan Brock	.03
236	Craig Heyward	.03
237	Vaughan Johnson	.03
238	Robert Massey	.03
239	Brett Maxie	.03
240	Rueben Mayes	.03
241	Pat Swilling	.03
242	Renaldo Turnbull	.03
243	Jim Mora (C)	.03
244	Kyle Clifton	.03
245	Jeff Criswell	.03
246	James Hasty	.03
247	Erik McMillan	.03
248	Scott Mersereau	.05
249	Ken O'Brien	.03
250	Blair Thomas (with NFLPA logo)	.30
250a	Blair Thomas (NFLPA logo removed)	.10
251	Al Toon	.03
252	Bruce Coslet (C)	.03
253	Eric Allen (AW, FC)	.03
254	Fred Barnett	.10
255	Keith Byars	.03
256	Randall Cunningham	.10
257	Seth Joyner	.03
258	Clyde Simmons	.03
259	Jessie Small	.03
260	Andre Waters	.03
261	Rich Kotite (C)	.03
262	Roy Green	.03
263	Ernie Jones	.03
264	Tim McDonald	.03
265	Timm Rosenbach	.03
266	Rod Saddler	.03
267	Luis Sharpe	.03
268	Anthony Thompson	.03
269	*Marcus Turner*	.08
270	Joe Bugel (C)	.03
271	Gary Anderson (Pit.)	.03
272	Dermontti Dawson	.03
273	Eric Green	.10
274	Merril Hoge	.03
275	Tunch Ilkin	.03
276	David Johnson	.03
277	Louis Lipps	.03
278	Rod Woodson	.05
279	Chuck Noll (C)	.03
280	Martin Bayless	.03
281	Marion Butts	.05
282	Gill Byrd	.03
283	Burt Grossman	.03
284	Courtney Hall	.03
285	Anthony Miller	.03
286	Leslie O'Neal	.03
287	Billy Joe Tolliver	.03
288	Dan Henning (C)	.03
289	Dexter Carter	.03
290	Michael Carter	.03
291	Mike Fagan	.03
292	Pierce Holt	.03
293	Guy McIntyre	.03
294	Tom Rathman	.03
295	John Taylor	.08
296	Steve Young	.50
297	George Seifert (C)	.03
298	Brian Blades	.03
299	Jeff Bryant	.03
300	Norm Johnson	.03
301	Tommy Kane	.03
302	Cortez Kennedy	.20
303	Bryan Millard	.03
304	John L. Williams	.03
306	Chuck Knox (C, with NFLPA logo)	.10
306a	Chuck Knox (NFLPA logo removed)	.40
307	Gary Anderson (T.B.)	.03
308	Reggie Cobb	.10
309	Randy Grimes	.03
310	Harry Hamilton	.03
311	Bruce Hill	.03
312	Eugene Marve	.03
313	Ervin Randle	.03
314	Vinny Testaverde	.08
315	Richard Williamson (C)	.03
316	Ernest Byner	.03
317	Gary Clark	.08
318	Andre Collins (with NFLPA logo)	.05
318a	Andre Collins (NFLPA logo removed)	.05
319	Darryl Grant	.03
320	Chip Lohmiller	.03
321	Martin Mayhew	.03
322	Mark Rypien	.08
323	Alvin Walton	.03
324	Joe Gibbs	.03
325	Jerry Glanville (R)	.03
326	Nate Odomes (with NFLPA logo)	.05
326a	Nate Odomes (NFLPA logo removed)	.05
327	Boomer Esiason	.03
328	Steve Tasker (with NFLPA logo)	.05
328a	Steve Tasker (NFLPA logo removed)	.05
329	Jerry Rice	.25
330	Jeff Rutledge	.03
331	KC defense (R)	.03
332	Rams (R)	.03
333	John Taylor (R)	.03
334	Randall Cunningham (with NFLPA logo)	.10
334a	Randall Cunningham (NFLPA logo removed)	.10
335	Bo Jackson	.10
336	Lawrence Taylor	.08
337	Warren Moon	.10
338	Alan Grant	.03
339	Steve DeBerg	.03
340	Playoff (Mark Clayton) (TM on Chief #27's shoulder)	.05
340a	Playoff (Mark Clayton) (TM away from Chief #27)	.05
341	Playoff (Jim Kelly) (with NFLPA logo)	.05
341a	Playoff (Jim Kelly) (NFLPA logo removed)	.05
342	NFC Championship (Matt Bahr) (R)	.03
343	*Robert Tisch*	.08
344	Sam Jankovich	.03
345	John Elway	.08
346	Bo Jackson	.08
347	Paul Tagliabue	.05
348	Ronnie Lott	.03
349	Super Bowl XXV Teleclinic	.03
350	Whitney Houston	.08
351	U.S. Troops	.08
352	Art McNally (O)	.03
353	Dick Jorgensen (O)	.03
354	Jerry Seeman (O)	.03
355	Jim Tunney (O)	.03
356	Gerry Austin (O)	.03
357	Gene Barth (O)	.03
358	Red Cashion (O)	.03
359	Tom Dooley (O)	.03
360	Johnny Grier (O)	.03
361	Pat Haggerty (O)	.03
362	Dale Hamer (O)	.03
363	Dick Hantak (O)	.03
364	Jerry Markbreit (O)	.03
365	Gordon McCarter (O)	.03
366	Bob McElwee (O)	.03
367	Howard Roe (O)	.03
368	Tom White (O)	.03
369	Norm Schachter (O)	.03
370	Warren Moon (small type)	.12
370a	Warren Moon (large type)	.10
371	Boomer Esiason (small type)	.05
371a	Boomer Esiason (large type)	.05
372	Troy Aikman (small type)	.50
372a	Troy Aikman (large type)	.50
373	Carl Banks (small type)	.05
373a	Carl Banks (large type)	.05
374	Jim Everett (small type)	.05
374a	Jim Everett (large type)	.05
375	Anthony Munoz (small type, error back: "dificul", "latrapar", error front: "Quadante," "Antony")	
375a	Anthony Munoz (small type, corrected back: "dicifil", "atrapar", error front: "Quadante," "Antony")	.05
375b	Anthony Munoz (large type, error front: "Quadante," "Antony")	.05
375c	Anthony Munoz (large type, corrected front: "Quedate," "Anthony")	.05
376	Ray Childress (small type)	.05
376a	Ray Childress (large type)	.05
377	Charles Mann (small type)	.05
377a	Charles Mann (large type)	.05
378	Jackie Slater (small type)	.05
378a	Jackie Slater (large type)	.05
379	Jerry Rice (NFC)	.25
380	Andre Rison (NFC)	.10
381	Jim Lachey (NFC)	.03
382	Jackie Slater (NFC)	.03
383	Randall McDaniel (NFC)	.03
384	Mark Bortz (NFC)	.03
385	Jay Hilgenberg (NFC)	.03
386	Keith Jackson (NFC)	.05
387	Joe Montana (NFC)	.50
388	Barry Sanders (NFC)	.50
389	Neal Anderson (NFC)	.03
390	Reggie White (NFC)	.05
391	Chris Doleman (NFC)	.03
392	Jerome Brown (NFC)	.03
393	Charles Haley (NFC)	.03
394	Lawrence Taylor (NFC)	.05
395	Pepper Johnson (NFC)	.03
396	Mike Singletary (NFC)	.03
397	Darrell Green (NFC)	.03
398	Carl Lee (NFC)	.03
399	Joey Browner (NFC)	.03
400	Ronnie Lott (NFC)	.05
401	Sean Landeta (NFC)	.03
402	Morten Andersen (NFC)	.03
403	Mel Gray (NFC)	.03
404	Reyna Thompson (NFC)	.03
405	Jimmy Johnson (NFC)	.03
406	Andre Reed	.05
407	Anthony Miller	.03
408	Anthony Munoz	.03
409	Bruce Armstrong	.03
410	Bruce Matthews	.03
411	Mike Munchak	.03
412	Kent Hull	.03
413	Rodney Holman	.03
414	Warren Moon	.10
415	Thurman Thomas	.15
416	Marion Butts	.05
417	Bruce Smith	.03
418	Greg Townsend	.03
419	Ray Childress	.03
420	Derrick Thomas	.08
421	Leslie O'Neal	.03
422	John Offerdahl	.03
423	Shane Conlan	.03
424	Rod Woodson	.04
425	Albert Lewis	.03
426	Steve Atwater	.03
427	David Fulcher	.03
428	Rohn Stark	.03
429	Nick Lowery	.03
430	Clarence Verdin	.03
431	Steve Tasker	.03
432	Art Shell	.03
433	Scott Case	.03
434	Tory Epps	.03
435	Mike Gann	.03
436	Brian Jordan	.03
437	Mike Kenn	.03
438	John Rade	.03
439	Andre Rison	.30
440	Mike Rozier	.03
441	Jessie Tuggle	.03
442	Don Beebe	.03
443	*John Davis*	.08
444	James Lofton	.08
445	Keith McKeller	.03
446	Frank Reich	.03
447	Scott Norwood	.03
448	Frank Reich	.03
449	Leon Seals	.03
450	Leonard Smith	.03
451	Neal Anderson	.03
452	Trace Armstrong	.03
453	Mark Bortz	.03
454	Wendell Davis	.03
455	Shaun Gayle	.03
456	Jay Hilgenberg	.03
457	Steve McMichael	.03
458	Mike Singletary	.03
459	Donnell Woolford	.03
460	Jim Breech	.03
461	Eddie Brown	.03
462	Barney Bussey	.03
463	Bruce Kozerski	.03
464	Tim Krumrie	.03
465	Bruce Reimers	.03
466	*Kevin Walker*	.08
467	Ickey Woods	.03
468	Carl Zander	.03
469	Mike Baab	.03
470	Brian Brennan	.03
471	*Rob Burnett*	.08
472	Raymond Clayborn	.03
473	Reggie Langhorne	.03
474	Kevin Mack	.03
475	Anthony Pleasant	.03
476	Joe Morris	.03
477	Dan Fike	.03
478	Ray Horton	.03
479	Jim Jeffcoat	.03
480	Jimmie Jones	.03
481	Kelvin Martin	.03
482	Nate Newton	.03
483	Danny Noonan	.03
484	Jay Novacek	.10
485	Emmitt Smith	2.00
486	*James Washington*	.08
487	Simon Fletcher	.03
488	Ron Holmes	.03
489	Mike Horan	.03
490	Vance Johnson	.03
491	Keith Kartz	.03
492	Greg Kragen	.03
493	Ken Lanier	.03
494	Warren Powers	.03
495	Dennis Smith	.03
496	Jeff Campbell	.03
497	Ken Dallafior	.03
498	Dennis Gibson	.03
499	Kevin Glover	.03
500	Mel Gray	.03
501	Eddie Murray	.03
502	Barry Sanders	1.25
503	Chris Spielman	.03
504	William White	.03
505	*Matt Brock*	.08
506	Robert Brown	.03
507	LeRoy Butler	.03
508	James Campen	.03
509	Jerry Holmes	.03
510	Perry Kemp	.03
511	Ken Ruettgers	.03
512	Scott Stephen	.03
513	Ed West	.03
514	*Cris Dishman*	.08
515	Curtis Duncan	.03
516	Drew Hill	.03
517	Haywood Jeffires	.10
518	Sean Jones	.03
519	Lamar Lathon	.03
520	Don Maggs	.03
521	Bubba McDowell	.03
522	Johnny Meads	.03
523	Chip Banks (error no text)	.03
523a	Chip Banks (corrected)	.03
524	Pat Beach	.03
525	Sam Clancy	.03
526	Eugene Daniel	.03
527	Jon Hand	.03
528	Jessie Hester	.03
529	Mike Prior (error no textual information)	.03
529a	Mike Prior (corrected)	.03
530	Keith Taylor	.03
531	Donnell Thompson	.03
532	Dino Hackett	.03
533	David Lutz	.03
534	Chris Martin	.03
535	Kevin Ross	.03
536	Dan Saleaumua	.03
537	Neil Smith	.05
538	Percy Snow	.03
539	Robb Thomas	.03
540	Barry Word	.08
541	Marcus Allen	.08
542	Eddie Anderson	.03
543	Scott Davis	.03
544	Mervyn Fernandez	.03
545	Ethan Horton	.03
546	Ronnie Lott	.08
547	Don Mosebar	.03
548	Jerry Robinson	.03
549	Aaron Wallace	.03
550	Flipper Anderson	.05
551	Cleveland Gary	.03
552	Damone Johnson	.03
553	Duval Love	.03
554	Irv Pankey	.03
555	Mike Piel	.03
556	Jackie Slater	.03
557	Michael Stewart	.03
558	Pat Terrell	.03
559	J.B. Brown	.03
560	Mark Clayton	.03
561	Ferrell Edmunds	.03
562	Harry Galbreath	.03
563	David Griggs	.03
564	Jim C. Jensen	.03
565	Louis Oliver	.03
566	Tony paige	.05
567	Keith Sims	.03
568	Joey Browner	.03
569	Anthony Carter	.05
570	Chris Doleman	.05
571	Rich Gannon	.05
572	Hassan Jones	.03
573	Steve Jordan	.03
574	Carl Lee	.03
575	Randall McDaniel	.03
576	Herschel Walker	.05
577	Ray Agnew	.03
578	Vincent Brown	.03
579	Irving Fryar	.03
580	Tim Goad	.03
581	Maurice Hurst	.03
582	Fred Marion	.03
583	Johnny Rembert	.03
584	Andre Tippett	.03
585	Brent Williams	.03
586	Morten Andersen	.03
587	*Toi Cook*	.08
588	Jim Dombrowski	.03
589	Dalton Hilliard	.05
590	Rickey Jackson	.03
591	Eric Martin	.03
592	Sam Mills	.03
593	Bobby Hebert	.03
594	Steve Walsh	.03
595	Ottis Anderson	.03
596	Pepper Johnson	.03
597	*Bob Kratch*	.05
598	Sean Landeta	.03
599	Doug Riesenberg	.03
600	William Roberts	.03
601	Phil Simms	.05
602	Lawrence Taylor	.08
603	Everson Walls	.03
604	Brad Baxter	.05
605	Dennis Byrd	.03
606	Jeff Lageman	.03
607	Pat Leahy	.03
608	Rob Moore	.08
609	Joe Mott	.03
610	Tony Stargell	.03
611	Brian Washington	.03
612	*Marvin Washington*	.15
613	David Alexander	.03
614	Jerome Brown	.03
615	Byron Evans	.03
616	Ron Heller	.03
617	Wes Hopkins	.03
618	Keith Jackson	.10
619	Heath Sherman	.03
620	Reggie White	.10
621	Calvin Williams	.10
622	Ken Harvey	.03
623	Eric Hill	.03
624	Johnny Johnson	.20
625	Freddie Joe Nunn	.03
626	Ricky Proehl	.08
627	Tootie Robbins	.03
628	Jay Taylor	.03
629	Tom Tupa	.03
630	*Jim Wahler*	.08
631	Bubby Brister	.03
632	Thomas Everett	.03
633	Bryan Hinkle	.03
634	Carnell Lake	.03
635	David Little	.03
636	Hardy Nickerson	.03
637	Gerald Williams	.03
638	Keith Willis	.03
639	Tim Worley	.03
640	Rod Bernstine	.03
641	Frank Cornish	.03
642	Gary Plummer	.03
643	*Henry Rolling*	.08
644	Sam Seale	.03
645	Junior Seau	.20
646	Billy Ray Smith	.03
647	Broderick Thompson	.03
648	*Derrick Walker*	.08
649	Todd Bowles	.03
650	Don Griffin	.03
651	Charles Haley	.03
652	Brent Jones	.03
653	Joe Montana	1.00
654	Jerry Rice	.75
655	Bill Romanowski	.03
656	Michael Walter	.03
657	Dave Waymer	.03
658	Jeff Chadwick	.03
659	Derrick Fenner	.03
660	Nesby Glasgow	.03
661	Jacob Green	.03
662	*Dwayne Harper*	.08
663	Andy Heck	.03
664	Dave Krieg	.03
665	Rufus Porter	.03
666	Eugene Robinson	.03
667	Mark Carrier	.03
668	Steve Christie	.03
669	Reuben Davis	.03
670	Paul Gruber	.03
671	Wayne Haddix	.03
672	Ron Hall	.03
673	Keith McCants	.03
674	Ricky Reynolds	.03
675	Mark Robinson	.03
676	Jeff Bostic	.03
677	Darrell Green	.05
678	Markus Koch	.03
679	Jim Lachey	.03
680	Charles Mann	.03
681	Wilber Marshall	.03
682	Art Monk	.03
683	Gerald Riggs	.03
684	Ricky Sanders	.03
685	Ray Handley replaces Bill Parcels	.03
686	NFL Announces Expansion	.03
687	Miami Gets Super Bowl XXIX	.03
688	George Young named NFL Executive of yea	.03
689	Five-millionth fan visits Pro FB HOF	.03
690	Sports Illustrated poll pro football #1	.03
691	American Bowl London	.03
692	American Bowl Berlin	.03
693	American Bowl Tokyo	.03
694	Joe Ferguson (LEG)	.03
695	Carl Hairston (LEG)	.03
696	Dan Hampton (LEG)	.03
697	Mike Haynes (LEG)	.03
698	Marty Lyons (LEG)	.03
699	Ozzie Newsome (LEG)	.08
700	Scott Studwell (LEG)	.03
701	Mike Webster (LEG)	.04
702	Dwayne Woodruff (LEG)	.03
703	Larry Kennan (CO)	.03
704	*Stan Gelbaugh*	.08
705	John Brantley	.03
706	Danny Lockett	.03
707	*Anthony Parker*	.08
708	Dan Crossman	.03
709	Eric Wilkerson	.03
710	*Judd Garrett*	.08
711	Tony Baker	.03
712	1st Place BW (Randall Cunningham)	.06
713	2nd Place BW (Mark Ingram)	.03
714	3rd Place BW (Pete Holohan, Barney Bussey, Carl Carter)	.03
715	1st Place Color Action (Sterling Sharpe)	.08
716	2nd Place Color Action (Jim Harbaugh)	.04
717	3rd Place Color Action (Anthony Miller, David Fulcher)	.03
718	1st Place Color Feature (Bill Parcels, Lawrence Taylor) (CO)	.03
719	Patriotic Crowd (2nd Place Color Feature)	.03
720	3rd Place Color Feature (Alfredo Roberts)	.03
721	Read And Study (Ray Bentley)	.03
722	Never Give Up (Earnest Byner)	.03
723	Steroids Destroy (Bill Fralic)	.03
724	Don't Polute (Joe Jacoby)	.03
725	AIDS Kills (Howie Long)	.03
726	School's The Ticket (Dan Marino)	.40
727	Leer Y Estudiar (Ron Rivera)	.03
728	Be The Best (Mike Singletary)	.05
729	Chill (Cornelius Bennett)	.03
730	Russell Maryland	.20
731	*Eric Turner*	.20
732	*Bruce Pickens*	.08
733	*Mike Croel*	.15
734	*Todd Lyght*	.15
735	*Eric Swann*	.10
736	*Charles McRae*	.10
737	*Antone Davis*	.10
738	*Stanley Richard*	.30
739	*Herman Moore*	3.50
740	*Pat Harlow*	.08
741	*Alvin Harper*	.30
742	*Mike Pritchard*	.50
743	*Leonard Russell*	.15
744	*Huey Richardson*	.04
745	*Dan McGwire*	.08
746	*Bobby Wilson*	.08
747	*Alfred Williams*	.10
748	*Vinnie Clark*	.08
749	*Kelvin Pritchett*	.10
750	*Harvey Williams*	1.00
751	*Stan Thomas*	.05
752	*Randal Hill*	.35
753	*Todd Marinovich*	.08
754	*Ted Washington*	.08

755	*Henry Jones*	.20
756	*Jarrod Bunch*	.10
757	*Mike Dumas*	.05
758	*Ed King*	.08
759	*Reggie Johnson*	.08
760	*Roman Phifer*	.10
761	*Mike Jones*	.05
762	*Brett Favre*	3.00
763	*Browning Nagle*	.20
764	*Esera Tuaolo*	.05
765	*George Thornton*	.03
766	*Dixon Edwards*	.05
767	*Darryll Lewis*	.03
768	*Eric Bieniemy*	.05
769	*Shane Curry*	.05
770	*Jerome Henderson*	.06
771	*Wesley Carroll*	.10
772	*Nick Bell*	.15
773	*John Flannery*	.03
774	*Ricky Watters*	1.50
775	*Jeff Graham*	.75
776	*Eric Moten*	.08
777	*Jesse Campbell*	.08
778	*Chris Zorich*	.05
779	*Joe Valerio*	.03
780	*Doug Thomas*	.05
781	*Lamar Rogers*	.04
782	*John Johnson*	.08
783	*Phil Hansen*	.08
784	*Kanavis McGhee*	.05
785	*Calvin Stephens*	.05
786	*James Jones*	.10
787	*Reggie Barrett*	.03
788	*Aeneas Williams*	.10
789	*Aaron Craver*	.10
790	*Keith Traylor*	.08
791	*Godfrey Myles*	.08
792	*Mo Lewis*	.08
793	*James Richard*	.03
794	*Carlos Jenkins*	.20
795	*Lawrence Dawsey*	.25
796	*Don Davey*	.04
797	*Jake Reed*	1.00
798	Dave McCloughan	.03
799	Eric Williams	.15
800	Steve Jackson	.10
801	Bob Dahl	.03
802	Ernie Mills	.10
803	David Daniels	.03
804	Rob Selby	.05
805	Ricky Ervins	.20
806	Tim Barnett	.20
807	Chris Gardocki	.04
808	Kevin Donnalley	.04
809	Robert Wilson	.04
810	Chuck Webb	.04
811	Darryl Wren	.08
812	Ed McCaffrey	2.00
813	Shula's 300th Victory	.05
814	Raiders-49ers Sell Out Coliseum	.03
815	NFL International	.03
816	*Moe Gardner*	.05
817	*Tim McKyer*	.05
818	*Tom Waddle*	.50
819	*Michael Jackson*	.75
820	Tony Casillas	.03
821	Gaston Green	.03
822	Kenny Walker	.08
823	Willie Green	.30
824	Erik Kramer	1.00
825	William Fuller	.05
826	Allen Pinkett	.04
827	Rick Venturi	.04
828	Bill Maas	.04
829	Jeff Jaeger	.04
830	Robert Delpino	.04
831	Mark Higgs	.50
832	Reggie Roby	.03
833	Terry Allen	1.50
834	Cris Carter	.25
835	John Randle	.40
836	Hugh Millen	.25
837	Jon Vaughn	.25
838	Gill Fenerty	.03
839	Floyd Turner	.03
840	Irv Eatman	.03
841	Lonnie Young	.03
842	Jim McMahon	.05
843	Randal Hill	.05
844	Barry Foster	.45
845	Neil O'Donnell	1.50
846	John Friesz	.10
847	Broderick Thomas	.03
848	Brian Mitchell	.10
849	*Mike Utley*	.15
850	Mike Croel	.08

1991 Pro Set WLAF Helmets

Each of these 10 cards features a helmet for a team in the World League of American Football in its initial season. The cards, random inserts in 1991 Pro Set Series I packs, are numbered on the back and include information about the team depicted on the front, plus a schedule.

		MT
Complete Set (10):		3.00
Common Helmet:		.30

1	Barcelona Dragons	.30
2	Birmingham Fire	.30
3	Frankfurt Galaxy	.30
4	London Monarchs	.30
5	Montreal Machine	.30
6	NY-NJ Knights	.30
7	Orlando Thunder	.30
8	Raleigh-Durham Skyhawks	.30
9	Sacramento Surge	.30
10	San Antonio Riders	.30

1991 Pro Set WLAF Inserts

These cards, featuring players from each of the 10 teams in the World League of American Football during its initial season in 1991, were random inserts in 1991 Pro Set Series I packs. Each team is represented by its quarterback and head coach, at least. The card front has the set's logo in an upper corner and indicates it is an official World League card. The back also has the set logo, plus a player profile and head shot. Card numbering includes "World League Collectible" above the number.

		MT
Complete Set (32):		6.00
Common Player:		.10

1	Mike Lynn	.35
2	Larry Kennan	.10
3	Jack Bicknell	.10
4	Scott Erney	.20
5	A.J. Green	.25
6	Chan Gailey	.10
7	Paul McGowan	.15
8	Brent Pease	.20
9	Jack Elway	.30
10	Mike Perez	.30
11	Mike Tetter	.10
12	Larry Kennan	.10
13	Corris Ervin	.10
14	John Witkowski	.25
15	Jacques Dussault	.10
16	Ray Savage	.10
17	Kevin Sweeney	.50
18	Mouse Davis	.50
19	Todd Hammel	.20
20	Anthony Parker	.30
21	Don Matthews	.15
22	Kerwin Bell	.30
23	Wayne Davis	.10
24	Roman Gabriel	.60
25	John Carter	.20
26	Mark Maye	.20
27	Kay Stephenson	.20
28	Ben Bennett	.50
29	Shawn Knight	.20
30	Mike Riley	.10
31	Jason Garrett	.15
32	Greg Gilbert	.20

1991 Pro Set Cinderella Story

This nine-card perforated sheet was available inside The Official NFL Pro Set Card Book. The card fronts are similar to the design Pro Set used for its 1991 set, except there are four cards which have black-and-white photos instead of color ones. Each card back is numbered indicating it is in the Cinderella Story set, which profiles players who have achieved success in the NFL despite formidable roadblocks in their paths. If a card is perforated from the sheet, it measures the standard 2-1/2" x 3-1/2".

		MT
Complete Set (9):		8.00
Common Player:		.60

1	Rocky Bleier	1.00
2	Tom Dempsey	.60
3	Dan Hampton	.75
4	Charlie Hennigan	.60
5	Dante Lavelli	.75
6	Jim Plunkett	.75
7	1968 New York Jets (Joe Namath Handing Off)	1.50
8	1981 San Francisco 49ers (Joe Montana Passing)	3.00
9	1979 Tampa Bay Bucs (Ricky Bell Running)	.60

A player's name in *italic* type indicates a rookie card.

1991 Pro Set National Banquet

Each of these cards can be identified by the National Sports Collectors Convention logo on the front. The cards, which feature full-bleed color photos, were given away during the convention, held in Anaheim, Calif. Each card back is numbered and includes a player profile, biographical information and a mug shot.

		MT
Complete Set (5):		5.00
Common Player:		.50

1	Ronnie Lott	1.50
2	Roy Firestone (Television celebrity)	1.25
3	Roger Craig	1.25
4	ProFiles Television Show (Craig James, Tim Brant)	1.00
5	Title Card	.50

1991 Pro Set Platinum

Pro Set issued this 315-card set in two series - 150 and 165 cards each. The glossy cards have full-bleed color action photos on the front, along with the Pro Set Platinum logo. The card backs use a horizontal format and include another action photo, plus the player's name, team and position. A "Platinum Performer" feature is also included, highlighting an outstanding performance by the player. Each series is numbered alphabetically by team, beginning with Atlanta. Subsets include "Special Teams" (#s 128-135), "Platinum Performance" (#s 136-150) and "Platinum Prospects" (#s 286-315). Random insert cards include "Special Collectibles" (numbered PC1-PC10) and redemption cards for a limited-edition Platinum card of Paul Brown or Emmitt Smith.

		MT
Complete Set (315):		12.00
Complete Series 1 (150):		5.00
Complete Series 2 (165):		7.00
Common Player:		.05
Wax Box:		6.00

1	Chris Miller	.05
2	Andre Rison	.25
3	Tim Green	.05
4	Jessie Tuggle	.05
5	Thurman Thomas	.40
6	Darryl Talley	.05
7	Kent Hull	.05
8	Bruce Smith	.05
9	Shane Conlan	.05
10	Jim Harbaugh	.08
11	Neal Anderson	.08
12	Mark Bortz	.05
13	Richard Dent	.05
14	Steve McMichael	.05
15	James Brooks	.05
16	Boomer Esiason	.08
17	Tim Krumrie	.05
18	James Francis	.05
19	Lewis Billups	.05
20	Eric Metcalf	.05
21	Kevin Mack	.05
22	Clay Matthews	.05
23	Mike Johnson	.05
24	Troy Aikman	1.00
25	Emmitt Smith	2.00
26	Daniel Stubbs	.05
27	Ken Norton	.05
28	John Elway	.40
29	Bobby Humphrey	.05
30	Simon Fletcher	.05
31	Karl Mecklenburg	.05
32	Rodney Peete	.05
33	Barry Sanders	1.00
34	Michael Cofer	.05
35	Jerry Ball	.05
36	Sterling Sharpe	.20
37	Tony Mandarich	.05
38	Brian Noble	.05
39	Tim Harris	.05
40	Warren Moon	.15
41	Ernest Givins	.05
42	Mike Munchak	.05
43	Sean Jones	.05
44	Ray Childress	.05
45	Jeff George	.30
46	Albert Bentley	.05
47	Duane Bickett	.05
48	Steve DeBerg	.05
49	Christian Okoye	.05
50	Neil Smith	.05
51	Derrick Thomas	.25
52	Willie Gault	.05
53	Don Mosebar	.05
54	Howie Long	.05
55	Greg Townsend	.05
56	Terry McDaniel	.05
57	Jackie Slater	.05
58	Jim Everett	.05
59	Cleveland Gary	.05
60	Mike Piel	.05
61	Jerry Gray	.05
62	Dan Marino	.75
63	Sammie Smith	.05
64	Richmond Webb	.05
65	Louis Oliver	.05
66	Ferrell Edmunds	.05
67	Jeff Cross	.05
68	Wade Wilson	.05
69	Chris Doleman	.05
70	Joey Browner	.05
71	Keith Millard	.05
72	John Stephens	.05
73	Andre Tippett	.05
74	Brent Williams	.05
75	Craig Heyward	.05
76	Eric Martin	.05
77	Pat Swilling	.05
78	Sam Mills	.05
79	Jeff Hostetler	.25
80	Ottis Anderson	.05
81	Lawrence Taylor	.10
82	Pepper Johnson	.05
83	Blair Thomas	.05
84	Al Toon	.05
85	Ken O'Brien	.05
86	Erik McMillan	.05
87	Dennis Byrd	.05
88	Randall Cunningham	.10
89	Fred Barnett	.15
90	Seth Joyner	.05
91	Reggie White	.15
92	Timm Rosenbach	.05
93	Johnny Johnson	.25
94	Tim McDonald	.05
95	Freddie Joe Nunn	.05
96	Bubby Brister	.08
97	Gary Anderson	.05
98	Merril Hoge	.05
99	Keith Willis	.05
100	Rod Woodson	.05
101	Billy Joe Tolliver	.05
102	Marion Butts	.08
103	Rod Benstine	.05
104	Lee Williams	.05
105	Burt Grossman	.05
106	Tom Rathman	.05
107	John Taylor	.10
108	Michael Carter	.05
109	Guy McIntyre	.05
110	Pierce Holt	.05
111	John L. Williams	.05
112	Dave Krieg	.05
113	Bryan Millard	.05
114	Cortez Kennedy	.30
115	Derrick Fenner	.05
116	Vinny Testaverde	.08
117	Reggie Cobb	.25
118	Gary Anderson	.05
119	Bruce Hill	.05
120	Wayne Haddix	.05
121	Broderick Thomas	.05
122	Keith McCants	.05
123	Andre Collins	.05
124	Earnest Byner	.05
125	Jim Lachey	.05
126	Mark Rypien	.10
127	Charles Mann	.05
128	Nick Lowery	.05
129	Chip Lohmiller	.05
130	Mike Horan	.05
131	Rohn Stark	.05
132	Sean Landeta	.05
133	Clarence Verdin	.05
134	Johnny Bailey	.05
135	Herschel Walker	.05
136	Bo Jackson	.40
137	Dexter Carter	.05
138	Warren Moon	.10
139	Joe Montana	1.00
140	Jerry Rice	.75
141	Deion Sanders	.30
142	Ronnie Lippett	.05
143	Terance Mathis	.05
144	Gaston Green	.05
145	Dean Biasucci	.05
146	Charles Haley	.05
147	Derrick Thomas	.25
148	Lawrence Taylor	.10
149	Art Shell	.05
150	Bill Parcells	.05
151	Steve Broussard	.05
152	Darion Conner	.05
153	Bill Fralic	.05
154	Mike Gann	.05
155	Tim McKyer	.05
156	Don Beebe	.05
157	Cornelius Bennett	.05
158	Andre Reed	.10
159	Leonard Smith	.05
160	Will Wolford	.05
161	Mark Carrier	.05
162	Wendell Davis	.10
163	Jay Hilgenberg	.05
164	Brad Muster	.05
165	Mike Singletary	.05
166	Eddie Brown	.05
167	David Fulcher	.05
168	Rodney Holman	.05
169	Anthony Munoz	.05
170	Craig Taylor	.05
171	Mike Baab	.05
172	David Grayson	.05
173	Reggie Langhorne	.05
174	Joe Morris	.05
175	Kevin Gogan	.10
176	Jack Del Rio	.05
177	Issiac Holt	.05
178	Michael Irvin	.60
179	Jay Novacek	.15
180	Steve Atwater	.05
181	Mark Jackson	.05
182	Ricky Nattiel	.05
183	Warren Powers	.05
184	Dennis Smith	.05
185	Bennie Blades	.05
186	Lomas Brown	.05
187	Robert Clark	.05
188	Mel Gray	.05
189	Chris Spielman	.05
190	Johnny Holland	.05
191	Don Majkowski	.05
192	Bryce Paup	.50
193	Darrell Thompson	.15
194	Ed West	.05
195	Cris Dishman	.15
196	Drew Hill	.05
197	Bruce Matthews	.05
198	Bubba McDowell	.05
199	Allen Pinkett	.05
200	Bill Brooks	.05
201	Jeff Herrod	.05
202	Anthony Johnson	.10
203	Mike Prior	.05
204	John Alt	.05
205	Stephone Paige	.05
206	Kevin Ross	.05
207	Dan Saleaumua	.05
208	Barry Word	.10
209	Marcus Allen	.05
210	Roger Craig	.05
211	Ronnie Lott	.10
212	Winston Moss	.05
213	Jay Schroeder	.05
214	Robert Delpino	.05
215	Henry Ellard	.05
216	Kevin Greene	.05
217	Tom Newberry	.05
218	Michael Stewart	.05
219	Mark Duper	.05
220	Mark Higgs	.30
221	John Offerdahl	.05
222	Keith Sims	.05
223	Anthony Carter	.05
224	Cris Carter	.05
225	Steve Jordan	.05
226	Randall McDaniel	.05
227	Al Noga	.05
228	Ray Agnew	.05
229	Bruce Armstrong	.05
230	Bruce Armstrong	.05
231	Greg McMurtry	.05
232	Chris Singleton	.05
233	Morten Andersen	.05
234	Vince Buck	.05
235	Gill Fenerty	.05
236	Rickey Jackson	.05
237	Vaughan Johnson	.05
238	Carl Banks	.05
239	Mark Collins	.05
240	Rodney Hampton	.50
241	David Meggett	.05
242	Bart Oates	.05
243	Kyle Clifton	.05
244	Jeff Lageman	.05
245	Freeman McNeil	.05
246	Rob Moore	.20
247	Eric Allen	.05
248	Keith Byars	.05
249	Keith Jackson	.10
250	Jim McMahon	.05
251	Andre Waters	.05
252	Ken Harvey	.05
253	Ernie Jones	.05
254	Luis Sharpe	.05
255	Anthony Thompson	.05
256	Tom Tupa	.05
257	Eric Green	.10
258	Barry Foster	.50
259	Bryan Hinkle	.05
260	Tunch Ilkin	.05
261	Louis Lipps	.05
262	Gill Byrd	.05
263	John Friesz	.10
264	Anthony Miller	.05
265	Junior Seau	.25
266	Ronnie Harmon	.05
267	Harris Barton	.05
268	Todd Bowles	.05
269	Don Griffin	.05
270	Bill Romanowski	.05
271	Steve Young	.50
272	Brian Blades	.05
273	Jacob Green	.05
274	Rufus Porter	.05
275	Eugene Robinson	.05
276	Mark Carrier	.05
277	Reuben Davis	.05
278	Paul Gruber	.05
279	Gary Clark	.10
280	Darrell Green	.05
281	Wilber Marshall	.05
282	Matt Millen	.05
283	Alvin Walton	.05
284	Joe Gibbs	.05
285	Don Shula	.05
286	*Larry Brown*	.15
287	*Mike Croel*	.30
288	*Antone Davis*	.10
289	*Ricky Ervins*	.25
290	*Brett Favre*	1.75
291	*Pat Harlow*	.10
292	*Michael Jackson*	.60
293	*Henry Jones*	.25
294	*Aaron Craver*	.10
295	*Nick Bell*	.25
296	*Todd Lyght*	.15
297	*Todd Marinovich*	.10
298	*Russell Maryland*	.35
299	*Kanavis McGhee*	.10
300	*Dan McGwire*	.15
301	*Charles McRae*	.15
302	*Eric Moten*	.10
303	*Jerome Henderson*	.10
304	*Browning Nagle*	.25
305	*Mike Pritchard*	.35
306	*Stanley Richard*	.30
307	*Randal Hill*	.25
308	*Leonard Russell*	1.00
309	*Eric Swann*	.15
310	*Phil Hansen*	.15
311	*Moe Gardner*	.15
312	*Jon Vaughn*	.15
313	*Aeneas Williams*	.10
314	*Alfred Williams*	.15
315	*Harvey Williams*	.35

1991 Pro Set Platinum PC

These 10 insert cards were randomly included in Series II Platinum packs. Each is numbered on the card back using a "PC" prefix. The card front has a full-bleed color action photo, plus the set logo. The back has another photo and player summary, all designed in a horizontal format. The cards were divided into three subsets - Platinum Profile, Platinum Photo and Platinum Game Breaker.

		MT
Complete Set (10):		10.00
Common Player:		.50

1	Bobby Hebert	.50
2	Art Monk	.50
3	Kenny Walker	.50
4	Low Fives	.50
5	Kevin Mack	.50
6	Neal Anderson	.50
7	Gaston Green	.50
8	Barry Sanders	3.00
9	Emmitt Smith	5.00
10	Thurman Thomas	1.50

Values quoted in this guide reflect the retail price of a card — the price a collector can expect to pay when buying a card from a dealer. The wholesale price — that which a collector can expect to receive when selling cards — will be significantly lower, depending on desirability and condition.

1991 Pro Set Spanish

These cards have the same photos on them as their regular 1991 Pro Set counterparts, but the card numbers have been changed. Also, the big difference is that all text and information on the card is in Spanish. Five insert cards (ES1–ES5) were also randomly included in packs.

		MT
Complete Set (300):		10.00
Common Player:		.03
1	Steve Broussard	.03
2	Darion Conner	.03
3	Tory Epps	.03
4	Bill Fralic	.03
5	Mike Gann	.03
6	Chris Miller	.15
7	Andre Rison	.20
8	Deion Sanders	.25
9	Jessie Tuggle	.03
10	Cornelius Bennett	.10
11	Shane Conlan	.05
12	Kent Hull	.03
13	Kirby Jackson	.03
14	James Lofton	.15
15	Andre Reed	.15
16	Bruce Smith	.15
17	Darryl Talley	.05
18	Thurman Thomas	.50
19	Neal Anderson	.15
20	Trace Armstrong	.03
21	Mark Carrier	.07
22	Wendell Davis	.03
23	Richard Dent	.15
24	Jim Harbaugh	.10
25	Ron Rivera	.03
26	Mike Singletary	.15
27	Lemuel Stinson	.03
28	James Brooks	.03
29	Eddie Brown	.03
30	Boomer Esiason	.15
31	James Francis	.03
32	David Fulcher	.03
33	Rodney Holman	.03
34	Anthony Munoz	.10
35	Bruce Reimers	.05
36	Ickey Woods	.05
37	Mike Baab	.03
38	Brian Brennan	.03
39	Raymond Clayborn	.03
40	Mike Johnson	.03
41	Clay Matthews	.05
42	Eric Metcalf	.07
43	Frank Minnifield	.03
44	Joe Morris	.03
45	Anthony Pleasant	.03
46	Troy Aikman	1.00
47	Jack Del Rio	.03
48	Issiac Holt	.03
49	Michael Irvin	.50
50	Jimmie Jones	.03
51	Nate Newton	.03
52	Danny Noonan	.03
53	Jay Novacek	.07
54	Emmitt Smith	2.00
55	Steve Atwater	.05
56	Michael Brooks	.03
57	John Elway	.25
58	Mike Horan	.03
59	Mark Jackson	.03
60	Karl Mecklenburg	.03
61	Warren Powers	.03
62	Dennis Smith	.03
63	Doug Widell	.03
64	Jerry Ball	.05
65	Bennie Blades	.03
66	Robert Clark	.03
67	Ken Dallafior	.03
68	Mel Gray	.07
69	Eddie Murray	.05
70	Rodney Peete	.05
71	Barry Sanders	.75
72	Chris Spielman	.05
73	Robert Brown	.03
74	LeRoy Butler	.07
75	Perry Kemp	.03
76	Don Majkowski	.03
77	Tony Mandarich	.03
78	Mark Murphy	.03
79	Brian Noble	.03
80	Sterling Sharpe	.50
81	Ed West	.03
82	Ray Childress	.03
83	Cris Dishman	.03
84	Ernest Givins	.07
85	Drew Hill	.05
86	Haywood Jeffires	.07
87	Lamar Lathon	.03
88	Bruce Matthews	.03
89	Bubba McDowell	.03
90	Warren Moon	.25
91	Chip Banks	.03
92	Albert Bentley	.05
93	Duane Bickett	.03
94	Bill Brooks	.03
95	Sam Clancy	.03
96	Ray Donaldson	.03
97	Jeff George	.25
98	Mike Prior	.03
99	Clarence Verdin	.03
100	Steve DeBerg	.05
101	Albert Lewis	.03
102	Christian Okoye	.05
103	Kevin Ross	.03
104	Stephone Paige	.03
105	Kevin Porter	.03
106	Percy Snow	.03
107	Derrick Thomas	.20
108	Barry Word	.20
109	Marcus Allen	.20
110	Mervyn Fernandez	.03
111	Howie Long	.05
112	Ronnie Lott	.15
113	Terry McDaniel	.03
114	Max Montoya	.03
115	Don Mosebar	.03
116	Jay Schroeder	.10
117	Greg Townsend	.03
118	Flipper Anderson	.05
119	Henry Ellard	.07
120	Jim Everett	.10
121	Kevin Greene	.03
122	Damone Johnson	.03
123	Buford McGee	.05
124	Tom Newberry	.03
125	Michael Stewart	.03
126	Alvin Wright	.03
127	Mark Clayton	.05
128	Jeff Cross	.05
129	Mark Duper	.05
130	Ferrell Edmunds	.03
131	Dan Marino	.75
132	Tim McKyer	.03
133	John Offerdahl	.05
134	Louis Oliver	.03
135	Sammie Smith	.03
136	Joey Browner	.05
137	Anthony Carter	.10
138	Chris Doleman	.05
139	Hassan Jones	.03
140	Steve Jordan	.05
141	Carl Lee	.03
142	Al Noga	.03
143	Henry Thomas	.03
144	Herschel Walker	.15
145	Ray Agnew	.03
146	Bruce Armstrong	.03
147	Marv Cook	.05
148	Irving Fryar	.07
149	Tommy Hodson	.07
150	Fred Marion	.03
151	Johnny Rembert	.03
152	Chris Singleton	.07
153	Andre Tippett	.05
154	Morten Andersen	.10
155	Toi Cook	.05
156	Craig Heyward	.05
157	Dalton Hilliard	.05
158	Rickey Jackson	.07
159	Vaughan Johnson	.07
160	Rueben Mayes	.05
161	Pat Swilling	.07
162	Bobby Hebert	.05
163	Ottis Anderson	.10
164	Carl Banks	.05
165	Rodney Hampton	.25
166	Jeff Hostetler	.15
167	Mark Ingram	.03
168	Leonard Marshall	.03
169	David Meggett	.07
170	Lawrence Taylor	.25
171	Everson Walls	.03
172	Brad Baxter	.03
173	Jeff Lageman	.03
174	Pat Leahy	.03
175	Erik McMillan	.03
176	Rob Moore	.10
177	Ken O'Brien	.07
178	Blair Thomas	.10
179	Al Toon	.03
180	Eric Allen	.07
181	Jerome Brown	.03
182	Keith Byars	.07
183	Randall Cunningham	.15
184	Byron Evans	.03
185	Keith Jackson	.05
186	Heath Sherman	.03
187	Clyde Simmons	.05
188	Reggie White	.20
189	Rich Camarillo	.03
190	Johnny Johnson	.15
191	Ernie Jones	.03
192	Tim McDonald	.03
193	Freddie Joe Nunn	.03
194	Luis Sharpe	.03
195	Jay Taylor	.03
196	Anthony Thompson	.05
197	Tom Tupa	.03
198		

199	Gary Anderson	.05
200	Bubby Brister	.10
201	Eric Green	.07
202	Bryan Hinkle	.03
203	Merril Hoge	.03
204	Carnell Lake	.03
205	Louis Lipps	.03
206	Keith Willis	.03
207	Rod Woodson	.10
208	Rod Bernstine	.05
209	Marion Butts	.07
210	Anthony Miller	.10
211	Leslie O'Neal	.03
212	Henry Rolling	.03
213	Junior Seau	.15
214	Billy Ray Smith	.03
215	Broderick Thompson	.03
216	Derrick Walker	.03
217	Dexter Carter	.03
218	Don Griffin	.03
219	Charles Haley	.05
220	Pierce Holt	.03
221	Joe Montana	1.00
222	Jerry Rice	.75
223	John Taylor	.10
224	Michael Walter	.03
225	Steve Young	.25
226	Brian Blades	.05
227	Jeff Bryant	.03
228	Jacob Green	.03
229	Tommy Kane	.05
230	Dave Krieg	.07
231	Bryan Millard	.03
232	Rufus Porter	.03
233	Eugene Robinson	.03
234	John L. Williams	.03
235	Gary Anderson	.05
236	Mark Carrier	.05
237	Reggie Cobb	.03
238	Rueben Davis	.03
239	Paul Gruber	.05
240	Harry Hamilton	.03
241	Keith McCants	.03
242	Ricky Reynolds	.03
243	Vinny Testaverde	.10
244	Earnest Byner	.05
245	Gary Clark	.10
246	Andre Collins	.03
247	Darrell Green	.07
248	Jim Lachey	.03
249	Charles Mann	.03
250	Wilber Marshall	.05
251	Art Monk	.10
252	Mark Rypien	.10
253	Russell Maryland	.15
254	Mike Croel	.03
255	Stanley Richard	.03
256	Leonard Russell	.03
257	Dan McGwire	.10
258	Todd Marinovich	.05
259	Eric Swann	.03
260	Mike Pritchard	.05
261	Alfred Williams	.03
262	Brett Favre	1.25
263	Browning Nagle	.07
264	Darryll Lewis	.03
265	Nick Bell	.03
266	Jeff Graham	.05
267	Eric Moten	.03
268	Roman Phifer	.03
269	Eric Bieniemy	.05
270	Phil Hansen	.03
271	Reggie Barrett	.03
272	Aeneas Williams	.07
273	Aaron Craver	.03
274	Lawrence Dawsey	.05
275	Ricky Ervins	.03
276	Jake Reed	.05
277	Eric Williams	.10
278	Tim Barnett	.10
279	Keith Traylor	.03
280	Jerry Rice	.25
281	Jim Lachey	.03
282	Barry Sanders	.50
283	Neal Anderson	.07
284	Reggie White	.15
285	Lawrence Taylor	.15
286	Mike Singletary	.10
287	Joey Browner	.05
288	Morten Andersen	.05
289	Andre Reed	.10
290	Anthony Munoz	.07
291	Warren Moon	.20
292	Thurman Thomas	.25
293	Ray Childress	.03
294	Derrick Thomas	.15
295	Rod Woodson	.05
296	Steve Atwater	.05
297	David Fulcher	.03
298	Anthony Munoz	.10
299	Ron Rivera	.03
300	Cornelius Bennett	.10
E1	Tom Flores	2.00
E2	Anthony Munoz	2.00
E3	Tony Casillas	2.00
E4	Super Bowl XXVI	2.00
E5	Felicidades	2.00

1991 Pro Set UK Sheets

Measuring 5-1/8" x 11-3/4", the five six-card strips were used as a promotion in a Middlesex, England, newspaper called Today. Released one strip per week in Sunday papers during Fall 1991, the unperforated strips were numbered 1-5. Each player card is numbered identically to his 1991 regular-issue cards.

		MT
Complete Set (5):		25.00
Common Player:		2.00
1	Quarterbacks (200 Jim Everett, 167 Warren Moon, 111 Boomer Esiason, 128 Troy Aikman, 726 Dan Marino, 138	10.00
2	Running Backs (576 Herschel Walker, 213 Sammie Smith, 722 Earnest Byner, 123 Eric Metcalf, 485 Emmitt	10.00
3	Receivers (209 Mark Duper, 654 Jerry Rice, 251 Al Toon, 161 Sterling Sharpe, 618 Keith Jackson, 115 Tim	6.00
4	Kickers (460 Jim Breech, 447 Scott Norwood, 489 Mike Horan, 300 Norm Johnson, 184 Nick Lowery, 401 Sean	2.00
5	Defensive (728 Mike Singletary, 56 Carl Banks, 98 Deion Sanders, 191 Howie Long, 131 Issiac Holt, 241 Pat	3.00

1991 Pro Set WLAF

PAUL BERARDELLI • GUARD
LONDON MONARCHS

These cards feature players from the World League of American Football. This logo and a notation that the card is an "Official World League Card" are on the front, which has a full-bleed color or action photo. The back has a card number, player profile, biographical information and a mug shot. Each back is designed in a horizontal format.

		MT
Complete Set (150):		5.00
Common Player:		.05
1	World League Logo	.15
2	Mike Lynn	.15
3	First Weekend	.15
4	World Bowl Trophy	.30
5	Jon Horton	.05
6	Stan Gelbaugh	.50
7	Dan Crossman	.05
8	Marlon Brown	.10
9	Judd Garrett	.25
10	Barcelona Dragons	.05
11	Birmingham Fire	.05
12	Frankfurt Galaxy	.05
13	London Monarchs	.05
14	Montreal Machine	.05
15	NY-NJ Knights	.05
16	Orlando Thunder	.05
17	Raleigh-Durham Skyhawks	.05
18	Sacramento Surge	.05
19	San Antonio Riders	.05
20	Eric Wilkerson	.05
21	Stan Gelbaugh	.35
22	Judd Garrett	.15
23	Tony Baker	.05
24	Byron Williams	.05
25	Chris Mohr	.10
26	Errol Tucker	.05
27	Carl Painter	.05
28	Anthony Parker	.10
29	Danny Lockett	.10
30	Scott Adams	.05
31	Jim Bell	.05
32	Lydell Carr	.15
33	Bruce Clark	.15
34	Demetrius Davis	.10
35	Scott Erney	.10
36	Ron Goetz	.05
37	Xisco Marcos	.05
38	Paul Palmer	.15
39	Tony Rice	.40
40	Bobby Sign	.05
41	Gene Taylor	.05
42	Barry Voorhees	.05
43	Jack Bicknell	.10
44	Kenny Bell	.05
45	Willie Bouyer	.05
46	John Brantley	.10
47	Elroy Harris	.05
48	James Henry	.05
49	John Holland	.10
50	Arhur Hunter	.05
51	Eric Jones	.05
52	Kirk Maggio	.05
53	Paul McGowan	.05
54	John Miller	.10
55	Maurice Oliver	.05
56	Darrel Phillips	.05
57	Chan Gailey	.05
58	Tony Baker	.10
59	Tim Broady	.05
60	Garry Frank	.05
61	Jason Johnson	.05
62	Stefan Maslo	.05
63	Mark Mraz	.05
64	Yepi Pau'u	.05
65	Mike Perez	.25
66	Mike Teeter	.05
67	Chris Williams	.05
68	Jack Elway	.20
69	Theo Adams	.05
70	Jeff Alexander	.05
71	Phillip Alexander	.05
72	Paul Berardelli	.10
73	Dana Brinson	.05
74	Marlon Brown	.05
75	Dedrick Dodge	.05
76	Victor Ebubedike	.05
77	Corris Ervin	.10
78	Steve Gabbard	.05
79	Judd Garrett	.15
80	Stan Gelbaugh	.75
81	Roy Hart	.05
82	Jon Horton	.05
83	Danny Lockett	.15
84	Doug Marrone	.05
85	Ken Sale	.05
86	Larry Kennan	.05
87	Mike Cadore	.05
88	K.D. Dunn	.05
89	Ricky Johnson	.05
90	Chris Mohr	.05
91	Bjorn Nittmo	.10
92	Michael Proctor	.05
93	Richard Shelton	.15
94	Tracy Simien	.30
95	Jacques Dussault	.05
96	Cornell Burbage	.10
97	Joe Campbell	.05
98	Monty Gilbreath	.05
99	Jeff Graham	.25
100	Kip Lewis	.05
101	Bob Lilljedah	.05
102	Falanda Newton	.10
103	Anthony Parker	.05
104	Caesar Rentie	.05
105	Ron Sancho	.10
106	Craig Schlicting	.10
107	Lonnie Turner	.05
108	Eric Wilkerson	.05
109	Tony Woods	.05
110	Darrell "Mouse" Davis	.15
111	Kerwin Bell	.30
112	Wayne Davis	.05
113	John Guerrero	.05
114	Myron Jones	.05
115	Eric Mitchel	.20
116	Billy Owens	.05
117	Carl Painter	.05
118	Rob Sterling	.05
119	Errol Tucker	.05
120	Byron Williams	.05
121	Mike Withycombe	.05
122	Don Matthews	.05
123	Jon Carter	.05
124	Marvin Hargrove	.05
125	Clarkston Hines	.05
126	Ray Jackson	.05
127	Bobby McAllister	.25
128	Darryl McGill	.05
129	Pat McGuirk	.10
130	Shawn Woodson	.05
131	Roman Gabriel	.25
132	Greg Couatte	.05
133	Mike Eklins	.15
134	Victor Floyd	.05
135	Shawn Knight	.10
136	Pete Najarian	.05
137	Carl Parker	.10
138	Richard Stephens	.05
139	Curtis Wilson	.05
140	Kay Stephenson	.10
141	Ricky Blake	.25
142	Donnie Gardner	.25
143	Jason Garrett	.25
144	Mike Johnson	.05
145	Undra Johnson	.05
146	John Layfield	.05
147	Mark Ledbetter	.05
148	Gary Richard	.05
149	Tim Walton	.05
150	Mike Riley	.05

1991 Pro Set WLAF World Bowl Combo 43

This set combines Pro Set's helmet and 32-card insert sets into one issue. Fans who attended the World Bowl Game in Wembley Stadium in London, England, received the set. The cards have been renumbered from the original sets, and the helmet cards can be identified by the chronological text which is on the back instead of a team schedule.

		MT
Complete Set (43):		15.00
Common Player:		.25
1	PRES (Mike Lynn)	.75
2	League Opener London 24, Frankfurt 11	.50
3	Jack Bicknell	.50
4	Scott Erney	.40
5	Anthony Greene	.50
6	Chan Gailey	.50
7	Paul McGowan	.25
8	Brent Pease	.25
9	Jack Elway	.80
10	Mike Perez	.75
11	Mike Teeter	.25
12	Larry Kennan	.25
13	Corris Ervin	.25
14	John Witkowski	.50
15	Jacques Dussault	.35
16	Ray Savage	.35
17	Kevin Sweeney	.65
18	Mouse Davis	.65
19	Todd Hammel	.50
20	Anthony Parker	.50
21	Don Matthews	.25
22	Kerwin Bell	.75
23	Wayne Davis	.25
24	Roman Gabriel	.75
25	Jon Carter	.50
26	Bobby McAllister	1.00
27	Kay Stephenson	.25
28	Mike Elkins	1.00
29	Shawn Knight	.50
30	Mike Riley	.25
31	Jason Garrett	.75
32	Greg Gilbert	.50
33	World Bowl Trophy	4.00
34	Barcelona Dragons Helmet	.60
35	Birmingham Fire Helmet	.60
36	Frankfurt Galaxy Helmet	.60
37	London Monarchs Helmet	.60
38	Montreal Machine Helmet	.60
39	NY-NJ Knights Helmet	.60
40	Orlando Thunder Helmet	.60
41	Ral.-Durham Skyhawks Helmet	.60
42	Sacramento Surge Helmet	.60
43	San Antonio Riders Helmet	.60

1991 Pro Set Super Bowl XXVI AMEX Binder

American Express sponsored this 49-card set which was sold to commemorate Super Bowl XXVI in Minneapolis. The cards were included in an album, which holds four cards per page. Representatives from the Super Bowl teams - the Buffalo Bills and Washington Redskins - are included in the set. The cards have the same photos and numbers as their regular set counterparts, except these are marked with an AFC or NFC Champs logo on the front.

		MT
Complete Set (49):		25.00
Common Player:		.40
1	The NFL Experience	1.00
2	Super Bowl XXVI	.50
3	AFC Standings	.50
4	NFC Standings	.50
5	The Metrodome	.50
6	Howard Ballard	.40
74	Cornelius Bennett	.75
75	Shane Conlan	.50
76	Kent Hull	.50
77	Kirby Jackson	.40

79	Mark Kelso	.40
80	Nate Odomes	.40
81	Andre Reed	.90
82	Jim Ritcher	.40
83	Bruce Smith	.75
84	Darryl Talley	.50
86	Thurman Thomas	3.00
88	Will Wolford	.40
89	Jeff Wright	.40
90	Marv Levy	.40
300	Cornelius Bennett	.60
316	Earnest Byner	.60
317	Gary Clark	.90
318	Andre Collins	.50
320	Chip Lohmiller	.40
321	Martin Mayhew	.40
322	Mark Rypien	.75
323	Alvin Walton	.40
324	Joe Gibbs	.50
370	Warren Moon	.75
444	James Lofton	.75
445	Keith McKeller	.50
449	Leon Seals	.40
450	Leonard Smith	.40
676	Jeff Bostic	.40
677	Darrell Green	.75
678	Markus Koch	.40
679	Jim Lachey	.50
680	Charles Mann	.50
681	Wilber Marshall	.50
682	Art Monk	.75
683	Gerald Riggs	.50
684	Ricky Sanders	.75
725	Howie Long	.75
726	Dan Marino	2.00
746	Bobby Wilson	.50
805	Ricky Ervins	.75
848	Brian Mitchell	.75
(1)	Jim Kelly	20.00
(1)	Jim Kelly	20.00

1992 Pro Set

DAVE KRIEG

Pro Set issued its 700-card 1992 set in two series - 400 and 300 cards. The fronts have full-bleed color action photos and the player's name and NFL/Pro Set logos at the bottom. The backs, using a horizontal format, offer statistics, a biography, career highlights and a close-up shot of the player. Subsets include Statistical Leaders, Milestones, Draft Day, Innovators, 1991 Replays, Super Bowl XXVI Replays, Pro Set Newsreel, Magic Numbers, Play Smart, NFC Spirit of the Game, AFC Pro Bowl Stars, NFC Pro Bowl Stars, and six miscellaneous cards. Insert cards include an Emmitt Smith hologram set of four cards (ES1-ES4), Hall of Fame 2000 (10 cards), Team MVPs (30 gold-foil stamped cards), a Santa Claus card, Ground Force, Hall of Fame Inductees and a Pro Set Emmitt Smith Power Preview special offer card.

		MT
Complete Set (700):		20.00
Complete Series 1 (400):		10.00
Complete Series 2 (300):		10.00
Common Player:		.05
Minor Stars:		.10
Series 1 Wax Box:		8.00
Series 2 Wax Box:		12.00
1	Mike Croel (LL)	.05
2	Thurman Thomas (LL)	.10
3	Wayne Fontes (CO) (LL)	.05
4	Anthony Munoz (LL)	.05
5	Steve Young (LL)	.25
6	Warren Moon (LL)	.10
7	Emmitt Smith (LL)	.50
8	Haywood Jeffires (LL)	.05
9	Marv Cook (LL)	.05
10	Michael Irvin (LL)	.10
11	Thurman Thomas (LL)	.10
12	Chip Lohmiller (LL)	.05
13	Barry Sanders (LL)	.75
14	Reggie Roby (LL)	.05
15	Mel Gray (LL)	.05
16	Ronnie Lott (LL)	.05
17	Pat Swilling (LL)	.05
18	Reggie White (LL)	.10
19	Haywood Jeffires (ML)	.05
20	Pat Leahy (ML)	.05
21	James Lofton (ML)	.05
22	Art Monk (ML)	.10
23	Don Shula (ML)	.05
24	Nick Lowery (ML)	.05
25	John Elway (ML)	.50
26	Chicago Bears (ML)	.05
27	Marcus Allen (ML)	.10
28	*Terrell Buckley*	.20
29	*Amp Lee*	.10
30	*Chris Mims*	.10
31	*Leon Searcy*	.10
32	*Jimmy Smith*	2.00
33	*Siran Stacy*	.10
34	Pete Gogolak	.05
35	Cheerleaders	.05
36	Houston Astrodome	.05
37	Christian Okoye (Week 1)	.05
38	Don Beebe (Week 2)	.05
39	Wendell Davis (Week 3)	.05
40	Don Shula (CO, Week 4)	.05
41	Ronnie Lott (Week 5)	.05
42	Art Monk (Week 6)	.10
43	Thurman Thomas (Week 7)	.10
44	John Stephens (Week 8)	.05
45	Herschel Walker (Week 9)	.05
46	Chris Burkett (Week 10)	.05
47	Line Play (Week 11)	.05
48	Andre Rison (Week 12)	.10
49	Steve Beuerlein, Michael Irvin (Week 13)	.10
50	Irving Fryar (Week 14)	.05
51	Bill's Defense (Week 15)	.05
52	Kelvin Martin (Week 16)	.05
53	Bruce Coslet (CO, Week 17)	.05
54	Fred Jones (AFC Wild Card)	.05
55	Oilers' Run-and-Shoot (AFC Wild Card)	.05
56	Bill Bates (NFC Wild Card)	.05
57	Michael Haynes (NFC Wild Card)	.05
58	Bronco Interception (AFC Divisional Playoff)	.05
59	Thurman Thomas (AFC Divisional Playoff)	.10
60	Erik Kramer (NFC Divisional Playoff)	.05
61	Darrell Green (NFC Divisional Playoff)	.05
62	Carlton Bailey (AFC Championship)	.05
63	Mark Rypien (NFC Championship)	.05
64	TD Reversed, FG Blocked	.05
65	Brad Edwards (Picks Off First of Two)	.05
66	Rypien to Byner, Rypien to Byner	.05
67	Riggs Puts Redskins Up	.05
68	Gouveia Interceptions Buries Bills	.05
69	Thurman Thomas	.20
70	Clark Catches Rypien's Second TD	.05
71	Bills Convert Late Break	.05
72	Redskins Run Out the Clock	.05
73	Jeff Bostic	.05
74	Earnest Byner	.05
75	Gary Clark	.05
76	Andre Collins	.05
77	Darrell Green	.05
78	Joe Jacoby	.05
79	Jim Lachey	.05
80	Chip Lohmiller	.05
81	Charles Mann	.05
82	Martin Mayhew	.05
83	Matt Millen	.05
84	Brian Mitchell	.05
85	Art Monk	.10
86	Gerald Riggs	.05
87	Mark Rypien	.05
88	Fred Stokes	.05
89	Bobby Wilson	.05
90	Joe Gibbs	.05
91	Howard Ballard	.05
92	Cornelius Bennett	.10
93	Kenneth Davis	.05
94	Al Edwards	.05
95	Kent Hull	.05
96	Kirby Jackson	.05
97	Mark Kelso	.05
98	James Lofton	.10
99	Keith McKeller	.05
100	Nate Odomes	.05
101	Jim Ritcher	.05
102	Leon Seals	.05
103	Steve Tasker	.05
104	Darryl Talley	.05
105	Thurman Thomas	.20
106	Will Wolford	.05
107	Jeff Wright	.05
108	Marv Levy	.05
109	Darion Conner	.05
110	Bill Fralic	.05
111	Moe Gardner	.05
112	Michael Haynes	.20
113	Chris Miller	.05
114	Eric Pegram	.05
115	Bruce Pickens	.05
116	Andre Rison	.20
117	Jerry Glanville	.05
118	Neal Anderson	.05
119	Trace Armstrong	.05
120	Wendell Davis	.05
121	Richard Dent	.10
122	Jay Hilgenberg	.05
123	Lemuel Stinson	.05
124	Stan Thomas	.05
125	Tom Waddle	.05
126	Mike Ditka	.10
127	James Brooks	.05
128	Eddie Brown	.05
129	David Fulcher	.05
130	Harold Green	.05
131	Tim Krumrie	.05
132	Anthony Munoz	.05
133	Craig Taylor	.05
134	Eric Thomas	.05
135	David Shula	.05
136	Mike Baab	.05
137	Brian Brennan	.05
138	Michael Jackson	.10
139	James Jones	.05
140	Ed King	.05
141	Clay Matthews	.05
142	Eric Metcalf	.05
143	Joe Morris	.05
144	Bill Belichick	.05
145	Steve Beuerlein	.05
146	Larry Brown	.05
147	Ray Horton	.05
148	Ken Norton	.05
150	Emmitt Smith	1.50
151	Mark Stepnoski	.05
152	Alexander Wright	.05
153	Jimmy Johnson	.10
154	Mike Croel	.05
155	John Elway	.75
156	Gaston Green	.05
157	Wymon Henderson	.05
158	Karl Mecklenburg	.05
159	Warren Powers	.05
160	Steve Sewell	.05
161	Doug Widell	.05
162	Dan Reeves	.05
163	Eric Andolsek	.05
164	Jerry Ball	.05
165	Bennie Blades	.05
166	Ray Crockett	.05
167	Willie Green	.05
168	Erik Kramer	.05
169	Barry Sanders	2.00
170	Chris Spielman	.05
171	Wayne Fontes	.05
172	Vinnie Clark	.05
173	Tony Mandarich	.05
174	Brian Noble	.05
175	Bryce Paup	.05
176	Sterling Sharpe	.20
177	Darrell Thompson	.05
178	Esera Tuaolo	.05
179	Ed West	.05
180	Mike Holmgren	.20
181	Ray Childress	.05
182	Cris Dishman	.05
183	Curtis Duncan	.05
184	William Fuller	.05
185	Lamar Lathon	.05
186	Warren Moon	.20
187	*Bo Orlando*	.10
188	Lorenzo White	.05
189	Jack Pardee	.05
190	Chip Banks	.05
191	Dean Biasucci	.05
192	Bill Brooks	.05
193	Ray Donaldson	.05
194	Jeff Herrod	.05
195	Mike Prior	.05
196	Mark Vander Poel	.05
197	Clarence Verdin	.05
198	Ted Marchibroda	.05
199	John Alt	.05
200	Deron Cherry	.05
201	Steve DeBerg	.05
202	Nick Lowery	.05
203	Neil Smith	.05
204	Derrick Thomas	.20
205	Joe Valerio	.05
206	Barry Word	.05
207	Marty Schottenheimer	.05
208	Marcus Allen	.20
209	Nick Bell	.05
210	Tim Brown	.20
211	Howie Long	.10
212	Ronnie Lott	.10
213	Todd Marinovich	.05
214	Greg Townsend	.05
215	Steve Wright	.05
216	Art Shell	.05
217	Flipper Anderson	.05
218	Robert Delpino	.05
219	Henry Ellard	.05
220	Kevin Greene	.05
221	Todd Lyght	.05
222	Tom Newberry	.05
223	Roman Phifer	.05
224	Michael Stewart	.05
225	Chuck Knox	.05
226	Aaron Craver	.05
227	Jeff Cross	.05
228	Mark Duper	.05
229	Ferrell Edmunds	.05
230	Jim C. Jensen	.05
231	Louis Oliver	.05
232	Reggie Roby	.05
233	Sammie Smith	.05
234	Don Shula	.10
235	Joey Browner	.05
236	Anthony Carter	.05
237	Chris Doleman	.05
238	Steve Jordan	.05
239	Kirk Lowdermilk	.05
240	Henry Thomas	.05
241	Herschel Walker	.10
242	Felix Wright	.05
243	Dennis Green	.10
244	Ray Agnew	.05
245	Marv Cook	.05
246	Irving Fryar	.10
247	Pat Harlow	.05
248	Hugh Millen	.05
249	Leonard Russell	.10
250	Andre Tippett	.05
251	Jon Vaughn	.05
252	Dick MacPherson	.05
253	Morten Andersen	.10
254	Bobby Hebert	.05
255	Joel Hilgenberg	.05
256	Vaughan Johnson	.05
257	Sam Mills	.05
258	Pat Swilling	.05
259	Floyd Turner	.05
260	Steve Walsh	.05
261	Jim Mora	.05
262	Stephen Baker	.05
263	Mark Collins	.05
264	Rodney Hampton	.10
265	Jeff Hostetler	.10
266	Erik Howard	.05
267	Sean Landeta	.05
268	Gary Reasons	.05
269	Everson Walls	.05
270	Ray Handley	.05
271	*Louis Aguiar*	.10
272	Brad Baxter	.05
273	Chris Burkett	.05
274	Irv Eatman	.05
275	Jeff Lageman	.05
276	Freeman McNeil	.05
277	Rob Moore	.20
278	Lonnie Young	.05
279	Bruce Coslet	.05
280	Jerome Brown	.05
281	Keith Byars	.05
282	Bruce Collie	.05
283	Keith Jackson	.10
284	James Joseph	.05
285	Seth Joyner	.05
286	Andre Waters	.05
287	Reggie White	.20
288	Rich Kotite	.05
289	Rich Camarillo	.05
290	Garth Jax	.05
291	Ernie Jones	.05
292	Tim McDonald	.05
293	Rod Saddler	.05
294	Anthony Thompson	.05
295	Tim Tupa	.05
296	Ron Wolfley	.05
297	Joe Bugel	.05
298	Gary Anderson	.05
299	Jeff Graham	.10
300	Bryan Hinkle	.05
301	Tunch Ilkin	.05
302	Louis Lipps	.05
303	Neil O'Donnell	.10
304	Rod Woodson	.05
305	Bill Cowher	.05
306	Eric Bieniemy	.05
307	Marion Butts	.05
308	John Friesz	.10
309	Courtney Hall	.05
310	Ronnie Harmon	.05
311	Henry Rolling	.05
312	Billy Ray Smith	.05
313	George Thornton	.05
314	Bobby Ross	.05
315	Todd Bowles	.05
316	Michael Carter	.05
317	Don Griffin	.05
318	Charles Haley	.05
319	Brent Jones	.05
320	John Taylor	.05
321	Ted Washington	.05
322	Steve Young	.50
323	George Seifert	.10
324	Brian Blades	.05
325	Jacob Green	.05
326	Patrick Hunter	.05
328	Tommy Kane	.05
329	Cortez Kennedy	.10
330	Dave Krieg	.05
331	Rufus Porter	.05
332	John L. Williams	.05
333	Tom Flores	.05
334	Gary Anderson	.05
335	Mark Carrier	.05
336	Reuben Davis	.05
337	Lawrence Dawsey	.05
338	Keith McCants	.05
339	Vinny Testaverde	.20
340	Broderick Thomas	.05
341	Robert Wilson	.05
342	Sam Wyche	.05
343	1991 Teacher of the Year	.05
344	Owners Reject Instant Replay	.05
345	NFL Experience Unveiled	.05
346	Noll Retires Tosses Coin	.05
347	Isaac Curtis, Tim McGee	.05
348	Drew Pearson, Michael Irvin	.10
349	Billy Sims, Barry Sanders	.50
350	Kenny Stabler, Todd Marinovich	.05
351	Craig James, Leonard Russell	.05
352	Bob Golic (Graffiti It's a Sign of Ignorance)	.05
353	Pat Harlow (Vote, Let Your Choice Be Heard)	.05
354	Esera Tuaolo (Stand Tall, Be Proud of Your Heritage)	.05
355	Mark Schlereth (Save the Environment Be a Team Player)	.05
356	Trace Armstrong (Drug Abuse Stay in Control)	.05
357	Eric Bieniemy (Save a Life Buckle Up)	.05
358	Bill Romanowski (Education Stay in School)	.05
359	Irv Eatman (Exercise Be Active)	.05
360	Jonathan Hayes (Diabetes Be Your Best)	.05
361	Atlanta Falcons	.05
362	Chicago Bears	.05
363	Dallas Cowboys	.05
364	Detroit Lions	.05
365	Green Bay Packers	.05
366	Los Angeles Rams	.05
367	Minnesota Vikings	.05
368	New Orleans Saints	.05
369	New York Giants	.05
370	Philadelphia Eagles	.05
371	Phoenix Cardinals	.05
372	San Francisco 49ers	.05
373	Tampa Bay Buccaneers	.05
374	Washington Redskins	.05
375	Steve Atwater	.05
376	Cornelius Bennett	.05
377	Tim Brown	.10
378	Marion Butts	.05
379	Ray Childress	.05
380	Mark Clayton	.05
381	Marv Cook	.05
382	Cris Dishman	.05
383	William Fuller	.05
384	Gaston Green	.05
385	Jeff Jaeger	.05
386	Haywood Jeffires	.05
387	James Lofton	.05
388	Ronnie Lott	.05
389	Karl Mecklenburg	.05
390	Warren Moon	.05
391	Anthony Munoz	.05
392	Dennis Smith	.05
393	Neil Smith	.05
394	Darryl Talley	.05
395	Derrick Thomas	.10
396	Thurman Thomas	.20
397	Greg Townsend	.05
398	Richmond Webb	.05
399	Rod Woodson	.05
400	Dan Reeves	.05
401	Troy Aikman (PB)	.30
403	PB (Eric Allen)	.05
404	PB (Bennie Blades)	.05
405	PB (Mark Carrier)	.05
406	PB (Gary Clark)	.05
407	PB (Mel Gray)	.05
408	PB (Michael Irvin)	.10
409	PB (Vaughan Johnson)	.05
410	PB (Vaughan Johnson)	.05
411	PB (Seth Joyner)	.05
412	PB (Jim Lachey)	.05
413	PB (Chip Lohmiller)	.05
414	PB (Charles Mann)	.05
415	PB (Chris Miller)	.05
416	PB (Sam Mills)	.05
417	PB (Bart Oates)	.05
418	PB (Jerry Rice)	.30
419	PB (Andre Rison)	.10
420	PB (Mark Rypien)	.05
421	PB (Barry Sanders)	.75
422	PB (Deion Sanders)	.10
423	PB (Mark Schlereth)	.05
424	PB (Mike Singletary)	.05
425	(Emmitt Smith PB)	.50
426	PB (Pat Swilling)	.05
427	PB (Reggie White)	.10
428	Rick Bryan	.05
429	Tim Green	.05
430	Drew Hill	.05
431	Norm Johnson	.05
432	Keith Jones	.05
433	Mike Pritchard	.10
434	Deion Sanders	.50
435	*Tony Smith*	.05
436	Jessie Tuggle	.05
437	Steve Christie	.05
438	Shane Conlan	.05
439	*Matt Darby*	.10
440	*John Fina*	.05
441	Henry Jones	.05
442	Jim Kelly	.20
443	Pete Metzelaars	.05
444	Andre Reed	.10
445	Bruce Smith	.10
446	*Troy Auzenne*	.10
447	Mark Carrier	.05
448	*Will Furrer*	.10
449	Jim Harbaugh	.05
450	Brad Muster	.05
451	Darren Lewis	.05
452	Mike Singletary	.10
453	*Alonzo Spellman*	.20
454	Chris Zorich	.05
455	Jim Breech	.05
456	Boomer Esiason	.10
457	James Francis	.05
458	Derrick Fenner	.05
459	*David Klingler*	.20
460	Tim McGee	.05
461	*Carl Pickens*	1.00
462	Alfred Williams	.05
463	*Darryl Williams*	.10
464	Mark Bavaro	.05
465	Jay Hilgenberg	.05
466	Leroy Hoard	.10
467	Bernie Kosar	.05
468	Michael Dean Perry	.10
469	Todd Philcox	.10
470	*Patrick Rowe*	.10
471	*Tommy Vardell*	.20
472	Everson Walls	.05
473	Troy Aikman	.75
474	*Kenneth Gant*	.10
475	Charles Haley	.05
476	Michael Irvin	.20
477	*Robert Jones*	.10
478	Russell Maryland	.10
479	Jay Novacek	.05
480	*Kevin Smith*	.10
481	Tony Tolbert	.05
482	Steve Atwater	.05
483	*Shane Dronett*	.10
484	Simon Fletcher	.05
485	Greg Lewis	.05
486	*Tommy Maddox*	.20
487	Shannon Sharpe	.20
488	Dennis Smith	.05
489	Sammie Smith	.05
490	Kenny Walker	.05
491	Lomas Brown	.05
492	Mike Farr	.05
493	Mel Gray	.05
494	*Jason Hanson*	.10
495	Herman Moore	.75
496	Rodney Peete	.05
497	*Robert Porcher*	.10
498	Kelvin Pritchett	.05
499	Andre Ware	.05
500	*Sanjay Beach*	.10
501	*Edgar Bennett*	.20
502	Lewis Billups	.05
503	Terrell Buckley	.20
504	*Ty Detmer*	.10
505	*Brett Favre*	2.50
506	Johnny Holland	.05
507	*Dexter McNabb*	.10
508	Vince Workman	.05
509	Cody Carlson	.05
510	Ernest Givins	.05
511	Jerry Gray	.05
512	Haywood Jeffires	.05
513	Bruce Matthews	.05
514	Bubba McDowell	.05
515	*Bucky Richardson*	.10
516	Webster Slaughter	.05
517	Al Smith	.05
518	Mel Agee	.05
519	*Ashley Ambrose*	.10
520	Kevin Call	.05
521	Ken Clark	.05
522	*Quentin Coryatt*	.20
523	*Steve Emtman*	.10
524	Jeff George	.05
525	Jessie Hester	.05
526	Anthony Johnson	.05
527	Tim Barnett	.05
528	Martin Bayless	.05
529	J.J. Birden	.05
530	*Dale Carter*	.20
531	Dave Krieg	.05

532	Albert Lewis	.05
533	Nick Lowery	.05
534	Christian Okoye	.05
535	Harvey Williams	.10
536	Aundray Bruce	.05
537	Eric Dickerson	.05
538	Willie Gault	.05
539	Ethan Horton	.05
540	Jeff Jaeger	.05
541	Napoleon McCallum	.05
542	*Chester McGlockton*	.10
543	Steve Smith	.05
544	Steve Wisniewski	.05
545	Marc Boutte	.05
546	Pat Carter	.05
547	Jim Everett	.05
548	Cleveland Gary	.05
549	*Sean Gilbert*	.20
550	Steve Israel	.05
551	*Todd Kinchen*	.20
552	Jackie Slater	.05
553	Tony Zendejas	.05
554	Robert Clark	.05
555	Mark Clayton	.10
556	*Marco Coleman*	.10
557	Bryan Cox	.05
558	(Keith Jackson) (Card says drafted in '88, but acquired as free agent in '92)	.05
559	Dan Marino	1.25
560	John Offerdahl	.05
561	*Troy Vincent*	.20
562	Richmond Webb	.05
563	Terry Allen	.20
564	Cris Carter	.50
565	Roger Craig	.10
566	Rich Gannon	.05
567	Hassan Jones	.05
568	Randall McDaniel	.05
569	Al Noga	.05
570	Steve Scott	.05
571	*Van Waiters*	.05
572	Bruce Armstrong	.05
573	Gene Chilton	.10
574	Eugene Chung	.10
575	Todd Collins	.05
576	Hart Lee Dykes	.05
577	David Howard	.05
578	Eugene Lockhart	.05
579	Greg McMurtry	.05
580	*Rodney Smith*	.05
581	Gene Atkins	.05
582	Vince Buck	.05
583	Wesley Carroll	.05
584	Jim Dombrowski	.05
585	*Vaughn Dunbar*	.10
586	Craig Heyward	.05
587	Dalton Hilliard	.05
588	Wayne Martin	.05
589	Renaldo Turnbull	.05
590	Carl Banks	.05
591	Derek Brown	.10
592	Jarrod Bunch	.05
593	Mark Ingram	.05
594	Ed McCaffrey	.30
595	Phil Simms	.10
596	*Phillippi Sparks*	.05
597	Lawrence Taylor	.20
598	Lewis Tillman	.05
599	Kyle Clifton	.05
600	Mo Lewis	.05
601	Terance Mathis	.05
602	Scott Mersereau	.05
603	*Johnny Mitchell*	.20
604	Browning Nagle	.10
605	Ken O'Brien	.05
606	Al Toon	.05
607	Marvin Washington	.05
608	Eric Allen	.05
609	Fred Barnett	.05
610	John Booty	.05
611	Randall Cunningham	.20
612	Rich Miano	.05
613	Clyde Simmons	.05
614	Siran Stacy	.05
615	Herschel Walker	.10
616	Calvin Williams	.05
617	Chris Chandler	.20
618	Randal Hill	.10
619	Johnny Johnson	.10
620	Lorenzo Lynch	.05
621	Robert Massey	.05
622	Ricky Proehl	.05
623	Timm Rosenbach	.05
624	*Tony Sacca*	.10
625	(Aeneas Williams) (name misspelled Aaneas)	.10
626	Bubby Brister	.05
627	Barry Foster	.05
628	Merril Hoge	.05
629	David Johnson	.05
630	David Little	.05
631	Greg Lloyd	.05
632	Ernie Mills	.05
633	*Leon Searcy*	.05
634	Dwight Stone	.05
635	*Sam Anno*	.10
636	Burt Grossman	.05
637	Stan Humphries	.10
638	Nate Lewis	.05
639	Anthony Miller	.05
640	Chris Mims	.05
641	*Marquez Pope*	.20
642	Stanley Richard	.05
643	Junior Seau	.20

644	*Brian Bollinger*	.05
645	*Steve Bono*	.30
646	Dexter Carter	.10
647	*Dana Hall*	.05
648	Amp Lee	.10
649	Joe Montana	1.25
650	Tom Rathman	.05
651	Jerry Rice	.75
652	Ricky Watters	.20
653	Robert Blackmon	.05
654	John Kasay	.05
655	*Ronnie Lee*	.10
656	Dan McGwire	.10
657	*Ray Roberts*	.10
658	Kelly Stouffer	.05
659	Chris Warren	.20
660	Tony Woods	.05
661	David Wyman	.05
662	*Reggie Cobb*	.05
663A	(Steve DeBerg) (incorrect career yardage 1,455; found in foil packs)	.05
663B	(Steve DeBerg) (correct career yardage 31,455; found in jumbo packs)	.05
664	*Santana Dotson*	.20
665	Craig Erickson	.10
666	Paul Gruber	.05
667	Ron Hall	.05
668	*Courtney Hawkins*	.10
669	Charles McRae	.05
670	Ricky Reynolds	.05
671	Monte Coleman	.05
672	Brad Edwards	.05
673	(James Geathers) (card says played in New Orleans '89; should say Washington)	.05
674	Kelly Goodburn	.05
675	Kurt Gouveia	.05
676	*Chris Hakel*	.10
677	Wilber Marshall	.05
678	Ricky Sanders	.05
679	Mark Schlereth	.05
680	Spirit of the Game (Rich Stadium)	.05
681	Spirit of the Game (Boomer Esiason) (with tiger cub)	.05
682	Spirit of the Game (The Dog Pound)	.05
683	Spirit of the Game (Bronco Statue)	.05
684	Spirit of the Game ("Luv Ya Blue")	.05
685	Spirit of the Game (Hoosier Dome)	.05
686	Spirit of the Game (Mack Lee Hill, Tracy Simien) (Mack Lee Hill Award)	.05
687	Spirit of the Game (The Team of the Decades)	.05
688	Spirit of the Game (Dolphins' helmet)	.05
689	Spirit of the Game (Francis J. Kilroy) (VP)	.05
690	Spirit of the Game (Team mascot)	.05
691	Spirit of the Game (Steelers' helmet)	.05
692	Spirit of the Game (Charger in parachute)	.05
693	Spirit of the Game (Kingdome)	.05
694	Play Smart (Stephen Baker)	.05
695	Hank Williams Jr.	.20
696	NEW (Brian Baldinger, Gary Baldinger, Rich Baldinger) (3 Brothers in NFL)	.05
697	NEW (Japan Bowl August 2, 1992)	.05
698	NEW (Georgia Dome)	.05
699	NEW (Theme Art Super Bowl XXVII)	.05
700	Super Bowl XXVI MVP (Mark Rypien)	.05
AU150	Emmitt Smith AUTO (Certified Autograph)	200.00
AU168	Erik Kramer AUTO (Certified Autograph)	40.00
NNO	Power Preview (Emmitt Smith)	1.00
NNO	Santa Claus (Spirit of the Game)	.50

1992 Pro Set Emmitt Smith Holograms

Dallas Cowboys' star running back Emmitt Smith is fea-tured on these four insert holograms offered randomly in 1992 Pro Set foil packs. Each card front represents a different part of Smith's career. The red, white and blue backs have player-e profile information, 1991 and projected stats and a career summary. Cards are numbered ES1-ES4, with those numbered ES1 being the easiest to find, while the ES4 cards were the most difficult to find.

		MT
Complete Set (4):		60.00
Common Smith:		7.00
1	Stats 1990-1999	7.00
2	Drafted by Cowboys	10.00
3	Rookie of the Year	20.00
4	NFL Rushing Leader	30.00

1992 Pro Set Gold MVPs

PAT SWILLING — Pro Set Most Valuable Player

A most valuable player from each of the 28 NFL teams has been selected for this insert set. Two coaches were also selected. Cards 1-15, Series I jumbo pack inserts, have full-bleed action photos, plus a diamond-shaped '92 MVP' emblem on the front. The player's name is stamped in gold foil near the Pro Set/NFL logo. The horizontal card backs have statistics, a career summary and close-up shot. Series II pack inserts, cards 16-30, have a two-toned stripe on the left, plus a gray box in the lower left corner which has 'MVP' stamped in gold foil. The backs are screened and have career information and a close-up shot of the player. All cards are numbered with an 'MVP' prefix; AFC players are cards 1-14; NFC cards are 16-29. Coaches' cards are Don Shula (15) and Jimmy Johnson (30).

		MT
Complete Set (30):		15.00
Common Player:		.10
Minor Stars:		.20
1	Thurman Thomas	.40
2	Anthony Munoz	.10
3	Clay Matthews	.10
4	John Elway	2.00
5	Warren Moon	.40
6	Bill Brooks	.10
7	Derrick Thomas	.20
8	Todd Marinovich	.10
9	Mark Higgs	.10
10	Leonard Russell	.20
11	Rob Moore	.40
12	Rod Woodson	.20
13	Marion Butts	.10
14	Brian Blades	.10
15	Don Shula	.20
16	Deion Sanders	1.00
17	Neal Anderson	.10
18	Emmitt Smith	3.00
19	Barry Sanders	4.00
20	Brett Favre	5.00
21	Kevin Greene	.10
22	Terry Allen	.40
23	Pat Swilling	.10
24	Rodney Hampton	.20
25	Randall Cunningham	.50
26	Randall Hill	.10
27	Jerry Rice	1.50
28	Vinny Testaverde	.40
29	Mark Rypien	.20
30	Jimmy Johnson	.20

1992 Pro Set Ground Force

These cards are identical to their counterparts in the regular 1992 Pro Set issue, except they are stamped with a "Ground Force" logo in gold foil on the front. They share the same number as their counterparts in the regular issue's Ground Force subset. The gold-foiled inserts were included in foil packs of numbered hobby cases only.

		MT
Complete Set (6):		50.00
Common Player:		3.00
86	Gerald Riggs	3.00
105	Thurman Thomas	8.00
118	Neal Anderson	3.00
150	Emmitt Smith	35.00
206	Barry Word	3.00
249	Leonard Russell	3.00

1992 Pro Set HOF Inductees

JOHN RIGGINS — RB, HALL OF FAME

These cards, numbered with an "SC" prefix, are a "Special Collectibles" subset that features the 1992 Pro Football Hall of Fame Inductees. The cards, random inserts in 1992 Pro Set packs, have the Hall of Fame's logo on the front, along with the Pro Set logo, and show an action photo of the player. The card back has a career summary and a portrait shot.

		MT
Complete Set (4):		1.50
Common Player:		.40
1	Lem Barney	.40
2	Al Davis	.40
3	John Mackey	.40
4	John Riggins	.50

1992 Pro Set HOF 2000

WARREN MOON — Houston Oilers

Randomly inserted in Series II foil packs, the 10-card set honors players which Pro Set said would be inducted into the Hall of Fame shortly after the year 2000. The card fronts are identical to the base cards, with the player's name in a white stripe along the left and his team name listed beneath it. The HOF-2000 logo appears on a 3-D band in the lower left. Card backs have HOF-2000 listed at the top, with the player's name, position and team printed below it. Inside a 3-D text box is a write-up on the player's career. The cards are numbered inside a small rectangle in the lower right.

		MT
Complete Set (10):		20.00
Common Player:		1.50
Minor Stars:		3.00
1	Marcus Allen	3.00
2	Richard Dent	1.50
3	Eric Dickerson	3.00
4	Ronnie Lott	1.50
5	Art Monk	1.50
6	Joe Montana	8.00
7	Warren Moon	3.00
8	Anthony Munoz	1.50
9	Mike Singletary	3.00
10	Lawrence Taylor	3.00

1992 Pro Set Club

This nine-card set was used as a football practice educational tool. The full-bleed card fronts include photos which deal with various football skills. The bottom of each card includes the card's caption inside a purple stripe. The Pro Set Club logo is located on the left side of the stripe. The card backs include details on the skill highlighted on the front. The text is printed inside a yellow box. Card numbers are printed inside an oval in the lower right.

		MT
Complete Set (9):		5.00
Common Player:		.75
1	Quarterback Throwing Pass	.75
2	Coach Reviewing Play Strategy	.75
3	Team Stretching	.75
4	Offensive Play	.75
5	Kickoff	.75
6	Player's Stance	.75
7	Football Is a Spectator Sport	.75
8	Defensive Practice	.75
9	Play in Motion	.75

1992 Pro Set Emmitt Smith Promo Sheet

Measuring 7" x 13" and numbered to 2,000, this five-card sheet was used to promote the signing of Emmitt Smith as the Pro Set spokesman. Showcased on the sheet are his 1990, 1991, 1991 Platinum, 1991 Platinum Game Breaker and 1992 cards with a checklist back.

		MT
Complete Set (1):		10.00
Common Sheet:		10.00
NNO	Emmitt Smith Sheet (five cards featured numberd of 2000)	10.00

1992 Pro Set Power

MICHAEL HAYNES

This 330-card UV-coated set features action photos on the fronts with a semi-ghosted background. The player's name is in red letters at the bottom. The backs are in a horizontal format and feature the team and player name printed in the team's colors. A player profile is also included. A 10-card insert set, "Power Combos," was also made and features pairs of teammates. The cards were random inserts in foil packs.

		MT
Complete Set (330):		15.00
Common Player:		.05
Wax Box:		15.00
1	Warren Moon	.30
2	Mike Horan	.05
3	Bobby Hebert	.05
4	Jim Harbaugh	.05
5	Sean Landeta	.05
6	Bubby Brister	.05
7	John Elway	.50
8	Troy Aikman	1.00
9	Rodney Peete	.05
10	Dan McGwire	.05
11	Mark Rypien	.10
12	Randall Cunningham	.20
13	Dan Marino	1.50
14	Vinny Testaverde	.05
15	Jeff Hostetler	.35
16	Joe Montana	1.00
17	Dave Krieg	.05
18	Jeff Jaeger	.05
19	Bernie Kosar	.05
20	Barry Sanders	1.00
21	Deion Sanders	.40
22	Emmitt Smith	2.00
23	Mel Gray	.05
24	Stanley Richard	.05
25	Brad Muster	.05
26	Rod Woodson	.10
27	Rodney Hampton	.50
28	Darrell Green	.05
29	Barry Foster	.50
30	Dave Meggett	.05
31	Lonnie Young	.05
32	Marcus Allen	.05
33	Merril Hoge	.05
34	Thurman Thomas	.25
35	Neal Anderson	.10
36	Bennie Blades	.05
37	Pat Terrell	.05
38	Nick Bell	.20
39	Johnny Johnson	.20
40	Bill Bates	.05
41	Keith Byars	.05
42	Ronnie Lott	.05
43	Elvis Patterson	.05
44	Lorenzo White	.05
45	Tony Stargell	.05
46	Tim McDonald	.05
47	Kirby Jackson	.05
48	Lionel Washington	.05
49	Dennis Smith	.05
50	Mike Singletary	.05
51	Mike Croel	.05
52	Pepper Johnson	.05
53	Vaughn Johnson	.05
54	Chris Spielman	.05
55	Junior Seau	.10
56	Lawrence Taylor	.15
57	Clay Matthews	.05
58	Derrick Thomas	.20
59	Seth Joyner	.05
60	Stan Thomas	.05
61	Nate Newton	.05
62	Matt Brock	.05
63	*Gene Chilton*	.15
64	Randall McDaniel	.05
65	Max Montoya	.05
66	Joe Jacoby	.05
67	Russell Maryland	.25
68	Ed King	.05
69	*Mark Schlereth*	.15
70	Charles McRae	.05
71	Charles Mann	.05
72	William Perry	.05
73	Simon Fletcher	.05
74	Paul Gruber	.05
75	Howie Long	.05
76	Steve McMichael	.05
77	Karl Mecklenburg	.05
78	Anthony Munoz	.05
79	Ray Childress	.05
80	Jerry Rice	1.00
81	Art Monk	.10
82	John Taylor	.10
83	Andre Reed	.25
84	Haywood Jeffires	.25
85	Mark Duper	.05
86	Fred Barnett	.25
87	Tom Waddle	.15
88	Michael Irvin	.25
89	Brian Blades	.05
90	Neil Smith	.05
91	Kevin Greene	.05
92	Reggie White	.30
93	Jerry Ball	.05
94	Charles Haley	.05
95	Richard Dent	.05
96	Clyde Simmons	.05
97	Cornelius Bennett	.05
98	Eric Swann	.05
99	Doug Smith	.05
100	Jim Kelly	.40
101	Michael Jackson	.30
102	Steve Christie	.05
103	Timm Rosenbach	.05
104	Brett Favre	1.25
105	Jeff Feagles	.05
106	Kevin Butler	.05
107	Boomer Esiason	.25
108	Steve Young	1.00
109	Norm Johnson	.05
110	Jay Schroeder	.05
111	Jeff George	.40
112	Chris Miller	.05
113	*Steve Bono*	1.00
114	Neil O'Donnell	.50
115	*David Klingler*	.35
116	Rich Gannon	.10
117	Chris Chandler	.05
118	Stan Gelbaugh	.05
119	Scott Mitchell	.50
120	Mark Carrier	.05
121	Terry Allen	.55
122	Tim McKyer	.05
123	Barry Word	.20
124	Freeman McNeil	.05
125	Louis Oliver	.05

126	Jarvis Williams	.05
127	Steve Atwater	.05
128	Cris Dishman	.05
129	Eric Dickerson	.05
130	Brad Baxter	.05
131	Frank Minnifield	.05
132	Ricky Watters	.50
133	David Fulcher	.05
134	Herschel Walker	.05
135	Christian Okoye	.05
136	Jerome Henderson	.05
137	Nate Odomes	.05
138	Todd Scott	.05
139	Robert Delpino	.05
140	Gary Anderson	.05
141	Todd Lyght	.05
142	Chris Warren	.30
143	*Mike Brim*	.15
144	Tom Rathman	.05
145	*Dexter McNabb*	.10
146	Vince Workman	.05
147	Anthony Jackson	.05
148	Brian Washington	.05
149	David Tate	.05
150	Johnny Holland	.05
151	Monte Coleman	.05
152	Keith McCants	.05
153	*Eugene Seale*	.10
154	Al Smith	.05
155	Andre Collins	.05
156	Pat Swilling	.05
157	Rickey Jackson	.05
158	Wilbur Marshall	.05
159	Kyle Clifton	.05
160	Fred Stokes	.05
161	Lance Smith	.05
162	Guy McIntyre	.05
163	Bill Maas	.05
164	Gerald Perry	.05
165	Bart Oates	.05
166	Tony Jones	.05
167	Moe Gardner	.05
168	Joe Wolf	.05
169	Tim Krumrie	.05
170	Leonard Marshall	.05
171	Kevin Call	.05
172	Keith Kartz	.05
173	Ron Heller	.05
174	Steve Wallace	.05
175	Tony Casillas	.05
176	Tim Irwin	.05
177	Pat Harlow	.05
178	Bruce Smith	.05
179	Jim Lachey	.05
180	Andre Rison	.50
181	Michael Haynes	.60
182	Rod Bernstine	.05
183	Mark Clayton	.05
184	Jay Novacek	.25
185	Rob Moore	.05
186	Willie Green	.20
187	Ricky Proehl	.05
188	Al Toon	.05
189	Webster Slaughter	.05
190	Tony Bennett	.05
191	Jeff Cross	.05
192	Michael Dean Perry	.05
193	Greg Townsend	.05
194	Alfred Williams	.05
195	William Fuller	.05
196	Cortez Kennedy	.05
197	Henry Thomas	.05
198	Esera Tuaolo	.05
199	Tim Green	.05
200	Keith Jackson	.15
201	Don Majkowski	.05
202	Steve Beuerlein	.40
203	Hugh Millen	.05
204	Browning Nagel	.15
205	Chip Lohmiller	.05
206	Phil Simms	.15
207	Jim Everett	.05
208	Erik Kramer	.05
209	Todd Marinovich	.05
210	Henry Jones	.15
211	Dwight Stone	.05
212	Andre Waters	.05
213	Darryl Henley	.05
214	Mark Higgs	.15
215	Dalton Hilliard	.05
216	Earnest Byner	.05
217	Eric Metcalf	.05
218	Gill Byrd	.05
219	*Robert Williams*	.10
220	Kenneth Davis	.05
221	Larry Brown	.05
222	Mark Collins	.05
223	Vinnie Clark	.05
224	Patrick Hunter	.05
225	Gaston Green	.05
226	Everson Walls	.05
227	Harold Green	.05
228	Albert Lewis	.05
229	Don Griffin	.05
230	Lorenzo Lynch	.05
231	Brian Mitchell	.05
232	Thomas Everett	.05
233	Leonard Russell	.50
234	Eric Bieniemy	.05
235	John L. Williams	.05
236	Leroy Hoard	.05
237	Darren Lewis	.05
238	Reggie Cobb	.15
239	Steve Broussard	.05
240	Marion Butts	.05
241	Mike Pritchard	.25
242	Dexter Carter	.05
243	Aeneas Williams	.05

244	Bruce Pickens	.05
245	Harvey Williams	.15
246	Bobby Humphrey	.05
247	Duane Bickett	.05
248	James Francis	.05
249	Broderick Thomas	.05
250	Chip Banks	.05
251	Bryan Cox	.05
252	Sam Mills	.05
253	Ken Norton	.05
254	Jeff Harrod	.05
255	John Roper	.05
256	Darryl Talley	.05
257	Andre Tippett	.05
258	Jeff Lageman	.05
259	Chris Doleman	.05
260	Shane Conlan	.05
261	Jessie Tuggle	.05
262	Eric Hill	.05
263	Bruce Armstrong	.05
264	Bill Fralic	.05
265	Alvin Harper	.60
266	Bill Brooks	.05
267	Henry Ellard	.05
268	Cris Carter	.05
269	Irving Fryar	.05
270	Lawrence Dawsey	.05
271	James Lofton	.05
272	Ernest Givins	.05
273	Terance Mathis	.05
274	Randal Hill	.15
275	Eddie Brown	.05
276	Tim Brown	.50
277	Anthony Carter	.05
278	Wendell Davis	.05
279	Mark Ingram	.05
280	Anthony Miller	.05
281	Clarence Verdin	.05
282	Willie Anderson	.05
283	Ricky Sanders	.05
284	Steve Jordan	.05
285	Gary Clark	.05
286	Sterling Sharpe	.20
287	Herman Moore	.65
288	Stephen Baker	.05
289	Marv Cook	.05
290	Ernie Jones	.05
291	Eric Green	.05
292	Mervyn Fernandez	.05
293	Greg McMurty	.05
294	Quinn Early	.05
295	Tim Harris	.05
296	*Will Furrer*	.25
297	*Jason Hanson*	.15
298	*Chris Hakel*	.15
299	*Ty Detmer*	.20
300	David Klingler	.30
301	*Amp Lee*	.30
302	*Troy Vincent*	.30
303	*Kevin Smith*	.30
304	*Terrell Buckley*	.20
305	*Dana Hall*	.25
306	*Tony Smith*	.25
307	*Steve Israel*	.25
308	*Vaughn Dunbar*	.20
309	*Ashley Ambrose*	.10
310	*Edgar Bennett*	.50
311	*Dale Carter*	.40
312	*Rodney Culver*	.25
313	*Matt Darby*	.15
314	*Tommy Vardell*	.30
315	*Quentin Coryatt*	.40
316	*Robert Jones*	.25
317	*Joe Bowden*	.10
318	*Eugene Chung*	.10
319	*Troy Auzenne*	.10
320	*Santana Dotson*	.25
321	*Greg Skrepenak*	.10
322	*Steve Emtman*	.20
323	*Carl Pickens*	2.00
324	*Johnny Mitchell*	.75
325	*Patrick Rowe*	.25
326	*Alonzo Spellman*	.35
327	*Robert Porcher*	.30
328	*Chris Mims*	.30
329	*Marc Boutte*	.10
330	*Shane Dronett*	.35

1992 Pro Set Power Power Combos

These cards feature top offensive and defensive combinations from the same team. The front of each card has a color photo of the two players together, with a ghosted background.

"Combos" and "Power" are written at the top of the card in holographic letters. The cards are numbered on the back and have a purple background which contains player biographical information and a summary of their roles with their team. This information is framed by a marble-like border all the way around the card. The cards were randomly included in Pro Set Power foil packs.

		MT
Complete Set (10):		45.00
Common Player:		3.00
1	Steve Emtman, Quentin Coryatt	5.00
2	Barry Word, Christian Okoye	3.00
3	Sam Mills, Vaughan Johnson	3.00
4	Broderick Thomas, Keith McCants	3.00
5	Michael Irvin, Emmitt Smith	30.00
6	Jerry Ball, Chris Spielman	3.00
7	Rickey Sanders, Gary Clark, Art Monk	4.00
8	Dave Johnson, Rod Woodson	4.50
9	Bill Fralic, Chris Hinton	3.00
10	Irving Fryar, Marv Cook	3.00

1992-93 Pro Set Super Bowl XXVII

Inserted into Super Bowl XXVII GTE seat cushions at the Super Bowl and available by mail - with either a Bills or Cowboys mini-binder - for $22, the 38-card set was packaged in two cello packs. Reports have said 7,000 sets were issued for the mail-in offer. The cards are identical to the regular-issue cards, with the exception of the Super Bowl XXVII logo and AFC or NFC Champions listed under the player's name on the card fronts. Card backs are numbered "XX-VII," except Marco Coleman who was named Pro Set Rookie of the Year. There are NFC and AFC logo cards and a Newsreel card included in the set.

		MT
Complete Set (38):		10.00
Common Player:		.20
1	AFC Logo	.20
2	Cornelius Bennett	.30
3	Steve Christie	.20
4	Shane Conlan	.20
5	Matt Darby	.20
6	Kenneth Davis	.20
7	John Fina	.20
8	Henry Jones	.20
9	Jim Kelly	.50
10	Marv Levy (CO)	.20
11	James Lofton	.30
12	Pete Metzelaars	.20
13	Nate Odomes	.20
14	Andre Reed	.40
15	Bruce Smith	.40
16	Darryl Talley	.20
17	Steve Tasker	.30
18	Thurman Thomas	.75
19	NFC Logo	.20
20	Troy Aikman	2.00
21	Steve Beuerlein	.30
22	(Tony Casillas)	.20
23	Kenneth Gant	.30
24	Charles Haley	.30
25	Alvin Harper	.30
26	Michael Irvin	.75
27	Jimmy Johnson (CO)	.30
28	Robert Jones	.20
29	Russell Maryland	.30
30	Nate Newton	.30
31	Ken Norton	.30
32	Jay Novacek	.40
33	Emmitt Smith	4.00
34	Kevin Smith	.30
35	Mark Stepnoski	.20
36	Tony Tolbert	.20
37	Newsreel Art, Super Bowl XXVII	.20
38	Marco Coleman (PS-ROY)	.30

1992-93 Pro Set Power Emmitt Smith

Produced as a premium for Pro Set Series II, the 10-card set honors Emmitt Smith's career. The set was offered through a chase card which was randomly seeded in Series II foil packs. The set was available through the mail in exchange for 10 1992 Pro Set first or second series wrappers and 10 1992 Pro Set Power wrappers, in addition to $7.50 for shipping. Those collectors who paid $20 more would receive one of 7,500 Smith-autographed cards. The card fronts have a borderless photo, with Pro Set Power printed in one of the upper corners. A blue stripe at the bottom includes Smith's name and card caption. The backs, numbered of "10," include a "Report Card" and highlights.

		MT
Complete Set (10):		20.00
Common Player:		2.50
1	Title Card (Emmitt Smith)	2.50
2	Drafted by the (Emmitt Smith)	2.50
3	Emmitt Scores Four Touchdowns (Emmitt Smith)	2.50
4	Pro Set Offensive Rookie of the Year (Emmitt Smith)	2.50
5	Cowboys Beat Undefeated Redskins (Emmitt Smith)	2.50
6	Cowboys Beat Chicago In Playoffs (Emmitt Smith)	2.50
7	Back-to-Back Rushing Titles (Emmitt Smith)	2.50
8	Emmitt's Three Pro Bowls (Emmitt Smith)	2.50
9	Emmitt's Super Day (Emmitt Smith)	2.50
10	Running Back of the 90's (Emmitt Smith)	2.50

1993 Pro Set Promos

Measuring 8" x 13-1/2", the 10-card unperforated sheets featuring six different cards were given to dealers, card show attendees and promoters. In addition, single cards were also handed out. The sheet included a bottom row of five Emmitt Smith cards. The card fronts have a full-bleed photo, with the player's name, team logo and 1993 Pro Set logo printed inside "a ripped away" area. Card backs feature a player photo at the top, with the player's name, position and team in the "ripped away" area along the left border. The player's bio, highlights and stats are printed underneath the photo.

		MT
Complete Set (6):		8.00
Common Player:		.75
1	Jerome Bettis	2.00
2	Reggie Brooks	1.00
3	Cortez Kennedy	1.00
4	Junior Seau	1.00
5	Emmitt Smith	4.00
6	Wade Wilson	.75

1993 Pro Set

Pro Set's 1993 set consists of one series of 449 cards featuring full-bleed photos on the fronts

and backs. The player's name and team logo appear at the bottom of the card over a gray slate panel that stretches along the left side of the back of the card. The backs include statistics for the past three years and lifetime totals, plus biographical information. Insert sets include prism cards for "All Rookie Forecast" (27 cards) and "Rookie Running Backs" (14); "College Connections" (10 cards, each featuring a pair of players from the same college) and "Rookie Quarterbacks" (6 cards).

		MT
Complete Set (449):		15.00
Common Player:		.05
Minor Stars:		.10
Wax Box:		15.00
1	Marco Coleman (LL)	.05
2	Steve Young (LL)	.25
3	Mike Holmgren (LL)	.10
4	John Elway (LL)	.40
5	Steve Young (LL)	.25
6	Dan Marino (LL)	.75
7	Emmitt Smith (LL)	.75
8	Sterling Sharpe (LL)	.10
9	Jay Novacek (LL)	.05
10	Sterling Sharpe (LL)	.10
11	Thurman Thomas (LL)	.10
12	Pete Stoyanovich (LL)	.05
13	Greg Montgomery (LL)	.05
14	Johnny Bailey (LL)	.05
15	Jon Vaughn (LL)	.05
16	Jones/McMillan, Jones/McMillan,	.05
17	Clyde Simmons (LL)	.05
18	Cortez Kennedy (LL)	.05
19	AFC Wildcard	.05
20	AFC Wildcard	.05
21	NFC Wildcard	.05
22	NFC Wildcard	.05
23	AFC Divisional	.05
24	AFC Divisional	.75
25	NFC Divisional	.50
26	NFC Divisional (Watters)	.10
27	AFC Championship	.05
28	NFC Championship	.05
29	SB 28 Theme Art	.05
30	Troy Aikman	.75
31	Thomas Everett	.05
32	Charles Haley	.05
33	Alvin Harper	.10
34	Michael Irvin	.20
35	Robert Jones	.05
36	Russell Maryland	.05
37	Ken Norton	.05
38	Jay Novacek	.05
39	Emmitt Smith	1.75
40	*Darrin Smith*	.20
41	Mark Stepnoski	.05
42	*Kevin Williams*	.20
43	Daryl Johnston	.05
44	*Derrick Lassic*	.10
45	Don Beebe	.05
46	Cornelius Bennett	.05
47	Bill Brooks	.05
48	Kenneth Davis	.05
49	Jim Kelly	.20
50	Andre Reed	.10
51	Bruce Smith	.05
52	*Thomas Smith*	.05
53	Darryl Talley	.05
54	Thurman Thomas	.10
55	*Reggie Copeland*	.20
56	Scott Christie	.05
57	Pete Metzelaars	.05
58	Frank Reich	.05
59	Henry Jones	.05
60	Vinny Clark	.05
61	Eric Dickerson	.05
62	Jumpy Geathers	.05
63	*Roger Harper*	.10
64	Michael Haynes	.10
65	Bobby Hebert	.05
66	*Lincoln Kennedy*	.05
67	Chris Miller	.10
68	Andre Rison	.10
69	Deion Sanders	.50
70	Jessie Tuggle	.05
71	*Ron George*	.10
72	Erric Pegram	.05
73	Melvin Jenkins	.05
74	Pierce Holt	.05
75	Neal Anderson	.05
76	Mark Carrier	.05
77	*Curtis Conway*	.75
78	Richard Dent	.05
79	Jim Harbaugh	.10
80	Craig Heyward	.05
81	Darren Lewis	.05
82	Alonzo Spellman	.05
83	Tom Waddle	.05
84	Wendall Davis	.05
85	Chris Zorich	.05
86	*Carl Simpson*	.10
87	*Chris Gedney*	.05
88	Trace Armstrong	.05
89	Peter Tom Willis	.05
90	*John Copeland*	.10
91	Derrick Fenner	.05

92	James Francis	.05
93	Harold Green	.05
94	David Klingler	.10
95	Tim Krumrie	.05
96	*Tony McGee*	.10
97	Carl Pickens	.75
98	Alfred Williams	.05
99	Doug Pelrey	.10
100	*Lance Gunn*	.10
101	Jay Schroeder	.05
102	*Steve Tovar*	.10
103	Jeff Query	.05
104	*Ty Parten*	.05
105	Jerry Ball	.05
106	Mark Carrier	.05
107	Rob Burnett	.05
108	Michael Jackson	.10
109	Mike Johnson	.05
110	Bernie Kosar	.05
111	Clay Matthews	.05
112	Eric Metcalf	.05
113	Michael Dean Perry	.05
114	*Vinny Testaverde*	.20
115	Eric Turner	.05
116	Tommy Vardell	.05
117	Leroy Hoard	.05
118	*Steve Everitt*	.10
119	Everson Walls	.05
120	Steve Atwater	.05
121	Rod Bernstine	.05
122	Mike Croel	.05
123	John Elway	1.00
124	Simon Fletcher	.05
125	*Glyn Milburn*	.20
126	*Reggie Rivers*	.20
127	Shannon Sharpe	.20
128	Dennis Smith	.05
129	*Dan Williams*	.10
130	*Rondell Jones*	.10
131	*Jason Elam*	.20
132	*Arthur Marshall*	.10
133	Gary Zimmerman	.05
134	Karl Mecklenburg	.05
135	Bennie Blades	.05
136	Lomas Brown	.05
137	Bill Fralic	.05
138	Mel Gray	.05
139	Willie Green	.05
140	*Ryan McNeil*	.05
141	Rodney Peete	.05
142	Barry Sanders	2.00
143	Chris Spielman	.05
144	Pat Swilling	.05
145	Andre Ware	.05
146	Herman Moore	.50
147	Tim McKyer	.05
148	Brett Perriman	.05
149	*Antonio London*	.10
150	Edgar Bennett	.05
151	Terrell Buckley	.05
152	Brett Favre	2.00
153	Jackie Harris	.05
154	Johnny Holland	.05
155	Sterling Sharpe	.10
156	*Tim Hauck*	.05
157	*George Teague*	.25
158	Reggie White	.20
159	Mark Clayton	.05
160	Ty Detmer	.10
161	*Wayne Simmons*	.05
162	*Mark Brunell*	3.00
163	Tony Bennett	.05
164	Brian Noble	.05
165	Cody Carlson	.05
166	Ray Childress	.05
167	Cris Dishman	.05
168	Curtis Duncan	.05
169	*Brad Hopkins*	.10
170	Haywood Jeffires	.05
171	Wilber Marshall	.05
172	*Michael Barrow*	.10
173	Bubba McDowell	.05
174	Warren Moon	.20
175	Webster Slaughter	.05
176	*Travis Hannah*	.10
177	Lorenzo White	.05
178	Ernest Givins	.05
179	Keith McCants	.05
180	Kerry Cash	.05
181	Quentin Coryatt	.05
182	Kirk Lowdermilk	.05
183	Rodney Cullver	.05
184	Rohn Stark	.05
185	Steve Emtman	.05
186	Jeff George	.20
187	Jeff Herrod	.05
188	Reggie Langhorne	.05
189	*Roosevelt Potts*	.10
190	Jack Trudeau	.05
191	Will Wolford	.05
192	Jessie Hester	.05
193	Anthony Johnson	.10
194	*Ray Buchanan*	.10
195	Dale Carter	.05
196	Willie Davis	.05
197	John Alt	.05
198	Joe Montana	1.00
199	*Will Shields*	.05
200	Neil Smith	.05
201	Derrick Thomas	.10
202	Harvey Williams	.05
203	Marcus Allen	.20
204	J.J. Birden	.05
205	Tim Barnett	.05
206	Albert Lewis	.05
207	Nick Lowery	.05
208	Dave Krieg	.05
209	Keith Cash	.05

#	Player	Price
210	Patrick Bates	.10
211	Nick Bell	.05
212	Tim Brown	.20
213	Willie Gault	.05
214	Ethan Horton	.05
215	Jeff Hostetler	.10
216	Howie Long	.05
217	Greg Townsend	.05
218	Rocket Ismail	.10
219	Alexander Wright	.05
220	Greg Robinson	.10
221	Billy Joe Hobert	.20
222	Steve Wisniewski	.05
223	Steve Smith	.05
224	Vince Evans	.05
225	Willie Anderson	.05
226	Jerome Bettis	1.50
227	Troy Drayton	.25
228	Henry Ellard	.05
229	Jim Everett	.10
230	Tony Zendejas	.05
231	Todd Lyght	.05
232	Todd Kinchen	.10
233	Jackie Slater	.05
234	Fred Stokes	.05
235	Russell White	.10
236	Cleveland Gary	.05
237	Sean Lachapelle	.20
238	Steve Israel	.05
239	Shane Conlan	.05
240	Keith Byars	.05
241	Marco Coleman	.05
242	Bryan Cox	.05
243	Irving Fryar	.05
244	Richmond Webb	.05
245	Mark Higgs	.05
246	Terry Kirby	.30
247	Mark Ingram	.05
248	John Offerdahl	.05
249	Keith Jackson	.05
250	Dan Marino	2.00
251	O.J. McDuffie	.75
252	Louis Oliver	.05
253	Pete Stoyanovich	.05
254	Troy Vincent	.10
255	Anthony Carter	.05
256	Cris Carter	.20
257	Roger Craig	.05
258	Jack Del Rio	.05
259	Chris Doleman	.05
260	Barry Word	.05
261	Qadry Ismail	.25
262	Jim McMahon	.05
263	Robert Smith	1.25
264	Fred Strickland	.05
265	Randall McDaniel	.05
266	Carl Lee	.05
267	Orlanda Truitt	.10
268	Terry Allen	.10
269	Audray McMillan	.05
270	Drew Bledsoe	3.00
271	Eugene Chug	.05
272	Marv Cook	.05
273	Pat Harlow	.05
274	Greg McMurty	.05
275	Leonard Russell	.05
276	Chris Slade	.10
277	Andre Tippett	.05
278	Vincent Brisby	.25
279	Ben Coates	.30
280	Sam Gash	.10
281	Bruce Armstrong	.05
282	Rod Smith	.20
283	Michael Timpson	.05
284	Scott Sisson	.10
285	Morten Anderson	.05
286	Reggie Freeman	.10
287	Dalton Hilliard	.05
288	Rickey Jackson	.05
289	Vaughan Johnson	.05
290	Eric Martin	.05
291	Sam Mills	.05
292	Brad Muster	.05
293	Willie Roaf	.20
294	Irv Smith	.20
295	Wade Wilson	.05
296	Derek Brown	.10
297	Quinn Early	.05
298	Steve Walsh	.05
299	Renaldo Turnbull	.05
300	Jessie Armstead	.10
301	Carlton Bailey	.05
302	Michael Brooks	.05
303	Rodney Hampton	.10
304	Ed McCaffrey	.10
305	Dave Meggett	.05
306	Bart Oates	.05
307	Mike Sherrard	.05
308	Phil Simms	.10
309	Lawrence Taylor	.10
310	Mark Jackson	.05
311	Jarrod Bunch	.05
312	Howard Cross	.05
313	Michael Strahan	.05
314	Marcus Buckley	.05
315	Brad Baxter	.05
316	Adrian Murrell	1.00
317	Boomer Esiason	.10
318	Johnny Johnson	.05
319	Marvin Jones	.20
320	Jeff Lageman	.05
321	Ronnie Lott	.10
322	Leonard Marshall	.05
323	Johnny Mitchell	.05
324	Rob Moore	.05
325	Browning Nagle	.05
326	Blair Thomas	.05
327	Brian Washington	.05

#	Player	Price
328	Terrance Mathis	.10
329	Kyle Clifton	.05
330	Eric Allen	.05
331	Victor Bailey	.10
332	Fred Barnett	.05
333	Mark Bavaro	.05
334	Randall Cunningham	.10
335	Ken O'Brien	.05
336	Seth Joyner	.05
337	Leonard Renfro	.10
338	Heath Sherman	.05
339	Clyde Simmons	.05
340	Herschel Walker	.10
341	Calvin Williams	.05
342	Bubby Brister	.05
343	Vaughn Hebron	.10
344	Keith Millard	.05
345	Johnny Bailey	.05
346	Steve Beuerlein	.10
347	Chuck Cecil	.05
348	Larry Centers	.20
349	Chris Chandler	.10
350	Ernest Dye	.05
351	Garrison Hearst	1.00
352	Randal Hill	.05
353	John Booty	.05
354	Gary Clark	.05
355	Ron Moore	.10
356	Ricky Proehl	.05
357	Eric Swann	.05
358	Ken Harvey	.05
359	Ben Coleman	.10
360	Deon Figures	.20
361	Barry Foster	.05
362	Jeff Graham	.05
363	Eric Green	.05
364	Kevin Greene	.05
365	Andre Hastings	.10
366	Greg Lloyd	.05
367	Neil O'Donnell	.05
368	Dwight Stone	.05
369	Mike Tomczak	.05
370	Rod Woodson	.10
371	Chad Brown	.20
372	Ernie Mills	.05
373	Darren Perry	.05
374	Leon Searcy	.05
375	Marion Butts	.05
376	John Carney	.05
377	Ronnie Harmon	.05
378	Stan Humphries	.10
379	Nate Lewis	.05
380	Natrone Means	1.00
381	Anthony Miller	.05
382	Chris Mims	.05
383	Leslie O'Neal	.05
384	Joe Coccozzo	.10
385	Junior Seau	.10
386	Jerrol Williams	.05
387	John Friesz	.05
388	Darrien Gordon	.10
389	Derrick Walker	.05
390	Dana Hall	.05
391	Brent Jones	.05
392	Todd Kelly	.10
393	Amp Lee	.10
394	Tim McDonald	.05
395	Jerry Rice	1.00
396	Dana Stubblefield	.40
397	John Taylor	.05
398	Ricky Watters	.20
399	Steve Young	.75
400	Steve Bono	.30
401	Adrian Hardy	.10
402	Tom Rathman	.05
403	Elvis Grbac	1.00
404	Bill Romanowski	.05
405	Brian Blades	.05
406	Ferrell Edmunds	.05
407	Carlton Gray	.10
408	Cortez Kennedy	.10
409	Kelvin Martin	.05
410	Dan McGwire	.05
411	Rick Mirer	.30
412	Rufus Porter	.05
413	Chris Warren	.20
414	Jon Vaughn	.05
415	John L. Williams	.05
416	Eugene Robinson	.05
417	Michael McCrary	.10
418	Michael Bates	.20
419	Stan Gelbaugh	.05
420	Reggie Cobb	.05
421	Eric Curry	.10
422	Lawrence Dawsey	.05
423	Santana Dotson	.05
424	Craig Erickson	.10
425	Ron Hall	.05
426	Courtney Hawkins	.05
427	Broderick Thomas	.05
428	Vince Workman	.05
429	Demetrius DuBose	.10
430	Lamar Thomas	.05
431	John Lynch	.20
432	Hardy Nickerson	.05
433	Horace Copeland	.20
434	Steve DeBerg	.05
435	Joe Jacoby	.05
436	Tom Carter	.05
437	Andre Collins	.05
438	Darrell Green	.05
439	Desmond Howard	.05
440	Chip Lohmiller	.05
441	Charles Mann	.05
442	Tim McGee	.05
443	Art Monk	.10
444	Mark Rypien	.05
445	Ricky Sanders	.05
446	Brian Mitchell	.05
447	Reggie Brooks	.10
448	Carl Banks	.05
449	Cary Conklin	.05

1993 Pro Set All-Rookies

These cards feature color action shots against a prism-like background. Twenty-seven of the NFL's top rookie prospects are featured on these cards, which were random inserts in 1993 Pro Set foil packs. The player's name is at the bottom of the card, while the set's name is in a brown stripe along the right side. The numbered card back is green and has a football field ghosted over it. A player biography and team logo are also included. The player's name and card number are inside a gray stripe running along the left side of the card.

		MT
Complete Set (27):		10.00
Common Player:		.20
Minor Stars:		.40
1	Rick Mirer	.40
2	Garrison Hearst	1.75
3	Jerome Bettis	1.75
4	Vincent Brisby	.20
5	O.J. McDuffie	.75
6	Curtis Conway	.75
7	Raghib Ismail	.20
8	Steve Everitt	.20
9	Ernest Dye	.20
10	Todd Rucci	.20
11	Willie Roaf	.40
12	Lincoln Kennedy	.20
13	Irv Smith	.20
14	Jason Elam	.20
15	Derrick Alexander	.20
16	John Copeland	.20
17	Eric Curry	.20
18	Dana Stubblefield	.20
19	Leonard Renfro	.20
20	Marvin Jones	.20
21	Demetrius DuBose	.20
22	Chris Slade	.20
23	Darrin Smith	.20
24	Deon Figures	.20
25	Darrien Gordon	.20
26	Patrick Bates	.20
27	George Teague	.20

1993 Pro Set College Connections

College teammates who've become stars in the NFL are featured on these insert cards, randomly included in 1993 jumbo packs. Each card front is horizontal and features two small color action photos of the teammates against a silver prism-like background. A gray stripe at the bottom has the set's name. Each back has two panels which compare the players and give biographical information about them. The cards are numbered with a "CC" prefix.

		MT
Complete Set (10):		35.00
Common Player:		1.00
Minor Stars:		2.00
1	Barry Sanders, Thurman Thomas	6.00
2	Jerome Bettis, Reggie Brooks	2.00
3	Neal Anderson, Emmitt Smith	5.00
4	Raghib Ismail, Tim Brown	1.00
5	Rodney Hampton, Garrison Hearst	2.00
6	Derrick Thomas, Cornelius Bennett	1.00
7	Steve Young, Jim McMahon	3.00
8	Rick Mirer, Joe Montana	5.00
9	Terrell Buckley, Deion Sanders	3.00
10	Drew Bledsoe, Mark Rypien	5.00

1993 Pro Set Rookie Quarterbacks

These cards, randomly inserted in 1993 Pro Set jumbo packs, have color action shots on them against a prism-like background. The set name is in a gray stripe along the right side; the player's name is at the bottom of the card. The pink backs have a team logo and career highlights and are numbered with a "RQ" prefix. The player's name is in a purple stripe which runs along the left side of the card.

		MT
Complete Set (6):		10.00
Common Player:		.20
1	Drew Bledsoe	3.00
2	Rick Mirer	.40
3	Mark Brunell	3.00
4	Billy Joe Hobert	.20
5	Trent Green	4.00
6	Elvis Grbac	.75

1993 Pro Set Rookie Running Backs

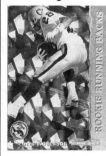

Fourteen promising rookie running backs are featured on these cards, which were random inserts in 1993 Pro Set foil packs. Each card front has a color action shot against a prism background. The player's name is at the bottom of the card; the set name runs along the right side in a brown stripe. The backs, numbered with a "RRB" prefix, are gray and have a light brown stripe along the left side containing the player's name. His career highlights, team, position and biography are also given.

		MT
Complete Set (14):		10.00
Common Player:		.20
Minor Stars:		.40
1	Derrick Lassic	.20
2	Reggie Brooks	.20
3	Garrison Hearst	1.75
4	Ron Moore	.20
5	Robert Smith	1.75
6	Jerome Bettis	1.75
7	Russell White	.20
8	Derek Brown	.20
9	Roosevelt Potts	.20
10	Terry Kirby	.40
11	Glyn Milburn	.40
12	Greg Robinson	.20
13	Natrone Means	1.50
14	Vaughn Hebron	.20

1993 Pro Set Power Prototypes

The 10-card set previewed the 1993 Pro Set Power series. The card fronts have the Pro Set Power logo in one of the upper corners, with the player's name and team listed in a red, white and blue box at the bottom of the full-bleed cards. The backs include a horizontal photo, along with a rating system and career highlights. The cards are numbered in the upper left. "Prototype" is printed at the bottom center.

		MT
Complete Set (10):		10.00
Common Player:		.50
20	Barry Sanders	2.00
22	Emmitt Smith	4.00
26	Rod Woodson	.50
32	Ricky Watters	.75
37	Larry Centers	.50
71	Santana Dotson	.50
80	Jerry Rice	2.00
138	Reggie Rivers	.50
193	Trace Armstrong	.50
NNO	Title/Ad Card	.50

1993 Pro Set Power

Pro Set Power's 1993 set has 200 cards. The fronts are similar to the 1992 look; the player is featured in a color action shot against a ghosted background. The player's name and team are at the bottom left; the foil-stamped Pro Set Power logo is in the upper right. The card back has a summary of the player's 1992 season, including statistics and a rating guide. His name appears at the top between team color-coded bars. Below that is an action photo. Insert sets include All-Power Defense (25 cards), Power Moves (30), Draft Picks (30), and Power Combos (10).

	MT
Complete Set (200):	7.00
Common Player:	.05
Minor Stars:	.10
Wax Box:	15.00
1 Warren Moon	.20
2 Steve Christie	.05
3 Jim Breech	.05
4 Brett Favre	1.00
5 Sean Landeta	.05
6 Jim Arnold	.05
7 John Elway	.50
8 Troy Aikman	1.00
9 Rodney Peete	.10
10 Pete Stoyanovich	.05
11 Mark Rypien	.05
12 Jim Kelly	.20
13 Dan Marino	1.25
14 Neil O'Donnell	.10
15 David Klingler	.05
16 Rich Gannon	.05
17 Dave Krieg	.05
18 Jeff Jaeger	.05
19 Bernie Kosar	.05
20 Barry Sanders	1.00
21 Deion Sanders	.40
22 Emmitt Smith	1.25
23 Barry Word	.05
24 Stanley Richard	.05
25 Louis Oliver	.05
26 Rod Woodson	.10
27 Rodney Hampton	.20
28 Cris Dishman	.05
29 Barry Foster	.10
30 Dave Meggett	.05
31 Kevin Ross	.05
32 Ricky Watters	.20
33 Darren Lewis	.05
34 Thurman Thomas	.20
35 Rodney Culver	.05
36 Bennie Blades	.05
37 Larry Centers	.20
38 Todd Scott	.05
39 Darren Perry	.05
40 Robert Massey	.05
41 Keith Byars	.05
42 Chris Warren	.10
43 Cleveland Gary	.05
44 Lorenzo White	.05
45 Tony Stargell	.05
46 Bennie Thompson	.05
47 A.J. Johnson	.05
48 Daryl Johnston	.05
49 Dennis Smith	.05
50 Johnny Holland	.05
51 Ken Norton Jr.	.05
52 Pepper Johnson	.05
53 Vaughn Johnson	.05
54 Chris Spielman	.05
55 Junior Seau	.20
56 Chris Doleman	.05
57 Rickey Jackson	.05
58 Derrick Thomas	.10
59 Seth Joyner	.05
60 Stan Thomas	.05
61 Nate Newton	.05
62 Matt Brock	.05
63 Mike Munchak	.05
64 Randall McDaniel	.05
65 Ron Hallstrom	.05
66 Andy Heck	.05
67 Russell Maryland	.05
68 Bruce Wilkerson	.05
69 Mark Schlereth	.05
70 John Fina	.05
71 Santana Dotson	.05
72 Don Mosebar	.05
73 Simon Fletcher	.05
74 Paul Gruber	.05
75 Howard Ballard	.05
76 John Alt	.05
77 Carlton Haselrig	.05
78 Bruce Smith	.05
79 Ray Childress	.05
80 Jerry Rice	.75
81 Art Monk	.10
82 John Taylor	.05
83 Andre Reed	.10
84 Sterling Sharpe	.10
85 Sam Graddy	.05
86 Fred Barnett	.05
87 Ricky Proehl	.05
88 Michael Irvin	.25
89 Webster Slaughter	.05
90 Tony Bennett	.05
91 Leslie O'Neal	.05
92 Michael Dean Perry	.05
93 Greg Townsend	.05
94 Anthony Smith	.05
95 Richard Dent	.05
96 Clyde Simmons	.05
97 Cornelius Bennett	.05
98 Eric Swann	.05
99 Cortez Kennedy	.05
100 Emmitt Smith	.75
101 Michael Jackson	.05
102 Lin Elliott	.05
103 Rohn Stark	.05
104 Jim Harbaugh	.05
105 Greg Davis	.05

106	Mike Cofer	.05
107	Morten Andersen	.05
108	Steve Young	.75
109	Norm Johnson	.05
110	Dan McGwire	.05
111	Jim Everett	.05
112	Randall Cunningham	.10
113	Steve Bono	.20
114	Cody Carlson	.05
115	Jeff Hostetler	.10
116	Rich Camarillo	.05
117	Chris Chandler	.05
118	Stan Gelbaugh	.05
119	Tony Sacca	.05
120	Henry Jones	.05
121	Terry Allen	.05
122	Amp Lee	.05
123	Mel Gray	.05
124	Jon Vaughn	.05
125	Bubba McDowell	.05
126	Audray McMilliam	.05
127	Terrell Buckley	.05
128	Dana Hall	.05
129	Eric Dickerson	.05
130	Martin Bayless	.05
131	Steve Israel	.05
132	Vaughn Dunbar	.05
133	Ronnie Harmon	.05
134	Dale Carter	.05
135	Neal Anderson	.05
136	Merton Hanks	.05
137	James Washington	.05
138	Reggie Rivers	.05
139	Bruce Pickens	.05
140	Gary Anderson	.05
141	Eugene Robinson	.05
142	Charles Mincy	.05
143	Matt Darby	.05
144	Tom Rathman	.05
145	Mike Prior	.05
146	Sean Lumpkin	.05
147	Greg Jackson	.05
148	Wes Hopkins	.05
149	David Tate	.05
150	James Francis	.05
151	Brian Cox	.05
152	Keith McCants	.05
153	Mark Stepnoski	.05
154	Al Smith	.05
155	Robert Jones	.05
156	Lawrence Taylor	.10
157	Clay Matthews	.05
158	Wilber Marshall	.05
159	Mike Johnson	.05
160	Adam Schreiber	.05
161	Tim Grunhard	.05
162	Mark Bortz	.05
163	Gene Chilton	.05
164	Jamie Dukes	.05
165	Bart Oates	.05
166	Kevin Gogan	.05
167	Kent Hull	.05
168	Ed King	.05
169	Eugene Chung	.05
170	Troy Auzenne	.05
171	Charles Mann	.05
172	William Perry	.05
173	Mike Lodish	.05
174	Bruce Matthews	.05
175	Tony Casillas	.05
176	Steve Wisenewski	.05
177	Karl Mecklenberg	.05
178	Richmond Webb	.05
179	Erik Williams	.05
180	Andre Rison	.10
181	Michael Haynes	.05
182	Don Beebe	.05
183	Anthony Miller	.05
184	Jay Novacek	.05
185	Rob Moore	.05
186	Willie Green	.05
187	Tom Waddle	.05
188	Keith Jackson	.05
189	Steve Tasker	.05
190	Marco Coleman	.05
191	Jeff Wright	.05
192	Burt Grossman	.05
193	Trace Armstrong	.05
194	Charles Haley	.05
195	Greg Lloyd	.05
196	Marc Boutte	.05
197	Rufus Porter	.05
198	Dennis Gibson	.05
199	Shane Dronett	.05
200	Joe Montana	1.00
H1	Emmitt Smith HOLO	25.00
H2	Emmitt Smith HOLO	25.00

1993 Pro Set Power Gold

Inserted one per pack, this set was a parallel to the Power base cards. The Power logo is printed in gold foil, which is very similar to the silver foil. If the card is held at the correct angle, the gold foil can be differentiated.

	MT
Complete Set (200):	20.00
Common Player:	.10
Gold Cards:	1x-2x

1993 Pro Set Power All-Power Defense

Twenty-five top NFL defensive players are featured on these cards, which were randomly inserted at a rate of two per jumbo pack. Each card front has a borderless color photo against a brown background. A black rectangle at the bottom includes the player's name in yellow letters. The back is also in brown, and includes the player's name, team, position and biography in a yellow box in the upper left corner. A career summary is also given in red lettering. Cards are numbered with an "APD" prefix. Scarcer gold-foil versions were also made for each card.

		MT
Complete Set (25):		5.00
Common Player:		.20
Minor Stars:		.40
Comp. Gold Set (25):		10.00
Gold Cards:		1x-2x
1	Clyde Simmons	.20
2	Anthony Smith	.20
3	Ray Childress	.20
4	Michael Dean Perry	.40
5	Bruce Smith	.40
6	Cortez Kennedy	.40
7	Charles Haley	.20
8	Marco Coleman	.20
9	Alonzo Spellman	.20
10	Junior Seau	.75
11	Ken Norton	.20
12	Derrick Thomas	.40
13	Wilber Marshall	.20
14	Chris Doleman	.20
15	Seth Joyner	.20
16	Al Smith	.20
17	Deion Sanders	.75
18	Rod Woodson	.40
19	Audray McMillian	.20
20	Dale Carter	.20
21	Terrell Buckley	.20
22	Bennie Thompson	.20
23	Chris Spielman	.20
24	Lawrence Taylor	.40
25	Tony Bennett	.20

1993 Pro Set Power Combos

Two players are featured on the front of each card in this Pro Set Power insert set. Cards were random inserts in foil packs. Each card front has a black, blue and purple border, along with the players' names in red in a black bar at the bottom. The card back has a purple rectangle at the top, which has the players' team name in it in yellow lettering. Their names, positions, uniform numbers, career summaries and highlights are featured on the back against a green background with borders in the same color as those on the front. Gold versions and prism versions, were also made for each card.

		MT
Complete Set (10):		6.00
Common Player:		.50
Minor Stars:		1.00
Comp. Gold Set (10):		12.00
Gold Cards:		1x-2x
Comp. Prism Set (10):		18.00
Prism Cards:		1x-3x
1	Emmitt Smith, Barry Sanders	3.00
2	Terrell Buckley, Sterling Sharpe	1.00
3	Junior Seau, Gary Plummer	1.00
4	Deion Sanders, Tim McKyer	1.00
5	Bruce Smith, Darryl Talley	.50
6	Warren Moon, Webster Slaughter	.50
7	Chris Doleman, Henry Thomas	.50
8	Karl Mecklenberg, Michael Brooks	.50
9	Ken Norton, Robert Jones	.50
10	Bryan Cox, Marco Coleman	

1993 Pro Set Power Draft Picks

These cards feature color action photos on the front against a black-and-white background. The cards, random inserts in 1993 Pro Set Power packs, feature top rookies in the NFL for the 1993 season; the player's name is in red at the bottom. The card back also has the player's name in red at the top, and is in a horizontal format. The player's name and player biography are also included. Cards are numbered with a "PDP" prefix. Gold foil versions were also made for each card.

		MT
Complete Set (30):		8.00
Common Player:		.10
Minor Stars:		.10
Comp. Gold Set (30):		16.00
Gold Cards:		1x-2x
1	Lincoln Kennedy	.10
2	Thomas Smith	.10
3	Robert Smith	1.00
4	John Copeland	.20
5	Dan Footman	.10
6	Darrin Smith	.20
7	Qadry Ismail	.50
8	Ryan McNeil	.10
9	George Teague	.20
10	Brad Hopkins	.10
11	Ernest Dye	.10
12	Jaime Fields	.10
13	Patrick Bates	.10
14	Jerome Bettis	1.00
15	O.J. McDuffie	.75
16	Gino Torretta	.10
17	Drew Bledsoe	2.50
18	Irv Smith	.10
19	Marcus Buckley	.10
20	Coleman Rudolph	.10
21	Leonard Renfro	.10
22	Garrison Hearst	1.00
23	Deon Figures	.20
24	Natrone Means	1.00
25	Todd Kelly	.10
26	Carlton Gray	.10
27	Eric Curry	.10
28	Tom Carter	.20
29	AFC Stars	.10
30	NFC Stars	.10

A card number in parentheses ( ) indicates the set is unnumbered.

1993 Pro Set Power Moves

These insert cards feature borderless color action photos on the front, with a ghosted version of the same photo on the back. The front has a red frame for a border, with the player's name in red at the bottom. The back has the set name in white in a black stripe along the left side, with the player's name and his team name in black in a gray plaque at the top. Cards are numbered with a "PM" prefix. Card numbers 1-30 were randomly inserted in 1993 Pro Set Power packs; cards 31-40 were random inserts in 1993 Pro Set Power jumbo packs. Scarcer gold-foil versions were also made for each card.

		MT
Complete Set (40):		5.00
Common Player:		.10
Minor Stars:		.20
Comp. Gold Set (40):		10.00
Gold Cards:		1x-2x
1	Bobby Hebert	.20
2	Billy Brooks	.10
3	Vinny Testaverde	.20
4	Hugh Millen	.10
5	Rod Berstine	.10
6	Robert Delpino	.10
7	Pat Swilling	.10
8	Reggie White	.30
9	Aaron Cox	.10
10	Joe Montana	2.00
11	Gaston Green	.10
12	Jeff Hostetler	.20
13	Shane Conlan	.10
14	Irv Eatman	.10
15	Mark Ingram	.10
16	Irving Fryar	.10
17	Don Majkowski (Will Wolford)	.10
18	Boomer Esiason	.20
19	Ronnie Lott	.10
20	Johnny Johnson	.10
21	Steve Beuerlein	.10
22	Chuck Cecil	.10
23	Gary Clark	.10
24	Kevin Greene	.10
25	Jerrol Williams	.10
26	Tim McDonald	.10
27	Ferrell Edmunds	.10
28	Kelvin Martin	.10
29	Hardy Nickerson	.10
30	Jerry Ball	.10
31	Jim McMahon	.10
32	Marcus Allen	.30
33	John Stephens	.10
34	John Booty	.10
35	Wade Wilson	.10
36	Mark Bavaro	.10
37	Bill Fralic	.10
38	Mark Clayton	.10
39	Mike Sherrard	.10

1993 Pro Set Power Update Power Moves

These insert cards feature color action photos on the front, with a purple border framed with blue and red lines. The player's name is at the bottom in yellow letters. The card backs, numbered with a "PMVD" prefix, have a biography and season highlights, plus a date when he was traded. Helmets for his old and new team appear at the top, too. The background has shades of purple and white. These inserts shared packs with 1993 Pro Set Power Power Prospects cards.

	MT
Complete Set (50):	4.00
Common Player:	.10

1993 Pro Set Power Moves

Minor Stars:		.20
Comp. Gold Set (50):		8.00
Gold Cards:		1x-2x
1	Bobby Hebert	.20
2	Bill Brooks	.10
3	Vinny Testaverde	.20
4	Hugh Millen	.10
5	Rod Bernstine	.10
6	Robert Delpino	.10
7	Pat Swilling	.10
8	Reggie White	.30
9	Aaron Cox	.10
10	Joe Montana	2.00
11	Vinnie Clark (Name misspelled Vinny on card)	.10
12	Jeff Hostetler	.20
13	Shane Conlan	.10
14	Irv Eatman	.10
15	Mark Ingram	.10
16	Irving Fryar	.10
17	Don Majkowski	.10
18	Will Wolford	.10
19	Boomer Esiason	.20
20	Ronnie Lott	.10
21	Johnny Johnson	.10
22	Steve Beuerlein	.10
23	Chuck Cecil	.10
24	Gary Clark	.10
25	Kevin Greene	.10
26	Jerrol Williams	.10
27	Tim McDonald	.10
28	Ferrell Edmunds	.10
29	Kelvin Martin	.10
30	Hardy Nickerson	.10
31	Jumpy Geathers	.10
32	Craig Heyward	.10
33	Tim McKyer	.10
34	Mark Carrier	.10
35	Gary Zimmerman	.10
36	Jay Schroeder	.10
37	Keith Millard	.10
38	Vince Workman	.10
39	Kirk Lowdermilk	.10
40	Fred Stokes	.10
41	Ernie Jones	.10
42	Keith Byars	.10
43	Carlton Bailey	.10
44	Michael Brooks	.10
45	Tim McGee	.10
46	Leonard Marshall	.10
47	Bubby Brister	.10
48	Mike Tomczak	.10
49	Mark Jackson	.10
50	Wade Wilson	.10

1993 Pro Set Power Update Power Prospects

These cards were included in packs containing 1993 Pro Set Power Update Power Moves cards. Each card has a color action photo framed by gray borders. A horizontally-patterned background is also used on the front. The player's name is in yellow at the bottom on the front, while it and his team helmet appear at the top in a panel on the back. The back is gray and contains a career summary and a number, which uses a "PP" prefix. Gold versions were also made for each card.

	MT
Complete Set (60):	10.00
Common Player:	.10
Minor Stars:	.20
1	Drew Bledsoe	2.50
2	Rick Mirer	.25
3	Trent Green	4.00
4	Mark Brunell	3.00
5	Billy Joe Hobert	.20
6	Ron Moore	.40
7	Elvis Grbac	.50
8	Garrison Hearst	1.00
9	Jerome Bettis	1.00
10	Reggie Brooks	.25
11	Robert Smith	1.00
12	Vaughn Hebron	.10
13	Derek Brown	.25
14	Roosevelt Potts	.20
15	Terry Kirby	.30
16	Glyn Milburn	.30
17	Greg Robinson	.10
18	Natrone Means	1.00
19	Curtis Conway	.50
20	James Jett	.75
21	O.J. McDuffie	.50
22	Raghib Ismail	.20
23	Qadry Ismail	.40
24	Kevin Williams	.60
25	Victor Bailey	.20
26	Vincent Brisby	.60
27	Irv Smith	.10
28	Troy Drayton	.40
29	Wayne Simmons	.10
30	Marvin Jones	.10
31	Demetrius DuBose	.10
32	Chad Brown	.40
33	Michael Barrow	.10
34	Darrin Smith	.20
35	Deon Figures	.20
36	Darrien Gordon	.20
37	Patrick Bates	.10
38	George Teague	.10
39	Lance Gunn	.10
40	Tom Carter	.20
41	Carlton Gray	.20
42	John Copeland	.20
43	Eric Curry	.25
44	Dana Stubblefield	.40
45	Leonard Renfro	.10
46	Dan Williams	.10
47	Todd Kelly	.10
48	Chris Slade	.40
49	Carl Simpson	.10
50	Coleman Rudolph	.10
51	Michael Strahan	.10
52	Dan Footman	.10
53	Steve Everitt	.10
54	Will Shields	.10
55	Ben Coleman	.10
56	William Roaf	.10
57	Lincoln Kennedy	.10
58	Brad Hopkins	.10
59	Ernest Dye	.10
60	Jason Elam	.10

1993 Pro Set Power Update Prospects Gold

Featuring a gold-foil stamp on the card fronts, this 60-card set is a parallel to the Power Update base set.

	MT
Complete Set (60):	25.00
Common Player:	.10
Gold Cards:	1x-2x

1993 Pro Set Power Update Combos

These inserts were randomly included in 1993 Pro Set Power Update packs. Each card front features two players on it, in a horizontal format. Their names are at the bottom in red letters. The backs are horizontal too, and include the players' names at the top, along with career highlights for them against a turf-like background. Cards are numbered with a "PC" prefix. Gold versions and prism versions.

		MT
Complete Set (10):		10.00
Common Player:		.50
Minor Stars:		1.00
Comp. Gold Set (10):		20.00
Gold Cards:		1x-2x
Comp. Prism Set (10):		30.00
Prism Cards:		1x-3x
1	Andre Rison, Michael Haynes, Mike Pritchard, Drew Hill	.50
2	Steve Young, Jerry Rice	3.00
3	Jim Kelly, Frank Reich	1.00
4	Alvin Harper, Michael Irvin	1.50
5	Rod Woodson, Deon Figures	.50
6	Bruce Smith, Cornelius Bennett	.50
7	Bryan Cox, Marco Coleman	.50
8	Troy Aikman, Emmitt Smith	4.00
9	Tim Brown, Raghib Ismail	1.00
10	Art Monk, Desmond Howard, Ricky Sanders	.50

1993 Pro Set Power Update Impact Rookies

These cards feature top rookies entering the 1993 season. Each card front has an action photo framed by a gold border. The player's name is in yellow at the bottom. The back is gray and includes the player's team name and helmet at the top, along with the college he attended, position and collegiate highlights underneath. Cards are numbered with an "IR" prefix.

		MT
Complete Set (15):		10.00
Common Player:		.25
Minor Stars:		.50
1	Rick Mirer	2.00
2	Drew Bledsoe	3.00
3	Jerome Bettis	1.00
4	Derek Brown	.50
5	Roosevelt Potts	.25
6	Glyn Milburn	.50
7	Adrian Murrell	.50
8	Victor Bailey	.25
9	Vincent Brisby	.50
10	O.J. McDuffie	1.00
11	James Jett	.50
12	Eric Curry	.25
13	Dana Stubblefield	.50
14	William Roaf	.25
15	Patrick Bates	.25

1994 Pro Set National Promos

Six of eight cards were handed out at the Pro Set booth at the 1994 National Sports Collectors Convention. The cards, numbered by a letter, were promos from either Pro Set football, Power football or Power racing. A title card, which was unnumbered, featured the National logo and was individually numbered "of 10,000." The Garrison Hearst and Richmond Webb cards were inserts in "Tuff Stuff" magazine. The card backs have "proto" printed inside a strip at the bottom.

		MT
Complete Set (8):		14.00
Common Player:		1.00
1	Fire Power (Jerome Bettis)	2.00
2	Drew Bledsoe	3.00
3	Green Bay Packers, Air Power (Brett Favre, Sterling Sharpe)	5.00
4	Ronald Moore	1.00
5	Power Line (Willie Roaf)	1.00
6	Garrison Hearst	1.50
7	Richmond Webb	1.00
NNO	Title Card (1994 National)	1.00

1991 Quarterback Legends

This 50-card set, produced by NFL Quarterback Legends,

comes in a special commemorative box. Each card front has a full-bleed color action photo, with the set logo and name given at the bottom of the card in a checkerboard pattern. The card back has the sponsors' logos, a card number, a color photo, statistics and a career summary. The design is horizontal. Cards were released at the Quarterback Legends Show in Nashville, Tenn., in January 1992.

		MT
Complete Set (50):		20.00
Common Player:		.25
1	Ken Anderson	.75
2	Steve Bartkowski	.35
3	George Blanda	1.50
4	Terry Bradshaw	2.00
5	Zeke Bratkowski	.25
6	John Brodie	.50
7	Charley Conerly	.50
8	Len Dawson	.50
9	Lynn Dickey	.25
10	Joe Ferguson	.25
11	Vince Ferragamo	.25
12	Tom Flores	.35
13	Dan Fouts	1.00
14	Roman Gabriel	.25
15	Otto Graham	.75
16	Bob Griese	1.25
17	Steve Grogan	.35
18	John Hadl	.35
19	James Harris	.25
20	Jim Hart	.25
21	Ron Jaworski	.25
22	Charlie Johnson	.25
23	Bert Jones	.35
24	Sonny Jurgensen	.75
25	Joe Kapp	.25
26	Billy Kilmer	.50
27	Daryle Lamonica	.35
28	Greg Landry	.25
29	Neil Lomax	.25
30	Archie Manning	.40
31	Earl Morrall	.35
32	Craig Morton	.35
33	Gifford Nielsen	.25
34	Dan Pastorini	.25
35	Jim Plunkett	.35
36	Norm Snead	.25
37	Ken Stabler	.75
38	Bart Starr	1.50
39	Roger Staubach	3.00
40	Joe Theismann	.75
41	Y.A. Tittle	.75
42	Johnny Unitas	1.50
43	Bill Wade	.25
44	Danny White	.35
45	Doug Williams	.25
46	Jim Zorn	.35
47	Legendary Feats (Otto Graham)	1.00
48	Legendary Feats (Johnny Unitas)	1.00
49	Legendary Feats (Bart Starr)	1.00
50	Legendary Feats (Terry Bradshaw)	1.75

1992 Quarterback Greats GE

Members of the Quarterback Club are represented in this 12-card set sponsored by General Electric. The QB Club, GE and NFL Team Players logos all appear on the card back, which is numbered. The card front has a color action photo against a red background. The player's name is at the top of the card in white letters. Quarterback Greats is also written on the card front. The back has a career summary and four statistics. Cards were available through a mail-in offer utilizing proofs of purchase seals. An unnumbered checklist card was also produced for the set.

		MT
Complete Set (12):		10.00
Common Player:		.50
1	Troy Aikman	5.00
2	Bubby Brister	.75
3	Randall Cunningham	1.00
4	John Elway	2.00
5	Boomer Esiason	.75
6	Jim Everett	.75
7	Jim Kelly	1.50
8	Bernie Kosar	.50
9	Dan Marino	4.00
10	Warren Moon	1.00
11	Phil Simms	.50
NNO	Title Card (Checklist)	.25

1993 Quarterback Legends

These cards feature color photos of some of the NFL's best quarterbacks, against a sepia-toned background. The set name runs vertically along the left side of the card, in bronze letters. The card back is numbered and includes a career summary and closeup shot of the player.

		MT
Complete Set (50):		15.00
Common Player:		.20
1	Checklist Card	.25
2	Ken Anderson	.50
3	Steve Bartkowski	.25
4	George Blanda	1.00
5	Terry Bradshaw	1.50
6	Zeke Bratkowski	.20
7	John Brodie	.50
8	Charley Conerly	.50
9	Len Dawson	.50
10	Lynn Dickey	.20
11	Joe Ferguson	.20
12	Vince Ferragamo	.20
13	Tom Flores	.25
14	Dan Fouts	.75
15	Roman Gabriel	.25
16	Otto Graham	.75
17	Bob Griese	1.00
18	Steve Grogan	.25
19	John Hadl	.25
20	James Harris	.20
21	Jim Hart	.20
22	Ron Jaworski	.20
23	Charlie Johnson	.20
24	Bert Jones	.25
25	Sonny Jurgensen	.50
26	Joe Kapp	.20
27	Billy Kilmer	.25
28	Daryle Lamonica	.25
29	Greg Landry	.20
30	Neil Lomax	.20
31	Archie Manning	.50
32	Earl Morrall	.25
33	Craig Morton	.25
34	Gifford Nielsen	.20
35	Dan Pastorini	.20
36	Jim Plunkett	.25
37	Norm Snead	.20
38	Ken Stabler	.75
39	Bart Starr	1.00
40	Roger Staubach	2.00
41	Joe Theismann	.75
42	Y.A. Tittle	.75
43	Johnny Unitas	1.00
44	Bill Wade	.20
45	Danny White	.25
46	Doug Williams	.20
47	Jim Zorn	.20
48	Miracle Streak (George Blanda)	.75
49	Perfect Season (Bob Griese, Earl Morrall)	.50
50	Record Setting Super Bowl XXII (Doug Williams)	.25

R

1935 R311-2 Premium Photos

Measuring 6" x 8", these 17 photos feature both collegiate and professional players. The black-and-white photos have blank backs. The photos could be ordered from National Chicle in exchange for 20 wrappers given to the retailer. The photos are listed in alphabetical order by the player's name or team.

		NM
Complete Set (17):		3000.
Common Player:		175.00
1	Joe Bach	175.00
2	Eddie Casey	175.00
3	George Christensen	175.00
4	Red Grange	525.00
5	TD Next Stop (Stan Kostka)	175.00
6	Fordham Back (Joe Maniaci) (26 with ball, shown trying to gain around left end)	175.00
7	Harry Newman	175.00
8	Walter Switzer (Cornell quarterback)	175.00

9	Chicago Bears, 1934 Western Champs	300.00
10	New York Giants, 1934 World's Champs	350.00
11	Notre Dame's Quick Kick Against Army, 1934	220.00
12	Pittsburgh in Rough Going Against the Navy 1945	175.00
13	Pittsburgh Pirates, 1935 Football Club	250.00
14	Touchdown! Morton of Yale	175.00
15	A Tight Spot	175.00
16	Cotton Goes Places	175.00
17	Boston Redskins, The Greatest Tackle Picture Ever Photographed (Ace Gutowky, Steve Hokuf)	220.00

1985 Raiders Shell Oil Posters

Measuring 11-5/8" x 18", the five posters were available at participating Southern California Shell gas stations during the 1985 season. Color artwork of Raider players in action are included on the poster fronts. The backs are blank, except for the Pro Bowl poster which has the Raiders and Shell logos and the release schedule of the posters.

		MT
Complete Set (5):		25.00
Common Player:		5.00
1	Pro Bowl (No release date)	6.00
2	Defensive Front (September)	6.00
3	Deep Secondary (October)	5.00
4	Big Offensive Line (November)	5.00
5	Scores (December)	5.00

1985 Raiders Smokey

Measuring 2-5/8" x 4-1/8", the four-card set is anchored by a photo on the front, with the player's name, position and team at the bottom. The Raiders' logo and Kodak logo are printed on the lower left and right, respectively. The card backs have the player's name and his highlights on the left. A fire safety tip and cartoon are included on the right. The cards are numbered on the backs. The sponsors and Kodak logos are printed at the bottom of the card backs.

		MT
Complete Set (4):		3.00
Common Player:		.35
1	Marcus Allen	1.50
2	Tom Flores (CO)	.50
3	Howie Long	1.25
4	Rod Martin	.35

1987 Raiders Smokey Color-Grams

This 14-page booklet includes 13 player drawings and one of Smokey and Huddles. Featured on a page are a 5-5/8" x 3-11/16" postcard and a perforated card which measures 2-1/2" x 3-11/16". Each booklet measures 8-1/8" x 3-11/16". The postcard fronts have "Arsonbusters" printed at the top, with a Smokey the Bear and two Raiders logos printed at the bottom. The cards, which are unnumbered, are listed by page number.

		MT
Complete Set (14):		25.00
Common Player:		1.25
1	Smokey and Huddles	1.25
2	Matt Millen	1.50
3	Rod Martin	1.50
4	Sean Jones	2.50
5	Dokie Williams	1.25

6	Don Mosebar	1.50
7	Todd Christensen	2.50
8	Bill Pickel	1.25
9	Marcus Allen	8.00
10	Charley Hannah	1.25
11	Howie Long	3.00
12	Vann McElroy	1.50
13	Reggie McKenzie	1.25
14	Mike Haynes	2.00

1988 Raiders Police

Measuring 2-3/4" x 4-1/8", the 12-card set is anchored by a large photo on the front, with "Los Angeles Raiders," Texaco logo and Raiders' logo printed at the top. The player's number, name and position are listed beneath the photo. The card backs, which are numbered, have the player's name, number, position, bio, safety tip and L.A.P.D. shield.

		MT
Complete Set (12):		8.00
Common Player:		.40
1	Vann McElroy	.40
2	Bill Pickel	.40
3	Marcus Allen	2.00
4	Rod Martin	1.00
5	Lionel Washington	.50
6	Don Mosebar	.50
7	Reggie McKenzie	.40
8	Todd Christensen	.75
9	Bo Jackson	2.50
10	James Lofton	1.25
11	Howie Long	1.00
12	Mike Shanahan (CO)	.75

1988 Raiders Smokey

Measuring 3" x 5", the 14-card set showcases "Arsonbusters" at the top of the photo. The player's name and position are printed at the bottom of the photo. The Smokey the Bear and Raiders' logos are printed at the bottom of the black-bordered card fronts. The unnumbered card backs have the player's name, position, bio and safety tip cartoon.

		MT
Complete Set (14):		10.00
Common Player:		.75
1	Marcus Allen	4.00
2	Todd Christensen	1.00
3	Bo Jackson	4.00
4	James Lofton	2.00
5	Howie Long	1.50
6	Rod Martin	1.00
7	Vann McElroy	.75
8	Don Mosebar	1.00
9	Bill Pickel	.75
10	Jerry Robinson	.75
11	Mike Shanahan (CO)	1.50
12	Smokey Bear	.75
13	Stacey Toran	.75
14	Greg Townsend	1.00

1989 Raiders Swanson

The three cards were printed on a perforated strip, which also included two Swanson Hungry-Man dinner coupons. The cards measure 2-1/2" x 3-3/4". The card fronts have a black-and-white player photo inside an oval, with "Hungry Man" printed in a stripe in the upper left corner. The player's name is printed at the bottom. The card backs, which are numbered, showcase the player's name, bio and highlights. The Swanson Hungry-Man logo is printed at the top of the horizontal card backs.

		MT
Complete Set (3):		8.00
Common Player:		2.50
1	Marcus Allen	5.00
2	Howie Long	3.00
3	Jim Plunkett	2.50

1990 Raiders Smokey

The 16-card set is anchored on the front with a large photo. "Los Angeles Raiders" is printed

above the photo, while the player's name and number are printed beneath the photo. The Smokey the Bear logo is in the lower left. The card fronts are bordered in black. The unnumbered card backs have the player's name, position, bio, Raiders' logos and safety tip cartoon.

		MT
Complete Set (16):		10.00
Common Player:		.75
1	Eddie Anderson	1.00
2	Tom Benson	.75
3	Mervyn Fernandez	1.25
4	Bob Golic	1.00
5	Jeff Gossett	.75
6	Rory Graves	.75
7	Jeff Jaeger	.75
8	Howie Long	2.00
9	Don Mosebar	1.00
10	Jay Schroeder	1.25
11	Art Shell (CO)	2.00
12	Greg Townsend	1.25
13	Lionel Washington	1.00
14	Steve Wisniewski	1.25
15	Commitment to Excellence (Helmet and Super Bowl trophies)	.75
16	Denise Franzen (Cheerleader)	.75

1990-91 Raiders Main Street Dairy

The six half-pint milk cartons have the Raiders logo, player head shot, his name, position, team and safety tip printed on a panel. The cartons measure 4-1/2" x 6" when they are collapsed. Released in the Los Angeles metro area, the cartons were produced in three colors -- brown (chocolate lowfat), red (vitamin D) and blue (two percent lowfat).

		MT
Complete Set (6):		15.00
Common Player:		2.50
1	Bob Golic (Blue)	3.50
2	Terry McDaniel (Brown)	2.50
3	Don Mosebar (Red)	2.50
4	Jay Schroeder (Blue)	3.50
5	Art Shell (CO) (Red)	5.00
6	Steve Wisniewski (Brown)	2.50

1991 Raiders Police

The 12-card set showcases a color action photo on the front, with the player's name printed in a gray stripe above the photo. The Raiders and sponsor logos are printed at the bottom of the card front. The card backs are numbered, have the player's name, position, bio and safety tip. The sponsors are listed at the bottom, and the card number is printed inside a football in the upper right.

		MT
Complete Set (12):		15.00
Common Player:		1.00
1	Art Shell (CO)	3.00
2	Marcus Allen	3.00
3	Mervyn Fernandez	1.50
4	Willie Gault	1.50
5	Howie Long	2.00
6	Don Mosebar	1.25
7	Winston Moss	1.00
8	Jay Schroeder	1.50
9	Steve Wisniewski	1.25
10	Ethan Horton	1.00
11	Lionel Washington	1.25
12	Greg Townsend	1.50

1991 Raiders Adohr Farms Dairy

These 10 half-pint milk cartons have the Raiders' logo, player headshot, safety tip, player's name, position and team printed on one of the panels. The cartons measure 4-1/2" x 6" when collapsed. The cartons were printed in two colors -- blue (two percent lowfat) and red (vitamin D). The Greg Townsend carton was the only one to be released in both colors. The cartons are unnumbered.

		MT
Complete Set (10):		25.00
Common Player:		2.50
1	Jeff Gossett (Red)	2.50
2	Ethan Horton (Blue)	2.50
3	Jeff Jaeger (Red)	2.50
4	Ronnie Lott (Blue)	5.00
5	Terry McDaniel (Red)	2.50
6	Don Mosebar (Red)	2.50
7	Jay Schroeder (Red)	3.50
8	Art Shell (CO) (Red)	5.00
9	Greg Townsend (Red or blue)	3.50
10	Steve Wisniewski (Red)	2.50

1993-94 Raiders Adohr Farms Dairy

The six half-pint milk cartons have the Raiders' logo, player headshot, safety tip, player's name and position printed on one of the panels. The cartons measure 4-1/2" x 6" when collapsed. According to reports, 2 million cartons were sold through Los Angeles area schools and hospitals during a two-week period. The cartons are unnumbered.

		MT
Complete Set (6):		15.00
Common Player:		2.50
1	Jeff Gossett	2.50
2	Ethan Horton	2.50
3	Terry McDaniel	2.50
4	Don Mosebar	2.50
5	Art Shell (CO)	5.00
6	Steve Wisniewski	2.50

1994-95 Raiders Adohr Farms Dairy

The four half-pint milk cartons showcase the Raiders' logo, player headshot, safety tip, player's name and position on one of the carton's panels. The cartons measure 4-1/2" x 6" when collapsed. Five million sets were distributed during a three-week period to hospitals, schools, airlines and the general public. The cartons are not numbered.

		MT
Complete Set (4):		15.00
Common Player:		3.50
1	Jeff Jaeger	3.50
2	Terry McDaniel	3.50
3	Art Shell (CO)	6.00
4	Steve Wisniewski	3.50

1950 Rams Admiral

Measuring 3-1/2" x 5-1/2", the 35-card set features a posed black-and-white photo on the front of the card, with "Your Admiral dealer presents..." and the player's name printed in a black area at the top. Beneath the photo are the card number and player bio. The backs have a Rams schedule on one half, while the other half is blank. Card Nos. 26-35 are blank-backed and are a bit smaller than the other cards in the set.

		NM
Complete Set (35):		110.00
Common Player:		20.00
1	Joe Stydahar (CO)	30.00
2	Hampton Pool (CO)	20.00
3	Fred Naumetz	20.00
4	Jack Finlay	20.00
5	Gil Bouley	20.00
6	Bob Reinhard	20.00
7	Bob Boyd	20.00
8	Bob Waterfield	100.00
9	Mel Hein (CO)	40.00
10	Howard Hickey (CO)	25.00
11	Ralph Pasquariello	20.00
12	Jack Zilly	20.00
13	Tom Kalmanir	20.00
14	Norm Van Brocklin	125.00
15	Woodley Lewis	30.00
16	Glenn Davis	50.00
17	Dick Hoerner	20.00
18	Bob Kelley (ANN)	20.00
19	Paul (Tank) Younger	30.00

20	George Sims	20.00
21	Dick Huffman	20.00
22	Tom Fears	50.00
23	Vitamin Smith	25.00
24	Elroy Hirsch	75.00
25	Don Paul	20.00
26	Bill Lange	20.00
27	Paul Barry	20.00
28	Deacon Dan Towler	30.00
29	Vic Vasicek	20.00
30	Bill Smyth	20.00
31	Larry Brink	20.00
32	Jerry Williams	20.00
33	Stan West	20.00
34	Art Statuto	20.00
35	Ed Champagne	20.00

1953 Rams Black Border

Measuring 4-1/4" x 6-3/8", the 36-card set is anchored by a large photo and bordered in black. A facsimile autograph is printed near the bottom of the photo. The unnumbered card backs have the player's name, bio and career highlights. The set was available from the Rams. Some cards from the 1953-55 and 1957 Rams Black Border sets are very similar, with the exception of different information on the card backs.

		NM
Complete Set (36):		175.00
Common Player:		3.00
1	Ben Agajanian	3.00
2	Bob Boyd (Born in Riverside)	3.00
3	Larry Brink	3.00
4	Rudy Bukich	5.00
5	Tom Dahms (4 text lines)	3.00
6	Dick Daugherty (Regular Ram ...)	3.00
7	Jack Dwyer (Played 1951 ...)	3.00
8	Tom Fears (1952 stats)	10.00
9	Bob Fry (Was sprinter ...)	3.00
10	Frank Fuller (Attended ...)	3.00
11	Norbert Hecker	3.00
12	Elroy Hirsch (1952 stats)	12.00
13	John Hock (Just completed ...)	3.00
14	Bob Kelley (ANN) (Signature in upper left of photo)	3.00
15	Dick Lane	12.00
16	Woodley Lewis (Ram utility ...)	4.00
17	Tom McCormick (Set three ...)	3.00
18	Lewis Bud McFadin (Came to Rams ...)	3.00
19	Leon McLaughlin (Played every ...)	3.00
20	Brad Myers	3.00
21	Don Paul (A five year ...)	4.00
22	Hampton Pool (CO) (Hampton Pool ...)	3.00
23	Duane Putnam (As rookie ...)	4.00
24	Volney Quinlan (Nickname ...)	4.00
25	Herb Rich	3.00
26	Andy Robustelli (Rams' regular ...)	10.00
27	Vitamin Smith	4.00
28	Harland Svare (Attended ...)	3.00
29	Len Teeuws	3.00
30	Harry Thompson (Used at ...)	3.00
31	Charley Toogood (Been defensive ...)	3.00
32	Deacon Dan Towler (National football)	7.00
33	Norm Van Brocklin (1952 stats)	20.00
34	Stan West (Rams' regular)	3.00
35	Paul (Tank) Younger (1952 stats)	6.00
36	Coaches (John Sauer, William Battles, Howard (Red) Hickey)	4.00

1954 Rams Black Border

Measuring 4-1/4" x 6-3/8", the front is anchored by a large black-and-white photo, bor-

dered in black. A facsimile autograph also appears near the bottom of the photo. The unnumbered backs have the player's name, bio and career highlights. The 36-card set was available from the Rams.

		NM
Complete Set (36):		175.00
Common Player:		3.00
1	Bob Boyd (One of fastest ...)	3.00
2	Bob Carey	3.00
3	Bobby Cross	3.00
4	Tom Dahms (5 text lines)	3.00
5	Don Doll	3.00
6	Jack Dwyer (Regular defensive ...)	3.00
7	Tom Fears (1953 stats)	20.00
8	Bob Griffin (All American ...)	3.00
9	Art Hauser (Was fastest ...)	3.00
10	Hall Haynes	3.00
11	Elroy Hirsch (1953 stats)	12.00
12	Ed Hughes	3.00
13	Bob Kelley (ANN) (Signature across photo)	3.00
14	Woodley Lewis (Established ...)	4.00
15	Gene Lipscomb	10.00
16	Tom McCormick (Rams' regular)	3.00
17	Bud McFadin (Although ...)	3.00
18	Leon McLaughlin (Started every ...)	3.00
19	Paul Miller (Lettered at ...)	3.00
20	Don Paul (One of two ...)	4.00
21	Hampton Pool (CO) (Since taking ...)	3.00
22	Duane Putnam (Offensive guard)	4.00
23	Volney Quinlan (Had best ...)	4.00
24	Les Richter (Rated one ...)	7.00
25	Andy Robustelli (L.A.'s regular ...)	10.00
26	Willard Sherman (Played at ...)	4.00
27	Harland Svare (An outside ...)	3.00
28	Harry Thompson (Played offensive ...)	3.00
29	Charley Toogood	3.00
30	Deacon Dan Towler (Since becoming ...)	7.00
31	Norm Van Brocklin (1953 stats)	20.00
32	Bill Wade (Selected as)	8.00
33	Duane Wardlow	3.00
34	Stan West (Virtually ...)	3.00
35	Paul (Tank) Younger (1953 stats)	7.00
36	Coaches (Bill Battles, Howard Hickey, John Sauer, Dick Voris, Buck Weaver, Hampton Pool)	4.00

1955 Rams Black Border

Measuring 4-1/4" x 6-3/8", the 37-card set is anchored by a large black-and-white photo on the front and bordered in black. A facsimile autograph appears near the bottom of the photo. The backs include the player's name, bio and career highlights. The cards are unnumbered and were available as a set from the Rams.

		NM
Complete Set (37):		175.00
Common Player:		3.00
1	Jack Bighead	3.00
2	Bob Boyd	3.00
3	Don Burroughs	3.00
4	Jim Cason	3.00
5	Bobby Cross	3.00
6	Jack Ellena	3.00
7	Tom Fears	10.00
8	Sid Fournet	3.00
9	Frank Fuller	4.00
10	Sid Gillman (and staff)	7.00
11	Bob Griffin	3.00
12	Art Hauser	3.00

13	Hall Haynes	3.00
14	Elroy Hirsch	12.00
15	John Hock	3.00
16	Glenn Holtzman	3.00
17	Ed Hughes	3.00
18	Woodley Lewis	4.00
19	Gene Lipscomb	10.00
20	Tom McCormick	3.00
21	Bud McFadin	3.00
22	Leon McLaughlin	3.00
23	Paul Miller	3.00
24	Larry Morris	3.00
25	Don Paul	4.00
26	Duane Putnam	4.00
27	Volney Quinlan	3.00
28	Les Richter	7.00
29	Andy Robustelli	10.00
30	Willard Sherman	4.00
31	Corky Taylor	3.00
32	Charley Toogood	3.00
33	Deacon Dan Towler	7.00
34	Norm Van Brocklin	20.00
35	Bill Wade	8.00
36	Ron Waller	3.00
37	Paul (Tank) Younger	7.00

1956 Rams White Border

Measuring 4-1/4" x 6-3/8", the 37-card set is anchored by a black-and-white photo on the front and bordered in white. A facsimile autograph appears near the bottom of the photo. The unnumbered card backs have the player's name, bio and career highlights. The set was available from the Rams.

		NM
Complete Set (37):		175.00
Common Player:		3.00
1	Bob Boyd	3.00
2	Rudy Bukich	5.00
3	Don Burroughs	3.00
4	Jim Cason	3.00
5	Leon Clarke	4.00
6	Dick Daugherty	3.00
7	Jack Ellena	3.00
8	Tom Fears	10.00
9	Sid Fournet	3.00
10	Bob Fry	3.00
11	Sid Gillman, Joseph Madro, Jack Faulkner, Joe Thomas, Lowell Storm (Coaches)	7.00
12	Bob Griffin	3.00
13	Art Hauser	3.00
14	Elroy Hirsch	12.00
15	John Hock	3.00
16	Bobby Holladay	3.00
17	Glenn Holtzman	3.00
18	Bob Kelley (ANN)	3.00
19	Joe Marconi	4.00
20	Bud McFadin	3.00
21	Paul Miller	3.00
22	Ron Miller	3.00
23	Larry Morris	3.00
24	John Morrow	3.00
25	Brad Myers	3.00
26	Hugh Pitts	3.00
27	Duane Putnam	3.00
28	Les Richter	7.00
29	Willard Sherman	4.00
30	Charley Toogood	3.00
31	Norm Van Brocklin	20.00
32	Bill Wade	7.00
33	Ron Waller	3.00
34	Duane Wardlow	3.00
35	Jesse Whittenton	4.00
36	Tom Wilson	4.00
37	Paul (Tank) Younger	7.00

1957 Rams Black Border

Measuring 4-1/4" x 6-3/8", the 38-card set is anchored by a large photo on the front bordered in black. A facsimile autograph appears near the bottom of the photo. The card backs include the player's name, bio and career highlights. The cards are unnumbered and were sold as a set by the Rams.

		NM
Complete Set (38):		175.00
Common Player:		3.00
1	Jon Arnett	8.00
2	Bob Boyd (Frequently called ...)	4.00
3	Alex Bravo	3.00
4	Bill Brundige (ANN)	3.00
5	Don Burroughs	3.00
6	Jerry Castete	3.00

7	Leon Clarke	4.00
8	Paige Cothren	3.00
9	Dick Daugherty (Has the ...)	3.00
10	Bob Dougherty	3.00
11	Bob Fry (One of the ...)	3.00
12	Frank Fuller (One of the ...)	3.00
13	Coaches (Sid Gillman, Joseph Madro, George Allen, Jack Faulkner, Lowell Storm)	10.00
14	Bob Griffin (After four ...)	3.00
15	Art Hauser (One of the ...)	3.00
16	Elroy Hirsch (A legendary ...)	12.00
17	John Hock (Teamed with ...)	3.00
18	Glenn Holtzman	3.00
19	John Houser	3.00
20	Bob Kelley (ANN) (Signature near right border of photo)	3.00
21	Lamar Lundy	8.00
22	Joe Marconi	3.00
23	Paul Miller (From a ...)	3.00
24	Larry Morris	3.00
25	Ken Panfil	3.00
26	Jack Pardee	12.00
27	Duane Putnam (Named to a ...)	4.00
28	Les Richter (One of the ...)	7.00
29	Willard Sherman (One of the ...)	4.00
30	Del Shofner	8.00
31	Bill Ray Smith	6.00
32	George Strugar	3.00
33	Norm Van Brocklin (When Van Brocklin ...)	25.00
34	Bill Wade (In the first ...)	7.00
35	Ron Waller	3.00
36	Jesse Whittenton	4.00
37	Tom Wilson	4.00
38	Paul (Tank) Younger (One of a ...)	7.00

1959 Rams Bell Brand

The 40-card set is anchored by a color photo on the front, with the player's name, position and team at the bottom. The numbered card backs have the player's name, position, bio and career highlights, along with an advertisement for Bell Snacks on the left side. The right side has an ad for fans to buy L.A. Rams' Signature Merchandise. The card number is located in the upper left corner. The cards were included in specially marked bags of Bell's potato chips and corn chips.

		NM
Complete Set (40):		1500.
Common Player:		30.00
1	Bill Wade	45.00
2	Buddy Humphrey	30.00
3	Frank Ryan	50.00
4	Ed Meador	40.00
5	Tom Wilson	30.00
6	Don Burroughs	30.00
7	Jon Arnett	45.00
8	Del Shofner	45.00
9	Jack Pardee	50.00
10	Ollie Matson	75.00
11	Joe Marconi	30.00
12	Jim Jones	30.00
13	Jack Morris	30.00
14	Willard Sherman	40.00
15	Clendon Thomas	40.00
16	Les Richter	40.00
17	John Morrow	30.00
18	Lou Michaels	40.00
19	Bob Reifsnyder	30.00
20	John Guzik	30.00
21	Duane Putnam	30.00
22	John Houser	30.00
23	Buck Lansford	30.00
24	Gene Selawski	30.00
25	John Baker	30.00
26	Bob Fry	30.00
27	John Lovetere	30.00
28	George Strugar	30.00
29	Roy Wilkins	30.00
30	Charley Bradshaw	30.00
31	Gene Brito	40.00
32	Jim Phillips	40.00
33	Leon Clarke	40.00
34	Lamar Lundy	45.00
35	Sam Williams	30.00

36	Sid Gillman (CO)	60.00
37	Jack Faulkner (CO)	30.00
38	Joseph Madro (CO)	30.00
39	Don Paul (CO)	30.00
40	Lou Rymkus (CO)	40.00

1960 Rams Bell Brand

The 39-card standard sized set features the identical design on the front and back as the 1959 set, except the fronts of the 1960 set has yellow borders (the 1959 set had white borders). Card Nos. 1-18, with the exception of No. 2, are duplicate photos from the 1959 set. These cards were also inserted into specially marked bags of Bell's Snacks. Card No. 2 of Gene Selawski was pulled from the set early in the season because he was waived from the team. However, the card was available from the company.

		NM
Complete Set (39):		2000.
Common Player (1-18):		25.00
Common Player (19-39):		50.00
1	Joe Marconi	25.00
2	Gene Selawski (SP)	1200.
3	Frank Ryan	40.00
4	Ed Meador	30.00
5	Tom Wilson	25.00
6	Gene Brito	35.00
7	Jon Arnett	35.00
8	Buck Lansford	25.00
9	Jack Pardee	45.00
10	Ollie Matson	65.00
11	John Lovetere	25.00
12	Bill Jolko	25.00
13	Jim Phillips	30.00
14	Lamar Lundy	35.00
15	Del Shofner	40.00
16	Les Richter	30.00
17	Bill Wade	35.00
18	Lou Michaels	30.00
19	Dick Bass	60.00
20	Charley Britt	50.00
21	Willard Sherman	60.00
22	George Strugar	50.00
23	Bob Long	50.00
24	Danny Villanueva	60.00
25	Jim Boeke	50.00
26	Clendon Thomas	50.00
27	Art Hunter	50.00
28	Carl Karilivacz	50.00
29	John Baker	50.00
30	Charley Bradshaw	50.00
31	John Guzik	50.00
32	Buddy Humphrey	50.00
33	Carroll Dale	60.00
34	Don Ellensick	50.00
35	Ray Hord	50.00
36	Charles Janerette	50.00
37	John Kenerson	50.00
38	Jerry Stalcup	50.00
39	Bob Waterfield (CO)	125.00

1973 Rams Team Issue

Measuring 7" x 8-3/4", the six sheets are anchored on the front by color photos. Bordered in white, the fronts have the player's name and team listed beneath the photo. The blank-backed cards are unnumbered.

		NM
Complete Set (6):		32.00
Common Player:		2.50
1	Jim Bertelsen	2.50
2	John Hadl	7.00
3	Harold Jackson	5.00
4	Merlin Olsen	10.00
5	Isiah Robertson	3.50
6	Jack Snow	3.50

1980 Rams Police

Measuring 2-5/8" x 4-1/8", the 14-card set is anchored by a large photo. The player's name, number, position and team are printed beneath the photo. The Rams' and Kiwanis' logos appear in the lower left and right, respectively, on the card fronts. The backs have Rams' tips inside a box, with the sponsors listed at the bottom. The cards are unnumbered. The cards were handed out by police officers for 14 weeks.

	NM
Complete Set (14):	20.00
Common Player:	1.00
11 Pat Haden	3.50
15 Vince Ferragamo	2.50
21 Nolan Cromwell	2.50
26 Wendell Tyler	2.50
32 Cullen Bryant	1.25
53 Jim Youngblood	1.25
59 Bob Brudzinski	1.00
61 Rich Saul	1.00
77 Doug France	1.00
82 Willie Miller	1.00
85 Jack Youngblood	4.00
88 Preston Dennard	1.00
90 Larry Brooks	1.00
xx0 Ray Malavasi (CO)	1.00

1985 Rams Smokey

Measuring 4" x 6", the 24-card set showcases the player's last name at the top of the card, with a photo of the player standing with Smokey the Bear printed in the center of the card front. The Rams' logo, helmet and Smokey' Bear logo are printed beneath the photo on the front. The backs include the card number, player name, position and bio, along with a safety tip cartoon.

	MT
Complete Set (24):	15.00
Common Player:	.50
1 George Andrews	.50
2 Bill Bain	.50
3 Russ Bolinger	.50
4 Jim Collins	.50
5 Nolan Cromwell	1.00
6 Reggie Doss	.50
7 Carl Ekern	.50
8 Vince Ferragamo	1.00
9 Gary Green	.50
10 Mike Guman	.50
11 David Hill	.50
12 LeRoy Irvin (SP)	4.00
13 Mark Jerue	.50
14 Johnnie Johnson	.75
15 Jeff Kemp	1.00
16 Mel Owens	.50
17 Irv Pankey	.50
18 Doug Smith	.75
19 Ivory Sully	.50
20 Jack Youngblood	1.50
21 Mike McDonald	.50
22 Norwood Vann	.50
23 Smokey Bear (Unnumbered)	.50
24 Smokey Bear (Reggie Doss, Gary Green, Johnnie Johnson, Carl Ekern) (Unnumbered)	.75

1987 Rams Jello/General Foods

Jello and Bird's Eye sponsored this 10-card set, which features a large photo, with the Rams' helmet in the upper left and the NFL shield in the upper right. The Jello and Bird's Eye logos are in the lower left and right, respectively, with the player's name and position printed in the bottom center of the card front. The card backs have the player's name and number at the top, with his bio inside an oval in the center. His career highlights are listed at the bottom of the card, along with the Jello and Bird's Eye logos. The cards are unnumbered.

	MT
Complete Set (10):	5.00
Common Player:	.35
1 Ron Brown	.50
2 Nolan Cromwell	.60
3 Eric Dickerson	2.00
4 Carl Ekern	.35
5 Jim Everett	2.00
6 Dennis Harrah	.35
7 LeRoy Irvin	.50
8 Mike Lansford	.35
9 Jackie Slater	.60
10 Doug Smith	.50

1987 Rams Oscar Mayer

This 19-card set celebrated the Rams Special Teams Player of the Week. The player's photo

appears inside a ripped-out hole in the center of the card. The Rams' helmet and Oscar Mayer logo are on the lower left and right, respectively. The player's name and position are listed beneath the photo. The fronts have a baby blue background. The unnumbered card backs have the player's name, bio Rams' helmet and Oscar Mayer logo.

	MT
Complete Set (19):	14.00
Common Player:	.75
1 Sam Anno	.75
2 Ron Brown	1.00
3 Nolan Cromwell	1.25
4 Henry Ellard	1.50
5 Jerry Gray	1.00
6 Kevin Greene	3.00
7 Mike Guman	.75
8 Dale Hatcher	.75
9 Clifford Hicks	.75
10 Mark Jerue	.75
11 Johnnie Johnson	1.00
12 Larry Kelm	.75
13 Mike Lansford	.75
14 Vince Newsome	.75
15 Michael Stewart	.75
16 Mickey Sutton	.75
17 Tim Tyrrell	.75
18 Norwood Vann	.75
19 Charles White	1.25

1989 Rams Police

Released as a 16-card perforated sheet, the cards have a photo of the player, with his name and position, along with the Rams' helmet and Frito-Lay logos beneath the helmet. The card backs, numbered "of 16," have the Rams' helmet and Frito-Lay logo in the upper corners, followed by the player's name, position and quote. McGruff the Crime Dog's safety tip is also included on the back. The 7-11 and police badge logos are in the lower corners, with the card number centered at the bottom.

	MT
Complete Set (16):	10.00
Common Player:	1.00
1 John Robinson	2.00
2 Jim Everett	2.50
3 Doug Smith	1.25
4 Duval Love	1.00
5 Henry Ellard	2.00
6 Mel Owens	1.00
7 Jerry Gray	1.25
8 Kevin Greene	2.00
9 Vince Newsome	1.00
10 Irv Pankey	1.00
11 Tom Newberry	1.25
12 Pete Holohan	1.00
13 Mike Lansford	1.00
14 Greg Bell	1.25
15 Jackie Slater	1.25
16 Dale Hatcher	1.00

1990 Rams Smokey

Full-bleed photos are on the fronts of this 12-card set, while the backs have a black-and-white photo of the player and his bio. The cards are unnumbered and sponsored by local fire departments. The cards measure 3-3/4" x 5-3/4".

	MT
Complete Set (12):	8.00
Common Player:	.75
1 Aaron Cox	.75
2 Henry Ellard	1.25
3 Jim Everett	1.50
4 Jerry Gray	.75
5 Kevin Greene	1.50
6 Pete Holohan	.75
7 Mike Lansford	.75
8 Vince Newsome	.75
9 Doug Reed	.75
10 Jackie Slater	1.00
11 Fred Strickland	.75
12 Mike Wilcher	.75

1992 Rams Carl's Jr.

The 21-card set is anchored on the front with a photo, with the Rams' helmet in the lower left, player's name, position and number in the lower center and "Drug abuse is life abuse" in the bottom right. The

card backs include a photo of the player in the upper left, with his name, position, number and bio printed beneath it. A safety message is printed to the right of the photo, with the card number printed inside a black box in the upper right. The player's stats and highlights are listed on the right side, along with Carl's Jr.'s logo and the other sponsors' logos. Reportedly, 80,000 sets were distributed.

	MT
Complete Set (21):	10.00
Common Player:	.60
1 Carl Karcher (Founder)	.60
2 Happy Star (Carl's Jr. symbol)	.75
3 Tony Zendejas	.60
4 Henry Ellard	1.25
5 Jackie Slater	.75
6 Bern Brostek	.60
7 Cleveland Gary	.75
8 Larry Kelm	.60
9 Roman Phifer	.75
10 Jim Everett	1.25
11 Anthony Newman	.60
12 Steve Israel	.60
13 Marc Boutte	.75
14 Darryl Henley	.60
15 Michael Stewart	.60
16 Flipper Anderson	1.25
17 Kevin Greene	1.25
18 Sean Gilbert	1.25
NNOOSkippy (Be Drug Free)	.75
NNOOSpike (Be Drug Free)	.75
NNOOWise Owl Mike (Be Drug Free)	.75

1994 Rams L.A. Times

Measuring 5-1/2" x 8-1/2", the 32-sheet set was printed by the Los Angeles Times on semi-gloss stock. Showcased on the fronts is a large color photo, with the player's last name printed along the right side. The "Collector Series" logo is located in the upper left, while the L.A. Rams' logo and helmet are printed inside a yellow stripe at the bottom of the card front. The sheets are numbered "of 32" on the fronts. The backs have the player's name in a stripe at the top, with his jersey number, position, bio, headshot, career highlights and 1994 Rams' schedule following underneath. The sheets were included in weekend editions of the L.A. Times.

	MT
Complete Set (32):	10.00
Common Player:	.40
1 Toby Wright	.40
2 Tim Lester	.40
3 Shane Conlan	.50
4 Troy Drayton	.50
5 Fred Stokes	.40
6 Jerome Bettis	1.25
7 Jimmie Jones	.40
8 Henry Rolling	.40
9 Anthony Newman	.40
10 Flipper Anderson	.75
11 Steve Israel	.40
12 Johnny Bailey	.40
13 Jackie Slater	.50
14 Chris Chandler	.50
15 Sean Landeta	.40
16 Bern Brostek	.40
17 Roman Phifer	.40
18 Robert Young	.50
19 Leo Goeas	.40
20 Chris Miller	.75
21 Darryl Ashmore	.40
22 Joe Kelly	.40
23 Wayne Gandy	.40
24 Tony Zendejas	.40
25 Tom Newberry	.40
26 David Lang	.40
27 Sean Gilbert	.50
28 Chris Martin	.40
29 Thomas Homco	.40
30 Chuck Knox (CO)	.50
31 Todd Lyght	.40
32 Jerome Bettis, Sean Gilbert	.75

> A card number in parentheses ( ) indicates the set is unnumbered.

1995 Rams Upper Deck McDonald's

Sold in five-card packs for 79 cents at St. Louis area McDonald's restaurants, the 26-card set featured the Upper Deck logo in the upper left and McDonald's logo in top right. The player's name is in the lower left, with the team name and his position at the bottom right. Printed along the left side of the photo is "Special Edition" and "Premiere Season." The backs, prefixed with "McD," have the player's name, team, position and bio at the top above the photo, while the player's stats are printed beneath the photo. Proceeds from the sales of this set went to the Ronald McDonald Children's Charities.

	MT
Complete Set (26):	8.00
Common Player:	.25
1 Johnny Bailey	.25
2 Jerome Bettis	.50
3 Isaac Bruce	2.00
4 Kevin Carter	.50
5 Shane Conlan	.25
6 Troy Drayton	.35
7 Wayne Gandy	.35
8 Sean Gilbert	.35
9 Jessie Hester	.25
10 Bern Brostek	.25
11 Jimmie Jones	.25
12 Todd Kinchen	.35
13 Sean Landeta	.25
14 Thomas Homco	.25
15 Todd Lyght	.25
16 Keith Lyle	.25
17 Chris Miller	.35
18 Toby Wright	.25
19 Anthony Parker	.25
20 Roman Phifer	.25
21 Leonard Russell	.35
22 Jackie Slater	.35
23 Fred Stokes	.25
24 Alexander Wright	.35
25 Robert Young	.35
NNO Checklist Card	.35

1996 Ravens Score Board/Exxon

Score Board produced this set which was distributed at Baltimore-area Exxon stations. The nine-card set was sold in four-card packs (three players and a checklist) and carried a "BR" prefix.

	MT
Complete Set (9):	2.50
Common Player:	.25
1 Vinny Testaverde	.40
2 Eric Zeier	.40
3 Earnest Byner	.25
4 Derrick Alexander	.75
5 Michael Jackson	.40
6 Jonathan Ogden	.25
7 Ray Lewis	.25
8 Eric Turner	.25
9 Ravens Checklist	.25

1939 Redskins Matchbooks

Measuring 1-1/2" x 4-1/2" when folded out, the 20-matchbooks have a black-and-white headshot of the player at the top, with his facsimile autograph, position, college and bio listed underneath. The back side says, "This is one of 20 autographed pictures of the Washington Redskins. Compliments of The Ross

Jewelry Co." The inside of the matchbook has the official 1939 Redskins schedule. The matchbooks are unnumbered.

	NM
Complete Set (20):	525.00
Common Matchbook:	10.00
1 Jim Barber (SP)	125.00
2 Sammy Baugh	65.00
3 Hal Bradley	10.00
4 Vic Carroll	10.00
5 Bud Erickson	10.00
6 Andy Farkas	12.00
7 Frank Filchock	12.00
8 Ray Flaherty (CO)	18.00
9 Don Irwin	10.00
10 Ed Justice	10.00
11 Jim Karcher	10.00
12 Max Krause	10.00
13 Charley Malone	10.00
14 Bob Masterson	10.00
15 Wayne Millner	20.00
16 Mickey Parks	10.00
17 Ernie Pinckert	10.00
18 Steve Slivinski (SP)	125.00
19 Clem Stralka	10.00
20 Jay Turner	10.00

1940 Redskins Matchbooks

This 20-matchbook set is very similar in design to the 1939 set. The 1940 set has a headshot of the player, a facsimile autograph, his position, college and bio showcased on the front. The backside of the matchbook states, "This is one of 20 autographed pictures of the Washington Redskins." The inside of the matchbooks have the official 1940 Redskins' schedule. Prices listed here are for matchbooks missing the matches, but with the strikers intact.

	NM
Complete Set (20):	225.00
Common Player:	10.00
1 Jim Barber	10.00
2 Sammy Baugh	45.00
3 Vic Carroll	10.00
4 Glen Edwards	25.00
5 Andy Farkas	12.00
6 Dick Farman	10.00
7 Bob Hoffman	10.00
8 Don Irwin	10.00
9 Charley Malone	10.00
10 Bob Masterson	10.00
11 Wayne Millner	20.00
12 Mickey Parks	10.00
13 Ernie Pinckert	12.00
14 Bo Russell	10.00
15 Steve Slivinski	10.00
16 Clem Stralka	10.00
17 Dick Todd	10.00
18 Bill Young	10.00
19 Roy Zimmerman	10.00

1941 Redskins Matchbooks

Measuring 1-1/2" x 4-1/2" when folded out, the 20 matchbooks have a headshot of the player at the top of the front, with his facsimile autograph, position, college and bio listed beneath. The backside of the cover states, "This is one of 20 autographed pictures of the Washington Redskins. Compliments of Home Laundry." The phone number Atlantic 2400 is also included. The inside features the 1941 official Redskins' schedule.

	NM
Complete Set (20):	195.00
Common Player:	8.00
1 Ki Aldrich	8.00
2 Jim Barber	8.00
3 Sammy Baugh	40.00
4 Vic Carroll	8.00
5 Fred Davis	8.00
6 Andy Farkas	10.00
7 Dick Farman	8.00
8 Frank Filchock	10.00
9 Ray Flaherty (CO)	12.00
10 Bob Masterson	8.00
11 Bob McChesney	8.00
12 Wayne Millner	15.00
13 Wilbur Moore	8.00
14 Bob Seymour	8.00
15 Clyde Shugart	8.00
16 Clem Stralka	8.00
17 Robert Titchenal	8.00
18 Dick Todd	10.00
19 Bill Young	8.00
20 Roy Zimmerman	8.00

1942 Redskins Matchbooks

Measuring 1-1/2" x 4-1/2" when folded out, the 20 matchbooks follow the same design as the previous sets. A player headshot is showcased on the front, with his facsimile signature, position, college and bio printed beneath. The back of the cover states, "This is one of 20 autographed pictures of the Washington Redskins. Compliments of Home Laundry Atlantic 2400." The inside of the covers have the official 1942 Redskins' schedule, plus an ad for Home Laundry.

	NM
Complete Set (20):	195.00
Common Player:	8.00
1 Ki Aldrich	10.00
2 Sammy Baugh	45.00
3 Joe Beinor	8.00
4 Vic Carroll	8.00
5 Ed Cifers	8.00
6 Fred Davis	8.00
7 Glen Edwards	16.00
8 Andy Farkas	10.00
9 Dick Farman	8.00
10 Ray Flaherty (CO)	12.00
11 Al Krueger	8.00
12 Bob Masterson	8.00
13 Bob McChesney	8.00
14 Wilbur Moore	8.00
15 Bob Seymour	8.00
16 Clyde Shugart	8.00
17 Clem Stralka	8.00
18 Dick Todd	10.00
19 Willie Wilkin	8.00
20 Bill Young	8.00

1951-52 Redskins Matchbooks

Measuring 1-1/2" x 4-1/2" when folded out, the 20 matchbooks have the player headshot on the front, followed by a facsimile signature, position, college and bio. The backs state, "This is one of 20 autographed pictures of the Washington Redskins. Compliments of Jack Blank, President, Arcade Pontiac Co. ADams 8500." The outside of the matchbooks have the Redskins' logo on black and gold. An advertisement for Arcade Pontiac is printed on the back, also in color. The matchbooks are unnumbered.

	NM
Complete Set (25):	225.00
Common Player:	8.00
1 John Badaczewski	8.00
2A Head Coach (Herman Ball) (CO)	8.00
2B Assistant Coach (Herman Ball) (CO)	8.00
3 Sammy Baugh	40.00
4 Ed Berrang (1951)	10.00
5 Dan Brown (1951)	10.00
6 Al DeMao	8.00
7 Harry Dowda (1952)	10.00
8 Chuck Drazenovich	8.00
9 Bill Dudley (1951)	15.00
10 Harry Gilmer	12.00
11 Robert Goode (1951)	10.00
12 Leon Heath (1952)	10.00
13 Charlie Justice (1952)	15.00
14 Lou Karras	8.00
15 Eddie LeBaron (1952)	12.00
16 Paul Lipscomb	8.00
17 Laurie Niemi	8.00
18 John Papit (1952)	10.00
19 James Peebles (1951)	10.00
20 Ed Quirk	8.00
21 Jim Ricca (1952)	10.00
22 James Staton (1951)	10.00
23 Hugh Taylor	10.00
24 Joe Tereshinski	10.00
25 Dick Todd (CO) (1952)	10.00

1958-59 Redskins Matchbooks

Measuring 1-1/2" x 4-1/2" when folded out, the 20 matchbooks went with a totally different design than in years past.

This set features a cutout of a player headshot printed below the Redskins' logo and "Famous Redskins." The years he played with the Redskins are listed to the left of the headshot. The back of the cover has an ad for First Federal Savings. The inside includes the player's name and bio, along with an ad for First Federal Savings. The matchbooks, which are unnumbered, are printed on gray cardboard.

		NM
Complete Set (20):		195.00
Common Player:		8.00
1	Steve Bagarus (58)	8.00
2	Cliff Battles (58)	15.00
3	Sammy Baugh (58)	40.00
4	Gene Brito (58)	10.00
5	Jim Castiglia (58)	8.00
6	Al DeMao (58)	8.00
7	Chuck Drazenovich (59)	10.00
8	Bill Dudley (59)	18.00
9	Al Fiorentino (59)	8.00
10	Don Irwin (59)	8.00
11	Eddie LeBaron (58)	10.00
12	Wayne Millner (58)	12.00
13	Wilbur Moore (58)	10.00
14	Jim Schrader (59)	8.00
15	Riley Smith (59)	8.00
16	Mike Sommer (58)	8.00
17	Joe Tereshinski (58)	8.00
18	Dick Todd (59)	10.00
19	Willie Wilkin (59)	8.00
20	Casimir Witucki	8.00

1960-61 Redskins Matchbooks

Measuring 1-1/2" x 4-1/2" when folded out, the 20 matchbooks are very similar in design to the 1958-59 set except this 1960-61 set is printed on off-white cardboard. The front has a headshot of the player, along with the Redskins' logo and "Famous Redskins." The player's bio is printed on the back, along with "This is one of twenty famous Redskins presented for you by your 1st Federal Savings and Loan Association of Washington, Bethesda Branch." The matchbooks are not numbered.

		NM
Complete Set (20):		175.00
Common Player:		8.00
1	Bill Anderson (61)	10.00
2	Don Bosseler (60)	10.00
3	Glen Edwards (60)	15.00
4	Ralph Guglielmi (61)	10.00
5	Bill Hartman (60)	8.00
6	Norbert Hecker (61)	8.00
7	Dick James (61)	10.00
8	Charlie Justice (60)	15.00
9	Ray Krause (61)	8.00
10	Ray Lemek (61)	8.00
11	Tommy Mont (60)	8.00
12	John Olszewski (61)	10.00
13	John Paluck (61)	8.00
14	Jim Peebles (60)	8.00
15	Bo Russell (60)	8.00
16	Jim Schrader (61)	8.00
17	Louis Stephens (61)	8.00
18	Ed Sutton (60)	8.00
19	Bob Toneff (60)	10.00
20	Lavern Torgeson (60)	10.00

1960 Redskins Jay Publishing

Measuring 5" x 7", the 12-card set is anchored by a black-and-white posed photo on the front. The cards are unnumbered and blank-backed. Originally, the cards were sold for 25 cents in 12-photo packs.

		NM
Complete Set (12):		50.00
Common Player:		5.00
1	Sam Baker	6.00
2	Don Bosseler	6.00
3	Gene Brito	5.00
4	Johnny Carson	5.00
5	Chuck Drazenovich	5.00
6	Ralph Guglielmi	6.00
7	Dick James	6.00
8	Eddie LeBaron	7.50
9	Jim Podoley	5.00
10	Jim Schrader	5.00
11	Ed Sutton	5.00
12	Albert Zagers	5.00

1969 Redskins High's Dairy

Measuring 8" x 10", the eight-card set includes Alex Fournier artwork on the front. The player's facsimile signature is printed near the bottom of the artwork. On the left side of the unnumbered card backs is the player's name, bio and stats, while on the right side is data on Fournier. The portraits were available two ways – they could be purchased at High's Dairy Stores or consumers could purchase two half gallons of milk and recieve a free portrait.

		NM
Complete Set (8):		100.00
Common Player:		6.00
1	Chris Hanburger	10.00
2	Len Hauss	8.00
3	Sam Huff	15.00
4	Sonny Jurgensen	25.00
5	Carl Kammerer	6.00
6	Brig Owens	6.00
7	Pat Richter	8.00
8	Charley Taylor	20.00

1972 Redskins Caricature

Dick Shuman and Compu-Set, Inc. produced this 15-card set. The 8" x 10" cards feature a caricature of a Washington Redskin player. The cards are unnumbered and blank-backed.

		NM
Complete Set (16):		130.00
Common Player:		8.00
1	Mike Bass	10.00
2	Verlon Biggs	8.00
3	Mike Bragg	8.00
4	Speedy Duncan	10.00
5	Pat Fischer	10.00
6	Chris Hanburger	10.00
7	Curt Knight	8.00
8	Ron McDole	8.00
9	Brig Owens	8.00
10	Jack Pardee	10.00
11	Richie Petibon	10.00
12	Myron Pottios	8.00
13	Manny Sistrunk	8.00
14	Diron Talbert	8.00
15	Ted Vactor	8.00
16	Cover Card (Jack Pardee, Mike Bass, Manny Sistrunk, Chris Hanburger)	10.00

1981 Redskins Frito-Lay Schedules

Measuring 3-1/2" x 7-1/2", the 30 schedules are anchored by a color photo on the inside. Included on the 1981 Redskins' schedule, player photo and his name and bio, along with sponsor logos. The schedules are unnumbered.

		MT
Complete Set (30):		30.00
Common Player:		.50
1	Coy Bacon	.75
2	Perry Brooks	.50
3	Dave Butz	.75
4	Rickey Claitt	.50
5	Monte Coleman	.75
6	Mike Connell	.50
7	Brad Dusek	.75
8	Ike Forte	.50
9	Clarence Harmon	.50
10	Terry Hermeling	.50
11	Wilbur Jackson	.50
12	Mike Kruczek	.50
13	Bob Kuziel	.50
14	Joe Lavender	.75
15	Karl Lorch	.50
16	LeCharls McDaniel	.50
17	Rich Milot	.50
18	Art Monk	3.00
19	Mark Moseley	1.00
20	Mark Murphy	.75
21	Mike Nelms	.50
22	Neal Olkewicz	.50
23	Lemar Parrish	.75
24	Tony Peters	.50
25	Ron Saul	.50
26	George Starke	.50
27	Joe Theismann	2.00
28	Ricky Thompson	.50
29	Don Warren	.75
30	Jeris White	.50

1982 Redskins Frito-Lay Schedules

Measuring 3-1/2" x 7-1/2", the 15 schedule set boasts a color photo of the player on the inside, with "Redskins '82 Schedule" printed on another panel. The player's name and bio are also included on the schedules.

		MT
Complete Set (15):		15.00
Common Player:		.50
1	Dave Butz	.75
2	Monte Coleman	.75
3	Brad Dusek	.50
4	Joe Lavender	.75
5	Art Monk	2.00
6	Mark Moseley	1.00
7	Mark Murphy	.75
8	Mike Nelms	.50
9	Neal Olkewicz	.50
10	Tony Peters	.50
11	John Riggins	3.00
12	George Starke	.50
13	Joe Theismann	2.00
14	Don Warren	.75
15	Joe Washington	1.00

1982 Redskins Police

Measuring 2-5/8" x 4-1/8", the 15-card set includes a photo of the player on the front, with the Redskins' helmet on the lower left. On the bottom right are the player's number, name, position and team. The backs have a boxed-in "Redskins/PACT Tips." The Frito-Lay and PACT logos appear at the bottom corners. The cards are numbered.

		MT
Complete Set (15):		10.00
Common Player:		.50
1	Dave Butz	.75
2	Art Monk	2.50
3	Mark Murphy	.50
4	Monte Coleman	.75
5	Mark Moseley	.75
6	George Starke	.50
7	Perry Brooks	.50
8	Joe Washington	.75
9	Don Warren	.75
10	Joe Lavender	.50
11	Joe Theismann	2.00
12	Tony Peters	.50
13	Neal Olkewicz	.50
14	Mike Nelms	.50
15	John Riggins	2.00

1983 Redskins Frito-Lay Schedules

Measuring 2-1/2" x 3-1/2", the 15-schedule set showcases an action photo, along with the player's name and bio. The schedules are unnumbered.

		MT
Complete Set (15):		15.00
Common Player:		.50
1	Charlie Brown	.75
2	Dave Butz	.75
3	The Hogs	.75
4	Dexter Manley	.75
5	Rich Milot	.75
6	Art Monk	1.50
7	Mark Moseley	.75
8	Mark Murphy	.50
9	Mike Nelms	.50
10	Neal Olkewicz	.50
11	Tony Peters	.50
12	John Riggins	1.25
13	Joe Theismann	2.00
14	Joe Washington	.75
15	Jeris White	.50

1983 Redskins Police

#81 · Art Monk Wide Receiver
Washington Redskins

Measuring 2-5/8" x 4-1/8", the 16-card set was handed out

one per week by police officers. The card fronts are anchored by a large photo, with the player's number, position, name and bio beneath it. The Redskins' helmet is in the lower left corner, with "Washington Redskins, Super Bowl XVII Champions" printed at the bottom right. The backs, numbered "of 16," have a boxed-in "Redskins PACT Tips" and the player's bio and highlights. The Frito-Lay and PACT logos are printed in the lower left and right corners, respectively. Jeris White's card is tough to locate, as his card was never handed out because he held out during the season.

		MT
Complete Set (16):		10.00
Common Player:		.50
1	Joe Washington	1.00
2	The Hogs (Offensive Line)	.75
3	Mark Moseley	1.00
4	Monte Coleman	.50
5	Neal Olkewicz	.50
6	Joe Theismann	3.00
7	Charlie Brown	.75
8	Dave Butz	.75
9	Jeris White (SP)	1.50
10	Mark Murphy	.50
11	Dexter Manley	.75
12	Art Monk	3.00
13	Rich Milot	.50
14	Vernon Dean	.50
15	John Riggins	2.00

1984 Redskins Frito-Lay Schedules

Measuring 3-1/2" x 7-1/2", the 15 schedules boast a color photo of the player, along with his name and bio. The schedules are unnumbered.

		MT
Complete Set (15):		15.00
Common Player:		.50
1	Charlie Brown	.75
2	Dave Butz	.75
3	Ken Coffey	.50
4	Clint Didier	.50
5	Darryl Grant	.50
6	Darrell Green	1.00
7	Jeff Hayes	.50
8	The Hogs	.75
9	Rich Milot	.50
10	Art Monk	1.50
11	Mark Murphy	.50
12	John Riggins	1.50
13	Joe Theismann	1.50
14	Don Warren	.75
15	Joe Washington	.75

1984 Redskins Police

Measuring 2-5/8" x 4-1/8", the 16-card set showcases a color photo on the front, with the player's name, number and position beneath the photo. The player's facsimile signature and "NFC Champion Redskins" is printed in the lower right. The Redskins' helmet is located in the lower left. The card backs, numbered "of 16," have the "Redskins/PACT Tip" at the top, while the player's name, bio and highlights are printed below. The Frito-Lay and PACT logos are printed in the lower left and right, respectively.

		MT
Complete Set (16):		8.00
Common Player:		.35
1	John Riggins	1.25
2	Darryl Grant	.35
3	Art Monk	1.50
4	Neal Olkewicz	.35
5	The Hogs	.50
6	Jeff Hayes	.50
7	Joe Theismann	1.25
8	Clint Didier	.35
9	Mark Murphy	.35
10	Don Warren	.50
11	Darrell Green	.50
12	Dave Butz	.50
13	Ken Coffey	.35
14	Rich Milot	.35
15	Charlie Brown	.50
16	Joe Washington	.50

1985 Redskins Frito-Lay Schedules

Measuring 3-1/2" x 7-1/2", the 16 schedules showcase a photo of a legendary Washington Redskins' player. The schedules are unnumbered.

		MT
Complete Set (16):		15.00
Common Player:		.50
1	Cliff Battles	.75
2	Sammy Baugh	1.50
3	Larry Brown	.75
4	Bill Dudley	.75
5	Turk Edwards	.75
6	Pat Fischer	.50
7	Chris Hanburger	.50
8	Len Hauss	.50
9	Ken Houston	.75
10	Sam Huff	1.00
11	Sonny Jurgenson	1.00
12	Billy Kilmer	.50
13	Wayne Millner	.50
14	Bobby Mitchell	.75
15	Brig Owens	.50
16	Charley Taylor	1.00

1985 Redskins Police

Measuring 2-5/8" x 4-1/8", the 16-card set has the Washington Redskins' logo at the top of the card front, with the player photo in the center. Beneath the photo are the player's number, position and name. The backs, numbered "of 16," have "Redskins/PACT Tips" at the top. Printed in the center of the back are the player's name, number, position, bio and career highlights. The Frito-Lay and PACT logos are located in the lower left and right, respectively.

		MT
Complete Set (16):		5.00
Common Player:		.35
1	Darrell Green	.75
2	Clint Didier	.35
3	Neal Olkewicz	.35
4	Darryl Grant	.35
5	Joe Jacoby	.50
6	Vernon Dean	.35
7	Joe Theismann	1.00
8	Mel Kaufman	.35
9	Calvin Muhammad	.35
10	Dexter Manley	.50
11	John Riggins	1.00
12	Mark May	.50
13	Dave Butz	.35
14	Art Monk	1.25
15	Russ Grimm	.50
16	Charles Mann	.50

1986 Redskins Frito-Lay Schedules

These 16 schedules feature the Redskins' 50th Anniversary logo on the front and Frito-Lay's logos on the back. When opened, the left panel contains the preseason and postseason schedules, the center panel has a player photo and the right panel features the regular season schedule. The other panel has basic player information. The schedules are un-numbered.

		MT
Complete Set (16):		20.00
Common Player:		1.00
1	Cliff Battles	1.50
2	Sammy Baugh	2.00
3	Larry Brown	1.00
4	Bill Dudley	1.50
5	Turk Edwards	1.00
6	Pat Fischer	1.00
7	Chris Hanburger	1.00
8	Len Hauss	1.00
9	Sam Huff	2.00
10	Ken Houston	1.50
11	Sonny Jurgensen	2.00
12	Billy Kilmer	1.50
13	Wayne Millner	1.50
14	Bobby Mitchell	2.00
15	Brig Owens	1.00
16	Charley Taylor	2.00

1986 Redskins Police

Measuring 2-5/8" x 4-1/8", the 16-card set has a Washington Redskins' pennant in the upper left corner of the front. Inside the pennant is a facsimile signature of the player. His number, name and position is printed to the right of the pen-

nant. The photo fills up the bottom portion of the card front. The backs, numbered "of 16," have the player's name inside a pennant at the top, with his number, position, bio and career highlights printed beneath it. Quick quiz and crime prevention tips are also included on the back. The Frito-Lay, PACT and WMAL radio logos are printed at the bottom.

		MT
Complete Set (16):		5.00
Common Player:		.35
1	Darrell Green	.75
2	Joe Jacoby	.50
3	Charles Mann	.50
4	Jay Schroeder	.50
5	Raphel Cherry	.35
6	Russ Grimm	.50
7	Mel Kaufman	.35
8	Gary Clark	1.25
9	Vernon Dean	.35
10	Mark May	.50
11	Dave Butz	.50
12	Jeff Bostic	.50
13	Dean Hamel	.35
14	Dexter Manley	.50
15	George Rogers	.50
16	Art Monk	1.00

1987 Redskins Frito-Lay Schedules

Measuring 3-1/2" x 7-1/2", the 16 schedule set includes an action photo of the player. The schedules are unnumbered.

		MT
Complete Set (16):		15.00
Common Player:		.50
1	Jeff Bostic	.75
2	Kelvin Bryant	.75
3	Dave Butz	.75
4	Gary Clark	1.00
5	Steve Cox	.50
6	Clint Didier	.50
7	Darryl Grant	.50
8	Darrell Green	.75
9	Joe Jacoby	.75
10	Dexter Manley	.75
11	Charles Mann	.75
12	Mark May	.75
13	Art Monk	1.00
14	Jay Schroeder	.75
15	Alvin Walton	.50
16	Don Warren	.75

1987 Redskins Police

Measuring 2-5/8" x 4-1/8", the 16-card set has the Washington Redskins' logo at the top, with the player photo anchoring the middle. The player's name is printed at the bottom of the card front. The backs, numbered "Week X of 16," have the player's number inside a football in the upper left. The player's name, position, bio and career highlights are also listed on the back. "Did you know?" and a tip from McGruff the Crime Dog round out the back, along with Frito-Lay and PACT logos at the bottom right.

		MT
Complete Set (16):		5.00
Common Player:		.30
1	Joe Jacoby	.40
2	Gary Clark	.75
3	Dexter Manley	.40
4	Darrell Green	.40
5	Alvin Walton	.30
6	Clint Didier	.30
7	Art Monk	1.00
8	Darryl Grant	.30
9	Kelvin Bryant	.40
10	Jay Schroeder	.40
11	Don Warren	.40
12	Steve Cox	.30
13	Mark May	.40
14	Jeff Bostic	.40
15	Charles Mann	.40
16	Dave Butz	.40

1988 Redskins Frito-Lay Schedules

Measuring 3-1/2" x 7-1/2", the 16 schedules boast an action photo of a player, with his name and bio. A photo of the Super Bowl trophy is showcased on these schedules, which are un-numbered.

		MT
Complete Set (16):		15.00
Common Player:		.50
1	Jeff Bostic	.75
2	Dave Butz	.75
3	Gary Clark	1.00
4	Brian Davis	.50
5	Joe Jacoby	.75
6	Markus Koch	.50
7	Charles Mann	.75
8	Wilbur Marshall	.75
9	Mark May	.75
10	Raleigh McKenzie	.50
11	Art Monk	1.00
12	Ricky Sanders	.75
13	Alvin Walton	.50
14	Don Warren	.75
15	Barry Wilburn	.50
16	Doug Williams	1.00

1988 Redskins Police

Measuring 2-5/8" x 4-1/8", the 16-card set has the Washington Redskins' logo (with the Vince Lombardi Super Bowl Trophy printed where the "i" in Redskins would appear) located in the upper left. The player's number and name are printed in the upper right. A color photo covers the remaining portion of the card front. The backs, numbered with a "Week X," have the player's name and number at the top, followed by his bio, career highlights and a safety tip. The logos printed at the bottom from left to right are Mobil, PACT and Jello.

		MT
Complete Set (16):		5.00
Common Player:		.30
1	Jeff Bostic	.40
2	Dave Butz	.40
3	Gary Clark	.75
4	Brian Davis	.30
5	Joe Jacoby	.40
6	Markus Koch	.30
7	Charles Mann	.40
8	Wilber Marshall	.40
9	Mark May	.40
10	Raleigh McKenzie	.30
11	Art Monk	1.00
12	Ricky Sanders	.75
13	Alvin Walton	.30
14	Don Warren	.40
15	Barry Wilburn	.30
16	Doug Williams	.75

1989 Redskins Mobil Schedules

Measuring 3-1/2" x 7-1/2", the 16 schedules showcase a color player photo, along with the 1989 schedule. These schedules are unnumbered.

		MT
Complete Set (16):		10.00
Common Player:		.40
1	Ravin Caldwell	.40
2	Gary Clark	1.00
3	Monte Coleman	.60
4	Brian Davis	.40
5	Joe Jacoby	.60
6	Jim Lachey	.60
7	Chip Lohmiller	.60
8	Charles Mann	.60
9	Wilbur Marshall	.60
10	Mark May	.60
11	Raleigh McKenzie	.40
12	Art Monk	1.00
13	Mark Rypien	.60
14	Ricky Sanders	.60
15	Don Warren	.60
16	Doug Williams	.75

1989 Redskins Police

Measuring 2-5/8" x 4-1/8", the 16-card set has "Washing-

---

ton" in a stripe at the top of the card front, with "Redskins" printed beneath it. The player photo has the player's name and number inside a stripe near the bottom. The unnumbered card backs have the player's number and name at the top, along with his bio, career highlights, safety tip and "Did you know?" The Mobil, PACT and Fox-TV 5 logos are printed at the bottom of the card backs.

		MT
Complete Set (16):		5.00
Common Player:		.30
11	Mark Rypien	.60
17	Doug Williams	.60
21	Earnest Byner	.40
22	Jamie Morris	.30
28	Darrell Green	.40
34	Brian Davis	.30
37	Gerald Riggs	.40
50	Ravin Caldwell	.30
52	Neal Olkewicz	.30
58	Wilber Marshall	.40
73	Mark May	.40
74	Markus Koch	.30
81	Art Monk	1.00
83	Ricky Sanders	.60
84	Gary Clark	.75
85	Don Warren	.40

1990 Redskins Mobil Schedules

Measuring 3-1/2" x 7-1/2", the 16 pocket schedules boast a color action photo of the player. The schedules are unnumbered.

		MT
Complete Set (16):		10.00
Common Player:		.40
1	Jeff Bostic	.60
2	Earnest Byner	.60
3	Gary Clark	.75
4	Darryl Grant	.40
5	Darrell Green	.60
6	Jim Lachey	.60
7	Chip Lohmiller	.60
8	Charles Mann	.60
9	Wilbur Marshall	.60
10	Ralf Mojsiejenko	.40
11	Art Monk	1.00
12	Gerald Riggs	.60
13	Mark Rypien	.60
14	Ricky Sanders	.60
15	Alvin Walton	.40
16	Don Warren	.60

1990 Redskins Police

Measuring 3-1/2" x 7-1/2", the 16-card set includes a Washington Redskins' logo at the top, with the player's name and number at the bottom of the card front. The unnumbered card backs have the player's name, number, bio, career highlights, safety tip and "Did you know?" Printed at the bottom of the card backs are the Mobil, PACT and Fox-TV 5 logos.

		MT
Complete Set (16):		5.00
Common Player:		.25
1	Todd Bowles	.25
2	Earnest Byner	.35
3	Ravin Caldwell	.25
4	Gary Clark	.60
5	Darrell Green	.35
6	Jimmie Johnson	.25
7	Jim Lachey	.35
8	Chip Lohmiller	.35
9	Charles Mann	.35
10	Greg Manusky	.25
11	Wilber Marshall	.35
12	Art Monk	.75
13	Gerald Riggs	.35
14	Mark Rypien	.35
15	Alvin Walton	.25
16	Don Warren	.35

1991 Redskins Mobil Schedules

Measuring 2-1/2" x 3-1/2", the 16 pocket schedules boast a photo of the player on the front. The player's name and bio also are printed on the unnumbered schedule.

		MT
Complete Set (16):		10.00
Common Player:		.40
1	Earnest Byner	.60
2	Gary Clark	.75
3	Andre Collins	.60
4	Kurt Gouveia	.40
5	Darrell Green	.60
6	Jimmie Johnson	.40
7	Markus Koch	.40
8	Jim Lachey	.60
9	Chip Lohmiller	.60
10	Charles Mann	.60
11	Martin Mayhew	.40
12	Art Monk	1.00
13	Mark Rypien	.60
14	Mark Schlereth	.40
15	Ed Simmons	.40
16	Eric Williams	.40

1991 Redskins Police

Measuring 2-5/8" x 4-1/8", the 16-card set has "Washington" printed inside a gold stripe at the top, while "Redskins" is printed vertically along the left side. The player photo is to the right of "Redskins." The player's number is printed inside a circle at the bottom, with his name inside a black stripe at the bottom. The backs have the player's name, number, bio, career highlights, safety tip and "Did you know?" The logos printed on the bottom, from left to right, are Mobil, PACT and Fox-TV 5. The cards are unnumbered.

		MT
Complete Set (16):		5.00
Common Player:		.25
1	John Brandes	.25
2	Earnest Byner	.35
3	Gary Clark	.60
4	Andre Collins	.35
5	Darrell Green	.35
6	Joey Howard	.25
7	Tim Johnson	.25
8	Jim Lachey	.35
9	Chip Lohmiller	.25
10	Charles Mann	.35
11	Art Monk	.75
12	Mark Rypien	.35
13	Mark Schlereth	.25
14	Fred Stokes	.25
15	Don Warren	.35
16	Eric Williams	.25

1992 Redskins Mobil Schedules

Measuring 2-1/2" x 3-1/2", the 16 pocket schedules have a color action photo of the player, along with his name and bio. The schedules are unnumbered.

		MT
Complete Set (16):		10.00
Common Player:		.40
1	Gary Clark	.75
2	Brad Edwards	.40
3	Ricky Ervins	.75
4	Jumpy Geathers	.40
5	Darrell Green	.60
6	Joe Jacoby	.60
7	Tim Johnson	.40
8	Charles Mann	.60
9	Wilbur Marshall	.60
10	Ron Middleton	.40
11	Brian Mitchell	.75
12	Art Monk	1.00
13	Jim Lachey	.60
14	Chip Lohmiller	.40
15	Mark Rypien	.60
16	Fred Stokes	.40

1992 Redskins Police

Measuring 2-1/2" x 4-1/8", the 16-card set has "Washing-

---

ton Redskins" printed in the upper right, with the Vince Lombardi Trophy in the upper left of the photo. The player's number is printed inside a circle on the lower left of the photo, while the player's name is printed inside the border at the bottom of the card front. The card backs, which are unnumbered, have the player's number, name, bio, career highlights and tip. The sponsor logos, from left to right, are Mobil, PACT and Fox-TV 5.

		MT
Complete Set (16):		5.00
Common Player:		.30
1	Jeff Bostic	.40
2	Earnest Byner	.40
3	Gary Clark	.60
4	Monte Coleman	.40
5	Andre Collins	.40
6	Danny Copeland	.30
7	Kurt Gouveia	.30
8	Darrell Green	.40
9	Jim Lachey	.40
10	Charles Mann	.40
11	Wilbur Marshall	.40
12	Raleigh McKenzie	.30
13	Art Monk	1.00
14	Mark Rypien	.40
15	Mark Schlereth	.30
16	Eric Williams	.30

1993 Redskins Mobil Schedules

Measuring 2-1/2" x 3-1/2", the 16 pocket schedules have an action photo on the front, along with the player's name and bio. The schedules are unnumbered.

		MT
Complete Set (16):		10.00
Common Player:		.40
1	Todd Bowles	.40
2	Earnest Byner	.60
3	Monte Coleman	.60
4	Andre Collins	.60
5	Shane Collins	.40
6	Danny Copeland	.40
7	Kurt Gouveia	.40
8	Darrell Green	.60
9	A.J. Johnson	.40
10	Jim Lachey	.40
11	Ron Middleton	.40
12	Brian Mitchell	.75
13	Mark Rypien	.60
14	Ricky Sanders	.60
15	Mark Schlereth	.40
16	Ed Simmons	.40

1993 Redskins Police

Measuring 2-3/4" x 4-1/8", the 16-card set has "Washington Redskins" printed at the top, with a photo in the middle. The Redskins' helmet is in the lower left, with the player's name and number printed beneath the photo to the right of the helmet. The unnumbered card backs have the player's name, number, bio, career highlights and safety tip. The sponsor logos printed at the bottom, from left to right, are Mobil, PACT and Cellular One.

		MT
Complete Set (16):		5.00
Common Player:		.30
1	Ray Brown	.30
2	Andre Collins	.40
3	Brad Edwards	.30
4	Matt Elliott	.30
5	Ricky Ervins	.40
6	Darrell Green	.60
7	Desmond Howard	.60

8	Joe Jacoby	.40
9	Tim Johnson	.30
10	Jim Lachey	.40
11	Chip Lohmiller	.30
12	Charles Mann	.40
14	Raleigh McKenzie	.30
14	Brian Mitchell	.50
15	Terry Orr	.30
16	Mark Rypien	.40

1994 Redskins Mobil Schedules

Measuring 2-1/2" x 3-1/2", the 16 pocket schedules showcase an action photo of the player, along with his name and bio. The schedules are unnumbered.

		MT
Complete Set (16):		10.00
Common Player:		.40
1	Reggie Brooks	.60
2	Ray Brown	.40
3	Tom Carter	.60
4	Shane Collins	.40
5	Darrell Green	.60
6	Ken Harvey	.60
7	Lamont Hollinquest	.40
8	Desmond Howard	.60
9	Tim Johnson	.40
10	Jim Lachey	.60
11	Chip Lohmiller	.60
12	Chip Lohmiller	.60
13	Sterling Palmer	.40
14	Heath Shuler	1.50
15	Bobby Wilson	.40
16	Frank Wycheck	.40

1995 Redskins Program Sheets

Measuring 8" x 10", the eight sheets were inserted into Redskins' GameDay programs during the regular season. The sheets showcase stadium photographs taken during championship games. The sheets are unnumbered.

		MT
Complete Set (8):		20.00
Common Player:		3.00
1	9/3/95 vs. Cardinals. Redskins vs. Bears, 1937, 1943. (Wrigley Field)	3.00
2	9/10/95 vs. Raiders. Redskins vs. Bears, 1940, 1942. (Griffith Stadium)	3.00
3	10/1/95 vs. Cowboys. Redskins vs. Rams, 1945. (Cleveland Stadium)	3.00
4	10/22/95 vs. Lions. Redskins vs. Dolphins, S.B. VII. (L.A. Coliseum)	3.00
5	10/29/95 vs. Giants. Redskins vs. Dolphins, S.B. XVII. (Rose Bowl)	3.00
6	11/19/95 vs. Seahawks. Redskins vs. Raiders, S.B. XVIII. (Tampa Stadium)	3.00
7	11/26/95 vs. Eagles. Skins vs. Broncos, S.B. XXII. (Jack Murphy Stadium)	3.00
8	12/24/95 vs. Panthers. Redskins vs. Bills, S.B. XXVI. (H.H.H. Metrodome)	3.00

1996 Redskins Score Board/Exxon

This nine-card set was produced by Score Board and distributed by Washington D.C. area Exxon stations. The cards were sold in four-card packs, which contained three player cards and one checklist. They have a "WR" prefix.

		MT
Complete Set (9):		3.00
Common Player:		.25
1	Gus Frerotte	.75
2	Terry Allen	.50
3	Henry Ellard	.50
4	Michael Westbrook	1.00
5	Brian Mitchell	.25

6	Sean Gilbert	.25
7	Ken Harvey	.25
8	Darrell Green	.50
9	Redskins Checklist	.25

1993 Rice Council

Athletes from football, baseball, swimming, bobsledding and tennis are honored in this 10-card set produced by the USA Rice Council in Houston, Texas. Troy Aikman and Warren Moon are the two football players featured in the set. Showcased on the fronts are a color photo, player's name and USA Rice Council logo. The fronts are bordered in red or blue. The backs, which are numbered in the upper right corner, have the player's name, team and position, along with his bio. A recipe also is included on the back.

		MT
Complete Set (10):		10.00
Common Player:		.25
1	Steve Sax	.50
2	Troy Aikman	4.00
3	Roger Clemens	1.50
4	Zina Garrison	.75
5	Warren Moon	1.50
6	Summer Sanders	.75
7	Steve Sax	.50
8	Brian Shimer	.25
9	Food Guide Pyramid	.25
10	Ten Tips to Healthy Eating for Kids	.25

1999 Sage

This was the premiere issue of Sage Football. It released a 50-card prospect set that included all of the top picks from 1999 except for Ricky Williams. Only 4,200 of each player was produced. Inserts included five different levels of autographs with Red, Bronze, Silver, Gold and Platinum.

		MT
Complete Set (50):		35.00
Common Player:		.25
Minor Stars:		.50
Wax Box:		120.00
1	Rahim Abdullah	.25
2	Jerry Azumah	.25
3	Champ Bailey	1.00
4	D'Wayne Bates	.50
5	Michael Bishop	1.00
6	David Boston	1.50
7	Fernando Bryant	.25
8	Tony Bryant	.25
9	Chris Claiborne	.50
10	Mike Cloud	.50
11	Cecil Collins	1.25
12	Tim Couch	5.00
13	Daunte Culpepper	2.50
14	Jared DeVries	.25
15	Adrian Dingle	.25
16	Antwan Edwards	.50
17	Troy Edwards	1.50
18	Kevin Faulk	1.00
19	Rufus French	.25
20	Martin Gramatica	.50
21	Torry Holt	1.50
22	Sedrick Irvin	.50
23	Edgerrin James	8.00
24	Jon Jansen	.25
25	Andy Katzenmoyer	.50
26	Jevon Kearse	1.50
27	Patrick Kerney	.25

28	Lamar King	.25
29	Shaun King	2.50
30	Jim Kleinsasser	.50
31	Rob Konrad	.25
32	Brian Kuklick	.25
33	Chris McAlister	.25
34	Darnell McDonald	.50
35	Reggie McGrew	.25
36	Donovan McNabb	2.50
37	Cade McNown	2.50
38	Dat Nguyen	.50
39	Solomon Page	.25
40	Mike Peterson	.25
41	Anthony Poindexter	.25
42	Peerless Price	1.00
43	Michael Rucker	.25
44	L.J. Shelton	.25
45	Akili Smith	2.50
46	John Tait	.25
47	Fred Vinson	.25
48	Al Wilson	.25
49	Antoine Winfield	.25
50	Damien Woody	.25

1999 Sage Autographs

This is a 50-card Autograph insert that has red borders and a hologram on the front with the player's autograph and sequentially numbered. Most players signed a total of 999 except for ten players.

		MT
Complete Set (50):		550.00
Common Player:		4.00
Minor Stars:		8.00
1	Rahim Abdullah 999	4.00
2	Jerry Azumah 999	4.00
3	Champ Bailey 999	12.00
4	D'Wayne Bates 999	8.00
5	Michael Bishop 999	12.00
6	David Boston 869	20.00
7	Fernando Bryant 999	4.00
8	Tony Bryant 999	4.00
9	Chris Claiborne 999	12.00
10	Mike Cloud 434	15.00
11	Cecil Collins 999	15.00
12	Tim Couch 999	60.00
13	Daunte Culpepper 419	40.00
14	Jared DeVries 887	4.00
15	Adrian Dingle 999	4.00
16	Antwan Edwards 999	8.00
17	Troy Edwards 999	20.00
18	Kevin Faulk 999	12.00
19	Rufus French 999	6.00
20	Martin Gramatica 999	8.00
21	Torry Holt 999	20.00
22	Sedrick Irvin 999	12.00
23	Edgerrin James 859	75.00
24	Jon Jansen 999	4.00
25	Andy Katzenmoyer 209	35.00
26	Jevon Kearse 999	15.00
27	Patrick Kerney 879	4.00
28	Lamar King 999	4.00
29	Shaun King 999	30.00
30	Jim Kleinsasser 999	8.00
31	Rob Konrad 999	8.00
32	Brian Kuklick 999	4.00
33	Chris McAlister 999	8.00
34	Darnell McDonald 999	15.00
35	Reggie McGrew 999	4.00
36	Donovan McNabb 999	30.00
37	Cade McNown 209	75.00
38	Dat Nguyen 999	8.00
39	Solomon Page 999	4.00
40	Mike Peterson 999	4.00
41	Anthony Poindexter 999	4.00
42	Peerless Price 232	30.00
43	Michael Rucker 999	4.00
44	L.J. Shelton 999	4.00
45	Akili Smith 419	40.00
46	John Tait 999	4.00
47	Fred Vinson 999	4.00
48	Al Wilson 999	4.00
49	Antoine Winfield 999	4.00
50	Damien Woody 999	4.00

1999 Sage Autographs Bronze

This insert is the same as the Red Autographs except for the borders are Bronze and the players only signed a total of 650. A few of the players signed less.

		MT
Complete Set (50):		725.00
Common Player:		6.00
Minor Stars:		12.00
1	Rahim Abdullah 650	12.00
2	Jerry Azumah 650	12.00
3	Champ Bailey 650	15.00
4	D'Wayne Bates 650	12.00
5	Michael Bishop 650	12.00
6	David Boston 565	30.00
7	Fernando Bryant 650	6.00
8	Tony Bryant 650	6.00
9	Chris Claiborne 650	12.00
10	Mike Cloud 280	20.00
11	Cecil Collins 650	18.00
12	Tim Couch 650	75.00
13	Daunte Culpepper 285	45.00
14	Jared DeVries 575	6.00
15	Adrian Dingle 650	6.00
16	Antwan Edwards 650	12.00
17	Troy Edwards 650	20.00
18	Kevin Faulk 650	15.00
19	Rufus French 650	6.00
20	Martin Gramatica 650	12.00
21	Torry Holt 650	20.00
22	Sedrick Irvin 650	12.00
23	Edgerrin James 570	100.00
24	Jon Jansen 650	6.00
25	Andy Katzenmoyer 140	45.00
26	Jevon Kearse 650	20.00
27	Patrick Kerney 585	12.00
28	Lamar King 650	6.00
29	Shaun King 650	30.00
30	Jim Kleinsasser 650	12.00
31	Rob Konrad 650	12.00
32	Brian Kuklick 650	6.00
33	Chris McAlister 650	12.00
34	Darnell McDonald 650	15.00
35	Reggie McGrew 650	6.00
36	Donovan McNabb 650	30.00
37	Cade McNown 140	85.00
38	Dat Nguyen 650	6.00
39	Solomon Page 650	6.00
40	Mike Peterson 650	6.00
41	Anthony Poindexter 999	
42	Peerless Price 150	35.00
43	Michael Rucker 650	6.00
44	L.J. Shelton 650	6.00
45	Akili Smith 285	45.00
46	John Tait 650	6.00
47	Fred Vinson 650	6.00
48	Al Wilson 650	6.00
49	Antoine Winfield 650	6.00
50	Damien Woody 650	6.00

1999 Sage Autographs Gold

This insert is the same as the Red set except for the bor-

ders are in gold and most players in the set signed only 200.

		MT
Common Player:		12.00
Minor Stars:		20.00
1	Rahim Abdullah 200	12.00
2	Jerry Azumah 200	12.00
3	Champ Bailey 200	25.00
4	D'Wayne Bates 200	20.00
5	Michael Bishop 200	25.00
6	David Boston 174	45.00
7	Fernando Bryant 200	12.00
8	Tony Bryant 200	12.00
9	Chris Claiborne 200	20.00
10	Mike Cloud 88	35.00
11	Cecil Collins 200	30.00
12	Tim Couch 200	125.00
13	Daunte Culpepper 90	75.00
14	Jared DeVries 185	20.00
15	Adrian Dingle 200	12.00
16	Antwan Edwards 200	20.00
17	Troy Edwards 200	25.00
18	Kevin Faulk 200	25.00
19	Rufus French 200	12.00
20	Martin Gramatica 200	20.00
21	Torry Holt 200	35.00
22	Sedrick Irvin 200	25.00
23	Edgerrin James 175	150.00
24	Jon Jansen 200	12.00
25	Andy Katzenmoyer 45	75.00
26	Jevon Kearse 200	30.00
27	Patrick Kerney 175	12.00
28	Lamar King 200	12.00
29	Shaun King 200	50.00
30	Jim Kleinsasser 200	20.00
31	Rob Konrad 200	20.00
32	Brian Kuklick 200	12.00
33	Chris McAlister 200	20.00
34	Darnell McDonald 200	25.00
35	Reggie McGrew 200	12.00
36	Donovan McNabb 200	50.00
37	Cade McNown 45	150.00
38	Dat Nguyen 200	12.00
39	Solomon Page 200	12.00
40	Mike Peterson 200	12.00
41	Anthony Poindexter 200	12.00
42	Peerless Price 46	60.00
43	Michael Rucker 200	12.00
44	L.J. Shelton 200	12.00
45	Akili Smith 90	75.00
46	John Tait 200	12.00
47	Fred Vinson 200	12.00
48	Al Wilson 200	12.00
49	Antoine Winfield 200	12.00
50	Damien Woody 200	12.00

1999 Sage Autographs Platinum

This insert is the same as the Red Autographs except most of the players only signed 50 cards and the borders are in platinum.

		MT
Common Player:		15.00
Minor Stars:		30.00
1	Rahim Abdullah 50	15.00
2	Jerry Azumah 50	15.00
3	Champ Bailey 50	35.00
4	D'Wayne Bates 50	30.00
5	Michael Bishop 50	35.00
6	David Boston 43	60.00
7	Fernando Bryant 50	15.00
8	Tony Bryant 50	15.00
9	Chris Claiborne 50	30.00
10	Mike Cloud 22	45.00
11	Cecil Collins 50	40.00
12	Tim Couch 50	175.00
13	Daunte Culpepper 25	130.00
14	Jared DeVries 47	15.00
15	Adrian Dingle 50	15.00
16	Antwan Edwards 50	40.00
17	Troy Edwards 50	55.00
18	Kevin Faulk 50	60.00
19	Rufus French 50	15.00
20	Martin Gramatica 50	15.00
21	Torry Holt 50	60.00
22	Sedrick Irvin 50	40.00
23	Edgerrin James 45	150.00
24	Jon Jansen 50	15.00
25	Andy Katzenmoyer 15	100.00
26	Jevon Kearse 50	45.00
27	Patrick Kerney 45	15.00
28	Lamar King 50	15.00
29	Shaun King 50	45.00
30	Jim Kleinsasser 50	15.00
31	Rob Konrad 50	40.00
32	Brian Kuklick 50	15.00
33	Chris McAlister 50	40.00
34	Darnell McDonald 50	40.00
35	Reggie McGrew 50	40.00
36	Donovan McNabb 50	80.00
37	Cade McNown 90	80.00
38	Dat Nguyen 400	15.00
39	Solomon Page 400	10.00
40	Mike Peterson 400	10.00
41	Anthony Poindexter 400	10.00
42	Peerless Price 93	50.00
43	Michael Rucker 400	10.00
44	L.J. Shelton 400	10.00
45	Akili Smith 180	65.00
46	John Tait 400	10.00
47	Fred Vinson 400	10.00
48	Al Wilson 400	10.00
49	Antoine Winfield 400	10.00
50	Damien Woody 400	10.00

1999 Sage Autographs Silver

This insert is the same as the Red Autographs except most of the players signed a total of 400 cards and the borders are in silver.

		MT
Common Player:		10.00
Minor Stars:		15.00
1	Rahim Abdullah 400	15.00
2	Jerry Azumah 400	15.00
3	Champ Bailey 400	20.00
4	D'Wayne Bates 400	15.00
5	Michael Bishop 400	30.00
6	David Boston 348	45.00
7	Fernando Bryant 400	15.00
8	Tony Bryant 400	10.00
9	Chris Claiborne 400	20.00
10	Mike Cloud 175	30.00
11	Cecil Collins 400	30.00
12	Tim Couch 400	100.00
13	Daunte Culpepper 180	75.00
14	Jared DeVries 355	10.00
15	Adrian Dingle 400	10.00
16	Antwan Edwards 400	15.00
17	Troy Edwards 400	30.00
18	Kevin Faulk 400	35.00
19	Rufus French 400	10.00
20	Martin Gramatica 400	10.00
21	Torry Holt 400	35.00
22	Sedrick Irvin 400	20.00
23	Edgerrin James 350	75.00
24	Jon Jansen 400	10.00
25	Andy Katzenmoyer 90	55.00
26	Jevon Kearse 400	25.00
27	Patrick Kerney 365	10.00
28	Lamar King 400	10.00
29	Shaun King 400	20.00
30	Jim Kleinsasser 400	10.00
31	Rob Konrad 400	15.00
32	Brian Kuklick 400	15.00
33	Chris McAlister 400	15.00
34	Darnell McDonald 400	20.00
35	Reggie McGrew 400	10.00
36	Donovan McNabb 400	50.00
37	Cade McNown 400	35.00
38	Dat Nguyen 400	15.00
39	Solomon Page 400	10.00
40	Mike Peterson 400	10.00
41	Anthony Poindexter 400	10.00
42	Peerless Price 93	50.00
43	Michael Rucker 400	10.00
44	L.J. Shelton 400	10.00
45	Akili Smith 180	65.00
46	John Tait 400	10.00
47	Fred Vinson 400	10.00
48	Al Wilson 400	10.00
49	Antoine Winfield 400	10.00
50	Damien Woody 400	10.00

1968-69 Saints 8x10

Measuring 8" x 10", the 35 black-and-white photo cards feature members of the 1968-69 Saints teams. The backs are unnumbered and blank.

		NM
Complete Set (35):		120.00
Common Player:		6.00
1	Dan Abramowicz	6.00
2	Doug Atkins	7.50
3	Tom Barrington	4.00
4	Jim Boeke	3.00
5	Johnny Brewer	3.00
6	Bo Burris	3.00
7	Bill Cody	3.00
8	Ted Davis	3.00
9	John Douglas	3.00
10	Charles Durkee	3.00
11	John Gilliam	4.00
12	Jim Hester	3.00
13	Gene Howard	3.00
14	Les Kelley	3.00
15	Jake Kupp	4.00
16	Earl Leggett	3.00
17	Archie Manning	20.00
18	Don McCall	3.00
19	Tom McNeill	3.00
20	Richard Neal	3.00
21	Dave Parks	4.00
22	Dave Parks (with small inset photo)	3.00
23	Ray Poage	3.00
24	David Rowe	3.00
25	Roy Schmidt	3.00
26	Randy Schultz	3.00
27	Brian Schweda	3.00
28	Monty Stickles	3.00
29	Steve Stonebreaker	4.00
30	Jerry Sturm	3.00
31	Mike Tilleman	3.00
32	Joe Wendryhoski	3.00
33	Ernie Wheelwright	4.00
34	Fred Whittingham	3.00
35	Del Williams	3.00

1974 Saints Circle Inset

Measuring 8" x 10", the 22 photos showcase a black-and-white action photo on the front, with a player headshot pictured inside a circle inset. Printed at the bottom of the card are the player's name, position and team name. The backs are un-numbered and blank.

		NM
Complete Set (22):		120.00
Common Player:		5.00
1	John Beasley	5.00
2	Tom Blanchard	6.00
3	Larry Cipa	5.00
4	Don Coleman	5.00
5	Wayne Colman	5.00
6	Jack DeGrenier	5.00
7	Rick Kingrea	5.00
8	Phil LaPorta	5.00
9	Odell Lawson	5.00
10	Archie Manning	20.00
11	Alvin Maxson	6.00
12	Bill McClard	5.00
13	Bill McNeill	5.00
14	Jim Merlo	6.00
15	Rick Middleton	5.00
16	Derland Moore	5.00
17	Jerry Moore	5.00
18	Joel Parker	5.00
19	Jess Phillips	5.00
20	Terry Schmidt	5.00
21	Paul Seal	5.00
22	Dave Thompson	5.00

1979 Saints Coke

The 45 cards are anchored by a black-and-white player headshot, with the Coca-Cola logo in an oval in the upper right. The Saints logo is in the lower left and the player's name is printed in the lower right. The fronts of the cards are bordered in red. The card backs have the card number inside a helmet in the upper left, while the player's name is to the right of the helmet. His position is printed inside a banner. Beneath the banner is the player's bio. The Coca-Cola logo is located at the bottom center.

		NM
Complete Set (45):		60.00
Common Player:		1.00
1	Archie Manning	8.00
2	Ed Burns	1.00
3	Bobby Scott	1.50
4	Russell Erxleben	1.50
5	Eric Felton	1.00
6	David Gray	1.00
7	Ricky Ray	1.00
8	Clarence Chapman	1.00
9	Kim Jones	1.00
10	Mike Strachan	1.00
11	Tony Galbreath	2.00
12	Tom Myers	1.50
13	Chuck Muncie	3.00
14	Jack Holmes	1.00
15	Don Schwartz	1.00
16	Ralph McGill	1.00
17	Ken Bordelon	1.00
18	Jim Kovach	1.00
19	Pat Hughes	1.00
20	Reggie Mathis	1.00
21	Jim Merlo	1.00
22	Joe Federspiel	1.00
23	Don Reese	1.00
24	Roger Finnie	1.00
25	John Hill	1.00
26	Barry Bennett	1.00
27	Dave Lafary	1.00
28	Robert Woods	1.50
29	Conrad Dobler	1.50
30	John Watson	1.00
31	Fred Sturt	1.00
32	J.T. Taylor	1.00
33	Mike Fultz	1.00
34	Joe Campbell	1.00
35	Derland Moore	1.00
36	Elex Price	1.00
37	Elois Grooms	1.00
38	Emanuel Zanders	1.00
39	Ike Harris	1.00
40	Tinker Owens	1.50
41	Rich Mauti	1.00
42	Henry Childs	1.50
43	Larry Hardy	1.00
44	Brooks Williams	1.00
45	Wes Chandler	3.50

1992 Saints McDag

Showcased on the front of the 32-card set is "Saints '92" inside a brown border on the left side. The photo is located on the right, with the Saints' logo in the lower left of the photo. The player's name is printed in a gold stripe at the bottom of the front. The backs, which are unnumbered, have the player's name, position, bio, number, career highlights and safety tips. The Behavioral Health and Saints logos are printed on the lower left and right, respectively. The cards were produced by McDag Productions.

		MT
Complete Set (32):		12.00
Common Player:		.25
1	Morten Andersen	.50
2	Gene Atkins	.40
3	Toi Cook	.25
4	Tommy Barnhardt	.25
5	Hoby Brenner	.40
6	Stan Brock	.25
7	Vince Buck	.40
8	Wesley Carroll	.40
9	Jim Dombrowski	.25
10	Vaughn Dunbar	.50
11	Quinn Early	.75
12	Bobby Hebert	.50
13	Craig Heyward	.60
14	Joel Hilgenberg	.25
15	Dalton Hilliard	.40
16	Rickey Jackson	.40
17	Vaughan Johnson	.25
18	Reginald Jones	.25
19	Eric Martin	.40
20	Wayne Martin	.25
21	Brett Maxie	.25
22	Fred McAfee	.40
23	Sam Mills	.50
24	Jim Mora (CO)	.40
25	Pat Swilling	.50
26	John Tice	.25
27	Renaldo Turnbull	.50
28	Floyd Turner	.40
29	Steve Walsh	.50
30	Frank Warren	.25
31	Jim Wilks	.25
32	Saints Cheerleaders	.40

1962 Salada Coins

These coins, featuring 154 pro football players, are color-color-coded according to the team the player plays for; each team has a specific rim color. The fronts feature a color head-and-shoulders shot of the player without his helmet on. The backs are numbered and contain advertising for Salada Tea and Junket brand desserts. Brief biographical information, including the collegiate school the player attended, is also given. Each coin measures 1-1/2" diameter. The set can sometimes be found as a complete set in its own custom box. Double- and triple-printed coins are indicated by (DP) and (TP) and are easier to find than the others.

		NM
	Complete Set (154):	3000.
	Common Player DP:	7.50
	Common Player SP:	25.00
1	Johnny Unitas	175.00
2	Lenny Moore	85.00
3	Jim Parker	50.00
4	Gino Marchetti	60.00
5	Dick Szymanski	25.00
6	Alex Sandusky	25.00
7	Raymond Berry	90.00
8	Jimmy Orr	30.00
9	Ordell Braase	25.00
10	Bill Pellington	25.00
11	Bob Boyd	25.00
12	Paul Hornung (DP)	25.00
13	Jim Taylor (DP)	20.00
14	Henry Jordan (DP)	8.00
15	Dan Currie (DP)	8.00
16	Bill Forester (DP)	8.00
17	Dave Hanner (DP)	8.00
18	Bart Starr (DP)	30.00
19	Max McGee (DP)	7.50
20	Jerry Kramer (DP)	9.00
21	Forrest Gregg (DP)	15.00
22	Jim Ringo (DP)	15.00
23	Billy Kilmer	55.00
24	Charlie Krueger	25.00
25	Bob St. Clair	50.00
26	Abe Woodson	25.00
27	Jimmy Johnson	65.00
28	Matt Hazeltine	25.00
29	Bruce Bosley	25.00
30	Dan Conners	25.00
31	John Brodie	80.00
32	J.D. Smith	25.00
33	Monty Stickles	25.00
34	Johnny Morris (DP)	9.00
35	Stan Jones (DP)	15.00
36	J.C. Caroline (DP)	8.00
37	Richie Petitbon (DP)	9.00
38	Joe Fortunato (DP)	9.00
39	Larry Morris (DP)	6.00
40	Doug Atkins (DP)	12.00
41	Billy Wade (DP)	7.50
42	Rick Casares (DP)	9.00
43	Willie Galimore (DP)	9.00
44	Angelo Coia (DP)	8.00
45	Ollie Matson	65.00
46	Carroll Dale	30.00
47	Ed Meador	30.00
48	Jon Arnett	35.00
49	Joe Marconi	25.00
50	John LoVetere	25.00
51	Red Phillips	25.00
52	Zeke Bratkowski	35.00
53	Dick Bass	30.00
54	Les Richter	30.00
55	Art Hunter (DP)	8.00
56	Jim Brown (TP)	65.00
57	Mike McCormack (DP)	12.00
58	Bob Gain (DP)	8.00
59	Paul Wiggin (DP)	7.50
60	Jim Houston (DP)	7.50
61	Ray Renfro (DP)	7.50
62	Galen Fiss (DP)	8.00
63	J.R. Smith (DP)	8.00
64	John Morrow (DP)	8.00
65	Gene Hickerson (DP)	8.00
66	Jim Ninowski (DP)	7.50
67	Tom Tracy	30.00
68	Buddy Dial	30.00
69	Mike Sandusky	30.00
70	Lou Michaels	30.00
71	Preston Carpenter	25.00
72	John Reger	25.00
73	John Henry Johnson	65.00
74	Gene Lipscomb	40.00
75	Mike Henry	30.00
76	George Tarasovic	25.00
77	Bobby Layne	70.00
78	Harley Sewell (DP)	8.00
79	Darris McCord (DP)	7.50
80	Yale Lary (DP)	12.00
81	Jim Gibbons (DP)	8.00
82	Gail Cogdill (DP)	8.00
83	Nick Pietrosante (DP)	9.00
84	Alex Karras (DP)	15.00
85	Dick Lane (DP)	12.00
86	Joe Schmidt (DP)	15.00
87	John Gordy (DP)	8.00
88	Milt Plum (DP)	7.50
89	Andy Stynchula	25.00
90	Bob Toneff	25.00
91	Bill Anderson	30.00
92	Sam Horner	25.00
93	Norm Snead	30.00
94	Bobby Mitchell	65.00
95	Billy Barnes	25.00
96	Rod Breedlove	25.00
97	Fred Hageman	25.00
98	Vince Promuto	25.00
99	Joe Rutgens	25.00
100	Maxie Baughan (DP)	9.00
101	Pete Retzlaff (DP)	7.50
102	Tom Brookshier (DP)	9.00
103	Sonny Jurgensen (DP)	25.00

104	Ed Khayat (DP)	6.00
105	Chuck Bednarik (DP)	15.00
106	Tommy McDonald (DP)	9.00
107	Bobby Walston (DP)	8.00
108	Ted Dean (DP)	8.00
109	Clarence Peaks (DP)	8.00
110	Jimmy Carr (DP)	8.00
111	Sam Huff (DP)	15.00
112	Erich Barnes (DP)	8.00
113	Del Shofner (DP)	9.00
114	Bob Gaiters (DP)	8.00
115	Alex Webster (DP)	9.00
116	Dick Modzelewski (DP)	7.50
117	Jim Katcavage (DP)	7.50
118	Roosevelt Brown (DP)	15.00
119	Y.A. Tittle (DP)	25.00
120	Andy Robustelli (DP)	12.00
121	Dick Lynch (DP)	7.50
122	Don Webb (DP)	8.00
123	Larry Eisenhauer (DP)	8.00
124	Babe Parilli (DP)	7.50
125	Charles Long (DP)	8.00
126	Billy Lott (DP)	8.00
127	Harry Jacobs (DP)	7.50
128	Bob Dee (DP)	8.00
129	Ron Burton (DP)	7.50
130	Jim Colclough (TP)	3.00
131	Gino Cappelletti (DP)	9.00
132	Tommy Addison (DP)	8.00
133	Larry Grantham (DP)	7.50
134	Dick Christy (DP)	8.00
135	Bill Mathis (DP)	7.50
136	Butch Songin (DP)	7.50
137	Dainard Paulson (DP)	8.00
138	Roger Ellis (DP)	8.00
139	Mike Hudock (DP)	8.00
140	Don Maynard (DP)	20.00
141	Al Dorow (DP)	7.50
142	Jack Klotz (DP)	8.00
143	Lee Riley (DP)	8.00
144	Bill Atkins (DP)	8.00
145	Art Baker (DP)	8.00
146	Stew Barber (DP)	8.00
147	Glen Bass (DP)	8.00
148	Al Bemiller (DP)	8.00
149	Richie Lucas (DP)	8.00
150	Archie Matsos (DP)	8.00
151	Warren Rabb (DP)	8.00
152	Ken Rice (DP)	8.00
153	Billy Shaw (DP)	7.50
154	Laverne Torczon (DP)	8.00

1959 San Giorgio Flipbooks

Measuring 5-3/4" x 3-9/16", the 17 flipbooks showcase movement of a player on 14 different photos. When the photos are separated and sorted, the photos go into motion when they are flipped. Players from the Washington Redskins, Philadelphia Eagles and Pittsburgh Steelers are pictured in the set. Many collectors prefer the flipbooks to be intact and uncut.

		NM
	Complete Set (17):	2500.
	Common Player:	150.00
1	Sam Baker	175.00
2	Bill Barnes	150.00
3	Chuck Bednarik	300.00
4	Don Bosseler	150.00
5	Darrell Brewster	150.00
6	Jack Butler	150.00
7	Proverb Jacobs	150.00
8	Eddie LeBaron	200.00
9	Tommy McDonald	175.00
10	Ed Meadows	150.00
11	Gern Nagler	150.00
12	Clarence Peaks	150.00
13	Pete Retzlaff	175.00
14	Mike Sommer	150.00
15	Tom Tracy	175.00
16	Bobby Walston	150.00
17	Chuck Weber	150.00

1989 Score Promos

These cards were used to promote Score's debut football set. They are basically identical to the 1989 regular issue, but these six promo cards can be distinguished from the regular set by the use of a registered symbol on them instead of a trademark symbol. Also, the stats on these promo cards are carried out to only one decimal place on the card back; the regular cards carry out the stats to two places. These cards were sent to dealers along with order forms for the 1989 set.

		MT
	Complete Set (6):	75.00
	Common Player:	5.00
1	Joe Montana	35.00
2	Bo Jackson	15.00
3	Boomer Esiason	12.00
4	Roger Craig	8.00
5	Too Tall Jones (Registered seven sacks, regular card issue has registered 7.0 sacks)	5.00
6	Phil Simms (Moorehead State, should say Morehead State; photo cropping has Score logo blocking part of the sacks)	8.00

1989 Score

Score's premier set of football cards, a 330-card edition, was released in August 1989. An additional 110 cards were released as a boxed updated set to hobby shops in January 1990 and were numbered 331-440 with an "S" following the number. Score expanded its print run and corrected several errors in the regular set: #101, Keith Jackson (wrong uniform number on back); #122, Ricky Sanders (wrong uniform number on back); #126, Ron Hall (wrong photos on front and back); #188 Mark Carrier (wrong photo -- original back showed Bruce Hill); #218, Willie Gault (photo showed Greg Townsend); #293, Keith Jackson's All Pro card (wrong uniform number on back); #305, Tim Brown (photo showed James Lofton); and #316, Eric Thomas (wrong uniform number on back). The corrected cards were issued in both wax boxes and in factory sets, a Score spokesman said. The corrected cards are scarcer than the error cards. Score was the first set to include the same year's first-round draft picks. Rookies in this set include Barry Sanders, Deion Sanders, Troy Aikman, Louis Oliver, Dave Meggett, and Erik McMillan and Don Majkowski.

		MT
	Complete Set (330):	240.00
	Comp. Factory Set (330):	250.00
	Common Player:	.10
	Minor Stars:	.20
	Wax Box:	500.00
1	Joe Montana	3.00
2	Bo Jackson	1.00
3	Boomer Esiason	.20
4	Roger Craig	.10
5	Ed Jones	.10
6	Phil Simms	.20
7	Dan Hampton	.10
8	John Settle	.10
9	Bernie Kosar	.20
10	Al Toon	.10
11	Bubby Brister	8.00
12	Mark Clayton	.10
13	Dan Marino	4.00
14	Joe Morris	.10
15	Warren Moon	1.00
16	Chuck Long	.10
17	Mark Jackson	.10
18	Michael Irvin	5.00
19	Bruce Smith	.10
20	Anthony Carter	.10
21	Charles Haley	.10

22	Dave Duerson	.10
23	Troy Stradford	.10
24	Freeman McNeil	.10
25	Jerry Gray	.10
26	Bill Maas	.10
27	Chris Chandler	6.00
28	Tom Newberry	.10
29	Albert Lewis	.10
30	Jay Schroeder	.10
31	Dalton Hilliard	.10
32	Tony Eason	.10
33	Rick Donnelly	.10
34	Herschel Walker	.20
35	Wesley Walker	.10
36	Chris Doleman	.20
37	Pat Swilling	.20
38	Joey Browner	.10
39	Shane Conlan	.10
40	Mike Tomczak	.10
41	Webster Slaughter	.10
42	Ray Donaldson	.10
43	Christian Okoye	.10
44	Jon Bosa	.10
45	Aaron Cox	.10
46	Bobby Hebert	.10
47	Carl Banks	.10
48	Jeff Fuller	.10
49	Gerald Willhite	.10
50	Mike Singletary	.10
51	Stanley Morgan	.10
52	Mark Bavaro	.10
53	Mickey Shuler	.10
54	Keith Millard	.10
55	Andre Tippett	.10
56	Vance Johnson	.10
57	Bennie Blades	.20
58	Tim Harris	.10
59	Hanford Dixon	.10
60	Chris Miller	1.50
61	Cornelius Bennett	.75
62	Neal Anderson	.10
63	Ickey Woods	.10
64	Gary Anderson	.10
65	Vaughan Johnson	.20
66	Ronnie Lippett	.10
67	Mike Quick	.10
68	Roy Green	.10
69	Tim Krumrie	.10
70	Mark Malone	.10
71	James Jones	.10
72	Cris Carter	25.00
73	Ricky Nattiel	.10
74	Jim Arnold	.10
75	Randall Cunningham	1.00
76	John L. Williams	.10
77	Paul Gruber	.10
78	Rod Woodson	4.00
79	Ray Childress	.10
80	Doug Williams	.10
81	Deron Cherry	.10
82	John Offerdahl	.10
83	Louis Lipps	.10
84	Neil Lomax	.10
85	Wade Wilson	.10
86	Tim Brown	8.00
87	Chris Hinton	.10
88	Stump Mitchell	.10
89	Tunch Ilkin	.10
90	Steve Pelluer	.10
91	Brian Noble	.10
92	Reggie White	.90
93	Aundray Bruce	.10
94	Garry James	.10
95	Drew Hill	.10
96	Anthony Munoz	.10
97	James Wilder	.10
98	Dexter Manley	.10
99	Lee Williams	.10
100	Dave Krieg	.10
101	Keith Jackson ERR (incorrect number 84)	1.00
101a	Keith Jackson COR (correct number 88)	1.00
102	Luis Sharpe	.10
103	Kevin Greene	.20
104	Duane Bickett	.10
105	Mark Rypien	.75
106	Curt Warner	.10
107	Jacob Green	.10
108	Gary Clark	.20
109	Bruce Matthews	.50
110	Bill Fralic	.10
111	Bill Bates	.10
112	Jeff Bryant	.10
113	Charles Mann	.10
114	Richard Dent	.10
115	Bruce Hill	.10
116	Mark May	.10
117	Mark Collins	.10
118	Ron Holmes	.10
119	Scott Case	.20
120	Tom Rathman	.10
121	Dennis McKinnon	.10
122	Ricky Sanders ERR (incorrect number 46)	.25
122a	Ricky Sanders COR (correct number 83)	.50
123	Michael Carter	.10
124	Ozzie Newsome	.10
125	Irving Fryar	.10
126	Ron Hall ERR (wrong photo)	.25
126a	Ron Hall COR (corrected photo)	.50

127	Clay Matthews	.10
128	Leonard Marshall	.10
129	Kevin Mack	.10
130	Art Monk	.20
131	Garin Veris	.10
132	Steve Jordan	.10
133	Frank Minnifield	.10
134	Eddie Brown	.10
135	Stacey Bailey	.10
136	Rickey Jackson	.10
137	Henry Ellard	.10
138	Jim Burt	.10
139	Jerome Brown	.10
140	Rodney Holman	.20
141	Sammy Winder	.10
142	Marcus Cotton	.10
143	Jim Jeffcoat	.10
144	Reuben Mayes	.10
145	Jim McMahon	.10
146	Reggie Williams	.10
147	John Anderson	.10
148	Harris Barton	.20
149	Philip Epps	.10
150	Jay Hilgenberg	.10
151	Earl Ferrell	.10
152	Andre Reed	.50
153	Dennis Gentry	.10
154	Max Montoya	.10
155	Darrin Nelson	.10
156	Jeff Chadwick	.10
157	James Brooks	.10
158	Keith Bishop	.10
159	Robert Awalt	.10
160	Marty Lyons	.10
161	Johnny Hector	.10
162	Tony Casillas	.10
163	Kyle Clifton	.20
164	Cody Risien	.10
165	Jamie Holland	.10
166	Merril Hoge	.10
167	Chris Spielman	3.00
168	Carlos Carson	.10
169	Jerry Ball	.20
170	Don Majkowski	.20
171	Everson Walls	.10
172	Mike Rozier	.10
173	Matt Millen	.10
174	Karl Mecklenberg	.10
175	Paul Palmer	.10
176	Brian Blades	1.00
177	Brent Fullwood	.10
178	Anthony Miller	1.00
179	Brian Sochia	.10
180	Stephen Baker	.20
181	Jesse Solomon	.10
182	John Grimsley	.10
183	Timmy Newsome	.10
184	Steve Sewell	.10
185	Dean Biasucci	.10
186	Alonzo Highsmith	.10
187	Randy Grimes	.10
188	Mark Carrier ERR (back shows Bruce Hill)	1.50
188a	Mark Carrier COR (corrected)	1.50
189	Vann McElroy	.10
190	Greg Bell	.10
191	Quinn Early	2.00
192	Lawrence Taylor	.50
193	Albert Bentley	.10
194	Ernest Givins	.20
195	Jackie Slater	.10
196	Jim Sweeney	.10
197	Freddie Joe Nunn	.10
198	Keith Byars	.10
199	Hardy Nickerson	1.50
200	Steve Beuerlein	5.00
201	Bruce Armstrong	.20
202	Lionel Manuel	.10
203	J.T. Smith	.10
204	Mark Ingram	1.00
205	Fred Smerlas	.10
206	Bryan Hinkle	.10
207	Steve McMichael	.10
208	Nick Lowery	.10
209	Jack Trudeau	.10
210	Lorenzo Hampton	.10
211	Thurman Thomas	8.00
212	Steve Young	2.00
213	James Lofton	.10
214	Jim Covert	.10
215	Ronnie Lott	.20
216	Stephone Paige	.10
217	Mark Duper	.10
218	Willie Gault ERR (shows Greg Townsend)	.25
218a	Willie Gault COR (corrected)	.50
219	Ken Ruettgers	.10
220	Kevin Ross	.10
221	Jerry Rice	3.00
222	Billy Ray Smith	.10
223	Jim Kelly	1.00
224	Vinny Testaverde	.40
225	Steve Largent	.75
226	Warren Williams	.10
227	Morten Andersen	.10
228	Bill Brooks	.10
229	Reggie Langhorne	.20
230	Pepper Johnson	.10
231	Pat Leahy	.10
232	Fred Marion	.10
233	Gary Zimmerman	.10
234	Marcus Allen	.20
235	Gaston Green	.20
236	John Stephens	.20

237	Terry Kinard	.10
238	John Taylor	1.50
239	Brian Bosworth	.10
240	Anthony Toney	.10
241	Ken O'Brien	.10
242	Howie Long	.10
243	Doug Flutie	2.00
244	Jim Everett	.30
245	Broderick Thomas	.20
246	Deion Sanders	20.00
247	Donnell Woolford	1.00
248	Wayne Martin	.75
249	David Williams	.10
250	Bill Hawkins	.10
251	Eric Hill	.10
252	Burt Grossman	.20
253	Tracy Rocker	.10
254	Steve Wisniewski	.20
255	Jessie Small	.10
256	David Braxton	.10
257	Barry Sanders	165.00
258	Derrick Thomas	4.00
259	Eric Metcalf	2.00
260	Keith DeLong	.20
261	Hart Lee Dykes	.20
262	Sammie Smith	.20
263	Steve Atwater	1.00
264	Eric Ball	.20
265	Don Beebe	1.00
266	Brian Williams	.10
267	Jeff Lageman	.30
268	Tim Worley	.20
269	Tony Mandarich	.10
270	Troy Aikman	40.00
271	Andy Heck	.20
272	Andre Rison	5.00
273	AFC Championship Game	.20
274	NFC Championship (Joe Montana)	1.00
275	Joe Montana, Jerry Rice	2.00
276	Rodney Carter	.10
277	Mark Jackson, Vance Johnson, Ricky Nattiel	.10
278	John Williams, Curt Warner	.10
279	Joe Montana, Jerry Rice	2.00
280	Roy Green, Neil Lomax	.10
281	Randall Cunningham, Keith Jackson	.20
282	Chris Doleman, Keith Millard	.10
283	Mark Duper, Mark Clayton	.10
284	Allen, Jackson	.50
285	Frank Minnifield (AP)	.10
286	Bruce Matthews (AP)	.10
287	Joey Browner (AP)	.10
288	Jay Hilgenberg (AP)	.10
289	Carl Lee (AP)	.10
290	Scott Norwood (AP)	.10
291	John Taylor (AP)	.50
292	Jerry Rice (AP)	1.00
293	Keith Jackson ERR (AP, incorrect number)	.50
293a	Keith Jackson COR (AP, corrected)	.50
294	Gary Zimmerman (AP)	.10
295	Lawrence Taylor (AP)	.20
296	Reggie White (AP)	.20
297	Roger Craig (AP)	.10
298	Boomer Esiason (AP)	.10
299	Cornelius Bennett (AP)	.10
300	Mike Horan (AP)	.10
301	Deron Cherry (AP)	.10
302	Tom Newberry (AP)	.10
303	Mike Singletary (AP)	.10
304	Shane Conlan (AP)	.10
305	Tim Brown ERR (AP, shows James Lofton)	2.00
305a	Tim Brown COR (AP, corrected)	2.00
306	Henry Ellard (AP)	.10
307	Bruce Smith (AP)	.10
308	Tim Krumrie (AP)	.10
309	Anthony Munoz (AP)	.10
310	Darrell Green (SB)	.10
311	Anthony Miller (SB)	.50
312	Wesley Walker (SB)	.10
313	Ron Brown (SB)	.10
314	Bo Jackson (SB)	.40
315	Philip Epps (SB)	.10
316	Eric Thomas ERR (SB, wrong number)	.25
316a	Eric Thomas COR (SB, corrected)	.50
317	Herschel Walker (SB)	.20
318	Jacob Green (PD)	.10
319	Andre Tippett	.10
320	Freddie Joe Nunn (PD)	.10
321	Reggie White (PD)	.20

322 Lawrence Taylor (PD) .20
323 Greg Townsend (PD) .10
324 Tim Harris (PD) .10
325 Bruce Smith (PD) .10
326 Tony Dorsett (RB) .30
327 Steve Largent (RB) .50
328 Tim Brown (RB) 2.00
329 Joe Montana (RB) 1.50
330 Tom Landry (Tribute) 1.00

1989 Score Supplemental

These 110 cards continue with numbers where the 1989 Score regular set left off at -330. The cards are numbered using an "S" prefix, however. The design is similar to the regular issue's, but the supplemental cards have purple borders. The cards were distributed as a complete, boxed set only.

	MT
Complete Set (110):	10.00
Common Player:	.05
Minor Stars:	.10

331 Herschel Walker .10
332 Allen Pinkett .05
333 Sterling Sharpe 4.00
334 Alvin Walton .05
335 Frank Reich .50
336 Jim Thornton .05
337 David Fulcher .05
338 Raul Allegre .05
339 John Elway 3.00
340 Michael Cofer .05
341 Jim Skow .05
342 Steve DeBerg .05
343 Mervyn Fernandez .05
344 Mike Lansford .05
345 Reggie Roby .05
346 Raymond Clayborn .05
347 Lonzell Hill .05
348 Ottis Anderson .05
349 Erik McMillan .05
350 Al Harris .05
351 Jack Del Rio 1.00
352 Gary Anderson .10
353 Jim McMahon .10
354 Keena Turner .05
355 Tony Woods .05
356 Donald Igwebuike .05
357 Gerald Riggs .05
358 Eddie Murray .05
359 Dino Hackett .05
360 Brad Muster .05
361 Paul Palmer .05
362 Jerry Robinson .05
363 Simon Fletcher .50
364 Tommy Kramer .05
365 Jim C. Jensen .05
366 Lorenzo White .50
367 Fredd Young .05
368 Ron Jaworski .05
369 Mel Owens .05
370 Dave Waymer .05
371 Sean Landeta .05
372 Sam Mills .05
373 Todd Blackledge .05
374 JoJo Townsell .05
375 Ron Wolfley .05
376 Ralf Mojsiejenko .05
377 Eric Wright .05
378 Newsby Glasgow .05
379 Darryl Talley .05
380 Eric Allen .40
381 Dennis Smith .05
382 John Tice .05
383 Jesse Solomon .05
384 Bo Jackson 1.50
385 Mike Merriweather .05
386 Maurice Carthon .05
387 Dave Grayson .05
388 Wilber Marshall .05
389 David Wyman .05
390 Thomas Everett .05
391 Alex Gordon .05
392 D.J. Dozier .05
393 Scott Radecic .05
394 Eric Thomas .05
395 Mike Gann .05
396 William Perry .05
397 Carl Hariston .05
398 Billy Ard .05
399 Donnell Thompson .05

400 Mike Webster .05
401 Scott Davis .05
402 Sean Farrell .05
403 Mike Golic .05
404 Mike Kenn .05
405 Keith Van Horne .05
406 Bob Golic .05
407 Neil Smith 2.50
408 Dermontti Dawson .05
409 Leslie O'Neal .10
410 Matt Bahr .05
411 Guy McIntyre .10
412 Bryan Millard .05
414 Rob Taylor .05
415 Tony Zendejas .05
416 Vai Sikahema .05
417 Gary Reasons .05
418 Shawn Collins .05
419 Mark Green .05
420 Courtney Hall .05
421 Bobby Humphrey .05
422 Myron Guyton .05
423 Darryl Ingram .05
424 Chris Jacke .10
425 Keith Jones .05
426 Robert Massey .05
427 Bubba McDowell .05
428 Dave Meggett 1.00
429 Louis Oliver .05
430 Danny Peebles .05
431 Rodney Peete 1.00
432 Jeff Query .10
433 Timm Rosenbach .05
434 Frank Stams .05
435 Lawyer Tillman .05
436 Billy Joe Tolliver .10
437 Floyd Turner .30
438 Steve Walsh .75
439 Joe Wolf .05
440 Trace Armstrong .05

1989 Score Franco Harris

This card, which has two versions, was given to those who received Franco Harris' autograph at the Super Bowl show in New Orleans. The unnumbered standard-size cards have identical fronts and are similar in design to Score's 1989 regular set. The difference on the card backs is in the text which describes Harris' status as a potential Hall of Famer. Earlier versions say Harris was a "sure-shot" to be elected to the Hall of Fame. He was elected during the show, so the text was changed to say "Hall of Famer." The "sure-shot" cards are scarcer.

	MT
Complete Set (2):	135.00
Common Player:	65.00

1A Franco Harris (Sure-shot) 80.00
1B Franco Harris (Hall of Famer) 65.00

1990 Score Promos

These cards were sent to dealers along with order forms for Score's 1990 regular set. The design is similar to the regular issue, except the photos are cropped tighter. They also use a registered symbol on them, not the trademark symbol which is used on the regular cards.

	MT
Complete Set (3):	18.00
Common Player:	2.50

20 Barry Sanders 14.00
184 Robert Delpino 2.50
256 Cornelius Bennett 5.00

1990 Score

Variations in the set include #134, Kevin Butler (uncorrected photo on back shows him wearing a helmet; corrected photo shows him without helmet), #136, Vai Sikahema (uncorrected photo on back shows him wearing a helmet; corrected photo shows him without a helmet), #147, Joey Browner (uncorrected back shows him looking into the sun; corrected back show more of a profile); #208, Ralf Mojsiejenko (uncorrected stats read "Chargers"; corrected stats read "Redskins."); and #600, Buck Buchanan (uncorrected back says he was the first player selected in the '83 AFL draft; it was corrected to read the '63 draft). Note: Rookie cards in the first series contained no information on which NFL team the player was drafted by; thus they are considered first cards, not rookie cards. (Key: HG - Hot Gun; GF - Ground Force; DP - draft pick)

	MT
Complete Set (660):	8.00
Complete Series 1 (1-330):	4.00
Complete Series 2 (331-660):	4.00
Common Player:	.04
Wax Box:	7.00

1 Joe Montana 1.00
2 Christian Okoye .04
3 Mike Singletary .04
4 Jim Everett .04
5 Phil Simms .10
6 Brent Fullwood .04
7 Bill Fralic .04
8 Leslie O'Neal .04
9 John Taylor .20
10 Bo Jackson .40
11 John Stephens .04
12 Art Monk .04
13 Dan Marino 1.50
14 John Settle .04
15 Don Majkowski .04
16 Bruce Smith .04
17 Brad Muster .04
18 Jason Buck .04
19 James Brooks .04
20 Barry Sanders 1.25
21 Troy Aikman 1.00
22 Allen Pinkett .04
23 Duane Bickett .04
24 Kevin Ross .04
25 John Elway .40
26 Jeff Query .04
27 Eddie Murray .04
28 Richard Dent .04
29 Lorenzo White .15
30 Eric Metcalf .10
31 Jeff Dellenbach .10
32 Leon White .04
33 Jim Jeffcoat .04
34 Herschel Walker .04
35 Mike Johnson .04
36 Joe Phillips .04
37 Willie Gault .04
38 Keith Millard .04
39 Fred Marion .04
40 Boomer Esiason .20
41 Dermontti Dawson .04
42 Dino Hackett .04
43 Reggie Roby .04
44 Roger Vick .04
45 Bobby Hebert .15
46 Don Beebe .15
47 Neal Anderson .10
48 Johnny Holland .04
49 Bobby Humphrey .04
50 Lawrence Taylor .10
51 Billy Ray Smith .04
52 Robert Perryman .04
53 Gary Anderson .04
54 Raul Allegre .04
55 Pat Swilling .04
56 Chris Doleman .04
57 Andre Reed .20
58 Seth Joyner .04
59 Bart Oates .04
60 Bernie Kosar .04
61 Dave Krieg .04
62 Lars Tate .04
63 Scott Norwood .04
64 Kyle Clifton .04
65 Alan Veingrad .04
66 Gerald Riggs .04
67 Tim Worley .04
68 Rodney Holman .04
69 Tony Zendejas .04
70 Chris Miller .10
71 Wilber Marshall .04
72 Skip McClendon .10
73 Jim Covert .04
74 Sam Mills .04
75 Chris Hinton .04
76 Irv Eatman .04
77 Bubba Paris .04
78 John Elliott .04
79 Thomas Everett .04
80 Steve Smith .04
81 Jackie Slater .04
82 Kelvin Martin .25
83 JoJo Townsell .04

84 Jim Jensen .04
85 Bobby Humphrey .04
86 Mike Dyal .04
87 Andre Rison .25
88 Brian Sochia .04
89 Greg Bell .04
90 Dalton Hilliard .04
91 Carl Banks .04
92 Dennis Smith .04
93 Bruce Matthews .04
94 Charles Haley .04
95 Deion Sanders .35
96 Stephone Paige .04
97 Marion Butts .10
98 Howie Long .04
99 Donald Igwebuike .04
100 Roger Craig .04
101 Charles Mann .04
102 Fredd Young .04
103 Chris Jacke .04
104 Scott Case .04
105 Warren Moon .25
106 Clyde Simmons .04
107 Steve Atwater .04
108 Morten Andersen .04
109 Eugene Marve .04
110 Thurman Thomas .40
111 Carnell Lake .04
112 Jim Kelly .30
113 Stanford Jennings .04
114 Jacob Green .04
115 Karl Mecklenberg .04
116 Ray Childress .04
117 Erik McMillan .04
118 Harry Newsome .04
119 James Dixon .04
120 Hassan Jones .04
121 Eric Allen .04
122 Felix Wright .04
123 Merril Hoge .04
124 Eric Ball .04
125 Willie Anderson .10
126 James Jefferson .04
127 Tim McDonald .04
128 Larry Kinnebrew .04
129 Mark Collins .04
130 Ickey Woods .04
131 Jeff Donaldson .04
132 Rich Camarillo .04
133 Melvin Bratton .04
134 Kevin Butler (helmet) .05
134a Kevin Butler (without helmet) .05
135 Albert Bentley .04
136 Vai Sikahema (helmet on back) .08
136a Vai Sikahema (without helmet) .08
137 Todd McNair .10
138 Alonzo Highsmith .04
139 Brian Blades .10
140 Jeff Lageman .04
141 Eric Thomas .04
142 Derek Hill .04
143 Rick Fenney .04
144 Herman Heard .04
145 Steve Young 1.00
146 Kent Hull .04
147 Joey Browner .04
148 Frank Minnifield .04
149 Robert Massey .04
150 Dave Meggett .10
151 Bubba McDowell .04
152 Rickey Dixon .10
153 Ray Donaldson .04
154 Alvin Walton .04
155 Mike Cofer .04
156 Darryl Talley .04
157 A.J. Johnson .04
158 Jerry Gray .04
159 Keith Byars .04
160 Andy Heck .04
161 Mike Munchak .04
162 Dennis Gentry .04
163 Timm Rosenbach .04
164 Randall McDaniel .04
165 Pat Leahy .04
166 Bubby Brister .10
167 Aundray Bruce .04
168 Bill Brooks .04
169 Eddie Anderson .10
170 Ronnie Lott .04
171 Jay Hilgenberg .04
172 Joe Nash .04
173 Simon Fletcher .04
174 Shane Conlan .04
175 Sean Landeta .04
176 John Alt .10
177 Clay Matthews .04
178 Anthony Munoz .04
179 Pete Holohan .04
180 Robert Awalt .04
181 Rohn Stark .04
182 Vance Johnson .04
183 Robert Delpino .04
184 Drew Hill .04
185 Reggie Langhorne .04
186 Lonzell Hill .04
187 Tom Rathman .04
188 Greg Montgomery .10
189 Leonard Smith .04
190 Chris Spielman .04
191 Tom Newberry .04
192 Cris Carter .35
193 Kevin Porter .04
194 Donnell Thompson .04
195 Vaughan Johnson .04

197 Steve McMichael .04
198 Jim Sweeney .04
199 Rich Karlis .04
200 Jerry Rice 1.00
201 Dan Hampton .04
202 Jim Lachey .04
203 Reggie White .15
204 Jerry Ball .04
205 Russ Grimm .04
206 Tim Green .08
207 Shawn Collins .04
208 Ralf Mojsiejenko (Chargers on back) .05
208a Ralf Mojsiejenko (Redskins on back) .05
209 Trace Armstrong .04
210 Keith Jackson .25
211 Jamie Holland .04
212 Mark Clayton .04
213 Jeff Cross .04
214 Bob Gagliano .04
215 Louis Oliver .04
216 Jim Arnold .04
217 Robert Clark .08
218 Gill Byrd .04
219 Rodney Peete .08
220 Anthony Miller .30
221 Steve Grogan .04
222 Vince Newsome .04
223 Tom Benson .04
224 Kevin Murphy .04
225 Henry Ellard .04
226 Richard Johnson .04
227 Jim Skow .04
228 Keith Jones .04
229 Dave Brown .04
230 Marcus Allen .04
231 Steve Walsh .04
232 Jim Harbaugh .10
233 Mel Gray .04
234 David Treadwell .04
235 John Offerdahl .04
236 Gary Reasons .04
237 Tim Krumrie .04
238 Dave Duerson .04
239 Gary Clark .10
240 Mark Jackson .04
241 Mark Murphy .04
242 Jerry Holmes .04
243 Tim McGee .04
244 Mike Tomczak .04
245 Sterling Sharpe .10
246 Bennie Blades .04
247 Ken Harvey .10
248 Ron Heller .04
249 Louis Lipps .04
250 Wade Wilson .04
251 Freddie Joe Nunn .04
252 Jerome Brown .04
253 Myron Guyton .04
254 Nate Odomes .25
255 Rod Woodson .25
256 Cornelius Bennett .04
257 Keith Woodside .04
258 Jeff Uhlenhake .04
259 Harry Hamilton .04
260 Mark Bavaro .04
261 Vinny Testaverde .10
262 Steve DeBerg .04
263 Steve Wisniewski .04
264 Pete Mandley .04
265 Tim Harris .04
266 Jack Trudeau .04
267 Mark Kelso .04
268 Brian Noble .04
269 Jessie Tuggle .20
270 Ken O'Brien .04
271 David Little .04
272 Pete Stoyanovich .04
273 Odessa Turner .10
274 Anthony Toney .04
275 Tunch Ilkin .04
276 Carl Lee .04
277 Hart Lee Dykes .04
278 Al Noga .04
279 Greg Lloyd .04
280 Billy Joe Tolliver .04
281 Kirk Lowdermilk .04
282 Earl Ferrell .04
283 Eric Sievers .04
284 Steve Jordan .04
285 Brent Grossman .04
286 Johnny Rembert .04
287 Jeff Jaeger .10
288 James Hasty .04
289 Tony Mandarich .04
290 Chris Singleton (DP) .10
291 Lynn James (DP, FC) .04
292 Andre Ware (DP) .20
293 Ray Agnew (DP) .04
294 Joel Smeenge (DP) .10
295 Marc Spindler (DP) .04
296 Renaldo Turnbull (DP) .40
297 Reggie Rembert (DP) .04
298 Jeff Alm (DP) .04
299 Cortez Kennedy (DP) .30
300 Blair Thomas (DP) .10
301 Pat Terrell (DP) .04
302 Junior Seau (DP) 1.00
303 Mohammed Elewonibi (DP) .04
304 Tony Bennett (DP) .35
305 Percy Snow (DP) .08

306 Richmond Webb (DP) .15
307 Rodney Hampton (DP) 1.00
308 Barry Foster (DP) .10
309 John Friesz (DP) .25
310 Ben Smith (DP) .08
311 Joe Montana (HG) .50
312 Jim Everett (HG) .04
313 Mark Rypien (HG) .08
314 Phil Simms (HG) .08
315 Don Majkowski (HG) .04
316 Boomer Esiason (HG) .10
317 Warren Moon (HG) .10
318 Jim Kelly (HG) .10
319 Bernie Kosar (HG) .04
320 Dan Marino (HG) .40
321 Christian Okoye (GF) .04
322 Thurman Thomas (GF) .20
323 James Brooks (GF) .04
324 Bobby Humphrey (GF) .04
325 Barry Sanders (GF) .75
326 Neal Anderson (GF) .04
327 Dalton Hilliard (GF) .04
328 Greg Bell (GF) .04
329 Roger Craig (GF) .04
330 Bo Jackson (GF) .20
331 Don Warren .04
332 Rufus Porter .04
333 Sammie Smith .04
334 Lewis Tillman .04
335 Michael Walter .04
336 Marc Logan .04
337 Ron Hallstrom .08
338 Stanley Morgan .04
339 Mark Robinson .04
340 Frank Reich .20
341 Chip Lohmiller .10
342 Steve Beuerlein .25
343 John L. Williams .04
344 Irving Fryar .04
345 Anthony Carter .04
346 Al Toon .04
347 J.T. Smith .04
348 Pierce Holt .10
349 Ferrell Edmunds .04
350 Mark Rypien .15
351 Paul Gruber .04
352 Ernest Givins .04
353 Ervin Randle .04
354 Guy McIntyre .04
355 Webster Slaughter .04
356 Reuben Davis .04
357 Rickey Jackson .04
358 Earnest Byner .04
359 Eddie Brown .04
360 Troy Stradford .04
361 Pepper Johnson .04
362 Ravin Caldwell .04
363 Chris Mohr .08
364 Jeff Bryant .04
365 Bruce Collie .04
366 Courtney Hall .04
367 Jerry Olsavsky .04
368 David Galloway .04
369 Wes Hopkins .04
370 Johnny Hector .04
371 Clarence Verdin .04
372 Nick Lowery .04
373 Tim Brown .45
374 Kevin Greene .04
375 Leonard Marshall .04
376 Roland James .04
377 Scott Studwell .04
378 Jarvis Williams .04
379 Mike Saxon .04
380 Kevin Mack .04
381 Joe Kelly .04
382 Tom Thayer .10
383 Roy Green .04
384 Michael Brooks .20
385 Michael Cofer .04
386 Ken Ruettgers .04
387 Dean Steinkuhler .04
388 Maurice Carthon .04
389 Ricky Sanders .04
390 Winton Moss .10
391 Tony Woods .04
392 Keith DeLong .04
393 David Wyman .04
394 Vencie Glenn .04
395 Harris Barton .04
396 Bryan Hinkle .04
397 Derek Kennard .04
398 Heath Sherman .20
399 Troy Benson .04
400 Gary Zimmerman .04
401 Mark Duper .04
402 Eugene Lockhart .04
403 Tim Manoa .04
404 Reggie Williams .04
405 Mark Bortz .10
406 Mike Kenn .04
407 John Grimsley .04
408 Bill Romanowski .10
409 Perry Kemp .04
410 Norm Johnson .04
411 Broderick Thomas .04
412 Joe Wolf .04
413 Andre Waters .04
414 Jason Staurovsky .04
415 Eric Martin .04
416 Joe Prokop .04
417 Steve Sewell .04
418 Cedric Jones .04

419	Alphonso Carreker	.04
420	Keith Willis	.04
421	Bobby Butler	.04
422	John Roper	.04
423	Tim Spencer	.04
424	*Jesse Sapolu*	.08
425	Ron Wolfley	.04
426	Doug Smith	.04
427	William Howard	.04
428	Keith Van Horne	.04
429	Tony Jordan	.04
430	Mervyn Fernandez	.04
431	*Shaun Gayle*	.10
432	Ricky Nattiel	.04
433	Albert Lewis	.04
434	*Fred Banks*	.10
435	Henry Thomas	.04
436	Chet Brooks	.04
437	Mark Ingram	.04
438	Jeff Gossett	.04
439	Mike Wilcher	.04
440	Deron Cherry	.04
441	Mike Rozier	.04
442	Jon Hand	.04
443	Ozzie Newsome	.10
444	Sammy Martin	.04
445	Luis Sharpe	.04
446	Lee Williams	.04
447	*Chris Martin*	.10
448	Kevin Fagan	.04
449	Gene Lang	.04
450	Greg Townsend	.04
451	Robert Lyles	.04
452	Eric Hill	.04
453	John Teltschik	.04
454	Vestee Jackson	.04
455	Bruce Reimers	.04
456	*Butch Rolle*	.10
457	Lawyer Tillman	.04
458	Andre Tippett	.04
459	James Thornton	.04
460	Randy Grimes	.04
461	Larry Roberts	.04
462	Ron Holmes	.04
463	Mike Wise	.04
464	*Danny Copeland*	.10
465	*Bruce Wilkerson*	.10
466	Mike Quick	.04
467	Mickey Shuler	.04
468	Mike Prior	.04
469	Ron Rivera	.04
470	Dean Biasucci	.04
471	Perry Williams	.04
472	Darren Comeaux	.04
473	Freeman McNeil	.04
474	Tyrone Braxton	.04
475	Jay Schroeder	.04
476	Naz Worthen	.04
477	Lionel Washington	.04
478	Carl Zander	.04
479	Al Baker	.04
480	Mike Merriweather	.04
481	Mike Gann	.04
482	Brent Williams	.04
483	Eugene Robinson	.04
484	Ray Horton	.04
485	Bruce Armstrong	.04
486	Jon Fourcade	.04
487	Lewis Billups	.04
488	Ken Sims	.04
489	Chris Chandler	.04
490	Mark Lee	.04
491	Johnny Meads	.04
492	Tim Irwin	.04
493	E.J. Junior	.04
494	Hardy Nickerson	.04
495	Rob McGovern	.04
496	*Fred Strickland*	.10
497	*Reggie Rutland*	.10
498	Mel Owens	.04
499	Derrick Thomas	.25
500	Jerrol Williams	.04
501	*Maurice Hurst*	.10
502	*Larry Kelm*	.10
503	Herman Fontenot	.04
504	Pat Beach	.04
505	*Haywood Jeffires*	.85
506	Neil Smith	.25
507	*Cleveland Gary*	.10
508	William Perry	.04
509	Michael Carter	.04
510	Walker Lee Ashley	.04
511	Bob Golic	.04
512	*Danny Villa*	.08
513	Matt Millen	.04
514	Don Griffin	.04
515	Jonathan Hayes	.04
516	*Gerald Williams*	.08
517	Scott Fulhage	.04
518	Irv Pankey	.04
519	*Randy Dixon*	.08
520	Terry McDaniel	.04
521	Dan Saleaumua	.04
522	Darrin Nelson	.04
523	Leonard Griffin	.04
524	Michael Ball	.04
525	*Ernie Jones*	.25
526	Tony Eason	.04
527	Ed Reynolds	.04
528	Gary Hogeboom	.04
529	Don Mosebar	.04
530	Ottis Anderson	.04
531	Bucky Scribner	.04
532	Aaron Cox	.04
533	Sean Jones	.04
534	Doug Flutie	.75
535	Leo Lewis	.04
536	Art Still	.04

538	Matt Bahr	.04
539	Keena Turner	.04
540	Sammy Winder	.04
541	Mike Webster	.04
542	*Doug Riesenberg*	.10
543	Dan Fike	.04
544	Clarence Kay	.04
545	Jim Burt	.04
546	Mike Horan	.04
547	Al Harris	.04
548	Maury Buford	.04
549	Jerry Robinson	.04
550	Tracy Rocker	.04
551	Karl Mecklenburg (CC)	.04
552	Lawrence Taylor (CC)	.08
553	Derrick Thomas (CC)	.20
554	Mike Singletary (CC)	.04
555	Tim Harris (CC)	.04
556	Jerry Rice (RM)	.40
557	Art Monk (RM)	.04
558	Mark Carrier (RM)	.04
559	Andre Reed (RM)	.08
560	Sterling Sharpe (RM)	.30
561	Herschel Walker (GF)	.04
562	Ottis Anderson (GF)	.04
563	Randall Cunningham (HG)	.08
564	John Elway (HG)	.20
565	David Fulcher (AP)	.04
566	Ronnie Lott (AP)	.04
567	Jerry Gray (AP)	.04
568	Albert Lewis (AP)	.04
569	Karl Mecklenburg (AP)	.04
570	Mike Singletary (AP)	.04
571	Lawrence Taylor (AP)	.08
572	Tim Harris (AP)	.04
573	Keith Millard (AP)	.04
574	Reggie White (AP)	.08
575	Chris Doleman (AP)	.04
576	Dave Meggett (AP)	.04
577	Rod Woodson (AP)	.04
578	Sean Landeta (AP)	.04
579	Eddie Murray (AP)	.04
580	Barry Sanders (AP)	.75
581	Christian Okoye (AP)	.04
582	Joe Montana (AP)	.50
583	Jay Hilgenberg (AP)	.04
584	Bruce Matthews (AP)	.04
585	Tom Newberry (AP)	.04
586	Gary Zimmerman (AP)	.04
587	Anthony Munoz (AP)	.04
588	Keith Jackson (AP)	.08
589	Sterling Sharpe (AP)	.30
590	Jerry Rice (AP)	.40
591	Bo Jackson (RB)	.15
592	Steve Largent (RB)	.10
593	Flipper Anderson (RB)	.04
594	Joe Montana (RB)	.50
595	Franco Harris (HOF)	.08
596	Bob St. Clair (HOF)	.04
597	Tom Landry (HOF)	.04
598	Jack Lambert (HOF)	.04
599	Ted Hendricks (HOF)	.04
600	Buck Buchanan (HOF, "drafted '83")	.05
600a	Buck Buchanan (HOF, "drafted '63")	.05
601	Bob Griese (HOF)	.04
602	Super Bowl	.04
603	Vince Lombardi	.04
604	Mark Carrier	.04
605	Randall Cunningham	.10
606	Percy Snow (C90)	.04
607	Andre Ware (C90)	.10
608	Blair Thomas (C90)	.10
609	Eric Green (C90)	.10
610	Reggie Rembert (C90)	.04
611	Richmond Webb (C90)	.10
612	Bern Brostek (C90)	.04
613	James Williams (C90)	.04
614	Mark Carrier (C90)	.04
615	Renaldo Turnbull (C90)	.20
616	Cortez Kennedy (C90)	.40
617	Keith McCants (C90)	.04
618	*Anthony Thompson* (DP)	.10
619	*LeRoy Butler* (DP)	.20
620	*Aaron Wallace* (DP)	.10
621	*Alexander Wright* (DP)	.15
622	*Keith McCants* (DP)	.10
623	*Jimmie Jones* (DP)	.10
624	*Anthony Johnson* (DP)	.20

625	Fred Washington (DP)	.04
626	Mike Bellamy (DP)	.04
627	Mark Carrier (DP)	.20
628	Harold Green (DP)	.25
629	*Eric Green* (DP)	.40
630	*Andre Collins* (DP)	.10
631	*Lamar Lathon* (DP)	.10
632	*Terry Wooden* (DP)	.10
633	Jesse Anderson (DP)	.04
634	*Jeff George* (DP)	1.25
635	*Carwell Gardner* (DP)	.10
636	*Darrell Thompson*	.25
637	Vince Buck (DP)	.10
638	Mike Jones (DP)	.04
639	*Charles Arbuckle* (DP)	.10
640	Dennis Brown (DP)	.10
641	*James Williams* (DP)	.10
642	*Bern Brostek* (DP)	.10
643	*Darion Conner* (DP)	.08
644	*Mike Fox* (DP)	.08
645	*Cary Conklin* (DP)	.40
646	*Tim Grunhard* (DP)	.08
647	*Ron Cox* (DP)	.08
648	*Keith Sims* (DP)	.08
649	*Alton Montgomery* (DP)	.10
650	*Greg McMurtry* (DP)	.10
651	*Scott Mitchell* (DP)	.75
652	*Tim Ryan* (DP)	.04
653	*Jeff Mills* (DP)	.04
654	*Ricky Proehl* (DP)	.50
655	*Steve Broussard* (DP)	.08
656	*Peter Tom Willis* (DP)	.15
657	*Dexter Carter* (DP)	.15
658	Tony Casillas	.04
659	Joe Morris	.04
660	Greg Kragen	.04

1990 Score Hot Card

Score test-marketed a 100-card football blister pack subset in August 1990, available only at select retail accounts. Blister packs featuring 100 assorted cards from Series I and Series II. As an incentive to buy the blister packs, one "Hot Card" was included in each blister pack.

		MT
	Complete Set (10):	30.00
	Common Player:	1.75
1	Joe Montana	6.00
2	Bo Jackson	2.50
3	Barry Sanders	6.00
4	Jerry Rice	6.00
5	Eric Metcalf	1.75
6	Don Majkowski	1.75
7	Christian Okoye	1.75
8	Bobby Humphrey	1.75
9	Dan Marino	12.00
10	Sterling Sharpe	3.00

1990 Score Update

These cards were sold in sets only to hobby stores and included traded players as well as rookies in team uniforms.

		MT
	Complete Set (110):	100.00
	Common Player:	.10
	Minor Stars:	.20
1	Marcus Dupree	.10
2	Jerry Kauric	.10
3	Everson Walls	.10
4	Elliott Smith	.10
5	*Donald Evans*	.10
6	Jerry Holmes	.10
7	*Dan Stryzinski*	.10
8	Gerald McNeil	.10
9	*Rick Tuten*	.10
10	Mickey Shuler	.10
11	Jay Novacek	1.00
12	*Eric Williams*	.20
13	Stanley Morgan	.10
14	*Wayne Haddix*	.20
15	Gary Anderson	.20
16	*Stan Humphries*	1.00
17	Raymond Clayborn	.10
18	*Mark Boyer*	.10
19	Dave Waymer	.10
20	Andre Rison	.50
21	Daniel Stubbs	.10
22	Mike Rozier	.10
23	Damian Johnson	.10
24	Don Smith	.10
25	Max Montoya	.10
26	Terry Kinard	.10
27	Herb Welch	.10
28	Cliff Odom	.10
29	John Kidd	.10
30	*Barry Word*	.20
31	Rich Karlis	.10
32	Mike Baab	.10
33	Ronnie Harmon	.10
34	Jeff Donaldson	.10
35	Riki Ellison	.10
36	Steve Walsh	.20
37	*Bill Lewis*	.10
38	Tim McKyer	.10
39	James Wilder	.10
40	Tony Paige	.10
41	*Derrick Fenner*	.20
42	Thane Gash	.10
43	Dave Duerson	.10
44	Clarence Weathers	.10
45	Matt Bahr	.10
46	Alonzo Highsmith	.10
47	Joe Kelly	.10
48	Chris Hinton	.10
49	Bobby Humphery	.10
50	Greg Bell	.10
51	Fred Smerlas	.10
52	Dennis McKinnon	.10
53	Jim Skow	.10
54	Renaldo Turnbull	.20
55	Bern Brostek	.10
56	*Charles Wilson*	.10
57	Keith McCants	.10
58	Alexander Wright	.20
59	*Ian Beckles*	.10
60	*Eric Davis*	.20
61	Chris Singleton	.10
62	*Rob Moore*	10.00
63	Darion Conner	.10
64	*Tim Grunhard*	.10
65	Junior Seau	4.00
66	Tony Stargell	.10
67	Anthony Thompson	.20
68	Cortez Kennedy	.50
69	Darrell Thompson	.10
70	*Calvin Williams*	.20
71	Rodney Hampton	1.50
72	Terry Wooden	.10
73	Leo Goeas	.10
74	Ken Willis	.10
75	Ricky Proehl	.75
76	*Steve Christie*	.50
77	Andre Ware	.20
78	Jeff George	3.00
79	Walter Wilson	.10
80	*Johnny Bailey*	.20
81	Harold Green	.20
82	Mark Carrier	.50
83	Frank Cornish	.10
84	James Williams	.10
85	*James Francis*	.20
86	Percy Snow	.10
87	Anthony Johnson	1.00
88	Tim Ryan	.10
89	*Dan Owens*	.20
90	Aaron Wallace	.10
91	Steve Broussard	.20
92	Eric Green	.50
93	Blair Thomas	.20
94	*Robert Blackmon*	.20
95	*Alan Grant*	.10
96	Andre Collins	.10
97	Dexter Carter	.20
98	*Reggie Cobb*	.20
99	Dennis Brown	.10
100	*Kenny Davidson*	.10
101	Emmitt Smith	80.00
102	Jeff Alm	.10
103	Alton Montgomery	.10
104	Tony Bennett	.20
105	Johnny Johnson	.50
106	*Leroy Hoard*	1.50
107	Ray Agnew	.10
108	Richmond Webb	.20
109	Keith Sims	.10
110	Barry Foster	.20

1990 Score 100 Hottest

These cards featuring 100 top NFL players, have the same photos on them as the regular issue 1990 Score cards, but they are numbered differently. Publications International published a magazine to accompany the set; the magazine offered additional information about the players.

		MT
	Complete Set (100):	15.00
	Common Player:	.10
1	Bo Jackson	.25
2	Joe Montana	2.00
3	Deion Sanders	.50
4	Dan Marino	1.25
5	Barry Sanders	1.00
6	Neal Anderson	.15
7	Phil Simms	.20
8	Bobby Humphrey	.10
9	Roger Craig	.20
10	John Elway	.60
11	James Brooks	.15
12	Ken O'Brien	.10
13	Thurman Thomas	.50
14	Troy Aikman	2.00
15	Karl Mecklenburg	.10
16	Dave Krieg	.10
17	Chris Spielman	.10
18	Tim Harris	.15
19	Tim Worley	.10
20	Clay Matthews	.15
21	Lars Tate	.10
22	Hart Lee Dykes	.10
23	Cornelius Bennett	.15
24	Anthony Miller	.15
25	Lawrence Taylor	.30
26	Jay Hilgenberg	.10
27	Tom Rathman	.15
28	Brian Blades	.25
29	David Fulcher	.10
30	Cris Carter	.40
31	Marcus Allen	.30
32	Eric Metcalf	.15
33	Bruce Smith	.15
34	Jim Kelly	.60
35	Wade Wilson	.15
36	Rich Camarillo	.10
37	Boomer Esiason	.20
38	John Offerdahl	.10
39	Vance Johnson	.10
40	Ronnie Lott	.20
41	Kevin Ross	.15
42	Greg Bell	.10
43	Erik McMillan	.10
44	Mike Singletary	.20
45	Roger Vick	.10
46	Keith Jackson	.30
47	Henry Ellard	.15
48	Gary Anderson	.15
49	Art Monk	.30
50	Jim Everett	.15
51	Anthony Munoz	.15
52	Ray Childress	.15
53	Howie Long	.20
54	Chris Hinton	.10
55	John Stephens	.20
56	Reggie White	.25
57	Rodney Peete	.15
58	Don Majkowski	.10
59	Michael Cofer	.10
60	Bubby Brister	.10
61	Jerry Gray	.10
62	Rodney Holman	.10
63	Vinny Testaverde	.20
64	Sterling Sharpe	.65
65	Keith Millard	.10
66	Jim Lachey	.10
67	Dave Meggett	.15
68	Brent Fullwood	.10
69	Bobby Hebert	.15
70	Joey Browner	.10
71	Flipper Anderson	.15
72	Tim McGee	.10
73	Eric Allen	.10
74	Charles Haley	.25
75	Christian Okoye	.15
76	Herschel Walker	.20
77	Kelvin Martin	.15
78	Bill Fralic	.10
79	Leslie O'Neal	.15
80	Bernie Kosar	.20
81	Eric Sievers	.10
82	Timm Rosenbach	.10
83	Steve DeBerg	.15
84	Duane Bickett	.10
85	Chris Doleman	.15
86	Carl Banks	.15
87	Vaughan Johnson	.10
88	Dennis Smith	.15
89	Billy Joe Tolliver	.15
90	Dalton Hilliard	.10
91	John Taylor	.20
92	Mark Rypien	.20
93	Chris Miller	.30
94	Mark Clayton	.25
95	Andre Reed	.25
96	Warren Moon	.50
97	Bruce Matthews	.10
98	Rod Woodson	.25
99	Pat Swilling	.15
100	Jerry Rice	1.25

1990 Score Young Superstars

JOHN ROPER

This 40-card glossy set was a 1990 Score mail-in offer featuring some of the top young players in the NFL. Each card front has an action photo framed by black borders. Each back has a full color close-up photo, plus statistics, a card number, team logo and career summary.

		MT
	Complete Set (40):	8.00
	Common Player:	.10
1	Barry Sanders	1.50
2	Bobby Humphrey	.40
3	Ickey Woods	.20
4	Shawn Collins	.10
5	Dave Meggett	.25
6	Keith Jackson	.25
7	Sterling Sharpe	.25
8	Troy Aikman	.75
9	Tim McDonald	.10
10	Tim Brown	.25
11	Trace Armstrong	.10
12	Eric Metcalf (Led Bears in rushing, should be Browns)	.20
13	Derrick Thomas	.35
14	Eric Hill	.10
15	Deion Sanders	.50
16	Steve Atwater	.15
17	Carnell Lake	.10
18	Andre Reed	.30
19	Chris Spielman	.15
20	Eric Allen	.10
21	Erik McMillan	.10
22	Louis Oliver	.10
23	Robert Massey	.10
24	John Roper	.10
25	Burt Grossman	.15
26	Chris Jacke	.10
27	Steve Wisniewski	.10
28	Alonzo Highsmith	.10
29	Mark Carrier	.20
30	Bruce Armstrong	.10
31	Jerome Brown	.10
32	Cornelius Bennett	.20
33	Flipper Anderson	.15
34	Brian Blades	.25
35	Anthony Miller	.20
36	Thurman Thomas	.90
37	Chris Miller	.35
38	Aundray Bruce	.15
39	Robert Clark	.15
40	Robert Delpino	.15

1990 Score Final Five

These five cards were inserted in 1990 Score Football factory sets and feature the last five picks in the 1990 NFL Draft. The "Final Five" logo is on each card front, along with a color photo of the player selected. The back has his name, position and summary of his collegiate accomplishments. Cards are numbered with a "B" prefix.

		MT
	Complete Set (5):	.50
	Common Player:	.05
1	Judd Garrett	.05
2	Matt Stover	.15
3	Ken McMichael	.05
4	Demetrius Davis	.05
5	Elliott Searcy	.05

Post-1980 cards in Near Mint condition will generally sell for about 75% of the quoted Mint value. Excellent-condition cards bring no more than 40%.

1990 Score Franco Harris

This card was given away to collectors who acquired Franco Harris' autograph at the Super Bowl Card Show in Tampa. The card is unnumbered and features a Leroy Nieman painting of Harris on the front with a picture of him celebrating a Super Bowl win on the back. Production of this card was estimated between 1,500 and 5,000.

	MT
Complete Set (1):	100.00
Common Player:	100.00
1 Franco Harris	100.00

1991 Score Promos

These six cards were designed to preview Score's 1991 regular set. The card numbers, which are on the card back, are identical to those in the regular set, except for Lawrence Taylor, who is #529 in the regular set. The prototype cards can be distinguished from the regular cards by several differences, including: the statistics on the back are in blue-green, not green; the promo cards omit the tiny trademark symbol next to the Team NFL logo; and cards 1, 5 and 7 are cropped slightly different.

	MT
Complete Set (6):	10.00
Common Player:	1.00
1 Joe Montana	5.00
4 Lawrence Taylor	1.25
5 Derrick Thomas	1.50
6 Mike Singletary	1.00
7 Boomer Esiason	1.25
12 Randall Cunningham	1.50

1991 Score

Score's 1991 first series was released in May 1991. The size increased by 15 cards over the previous year's Series I. Carried over from Score baseball was the "Dream Team" subset - this time featuring card-size profile shots with a smaller action insert. Artist Chris Greco worked on the MVP and Top Leader cards. Because Draft Pick cards carry no NFL team designation, they technically are not considered true rookie cards. (Key: DP - Draft Pick, 90 - 90-Plus Club, TL - Top Leader, DT - Dream Team)

	MT
Complete Set (686):	9.00
Factory Set (690):	9.00

Complete Series 1 (345):	4.50
Complete Series 2 (341):	4.50
Common Player:	.04
Wax Box:	5.00
1 Joe Montana	1.00
2 Eric Allen	.04
3 Rohn Stark	.04
4 Frank Reich	.04
5 Derrick Thomas	.25
6 Mike Singletary	.04
7 Boomer Esiason	.10
8 Matt Millen	.04
9 Chris Spielman	.04
10 Gerald McNeil	.04
11 Nick Lowery	.04
12 Randall Cunningham	.10
13 Marion Butts	.04
14 Tim Brown	.25
15 Emmitt Smith	1.75
16 Rich Camarillo	.04
17 Mike Merriweather	.04
18 Derrick Fenner	.10
19 Clay Matthews	.04
20 Barry Sanders	1.75
21 James Brooks	.04
22 Alton Montgomery	.04
23 Steve Atwater	.04
24 Ron Morris	.04
25 Brad Muster	.04
26 Andre Rison	.25
27 Brian Brennan	.04
28 Leonard Smith	.04
29 Kevin Butler	.04
30 Tim Harris	.04
31 Jay Novacek	.15
32 Eddie Murray	.04
33 Keith Woodside	.04
34 *Ray Crockett*	.10
35 Eugene Lockhart	.04
36 Bill Romanowski	.04
37 Eddie Brown	.04
38 Eugene Daniel	.04
39 Scott Fulhage	.04
40 Harold Green	.10
41 Mark Jackson	.04
42 Sterling Sharpe	.10
43 Mel Gray	.04
44 Jerry Holmes	.04
45 Allen Pinkett	.04
46 Warren Powers	.04
47 Rodney Peete	.04
48 Lorenzo White	.10
49 Dan Owens	.04
50 James Francis	.04
51 Ken Norton	.04
52 Ed West	.04
53 Andre Reed	.10
54 John Grimsley	.04
55 Michael Cofer	.04
56 Chris Doleman	.04
57 Pat Swilling	.04
58 Jessie Tuggle	.04
59 Mike Johnson	.04
60 Steve Walsh	.04
61 Sam Mills	.04
62 Don Mosebar	.04
63 Jay Hilgenberg	.04
64 Cleveland Gary	.04
65 Andre Tippett	.04
66 Tom Newberry	.04
67 Maurice Hurst	.04
68 Louis Oliver	.04
69 Fred Marion	.04
70 Christian Okoye	.04
71 Marv Cook	.04
72 Darryl Talley	.04
73 Rick Fenney	.04
74 Kelvin Martin	.04
75 Howie Long	.04
76 Steve Wisniewski	.04
77 Karl Mecklenburg	.04
78 Dan Saleaumua	.04
79 Ray Childress	.04
80 Henry Ellard	.04
81 Ernest Givins	.04
82 Ferrell Edmunds	.04
83 Steve Jordan	.04
84 Tony Mandarich	.04
85 Eric Martin	.04
86 Rich Gannon	.10
87 Irving Fryar	.04
88 Tom Rathman	.04
89 Dan Hampton	.04
90 Barry Word	.10
91 Kevin Greene	.04
92 Sean Landeta	.04
93 Trace Armstrong	.04
94 Dennis Byrd	.04
95 Timm Rosenbach	.04
96 Anthony Toney	.04
97 Tim Krumrie	.04
98 Jerry Ball	.04
99 Tim Green	.04
100 Bo Jackson	.35
101 Myron Guyton	.04
102 Mike Mularkey	.04
103 Jerry Gray	.04
104 Scott Stephen	.04
106 Lomas Brown	.04
107 David Little	.04
108 Brad Baxter	.10
109 Freddie Joe Nunn	.04
110 Dave Meggett	.04
111 Mark Rypien	.10
112 Warren Williams	.04
113 Ron Rivera	.04
114 Terance Mathis	.10

115 Anthony Munoz	.04
116 Jeff Bryant	.04
117 Issaic Holt	.04
118 Steve Sewell	.04
119 Tim Newton	.04
120 Emile Harry	.04
121 Gary Anderson (Pitt.)	.04
122 Mark Lee	.04
123 Alfred Anderson	.04
124 Tony Blaylock	.04
125 Ernest Byner	.04
126 Bill Maas	.04
127 Keith Taylor	.04
128 Cliff Odom	.04
129 Bob Golic	.04
130 Bart Oates	.04
131 Jim Arnold	.04
132 Jerr Herrod	.04
133 Bruce Armstrong	.04
134 Craig Heyward	.06
135 Joey Browner	.04
136 Darren Comeaux	.04
137 Pat Beach	.04
138 Dalton Hilliard	.06
139 David Treadwell	.04
140 Gary Anderson (T.B.)	.04
141 Eugene Robinson	.04
142 Scott Case	.04
143 Paul Farren	.04
144 Gill Fenerty	.04
145 Tim Irwin	.04
146 Norm Johnson	.04
147 Willie Gault	.06
148 Clarence Verdin	.04
149 Jeff Uhlenhake	.04
150 Erik McMillan	.04
151 Kevin Ross	.04
152 Pepper Johnson	.04
153 Bryan Hinkle	.04
154 Gary Clark	.08
155 Robert Delpino	.04
156 Doug Smith	.04
157 Chris Martin	.04
158 Ray Berry	.04
159 Steve Christie	.04
160 Don Smith	.04
161 Greg McMurtry	.04
162 Jack Del Rio	.04
163 Floyd Dixon	.04
164 Buford McGee	.04
165 Brett Maxie	.04
166 Morten Andersen	.06
167 Kent Hull	.04
168 Skip McClendon	.04
169 Keith Sims	.04
170 Leonard Marshall	.04
171 Tony Woods	.04
172 Byron Evans	.04
173 *Rob Burnett*	.15
174 Tory Epps	.04
175 *Toi Cook*	.10
176 John Elliott	.04
177 Tommie Agee	.04
178 Keith Van Horne	.04
179 Dennis Smith	.04
180 James Lofton	.08
181 Art Monk	.04
182 Anthony Carter	.04
183 Louis Lipps	.04
184 Bruce Hill	.04
185 Mike Young	.04
186 Eric Green	.10
187 *Barney Bussey*	.10
188 Curtis Duncan	.04
189 Robert Awalt	.04
190 Johnny Johnson	.20
191 Jeff Cross	.04
192 Keith McKeller	.04
193 Robert Brown	.04
194 Vincent Brown	.04
195 Calvin Williams	.20
196 Sean Jones	.04
197 Willie Drewrey	.04
198 Bubba McDowell	.04
199 Al Noga	.04
200 Ronnie Lott	.10
201 Warren Moon	.20
202 Chris Hinton	.04
203 Jim Sweeney	.04
204 Wayne Haddix	.04
205 *Tim Jorden*	.10
206 Marvin Allen	.04
207 *Jim Morrissey*	.10
208 Ben Smith	.04
209 William White	.04
210 Jim Jensen	.04
211 Doug Reed	.04
212 Ethan Horton	.04
213 Chris Jacke	.04
214 Johnny Hector	.04
215 Drew Hill	.04
216 Roy Green	.04
217 Dean Steinkuhler	.04
218 Cedric Mack	.04
219 Chris Miller	.04
220 Keith Byars	.04
221 Lewis Billups	.04
222 Roger Craig	.04
223 Shaun Gayle	.04
224 Mike Rozier	.04
225 Troy Aikman	1.00
226 Bobby Humphrey	.04
227 Eugene Marve	.04
228 Michael Carter	.04
229 Richard Johnson	.04
230 Billy Joe Tolliver	.08

231 Mark Murphy	.04
232 John L. Williams	.04
233 Ronnie Harmon	.08
234 Thurman Thomas	.40
235 Martin Mayhew	.04
236 Richmond Webb	.04
237 Gerald Riggs	.04
238 Mike Prior	.04
239 Mike Gann	.04
240 Alvin Walton	.04
241 Tim McGee	.04
242 Bruce Matthews	.04
243 Johnny Holland	.04
244 Martin Bayless	.04
245 Eric Metcalf	.04
246 John Alt	.04
247 Max Montoya	.04
248 Rod Bernstine	.04
249 Paul Gruber	.04
250 Charles Haley	.04
251 Scott Norwood	.04
252 Michael Haddix	.04
253 Ricky Sanders	.06
254 Ervin Randle	.04
255 Duane Bickett	.04
256 Mike Munchak	.04
257 Keith Jones	.04
258 Riki Ellison	.04
259 Vince Newsome	.04
260 Lee Williams	.04
261 Steve Smith	.04
262 Sam Clancy	.04
263 Pierce Holt	.04
264 Jim Harbaugh	.08
265 Dino Hackett	.04
266 Andy Heck	.04
267 Leo Goeas	.04
268 Russ Grimm	.04
269 Gill Byrd	.04
270 Neal Anderson	.08
271 Jackie Slater	.04
272 Joe Nash	.04
273 Todd Bowles	.04
274 D.J. Dozier	.04
275 Kevin Fagan	.04
276 Don Warren	.04
277 Jim Jeffcoat	.04
278 Bruce Smith	.08
279 Cortez Kennedy	.25
280 Thane Gash	.04
281 Perry Kemp	.04
282 John Taylor	.10
283 Stephone Paige	.04
284 Paul Skansi	.04
285 Shawn Collins	.04
286 Mervyn Fernandez	.04
287 Daniel Stubbs	.04
288 Chip Lohmiller	.04
289 Brian Blades	.04
290 Mark Carrier	.04
291 Carl Zander	.04
292 David Wyman	.04
293 Jeff Bostic	.04
294 Irv Pankey	.04
295 Keith Millard	.04
296 Jamie Mueller	.04
297 Bill Fralic	.04
298 Wendell Davis	.08
299 Ken Clarke	.04
300 Wymon Henderson	.04
301 Jeff Campbell	.04
302 *Cody Carlson*	.35
303 *Matt Brock*	.10
304 Maurice Carthon	.04
305 *Scott Mersereau*	.10
306 Steve Wright	.04
307 J.B. Brown	.04
308 Ricky Reynolds	.04
309 Darryl Pollard	.04
310 Donald Evans	.04
311 *Nick Bell* (DP)	.20
312 *Pat Harlow* (DP)	.10
313 *Dan McGwire* (DP)	.10
314 Mike Dumas (DP)	.04
315 *Mike Croel* (DP)	.20
316 Chris Smith (DP)	.04
317 *Kenny Walker* (DP)	.10
318 *Todd Lyght* (DP)	.10
319 Mike Stonebreaker (DP)	.04
320 Randall Cunningham (90)	.08
321 Terance Mathis (90)	.04
322 Gaston Green (90)	.04
323 Johnny Bailey (90)	.04
324 Donnie Elder (90)	.04
325 Dwight Stone (90)	.04
326 *J.J. Birden* (90)	.35
327 Alex Wright (90)	.04
328 Eric Metcalf (90)	.04
329 Andre Rison (TL)	.15
330 Warren Moon (TL)	.10
331 Steve Tasker, Reyna Thompson (DT)	.04
332 Mel Gray (DT)	.04
333 Nick Lowery (DT)	.04
334 Sean Landeta (DT)	.04
335 David Fulcher (DT)	.04
336 Joey Browner (DT)	.04
337 Albert Lewis (DT)	.04
338 Rod Woodson (DT)	.06
339 Shane Conlan (DT)	.04
340 Pepper Johnson (DT)	.04
341 Chris Spielman (DT)	.06
342 Derrick Thomas (DT)	.08

343 Ray Childress (DT)	.04
344 Reggie White (DT)	.08
345 Bruce Smith (DT)	.06
346 Darrell Green	.04
347 Ray Bentley	.04
348 Herschel Walker	.06
349 Rodney Holman	.04
350 Al Toon	.04
351 Harry Hamilton	.04
352 Albert Lewis	.04
353 Renaldo Turnbull	.04
354 Junior Seau	.25
355 Merril Hoge	.04
356 Shane Conlan	.04
357 Jay Schroeder	.04
358 Steve Broussard	.04
359 Mark Bavaro	.04
360 Jim Lachey	.04
361 Greg Townsend	.04
362 Dave Krieg	.04
363 Jessie Hester	.04
364 Steve Tasker	.04
365 Ron Hall	.04
366 Pat Leahy	.04
367 Jim Everett	.06
368 Felix Wright	.04
369 Ricky Proehl	.04
370 Anthony Miller	.05
371 Keith Jackson	.08
372 Pete Stoyanovich	.04
373 Tommy Kane	.04
374 Richard Johnson	.04
375 Randall McDaniel	.04
376 John Stephens	.04
377 Haywood Jeffires	.15
378 Rodney Hampton	.50
379 Tim Grunhard	.04
380 Jerry Rice	1.00
381 Ken Harvey	.04
382 Vaughan Johnson	.04
383 J.T. Smith	.04
384 Carnell Lake	.04
385 Dan Marino	1.75
386 Kyle Clifton	.04
387 Wilber Marshall	.04
388 Pete Holohan	.04
389 Gary Plummer	.04
390 William Perry	.04
391 Mark Robinson	.04
392 Nate Odomes	.06
393 Ickey Woods	.04
394 Reyna Thompson	.04
395 Deion Sanders	.40
396 Harris Barton	.04
397 Sammie Smith	.04
398 Vinny Testaverde	.04
399 Ray Donaldson	.04
400 Tim McKyer	.04
401 Nesby Glasgow	.04
402 Brent Williams	.04
403 Rob Moore	.10
404 Bubby Brister	.05
405 David Fulcher	.04
406 Reggie Cobb	.20
407 Jerome Brown	.04
408 Erik Howard	.04
409 Tony Paige	.04
410 John Elway	.35
411 Charles Mann	.04
412 Luis Sharpe	.04
413 Hassan Jones	.04
414 Frank Minnifield	.04
415 Steve DeBerg	.04
416 Mark Carrier	.04
417 Brian Jordan	.04
418 Reggie Langhorne	.04
419 Don Majkowski	.04
420 Marcus Allen	.04
421 Michael Brooks	.04
422 Vai Sikahema	.04
423 Dermontti Dawson	.04
424 Jacob Green	.04
425 Flipper Anderson	.04
426 Bill Brooks	.04
427 Keith McCants	.04
428 Ken O'Brien	.04
429 Fred Barnett	.10
430 Mark Duper	.04
431 Mark Kelso	.04
432 Leslie O'Neal	.04
433 Ottis Anderson	.05
434 Jesse Sapolu	.04
435 Gary Zimmerman	.04
436 Kevin Porter	.04
437 Anthony Thompson	.04
438 Robert Clark	.04
439 Chris Warren	.20
440 Gerald Williams	.04
441 Jim Skow	.04
442 Rick Donnelly	.04
443 Guy McIntyre	.04
444 Jeff Lageman	.04
445 John Offerdahl	.04
446 Clyde Simmons	.04
447 John Kidd	.04
448 Chip Banks	.04
449 Johnny Meads	.04
450 Rickey Jackson	.04
451 Lee Johnson	.04
452 Michael Irvin	.25
453 Leon Seals	.04
454 Darrell Thompson	.20
455 Everson Walls	.04
456 LeRoy Butler	.06
457 Marcus Dupree	.04
458 Kirk Lowdermilk	.04
459 Chris Singleton	.04
460 Seth Joyner	.04

461 (Rueben Mayes) (Hayes in bio should be Heyward)	.04
462 Ernie Jones	.04
463 Greg Kragen	.04
464 Bennie Blades	.04
465 Mark Bortz	.04
466 Tony Stargell	.04
467 Mike Cofer	.05
468 Randy Grimes	.04
469 Tim Worley	.04
470 Kevin Mack	.04
471 Wes Hopkins	.04
472 Will Wolford	.04
473 Sam Seale	.04
474 Jim Ritcher	.04
475 Jeff Hostetler	.20
476 Mitchell Price	.04
477 Ken Lanier	.04
478 Naz Worthen	.04
479 Ed Reynolds	.04
480 Mark Clayton	.05
481 Matt Bahr	.04
482 Gary Reasons	.04
483 Dave Szott	.04
484 Barry Foster	.45
485 Bruce Reimers	.04
486 Dean Biasucci	.04
487 Cris Carter	.05
488 Albert Bentley	.04
489 Robert Massey	.04
490 Al Smith	.04
491 Greg Lloyd	.08
492 Steve McMichael (Photo on back actually Dan Hampton)	.05
493 *Jeff Wright*	.08
494 Scott Davis	.04
495 Freeman McNeil	.04
496 Simon Fletcher	.04
497 Terry McDaniel	.04
498 Heath Sherman	.04
499 Jeff Jaeger	.04
500 Mark Collins	.04
501 Tim Goad	.04
502 Jeff George	.25
503 Jimmie Jones	.05
504 Henry Thomas	.04
505 Steve Young	.60
506 William Roberts	.04
507 Neil Smith	.04
508 Mike Saxon	.04
509 Johnny Bailey	.04
510 Broderick Thomas	.04
511 Wade Wilson	.04
512 Hart Lee Dykes	.04
513 Hardy Nickerson	.04
514 Tim McDonald	.05
515 Frank Cornish	.04
516 Jarvis Williams	.04
517 Carl Lee	.04
518 Carl Banks	.04
519 Mike Golic	.04
520 Brian Noble	.04
521 James Hasty	.04
522 Bubba Paris	.04
523 *Kevin Walker*	.08
524 William Fuller	.04
525 Eddie Anderson	.04
526 Roger Ruzek	.04
527 Robert Blackmon	.04
528 Vince Buck	.04
529 Lawrence Taylor	.10
530 Reggie Roby	.04
531 Doug Riesenberg	.04
532 Joe Jacoby	.04
533 Kirby Jackson	.04
534 Robb Thomas	.04
535 Don Griffin	.04
536 Andre Waters	.05
537 Marc Logan	.04
538 James Thornton	.04
539 Ray Agnew	.04
540 Frank Stams	.04
541 Brett Perriman	.05
542 Andre Ware	.10
543 Kevin Haverdink	.04
544 *Greg Jackson*	.08
545 Tunch Ilkin	.04
546 Dexter Carter	.04
547 Rod Woodson	.06
548 Donnell Woolford	.04
549 Mark Boyer	.04
550 Jeff Query	.04
551 Burt Grossman	.04
552 Mike Kenn	.04
553 Richard Dent	.04
554 Gaston Green	.04
555 Phil Simms	.10
556 Brent Jones	.05
557 Ronnie Lippett	.04
558 Mike Horan	.04
559 Danny Noonan	.04
560 Reggie White	.15
561 Rufus Porter	.04
562 Aaron Wallace	.04
563 Vance Johnson	.04
564 (Aaron Craver) (No copyright line on back)	.04
565A *Russell Maryland* (No copyright line on back)	.40
565B *Russell Maryland*	.40
566 Paul Justin	.04
567 Walter Dean	.04
568 *Herman Moore*	3.00

569	Bill Musgrave	.10	
570	Rob Carpenter	.10	
571	Greg Lewis	.10	
572	Ed King	.10	
573	Ernie Mills	.08	
574	Jake Reed	1.00	
575	Ricky Watters	2.00	
576	Derek Russell	.25	
577	Shawn Moore	.15	
578	Eric Bieniemy	.15	
579	Chris Zorich	.30	
580	Scott Miller	.10	
581	Jarrod Bunch	.10	
582	Ricky Ervins	.20	
583	Browning Nagle	.20	
584	Eric Turner	.20	
585	William Thomas	.08	
586	Stanley Richard	.30	
587	Adrian Cooper	.15	
588	Harvey Williams	.10	
589	Alvin Harper	.10	
590	John Carney	.04	
591	Mark Vander Poel	.04	
592	Mike Pritchard	.35	
593	Eric Moten	.08	
594	Moe Gardner	.10	
595	Wesley Carroll	.10	
596	Eric Swann	.10	
597	Joe Kelly	.05	
598	Steve Jackson	.10	
599	Kelvin Pritchett	.15	
600	Jesse Campbell	.08	
601	Darryll Lewis (Misspelled Darryl on card)	.08	
602	Howard Griffith	.04	
603	Blaise Bryant	.04	
604	Vinnie Clark	.08	
605	Mel Agee	.08	
606	Bobby Wilson	.08	
607	Kevin Donnalley	.04	
608	Randal Hill	.35	
609	Stan Thomas	.04	
610	Mike Heldt	.04	
611	Brett Favre	4.00	
612	Lawrence Dawsey	.25	
613	Dennis Gibson	.04	
614	Dean Dingman	.04	
615	Bruce Pickens	.08	
616	Todd Marinovich	.08	
617	Gene Atkins	.04	
618	Marcus Dupree (Comeback Player)	.04	
619	Warren Moon (Man of the Year)	.10	
620	Joe Montana (MVP)	.50	
621	Neal Anderson (Team MVP)	.05	
622	James Brooks (Team MVP)	.05	
623	Thurman Thomas (Team MVP)	.20	
624	Bobby Humphrey (Team MVP)	.04	
625	Kevin Mack (Team MVP)	.04	
626	Mark Carrier (Team MVP)	.04	
627	Johnny Johnson (Team MVP)	.08	
628	Marion Butts (Team MVP)	.05	
629	Steve DeBerg (Team MVP)	.05	
630	Jeff George (Team MVP)	.10	
631	Troy Aikman (MVP)	.50	
632	Dan Marino (MVP)	.25	
633	Randall Cunningham (Team MVP)	.08	
634	Andre Rison (Team MVP)	.08	
635	Pepper Johnson (Team MVP)	.04	
636	Pat Leahy (Team MVP)	.04	
637	Barry Sanders (MVP)	.50	
638	Warren Moon (Team MVP)	.08	
639	Sterling Sharpe (MVP)	.25	
640	Bruce Armstrong (Team MVP)	.04	
641	Bo Jackson (Team MVP)	.10	
642	Henry Ellard (Team MVP)	.05	
643	Earnest Byner (Team MVP)	.04	
644	Pat Swilling (Team MVP)	.04	
645	John L. Williams (Team MVP)	.04	
646	Rod Woodson (Team MVP)	.06	
647	Chris Doleman (Team MVP)	.04	
648	Joey Browner (Crunch Crew)	.04	
649	Erik McMillan (Crunch Crew)	.04	
650	David Fulcher (Crunch Crew)	.04	
651A	Ronnie Lott (Front 47, back 42)	.08	

651B	Ronnie Lott (Front 47, back 42 is now blacked out)	.05
652	Louis Oliver (Crunch Crew)	.04
653	Mark Robinson (Crunch Crew)	.04
654	Dennis Smith (Crunch Crew)	.04
655	Reggie White (Sack Attack)	.08
656	Charles Haley (Sack Attack)	.04
657	Leslie O'Neal (Sack Attack)	.04
658	Kevin Greene (Sack Attack)	.04
659	Dennis Byrd (Sack Attack)	.04
660	Bruce Smith (Sack Attack)	.08
661	Derrick Thomas (Sack Attack)	.10
662	Steve DeBerg (Top Leader)	.04
663	Barry Sanders (TL)	.50
664	Thurman Thomas (TL)	.20
665	Jerry Rice (TL)	.40
666	Derrick Thomas (Top Leader)	.10
667	Bruce Smith (Top Leader)	.08
668	Mark Carrier (Top Leader)	.04
669	Richard Johnson (Top Leader)	.04
670	Jan Stenerud (Hall of Fame)	.05
671	Stan Jones (Hall of Fame)	.05
672	John Hannah (Hall of Fame)	.05
673	Tex Schramm (Hall of Fame)	.05
674	Earl Campbell (Hall of Fame)	.10
675	Mark Carrier, Emmitt Smith (ROY ROY)	.25
676	Warren Moon (DT)	.10
677	Barry Sanders (DT)	.50
678	Thurman Thomas (DT)	.20
679	Andre Reed (DT)	.06
680	Andre Rison (DT)	.15
681	Keith Jackson (DT)	.05
682	Bruce Armstrong (DT)	.05
683	Jim Lachey (DT)	.04
684	Bruce Matthews (DT)	.04
685	Mike Munchak (DT)	.04
686	Don Mosebar (DT)	.04
1B	Super Bowl (Jeff Hostetler)	.25
2B	Super Bowl (Matt Bahr)	.05
3B	Super Bowl (Ottis Anderson)	.05
4B	Super Bowl (Ottis Anderson)	.05

1991 Score Dream Team Autographs

The 11-card, standard-size set was inserted every 5,000 packs of Series II packs. Each player autographed approximately 500 cards.

		MT
Complete Set (11):		850.00
Common Player:		25.00
676	Warren Moon	100.00
677	Barry Sanders	250.00
678	Thurman Thomas	125.00
679	Andre Reed	100.00
680	Andre Rison	100.00
681	Keith Jackson	50.00
682	Bruce Armstrong	25.00
683	Jim Lachey	25.00
684	Bruce Matthews	25.00
685	Mike Munchak	25.00
686	Don Mosebar	25.00

1991 Score Hot Rookie

1991 Score blister packs contained these random inserts which have card fronts showing action shots of the players in their collegiate uniforms against a hot pink/yellow background. The fronts are bordered in black. Each card back is numbered and includes a close-up shot of the player, plus a brief career summary.

		MT
Complete Set (10):		8.00
Common Player:		.80
1	Dan McGwire	2.00
2	Todd Lyght	1.00
3	Mike Dumas	.80
4	Pat Harlow	.80
5	Nick Bell	1.00
6	Chris Smith	.80
7	Mike Stonebreaker	.80
8	Mike Croel	1.00
9	Kenny Walker	1.00
10	Rob Carpenter	.80

1991 Score Supplemental

Rookies and players who were traded during the regular season are featured in this 110-card update set. The fronts have the same design as the regular cards do, except the borders shade from blue-green to white. The backs have a mug shot and player information in a horizontal format framed by a gold border. Card numbering is done on the back with a "T" suffix.

		MT
Complete Set (110):		8.00
Common Player:		.04
1	Ronnie Lott	.10
2	Matt Millen	.04
3	Tim McKyer	.04
4	Vince Newsome	.04
5	Gaston Green	.04
6	Brett Perriman	.08
7	Roger Craig	.06
8	Pete Holohan	.04
9	Tony Zendejas	.04
10	Lee Williams	.04
11	Mike Stonebreaker	.04
12	Felix Wright	.04
13	Lonnie Young	.04
14	Hugh Millen	.10
15	Roy Green	.04
16	Greg Davis	.10
17	Dexter Manley	.04
18	Ted Washington	.10
19	Norm Johnson	.04
20	Joe Morris	.04
21	Robert Perryman	.04
22	Mike Iaquaniello	.04
23	Gerald Perry	.10
24	Zeke Mowatt	.04
25	Rich Miano	.10
26	Nick Bell	.10
27	Terry Orr	.15
28	Matt Stover	.15
29	Bubba Paris	.04
30	Ron Brown	.04
31	Don Davey	.04
32	Lee Rouson	.04
33	Terry Hoage	.04
34	Tony Covington	.04
35	John Rienstra	.04
36	Charles Dimry	.08
37	Todd Marinovich	.08
38	Winston Moss	.04
39	Vestee Jackson	.04
40	Brian Hansen	.04
41	Irv Eatman	.04
42	Jarrod Bunch	.08
43	Kanavis McGhee	.10
44	Vai Sikahema	.04
45	Charles McRae	.10
46	Quinn Early	.04
47	Jeff Faulkner	.04
48	William Frizzell	.10
49	John Booty	.04
50	Tim Harris	.04
51	Derek Russell	.10
52	John Flannery	.10
53	Tim Barnett	.15
54	Alfred Williams	.15
55	Dan McGwire	.04
56	Ernie Mills	.10
57	Stanley Richard	.10
58	Huey Richardson	.10
59	Jerome Henderson	.10
60	Bryan Cox	.40
61	Russell Maryland	.25
62	Reggie Jones	.15
63	Mo Lewis	.10
64	Moe Gardner	.04
65	Wesley Carroll	.10
66	Michael Jackson	.25
67	Shawn Jefferson	.10
68	Chris Zorich	.10
69	Kenny Walker	.04
70	Erric Pegram	.10
71	Alvin Harper	.10
72	Harry Colon	.10
73	Scott Miller	.04
74	Lawrence Dawsey	.10
75	Phil Hansen	.15
76	Roman Phifer	.15
77	Greg Lewis	.04
78	Merton Hanks	.15
79	James Jones	.10
80	Vinnie Clark	.10
81	R.J. Kors	.04
82	Mike Pritchard	.25

83	Stan Thomas	.04
84	Lamar Rogers	.04
85	Erik Williams	.25
86	Keith Traylor	.10
87	Mike Dumas	.04
88	Mel Agee	.10
89	Harvey Williams	.25
90	Todd Lyght	.04
91	Jake Reed	.50
92	Pat Harlow	.04
93	Antone Davis	.10
94	Aeneas Williams	.10
95	Eric Bieniemy	.10
96	John Kasay	.10
97	Robert Wilson	.04
98	Ricky Ervins	.15
99	Mike Croel	.10
100	David Lang	.10
101	Esera Tuaolo	.10
102	Randal Hill	.20
103	Jon Vaughn	.25
104	Dave McCloughan	.04
105	David Daniels	.10
106	Eric Moten	.04
107	Anthony Morgan	.15
108	Ed King	.04
109	Leonard Russell	.10
110	Aaron Craver	.08

1991 Score National 10

These 10 cards were distributed at the 12th National Sports Collectors Covention in a cello wrapper. A panel on the card back indicates the cards were created for the convention. A mug shot, card number, biographical information and career summary are also provided on the back. The front has a color or action photo of the player, with a player/football pattern above and below the photo.

		MT
Complete Set (10):		10.00
Common Player:		.75
1	Emmitt Smith	8.00
2	Mark Carrier	1.00
3	Steve Broussard	1.00
4	Johnny Johnson	2.00
5	Steve Christie	1.00
6	Richmond Webb	.75
7	James Francis	.75
8	Jeff George	2.00
9	Rodney Hampton	3.00
10	Calvin Williams	1.00

1991 Score Young Superstars

These cards, available in October 1990 via a mail-in offer found on Score wax packs, featured up-and-coming stars of the game. Each front has game-day photography surrounded by black borders and team colors. The card back shows a head shot, a player profile and a scouting report quote.

		MT
Complete Set (40):		7.00
Common Player:		.10
1	Johnny Bailey	.15
2	Johnny Johnson	.20
3	Fred Barnett	.15
4	Keith McCants	.10
5	Brad Baxter	.10
6	Dan Owens	.10
7	Steve Broussard	.15
8	Ricky Proehl	.10
9	Marion Butts	.20
10	Reggie Cobb	.15
11	Dennis Byrd	.10
12	Emmitt Smith	3.00
13	Mark Carrier	.15
14	Keith Sims	.10
15	Dexter Carter	.15
16	Chris Singleton	.10
17	Steve Christie	.10

18	Frank Cornish	.10
19	Timm Rosenbach	.10
20	Sammie Smith	.10
21	Calvin Williams	.15
22	Merril Hoge	.10
23	Hart Lee Dykes	.10
24	Darrell Thompson	.10
25	James Francis	.10
26	John Elliott	.10
27	Jeff George	.25
28	Broderick Thomas	.15
29	Eric Green	.15
30	Steve Walsh	.10
31	Harold Green	.15
32	Andre Ware	.10
33	Richmond Webb	.10
34	Junior Seau	.40
35	Tim Grunhard	.10
36	Tim Worley	.10
37	Haywood Jeffires	.20
38	Rod Woodson	.20
39	Rodney Hampton	.20
40	Dave Szott	.10

1992 Score

This 550-card set features color action photos surrounded by a solid colored border. The player's position is on the bottom in a dark blue band; his name is at the top in a green band. The back has a mug shot, biography, statistics and profile. Subsets include Draft Picks, Crunch Crew, Rookie of the Year, Little Big Men, Sack Attack, Hall of Famers, and the 90 Plus Club. Two insert sets were also made - Dream Team (25 cards, in foil packs) and Gridiron Stars (45 cards), which were in jumbo packs.

		MT
Complete Set (550):		25.00
Common Player:		.05
Minor Stars:		.10
Wax Box:		8.00
1	Barry Sanders	2.00
2	Pat Swilling	.05
3	Moe Gardner	.05
4	Steve Young	1.50
5	Chris Spielman	.05
6	Richard Dent	.05
7	Anthony Munoz	.05
8	Martin Mayhew	.05
9	Terry McDaniel	.05
10	Thurman Thomas	.40
11	Ricky Sanders	.05
12	Steve Atwater	.05
13	Tony Tolbert	.05
14	Vince Workman	.05
15	Haywood Jeffires	.05
16	Duane Bickett	.05
17	Jeff Uhlenhake	.05
18	Tim McDonald	.05
19	Cris Carter	.10
20	Derrick Thomas	.10
21	Hugh Millen	.05
22	Bart Oates	.05
23	Eugene Robinson	.05
24	Jerrol Williams	.05
25	Reggie White	.10
26	Marion Butts	.05
27	Jim Sweeney	.05
28	Tom Newberry	.05
29	Pete Stoyanovich	.05
30	Ronnie Lott	.05
31	Simon Fletcher	.05
32	Dino Hackett	.05
33	Morten Andersen	.05
34	Clyde Simmons	.05
35	Mark Rypien	.05
36	Greg Montgomery	.05
37	Nate Lewis	.05
38	Henry Ellard	.05
39	Luis Sharpe	.05
40	Michael Irvin	.30
41	Louis Lipps	.05
42	John L. Williams	.05
43	Broderick Thomas	.05
44	Michael Haynes	.15
45	Don Majkowski	.05
46	William Perry	.05
47	David Fulcher	.05
48	Tony Bennett	.05

49	Clay Matthews	.05
50	Warren Moon	.10
51	Bruce Armstrong	.05
52	Harry Newsome	.05
53	Bill Brooks	.05
54	Greg Townsend	.05
55	Tom Rathman	.05
56	Sean Landeta	.05
57	Kyle Clifton	.05
58	Steve Broussard	.05
59	Mark Carrier	.05
60	Mel Gray	.05
61	Tim Krumrie	.05
62	Rufus Porter	.05
63	Kevin Mack	.05
64	Todd Bowles	.05
65	Emmitt Smith	3.00
66	Mike Croel	.05
67	Brian Mitchell	.05
68	Bennie Blades	.05
69	Carnell Lake	.05
70	Cornelius Bennett	.05
71	Darrell Thompson	.05
72	Wes Hopkins	.05
73	Jessie Hester	.05
74	Irv Eatman	.05
75	Marv Cook	.05
76	Tim Brown	.10
77	Pepper Johnson	.05
78	Mark Duper	.05
79	Robert Delpino	.05
80	Charles Mann	.05
81	Brian Jordan	.10
82	Wendell Davis	.05
83	Lee Johnson	.05
84	Ricky Reynolds	.05
85	Vaughan Johnson	.05
86	Brian Seale	.05
87	Sam Seale	.05
88	Ed King	.05
89	Gaston Green	.05
90	Christian Okoye	.05
91	Chris Jacke	.05
92	Rohn Stark	.05
93	Kevin Greene	.05
94	Jay Novacek	.10
95	Chip Lohmiller	.05
96	Cris Dishman	.05
97	Ethan Horton	.05
98	Pat Harlow	.05
99	Mark Ingram	.05
100	Mark Carrier	.05
101	Deron Cherry	.05
102	Sam Mills	.05
103	Mark Higgs	.05
104	Keith Jackson	.05
105	Steve Tasker	.05
106	Ken Harvey	.05
107	Bryan Hinkle	.05
108	Anthony Carter	.05
109	Johnny Hector	.05
110	Randall McDaniel	.05
111	Johnny Johnson	.05
112	Shane Conlan	.05
113	Ray Horton	.05
114	Sterling Sharpe	.10
115	Guy McIntyre	.05
116	Tom Waddle	.05
117	Albert Lewis	.05
118	Riki Ellison	.05
119	Chris Doleman	.05
120	Andre Rison	.05
121	Bobby Hebert	.05
122	Dan Owens	.05
123	Rodney Hampton	.10
124	Ron Holmes	.05
125	Ernie Jones	.05
126	Michael Carter	.05
127	Reggie Cobb	.05
128	Esera Tuaolo	.05
129	Wilber Marshall	.05
130	Mike Munchak	.05
131	Cortez Kennedy	.05
132	Lamar Lathon	.05
133	Todd Lyght	.05
134	Jeff Feagles	.05
135	Burt Grossman	.05
136	Mike Cofer	.05
137	Frank Warren	.05
138	Jarvis Williams	.05
139	Eddie Brown	.05
140	John Elliott	.05
141	Jim Everett	.05
142	Hardy Nickerson	.05
143	Eddie Murray	.05
144	Andre Tippett	.05
145	Heath Sherman	.05
146	Ronnie Harmon	.05
147	Eric Metcalf	.05
148	Tony Martin	.25
149	Chris Burkett	.05
150	Andre Waters	.05
151	Ray Donaldson	.05
152	Paul Gruber	.05
153	Chris Singleton	.05
154	Clarence Kay	.05
155	Ernest Givins	.05
156	Eric Hill	.05
157	Jesse Sapolu	.05
158	Jack Del Rio	.05
159	Erric Pegram	.10
160	Joey Browner	.05
161	Marcus Allen	.10
162	Eric Moten	.05
163	Donnell Thompson	.05
164	Chuck Cecil	.05
165	Matt Millen	.05
166	Barry Foster	.05

167	Kent Hull	.05
168	Tony Jones	.05
169	Mike Prior	.05
170	Neal Anderson	.05
171	Roger Craig	.05
172	Felix Wright	.05
173	James Francis	.05
174	Eugene Lockhart	.05
175	Dalton Hilliard	.05
176	Nick Lowery	.05
177	Tim McKyer	.05
178	Lorenzo White	.05
179	Jeff Hostetler	.10
180	*Jackie Harris*	.25
181	Ken Norton	.05
182	Flipper Anderson	.05
183	Don Warren	.05
184	Brad Baxter	.05
185	John Taylor	.05
186	Harold Green	.05
187	James Washington	.05
188	Aaron Craver	.05
189	Mike Merriweather	.05
190	Gary Clark	.05
191	Vince Buck	.05
192	Cleveland Gary	.05
193	Dan Saleaumua	.05
194	Gary Zimmerman	.05
195	Richmond Webb	.05
196	Gary Plummer	.05
197	Willie Green	.05
198	Chris Warren	.30
199	Mike Pritchard	.05
200	Art Monk	.05
201	Matt Stover	.05
202	Tim Grunhard	.05
203	Mervyn Fernandez	.05
204	Mark Jackson	.05
205	Freddie Joe Nunn	.05
206	Stan Thomas	.05
207	Keith McKeller	.05
208	Jeff Lageman	.05
209	Kenny Walker	.05
210	Dave Krieg	.05
211	Dean Clasucci	.05
212	Herman Moore	1.00
213	Jon Vaughn	.05
214	Howard Cross	.05
215	Greg Davis	.05
216	Bubby Brister	.05
217	John Kasay	.05
218	Ron Hall	.05
219	Mo Lewis	.05
220	Eric Green	.05
221	Scott Case	.05
222	Sean Jones	.05
223	Winston Moss	.05
224	Reggie Langhorne	.05
225	Greg Lewis	.05
226	Todd McNair	.05
227	Rod Bernstine	.05
228	Joe Jacoby	.05
229	Brad Muster	.05
230	Nick Bell	.05
231	Terry Allen	.40
232	Cliff Odom	.05
233	Brian Hansen	.05
234	William Fuller	.05
235	Issiac Holt	.05
236	Dexter Carter	.05
237	Gene Atkins	.05
238	Pat Beach	.05
239	Tim McGhee	.05
240	Dermontti Dawson	.05
241	Dan Fike	.05
242	Don Beebe	.05
243	Jeff Bostic	.05
244	Mark Collins	.05
245	Steve Sewell	.05
246	Steve Walsh	.05
247	Erik Kramer	.10
248	Scott Norwood	.05
249	Jesse Solomon	.05
250	Jerry Ball	.05
251	Eugene Daniel	.05
252	Michael Stewart	.05
253	Fred Barnett	.05
254	Rodney Holman	.05
255	Stephen Baker	.05
256	Don Griffin	.05
257	Will Wolford	.05
258	Perry Kemp	.05
259	Leonard Russell	.05
260	Jeff Gossett	.05
261	Dwayne Harper	.05
262	Vinny Testaverde	.05
263	Maurice Hurst	.05
264	Tony Casillas	.05
265	Louis Oliver	.05
266	Jim Morrissey	.05
267	Kenneth Davis	.05
268	John Alt	.05
269	*Michael Zordich*	.05
270	Brian Brennan	.05
271	Greg Kragen	.05
272	Andre Collins	.05
273	Dave Meggett	.05
274	Scott Fulhage	.05
275	Tony Zendejas	.05
276	Herschel Walker	.05
277	Keith Henderson	.05
278	Johnny Bailey	.05
279	Vince Newsome	.05
280	Chris Hinton	.05
281	Robert Blackmon	.05
282	James Hasty	.05
283	John Offerdahl	.05
284	Wesley Carroll	.05

285	Lomas Brown	.05
286	Neil O'Donnell	.25
287	Kevin Porter	.05
289	Carlton Bailey	.05
290	Leonard Marshall	.05
291	John Carney	.05
292	Bubba McDowell	.05
293	Nate Newton	.05
294	Dave Waymer	.05
295	Rob Moore	.05
296	Earnest Byner	.05
297	Jason Staurovsky	.05
298	Keith McCants	.05
299	Floyd Turner	.05
300	Steve Jordan	.05
301	Nate Odomes	.05
302	Gerald Riggs	.05
303	Marvin Washington	.05
304	Anthony Thompson	.05
305	Steve DeBerg	.05
306	Jim Harbaugh	.10
307	Larry Brown	.05
308	Roger Ruzek	.05
309	Jessie Tuggle	.05
310	Al Smith	.05
311	Mark Kelso	.05
312	Lawrence Dawsey	.05
313	*Steve Bono*	1.00
314	Greg Lloyd	.10
315	Steve Wisniewski	.05
316	Gill Fenerty	.05
317	Mark Stepnoski	.05
318	Derek Russell	.05
319	Chris Martin	.05
320	Shaun Gayle	.05
321	Bob Golic	.05
322	Larry Kelm	.05
323	*Mike Brim*	.05
324	Tommy Kane	.05
325	*Mark Schlereth*	.05
326	Ray Childress	.05
327	*Richard Brown*	.05
328	Vincent Brown	.05
329	Mike Farr	.05
330	Eric Swann	.05
331	Bill Fralic	.05
332	Rodney Peete	.10
333	Jerry Gray	.05
334	Ray Berry	.05
335	Dennis Smith	.05
336	Jeff Herrod	.05
337	Tony Mandarich	.05
338	Matt Bahr	.05
339	Mike Saxon	.05
340	Bruce Matthews	.05
341	Rickey Jackson	.05
342	Eric Allen	.05
343	Lonnie Young	.05
344	Steve McMichael	.05
345	Willie Gault	.05
346	Barry Word	.05
347	Rich Camarillo	.05
348	Bill Romanowski	.05
349	Jim Lachey	.05
350	Jim Ritcher	.05
351	Irving Fryar	.05
352	Gary Anderson	.05
353	Henry Rolling	.05
354	Mark Bortz	.05
355	Mark Clayton	.05
356	Keith Woodside	.05
357	Jonathan Hayes	.05
358	Derrick Fenner	.05
359	Keith Byars	.05
360	Drew Hill	.05
361	Harris Barton	.05
362	John Kidd	.05
363	Aeneas Williams	.05
364	Brian Washington	.05
365	John Stephens	.05
366	Norm Johnson	.05
367	Darryl Henley	.05
368	William White	.05
369	Mark Murphy	.05
370	Myron Guyton	.05
371	Leon Seals	.05
372	Rich Gannon	.05
373	Toi Cook	.05
374	Anthony Johnson	.05
375	Rod Woodson	.05
376	Alexander Wright	.05
377	Kevin Butler	.05
378	Neil Smith	.05
379	Gary Anderson	.05
380	Reggie Roby	.05
381	Jeff Bryant	.05
382	Ray Crockett	.05
383	Richard Johnson	.05
384	Hassan Jones	.05
385	Karl Mecklenburg	.05
386	Jeff Jaeger	.05
387	Keith Wills	.05
388	Phil Simms	.05
389	Kevin Ross	.05
390	Chris Miller	.05
391	Brian Noble	.05
392	*Jamie Dukes*	.05
393	George Jamison	.05
394	Rickey Dixon	.05
395	Carl Lee	.05
396	Jon Hand	.05
397	Kirby Jackson	.05
398	Pat Terrell	.05
399	Howie Long	.05
400	Mike Young	.05
401	Keith Sims	.05
402	Tommy Barnhardt	.05
403	Greg McMurty	.05

404	Keith Van Horne	.05
405	Seth Joyner	.05
406	Jim Jeffcoat	.05
407	Courtney Hall	.05
408	Tony Covington	.05
409	Jacob Green	.05
410	Charles Haley	.05
411	Darryl Talley	.05
412	Jeff Cross	.05
413	John Elway	.40
414	Donald Evans	.05
415	Jackie Slater	.05
416	John Friesz	.05
417	Anthony Smith	.05
418	Gill Byrd	.05
419	Willie Drewrey	.05
420	Jay Hilgenberg	.05
421	David Treadwell	.05
422	Curtis Duncan	.05
423	Sammie Smith	.05
424	Henry Thomas	.05
425	James Lofton	.05
426	Fred Marion	.05
427	Bryce Paup	.40
428	Eric Andolsek	.05
429	Reyna Thompson	.05
430	Mike Kenn	.05
431	Bill Maas	.05
432	Quinn Early	.05
433	Everson Walls	.05
434	Jimmie Jones	.05
435	Dwight Stone	.05
436	Harry Colon	.05
437	Don Mosebar	.05
438	Calvin Williams	.05
439	Tom Tupa	.05
440	Darrell Green	.05
441	Eric Thomas	.05
442	Terry Wooden	.05
443	Brett Perriman	.10
444	Todd Marinovich	.05
445	Jim Breech	.05
446	Eddie Anderson	.05
447	Jay Schroeder	.05
448	William Roberts	.05
449	Brad Edwards	.05
450	Tunch Ilkin	.05
451	Joe Ivy	.05
452	Robert Clark	.05
453	Tim Barnett	.05
454	Jarrod Bunch	.05
455	Tim Harris	.05
456	James Brooks	.05
457	Trace Armstrong	.05
458	Michael Brooks	.05
459	Andy Heck	.05
460	Greg Jackson	.05
461	Vance Johnson	.05
462	Kirk Lowdermilk	.05
463	Erik McMillan	.05
464	Scott Mersereau	.05
465	Jeff Wright	.05
466	Mike Tomczak	.05
467	David Alexander	.05
468	Bryan Millard	.05
469	John Randle	.05
470	Joel Hilgenberg	.05
471	*Bennie Thompson*	.05
472	Freeman McNeil	.05
473	Terry Orr	.05
474	Mike Horan	.05
475	Leroy Hoard	.05
476	*Patrick Rowe* (DP)	.05
477	*Siran Stacy* (DP)	.05
478	*Amp Lee* (DP)	.20
479	*Eddie Blake* (DP)	.05
480	*Joe Bowden* (DP)	.05
481	*Roderick Milstead* (DP)	.05
482	*Keith Hamilton* (DP)	.05
483	*Darryl Williams* (DP)	.05
484	*Robert Porcher* (DP)	.10
485	*Ed Cunningham* (DP)	.05
486	*Chris Mims* (DP)	.10
487	*Chris Hakel* (DP)	.05
488	*Jimmy Smith* (DP)	3.50
489	*Todd Harrison* (DP)	.05
490	*Edgar Bennett* (DP)	.75
491	*Dexter McNabb* (DP)	.05
492	*Leon Searcy* (DP)	.05
493	*Tommy Vardell* (DP)	.10
494	*Terrell Buckley* (DP)	.10
495	*Kevin Turner* (DP)	.05
496	*Russ Campbell* (DP)	.05
497	*Torrance Small* (DP)	.30
498	*Nate Turner* (DP)	.05
499	*Cornelius Benton* (DP)	.05
500	*Matt Elliott* (DP)	.05
501	*Robert Stewart* (DP)	.05
502	*Muhammad Shamsid-Deen* (DP)	.05
503	*George Williams* (DP)	.05
504	*Pumpy Tudors* (DP)	.05
505	*Matt LaBounty* (DP)	.05
506	*Darryl Hardy* (DP)	.05
507	*Derrick Moore* (DP)	.50
508	*Willie Clay* (DP)	.05
509	*Bob Whitfield* (DP)	.05

510	*Ricardo McDonald* (DP)	.05
511	*Carlos Huerta* (DP)	.05
512	*Selwyn Jones* (DP)	.05
513	*Steve Gordon* (DP)	.05
514	*Bob Meeks* (DP)	.05
515	Bennie Blades (CC)	.05
516	Andre Waters (CC)	.05
517	Bubba McDowell (CC)	.05
518	Kevin Porter (CC)	.05
519	Carnell Lake (CC)	.05
520	Leonard Russell (ROY)	.05
521	Mike Croel (ROY)	.05
522	Lawrence Dawsey (ROY)	.05
523	Moe Gardner (ROY)	.05
524	Steve Broussard (LBM)	.05
525	Dave Meggett (LBM)	.05
526	Darrell Green (LBM)	.05
527	Tony Jones (LBM)	.05
528	Barry Sanders (LBM)	1.00
529	Pat Swilling (SA)	.05
530	Reggie White (SA)	.05
531	William Fuller (SA)	.05
532	Simon Fletcher (SA)	.05
533	Derrick Thomas (SA)	.05
534	Mark Rypien (MOY)	.05
535	John Mackey (HOF)	.05
536	John Riggins (HOF)	.05
537	Lem Barney (HOF)	.05
538	Shawn McCarthy (90)	.05
539	Al Edwards (90)	.05
540	Alexander Wright (90)	.05
541	Ray Crockett (90)	.05
542	Steve Young (90)	.40
543	Nate Lewis (90)	.05
544	Dexter Carter (90)	.05
545	Reggie Rutland (90)	.05
546	Jon Vaughn (90)	.05
547	Chris Martin (90)	.05
548	Warren Moon (HL)	.05
549	Super Bowl logo	.05
550	Robb Thomas	.05

1992 Score NFL Follies

This three-card set was available exclusively through the purchase of NFL Football Card Follies, a tape produced by NFL Films and distributed by Polygram Video. It featured three of the game's wacky and wildest plays. The video was available in video stores nationwide for a suggested retail price of $19.95.

		MT
Complete Set (3):		30.00
Common Player:		8.00
1	Franco Harris	15.00
2	Garo Yepremian	8.00
3	Jim Marshall	8.00

1992 Score Dream Team

These cards have horizontal fronts which feature a full-bleed color action photo. The team logo

is in a diamond in the lower left corner, intersected by color-coded stripes which have the player's name and position (bottom) and set name (left side) in them. The set name is in gold foil. The card back has a portrait shot, team logo, player profile, statistics, biography and card number. Cards were randomly inserted in 1992 Score jumbo packs.

		MT
Complete Set (25):		85.00
Common Player:		1.50
Minor Stars:		3.00
1	Michael Irvin	3.00
2	Haywood Jeffires	1.50
3	Emmitt Smith	20.00
4	Barry Sanders	25.00
5	Marv Cook	1.50
6	Bart Oates	1.50
7	Steve Wisniewski	1.50
8	Randall McDaniel	1.50
9	Jim Lachey	1.50
10	Lomas Brown	1.50
11	Reggie White	4.00
12	Clyde Simmons	1.50
13	Derrick Thomas	3.00
14	Seth Joyner	1.50
15	Darryl Talley	1.50
16	Karl Mecklenburg	1.50
17	Sam Mills	1.50
18	Darrell Green	1.50
19	Steve Atwater	1.50
20	Mark Carrier	1.50
21	Jeff Gossett	1.50
22	Chip Lohmiller	1.50
23	Mel Gray	1.50
24	Steve Tasker	1.50
25	Mark Rypien	1.50

1992 Score Gridiron Stars

Each 1992 Score jumbo pack contained three of these cards, which are devoted to "Gridiron Stars." This is gold foil-stamped along the left side of the card front, which has an action photo of the player, plus his name, position and logo. The numbered card back includes a player profile shot, statistics and a career summary.

		MT
Complete Set (45):		12.00
Common Player:		.25
Minor Stars:		.50
1	Barry Sanders	3.00
2	Mike Croel	.25
3	Thurman Thomas	.50
4	Lawrence Dawsey	.25
5	Brad Baxter	.25
6	Moe Gardner	.25
7	Emmitt Smith	3.00
8	Sammie Smith	.25
9	Rodney Hampton	.50
10	Mark Carrier	.25
11	Mo Lewis	.25
12	Andre Rison	.50
13	Eric Green	.25
14	Richmond Webb	.25
15	Johnny Bailey	.25
16	Mike Pritchard	.25
17	John Friesz	.50
18	Leonard Russell	.50
19	Derrick Thomas	.50
20	Ken Harvey	.25
21	Fred Barnett	.25
22	Aeneas Williams	.25
23	Marion Butts	.25
24	Harold Green	.25
25	Michael Irvin	.50
26	Dan Owens	.25
27	Curtis Duncan	.25
28	Rodney Peete	.25
29	Brian Blades	.25
30	Marv Cook	.25
31	Burt Grossman	.25
32	Michael Haynes	.25
33	Bennie Blades	.25
34	Cornelius Bennett	.25
35	Louis Oliver	.25
36	Rod Woodson	.25
37	Steve Wisniewski	.25
38	Neil Smith	.25
39	Gaston Green	.25
40	Jeff Lageman	.25
41	Chip Lohmiller	.25
42	Tim McDonald	.25
43	John Elliott	.25
44	Steve Atwater	.25
45	Flipper Anderson	.25

1992 Score Young Superstars

Promising stars of the NFL are featured in this 40-card boxed set from Score. Each card front has a glossy, color action photo, framed by two

borders - a green one and a purple outer border with black specks inside. The Score logo, player's name and team name also appear on the card front. The back is numbered and includes a mug shot of the player, plus statistics, biographical information, a career summary and a scouting report analyzing the player's skills.

		MT
Complete Set (40):		5.00
Common Player:		.10
1	Michael Irvin	1.00
2	Cortez Kennedy	.30
3	Ken Harvey	.10
4	Bubba McDowell	.10
5	Mark Higgs	.35
6	Andre Rison	.50
7	Lamar Lathon	.10
8	Bennie Blades	.15
9	Anthony Johnson	.10
10	Vince Buck	.10
11	Pat Harlow	.10
12	Mike Croel	.10
13	Myron Guyton	.10
14	Curtis Duncan	.15
15	Michael Haynes	.25
16	Alexander Wright	.10
17	Greg Lewis	.10
18	Chip Lohmiller	.10
19	Nate Lewis	.10
20	Rodney Peete	.15
21	Marv Cook	.15
22	Lawrence Dawsey	.15
23	Pat Terrell	.10
24	John Friesz	.20
25	Tony Bennett	.15
26	Gaston Green	.10
27	Kevin Porter	.10
28	Mike Pritchard	.20
29	Keith Henderson	.10
30	Mo Lewis	.10
31	John Randle	.10
32	Aeneas Williams	.10
33	Floyd Turner	.10
34	Neil Smith	.15
35	Tom Waddle	.10
36	Jeff Lageman	.10
37	Cris Carter	.20
38	Leonard Russell	.25
39	Terry McDaniel	.10
40	Moe Gardner	.10

1993 Score Samples

The six-card, regular-size set was issued to preview the base 1993 set. The six cards are virtually identical to the first six cards in the base set, except for a "Promo" stamp on the lower right corner of the card backs.

		MT
Complete Set (6):		5.00
Common Player:		.50
1	Barry Sanders	3.00
2	Moe Gardner	.50
3	Ricky Watters	1.25
4	Todd Lyght	.50
5	Rodney Hampton	.75
6	Curtis Duncan	.50

1993 Score

Score's 440-card 1993 set

features subsets for Rookies, Super Bowl Highlights, Double Trouble, Rookie of the Year, 90 Plus Club, Highlights, and Hall of Famers. The card fronts have action photos with a white border. The player's team name is in a panel along the side in the appropriate colors, as is the player's name, which is at the bottom of the card. Backs have a profile, mug shot, statistics, biographical information and team logo. Insert sets include Dream Team (26 cards), Franchise (28 cards, one per team), and Men of Autumn (55) - a Score Pinnacle "Men Of Autumn" card which was not included in regular Pinnacle packs.

		MT
Complete Set (440):		15.00
Common Player:		.05
Minor Stars:		.10
Autograph Butkus:		25.00
Wax Box:		15.00
1	Barry Sanders	1.25
2	Moe Gardner	.05
3	Ricky Watters	.25
4	Todd Lyght	.05
5	Rodney Hampton	.10
6	Curtis Duncan	.05
7	Barry Word	.05
8	Reggie Cobb	.05
9	Mike Kenn	.05
10	Michael Irvin	.30
11	Bryan Cox	.05
12	Chris Doleman	.05
13	Rod Woodson	.10
14	Emmitt Smith	2.00
15	Pete Stoyanovich	.05
16	Steve Young	.75
17	Randall McDaniel	.05
18	Cortez Kennedy	.10
19	Mel Gray	.05
20	Barry Foster	.10
21	Tim Brown	.10
22	Todd McNair	.05
23	Anthony Johnson	.05
24	Nate Odomes	.05
25	Brett Favre	2.00
26	Jack Del Rio	.05
27	Terry McDaniel	.05
28	Haywood Jeffires	.05
29	Jay Novacek	.05
30	Wilber Marshall	.05
31	Richmond Webb	.05
32	Steve Atwater	.05
33	James Lofton	.05
34	Harold Green	.05
35	Eric Metcalf	.05
36	Bruce Matthews	.05
37	Albert Lewis	.05
38	Jeff Herrod	.05
39	Vince Workman	.05
40	John Elway	.50
41	Brett Perriman	.05
42	Jon Vaughn	.05
43	Terry Allen	.05
44	Clyde Simmons	.05
45	Bennie Thompson	.05
46	Wendall Davis	.05
47	Bobby Hebert	.05
48	John Offerdahl	.05
49	Jeff Graham	.05
50	Steve Wisniewski	.05
51	Louis Oliver	.05
52	Rohn Stark	.05
53	Cleveland Gary	.05
54	John Randle	.05
55	Jim Everett	.05
56	Donnell Woolford	.05
57	Pepper Johnson	.05
58	Irving Fryar	.05
59	Greg Townsend	.05
60	Chris Burkett	.05
61	Johnny Johnson	.05
62	Ronnie Harmon	.05
63	Don Griffin	.05
64	Wayne Martin	.05
65	John L. Williams	.05
66	Brad Edwards	.05
67	Toi Cook	.05
68	Lawrence Dawsey	.05
69	Johnny Bailey	.05
70	Mike Brim	.05
71	Andre Rison	.10
72	Cornelius Bennett	.05
73	Brad Muster	.05
74	Broderick Thomas	.05
75	Tom Waddle	.05
76	Paul Gruber	.05
77	Jackie Harris	.05
78	Kenneth Davis	.05
79	Norm Johnson	.05
80	Jim Jeffcoat	.05
81	Chris Warren	.10
82	Greg Kragen	.05
83	Ricky Reynolds	.05
84	Hardy Nickerson	.05
85	Brian Mitchell	.05
86	Rufus Porter	.05
87	Greg Jackson	.05
88	Seth Joyner	.05
89	Tim Grunhard	.05
90	Tim Harris	.05

91	Sterling Sharpe	.10
92	Daniel Stubbs	.05
93	Rob Burnett	.05
94	Rich Camarillo	.05
95	Al Smith	.05
96	Thurman Thomas	.10
97	Morten Andersen	.05
98	Reggie White	.10
99	Gill Byrd	.05
100	Pierce Holt	.05
101	Tim McGee	.05
102	Rickey Jackson	.05
103	Vince Newsome	.05
104	Chris Spielman	.05
105	Tim McDonald	.05
106	James Francis	.05
107	Andre Tippett	.05
108	Sam Mills	.05
109	Hugh Millen	.05
110	Brad Baxter	.05
111	Ricky Sanders	.05
112	Marion Butts	.05
113	Fred Barnett	.05
114	Wade Wilson	.05
115	Dave Meggett	.05
116	Kevin Greene	.05
117	Reggie Langhorne	.05
118	Simon Fletcher	.05
119	Tommy Vardell	.05
120	Darion Conner	.05
121	Darren Lewis	.05
122	Charles Mann	.05
123	David Fulcher	.05
124	Tommy Kane	.05
125	Richard Brown	.05
126	Nate Lewis	.05
127	Tony Tolbert	.05
128	Greg Lloyd	.05
129	Herman Moore	.50
130	Robert Massey	.05
131	Chris Jacke	.05
132	Keith Byars	.05
133	William Fuller	.05
134	Rob Moore	.05
135	Duane Bickett	.05
136	Jarrod Bunch	.05
137	Ethan Horton	.05
138	Leonard Russell	.05
139	Darryl Henley	.05
140	Tony Bennett	.05
141	Harry Newsome	.05
142	Kelvin Martin	.05
143	Audray McMillian	.05
144	Chip Lohmiller	.05
145	Henry Jones	.05
146	Rod Bernstine	.05
147	Darryl Talley	.05
148	Clarence Verdin	.05
149	Derrick Thomas	.10
150	Raleigh McKenzie	.05
151	Phil Hansen	.05
152	*Lin Elliott*	.05
153	Chip Banks	.05
154	Shannon Sharpe	.10
155	David Williams	.05
156	Gaston Green	.05
157	Trace Armstrong	.05
158	Todd Scott	.05
159	Stan Humphries	.10
160	Christian Okoye	.05
161	Dennis Smith	.05
162	Derek Kennard	.05
163	Melvin Jenkins	.05
164	Tommy Barnhardt	.05
165	Eugene Robinson	.05
166	Tom Rathman	.05
167	Chris Chandler	.05
168	Steve Broussard	.05
169	Wymon Henderson	.05
170	Bryce Paup	.05
171	Kent Hull	.05
172	Willie Davis	.05
173	Richard Dent	.05
174	Rodney Peete	.05
175	Clay Matthews	.05
176	Erik Williams	.05
177	Mike Cofer	.05
178	Mark Kelso	.05
179	Kurt Gouveia	.05
180	Keith McCants	.05
181	Jim Arnold	.05
182	Sean Jones	.05
183	Chuck Cecil	.05
184	Mark Rypien	.05
185	William Perry	.05
186	Mark Jackson	.05
187	Jim Dombrowski	.05
188	Heath Sherman	.05
189	Bubba McDowell	.05
190	Fuad Reveiz	.05
191	Darren Perry	.05
192	Karl Mecklenburg	.05
193	Frank Reich	.05
194	Tony Casillas	.05
195	Jerry Ball	.05
196	Jessie Hester	.05
197	David Lang	.05
198	Sean Landeta	.05
199	Jerry Gray	.05
200	Mark Higgs	.05
201	Bruce Armstrong	.05
202	Vaughan Johnson	.05
203	Calvin Williams	.05
204	Leonard Marshall	.05
205	Mike Munchak	.05
206	Kevin Ross	.05
207	Daryl Johnston	.05
208	Jay Schroeder	.05

209	Mo Lewis	.05
210	Carlton Haselrig	.05
211	Cris Carter	.10
212	Marv Cook	.05
213	Mark Duper	.05
214	Jackie Slater	.05
215	Mike Prior	.05
216	Warren Moon	.05
217	Mike Saxon	.05
218	Derrick Fenner	.05
219	Brian Washington	.05
220	Jessie Tuggle	.05
221	Jeff Hostetler	.10
222	Deion Sanders	.50
223	Neal Anderson	.05
224	Kevin Mack	.05
225	Tommy Maddox	.05
226	Neil Smith	.05
227	Ronnie Lott	.05
228	Willie Anderson	.05
229	Keith Jackson	.05
230	Pat Swilling	.05
231	Carl Banks	.05
232	Eric Allen	.05
233	Randal Hill	.05
234	Burt Grossman	.05
235	Jerry Rice	.75
236	Santana Dotson	.05
237	Andre Reed	.05
238	Troy Aikman	.75
239	Ray Childress	.05
240	Phil Simms	.05
241	Steve McMichael	.05
242	Browning Nagle	.05
243	Anthony Miller	.05
244	Earnest Byner	.05
245	Jay Hilgenberg	.05
246	Jeff George	.10
247	Marco Coleman	.05
248	Herschel Walker	.05
249	Howie Long	.05
250	Ed McCaffrey	.05
251	Jim Kelly	.10
252	Henry Ellard	.05
253	Joe Montana	1.25
254	Dale Carter	.05
255	John Elliott	.05
256	Gary Clark	.05
257	Carl Pickens	.75
258	Dave Krieg	.05
259	Russell Maryland	.05
260	Randall	.10
	Cunningham	
261	Leslie O'Neal	.05
262	Vinny Testaverde	.05
263	Ricky Ervins	.05
264	Chris Mims	.05
265	Dan Marino	2.00
266	Eric Martin	.05
267	Bruce Smith	.05
268	Jim Harbaugh	.05
269	Steve Emtman	.05
270	Ricky Proehl	.05
271	Vaughn Dunbar	.05
272	Junior Seau	.10
273	Sean Gilbert	.05
274	Jim Lachey	.05
275	Dalton Hilliard	.05
276	David Klingler	.05
277	Robert Jones	.05
278	David Treadwell	.05
279	Tracy Scroggins	.05
280	Terrell Buckley	.05
281	Quentin Coryatt	.05
282	Jason Hanson	.05
283	Desmond Howard	.05
284	Guy McIntyre	.05
285	Gary Zimmerman	.05
286	Marty Carter	.05
287	Jim Sweeney	.05
288	*Arthur Marshall*	.10
289	Eugene Chung	.05
290	Mike Pritchard	.05
291	Jim Ritcher	.05
292	Todd Marinovich	.05
293	Courtney Hall	.05
294	Mark Collins	.05
295	Troy Auzenne	.05
296	Aeneas Williams	.05
297	Andy Heck	.05
298	Shaun Gayle	.05
299	Kevin Fagan	.05
300	Carnell Lake	.05
301	Antone Davis	.05
302	Maurice Hurst	.05
303	Mike Merriweather	.05
304	Reggie Roby	.05
305	Darryl Williams	.05
306	*Jerome Bettis*	1.50
307	*Curtis Conway*	1.00
308	*Drew Bledsoe*	3.00
309	*John Copeland*	.10
310	*Eric Curry*	.10
311	*Lincoln Kennedy*	.10
312	*Dan Williams*	.10
313	*Patrick Bates*	.10
314	*Tom Carter*	.10
315	*Garrison Hearst*	1.50
316	*Joel Hilgenberg*	.05
317	Harris Barton	.05
318	Jeff Lageman	.05
319	*Charles Mincy*	.10
320	Ricardo McDonald	.05
321	Lorenzo White	.05
322	Troy Vincent	.05
323	Bennie Blades	.05
324	Dana Hall	.05
325	Ken Norton	.05

326	Will Wolford	.05
327	Neil O'Donnell	.10
328	Tracy Simien	.05
329	Darrell Green	.05
330	Kyle Clifton	.05
331	*Elbert Shelley*	.05
332	Jeff Wright	.05
333	Mike Johnson	.05
334	John Gesek	.05
335	Michael Brooks	.05
336	George Jamison	.05
337	Johnny Holland	.05
338	Lamar Lathon	.05
339	Bern Brostek	.05
340	Steve Jordan	.05
341	Gene Atkins	.05
342	Aaron Wallace	.05
343	Adrian Cooper	.05
344	Amp Lee	.05
345	Vincent Brown	.05
346	James Hasty	.05
347	Ron Hall	.05
348	Matt Elliott	.05
349	Tim Krumrie	.05
350	Mark Stepnoski	.05
351	Mat Stover	.05
352	James Washington	.05
353	Marc Spindler	.05
354	Frank Warren	.05
355	Vai Sikahema	.05
356	Dan Saleaumua	.05
357	Mark Clayton	.05
358	Brent Jones	.05
359	*Andy Harmon*	.05
360	Anthony Parker	.05
361	Chris Hinton	.05
362	Greg Montgomery	.05
363	Greg McMurtry	.05
364	Craig Heyward	.05
365	David Johnson	.05
366	Bill Romanowski	.05
367	Steve Christie	.05
368	Art Monk	.05
369	Howard Ballard	.05
370	Andre Collins	.05
371	Alvin Harper	.10
372	*Blaise Winter*	.05
373	Al Del Greco	.05
374	Eric Green	.05
375	Chris Mohr	.05
376	Tom Newberry	.05
377	Cris Dishman	.05
378	James Geathers	.05
379	Don Mosebar	.05
380	Andre Ware	.05
381	Marvin Washington	.05
382	Bobby Humphrey	.05
383	Marc Logan	.05
384	Lomas Brown	.05
385	Steve Tasker	.05
386	Chris Miller	.05
387	Tony Paige	.05
388	Charles Haley	.05
389	Rich Moran	.05
390	Mike Sherrard	.05
391	Nick Lowery	.05
392	Henry Thomas	.05
393	Keith Sims	.05
394	Thomas Everett	.05
395	Steve Wallace	.05
396	John Carney	.05
397	Tim Johnson	.05
398	Jeff Gossett	.05
399	Anthony Smith	.05
400	Kelvin Pritchett	.05
401	Dermontti Dawson	.05
402	Alfred Williams	.05
403	Michael Haynes	.05
404	Bart Oates	.05
405	Ken Lanier	.05
406	Vencie Glenn	.05
407	John Taylor	.05
408	Nate Newton	.05
409	Mark Carrier	.05
410	Ken Harvey	.05
411	Troy Aikman (SB)	.40
412	Charles Haley (SB)	.05
413	Warren Moon, Haywood Jeffires (DT)	.05
414	Henry Jones, Mark Kelso (DT)	.05
415	Rickey Jackson, Sam Mills (DT)	.05
416	Clyde Simmons, Reggie White (DT)	.05
417	Dale Carter (RY)	.05
418	Carl Pickens (RY)	.05
419	Vaughn Dunbar (RY)	.05
420	Santana Dotson (RY)	.05
421	Steve Emtman (90-plus)	.05
422	Louis Oliver (90-plus)	.05
423	Carl Pickens (90-plus)	.05
424	Eddie Anderson (90-plus)	.05
425	Deion Sanders (90-plus)	.20
426	Jon Vaughn (90-plus)	.05
427	Darren Lewis (90-plus)	.05
428	Kevin Ross (90-plus)	.05

429	David Brandon (90-plus)	.05
430	Dave Meggett (90-plus)	.05
431	Jerry Rice (H)	.35
432	Sterling Sharpe (H)	.10
433	Art Monk (H)	.05
434	James Lofton (H)	.05
435	Lawrence Taylor	.10
436	Bill Walsh (HF)	.05
437	Chuck Noll (HF)	.05
438	Dan Fouts (HF)	.05
439	Larry Little (HF)	.05
440	Steve Young (MY)	.30

1993 Score Dream Team

The best 13 offensive and 13 defensive players by position are represented in this 1993 Score insert set. Cards were randomly inserted in 1993 Score 35-card packs and were selections made by Score. The horizontal card front has a close-up shot of the player on the right side and an action shot of him on the left against a black panel. The card background is a cloudy sky tinted in brown. The card back has a photo identical to the action photo on the front, except it's bigger and fuzzier. A player profile appears at the bottom in a black panel. The back is numbered and also features a team logo.

		MT
Complete Set (26):		20.00
Common Player:		.50
Minor Stars:		1.00
1	Steve Young	5.00
2	Emmitt Smith	12.00
3	Barry Foster	1.00
4	Sterling Sharpe	1.00
5	Jerry Rice	5.00
6	Keith Jackson	.50
7	Steve Wallace	.50
8	Richmond Webb	.50
9	Guy McIntyre	.50
10	Carlton Haselrig	.50
11	Bruce Matthews	.50
12	Morten Andersen	.50
13	Rich Camarillo	.50
14	Deion Sanders	3.00
15	Steve Tasker	.50
16	Clyde Simmons	.50
17	Reggie White	1.00
18	Cortez Kennedy	.75
19	Rod Woodson	1.00
20	Terry McDaniel	.50
21	Chuck Cecil	.50
22	Steve Atwater	.50
23	Bryan Cox	.50
24	Derrick Thomas	1.00
25	Wilber Marshall	.50
26	Sam Mills	.50

1993 Score Franchise

A top player from each of the 28 NFL teams has been selected for this insert set. Cards were random inserts in 1993 Score foil packs at a rate of about one every 24 packs. The front has a color action photo and the set's logo; the numbered backs have a close-up shot of the player, plus a profile.

		MT
Complete Set (28):		175.00
Common Player:		2.00
Minor Stars:		4.00
1	Andre Rison	2.00
2	Thurman Thomas	4.00
3	Richard Dent	2.00
4	Harold Green	2.00
5	Eric Metcalf	2.00
6	Emmitt Smith	40.00
7	John Elway	25.00
8	Barry Sanders	40.00
9	Sterling Sharpe	4.00
10	Warren Moon	4.00
11	Jeff Herrod	2.00
12	Derrick Thomas	4.00
13	Steve Wisniewski	2.00
14	Cleveland Gary	2.00
15	Dan Marino	40.00
16	Chris Doleman	2.00
17	Marv Cook	2.00
18	Rickey Jackson	2.00
19	Rodney Hampton	2.00
20	Jeff Lageman	2.00
21	Clyde Simmons	2.00
22	Rich Camarillo	2.00
23	Rod Woodson	4.00
24	Ronnie Harmon	2.00
25	Steve Young	20.00
26	Cortez Kennedy	2.00
27	Reggie Cobb	2.00
28	Mark Rypien	2.00

1993 Score Ore-Ida QB Club

The 18-card, standard-size set was issued with specially marked Ore-Ida Bagel Bites, Twice Baked and Topped Baked Potatoes. Purchasers had to send in six proof-of-purchase seals and $1.50 for two nine-card packs. The cards are identical in design to cards in the base 1993 set, except for different numbering. Esiason (Jets) and Hostetler (Raiders) are pictured in their new uniforms.

		MT
Complete Set (18):		25.00
Common Player:		.75
1	John Elway	2.00
2	Steve Young	2.00
3	Warren Moon	1.25
4	Randall Cunningham	.75
5	Jeff Hostetler	.75
6	Phil Simms	1.00
7	Jim Everett	.75
8	David Klingler	.75
9	Brett Favre	6.00
10	Troy Aikman	3.50
11	Dan Marino	6.00
12	Mark Rypien	.75
13	Jim Kelly	1.25
14	Jim Harbaugh	1.00
15	Bernie Kosar	.75
16	Boomer Esiason	.75
17	Chris Miller	.75
18	Neil O'Donnell	.75

1994 Score Samples

The nine-card, standard-size set was issued to preview the 1994 base set and are identical in design to cards in the regular-issued set. The Glyn Milburn card is an example of the Gold Zone insert set.

		MT
Complete Set (9):		3.00
Common Player:		.25
21	Jerome Bettis	1.00
25	Steve Jordan	.25
50	Shannon Sharpe	.40
112	Glyn Milburn (FOIL)	.40
161	Ronnie Lott	.40
257	Derrick Thomas	.50
0	Generic Rookie Card	.25
NNO	Sample Redemption Card	.25
NNO	Score Ad Card	.25

A card number in parentheses ( ) indicates the set is unnumbered.

1994 Score

Score's 330-card 1994 set includes Rookie Redemption, Dream Team and Sophomore Showcase insert cards, plus a Gold Zone parallel set. The Gold Zone cards are identical to the regular set, except they are printed on gold foil; they are inserted one per pack. The card front has a full-color action photo with ragged, torn borders at the top and bottom of the card. The Score logo, player's name and position, and a team helmet are also on the front. Each card back has a mug shot, biographical information, player profile, and statistics. Subsets within the main set are devoted to checklists and 1994 rookies. Nine sample cards, each marked on the back as being a sample, were also made to preview the regular set.

		MT
Complete Set (330):		20.00
Common Player:		.05
Wax Box:		30.00
1	Barry Sanders	1.00
2	Troy Aikman	.75
3	Sterling Sharpe	.35
4	Deion Sanders	.15
5	Bruce Smith	.10
6	Eric Metcalf	.08
7	John Elway	.50
8	Bruce Matthews	.05
9	Rickey Jackson	.05
10	Cortez Kennedy	.05
11	Jerry Rice	.75
12	Stanley Richard	.05
13	Rod Woodson	.10
14	Eric Swann	.10
15	Eric Allen	.10
16	Richard Dent	.06
17	Carl Pickens	.08
18	Rohn Stark	.05
19	Marcus Allen	.10
20	Steve Wisniewski	.08
21	Jerome Bettis	.15
22	Darrell Green	.05
23	Lawrence Dawsey	.05
24	Larry Centers	.10
25	Steve Jordan	.08
26	Johnny Johnson	.08
27	Phil Simms	.10
28	Bruce Armstrong	.05
29	Willis Roaf	.08
30	Andre Rison	.10
31	Henry Jones	.05
32	Warren Moon	.10
33	Sean Gilbert	.08
34	Ben Coates	.05
35	Seth Joyner	.05
36	Ronnie Harmon	.08
37	Quentin Coryatt	.08
38	Ricky Sanders	.05
39	Gerald Williams	.05
40	Emmitt Smith	2.00
41	Jason Hanson	.05
42	Kevin Smith	.05
43	Irving Fryar	.10
44	Boomer Esiason	.08
45	Darryl Talley	.05
46	Paul Gruber	.05
47	Anthony Smith	.05
48	John Copeland	.05
49	Michael Jackson	.08
50	Shannon Sharpe	.15
51	Reggie White	.15
52	Andre Collins	.05
53	Jack Del Rio	.05
54	John Elliott	.05
55	Kevin Greene	.08
56	Steve Young	.75
57	Erric Pegram	.20
58	Donnell Woolford	.05
59	Darryl Williams	.05
60	Michael Irvin	.35
61	Mel Gray	.05
62	Greg Montgomery	.05
63	Neil Smith	.10
64	Andy Harmon	.05
65	Dan Marino	2.00
66	Leonard Russell	.10
67	Joe Montana	.75

68	John Taylor	.10
69	Cris Dishman	.08
70	Cornelius Bennett	.10
71	Harold Green	.08
72	Anthony Pleasant	.05
73	Dennis Smith	.05
74	Bryce Paup	.05
75	Jeff George	.08
76	Henry Ellard	.05
77	Randall McDaniel	.05
78	Derek Brown	.35
79	Johnny Mitchell	.10
80	Leroy Thompson	.05
81	Junior Seau	.08
82	Kelvin Martin	.05
83	Guy McIntyre	.05
84	Elbert Shelley	.05
85	Louis Oliver	.05
86	Tommy Vardell	.05
87	Jeff Harrod	.05
88	Edgar Bennett	.05
89	Reggie Langhorne	.05
90	Terry Kirby	.20
91	Marcus Robertson	.05
92	Mark Collins	.08
93	Calvin Williams	.08
94	Barry Foster	.15
95	Brent Jones	.05
96	Reggie Cobb	.08
97	Ray Childress	.05
98	Chris Miller	.10
99	John Carney	.05
100	Ricky Proehl	.05
101	Renaldo Turnbull	.08
102	John Randle	.05
103	Willie Anderson	.05
104	Scottie Graham	.50
105	Webster Slaughter	.08
106	Tyrone Hughes	.05
107	Ken Norton	.05
108	Jim Kelly	.25
109	Michael Haynes	.15
110	Mark Carrier	.05
111	Eddie Murray	.05
112	Glyn Milburn	.25
113	Jackie Harris	.15
114	Dean Biasucci	.05
115	Tim Brown	.15
116	Mark Higgs	.05
117	Steve Emtman	.05
118	Clay Matthews	.05
119	Clyde Simmons	.05
120	Howard Ballard	.05
121	Ricky Watters	.20
122	William Fuller	.05
123	Robert Brooks	.05
124	Brian Blades	.05
125	Leslie O'Neal	.05
126	Gary Clark	.08
127	Jim Sweeney	.05
128	Vaughan Johnson	.05
129	Gary Brown	.15
130	Todd Lyght	.05
131	Nick Lowery	.05
132	Ernest Givins	.05
133	Lomas Brown	.05
134	Craig Erickson	.05
135	James Francis	.05
136	Andre Reed	.08
137	Jim Everett	.08
138	Nate Odomes	.05
139	Tom Waddle	.08
140	Stevon Moore	.05
141	Rod Bernstine	.05
142	Brett Favre	2.00
143	Roosevelt Potts	.05
144	Chester McGlockton	.05
145	LeRoy Butler	.05
146	Charles Haley	.05
147	Rodney Hampton	.30
148	George Teague	.08
149	Gary Anderson	.05
150	Mark Stepnoski	.05
151	Courtney Hawkins	.05
152	Tim Grunhard	.05
153	David Klingler	.15
154	Erik Williams	.05
155	Herman Moore	.15
156	Daryl Johnston	.05
157	Chris Zorich	.05
158	Shane Conlan	.05
159	Santana Dotson	.05
160	Sam Mills	.08
161	Ronnie Lott	.08
162	Jesse Sapolu	.05
163	Marion Butts	.05
164	Eugene Robinson	.05
165	Mark Schlereth	.05
166	John L. Williams	.05
167	Anthony Miller	.15
168	Rich Camarillo	.05
169	Jeff Lageman	.05
170	Michael Brooks	.05
171	Scott Mitchell	.30
172	Duane Bickett	.05
173	Willie Davis	.05
174	Maurice Hurst	.05
175	Brett Perriman	.05
176	Jay Novacek	.05
177	Terry Allen	.05
178	Pete Metzelaars	.05
179	Erik Kramer	.10
180	Neal Anderson	.05
181	Ethan Horton	.05
182	Tony Bennett	.05
183	Gary Zimmerman	.05
184	Jeff Hostetler	.06
185	Jeff Cross	.05

186	Vincent Brown	.05
187	Herschel Walker	.05
188	Courtney Hall	.05
189	Norm Johnson	.05
190	Hardy Nickerson	.05
191	Greg Townsend	.05
192	Mike Munchak	.05
193	Dante Jones	.05
194	Vinny Testaverde	.08
195	Vance Johnson	.05
196	Chris Jacke	.05
197	Will Wolford	.05
198	Terry McDaniel	.05
199	Bryan Cox	.05
200	Nate Newton	.05
201	Keith Byars	.05
202	Neil O'Donnell	.15
203	Harris Barton	.05
204	Thurman Thomas	.25
205	Jeff Query	.05
206	Russell Maryland	.08
207	Pat Swilling	.05
208	Haywood Jeffires	.05
209	John Alt	.05
210	O.J. McDuffie	.30
211	Keith Sims	.05
212	Eric Martin	.05
213	Kyle Clifton	.05
214	Luis Sharpe	.05
215	Thomas Everett	.05
216	Chris Warren	.05
217	Chris Doleman	.05
218	Tony Jones	.05
219	Karl Mecklenburg	.05
220	Rob Moore	.10
221	Jessie Hester	.05
222	Jeff Jaeger	.05
223	Keith Jackson	.08
224	Mo Lewis	.05
225	Mike Horan	.05
226	Eric Green	.05
227	Jim Ritcher	.05
228	Eric Curry	.05
229	Stan Humphries	.05
230	Mike Johnson	.05
231	Alvin Harper	.10
232	Bennie Blades	.05
233	Cris Carter	.05
234	Morten Anderson	.05
235	Brian Washington	.05
236	Eric Hill	.05
237	Natrone Means	.40
238	Carlton Bailey	.05
239	Anthony Carter	.05
240	Jessie Tuggle	.05
241	Tim Irwin	.05
242	Mark Currier	.05
243	Steve Atwater	.05
244	Sean Jones	.05
245	Bernie Kosar	.05
246	Richmond Webb	.05
247	Dave Meggett	.05
248	Vincent Brisby	.35
249	Fred Barnett	.05
250	Greg Lloyd	.05
251	Tim McDonald	.05
252	Mike Pirtchard	.08
253	Greg Robinson	.05
254	Tony McGee	.10
255	Chris Spielman	.05
256	Keith Loneker	.10
257	Derrick Thomas	.15
258	Wayne Martin	.05
259	Art Monk	.05
260	Andy Heck	.05
261	Chip Lohmiller	.05
262	Simon Fletcher	.05
263	Ricky Reynolds	.05
264	Chris Hinton	.05
265	Ron Moore	.35
266	Raghib Ismail	.15
267	Pete Styanovich	.05
268	Mark Jackson	.05
269	Randall Cunningham	.10
270	Dermontti Dawson	.05
271	Bill Romanowski	.05
272	Tim Johnson	.05
273	Steve Tasker	.05
274	Keith Hamilton	.05
275	Pierce Holt	.05
276	Heath Shuler	.25
277	Marshall Faulk	3.00
278	Charles Johnson	.50
279	Sam Adams	.30
280	Trev Alberts	.25
281	Derrick Alexander	.25
282	Bryant Young	.25
283	Greg Hill	.50
284	Darnay Scott	1.00
285	Willie McGinest	.25
286	Thomas Randolph	.15
287	Errict Rhett	1.00
288	Lamar Smith	.25
289	William Floyd	.40
290	Johnnie Morton	.60
291	Jamir Miller	.30
292	David Palmer	.50
293	Dan Wilkinson	.60
294	Trent Dilfer	2.00
295	Antonio Langham	.30
296	Chuck Levy	.25
297	John Thierry	.25
298	Kevin Lee	.35
299	Aaron Glenn	.25
300	Charlie Garner	1.75
301	Lonnie Johnson	.15
302	LeShon Johnson	.45

303	Thomas Lewis	.50
304	Ryan Yarborough	.40
305	Mario Bates	.20
306	Bills/Cardinals Checklist	.05
307	Bengals/Falcons Checklist	.05
308	Browns/Bears Checklist	.05
309	Broncos/Cowboys Checklist	.05
310	Oilers/Lions Checklist	.05
311	Colts/Packers Checklist	.05
312	Chiefs/Rams Checklist	.05
313	Raiders/Vikings Checklist	.05
314	Dolphins/Saints Checklist	.05
315	Patriots/Giants Checklist	.05
316	Jets/Eagles Checklist	.05
317	Steelers/49ers Checklist	.05
318	Chargers/Bucs Checklist	.05
319	Seahawks/Redskins Checklist	.05
320	Garrison Hearst	.20
321	Drew Bledsoe	.75
322	Tyrone Hughes	.05
323	James Jett	.25
324	Tom Carter	.05
325	Reggie Brooks	.25
326	Dana Stubblefield	.25
327	Jerome Bettis	.15
328	Chris Slade	.15
329	Rick Mirer	.15
330	Emmitt Smith MVP	1.00

1994 Score Rookie Redemption

The 10-card, regular-sized set was inserted every 72 packs as a redemption card. The card fronts have metallic imaging while the backs have a player headshot and season highlights.

		MT
Complete Set (10):		150.00
Common Player:		10.00
1	Heath Shuler	10.00
2	Trent Dilfer	20.00
3	Marshall Faulk	50.00
4	Charlie Garner	15.00
5	LeShon Johnson	10.00
6	Charles Johnson	15.00
7	Errict Rhett	15.00
8	Lake Dawson	10.00
9	Bert Emanuel	15.00
10	Greg Hill	15.00

1994 Score Gold Zone

The 330-card, standard-size set is a parallel set with the card fronts having a metallic gold sheen.

		MT
Complete Set (330):		120.00
Common Player:		.30
Veteran Stars:		3x-6x
RCs:		1.5x-3x

1994 Score Dream Team

These cards were randomly inserted in 1994 Score packs at a rate of one every 72 packs. The cards have an animating hologram on the front, and feature 18 of the NFL's elite players. The hologram has an action shot and closeup photo of the player on the front, along with his name, Score logo, set logo and his team's name running across the card several times. The backs are numbered with a "DT" prefix and have a Score

Football Fifth Anniversary logo, along with the player's 1989 Score card.

		MT
Complete Set (18):		160.00
Common Player:		4.00
Minor Stars:		8.00
1	Troy Aikman	30.00
2	Steve Atwater	4.00
3	Cornelius Bennett	4.00
4	Tim Brown	8.00
5	Michael Irvin	8.00
6	Bruce Matthews	4.00
7	Eric Metcalf	4.00
8	Anthony Miller	4.00
9	Jerry Rice	30.00
10	Andre Rison	8.00
11	Barry Sanders	35.00
12	Deion Sanders	15.00
13	Sterling Sharpe	8.00
14	Neil Smith	4.00
15	Derrick Thomas	8.00
16	Thurman Thomas	8.00
17	Rod Woodson	8.00
18	Steve Young	30.00

1994 Score Sophomore Showcase

Eighteen of the NFL's top second-year players are featured on these cards, which were random inserts in one out of every four Score jumbo packs. The card front has a full-bleed color photo and the Score logo. The player's name and set logo are stamped in gold foil at the bottom. The card back has the player's name running in a marble-like panel along the left side. There's a closeup shot of the player, along with the set's logo, plus a brief career summary on the other side. Cards are numbered with an "SS" prefix.

		MT
Complete Set (18):		60.00
Common Player:		2.00
1	Jerome Bettis	8.00
2	Rick Mirer	4.00
3	Reggie Brooks	2.00
4	Drew Bledsoe	20.00
5	Ron Moore	2.00
6	Derek Brown	2.00
7	Roosevelt Potts	2.00
8	Terry Kirby	3.00
9	James Jett	2.00
10	Vincent Brisby	5.00
11	Tyrone Hughes	2.00
12	Rocket Ismail	3.00
13	Tony McGee	2.00
14	Garrison Hearst	8.00
15	Eric Curry	2.00
16	Dana Stubblefield	3.00
17	Tom Carter	2.00
18	Chris Slade	3.00

1995 Score Promos

The six-card, regular-size set was distributed in four-card packs as a preview for the 1995 base set. The card fronts have "Promo" stamps.

		MT
Complete Set (6):		10.00
Common Player:		.50
42	Drew Bledsoe	2.50
47	Barry Foster	.50
58	Steve Broussard	.50
211	Star Struck Card (Jerry Rice)	2.50
DT2	Dream Team Card (Troy Aikman)	5.00
NNO	Title Card	.50

1995 Score

Score's 1995 275-card football set includes two subsets (26 Draft Pick cards and 30 Star Struck cards), plus two parallel sets (Red Siege and Artist's Proofs). The regular cards have a color action photo on the front, with the player's name along the left side and his team's logo in the lower right corner. The card back has another color photo, plus a brief career summary and statistics. Red Siege cards (one in three packs) are the same, except they have a red-foil background and have "Red Siege" written on the back. The Artist's Proofs cards (one in 36) have an exclusive stamp on the Red Siege cards. Insert sets include Dream Team, Offense Inc., Pass Time and Reflextions.

		MT
Complete Set (275):		15.00
Common Player:		.05
Hobby Wax Box:		30.00
Retail Wax Box:		30.00
1	Steve Young	.50
2	Barry Sanders	1.00
3	Jerry Rice	.75
4	Marshall Faulk	.75
5	Terance Mathis	.05
6	Rod Woodson	.10
7	Seth Joyner	.05
8	Michael Timpson	.05
9	Deion Sanders	.30
10	Emmitt Smith	1.50
11	Cris Carter	.10
12	Jake Reed	.05
13	Reggie White	.10
14	Shannon Sharpe	.10
15	Troy Aikman	.75
16	Andre Reed	.10
17	Tyrone Hughes	.05
18	Sterling Sharpe	.05
19	Jerome Bettis	.30
20	Irving Fryar	.05
21	Warren Moon	.10
22	Ben Coates	.05
23	Frank Reich	.05
24	Henry Ellard	.05
25	Steve Atwater	.05
26	Willie Davis	.05
27	Michael Irvin	.10
28	Harvey Williams	.05
29	Aeneas Williams	.05
30	Errict Rhett	.15
31	Lorenzo White	.05
32	John Elway	.75
33	Rodney Hampton	.10
34	Webster Slaughter	.05
35	Eric Turner	.05
36	Dan Marino	1.50
37	Daryl Johnston	.05
38	Bruce Smith	.05
39	Ron Moore	.05
40	Larry Centers	.05
41	Curtis Conway	.10
42	Drew Bledsoe	.75
43	Quinn Early	.05
44	Marcus Allen	.10
45	Andre Rison	.10
46	Jeff Blake	.50

47	Barry Foster	.10
48	Antonio Langham	.05
49	Herman Moore	.10
50	Willie Anderson	.05
51	Rick Mirer	.30
52	Jay Novacek	.05
53	Tim Bowens	.05
54	Carl Pickens	.10
55	Lewis Tillman	.05
56	Lawrence Dawsey	.05
57	Leroy Hoard	.05
58	Steve Broussard	.05
59	Dave Krieg	.05
60	John Taylor	.05
61	Johnny Mitchell	.05
62	Jessie Hester	.05
63	Johnny Bailey	.05
64	Brett Favre	1.50
65	Bryce Paup	.05
66	J.J. Birden	.05
67	Steve Tasker	.05
68	Edgar Bennett	.05
69	Ray Buchanan	.05
70	Brent Jones	.05
71	Dave Meggett	.05
72	Jeff Graham	.05
73	Michael Brooks	.05
74	Ricky Ervins	.05
75	Chris Warren	.05
76	Natrone Means	.30
77	Tim Brown	.10
78	Jim Everett	.05
79	Chris Calloway	.05
80	John L. Williams	.05
81	Chris Chandler	.05
82	Tim McDonald	.05
83	Calvin Williams	.05
84	Tony McGee	.05
85	Erik Kramer	.05
86	Eric Green	.05
87	Nate Newton	.05
88	Leonard Russell	.05
89	Jeff George	.10
90	Raymont Harris	.10
91	Darnay Scott	.40
92	Brian Mitchell	.05
93	Craig Erickson	.05
94	Cortez Kennedy	.10
95	Derrick Alexander	.10
96	Charles Haley	.05
97	Randall Cunningham	.10
98	Haywood Jeffires	.05
99	Ronnie Harmon	.05
100	Dale Carter	.05
101	Dave Brown	.05
102	Michael Haynes	.05
103	Johnny Johnson	.05
104	William Floyd	.10
105	Jeff Hostetler	.05
106	Bernie Parmalee	.10
107	Mo Lewis	.05
108	Bam Morris	.10
109	Vincent Brisby	.05
110	John Randle	.05
111	Steve Walsh	.05
112	Terry Allen	.05
113	Greg Lloyd	.05
114	Merton Hanks	.05
115	Mel Gray	.05
116	Jim Kelly	.10
117	Don Beebe	.05
118	Floyd Turner	.05
119	Neil Smith	.05
120	Keith Byars	.05
121	Rocket Ismail	.05
122	Leslie O'Neal	.05
123	Mike Sherrard	.05
124	Marion Butts	.05
125	Andre Coleman	.05
126	Charles Johnson	.10
127	Derrick Fenner	.05
128	Vinny Testaverde	.05
129	Chris Spielman	.05
130	Bert Emanuel	.25
131	Craig Heyward	.05
132	Anthony Miller	.05
133	Rob Moore	.05
134	Gary Brown	.05
135	David Klingler	.05
136	Sean Dawkins	.10
137	Terry McDaniel	.05
138	Fred Barnett	.05
139	Bryan Cox	.05
140	Andrew Jordan	.05
141	Leroy Thompson	.05
142	Richmond Webb	.05
143	Kimble Anders	.05
144	Mario Bates	.25
145	Irv Smith	.05
146	Carnell Lake	.05
147	Mark Seay	.05
148	Dana Stubblefield	.05
149	Kelvin Martin	.05
150	Pete Metzelaars	.05
151	Roosevelt Potts	.05
152	Bubby Brister	.05
153	Trent Dilfer	.40
154	Ricky Proehl	.05
155	Aaron Glenn	.05
156	Eric Metcalf	.05
157	Kevin Williams	.05
158	Charlie Garner	.05
159	Glyn Milburn	.05
160	Fuad Reveiz	.05
161	Brett Perriman	.05
162	Neil O'Donnell	.05
163	Tony Martin	.05
164	Sam Adams	.05
165	John Friesz	.05

166	Bryant Young	.05
167	Junior Seau	.10
168	Ken Harvey	.05
169	Bill Brooks	.05
170	Eugene Robinson	.05
171	Ricky Sanders	.05
172	Rodney Peete	.05
173	Boomer Esiason	.05
174	Reggie Roby	.05
175	Michael Jackson	.05
176	Gus Frerotte	.10
177	Terry Kirby	.05
178	Jessie Tuggle	.05
179	Courtney Hawkins	.05
180	Heath Shuler	.20
181	Jack Del Rio	.05
182	O.J. McDuffie	.05
183	Ricky Watters	.05
184	Willie Roaf	.05
185	Glenn Foley	.05
186	Blair Thomas	.05
187	Darren Woodson	.05
188	Kevin Greene	.05
189	Jeff Burris	.05
190	Jay Schroeder	.05
191	Stan Humphries	.10
192	Irving Spikes	.05
193	Jim Harbaugh	.05
194	Robert Brooks	.05
195	Greg Hill	.05
196	Herschel Walker	.05
197	Brian Blades	.05
198	Mark Ingram	.05
199	Kevin Turner	.05
200	Lake Dawson	.10
201	Alvin Harper	.05
202	Derek Brown	.05
203	Qadry Ismail	.05
204	Reggie Brooks	.05
205	Steve Young (Starstruck)	.25
206	Emmitt Smith (Starstruck)	.50
207	Stan Humphries (Starstruck)	.10
208	Barry Sanders (Starstruck)	.50
209	Marshall Faulk (Starstruck)	.50
210	Drew Bledsoe (Starstruck)	.50
211	Jerry Rice (Starstruck)	.50
212	Tim Brown (Starstruck)	.10
213	Cris Carter (Starstruck)	.10
214	Dan Marino (Starstruck)	.75
215	Troy Aikman (Starstruck)	.30
216	Jerome Bettis (Starstruck)	.10
217	Deion Sanders (Starstruck)	.10
218	Junior Seau (Starstruck)	.10
219	John Elway (Starstruck)	.10
220	Warren Moon (Starstruck)	.10
221	Sterling Sharpe (Starstruck)	.10
222	Marcus Allen (Starstruck)	.10
223	Michael Irvin (Starstruck)	.10
224	Brett Favre (Starstruck)	.40
225	Rodney Hampton (Starstruck)	.10
226	Dave Brown (Starstruck)	.05
227	Ben Coates (Starstruck)	.05
228	Jim Kelly (Starstruck)	.10
229	Heath Shuler (Starstruck)	.40
230	Herman Moore (Starstruck)	.10
231	Jeff Hostetler (Starstruck)	.05
232	Rick Mirer (Starstruck)	.10
233	Bam Morris (Starstruck)	.10
234	Terance Mathis (Starstruck)	.05
235	Checklist	.05
236	Troy Aikman (CL)	.20
237	Jerry Rice (CL)	.20
238	Emmitt Smith (CL)	.40
239	Steve Young (CL)	.20
240	Drew Bledsoe (CL)	.25
241	Marshall Faulk (CL)	.25
242	Dan Marino (CL)	.25
243	Junior Seau (CL)	.05

244	*Ray Zellars*	.10
245	*Rob Johnson*	2.00
246	*Tony Boselli*	.10
247	*Kevin Carter*	.10
248	*Steve McNair*	3.00
249	*Tyrone Wheatley*	.50
250	*Steve Stenstrom*	.10
251	*Stoney Case*	.10
252	*Rodney Thomas*	.10
253	*Michael Westbrook*	1.00
254	*Derrick Alexander*	.10
255	*Kyle Brady*	.10
256	*Kerry Collins*	.10
257	*Rashaan Salaam*	.50
258	*Frank Sanders*	.25
259	*John Walsh*	.10
260	*Sherman Williams*	.10
261	*Ki-Jana Carter*	.30
262	*Jack Jackson*	.10
263	*J.J. Stokes*	.75
264	*Kordell Stewart*	2.50
265	*Dave Barr*	.10
266	*Eddie Goines*	.10
267	*Warren Sapp*	.10
268	*James Stewart*	1.50
269	*Joey Galloway*	1.50
270	*Tyrone Davis*	.10
271	*Napoleon Kaufman*	1.00
272	*Mark Bruener*	.30
273	*Todd Collins*	.10
274	*Billy Williams*	.10
275	*James Stewart*	.10

1995 Score Red Siege

The 275-card, regular-size parallel set, inserted every three packs, have a silver-foil background instead of a white background. A Red Siege logo is printed on the card backs.

	MT
Complete Set (275):	200.00
Common Player:	.30
Veteran Stars:	5x-10x
RCs:	2.5x-5x

1995 Score Red Siege Artist's Proof

The 275-card, regular-size set, inserted every 36 packs, parallels the Red Siege set with an Artist's Proof stamp on the card front.

	MT
Complete Set (275):	900.00
Common Player:	5.00
Veteran Stars:	30x-50x
RCs:	12x-25x

1995 Score Dream Team

These 1995 Score football inserts were included one per

72 packs, making them the most elusive set. Ten of the league's elite players are featured on gold-foiled cards which have the set logo in the upper right corner. A color action photo and a ghosted image appear on the front. The horizontally-designed back, numbered using a "DT" prefix, has a photo on the top half, with a brief player profile underneath.

		MT
Complete Set (10):		150.00
Common Player:		10.00
1	Steve Young	15.00
2	Troy Aikman	15.00
3	Dan Marino	30.00
4	Drew Bledsoe	15.00
5	Emmitt Smith	30.00
6	Barry Sanders	15.00
7	Jerry Rice	15.00
8	Marshall Faulk	10.00
9	Deion Sanders	10.00
10	John Elway	10.00

1995 Score Offense Inc.

These 1995 Score football insert cards could be found one per 16 packs. The cards feature 30 of the NFL's top offensive players. The card front has a large and small photo of the player, with a foiled set logo shield in the lower right corner. The card back, numbered using an "OF" prefix, reuses the shield, plus a mug shot, a season recap and key statistics from the 1994 season.

		MT
Complete Set (30):		90.00
Common Player:		2.00
1	Steve Young	6.00
2	Emmitt Smith	12.00
3	Dan Marino	12.00
4	Barry Sanders	7.00
5	Jeff Blake	2.00
6	Jerry Rice	6.00
7	Troy Aikman	6.00
8	Brett Favre	12.00
9	Marshall Faulk	2.00
10	Drew Bledsoe	6.00
11	Natrone Means	2.00
12	John Elway	4.00
13	Chris Warren	2.00
14	Michael Irvin	4.00
15	Mario Bates	2.00
16	Warren Moon	2.00
17	Jerome Bettis	4.00
18	Herman Moore	2.00
19	Barry Foster	2.00
20	Jeff George	2.00
21	Cris Carter	2.00
22	Sterling Sharpe	2.00
23	Jim Kelly	2.00
24	Heath Shuler	2.00
25	Marcus Allen	2.00
26	Dave Brown	2.00
27	Rick Mirer	2.00
28	Rodney Hampton	2.00
29	Errict Rhett	2.00
30	Ben Coates	2.00

Values quoted in this guide reflect the retail price of a card — the price a collector can expect to pay when buying a card from a dealer. The wholesale price — that which a collector can expect to receive when selling cards — will be significantly lower, depending on desirability and condition.

1995 Score Pass Time

These horizontally-formatted insert cards were included one per 18 1995 Score football jumbo packs. Each card front uses gold foil as a background and for the player's name and insert set logo. A larger head-and-shoulders shot and a smaller action photo are the main features. The player's position appears along the left side of the card, with his team logo included within the letters. The card back, numbered using a "PT" prefix, also has two photos, the set logo and a brief career summary.

		MT
Complete Set (18):		160.00
Common Player:		5.00
1	Steve Young	16.00
2	Dan Marino	30.00
3	Drew Bledsoe	16.00
4	Troy Aikman	16.00
5	Glenn Foley	5.00
6	John Elway	12.00
7	Brett Favre	30.00
8	Heath Shuler	5.00
9	Warren Moon	5.00
10	Rick Mirer	5.00
11	Stan Humphries	5.00
12	Jeff Hostetler	5.00
13	Jim Kelly	5.00
14	Randall Cunningham	5.00
15	Jeff Blake	5.00
16	Trent Dilfer	10.00
17	Jeff George	5.00
18	Dave Brown	5.00

1995 Score Reflextions

These horizontally-designed insert cards feature two players per card; each is his team's featured player at his position. Only one player's name is listed on the front; his photo is on the left; a photo of his idol is on the right, in a square next to "Reflextions," which is written along the right side. The card back, numbered using an "RF" prefix, has two photos of the players, plus a paragraph which indicates who the second player is. The set logo appears at the top, with the player's team name in a branching extension of the letter X. Cards were randomly included one per 36 hobby packs.

		MT
Complete Set (8):		130.00
Common Player:		5.00
1	Drew Bledsoe, Dan Marino	40.00
2	Charlie Garner, Barry Sanders	20.00
3	Rick Mirer, Warren Moon	5.00

4	Heath Shuler, Steve Young	15.00
5	Marshall Faulk, Emmitt Smith	40.00
6	Derrick Alexander, Jerry Rice	15.00
7	Barry Foster, Bam Morris	5.00
8	Natrone Means, Chris Warren	8.00

1995 Score Pin-Cards

The 40-card, regular-size set features a player from each team and three cards each for the expansion teams (Carolina, Jacksonville) and the new St. Louis Rams. Card No. 40 is a Super Bowl XXX card. Arizona, Atlanta, Carolina, Chicago, Cleveland, Houston, Indianapolis, Jacksonville, Kansas City and Tampa Bay are represented with a team-helmet card with a pin.

		MT
Complete Set (40):		30.00
Common Helmet Card:		.50
Common Player:		.75
1	Jacksonville Jaguars - History	
2	Jacksonville Jaguars - Stadium	.75
3	Jacksonville Jaguars - Logo Lore	
4	Carolina Panthers - History	.75
5	Carolina Panthers - Stadium	.75
6	Carolina Panthers - Logo Lore	.75
7	St. Louis Rams - History	.75
8	St. Louis Rams - Stadium	.75
9	St. Louis Rams - Logo Lore	.75
10	Drew Bledsoe	2.50
11	Dave Brown	.75
12	Randall Cunningham	.75
13	John Elway	1.25
14	Jim Everett	.75
15	Boomer Esiason	.75
16	Brett Favre	5.00
17	Jeff Hostetler	.75
18	Jim Kelly	1.00
19	David Klingler	.75
20	Dan Marino	5.00
21	Chris Miller	.75
22	Rick Mirer	1.00
23	Warren Moon	1.00
24	Neil O'Donnell	1.00
25	Jerry Rice	2.50
26	Barry Sanders	2.50
27	Junior Seau	1.00
28	Heath Shuler	1.50
29	Emmitt Smith	5.00
30	Arizona Cardinals	.50
31	Atlanta Falcons	.50
32	Carolina Panthers	.75
33	Chicago Bears	.75
34	Cleveland Browns	.75
35	Houston Oilers	.50
36	Indianapolis Colts	.50
37	Jacksonville Jaguars	.75
38	Kansas City Chiefs	.50
39	Tampa Bay Buccaneers	.50
40	Super Bowl XXX Logo	.50

1995 Score Young Stars

These cards were available at the 1995 NFL Experience Super Bowl Card Show. Pinnacle exchanged the cards for three or five Pinnacle wrappers. The four cards have Gold Zone (limited to 2,000) and Platinum versions (limited to 1,000). The cards are numbered with the "YSG" prefix.

		MT
Complete Set (4):		30.00
Common Player:		5.00
Platinum Cards:		2x
1	Marshall Faulk	8.00
2	Jeff Blake	8.00
3	Drew Bledsoe	12.00
4	Natrone Means	5.00

1995 Summit

Score's 1995 super-premium effort, Summitt, has 200 cards printed on 24-point stock, making them thicker than normal cards. Each card front has an action photo cutout against a white background. The player's name is stamped in gold foil in a banner at the bottom, alongside his team helmet, also stamped in gold. The horizontally-designed card back has a photo of the player on the left side, with a chart of his 1994 statistics on the right. A parallel set, Ground Zero, was also produced; all cards are reprinted on a prismatic foil. Three insert sets - Rookie Summit, Team Summit and Backfield Stars - were also produced.

		MT
Complete Set (200):		30.00
Common Player:		.10
Minor Stars:		.20
Wax Box:		30.00
1	Neil O'Donnell	.20
2	Jim Everett	.10
3	Craig Heyward	.10
4	Jeff Blake	.50
5	Alvin Harper	.20
6	Heath Shuler	1.00
7	Rodney Hampton	.20
8	Dave Krieg	.10
9	Mark Brunell	1.50
10	Rob Moore	.10
11	Daryl Johnston	.10
12	Marcus Allen	.20
13	Terance Mathis	.10
14	Frank Reich	.10
15	Gus Frerotte	.50
16	John Elway	.50
17	Amp Lee	.10
18	Chris Miller	.10
19	Leroy Hoard	.10
20	Stan Humphries	.20
21	Charlie Garner	.10
22	Jim Kelly	.30
23	Gary Brown	.10
24	Bam Morris	.10
25	Edgar Bennett	.10
26	Erik Kramer	.10
27	Dan Marino	3.00
28	Michael Haynes	.10
29	Lake Dawson	.25
30	Ben Coates	.10
31	Michael Jackson	.10
32	Brett Favre	3.00
33	Calvin Williams	.10
34	Steve Young	1.50
35	Troy Aikman	1.50
36	Greg Hill	.25
37	Leonard Russell	.10
38	Jeff George	.20
39	Herschel Walker	.20
40	Eric Green	.10
41	Haywood Jeffires	.10
42	Terry Kirby	.10
43	Darnay Scott	.50
44	Tim Brown	.20
45	Brian Mitchell	.10
46	Desmond Howard	.10
47	Warren Moon	.20
48	Andre Reed	.10
49	Ricky Proehl	.10
50	Marshall Faulk	.75
51	Lewis Tillman	.10
52	Don Beebe	.10
53	Jerome Bettis	.50
54	Brett Perriman	.20

55	Mario Bates	.30
56	Ronnie Harmon	.10
57	Isaac Bruce	1.00
58	Jackie Harris	.10
59	Dexter Carter	.10
60	Charles Johnson	.25
61	Herman Moore	.40
62	Craig Erickson	.10
63	Kenneth Davis	.10
64	Emmitt Smith	3.00
65	Brent Jones	.10
66	Ricky Watters	.20
67	Henry Ellard	.10
68	Vinny Testaverde	.10
69	Mark Pike	.10
70	Curtis Conway	.30
71	Michael Irvin	.40
72	Jay Novacek	.10
73	Howard Cross	.10
74	Drew Bledsoe	1.50
75	Steve Beuerlein	.10
76	Andre Rison	.20
77	Morten Andersen	.10
78	Trent Dilfer	.40
79	Cris Carter	.20
80	Natrone Means	.75
81	Bernie Parmalee	.30
82	Randall Cunningham	.10
83	Eric Metcalf	.10
84	Rick Mirer	.50
85	Mark Ingram	.10
86	David Klingler	.10
87	Kevin Williams	.10
88	Erric Pegram	.10
89	Keith Byars	.10
90	Sean Dawkins	.20
91	Chris Warren	.25
92	William Floyd	.40
93	Jeff Hostetler	.20
94	Carl Pickens	.20
95	Flipper Anderson	.10
96	Johnny Mitchell	.10
97	Larry Centers	.10
98	Shannon Sharpe	.10
99	Errict Rhett	.30
100	Fred Barnett	.10
101	Harold Green	.10
102	Scott Mitchell	.20
103	Jerry Rice	1.50
104	Shawn Jefferson	.10
105	Glyn Milburn	.10
106	Garrison Hearst	.20
107	John Taylor	.10
108	Keith Cash	.10
109	Robert Brooks	.20
110	Barry Sanders	2.00
111	Ernest Givins	.10
112	Steve Tasker	.10
113	Jeff Graham	.10
114	Chris Chandler	.10
115	Lorenzo Neal	.10
116	Bert Emanuel	.40
117	Mike Sherrard	.10
118	Harvey Williams	.10
119	Reggie Brooks	.10
120	Steve Walsh	.10
121	Leroy Thompson	.10
122	Dave Brown	.10
123	Lorenzo White	.10
124	Steve Bono	.25
125	Irving Fryar	.10
126	Jake Reed	.10
127	Boomer Esiason	.10
128	Rocket Ismail	.10
129	Vincent Brisby	.10
130	Robert Smith	.20
131	Anthony Miller	.10
132	Roosevelt Potts	.10
133	Dave Meggett	.10
134	Junior Seau	.20
135	Neil Smith	.10
136	Charles Haley	.10
137	Rod Woodson	.10
138	Deion Sanders	.75
139	Reggie White	.20
140	John Randle	.10
141	Greg Lloyd	.10
142	Cortez Kennedy	.10
143	Bruce Smith	.10
144	J.J. Stokes	1.50
145	Kyle Brady	.20
146	Frank Sanders	1.00
147	Michael Westbrook	1.50
148	Rob Johnson	4.00
149	Tyrone Poole	.20
150	Lovell Pinkney	.20
151	Tyrone Wheatley	1.00
152	Steve McNair	5.00
153	Napoleon Kaufman	4.00
154	Tamarick Vanover	1.00
155	Todd Collins	.20
156	Kevin Carter	.20
157	Rodney Thomas	.30
158	Stoney Case	.20
159	Kordell Stewart	6.00
160	Tony Boselli	.20
161	Sherman Williams	.20
162	Christian Fauria	.20
163	Ray Zellars	.20
164	Ki-Jana Carter	1.00
165	Terrell Fletcher	.20
166	Curtis Martin	5.00
167	Eric Zeier	.30
168	Joey Galloway	3.00
169	Warren Sapp	.30
170	Kerry Collins	2.00
171	Mark Bruener	.30

172	Chris Sanders	1.25
173	Rashaan Salaam	.50
174	Jerry Rice	.50
175	Marshall Faulk	.75
176	Drew Bledsoe	.75
177	Emmitt Smith	1.25
178	Tim Brown	.20
179	Steve Young	.50
180	Barry Sanders	1.00
181	Michael Irvin	.25
182	Dan Marino	1.25
183	Jeff George	.20
184	Chris Warren	.20
185	Herman Moore	.20
186	Andre Rison	.20
187	Bam Morris	.20
188	Troy Aikman	.50
189	Jim Kelly	.20
190	John Elway	.25
191	Cris Carter	.20
192	Shannon Sharpe	.10
193	Brett Favre	.50
194	Drew Bledsoe	.40
195	John Elway	.20
196	Dan Marino	.50
197	Brett Favre	.30
198	Troy Aikman	.30
199	Steve Young	.30
200	Randall Cunningham, Rick Mirer	.20

1995 Summit Ground Zero

Ground Zero was a 200-card parallel set to the 1995 Score Summit set, and was inserted one per seven packs. Card fronts featured a prismatic silver foil, while card backs contained the words "Ground Zero."

		MT
Complete Set (200):		450.00
Ground Zero Cards:		7x-15x

1995 Summit Backfield Stars

The 1995 Score Summit inserts were included one per 37 packs. They feature 20 of the best running backs on a holographic silver foil printing that gives each runner a dimensional-background effect. "Backfield Stars" is written along the left side of the card; the player's name is in the lower right corner. The numbered card back is horizontal and has a player photo on the left, with a brief career summary on the right. The player's name is at the top between two stars.

		MT
Complete Set (20):		110.00
Common Player:		5.00
1	Emmitt Smith	30.00
2	Marshall Faulk	10.00
3	Barry Sanders	20.00
4	Ricky Watters	5.00
5	Rodney Hampton	5.00
6	Chris Warren	5.00
7	Garrison Hearst	5.00
8	Tyrone Wheatley	5.00
9	Rashaan Salaam	5.00
10	Natrone Means	5.00
11	Bam Morris	5.00
12	Jerome Bettis	5.00
13	Errict Rhett	5.00
14	William Floyd	5.00
15	Edgar Bennett	5.00
16	Marcus Allen	5.00
17	Mario Bates	5.00
18	Lorenzo White	5.00
19	Gary Brown	5.00
20	Craig Heyward	5.00

A player's name in *italic* type indicates a rookie card.

1995 Summit Rookie Summit

These 1995 Score Summit inserts could be found one per 23 packs. The cards feature exclusive photography taken at Pinnacle's Rookie Photo Shoot before the season began. Each rookie is shown, in his team's NFL uniform, airborne against a goalpost background. Gold Rush foil is used on both sides. The numbered card back has a posed shot of the player in his NFL uniform, with a line describing one of his more recent accomplishments. The "Rookie Summit" logo appears on both sides.

		MT
Complete Set (18):		90.00
Common Player:		3.00
1	Kevin Carter	3.00
2	Sherman Williams	3.00
3	Kordell Stewart	16.00
4	Christian Fauria	3.00
5	J.J. Stokes	6.00
6	Joey Galloway	8.00
7	Michael Westbrook	6.00
8	James Stewart	5.00
9	Stoney Case	3.00
10	Kyle Brady	3.00
11	Terrell Fletcher	3.00
12	Todd Collins	3.00
13	Jimmy Oliver	3.00
14	Napoleon Kaufman	12.00
15	John Walsh	3.00
16	Kerry Collins	7.00
17	Ki-Jana Carter	5.00
18	Terrell Davis	30.00

1995 Summit Team Summit

These cards feature 12 of the league's top players, utilizing spectroetching on a holographic foil card. Cards were randomly included in every 91 packs of 1995 Score Summit football and are numbered.

		MT
Complete Set (12):		160.00
Common Player:		4.00
Minor Stars:		8.00
Inserted 1:91		
1	Dan Marino	20.00
2	Emmitt Smith	20.00
3	Drew Bledsoe	15.00
4	Troy Aikman	15.00
5	Bam Morris	4.00
6	Steve Young	12.00
7	Randall Cunningham	8.00
8	Natrone Means	8.00
9	Barry Sanders	30.00
10	Brett Favre	30.00
11	Errict Rhett	4.00
12	Jerry Rice	15.00

1996 Score

Score's regular 1996 football issue has 275 cards and two

parallel sets - Field Force and Artist's Proofs. Each regular card has a color action photo on the front, trimmed to look like a baseball diamond. The player's name and position are in white letters at the bottom in a black bar. The Score logo is in an upper corner. The horizontal back has a mug shot on one side, with the team name under it and a card number in the upper corner. Additional information on the back includes biographical and statistical data and a recap of the player's accomplishments. Field Force cards, found in every sixth pack, are printed on a matte finish. Artist's Proof cards, seeded one per 36 packs, have a gold stamp on a regular issue card. Insert sets include Dream Team, Footsteps, In the Zone, Numbers Game and Settle the Score.

		MT
Complete Set (275):		15.00
Common Player:		.05
Minor Stars:		.10
Wax Box:		20.00
1	Emmitt Smith	1.50
2	Flipper Anderson	.05
3	Kordell Stewart	1.00
4	Bruce Smith	.05
5	Marshall Faulk	.75
6	William Floyd	.05
7	Darren Woodson	.05
8	Lake Dawson	.05
9	Terry Allen	.05
10	Ki-Jana Carter	.25
11	Tony Boselli	.05
12	Christian Fauria	.05
13	Jeff George	.05
14	Dan Marino	1.50
15	Rodney Thomas	.30
16	Anthony Miller	.05
17	Chris Sanders	.30
18	Natrone Means	.10
19	Curtis Conway	.05
20	Ben Coates	.05
21	Alvin Harper	.05
22	Frank Sanders	.05
23	Boomer Esiason	.05
24	Lovell Pinkney	.05
25	Troy Aikman	.75
26	Quinn Early	.05
27	Adrian Murrell	.05
28	Chris Spielman	.05
29	Tyrone Wheatley	.30
30	Tim Brown	.05
31	Erik Kramer	.05
32	Warren Moon	.05
33	Jimmy Oliver	.05
34	Herman Moore	.20
35	Quentin Coryatt	.05
36	Heath Shuler	.25
37	Jim Kelly	.05
38	Chris Miller	.05
39	Harvey Williams	.05
40	Vinny Testaverde	.05
41	Steve McNair	.75
42	Jerry Rice	.75
43	Darick Holmes	.05
44	Kyle Brady	.05
45	Greg Lloyd	.05
46	Kerry Collins	.25
47	Willie McGinest	.05
48	Isaac Bruce	.40
49	Carnell Lake	.05
50	Charles Haley	.05
51	Troy Vincent	.05
52	Randall Cunningham	.05
53	Rashaan Salaam	.50
54	Willie Jackson	.05
55	Chris Warren	.15
56	Michael Irvin	.10
57	Mario Bates	.05
58	Warren Sapp	.05
59	John Elway	.25
60	Shannon Sharpe	.05
61	Bam Morris	.05
62	Robert Brooks	.05
63	Rodney Hampton	.05
64	Ken Norton Jr.	.05
65	Bryce Paup	.05
66	Eric Swann	.05
67	Rodney Peete	.05
68	Larry Centers	.05
69	Lamont Warren	.05
70	Jay Novacek	.05
71	Cris Carter	.05
72	Terrell Fletcher	.05
73	Andre Rison	.05
74	Ricky Watters	.05
75	Napoleon Kaufman	.05
76	Reggie White	.05
77	Yancey Thigpen	.40
78	Terry Kirby	.05
79	Deion Sanders	.50
80	Irving Fryar	.05
81	Marcus Allen	.05
82	Carl Pickens	.05
83	Drew Bledsoe	.75
84	Eric Metcalf	.05
85	Robert Smith	.05

86	Tamarick Vanover	.50
87	Henry Ellard	.05
88	Kevin Greene	.05
89	Mark Brunell	.50
90	Terrell Davis	.75
91	Brian Mitchell	.05
92	Aaron Bailey	.05
93	Rocket Ismail	.05
94	Dave Brown	.05
95	Rod Woodson	.05
96	Sean Gilbert	.05
97	Mark Seay	.05
98	Zack Crockett	.05
99	Scott Mitchell	.05
100	Erric Pegram	.05
101	David Palmer	.05
102	Vincent Brisby	.05
103	Brett Perriman	.05
104	Jim Everett	.05
105	Tony Martin	.05
106	Desmond Howard	.05
107	Stan Humphries	.05
108	Bill Brooks	.05
109	Neil Smith	.05
110	Michael Westbrook	.10
111	Herschel Walker	.05
112	Andre Coleman	.05
113	Derrick Alexander	.05
114	Jeff Blake	.60
115	Sherman Williams	.05
116	James Stewart	.05
117	Hardy Nickerson	.05
118	Elvis Grbac	.05
119	Brett Favre	1.50
120	Mike Sherrard	.05
121	Edgar Bennett	.05
122	Calvin Williams	.05
123	Brian Blades	.05
124	Jeff Graham	.05
125	Gary Brown	.05
126	Bernie Parmalee	.05
127	Kimble Anders	.05
128	Hugh Douglas	.05
129	James Stewart	.05
130	Eric Bjornson	.05
131	Ken Dilger	.05
132	Jerome Bettis	.05
133	Cortez Kennedy	.05
134	Bryan Cox	.05
135	Darnay Scott	.05
136	Bert Emanuel	.05
137	Steve Bono	.05
138	Charles Johnson	.05
139	Glyn Milburn	.05
140	Derrick Alexander	.05
141	Dave Meggett	.05
142	Trent Dilfer	.05
143	Eric Zeier	.05
144	Jim Harbaugh	.05
145	Antonio Freeman	.05
146	Orlanda Thomas	.05
147	Russell Maryland	.05
148	Chad May	.05
149	Craig Heyward	.05
150	Aeneas Williams	.05
151	Kevin Williams	.05
152	Charlie Garner	.05
153	J.J. Stokes	.10
154	Stoney Case	.05
155	Mark Chmura	.20
156	Mark Bruener	.05
157	Derek Loville	.05
158	Justin Armour	.05
159	Brent Jones	.05
160	Aaron Craver	.05
161	Terance Mathis	.05
162	Chris Zorich	.05
163	Glenn Foley	.05
164	Johnny Mitchell	.05
165	Junior Seau	.05
166	Willie Davis	.05
167	Rick Mirer	.05
168	Leroy Hoard	.05
169	Greg Hill	.05
170	Steve Tasker	.05
171	Tony Bennett	.05
172	Jeff Hostetler	.05
173	Dave Krieg	.05
174	Mark Carrier	.05
175	Michael Haynes	.05
176	Chris Chandler	.05
177	Ernie Mills	.05
178	Jake Reed	.05
179	Errict Rhett	.50
180	Garrison Hearst	.10
181	Derrick Thomas	.05
182	Aaron Hayden	.30
183	Jackie Harris	.05
184	Curtis Martin	1.50
185	Neil O'Donnell	.05
186	Derrick Moore	.05
187	Steve Young	.75
188	Pat Swilling	.05
189	Amp Lee	.05
190	Rob Johnson	.05
191	Todd Collins	.05
192	J.J. Birden	.05
193	O.J. McDuffie	.05
194	Shawn Jefferson	.05
195	Sean Dawkins	.05
196	Fred Barnett	.05
197	Roosevelt Potts	.05
198	Rob Moore	.05
199	Qadry Ismail	.05
200	Barry Sanders	1.00
201	Floyd Turner	.05
202	Wayne Chrebet	.05
203	Andre Reed	.05

204	Tyrone Hughes	.05
205	Keenan McCardell	.05
206	Gus Frerotte	.05
207	Daryl Johnston	.05
208	Haywood Jeffires	.05
209	Steve Atwater	.05
210	Michael Jackson	.05
211	Andre Hastings	.05
212	Joey Galloway	.75
213	Robert Green	.05
214	*Keyshawn Johnson*	2.00
215	Tony Brackens	.05
216	Stepfret Williams	.05
217	Mike Alstott	1.00
218	Terry Glenn	1.50
219	*Tim Biakabutuka*	.75
220	Eric Moulds	1.50
221	*Jeff Lewis*	.50
222	Bobby Engram	.50
223	Cedric Jones	.05
224	*Stanley Pritchett*	.05
225	*Kevin Hardy*	.20
226	*Alex Van Dyke*	.30
227	Willie Anderson	.05
228	*Regan Upshaw*	.05
229	Leeland McElroy	.20
230	*Marvin Harrison*	2.00
231	Eddie George	3.00
232	*Lawrence Phillips*	.50
233	Daryl Gardener	.05
234	Alex Molden	.05
235	*Derrick Mayes*	.75
236	John Mobley	.05
237	Isreal Ifeanyi	.05
238	Pete Kendall	.05
239	*Danny Kanell*	.50
240	Jonathan Ogden	.05
241	Reggie Brown	.05
242	Marcus Jones	.05
243	Jon Stark	.05
244	Barry Sanders	.50
245	Brett Favre	.30
246	John Elway	.15
247	Dan Marino	.75
248	Drew Bledsoe	.30
249	Michael Irvin	.05
250	Troy Aikman	.30
251	Emmitt Smith	.75
252	Steve Young	.30
253	Jerry Rice	.30
254	Jeff Blake	.25
255	Tim Brown	.05
256	Bam Morris	.05
257	Rodney Hampton	.05
258	Scott Mitchell	.05
259	Garrison Hearst	.05
260	Larry Centers	.05
261	Neil O'Donnell	.05
262	Orlanda Thomas	.05
263	Hugh Douglas	.05
264	Bill Brooks	.05
265	Harvey Williams	.05
266	Charles Haley	.05
267	Greg Lloyd	.05
268	Daryl Johnston	.05
269	Dan Marino	.30
270	Jeff Blake	.10
271	John Elway	.05
272	Emmitt Smith	.30
273	Brett Favre	.30
274	Jerry Rice	.30
275	Dan Marino, Jeff Blake, John Elway, Emmitt Smith, Brett Favre, Jerry Rice	.50

1996 Score Field Force

The 275-card, standard-size parallel set, features a matte finish instead of the gloss card-front finish of the base cards. The set was inserted every six packs; 1:3 for jumbo.

	MT
Complete Set (275):	300.00
Common Player:	.40
Veteran Stars:	5x-10x
RCs:	3x-6x

1996 Score Artist's Proofs

Darnay Scott WR

The 275-card, regular-sized parallel set, inserted every 36 packs, features an Artist's Proof logo on the card front. The set is inserted every 18 jumbo packs.

	MT
Complete Set (275):	1000.
Common Player:	4.00
Semistars:	6.00
Veteran Stars:	30x-50x
RCs:	12x-25x

1996 Score Dream Team

DREAM TEAM of Troy Aikman!

These 1996 Score football inserts feature 10 players who an NFL coach would love to build a team around. The cards were random inserts, one per 72 packs; they are the most exclusive card in 1996 Score.

		MT
Complete Set (10):		120.00
Common Player:		5.00
1	Troy Aikman	15.00
2	Michael Irvin	5.00
3	Emmitt Smith	30.00
4	John Elway	5.00
5	Barry Sanders	15.00
6	Brett Favre	30.00
7	Dan Marino	30.00
8	Drew Bledsoe	15.00
9	Jerry Rice	15.00
10	Steve Young	10.00

1996 Score Footsteps

ISAAC BRUCE

These 1996 Score football inserts were seeded one per 35 hobby packs. A top rookie from the 1995 season is paired with a top veteran he most wants to emulate. The 15 dual-player cards are printed with rainbow holographic highlights.

		MT
Complete Set (15):		100.00
Common Player:		2.00
1	Darick Holmes, Errict Rhett	4.00
2	Rashaan Salaam, Natrone Means	6.00
3	Ki-Jana Carter, Barry Sanders	15.00
4	Terrell Davis, Marshall Faulk	12.00
5	Rodney Thomas, Chris Warren	2.00
6	Curtis Martin, Emmitt Smith	25.00
7	Kerry Collins, Troy Aikman	15.00
8	Eric Zeier, Drew Bledsoe	10.00
9	Steve McNair, Brett Favre	15.00
10	Steve Young, Kordell Stewart	15.00
11	J.J. Stokes, Jerry Rice	12.00
12	Joey Galloway, Michael Irvin	5.00
13	Michael Westbrook, Cris Carter	5.00
14	Tamarick Vanover, Isaac Bruce	4.00
15	Orlanda Thomas, Deion Sanders	4.00

1996 Score Numbers Game

ELWAY QB
DENVER BRONCOS

These 25 cards were randomly inserted into every 17 packs of 1996 Score football. The card front has a color action photo on it, with a smaller photo on the right in four pieces. The player's name and position are stamped in gold under this photo. Gold foil stamping is also used for the set icon in the lower left corner. The player's team name is in black letters in the foil band at the bottom. The card back has a color photo of the player, with the rest of the full-bleed photo in black-and-white. The card number is in the upper left corner in a white rectangle; the player's name, position and team name run horizontally down the left side. Four rectangles on the right side each have a tidbit of statistical information.

		MT
Complete Set (25):		90.00
Common Player:		2.00
1	Barry Sanders	7.00
2	Drew Bledsoe	6.00
3	Brett Favre	12.00
4	John Elway	4.00
5	Dan Marino	12.00
6	Michael Irvin	2.00
7	Troy Aikman	6.00
8	Emmitt Smith	12.00
9	Steve Young	6.00
10	Jerry Rice	6.00
11	Chris Sanders	2.00
12	Herman Moore	3.00
13	Frank Sanders	2.00
14	Kordell Stewart	6.00
15	Jeff Blake	5.00
16	Robert Brooks	2.00
17	Marshall Faulk	4.00
18	Carl Pickens	2.00
19	Greg Lloyd	2.00
20	Curtis Conway	2.00
21	Chris Warren	2.00
22	Natrone Means	2.00
23	Deion Sanders	4.00
24	Neil O'Donnell	2.00
25	Ricky Watters	2.00

A card number in parentheses ( ) indicates the set is unnumbered.

1996 Score In the Zone

IN THE ZONE
Jerry Rice

This set features 20 offensive players who excel in getting into the end zone. Cards were exclusive to 1996 Score retail packs, every 33rd pack. The front has a color action photo, with red foil highlights for the set name along the right side and for the stadium background. The player's name is in the lower left corner; the Score logo is in the upper left corner. The numbered back has a color photo, with the player's name, a player profile and a set icon below the card number.

		MT
Complete Set (20):		140.00
Common Player:		2.00
1	Brett Favre	30.00
2	Warren Moon	2.00
3	Erik Kramer	2.00
4	Scott Mitchell	2.00
5	Jeff Blake	8.00
6	Steve Bono	2.00
7	Dan Marino	30.00
8	Troy Aikman	15.00
9	Emmitt Smith	30.00
10	Curtis Martin	20.00
11	Errict Rhett	10.00
12	Terrell Davis	18.00
13	Derek Loville	2.00
14	Rodney Hampton	2.00
15	Cris Carter	2.00
16	Herman Moore	6.00
17	Jerry Rice	15.00
18	Ben Coates	2.00
19	Michael Irvin	2.00
20	Carl Pickens	2.00

1996 Score Settle the Score

WATTERS vs. SMITH

These cards were random inserts in 1996 Score football, one every 36 jumbo packs. Each card features two players on it.

		MT
Complete Set (30):		500.00
Common Player:		5.00
1	Frank Sanders, Charlie Garner	5.00
2	Drew Bledsoe, Neil O'Donnell	12.00
3	Jerry Rice, Craig Heyward	18.00
4	Emmitt Smith, Rod Woodson	35.00
5	Darick Holmes, Dan Marino	35.00
6	Kerry Collins, Steve Young	18.00
7	Rashaan Salaam, Brett Favre	35.00
8	Curtis Conway, Barry Sanders	25.00
9	Troy Aikman, Dan Marino	40.00
10	Dan Marino, Neil O'Donnell	35.00

11	Eric Zeier, Steve McNair	8.00
12	Jeff Blake, Kordell Stewart	18.00
13	Troy Aikman, Heath Shuler	18.00
14	Michael Irvin, Jerry Rice	18.00
15	Emmitt Smith, Ricky Watters	35.00
16	John Elway, Steve Bono	8.00
17	John Elway, Rick Mirer	8.00
18	John Elway, Tim Brown	8.00
19	Barry Sanders, Brett Favre	45.00
20	Barry Sanders, Warren Moon	25.00
21	Brett Favre, Trent Dilfer	20.00
22	Rodney Thomas, James Stewart	5.00
23	Jim Harbaugh, Drew Bledsoe	14.00
24	Marcus Allen, Harvey Williams	5.00
25	Tamarick Vanover, Joey Galloway	8.00
26	Dan Marino, Drew Bledsoe	40.00
27	Mario Bates, Jerry Rice	18.00
28	Tyrone Wheatley, Michael Westbrook	8.00
29	Napoleon Kaufman, Junior Seau	5.00
30	J.J. Stokes, Isaac Bruce	8.00

1996 Summit

DREW BLEDSOE

The 200-card, regular-sized set came in seven-card packs and included three subsets: Rookies (35), Quarterhorses (15) and Checklists (4). The card fronts feature the player's name and team helmet in gold foil. The card backs include a headshot of the player with three statistical categories and the card number in the upper left corner. A parallel insert set, Ground Zero, is inserted every six packs and features prismatic foil renditions of the base set. Artist's Proofs, another 200-card parallel set, adds special holographic foil stamps to the base set and are inserted every 35 packs. Other insert sets in Summit are Turf Team, Inspirations, 3rd & Long and its parallel insert set - 3rd & Long Mirage.

		MT
Complete Set (200):		35.00
Common Player:		.10
Minor Stars:		.20
Wax Box:		35.00
1	Troy Aikman	1.25
2	Marshall Faulk	.50
3	Bruce Smith	.10
4	Jerome Bettis	.20
5	Bryan Cox	.10
6	Robert Brooks	.20
7	Dan Marino	2.50
8	Irving Fryar	.10
9	Jerry Rice	1.25
10	Ki-Jana Carter	.20
11	Herman Moore	.30
12	Derrick Thomas	.10
13	Curtis Martin	1.75
14	Jeff Hostetler	.10
15	Errict Rhett	.30
16	Emmitt Smith	2.50
17	Aaron Craver	.10
18	Kyle Brady	.10
19	Tony Martin	.10
20	Vinny Testaverde	.10
21	Charles Haley	.10
22	Rodney Thomas	.10
23	Jim Everett	.10
24	Brian Blades	.10
25	Frank Sanders	.10
26	Bryce Paup	.10
27	Anthony Miller	.10
28	Ken Dilger	.10
29	Orlando Thomas	.10
30	Rodney Hampton	.10
31	Ken Norton Jr.	.10
32	Darren Woodson	.10
33	Antonio Freeman	.10
34	Steve Bono	.10
35	Ben Coates	.10
36	Jeff George	.10
37	Curtis Conway	.10
38	Steve Atwater	.10
39	Fred Barnett	.10
40	Joey Galloway	1.25
41	Jim Kelly	.20
42	Michael Irvin	.20
43	Steve Tasker	.10
44	Warren Moon	.10
45	Hugh Douglas	.10
46	Steve Walsh	.10
47	Kerry Collins	.30
48	Barry Sanders	1.75
49	Steve Young	.75
50	Jim Harbaugh	.10
51	Tyrone Wheatley	.10
52	Boomer Esiason	.10
53	Deion Sanders	.75
54	Steve McNair	1.00
55	Willie McGinest	.10
56	Adrian Murrell	.10
57	Thurman Thomas	.20
58	John Elway	.75
59	William Floyd	.10
60	Eric Zeier	.10
61	Dave Krieg	.10
62	Eric Bjornson	.10
63	Brett Favre	2.50
64	Derrick Alexander	.10
65	Charlie Garner	.10
66	Stan Humphries	.10
67	Bert Emanuel	.10
68	Scott Mitchell	.10
69	Quentin Coryatt	.10
70	Eric Green	.10
71	Jeff Graham	.10
72	Ernie Mills	.10
73	Trent Dilfer	.20
74	Sherman Williams	.10
75	Tamarick Vanover	.10
76	Drew Bledsoe	1.25
77	Jay Novacek	.10
78	Edgar Bennett	.10
79	Tim Brown	.10
80	Greg Lloyd	.10
81	Darick Holmes	.10
82	Carl Pickens	.10
83	Flipper Anderson	.10
84	Bernie Kosar	.10
85	Dave Brown	.10
86	Calvin Williams	.10
87	Michael Westbrook	.20
88	Kevin Williams	.10
89	Chris Sanders	.10
90	Robert Smith	.10
91	Cris Carter	.20
92	Gus Frerotte	.10
93	Larry Centers	.10
94	Eric Metcalf	.10
95	Isaac Bruce	.50
96	Kordell Stewart	1.50
97	Ricky Watters	.20
98	Terrell Fletcher	.10
99	Bernie Parmalee	.10
100	Harvey Williams	.10
101	Hardy Nickerson	.10
102	Jeff Blake	.50
103	Terry Allen	.10
104	Yancey Thigpen	.30
105	Greg Hill	.10
106	Chris Warren	.10
107	Terrell Davis	1.50
108	Mark Brunell	1.00
109	Alvin Harper	.10
110	Marcus Allen	.20
111	Garrison Hearst	.10
112	Derek Loville	.10
113	Craig Heyward	.10
114	Kimble Anders	.10
115	O.J. McDuffie	.10
116	Junior Seau	.20
117	Terry Kirby	.10
118	Erric Pegram	.10
119	Rick Mirer	.10
120	Erik Kramer	.10
121	Brian Perriman	.10
122	Shawn Jefferson	.10
123	J.J. Stokes	.20
124	Kevin Greene	.10
125	Daryl Johnston	.10
126	Mark Chmura	.10
127	James Stewart	.10
128	Mario Bates	.10
129	Rodney Peete	.10
130	Quinn Early	.10
131	Shannon Sharpe	.10
132	Neil Smith	.10
133	Herschel Walker	.10
134	Aaron Bailey	.10
135	Rashaan Salaam	.40
136	Kevin Smith	.10
137	Sean Dawkins	.10
138	Jake Reed	.10
139	Neil O'Donnell	.20
140	Reggie White	.20
141	Vincent Brisby	.10
142	Napoleon Kaufman	.10
143	Brent Jones	.10

144	Mark Seay	.10
145	Heath Shuler	.10
146	Wayne Chrebet	.10
147	Leeland McElroy	.30
148	Tim Biakabutuka	1.00
149	John Mobley	.10
150	Tony Brackens	.20
151	Danny Kanell	.75
152	Eddie Kennison	.40
153	Jonathan Ogden	.20
154	Bobby Engram	.30
155	Chris Darkins	.10
156	Daryl Gardener	.10
157	Keyshawn Johnson	3.00
158	Mike Alstott	1.75
159	Simeon Rice	.20
160	Eric Moulds	2.50
161	Stepfret Williams	.10
162	Eddie George	4.00
163	Duane Clemons	.10
164	Amani Toomer	.20
165	Rickey Dudley	.30
166	Bobby Hoying	1.00
167	Lawrence Phillips	.50
168	Willie Anderson	.10
169	Derrick Mayes	1.00
170	Kevin Hardy	.20
171	Terry Glenn	1.75
172	Stephen Davis	4.00
173	Walt Harris	.20
174	Marvin Harrison	3.00
175	Karim Abdul-Jabbar	.75
176	Alex Molden	.10
177	Regan Upshaw	.10
178	Jerald Moore	.10
179	Alex Van Dyke	.20
180	Jeff Lewis	.75
181	Cedric Jones	.10
182	Jim Kelly	.10
183	Troy Aikman	.50
184	Jim Harbaugh	.10
185	Neil O'Donnell	.10
186	Steve Young	.30
187	Kerry Collins	.30
188	Scott Mitchell	.10
189	Drew Bledsoe	.50
190	Kordell Stewart	.75
191	Erik Kramer	.10
192	Brett Favre	1.00
193	Warren Moon	.10
194	Jeff Blake	.25
195	Mark Brunell	.50
196	John Elway	.25
197	Checklist (Emmitt Smith)	.30
198	Checklist (Dan Marino)	.30
199	Checklist (Brett Favre)	.30
200	Checklist (Jim Harbaugh)	.10

1996 Summit Ground Zero

Ground Zero is a 200-card prismatic foil rendition of the regular-issue set. These parallel cards are inserted every six packs.

	MT
Complete Set (200):	400.00
Ground Zero Cards:	6x-12x

1996 Summit Artist's Proofs

Artist's Proofs add a holographic Artist's Proof stamp to all 200 cards in the regular-issue set. These parallel cards are inserted at a rate of one per 35 packs.

	MT
Complete Set (200):	1400.
Artist's Proof Cards:	20x-40x

A card number in parentheses ( ) indicates the set is unnumbered.

1996 Summit Premium Stock

Premium Stock was available in hobby stores and was an upgraded version of Summit Football. In 13-card packs of Premium Stock, the regular-issue set was reprinted in a rainbow holographic foil version. In addition, Turf Team inserts also received special prismatic foil treatment. Other inserts were the same as the regular-issue product.

	MT
Complete Set (200):	50.00
Premium Stock Cards:	1.5x

1996 Summit Inspirations

The 18-card, regular-sized set was inserted in every 17 packs of Summit football. The cards feature foil printing and the production run was limited to 8,000.

		MT
Complete Set (18):		140.00
Common Player:		3.00
1	Jim Harbaugh	3.00
2	Alex Van Dyke	5.00
3	Mike Alstott	5.00
4	Jonathan Ogden	3.00
5	Brett Favre	30.00
6	Tony Brackens	3.00
7	Drew Bledsoe	15.00
8	Danny Kanell	3.00
9	Eric Moulds	5.00
10	John Elway	12.00
11	Eddie George	25.00
12	Karim Abdul-Jabbar	18.00
13	Tim Biakabutuka	10.00
14	Jeff Lewis	3.00
15	Terry Glenn	10.00
16	Jeff Blake	7.00
17	Kevin Hardy	3.00
18	Bobby Engram	7.00

1996 Summit Turf Team

The 16-card, regular-sized set, inserted in hobby packs of Summit football, features spot-embossed technology and is limited to a production run of 4,000.

		MT
Complete Set (16):		350.00
Common Player:		6.00
1	Emmitt Smith	50.00
2	Brett Favre	50.00
3	Curtis Martin	40.00
4	Steve Young	20.00
5	Kerry Collins	12.00
6	Barry Sanders	30.00
7	Dan Marino	50.00
8	Isaac Bruce	12.00
9	Troy Aikman	25.00
10	Marshall Faulk	18.00
11	Joey Galloway	20.00
12	Jeff Blake	6.00
13	Drew Bledsoe	25.00
14	John Elway	20.00
15	Jerry Rice	25.00
16	Michael Irvin	6.00

1996 Summit Third and Long

The 18-card, regular-sized set was inserted in hobby, retail and magazine packs and was limited to a production run of 2,000. The cards are printed on rainbow holographic foil with sequential numbering. An 18-card parallel insert set, Mirage, features a floating football hologram behind the player's image. Mirage is limited to 600 sets.

		MT
Complete Set (18):		500.00
Common Player:		7.50
Minor Stars:		15.00
Production 2,000 Sets		
Mirage Prize Cards:		2x
Production 600 Sets		
1	Michael Irvin	15.00
2	Dan Marino	45.00
3	Keyshawn Johnson	20.00
4	Chris Warren	7.50
5	Rashaan Salaam	7.50
6	Brett Favre	60.00
7	Terry Glenn	15.00
8	Steve Young	15.00
9	Kerry Collins	15.00
10	Emmitt Smith	45.00
11	Marvin Harrison	15.00
12	Jerry Rice	30.00
13	John Elway	45.00
14	Drew Bledsoe	30.00
15	Eddie Kennison	7.50
16	Troy Aikman	30.00
17	Barry Sanders	60.00
18	Terrell Davis	60.00

1996 Summit Hit The Hole

The 16-card, regular-sized set, limited to a production run of 1,000, was randomly inserted in five-card retail packs of 1996 Pinnacle Summit. The set features 16 top offensive players on all-foil printing.

		MT
Complete Set (16):		400.00
Common Player:		10.00
1	Rashaan Salaam	10.00
2	Marshall Faulk	20.00
3	Ricky Watters	10.00
4	Leeland McElroy	10.00
5	Emmitt Smith	70.00
6	Eddie George	50.00
7	Curtis Martin	50.00
8	Lawrence Phillips	25.00
9	Darick Holmes	10.00
10	Barry Sanders	40.00
11	Karim Abdul-Jabbar	35.00
12	Errict Rhett	20.00
13	Terrell Davis	40.00
14	Chris Warren	10.00
15	Rodney Thomas	10.00
16	Tim Biakabutuka	20.00

1997 Score

The 330-card set features a player photo in the center on the front, with the team and the player's position printed at the top. The Score logo is in the upper left of the photo, while goalposts appear on the center of each side of the photo. The player's name is printed at the bottom. The base set is paralleled by a Showcase Series and Artist's Proof version.

		MT
Complete Set (330):		15.00
Common Player:		.05
Minor Stars:		.10
Showcase Series:		4x-8x
Artist's Proofs:		20x-40x
Wax Box:		32.00
1	John Elway	.50
2	Drew Bledsoe	.75
3	Brett Favre	1.75
4	Emmitt Smith	1.50
5	Kerry Collins	.25
6	Jerry Rice	.75
7	Kordell Stewart	.75
8	Barry Sanders	1.25
9	Dan Marino	1.50
10	Steve Young	.50
11	Erik Kramer	.05
12	Warren Moon	.10
13	Chris Calloway	.05
14	Doug Evans	.05
15	Darren Woodson	.05
16	Alonzo Spellman	.05
17	Greg Hill	.05
18	Aaron Craver	.05
19	Jeff Hostetler	.05
20	William Thomas	.05
21	Marco Coleman	.05
22	Wayne Simmons	.05
23	Donnell Woolford	.05
24	Vinny Testaverde	.10
25	Ed McCaffrey	.05
26	Jim Everett	.05
27	Gilbert Brown	.05
28	Jason Dunn	.05
29	Stanley Pritchett	.05
30	Joey Galloway	.15
31	Amani Toomer	.05
32	Chris Penn	.05
33	Aeneas Williams	.05
34	Bobby Taylor	.05
35	Bryan Still	.05
36	Ty Law	.05
37	Shannon Sharpe	.05
38	Marty Carter	.05
39	Sam Mills	.05
40	William Floyd	.05
41	Brad Johnson	.05
42	Sean Dawkins	.05
43	Michael Irvin	.10
44	Jeff George	.10
45	Brent Jones	.05
46	Mark Brunell	.75
47	Rob Moore	.05
48	Hardy Nickerson	.05
49	Chris Chandler	.05
50	Willie Anderson	.05
51	Isaac Bruce	.15
52	Natrone Means	.10
53	Tony Banks	.15
54	Marshall Faulk	.15
55	Michael Westbrook	.05
56	Bruce Smith	.05
57	Jamal Anderson	.15
58	Jackie Harris	.05
59	Sean Gilbert	.05
60	Ki-Jana Carter	.05
61	Eric Moulds	.10
62	James Stewart	.05
63	Jeff Blake	.10
64	O.J. McDuffie	.05
65	Neil Smith	.05
66	Kevin Smith	.05
67	Terry Allen	.05
68	Sean LaChapelle	.05
69	Rashaan Salaam	.10
70	Jeff Graham	.05
71	Mark Carrier	.05
72	Allen Aldridge	.05
73	Keenan McCardell	.05
74	Willie McGinest	.05
75	Napoleon Kaufman	.10
76	Jerris McPhail	.05
77	Eric Swann	.05
78	Kimble Anders	.05
79	Charles Johnson	.05
80	Bryan Cox	.05
81	Johnnie Morton	.05
82	Andre Rison	.05
83	Corey Miller	.05
84	Troy Drayton	.05
85	Jim Harbaugh	.05
86	Wesley Walls	.05
87	Bryce Paup	.05
88	Curtis Martin	1.00
89	Michael Sinclair	.05
90	Chris T. Jones	.05
91	Jake Reed	.05
92	LeRoy Butler	.05
93	Reggie Tongue	.05
94	Bert Emanuel	.05
95	Stan Humphries	.05
96	Neil O'Donnell	.05
97	Troy Vincent	.05
98	Mike Alstott	.15
99	Chad Cota	.05
100	Marvin Harrison	.30
101	Terrell Owens	.30
102	Dave Brown	.05
103	Harvey Williams	.05
104	Desmond Howard	.05
105	Carl Pickens	.05
106	Kent Graham	.05
107	Michael Bates	.05
108	Terrell Davis	1.00
109	Marcus Allen	.10
110	Ray Zellars	.05
111	Chris Warren	.05
112	Phillippi Sparks	.05
113	Craig Erickson	.05
114	Eddie George	1.00
115	Daryl Johnston	.05
116	Ricky Watters	.10
117	Tedy Bruschi	.05
118	Mike Mamula	.05
119	Ken Harvey	.05
120	John Randle	.05
121	Mark Chmura	.05
122	Sam Gash	.05
123	John Kasay	.05
124	Barry Minter	.05
125	Raymont Harris	.05
126	Derrick Thomas	.05
127	Trent Dilfer	.10
128	Carnell Lake	.05
129	Brian Dawkins	.05
130	Tyronne Drakeford	.05
131	Daryl Gardener	.05
132	Fred Strickland	.05
133	Kevin Hardy	.05
134	Winslow Oliver	.05
135	Herman Moore	.15
136	Keith Byars	.05
137	Harold Green	.05
138	Ty Detmer	.05
139	Lamar Thomas	.05
140	Elvis Grbac	.05
141	Edgar Bennett	.05
142	Cornelius Bennett	.05
143	Tony Tolbert	.05
144	James Hasty	.05
145	Ben Coates	.05
146	Errict Rhett	.10
147	Jason Seahorn	.05
148	Michael Jackson	.05
149	John Mobley	.05
150	Walt Harris	.05
151	Terry Kirby	.05
152	Devin Wyman	.05
153	Ray Crockett	.05
154	Quinn Early	.05
155	Rodney Thomas	.05
156	Mark Seay	.05
157	Derrick Alexander	.05
158	Lamar Lathon	.05
159	Anthony Miller	.05
160	Shawn Wooden	.05
161	Antonio Freeman	.15
162	Cortez Kennedy	.05
163	Rickey Dudley	.10
164	Tony Carter	.05
165	Kevin Williams	.05
166	Reggie White	.10
167	Tim Bowens	.05
168	Roy Barker	.05
169	Adrian Murrell	.05
170	Anthony Johnson	.05
171	Terry Glenn	.25
172	Jeff Lewis	.05
173	Dorsey Levens	.10
174	Willie Jackson	.05
175	Willie Clay	.05
176	Richmond Webb	.05
177	Shawn Lee	.05
178	Joe Aska	.05
179	Rod Woodson	.05
180	Jim Schwantz	.05
181	Alfred Williams	.05
182	Ferric Collons	.05
183	Ken Norton Jr.	.05
184	Rick Mirer	.10
185	Leeland McElroy	.05
186	Rodney Hampton	.05
187	Ted Popson	.05
188	Fred Barnett	.05
189	Junior Seau	.10
190	Michael Barrow	.05
191	Corey Widmer	.05
192	Rodney Peete	.05
193	Rod Smith	.05
194	Muhsin Muhammad	.15
195	Keith Jackson	.05
196	Jimmy Smith	.05
197	Dave Meggett	.05
198	Lawrence Phillips	.10
199	Chad Brown	.05
200	Darrin Smith	.05
201	Larry Centers	.05
202	Kevin Greene	.05
203	Sherman Williams	.05
204	Chris Sanders	.05
205	Shawn Jefferson	.05
206	Thurman Thomas	.10
207	Keyshawn Johnson	.30
208	Bryant Young	.05
209	Tim Biakabutuka	.15
210	Troy Aikman	.75
211	Quentin Coryatt	.05
212	Karim Abdul-Jabbar	.50
213	Brian Blades	.05
214	Ray Farmer	.05
215	Simeon Rice	.05
216	Tyrone Braxton	.05
217	Jerome Woods	.05
218	Charles Way	.05
219	Garrison Hearst	.05
220	Bobby Engram	.10
221	Billy Davis	.05
222	Ken Dilger	.05
223	Robert Smith	.05
224	John Friesz	.05
225	Charlie Garner	.05
226	Jerome Bettis	.10
227	Darnay Scott	.05
228	Terance Mathis	.05
229	Brian Williams	.05
230	Cris Carter	.05
231	Michael Haynes	.05
232	Cedric Jones	.05
233	Danny Kanell	.05
234	Deion Sanders	.30
235	Steve Atwater	.05
236	Jonathan Ogden	.05
237	Lake Dawson	.05
238	Eric Allen	.05
239	Eddie Kennison	.30
240	Irving Fryar	.05
241	Michael Strahan	.05
242	Steve McNair	.40
243	Terrell Buckley	.05
244	Merton Hanks	.05
245	Jessie Armstead	.05
246	Dana Stubblefield	.05
247	Brett Perriman	.05
248	Mark Collins	.05
249	Willie Roaf	.05
250	Gus Frerotte	.05
251	William Fuller	.05
252	Tamarick Vanover	.10
253	Scott Mitchell	.05
254	Eric Metcalf	.05
255	Herschel Walker	.05
256	Robert Brooks	.05
257	Zach Thomas	.15
258	Alvin Harper	.05
259	Wayne Chrebet	.05
260	Bill Romanowski	.05
261	Willie Green	.05
262	Dale Carter	.05
263	Chris Slade	.05
264	J.J. Stokes	.05
265	Tim Brown	.05
266	Eric Davis	.05
267	Mark Carrier	.05
268	Tony Martin	.05
269	Tyrone Wheatley	.05
270	Eugene Robinson	.05
271	Curtis Conway	.05
272	Michael Timpson	.05
273	Orlando Pace	.50
274	Tiki Barber	1.00
275	Byron Hanspard	.25
276	Warrick Dunn	1.50
277	Rae Carruth	.05
278	Bryant Westbrook	.30
279	Antowain Smith	1.25
280	Peter Boulware	.05
281	Reidel Anthony	1.00
282	Troy Davis	.20
283	Jake Plummer	4.00
284	Chris Canty	.05
285	Dwayne Rudd	.05
286	Ike Hilliard	1.00
287	Reinard Wilson	.05
288	Corey Dillon	1.50
289	Tony Gonzalez	.50
290	Darnell Autry	.50
291	Kevin Lockett	.20
292	Darrell Russell	.05
293	Jim Druckenmiller	1.00
294	Scott Mitchell	.05
295	Joey Kent	.30
296	Shawn Springs	.05
297	James Farrior	.05
298	Sedrick Shaw	.05
299	Marcus Harris	.05
300	Danny Wuerffel	.30
301	Marc Edwards	.20
302	Michael Booker	.05
303	David LaFleur	.50
304	Mike Adams	.05
305	Pat Barnes	.05
306	George Jones	.05
307	Yatil Green	.05
308	Drew Bledsoe	.30
309	Troy Aikman	.40
310	Terrell Davis	.40
311	Jim Everett	.05
312	John Elway	.50
313	Barry Sanders	.50
314	Jim Harbaugh	.05
315	Steve Young	.20
316	Dan Marino	.75
317	Michael Irvin	.05
318	Emmitt Smith	.75
319	Jeff Hostetler	.05
320	Mark Brunell	.30
321	Jeff Blake	.05
322	Scott Mitchell	.05
323	Boomer Esiason	.05
324	Jerome Bettis	.05
325	Warren Moon	.05
326	Neil O'Donnell	.05
327	Checklist (Jim Kelly)	.05
328	Checklist (Dan Marino)	.75
329	Checklist (John Elway)	.20
330	Checklist (Drew Bledsoe)	.30

1997 Score Franchise

This 16-card set includes the Franchise players from various NFL teams, including Emmitt Smith and Barry Sanders.

Complete Set (16): 200.00 (MT)
Common Player: 4.00

1 Emmitt Smith 30.00
2 Barry Sanders 25.00
3 Brett Favre 35.00
4 Drew Bledsoe 15.00
5 Jerry Rice 15.00
6 Troy Aikman 15.00
7 Dan Marino 30.00
8 John Elway 10.00
9 Steve Young 10.00
10 Eddie George 18.00
11 Keyshawn Johnson 4.00
12 Terrell Davis 15.00
13 Marshall Faulk 4.00
14 Kerry Collins 6.00
15 Deion Sanders 8.00
16 Joey Galloway 4.00

1997 Score New Breed

This 18-card set features a player photo superimposed over a holographic background on the card front. "The New Breed" is printed at the top. A football's brown pebble grain is on the top and bottom border of the front. The Score logo is in the lower left, while his name, position and team are printed to the right of the logo. The backs are numbered in the upper left corner.

Complete Set (18): 75.00 (MT)
Common Player: .75

1 Eddie George 8.00
2 Terrell Davis 8.00
3 Curtis Martin 8.00
4 Tony Banks .75
5 Lawrence Phillips .75
6 Terry Glenn 1.50
7 Jerome Bettis .75
8 Karim Abdul-Jabbar 1.50
9 Napoleon Kaufman .75
10 Isaac Bruce .75
11 Keyshawn Johnson .75
12 Rickey Dudley .75
13 Eddie Kennison 3.00
14 Marvin Harrison 3.00
15 Emmitt Smith 10.00
16 Barry Sanders 10.00
17 Kerry Collins 1.50
18 Brett Favre 12.00

1997 Score The Specialist

The 18-card chase set features a holographic front, with the player over a background which repeats "The Specialist" many times. The player's name is printed in red at the bottom center. The cards are numbered on the back.

Complete Set (18): 75.00 (MT)
Common Player: .75

1 Brett Favre 12.00
2 Drew Bledsoe 6.00
3 Mark Brunell 6.00
4 Kerry Collins 1.50
5 John Elway 4.00
6 Barry Sanders 10.00
7 Troy Aikman 6.00
8 Jerry Rice 6.00
9 Dan Marino 10.00
10 Neil O'Donnell .75
11 Scott Mitchell .75
12 Jim Harbaugh .75
13 Emmitt Smith 10.00
14 Steve Young 4.00
15 Dave Brown .75
16 Jeff Blake 2.00
17 Jim Everett .75
18 Kordell Stewart 6.00

1998 Score

The 270-card base set is made up of 15 Off Season cards, 3 checklists, 20 rookies and 232 veterans. Three parallel sets that include Showcase, Artist's Proofs and One on One. The Showcase set includes only the top 110 players and were inserted 1:7 packs. The Artist's Proof set is made up of the best 50 players in the set and were found 1:35 packs. The last parallel set is the One on One set in which there is only one of each card in the 160-card set. A special hobby exclusive Ryan Leaf autographed card was added with only 200 signed.

Complete Set (270): 50.00 (MT)
Common Player: .10
Minor Stars: .20
Common Rookie: 1.00
Complete Showcase (110): 120.00
Showcase Cards: 2x-4x
Showcase Rookies: 2x
Inserted 1:7
Complete Artist's Proof (50): 250.00
AP Cards: 5x-10x
Inserted 1:35
Wax Box: 50.00

1 John Elway 1.00
2 Kordell Stewart .75
3 Warrick Dunn .75
4 Brad Johnson .30
5 Kerry Collins .20
6 Danny Kanell .10
7 Emmitt Smith 1.50
8 Jamal Anderson .50
9 Jim Harbaugh .20
10 Tony Martin .20
11 Rod Smith .30
12 Dorsey Levens .30
13 Steve McNair .40
14 Derrick Thomas .10
15 Rob Moore .20
16 Peter Boulware .10
17 Terry Allen .20
18 Joey Galloway .30
19 Jerome Bettis .30
20 Carl Pickens .20
21 Napoleon Kaufman .30
22 Troy Aikman 1.00
23 Curtis Conway .20
24 Adrian Murrell .20
25 Elvis Grbac .20
26 Garrison Hearst .30
27 Chris Sanders .10
28 Scott Mitchell .20
29 Junior Seau .20
30 Chris Chandler .20
31 Kevin Hardy .10
32 Terrell Davis 1.50
33 Keyshawn Johnson .30
34 Natrone Means .20
35 Antowain Smith .30
36 Jake Plummer .75
37 Isaac Bruce .20
38 Tony Banks .20
39 Reidel Anthony .20
40 Darren Woodson .10
41 Corey Dillon .50
42 Antonio Freeman .30
43 Eddie George .75
44 Yancey Thigpen .20
45 Tim Brown .20
46 Wayne Chrebet .30
47 Andre Rison .20
48 Michael Strahan .10
49 Deion Sanders .30
50 Eric Moulds .30
51 Mark Brunell .75
52 Rae Carruth .10
53 Warren Sapp .10
54 Mark Chmura .20
55 Darrell Green .10
56 Quinn Early .10
57 Barry Sanders 2.00
58 Neil O'Donnell .20
59 Tony Brackens .10
60 Willie Davis .10
61 Shannon Sharpe .30
62 Shawn Springs .10
63 Tony Gonzalez .20
64 Rodney Thomas .10
65 Terance Mathis .10
66 Brett Favre 2.00
67 Eric Swann .10
68 Kevin Turner .10
69 Tyrone Wheatley .10
70 Trent Dilfer .20
71 Bryan Cox .10
72 Lake Dawson .10
73 Will Blackwell .10
74 Fred Lane .20
75 Ty Detmer .10
76 Eddie Kennison .20
77 Jimmy Smith .30
78 Chris Calloway .10
79 Shawn Jefferson .10
80 Dan Marino 1.50
81 LeRoy Butler .10
82 William Roaf .10
83 Rick Mirer .10
84 Dermontti Dawson .10
85 Errict Rhett .10
86 Lamar Thomas .10
87 Lamar Lathon .10
88 John Randle .10
89 Darryl Williams .10
90 Keenan McCardell .20
91 Erik Kramer .10
92 Ken Dilger .10
93 Dave Meggett .10
94 Jeff Blake .20
95 Ed McCaffrey .20
96 Charles Johnson .10
97 Irving Spikes .10
98 Mike Alstott .30
99 Vincent Brisby .10
100 Michael Westbrook .20
101 Rickey Dudley .10
102 Bert Emanuel .10
103 Daryl Johnston .10
104 Lawrence Phillips .10
105 Eric Bieniemy .10
106 Bryant Westbrook .10
107 Rob Johnson .20
108 Ray Zellars .10
109 Anthony Johnson .10
110 Reggie White .30
111 Wesley Walls .10
112 Amani Toomer .10
113 Gary Brown .10
114 Brian Blades .10
115 Alex Van Dyke .10
116 Michael Haynes .10
117 Jessie Armstead .10
118 James Jett .10
119 Troy Drayton .10
120 Craig Heyward .10
121 Steve Atwater .10
122 Tiki Barber .10
123 Karim Abdul .10
124 Kimble Anders .10
125 Frank Sanders .10
126 David Sloan .10
127 Andre Hastings .10
128 Vinny Testaverde .20
129 Robert Smith .20
130 Horace Copeland .10
131 Larry Centers .10
132 J.J. Stokes .20
133 Ike Hilliard .20
134 Muhsin Muhammad .10
135 Sean Dawkins .10
136 Raymont Harris .10
137 Lamar Smith .10
138 David Palmer .10
139 Steve Young .75
140 Bryan Still .10
141 Keith Byars .10
142 Cris Carter .30
143 Charlie Garner .10
144 Drew Bledsoe 1.00
145 Simeon Rice .10
146 Merton Hanks .10
147 Aeneas Williams .10
148 Rodney Hampton .10
149 Zach Thomas .20
150 Mark Bruener .10
151 Jason Dunn .10
152 Danny Wuerffel .10
153 Jim Druckenmiller .20
154 Greg Hill .10
155 Earnest Byner .10
156 Greg Lloyd .10
157 John Mobley .10
158 Tim Biakabutuka .20
159 Terrell Owens .50
160 O.J. McDuffie .20
161 Glenn Foley .20
162 Derrick Brooks .10
163 Dave Brown .10
164 Ki-Jana Carter .10
165 Bobby Hoying .20
166 Randal Hill .10
167 Michael Irvin .20
168 Bruce Smith .10
169 Troy Davis .10
170 Derrick Mayes .10
171 Henry Ellard .10
172 Dana Stubblefield .10
173 Willie McGinest .10
174 Leeland McElroy .10
175 Edgar Bennett .10
176 Robert Porcher .10
177 Randall Cunningham .30
178 Jim Everett .10
179 Jake Reed .10
180 Quentin Coryatt .10
181 William Floyd .10
182 Jason Sehorn .10
183 Carnell Lake .10
184 Dexter Coakley .10
185 Derrick Alexander .10
186 Johnnie Morton .10
187 Irving Fryar .10
188 Warren Moon .20
189 Todd Collins .10
190 Ken Norton Jr. .10
191 Terry Glenn .20
192 Rashaan Salaam .20
193 Jerry Rice 1.00
194 James Stewart .10
195 David LaFleur .10
196 Eric Green .10
197 Gus Frerotte .20
198 Willie Green .10
199 Marshall Faulk .30
200 Brett Perriman .10
201 Darnay Scott .10
202 Marvin Harrison .20
203 Joe Aska .10
204 Darrien Gordon .10
205 Herman Moore .20
206 Curtis Martin .30
207 Derek Loville .10
208 Dale Carter .10
209 Heath Shuler .10
210 Jonathan Ogden .10
211 Leslie Shepherd .10
212 Tony Boselli .10
213 Eric Metcalf .10
214 Neil Smith .10
215 Anthony Miller .10
216 Jeff George .20
217 Charles Way .10
218 Mario Bates .10
219 Ben Coates .20
220 Michael Jackson .10
221 Thurman Thomas .20
222 Kyle Brady .10
223 Marcus Allen .20
224 Robert Brooks .10
225 Yatil Green .10
226 Byron Hanspard .10
227 Andre Reed .20
228 Chris Warren .10
229 Jackie Harris .10
230 Ricky Watters .20
231 Bobby Engram .10
232 Tamarick Vanover .10
233 *Peyton Manning* 8.00
234 *Curtis Enis* 3.00
235 *Randy Moss* 12.00
236 *Charles Woodson* 3.00
237 *Robert Edwards* 2.00
238 *Jacquez Green* 2.00
239 *Keith Brooking* 1.00
240 *Jerome Pathon* 1.50
241 *Kevin Dyson* 2.00
242 *Fred Taylor* 6.00
243 *Tavian Banks* 1.50
244 *Marcus Nash* 2.00
245 *Brian Griese* 4.00
246 *Andre Wadsworth* 1.50
247 *Ahman Green* 2.00
248 *Joe Jurevicius* 1.00
249 *Germane Crowell* 2.00
250 *Skip Hicks* 2.00
251 *Ryan Leaf* 5.00
252 *Hines Ward* 1.50
253 John Elway .50
254 Mark Brunell .30
255 Brett Favre 1.00
256 Troy Aikman .50
257 Warrick Dunn .30
258 Barry Sanders 1.00
259 Eddie George .30
260 Kordell Stewart .30
261 Emmitt Smith .75
262 Steve Young .25
263 Terrell Davis .75
264 Dorsey Levens .10
265 Dan Marino .75
266 Jerry Rice .50
267 Drew Bledsoe 1.00
268 Brett Favre 1.00
269 Barry Sanders 1.00
270 Terrell Davis .75

1998 Score Complete Players

Only 10 of the NFL's all-around athletes are included in this set that has three different cards highlighting three specific attributes on special cards with holographic foil stamping. Singles were inserted 1:11 packs.

Complete Set (30): 100.00 (MT)
Common Player: 2.50
Inserted 1:11

1a Brett Favre 8.00
1b Brett Favre 8.00
1c Brett Favre 8.00
2a John Elway 5.00
2b John Elway 5.00
2c John Elway 5.00
3a Emmitt Smith 6.00
3b Emmitt Smith 6.00
3c Emmitt Smith 6.00
4a Kordell Stewart 2.50
4b Kordell Stewart 2.50
4c Kordell Stewart 2.50
5a Dan Marino 6.00
5b Dan Marino 6.00
5c Dan Marino 6.00
6a Mark Brunell 3.00
6b Mark Brunell 3.00
6c Mark Brunell 3.00
7a Terrell Davis 7.00
7b Terrell Davis 7.00
7c Terrell Davis 7.00
8a Barry Sanders 8.00
8b Barry Sanders 8.00
8c Barry Sanders 8.00
9a Warrick Dunn 2.50
9b Warrick Dunn 2.50
9c Warrick Dunn 2.50
10a Jerry Rice 4.00
10b Jerry Rice 4.00
10c Jerry Rice 4.00

1998 Score Rookie Autographs

The 33-card set includes all of the top rookies from 1998. Each is hand signed and limited to 500.

Complete Set (33): 1600. (MT)
Common Player: 20.00
Minor Stars: 40.00
Production 500 Sets

Stephen Alexander 40.00
Tavian Banks 50.00
Charlie Batch 100.00
Keith Brooking 20.00
Thad Busby 20.00
John Dutton 20.00
Tim Dwight 50.00
Kevin Dyson 50.00
Robert Edwards 60.00
Greg Ellis 20.00
Curtis Enis 60.00
Chris Fuamatu-Ma'afala 40.00
Ahman Green 40.00
Jacquez Green 50.00
Brian Griese 70.00
Skip Hicks 50.00
Robert Holcombe 40.00
Tebucky Jones 20.00
Joe Jurevicius 30.00
Ryan Leaf 85.00
Leonard Little 20.00
Alonzo Mayes 20.00
Michael Myers 20.00
Randy Moss 250.00
Marcus Nash 50.00
Jerome Pathon 40.00
Jason Peter 40.00
Anthony Simmons 20.00
Tony Simmons 40.00
Takeo Spikes 30.00
Duane Starks 20.00
Fred Taylor 100.00
Hines Ward 40.00

1998 Score Star Salute

This set highlights the top 20 players in the NFL and puts each of them on a foil board with micro-etching. Singles were issued 1:35 packs.

Complete Set (20): 120.00 (MT)
Common Player: 4.00
Inserted 1:35

1 Terrell Davis 15.00
2 Barry Sanders 20.00
3 Steve Young 6.00
4 Drew Bledsoe 8.00
5 Kordell Stewart 8.00
6 Emmitt Smith 15.00
7 Dorsey Levens 4.00
8 Corey Dillon 4.00
9 Jerome Bettis 4.00
10 Herman Moore 4.00
11 Brett Favre 20.00
12 Antonio Freeman 5.00
13 Mark Brunell 8.00
14 John Elway 12.00
15 Terry Glenn 4.00
16 Warrick Dunn 7.00
17 Eddie George 8.00
18 Troy Aikman 10.00
19 Deion Sanders 4.00
20 Jerry Rice 10.00

1998 Score Rookie Preview

The 160-card Rookie Preview set was released before the 270-card Score set. The singles are identical to the Score set and included rookie cards of Ryan Leaf and Peyton Manning.

Complete Set (160): 20.00 (MT)
Common Player: .10
Minor Stars: .20

1 John Elway 1.00
2 Kordell Stewart .75
3 Warrick Dunn .75
4 Emmitt Smith 1.50
11 Rod Smith .20
12 Dorsey Levens .20
16 Steve McNair .50
16 Peter Boulware .10
17 Joey Galloway .30
19 Jerome Bettis .20
20 Carl Pickens .10
21 Napoleon Kaufman .30
22 Troy Aikman 1.00
24 Adrian Murrell .10
25 Elvis Grbac .10
27 Chris Sanders .10
28 Scott Mitchell .10
29 Junior Seau .20
30 Chris Chandler .10
31 Kevin Hardy .10
32 Terrell Davis 1.50
35 Antowain Smith .30
36 Jake Plummer .75
37 Isaac Bruce .20
38 Tony Banks .20
40 Darren Woodson .10
41 Corey Dillon .50
42 Antonio Freeman .30
43 Eddie George .75
48 Michael Strahan .10
51 Mark Brunell .75
56 Quinn Early .10
57 Barry Sanders 2.00
58 Neil O'Donnell .10
59 Tony Brackens .10
60 Willie Davis .10
61 Shannon Sharpe .20
62 Shawn Springs .10
63 Tony Gonzalez .10
64 Rodney Thomas .10
65 Terance Mathis .10
66 Brett Favre 2.00
68 Kevin Turner .10
69 Tyrone Wheatley .10
70 Trent Dilfer .20
71 Bryan Cox .10
72 Lake Dawson .10
74 Fred Lane .10
75 Ty Detmer .10
76 Eddie Kennison .10
78 Chris Calloway .10
79 Shawn Jefferson .10
80 Dan Marino 1.50
81 LeRoy Butler .10
82 William Roaf .10
83 Rick Mirer .10
84 Dermontti Dawson .10
87 Lamar Lathon .10
88 John Randle .10
89 Darryl Williams .10
91 Erik Kramer .10
92 Ken Dilger .10
93 Dave Meggett .10
94 Jeff Blake .20
97 Irving Spikes .10
98 Mike Alstott .30
99 Vincent Brisby .10
101 Rickey Dudley .10
102 Bert Emanuel .10
105 Eric Bieniemy .10
106 Bryant Westbrook .10
108 Ray Zellars .10
110 Reggie White .20
111 Wesley Walls .10

113 Gary Brown .10
114 Brian Blades .10
115 Alex Van Dyke .10
116 Michael Haynes .10
117 Jessie Armstead .10
118 James Jett .10
119 Troy Drayton .10
120 Craig Heyward .10
121 Steve Atwater .10
123 Karim Abdul .20
125 Frank Sanders .10
126 David Sloan .10
127 Andre Hastings .10
130 Horace Copeland .10
135 Sean Dawkins .10
137 Lamar Smith .10
138 David Palmer .10
139 Steve Young .75
140 Bryan Still .10
141 Keith Byars .10
142 Cris Carter .30
144 Drew Bledsoe 1.00
145 Simeon Rice .10
146 Merton Hanks .10
147 Aeneas Williams .10
148 Rodney Hampton .10
149 Zach Thomas .10
150 Mark Bruener .10
151 Jason Dunn .10
155 Earnest Byner .10
156 Greg Lloyd .10
157 John Mobley .10
160 O.J. McDuffie .20
161 Glenn Foley .20
162 Derrick Brooks .10
163 Dave Brown .10
166 Randal Hill .10
167 Michael Irvin .20
168 Bruce Smith .10
170 Derrick Mayes .10
171 Henry Ellard .10
172 Dana Stubblefield .10
173 Willie McGinest .10
175 Edgar Bennett .10
176 Robert Porcher .10
177 Randall Cunningham .30
178 Jim Everett .10
180 Quentin Coryatt .10
181 William Floyd .10
182 Jason Sehorn .10
183 Carnell Lake .10
184 Dexter Coakley .10
185 Derrick Alexander .10
186 Johnnie Morton .10
188 Warren Moon .20
189 Todd Collins .10
190 Ken Norton Jr. .10
191 Terry Glenn .30
193 Jerry Rice 1.00
194 James Stewart .10
196 Eric Green .10
198 Willie Green .10
200 Brett Perriman .10
201 Darnay Scott .10
203 Joe Aska .10
204 Darrien Gordon .10
205 Herman Moore .20
206 Curtis Martin .50
207 Derek Loville .10
208 Dale Carter .10
209 Heath Shuler .20
210 Jonathan Ogden .10
211 Leslie Shepherd .10
212 Tony Boselli .10
213 Eric Metcalf .10
214 Neil Smith .10
215 Anthony Miller .10
216 Jeff George .20
217 Charles Way .10
218 Mario Bates .10
222 Kyle Brady .10
228 Chris Warren .10
229 Jackie Harris .10
233 *Peyton Manning* 8.00
251 *Ryan Leaf* 5.00

1998 Score Rookie Preview Star Salute

Singles from this set were printed on silver foil stock and inserted 1:35 packs.

		MT
Complete Set (20):		120.00
Common Player:		4.00
1	Terrell Davis	15.00
2	Barry Sanders	20.00
3	Steve Young	6.00
4	Drew Bledsoe	8.00
5	Kordell Stewart	8.00
6	Emmitt Smith	15.00
7	Dorsey Levens	4.00
8	Corey Dillon	4.00
9	Jerome Bettis	4.00
10	Herman Moore	4.00
11	Brett Favre	20.00
12	Antonio Freeman	4.00
13	Mark Brunell	8.00
14	John Elway	12.00
15	Terry Glenn	4.00
16	Warrick Dunn	7.00
17	Eddie George	8.00
18	Troy Aikman	10.00
19	Deion Sanders	4.00
20	Jerry Rice	10.00

1999 Score

This is a 275-card set that had 55 short-printed cards found 1:3 hobby packs and 1:9 retail packs. The short-prints were of 40 Rookies, 10 All-Pros and 5 Great Combos. The base set is divided into three colors like the first set was in 1989. Red, blue and green gold borders with the short-prints in green. Inserts include: Showcase, Artist's Proofs, Reprints, Reprint Autographs, Complete Players, Franchise, Future Franchise, Millenium Men, Numbers Game, Rookie Preview Autographs, Scoring Core and Settle the Score.

		MT
Complete Set (275):		150.00
Common Player:		.10
Minor Stars:		.20
Common Rookie (221-260):		1.00
Common All-Pros (261-270):		1.00
Inserted 1:3		
Wax Box:		80.00
1	Randy Moss	2.50
2	Randall Cunningham	.50
3	Cris Carter	.50
4	Robert Smith	.20
5	Jake Reed	.10
6	Leroy Hoard	.10
7	John Randle	.10
8	Brett Favre	2.00
9	Antonio Freeman	.50
10	Dorsey Levens	.20
11	Robert Brooks	.20
12	Derrick Mayes	.10
13	Mark Chmura	.20
14	Darick Holmes	.10
15	Vonnie Holliday	.20
16	Mike Alstott	.50
17	Warrick Dunn	.75
18	Trent Dilfer	.20
19	Jacquez Green	.20
20	Reidel Anthony	.20
21	Warren Sapp	.10
22	Bert Emanuel	.10
23	Curtis Enis	.50
24	Curtis Conway	.20
25	Bobby Engram	.10
26	Erik Kramer	.10
27	Moses Moreno	.10
28	Edgar Bennett	.10
29	Barry Sanders	2.00
30	Charlie Batch	.75
31	Herman Moore	.50
32	Johnnie Morton	.10
33	Germane Crowell	.20
34	Terry Fair	.10
35	Gary Brown	.10
36	Kent Graham	.10
37	Kerry Collins	.20
38	Charles Way	.10
39	Tiki Barber	.20
40	Ike Hilliard	.10
41	Joe Jurevicius	.20
42	Michael Strahan	.10
43	Jason Sehorn	.10
44	Brad Johnson	.50
45	Terry Allen	.20
46	Skip Hicks	.50
47	Michael Westbrook	.20
48	Leslie Shepherd	.10
49	Stephen Alexander	.10
50	Albert Connell	.10
51	Darrell Green	.10
52	Jake Plummer	1.00
53	Adrian Murrell	.20
54	Frank Sanders	.20
55	Rob Moore	.20
56	Larry Centers	.10
57	Simeon Rice	.10
58	Andre Wadsworth	.20
59	Duce Staley	.10
60	Charles Johnson	.20
61	Charlie Garner	.10
62	Bobby Hoying	.10
63	Darryl Johnston	.10
64	Emmitt Smith	1.50
65	Troy Aikman	1.00
66	Michael Irvin	.20
67	Deion Sanders	.50
68	Chris Warren	.20
69	Darren Woodson	.10
70	Rod Woodson	.10
71	Travis Jervey	.10
72	Jerry Rice	1.00
73	Terrell Owens	.50
74	Steve Young	.75
75	Garrison Hearst	.20
76	J.J. Stokes	.20
77	Ken Norton	.10
78	R.W. McQuarters	.10
79	Bryant Young	.10
80	Jamal Anderson	.50
81	Chris Chandler	.20
82	Terrance Mathis	.10
83	Tim Dwight	.50
84	O.J. Santiago	.10
85	Chris Calloway	.10
86	Keith Brooking	.10
87	Eddie Kennison	.10
88	Willie Roaf	.10
89	Cameron Cleeland	.20
90	Lamar Smith	.10
91	Sean Dawkins	.10
92	Tim Biakabutuka	.20
93	Muhsin Muhammad	.10
94	Steve Beuerlein	.20
95	Rae Carruth	.10
96	Wesley Walls	.10
97	Kevin Greene	.10
98	Trent Green	.50
99	Tony Banks	.20
100	Greg Hill	.10
101	Robert Holcombe	.20
102	Isaac Bruce	.30
103	Amp Lee	.10
104	Az-Zahir Hakim	.20
105	Warren Moon	.20
106	Jeff George	.20
107	Raghib Ismail	.10
108	Kordell Stewart	.75
109	Jerome Bettis	.20
110	Courtney Hawkins	.10
111	Chris Fuamatu-Ma'afala	.20
112	Levon Kirkland	.10
113	Hines Ward	.20
114	Will Blackwell	.10
115	Corey Dillon	.50
116	Carl Pickens	.20
117	Neil O'Donnell	.20
118	Jeff Blake	.20
119	Darnay Scott	.10
120	Takeo Spikes	.10
121	Steve McNair	.75
122	Frank Wycheck	.10
123	Eddie George	.75
124	Chris Sanders	.10
125	Yancy Thigpen	.10
126	Kevin Dyson	.20
127	Blaine Bishop	.10
128	Fred Taylor	1.00
129	Mark Brunell	.75
130	Jimmy Smith	.20
131	Keenan McCardell	.10
132	Kyle Brady	.10
133	Tavian Banks	.20
134	James Stewart	.10
135	Kevin Hardy	.10
136	Jonathan Quinn	.10
137	Jermaine Lewis	.20
138	Priest Holmes	.50
139	Scott Mitchell	.20
140	Eric Zeier	.10
141	Patrick Johnson	.20
142	Ray Lewis	.10
143	Terry Kirby	.10
144	Ty Detmer	.10
145	Irv Smith	.10
146	Chris Spielman	.10
147	Antonio Langham	.10
148	Dan Marino	1.50
149	O.J. McDuffie	.20
150	Oronde Gadsden	.20
151	Karim Abdul	.30
152	Yatil Green	.10
153	Zach Thomas	.20
154	John Avery	.20
155	Lamar Thomas	.10
156	Drew Bledsoe	.75
157	Terry Glenn	.30
158	Ben Coates	.20
159	Shawn Jefferson	.10
160	Cedric Shaw	.10
161	Tony Simmons	.20
162	Ty Law	.10
163	Robert Edwards	.30
164	Curtis Martin	.50
165	Keyshawn Johnson	.50
166	Vinny Testaverde	.20
167	Aaron Glenn	.10
168	Wayne Chrebet	.20
169	Dedric Ward	.10
170	Peyton Manning	1.50
171	Marshall Faulk	.50
172	Marvin Harrison	.20
173	Jerome Pathon	.20
174	Ken Dilger	.10
175	E.G. Green	.20
176	Doug Flutie	.75
177	Thurman Thomas	.20
178	Andre Reed	.20
179	Eric Moulds	.50
180	Antowain Smith	.30
181	Bruce Smith	.20
182	Rob Johnson	.20
183	Terrell Davis	1.50
184	John Elway	1.50
185	Ed McCaffrey	.20
186	Rod Smith	.20
187	Shannon Sharpe	.20
188	Marcus Nash	.10
189	Brian Griese	.50
190	Neil Smith	.10
191	Bubby Brister	.20
192	Ryan Leaf	.50
193	Natrone Means	.50
194	Mikhael Ricks	.10
195	Junior Seau	.20
196	Jim Harbaugh	.20
197	Bryan Still	.10
198	Freddie Jones	.10
199	Andre Rison	.20
200	Elvis Grbac	.20
201	Bam Morris	.10
203	Rashaan Shehee	.10
204	Donnell Bennett	.10
205	Tony Gonzalez	.20
206	Derrick Alexander	.10
207	Jon Kitna	.50
208	Ricky Watters	.20
209	Joey Galloway	.50
210	Ahman Green	.10
211	Shawn Springs	.10
212	Michael Sinclair	.10
213	Napoleon Kaufman	.20
214	Tim Brown	.20
215	Charles Woodson	.50
216	Harvey Williams	.10
217	Jon Ritchie	.10
218	Rich Gannon	.10
219	Rickey Dudley	.20
220	James Jett	.10
221	*Tim Couch*	25.00
222	*Ricky Williams*	25.00
223	*Donovan McNabb*	12.00
224	*Edgerrin James*	25.00
225	*Torry Holt*	6.00
226	*Daunte Culpepper*	12.00
227	*Akili Smith*	10.00
228	*Champ Bailey*	5.00
229	*Chris Claiborne*	2.50
230	*Chris McAlister*	2.00
231	*Troy Edwards*	5.00
232	*Jevon Kearse*	5.00
233	*Shaun King*	8.00
234	*David Boston*	7.00
235	*Peerless Price*	5.00
236	*Cecil Collins*	6.00
237	*Rob Konrad*	2.00
238	*Cade McNown*	12.00
239	*Shawn Bryson*	1.00
240	*Kevin Faulk*	7.00
241	*Scott Covington*	2.00
242	*James Johnson*	4.00
243	*Mike Cloud*	2.00
244	*Aaron Brooks*	2.00
245	*Sedrick Irvin*	4.00
246	*Amos Zereoue*	5.00
247	*Jermaine Fazande*	1.00
248	*Joe Germaine*	4.00
249	*Brock Huard*	3.00
250	*Craig Yeast*	1.00
251	*Travis McGriff*	2.00
252	*D'Wayne Bates*	2.00
253	*Na Brown*	1.00
254	*Tai Streets*	2.00
255	*Andy Katzenmoyer*	2.00
256	*Kevin Johnson*	6.00
257	*Joe Montgomery*	2.00
258	*Karsten Bailey*	2.00
259	*De'Mond Parker*	2.00
260	*Reg Kelly*	1.00
261	*Eddie George*	2.00
262	*Jamal Anderson*	1.00
263	*Barry Sanders*	3.00
264	*Fred Taylor*	3.00
265	*Keyshawn Johnson*	1.00
266	*Jerry Rice*	3.50
267	*Doug Flutie*	2.50
268	*Deion Sanders*	1.00
269	*Randall Cunningham*	1.00
270	*Steve Young*	2.50
271	Terrell Davis, John Elway	5.00
272	Marshall Faulk, Peyton Manning	4.00
273	Brett Favre, Antonio Freeman	5.00
274	Troy Aikman, Emmitt Smith	4.00
275	Cris Carter, Randy Moss	6.00

1999 Score Anniversary Showcase

This is a parallel to the base with each card the same except for a gold foil border around the photo and a gold foil stamp on the front. The backs are sequentially numbered to 1989 and say Anniversary Showcase next to it.

	MT
Complete Set (275):	450.00
Showcase Cards:	3x-6x
Showcase Rookies:	1.5x
Showcase AP/GC:	2x
Production 1,989 Sets	

1999 Score Anniversary Artist Proof

This is a parallel to the base and each card is sequentially numbered to 10.

	MT
Production 10 Sets	

1999 Score 1989 Score Reprints

This was a 20-card reprint of the 1989 Score cards that included all of the top rookies and stars from the premiere release. These were only found in hobby product and were sequentially numbered to 1989. The first 150 of each card were autographed.

		MT
Complete Set (20):		80.00
Common Player:		3.00
Production 1,989 Sets		
1	Barry Sanders	20.00
2	Troy Aikman	10.00
3	John Elway	15.00
4	Cris Carter	8.00
5	Tim Brown	6.00
6	Doug Flutie	5.00
7	Chris Chandler	3.00
8	Thurman Thomas	3.00
9	Steve Young	6.00
10	Dan Marino	12.00
11	Derrick Thomas	3.00
12	Bubby Brister	5.00
13	Jerry Rice	10.00
14	Andre Rison	3.00
15	Randall Cunningham	5.00
16	Vinny Testaverde	3.00
17	Michael Irvin	3.00
18	Rod Woodson	3.00
19	Neil Smith	3.00
20	Deion Sanders	6.00

1999 Score 1989 Score Reprints Autographs

These are the same cards as the Reprint set except for each is autographed and has the words "Authentic Signature" down the side of the fronts of the cards. Only 150 of each were signed.

		MT
Complete Set (20):		1700.
Common Player:		40.00
Production 150 Sets		
1	Barry Sanders	375.00
2	Troy Aikman	200.00
3	John Elway	300.00
4	Cris Carter	80.00
5	Tim Brown	60.00
6	Doug Flutie	85.00
7	Chris Chandler	40.00
8	Thurman Thomas	40.00
9	Steve Young	85.00
10	Dan Marino	300.00
11	Derrick Thomas	40.00
12	Bubby Brister	60.00
13	Jerry Rice	200.00
14	Andre Rison	40.00
15	Randall Cunningham	75.00
16	Vinny Testaverde	50.00
17	Michael Irvin	40.00
18	Rod Woodson	40.00
19	Neil Smith	40.00
20	Deion Sanders	80.00

1999 Score Complete Players

These singles were found in both hobby (1:17) and retail (1:35) product. Each of the 30 cards is printed on foil board with foil stamping and have one large color photo of the player on the front along with four smaller shots in black and white on the side.

		MT
Complete Set (30):		75.00
Common Player:		1.50
Minor Stars:		3.00
Inserted 1:17		
1	Antonio Freeman	1.50
2	Troy Aikman	5.00
3	Jerry Rice	5.00
4	Brett Favre	10.00
5	Cris Carter	3.00
6	Jamal Anderson	1.50
7	John Elway	7.50
8	Mark Brunell	4.00
9	Steve McNair	3.00
10	Kordell Stewart	3.00
11	Drew Bledsoe	4.00
12	Tim Couch	12.00
13	Dan Marino	7.50
14	Akili Smith	5.00
15	Peyton Manning	5.00
16	Jake Plummer	4.00
17	Jerome Bettis	1.50
18	Randy Moss	10.00
19	Keyshawn Johnson	1.50
20	Barry Sanders	10.00
21	Ricky Williams	12.00
22	Emmitt Smith	7.50
23	Corey Dillon	1.50
24	Dorsey Levens	1.50
25	Donovan McNabb	1.50
26	Curtis Martin	1.50
27	Eddie George	3.00
28	Fred Taylor	3.50
29	Steve Young	3.50
30	Terrell Davis	7.50

1999 Score Franchise

This 31-card set was a retail exclusive (1:35) and picked a star player from each team. Each card is printed on holographic foil board and has a large color photo of the player on the front along with a smaller black and white next to it.

	MT
Complete Set (31):	125.00
Common Player:	2.00
Minor Stars:	4.00

Inserted 1:35
1	Brett Favre	15.00
2	Randy Moss	15.00
3	Mike Alstott	4.00
4	Barry Sanders	15.00
5	Curtis Enis	4.00
6	Ike Hilliard	2.00
7	Emmitt Smith	10.00
8	Jake Plummer	8.00
9	Brad Johnson	4.00
10	Duce Staley	2.00
11	Jamal Anderson	4.00
12	Steve Young	6.00
13	Eddie Kennison	2.00
14	Isaac Bruce	4.00
15	Muhsin Muhammad	2.00
16	Dan Marino	15.00
17	Drew Bledsoe	7.00
18	Curtis Martin	4.00
19	Doug Flutie	6.00
20	Peyton Manning	10.00
21	Kordell Stewart	5.00
22	Ty Detmer	2.00
23	Corey Dillon	4.00
24	Mark Brunell	7.00
25	Priest Holmes	4.00
26	Eddie George	5.00
27	John Elway	10.00
28	Natrone Means	4.00
29	Tim Brown	2.00
30	Andre Rison	2.00
31	Joey Galloway	4.00

1999 Score Future Franchise

This 31-card set was a hobby exclusive and included a rookie on one side and a star player on the other from the same team. Singles were found 1:35 packs and each were printed on holographic foil board.

		MT
Complete Set (31):		160.00
Common Player:		2.00
Minor Stars:		4.00

Inserted 1:35
1	Aaron Brooks, Brett Favre	12.00
2	Daunte Culpepper, Randy Moss	15.00
3	Shaun King, Mike Alstott	4.00
4	Sedrick Irvin, Barry Sanders	12.00
5	Cade McNown, Curtis Enis	10.00
6	Joe Montgomery, Ike Hilliard	2.00
7	Wayne McGarity, Emmitt Smith	8.00
8	David Boston, Jake Plummer	6.00
9	Champ Bailey, Brad Johnson	4.00
10	Donovan McNabb, Duce Staley	10.00
11	Reg Kelly, Jamal Anderson	2.00
12	Tai Streets, Steve Young	5.00
13	Ricky Williams, Eddie Kennison	25.00
14	Torry Holt, Isaac Bruce	6.00
15	Mike Rucker, Muhsin Muhammad	2.00
16	James Johnson, Dan Marino	8.00
17	Kevin Faulk, Drew Bledsoe	6.00
18	Randy Thomas, Curtis Martin	4.00
19	Peerless Price, Doug Flutie	5.00
20	Edgerrin James, Peyton Manning	12.00
21	Troy Edwards, Kordell Stewart	5.00
22	Tim Couch, Ty Detmer	25.00
23	Akili Smith, Corey Dillon	10.00
24	Fernando Bryant, Mark Brunell	5.00
25	Chris McAlister, Priest Holmes	4.00
26	Jevon Kearse, Eddie George	5.00
27	Travis McGriff, John Elway	8.00
28	Jermaine Fazande, Natrone Means	2.00
29	Dameane Douglas, Tim Brown	2.00
30	Mike Cloud, Andre Rison	2.00
31	Brock Huard, Joey Galloway	4.00

1999 Score Millenium Men

The Millennium Men set has Barry Sanders, representing ten years of NFL excellence with Ricky Williams, representing the outstanding future generation of running backs. Each player has an individual card and a back-to-back single in this 3-card set. Each is sequentially numbered to 1,000 and the first 100 of each are autographed. These were only found in retail product.

		MT
Complete Set (3):		60.00
Common Player:		20.00

Production 1,000 Sets
1	Barry Sanders	25.00
2	Ricky Williams	20.00
3	Barry Sanders, Ricky Williams	25.00
1AU	Barry Sanders AUTO	375.00
2AU	Ricky Williams AUTO	275.00
3AU	Barry Sanders, Ricky Williams AUTO	500.00

1999 Score Numbers Game

This was a 30-card set that was printed on holographic foil board with gold foil stamping. Each card is sequentially numbered to the player's specific stat.

		MT
Complete Set (30):		75.00
Common Player:		1.50

Numbered to Stat
1	Brett Favre 4212	7.00
2	Steve Young 4170	3.00
3	Jake Plummer 3737	3.50
4	Drew Bledsoe 3633	4.00
5	Dan Marino 3497	6.00
6	Peyton Manning 3739	6.00
7	Randall Cunningham 3704	1.50
8	John Elway 2806	3.00
9	Doug Flutie 2711	3.00
10	Mark Brunell 2601	3.00
11	Troy Aikman 2330	3.00
12	Terrell Davis 2008	8.00
13	Jamal Anderson 1846	1.50
14	Garrison Hearst 1570	1.50
15	Barry Sanders 1491	12.00
16	Emmitt Smith 1332	7.00
17	Marshall Faulk 1319	3.00
18	Eddie George 1294	3.00
19	Curtis Martin 1287	3.00
20	Fred Taylor 1223	6.00
21	Corey Dillon 1130	3.00
22	Antonio Freeman 1424	3.00
23	Eric Moulds 1368	3.00
24	Randy Moss 1313	12.00
25	Rod Smith 1222	1.50
26	Jerry Rice 1157	7.00
27	Keyshawn Johnson 1131	3.00
28	Terrell Owens 1097	3.00
29	Tim Brown 1012	1.50
30	Cris Carter 1011	3.00

1999 Score Rookie Preview Autographs

Each of these singles were randomly inserted into hobby packs with each player signing a total of 600 cards. Each card is printed on foil board with the signature on the bottom of the card.

		MT
Common Player:		10.00
Minor Stars:		20.00

Production 600 Sets
Ricky Williams	150.00
Donovan McNabb	75.00
Edgerrin James	85.00
Torry Holt	50.00
Daunte Culpepper	75.00
Akili Smith	60.00
Champ Bailey	30.00
Chris Claiborne	20.00
Chris McAlister	20.00
Troy Edwards	40.00
Jevon Kearse	35.00
David Boston	50.00
Peerless Price	40.00
Cecil Collins	40.00
Rob Konrad	20.00
Cade McNown	75.00
Shawn Bryson	10.00
Kevin Faulk	50.00
Corby Jones	20.00
James Johnson	30.00
Mike Cloud	20.00
Autrey Denson	25.00
Sedrick Irvin	30.00
Michael Bishop	40.00
Joe Germaine	30.00
De'Mond Parker	20.00
Shaun King	30.00
D'Wayne Bates	20.00
Na Brown	10.00
Tai Streets	25.00
Kevin Johnson	30.00
Jim Kleinsasser	30.00
Darnell McDonald	25.00
Travis McGriff	20.00

1999 Score Scoring Core

Scoring Core's holographic foil design highlights 30 players

who find their way into the end zone. Singles were found 1:17 hobby packs and 1:35 retail.

		MT
Complete Set (30):		75.00
Common Player:		1.50
Minor Stars:		3.00

Inserted 1:17
1	Antonio Freeman	1.50
2	Troy Aikman	5.00
3	Jerry Rice	5.00
4	Brett Favre	10.00
5	Cris Carter	3.00
6	Jamal Anderson	1.50
7	John Elway	7.50
8	Tim Brown	1.50
9	Mark Brunell	4.00
10	Terrell Owens	3.00
11	Drew Bledsoe	4.00
12	Tim Couch	12.00
13	Dan Marino	7.50
14	Marshall Faulk	1.50
15	Peyton Manning	5.00
16	Jake Plummer	4.00
17	Jerome Bettis	1.50
18	Randy Moss	10.00
19	Charlie Batch	3.00
20	Barry Sanders	10.00
21	Ricky Williams	12.00
22	Emmitt Smith	7.50
23	Joey Galloway	1.50
24	Herman Moore	1.50
25	Natrone Means	1.50
26	Mike Alstott	1.50
27	Eddie George	3.00
28	Fred Taylor	3.50
29	Steve Young	3.50
30	Terrell Davis	7.50

1999 Score Settle the Score

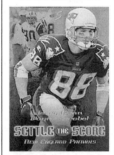

This retail exclusive insert is a dual-sided foil set that matches two players who need to settle the score between each other. Singles were inserted 1:17 packs.

		MT
Complete Set (30):		70.00
Common Player:		1.50
Minor Stars:		3.00

Inserted 1:17 Retail
1	Randall Cunningham, Brett Favre	10.00
2	Doug Flutie, Dan Marino	7.50
3	Terry Allen, Emmitt Smith	7.50
4	Warrick Dunn, Barry Sanders	10.00
5	Corey Dillon, Eddie George	3.00
6	Drew Bledsoe, Vinny Testaverde	4.00
7	Troy Aikman, Jake Plummer	5.00
8	Jamal Anderson, Terrell Davis	7.50
9	Chris Chandler, John Elway	7.50
10	Mark Brunell, Steve Young	4.00
11	Cris Carter, Herman Moore	1.50
12	Steve McNair, Kordell Stewart	3.00
13	Napoleon Kaufman, Natrone Means	1.50
14	Marshall Faulk, Curtis Martin	1.50
15	Antonio Freeman, Terrell Owens	3.00
16	Wayne Chrebet, Terry Glenn	1.50
17	Garrison Hearst, Dorsey Levens	1.50
18	Jon Kitna, Ryan Leaf	3.00
19	Mike Alstott, Robert Smith	1.50
20	Randy Moss, Jerry Rice	10.00
21	Charlie Batch, Peyton Manning	6.00
22	Jerome Bettis, Fred Taylor	4.00
23	Keyshawn Johnson, Eric Moulds	3.00
24	Tim Couch, Ricky Williams	20.00
25	Isaac Bruce, Carl Pickens	1.50
26	Deion Sanders, Charles Woodson	1.50
27	Tim Brown, Rod Smith	1.50
28	Daunte Culpepper, Donovan McNabb	8.00
29	Joey Galloway, Ed McCaffrey	1.50
30	Karim Abdul, Antowain Smith	1.50

1999 Score Supplemental

This was a 110-card set that could only be found in factory set form. The set included 24 Mid-Season Updates, 20 Star Salutes and 66 new Rookies. Each in-cluded two insert cards. Inserts included Behind the Numbers, In-scriptions, Quantum Leaf Pre-views and Zenith Z-Team. SRP was $24.99 per factory set.

		MT
Complete Set (110):		40.00
Common Player:		.10
Minor Stars:		.20
Common Rookie:		.50
1	Chris Griesen	2.00
2	Sherdrick Bonner	1.00
3	Joel Makovicka	2.00
4	Andy McCullough	1.00
5	Jeff Paulk	1.50
6	Brandon Stokley	1.50
7	Sheldon Jackson	1.00
8	Bobby Collins	2.00
9	Kamil Loud	1.00
10	Antoine Winfield	1.50
11	Jerry Azumah	1.00
12	James Allen	1.00
13	Nick Williams	1.00
14	Michael Basnight	1.00
15	Damon Griffin	1.50
16	Ronnie Powell	1.00
17	Darrin Chiaverini	2.00
18	Mark Campbell	1.00
19	Mike Lucky	1.00
20	Wane McGarity	2.00
21	Jason Tucker	4.00
22	Ebenezer Ekuban	1.50
23	Robert Thomas	1.00
24	Dat Nguyen	1.50
25	Olandis Gary	8.00
26	Desmond Clark	1.00
27	Andre Cooper	1.00
28	Chris Watson	1.25
29	Al Wilson	1.50
30	Cory Sauter	1.00
31	Brock Olivo	.50
32	Basil Mitchell	.50
33	Matt Snider	.50
34	Antwan Edwards	1.50
35	Mike McKenzie	1.50
36	Terrence Wilkins	4.00
37	Fernando Bryant	1.00
38	Larry Parker	1.00
39	Autry Denson	2.00
40	Jim Kleinsasser	2.00
41	Michael Bishop	2.50
42	Andy Katzenmoyer	2.00
43	Brett Bech	1.00
44	Sean Bennett	1.50
45	Dan Campbell	.50
46	Ray Lucas	8.00
47	Scott Dreisbach	1.50
48	Cecil Martin	1.00
49	Dameane Douglas	1.00
50	Jed Weaver	.50
51	Jerame Tuman	1.00
52	Steve Heiden	.50
53	Jeff Garcia	5.00
54	Terry Jackson	1.00
55	Charlie Rogers	1.00
56	Lamar King	.50
57	Kurt Warner	20.00
58	Dre' Bly	1.00
59	Justin Watson	1.00
60	Rabih Abdullah	.50
61	Martin Gramatica	1.00
62	Darnell McDonald	2.00
63	Anthony McFarland	1.00
64	Larry Brown	.50
65	Kevin Daft	1.50
66	Mike Sellers	.50
67	Ken Oxendine	.20
68	Errict Rhett	.20
69	Stoney Case	.10
70	Jonathon Linton	.20
71	Marcus Robinson	1.50
72	Shane Matthews	.20
73	Cade McNown	3.00
74	Akili Smith	3.00
75	Karim Abdul	.20
76	Tim Couch	6.00
77	Kevin Johnson	2.00
78	Ron Rivers	.10
79	Bill Schroeder	.10
80	Edgerrin James	8.00
81	Cecil Collins	2.00
82	Matthew Hatchette	.20
83	Daunte Culpepper	3.00
84	Ricky Williams	6.00
85	Tyrone Wheatley	.20
86	Donovan McNabb	3.00
87	Marshall Faulk	.50
88	Torry Holt	2.00
89	Stephen Davis	.50
90	Brad Johnson	.50
91	Jake Plummer	.50
92	Emmitt Smith	1.00
93	Troy Aikman	1.00
94	John Elway	1.00
95	Terrell Davis	1.00
96	Barry Sanders	1.50
97	Brett Favre	1.50
98	Antonio Freeman	.50
99	Peyton Manning	1.50
100	Fred Taylor	1.00
101	Mark Brunell	.50
102	Dan Marino	1.00
103	Randy Moss	1.50
104	Cris Carter	.50
105	Drew Bledsoe	.75
106	Terry Glenn	.40
107	Keyshawn Johnson	.40
108	Jerry Rice	1.00
109	Steve Young	.75
110	Eddie George	.50

1999 Score Supplemental Behind The Numbers

This 30-card insert included both veterans and rookies. Each single was printed on holograph-ic foil board with foil stamping. Singles were sequentially num-bered to 1,000. A parallel Gold version was also issued with each card numbered to the play-er's jersey number.

		MT
Complete Set (30):		250.00
Common Player:		5.00

Production 1,000 Sets
1	Kurt Warner	30.00
2	Tim Couch	20.00
3	Randy Moss	20.00
4	Brett Favre	20.00
5	Marvin Harrison	5.00
6	Terry Glenn	5.00
7	John Elway	15.00
8	Troy Aikman	12.00
9	Steve McNair	5.00
10	Kordell Stewart	5.00
11	Drew Bledsoe	8.00
12	Jon Kitna	5.00
13	Dan Marino	15.00
14	Jerry Rice	12.00
15	Edgerrin James	30.00
16	Jake Plummer	8.00
17	Antonio Freeman	5.00
18	Peyton Manning	15.00
19	Keyshawn Johnson	5.00
20	Barry Sanders	20.00
21	Cris Carter	5.00
22	Emmitt Smith	15.00
23	Steve Young	12.00
24	Ricky Williams	20.00
25	Doug Flutie	8.00
26	Mark Brunell	5.00
27	Eddie George	5.00
28	Fred Taylor	8.00
29	Donovan McNabb	12.00
30	Terrell Davis	15.00

1999 Score Supplemental Inscriptions

This 30-card insert includ-ed autographs of both past and

present players. The never-re-leased 1997 Inscriptions of Barry Sanders was randomly inserted into this product. The rest of the singles were found at one in three boxes.

		MT
Complete Set (30):		1000.
Common Player:		15.00
Minor Stars:		30.00
1	Eric Moulds	30.00
2	Chris Chandler	15.00
3	Thurman Thomas	30.00
4	Tim Brown	30.00
5	Priest Holmes	30.00
6	Wesley Walls	15.00
7	Corey Dillon	30.00
8	Duce Staley	30.00
9	Natrone Means	30.00
10	Isaac Bruce	30.00
11	Joey Galloway	30.00
12	Skip Hicks	30.00
13	Terrell Owens	30.00
14	Eric Moss	15.00
15	Kurt Warner	200.00
16	Johnny Unitas	125.00
17	Bart Starr	150.00
18	Earl Campbell	50.00
19	Jim Brown	150.00
20	Vinny Testaverde	30.00
21	Kordell Stewart	40.00
22	Steve McNair	40.00
23	Stephen Davis	30.00
24	Ricky Williams	125.00
25	Marvin Harrison	40.00
26	Brad Johnson	30.00
27	Dorsey Levens	30.00
28	Jon Kitna	30.00
29	Brian Griese	40.00
30	Tim Biakabutuka	15.00

1999 Score Supplemental Quantum Leaf Previews

This 18-card insert gave collectors a look at the first 2000 release. Each player was pictured on dot matrix hologram foil and randomly inserted.

		MT
Complete Set (18):		150.00
Common Player:		3.00
1	Barry Sanders	15.00
2	Ricky Williams	15.00
3	Terrell Davis	12.00
4	John Elway	12.00
5	Edgerrin James	25.00
6	Tim Couch	15.00
7	Peyton Manning	12.00
8	Kurt Warner	25.00
9	Randy Moss	15.00
10	Dan Marino	12.00
11	Brett Favre	15.00
12	Eddie George	3.00
13	Marvin Harrison	3.00
14	Jerry Rice	10.00
15	Emmitt Smith	12.00
16	Keyshawn Johnson	3.00
17	Drew Bledsoe	7.00
18	Marshall Faulk	3.00

1999 Score Supplemental Zenith Z-Team

This 20-card insert includ-ed the cream of the crop in the NFL. Each was pictured on clear plastic with holographic foil stamping and were sequentially numbered to 100.

		MT
Complete Set (20):		600.00
Common Player:		15.00
Production 100 Sets		
1	Steve Young	20.00
2	Barry Sanders	60.00
3	Fred Taylor	30.00

4	Marshall Faulk	15.00
5	Emmitt Smith	45.00
6	Brett Favre	60.00
7	Troy Aikman	30.00
8	Terrell Davis	45.00
9	Edgerrin James	85.00
10	Drew Bledsoe	20.00
11	Dan Marino	45.00
12	Randy Moss	60.00
13	Ricky Williams	60.00
14	Mark Brunell	20.00
15	Jake Plummer	25.00
16	Jerry Rice	30.00
17	Peyton Manning	45.00
18	Tim Couch	60.00
19	Eddie George	15.00
20	John Elway	45.00

1997 Score Board NFL Rookies

The 100-card set features the player's name at the top, while the logo of the teams that drafted him is included in a black stripe in the upper left corner. The '97 Rookies Score Board logo is in the lower center. The team's name is printed inside a black half oval at the bottom. The black stripe that runs along the left side of the back includes the various logos, player's name, bio and card number. To the right of the stripe is the player's photo, highlights and stats. The set was paralleled by the Dean's List, which was inserted 1:5 packs. Vintage rookie cards and auto-graphed rookie cards of current and ex-NFL players were also randomly inserted.

		MT
Complete Set (100):		10.00
Common Player:		.05
Minor Stars:		.10
1	Jake Plummer	2.00
2	Tony Gonzalez	.20
3	Trevor Pryce	.05
4	Greg Jones	.05
5	Koy Detmer	1.25
6	Rae Carruth	.75
7	Peter Boulware	.05
8	Warrick Dunn	2.00
9	Antowain Smith	.30
10	Troy Davis	1.00
11	David LaFleur	.30
12	Yatil Green	1.00
13	Michael Booker	.05
14	Shawn Springs	.30
15	Bryant Westbrook	.30
16	Byron Hanspard	.50
17	Darrell Russell	.05
18	Corey Dillon	1.00
19	Tyrus McCloud	.05
20	Reinard Wilson	.05
21	Adam Meadows	.05
22	Tremain Mack	.05
23	Ricky Parker	.05
24	George Jones	.05
25	Terry Battle	.05
26	Will Blackwell	.05
27	Jerald Sowell	.05
28	Isaac Byrd	.05
29	Chris Naeole	.05
30	Kevin Lockett	.05
31	Freddie Jones	.05
32	Pat Barnes	.05
33	Torrian Gray	.05
34	Brian Manning	.05
35	Dedric Ward	.05
36	Pete Monty	.05
37	Sam Madison	.05
38	Sedrick Shaw	.05
39	Mike Logan	.05
40	Albert Connell	.05
41	Canute Curtis	.05
42	Ronde Barber	.05
43	Orlando Pace	.75
44	Edward Perry	.05
45	Tiki Barber	.50
46	Kevin Jackson	.05
47	Jerry Wunsch	.05
48	Michael Hamilton	.05
49	Darnell Autry	.50
50	Jim Druckenmiller	1.25

51	James Farrior	.05
52	Derrick Mason	.05
53	Ty Howard	.05
54	Jason Taylor	.05
55	Reidel Anthony	1.00
56	Bert Berry	.05
57	Marc Edwards	.05
58	James Hamilton	.05
59	Ike Hilliard	1.00
60	Tommy Knight	.05
61	Walter Jones	.05
62	Chad Levitt	.05
63	Pratt Lyons	.05
64	Greg Clark	.05
65	Ryan Phillips	.05
66	Jason Martin	.05
67	Scott Sanderson	.05
68	Alshermond Singleton	.05
69	Duce Staley	.50
70	Jared Tomich	.05
71	Ross Verba	.05
72	Derrick Rodgers	.05
73	Mike Vrabel	.05
74	John Allred	.05
75	Bob Sapp	.05
76	Brad Otton	.05
77	Tarik Glenn	.05
78	Chad Scott	.05
79	Nathan Davis	.05
80	Henri Crockett	.05
81	Tarik Saleh	.05
82	Seth Payne	.05
83	Pete Chryplewicz	.05
84	Reidel Anthony	.50
85	Reinard Wilson	.05
86	Byron Hanspard	.20
87	Shawn Springs	.20
88	David LaFleur	.20
89	Troy Davis	.50
90	Warrick Dunn	1.00
91	Peter Boulware	.05
92	Rae Carruth	.20
93	Tony Gonzalez	.10
94	Jake Plummer	.25
95	Orlando Pace	.25
96	Ike Hilliard	.50
97	Kevin Jackson	.05
98	Jim Druckenmiller	.60
99	Shawn Springs	.20
100	Warrick Dunn	1.00

1997 Score Board NFL Rookies Dean's List

Dean's List is a parallel set of the NFL Rookies base cards. Dean's List cards were inserted one per five packs.

	MT
Dean's List Cards:	2x-3x

1997 Score Board NFL Rookies NFL War Room

The 20-card set was inserted 1:100 packs. It includes com-ments from NFL insiders on play-ers that were selected on draft day. The cards carry a "W" prefix.

	MT
Complete Set (20):	300.00

		MT
Common Player:		10.00
Minor Stars:		20.00
1	Yatil Green	45.00
2	Antowain Smith	20.00
3	Tony Gonzalez	20.00
4	Corey Dillon	30.00
5	Jake Plummer	30.00
6	Peter Boulware	10.00
7	Orlando Pace	30.00
8	Darrell Russell	10.00
9	Reinard Wilson	10.00
10	Shawn Springs	20.00
11	Bryant Westbrook	20.00
12	Rae Carruth	40.00
13	Warrick Dunn	80.00
14	David LaFleur	20.00
15	Byron Hanspard	30.00
16	Michael Booker	10.00
17	Reidel Anthony	45.00
18	Troy Davis	45.00
19	Chris Naeole	10.00
20	Jim Druckenmiller	60.00

1997 Score Board NFL Rookies Varsity Club

Inserted 1:36 packs, the 30-card set features the school pennant and team logo of the player's college or university. The cards are numbered and carry a "V" prefix.

		MT
Complete Set (30):		140.00
Common Player:		2.00
Minor Stars:		4.00
1	Tiki Barber	10.00
2	Sedrick Shaw	2.00
3	Kevin Lockett	2.00
4	Byron Hanspard	10.00
5	David LaFleur	6.00
6	Warrick Dunn	25.00
7	Yatil Green	15.00
8	Corey Dillon	6.00
9	Orlando Pace	10.00
10	Tony Gonzalez	4.00
11	Darrell Russell	2.00
12	Jake Plummer	10.00
13	Peter Boulware	2.00
14	Shawn Springs	6.00
15	Bryant Westbrook	6.00
16	Rae Carruth	12.00
17	Antowain Smith	6.00
18	Reidel Anthony	15.00
19	Michael Booker	2.00
20	Freddie Jones	2.00
21	Pat Barnes	2.00
22	Troy Davis	15.00
23	Walter Jones	2.00
24	Reinard Wilson	2.00
25	George Jones	2.00
26	Terry Battle	2.00
27	Tommy Knight	2.00
28	Tremain Mack	2.00
29	Jim Druckenmiller	20.00
30	Ike Hilliard	15.00

1997 Score Board Playbook By The Numbers

Playbook By The Numbers consists of a 50-card base set.

9	Jim Druckenmiller (Rookie)	2.50
10	Pat Barnes (Rookie)	.30

1997 Score Board Playbook Red Zone Stats

Red Zone Stats is a 10-card insert, seeded one per 20 packs. This insert has Silver Magnified (numbered to 1,000; inserted one per 21 packs) and Gold Magnified (numbered to 100; 1:210) parallel versions. They have a "RZ" prefix.

		MT
Complete Set (10):		75.00
Common Player:		2.50
Minor Stars:		5.00
Magnified Gold Cards:		4x-8x
Magnified Silver Cards:		1x
1	Emmitt Smith	15.00
2	Terry Allen	2.50
3	Troy Aikman	10.00
4	Brett Favre	20.00
5	John Elway	8.00
6	Drew Bledsoe	10.00
7	Terrell Davis	10.00
8	Karim Abdul-Jabbar	5.00
9	Curtis Martin	10.00
10	Warrick Dunn	10.00

1997 Score Board Playbook Standout Numbers

Standout Numbers is a 30-card insert which was inserted one per four packs. Standout Numbers also has Silver Magni-fied (numbered to 2,700, inserted one per three packs) and Gold Magnified (numbered to 270; 1:26) parallel versions. The cards are numbered with a "SN" prefix.

		MT
Complete Set (30):		75.00
Common Player:		1.00
Minor Stars:		2.00
Magnified Golds:		2x-4x
Magnified Silvers:		1x
1	Drew Bledsoe	5.00
2	Emmitt Smith	10.00
3	Cris Carter	1.00
4	Brett Favre	12.00
5	Jerome Bettis	2.00
6	Mark Brunell	5.00
7	John Elway	4.00
8	Troy Aikman	5.00
9	Steve Young	4.00
10	Kordell Stewart	5.00
11	Reggie White	2.00
12	Isaac Bruce	2.00
13	Dan Marino	10.00
14	Kevin Greene	1.00
15	Tim Brown	2.00
16	Terry Glenn	3.00
17	Ricky Watters	2.00
18	Carl Pickens	1.00
19	Keyshawn Johnson	2.00
20	Barry Sanders	5.00
21	Marshall Faulk	2.00
22	James Stewart	2.00
23	Jerry Rice	5.00
24	Curtis Martin	5.00
25	Herman Moore	2.00
26	Terry Allen	1.00
27	Eddie George	7.00
28	Warrick Dunn	5.00
29	Marcus Allen	5.00
30	Terrell Davis	5.00

1977 Seahawks Fred Meyer

The 13-card, 7-1/4" x 6" set, distributed by Fred Meyer

The base set is divided into five subsets: quarterbacks, running backs, wide receivers, defensive players and rookies. The base cards are numbered within their subset. Silver Magnified (se-quentially numbered to 2,000; inserted one per two packs) and Gold Magnified (numbered to 200; 1:21) parallel versions were also produced. Three insert sets were included in this product: Standout Numbers, Red Zone Stats and Master Signings.

		MT
Complete Set (50):		30.00
Common Player:		.10
Minor Stars:		.20
Gold Magnified Cards:		10x-20x
Silver Magnified Cards:		3x
Wax Box:		35.00
1	Troy Aikman (Quarterback)	1.00
2	Mark Brunell (Quarterback)	1.00
3	Dan Marino (Quarterback)	2.00
4	Brett Favre (Quarterback)	2.50
5	Kordell Stewart (Quarterback)	1.00
6	Drew Bledsoe (Quarterback)	1.00
7	John Elway (Quarterback)	.75
8	Kerry Collins (Quarterback)	.30
9	Steve Young (Quarterback)	.75
10	Jeff Blake (Quarterback)	.20
1	Emmitt Smith (Running Back)	2.00
2	Terrell Davis (Running Back)	1.00
3	Barry Sanders (Running Back)	1.00
4	Marshall Faulk (Running Back)	.20
5	Robert Smith (Running Back)	.10
6	Curtis Martin (Running Back)	1.00
7	Jerome Bettis (Running Back)	.20
8	Eddie George (Running Back)	1.50
9	Terry Allen (Running Back)	.10
10	Ricky Watters (Running Back)	.20
1	Carl Pickens (Wide Receiver)	.10
2	Michael Irvin (Wide Receiver)	.20
3	Herman Moore (Wide Receiver)	.20
4	Robert Brooks (Wide Receiver)	.10
5	Cris Carter (Wide Receiver)	.10
6	Terry Glenn (Wide Receiver)	.75
7	Tim Brown (Wide Receiver)	.10
8	Jerry Rice (Wide Receiver)	1.00
9	Keyshawn Johnson (Wide Receiver)	.30
10	Isaac Bruce (Wide Receiver)	.20
1	Simeon Rice (Defense)	.10
2	Peter Boulware (Defense)	.10
3	Bruce Smith (Defense)	.10
4	Deion Sanders (Defense)	.50
5	Reggie White (Defense)	.20
6	Darrell Russell (Defense)	.10
7	Greg Lloyd (Defense)	.10
8	Junior Seau (Defense)	.10
9	Shawn Springs (Defense)	.20
10	Cortez Kennedy (Defense)	.10
1	Tony Gonzalez (Rookie)	.30
2	Rae Carruth (Rookie)	.50
3	Warrick Dunn (Rookie)	4.00
4	Tiki Barber (Rookie)	.40
5	Antowain Smith (Rookie)	2.00
6	Corey Dillon (Rookie)	2.00
7	Troy Davis (Rookie)	.40
8	Danny Wuerffel (Rookie)	.60

Department Stores, feature a color action shot with a headshot inset in a lower corner (cards 3, 5, 12, and 13a have no insets). Seahawks quarterback Jim Zorn is represented on two No. 13 cards, one having no inset. All card backs are blank.

		NM
Complete Set (14):		75.00
Common Player:		5.00
1	Steve August	5.00
2	Autry Beamon	5.00
3	Terry Beeson	5.00
4	Dennis Boyd	5.00
5	Norm Evans	5.00
6	Sammy Green	5.00
7	Ron Howard	5.00
8	Steve Largent	20.00
9	Steve Myer	5.00
10	Steve Niehaus	5.00
11	Sherman Smith	5.00
12	Don Testerman	5.00
13A	Jim Zorn (No inset photo)	12.00
13B	Jim Zorn (With inset photo)	12.00

1977 Seahawks Team Issue

The 10-card, 5" x 7" set features black and white headshots of Seattle players with blank backs. A facsimile autograph also appears on each card front.

		NM
Complete Set (10):		75.00
Common Player:		5.00
1	Ron Howard	5.00
2	Steve Largent	25.00
3	John Leypoldt	5.00
4	Bob Lurtsema	5.00
5	Steve Myer	5.00
6	Steve Niehaus	5.00
7	Jack Patera (CO)	6.00
8	Sherman Smith	5.00
9	Don Testerman	5.00
10	Jim Zorn	12.00

1978-80 Seahawks Nalley's

The 24-card, 10-3/4" x 9" set was available on the box backs of eight-ounce Nalley's potato chip products. The color posed fronts feature a facsimile autograph with Seattle's schedule and player stats on the box sides. Prices are for complete boxes.

		NM
Complete Set (24):		750.00
Common Player (1-8):		25.00
Common Player (9-16):		20.00
Common Player (17-24):		15.00
1	Steve Largent	300.00
2	Autry Beamon	25.00
3	Jim Zorn	65.00
4	Sherman Smith	40.00
5	Ron Coder	25.00
6	Terry Beeson	25.00
7	Steve Niehaus	30.00
8	Ron Howard	25.00
9	Steve Myer	20.00
10	Tom Lynch	20.00
11	David Sims	20.00
12	John Yarno	20.00
13	Bill Gregory	25.00
14	Steve Raible	25.00
15	Dennis Boyd	20.00
16	Steve August	20.00
17	Keith Simpson	15.00
18	Michael Jackson	15.00
19	Manu Tuiasosopo	20.00
20	Sam McCullum	20.00
21	Keith Butler	15.00
22	Sam Akins	15.00
23	Dan Doornink	20.00
24	Dave Brown	20.00

1979 Seahawks Police

The 16-card, 2-5/8" x 4-1/8" set, sponsored by Coca-Cola, Kiwanis, the Washington State Crime Prevention Association and local law enforcement, contain "Tips from the Seahawks" on the card backs.

		NM
Complete Set (16):		12.00
Common Player:		.75
1	Steve August	.75
2	Autry Beamon	.75
3	Terry Beeson	.75
4	Dennis Boyd	.75
5	Dave Brown	.75
6	Efren Herrera	.75
7	Steve Largent	8.00
8	Tom Lynch	.75
9	Bob Newton	.75
10	Jack Patera (CO)	1.00
11	Sea Gal (Keri Truscan)	.75
12	Seahawk (Mascot)	.75
13	David Sims	.75
14	Sherman Smith	.75
15	John Yarno	.75
16	Jim Zorn	3.00

1980 Seahawks Police

The 16-card, 2-5/8" x 4-1/8" set, sponsored by local law enforcement, Coca-Cola, Kiwanis, the Washington State Crime Prevention Association and Ernst Home Centers, feature "tips from the Seahawks" on the card backs.

		NM
Complete Set (16):		10.00
Common Player:		.60
1	Sam McCullum	.60
2	Dan Doornink	.60
3	Sherman Smith	.60
4	Efren Herrera	.60
5	Bill Gregory	.60
6	Keith Simpson	.60
7	Manu Tuiasosopo	.60
8	Michael Jackson	.60
9	Steve Raible	.60
10	Steve Largent	6.00
11	Jim Zorn	2.00
12	Nick Bebout	.60
13	The Seahawk (mascot)	.60
14	Jack Patera (CO)	.75
15	Robert Hardy	.60
16	Keith Butler	.60

1980 Seahawks 7-Up

The 10-card, 2-3/8" x 3-1/4" set features a player closeup on the card fronts with player bio information on the card backs. Quarterback Jim Zorn and receiver Steve Largent do not appear due to their sponsorships with Darigold Dairy.

		NM
Complete Set (10):		125.00
Common Player:		12.00
1	Steve August	12.00
2	Terry Beeson	12.00
3	Dan Doornink	12.00
4	Michael Jackson	12.00
5	Tom Lynch	12.00
6	Steve Myer	12.00
7	Steve Raible	20.00
8	Sherman Smith	20.00
9	Manu Tuiasosopo	12.00
10	John Yarno	12.00

1981 Seahawks 7-Up

The 30-card, 3-1/2" x 5-1/2" set features color action shots and facsimile autographs on the card fronts. The card backs contain a brief player bio. As with the 1980 set, Zorn and Largent do not appear because of conflicting sponsorships.

		MT
Complete Set (30):		85.00
Common Player:		3.00
1	Sam Adkins	3.00
2	Steve August	3.00
3	Terry Beeson	3.00
4	Dennis Boyd	3.00
5	Dave Brown	4.00
6	Louis Bullard	3.00
7	Keith Butler	3.00
8	Peter Cronan	3.00
9	Dan Doornink	4.00
10	Jacob Green	6.00
11	Bill Gregory	3.00
12	Robert Hardy	3.00
13	Efren Herrera	3.00
14	Michael Jackson	3.00
15	Art Kuehn	3.00
16	Steve Largent	20.00
17	Tom Lynch	3.00
18	Sam McCullum	3.00
19	Steve Myer	3.00
20	Jack Patera (CO)	4.00
21	Steve Raible	3.00
22	The Sea Gals	3.00
23	The Seahawk Mascot	3.00
24	Keith Simpson	3.00
25	Sherman Smith	3.00
26	Manu Tuiasosopo	3.00
27	Herman Weaver	3.00
28	Cornell Webster	3.00
29	John Yarno	3.00
30	Jim Zorn	8.00

1982 Seahawks Police

The 16-card, 2-5/8" x 4-1/8" set, issued by the Washington State Crime Prevention Association, Kiwanis, Coca-Cola, local law enforcement and Ernst Home Centers, includes "Tips from the Seahawks" on the card backs and the set contains the card of team mascot Sea Gal (No. 4). Also, the cards of Sam McCullum and Jack Patera were distributed in lesser quantities.

		MT
Complete Set (16):		12.00
Common Player:		.40
1	Sam McCullum (SP)	2.00
2	Manu Tuiasosopo	.50
3	Sherman Smith	.60
4	Karen Godwin (Sea Gal)	.40
5	Dave Brown	.60
6	Keith Simpson	.40
7	Steve Largent	5.00
8	Michael Jackson	.40
9	Kenny Easley	.75
10	Dan Doornink	.40
11	Jim Zorn	2.00
12	Jack Patera (CO SP)	2.00
13	Jacob Green	.60
14	Dave Krieg	3.00
15	Steve August	.40
16	Keith Butler	.40

1982 Seahawks 7-Up

The 15-card, 3-1/2" x 5-1/2" set features color action shots on the card fronts with "Seahawks Fan Mail Courtesy" printed, as well as a facsimile autograph. The card backs include "Tips from the Seahawks" and the cards of Zorn and Largent are included with Darigold logo on the backs.

		MT
Complete Set (15):		75.00
Common Player:		3.00
1	Edwin Bailey	3.00
2	Dave Brown	3.00
3	Kenny Easley	5.00
4	Ron Essink	3.00
5	Jacob Green (No facsimile autograph)	5.00
6	Robert Hardy	3.00
7	John Harris	3.00
8	David Hughes	3.00
9	Paul Johns (HOR)	3.00
10	Kerry Justin	3.00
11	Dave Krieg	12.00
12	Steve Largent (Darigold logo or Gold-n-Soft)	20.00
13	Keith Simpson	3.00
14	Manu Tuiasosopo	3.00
15	Jim Zorn (HOR) (Darigold logo or Gold-n-Soft)	8.00

1984 Seahawks GTE

The 12-card, 3-1/2" x 5-1/2" set features a color shot with a headshot inset in a corner, along with a facsimile autograph on the card front. The card backs have a brief player bio.

		MT
Complete Set (12):		40.00
Common Player:		2.00
1	Kenny Easley	3.00
2	Jacob Green	3.00
3	John Harris	2.00
4	Norm Johnson	4.00
5	Chuck Knox (CO)	3.00
6	Dave Krieg	7.00
7	Steve Largent	16.00
8	Joe Nash	2.00
9	Keith Simpson	2.00
10	Mike Tice	2.00
11	Curt Warner	7.00
12	Charley Young	3.00

1984 Seahawks Nalley's

The four-card, 10-3/4" x 9" set was available on the box backs of Nalley's potato chips. The box sides contain Seattle's schedule and player bio information. Prices are for complete boxes.

		MT
Complete Set (4):		50.00
Common Player:		10.00
1	Kenny Easley	10.00
2	Dave Krieg	15.00
3	Steve Largent	25.00
4	Curt Warner	15.00

1985 Seahawks Police

The 16-card, 2-5/8" x 4-1/8" set was sponsored by Kiwanis, Coca-Cola, KOMO-TV4, Mc-Donald's, the Washington State Crime Prevention Association and local law enforcement. The card backs contain "Tips from the Seahawks."

		MT
Complete Set (16):		8.00
Common Player:		.40
1	Dave Brown	.50
2	Jeff Bryant	.50
3	Blair Bush	.50
4	Keith Butler	.40
5	Dan Doornink	.40
6	Kenny Easley	1.00
7	Jacob Green	.60
8	John Harris	.40
9	Norm Johnson	1.00
10	Chuck Knox (CO)	1.00
11	Dave Krieg	1.50
12	Steve Largent	3.00
13	Joe Nash	.50
14	Bruce Scholtz	.40
15	Curt Warner	1.25
16	Fredd Young	.60

1986 Seahawks Police

The 16-card, 2-5/8" x 4-1/8" set, sponsored by local law enforcement, contain "Tips from the Seahawks" on the card backs.

		MT
Complete Set (16):		8.00
Common Player:		.40
1	Edwin Bailey	.40
2	Dave Brown	.50
3	Jeff Bryant	.50
4	Blair Bush	.50
5	Keith Butler	.40
6	Kenny Easley	.60
7	Jacob Green	.60
8	Michael Jackson	.40
9	Chuck Knox (CO)	.60
10	Dave Krieg	1.50
11	Steve Largent	3.00
12	Joe Nash	.50
13	Bruce Scholtz	.40
14	Terry Taylor	.40
15	Curt Warner	.75
16	Fredd Young	.60

1987 Seahawks GTE

The 24-card, 3-5/8" x 5-1/2" set features color fronts with a facsimile player signature. The card backs have a career summary and a greeting from the player with another autograph.

		MT
Complete Set (24):		60.00
Common Player:		1.50
1	Edwin Bailey	1.50
2	Brian Bosworth	2.50
3	Dave Brown	2.00
4	Jeff Bryant	2.00
5	Bobby Joe Edmonds	3.00
6	Jacob Green	3.00
7	Michael Jackson	1.50
8	Norm Johnson	2.00
9	Jeff Kemp	2.50
10	Chuck Knox (CO)	3.00
11	Dave Krieg	5.00
12	Steve Largent	10.00
13	Ron Mattes	1.50
14	Bryan Millard	1.50
15	Paul Moyer	1.50
16	Eugene Robinson	2.00
17	Paul Skansi	1.50
18	Kelly Stouffer	1.50
19	Terry Taylor	1.50
20	Mike Tice	1.50
21	Daryl Turner	2.00
22	Curt Warner	4.00
23	John L. Williams	2.00
24	Fredd Young	2.00

1987 Seahawks Police

The 16-card, 2-5/8" x 4-1/8" set features a silver border with a blue/green Seahawks logo. The card backs contain a safety tip.

		MT
Complete Set (16):		5.00
Common Player:		.35
1	Jeff Bryant	.35
2	Kenny Easley	.60
3	Bobby Joe Edmonds	.35
4	Jacob Green	.60
5	Chuck Knox (CO)	.60
6	Dave Krieg	1.50
7	Steve Largent	2.50
8	Ron Mattes	.35
9	Bryan Millard	.35
10	Eugene Robinson	.60
11	Bruce Scholtz	.35
12	Paul Skansi	.35
13	Curt Warner	.75
14	John L. Williams	1.00
15	Mike Wilson	.35
16	Fredd Young	.35

1987 Seahawks Snyder's/Franz

The 12-card, standard-size set was distributed in the Spokane area (Snyder bread) and Portland area (Franz bread). The card fronts contain a color photo with blue borders while the backs feature a player career summary.

		MT
Complete Set (12):		60.00
Common Player:		5.00
1	Jeff Bryant	5.00
2	Keith Butler	5.00
3	Randy Edwards	5.00
4	Byron Franklin	5.00
5	Jacob Green	7.00
6	Dave Krieg	10.00
7	Bryan Millard	5.00
8	Paul Moyer	5.00
9	Eugene Robinson	7.00
10	Mike Tice	5.00
11	Daryl Turner	6.00
12	Curt Warner	8.00

1988 Seahawks Domino's

The 50-card, 2-1/2" x 8-1/2" set was distributed in panel strips with coupons for each Domino's pizza ordered. The first panel contained nine-cards and included a 12-1/2" x 8-1/2" team photo. Cards 10-13, 14-17, 18-21, 22-25, 26-29, 30-33, 34-38, 39-42, 43-46 and 47-50 were issued on a weekly basis.

		MT
Complete Set (51):		45.00
Common Player:		.60
1	Steve Largent	10.00
2	Kelly Stouffer	.75
3	Bobby Joe Edmonds	1.00
4	Patrick Hunter	.75
5	Ventrella/Valle/Gellos	.60
6	Edwin Bailey	.60
7	Alonzo Mitz	.60
8	Tommy Kane	1.00
9	Chuck Knox (CO)	1.00
10	Curt Warner	2.00
11	Alvin Powell	.60
12	Joe Nash	.60
13	Brian Blades	3.00
14	Blair Bush	.75
15	Melvin Jenkins	.60
16	Ruben Rodriguez	.60
17	Tommie Agee	.60
18	Eugene Robinson	.75
19	Dwayne Harper	.60
20	Raymond Butler	.60
21	Jeff Kemp	1.00
22	Norm Johnson	.75
23	Bryan Millard	.60
24	Tony Woods	1.00
25	Paul Skansi	.60
26	Jacob Green	1.00
27	Randall Morris	.60
28	Mike Tice	.60
29	Kevin Harmon	.60
30	Dave Krieg	2.50
31	Nesby Glasgow	.75
32	Bruce Scholtz	.60
33	John Spagnola	.60
34	Jeff Bryant	.75
35	Stan Eisenhooth	.60
36	Dave Wyman	.60
37	Greg Gaines	.60
38	Charlie Jones (NBC ANN)	
39	Terry Taylor	.60
40	Vernon Dean	.60
41	Mike Wilson	.60
42	Darrin Miller	.60
43	John L. Williams	2.50
44	Grant Feasel	.60
45	M.L. Johnson	.60
46	Ken Clarke	.75
47	Brian Bosworth	.75
48	Ron Mattes	.60
49	Paul Moyer	.60
50	Rufus Porter	1.00
NNO	Team Photo (Large size)	7.00

1988 Seahawks Police

The 16-card, 2-5/8" x 4-1/8" set features color photos with gray borders and the backs include safety tips. Terry Taylor's card was pulled from distribution after he was suspended from the team.

		MT
Complete Set (16):		10.00
Common Player:		.50
1	Brian Bosworth	1.00
2	Jeff Bryant	.60
3	Raymond Butler	.50
4	Jacob Green	1.00
5	Patrick Hunter	.60
6	Norm Johnson	.75
7	Chuck Knox (CO)	.75
8	Dave Krieg	1.50
9	Steve Largent	2.50
10	Ron Mattes	.50
11	Bryan Millard	.50
12	Paul Moyer	.50
13	Terry Taylor (SP)	2.50
14	Curt Warner	1.00
15	John L. Williams	1.25
16	Fredd Young (SP)	4.50

1988 Seahawks Snyder's/Franz

The 12-card, standard-size set was issued in the Spokane area in Snyder's bread and in the Portland area in Franz bread. The card fronts have a color photo with blue borders.

		MT
Complete Set (10):		125.00
Common Player:		12.00
1	Steve August	12.00
2	Terry Beeson	12.00
3	Dan Doornink	15.00
4	Michael Jackson	12.00
5	Tom Lynch	12.00
6	Steve Myer	12.00
7	Steve Raible	20.00
8	Sherman Smith	20.00
9	Manu Tuiasosopo	15.00
10	John Yarno	12.00

1989 Seahawks Oroweat

The 20-card, standard-size set was produced for Oroweat by Pacific and features silver borders. The horizontal backs contain player bio and stat information with career highlights. Each card was available in Oroweat's Oatnut Bread with a total distribution of 1.5 million.

		MT
Complete Set (20):		25.00
Common Player:		.60
1	Paul Moyer	.60
2	Dave Wyman	.60
3	Tony Woods	1.00
4	Kelly Stouffer	1.00
5	Brian Blades	3.00
6	Norm Johnson	1.50
7	Curt Warner	2.00
8	John L. Williams	2.00
9	Edwin Bailey	.60
10	Jacob Green	1.00
11	Paul Skansi	.60
12	Jeff Bryant	.75
13	Bruce Scholtz	.60
14	Dave Krieg	3.00
15	Steve Largent	8.00
16	Joe Nash	.75
17	Mike Wilson	.60
18	Ron Mattes	.60
19	Grant Feasel	.60
20	Bryan Millard	.60

1989 Seahawks Police

The 16-card, 2-5/8" x 4-1/8" set feature light blue borders with color action shots. The card backs contain safety tips, except for Largent's card, which lists his NFL records.

		MT
Complete Set (16):		5.00
Common Player:		.40
1	Brian Blades	1.00
2	Brian Bosworth	.50
3	Jeff Bryant	.50
4	Jacob Green	.60
5	Chuck Knox (CO)	.60
6	Dave Krieg	1.25
7	Steve Largent	2.00
8	Bryan Millard	.40
9	Rufus Porter	.50
10	Paul Moyer	.40
11	Eugene Robinson	.50
12	Ruben Rodriguez	.40
13	Kelly Stouffer	.50
14	Curt Warner	1.00
15	John L. Williams	1.00
16	Tony Woods	.60

1990 Seahawks Oroweat

The 50-card, regular-size set, produced by Pacific, was available in loaves of Oroweat's Oat Nut, Health Nut and Twelve Grain breads. The first 20 cards of the set were issued before the season with the remaining cards issued during the season. No card No. 25 was produced.

		MT
Complete Set (50):		30.00
Common Player (1-20):		.35
Common Player (21-50):		.50
1	Dave Krieg	1.50
2	Rick Donnelly	.35
3	Brian Blades	1.50
4	Cortez Kennedy	1.75
5	John L. Williams	1.50
6	Jeff Chadwick	.35
7	Thom Kaumeyer	.35
8	Bryan Millard	.35
9	Eugene Robinson	.50
10	Jacob Green	.50
11	Willie Bouyer	.35
12	Jeff Bryant	.50
13	Chris Warren	3.00
14	Derrick Fenner	.75
15	Paul Skansi	.35
16	Joe Cain	.35
17	Tommy Kane	.60
18	Tom Flores (GM)	.60

19	Terry Wooden	.50
20	Tony Woods	.60
21	Ricky Andrews	.50
22	Joe Tofflemire	.50
23	Ned Bolcar	.50
24A	Kelly Stouffer	1.00
24B	Melvin Jenkins	.50
26	Norm Johnson	.75
27	Eric Hayes	.50
28	Mike Morris	.50
29	Edwin Bailey	.50
30	Ron Heller	.50
31	Darren Comeaux	.60
32	Andy Heck	.60
33	Ronnie Lee	.50
34	Robert Blackmon	.60
35	Joe Nash	.60
36	Patrick Hunter	.60
37	Darrick Brilz	.50
38	Ron Mattes	.50
39	Nesby Glasgow	.60
40	Dwayne Harper	.50
41	Chuck Knox (CO)	.75
42	Travis McNeal	.60
43	Derek Loville	1.50
44	Dave Wyman	.50
45	Louis Clark	.50
46	Grant Feasel	.50
47	James Jones	.50
48	Rufus Porter	1.00
49	Jeff Kemp	1.00
50	James Jefferson	.60
NNO	Title Card	3.00
		.50

1990 Seahawks Police

Travis McNeal
Tight End 6'3" 248 lbs. Tennessee-Chat.

The 16-card, 2-5/8" x 4-1/8" set has green borders around a color action shot with safety tips appearing on the backs.

		MT
Complete Set (16):		5.00
Common Player:		.35
1	Brian Blades	.75
2	Grant Feasel	.35
3	Jacob Green	.75
4	Andy Heck	.50
5	James Jefferson	.50
6	Norm Johnson	.75
7	Cortez Kennedy	1.00
8	Chuck Knox (CO)	.75
9	Dave Krieg	1.00
10	Travis McNeal	.35
11	Bryan Millard	.35
12	Rufus Porter	.50
13	Paul Skansi	.50
14	John L. Williams	.75
15	Tony Woods	.50
16	David Wyman	.35

1991 Seahawks Oroweat

The 50-card, standard-size set, produced by Pacific, was distributed in loaves of Oroweat bread and in five-card packs at a Seattle home game. The cards are very similar to Pacific's 1991 inaugural NFL set, except for the Oroweat logo in the upper right corner of the card front.

		MT
Complete Set (50):		30.00
Common Player:		.50
1	Tommy Kane	.50
2	Norm Johnson	.75
3	Robert Blackmon	.50
4	Mike Tice	.50
5	Cortez Kennedy	1.50
6	Bryan Millard	.50
7	Tony Woods	.50
8	Paul Skansi	.50
9	John L. Williams	1.50
10	Terry Wooden	.50
11	Brian Blades	1.25
12	Jacob Green	.75
13	Joe Nash	.75

14	Eugene Robinson	.75
15	Rufus Porter	.75
16	Andy Heck	.50
17	Derrick Fenner	1.00
18	Nesby Glasgow	.50
19	Chris Warren	3.00
20	Dave Krieg	1.50
21	Vann McElroy	.50
22	Jeff Bryant	.50
23	Warren Wheat	.50
24	Marcus Cotton	.50
25	David Wyman	.50
26	Joe Cain	.50
27	Darrick Brilz	.50
28	Eric Hayes	.50
29	Ronnie Lee	.50
30	Louis Clark	.50
31	James Jones	.50
32	Dwayne Harper	.50
33	Grant Feasel	.50
34	Trey Junkin	.50
35	James Jefferson	.50
36	Edwin Bailey	.50
37	Derrick Loville	1.50
38	Travis McNeal	.50
39	Rick Donnelly	.50
40	Rod Stephens	.50
41	Darren Comeaux	.50
42	Brian Davis	.50
43	Bill Hitchcock	.50
44	Jeff Chadwick	.75
45	Patrick Hunter	.50
46	David Daniels	.50
47	Doug Thomas	.50
48	Dan McGwire	.75
49	John Kasay	.75
50	Jeff Kemp	.75
NNO	Title Card	2.50

1992 Seahawks Oroweat

The 50-card, regular-size set, produced by Pacific, was delivered in various loaves of Oroweat bread. The card design is very similar to the base 1992 Pacific set, except for the Oroweat and KIRO Newsradio logos.

		MT
Complete Set (51):		25.00
Common Player:		.50
1	Brian Blades	1.00
2	Patrick Hunter	.75
3	Jeff Bryant	.75
4	Robert Blackmon	.50
5	Joe Cain	.50
6	Grant Feasel	.50
7	Dan McGwire	.75
8	David Wyman	.50
9	Jacob Green	.75
10	Theo Adams	.50
11	Brian Davis	.50
12	Andy Heck	.50
13	Bill Hitchcock	.50
14	Joe Nash	.50
15	Rod Stephens	.50
16	John Hunter	.50
17	Paul Green	.50
18	James Jones	.50
19	Robb Thomas	.50
20	Tony Woods	.50
21	Dedrick Dodge	.50
22	Tracy Johnson	.50
23	Darrick Brilz	.50
24	Joe Tofflemire	.50
25	Louis Clark	.50
26	Rueben Mayes	.75
27	Natu Tuataloa	.50
28	Terry Wooden	.75
29	Tommy Kane	.50
30	Stan Gelbaugh	.75
31	Nesby Glasgow	.50
32	Kelly Stouffer	.50
33	Ray Roberts	.50
34	Doug Thomas	.50
35	David Daniels	.50
36	John Kasay	.75
37	Cortez Kennedy	.75
38	Tyrone Rodgers	.50
39	Bryan Millard	.50
40	Eugene Robinson	.75
41	Malcolm Frank	.50
42	Dwayne Harper	.50
43	Ron Heller	.50
44	Rick Tuten	.50
45	Trey Junkin	.50
46	Bob Spitulski	.50
47	Chris Warren	2.00
48	John L. Williams	.75
49	Ronnie Lee	.50
50	Rufus Porter	.75
NNO	Title/Ad Card	1.00

1993 Seahawks Oroweat

The 50-card, standard size set, sponsored by Oroweat and KIRO Newsradio, was produced by Pacific. The cards' design is very similar to Pacific's 1993

14	Eugene Robinson	.75
15	Rufus Porter	.75
16	Andy Heck	.50
17	Derrick Fenner	1.00
18	Nesby Glasgow	.50
19	Chris Warren	3.00
20	Dave Krieg	1.50
21	Vann McElroy	.50
22	Jeff Bryant	.50
23	Warren Wheat	.50
24	Marcus Cotton	.50
25	David Wyman	.50
26	Joe Cain	.50
27	Darrick Brilz	.50
28	Eric Hayes	.50
29	Ronnie Lee	.50
30	Louis Clark	.50
31	James Jones	.50
32	Dwayne Harper	.50
33	Grant Feasel	.50
34	Trey Junkin	.50
35	James Jefferson	.50
36	Edwin Bailey	.50
37	Derrick Loville	1.50
38	Travis McNeal	.50
39	Rick Donnelly	.50
40	Rod Stephens	.50
41	Darren Comeaux	.50
42	Brian Davis	.50
43	Bill Hitchcock	.50
44	Jeff Chadwick	.75
45	Patrick Hunter	.50
46	David Daniels	.50
47	Doug Thomas	.50
48	Dan McGwire	.75
49	John Kasay	.75
50	Jeff Kemp	.75
NNO	Title Card	2.50

base set and were included in various loaves of Oroweat bread.

		MT
Complete Set (50):		25.00
Common Player:		.50
1	Cortez Kennedy	1.00
2	Robb Thomas	.75
3	Rueben Mayes	.75
4	Rick Tuten	.50
5	Tracy Johnson	.50
6	Michael Bates	.50
7	Andy Heck	.50
8	Stan Gelbaugh	.75
9	Dan McGwire	.75
10	Mike Keim	.50
11	Grant Feasel	.50
12	Brian Blades	1.00
13	Tyrone Rodgers	.50
14	Paul Green	.50
15	Rafael Robinson	.50
16	John Kasay	.75
17	Chris Warren	2.00
18	Michael Sinclair	.50
19	John L. Williams	.75
20	Bob Spitolin	.50
21	Eugene Robinson	.75
22	Patrick Hunter	.75
23	Kevin Murphy	.50
24	Dave McCloughan	.50
25	Rick Mirer	5.00
26	Ray Donaldson	.75
27	E.J. Junior	.75
28	Jeff Bryant	.75
29	Ferrell Edmunds	.50
30	Tommy Kane	.50
31	Terry Wooden	.75
32	Doug Thomas	.75
33	Carlton Gray	.50
34	Kelvin Martin	.75
35	Rod Stephens	.50
36	Darrick Brilz	.50
37	Joe Tofflemire	.50
38	James Jefferson	.50
39	Rufus Porter	.75
40	Jeff Blackshear	.50
41	Dwayne Harper	.50
42	Ray Roberts	.50
43	Robert Blackmon	.50
44	Joe Nash	.50
45	Michael McCrary	.50
46	Trey Junkin	.50
47	Natu Tuatagaloa	.50
48	Bill Hitchcock	.50
49	Jon Vaughn	.75
50	Dean Wells	.50

1994 Seahawks Oroweat

CHRIS WARREN

The 50-card, standard-size set, produced by Pacific, was issued in various loaves of Oroweat bread in the Northwest area. The cards are almost identical in design to Pacific's 1994 football set, except for the Oroweat logo in the upper right corner of the card front.

		MT
Complete Set (50):		25.00
Common Player:		.50
1	Brian Blades	.75
2	Terrence Warren	.50
3	Carlton Gray	.50
4	Bob Spitulski	.50
5	Dean Wells	.50
6	Lamar Smith	.50
7	Michael Bates	.50
8	Duane Bickett	.60
9	Cortez Kennedy	1.00
10	Dave McCloughan	.50
11	Tracy Johnson	.50
12	Eugene Robinson	.60
13	Jeff Blackshear	.50
14	Tyrone Rodgers	.50
15	Trey Junkin	.50
16	Ferrell Edmunds	.50
17	Tony Brown	.50
18	Orlando Watters	.50
19	John Kasay	.60
20	Rafael Robinson	.50
21	Kelvin Martin	.60
22	Stan Gelbaugh	.50
23	Steve Smith	.50
24	Ray Donaldson	.60

25	Rufus Porter	.50
26	Patrick Hunter	.60
27	Terry Wooden	.60
28	Sam Adams	.60
29	Mack Strong	.60
30	Chris Warren	1.25
31	Bill Hitchcock	.50
32	David Brandon	.50
33	Michael McCrary	.50
34	Jon Vaughn	.60
35	Paul Green	.50
36	Mike Keim	.50
37	Joe Tofflemire	.50
38	Rick Tuten	.50
39	Rick Mirer	3.00
40	Rod Stephens	.50
41	Robert Blackmon	.50
42	Howard Ballard	.50
43	Michael Sinclair	.50
44	Kevin Mawae	.50
45	Brent Williams	.50
46	Ray Roberts	.50
47	Robb Thomas	.60
48	Antonio Edwards	.50
49	Dan McGwire	.50
50	Joe Nash	.50

1982 Sears-Roebuck

The 12-card, 5" x 7" set, issued by 37 different Sears district stores, closely resembles the Marketcom posters. The card backs contain bio and career highlight information with the Sears Roebuck logo on the card back bottom. Because of the football strike in 1982, many of the cards were not distributed and were either destroyed or thrown out.

		MT
Complete Set (12):		265.00
Common Player:		8.00
1	Ken Anderson	15.00
2	Terry Bradshaw	25.00
3	Earl Campbell	25.00
4	Dwight Clark	8.00
5	Cris Collinsworth	8.00
6	Tony Dorsett	20.00
7	Dan Fouts	18.00
8	Franco Harris	20.00
9	Joe Montana	75.00
10	Walter Payton	40.00
11	Randy White	15.00
12	Kellen Winslow	15.00

1993 Select

DREW BLEDSOE

Score's 1993 Select set includes 200 cards which are framed on two sides by green. A 10-card insert set, Gridiron Skills, was also produced; cards were randomly inserted in packs.

		MT
Complete Set (200):		40.00
Common Player:		.25
Minor Stars:		.50
Wax Box:		100.00
1	Steve Young	3.00
2	Andre Reed	.50
3	Deion Sanders	2.00
4	Harold Green	.25
5	Wendell Davis	.25
6	Mike Johnson	.25
7	Troy Aikman	3.00
8	Johnny Mitchell	.25
9	Dale Carter	.25
10	Bruce Matthews	.25
11	Terrell Buckley	.25
12	Steve Emtman	.25
13	Neil Smith	.25
14	Tim Brown	.50
15	Chris Doleman	.25
16	Dan Marino	6.00
17	Terry McDaniel	.25
18	Neal Anderson	.25
19	Phil Simms	.25
20	Jeff Lageman	.25
21	Jerry Rice	3.00
22	Dermontti Dawson	.25
23	Reggie Cobb	.25
24	Junior Seau	.50
25	Darrell Green	.25
26	Chris Warren	.25

27	Randall Cunningham	.50
28	Bruce Smith	.25
29	Bryan Cox	.25
30	David Klingler	.25
31	Chip Lohmiller	.25
32	Eric Metcalf	.25
33	Ken Norton	.25
34	John Elway	3.00
35	Harris Barton	.25
36	Tim Barnett	.25
37	Rodney Hampton	.50
38	Desmond Howard	.50
39	Tom Rathman	.25
40	Derrick Thomas	.50
41	Randal Hill	.25
42	Steve Wisniewski	.25
43	Brett Favre	8.00
44	Darryl Talley	.25
45	Shane Conlan	.25
46	Anthony Miller	.50
47	Randall McDaniel	.25
48	Rod Woodson	.25
49	Eric Martin	.25
50	Ronnie Lott	.25
51	Chris Spielman	.25
52	Vincent Brown	.25
53	Donnell Woolford	.25
54	Richmond Webb	.25
55	Emmitt Smith	6.00
56	Haywood Jeffires	.25
57	Jim Kelly	.25
58	James Francis	.25
59	Steve Wallace	.25
60	Jarrod Bunch	.25
61	Lawrence Dawsey	.25
62	Steve Atwater	.25
63	Art Monk	.50
64	Eric Green	.25
65	Lawrence Taylor	.50
66	Ronnie Harmon	.25
67	Fred Barnett	.25
68	Cortez Kennedy	.25
69	Mark Collins	.25
70	Howie Long	.50
71	Jackie Harris	.25
72	Irving Fryar	.25
73	Jim Everett	.25
74	Troy Vincent	.25
75	Cris Carter	.50
76	Boomer Esiason	.25
77	Sam Mills	.25
78	Lorenzo White	.25
79	Andre Rison	.50
80	Quentin Coryatt	.25
81	Steve McMichael	.25
82	Nick Lowery	.25
83	Michael Irvin	.50
84	Thurman Thomas	.50
85	Bill Romanowski	.25
86	Carl Pickens	2.00
87	Tim McDonald	.25
88	Bernie Kosar	.25
89	Greg Lloyd	.25
90	Barry Sanders	5.00
91	Shannon Sharpe	.50
92	Henry Thomas	.25
93	Barry Foster	.25
94	Antone Davis	.25
95	Stan Humphries	.50
96	Eric Swann	.25
97	Mike Pritchard	.25
98	Reggie White	.50
99	Jeff Hostetler	.25
100	Willie Anderson	.25
101	Gary Clark	.25
102	Morten Andersen	.25
103	Leonard Russell	.25
104	Chris Hinton	.25
105	John Stephens	.25
106	Byron Evans	.25
107	Warren Moon	.50
108	Marv Cook	.25
109	*Carlton Gray*	.25
110	Jay Novacek	.25
111	Gary Anderson	.25
112	Andre Tippett	.25
113	Cornelius Bennett	.25
114	Clyde Simmons	.25
115	Jeff George	.50
116	Audray McMillian	.25
117	Mark Carrier	.25
118	Vaughan Johnson	.25
119	Kevin Greene	.25
120	John Taylor	.25
121	Jerry Ball	.25
122	Pat Swilling	.25
123	*George Teague*	.50
124	Ricky Reynolds	.25
125	Marcus Allen	.50
126	Henry Jones	.25
127	Ricky Watters	.50
128	Leon Searcy	.25
129	Chris Miller	.25
130	Jim Harbaugh	.50
131	Luis Sharpe	.25
132	Simon Fletcher	.25
133	Eric Allen	.25
134	Carlton Haselrig	.25
135	Harvey Williams	.25
136	Leslie O'Neal	.25
137	Sterling Sharpe	.50
138	Tim Harris	.25
139	Mark Rypien	.25
140	Harry Galbreath	.25
141	Sean Gilbert	.25
142	Keith Jackson	.25
143	Mark Clayton	.25
144	Guy McIntyre	.25
145	Jessie Tuggle	.25

146	Leonard Marshall	.25
147	Willie Davis	.25
148	Herman Moore	2.00
149	Charles Haley	.25
150	Amp Lee	.25
151	Gary Zimmerman	.25
152	Bennie Blades	.25
153	Pierce Holt	.25
154	Edgar Bennett	.50
155	Joe Montana	4.00
156	Ted Washington	.25
157	Hardy Nickerson	.25
158	Rohn Stark	.25
159	Brent Jones	.25
160	Eugene Robinson	.25
161	Pepper Johnson	.25
162	Dan Saleaumua	.25
163	Seth Joyner	.25
165	Mike Munchak	.25
166	*Drew Bledsoe*	15.00
167	*Curtis Conway*	3.00
168	*Lincoln Kennedy*	.50
169	*Dana Stubblefield*	1.00
170	*Wayne Simmons*	.50
171	*Garrison Hearst*	5.00
172	*Jerome Bettis*	8.00
173	*Eric Curry*	.50
174	*Natrone Means*	5.00
175	*Glyn Milburn*	.50
176	*Marvin Jones*	.50
177	*O.J. McDuffie*	3.00
178	*Dan Williams*	.50
179	*Rick Mirer*	.75
180	*John Copeland*	.50
181	*Willie Roaf*	.50
182	*Patrick Bates*	.50
183	*Troy Drayton*	.75
184	*Vincent Brisby*	.50
185	*Iro Smith*	.50
186	Marion Butts	.25
187	Wayne Martin	.25
188	Brian Blades	.25
189	Mel Gray	.25
190	Mark Stepnoski	.25
191	Ernest Givins	.25
192	Steve Tasker	.25
193	Tim Grunhard	.25
194	Stanley Richard	.25
195	Jeff Wright	.25
196	Rodney Peete	.25
197	Tunch Ilkin	.25
198	Rich Camarillo	.25
199	Erik Williams	.25
200	Pete Stoyanovich	.25

1993 Select Gridiron Skills

These cards were random inserts in 1993 Score Select foil packs at a rate of about one every 72 packs. Five top wide receivers and five top quarterbacks are represented. The card front has a player action photo against a shiny, metallic-like background. The player's name and position are at the bottom in a red stripe, along with the set logo. The back has a player photo and a description of the skills he brings to the football field. Each card is numbered.

		MT
Complete Set (10):		250.00
Common Player:		5.00
Minor Stars:		10.00
1	Warren Moon	10.00
2	Steve Young	30.00
3	Dan Marino	60.00
4	John Elway	40.00
5	Troy Aikman	30.00
6	Sterling Sharpe	10.00
7	Jerry Rice	30.00
8	Andre Rison	10.00
9	Haywood Jeffires	5.00
10	Michael Irvin	10.00

1993 Select Young Stars

These metallic-like cards, sold as a set in a black box, use FX printing technology. Each card front has a color action photo against a tombstone-like background. The player's name and "Young Stars" are written at the top of the card, above the arch. The Select logo is in the lower left corner. The front and back use team colors in the design. The back has a team helmet in the center, above a player profile. Cards are numbered. There were 5,900 sets produced; each includes a certificate of authenticity which indicates the set's serial number.

		MT
Complete Set (38):		50.00
Common Player:		1.00
1	Brett Favre	10.00
2	Anthony Miller	1.00
3	Rodney Hampton	2.50
4	Cortez Kennedy	1.00
5	Junior Seau	2.50
6	Ricky Watters	2.50
7	Terry Allen	1.50
8	Drew Bledsoe	4.00
9	Rick Mirer	4.00
10	Jeff Graham	1.00
11	Barry Foster	1.00
12	Eric Green	1.00
13	Troy Aikman	10.00
14	Michael Haynes	1.00
15	Johnny Mitchell	1.00
16	Lawrence Dawsey	1.00
17	Mo Lewis	1.00
18	Andre Ware	1.00
19	Neil O'Donnell	2.00
20	Broderick Thomas	1.00
21	Tim Barnett	1.00
22	Fred Barnett	1.00
23	Carl Pickens	3.00
24	Santana Dotson	1.00
25	Sean Gilbert	1.00
26	Quentin Coryatt	1.00
27	Arthur Marshall	1.00
28	Dale Carter	1.00
29	Henry Jones	1.00
30	Terrell Buckley	1.00
31	Tommy Vardell	1.00
32	Russell Maryland	1.00
33	Steve Emtman	1.00
34	Jarrod Bunch	1.00
35	Alfred Williams	1.00
36	Brian Mitchell	1.00
37	Chris Warren	3.00
38	Deion Sanders	4.00

1994 Select Samples

The seven-card, regular-sized set was issued to preview the 1994 Select set. The cards are virtually identical to the base set and include a Canton Bound and Future Force insert sample. The card numbers are the same as the base card counterparts.

		MT
Complete Set (7):		10.00
Common Player:		1.00
5	Rod Woodson	1.00
19	Junior Seau	1.50
33	Mark Carrier (DB)	1.00
218	Charlie Garner	1.00
CB4	Barry Sanders	4.00
FF2	Drew Bledsoe	4.00
NNO	Title Card	1.00

Values quoted in this guide reflect the retail price of a card — the price a collector can expect to pay when buying a card from a dealer. The wholesale price — that which a collector can expect to receive from a dealer when selling cards — will be significantly lower, depending on desirability and condition.

1994 Select

Select consists of a 225-card base set. The cards feature a full-bleed photo and a small, oval-shaped, black and white photo with a gold-foil border on the front. A 25-card rookie subset is included in the base series. Insert sets in Select include Canton Bound (12 cards, 1:48) and Future Force (12 cards, 1:48).

		MT
Complete Set (225):		30.00
Common Player:		.15
Minor Stars:		.30
Wax Box:		80.00
1	Emmitt Smith	3.00
2	Bruce Smith	.15
3	Randall McDaniel	.15
4	Drew Bledsoe	2.50
5	Rod Woodson	.15
6	Richard Dent	.15
7	Norm Johnson	.15
8	Jim Everett	.15
9	Harold Green	.15
10	John Elway	3.00
11	Barry Sanders	4.00
12	Sterling Sharpe	.30
13	Marcus Robertson	.15
14	Steve Wisniewski	.15
15	Irving Fryar	.15
16	Tyrone Hughes	.15
17	Garrison Hearst	1.00
18	Randall Cunningham	.50
19	Junior Seau	.30
20	Rick Mirer	.30
21	Jerry Rice	2.00
22	Eric Metcalf	.15
23	Roosevelt Potts	.15
24	Neil Smith	.15
25	Jerome Bettis	1.00
26	Keith Hamilton	.15
27	Hardy Nickerson	.15
28	Steve Tasker	.15
29	Johnny Johnson	.15
30	Tom Carter	.15
31	Andre Rison	.30
32	Cortez Kennedy	.30
33	Mark Carrier	.15
34	Shannon Sharpe	.30
35	Eric Swann	.15
36	Steve Young	1.50
37	Johnny Mitchell	.15
38	Dermontti Dawson	.15
39	Mike Johnson	.15
40	Troy Aikman	2.00
41	Pierce Holt	.15
42	Derrick Thomas	.15
43	Reggie Cobb	.15
44	Michael Jackson	.15
45	Lomas Brown	.15
46	Jeff Hostetler	.15
47	Pete Stoyanovich	.15
48	Reggie White	.50
49	Quentin Coryatt	.15
50	Cris Carter	.75
51	Sean Gilbert	.15
52	Chris Slade	.15
53	Ronnie Harmon	.15
54	Renaldo Turnbull	.15
55	Fred Barnett	.15
56	John Elliott	.15
57	Deion Sanders	1.00
58	John Carney	.15
59	Louis Oliver	.15
60	Greg Lloyd	.15
61	Chris Hinton	.15
62	Ron Moore	.15
63	Vincent Brown	.15
64	Tony McGee	.15
65	Erik Williams	.15
66	Thurman Thomas	.30
67	Neil O'Donnell	.30
68	Scott Mitchell	.30
69	Keith Byars	.15
70	Henry Ellard	.15
71	Chris Spielman	.15
72	LeRoy Butler	.15
73	Tim Brown	.30
74	Darrell Green	.15
75	Bruce Matthews	.15
76	Stan Humphries	.30
77	Will Wolford	.15
78	John Taylor	.15
79	Joe Montana	3.00
80	Chris Warren	.30
81	Michael Brooks	.15
82	Vance Johnson	.15
83	Rob Moore	.30
84	Herschel Walker	.15
85	Alvin Harper	.15
86	Wayne Martin	.15
87	Leslie O'Neal	.15
88	Willie Anderson	.15
89	Tommy Vardell	.15
90	Mike Sherrard	.15
91	Chris Jacke	.15
92	Jim Kelly	.30
93	Jeff Graham, Thomas Everett	.15
94	Bryan Cox	.15
95	Michael Irvin	.30
96	Jeff Lageman	.15
97	Webster Slaughter	.15
98	Eugene Robinson	.15
99	Vencie Glenn	.15
100	Sean Jones	.15
101	Calvin Williams	.15
102	Jim Harbaugh	.30
103	Eric Curry	.15
104	Terry Allen	.30
105	Darryl Williams	.15
106	Gary Clark	.15
107	Marcus Allen	.50
108	Chip Lohmiller	.15
109	Vaughan Johnson	.15
110	Herman Moore	.75
111	Barry Foster	.15
112	Rocket Ismail	.15
113	Erric Pegram	.15
114	Anthony Miller	.15
115	Shane Conlan	.15
116	David Klingler	.15
117	Mark Collins	.15
118	Tony Bennett	.15
119	Donnell Woolford	.15
120	Reggie Brooks	.15
121	Sam Mills	.15
122	Greg Montgomery	.15
123	Kevin Greene	.15
124	Terry McDaniel	.15
125	Henry Jones	.15
126	Ricky Watters	.30
127	Dan Marino	3.00
128	Steve Atwater	.15
129	Ricky Proehl	.15
130	Ernest Givins	.15
131	John L. Williams	.15
132	John Randle	.15
133	Jay Novacek	.15
134	Boomer Esiason	.30
135	Jessie Hester	.15
136	Courtney Hawkins	.15
137	Ben Coates	.30
138	Stevon Moore	.15
139	Eric Allen	.15
140	Jessie Tuggle	.15
141	Marion Butts	.15
142	Brett Favre	4.00
143	Andre Reed	.30
144	Rodney Hampton	.30
145	Keith Sims	.15
146	Derek Brown	.15
147	Eric Green	.15
148	Greg Robinson	.15
149	Nate Newton	.15
150	Mark Higgs	.15
151	Nick Lowery	.15
152	Craig Erickson	.15
153	Anthony Carter	.15
154	Simon Fletcher	.15
155	Ronnie Lott	.30
156	Gary Brown	.15
157	Brent Jones	.15
158	Jim Sweeney	.15
159	Robert Brooks	.15
160	Keith Jackson	.15
161	Daryl Johnston	.15
162	Tom Waddle	.15
163	Eric Martin	.15
164	Cornelius Bennett	.15
165	Tim McDonald	.15
166	Chris Doleman	.15
167	Gary Zimmerman	.15
168	Al Smith	.15
169	Mark Carrier	.15
170	Harris Barton	.15
171	Ray Childress	.15
172	Darryl Talley	.15
173	James Jett	.15
174	Mark Stepnoski	.15
175	Jeff Query	.15
176	Charles Haley	.15
177	Rod Bernstine	.15
178	Richmond Webb	.15
179	Rich Camarillo	.15
180	Pat Swilling	.15
181	Chris Miller	.15
182	Mike Pritchard	.15
183	Checklist	.15
184	Natrone Means	.75
185	Erik Kramer	.15
186	Clyde Simmons	.15
187	Checklist	.15
188	Warren Moon	.30
189	Michael Haynes	.15
190	Terry Kirby	.30
191	Brian Blades	.15
192	Haywood Jeffires	.15
193	Checklist	.15
194	Morten Andersen	.15
195	Dana Stubblefield	.15
196	Ken Norton	.15
197	Art Monk	.15
198	*Seth Joyner*	.15
199	*Heath Shuler*	.40
200	*Marshall Faulk*	6.00
201	*Charles Johnson*	.40
202	*Derrick Alexander*	.40
203	*Greg Hill*	.50
204	*Darnay Scott*	1.50
205	*Willie McGinest*	.25
206	*Thomas Randolph*	.25
207	*Errict Rhett*	1.00
208	*William Floyd*	.50
209	*Johnnie Morton*	1.25
210	*David Palmer*	1.00
211	*Dan Wilkinson*	.50
212	*Trent Dilfer*	2.50
213	*Antonio Langham*	.50
214	*Chuck Levy*	.25
215	*John Thierry*	.25
216	*Kevin Lee*	.25
217	*Aaron Glenn*	.25
218	*Charlie Garner*	1.75
219	*Jeff Burris*	.25
220	*LeShon Johnson*	.25
221	*Thomas Lewis*	.25
222	*Ryan Yarborough*	.25
223	*Mario Bates*	.50
224	Checklist	.15
225	Checklist	.15
SR1	Marshall Faulk SR	40.00
SR2	Dan Wilkinson SR	10.00

1994 Select Canton Bound

Canton Bound is a 12-card insert featuring Dufex technology. The set features players destined for the Hall of Fame and was inserted 1:48.

		MT
Complete Set (12):		260.00
Common Player:		5.00
Minor Stars:		10.00
Inserted 1:48		
1	Emmitt Smith	45.00
2	Sterling Sharpe	10.00
3	Joe Montana	45.00
4	Barry Sanders	60.00
5	Jerry Rice	30.00
6	Ronnie Lott	5.00
7	Reggie White	10.00
8	Steve Young	20.00
9	Jerome Bettis	10.00
10	Bruce Smith	5.00
11	Troy Aikman	30.00
12	Thurman Thomas	10.00

1994 Select Future Force

Future Force is a 12-card insert which was seeded 1:48. The cards feature Dufex technology.

		MT
Complete Set (12):		75.00
Common Player:		3.00
Minor Stars:		6.00
Inserted 1:48		
1	Rick Mirer	6.00
2	Drew Bledsoe	30.00
3	Jerome Bettis	12.00
4	Reggie Brooks	3.00
5	Natrone Means	10.00
6	James Jett	3.00
7	Terry Kirby	6.00
8	Vincent Brisby	3.00
9	Gary Brown	3.00
10	Tyrone Hughes	3.00
11	Dana Stubblefield	3.00
12	Garrison Hearst	12.00

1994 Select Franco Harris

The standard-size Harris card was given away at Pinnacle's party at the 15th National Sports Card Convention. The card front features a metallic Harris image with his signature on the card's back. The card is numbered as "x of 5,000."

		MT
Complete Set (1):		25.00
Common Player:		25.00
1	Franco Harris	25.00

1995 Select Certified Promos

This three-card promo set was issued to give collectors and dealers a look at the designs for 1995 Select Certified. It included two base cards and one Gold Team insert.

		MT
Complete Set (3):		20.00
Common Player:		5.00
10	Steve Young	5.00
44	Troy Aikman	5.00
7	Dan Marino (Gold Team)	15.00

1995 Select Certified

These 1995 Select cards feature 24-point stock and double lamination for each card. The 135-card set includes 29 rookies. Gold foil printing is used for the player's name and the brand logo on the front, which has a full-bleed action photo on it. Each card is also reprinted using a gold mirror mylar foil technology to form a parallel set. These cards were randomly inserted into every fifth pack. Insert sets include Certified Future, Certified Gold Team and The Select Few.

		MT
Complete Set (135):		260.00
Common Player:		.25
Minor Stars:		.50
Comp. Checklist Set (7):		3.00
Wax Box:		425.00
1	Marshall Faulk	3.00
2	Heath Shuler	1.00
3	Garrison Hearst	1.00
4	Errict Rhett	1.00
5	Jeff George	.50
6	Jerome Bettis	2.00
7	Jim Kelly	.50
8	Rick Mirer	.50
9	Willie Davis	.25
10	Steve Young	3.00
11	Erik Kramer	.25
12	Natrone Means	1.00
13	*Jeff Blake*	1.50
14	Neil O'Donnell	.50
15	Andre Rison	.25
16	Randall Cunningham	.25
17	Emmitt Smith	6.00
18	Tim Brown	.50
19	Shannon Sharpe	.25
20	Boomer Esiason	.25
21	Barry Sanders	8.00
22	Rodney Hampton	.50
23	Robert Brooks	1.00
24	Jim Everett	.25
25	Gary Brown	.25
26	Drew Bledsoe	4.00
27	Desmond Howard	.25
28	Cris Carter	.50
29	Marcus Allen	.50
30	Dan Marino	6.00
31	Warren Moon	.50
32	Dave Krieg	.25
33	Ben Coates	.25
34	Terance Mathis	.25
35	Mario Bates	1.00
36	Andre Reed	.25
37	Dave Brown	.25
38	Jeff Graham	.25
39	Johnny Mitchell	.25
40	Carl Pickens	1.00
41	Jeff Hostetler	.25
42	Vinny Testaverde	.25
43	Ricky Watters	.50
44	Troy Aikman	4.00
45	Bam Morris	1.00
46	John Elway	3.00
47	Junior Seau	.50

48	Scott Mitchell	.50
49	Jerry Rice	4.00
50	Brett Favre	8.00
51	Chris Warren	.50
52	Chris Chandler	.25
53	Lorenzo White	.25
54	Craig Erickson	.25
55	Alvin Harper	.25
56	Steve Beuerlein	.25
57	Edgar Bennett	.25
58	Steve Bono	.50
59	Eric Green	.25
60	Jake Reed	.25
61	Terry Kirby	.25
62	Vincent Brisby	.25
63	Lake Dawson	.50
64	Torrance Small	.25
65	Mark Brunell	4.00
66	Haywood Jeffries	.25
67	Flipper Anderson	.25
68	Ron Moore	.25
69	LeShon Johnson	.25
70	Rocket Ismail	.25
71	Herman Moore	2.00
72	Charlie Garner	.25
73	Anthony Miller	.25
74	Greg Lloyd	.25
75	Michael Irvin	1.00
76	Stan Humphries	.50
77	Leroy Hoard	.25
78	Deion Sanders	4.00
79	Darnay Scott	1.50
80	Chris Miller	.25
81	Curtis Conway	.50
82	Trent Dilfer	1.00
83	Bruce Smith	.25
84	Reggie Brooks	.25
85	Frank Reich	.25
86	Henry Ellard	.25
87	Eric Metcalf	.25
88	Sean Gilbert	.25
89	Larry Centers	.25
90	Ricky Ervins	.25
91	Craig Heyward	.25
92	Rod Woodson	.25
93	Steve Walsh	.25
94	Fred Barnett	.25
95	William Floyd	1.00
96	Harvey Williams	.25
97	Greg Hill	.50
98	Irving Fryar	.25
99	Kevin Williams	.25
100	Herschel Walker	.25
101	Sean Dawkins	.25
102	Michael Haynes	.25
103	Reggie White	.50
104	Robert Smith	.25
105	Todd Collins	.50
106	Michael Westbrook	2.50
107	Frank Sanders	4.00
108	Christian Fauria	.50
109	Stoney Case	.50
110	Jimmy Oliver	.50
111	Mark Bruener	.50
112	Rodney Thomas	.50
113	Chris Jones	2.00
114	James Stewart	.50
115	Kevin Carter	.50
116	Eric Zeier	.50
117	Curtis Martin	18.00
118	James Stewart	8.00
119	Joe Aska	.50
120	Ken Dilger	.50
121	Tyrone Wheatley	1.50
122	Ray Zellars	.50
123	Kyle Brady	.50
124	Chad May	.50
125	Napoleon Kaufman	15.00
126	Terrell Davis	75.00
127	Warren Sapp	.50
128	Sherman Williams	.50
129	Kordell Stewart	25.00
130	Ki-Jana Carter	2.00
131	Terrell Fletcher	.50
132	Rashaan Salaam	2.00
133	J.J. Stokes	5.00
134	Kerry Collins	5.00
135	Joey Galloway	18.00

1995 Select Certified Mirror Golds

These cards are a parallel set to Select Certified's main set, except they use gold mirror mylar foil technology. Cards were seeded one per five packs.

		MT
Complete Set (135):		1200.
Common Player:		2.00
Minor Stars:		4.00
1	Marshall Faulk	10.00
2	Heath Shuler	4.00
3	Garrison Hearst	4.00
4	Errict Rhett	4.00
5	Jeff George	4.00
6	Jerome Bettis	8.00
7	Jim Kelly	4.00
8	Rick Mirer	4.00
9	Willie Davis	2.00
10	Steve Young	25.00
11	Erik Kramer	2.00
12	Natrone Means	4.00
13	Jeff Blake	6.00
14	Neil O'Donnell	2.00
15	Andre Rison	2.00
16	Randall Cunningham	4.00
17	Emmitt Smith	45.00
18	Tim Brown	4.00
19	Shannon Sharpe	2.00
20	Boomer Esiason	2.00
21	Barry Sanders	50.00
22	Rodney Hampton	2.00
23	Robert Brooks	2.00
24	Jim Everett	2.00
25	Gary Brown	2.00
26	Drew Bledsoe	30.00
27	Desmond Howard	2.00
28	Cris Carter	2.00
29	Marcus Allen	4.00
30	Dan Marino	45.00
31	Warren Moon	4.00
32	Dave Krieg	2.00
33	Ben Coates	2.00
34	Terance Mathis	2.00
35	Mario Bates	2.00
36	Andre Reed	2.00
37	Dave Brown	2.00
38	Jeff Graham	2.00
39	Johnny Mitchell	2.00
40	Carl Pickens	4.00
41	Jeff Hostetler	2.00
42	Vinny Testaverde	2.00
43	Ricky Watters	4.00
44	Troy Aikman	30.00
45	Bam Morris	2.00
46	John Elway	45.00
47	Junior Seau	4.00
48	Scott Mitchell	2.00
49	Jerry Rice	30.00
50	Brett Favre	50.00
51	Chris Warren	4.00
52	Chris Chandler	2.00
53	Lorenzo White	2.00
54	Craig Erickson	2.00
55	Alvin Harper	2.00
56	Steve Beuerlein	2.00
57	Edgar Bennett	2.00
58	Steve Bono	4.00
59	Eric Green	2.00
60	Jake Reed	2.00
61	Terry Kirby	2.00
62	Vincent Brisby	2.00
63	Lake Dawson	2.00
64	Torrance Small	2.00
65	Mark Brunell	30.00
66	Haywood Jeffries	2.00
67	Flipper Anderson	2.00
68	Ron Moore	2.00
69	LeShon Johnson	2.00
70	Rocket Ismail	2.00
71	Herman Moore	4.00
72	Charlie Garner	2.00
73	Anthony Miller	2.00
74	Greg Lloyd	2.00
75	Michael Irvin	4.00
76	Stan Humphries	2.00
77	Leroy Hoard	2.00
78	Deion Sanders	25.00
79	Darnay Scott	4.00
80	Chris Miller	2.00
81	Curtis Conway	4.00
82	Trent Dilfer	2.00
83	Bruce Smith	2.00
84	Reggie Brooks	2.00
85	Frank Reich	2.00
86	Henry Ellard	2.00
87	Eric Metcalf	2.00
88	Sean Gilbert	2.00
89	Larry Centers	2.00
90	Ricky Ervins	2.00
91	Craig Heyward	2.00
92	Rod Woodson	2.00
93	Steve Walsh	2.00
94	Fred Barnett	4.00
95	William Floyd	4.00
96	Harvey Williams	2.00
97	Greg Hill	2.00
98	Irving Fryar	2.00
99	Kevin Williams	2.00
100	Herschel Walker	2.00
101	Sean Dawkins	2.00
102	Michael Haynes	2.00
103	Reggie White	4.00
104	Robert Smith	4.00
105	Todd Collins	4.00
106	Michael Westbrook	30.00
107	Frank Sanders	15.00
108	Christian Fauria	4.00
109	Stoney Case	4.00
110	Jimmy Oliver	4.00
111	Mark Bruener	4.00
112	Rodney Thomas	4.00
113	Chris Jones	4.00
114	James Stewart	4.00
115	Kevin Carter	4.00
116	Eric Zeier	4.00
117	Curtis Martin	45.00
118	James Stewart	35.00
119	Joe Aska	4.00
120	Ken Dilger	4.00
121	Tyrone Wheatley	25.00
122	Ray Zellars	4.00
123	Kyle Brady	4.00
124	Chad May	4.00
125	Napoleon Kaufman	30.00
126	Terrell Davis	300.00
127	Warren Sapp	8.00
128	Sherman Williams	4.00
129	Kordell Stewart	50.00
130	Ki-Jana Carter	6.00
131	Terrell Fletcher	4.00
132	Rashaan Salaam	6.00
133	J.J. Stokes	12.00
134	Kerry Collins	15.00
135	Joey Galloway	50.00

1995 Select Certified Checklists

The seven-card, standard-size set was issued one per pack of Select Certified and features members of the Quarterback Club.

		MT
Complete Set (7):		4.00
Common Player:		.25
1	Drew Bledsoe	.75
2	John Elway	.40
3	Dan Marino	1.50
4	Brett Favre	1.50
5	Troy Aikman	.75
6	Steve Young	.60
7	Rick Mirer (UER), Randall Cunningham (Gold Team list incorrect)	.25

1995 Select Certified Future

These cards pay tribute to the 10 best rookies in the 1995 season. Each card is done in gold foil background. Cards were random inserts, one per 19 packs of 1995 Score Select Certified product.

		MT
Complete Set (10):		120.00
Common Player:		3.00
1	Ki-Jana Carter	6.00
2	Steve McNair	25.00
3	Kerry Collins	6.00
4	Michael Westbrook	6.00
5	Joey Galloway	10.00
6	J.J. Stokes	6.00
7	Rashaan Salaam	6.00
8	Tyrone Wheatley	3.00
9	Todd Collins	3.00
10	Curtis Martin	25.00

1995 Select Certified Gold Team

Ten of the NFL's biggest stars are featured on these 1995 Select Certified inserts. The cards use gold Dufex, with textured gold foil highlights on both sides of the card. Gold Team inserts were seeded one per 41 packs.

		MT
Complete Set (10):		400.00
Common Player:		20.00
1	Jerry Rice	35.00
2	Emmitt Smith	70.00
3	Drew Bledsoe	35.00
4	Marshall Faulk	20.00
5	Troy Aikman	35.00
6	Barry Sanders	35.00
7	Dan Marino	70.00
8	Errict Rhett	20.00
9	Brett Favre	70.00
10	Steve McNair	35.00

Post-1980 cards in Near Mint condition will generally sell for about 75% of the quoted Mint value. Excellent-condition cards bring no more than 40%.

1995 Select Certified Select Few

These cards, which appear one per 32 packs of 1995 Select Certified product, showcase 20 top talents. Another version of Select Few appears in a plastic holder and is inserted on the inside of sealed boxes.

		MT
Complete Set (20):		600.00
Common Player:		7.00
Cards are numbered of 2250		
Comp. 1028 Numb. Set (20):		1200.
1028 Numb. Cards:		1x-2x
1	Dan Marino	60.00
2	Emmitt Smith	60.00
3	Marshall Faulk	7.00
4	Barry Sanders	40.00
5	Drew Bledsoe	40.00
6	Brett Favre	60.00
7	Troy Aikman	40.00
8	Jerry Rice	40.00
9	Steve Young	30.00
10	Natrone Means	10.00
11	Bam Morris	7.00
12	Errict Rhett	7.00
13	John Elway	25.00
14	Heath Shuler	10.00
15	Ki-Jana Carter	10.00
16	Kerry Collins	14.00
17	Steve McNair	30.00
18	Rashaan Salaam	10.00
19	Tyrone Wheatley	7.00
20	J.J. Stokes	10.00

1996 Select Promos

The three-card, standard-size set was issued to preview the 1996 Select card set. Aikman's and Favre's cards are base cards while the Marino card previews the Prime Cut insert.

		MT
Complete Set (3):		8.00
Common Player:		1.50
1	Troy Aikman	1.50
10	Prime Cut card (Dan Marino)	5.00
19	Brett Favre	4.00

1996 Select

Only hobby shops were able to carry Select football. The 200-card set has five checklists, 30 top rookies, and 15 Fluid and Fleet cards. Each regular card is also featured in a parallel Artist's Proof set, seeded one card per 23 packs. Each regular card front is horizontal, with a gold-foil framed box with a mug shot on the left side, against a pigskin football background. The Select logo above the picture and the player's name below are also in gold foil. The right side of the card has a full-bleed color action photo. The back also uses a football motif for the background, along with a checkerboard pattern with a photo inside it. The Select logo is in one square, as is a team logo. A card number is in the upper right corner in a white square, with a player photo underneath. Statistics run along the bottom of the card. Insert sets are: Building Blocks, Four-midable and Prime Cut.

		MT
Complete Set (200):		25.00
Common Player:		.10
Minor Stars:		.20
Wax Box:		30.00
1	Troy Aikman	1.50
2	Marshall Faulk	1.00
3	Kordell Stewart	1.50
4	Larry Centers	.10
5	Tamarick Vanover	1.00
6	Ken Norton Jr.	.10
7	Steve Tasker	.10
8	Dan Marino	3.00
9	Heath Shuler	.50
10	Anthony Miller	.10
11	Mario Bates	.10
12	Natrone Means	.20
13	Darren Woodson	.10
14	Chris Sanders	.50
15	Chris Warren	.10
16	Eric Metcalf	.10
17	Quentin Coryatt	.10
18	Jeff Hostetler	.10
19	Brett Favre	3.00
20	Curtis Martin	2.50
21	Floyd Turner	.10
22	Curtis Conway	.10
23	Orlando Thomas	.10
24	Lee Woodall	.10
25	Darick Holmes	.10
26	Marcus Allen	.10
27	Ricky Watters	.10
28	Herman Moore	.30
29	Rodney Hampton	.10
30	Alvin Harper	.10
31	Jeff Blake	1.00
32	Wayne Chrebet	.10
33	Jerry Rice	1.50
34	Dave Krieg	.10
35	Mark Brunell	.75
36	Terry Allen	.10
37	Emmitt Smith	3.00
38	Bryan Cox	.10
39	Tony Martin	.10
40	John Elway	.50
41	Warren Moon	.10
42	Yancey Thigpen	1.00
43	Jeff George	.20
44	Rodney Thomas	.50
45	Joey Galloway	1.25
46	Jim Kelly	.10
47	Drew Bledsoe	1.50
48	Greg Lloyd	.10
49	Michael Irvin	.20
50	Quinn Early	.10
51	Brent Jones	.10
52	Rashaan Salaam	1.00
53	James Stewart	.10
54	Gus Frerotte	.10
55	Edgar Bennett	.10
56	Lamont Warren	.10
57	Napoleon Kaufman	.20
58	Kevin Williams	.10
59	Irving Fryar	.10
60	Trent Dilfer	.10
61	Eric Zeier	.10
62	Tyrone Wheatley	.10
63	Isaac Bruce	.75
64	Terrell Davis	1.00
65	Lake Dawson	.10
66	Carnell Lake	.10
67	Kerry Collins	.30
68	Kyle Brady	.10
69	Rodney Peete	.10
70	Carl Pickens	.20
71	Robert Smith	.10
72	Rod Woodson	.10
73	Deion Sanders	.75
74	Sean Dawkins	.10
75	William Floyd	.10
76	Barry Sanders	1.50
77	Ben Coates	.10
78	Neil O'Donnell	.10
79	Bill Brooks	.10
80	Steve Bono	.10
81	Jay Novacek	.10
82	Bernie Parmalee	.10
83	Derek Loville	.10
84	Frank Sanders	.20
85	Robert Brooks	.10
86	Jim Harbaugh	.10
87	Rick Mirer	.10
88	Craig Heyward	.10
89	Greg Hill	.10
90	Andre Coleman	.10
91	Shannon Sharpe	.10
92	Hugh Douglas	.10
93	Andre Hastings	.10
94	Bryce Paup	.10
95	Jim Everett	.10
96	Brian Mitchell	.10
97	Jeff Graham	.10
98	Steve McNair	1.00
99	Charlie Garner	.10
100	Willie McGinest	.10
101	Harvey Williams	.10
102	Daryl Johnston	.10
103	Cris Carter	.10
104	J.J. Stokes	.20
105	Garrison Hearst	.20
106	Mark Chmura	.50
107	Derrick Thomas	.10
108	Errict Rhett	.75
109	Terance Mathis	.10
110	Dave Brown	.10
111	Erric Pegram	.10
112	Scott Mitchell	.10
113	Aaron Bailey	.10
114	Stan Humphries	.10
115	Bruce Smith	.10
116	Rob Johnson	.10
117	O.J. McDuffie	.10
118	Brian Blades	.10
119	Steve Atwater	.10
120	Tyrone Hughes	.10
121	Michael Westbrook	.20
122	Ki-Jana Carter	.50
123	Adrian Murrell	.10
124	Steve Young	1.50
125	Charles Haley	.10
126	Vincent Brisby	.10
127	Jerome Bettis	.10
128	Erik Kramer	.10
129	Roosevelt Potts	.10
130	Tim Brown	.10
131	Reggie White	.10
132	Jake Reed	.10
133	Junior Seau	.10
134	Stoney Case	.10
135	Kimble Anders	.10
136	Brett Perriman	.10
137	Todd Collins	.10
138	Sherman Williams	.10
139	Hardy Nickerson	.10
140	Ernie Mills	.10
141	Glyn Milburn	.10
142	Terry Kirby	.10
143	Bert Emanuel	.10
144	Aeneas Williams	.10
145	Aaron Craver	.10
146	Jackie Harris	.10
147	Amp Lee	.10
148	Aaron Hayden	.50
149	Antonio Freeman	.10
150	Kevin Greene	.10
151	Kevin Hardy	.40
152	Eric Moulds	2.00
153	Tim Biakabutuka	1.00
154	Keyshawn Johnson	2.50
155	Jeff Lewis	.50
156	Stepfret Williams	.10
157	Tony Brackens	.20
158	Mike Alstott	1.50
159	Willie Anderson	.10
160	Marvin Harrison	3.00
161	Regan Upshaw	.10
162	Bobby Engram	.50
163	Leeland McElroy	.20
164	Alex Van Dyke	.20
165	Stanley Pritchett	.10
166	Cedric Jones	.10
167	Terry Glenn	1.75
168	Eddie George	4.00
169	Lawrence Phillips	.50
170	Jonathan Ogden	.10
171	Danny Kanell	.50
172	Alex Molden	.10
173	Daryl Gardener	.10
174	Derrick Mayes	1.00
175	Marco Battaglia	.10
176	Jon Stark	.10
177	Karim Abdul-Jabbar	.75
178	Stephen Davis	4.00
179	Rickey Dudley	.30
180	Eddie Kennison	.30
181	Barry Sanders	.75
182	Brett Favre	.50
183	John Elway	.30
184	Steve Young	.50
185	Michael Irvin	.10
186	Jerry Rice	.50
187	Emmitt Smith	1.00
188	Isaac Bruce	.20
189	Chris Warren	.10
190	Errict Rhett	.40
191	Herman Moore	.10
192	Carl Pickens	.10
193	Cris Carter	.10
194	Terrell Davis	.75
195	Rodney Thomas	.10
196	Dan Marino	.50
197	Drew Bledsoe	.20
198	Emmitt Smith	1.00
199	Jerry Rice	.30
200	John Elway, Barry Sanders	.30

1996 Select Artist's Proofs

The 200-card, standard-size set parallels the base set, inserted every 23 packs, with Artist's Proof printed in gold foil.

	MT
Complete Set (200):	1600.
Common Player:	5.00
Veteran Stars:	30x-50x
RCs:	12x-25x

1996 Select Building Blocks

This 1996 Score Select insert set features first- and second-year players who appear to be headed to stardom. The cards, seeded one per 48 packs, use all-foil Dufex print technology. The card front has a color action photo, with a background similar to a television display room; the "screens" have a smaller mug shot taken from the larger action photo. The player's name and "Building Blocks" are written in silver foil in the lower left corner. The vertical back has a color action photo on one half, with a card number in a black rectangle above. The other side has the brand logo, player's name, set name, position and team, and brief player profile.

		MT
Complete Set (20):		180.00
Common Player:		4.00
1	Curtis Martin	25.00
2	Terrell Davis	25.00
3	Darick Holmes	4.00
4	Rashaan Salaam	6.00
5	Ki-Jana Carter	6.00
6	Rodney Thomas	4.00
7	Kerry Collins	8.00
8	Eric Zeier	4.00
9	Steve McNair	15.00
10	Kordell Stewart	20.00
11	J.J. Stokes	6.00
12	Joey Galloway	10.00
13	Michael Westbrook	6.00
14	Mike Alstott	4.00
15	Tony Brackens	4.00
16	Terry Glenn	10.00
17	Kevin Hardy	4.00
18	Leeland McElroy	6.00
19	Tim Biakabutuka	12.00
20	Keyshawn Johnson	15.00

Post-1980 cards in Near Mint condition will generally sell for about 75% of the quoted Mint value. Excellent-condition cards bring no more than 40%.

1996 Select Four-midable

These 1996 Score Select inserts were seeded one per 18 packs. Each card front has a full-motion hologram which features crashing AFC and NFC helmets, as well as a color photo of a player who appeared in the championship games. The hologram is at the bottom; the color photo is in a conference color-coordinated panel at the top. Blue is used for the NFC; red is used for the AFC. The logos are included in the background. The brand name and set name are written in silver foil, as is the player's team name, which is repeated above the hologram. The horizontal back has a color action photo incorporated into a black-and-white stadium scene, plus a black rectangle which recaps the player's championship game performance. A card number is also given.

		MT
Complete Set (16):		70.00
Common Player:		2.00
1	Troy Aikman	10.00
2	Michael Irvin	4.00
3	Emmitt Smith	20.00
4	Deion Sanders	7.00
5	Brett Favre	20.00
6	Robert Brooks	2.00
7	Edgar Bennett	2.00
8	Reggie White	4.00
9	Kordell Stewart	10.00
10	Yancey Thigpen	5.00
11	Neil O'Donnell	2.00
12	Greg Lloyd	2.00
13	Jim Harbaugh	2.00
14	Sean Dawkins	2.00
15	Marshall Faulk	7.00
16	Quentin Coryatt	2.00

1996 Select Prime Cut

These cards are the highlight inserts in Score's 1996 Select football product. The cards are die-cut and feature 18 of the NFL's most elite players. The top of the card is die-cut around a football which has a facsimile autograph of the player. Below is a larger color action photo, flanked by two smaller ones. The player's name is in a bar at the bottom, along with "Prime Cut" and a team logo in the center. Cards were limited to 1,996 each and were inserted in every 80th pack.

		MT
Complete Set (18):		550.00
Common Player:		5.00
1	Emmitt Smith	70.00
2	Troy Aikman	40.00
3	Michael Irvin	5.00

4	Steve Young	30.00
5	Jerry Rice	40.00
6	Drew Bledsoe	30.00
7	Brett Favre	70.00
8	John Elway	30.00
9	Barry Sanders	40.00
10	Dan Marino	70.00
11	Isaac Bruce	15.00
12	Marshall Faulk	10.00
13	Errict Rhett	10.00
14	Chris Warren	5.00
15	Herman Moore	5.00
16	Deion Sanders	20.00
17	Joey Galloway	20.00
18	Curtis Martin	50.00

1996 Select Certified

The 125-card, regular-sized set was available in six-card packs. The card fronts feature a full mirror background with the color player action shot. The player's name is printed down the right border with in-depth statistics printed on the horizontal card back. Parallel versions of the base set are available in Certified Red (1:5) and Certified Blue (1:50). Mirror Red (1:100), Mirror Blue (1:200) and Mirror Gold (1:300) parallel inserts were also issued. Artist's Proof (1:18), Gold Team (1:38) and Thumbs Up (1:41) were the other inserts and each card was also available in Premium Stock, nine-card packs.

		MT
Complete Set (125):		50.00
Common Player:		.20
Minor Stars:		.40
Wax Box:		90.00
1	Isaac Bruce	1.00
2	Rick Mirer	.20
3	Jake Reed	.20
4	Reggie White	.40
5	Harvey Williams	.20
6	Jim Everett	.20
7	Tony Martin	.20
8	Craig Heyward	.20
9	Tamarick Vanover	1.25
10	Hugh Douglas	.20
11	Erik Kramer	.20
12	Charlie Garner	.20
13	Erric Pegram	.20
14	Scott Mitchell	.20
15	Michael Westbrook	.75
16	Robert Smith	.20
17	Kerry Collins	.75
18	Derek Loville	.20
19	Jeff Blake	.40
20	Terry Kirby	.20
21	Bruce Smith	.20
22	Stan Humphries	.20
23	Rodney Thomas	.20
24	Wayne Chrebet	.20
25	Napoleon Kaufman	.20
26	Marshall Faulk	1.00
27	Emmitt Smith	5.00
28	Natrone Means	.20
29	Neil O'Donnell	.20
30	Warren Moon	.40
31	Junior Seau	.40
32	Chris Sanders	.20
33	Barry Sanders	3.00
34	Jeff Graham	.20
35	Kordell Stewart	2.50
36	Jim Harbaugh	.20
37	Chris Warren	.20
38	Cris Carter	.20
39	J.J. Stokes	.75
40	Tyrone Wheatley	.40
41	Terrell Davis	6.00
42	Mark Brunell	1.50
43	Steve Young	2.00
44	Rodney Hampton	.20
45	Drew Bledsoe	2.00
46	Larry Centers	.20
47	Ken Norton Jr.	.20
48	Deion Sanders	2.00
49	Alvin Harper	.20
50	Trent Dilfer	.40
51	Steve McNair	2.00
52	Robert Brooks	.20
53	Edgar Bennett	.20

54	Troy Aikman	2.50
55	Dan Marino	5.00
56	Steve Bono	.20
57	Marcus Allen	.40
58	Rodney Peete	.20
59	Ben Coates	.40
60	Yancey Thigpen	.40
61	Tim Brown	.20
62	Jerry Rice	2.50
63	Quinn Early	.20
64	Ricky Watters	.40
65	Thurman Thomas	.40
66	Greg Lloyd	.20
67	Eric Metcalf	.20
68	Jeff George	.20
69	John Elway	2.00
70	Frank Sanders	.20
71	Curtis Conway	.20
72	Greg Hill	.20
73	Darick Holmes	.20
74	Herman Moore	.40
75	Carl Pickens	.20
76	Eric Zeier	.20
77	Curtis Martin	3.50
78	Rashaan Salaam	1.00
79	Joey Galloway	1.50
80	Jeff Hostetler	.20
81	Jim Kelly	.40
82	Dave Brown	.20
83	Errict Rhett	.75
84	Michael Irvin	.40
85	Brett Favre	5.00
86	Cedric Jones	.20
87	*Jeff Lewis*	2.00
88	Alex Van Dyke	.40
89	*Regan Upshaw*	.20
90	*Karim Abdul-Jabbar*	2.50
91	*Marvin Harrison*	10.00
92	*Stephen Davis*	15.00
93	*Terry Glenn*	5.00
94	*Kevin Hardy*	.40
95	*Stanley Pritchett*	.40
96	*Willie Anderson*	.20
97	*Lawrence Phillips*	2.50
98	*Bobby Hoying*	2.50
99	*Amani Toomer*	.40
100	*Eddie George*	15.00
101	*Stepfret Williams*	.20
102	*Eric Moulds*	6.00
103	*Simeon Rice*	.40
104	*John Mobley*	.20
105	*Keyshawn Johnson*	8.00
106	*Daryl Gardener*	.20
107	*Tony Banks*	3.00
108	*Bobby Engram*	.75
109	*Jonathan Ogden*	.40
110	*Eddie Kennison*	.75
111	*Danny Kanell*	1.50
112	*Tony Brackens*	.40
113	*Tim Biakabutuka*	3.00
114	*Leeland McElroy*	1.00
115	*Rickey Dudley*	1.00
116	Troy Aikman	1.00
117	Brett Favre	2.00
118	Drew Bledsoe	1.00
119	Steve Young	1.00
120	Kerry Collins	1.00
121	John Elway	1.00
122	Dan Marino	2.50
123	Kordell Stewart	1.25
124	Jeff Blake	.40
125	Jim Harbaugh	.20

1996 Select Certified Red

Certified Red parallel cards were a parallel set to the 125-card Select Certified set in 1996. They were inserted every five packs and feature a full red background.

	MT
Complete Set (125):	300.00
Certified Red Cards:	3x-6x

A card number in parentheses ( ) indicates the set is unnumbered.

1996 Select Certified Blue

This 125-card set paralleled the 1996 Select Certified set, but pictured each card on a full blue background. Certified Blue inserts were seeded every 50 packs.

	MT
Complete Set (125):	2500.
Certified Blue Cards:	25x-50x

1996 Select Certified Artist's Proofs

This 125-card set paralleled the 1996 Select Certified set, but includes a holographic Artist's Proof stamp on the front of the card. Artist's Proofs were seeded every 18 packs.

	MT
Complete Set (125):	1200.
Artist's Proof Cards:	12x-24x

1996 Select Certified Mirror Red

Mirror Red included all 125 cards in 1996 Select Certified, but featured roughly three-fourths of the background in red, with the remaining portion unchanged from regular-issue cards. The entire front then has a mirror effect. Mirror Red inserts were seeded every 100 packs.

	MT
Mirror Red Cards:	40x-80x

Post-1980 cards in Near Mint condition will generally sell for about 75% of the quoted Mint value. Excellent-condition cards bring no more than 40%.

1996 Select Certified Mirror Blue

This 125-card set featured a mostly blue background, with the rest still having the regular-issue background color, then a mirror background over the entire front. Mirror Blues parallel the regular-issue set and are seeded every 200 packs.

	MT
Mirror Blue Cards:	75x-150x

1996 Select Certified Mirror Gold

Mirror Golds parallel the 125-card base set and feature most of the background in gold, with the remaining portion in regular-issue card color. The entire front is put through a mirror process that gives it a holographic appearance. Mirror Gold inserts are found every 300 packs.

	MT
Mirror Gold Cards:	150x-300x

1996 Select Certified Gold Team

The Gold Team is an 18-card, regular-sized insert set that was found every 38 packs of 1996 Select Certified. The card fronts feature a full gold action shot while the backs, also in complete gold, are individually numbered.

		MT
Complete Set (18):		500.00
Common Player:		8.00
1	Emmitt Smith	60.00
2	Barry Sanders	30.00
3	Dan Marino	60.00
4	Steve Young	25.00
5	Troy Aikman	30.00
6	Jerry Rice	30.00
7	Rashaan Salaam	8.00
8	Marshall Faulk	15.00
9	Drew Bledsoe	30.00

10	Steve McNair	15.00
11	Brett Favre	60.00
12	Terrell Davis	30.00
13	Kordell Stewart	30.00
14	Keyshawn Johnson	15.00
15	Kerry Collins	15.00
16	Curtis Martin	45.00
17	Isaac Bruce	15.00
18	Terry Glenn	25.00

1996 Select Certified Thumbs Up

The 24-card, regular-sized set was inserted every 41 packs of Select Certified. The silver card fronts feature an actual thumbprint of the Quarterback Club member pictured. The card backs include another photo and the player's "Thumbs Up Moment" and are individually numbered.

		MT
Complete Set (24):		450.00
Common Player:		8.00
1	Steve Young	30.00
2	Jeff Blake	15.00
3	Dan Marino	60.00
4	Kerry Collins	15.00
5	John Elway	25.00
6	Neil O'Donnell	8.00
7	Brett Favre	60.00
8	Scott Mitchell	8.00
9	Troy Aikman	30.00
10	Jim Harbaugh	8.00
11	Drew Bledsoe	30.00
12	Jeff Hostetler	8.00
13	Marvin Harrison	15.00
14	Tim Biakabutuka	8.00
15	Eddie George	35.00
16	Tony Brackens	8.00
17	Karim Abdul-Jabbar	20.00
18	Daryl Gardener	8.00
19	Alex Van Dyke	8.00
20	Terry Glenn	30.00
21	Eric Moulds	8.00
22	Eddie Kennison	12.00
23	Regan Upshaw	8.00
24	Mike Alstott	10.00

1996 Select Certified Premium Stock

Premium Stock was an enhanced version of Select Certified that was available to the hobby only in jumbo nine-card packs. Premium Stock treated the base cards and the Mirror Red inserts with a micro-etching process, while all other inserts are the same. Packs of Premium Stock contained all of the inserts, but at easier insertion rates than regular packs. The odds in Premium Stock were: Certified Red (1:3), Certified Blue (1:33), Mirror Red (1:66), Mirror Blue (1:133), Mirror Gold (1:199), Artist's Proof (1:12), Gold Team (1:25) and Thumbs Up (1:27).

	MT
Complete Set (125):	100.00
Premium Stock Cards:	2x

1996 Select Certified Premium Stock Etched Mirror Red

Premium Stock Etched Mirror Red inserts paralleled the 125-card Select Certified set, but were available only in Premium Stock packs at a rate of one per 66 packs. This was the only insert that was changed in Premium Stock versus the regular-issue packs. The fronts of these cards have etched foil similar to the base set for Premium Stock.

	MT
Etched Mirror Red Cards:	150x-300x

1997 Pinnacle Certified

Pinnacle Certified consists of a 150-card base set, four parallels and two inserts. The base cards were printed on silver mirror board. The parallel sets include Certified Red (1:5), Mirror Red (1:99), Mirror Blue (1:199) and Mirror Blue (1:299). The inserts are Certified Team (20 cards, 1:19) and Epix (24 cards, 1:15). All cards in the set have a clear-coat protector.

		MT
Complete Set (150):		75.00
Common Player:		.25
Minor Stars:		.50
Certified Red Cards:		3x-6x
Certified Red Rookies:		2x-3x
Mirror Red Stars:		30x-60x
Mirror Red Rookies:		15x-30x
Mirror Blue Stars:		50x-100x
Mirror Blue Rookies:		25x-50x
Mirror Gold Stars:		100x-200x
Mirror Gold Rookies:		50x-100x
Wax Box:		90.00
1	Emmitt Smith	5.00
2	Dan Marino	5.00
3	Brett Favre	6.00
4	Steve Young	2.00
5	Kerry Collins	.75
6	Troy Aikman	2.50
7	Drew Bledsoe	2.50
8	Eddie George	4.00
9	Jerry Rice	3.00
10	John Elway	2.00
11	Barry Sanders	4.00
12	Mark Brunell	2.50
13	Elvis Grbac	.25
14	Tony Banks	1.50
15	Vinny Testaverde	.25
16	Rick Mirer	.25
17	Carl Pickens	.25
18	Deion Sanders	1.50
19	Terry Glenn	2.50
20	Heath Shuler	.25
21	Dave Brown	.25
22	Keyshawn Johnson	1.00
23	Jeff George	.50
24	Ricky Watters	.50
25	Kordell Stewart	2.50
26	Junior Seau	.25
27	Terrell Owens	2.00
28	Warren Moon	.50
29	Isaac Bruce	.50
30	Steve McNair	2.00
31	Gus Frerotte	.25
32	Trent Dilfer	.50
33	Shannon Sharpe	.25
34	Scott Mitchell	.25
35	Antonio Freeman	.50
36	Jim Harbaugh	.25
37	Natrone Means	.50
38	Marcus Allen	.50
39	Karim Abdul-Jabbar	1.75
40	Tim Biakabutuka	.50
41	Jeff Blake	.50
42	Michael Irvin	.50
43	Herschel Walker	.25
44	Curtis Martin	2.50
45	Eddie Kennison	.50
46	Napoleon Kaufman	.75
47	Larry Centers	.25
48	Jamal Anderson	.50
49	Derrick Alexander	.25
50	Bruce Smith	.25
51	Wesley Walls	.25
52	Rod Smith	.25
53	Keenan McCardell	.25
54	Robert Brooks	.25
55	Willie Green	.25
56	Jake Reed	.25
57	Joey Galloway	.50
58	Eric Metcalf	.25
59	Chris Sanders	.25
60	Jeff Hostetler	.25
61	Kevin Greene	.25
62	Frank Sanders	.25
63	Dorsey Levens	.50
64	Sean Dawkins	.25
65	Cris Carter	.25
66	Andre Hastings	.25
67	Amani Toomer	.25
68	Adrian Murrell	.50
69	Ty Detmer	.25
70	Yancey Thigpen	.25
71	Jim Everett	.25
72	Todd Collins	.25
73	Curtis Conway	.50
74	Herman Moore	.50
75	Neil O'Donnell	.25
76	Rod Woodson	.25
77	Tony Martin	.25
78	Kent Graham	.25
79	Andre Reed	.25
80	Reggie White	.50
81	Thurman Thomas	.50
82	Garrison Hearst	.25
83	Chris Warren	.25
84	Wayne Chrebet	.25
85	Chris T. Jones	.25
86	Anthony Miller	.25
87	Chris Chandler	.25
88	Terrell Davis	3.00
89	Mike Alstott	1.50
90	Terry Allen	.25
91	Jerome Bettis	.50
92	Stan Humphries	.25
93	Andre Rison	.25
94	Marshall Faulk	.50
95	Erik Kramer	.25
96	O.J. McDuffie	.25
97	Robert Smith	.25
98	Keith Byars	.25
99	Rodney Hampton	.25
100	Desmond Howard	.25
101	Lawrence Phillips	.50
102	Michael Westbrook	.25
103	Johnnie Morton	.25
104	Ben Coates	.25
105	J.J. Stokes	.50
106	Terance Mathis	.25
107	Errict Rhett	.25
108	Tim Brown	.25
109	Marvin Harrison	1.00
110	Muhsin Muhammad	.25
111	Bam Morris	.25
112	Mario Bates	.25
113	Jimmy Smith	.25
114	Irving Fryar	.25
115	Tamarick Vanover	.25
116	Brad Johnson	.25
117	Rashaan Salaam	.25
118	Ki-Jana Carter	.25
119	Tyrone Wheatley	.25
120	John Friesz	.25
121	*Orlando Pace*	.50
122	*Jim Druckenmiller*	6.00
123	*Byron Hanspard*	.75
124	*David LaFleur*	1.50
125	*Reidel Anthony*	3.00
126	*Antowain Smith*	4.00
127	*Bryant Westbrook*	.50
128	*Fred Lane*	2.00
129	*Tiki Barber*	4.00
130	*Shawn Springs*	.50
131	*Ike Hilliard*	3.00
132	*James Farrior*	.25
133	*Darrell Russell*	.25
134	*Walter Jones*	.25
135	*Tom Knight*	.25
136	*Yatil Green*	1.00
137	*Joey Kent*	.50
138	*Kevin Lockett*	.50
139	*Troy Davis*	1.00
140	*Darnell Autry*	.50
141	*Pat Barnes*	.75
142	*Rae Carruth*	3.00
143	*Will Blackwell*	.50
144	*Warrick Dunn*	7.00
145	*Corey Dillon*	7.00
146	*Dwayne Rudd*	.25
147	*Reinard Wilson*	.25
148	*Peter Boulware*	.25
149	*Tony Gonzalez*	1.50
150	*Danny Wuerffel*	4.00

1997 Pinnacle Certified Epix

Epix is a 24-card insert which features holographic effects. The set consists of Game, Moment and Season cards that highlight each player's top performances. Orange, Purple and Emerald versions of each card were produced. Epix was inserted 1:15.

		MT
Complete Set (24):		400.00
Common Moment (E1-E8):		12.00
Common Season (E9-E16):		8.00
Common Game (E17-E24):		4.00
1	Emmitt Smith	70.00
2	Troy Aikman	40.00
3	Terrell Davis	40.00
4	Drew Bledsoe	40.00
5	Jeff George	12.00
6	Kerry Collins	12.00
7	Antonio Freeman	12.00
8	Herman Moore	12.00
9	Barry Sanders	35.00
10	Brett Favre	50.00
11	Michael Irvin	8.00
12	Steve Young	20.00
13	Mark Brunell	25.00
14	Jerome Bettis	8.00
15	Deion Sanders	15.00
16	Jeff Blake	8.00
17	Dan Marino	30.00
18	Eddie George	20.00
19	Jerry Rice	15.00
20	John Elway	12.00
21	Curtis Martin	12.00
22	Kordell Stewart	20.00
23	Junior Seau	4.00
24	Reggie White	4.00

1997 Pinnacle Certified Team

Certified Team is a 20-card insert that was seeded 1:19 in packs of Certified Football. The cards were printed on silver mirror board. Gold (inserted 1:119) and Mirror Gold (25 numbered sets) parallels were also issued.

		MT
Complete Set (20):		250.00
Common Player:		5.00
Inserted 1:19		
Gold Cards:		2x-4x
Inserted 1:119		
Mirror Golds:		20x-40x
Production 25 Sets		
1	Brett Favre	30.00
2	Dan Marino	25.00
3	Emmitt Smith	25.00
4	Eddie George	20.00
5	Jerry Rice	15.00
6	Troy Aikman	15.00
7	Barry Sanders	18.00
8	Terrell Davis	15.00
9	Drew Bledsoe	15.00
10	Curtis Martin	15.00
11	Terry Glenn	7.00
12	John Elway	10.00
13	Kordell Stewart	15.00
14	Karim Abdul-Jabbar	8.00
15	Steve Young	10.00
16	Steve McNair	10.00
17	Terrell Owens	5.00
18	Keyshawn Johnson	5.00
19	Keyshawn Johnson	5.00
20	Mark Brunell	15.00

1997 Pinnacle Totally Certified Platinum Red

Platinum Red is considered the "base set" for Totally Certified. Each card in the 150-card set is sequentially-numbered to 4,999. The cards feature a micro-etched holographic mylar finish. Platinum Blue (one per pack) and Platinum Gold (1:79) parallels were also included in this series.

		MT
Complete Set (150):		500.00
Common Player:		1.25
Minor Stars:		2.50
Reds Sequentially #'d to 4,999		
Complete Blue Set (150):		1000.
Blue Cards:		2x
Blues Sequentially #'d to 2,499		
Wax Box:		120.00
1	Emmitt Smith	25.00
2	Dan Marino	25.00
3	Brett Favre	30.00
4	Steve Young	10.00
5	Kerry Collins	3.00
6	Troy Aikman	15.00
7	Drew Bledsoe	20.00
8	Eddie George	20.00
9	Jerry Rice	15.00
10	John Elway	12.00
11	Barry Sanders	15.00
12	Mark Brunell	12.00
13	Elvis Grbac	1.25
14	Tony Banks	7.50
15	Vinny Testaverde	1.25
16	Rick Mirer	1.25
17	Carl Pickens	1.25
18	Deion Sanders	8.00
19	Terry Glenn	3.00
20	Heath Shuler	1.25
21	Dave Brown	1.25
22	Keyshawn Johnson	4.00
23	Jeff George	2.50
24	Ricky Watters	2.50
25	Kordell Stewart	15.00
26	Junior Seau	1.25
27	Terrell Owens	7.50
28	Warren Moon	1.25
29	Isaac Bruce	2.50
30	Steve McNair	12.00
31	Gus Frerotte	1.25
32	Trent Dilfer	2.50
33	Shannon Sharpe	1.25
34	Scott Mitchell	1.25
35	Antonio Freeman	4.00
36	Jim Harbaugh	1.25
37	Natrone Means	2.50
38	Marcus Allen	2.50
39	Karim Abdul-Jabbar	7.50
40	Tim Biakabutuka	2.50
41	Jeff Blake	2.50
42	Michael Irvin	2.50
43	Herschel Walker	1.25
44	Curtis Martin	12.00
45	Eddie Kennison	4.00
46	Napoleon Kaufman	1.25
47	Larry Centers	1.25
48	Jamal Anderson	2.50
49	Derrick Alexander	1.25
50	Bruce Smith	1.25
51	Wesley Walls	1.25
52	Rod Smith	1.25
53	Keenan McCardell	1.25
54	Robert Brooks	1.25
55	Willie Green	1.25
56	Jake Reed	1.25
57	Joey Galloway	2.50
58	Eric Metcalf	1.25
59	Chris Sanders	1.25
60	Jeff Hostetler	1.25
61	Kevin Greene	1.25
62	Frank Sanders	1.25
63	Dorsey Levens	4.00
64	Sean Dawkins	1.25
65	Cris Carter	2.50
66	Andre Hastings	1.25
67	Amani Toomer	1.25
68	Adrian Murrell	2.50
69	Ty Detmer	1.25
70	Yancey Thigpen	1.25
71	Jim Everett	1.25
72	Todd Collins	1.25
73	Curtis Conway	1.25
74	Herman Moore	2.50
75	Neil O'Donnell	1.25
76	Rod Woodson	1.25
77	Tony Martin	1.25
78	Kent Graham	1.25
79	Andre Reed	1.25
80	Reggie White	2.50
81	Thurman Thomas	2.50
82	Garrison Hearst	1.25
83	Chris Warren	1.25
84	Wayne Chrebet	1.25
85	Chris T. Jones	1.25
86	Anthony Miller	1.25
87	Chris Chandler	1.25
88	Terrell Davis	15.00
89	Mike Alstott	7.50
90	Terry Allen	1.25
91	Jerome Bettis	2.50
92	Stan Humphries	1.25
93	Andre Rison	1.25
94	Marshall Faulk	2.50
95	Erik Kramer	1.25
96	O.J. McDuffie	1.25
97	Robert Smith	1.25
98	Keith Byars	1.25
99	Rodney Hampton	1.25
100	Desmond Howard	1.25
101	Lawrence Phillips	2.50
102	Michael Westbrook	1.25
103	Johnnie Morton	1.25
104	Ben Coates	1.25
105	J.J. Stokes	1.25
106	Terance Mathis	1.25
107	Errict Rhett	1.25
108	Tim Brown	1.25
109	Marvin Harrison	4.00
110	Muhsin Muhammad	1.25
111	Bam Morris	1.25
112	Mario Bates	1.25
113	Jimmy Smith	1.25
114	Irving Fryar	1.25
115	Tamarick Vanover	1.25
116	Brad Johnson	2.50
117	Rashaan Salaam	1.25
118	Ki-Jana Carter	1.25
119	Tyrone Wheatley	1.25
120	John Friesz	1.25
121	*Orlando Pace*	2.50
122	*Jim Druckenmiller*	18.00
123	*Byron Hanspard*	5.00
124	*David LaFleur*	7.50
125	*Reidel Anthony*	12.00
126	*Antowain Smith*	18.00
127	*Bryant Westbrook*	7.50
128	*Fred Lane*	7.50
129	*Tiki Barber*	12.00
130	*Shawn Springs*	1.25
131	*Ike Hilliard*	10.00
132	*James Farrior*	1.25
133	*Darrell Russell*	1.25
134	*Walter Jones*	1.25
135	*Tom Knight*	1.25
136	*Yatil Green*	7.00
137	*Joey Kent*	2.50
138	*Kevin Lockett*	1.25
139	*Troy Davis*	7.00
140	*Darnell Autry*	3.00
141	*Pat Barnes*	4.00
142	*Rae Carruth*	10.00
143	*Will Blackwell*	2.50
144	*Warrick Dunn*	30.00
145	*Corey Dillon*	18.00
146	*Dwayne Rudd*	1.25
147	*Reinard Wilson*	1.25
148	*Peter Boulware*	1.25
149	*Tony Gonzalez*	7.50
150	*Danny Wuerffel*	12.00

1997 Pinnacle Totally Certified Platinum Gold

Platinum Gold cards feature a micro-etched holographic mylar finish. Each card is sequentially-numbered to 30 and they were inserted 1:79.

		MT
Common Player:		60.00
Minor Stars:		125.00
Golds Sequentially #'d to 30		
1	Emmitt Smith	1250.
2	Dan Marino	1250.
3	Brett Favre	1500.
4	Steve Young	500.00

5	Kerry Collins	175.00
6	Troy Aikman	750.00
7	Drew Bledsoe	750.00
8	Eddie George	1000.
9	Jerry Rice	750.00
10	John Elway	600.00
11	Barry Sanders	900.00
12	Mark Brunell	600.00
13	Elvis Grbac	60.00
14	Tony Banks	125.00
15	Vinny Testaverde	60.00
16	Rick Mirer	60.00
17	Carl Pickens	60.00
18	Deion Sanders	400.00
19	Terry Glenn	150.00
20	Heath Shuler	60.00
21	Dave Brown	60.00
22	Keyshawn Johnson	200.00
23	Jeff George	125.00
24	Ricky Watters	125.00
25	Kordell Stewart	750.00
26	Junior Seau	60.00
27	Terrell Owens	375.00
28	Warren Moon	125.00
29	Isaac Bruce	125.00
30	Steve McNair	600.00
31	Gus Frerotte	60.00
32	Trent Dilfer	125.00
33	Shannon Sharpe	60.00
34	Scott Mitchell	60.00
35	Antonio Freeman	200.00
36	Jim Harbaugh	60.00
37	Natrone Means	125.00
38	Marcus Allen	125.00
39	Karim Abdul-Jabbar	150.00
40	Tim Biakabutuka	60.00
41	Jeff Blake	125.00
42	Michael Irvin	125.00
43	Herschel Walker	60.00
44	Curtis Martin	600.00
45	Eddie Kennison	200.00
46	Napoleon Kaufman	200.00
47	Larry Centers	60.00
48	Jamal Anderson	125.00
49	Derrick Alexander	60.00
50	Bruce Smith	60.00
51	Wesley Walls	60.00
52	Rod Smith	60.00
53	Keenan McCardell	60.00
54	Robert Brooks	60.00
55	Willie Green	60.00
56	Jake Reed	60.00
57	Joey Galloway	125.00
58	Eric Metcalf	60.00
59	Chris Sanders	60.00
60	Jeff Hostetler	60.00
61	Kevin Greene	60.00
62	Frank Sanders	60.00
63	Dorsey Levens	200.00
64	Sean Dawkins	60.00
65	Cris Carter	60.00
66	Andre Hastings	60.00
67	Amani Toomer	60.00
68	Adrian Murrell	125.00
69	Ty Detmer	60.00
70	Yancey Thigpen	60.00
71	Jim Everett	60.00
72	Todd Collins	60.00
73	Curtis Conway	60.00
74	Herman Moore	125.00
75	Neil O'Donnell	60.00
76	Rod Woodson	60.00
77	Tony Martin	60.00
78	Kent Graham	60.00
79	Andre Reed	60.00
80	Reggie White	125.00
81	Thurman Thomas	125.00
82	Garrison Hearst	60.00
83	Chris Warren	60.00
84	Wayne Chrebet	60.00
85	Chris T. Jones	60.00
86	Anthony Miller	60.00
87	Chris Chandler	60.00
88	Terrell Davis	750.00
89	Mike Alstott	375.00
90	Terry Allen	60.00
91	Jerome Bettis	125.00
92	Stan Humphries	60.00
93	Andre Rison	60.00
94	Marshall Faulk	125.00
95	Erik Kramer	60.00
96	O.J. McDuffie	60.00
97	Robert Smith	60.00
98	Keith Byars	60.00
99	Rodney Hampton	60.00
100	Desmond Howard	60.00
101	Lawrence Phillips	125.00
102	Michael Westbrook	60.00
103	Johnnie Morton	60.00
104	Ben Coates	60.00
105	J.J. Stokes	60.00
106	Terance Mathis	60.00
107	Errict Rhett	60.00
108	Tim Brown	60.00
109	Marvin Harrison	200.00
110	Muhsin Muhammad	60.00
111	Bam Morris	60.00
112	Mario Bates	60.00
113	Jimmy Smith	60.00
114	Irving Fryar	60.00
115	Tamarick Vanover	60.00
116	Brad Johnson	125.00
117	Rashaan Salaam	60.00
118	Ki-Jana Carter	60.00
119	Tyrone Wheatley	60.00
120	John Friesz	60.00
121	Orlando Pace	75.00
122	Jim Druckenmiller	450.00

123	Byron Hanspard	150.00
124	David LaFleur	200.00
125	Reidel Anthony	300.00
126	Antowain Smith	450.00
127	Bryant Westbrook	75.00
128	Fred Lane	200.00
129	Tiki Barber	300.00
130	Shawn Springs	60.00
131	Ike Hilliard	250.00
132	James Farrior	60.00
133	Darrell Russell	60.00
134	Walter Jones	60.00
135	Tom Knight	60.00
136	Yatil Green	150.00
137	Joey Kent	75.00
138	Kevin Lockett	60.00
139	Troy Davis	150.00
140	Darnell Autry	125.00
141	Pat Barnes	150.00
142	Rae Carruth	250.00
143	Will Blackwell	75.00
144	Warrick Dunn	750.00
145	Corey Dillon	450.00
146	Dwayne Rudd	60.00
147	Reinard Wilson	60.00
148	Peter Boulware	60.00
149	Tony Gonzalez	200.00
150	Danny Wuerffel	300.00

1996 Sentry Foods Packers-Bears Rivalry

This six-card set was issued through Sentry Foods stores in Wisconsin commemorating the past 23 years of the Green Bay Packers and Chicago Bears rivalry. The set was issued as a perforated sheet with color action photos and both team's helmets at the bottom along with a Sentry Foods logo in the lower left of the horizontal card. The card backs are unnumbered and include the date of the game, highlights and the box score. A full sheet also included coupons below the six cards.

			MT
Complete Set (6):			4.00
Common Player:			.50
1	Dec. 16, 1973 (John Brockington)		.50
2	Sep. 7, 1980 (Chester Marcol)		.50
3	Nov. 5, 1989 (Sterling Sharpe and many Packers celebra ting)		.50
4	Oct. 31, 1994 (Edgar Bennett)		.50
5	Nov. 12, 1995 (Brett Favre handing off to Edgar Bennett)		2.00
6	Oct. 6, 1996 (Packers defense)		.50

1997 Sentry Foods Packers-Vikings

This set was issued as a 10-card perforated sheet and included highlights from the past

30 years of the Green Bay Packers and Minnesota Vikings rivalry. Fronts feature a horizontal game action photo with the Sentry Foods logo in the upper left corner and "Packers vs. Vikings" across the bottom in a strip along with both team's logos. The black-and-white backs have the game's date, Sentry logo, highlights and a box score with a large Packers logo in the background. Cards are unnumbered with the bottom right card in an uncut sheet being an entry form for children to join the Junior Power Pack Club. The sheet was available at participating Sentry stores in Wisconsin.

		MT
Complete Set (9):		6.00
Common Player:		.50
1	Dec. 3, 1967 (Don Chandler kicks)	.50
2	Dec. 10, 1972 (Packer offense)	.50
3	Nov. 26, 1978 (Packer defense stops Chuck Foreman)	.50
4	Nov. 11, 1979 (Packer defense)	.50
5	Oct. 26, 1980 (Lynn Dickey)	.50
6	Nov. 13, 1983 (Packer offense)	.50
7	Dec. 13, 1987 (Paul Ott Carruth)	.50
8	Nov. 26, 1989 (Don Majkowski)	.50
9	Sep. 4, 1994 (Brett Favre handing off to Edgar Bennett)	2.00

1972 7-11 Slurpee Cups

Each of these 60 white plastic cups measures 5-1/4" tall, 3-1/4" in diameter at the mouth and 2" in diameter at the base. The fronts feature a color player portrait with his name and team name. Most of the cups feature a facsimile autograph between the portrait and the player's name. The backs include biographical information, the player's team helmet and the 7-Eleven logo. Another set of 80 cups was released in 1973. The cups are similar except the 1972 cups have a smaller typeface for the player's name (1/16") and do not have "Made in USA" printed on the sides.

		NM
Complete Set (60):		250.00
Common Player:		4.00
1	Donny Anderson	4.00
2	Elvin Bethea	5.00
3	Fred Biletnikoff	8.00
4	Bill Bradley	4.00
5	Terry Bradshaw	25.00
6	Larry Brown	4.00
7	Willie Brown	5.00
8	Norm Bulaich	4.00
9	Dick Butkus	15.00
10	Ray Chester	4.00
11	Bill Curry	4.00
12	Len Dawson	8.00
13	Willie Ellison	4.00
14	Ed Flanagan	4.00
15	Gary Garrison	4.00
16	Gale Gillingham	4.00
17	Joe Greene	8.00
18	Cedrick Hardman	4.00
19	Jim Hart	5.00
20	Ted Hendricks	5.00
21	Winston Hill	4.00
22	Ken Houston	5.00
23	Chuck Howley	4.00
24	Claude Humphrey	4.00
25	Roy Jefferson	4.00
26	Sonny Jurgensen	6.00
27	Leroy Kelly	5.00
28	Paul Krause	4.00
29	George Kunz	4.00
30	Jake Kupp	4.00
31	Ted Kwalick	4.00
32	Willie Lanier	5.00
33	Bob Lilly	6.00
34	Floyd Little	4.00
35	Larry Little	5.00
36	Tom Mack	4.00
37	Milt Morin	4.00
38	Mercury Morris	5.00
39	John Niland	4.00
40	Jim Otto	5.00
41	Steve Owens	4.00
42	Alan Page	5.00
43	Jim Plunkett	5.00

44	Mike Reid	5.00
45	Mel Renfro	5.00
46	Isiah Robertson	4.00
47	Andy Russell	5.00
48	Charlie Sanders	4.00
49	O.J. Simpson	15.00
50	Bubba Smith	5.00
51	Bill Stanfill	4.00
52	Jan Stenerud	5.00
53	Walt Sweeney	4.00
54	Bob Tucker	4.00
55	Jim Tyrer	4.00
56	Rick Volk	4.00
57	Gene Washington	4.00
58	Dave Wilcox	4.00
59	Del Williams	4.00
60	Ron Yary	4.00

1973 7-11 Slurpee Cups

This 80-cup series is similar to the 1972 series except the player's name is printed in larger type (1/8") and the words "Made in USA" are printed down the sides.

		NM
Complete Set (80):		450.00
Common Player:		5.00
1	Dan Abramowicz	6.00
2	Ken Anderson	10.00
3	Jim Beirne	5.00
4	Ed Bell	5.00
5	Bob Berry	5.00
6	Jim Bertelsen	5.00
7	Marlin Briscoe	5.00
8	John Brockington	6.00
9	Larry Brown	5.00
10	Buck Buchanan	7.50
11	Dick Butkus	25.00
12	Larry Carwell	5.00
13	Rich Caster	5.00
14	Bobby Douglass	5.00
15	Pete Duranko	5.00
16	Cid Edwards	5.00
17	Mel Farr	5.00
18	Pat Fischer	5.00
19	Mike Garrett	5.00
20	Walt Garrison	6.00
21	George Goeddeke	5.00
22	Bob Gresham	5.00
23	Jack Ham	10.00
24	Chris Hanburger	5.00
25	Franco Harris	20.00
26	Calvin Hill	6.00
27	J.D. Hill	5.00
28	Marv Hubbard	5.00
29	Scott Hunter	5.00
30	Harold Jackson	6.00
31	Randy Jackson	5.00
32	Bob Johnson	5.00
33	Jim Johnson	7.50
34	Ron Johnson	5.00
35	Leroy Keyes	5.00
36	Greg Landry	6.00
37	Gary Larsen	5.00
38	Frank Lewis	5.00
39	Bob Lilly	10.00
40	Dale Lindsey	5.00
41	Larry Little	7.50
42	Carl (Spider) Lockhart	5.00
43	Mike Lucci	5.00
44	Jim Lynch	5.00
45	Art Malone	5.00
46	Ed Marinaro	6.00
47	Jim Marshall	7.50
48	Ray May	5.00
49	Don Maynard	10.00
50	Don McCauley	5.00
51	Mike McCoy	5.00
52	Tom Mitchell	5.00
53	Tommy Nobis	7.50
54	Dan Pastorini	6.00
55	Mac Percival	5.00
56	Mike Phipps	6.00
57	Ed Podolak	5.00
58	John Reaves	5.00
59	Tim Rossovich	5.00
60	Bo Scott	5.00
61	Ron Sellers	5.00
62	Dennis Shaw	5.00
63	Mike Siani	5.00
64	O.J. Simpson	25.00
65	Bubba Smith	7.50
66	Larry Smith	5.00
67	Jackie Smith	7.50
68	Norm Snead	6.00
69	Jack Snow	5.00
70	Steve Spurrier	20.00
71	Doug Swift	5.00
72	Jack Tatum	7.50
73	Bruce Taylor	5.00
74	Otis Taylor	6.00
75	Bob Trumpy	6.00
76	Jim Turner	5.00
77	Phil Villapiano	5.00
78	Roger Wehrli	5.00
79	Ken Willard	5.00
80	Jack Youngblood	7.50

1983 7-11 Discs

These discs were available at participating 7-Eleven stores

in 1983. Each disc, which is numbered on the back as "x of Fifteen," has a portrait and an action picture on the front. The player's team name is at the top of the disc, while his name is at the bottom. His jersey number is on each side. The disc back has the player's career totals, pro honors, a Slurpee logo and the year, 1983.

		MT
Complete Set (15):		30.00
Common Player:		1.00
1	Franco Harris	5.00
2	Dan Fouts	3.00
3	Lee Roy Selmon	1.25
4	Nolan Cromwell	1.25
5	Marcus Allen	5.00
6	Joe Montana	10.00
7	Kellen Winslow	2.00
8	Hugh Green	1.00
9	Ted Hendricks	2.00
10	Danny White	1.50
11	Wes Chandler	1.00
12	Jimmie Giles	1.00
13	Jack Youngblood	2.00
14	Lester Hayes	1.00
15	Vince Ferragamo	1.00

1984 7-11 Discs

These discs, available at participating 7-Eleven stores, were available in two regions, East and West, as indicated by the card number prefix. The disc has a diameter of 1-3/4" and is designed like the previous year's issue, except the year on the back is 1984.

		MT
Complete Set (40):		60.00
Common Player:		.75
1E	Franco Harris	3.00
2E	Lawrence Taylor	2.00
3E	Mark Gastineau	.75
4E	Lee Roy Selmon	1.00
5E	Ken Anderson	1.50
6E	Walter Payton	4.00
7E	Ken Stabler	1.50
8E	Marcus Allen	2.00
9E	Fred Smerlas	.75
10E	Ozzie Newsome	1.25
11E	Steve Bartkowski	1.00
12E	Tony Dorsett	2.00
13E	John Riggins	1.50
14E	Billy Sims	.75
15E	Dan Marino	9.00
16E	Tony Collins	.75
17E	Curtis Dickey	.75
18E	Ron Jaworski	.75
19E	William Andrews	.75
20E	Joe Theismann	1.50
1W	Franco Harris	2.00
2W	Joe Montana	10.00
3W	Matt Blair	.75
4W	Warren Moon	6.00
5W	Marcus Allen	2.00
6W	John Riggins	1.50
7W	Walter Payton	4.00
8W	Vince Ferragamo	.75
9W	Billy Sims	.75
10W	Ken Anderson	1.25
11W	Lynn Dickey	.75
12W	Tony Dorsett	2.00
13W	Bill Kenney	.75
14W	Ottis Anderson	1.00
15W	Dan Fouts	1.50
16W	Eric Dickerson	3.00
17W	John Elway	6.00
18W	Ozzie Newsome	1.25
19W	Curt Warner	1.00
20W	Joe Theismann	1.50

1981 Shell Posters

The works of three different artists are featured on these 10-7/8" x 13-7/8" posters available at participating Shell Oil stations across the country in 1981. Each poster has a black-and-white drawing of the featured player, as rendered by either K. Atkins,

Nick Galloway or Tanenbawm (these signatures are on the corresponding poster fronts). There are, however, some posters which were not signed by the artist (#s 7, 11, 12 and 93). The posters are listed alphabetically by teams, then alphabetically by players. Team sets consist of six posters. A national set of six posters was also made (Payton, Griffin, Logan, Pearson, Campbell and O. Anderson) and was available in markets where a pro team did not exist.

		MT
Complete Set (96):		400.00
Common Player:		4.00
(1)	William Andrews	5.00
(2)	Steve Bartkowski	7.00
(3)	Buddy Curry	3.50
(4)	Wallace Francis	5.00
(5)	Mike Kenn	5.00
(6)	Jeff Van Note	4.00
(7)	Mike Barnes	4.00
(8)	Roger Carr	5.00
(9)	Curtis Dickey	5.00
(10)	Bert Jones	7.00
(11)	Bruce Laird	4.00
(12)	Randy McMillan	4.00
(13)	Brian Baschnagel	4.00
(15)	Vince Evans	5.00
(16)	Gary Fencik	5.00
(17)	Roland Harper	4.00
(18)	Alan Page	9.00
(19)	Walter Payton	10.00
(20)	Ken Anderson	8.00
(21)	Ross Browner	4.00
(22)	Archie Griffin	4.00
(23)	Pat McInally	5.00
(24)	Anthony Munoz	6.00
(25)	Reggie Williams	5.00
(26)	Lyle Alzado	6.00
(27)	Joe DeLamielleure	4.00
(28)	Doug Dieken	4.00
(29)	Dave Logan	4.00
(30)	Reggie Rucker	5.00
(31)	Brian Sipe	6.00
(32)	Benny Barnes	5.00
(33)	Bob Breunig	5.00
(34)	D.D. Lewis	5.00
(35)	Harvey Martin	6.00
(36)	Drew Pearson	7.00
(37)	Rafael Septien	4.00
(38)	Al (Bubba) Baker	5.00
(39)	Dexter Bussey	4.00
(40)	Gary Danielson	5.00
(41)	Freddie Scott	4.00
(42)	Billy Sims	6.00
(43)	Tom Skladany	4.00
(44)	Robert Brazile	6.00
(45)	Ken Burrough	6.00
(46)	Earl Campbell	9.00
(47)	Leon Gray	5.00
(48)	Carl Mauck	4.00
(49)	Ken Stabler	8.00
(50)	Bob Baumhower	5.00
(51)	Jimmy Cefalo	5.00
(52)	A.J. Duhe	6.00
(53)	Nat Moore	5.00
(54)	Ed Newman	4.00
(55)	Uwe Von Schamann	4.00
(56)	Steve Grogan	7.00
(57)	John Hannah	4.50
(58)	Don Hasselbeck	4.00
(59)	Mike Haynes	6.00
(60)	Harold Jackson	6.00
(61)	Steve Nelson	4.00
(62)	Elois Grooms	5.00
(63)	Rickey Jackson	7.50
(64)	Archie Manning	8.00
(65)	Tommy Myers	5.00
(66)	Benny Ricardo	5.00
(67)	George Rogers	6.00
(68)	Harry Carson	7.00
(69)	Dave Jennings	4.00
(70)	Gary Jeter	5.00
(71)	Phil Simms	8.00
(72)	Lawrence Taylor	12.00
(73)	Brad Van Pelt	5.00
(74)	Greg Buttle	4.00
(75)	Bruce Harper	4.00
(76)	Joe Klecko	5.00
(77)	Randy Rasmussen	5.00
(78)	Richard Todd	5.00
(79)	Wesley Walker	5.00
(80)	Ottis Anderson	4.00
(81)	Dan Dierdorf	9.00
(82)	Mel Gray	5.00
(83)	Jim Hart	6.00
(84)	E.J. Junior	5.00
(85)	Pat Tilley	5.00
(86)	Jimmie Giles	5.00
(87)	Charley Hannah	4.00
(88)	Bill Kollar	4.00
(89)	David Lewis	4.00
(90)	Lee Roy Selmon	6.00
(91)	Doug Williams	5.00
(92)	Joe Lavender	5.00
(93)	Mark Moseley	5.00
(94)	Mark Murphy	4.00
(95)	Lemar Parrish	5.00
(96)	John Riggins	9.00
(97)	Joe Washington	5.00

1994 Signature Rookies

The 60-card, standard-size set featured top NFL prospects in their collegiate uniforms. The player's name and position appear on the bottom edge and the cards are numbered as "x of 45,000" or "Authentic Signature" along the left edge in gold foil. Production was limited to 12,500 boxes. Inserts included Hottest Prospect, Gale Sayers, Charlie Ward and Tony Dorsett.

		MT
Complete Set (60):		8.00
Common Player:		.05
1	Sam Adams	.05
2	Trev Alberts	.05
3	Derrick Alexander	.25
4	Aubrey Beavers	.05
5	Lou Benfatti	.05
6	James Bostic	.05
7	Tim Bowens	.25
8	Rich Braham	.05
9	Isaac Bruce	1.50
10	Vaughn Bryant	.05
11	Brenston Buckner	.05
12	Jeff Burris	.10
13	Carlester Crumpler	.05
14	Lake Dawson	.30
15	Tyrone Drakeford	.05
16	Dan Eichloff	.05
17	Rob Fredrickson	.20
18	Gus Frerotte	.75
19	William Gaines	.05
20	Wayne Gandy	.05
21	Jason Gildon	.05
22	Lemanski Hall	.05
23	Shelby Hill	.05
24	LeShon Johnson	.15
25	Alan Kline	.05
26	Antonio Langham	.10
27	Keith Lyle	.05
28	Van Malone	.05
29	Jamir Miller	.10
30	Byron "Bam" Morris	.50
31	Jeremy Nunley	.05
32	Brad Ottis	.05
33	Joe Panos	.05
34	John Reece	.05
35	Tony Richardson	.05
36	Tim Ruddy	.05
37	Corey Sawyer	.05
38	Malcolm Seabron	.05
39	John Thierry	.05
40	Jason Seahorn	.05
41	Eric Zomalt	.05
42	Toby Wright	.05
43	Willie Jackson	.05
44	Tre Johnson	.05
45	Darren Krein	.05
46	Corey Louchiey	.05
47	Eric Mahlum	.05
48	Chris Maumalanga	.05
49	Jim Miller	.05
50	Aaron Mundy	.05
51	Turhon O'Brannon	.05
52	David Palmer	.10
53	Jim Pyne	.05
54	Errict Rhett	1.25
55	Sam Rogers	.05
56	Jason Winrow	.05
57	Ronnie Woolfork	.05
58	Rob Waldrop	.05
59	Ryan Yarborough	.05
60	Checklist	.05

Values quoted in this guide reflect the retail price of a card — the price a collector can expect to pay when buying a card from a dealer. The wholesale price — that which a collector can expect to receive from a dealer when selling cards — will be significantly lower, depending on desirability and condition.

1994 Signature Rookies Signatures

The 59-card, standard-size set was inserted in each six-card pack of Signature Rookies. Each card was numbered as "x of 7,750." Reportedly, 700 Errict Rhett cards are not actually signed by the running back, but that he had an aquaintance autograph the cards for him. Autographed Rhett cards could be sent in to Signature Rookies for verification.

		MT
Complete Set (59):		225.00
Common Autograph:		4.00
1	Sam Adams	4.00
2	Trev Alberts	4.00
3	Derrick Alexander (WR)	6.00
4	Larry Allen	4.00
5	Aubrey Beavers	4.00
6	Lou Benfatti	4.00
7	James Bostic	4.00
8	Tim Bowens	4.00
9	Rich Braham	4.00
10	Isaac Bruce	30.00
11	Vaughn Bryant	4.00
12	Brenston Buckner	4.00
13	Jeff Burris	4.00
14	Carlester Crumpler	6.00
15	Lake Dawson	6.00
16	Tyronne Drakeford	4.00
17	Dan Eichloff	4.00
18	Rob Fredrickson	4.00
19	Gus Frerotte	10.00
20	William Gaines	4.00
21	Wayne Gandy	4.00
22	Jason Gildon	4.00
23	Lemanski Hall	4.00
24	Shelby Hill	4.00
25	Willie Jackson	4.00
26	LeShon Johnson	6.00
27	Tre Johnson	4.00
28	Alan Kline	4.00
29	Darren Krein	4.00
30	Antonio Langham	6.00
31	Corey Louchiey	4.00
32	Keith Lyle	4.00
33	Eric Mahlum	4.00
34	Van Malone	4.00
35	Chris Maumalanga	4.00
36	Jamir Miller	4.00
37	Jim Miller	6.00
38	Byron "Bam" Morris	6.00
39	Aaron Mundy	4.00
40	Jeremy Nunley	4.00
41	Turhon O'Bannon	4.00
42	Brad Ottis	4.00
43	David Palmer	5.00
44	Joe Panos	4.00
45	Jim Pyne	4.00
46	John Reece	4.00
47	Errict Rhett	10.00
48	Tony Richardson	4.00
49	Sam Rogers	4.00
50	Tim Ruddy	4.00
51	Corey Sawyer	4.00
52	Malcolm Seabron	4.00
53	Jason Sehorn	4.00
54	John Thierry	4.00
55	Jason Winrow	4.00
56	Ronnie Woolfork	4.00
57	Toby Wright	4.00
58	Ryan Yarborough	4.00
59	Eric Zomalt	4.00

1994 Signature Rookies Bonus Signatures

The 15-card, standard-size set was hand-numbered out of 7,750 and the player's signature appeared on the bottom edge. Cards were randomly inserted in 1994 Tetrad packs.

	MT
Complete Set (15):	35.00

Common Signature:		3.00
Coupons Replace Some Cards		
1	Jamal Anderson	10.00
2	Myron Bell	3.00
3	Mitch Berger	3.00
4	Jocelyn Borgella	3.00
5	Chris Brantley	3.00
6	Ron Edwards	3.00
7	Rob Holmberg	3.00
8	Fred Lester	3.00
9	Joseph Patton	3.00
10	Eric Ravotti	3.00
11	Jim Reid	3.00
12	Jerry Reynolds	3.00
13	Bracey Walker	3.00
14	Gabe Wilkins	3.00
15	Brant Boyer	3.00

1994 Signature Rookies Tony Dorsett

The two-card, standard-size set, limited to 5,000, are numbered as out of 5,000 autographed 1,000 cards. Dallas Cowboys Hall of Fame running back.

	MT
Complete Set (2):	6.00
Common Player:	3.00
Complete Signature Set (2):	125.00
Tony Dorsett AU/1000	60.00

1994 Signature Rookies Hottest Prospects

The five-card, standard-size set was numbered out of 15,000 and featured the players in their collegiate uniforms. The cards are numbered and carry an "A" prefix.

		MT
Complete Set (5):		10.00
Common Player:		2.00
1	Willie McGinest	3.00
2	Bryant Young	4.00
3	DeWayne Washington	2.00
4	Aaron Taylor	2.00
5	Charles Johnson	2.50

1994 Signature Rookies Gale Sayers

The two-card, standard-size set was randomly inserted into packs and was limited to 5,000 of each card. The former Chicago Bears star autographed 1,000 of the cards.

	MT
Complete Set (2):	8.00
Common Sayers:	4.00
Comp. Signature Set (2):	150.00
Gale Sayers AU/1000	75.00

1994 Signature Rookies Charlie Ward

The five-card, standard-size set highlights Florida State's 1993 Heisman winner and 5,000 of each card was produced. Ward autographed 525 of his cards. The cards are numbered with a "C" prefix.

		MT
Complete Set (5):		4.00
Common Ward:		1.00
Complete Signed Set (5):		150.00
Charlie Ward AU/25		30.00
1	Charlie Ward (In throwing motion)	1.00
2	Charlie Ward (Ready to hand-off)	1.00
3	Charlie Ward (Posed football shot)	1.00
4	Charlie Ward (Holding basketball at waist)	1.00
5	Charlie Ward (holding basketball overhead)	1.00

A player's name in *italic type* indicates a rookie card.

1995 SR Auto-Phonex

The 40-card, standard-size set features card fronts with triple images of the key player in his collegiate uniform. The player's name appears in gold foil along the bottom edge with "1 of 19,000" printed on the bottom. Each case of Auto-Phonex features Hot Packs, which include an autographed phone card plus five additional autographed cards. J.J. Stokes was featured on the $5 card (1:287) while the $25 card (Kevin Carter) is inserted every 1,437. Ten Warren Sapp $100 cards (1:14,371) and eight $1,000 (Rashaan Salaam and Ki-Jana Carter) were included every 35,928 packs.

		MT
Complete Set (40):		10.00
Common Player:		.10
1	Warren Sapp	.30
2	Kevin Carter	.20
3	Ki-Jana Carter	.75
4	J.J. Stokes	1.00
5	Derrick Alexander	.20
6	Rashaan Salaam	1.25
7	Jamal Willis	.10
8	Frank Sanders	.60
9	Rob Johnson	.10
10	Derrick Brooks	.20
11	Sherman Williams	.30
12	Dave Barr	.10
13	Christian Fauria	.20
14	Stoney Case	.10
15	Rodney Thomas	.60
16	James A. Stewart	.20
17	Ray Zellars	.30
18	Jack Jackson	.10
19	Terrell Davis	1.25
20	Kyle Brady	.20
21	Ruben Brown	.20
22	Brent Moss	.10
23	John Sacca	.10
24	David Dunn	.20
25	Eddie Goines	.10
26	Curtis Martin	1.50
27	Billy Williams	.10
28	Steve Stenstrom	.10
29	Mark Bruener	.30
30	Kelvin Anderson	.10
31	Ellis Johnson	.20
32	Steve Ingram	.10
33	Larry Jones	.10
34	Bobby Taylor	.30
35	Joe Aska	.10
36	Jerrott Willard	.10
37	Chris T. Jones	.30
38	Mark Birchmeier	.10
39	Jimmy Hitchcock	.10
40	Tyrone Davis	.10
NNO	Ki-Jana Carter (CL)	.30

1995 SR Auto-Phonex Phone Card Signatures

The 40-card, 2-3/8" x 3-1/8" phone card set was inserted

in each pack of SR Auto-Phonex. The cards have rounded corners and the common card has $2 of calling time. $5 cards of J.J. Stokes (1:287), $25 cards of Kevin Carter (1:1,437) and $100 cards of Warren Sapp (1:14,371) were inserted, as were eight $1,000 cards of Ki-Jana Carter and Rashaan Salaam (1:35,928).

		MT
Complete Set (40):		250.00
Common Player:		3.00
1	Warren Sapp	8.00
2	Kevin Carter	4.00
3	Ki-Jana Carter	6.00
4	J.J. Stokes	15.00
5	Derrick Alexander	4.00
6	Rashaan Salaam	8.00
7	Jamal Willis	3.00
8	Frank Sanders	10.00
9	Eric Zeier	6.00
10	Derrick Brooks	4.00
11	Sherman Williams	5.00
12	Dave Barr	3.00
13	Christian Fauria	4.00
14	Stoney Case	3.00
15	Rodney Thomas	6.00
16	James A. Stewart	4.00
17	Ray Zellars	5.00
18	Jack Jackson	3.00
19	Terrell Davis	50.00
20	Kyle Brady	4.00
21	Ruben Brown	4.00
22	Brent Moss	3.00
23	John Sacca	3.00
24	David Dunn	4.00
25	Eddie Goines	3.00
26	Curtis Martin	30.00
27	Billy Williams	3.00
28	Steve Stenstrom	3.00
29	Mark Bruener	6.00
30	Kelvin Anderson	3.00
31	Ellis Johnson	4.00
32	Steve Ingram	3.00
33	Larry Jones	3.00
34	Bobby Taylor	5.00
35	Joe Aska	3.00
36	Jerrott Willard	3.00
37	Chris T. Jones	8.00
38	Mark Birchmeier	3.00
39	Jimmy Hitchcock	3.00
40	Tyrone Davis	3.00
NNO	J.J. Stokes $5 Card	40.00
NNO	Kevin Carter $25 Card	80.00

1995 SR Auto-Phonex Signatures

The 10-card, standard-size set was randomly inserted in Hot Packs and was also available through a mail-in redemption offer. The cards are identical in design to the regular-issue cards, except for the signatures.

		MT
Complete Set (10):		325.00
Common Player:		10.00
3A	Ki-Jana Carter	30.00
6A	Rashaan Salaam	30.00
8A	Frank Sanders	50.00
11A	Sherman Williams	20.00
12A	Dave Barr	10.00
14A	Stoney Case	20.00
16A	James A. Stewart	15.00
17A	Ray Zellars	20.00
20A	Kyle Brady	20.00
23A	John Sacca	10.00

1995 SR Draft Preview

The 80-card, standard-size set was issued in six-card packs for $5, and included an autographed card. Each player signed 7,750 of his own cards, and

39,000 of each card was produced. An international version was also produced, limited to a production total of 13,500, 2,750 of which were signed.

		MT
Complete Set (80):		15.00
Common Player:		.10
International:		1x-2x
1	Derrick Alexander	.15
2	Kelvin Anderson	.10
3	Antonio Armstrong	.10
4	Jamie Asher	.10
5	Joe Aska	.10
6	Dave Barr	.10
7	Brandon Bennett	.10
8	Tony Berti	.10
9	Mark Birchmeier	.10
10	Tony Boselli	.15
11	Derrick Brooks	.15
12	Anthony Brown	.10
13	Ruben Brown	.15
14	Mark Bruener	.30
15	Ontiwaun Carter	.10
16	Stoney Case	.10
17	Byron Chamberlain	.10
18	Shannon Clavelle	.10
19	Jamal Cox	.10
20	Zack Crockett	.15
21	Terrell Davis	1.50
22	Tyrone Davis	.10
23	Lee DeRamus	.10
24	Ken Dilger	.40
25	Hugh Douglas	.50
26	David Dunn	.15
27	Chad Eaton	.10
28	Hicham El-Mashtoub	.10
29	Christian Fauria	.15
30	Terrell Fletcher	.30
31	Antonio Freeman	.10
32	Eddie Goines	.10
33	Roger Graham	.10
34	Carl Greenwood	.10
35	Ed Hervey	.10
36	Jimmy Hitchcock	.10
37	Darius Holland	.10
38	Torey Hunter	.10
39	Steve Ingram	.10
40	Jack Jackson	.10
41	Trezelle Jenkins	.15
42	Ellis Johnson	.15
43	Eric Johnson	.10
44	Rob Johnson	.10
45	Chris T. Jones	.25
46	Larry Jones	.10
47	Shawn King	.10
48	Scotty Lewis	.10
49	Curtis Martin	2.00
50	Oscar McBride	.10
51	Kez McCorvey	.10
52	Bronzell Miller	.10
53	Pete Mitchell	.25
54	Brent Moss	.10
55	Craig Newsome	.15
56	Herman O'Berry	.10
57	Matt O'Dwyer	.10
58	Tyrone Poole	.15
59	Brian Pruitt	.10
60	Cory Raymer	.10
61	John Sacca	.10
62	Frank Sanders	.75
63	J.J. Smith	.10
64	Brendan Stai	.10
65	Steve Stenstrom	.10
66	James O. Stewart	.40
67	Kordell Stewart	1.50
68	Ben Talley	.10
69	Bobby Taylor	.25
70	Johnny Thomas	.10
71	Orlando Thomas	.15
72	Rodney Thomas	.10
73	Zach Wiegert	.10
74	Jerrott Willard	.10
75	Billy Williams	.10
76	Sherman Williams	.25
77	Jamal Willis	.10
78	Dave Wohlabaugh	.10
79	Eric Zeier	.75
80	Checklist	.10

1995 SR Draft Preview Signatures

The 79-card, standard-size parallel set (minus the checklist), was included in each pack of SR Draft Preview. Each player signed 7,750 cards out of the 39,000 produced, and 2,750 out of the 13,500 produced for the international set.

		MT
Complete Set (79):		250.00
Common Player:		2.50
International:		1x-2x
1	Derrick Alexander	3.00
2	Kelvin Anderson	2.50
3	Antonio Armstrong	2.50
4	Jamie Asher	2.50
5	Joe Aska	2.50
6	Dave Barr	2.50

7	Brandon Bennett	2.50
8	Tony Berti	2.50
9	Mark Birchmeier	2.50
10	Tony Boselli	3.00
11	Derrick Brooks	3.00
12	Anthony Brown	2.50
13	Ruben Brown	3.00
14	Mark Bruener	4.00
15	Ontiwaun Carter	2.50
16	Stoney Case	2.50
17	Byron Chamberlain	2.50
18	Shannon Clavelle	2.50
19	Jamal Cox	2.50
20	Zack Crockett	3.00
21	Terrell Davis	30.00
22	Tyrone Davis	2.50
23	Lee DeRamus	2.50
24	Ken Dilger	5.00
25	Hugh Douglas	5.00
26	David Dunn	3.00
27	Chad Eaton	2.50
28	Hicham El-Mashtoub	2.50
29	Christian Fauria	3.00
30	Terrell Fletcher	4.00
31	Antonio Freeman	20.00
32	Eddie Goines	2.50
33	Roger Graham	2.50
34	Carl Greenwood	2.50
35	Ed Hervey	2.50
36	Jimmy Hitchcock	2.50
37	Darius Holland	2.50
38	Torey Hunter	2.50
39	Steve Ingram	2.50
40	Jack Jackson	2.50
41	Trezelle Jenkins	2.50
42	Ellis Johnson	3.00
43	Eric Johnson	3.00
44	Rob Johnson	2.50
45	Chris T. Jones	8.00
46	Larry Jones	2.50
47	Shawn King	2.50
48	Scotty Lewis	2.50
49	Curtis Martin	20.00
50	Oscar McBride	2.50
51	Kez McCorvey	2.50
52	Bronzell Miller	2.50
53	Pete Mitchell	4.00
54	Brent Moss	2.50
55	Craig Newsome	3.00
56	Herman O'Berry	2.50
57	Matt O'Dwyer	2.50
58	Tyrone Poole	3.00
59	Brian Pruitt	2.50
60	Cory Raymer	2.50
61	John Sacca	2.50
62	Frank Sanders	8.00
63	J.J. Smith	2.50
64	Brendan Stai	2.50
65	Steve Stenstrom	2.50
66	James O. Stewart	5.00
67	Kordell Stewart	20.00
68	Ben Talley	2.50
69	Bobby Taylor	4.00
70	Johnny Thomas	2.50
71	Orlando Thomas	3.00
72	Rodney Thomas	5.00
73	Zach Wiegert	3.00
74	Jerrott Willard	2.50
75	Billy Williams	2.50
76	Sherman Williams	4.00
77	Jamal Willis	2.50
78	Dave Wohlabaugh	2.50
79	Eric Zeier	5.00

1995 SR Draft Preview Franchise Rookies

The 10-card, standard-size set was inserted every eight packs of SR Draft Preview. Production was limited to 10,000 sets with each player signing 2,500 of his own card. The cards are numbered with a "R" prefix.

		MT
Complete Set (10):		12.00
Common Player:		.50
1	Kyle Brady	.75
2	Kevin Carter	.50
3	Ki-Jana Carter	3.00
4	Luther Ellis	.50
5	Rashaan Salaam	4.00
6	Warren Sapp	.75

7	James A. Stewart	.50
8	J.J. Stokes	3.00
9	Michael Westbrook	2.00
10	Ray Zellars	.75

1995 SR Draft Preview Franchise Rookies Signatures

The 10-card, standard-size set was limited to 2,500 of each card and is identical in design to the Franchise Rookies insert set with the exception of the player's autograph on the card front. The cards carry a "R" prefix.

		MT
Complete Set (10):		75.00
Common Player:		4.00
1	Kyle Brady	5.00
2	Kevin Carter	4.00
3	Ki-Jana Carter	6.00
4	Luther Ellis	4.00
5	Rashaan Salaam	10.00
6	Warren Sapp (1125)	8.00
7	James A. Stewart	4.00
8	J.J. Stokes	12.00
9	Michael Westbrook	15.00
10	Ray Zellars	4.00

1995 SR Draft Preview International Franchise Duo

The 10-card, regular-size set was inserted every 10 packs and features one draft choice on each side of the card. "International" appears in the silver triangle and the player's name is divided (first and last) on the left and right sides.

		MT
Complete Set (10):		20.00
Common Player:		1.50
1	Ki-Jana Carter, Kevin Carter	3.00
2	Warren Sapp, Derrick Alexander	2.00
3	James A. Stewart, James O. Stewart	2.00
4	Michael Westbrook, J.J. Stokes	2.50
5	Kyle Brady, Kerry Collins	3.00
6	Steve McNair, Kerry Collins	5.00
7	Eric Zeier, Kordell Stewart	5.00
8	Rob Johnson, Stoney Case	1.50
9	Rashaan Salaam, Ki-Jana Carter	3.00
10	Ray Zellars, Sherman Williams	2.00

1995 SR Draft Preview Int'l Franchise Duo Signatures

The 16-card, standard-size set features one draft choice on each side of the card and is a parallel set in design with the International Franchise Duo insert set. Warren Sapp and James A. Stewart, included in the regular-issue set, did not sign and the set skips No. 12.

		MT
Complete Set (16):		700.00
Common Player:		15.00
1	Derrick Alexander (AU/200)	15.00
2	Kyle Brady (AU/242)	20.00
3	Kevin Carter (AU/315)	15.00
4	Ki-Jana Carter (AU/400)	30.00
5	Stoney Case (AU/200)	15.00
6	Kerry Collins (AU/600)	80.00
7	Rob Johnson (AU/309)	35.00
8	Steve McNair (AU/600)	70.00
9	Rashaan Salaam (AU/299)	100.00
10	Kordell Stewart (AU/309)	150.00
11	James O. Stewart (AU/200)	30.00

13	J.J. Stokes	80.00
14	Michael Westbrook (AU/284)	70.00
15	Sherman Williams (AU/312)	20.00
16	Eric Zeier (AU/314)	35.00
17	Ray Zellars (AU/310)	20.00

1995 SR Draft Preview Masters of the Mic

The five-card, standard-size set features some of the top announcers. Each announcer autographed 1,000 of his cards with 30,000 total sets produced. The card backs contain a brief announcer profile. An international version was also produced with the only difference being the silver-foil "International" stamp.

		MT
Complete Set (5):		10.00
Common Player:		2.00
International:		1x-2x

1995 SR Draft Preview Masters of the Mic Signatures

This five-card insert consists of autographed versions of the Masters of the Mic set. Each announcer signed 1,000 cards, which were inserted 1:4. The cards are numbered with a "M" prefix.

		MT
Complete Set (5):		75.00
Common Player:		15.00
1	Todd Christensen	15.00
2	Jerry Glanville	15.00
3	Howie Long	15.00
4	Dick Stockton	15.00
5	Joe Theismann UER	15.00

1995 SR Draft Preview Peripheral Vision

Peripheral Vision was a five-card insert that featured Rashaan Salaam and Ki-Jana Carter, each with two cards of their own as well as sharing the double sided card No. 5. These inserts are numbered "1 of 5,000," and carry a V1-V5 card number. Autographed versions of each card are also available and limited to 100 of each.

		MT
Complete Set (5):		15.00
Common Player:		2.50
1	Rashaan Salaam	4.00
2	Rashaan Salaam	4.00
3	Ki-Jana Carter	2.50
4	Ki-Jana Carter	2.50
5	Ki-Jana Carter, Rashaan Salaam	3.00

1995 SR Draft Preview Peripheral Vision Signatures

This five-card autographed set was inserted one per 24 packs.

		MT
Complete Set (5):		550.00
Common Player:		80.00
1/2	Rashaan Salaam	80.00
3/4	Ki-Jana Carter	80.00
5/6	Ki-Jana Carter, Rashaan Salaam	250.00
V2	Rashaan Salaam	150.00
V4	Ki-Jana Carter	90.00

1995 SR Draft Preview Old Judge Previews

Inserted 1:24, the cards in this five-card set measure 2" x 3".

They are designed to look like the old tobacco cards. The card fronts feature a color photo on a solid background with the words "Old Judge, T-95 Test Issue" printed across the top. The backs contain basic player information.

		MT
Complete Set (5):		20.00
Common Player:		1.50
1	Blake Brockemeyer	1.50
2	Kerry Collins	8.00
3	Steve McNair	8.00
4	J.J. O'Laughlin	1.50
5	John Walsh	1.50

1995 SR Draft Preview Old Judge Previews Signatures

An autographed version of Old Judge Previews, these cards were inserted 1:24. Each player signed 515 cards for this insert.

		MT
Complete Set (5):		200.00
Common Player:		15.00
1	Blake Brockemeyer	15.00
2	Kerry Collins	80.00
3	Steve McNair	80.00
4	J.J. O'Laughlin	15.00
5	John Walsh	15.00

1995 SR Signature Prime Previews

This five-card set was randomly inserted in packs of Basketball Autobilia. The cards are borderless and feature a color photo on both sides. The backs feature biographical information and college stats.

		MT
Complete Set (5):		12.00
Common Player:		1.00
1	Ki-Jana Carter	2.00
2	Kyle Brady	1.00
3	J.J. Stokes	2.50
4	Rashaan Salaam	3.00
5	Steve McNair	5.00

1995 SR Signature Prime

SR Signature Prime consists of a 50-card base set with one parallel and one insert. The base cards feature a borderless color photo on the front. The player's name is printed in gold in a red stripe on the left side of the card. The card backs contain another color photo, biographical information and college stats. The only insert is TD Club (1:1). Both the base set and TD Club have autographed versions as well.

		MT
Complete Set (50):		20.00
Common Player:		.15
Checklist (NNO)		.10
1	Justin Armour	.15
2	Joe Aska	.15
3	Henry Bailey	.15
4	Jay Barker	.15
5	Dave Barr	.15
6	Kevin Bouie	.15
7	Mark Bruener	.40
8	Stoney Case	.15
9	Curtis Ceaser	.15
10	Todd Collins	.75
11	Jerry Colquitt	.15
12	Terrell Davis	4.00
13	David Dunn	.40
14	O'Mar Ellison	.15
15	Christian Fauria	.40
16	Antonio Freeman	3.00
17	Eddie Goines	.15
18	Aaron Hayden	.40
19	William Henderson	.15
20	Kevin Hickman	.15
21	Jack Jackson	.15
22	Travis Jervey	.15
23	Rob Johnson	.40
24	Chris T. Jones	.75
25	Larry Jones	.15
26	Curtis Marsh	.15
27	Curtis Martin	4.00
28	Fred McCrary	.15
29	Mike Miller	.15
30	Shannon Myers	.15
31	Jimmy Oliver	.15
32	Dino Philyaw	.15
33	Lovell Pinkney	.15
34	Michael Roan	.15
35	Chris Sanders	.75

36	Frank Sanders	.75
37	Cory Schlesinger	.40
38	Charlie Simmons	.15
39	David Sloan	.40
40	Steve Stenstrom	.15
41	James A. Stewart	.15
42	Rodney Thomas	.40
43	A.C. Tellison	.15
44	Tamarick Vanover	.75
45	John Walsh	.15
46	Kendell Watkins	.15
47	Charles Way	.40
48	Craig Whelihan	.15
49	Eric Zeier	.40
50	Ray Zellars	.40

1995 SR Signature Prime Signatures

This set consists of autographed versions of the Signature Prime base set. The cards were inserted one per pack and sealed in a protective holder. Each player signed 3,000 of his cards which are numbered in the bottom right corner.

		MT
Complete Set (50):		275.00
Common Player:		4.00
1	Justin Armour	4.00
2	Joe Aska	4.00
3	Henry Bailey	4.00
4	Jay Barker	4.00
5	Dave Barr	4.00
6	Kevin Bouie	4.00
7	Mark Bruener	8.00
8	Stoney Case	4.00
9	Curtis Ceaser	4.00
10	Todd Collins	8.00
11	Jerry Colquitt	4.00
12	Terrell Davis	30.00
13	David Dunn	8.00
14	O'Mar Ellison	4.00
15	Christian Fauria	8.00
16	Antonio Freeman	20.00
17	Eddie Goines	4.00
18	Aaron Hayden	8.00
19	William Henderson	4.00
20	Kevin Hickman	4.00
21	Jack Jackson	4.00
22	Travis Jervey	4.00
23	Rob Johnson	4.00
24	Chris T. Jones	12.00
25	Larry Jones	4.00
26	Curtis Marsh	4.00
27	Curtis Martin	30.00
28	Fred McCrary	4.00
29	Mike Miller	4.00
30	Shannon Myers	4.00
31	Jimmy Oliver	4.00
32	Dino Philyaw	4.00
33	Lovell Pinkney	4.00
34	Michael Roan	4.00
35	Chris Sanders	12.00
36	Frank Sanders	12.00
37	Cory Schlesinger	8.00
38	Charlie Simmons	4.00
39	David Sloan	8.00
40	Steve Stenstrom	4.00
41	James A. Stewart	4.00
42	Rodney Thomas	8.00
43	A.C. Tellison	4.00
44	Tamarick Vanover	12.00
45	John Walsh	4.00
46	Kendell Watkins	4.00
47	Charles Way	8.00
48	Craig Whelihan	4.00
49	Eric Zeier	8.00
50	Ray Zellars	8.00

1995 SR Signature Prime TD Club

TD Club is a 10-card insert, limited to 15,000 cards per player. The fronts feature a player photo against a silver foil background and a "T" prefix.

		MT
Complete Set (10):		12.00
Common Player:		.50
1	Kyle Brady	.50
2	Ki-Jana Carter	1.50
3	Kerry Collins	3.00
4	Joey Galloway	2.00
5	Steve McNair	3.00
6	Rashaan Salaam	2.00
7	James O. Stewart	.75
8	J.J. Stokes	2.00
9	Michael Westbrook	2.00
10	Sherman Williams	.50

1995 SR Signature Prime TD Club Signatures

Each player in the TD Club insert signed 1,000 of their

cards for this parallel set. The cards are sequentially numbered carrying a "T" prefix and are sealed in a protective holder.

		MT
Complete Set (10):		300.00
Common Player:		15.00
1	Kyle Brady	15.00
2	Ki-Jana Carter	25.00
3	Kerry Collins	75.00
4	Joey Galloway	40.00
5	Steve McNair	75.00
6	Rashaan Salaam	30.00
7	James O. Stewart	25.00
8	J.J. Stokes	30.00
9	Michael Westbrook	30.00
10	Sherman Williams	15.00

1996 SR Autobilia

SR Autobilia consists of a 55-card base set featuring rookies from the 1995 and 1996 seasons. Instant win cards were randomly inserted in packs. The cards were redeemable for autographs and memorabilia.

		MT
Complete Set (55):		15.00
Common Player:		.10
1	Ruben Brown	.10
2	Kevin Carter	.10
3	Ki-Jana Carter	.25
4	Stoney Case	.10
5	Kerry Collins	.75
6	Terrell Davis	1.00
7	Antonio Freeman	.50
8	Joey Galloway	.75
9	Darick Holmes	.25
10	Jack Jackson	.10
11	Curtis Martin	1.00
12	O.J. McDuffie	.25
13	Steve McNair	.30
14	Byron "Bam" Morris	.50
15	Craig Newsome	.10
16	Errict Rhett	.50
17	Rashaan Salaam	.75
18	Frank Sanders	.25
19	James O. Stewart	.25
20	Kordell Stewart	.75
21	J.J. Stokes	.50
22	Rodney Thomas	.25
23	Tamarick Vanover	.50
24	Michael Westbrook	.50
25	Sherman Williams	.10
26	Eric Zeier	.40
27	Karim Abdul-Jabbar	1.50
28	Mike Alstott	1.00
29	Willie Anderson	.10
30	Tony Banks	1.25
31	Marco Battaglia	.40
32	Tim Biakabutuka	1.50
33	Stephen Davis	.60
34	Chris Doering	.10
35	Daryl Gardener	.10
36	Eddie George	2.50
37	Terry Glenn	2.50
38	Randall Godfrey	.10
39	Marvin Harrison	1.00
40	Aaron Hayden	.25
41	Mercury Hayes	.40
42	Dietrich Jells	.10
43	Cedric Jones	.10
44	Jeff Lewis	.30
45	Derrick Mayes	.75
46	Leland McElroy	1.00
47	Jerald Moore	.40
48	Eric Moulds	.75
49	Kendrick Nord	.10
50	Stanley Pritchett	.25
51	Jon Stark	.10
52	Steve Taneyhill	.10
53	Amani Toomer	.75
54	Stepfret Williams	.50
55	Checklist	.10

1992 SkyBox Impel Impact Prime Time Promos

These unnumbered promotional cards were distributed as a set in January 1992 during the Super Bowl XXVI show. The Earnest Byner card shows him in action on the front, with his name and number above the photo in maroon. A maroon bar along the right side of the card contains his team's name, in white letters. A Prime Time logo appears in the lower left corner. The card back, as does the one for Jim Kelly, says the card is a limited-edition commemorative card and includes an advertisement for Impel's Impact and Prime Time products. The Kelly card front shows him ready to pass. Because the cards were produced before Impel changed its name to SkyBox, subtle card front design changes can be detected on the later-released base brands.

	MT
Complete Set (2):	10.00
Common Player:	3.00
---- Impact (Jim Kelly)	7.50
---- PrimeTime (Earnest Byner)	3.00

1992 SkyBox Impact Promos

These three cards, available together in a promotional pack, preview the 1992 SkyBox Impact set. The cards' design is similar to the regular issue, except the numbers, which are on the card back. They use 001, 002 and 003.

		MT
Complete Set (3):		6.00
Common Player:		1.00
1	Jim Kelly	5.00
2	Michael Dean Perry	2.00
3	Reggie Roby	1.00

1992 SkyBox Impact

This 350-card set features full-bleed action photos with the players' names printed in block letters across the top. The back has an action photo, career highlights, stats, a biography and the player's position, as diagramed with Xs and Os. Subsets include Team Checklists, High Impact League Leaders, Sudden Impact Hardest Hitters, and Instant Impact Rookies. Insert sets include Major Impact (20 cards featuring top players) and Holograms (two feature Jim Kelly and Lawrence Taylor; the rest are mail-in offers).

		MT
Complete Set (350):		14.00
Common Player:		.05
Wax Box:		14.00
1	Jim Kelly	.25
2	Andre Rison	.25
3	Michael Dean Perry	.05
4	Herman Moore	.50
5	Fred McAfee	.15
6	Ricky Proehl	.05
7	Jim Everett	.05
8	Mark Carrier	.05
9	Eric Martin	.05
10	John Elway	1.00
11	Michael Irvin	.25
12	Keith McCants	.05
13	Greg Lloyd	.05
14	Lawrence Taylor	.10
15	Mike Tomczak	.05
16	Cortez Kennedy	.05
17	William Fuller	.05
18	James Lofton	.05
19	Kevin Fagan	.05
20	Bill Brooks	.05
21	Roger Craig	.05
22	Jay Novacek	.10
23	Steve Sewell	.05
24	William Perry	.05
25	Jerry Rice	1.00
26	James Joseph	.05
27	Timm Rosenbach	.05
28	Pat Terrell	.05
29	Jon Vaughn	.08
30	Steve Walsh	.05
31	James Hasty	.05
32	Dwight Stone	.05
33	Derrick Fenner	.05
34	Mark Bortz	.05
35	Dan Saleaumua	.05
36	Sammie Smith	.05
37	Antone Davis	.05
38	Steve Young	1.00
39	Mike Baab	.05
40	Rick Fenney	.05
41	Chris Hinton	.05
42	Bart Oates	.05
43	Bryan Hinkle	.05
44	James Francis	.05
45	Ray Crockett	.05
46	Eric Dickerson	.05
47	Hart Lee Dykes	.05
48	Percy Snow	.05
49	Ron Hall	.05
50	Warren Moon	.25
51	Ed West	.05
52	Clarence Verdin	.05
53	Eugene Lockhart	.05
54	Andre Reed	.15
55	Kevin Ross	.05
56	Al Noga	.05
57	Wes Hopkins	.05
58	Rufus Porter	.05
59	Brian Mitchell	.05
60	Reggie Roby	.05
61	Rodney Peete	.05
62	Jeff Herrod	.05
63	Anthony Smith	.05
64	Brad Muster	.05
65	Jessie Tuggle	.05
66	Al Smith	.05
67	Jeff Hostetler	.20
68	John L. Williams	.05
69	Paul Gruber	.05
70	Cornelius Bennett	.05
71	William White	.05
72	Tom Rathman	.05
73	Boomer Esiason	.10
74	Neil Smith	.05
75	Sterling Sharpe	.10
76	James Jones	.05
77	David Treadwell	.05
78	Flipper Anderson	.05
79	Eric Allen	.05
80	Joe Jacoby	.05
81	Keith Sims	.05
82	Bubba McDowell	.05
83	Ronnie Lippett	.05
84	Cris Carter	.15
85	Chris Burkett	.05
86	Issiac Holt	.05
87	Duane Bickett	.05
88	Leslie O'Neal	.05
89	Gill Fenerty	.05
90	Pierce Holt	.05
91	Willie Drewrey	.05
92	Brian Blades	.05
93	Tony Martin	.05
94	Jessie Hester	.05
95	John Stephens	.05
96	Keith Willis	.05
97	Vai Sikahema	.05
98	Mark Higgs	.15
99	Steve McMichael	.05
100	Deion Sanders	.15
101	Marvin Washington	.05
102	Ken Norton	.05
103	Barry Word	.10
104	Sean Jones	.05
105	Ronnie Harmon	.05
106	Donnell Woolford	.05
107	Ray Agnew	.05
108	Lemuel Stinson	.05
109	Dennis Smith	.05
110	Lorenzo White	.05
111	Craig Heyward	.05
112	Jeff Query	.05
113	Gary Plummer	.05
114	John Taylor	.08
115	Rohn Stark	.05
116	Tom Waddle	.05
117	Jeff Cross	.05
118	Tim Green	.05
119	Anthony Munoz	.05
120	Mel Gray	.05
121	Ray Donaldson	.05
122	Dennis Byrd	.05
123	Carnell Lake	.05
124	Broderick Thomas	.05
125	Charles Mann	.05
126	Darion Conner	.05
127	John Roper	.05
128	Jack Del Rio	.05
129	Rickey Dixon	.05
130	Eddie Anderson	.05
131	Steve Broussard	.05
132	Michael Young	.05
133	Lamar Lathon	.05
134	Rickey Jackson	.05
135	Billy Ray Smith	.05
136	Tony Casillas	.05
137	Ickey Woods	.05
138	Ray Childress	.05
139	Vance Johnson	.05
140	Brett Perriman	.05
141	Calvin Williams	.10
142	Dino Hackett	.05
143	Jacob Green	.05
144	Robert Delpino	.05
145	Marv Cook	.05
146	Dwayne Harper	.05
147	Ricky Ervins	.08
148	Kelvin Martin	.08
149	Leroy Hoard	.05
150	Dan Marino	1.25
151	Richard Johnson	.05
152	Henry Ellard	.05
153	Al Toon	.05
154	Dermontti Dawson	.05
155	Robert Blackmon	.05
156	Howie Long	.05
157	David Fulcher	.05
158	Mike Merriweather	.05
159	Gary Anderson	.05
160	John Friesz	.05
161	Eugene Robinson	.05
162	Brad Baxter	.05
163	Bennie Blades	.05
164	Harold Green	.05
165	Ernest Givins	.05
166	Deron Cherry	.05
167	Carl Banks	.05
168	Keith Jackson	.10
169	Pat Leahy	.05
170	Alvin Harper	.10
171	David Little	.05
172	Anthony Carter	.05
173	Willie Gault	.05
174	Bruce Armstrong	.05
175	Junior Seau	.15
176	Eric Metcalf	.05
177	Tony Mandarich	.05
178	Ernie Jones	.05
179	Albert Bentley	.05
180	Mike Pritchard	.15
181	Bubby Brister	.05
182	Vaughan Johnson	.05
183	Robert Clark	.05
184	Lawrence Dawsey	.05
185	Eric Green	.05
186	Jay Schroeder	.05
187	Andre Tippett	.05
188	Vinny Testaverde	.05
189	Wendell Davis	.05
190	Russell Maryland	.15
191	Chris Singleton	.05
192	Ken O'Brien	.05
193	Merril Hoge	.05
194	Steve Bono	.50
195	Earnest Byner	.05
196	Mike Singletary	.05
197	Gaston Green	.05
198	Mark Carrier	.05
199	Harvey Williams	.10
200	Randall Cunningham	.15
201	Cris Dishman	.05
202	Greg Townsend	.05
203	Christian Okoye	.05
204	Sam Mills	.05
205	Kyle Clifton	.05
206	Jim Harbaugh	.08
207	Anthony Thompson	.05
208	Rob Moore	.08
209	Irving Fryar	.05
210	Derrick Thomas	.15
211	Chris Miller	.05
212	Doug Smith	.05
213	Michael Haynes	.20
214	Phil Simms	.10
215	Charles Haley	.05
216	Burt Grossman	.05
217	Rod Bernstine	.05
218	Louis Lipps	.05
219	Dan McGwire	.05
220	Ethan Horton	.05
221	Michael Carter	.05
222	Neil O'Donnell	.10
223	Anthony Miller	.05
224	Eric Swann	.05
225	Thurman Thomas	.40
226	Jeff George	.25
227	Joe Montana	1.00
228	Leonard Marshall	.05
229	Haywood Jeffires	.10
230	Mark Clayton	.05
231	Chris Doleman	.05
232	Troy Aikman	1.50
233	Gary Anderson	.05
234	Pat Swilling	.05
235	Ronnie Lott	.07
236	Brian Jordan	.05
237	Bruce Smith	.07
238	Tony Jones	.05
239	Tim McKyer	.05
240	Gary Clark	.05
241	Mitchell Price	.05
242	John Kasay	.05
243	Stephone Paige	.05
244	Jeff Wright	.05
245	Shannon Sharpe	.15
246	Keith Byars	.05
247	Charles Dimry	.05
248	Steve Smith	.05
249	Eric Pegram	.15
250	Bernie Kosar	.05
251	Peter Tom Willis	.05
252	Mark Ingram	.05
253	Keith McKeller	.05
254	Lewis Billups	.05
255	Alton Montgomery	.05
256	Jimmie Jones	.05
257	Brent Williams	.05
258	Gene Atkins	.05
259	Reggie Rutland	.05
260	Sam Seale	.05
261	Andre Ware	.07
262	Fred Barnett	.10
263	Randal Hill	.10
264	Patrick Hunter	.05
265	Johnny Rembert	.05
266	Monte Coleman	.05
267	Aaron Wallace	.05
268	Ferrell Edmunds	.05
269	Stan Thomas	.05
270	Robb Thomas	.05
271	Martin Bayless	.05
272	Dean Biasucci	.05
273	Keith Henderson	.05
274	Vinnie Clark	.05
275	Emmitt Smith	2.00
276	Mark Rypien	.10
277	Atlanta Falcons Wing and a Prayer	.10
278	Buffalo Bills Machine Gun	.10
279	Chicago Bears Grizzly	.05
280	Cincinnati Bengals Price is Right	.05
281	Cleveland Browns Coasting	.05
282	Dallas Cowboys Gunned Down	.15
283	Denver Broncos The Drive II	.15
284	Detroit Lions Lions Roar	.05
285	Green Bay Packers Razor Sharpe	.15
286	Houston Oilers Oil's Well	.10
287	Indianapolis Colts Whew	.10
288	Kansas City Chiefs Ambush	.10
289	Los Angeles Raiders Lott of Defense	.05
290	Los Angeles Rams Ram It	.05
291	Miami Dolphins Miami Ice	.15
292	Minnesota Vikings Purple Blaze	.05
293	New England Patriots Surprise Attack	.05
294	New Orlean Saints Marching In	.05
295	New York Giants Almost Perfect	.05
296	New York Jets Playoff Bound	.05
297	Philadelphia Eagles Flying High	.05
298	Phoenix Cardinals	.05
299	Pittsburgh Steelers Steel Curtain	.05
300	San Diego Chargers Lightning	.05
301	San Francisco 49ers Instant Rice	.15
302	Seattle Seahawks Defense Never Rests	.05
303	Tampa Bay Buccaneers Stunned	.05
304	Washington Redskins Super	.05
305	Jim Kelly (LL)	.10
306	Steve Young (LL)	.15
307	Thurman Thomas (LL)	.20
308	Emmitt Smith (LL)	1.00
309	Haywood Jeffires (LL)	.05
310	Michael Irvin (LL)	.30
311	William Fuller (LL)	.05
312	Pat Swilling (LL)	.05
313	Ronnie Lott (LL)	.07
314	Deion Sanders (LL)	.07
315	Cornelius Bennett	.05
316	David Fulcher	.05
317	Ronnie Lott	.05
318	Pat Swilling	.05
319	Lawrence Taylor	.07
320	Derrick Thomas	.07
321	Steve Emtman	.15
322	Carl Pickens	1.50
323	David Klingler	.25
324	Dale Carter	.25
325	Mike Gaddis	.08
326	Quentin Coryatt	.35
327	Darryl Williams	.15
328	Jeremy Lincoln	.05
329	Robert Jones	.15
330	Bucky Richardson	.30
331	Tony Brooks	.05
332	Alonzo Spellman	.20
333	Robert Brooks	1.00
334	Marco Coleman	.20
335	Siran Stacy	.15
336	Tommy Maddox	.25
337	Steve Israel	.15
338	Vaughn Dunbar	.15
339	Shane Collins	.15
340	Kevin Smith	.25
341	Chris Mims	.25
342	Chester McGlockton	.25
343	Tracy Scroggins	.25
344	Howard Dinkins	.10
345	Levon Kirkland	.10
346	Terrell Buckley	.30
347	Marquez Pope	.10
348	Phillippi Sparks	.10
349	Joe Bowden	.10
350	Edgar Bennett	.75

1992 SkyBox Impact Holograms

These holograms were included as random inserts in foil packs (#s H1 and H2) or offered to those who responded to the mail-in offer which made them available (#s H3-H6). The card front has a full-bleed hologram photo, plus the player's last name. The back has a color photo and a career summary.

		MT
Complete Set (6):		15.00
Common Player:		2.00
1	Jim Kelly	3.00
2	Lawrence Taylor	2.50
3	Christian Okoye	2.00
4	Mark Rypien	3.00
5	Pat Swilling	3.00
6	Ricky Ervins	2.00

1992 SkyBox Impact Major Impact

These cards feature 20 players who have a tremendous impact on NFL games. Each borderless card front has a full-bleed color photo and the player's last name stamped in silver-foil block letters across the top. The back has an action shot and career summary. A blue stripe separates these items on the cards for NFC players (11-20), while a red stripe is used for AFC cards (1-10). Cards are numbered with an "M" prefix and were randomly inserted in 1992 SkyBox Impact jumbo packs.

		MT
Complete Set (20):		15.00
Common Player:		.50
Minor Stars:		1.00
1	Cornelius Bennett	.50
2	David Fulcher	.50
3	Haywood Jeffires	.50
4	Ronnie Lott	.50
5	Dan Marino	5.00
6	Warren Moon	1.00
7	Christian Okoye	.50
8	Andre Reed	.50
9	Derrick Thomas	1.00
10	Thurman Thomas	1.00
11	Troy Aikman	2.50
12	Randall Cunningham	.50
13	Michael Irvin	1.00
14	Jerry Rice	2.50
15	Joe Montana	2.50
16	Mark Rypien	.50
17	Deion Sanders	1.50
18	Emmitt Smith	5.00
19	Pat Swilling	.50
20	Lawrence Taylor	1.00

Post-1980 cards in Near Mint condition will generally sell for about 75% of the quoted Mint value. Excellent-condition cards bring no more than 40%.

1992 SkyBox Primetime Previews

This five-card set allowed collectors to see what the Primetime sets would look like and are exact replicas of the regular-issue cards, except for being numbered A-D, plus a title card. Five-card sets were originally packaged in cello packs.

		MT
Complete Set (5):		10.00
Common Player:		1.00
A	Jerry Rice	4.00
B	Deion Sanders	3.00
C	John Elway	2.00
D	Vaughn Dunbar	1.00
NNO	Title Card (Advertisement)	1.00

1992 SkyBox Primetime

This 360-card set features cards which use cut-out action photos superimposed against a grey background with thin black lines. The player's name is at the top, while his jersey number is included at the bottom in his team's colors. His team name is in a color-coded bar on the left. Half of the card back features an action photo; the rest has stats, a biography and career summary. A team color-coded band with the player's name separates the photo and the remaining information. A 28-card subset, Team MVP, was also made. Insert cards feature Costacos Brothers poster art (15 silver foil cards); a poster checklist; a Kelly hologram; and a Steve Emtman Horse-Power card. Five promo cards were also made and were available in cello packs.

		MT
Complete Set (360):		30.00
Common Player:		.10
Minor Stars:		.20
Wax Box:		25.00
1	Deion Sanders	1.25
2	Shane Collins	.20
3	James Patton	.10
4	Reggie Roby	.10
5	Merril Hoge	.10
6	Vinny Testaverde	.10
7	Boomer Esiason	.10
8	Troy Aikman	2.50
9	Tommy Jeter	.10
10	Brent Williams	.10
11	Mark Rypien	.10
12	Jim Kelly	.25
13	Dan Marino	4.00
14	Bill Cowher	.10
15	Leslie O'Neal	.10
16	Joe Montana	2.50
17	William Fuller	.10
18	Paul Gruber	.10
19	Bernie Kosar	.10
20	Rickey Jackson	.10

#	Player	Price
21	Earnest Byner	.10
22	Emmitt Smith	5.00
23	Neal Anderson	.10
24	Greg Lloyd	.20
25	Ronnie Harmon	.10
26	Ray Donaldson	.10
27	Kevin Ross	.10
28	Irving Fryar	.10
29	John Williams	.10
30	Chris Hinton	.10
31	*Tracy Scroggins*	.20
32	Rohn Stark	.10
33	David Fulcher	.10
34	Thurman Thomas	.50
35	Christian Okoye	.10
36	*Vaughn Dunbar*	.20
37	*Joel Steed*	.10
38	James Francis (card number on back is actually 354)	.10
39	Dermontti Dawson	.10
40	Mark Higgs	.10
41	Flipper Anderson	.10
42	Ronnie Lott	.10
43	Jim Everett	.10
44	Burt Grossman	.10
45	Charles Haley	.10
46	Ricky Proehl	.10
47	*Marquez Pope*	.10
48	David Treadwell	.10
49	William White	.10
50	John Elway	1.00
51	Mark Carrier	.10
52	Brian Blades	.10
53	Keith McKeller	.10
54	Art Monk	.20
55	Lamar Lathon	.10
56	Pat Swilling	.10
57	Steve Broussard	.10
58	Derrick Thomas	.20
59	Keith Jackson	.20
60	Leonard Marshall	.10
61	Eric Metcalf (card number on back is actually 350)	.10
62	Andy Heck	.10
63	Mark Carrier	.10
64	Neil O'Donnell	.10
65	Broderick Thomas	.10
66	Erik Kramer	.20
67	Joe Montana	1.25
68	Robert Delpino	.10
69	*Steve Israel*	.10
70	Herman Moore	1.25
71	Jacob Green	.10
72	Lorenzo White	.10
73	Nick Lowery	.10
74	Eugene Robinson	.10
75	Carl Banks	.10
76	Bruce Smith	.10
77	Mark Rypien	.10
78	Anthony Munoz	.10
79	*Clayton Holmes*	.10
80	Jerry Rice	2.50
81	Henry Ellard	.10
82	Tim McGee	.10
83	Al Toon	.10
84	Haywood Jeffires	.10
85	Mike Singletary	.10
86	Thurman Thomas	.25
87	Jessie Hester	.10
88	Michael Irvin	.50
89	Jack Del Rio	.10
90	Seth Joyner (No player photo)	.10
91	Jeff Herrod	.10
92	Michael Dean Perry	.10
93	Louis Oliver	.10
94	Dan McGwire	.10
95	Cris Carter	.20
96	*Dale Carter*	.50
97	Cornelius Bennett	.10
98	*Edgar Bennett*	.50
99	Steve Young	2.50
100	Warren Moon	.50
101	Deion Sanders	.50
102	Mel Gray	.10
103	Mark Murphy	.10
104	Jeff George	.10
105	Anthony Miller	.10
106	Tom Rathman	.10
107	*Fred McAfee*	.10
108	*Paul Siever*	.10
109	Lemuel Stinson	.10
110	Vance Johnson	.10
111	Jay Schroeder	.10
112	Calvin Williams	.10
113	Cortez Kennedy	.10
114	*Quentin Coryatt*	.30
115	Ronnie Lippett	.10
116	Brad Baxter	.10
117	Bubba McDowell	.10
118	Cris Carter	.20
119	John Stephens	.10
120	James Hasty	.10
121	Bubby Brister	.10
122	*Robert Jones*	.20
123	Sterling Sharpe	.20
124	*Jason Hanson*	.20
125	Sam Mills	.10
126	Ernie Jones	.10
127	*Chester McGlockton*	.50
128	*Troy Vincent*	.20
129	Chuck Smith	.10
130	Tim McKyer	.10
131	Tom Newberry	.10
132	*Leonard Wheeler*	.10
133	*Patrick Rowe*	.10
134	Eric Swann	.10
135	*Jeremy Lincoln*	.10
136	Brian Noble	.10
137	Allen Pinkett	.10
138	*Carl Pickens*	1.50
139	Eric Green	.10
140	Louis Lipps	.10
141	Chris Singleton	.10
142	Gary Clark	.10
143	Tim Green	.10
144	Dennis Green	.10
145	Gary Anderson	.10
146	Miami Dolphins	.10
147	Kelvin Martin	.10
148	*Mike Holmgren*	.10
149	Gaston Green	.10
150	*Terrell Buckley*	.10
151	*Robert Brooks*	1.50
152	Anthony Smith	.10
153	Jay Novacek	.10
154	Webster Slaughter	.10
155	John Roper	.10
156	*Steve Emtman*	.20
157	Tony Sacca	.10
158	Ray Crockett	.10
159	Jerry Rice	1.00
160	Alonzo Spellman	.20
161	Deion Sanders	.50
162	Robert Clark	.10
163	Mark Ingram	.10
164	*Ricardo McDonald*	.10
165	Emmitt Smith	3.00
166	*Tommy Maddox*	.20
167	*Tom Myslinski*	.10
168	Tony Bennett (No player photo on card)	.10
169	Ernest Givins	.10
170	Eugene Robinson	.10
171	Roger Craig	.10
172	Irving Fryar	.10
173	Jeff Herrod	.10
174	Chris Mims	.20
175	Bart Oates	.10
176	Michael Irvin	.50
177	Lawrence Dawsey	.10
178	Warren Moon	.10
179	Timm Rosenbach	.10
180	Bobby Ross	.10
181	Chris Burkett	.10
182	*Tony Brooks*	.10
183	Clarence Verdin	.10
184	Bernie Kosar	.10
185	Eric Martin	.10
186	Jeff Bryant	.10
187	Carnell Lake	.10
188	*Darren Woodson*	.40
189	Dwayne Harper	.10
190	Bernie Kosar	.10
191	Keith Sims	.10
192	Rich Gannon	.10
193	Broderick Thomas	.10
194	Michael Young	.10
195	Cris Dishman	.10
196	Wes Hopkins	.10
197	Christian Okoye	.10
198	David Little	.10
199	*Chris Crooms*	.10
200	Lawrence Taylor	.10
201	*Marc Boutte*	.10
202	Mark Carrier	.10
203	Keith McCants	.10
204	*Dwayne Sabb*	.10
205	Brian Mitchell	.10
206	Keith Byars	.10
207	Jeff Hostetler	.20
208	Percy Snow	.10
209	Lawrence Taylor	.10
210	*Troy Auzenne*	.10
211	Warren Moon	.10
212	Mike Pritchard	.10
213	Eric Dickerson	.10
214	Harvey Williams	.10
215	Phil Simms (Misspelled Sims on card front)	.10
216	Sean Lumpkin (Card number on back is actually 002)	.10
217	Marco Coleman	.10
218	*Phillippi Sparks*	.10
219	*Gerald Dixon*	.10
220	Steve Walsh	.10
221	Russell Maryland	.10
222	Eddie Anderson	.10
223	*Shane Dronett*	.10
224	*Todd Collins*	.10
225	*Leon Searcy*	.10
226	Andre Rison	.10
227	James Lofton	.10
228	Ken O'Brien	.10
229	Nick Bell	.10
230	Ben Smith	.10
231	Wendell Davis	.10
232	*Craig Thompson*	.10
233	*Craig Thompson*	.10
234	Dana Hall	.10
235	*Larry Webster*	.10
236	Jerry Rice	1.00
237	Rod Bernstine	.10
238	*David Klingler*	.20
239	*Greg Skrepenak*	.10
240	*Mark Wheeler*	.10
241	*Kevin Smith*	.10
242	Charles Mann	.20
243	Barry Sanders	.20
244	*Curtis Whitley*	.10
245	Ronnie Harmon	.10
246	Brent Jones	.10
247	*Robert Harris*	.10
248	Ted Marchibroda	.10
249	Willie Gault	.10
250	Siran Stacy	.10
251	Dennis Byrd	.10
252	Corey Harris	.10
253	Al Noga	.10
254	*David Shula*	.10
255	Rob Moore	.10
256	Marv Cook	.10
257	John Elway	.30
258	Harold Green	.10
259	Tom Flores	.10
260	Andre Reed	.10
261	Anthony Thompson	.10
262	Issiac Holt	.10
263	*Mike Evans*	.10
264	*Jimmy Smith*	3.50
265	Anthony Carter	.10
266	*Ashley Ambrose*	.10
267	John Fina (Card number on back is actually 357)	.10
268	*Sean Gilbert*	.40
269	Ken Norton Jr.	.10
270	Barry Word	.10
271	Pat Swilling	.10
272	Dan Marino	1.50
273	David Fulcher	.10
274	William Perry	.10
275	Ed West	.10
276	Gene Atkins	.10
277	Neal Anderson	.10
278	Dino Hackett	.10
279	Greg Townsend	.10
280	Andre Tippett	.10
281	*Darryl Williams*	.10
282	*Kurt Barber*	.10
283	Pat Terrell	.10
284	Derrick Thomas	.10
285	*Eddie Robinson*	.10
286	Howie Long	.10
287	Tim McDonald (No player photo)	.10
288	Thurman Thomas	.10
289	Wendell Davis	.10
290	Jeff Cross	.10
291	Duane Bickett	.10
292	*Tony Smith*	.10
293	Jerry Ball	.10
294	Jessie Tuggle	.10
295	Chris Burkett	.10
296	*Eugene Chung*	.10
297	Chris Miller	.10
298	Albert Bentley	.10
299	Richard Johnson	.10
300	Randall Cunningham	.10
301	*Courtney Hawkins*	.10
302	Ray Childress	.10
303	Rodney Peete	.10
304	Kevin Fagan	.10
305	Ronnie Lott	.10
306	Michael Carter	.10
307	Derrick Thomas	.10
308	Jarvis Williams	.10
309	Greg Lloyd	.10
310	Ethan Horton	.10
311	Ricky Ervins	.10
312	Bennie Blades	.10
313	Troy Aikman	1.00
314	Bruce Armstrong	.10
315	Leroy Hoard	.10
316	Gary Anderson	.10
317	Steve McMichael	.10
318	Junior Seau	.50
319	*Mark Thomas*	.10
320	Fred Barnett	.10
321	Mike Merriweather	.10
322	Keith Willis	.10
323	Brett Perriman	.10
324	Michael Haynes	.10
325	Jim Harbaugh	.10
326	Sammie Smith	.10
327	Robert Delpino	.10
328	Tony Mandarich	.10
329	Mark Bortz	.10
330	*Ray Etheridge*	.10
331	Jarvis Williams	.10
332	Dan Marino	1.50
333	Dwight Stone	.10
334	Billy Ray Smith	.10
335	Darion Connor	.10
336	*Howard Dinkins*	.10
337	*Robert Porcher*	.50
338	Chris Doleman	.10
339	Alvin Harper	.20
340	John Taylor	.10
341	Ray Agnew	.10
342	Jon Vaughn	.10
343	*James Brown*	.10
344	Michael Irvin	.50
345	Neil Smith	.10
346	Vaughn Johnson	.10
347	Checklist	.10
348	Checklist	.10
349	Checklist	.10
350	Checklist (See also number 61)	.10
351	Checklist	.10
352	Checklist	.10
353	Checklist	.10
354	Checklist (See also number 38)	.10
355	Checklist	.10
356	Checklist	.10
357	Checklist (See also number 267)	.10
358	Checklist (See also number 138)	.10
359	Checklist	.10
360	Checklist	.10

1992 SkyBox Primetime Poster Cards

These insert cards feature photos used on posters made by Costacos to capture the essence of the player's nickname, image or city he plays in. The cards, randomly inserted in 1992 Sky-Box Primetime foil packs, are identical to their counterparts in SkyBox's regular 1992 Primetime set, except the inserts have silver foil-stamped borders on the front. The cards were estimated to be two per 36-pack box of cards and were found in the 10,000 numbered cases distributed to the hobby only. Card backs have the Primetime logo in the upper left, along with a card number, which uses an "M" prefix, in the upper right. A photo, career summary and team logo also appear.

		MT
Complete Set (16):		55.00
Common Player:		1.25
1	Bernie Kosar	1.50
2	Mark Carrier	1.25
3	Neal Anderson	1.25
4	Thurman Thomas	5.50
5	Deion Sanders	6.00
6	Joe Montana	8.00
7	Jerry Rice	8.00
8	Jarvis Williams	1.25
9	Dan Marino	15.00
10	Derrick Thomas	2.25
11	Christian Okoye	1.25
12	Warren Moon	3.00
13	Michael Irvin	7.50
14	Troy Aikman	8.00
15	Emmitt Smith	15.00
16	Checklist	1.25

1993 SkyBox Premium

SkyBox Premium's 270-card set features silhouetted action photos highlighted by the contrast of the team color, two-tone background. Team logos, the player's name and a foil-stamped SkyBox Premium logo is also on the front. The back has a color action photo, a biography, four-year statistics, and career totals. Cards are UV-coated. Insert sets include Costacos Brothers posters (10 cards), Chris Mortensen's PrimeTime Rookies (10 cards) and Thunder and Lightning (nine dual team-mate cards).

		MT
Complete Set (270):		45.00
Common Player:		.10
Minor Stars:		.20
Wax Box:		45.00
1	Eric Martin	.10
2	Earnest Byner	.10
3	Ricky Proehl	.10
4	Mark Carrier	.10
5	Shannon Sharpe	.20
6	Anthony Thompson	.10
7	Drew Bledsoe	7.00
8	*Tom Carter*	.40
9	*Ryan McNeil*	.20
10	Troy Aikman	2.00
11	Robert Jones	.10
12	Rodney Peete	.10
13	Wendell Davis	.10
14	Thurman Thomas	.50
15	John Stephens	.10
16	Rodney Hampton	.25
17	Eric Bieniemy	.10
18	Santana Dotson	.10
19	Jeff George	.20
20	John L. Williams	.10
21	Barry Wood	.10
22	Chris Miller	.10
23	Jeff Hostetler	.20
24	Dwight Stone	.10
25	Brad Baxter	.10
26	Randall Cunningham	.20
27	Mark Higgs	.10
28	Vaughn Dunbar	.10
29	Ricky Ervins	.10
30	Johnny Bailey	.10
31	Michael Jackson	.10
32	Mike Croel	.10
33	Steve Young	2.00
34	*Deon Figures*	.20
35	*Robert Smith*	3.00
36	*Irv Smith*	.20
37	Charles Haley	.10
38	Cris Dishman	.10
39	Barry Sanders	3.00
40	Jim Harbaugh	.10
41	Darryl Talley	.10
42	Jackie Harris	.10
43	Phil Simms	.10
44	Marion Butts	.10
45	Anthony Munoz	.10
46	Steve Emtman	.10
47	Kelvin Martin	.10
48	Joe Montana	3.00
49	Andre Rison	.25
50	Ethan Horton	.10
51	Kevin Greene	.10
52	Browning Nagle	.10
53	Tim Harris	.10
54	Keith Byars	.10
55	Terry Allen	.10
56	Chip Lohmiller	.10
57	Robert Massey	.10
58	Michael Dean Perry	.10
59	Tommy Maddox	.10
60	Jerry Rice	2.00
61	*Lincoln Kennedy*	.10
62	*Jerome Bettis*	2.50
63	*Coleman Rudolph*	.10
64	Emmitt Smith	4.00
65	Curtis Duncan	.10
66	Andre Ware	.10
67	Neal Anderson	.10
68	Jim Kelly	.25
69	Reggie White	.25
70	Dave Meggett	.10
71	Junior Seau	.40
72	Courtney Hawkins	.10
73	Clarence Verdin	.10
74	Dale Carter	.10
75	Michael Haynes	.10
76	Willie Gault	.10
77	Eric Green	.10
78	Ronnie Lott	.10
79	Vai Sikahema	.10
80	Mark Ingram	.10
81	Anthony Carter	.10
82	Mark Rypien	.10
83	Gary Clark	.10
84	Bernie Kosar	.10
85	Cleveland Gary	.10
86	Tom Rathman	.10
87	*Tony McGee*	.40
88	*Rick Mirer*	.50
89	*John Copeland*	.50
90	Michael Irvin	.20
91	Wilber Marshall	.10
92	Mel Gray	.10
93	Craig Heyward	.10
94	Don Beebe	.10
95	Andre Tippett	.10
96	Derek Brown	.10
97	Ronnie Harmon	.10
98	Derrick Fenner	.10
99	Rodney Culver	.10
100	Cortez Kennedy	.20
101	Marcus Allen	.20
102	Steve Broussard	.10
103	Tim Brown	.25
104	Merril Hoge	.10
105	Chris Burkett	.10
106	Fred Barnett	.10
107	Dan Marino	4.00
108	Chris Doleman	.10
109	Art Monk	.10
110	Ernie Jones	.10
111	Jay Hilgenberg	.10
112	Jim Everett	.10
113	John Taylor	.10
114	*Steve Everett*	.25
115	*Carlton Gray*	.20
116	*Eric Curry*	.50
117	Ken Norton	.10
118	Lorenzo White	.10
119	Pat Swilling	.10
120	William Perry	.10
121	Brett Favre	4.00
122	Jon Vaughn	.10
123	Mark Jackson	.10
124	Stan Humphries	.20
125	Harold Green	.10
126	*Harold Green*	.10
127	Anthony Jackson	.10
128	Brian Blades	.10
129	Willie Davis	.10
130	Bobby Hebert	.10
131	Terry McDaniel	.10
132	Jeff Graham	.10
133	Jeff Lageman	.10
134	Andre Waters	.10
135	Steve Walsh	.10
136	Cris Carter	.20
137	Tim McGee	.10
138	Chuck Cecil	.10
139	John Elway	1.00
140	Todd Lyght	.10
141	Brent Jones	.10
142	*Patrick Bates*	.25
143	*Darrien Gordon*	.50
144	*Michael Strahan*	.10
145	Jay Novacek	.10
146	Warren Moon	.25
147	Rodney Holman	.10
148	Anthony Morgan	.10
149	Sterling Sharpe	.20
150	Leonard Russell	.10
151	Lawrence Taylor	.20
152	Leslie O'Neal	.10
153	Carl Pickens	1.00
154	Aaron Cox	.10
155	Ferrell Edmunds	.10
156	Neil O'Donnell	.20
157	Tony Smith	.10
158	James Lofton	.10
159	*George Teague*	.50
160	Boomer Esiason	.20
161	Eric Allen	.10
162	Floyd Turner	.10
163	Esera Tuaolo	.10
164	Darrell Green	.10
165	Steve Beuerlein	.10
166	Vance Johnson	.10
167	Willie Anderson	.10
168	Ricky Watters	.20
169	*Marvin Jones*	.20
170	*Dana Stubblefield*	.75
171	*Willie Roaf*	.25
172	Russell Maryland	.10
173	Ernest Givins	.10
174	Willie Green	.10
175	Bruce Smith	.10
176	Terrell Buckley	.10
177	Scott Zolak	.10
178	Mike Sherrard	.10
179	Lawrence Dawsey	.10
180	Jay Schroeder	.10
181	Quentin Coryatt	.10
182	Harvey Williams	.10
183	*Natrone Means*	3.00
184	Eric Dickerson	.20
185	Gaston Green	.10
186	*Thomas Smith*	.25
187	Johnny Johnson	.10
188	Marco Coleman	.10
189	Wade Wilson	.10
190	Rich Gannon	.10
191	Brian Mitchell	.10
192	Eric Metcalf	.10
193	Robert Delpino	.10
194	Shane Conlan	.10
195	Dexter Carter	.10
196	*Garrison Hearst*	3.00
197	*Chris Slade*	.20
198	*Troy Drayton*	.30
199	*Lin Elliot*	.10
200	Haywood Jeffires	.10
201	Herman Moore	1.00
202	Cornelius Bennett	.10
203	Mark Clayton	.10
204	Marv Cook	.10
205	Stephen Baker	.10
206	Gary Anderson	.10
207	Eddie Brown	.10
208	Will Wolford	.10
209	Derrick Thomas	.20
210	Seth Joyner	.10
211	Mike Pritchard	.10
212	Rod Woodson	.20
213	*Todd Kelly*	.20
214	Rob Moore	.10
215	Keith Jackson	.10
216	Wesley Carroll	.10
217	Steve Jordan	.10
218	Ricky Sanders	.10
219	Tommy Vardell	.10
220	Rod Bernstine	.10
221	Henry Ellard	.10
222	Amp Lee	.10
223	O.J. McDuffie	2.00
224	Carl Simpson	.10
225	*Dan Williams*	.20
226	Thomas Everett	.10
227	Webster Slaughter	.10
228	Trace Armstrong	.10
229	Kenneth Davis	.10
230	Tony Bennett	.10
231	Reyna Thompson	.10
232	Anthony Miller	.10
233	Reggie Cobb	.20
234	Mark Duper	.10
235	Chris Warren	.30
236	Christian Okoye	.10
237	Irving Fryar	.10
238	Deion Sanders	1.00
239	Barry Foster	.10
240	*Ernest Dye*	.10
241	Calvin Williams	.10
242	Louis Oliver	.10
243	Dalton Hilliard	.10
244	Roger Craig	.10

245 Randall Hill .10
246 Vinny Testaverde .10
247 Steve Atwater .10
248 Jim Price .10
249 *Martin Harrison* .20
250 *Curtis Conway* 2.00
251 *Demetrius DuBose* .20
252 *Leonard Renfro* .10
253 Alvin Harper .40
254 Leonard Harris .10
255 Tom Waddle .10
256 Andre Reed .20
257 Sanjay Beach .10
258 Michael Timpson .10
259 Nate Lewis .10
260 Steve DeBerg .10
261 David Klingler .10
262 Dan McGwire .10
263 Dave Krieg .10
264 Brad Muster .10
265 Nick Bell .10
266 Checklist 1 .10
267 Checklist 2 .10
268 Checklist 3 .10
269 Checklist 4 .10
270 Checklist 5 .10

1993 SkyBox Poster Art Cards

These cards were randomly inserted in SkyBox's 1993 packs. The front of each card pictures a sports poster created by the Costacos Brothers. Each reproduction is framed by a black border. The back has a photo at the top half, with a gold stripe underneath containing the player's name. A team logo and brief career summary are at the bottom against a white background. The cards are numbered with a "CB" prefix.

		MT
Complete Set (10):		7.00
Common Player:		.50
1	Cowboys Defense	.75
2	Cowboys Champs	3.00
3	Barry Foster	1.75
4	Art Monk	.50
5	Jerry Rice	2.00
6	Barry Sanders	2.50
7	Deion Sanders	.75
8	Junior Seau	.75
9	Derrick Thomas, Neil Smith	.75
10	Steve Young	1.25

1993 SkyBox Premium Rookies

PATRICK BATES
PRIMETIME ROOKIE

These 10 rookies were selected for this set by Chris Mortensen, of ESPN and The Sporting News. He predicted the players would be "prime timers" in 1993. The card front, which has a gold-and-black metallic background, shows the player in his collegiate uniform. A black stripe at the left contains the player's name, set title and Mortensen's facsimile signature. Mortensen is pictured on the bottom half of the card back, along with his player evaluation and the player's position. The top half has a photo of the player, plus his name, in a gold stripe, and a card number, which uses a "PR" prefix.

		MT
Complete Set (10):		60.00
Common Player:		5.00
1	Patrick Bates	5.00
2	Drew Bledsoe	25.00
3	Darrien Gordon	5.00
4	Garrison Hearst	15.00
5	Marvin Jones	5.00
6	Terry Kirby	5.00
7	Natrone Means	10.00
8	Rick Mirer	7.00
9	Willie Roaf	5.00
10	Dan Williams	5.00

1993 SkyBox Premium Thunder and Lightning

These cards are in a horizontal format and feature two teammates per card, one on each side. The player on the Thunder side is featured against a metallic black-and-gold background. Those on the Lightning side are featured against a black-and-silver metallic background with lightning bolts running through it. The player's name is in white lettering across the bottom. A TL prefix is used to number the cards; the number is on the Lightning side of the card. Cards were random inserts in every ninth 1993 SkyBox Premium 12-card foil pack.

		MT
Complete Set (9):		40.00
Common Player:		3.00
1	Jim Kelly, Thurman Thomas	3.00
2	Brett Favre, Sterling Sharpe	12.00
3	Dan Marino, Keith Jackson	12.00
4	Sam Mills, Vaughan Johnson	3.00
5	Warren Moon, Haywood Jeffires	3.00
6	Troy Aikman, Michael Irvin	10.00
7	Randall Cunningham, Fred Barnett	3.00
8	Steve Young, Jerry Rice	10.00
9	Dennis Smith, Steve Atwater	3.00

1993 SkyBox Celebrity Cycle Protypes

This four-card set includes three actual celebrities and one mystery card, which pictures a Harley-Davidson motorcycle against an American flag background. Backs are blank except for a large red stamp that reads "UNFINISHED SKYBOX PROTOTYPE."

		MT
Complete Set (4):		8.00
Common Player:		1.00
1	Mitch Frerotte	1.00
2	Jerry Glanville (CO)	1.00
3	Kenny Lofton (Cleveland Indians)	5.00
4	Mystery Celebrity Cycle Card	1.00

1993 SkyBox Impact Promos

This two-card promotional set was mailed to dealers to promote the 1993 Impact set, and was numbered IP1 and IP2. Cards contain the same design as the regular-issue product. Another version of the Jim Kelly card was distributed at the 1993 Chicago National, but is differentiated by a blue foil stamp commemorating the event.

		MT
Complete Set (2):		3.00
Common Player:		1.00
1	Jim Kelly	2.00
2	Lawrence Taylor	1.00

1993 SkyBox Impact

SkyBox's 1993 Impact set has 400 cards featuring full-bleed color action photos; the backgrounds are not in focus, so the player appears to stand out. The player's name and logo are at the bottom; SkyBox is written at the top. The back has a color photo, four-year statistics, a biography and career totals. Subsets include Class of '83, checklists, Rookies First Round and Rookies Second Round. Insert cards include redemption cards for a set of draft picks (29 cards) and a dual-sport card of Magic Johnson/Jim Kelley. SkyBox color foil cards were also created for each player in the 400-card set. Four different foil colors were used; each player is done in one color only. They can be collected to form a 400-card set. Two promo cards, using the same design as the regular 1993 SkyBox Impact set, were also produced.

	MT
Complete Set (400):	15.00
Common Player:	.03
Complete Set Colors (400):	50.00
Common Colors:	.20
Unlisted Color Stars:	2x-4x
Wax Box:	14.00

1 Steve Broussard .03
2 Michael Haynes .10
3 Tony Smith .03
4 Tory Epps .03
5 Chris Hinton .03
6 Bobby Hebert .03
7 Tim McKyer .03
8 Chris Miller .05
9 Bruce Pickens .03
10 Mike Pritchard .05
11 Andre Rison .20
12 Deion Sanders .10
13 Pierce Holt .03
14 Jessie Tuggle .03
15 Don Beebe .03
16 Cornelius Bennett .03
17 Kenneth Davis .03
18 Kent Hull .03
19 Jim Kelly .25
20 Mark Kelso .03
21 Keith McKellar .03
22 Andre Reed .10
23 Jim Richter .03
24 Bruce Smith .04
25 Thurman Thomas .10
26 Steve Christie .03
27 Darryl Talley .03
28 Pete Metzelaars .03
29 Steve Tasker .03
30 Henry Jones .03
31 Neal Anderson .05
32 Trace Armstrong .03
33 Mark Bortz .03
34 Mark Carrier .03
35 Wendell Davis .03
36 Richard Dent .03
37 Jim Harbaugh .05
38 Steve McMichael .03
39 Craig Heyward .03
40 William Perry .03
41 Donnell Woolford .03
42 Tom Waddle .05
43 Anthony Morgan .03
44 Jim Breech .03
45 David Klingler .15
46 Derrick Fenner .03
47 David Fulcher .03
48 James Francis .03
49 Harold Green .03
50 Carl Pickens .15
51 Jay Schroeder .03
52 Alex Gordon .03
53 Eric Ball .03
54 Eddie Brown .03
55 Jay Hilgenberg .03
56 Michael Jackson .05
57 Bernie Kosar .05
58 Kevin Mack .03
59 Eric Metcalf .03
60 Michael Dean Perry .03
61 Tommy Vardell .05
62 Leroy Hoard .03
63 Clay Matthews .03
64 Vinny Testaverde .05
65 Mark Carrier .03
66 Troy Aikman 1.00
67 *Lin Elliot* .08
68 Thomas Everett .03
69 Alvin Harper .25
70 Ray Horton .03
71 Michael Irvin .10
72 Russell Maryland .03
73 Jay Novacek .03
74 Emmitt Smith 2.00
75 Tony Casillas .03
76 Robert Jones .03
77 Ken Norton .03
78 Daryl Johnston .03
79 Charles Haley .03
80 *Leon Lett* .25
81 Steve Atwater .03
82 Mike Croel .05
83 John Elway 1.00
84 Simon Fletcher .03
85 Vance Johnson .03
86 Shannon Sharpe .08
87 Rod Bernstine .03
88 Robert Delpino .03
89 Karl Mecklenburg .03
90 Steve Sewell .03
91 Tommy Maddox .15
92 *Arthur Marshall* .25
93 Dennis Smith .03
94 Derek Russell .03
95 Bernie Blades .03
96 Michael Cofer .03
97 Willie Green .08
98 Herman Moore .40
99 Rodney Peete .05
100 Andre Ware .03
101 Barry Sanders 1.25
102 Chris Spielman .03
103 Jason Hanson .03
104 Mel Gray .03
105 Pat Swilling .03
106 Bill Fralic .03
107 Rodney Herman .03
108 Brett Favre 2.00
109 Sterling Sharpe .10
110 Derek Brown .10
111 Terrell Buckley .15
112 Sanjay Beach .03
113 Tony Bennett .03
114 Jackie Harris .15
115 Bryce Paup .03
116 Shawn Patterson .03
117 John Stephens .03
118 Cris Dishman .03
119 Haywood Jeffires .10
120 Ernest Givins .03
121 Lamar Lathon .03
122 Warren Moon .15
123 Lorenzo White .03
124 Curtis Duncan .03
125 Webster Slaughter .03
126 Cody Carlson .03
127 Leonard Harris .03
128 Bruce Matthews .03
129 Ray Childress .03
130 Al Smith .03
131 Jeff George .15
132 Anthony Johnson .03
133 Steve Emtman .08
134 Quentin Coryatt .08
135 Rodney Culver .03
136 Jessie Hester .03
137 Aaron Cox .03
138 Clarence Verdin .03
139 Joe Montana 1.25
140 Dave Krieg .03
141 Harvey Williams .03
142 Derrick Thomas .15
143 Barry Word .05
144 Christian Okoye .03
145 Nick Lowery .03
146 Dale Carter .03
147 Willie Davis .10
148 Tim Barnett .03
149 Neal Smith .03
150 Marcus Allen .06
151 Nick Bell .04
152 Tim Brown .35
153 Eric Dickerson .03
154 Willie Gault .03
155 Howie Long .03
156 Gaston Green .03
157 Chester McGlockton .03
158 Eddie Anderson .03
159 Ethan Horton .03
160 James Lofton .03
161 Jeff Hostetler .10
162 Terry McDaniel .03
163 Flipper Anderson .03
164 Shane Conlan .03
165 Jim Everett .05
166 Henry Ellard .03
167 Cleveland Gary .03
168 Todd Lyght .03
169 Sean Gilbert .03
170 Jim Price .03
171 Bill Hawkins .03
172 Mark Clayton .03
173 Mark Higgs .10
174 Dan Marino 2.00
175 Louis Oliver .03
176 Reggie Roby .03
177 Bobby Humphrey .03
178 Troy Vincent .10
179 Marco Coleman .05
180 Aaron Craver .05
181 Keith Jackson .10
182 Mark Duper .03
183 Pete Stoyanovich .03
184 Irving Fryar .03
185 Brian Cox .03
186 Terry Allen .06
187 Anthony Carter .03
188 Cris Carter .03
189 Chris Doleman .03
190 Rich Gannon .06
191 Sean Salisbury .03
192 Hassan Jones .03
193 Steve Jordan .03
194 Roger Craig .05
195 Todd Scott .03
196 Esera Tualo .03
197 Ray Agnew .03
198 Marv Cook .03
199 Tom Hodson .03
200 Chris Singleton .03
201 Michael Timpson .03
202 Jon Vaughn .03
203 Leonard Russell .10
204 Scott Zolak .03
205 Renya Thompson .03
206 Andre Tippett .03
207 Morten Andersen .03
208 Wesley Carroll .03
209 Vince Buck .03
210 Rickey Jackson .03
211 Vaughn Johnson .03
212 Eric Martin .03
213 Sam Mills .03
214 Steve Walsh .05
215 Wade Wilson .05
216 Vaughn Dunbar .03
217 Brad Muster .03
218 Dalton Hilliard .03
219 Floyd Turner .03
220 Stephen Baker .03
221 Mark Jackson .03
222 Jarrod Bunch .05
223 Mark Collins .03
224 Rodney Hampton .25
225 Phil Simms .05
226 Pepper Johnson .03
227 Dave Meggett .03
228 Derek Brown .03
229 Mike Sherrard .03
230 Lawrence Taylor .10
231 Leonard Marshall .03
232 Brad Baxter .03
233 Dennis Byrd .03
234 Ronnie Lott .05
235 Boomer Esiason .10
236 Browning Nagle .05
237 Rob Moore .05
238 Jeff Lageman .03
239 Johnny Mitchell .25
240 Chris Burkett .03
241 Eric Thomas .03
242 Johnny Johnson .10
243 Eric Allen .05
244 Fred Barnett .05
245 Keith Byars .03
246 Randall Cunningham .10
247 Heath Sherman .03
248 Calvin Williams .05
249 Erik McMillan .03
250 Byron Evans .03
251 Seth Joyner .03
252 Vai Sikahema .03
253 Andre Waters .03
254 Tim Harris .03
255 Mark Bavaro .03
256 Clyde Simmons .03
257 Steve Beuerlein .10
258 Randal Hill .05
259 Ernie Jones .03
260 Robert Massey .03
261 Rickey Proehl .05
262 Aeneas Williams .03
263 Johnny Bailey .03
264 Cris Chandler .03
265 Anthony Thompson .03
266 Gary Clark .05
267 Chuck Cecil .03
268 Rich Camarillo .03
269 Neil O'Donnell .25
270 Gerald Williams .03
271 Greg Lloyd .03
272 Eric Green .03
273 Merril Hoge .03
274 Ernie Mills .03
275 Rod Woodson .05
276 Gary Anderson .03
277 Barry Foster .10
278 Jeff Graham .03
279 Dwight Stone .03
280 Kevin Greene .05
281 Eric Bieniemy .03
282 Marion Butts .03
283 Gill Byrd .03
284 Stan Humphries .05
285 Anthony Miller .05
286 Leslie O'Neal .03
287 Junior Seau .15
288 Ronnie Harmon .03
289 Nate Lewis .03
290 John Kidd .03
291 Steve Young 1.00
292 John Taylor .06
293 Jerry Rice .75
294 Tim McDonald .03
295 Brent Jones .03
296 Tom Rathman .03
297 Dexter Carter .03
298 Mike Cofer .03
299 Ricky Watters .40
300 Mervyn Fernandez .03
301 Amp Lee .08
302 Kevin Fagan .03
303 Roy Foster .03
304 Bill Romanowski .03
305 Brian Blades .03
306 John L. Williams .03
307 Tommy Kane .03
308 John Kasay .03
309 Chris Warren .10
310 Rufus Porter .03
311 Cortez Kennedy .10
312 Dan McGwire .05
313 Stan Gelbaugh .03
314 Kelvin Martin .03
315 Ferrell Edmunds .03
316 Eugene Robinson .03
317 Gary Anderson .03
318 Reggie Cobb .05
319 Lawrence Dawsey .03
320 Courtney Hawkins .03
321 Santana Dotson .03
322 Ron Hall .03
323 Keith McCants .03
324 Martin Mayhew .03
325 Anthony Munoz .03
326 Steve DeBerg .03
327 Vince Workman .03
328 Earnest Byner .03
329 Ricky Ervins .03
330 Jim Lachey .03
331 Chip Lohmiller .03
332 Ricky Sanders .03
333 Brad Edwards .03
334 Tim McGee .03
335 Darrell Green .05
336 Charles Mann .03
337 Wilber Marshall .03
338 Brian Mitchell .03
339 Art Monk .05
340 Mark Rypien .08
341 John Elway (C83) .10
342 Jim Kelly (C83) .10
343 Dan Marino (C83) .20
344 Eric Dickerson (C83) .08
345 Willie Gault (C83) .05
346 Ken O'Brien (C83) .05
347 Darrell Green (C83) .05
348 Richard Dent (C83) .05
349 Karl Mecklenburg (C83) .03
350 Henry Ellard (C83) .03
351 Roger Craig (C83) .05
352 Charles Mann (C83) .03
353 Checklist A .03
354 Checklist B .03
355 Checklist C .03
356 Checklist D .03
357 Checklist E .03
358 Checklist F .03
359 Checklist G .03
360 Checklist (rookies) .03
361 *Drew Bledsoe* 2.50
362 *Rick Mirer* 1.00
363 *Garrison Hearst* 1.00
364 *Marvin Jones* .15
365 *John Copeland* .25
366 *Eric Curry* .25
367 *Curtis Conway* 1.00
368 *Willie Roaf* .15
369 *Lincoln Kennedy* .20
370 *Jerome Bettis* 1.00

371	Dan Williams	.10
372	Patrick Bates	.10
373	Brad Hopkins	.10
374	Steve Everett	.10
375	Wayne Simmons	.10
376	Tom Carter	.15
377	Ernest Dye	.10
378	Lester Holmes	.10
379	Irv Smith	.25
380	Robert Smith	1.00
381	Darrien Gordon	.20
382	Deon Figures	.20
383	O.J. McDuffie	.75
384	Dana Stubblefield	.50
385	Todd Kelly	.10
386	Thomas Smith	.10
387	George Teague	.25
388	Carlton Gray	.10
389	Chris Slade	.25
390	Ben Coleman	.10
391	Ryan McNeil	.10
392	Demetrius DuBose	.10
393	Carl Simpson	.10
394	Coleman Rudolph	.10
395	Tony McGee	.15
396	Roger Harper	.15
397	Troy Drayton	.25
398	Michael Strahan	.10
399	Natrone Means	1.00
400	Glyn Milburn	.60

1993 SkyBox Impact Kelly/Magic

SkyBox spokesmen Jim Kelly and Magic Johnson selected a team of their favorite players for this insert set. The cards are foil stamped and indicate which player selected them by either a Kelly's Heroes logo or Magic's Kingdom logo on it, in a small panel along the left which has a player portrait shot. An action photo and the player's name are on the right. Each card has selection by both players on opposite sides. The cards were random inserts in foil packs. The two spokesmen also autographed 500 cards which were offered to those who found individually numbered redemption certificates randomly included among packs. Those who obtained cards 12 and 32, the uniform numbers of Kelly and Johnson, were to receive the autographed cards personally from the players.

		MT
Complete Set (12):		20.00
Common Player:		1.00
Minor Stars:		2.00
Inserted 1:12		
1	Title card	1.00
2	Dan Marino,	5.00
	Jim Kelly	
3	Jay Novacek,	1.00
	Keith Jackson	
4	Thurman Thomas,	5.00
	Barry Sanders	
5	Barry Sanders,	5.00
	Emmitt Smith	
6	Jerry Rice,	3.00
	Sterling Sharpe	
7	Andre Reed,	3.00
	Jerry Rice	
8	Thurman Thomas,	2.00
	Patrick Swilling	
9	Darryl Talley,	2.00
	Lawrence Taylor	
10	Rod Woodson,	1.00
	Darrell Green	
11	Steve Tasker,	1.00
	Elvis Patterson	
12	Morten Andersen,	1.00
	Chip Lowery	

A card number in parentheses ( ) indicates the set is unnumbered.

1993 SkyBox Impact Update

This 20-card set could be obtained by sending five Impact wrappers plus $3.99 for postage and handling. The set focuses on players who switched teams through free agency and pictures the player in his new uniform in front of the player in his old uniform. Cards are numbered and have a "U" prefix.

		MT
Complete Set (20):		10.00
Common Player:		.25
Minor Stars:		.50
1	Pierce Holt	.25
2	Vinny Testaverde	.50
3	Rod Bernstine	.25
4	Reggie White	.50
5	Mark Clayton	.25
6	Joe Montana	5.00
7	Marcus Allen	.25
8	Jeff Hostetler	.25
9	Shane Conlan	.25
10	Brad Muster	.25
11	Mike Sherrard	.25
12	Ronnie Lott	.50
13	Steve Beuerlein	.25
14	Gary Clark	.25
15	Kevin Greene	.25
16	Tim McDonald	.25
17	Wilber Marshall	.25
18	Keith Byars	.25
19	Pat Swilling	.25
20	Boomer Esiason	.25

1993 SkyBox Impact Rookie Redemption

This 29-card set features all of the first round picks from the 1993 NFL Draft, excluding Sean Dawkins (16th), who signed an exclusive contract with Courtside. The set could be obtained either by pulling a redemption card (seeded one per 180 packs) or by a second chance drawing. Cards picture the players in their pro uniforms, with the name running up the left side and the draft position in the lower right corner. Cards are numbered with a "R" prefix.

		MT
Complete Set (29):		20.00
Common Player:		.50
Minor Stars:		1.00
1	Title Card/Checklist	2.50
	(Drew Bledsoe)	
2	Drew Bledsoe	5.00
3	Rick Mirer	3.00
4	Garrison Hearst	1.75
5	Marvin Jones	.50
6	John Copeland	.50
7	Eric Curry (UER)	.50
	(Card front states	
	he was selected in	
	sixth round instead	
	of sixth pick)	
8	Curtis Conway	1.25
9	Willie Roaf	.50

10	Lincoln Kennedy	.50
11	Jerome Bettis	1.75
12	Dan Williams	.50
13	Patrick Bates	.50
14	Brad Hopkins	.50
15	Steve Everitt	.50
16	Wayne Simmons	.50
17	Tom Carter	.50
18	Ernest Dye	.50
19	Lester Holmes	.50
20	Irv Smith	.50
21	Robert Smith	1.75
22	Darrien Gordon	.50
23	Deon Figures	.50
24	Leonard Renfro	.50
25	O.J. McDuffie	1.25
26	Dana Stubblefield	1.00
27	Todd Kelly	.50
28	Thomas Smith	.50
29	George Teague	.50
NNO	Rookie Redemption Card Expired	

1994 SkyBox Promos

Six different players and a commemorative card were issued for this set, which promotes the 1994 SkyBox Premium set. The cards are numbered S1-S6, with the commemorative card having no number.

		MT
Complete Set (7):		8.00
Common Player:		1.00
1	Tom Carter	1.00
2	Gary Clark	1.00
3	James Jett	1.00
4	Jim Kelly	2.00
5	Ronnie Lott	1.50
6	John Taylor	1.00
NNO	Sample Commemorative Game Card	

1994 SkyBox Premium

SkyBox released its 1994 premium football set in a single-series, 200-card issue. Cards have a borderless design on the front and show a player against an action background, highlighted with team colors. The flip side presents an up-close photo, biographical information, 1993 season and NFL career stats and a scouting report written by Chris Mortensen. The regular-issue set contains several subsets, including 23 Prime Movers and 40 rookies. SkyBox also had various randomly inserted sets, autographed cards and a sweepstakes game card. Insert sets were entitled SkyTech Stars, SkyBox Revolution and Prime Time Rookies.

		MT
Complete Set (200):		35.00
Common Player:		.10
Minor Stars:		.20

Wax Box:		90.00
1	Steve Beuerlein	.10
2	Gary Clark	.10
3	Garrison Hearst	1.00
4	Ron Moore	.10
5	Eric Swann	.10
6	Chuck Cecil	.10
7	Seth Joyner	.10
8	Clyde Simmons	.10
9	Andre Rison	.20
10	Deion Sanders	1.00
11	Erric Pegram	.10
12	Steve Broussard	.10
13	Chris Doleman	.10
14	Jeff George	.30
15	Cornelius Bennett	.10
16	Jim Kelly	.20
17	Andre Reed	.10
18	Bruce Smith	.10
19	Darryl Talley	.10
20	Thurman Thomas	.30
21	Mark Carrier	.10
22	Dante Jones	.10
23	Curtis Conway	.30
24	Tim Worley	.10
25	Erik Kramer	.10
26	John Copeland	.10
27	David Klingler	.10
28	Derrick Fenner	.10
29	Harold Green	.10
30	Carl Pickens	.50
31	Tony McGee	.10
32	Steve Everitt	.10
33	Michael Jackson	.10
34	Eric Metcalf	.10
35	Vinny Testaverde	.20
36	Michael Dean Perry	.10
37	Troy Aikman	2.00
38	Alvin Harper	.20
39	Michael Irvin	.60
40	Jay Novacek	.10
41	Emmitt Smith	4.00
42	Charles Haley	.10
43	Daryl Johnston	.10
44	Kevin Williams	.30
45	Rodney Peete	.10
46	John Elway	1.00
47	Shannon Sharpe	.20
48	Rod Bernstine	.10
49	Glyn Milburn	.20
50	Mike Pritchard	.10
51	Anthony Miller	.10
52	Herman Moore	1.50
53	Barry Sanders	3.50
54	Scott Mitchell	.20
55	Pat Swilling	.10
56	Willie Green	.10
57	Edgar Bennett	.10
58	Brett Favre	4.00
59	Sterling Sharpe	.20
60	Reggie White	.20
61	Sean Jones	.10
62	Reggie Cobb	.10
63	Haywood Jeffires	.10
64	Lorenzo White	.10
65	Webster Slaughter	.10
66	Gary Brown	.10
67	Steve Emtman	.10
68	Quentin Coryatt	.10
69	Sean Dawkins	.10
70	Jim Harbaugh	.10
71	Tony Bennett	.10
72	Marcus Allen	.20
73	Steve Bono	.20
74	Dale Carter	.10
75	Joe Montana	3.00
76	Neil Smith	.10
77	Derrick Thomas	.20
78	Keith Cash	.10
79	Tim Brown	.20
80	Raghib Ismail	.10
81	Jeff Hostetler	.20
82	Patrick Bates	.10
83	James Jett	.10
84	Jerome Bettis	1.00
85	Chris Miller	.10
86	Marc Boutte	.10
87	Sean Gilbert	.20
88	Keith Jackson	.10
89	Terry Kirby	.20
90	Dan Marino	4.00
91	Brian Cox	.10
92	Bernie Kosar	.10
93	Qadry Ismail	.20
94	Robert Smith	.25
95	Terry Allen	.10
96	Scottie Graham	.30
97	Warren Moon	.20
98	Drew Bledsoe	3.00
99	Ben Coates	.40
100	Leonard Russell	.10
101	Vincent Brisby	.40
102	Marion Butts	.10
103	Morten Andersen	.10
104	Derek Brown	.10
105	Michael Haynes	.10
106	Sam Mills	.10
107	Lorenzo Neal	.10
108	Willie Roaf	.10
109	Jim Everett	.10
110	Michael Brooks	.10
111	Rodney Hampton	.20
112	Dave Brown	.20
113	Dave Meggett	.10
114	Ronnie Lott	.20
115	Boomer Esiason	.10
116	Rob Moore	.10
117	Johnny Johnson	.10
118	Marvin Jones	.10
119	Johnny Mitchell	.10

120	Fred Barnett	.10
121	Randall Cunningham	.20
122	Herschel Walker	.10
123	Calvin Williams	.10
124	Neil O'Donnell	.20
125	Eric Green	.10
126	Leroy Thompson	.10
127	Rod Woodson	.20
128	Barry Foster	.20
129	Deon Figures	.10
130	John L. Williams	.10
131	Chris Mims	.10
132	Darrien Gordon	.10
133	Stan Humphries	.30
134	Natrone Means	1.00
135	Junior Seau	.30
136	Brent Jones	.10
137	Jerry Rice	3.00
138	Dana Stubblefield	.20
139	John Taylor	.10
140	Ricky Watters	.20
141	Steve Young	3.00
142	Ken Norton	.10
143	Brian Blades	.10
144	Cortez Kennedy	.20
145	Kelvin Martin	.10
146	Rick Mirer	.20
147	Chris Warren	.20
148	Eric Curry	.10
149	Santana Dotson	.10
150	Craig Erickson	.10
151	Hardy Nickerson	.10
152	Paul Gruber	.10
153	Reggie Brooks	.20
154	Tom Carter	.10
155	Desmond Howard	.10
156	Ken Harvey	.10
157	Dan Wilkinson	.40
158	Marshall Faulk	4.00
159	Heath Shuler	.50
160	Willie McGinest	.50
161	Trev Alberts	.20
162	Trent Dilfer	3.00
163	Bryant Young	.50
164	Sam Adams	.20
165	Antonio Langham	.20
166	Jamir Miller	.20
167	John Thierry	.20
168	Aaron Glenn	.20
169	Joe Johnson	.20
170	Bernard Williams	.20
171	Wayne Gandy	.20
172	Aaron Taylor	.20
173	Charles Johnson	.50
174	DeWayne Washington	.20
175	Todd Steussie	.20
176	Tim Bowens	.20
177	Johnnie Morton	1.50
178	Rob Fredrickson	.20
179	Shante Carver	.20
180	Thomas Lewis	.20
181	Greg Hill	1.00
182	Henry Ford	.20
183	Jeff Burris	.20
184	William Floyd	.50
185	Derrick Alexander	.50
186	Glenn Foley	1.50
187	Charlie Garner	2.50
188	Errict Rhett	1.00
189	Chuck Levy	.20
190	Bam Morris	1.00
191	Donnell Bennett	.75
192	LeShon Johnson	.20
193	Mario Bates	.50
194	David Palmer	.50
195	Darnay Scott	1.50
196	Lake Dawson	.50
197	Checklist	.10
198	Checklist	.10
199	Checklist	.10
200	Checklist for Insert Cards	.10

1994 SkyBox Premium Inside the Numbers

Inside the Numbers is a 20-card set that features a borderless design on gold foil. The set was inserted at a rate of one per retail pack.

		MT
Complete Set (20):		20.00
Common Player:		.40
1	Jim Kelly	.75
2	Ronnie Lott	.75
3	Morten Andersen	.40
4	Reggie White	1.25
5	Terry Kirby	.60
6	Marcus Allen	1.00
7	Thurman Thomas	1.00
8	Joe Montana	8.00
9	Tom Carter	.40
10	Jerome Bettis	2.00
11	Sterling Sharpe	.75
12	Andre Rison	.75
13	Reggie Brooks	.40
14	Hardy Nickerson	.60
15	Ricky Watters	.75
16	Gary Brown	.40
17	Natrone Means	1.50
18	LeShon Johnson	.60
19	Errict Rhett	.75
20	Trent Dilfer	1.75

1994 SkyBox Premium Revolution

This insert set provides an up-close look at 15 of the NFL's premium players. Each card front is printed with portrait photography on a pewter foil background. Revolution cards are numbered on the back with an "R" prefix and were inserted one every 20th pack of SkyBox Premium cards. The card back uses the player's team colors for a background, and includes a team logo and a player biography.

		MT
Complete Set (15):		125.00
Common Player:		4.00
Minor Stars:		8.00
1	Jim Kelly	4.00
2	Thurman Thomas	8.00
3	Troy Aikman	18.00
4	Michael Irvin	8.00
5	Emmitt Smith	30.00
6	John Elway	20.00
7	Barry Sanders	18.00
8	Sterling Sharpe	8.00
9	Joe Montana	18.00
10	Jerome Bettis	10.00
11	Dan Marino	30.00
12	Drew Bledsoe	18.00
13	Jerry Rice	18.00
14	Steve Young	15.00
15	Rick Mirer	10.00

1994 SkyBox Premium Rookies

Prime Time Rookies consists of 10 Chris Mortensen-selected rookies who were expected to make the biggest impact in the 1994 season. Cards from this set were randomly inserted at a rate of one every 96th pack of SkyBox Premium cards. Card backs are numbered with a "PT" prefix.

		MT
Complete Set (10):		180.00
Common Player:		10.00
1	Trent Dilfer	15.00
2	Heath Shuler	15.00
3	Marshall Faulk	40.00
4	Charlie Garner	10.00
5	Errict Rhett	15.00
6	Greg Hill	12.00
7	William Floyd	10.00
8	Charles Johnson	10.00
9	Derrick Alexander	10.00
10	David Palmer	10.00

1994 SkyBox Premium SkyTech Stars

SkyTech Stars were found in one of every six packs of SkyBox Premium cards. The set features 30 selected players printed over a foil background; cards are the same as they appear in the regular set except for the foil printing. Cards are numbered on the back with an "ST" prefix and include a photo, team logo, biography and statistics.

		MT
Complete Set (30):		100.00
Common Player:		2.00
Minor Stars:		4.00
1	Troy Aikman	8.00
2	Emmitt Smith	16.00
3	Michael Irvin	4.00
4	John Elway	7.00
5	Sterling Sharpe	4.00
6	Joe Montana	8.00
7	Drew Bledsoe	8.00
8	Rick Mirer	4.00
9	Junior Seau	4.00
10	Jerome Bettis	4.00
11	Rod Woodson	2.00
12	Tim Brown	2.00
13	Jeff George	4.00
14	Brett Favre	16.00
15	Reggie White	4.00
16	Cortez Kennedy	2.00
17	Ricky Watters	4.00
18	Shannon Sharpe	2.00
19	Reggie Brooks	2.00
20	Heath Shuler	5.00
21	Marshall Faulk	8.00
22	Thurman Thomas	4.00
23	Barry Foster	2.00
24	Sean Gilbert	2.00
25	Jerry Rice	8.00
26	Andre Rison	4.00
27	Barry Sanders	10.00
28	Jim Kelly	4.00
29	Steve Young	8.00
30	Dan Marino	16.00

1994 SkyBox Impact Promos

This six-card set was issued to preview the SkyBox Impact set and carried the same card designs as the regular-issue sets. The cards are numbered with an "S" prefix on the back. In addition, the cards were also issued as a 7-1/2 x 8-1/2" unperforated sheet at the 1994 National Sports Collectors Convention.

		MT
Complete Set (6):		8.00
Common Player:		1.00
1	Marcus Allen	2.00
2	Chris Doleman	1.00
3	Craig Erickson	1.00
4	Jim Kelly	3.00
5	Reggie Roby	1.00
6	Rod Woodson	1.50

1994 SkyBox Impact

These cards feature a borderless design which shows a player highlighted against a ghosted action background. The set's name is in one of the bottom corners; the player's name is in a top corner. The card back has an oversized action photo, biographical information, stats, a card number and a player profile. There are 30 rookies and five checklists included with the set. Insert cards included with the set are: Instant Impact Rookies (one in 30 packs); Ultimate Impact Players (one in 15 packs); and the SkyBox Impact NFL Rookie Exchange Card, found one in every 350 packs. This "IOU" card is redeemable for a limited-edition set of NFL first-round draft choice selections pictured in their NFL uni-

forms. There were also six promo cards created to preview the regular set. They have the same basic design, except they are numbered with an "S" prefix.

		MT
Complete Set (300):		20.00
Common Player:		.05
Minor Stars:		.10
Wax Box:		25.00
1	Johnny Bailey	.05
2	Steve Beuerlein	.05
3	Gary Clark	.05
4	Garrison Hearst	.50
5	Ron Moore	.05
6	Ricky Proehl	.05
7	Eric Swann	.05
8	Aeneas Williams	.05
9	Robert Massey	.05
10	Chuck Cecil	.05
11	Ken Harvey	.05
12	Michael Haynes	.05
13	Tony Smith	.05
14	Bobby Hebert	.05
15	Mike Pritchard	.05
16	Andre Rison	.10
17	Deion Sanders	.50
18	Pierce Holt	.05
19	Erric Pegram	.10
20	Jessie Tuggle	.05
21	Steve Broussard	.05
22	Don Beebe	.05
23	Cornelius Bennett	.05
24	Kenneth Davis	.05
25	Bill Brooks	.05
26	Jim Kelly	.10
27	Andre Reed	.05
28	Bruce Smith	.05
29	Darryl Talley	.05
30	Thurman Thomas	.10
31	Steve Tasker	.05
32	Neal Anderson	.05
33	Mark Carrier	.05
34	Richard Dent	.05
35	Jim Harbaugh	.10
36	Chris Gedney	.05
37	Tom Waddle	.05
38	Curtis Conway	.50
39	Dante Jones	.05
40	Donnell Woolford	.05
41	Tim Worley	.05
42	John Copeland	.05
43	David Klingler	.05
44	Derrick Fenner	.05
45	Harold Green	.05
46	Carl Pickens	.50
47	Tony McGee	.05
48	Darryl Williams	.05
49	Steve Everitt	.05
50	Michael Jackson	.05
51	Eric Metcalf	.05
52	Tommy Vardell	.05
53	Vinny Testaverde	.05
54	Mark Carrier	.05
55	Michael Dean Perry	.05
56	Eric Turner	.05
57	Troy Aikman	1.00
58	Alvin Harper	.10
59	Michael Irvin	.10
60	Leon Lett	.05
61	Russell Maryland	.05
62	Jay Novacek	.05
63	Emmitt Smith	2.00
64	Ken Norton Jr.	.05
65	Charles Haley	.05
66	Daryl Johnston	.05
67	Kevin Smith	.05
68	James Washington	.05
69	Kevin Williams	.30
70	Bernie Kosar	.05
71	Mike Croel	.05
72	John Elway	.50
73	Shannon Sharpe	.05
74	Rod Bernstine	.05
75	Simon Fletcher	.05
76	Arthur Marshall	.05
77	Glyn Milburn	.05
78	Dennis Smith	.05
79	Herman Moore	.50
80	Rodney Peete	.10
81	Barry Sanders	1.25
82	Mel Gray	.05
83	Erik Kramer	.10
84	Pat Swilling	.05
85	Willie Green	.05
86	Chris Spielman	.05
87	Robert Porcher	.05
88	Derrick Moore	.05
89	Edgar Bennett	.05
90	Tony Bennett	.05
91	LeRoy Butler	.05
92	Brett Favre	2.00
93	Jackie Harris	.05
94	Sterling Sharpe	.10
95	Darrell Thompson	.05
96	Reggie White	.10
97	Terrell Buckley	.05
98	Cris Dishman	.05
99	Ernest Givins	.05
100	Haywood Jeffires	.05
101	Warren Moon	.10
102	Lorenzo White	.05
103	Webster Slaughter	.05
104	Ray Childress	.05
105	Wilbur Marshall	.05
106	Gary Brown	.05
107	Mariusz Robertson	.05

108	Sean Jones	.05
109	Jeff George	.10
110	Steve Emtman	.05
111	Quentin Coryatt	.05
112	*Sean Dawkins*	.40
113	Jeff Herrod	.05
114	Roosevelt Potts	.05
115	Marcus Allen	.10
116	Kimble Anders	.05
117	Tim Barnett	.05
118	J.J. Birden	.05
119	Dale Carter	.05
120	Willie Davis	.05
121	Nick Lowery	.05
122	Joe Montana	1.00
123	Kevin Ross	.05
124	Neil Smith	.05
125	Derrick Thomas	.05
126	Keith Cash	.05
127	Tim Brown	.10
128	Raghib Ismail	.05
129	Ethan Horton	.05
130	Jeff Hostetler	.10
131	Patrick Bates	.05
132	Terry McDaniel	.05
133	Anthony Smith	.05
134	Greg Robinson	.05
135	James Jett	.05
136	Alexander Wright	.05
137	Willie Anderson	.05
138	Shane Conlan	.05
139	Jim Everett	.05
140	Henry Ellard	.05
141	Jerome Bettis	.25
142	Troy Drayton	.05
143	Sean Gilbert	.05
144	Chris Miller	.05
145	Keith Byars	.05
146	Marco Coleman	.05
147	Bryan Cox	.05
148	Irving Fryar	.05
149	Mark Ingram	.05
150	Keith Jackson	.05
151	Terry Kirby	.05
152	Dan Marino	2.00
153	O.J. McDuffie	.20
154	Scott Mitchell	.10
155	Anthony Carter	.05
156	Cris Carter	.10
157	Chris Doleman	.05
158	Steve Jordan	.05
159	Qadry Ismail	.05
160	Randall McDaniel	.05
161	John Randle	.05
162	Robert Smith	.20
163	Henry Thomas	.05
164	Terry Allen	.05
165	*Scottie Graham*	.10
166	Drew Bledsoe	1.00
167	Vincent Brown	.05
168	Ben Coates	.05
169	Leonard Russell	.05
170	Andre Tippett	.05
171	Vincent Brisby	.05
172	Michael Timpson	.05
173	Bruce Armstrong	.05
174	Morten Andersen	.05
175	Derek Brown	.05
176	Quinn Early	.05
177	Rickey Jackson	.05
178	Vaughan Johnson	.05
179	Lorenzo Neal	.05
180	Sam Mills	.05
181	Irv Smith	.05
182	Renaldo Turnbull	.05
183	Wade Wilson	.05
184	Willie Roaf	.05
185	Michael Brooks	.05
186	Mark Jackson	.05
187	Rodney Hampton	.10
188	Phil Simms	.05
189	Dave Meggett	.05
190	Mike Sherrard	.05
191	Chris Calloway	.05
192	Brad Baxter	.05
193	Ronnie Lott	.05
194	Boomer Esiason	.05
195	Rob Moore	.05
196	Johnny Johnson	.05
197	Marvin Jones	.10
198	Mo Lewis	.05
199	Johnny Mitchell	.05
200	Brian Washington	.05
201	Eric Allen	.05
202	Fred Barnett	.05
203	Mark Bavaro	.05
204	Randall Cunningham	.10
205	Vaughn Hebron	.05
206	Seth Joyner	.05
207	Clyde Simmons	.05
208	Herschel Walker	.05
209	Calvin Williams	.05
210	Neil O'Donnell	.10
211	Eric Green	.05
212	Leroy Thompson	.05
213	Rod Woodson	.05
214	Barry Foster	.05
215	Jeff Graham	.05
216	Kevin Greene	.05
217	Deon Figures	.05
218	Greg Lloyd	.05
219	Marion Butts	.05
220	Chris Mims	.05
221	Darrien Gordon	.05
222	Ronnie Harmon	.05
223	Stan Humphries	.05
224	Nate Lewis	.05

225	Natrone Means	.40
226	Anthony Miller	.05
227	Leslie O'Neal	.05
228	Junior Seau	.10
229	Brent Jones	.05
230	Tim McDonald	.05
231	Tom Rathman	.05
232	Jerry Rice	1.00
233	Dana Stubblefield	.10
234	John Taylor	.05
235	Ricky Watters	.10
236	Steve Young	1.00
237	Amp Lee	.05
238	Robert Blackmon	.05
239	Brian Blades	.05
240	Cortez Kennedy	.05
241	Kelvin Martin	.05
242	Rick Mirer	.25
243	Eugene Robinson	.05
244	Chris Warren	.10
245	John L. Williams	.05
246	Jon Vaughn	.05
247	Reggie Cobb	.05
248	Horace Copeland	.05
249	*Derrick Alexander*	.25
250	Santana Dotson	.05
251	Craig Erickson	.05
252	Courtney Hawkins	.05
253	Hardy Nickerson	.05
254	Vince Workman	.05
255	Paul Gruber	.05
256	Reggie Brooks	.05
257	Tom Carter	.05
258	Andre Collins	.05
259	Darrell Green	.05
260	Desmond Howard	.05
261	Tim McGee	.05
262	Brian Mitchell	.05
263	Art Monk	.05
264	John Friesz	.05
265	Ricky Sanders	.05
266	Checklist A	.05
267	Checklist B	.05
268	Checklist C	.05
269	Checklist D	.05
270	Checklist E	.05
271	Carolina Panthers	.20
272	Jacksonville Jaguars	.20
273	*Dan Wilkinson*	.10
274	*Marshall Faulk*	3.00
275	*Heath Shuler*	.25
276	*Willie McGinest*	.25
277	*Trev Alberts*	.10
278	*Trent Dilfer*	.50
279	*Bryant Young*	.40
280	*Sam Adams*	.10
281	*Antonio Langham*	.10
282	*Jamir Miller*	.10
283	*John Thierry*	.10
284	*Aaron Glenn*	.10
285	*Joe Johnson*	.10
286	*Bernard Williams*	.10
287	*Wayne Gandy*	.10
288	*Aaron Taylor*	.10
289	*Charles Johnson*	.50
290	*DeWayne Washington*	.10
291	*Todd Steussie*	.10
292	*Tim Bowens*	.10
293	*Johnnie Morton*	.50
294	*Rob Fredrickson*	.10
295	*Shante Carver*	.10
296	*Thomas Lewis*	.10
297	*Greg Hill*	.50
298	*Henry Ford*	.10
299	*Jeff Burris*	.10
300	*William Floyd*	.50
NNO	Carolina Panthers	30.00

1994 SkyBox Impact Instant Impact

Each of these card fronts features a full-bleed color photo against a faded background. The Instant Impact logo is stamped in gold foil in the lower right corner, while the player's name is in the upper left corner in team color-coded boxes. The backs are horizontal and have another action photo, plus a brief player profile. The player's name and team logo are in a color stripe at the top of the card, next to "Instant Impact," which is written in a black box. Cards, numbered with an "R" prefix, were randomly inserted one out of every 30th SkyBox Impact pack.

		MT
Complete Set (12):		35.00
Common Player:		2.00
1	Rick Mirer	3.00
2	Jerome Bettis	4.00
3	Reggie Brooks	2.00
4	Terry Kirby	2.00
5	Vincent Brisby	2.00
6	James Jett	2.00
7	Drew Bledsoe	10.00
8	Dana Stubblefield	2.00
9	Natrone Means	4.00

10	Curtis Conway	3.00
11	O.J. McDuffie	3.00
12	Garrison Hearst	5.00

1994 SkyBox Impact Quarterback Update

This 10-card set contains traded and rookie quarterbacks in their new uniforms and are identical to the Impact base card design. The set was available through a redemption offer, as well as a one per pack retail exclusive insert.

		MT
Complete Set (11):		5.00
Common Player:		.40
1	Warren Moon	.60
2	Trent Dilfer	.75
3	Jeff George	.60
4	Heath Shuler	.75
5	Jim Harbaugh	.60
6	Rodney Peete	.40
7	Chris Miller	.40
8	Jim Everett	.60
9	Scott Mitchell	.60
10	Erik Kramer	.40
NNO	Checklist	.40

1994 SkyBox Impact Rookie Redemption

This redemption set included the first 29 players chosen in the 1994 NFL Draft. The redemption card was randomly inserted into packs of 1994 SkyBox Impact.

		MT
Complete Set (30):		25.00
Common Player:		.25
Minor Stars:		.50
1	Dan Wilkinson	.50
2	Marshall Faulk	8.00
3	Heath Shuler	1.00
4	Willie McGinest	.50
5	Trev Alberts	.25
6	Trent Dilfer	5.00
7	Bryant Young	.50
8	Sam Adams	.25
9	Antonio Langham	.25
10	Jamir Miller	.25
11	John Thierry	.25
12	Aaron Glenn	.50
13	Joe Johnson	.25
14	Bernard Williams	.25
15	Wayne Gandy	.25
16	Aaron Taylor	.25
17	Charles Johnson	1.00
18	DeWayne Washington	.50
19	Todd Steussie	.50
20	Tim Bowens	.25
21	Johnnie Morton	1.00
22	Rob Fredrickson	.25
23	Shante Carver	.25
24	Thomas Lewis	.25
25	Greg Hill	1.00
26	Henry Ford	.25
27	Jeff Burris	.25
28	William Floyd	1.00
29	Derrick Alexander (WR)	1.00
NNO	Rookie Redemption Exp.	.50

1994 SkyBox Impact Ultimate Impact

These cards, randomly inserted in every 15th pack of 1994 SkyBox Impact cards, feature 15 top NFL players. Each card front has a color action photo against a borderless background. The player's name is spelled out in boxes at the top. The Ultimate logo is stamped in silver foil in the lower right corner. Each card back is

numbered with a "U" prefix and is in a horizontal format. A color action shot takes up more than half of the card. A player profile fills the rest.

		MT
Complete Set (15):		75.00
Common Player:		2.00
1	Troy Aikman	10.00
2	Emmitt Smith	20.00
3	Michael Irvin	2.00
4	Joe Montana	10.00
5	Jerry Rice	10.00
6	Sterling Sharpe	2.00
7	Steve Young	10.00
8	Ricky Watters	2.00
9	Barry Sanders	10.00
10	John Elway	12.00
11	Reggie White	2.00
12	Jim Kelly	2.00
13	Thurman Thomas	2.00
14	Dan Marino	20.00
15	Brett Favre	20.00

1995 SkyBox

SkyBox Premium football for 1995 includes 200 cards, comprised of 120 veteran players, 40 rookies, 10 Style Points, 10 Mirror Images and four each for the Jacksonville and Carolina expansion teams. Each card has a color action photo of the player on the left, with his team name and position along the right side in a sandpaper-colored panel. The player's name is in the lower left corner, with a gold foil Sky-Box logo sandwiched in between. The back has a mug shot, biographical information, 1994 and career stats, and a player profile, all against a background of his team's primary color. Insert sets include Paydirt, Quick-Strike, The Promise and Prime Time Rookies. Also, Premium Moments merchandise cards, offering collectors a chance to purchase autographed memorabilia, were included one per hobby pack. In every sixth retail pack, the cards are replaced by a decoder game card called Great Men Make Great Moments Make Great Cards, which could be decoded at special displays at participating hobby shops.

		MT
Complete Set (200):		20.00
Common Player:		.10
Minor Stars:		.20
Wax Box:		30.00
1	Garrison Hearst	.20
2	Dave Krieg	.10
3	Rob Moore	.10
4	Eric Swann	.10
5	Larry Centers	.10
6	Jeff George	.20
7	Craig Heyward	.10
8	Terance Mathis	.10
9	Eric Metcalf	.10
10	Jim Kelly	.20
11	Andre Reed	.10
12	Bruce Smith	.10
13	Thurman Thomas	.20
14	Randy Baldwin	.10
15	Don Beebe	.10
16	Barry Foster	.10
17	Lamar Lathon	.10
18	Frank Reich	.10
19	Jeff Graham	.10
20	Raymont Harris	.10
21	Lewis Tillman	.10
22	Michael Timpson	.10
23	*Jeff Blake*	.20
24	Carl Pickens	.20
25	Darnay Scott	.50
26	Dan Wilkinson	.10
27	Derrick Alexander	.25
28	Leroy Hoard	.10
29	Antonio Langham	.10

#	Player	MT
30	Andre Rison	.20
31	Eric Turner	.10
32	Troy Aikman	1.00
33	Michael Irvin	.30
34	Darryl Johnston	.10
35	Emmitt Smith	2.00
36	John Elway	.40
37	Glyn Milburn	.10
38	Anthony Miller	.10
39	Shannon Sharpe	.10
40	Scott Mitchell	.10
41	Herman Moore	.20
42	Barry Sanders	2.00
43	Chris Spielman	.10
44	Edgar Bennett	.10
45	Robert Brooks	.10
46	Brett Favre	2.00
47	Reggie White	.20
48	Mel Gray	.10
49	Haywood Jeffires	.10
50	Webster Slaughter	.10
51	Craig Erickson	.10
52	Quentin Coryatt	.10
53	Sean Dawkins	.10
54	Marshall Faulk	1.00
55	Steve Beuerlein	.10
56	Reggie Cobb	.10
57	Desmond Howard	.10
58	Ernest Givins	.10
59	Jeff Lageman	.10
60	Marcus Allen	.20
61	Steve Bono	.25
62	Greg Hill	.25
63	Derrick Thomas	.20
64	Tim Bowens	.10
65	Irving Fryar	.10
66	Eric Green	.10
67	Terry Kirby	.10
68	Dan Marino	2.00
69	O.J. McDuffie	.10
70	Bernie Parmalee	.25
71	Terry Allen	.10
72	Cris Carter	.20
73	Quadry Ismail	.10
74	Warren Moon	.20
75	Jake Reed	.10
76	Drew Bledsoe	1.00
77	Vincent Brisby	.10
78	Ben Coates	.10
79	Dave Meggett	.10
80	Mario Bates	.30
81	Jim Everett	.10
82	Michael Haynes	.10
83	Tyrone Hughes	.10
84	Dave Brown	.10
85	Rodney Hampton	.10
86	Thomas Lewis	.10
87	Herschel Walker	.10
88	Mike Sherrard	.10
89	Boomer Esiason	.10
90	Aaron Glenn	.10
91	Johnny Johnson	.10
92	Johnny Mitchell	.10
93	Ron Moore	.10
94	Tim Brown	.20
95	Raghib Ismail	.10
96	Jeff Hostetler	.20
97	Chester McGlockton	.10
98	Fred Barnett	.10
99	Randall Cunningham	.10
100	Charlie Garner	.10
101	Ricky Watters	.20
102	Calvin Williams	.10
103	Charles Johnson	.30
104	Bam Morris	.10
105	Neil O'Donnell	.10
106	Rod Woodson	.10
107	Jerome Bettis	.30
108	Troy Drayton	.10
109	Sean Gilbert	.10
110	Chris Miller	.10
111	Leonard Russell	.10
112	Ronnie Harmon	.10
113	Stan Humphries	.20
114	Shawn Jefferson	.10
115	Natrone Means	.20
116	Junior Seau	.20
117	William Floyd	.40
118	Brent Jones	.10
119	Jerry Rice	1.00
120	Deion Sanders	1.00
121	Dana Stubblefield	.10
122	Bryant Young	.10
123	Steve Young	1.00
124	Brian Blades	.10
125	Cortez Kennedy	.10
126	Rick Mirer	.40
127	Ricky Proehl	.10
128	Chris Warren	.10
129	Horace Copeland	.10
130	Trent Dilfer	.50
131	Alvin Harper	.20
132	Jackie Harris	.10
133	Hardy Nickerson	.10
134	Errict Rhett	.20
135	Henry Ellard	.10
136	Brian Mitchell	.10
137	Heath Shuler	.75
138	Tydus Winans	.10
139	Drew Bledsoe, Brett Favre	1.00
140	Marshall Faulk, William Floyd	1.00
141	Brett Favre, Trent Dilfer	.50
142	Dan Marino, Brett Favre	1.00
143	Errict Rhett, Trent Dilfer	.50
144	Jerry Rice, Eric Turner	.50
145	Andre Rison, Eric Turner	.10
146	Barry Sanders, Dave Meggett	.50
147	Emmitt Smith, Daryl Johnston	.75
148	Steve Young, Brett Favre	1.00
149	Emmitt Smith, Errict Rhett	.75
150	Barry Sanders, Marshall Faulk	1.00
151	Jerry Rice, Darnay Scott	.50
152	Daryl Johnston, William Floyd	.25
153	Dan Marino, Trent Dilfer	1.00
154	John Elway, Heath Shuler	.40
155	Natrone Means, Bam Morris	.30
156	Dan Wilkinson, Reggie White	.10
157	Rodney Hampton, Mario Bates	.10
158	Marvin Jones, Junior Seau	.10
159	Ki-Jana Carter	.50
160	Tony Boselli	.20
161	Steve McNair	4.00
162	Michael Westbrook	1.50
163	Kerry Collins	2.00
164	Kevin Carter	.20
165	Mike Mamula	.20
166	Joey Galloway	3.00
167	Kyle Brady	.20
168	J.J. Stokes	1.50
169	Warren Sapp	.20
170	Rob Johnson	4.00
171	Tyrone Wheatley	.75
172	Napoleon Kaufman	3.00
173	James Stewart	3.00
174	Joe Aska	.25
175	Rashaan Salaam	.40
176	Tyrone Poole	.20
177	Ty Law	.20
178	Dino Philyaw	.20
179	Mark Bruener	.20
180	Derrick Brooks	.20
181	Jack Jackson	.20
182	Ray Zellars	.20
183	Eddie Goines	.20
184	Chris Sanders	.40
185	Charlie Simmons	.20
186	Lee DeRamus	.20
187	Frank Sanders	.30
188	Rodney Thomas	.20
189	Steve Stenstrom	.25
190	Stoney Case	.25
191	Tyrone Davis	.20
192	Kordell Stewart	6.00
193	Christian Fauria	.25
194	Todd Collins	.20
195	Sherman Williams	.20
196	Lovell Pinckney	.20
197	Eric Zeier	.20
198	Zack Crockett	.20
199	Checklist A	.10
200	Checklist B	.10

1995 SkyBox Inside the Numbers

Inside the Numbers featured 20 players on a design that was very similar to the regular-issue set. These were seeded at a rate of one per retail pack.

		MT
	Complete Set (20):	25.00
	Common Player:	.40
1	William Floyd	.75
2	Marshall Faulk	1.50
3	Warren Moon	.75
4	Cris Carter	.75
5	Deion Sanders	1.50
6	Drew Bledsoe	2.50
7	Natrone Means	1.00
8	Herschel Walker	.40
9	Ben Coates	.75
10	Mel Gray	.40
11	Barry Sanders	3.00
12	Steve Young	2.00
13	Rashaan Salaam	2.00
14	Andre Reed	.40
15	Tyrone Hughes	.40
16	Eric Turner	.40
17	Ki-Jana Carter	2.00
18	Dan Marino	5.00
19	Errict Rhett	1.50
20	Jerry Rice	2.50

A card number in parentheses ( ) indicates the set is unnumbered.

1995 SkyBox Paydirt

These 1995 SkyBox Premium football inserts feature 30 of the top NFL players who can put the ball in the end zone. Each card front has a color action photo, with the player's name at the bottom in gold foil. Gold foil yard markers run along the left side of the card, which has a prismatic background which alternates between saying SkyBox and Paydirt. The card back is numbered with a "PD" prefix in the upper right corner and features a square in the upper right corner with a photo inside, plus a brief description of the player's talents below. "Paydirt" is written along the left side of the card. Cards were random inserts, one every four packs.

		MT
	Complete Set (30):	70.00
	Common Gold Player:	1.00
	Minor Gold Stars:	2.00
	Comp. Colors Set (30):	700.00
	Colors Cards:	5x-10x
1	Troy Aikman	4.00
2	J.J. Stokes	3.00
3	Ki-Jana Carter	3.00
4	Steve McNair	4.50
5	Jerome Bettis	1.00
6	Tim Brown	1.00
7	Cris Carter	1.00
8	John Elway	2.00
9	Marshall Faulk	2.00
10	Brett Favre	8.00
11	Michael Westbrook	2.50
12	Rodney Hampton	1.00
13	Michael Irvin	2.00
14	Dan Marino	8.00
15	Natrone Means	2.00
16	David Meggett	1.00
17	Joey Galloway	4.00
18	Herman Moore	2.00
19	Bam Morris	1.00
20	Carl Pickens	2.00
21	Errict Rhett	2.00
22	Kerry Collins	2.00
23	Barry Sanders	5.00
24	Deion Sanders	3.00
25	Emmitt Smith	8.00
26	Thurman Thomas	1.00
27	Ricky Watters	1.00
28	Rod Woodson	1.00
29	Chris Warren	2.00
30	Steve Young	4.00

1995 SkyBox The Promise

This 1995 SkyBox Premium insert set features 18 young stars. The cards, included one per 24 packs, have a color action photo on the front, with a large ghosted head shot as the background. The card has a gold metallic effect, and uses gold foil for the insert set name. The back is horizontal and includes a small photo and a brief summary of the player's accomplishments.

Cards are numbered with a "P" prefix in the upper right corner.

		MT
	Complete Set (14):	20.00
	Common Player:	2.00
	Minor Stars:	4.00
1	Derrick Alexander	4.00
2	Mario Bates	4.00
3	Trent Dilfer	4.00
4	Marshall Faulk	6.00
5	William Floyd	4.00
6	Aaron Glenn	4.00
7	Raymont Harris	4.00
8	Greg Hill	4.00
9	Charles Johnson	4.00
10	Bam Morris	4.00
11	Errict Rhett	2.00
12	Darnay Scott	2.00
13	Heath Shuler	2.00
14	Dan Wilkinson	4.00

1995 SkyBox Quick Strike

These 1995 SkyBox Premium inserts feature 10 of the NFL's most potent scoring threats. The cards were random inserts, one per 12 packs. The card front has an action photo of the player, against a metallic-like background which has the score of one of his team's wins in which he played a prominent role. The insert set and SkyBox logos are stamped in gold foil. The horizontal back has a photo and a brief summary of the game. Cards are numbered with a "Q" prefix.

		MT
	Complete Set (10):	40.00
	Common Player:	2.00
1	Chris Warren	2.00
2	Marshall Faulk	3.00
3	William Floyd	2.00
4	Jerry Rice	7.00
5	Eric Turner	2.00
6	Tim Brown	2.00
7	Deion Sanders	5.00
8	Emmitt Smith	14.00
9	Rod Woodson	2.00
10	Steve Young	7.00

1995 SkyBox Rookie Receivers

This eight-card set was inserted as a complete set in every retail box. The cards are identical in design to the rookies in the regular-issue set, except for the numbering which is "X" of 8.

		MT
	Complete Set (8):	5.00
	Common Player:	.50
1	Michael Westbrook	1.00
2	Joey Galloway	1.50
3	J.J. Stokes	1.00
4	Frank Sanders	.75
5	Chris Sanders	.75
6	Tyrone Davis	.50
7	Jimmy Oliver	.50
NNO	Cover/Checklist Card	.50

Values quoted in this guide reflect the retail price of a card — the price a collector can expect to pay when buying a card from a dealer. The wholesale price — that which a collector can expect to receive from a dealer when selling cards — will be significantly lower, depending on desirability and condition.

1995 SkyBox Prime Time Rookies

These 1995 SkyBox Premium inserts feature 10 rookies who might be destined for greatness in the NFL. These cards were included one per 96 packs and are numbered using a "PT" prefix. The card front has a photo of the player superimposed against a clockface. Gold foil stamping is used for the player's name and insert set name, which appears at the bottom of the card in script. The horizontal back has a photo on one side, and biographical and collegiate information on the other, all against a background of cogs.

		MT
	Complete Set (10):	190.00
	Common Player:	10.00
1	Ki-Jana Carter	10.00
2	Kerry Collins	15.00
3	Joey Galloway	20.00
4	Steve McNair	35.00
5	Rashaan Salaam	15.00
6	James Stewart	25.00
7	J.J. Stokes	15.00
8	Rodney Thomas	10.00
9	Michael Westbrook	15.00
10	Tyrone Wheatley	10.00

1995 SkyBox Impact

SkyBox Impact's 1995 NFL football set has 200 cards, including 30 top rookies, five cards each for the expansion Jacksonville Jaguars and Carolina Panthers, and subsets such as Specialists and Super Sophs. Each UV-coated front has a full-bleed color action photo, with the player's name and position at the bottom, flanked by a SkyBox logo. The player's first name is stamped in gold foil. The card back is horizontal, with a photo on the right with career stats printed over it. All 49ers cards have a Super Bowl Champion logo on them. The card number is in a black circle in the upper right corner. The left side of the card has the player's name at the top in team color-coded bars. Below follows a team logo and biographical information, then a brief player profile. Insert sets include the hobby-only Future Hall of Famers, Impact Power, Fox More Attitude, and Countdown to Impact. Included in each pack is a SkyBox/NFL on Fox Play Action Match & Win game card, which gave collectors a chance to win tickets and a VIP trip to the 1995-96 NFC Championship Game, NFL on Fox varsity jackets, T-shirts, caps and 1995 SkyBox Premium NFL packs. In addition, there is a redemption for a SkyMotion card, which captures three seconds of actual game action. There are two cards, both of Brett Favre (one running, one passing). One is available through the redemption card (one per 360 packs), the other through an on-wrapper offer.

		MT
	Complete Set (200):	15.00
	Common Player:	.05
	Minor Stars:	.10
	Hobby Wax Box:	30.00
	Retail Wax Box:	30.00
1	Garrison Hearst	.10
2	Ron Moore	.05
3	Eric Swann	.05
4	Aeneas Williams	.05
5	Jeff George	.05
6	Craig Heyward	.05
7	Terrance Mathis	.05
8	Andre Rison	.10
9	Cornelius Bennett	.05
10	Jim Kelly	.10
11	Andre Reed	.05
12	Bruce Smith	.05
13	Thurman Thomas	.15
14	Frank Reich	.05
15	Lamar Lathon	.05
16	Darrien Conner	.05
17	Randy Baldwin	.05
18	Don Beebe	.05
19	Mark Carrier	.05
20	Jeff Graham	.05
21	Raymont Harris	.15
22	Alonzo Spellman	.05
23	Lewis Tillman	.05
24	Steve Walsh	.05
25	Jeff Blake	.50
26	Carl Pickens	.05
27	Darnay Scott	.40
28	Dan Wilkinson	.05
29	Derrick Alexander	.20
30	Leroy Hoard	.05
31	Antonio Langham	.05
32	Vinny Testaverde	.05
33	Eric Turner	.05
34	Troy Aikman	.75
35	Charles Haley	.05
36	Alvin Harper	.05
37	Michael Irvin	.20
38	Daryl Johnston	.05
39	Jay Novacek	.05
40	Leon Lett	.05
41	Emmitt Smith	1.50
42	John Elway	.25
43	Glyn Milburn	.05
44	Anthony Miller	.05
45	Leonard Russell	.05
46	Shannon Sharpe	.10
47	Scott Mitchell	.05
48	Herman Moore	.10
49	Barry Sanders	1.00
50	Chris Spielman	.05
51	Edgar Bennett	.05
52	Robert Brooks	.05
53	Brett Favre	1.50
54	Bryce Paup	.05
55	Sterling Sharpe	.10
56	Reggie White	.10
57	Ray Childress	.05
58	Haywood Jeffires	.05
59	Webster Slaughter	.05
60	Lorenzo White	.05
61	Trev Alberts	.05
62	Quentin Coryatt	.05
63	Sean Dawkins	.15
64	Marshall Faulk	.50
65	Jeff Lageman	.05
66	Steve Beuerlein	.05
67	Desmond Howard	.05
68	Kelvin Martin	.05
69	Reggie Cobb	.05
70	Marcus Allen	.05
71	Greg Hill	.20
72	Joe Montana	.75
73	Neil Smith	.05
74	Derrick Thomas	.10
75	Tim Brown	.10
76	Rocket Ismail	.05
77	Jeff Hostetler	.05
78	Chester McGlockton	.05
79	Harvey Williams	.05
80	Tim Bowens	.05
81	Irving Fryar	.05
82	Keith Jackson	.05
83	Terry Kirby	.05
84	Dan Marino	1.50
85	O.J. McDuffie	.05
86	Bernie Parmalee	.15
87	Terry Allen	.05
88	Cris Carter	.10
89	Quadry Ismail	.05
90	Warren Moon	.10
91	Jake Reed	.05
92	Drew Bledsoe	1.00
93	Vincent Brisby	.05
94	Ben Coates	.05
95	Michael Timpson	.05
96	Jim Everett	.05
97	Michael Haynes	.05
98	Willie Roaf	.05

99	Michael Brooks	.05
100	Dave Brown	.05
101	Rodney Hampton	.05
102	Thomas Lewis	.05
103	Dave Meggett	.05
104	Boomer Esiason	.05
105	Johnny Johnson	.05
106	Johnny Mitchell	.05
107	Rob Moore	.05
108	Fred Barnett	.05
109	Randall Cunningham	.10
110	Charlie Garner	.05
111	Herschel Walker	.05
112	Barry Foster	.05
113	Eric Green	.05
114	Charles Johnson	.20
115	Greg Lloyd	.05
116	Bam Morris	.35
117	Neil O'Donnell	.10
118	Rod Woodson	.10
119	Willie Anderson	.05
120	Jerome Bettis	.25
121	Troy Drayton	.05
122	Sean Gilbert	.05
123	Ronnie Harmon	.05
124	Stan Humphries	.10
125	Shawn Jefferson	.05
126	Natrone Means	.30
127	Leslie O'Neal	.05
128	Junior Seau	.10
129	William Floyd	.25
130	Brent Jones	.05
131	Jerry Rice	.50
132	Deion Sanders	.10
133	Dana Stubblefield	.05
134	Ricky Watters	.10
135	Bryant Young	.05
136	Steve Young	.50
137	Brian Blades	.05
138	Cortez Kennedy	.10
139	Rick Mirer	.10
140	Chris Warren	.05
141	Horace Copeland	.05
142	Trent Dilfer	.30
143	Hardy Nickerson	.05
144	Errict Rhett	.05
145	Henry Ellard	.05
146	Brian Mitchell	.05
147	Heath Shuler	.25
148	Tydus Winans	.05
149	Steve Tasker	.05
150	Jeff Burris	.05
151	Tyrone Hughes	.05
152	Mel Gray	.05
153	Kevin Williams	.05
154	Andre Coleman	.05
155	Corey Sawyer	.05
156	Darrien Gordon	.05
157	Aaron Glenn	.05
158	Eric Metcalf	.05
159	Errict Rhett	.40
160	Marshall Faulk	.75
161	Darnay Scott	.05
162	William Floyd	.10
163	Charlie Garner	.05
164	Heath Shuler	.40
165	Trent Dilfer	.20
166	Willie McGinest	.05
167	Bam Morris	.20
168	Mario Bates	.05
169	*Ki-Jana Carter*	.50
170	*Tony Boselli*	.05
171	*Steve McNair*	2.50
172	*Michael Westbrook*	.75
173	*Kerry Collins*	1.00
174	*Kevin Carter*	.10
175	*Mike Mamula*	.05
176	*Joseph Galloway*	1.50
177	*Kyle Brady*	.10
178	*J.J. Stokes*	.75
179	*Warren Sapp*	.05
180	*Rob Johnson*	2.00
181	*Tyrone Wheatley*	.50
182	*Napoleon Kaufman*	2.00
183	*James Stewart*	1.25
184	*Dino Philyaw*	.10
185	*Rashaan Salaam*	.40
186	*Tyrone Poole*	.10
187	*Ty Law*	.10
188	*Joe Aska*	.10
189	*Mark Bruener*	.10
190	*Derrick Brooks*	.10
191	*Jack Jackson*	.10
192	*Ray Zellars*	.10
193	*Eddie Goines*	.10
194	*Chris Sanders*	.30
195	*Charlie Simmons*	.10
196	*Lee DeRamus*	.10
197	*Frank Sanders*	.30
198	*Rodney Thomas*	.30
199	Checklist A	.05
200	Checklist B	.05
M1	Brett Favre SKY (SkyMotion)	25.00

Post-1980 cards in Near Mint condition will generally sell for about 75% of the quoted Mint value. Excellent-condition cards bring no more than 40%.

1995 SkyBox Impact Countdown

These 10 cards address some of the more unique stats of the NFL's best players in a whole new way. For example, how many minutes did it actually take for Barry Sanders to run for a league-leading 1,883 yards? His insert card, like the rest, will provide the foiled answer on the front. The cards are horizontal, with the set logo and brand logo toward the bottom of the card. The player's name is in the upper right corner. The card back has a photo on one side, and a brief explanation of the unique stat which is being featured. A card number, using a "C" prefix, is in a red circle in the upper right corner.

		MT
Complete Set (10):		60.00
Common Player:		3.00
1	Barry Sanders	10.00
2	Jerry Rice	7.00
3	Steve Young	7.00
4	Troy Aikman	7.00
5	Dan Marino	15.00
6	Emmitt Smith	15.00
7	Junior Seau	3.00
8	Drew Bledsoe	7.00
9	Brett Favre	15.00
10	Deion Sanders	5.00

1995 SkyBox Impact Future Hall of Famers

This 1995 SkyBox Impact insert set presents eight solid candidates who are on their way to the Pro Football Hall of Fame. The cards were random inserts in hobby packs only, one per 60 packs. Cards are numbered using an "HF" prefix; fronts have "Hall of Fame" written on them.

		MT
Complete Set (7):		180.00
Common Player:		15.00
#2 was never made.		
1	Jerry Rice	25.00
3	Steve Young	25.00
4	John Elway	15.00
5	Dan Marino	50.00
6	Emmitt Smith	50.00
7	Barry Sanders	25.00
8	Troy Aikman	25.00

1995 SkyBox Impact Fox More Attitude

These 15 cards include seven young 1995 veterans and eight 1995 first-round draft picks who represent a fresh new attitude of SkyBox and the NFL on Fox. Cards were seeded one per nine packs of 1995 SkyBox Impact product. The card front has a color or action photo of the player with a football field for a background. "Same Game" and "More Attitude," in foil, are written along the left side of the card, as is the player's name, which is also stamped in foil. The "NFL on Fox" logo is stamped in foil in the lower right corner. The card back has a parallelogram in the center which contains a color photo towards the top, with a summary of the player's attitude underneath. There's biographical information along the left side of the card; a card number in the upper right in a black circle, and the player's name are along the right side. The card number uses an "F" prefix.

		MT
Complete Set (15):		40.00
Common Player:		2.00
1	Ki-Jana Carter	2.00
2	Steve McNair	6.00
3	Michael Westbrook	4.00
4	Kerry Collins	3.00
5	Joseph Galloway	3.00
6	J.J. Stokes	2.00
7	Tyrone Wheatley	3.00
8	Rashaan Salaam	3.00
9	Trent Dilfer	3.00
10	William Floyd	3.00
11	Marshall Faulk	3.00
12	Errict Rhett	3.00
13	Heath Shuler	3.00
14	Drew Bledsoe	7.00
15	Ben Coates	3.00

1995 SkyBox Impact Power

Thirty of the NFL's impact players are featured on these two insert sets. Cards IP1-IP10, DE-Terminators, are devoted to 10 defensive players who make big hits. Cards IP11-IP30, Stars of the Ozone, are devoted to 20 offensive stars who make big plays. There was, however, no card made for IP25. Cards were seeded one per three packs of 1995 SkyBox Impact product. The card fronts for each set are similar; both have foil backgrounds, have the set icon in the upper left corner and have the player's name in foil along the right side of the card. The backs are similar, too. There's a smaller color photo in a box in the upper right corner; a card number, using an "IP" prefix, is in a black circle in the opposite corner. The player's name and "Impact Power" are written along the left side. An assessment of the player's skills is below the photo.

		MT
Complete Set (30):		25.00
Common Player:		.50
Minor Stars:		1.00
IP25 was never made.		
1	Junior Seau	1.00
2	Reggie White	1.00
3	Eric Swann	.50
4	Bruce Smith	.50
5	Rod Woodson	.50
6	Derrick Thomas	1.00
7	Chester McGlockton	.50
8	Cortez Kennedy	.50
9	Deion Sanders	1.50
10	Bryan Cox	.50
11	Jerry Rice	3.00
12	Sterling Sharpe	1.00
13	Tim Brown	1.00
14	Marshall Faulk	1.00
15	Brett Favre	5.00
16	Chris Warren	.50
17	Herman Moore	.50
18	Steve Young	3.00
19	Andre Rison	1.00
20	Thurman Thomas	1.00
21	Marcus Allen	1.00
22	Michael Irvin	1.00
23	Emmitt Smith	5.00
24	John Elway	2.00
26	Barry Sanders	5.00
27	Troy Aikman	5.00
28	Natrone Means	1.00
29	Ben Coates	.50
30	Errict Rhett	1.00

1995 SkyBox Impact Rookie Running Backs

Rookie Running Backs was available as a set and inserted into each retail box. It included eight different rookies, with designs very similar to the rookies in the base set, except for the numbering (1-8), and one unnumbered header card.

		MT
Complete Set (9):		7.00
Common Player:		.50
1	Ki-Jana Carter	1.00
2	Tyrone Wheatley	.50
3	Napoleon Kaufman	.75
4	James O. Stewart	.50
5	Rashaan Salaam	1.25
6	Ray Zellars	.50
7	Rodney Thomas	.75
8	Curtis Martin	3.00
NNO	Cover/Checklist Card	.30

1995 SkyBox Impact Fox Announcers

This seven-card set featured FOX's NFL Sunday announcers and was done to promote SyBox's ties to the network. Fronts pictured teams of announcers, while the back contained information about them. There was also an unnumbered header card included.

		MT
Complete Set (8):		10.00
Common Player:		1.00
1	Pat Summerall, John Madden	3.00
2	James Brown, Jimmy Johnson, Terry Bradshaw, Howie Long	3.00
3	Dick Stockton, Matt Millen	1.00
4	Kevin Harlan, Jerry Glanville	1.00
5	Joe Buck, Tim Green	1.00
6	Kenny Albert, Anthony Munoz	1.50
7	Thom Brennaman, Ron Pitts	1.00
NNO	Cover Card	1.00

1996 SkyBox

SkyBox Premium was a 250-card set that marked the fifth anniversary of the product. The regular-issue set includes 178 regular player cards, 50 rookies (179-228), 10 Prime Time Rookie Retrospectives (229-238), which are quad cards, 10 Panorama (239-248) and two checklists (249-250). SkyBox Premium was issued in 10-card packs and contains the final two cards in the Brett Favre MVP Series (cards 1, 2, 3 were in Impact), side B of the Favre Lenticular Exchange card, six SkyBox spokesperson autographs and a Rubies parallel set. Inserts include: V, Next Big Thing, Thunder and Lightning, Close-Ups and Prime Time Rookies.

		MT
Complete Set (250):		25.00
Common Player:		.10
Minor Stars:		.20
Wax Box:		30.00
1	Larry Centers	.10
2	Boomer Esiason	.10
3	Garrison Hearst	.10
4	Rob Moore	.10
5	Frank Sanders	.20
6	Eric Swann	.10
7	Bert Emanuel	.10
8	Jeff George	.10
9	Craig Heyward	.10
10	Terance Mathis	.10
11	Eric Metcalf	.10
12	Derrick Alexander	.10
13	Leroy Hoard	.10
14	Michael Jackson	.10
15	Vinny Testaverde	.10
16	Eric Turner	.10
17	Darick Holmes	.40
18	Jim Kelly	.20
19	Bryce Paup	.10
20	Andre Reed	.10
21	Bruce Smith	.10
22	Thurman Thomas	.20
23	Tim Tindale	.10
24	Mark Carrier	.10
25	Kerry Collins	.50
26	Willie Green	.10
27	Lamar Lathon	.10
28	Tyrone Poole	.10
29	Curtis Conway	.10
30	Bryan Cox	.10
31	Erik Kramer	.10
32	Nate Lewis	.10
33	Rashaan Salaam	.75
34	Alonzo Spellman	.10
35	Michael Timpson	.10
36	Jeff Blake	.75
37	Ki-Jana Carter	.20
38	David Dunn	.10
39	Carl Pickens	.10
40	Darnay Scott	.10
41	Troy Aikman	1.50
42	Charles Haley	.10
43	Michael Irvin	.10
44	Daryl Johnston	.10
45	Jay Novacek	.10
46	Deion Sanders	1.00
47	Emmitt Smith	2.50
48	Kevin Williams	.10
49	Steve Atwater	.10
50	Terrell Davis	1.25
51	John Elway	.75
52	Anthony Miller	.10
53	Shannon Sharpe	.10
54	Mike Sherrard	.10
55	Scott Mitchell	.10
56	Herman Moore	.50
57	Johnnie Morton	.10
58	Brett Perriman	.10
59	Barry Sanders	1.75
60	Edgar Bennett	.10
61	Robert Brooks	.10
62	Mark Chmura	.25
63	Brett Favre	2.50
64	Antonio Freeman	.10
65	Keith Jackson	.10
66	Reggie White	.20
67	Chris Chandler	.10
68	Mel Gray	.10
69	Steve McNair	1.00
70	Chris Sanders	.40
71	Rodney Thomas	.30
72	Quentin Coryatt	.10
73	Sean Dawkins	.10
74	Ken Dilger	.10
75	Marshall Faulk	.75
76	Jim Harbaugh	.10
77	Lamont Warren	.10
78	Tony Boselli	.10
79	Mark Brunell	1.00
80	Willie Jackson	.10
81	Natrone Means	.10
82	James Stewart	.10
83	Marcus Allen	.10
84	Kimble Anders	.10
85	Steve Bono	.10
86	Lake Dawson	.10
87	Neil Smith	.10
88	Derrick Thomas	.10
89	Tamarick Vanover	.75
90	Fred Barnett	.10
91	Terry Kirby	.10
92	Dan Marino	2.50
93	O.J. McDuffie	.10
94	Bernie Parmalee	.10
95	Richmond Webb	.10
96	Cris Carter	.10
97	Qadry Ismail	.10
98	Scottie Graham	.10
99	Warren Moon	.10
100	Jake Reed	.10
101	Robert Smith	.10
102	Drew Bledsoe	1.25
103	Vincent Brisby	.10
104	Ben Coates	.10
105	Curtis Martin	2.00
106	David Meggett	.10
107	Chris Slade	.10
108	Mario Bates	.10
109	Jim Everett	.10
110	Michael Haynes	.10
111	Tyrone Hughes	.10
112	Renaldo Turnbull	.10
113	Dave Brown	.10
114	Chris Calloway	.10
115	Rodney Hampton	.10
116	Thomas Lewis	.10
117	Tyrone Wheatley	.10
118	Kyle Brady	.10
119	Hugh Douglas	.10
120	Aaron Glenn	.10
121	Jeff Graham	.10
122	Adrian Murrell	.10
123	Neil O'Donnell	.10
124	Tim Brown	.10
125	Nolan Harrison	.10
126	Billy Joe Hobert	.10
127	Jeff Hostetler	.10
128	Napoleon Kaufman	.30
129	Chester McGlockton	.10
130	Harvey Williams	.10
131	Charlie Garner	.10
132	Andy Harmon	.10
133	Chris T. Jones	.10
134	Mike Mamula	.10
135	Rodney Peete	.10
136	Bobby Taylor	.10
137	Ricky Watters	.10
138	Jerome Bettis	.20
139	Greg Lloyd	.10
140	Jim Miller	.10
141	Ernie Mills	.10
142	Kordell Stewart	1.25
143	Yancey Thigpen	.30
144	Rod Woodson	.10
145	Andre Coleman	.10
146	Terrell Fletcher	.10
147	*Aaron Hayden*	.30
148	Stan Humphries	.10
149	Junior Seau	.75
150	Isaac Bruce	.75
151	Kevin Carter	.10
152	Todd Kinchen	.10
153	Leslie O'Neal	.10
154	Mark Rypien	.10
155	William Floyd	.10
156	Merton Hanks	.10
157	Brent Jones	.10
158	Derek Loville	.10
159	Ken Norton	.10
160	Jerry Rice	1.50
161	J.J. Stokes	.75
162	Steve Young	1.00
163	Brian Blades	.10
164	Christian Fauria	.10
165	Joey Galloway	1.00
166	Rick Mirer	.10
167	Chris Warren	.20
168	Trent Dilfer	.10
169	Alvin Harper	.10
170	Jackie Harris	.10
171	Hardy Nickerson	.10
172	Errict Rhett	.50
173	Terry Allen	.10
174	Henry Ellard	.10
175	Gus Frerotte	.10
176	Brian Mitchell	.10
177	Heath Shuler	.10
178	Michael Westbrook	.75
179	*Karim Abdul-Jabbar*	.75
180	*Mike Alstott*	1.50
181	*Willie Anderson*	.10
182	*Marco Battaglia*	.10
183	*Tim Biakabutuka*	1.00
184	*Tony Brackens*	.10
185	*Duane Clemons*	.10
186	*Marcus Coleman*	.10
187	*Ernie Conwell*	.10
188	*Chris Darkins*	.10
189	*Stephen Davis*	4.00
190	*Brian Dawkins*	.10
191	*Rickey Dudley*	.30
192	*Jason Dunn*	.10
193	*Bobby Engram*	.30
194	*Daryl Gardener*	.10
195	*Eddie George*	4.00
196	*Terry Glenn*	2.00
197	*Kevin Hardy*	.10
198	*Walt Harris*	.20
199	*Marvin Harrison*	3.00
200	*Bobby Hoying*	1.00
201	*Isreal Ifeanyi*	.10
202	*DeRon Jenkins*	.10
203	*Keyshawn Johnson*	2.50
204	*Lance Johnstone*	.10
205	*Cedric Jones*	.30
206	*Marcus Jones*	.10
207	*Eddie Kennison*	.50
208	*Jevon Langford*	.10
209	*Dedric Mathis*	.10
210	*Jermaine Mayberry*	.10
211	*Leeland McElroy*	.30
212	*Johnny McWilliams*	.10
213	*Ray Mickens*	.10
214	*John Mobley*	.25
215	*Jerald Moore*	.25
216	*Eric Moulds*	2.00
217	*Mushin Muhammad*	1.00
218	*Jonathan Ogden*	.20
219	*Lawrence Phillips*	.75
220	*Kavika Pittman*	.10
221	*Stanley Pritchett*	.50
222	*Simeon Rice*	.10
223	*Detron Smith*	.10
224	*Bryan Still*	.10
225	*Amani Toomer*	.50
226	*Regan Upshaw*	.10
227	*Alex Van Dyke*	.20

228 *Stepfret Williams* .10
229 Retrospective .20
(Quentin Coryatt, Chester McGlockton, Carl Pickens, Robert Brooks)
230 Retrospective .40
(Dale Carter, Edgar Bennett, Drew Bledsoe, Garrison Hearst)
231 Retrospective .20
(Natrone Means, Rick Mirer, Jerome Bettis, Robert Smith)
232 Retrospective .20
(O.J. McDuffie, Curtis Conway, Marshall Faulk, Greg Hill)
233 Retrospective .20
(Heath Shuler, Trent Dilfer, William Floyd, Charles Johnson)
234 Retrospective .20
(Errict Rhett, Sean Dawkins, Mario Bates, Ki-Jana Carter)
235 Retrospective .40
(Kerry Collins, Steve McNair, Joey Galloway, Rashaan Salaam)
236 Retrospective .40
(J.J. Stokes, Michael Westbrook, Kyle Brady, Kordell Stewart)
237 Retrospective .20
(Keyshawn Johnson, Eddie George, Leeland McElroy, Lawrence Phillips)
238 Retrospective .20
(Bobby Engram, Rickey Dudley, Eric Moulds, Tim Biakabutuka)
239 Panorama Jan. 14, 1996 .40
(Kordell Stewart, Quentin Coryatt)
240 Panorama Nov. 26, 1995 .20
(Robert Brooks)
241 Panorama Nov. 12, 1995 .10
(Henry Jones, Terance Mathis)
242 Panorama Dec. 9, 1995 .10
(Mark Seay, Alfred Pupunu)
243 Panorama Sept. 17, 1995 .20
(Robert Brooks, Willie Beamon)
244 Panorama Oct. 29, 1995 - 49ers Halloween .10
245 Panorama Oct. 15, 1995 .10
246 Panorama Dec. 31, 1995 .20
(Zack Crockett, Junior Seau)
247 Panorama Jan. 14, 1996 .10
(Kevin Williams, Doug Evans)
248 Panorama Nov. 19, 1995 .20
(Tim Jacobs, Antonio Freeman)
249 Checklist (1-141) .10
250 Checklist (141-250) .10

1996 SkyBox Rubies

Rubies was a 248-card parallel set (250 minus check- lists) that were inserted into hobby boxes under the packs. Rubies awarded collectors that purchased sealed boxes since the person who opened the box would pull a Rubies insert. Rubies are distinguished by ruby foil in place of the gold foil found on common cards.

	MT
Complete Set (228):	1800.
Rubies:	20x-40x

1996 SkyBox V

Ten players who changed the game over the last five years are featured in V, which was seeded every 18 packs. This insert celebrates SkyBox's fifth anniversary with die-cut, V-shaped designs.

		MT
Complete Set (10):		40.00
Common Player:		1.50
1	Ki-Jana Carter	3.00
2	Kerry Collins	3.00
3	Trent Dilfer	1.50
4	Joey Galloway	8.00
5	Herman Moore	4.00
6	Errict Rhett	4.00
7	Rashaan Salaam	5.00
8	Deion Sanders	8.00
9	Thurman Thomas	1.50
10	Reggie White	1.50

1996 SkyBox Next Big Thing

Next Big Thing showcases 15 young players that are expected to produce big things through their careers. Inserted at a one per 40 rate, these inserts feature a multi-colored foil background with the words "Next Big Thing" in bold.

		MT
Complete Set (15):		120.00
Common Player:		4.00
1	Mark Brunell	10.00
2	Rickey Dudley	8.00
3	Bobby Engram	8.00
4	Antonio Freeman	4.00
5	Eddie George	30.00
6	Terry Glenn	15.00
7	Marvin Harrison	12.00
8	Keyshawn Johnson	10.00
9	Napoleon Kaufman	4.00
10	Steve McNair	10.00
11	Alex Molden	4.00
12	Frank Sanders	4.00
13	Kordell Stewart	20.00
14	Amani Toomer	4.00
15	Alex Van Dyke	4.00

A card number in parentheses ( ) indicates the set is unnumbered.

1996 SkyBox Thunder and Lightning

Thunder and Lightning was made up of 20 players featured on 10 different cards (numbered 1-10 a & b) who make lethal 1-2 combinations. Each card is actually a card-within-a-card where the "lightning" player is inserted into the "thunder" card. Thunder and Lightning inserts were found every 72 packs.

		MT
Complete Set (10):		200.00
Common Player:		8.00
1	Emmitt Smith, Troy Aikman	50.00
2	Barry Sanders, Scott Mitchell	25.00
3	Marshall Faulk, Jim Harbaugh	20.00
4	Dan Marino, O.J. McDuffie	40.00
5	Jerry Rice, Steve Young	30.00
6	Jeff Blake, Carl Pickens	8.00
7	Brett Favre, Edgar Bennett	40.00
8	Curtis Martin, Drew Bledsoe	30.00
9	Errict Rhett, Trent Dilfer	8.00
10	Rick Mirer, Chris Warren	8.00

1996 SkyBox Prime-Time Rookies

Prime Time Rookies returned to Premium as a hobby-only insert that showcased the top rookies from the 1996 NFL Draft. These inserts were found every 96 packs.

		MT
Complete Set (10):		170.00
Common Player:		12.00
1	Tim Biakabutuka	20.00
2	Rickey Dudley	12.00
3	Bobby Engram	14.00
4	Eddie George	40.00
5	Terry Glenn	35.00
6	Marvin Harrison	20.00
7	Keyshawn Johnson	25.00
8	Leeland McElroy	12.00
9	Eric Moulds	12.00
10	Lawrence Phillips	25.00

Post-1980 cards in Near Mint condition will generally sell for about 75% of the quoted Mint value. Excellent-condition cards bring no more than 40%.

1996 SkyBox Close-Ups

Ten NFL stars are featured in close-up shots in this retail exclusive insert, which was found every 30 packs.

		MT
Complete Set (10):		175.00
Common Player:		7.00
1	Troy Aikman	25.00
2	Drew Bledsoe	25.00
3	Isaac Bruce	12.00
4	Terrell Davis	30.00
5	John Elway	20.00
6	Barry Sanders	25.00
7	Emmitt Smith	50.00
8	Kordell Stewart	20.00
9	Tamarick Vanover	7.00
10	Ricky Watters	7.00

1996 SkyBox Autographs

The six spokesman for Fleer/SkyBox signed cards to be inserted into packs of Premium at a rate of one per 450. Highlighted by Brett Favre, the set also includes Trent Dilfer, Daryl Johnston, Eric Turner, Dave Meggett and William Floyd.

	MT
Complete Set (6):	350.00
Common Player:	20.00
Trent Dilfer	40.00
Brett Favre	250.00
William Floyd	20.00
Daryl Johnston	20.00
Dave Meggett	20.00
Eric Turner	20.00

1996 SkyBox Brett Favre MVP

Brett Favre MVP Series was a five-card insert devoted to SkyBox spokesman and NFL MVP Brett Favre. Cards 1-3A were found in Impact, with a one per 480 insert rate, while cards 3B-5 with a one per 240 insertion rate. Each card showed off a different technology, with No. 1 printed on foil, No. 2 printed on acrylic, No. 3 utilizing lenticular technology, No. 4 was die-cut and No. 5 was printed on leather. Card No. 3 required collectors to obtain sides A and B, from Impact and Premium, respectively, to redeem it for the actual lenticular card.

		MT
Complete Set (6):		180.00
Common Player:		30.00
1	Brett Favre Foil	40.00
2	Brett Favre Acrylic	40.00
3a	Brett Favre Exch.A	30.00
3b	Brett Favre Exch.B	40.00
3c	Brett Favre Prize	60.00
4	Brett Favre Die-Cut	30.00
5	Brett Favre Leather	30.00

1996 SkyBox Impact

Impact Football was a 200-card set that featured borderless action shots and commentary on card backs by Fox analyst Matt Millen. The set includes 148 veterans, 40 rookies (149-188), five Inspirations (189-193), five Brett Favre Highlights and two checklists. There were five different inserts sets - NFL on Fox, Excelerators, Intimidators, No Surrender and VersaTeam - and three Brett Favre MVP Series cards and a Favre SkyMint Exchange card.

		MT
Complete Set (200):		18.00
Common Player:		.05
Minor Stars:		.10
Wax Box:		20.00
1	Garrison Hearst	.05
2	Rob Moore	.05
3	Frank Sanders	.05
4	Eric Swann	.05
5	Aeneas Williams	.05
6	Bert Emanuel	.05
7	Jeff George	.05
8	Craig Heyward	.05
9	Terance Mathis	.05
10	Eric Metcalf	.05
11	Leroy Hoard	.05
12	Michael Jackson	.05
13	Andre Rison	.05
14	Vinny Testaverde	.05
15	Eric Turner	.05
16	Darrick Holmes	.05
17	Jim Kelly	.05
18	Bryce Paup	.05
19	Bruce Smith	.05
20	Thurman Thomas	.05
21	Mark Carrier	.05
22	Kerry Collins	.25
23	Derrick Moore	.05
24	Tyrone Poole	.05
25	Curtis Conway	.05
26	Jeff Graham (Jets)	.05
27	Erik Kramer	.05
28	Rashaan Salaam	.50
29	Jeff Blake	.60
30	Ki-Jana Carter	.25
31	Carl Pickens	.05
32	Darnay Scott	.05
33	Troy Aikman	.75
34	Charles Haley	.05
35	Michael Irvin	.10
36	Daryl Johnston	.05
37	Jay Novacek	.05
38	Deion Sanders	.50
39	Emmitt Smith	1.50
40	Steve Atwater	.05
41	Terrell Davis	.75
42	John Elway	.25
43	Anthony Miller	.05
44	Shannon Sharpe	.05
45	Scott Mitchell	.05
46	Herman Moore	.20
47	Brett Perriman	.05
48	Barry Sanders	1.00
49	Edgar Bennett	.05
50	Robert Brooks	.05
51	Mark Chmura	.20
52	Brett Favre	1.50
53	Reggie White	.10
54	Mel Gray	.05
55	Steve McNair	.75
56	Chris Sanders	.25
57	Rodney Thomas	.30
58	Quentin Coryatt	.05
59	Sean Dawkins	.05
60	Ken Dilger	.05
61	Marshall Faulk	.75
62	Jim Harbaugh	.05
63	Tony Boselli	.05
64	Mark Brunell	.50
65	Keenan McCardell	.05
66	James Stewart	.05
67	Marcus Allen	.05
68	Steve Bono	.05
69	Neil Smith	.05
70	Derrick Thomas	.05
71	Tamarick Vanover	.50
72	Bryan Cox (Bears)	.05
73	Irving Fryar (Eagles)	.05
74	Eric Green	.05
75	Dan Marino	1.50
76	O.J. McDuffie	.05
77	Bernie Parmalee	.05
78	Cris Carter	.05
79	Qadry Ismail	.05
80	Warren Moon	.05
81	Jake Reed	.05
82	Robert Smith	.05
83	Drew Bledsoe	.75
84	Ben Coates	.05
85	Curtis Martin	1.25
86	Willie McGinnest	.05
87	David Meggett	.05
88	Mario Bates	.05
89	Quinn Early (Bills)	.05
90	Jim Everett	.05
91	Michael Haynes	.05
92	Renaldo Turnbull	.05
93	Dave Brown	.05
94	Rodney Hampton	.05
95	Thomas Lewis	.05
96	Phillippi Sparks	.05
97	Tyrone Wheatley	.05
98	Kyle Brady	.05
99	Hugh Douglas	.05
100	Mo Lewis	.05
101	Adrian Murrell	.05
102	Tim Brown	.05
103	Jeff Hostetler	.05
104	Raghib Ismail	.05
105	Chester McGlockton	.05
106	Harvey Williams	.05
107	Fred Barnett (Dolphins)	.05
108	William Fuller	.05
109	Charlie Garner	.05
110	Rodney Peete	.05
111	Ricky Watters	.05
112	Calvin Williams	.05
113	Bam Morris	.05
114	Neil O'Donnell (Jets)	.05
115	Erric Pegram	.05
116	Kordell Stewart	1.00
117	Yancey Thigpen	.30
118	Rod Woodson	.05
119	Jerome Bettis (Steelers)	.05
120	Isaac Bruce	.40
121	Troy Drayton	.05
122	Leslie O'Neal	.05
123	*Aaron Hayden*	.30
124	Stan Humphries	.05
125	Natrone Means (Jaguars)	.10
126	Junior Seau	.05
127	William Floyd	.05
128	Brent Jones	.05
129	Derek Loville	.05
130	Ken Norton	.05
131	Jerry Rice	.75
132	J.J. Stokes	.10
133	Steve Young	.75
134	Brian Blades	.05
135	Joey Galloway	.75
136	Cortez Kennedy	.05
137	Rick Mirer	.10
138	Chris Warren	.15
139	Trent Dilfer	.05
140	Alvin Harper	.05
141	Jackie Harris	.05
142	Hardy Nickerson	.05
143	Errict Rhett	.50
144	Terry Allen	.05
145	Henry Ellard	.05
146	Brian Mitchell	.05
147	Heath Shuler	.25
148	Michael Westbrook	.05
149	*Karim Abdul-Jabbar*	.50
150	*Mike Alstott*	1.50
151	*Marco Battaglia*	.05
152	*Tim Biakabutuka*	.75
153	*Sean Boyd*	.05
154	*Tony Brackens*	.05
155	*Duane Clemons*	.05
156	*Marcus Coleman*	.05
157	*Chris Darkins*	.30
158	*Rickey Dudley*	.30
159	*Jason Dunn*	.20
160	*Bobby Engram*	.10
161	*Daryl Gardener*	.05
162	*Eddie George*	3.00
163	*Terry Glenn*	1.50
164	*Kevin Hardy*	.20
165	*Marvin Harrison*	2.00
166	*Dietrich Jells*	.05
167	*DeRon Jenkins*	.05
168	*Darrius Johnson*	.05
169	*Keyshawn Johnson*	2.00
170	*Lance Johnstone*	.05
171	*Cedric Jones*	.05
172	*Marcus Jones*	.05
173	*Danny Kanell*	.50
174	*Eddie Kennison*	.30
175	*Jevon Langford*	.05
176	*Markco Maddox*	.05
177	*Derrick Mayes*	.75
178	*Leeland McElroy*	.20
179	*Del McGee*	.05
180	*Johnny McWilliams*	.05

181	Alex Molden	.05
182	Eric Moulds	1.50
183	Jonathan Ogden	.05
184	Lawrence Phillips	.50
185	Simeon Rice	.20
186	Amani Toomer	.30
187	Regan Upshaw	.05
188	Jerome Woods	.05
189	Darrell Green (Inspirations)	.05
190	Daryl Johnston (Inspirations)	.05
191	Sam Mills (Inspirations)	.05
192	Earnest Byner (Inspirations)	.05
193	Herschel Walker (Inspirations)	.05
194	Brett Favre (Highlights)	.25
195	Brett Favre (Highlights)	.25
196	Brett Favre (Highlights)	.25
197	Brett Favre (Highlights)	.25
198	Brett Favre (Highlights)	.25
199	Checklist	.05
200	Checklist	.05

1996 SkyBox Impact Excelerators

Excelerators included 15 players who have breakaway speed. The word "Excelerators" is written across the top in foil, with the player's name across the bottom, with his last name in large letters, and flames rising up. These inserts were seeded every 12 packs.

		MT
Complete Set (15):		40.00
Common Player:		2.00
1	Robert Brooks	2.00
2	Isaac Bruce	4.00
3	William Floyd	2.00
4	Joey Galloway	6.00
5	Michael Irvin	2.00
6	Napoleon Kaufman	2.00
7	Anthony Miller	2.00
8	Herman Moore	2.00
9	Barry Sanders	8.00
10	Chris Sanders	2.00
11	Kordell Stewart	6.00
12	Rodney Thomas	2.00
13	Tamarick Vanover	2.00
14	Ricky Watters	2.00
15	Michael Westbrook	2.00

1996 SkyBox Impact Intimidators

Intimidators was a 10-card insert that displayed the NFL's toughest players against a shattered-looking background. The word "Intimidators" runs down the right side and gets smaller toward the bottom. Intimidators inserts were seeded every 20 packs of Impact.

		MT
Complete Set (10):		45.00
Common Player:		2.00
1	Terrell Davis	6.00
2	Hugh Douglas	2.00
3	Dan Marino	12.00
4	Curtis Martin	10.00
5	Carl Pickens	2.00
6	Errict Rhett	4.00
7	Jerry Rice	6.00
8	Emmitt Smith	12.00
9	Eric Swann	2.00
10	Chris Warren	3.00

1996 SkyBox Impact More Attitude

More Attitide was the easiest insert to get in Impact, with an insertion rate of one per three packs. The insert displayed 20 rookies from 1996 in their college uniforms with silver foil backgrounds.

		MT
Complete Set (20):		25.00
Common Player:		.50
1	Karim Abdul-Jabbar	3.00
2	Tim Biakabutuka	2.00
3	Bobby Engram	2.00
4	Daryl Gardener	.50
5	Eddie George	5.00
6	Terry Glenn	4.00
7	Kevin Hardy	.50
8	Marvin Harrison	2.50
9	DeRon Jenkins	.50
10	Keyshawn Johnson	3.00
11	Cedric Jones	.50
12	Eddie Kennison	1.50
13	Jevon Langford	.50
14	Leeland McElroy	1.50
15	Johnny McWilliams	.50
16	Eric Moulds	2.00
17	Lawrence Phillips	1.00
18	Jonathan Ogden	.50
19	Simeon Rice	.50
20	Amani Toomer	1.00

1996 SkyBox Impact No Surrender

No Surrender featured 20 top players in a horizontal format with the player's image embossed against a football background. The words "No Surrender" are written across the top of the card in red foil. This insert is seeded in every 40 hobby packs.

		MT
Complete Set (20):		150.00
Common Player:		5.00
1	Marcus Allen	5.00
2	Jeff Blake	10.00
3	Drew Bledsoe	15.00
4	Ben Coates	5.00
5	Brett Favre	30.00
6	Terry Glenn	18.00
7	Jim Harbaugh	5.00
8	Kevin Hardy	5.00
9	Keyshawn Johnson	16.00
10	Dan Marino	30.00
11	Leeland McElroy	10.00
12	Steve McNair	14.00
13	Herman Moore	7.00
14	Lawrence Phillips	10.00
15	Errict Rhett	10.00
16	Jerry Rice	15.00
17	Simeon Rice	5.00
18	Barry Sanders	20.00
19	Rodney Thomas	7.00
20	Tyrone Wheatley	5.00

1996 SkyBox Impact Versateam

This 10-card insert featured NFL stars that excel at multiple things. The cards, which are found every 120 packs, feature a color action shot of the player over a green tinted background. The background is split diagonally, with half containing the player's position and half with another shot of the player.

		MT
Complete Set (10):		200.00
Common Player:		10.00
1	Tim Brown	10.00
2	Terrell Davis	25.00
3	John Elway	16.00
4	Marshall Faulk	15.00
5	Joey Galloway	25.00
6	Curtis Martin	45.00
7	Deion Sanders	15.00
8	Kordell Stewart	35.00
9	Chris Warren	10.00
10	Steve Young	30.00

1996 SkyBox Impact Rookies

Although released in early 1997, Impact Rookies is generally considered a 1996 product due to its focus on 1996 rookies. The set consists of 150 cards, including 70 1996 rookies, 50 All-Time Impact Rookies, 20 Rookie Sleepers and 10 Rookie Record Holders. Ten-card packs had the following inserts: 1996 All-Rookie Team, Draft Board, Rookie Rewind, 1997 NFL Draft Exchange and 1996 Rookies. In addition, autographed versions of Karim Abdul-Jabbar, Rickey Dudley, Marvin Harrison, Lawrence Phillips, Eddie Kennison and Amani Toomer 1996 Rookies inserts were available through a case topper redemption offer. One redemption card was included in six-box cases, with two per 12-box case and three per 20-box cases.

		MT
Complete Set (150):		12.00
Common Player:		.05
Minor Stars:		.10
Wax Box:		20.00
1	Leeland McElroy	.10
2	Johnny McWilliams	.05
3	Simeon Rice	.10
4	DeRon Jenkins	.05
5	Jermaine Lewis	1.00
6	Ray Lewis	.05
7	Jonathan Ogden	.10
8	Eric Moulds	1.50
9	Tim Biakabutuka	.50
10	Muhsin Muhammad	.50
11	Winslow Oliver	.05
12	Bobby Engram	.20
13	Walt Harris	.10
14	Willie Anderson	.05
15	Marco Battaglia	.05
16	Jevon Langford	.05
17	Kavika Pittman	.05
18	Stepfret Williams	.05
19	Tory James	.05
20	Jeff Lewis	.50
21	John Mobley	.05
22	Detron Smith	.05
23	Derrick Mayes	.75
24	Eddie George	2.50
25	Marvin Harrison	2.00
26	Dedric Mathis	.05
27	Tony Brackens	.05
28	Kevin Hardy	.10
29	Jerome Woods	.05
30	Karim Abdul-Jabbar	.50
31	Daryl Gardener	.05
32	Jerris McPhail	.05
33	Stanley Pritchett	.05
34	Zach Thomas	.50
35	Duane Clemons	.05
36	Moe Williams	.05
37	Tedy Bruschi	.05
38	Terry Glenn	1.25
39	Alex Molden	.05
40	Ricky Whittle	.05
41	Cedric Jones	.05
42	Danny Kanell	.10
43	Amani Toomer	.10
44	Marcus Coleman	.05
45	Keyshawn Johnson	1.50
46	Ray Mickens	.05
47	Alex Van Dyke	.10
48	Rickey Dudley	.20
49	Lance Johnstone	.05
50	Brian Dawkins	.05
51	Jason Dunn	.05
52	Ray Farmer	.05
53	Bobby Hoying	.50
54	Jermaine Mayberry	.05
55	Bryan Still	.05
56	Tony Banks	.50
57	Ernie Conwell	.05
58	Eddie Kennison	.20
59	Jerald Moore	.05
60	Lawrence Phillips	.50
61	Isreal Ifeanyi	.05
62	Terrell Owens	3.00
63	Iheanyi Uwaezuoke	.10
64	Mike Alstott	1.25
65	Marcus Jones	.05
66	Nilo Silvan	.05
67	Regan Upshaw	.05
68	Stephen Davis	2.50
69	Troy Aikman	.50
70	Terry Allen	.05
71	Edgar Bennett	.05
72	Jerome Bettis	.10
73	Drew Bledsoe	.50
74	Tim Brown	.10
75	Mark Brunell	.50
76	Cris Carter	.10
77	Kerry Collins	.10
78	Terrell Davis	1.00
79	John Elway	.80
80	Marshall Faulk	.10
81	Brett Favre	1.00
82	Joey Galloway	.10
83	Rodney Hampton	.05
84	Jim Harbaugh	.05
85	Michael Irvin	.10
86	Chris T. Jones	.05
87	Napoleon Kaufman	.20
88	Jim Kelly	.10
89	Dan Marino	.75
90	Curtis Martin	.30
91	Terance Mathis	.05
92	Steve McNair	.30
93	Anthony Miller	.05
94	Scott Mitchell	.05
95	Herman Moore	.10
96	Brett Perriman	.05
97	Carl Pickens	.05
98	Jerry Rice	.50
99	Andre Rison	.05
100	Rashaan Salaam	.05
101	Barry Sanders	1.00
102	Chris Sanders	.05
103	Deion Sanders	.20
104	Frank Sanders	.05
105	Bruce Smith	.05
106	Emmitt Smith	.75
107	Robert Smith	.05
108	Kordell Stewart	.75
109	J.J. Stokes	.05
110	Yancey Thigpen	.05
111	Thurman Thomas	.05
112	Eric Turner	.05
113	Tamarick Vanover	.05
114	Chris Warren	.05
115	Ricky Watters	.10
116	Michael Westbrook	.05
117	Reggie White	.10
118	Steve Young	.30
119	Jeff Blake	.05
120	Robert Brooks	.05
121	Isaac Bruce	.10
122	Mark Chmura	.05
123	Wayne Chrebet	.10
124	Ben Coates	.05
125	Ken Dilger	.05
126	Bert Emanuel	.05
127	Gus Frerotte	.05
128	Kevin Greene	.05
129	Erik Kramer	.05
130	Greg Lloyd	.05
131	Tony Martin	.05
132	Brian Mitchell	.05
133	Bryce Paup	.05
134	Jake Reed	.05
135	Errict Rhett	.05
136	Yancey Thigpen	.05
137	Tamarick Vanover	.05
138	Chris Warren	.05
139	Marcus Allen	.10
140	Jerome Bettis	.10
141	Tim Brown	.10
142	Mark Carrier	.05
143	Marshall Faulk	.10
144	Tyrone Hughes	.05
145	Dan Marino	.75
146	Curtis Martin	.30
147	Barry Sanders	1.00
148	Orlando Thomas	.10
149	Checklist (1-107)	.05
150	Checklist (108-150/inserts)	.05

1996 SkyBox Impact Rookies All-Rookie Team

This 10-card insert includes some of the top rookies from the 1996 season. The fronts feature an embossed image of the player on a matte finish, with the words All-Rookie Team and the names of different members of the team printed in the background in white, embossed letters. All-Rookie Team inserts are numbered and inserted every six packs.

		MT
Complete Set (10):		20.00
Common Player:		1.00
1	Karim Abdul-Jabbar	4.00
2	Tim Biakabutuka	2.00
3	Eddie George	6.00
4	Marvin Harrison	3.00
5	Keyshawn Johnson	3.00
6	Eddie Kennison	2.00
7	Lawrence Phillips	1.00
8	Zach Thomas	2.00
9	Amani Toomer	1.00
10	Simeon Rice	1.00

1996 SkyBox Impact Rookies Draft Board

Draft Board has 20 cards that feature multiple players on the front in a horizontal format against a maroon background. The back explains the tie between the players - whether they were all late round picks or attended the same college - and are numbered. Draft Board inserts are found every 24 packs.

		MT
Complete Set (20):		170.00
Common Player:		4.00
1	Terry Glenn, Rickey Dudley, Bobby Hoying	12.00
2	Simeon Rice, Kevin Hardy	4.00
3	Emmitt Smith, Errict Rhett	30.00
4	Deion Sanders, Corey Sawyer, Derrick Brooks	10.00
5	Terry Allen, Marcus Allen	4.00
6	John Mobley, Andre Reed	4.00
7	Drew Bledsoe, Rick Mirer, Mark Brunell	14.00
8	John Elway, Jim Kelly, Dan Marino	30.00
9	Carl Pickens, Anthony Miller	4.00
10	Antonio Freeman, Robert Brooks, Chris T. Jones	4.00
11	Jerome Bettis, Ricky Watters, Tim Brown	4.00
12	Jerry Rice, Herman Moore, Michael Irvin	15.00
13	Terrell Davis, Rodney Hampton, Garrison Hearst	15.00
14	Kerry Collins, Ki-Jana Carter, Kyle Brady	10.00
15	Barry Sanders, Thurman Thomas	15.00
16	Jermaine Lewis, Jeff Lewis, Ray Lewis	4.00
17	Steve Young, Troy Aikman	15.00
18	Curtis Martin, Chris Warren, Jamal Anderson	20.00
19	Kordell Stewart, Rashaan Salaam, Michael Westbrook	8.00
20	Tony Banks, Muhsin Muhammad	6.00

1996 SkyBox Impact Rookies Rookie Rewind

Rookie Rewind looks back on past drafts to reflect their rise to stardom. Ten different players are featured over a swirl background with the words "Rookie Rewind" in gold foil across the bottom. Rookie Rewind inserts were found only in hobby packs and carried an insertion rate of one per 120.

		MT
Complete Set (10):		50.00
Common Player:		1.50
1	Jamal Anderson	3.00
2	Jeff Blake	3.00
3	Robert Brooks	1.50
4	Mark Brunell	8.00
5	Brett Favre	18.00
6	Aaron Hayden	1.50
7	Derek Loville	1.50
8	Emmitt Smith	18.00
9	Robert Smith	1.50
10	Tamarick Vanover	3.00

1996 SkyBox Impact Rookies 1996 Rookies

This insert showcased the top rookies of 1996 on cards that were individually numbered to 1,996. The 10 offensive stars included in this insert are found every 144 packs. Autographed versions of Abdul-Jabbar, Dudley, Harrison, Phillips, Kennison and Toomer were available as case toppers.

		MT
Complete Set (10):		200.00
Common Player:		8.00
1	Karim Abdul-Jabbar	30.00
2	Tim Biakabutuka	8.00
3	Rickey Dudley	8.00
4	Eddie George	45.00
5	Terry Glenn	35.00
6	Marvin Harrison	25.00
7	Keyshawn Johnson	25.00
8	Eddie Kennison	15.00
9	Lawrence Phillips	20.00
10	Amani Toomer	8.00

1996 SkyBox SkyMotion

SkyBox's 1996 SkyMotion set features the video work of NFL films to reproduce 3.5 seconds of game action on each card. No special lights or glasses are needed to get the full effect of the card; all it takes is a flick of the wrist. The cards provide the whole picture of how the play unfolds. The cards are laminated onto paper, enabling SkyBox to print stats and other information on the back for the first time. (Previous cards were plastic, printed on one side only.) In addition, there's a Replay parallel set of all 60 cards; these cards feature rounded edges with special foil stamping on the card back. One Replay card is included in each box. Two other insert sets were also made - Big Bang and Team Galaxy.

		MT
Complete Set (60):		150.00
Common Player:		1.50
Minor Stars:		3.00
Wax Box:		75.00
1	Troy Aikman	10.00
2	Marcus Allen	3.00
3	Jeff Blake	5.00
4	Drew Bledsoe	10.00
5	Tim Brown	1.50
6	Isaac Bruce	6.00
7	Mark Brunell	7.00
8	Cris Carter	1.50
9	Kerry Collins	4.00
10	Ben Coates	1.50
11	Curtis Conway	1.50
12	Terrell Davis	10.00
13	Trent Dilfer	1.50
14	Hugh Douglas	1.50
15	John Elway	6.00
16	Marshall Faulk	5.00
17	Brett Favre	15.00
18	William Floyd	1.50
19	Joey Galloway	7.00
20	Jeff George	1.50
21	Rodney Hampton	1.50
22	Jim Harbaugh	1.50
23	*Aaron Hayden*	3.00
24	Jeff Hostetler	1.50
25	Tyrone Hughes	1.50
26	Michael Irvin	3.00
27	Daryl Johnston	1.50
28	Jim Kelly	1.50
29	Greg Lloyd	1.50
30	Dan Marino	15.00
31	Curtis Martin	12.00
32	Chester McGlockton	1.50
33	Steve McNair	6.00
34	Eric Metcalf	1.50
35	Scott Mitchell	1.50
36	Herman Moore	4.00
37	Bryce Paup	1.50
38	Carl Pickens	1.50
39	Errict Rhett	4.00
40	Jerry Rice	10.00
41	Rashaan Salaam	4.00
42	Barry Sanders	10.00
43	Chris Sanders	1.50
44	Deion Sanders	6.00
45	Junior Seau	1.50
46	Heath Shuler	1.50
47	Bruce Smith	1.50
48	Emmitt Smith	15.00
49	Kordell Stewart	8.00
50	Eric Swann	1.50
51	Derrick Thomas	1.50
52	Thurman Thomas	3.00
53	Eric Turner	1.50
54	Tamarick Vanover	6.00
55	Chris Warren	3.00
56	Ricky Watters	1.50
57	Michael Westbrook	4.00
58	Reggie White	3.00
59	Rod Woodson	1.50
60	Steve Young	7.00

1996 SkyBox SkyMotion Gold

Actually called Replay, but referred to in the hobby as Golds, this 60-card parallel set featured rounded edges and special foil stamping on the card back to differentiate it from regular-issue cards. Gold parallels were inserted as a box topper into every other hobby box as a reward to box purchasers.

	MT
Complete Set (60):	1000.
Gold Cards:	4x-8x

1996 SkyBox SkyMotion Big Bang

These 1996 SkyBox Sky-Motion inserts have 10 top rookies against a background of exploding fireworks. The cards, using lenticular printing, were seeded one per every packs.

		MT
Complete Set (10):		100.00
Common Player:		4.00
1	Tim Biakabutuka	10.00
2	Rickey Dudley	8.00
3	Eddie George	25.00
4	Terry Glenn	20.00
5	Kevin Hardy	4.00
6	Marvin Harrison	15.00
7	Keyshawn Johnson	15.00
8	Leeland McElroy	8.00
9	Lawrence Phillips	8.00
10	Simeon Rice	4.00

1996 SkyBox SkyMotion Team Galaxy

These 1996 SkyBox Sky-Motion inserts showcase five of the NFL's top stars against a backdrop of planets and footballs. The cards, printed using lenticular printing, were seeded one per 35 packs.

		MT
Complete Set (5):		150.00
Common Player:		20.00
1	Karim Abdul-Jabbar	20.00
2	Brett Favre	50.00
3	Curtis Martin	40.00
4	Jerry Rice	35.00
5	Emmitt Smith	50.00

1997 SkyBox

This 250-card base set features 208 veterans, 40 rookies and two checklists. The base cards have a holographic foil design on 20 pt. card stock. The inserts for the set include Rookie Preview, Close Ups, PrimeTime Rookies, Premium Players, Larger Than Life, Autographics and Star Rubies.

		MT
Complete Set (250):		35.00
Common Player:		.10
Minor Stars:		.20
Ruby Cards:		50x-100x
Ruby Rookies:		25x-50x
Wax Box:		45.00
1	Brett Favre	3.00
2	Michael Bates	.10
3	Jeff Graham	.10
4	Terry Glenn	.30
5	Stephen Davis	.10
6	Wesley Walls	.10
7	Barry Sanders	1.50
8	Chris Sanders	.10
9	O.J. McDuffie	.10
10	Ken Dilger	.10
11	Kimble Anders	.10
12	Keenan McCardell	.10
13	Ki-Jana Carter	.10
14	Gary Brown	.10
15	Andre Rison	.10
16	Edgar Bennett	.10
17	Jerome Bettis	.20
18	Ted Johnson	.10
19	John Friez	.10
20	Tony Brackens	.10
21	Bryan Cox	.10
22	Eric Moulds	.10
23	Johnnie Morton	.10
24	Brad Johnson	.10
25	Bam Morris	.10
26	Anthony Johnson	.10
27	Jim Harbaugh	.10
28	Keyshawn Johnson	.20
29	Cary Blanchard	.10
30	Curtis Conway	.10
31	Herschel Walker	.10
32	Thurman Thomas	.20
33	Frank Sanders	.10
34	Lawrence Phillips	.20
35	Scottie Graham	.10
36	Jim Everett	.10
37	Dale Carter	.10
38	Ashley Ambrose	.10
39	Mark Chmura	.20
40	James Stewart	.10
41	John Mobley	.10
42	Terrell Davis	1.25
43	Ben Coates	.10
44	Jeff George	.10
45	Ty Detmer	.10
46	Isaac Bruce	.20
47	Chris Warren	.10
48	Steve Walsh	.10
49	Bruce Smith	.10
50	Cris Carter	.10
51	Jamal Anderson	.10
52	Tim Biakabutuka	.10
53	Steve Young	.75
54	Eric Turner	.10
55	Jessie Tuggle	.10
56	Chris T. Jones	.10
57	Daryl Johnston	.10
58	Randall Cunningham	.10
59	Trent Dilfer	.20
60	Mark Brunell	1.25
61	Warren Moon	.10
62	Terry Kirby	.10
63	Eddie George	1.75
64	Neil Smith	.10
65	Gilbert Brown	.10
66	Emmitt Smith	2.50
67	Chad Brown	.10
68	Jamie Asher	.10
69	Willie McGinest	.10
70	Tim Brown	.10
71	Quentin Coryatt	.10
72	Mario Bates	.10
73	Fred Barnett	.10
74	Hugh Douglas	.10
75	Eric Swann	.10
76	Chris Chandler	.10
77	Larry Centers	.10
78	Vinny Testaverde	.10
79	Jermaine Lewis	.10
80	Junior Seau	.10
81	Kevin Greene	.10
82	Ricky Watters	.20
83	Anthony Miller	.10
84	Michael Westbrook	.10
85	Charles Way	.10
86	Andre Reed	.10
87	Darrell Green	.10
88	Troy Aikman	1.25
89	Jim Pyne	.10
90	Dan Marino	2.50
91	Elvis Grbac	.10
92	Mel Gray	.10
93	Marcus Allen	.20
94	Terry Allen	.10
95	Karim Abdul-Jabbar	.30
96	Rick Mirer	.10
97	Bert Emanuel	.10
98	John Elway	.75
99	Tony Martin	.10
100	Zach Thomas	.10
101	Harvey Williams	.10
102	Jason Sehorn	.10
103	Lawyer Milloy	.10
104	Thomas Lewis	.10
105	Michael Irvin	.20
106	James Hundon	.10
107	Willie Green	.10
108	Bobby Engram	.10
109	Mike Alstott	.10
110	Greg Lloyd	.10
111	Shannon Sharpe	.10
112	Desmond Howard	.10
113	Jason Elam	.10
114	Qadry Ismail	.10
115	William Thomas	.10
116	Marshall Faulk	.10
117	Tyrone Wheatley	.10
118	Tommy Vardell	.10
119	Rashaan Salaam	.10
120	Brian Mitchell	.10
121	Terance Mathis	.10
122	Dorsey Levens	.20
123	Todd Collins	.10
124	Derrick Alexander	.10
125	Stan Humphries	.10
126	Kordell Stewart	1.25
127	Kent Graham	.10
128	Yancey Thigpen	.10
129	Bryan Still	.10
130	Carl Pickens	.10
131	Ray Lewis	.10
132	Curtis Martin	1.25
133	Kerry Collins	.30
134	Ed McCaffrey	.10
135	Darick Holmes	.10
136	Glyn Milburn	.10
137	Rickey Dudley	.10
138	Terrell Owens	.75
139	Kevin Williams	.10
140	Reggie White	.20
141	Darnay Scott	.10
142	Brett Perriman	.10
143	Neil O'Donnell	.20
144	Natrone Means	.20
145	Jerris McPhail	.10
146	Lamar Lathon	.10
147	Michael Jackson	.10
148	Simeon Rice	.10
149	Greg Hill	.10
150	Erik Kramer	.10
151	Quinn Early	.10
152	Tamarick Vanover	.10
153	Derrick Thomas	.10
154	Nilo Silvan	.10
155	Deion Sanders	.50
156	Lorenzo Neal	.10
157	Steve McNair	1.00
158	Levon Kirkland	.10
159	Bobby Hebert	.10
160	William Floyd	.20
161	Leeland McElroy	.10
162	Chester McGlockton	.10
163	Michael Haynes	.10
164	Aeneas Williams	.10
165	Hardy Nickerson	.10
166	Rodney Woodson	.10
167	Iheanyi Uwaezuoke	.10
168	Chris Slade	.10
169	Herman Moore	.20
170	Rob Moore	.10
171	Andre Hastings	.10
172	Antonio Freeman	.40
173	Tony Boselli	.10
174	Drew Bledsoe	1.25
175	Sam Mills	.10
176	Robert Smith	.10
177	Jimmy Smith	.10
178	Alex Molden	.10
179	Joey Galloway	.20
180	Irving Fryar	.10
181	Wayne Chrebet	.20
182	Dave Brown	.10
183	Robert Brooks	.20
184	Tony Banks	.30
185	Eric Metcalf	.10
186	Napoleon Kaufman	.20
187	Frank Wycheck	.10
188	Donnell Woolford	.10
189	Kevin Turner	.10
190	Eddie Kennison	.40
191	Cortez Kennedy	.10
192	Raymont Harris	.10
193	Ronnie Harmon	.10
194	Kevin Hardy	.10
195	Gus Frerotte	.10
196	Marvin Harrison	.40
197	Jeff Blake	.20
198	Mike Tomczak	.10
199	William Roaf	.10
200	Jerry Rice	1.25
201	Jake Reed	.10
202	Ken Norton	.10
203	Errict Rhett	.20
204	Adrian Murrell	.20
205	Rodney Hampton	.10
206	Scott Mitchell	.10
207	Jason Dunn	.10
208	Ray Zellars	.10
209	*Michael Adams*	.10
210	*John Allred*	.10
211	*Reidel Anthony*	1.50
212	*Darnell Autry*	.30
213	*Tiki Barber*	1.50
214	*Will Blackwell*	.20
215	*Peter Boulware*	.10
216	*Macey Brooks*	.10
217	*Rae Carruth*	1.50
218	*Troy Davis*	.30
219	*Corey Dillon*	2.50
220	*Jim Druckenmiller*	2.50
221	*Warrick Dunn*	3.00
222	*Marc Edwards*	.20
223	*James Farrior*	.10
224	*Tony Gonzalez*	.75
225	*Jay Graham*	.50
226	*Yatil Green*	.30
227	*Byron Hanspard*	.50
228	*Ike Hilliard*	1.25
229	*Leon Johnson*	.10
230	*Damon Jones*	.10
231	*Freddie Jones*	.50
232	*Joey Kent*	.50
233	*David LaFleur*	.75
234	*Kevin Lockett*	.20
235	*Sam Madison*	.10
236	*Brian Manning*	.10
237	*Ronnie McAda*	.10
238	*Orlando Pace*	.20
239	*Jake Plummer*	5.00
240	*Keith Poole*	.10
241	*Darrell Russell*	.10
242	*Sedrick Shaw*	.30
243	*Antowain Smith*	1.50
244	*Shawn Springs*	.50
245	*Duce Staley*	8.00
246	*Dedric Ward*	.50
247	*Bryant Westbrook*	.20
248	*Danny Wuerffel*	.75
249	Checklist	.10
250	Checklist	.10

1997 SkyBox Autographics

Inserted 1:240 packs, the cards featured signed fronts. In addition, an Autographics Century Marks parallel set was also randomly seeded.

	MT
Common Player:	15.00
Minor Stars:	30.00
Century Marks:	2x
Karim Abdul-Jabbar	80.00
Larry Allen	15.00
Terry Allen	30.00
Mike Alstott	75.00
Darnell Autry	45.00
Tony Banks	75.00
Pat Barnes	30.00
Jeff Blake	30.00
Michael Booker	15.00
Reuben Brown	15.00
Rae Carruth	60.00
Cris Carter	30.00
Ben Coates	30.00
Ernie Conwell	15.00
Terrell Davis	150.00
Ty Detmer	15.00
Ken Dilger	15.00
Corey Dillon	80.00
Jim Druckenmiller	125.00
Rick Dudley	30.00
Brett Favre CM	700.00
Antonio Freeman	50.00
Daryl Gardner	15.00
Chris Gedney	15.00
Eddie George	200.00
Hunter Goodwin	15.00
Marvin Harrison	60.00
Garrison Hearst	30.00
William Henderson	15.00
Michael Jackson	15.00
Tory James	15.00
Rob Johnson	30.00
Chris T. Jones	15.00
Pete Kendall	15.00
Eddie Kennison	60.00
David LaFleur	40.00
Jeff Lewis	30.00
Thomas Lewis	15.00
Keith Lockett	30.00
Brian Manning	15.00
Dan Marino	400.00
Ed McCaffrey	15.00
Keenan McCardell	30.00
Glyn Milburn	15.00
Alex Molden	15.00
Johnnie Morton	15.00
Winslow Oliver	15.00
Jerry Rice	350.00
Rashaan Salaam	30.00
Frank Sanders	15.00
Shannon Sharpe	30.00
Sedrick Shaw	40.00
Alex Smith	15.00
Antowain Smith	80.00
Emmitt Smith	350.00
Jimmy Smith	15.00
Shawn Springs	15.00
James Stewart	15.00
Kordell Stewart	150.00
Rodney Thomas	15.00
Amani Toomer	15.00
Floyd Turner	15.00
Alex Van Dyke	15.00
Mike Vrabel	15.00
Chris Warren	15.00
Charles Way	15.00
Reggie White (Century)	100.00
Rickey Whittle	15.00
Sherman Williams	15.00
John Wittman	15.00

1997 SkyBox Close Ups

This 18-card insert features head shots of young NFL players. Four more pictures are included on the card. Close Ups were inserted 1:18.

		MT
Complete Set (10):		100.00
Common Player:		3.00
1	Terrell Davis	15.00
2	Troy Aikman	15.00
3	Drew Bledsoe	15.00
4	Steve McNair	10.00
5	Jerry Rice	15.00
6	Kordell Stewart	15.00
7	Kerry Collins	6.00
8	John Elway	10.00
9	Deion Sanders	8.00
10	Joey Galloway	3.00

1997 SkyBox Larger Than Life

Larger Than Life is a 10-card insert featuring the legends of today. Larger Than Life cards were inserted one per 360 packs.

		MT
Complete Set (10):		450.00
Common Player:		15.00
1	Emmitt Smith	75.00
2	Barry Sanders	90.00
3	Curtis Martin	40.00
4	Dan Marino	75.00
5	Keyshawn Johnson	25.00
6	Marvin Harrison	15.00
7	Terry Glenn	20.00
8	Eddie George	60.00
9	Brett Favre	90.00
10	Karim Abdul-Jabbar	20.00

1997 SkyBox Premium Players

Premium Players is a 15-card insert set which was seeded one per 192 packs.

		MT
Complete Set (15):		800.00
Common Player:		8.00
1	Eddie George	85.00
2	Terry Glenn	25.00
3	Karim Abdul-Jabbar	25.00
4	Emmitt Smith	100.00
5	Dan Marino	100.00
6	Brett Favre	120.00
7	Keyshawn Johnson	8.00
8	Curtis Martin	60.00
9	Marvin Harrison	8.00
10	Barry Sanders	75.00
11	Jerry Rice	60.00
12	Terrell Davis	60.00
13	Troy Aikman	60.00
14	Drew Bledsoe	60.00
15	John Elway	40.00

1997 SkyBox PrimeTime Rookies

PrimeTime Rookies is a 10-card insert featuring the top rookies of 1997. This set is inserted one per 96 packs.

		MT
Complete Set (10):		175.00
Common Player:		7.00
1	Jim Druckenmiller	35.00
2	Antowain Smith	25.00
3	Rae Carruth	15.00
4	Yatil Green	15.00
5	Ike Hilliard	15.00
6	Reidel Anthony	20.00
7	Orlando Pace	7.00
8	Peter Boulware	7.00
9	Warrick Dunn	45.00
10	Troy Davis	15.00

A player's name in *italic* type indicates a rookie card.

1997 SkyBox Reebok Bronze

The Reebok Value Added set came in bronze, silver, gold, ruby and emerald versions. The overall insertion rate for the Reebok Value Added set was one per pack.

		MT
Complete Set (15):		4.00
Common Player:		.10
Gold:		4x
Green:		25x-50x
Red:		10x-20x
Silver:		2x
12	Keenan McCardell	.10
37	Dale Carter	.10
38	Ashley Ambrose	.10
43	Ben Coates	.10
66	Emmitt Smith	1.50
95	Karim Abdul-Jabbar	.50
98	John Elway	1.50
110	Greg Lloyd	.10
123	Todd Collins	.10
161	Leeland McElroy	.10
169	Herman Moore	.10
175	Sam Mills	.10
180	Irving Fryar	.10
202	Ken Norton	.10
205	Rodney Hampton	.10

1997 SkyBox Rookie Preview

These 15 embossed insert cards feature some of the top rookies of 1997. Rookie Preview cards were inserted 1:6.

		MT
Complete Set (15):		30.00
Common Player:		1.00
1	Reidel Anthony	3.00
2	Tiki Barber	3.00
3	Peter Boulware	1.00
4	Rae Carruth	2.50
5	Jim Druckenmiller	4.50
6	Warrick Dunn	6.00
7	James Farrior	1.00
8	Yatil Green	2.50
9	Byron Hanspard	2.00
10	Ike Hilliard	2.50
11	Orlando Pace	1.50
12	Darrell Russell	1.00
13	Antowain Smith	3.00
14	Shawn Springs	1.00
15	Bryant Westbrook	1.00

1997 E-X2000

E-X2000 consists of a 60-card base set with one parallel and four inserts. The base cards feature "SkyView" technology, with a die-cut image over a transparent window. The Essential Credentials parallel set consists of less than 100 numbered sets. The inserts include A Cut Above, Fleet of Foot, Star Date 2000 and Autographics.

		MT
Complete Set (60):		100.00
Common Player:		.40

		MT
Minor Stars:		.75
Credential Cards:		10x-20x
Credential Rookies:		5x-10x
Wax Box:		100.00
1	Jake Plummer	20.00
2	Jamal Anderson	.75
3	Rae Carruth	5.00
4	Kerry Collins	1.00
5	Darnell Autry	3.00
6	Rashaan Salaam	.75
7	Troy Aikman	5.00
8	Deion Sanders	2.50
9	Emmitt Smith	8.00
10	Herman Moore	.75
11	Barry Sanders	5.00
12	Mark Chmura	.75
13	Brett Favre	12.00
14	Antonio Freeman	.75
15	Reggie White	.75
16	Cris Carter	.40
17	Brad Johnson	.40
18	Troy Davis	.75
19	Danny Wuerffel	4.00
20	Dave Brown	.40
21	Ike Hilliard	5.00
22	Ty Detmer	.40
23	Ricky Watters	.75
24	Tony Banks	3.00
25	Eddie Kennison	2.50
26	Jim Druckenmiller	8.00
27	Jerry Rice	5.00
28	Steve Young	3.00
29	Trent Dilfer	.75
30	Warrick Dunn	8.00
31	Terry Allen	.40
32	Gus Frerotte	.40
33	Vinny Testaverde	.40
34	Antowain Smith	6.00
35	Thurman Thomas	.75
36	Jeff Blake	.75
37	Carl Pickens	.40
38	Terrell Davis	5.00
39	John Elway	3.00
40	Eddie George	7.00
41	Steve McNair	4.00
42	Marshall Faulk	.75
43	Marvin Harrison	2.50
44	Mark Brunell	5.00
45	Marcus Allen	.75
46	Elvis Grbac	.40
47	Karim Abdul-Jabbar	3.50
48	Dan Marino	10.00
49	Drew Bledsoe	5.00
50	Terry Glenn	4.00
51	Curtis Martin	5.00
52	Keyshawn Johnson	1.00
53	Tim Brown	.40
54	Jeff George	.40
55	Jerome Bettis	.75
56	Kordell Stewart	5.00
57	Stan Humphries	.40
58	Junior Seau	.75
59	Joey Galloway	.75
60	Chris Warren	.40

1997 E-X2000 A Cut Above

This 10-card insert features players on cards die-cut to look like saw blades. A Cut Above cards were inserted 1:288.

		MT
Complete Set (10):		600.00
Common Player:		15.00
1	Barry Sanders	75.00
2	Brett Favre	120.00
3	Dan Marino	100.00
4	Eddie George	80.00
5	Emmitt Smith	100.00
6	Jerry Rice	60.00
7	Joey Galloway	15.00
8	John Elway	40.00
9	Mark Brunell	60.00
10	Terrell Davis	60.00

1997 E-X2000 Fleet of Foot

The cards in this 20-card insert are die-cut to look like football cleats. They were inserted 1:20.

		MT
Complete Set (20):		220.00
Common Player:		3.00
1	Antonio Freeman	8.00
2	Barry Sanders	25.00
3	Carl Pickens	3.00
4	Chris Warren	3.00
5	Curtis Martin	20.00
6	Deion Sanders	12.00
7	Emmitt Smith	40.00
8	Jerry Rice	20.00
9	Joey Galloway	8.00
10	Karim Abdul-Jabbar	15.00
11	Kordell Stewart	20.00
12	Lawrence Phillips	3.00
13	Mark Brunell	20.00
14	Marvin Harrison	8.00
15	Rae Carruth	10.00
16	Ricky Watters	3.00
17	Steve Young	15.00
18	Terrell Davis	20.00
19	Terry Glenn	18.00
20	Shawn Springs	3.00

1997 E-X2000 Star Date 2000

This 15-card insert features young stars of the NFL. The cards were inserted 1:9.

		MT
Complete Set (15):		60.00
Common Player:		1.50
1	Curtis Martin	6.00
2	Darnell Autry	3.00
3	Darrell Russell	1.50
4	Eddie Kennison	3.00
5	Jim Druckenmiller	8.00
6	Karim Abdul-Jabbar	6.00
7	Kerry Collins	3.00
8	Keyshawn Johnson	3.00
9	Marvin Harrison	3.00
10	Orlando Pace	1.50
11	Pat Barnes	1.50
12	Reidel Anthony	5.00
13	Tim Biakabutuka	1.50
14	Warrick Dunn	12.00
15	Yatil Green	4.00

1997 SkyBox Impact

The 250-card set contains 207 player cards, three checklists and 40 rookies. The cards feature the player's photo superimposed over a jagged background, with the player's name printed in 3-D block letters at the top. The player's first and last name and team are printed at the bottom right in gold foil, while the Impact logo is in the lower left. The backs include the player's name, position, quote, Impact stats, bio, stats, photo and team helmet over a team-colored football background. A Rave parallel set was randomly seeded. SkyBox produced less than 150 Rave sets.

		MT
Complete Set (250):		25.00
Common Player:		.05
Minor Stars:		.10
Wax Box:		50.00
1	Carl Pickens	.05
2	Ray Lewis	.05
3	Darrell Green	.05
4	Brett Favre	1.75
5	Todd Collins	.05
6	Errict Rhett	.10
7	John Elway	.50
8	Troy Aikman	.75
9	Steve McNair	.75
10	Kordell Stewart	.75
11	Drew Bledsoe	.75
12	Kerry Collins	.25
13	Dan Marino	1.50
14	Ricky Watters	.10
15	Marvin Harrison	.30
16	Simeon Rice	.05
17	Qadry Ismail	.05
18	Andre Coleman	.05
19	Keyshawn Johnson	.30
20	Barry Sanders	1.25
21	Rickey Dudley	.10
22	Emmitt Smith	1.50
23	Erik Kramer	.05
24	Tony Boselli	.05
25	Steve Young	.50
26	Rod Woodson	.05
27	Eddie George	1.00
28	Curtis Martin	1.00
29	Amani Toomer	.05
30	Terrell Davis	1.00
31	Jim Everett	.05
32	Marcus Allen	.10
33	Karim Abdul-Jabbar	.50
34	Thurman Thomas	.10
35	Cortez Kennedy	.05
36	Jerome Bettis	.10
37	Kevin Carter	.05
38	Gilbert Brown	.05
39	Bert Emanuel	.05
40	Kyle Brady	.05
41	Trent Dilfer	.10
42	Garrison Hearst	.05

43	Kevin Greene	.05
44	Bryan Cox	.05
45	Desmond Howard	.05
46	Larry Centers	.05
47	Quentin Coryatt	.05
48	Michael Jackson	.05
49	John Randle	.05
50	Mark Brunell	.75
51	William Thomas	.05
52	Glyn Milburn	.05
53	Mike Alstott	.10
54	Chris Spielman	.05
55	Junior Seau	.10
56	Brian Blades	.05
57	Lamar Lathon	.05
58	Derrick Thomas	.05
59	Dave Brown	.05
60	Frank Wycheck	.05
61	Chris Slade	.05
62	Neil Smith	.05
63	Ashley Ambrose	.05
64	Alex Molden	.05
65	Edgar Bennett	.05
66	Alvin Harper	.05
67	Jamal Anderson	.15
68	Eddie Kennison	.30
69	Ken Norton	.05
70	Zach Thomas	.20
71	Leeland McElroy	.10
72	Terry Allen	.05
73	Raymont Harris	.05
74	Ken Dilger	.05
75	Jason Dunn	.05
76	Robert Smith	.05
77	William Roaf	.05
78	Bruce Smith	.05
79	Vinny Testaverde	.05
80	Jerry Rice	.75
81	Tim Brown	.05
82	James Stewart	.05
83	Andre Reed	.05
84	Herman Moore	.15
85	Stan Humphries	.05
86	Chris Warren	.05
87	Tyrone Wheatley	.05
88	Michael Irvin	.10
89	Dan Wilkinson	.05
90	Tony Banks	.20
91	Chester McGlockton	.05
92	Reggie White	.10
93	Elvis Grbac	.05
94	Willie Davis	.05
95	Greg Lloyd	.05
96	Ben Coates	.05
97	Rashaan Salaam	.10
98	Eric Swann	.05
99	Hugh Douglas	.05
100	Henry Ellard	.05
101	Rod Smith	.05
102	Tim Biakabutuka	.10
103	Chad Brown	.05
104	Kevin Hardy	.05
105	Chris T. Jones	.05
106	Antonio Freeman	.20
107	Lamont Warren	.05
108	Derrick Alexander	.05
109	Brett Perriman	.05
110	Antonio Langham	.05
111	Eric Moulds	.05
112	O.J. McDuffie	.05
113	Eric Metcalf	.05
114	Ray Zellars	.05
115	Marco Coleman	.05
116	Terry Kirby	.05
117	Darren Woodson	.05
118	Charles Johnson	.05
119	Sam Mills	.05
120	Rodney Hampton	.05
121	Rick Mirer	.10
122	Derrick Brooks	.05
123	Greg Hill	.05
124	John Mobley	.05
125	Chris Sanders	.05
126	Kent Graham	.05
127	Michael Westbrook	.05
128	Harvey Williams	.05
129	Keenan McCardell	.05
130	Neil O'Donnell	.05
131	LeRoy Butler	.05
132	Willie McGinest	.05
133	Ki-Jana Carter	.05
134	Robert Jones	.05
135	Jim Harbaugh	.05
136	Wesley Walls	.05
137	Jackie Harris	.05
138	Jermaine Lewis	.05
139	Jake Reed	.05
140	John Friesz	.05
141	Jerris McPhail	.05
142	Charlie Garner	.05
143	Bryce Paup	.05
144	Tony Martin	.05
145	Shannon Sharpe	.05
146	Terrell Owens	.50
147	Curtis Conway	.05
148	Jamie Asher	.05
149	Lawrence Phillips	.10
150	Deion Sanders	.30
151	Frank Sanders	.05
152	Joey Galloway	.20
153	Mel Gray	.05
154	Robert Brooks	.05
155	Jeff George	.05
156	Michael Haynes	.05
157	Chris Chandler	.05
158	Adrian Murrell	.05
159	Tamarick Vanover	.05
160	Marshall Faulk	.10

161	Thomas Lewis	.05
162	Ty Detmer	.05
163	Darnay Scott	.05
164	Bam Morris	.05
165	Scott Mitchell	.05
166	Brad Johnson	.05
167	Dave Meggett	.05
168	Bobby Engram	.05
169	Natrone Means	.10
170	Erric Pegram	.05
171	Leonard Russell	.05
172	Muhsin Muhammad	.05
173	Aeneas Williams	.05
174	Fred Barnett	.05
175	William Floyd	.05
176	Kimble Anders	.05
177	Darick Holmes	.05
178	Willie Green	.05
179	Rodney Thomas	.05
180	Derrick Alexander	.05
181	Sean Dawkins	.05
182	Dorsey Levens	.10
183	Napoleon Kaufman	.05
184	Mario Bates	.05
185	Yancey Thigpen	.05
186	Johnnie Morton	.05
187	Gus Frerotte	.05
188	Terance Mathis	.05
189	Tyrone Hughes	.05
190	Wayne Chrebet	.05
191	Tony Brackens	.05
192	Hardy Nickerson	.05
193	Daryl Johnston	.05
194	Irving Fryar	.05
195	Jeff Blake	.15
196	Charles Way	.05
197	Brian Mitchell	.05
198	Brent Jones	.05
199	Mark Chmura	.05
200	Terry Glenn	.30
201	Cris Carter	.05
202	Steve Atwater	.05
203	Rob Moore	.05
204	Anthony Johnson	.05
205	Warren Moon	.10
206	Darrien Gordon	.05
207	Isaac Bruce	.15
208	Reidel Anthony	1.00
209	Darnell Autry	.50
210	Tiki Barber	1.50
211	Pat Barnes	.30
212	Terry Battle	.10
213	Michael Booker	.10
214	Peter Boulware	.20
215	Chris Canty	.10
216	Rae Carruth	1.00
217	Troy Davis	.30
218	Corey Dillon	1.75
219	Jim Druckenmiller	2.00
220	Warrick Dunn	1.75
221	James Farrior	.10
222	Tarik Glenn	.10
223	Tony Gonzalez	.50
224	Yatil Green	.30
225	Byron Hanspard	.30
226	Ike Hilliard	1.00
227	Kenny Holmes	.10
228	Walter Jones	.10
229	Tom Knight	.10
230	David LaFleur	.40
231	Kenard Lang	.10
232	Kevin Lockett	.10
233	Tremain Mack	.10
234	Sam Madison	.10
235	Chris Naeole	.10
236	Orlando Pace	.40
237	Jake Plummer	4.00
238	Dwayne Rudd	.10
239	Darrell Russell	.25
240	Jamie Sharper	.10
241	Sedrick Shaw	.50
242	Antowain Smith	1.25
243	Shawn Springs	.50
244	Bryant Westbrook	.20
245	Reinard Wilson	.10
246	Danny Wuerffel	1.00
247	Renaldo Wynn	.10
248	Checklist	.05
249	Checklist	.05
250	Checklist	.05

1997 SkyBox Impact Raves

Rave is a parallel of the SkyBox Impact base set. The

Rave set parallels 247 cards (not the checklists) and was limited to 150 sets.

	MT
Rave Stars:	40x-80x
Rave Rookies:	20x-40x

1997 SkyBox Impact Boss

Inserted 1:6 packs, the 20-card set features the player's photo, name and team name embossed on the front. The backs have the player's name, team, position and highlights on the left side, while the Boss logo runs vertically along the right border. The cards are numbered "of 20" in the upper right corner. The Super Boss parallel set was inserted 1:36. The cards are identical to the base Boss, except the cards are printed on foil. The Super Boss logo appears in the lower left of the card front. The Super Boss cards also have an "SB" suffix with the card numbers on the back.

		MT
Complete Set (20):		40.00
Common Player:		1.00
Super Boss Cards:		2x-4x
1	Karim Abdul-Jabbar	2.00
2	Troy Aikman	3.00
3	Tim Biakabutuka	1.00
4	Mark Brunell	3.00
5	Rae Carruth	2.00
6	Kerry Collins	2.00
7	Corey Dillon	2.00
8	Jim Druckenmiller	3.00
9	Warrick Dunn	4.00
11	Brett Favre	6.00
12	Eddie George	4.00
13	Marvin Harrison	1.50
14	Keyshawn Johnson	1.50
15	Eddie Kennison	1.50
16	Dan Marino	5.00
17	Curtis Martin	3.00
18	Steve McNair	3.00
18	Orlando Pace	1.00
19	Barry Sanders	4.00
20	Steve Young	2.00

1997 SkyBox Impact Excelerators

The 12-card set was inserted 1:48 packs. The die-cut cards have the player's photo superimposed over a black and silver background, with a shield in the center. Excelerators is printed in red in the center of the background, while the player's name is printed in silver over the center of the player photo. The SkyBox logo is at the bottom center of the front. The backs have a player photo in the center, with his name and highlights printed inside the shield. The card numbers are printed "of 12."

		MT
Complete Set (12):		100.00
Common Player:		3.00
1	Mark Brunell	15.00
2	Rae Carruth	10.00
3	Terrell Davis	20.00
4	Joey Galloway	3.00
5	Marvin Harrison	6.00
6	Keyshawn Johnson	3.00
7	Eddie Kennison	6.00
8	Steve McNair	12.00
9	Jerry Rice	15.00
10	Emmitt Smith	30.00
11	Shawn Springs	6.00
12	Kordell Stewart	15.00

1997 SkyBox Impact Instant Impact

The 15-card set was inserted 1:24 packs. The player's last name is printed in black at the top inside a white stripe. The Impact logo is printed in silver in the lower right of the photo. A black stripe at the bottom includes "Instant Impact," player's name and team in silver foil. The team's helmet is located in the bottom center. The backs have the card number "of 15" printed at the top, while his highlights are printed in the center of the card. The black stripe on the bottom repeats the information from the front, without the silver foil.

		MT
Complete Set (15):		75.00
Common Player:		1.50
1	Reidel Anthony	10.00
2	Darnell Autry	3.00
3	Tiki Barber	3.00
4	Peter Boulware	1.50
5	Troy Davis	3.00
6	Jim Druckenmiller	12.00
7	Warrick Dunn	15.00
8	Yatil Green	8.00
9	Ike Hilliard	4.00
10	Orlando Pace	3.00
11	Darrell Russell	1.50
12	Sedrick Shaw	5.00
13	Shawn Springs	5.00
14	Bryant Westbrook	1.50
15	Danny Wuerffel	12.00

1997 SkyBox Impact Rave Reviews

Inserted 1:288 packs, the 12-card set includes a player photo superimposed over a ho-lofoil background of numbers. The Rave Reviews logo is printed above the player's name in the lower left corner. "Rave Review" is printed in holofoil vertically along the right border. The backs

have the player's name at the top, with a quote from Ronnie Lott along the left border. The player's photo is on the right. Lott's photo and description, along with the card number "of 12" are printed in the lower left.

		MT
Complete Set (12):		425.00
Common Player:		15.00
Inserted 1:288		
1	Terrell Davis	50.00
2	John Elway	30.00
3	Brett Favre	50.00
4	Joey Galloway	15.00
5	Eddie George	25.00
6	Terry Glenn	15.00
7	Dan Marino	40.00
8	Curtis Martin	20.00
9	Jerry Rice	25.00
10	Barry Sanders	50.00
11	Deion Sanders	15.00
12	Emmitt Smith	40.00

1997 SkyBox Impact Total Impact

Inserted 1:36 retail packs, the 10-card set is printed on plastic over a white background.

		MT
Complete Set (10):		75.00
Common Player:		5.00
1	Karim Abdul-Jabbar	7.00
2	Troy Aikman	12.00
3	Drew Bledsoe	12.00
4	Isaac Bruce	5.00
5	Kerry Collins	7.00
6	John Elway	10.00
7	Terry Glenn	7.00
8	Lawrence Phillips	5.00
9	Deion Sanders	8.00
10	Kordell Stewart	12.00

1998 E-X2001

Each of the 60 base cards in this set are holographic and gold-foil stamped with player-specific die-cuts mounted on durable, see-thru plastic stock exposed along a large portion of the card. The Essential Credentials Now parallel cards differ from the base set in color, holo-foil and scarcity. Each card is sequentially numbered according to the player's card number in the base set. Card #1 has only one single and card #60 has cards numbered to 60. The Essential Credentials Future is similar to the Now set except in color, holo-foil and the sequentially numbering is opposite the player's card number. For example, card #1 has 60 cards and card #60 only has one.

	MT
Complete Set (60):	125.00
Common Player:	.30

Minor Stars:		.60
Wax Box:		110.00
1	Kordell Stewart	3.00
2	Steve Young	2.50
3	Mark Brunell	3.00
4	Brett Favre	8.00
5	Barry Sanders	8.00
6	Warrick Dunn	3.00
7	Jerry Rice	4.00
8	Dan Marino	6.00
9	Emmitt Smith	6.00
10	John Elway	4.00
11	Eddie George	3.00
12	Jake Plummer	3.00
13	Terrell Davis	6.00
14	Curtis Martin	2.50
15	Troy Aikman	4.00
16	Terry Glenn	1.00
17	Mike Alstott	1.00
18	Drew Bledsoe	3.00
19	Keyshawn Johnson	.30
20	Dorsey Levens	.30
21	Elvis Grbac	.30
22	Ricky Watters	1.00
23	Robert Smith	1.00
24	Trent Dilfer	1.00
25	Joey Galloway	1.00
26	Rob Moore	.30
27	Steve McNair	1.50
28	Jim Harbaugh	.30
29	Troy Davis	.30
30	Rob Johnson	1.00
31	Shannon Sharpe	.30
32	Jerome Bettis	1.00
33	Tim Brown	.30
34	Kerry Collins	1.00
35	Garrison Hearst	.30
36	Antonio Freeman	1.00
37	Charlie Garner	.30
38	Glenn Foley	.30
39	Yatil Green	.30
40	Tiki Barber	.30
41	Bobby Hoying	.30
42	Corey Dillon	2.00
43	Antowain Smith	1.50
44	*Robert Edwards*	2.00
45	*Jammi German*	2.00
46	*Ahman Green*	6.00
47	*Hines Ward*	5.00
48	*Skip Hicks*	4.00
49	*Brian Griese*	10.00
50	*Charlie Batch*	12.00
51	*Jacquez Green*	6.00
52	*John Avery*	6.00
53	*Kevin Dyson*	6.00
54	*Peyton Manning*	25.00
55	*Randy Moss*	40.00
56	*Ryan Leaf*	12.00
57	*Curtis Enis*	10.00
58	*Charles Woodson*	10.00
59	*Robert Holcombe*	6.00
60	*Fred Taylor*	18.00

1998 E-X2001 Destination Honolulu

Hawaiian culture is celebrated on these wooden inserts, with five different statuesque die-cuts. Singles were inserted 1:720 packs.

		MT
Complete Set (10):		900.00
Common Player:		35.00
Inserted 1:720		
1	Peyton Manning	175.00
2	Terrell Davis	150.00
3	Corey Dillon	70.00
4	Jake Plummer	80.00
5	Eddie George	80.00
6	Emmitt Smith	150.00
7	Brett Favre	200.00
8	Antowain Smith	35.00
9	Barry Sanders	200.00
10	Ryan Leaf	100.00

1998 E-X2001 Helmet Heroes

Each single is die-cut around the helmet at the top of the cards. These team color-coded, thick plastic inserts featured some of the NFL's most dynamic players. They were found 1:24 packs.

		MT
Complete Set (20):		200.00
Common Player:		3.00
Inserted 1:24		
1	Barry Sanders	25.00
2	Emmitt Smith	18.00
3	Brett Favre	25.00
4	Mark Brunell	10.00
5	Jerry Rice	12.00
6	Steve Young	8.00
7	Warrick Dunn	10.00
8	Kordell Stewart	10.00
9	John Elway	12.00
10	Troy Aikman	12.00
11	Dan Marino	18.00
12	Curtis Martin	8.00
13	Dorsey Levens	3.00
14	Jake Plummer	10.00
15	Corey Dillon	7.00
16	Yancey Thigpen	3.00
17	Randy Moss	35.00
18	Curtis Enis	8.00
19	Charles Woodson	10.00
20	Fred Taylor	18.00

1998 E-X2001 Star Date 2001

The idea behind this set was to include the stars of tomorrow on a thick, plastic stock with flecks of foil running through it and highlighted with etched silver foil stamping. Singles were inserted 1:12 packs.

		MT
Complete Set (15):		70.00
Common Player:		1.50
Minor Stars:		3.00
Inserted 1:12		
1	Randy Moss	20.00
2	Fred Taylor	10.00
3	Corey Dillon	6.00
4	Jake Plummer	8.00
5	Antowain Smith	4.00
6	Wilmont Perry	1.50
7	Donald Hayes	1.50
8	Tavian Banks	8.00
9	John Dutton	1.50
10	Kevin Dyson	6.00
11	Germane Crowell	3.00
12	Bobby Hoying	1.50
13	Jerome Pathon	3.00
14	Ryan Leaf	8.00
15	Peyton Manning	15.00

1998 SkyBox

This 250-card included 195 veteran stars, 15 One for the Ages subset cards and 40 rookies seeded one per four packs. Each card featured a borderless design on the front, with the player's name, team, position and SkyBox logo printed in a prismatic gold foil. Backs contain a closeup of the player over a black background. Each card was paralleled in a Star Rubies parallel which was numbered to 50 sets. Insert sets include: Autographics, D'Stroyers, Intimidation Nation, Prime Time Rookies, Rap Show and Soul of the Game.

		MT
Complete Set (250):		250.00
Common Player:		.10
Minor Stars:		.20
Common Rookie (211-250):		1.50
Inserted 1:4		
Wax Box:		80.00
1	John Elway	1.25
2	Drew Bledsoe	1.25
3	Antonio Freeman	.50
4	Merton Hanks	.10
5	James Jett	.10
6	Ricky Proehl	.10
7	Deion Sanders	.50
8	Frank Sanders	.10
9	Bruce Smith	.10
10	Tiki Barber	.20
11	Isaac Bruce	.20
12	Mark Brunell	1.00
13	Quinn Early	.10
14	Terry Glenn	.20
15	Darrien Gordon	.10
16	Keith Byars	.10
17	Terrell Davis	1.25
18	Charlie Garner	.10
19	Eddie Kennison	.20
20	Keenan McCardell	.10
21	Eric Moulds	.10
22	Jimmy Smith	.20
23	Reidel Anthony	.20
24	Rae Carruth	.10
25	Michael Irvin	.50
26	Dorsey Levens	.20
27	Derrick Mayes	.10
28	Adrian Murrell	.20
29	Dwayne Rudd	.10
30	Leslie Shepherd	.10
31	Jamal Anderson	.20
32	Robert Brooks	.10
33	Sean Dawkins	.10
34	Cris Dishman	.10
35	Rickey Dudley	.10
36	Bobby Engram	.10
37	Chester McGlockton	.10
38	Terrell Owens	.20
39	Wayne Chrebet	.10
40	Dexter Coakley	.10
41	Kerry Collins	.20
42	Trent Dilfer	.20
43	Bobby Hoying	.10
44	Glyn Milburn	.10
45	Rob Moore	.10
46	Jake Reed	.10
47	Dana Stubblefield	.10
48	Reggie White	.20
49	Natrone Means	.20
50	Troy Aikman	1.25
51	Aaron Bailey	.10
52	William Floyd	.10
53	Eric Metcalf	.10
54	Warrick Dunn	1.00
55	Chad Lewis	.10
56	Curtis Martin	.75
57	Tony Martin	.10
58	John Randle	.10
59	Jeff Burris	.10
60	Larry Centers	.10
61	Bert Emanuel	.10
62	Sean Gilbert	.10
63	David Palmer	.10
64	Eric Bieniemy	.10
65	Peter Boulware	.10
66	Charles Johnson	.10
67	Jerris McPhail	.10
68	Scott Mitchell	.10
69	Chris Sanders	.10
70	Ken Dilger	.10
71	Brad Johnson	.20
72	Danny Kanell	.10
73	Fred Lane	.20
74	Warren Sapp	.10
75	Carl Pickens	.20
76	Cris Carter	.20
77	Marshall Faulk	.20
78	Keyshawn Johnson	.20
79	Tony McGee	.10
80	Muhsin Muhammad	.10
81	Kordell Stewart	1.00
82	Karl Williams	.10
83	Willie Davis	.10
84	David Dunn	.10
85	Marvin Harrison	.10
86	Michael Jackson	.10
87	John Mobley	.10
88	Shawn Springs	.10
89	Wesley Walls	.10
90	Jermaine Lewis	.10
91	Ed McCaffrey	.10
92	Chris Calloway	.10
93	Lamont Warren	.10
94	Ricky Watters	.20
95	Tony Banks	.20
96	Tony Brackens	.10
97	Gary Brown	.10
98	Howard Griffith	.10
99	Ray Lewis	.10
100	Jeff Blake	.20
101	Charlie Jones	.10
102	Glenn Foley	.20
103	Jay Graham	.10
104	James McKnight	.10
105	Steve McNair	.75
106	Chad Scott	.10
107	Rod Smith	.20
108	Jason Taylor	.10
109	Corey Dillon	1.00
110	Eddie George	1.00
111	Jim Harbaugh	.20
112	Warren Moon	.20
113	Shannon Sharpe	.20
114	Darnell Autry	.10
115	Brett Favre	2.50
116	Jeff George	.20
117	Tony Gonzalez	.10
118	Garrison Hearst	.20
119	Randal Hill	.10
120	Eric Swann	.10
121	Jamie Asher	.10
122	Tim Brown	.20
123	Stephen Davis	.10
124	Chris Chandler	.10
125	Jerry Rice	1.25
126	Troy Davis	.10
127	Ronnie Harmon	.10
128	Andre Rison	.10
129	Duce Staley	.10
130	Charles Way	.10
131	Bryant Westbrook	.10
132	Mike Alstott	.50
133	Gus Frerotte	.10
134	Travis Jervey	.10
135	Daryl Johnston	.10
136	Jake Plummer	1.00
137	Junior Seau	.10
138	Robert Smith	.20
139	Thurman Thomas	.20
140	Karim Abdul-Jabbar	.20
141	Jerome Bettis	.20
142	Byron Hanspard	.10
143	Raymont Harris	.10
144	Willie McGinest	.10
145	Barry Sanders	2.50
146	Irv Smith	.10
147	Michael Strahan	.10
148	Frank Wycheck	.10
149	Steve Broussard	.10
150	Joey Galloway	.50
151	Courtney Hawkins	.10
152	O.J. McDuffie	.10
153	Herman Moore	.20
154	Chris Penn	.10
155	O.J. Santiago	.10
156	Yancey Thigpen	.10
157	Jason Sehorn	.10
158	Ben Coates	.10
159	Ernie Conwell	.10
160	Dale Carter	.10
161	Jeff Graham	.10
162	Rob Johnson	.20
163	Damon Jones	.10
164	Mark Chmura	.20
165	Curtis Conway	.10
166	Elvis Grbac	.10
167	Andre Hastings	.10
168	Terry Kirby	.10
169	Aeneas Williams	.10
170	Derrick Alexander	.10
171	Troy Brown	.10
172	Irving Fryar	.10
173	Jerald Moore	.10
174	Andre Reed	.10
175	James Stewart	.20
176	Chris Warren	.10
177	Will Blackwell	.10
178	Erik Kramer	.10
179	Dan Marino	2.00
180	Terance Mathis	.10
181	Johnnie Morton	.10
182	J.J. Stokes	.20
183	Rodney Thomas	.10
184	Steve Young	.75
185	Kimble Anders	.10
186	Napoleon Kaufman	.50
187	Orlando Pace	.10
188	Antowain Smith	.75
189	Emmitt Smith	2.00
190	Terry Allen	.10
191	Mark Bruener	.10
191	Mark Bruener	.10
192	Rodney Harrison	.10
193	Billy Joe Hobert	.10
194	Leon Johnson	.10
195	Freddie Jones	.10
196	Super Bowl	.10
197	Super Bowl	.10
198	Super Bowl	.10
199	Super Bowl	.10
200	Super Bowl	.10
201	Super Bowl	.10
202	Super Bowl	.10
203	Super Bowl	.10
204	Super Bowl	.10
205	Super Bowl	.10
206	Super Bowl	.10
207	Super Bowl	.10
208	Super Bowl	.10
209	Super Bowl	.10
210	Super Bowl	.10
211	*(Robert Edwards)*	8.00
212	*Roland Williams*	1.50
213	*Joe Jurevicius*	3.00
214	*Wilmont Perry*	1.50
215	*Robert Holcombe*	6.00
216	*Larry Shannon*	1.50
217	*Skip Hicks*	6.00
218	*Patrick Johnson*	1.50
219	*Pat Palmer*	1.50

220	John Dutton	1.50
221	Az-Zahir Hakim	3.00
222	Mikhael Ricks	3.00
223	Rashaan Shehee	3.00
224	Ryan Leaf	15.00
225	Alvis Whitted	1.50
226	Marcus Nash	6.00
227	Fred Taylor	25.00
228	Hines Ward	6.00
229	Chris Fuamatu-Ma'afala	5.00
230	Jerome Pathon	3.00
231	Peyton Manning	45.00
232	Charles Woodson	15.00
233	Jon Ritchie	1.50
234	Scott Frost	1.50
235	John Avery	6.00
236	Jonathon Linton	1.50
237	Jacquez Green	6.00
238	Andre Wadsworth	3.00
239	Cam Quayle	1.50
240	Randy Moss	70.00
241	Raymond Priester	1.50
242	Donald Hayes	1.50
243	Brian Griese	15.00
244	Brian Alford	1.50
245	Kevin Dyson	8.00
246	Jammi German	1.50
247	Cameron Cleeland	4.00
248	Curtis Enis	15.00
249	Terry Hardy	1.50
250	Tony Simmons	4.00

1998 SkyBox Star Rubies

Star Rubies paralleled all 250 cards in SkyBox. The gold foil stamps of the regular cards were replaced by red foil and backs were numbered to 50.

	MT
Star Ruby Cards:	75x-150x
Star Ruby Rookies:	4x-8x

1998 SkyBox Autographics

A total of 73 different NFL players signed cards for Autographics in 1998. The program ran through Thunder, Metal Universe, SkyBox and E-X2001 products. Regular versions are signed in black ink, while Blue versions are individually numbered to 50. Cards were inserted 1:112 in Thunder, 1:68 in Metal Universe and Premium and 1:48 packs of E-X2001.

	MT
Common Player:	10.00
Minor Stars:	20.00
Inserted 1:48 E-X2001	
Inserted 1:68 Metal Universe	
Inserted 1:68 SkyBox Premium	
Inserted 1:112 Thunder	
Blue Signatures:	2x-4x
Production 50 Sets	
Kevin Abrams	10.00
Mike Alstott	35.00
Jamie Asher	10.00
Jon Avery	40.00
Tavian Banks	45.00
Pat Barnes	10.00
Jerome Bettis	30.00
Eric Bjornson	10.00
Peter Boulware	10.00
Troy Brown	10.00
Mark Breunner	10.00
Mark Brunell	85.00
Rae Carruth	10.00
Ray Crockett	10.00
Germane Crowell	10.00
Stephen Davis	20.00
Troy Davis	10.00
Sean Dawkins	10.00
Trent Dilfer	30.00
Corey Dillon	60.00
Jim Druckenmiller	30.00
Kevin Dyson	35.00
Marc Edwards	10.00

	Robert Edwards	60.00
	Bobby Engram	10.00
	Curtis Enis	70.00
	William Floyd	20.00
	Glenn Foley	20.00
	Chris Fuamatu-Ma'afal	30.00
	Joey Galloway	35.00
	Jeff George	30.00
	Ahman Green	40.00
	Jacquez Green	50.00
	Yatil Green	20.00
	Byron Hanspard	25.00
	Marvin Harrison	30.00
	Skip Hicks	35.00
	Robert Holcombe	40.00
	Bobby Hoying	25.00
	Travis Jervey	20.00
	Rob Johnson	30.00
	Freddie Jones	10.00
	Eddie Kennison	20.00
	Fred Lane	20.00
	Ryan Leaf	100.00
	Dorsey Levens	30.00
	Jeff Lewis	20.00
	Jermaine Lewis	20.00
	Dan Marino	225.00
	Curtis Martin	60.00
	Steve Matthews	10.00
	Alonzo Mayes	20.00
	Keenan McCardell	20.00
	Willie McGinnest	10.00
	James McKnight	20.00
	Glyn Milburn	10.00
	Warren Moon	35.00
	Randy Moss	250.00
	Marcus Nash	35.00
	Terrell Owens	40.00
	Jason Peter	20.00
	Jake Plummer	100.00
	John Randle	20.00
	Shannon Sharpe	40.00
	Jimmy Smith	20.00
	Lamar Smith	10.00
	Robert Smith	35.00
	Duce Staley	20.00
	Kordell Stewart	100.00
	Fred Taylor	125.00
	Rodney Thomas	10.00
	Kevin Turner	10.00
	Hines Ward	40.00
	Charles Way	10.00
	Frank Wycheck	10.00

1998 SkyBox D'stroyers

D'Stroyers was a 15-card insert that highlighted top young players in the league. The players were featured over a prismatic foil background and inserted one per six packs.

	MT
Complete Set (15):	35.00
Common Player:	.75
Minor Stars:	1.50
Inserted 1:6	
1 Antowain Smith	3.00
2 Corey Dillon	4.00
3 Charles Woodson	4.00
4 Randy Moss	12.00
5 Deion Sanders	1.50
6 Robert Edwards	5.00
7 Herman Moore	1.50
8 Mark Brunell	6.00
9 Dorsey Levens	.75
10 Curtis Enis	4.00
11 Drew Bledsoe	6.00
12 Steve McNair	3.00
13 Keyshawn Johnson	.75
14 Bobby Hoying	.75
15 Trent Dilfer	1.50

Post-1980 cards in Near Mint condition will generally sell for about 75% of the quoted Mint value. Excellent-condition cards bring no more than 40%.

1998 SkyBox Intimidation Nation

Intimidation Nation captured 15 of the top players in the league over a flaming background. This insert was the toughest to find in SkyBox and inserted one per 360 packs.

	MT
Complete Set (15):	750.00
Common Player:	20.00
Inserted 1:360	
1 Terrell Davis	75.00
2 Emmitt Smith	100.00
3 Barry Sanders	120.00
4 Brett Favre	120.00
5 Eddie George	45.00
6 Jerry Rice	60.00
7 John Elway	60.00
8 Mark Brunell	50.00
9 Troy Aikman	60.00
10 Peyton Manning	100.00
11 Ryan Leaf	50.00
12 Curtis Martin	20.00
13 Dan Marino	100.00
14 Warrick Dunn	45.00
15 Jake Plummer	45.00

1998 SkyBox Prime Time Rookies

Ten rookies were featured on this horizontal, multi-colored background insert set. The cards featured the rookie on the left side with a bullseye over the background. Prime Time Rookies were seeded one per 96 packs.

	MT
Complete Set (10):	200.00
Common Player:	6.00
Inserted 1:96	
1 Curtis Enis	15.00
2 Robert Edwards	15.00
3 Fred Taylor	25.00
4 Robert Holcombe	12.00
5 Ryan Leaf	20.00
6 Peyton Manning	40.00
7 Randy Moss	60.00
8 Charles Woodson	20.00
9 Andre Wadsworth	6.00
10 Kevin Dyson	6.00

1998 SkyBox Rap Show

This 15-card insert featured an action shot of the player with

a silver foil-stamped quote from one of his peers on the front. Rap Show inserts were seeded per 36 packs.

	MT
Complete Set (15):	150.00
Common Player:	5.00
Minor Stars:	8.00
Inserted 1:36	
1 John Elway	20.00
2 Drew Bledsoe	20.00
3 Corey Dillon	12.00
4 Brett Favre	40.00
5 Barry Sanders	40.00
6 Eddie George	15.00
7 Emmitt Smith	30.00
8 Jake Plummer	15.00
9 Joey Galloway	8.00
10 Ricky Watters	5.00
11 Mike Alstott	8.00
12 Kordell Stewart	15.00
13 Antonio Freeman	8.00
14 Terrell Davis	20.00
15 Warrick Dunn	15.00

1998 SkyBox Soul of the Game

Soul of the Game were horizontal inserts that resembled a record sleeve with the album half out. The cards were one solid piece of plastic and inserted one per 18 packs.

	MT
Complete Set (15):	80.00
Common Player:	3.00
Minor Stars:	5.00
Inserted 1:18	
1 Troy Aikman	15.00
2 Dorsey Levens	3.00
3 Deion Sanders	7.00
4 Antonio Freeman	5.00
5 Dan Marino	20.00
6 Keyshawn Johnson	3.00
7 Terry Glenn	5.00
8 Tim Brown	3.00
9 Curtis Martin	10.00
10 Bobby Hoying	3.00
11 Kordell Stewart	12.00
12 Jerry Rice	15.00
13 Steve McNair	10.00
14 Joey Galloway	5.00
15 Steve Young	10.00

1998 SkyBox Double Vision

Each single in this 32-card set measures 5-1/2" x 7" and has an interactive team color-coded slide on the front. So when you pull the tab the player goes from black and white to color. Along with another color picture of that player with his name, team and position.

	MT
Complete Set (32):	130.00
Common Player:	4.00
Production 5,000 Sets	
1 Dan Marino	12.00
2 John Elway	8.00
3 Troy Aikman	8.00
4 Steve Young	6.00
5 Terrell Davis	12.00
6 Barry Sanders	16.00
7 Jerry Rice	8.00
8 Kordell Stewart	6.00
9 Jake Plummer	6.00
10 Brett Favre	16.00
11 Drew Bledsoe	6.00
12 Tony Banks	4.00
13 Kerry Collins	4.00
14 Steve McNair	6.00
15 Warren Moon	4.00
16 Ryan Leaf	10.00
17 Peyton Manning	16.00
18 Elvis Grbac	4.00
19 Jeff Blake	4.00
20 Brad Johnson	4.00

21	Trent Dilfer	4.00
22	Scott Mitchell	4.00
23	Dan Marino	12.00
24	John Elway	8.00
25	Troy Aikman	8.00
26	Steve Young	6.00
27	Terrell Davis	12.00
28	Barry Sanders	16.00
29	Jerry Rice	8.00
30	Kordell Stewart	6.00
31	Jake Plummer	6.00
32	Brett Favre	16.00

1998 SkyBox Thunder

This 250-card set replaced Thunder in 1998 and arrived with 225 veterans and 25 rookies. Thunder was tiered, with 1-100 seeded 4:1 packs, 101-200 seeded 3:1 and 201-250 seeded 1:1. Cards featured a borderless artsy design with the color image of the player over it. The player's last name was foil stamped in large letters down either side. Each card was reprinted in both Rave and Super Rave parallel sets. Thunder also included five insert sets: Boss, Destination: End Zone, Number Crushers, Quick Strike, Autographics and StarBurst.

	MT
Complete Set (250):	50.00
Common Player (1-200):	.10
Minor Stars (1-200):	.20
Common Player (201-250):	.20
Minor Stars (201-250):	.40
Wax Box:	48.00
1 Reggie White	.20
2 Elvis Grbac	.10
3 Ed McCaffrey	.10
4 O.J. McDuffie	.10
5 Scott Mitchell	.10
6 Byron Hanspard	.20
7 John Randle	.10
8 Shawn Jefferson	.10
9 Peter Boulware	.10
10 Karl Williams	.10
11 Napoleon Kaufman	.50
12 Barry Minter	.10
13 Cris Dingman	.10
14 James Stewart	.10
15 Marcus Robertson	.10
16 Rodney Harrison	.10
17 Micheal Barrow	.10
18 Michael Sinclair	.10
19 DeWayne Washington	.10
20 Phillippi Sparks	.10
21 Ernie Conwell	.10
22 Ken Dilger	.10
23 Johnnie Morton	.10
24 Eric Swann	.10
25 Curtis Conway	.20
26 Duce Staley	.10
27 Darrell Green	.10
28 Quinn Early	.10
29 LeRoy Butler	.10
30 Winfred Tubbs	.10
31 Darren Woodson	.10
32 Marcus Allen	.20
33 Glenn Foley	.10
34 Tom Knight	.10
35 Sam Shade	.10
36 James McKnight	.10
37 Leeland McElroy	.10
38 Earl Holmes	.10
39 Ryan McNeil	.10
40 Cris Carter	.20
41 Jessie Armstead	.10
42 Bryce Paup	.10
43 Chris Slade	.10
44 Eric Metcalf	.10
45 Jim Harbaugh	.10
46 Terry Kirby	.10
47 Donnie Edwards	.10
48 Darryl Williams	.10
49 Neil Smith	.10
50 Warren Sapp	.10
51 Jason Taylor	.10
52 Irving Fryar	.10
53 Jeff George	.20

54	Yancey Thigpen	.10
55	Ricky Proehl	.10
56	Kevin Greene	.10
57	Joel Steed	.10
58	Larry Allen	.10
59	Thurman Thomas	.20
60	Aaron Glenn	.10
61	Natrone Means	.20
62	Chris Calloway	.10
63	Chuck Smith	.10
64	Chidi Ahanotu	.10
65	Mario Bates	.10
66	Jonathan Ogden	.10
67	Drew Bledsoe	1.00
68	John Mobley	.10
69	Antowain Smith	.60
70	Aeneas Williams	.10
71	Brian Williams	.10
72	Derrick Thomas	.10
73	Ted Johnson	.10
74	Troy Drayton	.10
75	Mike Pritchard	.10
76	Darnay Scott	.10
77	James Jett	.10
78	Dwayne Rudd	.10
79	Marvin Harrison	.20
80	Dermontti Dawson	.10
81	Keith Lyle	.10
82	Steve Atwater	.10
83	Tyrone Wheatley	.10
84	Tony Brackens	.10
85	Dale Carter	.10
86	Robert Porcher	.10
87	Merton Hanks	.10
88	Leon Johnson	.10
89	Simeon Rice	.10
90	Robert Brooks	.10
91	William Thomas	.10
92	Wesley Walls	.10
93	Chester McGlockton	.10
94	Chris Chandler	.10
95	Michael Strahan	.10
96	Ray Zellars	.10
97	Dexter Coakley	.10
98	Rob Johnson	.20
99	Eric Green	.10
100	Darrien Gordon	.10
101	Gary Brown	.10
102	Reidel Anthony	.20
103	Keenan McCardell	.10
104	Leslie O'Neal	.10
105	Bryant Westbrook	.10
106	Derrick Alexander	.10
107	Jeff Blake	.20
108	Ben Coates	.10
109	Shawn Springs	.10
110	Robert Smith	.20
111	Karim Abdul-Jabbar	.20
112	Willie Davis	.10
113	Mark Chmura	.20
114	Terry Allen	.10
115	Will Blackwell	.10
116	Jamal Anderson	.40
117	Dana Stubblefield	.10
118	Trent Dilfer	.20
119	Jermaine Lewis	.10
120	Chad Brown	.10
121	Tamarick Vanover	.10
122	Tony Martin	.10
123	Larry Centers	.10
124	J.J. Stokes	.10
125	Danny Kanell	.10
126	Wayne Chrebet	.20
127	Kerry Collins	.20
128	Tony Banks	.30
129	Randal Hill	.10
130	Jimmy Smith	.10
131	Tim Brown	.20
132	Zach Thomas	.10
133	Rod Smith	.20
134	Frank Wycheck	.10
135	Garrison Hearst	.20
136	Bruce Smith	.10
137	Hardy Nickerson	.10
138	Sean Dawkins	.10
139	Willie McGinest	.10
140	Kimble Anders	.10
141	Michael Westbrook	.10
142	Chris Doleman	.10
143	Ricky Watters	.20
144	Levon Kirkland	.10
145	Rob Moore	.20
146	Eddie Kennison	.20
147	Rickey Dudley	.10
148	Jay Graham	.10
149	Brad Johnson	.30
150	Bobby Hoying	.10
151	Sherman Williams	.10
152	Charles Way	.10
153	Adrian Murrell	.20
154	Chris Sanders	.10
155	Greg Hill	.10
156	Rae Carruth	.20
157	Mike Alstott	.50
158	Terance Mathis	.10
159	Antonio Freeman	.30
160	Junior Seau	.20
161	Chris Warren	.20
162	Shannon Sharpe	.20
163	Derrick Rodgers	.10
164	Charles Johnson	.10
165	Marshall Faulk	.20
166	Jamie Asher	.10
167	Michael Jackson	.10
168	Terrell Owens	.30
169	Jason Sehorn	.10
170	Raymont Harris	.10
171	Jake Reed	.10

172	Kevin Hardy	.10
173	Jerald Moore	.10
174	Michael Irvin	.20
175	Freddie Jones	.10
176	Steve McNair	.50
177	Carnell Lake	.10
178	Troy Brown	.10
179	Hugh Douglas	.10
180	Andre Rison	.20
181	Leslie Shepherd	.10
182	Andre Hastings	.10
183	Fred Lane	.20
184	Andre Reed	.10
185	Darrell Russell	.10
186	Frank Sanders	.10
187	Derrick Brooks	.10
188	Charlie Garner	.10
189	Bert Emanuel	.10
190	Terrell Buckley	.10
191	Carl Pickens	.10
192	Tiki Barber	.30
193	Pete Mitchell	.10
194	Gilbert Brown	.10
195	Isaac Bruce	.30
196	Ray Lewis	.10
197	Warren Moon	.20
198	Tony Gonzalez	.20
199	John Mobley	.10
200	Gus Frerotte	.10
201	Brett Favre	4.00
202	Terrell Davis	2.50
203	Dan Marino	3.50
204	Barry Sanders	4.00
205	Steve Young	1.00
206	Deion Sanders	1.00
207	Kordell Stewart	2.00
208	Eddie George	2.50
209	Jake Plummer	2.00
210	Warrick Dunn	2.00
211	John Elway	2.00
212	Terry Glenn	.40
213	Mark Brunell	2.00
214	Corey Dillon	1.50
215	Joey Galloway	.40
216	Dorsey Levens	.40
217	Troy Aikman	2.00
218	Keyshawn Johnson	.40
219	Jerome Bettis	.40
220	Curtis Martin	1.25
221	Herman Moore	.40
222	Emmitt Smith	3.50
223	Jerry Rice	2.00
224	Drew Bledsoe	2.00
225	Antowain Smith	1.25
226	*Stephen Alexander*	1.50
227	*John Avery*	1.50
228	*Kevin Dyson*	1.50
229	*Robert Edwards*	3.00
230	*Greg Ellis*	.20
231	*Curtis Enis*	4.00
232	*Chris Fuamatu-Ma'afal*	1.00
233	*Ahman Green*	2.00
234	*Jacquez Green*	2.00
235	*Az-Zahir Hakim*	.20
236	*Skip Hicks*	2.00
237	*Joe Jurevicius*	.50
238	*Ryan Leaf*	7.00
239	*Peyton Manning*	10.00
240	*Alonzo Mayes*	.50
241	*R.W. McQuarters*	.20
242	*Randy Moss*	20.00
243	*Marcus Nash*	2.00
244	*Jerome Pathon*	.20
245	*Jason Peter*	1.00
246	*Brian Simmons*	.50
247	*Takeo Spikes*	1.00
248	*Fred Taylor*	4.00
249	*Andre Wadsworth*	1.00
250	*Charles Woodson*	4.00

1998 SkyBox Thunder Rave

Rave was a 250-card parallel set to Thunder, and featured prismatic silver foil on the front to distinguish them from the base cards. Rave parallels were sequentially numbered to 150 on the back in silver foil and were found only in hobby packs.

	MT
Rave Cards (1-200):	40x-80x
Rave Stars (201-250):	20x-40x
Rave Rookies (201-250):	10x-20x

1998 SkyBox Thunder Super Rave

Super Rave was a 250-card parallel set that was found only in hobby packs. Cards were sequentially numbered to 25 sets.

	MT
Super Rave Cards (1-200):	125x-250x
Super Rave Stars (201-250):	100x-200x
Super Rave Rookies (201-250):	20x-40x

1998 SkyBox Thunder Boss

This insert featured 20 players on an embossed design. Backgrounds on the front were done in team colors with several quadrilaterals added. Boss cards were inserted one per eight packs and numbered with a "B" suffix.

		MT
Complete Set (20):		35.00
Common Player:		.75
Minor Stars:		1.50
1	Troy Aikman	6.00
2	Drew Bledsoe	6.00
3	Tim Brown	.75
4	Antonio Freeman	1.50
5	Joey Galloway	1.50
6	Terry Glenn	1.50
7	Bobby Hoying	.75
8	Michael Irvin	1.50
9	Keyshawn Johnson	.75
10	Dorsey Levens	1.50
11	Curtis Martin	5.00
12	John Mobley	.75
13	Jake Plummer	6.00
14	John Randle	.75
15	Deion Sanders	3.00
16	Junior Seau	.75
17	Shannon Sharpe	.75
18	Bruce Smith	.75
19	Robert Smith	.75
20	Dana Stubblefield	.75

1998 SkyBox Thunder Destination End Zone

This 15-card insert captured top scorers in the league on a green background. A small image of the player is placed in a bottom corner with his name in silver letters, and the insert name in red foil. These were inserted one per 96 packs and numbered with a "DE" suffix.

		MT
Complete Set (15):		200.00
Common Player:		5.00
1	Jerome Bettis	5.00
2	Mark Brunell	20.00
3	Terrell Davis	25.00
4	Corey Dillon	15.00
5	Warrick Dunn	20.00
6	John Elway	20.00
7	Brett Favre	50.00
8	Eddie George	20.00
9	Dorsey Levens	5.00
10	Curtis Martin	15.00
11	Herman Moore	5.00
12	Barry Sanders	50.00
13	Emmitt Smith	40.00
14	Kordell Stewart	25.00
15	Steve Young	15.00

1998 SkyBox Thunder Number Crushers

Number Crushers was a 10-card insert that featured the player on the front over a grid-like background. Backs were numbered with a "NC" suffix and included a Q&A section with a pull-out card that contained the answers. These were inserted one per 16 packs.

		MT
Complete Set (10):		45.00
Common Player:		2.00
Minor Stars:		4.00
1	Troy Aikman	6.00
2	Jerome Bettis	4.00
3	Tim Brown	2.00
4	Mark Brunell	6.00
5	Dan Marino	12.00
6	Herman Moore	4.00
7	Rob Moore	2.00
8	Jerry Rice	6.00
9	Shannon Sharpe	2.00
10	Emmitt Smith	12.00

1998 SkyBox Thunder Quick Strike

This 12-card, matchbook-like insert featured players on an olive background, with a black strip across the bottom resembling a match strike area. The card opened up to reveal another card of the player, while the back of the matchbook contained only the insert logo. Cards were inserted one per 300 packs and numbered with a "QS" suffix.

		MT
Complete Set (12):		550.00
Common Player:		25.00
1	Terrell Davis	50.00
2	John Elway	50.00
3	Brett Favre	80.00
4	Joey Galloway	25.00
5	Eddie George	50.00
6	Keyshawn Johnson	25.00
7	Dan Marino	70.00
8	Jerry Rice	50.00
9	Barry Sanders	80.00
10	Deion Sanders	30.00
11	Kordell Stewart	50.00
12	Steve Young	40.00

1998 SkyBox Thunder Star Burst

StarBurst was a 10-card insert featuring the player over a gold holofoil background that "bursts" against a regular background tinted in team colors. These were inserted one per 32 packs and numbered with a "SB" suffix.

		MT
Complete Set (10):		100.00
Common Player:		3.00
1	Tiki Barber	3.00
2	Corey Dillon	8.00
3	Warrick Dunn	10.00
4	Curtis Enis	8.00
5	Ryan Leaf	12.00
6	Peyton Manning	20.00
7	Randy Moss	30.00
8	Jake Plummer	10.00
9	Antowain Smith	6.00
10	Charles Woodson	8.00

1999 E-X Century

This was a 90-card set that included 30 rookie cards found 1:4 packs. Each base card was printed on clear plastic stock with holographic foil stamping. Parallel sets included Essential Credentials Future and Essential Credentials Now. Other inserts included: Authen-Kicks, Autographics, Bright Lites and E-Xtraordinary. SRP was $5.99 for three-card packs.

		MT
Complete Set (90):		175.00
Common Player:		.25
Minor Stars:		.50
Common Rookie:		1.50
Inserted 1:4		
Wax Box:		85.00
1	Keyshawn Johnson	1.00
2	Natrone Means	.50
3	Antonio Freeman	1.00
4	Muhsin Muhammad	.50
5	Curtis Martin	1.00
6	Chris Chandler	.50
7	Priest Holmes	1.00
8	Vinny Testaverde	.50
9	Tim Brown	.50
10	Eddie George	1.25
11	Brad Johnson	1.00
12	Mike Alstott	1.00
13	Dorsey Levens	1.00
14	Jamal Anderson	1.00
15	Herman Moore	1.00
16	Brett Favre	4.00
17	John Elway	3.00
18	Steve Young	1.50
19	Warrick Dunn	1.00
20	Fred Taylor	2.00
21	Charlie Batch	1.75
22	Jimmy Smith	1.00
23	Steve McNair	1.25
24	Jerry Rice	2.00
25	Dan Marino	3.00
26	Jake Plummer	2.00
27	Marshall Faulk	1.00
28	Garrison Hearst	.50

1999 E-X Century Essential Credentials Future

This was a 90-card parallel set that was sequentially numbered opposite of the player's card number.

		MT
Common Player:		7.50
Minor Stars:		15.00
1	Keyshawn Johnson 90	15.00
2	Natrone Means 89	7.50
3	Antonio Freeman 88	15.00
4	Muhsin Muhammad 87	7.50
5	Curtis Martin 86	15.00
6	Chris Chandler 85	7.50
7	Priest Holmes 84	15.00
8	Vinny Testaverde 83	7.50
9	Tim Brown 82	7.50
10	Eddie George 81	20.00
11	Brad Johnson 80	15.00
12	Mike Alstott 79	15.00
13	Dorsey Levens 78	15.00
14	Jamal Anderson 77	15.00
15	Herman Moore 76	15.00
16	Brett Favre 75	125.00
17	John Elway 74	100.00
18	Steve Young 73	30.00
19	Warrick Dunn 72	20.00
20	Fred Taylor 71	60.00
21	Charlie Batch 70	50.00
22	Jimmy Smith 69	15.00
23	Steve McNair 68	25.00
24	Jerry Rice 67	50.00
25	Dan Marino 66	125.00
26	Jake Plummer 65	75.00
27	Marshall Faulk 64	25.00
28	Garrison Hearst 63	15.00
29	Terrell Davis 62	100.00
30	Barry Sanders 61	150.00
31	Carl Pickens 60	7.50
32	Jerome Bettis 59	25.00
33	Scott Mitchell 58	7.50
34	Duce Staley 57	15.00
35	Robert Smith 56	15.00
36	Wayne Chrebet 55	20.00
37	Steve Beuerlein 54	15.00

1999 E-X Century Essential Credentials Now

This was a 90-card parallel set that was sequentially numbered to the player's card number.

		MT
Common Player:		7.50
Minor Stars:		15.00
1	Keyshawn Johnson 1	7.50
2	Natrone Means 2	7.50
3	Antonio Freeman 3	7.50
4	Muhsin Muhammad 4	7.50
5	Curtis Martin 5	7.50
6	Chris Chandler 6	7.50
7	Priest Holmes 7	7.50
8	Vinny Testaverde 8	7.50
9	Tim Brown 9	7.50
10	Eddie George 10	125.00
11	Brad Johnson 11	100.00
12	Mike Alstott 12	100.00
13	Dorsey Levens 13	85.00
14	Jamal Anderson 14	85.00
15	Herman Moore 15	85.00
16	Brett Favre 16	400.00
17	John Elway 17	350.00
18	Steve Young 18	175.00
19	Warrick Dunn 19	85.00
20	Fred Taylor 20	160.00
21	Charlie Batch 21	125.00
22	Jimmy Smith 22	50.00
23	Steve McNair 23	75.00
24	Jerry Rice 24	160.00
25	Dan Marino 25	250.00
26	Jake Plummer 26	130.00
27	Marshall Faulk 27	60.00
28	Garrison Hearst 28	40.00
29	Terrell Davis 29	175.00
30	Barry Sanders 30	275.00
31	Carl Pickens 31	30.00
32	Jerome Bettis 32	60.00
33	Scott Mitchell 33	25.00
34	Duce Staley 34	50.00
35	Robert Smith 35	35.00
36	Wayne Chrebet 36	45.00
37	Steve Beuerlein 37	20.00
38	Elvis Grbac 38	20.00
39	Troy Aikman 39	125.00
40	Emmitt Smith 40	140.00
41	Joey Galloway 41	45.00
42	Ryan Leaf 42	30.00
43	Skip Hicks 43	30.00
44	Cris Carter 44	45.00

(1999 E-X Century)

38	Elvis Grbac 53	15.00
39	Troy Aikman 52	110.00
40	Emmitt Smith 51	110.00
41	Joey Galloway 50	35.00
42	Ryan Leaf 49	30.00
43	Skip Hicks 48	25.00
44	Cris Carter 47	45.00
45	Shannon Sharpe 46	25.00
46	Mark Brunell 45	85.00
47	Kerry Collins 44	20.00
48	Corey Dillon 43	45.00
49	Kordell Stewart 42	60.00
50	Randy Moss 41	225.00
51	Jon Kitna 40	60.00
52	Deion Sanders 39	60.00
53	Rod Smith 38	25.00
54	Drew Bledsoe 37	110.00
55	Terrell Owens 36	60.00
56	Napoleon Kaufman 35	50.00
57	Trent Green 34	30.00
58	Ricky Watters 33	30.00
59	Randall Cunningham 32	50.00
60	Peyton Manning 31	160.00
61	Tim Couch 30	300.00
62	Amos Zereoue 29	75.00
63	Cade McNown 28	150.00
64	Donovan McNabb 27	150.00
65	Ricky Williams 26	300.00
66	Daunte Culpepper 25	150.00
67	Troy Edwards 24	100.00
68	Peerless Price 23	85.00
69	Edgerrin James 22	350.00
70	Champ Bailey 21	60.00
71	Akili Smith 20	125.00
72	Kevin Johnson 19	85.00
73	Cecil Collins 18	200.00
74	David Boston 17	125.00
75	Torry Holt 16	125.00
76	J.J. Johnson 15	100.00
77	Na Brown 14	75.00
78	Rob Konrad 13	75.00
79	Michael Cloud 12	80.00
80	Craig Yeast 11	80.00
81	Brock Huard 10	125.00
82	Chris McAlister 9	7.50
83	Shaun King 8	7.50
84	Dee Miller 7	7.50
85	Joe Germaine 6	7.50
86	D'Wayne Bates 5	7.50
87	Kevin Faulk 4	7.50
88	Antoine Winfield 3	7.50
89	Reggie Kelly 2	7.50
90	Antwan Edwards 1	7.50

(1998 SkyBox Thunder Rave — Rave Cards list continued)

5	Warrick Dunn	20.00
6	John Elway	20.00
7	Brett Favre	50.00
8	Eddie George	20.00
9	Dorsey Levens	5.00
10	Curtis Martin	15.00
11	Herman Moore	5.00
12	Barry Sanders	50.00
13	Emmitt Smith	40.00
14	Kordell Stewart	25.00
15	Steve Young	15.00

(1998 SkyBox Thunder Star Burst checklist — bottom of column 4)

29	Terrell Davis	3.00
30	Barry Sanders	4.00
31	Carl Pickens	.50
32	Jerome Bettis	1.00
33	Scott Mitchell	.25
34	Duce Staley	.75
35	Robert Smith	1.00
36	Wayne Chrebet	1.00
37	Steve Beuerlein	.50
38	Elvis Grbac	.50
39	Troy Aikman	2.00
40	Emmitt Smith	3.00
41	Joey Galloway	1.00
42	Ryan Leaf	1.00
43	Skip Hicks	.50
44	Cris Carter	1.00
45	Shannon Sharpe	.50
46	Mark Brunell	1.50
47	Kerry Collins	.50
48	Corey Dillon	1.00
49	Kordell Stewart	1.25
50	Randy Moss	4.00
51	Jon Kitna	1.25
52	Deion Sanders	1.00
53	Rod Smith	.50
54	Drew Bledsoe	1.50
55	Terrell Owens	1.00
56	Napoleon Kaufman	1.00
57	Trent Green	1.00
58	Ricky Watters	1.00
59	Randall Cunningham	1.00
60	Peyton Manning	3.00
61	Tim Couch	20.00
62	Amos Zereoue	5.00
63	Cade McNown	10.00
64	Donovan McNabb	10.00
65	Ricky Williams	20.00
66	Daunte Culpepper	10.00
67	Troy Edwards	7.00
68	Peerless Price	5.00
69	Edgerrin James	25.00
70	Champ Bailey	4.00
71	Akili Smith	10.00
72	Kevin Johnson	7.00
73	Cecil Collins	10.00
74	David Boston	7.00
75	Torry Holt	7.00
76	J.J. Johnson	6.00
77	Na Brown	1.50
78	Rob Konrad	3.00
79	Michael Cloud	3.00
80	Craig Yeast	1.50
81	Brock Huard	4.00
82	Chris McAlister	3.00
83	Shaun King	8.00
84	Dee Miller	1.50
85	Joe Germaine	4.00
86	D'Wayne Bates	3.00
87	Kevin Faulk	5.00
88	Antoine Winfield	3.00
89	Reggie Kelly	1.50
90	Antwan Edwards	1.50

45	Shannon Sharpe 45	25.00
46	Mark Brunell 46	80.00
47	Kerry Collins 47	20.00
48	Corey Dillon 48	45.00
49	Kordell Stewart 49	45.00
50	Randy Moss 50	175.00
51	Jon Kitna 51	35.00
52	Deion Sanders 52	35.00
53	Rod Smith 53	15.00
54	Drew Bledsoe 54	60.00
55	Terrell Owens 55	35.00
56	Napoleon Kaufman 56	25.00
57	Trent Green 57	20.00
58	Ricky Watters 58	15.00
59	Randall Cunningham 59	25.00
60	Peyton Manning 60	120.00
61	Tim Couch 61	200.00
62	Amos Zereoue 62	50.00
63	Cade McNown 63	100.00
64	Donovan McNabb 64	100.00
65	Ricky Williams 65	200.00
66	Daunte Culpepper 66	100.00
67	Troy Edwards 67	60.00
68	Peerless Price 68	50.00
69	Edgerrin James 69	200.00
70	Champ Bailey 70	40.00
71	Akili Smith 71	85.00
72	Kevin Johnson 72	50.00
73	Cecil Collins 73	75.00
74	David Boston 74	50.00
75	Torry Holt 75	50.00
76	J.J. Johnson 76	35.00
77	Na Brown 77	15.00
78	Rob Konrad 78	20.00
79	Michael Cloud 79	20.00
80	Craig Yeast 80	15.00
81	Brock Huard 81	35.00
82	Chris McAlister 82	15.00
83	Shaun King 83	35.00
84	Dee Miller 84	7.50
85	Joe Germaine 85	25.00
86	D'Wayne Bates 86	20.00
87	Kevin Faulk 87	35.00
88	Antoine Winfield 88	15.00
89	Reggie Kelly 89	7.50
90	Antwan Edwards 90	7.50

1999 E-X Century Authen-Kicks

This 12-card insert included swatches of game-worn shoes. Each player hand-numbered their cards with each to a different amount. Singles were randomly inserted.

		MT
Complete Set (12):		1000.
Common Player:		50.00
1	Travis McGriff 235	50.00
2	Trent Green 190	50.00
3	Brock Huard 280	50.00
4	Randall Cunningham 290	60.00
5	Donovan McNabb 210	125.00
6	Torry Holt 285	85.00
7	Joe Germaine 280	50.00
8	Cade McNown 260	125.00
9	Doug Flutie 215	85.00
10	O.J. McDuffie 285	50.00
11	Ricky Williams 215	225.00
12	Dan Marino 285	175.00

1999 E-X Century Bright Lites

This was a 20-card insert that included the game's best and pictured them on a green plastic stock with a glowing star background. Singles were found 1:24 packs. A parallel Orange version was also issued.

		MT
Complete Set (20):		160.00
Common Player:		3.00
Inserted 1:24		
1	Randy Moss	15.00
2	Tim Couch	20.00
3	Eddie George	6.00
4	Brett Favre	15.00
5	Steve Young	7.00
6	Barry Sanders	15.00
7	Troy Aikman	10.00
8	Jake Plummer	5.00
9	Edgerrin James	20.00
10	Terrell Davis	12.00
11	Warrick Dunn	3.00
12	Jerry Rice	10.00
13	Fred Taylor	10.00
14	Mark Brunell	7.00
15	Emmitt Smith	12.00
16	Ricky Williams	20.00
17	Charlie Batch	6.00
18	Jamal Anderson	3.00
19	Peyton Manning	12.00
20	Dan Marino	12.00

1999 E-X Century E-Xtraordinary

This 15-card insert included the top young players in the game and pictured them on lenticular stock with a team color coded background. Singles were inserted 1:9 packs.

		MT
Complete Set (15):		75.00
Common Player:		2.00
Inserted 1:9		
1	Ricky Williams	12.00
2	Corey Dillon	2.00
3	Charlie Batch	4.00
4	Terrell Davis	8.00
5	Edgerrin James	12.00
6	Jake Plummer	6.00
7	Tim Couch	12.00
8	Warrick Dunn	2.00
9	Akili Smith	6.00
10	Randy Moss	12.00
11	Cade McNown	6.00
12	Fred Taylor	5.00
13	Donovan McNabb	6.00
14	Torry Holt	4.00
15	Peyton Manning	8.00

1999 SkyBox Dominion

This was a 250-card set that included 50 unseeded rookie cards. Each base card included game-action photography with the player's name and team in silver foil. Insert sets included: Atlantattitude, Generation Next, Goal 2 Go, Hats Off and Hats Off Autographs. SRP was $1.89 for nine-card packs.

		MT
Complete Set (250):		45.00
Common Player:		.15
Minor Stars:		.30
Common Rookie:		.50
Wax Box:		65.00
1	Randy Moss	2.00
2	James Jett	.15
3	Lawyer Milloy	.15
4	Mike Alstott	.50
5	Courtney Hawkins	.15
6	Carl Pickens	.30
7	Marvin Harrison	.50
8	Robert Smith	.50
9	Fred Taylor	1.00
10	Barry Sanders	2.00
11	Tony Gonzalez	.15
12	Leroy Hoard	.15
13	Drew Bledsoe	.75
14	Cam Cleeland	.30
15	Steve Atwater	.15
16	Eric Moulds	.50
17	Herman Moore	.50
18	Rickey Dudley	.15
19	Jeff Blake	.30
20	Eddie George	.50
21	Antonio Freeman	.50
22	Stephen Alexander	.15
23	Larry Centers	.15
24	Chris Chandler	.30
25	James Stewart	.30
26	Randall Cunningham	.50
27	Mark Brunell	.75
28	David Palmer	.15
29	Eric Green	.15
30	Terry Glenn	.50
31	Jerry Rice	1.00
32	Ricky Proehl	.15
33	Tony Banks	.30
34	John Elway	1.50
35	Johnnie Morton	.15
36	Tony Simmons	.30
37	Jon Kitna	.50
38	Trent Green	.30
39	Peyton Manning	1.50
40	Emmitt Smith	1.50
41	Warrick Dunn	.50
42	Jerome Bettis	.50
43	Ricky Watters	.30
44	Raghib Ismail	.15
45	Ryan Leaf	.30
46	Jackie Harris	.15
47	Robert Holcombe	.15
48	Dorsey Levens	.50
49	Duce Staley	.30
50	Brett Favre	2.00
51	Andre Rison	.15
52	Curtis Conway	.30
53	Mark Chmura	.30
54	Doug Flutie	.75
55	Ernie Mills	.15
56	Jeff George	.30
57	Chris Warren	.15
58	Alonzo Mayes	.15
59	Freddie Jones	.15
60	Shannon Sharpe	.30
61	O.J. Santiago	.15
62	Shawn Springs	.15
63	Kent Graham	.15
64	Muhsin Muhammad	.15
65	Keith Poole	.15
66	Chris Spielman	.15
67	Curtis Enis	.30
68	Lamar Smith	.15
69	Charles Johnson	.15
70	Kerry Collins	.30
71	Charlie Batch	.75
72	Keenan McCardell	.30
73	Ty Detmer	.30
74	Mark Bruener	.15
75	Lamar Thomas	.15
76	Kwamie Lassiter	.15
77	Bam Morris	.15
78	Michael Sinclair	.15
79	Darnay Scott	.30
80	Napoleon Kaufman	.50
81	Ed McCaffery	.30
82	Reidel Anthony	.30
83	Kevin Greene	.15
84	Michael Irvin	.30
85	Charles Way	.15
86	Tim Brown	.30
87	Johnny McWilliams	.15
88	Brad Johnson	.50
89	Antonio Langham	.15
90	Bruce Smith	.15
91	Reggie Barlow	.15
92	Ty Law	.15
93	Bobby Engram	.15
94	Kimble Anders	.15
95	Dale Carter	.15
96	Jimmy Smith	.30
97	Marc Edwards	.15
98	Ken Dilger	.15
99	Adrian Murrell	.30
100	Terance Mathis	.15
101	Gary Anderson	.15
102	Garrison Hearst	.30
103	Ahman Green	.30
104	Daryl Johnston	.15
105	O.J. McDuffie	.30
106	Matthew Hatchette	.15
107	Chris Doleman	.15
108	Steve McNair	.50
109	Leon Johnson	.15
110	Terrell Davis	1.50
111	Rob Moore	.30
112	Troy Aikman	1.00
113	John Avery	.30
114	Frank Wycheck	.15
115	Curtis Martin	.50
116	Jim Harbaugh	.30
117	Sean Dawkins	.15
118	Glenn Foley	.30
119	Warren Sapp	.15
120	R.W. McQuarters	.15
121	Yancey Thigpen	.30
122	Frank Sanders	.15
123	Tim Dwight	.50
124	Pete Mitchell	.15
125	Steve Beuerlein	.30
126	Tyrone Davis	.15
127	Jamie Asher	.15
128	Corey Dillon	.50
129	Doug Pederson	.15
130	Deion Sanders	.50
131	J.J. Stokes	.30
132	Jermaine Lewis	.30
133	Gary Brown	.15
134	Derrick Alexander	.15
135	Tony McGee	.15
136	Kyle Brady	.15
137	Mikhael Ricks	.15
138	Germane Crowell	.30
139	Skip Hicks	.30
140	Ben Coates	.15
141	Will Blackwell	.15
142	Al Del Greco	.15
143	Jake Plummer	1.00
144	Marshall Faulk	.50
145	Antowain Smith	.50
146	Corey Fuller	.15
147	Keyshawn Johnson	.50
148	John Randle	.15
149	Terrell Buckley	.15
150	Terry Kirby	.15
151	Robert Brooks	.15
152	Karim Abdul	.30
153	Jason Seahorn	.15
154	Elvis Grbac	.30
155	Andre Reed	.15
156	Ike Hilliard	.15
157	Jamal Anderson	.50
158	Jake Reed	.15
159	Rich Gannon	.30
160	Michael Jackson	.15
161	Bert Emanuel	.15
162	Charles Woodson	.50
163	Ray Lewis	.30
164	Trent Dilfer	.30
165	Oronde Gadsden	.30
166	Wesley Walls	.15
167	Joey Galloway	.50
168	Mo Lewis	.15
169	Darren Woodson	.15
170	Cris Carter	.50
171	Brian Mitchell	.15
172	Tim Biakabutuka	.30
173	Michael Westbrook	.30
174	Dan Marino	1.50
175	Greg Hill	.15
176	Priest Holmes	.50
177	Fred Lane	.15
178	Isaac Bruce	.50
179	Erik Kramer	.15
180	Steve Young	.75
181	Terry Fair	.15
182	Brian Griese	.75
183	Leslie Shepherd	.15
184	Kordell Stewart	.75
185	Charlie Jones	.15
186	Chris Calloway	.15
187	Wayne Chrebet	.30
188	Natrone Means	.30
189	David LaFleur	.15
190	Rod Smith	.30
191	Kevin Dyson	.30
192	Scott Mitchell	.15
193	Andre Wadsworth	.15
194	Vinny Testaverde	.30
195	Az-Zahir Hakim	.15
196	Joe Jurevicius	.15
197	Junior Seau	.30
198	Jason Elam	.15
199	Terrell Owens	.50
200	Jacquez Green	.30
201	Tim Couch	8.00
202	Donovan McNabb	5.00
203	Cade McNown	5.00
204	Akili Smith	5.00
205	Kevin Faulk	2.00
206	Sedrick Irvin	1.50
207	Edgerrin James	8.00
208	Ricky Williams	8.00
209	D'Wayne Bates	1.00
210	David Boston	3.00
211	Torry Holt	3.00
212	Peerless Price	2.00
213	Daunte Culpepper	5.00
214	Troy Edwards	3.00
215	Rob Konrad	1.00
216	Joe Germaine	1.00
217	James Johnson	1.50
218	Brock Huard	1.50
219	Cecil Collins	5.00
220	Jeff Paulk, Eugene Baker	.50
221	Marty Booker, Jim Finn	.50
222	Scott Covington, Nick Williams	.50
223	Kevin Johnson, Darrin Chiaverini	3.00
224	Ebenezer Ekuban, Dat Nguyen	.75
225	Al Wilson, Chad Plummer	.50
226	Chris Claiborne, Aaron Gibson	.75
227	Aaron Brooks, De'Mond Parker	.75
228	John Tait, Michael Cloud	.75
229	Andy Katzenmoyer, Michael Bishop	1.50
230	Joe Montgomery, Dan Campbell	.75
231	Na Brown, Cecil Martin	.50
232	Amos Zereoue, Jerame Tuman	1.50
233	Jermaine Fazande, Steve Heiden	.50
234	Karsten Bailey, Charlie Rogers	.50
235	Shaun King, Martin Gramatica	4.00
236	Jevon Kearse, Kevin Daft	1.50
237	Champ Bailey, Tim Alexander	1.50
238	Karsten Bailey, Darnell McDonald	1.00
239	Lamarr Glenn, Terry Jackson	.50
240	Troy Smith, Malcolm Johnson	.50
241	Rondel Menendez, Craig Yeast	.50
242	Jed Weaver, James Dearth	.50
243	Joel Makovicka, Shawn Bryson	.50
244	Desmond Clark, Jim Kleinsasser	.75
245	Sean Bennett, Autry Denson	1.00
246	Billy Miller, Wane McGarity	.75
247	Mike Lucky, Justin Swift	.50
248	Travis McGriff, Mar Tay Jenkins	.75
249	Donald Driver, Larry Parker	.75
250	Antoine Winfield, Dre' Bly	.75

1999 SkyBox Dominion Atlantattitude

This 15-card insert set included players who had the chance to lead their team to Super Bowl XXXIV in Atlanta. Singles were inserted 1:24 packs. Parallel Plus sets (1:240) and Warp Tek (numbered to player's uniform number) were also issued.

		MT
Complete Set (15):		100.00
Common Player:		2.00
Minor Stars:		4.00
Inserted 1:24		
1	Charlie Batch	4.00
2	Mark Brunell	5.00
3	Tim Couch	15.00
4	Terrell Davis	10.00
5	Warrick Dunn	4.00
6	Brett Favre	15.00
7	Peyton Manning	10.00
8	Dan Marino	10.00
9	Randy Moss	15.00
10	Jake Plummer	7.00
11	Barry Sanders	15.00
12	Akili Smith	7.00
13	Emmitt Smith	10.00
14	Fred Taylor	7.00
15	Ricky Williams	15.00

Values quoted in this guide reflect the retail price of a card — the price a collector can expect to pay when buying a card from a dealer. The wholesale price — that which a collector can expect to receive from a dealer when selling cards — will be significantly lower, depending on desirability and condition.

1999 SkyBox Dominion Atlantattitude Plus

This was a 15-card insert set that paralleled the Atlantattitude insert. Singles from this insert were found 1:240 packs.

	MT
Plus Cards:	3x
Inserted 1:240	

1999 SkyBox Dominion Atlantattitude Warp Tek

This was a 15-card insert set that paralleled the Atlantattitude insert. Each single in this set was sequentially numbered to the player's jersey number.

		MT
Common Player:		50.00
Production to player's uniform number		
1	Charlie Batch 10	135.00
2	Mark Brunell 8	150.00
3	Tim Couch 2	500.00
4	Terrell Davis 30	140.00
5	Warrick Dunn 28	50.00
6	Brett Favre 4	400.00
7	Peyton Manning 18	225.00
8	Dan Marino 13	275.00
9	Randy Moss 84	100.00
10	Jake Plummer 16	150.00
11	Barry Sanders 20	275.00
12	Akili Smith 11	135.00
13	Emmitt Smith 22	175.00
14	Fred Taylor 28	125.00
15	Ricky Williams 34	200.00

1999 SkyBox Dominion Generation Next

This 20-card insert set included the hottest rookies from the 1999 season. Singles were inserted 1:3 packs. Two parallel sets were issued: Plus (1:30) and Warp Tek (1:300).

		MT
Complete Set (20):		25.00
Common Player:		.50
Minor Stars:		1.00
Inserted 1:3		
1	D'Wayne Bates	.50
2	David Boston	1.50
3	Cecil Collins	2.50
4	Tim Couch	5.00
5	Daunte Culpepper	2.50
6	Troy Edwards	1.50
7	Kevin Faulk	1.25
8	Joe Germaine	1.00
9	Torry Holt	1.50
10	Brock Huard	1.00
11	Sedrick Irvin	1.00
12	Edgerrin James	4.00

13	James Johnson	1.25
14	Kevin Johnson	1.50
15	Shaun King	1.25
16	Donovan McNabb	2.50
17	Cade McNown	2.50
18	Akili Smith	2.50
19	Ricky Williams	5.00
20	Amos Zereoue	1.25

1999 SkyBox Dominion Generation Next Plus

This was a 20-card insert set that paralleled the Generation Next insert. These singles were found 1:30 packs.

	MT
Plus Cards:	3x
Inserted 1:30	

1999 SkyBox Dominion Generation Next Warp Tek

This was a 20-card insert set that paralleled the Generation Next insert. These singles were found 1:300 packs.

		MT
Warp Tek Cards:		5x-10x
Inserted 1:300		
1	D'Wayne Bates	6.00
2	David Boston	10.00
3	Cecil Collins	8.00
4	Tim Couch	35.00
5	Daunte Culpepper	20.00
6	Troy Edwards	10.00
7	Kevin Faulk	8.00
8	Joe Germaine	6.00
9	Torry Holt	12.00
10	Brock Huard	6.00
11	Sedrick Irvin	8.00
12	Edgerrin James	50.00
13	James Johnson	8.00
14	Kevin Johnson	15.00
15	Shaun King	20.00
16	Donovan McNabb	20.00
17	Cade McNown	20.00
18	Akili Smith	15.00
19	Ricky Williams	35.00
20	Amos Zereoue	8.00

1999 SkyBox Dominion Goal 2 Go

This was a 10-card insert set that pictured two players on the same card with one on each side. Singles were inserted 1:9 packs. A Plus parallel (1:90) and Warp Tek parallel (1:900) were also issued.

		MT
Complete Set (10):		25.00
Common Player:		1.50
Inserted 1:9		
1	Terrell Davis, Jamal Anderson	4.00
2	Brett Favre, Jake Plummer	5.00
3	Randy Moss, Jerry Rice	5.00
4	Warrick Dunn, Barry Sanders	5.00
5	Eddie George, Fred Taylor	1.50
6	Emmitt Smith, Marshall Faulk	4.00
7	Keyshawn Johnson, Terrell Owens	1.50
8	Peyton Manning, Ryan Leaf	4.00
9	Dan Marino, John Elway	4.00
10	Cade McNown, Charlie Batch	3.00

1999 SkyBox Dominion Goal 2 Go Plus

This was a 10-card insert set that paralleled the Goal 2 Go insert. Singles were found 1:90 packs.

	MT
Plus Cards:	3x
Inserted 1:90	

1999 SkyBox Dominion Goal 2 Go Warp Tek

This was a 10-card insert set that paralleled the Goal 2 Go insert. Singles were inserted 1:900 packs.

		MT
Inserted 1:900		
1	Terrell Davis, Jamal Anderson	25.00
2	Brett Favre, Jake Plummer	40.00
3	Randy Moss, Jerry Rice	35.00
4	Warrick Dunn, Barry Sanders	35.00
5	Eddie George, Fred Taylor	20.00
6	Emmitt Smith, Marshall Faulk	25.00
7	Keyshawn Johnson, Terrell Owens	15.00
8	Peyton Manning, Ryan Leaf	35.00
9	Dan Marino, John Elway	35.00
10	Cade McNown, Charlie Batch	35.00

1999 SkyBox Dominion Hats Off

This six-card insert set included swatches of caps worn at the 1999 NFL Draft on April 10, 1999 in New York City by six NFL rookies. Each card has a different amount produced and singles were randomly inserted.

		MT
Complete Set (6):		750.00
Common Player:		100.00
1	Tim Couch 135	200.00
2	Donovan McNabb 130	120.00
3	Akili Smith 85	100.00
4	Ricky Williams 130	200.00
5	Daunte Culpepper 100	120.00
6	Cade McNown 120	120.00

1999 SkyBox Dominion Hats Off Autographs

This is a five-card insert set that parallels the Hats Off insert. Each of these singles was autographed. Tim Couch did not sign in this insert. Each player signed a total of 20 cards.

	MT
Complete Set (5):	2000.
Common Player:	300.00
Production 20 Sets	
Couch did not sign	
Donovan McNabb	400.00
Akili Smith	300.00
Ricky Williams	600.00
Daunte Culpepper	375.00
Cade McNown	400.00

1999 SkyBox Molten Metal

This 151-card set had a 26-card rookie subset that was inserted 1:5 packs. Each of the rookie cards had rounded corners and was printed on actual metal. Insert sets included: Autographics, Gridiron Gods, Patchworks, Perfect Fit and Top Notch. SRP was $2.99 for five-card packs.

		MT
Complete Set (151):		120.00
Common Player:		.25
Minor Stars:		.50
Common Rookie:		2.00
Inserted 1:5		
Wax Box:		85.00
1	Terrell Davis	4.50
2	Chris Chandler	.50
3	Terry Glenn	1.00
4	Jon Kitna	1.25
5	Bubby Brister	.50
6	Jermaine Lewis	.25
7	Doug Flutie	2.00
8	Napoleon Kaufman	1.00
9	Yancey Thigpen	.25
10	Bobby Engram	.25
11	Barry Sanders	6.00
12	Ben Coates	.50
13	Joey Galloway	1.00
14	Charlie Batch	2.00
15	Jerome Bettis	1.00
16	Brad Johnson	1.00
17	Brian Griese	2.50
18	Jeff Lewis	.25
19	Jake Plummer	2.50
20	Mark Brunell	2.50
21	Robert Smith	1.00
22	Steve Young	2.00
23	Derrick Mayes	.50
24	Wayne Chrebet	.75
25	Rich Gannon	.50
26	Steve McNair	1.25
27	Charles Johnson	.25
28	Stephen Alexander	.25
29	Jeff Blake	.50
30	Tony Gonzalez	.50
31	Eddie Kennison	.25
32	Hines Ward	.50
33	Isaac Bruce	1.00
34	Peyton Manning	4.50
35	Doug Pederson	.25
36	Stephen Davis	1.00
37	Terance Mathis	.25
38	Herman Moore	.50
39	Fred Taylor	3.00
40	Courtney Hawkins	.25
41	Michael Westbrook	.50
42	Vinny Testaverde	.50
43	Jacquez Green	.50
44	Rocket Ismail	.25
45	Curtis Martin	1.00
46	Tim Brown	.50
47	Kevin Dyson	.50
48	Steve Beuerlein	.50
49	Adrian Murrell	.50
50	Randall Cunningham	1.00
51	Jerry Rice	3.00
52	Tim Biakabutuka	.50
53	Muhsin Muhammad	.50
54	Antonio Freeman	1.00
55	Cris Carter	1.00
56	Lawrence Phillips	.50
57	Michael Irvin	.50
58	Terrell Owens	1.00
59	Warrick Dunn	1.00
60	Leslie Shepherd	.25
61	O.J. McDuffie	.50
62	Byron Hanspard	.25
63	Trent Dilfer	.50
64	Eric Moulds	1.00
65	Scott Mitchell	.25
66	Marc Edwards	.25
67	Dorsey Levens	1.00
68	Dan Marino	4.50
69	Jason Sehorn	.25
70	Junior Seau	.50
71	Reidel Anthony	.25
72	Rob Moore	.50
73	Deion Sanders	1.00
74	Rickey Dudley	.50
75	Keyshawn Johnson	1.00
76	Eddie George	1.25
77	E.G. Green	.50
78	Terry Kirby	.25
79	John Avery	.50
80	Pete Mitchell	.25
81	Natrone Means	.75
82	Mike Alstott	1.00
83	Carl Pickens	.50
84	Karim Abdul	.50
85	Kerry Collins	.50
86	Erik Kramer	.25
87	Robert Holcombe	.50
88	Willie Jackson	.25
89	Marcus Pollard	.25
90	Bam Morris	.25
91	Gary Brown	.25
92	Freddie Jones	.25
93	Kurt Warner	20.00
94	Priest Holmes	1.00
95	Duce Staley	1.00
96	Skip Hicks	.50
97	Frank Sanders	.50
98	Corey Dillon	1.00
99	Shannon Sharpe	.75
100	Randy Moss	6.00
101	Sean Dawkins	.25
102	Marshall Faulk	1.00
103	Mark Chmura	.50
104	Keenan McCardell	.50
105	Jimmy Smith	1.00
106	Jim Harbaugh	.50
107	Jamal Anderson	1.00
108	Elvis Grbac	.50
109	Ed McCaffrey	.75
110	Drew Bledsoe	2.50
111	Curtis Conway	.50
112	Billy Joe Tolliver	.25
113	J.J. Stokes	.50
114	Curtis Enis	1.00
115	Antowain Smith	1.00
116	Troy Aikman	3.00
117	Ricky Watters	.50
118	Kordell Stewart	1.00
119	Derrick Alexander	.25
120	Emmitt Smith	4.50
121	Billy Joe Hobert	.25
122	Johnnie Morton	.25
123	Rod Smith	.75
124	Marvin Harrison	1.00
125	Brett Favre	6.00
126	Craig Yeast	.50
127	Ricky Williams	15.00
128	Brandon Stokley	2.00
129	Akili Smith	7.00
130	Peerless Price	4.00
131	Joe Montgomery	2.00
132	Cade McNown	8.00
133	Donovan McNabb	8.00
134	Shaun King	8.00
135	J.J. Johnson	3.00
136	Kevin Johnson	5.00
137	Edgerrin James	25.00
138	Terry Jackson	2.00
139	Sedrick Irvin	2.00
140	Brock Huard	3.00
141	Torry Holt	5.00
142	Amos Zereoue	2.00
143	Kevin Faulk	5.00
144	Troy Edwards	5.00
145	Donald Driver	2.00
146	Daunte Culpepper	7.00
147	Tim Couch	15.00
148	Cecil Collins	5.00
149	David Boston	5.00
150	Champ Bailey	3.00
151	Olandis Gary	10.00

1999 SkyBox Molten Metal Gridiron Gods

This 20-card insert set included the top players in the NFL. Singles were inserted 1:6 packs. Parallel Silver (1:24), Gold (1:72) and Blue (numbered to 99) sets were also released.

		MT
Complete Set (20):		50.00
Common Player:		2.00
Inserted 1:6		
1	Randy Moss	6.00
2	Keyshawn Johnson	2.00
3	Mike Alstott	2.00
4	Brian Griese	3.00
5	Tim Couch	8.00
6	Troy Aikman	4.00
7	Warrick Dunn	2.00
8	Mark Brunell	3.00
9	Jerry Rice	4.00
10	Dorsey Levens	2.00
11	Fred Taylor	4.00
12	Emmitt Smith	5.00
13	Edgerrin James	12.00
14	Eddie George	2.50
15	Drew Bledsoe	3.00
16	Deion Sanders	2.00
17	Charlie Batch	2.50
18	Kordell Stewart	2.00
19	Brad Johnson	2.00
20	Akili Smith	3.50

1999 SkyBox Molten Metal Gridiron Gods Blue

This was a 20-card parallel to the Gridiron God insert set. Each of these singles was sequentially numbered to 99.

	MT
Blue Cards:	5x-10x
Production 99 Sets	

1999 SkyBox Molten Metal Gridiron Gods Gold

This was a 20-card parallel to the Gridiron Gods insert set. These singles were found 1:72 packs.

	MT
Gold Cards:	4x
Inserted 1:72	

1999 SkyBox Molten Metal Gridiron Gods Silver

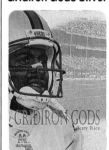

This was a 20-card parallel to the Gridiron Gods insert set. These singles were found 1:24 packs.

	MT
Silver Cards:	2x
Inserted 1:24	

1999 SkyBox Molten Metal Patchworks

This nine-card insert set included pieces of numbers, names or patches from player-worn jerseys. Singles were inserted 1:360 packs.

		MT
Complete Set (9):		1000.
Common Player:		50.00
Inserted 1:360		
1	Drew Bledsoe	100.00
2	Terrell Davis	125.00
3	Brett Favre	200.00
4	Peyton Manning	200.00
5	Dan Marino	175.00
6	Herman Moore	50.00
7	Randy Moss	250.00
8	Jerry Rice	125.00
9	Steve Young	85.00

1999 SkyBox Molten Metal Perfect Fit

This 10-card insert set included players who make their teams complete. Singles were inserted 1:24 packs. Parallel Silver (1:72), Gold (1:216) and Red (numbered to 25) versions were also released.

		MT
Complete Set (10):		70.00
Common Player:		5.00
Inserted 1:24		
1	Barry Sanders	12.00
2	Brett Favre	12.00
3	Dan Marino	10.00
4	Edgerrin James	20.00
5	Emmitt Smith	10.00
6	Fred Taylor	5.00
7	Randy Moss	12.00
8	Terrell Davis	12.00
9	Tim Couch	12.00
10	Peyton Manning	10.00

1999 SkyBox Molten Metal Perfect Fit Gold

This was a ten-card parallel to the Perfect Fit insert. Singles were found 1:216 packs.

	MT
Gold Cards:	4x
Inserted 1:216	

1999 SkyBox Molten Metal Perfect Fit Red

This was a ten-card parallel to the Perfect Fit insert set. Each single was sequentially numbered to 25.

	MT
Red Cards:	8x-16x
Production 25 Sets	

1999 SkyBox Molten Metal Perfect Fit Silver

This was a ten-card parallel to the Perfect Fit insert set. Singles were inserted 1:72 packs.

	MT
Silver Cards:	2x
Inserted 1:72	

1999 SkyBox Molten Metal Top Notch

This 15-card insert set included the top players in the NFL.

Singles were found 1:12 packs. Parallel Silver (1:36), Gold (1:108) and Green (numbered to 75) versions were also produced.

		MT
Complete Set (15):		60.00
Common Player:		2.00
Inserted 1:12		
1	Jake Plummer	5.00
2	Cade McNown	6.00
3	Tim Couch	10.00
4	Emmitt Smith	7.00
5	Charlie Batch	4.00
6	Donovan McNabb	6.00
7	Steve Young	4.00
8	Brian Griese	4.00
9	Doug Flutie	4.00
10	Edgerrin James	15.00
11	Fred Taylor	5.00
12	Keyshawn Johnson	2.00
13	Mark Brunell	4.00
14	Randy Moss	10.00
15	Ricky Williams	10.00

1999 SkyBox Molten Metal Top Notch Gold

This was a 15-card parallel to the Top Notch insert set. Each of these singles was inserted 1:108 packs.

	MT
Gold Cards:	4x
Inserted 1:108	

1999 SkyBox Molten Metal Top Notch Green

This was a 15-card parallel to the Top Notch insert set. Singles were sequentially numbered to 75.

	MT
Green Cards:	5x-10x
Production 75 Sets	

1999 SkyBox Molten Metal Top Notch Silver

This was a 15-card parallel to the Top Notch insert set. Singles were found 1:36 packs.

	MT
Silver Cards:	2x
Inserted 1:36	

1999 SkyBox Premium

This was a 290-card set that included 40 rookies with two different cards. One version wasn't

seeded while the other was found 1:8 packs. The seeded version pictured the rookies in an action photo, while the other version was posed. Insert sets included: Star Rubies, 2000 Men, Autographics, Box Tops, Deja Vu, Genuine Coverage, Prime Time Rookies and Year 2. SRP was $2.69 for eight-card packs.

		MT
Complete Set (290):		325.00
Common Player:		.15
Minor Stars:		.30
Common Rookie:		.50
Common SP:		1.50
SP in Action Photos		
Inserted 1:8		
Wax Box:		55.00
1	Randy Moss	2.50
2	Jamie Asher	.15
3	Joey Galloway	.50
4	Kent Graham	.15
5	Leslie Shepherd	.15
6	Levon Kirkland	.15
7	Marcus Pollard	.15
8	O.J. McDuffie	.15
9	Bill Romanowski	.15
10	Priest Holmes	.50
11	Tim Biakabutuka	.30
12	Duce Staley	.30
13	Isaac Bruce	.50
14	Jay Riemersma	.15
15	Karim Abdul	.30
16	Kevin Dyson	.30
17	Rickey Dudley	.30
18	Rocket Ismail	.15
19	Billy Davis	.15
20	James Jett	.15
21	Jerome Bettis	.50
22	Michael McCrary	.15
23	Michael Westbrook	.30
24	Oronde Gadsden	.30
25	Brad Johnson	.50
26	Shawn Springs	.15
27	Cris Carter	.50
28	Ed McCaffrey	.30
29	Gary Brown	.15
30	Hines Ward	.30
31	Hugh Douglas	.15
32	Jamir Miller	.15
33	Michael Bates	.15
34	Peyton Manning	2.00
35	Tony Banks	.30
36	Charles Way	.15
37	Charlie Batch	1.00
38	Jake Reed	.15
39	Mark Brunell	1.00
40	Skip Hicks	.30
41	Steve Young	.75
42	Wesley Walls	.15
43	Antonio Langham	.15
44	Antowain Smith	.50
45	Brian Griese	1.00
46	Jessie Armstead	.15
47	Thurman Thomas	.30
48	Jeff George	.50
49	Jessie Tuggle	.15
50	Jim Harbaugh	.30
51	Marvin Harrison	.50
52	Randall Cunningham	.50
53	Stephen Alexander	.15
54	Tiki Barber	.30
55	Billy Joe Tolliver	.15
56	Bruce Smith	.15
57	Eddie George	.75
58	Eugene Robinson	.15
59	John Elway	2.00
60	Ken Dilger	.15
61	Rodney Harrison	.15
62	Ty Detmer	.15
63	Andre Reed	.15
64	Dorsey Levens	.50
65	Eddie Kennison	.15
66	Freddie Jones	.15
67	Jacquez Green	.30
68	Jason Elam	.15
69	Marc Edwards	.15
70	Terance Mathis	.15
71	Alonzo Mayes	.15
72	Andre Wadsworth	.15
73	Barry Sanders	2.50
74	Derrick Alexander	.15
75	Garrison Hearst	.30
76	Leon Johnson	.15
77	Mike Alstott	.50
78	Shawn Jefferson	.15
79	Andre Hastings	.15
80	Eric Moulds	.50
81	Ryan Leaf	.50
82	Takeo Spikes	.15
83	Terrell Davis	2.00
84	Tim Dwight	.50
85	Trent Dilfer	.30
86	Vonnie Holliday	.30
87	Antonio Freeman	.50
88	Carl Pickens	.30
89	Chris Chandler	.30
90	Dale Carter	.15
91	La'Roi Glover	.15
92	Natrone Means	.30
93	Reidel Anthony	.15
94	Brett Favre	2.50
95	Bubby Brister	.30
96	Cameron Cleeland	.30
97	Chris Calloway	.15
98	Corey Dillon	.50
99	Greg Hill	.15
100	Vinny Testaverde	.30
101	Trent Green	.30
102	Sam Gash	.15
103	Mikhael Ricks	.15
104	Emmitt Smith	2.00
105	Doug Flutie	.75
106	Deion Sanders	.50
107	Charles Johnson	.15
108	Bam Morris	.15
109	Andre Rison	.30
110	Doug Pederson	.15
111	Marshall Faulk	.50
112	Tim Brown	.30
113	Warren Sapp	.15
114	Bryan Still	.15
115	Chris Penn	.15
116	Jamal Anderson	.50
117	Keyshawn Johnson	.50
118	Ricky Proehl	.15
119	Robert Brooks	.15
120	Tony Gonzalez	.30
121	Ty Law	.15
122	Elvis Grbac	.30
123	Jeff Blake	.30
124	Mark Chmura	.30
125	Junior Seau	.30
126	Mo Lewis	.15
127	Ray Buchanan	.15
128	Robert Holcombe	.30
129	Tony Simmons	.30
130	David Palmer	.15
131	Ike Hilliard	.30
132	Mike Vanderjagt	.15
133	Rae Carruth	.15
134	Sean Dawkins	.15
135	Shannon Sharpe	.30
136	Curtis Conway	.30
137	Darrell Green	.15
138	Germane Crowell	.30
139	J.J. Stokes	.30
140	Kevin Hardy	.15
141	Rob Moore	.30
142	Robert Smith	.50
143	Wayne Chrebet	.30
144	Yancey Thigpen	.30
145	Jerome Pathon	.15
146	John Mobley	.15
147	Kerry Collins	.30
148	Peter Boulware	.15
149	Matthew Hatchette	.15
150	Kordell Stewart	.50
151	Koy Detmer	.15
152	Sedrick Shaw	.15
153	Steve Beuerlein	.30
154	Zach Thomas	.30
155	Adrian Murrell	.30
156	Bobby Engram	.15
157	Bryan Cox	.15
158	Drew Bledsoe	1.00
159	Jerry Rice	1.25
160	Keenan McCardell	.30
161	Steve McNair	.50
162	Terry Fair	.15
163	Derrick Brooks	.15
164	Eric Green	.15
165	Erik Kramer	.15
166	Frank Sanders	.15
167	Fred Taylor	1.25
168	Johnnie Morton	.15
169	R.W. McQuarters	.15
170	Terry Glenn	.50
171	Frank Wycheck	.15
172	John Avery	.30
173	Kevin Turner	.15
174	Larry Centers	.15
175	Michael Irvin	.30
176	Rich Gannon	.30
177	Ricky Watters	.30
178	Rodney Thomas	.15
179	Scott Mitchell	.15
180	Chad Brown	.15
181	John Randle	.15
182	Michael Strahan	.15
183	Muhsin Muhammad	.30
184	Reggie Barlow	.15
185	Rod Smith	.30
186	Dan Marino	2.00
187	Dexter Coakley	.15
188	Jermaine Lewis	.30
189	Jon Kitna	.75
190	Napoleon Kaufman	.50
191	Will Blackwell	.15
192	Aaron Glenn	.15
193	Ben Coates	.30
194	Curtis Enis	.50
195	Herman Moore	.50
196	Jake Plummer	1.25
197	Jimmy Smith	.30
198	Terrell Owens	.50
199	Warrick Dunn	.50
200	Charles Woodson	.50
201	Ahman Green	.50
202	Mark Bruener	.15
203	Ray Lewis	.30
204	Tony Martin	.15
205	Troy Aikman	1.25
206	Curtis Martin	.50
207	Darnay Scott	.30
208	Derrick Mayes	.15
209	Keith Poole	.15
210	Warren Moon	.30
211	*Chris Claiborne*	1.00
211	Chris Claiborne SP	5.00
212	*Ricky Williams*	8.00
212	Ricky Williams SP	30.00
213	*Tim Couch*	8.00
213	Tim Couch SP	30.00
214	*Champ Bailey*	1.50
214	Champ Bailey SP	6.00
215	*Torry Holt*	2.50
215	Torry Holt SP	10.00
216	*Donovan McNabb*	4.00
216	Donovan McNabb SP	15.00
217	*David Boston*	2.50
217	David Boston SP	10.00
218	*Chris McAllister*	1.50
218	Chris McAllister SP	5.00
219	*Michael Bishop*	1.75
219	Michael Bishop SP	7.00
220	*Daunte Culpepper*	4.00
220	Daunte Culpepper SP	15.00
221	*Joe Germaine*	1.50
221	Joe Germaine SP	6.00
222	*Edgerrin James*	10.00
222	Edgerrin James SP	40.00
223	*Jevon Kearse*	2.50
223	Jevon Kearse SP	10.00
224	*Ebenezer Ekuban*	1.00
224	Ebenezer Ekuban SP	1.50
225	*Scott Covington*	.50
225	Scott Covington SP	1.50
226	*Aaron Brooks*	1.00
226	Aaron Brooks SP	5.00
227	*Cecil Collins*	4.00
227	Cecil Collins SP	15.00
228	*Akili Smith*	4.00
228	Akili Smith SP	15.00
229	*Shaun King*	3.00
229	Shaun King SP	12.00
230	*Chad Plummer*	.50
230	Chad Plummer SP	1.50
231	*Peerless Price*	1.75
231	Peerless Price SP	8.00
232	*Antoine Winfield*	.50
232	Antoine Winfield SP	3.00
233	*Antwan Edwards*	1.00
233	Antwan Edwards SP	3.00
234	*Rob Konrad*	1.00
234	Rob Konrad SP	3.00
235	*Troy Edwards*	2.50
235	Troy Edwards SP	10.00
236	*Terry Jackson*	.50
236	Terry Jackson SP	1.00
237	*Jimmy Kleinsasser*	1.00
237	Jim Kleinsasser SP	5.00
238	*Joe Montgomery*	1.50
238	Joe Montgomery SP	6.00
239	*Desmond Clark*	1.00
239	Desmond Clark SP	1.50
240	*Lamar King*	.50
240	Lamar King SP	1.50
241	*Dameane Douglas*	.50
241	Dameane Douglas SP	1.50
242	*Martin Gramatica*	1.25
242	Martin Gramatica SP	6.00
243	*James Finn*	.50
243	James Finn SP	1.50
244	*Andy Katzenmoyer*	1.25
244	Andy Katzenmoyer SP	5.00
245	*Dee Miller*	.50
245	Dee Miller SP	1.50
246	*D'Wayne Bates*	1.00
246	D'Wayne Bates SP	3.00
247	*Amos Zereoue*	2.00
247	Amos Zereoue SP	8.00
248	*Karsten Bailey*	1.00
248	Karsten Bailey SP	3.00
249	*Kevin Johnson*	2.50
249	Kevin Johnson SP	10.00
250	*Cade McNown*	4.00
250	Cade McNown SP	15.00

1999 SkyBox Premium Shining Star Rubies

This was a 290-card parallel to the base set. Each of the singles was sequentially numbered to 30 except for the seeded rookie cards which were numbered to 15.

	MT
Ruby Cards:	50x-100x
Ruby Rookies: 1	5x-30x
Production 30 Sets	
Ruby SP's:	5x-10x
Production 15 Sets	

1999 SkyBox Premium 2000 Men

This 15-card insert set included players who looked to be the stars for the next millennium. Each single was sequentially numbered to 100.

	MT
Complete Set (15):	650.00
Common Player:	20.00

Production 100 Sets		
1	Warrick Dunn	20.00
2	Tim Couch	80.00
3	Fred Taylor	40.00
4	Jake Plummer	40.00
5	Jerry Rice	40.00
6	Edgerrin James	80.00
7	Mark Brunell	40.00
8	Peyton Manning	60.00
9	Randy Moss	80.00
10	Terrell Davis	60.00
11	Charlie Batch	30.00
12	Dan Marino	60.00
13	Emmitt Smith	60.00
14	Brett Favre	80.00
15	Barry Sanders	80.00

1999 SkyBox Premium Autographics

This was a 79-card insert that was found in several Sky-Box products. Singles were issued in Dominion, E-X Century, Molten Metal, Metal Universe and SkyBox Premium at 1:68 hobby packs and 1:90 retail packs. Each single had the autograph on the front of the card and each also had a parallel Red version that was sequentially numbered to 50.

		MT
Common Player:		10.00
Minor Stars:		20.00
Inserted 1:68		
	Stephen Alexander	20.00
	Mike Alstott	40.00
	Champ Bailey	30.00
	Karsten Bailey	10.00
	Charlie Batch	50.00
	D'Wayne Bates	20.00
	Michael Bishop	35.00
	Dre' Bly	10.00
	David Boston	50.00
	Gary Brown	10.00
	Na Brown	10.00
	Tim Brown	30.00
	Troy Brown	10.00
	Mark Bruener	10.00
	Mark Brunell	50.00
	Shawn Bryson	10.00
	Wayne Chrebet	30.00
	Chris Claiborne	20.00
	Cam Cleeland	10.00
	Cecil Collins	75.00
	Daunte Culpepper	75.00
	Randall Cunningham	40.00
	Terrell Davis	85.00
	Ty Detmer	10.00
	Jared DeVries	10.00
	Troy Edwards	50.00
	Kevin Faulk	35.00
	Marshall Faulk	40.00
	Doug Flutie	50.00
	Oronde Gadsden	20.00
	Joey Galloway	35.00
	Eddie George	50.00
	Martin Gramatica	20.00
	Anthony Gray	10.00
	Ahman Green	20.00
	Brian Griese	70.00
	Howard Griffith	10.00
	Marvin Harrison	45.00
	Courtney Hawkins	10.00
	Vonnie Holliday	10.00
	Torry Holt	50.00
	Sedrick Irvin	10.00
	Edgerrin James	150.00
	Patrick Jeffers	30.00
	James Johnson	35.00
	Kevin Johnson	50.00
	Freddie Jones	10.00
	Jevon Kearse	35.00
	Shaun King	40.00
	Jon Kitna	35.00
	Rob Konrad	10.00
	Dorsey Levens	30.00
	Peyton Manning	100.00
	Darnell McDonald	10.00
	Donovan McNabb	75.00
	Cade McNown	75.00
	Eric Moss	10.00
	Randy Moss	175.00
	Eric Moulds	30.00
	Marcus Nash	20.00
	Terrell Owens	35.00
	Jerome Pathon	20.00
	Jake Plummer	75.00
	Peerless Price	35.00
	Mikhael Ricks	10.00
	Frank Sanders	20.00
	Tony Simmons	10.00
	Akili Smith	75.00
	Antowain Smith	35.00
	L.C. Stevens	10.00
	Michael Strahan	10.00
	Tai Streets	10.00
	Lamar Thomas	10.00
	Jerame Tuman	10.00
	Kevin Turner	10.00
	Tyrone Wheatley	10.00
	Ricky Williams	150.00
	Frank Wycheck	10.00
	Amos Zereoue	40.00

1999 SkyBox Premium Autographics Foil

This was a 79-card parallel to the Autographics insert set. Each of these singles was printed with red foil and sequentially numbered to 50.

	MT
Foil Cards:	2x
Production 50 Sets	

1999 SkyBox Premium Box Tops

This 15-card insert set included veterans from the NFL. Singles were inserted 1:12 packs.

		MT
Complete Set (15):		45.00
Common Player:		2.00
Inserted 1:12		
1	Terrell Davis	6.00
2	Troy Aikman	4.00
3	Peyton Manning	6.00
4	Mark Brunell	3.00
5	Eddie George	2.50
6	Corey Dillon	2.00
7	Dan Marino	6.00
8	Brett Favre	8.00
9	Barry Sanders	8.00
10	Emmitt Smith	6.00
11	Fred Taylor	4.00
12	Jerry Rice	4.00
13	Jamal Anderson	2.00
14	Joey Galloway	2.00
15	Randy Moss	8.00

1999 SkyBox Premium Deja Vu

This 15-card insert set included a draft pick paired with a veteran who was the same number pick in a previous draft. Singles were inserted 1:36 picks. A parallel die-cut version was also issued with each of those singles sequentially numbered to 99.

		MT
Complete Set (15):		50.00
Common Player:		2.00
Inserted 1:36		
1	Akili Smith, Barry Sanders	12.00
2	Cade McNown, Warrick Dunn	6.00
3	Cecil Collins, Jerris McPhail	6.00
4	Champ Bailey, Curtis Conway	2.00
5	Daunte Culpepper, Michael Irvin	6.00
6	David Boston, Tim Biakabutuka	3.00

		MT
7	Donovan McNabb, Marshall Faulk	6.00
8	Edgerrin James, Michael Westbrook	12.00
9	Kevin Faulk, Joey Kent	2.00
10	Kevin Johnson, Jerome Pathon	3.00
11	Ricky Williams, Deion Sanders	12.00
12	Shaun King, Germane Crowell	2.00
13	Tim Couch, Troy Aikman	12.00
14	Torry Holt, Tim Brown	3.00
15	Troy Edwards, Eric Metcalf	3.00

1999 SkyBox Premium Genuine Coverage

This was a six-card insert set that included a piece of a game-worn jersey. Each card had a different amount issued and was randomly inserted.

	MT
Complete Set (6):	600.00
Common Player:	50.00
Drew Bledsoe	85.00
Mark Brunell	85.00
Randall Cunningham	60.00
Brett Favre	175.00
Herman Moore	50.00
Randy Moss	225.00

1999 SkyBox Premium Prime Time Rookies

This 15-card insert set included the best rookies from 1999. Singles were found 1:96 packs. A parallel Autograph version was also issued with each of those singles sequentially numbered to 25.

		MT
Complete Set (15):		160.00
Common Player:		5.00
Inserted 1:96		
1	Ricky Williams	30.00
2	Tim Couch	30.00
3	Edgerrin James	30.00
4	Daunte Culpepper	15.00
5	David Boston	10.00
6	Akili Smith	15.00
7	Cecil Collins	15.00
8	Cade McNown	15.00
9	Torry Holt	10.00
10	Donovan McNabb	15.00
11	Kevin Johnson	10.00
12	Shaun King	8.00
13	Champ Bailey	5.00
14	Troy Edwards	10.00
15	Kevin Faulk	8.00

1999 SkyBox Premium Prime Time Rookies Autographs

This was a 15-card parallel to the Prime Time Rookie insert set. Each of these singles was autographed and sequentially numbered to 25.

		MT
Common Player:		100.00
Production 25 Sets		
1	Ricky Williams	400.00
2	Tim Couch	400.00
3	Edgerrin James	550.00
4	Daunte Culpepper	200.00
5	David Boston	150.00

6	Akili Smith	180.00
7	Cecil Collins	100.00
8	Cade McNown	200.00
9	Torry Holt	150.00
10	Donovan McNabb	200.00
11	Kevin Johnson	150.00
12	Shaun King	200.00
13	Champ Bailey	100.00
14	Troy Edwards	150.00
15	Kevin Faulk	100.00

1999 SkyBox Premium Year 2

This 15-card insert set included players who were in their second year as a pro. Singles were found 1:6 packs.

		MT
Complete Set (15):		15.00
Common Player:		.75
Minor Stars:		1.50
Inserted 1:6		
1	Ahman Green	.75
2	Terry Fair	.75
3	Charlie Batch	2.00
4	Ryan Leaf	1.50
5	Skip Hicks	1.50
6	John Avery	.75
7	Charles Woodson	1.50
8	Jacquez Green	.75
9	Kevin Dyson	.75
10	Marcus Nash	.75
11	Robert Holcombe	.75
12	Germane Crowell	1.50
13	Curtis Enis	1.50
14	Tim Dwight	1.50
15	Brian Griese	3.00

1992 Slam Thurman Thomas

Thurman Thomas was featured in this 11-card (10 cards, plus one promo) set. Slam reported the production run to be 25,000 total sets and included an autographed (limited to 1,000) edition card for every 25 sets ordered.

		MT
Complete Set (11):		10.00
Common Player:		1.00
1	Thurman Thomas (RB-Willowridge HS)	1.00
2	Thurman Thomas (HS-All American)	1.00
3	Thurman Thomas (Gator Bowl MVP)	1.00
4	Thurman Thomas (RB-Oklahoma State)	1.00
5	Thurman Thomas (All Big 8)	1.00
6	Thurman Thomas (1st Team All-American)	1.00
7	Thurman Thomas (RB-Buffalo)	1.00
8	Thurman Thomas (AFC All-Pro)	1.00
9	Thurman Thomas (AFC Rushing Champion)	1.00
10	Thurman Thomas (NFL Leader-Total Yards)	1.00
P1	Thurman Thomas (Promo 1)	1.00
AU	Thurman Thomas (Autographed)	80.00

1993 Slam Jerome Bettis

Jerome Bettis is featured in this six-card set (five cards, plus a promo) by Slam. Sets arrived with one autographed

card, 4 regular issue cards, plus the promo card. There is also a certificate of authenticity that lists the production number out of a total of 5,000 produced.

		MT
Complete Set (6):		12.00
Common Player:		2.00
1	Jerome Bettis (High School All-American)	2.00
2	Jerome Bettis (Freshman Notre Dame)	2.00
3	Jerome Bettis (1991 Notre Dame Co-MVP)	2.00
4	Jerome Bettis (All-American)	2.00
5	Jerome Bettis (10th Pick Overall)	2.00
P1	Jerome Bettis (Promo 1) (FB Notre Dame)	2.00
1AU	Jerome Bettis (High School All-American)	15.00
2AU	Jerome Bettis (Freshman Notre Dame)	15.00
3AU	Jerome Bettis (1991 Notre Dame Co-MVP)	15.00
4AU	Jerome Bettis (All-American)	20.00
5AU	Jerome Bettis (10th Pick Overall)	20.00

1978 Slim Jim

Specially-marked Slim Jim products in 1978 contained a 3" x 5-3/4" panel featuring two football player discs. The discs, featuring a player mug shot, biographical data, an NFLPA logo and "Slim Jim Collection" on the front, were issued by Michael Schechter Associates. MSA is also on the disc front. Each disc has a diameter of 2-3/8" and is perforated so it can be cut out from the panel. The same two players were always on the same panel. They are listed according to the pairs on the panel, starting with 1A and 1B and ending 69-70. Note: The prices for each disc are actually the value of the panel. So, 1A and 1B would be $20, not $40.

		NM
Complete Set (70):		350.00
Common Player:		8.00
1A	Lyle Alzado	20.00
1B	Archie Manning	20.00
2A	Bill Bergey	20.00
2B	John Riggins	20.00
3A	Fred Biletnikoff	20.00
3B	Dan Dierdorf	8.00
4A	John Cappelletti	8.00
4B	Bob Chandler	8.00
5A	Tommy Casanova	8.00
5B	Darryl Stingley	8.00
6A	Billy Joe Dupree	8.00
6B	Nat Moore	8.00
7A	John Dutton	8.00
7B	Paul Krause	8.00
8A	Leon Gray	8.00
8B	Richard Caster	8.00
9A	Mel Gray	8.00
9B	Claude Humphrey	8.00
10A	Joe Greene	12.00
10B	Dexter Bussey	12.00
11A	Jack Gregory	8.00
11B	Billy Johnson	8.00
12A	Steve Grogan	8.00
12B	Jerome Barkum	8.00
13A	Dan Hannah	10.00
13B	Isaac Curtis	10.00
14A	Jim Hart	9.00
14B	Otis Sistrunk	9.00
15A	Tommy Hart	8.00
15B	Ron Howard	8.00
16A	Wilbur Jackson	8.50
16B	Riley Odoms	8.50
17A	Ron Jaworski	10.00
17B	Mike Thomas	10.00
18A	Larry Little	12.00
18B	Isiah Robertson	12.00
19A	Ron McDole	8.00
19B	Willie Buchanon	8.00
20A	Lydell Mitchell	8.50
20B	Glen Edwards	8.50
21A	Robert Newhouse	8.00
21B	Glenn Doughty	8.00
22A	Alan Page	10.00
22B	Fred Carr	8.00
23A	Walter Payton	55.00
23B	Larry Csonka	55.00
24A	Greg Pruitt	8.00
24B	Doug Buffone	8.00
25A	Ahmad Rashad	8.00

25B	Jeff Van Note	12.00
26A	Golden Richards	10.00
26B	Rocky Bleier	10.00
27A	Clarence Scott	8.00
27B	Joe DeLamielleure	8.00
28A	Lee Roy Selmon	8.00
28B	Charlie Sanders	10.00
29A	Bruce Taylor	8.50
29B	Otis Armstrong	8.50
30A	Emmitt Thomas	8.00
30B	Elvin Bethea	8.00
31A	Brad Van Pelt	8.00
31B	Ted Washington	8.00
32A	Gene Washington	8.00
32B	Charlie Joiner	15.00
33A	Clarence Williams	8.00
33B	Lemar Parrish	8.00
34A	Roger Wehrli	12.00
34B	Gene Upshaw	12.00
35A	Don Woods	8.00
35B	Ron Jessie	8.00

1993 SP

These cards, sold only through hobby dealers, feature gold foil logos, a Premier Prospects subset printing using Light F/X and Electric printing processes, and full-bleed color photos. The borders are team color-coded, too. Gold foil is used for the player's name and set logo. The back has a photo, player stats, biographical information, a card number and a gold-foil Upper Deck hologram. Random foil packs had a card from the 15-card All-Pro insert set. Upper Deck also created a promo card to preview the design for its new set. The card features Kansas City Chiefs quarterback Joe Montana, but it is not identified as a promo card. However, the promo card's number, 19, is different from the number he is assigned in the regular set (#122). The promo card is worth $4.

		MT
Complete Set (270):		170.00
Common Player:		.25
Minor Stars:		.50
Foil Prospects:		1.00
Wax Box:		225.00
1	Curtis Conway	5.00
2	John Copeland	1.00
3	Kevin Williams	1.00
4	Dan Williams	1.00
5	Patrick Bates	1.00
6	Jerome Bettis	18.00
7	O.J. McDuffie	3.00
8	Robert Smith	15.00
9	Drew Bledsoe	70.00
10	Irv Smith	2.00
11	Marvin Jones	1.00
12	Victor Bailey	1.00
13	Garrison Hearst	15.00
14	Natrone Means	10.00
15	Todd Kelly	1.00
16	Rick Mirer	2.00
17	Eric Curry	1.00
18	Reggie Brooks	1.00
19	Eric Dickerson	.50
20	Roger Harper	.25
21	Michael Haynes	.25
22	Bobby Hebert	.25
23	Lincoln Kennedy	.50
24	Chris Miller	.25
25	Mike Pritchard	.25
26	Andre Rison	.75
27	Deion Sanders	2.00
28	Cornelius Bennett	.25
29	Kenneth Davis	.25
30	Henry Jones	.25
31	Jim Kelly	1.00
32	John Parrella	.25
33	Andre Reed	.50
34	Bruce Smith	.50
35	Thomas Smith	.25
36	Thurman Thomas	1.00
37	Neal Anderson	.25
38	Myron Baker	.25
39	Mark Carrier	.25

40	Richard Dent	.50
41	Chris Gedney	.25
42	Jim Harbaugh	.50
43	Craig Heyward	.25
44	Carl Simpson	.25
45	Alonzo Spellman	.25
47	Derrick Fenner	.25
48	Harold Green	.25
49	David Klingler	.25
50	Ricardo McDonald	.25
51	Tony McGee	.50
52	Carl Pickens	1.50
53	Steve Tovar	.25
54	Alfred Williams	.25
55	Darryl Williams	.25
56	Jerry Ball	.25
57	Michael Caldwell	.25
58	Mark Carrier	.25
59	Steve Everitt	.25
60	Dan Footman	.25
61	Pepper Johnson	.25
62	Bernie Kosar	.50
63	Eric Metcalf	.50
64	Michael Dean Perry	.50
65	Troy Aikman	3.00
66	Charles Haley	.50
67	Michael Irvin	1.00
68	Robert Jones	.25
69	Derrick Lassic	.50
70	Russell Maryland	.50
71	Ken Norton	.25
72	Darrin Smith	.50
73	Emmitt Smith	6.00
74	Steve Atwater	.25
75	Rod Bernstine	.25
76	Jason Elam	1.00
77	John Elway	3.00
78	Simon Fletcher	.25
79	Tommy Maddox	.25
80	Glyn Milburn	1.00
81	Derek Russell	.25
82	Shannon Sharpe	.50
83	Bennie Blades	.25
84	Willie Green	.25
85	Antonio London	.25
86	Ryan McNeil	.25
87	Herman Moore	1.50
88	Rodney Peete	.50
89	Barry Sanders	6.00
90	Chris Spielman	.25
91	Pat Swilling	.25
92	Mark Brunell	35.00
93	Terrell Buckley	.25
94	Brett Favre	6.00
95	Jackie Harris	.25
96	Sterling Sharpe	1.00
97	John Stephens	.25
98	Reggie White	1.00
99	Wayne Simmons	.50
100	George Teague	.50
101	Michael Barrow	.25
102	Cody Carson	.25
103	Ray Childress	.25
104	Brad Hopkins	.25
105	Haywood Jeffires	.25
106	Wilber Marshall	.25
107	Warren Moon	1.00
108	Webster Slaughter	.25
109	Lorenzo White	.25
110	John Baylor	.25
111	Duane Bickett	.25
112	Quentin Coryatt	.25
113	Steve Emtman	.25
114	Jeff George	1.00
115	Jessie Hester	.25
116	Anthony Johnson	.25
117	Reggie Langhorne	.25
118	Roosevelt Potts	.25
119	Marcus Allen	1.00
120	J.J. Birden	.25
121	Willie Davis	.25
122	Jaime Fields	.25
123	Joe Montana	4.00
124	Will Shields	.25
125	Neil Smith	.25
126	Derrick Thomas	.50
127	Harvey Williams	.25
128	Tim Brown	1.00
129	Billy Joe Hobert	1.50
130	Jeff Hostetler	.50
131	Ethan Horton	.25
132	Raghib Ismail	.25
133	Howie Long	.25
134	Terry McDaniel	.25
135	Greg Robinson	.25
136	Anthony Smith	.25
137	Willie Anderson	.25
138	Marc Boutte	.25
139	Shane Conlan	.25
140	Troy Drayton	.75
141	Henry Ellard	.25
142	Jim Everett	.25
143	Cleveland Gary	.25
144	Sean Gilbert	.25
145	David Lang	.25
146	Marco Coleman	.25
147	Bryan Cox	.25
148	Irving Fryar	.25
149	Keith Jackson	.25
150	Dan Marino	6.00
151	Scott Mitchell	.50
152	Troy Vincent	.25
153	Richmond Webb	.25
154	Anthony Carter	.25
155	Cris Carter	1.50
156	Roger Craig	.50
157	Chris Doleman	.25

158	Qadry Ismail	1.50
159	Steve Jordan	.25
160	Audray McMillian	.25
161	Gino Torretta	.25
162	Barry Word	.25
163	Vincent Brown	.25
164	Marv Cook	.25
165	Sam Gash	.25
166	Pat Harlow	.25
167	Greg McMurtry	.25
168	Todd Rucci	.25
169	Leonard Russell	.25
170	Scott Sisson	.25
171	Chris Slade	.50
172	Morten Andersen	.25
173	Derek Brown	.50
174	Reggie Freeman	.25
175	Rickey Jackson	.25
176	Eric Martin	.25
177	Wayne Martin	.25
178	Brad Muster	.25
179	Willie Roaf	.50
180	Renaldo Turnbull	.25
181	Derek Brown	.25
182	Marcus Buckley	.25
183	Jarrod Bunch	.25
184	Rodney Hampton	.50
185	Ed McCaffrey	1.00
186	Kanavis McGhee	.25
187	Phil Simms	.50
188	Michael Strahan	.50
189	Lawrence Taylor	1.00
190	Kurt Barber	.25
191	Boomer Esiason	.50
192	Johnny Johnson	.25
193	Ronnie Lott	.50
194	Johnny Mitchell	.25
195	Rob Moore	.50
196	Adrian Murrell	12.00
197	Coleman Rudolph	.25
198	Marvin Washington	.25
199	Eric Allen	.25
200	Fred Barnett	.25
201	Randall Cunningham	1.00
202	Byron Evans	.25
203	Lester Holmes	.25
204	Seth Joyner	.25
205	Leonard Renfro	.25
206	Heath Sherman	.25
207	Clyde Simmons	.25
208	Johnny Bailey	.25
209	Steve Beuerlein	.25
210	Chuck Cecil	.25
211	Larry Centers	1.50
212	Ben Coleman	.25
213	Ernest Dye	.25
214	Ken Harvey	.25
215	Randal Hill	.25
216	Ricky Proel	.25
217	Deon Figures	.50
218	Barry Foster	.25
219	Eric Green	.25
220	Kevin Greene	.50
221	Carlton Haselrig	.25
222	Andre Hasting	1.50
223	Greg Lloyd	.25
224	Neil O'Donnell	.50
225	Rod Woodson	.50
226	Marion Butts	.25
227	Darren Carrington	.25
228	Darrien Gordon	.50
229	Ronnie Harmon	.25
230	Stan Humphries	.50
231	Anthony Miller	.25
232	Chris Mims	.25
233	Leslie O'Neal	.25
234	Junior Seau	.75
235	Dana Hall	.25
236	Adrian Hardy	.25
237	Brent Jones	.25
238	Tim McDonald	.25
239	Tom Rathman	.25
240	Jerry Rice	3.00
241	Dana Stubblefield	1.00
242	Ricky Watters	1.00
243	Steve Young	2.50
244	Brian Blades	.25
245	Ferrell Edmunds	.25
246	Carlton Gray	.25
247	Cortez Kennedy	.25
248	Kelvin Martin	.25
249	Dan McGwire	.25
250	Jon Vaughn	.25
251	Chris Warren	.50
252	John L. Williams	.25
253	Reggie Cobb	.25
254	Horace Copeland	.50
255	Lawrence Dawsey	.25
256	Demetrius DuBose	.25
257	Craig Erickson	.50
258	Courtney Hawkins	.25
259	John Lynch	.50
260	Hardy Nickerson	.25
261	Lamar Thomas	.50
262	Carl Banks	.25
263	Tom Carter	.50
264	Brad Edwards	.25
265	Kurt Gouveia	.25
266	Darrell Green	.25
267	Charles Mann	.25
268	Art Monk	.50
269	Mark Rypien	.25
270	Ricky Sanders	.25

A player's name in *italic* type indicates a rookie card.

1993 SP All-Pros

These cards, using a die-cut technique, feature 15 All-Pros, as indicated by the "All-Pro" logo stamped in gold foil on the card front. The front has a color action photo against a black background, plus a statistical category which the player led the league in. His name is in the gold-foil arc at the top of the card. The back has another photo, along with the player's name and team, which run along the left side. Season highlights and a card number, using an "AP" prefix, are also given on the back. The cards were randomly included in 1993 Upper Deck SP packs.

		MT
Complete Set (15):		160.00
Common Player:		1.50
Minor Stars:		3.00
Inserted 1:15		
1	Steve Young	12.00
2	Warren Moon	3.00
3	Troy Aikman	15.00
4	Dan Marino	30.00
5	Barry Sanders	30.00
6	Barry Foster	1.50
7	Emmitt Smith	30.00
8	Thurman Thomas	3.00
9	Jerry Rice	15.00
10	Sterling Sharpe	3.00
11	Anthony Miller	1.50
12	Haywood Jeffires	1.50
13	Junior Seau	3.00
14	Reggie White	3.00
15	Derrick Thomas	1.50

1994 SP

This set has reduced in size from the 270 cards in 1993 to 200 in 1994, and also has a smaller print run. The set includes more than 40 rookies in it, too. Each card in the set has a 1994 game-action photograph, including players in their throwback uniforms. A strip down the right side contains the SP logo, fading from dark to light, with an Upper Deck hologram about two-thirds of the way up. The player's name and position is also in this strip. His team name is in the lower right corner. The back has a photo of the player in the top half, with statistics and a biography in the bottom half. A card number and Upper Deck are in the upper corners. The player's name and position are under the photo. Every card in the set is also reprinted using a die-cut design to form a parallel set. One die-cut card was included in each pack. These cards have a silver-foil hologram on the back, rather than a gold-foil hologram, which appears on the regular cards. A 40-card insert set, All-Pro/Future All-Pro, was also produced; cards were randomly included in every fifth pack. These cards were also produced in a die-cut version; they were randomly included in every 75th pack. Two commemorative record-breaker cards, honoring accomplishments by Dan Marino and Jerry Rice, were also produced. One of each card was included in every case made.

		MT
Complete Set (200):		65.00
Common Player:		.20
Minor Stars:		.40
Foil Prospects:		.75
Wax Box:		75.00
1	Dan Wilkinson	1.00
2	Heath Shuler	1.00
3	Marshall Faulk	35.00
4	Willie McGinest	1.00
5	Trent Dilfer	4.00
6	Bryant Young	1.00
7	Antonio Langham	.75
8	John Thierry	.75
9	Aaron Glenn	.75
10	Charles Johnson	1.00
11	DeWayne Washington	.75
12	Johnnie Morton	1.00
13	Greg Hill	1.00
14	William Floyd	1.25
15	Derrick Alexander	1.00
16	Darnay Scott	2.00
17	Errict Rhett	1.50
18	Charlie Garner	5.00
19	Thomas Lewis	.75
20	David Palmer	.75
21	Andre Reed	.40
22	Thurman Thomas	.50
23	Bruce Smith	.20
24	Jim Kelly	.50
25	Cornelius Bennett	.20
26	Bucky Brooks	.40
27	Jeff Burris	.75
28	Jim Harbaugh	.40
29	Tony Bennett	.20
30	Quentin Coryatt	.20
31	Floyd Turner	.20
32	Roosevelt Potts	.20
33	Jeff Herrod	.20
34	Irving Fryar	.20
35	Bryan Cox	.20
36	Dan Marino	5.00
37	Terry Kirby	.20
38	Michael Stewart	.20
39	Bernie Kosar	.20
40	Aubrey Beavers	.40
41	Vincent Brisby	.75
42	Ben Coates	.50
43	Drew Bledsoe	3.00
44	Marion Butts	.20
45	Chris Slade	.20
46	Michael Timpson	.20
47	Ray Crittenden	.40
48	Rob Moore	.20
49	Johnny Mitchell	.20
50	Art Monk	.40
51	Boomer Esiason	.20
52	Ronnie Lott	.20
53	Ryan Yarborough	.75
54	Carl Pickens	1.50
55	David Klingler	.20
56	Harold Green	.20
57	John Copeland	.20
58	(Louis Oliver)	.20
59	Corey Sawyer	.20
60	Michael Jackson	.20
61	Mark Rypien	.20
62	Vinny Testaverde	.20
63	Eric Metcalf	.20
64	Eric Turner	.20
65	Haywood Jeffires	.20
66	Michael Barrow	.20
67	Cody Carlson	.20
68	Gary Brown	.20
69	Bucky Richardson	.20
70	Al Smith	.20
71	Eric Green	.20
72	Neil O'Donnell	.40
73	Barry Foster	.20
74	Greg Lloyd	.20
75	Rod Woodson	.40
76	Bam Morris	1.00
77	John L. Williams	.20
78	Anthony Miller	.20
79	Mike Pritchard	.20
80	John Elway	2.00
81	Shannon Sharpe	.40
82	Steve Atwater	.20
83	Simon Fletcher	.20
84	Glyn Milburn	.20
85	Mark Collins	.20
86	Keith Cash	.20
87	Willie Davis	.20
88	Joe Montana	3.00
89	Marcus Allen	.40
90	Neil Smith	.20
91	Derrick Thomas	.40
92	Tim Brown	.40
93	Jeff Hostetler	.20
94	Terry McDaniel	.20
95	Raghib Ismail	.20
96	Rob Fredrickson	.75
97	Harvey Williams	.20
98	Steve Wisniewski	.20
99	Stan Humphries	.50
100	Leslie O'Neal	1.00
101	Leslie O'Neal	.20
102	Junior Seau	.50
103	Ronnie Harmon	.20
104	Shawn Jefferson	.20
105	Howard Ballard	.20
106	Rick Mirer	1.00
107	Cortez Kennedy	.20
108	Chris Warren	.40
109	Brian Blades	.20
110	Sam Adams	.50
111	Gary Clark	.20
112	Steve Beuerlein	.20
113	Ron Moore	.20
114	Eric Swann	.20
115	Clyde Simmons	.20
116	Seth Joyner	.20
117	Troy Aikman	3.00
118	Charles Haley	.20
119	Alvin Harper	.20
120	Michael Irvin	1.00
121	Daryl Johnston	.20
122	Emmitt Smith	5.00
123	Shante Carver	.40
124	Dave Brown	.20
125	Rodney Hampton	.40
126	Dave Meggett	.20
127	Chris Calloway	.20
128	Mike Sherrard	.20
129	Carlton Bailey	.20
130	Randall Cunningham	.40
131	William Fuller	.20
132	Eric Allen	.20
133	Calvin Williams	.40
134	Herschel Walker	.20
135	Bernard Williams	.20
136	Henry Ellard	.20
137	Ethan Horton	.20
138	Desmond Howard	.20
139	Reggie Brooks	.20
140	John Friesz	.20
141	Tom Carter	.20
142	Terry Allen	.20
143	Adrian Cooper	.20
144	Qadry Ismail	.20
145	Warren Moon	.40
146	Henry Thomas	.20
147	Todd Steussie	.40
148	Cris Carter	.40
149	Andy Heck	.20
150	Curtis Conway	1.50
151	Erik Kramer	.40
152	Lewis Tillman	.20
153	Dante Jones	.20
154	Alonzo Spellman	.20
155	Herman Moore	2.00
156	Broderick Thomas	.20
157	Scott Mitchell	.40
158	Barry Sanders	4.00
159	Chris Spielman	.20
160	Pat Swilling	.20
161	Bennie Blades	.20
162	Sterling Sharpe	.40
163	Brett Favre	5.00
164	Reggie Cobb	.20
165	Reggie White	.40
166	Sean Jones	.20
167	George Teague	.20
168	LeShon Johnson	.20
169	Courtney Hawkins	.20
170	Jackie Harris	.20
171	Craig Erickson	.20
172	Santana Dotson	.20
173	Eric Curry	.20
174	Hardy Nickerson	.20
175	Derek Brown	.20
176	Jim Everett	.20
177	Michael Haynes	.20
178	Tyrone Hughes	.20
179	Wayne Martin	.20
180	Willie Roaf	.20
181	Irv Smith	.20
182	Jeff George	.50
183	Andre Rison	.40
184	Erric Pegram	.20
185	Bert Emanuel	3.00
186	Chris Doleman	.20
187	Ron George	.20
188	Chris Miller	.20
189	Troy Drayton	.20
190	Chris Chandler	.20
191	Jerome Bettis	2.00
192	Jimmie Jones	.20
193	Sean Gilbert	.20
194	Jerry Rice	3.00
195	Brent Jones	.20
196	Deion Sanders	2.50
197	Steve Young	3.00
198	Ricky Watters	.40
199	Dana Stubblefield	.20
200	Ken Norton	.20
RB1	Dan Marino 300 TDs	45.00
RB2	Jerry Rice 127 TDs	25.00

1994 SP Die-Cuts

This set has reduced in size from the 270 cards in 1993 to 200 in 1994, and also has a smaller print run. The set includes more than 40 rookies in it, too. Each card in the set has a 1994 game-action photograph, including players in their throwback uniforms. A strip down the right side contains the SP logo, fading from dark to light, with an Upper Deck hologram about two-thirds of the way up. The player's name and position is also in this strip. His team name is in the lower right corner. The back has a photo of the player in the top half, with statistics and a biography in the bottom half. A card number and Upper Deck are in the upper corners. The player's name and position are under the photo. Every card in the set is also reprinted using a die-cut design to form a parallel set. One die-cut card was included in each pack. These cards have a silver-foil hologram on the back, rather than a gold-foil hologram, which appears on the regular cards. A 40-card insert set, All-Pro/Future All-Pro, was also produced; cards were randomly included in every fifth pack. These cards were also produced in a die-cut version; they were randomly included in every 75th pack. Two commemorative record-breaker cards, honoring accomplishments by Dan Marino and Jerry Rice, were also produced. One of each card was included in every case made.

		MT
Complete Set (200):		200.00
Common Player:		.50
Minor Stars:		1.00
1	Dan Wilkinson	3.00
2	Heath Shuler	20.00
3	Marshall Faulk	50.00
4	Willie McGinest	3.00
5	Trent Dilfer	15.00
6	Bryant Young	4.00
7	Antonio Langham	4.00
8	John Thierry	1.00
9	Aaron Glenn	1.00
10	Charles Johnson	8.00
11	DeWayne Washington	1.00
12	Johnnie Morton	3.00
13	Greg Hill	10.00
14	William Floyd	15.00
15	Derrick Alexander	8.00
16	Darnay Scott	8.00
17	Errict Rhett	20.00
18	Charlie Garner	8.00
19	Thomas Lewis	3.00
20	David Palmer	5.00
21	Andre Reed	1.00
22	Thurman Thomas	1.00
23	Bruce Smith	1.00
24	Jim Kelly	1.00
25	Cornelius Bennett	1.00
26	Bucky Brooks	3.00
27	Jeff Burris	3.00
28	Jim Harbaugh	.50
29	Tony Bennett	.50
30	Quentin Coryatt	.50
31	Floyd Turner	.50
32	Roosevelt Potts	.50
33	Jeff Herrod	.50
34	Irving Fryar	.50
35	Bryan Cox	.50
36	Dan Marino	20.00
37	Terry Kirby	.50
38	Michael Stewart	.50
39	Bernie Kosar	.50
40	Aubrey Beavers	1.00
41	Vincent Brisby	3.00
42	Ben Coates	1.00
43	Drew Bledsoe	20.00
44	Marion Butts	.50
45	Chris Slade	.50
46	Michael Timpson	.50
47	Ray Crittenden	1.00
48	Rob Moore	.50
49	Johnny Mitchell	.50
50	Art Monk	1.00
51	Boomer Esiason	.50
52	Ronnie Lott	1.00
53	Ryan Yarborough	1.00
54	Carl Pickens	1.00
55	David Klingler	.50
56	Harold Green	.50
57	John Copeland	.50
58	.20 (Louis Oliver)	.50
59	Corey Sawyer	.50
60	Michael Jackson	.50
61	Mark Rypien	.50
62	Vinny Testaverde	.50
63	Eric Metcalf	.50
64	Eric Turner	.50
65	Haywood Jeffires	.50
66	Michael Barrow	.50
67	Cody Carlson	.50
68	Gary Brown	.50
69	Bucky Richardson	.50
70	Al Smith	.50
71	Eric Green	.50
72	Neil O'Donnell	1.00
73	Barry Foster	1.00
74	Greg Lloyd	.50
75	Rod Woodson	1.00
76	Bam Morris	10.00
77	John L. Williams	.50
78	Anthony Miller	1.00
79	Mike Pritchard	.50
80	John Elway	5.00
81	Shannon Sharpe	1.00
82	Steve Atwater	.50
83	Simon Fletcher	.50
84	Glyn Milburn	1.00
85	Mark Collins	.50
86	Keith Cash	.50
87	Willie Davis	.50
88	Joe Montana	15.00
89	Marcus Allen	1.00
90	Neil Smith	1.00
91	Derrick Thomas	1.00
92	Tim Brown	1.00
93	Jeff Hostetler	.50
94	Terry McDaniel	.50
95	Raghib Ismail	1.00
96	Rob Fredrickson	3.00
97	Harvey Williams	.50
98	Steve Wisniewski	.50
99	Stan Humphries	1.00
100	Natrone Means	12.00
101	Leslie O'Neal	.50
102	Junior Seau	1.00
103	Ronnie Harmon	.50
104	Shawn Jefferson	.50
105	Howard Ballard	.50
106	Rick Mirer	6.00
107	Cortez Kennedy	1.00
108	Chris Warren	1.00
109	Brian Blades	.50
110	Sam Adams	1.00
111	Gary Clark	.50
112	Steve Beuerlein	.50
113	Ron Moore	1.00
114	Eric Swann	.50
115	Clyde Simmons	.50
116	Seth Joyner	.50
117	Troy Aikman	8.00
118	Charles Haley	.50
119	Alvin Harper	1.00
120	Michael Irvin	4.00
121	Daryl Johnston	.50
122	Emmitt Smith	20.00
123	Shante Carver	1.00
124	Dave Brown	1.00
125	Rodney Hampton	1.00
126	Dave Meggett	.50
127	Chris Calloway	.50
128	Mike Sherrard	.50
129	Carlton Bailey	.50
130	Randall Cunningham	1.00
131	William Fuller	.50
132	Eric Allen	.50
133	Calvin Williams	.50
134	Herschel Walker	.50
135	Bernard Williams	.50
136	Henry Ellard	.50
137	Ethan Horton	.50
138	Desmond Howard	.50
139	Reggie Brooks	.50
140	John Friesz	.50
141	Tom Carter	.50
142	Terry Allen	.50
143	Adrian Cooper	.50
144	Qadry Ismail	.50
145	Warren Moon	1.00
146	Henry Thomas	.50
147	Todd Steussie	1.00
148	Cris Carter	1.00
149	Andy Heck	.50
150	Curtis Conway	1.00
151	Erik Kramer	.50
152	Lewis Tillman	.50
153	Dante Jones	.50
154	Alonzo Spellman	.50
155	Herman Moore	1.00
156	Broderick Thomas	.50
157	Scott Mitchell	1.00
158	Barry Sanders	10.00
159	Chris Spielman	.50
160	Pat Swilling	.50
161	Bennie Blades	.50
162	Sterling Sharpe	1.50
163	Brett Favre	5.00
164	Reggie Cobb	.50
165	Reggie White	1.00
166	Sean Jones	.50
167	George Teague	.50
168	LeShon Johnson	1.00
169	Courtney Hawkins	.50
170	Jackie Harris	.50
171	Craig Erickson	1.00
172	Santana Dotson	.50
173	Eric Curry	.50
174	Hardy Nickerson	.50
175	Derek Brown	.50
176	Jim Everett	.50
177	Michael Haynes	.50
178	Tyrone Hughes	.50
179	Wayne Martin	.50
180	Willie Roaf	.50
181	Irv Smith	.50
182	Jeff George	1.00
183	Andre Rison	1.00
184	Erric Pegram	.50
185	Bert Emanuel	4.00
186	Chris Doleman	.50
187	Ron George	.50
188	Chris Miller	.50
189	Troy Drayton	.50
190	Chris Chandler	.50
191	Jerome Bettis	6.00
192	Jimmie Jones	.50
193	Sean Gilbert	.50
194	Jerry Rice	8.00
195	Brent Jones	.50
196	Deion Sanders	8.00
197	Steve Young	8.00
198	Ricky Watters	1.00
199	Dana Stubblefield	.50
200	Ken Norton	.50

1994 SP All-Pro Holoviews

This 40-card Upper Deck SP insert set, titled All-Pro and Future All-Pro, uses Upper Deck's new Holoview technology. To create these holograms, each player was videotaped on a rotating turntable. The individual frames were then synthesized to produce a three-dimensional picture of the player. These cards were inserted into every fifth pack. These insert cards were also reprinted in a version using a die-cut design and rainbow foil. These cards were inserted into packs at a rate of one per every 75 packs.

		MT
Complete Set (40):		60.00
Common Player:		1.00
Minor Stars:		2.00
Inserted 1:5		
1	Jamir Miller	1.00
2	Andre Rison	2.00
3	Bucky Brooks	1.00
4	Thurman Thomas	2.00
5	John Thierry	1.00
6	Dan Wilkinson	2.00
7	Darnay Scott	2.00
8	Antonio Langham	2.00
9	Troy Aikman	6.00
10	Emmitt Smith	10.00
11	John Elway	8.00
12	Barry Sanders	12.00
13	Johnnie Morton	2.00
14	Reggie White	2.00
15	Brett Favre	12.00
16	LeShon Johnson	1.00
17	Joe Montana	6.00
18	Greg Hill	1.00
19	Calvin Williams	1.00
20	Tim Brown	2.00
21	Isaac Bruce	4.00
22	Jerome Bettis	2.00
23	Dan Marino	10.00
24	O.J. McDuffie	2.00
25	Willie McGinest	1.00
26	Mario Bates	1.00
27	Rodney Hampton	1.00
28	Thomas Lewis	1.00
29	Aaron Glenn	1.00
30	Barry Foster	1.00
31	Charles Johnson	2.00
32	Steve Young	5.00
33	Jerry Rice	6.00
34	Bryant Young	1.00

35	William Floyd	1.00
36	Sam Adams	1.00
37	Rick Mirer	2.00
38	Errict Rhett	1.00
39	Reggie Brooks	1.00
40	Heath Shuler	2.00

1994 SP All-Pro Holoview Die-Cuts

This 40-card Upper Deck SP insert set, titled All-Pro and Future All-Pro, uses Upper Deck's new Holoview technology. To create these holograms, each player was videotaped on a rotating turntable. The individual frames were then synthesized to produce a three-dimensional picture of the player. These cards were inserted into every fifth pack. These insert cards were also reprinted in a version using a die-cut design and rainbow foil. These cards were inserted into packs at a rate of one per every 75 packs.

		MT
Complete Set (40):		1600.
Common Player:		15.00
Minor Stars:		30.00
1	Jamir Miller	15.00
2	Andre Rison	15.00
3	Bucky Brooks	15.00
4	Thurman Thomas	30.00
5	John Thierry	15.00
6	Dan Wilkinson	15.00
7	Darnay Scott	50.00
8	Antonio Langham	15.00
9	Troy Aikman	100.00
10	Emmitt Smith	200.00
11	John Elway	80.00
12	Barry Sanders	100.00
13	Johnnie Morton	15.00
14	Reggie White	30.00
15	Brett Favre	200.00
16	LeShon Johnson	15.00
17	Joe Montana	100.00
18	Greg Hill	30.00
19	Calvin Jones	15.00
20	Tim Brown	30.00
21	Isaac Bruce	100.00
22	Jerome Bettis	30.00
23	Dan Marino	200.00
24	O.J. McDuffie	30.00
25	Willie McGinest	15.00
26	Mario Bates	30.00
27	Rodney Hampton	15.00
28	Thomas Lewis	15.00
29	Aaron Glenn	15.00
30	Barry Foster	15.00
31	Charles Johnson	30.00
32	Steve Young	80.00
33	Jerry Rice	100.00
34	Bryant Young	15.00
35	William Floyd	30.00
36	Sam Adams	15.00
37	Rick Mirer	30.00
38	Errict Rhett	50.00
39	Reggie Brooks	15.00
40	Heath Shuler	30.00

1995 SP

Upper Deck's 1995 SP football contains 200 cards -

180 regular players and 20 Premier Prospects. Each regular card front has a full-bleed color photo on it, with the player's name stamped in copper foil on the right side. Copper foil is also used along the right side for the brand logo and a border between the photo and the logo. A second color photo appears on the card back, which includes biographical information, a career achievement and statistics. "Premier Prospects" are labeled on the fronts as being such. Insert cards here include: All-Pros, Holoview F/X and Special FX, and Joe Montana Trilogy (MT17-MT20). A special Dan Marino Record Breaker (DM1) insert and a Montana Tribute card were also produced.

		MT
Complete Set (200):		120.00
Common Player:		.20
Minor Stars:		.40
Wax Box:		200.00
1	Ki-Jana Carter	1.00
2	Eric Zeier	.40
3	Steve McNair	10.00
4	Michael Westbrook	2.00
5	Kerry Collins	3.00
6	Joey Galloway	8.00
7	Kevin Carter	.40
8	Mike Mamula	.40
9	Kyle Brady	.40
10	J.J. Stokes	2.50
11	Tyrone Poole	.40
12	Rashaan Salaam	1.00
13	Sherman Williams	.50
14	Luther Elliss	.20
15	James Stewart	4.00
16	Tamarick Vanover	1.50
17	Napoleon Kaufman	7.00
18	Curtis Martin	10.00
19	Tyrone Wheatley	1.00
20	Frank Sanders	.40
21	Devin Bush	.40
22	Terance Mathis	.20
23	Bert Emanual	.75
24	Eric Metcalf	.20
25	Craig Heyward	.20
26	Jeff George	.40
27	Mark Carrier	.20
28	Pete Metzelaars	.20
29	Frank Reich	.20
30	Sam Mills	.20
31	John Kasay	.20
32	Willie Green	.20
33	Jeff Graham	.20
34	Curtis Conway	.75
35	Steve Walsh	.20
36	Erik Kramer	.40
37	Michael Timpson	.20
38	Mark Carrier	.20
39	Troy Aikman	3.00
40	Michael Irvin	.40
41	Charles Haley	.20
42	Deion Sanders	2.50
43	Jay Novacek	.20
44	Emmitt Smith	6.00
45	Herman Moore	1.00
46	Scott Mitchell	.40
47	Bennie Blades	.20
48	Johnnie Morton	.20
49	Chris Spielman	.20
50	Barry Sanders	3.00
51	Edgar Bennett	.20
52	Reggie White	.40
53	Sean Jones	.20
54	Mark Ingram	.20
55	Robert Brooks	.40
56	Brett Favre	6.00
57	Lovell Pinkney	.20
58	Chris Miller	.20
59	Isaac Bruce	.50
60	Roman Phifer	.20
61	Sean Gilbert	.20
62	Jerome Bettis	1.00
63	Derrick Alexander	.20
64	Cris Carter	.40
65	Jake Reed	.20
66	Robert Smith	.20
67	David Palmer	.20
68	Warren Moon	.40
69	Ray Zellars	.40
70	Jim Everett	.20
71	Michael Haynes	.20
72	Quinn Early	.20
73	Willie Roaf	.20
74	Mario Bates	1.00
75	Mike Sherrard	.20
76	Chris Calloway	.20
77	Dave Brown	.20
78	Thomas Lewis	.20
79	Herschel Walker	.20
80	Rodney Hampton	.40
81	Fred Barnett	.20
82	Calvin Williams	.20
83	Randall Cunningham	.20
84	Charlie Garner	.20
85	Bobby Taylor	.20
86	Ricky Watters	.40
87	Dave Kreig	.20
88	Rob Moore	.20
89	Eric Swann	.20
90	Clyde Simmons	.20
91	Seth Joyner	.20
92	Garrison Hearst	.40
93	Jerry Rice	3.00
94	Bryant Young	.20
95	Brent Jones	.20
96	Ken Norton	.20
97	William Floyd	1.50
98	Steve Young	3.00
99	Warren Sapp	.40
100	Trent Dilfer	1.50
101	Alvin Harper	.40
102	Hardy Nickerson	.20
103	Derrick Brooks	.20
104	Errict Rhett	.40
105	Henry Ellard	.20
106	Ken Harvey	.20
107	Gus Frerotte	1.00
108	Brian Mitchell	.20
109	Terry Allen	.20
110	Heath Shuler	1.50
111	Jim Kelly	.40
112	Andre Reed	.20
113	Bruce Smith	.20
114	Darick Holmes	1.50
115	Bryce Paup	.20
116	Cornelius Bennett	.20
117	Carl Pickens	.50
118	Darnay Scott	1.25
119	Jeff Blake	2.00
120	Steve Tovar	.20
121	Tony McGee	.20
122	Dan Wilkinson	.20
123	Craig Powell	.20
124	Vinny Testaverde	.20
125	Eric Turner	.20
126	Leroy Hoard	.20
127	Lorenzo White	.20
128	Andre Rison	.40
129	Shannon Sharpe	.40
130	Terrell Davis	35.00
131	Anthony Miller	.20
132	Mike Pritchard	.20
133	Steve Atwater	.20
134	John Elway	2.00
135	Haywood Jeffires	.20
136	Gary Brown	.20
137	Al Smith	.20
138	Rodney Thomas	.50
139	Ray Childress	.20
140	Mel Gray	.20
141	Craig Erickson	.20
142	Sean Dawkins	.20
143	Ken Dilger	1.25
144	Ellis Johnson	.20
145	Quentin Coryatt	.20
146	Marshall Faulk	1.50
147	Tony Boselli	.40
148	Rob Johnson	7.00
149	Desmond Howard	.20
150	Steve Beuerlein	.20
151	Reggie Cobb	.20
152	Jeff Lageman	.20
153	Willie Davis	.20
154	Marcus Allen	.40
155	Neil Smith	.20
156	Greg Hill	.75
157	Steve Bono	.50
158	Derrick Thomas	.40
159	Jeff Hostetler	.20
160	Harvey Williams	.20
161	Raghib Ismail	.20
162	Chester McGlockton	.20
163	Terry McDaniel	.20
164	Tim Brown	.40
165	Terry Kirby	.20
166	Irving Fryar	.20
167	O.J. McDuffie	.20
168	Bryan Cox	.20
169	Eric Green	.20
170	Dan Marino	6.00
171	Ben Coates	.20
172	Vincent Brisby	.20
173	Chris Slade	.20
174	Ty Law	.20
175	Vincent Brown	.20
176	Drew Bledsoe	3.00
177	Johnny Mitchell	.20
178	Boomer Esiason	.20
179	Wayne Chrebet	7.00
180	Hugh Douglas	.20
181	Ron Moore	.20
182	Aaron Glenn	.20
183	Mark Bruener	1.00
184	Neil O'Donnell	.40
185	Charles Johnson	.75
186	Greg Lloyd	.40
187	Rod Woodson	.40
188	Bam Morris	1.50
189	Terrell Fletcher	1.00
190	Terrance Shaw	.40
191	Stan Humphries	.40
192	Junior Seau	.40
193	Leslie O'Neal	.20
194	Natrone Means	2.00
195	Christian Fauria	.20
196	Rick Mirer	1.00
197	Sam Adams	.20
198	Cortez Kennedy	.20
199	Eugene Robinson	.20
200	Chris Warren	.40
NNO	Dan Marino Tribute	70.00
NNO	Joe Montana Salute	40.00

1995 SP All-Pros

These All-Pro die-cut cards came in two versions - silver, which was randomly inserted one per every five packs, and gold, which was found one per every 62 packs. The top and bottom of the card are die-cut, with either silver or gold foil; the player's name is at the top, while his team name is at the bottom. All-Pro is written in foil on the left side of the card; the player's position is in foil on the right, along with the brand logo. Card backs, numbered with an "AP" prefix, have a close-up shot of the player, plus a brief summary of the player's achievements.

		MT
Complete Set (20):		60.00
Common Player:		2.50
Comp. Gold Set (20):		550.00
Gold Cards:		3x-6x
1	Marshall Faulk	5.00
2	Natrone Means	2.50
3	Emmitt Smith	8.00
4	Brett Favre	8.00
5	Michael Westbrook	3.00
6	Jerry Rice	5.00
7	John Elway	4.00
8	Troy Aikman	5.00
9	Rashaan Salaam	4.00
10	Jerome Bettis	2.50
11	Drew Bledsoe	5.00
12	Kerry Collins	3.00
13	Dan Marino	8.00
14	Tyrone Wheatley	3.00
15	Steve McNair	4.00
16	Steve Young	5.00
17	Eric Zeier	3.00
18	Errict Rhett	4.00
19	Michael Irvin	3.00
20	Barry Sanders	5.00

1995 SP Holoviews

Some of the NFL's top stars and promising rookies are showcased in this 40-card insert set. Cards were randomly included in 1995 Upper Deck football, one per every five packs. The horizontal card front features a glossy color photo on the right side, along with a rectangle which says "Holoview." A hologram of the player up close, plus his name, team name and position, are on the left side. The back is also horizontal and includes an action photo on the left, plus a summary of the player's accomplishments on the right. Cards are numbered using a fraction format - 13/40, etc. Each Holoview was also made in a die-cut version, seeded one per every 75 packs.

		MT
Complete Set (40):		125.00
Common Player:		1.00
Minor Stars:		2.00

Inserted 1:5

1	Joe Montana	10.00
2	Dan Marino	12.00
3	Drew Bledsoe	8.00
4	Ben Coates	1.00
5	Curtis Martin	8.00
6	Kyle Brady	1.00
7	Marshall Faulk	3.00
8	Ki-Jana Carter	2.00
9	Leroy Hoard	1.00
10	James O. Stewart	1.00
11	Mark Bruener	1.00
12	Charles Johnson	1.00
13	Rod Woodson	1.00
14	John Elway	10.00
15	Tim Brown	1.00
16	Napoleon Kaufman	8.00
17	Natrone Means	2.00
18	Jimmy Oliver	1.00
19	Christian Fauria	1.00
20	Joey Galloway	4.00
21	Chris Warren	1.00
22	Kerry Collins	3.00
23	Mario Bates	1.00
24	Jerome Bettis	2.00
25	William Floyd	1.00
26	Jerry Rice	8.00
27	J.J. Stokes	2.00
28	Steve Young	6.00
29	Troy Aikman	8.00
30	Michael Irvin	2.00
31	Emmitt Smith	12.00
32	Rodney Hampton	1.00
33	Heath Shuler	2.00
34	Michael Westbrook	2.00
35	Barry Sanders	15.00
36	Brett Favre	15.00
37	Cris Carter	3.00
38	Warren Moon	2.00
39	James A. Stewart	1.00
40	Errict Rhett	1.00

1995 SP Holoview Die-Cuts

These 40 1995 Upper Deck SP inserts are the same as the regular Holoview insert cards, except they are die-cut around the top of the card. They are seeded one per every 75 packs.

		MT
Complete Set (40):		1600.
Common Player:		7.00
1	Joe Montana	70.00
2	Dan Marino	125.00
3	Drew Bledsoe	70.00
4	Ben Coates	7.00
5	Curtis Martin	80.00
6	Kyle Brady	7.00
7	Marshall Faulk	20.00
8	Ki-Jana Carter	14.00
9	Leroy Hoard	7.00
10	James O. Stewart	14.00
11	Mark Bruener	7.00
12	Charles Johnson	7.00
13	Rod Woodson	7.00
14	John Elway	50.00
15	Tim Brown	14.00
16	Napoleon Kaufman	14.00
17	Natrone Means	14.00
18	Jimmy Oliver	7.00
19	Christian Fauria	7.00
20	Joey Galloway	40.00
21	Chris Warren	14.00
22	Kerry Collins	20.00
23	Mario Bates	14.00
24	Jerome Bettis	14.00
25	William Floyd	14.00
26	Jerry Rice	70.00
27	J.J. Stokes	25.00
28	Steve Young	50.00
29	Troy Aikman	70.00
30	Michael Irvin	14.00
31	Emmitt Smith	125.00
32	Rodney Hampton	14.00
33	Heath Shuler	14.00
34	Michael Westbrook	14.00
35	Barry Sanders	70.00
36	Brett Favre	125.00
37	Cris Carter	14.00
38	Warren Moon	14.00
39	James A. Stewart	14.00
40	Errict Rhett	16.00

1995 SP Championship

Upper Deck's debut SP Championship series has 225 cards, including 45 Future Champions subset cards. The Championship series of cards is the retail-only spinoff of Upper Deck's hobby-only SP product. All cards, inserts, wrappers and box designs are completely different in the retail and hobby versions. Each card front has a full-bleed color photo on it, plus a brand logo stamped in gold foil. The player's name and position are at the bottom, along with the team name, which is in an oval. Each card in the regular-issue set is also paralleled in a die-cut version that appears one per pack. One per every 15 packs holds a Showcase of the Playoffs insert card. This is a 20-card set of top NFL stars who could make an impact in the playoffs. This insert is also featured in a die-cut version that is seeded one card per every 40 packs.

		MT
Complete Set (225):		65.00
Common Player:		.15
Minor Stars:		.30
Inserted 1:1		
Wax Box:		150.00
1	Frank Sanders	2.50
2	Stoney Case	.30
3	Lorenzo Styles	.30
4	Todd Collins	.30
5	Darick Holmes	.60
6	Brian DeMarco	.30
7	Tyrone Poole	.30
8	Kerry Collins	2.00
9	Rashaan Salaam	.75
10	Steve Stenstrom	.30
11	Ki-Jana Carter	.75
12	Eric Zeier	1.25
13	Sherman Williams	.30
14	Terrell Davis	30.00
15	David Dunn	.30
16	Luther Elliss	.30
17	Craig Newsome	.30
18	Antonio Freeman	10.00
19	Steve McNair	6.00
20	Anthony Cook	.30
21	Rodney Thomas	.30
22	Ellis Johnson	.30
23	Ken Dilger	.30
24	James O. Stewart	.75
25	Pete Mitchell	.30
26	Tamarick Vanover	.60
27	Orlanda Thomas	.30
28	Corey Fuller	.30
29	Curtis Martin	7.00
30	Ty Law	.30
31	Roell Preston	.75
32	Mark Fields	.30
33	Tyrone Wheatley	1.00
34	Kyle Brady	.50
35	Napoleon Kaufman	5.00
36	Kordell Stewart	10.00
37	Mark Bruener	.75
38	Terrance Shaw	.30
39	Terrell Fletcher	.50
40	J.J. Stokes	1.50
41	Christian Fauria	.30
42	Joey Galloway	6.00
43	Kevin Carter	.30
44	Warren Sapp	.75
45	Michael Westbrook	1.50
46	Clyde Simmons	.15
47	Rob Moore	.15
48	Seth Joyner	.15
49	Dave Kreig	.15
50	Garrison Hearst	.40
51	Aeneas Williams	.15
52	Terance Mathis	.15
53	Bert Emanual	.50
54	Chris Doleman	.15
55	Craig Heyward	.15
56	Jeff George	.15
57	Eric Metcalf	.15
58	Jim Kelly	.30

59	Andre Reed	.15
60	Russell Copeland	.15
61	Bruce Smith	.15
62	Cornelius Bennett	.15
63	Jeff Burris	.15
64	Mark Carrier	.15
65	Pete Metzelaars	.15
66	Frank Reich	.15
67	Sam Mills	.15
68	John Kasay	.15
69	Willie Green	.15
70	Curtis Conway	.15
71	Erik Kramer	.15
72	Donnell Woolford	.15
73	Mark Carrier	.15
74	Jeff Graham	.15
75	Raymont Harris	.15
76	Carl Pickens	.30
77	Darnay Scott	.30
78	*Jeff Blake*	1.00
79	Dan Wilkinson	.15
80	Tony McGee	.15
81	Eric Bienemy	.15
82	Vinny Testaverde	.15
83	Eric Turner	.15
84	Leroy Hoard	.15
85	Lorenzo White	.15
86	Antonio Langham	.15
87	Andre Rison	.15
88	Troy Aikman	1.50
89	Michael Irvin	.50
90	Charles Haley	.15
91	Daryl Johnston	.15
92	Jay Novacek	.15
93	Emmitt Smith	3.00
94	Shannon Sharpe	.15
95	Anthony Miller	.15
96	Mike Pritchard	.15
97	Glyn Milburn	.15
98	Simon Fletcher	.15
99	John Elway	.75
100	Henry Thomas	.15
101	Herman Moore	.50
102	Scott Mitchell	.15
103	Bennie Blades	.15
104	Chris Spielman	.15
105	Barry Sanders	2.00
106	Mark Ingram	.15
107	Edgar Bennett	.15
108	Reggie White	.30
109	Sean Jones	.15
110	Robert Brooks	.30
111	Brett Favre	3.00
112	Chris Chandler	.15
113	Haywood Jeffires	.15
114	Gary Brown	.15
115	Al Smith	.15
116	Ray Childress	.15
117	Mel Gray	.15
118	Jim Harbaugh	.15
119	Sean Dawkins	.15
120	Roosevelt Potts	.15
121	Marshall Faulk	1.00
122	Tony Bennett	.15
123	Quentin Coryatt	.15
124	Desmond Howard	.15
125	Tony Boselli	.15
126	Steve Beuerlein	.15
127	Jeff Lageman	.15
128	*Rob Johnson*	3.00
129	Ernest Givins	.15
130	Willie Davis	.15
131	Marcus Allen	.30
132	Neil Smith	.15
133	Greg Hill	.50
134	Steve Bono	.30
135	Lake Dawson	.50
136	Dan Marino	3.00
137	Terry Kirby	.15
138	Irvin Fryar	.15
139	O.J. McDuffie	.15
140	Bryan Cox	.15
141	Eric Green	.15
142	Cris Carter	.15
143	Robert Smith	.15
144	John Randle	.15
145	Jake Reed	.15
146	DeWayne Washington	.15
147	Warren Moon	.30
148	Dave Meggett	.15
149	Ben Coates	.15
150	Vincent Brisby	.15
151	Willie McGinest	.15
152	Chris Slade	.15
153	Drew Bledsoe	2.00
154	Eric Allen	.15
155	Mario Bates	.50
156	Jim Everett	.15
157	Renaldo Turnbull	.15
158	Tyrone Hughes	.15
159	Michael Haynes	.15
160	Mike Sherrard	.15
161	Dave Brown	.15
162	Chris Calloway	.15
163	Keith Hamilton	.15
164	Rodney Hampton	.15
165	Herschel Walker	.15
166	Adrian Murrell	.50
167	Johnny Mitchell	.15
168	Boomer Esiason	.15
169	Mo Lewis	.15
170	Brad Baxter	.15
171	Aaron Glenn	.15
172	Jeff Hostetler	.15
173	Harvey Williams	.15
174	Tim Brown	.30
175	Terry McDaniel	.15

176	Pat Swilling	.15
177	Raghib Ismail	.15
178	Randall Cunningham	.15
179	Calvin Williams	.15
180	Ricky Watters	.30
181	Charlie Garner	.15
182	Fred Barnett	.15
183	Rodney Peete	.15
184	Neil O'Donnell	.30
185	Charles Johnson	.40
186	Rod Woodson	.15
187	Bam Morris	.75
188	Kevin Greene	.15
189	Greg Lloyd	.15
190	Chris Miller	.15
191	Isaac Bruce	1.50
192	Roman Phifer	.15
193	Jerome Bettis	.30
194	Carlos Jenkins	.15
195	Troy Drayton	.15
196	Andre Coleman	.15
197	Natrone Means	.75
198	Leslie O'Neal	.15
199	Junior Seau	.30
200	Tony Martin	.15
201	Stan Humphries	.15
202	Steve Young	2.00
203	Jerry Rice	2.00
204	Brent Jones	.15
205	Dana Stubblefield	.15
206	Lee Woodall	.15
207	Merton Hanks	.15
208	Rick Mirer	.30
209	Brian Blades	.15
210	Chris Warren	.30
211	Sam Adams	.15
212	Cortez Kennedy	.15
213	Eugene Robinson	.15
214	Alvin Harper	.15
215	Trent Dilfer	.50
216	Hardy Nickerson	.15
217	Errict Rhett	.30
218	Eric Curry	.15
219	Jackie Harris	.15
220	Henry Ellard	.15
221	Terry Allen	.15
222	Brian Mitchell	.15
223	Ken Harvey	.15
224	Gus Frerotte	.75
225	Heath Shuler	1.25

1995 SP Championship Die-Cuts

The 225-card, regular-size set was a parallel set to the SP Championship issue, inserted every pack. The cards are essentially identical, except for the die-cut card tops.

	MT
Complete Set (225):	150.00
Common Player (1-225):	.50
Die-Cut Cards:	2x-4x

1995 SP Championship Playoff Showcase

These cards feature a color action photo of a player in a box in the center. The set name is in foil at the bottom, along with the player's name and position. A gold-foiled brand logo is above the photo. Card backs are numbered using a "PS" prefix. Cards were randomly included in every 15th pack of 1995 Upper Deck SP Championship product. The inserts were also created in a die-cut version; these cards are seeded one per every 40 packs.

	MT
Complete Set (20):	100.00
Common Player:	1.00
Minor Stars:	2.00
Inserted 1:15	275.00
Die-Cut Cards:	2x
Inserted 1:20	
1 Troy Aikman	8.00
2 Jerry Rice	8.00
3 Isaac Bruce	2.00
4 Rodney Peete	1.00
5 Rashaan Salaam	2.00
6 Brett Favre	15.00
7 Alvin Harper	1.00
8 Cris Carter	2.00
9 Michael Westbrook	2.00
10 Jeff George	2.00
11 Natrone Means	2.00
12 Dan Marino	12.00
13 Steve Bono	2.00
14 Greg Lloyd	1.00
15 Jim Kelly	2.00
16 Jeff Hostetler	1.00
17 Marshall Faulk	3.00
18 John Elway	10.00
19 Jeff Blake	2.00
20 Andre Rison	1.00

1996 SP

The 188-card, regular-sized set was issued in eight-card packs and included the subset, Premiere Prospects. The release included a five-card SPX Force preview along with an autographed parallel version. Other inserts were: Focus On The Future, Explosive, Holoview and F/X Holoview. The base set cards include an action shot with a player headshot inset along the right border. The player's name appears on the top border with team nickname and position along the bottom.

	MT
Complete Set (188):	150.00
Common Player:	.20
Minor Stars:	.40
Wax Box:	225.00
1 *Keyshawn Johnson*	12.00
2 *Kevin Hardy*	.75
3 *Simeon Rice*	.75
4 *Jonathan Ogden*	.20
5 *Eddie George*	20.00
6 *Terry Glenn*	8.00
7 *Terrell Owens*	20.00
8 *Tim Biakabutuka*	6.00
9 *Lawrence Phillips*	5.00
10 *Alex Molden*	.20
11 *Regan Upshaw*	.20
12 *Rickey Dudley*	1.75
13 *Duane Clemons*	.20
14 *John Mobley*	.20
15 *Eddie Kennison*	3.00
16 *Karim Abdul-Jabbar*	3.00
17 *Eric Moulds*	12.00
18 *Marvin Harrison*	15.00
19 *Stepfret Williams*	.20
20 *Stephen Davis*	20.00
21 Deion Sanders	1.50
22 Emmitt Smith	5.00
23 Troy Aikman	2.50
24 Michael Irvin	.40
25 Herschel Walker	.20
26 Kavika Pittman	.20
27 Andre Hastings	.20
28 Jerome Bettis	.40
29 Mike Tomczak	.20
30 Kordell Stewart	2.00

31	Charles Johnson	.20
32	Greg Lloyd	.20
33	Brett Favre	5.00
34	Mark Chmura	.20
35	Edgar Bennett	.20
36	Robert Brooks	.20
37	Craig Newsome	.20
38	Reggie White	.40
39	Marshall Faulk	1.50
40	Jim Harbaugh	.20
41	Sean Dawkins	.20
42	Quentin Coryatt	.20
43	Ray Buchanan	.20
44	Ken Dilger	.20
45	Jerry Rice	2.50
46	J.J. Stokes	.40
47	Steve Young	2.00
48	Derek Loville	.20
49	Terry Kirby	.20
50	Ken Norton	.20
51	Tamarick Vanover	1.00
52	Steve Bono	.20
53	Marcus Allen	.40
54	Neil Smith	.20
55	Derrick Thomas	.20
56	Dale Carter	.20
57	Terance Mathis	.20
58	Eric Metcalf	.20
59	*Jamal Anderson*	45.00
60	Bert Emanuel	.20
61	Craig Heyward	.20
62	Cornelius Bennett	.20
63	Tony Martin	.20
64	Stan Humphries	.20
65	Andre Coleman	.20
66	Junior Seau	.20
67	Terrell Fletcher	.20
68	John Carney	.20
69	Charlie Jones	.20
70	Ricky Watters	.40
71	Charlie Garner	.20
72	*Bobby Hoying*	4.00
73	Jason Dunn	.20
74	Bobby Taylor	.20
75	Irving Fryar	.20
76	Jim Kelly	.40
77	Thurman Thomas	.40
78	Darick Holmes	.20
79	Bryce Paup	.20
80	Bruce Smith	.20
81	Andre Reed	.20
82	Glyn Milburn	.20
83	Brett Perriman	.20
84	Herman Moore	.75
85	Scott Mitchell	.20
86	Barry Sanders	3.00
87	Johnnie Morton	.20
88	Dan Marino	5.00
89	O.J. McDuffie	.20
90	Stanley Pritchett	.20
91	*Zach Thomas*	2.50
92	Daryl Gardner	.20
93	Rashaan Salaam	.75
94	Erik Kramer	.20
95	Curtis Conway	.20
96	*Bobby Engram*	.75
97	Walt Harris	.20
98	Bryan Cox	.20
99	John Elway	2.00
100	Terrell Davis	5.00
101	Anthony Miller	.20
102	Shannon Sharpe	.20
103	Steve Atwater	.20
104	Jeff Lewis	.20
105	Joey Galloway	1.50
106	Chris Warren	.20
107	Rick Mirer	.20
108	Cortez Kennedy	.20
109	Michael Sinclair	.20
110	John Friesz	.20
111	Warren Moon	.20
112	Cris Carter	.20
113	Jake Reed	.20
114	Robert Smith	.20
115	John Randle	.20
116	Orlanda Thomas	.20
117	Jeff Hostetler	.20
118	Tim Brown	.20
119	Joe Aska	.20
120	Napoleon Kaufman	.20
121	Terry McDaniel	.20
122	Harvey Williams	.20
123	Trent Dilfer	.20
124	Reggie Brooks	.20
125	Alvin Harper	.20
126	*Mike Alstott*	5.00
127	Hardy Nickerson	.20
128	Mario Bates	.20
129	Jim Everett	.20
130	Tyrone Hughes	.20
131	Michael Haynes	.20
132	Eric Allen	.20
133	Isaac Bruce	1.50
134	Kevin Carter	.20
135	Leslie O'Neal	.20
136	*Tony Banks*	6.00
137	Chris Chandler	.20
138	Steve McNair	2.00
139	Chris Sanders	.20
140	Ronnie Harmon	.20
141	Willie Davis	.20
142	Michael Westbrook	.40
143	Terry Allen	.20
144	Brian Mitchell	.20
145	Henry Ellard	.20
146	Gus Frerotte	.20
147	Kerry Collins	.50
148	Sam Mills	.20

149	Wesley Walls	.20
150	Kevin Greene	.20
151	*Mushin Muhammad*	8.00
152	Winslow Oliver	.20
153	Jeff Blake	.50
154	Carl Pickens	.20
155	Darnay Scott	.20
156	Garrison Hearst	.20
157	Marco Battaglia	.20
158	Drew Bledsoe	2.00
159	Curtis Martin	4.00
160	Shawn Jefferson	.20
161	Ben Coates	.20
162	Lawyer Milloy	.20
163	Tyrone Wheatley	.20
164	Rodney Hampton	.20
165	Chris Calloway	.20
166	Dave Brown	.20
167	*Amani Toomer*	.40
168	Vinny Testaverde	.20
169	Michael Jackson	.20
170	Eric Turner	.20
171	DeRon Jenkins	.20
172	*Jermaine Lewis*	2.00
173	Frank Sanders	.20
174	Rob Moore	.20
175	Kent Graham	.20
176	*Leeland McElroy*	.50
177	Larry Centers	.20
178	Eric Swann	.20
179	Mark Brunell	1.50
180	Willie Jackson	.20
181	James O. Stewart	.20
182	Natrone Means	.20
183	*Tony Brackens*	.75
184	Adrian Murrell	.20
185	Neil O'Donnell	.20
186	Hugh Douglas	.20
187	Jeff Graham	.20
188	*Alex Van Dyke*	.40

1996 SP Explosive

The 20-card, regular-sized, die-cut set was inserted every 360 packs of 1996 Upper Deck SP football. The die-cut cards are in the shape of an "X" and feature a circular headshot of the player over a black-and-white background. The player's first name appears in the lower left corner in lowercase letters with the last name in the upper right corner, also in lowercase. The card backs are numbered with the "X" prefix.

	MT
Complete Set (20):	1700.
Common Player:	25.00
1 Emmitt Smith	250.00
2 Jerry Rice	125.00
3 Rashaan Salaam	25.00
4 Brett Favre	250.00
5 Tim Brown	25.00
6 Tim Biakabutuka	75.00
7 John Elway	100.00
8 Steve Young	100.00
9 Napoleon Kaufman	25.00
10 Troy Aikman	125.00
11 Drew Bledsoe	125.00
12 Carl Pickens	25.00
13 Dan Marino	250.00
14 Eddie George	150.00
15 Joey Galloway	75.00
16 Deion Sanders	75.00
17 Curtis Martin	150.00
18 Marshall Faulk	60.00
19 Keyshawn Johnson	75.00
20 Barry Sanders	160.00

Values quoted in this guide reflect the retail price of a card — the price a collector can expect to pay when buying a card from a dealer. The wholesale price — that which a collector can expect to receive from a dealer when selling cards — will be significantly lower, depending on desirability and condition.

1996 SP Focus on the Future

The 30-card, regular-sized, die-cut set was inserted every 30 packs of SP football. The card fronts feature a color player shot over a gold background with a slide film-type addition on the right side. The cel contains a color headshot of the player with the photographer listed along the right border. The card backs are numbered with the "F" prefix.

	MT
Complete Set (30):	300.00
Common Player:	6.00
1 Leeland McElroy	6.00
2 Frank Sanders	6.00
3 Darick Holmes	6.00
4 Eric Moulds	12.00
5 Kerry Collins	6.00
6 Tim Biakabutuka	15.00
7 Ki-Jana Carter	6.00
8 Jeff Blake	10.00
9 John Mobley	6.00
10 Johnnie Morton	6.00
11 Eddie George	40.00
12 Steve McNair	20.00
13 Marshall Faulk	8.00
14 Kevin Hardy	6.00
15 Greg Hill	6.00
16 Tamarick Vanover	6.00
17 Karim Abdul-Jabbar	30.00
18 Drew Bledsoe	30.00
19 Curtis Martin	40.00
20 Danny Kanell	6.00
21 Keyshawn Johnson	20.00
22 Napoleon Kaufman	6.00
23 Rickey Dudley	8.00
24 Kordell Stewart	30.00
25 Lawrence Phillips	15.00
26 Isaac Bruce	15.00
27 J.J. Stokes	6.00
28 Joey Galloway	25.00
29 Errict Rhett	8.00
30 Mike Alstott	8.00

1996 SP Holoview

The 48-card, regular-sized set was inserted every seven packs of SP football. The card fronts feature a color player shot over a Holoview image headshot and multiple team logo. The player's name, position and team nickname appears in the upper right quadrant. A 48-card, die-cut parallel version was inserted every 75 packs. The cards also feature the same Holoview image but have a gold top border instead of a team-color top border.

	MT
Complete Set (48):	250.00
Common Player:	2.00
1 Jerry Rice	12.00
2 Herman Moore	4.00
3 Kerry Collins	4.00
4 Brett Favre	25.00
5 Junior Seau	2.00
6 Troy Aikman	12.00

7	John Elway	8.00
8	Steve Young	8.00
9	Reggie White	4.00
10	Kordell Stewart	12.00
11	Drew Bledsoe	12.00
12	Jeff Blake	4.00
13	Dan Marino	25.00
14	Curtis Martin	15.00
15	Marshall Faulk	6.00
16	Greg Lloyd	2.00
17	Cris Carter	2.00
18	Isaac Bruce	6.00
19	Joey Galloway	8.00
20	Barry Sanders	12.00
21	Emmitt Smith	25.00
22	Edgar Bennett	2.00
23	Rashaan Salaam	4.00
24	Steve McNair	8.00
25	Tamarick Vanover	4.00
26	Deion Sanders	6.00
27	Keyshawn Johnson	6.00
28	Kevin Hardy	2.00
29	Simeon Rice	2.00
30	Lawrence Phillips	6.00
31	Tim Biakabutuka	6.00
32	Terry Glenn	12.00
33	Rickey Dudley	4.00
34	Regan Upshaw	2.00
35	Eddie George	15.00
36	John Mobley	2.00
37	Eddie Kennison	8.00
38	Marvin Harrison	8.00
39	Leeland McElroy	4.00
40	Eric Moulds	4.00
41	Alex Van Dyke	4.00
42	Mike Alstott	5.00
43	Jeff Lewis	2.00
44	Bobby Engram	4.00
45	Derrick Mayes	2.00
46	Karim Abdul-Jabbar	10.00
47	Stepfret Williams	2.00
48	Stephen Davis	4.00

1996 SP Holoview Die-Cuts

Holoview Die-Cuts are a parallel set to the Holoview Collection, and seeded one per 74 packs. The 48 regular Holoviews are double die-cut on the top and bottom and have gold foil added to them.

	MT
Complete Set (48):	1000.
Holoview Die-Cuts:	2x-4x

1996 SP SPx Force

The five-card, regular-size die-cut set was inserted every 950 packs of 1996 SP football. Each card contained four Holoview images of top players at quarterback, running back, wide receiver and rookies. The fifth card features Holoviews of the top four at each position (and rookies) and will have an autographed parallel version (1:8,820).

	MT
Complete Set (4):	300.00
Common Player:	50.00

Set price does not include Autographs.

1	Keyshawn Johnson, Lawrence Phillips, Terry Glenn, Tim Biakabutuka	50.00
2	Barry Sanders, Emmitt Smith, Marshall Faulk, Curtis Martin	90.00
3	Dan Marino, Brett Favre, Drew Bledsoe, Troy Aikman	100.00
4	Jerry Rice, Herman Moore, Carl Pickens, Isaac Bruce	60.00
5A	Keyshawn Johnson AUTO	350.00
5B	Dan Marino AUTO	1600.

1996 SPx

This 50-card die-cut Upper Deck set utilizes Holoview technology on 32-point stock. It combines the top stars of the NFL with the top rookies of the 1995 season. To make a Holoview card, each athlete is videotaped while on a turntable. More than seven seconds - or 200 frames - of videotape are then synthesized to produce a 50-degree, 3D picture. A mug shot also appears in the card, which has an oval (using the team's primary color) that has the player's name at the top and team name below. A small color photo is also on the card front. The card back has a rectangle that includes a color photo, biographical and statistical information, and a recap of his accomplishments. Each card in the regular issue is also reprinted in a Gold parallel set; they are inserted one per every seven packs. Insert cards include a Joe Montana Tribute card (one in 95), a Dan Marino Record Breaker card (one in 81), autographed versions of the Marino and Montana cards (one in 433), and HoloFame Collection.

	MT
Complete Set (50):	150.00
Common Player:	1.50
Minor Stars:	3.00
Marino Auto:	300.00
Montana Auto:	225.00
Wax Box:	100.00

1	Frank Sanders	3.00
2	Terance Mathis	1.50
3	Todd Collins	3.00
4	Kerry Collins	4.00
5	Carl Pickens	3.00
6	Darnay Scott	3.00
7	Ki-Jana Carter	3.00
8	Eric Zeier	3.00
9	Andre Rison	1.50
10	Sherman Williams	3.00
11	Troy Aikman	8.00
12	Michael Irvin	3.00
13	Emmitt Smith	15.00
14	Shannon Sharpe	1.50
15	John Elway	5.00
16	Barry Sanders	10.00
17	Brett Favre	15.00
18	Rodney Thomas	4.00
19	Marshall Faulk	8.00
20	James O. Stewart	3.00
21	Greg Hill	1.50
22	Tamarick Vanover	3.00
23	Dan Marino	15.00
24	Cris Carter	1.50
25	Warren Moon	1.50
26	Drew Bledsoe	10.00
27	Ben Coates	1.50
28	Curtis Martin	15.00
29	Mario Bates	3.00
30	Tyrone Wheatley	3.00
31	Rodney Hampton	1.50
32	Kyle Brady	1.50
33	Jeff Hostetler	1.50
34	Napoleon Kaufman	4.00
35	Tim Brown	1.50
36	Charles Johnson	3.00
37	Rod Woodson	1.50
38	Natrone Means	4.00
39	J.J. Stokes	7.00
40	Steve Young	8.00
41	Brent Jones	1.50
42	Jerry Rice	8.00
43	Joe Montana	8.00
44	Rick Mirer	3.00
45	Chris Warren	1.50
46	Joey Galloway	10.00
47	Isaac Bruce	3.00
48	Jerome Bettis	3.00
49	Errict Rhett	3.00
50	Michael Westbrook	5.00
5C	Jerry Rice AUTO	1000.
5D	Barry Sanders AUTO	1000.

1996 SPx Gold

The 50-card, regular-size set was the parallel gold version of the SPx set.

	MT
Complete Set (50):	500.00
Common Player:	4.00
Gold Cards:	2x

1996 SPx Holofame

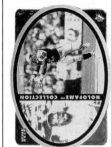

These 1996 Upper Deck SPx insert cards were seeded one per every 24 packs. They showcase players who are likely to be enshrined in the Hall of Fame someday. Cards are numbered using an "Hx" prefix.

	MT
Complete Set (10):	150.00
Common Player:	7.00

1	Troy Aikman	15.00
2	Emmitt Smith	30.00
3	Barry Sanders	16.00
4	Steve Young	10.00
5	Jerry Rice	15.00
6	John Elway	12.00
7	Marshall Faulk	10.00
8	Dan Marino	30.00
9	Drew Bledsoe	15.00
10	Natrone Means	7.00

1997 SP Authentic

SP Authentic Football is a 198-card set featuring 168 veterans and a subset called Future Watch which contains 30 of the year's top rookies. The front of the cards features an action shot with the player's name in the bottom right corner and team name in the upper left. The card backs feature another action shot and career stats. The inserts include Aikman PowerDeck Audio Cards, ProFiles, Sign of the Times, Mark of a Legend, Tradition, SP Authentics, and SP Authentics Collection.

	MT
Complete Set (198):	150.00
Common Player:	.30
Minor Stars:	.60
Wax Box:	180.00

1	Orlando Pace	1.00
2	Darrell Russell	2.00
3	Shawn Springs	2.00
4	Peter Boulware	.75
5	Bryant Westbrook	1.00
6	Walter Jones	.75
7	Ike Hilliard	6.00
8	James Farrior	.75
9	Tom Knight	.75
10	Warrick Dunn	15.00
11	Tony Gonzalez	20.00
12	Reinard Wilson	1.00
13	Yatil Green	.75
14	Reidel Anthony	6.00
15	Kenny Holmes	.75
16	Dwayne Rudd	.75
17	Renaldo Wynn	.75
18	David LaFleur	2.50
19	Antowain Smith	10.00
20	Jim Druckenmiller	6.00
21	Rae Carruth	3.00
22	Byron Hanspard	5.00
23	Jake Plummer	75.00
24	Joey Kent	.75
25	Corey Dillon	15.00
26	Danny Wuerffel	3.00
27	Will Blackwell	2.00
28	Troy Davis	1.00
29	Darnell Autry	.75
30	Pat Barnes	2.00
31	Kent Graham	.30
32	Simeon Rice	.30
33	Frank Sanders	.30
34	Rob Moore	.30
35	Eric Swann	.30
36	Chris Chandler	.30
37	Jamal Anderson	.60
38	Terance Mathis	.30
39	Bert Emanuel	.30
40	Michael Booker	.30
41	Vinny Testaverde	.30
42	Bam Morris	.30
43	Michael Jackson	.30
44	Derrick Alexander	.30
45	Jamie Sharper	.30
46	Kim Herring	.30
47	Todd Collins	.30
48	Thurman Thomas	.60
49	Andre Reed	.30
50	Quinn Early	.30
51	Bryce Paup	.30
52	Marcellus Wiley	.30
53	Kerry Collins	.75
54	Anthony Johnson	.30
55	Tshimanga Biakabutuka	.30
56	Muhsin Muhammad	.30
57	Sam Mills	.30
58	Wesley Walls	.30
59	Rick Mirer	.30
60	Raymont Harris	.30
61	Curtis Conway	.60
62	Bobby Engram	.30
63	Bryan Cox	.30
64	John Allred	.30
65	Jeff Blake	.60
66	Ki-Jana Carter	.30
67	Darnay Scott	.30
68	Carl Pickens	.30
69	Dan Wilkerson	.30
70	Troy Aikman	3.00
71	Emmitt Smith	5.00
72	Michael Irvin	.60
73	Deion Sanders	1.50
74	Anthony Miller	.30
75	Antonio Anderson	.30
76	John Elway	1.75
77	Terrell Davis	3.00
78	Rod Smith	.30
79	Shannon Sharpe	.30
80	Neil Smith	.30
81	Trevor Pryce	.30
82	Scott Mitchell	.30
83	Barry Sanders	3.00
84	Herman Moore	.60
85	Johnnie Morton	.30
86	Matt Russell	.30
87	Brett Favre	6.00
88	Edgar Bennett	.30
89	Robert Brooks	.30
90	Antonio Freeman	.60
91	Reggie White	.60
92	Craig Newsome	.30
93	Jim Harbaugh	.30
94	Marshall Faulk	.60
95	Sean Dawkins	.30
96	Marvin Harrison	.60
97	Quentin Coryatt	.30
98	Tarik Glenn	.30
99	Mark Brunell	3.00
100	Natrone Means	.30
101	Keenan McCardell	.30
102	Jimmy Smith	.30
103	Tony Brackens	.30
104	Kevin Hardy	.30
105	Elvis Grbac	.60
106	Marcus Allen	.60
107	Greg Hill	.30
108	Derrick Thomas	.30
109	Dale Carter	.30
110	Dan Marino	5.00
111	Karim Abdul-Jabbar	1.75
112	Brian Manning	.30
113	Quadry Ismail	.30
114	Troy Drayton	.30
115	Zach Thomas	.60
116	Jason Taylor	.30
117	Brad Johnson	.60
118	Robert Smith	.30
119	John Randle	.30
120	Cris Carter	.60
121	Jake Reed	.30
122	Randall Cunningham	.30
123	Drew Bledsoe	3.00
124	Curtis Martin	3.00
125	Terry Glenn	2.50
126	Willie McGinest	.30
127	Chris Canty	.30
128	Sedrick Shaw	.30
129	Heath Shuler	.30
130	Mario Bates	.30
131	Ray Zellars	.30
132	Andre Hastings	.30
133	Dave Brown	.30
134	Tyrone Wheatley	.30
135	Rodney Hampton	.30
136	Chris Calloway	.30
137	Tiki Barber	5.00
138	Neil O'Donnell	.30
139	Adrian Murrell	.60
140	Wayne Chrebet	.30
141	Keyshawn Johnson	.60
142	Hugh Douglas	.30
143	Jeff George	.30
144	Napoleon Kaufman	.60
145	Tim Brown	.30
146	Desmond Howard	.30
147	Rickey Dudley	.30
148	Terry McDaniel	.30
149	Ty Detmer	.30
150	Ricky Watters	.60
151	Chris T. Jones	.30
152	Irving Fryar	.30
153	Mike Mamula	.30
154	Jon Harris	.30
155	Kordell Stewart	3.00
156	Jerome Bettis	.60
157	Charles Johnson	.30
158	Greg Lloyd	.30
159	George Jones	.30
160	Terrell Fletcher	.30
161	Stan Humphries	.30
162	Tony Martin	.30
163	Eric Metcalf	.30
164	Junior Seau	.30
165	Rod Woodson	.30
166	Steve Young	1.75
167	Terry Kirby	.30
168	Garrison Hearst	.30
169	Jerry Rice	3.00
170	Ken Norton	.30
171	Kevin Greene	.30
172	Lamar Smith	.30
173	Warren Moon	.30
174	Chris Warren	.30
175	Cortez Kennedy	.30
176	Joey Galloway	.60
177	Tony Banks	1.25
178	Isaac Bruce	.60
179	Eddie Kennison	.60
180	Kevin Carter	.30
181	Craig Heyward	.30
182	Trent Dilfer	.60
183	Errict Rhett	.30
184	Mike Alstott	.60
185	Hardy Nickerson	.30
186	Ronde Barber	.30
187	Steve McNair	2.00
188	Eddie George	4.50
189	Chris Sanders	.30
190	Blaine Bishop	.30
191	Derrick Mason	.30
192	Gus Frerotte	.30
193	Terry Allen	.30
194	Brian Mitchell	.30
195	Alvin Harper	.30
196	Jeff Hostetler	.30
197	Lesley Sheppard	.30
198	Stephen Davis	.30
A1	Aikman Audio Blue	10.00
A2	Aikman Audio Pro Bowl	25.00
A3	Aikman Audio White/500	100.00

1997 SP Authentic Mark of a Legend

This seven-card collection features autographs from some of the NFL's greatest players. The inserts are seeded 1:168 packs. They have a "ML" prefix.

	MT
Complete Set (7):	600.00
Common Player:	50.00

1	Bob Griese	50.00
2	Roger Staubach	150.00
3	Joe Montana	200.00
4	Franco Harris	50.00
5	Gale Sayers	75.00
6	Steve Largent	50.00
7	Tony Dorsett	50.00

1997 SP Authentic ProFiles

ProFiles is a three-tiered, 40-card insert. The first tier has an action shot of the player with the NFL logo in the background and is inserted 1:5. The second tier card is a die-cut version of tier one and is inserted 1:12. Tier one cards are sequentially numbered to 100.

	MT
Complete Set (40):	150.00
Common Player:	1.50
Die-Cut Cards:	2x
Inserted 1:12	
Die-Cut 100's:	7x-14x
Production 100 Sets	

1	Dan Marino	10.00
2	Kordell Stewart	6.00
3	Emmitt Smith	10.00
4	Brett Favre	12.00
5	Marcus Allen	1.50
6	Jerry Rice	6.00
7	Jeff George	1.50
8	Mark Brunell	6.00
9	Eddie George	8.00
10	Cris Carter	1.50
11	Tshimanga Biakabutuka	1.50
12	Ike Hilliard	4.00
13	Darrell Russell	1.50
14	Jim Druckenmiller	8.00
15	Rae Carruth	4.00
16	Warrick Dunn	12.00
17	Herman Moore	1.50
18	Deion Sanders	3.00
19	Drew Bledsoe	6.00
20	Jeff Blake	1.50
21	Keyshawn Johnson	1.50
22	Curtis Martin	6.00
23	Michael Irvin	1.50
24	Barry Sanders	10.00
25	Carl Pickens	1.50
26	Steve McNair	5.00
27	Terry Allen	1.50
28	Terrell Davis	6.00
29	Lawrence Phillips	1.50
30	Marshall Faulk	1.50
31	Karim Abdul-Jabbar	4.00
32	Steve Young	5.00
33	Tim Brown	1.50
34	Antowain Smith	6.00
35	Kerry Collins	3.00
36	Reggie White	1.50
37	John Elway	5.00
38	Jerome Bettis	1.50
39	Troy Aikman	6.00
40	Junior Seau	1.50

1997 SP Authentic Sign of the Times

This 30-card insert consists of cards autographed by current NFL players. They were inserted once in 24 packs.

	MT
Complete Set (28):	2000.
Common Player:	20.00

Jeff Blake	40.00
Kerry Collins	60.00
Warrick Dunn	125.00
Rae Carruth	30.00
Karim Abdul-Jabbar	40.00
Reidel Anthony	50.00
Terrell Davis	125.00
Joey Galloway	40.00
Marshall Faulk	40.00
Robert Brooks	20.00
Will Blackwell	20.00
Emmitt Smith	325.00
Herman Moore	40.00
Napoleon Kaufman	50.00
Antowain Smith	60.00
Terry Allen	20.00
Tim Brown	30.00
Jerome Bettis	30.00
Rashaan Salaam	50.00
Jim Druckenmiller	50.00
George Jones	20.00
Isaac Bruce	30.00
Tony Gonzalez	20.00
Troy Aikman	200.00
Dan Marino	325.00
Jerry Rice	275.00
Curtis Martin	100.00
Eddie George	125.00

1997 SP Authentic Traditions

Tradition is a six-card insert. The cards feature two autographs, one from an NFL legend and the other from a proven superstar, both from the same team. Tradition was inserted once per 1,440 packs. The cards carry a "TD" prefix.

	MT
Complete Set (6):	2800.
Common Player:	150.00

1	Dan Marino, Bob Griese	500.00
2	Troy Aikman, Roger Staubach	450.00
3	Jerry Rice, Joe Montana	1200.
4	Jerome Bettis, Franco Harris	150.00
5	Emmitt Smith, Tony Dorsett	500.00
6	Joey Galloway, Steve Largent	175.00

1997 SPx

The 50-card, regular-sized, die-cut set was available in one-card packs. The card fronts a hologram panorama-type head-shot on the right half of the horizontal card with a color action shot on the left half. The cards are die-cut in the shape of an "X" on the right side.

		MT
Complete Set (50):		130.00
Common Player:		1.00
Minor Stars:		2.00
Wax Box:		100.00
1	Jerry Rice	6.00
2	Steve Young	4.00
3	Karim Abdul-Jabbar	3.00
4	Dan Marino	12.00
5	Bobby Engram	2.00
6	Rashaan Salaam	2.00
7	Marvin Harrison	5.00
8	Jim Harbaugh	1.00
9	Marshall Faulk	3.00
10	Eric Moulds	2.00
11	Thurman Thomas	2.00
12	Tamarick Vanover	2.00
13	Steve Bono	1.00
14	Warren Moon	1.00
15	Cris Carter	1.00
16	Carl Pickens	1.00
17	Ki-Jana Carter	1.00
18	Jeff Blake	2.00
19	Tim Biakabutuka	3.00
20	Kerry Collins	3.00
21	Leeland McElroy	2.00
22	Simeon Rice	1.00
23	John Elway	5.00
24	Terrell Davis	8.00
25	Jeff Lewis	1.00
26	Terry Glenn	3.00
27	Curtis Martin	10.00
28	Drew Bledsoe	6.00
29	Lawrence Phillips	3.00
30	Isaac Bruce	3.00
31	Eddie Kennison	2.00
32	Keyshawn Johnson	5.00
33	Stepfret Williams	1.00
34	Emmitt Smith	12.00
35	Troy Aikman	6.00
36	Deion Sanders	4.00
37	Joey Galloway	3.00
38	Rick Mirer	1.00
39	Rickey Dudley	2.00
40	Jeff Hostetler	1.00
41	Junior Seau	1.00
42	Derrick Mayes	1.00
43	Brett Favre	12.00
44	Edgar Bennett	1.00
45	Barry Sanders	8.00
46	Herman Moore	2.00
47	Kordell Stewart	6.00
48	Jerome Bettis	2.00
49	Eddie George	12.00
50	Steve McNair	4.00

1997 SPx Gold

This 50-card set featured the same die-cut design as the base set, but instead of the border being printed in team colors it was printed in gold. Gold parallels were inserted every nine packs.

	MT
Complete Set (50):	375.00
Gold Cards:	3x

1997 SPx Holofame

The 10-card, regular-sized set was inserted every 75 packs of Upper Deck's 1997 SPx football. The cards are numbered and carry the "HF" prefix.

		MT
Complete Set (20):		600.00
Common Player:		10.00
1	Jerry Rice	45.00
2	Emmitt Smith	90.00
3	Karim Abdul-Jabbar	15.00
4	Brett Favre	90.00
5	Curtis Martin	60.00
6	Eddie Kennison	20.00
7	Troy Aikman	45.00
8	Steve Young	35.00
9	Tim Biakabutuka	10.00
10	Reggie White	10.00
11	Terry Glenn	15.00
12	Lawrence Phillips	10.00
13	Dan Marino	90.00
14	Deion Sanders	25.00
15	Terrell Davis	50.00
16	Marvin Harrison	25.00
17	Eddie George	50.00
18	Marshall Faulk	10.00
19	Keyshawn Johnson	10.00
20	Barry Sanders	45.00

1997 SPx ProMotion

The six-card, regular-sized set was inserted every 433 packs of Upper Deck's 1997 SPx football. They are numbered with a "P" prefix.

		MT
Complete Set (6):		500.00
Common Player:		70.00
1	Dan Marino	150.00
2	Joe Montana	100.00
3	Troy Aikman	85.00
4	Barry Sanders	85.00
5	Karim Abdul-Jabbar	70.00
6	Eddie George	100.00

1997 SPx ProMotion Autographs

This insert included autographed versions of each of the six ProMotion inserts. Cards were autographed on the front and sequentially numbered to 100 on the back.

		MT
Complete Set (6):		3500.
Common Player:		300.00
1	Dan Marino	1000.
2	Joe Montana	700.00
3	Troy Aikman	600.00
4	Barry Sanders	700.00
5	Karim Abdul-Jabbar	300.00
6	Eddie George	600.00

A card number in parentheses ( ) indicates the set is unnumbered.

1998 SP Authentic

The 126-card regular set features top-notch photography of the league's best players, along with subsets Future Watch and Time Warp. The 30-card Future Watch set is made up of the top rookies from 1998 and each player is sequentially numbered to 2,000. The 12-card Time Warp set pictures today's top stars shown in action during their respective rookie campaigns. This set is also numbered to 2,000. Each single in this set has a parallel Die-Cut card that is numbered to 500.

		MT
Complete Set (126):		2000.
Common Player:		.25
Minor Stars:		.50
Die-Cut Cards:		5x-10x
Common Rookie (1-30):		15.00
Production 2,000 Sets		
Die-Cut Rookies:		1x
Production 500 Sets		
Common Time Warp (31-42):		5.00
Production 2,000 Sets		
Die-Cut Time Warps:		2x
Wax Box:		525.00
1	Andre Wadsworth	20.00
2	Corey Chavous	15.00
3	Keith Brooking	15.00
4	Duane Starks	15.00
5	Patrick Johnson	20.00
6	Jason Peter	15.00
7	Curtis Enis	75.00
8	Takeo Spikes	15.00
9	Greg Ellis	15.00
10	Marcus Nash	30.00
11	Brian Griese	185.00
12	Germane Crowell	60.00
13	Vonnie Holliday	25.00
14	Peyton Manning	450.00
15	Jerome Pathon	20.00
16	Fred Taylor	250.00
17	John Avery	40.00
18	Randy Moss	450.00
19	Robert Edwards	25.00
20	Tony Simmons	20.00
21	Shaun Williams	15.00
22	Joe Jurevicius	20.00
23	Charles Woodson	60.00
24	Tre Thomas	20.00
25	Grant Wistrom	15.00
26	Ryan Leaf	60.00
27	Ahman Green	40.00
28	Jacquez Green	40.00
29	Kevin Dyson	50.00
30	Stephen Alexander	25.00
31	John Elway	15.00
32	Jerry Rice	15.00
33	Emmitt Smith	20.00
34	Steve Young	10.00
35	Jerome Bettis	7.00
36	Deion Sanders	7.00
37	Andre Rison	5.00
38	Warren Moon	7.00
39	Mark Brunell	10.00
40	Ricky Watters	7.00
41	Dan Marino	20.00
42	Brett Favre	30.00
43	Jake Plummer	1.50
44	Adrian Murrell	.25
45	Eric Swann	.25
46	Jamal Anderson	.75
47	Chris Chandler	.50
48	Jim Harbaugh	.25
49	Michael Jackson	.25
50	Jermaine Lewis	.25
51	Rob Johnson	.50
52	Antowain Smith	.75
53	Thurman Thomas	.50
54	Kerry Collins	.50
55	Fred Lane	.25
56	Rae Carruth	.25
57	Erik Kramer	.25
58	Curtis Conway	.25
59	Corey Dillon	1.00
60	Neil O'Donnell	.25
61	Carl Pickens	.50
62	Troy Aikman	2.00
63	Emmitt Smith	3.00
64	Deion Sanders	.75
65	Terrell Davis	3.00
66	John Elway	2.00
67	Rod Smith	.50
68	Scott Mitchell	.25
69	Barry Sanders	4.00
70	Herman Moore	.50
71	Brett Favre	4.00
72	Dorsey Levens	.50
73	Antonio Freeman	.75
74	Marshall Faulk	.75
75	Marvin Harrison	.50
76	Mark Brunell	1.50
77	Keenan McCardell	.25
78	Jimmy Smith	.50
79	Andre Rison	.25
80	Elvis Grbac	.25
81	Derrick Alexander	.25
82	Dan Marino	3.00
83	Kareem Abdul-Jabbar	.50
84	O.J. McDuffie	.25
85	Brad Johnson	.75
86	Cris Carter	.75
87	Robert Smith	.50
88	Drew Bledsoe	1.50
89	Terry Glenn	.50
90	Ben Coates	.25
91	Lamar Smith	.25
92	Danny Wuerffel	.25
93	Tiki Barber	.50
94	Danny Kanell	.25
95	Ike Hilliard	.25
96	Curtis Martin	.75
97	Keyshawn Johnson	.75
98	Glenn Foley	.25
99	Jeff George	.50
100	Tim Brown	.50
101	Napoleon Kaufman	.75
102	Bobby Hoying	.25
103	Charlie Garner	.25
104	Irving Fryar	.25
105	Kordell Stewart	1.25
106	Jerome Bettis	.50
107	Charles Johnson	.25
108	Tony Banks	.50
109	Isaac Bruce	.50
110	Natrone Means	.50
111	Junior Seau	.50
112	Steve Young	1.00
113	Jerry Rice	2.00
114	Garrison Hearst	.50
115	Ricky Watters	.50
116	Warren Moon	.50
117	Joey Galloway	.75
118	Trent Dilfer	.50
119	Warrick Dunn	1.50
120	Mike Alstott	.75
121	Steve McNair	.75
122	Eddie George	1.50
123	Yancey Thigpen	.25
124	Gus Frerotte	.25
125	Terry Allen	.25
126	Michael Westbrook	.25

1998 SP Authentic Maximum Impact

This set was made up of the 30 players who provide the greatest contribution to their team's overall success. Singles were inserted 1:4 packs.

		MT
Complete Set (30):		75.00
Common Player:		.50
Minor Stars:		1.00
Inserted 1:4		
MI1	Brett Favre	6.00
MI2	Warrick Dunn	2.00
MI3	Junior Seau	.50
MI4	Steve Young	1.50
MI5	Herman Moore	.50
MI6	Antowain Smith	1.00
MI7	John Elway	3.00
MI8	Troy Aikman	3.00
MI9	Dorsey Levens	.50
MI10	Kordell Stewart	2.00
MI11	Peyton Manning	8.00
MI12	Eddie George	2.00
MI13	Dan Marino	4.50
MI14	Joey Galloway	1.00
MI15	Mark Brunell	2.00
MI16	Jake Plummer	2.00
MI17	Curtis Enis	4.00
MI18	Corey Dillon	1.50
MI19	Rob Johnson	1.00
MI20	Barry Sanders	6.00
MI21	Deion Smith	1.25
MI22	Napoleon Kaufman	1.00
MI23	Ryan Leaf	5.00
MI24	Jerry Rice	3.00
MI25	Drew Bledsoe	2.00
MI26	Jerome Bettis	1.00
MI27	Emmitt Smith	4.50
MI28	Tim Brown	1.00
MI29	Curtis Martin	1.25
MI30	Terrell Davis	4.50

1998 SP Authentic Memorabilia

Each card appears in different quanities and could be redeemed for a special piece of autographed memorabilia from the NFL's top rookies.

		MT
Common Player:		50.00
Inserted 1:864		
M1	Curtis Enis Ball (signed NFL game football)	85.00
M2	Ryan Leaf Ball (signed NFL game football)	125.00
M3	Randy Moss Ball (signed NFL game football)	300.00
M4	Takeo Spikes Ball (signed NFL game football)	50.00
M5	Andre Wadsworth Ball (signed NFL game football)	65.00
M6	Marcus Nash Ball (signed NFL game football)	75.00
M7	Curtis Enis Mini FB (signed mini football)	60.00
M8	Ryan Leaf Mini FB (signed mini football)	90.00
M9	Randy Moss Mini FB (signed mini football)	200.00
M10	Takeo Spikes Mini FB (signed mini football)	50.00
M11	Andre Wadsworth Mini FB (signed mini football)	50.00
M12	Marcus Nash Mini FB (signed mini football)	50.00
M13	Curtis Enis Helmet (signed NFL helmet)	125.00
M14	Ryan Leaf Helmet (signed NFL helmet)	200.00
M15	Randy Moss Helmet (signed NFL helmet)	400.00
M16	Takeo Spikes Helmet (signed NFL helmet)	85.00
M17	Andre Wadsworth Helmet (signed NFL helmet)	85.00
M18	Marcus Nash Helmet (signed NFL helmet)	100.00
M19	Curtis Enis Mini Helmet (signed mini helmet)	60.00
M20	Ryan Leaf Mini Helmet (signed mini helmet)	85.00
M21	Randy Moss Mini Helmet (signed mini helmet)	200.00
M22	Takeo Spikes Mini Helmet (signed mini helmet)	50.00
M23	Andre Wadsworth Mini Helmet (signed mini helmet)	50.00
M24	Marcus Nash Mini Helmet (signed mini helmet)	50.00
M25	"Players Ink" Autograph Collection	50.00
M26	Brett Favre (game-worn authentics ("1-of-1's"))	50.00
M27	Terrell Davis (game-worn authentics ("1-of-1's"))	50.00
M28	Dan Marino (game-worn authentics ("1-of-1's"))	50.00
M29	Jerry Rice (game-worn authentics ("1-of-1's"))	50.00
M30	Mark Brunell (game-worn authentics ("1-of-1's"))	50.00

1998 SP Authentic Player's Ink

This autographed insert comes in three versions. The base set has the green background, aren't numbered and were inserted 1:23 packs. The first parallel are the Silver cards and each single was sequentially numbered to 100. The last parallel was the Gold version in which each single was numbered to the players jersey number. Some singles were through redemption cards only.

		MT
Common Player:		20.00
Inserted 1:23		
Silver Cards:		2x
Production 100 Sets		
TA	Troy Aikman	120.00
BF	Brett Favre	240.00
RL	Ryan Leaf	75.00
DM	Dan Marino	200.00
JR	Jerry Rice	120.00
KS	Kordell Stewart	100.00
JP	Jake Plummer	70.00
KJ	Keyshawn Johnson	50.00
SS	Shannon Sharpe	40.00
MA	Mike Alstott	40.00
BH	Bobby Hoying	20.00
RM	Randy Moss	250.00
KM	Keenan McCardell	20.00
JM	Johnnie Morton	20.00
JA	Jamal Anderson	50.00
OE	Curtis Enis	50.00
MJ	Michael Jackson	50.00
AW	Andre Wadsworth	30.00
GC	Germane Crowell	40.00
BG	Brian Griese	80.00
SH	Skip Hicks	40.00
MN	Marcus Nash	40.00
JP	Jerome Pathon	25.00
TS	Takeo Spikes	25.00
FT	Fred Taylor	100.00
CD	Corey Dillon	30.00
RE	Robert Edwards	45.00
EG	Eddie George	60.00
DL	Dorsey Levens	30.00
TV	Tamarick Vanover	20.00

1998 SP Authentic Special Forces

The top specialists in the NFL were showcased in this premium collection set. Each single was sequentially numbered to 1,000.

		MT
Complete Set (30):		375.00
Common Player:		3.00
Minor Stars:		6.00
Production 1,000 Sets		
S1	Kordell Stewart	12.00
S2	Charles Woodson	15.00
S3	Terrell Davis	20.00
S4	Brett Favre	30.00
S5	Joey Galloway	6.00
S6	Warrick Dunn	10.00
S7	Ryan Leaf	20.00
S8	Drew Bledsoe	12.00
S9	Takeo Spikes	6.00

S10	Barry Sanders	30.00
S11	Troy Aikman	15.00
S12	John Elway	15.00
S13	Jerome Bettis	6.00
S14	Karim Abdul-Jabbar	6.00
S15	Tony Gonzalez	3.00
S16	Steve Young	10.00
S17	Napoleon Kaufman	6.00
S18	Andre Wadsworth	6.00
S19	Herman Moore	6.00
S20	Fred Taylor	25.00
S21	Deion Sanders	6.00
S22	Peyton Manning	45.00
S23	Jerry Rice	15.00
S24	Dan Marino	20.00
S25	Antonio Freeman	6.00
S26	Curtis Enis	12.00
S27	Jake Plummer	10.00
S28	Steve McNair	6.00
S29	Mark Brunell	12.00
S30	Robert Edwards	10.00

1998 SPx

SPx Football features Holoview cards. The 50-card base set utilizes decorative foil and Light F/X on 32-point card stock. Each card features three player photos on the front. SPx Football also has five parallel sets and three inserts. The parallels are Steel Parallel Universe (1:1), Bronze Parallel Universe (1:3), Silver Parallel Universe (1:6), Gold Parallel Universe (1:17) and Grand Finale Parallel Universe (50 total sets). The insert sets are HoloFame (1:54), ProMotion (1:252) and Piece of History (500 total cards). Piece of History cards could be redeemed for a framed, un-cut, numbered HoloFame Holoview sheet.

		MT
Complete Set (50):		70.00
Common Player:		.50
Minor Stars:		1.00
Wax Box:		75.00
1	Jake Plummer	4.00
2	Byron Hanspard	1.00
3	Vinny Testaverde	.50
4	Antowain Smith	2.50
5	Kerry Collins	2.00
6	Rae Carruth	1.00
7	Darnell Autry	1.00
8	Rick Mirer	.50
9	Jeff Blake	.50
10	Carl Pickens	.50
11	Troy Aikman	3.50
12	Emmitt Smith	5.00
13	Deion Sanders	1.50
14	John Elway	3.00
15	Terrell Davis	3.50
16	Herman Moore	1.00
17	Barry Sanders	5.00
18	Brett Favre	7.00
19	Reggie White	1.00
20	Marshall Faulk	1.00
21	Mark Brunell	2.50
22	Elvis Grbac	.50
23	Marcus Allen	1.00
24	Karim Abdul-Jabbar	1.00
25	Dan Marino	6.00
26	Cris Carter	.50
27	Drew Bledsoe	3.00
28	Curtis Martin	2.50
29	Heath Shuler	.50
30	Ike Hilliard	1.00
31	Keyshawn Johnson	1.00
32	Jeff George	.50
33	Napoleon Kaufman	1.00
34	Darrell Russell	.50
35	Ricky Watters	1.00
36	Kordell Stewart	3.00
37	Jerome Bettis	1.00
38	Junior Seau	.50
39	Steve Young	2.00
40	Jerry Rice	3.00
41	Joey Galloway	1.00
42	Chris Warren	.50
43	Orlando Pace	1.00
44	Isaac Bruce	1.00
45	Tony Banks	1.00
46	Trent Dilfer	1.00
47	Warrick Dunn	5.00
48	Steve McNair	2.50
49	Eddie George	3.50
50	Terry Allen	.50

1998 SPx Bronze/Gold/Silver/Steel

The SPx base set had five parallels, including Steel (1:1), Bronze (1:3), Silver (1:6) and Gold (1:17).

	MT
Bronze Cards:	2x
Gold Cards:	4x-8x
Silver Cards:	2x-4x
Steel Cards:	1.5x

1998 SPx Grand Finale

Grand Finale parallels the SPx base set. The all-gold Holoview cards commemorate the final SPx Holoview set. Only 50 sets were produced.

		MT
Common Player:		25.00
Minor Stars:		50.00
1	Jake Plummer	175.00
2	Byron Hanspard	100.00
3	Vinny Testaverde	25.00
4	Antowain Smith	125.00
5	Kerry Collins	175.00
6	Rae Carruth	50.00
7	Darnell Autry	50.00
8	Rick Mirer	25.00
9	Jeff Blake	50.00
10	Carl Pickens	25.00
11	Troy Aikman	200.00
12	Emmitt Smith	350.00
13	Deion Sanders	125.00
14	John Elway	200.00
15	Terrell Davis	225.00
16	Herman Moore	50.00
17	Barry Sanders	325.00
18	Brett Favre	450.00
19	Reggie White	50.00
20	Marshall Faulk	50.00
21	Mark Brunell	175.00
22	Elvis Grbac	25.00
23	Marcus Allen	50.00
24	Karim Abdul-Jabbar	100.00
25	Dan Marino	400.00
26	Cris Carter	25.00
27	Drew Bledsoe	200.00
28	Curtis Martin	175.00
29	Heath Shuler	25.00
30	Ike Hilliard	100.00
31	Keyshawn Johnson	50.00
32	Jeff George	25.00
33	Napoleon Kaufman	50.00
34	Darrell Russell	25.00
35	Ricky Watters	50.00
36	Kordell Stewart	200.00
37	Jerome Bettis	50.00
38	Junior Seau	25.00
39	Steve Young	175.00
40	Jerry Rice	225.00
41	Joey Galloway	50.00
42	Chris Warren	25.00
43	Orlando Pace	50.00
44	Isaac Bruce	50.00
45	Tony Banks	100.00
46	Trent Dilfer	50.00
47	Warrick Dunn	250.00
48	Steve McNair	150.00
49	Eddie George	200.00
50	Terry Allen	25.00

1998 SPx HoloFame

HoloFame is a 20-card insert, seeded one per 54 packs. The cards feature top players embossed on Holoview cards with silver decorative foil. Cards are numbered with a "HF" prefix.

		MT
Complete Set (20):		325.00
Common Player:		10.00
1	Troy Aikman	30.00
2	Emmitt Smith	50.00
3	John Elway	25.00
4	Terrell Davis	30.00
5	Herman Moore	10.00
6	Reggie White	10.00
7	Brett Favre	50.00
8	Napoleon Kaufman	10.00
9	Dan Marino	50.00
10	Karim Abdul-Jabbar	10.00
11	Cris Carter	10.00
12	Drew Bledsoe	30.00
13	Curtis Martin	25.00
14	Kordell Stewart	30.00
15	Junior Seau	10.00
16	Steve Young	20.00
17	Jerry Rice	30.00
18	Marshall Faulk	10.00
19	Eddie George	30.00
20	Terry Allen	10.00

1998 SPx ProMotion

ProMotion is a 10-card insert (1:252) produced on copper and silver Holoview cards. Cards are numbered with a "P" prefix.

		MT
Complete Set (10):		600.00
Common Player:		30.00
1	Troy Aikman	60.00
2	Emmitt Smith	85.00
3	Terrell Davis	60.00
4	Brett Favre	100.00
5	Marcus Allen	30.00
6	Dan Marino	100.00
7	Drew Bledsoe	60.00
8	Ike Hilliard	30.00
9	Warrick Dunn	60.00
10	Eddie George	60.00

1998 SPx Finite

SPx Finite Series One consists of a 190-card base set built from five subsets. The base cards feature silver foil. The set consists of 90 regular cards (numbered to 7,600), 30 Playmakers (5,500), 30 Youth Movement (3,000), 20 Pure Energy (2,500) and 10 Heroes of the Game (1,250). Ten rookie cards were also added to SPx Finite, numbered to 1,998.

		MT
Complete Set (370):		2500.
Complete Series 1 (190):		1200.
Complete Series 2 (180):		1300.
Common Player (1-90):		1.00
Minor Stars (1-90):		2.00
Production 7,600 Sets		
Common Player (91-120):		1.50
Minor Stars (91-120):		3.00
Production 5,500 Sets		
Common Player (121-150):		2.00
Minor Stars (121-150):		4.00
Production 3,000 Sets		
Common Player (151-170):		2.50
Minor Stars (151-170):		5.00
Production 2,500 Sets		
Common Player (171-180):		6.00
Production 1,250 Sets		
Common Player (181-190):		12.00
Production 1,998 Sets		
Common Player (191-280):		.50
Minor Stars (191-280):		1.00
Common Rookie (191-280):		1.00
Production 10,100 Sets		
Production 1,998 for #218,221,239		
Common Player (281-310):		.75
Minor Stars (281-310):		1.50
Production 7,200 Sets		
Common Player (311-340):		1.50
Minor Stars (311-340):		3.00
Production 4,000 Sets		
Production 1,700 for #321,338,339		
Common Player (341-360):		1.50

		MT
Common Player (361-370):		5.00
Production 1,620 Sets		
Series 1 Wax Box:		100.00
Series 2 Wax Box:		90.00
1	Jake Plummer	5.00
2	Eric Swann	1.00
3	Rob Moore	1.00
4	Jamal Anderson	3.00
5	Byron Hanspard	1.00
6	Cornelius Bennett	1.00
7	Michael Jackson	1.00
8	Peter Boulware	1.00
9	Jermaine Lewis	1.00
10	Antowain Smith	1.00
11	Bruce Smith	1.00
12	Bryce Paup	1.00
13	Rae Carruth	1.00
14	Michael Bates	1.00
15	Fred Lane	2.00
16	Darnell Autry	1.00
17	Curtis Conway	1.00
18	Erik Kramer	1.00
19	Corey Dillon	3.50
20	Darnay Scott	1.00
21	Reinard Wilson	1.00
22	Troy Aikman	6.00
23	David LaFleur	1.00
24	Emmitt Smith	8.00
25	John Elway	5.00
26	John Mobley	1.00
27	Terrell Davis	8.00
28	Rod Smith	2.00
29	Bryant Westbrook	1.00
30	Scott Mitchell	1.00
31	Barry Sanders	12.00
32	Dorsey Levens	2.00
33	Antonio Freeman	2.00
34	Reggie White	2.00
35	Marshall Faulk	2.00
36	Marvin Harrison	2.00
37	Ken Dilger	1.00
38	Mark Brunell	5.00
39	Keenan McCardell	1.00
40	Renaldo Wynn	1.00
41	Marcus Allen	2.00
42	Elvis Grbac	1.00
43	Andre Rison	1.00
44	Yatil Green	1.00
45	Zach Thomas	2.00
46	Karim Abdul-Jabbar	2.00
47	John Randle	1.00
48	Brad Johnson	2.00
49	Jake Reed	1.00
50	Danny Wuerffel	1.00
51	Andre Hastings	1.00
52	Drew Bledsoe	5.00
53	Terry Glenn	2.00
54	Ty Law	1.00
55	Danny Kanell	1.00
56	Tiki Barber	2.00
57	Jesse Armstead	1.00
58	Glenn Foley	1.00
59	James Farrior	1.00
60	Wayne Chrebet	2.00
61	Tim Brown	2.00
62	Napoleon Kaufman	3.00
63	Darrell Russell	1.00
64	Bobby Hoying	1.00
65	Irving Fryar	1.00
66	Charlie Garner	1.00
67	Will Blackwell	1.00
68	Kordell Stewart	5.00
69	Levon Kirkland	1.00
70	Tony Banks	2.00
71	Ryan McNeil	1.00
72	Isaac Bruce	2.00
73	Tony Martin	1.00
74	Junior Seau	2.00
75	Natrone Means	1.00
76	Jerry Rice	6.00
77	Garrison Hearst	2.00
78	Terrell Owens	2.00
79	Warren Moon	2.00
80	Joey Galloway	2.00
81	Chad Brown	1.00
82	Warrick Dunn	5.00
83	Mike Alstott	2.00
84	Hardy Nickerson	1.00
85	Steve McNair	3.00
86	Chris Sanders	1.00
87	Darryll Lewis	1.00
88	Gus Frerotte	1.00
89	Terry Allen	1.00
90	Chris Dishman	1.00
91	Kordell Stewart	7.00
92	Jerry Rice	8.00
93	Michael Irvin	3.00
94	Brett Favre	15.00
95	Jeff George	3.00
96	Joey Galloway	3.00
97	John Elway	8.00
98	Troy Aikman	8.00
99	Steve Young	5.00
100	Andre Rison	1.50
101	Ben Coates	1.50
102	Robert Brooks	1.50
103	Dan Marino	12.00
104	Isaac Bruce	3.00
105	Junior Seau	3.00
106	Jake Plummer	7.00
107	Curtis Conway	3.00
108	Jeff Blake	3.00
109	Rod Smith	3.00
110	Barry Sanders	15.00
111	Deion Sanders	4.00
112	Drew Bledsoe	7.00
113	Emmitt Smith	12.00

		MT
114	Herman Moore	3.00
115	Dorsey Levens	3.00
116	Jimmy Smith	1.50
117	Tony Martin	1.50
118	Carl Pickens	1.50
119	Keyshawn Johnson	3.00
120	Cris Carter	3.00
121	Warrick Dunn	10.00
122	Marshall Faulk	4.00
123	Trent Dilfer	4.00
124	Napoleon Kaufman	5.00
125	Corey Dillon	7.00
126	Darrell Russell	2.00
127	Danny Kanell	2.00
128	Reidel Anthony	2.00
129	Steve McNair	6.00
130	Ike Hilliard	2.00
131	Tony Banks	4.00
132	Yatil Green	2.00
133	J.J. Stokes	2.00
134	Fred Lane	4.00
135	Bryant Westbrook	2.00
136	Jake Plummer	10.00
137	Byron Hanspard	2.00
138	Rae Carruth	2.00
139	Keyshawn Johnson	4.00
140	Jim Druckenmiller	2.00
141	Amani Toomer	2.00
142	Troy Davis	2.00
143	Antowain Smith	6.00
144	Shawn Springs	2.00
145	Rickey Dudley	2.00
146	Terry Glenn	4.00
147	Johnnie Morton	2.00
148	David LaFleur	2.00
149	Eddie Kennison	4.00
150	Bobby Hoying	2.00
151	Junior Seau	5.00
152	Shannon Sharpe	5.00
153	Bruce Smith	2.50
154	Brett Favre	25.00
155	Emmitt Smith	15.00
156	Keenan McCardell	2.50
157	Kordell Stewart	10.00
158	Troy Aikman	12.00
159	Steve Young	8.00
160	Tim Brown	5.00
161	Eddie George	10.00
162	Herman Moore	5.00
163	Dan Marino	15.00
164	Dorsey Levens	5.00
165	Jerry Rice	12.00
166	Warren Sapp	2.50
167	Robert Smith	5.00
168	Mark Brunell	10.00
169	Terrell Davis	15.00
170	Jerome Bettis	5.00
171	Dan Marino	30.00
172	Barry Sanders	40.00
173	Marcus Allen	6.00
174	Brett Favre	40.00
175	Warrick Dunn	20.00
176	Eddie George	20.00
177	John Elway	20.00
178	Troy Aikman	20.00
179	Cris Carter	6.00
180	Terrell Davis	25.00
181	*Peyton Manning*	100.00
182	*Ryan Leaf*	35.00
183	*Andre Wadsworth*	20.00
184	*Charles Woodson*	35.00
185	Curtis Enis	35.00
186	*Grant Wistrom*	12.00
187	*Fred Taylor*	60.00
188	*Takeo Spikes*	25.00
189	*Kevin Dyson*	30.00
190	*Robert Edwards*	25.00
191	Adrian Murrell	1.00
192	Simeon Rice	.50
193	Frank Sanders	.50
194	Chris Chandler	1.00
195	Terrance Mathis	.50
196	Keith Brooking	1.50
197	Jim Harbaugh	1.00
198	Errict Rhett	.50
199	*Patrick Johnson*	2.00
200	Rob Johnson	1.00
201	Andre Reed	1.00
202	Thurman Thomas	1.00
203	Kerry Collins	1.00
204	William Floyd	.50
205	Sean Gilbert	.50
206	Bobby Engram	.50
207	Edgar Bennett	.50
208	Walt Harris	.50
209	Carl Pickens	1.00
210	Neil O'Donnell	1.00
211	Tony McGee	.50
212	Deion Sanders	1.50
213	Michael Irvin	1.00
214	*Greg Ellis*	1.50
215	Shannon Sharpe	2.00
216	Neil Smith	1.00
217	*Marcus Nash*	4.00
218	*Brian Griese*	50.00
219	Johnnie Morton	1.00
220	Herman Moore	1.00
221	*Charlie Batch*	40.00
222	Robert Brooks	.50
223	Mark Chmura	1.00
224	Brett Favre	6.00
225	*Jerome Pathon*	2.00
226	Zack Crockett	.50
227	Dan Footman	.50
228	Jimmy Smith	1.00
229	Bryce Paup	.50
230	James Stewart	.50
231	Derrick Thomas	.50

		MT
232	Derrick Alexander	.50
233	Tony Gonzalez	.50
234	Dan Marino	4.50
235	O.J. McDuffie	.50
236	Troy Drayton	.50
237	Cris Carter	1.00
238	Robert Smith	1.00
239	*Randy Moss*	160.00
240	Lamar Smith	.50
241	Sean Dawkins	.50
242	Alex Molden	.50
243	Ben Coates	1.00
244	Ted Johnson	.50
245	Sedrick Shaw	.50
246	Ike Hilliard	.50
247	Jason Sehorn	.50
248	Michael Strahan	.50
249	Keyshawn Johnson	1.00
250	Curtis Martin	1.50
251	Jeff George	1.00
252	Rickey Dudley	.50
253	James Jett	.50
254	Bobby Taylor	.50
255	Rodney Peete	.50
256	William Thomas	.50
257	Jerome Bettis	1.00
258	Charles Johnson	.50
259	*Chris Fuamatu-Ma'afala*	2.50
260	Eddie Kennison	.50
261	*Az-Zahir Hakim*	2.00
262	*Robert Holcombe*	3.00
263	Bryan Still	.50
264	*Mikhael Ricks*	2.00
265	Charlie Jones	.50
266	J.J. Stokes	1.00
267	Marc Edwards	.50
268	Steve Young	2.00
269	Ricky Watters	1.00
270	Cortez Kennedy	.50
271	Shawn Springs	.50
272	Trent Dilfer	1.00
273	Warren Sapp	.50
274	Reidel Anthony	1.00
275	Yancey Thigpen	.50
276	Chris Sanders	.50
277	Eddie George	2.50
278	Leslie Shepherd	.50
279	*Skip Hicks*	4.00
280	Dana Stubblefield	.50
281	John Elway	4.00
282	Brett Favre	8.00
283	Junior Seau	1.50
284	Barry Sanders	8.00
285	Jerry Rice	4.00
286	Antonio Freeman	1.50
287	Peyton Manning	20.00
288	Warrick Dunn	3.00
289	Steve Young	2.00
290	Dan Marino	6.00
291	Jerome Bettis	1.50
292	Ryan Leaf	8.00
293	Deion Sanders	1.50
294	Eddie George	3.00
295	Joey Galloway	1.50
296	Troy Aikman	4.00
297	Andre Wadsworth	1.50
298	Terrell Davis	6.00
299	Steve McNair	2.00
300	Jake Plummer	3.00
301	Emmitt Smith	6.00
302	Isaac Bruce	1.50
303	Kordell Stewart	3.00
304	Dorsey Levens	1.50
305	Antowain Smith	1.75
306	Drew Bledsoe	3.00
307	Marshall Faulk	1.50
308	Herman Moore	1.50
309	Mark Brunell	3.00
310	Charles Woodson	2.00
311	Peyton Manning	30.00
312	Curtis Enis	10.00
313	*Terry Fair*	7.00
314	Andre Wadsworth	5.00
315	*Anthony Simmons*	4.00
316	*Jacquez Green*	12.00
317	Takeo Spikes	4.00
318	*Vonnie Holliday*	7.00
319	*Kyle Turley*	2.00
320	Keith Brooking	4.00
321	Randy Moss	125.00
322	*Shaun Williams*	2.00
323	Greg Ellis	2.00
324	Mikhael Ricks	5.00
325	Charles Woodson	10.00
326	*Corey Chavous*	2.00
327	*Stephen Alexander*	7.00
328	Marcus Nash	7.00
329	*Tre Thomas*	2.00
330	*Duane Starks*	7.00
331	*John Avery*	12.00
332	Kevin Dyson	7.00
333	Fred Taylor	15.00
334	Grant Wistrom	2.00
335	Ryan Leaf	15.00
336	Robert Edwards	12.00
337	*Jason Peter*	4.00
338	Brian Griese	25.00
339	Charlie Batch	25.00
340	Patrick Johnson	2.00
341	John Elway	10.00
342	Curtis Enis	10.00
343	Antonio Freeman	3.00
344	Mark Brunell	6.00
345	Robert Edwards	12.00
346	Ryan Leaf	15.00
347	Steve Young	5.00
348	Jerome Bettis	3.00

349	Antowain Smith	3.00
350	Tim Brown	3.00
351	Peyton Manning	30.00
352	Troy Aikman	8.00
353	Natrone Means	1.50
354	Dan Marino	15.00
355	Junior Seau	1.50
356	Brad Johnson	3.00
357	Jerry Rice	8.00
358	Drew Bledsoe	6.00
359	Fred Taylor	15.00
360	Emmitt Smith	12.00
361	Terrell Davis	20.00
362	Kordell Stewart	10.00
363	Barry Sanders	25.00
364	Jake Plummer	10.00
365	Brett Favre	25.00
366	Curtis Enis	18.00
367	Eddie George	10.00
368	Napoleon Kaufman	5.00
369	Randy Moss	125.00
370	Warrick Dunn	10.00

1998 SPx Finite Radiance

Radiance is a gold-foil parallel of the SPx Finite base set. Regular cards are numbered to 3,800, Playmakers to 2,750, Youth Movement to 1,500, Pure Energy to 1,000 and Heroes of the Game to 100. The ten rookie cards are numbered to 50 in this set.

	MT
Cards (1-90):	2x
Production 3,800 Sets	
Cards (91-120):	2x
Production 2,750 Sets	
Cards (121-150):	2x
Production 1,500 Sets	
Cards (151-170):	2x
Production 1,000 Sets	
Cards (171-180):	5x
Production 100 Sets	
Cards (181-190):	4x
Production 50 Sets	
Cards (191-280):	2x
Production 5,050 Sets	
Production 500 for #218,221,239	
Cards (281-310):	2x
Production 3,600 Sets	
Cards (311-340):	2x
Production 1,885 Sets	
Production 350 for #321,338,339	
Cards (341-360):	2x
Production 900 Sets	
Cards (361-370):	2x
Production 540 Sets	

1998 SPx Finite Spectrum

Spectrum is a rainbow foil version of the SPx Finite base set. Regular cards are numbered to 1,900, Playmakers to 1,375, Youth Movement to 750, Pure Energy to 50 and Heroes of the Game is a 1-of-1 set. The ten rookie cards are also 1-of-1 in this parallel.

	MT
Cards (1-90):	3x
Production 1,900 Sets	

Cards (91-120):	3x
Production 1,375 Sets	
Cards (121-150):	4x
Production 750 Sets	
Cards (151-170):	15x-20x
Production 50 Sets	
Cards (171-190):	
Production 1 Set	
Cards (191-280):	4x-8x
Rookies (191-280):	1.5x-3x
Production 325 Sets	
Cards (281-310):	5x-10x
Rookies (281-310):	1.5x-3x
Production 150 Sets	
Cards (311-340):	4x-8x
#321,338,339:	2x-4x
Production 50 Sets	
Cards (341-360):	15x-30x
Rookies (341-360):	6x-12x
Production 25 Sets	
Cards (361-370):	
Production 1 Set	

1999 SP Authentic

This 145-card set included 55 rookies that were sequentially numbered to 1,999. Parallel sets included Excitement and Excitement Gold. Other insert sets include: Authentic Athletic, Buy Back Autographs, Maximum Impact, New Classics, NFL Headquarters, Player's Ink, Rookie Blitz and Supremacy. SRP was $4.99 for five-card packs.

		MT
Complete Set (145):		2000.
Common Player:		.25
Minor Stars:		.50
Common Rookie:		15.00
Production 1,999 Sets		
Wax Box:		220.00
1	Jake Plummer	1.50
2	Adrian Murrell	.25
3	Frank Sanders	.50
4	Jamal Anderson	.75
5	Chris Chandler	.50
6	Terance Mathis	.25
7	Priest Holmes	.75
8	Jermaine Lewis	.25
9	Antowain Smith	.75
10	Doug Flutie	1.25
11	Eric Moulds	.75
12	Muhsin Muhammad	.75
13	Tim Biakabutuka	.50
14	Wesley Walls	.50
15	Curtis Enis	.75
16	Bobby Engram	.25
17	Corey Dillon	.75
18	Darnay Scott	.50
19	Terry Kirby	.25
20	Ty Detmer	.25
21	Troy Aikman	2.00
22	Michael Irvin	.50
23	Emmitt Smith	3.00
24	Terrell Davis	3.00
25	Brian Griese	1.50
26	Rod Smith	.75
27	Shannon Sharpe	.75
28	Barry Sanders	4.00
29	Charlie Batch	1.25
30	Herman Moore	.75
31	Johnnie Morton	.25
32	Brett Favre	4.00
33	Antonio Freeman	.75
34	Dorsey Levens	.75
35	Mark Chmura	.50
36	Peyton Manning	3.00
37	Marvin Harrison	.75
38	Mark Brunell	1.25
39	Fred Taylor	2.00
40	Jimmy Smith	.75
41	Elvis Grbac	.50
42	Andre Rison	.50
43	Dan Marino	3.00
44	O.J. McDuffie	.25
45	Yatil Green	.25
46	Randall Cunningham	.75
47	Randy Moss	4.00
48	Robert Smith	.75
49	Cris Carter	.75
50	Drew Bledsoe	1.25
51	Ben Coates	.50
52	Terry Glenn	.75
53	Eddie Kennison	.25

54	Cam Cleeland	.50
55	Ike Hilliard	.50
56	Gary Brown	.25
57	Kerry Collins	.50
58	Vinny Testaverde	.50
59	Keyshawn Johnson	.75
60	Wayne Chrebet	.75
61	Curtis Martin	.75
62	Tim Brown	.50
63	Napoleon Kaufman	.75
64	Charles Woodson	.75
65	Duce Staley	.75
66	Charles Johnson	.25
67	Kordell Stewart	.75
68	Jerome Bettis	.75
69	Marshall Faulk	.75
70	Isaac Bruce	.75
71	Trent Green	.75
72	Jim Harbaugh	.50
73	Junior Seau	.50
74	Natrone Means	.50
75	Steve Young	1.25
76	Jerry Rice	2.00
77	Terrell Owens	.75
78	Lawrence Phillips	.25
79	Joey Galloway	.75
80	Ricky Watters	.50
81	Jon Kitna	1.00
82	Warrick Dunn	.75
83	Trent Dilfer	.50
84	Mike Alstott	.75
85	Eddie George	1.00
86	Steve McNair	1.00
87	Yancey Thigpen	.25
88	Brad Johnson	.75
89	Skip Hicks	.50
90	Michael Westbrook	.50
91	*Ricky Williams*	300.00
92	*Tim Couch*	300.00
93	*Akili Smith*	125.00
94	*Edgerrin James*	425.00
95	*Donovan McNabb*	125.00
96	*Torry Holt*	75.00
97	*Cade McNown*	125.00
98	*Shaun King*	125.00
99	*Daunte Culpepper*	130.00
100	*Brock Huard*	45.00
101	*Chris Claiborne*	20.00
102	*James Johnson*	45.00
103	*Rob Konrad*	20.00
104	*Peerless Price*	50.00
105	*Kevin Faulk*	50.00
106	*Andy Katzenmoyer*	20.00
107	*Troy Edwards*	75.00
108	*Kevin Johnson*	75.00
109	*Mike Cloud*	20.00
110	*David Boston*	60.00
111	*Champ Bailey*	45.00
112	*D'Wayne Bates*	20.00
113	*Joe Germaine*	35.00
114	*Antoine Winfield*	20.00
115	*Fernando Bryant*	15.00
116	*Jevon Kearse*	70.00
117	*Chris McAlister*	20.00
118	*Brandon Stokley*	15.00
119	*Karsten Bailey*	20.00
120	*Daylon McCutcheon*	15.00
121	*Jermaine Fazande*	25.00
122	*Joel Makovicka*	15.00
123	*Ebenezer Ekuban*	20.00
124	*Joe Montgomery*	25.00
125	*Sean Bennett*	25.00
126	*Na Brown*	15.00
127	*De'Mond Parker*	35.00
128	*Sedrick Irvin*	35.00
129	*Terry Jackson*	20.00
130	*Jeff Paulk*	20.00
131	*Cecil Collins*	75.00
132	*Bobby Collins*	15.00
133	*Amos Zereoue*	30.00
134	*Travis McGriff*	20.00
135	*Larry Parker*	15.00
136	*Wane McGarity*	20.00
137	*Cecil Martin*	15.00
138	*Al Wilson*	15.00
139	*Jim Kleinsasser*	25.00
140	*Dat Nguyen*	20.00
141	*Marty Booker*	25.00
142	*Reggie Kelly*	15.00
143	*Scott Covington*	20.00
144	*Antwan Edwards*	20.00
145	*Craig Yeast*	20.00

1999 SP Authentic Excitement

This was a 145-card parallel to the base set. Each single was sequentially numbered to 250 and printed on the front of the cards.

	MT
Excitement Cards:	7x-14x
Excitement Rookies:	1.5x
Production 250 Sets	

1999 SP Authentic Excitement Gold

This was a 145-card parallel to the base set. Each single was sequentially numbered to 25 and printed on the front of the singles.

	MT
Excitement Cards:	40x-80x
Excitement Rookies:	3x
Production 25 Sets	

1999 SP Authentic Athletic

This 10-card insert set included the most exciting and athletic players in the NFL. Singles were inserted 1:10 packs.

		MT
Complete Set (10):		35.00
Common Player:		2.50
Inserted 1:10		
1	Randy Moss	10.00
2	Steve McNair	2.50
3	Jamal Anderson	2.50
4	Curtis Martin	2.50
5	Kordell Stewart	2.50
6	Barry Sanders	10.00
7	Fred Taylor	6.00
8	Doug Flutie	3.50
9	Emmitt Smith	6.00
10	Steve Young	3.50

1999 SP Authentic Maximum Impact

This 10-card insert set included players who provide the greatest contribution to their team's overall success. Singles were inserted 1:4 packs.

		MT
Complete Set (10):		12.00
Common Player:		1.00
Inserted 1:4		
1	Jerry Rice	3.00
2	Eddie George	1.50
3	Marshall Faulk	1.00
4	Keyshawn Johnson	1.00
5	Terrell Davis	4.50
6	Warrick Dunn	1.00
7	Jerome Bettis	1.00
8	Drew Bledsoe	2.00
9	Curtis Martin	1.00
10	Brett Favre	6.00

1999 SP Authentic New Classics

This 10-card insert set included players to watch for the future. Singles were inserted 1:23 packs.

		MT
Complete Set (10):		60.00
Common Player:		3.00
Inserted 1:23		
1	Steve McNair	3.00
2	Jon Kitna	3.00
3	Curtis Enis	3.00
4	Peyton Manning	10.00
5	Fred Taylor	8.00
6	Randy Moss	15.00
7	Donovan McNabb	10.00
8	Terrell Owens	3.00
9	Keyshawn Johnson	3.00
10	Ricky Williams	15.00

1999 SP Authentic NFL Headquarters

This 10-card insert set included the game's hottest quarterbacks. Singles were inserted 1:10 packs.

		MT
Complete Set (10):		45.00
Common Player:		3.00
Inserted 1:10		
1	Brett Favre	12.00
2	Jake Plummer	5.00
3	Charlie Batch	4.00
4	Akili Smith	6.00
5	Troy Aikman	6.00
6	Drew Bledsoe	5.00
7	Dan Marino	10.00
8	Jon Kitna	3.00
9	Mark Brunell	5.00
10	Tim Couch	12.00

1999 SP Authentic Player's Ink

This 40-card insert set included autographs of the top players in the NFL. Many of the rookies were included and singles were inserted 1:23 packs. A parallel Level 2 version was also released and each was sequentially numbered to 100.

		MT
Complete Set (40):		2000.
Common Player:		25.00
Inserted 1:23		
Version 2 Cards:		2x
Production 100 Cards		
TA	Troy Aikman	125.00
JA	Jamal Anderson	25.00
CB	Champ Bailey	25.00
CH	Charlie Batch	35.00
JB	Jerome Bettis	25.00
MB	Michael Bishop	35.00
DR	Drew Bledsoe	75.00
DB	David Boston	45.00
BR	Mark Brunell	75.00
WC	Wayne Chrebet	25.00
CL	Michael Cloud	25.00
TC	Tim Couch	150.00
DC	Daunte Culpepper	60.00
TD	Terrell Davis	100.00
CD	Corey Dillon	35.00
TE	Troy Edwards	45.00
KF	Kevin Faulk	40.00
MF	Marshall Faulk	40.00
DF	Doug Flutie	50.00
AF	Antonio Freeman	25.00
JG	Joey Galloway	25.00
EG	Eddie George	40.00
TH	Torry Holt	45.00
BH	Brock Huard	30.00
EJ	Edgerrin James	200.00
BJ	Brad Johnson	30.00
SK	Shaun King	45.00
PM	Peyton Manning	125.00
DM	Dan Marino	225.00
ED	Ed McCaffrey	25.00
CM	Cade McNown	60.00
NM	Natrone Means	25.00
HM	Herman Moore	25.00
RM	Randy Moss	150.00
EM	Eric Moulds	25.00
TO	Terrell Owens	25.00
JP	Jake Plummer	50.00
JR	Jerry Rice	125.00
SS	Shannon Sharpe	25.00
AS	Akili Smith	60.00

1999 SP Authentic Rookie Blitz

This 19-card insert set included the top rookies from the 1999 season. Singles were inserted 1:11 packs.

		MT
Complete Set (19):		85.00
Common Player:		2.00
Inserted 1:11		
1	Edgerrin James	20.00
2	Tim Couch	15.00
3	Daunte Culpepper	8.00
4	Champ Bailey	3.00
5	Donovan McNabb	8.00
6	Kevin Johnson	6.00
7	Shaun King	6.00
8	Peerless Price	5.00
9	David Boston	6.00
10	Ricky Williams	15.00
11	Akili Smith	8.00
12	Kevin Faulk	4.00
13	D'Wayne Bates	2.00
14	Brock Huard	3.00
15	Rob Konrad	2.00
16	Torry Holt	6.00
17	Troy Edwards	6.00
18	Cade McNown	8.00
19	Cecil Collins	6.00

1999 SP Authentic Supremacy

This 12-card insert set included the premier performers in the NFL. Singles were inserted 1:23 packs.

		MT
Complete Set (12):		85.00
Common Player:		3.00
Inserted 1:23		
1	Terrell Davis	10.00
2	Joey Galloway	3.00
3	Dan Marino	10.00
4	Brett Favre	15.00
5	Emmitt Smith	10.00
6	Barry Sanders	15.00
7	Curtis Martin	3.00
8	Jamal Anderson	3.00
9	Jake Plummer	6.00
10	Randy Moss	15.00
11	Tim Couch	15.00
12	Peyton Manning	10.00

1999 SP Authentic Walter Payton

A total of 100 Payton autographed cards were released along with 34 Payton Game-Jersey autographed cards. Each card was randomly inserted.

		MT
WPA	Walter Payton AUTO/100	350.00
WPSP	Walter Payton JER/AUTO 34	3000.

1999 SP Signature

This 180-card release from Upper Deck includes both past and present stars from the NFL. The last 10 cards in the set never made it into the product and were later released to dealers from the manufacture. Inserts include: Autographs and Montana Great Performances.

		MT
Complete Set (180):		500.00
Common Player:		.50
Minor Stars:		1.00
Wax Box:		200.00
1	Jake Plummer	2.50
2	Mario Bates	.50
3	Adrian Murrell	.50
4	Jamal Anderson	1.50
5	Chris Chandler	1.00
6	Bob Christian	.50
7	O.J. Santiago	.50
8	Jim Harbaugh	1.00
9	Priest Holmes	1.50
10	Ray Lewis	.50
11	Michael Jackson	.50
12	Tony Siragusa	.50
13	Doug Flutie	2.00
14	Antowain Smith	1.25
15	Eric Moulds	1.25
16	William Floyd	.50
17	Fred Lane	.50
18	Muhsin Muhammad	.50
19	Bobby Engram	.50
20	Curtis Enis	1.50
21	Curtis Conway	1.00
22	Corey Dillon	1.50
23	Carl Pickens	1.00
24	Ashley Ambrose	.50
25	Darnay Scott	.50
26	Troy Aikman	3.00
27	Jason Garrett	.50
28	Emmitt Smith	4.50
29	Deion Sanders	1.25
30	John Elway	4.50
31	Terrell Davis	4.50
32	Ed McCaffrey	1.00
33	John Mobley	.50
34	Maa Tanuvasa	.50
35	Ray Crockett	.50
36	Barry Sanders	6.00
37	Herman Moore	1.00
38	Charlie Batch	2.00
39	Robert Porcher	.50
40	Tommy Vardell	.50
41	Brett Favre	6.00
42	Antonio Freeman	1.50
43	Darick Holmes	.50
44	Robert Brooks	.50
45	Peyton Manning	5.00
46	Marshall Faulk	1.25
47	Torrance Small	.50
48	Lamont Warren	.50
49	Zack Crockett	.50
50	Mark Brunell	2.00
51	Pete Mitchell	.50
52	Fred Taylor	4.00
53	Jimmy Smith	1.00
54	Andre Rison	.50
55	Rich Gannon	.50
56	Donnell Bennett	.50
57	Dan Marino	4.50
58	Karim Abdul	1.00
59	Troy Drayton	.50
60	Jason Taylor	.50
61	Cris Carter	1.25
62	Randy Moss	8.00
63	Robert Smith	1.00

64	Leroy Hoard	.50
65	Randall Cunningham	1.25
66	Derrick Alexander	.50
67	Drew Bledsoe	2.00
68	Robert Edwards	1.25
69	Willie McGinest	.50
70	Chris Slade	.50
71	Terry Glenn	1.00
72	Ty Law	.50
73	Kerry Collins	1.00
74	Sean Dawkins	.50
75	Cameron Cleeland	1.00
76	Sammy Knight	.50
77	Danny Kanell	.50
78	Gary Brown	.50
79	Chris Calloway	.50
80	Curtis Martin	1.25
81	Keyshawn Johnson	1.25
82	Vinny Testaverde	.50
83	Leon Johnson	.50
84	Kyle Brady	.50
85	Tim Brown	1.00
86	Jeff George	1.00
87	Rickey Dudley	.50
88	Napoleon Kaufman	1.25
89	James Jett	.50
90	Harvey Williams	.50
91	Koy Detmer	.50
92	Duce Staley	.50
93	Charlie Garner	.50
94	Jerome Bettis	1.00
95	Kordell Stewart	1.75
96	Courtney Hawkins	1.00
97	Hines Ward	1.00
98	Isaac Bruce	1.00
99	Tony Banks	1.00
100	Greg Hill	.50
101	Keith Lyle	.50
102	Ryan Leaf	2.00
103	Craig Whelihan	.50
104	Charlie Jones	.50
105	Junior Seau	1.00
106	Natrone Means	1.00
107	Rodney Harrison	.50
108	Steve Young	2.00
109	Garrison Hearst	1.00
110	Jerry Rice	3.00
111	Chris Doleman	.50
112	Roy Barker	.50
113	Ricky Watters	1.00
114	Jon Kitna	1.50
115	Joey Galloway	1.25
116	Chad Brown	.50
117	Michael Sinclair	.50
118	Warrick Dunn	1.50
119	Mike Alstott	1.25
120	Bert Emanuel	.50
121	Hardy Nickerson	.50
122	Eddie George	1.50
123	Steve McNair	1.25
124	Yancey Thigpen	.50
125	Frank Wycheck	.50
126	Jackie Harris	.50
127	Terry Allen	1.00
128	Trent Green	1.25
129	Jamie Asher	.50
130	Brian Mitchell	.50
131	Lance Alworth	1.00
132	Fred Biletnikoff	1.25
133	Mel Blount	.50
134	Cliff Branch	.50
135	Harold Carmichael	.50
136	Larry Csonka	1.25
137	Eric Dickerson	1.00
138	Randy Gradishar	.50
139	Joe Greene	1.00
140	Jack Ham	.50
141	Ted Hendricks	.50
142	Charlie Joiner	1.00
143	Ed Jones	.50
144	Billy Kilmer	.50
145	Paul Krause	.50
146	James Lofton	.50
147	Archie Manning	1.00
148	Don Maynard	1.00
149	Ozzie Newsome	.50
150	Jim Otto	.50
151	Lee Roy Selmon	.50
152	Billy Sims	1.00
153	Mike Singletary	1.00
154	Ken Stabler	1.50
155	John Stallworth	1.00
156	Roger Staubach	2.00
157	Charley Taylor	.50
158	Paul Warfield	1.25
159	Kellen Winslow	1.00
160	Jack Youngblood	.50
161	Bill Bergey	.50
162	Raymond Berry	.50
163	Chuck Howley	.50
164	Rocky Bleier	.50
165	Russ Francis	.50
166	Drew Pearson	.50
167	Mercury Morris	.50
168	Dick Anderson	.50
169	Earl Morrall	.50
170	Jim Hart	.50
171	*Ricky Williams*	100.00
172	*Cade McNown*	50.00
173	*Tim Couch*	100.00
174	*Daunte Culpepper*	50.00
175	*Akili Smith*	40.00
176	*Brock Huard*	20.00
177	*Donovan McNabb*	50.00
178	*Michael Bishop*	20.00
179	*Shaun King*	35.00
180	*Tory Holt*	30.00

1999 SP Signature Autographs

Cards in this insert are the same as the base except for the signature on the front. The backs are different then the regular base card. Singles were inserted one-per-pack. A Gold parallel was produced and inserted 1:59 packs.

		MT
Common Player:		10.00
Minor Stars:		20.00
Inserted 1:1		
Gold Cards:		2x
Inserted 1:59		
KA	Karim Abdul	20.00
TA	Troy Aikman	250.00
DA	Derrick Alexander	10.00
MA	Mike Alstott	50.00
AA	Ashley Ambrose	10.00
AN	Dick Anderson	10.00
TE	Jamie Asher	10.00
DE	Roy Barker	10.00
CB	Charlie Batch	60.00
MB	Mario Bates	10.00
DB	Donnell Bennett	10.00
BB	Bill Bergey	10.00
RY	Raymond Berry	25.00
MI	Michael Bishop	150.00
ML	Mel Blount	20.00
KB	Kyle Brady	10.00
RB	Robert Brooks	30.00
LB	Chad Brown	10.00
GB	Gary Brown	10.00
TB	Tim Brown	35.00
IB	Isaac Bruce	35.00
MK	Mark Brunell	125.00
CY	Chris Calloway	10.00
HC	Harold Carmichael	30.00
CC	Chris Chandler	30.00
BC	Bob Christian	10.00
CL	Cameron Cleeland	20.00
CW	Curtis Conway	20.00
TC	Tim Couch	325.00
CK	Ray Crockett	10.00
ZC	Zack Crockett	10.00
DC	Daunte Culpepper	175.00
NO	Sean Dawkins	10.00
KD	Koy Detmer	10.00
CD	Corey Dillon	35.00
TR	Troy Drayton	10.00
RD	Rickey Dudley	10.00
RE	Robert Edwards	25.00
JE	John Elway	300.00
BT	Bert Emanuel	20.00
BE	Bobby Engram	10.00
CE	Curtis Enis	30.00
MF	Marshall Faulk	40.00
BF	Brett Favre	300.00
WF	William Floyd	10.00
RF	Russ Francis	10.00
AF	Antonio Freeman	75.00
GA	Joey Galloway	70.00
CG	Charlie Garner	20.00
JG	Jason Garrett	10.00
EG	Eddie George	85.00
GE	Jeff George	20.00
GR	Randy Gradishar	10.00
GN	Trent Green	25.00
JH	Jack Ham	20.00
JK	Jackie Harris	10.00
RH	Rodney Harrison	10.00
HT	Jim Hart	20.00
GH	Garrison Hearst	25.00
TH	Ted Hendricks	20.00
HL	Greg Hill	10.00
LH	Leroy Hoard	10.00
DH	Darick Holmes	10.00
PH	Priest Holmes	30.00
WP	Torry Holt	150.00
HY	Chuck Howley	20.00
BH	Brock Huard	85.00
MJ	Michael Jackson	20.00
JJ	James Jett	20.00
KJ	Keyshawn Johnson	50.00
LJ	Leon Johnson	10.00
CJ	Charlie Joiner	20.00
SD	Charlie Jones	20.00
EJ	Ed Jones	20.00
NK	Napoleon Kaufman	50.00
SH	Shaun King	60.00
KI	Jon Kitna	30.00
SK	Sammy Knight	20.00
PK	Paul Krause	20.00
FL	Fred Lane	20.00

TL	Ty Law	10.00
RL	Ray Lewis	10.00
JL	James Lofton	20.00
KL	Keith Lyle	10.00
MG	Archie Manning	30.00
DM	Dan Marino	375.00
NY	Don Maynard	20.00
WM	Willie McGinest	10.00
MN	Donovan McNabb	175.00
QB	Cade McNown	175.00
NM	Natrone Means	30.00
KR	Brian Mitchell	10.00
PT	Pete Mitchell	10.00
JM	John Mobley	10.00
HM	Herman Moore	35.00
MO	Earl Morrall	20.00
MY	Mercury Morris	20.00
RM	Randy Moss	350.00
EM	Eric Moulds	40.00
MM	Muhsin Muhammad	10.00
AM	Adrian Murrell	10.00
HN	Hardy Nickerson	10.00
OZ	Ozzie Newsome	25.00
DP	Drew Pearson	25.00
JP	Jake Plummer	100.00
RP	Robert Porcher	10.00
OJ	O.J. Santiago	10.00
JR	Junior Seau	20.00
LS	Lee Roy Selmon	20.00
MS	Michael Sinclair	10.00
SY	Mike Singletary	25.00
TS	Tony Siragusa	10.00
CS	Chris Slade	10.00
TO	Torrance Small	10.00
AK	Akili Smith	150.00
AS	Antowain Smith	25.00
ES	Emmitt Smith	250.00
JS	Jimmy Smith	20.00
KS	Ken Stabler	40.00
ST	Duce Staley	10.00
SW	John Stallworth	25.00
MT	Maa Tanuvasa	10.00
CT	Charley Taylor	20.00
FT	Fred Taylor	125.00
JT	Jason Taylor	10.00
TV	Tommy Vardell	10.00
HW	Hines Ward	20.00
PW	Paul Warfield	25.00
LW	Lamont Warren	10.00
ND	Ricky Watters	40.00
WH	Craig Whelihan	10.00
HV	Harvey Williams	10.00
RW	Ricky Williams	325.00
KW	Kellen Winslow	25.00
FW	Frank Wycheck	10.00
JY	Jack Youngblood	20.00

1999 SP Signature Montana Great Performances

This was a 10-card set that highlights the career of Montana. Singles were randomly inserted. A parallel Autographed version was also produced and found 1:47 packs and a Gold Autographed parallel was made and found 1:880 packs.

		MT
Complete Set (10):		50.00
Common Player:		5.00
Randomly Inserted		
Signature Cards:		25x
Inserted 1:47		
Gold Signature Cards:		160x
Inserted 1:880		
1	Joe Montana	5.00
2	Joe Montana	5.00
3	Joe Montana	5.00
4	Joe Montana	5.00
5	Joe Montana	5.00
6	Joe Montana	5.00
7	Joe Montana	5.00
8	Joe Montana	5.00
9	Joe Montana	5.00
10	Joe Montana	5.00

> A card number in parentheses ( ) indicates the set is unnumbered.

1999 SPx

This was a 135-card set that included 45 sequentially numbered rookie cards. A total of 21 of the rookies were numbered to 1,999 and were autographed, 19 rookies were unsigned and numbered to 1,999 and only five were autographed and numbered to 500. Each single had a parallel Radiance and Spectrum single. Other inserts included: Highlight Heroes, Masters, Prolifics, SPxcitement, SPxtreme, Starscape and Winning Materials. SRP was $5.99 for three-card packs.

		MT
Complete Set (135):		2000.
Common Player:		.25
Minor Stars:		.50
Common Rookie:		6.00
Production 1,999 Sets		
Wax Box:		140.00
1	Jake Plummer	2.00
2	Adrian Murrell	.50
3	Frank Sanders	.50
4	Jamal Anderson	1.00
5	Chris Chandler	.50
6	Terance Mathis	.25
7	Tony Banks	.25
8	Priest Holmes	1.00
9	Jermaine Lewis	.50
10	Antowain Smith	1.00
11	Doug Flutie	1.75
12	Eric Moulds	1.00
13	Tshimanga Biakabutuka	.50
14	Steve Beuerlein	.50
15	Muhsin Muhammad	.25
16	Bobby Engram	.25
17	Curtis Conway	.50
18	Curtis Enis	.50
19	Corey Dillon	1.00
20	Jeff Blake	.50
21	Carl Pickens	.50
22	Ty Detmer	.25
23	Terry Kirby	.25
24	Leslie Shepherd	.25
25	Troy Aikman	2.50
26	Emmitt Smith	3.50
27	Deion Sanders	.50
28	Terrell Davis	3.50
29	Rod Smith	.50
30	Bubby Brister	.50
31	Barry Sanders	5.00
32	Herman Moore	1.00
33	Charlie Batch	1.50
34	Brett Favre	5.00
35	Antonio Freeman	1.00
36	Dorsey Levens	1.00
37	Peyton Manning	3.50
38	Marvin Harrison	1.00
39	Jerome Pathon	.25
40	Mark Brunell	2.00
41	Jimmy Smith	.50
42	Fred Taylor	2.50
43	Elvis Grbac	.50
44	Andre Rison	.25
45	Warren Moon	.50
46	Dan Marino	3.50
47	Karim Abdul	.75
48	O.J. McDuffie	.50
49	Randall Cunningham	1.00
50	Robert Smith	1.00
51	Randy Moss	5.00
52	Drew Bledsoe	2.00
53	Terry Glenn	1.00
54	Tony Simmons	.50
55	Danny Wuerffel	.50
56	Cameron Cleeland	.50
57	Kerry Collins	.50
58	Gary Brown	.25
59	Ike Hilliard	.50
60	Vinny Testaverde	.50
61	Curtis Martin	1.00
62	Keyshawn Johnson	.50
63	Rich Gannon	.25
64	Napoleon Kaufman	.50
65	Tim Brown	.50
66	Duce Staley	.50
67	Doug Pederson	.25
68	Charles Johnson	.25
69	Kordell Stewart	1.00
70	Jerome Bettis	1.00
71	Trent Green	.75
72	Marshall Faulk	1.00

73	Ryan Leaf	1.25
74	Natrone Means	1.00
75	Jim Harbaugh	.50
76	Steve Young	1.75
77	Garrison Hearst	.50
78	Jerry Rice	2.50
79	Terrell Owens	1.00
80	Ricky Watters	.75
81	Joey Galloway	1.00
82	Jon Kitna	1.25
83	Warrick Dunn	1.25
84	Trent Dilfer	.50
85	Mike Alstott	1.25
86	Steve McNair	1.25
87	Eddie George	1.25
88	Yancey Thigpen	.50
89	Skip Hicks	.75
90	Michael Westbrook	.75
91	*Amos Zereoue*	15.00
92	*Chris Claiborne AUTO 1,999*	20.00
93	*Scott Covington*	8.00
94	*Jeff Paulk*	6.00
95	*Brandon Stokley AUTO 1,999*	15.00
96	*Antoine Winfield*	6.00
97	*Reginald Kelly*	6.00
98	*Jermaine Fazande AUTO 1,999*	15.00
99	*Andy Katzenmoyer*	10.00
100	*Craig Yeast*	6.00
101	*Joe Montgomery*	10.00
102	*Darrin Chiaverini*	6.00
103	*Travis McGriff*	8.00
104	*Jevon Kearse AUTO 1,999*	50.00
105	*Joel Makovicka AUTO 1,999*	15.00
106	*Aaron Brooks*	10.00
107	*Chris McAlister*	6.00
108	*Jim Kleinsasser*	10.00
109	*Ebenezer Ekuban*	6.00
110	*Karsten Bailey*	6.00
111	*Sedrick Irvin*	30.00
112	*D'Wayne Bates AUTO 1,999*	20.00
113	*Joe Germaine AUTO 1,999*	30.00
114	*Cecil Collins AUTO 1,999*	75.00
115	*Michael Cloud*	10.00
116	*James Johnson*	15.00
117	*Champ Bailey AUTO 1,999*	35.00
118	*Rob Konrad*	10.00
119	*Peerless Price AUTO 1,999*	45.00
120	*Kevin Faulk*	40.00
121	*Dameane Douglas AUTO 1,999*	6.00
122	*Kevin Johnson AUTO 1,999*	60.00
123	*Troy Edwards AUTO 1,999*	50.00
124	*Edgerrin James AUTO 1,999*	325.00
125	*David Boston AUTO 1,999*	50.00
126	*Michael Bishop AUTO 1,999*	35.00
127	*Shaun King AUTO SP*	300.00
127A	*Shaun King Trade*	75.00
128	*Brock Huard AUTO 1,999*	30.00
129	*Torry Holt AUTO 1,999*	70.00
130	*Cade McNown AUTO 500*	300.00
131	*Tim Couch AUTO 500*	400.00
132	*Donovan McNabb AUTO 1,999*	75.00
133	*Akili Smith AUTO 500*	180.00
134	*Daunte Culpepper AUTO 500*	250.00
135	*Ricky Williams AUTO 500*	400.00

1999 SPx Radiance

This was a 135-card parallel to the base set including unsigned versions of the autographed rookie cards. Each single was printed with a holographic green-foil treatment and was sequentially numbered to 100.

	MT
Radiance Cards (1-90):	15x-30x
Radiance Rookies (1,999):	3x
Radiance Rookies (Auto.):	2x
Radiance Rookies (Auto. 500):	1x
Production 100 Sets	

1999 SPx Spectrum

This was a 135-card parallel to the base set and each was printed with a holographic red-foil treatment and numbered one-of-one.

	MT
Production 1 Set	

1999 SPx Highlight Heroes

This was a 10-card insert set that included mostly quarterbacks. Singles were inserted 1:9 packs.

		MT
Complete Set (10):		20.00
Common Player:		2.00
Inserted 1:9		
1	Jake Plummer	6.00
2	Doug Flutie	4.00
3	Garrison Hearst	2.00
4	Fred Taylor	6.00
5	Dorsey Levens	2.00
6	Kordell Stewart	3.00
7	Marshall Faulk	2.00
8	Steve Young	4.00
9	Troy Aikman	6.00
10	Jerome Bettis	2.00

1999 SPx Masters

This was a 15-card insert set that included the best players at their respective positions. Singles were inserted 1:17 packs.

		MT
Complete Set (15):		75.00
Common Player:		3.00
Inserted 1:17		
1	Dan Marino	10.00
2	Barry Sanders	12.00
3	Peyton Manning	10.00
4	Joey Galloway	3.00
5	Steve Young	5.00
6	Warrick Dunn	4.00
7	Deion Sanders	3.00
8	Fred Taylor	6.00
9	Charlie Batch	4.00
10	Jamal Anderson	3.00
11	Jake Plummer	6.00
12	Terrell Davis	10.00
13	Eddie George	4.00
14	Mark Brunell	5.00
15	Randy Moss	12.00

1999 SPx Prolifics

This was a 15-card insert set that included stars who had the ability to score points, yards

and wins. Singles were inserted 1:17 packs.

		MT
Complete Set (15):		50.00
Common Player:		3.00
Inserted 1:17		
1	John Elway	10.00
2	Barry Sanders	12.00
3	Jamal Anderson	3.00
4	Terrell Owens	4.00
5	Marshall Faulk	3.00
6	Napoleon Kaufman	3.00
7	Antonio Freeman	3.00
8	Doug Flutie	5.00
9	Vinny Testaverde	3.00
10	Jerry Rice	6.00
11	Eric Moulds	3.00
12	Emmitt Smith	10.00
13	Brett Favre	12.00
14	Randall Cunningham	3.00
15	Keyshawn Johnson	3.00

1999 SPx SPxcitement

This was a 20-card insert set who featured players who provide non-stop thrills. Singles were inserted 1:3 packs.

		MT
Complete Set (20):		30.00
Common Player:		1.00
Inserted 1:3		
1	Troy Aikman	4.00
2	Edgerrin James	6.00
3	Jerry Rice	4.00
4	Daunte Culpepper	4.00
5	Antowain Smith	1.00
6	Kevin Faulk	2.00
7	Steve McNair	1.00
8	Antonio Freeman	1.00
9	Torry Holt	3.00
10	Napoleon Kaufman	1.00
11	Curtis Martin	1.00
12	Randall Cunningham	1.00
13	Eric Moulds	1.00
14	Priest Holmes	1.00
15	David Boston	3.00
16	Herman Moore	1.00
17	Champ Bailey	1.50
18	Vinny Testaverde	1.00
19	Garrison Hearst	1.00
20	Jon Kitna	1.00

1999 SPx SPxtreme

This 20-card insert set highlighted the most collectible stars and saluted their extreme talents to the game. Singles were inserted 1:6 packs.

		MT
Complete Set (20):		45.00
Common Player:		1.50
Inserted 1:6		
1	Emmitt Smith	7.00
2	Brock Huard	2.50
3	David Boston	4.00
4	Edgerrin James	10.00
5	Kevin Faulk	2.50
6	Daunte Culpepper	6.00

		MT
7	Charlie Batch	2.50
8	Torry Holt	4.00
9	Andre Rison	1.50
10	Karim Abdul	1.50
11	Kordell Stewart	2.50
12	Curtis Enis	1.50
13	Terrell Owens	1.50
14	Curtis Martin	1.50
15	Ricky Watters	1.50
16	Corey Dillon	1.50
17	Tim Brown	1.50
18	Warrick Dunn	1.50
19	Drew Bledsoe	5.00
20	Eddie George	2.50

1999 SPx Starscape

This was a 10-card insert set that featured ten superstars and highlighted their spectacular achievement to date. Singles were inserted 1:9 packs.

		MT
Complete Set (10):		20.00
Common Player:		2.00
Inserted 1:9		
1	Randy Moss	10.00
2	Keyshawn Johnson	2.00
3	Curtis Enis	2.00
4	Jerome Bettis	2.00
5	Mark Brunell	4.00
6	Antowain Smith	2.00
7	Joey Galloway	2.00
8	Drew Bledsoe	4.00
9	Corey Dillon	2.00
10	Steve McNair	2.00

1999 SPx Winning Materials

This 10-card insert set featured two pieces of game-used memorabilia (jersey swatch and football) of the featured player. Singles were inserted 1:252 packs.

		MT
Complete Set (10):		1300.
Common Player:		75.00
Inserted 1:252		
DB	David Boston	75.00
TC	Tim Couch	225.00
DC	Daunte Culpepper	120.00
BF	Brett Favre	250.00
TH	Torry Holt	75.00
DM	Dan Marino	200.00
MC	Donovan McNabb	120.00
CM	Cade McNown	120.00
JR	Jerry Rice	150.00
RW	Ricky Williams	225.00

1993 Spectrum QB Club Tribute Sheet Promos

The two-sheet, 8-1/2" x 11" set, featuring Aikman and Marino, was issued as a preview for the 1993 Spectrum Quarterback Club Tribute Sheets. Production was limited to 5,000 sheets each.

		MT
Complete Set (2):		10.00
Common Player:		4.00
1	Troy Aikman	4.00
2	Dan Marino	6.00

Post-1980 cards in Near Mint condition will generally sell for about 75% of the quoted Mint value. Excellent-condition cards bring no more than 40%.

1993 Spectrum QB Club Tribute Sheets

The 12-sheet, 8-1/2" x 11" set featured 12 top quarterbacks with color photos over a black marble background with the player's signature in 24 kt. gold foil. As with the promos, the backs are blank and are limited to a production of 5,000.

		MT
Complete Set (12):		30.00
Common Player:		1.50
1	Troy Aikman	4.00
2	Randall Cunningham	1.50
3	John Elway	3.00
4	Boomer Esiason	1.50
5	Brett Favre	8.00
6	Jim Kelly	2.00
7	Dan Marino	8.00
8	Warren Moon	2.00
9	Phil Simms	1.50
10	Steve Young	3.00
11	AFC Stars (Jeff Hostetler, Bernie Kosar, Neil O'Donnell)	1.50
12	NFC Stars (Jim Everett, Chris Miller, Mark Rypien)	1.50

1993 Spectrum/ Front Row Promos

The five-card, standard-size set was issued as a preview of Spectrum Holdings Group and its purchase of the Front Row trademark. The fronts feature action color shots with the backs containing bio and stat information inset over another player shot. An oval with "For Promotional Use Only" printed inside was featured on the card backs.

		MT
Complete Set (5):		8.00
Common Player:		1.50
1	Eric Curry	1.50
2	Andre Hastings	1.50
3	Qadry Ismail	2.00
4	Lincoln Kennedy	1.50
5	O.J. McDuffie	2.50

1993 Spectrum/ Front Row Tribute Sheet

The 8-1/2" x 11" sheet was issued to promote Spectrum Holdings Group and its purchase of the Front Row trademark. A gold-foil bar edged in purple contains "Outstanding Players of the 1993 Draft" over a black granite-like background. Production run was 5,000 and the backs were blank.

		MT
Complete Set (1):		2.00
Common Panel:		2.00
1	Qadry Ismail, Lincoln Kennedy, O.J. McDuffie, Andre Hastings, Eric Curry	2.00

1992 Sport Decks Promo Aces

These four playing card Aces were produced by Junior Card and Toy Inc. to promote

the premier edition of Sport Decks NFL playing cards. One standard-size card was given away during each of the four days of the National Sports Collectors Convention in Atlanta. The front has a color action photo on it against a full-bleed metallic-sheen background. The card number and suit are in the upper left corner; a Team NFL logo is in the upper right corner. These are situated on a metallic bar running across the top. A similar bar runs along the bottom. It contains a team helmet, the player's name and position, and a Sport Decks logo. There were reportedly 6,000 silver-barred cards and 1,000 gold-barred cards made (three times more valuable than the values listed below for silver ones). The card backs are white, with pink and black lettering which provides advertisements, logos and the players who will be featured in the suit corresponding to the pictured player.

		MT
Complete Set (4):		12.00
Common Player:		1.00
AC	Emmitt Smith	6.00
AD	Thurman Thomas	2.00
AH	Dan Marino	5.00
AS	Mark Rypien	1.00

1992 Sport Decks

This 55-card deck of playing cards was produced after Sport Decks debuted the set at the 1992 National Sports Collectors Convention in Atlanta. Each card front has rounded corners and features a full-bleed color action shot. A stripe at the top contains a card number and suit in the upper left corner, with a Team NFL logo in the upper right corner. The bottom stripe contains a team helmet, player's name and position and card number and suit. The back has a white-bordered blue-green football field which has an "Official 1992 Season Football Star Cards" logo in the middle of a goal post.

		MT
Complete Set (55):		5.00
Common Player:		.05
AC	Troy Aikman	.75
2C	Rodney Peete	.07
3C	Cris Carter	.10
4C	Randal Hill	.07
5C	Jeff Hostetler	.07
6C	Flipper Anderson	.05
7C	Chris Miller	.10
8C	Anthony Carter	.07
9C	Timm Rosenbach	.05
10C	Sterling Sharpe	.25
JC	Ricky Ervins	.05
QC	Jerry Rice	.50
KC	Emmitt Smith	1.00
AD	Jim Kelly	.25
2D	John Friesz	.10
3D	Gaston Green	.05
4D	Hugh Millen	.05
5D	Dan McGwire	.05
6D	Eric Green	.07
7D	Christian Okoye	.07
8D	Ronnie Lott	.10
9D	Rob Moore	.07
10D	Mark Clayton	.05
JD	Thurman Thomas	.25
QD	John Elway	.45
KD	Warren Moon	.30
AH	Dan Marino	.75
2H	Anthony Munoz	.10
3H	Nick Bell	.05
4H	Michael Dean Perry	.05
5H	Haywood Jeffires	.05
6H	Bubby Brister	.05
7H	Andre Reed	.10
8H	Anthony Miller	.07
9H	Ken O'Brien	.07
10H	Bernie Kosar	.10
JH	Derrick Thomas	.15
QH	Jeff George	.10
KH	Boomer Esiason	.15
AS	Mark Rypien	.10
2S	Phil Simms	.10
3S	Pat Swilling	.07
4S	Jim Harbaugh	.15
5S	Mike Singletary	.15
6S	Lawrence Taylor	.15
7S	John Taylor	.10
8S	Keith Jackson	.10
9S	Vinny Testaverde	.10
10S	Andre Rison	.10
JS	Michael Irvin	.25
QS	Earnest Byner	.05
KS	Randall Cunningham	.10
JK	Eric Dickerson	.10
JK	Jim Everett	.10
xx	Title card	.05

1999 Sports Illustrated

This was a 150-card release that included 90 stars of yesterday and today, 30 Fresh Faces (impact rookies of 1998) and 30 Super Bowl MVP's. Top inserts include: Autographs, Canton Calling and SI Covers.

		MT
Complete Set (150):		100.00
Common Player:		.15
Minor Stars:		.30
Common Rookie:		1.00
Wax Box:		210.00
1	Bart Starr	.50
2	Bart Starr	.50
3	Joe Namath	.50
4	Len Dawson	.30
5	Chuck Howley	.15
6	Roger Staubach	.50
7	Jake Scott	.15
8	Larry Csonka	.30
9	Franco Harris	.30
10	Fred Biletnikoff	.15
11	Harvey Martin, Randy White	.15
12	Terry Bradshaw	.50
13	Terry Bradshaw	.50
14	Jim Plunkett	.30
15	Joe Montana	1.00
16	Marcus Allen	.50
17	Joe Montana	1.00
18	Richard Dent	.15
19	Phil Simms	.30
20	Doug Williams	.15
21	Jerry Rice	1.00
22	Joe Montana	1.00
23	Ottis Anderson	.30
24	Mark Rypien	.15
25	Troy Aikman	1.00
26	Emmitt Smith	1.50
27	Steve Young	.50
28	Larry Brown	.15
29	Desmond Howard	.15
30	Terrell Davis	1.50
31	Y.A. Tittle	.30
32	Paul Hornung	.50
33	Gale Sayers	.50
34	Garo Yepremian	.15
35	Bert Jones	.30
36	Joe Washington	.15
37	Joe Theismann	.30
38	Roger Craig	.30
39	Mike Singletary	.30
40	Bobby Bell	.15
41	Ken Houston	.15
42	Lenny Moore	.15
43	Mark Moseley	.15
44	Chuck Bednarik	.15
45	Ted Hendricks	.15
46	Steve Largent	.50
47	Bob Lilly	.15
48	Don Maynard	.50
49	John Mackey	.15
50	Anthony Munoz	.15
51	Bobby Mitchell	.15
52	Jim Brown	.50
53	Otto Graham	.50
54	Earl Morrall	.15
55	Danny White	.30
56	Karim Abdul-Jabbar	.50
57	Charlie Garner	.15
58	Jeff Blake	.30
59	Reggie White	.50
60	Derrick Thomas	.15
61	Duce Staley	.15
62	Tim Brown	.30
63	Elvis Grbac	.30
64	Tony Banks	.30
65	Rob Johnson	.30
66	Danny Kanell	.15
67	Marshall Faulk	.50
68	Warrick Dunn	1.25
69	Dan Marino	3.00
70	Jimmy Smith	.50
71	John Elway	2.50

72	Charles Way	.15
73	Ricky Watters	.30
74	Terry Glenn	.50
75	Bobby Hoying	.30
76	Curtis Martin	.50
77	Trent Dilfer	.30
78	Emmitt Smith	3.00
79	Irving Fryar	.15
80	Troy Aikman	2.00
81	Barry Sanders	4.00
82	Brett Favre	4.00
83	Robert Smith	.50
84	Dorsey Levens	.50
85	Cris Carter	.50
86	Jeff George	.30
87	Jerome Bettis	.30
88	Warren Moon	.30
89	Steve Young	.75
90	Fred Lane	.30
91	Jerry Rice	2.00
92	Natrone Means	.50
93	Mike Alstott	.50
94	Kordell Stewart	1.50
95	Jake Plummer	1.75
96	Jamal Anderson	.75
97	Corey Dillon	1.00
98	Deion Sanders	.50
99	Mark Brunell	1.50
100	Garrison Hearst	.50
101	Andre Rison	.15
102	Antowain Smith	.75
103	Drew Bledsoe	1.50
104	Eddie George	1.50
105	Keyshawn Johnson	.50
106	Isaac Bruce	.30
107	Rob Moore	.30
108	Steve McNair	.75
109	Terrell Davis	3.00
110	Carl Pickens	.50
111	Wayne Chrebet	.50
112	Kerry Collins	.30
113	Eric Metcalf	.15
114	Joey Galloway	.50
115	Shannon Sharpe	.30
116	Robert Brooks	.15
117	Glenn Foley	.30
118	Yancey Thigpen	.30
119	Frank Sanders	.30
120	Herman Moore	.50
121	Antonio Freeman	.75
122	Michael Irvin	.30
123	Brad Johnson	.50
124	James Stewart	.15
125	Jim Harbaugh	.30
126	Peyton Manning	12.00
127	Ryan Leaf	6.00
128	Curtis Enis	4.00
129	Fred Taylor	10.00
130	Randy Moss	25.00
131	John Avery	3.00
132	Charles Woodson	5.00
133	Robert Edwards	3.50
134	Charlie Batch	8.00
135	Brian Griese	5.00
136	Skip Hicks	3.00
137	Jacquez Green	3.00
138	Robert Holcombe	2.00
139	Kevin Dyson	3.00
140	Rodney Williams	1.00
141	Ahman Green	2.00
142	Tavian Banks	2.00
143	Donald Hayes	1.00
144	Tony Simmons	3.00
145	Patrick Johnson	2.00
146	Marcus Nash	3.00
147	Germane Crowell	3.00
148	R.W. McQuarters	2.00
149	Jonathan Quinn	2.00
150	Andre Wadsworth	2.00

1999 Sports Illustrated Autographs

A total of 35 players from the past signed cards in this insert with numbers unknown. Singles were found one-per-pack.

	MT
Complete Set (35):	3000.00
Common Player:	10.00
Minor Stars:	20.00
Inserted 1:1	
Ottis Anderson	20.00
Chuck Bednarik	10.00
Bobby Bell	10.00
Terry Bradshaw	400.00
Jim Brown	250.00

Roger Craig	25.00
Len Dawson	175.00
Otto Graham	30.00
Franco Harris	175.00
Ted Hendricks	10.00
Paul Hornung	185.00
Ken Houston	10.00
Bert Jones	10.00
Steve Largent	35.00
Bob Lilly	10.00
John Mackey	10.00
Don Maynard	20.00
Bobby Mitchell	10.00
Joe Montana	425.00
Lenny Moore	10.00
Earl Morrall	10.00
Mark Moseley	10.00
Anthony Munoz	20.00
Joe Namath	450.00
Jim Plunkett	20.00
Gale Sayers	35.00
Mike Singletary	100.00
Bart Starr	400.00
Roger Staubach	200.00
Joe Theismann	85.00
Y.A. Tittle	100.00
Joe Washington	10.00
Danny White	10.00
Doug Williams	100.00
Garo Yepremian	10.00

1999 Sports Illustrated Canton Calling

This was an 8-card set that included players who are on their way to the Hall of Fame. Singles were inserted 1:12 packs and a parallel Gold insert was also produced and found 1:120 packs.

	MT
Complete Set (8):	60.00
Common Player:	3.00
Inserted 1:12	
Gold Cards:	3x-6x
Inserted 1:120	
1 Warren Moon	3.00
2 Emmitt Smith	10.00
3 Jerry Rice	8.00
4 Brett Favre	15.00
5 Barry Sanders	15.00
6 Dan Marino	10.00
7 John Elway	10.00
8 Troy Aikman	8.00

1999 Sports Illustrated Covers

This was a 60-card set that took the best covers from the past and reproduced them on a card. Singles were found one-per-pack.

	MT
Complete Set (60):	30.00
Common Player:	.25
Minor Stars:	.50
Inserted 1:1	
1 Jim Brown	.50
2 Y.A. Tittle	.25
3 Dallas Cowboys	.25
4 Joe Namath	.75
5 Bart Starr	.50
6 Earl Morrall	.25

7	Minnesota Vikings	.25
8	Kansas City Chiefs	.25
9	Len Dawson	.25
10	Monday Night Football	.25
11	Jim Plunkett	.25
12	Garo Yepremian	.25
13	Larry Csonka	.25
14	Terry Bradshaw	.50
15	Franco Harris	.25
16	Bert Jones	.25
17	Harvey Martin, Randy White	.25
18	Roger Staubach	.50
19	Marcus Allen	.50
20	Joe Washington	.25
21	Dan Marino	2.50
22	Joe Theismann	.25
23	Roger Craig	.25
24	Mike Singletary	.25
25	Chicago Bears	.25
26	Phil Simms	.25
27	Vinny Testaverde	.25
28	Doug Williams	.25
29	Jerry Rice	1.50
30	Hershel Walker	.25
31	Joe Montana	1.75
32	Ottis Anderson	.25
33	Rocket Ismail	.25
34	Bruce Smith	.25
35	Thurman Thomas	.25
36	Mark Rypien	.25
37	Jim Harbaugh	.25
38	Randall Cunningham	.50
39	Troy Aikman	1.50
40	Reggie White	.50
41	Junior Seau	.25
42	Emmitt Smith	2.50
43	Natrone Means	.25
44	Ricky Watters	.25
45	Pittsburgh Steelers	.25
46	Steve Young, Troy Aikman	1.00
47	Steve Young	1.00
48	Deion Sanders	.50
49	Elvis Grbac	.25
50	Green Bay Packers	.25
51	Brett Favre	3.00
52	Mark Brunell, Kerry Collins	1.00
53	Antonio Freeman	.75
54	Desmond Howard	.25
55	AFC Central Quarterbacks	.25
56	Warrick Dunn	.50
57	Jerome Bettis	.25
58	John Elway	2.00
59	Brent Jones	.25
60	Terrell Davis	3.00

1976 Sportstix

The 10-sticker, 3-1/2" in diameter set was numbered as a continuation of non-sport issues. The helmet logos on the stickers have been erased and two major errors exist: Drew Pearson's card actually has Gloster Richardson on the card while Fred Biletnikoff's last name is spelled wrong on card No. 32.

	NM
Complete Set (11):	200.00
Common Player:	10.00
31 Carl Eller	20.00
32 Fred Biletnikoff (UER, Misspelled Belitnikoff)	30.00
33 Terry Metcalf	15.00
34 Gary Huff	10.00
35 Steve Bartkowski	20.00
36 Dan Pastorini	15.00
37 Drew Pearson (UER, photo is of Gloster Richardson)	20.00
38 Bert Jones	15.00
39 Otis Armstrong	15.00
40 Don Woods	10.00
C Dick Butkus	60.00

1991 Stadium Club

Topps made its premiere edition debut with its 1991 Stadium Club set of 500 cards. The glossy cards feature full-bleed action photos on the front. The player's name is at the bottom in an aqua stripe that is bordered with gold. The back uses a horizontal format with a football field and stadium for a background. A biography, Sporting News Football Analysis Report and miniature replica of the player's Topps rookie card are also included on the back.

	MT
Complete Set (500):	90.00
Common Player:	.20
Minor Stars:	.40
Wax Box:	90.00
1 Pepper Johnson	.20
2 Emmitt Smith	10.00
3 Deion Sanders	3.00
4 Andre Collins	.20
5 Eric Metcalf	.30
6 Richard Dent	.30
7 Eric Martin	.20
8 Marcus Allen	.50
9 Gary Anderson	.20
10 Joey Browner	.20
11 Lorenzo White	.20
12 Bruce Smith	.20
13 Mark Boyer	.20
14 Mike Piel	.20
15 Albert Bentley	.20
16 Bennie Blades	.20
17 Jason Staurovsky	.20
18 Anthony Toney	.20
19 Dave Krieg	.20
20 *Harvey Williams*	2.00
21 Bubba Paris	.20
22 Tim McGee	.20
23 Brian Noble	.20
24 Vinny Testaverde	.30
25 Doug Widell	.20
26 John Jackson	.20
27 Marion Butts	.20
28 Deron Cherry	.20
29 Don Warren	.20
30 Rod Woodson	.75
31 Mike Baab	.20
32 Greg Jackson	.20
33 Jerry Robinson	.20
34 Dalton Hilliard	.20
35 Brian Jordan	.20
36 James Thornton (Misspelled Thorton on cards back)	.20
37 Michael Irvin	1.00
38 Billy Joe Tolliver	.20
39 Jeff Herrod	.20
40 Scott Norwood	.20
41 Ferrell Edmunds	.20
42 Andre Waters	.20
43 Kevin Glover	.20
44 Ray Berry	.20
45 Timm Rosenbach	.20
46 Reuben Davis	.20
47 Charles Wilson	.20
48 *Todd Marinovich*	.20
49 Harris Barton	.20
50 Jim Breech	.20
51 Ron Holmes	.20
52 Chris Singleton	.20
53 Pat Leahy	.20
54 Tom Newberry	.20
55 Greg Montgomery	.20
56 Robert Blackmon	.20
57 Jay Hilgenberg	.20
58 Rodney Hampton	1.00
59 Brett Perriman	.75
60 *Ricky Watters*	7.00
61 Howie Long	.20
62 Frank Cornish	.20
63 Chris Miller	.20
64 Keith Taylor	.20
65 Tony Paige	.20
66 Gary Zimmerman	.20
67 Mark Royals	.20
68 Ernie Jones	.20
69 David Grant	.20
70 Shane Conlan	.20
71 Jerry Rice	5.00
72 Christian Okoye	.20
73 Eddie Murray	.20
74 Reggie White	.75
75 *Jeff Graham*	2.00
76 Mark Jackson	.20
77 David Grayson	.20
78 Dan Stryzinski	.20
79 Sterling Sharpe	.75
80 Cleveland Gary	.20
81 Johnny Meads	.20
82 Howard Cross	.20
83 Ken O'Brien	.20
84 Brian Blades	.20
85 Ethan Horton	.20
86 Bruce Armstrong	.20
87 *James Washington*	.40
88 Eugene Daniel	.20
89 James Lofton	.20
90 Louis Oliver	.20
91 Boomer Esiason	.30
92 Seth Joyner	.20
93 Mark Carrier	.20
94 *Brett Favre* (Favre misspelled as Farve)	70.00
95 Lee Williams	.20

96 Neal Anderson	.20
97 Brent Jones	.20
98 John Alt	.20
99 Rodney Peete	.20
100 Steve Broussard	.20
101 Cedric Mack	.20
102 Pat Swilling	.20
103 Stan Humphries	2.00
104 Darrell Thompson	.20
105 Reggie Langhorne	.20
106 Kenny Davidson	.20
107 Jim Everett	.30
108 Keith Millard	.20
109 Garry Lewis	.20
110 Jeff Hostetler	1.00
111 Lamar Lathon	.20
112 Johnny Bailey	.20
113 Cornelius Bennett	.20
114 Travis McNeal	.20
115 Jeff Lageman	.20
116 *Nick Bell*	.20
117 Calvin Williams	.50
118 Shawn Lee	.20
119 Anthony Munoz	.20
120 Jay Novacek	.40
121 Kevin Fagan	.20
122 Leo Goeas	.20
123 Vance Johnson	.20
124 Brent Williams	.20
125 Clarence Verdin	.20
126 Luis Sharpe	.20
127 Darrell Green	.20
128 Barry Word	.20
129 Steve Walsh	.40
130 Bryan Hinkle	.20
131 Ed West	.20
132 Jeff Campbell	.20
133 Dennis Byrd	.20
134 Nate Odomes	.20
135 Trace Armstrong	.20
136 Jarvis Williams	.20
137 Warren Moon	1.00
138 *Eric Moten*	.20
139 Tony Woods	.20
140 Phil Simms	.20
141 Ricky Reynolds	.20
142 Frank Stams	.20
143 Kevin Mack	.20
144 Wade Wilson	.20
145 Shawn Collins	.20
146 Roger Craig	.20
147 Jeff Feagles	.20
148 Norm Johnson	.20
149 Terrance Mathis	2.00
150 Reggie Cobb	.20
151 Chip Banks	.20
152 Darryl Pollard	.20
153 Karl Mecklenburg	.20
154 Ricky Proehl	.20
155 Pete Stoyanovich	.20
156 John Stephens	.20
157 Ron Morris	.20
158 Steve DeBerg	.20
159 Mike Munchak	.20
160 Brett Maxie	.20
161 Don Beebe	.20
162 Martin Mayhew	.20
163 Merril Hoge	.20
164 Kelvin Pritchett	.20
165 Jim Jeffcoat	.20
166 Myron Guyton	.20
167 Ickey Woods	.20
168 Andre Ware	.20
169 Gary Plummer	.20
170 Henry Ellard	.20
171 Scott Davis	.20
172 Randall McDaniel	.20
173 *Randal Hill*	1.00
174 Anthony Bell	.20
175 Gary Anderson	.20
176 Byron Evans	.20
177 Tony Mandarich	.20
178 Jeff George	2.00
179 Art Monk	.40
180 Mike Kenn	.20
181 Sean Landeta	.20
182 Shaun Gayle	.20
183 Michael Carter	.20
184 Robb Thomas	.20
185 Richmond Webb	.20
186 Carnell Lake	.20
187 Rueben Mayes	.20
188 Issiac Holt	.20
189 Leon Seals	.20
190 Al Smith	.20
191 Steve Atwater	.20
192 Greg McMurtry	.20
193 Al Toon	.20
194 Cortez Kennedy	.40
195 Gill Byrd	.20
196 Carl Zander	.20
197 Robert Brown	.20
198 Buford McGee	.20
199 Mervyn Fernandez	.20
200 Mike Dumas	.20
201 *Rob Burnett*	.40
202 Brian Mitchell	.20
203 Randall Cunningham	.50
204 Sammie Smith	.20
205 Ken Clarke	.20
206 Floyd Dixon	.20
207 Ken Norton	.20
208 Tony Siragusa	.20
209 Louis Lipps	.20
210 Chris Martin	.20
211 Jamie Mueller	.20
212 Dave Waymer	.20

213 Donnell Woolford	.20
214 Paul Gruber	.20
215 Ken Harvey	.20
216 *Henry Jones*	.40
217 Tommy Barnhardt	.20
218 Arthur Cox	.20
219 Pat Terrell	.20
220 Curtis Duncan	.20
221 Jeff Jaeger	.20
222 Scott Stephen	.20
223 Rob Moore	.20
224 Chris Hinton	.20
225 Marv Cook	.20
226 Patrick Hunter	.20
227 Earnest Byner	.20
228 Troy Aikman	4.00
229 Kevin Walker	.20
230 Keith Jackson	.20
231 *Russell Maryland*	.75
232 Charles Haley	.20
233 Nick Lowery	.20
234 Erik Howard	.20
235 Leonard Smith	.20
236 Tim Irwin	.20
237 Simon Fletcher	.20
238 Thomas Everett	.20
240 Leroy Hoard	.20
241 Wayne Haddix	.20
242 Gary Clark	.20
243 Eric Andolsek	.20
244 Jim Wahler	.20
245 Vaughan Johnson	.20
246 Kevin Butler	.20
247 Steve Tasker	.20
248 LeRoy Butler	.20
250 *Eric Turner*	1.00
251 Kevin Ross	.20
252 Stephen Baker	.20
253 Harold Green	.20
254 Rohn Stark	.20
255 Joe Nash	.20
256 Jesse Sapolu	.20
257 Willie Gault	.20
258 Jerome Brown	.20
259 Ken Willis	.20
260 Courtney Hall	.20
261 Hart Lee Dykes	.20
262 William Fuller	.20
263 Stan Thomas	.20
264 Dan Marino	6.00
265 Ron Cox	.20
266 Eric Green	.50
267 Anthony Carter	.20
268 Jerry Ball	.20
269 Ron Hall	.20
270 Dennis Smith	.20
271 Eric Hill	.20
272 *Dan McGwire*	.20
273 Lewis Billups	.20
274 Rickey Jackson	.20
275 Jim Sweeney	.20
276 Pat Beach	.20
277 Kevin Porter	.20
278 Mike Sherrard	.20
279 Andy Heck	.20
280 Ron Brown	.20
281 Lawrence Taylor	.50
282 Anthony Pleasant	.20
283 Wes Hopkins	.20
284 Jim Lachey	.20
285 Tim Harris	.20
286 Tony Epps	.20
287 Wendell Davis	.20
288 Bubba McDowell	.20
289 Reggie Roby, Bubby Brister	.20
290 *Chris Zorich*	1.00
291 Mike Merriweather	.20
292 Burt Grossman	.20
293 Eric McMillan	.20
294 John Elway	2.00
295 Toi Cook	.20
297 Matt Bahr	.20
298 Chris Spielman	.20
299 Freddie Joe Nunn (Troy Aikman and Emmitt Smith shown in background)	.30
300 Jim C. Jenson	.20
301 David Fulcher (Rookie card should be '88, not '89)	.20
302 Tommy Hodson	.20
303 Stephone Page	.20
304 Greg Townsend	.20
305 Dean Biasucci	.20
306 Jimmie Jones	.20
307 Eugene Marve	.20
308 Flipper Anderson	.20
309 Darryl Talley	.20
310 *Mike Croel*	.40
311 Thane Gash	.20
312 Perry Kemp	.20
313 Heath Sherman	.20
314 Mike Singletary	.20
315 Chip Lohmiller	.20
316 Tunch Ilkin	.20
317 Junior Seau	2.00
318 Mike Gann	.20
319 Tim McDonald	.20
320 Kyle Clifton	.20
321 Dan Owens	.20
322 Tim Grunhard	.20
323 Stan Brock	.20
324 Rodney Holman	.20
325 Mark Ingram	.20
326 *Browning Nagle*	.40

327	Joe Montana	5.00
328	Carl Lee	.20
329	John L. Williams	.20
330	David Griggs	.20
331	Clarence Kay	.20
332	Irving Fryar	.20
333	Doug Smith	.20
334	Kent Hull	.20
335	Mike Wilcher	.20
336	Ray Donaldson	.20
337	Mark Carrier (Rookie card should be '90, not '89)	.20
338	Kelvin Martin	.20
339	Keith Byars	.20
340	Wilber Marshall	.20
341	Ronnie Lott	.20
342	Blair Thomas	.20
343	Ronnie Harmon	.20
344	Brian Brennan	.20
345	*Charles McRae*	.20
346	Michael Cofer	.20
347	Keith Willis	.20
348	Bruce Kozerski	.20
349	Dave Meggett	.20
350	John Taylor	.20
351	Johnny Holland	.20
352	Steve Christie	.20
353	*Ricky Ervins*	1.00
354	Robert Massey	.20
355	Derrick Thomas	.50
356	Tommy Kane	.20
357	Melvin Bratton	.20
358	Bruce Matthews	.20
359	Mark Duper	.20
360	Jeff Wright	.20
361	Barry Sanders	6.00
362	Chuck Webb	.20
363	Darryl Grant	.20
364	William Roberts	.20
365	Reggie Rutland	.20
366	Clay Matthews	.20
367	Anthony Miller	.20
368	Mike Prior	.20
369	Jessie Tuggle	.20
370	Brad Muster	.20
371	Jay Schroeder	.20
372	Greg Lloyd	.20
373	Mike Cofer	.20
374	James Brooks	.20
375	Danny Noonan (Misspelled Noonen on card back)	.20
376	Latin Berry	.20
377	Brad Baxter	.20
378	Godfrey Myles	.20
379	Morten Andersen	.20
380	Keith Woodside	.20
381	Bobby Humphrey	.20
382	Mike Golic	.20
383	Keith McCants	.20
384	Anthony Thompson	.20
385	Mark Clayton	.20
386	Neil Smith	.20
387	Bryan Millard	.20
388	Mel Gray (Wrong Mel Gray pictured on card back)	.20
389	Ernest Givins	.20
390	Reyna Thompson	.20
391	*Eric Bieniemy*	.40
392	Jon Hand	.20
393	Mark Rypien	.20
394	Bill Romanowski	.20
395	Thurman Thomas	1.50
396	Jim Harbaugh	.20
397	Don Mosebar	.20
398	Andre Rison	.50
399	Mike Johnson	.20
400	Dermontti Dawson	.20
401	Herschel Walker	.30
402	Joe Prokop	.20
403	Eddie Brown	.20
404	Nate Newton	.20
405	Damone Johnson	.20
406	Jessie Hester	.20
407	Jim Arnold	.20
408	Ray Agnew	.20
409	Michael Brooks	.20
410	Keith Sims	.20
411	Carl Banks	.20
412	Jonathan Hayes	.20
413	Richard Johnson	.20
414	*Darryll Lewis*	.20
415	Jeff Bryant	.20
416	Leslie O'Neal	.20
417	Andre Reed	.30
418	Charles Mann	.20
419	Keith DeLong	.20
420	Bruce Hill	.20
421	Matt Brock	.20
422	Johnny Johnson	.30
423	Mark Bortz	.20
424	Ben Smith	.20
425	Jeff Cross	.20
426	Irv Pankey	.20
427	Hassan Jones	.20
428	Andre Tippett	.20
429	Tim Worley	.20
430	Daniel Stubbs	.20
431	Max Montoya	.20
432	Jumbo Elliott	.20
433	Duane Bickett	.20
434	*Nate Lewis*	
435	*Leonard Russell*	1.00
436	Hoby Brenner	.20
437	Ricky Sanders	.20
438	Pierce Holt	.20
439	Derrick Fenner	.20

440	Drew Hill	.20
441	Will Wolford	.20
442	Albert Lewis	.20
443	James Francis	.20
444	Chris Jackie (Jacke)	.20
445	Mike Farr	.20
446	Stephen Braggs	.20
447	Michael Haynes	1.00
448	Freeman McNeil (2008 pounds, sic)	.20
449	Kevin Donnalley	.20
450	John Offerdahl	.20
451	Eric Allen	.20
452	Keith McKeller	.20
453	Kevin Greene	.20
454	Ronnie Lippett	.20
455	Ray Childress	.20
456	Mike Saxon	.20
457	Mark Robinson	.20
458	Greg Kragen	.20
459	Steve Jordan	.20
460	John Johnson	.20
461	Sam Mills	.20
462	Bo Jackson	.40
463	Mark Collins	.20
464	Percy Snow	.20
465	Jeff Bostic	.20
466	Jacob Green	.20
467	Dexter Carter	.20
468	Rich Camarillo	.20
469	Bill Brooks	.20
470	John Carney	.20
471	Don Majkowski	.20
472	Ralph Tamm	.20
473	Fred Barnett	1.00
474	Jim Covert	.20
475	Kenneth Davis	.20
476	Jerry Gray	.20
477	Broderick Thomas	.20
478	Chris Doleman	.20
479	Haywood Jeffires	.40
480	Craig Heyward	.20
481	Markus Koch	.20
482	Tim Krumrie	.20
483	Robert Clark	.20
484	Mike Rozier	.20
485	Danny Villa	.20
486	Gerald Williams	.20
487	Steve Wisniewski	.20
488	J.B. Brown	.20
489	Eugene Robinson	.20
490	Ottis Anderson	.20
491	Tony Stargell	.20
492	Jack Del Rio	.20
493	Lamar Rogers	.20
494	Ricky Nattiel	.20
495	Dan Saleaumua	.20
496	Checklist Card	.20
497	Checklist Card	.20
498	Checklist Card	.20
499	Checklist Card	.20
500	Checklist Card	.20

1992 Stadium Club Promo Sheet

This nine-card promotional sheet was distributed at the 13th National Sports Collector's Convention in 1992. The sheet pictures the cards in a larger-than-the-finished- product format, but has a gold foil line framing the card that reveals the standard sized card. Sheet backs have a large logo promoting the event.

		MT
	Complete Set (1):	10.00
	Common Player:	10.00
NNO	Promo Sheet (Barry Sanders, Gene Atkins, Louis Oliver, Paul Gruber, Emmitt Smith, Steve Jordan, Warren, (Ronnie Lott))	10.00

1992 Stadium Club

This three-card series contains 700 cards. Each glossy card has a full-bleed color photo on the front, with a Stadium Club logo and player's name at the bottom. The team name is between two gold foil stripes. The back is done horizontally and includes a career summary, Sporting News Skills Rating System report and a miniature version of the player's Topps rookie card. The set has 30 Members Choice cards (#s 291-310 and 601-610), which are labeled on the card fronts.

		MT
	Complete Set (700):	150.00
	Complete Series 1 (300):	15.00
	Complete Series 2 (300):	15.00
	Complete Hi Series (100):	125.00
	Common Player:	.10
	Common Player (601-700):	.30
	Series 1 or 2 Wax Box:	15.00
	Series 3 Wax Box:	450.00
1	Mark Rypien	.10
2	*Carlton Bailey*	.15
3	Kevin Glover	.10
4	Vance Johnson	.10
5	Jim Jeffcoat	.10
6	Dan Saleaumua	.10
7	Darion Conner	.10
8	Don Maggs	.10
9	Richard Dent	.15
10	Mark Murphy	.10
11	Wesley Carroll	.10
12	Chris Burkett	.10
13	Steve Wallace	.10
14	Jacob Green	.10
15	Roger Ruzek	.10
16	J.B. Brown	.10
17	Dave Meggett	.10
18	David Johnson	.10
19	Rich Gannon	.10
20	Kevin Mack	.10
21	Reggie Cobb	.10
22	Nate Lewis	.10
23	Doug Smith	.10
24	Irving Fryar	.10
25	Anthony Thompson	.10
26	Duane Bickett	.10
27	Don Majkowski	.10
28	Mark Schlereth	.10
29	Melvin Jenkins	.10
30	Michael Haynes	.15
31	Greg Lewis	.10
32	Kenneth Davis	.10
33	Derrick Thomas	.20
34	David Williams	.10
35	Neal Anderson	.10
36	Andre Collins	.10
37	Jesse Solomon	.10
38	Barry Sanders	3.00
39	Jeff Gossett	.10
40	Rickey Jackson	.10
41	Ray Berry	.10
42	Leroy Hoard	.10
43	Eric Thomas	.10
44	Brian Washington	.10
45	Pat Terrell	.10
46	Eugene Robinson	.10
47	Luis Sharpe	.10
48	Jerome Brown	.10
49	Mark Collins	.10
50	Johnny Holland	.10
51	Tony Paige	.10
52	Willie Green	.10
53	Steve Atwater	.10
54	Brad Muster	.10
55	Cris Dishman	.10
56	Sam (Eddie Anderson)	.10
57	Sam Mills	.10
58	Donald Evans	.10
59	Jon Vaughn	.10
60	Marion Butts	.10
61	Rodney Holman	.10
62	*Dwayne White*	.10
63	Martin Mayhew	.10
64	Jonathan Hayes	.15
65	Andre Rison	.15
66	Calvin Williams	.10
67	James Washington	.10
68	Tim Harris	.10
69	Jim Richter	.10
70	Johnny Johnson	.10
71	John Offerdahl	.10
72	Herschel Walker	.10
73	Perry Kemp	.10
74	Erik Howard	.10
75	Lamar Lathon	.10
76	Greg Kragen	.10
77	Jay Schroeder	.10
78	Jim Arnold	.10
79	Chris Miller	.10
80	Deron Cherry	.10
81	Jim Harbaugh	.20
82	Gill Fenerty	.10
83	Fred Stokes	.10
84	Roman Phifer	.10
85	Clyde Simmons	.10
86	Vince Newsome	.10
87	Lawrence Dawsey	.10
88	Eddie Brown	.10
89	Greg Montgomery	.10
90	Jeff Lageman	.10
91	Terry Wooden	.10
92	Nate Newton	.10

93	David Richards	.10
94	Derek Russell	.10
95	Steve Jordan	.10
96	Hugh Millen	.10
97	Mark Duper	.10
98	Sean Landeta	.10
99	James Thornton	.10
100	Darrell Green	.10
101	Harris Barton	.10
102	John Alt	.10
103	Mike Farr	.10
104	Bob Golic	.10
105	Gene Atkins	.10
106	Gary Anderson	.10
107	Norm Johnson	.10
108	Eugene Daniel	.10
109	Kent Hull	.10
110	John Elway	1.00
111	Rich Camarillo	.10
112	Charles Wilson	.10
113	Matt Bahr	.10
114	Mark Carrier	.10
115	Richmond Webb	.10
116	Charles Mann	.10
117	Tim McGee	.10
118	Wes Hopkins	.10
119	Mo Lewis	.10
120	Warren Moon	.25
121	Damone Johnson	.10
122	Kevin Gogan	.10
123	Joey Browner	.10
124	Tommy Kane	.10
125	Vincent Brown	.10
126	Barry Word	.10
127	Michael Brooks	.10
128	Jumbo Elliot	.10
129	Marcus Allen	.25
130	Tom Waddle	.10
131	Jim Dombrowski	.10
132	Aeneas Williams	.10
133	Clay Matthews	.10
134	Thurman Thomas	.50
135	Dean Biasucci	.10
136	Moe Gardner	.10
137	James Campen	.10
138	Tim Johnson	.10
139	Erik Kramer	.15
140	Keith McCants	.10
141	John Carney	.10
142	Tunch Ilkin	.10
143	Louis Oliver	.10
144	Bill Maas	.10
145	Wendell Davis	.10
146	Pepper Johnson	.10
147	Howie Long	.10
148	Brett Maxie	.10
149	Tony Casillas	.10
150	Michael Carter	.10
151	Byron Evans	.10
152	Lorenzo White	.10
153	Larry Kelm	.10
154	Andy Heck	.10
155	Harry Newsome	.10
156	Chris Singleton	.10
157	Mike Kenn	.10
158	Jeff Faulkner	.10
159	Ken Lanier	.10
160	Darryl Talley	.10
161	*Louie Aguiar*	.10
162	Danny Copeland	.10
163	Kevin Porter	.10
164	Trace Armstrong	.10
165	Dermontti Dawson	.10
166	*Fred McAfee*	.10
167	Ronnie Lott	.20
168	Tony Mandarich	.10
169	Howard Cross	.10
170	Vestee Jackson	.10
171	Jeff Herrod	.10
172	*Randy Hilliard*	.10
173	Robert Wilson	.10
174	*Joe Walter*	.10
175	Chris Spielman	.10
176	Darryl Henley	.10
177	Jay Hilgenberg	.10
178	John Kidd	.10
179	Doug Widell	.10
180	Seth Joyner	.10
181	Nick Bell	.10
182	Don Griffin	.10
183	Johnny Meads	.10
184	Jeff Bostic	.10
185	Johnny Hector	.10
186	Jessie Tuggle	.10
187	Robb Thomas	.10
188	Shane Conlan	.10
189	*Michael Zordich*	.10
190	Emmitt Smith	5.00
191	Robert Blackmon	.10
192	Carl Lee	.10
193	Harry Galbreath	.10
194	Ed King	.10
195	Stan Thomas	.10
196	Andre Waters	.10
197	Pat Harlow	.10
198	Zefross Moss	.10
199	Bobby Hebert	.10
200	Doug Riesenberg	.10
201	Mike Croel	.10
202	Jeff Jaeger	.10
203	Gary Plummer	.10
204	Chris Jacke	.10
205	Neil O'Donnell	.50
206	Mark Bortz	.10
207	Tim Barnett	.10
208	Jerry Ball	.10
209	Chip Lohmiller	.10
210	Jim Everett	.10

211	Tim McKyer	.10
212	Aaron Craver	.10
213	John L. Williams	.10
214	Simon Fletcher	.10
215	Walter Reeves	.10
216	Terance Mathis	.10
217	Mike Pitts	.10
218	Bruce Matthews	.10
219	Howard Ballard	.10
220	Leonard Russell	.10
221	Michael Stewart	.10
222	Mike Merriweather	.10
223	Ricky Sanders	.10
224	Ray Horton	.10
225	Michael Jackson	.10
226	Bill Romanowski	.10
227	Steve McMichael	.10
228	Chris Martin	.10
229	Tim Green	.10
230	Karl Mecklenburg	.10
231	Felix Wright	.10
232	Charles McRae	.10
233	Pete Stoyanovich	.10
234	Stephen Baker	.10
235	Herman Moore	1.50
236	Terry McDaniel	.10
237	Dalton Hilliard	.10
238	Gill Byrd	.10
239	Leron Seals	.10
240	Rod Woodson	.15
241	Curtis Duncan	.10
242	Keith Jackson	.10
243	Mark Stepnoski	.10
244	Art Monk	.10
245	Matt Stover	.10
246	John Roper	.10
247	Rodney Hampton	.40
248	Steve Wisniewski	.10
249	Bryan Millard	.10
250	Todd Lyght	.10
251	Marvin Washington	.10
252	Eric Swann	.10
253	Bruce Kozerski	.10
254	Jon Hand	.10
255	Scott Fulhage	.10
256	Chuck Cecil	.10
257	Eric Martin	.10
258	Eric Metcalf	.10
259	T.J. Turner	.10
260	Kirk Lowdermilk	.10
261	Keith McKeller	.10
262	Wymon Henderson	.10
263	David Alexander	.10
264	George Jamison	.10
265	Ken Norton	.10
266	Jim Lachey	.10
267	*Bo Orlando*	.10
268	Nick Lowery	.10
269	Keith Van Horne	.10
270	Dwight Stone	.10
271	Kerith DeLong	.10
272	James Francis	.10
273	Greg McMurtry	.10
274	Ethan Horton	.10
275	Stan Brock	.10
276	Ken Harvey	.10
277	Ronnie Harmon	.10
278	Mike Pritchard	.10
279	Kyle Clifton	.10
280	Anthony Johnson	.10
281	Esera Tuaolo	.10
282	Vernon Turner	.10
283	David Griggs	.10
284	Dino Hackett	.10
285	Carwell Gardner	.10
286	Ron Hall	.10
287	Reggie White	.20
288	S.C. Checklist 1-100	.10
289	S.C. Checklist 101-200	.10
290	S.C. Checklist 201-300	.10
291	Mark Clayton	.10
292	Pat Swilling	.10
293	Ernest Givins	.10
294	Broderick Thomas	.10
295	John Friesz	.10
296	Cornelius Bennett	.10
297	Anthony Carter	.10
298	Earnest Byner	.10
299	Michael Irvin	.50
300	Cortez Kennedy	.10
301	Barry Sanders	2.00
302	Mike Croel	.10
303	Emmitt Smith	3.00
304	Leonard Russell	.10
305	Neal Anderson	.10
306	Derrick Thomas	.15
307	Mark Rypien	.10
308	Reggie White	.20
309	Rod Woodson	.15
310	Rodney Hampton	.10
311	Carnell Lake	.10
312	Robert Delpino	.10
313	Brian Blades	.10
314	Marc Spindler	.10
315	Scott Norwood	.10
316	Frank Warren	.10
317	David Treadwell	.10
318	Steve Broussard	.10
319	Lorenzo Lynch	.10
320	Ray Agnew	.10
321	Derrick Walker	.10
322	*Vinson Smith*	.10
323	Gary Clark	.10
324	Charles Haley	.10
325	Keith Byars	.10
326	Winston Moss	.10

327	*Paul McJulien*	.10
328	Tony Covington	.10
329	Mark Carrier	.10
330	Mark Tuinei	.10
331	*Tracy Simien*	.10
332	Jeff Wright	.10
333	Bryan Cox	.10
334	Lonnie Young	.10
335	Clarence Verdin	.10
336	Dan Fike	.10
337	Steve Sewell	.10
338	Gary Zimmerman	.10
339	Barney Bussey	.10
340	William Perry	.10
341	Jeff Hostetler	.15
342	Doug Smith	.10
343	Cleveland Gary	.10
344	Todd Marinovich	.10
345	Rich Moran	.10
346	Tony Woods	.10
347	Vaughan Johnson	.10
348	Marv Cook	.10
349	Pierce Holt	.10
350	Gerald Williams	.10
351	Kevin Butler	.10
352	William White	.10
353	Henry Rolling	.10
354	James Joseph	.10
355	Vinny Testaverde	.10
356	Scott Radecic	.10
357	Lee Johnson	.10
358	Steve Tasker	.10
359	David Lutz	.10
360	Audrey McMillan	.10
361	Brad Baxter	.10
362	Mark Dennis	.10
363	Erric Pegram	.15
364	Sean Jones	.10
365	William Roberts	.10
366	Steve Young	1.75
367	Joe Jacoby	.10
368	*Richard Brown*	.10
369	Keith Kartz	.10
370	Freddie Joe Nunn	.10
371	Darren Comeaux	.10
372	Larry Brown	.10
373	Haywood Jeffires	.10
374	Tom Newberry	.10
375	*Steve Bono*	1.25
376	Kevin Ross	.10
377	Kelvin Pritchett	.10
378	Jessie Hester	.10
379	Mitchell Price	.10
380	Barry Foster	.10
381	Reyna Thompson	.10
382	Cris Carter	.20
383	Lemuel Stinson	.10
384	Rod Bernstine	.10
385	James Lofton	.10
386	Kevin Murphy	.10
387	Greg Townsend	.10
388	*Edgar Bennett*	.75
389	Rob Moore	.10
390	Eugene Lockhart	.10
391	Bern Brostek	.10
392	Craig Heyward	.10
393	Ferrell Edmunds	.10
394	John Kasay	.10
395	Jesse Sapolu	.10
396	Jim Breech	.10
397	Neil Smith	.10
398	Bryce Paup	.40
399	Tony Tolbert	.10
400	Bubby Brister	.10
401	Dennis Smith	.10
402	Dan Owens	.10
403	Steve Beuerlein	.10
404	Rick Tuten	.10
405	Eric Allen	.10
406	Eric Hill	.10
407	Don Warren	.10
408	Greg Jackson	.10
409	Chris Doleman	.10
410	Anthony Munoz	.10
411	Michael Young	.10
412	Cornelius Bennett	.10
413	Ray Childress	.10
414	Kevin Call	.10
415	Burt Grossman	.10
416	Scott Miller	.10
417	Tim Newton	.10
418	Robert Young	.10
419	*Tommy Vardell*	.15
420	Michael Walter	.10
421	*Chris Port*	.10
422	Carlton Haselrig	.10
423	Rodney Peete	.10
424	Scott Stephen	.10
425	Chris Warren	1.00
426	*Scott Galbraith*	.10
427	Fuad Reveiz	.10
428	Irv Eatman	.10
429	David Szott	.10
430	Brent Williams	.10
431	Mike Horan	.10
432	Brent Jones	.10
433	Paul Gruber	.10
434	Carlos Huerta	.10
435	Scott Case	.10
436	Greg Davis	.10
437	Ken Clarke	.10
438	Alfred Williams	.10
439	Jim Jensen	.10
440	Louis Lipps	.10
441	Larry Roberts	.10
442	James Jones	.10
443	Don Mosebar	.10
444	Quinn Early	.10

#	Player	Price
445	Robert Brown	.10
446	Tom Thayer	.10
447	Michael Irvin	.40
448	Jarrod Bunch	.10
449	Riki Ellison	.10
450	Joe Phillips	.10
451	Ernest Givins	.10
452	Glenn Parker	.10
453	Brett Perriman	.25
454	Jayice Pearson	.10
455	Mark Jackson	.10
456	Siran Stacy	.10
457	Rufus Porter	.10
458	Michael Ball	.10
459	Craig Taylor	.10
460	George Thomas	.10
461	Alvin Wright	.10
462	Ron Hallstrom	.10
463	Mike Mooney	.10
464	Dexter Carter	.10
465	Marty Carter	.10
466	Pat Swilling	.10
467	Mike Golic	.10
468	Reggie Roby	.10
469	Randall McDaniel	.10
470	John Stephens	.10
471	Ricardo McDonald	.10
472	Wilber Marshall	.10
473	Jim Sweeney	.10
474	Ernie Jones	.10
475	Bennie Blades	.10
476	Don Beebe	.10
477	Grant Feasel	.10
478	Ernie Mills	.10
479	Tony Jones	.10
480	Jeff Uhlenhake	.10
481	Gaston Green	.10
482	John Taylor	.10
483	Anthony Smith	.10
484	Tony Bennett	.10
485	David Brandon	.10
486	Shawn Jefferson	.10
487	Christian Okoye	.10
488	Leonard Marshall	.10
489	Jay Novacek	.10
490	Harold Green	.10
491	Bubba McDowell	.10
492	Gary Anderson	.10
493	Terrell Buckley	.20
494	Jamie Dukes	.10
495	Morten Andersen	.10
496	Henry Thomas	.10
497	Bill Lewis	.10
498	Jeff Cross	.10
499	Hardy Nickerson	.10
500	Henry Ellard	.10
501	Joe Bowden	.10
502	Brian Noble	.10
503	Mike Cofer	.10
504	Jeff Bryant	.10
505	Lomas Brown	.10
506	Chip Banks	.10
507	Keith Taylor	.10
508	Mark Kelso	.10
509	Dexter McNabb	.10
510	Gene Chilton	.10
511	George Thornton	.10
512	Jeff Criswell	.10
513	Brad Edwards	.10
514	Ron Heller	.10
515	Tim Brown	.20
516	Keith Hamilton	.10
517	Mark Higgs	.10
518	Tommy Barnhardt	.10
519	Brian Jordan	.10
520	Ray Crockett	.10
521	Karl Wilson	.10
522	Ricky Reynolds	.10
523	Max Montoya	.10
524	David Little	.10
525	Alonzo Mitz	.10
526	Darryll Lewis	.10
527	Keith Henderson	.10
528	Leroy Butler	.10
529	Rob Burnett	.10
530	Chris Chandler	.10
531	Maury Buford	.10
532	Mark Ingram	.10
533	Mike Saxon	.10
534	Bill Fralic	.10
535	Craig Patterson	.10
536	John Randle	.10
537	Dwayne Harper	.10
538	Chris Hakel	.10
539	Maurice Hurst	.10
540	Warren Powers	.10
541	Will Wolford	.10
542	Dennis Gibson	.10
543	Jackie Slater	.10
544	Floyd Turner	.10
545	Guy McIntyre	.10
546	Eric Green	.10
547	Rohn Stark	.10
548	William Fuller	.10
549	Alvin Harper	.20
550	Mark Clayton	.10
551	Natu Tuatagaloa	.10
552	Fred Barnett	.10
553	Bob Whitfield	.10
554	Courtney Hall	.10
555	Brian Mitchell	.10
556	Patrick Hunter	.10
557	Rick Bryan	.10
558	Anthony Carter	.10
559	Jim Wahler	.10
560	Joe Morris	.10
561	Tony Zendejas	.10
562	Mervyn Fernandez	.10
563	Jamie Williams	.10
564	Darrell Thompson	.10
565	Adrian Cooper	.10
566	Chris Goode	.10
567	Jeff Davidson	.10
568	James Hasty	.10
569	Chris Mims	.50
570	Ray Seals	.15
571	Myron Guyton	.10
572	Todd McNair	.10
573	Andre Tippett	.10
574	Kirby Jackson	.10
575	Mel Gray	.10
576	Stephone Paige	.10
577	Scott Davis	.10
578	John Gesek	.10
579	Earnest Byner	.10
580	John Friesz	.10
581	Al Smith	.10
582	Flipper Anderson	.10
583	Amp Lee	.25
584	Greg Lloyd	.15
585	Cortez Kennedy	.10
586	Keith Sims	.10
587	Terry Allen	.50
588	David Fulcher	.10
589	Chris Hinton	.10
590	Tim McDonald	.10
591	Bruce Armstrong	.10
592	Sterling Sharpe	.20
593	Tom Rathman	.10
594	Bill Brooks	.10
595	Broderick Thomas	.10
596	Jim Wilks	.10
597	Tyrone Braxton	.10
598	Checklist 301-400	.10
599	Checklist 401-500	.10
600	Checklist 501-600	.10
601	Andre Reed (MC)	.50
602	Troy Aikman (MC)	3.00
603	Dan Marino (MC)	6.00
604	Randall Cunningham (MC)	.50
605	Jim Kelly (MC)	1.00
606	Deion Sanders (MC)	2.00
607	Junior Seau (MC)	1.00
608	Jerry Rice (MC)	3.00
609	Bruce Smith (MC)	.50
610	Lawrence Taylor (MC)	.50
611	Todd Collins	.50
612	Ty Detmer	2.00
613	Browning Nagle	.30
614	Tony Sacca	.30
615	Boomer Esiason	.30
616	Billy Joe Tolliver	.30
617	Leslie O'Neal	.30
618	Mark Wheeler	.30
619	Eric Dickerson	.30
620	Phil Simms	.30
621	Troy Vincent	1.00
622	Jason Hanson	.50
623	Andre Reed	.50
624	Russell Maryland	.50
625	Steve Emtman	1.00
626	Sean Gilbert	1.50
627	Dana Hall	1.00
628	Dan McGwire	.30
629	Lewis Billups	.30
630	Darryl Williams	.50
631	Dwayne Sabb	.30
632	Mark Royals	.30
633	Cary Conklin	.30
634	Al Toon	.30
635	Junior Seau	1.50
636	Greg Skrepenak	.30
637	Deion Sanders	3.00
638	Steve DeOssie	.30
639	Randall Cunningham	.50
640	Jim Kelly	1.00
641	Michael Brandon	.30
642	Clayton Holmes	.30
643	Webster Slaughter	.30
644	Ricky Proehl	.30
645	Jerry Rice	5.00
646	Carl Banks	.30
647	J.J. Birden	.30
648	Tracy Scroggins	1.00
649	Alonzo Spellman	.50
650	Joe Montana	5.00
651	Courtney Hawkins	1.00
652	Corey Widmer	.30
653	Robert Brooks	7.00
654	Darren Woodson	1.00
655	Derrick Bengals	.30
656	Steve Christie	.30
657	Chester McGlockton	3.00
658	Steve Israel	.30
659	Robert Harris	.30
660	Dan Marino	10.00
661	Ed McCaffrey	2.50
662	Johnny Mitchell	1.00
663	Timm Rosenbach	.30
664	Anthony Miller	.30
665	Merril Hoge	.30
666	Eugene Chung	.30
667	Rueben Mayes	.30
668	Martin Bayless	.30
669	Ashley Ambrose	.30
670	Michael Cofer	.30
671	Shane Dronett	.30
672	Bernie Kosar	.50
673	Mike Singletary	.50
674	Mike Lodish	.30
675	Phillippi Sparks	.50
676	Joel Steed	.30
677	Kevin Fagan	.30
678	Randal Hill	.30
679	Ken O'Brien	.30
680	Lawrence Taylor	.50
681	Harvey Williams	.50
682	Quentin Coryatt	1.00
683	Brett Favre	100.00
684	Robert Jones	1.00
685	Michael Dean Perry	.50
686	Bruce Smith	.50
687	Troy Auzenne	.30
688	Thomas McLemore	.30
689	Dale Carter	1.50
690	Marc Boutte	.30
691	Jeff George	2.00
692	Dion Lambert	.30
693	Vaughn Dunbar	.30
694	Derek Brown	.30
695	Troy Aikman	5.00
696	John Fina	.30
697	Kevin Smith	1.00
698	Corey Miller	.30
699	Lance Olberding	.30
700	Checklist 601-700	.50

1993 Stadium Club Promo Sheet

This nine-card promo sheet was distributed at the 1993 National Sports Collectors Convention in Chicago. Similar to the 1992 sheet, the photos are shown larger than normal and contain a gold line that reveals the true standard size card. Sheet backs contain a large logo celebrating the event.

	MT
Complete Set (1):	8.00
Common Player:	8.00
NNO Promo Sheet	8.00

(Johnny Bailey, Vai Sikahema, Richard Dent, Sterling Sharpe, Tommy Barnhardt, Cris Carter, , (Reggie Cobb)

1992 Stadium Club No.1 Draft Picks

This four-card insert set features three former #1 draft picks, plus Rocket Ismail. Cards were randomly inserted in 1992 Topps Stadium Club Series II packs, and are numbered on the back. Each card front has a full-bleed photo, along with the player's name, Stadium Club logo and #1 symbol at the bottom. A football in the top upper right has the year the player was selected in it. The card back has a closeup shot of the player, a player biography and set logo.

	MT
Complete Set (4):	30.00
Common Player:	7.00
1 Jeff George	10.00
2 Russell Maryland	7.00
3 Steve Emtman	7.00
4 Raghib Ismail	7.00

1992 Stadium Club QB Legends

These cards, featuring six Hall of Fame quarterbacks, were random inserts in 1992 Topps Stadium Club Series II packs, one per every 72 packs. The card front has a color action photo, along with the player's name and Stadium Club logo at the bottom. The set's name is given in a blue bar at the bottom, too, adjacent to a gold foil football helmet on the left. A lime green football appears in the upper right corner, with the year the player was inducted into the Hall of Fame inside it. The football is edged in gold foil and has three gold-foil stripes running down from it. The horizontal backs have a green and black background which includes a player photo, career statistics, a mini version of the player's first Topps card, and the player's facsimile autograph stamped in gold foil. Each card back is also numbered.

	MT
Complete Set (6):	15.00
Common Player:	3.00
1 Y.A. Tittle	3.00
2 Bart Starr	4.00
3 John Unitas	4.00
4 George Blanda	3.00
5 Roger Staubach	5.00
6 Terry Bradshaw	5.00

1993 Stadium Club

1993 Stadium Club football cards were issued in two 250-card series. Each card front has a full-bleed color photo and the player's name is foil stamped in gold at the bottom in a green stripe. The backs have statistics, a Football News Skills Rating Systems review and a miniature version of the player's Topps rookie card. A high-number series (#s 501-550) was also issued and includes Members Choice cards, Draft Picks, 1st-Year Players and Key Acquisitions. Super Team cards were randomly inserted into packs, one per every 24 packs. If the team pictured on a Super Team card wins a division title, conference championship or the Super Bowl, the card can be redeemed for special prizes. Other insert cards include First Day Production (silver foil) and Master Photo winner cards, which can be redeemed for a group of three Stadium Club Master Photos.

	MT
Complete Set (550):	50.00
Complete Series 1 (250):	25.00
Complete Series 2 (250):	15.00
Complete High Series (50):	10.00
Common Player:	.10
Minor Stars:	.20
Series 1 Wax Box:	50.00
Series 2 Wax Box:	20.00

#	Player	Price
1	Sterling Sharpe	.50
2	Chris Burkett	.10
3	Santana Dotson	.10
4	Michael Jackson	.10
5	Neal Anderson	.10
6	Bryan Cox	.10
7	Dennis Gibson	.10
8	Jeff Graham	.10
9	Roger Ruzek	.10
10	Duane Bickett	.10
11	Charles Mann	.10
12	Tommy Maddox	.15
13	Vaughn Dunbar	.10
14	Gary Plummer	.10
15	Chris Miller	.75
16	Chris Warren	.75
17	Alvin Harper	.20
18	Eric Dickerson	.10
19	Mike Jones	.10
20	Ernest Givins	.10
21	Natrone Means	2.00
22	Doug Riesenberg	.10
23	Barry Word	.10
24	Sean Salisbury	.10
25	Derrick Fenner	.10
26	David Howard	.10
27	Mark Kelso	.10
28	Todd Lyght	.10
29	Dana Hall	.10
30	Eric Metcalf	.10
31	Jason Hanson	.10
32	Dwight Stone	.10
33	Johnny Mitchell	.20
34	Reggie Roby	.10
35	Terrell Buckley	.15
36	Steve McMichael	.10
37	Marty Carter	.10
38	Seth Joyner	.10
39	Rohn Stark	.10
40	Eric Curry	.50
41	Tommy Barnhardt	.10
42	Karl Mecklenburg	.10
43	Darion Conner	.10
44	Ronnie Harmon	.10
45	Cortez Kennedy	.20
46	Tim Brown	.10
47	Bill Lewis	.10
48	Randall McDaniel	.10
49	Curtis Duncan	.10
50	Troy Aikman	3.00
51	David Klingler	.20
52	Brent Jones	.10
53	Dave Krieg	.10
54	Bruce Smith	.10
55	Vincent Brown	.10
56	O.J. McDuffie	2.25
57	Cleveland Gary	.10
58	Larry Centers	.75
59	Pepper Johnson	.10
60	Dan Marino	4.00
61	Robert Porcher	.10
62	Jim Harbaugh	.10
63	Sam Mills	.10
64	Gary Anderson	.10
65	Neil O'Donnell	.50
66	Keith Byars	.10
67	Jeff Herrod	.10
68	Marion Butts	.10
69	Terry McDaniel	.10
70	John Elway	1.00
71	Steve Broussard	.10
72	Kelvin Martin	.10
73	Tom Carter	.20
74	Bryce Paup	.10
75	Jim Kelly	.50
76	Bill Romanowski	.10
77	Andre Collins	.10
78	Mike Farr	.10
79	Henry Ellard	.10
80	Dale Carter	.10
81	Johnny Bailey	.10
82	Garrison Hearst	2.50
83	Brent Williams	.10
84	Richard McDonald	.10
85	Emmitt Smith	4.00
86	Vai Sikahema	.10
87	Jackie Harris	.20
88	Alonzo Spellman	.10
89	Mark Wheeler	.10
90	Dalton Hilliard	.10
91	Mark Higgs	.20
92	Aaron Wallace	.10
93	Earnest Byner	.10
94	Stanley Richard	.10
95	Cris Carter	.10
96	Bobby Houston	.20
97	Craig Heyward	.10
98	Bernie Kosar	.10
99	Mike Croel	.10
100	Deion Sanders	1.00
101	Warren Moon	.20
102	Christian Okoye	.10
103	Ricky Watters	.50
104	Eric Swann	.10
105	Rodney Hampton	.20
106	Daryl Johnston	.10
107	Andre Reed	.10
108	Jerome Bettis	2.50
109	Eugene Daniel	.10
110	Leonard Russell	.15
111	Darryl Williams	.10
112	Rod Woodson	.20
113	Boomer Esiason	.20
114	James Hasty	.10
115	Marc Boutte	.10
116	Tom Waddle	.10
117	Lawrence Dawsey	.10
118	Mark Collins	.10
119	Willie Gault	.10
120	Barry Sanders	2.50
121	Leroy Hoard	.10
122	Anthony Munoz	.10
123	Jesse Sapolu	.10
124	Art Monk	.10
125	Randal Hill	.10
126	John Offerdahl	.10
127	Carlos Jenkins	.10
128	Al Smith	.10
129	Michael Irvin	.50
130	Kenneth Davis	.10
131	Curtis Conway	2.00
132	Steve Atwater	.10
133	Neil Smith	.10
134	Steve Everitt	.20
135	Chris Mims	.10
136	Rickey Jackson	.10
137	Edgar Bennett	.60
138	Mike Pritchard	.10
139	Richard Dent	.10
140	Barry Foster	.10
141	Eugene Robinson	.10
142	Jackie Slater	.10
143	Paul Gruber	.10
144	Rob Moore	.20
145	Robert Smith	3.00
146	Lorenzo White	.10
147	Tommy Vardell	.10
148	Dave Meggett	.10
149	Vince Workman	.10
150	Terry Allen	.15
151	Howie Long	.10
152	Charles Haley	.10
153	Pete Metzelaars	.10
154	John Copeland	.50
155	Aeneas Williams	.10
156	Ricky Sanders	.10
157	Andre Ware	.10
158	Tony Paige	.10
159	Jerome Henderson	.10
160	Harold Green	.10
161	Wymon Henderson	.10
162	Andre Rison	.20
163	Donald Evans	.10
164	Todd Scott	.10
165	Steve Emtman	.20
166	William Fuller	.10
167	Michael Dean Perry	.10
168	Randall Cunningham	.20
169	Toi Cook	.10
170	Browning Nagle	.10
171	Darryl Henley	.10
172	George Teague	.40
173	Derrick Thomas	.20
174	Jay Novacek	.10
175	Mark Carrier	.10
176	Kevin Fagan	.10
177	Nate Lewis	.10
178	Courtney Hawkins	.20
179	Robert Blackmon	.10
180	Rick Mirer	.50
181	Mike Lodish	.10
182	Jarrod Bunch	.10
183	Anthony Smith	.10
184	Brian Noble	.10
185	Eric Bieniemy	.10
186	Keith Jackson	.20
187	Eric Martin	.10
188	Vance Johnson	.10
189	Kevin Mack	.10
190	Rich Camarillo	.10
191	Ashley Ambrose	.10
192	Jim Arnold	.10
193	Ricky Ervins	.10
194	Gary Anderson	.10
195	Eric Allen	.10
196	Roger Craig	.10
197	Jon Vaughn	.10
198	Tim McDonald	.10
199	Broderick Thomas	.10
200	Jessie Tuggle	.10
201	Alonzo Mitz	.10
202	Harvey Williams	.10
203	Russell Maryland	.10
204	Marvin Washington	.10
205	Jim Everett	.10
206	Trace Armstrong	.10
207	Steve Young	2.00
208	Tony Woods	.10
209	Brett Favre	4.00
210	Nate Odomes	.10
211	Ricky Proehl	.10
212	Jim Dombrowski	.10
213	Anthony Carter	.10
214	Tracy Simien	.10
215	Clay Matthews	.10
216	Patrick Bates	.35
217	Jeff George	.25
218	David Fulcher	.10
219	Phil Simms	.15
220	Eugene Chung	.10
221	Reggie Cobb	.10
222	Jim Sweeney	.10
223	Greg Lloyd	.10
224	Sean Jones	.10
225	Marvin Jones	.40
226	Bill Brooks	.10
227	Moe Gardner	.10
228	Louis Oliver	.10
229	Flipper Anderson	.10
230	Marc Spindler	.10
231	Jerry Rice	2.00
232	Chip Lohmiller	.10
233	Nolan Harrison	.10
234	Heath Sherman	.10
235	Reyna Thompson	.10
236	Derrick Walker	.10
237	Rufus Porter	.10
238	Checklist 1-125	.10
239	Checklist 126-250	.10
240	John Elway	.40
241	Troy Aikman	1.25
242	Steve Emtman	.15
243	Ricky Watters	.50
244	Barry Foster	.20
245	Dan Marino	1.50
246	Reggie White	.15
247	Thurman Thomas	.60
248	Broderick Thomas	.10
249	Joe Montana	2.00
250	Tim Goad	.10
251	Joe Nash	.10
252	Anthony Johnson	.10
253	Carl Pickens	1.00
254	Steve Beuerlein	.15
255	Anthony Newman	.10
256	Corey Miller	.10
257	Steve DeBerg	.10
258	Johnny Holland	.10
259	Jerry Ball	.10
260	Siupeli Malamala	.15
261	Steve Wisniewski	.10

No.	Player	Price
263	Kelvin Pritchett	.10
264	Chris Gardocki	.10
265	Henry Thomas	.10
266	Arthur Marshall	.40
267	Quinn Early	.10
268	Jonathan Hayes	.10
269	Erric Pegram	.40
270	Clyde Simmons	.10
271	Eric Moten	.10
272	Brian Mitchell	.10
273	Adrian Cooper	.10
274	Gaston Green	.10
275	John Taylor	.10
276	Jeff Uhlenhake	.10
277	Phil Hansen	.10
278	Kevin Williams	.50
279	Robert Massey	.10
280a	Drew Bledsoe	7.00
280b	Drew Bledsoe Err.	15.00
281	Walter Reeves	.10
282	Carlton Gray	.20
283	Derek Brown	.10
284	Martin Mayhew	.10
285	Sean Gilbert	.10
286	Jessie Hester	.10
287	Mark Clayton	.10
288	Blair Thomas	.10
289	J.J. Birden	.10
290	Shannon Sharpe	.20
291	Richard Fain	.15
292	Gene Atkins	.10
293	Burt Grossman	.10
294	Chris Doleman	.10
295	Pat Swilling	.10
296	Mike Kenn	.10
297	Merril Hoge	.10
298	Don Mosebar	.10
299	Kevin Smith	.10
300	Darrell Green	.10
301	Dan Footman	.20
302	Vestee Jackson	.10
303	Carwell Gardner	.10
304	Amp Lee	.10
305	Bruce Matthews	.10
306	Antone Davis	.10
307	Dean Biasucci	.10
308	Maurice Hurst	.10
309	John Kasay	.10
310	Lawrence Taylor	.15
311	Ken Harvey	.10
312	Willie Davis	.15
313	Tony Bennett	.15
314	Jay Schroeder	.10
315	Darren Perry	.10
316	Troy Drayton	1.00
317	Dan Williams	.20
318	Michael Haynes	.15
319	Renaldo Turnbull	.10
320	Junior Seau	.15
321	Ray Crockett	.10
322	Will Furrer	.10
323	Byron Evans	.10
324	Jim McMahon	.10
325	Robert Jones	.10
326	Eric Davis	.10
327	Jeff Cross	.10
328	Kyle Clifton	.10
329	Haywood Jeffires	.15
330	Jeff Hostetler	.15
331	Darryl Talley	.10
332	Keith McCants	.10
333	Mo Lewis	.10
334	Matt Stover	.10
335	Ferrell Edmunds	.10
336	Matt Brock	.10
337	Ernie Mills	.10
338	Shane Dronett	.10
339	Brad Muster	.10
340	Jesse Solomon	.10
341	John Randle	.10
342	Chris Spielman	.10
343	David Whitmore	.10
344	Glenn Parker	.10
345	Marco Coleman	.10
346	Kenneth Gant	.10
347	Cris Dishman	.10
348	Kenny Walker	.10
349	Roosevelt Potts	.45
350	Reggie White	.30
351	Gerald Robinson	.10
352	Mark Rypien	.15
353	Stan Humphries	.15
354	Chris Singleton	.10
355	Herschel Walker	.10
356	Ron Hall	.10
357	Ethan Horton	.10
358	Anthony Pleasant	.10
359	Thomas Smith	.20
360	Audray McMillian	.10
361	D.J. Johnson	.10
362	Ron Heller	.10
363	Bern Brostek	.10
364	Ronnie Lott	.10
365	Reggie Johnson	.10
366	Lin Elliott	.15
367	Lemuel Stinson	.10
368	William White	.10
369	Ernie Jones	.10
370	Tom Rathman	.10
371	Tommy Kane	.10
372	David Brandon	.10
373	Lee Johnson	.10
374	Wade Wilson	.10
375	Nick Lowery	.10
376	Bubba McDowell	.10
377	Wayne Simmons	.15
378	Calvin Williams	.10
379	Courtney Hall	.10

No.	Player	Price
380	Troy Vincent	.10
381	Tim McGee	.10
382	Russell Freeman	.15
383	Steve Tasker	.10
384	Michael Strahan	.15
385	Greg Skrepenak	.10
386	Jake Reed	.10
387	Pete Stoyanovich	.10
388	Levon Kirkland	.15
389	Mel Gray	.10
390	Brian Washington	.10
391	Don Griffin	.10
392	Desmond Howard	.50
393	Luis Sharpe	.10
394	Mike Johnson	.10
395	Andre Tippett	.10
396	Donnell Woolford	.10
397	Demetrius DuBose	.20
398	Pat Terrell	.10
399	Todd McNair	.10
400	Ken Norton	.10
401	Keith Hamilton	.10
402	Andy Heck	.10
403	Jeff Gossett	.10
404	Dexter McNabb	.10
405	Richmond Webb	.10
406	Irving Fryar	.10
407	Brian Hansen	.10
408	David Little	.10
409	Glyn Milburn	.25
410	Doug Dawson	.10
411	Scott Mersereau	.10
412	Don Beebe	.10
413	Vaughan Johnson	.10
414	Jack Del Rio	.10
415	Darrien Gordon	.20
416	Mark Schlereth	.10
417	Lomas Brown	.10
418	William Thomas	.10
419	James Francis	.10
420	Quentin Coryatt	.15
421	Tyji Armstrong	.10
422	Hugh Millen	.10
423	Adrian White	.15
424	Eddie Anderson	.10
425	Mark Ingram	.10
426	Ken O'Brien	.10
427	Simon Fletcher	.10
428	Tim McKyer	.10
429	Leonard Marshall	.10
430	Eric Green	.10
431	Leonard Harris	.10
432	Darin Jordan	.15
433	Erik Howard	.10
434	David Lang	.10
435	Eric Turner	.10
436	Michael Cofer	.10
437	Jeff Bryant	.10
438	Charles McRae	.10
439	Henry Jones	.10
440	Joe Montana	3.00
441	Morten Andersen	.10
442	Jeff Jaeger	.10
443	Leslie O'Neal	.10
444	Leroy Butler	.10
445	Steve Jordan	.10
446	Brad Edwards	.10
447	J.B. Brown	.10
448	Kerry Cash	.10
449	Mark Tuinei	.10
450	Rodney Peete	.10
451	Sheldon White	.10
452	Wesley Carroll	.10
453	Brad Baxter	.10
454	Mike Pitts	.10
455	Greg Montgomery	.10
456	Kenny Davidson	.10
457	Scott Fulhage	.10
458	Greg Townsend	.10
459	Rod Bernstine	.10
460	Gary Clark	.10
461	Hardy Nickerson	.10
462	Sean Landeta	.10
463	Rob Burnett	.10
464	Fred Barnett	.10
465	John L. Williams	.10
466	Anthony Miller	.15
467	Roman Phifer	.10
468	Rich Moran	.10
469	Willie Roaf	.50
470	William Perry	.10
471	Marcus Allen	.15
472	Carl Lee	.10
473	Kurt Gouveia	.10
474	Jarvis Williams	.10
475	Alfred Williams	.10
476	Mark Stepnoski	.10
477	Steve Wallace	.10
478	Pat Harlow	.10
479	Chip Banks	.10
480	Cornelius Bennett	.10
481	Ryan McNeil	.20
482	Norm Johnson	.10
483	Dermontti Dawson	.10
484	Dwayne White	.10
485	Derek Russell	.10
486	Lionel Washington	.10
487	Eric Hill	.10
488	Michael Barrow	.15
489	Checklist 251-375	.10
490	Checklist 376-500	.10
491	Emmitt Smith (MC)	2.00
492	Derrick Thomas (MC)	.15
493	Deion Sanders (MC)	.50
494	Randall Cunningham (MC)	.15
495	Sterling Sharpe (MC)	.20

No.	Player	Price
496	Barry Sanders (MC)	1.25
497	Thurman Thomas	.50
498	Brett Favre (MC)	1.50
499	Vaughan Johnson (MC)	.10
500	Steve Young (MC)	1.00
501	Marvin Jones	.20
502	Reggie Brooks	.20
503	Eric Curry	.10
504	Drew Bledsoe	2.00
505	Glyn Milburn	.50
506	Jerome Bettis	1.00
507	Robert Smith	.75
508	Dana Stubblefield	.50
509	Tom Carter	.10
510	Rick Mirer	.50
511	Russell Copeland	1.00
512	Deon Figures	.30
513	Tony McGee	.50
514	Derrick Lassic	.30
515	Everett Lindsay	.10
516	Derek Brown	1.00
517	Harold Alexander	.10
518	Tom Scott	.10
519	Elvis Grbac	3.00
520	Terry Kirby	1.00
521	Doug Pelfrey	.10
522	Horace Copeland	.75
523	Irv Smith	.20
524	Lincoln Kennedy	.40
525	Jason Elam	.10
526	Qadry Ismail	.75
527	Artie Smith	.10
528	Tyrone Hughes	1.00
529	Lance Gunn	.10
530	Vincent Brisby	1.00
531	Patrick Robinson	.10
532	Raghib Ismail	.50
533	Willie Beamon	.10
534	Vaughn Hebron	.25
535	Darren Drozdov	.10
536	James Jett	.75
537	Michael Bates	.50
538	Tom Rouen	.10
539	Michael Husted	.10
540	Greg Robinson	.50
541	Carl Banks	.10
542	Kevin Greene	.10
543	Scott Mitchell	.50
544	Michael Brooks	.10
545	Shane Conlan	.10
546	Vinny Testaverde	.10
547	Robert Delpino	.10
548	Bill Fralic	.10
549	Carlton Bailey	.10
550	Johnny Johnson	.10
NNO	Jerry Rice	15.00

1993 Stadium Club First Day Cards

ERIC DICKERSON

1993 Stadium Club football cards were issued in two 250-card series. Each card front has a full-bleed color photo and the player's name is foil stamped in gold at the bottom in a green stripe. The backs have statistics, a Football News Skills Rating Systems review and a miniature version of the player's Topps rookie card. A high-number series (#s 501-550) was also issued and includes Members Choice cards, Draft Picks, 1st-Year Players and Key Acquisitions. Super Team cards were randomly inserted into packs, one per every 24 packs. If the team pictured on a Super Team card wins a division title, conference championship or the Super Bowl, the card can be redeemed for special prizes. Other insert cards include First Day Production (silver foil) and Master Photo to winner cards, which can be redeemed for a group of three Stadium Club Master Photos.

MT

	MT
Complete Set (550):	2000.
Complete Series 1 (250):	1100.
Complete Series 2 (250):	600.00

No.	Player	Price
Complete Hi Series (50):		300.00
Common Player:		2.00
Minor Stars:		5.00
1	Sterling Sharpe	10.00
2	Chris Burkett	2.00
3	Santana Dotson	2.00
4	Michael Jackson	2.00
5	Neal Anderson	2.00
6	Bryan Cox	2.00
7	Dennis Gibson	2.00
8	Jeff Graham	2.00
9	Roger Ruzek	2.00
10	Duane Bickett	2.00
11	Charles Mann	2.00
12	Tommy Maddox	2.00
13	Vaughn Dunbar	2.00
14	Gary Plummer	2.00
15	Chris Miller	2.00
16	Chris Warren	10.00
17	Alvin Harper	10.00
18	Eric Dickerson	5.00
19	Mike Jones	2.00
20	Ernest Givins	2.00
21	Natrone Means	15.00
22	Doug Riesenberg	2.00
23	Barry Word	2.00
24	Sean Salisbury	2.00
25	Derrick Fenner	2.00
26	David Howard	2.00
27	Mark Kelso	2.00
28	Todd Lyght	2.00
29	Dana Hall	2.00
30	Eric Metcalf	5.00
31	Jason Hanson	2.00
32	Dwight Stone	2.00
33	Johnny Mitchell	5.00
34	Reggie Roby	2.00
35	Terrell Buckley	2.00
36	Steve McMichael	2.00
37	Marty Carter	2.00
38	Seth Joyner	2.00
39	Rohn Stark	2.00
40	Eric Curry	8.00
41	Tommy Barnhardt	2.00
42	Karl Mecklenburg	2.00
43	Darion Conner	2.00
44	Ronnie Harmon	2.00
45	Cortez Kennedy	5.00
46	Tim Brown	5.00
47	Bill Lewis	2.00
48	Randall McDaniel	2.00
49	Curtis Duncan	2.00
50	Troy Aikman	90.00
51	David Klingler	5.00
52	Brent Jones	2.00
53	Dave Krieg	2.00
54	Bruce Smith	2.00
55	Vincent Brown	2.00
56	O.J. McDuffie	40.00
57	Cleveland Gary	2.00
58	Larry Centers	8.00
59	Pepper Johnson	2.00
60	Dan Marino	125.00
61	Robert Porcher	2.00
62	Jim Harbaugh	2.00
63	Sam Mills	2.00
64	Gary Anderson	2.00
65	Neil O'Donnell	8.00
66	Keith Byars	2.00
67	Jeff Herrod	2.00
68	Marion Butts	2.00
69	Terry McDaniel	2.00
70	Steve Broussard	2.00
71	Kelvin Martin	2.00
72	Tom Carter	6.00
73	Bryce Paup	2.00
74	Jim Kelly	10.00
75	Bill Romanowski	2.00
76	Andre Collins	2.00
77	Mike Farr	2.00
78	Henry Ellard	2.00
79	Dale Carter	2.00
80	Johnny Bailey	2.00
81	Garrison Hearst	30.00
82	Brent Williams	2.00
83	Richard McDonald	2.00
84	Emmitt Smith	125.00
85	Vai Sikahema	2.00
86	Jackie Harris	2.00
87	Alonzo Spellman	2.00
88	Mark Wheeler	2.00
89	Dalton Hilliard	2.00
90	Mark Higgs	2.00
91	Aaron Wallace	2.00
92	Earnest Byner	2.00
93	Stanley Richard	2.00
94	Cris Carter	5.00
95	Bobby Houston	2.00
96	Craig Heyward	2.00
97	Bernie Kosar	5.00
98	Mike Croel	2.00
99	Deion Sanders	20.00
100	Warren Moon	10.00
101	Christian Okoye	2.00
102	Ricky Watters	10.00
103	Eric Swann	2.00
104	Rodney Hampton	10.00
105	Daryl Johnston	2.00
106	Andre Reed	5.00
107	Jerome Bettis	60.00
108	Eugene Daniel	2.00
109	Leonard Russell	2.00
110	Darryl Williams	2.00
111	Rod Woodson	5.00
112	Boomer Esiason	5.00
113	James Hasty	2.00
114	Marc Boutte	2.00

No.	Player	Price
116	Tom Waddle	2.00
117	Lawrence Dawsey	2.00
118	Mark Collins	2.00
119	Willie Gault	2.00
120	Barry Sanders	80.00
121	Leroy Hoard	2.00
122	Anthony Munoz	2.00
123	Jesse Sapolu	2.00
124	Art Monk	5.00
125	Randal Hill	5.00
126	John Offerdahl	2.00
127	Carlos Jenkins	2.00
128	Al Smith	2.00
129	Michael Irvin	30.00
130	Kenneth Davis	2.00
131	Curtis Conway	15.00
132	Steve Atwater	2.00
133	Neil Smith	5.00
134	Steve Everitt	5.00
135	Chris Mims	2.00
136	Rickey Jackson	2.00
137	Edgar Bennett	2.00
138	Mike Pritchard	2.00
139	Richard Dent	5.00
140	Barry Foster	10.00
141	Eugene Robinson	2.00
142	Jackie Slater	2.00
143	Paul Gruber	2.00
144	Rob Moore	5.00
145	Robert Smith	40.00
146	Lorenzo White	2.00
147	Tommy Vardell	2.00
148	Dave Meggett	5.00
149	Vince Workman	2.00
150	Terry Allen	2.00
151	Howie Long	2.00
152	Charles Haley	2.00
153	Pete Metzelaars	2.00
154	John Copeland	5.00
155	Aeneas Williams	2.00
156	Ricky Sanders	2.00
157	Andre Ware	2.00
158	Tony Paige	2.00
159	Jerome Henderson	2.00
160	Harold Green	2.00
161	Wymon Henderson	2.00
162	Andre Rison	5.00
163	Donald Evans	2.00
164	Todd Scott	2.00
165	Steve Emtman	2.00
166	William Fuller	2.00
167	Michael Dean Perry	2.00
168	Randall Cunningham	10.00
169	Toi Cook	2.00
170	Browning Nagle	2.00
171	Darryl Henley	2.00
172	George Teague	6.00
173	Derrick Thomas	10.00
174	Jay Novacek	2.00
175	Mark Carrier	2.00
176	Kevin Fagan	2.00
177	Nate Lewis	2.00
178	Courtney Hawkins	2.00
179	Robert Blackmon	2.00
180	Rick Mirer	6.00
181	Mike Lodish	2.00
182	Jarrod Bunch	2.00
183	Anthony Smith	2.00
184	Brian Noble	2.00
185	Eric Bieniemy	2.00
186	Keith Jackson	2.00
187	Eric Martin	2.00
188	Vance Johnson	2.00
189	Kevin Mack	2.00
190	Rich Camarillo	2.00
191	Ashley Ambrose	2.00
192	Ray Childress	2.00
193	Jim Arnold	2.00
194	Ricky Ervins	2.00
195	Gary Anderson	2.00
196	Eric Allen	2.00
197	Roger Craig	2.00
198	Jon Vaughn	2.00
199	Tim McDonald	2.00
200	Broderick Thomas	2.00
201	Jessie Tuggle	2.00
202	Alonzo Mitz	2.00
203	Harvey Williams	2.00
204	Russell Maryland	2.00
205	Marvin Washington	2.00
206	Jim Everett	2.00
207	Trace Armstrong	2.00
208	Steve Young	50.00
209	Tony Woods	2.00
210	Brett Favre	125.00
211	Nate Odomes	2.00
212	Ricky Proehl	2.00
213	Jim Dombrowski	2.00
214	Anthony Carter	2.00
215	Tracy Simien	2.00
216	Clay Matthews	2.00
217	Patrick Bates	5.00
218	Jeff George	8.00
219	David Fulcher	2.00
220	Phil Simms	5.00
221	Eugene Chung	2.00
222	Reggie Cobb	2.00
223	Jim Sweeney	2.00
224	Greg Lloyd	2.00
225	Sean Jones	2.00
226	Marvin Jones	5.00
227	Bill Brooks	2.00
228	Moe Gardner	2.00
229	Louis Oliver	2.00
230	Flipper Anderson	2.00
231	Marc Spindler	2.00
232	Jerry Rice	100.00

No.	Player	Price
233	Chip Lohmiller	2.00
234	Nolan Harrison	2.00
235	Heath Sherman	2.00
236	Reyna Thompson	2.00
237	Derrick Walker	2.00
238	Rufus Porter	2.00
239	Checklist 1-125	2.00
240	Checklist 126-250	2.00
241	John Elway	10.00
242	Troy Aikman	35.00
243	Steve Emtman	2.00
244	Ricky Watters	7.00
245	Barry Foster	5.00
246	Dan Marino	90.00
247	Reggie White	5.00
248	Thurman Thomas	8.00
249	Broderick Thomas	2.00
250	Joe Montana	70.00
251	Tim Goad	2.00
252	Joe Nash	2.00
253	Anthony Johnson	2.00
254	Carl Pickens	2.00
255	Steve Beuerlein	2.00
256	Anthony Newman	2.00
257	Corey Miller	2.00
258	Steve DeBerg	2.00
259	Johnny Holland	2.00
260	Jerry Ball	2.00
261	Siupeli Malamala	2.00
262	Steve Wisniewski	2.00
263	Kelvin Pritchett	2.00
264	Chris Gardocki	2.00
265	Henry Thomas	2.00
266	Arthur Marshall	5.00
267	Quinn Early	2.00
268	Jonathan Hayes	2.00
269	Erric Pegram	5.00
270	Clyde Simmons	2.00
271	Eric Moten	2.00
272	Brian Mitchell	2.00
273	Adrian Cooper	2.00
274	Gaston Green	2.00
275	John Taylor	5.00
276	Jeff Uhlenhake	2.00
277	Phil Hansen	2.00
278	Kevin Williams	20.00
279	Robert Massey	2.00
280	Drew Bledsoe	150.00
281	Walter Reeves	2.00
282	Carlton Gray	5.00
283	Derek Brown	2.00
284	Martin Mayhew	2.00
285	Sean Gilbert	2.00
286	Jessie Hester	2.00
287	Mark Clayton	2.00
288	Blair Thomas	2.00
289	J.J. Birden	2.00
290	Shannon Sharpe	6.00
291	Richard Fain	2.00
292	Gene Atkins	2.00
293	Burt Grossman	2.00
294	Chris Doleman	2.00
295	Pat Swilling	2.00
296	Mike Kenn	2.00
297	Merril Hoge	2.00
298	Don Mosebar	2.00
299	Kevin Smith	2.00
300	Darrell Green	2.00
301	Dan Footman	2.00
302	Vestee Jackson	2.00
303	Carwell Gardner	2.00
304	Amp Lee	2.00
305	Bruce Matthews	2.00
306	Antone Davis	2.00
307	Dean Biasucci	2.00
308	Maurice Hurst	2.00
309	John Kasay	2.00
310	Lawrence Taylor	5.00
311	Ken Harvey	2.00
312	Willie Davis	2.00
313	Tony Bennett	2.00
314	Jay Schroeder	2.00
315	Darren Perry	2.00
316	Troy Drayton	10.00
317	Dan Williams	5.00
318	Michael Haynes	2.00
319	Renaldo Turnbull	2.00
320	Junior Seau	8.00
321	Ray Crockett	2.00
322	Will Furrer	2.00
323	Byron Evans	2.00
324	Jim McMahon	2.00
325	Robert Jones	2.00
326	Eric Davis	2.00
327	Jeff Cross	2.00
328	Kyle Clifton	2.00
329	Haywood Jeffires	5.00
330	Jeff Hostetler	5.00
331	Darryl Talley	2.00
332	Keith McCants	2.00
333	Mo Lewis	2.00
334	Matt Stover	2.00
335	Ferrell Edmunds	2.00
336	Matt Brock	2.00
337	Ernie Mills	2.00
338	Shane Dronett	2.00
339	Brad Muster	2.00
340	Jesse Solomon	2.00
341	John Randle	2.00
342	Chris Spielman	2.00
343	David Whitmore	2.00
344	Glenn Parker	2.00
345	Marco Coleman	2.00
346	Kenneth Gant	2.00
347	Cris Dishman	2.00
348	Kenny Walker	2.00
349	Roosevelt Potts	5.00
350	Reggie White	5.00

351	Gerald Robinson	2.00
352	Mark Rypien	2.00
353	Stan Humphries	5.00
354	Chris Singleton	2.00
355	Herschel Walker	5.00
356	Ron Hall	2.00
357	Ethan Horton	2.00
358	Anthony Pleasant	2.00
359	*Thomas Smith*	5.00
360	Audray McMillian	2.00
361	D.J. Johnson	2.00
362	Ron Heller	2.00
363	Bern Brostek	2.00
364	Ronnie Lott	5.00
365	Reggie Johnson	2.00
366	*Lin Elliott*	2.00
367	Lemuel Stinson	2.00
368	William White	2.00
369	Ernie Jones	2.00
370	Tom Rathman	2.00
371	Tommy Kane	2.00
372	David Brandon	2.00
373	Lee Johnson	2.00
374	Wade Wilson	2.00
375	Nick Lowery	2.00
376	Bubba McDowell	2.00
377	*Wayne Simmons*	2.00
378	Calvin Williams	2.00
379	Courtney Hall	2.00
380	Troy Vincent	2.00
381	Tim McGee	2.00
382	*Russell Freeman*	2.00
383	Steve Tasker	2.00
384	*Michael Strahan*	2.00
385	Greg Skrepenak	2.00
386	Jake Reed	2.00
387	Pete Stoyanovich	2.00
388	*Levon Kirkland*	2.00
389	Mel Gray	2.00
390	Brian Washington	2.00
391	Don Griffin	2.00
392	Desmond Howard	5.00
393	Luis Sharpe	2.00
394	Mike Johnson	2.00
395	Andre Tippett	2.00
396	Donnell Woolford	2.00
397	*Demetrius DuBose*	5.00
398	Pat Terrell	2.00
399	Todd McNair	2.00
400	Ken Norton	2.00
401	Keith Hamilton	2.00
402	Andy Heck	2.00
403	Jeff Gossett	2.00
404	Dexter McNabb	2.00
405	Richmond Webb	2.00
406	Irving Fryar	2.00
407	Brian Hansen	2.00
408	David Little	2.00
409	*Glyn Milburn*	10.00
410	Doug Dawson	2.00
411	Scott Mersereau	2.00
412	Don Beebe	2.00
413	Vaughan Johnson	2.00
414	Jack Del Rio	2.00
415	*Darrien Gordon*	5.00
416	Mark Schlereth	2.00
417	Lomas Brown	2.00
418	William Thomas	2.00
419	James Francis	2.00
420	Quentin Coryatt	2.00
421	Tyji Armstrong	2.00
422	Hugh Millen	2.00
423	*Adrian White*	2.00
424	Eddie Anderson	2.00
425	Mark Ingram	2.00
426	Ken O'Brien	2.00
427	Simon Fletcher	2.00
428	Tim McKyer	2.00
429	Leonard Marshall	2.00
430	Eric Green	2.00
431	Leonard Harris	2.00
432	*Darin Jordan*	2.00
433	Erik Howard	2.00
434	David Lang	2.00
435	Eric Turner	2.00
436	Michael Cofer	2.00
437	Jeff Bryant	2.00
438	Charles McRae	2.00
439	Henry Jones	2.00
440	Joe Montana	100.00
441	Morten Andersen	2.00
442	Jeff Jaeger	2.00
443	Leslie O'Neal	2.00
444	Leroy Butler	2.00
445	Steve Jordan	2.00
446	Brad Edwards	2.00
447	J.B. Brown	2.00
448	Kerry Cash	2.00
449	Mark Tuinei	2.00
450	Rodney Peete	2.00
451	Sheldon White	2.00
452	Wesley Carroll	2.00
453	Brad Baxter	2.00
454	Mike Pitts	2.00
455	Greg Montgomery	2.00
456	Kenny Davidson	2.00
457	Scott Fulhage	2.00
458	Greg Townsend	2.00
459	Rod Bernstine	2.00
460	Gary Clark	2.00
461	Hardy Nickerson	2.00
462	Sean Landeta	2.00
463	Rob Burnett	2.00
464	Fred Barnett	2.00
465	John L. Williams	2.00
466	Anthony Miller	5.00
467	Roman Phifer	2.00
468	Rich Moran	2.00

469	*Willie Roaf*	5.00
470	William Perry	2.00
471	Marcus Allen	10.00
472	Carl Lee	2.00
473	Kurt Gouveia	2.00
474	Jarvis Williams	2.00
475	Alfred Williams	2.00
476	Mark Stepnoski	2.00
477	Steve Wallace	2.00
478	Pat Harlow	2.00
479	Chip Banks	2.00
480	Cornelius Bennett	5.00
481	*Ryan McNeil*	2.00
482	Norm Johnson	2.00
483	Dermontti Dawson	2.00
484	Dwayne White	2.00
485	Derek Russell	2.00
486	Lionel Washington	2.00
487	Eric Hill	2.00
488	*Michael Barrow*	2.00
489	Checklist 251-375	2.00
490	Checklist 376-500	2.00
491	Emmitt Smith (MC)	75.00
492	Derrick Thomas (MC)	5.00
493	Deion Sanders (MC)	10.00
494	Randall Cunningham (MC)	5.00
495	Sterling Sharpe (MC)	5.00
496	Barry Sanders (MC)	40.00
497	Thurman Thomas (MC)	10.00
498	Brett Favre (MC)	14.00
499	Vaughan Johnson (MC)	2.00
500	Steve Young (MC)	15.00
501	Marvin Jones	2.00
502	*Reggie Brooks*	6.00
503	Eric Curry	2.00
504	Drew Bledsoe	75.00
505	Glyn Milburn	5.00
506	Jerome Bettis	15.00
507	Robert Smith	5.00
508	Dana Stubblefield	10.00
509	Tom Carter	2.00
510	Rick Mirer	20.00
511	Russell Copeland	2.00
512	*Deon Figures*	8.00
513	*Tony McGee*	5.00
514	*Derrick Lassic*	2.00
515	Everett Lindsay	2.00
516	*Derek Brown*	10.00
517	Harold Alexander	2.00
518	Tom Scott	2.00
519	*Elvis Grbac*	10.00
520	*Terry Kirby*	10.00
521	Doug Pelfrey	2.00
522	*Horace Copeland*	6.00
523	*Irv Smith*	6.00
524	*Lincoln Kennedy*	5.00
525	Jason Elam	2.00
526	*Qadry Ismail*	20.00
527	Artie Smith	2.00
528	*Tyrone Hughes*	20.00
529	Lance Gunn	2.00
530	*Vincent Brisby*	30.00
531	Patrick Robinson	2.00
532	Raghib Ismail	5.00
533	Willie Beamon	2.00
534	*Vaughn Hebron*	5.00
535	Darren Drozdov	2.00
536	*James Jett*	7.00
537	*Michael Bates*	5.00
538	Tom Rouen	2.00
539	Michael Husted	2.00
540	*Greg Robinson*	2.00
541	Carl Banks	2.00
542	Kevin Greene	2.00
543	Scott Mitchell	5.00
544	Michael Brooks	2.00
545	Shane Conlan	2.00
546	Vinny Testaverde	2.00
547	Robert Delpino	2.00
548	Bill Fralic	2.00
549	Carlton Bailey	2.00
550	Johnny Johnson	2.00

1993 Stadium Club Master Photos I

Master Photos were available through redemption cards inserted every 24 packs of Stadium Club. The redemption cards offered three Master Photos, with the entire set containing 12 players. The fronts were larger than the normal cards, but contained a gold border to reveal a standard sized card. Backs were full of text and statistics, with the player's name printed in a strip down the middle.

		MT
Complete Set (12):		15.00
Common Player:		.75
Minor Stars:		1.50
1	Barry Foster	.75
2	Barry Sanders	6.00
3	Reggie Cobb	.75
4	Cortez Kennedy	.75
5	Steve Young	3.00
6	Ricky Watters	1.50
7	Rob Moore	1.50

8	Derrick Thomas	1.50
9	Jeff George	1.50
10	Sterling Sharpe	1.50
11	Bruce Smith	.75
12	Deion Sanders	2.00

1993 Stadium Club Master Photos II

Similar to the Series I Master Photos, every 24 packs of Series II also had redemption cards that could be redeemed for three Master Photos. There were also redemption cards for complete sets. This 12-card set was 5" x 7" and contained larger than normal cards that contain gold borders to reveal the standard sized cards.

		MT
Complete Set (12):		10.00
Common Player:		.75
Minor Stars:		1.50
1	Morten Andersen	.75
2	Ken Norton Jr	.75
3	Clyde Simmons	.75
4	Roman Phifer	.75
5	Greg Townsend	.75
6	Darryl Talley	.75
7	Herschel Walker	.75
8	Reggie White	1.50
9	Jesse Solomon	.75
10	Joe Montana	5.00
11	John Taylor	.75
12	Cornelius Bennett	.75

1993 Stadium Club Super Teams

Twenty-eight different NFL teams had Super Team cards that were inserted into Stadium Club Series II Football. Team cards featuring division winners (Cowboys, 49ers, Lions, Bills, Oilers, Chiefs), conference championship teams (Cowboys, Bills) or Super Bowl XXVII winner (Cowboys) were redeemable for prizes. Division winners could get embossed, gold foil Stadium Club cards of that team with a division winner logo. Conference Champion cards were redeemable for 12 special embossed gold Master Photos of that team. Super Bowl cards were redeemable for a 500-card complete set of Stadium Club cards with a Super Bowl logo.

		MT
Complete Set (28):		75.00
Common Player:		2.00
Minor Stars:		4.00
Inserted 1:24		
1	Jim Harbaugh	4.00
2	David Klingler	2.00
3	Jim Kelly	4.00
4	John Elway	10.00
5	Bernie Kosar	2.00
6	Reggie Cobb	2.00
7	Eric Swann	2.00
8	Stan Humphries	2.00
9	Derrick Thomas	4.00
10	Steve Emtman	2.00
11	Emmitt Smith	20.00
12	Dan Marino	12.00
13	Randall Cunningham	4.00
14	Deion Sanders	4.00
15	Steve Young	8.00
16	Lawrence Taylor	4.00
17	Brad Baxter	2.00
18	Barry Sanders	15.00
19	Warren Moon	4.00
20	Brett Favre	15.00
21	Brent Williams	2.00
22	Howie Long	2.00
23	Cleveland Gary	2.00
24	Mark Rypien	2.00
25	Sam Mills	2.00

26	Cortez Kennedy	2.00
27	Barry Foster	2.00
28	Terry Allen	2.00

1993 Stadium Club Super Teams Division Winners

Super Team Division Winners were available to those collectors who had the Cowboys, 49ers, Lions, Bills, Oilers and Chiefs team cards and redeemed them for the team set. The cards are similar to the base cards in Stadium Club, but contain a logo reading "Division Winner" on the front.

		MT
Complete Bag Bills (13):		8.00
Complete Bag Chiefs (13):		10.00
Complete Bag Cowboys (13):		15.00
Complete Bag 49ers (13):		12.00
Complete Bag Lions (13):		8.00
Complete Bag Oilers (13):		8.00
Common Player:		.50
B27	Mark Kelso	.50
B54	Bruce Smith	1.00
B75	Jim Kelly	1.25
B107	Andre Reed	1.00
B153	Pete Metzelaars	.50
B211	Nate Odomes	.50
B227	Bill Brooks	.50
B331	Darryl Talley	.50
B383	Steve Tasker	.50
B412	Don Beebe	.50
B439	Henry Jones	.50
B480	Cornelius Bennett	.75
F29	Dana Hall	.50
F52	Brent Jones	.50
F76	Bill Romanowski	.50
F103	Ricky Watters	1.25
F176	Kevin Fagan	.50
F199	Tim McDonald	.50
F208	Steve Young	3.00
F232	Jerry Rice	3.00
F275	John Taylor	.75
F326	Eric Davis	.50
F370	Tom Rathman	.50
L7	Dennis Gibson	.50
L31	Jason Hanson	.50
L61	Robert Porcher	.50
L120	Barry Sanders	3.00
L231	Marc Spindler	.50
L263	Kelvin Pritchett	.50
L295	Pat Swilling	.75
L321	Ray Crockett	.50
L342	Chris Spielman	.75
L368	William White	.50
L389	Mel Gray	.50
L450	Rodney Peete	.50
O20	Ernest Givins	.75
O101	Warren Moon	1.25
O128	Al Smith	.50
O146	Lorenzo White	.50
O166	William Fuller	.50
O192	Ray Childress	.50
O225	Sean Jones	.50
O305	Bruce Mathews	.50
O329	Haywood Jeffires	.75
O347	Cris Dishman	.50
O376	Bubba McDowell	.50
O455	Greg Montgomery	.50
CH80	Dale Carter	.75
CH133	Neil Smith	.75
CH173	Derrick Thomas	1.00
CH203	Harvey Williams	.75
CH215	Tracy Simien	.50
CH268	Jonathan Hayes	.50
CH289	J.J. Birden	.50
CH312	Willie Davis	.75
CH375	Nick Lowery	.50
CH399	Todd McNair	.50
CH440	Joe Montana	3.00
CH471	Marcus Allen	2.00
CO17	Alvin Harper	.75
CO50	Troy Aikman	3.00
CO85	Emmitt Smith	5.00
CO106	Daryl Johnston	.75
CO129	Michael Irvin	1.50
CO152	Charles Haley	.75
CO174	Jay Novacek	.75
CO204	Russell Maryland	.50
CO278	Kevin Williams (WR)	1.00
CO299	Kevin Smith	.50
CO325	Robert Jones	.50
CO400	Ken Norton Jr	.50
DW3	Bills Super Team DW (Jim Kelly)	1.00
DW9	Chiefs Super Team DW (Derrick Thomas)	
DW11	Cowboys Super Team DW (Emmitt Smith)	3.00
DW15	49ers Super Team DW (Barry Sanders)	1.75
DW18	Lions Super Team DW (Barry Sanders)	1.75
DW19	Oilers Super Team DW (Warren Moon)	1.00

1993 Stadium Club Super Teams Super Bowl

Collectors holding the Cowboys Super Team card from 1993 Stadium Club could redeem that card for a 500-card Stadium Club set stamped with

1993 Stadium Club Super Teams Conference Winners

Super Team Division Winners were available to those collectors who redeemed their 1993 Super Team cards of Cowboys or Bills. Collectors received a 12-card set stamped with a gold foil conference logo, as well as a Master Photo set of the team. The cards are similar to base cards in Stadium Club, except for the conference champions logo on the front.

		MT
Complete Bag Bills (13):		7.00
Complete Bag Cowboys (13):		15.00
Common Player:		.50
B27	Mark Kelso	.50
B54	Bruce Smith	1.00
B75	Jim Kelly	1.25
B107	Andre Reed	1.00
B153	Pete Metzelaars	.50
B211	Nate Odomes	.50
B227	Bill Brooks	.50
B331	Darryl Talley	.50
B383	Steve Tasker	.50
B412	Don Beebe	.50
B439	Henry Jones	.50
B480	Cornelius Bennett	.75
CO17	Alvin Harper	.75
CO50	Troy Aikman	3.00
CO85	Emmitt Smith	5.00
CO106	Daryl Johnston	.75
CO129	Michael Irvin	1.50
CO152	Charles Haley	.75
CO174	Jay Novacek	.75
CO204	Russell Maryland	.50
CO278	Kevin Williams (WR)	1.50
CO299	Kevin Smith	.50
CO325	Robert Jones	.50
CO400	Ken Norton Jr.	.50
CW3	Cowboys Super Team CW (Emmitt Smith)	3.00
CW11	Bills Super Team CW (Jim Kelly)	1.00

1993 Stadium Club Super Team Master Photos

Super Team Master Photos were available to those collectors with either a Bills or Cowboys Super Team card. Along with a specially stamped team set, collectors also received these 5" x 7", uncropped Master Photos. The sets arrived in a bag and had blank backs and either a gold foil "N" for NFC or "A" for AFC edged by stars beneath the player photo.

		MT
Complete Bag Bills (12):		10.00
Complete Bag Cowboys (12):		20.00
Common Player:		.75
B1	Don Beebe	.75
B2	Cornelius Bennett	.75
B3	Bill Brooks	.75
B4	Henry Jones	.75
B5	Jim Kelly	1.50
B6	Mark Kelso	.75
B7	Pete Metzelaars	.75
B8	Nate Odomes	.75
B9	Andre Reed	1.25
B10	Bruce Smith	1.25
B11	Darryl Talley	.75
B12	Steve Tasker	.75
CO1	Troy Aikman	4.00
CO2	Charles Haley	1.00
CO3	Alvin Harper	1.00
CO4	Michael Irvin	1.00
CO5	Daryl Johnston	1.00
CO6	Robert Jones	.75
CO7	Russell Maryland	.75
CO8	Ken Norton Jr	.75
CO9	Jay Novacek	1.00
CO10	Emmitt Smith	7.50
CO11	Kevin Smith	.75
CO12	Kevin Williams (WR)	2.00

a gold foil Super Bowl XXVIII logo stamped on the front. The set arrived with the redeemed Super Team Cowboys card that also has a Super Bowl logo.

	MT
Complete Set (501):	75.00
Common Player (1-500):	.15
Semistars:	.30
SB3 Cowboys Super Team SB (Emmitt Smith)	4.00

1993 Stadium Club Members Only

Only Stadium Club members could purchase this 579-card set from Topps that included the entire 550-card Stadium Club set, along with 28 Super Teams and a signed Jerry Rice Record Breaker card. Production was limited to 10,000 factory sets, with each costing $199. The cards are identical to the regular-issue cards, except for a gold-foil "Members Only" logo.

	MT
Complete Set (579):	200.00
Common Player (1-550):	.20
Semistars:	.40
NNO Jerry Rice (RB Auto) (signed card)	50.00

1994 Stadium Club

Stadium Club Football Series I contains 270 cards, including several new subsets, like Chalk Talk, Chain Gang, Great Expectations and Topps Best cards. Chalk Talk (221-229) offers players that frequently move the chains. Chalk Talk cards (71-74) display photographs on the fronts and illustrations on the backs. Great Expectations (182-190) highlight the best rookies of 1993, while Topps Best utilizes Topps Finest technology to showcase the top players at each position. Topps Stadium Club Football also has a three-card insert set called Dynasty and Destiny, as well as 1st Day Production and Super Team cards. Stadium Club cards have a borderless, high-gloss look on the front with the players name centered on the bottom. The backs feature a shot of the player and statistics. Series II also had 270 cards (#s 271-540) and three insert sets. 1st Day Production cards were once again offered in Series II packs. Two new insert sets - Ring Leaders and Frequent Scorers - were also produced. A 90-card High series was also issued, featuring rookies and veterans in their NFL 75th anniversary throwback uniforms. Each card is also available in a parallel 1st Day Issue set, seeded one per every 12 packs. Three insert sets were also made, utilizing Finest's chromium technology. The sets are Bowman's Best Black (veteran stars), Bowman's Best Blue (Rookies) and Bowman's Best Mirror Images (veteran and a rookie on the same card). These three insert types were each seeded at a rate of one per every three packs. A parallel

Bowman's Refractors set of the 45 cards was also made; they were seeded one per every 12 packs. In addition, each 24th pack contained one of six Expansion Team Redemption cards - offense, defense or special teams - for the Carolina Panthers and Jacksonville Jaguars. The cards entitled the finders to a 22-card Topps Finest set of the players for the team depicted on the redemption card, or both teams.

	MT
Complete Set (630):	70.00
Complete Series 1 (270):	30.00
Complete Series 2 (270):	25.00
Complete High Series (90):	15.00
Common Player:	.10
Minor Stars:	.20
Series 1 Wax Box:	35.00
Series 2 Wax Box:	35.00
Series 3 Wax Box:	60.00

No.	Player	MT
1	Dan Wilkinson	.20
2	Chip Lohmiller	.10
3	Roosevelt Potts	.10
4	Martin Mayhew	.10
5	Shane Conlan	.10
6	Sam Adams	.20
7	Mike Kenn	.10
8	Tim Goad	.10
9	Tony Jones	.10
10	Ron Moore	.25
11	Mark Bortz	.10
12	Darren Carrington	.10
13	Eric Martin	.10
14	Eric Allen	.10
15	Aaron Glenn	.25
16	Bryan Cox	.10
17	Levon Kirkland	.10
18	Qadry Ismail	.20
19	Shane Dronett	.10
20	Chris Spielman	.10
21	Rob Fredrickson	.20
22	Wayne Simmons	.10
23	Glenn Montgomery	.20
24	Jason Sehorn	.10
25	Nick Lowery	.10
26	Dennis Brown	.10
27	Kenneth Davis	.10
28	Shante Carver	.25
29	Ryan Yarborough	.20
30	Cortez Kennedy	.20
31	Anthony Pleasant	.10
32	Jessie Tuggle	.10
33	Herschel Walker	.20
34	Andre Collins	.10
35	William Floyd	.50
36	Harold Green	.10
37	Courtney Hawkins	.10
38	Curtis Conway	.20
39	Ben Coates	.20
40	Natrone Means	.50
41	Eric Hill	.10
42	Keith Kartz	.10
43	Alexander Wright	.10
44	William Roaf	.10
45	Vencie Glenn	.10
46	Ronnie Lott, David Lutz	.10
47	George Koonce, Kelvin Martin	.10
48	Rod Woodson	.20
49	Tim Grunhard	.10
50	Cody Carlson	.10
51	Bryant Young	.75
52	Jay Novacek	.10
53	Darryl Talley	.10
54	Gary Anderson, Harry Colon	.10
55	David Meggett	.10
56	Aubrey Beavers	.25
57	James Folston	.10
58	Willie Davis	.10
59	Jason Elam	.10
60	Eric Metcalf	.10
61	Bruce Armstrong	.10
62	Ron Heller	.10
63	LeRoy Butler	.10
64	Terry Obee	.10
65	Kurt Gouveia	.10
66	Pierce Holt	.10
67	David Alexander	.10
68	Deral Boykin	.20
69	Carl Pickens	.10
70	Broderick Thomas	.10
71	Barry Sanders	1.25
72	Qadry Ismail	.20
73	Thurman Thomas	.25
74	Junior Seau, Bob Dahl	.10
75	Vinny Testaverde	.10
76	Tyrone Hughes	.10
77	Nate Newton	.10
78	Eric Swann	.10
79	Brad Baxter	.10
80	Dana Stubblefield	.10
81	John Elliott	.10
82	Steve Wisniewski	.10
83	Eddie Robinson	.10
84	Isaac Davis	.20
85	Cris Carter	.20
86	Mel Gray	.10
87	Cornelius Bennett	.10
88	Neil O'Donnell	.20
89	Jon Hand	.10
90	John Elway	.75
91	Bill Hitchcock	.10
92	Neil Smith	.10
93	Joe Johnson	.20
94	Edgar Bennett	.10
95	Vincent Brown	.10
96	Tommy Vardell	.10
97	Donnell Woolford	.10
98	Lincoln Kennedy	.10
99	O.J. McDuffie	.50
100	Heath Shuler	.50
101	Jerry Rice	1.00
102	Erik Williams	.10
103	Randall McDaniel	.10
104	Dermontti Dawson	.10
105	Nate Newton	.10
106	Harris Barton	.10
107	Shannon Sharpe	.20
108	Sterling Sharpe	.20
109	Steve Young	1.00
110	Emmitt Smith	2.00
111	Thurman Thomas	.20
112	Kyle Clifton	.10
113	Desmond Howard	.20
114	Quinn Early	.10
115	David Klingler	.10
116	Bern Brostek	.10
117	Gary Clark	.10
118	Courtney Hall	.10
119	Joe King	.10
120	Quentin Coryatt	.10
121	Johnnie Morton	.50
122	Andre Reed	.20
123	Eric Davis	.10
124	Jack Del Rio	.10
125	Greg Lloyd	.10
126	Bubba McDowell	.10
127	Mark Jackson	.10
128	Jeff Jaeger	.10
129	Chris Warren	.20
130	Tom Waddle	.10
131	Tony Smith	.10
132	Todd Collins	.10
133	Mark Bavaro	.10
134	Joe Phillips	.10
135	Chris Jacke	.10
136	Glyn Milburn	.20
137	Keith Jackson	.20
138	Steve Tovar	.10
139	Tim Johnson	.10
140	Brian Washington	.10
141	Troy Drayton	.10
142	DeWayne Washington	.25
143	Erik Williams	.10
144	Eric Turner	.10
145	John Taylor	.20
146	Richard Cooper	.10
147	Van Malone	.10
148	Tim Ruddy	.20
149	Henry Jones	.10
150	Tim Brown	.20
151	Stan Humphries	.10
152	Harry Newsome	.10
153	Craig Erickson	.20
154	Gary Anderson	.10
155	Ray Childress	.10
156	Howard Cross	.10
157	Heath Sherman	.10
158	Terrell Buckley	.10
159	J.B. Brown	.10
160	Joe Montana	2.50
161	David Wyman	.10
162	Norm Johnson	.10
163	Rod Stephens	.10
164	Willie McGinest	.50
165	Barry Sanders	2.50
166	Marc Logan	.10
167	Anthony Newman	.10
168	Russell Maryland	.10
169	Luis Sharpe	.10
170	Jim Kelly	.25
171	Tre' Johnson	.10
172	Johnny Mitchell	.10
173	David Palmer	.50
174	Bob Dahl	.10
175	Aaron Wallace	.10
176	Chris Gardocki	.10
177	Hardy Nickerson	.10
178	Jeff Query	.10
179	Leslie O'Neal	.10
180	Kevin Greene	.10
181	Alonzo Spellman	.10
182	Reggie Brooks	.10
183	Dana Stubblefield	.10
184	Tyrone Hughes	.10
185	Drew Bledsoe	1.00
186	Ron Moore	.10
187	Jason Elam	.10
188	Rick Mirer	.50
189	William Roaf	.10
190	Jerome Bettis	.50
191	Bob Hopkins	.10
192	Derek Brown	.10
193	Nolan Harrison	.10
194	Jon Randle	.10
195	Carlton Bailey	.10
196	Kevin Williams	.25
197	Greg Hill	1.00
198	Mark McMillian	.10
199	Brad Edwards	.10
200	Dan Marino	4.00
201	Ricky Watters	.20
202	George Teague	.10
203	Steve Beuerlein	.10
204	Jeff Burris	.20
205	Steve Atwater	.10
206	John Thierry	.50
207	Patrick Hunter	.10
208	Wayne Gandy	.10
209	Derrick Moore	.10
210	Phil Simms	.10
211	Kirk Lowdermilk	.10
212	Patrick Robinson	.10
213	Kevin Mitchell	.10
214	Jonathan Hayes	.10
215	Michael Dean Perry	.10
216	John Fina	.10
217	Anthony Smith	.10
218	Paul Gruber	.10
219	Carnell Lake	.10
220	Carl Lee	.10
221	Steve Christie	.10
222	Greg Montgomery	.10
223	Reggie Brooks	.10
224	Derrick Thomas	.20
225	Eric Metcalf	.10
226	Michael Haynes	.10
227	Bobby Hebert	.10
228	Tyrone Hughes	.10
229	Donald Frank	.10
230	Vaughan Johnson	.10
231	Eric Thomas	.10
232	Ernest Givins	.10
233	Charles Haley	.10
234	Darrell Green	.10
235	Harold Alexander	.10
236	Dwayne Sabb	.10
237	Harris Barton	.10
238	Randall Cunningham	.20
239	Ray Buchanan	.10
240	Sterling Sharpe	.20
241	Chris Mims	.10
242	Mark Carrier	.10
243	Ricky Proehl	.10
244	Michael Brooks	.10
245	Sean Gilbert	.10
246	David Lutz	.10
247	Kelvin Martin	.10
248	Scottie Graham	.50
249	Irving Fryar	.10
250	Ricardo McDonald	.10
251	Marvcus Patton	.10
252	Errict Rhett	1.00
253	Winston Moss	.10
254	Rod Vernstine	.10
255	Terry Wooden	.10
256	Antonio Langham	.50
257	Tommy Barnhardt	.10
258	Marvin Washington	.10
259	Bo Orlando	.10
260	Marcus Allen	.20
261	Mario Bates	.25
262	Marco Coleman	.10
263	Doug Riesenberg	.10
264	Jesse Sapolu	.10
265	Dermontti Dawson	.10
266	Fernando Smith	.20
267	David Szott	.10
268	Steve Christie	.10
269	Bruce Matthews	.10
270	Michael Irvin	.50
271	Seth Joyner	.10
272	Santana Dotson	.10
273	Vincent Brisby	.50
274	Rohn Stark	.10
275	John Copeland	.10
276	Toby Wright	.10
277	David Griggs	.10
278	Aaron Taylor	.20
279	Chris Doleman	.10
280	Reggie Brooks	.10
281	Willie Anderson	.10
282	Alvin Harper	.20
283	Chris Hinton	.10
284	Kelvin Pritchett	.10
285	Russell Copeland	.10
286	Dwight Stone	.10
287	Jeff Gossett	.10
288	Larry Allen	.10
289	Kevin Mawae	.10
290	Mark Collins	.10
291	Chris Zorich	.10
292	Vince Buck	.10
293	Gene Atkins	.10
294	Webster Slaughter	.10
295	Steve Young	1.50
296	Dan Williams	.10
297	Jesse Armstead	.10
298	Victor Bailey	.10
299	John Carney	.10
300	Emmitt Smith	4.00
301	Bucky Brooks	.50
302	Mo Lewis	.10
303	Eugene Daniel	.10
304	Tyji Armstrong	.10
305	Eugene Chung	.10
306	Raghib Ismail	.20
307	Sean Jones	.10
308	Rick Cunningham	.10
309	Ken Harvey	.10
310	Jeff George	.20
311	Jon Vaughn	.10
312	Roy Barker	.10
313	Michael Barrow	.10
314	Ryan McNeil	.10
315	Pete Stoyanovich	.10
316	Darryl Williams	.10
317	Renaldo Turnbull	.10
318	Eric Green	.10
319	Nate Lewis	.10
320	Mike Flores	.10
321	Derek Russell	.10
322	Marcus Spears	.10
323	Corey Miller	.10
324	Derrick Thomas	.20
325	Steve Everitt	.10
326	Brent Jones	.10
327	Marshall Faulk	8.00
328	Don Beebe	.10
329	Harry Swayne	.10
330	Boomer Esiason	.10
331	Don Mosebar	.10
332	Isaac Bruce	5.00
333	Rickey Jackson	.10
334	Daryl Johnston	.10
335	Lorenzo Lynch	.10
336	Brian Blades	.10
337	Michael Timpson	.10
338	Reggie Cobb	.10
339	Joe Walter	.10
340	Barry Foster	.20
341	Richmond Webb	.10
342	Pat Swilling	.10
343	Shaun Gayle	.10
344	Reggie Roby	.10
345	Chris Calloway	.10
346	Doug Dawson	.10
347	Rob Burnett	.10
348	Dana Hall	.10
349	Horace Copeland	.10
350	Shannon Sharpe	.20
351	Rich Miano	.10
352	Henry Thomas	.10
353	Dan Saleaumua	.10
354	Kevin Ross	.10
355	Morten Andersen	.10
356	Anthony Blaylock	.10
357	Stanley Richard	.10
358	Albert Lewis	.10
359	Darren Woodson	.10
360	Drew Bledsoe	2.00
361	Eric Mahlum	.10
362	Trent Dilfer	3.00
363	William Roberts	.10
364	Robert Brooks	.10
365	Jason Hanson	.10
366	Troy Vincent	.10
367	William Thomas	.10
368	Lonnie Johnson	.10
369	Jamir Miller	.20
370	Michael Jackson	.10
371	Charlie Ward	1.25
372	Shannon Sharpe	.20
373	Jackie Slater	.10
374	Steve Young	.20
375	Bobby Wilson	.10
376	Paul Frase	.10
377	Dale Carter	.10
378	Robert Delpino	.10
379	Bert Emanuel	2.00
380	Rick Mirer	.50
381	Carlos Jenkins	.10
382	Gary Brown	.10
383	Doug Pelfrey	.10
384	Dexter Carter	.10
385	Chris Miller	.10
386	Charles Johnson	1.00
387	James Joseph	.10
388	Darrin Smith	.10
389	James Jett	.10
390	Junior Seau	.20
391	Chris Slade	.10
392	Jim Harbaugh	.10
393	Herman Moore	.75
394	Thomas Randolph	.10
395	Lamar Thomas	.10
396	Reggie Rivers	.10
397	Larry Centers	.10
398	Chad Brown	.10
399	Terry Kirby	.20
400	Bruce Smith	.10
401	Keenan McCardell	2.50
402	Tim McDonald	.10
403	Robert Smith	.10
404	Matt Brock	.10
405	Tony McGee	.10
406	Ethan Horton	.10
407	Michael Haynes	.10
408	Steve Jackson	.10
409	Erik Kramer	.10
410	Jerome Bettis	1.00
411	D.J. Johnson	.10
412	John Alt	.10
413	Jeff Lageman	.10
414	Rick Tuten	.10
415	Jeff Robinson	.10
416	Kevin Lee	.20
417	Thomas Lewis	.20
418	Kerry Cash	.10
419	Chuck Levy	.10
420	Mark Ingram	.10
421	Dennis Gibson	.10
422	Tyronne Drakeford	.10
423	James Washington	.10
424	Dante Jones	.10
425	Eugene Robinson	.10
426	Johnny Johnson	.10
427	Brian Mitchell	.10
428	Charles Mincy	.10
429	Mark Carrier	.10
430	Vince Workman	.10
431	James Francis	.10
432	Clay Matthews	.10
433	Randall McDaniel	.10
434	Brad Ottis	.10
435	Bruce Smith	.10
436	Cortez Kennedy	.20
437	John Randle	.10
438	Neil Smith	.10
439	Cornelius Bennett	.10
440	Junior Seau	.20
441	Derrick Thomas	.20
442	Rod Woodson	.20
443	Terry McDaniel	.10
444	Tim McDonald	.10
445	Mark Carrier	.10
446	Irv Smith	.10
447	Steve Wallace	.10
448	Cris Dishman	.10
449	Bill Brooks	.10
450	Jeff Hostetler	.10
451	Brenston Buckner	.10
452	Ken Ruettgers	.10
453	Marc Boutte	.10
454	John Offerdahl	.10
455	Allen Aldridge	.10
456	Steve Emtman	.10
457	Andre Rison	.20
458	Shawn Jefferson	.10
459	Todd Steussie	.20
460	Scott Mitchell	.20
461	Tom Carter	.10
462	Donnell Bennett	.20
463	James Jones	.10
464	Antone Davis	.10
465	Jim Everett	.10
466	Tony Tolbert	.10
467	Merril Hoge	.10
468	Michael Bates	.10
469	Phil Hansen	.10
470	Rodney Hampton	.20
471	Aeneas Williams	.10
472	Al Del Greco	.10
473	Todd Lyght	.10
474	Joel Steed	.10
475	Merton Hanks	.10
476	Tony Stargell	.10
477	Greg Robinson	.10
478	Roger Duffy	.10
479	Simon Fletcher	.10
480	Reggie White	.20
481	Lee Johnson	.10
482	Wayne Martin	.10
483	Thurman Thomas	.20
484	Warren Moon	.20
485	Sam Rogers	.10
486	Erric Pegram	.10
487	Will Wolford	.10
488	Duane Young	.10
489	Keith Hamilton	.10
490	Haywood Jeffires	.10
491	Trace Armstrong	.10
492	J.J. Birden	.10
493	Ricky Ervins	.10
494	Robert Blackmon	.10
495	William Perry	.10
496	Robert Massey	.10
497	Jim Jeffcoat	.10
498	Pat Harlow	.10
499	Jeff Cross	.10
500	Jerry Rice	1.25
501	Darnay Scott	2.00
502	Clyde Simmons	.10
503	Henry Rolling	.10
504	James Hasty	.10
505	Leroy Thompson	.10
506	Darrell Thompson	.10
507	Tim Bowens	.10
508	Gerald Perry	.10
509	Mike Croel	.10
510	Sam Mills	.10
511	Steve Young	.50
512	Hardy Nickerson	.10
513	Cris Carter	.20
514	Boomer Esiason	.10
515	Bruce Smith	.10
516	Emmitt Smith	2.00
517	Eugene Robinson	.10
518	Gary Brown	.10
519	Jerry Rice	.75
520	Troy Aikman	1.00
521	Marcus Allen	.20
522	Junior Seau	.20
523	Sterling Sharpe	.20
524	Dana Stubblefield	.10
525	Tom Carter	.10
526	Pete Metzelaars	.10
527	Russell Freeman	.10
528	Keith Cash	.10
529	Willie Drewrey	.10
530	Randal Hill	.10
531	Pepper Johnson	.10
532	Rob Moore	.20
533	Todd Kelly	.10
534	Keith Byars	.10
535	Mike Fox	.10
536	Brett Favre	4.00
537	Terry McDaniel	.10
538	Darren Perry	.10
539	Maurice Hurst	.10
540	Troy Aikman	2.00
541	Junior Seau	.20
542	Steve Broussard	.10
543	Lorenzo White	.10
544	Terry McDaniel	.10
545	Henry Thomas	.10
546	Tyrone Hughes	.10
547	Mark Collins	.10
548	Gary Anderson	.10
549	Darrell Green	.10
550	Jerry Rice	1.50
551	Cornelius Bennett	.10
552	Aeneas Williams	.10
553	Eric Metcalf	.10
554	John Elliott	.10
555	Mo Lewis	.10
556	Darren Carrington	.10
557	Kevin Greene	.10
558	John Elway	.50
559	Eugene Robinson	.10
560	Drew Bledsoe	2.00
561	Fred Barnett	.10
562	Bernie Parmalee	1.00
563	Bryce Paup	.10
564	Donnell Woolford	.10
565	Terance Mathis	.20
566	Santana Dotson	.10
567	Randall McDaniel	.10
568	Stanley Richard	.10
569	Brian Blades	.10
570	Jerome Bettis	1.00
571	Neil Smith	.10
572	Andre Reed	.20
573	Michael Bankston	.10
574	Dana Stubblefield	.10
575	Rod Woodson	.20
576	Ken Harvey	.10
577	Andre Rison	.20
578	Darion Conner	.10
579	Michael Strahan	.10
580	Barry Sanders	2.00
581	Pepper Johnson	.10
582	Lewis Tillman	.10
583	Jeff George	.20
584	Michael Haynes	.10
585	Herschel Walker	.20
586	Tim Brown	.20
587	Jim Kelly	.20
588	Ricky Watters	.20
589	Randall Cunningham	.20
590	Troy Aikman	2.00
591	Ken Norton	.10
592	Cortez Kennedy	.20
593	Ricky Ervins	.10
594	Cris Carter	.20
595	Sterling Sharpe	.20
596	John Randle	.10
597	Shannon Sharpe	.20
598	Ray Crittenden	.20
599	Barry Foster	.25
600	Deion Sanders	1.00
601	Seth Joyner	.10
602	Chris Warren	.20
603	Tom Rathman	.10
604	Brett Favre	3.00
605	Marshall Faulk	2.00
606	Terry Allen	.10
607	Ben Coates	.50
608	Brian Washington	.10
609	Henry Ellard	.10
610	David Meggett	.10
611	Stan Humphries	.10
612	Warren Moon	.20
613	Marcus Allen	.20
614	Ed McDaniel	.10
615	Joe Montana	2.00
616	Jeff Hostetler	.10
617	Johnny Johnson	.10
618	Andre Coleman	.10
619	Willie Davis	.10
620	Rick Mirer	.50
621	Dan Marino	3.00
622	Rob Moore	.20
623	Byron Morris	.50
624	Natrone Means	.50
625	Steve Young	1.00
626	Jim Everett	.10
627	Michael Brooks	.10
628	Dermontti Dawson	.10
629	Reggie White	.20
630	Emmitt Smith	2.50

1994 Stadium Club First Day Cards

First Day Issues parallel cards were inserted one per 12 packs, and parallel the 630-card base set. The cards are distinguished by a gold foil "First Day" stamp on front.

	MT
Complete Set (630):	3000.
Complete Series 1 (270):	1200.
Complete Series 2 (270):	1200.
Complete High Series (90):	600.00
Common Player:	2.00
Minor Stars:	5.00

No.	Player	MT
1	Dan Wilkinson	10.00
2	Chip Lohmiller	2.00
3	Roosevelt Potts	2.00
4	Martin Mayhew	2.00
5	Shane Conlan	2.00
6	Sam Adams	8.00

No.	Player	Price
7	Mike Kenn	2.00
8	Tim Goad	2.00
9	Tony Jones	2.00
10	Ron Moore	8.00
11	Mark Bortz	2.00
12	Darren Carrington	2.00
13	Eric Martin	2.00
14	Eric Allen	2.00
15	*Aaron Glenn*	6.00
16	Bryan Cox	2.00
17	Levon Kirkland	2.00
18	Qadry Ismail	5.00
19	Shane Dronett	2.00
20	Chris Spielman	2.00
21	*Rob Fredrickson*	8.00
22	Wayne Simmons	2.00
23	Glenn Montgomery	5.00
24	*Jason Sehorn*	5.00
25	Nick Lowery	2.00
26	Dennis Brown	2.00
27	Kenneth Davis	2.00
28	*Shante Carver*	5.00
29	*Ryan Yarborough*	7.00
30	Cortez Kennedy	5.00
31	Anthony Pleasant	2.00
32	Jessie Tuggle	2.00
33	Herschel Walker	5.00
34	Andre Collins	2.00
35	*William Floyd*	40.00
36	Harold Green	2.00
37	Courtney Hawkins	2.00
38	Curtis Conway	5.00
39	Ben Coates	2.00
40	Natrone Means	45.00
41	Eric Hill	2.00
42	Keith Kartz	2.00
43	Alexander Wright	2.00
44	William Roaf	2.00
45	Vencie Glenn	2.00
46	Ronnie Lott, David Lutz	2.00
47	George Koonce, Kelvin Martin	2.00
48	Rod Woodson	5.00
49	Tim Grunhard	2.00
50	Cody Carlson	2.00
51	*Bryant Young*	18.00
52	Jay Novacek	2.00
53	Darryl Talley	2.00
54	Gary Anderson, Harry Colon	2.00
55	David Meggett	2.00
56	*Aubrey Beavers*	5.00
57	James Folston	2.00
58	Willie Davis	2.00
59	Jason Elam	2.00
60	Eric Metcalf	2.00
61	Bruce Armstrong	2.00
62	Ron Heller	2.00
63	LeRoy Butler	2.00
64	Terry Obee	2.00
65	Kurt Gouveia	2.00
66	Pierce Holt	2.00
67	David Alexander	2.00
68	*Deral Boykin*	2.00
69	Carl Pickens	2.00
70	Broderick Thomas	2.00
71	Barry Sanders	25.00
72	Qadry Ismail	5.00
73	Thurman Thomas	8.00
74	Junior Seau, Bob Dahl	2.00
75	Vinny Testaverde	2.00
76	Tyrone Hughes	2.00
77	Nate Newton	2.00
78	Eric Swann	2.00
79	Brad Baxter	2.00
80	Dana Stubblefield	2.00
81	John Elliott	2.00
82	Steve Wisniewski	2.00
83	Eddie Robinson	2.00
84	*Isaac Davis*	5.00
85	Cris Carter	5.00
86	Mel Gray	2.00
87	Cornelius Bennett	2.00
88	Neil O'Donnell	5.00
89	Jon Hand	2.00
90	John Elway	20.00
91	Bill Hitchcock	2.00
92	Neil Smith	2.00
93	*Joe Johnson*	2.00
94	Edgar Bennett	2.00
95	Vincent Brown	5.00
96	Tommy Vardell	2.00
97	Donnell Woolford	2.00
98	Lincoln Kennedy	2.00
99	O.J. McDuffie	10.00
100	*Heath Shuler*	12.00
101	Jerry Rice	25.00
102	Erik Williams	2.00
103	Randall McDaniel	2.00
104	Dermontti Dawson	2.00
105	Nate Newton	2.00
106	Harris Barton	2.00
107	Shannon Sharpe	5.00
108	Sterling Sharpe	5.00
109	Steve Young	25.00
110	Emmitt Smith	45.00
111	Thurman Thomas	7.00
112	Kyle Clifton	2.00
113	Desmond Howard	2.00
114	Quinn Early	2.00
115	David Klingler	2.00
116	Bern Brostek	2.00
117	Gary Clark	2.00
118	Courtney Hall	2.00
119	*Joe King*	2.00
120	Quentin Coryatt	2.00
121	*Johnnie Morton*	6.00
122	Andre Reed	5.00
123	Eric Davis	2.00
124	Jack Del Rio	2.00
125	Greg Lloyd	2.00
126	Bubba McDowell	2.00
127	Mark Jackson	2.00
128	Jeff Jaeger	2.00
129	Chris Warren	5.00
130	Tom Waddle	2.00
131	Tony Smith	2.00
132	Todd Collins	2.00
133	Mark Bavaro	2.00
134	Joe Phillips	2.00
135	Chris Jacke	2.00
136	Glyn Milburn	5.00
137	Keith Jackson	2.00
138	Steve Tovar	2.00
139	Tim Johnson	2.00
140	Brian Washington	2.00
141	Troy Drayton	2.00
142	*DeWayne Washington*	5.00
143	Erik Williams	2.00
144	Eric Turner	2.00
145	John Taylor	5.00
146	Richard Cooper	2.00
147	*Van Malone*	2.00
148	*Tim Ruddy*	2.00
149	Henry Jones	2.00
150	Tim Brown	5.00
151	Stan Humphries	5.00
152	Harry Newsome	2.00
153	Craig Erickson	5.00
154	Gary Anderson	2.00
155	Ray Childress	2.00
156	Howard Cross	2.00
157	Heath Sherman	2.00
158	Terrell Buckley	2.00
159	J.B. Brown	2.00
160	Joe Montana	60.00
161	David Wyman	2.00
162	Norm Johnson	2.00
163	Rod Stephens	2.00
164	*Willie McGinest*	5.00
165	Barry Sanders	50.00
166	Marc Logan	2.00
167	Anthony Newman	2.00
168	Russell Maryland	2.00
169	Luis Sharpe	2.00
170	Jim Kelly	8.00
171	*Tre' Johnson*	2.00
172	Johnny Mitchell	2.00
173	*David Palmer*	6.00
174	Bob Dahl	2.00
175	Aaron Wallace	2.00
176	Chris Gardocki	2.00
177	Hardy Nickerson	2.00
178	Jeff Query	2.00
179	Leslie O'Neal	2.00
180	Kevin Greene	2.00
181	Alonzo Spellman	2.00
182	Reggie Brooks	2.00
183	Dana Stubblefield	2.00
184	Tyrone Hughes	2.00
185	Drew Bledsoe	35.00
186	Ron Moore	5.00
187	Jason Elam	2.00
188	Rick Mirer	15.00
189	William Roaf	2.00
190	Jerome Bettis	15.00
191	Brad Hopkins	2.00
192	Derek Brown	2.00
193	Nolan Harrison	2.00
194	Jon Randle	2.00
195	Carlton Bailey	2.00
196	Kevin Williams	5.00
197	*Greg Hill*	25.00
198	Mark McMillian	2.00
199	Brad Edwards	2.00
200	Dan Marino	90.00
201	Ricky Watters	5.00
202	George Teague	2.00
203	Steve Beuerlein	2.00
204	*Jeff Burris*	8.00
205	Steve Atwater	2.00
206	*John Thierry*	5.00
207	Patrick Hunter	2.00
208	*Wayne Gandy*	2.00
209	Derrick Moore	2.00
210	Phil Simms	2.00
211	Kirk Lowdermilk	2.00
212	Patrick Robinson	2.00
213	Kevin Mitchell	2.00
214	Jonathan Hayes	2.00
215	Michael Dean Perry	2.00
216	John Fina	2.00
217	Anthony Smith	2.00
218	Paul Gruber	2.00
219	Carnell Lake	2.00
220	Carl Lee	2.00
221	Steve Christie	2.00
222	Greg Montgomery	2.00
223	Reggie Brooks	2.00
224	Derrick Thomas	5.00
225	Eric Metcalf	2.00
226	Bobby Hebert	2.00
227	Tyrone Hughes	2.00
228	Donald Frank	2.00
229	Vaughan Johnson	2.00
230	Vaughan Johnson	2.00
231	Eric Thomas	2.00
232	Ernest Givins	2.00
233	Charles Haley	2.00
234	Darrell Green	2.00
235	Harold Alexander	2.00
236	Dwayne Sabb	2.00
237	Harris Barton	2.00
238	Randall Cunningham	6.00
239	Ray Buchanan	2.00
240	Sterling Sharpe	10.00
241	Chris Mims	2.00
242	Mark Carrier	2.00
243	Ricky Proehl	2.00
244	Michael Brooks	2.00
245	Sean Gilbert	2.00
246	David Lutz	2.00
247	Kelvin Martin	2.00
248	*Scottie Graham*	5.00
249	Irving Fryar	2.00
250	Ricardo McDonald	2.00
251	Marvcus Patton	2.00
252	*Errict Rhett*	40.00
253	Winston Moss	2.00
254	Rod Vernstine	2.00
255	Terry Wooden	2.00
256	*Antonio Langham*	10.00
257	Tommy Barnhardt	2.00
258	Marvin Washington	2.00
259	Bo Orlando	2.00
260	Marcus Allen	2.00
261	*Mario Bates*	30.00
262	Marco Coleman	2.00
263	Doug Riesenberg	2.00
264	Jesse Sapolu	2.00
265	Dermontti Dawson	2.00
266	*Fernando Smith*	2.00
267	David Szott	2.00
268	Steve Christie	2.00
269	Bruce Matthews	2.00
270	Michael Irvin	20.00
271	Seth Joyner	2.00
272	Santana Dotson	2.00
273	Vincent Brisby	10.00
274	Rohn Stark	2.00
275	John Copeland	2.00
276	Toby Wright	2.00
277	David Griggs	2.00
278	*Aaron Taylor*	2.00
279	Chris Doleman	2.00
280	Reggie Brooks	2.00
281	Willie Anderson	2.00
282	Alvin Harper	5.00
283	Chris Hinton	2.00
284	Kelvin Pritchett	2.00
285	Russell Copeland	2.00
286	Dwight Stone	2.00
287	Jeff Gossett	2.00
288	Larry Allen	2.00
289	Kevin Mawae	2.00
290	Mark Collins	2.00
291	Chris Zorich	2.00
292	Vince Buck	2.00
293	Gene Atkins	2.00
294	Webster Slaughter	2.00
295	Steve Young	35.00
296	Dan Williams	2.00
297	Jesse Armstead	2.00
298	Victor Bailey	2.00
299	John Carney	2.00
300	Emmitt Smith	90.00
301	*Bucky Brooks*	5.00
302	Mo Lewis	2.00
303	Eugene Daniel	2.00
304	Tyji Armstrong	2.00
305	Eugene Chung	2.00
306	Raghib Ismail	5.00
307	Sean Jones	2.00
308	Rick Cunningham	2.00
309	Ken Harvey	2.00
310	Jeff George	5.00
311	Jon Vaughn	2.00
312	Roy Barker	2.00
313	Michael Barrow	2.00
314	Ryan McNeil	2.00
315	Pete Stoyanovich	2.00
316	Darryl Williams	2.00
317	Renaldo Turnbull	2.00
318	Eric Green	2.00
319	Nate Lewis	2.00
320	Mike Flores	2.00
321	Derek Russell	2.00
322	Marcus Spears	2.00
323	Corey Miller	2.00
324	Derrick Thomas	5.00
325	Steve Everitt	2.00
326	Brent Jones	2.00
327	*Marshall Faulk*	100.00
328	Don Beebe	2.00
329	Harry Swayne	2.00
330	Boomer Esiason	2.00
331	Don Mosebar	2.00
332	*Isaac Bruce*	60.00
333	Rickey Jackson	2.00
334	Daryl Johnston	2.00
335	Lorenzo Lynch	2.00
336	Brian Blades	2.00
337	Michael Timpson	2.00
338	Reggie Cobb	2.00
339	Joe Walter	2.00
340	Barry Foster	7.00
341	Richmond Webb	2.00
342	Pat Swilling	2.00
343	Shaun Gayle	2.00
344	Reggie Roby	2.00
345	Chris Calloway	2.00
346	Doug Dawson	2.00
347	Rob Burnett	2.00
348	Dana Hall	2.00
349	Horace Copeland	2.00
350	Shannon Sharpe	5.00
351	Rich Miano	2.00
352	Henry Thomas	2.00
353	Dan Saleaumua	2.00
354	Kevin Ross	2.00
355	Morten Andersen	2.00
356	Anthony Blaylock	2.00
357	Stanley Richard	2.00
358	Albert Lewis	2.00
359	Darren Woodson	2.00
360	Drew Bledsoe	60.00
361	Eric Mahlum	2.00
362	*Trent Dilfer*	35.00
363	William Roberts	2.00
364	Robert Brooks	2.00
365	Jason Hanson	2.00
366	Troy Vincent	2.00
367	William Thomas	2.00
368	Lonnie Johnson	2.00
369	*Jamir Miller*	5.00
370	Michael Jackson	2.00
371	*Charlie Ward*	20.00
372	Shannon Sharpe	5.00
373	Jackie Slater	2.00
374	Steve Young	5.00
375	Bobby Wilson	2.00
376	Paul Frase	2.00
377	Dale Carter	2.00
378	Robert Delpino	2.00
379	*Bert Emanuel*	25.00
380	Rick Mirer	20.00
381	Carlos Jenkins	2.00
382	Gary Brown	2.00
383	Doug Pelfrey	2.00
384	Dexter Carter	2.00
385	Chris Miller	2.00
386	*Charles Johnson*	25.00
387	James Joseph	2.00
388	Darrin Smith	2.00
389	James Jett	2.00
390	Junior Seau	5.00
391	Chris Slade	2.00
392	Jim Harbaugh	2.00
393	Herman Moore	15.00
394	Thomas Randolph	2.00
395	Lamar Thomas	2.00
396	Reggie Rivers	2.00
397	Larry Centers	2.00
398	Chad Brown	2.00
399	Terry Kirby	5.00
400	Bruce Smith	2.00
401	Keenan McCardell	25.00
402	Tim McDonald	2.00
403	Robert Smith	2.00
404	Matt Brock	2.00
405	Tony McGee	2.00
406	Ethan Horton	2.00
407	Michael Haynes	2.00
408	Steve Jackson	2.00
409	Erik Kramer	2.00
410	Jerome Bettis	20.00
411	D.J. Johnson	2.00
412	John Alt	2.00
413	Jeff Lageman	2.00
414	Rick Tuten	2.00
415	Jeff Robinson	2.00
416	*Kevin Lee*	5.00
417	*Thomas Lewis*	8.00
418	Kerry Cash	2.00
419	*Chuck Levy*	2.00
420	Mark Ingram	2.00
421	Dennis Gibson	2.00
422	Tyronne Drakeford	2.00
423	James Washington	2.00
424	Dante Jones	2.00
425	Eugene Robinson	2.00
426	Johnny Johnson	2.00
427	Brian Mitchell	2.00
428	Charles Mincy	2.00
429	Mark Carrier	2.00
430	Vince Workman	2.00
431	James Francis	2.00
432	Clay Matthews	2.00
433	Randall McDaniel	2.00
434	Brad Ottis	2.00
435	Bruce Smith	2.00
436	Cortez Kennedy	5.00
437	John Randle	2.00
438	Neil Smith	2.00
439	Cornelius Bennett	2.00
440	Junior Seau	5.00
441	Derrick Thomas	2.00
442	Rod Woodson	5.00
443	Terry McDaniel	2.00
444	Tim McDonald	2.00
445	Mark Carrier	2.00
446	Irv Smith	2.00
447	Steve Wallace	2.00
448	Cris Dishman	2.00
449	Bill Brooks	2.00
450	Jeff Hostetler	2.00
451	Brenston Buckner	2.00
452	Ken Ruettgers	2.00
453	Marc Boutte	2.00
454	John Offerdahl	2.00
455	Allen Aldridge	2.00
456	Steve Emtman	2.00
457	Andre Rison	5.00
458	Shawn Jefferson	2.00
459	*Todd Steussie*	2.00
460	Scott Mitchell	5.00
461	Tom Carter	2.00
462	*Donnell Bennett*	2.00
463	James Jones	2.00
464	Antone Davis	2.00
465	Jim Everett	2.00
466	Tony Tolbert	2.00
467	Merril Hoge	2.00
468	Michael Bates	2.00
469	Phil Hansen	2.00
470	Rodney Hampton	5.00
471	Aeneas Williams	2.00
472	Al Del Greco	2.00
473	Todd Lyght	2.00
474	Joel Steed	2.00
475	Merton Hanks	2.00
476	Tony Stargell	2.00
477	Greg Robinson	2.00
478	Roger Duffy	2.00
479	Simon Fletcher	2.00
480	Reggie White	5.00
481	Lee Johnson	2.00
482	Wayne Martin	2.00
483	Thurman Thomas	8.00
484	Warren Moon	6.00
485	Sam Rogers	2.00
486	Erric Pegram	2.00
487	Will Wolford	2.00
488	Duane Young	2.00
489	Keith Hamilton	2.00
490	Haywood Jeffires	2.00
491	Trace Armstrong	2.00
492	J.J. Birden	2.00
493	Ricky Ervins	2.00
494	Robert Blackmon	2.00
495	William Perry	2.00
496	Robert Massey	2.00
497	Jim Jeffcoat	2.00
498	Pat Harlow	2.00
499	Jeff Cross	2.00
500	Jerry Rice	45.00
501	*Darnay Scott*	40.00
502	Clyde Simmons	2.00
503	Henry Rolling	2.00
504	James Hasty	2.00
505	Leroy Thompson	2.00
506	Darrell Thompson	2.00
507	Tim Bowens	2.00
508	Gerald Perry	2.00
509	Mike Croel	2.00
510	Sam Mills	2.00
511	Steve Young	20.00
512	Hardy Nickerson	2.00
513	Cris Carter	5.00
514	Boomer Esiason	2.00
515	Bruce Smith	2.00
516	Emmitt Smith	50.00
517	Eugene Robinson	2.00
518	Gary Brown	2.00
519	Jerry Rice	20.00
520	Troy Aikman	20.00
521	Marcus Allen	5.00
522	Junior Seau	2.00
523	Sterling Sharpe	5.00
524	Dana Stubblefield	2.00
525	Tom Carter	2.00
526	Pete Metzelaars	2.00
527	Russell Freeman	2.00
528	Keith Cash	2.00
529	Willie Drewrey	2.00
530	Randal Hill	2.00
531	Pepper Johnson	2.00
532	Rob Moore	5.00
533	Todd Kelly	2.00
534	Keith Byars	2.00
535	Mike Fox	2.00
536	Brett Favre	90.00
537	Terry McDaniel	2.00
538	Darren Perry	2.00
539	Maurice Hurst	2.00
540	Troy Aikman	45.00
541	Junior Seau	7.00
542	Steve Broussard	2.00
543	Lorenzo White	2.00
544	Terry McDaniel	2.00
545	Henry Thomas	2.00
546	Tyrone Hughes	2.00
547	Mark Collins	2.00
548	Gary Anderson	2.00
549	Darrell Green	2.00
550	Jerry Rice	45.00
551	Cornelius Bennett	2.00
552	Aeneas Williams	2.00
553	Eric Metcalf	2.00
554	John Elliott	2.00
555	Mo Lewis	2.00
556	Darren Carrington	2.00
557	Kevin Greene	2.00
558	John Elway	20.00
559	Eugene Robinson	2.00
560	Drew Bledsoe	45.00
561	Fred Barnett	2.00
562	*Bernie Parmalee*	30.00
563	Bryce Paup	2.00
564	Donnell Woolford	2.00
565	Terance Mathis	2.00
566	Santana Dotson	2.00
567	Randall McDaniel	2.00
568	Stanley Richard	2.00
569	Brian Blades	2.00
570	Jerome Bettis	20.00
571	Neil Smith	2.00
572	Andre Reed	5.00
573	Michael Bankston	2.00
574	Dana Stubblefield	2.00
575	Rod Woodson	5.00
576	Ken Harvey	2.00
577	Andre Rison	2.00
578	Darion Conner	2.00
579	Michael Strahan	2.00
580	Barry Sanders	35.00
581	Pepper Johnson	2.00
582	Lewis Tillman	2.00
583	Jeff George	2.00
584	Michael Haynes	2.00
585	Herschel Walker	5.00
586	Tim Brown	6.00
587	Jim Kelly	6.00
588	Ricky Watters	2.00
589	Randall Cunningham	5.00
590	Troy Aikman	45.00
591	Ken Norton	2.00
592	Cortez Kennedy	5.00
593	Ricky Ervins	2.00
594	Cris Carter	5.00
595	Sterling Sharpe	10.00
596	John Randle	2.00
597	Shannon Sharpe	5.00
598	*Ray Crittenden*	2.00
599	Barry Foster	6.00
600	Deion Sanders	35.00
601	Seth Joyner	2.00
602	Chris Warren	5.00
603	Tom Rathman	2.00
604	Brett Favre	25.00
605	Marshall Faulk	45.00
606	Terry Allen	2.00
607	Ben Coates	10.00
608	Brian Washington	2.00
609	Henry Ellard	2.00
610	David Meggett	2.00
611	Stan Humphries	5.00
612	Warren Moon	5.00
613	Marcus Allen	5.00
614	Ed McDaniel	2.00
615	Joe Montana	60.00
616	Jeff Hostetler	2.00
617	Johnny Johnson	2.00
618	Andre Coleman	2.00
619	Willie Davis	2.00
620	Rick Mirer	20.00
621	Dan Marino	90.00
622	Rob Moore	2.00
623	*Byron Morris*	40.00
624	Natrone Means	40.00
625	Steve Young	30.00
626	Jim Everett	2.00
627	Michael Brooks	2.00
628	Dermontti Dawson	2.00
629	Reggie White	5.00
630	Emmitt Smith	75.00

1994 Stadium Club Bowman Black

These 17 insert cards, featuring NFL veterans, were included in 1994-95 Stadium Club Football High series packs, one per every three packs. The cards utilize Finest chromium technology and have a black tint to them. "Bowman's Best" is written on the front. The back has a card number, close-up shot and summaries of the player's stats and skills. Refractor versions were also made for each Blue card; they were seeded one per every 12 packs.

	MT
Complete Set (17):	90.00
Common Player:	1.00
Comp. Refr. Set (17):	275.00
Refractor Cards:	1x-3x

No.	Player	Price
1	Jerry Rice	6.00
2	Deion Sanders	4.00
3	Reggie White	1.00
4	Dan Marino	10.00
5	Natrone Means	2.00
6	Rick Mirer	2.00
7	Michael Irvin	2.00
8	John Elway	4.00
9	Junior Seau	1.00
10	Drew Bledsoe	5.00
11	Sterling Sharpe	1.00
12	Brett Favre	10.00
13	Troy Aikman	7.00
14	Barry Sanders	7.00
15	Steve Young	2.00
16	Emmitt Smith	10.00
17	Joe Montana	5.00

1994 Stadium Club Bowman Blue

These 1994-95 Topps Stadium Club High Series inserts feature 17 of the NFL's most promising rookies. Cards, which use the Finest chromium technology, were seeded one per three packs. The cards are similar in design to the Bowman Black inserts, except these have a blue tint to them. There were also Refractors made for each Blue card; they are seeded one per every 12 packs.

	MT
Complete Set (17):	40.00
Common Player:	1.00
Comp. Refr. Set (17):	125.00
Refractor Cards:	1x-3x
1 Marshall Faulk	6.00
2 Derrick Alexander	1.00
3 Darnay Scott	2.00
4 Gus Frerotte	2.00
5 Jeff Blake	6.00
6 Charles Johnson	2.00
7 Thomas Lewis	1.00
8 Charlie Garner	1.00
9 Aaron Glenn	1.00
10 William Floyd	2.00
11 Antonio Langham	1.00
12 Errict Rhett	3.00
13 Heath Shuler	3.00
14 Jeff Burris	1.00
15 Dan Wilkinson	1.00
16 Rob Fredrickson	1.00
17 Tim Bowens	1.00

1994 Stadium Club Bowman Mirror Images

These cards match a top NFL veteran with a promising rookie. The horizontal front, using Finest chromium technology, shows both players, with their names underneath. The cards were random inserts in 1994-95 Topps Stadium High Series packs, one per every three packs. Refractor versions were also made; they could be found one per every 12 packs.

	MT
Complete Set (11):	45.00
Common Player:	1.00
Comp. Refrac. Set (11):	130.00
Refractor Cards:	1x-3x
18 Deion Sanders, Aaron Glenn	3.00
19 Barry Sanders, Marshall Faulk	7.00
20 Darryl Johnston, William Floyd	2.00
21 Reggie White, Tim Bowens	1.00
22 Troy Aikman, Heath Shuler	6.00
23 Donnell Woolford, Antonio Langham	1.00
24 Rodney Hampton, Errict Rhett	6.00
25 Tyrone Hughes, Jeff Burris	1.00
26 Henry Thomas, Dan Wilkinson	1.00
27 Jerry Rice, Derrick Alexander	5.00
28 Emmitt Smith, Bam Morris	10.00

1994 Stadium Club Dynasty and Destiny

Dynasty and Destiny is a Stadium Club insert set which compares former NFL players who are or will be Hall of Fame members with current players. Three cards appeared in Series I and three more followed in Series II. Each card front shows both players, with their names, the set name and Stadium Club logo stamped in gold foil. Destiny and Dynasty are also written on the card front. The back, numbered 1 of 6, etc., com-

pares statistics for both players from their first year in the league and their career totals. Mug shots are also given.

	MT
Complete Set (6):	25.00
Common Player:	5.00
1 Walter Payton, Emmitt Smith	12.00
2 Steve Largent, Tom Waddle	5.00
3 Randy White, Cortez Kennedy	5.00
4 Dan Fouts, Troy Aikman	8.00
5 Mike Singletary, Junior Seau	5.00
6 Ozzie Newsome, Shannon Sharpe	5.00

1994 Stadium Club Expansion Team Redemption

This 44-card Finest set was available through redemption cards in Stadium Club Series III, seeded one per 24 packs. The set introduced the two new expansion teams - Jacksonville Jaguars and Carolina Panthers with three redemption cards per franchise, labeled offense, defense and special teams, which could be redeemed for that group of players in their new uniforms. There was also a complete set redemption card found every 336 packs. The deadline for redemptions was February 20, 1996.

	MT
Jaguars Prize Set (22):	20.00
Panthers Prize Set (22):	25.00
Common Jaguar (J1-J22):	.75
Common Panther (P1-P22):	.75
Comp. Trade Card Set (6):	3.00
J1 James O. Stewart	2.00
J2 Kelvin Pritchett	.75
J3 Mike Dumas	.75
J4 Brian DeMarco	.75
J5 James Williams	.75
J6 Ernest Givins	.75
J7 Harry Colon	.75
J8 Derek Brown	.75
J9 Santo Stephens	.75
J10 Jeff Lageman	.75
J11 Bryan Barker	.75
J12 Dave Widell	.75
J13 Willie Jackson	1.00
J14 Vinnie Clark	.75
J15 Mickey Washington	.75
J16 Le'Shai Maston	.75
J17 Darren Carrington	.75
J18 Steve Beuerlein	.75
J19 Mark Williams	.75
J20 Keith Goganious	.75
J21 Shawn Bouwens	.75
J22 Chris Hudson	.75
P1 Kerry Collins	8.00
P2 Rod Smith	.75
P3 Willie Green	.75
P4 Greg Kragen	.75
P5 Blake Brockermeyer	.75
P6 Bob Christian	.75
P7 Carlton Bailey	.75
P8 Bubba McDowell	.75
P9 Matt Elliott	.75
P10 Tyrone Poole	1.00
P11 John Kasay	.75
P12 Gerald Williams	.75
P13 Derrick Moore	.75
P14 Don Beebe	.75
P15 Sam Mills	.75
P16 Darion Conner	.75
P17 Eric Guliford	.75
P18 Mike Fox	.75
P19 Pete Metzelaars	.75
P20 Frank Reich	1.00
P21 Mark Carrier	.75
P22 Vince Workman	.75
NNO Jacksonville Jaguars Defense Redemption Card	.50
NNO Jacksonville Jaguars Offense Redemption Card	.50
NNO Jacksonville Jaguars Special Teams Redemption Card	.50
NNO Carolina Panthers Defense Redemption Card	.50
NNO Carolina Panthers Offense Redemption Card	.50
NNO Carolina Panthers Special Teams Redemption Card	.50
NNO Carolina Panthers Complete Set Redemption	.50

1994 Stadium Club Frequent Scorers

These Stadium Club Series II inserts feature 10 different players, each having five different point cards, worth six points each. Collectors can receive a Finest quality upgrade set of the player by sending in 30 Frequent Scorer point cards of him. The point cards were included one per every three packs.

	MT
Complete Set (10):	150.00
Common Player:	6.00
1 Chris Warren	9.00
2 Marshall Faulk	25.00
3 Drew Bledsoe	25.00
4 Dan Marino	35.00
5 Vinny Testaverde	6.00
6 Jeff George	9.00
7 Steve Young	20.00
8 Dave Meggett	6.00
9 Stan Humphries	9.00
10 Rick Mirer	15.00

1994 Stadium Club Ring Leaders

These Stadium Club Series II inserts feature active players who have played in a Pro Bowl and have led the league in a statistical category. Topps used a "Power Matrix" technology that "makes the cards shine beyond belief." These cards were randomly included in every 24th pack.

	MT
Complete Set (12):	50.00
Common Player:	4.00
1 Emmitt Smith	20.00
2 Steve Young	10.00
3 Deion Sanders	7.00
4 Warren Moon	4.00
5 Thurman Thomas	4.00
6 Jerry Rice	10.00
7 Sterling Sharpe	4.00
8 Barry Sanders	12.00
9 Reggie White	4.00
10 Michael Irvin	4.00
11 Ronnie Lott	4.00
12 Herschel Walker	4.00

1994 Stadium Club Super Teams

Stadium Club Football also inserted Super Team cards into one of every 24 packs. The cards feature a wide-angle action shot of the team. If the team pictured won the Super Bowl, conference title or division championship, the Super Team card could be redeemed for additional cards that formed a parallel set but had either Super Bowl logo, conference champi-

onship logo or division winner logo, respectively.

	MT
Complete Set (28):	125.00
Common Player:	2.00
1 Cardinals	2.00
2 Falcons	2.00
3 Bills	2.00
4 Bears	2.00
5 Bengals	2.00
6 Browns	2.00
7 Cowboys	10.00
8 Broncos	6.00
9 Lions	6.00
10 Packers	10.00
11 Oilers	2.00
12 Colts	2.00
13 Chiefs	7.00
14 Raiders	2.00
15 Rams	2.00
16 Dolphins	5.00
17 Vikings	5.00
18 Patriots	6.00
19 Saints	2.00
20 Giants	2.00
21 Jets	2.00
22 Eagles	2.00
23 Steelers	4.00
24 Chargers	6.00
25 49ers	12.00
26 Seahawks	4.00
27 Buccaneers	2.00
28 Redskins	2.00

1994 Stadium Club Super Teams Division Winners

Collectors who had Super Team cards of the Cowboys, 49ers, Vikings, Chargers, Steelers and Dolphins could redeem the cards for a 10-card team bag set via mail. The cards were essentially the same as regular-issue cards, except for a division winner gold foil logo.

	MT
Complete Bag Chargers (11):	5.00
Complete Bag Cowboys (11):	12.00
Complete Bag Dolphins (11):	10.00
Complete Bag 49ers (11):	12.00
Complete Bag Vikings (11):	6.00
Complete Bag Steelers (11):	6.00
Common Player:	.40
7DW Cowboys Super Team DW (Emmitt Smith, Troy Aikman)	2.50
16DW Dolphins Super Team DW (Irving Fryar)	.75
17DWDW Vikings Super Team DW (Cris Carter)	.75
23DWSteelers Super Team DW (Neil O'Donnell)	.75
24DWChargers Super Team DW (Natrone Means)	.75
25DW49ers Super Team DW (Jerry Rice, Steve Young, Ricky Watters)	1.50
D16 Bryan Cox	.40
D56 Aubrey Beavers	.40
D99 O.J. McDuffie	1.00
D200 Dan Marino	4.00
D249 Irving Fryar	.60
D262 Marco Coleman	.40
D341 Richmond Webb	.40
D399 Terry Kirby	.60
D507 Tim Bowens	.60
D562 Bernie Parmalee	1.50
F35 William Floyd	2.00
F51 Bryant Young	1.25
F80 Dana Stubblefield	1.00
F201 Ricky Watters	.60
F295 Steve Young	2.50
F326 Brent Jones	.60
F402 Tim McDonald	.40
F475 Merton Hanks	.40
F500 Jerry Rice	2.50
F600 Deion Sanders	1.50
V18 Qadry Ismail	1.00
V85 Cris Carter	.60
V124 Jack Del Rio	.40
V142 DeWayne Washington	.60
V173 David Palmer	.60
V194 John Randle	.40
V352 Henry Thomas	.40
V433 Randall McDaniel	.40
V459 Todd Steussie	.60
V484 Warren Moon	1.00
CH12 Darren Carrington	.40
CH40 Natrone Means	.75
CH84 Isaac Davis	.40
CH151 Stan Humphries	1.00
CH179 Leslie O'Neal	.60

	MT
CH299 John Carney	.40
CH357 Stanley Richard	.40
CH390 Junior Seau	1.00
CH421 Dennis Gibson	.40
CH458 Shawn Jefferson	.60
CO52 Jay Novacek	.60
CO168 Russell Maryland	.40
CO233 Charles Haley	.60
CO270 Michael Irvin	1.00
CO282 Alvin Harper	.60
CO300 Emmitt Smith	4.00
CO334 Daryl Johnston	.60
CO359 Darren Woodson	.40
CO423 James Washington	.40
CO540 Troy Aikman	2.50

1994 Stadium Club Super Teams Master Photos

Super Team cards of the AFC and NFC Champions - the Chargers and 49ers - were redeemable for this 10-card team bag set of Master Photos of that respective team. The Master Photos were essentially the same as the base cards, but were printed on an oversized card, with a white border around the photo, and they have a conference winner gold foil logo.

	MT
Complete Bag Chargers (11):	7.50
Complete Bag 49ers (11):	15.00
Common Player:	.50
24CWChargers Super Team CW (Natrone Means)	.75
25CW49ers Super Team CW (Jerry Rice, Steve Young, Ricky Watters)	1.50
F35 William Floyd	2.50
F51 Bryant Young	1.50
F80 Dana Stubblefield	1.25
F201 Ricky Watters	.75
F295 Steve Young	3.00
F326 Brent Jones	.75
F402 Tim McDonald	.75
F475 Merton Hanks	.50
F500 Jerry Rice	3.00
F600 Deion Sanders	1.75
CH12 Darren Carrington	.50
CH40 Natrone Means	1.00
CH84 Isaac Davis	.50
CH151 Stan Humphries	1.25
CH179 Leslie O'Neal	.75
CH299 John Carney	.50
CH357 Stanley Richard	.50
CH390 Junior Seau	1.25
CH421 Dennis Gibson	.50
CH458 Shawn Jefferson	.75

1994 Stadium Club Super Teams Super Bowl

Super Team cards of the Super Bowl XXIX Champion 49ers could be redeemed for a 540-card parallel set to the regular-issue Stadium Club set. The cards are essentially the same as regular-issue cards, except for a "Super Bowl XXIX" logo on the front. The sets also came with a 49ers Super Team card that also had a "Super Bowl XXIX" logo on the front.

	MT
Complete Set (541):	60.00
Common Player (1-540):	.10
SB25 49ers Super Team SB (Jerry Rice, Steve Young, Ricky Watters)	2.00

1994 Stadium Club Members Only

Stadium Club Members Only parallel sets were only available directly from Topps to Stadium Club members. The sets include all base cards and inserts, and are essentially the same as regular-issue cards, except for a special "Members Only" logo on the front.

	MT
Complete Fact. Set (722):	250.00
Common Player (1-630):	.25
Common Player (DD1-DD6):	.25

	MT
Common Player (RL1-RL12):	.50
Common Player (ST1-ST28):	.25
DD1 Emmitt Smith, Walter Payton	8.00
DD2 Steve Largent, Tom Waddle	.25
DD3 Randy White, Cortez Kennedy	.40
DD4 Troy Aikman, Dan Fouts	5.00
DD5 Junior Seau, Mike Singletary	.40
DD6 Shannon Sharpe, Ozzie Newsome	.25
RL1 Emmitt Smith	12.00
RL2 Steve Young	6.00
RL3 Deion Sanders	4.00
RL4 Warren Moon	.75
RL5 Thurman Thomas	.75
RL6 Jerry Rice	8.00
RL7 Sterling Sharpe	.75
RL8 Barry Sanders	8.00
RL9 Reggie White	.75
RL10 Michael Irvin	.75
RL11 Ronnie Lott	.50
RL12 Herschel Walker	.50
ST1 Steve Beuerlein	.25
ST2 Drew Hill	.25
ST3 Jim Kelly	.40
ST4 Joe Cain	.25
ST5 Derrick Fenner	.25
ST6 Tommy Vardell	.25
ST7 Emmitt Smith	12.00
ST8 John Elway	4.00
ST9 Barry Sanders	8.00
ST10 Brent Favre	8.00
ST11 Gary Brown	.25
ST12 Zefross Moss	.25
ST13 Joe Montana	8.00
ST14 Howie Long	.40
ST15 Jerome Bettis	2.50
ST16 Irving Fryar	.40
ST17 Cris Carter	.40
ST18 Drew Bledsoe	6.00
ST19 Rickey Jackson	.25
ST20 Phil Simms	.40
ST21 Boomer Esiason	.40
ST22 Herschel Walker	.25
ST23 Neil O'Donnell	1.00
ST24 Natrone Means	2.50
ST25 Jerry Rice, Steve Young	8.00
ST26 Rick Mirer	2.50
ST27 Craig Erickson	.25
ST28 Reggie Brooks	.25

1994 Stadium Club Members Only 50

This 50-card set was exclusively available to Stadium Club members and contained 45 regular Stadium Club cards and five Finest cards. The words "Topps Stadium Club Members Only" appear in gold foil in one of the top corners.

	MT
Complete Set (50):	25.00
Common Player:	.25
1 Jerry Rice	4.00
2 Erik Williams	.25
3 Nate Newton	.25
4 Jesse Sapolu	.25
5 Randall McDaniel	.25
6 Harris Barton	.25
7 Jay Novacek	.40
8 Michael Irvin	.75
9 Steve Young	2.50
10 Jerome Bettis	1.50
11 Daryl Johnston	.40
12 Neil Smith	.40
13 Cortez Kennedy	.40
14 Ray Childress	.25
15 Leslie O'Neal	.40
16 Derrick Thomas	.40
17 Junior Seau	.75
18 Greg Lloyd	.40
19 Rod Woodson	.40
20 Nate Odomes	.25
21 Dennis Smith	.25
22 Steve Atwater	.25
23 Reggie White	.75
24 John Randle	.25
25 Sean Gilbert	.25
26 Richard Dent	.40
27 Rickey Jackson	.25
28 Hardy Nickerson	.25
29 Renaldo Turnbull	.25
30 Deion Sanders	2.00
31 Eric Allen	.25
32 Tim McDonald	.25
33 Mark Carrier (DB)	.25
34 Tim Brown	.75
35 Richmond Webb	.25
36 Keith Sims	.25
37 Bruce Matthews	.25
38 Steve Wisniewski	.25
39 Howard Ballard	.25
40 Shannon Sharpe	.40
41 Anthony Miller	.40
42 John Elway	2.50
43 Thurman Thomas	.75
44 Marcus Allen	.60
45 Andre Rison	.40

46	Drew Bledsoe	.25
47	Willie Roaf	.25
48	Reggie Brooks	.40
49	Dana Stubblefield	.40
50	Rick Mirer	1.25

1995 Stadium Club

Topps released its 1995 Stadium Club issue in two 225-card series. Series I has 180 regular cards of the top NFL players, plus 15 Draft Picks and 30 Extreme Corps subset cards. Series II has two subsets also - Xpansion Team and Draft Pixs. Each regular card front has full-bleed photography and is stamped with textured foil. Regular cards are stamped with gold; subset cards are emblazoned with rainbow and silver foil. Card backs have a second full-bleed photo, biographical data, 1994 and career stats, Skills Ratings and Trench Talk, an assessment of the player's strengths and career highlights. In addition, hobbyists can see the winners of Stadium Club's Extreme Fans contest from 1994. Four different fans can be found on the back of each regular card holding up one of the Skills Ratings cards. Series I inserts include Power Surge, Metalists, Nemeses, and Nightmares (hobby only). Series II inserts include MVPs, Power Surge, Ground Attack and Nightmares II (hobby only.) Also, as a special to Series II jumbo and rack packs, parallel sets have been created for the Draft Pix and Extreme Corps cards. These double foil-stamped (green and gold vs. the regular rainbow and silver) theme cards use diffraction foil and are in every jumbo and rack pack.

		MT
Complete Set (450):		100.00
Comp. Series 1 (225):		60.00
Comp. Series 2 (225):		40.00
Common Player:		.10
Minor Stars:		.20
Series 1 Hobby Box:		30.00
Series 2 Hobby Box:		30.00
Series 1 or 2 Retail Box:		40.00
1	Steve Young	1.00
2	Stan Humphries	.25
3	Chris Boniol	.20
4	Darren Perry	.10
5	Vinny Testaverde	.10
6	Aubrey Beavers	.10
7	DeWayne Washington	.10
8	Marion Butts	.10
9	George Koonce	.10
10	Joe Cain	.10
11	Mike Johnson	.10
12	Dale Carter	.10
13	Greg Biekert	.10
14	Aaron Pierce	.10
15	Aeneas Williams	.10
16	Steve Grant	.10
17	Henry Jones	.10
18	James Williams	.10
19	Andy Harmon	.10
20	Anthony Miller	.10
21	Kevin Ross	.10
22	Erik Howard	.10
23	Brian Blades	.10
24	Trent Dilfer	.50
25	Roman Phifer	.10
26	Bruce Kozerski	.10
27	Henry Ellard	.10
28	Rich Camarillo	.10
29	Richmond Webb	.10
30	George Teague	.10
31	Antonio Langham	.10
32	Barry Minter	.10
33	Bruce Armstrong	.10
34	Tim McDonald	.10
35	James Harris	.10
36	Lomas Brown	.10
37	Jay Novacek	.10
38	John Thierry	.10
39	John Elliott	.10

40	Terry McDaniel	.10
41	Shawn Lee	.10
42	Shane Dronett	.10
43	Cornelius Bennett	.10
44	Steve Bono	.20
45	Byron Evans	.10
46	Eugene Robinson	.10
47	Tony Bennett	.10
48	Michael Bankston	.10
49	William Roaf	.10
50	Bobby Houston	.10
51	Ken Harvey	.10
52	Bruce Matthews	.10
53	Lincoln Kennedy	.10
54	Todd Lyght	.10
55	Paul Gruber	.10
56	Corey Sawyer	.10
57	Myron Guyton	.10
58	John Jackson	.10
59	Sean Jones	.10
60	Pepper Johnson	.10
61	Steve Walsh	.10
62	Corey Miller	.10
63	Fuad Reveiz	.10
64	Rickey Jackson	.10
65	Scott Mitchell	.10
66	Michael Irvin	.30
67	Andre Reed	.10
68	Mark Seay	.10
69	Keith Byars	.10
70	Marcus Allen	.20
71	Shannon Sharpe	.20
72	Eric Hill	.10
73	James Washington	.10
74	Greg Jackson	.10
75	Chris Warren	.20
76	Will Wolford	.10
77	Anthony Smith	.10
78	Cris Dishman	.10
79	Carl Pickens	.10
80	Tyrone Hughes	.10
81	Chris Miller	.10
82	Clay Matthews	.10
83	Lonnie Marts	.10
84	Jerome Henderson	.10
85	Ben Coates	.10
86	Deon Figures	.10
87	Anthony Pleasant	.10
88	Guy McIntyre	.10
89	Jake Reed	.10
90	Rodney Hampton	.20
91	Santana Dotson	.10
92	Jeff Blackshear	.10
93	Willie Clay	.10
94	Nate Newton	.10
95	Bucky Brooks	.10
96	Lamar Lathon	.10
97	Tim Grunhard	.10
98	Harris Barton	.10
99	Brian Mitchell	.10
100	Natrone Means	.75
101	Sean Dawkins	.10
102	Chris Slade	.10
103	Tom Rathman	.10
104	Fred Barnett	.10
105	Gary Brown	.10
106	Leonard Russell	.10
107	Alfred Williams	.10
108	Kelvin Martin	.10
109	Alexander Wright	.10
110	O.J. McDuffie	.10
111	Mario Bates	.40
112	Tony Casillas	.10
113	Michael Timpson	.10
114	Robert Brooks	.10
115	Rob Burnett	.10
116	Mark Collins	.10
117	Chris Calloway	.10
118	Courtney Hawkins	.10
119	Marvcus Patton	.10
120	Greg Lloyd	.10
121	Ryan McNeil	.10
122	Gary Plummer	.10
123	Dwayne Sabb	.10
124	Jessie Hester	.10
125	Terance Mathis	.10
126	Steve Atwater	.10
127	Lorenzo Lynch	.10
128	James Francis	.10
129	John Fina	.10
130	Emmitt Smith	3.00
131	Bryan Cox	.10
132	Robert Blackmon	.10
133	Kenny Davidson	.10
134	Eugene Daniel	.10
135	Vince Buck	.10
136	Leslie O'Neal	.10
137	James Jett	.10
138	Johnny Johnson	.10
139	Michael Zordich	.10
140	Warren Moon	.25
141	William White	.10
142	Carl Banks	.10
143	Marty Carter	.10
144	Keith Hamilton	.10
145	Alvin Harper	.20
146	Corey Harris	.10
147	Elijah Alexander	.25
148	Darrell Green	.10
149	*Yancey Thigpen*	1.50
150	Deion Sanders	.75
151	Burt Grossman	.10
152	J.B. Brown	.10
153	Johnny Bailey	.10
154	Harvey Williams	.10
155	*Jeff Blake*	.50
156	Al Smith	.10
157	Chris Doleman	.10
158	Garrison Hearst	.20
159	Bryce Paup	.10
160	Herman Moore	.20

161	Cortez Kennedy	.10
162	Marquez Pope	.10
163	Quinn Early	.10
164	Broderick Thomas	.10
165	Jeff Herrod	.10
166	Robert Jones	.10
167	Mo Lewis	.10
168	Ray Crittenden	.10
169	Raymont Harris	.20
170	Bruce Smith	.10
171	Dana Stubblefield	.10
172	Charles Haley	.10
173	Charles Johnson	.40
174	Shawn Jefferson	.10
175	Leroy Hoard	.10
176	Bernie Parmalee	.30
177	Scottie Graham	.10
178	Edgar Bennett	.10
179	Aubrey Matthews	.10
180	Don Beebe	.10
181	Eric Swann (Extreme Corps)	.10
182	Jeff George (Extreme Corps)	.20
183	Jim Kelly (Extreme Corps)	.20
184	Sam Mills (Extreme Corps)	.10
185	Mark Carrier (Extreme Corps)	.10
186	Dan Wilkinson (Extreme Corps)	.10
187	Eric Turner (Extreme Corps)	.10
188	Troy Aikman (Extreme Corps)	2.50
189	John Elway (Extreme Corps)	1.00
190	Barry Sanders (Extreme Corps)	2.50
191	Brett Favre (Extreme Corps)	4.00
192	Michael Barrow (Extreme Corps)	.10
193	Marshall Faulk (Extreme Corps)	1.00
194	Steve Beuerlein (Extreme Corps)	.10
195	Neil Smith (Extreme Corps)	.10
196	Jeff Hostetler (Extreme Corps)	.20
197	Jerome Bettis (Extreme Corps)	.75
198	Dan Marino (Extreme Corps)	4.00
199	Cris Carter (Extreme Corps)	.20
200	Drew Bledsoe (Extreme Corps)	2.50
201	Jim Everett (Extreme Corps)	.20
202	Dave Brown (Extreme Corps)	.10
203	Boomer Esiason (Extreme Corps)	.10
204	Randall Cunningham (Extreme Corps)	.20
205	Rod Woodson (Extreme Corps)	.10
206	Junior Seau (Extreme Corps)	.20
207	Jerry Rice (Extreme Corps)	2.50
208	Rick Mirer (Extreme Corps)	1.00
209	Errict Rhett (Extreme Corps)	.30
210	Heath Shuler (Extreme Corps)	.50
211	*Bobby Taylor* (Draft Picks)	.20
212	*Jesse James* (Draft Picks)	.20
213	*Devin Bush* (Draft Picks)	.20
214	*Luther Elliss* (Draft Picks)	.20
215	*Kerry Collins* (Draft Picks)	2.00
216	*Derrick Alexander* (Draft Picks)	.20
217	*Rashaan Salaam* (Draft Picks)	.50
218	*J.J. Stokes* (Draft Picks)	2.00
219	*Todd Collins* (Draft Picks)	.20
220	*Ki-Jana Carter* (Draft Picks)	.50
221	*Kyle Brady* (Draft Picks)	1.00
222	*Kevin Carter* (Draft Picks)	.20
223	*Tony Boselli* (Draft Picks)	.20
224	*Scott Gragg* (Draft Picks)	.20
225	*Warren Sapp* (Draft Picks)	.20

235	Steve Tasker	.10
236	Howard Cross	.10
237	Charles Wilson	.10
238	Rob Fredrickson	.10
239	Russell Maryland	.10
240	Dan Marino	3.00
241	Rafael Robinson	.10
242	Ed McDaniel	.10
243	Brett Perriman	.20
244	Chuck Levy	.10
245	Errict Rhett	1.50
246	Tracy Simien	.10
247	Steve Everitt	.10
248	John Jurkovic	.10
249	Johnny Mitchell	.10
250	Mark Carrier	.10
251	Merton Hanks	.10
252	Joe Johnson	.10
253	Andre Coleman	.10
254	Ray Buchanan	.10
255	Jeff George	.20
256	Shane Conlan	.10
257	Gus Frerotte	.50
258	Doug Pelfrey	.10
259	Glenn Montgomery	.10
260	John Elway	.50
261	Larry Centers	.10
262	Calvin Williams	.10
263	Gene Atkins	.10
264	Tim Brown	.20
265	Leon Lett	.10
266	Martin Mayhew	.10
267	Arthur Marshall	.10
268	Maurice Hurst	.10
269	Greg Hill	.40
270	Junior Seau	.40
271	Rick Mirer	.40
272	Jack Del Rio	.10
273	Lewis Tillman	.10
274	Renaldo Turnbull	.10
275	Dan Footman	.10
276	John Taylor	.10
277	Russell Copeland	.10
278	Tracy Scroggins	.10
279	Lou Benfatti	.10
280	Rod Woodson	.10
281	Troy Drayton	.10
282	Quentin Coryatt	.10
283	Craig Heyward	.10
284	Jeff Cross	.10
285	Hardy Nickerson	.10
286	Dorsey Levens	.75
287	Derek Russell	.10
288	Seth Joyner	.10
289	Kimble Anders	.10
290	Drew Bledsoe	1.00
291	Bryant Young	.10
292	Chris Zorich	.10
293	Michael Strahan	.10
294	Kevin Greene	.10
295	Aaron Glenn	.10
296	Jimmy Spencer	.10
297	Eric Turner	.10
298	William Thomas	.10
299	Dan Wilkinson	.10
300	Troy Aikman	1.00
301	Terry Wooden	.10
302	Heath Shuler	1.00
303	Jeff Burris	.10
304	Mark Stepnoski	.10
305	Chris Mims	.10
306	Todd Steussie	.10
307	Johnnie Morton	.10
308	Darryl Talley	.10
309	Nolan Harrison	.10
310	Dave Brown	.10
311	Brent Jones	.10
312	Curtis Conway	.10
313	Ronald Humphrey	.10
314	Richie Anderson	.10
315	Jim Everett	.10
316	Willie Davis	.10
317	Ed Cunningham	.10
318	Willie McGinest	.10
319	Sean Gilbert	.10
320	Brett Favre	3.00
321	Bennie Thompson	.10
322	Neil O'Donnell	.20
323	Vince Workman	.10
324	Terry Kirby	.10
325	Simon Fletcher	.10
326	Ricardo McDonald	.10
327	Duane Young	.10
328	Jim Harbaugh	.20
329	D.J. Johnson	.10
330	Boomer Esiason	.10
331	Donnell Woolford	.10
332	Mike Sherrard	.10
333	Tyrone Legette	.10
334	Larry Brown	.10
335	William Floyd	.40
336	Reggie Brooks	.10
337	Patrick Bates	.10
338	Jim Jeffcoat	.10
339	Ray Childress	.10
340	Cris Carter	.20
341	Charlie Garner	.10
342	Bill Hitchcock	.10
343	Levon Kirkland	.10
344	Robert Porcher	.10
345	Darryl Williams	.10
346	Vincent Brisby	.10
347	Kenyon Rasheed	.10
348	Floyd Turner	.10
349	Bob Whitefield	.10
350	Jerome Bettis	.40
351	Brad Baxter	.10
352	Darrin Smith	.10
353	Lamar Thomas	.10
354	Lorenzo Neal	.10
355	Erik Kramer	.10

356	Dwayne Harper	.10
357	Doug Evans	.10
358	Jeff Feagles	.10
359	Ray Crockett	.10
360	Neil Smith	.10
361	Troy Vincent	.10
362	Don Griffin	.10
363	Michael Brooks	.10
364	Carlton Gray	.10
365	Thomas Smith	.10
366	Ken Norton	.10
367	Tony McGee	.10
368	Eric Metcalf	.10
369	Mel Gray	.10
370	Barry Sanders	2.50
371	Raghib Ismail	.10
372	Chad Brown	.20
373	Qadry Ismail	.10
374	Anthony Prior	.10
375	Kevin Lee	.10
376	Robert Young	.10
377	Kevin Williams	.10
378	Tydus Winans	.10
379	Ricky Watters	.20
380	Jim Kelly	.20
381	Eric Swann	.10
382	Mike Pritchard	.10
383	Derek Brown	.10
384	Dennis Gibson	.10
385	Byron Morris	.10
386	Reggie White	.20
387	Jeff Graham	.10
388	Marshall Faulk	1.00
389	Joe Phillips	.10
390	Jeff Hostetler	.10
391	Irving Fryar	.10
392	Stevon Moore	.10
393	Bert Emanuel	.40
394	Leon Searcy	.10
395	Robert Smith	.10
396	Michael Bates	.10
397	Thomas Lewis	.10
398	Joe Bowden	.10
399	Steve Tovar	.10
400	Jerry Rice	1.25
401	Toby Wright	.10
402	Daryl Johnston	.10
403	Vincent Brown	.10
404	Marvin Washington	.10
405	Chris Spielman	.10
406	Willie Jackson	.10
407	Harry Boatswain	.10
408	Kelvin Pritchett	.10
409	Dave Widell	.10
410	Frank Reich	.10
411	Corey Mayfield	.10
413	Keith Goganious	.10
414	John Kasay	.10
415	Ernest Givins	.10
416	Randy Baldwin	.10
417	Shawn Bouwens	.10
418	Mike Fox	.10
419	Mark Carrier	.10
420	Steve Beuerlein	.10
421	Steve Lofton	.10
422	Jeff Lageman	.10
423	Paul Butcher	.10
424	Mark Brunell	3.00
425	Vernon Turner	.10
426	Tim McKyer	.10
427	James Williams	.10
428	Tommy Barnhardt	.10
429	Rogerick Green	.10
430	Desmond Howard	.10
431	Darion Conner	.10
432	Reggie Clark	.10
433	Eric Guilford	.10
434	*Rob Johnson*	3.00
435	Sam Mills	.10
436	*Kordell Stewart*	6.00
437	*James Stewart*	3.00
438	*Zach Wiegert*	.10
439	*Ellis Johnson*	.10
440	*Matt O'Dwyer*	.10
441	*Anthony Cook*	.10
442	*Ron Davis*	.10
443	*Chris Hudson*	.10
444	*Hugh Douglas*	.20
445	*Tyrone Poole*	.10
446	*Korey Stringer*	.10
447	*Ruben Brown*	.10
448	*Brian DeMarco*	.10
449	*Michael Westbrook*	1.50
450	*Steve McNair*	5.00

1995 Stadium Club Ground Attack

These 1995 Topps Stadium Club Series II inserts feature 10 of the NFL's best backfield combinations together on one card. Etched foil is used on both sides. Cards are random inserts, one per every 14 retail and one per every 18 hobby packs.

		MT
Complete Set (15):		45.00
Common Player:		1.50
Minor Stars:		3.00
Inserted 1:18 Hobby		
1	Emmitt Smith, Daryl Johnston	10.00
2	Edgar Bennett, Brett Favre	12.00
3	Bernie Parmalee, Irving Spikes	1.50
4	John Elway, Glyn Milburn	10.00
5	Chris Warren, Rick Mirer	1.50
6	Marcus Allen, Greg Hill	3.00
7	Errict Rhett, Vince Workman	3.00
8	Byron Morris, Erric Pegram	1.50
9	Mario Bates, Derek Brown	1.50
10	William Floyd, Steve Young	6.00
11	Charlie Garner, Randall Cunningham	3.00
12	Lewis Tillman, Raymont Harris	1.50
13	Harvey Williams, Jeff Hostetler	1.50
14	Larry Centers, Garrison Hearst	3.00
15	Marshall Faulk, Roosevelt Potts	3.00

1995 Stadium Club Metalists

These cards, Topps' first ever laser-cut cards, feature eight players who have won multiple awards in their distinguished careers. The laser process allows for more precise and detailed cutting on the inside of the cards, giving them a unique look which is patterned after the color photo on the front. "Metalists" is written at the top of the card; the player's name is written along the bottom. The brand logo is also on the card front. The back, numbered using an "M" prefix, has the laser-cut image on one side, flanked by a brief recap of the awards the player won. Cards were seeded one per every 18 retail packs and one per every 24 hobby packs of 1995 Topps Stadium Club Series I product.

		MT
Complete Set (8):		75.00
Common Player:		5.00
1	Jerry Rice	15.00
2	Barry Sanders	15.00
3	John Elway	7.00
4	Dana Stubblefield	5.00
5	Emmitt Smith	25.00
6	Deion Sanders	7.00
7	Marshall Faulk	7.00
8	Steve Young	8.00

226	Ricky Reynolds	.10
227	Roosevelt Potts	.10
228	Jessie Tuggle	.10
229	Anthony Newman	.10
230	Randall Cunningham	.20
231	Jason Elam	.10
232	Darnay Scott	.50
233	Tom Carter	.10
234	Michael Barrow	.10

1995 Stadium Club MVPs

These eight cards celebrate the achievements of several players who have become the best of the best in the NFL while on their way to the Hall of Fame. The cards, seeded one per every 18 retail and one per every 24 hobby packs of 1995 Topps Stadium Club Series II product, are laser cut and highlight gold foil stamping on chromium stock. The player's name is laser cut along the left side of the card. Foil stamping is used for the MVP logo at the bottom of the card.

	MT
Complete Set (8):	40.00
Common Player:	2.00
1 Jerry Rice	5.00
2 Boomer Esiason	2.00
3 Randall Cunningham	2.00
4 Marcus Allen	2.00
5 John Elway	4.00
6 Dan Marino	10.00
7 Emmitt Smith	10.00
8 Steve Young	4.00

1995 Stadium Club Nemeses

Fifteen cards highlighting football's top rivalries make up this 1995 Topps Stadium Club Series I insert set. Complete with etched foil on both sides, the cards match up two players who are known for their classic confrontations, one on each side. Nemeses is written at the top of the card; the player's name, position and team helmet are at the bottom. The cards were seeded one per every 24th pack.

	MT
Complete Set (15):	130.00
Common Player:	5.00
1 Barry Sanders, Jack Del Rio	15.00
2 Reggie White, Lomas Brown	5.00
3 Terry McDaniel, Anthony Miller	5.00
4 Brett Favre, Chris Spielman	25.00
5 Junior Seau, Chris Warren	5.00
6 Cortez Kennedy, Steve Wisniewski	5.00
7 Rod Woodson, Tim Brown	5.00
8 Troy Aikman, Michael Brooks	15.00
9 Bruce Smith, Bruce Armstrong	5.00
10 Jerry Rice, Donnell Woolford	15.00
11 Emmitt Smith, Seth Joyner	25.00

12 Dan Marino, Cornelius Bennett	25.00
13 Marshall Faulk, Bryan Cox	8.00
14 Stan Humphries, Greg Lloyd	5.00
15 Michael Irvin, Deion Sanders	5.00

1995 Stadium Club Nightmares

This 30-card series was released as two 15-card insert sets; cards 1-15 were in 1995 Topps Stadium Club Series I hobby packs only (1 in 24), while 16-30 were in Series II hobby packs (1 in 18). "Biting" commentary on each player is provided by Vampirella, Topps' original "bad girl" comic character, who describes how the player terrorizes his opponents. The Series II Nightmare cards, which premiere artwork from the "Vampirella Gallery" release, feature a new etched foil design.

	MT
Complete Set (30):	200.00
Comp. Series 1 (15):	130.00
Comp. Series 2 (15):	70.00
Common Player:	4.00
1 Drew Bledsoe	15.00
2 Barry Sanders	15.00
3 Reggie White	4.00
4 Michael Irvin	4.00
5 Jerry Rice	15.00
6 Jerome Bettis	4.00
7 Dan Marino	25.00
8 Bruce Smith	4.00
9 Steve Young	15.00
10 Junior Seau	4.00
11 Emmitt Smith	25.00
12 Deion Sanders	10.00
13 Rod Woodson	4.00
14 Marshall Faulk	7.00
15 Troy Aikman	15.00
16 Stan Humphries	4.00
17 Chris Warren	4.00
18 Jack Del Rio	4.00
19 Randall Cunningham	4.00
20 Natrone Means	4.00
21 Dana Stubblefield	4.00
22 Jim Kelly	4.00
23 Cris Carter	4.00
24 Cornelius Bennett	4.00
25 Errict Rhett	10.00
26 Terry McDaniel	4.00
27 Rodney Hampton	4.00
28 Brett Favre	25.00
29 Bryan Cox	4.00
30 John Elway	10.00

1995 Stadium Club Power Surge

These 12 cards feature Topps' foil technology called Power Matrix. The cards, random inserts in 1995 Topps Stadium Club Series I packs, showcase the NFL's best players when the game is on the line. Cards were inserted one per every 18 packs.

	MT
Complete Set (24):	125.00
Comp. Series 1 (12):	75.00
Comp. Series 2 (12):	50.00
Common Player:	4.00
P1 Steve Young	10.00
P2 Natrone Means	8.00
P3 Cris Carter	4.00
P4 Junior Seau	6.00
P5 Barry Sanders	15.00
P6 Michael Irvin	6.00
P7 John Elway	8.00
P8 Emmitt Smith	20.00
P9 Greg Lloyd	4.00
P10 Jerry Rice	13.00
P11 Marshall Faulk	6.00
P12 Drew Bledsoe	10.00
PS1 Dan Marino	20.00
PS2 Ken Harvey	4.00
PS3 Chris Warren	6.00
PS4 Henry Ellard	4.00
PS5 Marshall Faulk	6.00
PS6 Irving Fryar	4.00
PS7 Kevin Ross	4.00
PS8 Vince Workman	4.00
PS9 Ray Buchanan	4.00
PS10 Tony Martin	4.00
PS11 D.J. Johnson	4.00
PS12 Steve Young	10.00

1995 Stadium Club Members Only

The 550-card, standard-size set was a parallel issue to the base 1995 Stadium Club issue and was released in two, 275-card series, available only through the Members Only Club. Just 2,000 sets were produced and were available for $99.95 for each series in a factory box that also included parallels of each insert. The cards are differentiated with the base cards by a gold-foil Members Only stamp. Each complete set order also came with three-pin set and a replica game ticket of the 1995 Pro Football Hall of Fame game between Jacksonville and Carolina.

	MT
Complete Set (550):	300.00
Common Player (1-450):	.20
Common Player (GA1-GA15):	.35
Common Player (ME1-ME8):	35.00
Common Player (MV1-MV8):	.35
Common Player (NE1-NE15):	.35
Common Player (NM1-NM30):	.35
Common Player (P1-P12/ PS1-PS12):	.35
P1 Steve Young	3.00
P2 Natrone Means	.50
P3 Cris Carter	.50
P4 Junior Seau	.50
P5 Barry Sanders	4.00
P6 Michael Irvin	1.00
P7 John Elway	2.50
P8 Emmitt Smith	8.00
P9 Greg Lloyd	.35
P10 Jerry Rice	4.00
P11 Marshall Faulk	3.00
P12 Drew Bledsoe	3.00
GA1 Emmitt Smith	8.00
GA2 Brett Favre	4.00
GA4 John Elway	2.50
GA5 Rick Mirer	.50
GA6 Greg Hill	.50
GA7 Errict Rhett	3.00
GA8 Byron "Bam" Morris	.35
GA9 Derek Brown (RB)	.35
GA10 Steve Young	3.00
GA11 Charlie Garner	.35
GA12 Lewis Tillman	.35
GA13 Harvey Williams	.35
GA14 Garrison Hearst	.75
GA15 Marshall Faulk	3.00
ME1 Jerry Rice	4.00
ME2 Jerry Rice	4.00
ME3 John Elway	2.50
ME4 Dana Stubblefield	.35
ME5 Emmitt Smith	8.00
ME6 Deion Sanders	2.50
ME7 Marshall Faulk	3.00
ME8 Steve Young	3.00
MV1 Jerry Rice	4.00
MV2 Boomer Esiason	.35
MV3 Randall Cunningham	.35
MV4 Marcus Allen	.50
MV5 John Elway	2.50
MV6 Dan Marino	8.00
MV7 Emmitt Smith	8.00
MV8 Steve Young	3.00
NE1 Barry Sanders, Jack Del Rio	4.00
NE2 Reggie White, Lomas Brown	.50

NE3 Terry McDaniel, Anthony Miller	.35
NE4 Brett Favre, Chris Spielman	4.00
NE5 Junior Seau, Chris Warren	.50
NE6 Cortez Kennedy, Steve Wisniewski	.35
NE7 Rod Woodson	.50
NE8 Troy Aikman, Michael Brooks	4.00
NE9 Bruce Smith, Bruce Armstrong	.50
NE10 Jerry Rice, Donnell Woolford	4.00
NE11 Emmitt Smith, Seth Joyner	8.00
NE12 Dan Marino, Cornelius Bennett	8.00
NE13 Marshall Faulk, Bryan Cox	3.00
NE14 Stan Humphries, Greg Lloyd	.50
NE15 Michael Irvin, Deion Sanders	.75
NM1 Drew Bledsoe	3.00
NM2 Barry Sanders	4.00
NM3 Reggie White	.50
NM4 Michael Irvin	1.00
NM5 Jerry Rice	.50
NM6 Jerome Bettis	.50
NM7 Dan Marino	8.00
NM8 Bruce Smith	.35
NM9 Steve Young	3.00
NM10 Junior Seau	.50
NM11 Emmitt Smith	8.00
NM12 Deion Sanders	2.50
NM13 Rod Woodson	3.00
NM14 Marshall Faulk	3.00
NM15 Troy Aikman	4.00
NM16 Stan Humphries	.50
NM17 Chris Warren	.50
NM18 Jack Del Rio	.35
NM19 Randall Cunningham	.35
NM20 Natrone Means	.50
NM21 Dana Stubblefield	.35
NM22 Jim Kelly	.50
NM23 Cris Carter	.50
NM24 Cornelius Bennett	.35
NM25 Errict Rhett	3.00
NM26 Terry McDaniel	.35
NM27 Rodney Hampton	.50
NM28 Brett Favre	4.00
NM29 Bryan Cox	.35
NM30 John Elway	2.50
PS1 Dan Marino	8.00
PS2 Ken Harvey	.35
PS3 Chris Warren	.50
PS4 Henry Ellard	.35
PS5 Marshall Faulk	3.00
PS6 Irving Fryar	.35
PS7 Kevin Ross	.35
PS8 Vince Workman	.35
PS9 Ray Buchanan	.35
PS10 Tony Martin	.50
PS11 D.J. Johnson	.35
PS12 Steve Young	3.00

1995 Stadium Club Members Only 50

The 50-card, standard-size boxed set featured the 44 starting players from the 1995 Pro Bowl and five Finest cards of the top rookies from the 1994 class. The remaining card was of Jerry Rice and Emmitt Smith who were elected to start in the Pro Bowl, but missed it due to injuries. The set was available to Members Only club members.

	MT
Complete Set (50):	20.00
Common Player:	.25
1 Tim Brown	.40
2 Richmond Webb	.25
3 Keith Sims	.25
4 Dermontti Dawson	.25
5 Duval Love	.25
6 Bruce Armstrong	.25
7 Ben Coates	.40
8 Andre Reed	.40
9 John Elway	.25
10 Marshall Faulk	.40
11 Natrone Means	.40
12 Charles Haley	.25
13 John Randle	.25
14 Leon Lett	.25
15 William Fuller	.25
16 Ken Harvey	.25
17 Chris Spielman	.25
18 Bryce Paup	.40
19 Deion Sanders	1.50
20 Aeneas Williams	.25
21 Darren Woodson	.25
22 Merton Hanks	.25
23 Michael Irvin	.75
24 William Roaf	.25
25 Nate Newton	.25
26 Mark Stepnoski	.25
27 Randall McDaniel	.25

28 Lomas Brown	.25
29 Brent Jones	.40
30 Cris Carter	.40
31 Steve Young	2.00
32 Barry Sanders	4.00
33 Jerome Bettis	.75
34 Bruce Smith	.40
35 Michael Dean Perry	.25
36 Cortez Kennedy	.40
37 Leslie O'Neal	.40
38 Derrick Thomas	.40
39 Junior Seau	.75
40 Greg Lloyd	.40
41 Rod Woodson	.40
42 Terry McDaniel	.25
43 Eric Turner	.25
44 Carnell Lake	.25
45 Jerry Rice, Emmitt Smith	6.00
46 William Floyd	1.00
47 Tim Bowens	.40
48 Heath Shuler	1.50
49 Bryant Young	.75
50 Marshall Faulk	2.50

1996 Stadium Club

Topps' 1996 Stadium Club football has 180 cards in its initial series. Insert sets include Contact Prints, Dot Matrix Parallel, Pro Bowl Embossed, Laser Sites, Cut Backs, and three versions of Extreme Player cards (bronze, silver and gold). Series II also has 180 cards in it, featuring 45 of the league's top rookies and traded players in their new uniforms. All regular cards in both series have etched gold foil and are UV coated. Series II inserts include Photo Gallery, New Age, TSC Matrix Parallel, NFL Playoff Box, Fusion Laser Cut (hobby exclusive) and Brace Yourself (retail only). Interactive game cards (Sunday Night Box, in Series I, and NFL Playoff Box, in Series II) were seeded in packs (one in 12 and 1 in 24 packs, respectively). Those who find the cards were eligible to win prizes based on the final scores of selected games.

	MT
Complete Set (360):	80.00
Complete Series 1 (180):	40.00
Complete Series 2 (180):	40.00
Common Player:	.10
Minor Stars:	.20
Wax Box Series 1:	50.00
Wax Box Series 2:	50.00
1 Kyle Brady (TSC Matrix Parallel Set)	.10
2 Mickey Washington	.10
3 Seth Joyner	.10
4 Vinny Testaverde	.10
5 Thomas Randolph	.10
6 Heath Shuler (TSC Matrix Parallel Set)	.20
7 Ty Law	.10
8 Blake Brockermeyer	.10
9 Darryll Lewis	.10
10 Jeff Blake (TSC Matrix Parallel Set)	.75
11 Tyrone Hughes (TSC Matrix Parallel Set)	.10
12 Horace Copeland	.10
13 Roman Phifer	.10
14 Eugene Robinson	.10
15 Anthony Miller (TSC Matrix Parallel Set)	.10
16 Robert Smith	.10
17 Chester McGlockton	.10
18 Marty Carter	.10
19 Scott Mitchell (TSC Matrix Parallel Set)	.10
20 O.J. McDuffie	.10
21 Stan Humphries (TSC Matrix Parallel Set)	.10

22 Eugene Daniel	.10
23 Devin Bush	.10
24 Darick Holmes	.10
25 Ricky Watters (TSC Matrix Parallel Set)	.10
26 J.J. Stokes (TSC Matrix Parallel Set)	.20
27 George Koonce	.10
28 Tamarick Vanover (TSC Matrix Parallel Set)	.75
29 Yancey Thigpen (TSC Matrix Parallel Set)	.50
30 Troy Aikman (TSC Matrix Parallel Set)	1.25
31 Rashaan Salaam (TSC Matrix Parallel Set)	.50
32 Anthony Cook	.10
33 Tim McKyer	.10
34 Dale Carter	.10
35 Marvin Washington	.10
36 Terry Allen	.10
37 Keith Goganious	.10
38 Pepper Johnson	.10
39 Dave Brown	.10
40 Levon Kirkland	.10
41 Ken Dilger	.10
42 Harvey Williams (TSC Matrix Parallel Set)	.10
43 Robert Blackmon	.10
44 Kevin Carter	.10
45 Warren Moon (TSC Matrix Parallel Set)	.10
46 Allen Aldridge	.10
47 Terance Mathis (TSC Matrix Parallel Set)	.10
48 Junior Seau (TSC Matrix Parallel Set)	.10
49 William Fuller	.10
50 Lee Woodall (TSC Matrix Parallel Set)	.10
51 Aeneas Williams (TSC Matrix Parallel Set)	.10
52 Thomas Smith	.10
53 Chris Slade	.10
54 Eric Allen (TSC Matrix Parallel Set)	.10
55 David Sloan	.10
56 Hardy Nickerson	.10
57 Michael Irvin (TSC Matrix Parallel Set)	.20
58 Corey Sawyer	.10
59 Eric Green	.10
60 Reggie White (TSC Matrix Parallel Set)	.10
61 Isaac Bruce (TSC Matrix Parallel Set)	.75
62 Darrell Green	.10
63 Aaron Glenn	.10
64 Mark Brunell (TSC Matrix Parallel Set)	1.00
65 Mark Carrier	.10
66 Mel Gray	.10
67 Phillippi Sparks	.10
68 Ernie Mills	.10
69 Rick Mirer (TSC Matrix Parallel Set)	.10
70 Neil Smith (TSC Matrix Parallel Set)	.10
71 Terry McDaniel	.10
72 Terrell Davis (TSC Matrix Parallel Set)	2.00
73 Alonzo Spellman	.10
74 Jessie Tuggle	.10
75 Terry Kirby	.10
76 David Palmer	.10
77 Calvin Williams	.10
78 Shaun Gayle	.10
79 Bryant Young	.10
80 Jim Harbaugh (TSC Matrix Parallel Set)	.10
81 Michael Jackson (TSC Matrix Parallel Set)	.10
82 David Meggett (TSC Matrix Parallel Set)	.10
83 Henry Thomas	.10
84 Jim Kelly (TSC Matrix Parallel Set)	.10
85 Frank Sanders (TSC Matrix Parallel Set)	.10
86 Daryl Johnston	.10
87 Alvin Harper	.10
88 John Copeland	.10
89 Mark Chmura (TSC Matrix Parallel Set)	.25
90 Jim Everett (TSC Matrix Parallel Set)	.10
91 Bobby Houston	.10
92 Willie Jackson	.10
93 Carlton Bailey	.10
94 Todd Lyght	.10
95 Ken Harvey	.10
96 Erric Pegram	.10
97 Anthony Smith	.10
98 Kimble Anders	.10
99 Steve McNair (TSC Matrix Parallel Set)	.75
100 Jeff George (TSC Matrix Parallel Set)	.20
101 Michael Timpson	.10

102	Brent Jones	.10
103	Mike Mamula	.10
104	Jeff Cross	.10
105	Craig Newsome	.10
106	Howard Cross	.10
107	Terry Wooden	.10
108	Randall McDaniel	.10
109	Andre Reed	.10
110	Steve Atwater	.10
111	Larry Centers	.10
112	Tony Bennett	.10
113	Drew Bledsoe (TSC Matrix Parallel Set)	1.25
114	Terrell Fletcher	.10
115	Warren Sapp	.10
116	Deion Sanders (TSC Matrix Parallel Set)	.75
117	Bryce Paup (TSC Matrix Parallel Set)	.10
118	Mario Bates	.10
119	Steve Tovar	.10
120	Barry Sanders (TSC Matrix Parallel Set)	2.00
121	Tony Boselli	.10
122	Michael Barrow	.10
123	Sam Mills (TSC Matrix Parallel Set)	.10
124	Tim Brown (TSC Matrix Parallel Set)	.10
125	Darren Perry	.10
126	Brian Blades	.10
127	Tyrone Wheatley	.10
128	Derrick Thomas (TSC Matrix Parallel Set)	.10
129	Edgar Bennett	.10
130	Cris Carter (TSC Matrix Parallel Set)	.10
131	Steve Grant	.10
132	Kevin Williams	.10
133	Darnay Scott	.20
134	Rod Stephens	.10
135	Ken Norton (TSC Matrix Parallel Set)	.10
136	Tim Biakabutuka (Draft Pick)	1.00
137	Willie Anderson (Draft Pick)	.10
138	Lawrence Phillips (Draft Pick)	.75
139	Jonathan Ogden (Draft Pick)	.10
140	Simeon Rice (Draft Pick)	.25
141	Alex Van Dyke (Draft Pick)	.20
142	Jerome Woods (Draft Pick)	.10
143	Eric Moulds (Draft Pick)	2.00
144	Mike Alstott (Draft Pick)	1.50
145	Marvin Harrison (Draft Pick)	3.00
146	Duane Clemons (Draft Pick)	.10
147	Regan Upshaw (Draft Pick)	.10
148	Eddie Kennison (Draft Pick)	.50
149	John Mobley (Draft Pick)	.10
150	Keyshawn Johnson (Draft Pick)	2.50
151	Marco Battaglia (Draft Pick)	.10
152	Rickey Dudley (Draft Pick)	.50
153	Kevin Hardy (Draft Pick)	.20
154	Curtis Martin (Shining Moments)	2.00
155	Dan Marino (Shining Moments)	2.00
156	Rashaan Salaam (Shining Moments)	.50
157	Joey Galloway (Shining Moments)	.75
158	John Elway (Shining Moments)	.40
159	Marshall Faulk (Shining Moments)	.50
160	Jerry Rice (Shining Moments)	1.00
161	Darren Bennett (Shining Moments)	.10
162	Tamarick Vanover (Shining Moments)	.50
163	Orlando Thomas (Shining Moments)	.10
164	Jim Kelly (Shining Moments)	.10
165	Larry Brown (Shining Moments)	.10
166	Errict Rhett (Shining Moments)	.40
167	Warren Moon (Shining Moments)	.10
168	Hugh Douglas (Shining Moments)	.10
169	Jim Everett (Shining Moments)	.10
170	AFC Championship Game (Shining Moments)	.10

171	Larry Centers (Shining Moments)	.10
172	Marcus Allen (Golden Moments)	.10
173	Morten Andersen (Golden Moments)	.10
174	Brett Favre (Golden Moments)	2.00
175	Jerry Rice (Golden Moments)	.75
176	Glyn Milburn (Golden Moments)	.10
177	Thurman Thomas (Golden Moments)	.10
178	Michael Irvin (Golden Moments)	.10
179	Barry Sanders (Golden Moments)	2.00
180	Dan Marino (Golden Moments)	2.00
181	Joey Galloway	1.00
182	Dwayne Harper	.10
183	Antonio Langham	.10
184	Chris Zorich	.10
185	Willie McGinest	.10
186	Wayne Chrebet	.10
187	Dermontti Dawson	.10
188	Charlie Garner	.10
189	Quentin Coryatt	.10
190	Rodney Hampton	.10
191	Kelvin Pritchett	.10
192	Willie Green	.10
193	Garrison Hearst	.10
194	Tracy Scroggins	.10
195	Raghib Ismail	.10
196	Michael Westbrook	.30
197	Troy Drayton	.10
198	Rob Fredrickson	.10
199	Sean Lumpkin	.10
200	John Elway	.75
201	Bernie Parmalee	.10
202	Chris Chandler	.10
203	Lake Dawson	.10
204	Orlando Thomas	.10
205	Carl Pickens	.20
206	Kurt Schulz	.10
207	Clay Matthews	.10
208	Winston Moss	.10
209	Sean Dawkins	.10
210	Emmitt Smith	2.50
211	Mark Carrier	.10
212	Clyde Simmons	.10
213	Derrick Brooks	.10
214	William Floyd	.20
215	Aaron Hayden	.10
216	Brian DeMarco	.10
217	Ben Coates	.10
218	Renaldo Turnbull	.10
219	Adrian Murrell	.10
220	Marcus Allen	.20
221	Brett Maxie	.10
222	Trev Alberts	.10
223	Darren Woodson	.10
224	Brian Mitchell	.10
225	Michael Haynes	.10
226	Sean Jones	.10
227	Eric Zeier	.10
228	Herman Moore	.30
229	Shane Conlan	.10
230	Chris Warren	.20
231	Dana Stubblefield	.10
232	Andre Coleman	.10
233	Kordell Stewart	1.25
234	Ray Crockett	.10
235	Craig Heyward	.10
236	Mike Fox	.10
237	Derek Brown	.10
238	Thomas Lewis	.10
239	Hugh Douglas	.10
240	Tom Carter	.10
241	Toby Wright	.10
242	Jason Belser	.10
243	Rodney Peete	.10
244	Napoleon Kaufman	.10
245	Merton Hanks	.10
246	Harry Colon	.10
247	Greg Hill	.10
248	Vincent Brisby	.10
249	Eric Hill	.10
250	Brett Favre	2.50
251	Leroy Hoard	.10
252	Eric Guliford	.10
253	Stanley Richard	.10
254	Carlos Jenkins	.10
255	D'Marco Farr	.10
256	Carlton Gray	.10
257	Derek Loville	.10
258	Ray Buchanan	.10
259	Jake Reed	.10
260	Dan Marino	2.50
261	Brad Baxter	.10
262	Pat Swilling	.10
263	Andy Harmon	.10
264	Harold Green	.10
265	Shannon Sharpe	.10
266	Erik Kramer	.10
267	Lamar Lathon	.10
268	Stevon Moore	.10
269	Tony Martin	.10
270	Bruce Smith	.10
271	James Washington	.10
272	Tyrone Poole	.10
273	Eric Swann	.10
274	Dexter Carter	.10
275	Greg Lloyd	.10
276	Michael Zordich	.10
277	Steve Wisniewski	.10
278	Chris Calloway	.10

279	Irv Smith	.10
280	Steve Young	1.00
281	James Stewart	.10
282	Blaine Bishop	.10
283	Rob Moore	.10
284	Eric Metcalf	.10
285	Kerry Collins	.30
286	Dan Wilkinson	.10
287	Curtis Conway	.10
288	Jay Novacek	.10
289	Henry Ellard	.10
290	Curtis Martin	2.00
291	Brett Perriman	.10
292	Jeff Lageman	.10
293	Trent Dilfer	.10
294	Cortez Kennedy	.10
295	Jeff Hostetler	.10
296	Mark Fields	.10
297	Qadry Ismail	.10
298	Steve Bono	.10
299	Tony Tolbert	.10
300	Jerry Rice	1.25
301	Marvcus Patton	.10
302	Robert Brooks	.20
303	Terry Ray	.10
304	John Thierry	.10
305	Errict Rhett	.30
306	Ricardo McDonald	.10
307	Antonio London	.10
308	Lonnie Johnson	.10
309	Mark Collins	.10
310	Marshall Faulk	.50
311	Anthony Pleasant	.10
312	Howard Griffith	.10
313	Roosevelt Potts	.10
314	Jim Flanigan	.10
315	'Omar Ellison	.10
316	Boomer Esiason	.10
317	Leslie O'Neal	.10
318	Jerome Bettis	.20
319	Larry Brown	.10
320	Neil O'Donnell	.10
321	Andre Rison	.10
322	Cornelius Bennett	.10
323	Quinn Early	.10
324	Bryan Cox	.10
325	Irving Fryar	.10
326	Eddie Robinson	.10
327	Chris Doleman	.10
328	Sean Gilbert	.10
329	Steve Walsh	.10
330	Kevin Greene	.10
331	Chris Spielman	.10
332	Jeff Graham	.10
333	Anthony Dorsett Jr.	.10
334	Amani Toomer	.50
335	Walt Harris	.20
336	Ray Mickens	.10
337	Danny Kanell	.50
338	Daryl Gardener	.10
339	Jonathan Ogden	.10
340	Eddie George	5.00
341	Jeff Lewis	.75
342	Terrell Owens	5.00
343	Brian Dawkins	.10
344	Tim Biakabutuka	.50
345	Marvin Harrison	1.50
346	Lawyer Milloy	.10
347	Eric Moulds	1.00
348	Alex Van Dyke	.20
349	John Mobley	.10
350	Kevin Hardy	.10
351	Ray Lewis	.10
352	Lawrence Phillips	.30
353	Stepfret Williams	.10
354	Bobby Engram	.50
355	Leeland McElroy	.30
356	Marco Battaglia	.10
357	Rickey Dudley	.20
358	Bobby Hoying	1.00
359	Cedric Jones	.10
360	Keyshawn Johnson	1.00

per every 12 packs in the corresponding series. The TSC logo is on the card front.

		MT
Complete Set (90):		85.00
Common Player:		1.00
1	Kyle Brady	1.00
6	Heath Shuler	1.00
10	Jeff Blake	6.00
11	Tyrone Hughes	1.00
15	Anthony Miller	1.00
19	Scott Mitchell	1.00
21	Stan Humphries	1.00
25	Ricky Watters	1.00
26	J.J. Stokes	6.00
28	Tamarick Vanover	7.00
29	Yancey Thigpen	5.00
30	Troy Aikman	12.00
31	Rashaan Salaam	5.00
42	Harvey Williams	1.00
45	Warren Moon	1.00
47	Terance Mathis	1.00
48	Junior Seau	1.00
50	Lee Woodall	1.00
51	Aeneas Williams	1.00
54	Eric Allen	1.00
57	Michael Irvin	2.00
60	Reggie White	3.00
61	Isaac Bruce	5.00
64	Mark Brunell	5.00
69	Rick Mirer	2.00
70	Neil Smith	1.00
72	Terrell Davis	15.00
80	Jim Harbaugh	1.00
81	Michael Jackson	1.00
82	David Meggett	1.00
84	Jim Kelly	2.00
85	Frank Sanders	1.00
89	Mark Chmura	1.00
90	Jim Everett	1.00
99	Steve McNair	10.00
100	Jeff George	1.00
113	Drew Bledsoe	10.00
116	Deion Sanders	10.00
117	Bryce Paup	1.00
120	Barry Sanders	20.00
123	Sam Mills	1.00
124	Tim Brown	1.00
128	Derrick Thomas	1.00
130	Cris Carter	1.00
135	Ken Norton	1.00
181	Joey Galloway	10.00
182	Chris Zorich	1.00
185	Willie McGinest	1.00
186	Wayne Chrebet	1.00
190	Rodney Hampton	1.00
196	Michael Westbrook	5.00
200	John Elway	10.00
204	Orlando Thomas	1.00
205	Carl Pickens	1.00
210	Emmitt Smith	25.00
213	Derrick Brooks	1.00
217	Ben Coates	1.00
220	Marcus Allen	2.00
224	Brian Mitchell	1.00
227	Eric Zeier	1.00
228	Herman Moore	4.00
230	Chris Warren	1.00
233	Kordell Stewart	12.00
235	Craig Heyward	1.00
239	Hugh Douglas	1.00
240	Tom Carter	1.00
243	Rodney Peete	1.00
244	Napoleon Kaufman	1.00
250	Brett Favre	25.00
260	Dan Marino	25.00
265	Shannon Sharpe	1.00
266	Erik Kramer	1.00
267	Lamar Lathon	1.00
270	Bruce Smith	1.00
275	Greg Lloyd	1.00
280	Steve Young	10.00
282	Blaine Bishop	1.00
284	Eric Metcalf	1.00
285	Kerry Collins	15.00
286	Dan Wilkinson	1.00
287	Curtis Conway	1.00
288	Jay Novacek	1.00
290	Curtis Martin	20.00
293	Trent Dilfer	1.00
295	Jeff Hostetler	1.00
298	Steve Bono	1.00
300	Jerry Rice	12.00
302	Robert Brooks	2.00
305	Errict Rhett	3.00
310	Marshall Faulk	5.00

1996 Stadium Club Dot Matrix

Ninety of the cards from Topps' 1996 Stadium Club set have been duplicated for a parallel insert set. Forty-five cards from Series I have been selected, using dot matrix foil for the design. There were also 45 Series II cards chosen; these cards also have holographic foil in the design. Cards were seeded one

1996 Stadium Club Brace Yourself

These cards are Stadium Club's retail-only inserts in Series II. Each card features a gridiron great on an embossed, holographic foil card. The front has a photo in the middle, with a bull's-eye as the background. The TSC logo is in the upper right corner; the player's name is in the lower left corner. "Brace Yourself" is written along the right side. The card back repeats the bull's-eye pattern as the background, with the player's name, team name, position and card number (using a "BY" prefix) toward the top. The middle of the card comments about the player's talents. Cards were seeded one per every 24 packs.

		MT
Complete Set (10):		125.00
Common Player:		3.00
1	Dan Marino	30.00
2	Marshall Faulk	10.00
3	Greg Lloyd	3.00
4	Steve Young	20.00
5	Emmitt Smith	30.00
6	Junior Seau	3.00
7	Chris Warren	3.00
8	Jerry Rice	20.00
9	Troy Aikman	20.00
10	Barry Sanders	20.00

1996 Stadium Club Contact Prints

These 10 cards were included in 1996 Topps Stadium Club Series I packs, one per every 12 packs. The cards feature a bone-jarring hit on the front in color, against a contact sheet which shows several smaller black-and-white prints of cards from the set as the background. "Contact Print" is in red foil along the left side of the card; "Takedown" is in blue foil along the bottom. The TSC logo is stamped in the upper right corner of the horizontally-designed front. The horizontal back has a closeup photo of one of the players featured on the front, along with an extended cut-line on the right side about the photo on the front. The name of the featured player is in white letters at the top; the name of the player being hit is in smaller white letters next to it. "Takedown" is written along the bottom of the card, with a card number (using a "CP" prefix) next to it.

	MT
Complete Set (10):	20.00
Common Player:	2.00

1996 Stadium Club Match Proofs

Match Proofs are a parallel set that runs through all 270 cards from Series I and II. This parallel set features identical fronts, but has different backs. Production of Match Proofs was limited to only 100 sets.

	MT
Proof Cards:	20x-40x

1996 Stadium Club Cut Backs

These eight cards were randomly included in 1996 Topps Stadium Club Series I hobby packs only, one per every 36 packs. Speedster running backs such as Curtis Martin and Barry Sanders are featured on these precisely-cut laser designed cards.

		MT
Complete Set (8):		60.00
Common Player:		3.00
1	Emmitt Smith	25.00
2	Barry Sanders	18.00
3	Curtis Martin	18.00
4	Chris Warren	5.00
5	Errict Rhett	10.00
6	Rodney Hampton	3.00
7	Ricky Watters	3.00
8	Terry Allen	3.00

1996 Stadium Club Fusion

These cards were found exclusively in 1996 Topps Stadium Club Series II packs, one per every 24 packs. Cards, which are laser cut along one side, are intended to be "fused" together to match up a pair of teammates, forming a larger image. Eight different dynamic duos are spotlighted in this set.

		MT
Complete Set (16):		135.00
Common Player:		4.00
1A	Steve Young	16.00
1B	Jerry Rice	20.00
2A	Drew Bledsoe	20.00
2B	Curtis Martin	25.00
3A	Trent Dilfer	4.00
3B	Errict Rhett	8.00
4A	Jeff Hostetler	4.00
4B	Tim Brown	4.00
5A	Brett Favre	30.00
5B	Robert Brooks	4.00
6A	Jim Harbaugh	4.00
6B	Marshall Faulk	10.00
7A	Erik Kramer	4.00
7B	Rashaan Salaam	8.00
8A	Scott Mitchell	4.00
8B	Barry Sanders	25.00

A card number in parentheses ( ) indicates the set is unnumbered.

1	Ken Norton	2.00
2	Chris Zorich	2.00
3	Corey Harris	2.00
4	Sam Mills	2.00
5	Bryce Paup	2.00
6	Rob Fredrickson	2.00
7	Darnell Walker	2.00
8	Derrick Thomas	2.00
9	Hardy Nickerson	2.00
10	Reggie White	3.00

1996 Stadium Club Laser Sites

These eight cards were inserted one per every 36 hobby packs of 1996 Topps Stadium Club Series I football. Each card has an intricate laser cut design, polished off with diffraction foil stamping. Eight top quarterbacks were selected for the set.

		MT
Complete Set (8):		70.00
Common Player:		3.00
1	Brett Favre	25.00
2	Dan Marino	25.00
3	Steve Young	13.00
4	Troy Aikman	13.00
5	Jim Harbaugh	3.00
6	Scott Mitchell	3.00
7	Erik Kramer	3.00
8	Warren Moon	3.00

1996 Stadium Club Namath Finest

Following on the heels of the Joe Namath reprints in 1996 Topps packs, Finest and Finest Refractor versions of these 10 cards were included in 1996 Topps Stadium Club Series I packs. Finest cards were seeded one per every 24 packs; Refractor versions were one per every 96 packs. Cards are labeled on the back as being part of a reprint set, with a number (1 of 10, etc.) also included. The Refractors are also labeled on the back as being such.

		MT
Complete Set (10):		100.00
Common Player:		10.00
1	1965	15.00
2	1966	10.00
3	1967	10.00
4	1968	10.00
5	1969	10.00
6	1970	10.00
7	1971	10.00
8	1972	10.00
9	1972	10.00
10	1973	10.00

1996 Stadium Club Namath Finest Refractors

This 10-card insert is a parallel to the Finest Namath Reprints, with Refractor versions seeded every 96 packs. Namath Reprints first appeared in Topps Football and were then reprinted in Finest technology for Stadium Club Series I packs. The insert showcases some of

Namath's top cards throughout his career.

	MT
Complete Set (10):	300.00
Refractors:	3x

1996 Stadium Club New Age

These cards were seeded one per every 24 packs of 1996 Topps Stadium Club Series II product. Twenty 1996 NFL draft picks and first-year rookies are spotlighted on the cards, which use etched dot matrix technology for the front. The front also has a color photo in the middle with a frame around it. A team logo is in the upper left corner of the frame. A TSC logo is at the top of the card; the player's name is along the bottom. The card back has a rectangle in the middle which has the player's name, team name and position toward the top, just below a card number (which uses an "NA" prefix). Inside the rectangle is a recap of the player's collegiate accomplishments. "New Age" is at the top of the card.

		MT
Complete Set (21):		150.00
Common Player:		2.00
1	Emmitt Smith	25.00
2	Jeff Blake	5.00
3	Junior Seau	2.00
4	Robert Brooks	2.00
5	Barry Sanders	18.00
6	Drew Bledsoe	13.00
7	Joey Galloway	10.00
8	Marshall Faulk	8.00
9	Mark Brunell	10.00
10	Jerry Rice	13.00
11	Rashaan Salaam	6.00
12	Troy Aikman	13.00
13	Steve Young	10.00
14	Tim Brown	2.00
15	Brett Favre	25.00
16	Kerry Collins	5.00
17	John Elway	10.00
18	Curtis Martin	18.00
19	Deion Sanders	10.00
20	Dan Marino	25.00
21	Chris Warren	2.00

1996 Stadium Club Pro Bowl

These 20 embossed cards were seeded one per every 24 retail packs of 1996 Topps Stadium Club Series I product. The cards used etched Power Matrix technology. Twenty participants in the 1996 Pro Bowl game are featured in the set.

		MT
Complete Set (20):		150.00
Common Player:		3.00
Minor Stars:		6.00
Inserted 1:24 Retail		
1	Brett Favre	30.00
2	Bruce Smith	3.00
3	Ricky Watters	6.00
4	Yancey Thigpen	6.00
5	Barry Sanders	30.00
6	Jim Harbaugh	3.00
7	Michael Irvin	6.00
8	Chris Warren	3.00
9	Dana Stubblefield	3.00
10	Jeff Blake	6.00
11	Emmitt Smith	20.00
12	Bryce Paup	3.00
13	Steve Young	10.00
14	Kevin Greene	3.00
15	Jerry Rice	15.00
16	Curtis Martin	10.00
17	Reggie White	6.00
18	Derrick Thomas	3.00
19	Cris Carter	6.00
20	Greg Lloyd	3.00

1996 Stadium Club Photo Gallery

These cards were seeded one per every 18 packs of 1996 Topps Stadium Club Series II product. Each card features a customized design that complements the outstanding photography, and is printed on smooth cast-coated stock with an exclusive Topps high gloss laminate. The Photo Gallery logo, player's name, opponent, and game date from when the picture was taken are stamped in red, blue or silver foil on the front. The card back has the player's team name and position listed at the top, with the player's name below. The date of the game is under his name, with a recap of the game below, on one side. A color or photo is on the other side. The card number, using a "PG" prefix, is in the lower left corner.

	MT
Complete Set (476):	300.00
Common Player (1-360):	.20
Common Player (C1-C8):	.35

Common Player (F1A-F8B):	.35
Common Player (N1-N10):	1.00
Common Player (BY1-BY10):	.35
Common Player (CP1-CP10):	.35
Common Player (NA1-NA20):	.35
Common Player (PB1-PB20):	.35
Common Player (PG1-PG20):	.50

C1	Emmitt Smith	8.00
C2	Barry Sanders	5.00
C3	Curtis Martin	4.00
C4	Chris Warren	.50
C5	Errict Rhett	.50
C6	Rodney Hampton	.35
C7	Ricky Watters	.50
C8	Terry Allen	.50
F1A	Steve Young	3.00
F1B	Jerry Rice	4.00
F2A	Drew Bledsoe	4.00
F2B	Curtis Martin	4.00
F3A	Trent Dilfer	.50
F3B	Errict Rhett	.50
F4A	Jeff Hostetler	.35
F4B	Tim Brown	.50
F5A	Brett Favre	10.00
F5B	Robert Brooks	.75
F6A	Jim Harbaugh	.50
F6B	Marshall Faulk	.75
F7A	Rashaan Salaam	.75
F7B	Erik Kramer	.35
F8A	Scott Mitchell	.35
F8B	Barry Sanders	5.00
N1	Joe Namath 1965	1.00
N2	Joe Namath 1966	1.00
N3	Joe Namath 1967	1.00
N4	Joe Namath 1968	1.00
N5	Joe Namath 1969	1.00
N6	Joe Namath 1970	1.00
N7	Joe Namath 1971	1.00
N8	Joe Namath 1972	1.00
N9	Joe Namath 1972	1.00
N10	Joe Namath 1973	1.00
BY1	Dan Marino	8.00
BY2	Marshall Faulk	.75
BY3	Greg Lloyd	.35
BY4	Steve Young	3.00
BY5	Emmitt Smith	8.00
BY6	Junior Seau	.50
BY7	Chris Warren	.50
BY8	Jerry Rice	4.00
BY9	Troy Aikman	4.00
BY10	Barry Sanders	5.00
CP1	Ken Norton, Drew Bledsoe	3.00
CP2	Chris Zorich, Barry Sanders	3.00
CP3	Corey Harris, Harvey Williams	.35
CP4	Sam Mills, Thurman Thomas	.75
CP5	Bryce Paup, Derrick Moore	.35
CP6	Rob Fredrickson, Chris Warren	.50
CP7	Darnell Walker, Bernie Parmalee	.35
CP8	Derrick Thomas, Gus Frerotte	.50
CP9	Hardy Nickerson, Harvey Williams	.35
CP10	Reggie White, Dave Brown	.75
NA1	Alex Van Dyke	.50
NA2	Lawrence Phillips	1.00
NA3	Tim Biakabutuka	1.00
NA4	Reggie Brown	.35
NA5	Duane Clemons	.35
NA6	Marco Battaglia	.35
NA7	Cedric Jones	.35
NA8	Jerome Woods	.35
NA9	Eric Moulds	1.00
NA10	Kevin Hardy	.35
NA11	Rickey Dudley	.50
NA12	Regan Upshaw	.35
NA13	Eddie Kennison	2.50
NA14	Jonathan Ogden	.35
NA15	John Mobley	.35
NA16	Mike Alstott	1.50
NA17	Alex Molden	.35
NA18	Marvin Harrison	2.50
NA19	Simeon Rice	.35
NA20	Keyshawn Johnson	2.50
PB1	Brett Favre	10.00
PB2	Bruce Smith	.50
PB3	Ricky Watters	.50
PB4	Yancey Thigpen	.50
PB5	Barry Sanders	5.00
PB6	Jim Harbaugh	.50
PB7	Michael Irvin	.75
PB8	Chris Warren	.50
PB9	Dana Stubblefield	.35
PB10	Jeff Blake	.50
PB11	Emmitt Smith	8.00
PB12	Bryce Paup	.35
PB13	Steve Young	3.00
PB14	Kevin Greene	.35
PB15	Jerry Rice	4.00
PB16	Curtis Martin	4.00
PB17	Reggie White	.75
PB18	Derrick Thomas	.50
PB19	Cris Carter	.50
PB20	Greg Lloyd	.50
PG1	Emmitt Smith	8.00
PG2	Jeff Blake	.50
PG3	Junior Seau	.50
PG4	Robert Brooks	.50
PG5	Barry Sanders	5.00
PG6	Drew Bledsoe	4.00
PG7	Joey Galloway	.75
PG8	Marshall Faulk	.75
PG9	Mark Brunell	4.00
PG10	Jerry Rice	4.00
PG11	Rashaan Salaam	.75
PG12	Troy Aikman	4.00
PG13	Steve Young	3.00
PG14	Tim Brown	.50
PG15	Brett Favre	10.00
PG16	Kerry Collins	3.00
PG17	John Elway	3.00
PG18	Curtis Martin	4.00
PG19	Deion Sanders	2.00
PG20	Dan Marino	8.00
PG21	Chris Warren	.50

1996 Stadium Club Namath Finest

(see upper left column for set details)

1996 Stadium Club Pro Bowl

		MT
Complete Set (20):		100.00
Common Player:		3.00
1	Alex Van Dyke	5.00
2	Lawrence Phillips	10.00
3	Tim Biakabutuka	10.00
4	Reggie Brown	3.00
5	Duane Clemons	3.00
6	Marco Battaglia	3.00
7	Cedric Jones	3.00
8	Jerome Woods	3.00
9	Eric Moulds	10.00
10	Kevin Hardy	3.00
11	Rickey Dudley	5.00
12	Regan Upshaw	3.00
13	Eddie Kennison	6.00
14	Jonathan Ogden	3.00
15	John Mobley	3.00
16	Mike Alstott	10.00
17	Alex Molden	3.00
18	Marvin Harrison	15.00
19	Simeon Rice	3.00
20	Keyshawn Johnson	15.00

1996 Stadium Club Members Only

This set is a complete parallel of the 1996 Stadium Club set. It was sold through Topps' Members Only Club. This issue was available in factory set form and included all the base set and insert cards. Club members could purchase the entire set or an individual series. Each card featured a special Members Only stamp.

1996 Stadium Club Sunday Night Redemption

Sunday Night Redemption cards were inserted in Stadium Club Series One packs (1:24 hobby and retail; 1:20 jumbo). The cards were designated for a certain week of the NFL season and if the score of that week's Sunday night game matched the two numbers on the card, collectors could mail the card in and receive two jumbo Finest cards featuring players in that week's game.

		MT
Complete Set (32):		250.00
Common Player:		5.00
1A	Rodney Hampton	5.00
1B	Jim Kelly	8.00
2A	Dan Marino	25.00
2B	Frank Sanders	5.00
3A	Trent Dilfer	7.00
3B	John Elway	12.00
4A	Eric Metcalf	5.00
4B	Ricky Watters	6.00
5A	Terry Allen	6.00
5B	Keyshawn Johnson	8.00
6A	Jeff Blake	8.00
6B	Steve McNair	10.00
7A	Marshall Faulk	8.00
7B	Eric Zeier	5.00
9A	Drew Bledsoe	15.00
9B	Bruce Smith	5.00
10A	Jim Everett	5.00
10B	Steve Young	12.00
11A	Dave Brown	5.00
11B	Kerry Collins	12.00
12A	Tim Brown	6.00
12B	Cris Carter	6.00
13A	Isaac Bruce	8.00
13B	Brett Favre	30.00
14A	Curtis Martin	15.00
14B	Junior Seau	6.00
15A	Warren Moon	6.00
15B	Barry Sanders	18.00
16A	Mark Brunell	15.00
16B	Chris Warren	5.00
17A	Terrell Davis	15.00
17B	Stan Humphries	5.00

1997 Stadium Club

The 170-card Series I set included a full-bleed photo on the front, with the Stadium Club logo

at the top and a "wave" on the bottom that included the player's name and position. The backs included an action shot, with the player's name, bio and highlights on the left side in a "ripped out" area. The stats appear in a box in the lower right, along with one highlight. There are three parallel sets. Printing Plates (cyan, yellow, magenta and black plates of each card for a total of 640 cards) were inserted in Home Team Advantage packs. One-of-a-Kind parallel cards were seeded 1:48 packs, while First Day Issue parallel cards were found 1:24 retail packs. Series II also had 170 cards and the same three parallel sets. The base set did include a 20-card Transaction subset, featuring important off-season moves.

	MT
Complete Set (340):	60.00
Complete Series 1 (170):	30.00
Complete Series 2 (170):	30.00
Common Player:	.10
Minor Stars:	.20
Series 1 Wax Box:	65.00
Series 2 Wax Box:	40.00

1	Junior Seau	.20
2	Michael Irvin	.20
3	Marcus Allen	.20
4	Dale Carter	.10
5	Darnell Autry	.40
6	Isaac Bruce	.20
7	Darrell Green	.10
8	Steve Atwater	.10
9	Kordell Stewart	1.50
10	Tony Brackens	.10
11	Gus Frerotte	.10
12	Henry Ellard	.10
13	Charles Way	.10
14	Jim Druckenmiller	2.00
15	Orlando Thomas	.10
16	Terrell Davis	1.25
17	Jim Schwantz	.10
18	Derrick Thomas	.10
19	Curtis Martin	1.50
20	Deion Sanders	.50
21	Bruce Smith	.10
22	Jake Reed	.10
23	Leeland McElroy	.10
24	Jerome Bettis	.20
25	Neil Smith	.10
26	Terry Allen	.10
27	Gilbert Brown	.10
28	Steve McNair	.75
29	Kerry Collins	.30
30	Thurman Thomas	.20
31	Kenny Holmes	.10
32	Karim Abdul-Jabbar	.30
33	Steve Young	1.00
34	Jerry Rice	1.25
35	Jeff George	.10
36	Errict Rhett	.20
37	Mike Alstott	.20
38	Tim Brown	.10
39	Keyshawn Johnson	.20
40	Jim Harbaugh	.10
41	Kevin Hardy	.10
42	Kevin Greene	.10
43	Eric Metcalf	.10
44	Troy Aikman	1.25
45	Marshall Faulk	.20
46	Shannon Sharpe	.10
47	Warren Moon	.10
48	Mark Brunell	1.25
49	Dan Marino	3.00
50	Byron Hanspard	1.00
51	Chris Chandler	.10
52	Wayne Chrebet	.10
53	Antonio Langham	.10
54	Barry Sanders	2.00
55	Curtis Conway	.10
56	Ricky Watters	.20
57	William Thomas	.10
58	Chris Warren	.10
59	Terry Glenn	.30
60	Peter Boulware	.10
61	Chad Cota	.10
62	Eddie Kennison	.50
63	Lamar Smith	.10
64	Brett Favre	3.00
65	Michael Westbrook	.10
66	Larry Centers	.10
67	Trent Dilfer	.20
68	Stevon Moore	.10
69	John Elway	1.00
70	Bryce Paup	.10
71	Quentin Coryatt	.10
72	Rashaan Salaam	.20
73	Thomas Lewis	.10
74	Drew Bledsoe	1.25
75	Cris Carter	.10
76	Joe Bowden	.10
77	Allen Aldridge	.10
78	Zach Thomas	.30
79	Emmitt Smith	3.00
80	Daryl Johnston	.10
81	Vinny Testaverde	.10
82	James Stewart	.10
83	Edgar Bennett	.10
84	Shawn Springs	.30
85		

No	Player	Price
86	Elvis Grbac	.10
87	Levon Kirkland	.10
88	Jeff Graham	.10
89	Terrell Fletcher	.10
90	Eddie George	2.00
91	Jessie Tuggle	.10
92	Terrell Owens	.75
93	Wayne Martin	.10
94	Dwayne Harper	.10
95	Mark Collins	.10
96	Marvcus Patton	.10
97	Napoleon Kaufman	.10
98	Keenan McCardell	.10
99	Ty Detmer	.10
100	Reggie White	.20
101	William Floyd	.10
102	Scott Mitchell	.10
103	Robert Blackmon	.10
104	Dan Wilkinson	.10
105	Warren Sapp	.10
106	Raymont Harris	.10
107	Brian Mitchell	.10
108	Tyrone Poole	.10
109	Derrick Alexander	.10
110	David Palmer	.10
111	James Farrior	.10
112	Daryl Gardener	.10
113	Marty Carter	.10
114	Lawrence Phillips	.20
115	Wesley Walls	.10
116	John Friesz	.10
117	Roman Phifer	.10
118	Jason Sehorn	.10
119	Henry Thomas	.10
120	Natrone Means	.20
121	Ty Law	.10
122	*Tony Gonzalez*	1.00
123	Kevin Williams	.10
124	Regan Upshaw	.10
125	Antonio Freeman	.30
126	Jessie Armstead	.10
127	*Pat Barnes*	.30
128	Charlie Garner	.10
129	Irving Fryar	.10
130	Rickey Dudley	.10
131	Rodney Harrison	.10
132	Brent Jones	.10
133	Neil O'Donnell	.10
134	Darryll Lewis	.10
135	Jason Belser	.10
136	Mark Chmura	.10
137	Seth Joyner	.10
138	Herschel Walker	.10
139	Santana Dotson	.10
140	Carl Pickens	.10
141	Terance Mathis	.10
142	Walt Harris	.10
143	John Mobley	.10
144	Gabe Northern	.10
145	Herman Moore	.20
146	Michael Jackson	.10
147	Chris Sanders	.10
148	LeShon Johnson	.10
149	Darrell Russell	.10
150	Winslow Oliver	.10
151	Tamarick Vanover	.10
152	Tony Martin	.10
153	Lamar Lathon	.10
154	Stanley Richard	.10
155	Derrick Brooks	.10
156	*Warrick Dunn*	3.00
157	Tim McDonald	.10
158	Keith Lyle	.10
159	Terry McDaniel	.10
160	Andre Hastings	.10
161	Phillippi Sparks	.10
162	Tedy Bruschi	.10
163	*Bryant Westbrook*	.20
164	Victor Green	.10
165	Jimmy Smith	.10
166	Greg Biekert	.10
167	Frank Sanders	.10
168	Chris Doleman	.10
169	Phil Hansen	.10
170	Walter Jones	.10
171	Mark Carrier	.10
172	Greg Hill	.10
173	Erik Kramer	.10
174	Chris Spielman	.10
175	Tom Knight	.10
176	Sam Mills	.10
177	Robert Smith	.10
178	Dorsey Levens	.20
179	Chris Slade	.10
180	Troy Vincent	.10
181	Mario Bates	.10
182	Ed McCaffrey	.10
183	Mike Mamula	.10
184	Chad Hennings	.10
185	Stan Humphries	.10
186	Reinard Wilson	.10
187	Kevin Carter	.10
188	Qadry Ismail	.10
189	Cortez Kennedy	.10
190	Eric Swann	.10
191	*Corey Dillon*	3.00
192	Renaldo Wynn	.10
193	Bobby Hebert	.10
194	Fred Barnett	.10
195	Ray Lewis	.10
196	Robert Jones	.10
197	Brian Williams	.10
198	Willie McGinest	.10
199	*Jake Plummer*	8.00
200	Aeneas Williams	.10
201	Ashley Ambrose	.10
202	Cornelius Bennett	.10
203	Mo Lewis	.10
204	James Hasty	.10
205	Carnell Lake	.10
206	Heath Shuler	.10
207	Dana Stubblefield	.10
208	Corey Miller	.10
209	*Ike Hilliard*	1.50
210	Bryant Young	.10
211	Hardy Nickerson	.10
212	Blaine Bishop	.10
213	Marcus Robertson	.10
214	Tony Bennett	.10
215	Kent Graham	.10
216	Steve Bono	.10
217	*Will Blackwell*	.50
218	Tyrone Braxton	.10
219	Eric Moulds	.20
220	Rod Woodson	.10
221	Anthony Johnson	.10
222	Willie Davis	.10
223	Darrin Smith	.10
224	Rick Mirer	.10
225	Marvin Harrison	.50
226	Dixon Edwards	.10
227	Joe Aska	.10
228	*Yatil Green*	.50
229	William Fuller	.10
230	Eddie Robinson	.10
231	Brian Blades	.10
232	Michael Sinclair	.10
233	Ken Harvey	.10
234	Harvey Williams	.10
235	Simeon Rice	.10
236	Chris T. Jones	.10
237	Bert Emanuel	.10
238	Corey Sawyer	.10
239	Chris Calloway	.10
240	Jeff Blake	.20
241	Alonzo Spellman	.10
242	Bryan Cox	.10
243	*Antowain Smith*	2.50
244	Tim Biakabutuka	.10
245	Ray Crockett	.10
246	Dwayne Rudd	.10
247	Glyn Milburn	.10
248	Gary Plummer	.10
249	O.J. McDuffie	.10
250	Willie Clay	.10
251	Jim Everett	.10
252	Eugene Daniel	.10
253	Jessie Armstead	.10
254	Mel Gray	.10
255	Ken Norton	.10
256	Johnnie Morton	.10
257	Courtney Hawkins	.10
258	Ricardo McDonald	.10
259	Todd Lyght	.10
260	Michael Barrow	.10
261	Aaron Glenn	.10
262	Clay Matthews	.10
263	*Troy Davis*	.30
264	Eric Hill	.10
265	Darrien Gordon	.10
266	Lake Dawson	.10
267	John Randle	.10
268	Lamar Thomas	.10
269	Mickey Washington	.10
270	Amani Toomer	.10
271	Steve Grant	.10
272	Adrian Murrell	.20
273	Derrick Witherspoon	.10
274	Michael Zordich	.10
275	Ben Coates	.10
277	Jim Schwantz	.10
278	Aaron Hayden	.10
279	Ryan McNeil	.10
280	LeRoy Butler	.10
281	Craig Newsome	.10
282	Bill Romanowski	.10
283	Michael Bankston	.10
284	Kevin Smith	.10
285	Byron Morris	.10
286	Darnay Scott	.10
287	*David LaFleur*	.50
288	Randall Cunningham	.20
289	Eric Davis	.10
290	Todd Collins	.10
291	Steve Tovar	.10
292	Jermaine Lewis	.10
293	Alfred Williams	.10
294	Brad Johnson	.20
295	Charles Johnson	.10
296	Ted Johnson	.10
297	Merton Hanks	.10
298	Andre Coleman	.10
299	Keith Jackson	.10
300	Terry Kirby	.10
301	Tony Banks	.30
302	Terrance Shaw	.10
303	Bobby Engram	.10
304	Hugh Douglas	.10
305	Lawyer Milloy	.10
306	James Jett	.10
307	*Joey Kent*	.50
308	Rodney Hampton	.10
309	DeWayne Washington	.10
310	Kevin Lockett	.10
311	Ki-Jana Carter	.10
312	Jeff Lageman	.10
313	Don Beebe	.10
314	Willie Williams	.10
315	Tyrone Wheatley	.10
316	Leslie O'Neal	.10
317	Quinn Early	.10
318	Sean Gilbert	.10
319	Tim Bowens	.10
320	Sean Dawkins	.10
321	Ken Dilger	.10
322	George Koonce	.10
323	Jevon Langford	.10
324	Mike Caldwell	.10
325	*Orlando Pace*	.50
326	Garrison Hearst	.10
327	Mike Tomczak	.10
328	Rob Moore	.10
329	Andre Reed	.10
330	Kimble Anders	.10
331	Qadry Ismail	.10
333	Dave Brown	.10
334	Bennie Blades	.10
335	Jamal Anderson	.20
336	John Lynch	.10
337	Tyrone Hughes	.10
338	Ronnie Harmon	.10
339	*Rae Carruth*	1.25
340	Robert Brooks	.10

1997 Stadium Club First Day

First Day Issue is a retail-only parallel of the Stadium Club Series base set which was inserted one per 24 packs. Each card was marked with a gold foil logo with the parallel name on the front of the card.

	MT
First Day Stars:	20x-40x
First Day Rookies:	10x-20x

1997 Stadium Club One of a Kind

One of a Kind is a hobby-only parallel which was seeded one per 48 packs. Each card is marked with a special security stamp. All 340 cards from Series I and II are paralleled.

	MT
One of a Kind Stars:	30x-60x
One of a Kind Rookies:	15x-30x

1997 Stadium Club Aerial Assault

The 10-card set was inserted 1:12 packs. A player photo is superimposed over a holographic background of the United States, with the team's city targeted. "Aerial Assault" is printed at the top left, while the Stadium Club logo and the player's name is in the lower right. The backs, which are numbered with an "AA" prefix, has the player photo on the left, with the player's name, team and 1996 passing stats all to the right.

	MT
Complete Set (10):	40.00
Common Player:	1.50
1 Dan Marino	10.00
2 Mark Brunell	5.00
3 Troy Aikman	5.00
4 Ty Detmer	1.50
5 John Elway	3.00
6 Drew Bledsoe	5.00
7 Steve Young	3.00
8 Vinny Testaverde	1.50
9 Kerry Collins	3.00
10 Brett Favre	12.00

1997 Stadium Club Bowman's Best Previews

The 15-card set was a sneak peek at the 1997 set. The cards were inserted at a 1:24 rate. The foil cards have a Bowman's Best logo in the upper left, with the player's name and team logo in the lower right. The backs, which are numbered with a "BBP" prefix, have the player photo on the left, with his name, bio, stats and highlights on the right. A Refractor parallel version was seeded 1:96 packs, while an Atomic Refractor version was found 1:192 packs.

	MT
Complete Set (15):	110.00
Common Player:	3.00
Refractors:	2x-3x
Atomic Refractors:	3x-6x
1 Dan Marino	20.00
2 Terry Allen	3.00
3 Jerome Bettis	3.00
4 Kevin Greene	3.00
5 Junior Seau	3.00
6 Brett Favre	25.00
7 Isaac Bruce	6.00
8 Michael Irvin	3.00
9 Kerry Collins	3.00
10 Karim Abdul-Jabbar	6.00
11 Keenan McCardell	3.00
12 Ricky Watters	3.00
13 Mark Brunell	12.00
14 Jerry Rice	12.00
15 Drew Bledsoe	12.00

1997 Stadium Club Bowman's Best Rookie Preview

These 15 chromium cards feature top rookies from 1997. The cards were inserted 1:24, with Refractor (1:96) and Atomic Refractor (1:192) versions also available. Cards are numbered with a "BBP" prefix.

	MT
Complete Set (15):	100.00
Common Player:	3.00
Refractors:	2x-3x
Atomic Refractors:	3x-6x
1 Orlando Pace	3.00
2 David LaFleur	6.00
3 James Farrior	3.00
4 Tony Gonzalez	6.00
5 Ike Hilliard	6.00
6 Antowain Smith	15.00
7 Tom Knight	3.00
8 Troy Davis	6.00
9 Yatil Green	3.00
10 Jim Druckenmiller	20.00
11 Bryant Westbrook	3.00
12 Darrell Russell	3.00
13 Rae Carruth	10.00
14 Shawn Springs	3.00
15 Peter Boulware	3.00

1997 Stadium Club Co-Signers

Seventy-two NFL players autographed these two-sided cards. There are 108 Co-Signers matchups. Co-Signers were found one per 63 Series I packs and one per 68 Series II packs.

	MT
Common Player (1-36):	75.00
Common Player (37-72):	50.00
Common Player (73-108):	25.00

No	Players	Price
1	Karim Abdul-Jabbar, Eddie George	400.00
2	Trace Armstrong, Alonzo Spellman	75.00
3	Steve Atwater, Kevin Hardy	75.00
4	Fred Barnett, Lake Dawson	75.00
5	Blaine Bishop, Darrell Green	75.00
6	Jeff Blake, Gus Frerotte	150.00
7	Steve Bono, Cris Carter	125.00
8	Tim Brown, Isaac Bruce	150.00
9	Wayne Chrebet, Mickey Washington	75.00
10	Curtis Conway, Eddie Kennison	150.00
11	Eric Davis, Jason Sehorn	75.00
12	Terrell Davis, Thurman Thomas	180.00
13	Ken Dilger, Kent Graham	75.00
14	Stephen Grant, Marvcus Patton	75.00
15	Keith Hamilton, Mike Tomczak	75.00
16	Rodney Hampton, David Meggett	75.00
17	Merton Hanks, Aeneas Williams	75.00
18	No Card	
19	Brent Jones, Wesley Walls	75.00
20	Carnell Lake, Tim McDonald	75.00
21	Thomas Lewis, Keith Lyle	75.00
22	Leeland McElroy, Jeff Lageman	75.00
23	Ray Mickens, Willie Davis	75.00
24	Herman Moore, Desmond Howard	150.00
25	Stevon Moore, William Thomas	75.00
26	Adrian Murrell, Levon Kirkland	125.00
27	Simeon Rice, Winslow Oliver	75.00
28	Bill Romanowski, Gary Plummer	75.00
29	Junior Seau, Chris Spielman	75.00
30	Chris Slade, Kevin Greene	75.00
31	Derrick Thomas, Chris T. Jones	75.00
32	Orlando Thomas, Bobby Engram	75.00
33	Amani Toomer, Thomas Randolph	75.00
34	Steve Tovar, Ellis Johnson	75.00
35	Herschel Walker, Anthony Johnson	75.00
36	Darren Woodson, Aaron Glenn	75.00
37	Karim Abdul-Jabbar, Thurman Thomas	125.00
38	Blaine Bishop, Tim McDonald	50.00
39	Jeff Blake, Derrick Thomas	80.00
40	No Card	
41	Cris Carter, Marvin Harrison	125.00
42	Curtis Conway, Wesley Walls	50.00
43	Willie Davis, Amani Toomer	50.00
44	Lake Dawson, Ray Mickens	50.00
45	Ken Dilger, Ellis Johnson	50.00
46	Bobby Engram, Thomas Lewis	50.00
47	Gus Frerotte, Chris T. Jones	75.00
48	Eddie George, Terrell Davis	250.00
49	Aaron Glenn, Eric Davis	50.00
50	Kent Graham, Steve Tovar	50.00
51	Darrell Green, Carnell Lake	50.00
52	Kevin Greene, Steve Atwater	50.00
53	Rodney Hampton, Anthony Johnson	50.00
54	Kevin Hardy, Merton Hanks	50.00
55	Desmond Howard, Tim Brown	80.00
56	Eddie Kennison, Brent Jones	100.00
57	Levon Kirkland, Simeon Rice	50.00
58	Jeff Lageman, Adrian Murrell	75.00
59	Keith Lyle, Wayne Chrebet	50.00
60	David Meggett, Herschel Walker	50.00
61	Herman Moore, Isaac Bruce	125.00
62	Winslow Oliver, Leeland McElroy	50.00
63	Marvcus Patton, Keith Hamilton	50.00
64	Gary Plummer, Junior Seau	50.00
65	Thomas Randolph, Fred Barnett	50.00
66	Alonzo Spellman, Stephen Grant	50.00
67	Chris Spielman, Stevon Moore	50.00
68	William Thomas, Bill Romanowski	50.00
69	Mike Tomczak, Trace Armstrong	50.00
70	Mickey Washington, Orlando Thomas	50.00
71	Aeneas Williams, Chris Slade	50.00
72	Darren Woodson, Jason Sehorn	50.00
73	Trace Armstrong, Keith Hamilton	25.00
74	Isaac Bruce, Desmond Howard	75.00
75	Terrell Davis, Karim Abdul-Jabbar	250.00
76	Tim Brown, Herman Moore	100.00
77	Derrick Thomas, Gus Frerotte	40.00
78	Thurman Thomas, Eddie George	150.00
79	Steve Atwater, Chris Slade	25.00
80	Merton Hanks, Kevin Greene	25.00
81	Marvin Harrison, Steve Bono	75.00
82	Anthony Johnson, David Meggett	25.00
83	Stephen Grant, Mike Tomczak	25.00
84	Herschel Walker, Rodney Hampton	25.00
85	Aeneas Williams, Kevin Hardy	25.00
86	Anthony Johnson, David Meggett	25.00
87	Brent Jones, Curtis Conway	25.00
88	Carnell Lake, Blaine Bishop	25.00
89	Tim McDonald, Darrell Green	25.00
90	Trace Armstrong, Keith Hamilton	25.00
91	Winslow Oliver, Levon Kirkland	25.00
92	Simeon Rice, Jeff Lageman	25.00
93	Wesley Walls, Eddie Kennison	40.00
94	Adrian Murrell, Leeland McElroy	40.00
95	Winslow Oliver, Levon Kirkland	25.00
96	Marvcus Patton, Alonzo Spellman	25.00
97	No Card	
98	Ray Mickens, Thomas Randolph	25.00
99	Junior Seau, Bill Romanowski	25.00
100	Marvcus Patton, Alonzo Spellman	25.00
101	Derrick Thomas, Gus Frerotte	40.00
102	Orlando Thomas, Keith Lyle	25.00
103	Thurman Thomas, Eddie George	150.00
104	Wayne Chrebet, Thomas Lewis	25.00
105	Steve Tovar, Ken Dilger	25.00
106	Ellis Johnson, Kent Graham	25.00
107	Wesley Walls, Eddie Kennison	40.00
108	Aeneas Williams, Kevin Hardy	25.00

1997 Stadium Club Grid Kids

Inserted 1:36 packs, 20 1997 NFL Draft picks are showcased in their game uniforms in the set. The cards are numbered with a "GK" prefix.

		MT
Complete Set (20):		150.00
Common Player:		3.00
Minor Stars:		6.00
1	Orlando Pace	3.00
2	Darrell Russell	3.00
3	Shawn Springs	6.00
4	Peter Boulware	3.00
5	Bryant Westbrook	6.00
6	Darnell Autry	8.00
7	Ike Hilliard	10.00
8	James Farrior	3.00
9	Jake Plummer	18.00
10	Tony Gonzalez	8.00
11	Yatil Green	10.00
12	Corey Dillon	15.00
13	Dwayne Rudd	3.00
14	Renaldo Wynn	3.00
15	David LaFleur	8.00
16	Antowain Smith	12.00
17	Jim Druckenmiller	15.00
18	Rae Carruth	3.00
19	Tom Knight	3.00
20	Byron Hanspard	8.00

1997 Stadium Club Never Compromise

This 40-card insert features 10 veterans and 30 rookies. The cards could be found every 12 packs. They are numbered with a "NC" prefix.

		MT
Complete Set (40):		225.00
Common Player:		1.50
Minor Stars:		3.00
1	Orlando Pace	3.00
2	Corey Dillon	15.00
3	Tony Gonzalez	3.00
4	Tom Knight	1.50
5	Deion Sanders	10.00
6	Dwayne Rudd	1.50
7	Warrick Dunn	25.00
8	Kenny Holmes	1.50
9	Will Blackwell	1.50
10	Shawn Springs	1.50
11	Rae Carruth	8.00
12	Edgar Bennett	1.50
13	Walter Jones	1.50
14	Reidel Anthony	8.00
15	Troy Davis	3.00
16	Mark Brunell	15.00
17	Pat Barnes	6.00
18	Reggie White	3.00
19	Darrell Russell	1.50
20	Ike Hilliard	3.00
21	Emmitt Smith	30.00
22	David LaFleur	6.00
23	Yatil Green	3.00
24	Barry Sanders	20.00
25	Bryant Westbrook	1.50
26	Lawrence Phillips	1.50
27	Peter Boulware	1.50
28	Joey Kent	3.00
29	Kevin Lockett	1.50
30	Derrick Thomas	1.50
31	Antowain Smith	15.00
32	James Farrior	1.50
33	Kordell Stewart	15.00
34	Byron Hanspard	6.00
35	Jim Druckenmiller	15.00
36	Reinard Wilson	1.50
37	Darnell Autry	6.00
38	Steve Young	10.00
39	Renaldo Wynn	1.50
40	Jake Plummer	15.00

1997 Stadium Club Offensive Strikes

Inserted 1:12 packs, the top five running backs and wide receivers from 1996 are featured in this set. The cards are borderless foilboard.

		MT
Complete Set (10):		45.00
Common Player:		1.50
AF1	Jerry Rice (Air Force)	5.00
AF2	Carl Pickens (Air Force)	1.50
AF3	Shannon Sharpe (Air Force)	1.50
AF4	Herman Moore (Air Force)	1.50
AF5	Terry Glenn (Air Force)	3.00
GC1	Barry Sanders (Ground Control)	8.00
GC2	Curtis Martin (Ground Control)	5.00
GC3	Emmitt Smith (Ground Control)	10.00
GC4	Terrell Davis (Ground Control)	5.00
GC5	Eddie George (Ground Control)	8.00

1997 Stadium Club Triumvirate

Exclusive to retail packs, the laser-cut cards featured a trio of leading NFL offensive teammates fused together. There are six different complete cards made up of three players per, each player card is seeded at a 1:36 pack ratio. Refractor versions were found 1:96, while Atomic Refractor versions were seeded 1:192.

		MT
Complete Set (18):		200.00
Common Player:		5.00
Refractors:		2x-4x
Atomic Refractors:		3x-6x
T1A	Emmitt Smith	30.00
T1B	Troy Aikman	15.00
T1C	Michael Irvin	5.00
T2A	Curtis Martin	15.00
T2B	Drew Bledsoe	15.00
T2C	Terry Glenn	7.00
T3A	Barry Sanders	20.00
T3B	Scott Mitchell	5.00
T3C	Herman Moore	5.00
T4A	William Floyd	5.00
T4B	Steve Young	10.00
T4C	Jerry Rice	15.00
T5A	Terrell Davis	15.00
T5B	John Elway	10.00
T5C	Shannon Sharpe	5.00
T6A	Edgar Bennett	5.00
T6B	Brett Favre	30.00
T6C	Antonio Freeman	8.00

> Post-1980 cards in Near Mint condition will generally sell for about 75% of the quoted Mint value. Excellent-condition cards bring no more than 40%.

1997 Stadium Club Triumvirate II

This 18-card, laser-cut insert consists of six trios of players, whose cards can be fit together. Triumvirate was seeded 1:36, with Refractor (1:144) and Atomic Refractor (1:288) also created.

		MT
Complete Set (18):		200.00
Common Player:		5.00
Refractors:		2x-3x
Atomic Refractors:		3x-6x
T1A	John Elway	10.00
T1B	Drew Bledsoe	15.00
T1C	Dan Marino	25.00
T2A	Troy Aikman	15.00
T2B	Brett Favre	30.00
T2C	Steve Young	10.00
T3A	Terrell Davis	15.00
T3B	Eddie George	20.00
T3C	Curtis Martin	15.00
T4A	Emmitt Smith	25.00
T4B	Ricky Watters	5.00
T4C	Barry Sanders	20.00
T5A	Shannon Sharpe	5.00
T5B	Terry Glenn	5.00
T5C	Carl Pickens	5.00
T6A	Jake Plummer	10.00
T6B	Orlando Pace	5.00
T6C	Jim Druckenmiller	15.00

1998 Stadium Club

Stadium Club was issued in a single-series, 195-card set in 1998, with a 30-card Star Rookies subset seeded one per two packs (1:1 jumbo pack). Cards featured a borderless design with embossed, holographic foil on 20-point stock. Stadium Club was paralleled in three different sets, with each exclusive to specific packs: First Day Issue (retail), One of a Kind (hobby) and Printing Plates (Home Team Advantage). Inserts include: Chrome, Chrome Refractors, Co-Signers (hobby), Double Threat, Leading Legends (retail), Prime Rookies, Triumvirates (hobby) and SuperChrome Oversized cards.

		MT
Complete Set (195):		110.00
Common Player:		.15
Minor Stars:		.30
Common Rookie (166-195):		1.50
Inserted 1:2		
Wax Box:		65.00
1	Barry Sanders	3.00
2	Tony Martin	.15
3	Fred Lane	.30
4	Darren Woodson	.15
5	Andre Reed	.30
6	Blaine Bishop	.15
7	Robert Brooks	.30
8	Tony Banks	.30
9	Charles Way	.15
10	Mark Brunell	1.25
11	Darrell Green	.15
12	Aeneas Williams	.15
13	Rob Johnson	.30
14	Deion Sanders	.50
15	Marshall Faulk	.30
16	Stephen Boyd	.15
17	Adrian Murrell	.30
18	Wayne Chrebet	.15
19	Michael Sinclair	.15
20	Dan Marino	2.00
21	Willie Davis	.15
22	Chris Warren	.30
23	John Mobley	.15
24	Shannon Sharpe	.30
25	Thurman Thomas	.30
26	Corey Dillon	1.00
27	Zach Thomas	.30
28	James Jett	.15
29	Eric Metcalf	.15
30	Drew Bledsoe	1.25
31	Scott Greene	.15
32	Simeon Rice	.15
33	Robert Smith	.30
34	Keenan McCardell	.15
35	Jessie Armstead	.15
36	Jerry Rice	1.50
37	Eric Green	.15
38	Terrell Owens	.50
39	Tim Brown	.30
40	Vinny Testaverde	.15
41	Brian Stablein	.15
42	Bert Emanuel	.15
43	Terry Glenn	.30
44	Chad Cota	.15
45	Jermaine Lewis	.15
46	Derrick Thomas	.30
47	O.J. McDuffie	.15
48	Frank Wycheck	.15
49	Steve Broussard	.15
50	Terrell Davis	2.00
52	Napoleon Kaufman	.50
53	Dan Wilkinson	.15
54	Kerry Collins	.30
55	Frank Sanders	.15
56	Jeff Burris	.15
57	Michael Westbrook	.15
58	Michael McCrary	.15
59	Bobby Hoying	.15
60	Jerome Bettis	.30
61	Amp Lee	.15
62	Levon Kirkland	.15
63	Dana Stubblefield	.15
64	Terance Mathis	.15
65	Mark Chmura	.15
66	Bryant Westbrook	.15
67	Rod Smith	.30
68	Derrick Alexander	.15
69	Jason Taylor	.15
70	Eddie George	1.25
71	Elvis Grbac	.15
72	Junior Seau	.30
73	Marvin Harrison	.30
74	Neil O'Donnell	.15
75	Johnnie Morton	.15
76	John Randle	.15
77	Danny Kanell	.15
78	Charlie Garner	.15
79	J.J. Stokes	.15
80	Troy Aikman	1.50
81	Gus Frerotte	.15
82	Jake Plummer	1.25
83	Andre Hastings	.15
84	Steve Atwater	.15
85	Larry Centers	.15
86	Kevin Hardy	.15
87	Willie McGinest	.15
88	Joey Galloway	.30
89	Charles Johnson	.15
90	Warrick Dunn	1.25
91	Derrick Rodgers	.15
92	Aaron Glenn	.15
93	Shawn Jefferson	.15
94	Antonio Freeman	.30
95	Jake Reed	.15
96	Reidel Anthony	.15
97	Cris Dishman	.15
98	Jason Sehorn	.15
99	Herman Moore	.30
100	John Elway	1.50
101	Brad Johnson	.30
102	Jeff George	.30
103	Emmitt Smith	2.00
104	Steve McNair	.75
105	Ed McCaffrey	.15
106	Errict Rhett	.15
107	Dorsey Levens	.30
108	Michael Jackson	.15
109	Carl Pickens	.15
110	James Stewart	.15
111	Karim Abdul-Jabbar	.30
112	Jim Harbaugh	.15
113	Yancey Thigpen	.15
114	Chad Brown	.15
115	Chris Sanders	.15
116	Cris Carter	.30
117	Glenn Foley	.15
118	Ben Coates	.15
119	Jamal Anderson	.30
120	Steve Young	.75
121	Scott Mitchell	.15
122	Rob Moore	.15
123	Bobby Engram	.15
124	Rod Woodson	.15
125	Terry Allen	.15
126	Warren Sapp	.15
127	Irving Fryar	.15
128	Isaac Bruce	.30
129	Rae Carruth	.15
130	Sean Dawkins	.15
131	Andre Rison	.15
132	Kevin Greene	.15
133	Warren Moon	.30
134	Keyshawn Johnson	.30
135	Jay Graham	.15
136	Mike Alstott	.50
137	Peter Boulware	.15
138	Doug Evans	.15
139	Jimmy Smith	.30
140	Kordell Stewart	1.25
141	Tamarick Vanover	.15
142	Chris Slade	.15
143	Freddie Jones	.15
144	Erik Kramer	.15
145	Ricky Watters	.30
146	Chris Chandler	.15
147	Garrison Hearst	.30
148	Trent Dilfer	.30
149	Bruce Smith	.15
150	Brett Favre	3.00
151	Will Blackwell	.15
152	Rickey Dudley	.15
153	Natrone Means	.30
154	Curtis Conway	.30
155	Tony Gonzalez	.30
156	Jeff Blake	.30
157	Michael Irvin	.30
158	Curtis Martin	.75
159	Tim McDonald	.15
160	Wesley Walls	.15
161	Michael Strahan	.15
162	Reggie White	.30
163	Jeff Graham	.15
164	Ray Lewis	.15
165	Antowain Smith	.75
166	*Ryan Leaf*	8.00
167	*Jerome Pathon*	1.50
168	*Duane Starks*	1.50
169	*Brian Simmons*	1.50
170	*Patrick Johnson*	1.50
171	*Keith Brooking*	1.50
172	*Kevin Dyson*	4.00
173	*Robert Edwards*	6.00
174	*Grant Wistrom*	1.50
175	*Curtis Enis*	6.00
176	*John Avery*	4.00
177	*Jason Peter*	1.50
178	*Brian Griese*	8.00
179	*Tavian Banks*	4.00
180	*Andre Wadsworth*	2.50
181	*Skip Hicks*	4.00
182	*Hines Ward*	4.00
183	*Greg Ellis*	2.00
184	*Robert Holcombe*	4.00
185	*Joe Jurevicius*	2.00
186	*Takeo Spikes*	2.00
187	*Ahman Green*	4.00
188	*Jacquez Green*	4.00
189	*Randy Moss*	25.00
190	*Charles Woodson*	7.00
191	*Fred Taylor*	8.00
192	*Marcus Nash*	4.00
193	*Germane Crowell*	4.00
194	*Tim Dwight*	2.50
195	*Peyton Manning*	15.00

1998 Stadium Club First Day Issue

First Day Issue cards parallel the 195-card regular-issue set, but are distinguished by a gold foil "First Day Issue" stamp on the front. These parallels were exclusive to retail packs, are numbered to 200 in gold foil on the back and inserted one per 47 packs.

	MT
First Day Issue Cards:	20x-40x
First Day Issue Rookies:	2x-4x

> Values quoted in this guide reflect the retail price of a card — the price a collector can expect to pay when buying a card from a dealer. The wholesale price — that which a collector can expect to receive when selling cards — will be significantly lower, depending on desirability and condition.

1998 Stadium Club One of a Kind

One of a Kind cards paralleled the 195-card base set in Stadium Club, but added a darkened, foil finish the front, with the insert name below the Stadium Club logo in the lower left corner. These parallel cards were exclusive to hobby packs, numbered on the back to 150 in gold foil and inserted one per 32 packs.

	MT
One of a Kind Cards:	30x-60x
One of a Kind Rookies:	3x-6x

1998 Stadium Club Chrome

This 20-card insert was seeded one per 12 packs of Stadium Club. Cards previewed the upcoming Chrome set, however with a different design. While normal Chrome cards were patterned after Topps cards, these inserts were chromium versions of the Stadium Club base cards. Chrome inserts were numbered with a "SCC" prefix and also had Refractor versions seeded one per 48 packs.

		MT
Complete Set (20):		100.00
Common Player:		2.00
Minor Stars:		4.00
Inserted 1:12		
Refractors:		2x
Inserted 1:48		
1	John Elway	6.00
2	Mark Brunell	6.00
3	Jerome Bettis	4.00
4	Steve Young	5.00
5	Herman Moore	4.00
6	Emmitt Smith	10.00
7	Warrick Dunn	6.00
8	Dan Marino	10.00
9	Kordell Stewart	8.00
10	Barry Sanders	15.00
11	Tim Brown	2.00
12	Dorsey Levens	4.00
13	Eddie George	6.00
14	Jerry Rice	8.00
15	Terrell Davis	8.00
16	Napoleon Kaufman	5.00
17	Troy Aikman	8.00
18	Drew Bledsoe	8.00
19	Antonio Freeman	4.00
20	Brett Favre	15.00

1998 Stadium Club Co-Signers

This 12-card hobby exclusive insert featured eight total players with both autographs on the same side of the card. Each arrived with a gold foil Topps "Certified Autograph Issue" stamp. Cards 1-4 were inserted 1:9,400 hobby and 1:5,640 jumbos, 5-8 were inserted 1:3,133 hobby and 1:1,880 jumbos and 9-12 were inserted one per 261 hobby and 1:141 jumbo packs. Co-Signers were numbered with a "CO" prefix.

		MT
Complete Set (12):		3000.
Common Player:		50.00
CO1	Peyton Manning, Ryan Leaf	550.00
CO2	Dan Marino, Kordell Stewart	550.00
CO3	Eddie George, Corey Dillon	250.00
CO4	Dorsey Levens, Mike Alstott	225.00
CO5	Ryan Leaf, Dan Marino	400.00
CO6	Peyton Manning, Kordell Stewart	350.00
CO7	Eddie George, Mike Alstott	150.00
CO8	Dorsey Levens, Corey Dillon	125.00
CO9	Peyton Manning, Dan Marino	200.00
CO10	Ryan Leaf, Kordell Stewart	100.00
CO11	Eddie George, Dorsey Levens	70.00
CO12	Mike Alstott, Corey Dillon	50.00

1998 Stadium Club Double Threat

This 10-card insert features two top tandems from 10 different NFL teams. Each player takes up half the card and contains the insert name printed repeatedly across the background along with the team logo. Double Threat inserts are seeded one per eight packs and are numbered with a "DT" prefix.

		MT
Complete Set (10):		50.00
Common Player:		1.50
Inserted 1:8		
1	Marshall Faulk, Peyton Manning	15.00
2	Curtis Conway, Curtis Enis	6.00
3	Drew Bledsoe, Robert Edwards	7.00
4	Warrick Dunn, Jacquez Green	6.00
5	John Elway, Marcus Nash	7.00
6	Mark Brunell, Fred Taylor	8.00
7	Eddie George, Kevin Dyson	6.00
8	Michael Jackson, Patrick Johnson	1.50
9	Terry Glenn, Tony Simmons	1.50
10	Natrone Means, Ryan Leaf	7.00

1998 Stadium Club Leading Legends

Leading Legends was a retail-exclusive insert that dis-
played the NFL's current record-holders among quarterbacks, wide receivers and running backs. The cards are printed on plastic with a gold foil background and card back. These were inserted one per 12 packs and unnumbered.

		MT
Complete Set (10):		40.00
Common Player:		2.00
Inserted 1:12 Retail		
1	Jerry Rice	5.00
2	Bruce Smith	2.00
3	Reggie White	3.00
4	Warren Moon	2.00
5	Dan Marino	7.00
6	John Elway	5.00
7	Emmitt Smith	7.00
8	Brett Favre	10.00
9	Steve Young	4.00
10	Barry Sanders	10.00

1998 Stadium Club Prime Rookies

This 10-card insert displayed the top draft picks in 1998 on a silver foil finish, with the insert name running up the right side. Prime Rookies were inserted one per eight packs and numbered with a "PR" prefix.

		MT
Complete Set (10):		50.00
Common Player:		1.50
Inserted 1:8		
1	Ryan Leaf	6.00
2	Andre Wadsworth	3.00
3	Fred Taylor	8.00
4	Kevin Dyson	4.00
5	Charles Woodson	6.00
6	Robert Edwards	5.00
7	Grant Wistrom	1.50
8	Curtis Enis	6.00
9	Randy Moss	20.00
10	Peyton Manning	15.00

1998 Stadium Club Super Chrome

SuperChrome featured 3-1/4" x 4-9/16" versions of the 20-card Chrome insert. These were inserted one per hobby box, with Refractor versions every 12 Home Team Advantage/Hobby Collector Pack boxes.

		MT
Complete Set (20):		100.00
Common Player:		2.00
Minor Stars:		4.00
Refractors:		2x
1	John Elway	6.00
2	Mark Brunell	6.00
3	Jerome Bettis	4.00
4	Steve Young	5.00
5	Herman Moore	4.00
6	Emmitt Smith	10.00
7	Warrick Dunn	6.00
8	Dan Marino	10.00
9	Kordell Stewart	8.00
10	Barry Sanders	15.00
11	Tim Brown	2.00
12	Dorsey Levens	4.00
13	Eddie George	6.00
14	Jerry Rice	8.00
15	Terrell Davis	8.00
16	Napoleon Kaufman	5.00
17	Troy Aikman	8.00
18	Drew Bledsoe	8.00
19	Antonio Freeman	4.00
20	Brett Favre	15.00

Post-1980 cards in Near Mint condition will generally sell for about 75% of the quoted Mint value. Excellent-condition cards bring no more than 40%.

1998 Stadium Club Triumvirate Luminous

Triumvirate was a 15-card, hobby-only insert in 1998. It featured three teammates on die-cut, fit-together cards numbered with a "T" prefix and either an A, B or C suffix. Regular, Luminous versions were seeded one per 24 packs, Luminescent versions were one per 96 and Illuminators were one per 192 packs.

		MT
Complete Set (15):		100.00
Common Player:		3.00
Minor Stars:		6.00
Inserted 1:24 Hobby		
Luminescent Cards:		2x
Inserted 1:96 Hobby		
Illuminator Cards:		5x
Inserted 1:192 Hobby		
T1A	Terrell Davis	10.00
T1B	John Elway	10.00
T1C	Shannon Sharpe	3.00
T2A	Barry Sanders	20.00
T2B	Scott Mitchell	3.00
T2C	Herman Moore	6.00
T3A	Dorsey Levens	6.00
T3B	Brett Favre	20.00
T3C	Antonio Freeman	6.00
T4A	Emmitt Smith	15.00
T4B	Troy Aikman	10.00
T4C	Michael Irvin	6.00
T5A	Napoleon Kaufman	6.00
T5B	Jeff George	3.00
T5C	Tim Brown	3.00

1999 Stadium Club

This was a 200-card set that included two subsets consisting of 25 Transactions and 25 Draft Picks found 1:3 packs. Each card was embossed and printed full-bleed on 20-point stock with a holographic foil logo. Two parallel sets were issued: First Day and One of a Kind. Other inserts included: Chrome Previews, Co-Signers, Emperors of the Zone, Lone Star Autographs, 3x3 Luminous and Never Compromise. SRP was $2.00 for six-card packs.

		MT
Complete Set (200):		85.00
Common Player:		.15
Minor Stars:		.30
Common Rookie:		1.00
Inserted 1:3		
Wax Box:		40.00
1	Dan Marino	2.00
2	Andre Reed	.15
3	Michael Westbrook	.30
4	Isaac Bruce	.50
5	Curtis Martin	.50
6	Courtney Hawkins	.15
7	Charles Way	.15
8	Terrell Owens	.50
9	Warrick Dunn	.50
10	Jake Plummer	1.50
11	Chad Brown	.15
12	Yancey Thigpen	.30
13	Lamar Thomas	.15
14	Keenan McCardell	.30
15	Shannon Sharpe	.30
16	Robert Brooks	.15
17	Cameron Cleeland	.30
18	Derrick Thomas	.15
19	Mark Brunell	1.00
20	Jamal Anderson	.50
21	Germane Crowell	.30
22	Rod Smith	.30
23	Ty Law	.15
24	Cris Carter	.50
25	Terrell Davis	2.00
26	Takeo Spikes	.15
27	Tim Biakabutuka	.30
28	Jermaine Lewis	.30
29	Adrian Murrell	.30
30	Doug Flutie	.75
31	Curtis Enis	.50
32	Skip Hicks	.30
33	Steve McNair	.75
34	Charles Woodson	.50
35	Jessie Armstead	.15
36	Shawn Springs	.15
37	Levon Kirkland	.15
38	Freddie Jones	.30
39	Warren Sapp	.15
40	Emmitt Smith	2.00
41	Reidel Anthony	.30
42	Tony Simmons	.30
43	Andre Hastings	.15
44	Byron Morris	.15
45	Jimmy Smith	.30
46	Antonio Freeman	.50
47	Herman Moore	.50
48	Muhsin Muhammad	.30
49	Chris Chandler	.30
50	John Elway	2.00
51	Aeneas Williams	.15
52	Bobby Engram	.15
53	Billy Davis	.15
54	Zach Thomas	.30
55	Mike Alstott	.50
56	Junior Seau	.30
57	Aaron Glenn	.15
58	Darrell Green	.15
59	Thurman Thomas	.30
60	Troy Aikman	1.50
61	Bill Romanowski	.15
62	Wesley Walls	.15
63	Andre Wadsworth	.15
64	Robert Smith	.50
65	Elvis Grbac	.30
66	Terry Fair	.15
67	Ben Coates	.30
68	Bert Emanuel	.15
69	Jacquez Green	.30
70	Barry Sanders	3.00
71	James Jett	.15
72	Gary Brown	.15
73	Stephen Alexander	.15
74	Wayne Chrebet	.50
75	Drew Bledsoe	1.00
76	John Lynch	.15
77	Jake Reed	.30
78	Marvin Harrison	.50
79	Johnnie Morton	.15
80	Brett Favre	3.00
81	Charlie Batch	1.00
82	Antowain Smith	.50
83	O.J. Santiago	.15
84	Larry Centers	.15
85	John Mobley	.15
86	Ernie Mills	.15
87	Jeff Blake	.30
88	Curtis Conway	.30
89	Bruce Smith	.15
90	Peyton Manning	2.00
91	Ray Lewis	.15
92	Ray Buchanan	.15
93	Tim Dwight	.50
94	O.J. McDuffie	.30
95	Vonnie Holliday	.30
96	Jon Kitna	.75
97	Trent Dilfer	.30
98	Jerome Bettis	.50
99	Dedric Ward	.15
100	Fred Taylor	1.50
101	Ike Hilliard	.15
102	Frank Wycheck	.15
103	Eric Moulds	.50
104	Rob Moore	.30
105	Ed McCaffrey	.50
106	Carl Pickens	.30
107	Priest Holmes	.50
108	Kevin Hardy	.15
109	Terry Glenn	.50
110	Keyshawn Johnson	.50
111	Karim Abdul	.30
112	Stephen Boyd	.15
113	Ahman Green	.30
114	Duce Staley	.50
115	Vinny Testaverde	.30
116	Napoleon Kaufman	.50
117	Frank Sanders	.15
118	Peter Boulware	.15
119	Kevin Greene	.15
120	Steve Young	.75
121	Darnay Scott	.30
122	Deion Sanders	.50
123	Corey Dillon	.50
124	Randall Cunningham	.50
125	Eddie George	.75
126	Derrick Alexander	.15
127	Mark Chmura	.30
128	Michael Sinclair	.15
129	Rickey Dudley	.15
130	Joey Galloway	.50
131	Michael Strahan	.15
132	Ricky Proehl	.15
133	Natrone Means	.30
134	Dorsey Levens	.50
135	Andre Rison	.30
136	John Avery	.30
137	John Randle	.15
138	Terance Mathis	.15
139	Erik Kramer	.15
140	Jerry Rice	1.50
141	Michael Irvin	.30
142	Oronde Gadsden	.30
143	Jerome Pathon	.15
144	Ricky Watters	.50
145	J.J. Stokes	.30
146	Kordell Stewart	.75
147	Tim Brown	.30
148	Garrison Hearst	.50
149	Tony Gonzalez	.30
150	Randy Moss	3.00
151	Daunte Culpepper	8.00
152	Amos Zereoue	4.00
153	Champ Bailey	3.00
154	Peerless Price	4.00
155	Edgerrin James	20.00
156	Joe Germaine	3.00
157	David Boston	5.00
158	Kevin Faulk	4.00
159	Troy Edwards	5.00
160	Akili Smith	5.00
161	Kevin Johnson	5.00
162	Rob Konrad	3.00
163	Shaun King	6.00
164	James Johnson	4.00
165	Donovan McNabb	8.00
166	Torry Holt	5.00
167	Michael Cloud	2.00
168	Sedrick Irvin	3.00
169	Cade McNown	8.00
170	Ricky Williams	15.00
171	Karsten Bailey	1.00
172	Cecil Collins	8.00
173	Brock Huard	3.00
174	D'Wayne Bates	2.00
175	Tim Couch	15.00
176	Transactions (Torrance Small)	.15
177	Transactions (Warren Moon)	.30
178	Transactions (Raghib Ismail)	.15
179	Transactions (Marshall Faulk)	.50
180	Transactions (Trent Green)	.50
181	Transactions (Sean Dawkins)	.15
182	Transactions (Pete Mitchell)	.15
183	Transactions (Jeff Graham)	.15
184	Transactions (Eddie Kennison)	.15
185	Transactions (Kerry Collins)	.30
186	Transactions (Eric Green)	.15
187	Transactions (Kyle Brady)	.15
188	Transactions (Tony Martin)	.15
189	Transactions (Jim Harbaugh)	.30
190	Transactions (Carnell Lake)	.15
191	Transactions (Steve Atwater)	.15
192	Transactions (Dale Carter)	.15
193	Transactions (Charles Johnson)	.15
194	Transactions (Tony Banks)	.15
195	Transactions (Jeff George)	.15
196	Transactions (Scott Mitchell)	.15
197	Transactions (Chris Calloway)	.15
198	Transactions (Rich Gannon)	.15
199	Transactions (Leslie Shepherd)	.15
200	Transactions (Brad Johnson)	.50

1999 Stadium Club First Day Issue

This 200-card insert set was a parallel to the base set and was a retail exclusive. Each single had the "First Day Issue" foil stamp on the fronts. Singles were sequentially numbered to 150 and found 1:38 packs.

	MT
First Day Cards:	10x-20x
First Day Rookies:	2x-4x
Production 150 Sets	
Inserted 1:38 Retail	

1999 Stadium Club One of a Kind

This was a 200-card insert set that was a hobby exclusive and paralleled the base set. Singles were sequentially numbered to 150 and inserted 1:48 packs.

	MT
One of a Kind Cards:	10x-20x
One of a Kind Rookies:	2x-4x
Production 150 Sets	
Inserted 1:48 Hobby	

1999 Stadium Club Chrome Preview

This was a 20-card insert set that included the hottest players from the Stadium Club set and pictured them with chromium stock. Singles were inserted 1:24 packs. A parallel Refractor version was made and inserted 1:96 packs. A Jumbo version was issued and found one-per-box and a Jumbo Refractor version was issued one every twelve boxes.

		MT
Complete Set (20):		100.00
Common Player:		3.00
Inserted 1:24		
Refractors:		2x
Inserted 1:96		
Jumbos:		1x
Inserted 1:box		
Jumbo Refractors:		3x
Inserted 1:12 boxes		
1	Randy Moss	12.00
2	Terrell Davis	8.00
3	Peyton Manning	8.00
4	Fred Taylor	6.00
5	John Elway	8.00
6	Steve Young	8.00
7	Brett Favre	12.00
8	Jamal Anderson	4.00
9	Barry Sanders	12.00
10	Dan Marino	8.00
11	Jerry Rice	6.00
12	Emmitt Smith	8.00
13	Randall Cunningham	3.00
14	Troy Aikman	6.00
15	Akili Smith	6.00
16	Donovan McNabb	6.00
17	Edgerrin James	12.00
18	Torry Holt	4.00
19	Ricky Williams	12.00
20	Tim Couch	12.00

1999 Stadium Club Co-Signers

This six-card insert set was a hobby exclusive and showcased six different double-autographed cards. Both players and their autographs were pictured on the same side of the card. Each single included the gold foil Topps "Certified Autograph Issue" stamp. Cards #1 and #2 were inserted 1:2,854 packs and cards #3-#6 were issued 1:1,189.

		MT
Complete Set (6):		1500.
Common Player:		150.00
Inserted 1:2,854 (1-3)		
Inserted 1:1,189 (4-6)		
1	Ricky Williams, Terrell Davis	325.00
2	Edgerrin James, Terrell Davis	325.00
3	Tim Couch, Dan Marino	325.00
4	Tim Couch, Peyton Manning	300.00
5	Randy Moss, Jerry Rice	300.00
6	Vinny Testaverde, Dan Marino	150.00

1999 Stadium Club Emperors of the Zone

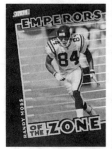

This 10-card insert set included the best touchdown producers in the NFL. Each was featured on a solid black styrene card with silver foil. Singles were inserted 1:12 packs.

		MT
Complete Set (10):		30.00
Common Player:		1.00
Inserted 1:12		
1	Ricky Williams	6.00
2	Brett Favre	6.00
3	Donovan McNabb	3.00
4	Peyton Manning	4.00
5	Terrell Davis	4.00
6	Jamal Anderson	1.00
7	Edgerrin James	6.00
8	Fred Taylor	4.00
9	Tim Couch	6.00
10	Randy Moss	6.00

1999 Stadium Club Lone Star Autographs

This 11-card insert set included autographs from some of the top players in the NFL. Each single included the Topps "Certified Autograph Issue" stamp. Singles were found 1:697 packs.

		MT
Complete Set (11):		1000.
Common Player:		30.00
Inserted 1:697		
1	Randy Moss	200.00
2	Jerry Rice	150.00
3	Peyton Manning	175.00
4	Vinny Testaverde	30.00
5	Tim Couch	200.00
6	Dan Marino	175.00
7	Edgerrin James	200.00
8	Fred Taylor	100.00
9	Garrison Hearst	30.00
10	Antonio Freeman	30.00
11	Torry Holt	75.00

A card number in parentheses ( ) indicates the set is unnumbered.

1999 Stadium Club 3 X 3 Luminous

This 15-card insert set featured three stars on three different technologies, Luminous, Luminescent and Illuminator, with each combination arranged by position and conference. Each single is featured on a laser-cut design where the collector could fuse three players together to form one oversized card. Luminous singles were found 1:36 packs. The Luminescent parallel singles were found 1:144 packs and the Illuminator cards were inserted 1:288 packs.

		MT
Complete Set (15):		85.00
Common Player:		3.00
Inserted 1:36		
Luminescent Cards:		3x
Inserted 1:144		
Illuminator Cards:		4x
Inserted 1:288		
1A	Brett Favre	12.00
1B	Troy Aikman	6.00
1C	Jake Plummer	6.00
2A	Jamal Anderson	3.00
2B	Emmitt Smith	8.00
2C	Barry Sanders	12.00
3A	Antonio Freeman	3.00
3B	Randy Moss	12.00
3C	Jerry Rice	6.00
4A	Peyton Manning	8.00
4B	John Elway	8.00
4C	Dan Marino	8.00
5A	Fred Taylor	6.00
5B	Terrell Davis	8.00
5C	Curtis Martin	3.00

1999 Stadium Club Never Compromise

This 30-card insert set was divided into three different subsets. The Rookies featured ten hot newcomers, The ten Stars included current NFL stars at the pinnacle of their success and the Legends featured ten Canton-bound season veterans whose play should enshrine them in the Hall of Fame. They were inserted 1:12 packs.

		MT
Complete Set (30):		80.00
Common Player:		1.00
Minor Stars:		2.00
Inserted 1:12		
1	Tim Couch	8.00
2	David Boston	2.50
3	Daunte Culpepper	4.00
4	Donovan McNabb	4.00
5	Ricky Williams	8.00
6	Troy Edwards	2.50
7	Akili Smith	4.00
8	Torry Holt	2.50
9	Cade McNown	4.00
10	Edgerrin James	8.00
11	Randy Moss	8.00

1999 Stadium Club Chrome

This was a 150-card set that utilized Chrome technology and each single was printed on 23-point stock. Parallel sets included First Day Issues and Refractors. Other inserts included: Clear Shots, Eyes of the Game, Never Compromise and True Colors. SRP was $4.00 for five-card packs.

		MT
Complete Set (150):		100.00
Common Player:		.25
Minor Stars:		.50
Common Rookie:		2.00
Wax Box:		70.00
1	Dan Marino	3.00
2	Andre Reed	.50
3	Michael Westbrook	.50
4	Isaac Bruce	1.00
5	Curtis Martin	1.00
6	Terrell Owens	1.00
7	Warrick Dunn	1.00
8	Jake Plummer	1.50
9	Chad Brown	.25
10	Yancey Thigpen	.50
11	Keenan McCardell	.50
12	Shannon Sharpe	.50
13	Cameron Cleeland	.50
14	Mark Brunell	1.50
15	Jamal Anderson	1.00
16	Germane Crowell	.50
17	Rod Smith	.75
18	Cris Carter	1.00
19	Terrell Davis	3.00
20	Tim Biakabutuka	.50
21	Jermaine Lewis	.25
22	Adrian Murrell	.50
23	Doug Flutie	1.25
24	Curtis Enis	1.00
25	Skip Hicks	.50
26	Steve McNair	1.25
27	Charles Woodson	1.00
28	Freddie Jones	.25
29	Warren Sapp	.25
30	Emmitt Smith	3.00
31	Reidel Anthony	.50
32	Tony Simmons	.50
33	Andre Hastings	.25
34	Byron Morris	.25
35	Jimmy Smith	1.00
36	Antonio Freeman	1.00
37	Herman Moore	1.00
38	Muhsin Muhammed	.50
39	Chris Chandler	.50
40	John Elway	3.00
41	Bobby Engram	.25
42	Keith Poole	.25
43	Mike Alstott	1.00
44	Junior Seau	.50
45	Thurman Thomas	.50
46	Troy Aikman	2.00
47	Wesley Walls	.50
48	Robert Smith	1.00
49	Elvis Grbac	.50
50	Ben Coates	.50
51	Bert Emanuel	.25
52	Jacquez Green	.50
53	Barry Sanders	4.00
54	James Jett	.25
55	Gary Brown	.25
56	Stephen Alexander	.25
57	Wayne Chrebet	1.00
58	Drew Bledsoe	1.50
59	Jake Reed	.50
60	Marvin Harrison	1.00
61	Johnnie Morton	.25
62	Brett Favre	4.00
63	Charlie Batch	1.25
64	Antowain Smith	1.00
65	Ernie Mills	.25
66	Jeff Blake	.50
67	Curtis Conway	.50
68	Bruce Smith	.25
69	Peyton Manning	3.00
70	Tim Dwight	1.00
71	O.J. McDuffie	.50
72	Jon Kitna	1.00
73	Trent Dilfer	.50
74	Jerome Bettis	1.00
75	Dedric Ward	.25
76	Fred Taylor	2.00
77	Ike Hilliard	.50
78	Frank Wycheck	.25
79	Eric Moulds	1.00
80	Rob Moore	.75
81	Ed McCaffrey	.75
82	Carl Pickens	.50
83	Priest Holmes	1.00
84	Terry Glenn	1.00
85	Keyshawn Johnson	1.00
86	Karim Abdul	.50
87	Ahman Green	.50
88	Duce Staley	1.00
89	Vinny Testaverde	.50
90	Napoleon Kaufman	1.00
91	Frank Sanders	.50
92	Steve Young	1.25
93	Darnay Scott	.50
94	Deion Sanders	1.00
95	Corey Dillon	1.00
96	Randall Cunningham	1.00
97	Eddie George	1.25
98	Derrick Alexander	.25
99	Mark Chmura	.50
100	Rickey Dudley	.50
101	Joey Galloway	1.00
102	Ricky Proehl	.25
103	Natrone Means	.75
104	Dorsey Levens	1.00
105	Andre Rison	.50
106	John Avery	.50
107	Terance Mathis	.25
108	Rae Carruth	.25
109	Jerry Rice	2.00
110	Michael Irvin	.50
111	Oronde Gadsden	.50
112	Jerome Pathon	.25
113	Ricky Watters	.50
114	J.J. Stokes	.50
115	Kordell Stewart	1.00
116	Tim Brown	.50
117	Tony Gonzalez	.50
118	Randy Moss	4.00
119	Daunte Culpepper	10.00
120	Amos Zereoue	3.00
121	Champ Bailey	4.00
122	Peerless Price	4.00
123	Edgerrin James	25.00
124	Joe Germaine	3.00
125	David Boston	6.00
126	Kevin Faulk	4.00
127	Troy Edwards	6.00
128	Akili Smith	8.00
129	Kevin Johnson	6.00
130	Rob Konrad	2.00
131	Shawn King	10.00
132	James Johnson	4.00
133	Donovan McNabb	10.00
134	Torry Holt	6.00
135	Michael Cloud	2.00
136	Sedrick Irvin	3.00
137	Cade McNown	10.00
138	Ricky Williams	15.00
139	Karsten Bailey	2.00
140	Cecil Collins	4.00
141	Brock Huard	4.00
142	D'Wayne Bates	2.00
143	Tim Couch	15.00
144	Raghib Ismail	.25
145	Marshall Faulk	1.00
146	Trent Green	.50
147	Tony Martin	.25
148	Jim Harbaugh	.25
149	Rich Gannon	.25
150	Brad Johnson	.75

1999 Stadium Club Chrome First Day

This was a 150-card parallel to the base set. Each single included the "First Day Issue" stamp and was sequentially numbered to 100. They were inserted 1:59 packs. A parallel Refractor version was also released and each of those was sequentially numbered to 25 and inserted 1:235 packs.

	MT
First Day Cards:	15x-30x
First Day Rookies:	4x-8x
Inserted 1:59	
Production 100 Sets	

1999 Stadium Club Chrome Refractors

This was a 150-card parallel to the base set. Each single was printed with iridescent technology and inserted 1:12 packs.

	MT
Refractor Cards:	3x-6x
Refractor Rookies:	2x
Inserted 1:12	

1999 Stadium Club Chrome Clear Shots

This nine-card insert set was an exclusive to the Stadium Club Chrome product. Each single was printed on a clear polycarbonate stock and was die cut. Singles were inserted 1:22 packs. A Refractor version was also released with each of those singles inserted 1:110 packs.

		MT
Complete Set (9):		45.00
Common Player:		2.00
Inserted 1:22		
Refractor Cards:		3x
Inserted 1:110		
1	David Boston	4.00
2	Edgerrin James	20.00
3	Chris Claiborne	2.00
4	Torry Holt	4.00
5	Tim Couch	12.00
6	Donovan McNabb	7.00
7	Akili Smith	5.00
8	Champ Bailey	3.00
9	Troy Edwards	4.00

1999 Stadium Club Chrome Eyes of the Game

This seven-card insert set was an exclusive insert to Stadium Club Chrome Football. A mix of rookies and veterans was included in this set. Singles were inserted 1:20 packs. A parallel Refractor version was also issued and found 1:100 packs.

		MT
Complete Set (7):		45.00
Common Player:		5.00
Inserted 1:20		
Refractor Cards:		3x
Inserted 1:100		
1	Tim Couch	10.00
2	Ricky Williams	10.00
3	Barry Sanders	10.00
4	Brett Favre	10.00
5	Terrell Davis	5.00
6	Peyton Manning	10.00
7	Randy Moss	10.00

A card number in parentheses ( ) indicates the set is unnumbered.

1999 Stadium Club Chrome Never Compromise

This 40-card insert set included 20 rookies and 20 veterans. Singles were inserted 1:6 packs. A parallel Refractor version was issued and inserted 1:30 packs.

		MT
Complete Set (40):		150.00
Common Player:		1.50
Minor Stars:		3.00
Inserted 1:6		
Refractor Cards:		3x
Inserted 1:30		
1	Tim Couch	10.00
2	David Boston	3.00
3	Daunte Culpepper	6.00
4	Donovan McNabb	6.00
5	Ricky Williams	10.00
6	Troy Edwards	3.00
7	Akili Smith	5.00
8	Torry Holt	4.00
9	Cade McNown	4.00
10	Edgerrin James	15.00
11	Cecil Collins	3.00
12	Peerless Price	1.50
13	Kevin Johnson	4.00
14	Champ Bailey	3.00
15	Kevin Faulk	3.00
16	D'Wayne Bates	1.50
17	Shaun King	6.00
18	Sedrick Irvin	3.00
19	James Johnson	3.00
20	Rob Konrad	1.50
21	Randy Moss	12.00
22	Peyton Manning	12.00
23	Eddie George	4.00
24	Fred Taylor	6.00
25	Jamal Anderson	1.50
26	Joey Galloway	1.50
27	Terrell Davis	8.00
28	Keyshawn Johnson	1.50
29	Antonio Freeman	1.50
30	Jake Plummer	5.00
31	Steve Young	4.00
32	Barry Sanders	12.00
33	Dan Marino	10.00
34	Emmitt Smith	10.00
35	Brett Favre	12.00
36	Randall Cunningham	1.50
37	John Elway	10.00
38	Drew Bledsoe	5.00
39	Jerry Rice	6.00
40	Troy Aikman	6.00

1999 Stadium Club Chrome True Colors

This was a 10-card insert set that was an exclusive to the Stadium Club Chrome product. Singles were inserted 1:24 packs. A parallel Refractor version was also released and found 1:120 packs.

	MT
Complete Set (10):	65.00
Common Player:	5.00
Inserted 1:24	
Refractor Cards:	3x

Inserted 1:120

1	Doug Flutie	5.00
2	Steve Young	5.00
3	Jake Plummer	7.00
4	Jerry Rice	8.00
5	Randy Moss	12.00
6	Fred Taylor	8.00
7	Peyton Manning	12.00
8	Dan Marino	10.00
9	Brett Favre	12.00
10	Terrell Davis	8.00

1963 Stancraft Playing Cards

This 54-card set, titled "Official NFL All-Time Greats," commemorates the opening of the Pro Football Hall of Fame in Canton, Ohio. Each of the cards, designed as playing cards, features an artistic drawing of the player, with his name, position, team name and years played below the picture, which is done in brown ink. The Aces and Jokers, however, have NFL logos on them instead of artwork. Two styles were used for the card backs - an NFL logo in the center surrounded by the 14 NFL team logos in a checkerboard pattern, all against a red background, or a green background with the 14 team helmets contained within it. Cards, 2-1/4" x 3-1/2" with rounded corners, came in a plastic box.

		NM
	Complete Set (54):	125.00
	Common Player:	1.50
AC	NFL Logo	1.50
2C	Johnny Blood McNally	2.00
3C	Bobby Mitchell	3.00
4C	Bill Howton	1.50
5C	Wilbur Fats Henry	2.00
6C	Tony Canedeo	2.00
7C	Bulldog Turner	3.00
8C	Charlie Trippi	2.00
9C	Tommy Mason	1.50
10C	Earl "Dutch" Clark	2.00
JC	Y.A. Tittle	5.00
QC	Lou Groza	5.00
KC	Bobby Layne	6.00
AD	NFL Logo	1.50
2D	Frankie Albert	1.50
3D	Del Shofner	1.50
4D	Ollie Matson	4.00
5D	Mike Ditka	8.00
6D	Otto Graham	6.00
7D	Chuck Bednarik	4.00
8D	Jim Taylor	3.00
9D	Mel Hein	2.00
10D	Eddie Price	1.50
JD	Sonny Randle	1.50
QD	Joe Perry	4.00
KD	Bob Waterfield	5.00
AH	NFL Logo	1.50
2H	Paul Hornung	5.00
3H	Johnny Unitas	10.00
4H	Doak Walker	5.00
5H	Tom Fears	3.00
6H	Jim Thorpe	10.00
7H	Gino Marchetti	3.00
8H	Claude Buddy Young	1.50
9H	Jim Benton	2.00
10H	Jim Brown	12.00
JH	George Halas	1.50
QH	Sammy Baugh	4.00
KH	Bill Dudley	2.50
1S	NFL Logo	1.50
2S	Eddie LeBaron	2.00
3S	Don Hutson	3.50
4S	Clarke Hinkle	2.00
5S	Charley Conerly	2.50
6S	Earl Curly Lambeau	2.00
7S	Sid Luckman	5.00
8S	Pete Pihos	2.00
9S	Dante Lavelli	2.00
10S	Norm Van Brocklin	4.00
11S	Cloyce Box	1.50
12S	Joe Schmidt	3.00
13S	Elroy Hirsch	3.00
xx	Joker (NFL logo)	2.00
xx	Joker (NFL logo)	2.00
1D	NFL Logo	1.50
2D	Frankie Albert	1.50
3D	Del Shofner	1.50
4D	Ollie Matson	4.00
5D	Mike Ditka	8.00
6D	Otto Graham	6.00
7D	Chuck Bednarik	4.00
8D	Jim Taylor	3.00
9D	Mel Hein	2.00
10D	Eddie Price	1.50
11D	Sonny Randle	1.50
12D	Joe Perry	4.00
13D	Bob Waterfield	5.00
1H	NFL Logo	1.50
2H	Paul Hornung	5.00
3H	Johnny Unitas	10.00
4H	Doak Walker	5.00
5H	Tom Fears	3.00
6H	Jim Thorpe	10.00
7H	Gino Marchetti	3.00
8H	Claude Buddy Young	1.50
9H	Jim Benton	2.00
10H	Jim Brown	12.00
JH	George Halas	1.50
QH	Sammy Baugh	4.00
KH	Bill Dudley	2.50
1S	NFL Logo	1.50
2S	Eddie LeBaron	2.00
3S	Don Hutson	3.50
4S	Clarke Hinkle	2.00
5S	Charley Conerly	2.50
6S	Earl (Curly) Lambeau	2.00
7S	Sid Luckman	5.00
8S	Pete Pihos	2.00
9S	Dante Lavelli	2.00
10S	Norm Van Brocklin	4.00
JS	Cloyce Box	1.50
QS	Joe Schmidt	3.00
KS	Elroy Hirsch	3.00

1991 Star Pics Promos

Star Pics issued these cards to promote their 1991 set. They were distributed in two-card panels and inserted in an issue of Pro Football Weekly. The card fronts feature a color photo with a football border. The backs are green and include basic player information and a close-up photo.

		MT
	Complete Set (4):	4.00
	Common Player:	1.00
1	Mark Carrier DB	1.00
2	Aaron Craver	1.00
3	Dan McGwire	1.00
4	Eric Turner	1.00

1991 Star Pics

The company's first set of college prospects was released in June 1991. The set features 44 out of 55 first- and second-round picks from the 1991 draft. All 91 players in the set -- the roster of which was set before the draft -- were selected. Subsets include the nine-card flashback issue (NFL players in college uniforms) and Top Pick Agents, featuring player representatives. At least one in 50 sets contained a randomly- inserted autograph. (Key: FL - flashback, A - agent.) Two promo panels, were also produced to preview the regular 1991 set's design. The players paired together were 1) Mark Carrier, $1, and 2) Aaron Craver, $1, and 3) Dan McGwire, $1, and 4) Eric Turner, $1.

		MT
	Complete Set (112):	6.00
	Common Player:	.05
	Common Autograph:	6.00
	Autograph Cards:	20x-40x
	NFL Autographs:	200x-400x
1	1991 NFL Draft Overview	.05
2	Barry Sanders (FL)	.10
3	Nick Bell	.10
4	Kevin Pritchett	.05
5	Huey Richardson	.05
6	Mike Croel	.05
7	Paul Justin	.05
8	Ivory Lee Brown	.05
9	Herman Moore	1.25
10	Derrick Thomas (FL)	.15
11	Keith Taylor	.05
12	Joe Johnson	.05
13	Dan McGwire	.10
14	Harvey Williams	.50
15	Eric Moten	.05
16	Steve Zucker	.05
17	Randal Hill	.20
18	Browning Nagle	.05
19	Stan Thomas	.05
20	Emmitt Smith (FL)	.50
21	Ted Washington	.05
22	Lamar Rogers	.05
23	Kenny Walker	.05
24	Howard Griffith	.05
25	Reggie Johnson	.05
26	Lawrence Dawsey	.05
27	Joe Garten	.05
28	Moe Gardner	.05
29	Michael Stonebreaker	.05
30	Jeff George (FL)	.15
31	Leigh Steinberg (A)	.05
32	John Flannery	.05
33	Pat Harlow	.05
34	Kanavis McGhee	.05
35	Michael Dumas	.05
36	Godfrey Myles	.05
37	Shawn Moore	.05
38	Jeff Graham	.50
39	Ricky Watters	1.00
40	Andre Ware (FL)	.05
41	Henry Jones	.10
42	Eric Turner	.30
43	Bob Wolf (A)	.05
44	Randy Baldwin	.05
45	Morris Lewis	.05
46	Jerry Evans	.05
47	Derek Russell	.05
48	Merton Hanks	.40
49	Kevin Donnalley	.05
50	Troy Aikman (FL)	.30
51	William Thomas	.05
52	Chris Thome	.05
53	Ricky Ervins	.10
54	Jake Reed	.25
55	Jerome Henderson	.05
56	Mark Vander Poel	.05
57	Bernard Ellison	.05
58	Jack Mills (A)	.05
59	Jarrod Bunch	.05
60	Mark Carrier (FL)	.05
61	Rocen Keeton	.05
62	Louis Riddick	.05
63	Bobby Wilson	.05
64	Steve Jackson	.05
65	Brett Favre	2.50
66	Ernie Mills	.20
67	Joe Valerio	.05
68	Chris Smith	.05
69	Ralph Cindrich	.05
70	Christian Okoye (FL)	.05
71	Charles McRae	.05
72	Jon Vaughn	.05
73	Eric Swann	.30
74	Bill Musgrave	.05
75	Eric Bieniemy	.20
76	Pat Tyrance	.05
77	Vince Clark	.05
78	Eugene Williams	.05
79	Rob Carpenter	.05
80	Deion Sanders (FL)	.25
81	Roman Phifer	.10
82	Greg Lewis	.05
83	John Johnson	.05
84	Richard Howell (A)	.05
85	Jesse Campbell	.05
86	Stanley Richard	.05
87	Alfred Williams	.05
88	Mike Pritchard	.25
89	Mel Agee	.05
90	Aaron Craver	.05
91	Tim Barnett	.05
92	Wesley Carroll	.05
93	Kevin Scott	.05
94	Darren Lewis	.05
95	Tim Bruton	.05
96	Tim James	.05
97	Darryl Lewis	.05
98	Shawn Jefferson	.20
99	Mitch Donahue	.05
100	Marvin Demoff (A)	.05
101	Adrian Cooper	.05
102	Bruce Pickens	.05
103	Scott Zolak	.05
104	Phil Hansen	.05
105	Ed King	.05
106	Mike Jones	.05
107	Alvin Harper	.50
108	Robert Young	.05
109	Offensive Top Prospects	.05
110	Defensive Top Prospects	.10

Values quoted in this guide reflect the retail price of a card — the price a collector can expect to pay when buying a card from a dealer. The wholesale price — that which a collector can expect to receive from a dealer when selling cards — will be significantly lower, depending on desirability and condition.

1992 Star Pics

The top collegiate pro prospects are featured in this 100-card set from Star Pics. Each card front has a glossy color action photo on the front, with a white border. The player's name and position run vertically along the left side of the card. A Star Pics logo appears in the lower right corner. The card back has a mug shot of the player, and summarizes his collegiate accomplishments. A scouting report, which lists the player's strengths and weaknesses, is also given. A card number appears in the upper left corner. Cards are sold as a factory set, or in 10-card packs. Subsets in the main set included five Flashback cards (#s 10, 20, 30, 50 and 70) and 10 StarStat cards. Two StarStat cards (#s 1 and 65) were included in the factory sets. The eight others were random inserts in packs.

		MT
	Complete Set (100):	6.00
	Common Player:	.05
	Common Autograph:	6.00
	Autograph Cards:	20x-40x
	NFL Autographs:	100x-200x
1	Steve Emtman	.10
2	Chris Hakel	.05
3	Phillippi Sparks	.05
4	Howard Dinkins	.05
5	Robert Brooks	.75
6	Chris Pederson	.05
7	Bucky Richardson	.10
8	Keith Goganious	.05
9	Robert Porcher	.05
10	Andre Rison	.20
11	Jason Hanson	.30
12	Tommy Vardell	.10
13	Bernard Dafney	.05
14	Levon Kirkland	.05
15	Corey Widmer	.05
16	Santana Dotson	.10
17	Chris Holder	.05
18	Elbert Turner	.05
19	Mike Croel	.10
20	Darren Perry	.10
21	Troy Vincent	.10
22	Quentin Coryatt	.40
23	John Brown III	.05
24	John Ray	.05
25	Vaughn Dunbar	.10
26	Stacey Dillard	.05
27	Alonzo Spellman	.20
28	Darren Woodson	.10
29	Pat Swilling	.10
64	Keith Hamilton	.05
65	Vaughn Dunbar	.10
66	Willie Clay	.05
67	Robert Jones	.05
68	Leon Searcy Jr.	.05
69	Elliot Pilton	.05
70	Thurman Thomas	.20
71	Mark Wheeler	.05
72	Jeremy Lincoln	.10
73	Tony McCoy	.05
74	Charles Davenport	.05
75	Patrick Rowe	.05
76	Tommy Jeter	.05
77	Rod Smith	.05
78	Johnny Mitchell	.25
79	Corey Barlow	.05
80	Scottie Graham	.15
81	Mark Bounds	.05
82	Chester McGlockton	.05
83	Ray Roberts	.05
84	Dale Carter	.10
85	James Patton	.05
86	Tyrone Legette	.05
87	Leodis Flowers	.05
88	Rico Smith	.05
89	Kevin Turner	.10
90	Steve Emtman	.10
91	Rodney Culver	.10
92	Chris Mims	.15
93	Carlos Snow	.05
94	Corey Harris	.05
95	Nate Williams	.05
96	Timothy Roberts	.05
97	Steve Israel	.05
98	Tony Smith	.05
99	Dwayne Sabb	.05
100	Checklist	.05

1992 Star Pics StarStat Bonus

Eight top collegiate NFL prospects are featured in this insert set. Cards were random inserts in 10-card foil StarPaks and compare the players' collegiate statistics to those of NFL greats. Fronts have the "Star-Stats" logo on them; backs have the card number. Two additional StarStat cards, for Steve Emtman and Vaughn Dunbar, were also made and were included in the 1992 Star Pics factory set.

		MT
	Complete Set (8):	8.00
	Common Player:	.50
1	Dale Carter	1.00
2	Carl Pickens	6.00
3	Alonzo Spellman	1.00
4	Jimmy Smith	1.25
5	Quentin Coryatt	2.00
6	Troy Vincent	.50
7	Darryl Williams	.50
8	Courtney Hawkins	.50

1989 Star-Cal Decals

The 54-card, 3" x 4-1/2" sticker set featured players from six NFL teams, and was licensed by the NFL and the NFL Players' Association. The cards have rounded edges with a silver logo (First Edition 1989) in the upper left corner. Each decal also came with a pennant-shaped mini team banner decal in the player's team colors.

		MT
	Complete Set (54):	80.00
	Common Player:	1.00
1	Raul Allegre	1.00
2	Carl Banks	1.00
3	Cornelius Bennett	1.50
4	Brian Blades	1.50
5	Kevin Butler	1.00
6	Harry Carson	1.00
7	Anthony Carter	1.00
8	Michael Carter	1.00
9	Shane Conlan	1.00
10	Roger Craig	1.50
11	Richard Dent	1.25
12	Chris Doleman	1.00
13	Tony Dorsett	4.00
14	Dave Duerson	1.00
15	Charles Haley	1.50
16	Dan Hampton	1.00
17	Al Harris	1.00
18	Mark Jackson	1.00
19	Kevin Smith	1.00
20	Vance Johnson	1.00
21	Clarence Kay	1.00
22	Jim Kelly	4.00
23	Tommy Kramer	1.00
24	Ronnie Lott	2.00
25	Lionel Manuel	1.00
26	Guy McIntyre	1.00
27	Steve McMichael	1.25
28	Karl Mecklenburg	1.25
29	Orson Mobley	1.00
30	Joe Montana	20.00
31	Joe Morris	1.00
32	Joe Nash	1.00
33	Ricky Nattiel	1.00
34	Chuck Nelson	1.00
35	Darrin Nelson	1.00
36	Karl Nelson	1.00
37	Scott Norwood	1.00
38	Bart Oates	1.00
39	Rufus Porter	1.00
40	Andre Reed	2.00
41	Phil Simms	2.00
42	Mike Singletary	1.50
43	Fred Smerlas	1.00
44	Bruce Smith	2.00
45	Kelly Stouffer	1.00
46	Scott Studwell	1.00
47	Matt Suhey	1.00
48	Steve Tasker	1.00
49	Keena Turner	1.00
50	John L. Williams	1.25
51	Wade Wilson	1.00
52	Sammy Winder	1.00
53	Tony Woods	1.00
54	Eric Wright	1.00

1990 Star-Cal Decals Prototypes

The four-card, 3" x 4-1/2" set was issued as a preview to the 1990 94-card decal set.

		MT
	Complete Set (4):	5.00
	Common Player:	1.00
1	Jeff Hostetler	1.00
2	Mike Kenn	1.00
3	Freeman McNeil	1.00
4	Steve Young	3.00

1990 Star-Cal Decals

The 94-card, 3" x 4-1/2" decal set was similar to the 1989 release, complete with facsimile autographs. Six players each from 12 of the league's top teams are featured. Each player decal was issued with a pennant-shaped mini team banner (3-1/2" x 2"). The set is also known as the Grid-Star decal set.

		MT
	Complete Set (94):	160.00
	Common Player:	1.00
1	Eric Allen	1.00
2	Marcus Allen	2.00
3	Flipper Anderson	1.00
4A	Neal Anderson (printed name in black letters)	1.00
4B	Neal Anderson (printed name in white letters)	1.00
5A	Carl Banks (printed name in black letters)	1.00
5B	Carl Banks (printed name in white letters)	1.00
6	Mark Bavaro	1.00
7	Cornelius Bennett	1.50
8	Brian Blades	1.00
9	Joey Browner	1.00
10	Keith Byars	1.00
11A	Anthony Carter (printed name in black letters)	1.00
11B	Anthony Carter (printed name in white letters)	1.00
12	Cris Carter	2.00
13	Michael Carter	1.00
14	Gary Clark	1.00
15	Mark Collins	1.00
16	Shane Conlan	1.00
17	Jim Covert	1.00
18A	Roger Craig (printed name in black letters)	1.50
18B	Roger Craig (printed name in white letters)	1.50
19	Richard Dent	1.25
20	Chris Doleman	1.00
21	Dave Duerson	1.00
22	Henry Ellard	1.50
23A	John Elway (printed name in black letters)	6.00
23B	John Elway (printed name in white letters)	8.00
24	Jim Everett	1.25
25	Mervyn Fernandez	1.00
26	Willie Gault	1.25
27	Bob Golic	1.00
28	Darrell Green	1.25
29	Kevin Greene	1.25
30	Charles Haley	1.25
31	Jay Hilgenberg	1.00
32	Pete Holohan	1.00

33	Kent Hull	1.00
34	Bobby Humphrey	1.00
35A	Bo Jackson (printed name in black letters)	2.00
35B	Bo Jackson (printed name in white letters)	2.00
36	Keith Jackson	1.25
37	Mark Jackson	1.25
38	Joe Jacoby	1.00
39	Vance Johnson	1.00
40	Jim Kelly	3.00
41	Bernie Kosar	1.25
42	Greg Kragen	1.00
43	Jeff Lageman	1.00
44	Pat Leahy	1.00
45	Howie Long	1.25
46A	Ronnie Lott (serial numbered 11419)	1.50
46B	Ronnie Lott (serial numbered 11414)	1.50
47	Kevin Mack	1.00
48	Charles Mann	1.00
49	Leonard Marshall	1.00
50	Clay Matthews	1.25
51	Eric McMillan	1.00
52	Karl Mecklenburg	1.25
53	Dave Meggett (UER) (name misspelled Megget)	1.25
54A	Eric Metcalf (serial numbered 11414)	2.00
54B	Eric Metcalf (serial numbered 11424)	1.50
55	Keith Millard	1.00
56	Frank Minnifield	1.00
57A	Joe Montana (printed name in black letters autograph covers only left leg)	12.00
57B	Joe Montana (printed name in black letters autograph covers both legs)	15.00
57C	Joe Montana (printed name in white letters autograph covers only left leg)	20.00
58	Joe Nash	1.00
59	Ken O'Brien	1.25
60	Rufus Porter	1.00
61	Andre Reed	1.50
62	Mark Rypien	1.25
63	Gerald Riggs	1.00
64	Mickey Shuler	1.00
65	Clyde Simmons	1.25
66A	Phil Simms (printed name in black letters)	1.50
66B	Phil Simms (printed name in white letters)	1.50
67A	Mike Singletary (printed name in black letters)	1.50
67B	Mike Singletary (printed name in white letters)	1.50
68	Jackie Slater	1.00
69	Bruce Smith	1.50
70A	Kelly Stouffer (serial numbered 11414)	1.00
70B	Kelly Stouffer (serial numbered 11427)	1.00
71	Jim Taylor	1.25
72	Lawyer Tillman	1.00
73	Al Toon	1.25
74A	Herschel Walker (printed name in black letters)	1.50
74B	Herschel Walker (printed name in white letters)	1.50
75	Reggie White	2.00
76A	John L. Williams (printed name in black letters autograph below knees)	1.00
76B	John L. Williams (printed name in black letters autograph above knees)	1.00
76C	John L. Williams (printed name in white letters autograph below knees)	1.00
77	Tony Woods	1.00
78	Gary Zimmerman	1.00

1988 Starline Prototypes

The four-card, regular-size set was never issued to the public and just 75 sets were produced. Each card in the set features a color photo with a blue border.

		MT
Complete Set (4):		500.00
Common Player:		75.00
1	John Elway	150.00
2	Bernie Kosar	75.00
3	Joe Montana	275.00
4	Phil Simms	75.00

1961 Steelers Jay Publishing

The 12-card, 5" x 7" features black and white photos with blank backs and were issued in 12-card packs for 25 cents.

		NM
Complete Set (12):		30.00
Common Player:		2.50
1	Preston Carpenter	2.50
2	Dean Derby	2.50
3	Buddy Dial	2.50
4	John Henry Johnson	2.50
5	Bobby Layne	2.50
6	Gene Lipscomb	2.50
7	Bill Mack	2.50
8	Fred Mautino	2.50
9	Lou Michaels	2.50
10	Buddy Parker (CO)	2.50
11	Myron Pottios	2.50
12	Tom Tracy	2.50

1963 Steelers IDL

The 26-card, 4" x 5" set features black and white photos with white borders and an IDL logo in the bottom left corner. The backs are blank.

		NM
Complete Set (26):		75.00
Common Player:		3.00
1	Frank Atkinson	3.00
2	Jim Bradshaw	3.00
3	Ed Brown	3.00
4	John Burrell	3.00
5	Preston Carpenter	3.00
6	Lou Cordileone	3.00
7	Buddy Dial	3.00
8	Bob Ferguson	3.00
9	Glenn Glass	3.00
10	Dick Haley	3.00
11	Dick Hoak	3.00
12	John Henry Johnson	3.00
13	Brady Keys	3.00
14	Joe Krupa	3.00
15	Ray Lemek	3.00
16	Bill Mack	3.00
17	Lou Michaels	3.00
18	Bill Nelsen	3.00
19	Buzz Nutter	3.00
20	Myron Pottios	3.00
21	John Reger	3.00
22	Mike Sandusky	3.00
23	Ernie Stautner	3.00
24	George Tarasovic	3.00
25	Clendon Thomas	3.00
26	Tom Tracy	3.00

1968 Steelers KDKA

The 15-card, 2-3/8" x 4-1/8" set featured multiple players on each horizontal card front by position.

		NM
Complete Set (15):		30.00
Common Player:		2.50
1	Centers: (John Knight, Ray Mansfield)	2.50
2	Coaches: (Bill Austin (Head), Fletcher, Torgeson, McLaughlin, Taylor, Heinrich, DePasqua)	2.50
3	Defensive Backs: (Bob Hohn, Paul Martha, Marv Woodson)	2.50
4	Defensive Backs: (John Foruria, Clendon Thomas, Bob Morgan)	2.50
5	Defensive Linemen: (Ben McGhee, Chuck Hinton, Dick Arndt, Ken Kortas, Lloyd Voss)	2.50
6	Flankers: (Roy Jefferson, Ken Hebert (End-Kicker))	2.50
7	Fullbacks: (Earl Gros, Bill Asbury)	2.50
8	Guards: (Larry Granger, Sam Davis, Bruce Van Dyke)	2.50
9	Linebackers: (Andy Russell, Bill Saul, John Campbell, Ray May)	2.50
10	Quarterbacks: (Dick Shiner, Kent Nix)	2.50
11	Rookies: (Ken Hebert, Ernie Ruple, Mike Taylor)	2.50
12	Running Backs: (Dick Hoak, Don Shy, Jim Butler)	2.50
13	Split Ends: (J.R. Wilburn, Dick Compton)	2.50
14	Tackles: (Fran O'Brien, Mike Haggerty, John Brown)	2.50
15	Tight Ends: (John Hilton, Chet Anderson)	2.50

1972 Steelers Photo Sheets

The eight-card, 2" x 3" set was issued in 10" x 8" sheets. The card fronts feature a black and white photo with the Steelers helmet appearing in the lower left corner. The backs are blank.

		NM
Complete Set (8):		30.00
Common Player:		1.50
1	Ralph Anderson, Jim Clack, Bobby Maples, Henry Davis, Jon Kolb, Ray Mansfield, Sam Davis, Chuck Allen	1.50
2	Jim Brumfield, Chuck Beatty, Bobby Walden, Frank Lewis, Lee Calland, Warren Bankston, Mel Blount, John	1.50
3	Bud Carson (CO), Bob Fry (CO), Dick Hoak (CO), Babe Parilli (CO), George Perles (CO), Lou Riecke (CO), Charley	1.50
4	Jack Ham, Ben McGee, Brian Stenger, Lloyd Voss, Bruce Van Dyke, L.C. Greenwood, Gerry Mullins, John Brown	1.50
5	Joe Greene, Bert Askson (UER), Mel Holmes, Dwight White, Bob Adams, Larry Brown, Dave Smith, John	1.50
6	Chuck Noll (CO), Jon Staggers, Terry Hanratty, Roy Gerela, Terry Bradshaw, Bob Leahy, Joe Gilliam, Rocky	1.50
7	Dick Post, Franco Harris, Dennis Meyer, Lorenzo Brinkley, Steve Furness, Gordon Gravelle, Rick Sharp, Dave	1.50
8	Mike Wagner, Ron Shanklin, Preston Pearson, Glen Edwards, Al Young, John Fuqua, Andy Russell, Steve Davis	1.50

1978 Steelers Team Issue

This set consists of eight 8" x 10" sheets which feature eight black-and-white photos each. Each player photo measures 2" x 3". The sheets are blank-backed and unnumbered.

		NM
Complete Set (8):		80.00
Common Panel:		10.00
1	B. Carr, Reggie Harrison RB, Mel Blount, Doug Becker, Tom Brzoza, Loren Toews, Mike Webster, Dennis Winston	12.00
2	Jack Deloplaine, Wentford Gains, Sidney Thornton, Rick Moser, Randy Reutershan, Nat Terry, Frank Lewis, Brad	10.00
3	Willie Fry, Steve Furness, Tom Beasley, Ted Petersen, Gary Dunn, L.C. Greenwood, Fred Anderson, Lance	12.00
4	Dave LaCrosse, Jon Kolb, Robin Cole, Sam Davis G, Jack Lambert, Jack Ham, Brad Cousina, John Hicks	12.00
5	Gerry Mullins, Dave Pureifory, Ray Pinney, Joe Greene, John Banaszak, Steve Courson, Dwight White, Larry	12.00
6	Chuck Noll CO, Craig Colquitt, Roy Gerela, Terry Bradshaw, Mike Kruczek, Cliff Stoudt, Rocky Bleier, Tony	18.00
7	John Stallworth, Theo Bell, Randy Grossman, Andre Keys, Jim Smith, L. McCarthey, Lynn Swann, Bennie	15.00
8	Mike Wagner, R. Scott, Glen Edwards, Alvin Maxson, Ron Johnson DB, Larry Anderson, Donnie Shell, Franco	12.00

1981 Steelers Police

The 16-card, 2-5/8" x 4-1/8" set was sponsored by the Steelers, Kiwanis, Coca-Cola and local law enforcement. The card fronts feature an action shot with the player's name, position, uniform number, height and weight. The card backs have "Steeler's Tips."

		MT
Complete Set (16):		25.00
Common Player:		.75
9	Matt Bahr	1.25
12	Terry Bradshaw (Passing)	10.00
31	Donnie Shell (Referee back)	1.50
32	Franco Harris (Running with ball)	6.00
47	Mel Blount (Running without ball)	3.00
52	Mike Webster (Standing)	1.50
57	Sam Davis	.75
58	Jack Lambert (Facing left)	5.00
9	Jack Ham (Sportsmanship back)	3.00
64	Steve Furness	.75
68	L.C. Greenwood	2.00
75	Joe Greene	5.00
76	John Banaszak	.75
79	Larry Brown (Chin 7/16" from bottom)	.75
82	John Stallworth (Running with ball)	2.50
88	Lynn Swann (Double coverage back)	6.00

1982 Steelers Police

The 16-card, 2-5/8" x 4-1/8" set is virtually identical in design with the 1981 set. The cards are sponsored by Coca-Cola, local law enforcement, Kiwanis and the Steelers. The card backs contain "Steeler's Tips."

		MT
Complete Set (16):		12.00
Common Player:		.40
12	Terry Bradshaw (Portrait)	5.00
31	Donnie Shell (Double Coverage back)	.60
32	Franco Harris (Portrait)	2.50
44	Frank Pollard	.40
47	Mel Blount (Running with ball)	1.50
52	Mike Webster (Portrait)	.75
58	Jack Lambert (Facing forward)	2.50
59	Jack Ham (Teamwork back)	1.50
65	Tom Beasley	.40
67	Gary Dunn	.40
74	Ray Pinney	.40
79	Larry Brown (Chin 5/16" from bottom)	.40
82	John Stallworth (Posed shot)	1.25
88	Lynn Swann (Sportsmanship back)	3.00
89	Bennie Cunningham	.50
90	Bob Kohrs	.40

1983 Steelers Police

The 17-card, 2-5/8" x 4-1/8" set is similar to the Police sets from 1981 and 1982. Card No. 2 has two variations of the spelling of coach Chuck Noll's last name.

		MT
Complete Set (16):		8.00
Common Player:		.25
1	Walter Abercrombie	.35
2	Gary Anderson (K)	.50
3	Mel Blount	.75
4	Terry Bradshaw	3.00
5	Robin Cole	.25
6	Steve Courson	.25
7	Bennie Cunningham	.35
8	Franco Harris	2.00
9	Greg Hawthorne	.25
10	Jack Lambert	1.00
11A	Chuck Noll (CO ERRM) (Misspelled Knoll)	5.00
11B	Chuck Noll (CO COR)	1.00
12	Donnie Shell	.35
13	John Stallworth	1.00
14	Mike Webster	.75
15	Dwayne Woodruff	.25
16	Rick Woods	.25

1984 Steelers Police

The 16-card, 2-5/8" x 4-1/8" set, sponsored by McDonald's, Kiwanis, the Steelers and local law enforcement, features action shots with "Steeler Tips" on the card backs. The cards are similar to the previous Police sets, except for the McDonald's and Kiwanis logos on the card fronts.

		MT
Complete Set (16):		8.00
Common Player:		.40
1	Gary Anderson (K)	.40
16	Mark Malone	.60
19	David Woodley	.60
30	Frank Pollard	.40
32	Franco Harris	2.00
34	Walter Abercrombie	.50
49	Dwayne Woodruff	.40
52	Mike Webster	.75
57	Mike Merriweather	.60
58	Jack Lambert	1.50
67	Gary Dunn	.40
73	Craig Wolfley	.40
82	John Stallworth	1.50
83	Louis Lipps	1.00
92	Keith Gary	.40
92	Keith Willis	.50

1985 Steelers Police

The 16-card, 2-5/8" x 4-1/8" set was sponsored by local law enforcement, Giant Eagle, the Steelers and Kiwanis. The card backs have "Steeler Tips."

		MT
Complete Set (16):		5.00
Common Player:		.40
1	Gary Anderson K (Kickoff back)	.50
16	Mark Malone (Playbook back)	.50
21	Eric Williams	.40
30	Frank Pollard (Second Effort back)	.40
31	Donnie Shell (Zone back)	.50
34	Walter Abercrombie (Teamwork back)	.50
49	Dwayne Woodruff (Turnover back)	.40
50	David Little	.50
52	Mike Webster (Offside back)	.75
53	Bryan Hinkle (Blindside back)	.40
56	Robin Cole (Timeout back)	.40
57	Mike Merriweather (Blitz back)	.60
82	John Stallworth (Captains back)	1.50
83	Louis Lipps (Pride back)	.60
93	Keith Willis (QB Sack card)	.40
NNO	Chuck Noll CO (Coach back)	1.25

1986 Steelers Police

The 15-card, 2-5/8" x 4-1/8" set was issued by Kiwanis, Giant Eagle, local law enforcement and the Steelers. The card fronts are virtually identical to the 1985 set, with the Giant Eagle and Kiwanis logos found in the top corners and brief bio information located along the bottom edge. The card backs contain "Steeler Tips."

		MT
Complete Set (15):		5.00
Common Player:		.35
1	Gary Anderson (K) (Field Goal back)	.60
16	Mark Malone (Quarterback back)	.60
24	Rich Erenberg	.50
30	Frank Pollard (Running Back back)	.50
31	Donnie Shell (Interception back)	.60
34	Walter Abercrombie (Penalty back)	.50
49	Dwayne Woodruff	.35
52	Mike Webster (Possession back)	.75
53	Bryan Hinkle (Prevent back)	.35
56	Robin Cole (Equipmen back)	.35
57	Mike Merriweather (Linebacker back)	.50
62	Tunch Ilkin	.50
67	Edmund Nelson	.35
67	Gary Dunn (Defensive Holding back)	.35
82	John Stallworth (Victory back)	1.00
83	Louis Lipps (Receiver back)	.75

1987 Steelers Police

CHUCK NOLL
Head Coach

The 16-card, 2-5/8" x 4-1/8" set has basically the same design as the 1985 and 1986 sets, complete with Kiwanis and Giant Eagle logos and "Steeler Tips."

		MT
Complete Set (16):		5.00
Common Player:		.35
1	Walter Abercrombie (Option Pass back)	.50
2	Gary Anderson (K) (Extra Point back)	.60
3	Bubby Brister	.90
4	Gary Dunn (Neutral Zone back)	.35
5	Preston Gothard	.35
6	Bryan Hinkle (Outside Linebackers back)	.50
7	Earnest Jackson	.50
8	Louis Lipps (Corner Pattern back)	.75
9	Mark Malone (Adverse Conditions back)	.60
10	Mike Merriweather (Instant Replay back)	.50
11	Chuck Noll (CO) (Referee back)	.75
12	John Rienstra	.35
13	Donnie Shell (Defense back)	.60
14	John Stallworth (Crackback Block back)	1.00
15	Mike Webster (Sportsmanship back)	.75
16	Keith Willis (Down back)	.35

1988 Steelers Police

The 16-card, 2-5/8" x 4-1/8" set is similar in design to the previous mid-1980s Steelers Police set as it is sponsored by Giant Eagle and Kiwanis and features "Steeler Tips" on the card backs. The Steelers helmet on the card backs has three white diamonds as opposed to the previous three years' helmets which had two black diamonds.

		MT
Complete Set (16):		5.00
Common Player:		.35
1	Gary Anderson (K)	.60
2	Bubby Brister	.75
3	Thomas Everett	.60
4	Delton Hall	.35
5	Bryan Hinkle	.50
6	Tunch Ilkin	.35
7	Earnest Jackson	.50
8	Louis Lipps	.60
9	David Little	.35
10	Mike Merriweather	.50
11	Frank Pollard	.35
12	John Rienstra	.35
13	Mike Webster	.75
14	Keith Willis	.35
15	Craig Wolfley	.35
16	Rod Woodson	1.50

1989 Steelers Police

The 16-card, 2-5/8" x 4-1/8" set is virtually identical to previous Police sets with sponsorships by Kiwanis and Giant Eagle. The card backs contain "Steeler Tips '89."

		MT
Complete Set (16):		5.00
Common Player:		.40
1	Gary Anderson	.60
6	Bubby Brister	.60
18	Harry Newsome	.40
44	Rodney Carter	.40
26	Rod Woodson	1.00
27	Thomas Everett	.60
33	Merril Hoge	.40
53	Bryan Hinkle	.40
54	Hardy Nickerson	.75
62	Tunch Ilkin	.40
63	Dermontti Dawson	.60
74	Terry Long	.40
78	Tim Johnson	.40
83	Louis Lipps	.75
97	Aaron Jones	.40
98	Gerald Williams	.40

1990 Steelers Police

The 16-card, 2-5/8" x 4-1/8" set features identical front designs as previous Police sets, with the Kiwanis and Giant Eagle

logos. The card backs have "Steelers '90 Tips."

		MT
Complete Set (16):		5.00
Common Player:		.35
1	Gary Anderson (K)	.35
2	Bubby Brister	.60
3	Thomas Everett	.35
4	Merril Hoge	.35
5	Tunch Ilkin	.35
6	Carnell Lake	.50
7	Louis Lipps	.75
8	David Little	.35
9	Greg Lloyd	.75
10	Mike Mularkey	.35
11	Hardy Nickerson	.75
12	Chuck Noll (CO)	.75
13	John Rienstra	.35
14	Keith Willis	.35
15	Rod Woodson	.90
16	Tim Worley	.50

1991 Steelers Police

The 16-card, 2-5/8" x 4-1/8" set features front and back designs which are similar to previous Police sets. The card backs contain "Steelers Tips '91" while the Giant Eagle and Kiwanis logos appear on both sides.

		MT
Complete Set (16):		5.00
Common Player:		.35
1	Gary Anderson (K)	.35
2	Bubby Brister	.60
3	Dermontti Dawson	.35
4	Eric Green	.75
5	Bryan Hinkle	.35
6	Merril Hoge	.50
7	John Jackson	.35
8	D.J. Johnson	.35
9	Carnell Lake	.50
10	Louis Lipps	.60
11	Greg Lloyd	1.00
12	Mike Mularkey	.35
13	Chuck Noll (CO)	.75
14	Dan Stryzinski	.35
15	Gerald Williams	.35
16	Rod Woodson	.90

1992 Steelers Police

The 16-card, 2-5/8" x 4-3/16" set was sponsored by Kiwanis and Giant Eagle and featured a color shot on the card front. The player's height, weight and position appear below his name with "Steelers Tips '92" and the Steelers' 60th anniversary logo featured on the card backs.

		MT
Complete Set (16):		5.00
Common Player:		.35
1	Gary Anderson (K)	.35
2	Bubby Brister	.50
3	Bill Cowher (CO)	.75
4	Dermontti Dawson	.35
5	Eric Green	.50
6	Carlton Haselrig	.35
7	Merril Hoge	.35
8	John Jackson	.35
9	Carnell Lake	.50
10	Louis Lipps	.60
11	Greg Lloyd	.75
12	Neil O'Donnell	1.00
13	Tom Ricketts	.35
14	Gerald Williams	.35
15	Jerrol Williams	.35
16	Rod Woodson	.75

1993 Steelers Police

The 16-card, 2-1/2" x 4" set, sponsored by Giant Eagle and Kiwanis, features a color action shot on the card front with "Steelers Tips '93" on the back. The Kiwanis and Giant Eagle logos appear on both the card front and back.

		MT
Complete Set (16):		5.00
Common Player:		.30
1	Gary Anderson (K)	.30
2	Adrian Cooper	.30
3	Bill Cowher (CO)	.50
4	Dermontti Dawson	.30
5	Donald Evans	.30
6	Eric Green	.50
7	Bryan Hinkle	.30
8	Merril Hoge	.30
9	Garry Howe	.30
10	Greg Lloyd	.75
11	Neil O'Donnell	1.00
12	Jerry Olsavsky	.30
13	Leon Searcy	.30
14	Dwight Stone	.30

| 15 | Gerald Williams | .30 |
| 16 | Rod Woodson | .75 |

1995 Steelers Eat'n Park

The four-strip card set was issued by Eat'n Park during a four-week window and each strip contained three peel-off player cards. The card fronts feature a color image over a silver background. Each strip was sold for 99 cents.

		MT
Complete Set (4):		5.00
Common Player:		1.00
1	Darren Perry, Rod Woodson, Greg Lloyd	1.50
2	Ray Seals, Carnell Lake, Kevin Greene	1.00
3	Dermontti Dawson, Erric Pegram, Mark Bruener	1.00
4	Kordell Stewart, Yancey Thigpen, Neil O'Donnell	2.50

1995 Steelers Giant Eagle Coins

The nine-coin set was distributed by Giant Eagle and was produced by Classic Pro Line. The coins were available in packs with cards for $1.89. The coins/cards were issued over a nine-week period beginning Sept. 3. The coin fronts have the player's face while the backs have the Pittsburgh team logo.

		MT
Complete Set (9):		10.00
Common Player:		1.00
1	Mel Blount	1.00
2	Bill Cowher (CO)	1.00
3	Joe Greene	1.50
4	Kevin Greene	1.00
5	Franco Harris	1.50
6	Jack Lambert	1.50
7	Greg Lloyd	1.50
8	Byron "Bam" Morris	1.00
9	Rod Woodson	1.50

1995 Steelers Giant Eagle ProLine

The nine-card, standard-size set, issued by Giant Eagle and produced by Classic Pro Line, was distributed in packs with the nine-coin set. The card fronts feature a color action shot with the Steelers logo appearing in the lower left corner. The card backs have a checklist of the nine players.

		MT
Complete Set (9):		8.00
Common Player:		.75
1	Kevin Greene	.75
2	Franco Harris	1.00
3	Greg Lloyd	1.00

4	Joe Greene	1.00
5	Byron "Bam" Morris	.75
6	Jack Lambert	1.00
7	Rod Woodson	1.00
8	Mel Blount	.75
9	Bill Cowher (CO)	.75

1996 Steelers Kids Club

The Steelers sponsored this four-card set. The cards feature color photography and black and yellow borders.

		MT
Complete Set (4):		5.00
Common Player:		1.00
1	Bill Cowher CO	1.50
2	Greg Lloyd	1.00
3	Kordell Stewart	3.00
4	Rod Woodson	1.00

1979 Stop 'N' Go

These 18 3D cards were available at Stop 'N' Go markets in 1979. Each front has a 3D effect player photo on the front, along with his team's helmet at the top. His name and team name are in a panel at the bottom of the card; "NFL 3-D Football Stars" is written at the top. The back of the card is numbered 1 of 18, etc., and includes yearly stats, plus summaries of the player's professional and collegiate accomplishments. The Stop 'N' Go logo is also on the card back. The cards measure 2-1/8" x 3-1/4".

		NM
Complete Set (18):		45.00
Common Player:		1.25
1	Gregg Bingham	1.25
2	Ken Burrough	1.50
3	Preston Pearson	1.50
4	Sam Cunningham	2.00
5	Robert Newhouse	2.00
6	Walter Payton	13.00
7	Robert Brazile	1.50
8	Rocky Bleier	2.50
9	Toni Fritsch	1.25
10	Jack Ham	3.00
11	Jay Saldi	1.25
12	Roger Staubach	15.00
13	Franco Harris	8.00
14	Otis Armstrong	2.00
15	Lyle Alzado	2.00
16	Billy Johnson	1.50
17	Elvin Bethea	1.50
18	Joe Greene	5.00

1980 Stop 'N' Go

These 3D cards were available with beverage purchases at participating Stop 'N' Go markets in 1980. The card design is similar to the previous year's design, except the card front has a star on each side of the panel at the bottom where the player's name is. The card back is somewhat different, however, with the main difference being the 1979 statistics and a 1980 copyright logo.

		NM
Complete Set (48):		50.00
Common Player:		.75
1	John Jefferson	1.00
2	Herbert Scott	.75
3	Pat Donovan	.75
4	William Andrews	1.25
5	Frank Corral	.75
6	Fred Dryer	1.50
7	Franco Harris	5.00
8	Leon Gray	.75
9	Gregg Bingham	.75
10	Louis Kelcher	.75
11	Robert Newhouse	1.25
12	Preston Pearson	1.00
13	Wallace Francis	1.00
14	Pat Haden	2.00
15	Jim Youngblood	.75
16	Rocky Bleier	1.50
17	Gifford Nielsen	.75
18	Elvin Bethea	1.00
19	Charlie Joiner	3.00
20	Tony Hill	1.00
21	Drew Pearson	1.25
22	Alfred Jenkins	1.00
23	Dave Elmendorf	.75
24	Jack Reynolds	1.25
25	Joe Greene	3.00
26	Robert Brazile	1.00

4	Joe Greene	1.00
5	Byron "Bam" Morris	.75
6	Jack Lambert	1.00
7	Rod Woodson	1.00
8	Mel Blount	.75
9	Bill Cowher (CO)	.75

1996 Steelers Kids Club (cont.)

27	Mike Reinfeldt	.75
28	Bob Griese	4.50
29	Harold Carmichael	1.50
30	Ottis Anderson	4.00
31	Ahmad Rashad	3.50
32	Archie Manning	1.50
33	Ricky Bell	1.00
34	Jay Saldi	.75
35	Ken Burrough	1.00
36	Don Woods	.75
37	Henry Childs	.75
38	Wilbur Jackson	.75
39	Steve DeBerg	1.50
40	Ron Jessie	.75
41	Mel Blount	2.50
42	Cliff Branch	1.50
43	Chuck Muncie	1.25
44	Ken MacAfee	.75
45	Charley Young	1.00
46	Cody Jones	.75
47	Jack Ham	2.00
48	Ray Guy	1.50

1976 Sunbeam NFL Die Cuts

The 28-card, standard-sized set is die-cut so that each card can stand up when perforated. The team's helmet, name and player drawing appear on the card fronts while the backs have a brief team history with the Sunbeam logo. The cards were printed on white or gray stock, with or without the Sunbeam logo.

		NM
Complete Set (29):		200.00
Common Player:		8.00
1	Atlanta Falcons	8.00
2	Baltimore Colts	8.00
3	Buffalo Bills	8.00
4	Chicago Bears	8.00
5	Cincinnati Bengals	8.00
6	Cleveland Browns	8.00
7	Dallas Cowboys	10.00
8	Denver Broncos	8.00
9	Detroit Lions	8.00
10	Green Bay Packers	10.00
11	Houston Oilers	8.00
12	Kansas City Chiefs	8.00
13	Los Angeles Rams	8.00
14	Miami Dolphins	10.00
15	Minnesota Vikings	8.00
16	New England Patriots	8.00
17	New Orleans Saints	8.00
18	New York Giants	8.00
19	New York Jets	8.00
20	Oakland Raiders	10.00
21	Philadelphia Eagles	8.00
22	Pittsburgh Steelers	8.00
23	St. Louis Cardinals	8.00
24	San Diego Chargers	8.00
25	San Francisco 49ers	10.00
26	Seattle Seahawks	8.00
27	Tampa Bay Buccaneers	8.00
28	Washington Redskins	10.00
NNO	NFL Logo (Blankbacked)	8.00

1976 Sunbeam SEC Die Cuts

The 20-card, standard-size set was die-cut so when each card was perforated, it could stand up. The set is similar in design to the NFL set of the same year, except with SEC teams. The card fronts feature the school's logo with the backs containing the school's 1976 schedule. The cards were distributed in Sunbeam bread packages.

		NM
Complete Set (20):		125.00
Common Player:		5.00
1	Alabama Crimson Tide (Team Profile)	10.00
	Alabama Crimson Tide (Schedule)	10.00
2	Auburn War Eagle (Team Profile)	6.00
	Auburn War Eagle (Schedule)	6.00
3	Florida Gators (Team Profile)	7.00
	Florida Gators (Schedule)	7.00
4	Georgia Bulldogs (Team Profile)	6.00
	Georgia Bulldogs (Schedule)	6.00

9	Kentucky Wildcats (Team Profile)	6.00
10	Kentucky Wildcats (Schedule)	6.00
11	Louisiana St. Tigers (Team Profile)	6.00
12	Louisiana St. Tigers (Schedule)	6.00
13	Miss. St. Bulldogs (Team Profile)	5.00
14	Miss. St. Bulldogs (Schedule)	5.00
15	Ole Miss Rebels (Team Profile)	5.00
16	Ole Miss Rebels (Schedule)	5.00
17	Tennessee Volunteers (Team Profile)	7.00
18	Tennessee Volunteers (Schedule)	7.00
19	Vanderbilt Commodores (Team Profile)	5.00
20	Vanderbilt Commodores (Schedule)	5.00

1972 Sunoco Stamps

Each NFL team is represented by 24 players in this 624-stamp set - 12 offensive and 12 defensive players have been chosen. The stamps measure 1-5/8" x 2-3/8" and were given away in perforated sheets of nine at participating Sun Oil Co. gas stations. Each stamp, featuring an oval with a player photo inside against a corresponding team color-coded background, is unnumbered. Two albums were issued to hold the stamps - a 56-page "NFL Action '72" album and a 128-page album. The albums had specific spots for each sticker, as indicated by a square providing the player's name, uniform number, age, height, weight and college he attended. There were 16 additional perforated sheets inside the album, too. The stamps could be placed inside the album by using the tabs which were provided with the album, instead of licking them.

		NM
Complete Set (624):		125.00
Common Player:		.10
(1)	Ken Burrow	.15
(2)	Bill Sandeman	.10
(3)	Andy Maurer	.10
(4)	Jeff Van Note	.20
(5)	Malcolm Snider	.10
(6)	George Kunz	.25
(7)	Jim Mitchell	.10
(8)	Wes Chesson	.10
(9)	Bob Berry	.20
(10)	Dick Shiner	.10
(11)	Jim Butler	.10
(12)	Art Malone	.10
(13)	Claude Humphrey	.25
(14)	John Small	.10
(15)	Glen Condren	.10
(16)	John Zook	.20
(17)	Don Hansen	.10
(18)	Tommy Nobis	1.25
(19)	Greg Brezina	.20
(20)	Ken Reaves	.10
(21)	Tom Hayes	.10
(22)	Tom McCauley	.10
(23)	Bill Bell	.15
(24)	Bill Lothridge	.20
(25)	Ed Hinton	.10
(26)	Bob Vogel	.10
(27)	Glenn Ressler	.10
(28)	Bill Curry	.30
(29)	John Williams	.10
(30)	Dan Sullivan	.10
(31)	Tom Mitchell	.10
(32)	John Mackey	1.50
(33)	Ray Perkins	2.00
(34)	John Unitas	6.00
(35)	Tom Matte	.30
(36)	Norm Bulaich	.25
(37)	Bubba Smith	1.00
(38)	Bill Newsome	.10
(39)	Fred Miller	.10
(40)	Roy Hinton	.10
(41)	Ray May	.10
(42)	Ted Hendricks	1.50
(43)	Charlie Stukes	.10
(44)	Rex Kern	.30
(45)	Jerry Logan	.10
(46)	Rick Volk	.20
(47)	David Lee	.10
(48)	Jim O'Brien	.25
(49)	J.D. Hill	.20
(50)	Willie Young	.10
(51)	Jim Reilly	.10

(52) Bruce Jarvis .15
(53) Levert Carr .10
(54) Donnie Green .10
(55) Jan White .20
(56) Marlin Briscoe .40
(57) Dennis Shaw .15
(58) O.J. Simpson 12.00
(59) Wayne Patrick .10
(60) John Leypoldt .10
(61) Al Cowlings .75
(62) Jim Dunaway .20
(63) Bob Tatarek .10
(64) Cal Snowden .10
(65) Paul Guidry .10
(66) Edgar Chandler .20
(67) Al Andrews .10
(68) Robert James .10
(69) Alvin Wyatt .10
(70) John Pitts .10
(71) Pete Richardson .10
(72) Spike Jones .10
(73) Dick Gordon .20
(74) Randy Jackson .10
(75) Glen Holloway .10
(76) Rick Coady .10
(77) Jim Cadile .10
(78) Steve Wright .10
(79) Bob Wallace .10
(80) George Farmer .15
(81) Bobby Douglass .40
(82) Don Shy .10
(83) Cyril Pinder .10
(84) Mac Percival .10
(85) Willie Holman .10
(86) George Seals .15
(87) Bill Staley .10
(88) Ed O'Bradovich .20
(89) Doug Buffone .10
(90) Dick Butkus 3.00
(91) Ross Brupbacher .20
(92) Charlie Ford .10
(93) Joe Taylor .10
(94) Ron Smith .20
(95) Jerry Moore .10
(96) Bobby Joe Green .15
(97) Chip Myers .10
(98) Rufus Mayes .10
(99) Howard Fest .10
(100) Bob Johnson .30
(101) Pat Matson .10
(102) Vern Holland .10
(103) Bruce Coslet .75
(104) Bob Trumpy 1.00
(105) Virgil Carter .20
(106) Fred Willis .10
(107) Jess Phillips .10
(108) Horst Muhlmann .15
(109) Royce Berry .10
(110) Mike Reid .50
(111) Steve Chomyszak .10
(112) Ron Carpenter .10
(113) Al Beauchamp .10
(114) Bill Bergey .50
(115) Ken Avery .10
(116) Lemar Parrish .40
(117) Ken Riley .40
(118) Sandy Durko .10
(119) Dave Lewis .10
(120) Paul Robinson .20
(121) Fair Hooker .20
(122) Doug Dieken .10
(123) John Demarie .10
(124) Jim Copeland .10
(125) Gene Hickerson .10
(126) Bob McKay .10
(127) Milt Morin .10
(128) Frank Pitts .10
(129) Mike Phipps .50
(130) Leroy Kelly 1.50
(131) Bo Scott .20
(132) Don Cockroft .10
(133) Ron Snidow .10
(134) Walter Johnson .10
(135) Jerry Sherk .30
(136) Jack Gregory .10
(137) Jim Houston .10
(138) Dale Lindsey .10
(139) Bill Andrews .25
(140) Clarence Scott .20
(141) Ernie Kellerman .10
(142) Walt Sumner .10
(143) Mike Howell .10
(144) Reece Morrison .10
(145) Bob Hayes 1.00
(146) Ralph Neely .20
(147) John Niland .10
(148) Dave Manders .10
(149) Blaine Nye .10
(150) Rayfield Wright .20
(151) Billy Truax .10
(152) Lance Alworth 3.00
(153) Roger Staubach 10.00
(154) Duane Thomas .50
(155) Walt Garrison .30
(156) Mike Clark .10
(157) Larry Cole .10
(158) Jethro Pugh .20
(159) Bob Lilly 2.00
(160) George Andrie .20
(161) Dave Edwards .10
(162) Lee Roy Jordan .90
(163) Chuck Howley .30
(164) Herb Adderley 1.00
(165) Mel Renfro .75
(166) Cornell Green .30
(167) Cliff Harris .20
(168) Ron Widby .10
(169) Jerry Simmons .10

(170) Roger Shoals .10
(171) Larron Jackson .10
(172) George Goeddeke .10
(173) Mike Schnitker .10
(174) Mike Current .10
(175) Billy Masters .15
(176) Jack Gehrke .10
(177) Don Horn .20
(178) Floyd Little 1.00
(179) Bobby Anderson .30
(180) Jim Turner .20
(181) Rich Jackson .10
(182) Paul Smith .10
(183) Dave Costa .10
(184) Lyle Alzado 1.00
(185) Olen Underwood .10
(186) Fred Forsberg .10
(187) Chip Myrtle .10
(188) Leroy Mitchell .10
(189) Billy Thompson .20
(190) Charlie Greer .10
(191) George Saimes .20
(192) Billy Van Heusen .20
(193) Earl McCullouch .20
(194) Jim Yarbrough .10
(195) Chuck Walton .15
(196) Ed Flanagan .10
(197) Frank Gallagher .10
(198) Rockne Freitas .10
(199) Charlie Sanders .25
(200) Larry Walton .10
(201) Greg Landry .40
(202) Altie Taylor .20
(203) Steve Owens .40
(204) Errol Mann .10
(205) Joe Robb .10
(206) Dick Evey .10
(207) Jerry Rush .10
(208) Larry Hand .15
(209) Paul Naumoff .20
(210) Mike Lucci .20
(211) Wayne Walker .10
(212) Lem Barney 1.00
(213) Dick LeBeau .20
(214) Mike Weger .10
(215) Wayne Rasmussen .10
(216) Herman Weaver .10
(217) John Spilis .10
(218) Francis Peay .10
(219) Bill Lueck .10
(220) Ken Bowman .10
(221) Gale Gillingham .20
(222) Dick Himes .10
(223) Rich McGeorge .10
(224) Carroll Dale .20
(225) Bart Starr 3.50
(226) Scott Hunter .30
(227) John Brockington .30
(228) Dave Hampton .20
(229) Clarence Williams .10
(230) Mike McCoy .20
(231) Bob Brown .20
(232) Alden Roche .10
(233) Dave Robinson .25
(234) Jim Carter .20
(235) Fred Carr .20
(236) Ken Ellis .15
(237) Doug Hart .10
(238) Al Randolph .10
(239) Al Matthews .10
(240) Tim Webster .10
(241) Jim Beirne .10
(242) Bob Young .10
(243) Elbert Drungo .10
(244) Sam Walton .20
(245) Alvin Reed .10
(246) Charlie Joiner 1.50
(247) Dan Pastorini .30
(248) Charlie Johnson .30
(249) Lynn Dickey .40
(250) Woody Campbell .10
(251) Robert Holmes .20
(252) Mark Moseley .30
(253) Pat Holmes .10
(254) Mike Tilleman .10
(255) Leo Brooks .10
(256) Elvin Bethea .30
(257) George Webster .30
(258) Garland Boyette .10
(259) Ron Pritchard .15
(260) Zeke Moore .10
(261) Willie Alexander .10
(262) Ken Houston 1.00
(263) John Charles .10
(264) Linzy Cole .10
(265) Elmo Wright .25
(266) Jim Tyrer .20
(267) Ed Buddle .20
(268) Jack Rudnay .10
(269) Mo Moorman .10
(270) Dave Hill .10
(271) Morris Stroud .10
(272) Otis Taylor .40
(273) Len Dawson 3.00
(274) Ed Podolak .30
(275) Wendell Hayes .10
(276) Jan Stenerud 1.25
(277) Marvin Upshaw .10
(278) Curley Culp .30
(279) Buck Buchanan 1.00
(280) Aaron Brown .10
(281) Bobby Bell 1.25
(282) Willie Lanier 1.50
(283) Jim Lynch .20
(284) Jim Marsalis .10
(285) Emmitt Thomas .20
(286) Jim Kearney .10
(287) Johnny Robinson .40

(288) Jerrel Wilson .10
(289) Jack Snow .35
(290) Charlie Cowan .10
(291) Tom Mack .50
(292) Ken Iman .10
(293) Joe Scibelli .10
(294) Harry Schuh .10
(295) Rob Klein .20
(296) Lance Rentzel .35
(297) Roman Gabriel .60
(298) Les Josephson .20
(299) Willie Ellison .20
(300) David Ray .10
(301) Jack Youngblood 1.25
(302) Merlin Olsen 1.75
(303) Phil Olsen .10
(304) Coy Bacon .10
(305) Jim Purnell .10
(306) Marlin McKeever .20
(307) Isiah Robertson .30
(308) Jim Nettles .10
(309) Gene Howard .10
(310) Kermit Alexander .20
(311) Dave Elmendorf .10
(312) Pat Studstill .20
(313) Paul Warfield 1.50
(314) Doug Crusan .10
(315) Bob Kuechenberg .50
(316) Bob DeMarco .10
(317) Larry Little 1.00
(318) Norm Evans .20
(319) Marv Fleming .20
(320) Howard Twilley .30
(321) Bob Griese 2.50
(322) Jim Klick .60
(323) Larry Csonka 2.00
(324) Garo Yepremian .30
(325) Jim Riley .10
(326) Manny Fernandez .30
(327) Bob Heinz .10
(328) Bill Stanfill .30
(329) Doug Swift .10
(330) Nick Buoniconti 1.00
(331) Mike Kolen .10
(332) Tim Foley .30
(333) Curtis Johnson .10
(334) Dick Anderson .40
(335) Jake Scott .50
(336) Larry Seiple .10
(337) Gene Washington .20
(338) Grady Alderman .10
(339) Ed White .25
(340) Mick Tingelhoff .20
(341) Milt Sunde .10
(342) Ron Yary .50
(343) John Beasley .10
(344) John Henderson .10
(345) Fran Tarkenton 4.00
(346) Clint Jones .20
(347) Dave Osborn .20
(348) Fred Cox .20
(349) Carl Eller .50
(350) Gary Larsen .10
(351) Alan Page 1.00
(352) Jim Marshall 1.00
(353) Roy Winston .20
(354) Lonnie Warwick .10
(355) Wally Hilgenberg .10
(356) Bobby Bryant .15
(357) Ed Sharockman .10
(358) Charlie West .10
(359) Paul Krause .60
(360) Bob Lee .20
(361) Randy Vataha .40
(362) Mike Montler .10
(363) Halvor Hagen .10
(364) Jon Morris .10
(365) Len St. Jean .10
(366) Tom Neville .10
(367) Tom Beer .15
(368) Ron Sellers .20
(369) Jim Plunkett 1.00
(370) Carl Garrett .20
(371) Jim Nance .30
(372) Charlie Gogolak .20
(373) Ike Lassiter .10
(374) Dave Rowe .10
(375) Julius Adams .20
(376) Dennis Wirgowski .10
(377) Ed Weisacosky .10
(378) Jim Cheyunski .10
(379) Steve Kiner .10
(380) Larry Carwell .10
(381) John Outlaw .10
(382) Rickie Harris .10
(383) Don Webb .10
(384) Tom Janik .10
(385) Al Dodd .20
(386) Don Morrison .10
(387) Jake Kupp .10
(388) John Didion .10
(389) Del Williams .10
(390) Glen Ray Hines .10
(391) Dave Parks .20
(392) Dan Abramowicz .40
(393) Archie Manning 2.00
(394) Bob Gresham .10
(395) Virgil Robinson .10
(396) Charlie Durkee .10
(397) Richard Neal .10
(398) Bob Pollard .10
(399) Dave Long .10
(400) Joe Owens .10
(401) Carl Cunningham .10
(402) Jim Flanigan .15
(403) Wayne Colman .10
(404) D'Artagnan Martin .10
(405) Delles Howell .10

(406) Hugo Hollas .10
(407) Doug Wyatt .10
(408) Julian Fagan .10
(409) Don Hermann .10
(410) Willie Young .10
(411) Bob Hyland .10
(412) Greg Larson .10
(413) Doug Van Horn .10
(414) Charlie Harper .10
(415) Bob Tucker .25
(416) Joe Morrison .20
(417) Randy Johnson .20
(418) Tucker Frederickson .30
(419) Ron Johnson .30
(420) Pete Gogolak .20
(421) Henry Reed .10
(422) Jim Kanicki .10
(423) Roland Lakes .10
(424) John Douglas .10
(425) Ron Hornsby .10
(426) Jim Files .10
(427) Willie Williams .10
(428) Otto Brown .10
(429) Scott Eaton .10
(430) Carl Lockhart .20
(431) Tom Blanchard .10
(432) Rocky Thompson .20
(433) Rich Caster .30
(434) Randy Rasmussen .10
(435) John Schmitt .10
(436) Dave Herman .20
(437) Winston Hill .20
(438) Pete Lammons .20
(439) Don Maynard 2.00
(440) Joe Namath 10.00
(441) Emerson Boozer .30
(442) John Riggins 4.00
(443) George Nock .10
(444) Bobby Howfield .10
(445) Gerry Philbin .20
(446) John Little .10
(447) Chuck Hinton .10
(448) Mark Lomas .10
(449) Ralph Baker .10
(450) Al Atkinson .10
(451) Larry Grantham .20
(452) John Dockery .10
(453) Earlie Thomas .10
(454) Phil Wise .10
(455) W.K. Hicks .10
(456) Steve O'Neal .15
(457) Drew Buie .10
(458) Art Shell 2.00
(459) Gene Upshaw 2.00
(460) Jim Otto .75
(461) George Buehler .10
(462) Bob Brown .40
(463) Ray Chester .40
(464) Fred Biletnikoff 2.00
(465) Daryle Lamonica .60
(466) Marv Hubbard .20
(467) Clarence Davis .20
(468) George Blanda 2.00
(469) Tony Cline .10
(470) Art Thoms .10
(471) Tom Keating .10
(472) Ben Davidson 1.00
(473) Phil Villapiano .40
(474) Dan Conners .10
(475) Duane Benson .10
(476) Nemiah Wilson .10
(477) Willie Brown 1.00
(478) George Atkinson .20
(479) Jack Tatum .40
(480) Jerry DePoyster .10
(481) Harold Jackson .50
(482) Wade Key .10
(483) Henry Allison .10
(484) Mike Evans .10
(485) Steve Smith .10
(486) Harold Carmichael 1.25
(487) Ben Hawkins .20
(488) Pete Liske .40
(489) Rick Arrington .10
(490) Lee Bouggess .10
(491) Tom Woodeshick .20
(492) Tom Dempsey .50
(493) Richard Harris .20
(494) Don Hultz .10
(495) Ernie Calloway .15
(496) Mel Tom .10
(497) Steve Zabel .10
(498) Tim Rossovich .20
(499) Ron Porter .10
(500) Al Nelson .10
(501) Nate Ramsey .10
(502) Leroy Keyes .40
(503) Bill Bradley .50
(504) Tom McNeill .10
(505) Dave Smith .10
(506) Jon Kolb .10
(507) Gerry Mullins .10
(508) Ray Mansfield .10
(509) Bruce Van Dyke .10
(510) John Brown .10
(511) Ron Shanklin .30
(512) Terry Bradshaw 7.50
(513) Terry Hanratty .40
(514) Preston Pearson .40
(515) John Fuqua .20
(516) Roy Gerela .10
(517) L.C. Greenwood .75
(518) Joe Greene 2.50
(519) Lloyd Voss .10
(520) Dwight White .30
(521) Jack Ham 2.50
(522) Chuck Allen .10
(523) Brian Stenger .10

(524) Andy Russell .75
(525) John Rowser .10
(526) Mel Blount 2.00
(527) Mike Wagner .20
(528) Bobby Walden .10
(529) Mel Gray .30
(530) Bob Reynolds .10
(531) Dan Dierdorf .60
(532) Wayne Mulligan .10
(533) Clyde Williams .10
(534) Ernie McMillan .10
(535) Jackie Smith 1.00
(536) John Gilliam .20
(537) Jim Hart .50
(538) Pete Beathard .40
(539) Johnny Roland .30
(540) Jim Bakken .30
(541) Ron Yankowski .10
(542) Fred Heron .15
(543) Bob Rowe .10
(544) Chuck Walker .10
(545) Larry Stallings .20
(546) Jamie Rivers .10
(547) Mike McGill .10
(548) Miller Farr .10
(549) Roger Wehrli .30
(550) Larry Willingham .10
(551) Larry Wilson 1.00
(552) Chuck Latourette .10
(553) Billy Parks .20
(554) Terry Owens .25
(555) Doug Wilkerson .10
(556) Carl Mauck .10
(557) Walt Sweeney .10
(558) Russ Washington .10
(559) Pettis Norman .20
(560) Gary Garrison .20
(561) John Hadl .60
(562) Mike Montgomery .10
(563) Mike Garrett .30
(564) Dennis Partee .10
(565) Deacon Jones 1.00
(566) Ron East .10
(567) Kevin Hardy .10
(568) Steve DeLong .20
(569) Rick Redman .10
(570) Bob Babich .15
(571) Pete Barnes .10
(572) Bob Howard .10
(573) Joe Beauchamp .10
(574) Bryant Salter .10
(575) Chris Fletcher .10
(576) Jerry LeVias .20
(577) Dick Witcher .10
(578) Len Rohde .12
(579) Randy Beisler .10
(580) Forrest Blue .20
(581) Woody Peoples .10
(582) Cas Banaszek .10
(583) Ted Kwalick .40
(584) Gene Washington .50
(585) John Brodie 1.25
(586) Ken Willard .40
(587) Vic Washington .20
(588) Bruce Gossett .10
(589) Tommy Hart .15
(590) Charlie Krueger .20
(591) Earl Edwards .10
(592) Cedric Hardman .20
(593) Dave Wilcox .25
(594) Frank Nunley .10
(595) Skip Vanderbundt .10
(596) Jimmy Johnson .60
(597) Bruce Taylor .30
(598) Mel Phillips .10
(599) Rosey Taylor .20
(600) Steve Spurrier 2.50
(601) Charley Taylor 1.50
(602) Jim Snowden .10
(603) Ray Schoenke .10
(604) Len Hauss .10
(605) John Wilbur .10
(606) Walt Rock .10
(607) Jerry Smith .20
(608) Roy Jefferson .20
(609) Bill Kilmer 1.00
(610) Larry Brown 1.00
(611) Charlie Harraway .10
(612) Curt Knight .10
(613) Ron McDole .10
(614) Manuel Sistrunk .10
(615) Diron Talbert .20
(616) Verlon Biggs .20
(617) Jack Pardee .75
(618) Myron Pottios .20
(619) Chris Hanburger .50
(620) Pat Fischer .20
(621) Mike Bass .10
(622) Richie Petitbon .20
(623) Brig Owens .10
(624) Mike Bragg .15

1972 Sunoco Stamps Update

These unnumbered 1-5/8" x 2-3/8" stamps are identical to the 1972 Sunoco stamps, but were not listed in the album which was produced to house the stamps. They were issued as team sheets later in the year.

NM
Complete Set (82): 75.00

Common Player: 1.00
(1) Clarence Ellis 1.00
(2) Dave Hampton 1.50
(3) Dennis Havig 1.00
(4) John James 1.00
(5) Joe Profit 1.00
(6) Lonnie Hepburn 1.00
(7) Dennis Nelson 1.00
(8) Mike McBath 1.00
(9) Walt Patulski 1.00
(10) Bob Asher 1.00
(11) Steve DeLong 1.00
(12) Tony McGee 1.00
(13) James Osborne 1.00
(14) Jim Seymour 1.00
(15) Tommy Casanova 1.50
(16) Neil Craig 1.00
(17) Essex Johnson 1.25
(18) Sherman White 1.00
(19) Bob Briggs 1.00
(20) Thom Darden 1.25
(21) Marv Bateman 1.00
(22) Toni Fritsch 1.00
(23) Calvin Hill 3.00
(24) Pat Toomay 1.25
(25) Pete Duranko 1.00
(26) Marv Montgomery 1.00
(27) Rod Sherman 1.00
(28) Bob Kowalkowski 1.00
(29) Jim Mitchell 1.00
(30) Larry Woods 1.00
(31) Willie Buchanon 1.50
(32) Leland Glass 1.00
(33) MacArthur Lane 1.50
(34) Chester Marcol 1.00
(35) Ron Widby 1.00
(36) Ken Burrough 1.50
(37) Calvin Hunt 1.00
(38) Ron Saul 1.00
(39) Greg Simpson 1.00
(40) Mike Sensibaugh 1.00
(41) Dave Chapple 1.00
(42) Jim Langer 6.00
(43) Mike Eischeid 1.00
(44) John Gilliam 1.25
(45) Ron Acks 1.00
(46) Bob Gladieux 1.00
(47) Honor Jackson 1.00
(48) Reggie Rucker 1.50
(49) Pat Studstill 1.00
(50) Bob Windsor 1.00
(51) Joe Federspiel 1.00
(52) Bob Newland 4.00
(53) Pete Athas 1.00
(54) Charlie Evans 1.00
(55) Jack Gregory 1.00
(56) John Mendenhall 1.00
(57) Ed Bell 1.00
(58) John Elliott 1.00
(59) Chris Farasopoulos 1.00
(60) Bob Svihus 1.00
(61) Steve Tannen 1.00
(62) Cliff Branch 3.00
(63) Gus Otto 1.00
(64) Otis Sistrunk 1.25
(65) Charlie Smith 1.00
(66) John Reaves 1.00
(67) Larry Watkins 1.00
(68) Henry Davis 1.00
(69) Ben McGee 1.00
(70) Donny Anderson 1.25
(71) Walker Gillette 1.00
(72) Martin Imhoff 1.00
(73) Bobby Moore (aka Ahmad Rashad) 8.00
(74) Norm Thompson 1.00
(75) Lionel Aldridge 1.00
(76) Dave Costa 1.00
(77) Cid Edwards 1.00
(78) Tim Rossovich 1.00
(79) Dave Williams 1.00
(80) Johnny Fuller 1.00
(81) Terry Hermeling 1.00
(82) Paul Laaveg 1.00

1995 Superior Pix Promos

This four-card preview of the 1995 Superior Pix set was distributed through mail and at the 1995 National. The cards are identical to the Superior Pix set except that the promo cards have the National logo on the back.

		MT
Complete Set (4):		8.00
Common Player:		1.00
1	Steve McNair	3.00
2	Kerry Collins	2.00
3	Tyrone Wheatley	1.00
4	Joey Galloway	2.00

1995 Superior Pix

Superior Pix consists of a 110-card base set, an autographed variant and four insert sets. The base cards include the words "95 Draft" printed in gold foil on the front. The inserts include Deep Threat (five cards, 1:9), Instant Impact (five cards, 1:18), Open Field (five cards, 1:18) and Top Defender (five cards, 1:9).

		MT
Complete Set (110):		10.00
Common Player:		.05
1	Ki-Jana Carter	.25
2	Tony Boselli	.25
3	Steve McNair	1.50
4	Michael Westbrook	.50
5	Kerry Collins	1.50
6	Terrell Davis	2.00
7	Kevin Bouie	.05
8	Brian Williams	.05
9	Kez McCorvey	.05
10	Kyle Brady	.25
11	Rob Johnson	.50
12	Carl Greenwood	.05
13	Mark Fields	.05
14	Andrew Greene	.05
15	Orlando Thomas	.05
16	Don Sasa	.05
17	Brent Moss	.05
18	Jamal Willis	.05
19	Michael Hendricks	.05
20	Rashaan Salaam	.50
21	John Sacca	.05
22	Cory Raymer	.05
23	Kirby Dar Dar	.05
24	Lee DeRamus	.05
25	Joey Galloway	.75
26	Mike Frederick	.05
27	Todd Collins	.50
28	Stoney Case	.05
29	Devin Bush	.05
30	Chad May	.05
31	Darick Holmes	.25
32	Johnny Thomas	.05
33	Luther Ellis	.05
34	Tyrone Wheatley	.25
35	Terry Connealy	.05
36	Ruben Brown	.05
37	Kelvin Anderson	.05
38	Tony Berti	.05
39	Steve Ingram	.05
40	Kevin Carter	.25
41	Dave Wohlabaugh	.05
42	Mike Morton	.05
43	Steve Stenstrom	.05
44	Zach Wiegert	.05
45	Rodney Thomas	.10
46	Eddie Goines	.05
47	Kenny Gales	.05
48	Jamal Ellis	.05
49	Demetrius Edwards	.05
50	Justin Armour	.05
51	Billy Williams	.05
52	Ed Hervey	.05
53	Antonio Armstrong	.05
54	Oliver Gibson	.05
55	David Dunn	.10
56	Tyrone Davis	.05
57	Craig Newsome	.05
58	William Strong	.05
59	Sherman Williams	.05
60	James O. Stewart	.05
61	Bryan Schwartz	.05
62	Frank Sanders	.25
63	Barrett Robbins	.05
64	Bronzell Miller	.05
65	Curtis Martin	2.00
66	Chris T. Jones	.50
67	Dave Barr	.05
68	Anthony Brown	.05
69	Ken Dilger	.25
70	Warren Sapp	.25
71	James A. Stewart	.05
72	Corey Fuller	.05
73	Christian Fauria	.25
74	Brian DeMarco	.05
75	J.J. Stokes	.50
76	Hicham El-Mashtoub	.05
77	Anthony Cook	.05
78	Mark Bruener	.25
79	Blake Brockemeyer	.05
80	Derrick Brooks	.25
81	Joe Aska	.05
82	Lance Brown	.05
83	Pete Mitchell	.05
84	Kordell Stewart	2.00
85	Bobby Taylor	.25
86	Jimmy Hitchcock	.05
87	Jack Jackson	.05
88	Ray Zellars	.05
89	Darius Holland	.05
90	Derrick Alexander	.25

91	Torey Hunter	.05
92	Scotty Lewis	.05
93	Carl Reeves	.05
94	Terrell Fletcher	.05
95	Ontiwaun Carter	.05
96	Trezelle Jenkins	.05
97	Mark Birchmeier	.05
98	Len Raney	.05
99	Ronald Cherry	.05
100	Tyrone Wheatley	.25
101	John Jones	.05
102	Zack Crockett	.05
103	Larry Jones	.05
104	Michael McCoy	.05
105	Ellis Johnson	.05
106	Jerrott Willard	.05
107	Jason James	.05
108	J.J. Smith	.05
109	Mike Mamula	.05
110	Checklist	.05

1995 Superior Pix Autographs

This set is a parallel of the Superior Pix base set. Each player autographed a number of their cards. The card fronts have "authentic signature" printed on them and are individually numbered. They were inserted one per pack.

		MT
Complete Set (109):		300.00
Common Player:		2.00
1	Ki-Jana Carter/1000	20.00
2	Tony Boselli/4000	3.00
3	Steve McNair/3000	15.00
4	Michael Westbrook/4000	7.00
5	Kerry Collins/3000	15.00
6	Terrell Davis/5000	18.00
7	Kevin Bouie	2.00
8	Brian Williams	2.00
9	Kez McCorvey/6500	2.00
10	Kyle Brady/3500	3.00
11	Rob Johnson/3000	8.00
12	Carl Greenwood	2.00
13	Mark Fields/5000	2.00
14	Andrew Greene/5000	2.00
15	Orlando Thomas/6000	2.00
16	Don Sasa/6500	2.00
17	Brent Moss	2.00
18	Jamal Willis	2.00
19	Michael Hendricks	2.00
20	Rashaan Salaam/3500	7.00
21	John Sacca	2.00
22	Cory Raymer/6000	2.00
23	Kirby Dar Dar	2.00
24	Lee DeRamus/6500	2.00
25	Joey Galloway/4000	10.00
26	Mike Frederick/6000	2.00
27	Todd Collins/5000	3.00
28	Stoney Case/4000	2.00
29	Devin Bush/5000	2.00
30	Chad May/4000	2.00
31	Darick Holmes/5500	8.00
32	Johnny Thomas/6500	2.00
33	Luther Ellis/5000	2.00
34	Tyrone Wheatley/5000	3.00
35	Terry Connealy/6500	2.00
36	Ruben Brown/3500	2.00
37	Kelvin Anderson	2.00
38	Tony Berti	2.00
39	Steve Ingram	2.00
40	Kevin Carter/4000	3.00
41	Dave Wohlabaugh/6500	2.00
42	Mike Morton/4000	2.00
43	Steve Stenstrom/5000	2.00
44	Zach Wiegert/5000	2.00
45	Rodney Thomas/5000	3.00
46	Eddie Goines	2.00
47	Kenny Gales/6500	2.00
48	Jamal Ellis/6500	2.00
49	Demetrius Edwards/6500	2.00
50	Justin Armour/6500	2.00
51	Billy Williams	2.00
52	Ed Hervey	2.00
53	Antonio Armstrong	2.00
54	Oliver Gibson	2.00
55	Tyrone Davis	2.00
56	Tyrone Davis	2.00
57	Craig Newsome/4000	2.00
58	William Strong	2.00
59	Sherman Williams/3500	2.00
60	James O. Stewart/4000	3.00

61	Bryan Schwartz/6000	2.00
62	Frank Sanders/5000	7.00
63	Barrett Robbins/6000	2.00
64	Bronzell Miller	2.00
65	Curtis Martin/4000	18.00
66	Chris T. Jones/4000	7.00
67	Dave Barr/5000	2.00
68	Anthony Brown/6500	2.00
69	Ken Dilger/6000	3.00
70	Warren Sapp/6500	3.00
71	James A. Stewart	2.00
72	Corey Fuller/5000	2.00
73	Christian Fauria/5000	2.00
74	Brian DeMarco/6000	2.00
75	J.J. Stokes/1000	16.00
76	Hicham El-Mashtoub	2.00
77	Anthony Cook/6000	2.00
78	Mark Bruener/4000	3.00
79	Blake Brockermeyer/4000	2.00
80	Derrick Brooks/4000	2.00
81	Joe Aska/4000	2.00
82	Lance Brown/6500	2.00
83	Pete Mitchell/6500	2.00
84	Kordell Stewart/6500	15.00
85	Bobby Taylor/4000	3.00
86	Jimmy Hitchcock	2.00
87	Jack Jackson/5000	2.00
88	Ray Zellars/4000	3.00
89	Darius Holland	2.00
90	Derrick Alexander/4000	3.00
91	Torey Hunter/6000	2.00
92	Scotty Lewis/6500	2.00
93	Carl Reeves	2.00
94	Terrell Fletcher/6000	3.00
95	Ontiwaun Carter/6500	2.00
96	Trezelle Jenkins/5000	2.00
97	Mark Birchmeier	2.00
98	Len Raney	2.00
99	Ronald Cherry/6500	2.00
100	Tyrone Wheatley/6500	3.00
101	John Jones	2.00
102	Zack Crockett/6000	2.00
103	Larry Jones/4000	2.00
104	Michael McCoy	2.00
105	Ellis Johnson/3500	2.00
106	Jerrott Willard/5000	2.00
107	Jason James	2.00
108	J.J. Smith	2.00
109	Mike Mamula/4000	2.00

1995 Superior Pix Deep Threat

This five-card insert (1:9) features the top wide receiver prospects from the 1995 Draft. The card fronts have a player photo on a prism background, with the words "1995 Draft Pix Series" at the top.

		MT
Complete Set (5):		8.00
Common Player:		1.00
1	Michael Westbrook	2.00
2	Joey Galloway	2.50
3	J.J. Stokes	2.00
4	Kyle Brady	1.00
5	Frank Sanders	2.00

1995 Superior Pix Instant Impact

Instant Impact is a five-card insert (1:18). The fronts have a split blue/silver/green foil background.

		MT
Complete Set (5):		8.00
Common Player:		.75
1	Steve McNair	3.00
2	Kerry Collins	3.00
3	Tyrone Wheatley	.75
4	Joey Galloway	1.50
5	Tony Boselli	.75

1995 Superior Pix Open Field

Open Field features the top running back prospects from the 1995 Draft on a split-color prism background. This five-card set was inserted 1:18.

		MT
Complete Set (5):		5.00
Common Player:		.75
1	Ki-Jana Carter	1.25
2	Tyrone Wheatley	.75
3	James O. Stewart	1.25
4	Rashaan Salaam	1.50
5	Ray Zellars	.75

1995 Superior Pix Top Defender

The top defensive linemen from the 1995 Draft are featured in this five-card set (1:9). The players are pictured on a blue and gold wood grain background.

		MT
Complete Set (5):		4.00
Common Player:		1.00
1	Kevin Carter	1.00
2	Derrick Alexander	1.00
3	Warren Sapp	1.00
4	Derrick Brooks	1.00
5	Mike Mamula	1.00

1991 Surge WLAF Police

The 39-card, 2-3/8" x 3-1/2" set, sponsored by American Airlines, features players from the WLAF Sacramento Surge team. The card fronts feature a color photo with an American Airlines logo appearing along the top border. The lower right corner contains a triangle with the Surge helmet. The card backs give bio information and a safety tip.

		MT
Complete Set (39):		20.00
Common Player:		.60
1	Mike Adams	.75
2	Sam Archer	.60
3	John Buddenberg	.60
4	Jon Burman	.60
5	Tony Burse	.75
6	Ricardo Cartwright	.60
7	Greg Coauette	.60
8	Paco Craig	.60
9	John Dominic	.60
10	Mike Elkins	1.00
11	Oliver Erhorn	.60
12	Mel Farr	1.00
13	Victor Floyd	.60
14	Byron Forsythe	.60
15	Paul Frazier	.60
16	Tom Gerhart	.60
17	Mike Hall	.60
18	Anthony Henton	.60
19	Nate Hill	.60
20	Kubanai Kalombo	.60
21	Shawn Knight	1.00
22	Sean Kugler	.60
23	Matti Lindholm	.60
24	Art Malone	.75
25	Robert McWright	.60
26	Tim Moore	.60
27	Pete Najarian	.60
28	Mark Nua	.60
29	Carl Parker	.60
30	Leon Perry	.60
31	Juha Salo	.60
32	Saute Sapolu	.60
33	Paul Soltis	.60
34	Richard Stephens	.60
35	Kay Stephenson (CO)	.75
36	Kendall Trainor	.75
37	Mike Wallace	.60
38	Curtis Wilson	.60
39	Rick Zumwalt	.60

1988 Swell Football Greats

Swell's first set picturing members of the Pro Football

Hall of Fame featured 144 players, coaches and executives. The set was released in 10-card wax packs and in complete sets in August 1988. A separate checklist was included. The standard-size cards feature full-color photos or sepia-toned black-and-white photos (in the case of older players) enclosed in a blue border. A red Swell logo is seen in the upper left corner; the Hall of Fame's 25th Anniversary logo is in the lower left, and the player's name and position is in white type in a red box in the lower right corner. Card backs feature blue borders and the player's biographical notes and career statistics in a white rectangle. Cards are printed on white cardboard stock. There have been some reports of small nicks and notches along the tops of some of the cards in the factory-issued sets.

		MT
Complete Set (144):		15.00
Common Player:		.10
1	Pete Rozelle	.30
2	Joe Namath	1.50
3	Frank Gatski	.10
4	O.J. Simpson	2.00
5	Roger Staubach	1.50
6	Herb Adderly	.10
7	Lance Alworth	.25
8	Doug Atkins	.10
9	Red Badgro	.10
10	Cliff Battles	.10
11	Sammy Baugh	.35
12	Raymond Berry	.15
13	Charles Bidwell, Sr.	.10
14	Chuck Bednarik	.15
15	Bert Bell	.10
16	Bobby Bell	.10
17	George Blanda	.15
18	Jim Brown	1.00
19	Paul Brown	.15
20	Roosevelt Brown	.10
21	Ray Flaherty	.10
22	Len Ford	.15
23	Dan Fortmann	.10
24	Bill George	.10
25	Art Donovan	.15
26	John (Paddy) Driscoll	.10
27	Jimmy Conzelman	.10
28	Willie Davis	.15
29	Earl "Dutch" Clark	.10
30	George Connor	.10
31	Guy Chamberlain	.10
32	Jack Christiansen	.10
33	Tony Canadeo	.15
34	Joe Carr	.10
35	Willie Brown	.15
36	Dick Butkus	.35
37	Bill Dudley	.10
38	Turk Edwards	.10
39	Weeb Ewbank	.20
40	Tom Fears	.10
41	Otto Graham	.40
42	Red Grange	.50
43	Frank Gifford	.60
44	Sid Gillman	.10
45	Forrest Gregg	.15
46	Lou Groza	.25
47	Joe Guyon	.10
48	George Halas	.20
49	Ed Healy	.10
50	Mel Hein	.10
52	Pete Henry	.10
52	Arnie Herber	.10
53	Bill Hewitt	.10
54	Clark Hinkle	.10
55	Elroy Hirsch	.25
56	Robert Hubbard	.10
57	Sam Huff	.15
58	Lamar Hunt	.15
59	Don Hutson	.20
60	Deacon Jones	.10
61	Sonny Jurgensen	.15
62	Walt Kiesling	.10
63	Frank Kinard	.10
64	Curley Lambeau	.10
65	Dick Lane	.10
66	Yale Lary	.10
67	Dante Lavelli	.10
68	Bobby Lane	.20
69	Alphonse Leemans	.15
70	Bob Lilly	.15
71	Vince Lombardi	.35
72	Sid Luckman	.20
73	William Roy Lyman	.10
74	Tim Mara	.10
75	Gino Marchetti	.15
76	George Preston Marshall	.10
77	Ollie Matson	.15
78	George McAfee	.10
79	Mike McCormack	.10
80	Hugh McElhenny	.15
81	John McNally	.15
82	Mike Michalske	.10
83	Wayne Millner	.10
84	Bobby Mitchell	.10

85	Ron Mix	.15
86	Lenny Moore	.15
87	Marion Motley	.15
88	George Musso	.10
89	Bronko Nagurski	.35
90	Earle Neale	.10
91	Ernie Nevers	.20
92	Ray Nitschke	.15
93	Leo Nomellini	.10
94	Merlin Olsen	.15
95	Jim Otto	.10
96	Steve Owen	.10
97	Clarence Parker	.10
98	Jim Parker	.10
99	Joe Perry	.15
100	Pete Pihos	.10
101	Hugh Ray	.10
102	Dan Reeves	.10
103	Jim Ringo	.10
104	Andy Robustelli	.10
105	Art Rooney	.10
106	Gale Sayers	.50
107	Joe Schmidt	.10
108	Bart Starr	.75
109	Ernie Stautner	.15
110	Ken Strong	.10
111	Joe Stydahar	.10
112	Charley Taylor	.15
113	Jim Taylor	.15
114	Jim Thorpe	.75
115	Y.A. Tittle	.35
116	George Trafton	.10
117	Charley Trippi	.10
118	Emlen Tunnell	.10
119	Clyde Turner	.10
120	Johnny Unitas	1.75
121	Norm Van Brocklin	.20
122	Steve Van Buren	.10
123	Paul Warfield	.10
124	Bob Waterfield	.20
125	Arnie Weinmeister	.10
126	Bill Willis	.10
127	Larry Wilson	.10
128	Alex Wojciechowicz	.10
129	Doak Walker	.25
130	Willie Lanier	.10
131	Paul Hornung	.25
132	Ken Houston	.10
133	Fran Tarkenton	.50
134	Don Maynard	.15
135	Larry Csonka	.30
136	Joe Greene	.15
137	Len Dawson	.15
138	Gene Upshaw	.10
139	Jim Langer	.10
140	John Henry Johnson	.10
141	Fred Biletnikoff	.15
142	Mike Ditka	.50
143	Jack Ham	.15
144	Alan Page	.15

1989 Swell Football Greats

The 1989 edition of Swell Football Greats again included every member of the Pro Football Hall of Fame inducted through 1989. Swell had released its initial set of HOFers in 1988. The standard-size cards featured white borders with red striping. The Swell logo is in the upper left corner, and a blue flag carries the "Football Greats" slogan across the bottom of the card, just above the player's name and position. Most of the photos are in color. Those that feature early greats are sepia-toned. Backs are printed in two colors and contain biographical notes and career highlights as well as the year of Hall of Fame induction. Cards, which were released in late August 1989, were issued in wax packs of 10 cards each. Collector's Sets were also released by Swell, which is a division of the Philadelphia Chewing Gum Corp. One variation exists in the set: In the upper right corner of card

#27, Sid Luckman. The scarcer error card shows "Sid" and the first part of "Chicago" printed in white. This was air-brushed out in later versions. The set has so little collector interest, however, that the error has no real additional value.

		MT
Complete Set (150):		15.00
Common Player:		.10
1	Terry Bradshaw	1.00
2	Bert Bell	.10
3	Joe Carr	.10
4	Earl "Dutch" Clark	.10
5	Harold "Red" Grange	.60
6	Wilbur "Pete" Henry	.10
7	Mel Hein	.10
8	Cal Hubbard	.10
9	George Halas	.30
10	Don Hutson	.15
11	Curley Lambeau	.10
12	Tim Mara	.10
13	George Preston Marshall	.10
14	John McNally	.10
15	Bronko Nagurski	.40
16	Ernie Nevers	.15
17	Jim Thorpe	.50
18	Ed Healy	.10
19	Clarke Hinkle	.10
20	Link Lyman	.10
21	Mike Michalske	.10
22	George Trafton	.10
23	Guy Chamberlain	.15
24	John "Paddy" Driscoll	.10
25	Dan Fortmann	.10
26	Otto Graham	.40
27A	Sid Luckman	.35
27B	Sid Luckman (corrected)	1.25
28	Steve Van Buren	.15
29	Bob Waterfield	.20
30	Bill Dudley	.15
31	Joe Guyon	.10
32	Arnie Herber	.10
33	Walt Kiesling	.10
34	Jimmy Conzelman	.10
35	Art Rooney	.10
36	Willie Wood	.10
37	Art Shell	.25
38	Sammy Baugh	.45
39	Mel Blount	.10
40	Lamar Hunt	.15
41	Norm Van Brocklin	.30
42	Y.A. Tittle	.35
43	Andy Robustelli	.10
44	Vince Lombardi	.35
45	Frank Kinard	.10
46	Bill Hewitt	.10
47	Jim Brown	1.00
48	Pete Pihos	.10
49	Hugh McElhenny	.15
50	Tom Fears	.10
51	Jack Christiansen	.10
52	Ernie Stautner	.15
53	Joe Perry	.15
54	Leo Nomellini	.15
55	Earl "Greasy" Neale	.10
56	Turk Edwards	.10
57	Alex Wojciechowicz	.10
58	Charley Trippi	.10
59	Marion Motley	.20
60	Wayne Miller	.10
61	Elroy Hirsch	.15
62	Art Donovan	.10
63	Cliff Battles	.10
64	Emlen Tunnell	.15
65	Joe Stydahar	.10
66	Ken Strong	.10
67	Dan Reeves	.10
68	Bobby Layne	.30
69	Paul Brown	.20
70	Charles Bidwell, Sr.	.10
71	Chuck Bednarik	.15
72	Bulldog Turner	.10
73	Hugh "Shorty" Ray	.10
74	Steve Owen	.10
75	George McAfee	.10
76	Forrest Gregg	.15
77	Frank Gifford	.50
78	Jim Taylor	.15
79	Len Ford	.10
80	Ray Flaherty	.10
81	Lenny Moore	.15
82	Dante Lavelli	.15
83	George Connor	.15
84	Roosevelt Grier	.10
85	Dick Lane	.10
86	Lou Groza	.30
87	Bill George	.10
88	Tony Canadeo	.10
89	Joe Schmidt	.10
90	Jim Parker	.10
91	Wayne Millner	.10
92	Raymond Berry	.15
93	Ollie Matson	.15
94	Gino Marchetti	.15
95	Larry Wilson	.10
96	Ray Nitschke	.25
97	Tuffy Leemans	.10
98	Weeb Ewbank	.10
99	Lance Alworth	.30
100	Bill Willis	.10

101	Bart Starr	.35
102	Gale Sayers	.35
103	Herb Adderly	.10
104	Johnny Unitas	1.00
105	Ron Mix	.10
106	Yale Lary	.10
107	Red Badgro	.10
108	Jim Otto	.10
109	Bob Lilly	.15
110	Deacon Jones	.15
111	Doug Atkins	.10
112	Jim Ringo	.10
113	Willie Davis	.10
114	George Blanda	.35
115	Bobby Bell	.10
116	Merlin Olsen	.15
117	George Musso	.10
118	Sam Huff	.15
119	Paul Warfield	.25
120	Bobby Mitchell	.10
121	Sonny Jurgensen	.25
122	Sid Gilman	.10
123	Arnie Weinmeister	.10
124	Charley Taylor	.10
125	Mike McCormack	.10
126	Willie Brown	.10
127	O.J. Simpson	1.50
128	Pete Rozelle	.25
129	Joe Namath	1.25
130	Frank Gatski	.10
131	Willie Lanier	.10
132	Ken Houston	.10
133	Paul Hornung	.25
134	Roger Staubach	1.25
135	Len Dawson	.15
136	Larry Csonka	.30
137	Doak Walker	.15
138	Fran Tarkenton	.60
139	Don Maynard	.15
140	Jim Langer	.15
141	John Henry Johnson	.10
142	Joe Greene	.20
143	Jack Ham	.10
144	Mike Ditka	.75
145	Alan Page	.10
146	Fred Biletnikoff	.15
147	Gene Upshaw	.10
148	Dick Butkus	.50
149	Checklist 1 & 2	.10
150	Checklist 3 & 4	.10

1990 Swell Football Greats

BOBBY LAYNE QUARTERBACK

Swell, which had released two straight sets of Pro Football Hall of Famers, returned with this 160-card set, also featuring HOFers. Produced by the Philadelphia Gum Co., the set includes 155 HOFers, two checklists, and three Hall of Fame cards. Cards are standard size, with a white border and blue and yellow lines. As in previous issues, some cards of the older players may have sepia-toned, rather than full-color, photos.

		MT
Complete Set (160):		15.00
Common Player:		.10
1	Terry Bradshaw	1.00
2	Bert Bell	.10
3	Joe Carr	.10
4	Dutch Clark	.15
5	Red Grange	.40
6	Pete Henry	.10
7	Mel Hein	.10
8	Cal Hubbard	.10
9	George Halas	.25
10	Don Hutson	.15
11	Curly Lambeau	.10
12	Tim Mara	.10
13	G. Preston Marshall	.10
14	John McNally	.10
15	Bronko Nagurski	.35
16	Ernie Nevers	.15
17	Jim Thorpe	.75
18	Ed Healy	.10
19	Clark Hinkle	.10
20	Link Lyman	.10
21	Mike Michalske	.10
22	George Trafton	.10
23	Guy Chamberlain	.10
24	Paddy Driscoll	.10
25	Dan Fortmann	.10
26	Otto Graham	.50
27	Sid Luckman	.40
28	Steve Van Buren	.15
29	Bob Waterfield	.25
30	Bill Dudley	.10
31	Joe Guyon	.10
32	Arnie Herber	.10
33	Walt Kiesling	.10
34	Jimmy Conzelman	.10
35	Art Rooney	.15
36	Willie Wood	.10
37	Art Shell	.15
38	Sammy Baugh	.40
39	Mel Blount	.10
40	Lamar Hunt	.15
41	Norm Van Brocklin	.25
42	Y.A. Tittle	.30
43	Andy Robustelli	.10
44	Vince Lombardi	.25
45	Bruiser Kinard	.10
46	Bill Hewitt	.10
47	Jim Brown	1.00
48	Pete Pihos	.10
49	Hugh McElhenny	.15
50	Tom Fears	.10
51	Jack Christiansen	.10
52	Ernie Stautner	.15
53	Joe Perry	.15
54	Leo Nomellini	.15
55	Turk Edwards	.10
56	Alex Wojciechowicz	.10
57	Charley Trippi	.10
58	Charlie Trippi	.10
59	Marion Motley	.15
60	Wayne Miller	.10
61	Elroy Hirsch	.20
62	Art Donovan	.10
63	Cliff Battles	.10
64	Emlen Tunnell	.10
65	Joe Stydahar	.10
66	Ken Strong	.10
67	Dan Reeves	.15
68	Bobby Layne	.25
69	Paul Brown	.20
70	Charles Bidwell, Sr.	.10
71	Chuck Bednarik	.15
72	Bulldog Turner	.10
73	Shorty Ray	.10
74	Steve Owen	.10
75	George McAfee	.10
76	Forrest Gregg	.15
77	Frank Gifford	.40
78	Jim Taylor	.15
79	Len Ford	.10
80	Ray Flaherty	.10
81	Lenny Moore	.15
82	Dante Lavelli	.10
83	George Connor	.15
84	Roosevelt Brown	.10
85	Dick Lane	.10
86	Lou Groza	.20
87	Bill George	.10
88	Tony Canadeo	.10
89	Joe Schmidt	.15
90	Jim Parker	.10
91	Raymond Berry	.15
92	Ace Parker	.10
93	Ollie Matson	.15
94	Gino Marchetti	.10
95	Larry Wilson	.10
96	Ray Nitschke	.15
97	Tuffy Leemans	.10
98	Weeb Ewbank	.10
99	Lance Alworth	.20
100	Bill Willis	.10
101	Bart Starr	.30
102	Gale Sayers	.30
103	Herb Adderly	.10
104	Johnny Unitas	1.00
105	Ron Mix	.10
106	Yale Lary	.10
107	Red Badgro	.10
108	Jim Otto	.10
109	Bob Lilly	.15
110	Deacon Jones	.10
111	Doug Atkins	.10
112	Jim Ringo	.15
113	Willie Davis	.10
114	George Blanda	.35
115	Bobby Bell	.10
116	Merlin Olsen	.15
117	George Musso	.10
118	Sam Huff	.10
119	Paul Warfield	.15
120	Bobby Mitchell	.10
121	Sonny Jurgensen	.15
122	Sid Gilman	.10
123	Arnie Weinmeister	.10
124	Charley Taylor	.10
125	Mike McCormack	.10
126	Willie Brown	.10
127	O.J. Simpson	1.50
128	Pete Rozelle	.25
129	Joe Namath	1.25
130	Frank Gatski	.10
131	Willie Lanier	.10
132	Ken Houston	.10
133	Paul Hornung	.25
134	Roger Staubach	1.00
135	Len Dawson	.15
136	Larry Csonka	.25
137	Doak Walker	.15
138	Fran Tarkenton	.40
139	Don Maynard	.15
140	Jim Langer	.10
141	John H. Johnson	.10
142	Joe Greene	.20
143	Jack Ham	.10
144	Mike Ditka	.50
145	Alan Page	.10
146	Fred Biletnikoff	.15
147	Gene Upshaw	.10
148	Dick Butkus	.30
149	Buck Buchanan	.10
150	Franco Harris	.30
151	Tom Landry	.35
152	Ted Hendricks	.10
153	Bob St. Clair	.10
154	Jack Lambert	.20
155	Bob Griese	.20
156	Admission Coupon	.10
157	Enshrinement Day	.10
158	Hall of Fame	.10
159	Checklist 1 & 2	.10
160	Checklist 3 & 4	.10

T

1962 Tang Team Photos

The 14-card, 8" x 10" set features a team photo with the players' names along the bottom border. The backs are blank. The set was available for 50 cents back in 1962 with a Tang seal. Reprints have been made in recent years.

		NM
Complete Set (14):		100.00
Common Player:		8.00
1	Baltimore Colts	8.00
2	Chicago Bears	8.00
3	Cleveland Browns	8.00
4	Dallas Cowboys	15.00
5	Detroit Lions	8.00
6	Green Bay Packers	15.00
7	Los Angeles Rams	8.00
8	Minnesota Vikings	12.00
9	New York Giants	8.00
10	Philadelphia Eagles	8.00
11	Pittsburgh Steelers	12.00
12	St. Louis Cardinals	8.00
13	San Francisco 49ers	12.00
14	Washington Redskins	12.00

1981 TCMA Greats

These standard-size cards were issued by TCMA in 1981. Each card front has a color photo of a player from the 1950s or '60s, framed by a white border. The card back is white and uses black ink to provide a career summary, biographical information, a TCMA copyright and a card number. Some cards, however, went unnumbered and command values about 2 times more than their numbered counterparts.

		MT
Complete Set (78):		25.00
Common Player:		.25
1	Alex Karras	1.00
2	Fran Tarkenton	3.00
3	John Unitas	4.50
4	Bobby Layne	2.00
5	Roger Staubach	6.00
6	Joe Namath	6.00
7	1954 New York Giants	.50
8	Jimmy Brown	6.00
9	Ray Wietecha	.25
10	R.C. Owens	.25
11	Alex Webster	.35
12	Jim Otto	1.00
13	Jim Taylor	1.00
14	Kyle Rote	.75
15	Roger Ellis	.25
16	Nick Pietrosante	.35
17	Milt Plum	.30
18	Eddie LeBaron	.50
19	Jimmy Patton	.25
20	Yale Lary	1.00
21	Leo Nomellini	1.25
22	Johnny Olszewski	.25
23	Ernie Koy	.35
24	Bill Wade	.35
25	Billy Wells	.25
26	Ron Waller	.25
27	Pat Summerall	.60
28	Joe Schmidt	1.25
29	Bob St. Clair	.75
30	Dick Lynch	.35
31	Tommy McDonald	.50
32	Earl Morrall	.50
33	Jim Martin	.25
34	Dick Modzelewski	.30
35	Dick LeBeau	.35
36	Dick Post	.25
37	Les Richter	.25
38	Andy Robustelli	.75
39	Pete Retzlaff	.35
40	Fred Biletnikoff	1.50
41	Timmy Brown	.35
42	Babe Parilli	.35
43	Lance Alworth	1.75
44	Sammy Baugh	1.75
45	Paul (Tank) Younger	.35
46	Chuck Bednarik	1.50
47	Art Donovan	1.25
48	Len Dawson	2.00
49	Don Maynard	1.25
50	Joe Morrison	.35
51	John Eliott	.25
52	Jim Ringo	.85
53	Max McGee	.35
54	Art Powell	.35
55	Galen Fiss	.25
56	Jack Stroud	.25
57	Bake Turner	.35
58	Mike McCormack	.75
59	L.G. Dupre	.35
60	Bill McPeak	.35
61	Art Spinney	.25
62	Fran Rogel	.25
63	Ollie Matson	1.25
64	Doak Walker	1.25
65	Lenny Moore	1.25
66	George Shaw, Bert Rechichar	.25
67	Kyle Rote, Jim Lee Howell, Ray Krause	.35
68	Andy Robustelli, Roosevelt Grier, Dick Modzelewski, Jim Katcavage	.65
69	Tucker Frederickson, Ernie Koy	.35
70	Gino Marchetti	1.00
71	Earl Morrall, Allie Sherman	.50
72	Roosevelt Brown	.75
73	Howard Cassady (Hopalong)	.25
74	Don Chandler	.35
75	Joe Childress	.25
76	Rick Casares	.35
77	Charley Conerly	1.00
78	1958 Giants QB's (Don Heinrich, Tom Dublinski, Charlie Conerly)	.50

1987 TCMA Update

This set, produced by TCMA's successor (CMC), is a re-issue of TCMA's 1981 set, but 12 additional cards were added. The extra cards were numbered from where the first issue ended, at 79. The copyright on the card back is CMC 1987.

		MT
Complete Set (12):		20.00
Common Player:		.75
79	Fred Dryer	1.00
80	Ed Marinaro	1.00
81	O.J. Simpson	10.00
82	Joe Theismann	2.50
83	Roman Gabriel	1.00
84	Terry Metcalf	.75
85	Lyle Alzado	1.50
86	Jake Scott	.75
87	Cliff Branch	1.50
88	Rocky Bleier	1.00
89	Cliff Harris	.75
90	Archie Manning	2.00

1960 Texans 7-Eleven

The standard-sized cards feature a black and white photo of the player with his name, position and team along the bottom edge. The horizontal card backs have player highlights in typewriter-style print. Even though there are 11 cards checklisted, there may have been more in the unnumbered set.

		NM
Complete Set (11):		400.00
Common Player:		35.00
1	Max Boydston	35.00
2	Mel Branch	35.00
3	Chris Burford	35.00
4	Ray Collins (UER) (No team name on front)	35.00
5	Cotton Davidson	35.00
6	Abner Haynes	60.00
7	Sherrill Headrick	35.00
8	Bill Krisher	35.00
9	Paul Miller	35.00
10	Johnny Robinson	60.00
11	Jack Spikes	35.00

1992 Thunderbolts Arena

Area Temps sponsored this set featuring the Cleveland Thunderbolts of the Arena Football League. The 24 cards are printed on plain white card stock. The fronts feature a black and white player photo framed by a purple line. The backs contain basic player information. Both sides feature the Area Temps logo. The cards are unnumbered.

		MT
Complete Set (24):		20.00
Common Player:		.60
1	Eric Anderson	.60
2	Robert Banks	.60
3	Bobby Bounds	.60
4	Marvin Bowman	.60
5	George Cooper	.60
6	Michael Denbrock ACO	.60
7	Chris Drennan	.60
8	Dennis Fitzgerald ACO	.60
9	John Fletcher	.60
10	Andre Giles	.60
11	Chris Harkness	.60
12	Major Harris	5.00
13	Luther Johnson	.60
14	Marvin Mattox	.60
15	Cedric McKinnon	.60
16	Cleo Miller ACO	.75
17	Tony Missick	.60
18	Anthony Newsom	.60
19	Phil Poirier	.60
20	Alvin Powell	.60
21	Ray Puryear	.60
22	Dave Whinham CO	.60
23	Brian Williams	.60
24	Kennedy Wilson	.60

1961 Titans Jay Publishing

The 12-card, 5" x 7" set features black and white photos of the New York Titans, an original AFL team that eventually became the New York Jets. The cards were originally packaged 12 to a pack and sold for 25 cents. The backs are blank.

		NM
Complete Set (12):		75.00
Common Player:		5.00
1	Al Dorow	5.00
2	Larry Grantham	6.00
3	Mike Hagler	5.00
4	Mike Hudock	5.00
5	Bob Jewett	5.00
6	Jack Klotz	5.00
7	Don Maynard	20.00
8	John McMullan	5.00
9	Bob Mischak	5.00
10	Art Powell	10.00
11	Bob Reifsnyder	5.00
12	Sid Youngelman	6.00

1995 Tombstone Pizza

The 12-card, standard-size set was randomly inserted in specially marked Tombstone pizzas. The entire set was available for $1 and three Tombstone proof of purchase seals. The card fronts feature a color photo with the quarterback's last name along the top border in large print. The card backs include career statistics and a player quote.

	MT
Complete Set (12):	20.00
Common Player:	1.00
1 Ken Anderson	1.00
2 Terry Bradshaw	4.00
3 Len Dawson	1.50
4 Dan Fouts	1.50
5 Bob Griese	2.00
6 Billy Kilmer	1.00
7 Joe Namath	6.00
8 Jim Plunkett	1.00
9 Ken Stabler	2.50
10 Bart Starr	2.00
11 Joe Theismann	1.00
12 Johnny Unitas	3.00

1995 Tombstone Pizza Autographs

The 12-card, standard-size set was a parallel to the base Classic Quarterback Series. Each quarterback signed 10,000 of his own cards.

	MT
Complete Set (12):	300.00
Common Player:	15.00
1 Ken Anderson	15.00
2 Terry Bradshaw	45.00
3 Len Dawson	25.00
4 Dan Fouts	25.00
5 Bob Griese	25.00
6 Billy Kilmer	15.00
7 Joe Namath	60.00
8 Jim Plunkett	15.00
9 Ken Stabler	35.00
10 Bart Starr	35.00
11 Joe Theismann	15.00
12 Johnny Unitas	40.00

1996 Tombstone Pizza Quarterback Club Caps

The 14-card, 1-5/8" cap set was distributed by Tombstone Pizza and produced by Pinnacle. The caps were issued on a punch-out board (8-1/2" x 11"). A black plastic slammer was also included with the set.

	MT
Complete Set (14):	15.00
Common Player:	.50
1 Steve Young	1.00
2 Emmitt Smith	2.50
3 Junior Seau	.50
4 Barry Sanders	1.25
5 Jerry Rice	1.25
6 Dan Marino	2.50
7 Jim Kelly	.60
8 Michael Irvin	.60
9 Brett Favre	1.25
10 Marshall Faulk	1.00
11 John Elway	.75
12 Randall Cunningham	.50
13 Drew Bledsoe	1.00
14 Troy Aikman	1.25

Values quoted in this guide reflect the retail price of a card — the price a collector can expect to pay when buying a card from a dealer. The wholesale price — that which a collector can expect to receive from a dealer when selling cards — will be significantly lower, depending on desirability and condition.

1950 Topps Felt Backs

BILLY CONN
All-American Halfback
GEORGETOWN U.

These 7/8" x 1-7/16" cards feature several top collegiate players of the era on the front; a mug shot has the player's name, position and college under it. The card back is felt and includes his college's team pennant. Cards come with either brown or yellow backgrounds; yellow backgrounds are generally twice the listed values. The following cards come in both versions: 5, 6, 9, 13, 30, 35, 36, 39, 46, 51, 52, 54, 55, 57, 61, 66, 71, 75, 76, 78, 84, 86, 87, 92, and 100.

	NM
Complete Set (100):	4800.
Common Player:	40.00
(1) Lou Allen	40.00
(2) Morris Bailey	40.00
(3) George Bell	40.00
(4) Lindy Berry	40.00
(5) Mike Boldin	40.00
(6) Bernie Botula	40.00
(7) Bob Bowlby	40.00
(8) Bob Bucher	40.00
(9) Al Burnett	40.00
(10) Don Burson	40.00
(11) Paul Campbell	40.00
(12) Herb Carey	40.00
(13) Bimbo Cecconi	40.00
(14) Bill Chauncey	40.00
(15) Dick Clark	40.00
(16) Tom Coleman	40.00
(17) Billy Conn	40.00
(18) John Cox	40.00
(19) Lou Creekmur	45.00
(20) Glen Davis	50.00
(21) Warren Davis	40.00
(22) Bob Deuber	40.00
(23) Ray Dooney	45.00
(24) Tom Dublinski	40.00
(25) Jeff Fleischman	40.00
(26) Jack Friedland	40.00
(27) Bob Fuchs	40.00
(28) Arnold Galiffa	40.00
(29) Dick Gilman	40.00
(30) Frank Gitschier	40.00
(31) Gene Glick	40.00
(32) Bill Gregus	45.00
(33) Harold Hagan	40.00
(34) Charles Hall	40.00
(35) Leon Hart	60.00
(36) Bob Hester	40.00
(37) George Hughes	40.00
(38) Levi Jackson	40.00
(39) Jackie Jensen	125.00
(40) Charlie Justice	100.00
(41) Gary Kerkorian	40.00
(42) Bernie Krueger	40.00
(43) Bill Kuhn	40.00
(44) Dean Laun	40.00
(45) Chet Leach	40.00
(46) Bobby Lee	40.00
(47) Roger Lehew	40.00
(48) Glenn Lippman	40.00
(49) Melvin Lyle	40.00
(50) Len Makowski	40.00
(51) Al Malekoff	40.00
(52) Jim Martin	50.00
(53) Frank Mataya	40.00
(54) Ray Matthews	45.00
(55) Dick McKissack	40.00
(56) Frank Miller	40.00
(57) John Miller	40.00
(58) Ed Modzelewski	45.00
(59) Don Mouser	40.00
(60) James Murphy	40.00
(61) Ray Nagle	45.00
(62) Leo Nomellini	140.00
(63) James O'Day	40.00
(64) Joe Paterno	375.00
(65) Andy Pavich	40.00
(66) Pete Perini	40.00
(67) Jim Powers	40.00
(68) Dave Rakestraw	45.00
(69) Herb Rich	40.00
(70) Fran Rogel	40.00
(71) Darrell Royal	80.00
(72) Steve Sawle	40.00
(73) Nick Sebeck	40.00
(74) Herb Seidell	40.00
(75) Charles Shaw	40.00
(76) Emil Sitko	40.00
(77) Ed (Butch) Songin	45.00
(78) Mariano Stalloni	40.00
(79) Ernie Stautner	135.00
(80) Don Stehley	40.00
(81) Gil Stevenson	45.00
(82) Bishop Strickland	40.00
(83) Harry Szulborski	40.00
(84) Wally Teninga	40.00
(85) Clayton Tonnemaker	40.00
(86) Deacon Dan Towler	55.00
(87) Bert Turek	40.00
(88) Harry Ulinski	40.00
(89) Leon Van Billingham	40.00
(90) Langdon Viracola	40.00
(91) Leo Wagner	40.00
(92) Doak Walker	150.00
(93) Jim Ward	40.00
(94) Art Weiner	45.00
(95) Dick Weiss	40.00
(96) Froggie Williams	40.00
(97) Robert (Red) Wilson	45.00
(98) Roger (Red) Wilson	40.00
(99) Carl Wren	40.00
(100) Pete Zinaich	40.00

1951 Topps

Refered to as the 1951 Topps "Magic" set, this 1951 issue was Topps' first major football card set. The 75-card set featured the nation's top college players. The backs of the cards include a football trivia question with the answer concealed under a scratch-off area.

	NM
Complete Set (75):	1000.
Common Player:	16.00
1 Jimmy Monahan	25.00
2 Bill Wade	45.00
3 Bill Reichardt	16.00
4 Babe Parilli	35.00
5 Billie Burkhalter	16.00
6 Ed Weber	16.00
7 Tom Scott	16.00
8 Frank Guthridge	16.00
9 John Karras	16.00
10 Vic Janowicz	100.00
11 Lloyd Hill	16.00
12 Jim Weatherall	20.00
13 Howard Hansen	16.00
14 Lou D'Achille	16.00
15 Johnny Turco	16.00
16 Jerrell Price	16.00
17 John Coatta	16.00
18 Bruce Patton	16.00
19 Marion Campbell	32.00
20 Blaine Earon	16.00
21 Dewey McConnell	16.00
22 Ray Beck	16.00
23 Jim Prewett	16.00
24 Bob Steele	16.00
25 Art Betts	16.00
26 Walt Trillhaase	16.00
27 Gil Bartosh	16.00
28 Bob Bestwick	16.00
29 Tom Rushing	16.00
30 Bert Rechichar	32.00
31 Bill Owens	16.00
32 Mike Goggins	16.00
33 John Petitbon	16.00
34 Byron Townsend	16.00
35 Ed Rotticci	16.00
36 Steve Wadiak	16.00
37 Bobby Marlow	17.00
38 Bill Fuchs	16.00
39 Ralph Staub	16.00
40 Bill Vesprini	16.00
41 Zack Jordan	16.00
42 Bob Smith	16.00
43 Charles Hanson	16.00
44 Glenn Smith	16.00
45 Armand Kitto	16.00
46 Vinnie Drake	16.00
47 Bill Putich	16.00
48 George Young	40.00
49 Don McRae	16.00
50 Frank Smith	16.00
51 Dick Hightower	16.00
52 Clyde Pickard	16.00
53 Bob Reynolds	16.00
54 Dick Gregory	16.00
55 Dale Samuels	16.00
56 Gale Galloway	16.00
57 Vic Pujo	16.00
58 Dave Waters	16.00
59 Joe Ernest	16.00
60 Elmer Costa	16.00
61 Nick Liotta	16.00
62 John Dottley	16.00
63 Hi Faubion	16.00
64 David Harr	16.00
65 Bill Matthews	16.00
66 Carroll McDonald	16.00
67 Dick Dewing	16.00
68 Joe Johnson	16.00
69 Arnold Burwitz	16.00
70 Ed Dobrowolski	16.00
71 Joe Dudeck	16.00
72 John Bright	20.00
73 Harold Loehlein	16.00
74 Lawrence Hairston	16.00
75 Bob Carey	20.00

1955 Topps All-American

BILL DUDLEY
Halfback

This was the last Topps set to have college stars. The 100-card All-American set includes past and contemporary college stars. Cards measure 2-5/8" x 3-5/8" and feature a horizontal format. A number of the cards were short-printed in this set. Because the set featured many stars of the past, this set includes the only "regular issue" cards of several Hall of Famers (though technically these cards shouldn't qualify as "regular issue" cards since they weren't released during the player's career). Some of these rookie cards include Red Grange, Mel Hein, Jim Thorpe, Ernie Nevers, Bruiser Kinard, Ace parker, Don Hutson and Pete Henry. The only card issued of the Four Horsemen also appears in this set. The second (and last) "regular issue" cards of these players appear in this set: Knute Rockne, Ken Strong, Turk Edwards, and Alex Wojciechowicz. This set also includes the last cards of Bill Dudley, Otto Graham, Whizzer White (his second-year card, which actually should be his rookie card, since the 1954 Bowman card showed not Byron "Whizzer" White but Wilford White) and Sid Luckman. Two variations exist in the set. The backs on #14 Gaynell Tinsley and #21 Whizzer White were switched. The corrected versions are more plentiful than the errors. (Key: SP - short-printed)

	NM
Complete Set (100):	3500.
Common Player:	15.00
SP Cards:	17.50
1 Herman Hickman	90.00
2 John Kimbrough	15.00
3 Ed Weir	15.00
4 Ernie Pinckert	15.00
5 Bobby Grayson	15.00
6 Niles Kinnick	70.00
7 Andy Bershak	15.00
8 George Cafego	15.00
9 Tom Hamilton (SP)	35.00
10 Bill Dudley	30.00
11 Bobby Dodd (SP)	35.00
12 Otto Graham	175.00
13 Aaron Rosenberg	15.00
14 Gaynell "Gus" Tinsley (Whizzer White back)	25.00
14a Gaynell "Gus" Tinsley	25.00
15 Ed Kaw (SP)	35.00
16 Knute Rockne	325.00
17 Bob Reynolds	15.00
18 Pudge Heffelfinger (SP)	35.00
19 Bruce A. Smith	25.00
20 Sammy Baugh	200.00
21 Whizzer White (SP, Gaynell Tinsley back)	70.00
21a Whizzer White (SP)	70.00
22 Brick Muller	15.00
23 Dick Kazmaier	25.00
24 Ken Strong	30.00
25 Casimir Myslinski (SP)	35.00
26 Larry Kelley (SP)	35.00
27 Red Grange	350.00
28 Mel Hein (SP)	40.00
29 Leo Nomellini (SP)	50.00
30 Wes E. Fesler	15.00
31 George Sauer Sr.	20.00
32 Hank Foldberg	15.00
33 Bob Higgins	15.00
34 Davey O'Brien	25.00
35 Tom Harmon	50.00
36 Turk Edwards (SP)	40.00
37 Jim Thorpe	375.00
38 Amos Alonzo Stagg	60.00
39 Jerome Holland	15.00
40 Donn Moomaw	15.00
41 Joseph Alexander (SP)	35.00
42 J. Edward Tryon (SP)	35.00
43 George Savitsky	15.00
44 Ed Garbisch	15.00
45 Elmer Oliphant	15.00
46 Arnold Lassman	15.00
47 Bo McMillan	15.00
48 Ed Widseth	15.00
49 Don Zimmerman	15.00
50 Ken Kavanaugh	15.00
51 Duane Purvis (SP)	35.00
52 John Lujack	50.00
53 John F. Green	15.00
54 Edwin Dooley (SP)	35.00
55 Frank Merritt (SP)	35.00
56 Ernie Nevers	50.00
57 Vic Hanson (SP)	35.00
58 Ed Franco	15.00
59 Doc Blanchard	45.00
60 Dan Hill	15.00
61 Charles Brickley (SP)	35.00
62 Harry Newman	15.00
63 Charlie Justice	30.00
64 Benny Friedman	15.00
65 Joe Donchess (SP)	35.00
66 Bruiser Kinard	20.00
67 Frankie Albert	15.00
68 Four Horsemen (SP)	475.00
69 Frank Sinkwich	18.00
70 Bill Daddio	15.00
71 Bob Wilson	15.00
72 Chub Peabody	15.00
73 Hugh Governali	15.00
74 Gene McEver	15.00
75 Hugh Gallarneau	15.00
76 Angelo Bertelli	18.00
77 Bowden Wyatt (SP)	35.00
78 Jay Berwanger	20.00
79 Pug Lund	15.00
80 Bennie Oosterbaan	15.00
81 Cotton Warburton	15.00
82 Alex Wojciechowicz	25.00
83 Ted Coy (SP)	35.00
84 Ace Parker (SP)	40.00
85 Sid Luckman	85.00
86 Albie Booth (SP)	35.00
87 Adolph Schultz (SP)	35.00
88 Ralph G. Kercheval	15.00
89 Marshall Goldberg	15.00
90 Charlie O'Rourke	15.00
91 Bob Odell	15.00
92 Biggie Munn	15.00
93 Willie Heston (SP)	35.00
94 Joe Bernard (SP)	35.00
95 Red Cagle (SP)	35.00
96 Bill Hollenbeck (SP)	35.00
97 Don Hutson (SP)	225.00
98 Beattie Feathers (SP)	75.00
99 Don Witmire (SP)	35.00
100 Wilbur "Fats" Henry	150.00

1956 Topps

This set of 120 cards plus an unnumbered (and probably short-printed) checklist was oversized, measuring 2-5/8" x 3-5/8". This was Topps' first set to feature only professional football players. Most notable about this set was the inclusion of the first team cards by any company (cards of the Chicago Cardinals and Washington Redskins players, however, were short-printed). Rookies in this set include Hall of Famers Roosevelt Brown, Joe Schmidt, Bill George and Lenny Moore, plus Rosey Grier. Second-year cards in this set are those of Alan Ameche, Art Donovan and Mike McCormack.

	NM
Complete Set (120):	1500.
Common Player:	5.00
SP Cards:	30.00
Team Cards:	17.00
Checklist:	375.00
1 Jack Carson	75.00
2 Gordon Soltau	5.00
3 Frank Varrichione	5.00
4 Eddie Bell	5.00
5 Alex Webster	15.00
6 Norm Van Brocklin	30.00
7 Green Bay Packers	17.00
8 Lou Creekmur	5.00
9 Lou Groza	25.00
10 Tom Bienemann	30.00
11 George Blanda	50.00
12 Alan Ameche	10.00
13 Vic Janowicz	40.00
14 Dick Moegle	5.00
15 Fran Rogel	5.00
16 Harold Giancanelli	5.00
17 Emlen Tunnell	15.00
18 Tank Younger	5.00
19 Bill Howton	8.00
20 Jack Christiansen	15.00
21 Darrell Brewster	5.00
22 Chicago Cardinals	100.00
23 Ed Brown	5.00
24 Joe Campanella	5.00
25 Leon Heath	30.00
26 San Francisco 49ers	17.00
27 Dick Flanagan	5.00
28 Chuck Bednarik	25.00
29 Kyle Rote	15.00
30 Les Richter	5.00
31 Howard Ferguson	5.00
32 Dorne Dibble	5.00
33 Kenny Konz	5.00
34 Dave Mann	30.00
35 Rick Casares	5.00
36 Art Donovan	25.00
37 Chuck Drazenovich	30.00
38 Joe Arenas	5.00
39 Lynn Chandnois	5.00
40 Philadelphia Eagles	17.00
41 Roosevelt Brown	40.00
42 Tom Fears	15.00
43 Gary Knafelc	5.00
44 Joe Schmidt	45.00
45 Cleveland Browns	17.00
46 Len Teeuws	30.00
47 Bill George	35.00
48 Baltimore Colts	17.00
49 Eddie LeBaron	40.00
50 Hugh McElhenny	25.00
51 Ted Marchibroda	5.00
52 Adrian Burk	5.00
53 Frank Gifford	60.00
54 Charley Toogood	5.00
55 Tobin Rote	8.00
56 Bill Stits	5.00
57 Don Colo	5.00
58 Ollie Matson	75.00
59 Harlon Hill	5.00
60 Lenny Moore	85.00
61 Washington Redskins	85.00
62 Billy Wilson	5.00
63 Pittsburgh Steelers	17.00
64 Bob Pellegrini	5.00
65 Ken MacAfee	5.00
66 Willard Sherman	5.00
67 Roger Zatkoff	5.00
68 Dave Middleton	5.00
69 Ray Renfro	5.00
70 Don Stonesifer	30.00
71 Stan Jones	30.00
72 Jim Mutscheller	5.00
74 Leo Nomellini	20.00
73 Volney Peters	30.00
75 Ray Mathews	5.00
76 Dick Bielski	5.00
77 Charley Conerly	25.00
78 Elroy Hirsch	25.00
79 Bill Forester	8.00
81 Jim Doran	5.00
82 Fred Morrison	5.00
83 Jack Simmons	30.00
84 Bill McColl	5.00
85 Bert Rechichar	5.00
86 Joe Scudero	30.00
87 Y.A. Tittle	40.00
88 Ernie Stautner	20.00
89 Norm Willey	5.00
90 Bob Schnelker	5.00
91 Dan Towler	8.00
92 John Martinkovic	5.00
93 Detroit Lions	17.00
94 George Ratterman	5.00
95 Chuck Ulrich	30.00
96 Bobby Watkins	5.00
97 Buddy Young	5.00
98 Billy Wells	30.00
99 Bob Toneff	5.00
100 Bill McPeak	5.00
101 Bobby Thompson	5.00
102 Roosevelt Grier	30.00
103 Ron Waller	5.00
104 Bobby Dillon	5.00
105 Leon Hart	8.00
106 Mike McCormack	15.00
107 John Olszewski	30.00
108 Bill Wightkin	5.00

108	George Shaw 8.00
109	Dale Atkeson 30.00
110	Joe Perry 20.00
111	Dale Dodrill 5.00
112	Tom Scott 5.00
113	New York Giants 17.00
114	Los Angeles Rams 17.00
115	Al Carmichael 5.00
116	Bobby Layne 40.00
117	Ed Modzelewski 5.00
118	Lamar McHan 30.00
119	Chicago Bears 17.00
120	Billy Vessels 35.00

1957 Topps

This 154-card set (not including the unnumbered checklist) has a horizontal format with two different pictures of the player on each side -- a head shot and a posed action shot. Issued in two series, the second series is more difficult to obtain than the first. Rookie cards in this set include Night Train Lane, Ray Berry, Earl Morrall, Bart Starr, John Unitas and Paul Hornung. Second-year cards include Roosevelt Brown, Pat Summerall, John Henry Johnson, Bob St. Clair, Lenny Moore and Len Ford (this is also his last regular-issued card). The final regular-issue card of Elroy Hirsch is also in this set. One variation does exist: The scarcer uncorrected card #58, Willard Sherman, has no team name on the front. The corrected version reads "Los Angeles Rams." It's believed that a number of the high series cards are short-printed, including Starr, Unitas and Hornung.

		NM
Complete Set (155):		2400.
Common Player (1-88):		4.50
Common Player (89-154):		6.50
Checklist:		700.00
1	Eddie LeBaron	30.00
2	Pete Retzlaff	8.00
3	Mike McCormack	10.00
4	Lou Baldacci	4.50
5	Gino Marchetti	14.00
6	Leo Nomellini	13.00
7	Bobby Watkins	6.00
8	Dave Middleton	6.00
9	Bobby Dillon	6.00
10	Les Richter	6.00
11	Roosevelt Brown	13.00
12	Lavern Torgeson	6.00
13	Dick Bielski	4.50
14	Pat Summerall	15.00
15	Jack Butler	7.00
16	John Henry Johnson	13.00
17	Art Spinney	4.50
18	Bob St. Clair	10.00
19	Perry Jeter	4.50
20	Lou Creekmur	4.50
21	Dave Hanner	4.50
22	Norm Van Brocklin	25.00
23	Don Chandler	6.50
24	Al Dorow	4.50
25	Tom Scott	4.50
26	Ollie Matson	16.00
27	Fran Rogel	4.50
28	Lou Groza	20.00
29	Billy Vessels	4.50
30	Y.A. Tittle	32.50
31	George Blanda	45.00
32	Bobby Layne	30.00
33	Bill Howton	4.50
34	Bill Wade	4.50
35	Emlen Tunnell	12.00
36	Leo Elter	4.50
37	Clarence Peaks	6.00
38	Don Stonesifer	4.50
39	George Tarasovic	4.50
40	Darrell Brewster	4.50
41	Bert Rechichar	4.50
42	Billy Wilson	4.50
43	Ed Brown	4.50
44	Gene Gedman	4.50
45	Gary Knafelc	4.50
46	Elroy Hirsch	20.00
47	Don Heinrich	4.50
48	Gene Brito	4.50
49	Chuck Bednarik	15.00
50	Dave Mann	4.50
51	Bill McPeak	4.50
52	Kenny Konz	4.50
53	Alan Ameche	8.00
54	Gordon Soltau	4.50
55	Rick Casares	4.50
56	Charlie Ane	4.50
57	Al Carmichael	4.50
58	Willard Sherman (no team name on front)	5.00
58a	Willard Sherman (Rams on front)	150.00
59	Kyle Rote	8.00
60	Chuck Drazenovich	4.50
61	Bobby Walston	4.50
62	John Olszewski	4.50
63	Ray Mathews	4.50
64	Maurice Bassett	4.50
65	Art Donovan	20.00
66	Joe Arenas	4.50
67	Harlon Hill	4.50
68	Yale Lary	10.00
69	Bill Forester	4.50
70	Bob Boyd	4.50
71	Andy Robustelli	13.00
72	Sam Baker	7.00
73	Bob Pellegrini	4.50
74	Leo Sanford	4.50
75	Sid Watson	4.50
76	Ray Renfro	4.50
77	Carl Taseff	4.50
78	Clyde Conner	4.50
79	J.C. Caroline	4.50
80	Howard Cassady	10.00
81	Tobin Rote	6.00
82	Ron Waller	4.50
83	Jim Patton	7.00
84	Volney Peters	4.50
85	Dick Lane	40.00
86	Royce Womble	4.50
87	Duane Putnam	6.00
88	Frank Gifford	85.00
89	Steve Meilinger	6.50
90	Buck Lansford	6.50
91	Lindon Crow	6.50
92	Ernie Stautner	15.00
93	Preston Carpenter	10.00
94	Raymond Berry	125.00
95	Hugh McElhenny	25.00
96	Stan Jones	12.00
97	Dorne Dibble	6.50
98	Joe Scudero	6.50
99	Eddie Bell	6.50
100	Joe Childress	6.50
101	Elbert Nickel	6.50
102	Walt Michaels	6.50
103	Jim Mutscheller	6.50
104	Earl Morrall	50.00
105	Larry Strickland	6.50
106	Jack Christiansen	15.00
107	Fred Cone	6.50
108	Bud McFadin	10.00
109	Charley Conerly	25.00
110	Tom Runnels	6.50
111	Ken Keller	6.50
112	James Root	6.50
113	Ted Marchibroda	6.50
114	Don Paul	6.50
115	George Shaw	6.50
116	Dick Moegle	6.50
117	Don Bingham	6.50
118	Leon Hart	10.00
119	Bart Starr	400.00
120	Paul Miller	6.50
121	Alex Webster	10.00
122	Ray Wietecha	6.50
123	Johnny Carson	6.50
124	Tommy McDonald	14.00
125	Jerry Tubbs	10.00
126	Jack Scarbath	6.50
127	Ed Modzelewski	6.50
128	Lenny Moore	45.00
129	Joe Perry	25.00
130	Bill Wightkin	6.50
131	Jim Doran	6.50
132	Howard Ferguson	6.50
133	Tom Wilson	6.50
134	Dick James	6.50
135	Jimmy Harris	6.50
136	Chuck Ulrich	6.50
137	Lynn Chandnois	6.50
138	Johnny Unitas	450.00
139	Jim Ridlon	6.50
140	Zeke Bratkowski	10.00
141	Ray Krouse	6.50
142	John Martinkovic	6.50
143	Jim Cason	6.50
144	Ken MacAfee	6.50
145	Sid Youngelman	10.00
146	Paul Larson	6.50
147	Len Ford	15.00
148	Bob Toneff	6.50
149	Ronnie Knox	6.50
150	Jim David	10.00
151	Paul Hornung	400.00
152	Tank Younger	6.50
153	Bill Svoboda	6.50
154	Fred Morrison	40.00

1958 Topps

This 132-card set features an oval photo of the player on the front and a bright red background on the back. The card set also includes team cards, which had been missing from the previous year's set. Rookies here include Jim Brown and Sonny Jurgensen. Second-year cards are those of Bart Starr, Jim Ringo (his rookie was in '55), Bill George, and Ray Berry. This set also includes the last Topps card of Jack Christiansen.

		NM
Complete Set (132):		1300.
Common Player:		3.75
1	Gene Filipski	14.00
2	Bobby Layne	25.00
3	Joe Schmidt	9.00
4	Bill Barnes	3.75
5	Milt Plum	8.00
6	Billie Howton	2.00
7	Howard Cassady	4.00
8	James Dooley	2.00
9	Cleveland Browns Team	6.50
10	Lenny Moore	15.00
11	Pete Brewster	3.75
12	Alan Ameche	5.00
13	Jim David	3.75
14	Jim Mutscheller	3.75
15	Andy Robustelli	9.00
16	Gino Marchetti	9.00
17	Ray Renfro	2.00
18	Yale Lary	8.50
19	Gary Glick	3.75
20	Jon Arnett	8.00
21	Bob Boyd	3.75
22	Johnny Unitas	115.00
23	Zeke Bratkowski	4.00
24	Sid Youngelman	3.75
25	Leo Elter	3.75
26	Ken Konz	3.75
27	Washington Redskins Team	7.00
28	C. Brettschneider	3.75
29	Chicago Bears Team	7.00
30	Alex Webster	4.00
31	Al Carmichael	3.75
32	Bobby Dillon	3.75
33	Steve Meilinger	3.75
34	Sam Baker	2.00
35	Chuck Bednarik	15.00
36	Vic Zucco	3.75
37	George Tarasovic	3.75
38	Bill Wade	3.75
39	Dick Stanfell	3.75
40	Jerry Norton	3.75
41	San Francisco 49ers Team	7.00
42	Emlen Tunnell	9.00
43	Jim Doran	3.75
44	Ted Marchibroda	3.75
45	Chet Hanulak	3.75
46	Dale Dodrill	3.75
47	John Carson	3.75
48	Dick Deschaine	3.75
49	Billy Wells	3.75
50	Larry Morris	3.75
51	Jack McClairen	3.75
52	Lou Groza	15.00
53	Rick Casares	3.75
54	Don Chandler	3.75
55	Duane Putnam	3.75
56	Gary Knafelc	3.75
57	Earl Morrall	10.00
58	Ron Kramer	4.00
59	Mike McCormack	8.00
60	Gern Nagler	3.75
61	New York Giants Team	7.00
62	Jim Brown	400.00
63	Joe Marconi	4.00
64	R.C. Owens	4.00
65	Jimmy Carr	4.00
66	Bart Starr	95.00
67	Tom Wilson	3.75
68	Lamar McHan	2.00
69	Chicago Cardinals Team	7.00
70	Jack Christiansen	8.00
71	Don McElhenny	4.00
72	Ron Waller	3.75
73	Frank Gifford	50.00
74	Bert Rechichar	3.75
75	John H. Johnson	10.00
76	Jack Butler	3.75
77	Frank Varrichione	3.75
78	Ray Mathews	3.75
79	Mary Matsuzak	3.75
80	Harlon Hill	3.75
81	Lou Creekmur	3.75
82	Woody Lewis	3.75
83	Don Heinrich	2.00
84	Charley Conerly	15.00
85	Los Angeles Rams Team	7.00
86	Y.A. Tittle	30.00
87	Bob Walston	3.75
88	Earl Putnam	3.75
89	Leo Nomellini	8.50
90	Sonny Jurgensen	100.00
91	Don Paul	3.75
92	Paige Cothren	3.75
93	Joe Perry	13.00
94	Tobin Rote	4.00
95	Billy Wilson	3.75
96	Green Bay Packers Team	7.00
97	Torgy Torgeson	3.75
98	Milt Davis	3.75
99	Larry Strickland	3.75
100	Matt Hazeltine	4.00
101	Walt Yowarski	3.75
102	Roosevelt Brown	8.00
103	Jim Ringo	8.00
104	Joe Krupa	3.75
105	Les Richter	3.75
106	Art Donovan	15.00
107	John Olszewski	3.75
108	Ken Keller	3.75
109	Philadelphia Eagles Team	5.50
110	Baltimore Colts Team	7.00
111	Dick Bielski	3.75
112	Eddie LeBaron	4.00
113	Gene Brito	3.75
114	William Galimore	12.00
115	Detroit Lions Team	7.00
116	Pittsburgh Steelers Team	7.00
117	L.G. Dupre	3.75
118	Babe Parilli	4.00
119	Bill George	8.00
120	Raymond Berry	30.00
121	Jim Podoley	3.75
122	Hugh McElhenny	15.00
123	Ed Brown	3.75
124	Dicky Moegle	3.75
125	Tom Scott	3.75
126	Tom McDonald	4.00
127	Ollie Matson	15.00
128	Preston Carpenter	3.75
129	George Blanda	35.00
130	Gordy Soltau	3.75
131	Dick Nolan	4.00
132	Don Bosseler	16.00

1959 Topps

JOHNNY UNITAS
QUARTERBACK   BALTIMORE COLTS

This 176-card set, featuring alternating blue and red letters for player names, was issued in two series, with the first being more valuable than the second. Team cards also included checklists on the back of each, and pennant cards were included and numbered as part of the set. This set showcases the rookie cards of Max McGee, Sam Huff, Alex Karras, John David Crow, Jerry Kramer, Jim Parker, Bobby Mitchell, and Jim Taylor (actually not the HOFer; see below). Second-year cards in the set are those of Paul Hornung and Jim Brown. Card #155, Jim Taylor, does not show the HOF running back for the Packers, as the card reads; instead, it shows Chicago Cardinal linebacker Jim Taylor. This mistake was repeated the following year, meaning a card actually depicting Taylor did not appear until 1961.

		NM
Complete Set (176):		1000.
Common Player (1-88):		2.50
Common Player (89-176):		2.00
Team Cards:		5.00
1	Johnny Unitas	100.00
2	Gene Brito	2.50
3	Detroit Lions Team Card	5.00
4	Max McGee	20.00
5	Hugh McElhenny	12.00
6	Joe Schmidt	8.00
7	Kyle Rote	5.00
8	Clarence Peaks	2.50
9	Pittsburgh Steelers Pennant Card	5.00
10	Jim Brown	125.00
11	Ray Mathews	2.50
12	Bobby Dillon	2.50
13	Joe Childress	2.50
14	Terry Barr	2.50
15	Del Shofner	4.50
16	Bob Pellegrini	2.50
17	Baltimore Colts Team Card	5.00
18	Preston Carpenter	2.50
19	Leo Nomellini	7.00
20	Frank Gifford	30.00
21	Charlie Ane	2.50
22	Jack Butler	2.50
23	Bart Starr	55.00
24	Chicago Cardinals Pennant Card	2.50
25	Bill Barnes	2.50
26	Walt Michaels	2.50
27	Clyde Conner	2.50
28	Paige Cothren	2.50
29	Roosevelt Grier	5.00
30	Alan Ameche	5.00
31	Philadelphia Eagles Team Card	5.00
32	Dick Nolan	2.00
33	R.C. Owens	2.50
34	Dale Dodrill	2.50
35	Gene Gedman	2.50
36	Gene Lipscomb	8.00
37	Ray Renfro	2.50
38	Cleveland Brown Pennant Card	2.50
39	Bill Forester	2.50
40	Bobby Layne	25.00
41	Pat Summerall	8.50
42	Jerry Mertens	2.50
43	Steve Myhra	2.50
44	John Henry Johnson	7.00
45	Woody Lewis	2.50
46	Green Bay Packers Team Card	5.00
47	Don Owens	2.50
48	Ed Beatty	2.50
49	Don Chandler	2.00
50	Ollie Matson	12.00
51	Sam Huff	40.00
52	Tom Miner	2.50
53	New York Giants Pennant Card	2.50
54	Kenny Konz	2.50
55	Raymond Berry	15.00
56	Howard Ferguson	2.50
57	Chuck Ulrich	2.50
58	Bob St. Clair	5.00
59	Don Burroughs	3.00
60	Lou Groza	15.00
61	San Francisco 49ers Team Card	5.00
62	Andy Nelson	2.50
63	Hal Bradley	2.50
64	Dave Hanner	2.50
65	Chuck Connerly	11.00
66	Gene Cronin	2.50
67	Duane Putnam	2.50
68	Baltimore Colts Pennant Card	2.50
69	Ernie Stautner	8.00
70	Jon Arnett	3.00
71	Ken Panfil	2.50
72	Matt Hazeltine	2.50
73	Harley Sewell	2.50
74	Mike McCormack	5.00
75	Jim Ringo	5.00
76	Los Angeles Rams Team Card	5.00
77	Bob Gain	3.00
78	Buzz Nutter	2.50
79	Jerry Norton	2.50
80	Joe Perry	12.00
81	Carl Brettschneider	2.50
82	Paul Hornung	60.00
83	Philadelphia Eagles Pennant Card	2.50
84	Les Richter	2.50
85	Howard Cassady	2.00
86	Art Donovan	8.00
87	Jim Patton	2.50
88	Pete Retzlaff	3.50
89	Jim Mutscheller	2.00
90	Zeke Bratkowski	3.00
91	Washington Redskins Team Card	5.00
92	Art Hunter	2.00
93	Gern Nagler	2.00
94	Chuck Weber	2.00
95	Lew Carpenter	2.00
96	Stan Jones	5.00
97	Ralph Guglielmi	2.00
98	Green Bay Packer Pennant Card	2.50
99	Ray Wietecha	2.00
100	Lenny Moore	10.00
101	Jim Ray Smith	3.00
102	Abe Woodson	5.00
103	Alex Karras	40.00
104	Chicago Bears Team Card	5.00
105	Johnny Crow	10.00
106	Joe Fortunato	5.00
107	Babe Parilli	3.00
108	Proverb Jacobs	2.00
109	Gino Marchetti	8.00
110	Bill Wade	2.00
111	San Francisco 49ers Pennant Card	2.50
112	Karl Rubke	2.00
113	Dave Middleton	2.00
114	Roosevelt Brown	5.00
115	John Olszewski	2.00
116	Jerry Kramer	25.00
117	King Hill	3.50
118	Chicago Cardinals Team Card	5.00
119	Frank Viarrichione	2.00
120	Rick Casares	2.50
121	George Strugar	2.00
122	Bill Glass	2.50
123	Don Bosseler	2.50
124	John Reger	2.50
125	Jim Ninowski	3.00
126	Los Angeles Rams Pennant Card	2.50
127	Willard Sherman	2.00
128	Bob Schnelker	2.00
129	Ollie Spencer	2.00
130	Y.A. Tittle	25.00
131	Yale Lary	6.00
132	Jim Parker	20.00
133	New York Giants Team Card	5.00
134	Jim Schrader	2.00
135	M.C. Reynolds	2.00
136	Mike Sandusky	2.00
137	Ed Brown	2.00
138	Al Barry	2.00
139	Detroit Lions Pennant Card	2.50
140	Bobby Mitchell	35.00
141	Larry Morris	2.00
142	Jim Phillips	3.00
143	Jim David	2.00
144	Joe Krupa	2.00
145	Willie Galimore	3.00
146	Pittsburgh Steelers Team Card	2.50
147	Andy Robustelli	7.50
148	Bill Wilson	2.00
149	Leo Sanford	2.00
150	Eddie LeBaron	5.00
151	Bill McColl	2.00
152	Buck Lansford	2.00
153	Chicago Bears Pennant Card	2.50
154	Leo Sugar	2.00
155	Jim Taylor	17.00
156	Lindon Crow	2.00
157	Jack McClairen	2.00
158	Vince Costello	2.50
159	Stan Wallace	2.00
160	Mel Triplett	3.00
161	Cleveland Browns Team Card	5.00
162	Dan Currie	2.00
163	L.G. Dupre	2.00
164	John Morrow	2.00
165	Jim Podoley	2.00
166	Bruce Bosley	2.50
167	Harlon Hill	2.00
168	Washington Redskins Pennant Card	2.50
169	Junior Wren	2.00
170	Tobin Rote	2.50
171	Art Spinney	2.00
172	Chuck Drazenovich	2.00
173	Bobby Joe Conrad	5.00
174	Jesse Richardson	2.00
175	Sam Baker	2.00
176	Tom Tracy	8.00

1960 Topps

This 132-card set by Topps, featuring NFL players only (Fleer picked up teams from the AFL in its 1960 set), showcased the inclusion of the expansion Dallas Cowboys. Cards are again numbered alphabetically according to city name. Card backs had a "Football Funnies" quiz which revealed the answer underneath a scratch-off area. This set marks the rookie cards of HOFer Forrest Gregg, future announcer Tom Brookshier, and former Jets coach Joe Walton. Second-year cards in the set include Jim Parker, Doug Atkins (his rookie card was six years prior to his second-year card), Bobby Mitchell, and Sam Huff. There are three errors in the set. Card #52, Jim Taylor, shows not the HOF running back of the Packers, as advertised; it again shows Cardinals linebacker Jim Taylor. This mistake was made in the 1959 set as well. The other errors are reversed negatives; on the card of #97, Frank Varrichione, and on card #20, Doug Atkins.

	NM
Complete Set (132):	625.00
Common Player:	1.75
Team Cards:	5.00
1 Johnny Unitas	80.00
2 Alan Ameche	5.00
3 Lenny Moore	7.00
4 Raymond Berry	7.00
5 Jim Parker	7.00
6 George Preas	1.75
7 Art Spinney	1.75
8 Bill Pellington	2.50
9 Johnny Sample	2.50
10 Gene Lipscomb	3.50
11 Baltimore Colts Team Card (Checklist 67-132)	5.00
12 Ed Brown	1.75
13 Rick Casares	1.75
14 Willie Galimore	1.75
15 Jim Dooley	1.75
16 Harlon Hill	1.75
17 Stan Jones	4.50
18 Bill George	4.50
19 Erich Barnes	3.00
20 Doug Atkins	5.50
21 Chicago Bears Team Card (Checklist 1-66)	5.00
22 Milt Plum	2.50
23 Jim Brown	85.00
24 Sam Baker	1.75
25 Bobby Mitchell	10.00
26 Ray Renfro	1.75
27 Billy Howton	1.75
28 Jim Ray Smith	3.50
29 Jim Shofner	3.50
30 Bob Gain	1.75
31 Cleveland Browns Team Card (Checklist 1-66)	5.00
32 Don Heinrich	1.75
33 Ed Modzelewski	1.75
34 Fred Cone	1.75
35 L.G. Dupre	1.75
36 Dick Bielski	1.75
37 Charlie Ane	1.75
38 Jerry Tubbs	1.75
39 Doyle Nix	1.75
40 Ray Krouse	1.75
41 Earl Morrall	5.00
42 Hopalong Cassady	1.75
43 Dave Middleton	1.75
44 Jim Gibbons	2.50
45 Darris McCord	1.75
46 Joe Schmidt	5.50
47 Terry Barr	1.75
48 Yale Lary	5.00
49 Gil Mains	1.75
50 Detroit Lions Team Card (Checklist 1-66)	5.00
51 Bart Starr	40.00
52 Jim Taylor	8.00
53 Lew Carpenter	1.75
54 Paul Hornung	35.00
55 Max McGee	3.00
56 Forrest Gregg	28.00
57 Jim Ringo	5.50
58 Bill Forester	1.75
59 Dave Hanner	1.75
60 Green Bay Packers Team Card (Checklist 67-132)	5.00
61 Bill Wade	1.75
62 Frank Ryan	8.00
63 Ollie Matson	8.00
64 Jon Arnett	1.75
65 Del Shofner	1.75
66 Jim Phillips	1.75
67 Art Hunter	1.75
68 Les Richter	1.75
69 Lou Michaels	3.00
70 John Baker	1.75
71 Los Angeles Rams Team Card (Checklist 1-66)	5.00
72 Charley Conerly	10.00
73 Mel Triplett	1.75
74 Frank Gifford	45.00
75 Alex Webster	1.75
76 Bob Schnelker	1.75
77 Pat Summerall	7.00
78 Roosevelt Brown	5.50
79 Jimmy Patton	1.75
80 Sam Huff	15.00
81 Andy Robustelli	6.00
82 New York Giants Team Card (Checklist 1-66)	5.00
83 Clarence Peaks	1.75
84 Bill Barnes	1.75
85 Pete Retzlaff	1.75
86 Bobby Walston	1.75
87 Chuck Bednarik	7.00
88 Bob Pellagrini	1.75
89 Tom Brookshier	6.00
90 Marion Campbell	1.75
91 Jesse Richardson	1.75
92 Philadelphia Eagles Team Card (Checklist 1-66)	5.00
93 Bobby Layne	23.00
94 John Henry Johnson	5.50
95 Tom Tracy	1.75
96 Preston Carpenter	1.75
97 Frank Varrichione	1.75
98 John Nisby	1.75
99 Dean Derby	1.75
100 George Tarasovic	1.75
101 Ernie Stautner	6.00
102 Pittsburgh Steelers Team Card (Checklist 67-132)	5.00
103 King Hill	1.75
104 Mal Hammack	1.75
105 John Crow	3.50
106 Bobby Joe Conrad	1.75
107 Woodley Lewis	1.75
108 Don Gillis	1.75
109 Carl Brettschneider	1.75
110 Leo Sugar	1.75
111 Frank Fuller	1.75
112 St. Louis Cardinals Team Card (Checklist 67-132)	5.00
113 Y.A. Tittle	22.00
114 Joe Perry	7.00
115 J.D. Smith	3.00
116 Hugh McElhenny	8.00
117 Billy Wilson	1.75
118 Bob St. Clair	3.50
119 Matt Hazeltine	1.75
120 Abe Woodson	1.75
121 Leo Nomellini	5.00
122 San Francisco 49ers Team Card (Checklist 67-132)	5.00
123 Ralph Guglielmi	1.75
124 Don Bosseler	1.75
125 Johnny Olszewski	1.75
126 Bill Anderson	1.75
127 Joe Walton	3.50
128 Jim Schrader	1.75
129 Ralph Felton	1.75
130 Gary Glick	1.75
131 Bob Toneff	1.75
132 Washington Redskins	25.00

1960 Topps Team Emblem Stickers

One of each of these 33 metallic inserts was included in a wax pack of 1960 Topps football cards. The team emblem stickers are unnumbered and included NFL teams (1-13) and college teams (14-33). This was Topps' first football insert set. Future Topps inserts in the early '60s would also include college teams. These sticker fronts are bordered in black and show either a blue, silver or gold background. The stickers measure about 2" x 3".

	NM
Complete Set (33):	175.00
Common Pro Team:	4.50
Common College Team:	4.50
(1) Baltimore Colts	6.00
(2) Chicago Bears	6.00
(3) Cleveland Browns	6.00
(4) Dallas Cowboys	8.00
(5) Detroit Lions	6.00
(6) Green Bay Packers	6.00
(7) Los Angeles Rams	6.00
(8) New York Giants	6.00
(9) Philadelphia Eagles	6.00
(10) Pittsburgh Steelers	6.00
(11) St. Louis Cardinals	6.00
(12) San Francisco 49ers	6.00
(13) Washington Redskins	8.00
(14) Air Force	4.50
(15) Army	4.50
(16) California	4.50
(17) Dartmouth	4.50
(18) Duke	4.50
(19) LSU	4.50
(20) Michigan	4.50
(21) Mississippi	4.50
(22) Navy	4.50
(23) Notre Dame	15.00
(24) SMU	4.50
(25) USC	4.50
(26) Syracuse	4.50
(27) Tennessee	4.50
(28) Texas	4.50
(29) UCLA	4.50
(30) Minnesota	4.50
(31) Washington	4.50
(32) Wisconsin	4.50
(33) Yale	4.50

Values quoted in this guide reflect the retail price of a card — the price a collector can expect to pay when buying a card from a dealer. The wholesale price — that which a collector can expect to receive from a dealer when selling cards — will be significantly lower, depending on desirability and condition.

1961 Topps

PAUL HORNUNG
HALFBACK — GREEN BAY PACKERS

This set of 198 cards was the last full Topps set to include both AFL players and NFL players. The AFL segment of the set (133-197) does not include team checklists. Cards are similar to the 1961 Topps baseball issue and feature a ruboff game on the back. The set is once again numbered in order of teams - alphabetically by city. Rookies in this set include John Brodie, Don Maynard, Jim Otto and Tom Flores. Second-year cards include Alex Karras, Henry Jordan, Sonny Jurgensen (three years after his rookie card debuted), Abner Haynes, Jack Kemp and Ron Mix. This set included the last regular-issue cards of Alan Ameche, Charley Conerly, Kyle Rote, Chuck Bednarik and Tom Brookshier. Card #41 could actually be considered Packer running back Jim Taylor's rookie card. His rookie and second-year cards Topps printed in 1959 and 1960 actually depicted Cardinal linebacker Jim Taylor instead of HOFer Jim Taylor.

	NM
Complete Set (198):	1100.
Common Player:	2.00
1 Johnny Unitas	90.00
2 Lenny Moore	7.00
3 Alan Ameche	4.00
4 Raymond Berry	7.00
5 Jim Mutscheller	2.00
6 Jim Parker	4.50
7 Gino Marchetti	5.50
8 Gene Lipscomb	3.00
9 Baltimore Colts	4.00
10 Bill Wade	2.00
11 Johnny Morris	6.00
12 Rick Casares	2.00
13 Harlon Hill	2.00
14 Stan Jones	4.50
15 Doug Atkins	5.00
16 Bill George	4.50
17 J.C. Caroline	2.00
18 Chicago Bears	4.00
19 Big Time Football comes to Texas (Eddie LeBaron)	3.25
20 Eddie LeBaron	3.00
21 Don McElhenny	2.00
22 L.G. Dupre	2.00
23 Jim Doran	2.00
24 Billy Howton	2.00
25 Buzz Guy	2.00
26 Jack Patera	2.00
27 Tom Frankauser	2.00
28 Dallas Cowboys	10.00
29 Jim Ninowski	2.00
30 Dan Lewis	2.00
31 Nick Pietrosante	3.00
32 Gail Cogdill	2.00
33 Jim Gibbons	2.00
34 Jim Martin	2.00
35 Alex Karras	20.00
36 Joe Schmidt	5.00
37 Detroit Lions	4.00
38 Set Scoring Record (Paul Hornung)	10.00
39 Bart Starr	40.00
40 Paul Hornung	28.00
41 Jim Taylor	24.00
42 Max McGee	2.00
43 Boyd Dowler	5.00
44 Jim Ringo	4.25
45 Henry Jordan	15.00
46 Bill Forester	2.00
47 Green Bay Packers	4.00
48 Frank Ryan	2.00
49 Jon Arnett	2.00
50 Ollie Matson	6.50
51 Jim Phillips	2.00
52 Del Shofner	2.00
53 Art Hunter	2.00
54 Gene Brito	2.00
55 Lindon Crow	2.00
56 Los Angeles Rams	4.00
57 25-TD Passes (Johnny Unitas)	15.00
58 Y.A. Tittle	22.00
59 John Brodie	40.00
60 J.D. Smith	2.00
61 R.C. Owens	2.00
62 Clyde Conner	2.00
63 Bob St. Clair	4.00
64 Leo Nomellini	5.00
65 Abe Woodson	2.00
66 San Francisco 49ers	4.00
67 Checklist	50.00
68 Milt Plum	2.00
69 Ray Renfro	2.00
70 Bobby Mitchell	7.00
71 Jim Brown	85.00
72 Mike McCormack	4.00
73 Jim Ray Smith	2.00
74 Sam Baker	2.00
75 Walt Michaels	2.00
76 Cleveland Browns	2.00
77 (Jim Brown IA)	35.00
78 George Shaw	2.00
79 Hugh McElhenny	6.00
80 Clancy Osborne	2.00
81 Dave Middleton	2.00
82 Frank Youso	2.00
83 Don Joyce	2.00
84 Ed Culpepper	2.00
85 Charley Conerly	8.00
86 Mel Triplett	2.00
87 Kyle Rote	4.00
88 Roosevelt Brown	4.50
89 Ray Wietecha	2.00
90 Andy Robustelli	6.00
91 Sam Huff	7.50
92 Jim Patton	2.00
93 New York Giants	4.00
94 Leads Giants for 13th Year (Chas Conerly)	5.00
95 Sonny Jurgensen	20.00
96 Tommy McDonald	2.00
97 Billy Barnes	2.00
98 Bobby Walston	2.00
99 Pete Retzlaff	2.00
100 Jim McCusker	2.00
101 Chuck Bednarik	7.00
102 Tom Brookshier	3.00
103 Philadephia Eagles	4.00
104 Bobby Layne	20.00
105 John Henry Johnson	5.00
106 Tom Tracy	2.00
107 Buddy Dial	3.00
108 Jim Orr	3.50
109 Mike Sandusky	2.00
110 John Reger	2.00
111 Junior Wren	2.00
112 Pittsburgh Steelers	4.00
113 Sets New Passing Record (Bobby Layne)	7.00
114 John Roach	2.00
115 Sam Etcheverry	3.00
116 John David Crow	3.00
117 Mal Hammack	2.00
118 Sonny Randle	2.00
119 Leo Sugar	2.00
120 Jerry Norton	2.00
121 St. Louis Cardinals	4.00
122 Checklist	35.00
123 Ralph Guglielmi	2.00
124 Dick James	2.00
125 Don Bosseler	2.00
126 Joe Walton	2.00
127 Bill Anderson	2.00
128 Vince Promuto	2.25
129 Bob Toneff	2.00
130 John Paluck	2.00
131 Washington Redskins	4.00
132 Wins NFL Passing Title (Milt Plum)	3.00
133 Abner Haynes	3.50
134 Mel Branch	2.00
135 Jerry Cornelison	2.00
136 Bill Krisher	2.00
137 Paul Miller	2.00
138 Jack Spikes	2.00
139 Johnny Robinson	6.00
140 Cotton Davidson	4.00
141 Dave Smith	2.00
142 Bill Groman	2.00
143 Rich Michael	2.00
144 Mike Dukes	2.00
145 George Blanda	26.00
146 Billy Cannon	4.00
147 Dennit Morris	2.00
148 Jacky Lee	2.00
149 Al Dorrow	2.00
150 Don Maynard	50.00
151 Art Powell	6.00
152 Sid Youngelman	2.00
153 Bob Mischak	2.00
154 Larry Grantham	2.00
155 Tom Saidock	2.00
156 Roger Donnahoo	2.00
157 Lavern Torczon	2.00
158 Archie Matsos	2.00
159 Elbert Dubenion	3.00
160 Wray Carlton	2.00
161 Rich McCabe	2.00
162 Ken Rice	2.00
163 Art Baker	2.00
164 Tom Rychlec	2.00
165 Mack Yoho	2.00
166 Jack Kemp	150.00
167 Paul Lowe	3.25
168 Ron Mix	9.00
169 Paul Maguire	3.00
170 Volney Peters	2.00
171 Ernie Wright	2.00
172 Ron Nery	2.00
173 Dave Kocourek	2.00
174 Jim Colclough	2.00
175 Babe Parilli	3.25
176 Billy Lott	2.00
177 Fred Bruney	2.00
178 Ross O'Hanley	2.00
179 Walt Cudzik	2.00
180 Charles Leo	2.00
181 Bob Dee	2.00
182 Jim Otto	40.00
183 Eddie Macon	2.00
184 Dick Christy	2.00
185 Alan Miller	2.00
186 Tom Flores	25.00
187 Joe Cannavino	2.00
188 Don Manoukian	2.00
189 Bob Coolbaugh	2.00
190 Lionel Taylor	7.00
191 Bud McFadin	2.00
192 Goose Gonsoulin	2.00
193 Frank Tripucka	2.75
194 Gene Mingo	3.00
195 Eldon Danenhauer	2.00
196 Bob McNamara	2.00
197 Dave Rolle	2.00
198 Checklist	90.00

1961 Topps Stickers

This set of 48 stickers was included one per pack in the 1961 Topps football set. Stickers are unnumbered and are grouped according to NFL (1-15), AFL (16-24), and colleges (25-48). The stickers were issued with tabs that could be peeled off. For the sticker to be considered Mint, tabs would have to be intact.

	NM
Complete Set (48):	175.00
Common Pro Team:	6.00
Common College Team:	3.50
(1) NFL Emblem	6.00
(2) Baltimore Colts	6.00
(3) Chicago Bears	6.00
(4) Cleveland Browns	6.00
(5) Dallas Cowboys	8.00
(6) Detroit Lions	6.00
(7) Green Bay Packers	8.00
(8) Los Angeles Rams	6.00
(9) Minnesota Vikings	6.00
(10) New York Giants	6.00
(11) Philadelphia Eagles	6.00
(12) Pittsburgh Steelers	6.00
(13) San Francisco 49ers	6.00
(14) St. Louis Cardinals	6.00
(15) Washington Redskins	8.00
(16) AFL Emblem	8.00
(17) Boston Patriots	6.00
(18) Buffalo Bills	8.00
(19) Dallas Texans	8.00
(20) Denver Broncos	6.00
(21) Houston Oilers	6.00
(22) Oakland Raiders	6.00
(23) San Diego Chargers	6.00
(24) Titans of New York	6.00
(25) Air Force	3.50
(26) Alabama	6.00
(27) Arkansas	3.50
(28) Army	5.00
(29) Baylor	3.50
(30) California	3.50
(31) Georgia Tech	3.50
(32) Illinois	3.50
(33) Kansas	3.50
(34) Kentucky	3.50
(35) Miami	6.00
(36) Michigan	6.00
(37) Missouri	3.50
(38) Navy	5.00
(39) Oregon	3.50
(40) Penn State	6.00
(41) Pittsburgh	3.50
(42) Purdue	3.50
(43) USC	6.00
(44) Stanford	3.50
(45) TCU	3.50
(46) Virginia	3.50
(47) Washington	3.50
(48) Washington State	3.50

Post-1980 cards in Near Mint condition will generally sell for about 75% of the quoted Mint value. Excellent-condition cards bring no more than 40%.

A card number in parentheses ( ) indicates the set is unnumbered.

1962 Topps

NORM SNEAD   WASHINGTON REDSKINS QUARTERBACK

This 176-card set is one of the decade's toughest to complete in mint condition because of the easily-scuffed black borders. Like many of the Topps sets of this era, a good number of the cards in the set are short-printed, probably because the number of cards in the set didn't exactly match the amount that would fit onto printing sheets. Cards are again grouped by teams, which are listed in alphabetical order by city. This was the first time in five years Topps tried a horizontal format; Topps would try it again in 1966. Rookies in this set include Mike Ditka, Ernie Davis (his only regular-issue card), Roman Gabriel, Fran Tarkenton, Bill Kilmer and Norm Snead. Second-year cards in the set include Don Meredith (his first Topps card) and John Brodie. Last-year cards in the set include Max McGee and Hall of Famers Joe Perry, Ollie Matson and Bobby Layne. The last Topps cards of Frank Gifford and Andy Robustelli are also included. (Key: SP - short printed)

	NM
Complete Set (176):	1700.
Common Player:	3.50
SP Cards:	7.50
1 Johnny Unitas	125.00
2 Lenny Moore	9.00
3 Alex Hawkins (SP)	8.00
4 Joe Perry	9.00
5 Raymond Berry (SP)	20.00
6 Steve Myhra	3.50
7 Tom Gilburg (SP)	7.50
8 Gino Marchetti	7.50
9 Bill Pellington	3.50
10 Andy Nelson	3.50
11 Wendell Harris (SP)	7.50
12 Baltimore Colts Team	3.50
13 Billy Wade (SP)	7.50
14 Willie Galimore	3.50
15 Johnny Morris (SP)	7.50
16 Rick Casares	3.50
17 Mike Ditka	225.00
18 Stan Jones	4.50
19 Roger LeClerc	3.50
20 Angelo Coia	3.50
21 Doug Atkins	7.50
22 Bill George	5.00
23 Richie Petitbon	5.00
24 Ron Bull (SP)	8.00
25 Chicago Bears Team	3.50
26 Howard Cassady	3.50
27 Ray Renfro (SP)	7.50
28 Jim Brown	125.00
29 Rick Kreitling	3.50
30 Jim Ray Smith	3.50
31 John Morrow	3.50
32 Lou Groza	12.00
33 Bob Gain	3.50
34 Bernie Parrish	3.50
35 Jim Shofner	3.50
36 Ernie Davis (SP)	110.00
37 Cleveland Browns Team	3.50
38 Eddie LeBaron	3.50
39 Don Meredith (SP)	80.00
40 J.W. Lockett (SP)	7.50
41 Don Perkins	7.50
42 Billy Howton	3.50
43 Dick Bielski	3.50
44 Mike Connelly	3.00
45 Jerry Tubbs (SP)	7.50
46 Don Bishop (SP)	7.50
47 Dick Moegle	3.50
48 Bobby Plummer (SP)	7.50
49 Dallas Cowboys Team	10.00
50 Milt Plum	3.50
51 Dan Lewis	3.50
52 Nick Pietrosante (SP)	7.50

53	Gail Cogdill	3.50
54	Jim Gibbons	3.50
55	Jim Martin	3.50
56	Yale Lary	7.50
57	Darris McCord	3.50
58	Alex Karras	15.00
59	Joe Schmidt	7.50
60	Dick Lane	6.00
61	John Lomakoski (SP)	7.50
62	Detroit Lions Team (SP)	15.00
63	Bart Starr (SP)	70.00
64	Paul Hornung (SP)	50.00
65	Tom Moore (SP)	7.50
66	Jim Taylor (SP)	30.00
67	Max McGee (SP)	7.50
68	Jim Ringo (SP)	15.00
69	Fuzzy Thurston (SP)	15.00
70	Forrest Gregg	7.50
71	Boyd Dowler	3.50
72	Henry Jordan (SP)	6.50
73	Bill Forester (SP)	7.50
74	Earl Gros (SP)	7.50
75	Green Bay Packers (SP)	20.00
76	Checklist	80.00
77	Zeke Bratkowski (SP)	7.50
78	Jon Arnett (SP)	7.50
79	Ollie Matson (SP)	20.00
80	Dick Bass (SP)	7.50
81	Jim Phillips	3.50
82	Carroll Dale	4.00
83	Frank Varrichione	3.50
84	Art Hunter	3.50
85	Danny Villanueva	3.00
86	Les Richter (SP)	7.50
87	Lindon Crow	3.50
88	Roman Gabriel (SP)	50.00
89	Los Angeles Rams (SP)	15.00
90	Fran Tarkenton	200.00
91	Jerry Reichow (SP)	7.50
92	Hugh McElhenny (SP)	20.00
93	Mel Triplett (SP)	7.50
94	Tommy Mason (SP)	7.00
95	Dave Middleton (SP)	7.50
96	Frank Youso (SP)	7.50
97	Mike Mercer (SP)	7.50
98	Rip Hawkins (SP)	7.50
99	Cliff Livingston (SP)	7.50
100	Roy Winston (SP)	7.00
101	Minnesota Vikings Team (SP)	20.00
102	Y.A. Tittle	30.00
103	Joe Walton	3.50
104	Frank Gifford	40.00
105	Alex Webster	3.50
106	Del Shofner	3.50
107	Don Chandler	3.50
108	Andy Robustelli	3.50
109	Jim Katcavage	3.50
110	Sam Huff (SP)	20.00
111	Erich Barnes	3.50
112	Jimmy Patton	3.50
113	Jerry Hillebrand	7.50
114	New York Giants Team	3.50
115	Sonny Jurgensen	20.00
116	Tommy McDonald	3.50
117	Ted Dean (SP)	7.50
118	Clarence Peaks	3.50
119	Bobby Walston	3.50
120	Pete Retzlaff (SP)	7.50
121	Jim Schrader (SP)	7.50
122	J.D. Smith	3.50
123	King Hill	3.50
124	Maxie Baughan	3.50
125	Pete Case (SP)	7.50
126	Philadelphia Eagles Team	3.50
127	Bobby Layne	25.00
128	Tom Tracy	3.50
129	John Henry Johnson	7.00
130	Buddy Dial (SP)	7.50
131	Preston Carpenter	3.50
132	Lou Michaels (SP)	7.50
133	Gene Lipscomb (SP)	8.00
134	Ernie Stautner (SP)	15.00
135	John Reger (SP)	7.50
136	Myron Pottios	3.50
137	Bob Ferguson (SP)	7.50
138	Pittsburgh Steelers Team	3.50
139	Sam Etcheverry	3.50
140	John David Crow (SP)	7.50
141	Bobby Joe Conrad (SP)	7.50
142	Prentice Gautt (SP)	8.00
143	Frank Mestnik	3.50
144	Sonny Randle	3.50
145	Gerry Perry	3.50
146	Jerry Norton	3.50
147	Jimmy Hill	3.50
148	Bill Stacy	3.50
149	Fate Echols (SP)	7.50
150	St. Louis Cardinals Team	3.50
151	Bill Kilmer	25.00
152	John Brodie	15.00
153	J.D. Smith	3.50
154	C.R. Roberts (SP)	7.50
155	Monty Stickles	3.50
156	Clyde Conner	3.50
157	Bob St. Clair	7.50
158	Tommy Davis	3.50
159	Leo Nomellini	5.50
160	Matt Hazeltine	3.50
161	Abe Woodson	3.50
162	Dave Baker	3.50
163	San Francisco 49ers Team	3.50
164	Norm Snead (SP)	30.00
165	Dick James	3.50
166	Bobby Mitchell	8.00
167	Sam Horner	3.50
168	Bill Barnes	3.50
169	Bill Anderson	3.50
170	Fred Dugan	3.50
171	John Aveni (SP)	7.50
172	Bob Toneff	3.50
173	Jim Kerr	3.50
174	Leroy Jackson (SP)	7.50
175	Washington Redskins Team	3.50
176	Checklist	100.00

1962 Topps Bucks

This 48-card set was issued one per wax pack in the 1962 Topps football issue. The 1-1/4" x 4-1/4" "cards" have a dollar bill motif with the player's head in the middle and his name underneath. Backs show the same motif, with the NFL and team logo encircled. The Topps Bucks were printed on white paper.

		NM
	Complete Set (48):	400.00
	Common Player:	4.50
1	J.D. Smith	4.50
2	Bart Starr	25.00
3	Dick James	4.50
4	Alex Webster	6.00
5	Paul Hornung	18.00
6	John David Crow	6.00
7	Jimmy Brown	60.00
8	Don Perkins	4.50
9	Bobby Walston	4.50
10	Jim Phillips	4.50
11	Y.A. Tittle	20.00
12	Sonny Randle	4.50
13	Jerry Reichow	4.50
14	Yale Lary	7.00
15	Buddy Dial	4.50
16	Ray Renfro	4.50
17	Norm Snead	4.50
18	Leo Nomellini	6.00
19	Hugh McElhenny	8.00
20	Eddie LeBaron	4.50
21	Bill Howton	4.50
22	Bobby Mitchell	9.00
23	Nick Pietrosante	4.50
24	John Unitas	30.00
25	Raymond Berry	9.00
26	Billy Kilmer	9.00
27	Lenny Moore	8.00
28	Tommy McDonald	4.50
29	Del Shofner	4.50
30	Jim Taylor	12.00
31	Joe Schmidt	7.00
32	Bill George	6.00
33	Fran Tarkenton	65.00
34	Willie Galimore	4.50
35	Bobby Layne	17.00
36	Max McGee	4.50
37	Jon Arnett	4.50
38	Lou Groza	10.00
39	Frank Varrichione	4.50
40	Milt Plum	4.50
41	Prentice Gautt	4.50
42	Billy Wade	6.00
43	Gino Marchetti	7.00
44	John Brodie	10.00
45	Sonny Jurgensen	10.00
46	Clarence Peaks	4.50
47	Mike Ditka	20.00
48	John Henry Johnson	7.00

1963 Topps

FRAN TARKENTON — MINNESOTA VIKINGS — QUARTERBACK

Topps' 170-card set of NFL players features teams grouped in alphabetical order by city name. As with many Topps sets in this era, numerous cards were short-printed because the number of cards didn't match the size of Topps' printing sheets, meaning some were produced in more quantities than others. Rookies in this set include Hall of Famers Deacon Jones, Bob Lilly, Willie Wood, and Ray Nitschke. Other important rookie cards include Jim Marshall and Charlie Johnson. The set also features the second-year cards of Roman Gabriel, Mike Ditka, Fran Tarkenton and Bill Kilmer. Last-year cards here include Eddie LeBaron, Fuzzy Thurston, Hugh McElhenny, Ernie Stautner and Leo Nomellini. The final Topps cards of such players as Night Train Lane, Yale Lary, Joe Schmidt, Y.A. Tittle, Rosey Grier, Sam Huff, John Henry Johnson and Bob St. Clair are also in this set. (Key: SP - short printed)

		NM
	Complete Set (170):	1300.
	Common Player:	2.00
1	Johnny Unitas	100.00
2	Lenny Moore	7.00
3	Jimmy Orr	2.00
4	Raymond Berry	7.00
5	Jim Parker	5.00
6	Alex Sandusky	2.00
7	Dick Szymanski	2.00
8	Gino Marchetti	5.00
9	Billy Ray Smith	3.00
10	Bill Pellington	2.00
11	Bob Boyd	2.00
12	Baltimore Colts Team (SP)	8.50
13	Frank Ryan (SP)	6.00
14	Jim Brown (SP)	200.00
15	Ray Renfro (SP)	4.50
16	Rich Kreitling (SP)	4.50
17	Mike McCormack (SP)	9.00
18	Jim Ray Smith (SP)	4.50
19	Lou Groza (SP)	17.00
20	Bill Glass (SP)	4.50
21	Galen Fiss (SP)	4.50
22	Don Fleming (SP)	6.00
23	Bob Gain (SP)	4.50
24	Cleveland Browns Team (SP)	8.50
25	Milt Plum	2.00
26	Dan Lewis	2.00
27	Nick Pietrosante	2.00
28	Gail Cogdill	2.00
29	Harley Sewell	2.00
30	Jim Gibbons	2.00
31	Carl Brettschneider	2.00
32	Dick Lane	3.50
33	Yale Lary	4.00
34	Roger Brown	3.00
35	Joe Schmidt	4.75
36	Detroit Lions Team	8.50
37	Roman Gabriel	7.00
38	Zeke Bratkowski	2.00
39	Dick Bass	2.00
40	Jon Arnett	2.00
41	Jim Phillips	2.00
42	Frank Varrichione	2.00
43	Danny Villanueva	2.00
44	Deacon Jones	50.00
45	Lindon Crow	2.00
46	Marlin McKeever	2.00
47	Ed Meador	2.50
48	Los Angeles Rams Team	4.00
49	Y.A. Tittle (SP)	40.00
50	Del Shofner (SP)	3.50
51	Alex Webster (SP)	6.00
52	Phil King	4.50
53	Jack Stroud	4.50
54	Darrell Dess	4.50
55	Jim Katcavage (SP)	4.50
56	Roosevelt Grier (SP)	8.00
57	Erich Barnes (SP)	4.50
58	Jim Patton (SP)	4.50
59	Sam Huff (SP)	14.00
60	New York Giants Team	4.00
61	Bill Wade	2.00
62	Mike Ditka	60.00
63	Johnny Morris	2.00
64	Roger LeClerc	2.00
65	Roger Davis	2.00
66	Joe Marconi	2.00
67	Herman Lee	2.00
68	Doug Atkins	5.00
69	Joe Fortunato	2.00
70	Bill George	4.75
71	Richie Petitbon	5.00
72	Chicago Bears Team (SP)	8.50
73	Eddie LeBaron (SP)	6.00
74	Don Meredith (SP)	50.00
75	Don Perkins (SP)	6.00
76	Amos Marsh (SP)	4.50
77	Bill Howton (SP)	4.50
78	Andy Cverko (SP)	4.50
79	Sam Baker (SP)	4.50
80	Jerry Tubbs (SP)	4.50
81	Don Bishop (SP)	4.50
82	Bob Lilly	125.00
83	Jerry Norton (SP)	4.50
84	Dallas Cowboys	16.00
85	Checklist	25.00
86	Bart Starr	40.00
87	Jim Taylor	16.00
88	Boyd Dowler	2.00
89	Forrest Gregg	5.25
90	Fuzzy Thurston	3.00
91	Jim Ringo	4.75
92	Ron Kramer	2.00
93	Hank Jordan	2.00
94	Bill Forester	2.00
95	Willie Wood	27.00
96	Ray Nitschke	80.00
97	Green Bay Packers Team	4.00
98	Fran Tarkenton	50.00
99	Tommy Mason	2.00
100	Mel Triplett	2.00
101	Jerry Reichow	2.00
102	Frank Youso	2.00
103	Hugh McElhenny	7.00
104	Gerry Huth	2.00
105	Ed Sharockman	2.00
106	Rip Hawkins	2.00
107	Jim Marshall	25.00
108	Jim Prestel	2.00
109	Minnesota Vikings Team	4.00
110	Sonny Jurgensen (SP)	22.00
111	Timmy Brown (SP)	8.00
112	Tommy McDonald (SP)	4.50
113	Clarence Peaks (SP)	4.50
114	Pete Retzlaff (SP)	4.50
115	Jim Schrader (SP)	4.50
116	Jim McCusker (SP)	4.50
117	Don Burroughs (SP)	4.50
118	Maxie Buaghan (SP)	4.50
119	Riley Gunnels (SP)	4.50
120	Jimmy Carr (SP)	4.50
121	Philadelphia Eagles	8.50
122	Ed Brown (SP)	4.50
123	John Henry Johnson	12.00
124	Buddy Dial (SP)	4.50
125	Red Mack (SP)	4.50
126	Preston Carpenter (SP)	4.50
127	Ray Lemek (SP)	4.50
128	Buzz Nutter (SP)	4.50
129	Ernie Stautner (SP)	12.00
130	Lou Michaels (SP)	4.50
131	Clendon Thomas (SP)	6.00
132	Tom Bettis (SP)	4.50
133	Pittsburgh Steelers (SP)	8.50
134	John Brodie	10.00
135	J.D. Smith	2.00
136	Bill Kilmer	5.00
137	Bernie Casey	4.50
138	Tommy Davis	2.00
139	Ted Connolly	2.00
140	Bob St. Clair	5.00
141	Abe Woodson	2.00
142	Matt Hazeltine	2.00
143	Leo Nomellini	5.50
144	Dan Colchico	2.00
145	San Francisco 49ers	8.50
146	Charlie Johnson	8.00
147	John David Crow	2.00
148	Bobby Joe Conrad	2.00
149	Sonny Randle	2.00
150	Prentice Gautt	2.00
151	Taz Anderson	2.00
152	Ernie McMillan	2.00
153	Jimmy Hill	2.00
154	Bill Koman	2.00
155	Larry Wilson	25.00
156	Don Owens	2.00
157	St. Louis Cardinals (SP)	8.50
158	Norm Snead	8.00
159	Bobby Mitchell	14.00
160	Billy Barnes (SP)	4.50
161	Fred Dugan (SP)	4.50
162	Don Bosseler (SP)	4.50
163	John Nisby (SP)	4.50
164	Riley Mattson (SP)	4.50
165	Bob Toneff (SP)	4.50
166	Rod Breedlove (SP)	4.50
167	Dick James (SP)	4.50
168	Claud Crabb (SP)	4.50
169	Washington Redskins Team (SP)	8.50
170	Checklist	60.00

1964 Topps

LEN DAWSON — KANSAS CITY CHIEFS — QB

Considered to be one of the toughest sets of the decade, this 176-card set was Topps' first to feature only American Football League players. Because of the awkward size of the set and the inability to print the cards on two sheets, some of the cards in the set are short-printed. Cards are numbered by city and by player. This set contains the rookie cards of Daryle Lamonica, Buck Buchanan, John Hadi, and Hall of Famers Bobby Bell and Matt Snell. Second-year cards in the set include Nick Buoniconti, Len Dawson and Lance Alworth. An interesting error exists in the set: Bo Roberson, #151, has a helmet with the Raiders logo at the bottom of the card. Helmets were not part of the card design, and logos were always airbrushed. (Key: SP - short printed)

		NM
	Complete Set (176):	1500.
	Common Player:	3.00
	SP Cards:	6.00
1	Tommy Addison (SP)	30.00
2	Houston Antwine	4.00
3	Nick Buoniconti	12.00
4	Ron Burton (SP)	6.00
5	Gino Cappelletti	6.00
6	Jim Colclough (SP)	6.00
7	Bob Dee (SP)	6.00
8	Larry Eisenhauer	3.00
9	Dick Felt (SP)	6.00
10	Larry Garron	3.00
11	Art Graham	3.00
12	Ron Hall	3.00
13	Charles Long	3.00
14	Don McKinnon	3.00
15	Don Oakes (SP)	6.00
16	Ross O'Hanley (SP)	6.00
17	Babe Parilli (SP)	6.00
18	Jesse Richardson	6.00
19	Jack Rudolph (SP)	6.00
20	Don Webb	4.00
21	Boston Patriots Team	4.50
22	Ray Abbruzzese	3.00
23	Stew Barber	4.00
24	Dave Behrman	3.00
25	Al Bemiller	3.00
26	Elbert Dubenion	6.00
27	Jim Dunaway (SP)	10.00
28	Booker Edgerson	6.00
29	Cookie Gilchrist (SP)	15.00
30	Jack Kemp (SP)	200.00
31	Daryle Lamonica (SP)	60.00
32	Bill Miller	3.00
33	Herb Paterra	4.00
34	Ken Rice	6.00
35	Ed Rutkowski	3.00
36	George Saimes	4.00
37	Tom Sestak	3.00
38	Billy Shaw (SP)	6.00
39	Mike Stratton	3.00
40	Gene Sykes	3.00
41	John Tracey (SP)	6.00
42	Sid Youngelman	6.00
43	Buffalo Bills Team	4.50
44	Eldon Danenhauer (SP)	6.00
45	Jim Fraser (SP)	6.00
46	Chuck Gavin (SP)	6.00
47	Goose Gonsoulin (SP)	6.00
48	Ernie Barnes	4.00
49	Tom Janik	3.00
50	Billy Joe	4.00
51	Ike Lassiter	6.00
52	John McCormick (SP)	6.00
53	Lewis Bud McFadin	3.00
54	Gene Mingo (SP)	3.00
55	Charlie Mitchell	3.00
56	John Nocera (SP)	6.00
57	Tom Nomina	3.00
58	Harold Olson (SP)	6.00
59	Bob Scarpitto	3.00
60	John Sklopan	3.00
61	Mickey Slaughter	3.00
62	Don Stone	3.00
63	Jerry Sturm	3.00
64	Lionel Taylor (SP)	12.00
65	Denver Broncos Team	17.00
66	Scott Appleton	4.00
67	Tony Banfield	3.00
68	George Blanda	60.00
69	Billy Cannon	4.50
70	Doug Cline (SP)	6.00
71	Gary Cutsinger (SP)	6.00
72	Willard Dewveall (SP)	6.00
73	Don Floyd (SP)	6.00
74	Freddy Gick (SP)	6.00
75	Charlie Hennigan (SP)	10.00
76	Ed Husmann (SP)	6.00
77	Bobby Jancik (SP)	6.00
78	Jacky Lee (SP)	6.00
79	Bob McLeod (SP)	6.00
80	Rich Michael (SP)	6.00
81	Larry Onesti	4.00
82	Checklist	50.00
83	Bob Schmidt (SP)	6.00
84	Walt Suggs (SP)	6.00
85	Bob Talamini (SP)	6.00
86	Charley Tolar (SP)	6.00
87	Don Trull	5.00
88	Houston Oilers Team	4.50
89	Fred Arbanas	3.00
90	Bobby Bell	35.00
91	Mel Branch (SP)	6.00
92	Buck Buchanan	35.00
93	Ed Budde	6.00
94	Chris Burford (SP)	6.00
95	Walt Corey	6.00
96	Len Dawson	75.00
97	Dave Grayson	4.00
98	Abner Haynes	4.00
99	Sherrill Headrick	6.00
100	E.J. Holub	3.00
101	Bobby Hunt	3.00
102	Frank Jackson (SP)	6.00
103	Curtis McClinton	3.00
104	Jerry Mays (SP)	3.00
105	Johnny Robinson	6.75
106	Jack Spikes (SP)	6.00
107	Smokey Stover (SP)	6.00
108	Jim Tyrer	6.00
109	Duane Wood (SP)	6.00
110	Kansas City Chiefs Team	4.50
111	Dick Christy (SP)	6.00
112	Dan Ficca (SP)	6.00
113	Larry Grantham	3.00
114	Curley Johnson (SP)	7.00
115	Gene Heeter	3.00
116	Jack Klotz	3.00
117	Pete Liske	4.00
118	Bob McAdam	3.00
119	Dee Mackey (SP)	6.00
120	Bill Mathis (SP)	6.00
121	Don Maynard	30.00
122	Dainard Paulson	6.00
123	Gerry Philbin	4.00
124	Mark Smolinski	6.00
125	Matt Snell	15.00
126	Mike Taliaferro	3.00
127	Bake Turner (SP)	12.00
128	Jeff Ware	3.00
129	Clyde Washington	3.00
130	Dick Wood	4.00
131	New York Jets Team	4.50
132	Dalva Allen (SP)	6.00
133	Dan Birdwell	3.00
134	Dave Costa	4.00
135	Dobie Craig	3.00
136	Clem Daniels	6.00
137	Cotton Davidson (SP)	3.00
138	Claude Gibson	6.00
139	Tom Flores	15.00

#	Player	Price
140	Wayne Hawkins (SP)	6.00
141	Ken Herock	3.00
142	Jon Jelacic (SP)	6.00
143	Joe Krakoski	3.00
144	Archie Matsos (SP)	6.00
145	Mike Mercer	3.00
146	Alan Miller (SP)	6.00
147	Bob Mischak (SP)	6.00
148	Jim Otto (SP)	25.00
149	Clancy Osborne (SP)	6.00
150	Art Powell (SP)	9.00
151	Bo Roberson	3.00
152	Fred Williamson (SP)	10.00
153	Oakland Raiders Team	4.50
154	*Chuck Allen (SP)*	10.00
155	Lance Alworth	40.00
156	George Blair	3.00
157	Earl Faison	3.00
158	Sam Gruniesen	3.00
159	*John Hadl*	35.00
160	Dick Harris (SP)	6.00
161	Emil Karas (SP)	6.00
162	Dave Kocourek (SP)	6.00
163	Ernie Ladd	6.00
164	Keith Lincoln	6.00
165	Paul Lowe (SP)	10.00
166	Charles McNeil	3.00
167	Jacque MacKinnon (SP)	6.00
168	Ron Mix (SP)	15.00
169	Don Norton (SP)	6.00
170	Don Rogers (SP)	6.00
171	Tobin Rote (SP)	10.00
172	Henry Schmidt (SP)	6.00
173	Bud Whitehead	3.00
174	Ernie Wright (SP)	6.00
175	San Diego Chargers Team	4.50
176	Checklist (SP)	150.00

1964 Topps Pennant Stickers

These 24 peel-off stickers (they measure about 2" x 4-1/2") were inserted one per wax pack of the 1964 Topps football cards. The unnumbered pennants covered AFL teams and major college teams. Since stickers were folded to fit into the backs, all of them are found with a crease.

		NM
	Complete Set (24):	240.00
	AFL Team:	12.00
	College Team:	7.00
(1)	Boston Patriots	12.00
(2)	Buffalo Bills	12.00
(3)	Denver Broncos	12.00
(4)	Houston Oilers	12.00
(5)	K.C. Chiefs	12.00
(6)	New York Jets	12.00
(7)	Oakland Raiders	12.00
(8)	San Diego Chargers	12.00
(9)	Air Force	7.00
(10)	Army	7.00
(11)	Dartmouth	7.00
(12)	Duke	7.00
(13)	Michigan	7.00
(14)	Minnesota	7.00
(15)	Mississippi	7.00
(16)	Navy	7.00
(17)	Notre Dame	15.00
(18)	SMU	7.00
(19)	USC	7.00
(20)	Syracuse	7.00
(21)	Texas	7.00
(22)	Washington	7.00
(23)	Wisconsin	7.00
(24)	Yale	7.00

1965 Topps

Topps' second set featuring only AFL players is easily the most valued set of the decade for several reasons - the oversized (about 2-1/2" x 5") cards are attractive; it includes Joe Namath's rookie card; and Topps' unorthodox printing method created an abundance of certain cards, but a scarcity of others - all throughout the 176-card set, too, not just in one sequentially-numbered series. There may be a variation on Namath's rookie card as well. There's a report of a card showing Broadway Joe with a butterfly tattoo on his arm; on other cards, this tattoo is airbrushed off. It's uncertain how many, or even if, this variation exists. Besides Namath, other rookies in this set include Fred Biletnikoff, Willie Brown, and Ben Davidson. Second-year cards include those of Daryle Lamonica, Bobby Bell, Buck Buchanon, Matt Snell and John Hadl. (Key: SP - short printed)

		NM
	Complete Set (176):	3800.
	Common Player:	6.50
	SP Cards:	11.50
1	Tommy Addison (SP)	35.00
2	Houston Antwine (SP)	11.50
3	Nick Buoniconti (SP)	24.00
4	Ron Burton (SP)	11.50
5	Gino Cappelletti (SP)	20.00
6	Jim Colclough	6.50
7	Bob Dee (SP)	11.50
8	Larry Eisenhauer (SP)	6.50
9	J.D. Garrett (SP)	6.50
10	Larry Garron (SP)	6.50
11	Art Graham (SP)	11.50
12	Ron Hall	6.50
13	Charles Long (SP)	6.50
14	*Jon Morris*	11.50
15	Bill Neighbors (SP)	11.50
16	Ross O'Hanley	6.50
17	Babe Parilli (SP)	11.50
18	Tony Romeo (SP)	11.50
19	Jack Rudolph (SP)	11.50
20	Bob Schmidt	6.50
21	Don Webb (SP)	11.50
22	Jim Whalen (SP)	11.50
23	Stew Barber	6.50
24	Glenn Bass (SP)	11.50
25	Al Bemiller (SP)	11.50
26	Wray Carlton (SP)	11.50
27	Tom Day	6.50
28	Elbert Dubenion (SP)	11.50
29	Jim Dunaway	6.50
30	*Pete Gogolak (SP)*	19.00
31	Dick Hudson (SP)	11.50
32	Harry Jacobs (SP)	11.50
33	Billy Joe (SP)	11.50
34	*Tom Keating (SP)*	17.00
35	Jack Kemp (SP)	200.00
36	Daryle Lamonica (SP)	40.00
37	Paul Maguire (SP)	20.00
38	*Ron McDole (SP)*	15.00
39	George Saimes (SP)	11.50
40	Tom Sestak (SP)	11.50
41	Billy Shaw (SP)	11.50
42	Mike Stratton (SP)	11.50
43	John Tracey (SP)	11.50
44	Ernie Warlick	6.50
45	Odell Barry	6.50
46	*Willie Brown (SP)*	65.00
47	Gerry Bussell (SP)	11.50
48	Eldon Danehauer (SP)	11.50
49	Al Denson (SP)	11.50
50	*Hewritt Dixon (SP)*	19.00
51	Cookie Gilchrist (SP)	25.00
52	Goose Gonsoulin (SP)	11.50
53	Abner Haynes (SP)	18.00
54	Jerry Hopkins (SP)	11.50
55	Ray Jacobs (SP)	11.50
56	Jacky Lee (SP)	11.50
57	John McCormick (SP)	6.50
58	Bob McCullough (SP)	11.50
59	John McGeever (SP)	6.50
60	Charlie Mitchell (SP)	11.50
61	Jim Perkins (SP)	11.50
62	Bob Scarpitto (SP)	11.50
63	Mickey Slaughter (SP)	11.50
64	Jerry Sturm (SP)	11.50
65	Lionel Taylor (SP)	20.00
66	Scott Appleton	11.50
67	Johnny Baker (SP)	11.50
68	Sonny Bishop (SP)	11.50
69	George Blanda (SP)	90.00
70	Sid Blanks (SP)	11.50
71	Ode Burrell (SP)	11.50
72	Doug Cline (SP)	11.50
73	Willard Dewveall (SP)	6.50
74	*Larry Elkins (SP)*	10.00
75	Don Floyd (SP)	11.50
76	Freddy Glick (SP)	6.50
77	Tom Goode (SP)	11.50
78	Charlie Hennigan (SP)	18.00
79	Ed Husmann	6.50
80	Bobby Jancik (SP)	11.50
81	Bud McFadin (SP)	11.50
82	Bob McLeod (SP)	11.50
83	Jim Norton (SP)	11.50
84	Walt Suggs	6.50
85	Bob Talamini	6.50
86	Charley Tolar (SP)	11.50
87	Checklist 1-88 (SP)	145.00
88	Don Trull (SP)	11.50
89	Fred Arbanas (SP)	11.50
90	*Pete Beathard (SP)*	22.00
91	Bobby Bell (SP)	11.50
92	Mel Branch (SP)	11.50
93	Tommy Brooker (SP)	11.50
94	Buck Buchanan (SP)	25.00
95	Ed Budde (SP)	11.50
96	Chris Burford (SP)	11.50
97	Walt Corey	6.50
98	Jerry Cornelison	6.50
99	Len Dawson (SP)	80.00
100	Jon Gilliam (SP)	11.50
101	Sherrill Headrick (SP)	11.50
102	Dave Hill (SP)	11.50
103	E.J. Holub (SP)	11.50
104	Bobby Hunt (SP)	11.50
105	Frank Jackson (SP)	11.50
106	Jerry Mays	6.50
107	Curtis McClinton (SP)	11.50
108	Bobby Ply (SP)	11.50
109	Johnny Robinson (SP)	11.50
110	Jim Tyrer (SP)	11.50
111	Bill Baird (SP)	11.50
112	*Ralph Baker (SP)*	15.00
113	Sam DeLuca (SP)	11.50
114	Larry Grantham (SP)	11.50
115	Gene Heeter (SP)	11.50
116	*Winston Hill (SP)*	15.00
117	*John Huarte (SP)*	30.00
118	Cosmo Iacavazzi	11.50
119	Curley Johnson (SP)	11.50
120	Dee Mackey	6.50
121	Don Maynard	35.00
122	*Joe Namath (SP)*	1650.
123	Dainard Paulson	6.50
124	Gerry Philbin (SP)	11.50
125	Sherman Plunkett	19.00
126	Mark Smolinski	6.50
127	Matt Snell (SP)	25.00
128	Mike Taliaferro (SP)	11.50
129	Bake Turner (SP)	15.00
130	Clyde Washington	11.50
131	*Verlon Biggs (SP)*	15.00
132	Dalva Allen	6.50
133	*Fred Biletnikoff (SP)*	200.00
134	Billy Cannon (SP)	20.00
135	Dave Costa (SP)	11.50
136	Clem Daniels (SP)	11.50
137	Ben Davidson (SP)	50.00
138	Cotton Davidson (SP)	11.50
139	Tom Flores (SP)	27.00
140	Claude Gibson	6.50
141	Wayne Hawkins	6.50
142	Archie Matsos (SP)	11.50
143	Mike Mercer (SP)	11.50
144	Bob Mischak (SP)	11.50
145	Jim Otto	25.00
146	Art Powell (SP)	13.00
147	Warren Powers (SP)	11.50
148	Ken Rice (SP)	11.50
149	Bo Roberson (SP)	11.50
150	Harry Schuh	12.00
151	Larry Todd (SP)	11.50
152	Fred Williamson (SP)	20.00
153	J.R. Williamson	6.50
154	Chuck Allen	6.50
155	Lance Alworth	65.00
156	Frank Buncom	6.50
157	*Steve DeLong (SP)*	17.00
158	Earl Faison (SP)	11.50
159	Kenny Graham (SP)	11.50
160	George Gross (SP)	11.50
161	John Hadl (SP)	28.00
162	Emil Karas (SP)	11.50
163	Dave Kocourek (SP)	11.50
164	Ernie Ladd (SP)	20.00
165	Keith Lincoln (SP)	20.00
166	Paul Lowe (SP)	20.00
167	Jacque MacKinnon	6.50
168	Ron Mix	20.00
169	Don Norton (SP)	11.50
170	Bob Petrich	6.50
171	Rick Redman (SP)	11.50
172	Pat Shea	6.50
173	*Walt Sweeney (SP)*	15.00
174	*Dick Westmoreland*	12.00
175	Ernie Wright (SP)	11.50
176	Checklist 89-176 (SP)	200.00

1965 Topps Rub-Offs

This 36-card, unnumbered set was included one per pack in wax packs of 1965 Topps football. The set, which measures two by three inches, includes the eight American Football League teams plus 28 college team emblems. Similar in design to the 1961 Topps baseball rub-offs, the fronts carried a team logo and team name in reverse type, while the backs carried instructions on how to use the rub-offs.

		NM
	Complete Set (36):	400.00
	Common AFL Team:	15.00
	Common College Team:	10.00
(1)	Boston Patriots	15.00
(2)	Buffalo Bills	20.00
(3)	Denver Broncos	25.00
(4)	Houston Oilers	20.00
(5)	Kansas City Chiefs	15.00
(6)	New York Jets	20.00
(7)	Oakland Raiders	35.00
(8)	San Diego Chargers	15.00
(9)	Alabama	15.00
(10)	Air Force Academy	10.00
(11)	Arkansas	15.00
(12)	Army	15.00
(13)	Boston College	15.00
(14)	Duke	15.00
(15)	Illinois	10.00
(16)	Kansas	15.00
(17)	Kentucky	15.00
(18)	Maryland	10.00
(19)	Miami	15.00
(20)	Minnesota	15.00
(21)	Mississippi	15.00
(22)	Navy	15.00
(23)	Nebraska	15.00
(24)	Notre Dame	35.00
(25)	Penn State	15.00
(26)	Purdue	15.00
(27)	Southern California	10.00
(28)	Southern Methodist	10.00
(29)	Stanford	10.00
(30)	Syracuse	10.00
(31)	Texas	15.00
(32)	Texas Christian	10.00
(33)	Virginia	10.00
(34)	Washington	15.00
(35)	Wisconsin	10.00
(36)	Yale	10.00

1966 Topps

This set, which shows AFL players only (Topps' third straight) is quite popular with collectors. It uses a TV motif. Cards were once again grouped in alphabetical order by city name, then by the player's last name. Joe Namath's second-year card is the set's biggest selling player card, but "card" #15, the Funny Ring checklist, is a very difficult find and is easily the most expensive card in the set. Other key cards include rookie cards of Otis Taylor, Jim Turner and George Sauer Jr., second-year cards of Fred Biletnikoff and Ben Davidson, and cards showing Hall of Famers George Blanda, Bobby Bell, Len Dawson, Don Maynard, Ron Mix, Jim Otto and Lance Alworth. A Jack Kemp card is the set's third most expensive card; other high-priced cards are checklists, which are hard to find in mint.

#	Player	Price
	Complete Set (132):	1300.
	Common Player:	4.00
1	Tom Addison	20.00
2	Houston Antwine	4.00
3	Nick Buoniconti	9.00
4	Gino Cappelletti	6.00
5	Bob Dee	4.00
6	Larry Garron	4.00
7	Art Graham	4.00
8	Ron Hall	4.00
9	Charles Long	4.00
10	Jon Morris	4.00
11	Don Oakes	4.00
12	Babe Parilli	4.00
13	Don Webb	4.00
14	Jim Whalen	4.00
15	Funny Ring CL	275.00
16	Stew Barber	4.00
17	Glenn Bass	4.00
18	Dave Behrman	4.00
19	Al Bemiller	4.00
20	*Butch Byrd*	5.00
21	Wray Carlton	4.00
22	Tom Day	4.00
23	Elbert Dubenion	4.00
24	Jim Dunaway	4.00
25	Dick Hudson	4.00
26	Jack Kemp	170.00
27	Daryle Lamonica	10.00
28	Tom Sestak	4.00
29	Billy Shaw	4.00
30	Mike Stratton	4.00
31	Eldon Danehauer	4.00
32	Cookie Gilchrist	7.00
33	Goose Gonsoulin	4.00
34	*Wendell Hayes*	8.00
35	Abner Haynes	4.00
36	Jerry Hopkins	4.00
37	Ray Jacobs	4.00
38	Charlie Janerette	4.00
39	Ray Kubala	4.00
40	John McCormick	4.00
41	Leroy Moore	4.00
42	Bob Scarpitto	4.00
43	Mickey Slaughter	4.00
44	Jerry Sturm	4.00
45	Lionel Taylor	6.50
46	Scott Appleton	4.00
47	Johnny Baker	4.00
48	George Blanda	40.00
49	Sid Blanks	4.00
50	Danny Brabham	4.00
51	Ode Burrell	4.00
52	Gary Cutsinger	4.00
53	Larry Elkins	4.00
54	Don Floyd	4.00
55	*Willie Frazier*	6.00
56	Freddy Glick	4.00
57	Charles Henningan	5.00
58	Bobby Jancik	4.00
59	Rich Michael	4.00
60	Don Trull	4.00
61	Checklist	40.00
62	Fred Arbanas	4.00
63	Pete Beathard	5.00
64	Bobby Bell	8.00
65	Ed Budde	4.00
66	Chris Burford	4.00
67	Len Dawson	35.00
68	Jon Gilliam	4.00
69	Sherrill Headrick	4.00
70	E.J. Holub	4.00
71	Bobby Hunt	4.00
72	Curtis McClinton	4.00
73	Jerry Mays	5.00
74	Johnny Robinson	5.00
75	Otis Taylor	17.00
76	Tom Erlandson	4.00
77	Norman Evans	8.00
78	Tom Goode	4.00
79	Mike Hudock	4.00
80	Frank Jackson	4.00
81	Billy Joe	4.00
82	Dave Kocourek	4.00
83	Bo Roberson	4.00
84	Jack Spikes	4.00
85	*Jim Warren*	8.00
86	Willie West	5.00
87	Dick Westmoreland	4.00
88	Eddie Wilson	4.00
89	Dick Wood	4.00
90	Verlon Biggs	4.00
91	Sam DeLuca	4.00
92	Winston Hill	4.00
93	Dee Mackey	4.00
94	Bill Mathis	4.00
95	Don Maynard	25.00
96	Joe Namath	340.00
97	Dainard Paulson	4.00
98	Gerry Philbin	4.00
99	Sherman Plunkett	4.00
100	Paul Rochester	4.00
101	*George Sauer Jr.*	12.00
102	Matt Snell	7.00
103	*Jim Turner*	4.00
104	Fred Biletnikoff	50.00
105	Bill Budness	4.00
106	Billy Cannon	6.00
107	Clem Daniels	4.00
108	Ben Davidson	10.00
109	Cotton Davidson	4.00
110	Claude Gibson	4.00
111	Wayne Hawkins	4.00
112	Ken Herock	4.00
113	Bob Mischak	4.00
114	Gus Otto	4.00
115	Jim Otto	15.00
116	Art Powell	6.00
117	Harry Schuh	4.00
118	Chuck Allen	4.00
119	Lance Alworth	30.00
120	Frank Buncom	4.00
121	Steve DeLong	4.50
122	John Farris	4.00
123	Ken Graham	4.00
124	Sam Gruneison	4.00
125	John Hadl	8.00
126	Walt Sweeney	4.00
127	Keith Lincoln	4.00
128	Ron Mix	9.00
129	Don Norton	4.00
130	Pat Shea	4.00
131	Ernie Wright	4.00
132	Checklist	90.00

1966 Topps Funny Rings

The 24-card, 1-1/4" x 3" set was issued in each pack of 1966 Topps Football. The card fronts feature a ring that can be punched out and folded to make a ring. The backs are blank.

#	Player	Price
	Complete Set (24):	500.00
	Common Player:	25.00
1	Funny Ring - Kiss Me	25.00
2	Funny Ring - Bloodshot Eye	25.00
3	Funny Ring - Big Mouth	25.00
4	Funny Ring - Tooth-ache	25.00
5	Funny Ring - Fish eats Fish	25.00
6	Funny Ring - Mrs. Skull	25.00
7	Funny Ring - Hot Dog	25.00
8	Funny Ring - Head with Nail	25.00
9	Funny Ring - Ah	25.00
10	Funny Ring - Apple with Worm	25.00
11	Funny Ring - Snake	25.00
12	Funny Ring - Yicch	25.00
13	Funny Ring - If You Can Read This	25.00
14	Funny Ring - Nuts to You	25.00
15	Funny Ring - Get Lost	25.00
16	Funny Ring - You Fink	25.00
17	Funny Ring - Hole in Shoe	25.00
18	Funny Ring - Head with One Eye	25.00
19	Funny Ring - Mr. Ugly	25.00
20	Funny Ring - Mr. Fang	25.00
21	Funny Ring - Mr. Fright	25.00
22	Funny Ring - Mr. Boo	25.00
23	Funny Ring - Mr. Glug	25.00
24	Funny Ring - Mr. Blech	25.00

1967 Topps

This 132-card set is the last AFL-only set issued by Topps. Best-known for the inclusion of Joe-Namath's second-year card, the set also features another Jack Kemp card. Wahoo McDaniels' only card is also in this set. Cards are grouped according to each of the nine AFL teams. It's very difficult to find an unmarked checklist; consequently, prices are pretty high on those two cards.

#	Player	Price
	Complete Set (132):	650.00
	Common Player:	2.50
1	John Huarte	10.00
2	Babe Parilli	2.50
3	Gino Cappelletti	3.00
4	Larry Garron	2.50
5	Tom Addison	2.50
6	Jon Morris	2.50
7	Houston Antwine	2.50
8	Don Oakes	2.50
9	Larry Eisenhauer	2.50
10	Jim Hunt	2.50
11	Jim Whalen	2.50
12	Art Graham	2.50
13	Nick Buoniconti	6.00
14	Bob Dee	2.50
15	Keith Lincoln	4.00
16	Tom Flores	5.50
17	Art Powell	3.00
18	Stew Barber	2.50
19	Wray Carlton	2.50
20	Elbert Dubenion	2.50
21	Jim Dunaway	2.50
22	Dick Hudson	2.50
23	Harry Jacobs	2.50
24	Jack Kemp	100.00
25	Ron McDole	2.50
26	George Saimes	2.50

27	Tom Sestak	2.50
28	Billy Shaw	2.50
29	Mike Stratton	2.50
30	*Nemiah Wilson*	3.00
31	John McCormick	2.50
32	Rex Mirich	2.50
33	Dave Costa	2.50
34	Goose Gonsoulin	2.50
35	Abner Haynes	3.50
36	Wendell Hayes	2.50
37	Archie Matsos	2.50
38	John Bramlett	2.50
39	Jerry Sturm	2.50
40	Max Leetzow	2.50
41	Bob Scarpitto	2.50
42	Lionel Taylor	3.50
43	Al Denson	2.50
44	*Miller Farr*	3.50
45	Don Trull	1.50
46	Jacky Lee	2.50
47	Bobby Jancik	2.50
48	Ode Burrell	2.50
49	Larry Elkins	2.50
50	W.K. Hicks	2.50
51	Sid Blanks	2.50
52	Jim Norton	2.50
53	*Bobby Maples*	3.00
54	Bob Talamini	2.50
55	Walter Suggs	2.50
56	Gary Cutsinger	2.50
57	Danny Brabham	2.50
58	Ernie Ladd	4.00
59	Checklist	40.00
60	Pete Beathard	2.50
61	Len Dawson	20.00
62	Bobby Hunt	2.50
63	Bert Coan	2.50
64	Curtis McClinton	2.50
65	Johnny Robinson	2.50
66	E.J. Holub	2.50
67	Jerry Mays	2.50
68	Jim Tyrer	2.50
69	Bobby Bell	5.50
70	Fred Arbanas	2.50
71	Buck Buchanan	5.50
72	Chris Burford	2.50
73	Otis Taylor	4.00
74	Cookie Gilchrist	5.00
75	Earl Faison	2.50
76	George Wilson Jr.	2.50
77	Rick Norton	2.50
78	Frank Jackson	2.50
79	Joe Auer	2.50
80	Willie West	2.50
81	Jim Warren	2.50
82	*Wahoo McDaniel*	30.00
83	Ernie Park	2.50
84	Bill Neighbors	2.50
85	Norm Evans	2.50
86	Tom Nomina	2.50
87	Rich Zecher	2.50
88	Dave Kocourek	2.50
89	Bill Baird	2.50
90	Ralph Baker	2.50
91	Verlon Biggs	2.50
92	Sam DeLuca	2.50
93	Larry Grantham	2.50
94	Jim Harris	2.50
95	Winston Hill	2.50
96	Bill Mathis	2.50
97	Don Maynard	20.00
98	Joe Namath	185.00
99	Gerry Philbin	2.50
100	Paul Rochester	2.50
101	George Sauer	3.50
102	Matt Snell	3.50
103	Daryle Lamonica	6.00
104	Glenn Bass	2.50
105	Jim Otto	6.00
106	Fred Biletnikoff	30.00
107	Cotton Davidson	2.50
108	Larry Todd	2.50
109	Billy Cannon	3.00
110	Clem Daniels	2.50
111	Dave Grayson	2.50
112	*Kent McCloughan*	2.50
113	Bob Svihus	2.50
114	Isaac Lassiter	2.50
115	Harry Schuh	2.50
116	Ben Davidson	6.00
117	Tom Day	2.50
118	Scott Appleton	2.50
119	*Steve Tensi*	3.00
120	John Hadl	5.00
121	Paul Lowe	3.00
122	Jim Allison	2.50
123	Lance Alworth	25.00
124	Jacque MacKinnon	2.50
125	Ron Mix	5.50
126	Bob Petrich	2.50
127	Howard Kindig	2.50
128	Steve DeLong	2.50
129	Chuck Allen	2.50
130	Frank Buncom	2.50
131	*Speedy Duncan*	5.00
132	Checklist	60.00

1967 Topps Comic Pennants

The 31-card, standard-size sticker set was issued in packs of 1967 Topps and is considered to be scarce - the set was probably discontinued before the end of the shipping. The cards contain juvenile humor (Denver girls look like Broncos). The cards are numbered in the upper right corner.

		NM
Complete Set (31):		600.00
Common Player:		20.00
1	Navel Academy	20.00
2	City College of Useless Knowledge	20.00
3	Notre Dame (Hunchback of)	40.00
4	Psychedelic State	20.00
5	Minneapolis Mini-skirts	20.00
6	School of Art - Go, Van Gogh	20.00
7	Washington Is Dead	25.00
8	School of Hard Knocks	20.00
9	Alaska (If I See Her ...)	20.00
10	Confused State	20.00
11	Yale Locks Are Tough to Pick	20.00
12	University of Transylvania	20.00
13	Down With Teachers	20.00
14	Cornell Caught Me Cheating	20.00
15	Houston Oilers (You're a Fink)	25.00
16	Harvard (Flunked Out)	25.00
17	Diskotech	20.00
18	Dropout U	20.00
19	Air Force (Gas Masks)	20.00
20	Nutstu U	20.00
21	Michigan State Pen	20.00
22	Denver Broncos (Girls Look Like)	25.00
23	Buffalo Bills (Without Paying My)	25.00
24	Army of Dropouts	20.00
25	Miami Dolphins (Bitten by Two)	30.00
26	Kansas City (Has Too Few Workers And Too Many) Chiefs	20.00
27	Boston Patriots (Banned In)	20.00
28	(Fat People) in Oakland (Are Usually Icebox) Raiders	30.00
29	(I'd Go) West (If I'd Just) Point (In The Right Direction)	20.00
30	New York Jets (Skies Are Crowded With)	25.00
31	San Diego Chargers (Police Will Press)	20.00

1968 Topps

GALE SAYERS — CHICAGO BEARS — RUNNING BACK

Topps' first set to clear 200 cards in number was also its first set in five years to feature NFL players as well as AFL players. Released in two series, the second series is a little tougher to find. First-series cards show blue printing on the backs, while second series issues have green. The 219-card set features a special design for cards of players from the Super Bowl teams, the Oakland Raiders and Green Bay Packers. Cards of players from these teams show players in a horizontal format set against a stylized football backdrop. Remaining cards are in a vertical format. Each carries a player photo inside a white frame with the players name, position and team in an oval at the card bottom. A number of second-series card backs can be pieced together to show a picture of Bart Starr or Len Dawson (10 cards per player). Puzzle-piece card backs are found on cards 141, 145, 146, 148, 151-53, 155, 163, 168, 170, 172, 186, 195 and 197. One error in the set is on #12, Kent McCloughan. The back spells his name "McCloughlan." Another mix-up occurs on card #70, Dick Van Raaphorst's card. The back lists his name as "Van Raap Horst." Also, there are two different checklist cards; the back of one is blue, the back of the other is green. Rookies in this set include Bob Griese, Jim Hart, Craig Morton, Joe Kapp, Jim Grabowski, Jack Snow, and Donny Anderson. Other valuable cards include Bart Starr, Don Meredith, Joe Namath, Gale Sayers, John Unitas, Dick Butkis, George Blanda, Jack Kemp, and Fran Tarkenton. This set featured the final regular-issue cards of Hall of Famers Mike Ditka and Jim Taylor.

		NM
Complete Set (219):		575.00
Common Player (1-131):		.80
Common Player (132-219):		1.50
1	Bart Starr	35.00
2	Dick Bass	.80
3	Grady Alderman	1.25
4	Obert Logan	1.25
5	*Ernie Koy*	1.50
6	Don Hultz	1.25
7	Earl Gros	1.25
8	Jim Bakken	.80
9	George Mira	.80
10	Carl Kammerer	1.25
11	Willie Frazier	.80
12	Kent McCloughan	1.25
13	George Sauer	1.50
14	Jack Clancy	.80
15	Jim Tyrer	.80
16	Bobby Maples	1.25
17	Bo Hickey	1.25
18	Frank Buncom	1.25
19	Keith Lincoln	1.50
20	Jim Whalen	.80
21	Junior Coffey	1.25
22	Billy Ray Smith	1.50
23	Johnny Morris	1.50
24	Ernie Green	1.25
25	Don Meredith	21.00
26	Wayne Walker	.80
27	Carroll Dale	.80
28	Bernie Casey	.80
29	*Dave Osborn*	1.50
30	Ray Poage	1.25
31	Homer Jones	.80
32	Sam Baker	.80
33	Bill Saul	1.25
34	Ken Willard	.80
35	Bobby Mitchell	4.00
36	Gary Garrison	1.50
37	Billy Cannon	1.50
38	Ralph Baker	1.25
39	*Howard Twilley*	3.50
40	Wendell Hayes	.80
41	Jim Norton	1.25
42	Tom Beer	1.25
43	Chris Burford	.80
44	Stew Barber	1.25
45	Leroy Mitchell	1.25
46	Dan Grimm	1.25
47	Jerry Logan	1.25
48	Andy Livingston	1.25
49	Paul Warfield	10.00
50	Don Perkins	1.25
51	Ron Kramer	.80
52	Bob Jeter	.80
53	*Les Josephson*	1.50
54	Bobby Walden	1.25
55	Checklist	15.00
56	Walter Roberts	1.25
57	Henry Carr	.80
58	Gary Ballman	.80
59	J.R. Wilburn	1.25
60	*Jim Hart*	8.00
61	Jimmy Johnson	.80
62	Chris Hanburger	1.50
63	John Hadl	3.00
64	Hewritt Dixon	1.25
65	Joe Namath	80.00
66	Jim Warren	1.25
67	Curtis McClinton	.80
68	Bob Talamini	.80
69	Steve Tensi	1.25
70	Dick Van Raaphorst	1.25
71	Art Powell	1.50
72	*Jim Nance*	3.50
73	Bob Riggle	1.25
74	John Mackey	3.50
75	Gale Sayers	50.00
76	Gene Hickerson	1.25
77	Dan Reeves	10.00
78	Tom Nowatzke	1.25
79	Elijah Pitts	.80
80	Lamar Lundy	1.25
81	Paul Flatley	1.25
82	Dave Whitsell	1.25
83	Spider Lockhart	.80
84	Dave Lloyd	1.25
85	Roy Jefferson	.80
86	Jackie Smith	5.00
87	John David Crow	1.50
88	Sonny Jurgensen	6.50
89	Ron Mix	3.50
90	Clem Daniels	.80
91	Cornell Gordon	1.25
92	Tom Goode	1.25
93	Bobby Bell	3.50
94	Walt Suggs	1.25
95	Eric Crabtree	1.25
96	Sherrill Headrick	.80
97	Wray Carlton	.80
98	Gino Cappelletti	1.50
99	Tommy McDonald	.80
100	Johnny Unitas	25.00
101	Richie Petitbon	1.50
102	Erich Barnes	.80
103	Bob Hayes	3.00
104	Milt Plum	1.50
105	Boyd Dowler	.80
106	Ed Meador	.80
107	Fred Cox	.80
108	*Steve Stonebreaker*	1.50
109	Aaron Thomas	1.25
110	Norm Snead	1.50
111	*Paul Martha*	1.50
112	Jerry Stovall	.80
113	Kay McFarland	1.25
114	Pat Richter	1.25
115	Rick Redman	1.25
116	Tom Keating	1.25
117	Matt Snell	2.50
118	Dick Westmoreland	1.25
119	Jerry Mays	.80
120	Sid Blanks	1.25
121	Al Denson	1.25
122	Bobby Hunt	1.25
123	Mike Mercer	1.25
124	Nick Buoniconti	3.00
125	*Ron Vanderkelen*	.80
126	Ordell Braase	1.25
127	Dick Butkus	36.00
128	Gary Collins	.80
129	Mel Renfro	1.50
130	Alex Karras	6.00
131	Herb Adderley	3.00
132	Roman Gabriel	3.50
133	Bill Brown	1.50
134	Kent Kramer	1.50
135	Tucker Frederickson	1.50
136	Nate Ramsey	1.50
137	Marv Woodson	1.50
138	Ken Gray	1.50
139	John Brodie	7.00
140	Jerry Smith	1.50
141	Brad Hubbert	1.50
142	George Blanda	23.00
143	*Pete Lammons*	1.50
144	Doug Moreau	1.50
145	E.J. Holub	1.50
146	Ode Burrell	1.50
147	Bob Scarpitto	1.50
148	Andre White	1.50
149	Jack Kemp	60.00
150	Art Graham	1.50
151	Tommy Nobis	4.00
152	*Willie Richardson*	1.50
153	Jack Concannon	1.50
154	Bill Glass	1.50
155	*Craig Morton*	12.00
156	Pat Studstill	1.50
157	Ray Nitschke	5.00
158	Roger Brown	1.50
159	Joe Kapp	5.00
160	Jim Taylor	10.00
161	Fran Tarkenton	20.00
162	Mike Ditka	25.00
163	*Andy Russell*	5.00
164	Larry Wilson	4.00
165	Tommy Davis	1.50
166	Paul Krause	1.35
167	Leslie Duncan	1.50
168	Fred Biletnikoff	11.00
169	Don Maynard	10.00
170	Frank Emanuel	1.50
171	Len Dawson	13.00
172	Miller Farr	1.50
173	*Floyd Little*	20.00
174	Lonnie Wright	1.50
175	Paul Costa	1.50
176	Don Trull	1.50
177	Jerry Simmons	1.50
178	Tom Matte	1.50
179	Bennie McRae	1.50
180	Jim Kanicki	1.50
181	Bob Lilly	7.00
182	Tom Watkins	1.50
183	*Jim Grabowski*	2.00
184	*Jack Snow*	4.50
185	*Gary Cuozzo*	3.00
186	Billy Kilmer	4.00
187	Jim Katcavage	1.50
188	Floyd Peters	1.50
189	Bill Nelsen	1.50
190	Bobby J. Conrad	1.50
191	Kermit Alexander	1.50
192	Charley Taylor	6.00
193	Lance Alworth	13.00
194	Daryle Lamonica	5.00
195	Al Atkinson	1.50
196	*Bob Griese*	85.00
197	Buck Buchanan	4.00
198	Pete Beathard	1.50
199	Nemiah Wilson	1.50
200	Ernie Wright	1.50
201	George Saimes	1.50
202	John Charles	1.50
203	Randy Johnson	1.50
204	Tony Lorick	1.50
205	Dick Evey	1.50
206	Leroy Kelly	7.50
207	Lee Roy Jordan	5.00
208	Jim Gibbons	1.50
209	*Donny Anderson*	4.00
210	Maxie Baughan	1.50
211	Joe Morrison	1.50
212	Jim Snowden	1.50
213	Lenny Lyles	1.50
214	Bobby Joe Green	1.50
215	Frank Ryan	1.35
216	Cornell Green	1.50
217	Karl Sweetan	1.50
218	Dave Williams	1.50
219	Checklist (blue)	20.00

1968 Topps Posters

Sixteen players from both the AFL and NFL are included in this set. Posters, printed on paper, measure about 5" x 7" and were issued in gum packs, similar to the Topps baseball posters of the same year. A full-color posed action shot is on the front, with the players, name, team and position shown in an oval at the bottom of the front. Backs are blank.

		NM
Complete Set (16):		50.00
Common Player:		1.50
1	Johnny Unitas	9.00
2	Leroy Kelly	1.50
3	Bob Hayes	1.50
4	Bart Starr	5.00
5	Charley Taylor	1.50
6	Fran Tarkenton	4.50
7	Jim Bakken	1.50
8	Gale Sayers	6.00
9	Gary Cuozzo	1.50
10	Les Josephson	1.50
11	Jim Nance	1.50
12	Brad Hubbert	1.50
13	Keith Lincoln	1.50
14	Don Maynard	2.00
15	Len Dawson	3.00
16	Jack Clancy	1.50

1968 Topps Stand-Ups

These 22 unnumbered card-size (2-1/2" x 3-1/2") issues were meant to be punched and folded in order to make them stand. Cards lose much of their value if they're not complete; obviously, not too many complete sets have been found. Cards show a head shot of the player, with his name beneath the photo. Backs are blank. Cards are listed below in alphabetical order.

		NM
Complete Set (22):		225.00
Common Player:		5.00
(1)	Sid Blanks	5.00
(2)	John Brodie	12.00
(3)	Jack Concannon	5.00
(4)	Roman Gabriel	7.00
(5)	Art Graham	5.00
(6)	Jim Grabowski	5.00
(7)	John Hadl	7.00
(8)	Jim Hart	7.00
(9)	Homer Jones	5.00
(10)	Sonny Jurgensen	15.00
(11)	Alex Karras	9.00
(12)	Billy Kilmer	7.00
(13)	Daryle Lamonica	5.00
(14)	Floyd Little	5.00
(15)	Curtis McClinton	5.00
(16)	Don Meredith	35.00
(17)	Joe Namath	85.00
(18)	Bill Nelsen	5.00
(19)	Dave Osborn	5.00
(20)	Willie Richardson	5.00
(21)	Frank Ryan	5.00
(22)	Norm Snead	5.00

1968 Topps Test Teams

These were printed in an extremely limited number by Topps. Cards are a bit oversize - about 2-1/2" x 4-5/8" -- and show a posed shot of the entire team on the front. A nameplate is beneath the picture, and a "frame" features footballs in each of the corners. The back is a guide to the photo, complete with little footballs to indicate each row. Cards were issued in alphabetical order by city name, and are numbered on the back.

		NM
Complete Set (25):		2700.
Common Team:		100.00
1	Atlanta Falcons	100.00
2	Baltimore Colts	100.00
3	Buffalo Bills	100.00
4	Chicago Bears	135.00
5	Cleveland Browns	100.00
6	Dallas Cowboys	135.00
7	Denver Broncos	135.00
8	Detroit Lions	100.00
9	Green Bay Packers	135.00
10	Houston Oilers	100.00
11	Kansas City Chiefs	100.00
12	Los Angeles Rams	100.00
13	Miami Dolphins	135.00
14	Minnesota Vikings	100.00
15	New England Patriots	100.00
16	New Orleans Saints	100.00
17	New York Giants	135.00
18	New York Jets	135.00
19	Oakland Raiders	135.00
20	Philadelphia Eagles	100.00
21	Pittsburgh Steelers	135.00
22	St. Louis Cardinals	100.00
23	San Diego Chargers	100.00
24	San Francisco 49ers	135.00
25	Washington Redskins	100.00

1968 Topps Team Patch/Stickers

These patches, inserted into packs of Topps test team cards, feature team logos for each NFL team. One test team card and a sticker were in each pack; the stickers were supposed to be the main item inside, according to the wrapper. The stickers measure 2-1/2" x 3-1/2".

		NM
Complete Set (44):		1600.
Common Sticker:		10.00
1	1 and 2	15.00
2	3 and 4	10.00
3	5 and 6	12.00
4	7 and 8	10.00
5	9 and 0	10.00
6	A and B	12.00
7	C and D	10.00
8	E and F	10.00
9	G and H	12.00
10	I and W	10.00
11	J and X	10.00
12	Atlanta Falcons	60.00
13	Baltimore Colts	65.00
14	Chicago Bears	80.00
15	Cleveland Browns	60.00
16	Dallas Cowboys	140.00
17	Detroit Lions	60.00
18	Green Bay Packers	75.00
19	Los Angeles Rams	60.00
20	Minnesota Vikings	65.00
21	New Orleans Saints	60.00
22	New York Giants	75.00
23	K and L	10.00
24	M and O	12.00
25	N and P	10.00
26	Q and R	10.00
27	S and T	12.00
28	U and V	10.00
29	Y and Z	10.00
30	Philadelphia Eagles	60.00
31	Pittsburgh Steelers	80.00
32	St. Louis Cardinals	60.00
33	San Francisco 49ers	75.00
34	Washington Redskins	120.00
35	Boston Patriots	60.00
36	Buffalo Bills	75.00
37	Denver Broncos	120.00
38	Houston Oilers	75.00
39	Kansas City Chiefs	60.00
40	Miami Dolphins	110.00
41	New York Jets	75.00
42	Oakland Raiders	140.00
43	San Diego Chargers	60.00
44	Cincinnati Bengals	70.00

Post-1980 cards in Near Mint condition will generally sell for about 75% of the quoted Mint value. Excellent-condition cards bring no more than 40%.

1969 Topps

Bryon **PICCOLO**
CHICAGO BEARS • RUNNING BACK

This 263-card set was printed in two series and in two different styles. The first series cards (1-132) have no borders, while the second series has white borders. In the borderless version, a player photo is set against a brightly colored background. A large team logo is in the lower right hand corner, and a player name and position and team name are in a white box at the card bottom. Second-series cards are of identical design, except for a white border around the player photo. This development is not pleasing to collectors searching for the first series in mint condition, since the lack of borders makes it tough to find any in superb condition. The variation in the set is the checklist card, #132, which is found with and without borders, depending on the series in which it was printed. Another variation in the set involved card #18, Tom Beer. In some versions of the card, the "B" in his last name is slightly raised above the rest of the name on the card front. Versions of each have been reported. The key card in this set is Brian Piccolo's rookie card; this and his Four In One issue are the only cards on which he appears. Other rookies in this set include Larry Csonka, Lance Rentzel, and Mike Curtis. Hall of Famers Doug Atkins and Bobby Mitchell were featured on their final regular-issue cards.

	NM
Complete Set (263):	550.00
Common Player (1-132):	1.00
Common Player (133-263):	1.15
1 LeRoy Kelly	12.00
2 Paul Flatley	1.00
3 Jim Cadile	1.00
4 Erich Barnes	1.00
5 Willie Richardson	1.00
6 Bob Hayes	3.00
7 Bob Jeter	1.00
8 Jim Colclough	1.00
9 Sherrill Headrick	1.00
10 Jim Dunaway	1.00
11 Bill Munson	1.00
12 Jack Pardee	1.75
13 Jim Lindsey	1.00
14 Dave Whitsell	1.00
15 Tucker Frederickson	1.00
16 Alvin Haymond	1.00
17 Andy Russell	1.00
18 Tom Beer	1.00
19 Bobby Maples	1.00
20 Len Dawson	8.00
21 Willis Crenshaw	1.00
22 Tommy Davis	1.00
23 Rickie Harris	1.00
24 Jerry Simmons	1.00
25 Johnny Unitas	25.00
26 Brian Piccolo	75.00
27 Bob Matheson	1.00
28 Howard Twilley	1.00
29 Jim Turner	1.00
30 *Pete Banaszak*	1.50
31 Lance Rentzel	1.50
32 Bill Triplett	1.00
33 Boyd Dowler	1.00
34 Merlin Olsen	5.00
35 Joe Kapp	1.50
36 *Dan Abramowicz*	3.00
37 Spider Lockhart	1.00
38 Tom Day	1.00
39 Art Graham	1.00
40 Bob Cappadona	1.00
41 Gary Ballman	1.00
42 Clendon Thomas	1.00
43 Jackie Smith	3.00
44 Dave Wilcox	1.00
45 Jerry Smith	1.00
46 Dan Grimm	1.00

47 Tom Matte	1.00
48 John Stofa	1.00
49 Rex Mirich	1.00
50 Milloer Farr	1.00
51 Gale Sayers	50.00
52 Bill Nelsen	1.00
53 Bob Lilly	6.00
54 Wayne Walker	1.00
55 Ray Nitschke	5.00
56 Ed Meador	1.00
57 Lonnie Warwick	1.00
58 Wendell Hayes	1.00
59 *Dick Anderson*	3.00
60 Don Maynard	6.00
61 Tony Lorick	1.00
62 Pete Gogolak	1.00
63 Nate Ramsey	1.00
64 Dick Shiner	1.00
65 Larry Wilson	3.25
66 Ken Willard	1.00
67 Charley Taylor	5.50
68 Billy Cannon	1.00
69 Lance Alworth	8.00
70 Jim Nance	1.00
71 Nick Rassas	1.00
72 Lenny Lyles	1.00
73 Bennie McRae	1.00
74 Bill Glass	1.00
75 Don Meredith	20.00
76 Dick LeBeau	1.00
77 Carroll Dale	1.00
78 Ron McDole	1.00
79 Charley King	1.00
80 Checklist 1-132	14.00
81 Dick Bass	1.00
82 Roy Winston	1.00
83 Don McCall	1.00
84 Jim Katcavage	1.00
85 Norm Snead	3.00
86 Earl Gros	1.00
87 Don Brumm	1.00
88 Sonny Bishop	1.00
89 Fred Arbanas	1.00
90 Karl Noonan	1.00
91 Dick Witcher	1.00
92 Vince Promuto	1.00
93 Tommy Nobis	3.00
94 Jerry Hill	1.00
95 *Ed O'Bradovich*	1.75
96 Ernie Kellerman	1.00
97 Chuck Howley	1.00
98 Hewritt Dixon	1.00
99 Ron Mix	3.25
100 Joe Namath	80.00
101 Billy Gambrell	1.00
102 Elijah Pitts	1.00
103 Billy Truax	1.00
104 Ed Sharockman	1.00
105 Doug Atkins	3.25
106 Greg Larson	1.00
107 Israel Lang	1.00
108 Houston Antwine	1.00
109 Paul Guidry	1.00
110 Al Denson	1.00
111 Roy Jefferson	1.00
112 Chuck LaTourette	1.00
113 Jimmy Johnson	1.00
114 Bobby Mitchell	4.00
115 Randy Johnson	1.00
116 Lou Michaels	1.00
117 Rudy Kuechenberg	1.00
118 Walt Suggs	1.00
119 Goldie Sellers	1.00
120 *Larry Csonka*	80.00
121 Jim Houston	1.00
122 Craig Baynham	1.00
123 Alex Karras	6.00
124 Jim Grabowski	1.25
125 Roman Gabriel	3.00
126 Larry Bowie	1.00
127 Dave Parks	1.00
128 Ben Davidson	2.00
129 Steve DeLong	1.00
130 Fred Hill	1.00
131 Ernie Koy	1.00
132 Checklist 133-263	15.00
133 Dick Hoak	1.15
134 *Larry Stallings*	1.50
135 *Clifton McNeil*	1.50
136 Walter Rock	1.15
137 Billy Lothridge	1.15
138 Bob Vogel	1.15
139 Dick Butkus	25.00
140 Frank Ryan	1.50
141 Larry Garron	1.15
142 George Saimes	1.15
143 Frank Buncom	1.15
144 Don Perkins	1.50
145 Johnny Robinson	1.15
146 Lee Roy Caffey	1.15
147 Bernie Casey	1.15
148 Billy Martin	1.15
149 Gene Howard	1.15
150 Fran Tarkenton	20.00
151 Eric Crabtree	1.15
152 W.K. Hicks	1.15
153 Bobby Bell	4.00
154 Sam Baker	1.15
155 Marv Woodson	1.15
156 Dave Williams	1.15
157 Bruce Bosley	1.15
158 Carl Kammerer	1.15
159 Jim Burson	1.15
160 Roy Hilton	1.15
161 Bob Grise	30.00
162 Bob Talamini	1.15
163 Jim Otto	3.75
164 Ron Bull	1.15

165 Walter Johnson	1.50
166 Lee Roy Jordan	3.50
167 Mike Lucci	1.15
168 Willie Wood	3.50
169 Maxie Baughan	1.15
170 Bill Brown	1.15
171 John Hadl	3.00
172 Gino Cappelletti	1.75
173 George Byrd	1.15
174 Steve Stonebreaker	1.15
175 Joe Morrison	1.15
176 Joe Scarpati	1.15
177 Bobby Walden	1.15
178 Roy Shivers	1.15
179 Kermit Alexander	1.15
180 Pat Richter	1.15
181 Pete Perreault	1.15
182 Pete Duranko	1.15
183 Leroy Mitchell	1.15
184 Jim Simon	1.15
185 Billy Ray Smith	1.15
186 Jack Concannon	1.15
187 Ben Davis	1.15
188 Mike Clark	1.15
189 Jim Gobbons	1.15
190 Dave Robinson	1.15
191 Otis Taylor	2.00
192 Nick Buoniconti	2.75
193 Matt Snell	2.00
194 Bruce Gossett	1.15
195 Mick Tingelhoff	1.50
196 Earl Leggett	1.15
197 Pete Case	1.15
198 *Tom Woodeshick*	1.50
199 Ken Kortas	1.15
200 Jim Hart	3.00
201 Fred Biletnikoff	10.00
202 Jacque MacKinnon	1.15
203 Jim Whalen	1.15
204 Matt Hazeltine	1.15
205 Charlie Gogolak	1.15
206 Ray Ogden	1.15
207 John Mackey	3.75
208 Rosey Taylor	1.15
209 Gene Hickerson	1.15
210 *Dave Edwards*	1.50
211 Tom Sestak	1.15
212 Ernie Wright	1.15
213 Dave Costa	1.15
214 Tom Vaughn	1.15
215 Bart Starr	25.00
216 Les Josephson	1.15
217 Fred Cox	1.15
218 Mike Tilleman	1.15
219 Darrell Dess	1.15
220 Dave Lloyd	1.15
221 Pete Beathard	1.00
222 Buck Buchanan	3.50
223 Frank Emanuel	1.15
224 Paul Martha	1.15
225 Johnny Roland	1.15
226 Gary Lewis	1.15
227 Sonny Jurgensen	7.00
228 Jim Butler	1.15
229 *Mike Curtis*	4.00
230 Richie Petitbon	1.50
231 George Sauer Jr.	1.15
232 George Blanda	20.00
233 Gary Garrison	1.15
234 Gary Collins	1.15
235 Craig Morton	4.00
236 Tom Nowatzke	1.15
237 Donny Anderson	1.15
238 Deacon Jones	4.00
239 Grady Alderman	1.15
240 Bill Kilmer	3.00
241 Mike Taliaferro	1.15
242 Stew Barber	1.15
243 Bobby Hunt	1.15
244 Homer Jones	1.15
245 Bob Brown	1.15
246 Bill Asbury	1.15
247 Charley Johnson	1.75
248 Chris Hanburger	1.15
249 John Brodie	8.00
250 Earl Morrall	2.00
251 Floyd Little	5.00
252 Jerrell Wilson	1.50
253 Jim Keyes	1.15
254 Mel Renfro	1.50
255 Herb Adderley	4.00
256 Jack Snow	1.15
257 Charlie Durkee	1.15
258 Charlie Harper	1.15
259 J.R. Wilburn	1.15
260 Charlie Krueger	1.15
261 Pete Jacquess	1.15
262 Gerry Philbin	1.15
263 Daryle Lamonica	12.00

Values quoted in this guide reflect the retail price of a card — the price a collector can expect to pay when buying a card from a dealer. The wholesale price — that which a collector can expect to receive from a dealer when selling a card — will be significantly lower, depending on desirability and condition.

1969 Topps Four In Ones

Issued one per pack in the 1969 Topps football wax packs, each "card" contained four perforated cards of NFL players which could be punched out and inserted into each team's mini-album. The cards are unnumbered, but appear here in alphabetical order according to the last name of the player who appears in the upper left corner of the card. One variation does exist: Cards #27 and 28 show the same four players, but Charlie Johnson on #27 has a red logo while #28 gives him a white one. Bill Triplett on #27 has a white logo, while #28 is red. Both seem to have been issued in equal quantities. Most of the cards in this set are of the key players, including Brian Piccolo and Larry Csonka rookies. A few of the lesser-known NFL players appeared in this set only and not the regular 1969 set (and vice versa). An important note: the entire card is priced here. The small, individual cards have very little value when separated from the rest of the card, as is the case with Topps' 1980-81 basketball issue.

	NM
Complete Set (66):	185.00
Common Card:	1.00
(1) Grady Alderman, Jerry Smith, Gale Sayers, Dick LeBeau	6.00
(2) Jim Allison, Frank Buncom, Frank Emanuel, George Sauer Jr.	1.00
(3) Lance Alworth, Don Maynard, Ron McDole, Billy Cannon	3.00
(4) Dick Anderson, Mike Taliaferro, Fred Biletnikoff, Otis Taylor	2.25
(5) Ralph Baker, Les Duncan, Eric Crabtree, Bobby Bell	1.00
(6) Gary Ballman, Jerry Hill, Roy Jefferson, Boyd Dowler	1.00
(7) Tom Beer, Miller Farr, Jim Colclough, Steve DeLong	1.00
(8) Sonny Bishop, Pete Banaszak, Paul Guidry, Tom Day	1.00
(9) Bruce Bosley, J.R. Wilburn, Tom Nowatzke, Jim Simon	1.00
(10) Larry Bowie, Willis Crenshaw, Tommy Davis, Paul Flatley	1.00
(11) Nick Buoniconti, George Saimes, Jacque MacKinnon, Pete Duranko	1.00
(12) Jim Burson, Dan Abramowicz, Ed O'Bradovich, Dick Witcher	1.00
(13) Reg Carolan, Larry Garron, W.K. Hicks, Pete Jacques	1.00
(14) Bert Coan, John Hadl, Dan Birdwell, Sam Brunelli	1.00
(15) Hewritt Dixon, Goldie Sellers, Joe Namath, Howard Twilley	20.00

(16) Charlie Durkee, Clinton McNeil, Maxie Baughan, Fran Tarkenton	6.00
(17) Pete Gogolak, Ron Bull, Chuck LaTourette, Willie Richardson	1.00
(18) Bob Griese, Jim Lemoine, Dave Grayson, Walt Sweeney	4.00
(19) Jim Hart, Darrell Dess, Kermit Alexander, Mick Tingelhoff	1.00
(20) Alvin Haymond, Elijah Pitts, Billy Ray Smith, Ken Willard	1.00
(21) Gene Hickerson, Donny Anderson, Dick Butkus, Mike Lucci	4.00
(22) Fred Hill, Ernie Koy, Tommy Nobis, Bennie McRae	1.00
(23) Dick Hoak, Roman Gabriel, Ed Sharockman, Dave Williams	1.00
(24) Jim Houston, Roy Shivers, Carroll Dale, Bill Asbury	1.00
(25) Gene Howard, Joe Morrison, Billy Martin, Ben Davis	1.00
(26) Chuck Howley, Brian Piccolo, Chris Hanburger, Erich Barnes	14.00
(27) Charlie Johnson, Jim Katcavage, Gary Lewis, Bill Triplett (red white)	4.00
(28) Charlie Johnson, Jim Katcavage, Gary Lewis, Bill Triplett (white red)	4.00
(29) Walter Johnson, Tucker Frederickson, Dave Lloyd, Bobby Walden	1.00
(30) Sonny Jurgensen, Dick Bass, Paul Martha, Dave Parks	3.00
(31) Leroy Kelly, Ed Meador, Bart Starr, Ray Ogden	6.00
(32) Charlie King, Bob Cappadona, Fred Arbanas, Ben Davidson	1.00
(33) Daryle Lamonica, Carl Cunningham, Bobby Hunt, Stew Barber	1.00
(34) Israel Lang, Bob Lilly, Jim Butler, John Brodie	4.00
(35) Jim Lindsey, Ray Nitschke, Rickie Harris, Bob Vogel	1.00
(36) Billy Lothridge, Herb Adderly, Charlie Gogolak, John Mackey	2.00
(37) Bobby Maples, Karl Noonan, Houston Antwine, Wendell Hayes	1.00
(38) Don Meredith, Gary Collins, Homer Jones, Marv Woodson	6.00
(39) Rex Mirich, Art Graham, Jim Turner, John Stofa	1.00
(40) Leroy Mitchell, Sid Blanks, Paul Rochester, Pete Perreault	1.00
(41) Jim Nance, Jim Dunaway, Larry Csonka, Ron Mix	2.00
(42) Bill Nelsen, Bill Munson, Nate Ramsey, Mike Curtis	1.00
(43) Jim Otto, Dave Herman, Dave Costa, Dennis Randall	1.00
(44) Jack Pardee, Norm Snead, Craig Baynham	1.00
(45) Richie Petitbon, John Robinson, Mike Clark, Jack Snow	1.00

(46) Nick Rassas, Tom Matte, Lance Rentzel, Bobby Mitchell	1.00
(47) Pat Richter, Dave Whitsell, Joe Kapp, Bill Glass	1.00
(48) Johnny Roland, Craig Morton, Bill Brown, Sam Baker	1.00
(49) Andy Russell, Randy Johnson, Bob Matheson, Alex Karras	2.00
(50) Joe Scarpati, Walter Rock, Jack Concannon, Bernie Casey	1.00
(51) Tom Sestak, Ernie Wright, Doug Moreau, Matt Snell	1.00
(52) Jerry Simmons, Bob Hayes, Doug Atkins, Spider Lockhart	1.00
(53) Jackie Smith, Jim Grabowski, Jim Johnson, Charley Taylor	2.00
(54) Larry Stallings, Roosevelt Taylor, Jim Gibbons, Bob Brown	1.00
(55) Mike Stratton, Marion Rushing, Soloman Brannan, Jim Keyes	1.00
(56) Walt Suggs, Len Dawson, Sherrill Headrick, Al Denson	2.00
(57) Bob Talamini, George Blanda, Jim Whalen, Jack Kemp	22.00
(58) Clendon Thomas, Don McCall, Earl Morrall, Lonnie Warwick	1.00
(59) Don Trull, Gerry Philbin, Gary Garrison, Buck Buchanan	1.00
(60) John Unitas, Les Josephson, Fred Cox, Mel Renfro	9.00
(61) Wayne Walker, Tony Lorick, Dave Wilcox, Merlin Olsen	2.00
(62) Willie West, Ken Herock, George Byrd, Gino Cappelletti	1.00
(63) Jerrel Wilson, John Bramlett, Pete Beathard, Floyd Little	1.00
(64) Larry Wilson, Lou Michaels, Billy Gambrell, Earl Gros	1.00
(65) Willie Wood, Steve Stonebreaker, Vince Promuto, Jim Cadile	1.00
(66) Tom Woodeshick, Greg Larson, Billy Kilmer, Don Perkins	1.50

1969 Topps mini-albums

The 26 team booklets were intended as stamp books for the 1969 Topps Four In Ones. You punched out the four players on the card and stuck them into this 2-1/2" x 3-1/2" book, right over the picture of the player. The booklets are numbered on the back and arranged in alphabetical order by city name. Aside from its condition, in order for a book to be considered mint, there must be no stamps in it.

	NM
Complete Set (26):	50.00
Common Booklet:	2.00
1 Atlanta Falcons	2.00
2 Baltimore Colts	2.00
3 Chicago Bears	4.00
4 Cleveland Browns	2.00
5 Dallas Cowboys	5.00
6 Detroit Lions	2.00
7 Green Bay Packers	5.00
8 Los Angeles Rams	2.00
9 Minnesota Vikings	2.00
10 New Orleans Saints	2.00
11 New York Giants	4.00
12 Philadelphia Eagles	2.00
13 Pittsburgh Steelers	4.00

14	St. Louis Cardinals	2.00
15	San Francisco 49ers	4.00
16	Washington Redskins	4.00
17	Boston Patriots	2.00
18	Buffalo Bills	4.00
19	Cincinnati Bengals	2.00
20	Denver Broncos	5.00
21	Houston Oilers	4.00
22	Kansas City Chiefs	2.00
23	Miami Dolphins	4.00
24	New York Jets	4.00
25	Oakland Raiders	5.00
26	San Diego Chargers	2.00

1970 Topps

The 1970 Topps set, which included 263 cards, was printed in two series. The second series is a little tougher to find than the first, since it was printed in lesser quantities. One variation that appears in the set is #113, Lance Rentzel. His name appears in red on the "common" card; on the hard-to-find variation, his name appears in black. Card #132, the second-series checklist card, was double-printed, a common practice for Topps during its multi-series production days. The set is best known for its inclusion of the O.J. Simpson rookie card, but other rookies in the set are Leroy Brown, Jan Stenerud, Alan Page, Bob Trumpy, Bubba Smith, Bill Bergey, Calvin Hill and Fred Dryer.

		NM
Complete Set (263):		450.00
Common Player (1-132):		.50
Common Player (133-263):		.75
1	Len Dawson	15.00
2	Doug Hart	.50
3	Verlon Biggs	.50
4	Ralph Neely	.75
5	Harmon Wages	.50
6	Dan Conners	.50
7	Gino Cappelletti	1.00
8	Erich Barnes	.75
9	Checklist 1-132	7.50
10	Bob Griese	15.00
11	Ed Flanagan	.50
12	George Seals	.50
13	Harry Jacobs	.50
14	Mike Haffner	.50
15	Bob Vogel	.50
16	Bill Peterson	.50
17	Spider Lockhart	.50
18	Billy Truax	.50
19	Jim Beirne	.50
20	Leroy Kelly	4.00
21	Dave Lloyd	.50
22	Mike Tilleman	.50
23	Gary Garrison	.50
24	Larry Brown	7.00
25	Jan Stenerud	12.00
26	Rolf Krueger	.50
27	Roland Lakes	.50
28	Dick Hoak	.50
29	Gene Washington (Vikings)	.75
30	Bart Starr	20.00
31	Dave Grayson	.50
32	Jerry Rush	.50
33	Len St. Jean	.50
34	Randy Edmunds	.50
35	Matt Snell	1.50
36	Paul Costa	.50
37	Mike Pyle	.50
38	Roy Hilton	.50
39	Steve Tensi	.50
40	Tommy Nobis	2.00
41	Pete Case	.50
42	Andy Rice	.50
43	Elvin Bethea	3.50
44	Jack Snow	.50
45	Mel Renfro	1.00
46	Andy Livingston	.50
47	Gary Ballman	.50
48	Bob DeMarco	.50
49	Steve DeLong	.50
50	Daryle Lamonica	3.50
51	Jim Lynch	.75
52	Mel Farr	.75
53	Bob Long	.50
54	John Elliott	.50
55	Ray Nitschke	4.00
56	Jim Shorter	.50
57	Dave Wilcox	.50
58	Eric Crabtree	.50
59	Alan Page	40.00
60	Jim Nance	.50
61	Glen Ray Hines	.50
62	John Mackey	3.00
63	Ron McDole	.50
64	Tom Beier	.50
65	Bill Nelsen	.65
66	Paul Flatley	.50
67	Sam Brunelli	.50
68	Jack Pardee	1.50
69	Brig Owens	.50
70	Gale Sayers	35.00
71	Lee Roy Jordan	2.00
72	Harold Jackson	8.00
73	John Hadl	2.50
74	Dave Parks	.50
75	Lem Barney	15.00
76	Johnny Roland	.50
77	Ed Budde	.50
78	Ben McGee	.50
79	Ken Bowman	.50
80	Fran Tarkenton	20.00
81	Gene Washington	4.00
82	Larry Grantham	.50
83	Bill Brown	.50
84	John Charles	.50
85	Fred Biletnikoff	7.00
86	Royce Berry	.50
87	Bob Lilly	4.50
88	Earl Morrall	2.00
89	Jerry LeVias	.50
90	O.J. Simpson	80.00
91	Mike Howell	.50
92	Ken Gray	.50
93	Chris Hanburger	.50
94	Larry Seiple	.75
95	Rich Jackson	.75
96	Rockne Freitas	.50
97	Dick Post	.75
98	Ben Hawkins	.50
99	Ken Reaves	.50
100	Roman Gabriel	2.50
101	Dave Rowe	.50
102	Dave Robinson	.50
103	Otis Taylor	1.50
104	Jim Turner	.50
105	Joe Morrison	.50
106	Dick Evey	.50
107	Ray Mansfield	.50
108	Grady Alderman	.50
109	Bruce Gossett	.50
110	Bob Trumpy	5.00
111	Jim Hunt	.50
112	Larry Stallings	.50
113	Lance Rentzel (red)	1.50
113a	Lance Rentzel (black)	1.50
114	Bubba Smith	25.00
115	Norm Snead	.75
116	Jim Otto	2.50
117	Bo Scott	.75
118	Rick Redman	.50
119	George Byrd	.50
120	George Webster	2.00
121	Chuck Walton	.50
122	Dave Costa	.50
123	Al Dodd	.50
124	Len Hauss	.50
125	Deacon Jones	3.50
126	Randy Johnson	.50
127	Ralph Heck	.50
128	Emerson Boozer	2.50
129	Johnny Robinson	.65
130	John Brodie	6.00
131	Gale Gillingham	1.00
132	Checklist 133-263 (DP)	8.00
133	Chuck Walker	.75
134	Bennie McRae	.75
135	Paul Warfield	6.00
136	Dan Darragh	.75
137	Paul Robinson	1.00
138	Ed Philpott	.75
139	Craig Morton	2.00
140	Tom Dempsey	5.00
141	Al Nelson	.75
142	Tom Matte	.75
143	Dick Schafrath	.75
144	Willie Brown	4.00
145	Charley Taylor	4.50
146	John Huard	.75
147	Dave Osborn	.75
148	Gene Mingo	.75
149	Larry Hand	.75
150	Joe Namath	50.00
151	Tom Mack	7.00
152	Kenny Graham	.75
153	Don Herrmann	.75
154	Bobby Bell	3.75
155	Hoyle Granger	.75
156	Claude Humphrey	1.25
157	Clifton McNeil	.75
158	Mick Tingelhoff	1.00
159	Don Horn	1.00
160	Larry Wilson	3.00
161	Tom Neville	.75
162	Larry Csonka	25.00
163	Doug Buffone	.75
164	Cornell Green	.75
165	Haven Moses	2.50
166	Bill Kilmer	2.50
167	Tim Rossovich	.75
168	Bill Bergey	5.00
169	Gary Collins	.75
170	Floyd Little	3.00
171	Tom Keating	.75
172	Pat Fischer	.75
173	Walt Sweeney	.75
174	Greg Larson	.75
175	Carl Eller	3.00
176	George Sauer	.75
177	Jim Hart	2.00
178	Bob Brown	.75
179	Mike Garrett	4.00
180	Johnny Unitas	22.00
181	Tom Regner	.75
182	Bob Jeter	.75
183	Gail Cogdill	.75
184	Earl Gros	.75
185	Dennis Partee	.75
186	Charlie Krueger	.75
187	Martin Baccaglio	.75
188	Charlie Long	.75
189	Bob Hayes	3.00
190	Dick Butkus	13.00
191	Al Bemiller	.75
192	Dick Westmoreland	.75
193	Joe Scarpati	.75
194	Ron Snidow	.75
195	Earl McCullough	1.00
196	Jake Kupp	.75
197	Bob Lurtsema	.75
198	Mike Current	.75
199	Charlie Smith	.75
200	Sonny Jurgensen	6.50
201	Mike Curtis	.75
202	Aaron Brown	.75
203	Richie Petitbon	1.00
204	Walt Suggs	.75
205	Roy Jefferson	.75
206	Russ Washington	1.00
207	Woody Peoples	1.00
208	Dave Williams	.75
209	John Zook	1.00
210	Tom Woodeshick	.75
211	Howard Fest	.75
212	Jack Concannon	.75
213	Jim Marshall	2.75
214	Jon Morris	.75
215	Dan Abramowicz	.75
216	Paul Martha	.75
217	Ken Willard	.75
218	Walter Rock	.75
219	Garland Boyette	.75
220	Buck Buchanan	3.75
221	Bill Munson	.75
222	David Lee	1.00
223	Karl Noonan	.75
224	Harry Schuh	.75
225	Jackie Smith	1.25
226	Gerry Philbin	.75
227	Ernie Koy	.75
228	Chuck Howley	.75
229	Billy Shaw	.75
230	Jerry Hillebrand	.75
231	Bill Thompson	1.50
232	Carroll Dale	.75
233	Gene Hickerson	.75
234	Jim Butler	.75
235	Greg Cook	1.50
236	Lee Roy Caffey	.75
237	Merlin Olsen	4.50
238	Fred Cox	.75
239	Nate Ramsey	.75
240	Lance Alworth	6.00
241	Chuck Hinton	.75
242	Jerry Smith	.75
243	Tony Baker	.75
244	Nick Buoniconti	2.50
245	Jim Johnson	.75
246	Willie Richardson	.75
247	Fred Dryer	15.00
248	Bobby Maples	.75
249	Alex Karras	5.50
250	Joe Kapp	2.00
251	Ben Davidson	2.50
252	Mike Stratton	.75
253	Les Josephson	.75
254	Don Maynard	6.00
255	Houston Antwine	.75
256	Mac Percival	1.00
257	George Goeddeke	.75
258	Homer Jones	.75
259	Bob Berry	.75
260	Calvin Hill	10.00
261	Willie Wood	3.00
262	Ed Weisacosky	.75
263	Jim Tyrer	3.00

1970 Topps Super Glossy

A collector favorite, this 33-card set is among the decade's most expensive subsets. These were found in the second series of 1970 Topps football wax packs and had full-color action-pose glossy fronts, heavy white cardboard stock, and rounded corners. The only information on the white backs is the player's name, team, position and card number.

		NM
Complete Set (33):		300.00
Common Player:		3.00
1	Tommy Nobis	3.00
2	John Unitas	27.50
3	Tom Matte	3.00
4	Mac Percival	3.00
5	Leroy Kelly	3.00
6	Mel Renfro	3.00
7	Bob Hayes	3.00
8	Earl McCullouch	3.00
9	Bart Starr	22.00
10	Willie Wood	7.00
11	Jack Snow	3.00
12	Joe Kapp	5.00
13	Dave Osborn	3.00
14	Dan Abramowicz	3.00
15	Fran Tarkenton	22.00
16	Tom Woodeshick	3.00
17	Roy Jefferson	3.00
18	Jackie Smith	3.00
19	Jim Johnson	3.00
20	Sonny Jurgensen	12.00
21	Houston Antwine	3.00
22	O.J. Simpson	60.00
23	Greg Cook	3.00
24	Floyd Little	4.00
25	Rich Jackson	3.00
26	George Webster	3.00
27	Len Dawson	9.00
28	Bob Griese	14.00
29	Joe Namath	70.00
30	Matt Snell	3.00
31	Daryle Lamonica	4.00
32	Fred Biletnikoff	7.00
33	Dick Post	3.00

1970 Topps posters

This 24-poster set was included one per pack in the first series of 1970 Topps football wax packs. The posters, which measure about 8" x 10", were folded several times; it's very difficult to find any in top condition.

		NM
Complete Set (24):		50.00
Common Player:		1.00
1	Gale Sayers	4.50
2	Bobby Bell	3.00
3	Roman Gabriel	3.25
4	Jim Tyrer	1.00
5	Willie Brown	3.00
6	Carl Eller	3.00
7	Tom Mack	1.50
8	Deacon Jones	3.00
9	Johnny Robinson	1.00
10	Jan Stenerud	2.00
11	Dick Butkus	5.00
12	Lem Barney	1.00
13	David Lee	1.00
14	Larry Wilson	2.00
15	Gene Hickerson	1.00
16	Lance Alworth	3.00
17	Merlin Olsen	3.00
18	Bob Trumpy	2.00
19	Bob Lilly	3.00
20	Mick Tingelhoff	1.50
21	Calvin Hill	2.00
22	Paul Warfield	3.00
23	Chuck Howley	1.00
24	Bob Brown	1.00

1970 Topps Supers

A 35-card set issued three per pack with a stick of gum, the cards featured an action pose of an NFL star with a facsimile autograph. No other identification is on the front. Card backs show the reverse of the player's regular 1970 card. These were printed on heavy white cardboard stock and measure about 3-1/8" x 5-1/4". The final seven in the set were apparently short-printed (possibly added late) and are much harder to find than the first 28 cards.

		NM
Complete Set (35):		300.00
Common Player:		2.75
1	Fran Tarkenton	16.00
2	Floyd Little	3.00
3	Bart Starr	16.00
4	Len Dawson	8.50
5	Dick Post	2.75
6	Sonny Jurgensen	8.50
7	Deacon Jones	5.00
8	Leroy Kelly	2.75
9	Larry Wilson	2.75
10	Greg Cook	2.75
11	Carl Eller	4.50
12	Lem Barney	2.75
13	Lance Alworth	7.00
14	Dick Butkus	12.00
15	John Unitas	25.00
16	Roy Jefferson	2.75
17	Bobby Bell	5.00
18	John Brodie	9.00
19	Dan Abramowicz	2.75
20	Matt Snell	2.75
21	Tom Matte	2.75
22	Gale Sayers	20.00
23	Tom Woodeshick	2.75
24	O.J. Simpson	50.00
25	Roman Gabriel	5.00
26	Jim Nance	2.75
27	Joe Morrison	2.75
28	Calvin Hill	2.75
29	Tommy Nobis	6.50
30	Bob Hayes	6.50
31	Joe Kapp	6.50
32	Daryle Lamonica	6.50
33	Joe Namath	65.00
34	George Webster	6.50
35	Bob Griese	15.00

1971 Topps

This 263-card set was released in two series, with the first containing cards #1-132 and the second with cards #133-263. The second-series checklist (card #106) is double-printed. There aren't any subsets in the 1971 issue, but the NFC players are designated by red borders and AFC players have blue borders. All-stars have blue borders. This, incidentally, is the last Topps set that would not contain some type of subset. Hall of Famers with rookie cards in this set include Terry Bradshaw, Joe Greene, Willie Lanier, and Ken Houston. Other rookies include Duane Thomas, Ron Johnson, Mercury Morris, Garo Yepremian, Mark Mosley, and Charlie Sanders.

		NM
Complete Set (263):		500.00
Common Player (1-132):		.50
Common Player (133-263):		.75
1	Johnny Unitas	30.00
2	Jim Butler	.50
3	Marty Schottenheimer	20.00
4	Joe O'Donnell	.50
5	Tom Dempsey	1.00
6	Chuck Allen	.50
7	Ernie Kellerman	.50
8	Walt Garrison	2.50
9	Bill Van Heusen	.50
10	Lance Alworth	5.00
11	Greg Landry	5.00
12	Larry Krause	.50
13	Buck Buchanan	2.50
14	Roy Gerela	1.00
15	Clifton McNeil	.50
16	Bob Brown	.50
17	Lloyd Mumphord	.50
18	Gary Cuozzo	.50
19	Don Maynard	5.00
20	Larry Wilson	2.50
21	Charlie Smith	.50
22	Ken Avery	.50
23	Billy Walik	.50
24	Jim Johnson	2.00
25	Dick Butkus	20.00
26	Charley Taylor	4.25
27	Checklist 1-132	8.00
28	Lionel Aldridge	1.00
29	Billy Lothridge	.50
30	Terry Hanratty	1.25
31	Lee Roy Jordan	2.00
32	Rick Volk	.75
33	Howard Kindig	.50
34	Carl Garrett	1.00
35	Bobby Bell	2.50
36	Gene Hickerson	.50
37	Dave Parks	.50
38	Paul Martha	.50
39	George Blanda	15.00
40	Tom Woodeshick	.50
41	Alex Karras	4.00
42	Rich Redman	.50
43	Zeke Moore	.50
44	Jack Snow	.50
45	Larry Csonka	12.00
46	Karl Kassulke	.50
47	Jim Hart	2.00
48	Al Atkinson	.50
49	Horst Muhlmann	.75
50	Sonny Jurgensen	6.00
51	Ron Johnson	2.50
52	Cas Banaszek	.50
53	Bubba Smith	8.00
54	Bobby Douglass	1.50
55	Willie Wood	2.50
56	Bake Turner	.50
57	Mike Morgan	.50
58	George Byrd	.50
59	Don Horn	2.00
60	Tommy Nobis	3.00
61	Jan Stenerud	3.00
62	Altie Taylor	.75
63	Gary Pettigrew	.50
64	Spike Jones	.50
65	Duane Thomas	2.50
66	Marty Domres	.75
67	Dick Anderson	.50
68	Ken Iman	.50
69	Miller Farr	.50
70	Daryle Lamonica	2.50
71	Alan Page	8.00
72	Pat Matson	.50
73	Emerson Boozer	1.00
74	Pat Fischer	.50
75	Gary Collins	.50
76	John Fuqua	1.00
77	Bruce Gossett	.50
78	Ed O'Bradovich	.50
79	Bob Tucker	1.50
80	Mike Curtis	.50
81	Rich Jackson	.50
82	Tom Janik	.50
83	Gale Gillingham	.50
84	Jim Mitchell	.50
85	Charlie Johnson	1.00
86	Edgar Chandler	.50
87	Cyril Pinder	.50
88	Johnny Robinson	.50
89	Ralph Neely	.50
90	Dan Abramowicz	.50
91	Mercury Morris	6.00
92	Steve DeLong	.50
93	Larry Stallings	.50
94	Tom Mack	2.50
95	Hewritt Dixon	.50
96	Fred Cox	.50
97	Chris Hanburger	.50
98	Gerry Philbin	.50
99	Ernie Wright	.50
100	John Brodie	5.00
101	Tucker Frederickson	.50
102	Bobby Walden	.50
103	Dick Gordon	.50
104	Walter Johnson	.50
105	Mike Lucci	.50
106	Checklist 133-263	6.00
107	Ron Berger	.50
108	Dan Sullivan	.50
109	George Kunz	2.00
110	Floyd Little	2.50
111	Zeke Bratkowski	.50
112	Haven Moses	.50
113	Ken Houston	20.00
114	Willie Lanier	20.00
115	Larry Brown	2.00
116	Tim Rossovich	.50
117	Errol Linden	.50
118	Mel Renfro	1.25
119	Mike Garrett	1.00
120	Fran Tarkenton	20.00
121	Garo Yepremian	3.00
122	Glen Condren	.50
123	Johnny Roland	.50
124	Dave Herman	.50
125	Merlin Olsen	4.00
126	Doug Buffone	.50
127	Earl McCullouch	.50
128	Spider Lockhart	.50
129	Ken Willard	.50
130	Gene Washington (MN)	.50
131	Mike Phipps	1.75
132	Andy Russell	.50
133	Ray Nitschke	4.50
134	Jerry Logan	.75
135	MacArthur Lane	2.00
136	Jim Turner	.75
137	Kent McCloughan	.75
138	Paul Guidry	.75
139	Otis Taylor	1.50
140	Virgil Carter	1.00
141	Joe Dawkins	.75
142	Steve Preece	.75
143	Mike Bragg	.75
144	Bob Lilly	4.50
145	Joe Kapp	1.25
146	Al Dodd	.75
147	Nick Buoniconti	2.50
148	Speedy Duncan	.75
149	Cedrick Hardman	1.00
150	Gale Sayers	30.00
151	Jim Otto	3.00
152	Billy Truax	.75
153	John Elliott	.75
154	Dick LeBeau	.75
155	Bill Bergey	1.75

156	*Terry Bradshaw*	175.00
157	Leroy Kelly	4.50
158	Paul Krause	2.00
159	Ted Vactor	.75
160	Bob Griese	12.00
161	Ernie McMillan	.75
162	Donny Anderson	.75
163	John Pitts	.75
164	Dave Costa	.75
165	Gene Washington (SF)	1.50
166	John Zook	.55
167	Pete Gogolak	.75
168	Erich Barnes	.55
169	Alvin Reed	.75
170	Jim Nance	.75
171	Craig Morton	2.00
172	Gary Garrison	.75
173	Joe Scarpati	.75
174	Adrian Young	.75
175	John Mackey	2.50
176	Mac Percival	.75
177	*Preston Pearson*	4.00
178	Fred Biletnikoff	6.00
179	*Mike Battle*	1.00
180	Len Dawson	7.00
181	Les Josephson	.75
182	Royce Berry	.75
183	Herman Weaver	.75
184	Norm Snead	1.25
185	Sam Brunelli	.75
186	*Jim Kiick*	4.00
187	Austin Denney	.75
188	*Roger Wehrli*	3.00
189	Dave Wilcox	.75
190	Bob Hayes	2.00
191	Joe Morrison	.75
192	Manny Sistrunk	.75
193	*Don Cockroft*	1.50
194	Lee Bouggess	.75
195	Bob Berry	.75
196	Ron Sellers	.75
197	George Webster	.75
198	Hoyle Granger	.75
199	Bob Vogel	.75
200	Bart Starr	22.00
201	Mike Mercer	.75
202	Dave Smith	.75
203	Lee Roy Caffey	.75
204	Mick Tingelhoff	.75
205	Matt Snell	1.50
206	Jim Tyrer	.75
207	Willie Brown	3.50
208	*Bob Johnson*	1.50
209	Deacon Jones	3.00
210	*Charlie Sanders*	4.50
211	*Jake Scott*	5.00
212	*Bob Anderson*	2.00
213	Charlie Krueger	.75
214	Jim Bakken	.75
215	Harold Jackson	2.50
216	Bill Brundige	.75
217	Calvin Hill	2.00
218	Claude Humphrey	.75
219	Glen Ray Hines	.75
220	Bill Nelsen	.75
221	Roy Hilton	.75
222	Don Herrmann	.75
223	John Bramlett	.75
224	Ken Ellis	.75
225	Dave Osborn	.75
226	*Edd Hargett*	.75
227	Gene Mingo	.75
228	Larry Grantham	.75
229	Dick Post	.75
230	Roman Gabriel	3.00
231	Mike Eischeid	.75
232	Jim Lynch	.75
233	*Lemar Parrish*	3.00
234	Cecil Turner	.75
235	*Dennis Shaw*	1.00
236	Mel Farr	.75
237	Curt Knight	.75
238	Chuck Howley	.75
239	*Bruce Taylor*	1.00
240	Jerry LeVias	.75
241	Bob Lurtsema	.75
242	Earl Morrall	2.00
243	Kermit Alexander	.75
244	Jackie Smith	1.00
245	*Joe Greene*	50.00
246	Harmon Wages	.75
247	Errol Mann	.75
248	Mike McCoy	.75
249	*Milt Morin*	1.00
250	Joe Namath	50.00
251	Jackie Burkett	.75
252	Steve Chomyszak	.75
253	Ed Sharockman	.75
254	*Robert Holmes*	1.00
255	John Hadl	2.00
256	Cornell Gordon	.75
257	*Mark Moseley*	5.00
258	Gus Otto	.75
259	Mike Taliaferro	.75
260	O.J. Simpson	25.00
261	Paul Warfield	7.00
262	Jack Concannon	.75
263	Tom Matte	3.00

Post-1980 cards in Near Mint condition will generally sell for about 75% of the quoted Mint value. Excellent-condition cards bring no more than 40%.

1971 Topps Game Cards

The 53 cards in this set came one per pack inside wax packs of 1971 Topps football cards. Intended for use in a card game, these cards are similar to playing cards and carry a head "Action" shot of the player, his name and team in a diagonal stripe across the front, and a play (such as "Interception," "Touchdown" and "Fumble") on the top and bottom. Card backs are light blue and show the Topps logo inside a football helmet surrounding a football. The set has 52 "playing cards" plus a "first down/field marker" for use with the game. Six of the cards in the series were double-printed: Dick Butkus, Bob Berry, Joe Namath, Andy Russell, Tom Woodeshick, and Bart Starr. (Key: DP -- double-printed)

		NM
Complete Set (53):		125.00
Common Player:		.50
1	Dick Butkus (DP)	4.00
2	Bob Berry (DP)	.50
3	Joe Namath (DP)	17.00
4	Mike Curtis	.50
5	Jim Nance	.50
6	Ron Berger	.50
7	O.J. Simpson	20.00
8	Haven Moses	.50
9	Tommy Nobis	.50
10	Gale Sayers	9.00
11	Virgil Carter	.50
12	Andy Russell (DP)	.50
13	Bill Nelsen	.50
14	Gary Collins	.50
15	Duane Thomas	.50
16	Bob Hayes	.80
17	Floyd Little	.80
18	Sam Brunelli	.50
19	Charlie Sanders	.50
20	Mike Lucci	.50
21	Gene Washington (SF)	.80
22	Willie Wood	3.00
23	Jerry LeVias	.50
24	Charlie Johnson	.80
25	Len Dawson	3.00
26	Bobby Bell	2.00
27	Merlin Olsen	3.00
28	Roman Gabriel	2.00
29	Bob Griese	4.00
30	Larry Csonka	4.00
31	Dave Osborn	.50
32	Gene Washington (MN)	.50
33	Dan Abramowicz	.50
34	Tom Dempsey	.50
35	Fran Tarkenton	9.00
36	Clifton McNeil	.50
37	Johnny Unitas	12.00
38	Matt Snell	.50
39	Daryle Lamonica	.80
40	Hewritt Dixon	.50
41	Tom Woodeshick (DP)	.50
42	Harold Jackson	.50
43	Terry Bradshaw	20.00
44	Ken Avery	.50
45	MacArthur Lane	.50
46	Larry Wilson	1.00
47	John Hadl	1.00
48	Lance Alworth	2.00
49	John Brodie	4.00
50	Bart Starr (DP)	9.00
51	Sonny Jurgensen	6.00
52	Larry Brown	.50
53	Field Marker	.50

A card number in parentheses ( ) indicates the set is unnumbered.

A player's name in *italic* type indicates a rookie card.

1971 Topps Pin-Ups

These mini-posters (about 5" x 7") were folded twice and inserted into wax packs. The front features a head shot of the player, with his name in bold capitals above the photo and his team in smaller type at the bottom. Backs showed a football field with side markers, as well as the accompanying instructions. Because these posters were folded, it's very difficult, if not impossible, to find any in Mint condition.

		NM
Complete Set (32):		40.00
Common Player:		.65
1	Gene Washington	.75
2	Andy Russell	.65
3	Harold Jackson	.65
4	Joe Namath	12.00
5	Fran Tarkenton	5.00
6	Dave Osborn	.65
7	Bob Griese	2.50
8	Roman Gabriel	1.00
9	Jerry LeVias	.65
10	Bart Starr	5.00
11	Bob Hayes	1.00
12	Gale Sayers	5.50
13	O.J. Simpson	7.50
14	Sam Brunelli	.65
15	Jim Nance	.65
16	Bill Nelsen	.65
17	Sonny Jurgensen	2.50
18	John Brodie	2.50
19	Lance Alworth	1.50
20	Larry Wilson	1.00
21	Daryle Lamonica	.75
22	Dan Abramowicz	.65
23	Gene Washington (Minn)	.65
24	Bobby Bell	1.50
25	Merlin Olsen	2.00
26	Charlie Sanders	.65
27	Virgil Carter	.65
28	Dick Butkus	2.50
29	Johnny Unitas	7.00
30	Tommy Nobis	.75
31	Floyd Little	.65
32	Larry Brown	.65

1972 Topps

The 1972 set, a 351-card edition, was Topps' last to be issued in series form. The first series includes cards #1-132; the second - somewhat harder to find than the first - includes cards #133-263; and the final series - the difficult series - shows cards #264-351. Because of the difficulty in acquiring a complete set, this is easily the most expensive Topps set of the 1970s. Subsets included in this issue include statistical leaders, playoffs, All-Pros and In Action cards. Rookies in the set include John Riggins, Archie Manning, Jim Plunkett, John Brockington, Ted Hendricks, L.C. Greenwood, Lyle Alzado, Dan Pastorini, Gene Upshaw, Roger Staubach, Charlie Joiner and Steve Spurrier. (Key: IA - in action, AP - All Pro)

		NM
Complete Set (351):		2300.
Common Player (1-132):		.50
Common Player (133-263):		.50
Comm Player (264-351):		20.00
1	AFC rushing leaders (Floyd Little, Larry Csonka)	3.50
2	NFC rushing leaders (John Brockington, Steve Owens, Willie Ellison)	1.00
3	AFC passing leaders (Bob Griese, Len Dawson)	2.00
4	NFC passing leaders (Roger Staubach, Bill Kilmer)	4.00
5	AFC receiving leaders (Fred Biletnikoff, Otis Taylor, Randy Vataha)	1.00
6	NFC receiving leaders (Bob Tucker, Ted Kwalick, Harold Jackson, Roy Jefferson)	1.00
7	AFC scoring leaders (Garo Yepremian, Jan Stenerud)	1.50
8	NFC scoring leaders (Curt Knight, Errol Mann, Bruce Gossett)	1.00
9	Jim Kiick	1.25
10	Otis Taylor	1.25
11	Bobby Joe Green	.50
12	Ken Ellis	.50
13	*John Riggins*	32.00
14	Dave Parks	.50
15	John Hadl	1.50
16	Ron Hornsby	.50
17	Chip Myers	.50
18	Bill Kilmer	1.50
19	Fred Hoaglin	.50
20	Carl Eller	1.50
21	Steve Zabel	.50
22	*Vic Washington*	.75
23	Len St. Jean	.50
24	Bill Thompson	.50
25	*Steve Owens*	2.50
26	*Ken Burrough*	1.50
27	Mike Clark	.50
28	Willie Brown	3.00
29	Checklist 1-132	6.00
30	Marlin Briscoe	.50
31	Jerry Logan	.50
32	Donny Anderson	.50
33	Rich McGeorge	.50
34	Charlie Durkee	.50
35	Willie Lanier	4.00
36	Chris Farasopoulos	.50
37	Ronnie Shanklin	.50
38	Forrest Blue	1.25
39	Ken Reaves	.50
40	Roman Gabriel	2.00
41	Mac Percival	.50
42	Lem Barney	3.00
43	Nick Buoniconti	1.75
44	Charlie Gogolak	.50
45	*Bill Bradley*	2.00
46	Joe Jones	.50
47	Dave Williams	.50
48	Pete Athas	.50
49	Virgil Carter	.50
50	Floyd Little	2.00
51	Curt Knight	.50
52	Bobby Maples	.50
53	Charlie West	.50
54	*Marv Hubbard*	1.25
55	*Archie Manning*	15.00
56	*Jim O'Brien*	1.00
57	Wayne Patrick	.50
58	Ken Bowman	.50
59	Roger Wehrli	.50
60	Charlie Sanders	1.00
61	Jan Stenerud	2.00
62	Willie Ellison	.50
63	Walt Sweeney	.50
64	Ron Smith	.50
65	*Jim Plunkett*	15.00
66	Herb Adderly	2.50
67	*Mike Reid*	4.00
68	*Richard Caster*	1.50
69	Dave Wilcox	.50
70	Leroy Kelly	2.50
71	*Bob Lee*	1.00
72	Verlon Biggs	.50
73	Henry Allison	.50
74	Steve Ramsey	.50
75	Claude Humphrey	.50
76	*Bob Grim*	1.00
77	John Fuqua	.50
78	Ken Houston	4.00
79	Checklist 133-263	4.50
80	Bob Griese	8.00

81	Lance Rentzel	.50
82	*Ed Podolak*	1.75
83	Ike Hill	.50
84	George Farmer	.50
85	*John Brockington*	4.00
86	Jim Otto	2.00
87	Richard Neal	.50
88	Jim Hart	1.50
89	Bob Babich	.50
90	Gene Washington (S.F.)	.75
91	John Zook	.50
92	Bobby Duhon	.50
93	*Ted Hendricks*	20.00
94	Rockne Freitas	.50
95	Larry Brown	1.50
96	Mike Phipps	1.00
97	Julius Adams	.50
98	Dick Anderson	.50
99	Fred Willis	.50
100	Joe Namath	35.00
101	*L.C. Greenwood*	20.00
102	Mark Nordquist	.50
103	Robert Holmes	.50
104	*Ron Yary*	3.50
105	Bob Hayes	1.75
106	Lyle Alzado	14.00
107	Bob Berry	.50
108	Phil Villapiano	2.00
109	Dave Elmendorf	.50
110	Gale Sayers	22.00
111	Jim Tyrer	.50
112	*Mel Gray*	4.00
113	Gerry Philbin	.50
114	Bob James	.50
115	Garo Yepremian	1.00
116	Dave Robinson	.50
117	Jeff Queen	.50
118	Norm Snead	.50
119	Jim Nance (IA)	.50
120	Terry Bradshaw (IA)	15.00
121	Jim Kiick (IA)	.50
122	Roger Staubach (IA)	20.00
123	Bo Scott (IA)	.50
124	John Brodie (IA)	2.00
125	Rick Volk (IA)	.50
126	John Riggins (IA)	8.00
127	Bubba Smith (IA)	1.75
128	Roman Gabriel (IA)	1.00
129	Calvin Hill (IA)	.50
130	Bill Nelsen (IA)	.50
131	Tom Matte (IA)	.50
132	Bob Griese (IA)	3.50
133	AFC semi-final	1.50
134	NFC semi-final (Duane Thomas)	1.50
135	AFC semi-final (Don Nottingham)	1.50
136	NFC semi-final	1.50
137	AFC Championship	2.50
138	NFC Championship	2.50
139	Super Bowl	5.00
140	Larry Csonka	7.00
141	Rick Volk	.75
142	Roy Jefferson	.75
143	*Raymond Chester*	1.50
144	Bobby Douglass	.75
145	Bob Lilly	4.00
146	Harold Jackson	2.00
147	Pete Gogolak	.75
148	Art Malone	.75
149	Ed Flanagan	.75
150	Terry Bradshaw	45.00
151	MacArthur Lane	.75
152	Jack Snow	.75
153	Al Beauchamp	.75
155	*Ted Kwalick*	1.75
156	Bob Anderson	.75
157	*Dan Pastorini*	2.00
158	*Emmitt Thomas*	1.50
159	*Randy Vataha*	1.25
160	Al Atkinson	.75
160	O.J. Simpson	15.00
161	Jackie Smith	1.00
162	Ernie Kellerman	.75
163	Dennis Partee	.75
164	Jake Kupp	.75
165	Johnny Unitas	20.00
166	Clint Jones	.75
167	Paul Warfield	6.00
168	Roland McDole	.75
169	Daryle Lamonica	2.25
170	Dick Butkus	10.00
171	Jim Butler	.75
172	Mike McCoy	.75
173	Dave Smith	.75
174	Greg Landry	1.50
175	Tom Dempsey	.75
176	John Charles	.75
177	Bobby Bell	2.50
178	Don Horn	.75
179	Bob Trumpy	2.00
180	Duane Thomas	1.25
181	Merlin Olsen	3.50
182	Dave Herman	.75
183	Jim Nance	.75
184	Pete Beathard	.75
185	Bob Tucker	.75
186	*Gene Upshaw*	14.00
187	Bo Scott	.75
188	*J.D. Hill*	1.25
189	Bruce Gossett	.75
190	Bubba Smith	3.50
191	Edd Hargett	1.00
192	Gary Garrison	.75
193	Jake Scott	1.25
194	Fred Cox	.75
195	Sonny Jurgensen	4.50

196	*Greg Brezina*	1.00
197	Ed O'Bradovich	.75
198	John Rowser	.75
199	Altie Taylor	.75
200	*Roger Staubach*	160.00
201	Leroy Keyes	1.50
202	Garland Boyette	.75
203	Tom Beer	.75
204	Buck Buchanan	2.50
205	Larry Wilson	2.50
206	*Scott Hunter*	1.00
208	Ron Johnson	.75
208	Sam Brunelli	.75
209	Deacon Jones	2.50
210	Fred Biletnikoff	5.00
211	Bill Nelson	.75
212	George Nock	.75
213	Dan Abramowicz	.75
214	Irv Goode	.75
215	*Isiah Robertson*	2.00
216	Tom Matte	.75
217	Pat Fischer	.75
218	Gene Washington	.75
219	Paul Robinson	.75
220	John Brodie	4.00
221	*Manny Fernandez*	2.00
222	Errol Mann	.75
223	Dick Gordon	.75
224	Calvin Hill	1.75
225	Fran Tarkenton	16.00
226	Jim Turner	.75
227	Jim Mitchell	.75
228	Pete Liske	.75
229	Carl Garrett	.75
230	Joe Greene	17.00
231	Gale Gillingham	.75
232	*Norm Bulaich*	1.25
233	Spider Lockhart	.75
234	Ken Willard	.75
235	George Blanda	11.00
236	Wayne Mulligan	.75
237	Dave Lewis	.75
238	Dennis Shaw	.75
239	Fair Hooker	.75
240	*Larry Little*	17.00
241	Mike Garrett	1.00
242	Glen Ray Hines	.75
243	Myron Pottios	.75
244	*Charlie Joiner*	25.00
245	Len Dawson	6.50
246	W.K. Hicks	.75
247	Les Josephson	.75
248	Lance Alworth	6.00
249	Frank Nunley	.75
250	Mel Farr (IA)	.75
251	Johnny Unitas (IA)	8.00
252	George Farmer (IA)	.75
253	Duane Thomas (IA)	.75
254	John Hadl (IA)	1.00
255	Vic Washington (IA)	.75
256	Don Horn (IA)	.75
257	L.C. Greenwood (IA)	3.00
258	Bob Lee (IA)	.75
259	Larry Csonka (IA)	3.50
260	Mike McCoy (IA)	.75
261	Greg Landry (IA)	.75
262	Ray May (IA)	.75
263	Bobby Douglass (IA)	.75
264	Charlie Sanders (AP)	22.00
265	Ron Yary (AP)	27.50
266	Rayfield Wright (AP)	20.00
267	Larry Little (AP)	40.00
268	John Niland (AP)	20.00
269	Forrest Blue (AP)	20.00
270	Otis Taylor (AP)	20.00
271	Paul Warfield (AP)	60.00
272	Bob Griese (AP)	75.00
273	John Brockington (AP)	20.00
274	Floyd Little (AP)	27.00
275	Garo Yepremian (AP)	30.00
276	Jerrel Wilson (AP)	20.00
277	Carl Eller (AP)	30.00
278	Bubba Smith (AP)	40.00
279	Alan Page (AP)	40.00
280	Bob Lilly (AP)	45.00
281	Ted Hendricks (AP)	45.00
282	Dave Wilcox (AP)	20.00
283	Willie Lanier (AP)	27.50
284	Jim Johnson (AP)	20.00
285	Willie Brown (AP)	27.50
286	Bill Bradley (AP)	20.00
287	Ken Houston (AP)	27.50
288	Mel Farr	20.00
289	Kermit Alexander	20.00
290	*John Gilliam*	25.00
291	*Steve Spurrier*	140.00
292	Walter Johnson	20.00
293	Jack Pardee	20.00
294	Checklist 264-351	80.00
295	Winston Hill	20.00
296	Hugo Hollas	20.00
297	*Ray May*	25.00
298	Jim Bakken	20.00
299	Larry Carwell	20.00
300	Alan Page	50.00
301	Walt Garrison	25.00
302	Mike Lucci	20.00
303	Nemiah Wilson	20.00
304	Carroll Dale	20.00
305	Jim Kanicki	20.00
306	Preston Pearson	25.00
307	Lemar Parrish	20.00
308	Earl Morrall	22.00
309	Tommy Nobis	25.00

#	Player	NM
310	Rich Jackson	20.00
311	Doug Cunningham	20.00
312	Jim Marsalis	20.00
313	Jim Beirne	20.00
314	Tom McNeill	20.00
315	Milt Morin	20.00
316	*Rayfield Wright*	24.00
317	Jerry LeVias	20.00
318	*Travis Williams*	27.50
319	Edgar Chandler	20.00
320	Bob Wallace	20.00
321	Delles Howell	20.00
322	Emerson Boozer	20.00
323	*George Atkinson*	22.00
324	Mike Montler	20.00
325	Randy Johnson	20.00
326	Mike Curtis	20.00
327	Miller Farr	20.00
328	Horst Muhlmann	20.00
329	*John Niland*	25.00
330	Andy Russell	20.00
331	Mercury Morris	35.00
332	Jim Johnson	20.00
333	Jerrel Wilson	20.00
334	Charley Taylor	40.00
335	Dick LeBeau	20.00
336	Jim Marshall	25.00
337	Tom Mack	20.00
338	Steve Spurrier (IA)	60.00
339	Floyd Little (IA)	25.00
340	Len Dawson (IA)	40.00
341	Dick Butkus (IA)	70.00
342	Larry Brown (IA)	27.50
343	Joe Namath (IA)	335.00
344	Jim Turner (IA)	20.00
345	Doug Cunningham (IA)	20.00
346	Edd Hargett (IA)	20.00
347	Steve Owens (IA)	21.00
348	George Blanda (IA)	45.00
349	Ed Podolak (IA)	20.00
350	Rich Jackson (IA)	20.00
351	Ken Willard (IA)	35.00

1973 Topps

MEL RENFRO — CORNERBACK — COWBOYS

This issue might have been Topps' most important of the decade for a number of reasons. The 1973 set was Topps' first of 10 consecutive football sets at 528 cards, and its first major set that was issued all at once instead of in a series. This coincides with its cutback in baseball cards (787 to 660) and emphasis on football and basketball; it also signaled the end of Topps' high-series release. Subsets in the 1973 release include the usual statistical leaders and playoffs, plus three cards depicting childhood photos of NFL stars. Rookies in this set include Ken Anderson, Lydell Mitchell, Franco Harris, Jack Ham, Art Shell, Ken Riley, Jack Tatum, Dan Dierdorf, Jim Langer, Jack Youngblood and Ken Stabler. Though he went on to play several more years with the Rams and Jets, Joe Namath's final regular-issue card appears in this set. Like Earl Campbell several years later, he apparently was unable to reach a contract agreement after this season. One other item of note: this set has a few of the most unique player names of any football issue: Chip Glass, Happy Feller, and the immortal Remi Prudhomme.

		NM
	Complete Set (528):	425.00
	Common Player:	.40
1	Rushing Leaders (Larry Brown, O.J. Simpson)	6.00
2	Passing Leaders (Norm Snead, Earl Morrall)	.75
3	Receiving Leaders (Harold Jackson, Fred Biletnikoff)	1.00

#	Player	Price
4	Scoring Leaders (Chester Marcol, Bobby Howfield)	.75
5	Interception Leaders (Bill Bradley, Mike Sensibaugh)	.75
6	Punting Leaders (Dave Chapple, Jerrell Wilson)	.75
7	Bob Trumpy	1.25
8	Mel Tom	.40
9	Clarence Ellis	.40
10	John Niland	.40
11	Randy Jackson	.40
12	Greg Landry	1.00
13	Cid Edwards	.40
14	Phil Olsen	.40
15	Terry Bradshaw	25.00
16	*Al Cowlings*	2.00
17	Walker Gillette	.40
18	Bob Atkins	.40
19	*Diron Talbert*	1.00
20	*Jim Johnson*	1.00
21	Howard Twilley	.40
22	Dick Enderle	.40
23	Wayne Colman	.40
24	John Schmitt	.40
25	George Blanda	7.50
26	Milt Morin	.40
27	Mike Current	.40
28	Rex Kern	.60
29	MacArthur Lane	.40
30	Alan Page	3.00
31	Randy Vataha	.40
32	Jim Kearney	.40
33	Steve Smith	.40
34	Ken Anderson	20.00
35	Calvin Hill	1.00
36	Andy Maurer	.40
37	Joe Taylor	.40
38	Deacon Jones	2.50
39	Mike Weger	.40
40	Roy Gerela	.40
41	Les Josephson	.40
42	Dave Washington	.40
43	Bill Curry	1.00
44	Fred Heron	.40
45	John Brodie	4.00
46	Roy Winston	.40
47	Mike Bragg	.40
48	Mercury Morris	1.25
49	Jim Files	.40
50	Gene Upshaw	3.50
51	Hugo Hollas	.40
52	Rod Sherman	.40
53	Ron Snidow	.40
54	Steve Tannen	.40
55	Jim Carter	.40
56	*Lydell Mitchell*	3.00
57	*Jack Rudnay*	.60
58	Halvor Hagen	.40
59	Tom Dempsey	.40
60	Fran Tarkenton	15.00
61	Lance Alworth	3.50
62	Vern Holland	.40
63	Steve DeLong	.40
64	Art Malone	.40
65	Isiah Robertson	.40
66	Jerry Rush	.40
67	Bryant Salter	.40
68	Checklist 1-132	4.00
69	J.D. Hill	.40
70	Forrest Blue	.40
71	Myron Pottios	.40
72	*Norm Thompson*	.60
73	Paul Robinson	.40
74	Larry Grantham	.40
75	Manny Fernandez	.40
76	Kent Nix	.40
77	*Art Shell*	20.00
78	George Saimes	.40
79	Don Cockroft	.40
80	Bob Tucker	.40
81	*Don McCauley*	1.00
82	Bob Brown	.40
83	Larry Carwell	.40
84	Mo Moorman	.40
85	John Gilliam	.40
86	Wade Key	.40
87	Ross Brupbacher	.40
88	Dave Lewis	.40
89	*Franco Harris*	50.00
90	Tom Mack	.40
91	Mike Tilleman	.40
92	Carl Mauck	.40
93	Larry Hand	.40
94	Dave Foley	.40
95	Frank Nunley	.40
96	John Charles	.40
97	Jim Bakken	.40
98	Pat Fischer	.40
99	Randy Rasmussen	.40
100	Larry Csonka	5.00
101	*Mike Siani*	.75
102	Tom Roussel	.40
103	*Clarence Scott*	.75
104	Charlie Johnson	.60
105	Rick Volk	.40
106	Willie Young	.40
107	Emmitt Thomas	.40
108	Jon Morris	.40
109	Clarence Williams	.40
110	Rayfield Wright	.40
111	Norm Bulaich	.40
112	Mike Eischeid	.40
113	Speedy Thomas	.40
114	Glen Holloway	.40
115	*Jack Ham*	25.00
116	Jim Nettles	.40
117	Errol Mann	.40
118	John Mackey	2.00
119	George Kunz	.40
120	Bob James	.40
121	Garland Boyette	.40
122	Mel Phillips	.40
123	Johnny Roland	.40
124	Doug Swift	.40
125	Archie Manning	2.50
126	Dave Herman	.40
127	Carleton Oats	.40
128	Bill Van Heusen	.40
129	Rich Jackson	.40
130	Len Hauss	.40
131	*Billy Parks*	.75
132	Ray May	.40
133	NFC Semi-Final (Roger Staubach)	3.00
134	AFC Semi-Final	1.50
135	NFC Semi-Final	.75
136	AFC Semi-Final (Bob Griese, Larry Csonka)	2.00
137	NFC Championship (Bill Kilmer, Larry Brown)	1.50
138	AFC Championship	.75
139	Super Bowl	1.50
140	Dwight White	2.00
141	Jim Marsalis	.40
142	Doug Van Horn	.40
143	Al Matthews	.40
144	Bob Windsor	.40
145	Dave Hampton	.75
146	Horst Muhlmann	.40
147	Wally Hilgenberg	1.00
148	Ron Smith	.40
149	*Coy Bacon*	1.50
150	Winston Hill	.40
151	*Ron Jessie*	1.25
152	Ken Iman	.40
153	Ron Saul	.40
154	*Jim Braxton*	.75
155	Bubba Smith	3.00
156	Gary Cuozzo	.40
157	Charlie Krueger	.40
158	*Tim Foley*	.75
159	Lee Roy Jordan	2.00
160	Bob Brown	.40
161	Margene Adkins	.40
162	Ron Widby	.40
163	Jim Houston	.40
164	Joe Dawkins	.40
165	L.C. Greenwood	3.50
166	Richmond Flowers	.40
167	Curley Culp	2.00
168	Len St. Jean	.40
169	Walter Rock	.40
170	Bill Bradley	.40
171	Ken Riley	2.50
172	Rich Coady	.40
173	Don Hansen	.40
174	Lionel Aldridge	.40
175	Don Maynard	3.00
176	Dave Osborn	.40
177	Jim Bailey	.40
178	John Pitts	.40
179	Dave Parks	.40
180	*Chester Marcol*	.75
181	Len Rohde	.40
182	Jeff Staggs	.40
183	Gene Hickerson	.40
184	Charlie Evans	.40
185	Mel Renfro	1.00
186	Marvin Upshaw	.40
187	George Atkinson	.40
188	Norm Evans	.40
189	Steve Ramsey	.40
190	Dave Chapple	.40
191	Gerry Mullins	.40
192	John Didion	.40
193	Bob Gladieux	.40
194	Don Hultz	.40
195	Mike Lucci	.40
196	John Wilbur	.40
197	George Farmer	.40
198	*Tommy Casanova*	1.25
199	Russ Washington	.40
200	Claude Humphrey	.40
201	Pat Hughes	.40
202	Zeke Moore	.40
203	Chip Glass	.40
204	Glenn Ressler	.40
205	Willie Ellison	.40
206	John Leypoldt	.40
207	Johnny Fuller	.40
208	Bill Hayhoe	.40
209	Ed Bell	.40
210	Willie Brown	2.00
211	Carl Eller	1.50
212	Mark Nordquist	.40
213	Larry Willingham	.40
214	Nick Buoniconti	1.75
215	John Hadl	1.25
216	*Jethro Pugh*	1.50
217	Leroy Mitchell	.40
218	Billy Newsome	.40
219	John McMakin	.40
220	Larry Brown	1.25
221	Clarence Scott	.40
222	Paul Naumoff	.40
223	Ted Fritsch	.40
224	Checklist 133-264	4.00
225	Dan Pastorini	1.00
226	Joe Beauchamp	.40
227	Pat Matson	.40
228	Tony McGee	.40
229	Mike Phipps	.40
230	Harold Jackson	1.25
231	Willie Williams	.40
232	Spike Jones	.40
233	Jim Tyrer	.40
234	Roy Hilton	.40
235	Phil Villapiano	.40
236	Charley Taylor	4.00
237	Malcolm Snider	.40
238	Vic Washington	.40
239	Grady Alderman	.40
240	Dick Anderson	.40
241	Ron Yankowski	.40
242	Billy Masters	.40
243	Herb Adderly	2.25
244	David Ray	.40
245	John Riggins	9.00
246	*Mike Wagner*	2.00
247	Don Morrison	.40
248	Earl McCullouch	.40
249	Dennis Wirgowski	.40
250	Chris Hanburger	.40
251	*Pat Sullivan*	2.00
252	Walt Sweeney	.40
253	Willie Alexander	.40
254	Doug Dressler	.40
255	Walter Johnson	.40
256	Ron Hornsby	.40
257	Ben Hawkins	.40
258	Donnie Green	.40
259	Fred Hoaglin	.40
260	Jerrill Wilson	.40
261	Horace Jones	.40
262	Woody Peoples	.40
263	Jim Hill	.40
264	John Fuqua	.40
265	Childhood Photo: (Donny Anderson)	.50
266	Childhood Photo: (Roman Gabriel)	1.00
267	Childhood Photo: (Mike Garrett)	.50
268	Rufus Mayes	.60
269	Chip Myrtle	.40
270	*Bill Stanfill*	1.00
271	Clint Jones	.40
272	Miller Farr	.40
273	Harry Schuh	.40
274	Bob Hayes	1.25
275	Bobby Douglass	.40
276	Gus Hollomon	.40
277	Del Williams	.40
278	Julius Adams	.40
279	Herman Weaver	.40
280	Joe Greene	6.00
281	Wes Chesson	.40
282	Charlie Harraway	.40
283	Paul Guidry	.40
284	Terry Owens	.40
285	Jan Stenerud	1.50
286	Pete Athas	.40
287	Dale Lindsey	.40
288	*Jack Tatum*	7.00
289	Floyd Little	1.50
290	Bob Johnson	.40
291	Tommy Hart	.40
292	Tom Mitchell	.40
293	*Walt Patulski*	.90
294	Jim Skaggs	.40
295	Bob Griese	7.00
296	Mike McCoy	.40
297	Mel Gray	1.00
298	Bobby Bryant	.40
299	*Blaine Nye*	.40
300	Dick Butkus	6.00
301	Charlie Cowan	.40
302	Mark Lomas	.40
303	Josh Ashton	.40
304	Happy Feller	.40
305	Ronnie Shanklin	.40
306	Wayne Rasmussen	.40
307	Jerry Smith	.40
308	Ken Reaves	.40
309	Ron East	.40
310	Otis Taylor	1.00
311	John Garlington	.40
312	Lyle Alzado	3.50
313	Remi Prudhomme	.40
314	Cornelius Johnson	.40
315	Lemar Parrish	.40
316	Jim Kiick	.40
317	Steve Zabel	.40
318	Alden Roche	.40
319	Tom Blanchard	.40
320	Fred Biletnikoff	4.00
321	Ralph Neely	.40
322	*Dan Dierdorf*	20.00
323	Richard Caster	.40
324	Gene Howard	.40
325	Elvin Bethea	.40
326	Carl Garrett	.40
327	Ron Billingsley	.40
328	Charlie West	.40
329	Tom Neville	.40
330	Ted Kwalick	.40
331	Rudy Redmond	.40
332	Henry Davis	.40
333	John Zook	.40
334	Jim Turner	.40
335	Len Dawson	3.50
336	*Bob Chandler*	1.25
337	Al Beauchamp	.40
338	Tom Matte	.40
339	Paul Laaveg	.40
340	Ken Ellis	.40
341	*Jim Langer*	13.00
342	Ron Porter	.40
343	*Jack Youngblood*	15.00
344	Cornell Green	.40
345	Marv Hubbard	.40
346	Bruce Taylor	.40
347	Sam Havrilak	.40
348	Walt Sumner	.40
349	Steve O'Neal	.40
350	Ron Johnson	.40
351	Rockne Freitas	.40
352	Larry Stallings	.40
353	Jim Cadile	.40
354	Ken Burrough	.40
355	Jim Plunkett	4.00
356	Dave Long	.40
357	Ralph Anderson	.40
358	Checklist 265-396	4.00
359	Gene Washington	.40
360	Dave Wilcox	.40
361	Paul Smith	.40
362	Alvin Wyatt	.40
363	Charlie Smith	.40
364	Royce Berry	.40
365	Dave Elmendorf	.40
366	Scott Hunter	.40
367	*Bob Kuechenberg*	3.00
368	Pete Gogolak	.40
369	Dave Edwards	.40
370	Lem Barney	2.50
371	Verlon Biggs	.40
372	*John Reaves*	.60
373	Ed Podolak	.40
374	Chris Farasopoulos	.40
375	Gary Garrison	.40
376	Tom Funchess	.40
377	Bobby Joe Green	.40
378	Don Brumm	.40
379	Jim O'Brien	.40
380	Paul Krause	1.25
381	Leroy Kelly	2.00
382	Ray Mansfield	.40
383	Dan Abramowicz	.40
384	*John Outlaw*	.60
385	Tommy Nobis	1.50
386	Tom Domres	.40
387	Ken Willard	.40
388	Mike Stratton	.40
389	Fred Dryer	3.00
390	Jake Scott	.40
391	Rich Houston	.40
392	Virgil Carter	.40
393	Tody Smith	.40
394	Ernie Calloway	.40
395	Charlie Sanders	.40
396	Fred Willis	.40
397	Curt Knight	.40
398	Nemiah Wilson	.40
399	Carroll Dale	.40
400	Joe Namath	30.00
401	Wayne Mulligan	.40
402	Jim Harrison	.40
403	Tim Rossovich	.40
404	David Lee	.40
405	Frank Pitts	.40
406	Jim Marshall	1.50
407	Bob Brown	.40
408	John Rowser	.40
409	Mike Montler	.40
410	Willie Lanier	2.00
411	Bill Bell	.40
412	Cedrick Hardman	.40
413	Bob Anderson	.40
414	*Earl Morrall*	1.25
415	Ken Houston	1.75
416	Jack Snow	.40
417	Dick Cunningham	.40
418	Greg Larson	.40
419	Mike Bass	.40
420	Mike Reid	2.00
421	Walt Garrison	.40
422	Pete Liske	.40
423	Jim Yarbrough	.40
424	Rich McGeorge	.40
425	Bobby Howfield	.40
426	Pete Banaszak	.40
427	Willie Holman	.40
428	Dale Hackbart	.40
429	Fair Hooker	.40
430	Ted Hendricks	4.00
431	Mike Garrett	.40
432	Glen Ray Hines	.40
433	Fred Cox	.40
434	Bobby Walden	.40
435	Bobby Bell	2.00
436	David Rowe	.40
437	Bob Berry	.40
438	Bill Thompson	.40
439	Jim Beirne	.40
440	Larry Little	3.00
441	Rocky Thompson	.40
442	Brig Owens	.40
443	Richard Neal	.40
444	Al Nelson	.40
445	Chip Myers	.40
446	Ken Bowman	.40
447	Jim Purnell	.40
448	Altie Taylor	.40
449	Linzy Cole	.40
450	Bob Lilly	4.00
451	Charlie Ford	.40
452	Milt Sunde	.40
453	Doug Wyatt	.40
454	*Don Nottingham*	.75
455	Johnny Unitas	18.00
456	*Frank Lewis*	1.50
457	Roger Wehrli	.40
458	Jim Cheyunski	.40
459	*Jerry Sherk*	1.00
460	Gene Washington	.40
461	Jim Otto	2.25
462	Ed Budde	.40
463	Jim Mitchell	.40
464	Emerson Boozer	.40
465	Garo Yepremian	.40
466	Pete Duranko	.40
467	Charlie Joiner	6.00
468	Spider Lockhart	.40
469	Marty Domres	.40
470	John Brockington	1.00
471	Ed Flanagan	.40
472	Roy Jefferson	.40
473	Julian Fagan	.40
474	Bill Brown	.40
475	Roger Staubach	40.00
476	Jan White	.40
477	Pat Holmes	.40
478	Bob DeMarco	.40
479	Merlin Olsen	3.50
480	Andy Russell	.40
481	Steve Spurrier	8.00
482	Nate Ramsey	.40
483	Dennis Partee	.40
484	Jerry Simmons	.40
485	Donny Anderson	.40
486	Ralph Baker	.40
487	*Ken Stabler*	60.00
488	Ernie McMillan	.40
489	Ken Burrow	.40
490	*Jack Gregory*	.60
491	Larry Seiple	.40
492	Mick Tingelhoff	.40
493	Craig Morton	1.50
494	Cecil Turner	.40
495	Steve Owens	.50
496	Richie Harris	.40
497	Buck Buchanan	2.00
498	Checklist 397-528	4.00
499	Bill Kilmer	1.50
500	O.J. Simpson	15.00
501	Bruce Gossett	.40
502	Art Thoms	.40
503	Larry Kaminski	.40
504	Larry Smith	.40
505	Bruce Van Dyke	.40
506	Alvin Reed	.40
507	Delles Howell	.40
508	Leroy Keyes	.40
509	Bo Scott	.40
510	Ron Yary	1.00
511	Paul Warfield	5.00
512	Mac Percival	.40
513	Essex Johnson	.40
514	Jackie Smith	1.00
515	Norm Snead	.40
516	Charlie Stukes	.40
517	*Reggie Rucker*	1.50
518	Bill Sandeman	.40
519	Mel Farr	.40
520	Raymond Chester	.40
521	*Fred Carr*	1.00
522	Jerry LeVias	.40
523	Jim Strong	.40
524	Roland McDole	.40
525	Dennis Shaw	.40
526	Dave Manders	.40
527	Skip Vanderbundt	.40
528	*Mike Sensibaugh*	1.25

1973 Topps Team Checklists

This was the first time Topps issued separate team checklists in its 528-card sets, a practice that would end with the 1974 set. The cards showed an anonymous action shot at the top of the card, with a Topps logo in a football helmet facing the team name. The checklist was beneath all that, and showed the card number, name, uniform number and position (as it would in 1974). Card backs carried pieces to a puzzle of either Larry Brown or Joe Namath; or they carried a message that read, "Collect all 26 Team Checklists and complete your Joe Namath & Larry Brown Puzzles."

		NM
	Complete Set (26):	35.00
	Common Team:	1.50
1	Atlanta Falcons	1.50
2	Baltimore Colts	1.50
3	Buffalo Bills	1.50
4	Chicago Bears	1.50
5	Cincinnati Bengals	1.50
6	Cleveland Browns	1.50
7	Dallas Cowboys	1.50
8	Denver Broncos	1.50
9	Detroit Lions	1.50
10	Green Bay Packers	1.50
11	Houston Oilers	1.50
12	Kansas City Chiefs	1.50
13	Los Angeles Rams	1.50
14	Miami Dolphins	1.50
15	Minnesota Vikings	1.50
16	New England Patriots	1.50
17	New Orleans Saints	1.50
18	New York Giants	1.50
19	New York Jets	1.50

20	Oakland Raiders	1.50
21	Philadelphia Eagles	1.50
22	Pittsburgh Steelers	1.50
23	St. Louis Cardinals	1.50
24	San Diego Chargers	1.50
25	San Francisco 49ers	1.50
26	Washington Redskins	1.50

1974 Topps

DAN DIERDORF GUARD
CARDINALS

This was Topps' second 528-card set, and marked the second and last time team checklists would be issued un-numbered and separate from the set. Rookies in this set include Ahmad Rashad, Greg Pruitt, Chuck Foreman, Harold Carmichael, Ray Guy, John Matuszak, Conrad Dobler, Ed Marinaro, Darryl Stingley, Lynn Dickey, Billy Joe DuPree, D.D. Lewis, John Hannah, Terry Metcalf, Joe Ferguson and Bert Jones. In addition, this set features the last regularly-issued card of Johnny Unitas. All Pro cards showing individual players are found on cards 121-144. Other subsets include statistical leader and playoff cards. There is one error in the set, on card #265, Bob Lee. The back of the card lists his team as the Atlanta Hawks instead of the Falcons.

		NM
Complete Set (528):		325.00
Common Player:		.35
1	O.J. Simpson	20.00
2	Blaine Nye	.35
3	Don Hansen	.35
4	Ken Bowman	.35
5	Carl Eller	1.00
6	Jerry Smith	.35
7	Ed Podolak	.35
8	Mel Gray	.35
9	Pat Matson	.35
10	Floyd Little	1.25
11	Frank Pitts	.35
12	*Vern Den Herder*	.75
13	John Fuqua	.35
14	Jack Tatum	1.50
15	Winston Hill	.35
16	John Beasley	.35
17	David Lee	.35
18	Rich Coady	.35
19	Ken Willard	.35
20	Coy Bacon	.35
21	Ben Hawkins	.35
22	Paul Guidry	.35
23	Norm Snead	.75
24	Jim Yarbrough	.35
25	*Jack Reynolds*	2.25
26	Josh Ashton	.35
27	Donnie Green	.35
28	Bob Hayes	1.00
29	John Zook	.35
30	Bobby Bryant	.35
31	Scott Hunter	.35
32	Dan Dierdorf	5.00
33	Curt Knight	.35
34	*Elmo Wright*	.60
35	Essex Johnson	.35
36	Walt Sumner	.35
37	Marv Montgomery	.35
38	Tim Foley	.35
39	Mike Siani	.35
40	Joe Greene	6.00
41	Bobby Howfield	.35
42	Del Williams	.35
43	Don McCauley	.35
44	Randy Jackson	.35
45	Ron Smith	.35
46	Gene Washington	.50
47	Po James	.35
48	Soloman Freelon	.35
49	Bob Windsor	.35
50	John Hadl	1.00
51	Greg Larson	.35
52	Steve Owens	.35
53	Jim Cheyunski	.35
54	Rayfield Wright	.35
55	Dave Hampton	.35
56	Ron Widby	.35

57	Milt Sunde	.35
58	Bill Kilmer	1.25
59	Bobby Bell	1.50
60	Jim Bakken	.50
61	Rufus Mayes	.35
62	Vic Washington	.35
63	Gene Washington	.35
64	Clarence Scott	.35
65	Gene Upshaw	2.00
66	Larry Seiple	.35
67	John McMakin	.35
68	Ralph Baker	.35
69	Lydell Mitchell	1.00
70	Archie Manning	1.75
71	George Farmer	.35
72	Ron East	.35
73	Al Nelson	.35
74	Pat Hughes	.35
75	Fred Willis	.35
76	Larry Walton	.35
77	Tom Neville	.35
78	Ted Kwalick	.35
79	Walt Patulski	.35
80	John Niland	.35
81	Ted Fritsch	.35
82	Paul Krause	1.00
83	Jack Snow	.35
84	Mike Bass	.35
85	Jim Tyrer	.35
86	Ron Yankowski	.35
87	Mike Phipps	.35
88	Al Beauchamp	.35
89	*Riley Odoms*	2.00
90	MacArthur Lane	.35
91	Art Thoms	.35
92	Marlin Briscoe	.35
93	Bruce Van Dyke	.35
94	Tom Myers	.35
95	Calvin Hill	.75
96	Bruce Laird	.35
97	Tony McGee	.35
98	Len Rohde	.35
99	Tom McNeill	.35
100	Delles Howell	.35
101	Gary Garrison	.35
102	Dan Goich	.35
103	Len St. Jean	.35
104	Zeke Moore	.35
105	*Ahmad Rashad*	15.00
106	Mel Renfro	1.00
107	Jim Mitchell	.35
108	Ed Budde	.35
109	Harry Schuh	.35
110	*Greg Pruitt*	4.00
111	Ed Flanagan	.35
112	Larry Stallings	.35
113	*Chuck Foreman*	4.00
114	Royce Berry	.35
115	Gale Gillingham	.35
116	Charlie Johnson	.75
117	Checklist 1-132	2.50
118	Bill Butler	.35
119	Roy Jefferson	.35
120	Bobby Douglass	.35
121	*Harold Carmichael*	15.00
122	George Kuntz (AP)	.35
123	Larry Little (AP)	1.50
124	Forrest Blue (AP)	.35
125	Ron Yary (AP)	.75
126	Tom Mack (AP)	.35
127	Bob Tucker (AP)	.35
128	Paul Warfield (AP)	4.00
129	Fran Tarkenton (AP)	10.00
130	O.J. Simpson (AP)	15.00
131	Larry Csonka (AP)	3.50
132	Bruce Gossett (AP)	.35
133	Bill Stanfill (AP)	.35
134	Alan Page (AP)	2.25
135	Paul Smith (AP)	.35
136	Claude Humphrey (AP)	.35
137	Jack Ham (AP)	7.00
138	Lee Roy Jordan (AP)	1.50
139	Phil Villapiano (AP)	.35
140	Ken Ellis (AP)	.35
141	Willie Brown (AP)	1.25
142	Dick Anderson (AP)	.35
143	Bill Bradley (AP)	.35
144	Jerrel Wilson (AP)	.35
145	Reggie Rucker	.60
146	Marty Domres	.35
147	Bob Kowalkowski	.35
148	*John Matuszak*	4.00
149	*Mike Adamle*	.75
150	Johnny Unitas	16.00
151	Charlie Ford	.35
152	*Bob Klein*	.60
153	Jim Merlo	.35
154	Willie Young	.35
155	Donny Anderson	.35
156	Brig Owens	.35
157	Bruce Jarvis	.35
158	Ron Carpenter	.35
159	Don Cockroft	.35
160	Tommy Nobis	1.25
161	Craig Morton	1.25
162	Jon Staggers	.35
163	Mike Eischeid	.35
164	*Jerry Sisemore*	.60
165	Cedric Hardman	.35
166	Bill Thompson	.35
167	Jim Lynch	.35
168	Bob Moore	.35
169	Glen Edwards	.35
170	Mercury Morris	1.00
171	Julius Adams	.35
172	Cotton Speyrer	.35
173	Bill Munson	.35

174	Benny Johnson	.35
175	*Burgess Owens*	.60
176	Cid Edwards	.35
177	Doug Buffone	.35
178	Charlie Cowan	.35
179	Bob Newland	.35
180	Ron Johnson	.35
181	Bob Rowe	.35
182	Len Hauss	.35
183	*Joe DeLamielleure*	2.00
184	*Sherman White*	.75
185	Fair Hooker	.35
186	Nick Mike-Mayer	.35
187	Ralph Neely	.35
188	Rich McGeorge	.35
189	*Ed Marinaro*	4.50
190	Dave Wilcox	.35
191	Joe Owens	.35
192	Bill Van Heusen	.35
193	Jim Kearney	.35
194	*Otis Sistrunk*	3.00
195	Ronnie Shanklin	.35
196	Bill Lenkaitis	.35
197	Tom Drougas	.35
198	Larry Hand	.35
199	Mack Alston	.35
200	Bob Griese	5.00
201	Earlie Thomas	.35
202	Carl Gersbach	.35
203	Jim Harrison	.35
204	Jake Kupp	.35
205	Merlin Olsen	3.50
206	Spider Lockhart	.35
207	Walter Gillette	.35
208	Verlon Biggs	.35
209	Bob James	.35
210	Bob Trumpy	1.00
211	Jerry Sherk	.35
212	Andy Maurer	.35
213	Fred Carr	.35
214	Mick Tingelhoff	.35
215	Steve Spurrier	7.00
216	Richard Harris	.35
217	Charlie Greer	.35
218	Buck Buchanan	2.00
219	*Ray Guy*	10.00
220	Franco Harris	20.00
221	*Darryl Stingley*	2.50
222	Rex Kern	.35
223	Toni Fritsch	.35
224	Levi Johnson	.35
225	Bob Kuechenberg	.60
226	Elvin Bethea	.35
227	*Al Woodall*	.50
228	Terry Owens	.35
229	Bivian Lee	.35
230	Dick Butkus	6.00
231	*Jim Bertelsen*	.60
232	*John Mendenhall*	.50
233	*Conrad Dobler*	2.50
234	J.D. Hill	.35
235	Ken Houston	1.50
236	Dave Lewis	.35
237	John Garlington	.35
238	Bill Sandeman	.35
239	Alden Roche	.35
240	John Gilliam	.35
241	Bruce Taylor	.35
242	Vern Winfield	.35
243	Bobby Maples	.35
244	Wendell Hayes	.35
245	George Blanda	7.00
246	Dwight White	.35
247	Sandy Durko	.35
248	Tom Mitchell	.35
249	Chuck Walton	.35
250	Bob Lilly	4.00
251	Doug Swift	.35
252	*Lynn Dickey*	3.00
253	*Jerome Barkum*	1.50
254	Clint Jones	.35
255	Billy Newsome	.35
256	Bob Asher	.35
257	Joe Scibelli	.35
258	Tom Blanchard	.35
259	Norm Thompson	.35
260	Larry Brown	1.00
261	Paul Seymour	.35
262	Checklist 133-264	2.50
263	*Doug Dieken*	.75
264	Lemar Parrish	.35
265	Bob Lee	.35
266	Bob Brown	.35
267	Roy Winston	.35
268	Randy Beisler	.35
269	Joe Dawkins	.35
270	Tom Dempsey	.35
271	Jack Rudnay	.35
272	Art Shell	6.00
273	Mike Wagner	.75
274	Rick Cash	.35
275	Greg Landry	1.00
276	Glenn Ressler	.35
277	*Billy Joe DuPree*	4.00
278	Norm Evans	.35
279	Billy Parks	.35
280	John Riggins	6.00
281	Lionel Aldridge	.35
282	Steve O'Neal	.35
283	Craig Clemons	.35
284	Willie Williams	.35
285	Isiah Robertson	.35
286	Dennis Shaw	.35
287	Bill Brundige	.35
288	John Leypoldt	.35
289	John DeMarie	.35
290	Mike Reid	1.25
291	Greg Brezina	.35

292	*Willie Buchanon*	1.00
293	Dave Osborn	.35
294	Mel Phillips	.35
295	Haven Moses	.35
296	Wade Key	.35
297	Marvin Upshaw	.35
298	Ray Mansfield	.35
299	Edgar Chandler	.35
300	Marv Hubbard	.35
301	Herman Weaver	.35
302	Jim Bailey	.35
303	*D.D. Lewis*	1.50
304	Ken Burrough	.35
305	Jake Scott	.35
306	Randy Rasmussen	.35
307	Pettis Norman	.35
308	Carl Johnson	.35
309	Joe Taylor	.35
310	Pete Gogolak	.35
311	Tony Baker	.35
312	John Richardson	.35
313	Dave Robinson	.35
314	*Reggie McKenzie*	2.50
315	*Isaac Curtis*	3.00
316	Tom Darden	.35
317	Ken Reaves	.35
318	Malcolm Snider	.35
319	*Jeff Siemon*	1.50
320	Dan Abramowicz	.35
321	Lyle Alzado	2.50
322	John Reaves	.35
323	Morris Stroud	.35
324	Bobby Walden	.35
325	Randy Vataha	.35
326	Nemiah Wilson	.35
327	Paul Naumoff	.35
328	Rushing Leaders	5.00
	(O.J. Simpson,	
	John Brockington)	
329	Passing Leaders	4.00
	(Ken Stabler,	
	Roger Staubach)	
330	Receiving Leaders	1.25
	(Fred Willis,	
	Harold Carmichael)	
331	Scoring Leaders	.60
	(Roy Gerela,	
	David Ray)	
332	Interception	.60
	Leaders	
	(Dick Anderson,	
	Mike Wagner,	
	Bobby Bryan t)	
333	Punting Leaders	.60
	(Jerrell Wilson,	
	Tom Wittum)	
334	Dennis Nelson	.35
335	Walt Garrison	.35
336	Tody Smith	.35
337	Ed Bell	.35
338	Bryant Salter	.35
339	Wayne Colman	.35
340	Garo Yepremian	.35
341	Bob Newton	.35
342	*Vince Clements*	.50
343	Ken Iman	.35
344	Jim Tolbert	.35
345	Chris Hanburger	.35
346	Dave Foley	.35
347	Tommy Casanova	.60
348	John James	.35
349	Clarence Williams	.35
350	Leroy Kelly	1.00
351	*Stu Voigt*	.75
352	Skip Vanderbundt	.35
353	Pete Duranko	.35
354	John Outlaw	.35
355	Jan Stenerud	1.25
356	Barry Pearson	.35
357	Brian Dowling	.50
358	Dan Conners	.35
359	Bob Bell	.35
360	Rick Volk	.35
361	Pat Toomay	.35
362	Bob Gresham	.35
363	John Schmitt	.35
364	Mel Rogers	.35
365	Manny Fernandez	.35
366	Ernie Jackson	.35
367	*Gary Huff*	1.00
368	Bob Grim	.35
369	Ernie McMillan	.35
370	Dave Elmendorf	.35
371	Mike Bragg	.35
372	John Skorupan	.35
373	Howard Fest	.35
374	*Jerry Tagge*	1.00
375	Art Malone	.35
376	Bob Babich	.35
377	Jim Marshall	1.25
378	Bob Hoskins	.35
379	Dan Zimmerman	.35
380	Ray May	.35
381	Emmitt Thomas	.35
382	Terry Hanratty	.35
383	*John Hannah*	15.00
384	George Atkinson	.35
385	Ted Hendricks	3.00
386	Jim O'Brien	.35
387	Jethro Pugh	.35
388	Elbert Drungo	.35
389	Richard Caster	.35
390	Deacon Jones	2.25
391	Checklist 265-396	2.50
392	Jess Phillips	.35
393	Gary Lyle	.35
394	Jim Files	.35
395	Jim Hart	1.50

396	Dave Chapple	.35
397	Jim Langer	2.50
398	John Wilbur	.35
399	Dwight Harrison	.35
400	John Brockington	.60
401	Ken Anderson	6.50
402	Mike Tilleman	.35
403	Charlie Hall	.35
404	Tommy Hart	.35
405	Norm Bulaich	.35
406	Jim Turner	.35
407	Mo Moorman	.35
408	Ralph Anderson	.35
409	Jim Otto	2.00
410	Andy Russell	.35
411	Glenn Doughty	.35
412	Altie Taylor	.35
413	Marv Bateman	.35
414	Willie Alexander	.35
415	Bill Zapalac	.35
416	Russ Washington	.35
417	Joe Federspiel	.35
418	Craig Cotton	.35
419	Randy Johnson	.35
420	Harold Jackson	1.00
421	Roger Wehrli	.35
422	Charlie Harraway	.35
423	Spike Jones	.35
424	Bob Johnson	.35
425	Mike McCoy	.35
426	Dennis Havig	.35
427	Bob McKay	.35
428	Steve Zabel	.35
429	Horace Jones	.35
430	Jim Johnson	1.00
431	Roy Gerela	.35
432	Tom Graham	.35
433	Curley Culp	.35
434	Ken Mendenhall	.35
435	Jim Plunkett	3.00
436	Julian Fagan	.35
437	Mike Garrett	.35
438	Bobby Joe Green	.35
439	Jack Gregory	.35
440	Charlie Sanders	.35
441	Bill Curry	.35
442	Bob Pollard	.35
443	David Ray	.35
444	*Terry Metcalf*	4.50
445	Pat Fischer	.35
446	Bob Chandler	.35
447	Bill Bergey	1.00
448	Walter Johnson	.35
449	*Charlie Young*	1.50
450	Chester Marcol	.35
451	Ken Stabler	20.00
452	Preston Pearson	.75
453	Mike Current	.35
454	Ron Bolton	.35
455	Mark Lomas	.35
456	Raymond Chester	.35
457	Jerry LeVias	.35
458	Skip Butler	.35
459	*Mike Livingston*	.75
460	AFC Semi-finals	.75
461	NFC Semi-finals	3.00
	(Roger Staubach)	
462	Playoff	2.50
	Championship	
	(Ken Stabler,	
	Fran Tarkenton)	
463	Super Bowl	2.00
464	Wayne Mulligan	.35
465	Horst Muhlmann	.35
466	Milt Morin	.35
467	Don Parish	.35
468	Richard Neal	.35
469	Ron Jessie	.35
470	Terry Bradshaw	20.00
471	Fred Dryer	2.50
472	Jim Carter	.35
473	Ken Burrow	.35
474	*Wally Chambers*	1.00
475	Dan Pastorini	.75
476	Don Morrison	.35
477	Carl Mauck	.35
478	*Larry Cole*	.75
479	Jim Kiick	.35
480	Willie Lanier	1.50
481	Don Herrmann	.35
482	George Hunt	.35
483	Bob Howard	.35
484	Myron Pottios	.35
485	Jackie Smith	1.00
486	Vern Holland	.35
487	Jim Braxton	.35
488	Joe Reed	.35
489	Wally Hilgenberg	.35
490	Fred Biletnikoff	3.50
491	Bob DeMarco	.35
492	Mark Nordquist	.35
493	Larry Brooks	.35
494	Pete Athas	.35
495	Emerson Boozer	.35
496	L.C. Greenwood	1.50
497	Rockne Freitas	.35
498	Checklist 397-528	2.50
499	Joe Schmiesing	.35
500	Roger Staubach	28.00
501	Al Cowlings	1.00
502	*Sam Cunningham*	2.00
503	Dennis Partee	.35
504	John Didion	.35
505	Nick Buoniconti	1.25
506	Carl Garrett	.35
507	Doug Van Horn	.35
508	Jamie Rivers	.35
509	Jack Youngblood	3.50

510	Charley Taylor	2.50
511	Ken Riley	.60
512	*Joe Ferguson*	2.50
513	Bill Lueck	.35
514	Ray Brown	.35
515	Fred Cox	.35
516	Joe Jones	.35
517	Larry Schreiber	.35
518	Dennis Wirgowski	.35
519	Leroy Mitchell	.35
520	Otis Taylor	.75
521	Henry Davis	.35
522	Bruce Barnes	.35
523	Charlie Smith	.35
524	*Bert Jones*	5.00
525	Lem Barney	2.00
526	*John Fitzgerald*	.50
527	Tom Funchess	.35
528	Steve Tannen	.60

1974 Topps Team Checklists

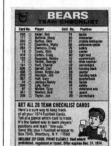

These unnumbered checklists were issued in wax packs of 1974 Topps cards. At the bottom of the card was an ad for a sendaway offer where collectors could buy the entire run of checklists through Topps. The back of the card carried instructions for a game that could be played with football cards. This was the last time Topps would issue team checklists separate from the rest of the set.

		NM
Complete Set (26):		35.00
Common Team:		1.50
(1)	Atlanta Falcons	1.50
(2)	Baltimore Colts	1.50
(3)	Buffalo Bills	1.50
(4)	Chicago Bears	1.50
(5)	Cincinnati Bengals	1.50
(6)	Cleveland Browns	1.50
(7)	Dallas Cowboys	1.50
(8)	Denver Broncos	1.50
(9)	Detroit Lions	1.50
(10)	Green Bay Packers	1.50
(11)	Houston Oilers	1.50
(12)	Kansas City Chiefs	1.50
(13)	Los Angeles Rams	1.50
(14)	Miami Dolphins	1.50
(15)	Minnesota Vikings	1.50
(16)	New England Patriots	1.50
(17)	New Orleans Saints	1.50
(18)	New York Giants	1.50
(19)	New York Jets	1.50
(20)	Oakland Raiders	1.50
(21)	Philadelphia Eagles	1.50
(22)	Pittsburgh Steelers	1.50
(23)	St. Louis Cardinals	1.50
(24)	San Diego Chargers	1.50
(25)	San Francisco 49ers	1.50
(26)	Washington Redskins	1.50

1975 Topps

FRED DRYER

The 528-card 1975 issue was arguably Topps' most attractive offering of the decade. Its clean design and white borders leaves room for the photo, player's name, a pennant with the team name, and the player's position in a green helmet. Most notable for the inclusion of the Dan Fouts rookie card, other rookies in this set are Mel Blount, Rocky Bleier, Drew Pearson, Lynn Swann, James Harris, Otis Armstrong, Lawrence McCutcheon and Joe Theismann. One feature of this set is the larger number of separate All-Pro cards, numbered 201-225. Each shows two star players. Other subsets include Statistical Leaders, Record Breakers, Highlights and Playoff Action. George Blanda has two "honorary" cards in this set, numbers 7 and 8. The first shows him in a black jersey and lists his career highlights on the back; the second shows him in a white Oakland jersey and documents his career statistics. No team checklists were issued for this set.

		NM
Complete Set (528):		325.00
Common Player:		.30
1	Rushing Leaders (Lawrence McCutcheon, Otis Armstrong)	1.75
2	Passing Leaders (Sonny Jurgensen, Ken Anderson)	1.50
3	Receiving Leaders (Charley Young, Lydell Mitchell)	.60
4	Scoring Leaders (Chester Marcol, Roy Gerela)	.60
5	Interception Leaders (Ray Brown, Emmitt Thomas)	.60
6	Punting Leaders (Tom Blanchard, Ray Guy)	.60
7	George Blanda (highlights, black jersey)	5.00
8	George Blanda (career, white jersey)	5.00
9	Ralph Baker	.30
10	Don Woods	.30
11	Bob Asher	.30
12	*Mel Blount*	25.00
13	Sam Cunningham	.60
14	Jackie Smith	.75
15	Greg Landry	.75
16	Buck Buchanan	1.50
17	Haven Moses	.30
18	Clarence Ellis	.30
19	Jim Carter	.30
20	Charley Taylor	2.25
21	Jess Phillips	.30
22	Larry Seiple	.30
23	Doug Dieken	.30
24	Ron Saul	.30
25	Isaac Curtis	.75
26	*Gary Larsen*	.75
27	Bruce Jarvis	.30
28	Steve Zabel	.30
29	John Mendenhall	.30
30	Rick Volk	.30
31	Checklist 1-132	2.50
32	Dan Abramowicz	.30
33	Bubba Smith	2.00
34	David Ray	.30
35	Dan Dierdorf	2.00
36	Randy Rasmussen	.30
37	Bob Howard	.30
38	Gary Huff	.30
39	Rocky Bleier	15.00
40	Mel Gray	.30
41	Tony McGee	.30
42	Larry Hand	.30
43	Wendell Hayes	.30
44	*Doug Wilkerson*	.50
45	Paul Smith	.30
46	Dave Robinson	.30
47	Bivian Lee	.30
48	*Jim Mandich*	.50
49	Greg Pruitt	1.00
50	Dan Pastorini	.60
51	Ron Pritchard	.30
52	Dan Conners	.30
53	Fred Cox	.30
54	Tony Greene	.30
55	Craig Morton	1.00
56	Jerry Sisemore	.30
57	Glenn Doughty	.30
58	Larry Schreiber	.30
59	*Charlie Waters*	4.00
60	Jack Youngblood	1.50
61	Bill Lenkaitis	.30
62	Greg Brezina	.30
63	Bob Pollard	.30
64	Mack Alston	.30
65	*Drew Pearson*	12.00
66	Charlie Stukes	.30
67	Emerson Boozer	.30

68	Dennis Partee	.30
69	Bob Newton	.30
70	Jack Tatum	.30
71	Frank Lewis	.30
72	Bob Young	.30
73	Julius Adams	.30
74	Paul Naumoff	.30
75	Otis Taylor	.60
76	Dave Hampton	.30
77	Mike Current	.30
78	Brig Owens	.30
79	Bobby Scott	.30
80	Harold Carmichael	4.00
81	Bill Stanfill	.30
82	Bob Babich	.30
83	Vic Washington	.30
84	Mick Tingelhoff	.30
85	Bob Trumpy	1.00
86	Earl Edwards	.30
87	Ron Hornsby	.30
88	Don McCauley	.30
89	Jimmy Johnson	.30
90	Andy Russell	.30
91	Cornell Green	.30
92	Charlie Cowan	.30
93	Jon Staggers	.30
94	Billy Newsome	.30
95	Willie Brown	1.25
96	Carl Mauck	.30
97	Doug Buffone	.30
98	Preston Pearson	.60
99	Jim Bakken	.30
100	Bob Griese	5.00
101	Bob Windsor	.30
102	Rockne Freitas	.30
103	Jim Marsalis	.30
104	Bill Thompson	.30
105	Ken Burrow	.30
106	Diron Talbert	.30
107	Joe Federspiel	.30
108	Norm Bulaich	.30
109	Bob DeMarco	.30
110	Tom Wittum	.30
111	Larry Hefner	.30
112	Tody Smith	.30
113	Stu Voigt	.30
114	Horst Muhlmann	.30
115	Ahmad Rashad	5.00
116	Joe Dawkins	.30
117	George Kunz	.30
118	D.D. Lewis	.30
119	Levi Johnson	.30
120	Len Dawson	3.50
121	Jim Bertelsen	.30
122	Ed Bell	.30
123	Art Thoms	.30
124	Joe Beauchamp	.30
125	Jack Ham	5.00
126	Carl Garrett	.30
127	Roger Finnie	.30
128	Howard Twilley	.30
129	Bruce Barnes	.30
130	Nate Wright	.30
131	Jerry Tagge	.30
132	Floyd Little	1.25
133	John Zook	.30
134	Len Hauss	.30
135	Archie Manning	1.50
136	Po James	.30
137	Walt Sumner	.30
138	Randy Beisler	.30
139	Willie Alexander	.30
140	Garo Yepremian	.30
141	Chip Myers	.30
142	Jim Braxton	.30
143	Doug Van Horn	.30
144	Stan White	.30
145	Roger Staubach	25.00
146	Herman Weaver	.30
147	Marvin Upshaw	.30
148	Bob Klein	.30
149	Earlie Thomas	.30
150	John Brockington	.30
151	Mike Siani	.30
152	Sam Davis	.30
153	Mike Wagner	.30
154	Larry Stallings	.30
155	Wally Chambers	.30
156	Randy Vataha	.30
157	Jim Marshall	1.00
158	Jim Turner	.30
159	Walt Sweeney	.30
160	Ken Anderson	3.50
161	Ray Brown	.30
162	John Didion	.30
163	Tom Dempsey	.30
164	Clarence Scott	.30
165	Gene Washington	.30
166	Willie Rodgers	.30
167	Doug Swift	.30
168	Rufus Mayes	.30
169	Marv Bateman	.30
170	Lydell Mitchell	.30
171	Ron Smith	.30
172	Bill Munson	.30
173	Bob Grim	.30
174	Ed Budde	.30
175	Bob Lilly	3.50
176	*Jim Youngblood*	2.00
177	Steve Tannen	.30
178	Rich McGeorge	.30
179	Jim Tyrer	.30
180	Forrest Blue	.30
181	Jerry LeVias	.30
182	*Joe Gilliam*	.60
183	Jim Otis	1.25
184	Mel Tom	.30
185	Paul Seymour	.30

186	George Webster	.30
187	Pete Duranko	.30
188	Essex Johnson	.30
189	Bob Lee	.30
190	Gene Upshaw	1.50
191	Tom Myers	.30
192	Don Zimmerman	.30
193	John Garlington	.30
194	Skip Butler	.30
195	Tom Mitchell	.30
196	Jim Langer	1.50
197	Ron Carpenter	.30
198	Dave Foley	.30
199	Bert Jones	1.50
200	Larry Brown	.75
201	All Pro Receivers (Charley Taylor, Fred Biletnikoff)	2.00
202	All Pro Tackles (Russ Washington, Rayfield Wright)	.50
203	All Pro Guards (Tom Mack, Larry Little)	1.00
204	All Pro Centers (Jeff Van Note, Jack Rudnay)	.30
205	All Pro Guards (Gale Gillingham, John Hannah)	1.00
206	All Pro Tackles (Winston Hill, Dan Dierdorf)	.50
207	All Pro Tight Ends (Riley Odoms, Charley Young)	.50
208	All Pro Quarterbacks (Fran Tarkenton, Ken Stabler)	3.00
209	All Pro Backs (Lawrence McCutcheon, O.J. Simpson)	5.00
210	All Pro Backs (Otis Armstrong, Terry Metcalf)	.50
211	All Pro Receivers (Isaac Curtis, Mel Gray)	.50
212	All Pro Kickers (Roy Gerela, Chester Marcol)	.50
213	All Pro Ends (Elvin Bethea, Jack Youngblood)	.50
214	All Pro Tackles (Otis Sistrunk, Alan Page)	.50
215	All Pro Tackles (Merlin Olsen, Mike Reid)	1.25
216	All Pro Ends (Carl Eller, Lyle Alzado)	1.00
217	All Pro Linebackers (Ted Hendricks, Phil Villapiano)	1.00
218	All Pro Linebackers (Willie Lanier, Lee Roy Jordan)	1.00
219	All Pro Linebackers (Andy Russell, Isiah Robertson)	.50
220	All Pro Cornerbacks (Emmitt Thomas, Nate Wright)	.50
221	All Pro Cornerbacks (Lemar Parrish, Willie Buchanon)	.50
222	All Pro Safeties (Ken Houston, Dick Anderson)	1.00
223	All Pro Safeties (Cliff Harris, Jack Tatum)	1.00
224	All Pro Punters (Tom Wittum, Ray Guy)	.50
225	All Pro Returners (Greg Pruitt, Terry Metcalf)	.50
226	Ted Kwalick	.30
227	Spider Lockhart	.30
228	Mike Livingston	.30
229	Larry Cole	.30
230	Gary Garrison	.30
231	Larry Brooks	.30
232	Bobby Howfield	.30
233	Fred Carr	.30
234	Norm Evans	.30
235	Dwight White	.30
236	Conrad Dobler	.30
237	Garry Lyle	.30
238	Darryl Stingley	1.00
239	Tom Graham	.30
240	Chuck Foreman	1.00
241	Ken Riley	.30
242	Don Morrison	.30
243	Lynn Dickey	.75
244	Don Cockroft	.30
245	Claude Humphrey	.30
246	John Skorupan	.30
247	Raymond Chester	.30
248	Cas Banaszek	.30
249	Art Malone	.30

250	Ed Flanagan	.30
251	Checklist 133-264	2.50
252	Nemiah Wilson	.30
253	Ron Jessie	.30
254	Jim Lynch	.30
255	Bob Tucker	.30
256	Terry Owens	.30
257	John Fitzgerald	.30
258	Jack Snow	.30
259	Garry Puetz	.30
260	Mike Phipps	.30
261	Al Matthews	.30
262	Bob Kuechenberg	.30
263	Ron Yankowski	.30
264	Ron Shanklin	.30
265	Bobby Douglass	.30
266	Josh Ashton	.30
267	Bill Van Heusen	.30
268	Jeff Siemon	.30
269	Bob Newland	.30
270	Gale Gillingham	.30
271	Zeke Moore	.30
272	Mike Tilleman	.30
273	John Leypoldt	.30
274	Ken Mendenhall	.30
275	Norm Snead	.30
276	Bill Bradley	.30
277	Jerry Smith	.30
278	Clarence Davis	.30
279	Jim Yarbrough	.30
280	Lemar Parrish	.30
281	Bobby Bell	1.50
282	*Lynn Swann*	45.00
283	John Hicks	.30
284	Coy Bacon	.30
285	Lee Roy Jordan	1.25
286	Willie Buchanon	.30
287	Al Woodall	.30
288	Reggie Rucker	.30
289	John Schmitt	.30
290	Carl Eller	1.00
291	Jake Scott	.30
292	Donny Anderson	.30
293	Charley Wade	.30
294	John Tanner	.30
295	Charley Johnson	.30
296	Tom Blanchard	.30
297	Curley Culp	.30
298	*Jeff Van Note*	1.25
299	Bob James	.30
300	Franco Harris	12.00
301	Tim Berra	.30
302	Bruce Gossett	.30
303	Berlon Biggs	.30
304	Bob Kowalkowski	.30
305	Marv Hubbard	.30
306	Ken Avery	.30
307	Mike Adamle	.30
308	Don Herrmann	.30
309	Chris Fletcher	.30
310	Roman Gabriel	1.25
311	Billy Joe DuPree	1.00
312	Fred Dryer	2.00
313	John Riggins	5.00
314	Bob McKay	.30
315	Ted Hendricks	1.50
316	Bobby Bryant	.30
317	Don Nottingham	.30
318	John Hannah	4.00
319	Rich Coady	.30
320	Phil Villapiano	.30
321	Jim Plunkett	2.00
322	Lyle Alzado	1.25
323	Ernie Jackson	.30
324	Billy Parks	.30
325	Willie Lanier	1.50
326	John James	.30
327	Joe Ferguson	1.00
328	*Ernie Holmes*	1.00
329	Bruce Laird	.30
330	Chester Marcol	.30
331	Dave Wilcox	.30
332	Pat Fischer	.30
333	Steve Owens	.30
334	Royce Berry	.30
335	Russ Washington	.30
336	Walker Gillette	.30
337	Mark Nordquist	.30
338	*James Harris*	1.00
339	Warren Koegel	.30
340	Emmitt Thomas	.30
341	Walt Garrison	.30
342	Thom Darden	.30
343	Mike Eischeid	.30
344	Ernie McMillan	.30
345	Nick Buoniconti	1.00
346	George Farmer	.30
347	Sam Adams	.30
348	Larry Cipa	.30
349	Bob Moore	.30
350	*Otis Armstrong*	4.00
351	George Blanda (RH)	2.50
352	Fred Cox (RH)	.60
353	Tom Dempsey (RH)	.60
354	Ken Houston (RH)	.60
355	O.J. Simpson (RH)	7.00
356	Ron Smith (RH)	.60
357	Bob Atkins	.30
358	Pat Sullivan	.30
359	Joe DeLamielleure	.60
360	*L. McCutcheon*	2.50
361	David Lee	.30
362	Mike McCoy	.30
363	Skip Vanderbundt	.30
364	Mark Moseley	.75
365	Lem Barney	1.50
366	Doug Dressler	.30
367	*Dan Fouts*	50.00

368	Bob Hyland	.30
369	John Outlaw	.30
370	Roy Gerela	.30
371	Isiah Robertson	.30
372	Jerome Barkum	.30
373	Ed Podolak	.30
374	Milt Morin	.30
375	John Niland	.30
376	Checklist 265-396	2.50
377	Ken Iman	.30
378	Manny Fernandez	.30
379	Dave Gallagher	.30
380	Ken Stabler	14.00
381	Mack Herron	.30
382	Bill McClard	.30
383	Ray May	.30
384	Don Hansen	.30
385	Elvin Bethea	.30
386	Joe Scibelli	.30
387	Neal Craig	.30
388	Marty Domres	.30
389	Ken Ellis	.30
390	Charley Young	.30
391	Tommy Hart	.30
392	Moses Denson	.30
393	Larry Walton	.30
394	Dave Green	.30
395	Ron Johnson	.30
396	Ed Bradley	.30
397	J.T. Thomas	.30
398	Jim Bailey	.30
399	Barry Pearson	.30
400	Fran Tarkenton	8.50
401	Jack Rudnay	.30
402	Rayfield Wright	.30
403	Roger Wehrli	.30
404	Vern Den Herder	.30
405	Fred Biletnikoff	3.00
406	Ken Grandberry	.30
407	Bob Adams	.30
408	Jim Merlo	.30
409	John Pitts	.30
410	Dave Osborn	.30
411	Dennis Havig	.30
412	Bob Johnson	.30
413	Ken Burrow	.30
414	Jim Cheyunski	.30
415	MacArthur Lane	.30
416	*Joe Theismann*	25.00
417	*Mike Boryla*	.50
418	Bruce Taylor	.30
419	Chris Hanburger	.30
420	Tom Mack	.30
421	Errol Mann	.30
422	Jack Gregory	.30
423	Harrison Davis	.30
424	Burgess Owens	.30
425	Joe Greene	4.00
426	Morris Stroud	.30
427	John DeMarie	.30
428	Mel Renfro	.75
429	Cid Edwards	.30
430	Mike Reid	1.00
431	Jack Mildren	.30
432	Jerry Simmons	.30
433	Ron Yary	.30
434	Howard Stevens	.30
435	Ray Guy	1.75
436	Tommy Nobis	1.00
437	Solomon Freelon	.30
438	J.D. Hill	.30
439	Toni Linhart	.30
440	Dick Anderson	.30
441	Guy Morriss	.30
442	Bob Hoskins	.30
443	John Hadl	1.00
444	Roy Jefferson	.30
445	Charlie Sanders	.30
446	Pat Curran	.30
447	David Knight	.30
448	Bob Brown	.30
449	Pete Gogolak	.30
450	Terry Metcalf	1.00
451	Bill Bergey	.75
452	(Dan Abramowicz) (HL)	.60
453	Otis Armstrong (HL)	1.00
454	Cliff Branch (HL)	1.50
455	John James (HL)	.60
456	Lydell Mitchell (HL)	.60
457	Lemar Parrish (HL)	.60
458	Ken Stabler (HL)	4.00
459	Lynn Swann (HL)	7.00
460	Emmitt Thomas (HL)	.60
461	Terry Bradshaw	15.00
462	Jerrel Wilson	.30
463	Walter Johnson	.30
464	Golden Richards	.30
465	Tommy Casanova	.30
466	Randy Jackson	.30
467	Ron Bolton	.30
468	Joe Owens	.30
469	Wally Hilgenberg	.30
470	Riley Odoms	.50
471	Otis Sistrunk	.50
472	Eddie Ray	.30
473	Reggie McKenzie	.75
474	Elbert Drungo	.30
475	Mercury Morris	.75
476	Dan Dickel	.30
477	Merritt Kersey	.30
478	Mike Holmes	.30
479	Clarence Williams	.30
480	Bill Kilmer	.50
481	Altie Taylor	.30
482	Dave Elmendorf	.30
483	Bob Rowe	.30

484	Pete Athas	.30
485	Winston Hill	.30
486	Bo Mathews	.30
487	Earl Thomas	.30
488	Jan Stenerud	1.25
489	Steve Holden	.30
490	*Cliff Harris*	4.00
491	*Boobie Clark*	.50
492	Joe Taylor	.30
493	Tom Neville	.30
494	Wayne Colman	.30
495	Jim Mitchell	.30
496	Paul Krause	.75
497	Jim Otto	2.00
498	John Rowser	.30
499	Larry Little	1.00
500	O.J. Simpson	12.00
501	*John Dutton*	1.50
502	Pat Hughes	.30
503	Malcolm Snider	.30
504	Fred Willis	.30
505	Harold Jackson	.90
506	Mike Bragg	.30
507	Jerry Sherk	.30
508	Mirro Roder	.30
509	Tom Sullivan	.30
510	Jim Hart	1.00
511	Cedrick Hardman	.30
512	Blaine Nye	.30
513	Elmo Wright	.30
514	Herb Orvis	.30
515	Richard Caster	.30
516	*Doug Kotar*	.50
517	Checklist 397-528	2.50
518	Jesse Freitas	.30
519	Ken Houston	1.25
520	Alan Page	1.75
521	Tim Foley	.30
522	Bill Olds	.30
523	Bobby Maples	.30
524	*Cliff Branch*	10.00
525	Merlin Olsen	3.00
526	AFC Champions (Terry Bradshaw, Franco Harris)	2.50
527	NFC Champions (Chuck Foreman)	1.00
528	Super Bowl (Terry Bradshaw)	4.00

1975 Topps Team Checklists

Each of the 26 NFL teams is represented in this set, which was available as a mail-in offer from Topps as an uncut sheet. Each card is standard size, and shows the team's 1975 schedule on the front. The card back is unnumbered and contains a checklist for the players in the team set.

		NM
Complete Set (26):		195.00
Common Player:		8.00
(1)	Atlanta Falcons	8.50
(2)	Baltimore Colts	8.00
(3)	Buffalo Bills	8.00
(4)	Chicago Bears	9.00
(5)	Cincinnati Bengals	8.00
(6)	Cleveland Browns	9.00
(7)	Dallas Cowboys	9.00
(8)	Denver Broncos	10.00
(9)	Detroit Lions	8.00
(10)	Green Bay Packers	8.00
(11)	Houston Oilers	8.00
(12)	Kansas City Chiefs	8.00
(13)	Los Angeles Rams	9.00
(14)	Miami Dolphins	10.00
(15)	Minnesota Vikings	9.00
(16)	New England Patriots	8.00
(17)	New York Giants	9.00
(18)	New York Jets	9.00
(19)	New Orleans Saints	9.00
(20)	Oakland Raiders	10.00
(21)	Philadelphia Eagles	8.00
(22)	Pittsburgh Steelers	9.00
(23)	St. Louis Cardinals	9.00
(24)	San Diego Chargers	8.00
(25)	San Francisco 49ers	9.00
(26)	Washington Redskins	10.00

1976 Topps

This is the most valuable of the 528-card sets issued by Topps, primarily because of the inclusion of Walter Payton's rookie card. Other rookies in this set include Steve Bartkowski, Harvey Martin, Russ Francis, Randy White, Jack Lambert, Randy Gradishar, Steve Grogan, and Ron Jaworski. The set also features the second-year card of Dan Fouts. Hall of Famers (and future Hall of Famers) showing up in the 1976 Topps issue include Payton, Fouts, Martin, White, Lambert, Willie Lanier, Fred Biletnikoff, Ray Guy, Alan Page, Bob Griese, Franco Harris, O.J. Simpson, John Riggins, Len Dawson, Paul Warfield, George Blanda, Roger Staubach, Ken Stabler, Larry Csonka, Charley Taylor and Fran Tarkenton. (Key: AP - All Pro)

		NM
Complete Set (528):		350.00
Common Player:		.25
Team cards:		1.25
1	George Blanda	5.00
2	Neil Colzie	.50
3	Chuck Foreman	.50
4	Jim Marshall	.50
5	Terry Metcalf	.50
6	O.J. Simpson	3.00
7	Fran Tarkenton	3.00
8	Charley Taylor	1.00
9	Ernie Holmes	.25
10	Ken Anderson (AP)	2.00
11	Bobby Bryant	.25
12	Jerry Smith	.25
13	David Lee	.25
14	*Robert Newhouse*	1.25
15	Vern Den Herder	.25
16	John Hannah	2.00
17	J.D. Hill	.25
18	James Harris	.25
19	Willie Buchanon	.25
20	Charley Young (AP)	.25
21	Jim Yarbrough	.25
22	Ronnie Coleman	.25
23	Don Cockroft	.25
24	Willie Lanier	1.00
25	Fred Biletnikoff	3.00
26	Ron Yankowski	.25
27	Spider Lockhart	.25
28	Bob Johnson	.25
29	J.T. Thomas	.25
30	Ron Yary (AP)	.25
31	*Brad Dusek*	.50
32	Raymond Chester	.25
33	Larry Little	.75
34	*Pat Leahy*	1.00
35	*Steve Bartkowski*	4.00
36	Tom Myers	.25
37	Bill Van Heusen	.25
38	Russ Washington	.25
39	Tom Sullivan	.25
40	Curley Culp (AP)	.25
41	Johnnie Gray	.25
42	Bob Klein	.25
43	Lem Barney	1.00
44	*Harvey Martin*	4.00
45	Reggie Rucker	.25
46	Neil Clabo	.25
47	Ray Hamilton	.25
48	Joe Ferguson	.75
49	Ed Podolak	.25
50	Ray Guy (AP)	1.50
51	Glen Edwards	.25
52	Jim LeClair	.25
53	Mike Barnes	.25
54	*Nat Moore*	4.00
55	Bill Kilmer	.75
56	Larry Stallings	.25
57	Jack Gregory	.25
58	Steve Mike-Mayer	.25
59	Virgil Livers	.25
60	Jerry Sherk (AP)	.25
61	Guy Morriss	.25
62	Barty Smith	.25
63	Jerome Barkum	.25
64	Ira Gordon	.25
65	Paul Krause	.60
66	John McMakin	.25

67	Checklist 1-132	2.00
68	Charley Johnson	.25
69	Tommy Nobis	.75
70	Lydell Mitchell	.25
71	Vern Holland	.25
72	Tim Foley	.25
73	Golden Richards	.25
74	Bryant Salter	.25
75	Terry Bradshaw	14.00
76	Ted Hendricks	1.25
77	*Rich Saul*	.35
78	John Smith	.25
79	Altie Taylor	.25
80	Cedrick Hardman (AP)	.25
81	Ken Payne	.25
82	Zeke Moore	.25
83	Alvin Maxson	.25
84	Wally Hilgenberg	.25
85	John Niland	.25
86	Mike Sensibaugh	.25
87	Ron Johnson	.25
88	Winston Hill	.25
89	Charlie Joiner	2.00
90	Roger Wehrli (AP)	.75
91	Mike Bragg	.25
92	Dan Dickel	.25
93	Earl Morrall	.75
94	Pat Toomay	.25
95	Gary Garrison	.25
96	Ken Geddes	.25
97	Mike Current	.25
98	Bob Avellini	.35
99	Dave Pureifory	.25
100	Franco Harris (AP)	7.00
101	Randy Logan	.25
102	John Fitzgerald	.25
103	*Gregg Bingham*	.40
104	Jim Plunkett	1.50
105	Carl Eller	.75
106	Larry Walton	.25
107	Clarence Scott	.25
108	Skip Vanderbundt	.25
109	Boobie Clark	.25
110	Tom Mack (AP)	.25
111	Bruce Laird	.25
112	*Dave Dalby*	.60
113	John Leypoldt	.25
114	Barry Pearson	.25
115	Larry Brown	.60
116	Jackie Smith	.25
117	Pat Hughes	.25
118	Al Woodall	.25
119	John Zook	.25
120	Jake Scott (AP)	.25
121	Rich Glover	.25
122	Ernie Jackson	.25
123	Otis Armstrong	1.00
124	Bob Grim	.25
125	Jeff Siemon	.25
126	Harold Hart	.25
127	John DeMarie	.25
128	Dan Fouts	10.00
129	Jim Kearney	.25
130	John Dutton (AP)	.40
131	Calvin Hill	.50
132	Toni Fritsch	.25
133	Ron Jessie	.25
134	Don Nottingham	.25
135	Lemar Parrish	.25
136	*Russ Francis*	4.00
137	Joe Reed	.25
138	C.L. Whittington	.25
139	Otis Sistrunk	.25
140	Lynn Swann (AP)	15.00
141	Jim Carter	.25
142	Mike Montler	.25
143	Walter Johnson	.25
144	Doug Kotar	.25
145	Roman Gabriel	1.00
146	Billy Newsome	.25
147	Ed Bradley	.25
148	Walter Payton	200.00
149	Johnny Fuller	.25
150	Alan Page (AP)	1.50
151	Frank Grant	.25
152	Dave Green	.25
153	Nelson Munsey	.25
154	Jim Mandich	.25
155	Lawrence McCutcheon	.75
156	Steve Ramsey	.25
157	Ed Flanagan	.25
158	*Randy White*	25.00
159	Gerry Mullins	.25
160	Jan Stenerud (AP)	.75
161	Steve Odom	.25
162	Roger Finnie	.25
163	Norm Snead	.25
164	Jeff Van Note	.40
165	Bill Bergey	.60
166	Allen Carter	.25
167	Steve Holden	.25
168	Sherman White	.25
169	Bob Berry	.25
170	Ken Houston (AP)	1.00
171	Bill Olds	.25
172	Larry Seiple	.25
173	Cliff Branch	3.00
174	Reggie McKenzie	.25
175	Dan Pastorini	.50
176	Paul Naumoff	.25
177	Checklist 133-265	2.00
178	Durwood Keeton	.25
179	Earl Thomas	.25
180	L.C. Greenwood (AP)	.85
181	John Outlaw	.25

182	Frank Nunley	.25
183	*Dave Jennings*	1.00
184	McArthur Lane	.25
185	Chester Marcol	.25
186	J.J. Jones	.25
187	Tom DeLeone	.25
188	Steve Zabel	.25
189	Ken Johnson	.25
190	Rayfield Wright (AP)	.25
191	Brent McClanahan	.25
192	Pat Fischer	.25
193	*Roger Carr*	1.00
194	Manny Fernandez	.25
195	Roy Gerela	.25
196	Dave Elmendorf	.25
197	Bob Kowalkowski	.25
198	Phil Villapiano	.25
199	Will Wynn	.25
200	*Terry Metcalf*	.50
201	Passing Leaders: (Ken Anderson, Fran Tarkenton)	2.00
202	Receiving Leaders: (Reggie Rucker, Lydell Mitchell, Chuck Foreman)	.50
203	Rushing Leaders: (O.J. Simpson, Jim Otis)	3.00
204	Scoring Leaders: (O.J. Simpson, Chuck Foreman)	3.00
205	Interception Leaders: (Mel Blount, Paul Krause)	.75
206	Punting Leaders: (Ray Guy, Herman Weaver)	.50
207	Ken Ellis	.25
208	Ron Saul	.25
209	Toni Linhart	.25
210	Jim Langer (AP)	1.25
211	Jeff Wright	.25
212	Moses Denson	.25
213	Earl Edwards	.25
214	Walker Gillette	.25
215	Bob Trumpy	.50
216	Emmitt Thomas	.25
217	Lyle Alzado	1.25
218	Carl Garrett	.25
219	Van Green	.25
220	*Jack Lambert (AP)*	28.00
221	Spike Jones	.25
222	John Hadl	.75
223	*Billy Johnson*	2.50
224	Tony McGee	.25
225	Preston Pearson	.50
226	Isiah Robertson	.25
227	Errol Mann	.25
228	Paul Seal	.25
229	*Roland Harper*	.75
230	*Ed White*	.25
231	Joe Theismann	6.50
232	Jim Cheyunski	.25
233	Bill Stanfill	.25
234	Marv Hubbard	.25
235	Tommy Casanova	.25
236	Bob Hyland	.25
237	Jesse Freitas	.25
238	Norm Thompson	.25
239	Charlie Smith	.25
240	John James (AP)	.25
241	Alden Roche	.25
242	Gordon Jolley	.25
243	Larry Ely	.25
244	Richard Caster	.25
245	Joe Greene	3.25
246	Larry Schreiber	.25
247	Terry Schmidt	.25
248	Jerrel Wilson	.25
249	Marty Domres	.25
250	Isaac Curtis (AP)	.25
251	Harold McLinton	.25
252	Fred Dryer	2.00
253	Bill Lenkaitis	.25
254	Don Hardeman	.25
255	Bob Griese	4.00
256	*Oscar Roan*	.40
257	Randy Gradishar	3.00
258	*Bob Thomas*	.50
259	Joe Owens	.25
260	Cliff Harris (AP)	1.00
261	Frank Lewis	.25
262	Mike McCoy	.25
263	*Rickey Young*	.60
264	*Brian Kelley*	.40
265	Charlie Sanders	.25
266	Jim Hart	1.00
267	Gregg Gantt	.25
268	John Ward	.25
269	Al Beauchamp	.25
270	Jack Tatum (AP)	.25
271	Jim Lash	.25
272	Diron Talbert	.25
273	Checklist 265-396	2.00
274	Steve Spurrier	4.00
275	Greg Pruitt	.60
276	Jim Mitchell	.25
277	Jack Rudnay	.25
278	*Freddie Solomon*	1.00
279	Frank LeMaster	.25
280	Wally Chambers (AP)	.25
281	Mike Collier	.25
282	Clarence Williams	.25
283	Mitch Hoopes	.25
284	Ron Bolton	.25

285	Harold Jackson	.75
286	Greg Landry	.60
287	Tony Greene	.25
288	Howard Stevens	.25
289	Roy Jefferson	.25
290	Jim Bakken (AP)	.25
291	Doug Sutherland	.25
292	Marvin Cobb	.25
293	Mack Alston	.25
294	Rod McNeil	.25
295	Gene Upshaw	1.00
296	Dave Gallagher	.25
297	Larry Ball	.25
298	Ron Howard	.25
299	*Don Strock*	1.50
300	O.J. Simpson (AP)	10.00
301	Ray Mansfield	.25
302	Larry Marshall	.25
303	Dick Himes	.25
304	*Ray Wersching*	.40
305	John Riggins	4.00
306	Bob Parsons	.25
307	Ray Brown	.25
308	Len Dawson	3.00
309	Andy Maurer	.25
310	Jack Youngblood (AP)	1.00
311	Essex Johnson	.25
312	Stan White	.25
313	Drew Pearson	4.00
314	Rockne Freitas	.25
315	Mercury Morris	.60
316	Willie Alexander	.25
317	Paul Warfield	3.00
318	Bob Chandler	.25
319	Bobby Walden	.25
320	Riley Odoms (AP)	.25
321	Mike Boryla	.25
322	Bruce Van Dyke	.25
323	Pete Banaszak	.25
324	Darryl Stingley	.50
325	John Mendenhall	.25
326	Dan Dierdorf	1.50
327	Bruce Taylor	.25
328	Don McCauley	.25
329	John Reaves	.25
330	Chris Hanburger (AP)	.25
331	NFC Champions (Roger Staubach)	3.00
332	AFC Champions (Franco Harris)	2.00
333	Super Bowl X (Terry Bradshaw)	2.25
334	Godwin Turk	.25
335	Dick Anderson	.25
336	Woody Green	.25
337	Pat Curran	.25
338	Council Rudolph	.25
339	Joe Lavender	.25
340	John Gilliam (AP)	.25
341	*Steve Furness*	.75
342	D.D. Lewis	.25
343	Duane Carrell	.25
344	Jon Morris	.25
345	John Brockington	.25
346	Mike Phipps	.25
347	*Lyle Blackwood*	.60
348	Julius Adams	.25
349	Terry Hermeling	.25
350	*Rolland Lawrence* (AP)	.50
351	Glenn Doughty	.25
352	Doug Swift	.25
353	Mike Strachan	.25
354	Craig Morton	.50
355	George Blanda	5.00
356	Garry Puetz	.25
357	Carl Mauck	.25
358	Walt Patulski	.25
359	Stu Voigt	.25
360	Fred Carr (AP)	.25
361	Po James	.25
362	Otis Taylor	.50
363	Jeff West	.25
364	Gary Huff	.25
365	Dwight White	.25
366	Dan Ryczek	.25
367	*Jon Keyworth*	.50
368	Mel Renfro	.60
369	*Bruce Coslet*	1.00
370	Len Hauss (AP)	.25
371	Rick Volk	.25
372	Howard Twilley	.25
373	*Cullen Bryant*	.60
374	Bob Babich	.25
375	Herman Weaver	.25
376	*Steve Grogan*	8.00
377	Bubba Smith	1.50
378	Burgess Owens	.25
379	Alvin Matthews	.25
380	Art Shell	2.00
381	Larry Brown	.25
382	Horst Muhlmann	.25
383	Ahmad Rashad	2.50
384	Bobby Maples	.25
385	Jim Marshall	.90
386	Joe Dawkins	.25
387	Dennis Partee	.25
388	Eddie McMillan	.25
389	Randy Johnson	.25
390	Bob Kuechenberg (AP)	.25
391	Rufus Mayes	.25
392	Lloyd Mumphord	.25
393	Ike Harris	.25
394	Dave Hampton	.25
395	Roger Staubach	15.00

396	Doug Buffone	.25
397	Howard Fest	.25
398	Wayne Mulligan	.25
399	Bill Bradley	.25
400	Chuck Foreman (AP)	.60
401	Jack Snow	.25
402	Bob Howard	.25
403	Jim Matuszak	1.00
404	Bill Munson	.25
405	Andy Russell	.25
406	Skip Butler	.25
407	Hugh McKinnis	.25
408	Bob Penchion	.25
409	Mike Bass	.25
410	George Kunz (AP)	.25
411	Ron Pritchard	.25
412	Barry Smith	.25
413	Norm Bulaich	.25
414	Marv Bateman	.25
415	Ken Stabler	8.00
416	Conrad Dobler	.25
417	Bob Tucker	.25
418	Gene Washington	.25
419	Ed Marinaro	1.00
420	Jack Ham (AP)	3.25
421	Jim Turner	.25
422	Chris Fletcher	.25
423	Carl Barzilauskas	.25
424	*Robert Brazile*	2.50
425	Harold Carmichael	1.50
426	*Ron Jaworski*	4.00
427	Ed "Too Tall" Jones	20.00
428	Larry McCarren	.25
429	*Mike Thomas*	.50
430	Joe DeLamielleure (AP)	.25
431	Tom Blanchard	.25
432	Ron Carpenter	.25
433	Levi Johnson	.25
434	Sam Cunningham	.25
435	Garo Yapremian	.25
436	Mike Livingston	.25
437	Larry Csonka	3.00
438	Doug Dieken	.25
439	Bill Lueck	.25
440	Tom MacLeod (AP)	.25
441	Mick Tingelhoff	.25
442	Terry Hanratty	.25
443	Mike Siani	.25
444	Dwight Harrison	.25
445	Jim Otis	.25
446	Jack Reynolds	.25
447	*Jean Fugett*	.40
448	Dave Beverly	.25
449	*Bernard Jackson*	1.00
450	Charley Taylor	2.00
451	Atlanta Falcons Team	1.50
452	Baltimore Colts Team	1.50
453	Buffalo Bills Team	1.50
454	Chicago Bears Team	1.50
455	Cincinnati Bengals Team	1.50
456	Cleveland Browns Team	1.50
457	Dallas Cowboys Team	1.50
458	Denver Broncos Team	1.50
459	Detroit Lions Team	1.50
460	Green Bay Packers Team	1.50
461	Houston Oilers Team	1.50
462	Kansas City Chiefs Team	1.50
463	Los Angeles Rams Team	1.50
464	Miami Dolphins Team	1.50
465	Minnesota Vikings Team	1.50
466	New England Patriots Team	1.50
467	New Orleans Saints Team	1.50
468	New York Giants Team	1.50
469	New York Jets Team	1.50
470	Oakland Raiders Team	1.50
471	Philadelphia Eagles Team	1.50
472	Pittsburgh Steelers Team	1.50
473	St. Louis Cardinals Team	1.50
474	San Diego Chargers Team	1.50
475	San Francisco 49ers Team	1.50
476	Seattle Seahawks Team	1.50
477	Tampa Bay Bucaneers Team	1.50
478	Washington Redskins Team	1.50
479	Fred Cox	.25
480	Mel Blount (AP)	5.00
481	John Bunting	.25
482	Ken Mendenhall	.25
483	Will Harrell	.25
484	Marlin Briscoe	.25
485	Archie Manning	.25

486	Tody Smith	.25
487	George Hunt	.25
488	Roscoe Word	.25
489	Paul Seymour	.25
490	Lee Roy Jordan (AP)	1.00
491	Chip Myers	.25
492	Norm Evans	.25
493	Jim Bertelsen	.25
494	Mark Moseley	.50
495	George Buehler	.25
496	Charlie Hall	.25
497	Marvin Upshaw	.25
498	*Tom Banks*	.50
499	Randy Vataha	.25
500	Fran Tarkenton (AP)	7.00
501	Mike Wagner	.25
502	Art Malone	.25
503	Fred Cook	.25
504	Rich McGeorge	.25
505	Ken Burrough	.25
506	Nick Mike-Mayer	.25
507	Checklist 397-528	2.00
508	Steve Owens	.25
509	*Brad Van Pelt*	.75
510	Ken Riley (AP)	.25
511	Art Thoms	.25
512	Ed Bell	.25
513	Tom Wittum	.25
514	Jim Braxton	.25
515	Nick Buoniconti	.60
516	*Brian Sipe*	2.00
517	Jim Lynch	.25
518	Prentice McCray	.25
519	Tom Dempsey	.25
520	Mel Gray (AP)	.25
521	Nate Wright	.25
522	Rocky Bleier	3.00
523	Dennis Johnson	.25
524	Jerry Sisemore	.25
525	Bert Jones	1.00
526	Perry Smith	.25
527	Blaine Nye	.25
528	Bob Moore	.50

1976 Topps Team Checklists

The 30-card, standard-size set includes team checklist for each of the 28 NFL teams and two checklists. The set was available in uncut sheets from Topps and was unnumbered. The cards parallel the team checklists in the base sets (451-478), but come in thinner stock.

		NM
Complete Set (30):		130.00
Common Player:		5.00
1	Atlanta Falcons	5.00
2	Baltimore Colts	5.00
3	Buffalo Bills	5.00
4	Chicago Bears	7.50
5	Cincinnati Bengals	5.00
6	Cleveland Browns	5.00
7	Dallas Cowboys	10.00
8	Denver Broncos	5.00
9	Detroit Lions	5.00
10	Green Bay Packers	5.00
11	Houston Oilers	5.00
12	Kansas City Chiefs	5.00
13	Los Angeles Rams	5.00
14	Miami Dolphins	7.50
15	Minnesota Vikings	5.00
16	New England Patriots	5.00
17	New York Giants	5.00
18	New York Jets	5.00
19	New Orleans Saints	5.00
20	Oakland Raiders	7.50
21	Philadelphia Eagles	5.00
22	Pittsburgh Steelers	7.50
23	St. Louis Cardinals	5.00
24	San Diego Chargers	5.00
25	San Francisco 49ers	7.50
26	Seattle Seahawks	5.00
27	Tampa Bay Buccaneers	5.00
28	Washington Redskins	7.50
29	Checklist 1-132	5.00
30	Checklist 133-264	5.00

1977 Topps

Known primarily for containing Steve Largent's rookie issue, this set of 528 cards also has the second-year card of Walter Payton. Other rookie cards included in the set are Pat Haden, Jim Zorn, John Cappelletti, Richard Todd, Harry Carson, Chuck Muncie, Archie Griffin and Dave Casper. All-Pro designations were once again placed on the regular-issued card. Of the subsets, the "Record" run appears in the middle of the set; AFC/NFC championship and the Super Bowl card are the last three in the set; and the statistical leader cards are the first six. This was the last year in which team checklists were issued; future cards would show team leaders with the checklists.

No.	Player	NM
	Complete Set (528):	230.00
	Common Player:	.20
1	Passing Leaders: (James Harris, Ken Stabler)	1.75
2	Receiving Leaders: (Drew Pearson, MacArthur Lane)	.50
3	Rushing Leaders: (Walter Payton, O.J. Simpson)	9.00
4	Scoring Leaders: (Mark Moseley, Toni Linhart)	.35
5	Interception Leaders: (Monte Jackson, Ken Riley)	.35
6	Punting Leaders: (John James, Marv Bateman)	.35
7	Mike Phipps	.20
8	Rick Volk	.20
9	Steve Furness	.20
10	Isaac Curtis	.20
11	Nate Wright	.20
12	Jean Fugett	.20
13	Ken Mendenhall	.20
14	Sam Adams	.20
15	Charlie Waters	1.00
16	Bill Stanfill	.20
17	John Holland	.20
18	*Pat Haden*	3.00
19	Bob Young	.20
20	Wally Chambers (AP)	.20
21	Lawrence Gaines	.20
22	Larry McCarren	.20
23	Horst Muhlmann	.20
24	Phil Villapiano	.40
25	Greg Pruitt	.40
26	Ron Howard	.20
27	Craig Morton	.75
28	Rufus Mayes	.20
29	*Lee Roy Selmon*	7.00
30	Ed White (AP)	.20
31	Harold McLinton	.20
32	Glenn Doughty	.20
33	Bob Kuechenberg	.20
34	Duane Carrell	.20
35	Riley Odoms	.20
36	Bobby Scott	.20
37	Nick Mike-Mayer	.20
38	Bill Lenkaitis	.20
39	Roland Harper	.20
40	Tommy Hart (AP)	.20
41	Mike Sensibaugh	.20
42	Rusty Jackson	.20
43	Levi Johnson	.20
44	Mike McCoy	.20
45	Roger Staubach	10.00
46	Fred Cox	.20
47	Bob Babich	.20
48	Reggie McKenzie	.20
49	Dave Jennings	.20
50	*Mike Haynes* (AP)	5.00
51	Larry Brown	.20
52	Marvin Cobb	.20
53	Fred Cook	.20
54	Freddie Solomon	.30
55	John Riggins	2.50
56	John Bunting	.20
57	Ray Wersching	.20
58	Mike Livingston	.20
59	Billy Johnson	.50
60	Mike Wagner (AP)	.20
61	Waymond Bryant	.20
62	Jim Otis	.20
63	Ed Galigher	.20
64	Randy Vataha	.20
65	*Jim Zorn*	4.00
66	John Keyworth	.20
67	Checklist 1-132	1.50
68	Henry Childs	.20
69	Thom Darden	.20
70	George Kunz (AP)	.20
71	Lenvil Elliott	.20
72	Curtis Johnson	.20
73	Doug Van Horn	.20
74	Joe Theismann	4.00
75	Dwight White	.20
76	Scott Laidlaw	.20
77	Monte Johnson	.20
78	Dave Beverly	.20
79	Jim Mitchell	.20
80	Jack Youngblood (AP)	.75
81	Mel Gray	.20
82	Dwight Harrison	.20
83	John Hadl	.50
84	Matt Blair	2.00
85	Charlie Sanders	.20
86	Noah Jackson	.20
87	Ed Marinaro	.40
88	Bob Howard	.20
89	John McDaniel	.20
90	Dan Dierdorf (AP)	1.25
91	Mark Moseley	.35
92	Cleo Miller	.20
93	Andre Tillman	.20
94	Bruce Taylor	.20
95	Bert Jones	1.00
96	*Anthony Davis*	1.00
97	Don Goode	.20
98	Ray Rhodes	5.00
99	*Mike Webster*	8.00
100	O.J. Simpson (AP)	5.00
101	*Doug Plank*	.75
102	Efren Herrera	.20
103	Charlie Smith	.20
104	Carlos Brown	.20
105	Jim Marshall	.70
106	Paul Naumoff	.20
107	Walter White	.20
108	*John Cappelletti*	2.50
109	Chip Myers	.20
110	Ken Stabler (AP)	8.00
111	Joe Ehrmann	.20
112	Rick Engles	.20
113	Jack Dolbin	.20
114	Ron Bolton	.20
115	Mike Thomas	.20
116	Mike Fuller	.20
117	John Hill	.20
118	*Richard Todd*	1.00
119	*Duriel Harris*	.50
120	John James (AP)	.20
121	Lionel Antoine	.20
122	John Skorupan	.20
123	Skip Butler	.20
124	Bob Tucker	.20
125	Paul Krause	.50
126	Dave Hampton	.20
127	Tom Wittum	.20
128	Gary Huff	.20
129	Emmitt Thomas	.20
130	Drew Pearson (AP)	2.00
131	Ron Saul	.20
132	Steve Niehaus	.20
133	Fred Carr	.20
134	Norm Bulaich	.20
135	Bob Trumpy	.40
136	Greg Landry	.30
137	George Buehler	.20
138	Reggie Rucker	.20
139	Julius Adams	.20
140	Jack Ham (AP)	2.50
141	Wayne Morris	.20
142	Marv Bateman	.20
143	Bobby Maples	.20
144	Harold Carmichael	1.00
145	Bob Avellini	.20
146	*Harry Carson*	7.00
147	Lawrence Pillers	.20
148	Ed Williams	.20
149	Dan Pastorini	.40
150	Ron Yary (AP)	.20
151	Joe Lavender	.20
152	Pat McInally	.75
153	Lloyd Mumphord	.20
154	Cullen Bryant	.20
155	Willie Lanier	.75
156	Gene Washington	.30
157	Scott Hunter	.20
158	Jim Merlo	.20
159	Randy Grossman	.20
160	Blaine Nye (AP)	.20
161	Ike Harris	.20
162	Doug Dieken	.20
163	Guy Morriss	.20
164	Bob Parsons	.20
165	Steve Grogan	2.00
166	John Brockington	.20
167	Charlie Joiner	1.50
168	Ron Carpenter	.20
169	Jeff Wright	.20
170	Chris Hanburger (AP)	.20
171	*Roosevelt Leaks*	.40
172	Larry Little	.60
173	John Matuszak	.30
174	Joe Ferguson	.50
175	Brad Van Pelt	.30
176	*Dexter Bussey*	.30
177	*Steve Largent*	50.00
178	Dewey Selmon	.20
179	Randy Gradishar	1.00
180	Mel Blount (AP)	3.00
181	Dan Neal	.20
182	Rich Szaro	.20
183	Mike Boryla	.20
184	Steve Jones	.20
185	Paul Warfield	2.00
186	*Greg Buttle*	.40
187	Rich McGeorge	.20
188	*Leon Gray*	.50
189	John Shinners	.20
190	Toni Linhart (AP)	.20
191	Robert Miller	.20
192	Jake Scott	.20
193	Jon Morris	.20
194	Randy Crowder	.20
195	Lynn Swann	10.00
196	Marsh White	.20
197	*Rod Perry*	.30
198	Willie Hall	.20
199	Mike Hartenstine	.20
200	Jim Bakken (AP)	.20
201	Atlanta Falcons Team	1.00
202	Baltimore Colts Team	1.00
203	Buffalo Bills Team	1.00
204	Chicago Bears Team	1.00
205	Cincinnati Bengals Team	1.00
206	Cleveland Browns Team	1.00
207	Dallas Cowboys Team	1.00
208	Denver Broncos Team	1.00
209	Detroit Lions Team	1.00
210	Green Bay Packers Team	1.00
211	Houston Oilers Team	1.00
212	Kansas City Chiefs Team	1.00
213	Los Angeles Rams Team	1.00
214	Miami Dolphins Team	1.00
215	Minnesota Vikings Team	1.00
216	New England Patriots Team	1.00
217	New Orleans Saints Team	1.00
218	New York Giants Team	1.00
219	New York Jets Team	1.00
220	Oakland Raiders Team	1.00
221	Philadelphia Eagles Team	1.00
222	Pittsburgh Steelers Team	1.00
223	St. Louis Cardinals Team	1.00
224	San Diego Chargers Team	1.00
225	San Francisco 49ers Team	1.00
226	Seattle Seahawks Team	1.00
227	Tampa Bay Buccaneers Team	1.00
228	Washington Redskins Team	1.00
229	Sam Cunningham	.20
230	Alan Page (AP)	1.25
231	Eddie Brown	.20
232	Stan White	.20
233	Vern Den Herder	.20
234	Clarence Davis	.20
235	Ken Anderson	1.75
236	Karl Chandler	.20
237	Will Harrell	.20
238	Clarence Scott	.20
239	Bo Rather	.20
240	Robert Brazile (AP)	.40
241	Bob Bell	.20
242	Rolland Lawrence	.20
243	Tom Sullivan	.20
244	Larry Brunson	.20
245	Terry Bradshaw	7.00
246	Rich Saul	.20
247	Cleveland Elam	.20
248	Don Woods	.20
249	Bruce Laird	.20
250	Coy Bacon (AP)	.20
251	Russ Francis	.60
252	Jim Braxton	.20
253	Perry Smith	.20
254	Jerome Barkum	.20
255	Garo Yepremian	.20
256	Checklist 133-264	1.50
257	*Tony Galbreath*	.50
258	Troy Archer	.20
259	Brian Sipe	1.00
260	Billy Joe DuPree (AP)	.50
261	Bobby Walden	.20
262	Larry Marshall	.20
263	Ted Fritsch	.20
264	Larry Hand	.20
265	Tom Mack	.30
266	Ed Bradley	.20
267	Pat Leahy	.75
268	Louis Carter	.20
269	*Archie Griffin*	5.00
270	Art Shell (AP)	1.50
271	Stu Voigt	.20
272	Prentice McCray	.20
273	MacArthur Lane	.20
274	Dan Fouts	5.00
275	Charley Young	.20
276	*Wilbur Jackson*	.50
277	John Hicks	.20
278	Nat Moore	.60
279	Virgil Livers	.20
280	Curley Culp (AP)	.20
281	Rocky Bleier	1.00
282	John Zook	.20
283	Tom DeLeone	.20
284	Danny White	5.00
285	Otis Armstrong	.40
286	Larry Walton	.20
287	Jim Carter	.20
288	Don McCauley	.20
289	Frank Grant	.20
290	Roger Wehrli (AP)	.20
291	Mick Tingelhoff	.20
292	Bernard Jackson	.20
293	*Tom Owen*	.30
294	Mike Esposito	.20
295	Fred Biletnikoff	2.00
296	*Revie Sorey*	.30
297	John McMakin	.20
298	Dan Ryczek	.20
299	Wayne Moore	.20
300	Franco Harris (AP)	4.00
301	*Rick Upchurch*	2.00
302	Jim Stienke	.20
303	Charlie Davis	.20
304	Don Cockroft	.20
305	Ken Burrough	.20
306	Clark Gaines	.20
307	Bobby Douglass	.20
308	Ralph Perretta	.20
309	Wally Hilgenberg	.20
310	Monte Jackson (AP)	.40
311	*Chris Bahr*	.50
312	Jim Cheyunski	.20
313	Mike Patrick	.20
314	Ed "Too Tall" Jones	5.00
315	Bill Bradley	.20
316	Benny Malone	.20
317	Paul Seymour	.20
318	Jim Laslavic	.20
319	Frank Lewis	.20
320	Ray Guy (AP)	.75
321	Allen Ellis	.20
322	Conrad Dobler	.30
323	Chester Marcol	.20
324	Doug Kotar	.20
325	Lemar Parrish	.20
326	Steve Holden	.20
327	Jeff Van Note	.20
328	Howard Stevens	.20
329	Brad Dusek	.20
330	Joe DeLamielleure (AP)	.20
331	Jim Plunkett	1.00
332	Checklist 265-396	1.50
333	Lou Piccone	.20
334	Ray Hamilton	.20
335	Jan Stenerud	.60
336	Jeris White	.20
337	*Sherman Smith*	.35
338	Dave Green	.20
339	Terry Schmidt	.20
340	*Sammie White* (AP)	1.25
341	*Jon Kolb*	.20
342	Randy White	7.00
343	Bob Klein	.20
344	Bob Kowalkowski	.20
345	Terry Metcalf	.30
346	Joe Danelo	.20
347	Ken Payne	.20
348	Neal Craig	.20
349	Dennis Johnson	.20
350	Bill Bergey (AP)	.50
351	Raymond Chester	.20
352	Bob Matheson	.20
353	Mike Kadish	.20
354	*Mark Van Eeghen*	.75
355	L.C. Greenwood	.60
356	Sam Hunt	.50
357	Darrell Austin	.20
358	Jim Turner	.20
359	Ahmad Rashad	2.00
360	Walter Payton (AP)	35.00
361	Mark Arneson	.20
362	Jerrel Wilson	.20
363	Steve Bartkowski	1.00
364	John Watson	.20
365	Ken Riley	.20
366	Gregg Bingham	.20
367	Golden Richards	.20
368	Clyde Powers	.20
369	Diron Talbert	.20
370	Lydell Mitchell	.30
371	Bob Jackson	.20
372	Jim Mandich	.20
373	Frank LeMaster	.20
374	Benny Ricardo	.20
375	Lawrence McCutcheon	.30
376	Lynn Dickey	.50
377	Phil Wise	.20
378	Tony McGee	.20
379	Norm Thompson	.20
380	*Dave Casper* (AP)	5.00
381	Glen Edwards	.20
382	Bob Thomas	.20
383	Bob Chandler	.20
384	Rickey Young	.20
385	Carl Eller	.60
386	Lyle Alzado	1.00
387	John Leypoldt	.20
388	Gordon Bell	.20
389	Mike Bragg	.20
390	Jim Langer (AP)	1.00
391	Vern Holland	.20
392	Nelson Munsey	.20
393	Mack Mitchell	.20
394	Tony Adams	.20
395	Preston Pearson	.35
396	Emanuel Zanders	.20
397	Vince Papale	.20
398	*Joe Fields*	.30
399	Craig Clemons	.20
400	Fran Tarkenton (AP)	6.00
401	Andy Johnson	.20
402	Willie Buchanon	.20
403	Pat Curran	.20
404	Ray Jarvis	.20
405	Joe Greene	2.00
406	Bill Simpson	.20
407	Ronnie Coleman	.20
408	J.K. McKay	.20
409	Pat Fischer	.20
410	John Dutton (AP)	.20
411	Boobie Clark	.20
412	*Pat Tilley*	1.00
413	Don Strock	.30
414	Brian Kelley	.20
415	Gene Upshaw	1.00
416	Mike Montler	.20
417	Checklist 397-528	1.50
418	John Gilliam	.20
419	Brent McClanahan	.20
420	Jerry Sherk (AP)	.20
421	Roy Gerela	.20
422	Tim Fox	.20
423	John Ebersole	.20
424	James Scott	.20
425	*Delvin Williams*	.20
426	Spike Jones	.20
427	Harvey Martin	1.25
428	Don Herrmann	.20
429	Calvin Hill	.40
430	Isiah Robertson (AP)	.20
431	Tony Greene	.20
432	Bob Johnson	.20
433	Lem Barney	.90
434	Eric Torkelson	.20
435	John Mendenhall	.20
436	Larry Seiple	.20
437	Art Kuehn	.20
438	John Vella	.20
439	Greg Latta	.20
440	Roger Carr (AP)	.20
441	Doug Sutherland	.20
442	Mike Kruczek	.20
443	Steve Zabel	.20
444	*Mike Pruitt*	1.00
445	Harold Jackson	.20
446	George Jakowenko	.20
447	John Fitzgerald	.20
448	Terry Joyce	.20
449	Jim LeClair	.20
450	Ken Houston (AP)	.75
451	Record: (Steve Grogan)	.40
452	Record: (Jim Marshall)	.40
453	Record: (Terry Schmidt)	5.00
454	Record: (O.J. Simpson)	3.00
455	Record: (Jim Zorn)	.40
456	Robert Pratt	.20
457	Walker Gillette	.20
458	Charlie Hall	.20
459	Robert Newhouse	.30
460	John Hannah (AP)	1.25
461	Ken Reaves	.20
462	Herman Weaver	.20
463	James Harris	.20
464	Howard Twilley	.20
465	Jeff Siemon	.20
466	John Outlaw	.20
467	*Chuck Muncie*	1.50
468	Bob Moore	.20
469	Robert Woods	.20
470	Cliff Branch (AP)	1.50
471	Johnnie Gray	.20
472	Don Hardeman	.20
473	Steve Ramsey	.20
474	Steve Mike-Mayer	.20
475	Gary Garrison	.20
476	Walter Johnson	.20
477	Neil Clabo	.20
478	Len Hauss	.20
479	Darryl Stingley	.40
480	Jack Lambert (AP)	7.00
481	Mike Adamle	.20
482	David Lee	.20
483	Tom Mullen	.20
484	Claude Humphrey	.20
485	Jim Hart	.60
486	Bobby Thompson	.20
487	Jack Rudnay	.20
488	Rich Saul	.20
489	Reuben Gant	.20
490	Cliff Harris (AP)	.75
491	Bob Brown	.20
492	Don Nottingham	.20
493	Ron Jessie	.20
494	Otis Sistrunk	.30
495	Bill Kilmer	.60
496	Oscar Roan	.20
497	Bill Van Heusen	.20
498	Randy Logan	.20
499	John Smith	.20
500	Chuck Foreman (AP)	.50
501	J.T. Thomas	.20
502	Steve Schubert	.20
503	Mike Barnes	.20
504	J.V. Cain	.20
505	Larry Csonka	2.00
506	Elvin Bethea	.20
507	Ray Easterling	.20
508	Joe Reed	.20
509	Steve Odom	.20
510	Tommy Casanova (AP)	.20
511	Dave Dalby	.20
512	Richard Caster	.20
513	Fred Dryer	1.50
514	Jeff Kinney	.20
515	Bob Griese	4.00
516	*Butch Johnson*	.75
517	Gerald Irons	.20
518	Don Calhoun	.20
519	Jack Gregory	.20
520	Tom Banks (AP)	.20
521	Bobby Bryant	.20
522	Reggie Harrison	.20
523	Terry Hermeling	.20
524	David Taylor	.20
525	*Brian Baschnagel*	.50
526	AFC Championship: (Ken Stabler)	.40
527	NFC Championship	.40
528	Super Bowl XI	1.50

1977 Topps Holsum Packers/Vikings

CHESTER MARCOL PACKERS

The 22-card, standard-size set featuring 11 Green Bay players (1-11) and 11 Minnesota players (12-22) was issued in Holsum Bread packages. For an unapparent reason, Holsum did not print its name or logo anywhere on the cards.

No.	Player	NM
	Complete Set (22):	45.00
	Common Player:	1.00
1	Lynn Dickey	3.00
2	John Brockington	2.00
3	Will Harrell	1.00
4	Ken Payne	1.00
5	Rich McGeorge	1.00
6	Steve Odom	1.00
7	Jim Carter	1.00
8	Fred Carr	1.00
9	Willie Buchanon	1.00
10	Mike McCoy	1.00
11	Chester Marcol	1.00
12	Chuck Foreman	4.00
13	Ahmad Rashad	7.00
14	Sammie White	3.00
15	Stu Voigt	1.00
16	Fred Cox	1.00
17	Carl Eller	4.00
18	Alan Page	6.00
19	Jeff Siemon	1.00
20	Bobby Bryant	1.00
21	Paul Krause	3.00
22	Ron Yary	2.00

1977 Topps Mexican

The 528-card, standard-size set is the Spanish parallel set to the standard 1977 Topps set. All text on the card fronts and backs is in Spanish. The wrappers are also deemed collectible as they depict various NFL stars.

	NM
Complete Set (528):	6000.
Common Player:	8.00
Common Checklist:	12.00

		NM
	Semistars:	10.00
1	Passing Leaders (James Harris, Ken Stabler)	100.00
2	Receiving Leaders (Drew Pearson, MacArthur Lane)	15.00
3	Rushing Leaders (Walter Payton, O.J. Simpson)	180.00
4	Scoring Leaders (Mark Moseley, Toni Linhart)	25.00
18	Pat Haden	30.00
29	Lee Roy Selmon (UER) (Misspelled Leroy)	75.00
45	Roger Staubach	100.00
50	Mike Haynes (AP)	25.00
55	John Riggins	30.00
65	Jim Zorn	30.00
74	Joe Theismann	40.00
80	Jack Youngblood (AP)	15.00
90	Dan Dierdorf (AP)	20.00
95	Bert Jones	15.00
96	Anthony Davis	20.00
98	Ray Rhodes	25.00
99	Mike Webster	50.00
100	O.J. Simpson (AP)	100.00
108	John Cappelletti	20.00
110	Ken Stabler (AP)	100.00
130	Drew Pearson (AP)	25.00
140	Jack Ham (AP)	30.00
144	Harold Carmichael	15.00
146	Harry Carson	40.00
165	Steve Grogan	20.00
167	Charlie Joiner	20.00
173	John Matuszak	20.00
177	Steve Largent	550.00
179	Randy Gradishar	15.00
180	Mel Blount (AP)	30.00
185	Paul Warfield	30.00
195	Lynn Swann	100.00
230	Alan Page (AP)	15.00
235	Ken Anderson	20.00
245	Terry Bradshaw	100.00
259	Brian Sipe	15.00
269	Archie Griffin	50.00
270	Art Shell	15.00
274	Dan Fouts	60.00
281	Rocky Bleier	30.00
284	Danny White	50.00
295	Fred Biletnikoff	50.00
300	Franco Harris (AP)	50.00
314	Ed "Too Tall" Jones	75.00
320	Ray Guy (AP)	15.00
331	Jim Plunkett	15.00
342	Randy White	60.00
359	Ahmad Rashad	20.00
360	Walter Payton (AP)	400.00
380	Dave Casper (AP)	40.00
386	Lyle Alzado	15.00
400	Fran Tarkenton (AP)	60.00
405	Joe Greene	30.00
412	Pat Tilley	20.00
415	Gene Upshaw	20.00
427	Harvey Martin	20.00
433	Lem Barney	15.00
444	Mike Pruitt	20.00
450	Ken Houston (AP)	20.00
453	O.J. Simpson (RB)	70.00
454	Most Yardage, Passing, Lifetime (Fran Tarkenton) (RB)	35.00
455	Most Passing Yards Season, Rookie (Jim Zorn) (RB)	25.00
460	John Hannah (AP)	15.00
467	Chuck Muncie	15.00
470	Cliff Branch	30.00
480	Jack Lambert (AP)	60.00
505	Larry Csonka	45.00
515	Bob Griese	45.00
526	AFC Championship (Ken Stabler)	75.00
527	NFC Championship	15.00
528	Super Bowl XI	200.00

1977 Topps Team Checklists

The 30-card, standard-size set contains a 28 team checklist and two checklist cards and was available through Topps as an uncut sheet. The cards are identical to the checklists in the base set, except for the thinner stock.

		NM
	Complete Set (30):	120.00
	Common Player:	5.00
1	Atlanta Falcons	5.00
2	Baltimore Colts	5.00
3	Buffalo Bills	5.00
4	Chicago Bears	8.00
5	Cincinnati Bengals	5.00
6	Cleveland Browns	5.00
7	Dallas Cowboys	10.00
8	Denver Broncos	5.00
9	Detroit Lions	5.00
10	Green Bay Packers	8.00
11	Houston Oilers	5.00
12	Kansas City Chiefs	5.00
13	Los Angeles Rams	5.00
14	Miami Dolphins	8.00
15	Minnesota Vikings	5.00
16	New England Patriots	5.00
17	New York Giants	5.00
18	New York Jets	5.00
19	New Orleans Saints	5.00
20	Oakland Raiders	8.00
21	Philadelphia Eagles	5.00
22	Pittsburgh Steelers	8.00
23	St. Louis Cardinals	5.00
24	San Diego Chargers	5.00
25	San Francisco 49ers	8.00
26	Seattle Seahawks	5.00
27	Tampa Bay Buccaneers	5.00
28	Washington Redskins	8.00
NN01	Checklist 1-132	5.00
NN02	Checklist 133-264	5.00

1978 Topps

Topps' fourth 528-card set featured a colorful design, with the team name in white inside a solid border of color down the left side of the card. The subsets in the 1978 set include highlights, conference leader cards, and team leader cards (the last cards in the set; the team leader cards are arranged alphabetically by city name). This is the first time Topps pictured the actual team leaders on its team cards. The set is most notable for the inclusion of the Dorsett rookie card, the Largent second-year card, and the Payton third-year card. Other rookies in the set include Johnny Rodgers, Joe Klecko, John Stallworth, Wesley Walker, Stanley Morgan and Pete Johnson. (Key: AP - All Pro)

		NM
	Complete Set (528):	140.00
	Common Player:	.15
1	Gary Huff (HL)	.25
2	Craig Morton (HL)	.25
3	Walter Payton (HL)	6.00
4	O.J. Simpson (HL)	3.00
5	Fran Tarkenton (HL)	2.00
6	Bob Thomas (HL)	.25
7	Joe Pisarcik	.15
8	Skip Thomas	.15
9	Roosevelt Leaks	.15
10	Ken Houston (AP)	.75
11	Tom Blanchard	.15
12	Jim Turner	.15
13	Tom DeLeone	.15
14	Jim LeClair	.15
15	Bob Avellini	.15
16	Tony McGee	.15
17	James Harris	.15
18	Terry Nelson	.15
19	Rocky Bleier	.75
20	Joe DeLamielleure (AP)	.15
21	Richard Caster	.15
22	*A.J. Duhe*	1.00
23	John Outlaw	.15
24	Danny White	1.50
25	Larry Csonka	1.50
26	David Hill	.15
27	Mark Arneson	.15
28	Jack Tatum	.15
29	Norm Thompson	.15
30	Sammie White	.30
31	Dennis Johnson	.15
32	Robin Earl	.15
33	Don Cockroft	.15
34	Bob Johnson	.15
35	John Hannah	.75
36	Scott Hunter	.15
37	Ken Burrough	.15
38	Wilbur Jackson	.15
39	Rich McGeorge	.15
40	Lyle Alzado (AP)	.75
41	John Ebersole	.15
42	*Gary Green*	.15
43	Art Kuehn	.15
44	Glen Edwards	.15
45	Lawrence McCutcheon	.15
46	Duriel Harris	.15
47	Rich Szaro	.15
48	Mike Washington	.15
49	Stan White	.15
50	Dave Casper (AP)	1.00
51	Len Hauss	.15
52	James Scott	.15
53	Brian Sipe	.60
54	Gary Shirk	.15
55	Archie Griffin	.60
56	Mike Patrick	.15
57	Mario Clark	.15
58	Jeff Siemon	.15
59	Steve Mike-Mayer	.15
60	Randy White (AP)	2.50
61	Darrell Austin	.15
62	Tom Sullivan	.15
63	*Johnny Rodgers*	1.75
64	Ken Reaves	.15
65	Terry Bradshaw	6.00
66	Fred Steinfort	.15
67	Curley Culp	.15
68	Ted Hendricks	.75
69	Raymond Chester	.15
70	Jim Langer (AP)	.75
71	Calvin Hill	.30
72	Mike Hartenstine	.15
73	Gerald Irons	.15
74	Billy Brooks	.15
75	John Mendenhall	.15
76	Andy Johnson	.15
77	Tom Wittum	.15
78	Lynn Dickey	.25
79	Carl Eller	.40
80	Tom Mack	.15
81	Clark Gaines	.15
82	Lem Barney	.75
83	Mike Montler	.15
84	Jon Kolb	.15
85	Bob Chandler	.15
86	Robert Newhouse	.15
87	Frank LeMaster	.15
88	Jeff West	.15
89	Lyle Blackwood	.15
90	Gene Upshaw (AP)	.15
91	Frank Grant	.50
92	Tom Hicks	.15
93	Mike Pruitt	.35
94	Chris Bahr	.15
95	Russ Francis	.35
96	Norris Thomas	.15
97	*Gary Barbaro*	.40
98	Jim Merlo	.15
99	Karl Chandler	.15
100	Fran Tarkenton	4.00
101	Abdul Salaam	.15
102	Marv Kellum	.15
103	Herman Weaver	.15
104	Roy Gerela	.15
105	Harold Jackson	.50
106	Dewey Selmon	.15
107	Checklist 1-132	1.00
108	Clarence Davis	.15
109	Robert Pratt	.15
110	Harvey Martin (AP)	.60
111	Brad Dusek	.15
112	Greg Latta	.15
113	Tony Peters	.15
114	Jim Braxton	.15
115	Ken Riley	.15
116	Steve Nelson	.15
117	Rick Upchurch	.35
118	Spike Jones	.15
119	Doug Kotar	.15
120	Bob Griese (AP)	3.00
121	Burgess Owens	.15
122	Rolf Benirschke	.60
123	Haskel Stanback	.15
124	J.T. Thomas	.15
125	Ahmad Rashad	1.25
126	Rick Kane	.15
127	Elvin Bethea	.15
128	Dave Dalby	.15
129	Mike Barnes	.15
130	Isiah Robertson	.15
131	Jim Plunkett	.75
132	Allan Ellis	.15
133	Mike Bragg	.15
134	Bob Jackson	.15
135	Coy Bacon	.15
136	John Smith	.15
137	Chuck Muncie	.35
138	Johnnie Gray	.15
139	Jimmy Robinson	.15
140	Tom Banks	.15
141	*Marvin Powell*	.40
142	Jerrell Wilson	.15
143	Ron Howard	.15
144	*Rob Lytle*	.35
145	L.C. Greenwood	.50
146	Morris Owens	.15
147	Joe Reed	.15
148	Mike Kadish	.15
149	Phil Villapiano	.15
150	Lydell Mitchell	.15
151	Randy Logan	.15
152	Mike Williams	.15
153	Jeff Van Note	.15
154	Steve Schubert	.15
155	Bill Kilmer	.50
156	Boobie Clark	.15
157	Charlie Hall	.15
158	*Raymond Clayborn*	.60
159	Jack Gregory	.15
160	Cliff Harris (AP)	.50
161	Joe Fields	.15
162	Don Nottingham	.15
163	Ed White	.15
164	Toni Fritsch	.15
165	Jack Lambert	3.00
166	NFC Champions (Roger Staubach)	1.50
167	AFC Champions: (Rob Lytle)	.30
168	Super Bowl XII (Tony Dorsett)	2.50
169	Neal Colzie	.20
170	Cleveland Elam (AP)	.15
171	David Lee	.15
172	Jim Otis	.15
173	Archie Manning	.75
174	Jim Carter	.15
175	Jean Fugett	.15
176	Willie Parker	.15
177	Haven Moses	.15
178	Horace King	.15
179	Bob Thomas	.15
180	Monte Jackson	.15
181	Steve Zabel	.15
182	John Fitzgerald	.15
183	Mike Livingston	.15
184	Larry Poole	.15
185	Isaac Curtis	.15
186	Chuck Ramsey	.15
187	Bob Klein	.15
188	Ray Rhodes	.15
189	Otis Sistrunk	.15
190	Bill Bergey	.30
191	Sherman Smith	.15
192	Dave Green	.15
193	Carl Mauck	.15
194	Reggie Harrison	.15
195	Roger Carr	.15
196	Steve Bartkowski	.75
197	Ray Wershing	.15
198	Willie Buchanon	.15
199	Neil Clabo	.15
200	Walter Payton (AP)	20.00
201	Sam Adams	.15
202	Larry Gordon	.15
203	Pat Tilley	.15
204	Mack Mitchell	.15
205	Ken Anderson	1.25
206	Scott Dierking	.15
207	Jack Rudnay	.15
208	Jim Stienke	.15
209	Bill Simpson	.15
210	Errol Mann	.15
211	Bucky Dilts	.15
212	Reuben Gant	.15
213	*Thomas Henderson*	.50
214	Steve Furness	.15
215	John Riggins	2.00
216	Keith Krepfle	.35
217	*Fred Dean*	1.25
218	Emanuel Zanders	.15
219	Don Testerman	.15
220	George Kunz	.15
221	Darryl Stingley	.25
222	Ken Sanders	.15
223	Gary Huff	.15
224	Gregg Bingham	.15
225	Jerry Sherk	.15
226	Doug Plank	.15
227	Ed Taylor	.15
228	Emery Moorehead	.15
229	*Reggie Williams*	2.50
230	Claude Humphrey	.15
231	*Randy Cross*	2.50
232	Jim Hart	.50
233	Bobby Bryant	.15
234	Larry Brown	.15
235	Mark Van Eeghen	.15
236	Terry Hermeling	.15
237	Steve Odom	.15
238	Jan Stenerud	.50
239	Andre Tillman	.15
240	*Tom Jackson* (AP)	4.00
241	Ken Mendenhall	.15
242	Tim Fox	.15
243	Don Herrmann	.15
244	Eddie McMillan	.15
245	Greg Pruitt	.30
246	J.K. McKay	.15
247	Larry Keller	.15
248	Dave Jennings	.15
249	Bo Harris	.15
250	Revie Sorey	.15
251	Tony Greene	.15
252	Butch Johnson	.35
253	Paul Naumoff	.15
254	Rickey Young	.15
255	Dwight White	.15
256	Joe Lavender	.15
257	Checklist 133-264	1.00
258	Ronnie Coleman	.15
259	Charlie Smith	.15
260	Ray Guy (AP)	.50
261	David Taylor	.15
262	Bill Lenkaitis	.15
263	Jim Mitchell	.15
264	Delvin Williams	.15
265	Jack Youngblood	.60
266	Chuck Crist	.15
267	Richard Todd	.30
268	*Dave Logan*	.35
269	Rufus Mayes	.15
270	Brad Van Pelt	.15
271	Chester Marcol	.15
272	J.V. Cain	.15
273	Larry Seiple	.15
274	Brent McClanahan	.15
275	Mike Wagner	.15
276	Diron Talbert	.15
277	Brian Baschnagel	.15
278	Ed Podolak	.15
279	Don Goode	.15
280	John Dutton	.15
281	Don Calhoun	.15
282	Monte Johnson	.15
283	Ron Jessie	.15
284	Jon Morris	.15
285	Riley Odoms	.15
286	Marv Bateman	.15
287	*Joe Klecko*	2.00
288	Oliver Davis	.15
289	John McDaniel	.15
290	Roger Staubach	8.00
291	Brian Kelley	.15
292	Mike Hogan	.15
293	John Leypoldt	.15
294	Jack Novak	.15
295	Joe Greene	1.50
296	John Hill	.15
297	Danny Buggs	.15
298	Ted Albrecht	.15
299	Nelson Munsey	.15
300	Chuck Foreman	.40
301	Dan Pastorini	.30
302	Tommy Hart	.15
303	Dave Beverly	.15
304	*Tony Reed*	.30
305	Cliff Branch	1.00
306	Clarence Duren	.15
307	Randy Rasmussen	.15
308	Oscar Roan	.15
309	Lenvil Elliott	.15
310	Dan Dierdorf (AP)	1.00
311	Johnny Perkins	.15
312	*Rafael Septien*	.30
313	Terry Beeson	.15
314	Lee Roy Selmon	.50
315	*Tony Dorsett*	35.00
316	Greg Landry	.30
317	Jake Scott	.15
318	Dan Peiffer	.15
319	John Bunting	.15
320	*John Stallworth*	20.00
321	Bob Howard	.15
322	Larry Little	.50
323	Reggie McKenzie	.15
324	Duane Carrell	.15
325	Ed Simonini	.15
326	John Vella	.15
327	*Wesley Walker*	3.50
328	Jon Keyworth	.15
329	Ron Bolton	.15
330	Tommy Casanova	.15
331	Passing Leaders: (Bob Griese, Roger Staubach)	3.50
332	Receiving Leaders: (Lydell Mitchell, Ahmad Rashad)	.25
333	Rushing Leaders: (Mark Van Eeghen, Walter Payton)	2.25
334	Scoring Leaders: (Errol Mann, Walter Payton)	2.25
335	Interception Leaders: (Lyle Blackwood, Rolland Lawrence)	.25
336	Punting Leaders: (Ray Guy, Tom Blanchard)	.25
337	Robert Brazile	.15
338	Charlie Joiner	1.00
339	Joe Ferguson	.30
340	Bill Thompson	.15
341	Sam Cunningham	.15
342	Curtis Johnson	.15
343	Jim Marshall	.50
344	Charlie Sanders	.15
345	Willie Hall	.15
346	Pat Haden	.75
347	Jim Bakken	.15
348	Bruce Taylor	.15
349	Barty Smith	.15
350	Drew Pearson	1.00
351	Mike Webster	2.00
352	Bobby Hammond	.15
353	Dave Mays	.15
354	Pat McInally	.15
355	Toni Linhart	.15
356	Larry Hand	.15
357	Ted Fritsch	.15
358	Larry Marshall	.15
359	Waymond Bryant	.15
360	*Louie Kelcher*	.35
361	*Stanley Morgan*	4.00
362	*Bruce Harper*	.30
363	Bernard Jackson	.15
364	Walter White	.15
365	Ken Stabler	6.00
366	Fred Dryer	1.00
367	Ike Harris	.15
368	Norm Bulaich	.15
369	Merv Krakau	.15
370	John James	.15
371	*Bennie Cunningham*	.30
372	Doug Van Horn	.15
373	Thom Darden	.15
374	*Eddie Edwards*	.15
375	Mike Thomas	.15
376	Fred Cook	.15
377	Mike Phipps	.15
378	Paul Krause	.15
379	Harold Carmichael	.75
380	Mike Haynes (AP)	1.00
381	Wayne Morris	.15
382	Greg Buttle	.15
383	Jim Zorn	.50
384	Jack Dolbin	.15
385	Charlie Waters	.50
386	Dan Ryczek	.15
387	*Joe Washington*	1.00
388	Checklist 265-396	1.00
389	James Hunter	.15
390	Billy Johnson	.15
391	Jim Allen	.15
392	George Buehler	.15
393	Harry Carson	1.25
394	Cleo Miller	.15
395	Gary Burley	.15
396	Mark Moseley	.25
397	Virgil Livers	.15
398	Joe Ehrmann	.15
399	Freddie Solomon	.15
400	O.J. Simpson	5.00
401	Julius Adams	.15
402	Artimus Parker	.15
403	Gene Washington	.15
404	Herman Edwards	.15
405	Craig Morton	.50
406	Alan Page	.75
407	Larry McCarren	.15
408	Tony Galbreath	.15
409	Roman Gabriel	.60
410	Efren Herrera (AP)	.15
411	*Jim Smith*	.60
412	Bill Bryant	.15
413	Doug Dieken	.15
414	Marvin Cobb	.15
415	Fred Biletnikoff	1.50
416	Joe Theismann	2.50
417	Roland Harper	.15
418	Derrel Luce	.15
419	Ralph Perretta	.15
420	*Louis Wright*	1.00
421	Prentice McCray	.15
422	Garry Puetz	.15
423	*Alfred Jenkins*	.50
424	Paul Seymour	.15
425	Garo Yepremian	.15
426	Emmitt Thomas	.15
427	Dexter Bussey	.15
428	John Sanders	.15
429	Ed "Too Tall" Jones	2.00
431	Frank Lewis	.15
432	Jerry Golsteyn	.15
433	Clarence Scott	.15
434	Pete Johnson	.50
435	Charley Young	.15
436	Harold McLinton	.15
437	Noah Jackson	.15
438	Bruce Laird	.15
439	John Matuszak	.15
440	Nat Moore (AP)	.35
441	Leon Gray	.15
442	Jerome Barkum	.15
443	Steve Largent	15.00
444	John Zook	.15
445	Preston Pearson	.30
446	Conrad Dobler	.15
447	Wilbur Summers	.15
448	Lou Piccone	.15
449	Ron Jaworski	.60
450	Jack Ham (AP)	1.50
451	Mick Tingelhoff	.15
452	Clyde Powers	.15
453	John Cappelletti	.50
454	Dick Ambrose	.15
455	Lemar Parrish	.15
456	Ron Saul	.15
457	Bob Parsons	.15
458	Glenn Doughty	.15
459	Don Woods	.15
460	Art Shell (AP)	1.00
461	Sam Hunt	.15
462	Lawrence Pillers	.15
463	Henry Childs	.15
464	Roger Wehrli	.15
465	Otis Armstrong	.30
466	*Bob Baumhower*	.75
467	Ray Jarvis	.15
468	Guy Morriss	.15
469	Matt Blair	.35
470	Bill Joe DuPree	.35
471	Roland Hooks	.15
472	Joe Danelo	.15
473	Reggie Rucker	.15
474	Vern Holland	.15
475	Mel Blount	1.25
476	Eddie Brown	.15
477	Bo Rather	.15
478	Don McCauley	.15
479	Glen Walker	.15
480	Randy Gradishar	.90
481	Dave Rowe	.15
482	Pat Leahy	.40
483	Mike Fuller	.15
484	David Lewis	.15
485	Steve Grogan	.75
486	Mel Gray	.15
487	*Eddie Payton*	.30
488	Checklist 397-528	1.00
489	Stu Voigt	.15
490	Rolland Lawrence (AP)	.15
491	Nick Mike-Mayer	.15
492	Troy Archer	.15
493	Benny Malone	.15
494	Golden Richards	.15
495	Chris Hanburger	.15
496	Dwight Harrison	.15

497 *Gary Fencik* .75
498 Rich Saul .15
499 Dan Fouts 5.00
500 Franco Harris (AP) 2.50
501 Atlanta Falcons Team: .50 (Haskel Stanback, Alfred Jenkins, Claude Humphrey, Jeff Merrow, Rolland)
502 Baltimore Colts Team: .50 (Lydell Mitchell, Lyle Blackwood, Fred Cook)
503 Buffalo Bills Team: 2.00 (Bob Chandler, O.J. Simpson, Tony Greene, Sherman White)
504 Chicago Bears 1.75 (James Scott, Allan Ellis, Ron Rydalch, Walter Payton)
505 Cincinnati Bengals Team: .75 (Billy Brooks, Lemar Parrish, Reggie Williams, Gary Burley, Pete Johnson)
506 Cleveland Browns Team: .50 (Reggie Rucker, Thom Darden, Mack Mitchell, Greg Pruitt)
507 Dallas Cowboys Team: 2.00 (Drew Pearson, Cliff Harris, Harvey Martin, Tony Dorsett)
508 Denver Broncos Team: .50 (Otis Armstrong, Haven Moses, Bill Thompson, Rick Upchurch)
509 Detroit Lions Team: .50 (Horace King, David Hill, James Hunter, Ken Sanders)
510 Green Bay Packers Team: .50 (Barty Smith, Steve Odom, Steve Luke, M.C. McCoy, Dave Pureifory, Dave
511 Houston Oilers Team: .50 (Ronnie Coleman, Ken Burrough, Mike Reinfeldt, James Young)
512 Kansas City Chiefs Team: .50 (Ed Podolak, Walter White, Gary Barbaro, Wilbur Young)
513 Los Angeles Rams Team: .50 (Lawrence McCutcheon, Harold Jackson, Bill Simpson, Jack Youngblood)
514 Miami Dolphins Team: .50 (Benny Malone, Nat Moore, Curtis Johnson, A.J. Duhe)
515 Minnesota Vikings Team: .50 (Chuck Foreman, Sammie White, Bobby Bryant, Carl Eller)
516 New England Patriots Team: .50 (Sam Cunningham, Darryl Stingley, Mike Haynes, Tony McGee)
517 New Orleans Saints Team: .50 (Chuck Muncie, Don Herrmann, Chuck Crist, Elois Grooms)
518 New York Giants Team: .50 (Bobby Hammond, Jimmy Robinson, Bill Bryant, John Mendenhall)
519 New York Jets Team: .75 (Clark Gaines, Wesley Walker, Burgess Owens, Joe Klecko)
520 Oakland Raiders Team: .50 (Mark Van Eeghen, Dave Casper, Jack Tatum, Neal Colzie)
521 Philadelphia Eagles Team: .50 (Mike Hogan, Harold Carmichael, Herman Edwards, John Sanders, Lem
522 Pittsburgh Steelers Team: 1.00 (Jim Smith, Mel Blount, Steve Furness, Franco Harris)
523 St. Louis Cardinals Team: .50 (Terry Metcalf, Mel Gray, Roger Wehrli, Mike Dawson)
524 San Diego Chargers Team: .50 (Rickey Young, Charlie Joiner, Mike Fuller, Gary Johnson)
525 San Francisco 49ers Team: .50 (Delvin Williams, G. Washington, Mel Phillips, Dave Washington, Cleveland
526 Seattle Seahawks Team: 1.50 (Steve Largent, Autry Beamon, Walter Packer, Sherman Smith)
527 Tampa Bay Buccaneers Team: .50 (Morris Owens, Isaac Hagins, Mike Washington, Lee Roy Selmon)
528 Washington Redskins Team: 1.00 (Jean Fugett, Ken Houston, Dennis Johnson, Mike Thomas)

1978 Topps Holsum

The 33-card, standard-size set was produced by Topps and distributed with loaves of Holsum Bread. For whatever reason, the cards do not have the Holsum name or logo printed anywhere on the card. As with the 1977 Packers/Vikings Holsum set, an uncut sheet was offered by Topps at an archives auction in 1989.

		NM
Complete Set (33):		250.00
Common Player:		3.00
1	Rolland Lawrence	3.00
2	Walter Payton	80.00
3	Lydell Mitchell	4.00
4	Joe DeLamielleure	3.00
5	Ken Anderson	10.00
6	Greg Pruitt	4.00
7	Harvey Martin	5.00
8	Tom Jackson	5.00
9	Chester Marcol	3.00
10	Jim Carter	3.00
11	Will Harrell	3.00
12	Greg Landry	4.00
13	Billy Johnson	4.00
14	Jan Stenerud	5.00
15	Lawrence McCutcheon	4.00
16	Bob Griese	20.00
17	Chuck Foreman	4.00
18	Sammie White	4.00
19	Jeff Siemon	3.00
20	Mike Haynes	4.00
21	Archie Manning	6.00
22	Brad Van Pelt	3.00
23	Richard Todd	4.00
24	Dave Casper	4.00
25	Bill Bergey	4.00
26	Franco Harris	20.00
27	Mel Gray	4.00
28	Louie Kelcher	3.00
29	O.J. Simpson	30.00
30	Jim Zorn	4.00
31	Lee Roy Selmon	6.00
32	Ken Houston	6.00
33	Checklist Card	8.00

A card number in parentheses ( ) indicates the set is unnumbered.

1979 Topps

Topps' fifth 528-card set was similar in design to its 1973 set, which also showed a small flag. This set, though, showed only the lower half of the flag in solid color, and showed the player's position in a football superimposed over the flag. The team name appeared in any one of a number of colors in capital letters above the photo. Subsets in this year's issue include conference leaders and playoff results. This set is notable for the inclusion of the only four cards Topps issued depicting running back Earl Campbell. Topps was apparently unable to reach a contract agreement with Campbell after this season - possibly similar to the Joe Namath situation after 1973. In addition to Campbell, other rookie cards in this set include Doug Williams, Steve DeBerg, Wilbert Montgomery, Tony Hill, James Jefferson, Ozzie Newsome, and James Lofton. This set also contains the second-year card of Tony Dorsett. (Key: AP - All Pro)

		NM
Complete Set (528):		140.00
Common Player:		.15
1	Passing Leaders (Roger Staubach, Terry Bradshaw)	5.00
2	Receiving Leaders (Rickey Young, Steve Largent)	.75
3	Rushing Leaders (Walter Payton, Earl Campbell)	7.00
4	Scoring Leaders (Frank Corral, Pat Leahy)	.25
5	Interception Leaders (Willie Buchanon, Ken Stone, Thom Darden)	.25
6	Punting Leaders (Tom Skladany, Pat McInally)	.25
7	Johnny Perkins	.15
8	Charles Phillips	.15
9	Derrel Luce	.15
10	John Riggins	1.50
11	Chester Marcol	.15
12	Bernard Jackson	.15
13	Dave Logan	.15
14	Bo Harris	.15
15	Alan Page	.75
16	John Smith	.15
17	Dwight McDonald	.15
18	John Cappelletti	.25
19	Pittsburgh Steelers Team (Franco Harris, Larry Anderson, Tim Dungy, L.C. Greenwood)	.75
20	Bill Bergey (AP)	.25
21	Jerome Barkum	.15
22	Larry Csonka	1.25
23	Joe Ferguson	.25
24	Ed "Too Tall" Jones	1.00
25	Dave Jennings	.15
26	Horace King	.15
27	Steve Little	.15
28	Morris Bradshaw	.15
29	Joe Ehrmann	.15
30	Ahmad Rashad (AP)	.75
31	Joe Lavender	.15
32	Dan Neal	.15
33	Johnny Evans	.15
34	Pete Johnson	.15
35	Mike Haynes (AP)	.40
36	Tim Mazzetti	.15
37	*Mike Barber*	.15
38	San Francisco 49ers Team (O.J. Simpson, Freddie Solomon, Chuck Crist, Cedrick Hardman)	1.75
39	Bill Gregory	.15
40	Randy Gradishar (AP)	.50
41	Richard Todd	.25
42	Henry Marshall	.15
43	John Hill	.15
44	Sidney Thornton	.15
45	Ron Jessie	.15
46	Bob Baumhower	.15
47	Johnnie Gray	.15
48	*Doug Williams*	2.00
49	Don McCauley	.15
50	Ray Guy (AP)	.30
51	Bob Klein	.15
52	Golden Richards	.15
53	Mark Miller	.15
54	John Sanders	.15
55	Gary Burley	.15
56	Steve Nelson	.15
57	Buffalo Bills Team (Miller, Frank Lewis, Mario Clark, Lucius Sanford)	.50
58	Bobby Bryant	.15
59	Rick Kane	.15
60	Larry Little	.35
61	Ted Fritsch	.15
62	Larry Mallory	.15
63	Marvin Powell	.15
64	Jim Hart	.30
65	Joe Greene (AP)	1.25
66	Walter White	.15
67	Gregg Bingham	.15
68	Errol Mann	.15
69	Bruce Laird	.15
70	Drew Pearson	.75
71	Steve Bartkowski	.60
72	Ted Albrecht	.15
73	Charlie Hall	.15
74	Pat McInally	.15
75	*Al Baker* (AP)	1.00
76	New England Patriots Team (Sam Cunningham, Stanley Morgan, Mike Haynes, Tony McGee)	.50
77	*Steve DeBerg*	4.00
78	John Yarno	.15
79	Stu Voight	.15
80	Frank Corral (AP)	.15
81	Troy Archer	.15
82	Bruce Harper	.15
83	Tom Jackson	.75
84	Larry Brown	.15
85	*Wilbert Montgomery*	1.00
86	Butch Johnson	.15
87	Mike Kadish	.15
88	Ralph Perretta	.15
89	David Lee	.15
90	Mark Van Eeghen	.15
91	John McDaniel	.15
92	Gary Fencik	.15
93	Mack Mitchell	.15
94	Cincinnati Bengals Team (Pete Johnson, Isaac Curtis, Dick Jauron, Ross Browner)	.50
95	Steve Grogan	.50
96	Garo Yepremian	.15
97	Barty Smith	.15
98	Frank Reed	.15
99	Jim Clark	.15
100	Chuck Foreman	.30
101	Joe Klecko	.75
102	Pat Tilley	.15
103	Conrad Dobler	.15
104	Craig Colquitt	.15
105	Dan Pastorini	.20
106	Rod Perry (AP)	.15
107	Nick Mike-Mayer	.15
108	John Matuszak	.15
109	David Taylor	.15
110	Billy Joe DuPree (AP)	.15
111	Harold McLinton	.15
112	Virgil Livers	.15
113	Cleveland Browns Team (Greg Pruitt, Thom Darden, Reggie Rucker, Mack Mitchell)	.50
114	Checklist 1-132	1.00
115	Ken Anderson	1.25
116	Bill Lenkaitis	.15
117	Bucky Dilts	.15
118	Tony Greene	.15
119	Bobby Hammond	.15
120	Nat Moore	.15
121	Pat Leahy (AP)	.30
122	James Harris	.15
123	Lee Roy Selmon	.25
124	Bennie Cunningham	.15
125	Matt Blair (AP)	.15
126	Jim Allen	.15
127	Alfred Jenkins	.15
128	Arthur Whittington	.15
129	Norm Thompson	.15
130	Pat Haden	.40
131	Freddie Solomon	.15
132	Chicago Bears Team (Walter Payton, James Scott, Gary Scott, Alan Page)	2.00
133	Mark Moseley	.15
134	Cleo Miller	.15
135	*Ross Browner*	.30
136	Don Calhoun	.15
137	David Whitehurst	.15
138	Terry Beeson	.15
139	Ken Stone	.15
140	Brad Van Pelt AP	.15
141	Wesley Walker (AP)	.75
142	Jan Stenerud	.50
143	Henry Childs	.15
144	Otis Armstrong	.25
145	Dwight White	.15
146	Steve Wilson	.15
147	Tom Skladany (AP)	.15
148	Lou Piccone	.15
149	Monte Johnson	.15
150	Joe Washington	.20
151	Philadelphia Eagles Team (Wilbert Montgomery, Harold Carmichael, Herman Edwards, Dennis Harrison)	.60
152	Fred Dean	.25
153	Rolland Lawrence	.15
154	Brian Baschnagel	.15
155	Joe Theismann	1.50
156	Marvin Cobb	.15
157	Dick Ambrose	.15
158	Mike Patrick	.15
159	Gary Shirk	.15
160	Tony Dorsett	8.00
161	Greg Buttle	.15
162	A.J. Duhe	.15
163	Mick Tingelhoff	.15
164	Ken Burrough	.15
165	Mike Wagner	.15
166	AFC Championship (Franco Harris)	1.00
167	NFC Championship (Franco Harris)	.30
168	Super Bowl XII (Franco Harris)	1.25
169	Oakland Raiders Team (Mark Van Eeghen, Dave Casper, Charles Phillips, Ted Hendricks)	.60
170	O.J. Simpson	4.00
171	Doug Nettles	.15
172	Dan Dierdorf (AP)	.75
173	Dave Beverly	.15
174	Jim Zorn	.35
175	Mike Thomas	.15
176	John Outlaw	.15
177	Jim Turner	.15
178	Freddie Scott	.15
179	Mike Phipps	.15
180	Jack Youngblood (AP)	.50
181	Sam Hunt	.15
182	*Tony Hill*	1.00
183	Gary Barbaro	.15
184	Archie Griffin	.40
185	Jerry Sherk	.15
186	Bobby Jackson	.15
187	Don Woods	.15
188	New York Giants Team (Doug Kotar, Jimmy Robinson, Terry Jackson, George Martin)	.15
189	Raymond Chester	.15
190	Joe DeLamielleure (AP)	.15
191	Tony Galbreath	.15
192	Robert Brazile (AP)	.15
193	Neil O'Donoghue	.15
194	Mike Webster	.75
195	Ed Simonini	.15
196	Denny Malone	.15
197	Tom Wittum	.15
198	Steve Largent (AP)	8.00
199	Tommy Hart	.15
200	Fran Tarkenton	4.00
201	Leon Gray (AP)	.15
202	Leroy Harris	.15
203	Eric Williams	.15
204	Thom Darden (AP)	.15
205	Ken Riley	.15
206	Clark Gaines	.15
207	Kansas City Chiefs Team (Tony Reed, Tim Gray, Art Still)	.50
208	Joe Danelo	.15
209	Glen Walker	.15
210	Art Shell	1.00
211	Jon Keyworth	.15
212	Herman Edwards	.15
213	John Fitzgerald	.15
214	Jim Smith	.15
215	Coy Bacon	.15
216	Dennis Johnson	.15
217	*John Jefferson*	3.00
218	Gary Weaver	.15
219	Tom Blanchard	.15
220	Bert Jones	.50
221	Stanley Morgan	1.50
222	James Hunter	.15
223	Jim O'Bradovich	.15
224	Carl Mauck	.15
225	Chris Bahr	.15
226	New York Jets Team (Kevin Long, Wesley Walker, Bobby Jackson, Burgess Owens, Joe Klecko)	.60
227	Roland Harper	.15
228	Randy Dean	.15
229	Bob Jackson	.15
230	Sammie White	.25
231	Mike Dawson	.15
232	Checklist 133-264	1.00
233	Ken MacAfee	.15
234	Jon Kolb (AP)	.15
235	Willie Hall	.15
236	Ron Saul (AP)	.15
237	Haskel Stanback	.15
238	Zenon Andrusyshyn	.15
239	Norris Thomas	.15
240	Rick Upchurch	.30
241	Robert Pratt	.15
242	Julius Adams	.15
243	Rich McGeorge	.15
244	Seattle Seahawks Team (Sherman Smith, Steve Largent, Cornell Webster, Bill Gregory)	1.00
245	Blair Bush	.15
246	Billy Johnson	.15
247	Randy Rasmussen	.15
248	Brian Kelley	.15
249	Mike Pruitt	.15
250	Harold Carmichael (AP)	.60
251	Mike Hartenstine	.15
252	Robert Newhouse	.15
253	Gary Danielson	.30
254	Mike Fuller	.15
255	L.C. Greenwood (AP)	.40
256	Lemar Parrish	.15
257	Ike Harris	.15
258	*Ricky Bell*	1.00
259	Willie Parker	.15
260	Gene Upshaw	.50
261	Glenn Doughty	.15
262	Steve Zabel	.15
263	Atlanta Falcons Team (Bubba Bean, Wallace Francis, Rolland Lawrence, Greg Brezina)	1.00
264	Ray Wersching	.15
265	Lawrence McCutcheon	.15
266	Willie Buchanon (AP)	.15
267	Matt Robinson	.15
268	Reggie Rucker	.15
269	Doug Van Horn	.15
270	Lydell Mitchell	.15
271	Vern Holland	.15
272	Eason Ramson	.15
273	Steve Towle	.15
274	Jim Marshall	.40
275	Mel Blount	1.00
276	Bob Kuziel	.15
277	James Scott	.15
278	Tony Reed	.15
279	Dave Green	.15
280	Toni Linhart	.15
281	Andy Johnson	.15
282	Los Angeles Rams Team (Cullen Bryant, Willie Miller, Rod Perry, Pat Thomas, Larry Brooks)	1.00
283	Phil Villapiano	.15
284	Dexter Bussey	.15
285	Craig Morton	.50
286	Guy Morriss	.15
287	Lawrence Pillers	.15
288	Gerald Irons	.15
289	Scott Perry	.15
290	Randy White	2.00
291	Jack Gregory	.15
292	Bob Chandler	.15
293	Rich Szaro	.15
294	Sherman Smith	.15
295	Tom Banks (AP)	.15
296	Revie Sorey (AP)	.15
297	Ricky Thompson	.15
298	Ron Yary	.15
299	Lyle Blackwood	.15
300	Franco Harris	2.00
301	Houston Oilers Team (Earl Campbell, Ken Burrough, Willie Alexander, Elvin Bethea)	3.00
302	Scott Bull	.15
303	Dewey Selmon	.15
304	Jack Rudnay	.15
305	Fred Biletnikoff	1.25
306	Jeff West	.15
307	Shafer Suggs	.15
308	Ozzie Newsome	15.00
309	Boobie Clark	.15
310	James Lofton	15.00
311	Joe Pisarcik	.15
312	Bill Simpson (AP)	.15
313	Haven Moses	.15

No.	Name	Price
314	Jim Merlo	.15
315	Preston Pearson	.15
316	Larry Tearry	.15
317	Tom Dempsey	.15
318	Greg Latta	.15
319	Washington Redskins Team (John Riggins, John McDaniel, Jake Scott, Coy Bacon)	.75
320	Jack Ham (AP)	1.25
321	Harold Jackson	.30
322	George Roberts	.15
323	Ron Jaworski	.40
324	Jim Otis	.15
325	Roger Carr	.15
326	Jack Tatum	.15
327	Derrick Gaffney	.15
328	Reggie Williams	.50
329	Doug Dieken	.15
330	Efren Herrea	.15
331	Record: (Campbell)	5.50
332	Record: (Tony Galbreath)	.25
333	Record: (Bruce Harper)	.25
334	Record: (John James)	.25
335	Record: (Walter Payton)	3.00
336	Record: (Rickey Young)	.15
337	Jeff Van Note	.15
338	San Diego Chargers Team (Lydell Mitchell, John Jefferson, Mike Fuller, Fred Dean)	.60
339	Stan Walters (AP)	.20
340	Louis Wright (AP)	.15
341	Horace Ivory	.15
342	Andre Tillman	.15
343	Greg Coleman	.15
344	Doug English (AP)	.60
345	Ted Hendricks	.50
346	Rich Saul	.15
347	Mel Gray	.15
348	Toni Fritsch	.15
349	Cornell Webster	.15
350	Ken Houston	.50
351	Ron Johnson	.15
352	Doug Kotar	.15
353	Brian Sipe	.40
354	Billy Brooks	.15
355	John Dutton	.15
356	Don Goode	.15
357	Detroit Lions Team (Dexter Bussey, David Hill, Jim Allen, Al Baker)	1.00
358	Reuben Gant	.15
359	Bob Parsons	.15
360	Cliff Harris	.35
361	Raymond Clayborn	.20
362	Scott Dierking	.15
363	Bill Bryan	.15
364	Mike Livingston	.15
365	Otis Sistrunk	.15
366	Charley Young	.15
367	Kent Wortman	.15
368	Checklist 265-396	1.00
369	Mike Michel	.15
370	Delvin Williams	.15
371	Steve Furness	.15
372	Emery Moorehead	.15
373	Clarence Scott	.15
374	Rufus Mayes	.15
375	Chris Hanberger	.15
376	Baltimore Colts Team (Joe Washington, Roger Carr, Norm Thompson, John Dutton)	.50
377	Bob Avellini	.15
378	Jeff Siemon	.15
379	Roland Hooks	.15
380	Russ Francis	.15
381	Roger Wehrli	.15
382	Joe Fields	.15
383	Archie Manning	.50
384	Rob Lytle	.15
385	Thomas Henderson	.15
386	Morris Owens	.15
387	Dan Fouts	4.00
388	Chuck Crist	.15
389	Ed O'Neil	.15
390	Earl Campbell (AP)	30.00
391	Randy Grossman	.15
392	Monte Jackson	.15
393	John Mendenhall	.15
394	Miami Dolphins Team (Delvin Williams, Duriel Harris, Tim Foley, Vern Den Herder)	.50
395	Isaac Curtis	.15
396	Mike Bragg	.15
397	Doug Plank	.15
398	Mike Barnes	.15
399	Calvin Hill	.20
400	Roger Staubach (AP)	8.00
401	Doug Beaudoin	.15
402	Chuck Ramsey	.15
403	Mike Hogan	.15
404	Mario Clark	.15
405	Riley Odoms	.15
406	Carl Eller	.30
407	Green Bay Packers Team (Terdell Middleton, James Lofton, Willie Buchanon, Ezra Johnson)	2.75
408	Mark Arenson	.15
409	Vince Ferragamo	.60
410	Cleveland Elam	.15
411	Donnie Shell	3.00
412	Ray Rhodes	.15
413	Don Cockroft	.15
414	Don Bass	.15
415	Cliff Branch	.75
416	Diron Talbert	.15
417	Tom Hicks	.15
418	Roosevelt Leaks	.15
419	Charlie Joiner	.75
420	Lyle Alzado (AP)	.75
421	Sam Cunningham	.15
422	Larry Keller	.15
423	Jim Mitchell	.15
424	Randy Logan	.15
425	Jim Langer	.40
426	Gary Green	.15
427	Luther Blue	.15
428	Dennis Johnson	.15
429	Danny White	.75
430	Roy Gerela	.15
431	Jimmy Robinson	.15
432	Minnesota Vikings Team (Chuck Foreman, Ahmad Rashad, Bobby Bryant, Mark Mullaney)	.50
433	Oliver Davis	.15
434	Lenvill Elliott	.15
435	Willie Miller	.15
436	Brad Dusek	.15
437	Bob Thomas	.15
438	Ken Mendenhall	.15
439	Clarence Davis	.15
440	Bob Griese	2.00
441	Tony McGee	.15
442	Ed Taylor	.15
443	Ron Howard	.15
444	Wayne Morris	.15
445	Charlie Waters	.35
446	Rick Danmeier	.15
447	Paul Naumoff	.15
448	Keith Krepfle	.15
449	Rusty Jackson	.15
450	John Stallworth	3.00
451	New Orleans Saints Team (Tony Galbreath, Henry Childs, Tom Myers, Elex Price)	.50
452	Ron Mikolajczyk	.15
453	Fred Dryer	.75
454	Jim LeClair	.15
455	Greg Pruitt	.25
456	Jake Scott	.15
457	Steve Schubert	.15
458	George Kunz	.15
459	Mike Williams	.15
460	Dave Casper (AP)	.15
461	Sam Adams	.15
462	Abdul Salaam	.15
463	Terdell Middleton	.15
464	Mike Wood	.15
465	Bill Thompson (AP)	.15
466	Larry Gordon	.15
467	Benny Ricardo	.15
468	Reggie McKenzie	.15
469	Dallas Cowboys Team (Tony Dorsett, Tony Hill, Benny Barnes, Randy White)	1.00
470	Rickey Young	.15
471	Charlie Smith	.15
472	Al Dixon	.15
473	Tom DeLeone	.15
474	Louis Breeden	.15
475	Jack Lambert	2.00
476	Terry Hermeling	.15
477	J.K. McKay	.15
478	Stan White	.15
479	Terry Nelson	.15
480	Walter Payton (AP)	12.00
481	Dave Dalby	.15
482	Burgess Owens	.15
483	Rolf Benirschke	.15
484	Jack Dolbin	.15
485	John Hannah (AP)	.60
486	Checklist 397-528	1.00
487	Greg Landry	.20
488	St. Louis Cardinals Team (Jim Otis, Pat Tilley, Ken Stone, Mike Dawson)	.50
489	Paul Krause	.15
490	John James	.15
491	Merv Krakau	.15
492	Dan Doornink	.15
493	Curtis Johnson	.15
494	Rafael Septien	.15
495	Jean Fugett	.15
496	Frank LeMaster	.15
497	Allan Ellis	.15
498	Billy Waddy	.20
499	Hank Bauer	.15
500	Terry Bradshaw (AP)	5.50
501	Larry McCarren	.15
502	Fred Cook	.15
503	Chuck Muncie	.20
504	Herman Weaver	.15
505	Eddie Edwards	.15
506	Tony Peters	.15
507	Denver Broncos Team (Lonnie Perrin, Riley Odoms, Steve Foley, Bernard Jackson, Lyle Alzado)	.50
508	Jimbo Elrod	.15
509	David Hill	.15
510	Harvey Martin	.35
511	Terry Miller	.15
512	June Jones	1.00
513	Randy Cross	.30
514	Duriel Harris	.15
515	Harry Carson	.75
516	Tim Fox	.15
517	John Zook	.15
518	Bob Tucker	.15
519	Kevin Long	.15
520	Ken Stabler	4.00
521	John Bunting	.15
522	Rocky Bleier	.75
523	Noah Jackson	.15
524	Cliff Parsley	.15
525	Louie Kelcher (AP)	.15
526	Tampa Bay Buccaneers (Ricky Bell, Morris Owens, Cedric Brown, Lee Roy Selmon)	.60
527	Bob Brudzinski	.15
528	Danny Buggs	.15

1980 Topps

The cards in this set feature a football at the bottom of the card with the team name and position on either side of the player's name. The 528-card set has subsets featuring, as usual, record breakers and the previous year's playoff decisions. Rookies in this set include Ottis Anderson, Tommy Kramer, Phil Simms and Wes Chandler. (Key: AP - All Pro)

No.	Name	NM
	Complete Set (528):	65.00
	Common Player:	.08
1	Record: (O. Anderson)	1.00
2	Record: (Harold Carmichael)	.15
3	Record: (Dan Fouts	1.00
4	Record: (Paul Krause)	.15
5	Record: (Rick Upchurch)	.15
6	Record: (Garo Yepremian)	.15
7	Harold Jackson	.25
8	Mike Williams	.08
9	Calvin Hill	.15
10	Jack Ham	1.00
11	Dan Melville	.08
12	Matt Robinson	.08
13	Billy Campfield	.08
14	Phil Tabor	.08
15	Randy Hughes	.08
16	Andre Tillman	.08
17	Isaac Curtis	.08
18	Charley Hannah	.08
19	Washington Redskins Team (John Riggins, Danny Buggs, Joe Lavender, Coy Bacon)	.50
20	Jim Zorn	.30
21	Brian Baschnagel	.08
22	Jon Keyworth	.08
23	Phil Villapiano	.08
24	Richard Osborne	.08
25	Rich Saul (AP)	.08
26	Doug Beaudoin	.08
27	Cleveland Elam	.08
28	Charlie Joiner	.65
29	Dick Ambrose	.08
30	Mike Reinfeldt (AP)	.11
31	Matt Bahr	1.75
32	Keith Krepfle	.08
33	Herbert Scott	.08
34	Doug Kotar	.08
35	Bob Griese	1.75
36	Jerry Butler	.40
37	Rolland Lawrence	.08
38	Gary Weaver	.08
39	Kansas City Chiefs Team (Ted McKnight, J.T. Smith, Gary Barbaro, Art Still)	.40
40	Chuck Muncie	.08
41	Mike Hartenstine	.08
42	Sammie White	.20
43	Ken Clark	.08
44	Clarence Harmon	.08
45	Bert Jones	.30
46	Mike Washington	.08
47	Joe Fields	.08
48	Mike Wood	.08
49	Oliver Davis	.08
50	Stan Walters (AP)	.08
51	Riley Odoms	.08
52	Steve Pisarkiewicz	.08
53	Tony Hill	.40
54	Scott Perry	.08
55	George Martin	.40
56	George Roberts	.08
57	Seattle Seahawks Team (Sherman Smith, Steve Largent, Dave Brown, Manu Tuiasosopo)	.75
58	Billy Johnson	.08
59	Reuben Johnson	.08
60	Dennis Harrah (AP)	.20
61	Rocky Bleier	.35
62	Sam Hunt	.08
63	Allan Ellis	.08
64	Ricky Thompson	.08
65	Ken Stabler	1.50
66	Dexter Bussey	.08
67	Ken Mendenhall	.08
68	Woodrow Lowe	.08
69	Thom Darden	.08
70	Randy White (AP)	1.50
71	Ken MacAfee	.08
72	Ron Jaworski	.30
73	William Andrews	1.00
74	Jimmy Robinson	.08
75	Roger Wehrli (AP)	.08
76	Miami Dolphins Team (Larry Csonka, Nat Moore, Neal Colzie, Gerald Small, Vern Den Herder)	.50
77	Jack Rudnay	.08
78	James Lofton	4.00
79	Robert Brazile	.08
80	Russ Francis	.08
81	Ricky Bell	.30
82	Bob Avellini	.08
83	Bobby Jackson	.08
84	Mike Bragg	.08
85	Cliff Branch	.50
86	Blair Bush	.08
87	Sherman Smith	.08
88	Glen Edwards	.08
89	Don Cockroft	.08
90	Louis Wright (AP)	.15
91	Randy Grossman	.08
92	Carl Hairston	.75
93	Archie Manning	.40
94	New York Giants Team (Billy Taylor, Earnest Gray, George Martin)	.30
95	Preston Pearson	.08
96	Rusty Chambers	.08
97	Greg Coleman	.08
98	Charley Young	.08
99	Matt Cavanaugh	.30
100	Jesse Baker	.08
101	Doug Plank	.08
102	Checklist 1-132	.65
103	Luther Bradley	.11
104	Bob Kuziel	.08
105	Craig Morton	.35
106	Sherman White	.08
107	Jim Breech	.75
108	Hank Bauer	.08
109	Tom Blanchard	.08
110	Ozzie Newsome (AP)	4.00
111	Steve Furness	.08
112	Frank LeMaster	.08
113	Dallas Cowboys Team (Tony Dorsett, Tony Hill, Harvey Martin)	.75
114	Doug Van Horn	.08
115	Delvin Williams	.08
116	Lyle Blackwood	.08
117	Derrick Gaffney	.08
118	Cornell Webster	.08
119	Sam Cunningham	.08
120	Jim Youngblood (AP)	.08
121	Bob Thomas	.08
122	Jack Thompson	.15
123	Randy Cross	.08
124	Karl Lorch	.08
125	Mel Gray	.08
126	John James	.08
127	Terdell Middleton	.08
128	Leroy Jones	.08
129	Tom DeLeone	.08
130	John Stallworth (AP)	1.00
131	Jimmie Giles	.30
132	Philadelphia Eagles Team (Wilbert Montgomery, Harold Carmichael, Brenard Wilson, Carl Hairston)	.30
133	Gary Green	.08
134	John Dutton	.08
135	Harry Carson (AP)	.50
136	Bob Kuechenberg	.08
137	Ike Harris	.08
138	Tommy Kramer	1.00
139	Sam Adams	.08
140	Doug English (AP)	.15
141	Steve Schubert	.08
142	Rusty Jackson	.08
143	Reese McCall	.08
144	Scott Dierking	.08
145	Ken Houston (AP)	.50
146	Bob Martin	.08
147	Sam McCullum	.08
148	Tom Banks	.08
149	Willie Buchanon	.08
150	Greg Pruitt	.20
151	Denver Broncos Team (Otis Armstrong, Rick Upchurch, Steve Foley, Brison Manor)	.30
152	Don Smith	.08
153	Pete Johnson	.08
154	Charlie Smith	.08
155	Mel Blount	.75
156	John Mendenhall	.08
157	Danny White	.08
158	Jimmy Cefalo	.30
159	Richard Bishop (AP)	.08
160	Walter Payton (AP)	8.00
161	Dave Dalby	.08
162	Preston Dennard	.08
163	Johnnie Gray	.08
164	Russell Erxleben	.08
165	Toni Fritsch (AP)	.08
166	Terry Hermeling	.08
167	Roland Hooks	.08
168	Roger Carr	.08
169	San Diego Chargers Team (Clarence Williams, John Jefferson, Woodrow Lowe, Ray Preston, Wilbur	.30
170	Ottis Anderson (AP)	5.00
171	Brian Sipe	.30
172	Leonard Thompson	.08
173	Tony Reed	.08
174	Bob Tucker	.08
175	Joe Greene	1.00
176	Jack Dolbin	.08
177	Chuck Ramsey	.08
178	Paul Hofer	.08
179	Randy Logan	.08
180	David Lewis (AP)	.08
181	Duriel Harris	.08
182	June Jones	.50
183	Larry McCarren	.08
184	Ken Johnson	.08
185	Charlie Waters	.30
186	Noah Jackson	.08
187	Reggie Williams	.25
188	New England Patriots Team (Sam Cunningham, Harold Jackson, Raymond Clayborn, Tony McGee)	.30
189	Carl Eller	.35
190	Ed White (AP)	.08
191	Mario Clark	.08
192	Roosevelt Leaks	.08
193	Ted McKnight	.08
194	Danny Buggs	.08
195	Lester Hayes	1.50
196	Clarence Scott	.08
197	New Orleans Saints Team (Chuck Muncie, Wes Chandler, Tom Myers, Elois Grooms, Don Reese)	.30
198	Richard Caster	.08
199	Louie Giammona	.08
200	Terry Bradshaw	2.75
201	Ed Newman	.08
202	Fred Dryer	.50
203	Dennis Franks	.08
204	Bob Breunig	.40
205	Alan Page	.50
206	Earnest Gray	.15
207	Minnesota Vikings Team (Rickey Young, Ahmad Rashad, Tommy Hannon, Nate Wright, Mark Mullaney)	.40
208	Horace Ivory	.08
209	Isaac Hagins	.08
210	Gary Johnson (Chargers, AP)	.08
211	Kevin Long	.08
212	Bill Thompson	.08
213	Don Bass	.08
214	George Starke	.20
215	Efren Herrera	.08
216	Theo Bell	.08
217	Monte Jackson	.08
218	Reggie McKenzie	.08
219	Bucky Dilts	.08
220	Lyle Alzado	.50
221	Tim Foley	.08
222	Mark Arneson	.08
223	Fred Quillan	.08
224	Benny Ricardo	.08
225	Phil Simms	15.00
226	Chicago Bears Team (Walter Payton, Brian Baschnagel, Gary Fencik, Terry Schmidt, Jon Osborne)	1.00
227	Max Runager	.08
228	Barty Smith	.08
229	Jay Saldi	.08
230	John Hannah (AP)	.50
231	Tim Wilson	.08
232	Jeff Van Note	.08
233	Henry Marshall	.08
234	Diron Talbert	.08
235	Garo Yepremian	.08
236	Larry Brown	.08
237	Clarence Williams	.08
238	Burgess Owens	.08
239	Vince Ferragamo	.25
240	Rickey Young	.08
241	Dave Logan	.08
242	Larry Gordon	.08
243	Terry Miller	.08
244	Baltimore Colts Team (Joe Washington, Fred Cook)	.30
245	Steve DeBerg	1.75
246	Checklist 133-264	.65
247	Greg Latta	.08
248	Raymond Clayborn	.08
249	Jim Clack	.08
250	Drew Pearson	.50
251	John Bunting	.08
252	Rob Lytle	.08
253	Jim Hart	.25
254	John McDaniel	.08
255	Dave Pear (AP)	.08
256	Donnie Shell	.50
257	Dan Doornink	.08
258	Wallace Francis	.35
259	Dave Beverly	.08
260	Lee Roy Selmon (AP)	.25
261	Doug Dieken	.08
262	Gary David	.08
263	Bob Rush	.08
264	Buffalo Bills Team (Curtis Brown, Frank Lewis, Keith Moody, Sherman White)	.30
265	Greg Landry	.20
266	Jan Stenerud	.40
267	Tom Hicks	.08
268	Pat McInally	.08
269	Tim Fox	.08
270	Harvey Martin	.30
271	Dan Lloyd	.08
272	Mike Barber	.08
273	Wendell Tyler	.60
274	Jeff Komlo	.08
275	Wes Chandler	2.50
276	Brad Dusek	.08
277	Charlie Johnson	.08
278	Dennis Swilley	.08
279	Johnny Evans	.08
280	Jack Lambert (AP)	1.25
281	Vern Den Herder	.08
282	Tampa Bay Bucaneers Team (Ricky Bell, Isaac Hagins, Lee Roy Selmon)	.30
283	Bob Klein	.08
284	Jim Turner	.08
285	Marvin Powell (AP)	.08
286	Aaron Kyle	.08
287	Dan Neal	.08
288	Wayne Morris	.08
289	Steve Bartkowski	.35
290	Dave Jennings	.08
291	John Smith	.08
292	Bill Gregory	.08
293	Frank Lewis	.08
294	Fred Cook	.08
295	David Hill (AP)	.08
296	Wade Key	.08
297	Sidney Thornton	.08
298	Charlie Hall	.08
299	Joe Lavender	.08

#	Player	Price
300	Tom Rafferty	.15
301	Mike Renfro	.15
302	Wilbut Jackson	.08
303	Green Bay Packers Team (Terdell Middleton, James Lofton, Johnnie Gray, Robert Barber, Ezra Johnson)	1.00
304	Henry Childs	.08
305	Russ Washington (AP)	.08
306	Jim LeClair	.08
307	Tommy Hart	.08
308	Gary Barbaro	.08
309	Billy Taylor	.08
310	Ray Guy	.25
311	Don Hasselbeck	.08
312	Doug Williams	.75
313	Nick Mike-Mayer	.08
314	Don McCauley	.08
315	Wesley Walker	.40
316	Dan Dierdorf	.50
317	Dave Brown	.08
318	Leroy Harris	.08
319	Pittsburgh Steelers Team (Franco Harris, John Stallworth, Jack Lambert, Steve Furness, L.C.	.75
320	Mark Moseley (AP)	.08
321	Mark Dennard	.08
322	Terry Nelson	.08
323	Tom Jackson	.50
324	Rick Kane	.08
325	Jerry Sherk	.08
326	Ray Preston	.08
327	Golden Richards	.08
328	Randy Dean	.08
329	Rick Danmeier	.08
330	Tony Dorsett	4.50
331	Passing Leaders (Dan Fouts, Roger Staubach)	2.00
332	Receiving Leaders (Joe Washington, Ahmad Rashad)	.15
333	Sack Leaders (Jesse Baker, Al Baker, Jack Youngblood)	.15
334	Scoring Leaders (John Smith, Jack Moseley)	.15
335	Interception Leaders (Mike Reinfeldt, Lemar Parrish)	.15
336	Punting Leaders (Bob Grupp, Dave Jennings)	.15
337	Freddie Solomon	.08
338	Cincinnati Bengals Team (Pete Johnson, Don Bass, Dick Jauron, Gary Burley)	.30
339	Ken Stone	.08
340	Greg Buttle (AP)	.08
341	Bob Baumhower	.08
342	Billy Waddy	.08
343	Cliff Parsley	.08
344	Walter White	.08
345	Mike Thomas	.08
346	Neil O'Donoghue	.08
347	Freddie Scott	.08
348	Joe Ferguson	.20
349	Doug Nettles	.08
350	Mike Webster (AP)	.50
351	Ron Saul	.08
352	Julius Adams	.08
353	Rafael Septien	.08
354	Cleo Miller	.08
355	Keith Simpson (AP)	.08
356	Johnny Perkins	.08
357	Jerry Sisemore	.08
358	Arthur Wittington	.08
359	St. Louis Cardinals Team (Ottis Anderson, Pat Tilley, Ken Stone, Bob Pollard)	.60
360	Rick Upchurch	.08
361	Kim Bokamper	.20
362	Roland Harper	.08
363	Pat Leahy	.08
364	Louis Breeden	.08
365	John Jefferson	.75
366	Jerry Eckwood	.08
367	David Whitehurst	.08
368	Willie Parker	.08
369	Ed Simonini	.08
370	Jack Youngblood (AP)	.40
371	Don Warren	1.50
372	Andy Johnson	.08
373	D.D. Lewis	.08
374	Beasley Reece	.30
375	L.C. Greenwood	.30
376	Cleveland Browns Team (Mike Pruitt, Dave Logan, Thom Darden, Jerry Sherk)	.30
377	Herman Edwards	.08
378	Rob Carpenter	.25
379	Herman Weaver	.08
380	Gary Fencik (AP)	.11
381	Don Strock	.08
382	Art Shell	.50
383	Tim Mazzetti	.08
384	Bruce Harper	.08
385	Al Baker	.08
386	Conrad Dobler	.08
387	Stu Voight	.08
388	Ken Anderson	.75
389	Pat Tilley	.08
390	John Riggins	1.25
391	Checklist 265-396	.65
392	Fred Dean (AP)	.15
393	Benny Barnes	.15
394	Los Angeles Rams Team (Wendell Tyler, Preston Dennard, Nolan Cromwell, Jim Youngblood)	.30
395	Brad Van Pelt	.08
396	Eddie Hare	.08
397	John Sciarra	.15
398	Bob Jackson	.08
399	John Yarno	.08
400	Franco Harris (AP)	1.75
401	Ray Wersching	.08
402	Virgil Livers	.08
403	Raymond Chester	.08
404	Leon Gray	.08
405	Richard Todd	.20
406	Larry Little	.25
407	Ted Fritsch	.08
408	Larry Mucker	.08
409	Jim Allen	.08
410	Randy Grandishar	.40
411	Atlanta Falcons Team (William Andrews, Wallace Francis, Rolland Lawrence, Don Smith)	.30
412	Louie Kelcher	.08
413	Robert Newhouse	.08
414	Gary Shirk	.08
415	Mike Haynes (AP)	.25
416	Craig Colbert	.08
417	Lou Piccone	.08
418	Clay Matthews	3.00
419	Marvin Cobb	.08
420	Harold Carmichael (AP)	.50
421	Uwe Von Schamann	.08
422	Mike Phipps	.08
423	Nolan Cromwell	1.00
424	Glenn Doughty	.08
425	Bob Young (AP)	.08
426	Tony Galbreath	.08
427	Luke Prestridge	.08
428	Terry Beeson	.08
429	Jack Tatum	.08
430	Lemar Parrish (AP)	.08
431	Chester Marcol	.08
432	Houston Oilers Team (Dan Pastorini, Ken Burrough, Mike Reinfeldt, Jesse Baker)	.30
433	John Fitzgerald	.08
434	Gary Jeter	.40
435	Steve Grogan	.40
436	Jon Kolb	.08
437	Jim O'Bradovich	.08
438	Gerald Irons	.08
439	Jeff West	.08
440	Wilbert Montgomery	.30
441	Norris Thomas	.08
442	James Scott	.08
443	Curtis Brown	.08
444	Ken Fantetti	.08
445	Pat Haden	.30
446	Carl Mauck	.08
447	Bruce Laird	.08
448	Otis Armstrong	.20
449	Gene Upshaw	.30
450	Steve Largent (AP)	4.50
451	Benny Malone	.08
452	Steve Nelson	.08
453	Mark Cotney	.08
454	Joe Danelo	.08
455	Billy Joe DuPree	.15
456	Ron Johnson	.08
457	Archie Griffin	.25
458	Reggie Rucker	.08
459	Claude Humphrey	.08
460	Lydell Mitchell	.08
461	Steve Towle	.08
462	Revie Sorey	.08
463	Tom Skladany	.08
464	Clark Gaines	.08
465	Frank Corral	.08
466	Steve Fuller	.25
467	Ahmad Rashad (AP)	.75
468	Oakland Raiders Team (Mark Van Eeghen, Cliff Branch, Lester Hayes, Willie Jones)	.30
469	Brian Peets	.08
470	Pat Donovan (AP)	.20
471	Ken Burrough	.08
472	Don Calhoun	.08
473	Bill Bryan	.08
474	Terry Jackson	.08
475	Joe Theismann	1.50
476	Jim Smith	.08
477	Joe DeLamielleure	.08
478	Mike Pruitt (AP)	.08
479	Steve Mike-Mayer	.08
480	Bill Bergey	.15
481	Mike Fuller	.08
482	Bob Parsons	.08
483	Billy Brooks	.08
484	Jerome Barkum	.08
485	Larry Csonka	1.00
486	John Hill	.08
487	Mike Dawson	.08
488	Detroit Lions Team (Dexter Bussey, Freddie Scott, Jim Allen, Luther Bradley, Al Baker)	.30
489	Ted Hendricks	.50
490	Dan Pastorini	.15
491	Stanley Morgan	.75
492	AFC Championship (Rocky Bleier)	.20
493	NFC Championship (Vince Ferragamo)	.20
494	Super Bowl XIV	.50
495	Dwight White	.08
496	Haven Moses	.08
497	Guy Morriss	.08
498	Dewey Selmon	.08
499	Dave Butz	1.50
500	Chuck Foreman	.20
501	Chris Bahr	.08
502	Mark Miller	.08
503	Tony Greene	.08
504	Brian Kelley	.08
505	Joe Washington	.15
506	Butch Johnson	.08
507	New York Jets Team (Clark Gaines, Wesley Walker, Burgess Owens, Joe Klecko)	.30
508	Steve Little	.08
509	Checklist 397-528	.65
510	Mark Van Eeghen	.08
511	Gary Danielson	.08
512	Manu Tuiasosopo	.08
513	Paul Coffman	.40
514	Cullen Bryant	.08
515	Nat Moore	.08
516	Bill Lenkaitis	.08
517	Lynn Cain	.25
518	Gregg Bingham	.08
519	Ted Albrecht	.08
520	Dan Fouts (AP)	2.00
521	Bernard Jackson	.08
522	Coy Bacon	.08
523	Tony Franklin	.25
524	Bo Harris	.08
525	Bob Grupp (AP)	.08
526	San Francisco 49ers Team (Paul Hofer, Freddie Solomon, James Owens, Dwaine Board)	.30
527	Steve Wilson	.08
528	Bennie Cunningham	.08

1980 Topps Super

Printed on heavy white cardboard stock, these oversize (around 5" x 7") cards featured 30 NFL stars. The front displays a color photo of the player and his name appears in a gold plaque atop the card; the back lists his name, position and team with the Topps logo in the center of the card. This is a set similar to the 1980 Topps Superstar Photo Baseball set.

#	Player	NM
	Complete Set (30):	15.00
	Common Player:	.30
1	Franco Harris	1.00
2	Bob Griese	1.00
3	Archie Manning	.30
4	Harold Carmichael	.30
5	Wesley Walker	.30
6	Richard Todd	.30
7	Dan Fouts	.90
8	Ken Stabler	.60
9	Jack Youngblood	.30
10	Jim Zorn	.30
11	Tony Dorsett	1.50
12	Lee Roy Selmon	.30
13	Russ Francis	.30
14	John Stallworth	.30
15	Terry Bradshaw	1.50
16	Joe Theismann	1.00
17	Ottis Anderson	.30
18	John Jefferson	.30
19	Jack Ham	.30
20	Joe Greene	.30
21	Chuck Muncie	.30
22	Ron Jaworski	.30
23	John Hannah	.30
24	Randy Gradishar	.30
25	Jack Lambert	.30
26	Ricky Bell	.30
27	Drew Pearson	.30
28	Rick Upchurch	.30
29	Brad Van Pelt	.30
30	Walter Payton	3.50

1981 Topps

Just one phrase describes this set: Joe Montana rookie. Other rookie cards in this set include Mark Gastineau, Art Monk, Billy Sims, Kellen Winslow, Joe Cribbs, Dwight Clark, Curtis Dickey and Charles White. The 528-card set is bordered in white. Around the photos is black piping which leads to a colored scroll at the bottom of the card showing the team and player. Super Action cards in this set - included along with the player's regular card - show the major stars in action. (Key: SA - Super Action, AP - All Pro)

#	Player	MT
	Complete Set (528):	250.00
	Common Player:	.08
	Wax Box:	400.00
1	Passing Leaders	.50
2	Receiving Leaders	.50
3	Sack Leaders	.10
4	Scoring Leaders	.10
5	Interception Leaders	.10
6	Punting Leaders	.10
7	Don Calhoun	.08
8	Jack Tatum	.08
9	Reggie Rucker	.08
10	Mike Webster (AP)	.25
11	Vince Evans	1.00
12	Ottis Anderson	.75
13	Leroy Harris	.08
14	Gordon King	.08
15	Harvey Martin	.15
16	Johnny Lam Jones	.15
17	Ken Greene	.08
18	Frank Lewis	.08
19	Seattle Seahawks Team	.65
20	Lester Hayes (AP)	.25
21	Uwe Von Schamann	.08
22	Joe Washington	.08
23	Louie Kelcher	.08
24	Willie Miller	.08
25	Steve Grogan	.25
26	John Hill	.08
27	Stan White	.08
28	William Andrews (SA)	.08
29	Clarence Scott	.08
30	Leon Gray (AP)	.08
31	Craig Colquitt	.08
32	Doug Williams	.25
33	Bob Breunig	.08
34	Billy Taylor	.08
35	Harold Carmichael	.50
36	Ray Wersching	.08
37	Dennis Johnson	.08
38	Archie Griffin	.15
39	Los Angeles Rams Team (Cullen Bryant, Billy Waddy, Nolan Cromwell, Jack Youngblood)	.08
40	Gary Fencik (AP)	.08
41	Lynn Dickey	.15
42	Steve Bartkowski (SA)	.08
43	Art Shell	.50
44	Wilbur Jackson	.08
45	Frank Corral	.08
46	Ted McKnight	.08
47	Joe Klecko	.15
48	Don Doornink	.08
49	Doug Dieken	.08
50	Jerry Robinson (AP)	.08
51	Wallace Francis	.08
52	Dave Preston	.08
53	Jay Saldi	.08
54	Rush Brown	.08
55	Phil Simms	5.00
56	Nick Mike-Mayer	.08
57	Washington Redskins Team	2.00
58	Mike Renfro	.08
59	Ted Brown (SA)	.08
60	Steve Nelson (AP)	.08
61	Sidney Thornton	.08
62	Kent Hill	.08
63	Don Bessillieu	.10
64	Fred Cook	.08
65	Raymond Chester	.08
66	Rick Kane	.08
67	Mike Fuller	.08
68	Dewey Selmon	.10
69	Charles White	1.00
70	Jeff Van Note (AP)	.08
71	Robert Newhouse	.08
72	Roynell Young	.20
73	Lynn Cain (SA)	.08
74	Mike Friede	.08
75	Earl Cooper	.08
76	New Orleans Saints Team	.15
77	Rick Danmeier	.08
78	Darrol Ray	.08
79	Gregg Bingham	.08
80	John Hannah (AP)	.40
81	Jack Thompson	.08
82	Rick Upchurch	.08
83	Mike Butler	.08
84	Don Warren	.25
85	Mark Van Eeghen	.08
86	J.T. Smith	1.00
87	Herman Weaver	.08
88	Terry Bradshaw (SA)	1.00
89	Charlie Hall	.08
90	Donnie Shell	.30
91	Ike Harris	.08
92	Charlie Johnson	.08
93	Rickey Watts	.08
94	New England Patriots Team	.15
95	Drew Pearson	.60
96	Neil O'Donoghue	.08
97	Conrad Dobler	.08
98	Jewerl Thomas	.08
99	Mike Barber	.08
100	Billy Sims (AP)	1.50
101	Vern Den Herder	.08
102	Greg Landry	.15
103	Joe Cribbs (SA)	.15
104	Mark Murphy	.20
105	Chuck Muncie	.08
106	Alfred Jackson	.08
107	Chris Bahr	.08
108	Gordon Jones	.08
109	Willie Harper	.10
110	Dave Jennings (AP)	.08
111	Bennie Cunningham	.08
112	Jerry Sisemore	.08
113	Cleveland Browns Team	.20
114	Rickey Young	.08
115	Ken Anderson	.75
116	Randy Gradishar	.20
117	Eddie Lee Ivery	.08
118	Wesley Walker	.20
119	Chuck Foreman	.20
120	Nolan Cromwell (AP)	.20
121	Curtis Dickey (SA)	.08
122	Wayne Morris	.08
123	Greg Stemrick	.08
124	Coy Bacon	.08
125	Jim Zorn	.20
126	Henry Childs	.08
127	Checklist 1-132	.25
128	Len Waltersheid	.08
129	Johnny Evans	.08
130	Gary Barbaro (AP)	.08
131	Jim Smith	.08
132	New York Jets Team	.15
133	Curtis Brown	.08
134	D.D Lewis	.08
135	Jim Plunkett	.50
136	Nat Moore	.08
137	Don McCauley	.08
138	Tony Dorsett (SA)	.75
139	Julius Adams	.08
140	Ahmad Rashad (AP)	.40
141	Rich Saul	.08
142	Ken Fantetti	.08
143	Kenny Johnson	.08
144	Clark Gaines	.08
145	Mark Moseley	.08
146	Vernon Perry	.15
147	Jerry Sherk	.08
148	Freddie Solomon	.08
149	Jerry Sherk	.08
150	Kellen Winslow (AP)	10.00
151	Green Bay Packers Team	.25
152	Ross Browner	.08
153	Dan Fouts (SA)	.60
154	Woody Peoples	.08
155	Jack Lambert	1.00
156	Mike Dennis	.08
157	Rafael Septien	.08
158	Archie Manning	.20
159	Don Hasselbeck	.08
160	Alan Page (AP)	.50
161	Arthur Whittington	.08
162	Billy Waddy	.08
163	Horace Belton	.08
164	Luke Prestridge	.08
165	Joe Theismann	.75
166	Morris Towns	.08
167	Dave Brown	.08
168	Ezra Johnson	.08
169	Tampa Bay Buccaneers Team	.10
170	Joe DeLamielleure (AP)	.08
171	Earnest Gray (SA)	.08
172	Mike Thomas	.08
173	Jim Haslett	.08
174	David Woodley	.10
175	Al Bubba Baker	.20
176	Nesby Glasgow	.20
178	Ton Brahaney	.08
179	Herman Edwards	.08
180	Junior Miller (AP)	.08
181	Richard Wood	.08
182	Lenvil Elliott	.08
183	Sammie White	.20
184	Russell Erxieben	.08
185	Ed "Too Tall" Jones	.75
186	Ray Guy (SA)	.08
187	Haven Moses	.08
188	New York Giants Team	.20
189	David Whitehurst	.08
190	John Jefferson (SA)	.20
191	Terry Beeson	.08
192	Dan Ross	.25
193	Dave Williams	.08
194	Art Monk	12.00
195	Roger Wehrli	.08
196	Rickey Feacher	.08
197	Miami Dolphins Team (Tony Nathan, Gerald Small, Kim Bokamper, A.J. Duhe)	.08
198	Carl Roaches	.08
199	Cilly Campfield	.08
200	Ted Hendricks (AP)	.15
201	Fred Smerlas	.75
202	Walter Payton (SA)	2.00
203	Luther Bradley	.08
204	Herbert Scott	.08
205	Jack Youngblood	.25
206	Danny Pittman	.08
207	Houston Oilers Team (Carl Roaches, Mike Barber, Jack Tatum, Jesse Baker, Robert Brazile)	.08
208	Vagas Ferguson	.08
209	Mark Dennard	.08
210	Lemar Parrish (AP)	.08
211	Bruce Harper	.08
212	Ed Simonini	.08
213	Nick Lowery	1.00
214	Kevin House	.20
215	Mike Kenn	1.50
216	Joe Montana	175.00
217	Joe Senser	.08
218	Lester Hayes (SA)	.08
219	Gene Upshaw	.20
220	Franco Harris	1.50
221	Ron Bolton	.08
222	Charles Alexander	.08
223	Matt Robinson	.08
224	Ray Oldham	.08
225	George Martin	.08
226	Buffalo Bills Team	.20
227	Tony Franklin	.08
228	George Cumby	.08
229	Butch Johnson	.08
230	Mike Haynes (AP)	.08
231	Rob Carpenter	.08
232	Steve Fuller	.08
233	John Sawyer	.08
234	Kenny King	.60
235	Jack Ham	.60
236	Jimmy Rogers	.08
237	Bob Parsons	.08
238	Marty Lyons	.50
239	Pat Tilley	.08
240	Dennis Harrah (AP)	.08
241	Thom Darden	.08
242	Rolf Benirschke	.08
243	Gerald Small	.08
244	Atlanta Falcons Team	.15
245	Roger Carr	.08
246	Sherman White	.08
247	Ted Brown	.08
248	Matt Cavanaugh	.08
249	John Dutton	.08
250	Bill Bergey (AP)	.15
251	Jim Allen	.08
252	Mike Nelms (SA)	.08
253	Tom Blanchard	.08
254	Ricky Thompson	.08
255	John Matuszak	.08
256	Randy Grossman	.08
257	Ray Griffin	.08
258	Lynn Cain	.08
259	Checklist 133-164	.25
260	Mike Pruitt (AP)	.08
261	Chris Ward	.08
262	Fred Steinfort	.08
263	James Owens	.08
264	Chicago Bears Team	1.50
265	Dan Fouts	1.50
266	Arnold Morgado	.08
267	John Jefferson (SA)	.08

#	Player	Price
268	Bill Lenkaitis	.08
269	James Jones	.08
270	Brad Van Pelt	.08
271	Steve Largent	1.75
272	Elvin Bethea	.08
273	Cullen Bryant	.08
274	Gary Danielson	.08
275	Tony Galbreath	.08
276	Dave Butz	.20
277	Steve Mike-Mayer	.08
278	Ron Johnson	.08
279	Tom DeLeone	.08
280	Ron Jaworski	.08
281	Mel Gray	.08
282	San Diego Chargers Team	.15
283	Mark Brammer	.08
284	Alfred Jenkins (SA)	.08
285	Greg Buttle	.08
286	Randy Hughes	.08
287	Delvin Williams	.08
288	Brian Baschnagel	.08
289	Gary Jeter	.08
290	Stanley Morgan (AP)	.50
291	Gerry Ellis	.08
292	Al Richardson	.08
293	Jimmie Giles	.08
294	Dave Jennings (SA)	.08
295	Wilbert Montgomery	.15
296	Dave Pureifory	.08
297	Greg Hawthorne	.08
298	Dick Ambrose	.08
299	Terry Hermeling	.08
300	Danny White	.40
301	Ken Burrough	.08
302	Paul Hofer	.08
303	Denver Broncos Team	.15
304	Eddie Payton	.08
305	Isaac Curtis	.08
306	Benny Ricardo	.08
307	Riley Odoms	.08
308	Bob Chandler	.08
309	Larry Heater	.08
310	Art Still (AP)	.50
311	Harold Jackson	.20
312	Charlie Joiner (SA)	.25
313	Jeff Nixon	.08
314	Aundra Thompson	.08
315	Richard Todd	.10
316	Dan Hampton	4.00
317	Doug Marsh	.08
318	Louie Giammona	.08
319	San Francisco 49ers Team	.50
320	Manu Tuiasosopo	.08
321	Rich Milot	.08
322	Mike Guman	.08
323	Bob Kuechenberg	.08
324	Tom Skladany	.08
325	Dave Logan	.08
326	Bruce Laird	.08
327	James Jones (SA)	.08
328	Joe Danelo	.08
329	Kenny King	.20
330	Pat Donovan (Ap)	.08
331	Record: (Earl Cooper)	.10
332	Record: (John Jefferson)	.10
333	Record: (Kenny King)	.10
334	Record: (Rod Martin)	.10
335	Record: (Jim Plunkett)	.10
336	Record: (Bill Thompson)	.10
337	John Cappelletti	.10
338	Detroit Lions Team	.20
339	Don Smith	.08
340	Rod Perry (AP)	.08
341	David Lewis	.08
342	Mark Gastineau	.75
343	Steve Largent (SA)	.85
344	Charley Young	.08
345	Toni Fritsch	.08
346	Matt Blair	.08
347	Don Bass	.08
348	Jim Jensen	.08
349	Karl Lorch	.08
350	Brian Sipe (AP)	.20
351	Theo Bell	.08
352	Sam Adams	.08
353	Paul Coffman	.08
354	Eric Harris	.08
355	Tony Hill	.20
356	J.T. Turner	.08
357	Frank LeMaster	.08
358	Jim Jodat	.08
359	Oakland Raiders Team	.25
360	Joe Cribbs (AP)	1.00
361	James Lofton (SA)	1.00
362	Dexter Bussey	.08
363	Bobby Jackson	.08
364	Steve DeBerg	1.00
365	Ottis Anderson	1.50
366	Tom Myers	.08
367	John James	.08
368	Reese McCall	.08
369	Jack Reynolds	.08
370	Gary Jonson (AP)	.08
371	Jimmy Cefalo	.08
372	Horace Ivory	.08
373	Garo Yepremian	.08

#	Player	Price
374	Brian Kelley	.08
375	Terry Bradshaw	2.50
376	Dallas Cowboys Team	.50
377	Randy Logan	.08
378	Tim Wilson	.08
379	Archie Manning (SA)	.08
380	Revie Sorey (AP)	.08
381	Randy Holloway	.08
382	Henry Lawrence	.08
383	Pat McInally	.08
384	Kevin Long	.08
385	Louis Wright	.08
386	Leonard Thompson	.08
387	Jan Stenerud	.20
388	Raymond Butler	.20
389	Checklist 265-396	.08
390	Steve Bartkowski (Ap)	.20
391	Clarence Harmon	.08
392	Wilbert Montgomery (SA)	.08
393	Billy Joe DuPree	.20
394	Kansas City Chiefs Team (Ted McKnight, Henry Marshall, Gary Barbaro, Art Still)	.08
395	Earnest Gray	.08
396	Ray Hamilton	.08
397	Brenard Wilson	.08
398	Calvin Hill	.10
399	Robin Cole	.08
400	Walter Payton (AP)	4.50
401	Jim Hart	.20
402	Ron Yary	.08
403	Cliff Branch	.40
404	Roland Hooks	.08
405	Ken Stabler	1.00
406	Chuck Ramsey	.08
407	Mike Nelms	.08
408	Ron Jaworski (SA)	.08
409	James Hunter	.08
410	Lee Roy Selmon	.08
411	Baltimore Colts Team (Curtis Dickey, Roger Carr, Bruce Laird, Mike Barnes)	.08
412	Henry Marshall	.08
413	Preston Pearson	.08
414	Richard Bishop	.08
415	Greg Pruitt	.08
416	Matt Bahr	.20
417	Tony Mullady	.08
418	Glen Edwards	.08
419	Sam McCullum	.08
420	Stan Walters (AP)	.08
421	George Roberts	.08
422	Dwight Clark	4.00
423	Pat Thomas	.10
424	Bruce Harper (SA)	.08
425	Craig Morton	.20
426	Derrick Gaffney	.08
427	Pete Johnson	.08
428	Wes Chandler	.50
429	Burgess Owens	.08
430	James Lofton (AP)	3.50
431	Tony Reed	.08
432	Minnesota Vikings Team	.40
433	Ron Springs	.10
434	Tim Fox	.08
435	Ozzie Newsome	3.00
436	Steve Furness	.08
437	Will Lewis	.08
438	Mike Hartenstine	.08
439	John Bunting	.08
440	Eddie Murray	2.00
441	Mike Pruitt	.08
442	Larry Swider	.08
443	Steve Freeman	.08
444	Bruce Hardy	.08
445	Pat Haden	.20
446	Curtis Dickey	.20
447	Doug Wilkerson	.08
448	Alfred Jenkins	.08
449	Dave Dalby	.08
450	Robert Brazile (AP)	.08
451	Bobby Hammond	.08
452	Raymond Clayborn	.08
453	Jim Miller	.08
454	Roy Simmons	.08
455	Charlie Waters	.20
456	Ricky Bell	.08
457	Ahmad Rashad (SA)	.25
458	Don Cockroft	.08
459	Keith Krepfle	.08
460	Marvin Powell (AP)	.08
461	Tommy Kramer	.08
462	Jim LeClair	.08
463	Freddie Scott	.08
464	Rob Lytle	.08
465	Johnnie Gray	.08
466	Doug France	.15
467	Carlos Carson	.25
468	St. Louis Cardinals Team	.25
469	Efren Herrera	.08
470	Randy White (AP)	.75
471	Richard Caster	.08
472	Andy Johnson	.08
473	Billy Sims (SA)	.25
474	Joe Lavender	.08
475	Harry Carson	.40
476	John Stallworth	.75

#	Player	Price
477	Bob Thomas	.08
478	Keith Wright	.08
479	Ken Stone	.08
480	Carl Hariston (AP)	.08
481	Reggie McKenzie	.08
482	Bob Griese	1.00
483	Mike Bragg	.08
484	Scott Dierking	.08
485	David Hill	.08
486	Brian Sipe (SA)	.20
487	Rod Martin	.25
488	Cincinnati Bengals Team (Pete Johnson, Dan Ross, Louis Breeden, Eddie Edwards)	.08
489	Preston Dennard	.08
490	John Smith (AP)	.08
491	Mike Reinfeldt	.08
492	NFC Championship (Ron Jaworski)	.08
493	AFC Championship (Jim Plunkett)	.08
494	Super Bowl XV (Jim Plunkett, King)	.40
495	Joe Greene	1.00
496	Charlie Joiner	.60
497	Rolland Lawrence	.08
498	Bubba Baker (SA)	.08
499	Brad Dusek	.08
500	Tony Dorsett	2.50
501	Robin Earl	.08
502	Theotis Brown	.08
503	Joe Ferguson	.15
504	Bealsey Reece	.08
505	Lyle Alzado	.20
506	Tony Nathan	.40
507	Philadelphia Eagles Team (Wilbert Montgomery, Charlie Smith, Brenard Wilson, Claude Humphrey)	.08
508	Herb Orvis	.08
509	Clarence Williams	.08
510	Ray Guy (AP)	.25
511	Jeff Komlo	.08
512	Freddie Solomon (SA)	.08
513	Tim Mazzetti	.08
514	Elvis Peacock	.08
515	Russ Francis	.08
516	Roland Harper	.08
517	Checklist 397-528	.25
518	Billy Johnson	.08
519	Dan Dierdorf	.40
520	Fred Dean (AP)	.08
521	Jerry Butler	.08
522	Ron Saul	.08
523	Charlie Smith	.08
524	Kellen Winslow (SA)	3.00
525	Bert Jones	.20
526	Pittsburgh Steelers Team	.75
527	Duriel Harris	.08
528	William Andrews	.25

1981 Topps Stickers

These stickers, which measure 1-15/16" x 2-9/16", are numbered alphabetically by teams within divisions. The front has a color photo with a white frame, plus the sticker number. That number is also on the back, along with the player's name, position, team and instructions on how to apply the sticker. A sticker album was also made available as a mail-in offer. The album cover features a Buffalo Bills player.

	MT
Complete Set (262):	25.00
Common Player:	.05

#	Player	Price
1	AFC Passing Leader (Brian Sipe)	.10
2	AFC Passing Yardage Leader (Dan Fouts)	.50
3	AFC Receiving Yardage Leader (John Jefferson)	.08
4	AFC Kickoff Return Yardage Leader (Bruce Harper)	.05
5	AFC Punt Return Yardage Leader (J.T. Smith)	.05
6	AFC Punting Leader (Luke Prestige)	.05
7	AFC Interceptions Leader (Lester Hayes)	.05
8	AFC Sacks Leader (Gary Johnson)	.05
9	Bert Jones	.15
10	Fred Cook	.05
11	Roger Carr	.10
12	Greg Landry	.08
13	Raymond Butler	.08
14	Bruce Laird	.05
15	Ed Simonini	.05
16	Curtis Dickey	.10
17	Joe Cribbs	.15
18	Joe Ferguson	.15
19	Ben Williams	.05
20	Jerry Butler	.08
21	Roland Hooks	.05
22	Fred Smerlas	.05
23	Frank Lewis	.05
24	Mark Brammer	.05
25	Dave Woodley	.08
26	Nat Moore	.10
27	Uwe Von Schamann	.05
28	Vern Den Herder	.05
29	Tony Nathan	.10
30	Duriel Harris	.08
31	Don McNeal	.05
32	Delvin Williams	.05
33	Stanley Morgan	.15
34	John Hannah	.15
35	Horace Ivory	.05
36	Steve Nelson	.05
37	Steve Grogan	.15
38	Vagas Ferguson	.10
39	John Smith	.05
40	Mike Haynes	.12
41	Mark Gastineau	.15
42	Wesley Walker	.15
43	Joe Klecko	.10
44	Chris Ward	.05
45	Johnny Lam Jones	.08
46	Marvin Powell	.05
47	Richard Todd	.15
48	Greg Buttle	.08
49	Eddie Edwards	.05
50	Dan Ross	.08
51	Ken Anderson	.50
52	Ross Browner	.08
53	Don Bass	.08
54	Jim LeClair	.05
55	Pete Johnson	.08
56	Anthony Munoz	1.25
57	Brian Sipe	.12
58	Mike Pruitt	.10
59	Greg Pruitt	.15
60	Thom Darden	.05
61	Ozzie Newsome	.40
62	Dave Logan	.05
63	Lyle Alzado	.15
64	Reggie Rucker	.08
65	Robert Brazile	.08
66	Mike Barber	.08
67	Carl Roaches	.10
68	Ken Stabler	.30
69	Gregg Bingham	.08
70	Mike Renfro	.08
71	Leon Gray	.05
72	Rob Carpenter	.10
73	Franco Harris	.50
74	Jack Lambert	.30
75	Jim Smith	.05
76	Mike Webster	.15
77	Sidney Thornton	.05
78	Joe Greene	.40

#	Player	Price
79	John Stallworth	.20
80	Tyrone McGriff	.05
81	Randy Gradishar	.12
82	Haven Moses	.08
83	Riley Odoms	.10
84	Matt Robinson	.05
85	Craig Morton	.12
86	Rulon Jones	.05
87	Rick Upchurch	.10
88	Jim Jensen	.05
89	Art Still	.12
90	J.T. Smith	.12
91	Steve Fuller	.05
92	Gary Barbaro	.05
93	Ted McKnight	.05
94	Bob Grupp	.05
95	Henry Marshall	.05
96	Mike Williams	.05
97	Jim Plunkett	.25
98	Lester Hayes	.12
99	Cliff Branch	.20
100	John Matuszak	.10
101	Matt Millen	.10
102	Kenny King	.05
103	Ray Guy	.15
104	Ted Hendricks	.20
105	John Jefferson	.12
106	Fred Dean	.12
107	Dan Fouts	.35
108	Charlie Joiner	.25
109	Kellen Winslow	1.25
110	Gary Johnson	.08
111	Mike Thomas	.05
112	Louie Kelcher	.12
113	Jim Zorn	.12
114	Terry Beeson	.05
115	Jacob Green	.35
116	Steve Largent	1.25
117	Dan Doornink	.05
118	Manu Tuiasosopo	.05
119	John Sawyer	.05
120	Jim Jodat	.05
121	Walter Payton (All-Pro)	2.00
122	Brian Sipe (All-Pro)	.25
123	Joe Cribbs (All-Pro)	.25
124	James Lofton (All-Pro)	.60
125	John Jefferson (All-Pro)	.25
126	Leon Gray (All-Pro)	.15
127	Joe DeLamielleure (All-Pro)	.20
128	Mike Webster (All-Pro)	.30
129	John Hannah (All-Pro)	.30
130	Mike Kenn (All-Pro)	.20
131	Kellen Winslow (All-Pro)	1.50
132	Lee Roy Selmon (All-Pro)	.30
133	Randy White (All-Pro)	.30
134	Gary Johnson (All-Pro)	.15
135	Art Still (All-Pro)	.20
136	Robert Brazile (All-Pro)	.20
137	Nolan Cromwell (All-Pro)	.20
138	Ted Hendricks (All-Pro)	.50
139	Lester Hayes (All-Pro)	.25
140	Randy Gradishar (All-Pro)	.35
141	Lemar Parrish (All-Pro)	.15
142	Donnie Shell (All-Pro)	.20
143	NFC Passing Leader (Ron Jaworski)	.12
144	NFC Passing Leader (Archie Manning)	
145	NFC Rushing Yardage Leader (Walter Payton)	.75
146	NFC Rushing Touchdowns Leader (Billy Sims)	.25
147	NFC Receiving Yardage Leader (James Lofton)	.25
148	NFC Punting Leader (Dave Jennings)	.05
149	NFC Interceptions Leader (Nolan Cromwell)	.08
150	NFC Sacks Leader (Al (Bubba) Baker)	.08
151	Tony Dorsett	.50
152	Harvey Martin	.15
153	Danny White	.25
154	Pat Donovan	.05
155	Drew Pearson	.15
156	Robert Newhouse	.10
157	Randy White	.40
158	Butch Johnson	.10
159	Dave Jennings	.05
160	Brad Van Pelt	.05
161	Phil Simms	.40
162	Mike Friede	.05

#	Player	Price
163	Billy Taylor	.08
164	Gary Jeter	.08
165	George Martin	.05
166	Earnest Gray	.05
167	Ron Jaworski	.15
168	Bill Bergey	.08
169	Wilbert Montgomery	.08
170	Charlie Smith	.05
171	Jerry Robinson	.05
172	Herman Edwards	.05
173	Harold Carmichael	.15
174	Claude Humphrey	.10
175	Ottis Anderson	.30
176	Jim Hart	.15
177	Pat Tilley	.08
178	Rush Brown	.05
179	Tom Brahaney	.05
180	Dan Dierdorf	.25
181	Wayne Morris	.05
182	Doug Marsh	.05
183	Art Monk	3.00
184	Clarence Harmon	.05
185	Lemar Parrish	.12
186	Joe Theismann	.35
187	Joe Lavender	.05
188	Wilbur Jackson	.05
189	Dave Butz	.05
190	Coy Bacon	.05
191	Walter Payton	1.50
192	Alan Page	.15
193	Vince Evans	.20
194	Roland Harper	.05
195	Dan Hampton	.80
196	Gary Fencik	.08
197	Mike Hartenstine	.05
198	Robin Earl	.05
199	Billy Sims	.25
200	Leonard Thompson	.05
201	Jeff Komlo	.05
202	Al (Bubba) Baker	.10
203	Ed Murray	.15
204	Dexter Bussey	.05
205	Tom Ginn	.05
206	Freddie Scott	.05
207	James Lofton	.50
208	Mike Butler	.05
209	Lynn Dickey	.12
210	Gerry Ellis	.05
211	Edd Lee Ivery	.10
212	Ezra Johnson	.05
213	Paul Coffman	.05
214	Aundra Thompson	.05
215	Ahmad Rashad	.25
216	Tommy Kramer	.08
217	Matt Blair	.08
218	Sammie White	.08
219	Ted Brown	.08
220	Joe Senser	.05
221	Rickey Young	.05
222	Randy Holloway	.05
223	Lee Roy Selmon	.15
224	Doug Williams	.10
225	Ricky Bell	.10
226	David Lewis	.05
227	Gordon Jones	.05
228	Dewey Selmon	.05
229	Jimmie Giles	.05
230	Mike Washington	.05
231	William Andrews	.15
232	Jeff Van Note	.08
233	Steve Bartkowski	.15
234	Junior Miller	.08
235	Lynn Cain	.08
236	Joel Williams	.05
237	Alfred Jenkins	.08
238	Kenny Johnson	.05
239	Jack Youngblood	.20
240	Elvis Peacock	.08
241	Cullen Bryant	.10
242	Dennis Harrah	.05
243	Billy Waddy	.05
244	Nolan Cromwell	.10
245	Doug France	.05
246	Johnnie Johnson	.08
247	Archie Manning	.25
248	Tony Galbreath	.08
249	Wes Chandler	.15
250	Stan Brock	.05
251	Ike Harris	.05
252	Russell Erxleben	.05
253	Jimmy Rogers	.05
254	Tom Myers	.05
255	Dwight Clark	.75
256	Earl Cooper	.05
257	Steve DeBerg	.25
258	Randy Cross	.10
259	Freddie Solomon	.08
260	Jim Miller	.05
261	Charley Young	.08
262	Bobby Leopold	.05

1981 Topps Red Border Stickers

These stickers came in their own little containers and measure 1-15/16" x 2-9/16". Each of the 28 NFL teams is represented in the set, which features red borders on the front, framing a color photo. The player's name and position are also listed. The sticker back has the sticker number, player name, position and team, biographical information and instructions on how to apply the sticker.

	MT
Complete Set (28):	20.00
Common Player:	.40

#	Player	Price
1	Steve Bartkowski	1.00
2	Bert Jones	1.00
3	Joe Cribbs	.60
4	Walter Payton	5.00
5	Ross Browner	.40
6	Brian Sipe	.75
7	Tony Dorsett	2.50
8	Randy Gradishar	.60
9	Billy Sims	1.00
10	James Lofton	1.75
11	Mike Barber	.40
12	Art Still	.40
13	Jack Youngblood	.75
14	Dave Woodley	.50
15	Ahmad Rashad	1.25
16	Russ Francis	.50
17	Archie Manning	.75
18	Dave Jennings	.40
19	Richard Todd	.50
20	Lester Hayes	.60
21	Ron Jaworski	.50
22	Franco Harris	2.00
23	Ottis Anderson	1.00
24	John Jefferson	.50
25	Freddie Solomon	.40
26	Steve Largent	3.50
27	Lee Roy Selmon	.75
28	Art Monk	8.00

Values quoted in this guide reflect the retail price of a card — the price a collector can expect to pay when buying a card from a dealer. The wholesale price — that which a collector can expect to receive from a dealer when selling cards — will be significantly lower, depending on desirability and condition.

1982 Topps

Topps' last 528-card set was issued in 1982, and the design was nearly a duplicate of the 1975 football set. Football helmets featuring the team's helmet design appeared on these cards for the first time. Also included in this set were in-action cards of top stars and a subset featuring NFL brother tandems. Cards are numbered alphabetically by team and by the last name of the player. Notable rookies in this set include Cris Collinsworth, Anthony Munoz, Freeman McNeil, George Rogers, Ronnie Lott, Lawrence Taylor and Neil Lomax. (Key: AP - All Pro, IA - In Action.)

		MT
	Complete Set (528):	90.00
	Common Player:	.05
	Wax Box:	150.00
1	Ken Anderson (RB)	.50
2	Dan Fouts (RB)	.50
3	LeRoy Irvin (RB)	.10
4	Stump Mitchell (RB)	.10
5	George Rogers (RB)	.15
6	Dan Ross (RB)	.05
7	AFC Championship (Ken Anderson, Pete Johnson)	.15
8	NFC Championship (Earl Cooper)	.15
9	Super Bowl XVI (Anthony Munoz)	.75
10	Baltimore Colts Team	.15
11	Raymond Butler	.05
12	Roger Carr	.05
13	Curtis Dickey	.05
14	Zachary Dixon	.05
15	Nesby Glasgow	.05
16	Bert Jones	.10
17	Bruce Laird	.05
18	Reese McCall	.05
19	Randy McMillan	.05
20	Ed Simonini	.05
21	Buffalo Bills Team	.15
22	Mark Brammer	.05
23	Curtis Brown	.05
24	Jerry Butler	.05
25	Mario Clark	.05
26	Joe Cribbs	.15
27	Joe Cribbs (IA)	.05
28	Joe Ferguson	.15
29	Jim Haslett	.05
30	Frank Lewis (AP)	.05
31	Frank Lewis (IA)	.05
32	Shane Nelson	.05
33	Charles Romes	.05
34	Bill Simpson	.05
35	Fred Smerlas	.05
36	Cincinnati Bengals Team	.15
37	Charles Alexander	.05
38	Ken Anderson (AP)	.50
39	Ken Anderson (IA)	.20
40	Jim Breech	.05
41	Jim Breech (IA)	.05
42	Louis Breeden	.05
43	Ross Browner	.05
44	Cris Collinsworth	1.00
45	Cris Collinsworth IA (IA)	.50
46	Isaac Curtis	.05
47	Pete Johnson	.05
48	Pete Johnson (IA)	.05
49	Steve Kreider	.05
50	Pat McInally (AP)	.05
51	Anthony Munoz (AP)	7.00
52	Dan Ross	.05
53	David Verser	.05
54	Reggie Williams	.05
55	Cleveland Browns Team	.20
56	Lyle Alzado	.20
57	Dick Ambrose	.05
58	Ron Bolton	.05
59	Steve Cox	.05
60	Joe DeLamielleure	.05
61	Tom DeLeone	.05
62	Doug Dieken	.05
63	Ricky Feacher	.05
64	Don Goode	.05
65	Robert L. Jackson	.05
66	Dave Logan	.05
67	Ozzie Newsome	1.50
68	Ozzie Newsome (IA)	.75
69	Greg Pruitt	.10
70	Mike Pruitt	.05
71	Mike Pruitt (IA)	.05
72	Reggie Rucker	.05
73	Clarence Scott	.05
74	Brian Sipe	.10
75	Charles White	.15
76	Denver Broncos Team	.15
77	Rubin Carter	.05
78	Steve Foley	.05
79	Randy Gradishar	.25
80	Tom Jackson	.25
81	Craig Morton	.25
82	Craig Morton (IA)	.10
83	Riley Odoms	.05
84	Rick Parros	.05
85	Dave Preston	.05
86	Tony Reed	.05
87	Bob Swenson	.05
88	Bill Thompson	.05
89	Rick Upchurch	.05
90	Steve Watson (AP)	.25
91	Steve Watson (IA)	.10
92	Houston Oilers Team	.15
93	Mike Barber	.05
94	Elvin Bethea	.05
95	Gregg Bingham	.05
96	Robert Brazile (AP)	.05
97	Ken Burrough	.05
98	Toni Fritsch	.05
99	Leon Gray	.05
100	Gifford Nielsen	.15
101	Vernon Perry	.05
102	Mike Reinfeldt	.05
103	Mike Renfro	.05
104	Carl Roaches (AP)	.05
105	Ken Stabler	1.00
106	Greg Stemrick	.05
107	J.C. Wilson	.05
108	Tim Wilson	.05
109	Kansas City Chiefs	.15
110	Gary Barbaro (AP)	.05
111	Brad Budde (AP)	.05
112	Joe Delaney (AP)	.25
113	Joe Delaney (IA)	.10
114	Steve Fuller	.05
115	Gary Green	.05
116	James Hadnot	.05
117	Eric Harris	.05
118	Billy Jackson	.05
119	Bill Kenney	.05
120	Nick Lowery (AP)	1.50
121	Nick Lowery (IA)	.60
122	Henry Marshall	.05
123	J.T. Smith	.25
124	Art Still	.05
125	Miami Dolphins Team	.15
126	Bob Baumhower (AP)	.05
127	Glenn Blackwood	.05
128	Jimmy Cefalo	.05
129	A.J. Duhe	.05
130	Andra Franklin	.10
131	Duriel Harris	.05
132	Nat Moore	.05
133	Tony Nathan	.05
134	Ed Newman	.05
135	Earnie Rhone	.05
136	Don Strock	.05
137	Tommy Vigorito	.05
138	Uwe Von Schamann	.05
139	Uwe Von Schamann (IA)	.05
140	David Woodley	.10
141	New England Patriots Team	.10
142	Julius Adams	.05
143	Richard Bishop	.05
144	Matt Cavanaugh	.05
145	Raymond Clayborn	.05
146	Tony Collins	.20
147	Vagas Ferguson	.05
148	Tim Fox	.05
149	Steve Grogan	.25
150	John Hannah	.25
151	John Hannah (IA)	.10
152	Don Hasselbeck	.05
153	Mike Haynes	.05
154	Harold Jackson	.10
155	Andy Johnson	.05
156	Stanley Morgan	.10
157	Stanley Morgan (IA)	.10
158	Steve Nelson	.05
159	Rod Shoate	.05
160	New York Jets Team	.25
161	Dan Alexander	.05
162	Mike Augustyniak	.05
163	Jerome Barkum	.05
164	Greg Buttle	.05
165	Scott Dierking	.05
166	Joe Fields	.05
167	Mark Gastineau (AP)	.20
168	Mark Gastineau (IA)	.10
169	Bruce Harper	.05
170	Johnny Lam Jones	.05
171	Joe Klecko (AP)	.10
172	Joe Klecko (IA)	.05
173	Pat Leahy	.05
174	Pat Leahy (IA)	.05
175	Marty Lyons	.10
176	Freeman McNeil	1.00
177	Marvin Powell AP	.05
178	Chuck Ramsey	.05
179	Darrol Ray	.05
180	Abdul Salaam	.05
181	Richard Todd	.10
182	Richard Todd (IA)	.05
183	Wesley Walker	.20
184	Chris Ward	.05
185	Oakland Raiders Team	.15
186	Cliff Branch	.25
187	Bob Chandler	.05
188	Ray Guy	.25
189	Lester Hayes (AP)	.05
190	Ted Hendricks (AP)	.05
191	Monte Jackson	.05
192	Derrick Jensen	.05
193	Kenny King	.05
194	Rod Martin	.05
195	John Matuszak	.05
196	Matt Millen	1.25
197	Derrick Ramsey	.05
198	Art Shell	.40
199	Mark Van Eeghen	.05
200	Arthur Whittington	.05
201	Marc Wilson	.20
202	Pittsburgh Steelers Team	.50
203	Mel Blount (AP)	.75
204	Terry Bradshaw	1.50
205	Terry Bradshaw (IA)	.75
206	Craig Colquitt	.05
207	Bennie Cunningham	.05
208	Russell Davis	.05
209	Gary Dunn	.05
210	Jack Ham	.75
211	Franco Harris	.75
212	Franco Harris (IA)	.75
213	Jack Lambert (AP)	.75
214	Jack Lambert (IA)	.25
215	Mark Malone	.20
218	Jim Smith	.05
219	John Stallworth	.60
220	John Stallworth (IA)	.30
221	David Trout	.05
222	Mike Webster (AP)	.20
223	San Diego Chargers Team	.15
224	Rolf Bernirschke	.05
225	Rolf Benirschke (IA)	.05
226	James Brooks	1.00
227	Willie Buchanon	.05
228	Wes Chandler	.15
229	Wes Chandler (IA)	.10
230	Dan Fouts	1.00
231	Dan Fouts (IA)	.50
232	Gary Johnson (AP)	.05
233	Charlie Joiner	.40
234	Charlie Joiner (IA)	.20
235	Louie Kelcher	.05
236	Chuck Muncie (AP)	.05
237	Chuck Muncie (IA)	.05
238	George Roberts	.05
239	Ed White	.05
240	Doug Wilkerson (AP)	.05
241	Kellen Winslow (AP)	2.00
242	Kellen Winslow IA (IA)	1.00
243	Seattle Seahawks Team	.20
244	Theotis Brown	.05
245	Don Doornink	.05
246	John Harris	.05
247	Efren Herrera	.05
248	David Hughes	.05
249	Steve Largent	1.75
250	Steve Largent (IA)	.90
251	Sam McCullum	.05
252	Sherman Smith	.05
253	Manu Tuiasosopo	.05
254	John Yarno	.05
255	Jim Zorn	.10
256	Jim Zorn (IA)	.05
257	(Joe Montana, Ken Anderson)	2.00
258	Receiving Leaders (Kellen Winslow, Dwight Clark)	.50
259	Sack Leaders (Joe Klecko, Curtis Greer)	.10
260	Scoring Leaders (Jim Breech, Nick Lowery, Ed Murray, Rafael Septien)	.10
261	Interception Leaders (John Harris, Everson Walls)	.20
262	Punting Leaders (Pat McInally, Tom Skladany)	.10
263	Brothers: (Chris Bahr, Matt Bahr)	.10
264	Brothers: (Lyle Blackwood, Glenn Blackwood)	.10
265	Brothers: (Pete Brock, Stan Brock)	.10
266	Brothers: (Archie Griffin, Ray Griffin)	.10
267	Brothers: (John Hannah, Charley Hannah)	.20
268	Brothers: (Monte Jackson, Terry Jackson)	.10
269	Brothers: (Eddie Payton, Walter Payton)	1.00
270	Brothers: (Dewey Selmon, Lee Roy Selmon)	.10
271	Atlanta Falcons Team	.15
272	Williams Andrews	.05
273	William Anderws (IA)	.05
274	Steve Bartkowski	.25
275	Steve Bartkowski	.05
276	Bobby Butler	.05
277	Lynn Cain	.05
278	Wallace Francis	.05
279	Alfred Jackson	.05
280	John James	.05
281	Alfred Jenkins (AP)	.05
282	Alfred Jenkins (IA)	.05
283	Kenny Johnson	.05
284	Mike Kenn (AP)	.25
285	Fulton Kuykendall	.05
286	Mike Luckhurst	.05
287	Mick Luckhurst (IA)	.05
288	Junior Miller	.05
289	Al Richardson	.05
290	R.C. Thielemann	.05
291	Jeff Van Note	.05
292	Chicago Bears Team	.75
293	Brian Baschnagel	.05
294	Robin Earl	.05
295	Vince Evans	.20
296	Gary Fencik (AP)	.05
297	Dan Hampton	1.00
298	Noah Jackson	.05
299	Ken Margerum	.05
300	Jim Osborne	.05
301	Bob Parsons	.05
302	Walter Payton	4.00
303	Walter Payton IA (IA)	2.00
304	Revie Sorey	.05
305	Matt Suhey	.25
306	Rickey Watts	.05
307	Dallas Cowboys Team	.60
308	Bob Breunig	.05
309	Doug Cosbie	.25
310	Pat Donovan (AP)	.05
311	Tony Dorsett	1.00
312	Tony Dorsett (IA)	.60
313	Michael Downs	.05
314	Billy Joe DuPree	.15
315	John Dutton	.05
316	Tony Hill	.05
317	Butch Johnson	.05
318	Ed "Too Tall" Jones	.60
319	James Jones	.05
320	Harvey Martin	.15
321	Drew Pearson	.40
322	Herbert Scott (AP)	.05
323	Rafael Septien (AP)	.05
324	Rafael Septien (IA)	.05
325	Ron Springs	.05
326	Dennis Thurman	.10
327	Everson Walls	.50
328	Everson Walls (IA)	.25
329	Danny White	.25
330	Danny White (IA)	.10
331	Randy White (AP)	.60
332	Randy White (IA)	.25
333	Detroit Lions Team	.15
334	Jim Allen	.05
335	Al Bubba Baker	.05
336	Dexter Bussey	.05
337	Doug English (AP)	.05
338	Ken Fantetti	.05
339	William Gay	.05
340	David Hill	.05
341	Eric Hipple	.10
342	Rick Kane	.05
343	Ed Murray	.40
344	Ed Murray (IA)	.20
345	Ray Oldham	.05
346	Dave Pureifory	.05
347	Freddie Scott	.05
348	Freddie Scott (IA)	.05
349	Billy Sims (AP)	.30
350	Billy Sims (IA)	.15
351	Tom Skladany (AP)	.05
352	Leonard Thompson	.05
353	Stan White	.05
354	Green Bay Packers Team	.40
355	Paul Coffman	.05
356	George Cumby	.05
357	Lynn Dickey	.10
358	Lynn Dickey (IA)	.05
359	Gerry Ellis	.05
360	Maurice Harvey	.05
361	Harlan Huckleby	.05
362	John Jefferson	.20
363	Mark Lee	.05
364	James Lofton (AP)	1.75
365	James Lofton (IA)	.75
366	Jan Stenerud	.25
367	Jan Stenerud (IA)	.10
368	Rich Wingo	.05
369	Los Angeles Rams Team	.20
370	Frank Corral	.05
371	Nolan Cromwell (AP)	.25
372	Nolan Cromwell (IA)	.10
373	Preston Dennard	.05
374	Mike Fanning	.05
375	Doug France	.05
376	Mike Guman	.05
377	Pat Haden	.25
378	Dennis Harrah	.05
379	Drew Hill	2.00
380	LeRoy Irvin	.40
381	Cody Jones	.05
382	Rod Perry	.05
383	Rich Saul (AP)	.05
384	Pat Thomas	.05
385	Wendell Tyler	.08
386	Wendell Tyler (IA)	.05
387	Billy Waddy	.05
388	Jack Youngblood	.25
389	Minnesota Vikings Team	.15
390	Matt Blair (AP)	.05
391	Ted Brown	.08
392	Ted Brown (IA)	.05
393	Rick Danmeier	.05
394	Tommy Kramer	.25
395	Mark Mullaney	.05
396	Eddie Payton	.05
397	Ahmad Rashad	.40
398	Joe Senser	.08
399	Joe Senser (IA)	.05
400	Sammy White	.05
401	Sammy White (IA)	.05
402	Ron Yary	.05
403	Rickey Young	.05
404	New Orleans Saints Team	.50
405	Russell Erxieben	.05
406	Elois Grooms	.05
407	Jack Holmes	.05
408	Archie Manning	.25
409	Derland Moore	.05
410	George Rogers	1.00
411	George Rogers (IA)	.40
412	Toussaint Tyler	.05
413	Dave Waymer	.20
414	Wayne Wilson	.05
415	New York Giants Team	.15
416	Scott Brunner	.10
417	Rob Carpenter	.05
418	Harry Carson (AP)	.25
419	Bill Currier	.05
420	Joe Danelo	.05
421	Joe Danelo (IA)	.05
422	Mark Haynes	.35
423	Terry Jackson	.05
424	Dave Jennings	.05
425	Gary Jeter	.05
426	Brian Kelley	.05
427	George Martin	.05
428	Curtis McGriff	.05
429	Bill Neill	.05
430	Johnny Perkins	.05
431	Beasley Reece	.07
432	Gary Shirk	.05
433	Phil Simms	1.50
434	Lawrence Taylor	30.00
435	Lawrence Taylor IA (IA)	10.00
436	Brad Van Pelt	.05
437	Philadelphia Eagles Team	.15
438	John Bunting	.05
439	Billy Campfield	.05
440	Harold Carmichael	.25
441	Harold Carmichael (IA)	.10
442	Herman Edwards	.05
443	Tony Franklin	.05
444	Tony Franklin (IA)	.05
445	Carl Hairston	.05
446	Dennis Harrison	.05
447	Ron Jaworski	.15
448	Charlie Johnson	.05
449	Keith Krepfle	.05
450	Frank LeMaster	.05
451	Randy Logan	.05
452	Wilbert Montgomery	.07
453	Wilbert Montgomery (IA)	.05
454	Hubert Oliver	.05
455	Jerry Robinson	.05
456	Jerry Robinson (IA)	.05
457	Jerry Sisemore	.05
458	Charlie Smith	.05
459	Stan Walters	.05
460	Brenard Wilson	.05
461	Roynell Young (AP)	.05
462	St. Louis Cardinals Team	.25
463	Ottis Anderson	1.00
464	Ottis Anderson (IA)	.60
465	Carl Birdsong	.05
466	Rush Brown	.05
467	Mel Gray	.05
468	Ken Greene	.05
469	Jim Hart	.15
470	E.J. Junior	.60
471	Neil Lomax	.75
472	Stump Mitchell	.40
473	Wayne Morris	.05
474	Neil O'Donoghue	.05
475	Pat Tilley	.05
476	Pat Tilley (IA)	.05
477	San Francisco 49ers Team	.40
478	Dwight Clark	1.00
479	Dwight Clark (IA)	.40
480	Earl Cooper	.05
481	Randy Cross (AP)	.05
482	Johnny Davis	.05
483	Fred Dean	.05
484	Fred Dean (IA)	.05
485	Dwight Hicks	.25
486	Ronnie Lott (AP)	15.00
487	Ronnie Lott IA (IA)	6.00
488	Joe Montana (AP)	30.00
489	Joe Montana IA (IA)	10.00
490	Ricky Patton	.05
491	Jack Reynolds	.05
492	Freddie Solomon	.05
493	Ray Wersching	.05
494	Charley Young	.05
495	Tampa Bay Buccaneers Team	.15
496	Cedric Brown	.05
497	Neal Colzie	.05
498	Jerry Eckwood	.05
499	Jimmy Giles (AP)	.05
500	Hugh Green	.60
501	Kevin House	.05
502	Kevin House (IA)	.05
503	Cecil Johnson	.05
504	James Owens	.05
505	Lee Roy Selmon (AP)	.15
506	Mike Washington	.05
507	James Wilder	.65
508	Doug Williams	.25
509	Washington Redskins Team	.75
510	Perry Brooks	.05
511	Dave Butz	.05
512	Wilbur Jackson	.05
513	Joe Lavender	.05
514	Terry Metcalf	.15
515	Art Monk	4.00
516	Frank Pollard, Mark Moseley	.05
517	Donnie Shell, Mark Murphy (AP)	.05
518	Mike Neims (AP)	.05
519	Lemar Parrish	.05
520	John Riggins	1.00
521	Joe Theismann	1.00
522	Ricky Thompson	.05
523	Don Warren	.15
524	Joe Washington	.25
525	Checklist 1-132	.25
526	Checklist 133-264	.25
527	Checklist 265-396	.25
528	Checklist 397-528	.25

1982 Topps "Coming Soon" Stickers

These stickers were inserted in 1982 Topps football card packs. They are 1-15/16" x 2-9/16", making them the same size as Topps' regular 1982 stickers. They also share the same card numbers, which is why the set is skip-numbered. The card number is on the back, along with the words "Coming Soon!" The fronts of the stickers are gold-bordered foil stickers.

		MT
	Complete Set (16):	5.00
	Common Player:	.10
5	MVP Super Bowl XVI (Joe Montana)	2.00
6	NFC Championship	.10
9	Super Bowl XVI (Joe Montana)	1.50
73	Tommy Kramer	.30
75	George Rogers	.30
139	Tom Skladany	.10
143	Nolan Cromwell	.30
144	Jack Lambert	.50
150	Lawrence Taylor	1.75
159	Billy Sims	.40
160	Ken Anderson	.50
221	John Hannah	.40
222	Anthony Munoz	.75
220	Ken Anderson	.50
221	Dan Fouts	.50
222	Frank Lewis	.10

Post-1980 cards in Near Mint condition will generally sell for about 75% of the quoted Mint value. Excellent-condition cards bring no more than 40%.

1982 Topps Stickers

These stickers follow the same format as the 1981 stickers, complete with an album featuring Joe Montana on the cover. However, these stickers have yellow borders and a 1982 copyright date on the back. Foil stickers were also produced again (#s 1-10, 70-77, 139-160, 220-227). Stickers 1 and 2 combine as a puzzle to form a picture of the San Francisco 49ers; 3 and 4 show Super Bowl theme art.

		MT
Complete Set (288):		30.00
Common Player"		.05
1	Super Bowl XVI (49er Team)	.35
2	Super Bowl XVI (49er Team)	.15
3	Super Bowl XVI (Theme Art Trophy)	.15
4	Super Bowl XVI (Theme Art Trophy)	.15
5	MVP Super Bowl XVI (Joe Montana)	3.50
6	1981 NFC Champions 49ers	.15
7	1981 AFC Champions (Ken Anderson)	.25
8	Super Bowl XVI (Ken Anderson)	.25
9	Super Bowl XVI (Joe Montana)	3.00
10	Super Bowl XVI (line blocking)	.15
11	Steve Bartkowski	.15
12	William Andrews	.10
13	Lynn Cain	.08
14	Wallace Francis	.08
15	Alfred Jackson	.08
16	Alfred Jenkins	.10
17	Mike Kenn	.08
18	Junior Miller	.10
19	Vince Evans	.10
20	Walter Payton	1.25
21	Dave Williams	.05
22	Brian Baschnagel	.05
23	Rickey Watts	.05
24	Ken Margerum	.08
25	Revie Sorey	.05
26	Gary Fencik	.05
27	Matt Suhey	.05
28	Danny White	.20
29	Tony Dorsett	.50
30	Drew Pearson	.25
31	Rafael Septien	.08
32	Pat Donovan	.05
33	Herbert Scott	.05
34	Ed "Too Tall" Jones	.20
35	Randy White	.25
36	Tony Hill	.08
37	Eric Hipple	.08
38	Billy Sims	.25
39	Dexter Bussey	.05
40	Freddie Scott	.08
41	David Hill	.05
42	Ed Murray	.10
43	Tom Skladany	.05
44	Doug English	.08
45	Al (Bubba) Baker	.12
46	Lynn Dickey	.12
47	Gerry Ellis	.05
48	Harlan Huckleby	.05
49	James Lofton	.40
50	John Jefferson	.25
51	Paul Coffman	.05
52	Jan Stenerud	.20
53	Rich Wingo	.05
54	Wendell Tyler	.10
55	Preston Dennard	.05
56	Billy Waddy	.05
57	Frank Corral	.05
58	Jack Youngblood	.15
59	Pat Thomas	.05
60	Rod Perry	.08
61	Nolan Cromwell	.08
62	Tommy Kramer	.10
63	Rickey Young	.05
64	Ted Brown	.05
65	Ahmad Rashad	.25
66	Sammie White	.08
67	Joe Senser	.05
68	Ron Yary	.08
69	Matt Blair	.08

70	NFC Passing Leader (Joe Montana)	3.50
71	NFC Passing Yardage Leader (Tommy Kramer)	.20
72	NFC Receiving Yardage Leader (Alfred Jenkins)	.15
73	NFC Rushing Yardage Leader (George Rogers)	.25
74	NFC Rushing Touchdowns Leader (Wendell Tyler)	.30
75	NFC Punting Leader (Tom Skladany)	.15
76	NFC Interceptions Leader (Everson Walls)	.35
77	MFC Sacks Leader (Curtis Greer)	.15
78	Archie Manning	.25
79	Dave Waymer	.08
80	George Rogers	.20
81	Jack Holmes	.05
82	Toussaint Tyler	.05
83	Wayne Wilson	.05
84	Russell Erxleben	.05
85	Elois Grooms	.05
86	Phil Simms	.20
87	Scott Brunner	.10
88	Rob Carpenter	.08
89	Johnny Perkins	.05
90	Dave Jennings	.05
91	Harry Carson	.12
92	Lawrence Taylor	2.50
93	Beasley Reece	.05
94	Mark Haynes	.05
95	Ron Jaworski	.12
96	Wilbert Montgomery	.08
97	Hubert Oliver	.05
98	Harold Carmichael	.10
99	Jerry Robinson	.08
100	Stan Walters	.05
101	Charlie Johnson	.05
102	Roynell Young	.05
103	Tony Franklin	.05
104	Neil Lomax	.15
105	Jim Hart	.15
106	Ottis Anderson	.20
107	Stump Mitchell	.12
108	Pat Tilley	.08
109	Rush Brown	.05
110	E.J. Junior	.05
111	Ken Greene	.05
112	Mel Gray	.08
113	Joe Montana	2.50
114	Ricky Patton	.05
115	Earl Cooper	.05
116	Dwight Clark	.08
117	Freddie Solomon	.08
118	Randy Cross	.10
119	Fred Dean	.08
120	Ronnie Lott	1.75
121	Dwight Hicks	.15
122	Doug Williams	.15
123	Jerry Eckwood	.08
124	James Owens	.08
125	Kevin House	.08
126	Jimmie Giles	.05
127	Charley Hannah	.05
128	Lee Roy Selmon	.15
129	Hugh Green	.12
130	Joe Theismann	.30
131	Joe Washington	.08
132	John Riggins	.25
133	Art Monk	.50
134	Ricky Thompson	.05
135	Don Warren	.08
136	Perry Brooks	.05
137	Mike Nelms	.05
138	Mark Moseley	.05
139	Nolan Cromwell (All-Pro)	.20
140	Dwight Hicks (All-Pro)	.15
141	Ronnie Lott (All-Pro)	2.00
142	Harry Carson (All-Pro)	.20
143	Jack Lambert (All-Pro)	.40
144	Lawrence Taylor (All-Pro)	2.50
145	Mel Blount (All-Pro)	.30
146	Joe Klecko (All-Pro)	.15
147	Randy White (All-Pro)	.35
148	Doug English (All-Pro)	.10
149	Fred Dean (All-Pro)	.20
150	Billy Sims (All-Pro)	.25
151	Tony Dorsett (All-Pro)	.75
152	James Lofton (All-Pro)	.75
153	Alfred Jenkins (All-Pro)	.20
154	Ken Anderson (All-Pro)	.35
155	Kellen Winslow (All-Pro)	.50
156	Marvin Powell (All-Pro)	.10

157	Randy Cross (All-Pro)	.20
158	Mike Webster (All-Pro)	.30
159	John Hannah (All-Pro)	.30
160	Anthony Munoz	1.25
161	Curtis Dickey	.08
162	Randy McMillan	.08
163	Roger Carr	.08
164	Raymond Butler	.05
165	Reese McCall	.05
166	Ed Simonini	.05
167	Herb Oliver	.05
168	Nesby Glasgow	.05
169	Joe Ferguson	.08
170	Joe Cribbs	.08
171	jerry Butler	.08
172	Frank Lewis	.05
173	Mark Brammer	.05
174	Fred Smerlas	.10
175	Jim Haslett	.05
176	Charles Alexander	.05
177	Bill Simpson	.05
178	Ken Anderson	.20
179	Charles Alexander	.05
180	Pete Johnson	.05
181	Isaac Curtis	.05
182	Cris Collinsworth	.35
183	Pat McInally	.08
184	Anthony Munoz	.50
185	Louis Breeden	.05
186	Jim Breech	.05
187	Brian Sipe	.10
188	Charles White	.10
189	Mike Pruitt	.08
190	Reggie Rucker	.12
191	Dave Logan	.05
192	Ozzie Newsome	.30
193	Dick Ambrose	.05
194	Joe DeLamielleure	.05
195	Ricky Feacher	.05
196	Craig Morton	.12
197	Dave Preston	.05
198	Rick Parros	.05
199	Rick Upchurch	.08
200	Steve Watson	.10
201	Riley Odoms	.08
202	Randy Gradishar	.10
203	Steve Foley	.05
204	Ken Stabler	.30
205	Gifford Nielsen	.08
206	Tim Wilson	.05
207	Ken Burrough	.10
208	Mike Renfro	.05
209	Greg Stemrick	.05
210	Robert Brazile	.08
211	Gregg Bingham	.08
212	Steve Fuller	.08
213	Bill Kenney	.08
214	Joe Delaney	.08
215	Henry Marshall	.05
216	Nick Lowery	.10
217	Art Still	.08
218	Gary Green	.05
219	Gary Barbaro	.08
220	AFC PAssing Leader (Ken Anderson)	.35
221	AFC PAssing Yardage Leader (Dan Fouts)	.50
222	AFC Receiving Yardage Leader (Frank Lewis)	.20
223	AFC Kickoff Return Yardage Leader (James Brooks)	.75
224	AFC RUshing Touchdowns Leader (Chuck Muncie)	.20
225	AFC Punting Leader (Pat McInally)	.20
226	AFC Interceptions Leader (John Harris)	.20
227	AFC Sacks Leader (Joe Klecko)	.20
228	Dave Woodley	.08
229	Tony Nathan	.08
230	Andra Franklin	.05
231	Nat Moore	.08
232	Duriel Harris	.05
233	Uwe Von Schamann	.05
234	Bob Baumhower	.10
235	Glenn Blackwood	.10
236	Tommy Vigorito	.05
237	Steve Grogan	.12
238	Matt Cavanaugh	.05
239	Tony Collins	.08
240	Vagas Ferguson	.10
241	John Smith	.05
242	Stanley Morgan	.10
243	John Hannah	.15
244	Steve Nelson	.05
245	Don Hasselback	.05
246	Richard Todd	.12
247	Bruce Harper	.05
248	Wesley Walker	.12
249	Jerome Barkum	.05
250	Marvin Powell	.08
251	Mark Gastineau	.10
252	Joe Klecko	.08
253	Darrol Ray	.05
254	Marty Lyons	.08

255	Marc Wilson	.10
256	Kenny King	.08
257	Mark Van Eeghen	.08
258	Cliff Branch	.12
259	Bob Chandler	.08
260	Ray Guy	.15
261	Ted Hendricks	.20
262	Lester Hayes	.20
263	Terry Bradshaw	.60
264	Franco Harris	.35
265	John Stallworth	.15
266	Jim Smith	.05
267	Mike Webster	.12
268	Jack Lambert	.20
269	Mel Blount	.15
270	Donnie Shell	.12
271	Bennie Cunningham	.08
272	Dan Fouts	.40
273	Chuck Muncie	.10
274	james Brooks	.65
275	Charlie Joiner	.20
276	Wes Chandler	.12
277	Kellen Winslow	.25
278	Doug Wilkerson	.05
279	Gary Johnson	.08
280	Rolf Benirschke	.08
281	Jim Zorn	.12
282	Theotis Brown	.08
283	Dan Doornink	.05
284	Steve Largent	1.25
285	Sam McCullum	.08
286	Efren Herrera	.05
287	Manu Tuiasosopo	.05
288	John Harris	.05

1983 Topps

Presumably adjusting for an increase in the size of its baseball card set, Topps cut the number of cards in its annual football card set in 1983 from 528 to 396. Because Topps still printed the cards on four sheets, one-third of the cards were double-printed - accounting for some of the apparent price discrepancies in the list below. Cards in the set are bordered in white and feature the team name in white block letters at the top of the card. The player's name and position are found in a white rectangle near the bottom. All-Pro designations are found above this box. This set is notable for several rookies: Gerald Riggs, Jim McMahon, Mike Singletary, Roy Green and Marcus Allen. It also features Lawrence Taylor's second-year card. Cards are again listed alphabetically by city name and by player number. (Key: PB - Pro Bowl)

		MT
Complete Set (396):		50.00
Common Player:		.05
Wax Box:		50.00
1	Ken Anderson (RB)	.25
2	Tony Dorsett (RB)	.40
3	Dan Fouts (RB)	.25
4	Joe Montana (RB)	2.00
5	Mark Moseley (RB)	.10
6	Mike Nelms (RB)	.10
7	Darrol Ray (RB)	.10
8	John Riggins (RB)	.25
9	Fulton Walker (RB)	.10
10	NFC Championship (John Riggins)	.10
11	AFC Championship (John Riggins)	.10
12	Super Bowl XVII	.25
13	Atlanta Falcons Team (William Andrews)	.10
14	William Andrews (PB)	.05
15	Steve Bartkowski	.25
16	Bobby Butler	.05
17	Buddy Curry	.05
18	Alfred Jackson	.05
19	Alfred Jenkins	.05
20	Kenny Johnson	.05
21	Mike Kenn (PB)	.05

22	Mick Luckhurst	.05
23	Junior Miller	.05
24	Al Richardson	.05
25	Gerald Riggs	.75
26	R.C. Thielemann	.05
27	Jeff Van Note (PB)	.05
28	Walter Payton (TL)	.75
29	Brian Baschnagel	.05
30	Dan Hampton (PB)	.50
31	Mike Hartenstine	.05
32	Noah Jackson	.05
33	Jim McMahon	3.00
34	Emery Moorehead	.05
35	Bob Parsons	.05
36	Walter Payton	2.00
37	Terry Schmidt	.05
38	Mike Singletary	7.00
39	Matt Suhey	.05
40	Rickey Watts	.05
41	Otis Wilson	.15
42	Tony Dorsett (TL)	.25
43	Bob Breunig (PB)	.05
44	Doug Cosbie	.05
45	Pat Donovan (PB)	.05
46	Tony Dorsett (PB)	.75
47	Tony Hill	.05
48	Butch Johnson	.05
49	Ed "Too Tall" Jones (PB)	.20
50	Harvey Martin	.10
51	Drew Pearson	.25
52	Rafael Septien	.05
53	Ron Springs	.05
54	Dennis Thurman	.05
55	Everson Walls (PB)	.40
56	Danny White (PB)	.15
57	Randy White (PB)	.60
58	Detroit Lions Team (Billy Sims)	.05
59	Al "Bubba" Baker	.05
60	Dexter Bussey	.05
61	Gary Danielson	.05
62	Keith Dorney (PB)	.05
63	Doug English (PB)	.05
64	Ken Fantetti	.05
65	Alvin Hall	.05
66	David Hill	.05
67	Eric Hipple	.05
68	Ed Murray	.10
69	Freddie Scott	.05
70	Billy Sims (PB)	.10
71	Tom Skladany	.05
72	Leonard Thompson	.05
73	Bobby Watkins	.05
74	Green Bay Packers Team (Eddie Lee Ivery)	.10
75	John Anderson	.05
76	Paul Coffman (PB)	.05
77	Lynn Dickey	.05
78	Mike Douglass	.05
79	Eddie Lee Ivery	.05
80	John Jefferson (PB)	.05
81	Ezra Johnson	.05
82	Mark Lee	.05
83	James Lofton (PB)	1.00
84	Larry McCarren (PB)	.05
85	Jan Stenerud	.10
86	Los Angeles Rams Team (Wendell Tyler)	.05
87	Bill Bain	.05
88	Nolan Cromwell (PB)	.05
89	Preston Dennard	.05
90	Vince Ferragamo	.05
91	Mike Guman	.05
92	Kent Hill (PB)	.05
93	Mike Lansford	.05
94	Rod Perry	.05
95	Pat Thomas	.05
96	Jack Youngblood	.15
97	Minnesota Vikings Team (Ted Brown)	.10
98	Matt Blair (PB)	.05
99	Ted Brown	.05
100	Greg Coleman	.05
101	Randy Holloway	.05
102	Tommy Kramer	.10
103	Doug Martin	.05
104	Mark Mullaney	.05
105	Joe Senser	.05
106	Willie Teal	.05
107	Sammy White	.05
108	Rickey Young	.05
109	New Orleans Saints Team (George Rogers)	.10
110	Stan Brock	.40
111	Bruce Clark	.05
112	Russell Erxleben	.05
113	Russell Gary	.05
114	Jeff Groth	.05
115	John Hill	.05
116	Derland Moore	.05
117	George Rogers (PB)	.20
118	Ken Stabler	.75
119	Wayne Wilson	.05
120	New York Giants Team (Butch Woolfolk)	.05
121	Scott Brunner	.05
122	Rob Carpenter	.05
123	Harry Carson (PB)	.05
124	Joe Danelo	.05
125	Earnest Gray	.05
126	Mark Haynes (PB)	.05
127	Terry Jackson	.05

128	Dave Jennings (PB)	.05
129	Brian Kelley	.05
130	George Martin	.05
131	Tom Mullady	.05
132	Johnny Perkins	.05
133	Lawrence Taylor (PB)	5.00
134	Brad Van Pelt	.05
135	Butch Woolfolk	.05
136	Philadelphia Eagles Team (Wilbert Montgomery)	.10
137	Harold Carmichael	.25
138	Herman Edwards	.05
139	Tony Franklin	.05
140	Carl Hairston	.05
141	Dennis Harrison (PB)	.05
142	Ron Jaworski	.25
143	Frank LeMaster	.05
144	Wilbert Montgomery	.07
145	Guy Morriss	.05
146	Jerry Robinson	.05
147	Max Runager	.05
148	Ron Smith	.05
149	John Spagnola	.05
150	Stan Walters	.05
151	Roynell Young	.05
152	St. Louis Cardinals Team (Ottis Anderson)	.20
153	Ottis Anderson	.40
154	Carl Birdsong	.05
155	Dan Dierdorf	.15
156	Roy Green	.75
157	Elois Grooms	.05
158	Neil Lomax	.10
159	Wayne Morris	.05
160	James Robbins	.05
161	Luis Sharpe	.20
162	Pat Tilley	.05
163	San Francisco 49ers Team (Jeff Moore)	.15
164	Dwight Clark (PB)	.40
165	Randy Cross (PB)	.05
166	Russ Francis	.05
167	Dwight Hicks (PB)	.05
168	Ronnie Lott (PB)	3.00
169	Joe Montana	7.00
170	Jeff Moore	.05
171	Renaldo Nehemiah	.10
172	Freddie Solomon	.05
173	Ray Wersching	.05
174	Tampa Bay Buccaneers Team (James Wilder)	.10
175	Cedric Brown	.05
176	Bill Capece	.05
177	Neal Colzie	.05
178	Jimmie Giles (PB)	.07
179	Hugh Green (PB)	.07
180	Kevin House	.05
181	James Owens	.05
182	Lee Roy Selmon (PB)	.07
183	Mike Washington	.05
184	James Wilder	.10
185	Doug Williams	.10
186	Washington Redskins Team (John Riggins)	.25
187	Jeff Bostic	.05
188	Charlie Brown (PB)	.05
189	Vernon Dean	.05
190	Joe Jacoby	.75
191	Dexter Manley	.25
192	Rich Milot	.05
193	Art Monk	1.00
194	Mark Mosely (PB)	.05
195	Mike Nelms (PB)	.05
196	Neal Olkewicz	.05
197	Tony Peters (PB)	.05
198	John Riggins	.60
199	Joe Theismann (PB)	.60
200	Don Warren	.05
201	Jeris White	.05
202	Passing Leaders (Joe Theismann, Ken Anderson)	.20
203	Receiving Leaders (Dwight Clark, Kellen Winslow)	.10
204	Rushing Leaders (Tony Dorsett, Freeman McNeil)	.40
205	Scoring Leaders (Marcus Allen, Wendell Tyler)	.80
206	Interception Leaders (Everson Walls)	.10
207	Punting Leaders (Carl Birdsong, Luke Prestridge)	.10
208	Baltimore Colts Team (Randy McMillan)	
209	Matt Bouza	.05
210	Johnnie Cooks	.05
211	Curtis Dickey	.05
212	Nesby Glasgow	.05
213	Derrick Hatchett	.05
214	Randy McMillan	.05
215	Mike Pagel	.10
216	Rohn Stark	.20
217	Donnell Thompson	.05
218	Leo Wisniewski	.05
219	Buffalo Bills Team (Joe Cribbs)	.10

220	Curtis Brown	.05
221	Jerry Butler	.05
222	Greg Cater	.05
223	Joe Cribbs	.10
224	Joe Ferguson	.10
225	Roosevelt Leaks	.05
226	Frank Lewis	.05
227	Eugene Marve	.05
228	Fred Smerlas (PB)	.08
229	Ben Williams (PB)	.05
230	Cincinnati Bengals Team (Pete Johnson)	.10
231	Charles Alexander	.05
232	Ken Anderson (PB)	.25
233	Jim Breech	.05
234	Ross Browner	.05
235	Cris Collinsworth (PB)	.25
236	Isaac Curtis	.05
237	Pete Johnson	.05
238	Steve Kreider	.05
239	Max Montoya	.05
240	Anthony Munoz (PB)	1.50
241	Ken Riley	.05
242	Dan Ross (PB)	.07
243	Reggie Williams	.05
244	Cleveland Browns Team (Mike Pruitt)	.10
245	*Chip Banks (PB)*	.25
246	Tom Cousineau	.05
247	Joe DeLamielleure	.05
248	Doug Dieken	.05
249	*Hanford Dixon*	.15
250	Ricky Feacher	.05
251	Lawrence Johnson	.05
252	Dave Logan	.05
253	Paul McDonald	.05
254	Ozzie Newsome	.60
255	Mike Pruitt	.05
256	Clarence Scott	.05
257	Brian Sipe	.10
258	Dwight Walker	.05
259	Charles White	.05
260	Denver Broncos Team (Gerald Wilhite)	.10
261	Steve DeBerg	.50
262	Randy Gradishar (PB)	.07
263	Rulon Jones	.05
264	Rick Karlis	.05
265	Don Latimer	.05
266	Rick Parros	.05
267	Luke Prestridge (PB)	.07
268	Rick Upchurch (PB)	.05
269	Steve Watson	.05
270	Gerald Wilhite	.05
271	Houston Oilers Team (Gifford Nielson)	.10
272	Harold Bailey	.05
273	Jesse Baker	.05
274	Gregg Bingham	.05
275	Robert Brazile (PB)	.05
276	Donnie Craft	.05
277	Daryl Hunt	.05
278	Archie Manning	.10
279	Gifford Nielsen	.05
280	Mike Renfro	.05
281	Carl Roaches	.05
282	Kansas City Chiefs Team (Joe Delaney)	.10
283	Gary Barbaro (PB)	.07
284	Joe Delaney	.05
285	*Jeff Gossett*	.60
286	Gary Green (PB)	.05
287	Eric Harris	.05
288	Billy Jackson	.05
289	Bill Kenney	.05
290	Nick Lowery	.60
291	Henry Marshall	.05
292	Art Still (PB)	.05
293	Marcus Allen (TL)	2.00
294	*Marcus Allen (PB)*	25.00
295	Lyle Alzado	.25
296	Chris Bahr	.05
297	Cliff Branch	.25
298	*Todd Christensen*	2.00
299	Ray Guy	.10
300	Frank Hawkins	.05
301	Lester Hayes (PB)	.05
302	Ted Hendricks (PB)	.15
303	Kenny King	.05
304	Rod Martin	.05
305	Matt Millen	.15
306	Burgess Owens	.05
307	Jim Plunkett	.25
308	Miami Dolphins Team (Andra Franklin)	.10
309	Bob Baumhower (PB)	.07
310	Glenn Blackwood	.05
311	Lyle Blackwood	.05
312	A.J. Duhe	.05
313	Andra Franklin (PB)	.07
314	Duriel Harris	.05
315	Bob Kuechenberg (PB)	.07
316	Don McNeal	.05
317	Tony Nathan	.05
318	Ed Newman (PB)	.05
319	Earnie Rhone	.05
320	Joe Rose	.05
321	Don Strock	.07
322	Uwe Von Schamann	.05

323	David Woodley	.05
324	New England Patriots Team (Tony Collins)	.10
325	Julius Adams	.05
326	Pete Brock	.05
327	*Rich Camarillo*	.25
328	Tony Collins	.05
329	Steve Grogan	.25
330	John Hannah (PB)	.25
331	Don Hasselbeck	.05
332	Mike Haynes (PB)	.05
333	Roland James	.05
334	Stanley Morgan	.75
335	Steve Nelson	.05
336	Kenneth Sims	.05
337	Mark Van Eeghen	.05
338	New York Jets Team (Freeman McNeil)	.10
339	Greg Buttle	.05
340	Joe Fields (PB)	.05
341	Mark Gastineau (PB)	.08
342	Bruce Harper	.05
343	Bobby Jackson	.05
344	Bobby Jones	.05
345	Johnny "Lam" Jones	.07
346	Joe Klecko	.10
347	Marty Lyons	.05
348	Freeman McNeil (PB)	.60
349	Lance Mehl	.05
350	Marvin Powell (PB)	.05
351	Darrol Ray	.05
352	Abdul Salaam	.05
353	Richard Todd	.10
354	Wesley Walker (PB)	.25
355	Pittsburgh Steelers Team (Franco Harris)	.25
356	*Gary Anderson*	.75
357	Mel Blount	.25
358	Terry Bradshaw	.75
359	Larry Brown (PB)	.05
360	Bennie Cunningham	.05
361	Gary Dunn	.05
362	Franco Harris	.75
363	Jack Lambert (PB)	.60
364	Frank Pollard	.05
365	Donnie Shell (PB)	.08
366	John Stallworth (PB)	.25
367	Loren Toews	.05
368	Mike Webster (PB)	.05
369	*Dwayne Woodruff*	.10
370	San Diego Chargers Team (Chuck Muncie)	.10
371	Rolf Benirschke (PB)	.05
372	James Brooks	.75
373	Wes Chandler (PB)	.05
374	Dan Fouts (PB)	.75
375	Tim Fox	.05
376	Gary Johnson (PB)	.05
377	Charlie Joiner	.25
378	Louie Kelcher	.05
379	Chuck Muncie (PB)	.07
380	Cliff Thrift	.05
381	Doug Wilkerson (PB)	.05
382	Kellen Winslow (PB)	.75
383	Seattle Seahawks Team (Sherman Smith)	.10
384	*Kenny Easley (PB)*	.40
385	*Jacob Green*	.50
386	John Harris	.05
387	Mike Jackson	.05
388	*Norm Johnson*	.50
389	Steve Largent	.85
390	Keith Simpson	.05
391	Sherman Smith	.05
392	Jeff West	.05
393	Jim Zorn	.05
394	Checklist 1-132	.25
395	Checklist 133-264	.25
396	Checklist 265-396	.25

1983 Topps Sticker Inserts

These 33 different inserts, which came in each wax pack of 1983 Topps football cards, pic-tured an NFL star on the front and a piece to one of three dif-ferent puzzles on the backs. A gold plaque at the bottom of the card identifies the player.

		MT
	Complete Set (33):	20.00
	Common Player:	.35
1	Marcus Allen	5.00
2	Ken Anderson	.50
3	Ottis Anderson	.35
4	William Andrews	.35
5	Terry Bradshaw	1.25
6	Wes Chandler	.35
7	Dwight Clark	.50
8	Cris Collinsworth	.35
9	Joe Cribbs	.35
10	Nolan Cromwell	.35
11	Tony Dorsett	1.50
12	Dan Fouts	1.00
13	Mark Gastineau	.35
14	Jimmie Giles	.35
15	Franco Harris	1.00
16	Ted Hendricks	.60
17	Tony Hill	.35
18	John Jefferson	.35
19	James Lofton	1.00
20	Freeman McNeil	.50
21	Joe Montana	6.00
22	Mark Moseley	.35
23	Ozzie Newsome	1.00
24	Walter Payton	3.00
25	John Riggins	1.00
26	Billy Sims	.35
27	John Stallworth	.50
28	Lawrence Taylor	3.00
29	Joe Theismann	1.25
30	Richard Todd	.35
31	Wesley Walker	.35
32	Danny White	.35
33	Kellen Winslow	.50

1983 Topps Stickers

These stickers are similar to those issued in previous years, but can be identified by the rounded frame around the picture on the front and the ref-erence on the back to the 1983 sticker album which was pro-duced. Once again, Topps in-cluded foil stickers in the set (#s 1-4, 73-80, 143-152 and 264-271. Foil stickers 1-2 are right and left sides of Franco Harris; 3 and 4 portray Walter Payton.

		MT
	Complete Set (330):	30.00
	Common Player:	.05
1	Franco Harris	.50
2	Franco Harris	.50
3	Walter Payton	1.25
4	Walter Payton	1.25
5	John Riggins	.35
6	Tony Dorsett	.40
7	Mark Van Eeghen	.05
8	Chuck Muncie	.08
9	Wilbert Montgomery	.08
10	Greg Pruitt	.08
11	Sam Cunningham	.10
12	Ottis Anderson	.20
13	Mike Pruitt	.08
14	Dexter Bussey	.05
15	Mike Pagel	.05
16	Curtis Dickey	.08
17	Randy McMillan	.08
18	Raymond Butler	.05
19	Nesby Glasgow	.05
20	Zachary Dixon	.05
21	Matt Bouza	.05
22	Johnie Cooks	.05
23	Curtis Brown	.05
24	Joe Cribbs	.08
25	Roosevelt Leaks	.08
26	Jerry Butler	.08
27	Frank Lewis	.08
28	Fred Smerlas	.05
29	Ben Williams	.05
30	Joe Ferguson	.15
31	Isaac Curtis	.08
32	Cris Collinsworth	.15
33	Anthony Munoz	.20
34	Max Montoya	.05

35	Ross Browner	.08
36	Reggie Williams	.10
37	Ken Riley	.10
38	Pete Johnson	.08
39	Ken Anderson	.20
40	Charles White	.10
41	Dave Logan	.05
42	Doug Dieken	.05
43	Ozzie Newsome	.20
44	Tom Cousineau	.05
45	Bob Golic	.08
46	Brian Sipe	.10
47	Paul McDonald	.05
48	Mike Pruitt	.10
49	Luke Prestridge	.05
50	Randy Gradishar	.10
51	Rulon Jones	.05
52	Rick Parros	.05
53	Steve DeBerg	.15
54	Tom Jackson	.10
55	Rick Upchurch	.08
56	Steve Watson	.08
57	Robert Brazile	.10
58	Willie Tullis	.05
59	Archie Manning	.15
60	Gifford Nielsen	.08
61	Harold Bailey	.05
62	Carl Roaches	.08
63	Gregg Bingham	.05
64	Daryl Hunt	.05
65	Gary Green	.05
66	Gary Barbaro	.08
67	Bill Kenney	.08
68	Joe Delaney	.10
69	Henry Marshall	.05
70	Nick Lowery	.10
71	Jeff Gossett	.05
72	Art Still	.10
73	AFC Passing Leader (Ken Anderson)	.40
74	AFC PAssing Yardage Leader (Dan Fouts)	.50
75	AFC Receiving Yardage Leader (Wes Chandler)	.25
76	AFC Kickoff Return Yardage Leader (James Brooks)	.40
77	AFC Punt Return Yardage Leader (Rick Upchurch)	.30
78	AFC Punting Leader (Luke Prestridge)	.15
79	AFC Sacks Leader (Jesse Baker)	.15
80	AFC Rushing Yardage Leader (Freeman McNeil)	.30
81	Ray Guy	.15
82	Jim Plunkett	.15
83	Lester Hayes	.08
84	Kenny King	.05
85	Cliff Branch	.12
86	Todd Christensen	.12
87	Lyle Alzado	.15
88	Ted Hendricks	.20
89	Rod Martin	.10
90	Dave Woodley	.10
91	Ed Newman	.05
92	Earnie Rhone	.05
93	Don McNeal	.05
94	Glenn Blackwood	.08
95	Andra Franklin	.05
96	Nat Moore	.12
97	Lyle Blackwood	.08
98	A.J. Duhe	.10
99	Tony Collins	.08
100	Stanley Morgan	.10
101	Pete Brock	.05
102	Steve Nelson	.05
103	Steve Grogan	.15
104	Mark Van Eeghen	.08
105	Don Hasselbeck	.05
106	John Hannah	.15
107	Mike Haynes	.15
108	Wesley Walker	.10
109	Marvin Powell	.05
110	Joe Klecko	.05
111	Bobby Jackson	.05
112	Richard Todd	.10
113	Lance Mehl	.05
114	Johnny Lam Jones	.10
115	Mark Gastineau	.10
116	Freeman McNeil	.15
117	Franco Harris	.30
118	Mike Webster	.15
119	Mel Blount	.15
120	Donnie Shell	.10
121	Terry Bradshaw	.75
122	John Stallworth	.12
123	Jack Lambert	.25
124	Dwayne Woodruff	.05
125	Bennie Cunningham	.05
126	Charlie Joiner	.20
127	Kellen Winslow	.20
128	Rolf Benirschke	.05
129	Louis Kelcher	.08
130	Chuck Muncie	.08
131	Wes Chandler	.10
132	Gary Johnson	.08
133	James Brooks	.15
134	Dan Fouts	.35

135	Jacob Green	.10
136	Michael Jackson	.05
137	Jim Zorn	.12
138	Sherman Smith	.08
139	Keith Simpson	.05
140	Steve Largent	1.25
141	John Harris	.08
142	Jeff West	.05
143	Ken Anderson (top)	.45
144	Ken Anderson (bottom)	.45
145	Tony Dorsett (top)	.40
146	Tony Dorsett (bottom)	.40
147	Dan Fouts (top)	.40
148	Dan Fouts (bottom)	.40
149	Joe Montana (top)	2.00
150	Joe Montana (bottom)	2.00
151	Mark Moseley (top)	.15
152	Mark Moseley (bottom)	.15
153	Richard Todd	.10
154	Butch Johnson	.10
155	Bill (Gary) Hogeboom	.08
156	A.J. Duhe	.08
157	Kurt Sohn	.05
158	Drew Pearson	.10
159	John Riggins	.35
160	Pat Donovan	.05
161	John Hannah	.15
162	Jeff Van Note	.10
163	Randy Cross	.10
164	Marvin Powell	.08
165	Kellen Winslow	.25
166	Dwight Clark	.20
167	Wes Chandler	.08
168	Tony Dorsett	.40
169	Freeman McNeil	.12
170	Ken Anderson	.25
171	Mark Moseley	.05
172	Mark Gastineau	.05
173	Gary Johnson	.05
174	Randy White	.30
175	Ed "Too Tall" Jones	.12
176	Hugh Green	.08
177	Harry Carson	.10
178	Lawrence Taylor	.30
179	Lester Hayes	.08
180	Mark Haynes	.05
181	Dave Jennings	.05
182	Nolan Cromwell	.08
183	Tony Peters	.05
185	Jimmy Cefalo	.05
185	A.J. Duhe	.08
186	John Riggins	.35
187	Charlie Brown	.05
188	Mike Nelms	.05
189	Mark Murphy	.05
190	Fulton Walker	.05
191	Marcus Allen	2.50
192	Chip Banks	.05
193	Charlie Brown	.05
194	Bob Crable	.05
195	Vernon Dean	.05
196	Jim McMahon	.75
197	James Robbins	.08
198	Luis Sharpe	.08
199	Rohn Stark	.05
200	Lester Williams	.05
201	Leo Wisniewski	.05
202	Butch Woolfolk	.05
203	Mike Kenn	.05
204	R.C. Thielemann	.05
205	Buddy Curry	.05
206	Steve Bartkowski	.12
207	Alfred Jenkins	.08
208	Don Smith	.05
209	Alfred Jenkins	.08
210	Fulton Kuykendall	.05
211	William Andrews	.08
212	Gary Fencik	.08
213	Walter Payton	1.50
214	Mike Singletary	1.50
215	Otis Wilson	.08
216	Matt Suhey	.05
217	Dan Hampton	.20
218	Mike Moorehead	.05
219	Mike Hartenstine	.05
220	Danny White	.25
221	Drew Pearson	.10
222	Rafael Septien	.05
223	Ed "Too Tall" Jones	.10
224	Everson Walls	.10
225	Randy White	.20
226	Harvey Martin	.10
227	Tony Hill	.10
228	John Jefferson	.30
229	Billy Sims	.20
230	Leonard Thompson	.05
231	Ed Murray	.05
232	Doug English	.05
233	Ken Fantetti	.05
234	Tom Skladany	.05
235	Freddie Scott	.05
236	Eric Hipple	.08
237	David Hill	.05
238	John Jefferson	.08
239	Paul Coffman	.05
240	Ezra Johnson	.05
241	Mike Douglass	.05
242	Mark Lee	.05
243	John Anderson	.10
244	Jan Stenerud	.15
245	Lynn Dickey	.10

246	James Lofton	.30
247	Vince Ferragamo	.12
248	Preston Dennard	.05
249	Jack Youngblood	.15
250	Mike Guman	.05
251	LeRoy Irvin	.08
252	Mike Lansford	.05
253	Kent Hill	.05
254	Nolan Cromwell	.05
255	Doug Martin	.05
256	Greg Coleman	.05
257	Ted Brown	.05
258	Mark Mullaney	.05
259	Joe Senser	.08
260	Randy Holloway	.05
261	Matt Blair	.08
262	Sammie White	.10
263	Tommy Kramer	.10
264	NFC Passing Leader (Joe Theismann)	.40
265	NFC Passing Yardage Leader (Joe Montana)	1.50
266	NFC Receiving Yardage Leader (Dwight Clark)	.25
267	NFC Kickoff Return Yardage Leader (Mike Nelms)	.10
268	NFC Punting Leader (Carl Birdsong)	.10
269	NFC Interceptions Leader (Everson Walls)	.20
270	NFC Sacks Leader (Doug Martin)	.15
271	NFC Rushing Yardage Leader (Tony Dorsett)	.40
272	Russell Erxleben	.05
273	Stan Brock	.05
274	Jeff Groth	.05
275	Bruce Clark	.05
276	Ken Stabler	.30
277	George Rogers	.10
278	Derland Moore	.05
279	Wayne Wilson	.05
280	Lawrence Taylor	.35
281	Harry Carson	.10
282	Brian Kelley	.05
283	Brad Van Pit	.05
284	Earnest Gray	.05
285	Dave Jennings	.05
286	Rob Carpenter	.05
287	Scott Brunner	.05
288	Ron Jaworski	.15
289	Jerry Robinson	.08
290	Frank LeMaster	.05
291	Wilbert Montgomery	.05
292	Tony Franklin	.05
293	Harold Carmichael	.15
294	John Spagnola	.05
295	Herman Edwards	.05
296	Ottis Anderson	.15
297	Carl Birdsong	.05
298	Doug Marsh	.05
299	Neil Lomax	.12
300	Rush Brown	.05
301	Pat Tilley	.08
302	Wayne Morris	.05
303	Dan Dierdorf	.20
304	Roy Green	.30
305	Joe Montana	1.75
306	Randy Cross	.10
307	Freddie Solomon	.05
308	Jack Reynolds	.10
309	Ronnie Lott	.50
310	Renaldo Nehemiah	.15
311	Russ Francis	.08
312	Dwight Clark	.20
313	Doug Williams	.12
314	Bill Capece	.05
315	Mike Washington	.05
316	Hugh Green	.10
317	Kevin House	.05
318	Lee Roy Selmon	.12
319	Neal Colzie	.10
320	Jimmie Giles	.08
321	Cedric Brown	.05
322	Tony Peters	.05
323	Neal Olkewicz	.05
324	Dexter Manley	.05
325	Joe Theismann	.30
326	Rich Milot	.05
327	Mark Moseley	.08
328	Art Monk	.40
329	Mike Nelms	.08
330	John Riggins	.35

Values quoted in this guide reflect the retail price of a card — the price a collector can expect to pay when buying a card from a dealer. The wholesale price — that which a collector can expect to receive from a dealer when selling cards — will be significantly lower, depending on desirability and condition.

1983 Topps Sticker Boxes

These boxes contained 35 stickers inside, but also had two 2-1/2" x 3-1/2" on them; an offensive player was on each box. The cards are not numbered, and there was no issue for #10, but the box is numbered with a tab. The prices below are for an uncut box.

		MT
Complete Set (12):		15.00
Common Player:		.75
1	Pat Donovan, Mark Gastineau	.75
2	Wes Chandler, Nolan Cromwell	1.25
3	Marvin Powell, Ed "Too Tall" Jones	1.25
4	Ken Anderson, Tony Peters	1.25
5	Freeman McNeil, Lawrence Taylor	2.00
6	Mark Moseley, Dave Jennings	.75
7	Dwight Clark, Mark Haynes	1.50
8	Jeff Van Note, Harry Carson	.75
9	Tony Dorsett, Hugh Green	2.00
11	Randy Cross, Gary Johnson	1.00
12	Kellen Winslow, Lester Hayes	1.25
13	John Hannah, Randy White	2.00

1984 Topps

Topps' most sought-after NFL set of the decade is notable for its excellent array of rookies: Dickerson, Elway, Marino, Curt Warner, Mark Duper, Willie Gault and Roger Craig are among them. This is one of the better-designed sets of the decade as well. The 396-card set is numbered alphabetically by city and by player name; AFC teams are listed first, while NFC teams are listed after the NFL leaders. Team leader cards, which had for years shown team leaders in several categories, this year showed just one leader. Card fronts show an angled photo in a yellow stripe. The team logo and name appear at the bottom also at an angle. The Pro Bowl designation appears above the team name. Instant Replay cards issued in this set in addition to the player's regular card featured NFL stars in action poses. The score on the Super Bowl card (#9) is incorrect: instead of 28-9, it should read 38-9. (Key: PB - Pro Bowl, IR - Instant Replay)

		MT
Complete Set (396):		230.00
Common Player:		.05
Wax Box:		500.00
1	Eric Dickerson (RB)	.75
2	Ali Haji-Sheikh (RB)	.10
3	Franco Harris (RB)	.25
4	Mark Moseley (RB)	.15
5	John Riggins (RB)	.25
6	Jan Stenerud (RB)	.10
7	AFC Championship	.10
8	NFC Championship	.10
9	Super Bowl XVIII	.25
10	Indianapolis Colts Team: (Curtis Dickey)	.10
11	Raul Allegre	.10
12	Curtis Dickey	.05
13	Ray Donaldson	.10
14	Nesby Glasgow	.05
15	Chris Hinton (PB)	1.50
16	Vernon Maxwell	.15
17	Randy McMillan	.05
18	Mike Pagel	.05
19	Rohn Stark	.05
20	Leo Wisniewski	.05
21	Buffalo Bills Team: (Joe Cribbs)	.10
22	Jerry Butler	.05
23	Joe Danelo	.05
24	Joe Ferguson	.10
25	Steve Freeman	.05
26	Roosevelt Leaks	.05
27	Frank Lewis	.05
28	Eugene Marve	.05
29	Booker Moore	.05
30	Fred Smerlas (PB)	.07
31	Ben Williams	.05
32	Cincinnati Bengals Team: (Cris Collinsworth)	.10
33	Charles Alexander	.05
34	Ken Anderson	.25
35	Ken Anderson (IR)	.10
36	Jim Breech	.05
37	Cris Collinsworth (PB)	.10
38	Cris Collinsworth (IR)	.06
39	Isaac Curtis	.05
40	Eddie Edwards	.05
41	Ray Horton	.20
42	Pete Johnson	.05
43	Steve Kreider	.05
44	Max Montoya	.05
45	Anthony Munoz (PB)	.75
46	Reggie Williams	.05
47	Cleveland Browns Team: (Mike Pruitt)	.10
48	Matt Bahr	.05
49	Chip Banks (PB)	.15
50	Tom Cousineau	.05
51	Joe DeLamielleure	.05
52	Doug Dieken	.05
53	Bob Golic	.50
54	Bobby Jones	.05
55	Dave Logan	.05
56	Clay Matthews	1.00
57	Paul McDonald	.05
58	Ozzie Newsome	.50
59	Ozzie Newsome (IR)	.20
60	Mike Pruitt	.05
61	Steve Watson	.05
62	Barney Chavous	.20
63	John Elway	125.00
64	Steve Foley	.05
65	Tom Jackson	.15
66	Rick Karlis	.05
67	Luke Prestridge	.05
68	Zack Thomas	.05
69	Rick Upchurch	.05
70	Steve Watson	.05
71	Sammy Winder	.25
72	Louis Wright (PB)	.05
73	Houston Oilers Team: (Tim Smith)	.10
74	Jesse Baker	.05
75	Gregg Bingham	.05
76	Robert Brazile	.07
77	Steve Brown	.05
78	Chris Dressel	.05
79	Doug France	.05
80	Florian Kempf	.05
81	Carl Roaches	.05
82	Tim Smith	.15
83	Willie Tullis	.05
84	Kansas City Chiefs Team: (Carlos Carson)	.10
85	Mike Bell	.05
86	Theotis Brown	.05
87	Carlos Carson (PB)	.10
88	Carlos Carson (IR)	.06
89	Deron Cherry (PB)	.75
90	Gary Green (PB)	.05
91	Billy Jackson	.05
92	Bill Kenney	.05
93	Bill Kenney (IR)	.05
94	Nick Lowery	.25
95	Henry Marshall	.05
96	Art Still	.07
97	Los Angeles Raiders Team: (Todd Christensen)	.10
98	Marcus Allen	4.00
99	Marcus Allen IR (IR)	2.00
100	Lyle Alzado	.20
101	Lyle Alzado (IR)	.08
102	Chris Bahr	.05
103	Malcolm Barnwell	.05
104	Cliff Branch	.25
105	Todd Christensen (PB)	.50
106	Todd Christensen (IR)	.20
107	Ray Guy	.20
108	Frank Hawkins	.05
109	Lester Hayes (PB)	.07
110	Ted Hendricks (PB)	.20
111	Howie Long (PB)	6.00
112	Rod Martin (PB)	.05
113	Vann McElroy (PB)	.15
114	Jim Plunkett	.15
115	Greg Pruitt (PB)	.10
116	Miami Dolphins Team: (Mark Duper)	.05
117	Bobb Baumhower (PB)	.05
118	Doug Betters (PB)	.10
119	A.J. Duhe	.05
120	Mark Duper (PB)	1.50
121	Andre Franklin (Andra)	.05
122	William Judson	.05
123	Dan Marino (PB)	140.00
124	Dan Marino IR (IR)	15.00
125	Nat Moore	.05
126	Ed Newman (PB)	.05
127	Reggie Roby	.60
128	Gerald Small	.05
129	Dwight Stephenson	.75
130	Uwe Von Schamann	.05
131	New England Patriots Team: (Tony Collins)	.10
132	Rich Camarillo (PB)	.05
133	Tony Collins (PB)	.05
134	Tony Collins (IR)	.05
135	Bob Cryder	.05
136	Steve Grogan	.10
137	John Hannah (PB)	.15
138	Brian Holloway (PB)	.15
139	Roland James	.05
140	Stanley Morgan	.25
141	Rick Sanford	.05
142	Mosi Tatupu	.05
143	Andre Tippett	1.00
144	New York Jets Team: (Wesley Walker)	.10
145	Jerome Barkum	.05
146	Mark Gastineau (PB)	.05
147	Mark Gastineau (IR)	.05
148	Bruce Harper	.05
149	Johnny "Lam" Jones	.05
150	Joe Klecko (PB)	.07
151	Pat Leahy	.05
152	Freeman McNeil	.20
153	Lance Mehl	.05
154	Marvin Powell (PB)	.05
155	Darrol Ray	.05
156	Pat Ryan	.05
157	Kirk Springs	.05
158	Wesley Walker	.15
159	Pittsburgh Steelers Team: (Franco Harris)	.25
160	Walter Abercrombie	.15
161	Gary Anderson (PB)	.05
162	Terry Bradshaw	1.00
163	Craig Colquitt	.05
164	Bennie Cunningham	.05
165	Franco Harris	.75
166	Franco Harris (IR)	.30
167	Jack Lambert (PB)	.60
168	Jack Lambert (IR)	.25
169	Frank Pollard	.05
170	Donnie Shell	.05
171	Mike Webster (PB)	.15
172	Keith Willis	.05
173	Rick Woods	.05
174	San Diego Chargers Team: (Kellen Winslow)	.20
175	Rolf Benirschke	.05
176	James Brooks	.20
177	Maury Buford	.05
178	Wes Chandler (PB)	.05
179	Dan Fouts (PB)	.75
180	Dan Fouts (IR)	.50
181	Charlie Joiner	.25
182	Linden King	.05
183	Chuck Muncie	.05
184	Billy Ray Smith	.25
185	Danny Walters	.05
186	Kellen Winslow (PB)	.60
187	Kellen Winslow (IR)	.25
188	Seattle Seahawks Team: (Curt Warner)	.10
189	Steve August	.05
190	Dave Brown	.05
191	Zachary Dixon	.05
192	Kenny Easley	.10
193	Jacob Green	.15
194	Norm Johnson	.05
195	Dave Krieg	3.50
196	Steve Largent	.80
197	Steve Largent (IR)	.60
198	Curt Warner (PB)	.50
199	Curt Warner (IR)	.20
200	Jeff West	.05
201	Charley Young	.05
202	Passing Leaders: (Dan Marino, Steve Bartkowski) (LL)	4.00
203	Receiving Leaders: (Todd Christensen, Charlie Brown, Earnest Gray, Roy Green)	.10
204	Rushing Leaders: (Curt Warner, Eric Dickerson)	.40
205	Scoring Leaders: (Gary Anderson, Mark Moseley)	.10
206	Interception Leaders: (Vann McElroy, Ken Riley, Mark Murphy)	.10
207	Punting Leaders: (Rich Camarillo, Greg Coleman)	.10
208	Atlanta Falcons Team: (William Andrews)	.10
209	William Andrews (PB)	.05
210	William Andrews (IR)	.05
211	Stacey Bailey	.15
212	Steve Bartkowski	.15
213	Steve Barkowski (IR)	.05
214	Ralph Giacomarro	.05
215	Billy Johnson (PB)	.07
216	Mike Kenn (PB)	.05
217	Mick Luckhurst	.05
218	Gerald Riggs	.10
219	R.C. Thielemann (PB)	.05
220	Jeff Van Note	.05
221	Walter Payton (TL)	.75
222	Jim Covert	.75
223	Leslie Frazier	.05
224	Willie Gault	.50
225	Mike Hartenstine	.05
226	Noah Jackson	.05
227	Jim McMahon	1.50
228	Walter Payton (PB)	2.00
229	Walter Payton IR (IR)	1.00
230	Mike Richardson	.10
231	Terry Schmidt	.05
232	Mike Singletary (PB)	1.75
233	Matt Suhey	.05
234	Bob Thomas	.05
235	Dallas Cowboys Team: (Tony Dorsett)	.25
236	Bob Breunig	.05
237	Doug Cosbie (PB)	.05
238	Tony Dorsett (PB)	.60
239	Tony Dorsett (IR)	.25
240	John Dutton	.05
241	Tony Hill	.05
242	Ed "Too Tall" Jones (PB)	.20
243	Drew Pearson	.20
244	Rafael Septien	.05
245	Ron Springs	.05
246	Dennis Thurman	.05
247	Everson Walls (PB)	.15
248	Danny White	.25
249	Randy White (PB)	.60
250	Detroit Lions Team: (Billy Sims)	.10
251	Jeff Chadwick	.25
252	Garry Cobb	.05
253	Doug English (PB)	.05
254	William Gay	.05
255	Eric Hipple	.05
256	James Jones	.25
257	Bruce McNorton	.05
258	Ed Murray	.05
259	Ulysses Norris	.05
260	Billy Sims	.15
261	Billy Sims (IR)	.08
262	Leonard Thompson	.05
263	Green Bay Packers Team: (James Lofton)	.25
264	John Anderson	.05
265	Paul Coffman (PB)	.05
266	Lynn Dickey	.07
267	Gerry Ellis	.05
268	John Jefferson	.05
269	John Jefferson (IR)	.05
270	Ezra Johnson	.05
271	Tim Lewis	.05
272	James Lofton (PB)	1.50
273	James Lofton (IR)	.75
274	Larry McCarren (PB)	.05
275	Jan Stenerud	.05
276	Eric Dickerson (TL)	.75
277	Mike Barber	.05
278	Jim Collins	.05
279	Nolan Cromwell (PB)	.05
280	Eric Dickerson (PB)	7.00
281	Eric Dickerson IR (IR)	2.00
282	George Farmer	.05
283	Vince Ferragamo	.10
284	Kent Hill (PB)	.05
285	John Misko	.05
286	Jackie Slater (PB)	2.00
287	Jack Youngblood	.20
288	Minnesota Vikings Team: (Darrin Nelson)	.10
289	Ted Brown	.05
290	Greg Coleman	.05
291	Steve Dils	.05
292	Tony Galbreath	.05
293	Tommy Kramer	.10
294	Doug Martin	.05
295	Darrin Nelson	.25
296	Benny Ricardo	.05
297	John Swain	.05
298	John Turner	.05
299	New Orleans Saints Team: (George Rogers)	.10
300	Morten Andersen	3.00
301	Russell Erxleben	.05
302	Jeff Groth	.05
303	Rickey Jackson (PB)	3.00
304	Johnnie Poe	.05
305	George Rogers	.10
306	Richard Todd	.05
307	Jim Wilks	.05
308	Dave Wilson	.05
309	Wayne Wilson	.05
310	New York Giants Team: (Earnest Gray)	.10
311	Leon Bright	.05
312	Scott Brunner	.05
313	Rob Carpenter	.05
314	Harry Carson (PB)	.20
315	Earnest Gray	.05
316	Ali Haji-Sheikh (PB)	.05
317	Mark Haynes (PB)	.08
318	Dave Jennings	.05
319	Brian Kelley	.05
320	Phil Simms	1.00
321	Lawrence Taylor (PB)	3.00
322	Lawrence Taylor IR (IR)	2.00
323	Brad Van Pelt	.05
324	Butch Woolfolk	.05
325	Philadelphia Eagles Team: (Mike Quick)	.15
326	Harold Carmichael	.20
327	Herman Edwards	.05
328	Michael Haddix	.10
329	Dennis Harrison	.05
330	Ron Jaworski	.10
331	Wilbert Montgomery	.07
332	Hubert Oliver	.05
333	Mike Quick (PB)	.75
334	Jerry Robinson	.05
335	Max Runager	.05
336	Michael Williams	.05
337	St. Louis Cardinals Team: (Ottis Anderson)	.15
338	Ottis Anderson	.50
339	Al "Bubba" Baker	.05
340	Carl Birdsong (PB)	.05
341	David Galloway	.05
342	Roy Green (PB)	.25
343	Roy Green (IR)	.10
344	Curtis Greer	.10
345	Neil Lomax	.10
346	Doug Marsh	.05
347	Stump Mitchell	.05
348	Lionel Washington	.50
349	San Francisco 49ers Team: (Dwight Clark)	.15
350	Dwaine Board	.05
351	Dwight Clark	.25
352	Dwight Clark (IR)	.10
353	Roger Craig	5.00
354	Fred Dean	.05
355	Fred Dean (IR)	.10
356	Dwight Hicks (PB)	.05
357	Ronnie Lott (PB)	1.50
358	Joe Montana (PB)	9.00
359	Joe Montana IR (IR)	4.00
360	Freddie Solomon	.05
361	Wendell Tyler	.05
362	Ray Wersching	.05
363	Eric Wright	.15
364	Tampa Bay Buccaneers Team: (Kevin House)	.10
365	Gerald Carter	.05
366	Hugh Green (PB)	.07
367	Kevin House	.05
368	Michael Morton	.05
369	James Owens	.05
370	Booker Reese	.05
371	Lee Roy Selmon (PB)	.07
372	Jack Thompson	.05
373	James Wilder	.10
374	Steve Wilson	.05
375	Washington Redskins Team: (John Riggins)	.20
376	Jeff Bostic (PB)	.05
377	Charlie Brown (PB)	.05
378	Charlie Brown (IR)	.05
379	Dave Butz (PB)	.05
380	Darrell Green	2.00
381	Russ Grimm (PB)	.50
382	Joe Jacoby (PB)	.05
383	Dexter Manley	.05
384	Art Monk	1.00
385	Mark Moseley	.05
386	Mark Murphy (PB)	.05
387	Mike Nelms	.05
388	John Riggins	.60
389	John Riggins (IR)	.25
390	Joe Theismann (PB)	.25
391	Joe Theismann (IR)	.25
392	Don Warren	.05
393	Joe Washington	.05
394	Checklist 1-132	.25
395	Checklist 133-264	.25
396	Checklist 265-396	.25

1984 Topps NFL Stars

This 11-card set was included, one per pack, in the 1984 Topps football card wax packs. Styled almost exactly as the 1985 NFL Stars set a year later, the glossy cards included an action photo of the player bordered in blue, plus the NFL logo and the player name at the bottom of the card. Cards were printed on heavy white cardboard stock.

		MT
Complete Set (11):		6.00
Common Player:		.25
1	Curt Warner	.40
2	Eric Dickerson	2.50
3	Dan Marino	2.00
4	Steve Bartkowski	.25
5	Todd Christensen	.25
6	Roy Green	.25
7	Charlie Brown	.25
8	Earnest Gray	.25
9	Mark Gastineau	.25
10	Fred Dean	.25
11	Lawrence Taylor	.40

1984 Topps Play Cards

The 27-card, standard-size set was inserted in each pack of 1984 Topps Football. The card fronts describe prizes for the collectors and game rules, as well as the number of yards gained. Collectors had to collect at least 25 yards for five 1984 Glossy inserts. The card backs of the Play Cards contain game rules.

		MT
Complete Set (27):		15.00
Common Player:		.60
1	Houston Oilers (2 yards gained)	.60
2	Houston Oilers (3 yards gained)	.60
3	Cleveland Browns (4 yards gained)	.60
4	Cleveland Browns (5 yards gained)	.60
5	Cincinnati Bengals (6 yards gained)	.60
6	Pittsburgh Steelers (7 yards gained)	.75
7	New Orleans Saints (8 yards gained)	.75
8	New York Giants (2 yards gained)	.60
9	Washington Redskins (3 yards gained)	.75

10	Green Bay Packers (4 yards gained)	.60
11	Atlanta Falcons (5 yards gained)	.60
12	Detroit Lions (6 yards gained)	.60
13	New England Patriots (7 yards gained)	.60
14	New York Jets (8 yards gained)	.75
15	Buffalo Bills (2 yards gained)	.60
16	Kansas City Chiefs (3 yards gained)	.60
17	Miami Dolphins (4 yards gained)	.75
18	San Diego Chargers (5 yards gained)	.60
19	Seattle Seahawks (6 yards gained)	.60
20	Seattle Seahawks (7 yards gained)	.60
21	Dallas Cowboys (8 yards gained)	1.00
22	St. Louis Cardinals (2 yards gained)	.60
23	Chicago Bears (3 yards gained)	.60
24	San Francisco 49ers (4 yards gained)	1.00
25	Philadelphia Eagles (5 yards gained)	.60
26	Minnesota Vikings (6 yards gained)	.60
27	Los Angeles Rams (7 yards gained)	.75

1984 Topps Glossy Send-In

This 30-card set was available only through a mail-in offer. Cards show an action pose of the player on the front with a blackboard diagram as a background. His name, team and position are at the bottom. Backs identify the player, set and card number.

		MT
	Complete Set (30):	14.00
	Common Player:	.25
1	Marcus Allen	1.25
2	John Riggins	.40
3	Walter Payton	2.00
4	Tony Dorsett	1.00
5	Franco Harris	.75
6	Curt Warner	.40
7	Eric Dickerson	2.50
8	Mike Pruitt	.25
9	Ken Anderson	.25
10	Dan Fouts	.50
11	Terry Bradshaw	.75
12	Joe Theismann	.40
13	Joe Montana	2.00
14	Danny White	.25
15	Kellen Winslow	.25
16	Wesley Walker	.25
17	Drew Pearson	.25
18	James Lofton	.25
19	Cris Collinsworth	.25
20	Dwight Clark	.25
21	Mark Gastineau	.25
22	Lawrence Taylor	.40
23	Randy White	.25
24	Ed "Too Tall" Jones	.25
25	Jack Lambert	.25
26	Fred Dean	.25
27	Jan Stenerud	.40
28	Bruce Harper	.25
29	Todd Christensen	.25
30	Greg Pruitt	.25

Post-1980 cards in Near Mint condition will generally sell for about 75% of the quoted Mint value. Excellent-condition cards bring no more than 40%.

1984 Topps Stickers

Topps has followed its same format for these stickers, except some of the stickers come in pairs, which are listed in parentheses. Those without are full stickers, comprising the entire card. An album, featuring Charlie Joiner on the front and Dan Fouts on the back, was also issued, as were foil stickers.

		MT
	Complete Set (283):	35.00
	Common Player:	.05
1	Super Bowl XVIII (Plunkett/Allen)	.35
2	Super Bowl XVIII (Plunkett/Allen)	.15
3	Super Bowl XVIII (Plunkett/Allen)	.15
4	Super Bowl XVIII (Plunkett/Allen)	.15
5	Marcus Allen (Super Bowl MVP)	.75
6	Walter Payton	1.00
7	Mike Richardson (157)	.03
8	Jim McMahon (158)	.10
9	Mike Hartenstine (159)	.05
10	Mike Singletary	.20
11	Willie Gault	.10
12	Terry Schmidt (162)	.05
13	Emery Moorehead (163)	.05
14	Leslie Frazier (164)	.06
15	Jack Thompson (165)	.05
16	Booker Reese (166)	.05
17	James Wilder (166)	.05
18	Lee Roy Selmon (167)	.08
19	Hugh Green	.06
20	Gerald Carter (170)	.05
21	Steve Wilson (171)	.05
22	Michael Morton (172)	.05
23	Kevin House	.05
24	Ottis Anderson	.12
25	Lionel Washington	.08
26	Pat Tilley (176)	.05
27	Curtis Greer (177)	.05
28	Roy Green	.08
29	Carl Bridsong	.05
30	Neil Lomax (180)	.06
31	Lee Nelson (181)	.05
32	Stump Mitchell (182)	.04
33	Tony Hill (183)	.05
34	Everson Walls (184)	.05
35	Danny White (185)	.08
36	Tony Dorsett	.40
37	Ed "Too Tall" Jones	.12
38	Rafael Septien (188)	.05
39	Doug Crosbie (189)	.05
40	Drew Pearson (190)	.06
41	Randy White	.20
42	Ron Jaworski	.10
43	Anthony Griggs (193)	.05
44	Hubert Oliver (194)	.05
45	Wilbert Montgomery (195)	.05
46	Dennis Harrison	.05
47	Mike Quick	.08
48	Jerry Robinson (198)	.04
49	Michael Williams (199)	.05
50	Herman Edwards (200)	.05
51	Steve Bartkowski (201)	.06
52	Mick Luckhurst (202)	.05
53	Mike Pitts (203)	.05
54	William Andrews	.10
55	R.C. Thielemann	.05
56	Buddy Curry (206)	.05
57	Billy Johnson (207)	.04
58	Ralph Giacomaro (208)	.05
59	Mike Kenn	.08
60	Joe Montana	1.75
61	Fred Dean (211)	.05
62	Dwight Clark (212)	.10
63	Wendell Tyler (213)	.05
64	Dwight Hicks	.05
65	Ronnie Lott	.25
66	Roger Craig (216)	.40
67	Fred Solomon (217)	.05
68	Ray Wersching (218)	.05
69	Brad Van Pelt (219)	.05
70	Butch Woolfolk (220)	.05
71	Terry Kinard (221)	.05
72	Lawrence Taylor	.35
73	Aji Haji-Sheikh	.05
74	Mark Haynes (224)	.05
75	Rob Carpenter (225)	.05
76	Earnest Gray (226)	.05
77	Harry Carson	.10
78	Billy Sims	.15
79	Ed Murray (229)	.05
80	William Gay (230)	.05
81	Leonard Thompson (231)	.05
82	Doug English	.08
83	Eric Hipple	.08
84	Ken Fantetti (234)	.05
85	Bruce McNorton (235)	.05
86	James Jones (236)	.05
87	Lynn Dickey (237)	.06
88	Ezra Johnson (238)	.05
89	Jan Stenerud (239)	.08
90	James Lofton	.20
91	Larry McCarren	.05
92	John Jefferson (242)	.05
93	Mike Douglass (243)	.05
94	Gerry Ellis (244)	.05
95	Paul Coffman	.05
96	Eric Dickerson	1.00
97	Jackie Slater (247)	.20
98	Carl Ekern (248)	.05
99	Vince Ferragamo (249)	.06
100	Kent Hill	.05
101	Nolan Cromwell	.08
102	Jack Youngblood (252)	.10
103	John Misko (253)	.05
104	Mike Barber (254)	.07
105	Jeff Bostic (255)	.05
106	Mark Murphy (256)	.05
107	Joe Jacoby (257)	.05
108	John Riggins	.25
109	Joe Theismann	.30
110	Russ Grimm (260)	.05
111	Neal Olkewicz (261)	.07
112	Charlie Brown (262)	.05
113	Dave Butz	.08
114	George Rogers	.10
115	Jim Kovach (265)	.05
116	Dave Wilson (266)	.05
117	Johnnie Poe (267)	.05
118	Russell Erxleben	.05
119	Rickey Jackson	.50
120	Jeff Groth (270)	.05
121	Richard Todd (271)	.06
122	Wayne Wilson (272)	.05
123	Steve Dils (273)	.05
124	Benny Ricardo (274)	.05
125	John Turner (275)	.05
126	Ted Brown	.05
127	Greg Coleman	.05
128	Darrin Nelson (278)	.05
129	Scott Studwell (279)	.06
130	Tommy Kramer (280)	.06
131	Doug Martin	.05
132	Nolan Cromwell	7.50
133	Carl Birdsong (145, All-Pro)	.10
134	Deron Cherry (146, All-Pro)	.20
135	Ronnie Lott (147, All-Pro)	.30
136	Lester Hayes (148, All-Pro)	.10
137	Lawrence Taylor (149, All-Pro)	.30
138	Jack Lambert (150, All-Pro)	.20
139	Chip Banks (151, All-Pro)	.10
140	Lee Roy Selmon (152, All-Pro)	.15
141	Fred Smerlas (153, All-Pro)	.10
142	Doug English (154, All-Pro)	.10
143	Doug Betters (155, All-Pro)	.10
144	Dan Marino (132, All-Pro)	3.00
145	Ali Haji-Sheikh (133, All-Pro)	.10
146	Eric Dickerson (134, All-Pro)	.65
147	Curt Warner (135, All-Pro)	.15
148	James Lofton (136, All-Pro)	.25
149	Todd Christensen (All-Pro)	.15
150	Cris Collinsworth (All-Pro)	.20
151	Mike Kenn (139, All-Pro)	.10
152	Russ Grimm (140, All-Pro)	.10
153	Jeff Bostic (141, All-Pro)	.10
154	John Hannah (142, All-Pro)	.15
155	Anthony Munoz (143, All-Pro)	.20
156	Ken Anderson	.35
157	Pete Johnson (7)	.05
158	Reggie Williams (8)	.06
159	Isaac Curtis (9)	.05
160	Anthony Munoz	.20
161	Cris Collinsworth	.15
162	Charles Alexander (12)	.05
163	Ray Horton (13)	.10
164	Steve Keider (14)	.05
165	Ben Williams (15)	.05
166	Frank Lewis (16)	.08
167	Roosevelt Leaks (17)	.05
168	Joe Ferguson	.08
169	Fred Smerlas	.05
170	Joe Danelo (20)	.05
171	Chris Keating (21)	.05
172	Jerry Butler (22)	.05
173	Eugene Marve	.05
174	Louis Wright	.08
175	Barney Chavous (25)	.10
176	Zack Thomas (26)	.05
177	Luke Prestridge (27)	.05
178	Steve Watson	.08
179	John Elway	5.00
180	Steve Foley (30)	.05
181	Sammy Winder (31)	.10
182	Rick Upchurch (32)	.05
183	Bobby Jones (33)	.08
184	Matt Bahr (34)	.05
185	Doug Dieken (35)	.05
186	Mike Pruitt	.08
187	Chip Banks	.10
188	Tom Cousineau (38)	.05
189	Paul McDonald (39)	.05
190	Clay Matthews (40)	.08
191	Ozzie Newsome	.20
192	Dan Fouts	.40
193	Chuck Muncie (43)	.05
194	Linden King (44)	.05
195	Charlie Joiner (45)	.08
196	Wes Chandler	.08
197	Kellen Winslow	.20
198	James Brooks (48)	.10
199	Mike Green (49)	.05
200	Rolf Benirschke (58)	.05
201	Henry Marshall (51)	.05
202	Nick Lowery (52)	.06
203	Jerry Blanton (53)	.05
204	Bill Kenney	.08
205	Carlos Carson	.08
206	Billy Jackson (56)	.05
207	Art Still (57)	.05
208	Theotis Brown (58)	.05
209	Deron Cherry	.25
210	Curtis Dickey	.08
211	Nesby Glasgow (61)	.05
212	Mike Pagel (62)	.05
213	Ray Donaldson (63)	.05
214	Raul Allegre	.05
215	Chris Hinton	.30
216	Rohn Stark (66)	.05
217	Randy McMillan (67)	.08
218	Vernon Maxwell (68)	.05
219	A.J. Duhe (69)	.10
220	Andra Franklin (70)	.05
221	Ed Newman (71)	.05
222	Dan Marino	7.50
223	Doug Betters	.08
224	Bob Baumhower (74)	.05
225	Reggie Roby (75)	.08
226	Dwight Stephenson (76)	.08
227	Mark Duper	.40
228	Mark Gastineau	.15
229	Freeman McNeil (79)	.08
230	Bruce Harper (80)	.05
231	Wesley Walker (81)	.06
232	Marvin Powell	.05
233	Joe Klecko	.08
234	Johnny Lam Jones (84)	.05
235	Lance Mehl (85)	.05
236	Pat Ryan (86)	.05
237	Florian Kempf (87)	.05
238	Carl Roaches (88)	.05
239	Gregg Bigham (89)	.05
240	Tim Smith	.05
241	Jesse Baker	.05
242	Doug France (92)	.05
243	Chris Dressel (93)	.05
244	Willie Tullis (94)	.05
245	Robert Brazile	.08
246	Tony Collins	.05
247	Brian Holloway (97)	.05
248	Stanley Morgan (98)	.06
249	Rick Sanford (99)	.05
250	John Hannah	.15
251	Rich Camarillo	.08
252	Andre Tippett (102)	.08
253	Steve Grogan (103)	.08
254	Clayton Weishuhn (104)	.05
255	Jim Plunkett (105)	.08
256	Rod Martin (106)	.05
257	Lester Hayes (107)	.05
258	Marcus Allen	.50
259	Todd Chistensen	.10
260	Ted Hendricks (110)	.08
261	Greg Pruitt (111)	.05
262	Howie Long (112)	.50
263	Vann McElroy	.05
264	Curt Warner	.25
265	Jacob Green (115)	.06
266	Bruce Scholtz (116)	.05
267	Steve Largent (117)	.50
268	Kenny Easley (118)	.08
269	Dave Krieg	.35
270	Dave Brown (120)	.05
271	Zachary Dixon (121)	.05
272	Norm Johnson (122)	.05
273	Terry Bradshaw (123)	.30
274	Keith Willis (124)	.05
275	Gary Anderson (125)	.05
276	Franco Harris	.35
277	Mike Webster	.15
278	Calvin Sweeney (128)	.05
279	Rick Woods (129)	.05
280	Bennie Cunningham (130)	.08
281	Jack Lambert	.15
282	Curt Warner (283)	.35
283	Todd Christensen (282)	.15

1984 Topps USFL

This 132-card set was Topps' first issue of United States Football League cards, and it's proven to be the most valuable set Topps issued in the 1980s. Several key rookie cards can be found in this set, including Jim Kelly, Herschel Walker, Reggie White, Anthony Carter, Bobby Hebert, Kelvin Bryant and Mike Rozier. Issued as a factory set, cards were printed on white cardboard stock. Bordered in red and blue piping over white space with the USFL logo and "Premier Edition" at the top of the card, a team helmet appears at lower left with the team name in red and the player name in black over a yellow background below the photo. Cards were numbered alphabetically by city name and by the player's last name.

		MT
	Complete Set (132):	375.00
	Common Player:	1.50
1	Luther Bradley	1.50
2	Frank Corral	1.50
3	Trumaine Johnson	1.50
4	Greg Landry	1.50
5	Kit Lathrop	1.50
6	Kevin Long	1.50
7	Tim Spencer	1.50
8	Stan White	1.50
9	Buddy Aydelette	1.50
10	Tom Banks	1.50
11	Fred Bohannon	1.50
12	Joe Cribbs	1.50
13	Joey Jones	1.50
14	Scott Norwood	1.50
15	Jim Smith	1.50
16	Cliff Stoudt	1.50
17	Vince Evans	2.00
18	Vagas Ferguson	1.50
19	John Gillen	1.50
20	Kris Haines	1.50
21	Glenn Hyde	1.50
22	Mark Keel	1.50
23	Gary Lewis	1.50
24	Doug Plank	1.50
25	Neil Balholm	1.50
26	David Dumars	1.50
27	David Martin	1.50
28	Craig Penrose	1.50
29	Dave Stalls	1.50
30	*Harry Sydney*	1.00
31	Vincent White	1.50
32	George Yarno	1.50
33	Kiki DeAyala	1.50
34	Sam Harrell	1.50
35	Mike Hawkins	1.50
36	*Jim Kelly*	100.00
37	Mark Rush	1.50
38	*Ricky Sanders*	10.00
39	Paul Bergmann	1.50
40	Tom Dinkel	1.50
41	Wyatt Henderson	1.50
42	*Vaughan Johnson*	5.00
43	Willie McClendon	1.50
44	Matt Robinson	1.50
45	George Achica	1.50
46	Mark Adickes	1.50
47	Howard Carson	1.50
48	Kevin Nelson	1.50
49	Jeff Partridge	1.50
50	JoJo Townsell	1.50
51	Eddie Weaver	1.50
52	*Steve Young*	250.00
53	Derrick Crawford	1.50
54	Walter Lewis	1.50
55	Phil McKinnely	1.50
56	Vic Minore	1.50
57	Gary Shirk	1.50
58	*Reggie White*	100.00
59	Anthony Carter	15.00
60	John Corker	1.50
61	David Greenwood	1.50
62	*Bobby Hebert*	10.00
63	Derek Holloway	1.50
64	Ken Lacy	1.50
65	Tyrone McGriff	1.50
66	Ray Pinney	1.50
67	Gary Barbaro	1.50
68	Sam Bowers	1.50
69	Clarence Collins	1.50
70	Willie Harper	1.50
71	Jim LeClair	1.50
72	Bob Leopold	1.50
73	Brian Sipe	2.00
74	*Herschel Walker*	25.00
75	*Junior Ah You*	1.50
76	*Marcus Dupree*	2.00
77	Marcus Marek	1.50
78	Tim Mazzetti	1.50
79	Mike Robinson	1.50
80	Dan Ross	1.50
81	Mark Schellen	1.50
82	Johnnie Walton	1.50
83	Gordon Banks	1.50
84	Fred Besana	1.50
85	Dave Browning	1.50
86	Eric Jordan	1.50
87	Frank Manumaleuga	1.50
88	*Gary Plummer*	4.00
89	Stan Talley	1.50
90	Arthur Whittington	1.50
91	Terry Beeson	1.50
92	*Mel Gray*	2.00
93	Mike Katolin	1.50
94	Dewey McClain	1.50
95	Sidney Thorton	1.50
96	Doug Williams	2.50
97	*Kelvin Bryant*	2.50
98	John Bunting	1.50
99	*Irv Eatman*	2.00
100	Scott Fitzkee	1.50
101	Chuck Fusina	1.50
102	*Sean Landeta*	3.00
103	David Trout	1.50
104	Scott Woerner	1.50
105	Glenn Carano	1.50
106	Ron Crosby	1.50
107	Jerry Holmes	1.50
108	Bruce Huther	1.50
109	*Mike Rozier*	4.00
110	Larry Swider	1.50
111	Danny Buggs	1.50
112	Putt Choate	1.50
113	Rich Garza	1.50
114	Joey Hackett	1.50
115	Rick Neuheisel	1.50
116	Mike St. Clair	1.50
117	*Gary Anderson*	4.00
118	Zenon Andrusyshyn	1.50
119	Doug Beaudoin	1.50
120	Mike Butler	1.50
121	Willie Gillespie	1.50
122	Fred Nordgren	1.50
123	John Reaves	1.50
124	Eric Truvillon	1.50
125	Reggie Collier	1.50
126	Mike Guess	1.50
127	Mike Hohensee	1.50
128	*Craig James*	4.00
129	Eric Robinson	1.50
130	Billy Taylor	1.50
131	Joey Walters	1.50
132	Checklist 1-132	1.50

Values quoted in this guide reflect the retail price of a card — the price a collector can expect to pay when buying a card from a dealer. The wholesale price — that which a collector can expect to receive from a dealer when selling cards — will be significantly lower, depending on desirability and condition.

1985 Topps

This was Topps' most radical card design in football cards in decades. Player photos were mounted horizontally in this 396-card set, with black borders surrounding the photo. The player's last name appeared in large white letters across the bottom of the card, with his first name in smaller letters in the middle of his last name. The team name appeared in smaller, darker type in the upper left corner. Cards in this issue were numbered alphabetically according to city name and conference, with NFC teams listed first and AFC teams listed after the league leader cards. This set includes rookie cards of Richard Dent, Henry Ellard, Joe Morris, Warren Moon, Mark Clayton, Tony Eason, Ken O'Brien and Louis Lipps. (Key: AP - All Pro)

		MT
Complete Set (396):		80.00
Common Player:		.05
Wax Box:		125.00
1	Record:	.60
	(Mark Clayton)	
2	Record:	.50
	(Eric Dickerson)	
3	Record:	.15
	(Charlie Joiner)	
4	Record: (Dan Marino RB)	8.00
5	Record: (Art Monk)	.30
6	Record: (Walter Payton RB)	1.00
7	NFC Championship:	.10
	(Matt Suhey)	
8	AFC Championship:	.10
	(Bennett)	
9	Super Bowl XIX:	.15
	(Wendell Tyler)	
10	Atlanta Falcons	.10
	Team:	
	(Gerald Riggs)	
11	William Andrews	.05
12	Stacey Bailey	.05
13	Steve Bartkowski	.15
14	Rick Bryan	.25
15	Alfred Jackson	.05
16	Kenny Johnson	.05
17	Mike Ken (AP)	.05
18	Mike Pitts	.25
19	Gerald Riggs	.05
20	Sylvester Stamps	.05
21	R.C. Theilemann	.05
22	Chicago Bears	.75
	Team:	
23	Todd Bell (AP)	.12
24	Richard Dent (AP)	4.00
25	Gary Fencik	.05
26	Dave Finzer	.05
27	Leslie Frazier	.05
28	Steve Fuller	.05
29	Willie Gault	.40
30	Dan Hampton (AP)	.60
31	Jim McMahon	.60
32	Steve McMichael	1.00
33	Walter Payton (AP)	1.75
34	Mike Singletary	.75
35	Matt Suhey	.05
36	Bob Thomas	.05
37	Dallas Cowboys	.25
	Team:	
	(Tony Dorsett)	
38	Bill Bates	1.00
39	Doug Cosbie	.05
40	Tony Dorsett	.60
41	Michael Downs	.05
42	Mike Hegman	.05
43	Tony Hill	.05
44	Gary Hogeboom	.10
45	Jim Jeffcoat	.05
46	Ed "Too Tall" Jones	.25
47	Mike Renfro	.05
48	Rafael Septien	.05
49	Dennis Thurman	.05
50	Everson Walls	.05
51	Danny White	.20
52	Randy White	.50
53	Detroit Lions Team	.10
54	Jeff Chadwick	.05
55	Mike Cofer	.25
56	Gary Danielson	.05
57	Keith Dorney	.05

58	Doug English	.05
59	William Gay	.05
60	Ken Jenkins	.05
61	James Jones	.05
62	Ed Murray	.05
63	Billy Sims	.12
64	Leonard Thompson	.05
65	Bobby Watkins	.05
66	Green Bay Packers Team:	.10
	(Lynn Dickey)	
67	Paul Coffman	.05
68	Lynn Dickey	.05
69	Mike Douglass	.05
70	Tom Flynn	.05
71	Eddie Lee Ivery	.05
72	Ezra Johnson	.05
73	Mark Lee	.05
74	Tim Lewis	.05
75	James Lofton	.50
76	Bucky Scribner	.05
77	Los Angeles Rams Team:	.40
	(Eric Dickerson)	
78	Nolan Cromwell	.05
79	Eric Dickerson (AP)	1.00
80	Henry Ellard	5.00
81	Kent Hill	.05
82	LeRoy Irvin	.05
83	Jeff Kemp	.35
84	Mike Lansford	.05
85	Barry Redden	.05
86	Jackie Slater	.40
87	Doug Smith	.50
88	Jack Youngblood	.15
89	Minnesota Vikings Team	.10
90	Alfred Anderson	.15
91	Ted Brown	.05
92	Greg Coleman	.05
93	Tommy Hannon	.05
94	Tommy Kramer	.10
95	Leo Lewis	.20
96	Doug Martin	.05
97	Darrin Nelson	.05
98	Jan Stenerud (AP)	.05
99	Sammy White	.05
100	New Orleans Saints Team	.10
101	Morten Anderson	.75
102	Hoby Brenner	.15
103	Bruce Clark	.05
104	Hokie Gajan	.05
105	Brian Hansen	.15
106	Rickey Jackson	1.00
107	George Rogers	.15
108	Dave Wilson	.05
109	Tyrone Young	.05
110	New York Giants Team	.10
111	Carl Banks	1.00
112	Jim Burt	.40
113	Rob Carpenter	.05
114	Harry Carson	.15
115	Earnest Gray	.05
116	Ali Haji-Sheikh	.05
117	Mark Haynes (AP)	.05
118	Bobby Johnson	.05
119	Lionel Manuel	.12
120	Joe Morris	.75
121	Zeke Mowatt	.10
122	Jeff Rutledge	.20
123	Phil Simms	.60
124	Lawrence Taylor (AP)	1.25
125	Philadelphia Eagles Team: (Wilbert Montgomery)	.10
126	Greg Brown	.05
127	Ray Ellis	.05
128	Dennis Harrison	.05
129	Wes Hopkins	.50
	Marvin Harvey	
130	Mike Horan	.05
131	Kenny Jackson	.15
132	Ron Jaworski	.12
133	Paul McFadden	.05
134	Wilbert Montgomery	.05
135	Mike Quick	.12
136	John Spagnola	.05
137	St. Louis Cardinals Team	.10
138	Ottis Anderson	.30
139	Al "Bubba" Baker	.05
140	Roy Green	.15
141	Curtis Greer	.05
142	E.J. Junior (AP)	.05
143	Neil Lomax	.05
144	Stump Mitchell	.05
145	Neil O'Donoghue	.05
146	Pat Tilley	.05
147	Lionel Washington	.05
148	San Francisco 49ers	1.00
149	Dwaine Board	.05
150	Dwight Clark	.20
151	Roger Craig	1.25
152	Randy Cross (AP)	.05
153	Fred Dean	.05
154	Keith Fahnhorst	.05
155	Dwight Hicks	.05
156	Ronnie Lott	.50
157	Joe Montana	7.00
158	Renaldo Nehemiah	.05
159	Fred Quillan	.05
160	Jack Reynolds	.05
161	Freddie Solomon	.05
162	Keena Turner	.50

163	Wendell Tyler	.05
164	Ray Wersching	.05
165	Carlton Williamson	.05
166	Tampa Bay Buccaneers Team: (Steve DeBerg)	.10
167	Gerald Carter	.05
168	Mark Cotney	.05
169	Steve DeBerg	.40
170	Sean Farrell	.05
171	Hugh Green	.05
172	Kevin House	.05
173	David Logan	.05
174	Michael Morton	.05
175	Lee Roy Selmon	.05
176	James Wilder	.05
177	Washington Redskins Team: (John Riggins)	.20
178	Charlie Brown	.05
179	Monte Coleman	.75
180	Vernon Dean	.05
181	Darrell Green	.65
182	Russ Grimm	.15
183	Joe Jacoby	.05
184	Dexter Manley	.05
185	Art Monk	1.00
186	Mark Moseley	.05
187	Calvin Muhammad	.05
188	Mike Nelms	.05
189	John Riggins	.50
190	Joe Theismann	.50
191	Joe Washington	.05
192	Passing Leaders:	13.00
	(Joe Montana, Dan Marino)	
193	Receiving Leaders:	.35
	(Ozzie Newsome, Art Monk)	
194	Rushing Leaders:	.40
	(Earnest Jackson, Eric Dickerson)	
195	Scoring Leaders:	.10
	(Gary Anderson, Ray Wersching)	
196	Interception Leaders:	.10
	(Kenny Easley, Tom Flynn)	
197	Punting Leaders:	.10
	(Jim Arnold, Brian Hansen)	
198	Buffalo Bills Team:	.10
	(Greg Bell)	
199	Greg Bell	.85
200	Preston Dennard	.05
201	Joe Ferguson	.10
202	Byron Franklin	.05
203	Steve Freeman	.05
204	Jim Haslett	.05
205	Charles Romes	.05
206	Fred Smerlas	.05
207	Darryl Talley	2.00
208	Van Williams	.05
209	Cincinnati Bengals Team:	.10
	(Ken Anderson, Larry Kinnebrew)	
210	Ken Anderson	.20
211	Jim Breech	.05
212	Louis Breeden	.05
213	James Brooks	.25
214	Ross Browner	.05
215	Eddie Edwards	.05
216	M.L. Harris	.05
217	Bobby Kemp	.05
218	Larry Kinnebrew	.10
219	Anthony Munoz (AP)	.40
220	Reggie Williams	.05
221	Cleveland Browns Team:	.10
	(Boyce Green)	
222	Matt Bahr	.05
223	Chip Banks	.05
224	Reggie Camp	.05
225	Tom Cousineau	.05
226	Joe DeLamielleure	.05
227	Ricky Feacher	.05
228	Boyce Green	.05
229	Al Gross	.05
230	Clay Matthews	.50
231	Paul McDonald	.05
232	Ozzie Newsome (AP)	.35
233	Mike Pruitt	.05
234	Don Rogers	.05
235	Denver Broncos Team:	.70
	(John Elway, Sammy Winder)	
236	Rubin Carter	.05
237	Barney Chavous	.05
238	John Elway	15.00
239	Steve Foley	.05
240	Mike Harden	.05
241	Tom Jackson	.15
242	Butch Johnson	.05
243	Rulon Jones	.05
244	Rick Karlis	.05
245	Steve Watson	.05
246	Gerald Wilhite	.05
247	Sammy Winder	.05
248	Houston Oilers Team:	.10
	(Larry Moriarty)	
249	Jesse Baker	.05
250	Carter Hartwig	.05
251	Warren Moon	20.00

252	Larry Moriarty	.10
253	Mike Munchak	.50
254	Carl Roaches	.05
255	Tim Smith	.05
256	Willie Tullis	.05
257	Jamie Williams	.05
258	Indianapolis Colts Team: (Art Schlichter)	.10
259	Raymond Butler	.05
260	Johnie Cooks	.05
261	Eugene Daniel	.05
262	Curtis Dickey	.05
263	Chris Hinton	.20
264	Vernon Maxwell	.05
265	Randy McMillan	.05
266	Art Schlichter	.15
267	Rohn Stark	.05
268	Leo Wisniewski	.05
269	Kansas City Chiefs Team: (Bill Kenney)	.10
270	Jim Arnold	.05
271	Mike Bell	.05
272	Todd Blackledge	.15
273	Carlos Carson	.05
274	Deron Cherry	.25
275	Herman Heard	.10
276	Bill Kenney	.05
277	Nick Lowery	.30
278	Bill Maas	.30
279	Henry Marshall	.05
280	Art Still	.05
281	Los Angeles Raiders Team: (Marcus Allen)	.30
282	Marcus Allen	2.00
283	Lyle Alzado	.20
284	Chris Bahr	.05
285	Malcolm Barnwell	.05
286	Cliff Branch	.15
287	Todd Christensen	.05
288	Ray Guy	.15
289	Lester Hayes	.05
290	Mike Haynes (AP)	.05
291	Henry Lawrence	.05
292	Howie Long	2.00
293	Rod Martin (AP)	.05
294	Vann McElroy	.05
295	Matt Millen	.05
296	Bill Pickel	.15
297	Jim Plunkett	.20
298	Dokie Williams	.10
299	Marc Wilson	.05
300	Miami Dolphins Team: (Mark Duper)	.15
301	Bob Baumhower	.05
302	Doug Betters	.05
303	Glenn Blackwood	.05
304	Lyle Blackwood	.05
305	Kim Bokamper	.05
306	Charles Bowser	.05
307	Jimmy Cefalo	.05
308	Mark Clayton (AP)	1.00
309	A.J. Duhe	.05
310	Mark Duper	.50
311	Andra Franklin	.05
312	Bruce Hardy	.05
313	Pete Johnson	.05
314	Dan Marino (AP)	30.00
315	Tony Nathan	.05
316	Ed Newman	.05
317	Reggie Roby (AP)	.15
318	Dwight Stephenson (AP)	.05
319	Uwe Von Schamann	.05
320	New England Patriots Team: (Tony Collins)	.10
321	Raymond Clayborn	.05
322	Tony Collins	.05
323	Tony Eason	.30
324	Tony Franklin	.05
325	Irving Fryar	4.00
326	John Hannah (AP)	.15
327	Brian Holloway	.05
328	Craig James	.50
329	Stanley Morgan	.20
330	Steve Nelson	.05
331	Derrick Ramsey	.05
332	Stephen Starring	.05
333	Mosi Tatupu	.05
334	Andre Tippett	.50
335	New York Jets Team: (Mark Gastineau, Ferguson)	.10
336	Russell Carter	.05
337	Mark Gastineau (AP)	.05
338	Bruce Harper	.05
339	Bobby Humphery	.05
340	Johnny "Lam" Jones	.05
341	Joe Klecko	.05
342	Pat Leahy	.05
343	Marty Lyons	.05
344	Freeman McNeil	.20
345	Lance Mehl	.05
346	Ken O'Brien	.50
347	Marvin Powell	.05
348	Pat Ryan	.05
349	Mickey Shuler	.40
350	Wesley Walker	.05
351	Pittsburgh Steelers Team (Mark Malone)	.15

352	Walter Abercrombie	.05
353	Gary Anderson	.05
354	Robin Cole	.05
355	Bennie Cunningham	.05
356	Rich Erenberg	.05
357	Jack Lambert	.40
358	Louis Lipps	.50
359	Mark Malone	.05
360	Mike Merriweather	.60
361	Frank Pollard	.05
362	Donnie Shell	.15
363	John Stallworth	.15
364	Sam Washington	.05
365	Mike Webster	.20
366	Dwayne Woodruff	.05
367	San Diego Chargers Team	.10
368	Rolf Benirschke	.05
369	Gill Byrd	1.00
370	Wes Chandler	.05
371	Bobby Duckworth	.05
372	Dan Fouts	.60
373	Mike Green	.05
374	Pete Holohan	.60
375	Earnest Jackson	.20
376	Lionel James	.20
377	Charlie Joiner	.30
378	Billy Ray Smith	.05
379	Kellen Winslow	.30
380	Seattle Seahawks Team (Dave Krieg)	.10
381	Dave Brown	.05
382	Jeff Bryant	.05
383	Dan Doornink	.05
384	Kenny Easley (AP)	.05
385	Jacob Green	.05
386	David Hughes	.05
387	Norm Johnson	.05
388	Dave Krieg	.75
389	Steve Largent	.80
390	Joe Nash	.20
391	Daryl Turner	.05
392	Curt Warner	.15
393	Fredd Young	.20
394	Checklist 1-132	.15
395	Checklist 133-264	.15
396	Checklist 265-396	.15

1985 Topps Box Bottoms

The bottoms of 1985 Topps wax pack boxes featured these cards, which are numbered using a letter instead of a number. The design is the same as a regular 1985 Topps card, except the front border is red and "Topps Superstars" is printed at the top. The backs are identical to the regular cards' backs except for the letters used as card numbers.

		MT
Complete Set (16):		15.00
Common Player:		.30
A	Marcus Allen	1.50
B	Ottis Anderson	.30
C	Mark Clayton	1.00
D	Eric Dickerson	1.00
E	Tony Dorsett	.75
F	Dan Fouts	.75
G	Mark Gastineau	.30
H	Charlie Joiner	.50
I	James Lofton	.75
J	Neil Lomax	.30
K	Dan Marino	6.00
L	Art Monk	.75
M	Joe Montana	6.00
N	Walter Payton	2.50
O	John Stallworth	.30
P	Lawrence Taylor	.75

1985 Topps Star Set

This 11-card glossy set was a follow-up to the 1984 insert set. Cards were printed on heavy white cardboard stock, with red borders surrounding an action picture of each player. Cards were issued one per wax

pack with the 1985 cards. Card backs were printed in blue and red and show pretty much the same design, front and back, as the 1984 insert set, but with smaller type indicating the year of issue on the back. This was the second and final year of Topps' production of United States Football League cards. The 132-card set was issued as a factory set. Cards were numbered alphabetically according to city and according to the player's last name. Printed on white cardboard stock, fronts show a bright red border with a white and blue stripe across the middle; the USFL logo appears in the upper right corner. The team name appears in heavy red type at the bottom of the card, and the player's name and position is in a yellow football above the team name. Card backs show a goalpost design in blue and red. The set includes rookie cards Doug Flutie, Gary Clark and Gerald McNeill; plus Herschel Walker's second-year card.

		MT
Complete Set (11):		6.50
Common Player:		.25
1	Mark Clayton	.25
2	Eric Dickerson	1.75
3	John Elway	1.00
4	Mark Gastineau	.25
5	Ronnie Lott	.40
6	Dan Marino	1.25
7	Joe Montana	1.50
8	Walter Payton	1.50
9	John Riggins	.35
10	John Stallworth	.25
11	Lawrence Taylor	.35

1985 Topps "Coming Soon" Stickers

These stickers say "Coming Soon" on the backs and share identical card numbers with their counterparts in Topps' regular 1985 sticker set; thus, the checklist is skip-numbered. These stickers, which were random inserts in 1985 Topps football packs, measure 2-1/8" x 3" each but, unlike many of the regular stickers, feature only one player per sticker. The stickers have a colored photo on the front with a color frame and white border surrounding it.

		MT
Complete Set (30):		5.00
Common Player:		.08
6	Ken Anderson	.30
15	Greg Bell	.15
24	John Elway	.75
33	Ozzie Newsome	.25
42	Charlie Joiner	.25
51	Bill Kenney	.15
60	Randy McMillan	.08
69	Dan Marino	2.00
77	Mark Clayton	.50
78	Mark Gastineau	.08
87	Warren Moon	2.00
96	Tony Eason	.15
105	Marcus Allen	.50
114	Steve Largent	.60
123	John Stallworth	.20
156	Walter Payton	1.00
165	James Wilder	.12
174	Neil Lomax	.15
183	Tony Dorsett	.35
192	Mike Quick	.15
201	William Andrews	.10
210	Joe Montana	2.50
214	Dwight Clark	.35
219	Lawrence Taylor	.35
228	Billy Sims	.15
237	James Lofton	.30
246	Eric Dickerson	.50
255	John Riggins	.25
268	George Rogers	.12
281	Tommy Kramer	.08

1985 Topps Stickers

These stickers are different than those issued in previous years, because no foil stickers were produced. However, there were stickers issued in pairs on some cards; they are noted as being partners by the parenthesis which follows the player's name in the checklist. Charlie Joiner, Art Monk, Joe Montana, Dan Marino, Walter Payton and Eric Dickerson are all featured on the album cover; the 49ers team is on the back.

		MT
Complete Set (285):		20.00
Common Player:		.05
1	Super Bowl XIX	1.50
2	Super Bowl XIX	1.00
3	Super Bowl XIX	.10
4	Super Bowl XIX	.10
5	Super Bow XIX	.08
6	Ken Anderson	.30
7	M.L. Harris (157)	.05
8	Eddie Edwards (157)	.05
9	Louis Breeden (159)	.05
10	Larry Kinnebrew	.05
11	Isaac Curtis (161)	.06
12	James Brooks (162)	.12
13	Jim Breech (163)	.05
14	Boomer Esiason (164)	.75
15	Greg Bell	.10
16	Fred Smerlas (166)	.05
17	Joe Ferguson (167)	.06
18	Ken Johnson (168)	.05
19	Darryl Talley (169)	.25
20	Preston Dennard (170)	.05
21	Charles Romes (171)	.05
22	Jim Haslett (172)	.05
23	Byron Franklin	.05
24	John Elway	1.25
25	Rulon Jones (175)	.05
26	Butch Johnson (176)	.05
27	Rick Karlis (177)	.05
28	Sammy Winder	.05
29	Tom Jackson (179)	.10
30	Mike Harden (180)	.05
31	Steve Watson (181)	.05
32	Steve Foley (182)	.05
33	Ozzie Newsome	.25
34	Al Gross (184)	.05
35	Paul McDonald (185)	.05
36	Matt Bahr (186)	.07
37	Charles White (187)	.06
38	Don Rogers (188)	.05
39	Mike Pruitt (189)	.05
40	Reggie Camp (190)	.05
41	Boyce Green	.05
42	Charlie Joiner	.20
43	Dan Fouts (193)	.25
44	Keith Ferguson (194)	.05
45	Pete Holohan (195)	.05
46	Earnest Jackson	.08
47	Wes Chandler (197)	.06
48	Gill Byrd (198)	.15
49	Kellen Winslow (199)	.15
50	Billy Ray Smith (200)	.06
51	Bill Kenney	.08
52	Herman Heard (202)	.05
53	Art Still (203)	.05
54	Nick Lowery (204)	.05
55	Deron Cherry (205)	.08
56	Jenry Marshall (206)	.05
57	Mike Bell (207)	.05
58	Todd Blackledge (208)	.05
59	Carlos Carson	.08
60	Randy McMillan	.05
61	Donnell Thompson (211)	.05
62	Raymond Butler (212)	.05

63	Ray Donaldson (213)	.05
64	Art Schlichter	.15
65	Rohn Stark (215)	.05
66	Johnie Cooks (216)	.05
67	Mike Pagel (217)	.05
68	Eugene Daniel (218)	.05
69	Dan Marino	2.00
70	Pete Johnson (220)	.05
71	Tony Nathan (221)	.05
72	Glenn Blackwood (222)	.05
73	Woody Bennett (223)	.05
74	Dwight Stephenson (224)	.05
75	Mark Duper (225)	.10
76	Doug Betters (226)	.05
77	Mark Clayton	.50
78	Mark Gastineau	.08
79	Johnny Lam Jones (229)	.05
80	Mickey Shuler (230)	.05
81	Tony Paige (231)	.15
82	Freeman McNeil	.15
83	Russell Carter (233)	.06
84	Wesley Walker (234)	.06
85	Bruce Harper (235)	.05
86	Ken O'Brien (236)	1.75
87	Warren Moon	.05
88	Jesse Baker (238)	.05
89	Carl Roaches (239)	.05
90	Carter Hartwig (240)	.05
91	Larry Moriarity (241)	.05
92	Robert Brazile (242)	.05
93	Oliver Luck (243)	.05
94	Willie Tullis (244)	.05
95	Tim Smith	.05
96	Tony Eason	.12
97	Stanley Morgan (247)	.10
98	Mosi Tatupu (248)	.05
99	Raymond Clayborn (249)	.08
100	Andre Tippett	.10
101	Craig James (251)	.15
102	Derrick Ramsey (252)	.05
103	Tony Collins (253)	.05
104	Tony Franklin (254)	.05
105	Marcus Allen	.40
106	Chris Bahr (256)	.05
107	Marc Wilson (257)	.05
108	Howie Long (258)	.10
109	Bill Pickel (259)	.05
110	Mike Haynes (260)	.08
111	Malcolm Barnwell (261)	.05
112	Rod Martin (262)	.05
113	Todd Christensen	.10
114	Steve Largent	.75
115	Curt Warner (265)	.08
116	Kenny Easley (266)	.05
117	Jacob Green (267)	.05
118	Daryl Turner	.05
119	Norm Johnson (269)	.05
120	Dave Krieg (270)	.10
121	Eric Lane (271)	.05
122	Jeff Bryant (272)	.05
123	John Stallworth	.12
124	Donnie Shell (274)	.05
125	Gary Anderson (275)	.05
126	Mark Malone (276)	.05
127	Sam Washington (277)	.05
128	Frank Pollard (278)	.05
129	Mike Merriweather (279)	.05
130	Walter Abercrombie (280)	.05
131	Louis Lipps	.30
132	Mark Clayton (144)	.35
133	Randy Cross (145)	.06
134	Eric Dickerson (146)	.35
135	John Hannah (147)	.10
136	Mike Kenn (148)	.05
137	Dan Marino (149)	1.50
138	Art Monk (151)	.15
139	Anthony Munoz (151)	.10
140	Ozzie Newsome (152)	.10
141	Walter Payton (153)	.40
142	Jan Stenerud (154)	.08
143	Dwight Stephenson (155)	.05
144	Todd Bell (132)	.05
145	Richard Dent (133)	.50
146	Kenny Easley (134)	.05
147	Mark Gastineau (135)	.06
148	Dan Hampton (136)	.10
149	Mark Haynes (137)	.05
150	Mike Haynes (138)	.06
151	E.J. Junior (139)	.05
152	Rod Martin (140)	.10
153	Steve Nelson (141)	.05
154	Reggie Roby (142)	.05

155	Lawrence Taylor (143)	.15
156	Walter Payton	.60
157	Dan Hampton (7)	.08
158	Willie Gault (8)	.06
159	Matt Suhey (9)	.05
160	Richard Dent	1.00
161	Mike Singletary (11)	.10
162	Gary Fencik (12)	.05
163	Jim McMahon (13)	.10
164	Bob Thomas (14)	.05
165	James Wilder	.08
166	Steve DeBerg (16)	.08
167	Mark Cotney (17)	.05
168	Adger Armstrong (18)	.05
169	Gerald Carter (19)	.05
170	David Logari (20)	.05
171	Hugh Green (21)	.05
172	Lee Roy Selmon (22)	.06
173	Kevin House	.10
174	Neil Lomax	.12
175	Ottis Anderson (25)	.10
176	Al (Bubba) Baker (26)	.05
177	E.J. Junior (27)	.08
178	Roy Green	.10
179	Pat Tilley (29)	.05
180	Stump Mitchell (30)	.05
181	Lionel Washington (31)	.05
182	Curtis Greer (32)	.05
183	Tony Dorsett	.25
184	Gary Hogeboom (34)	.06
185	Jim Jeffcoat (35)	.05
186	Danny White (36)	.08
187	Michael Downs (37)	.05
188	Doug Cosbie (38)	.08
189	Tony Hill (39)	.05
190	Rafael Septien (40)	.05
191	Randy White	.15
192	Mike Quick	.08
193	Ray Ellis (43)	.05
194	John Spagnola (44)	.05
195	Dennis Harrison (45)	.05
196	Wilbert Montgomery	.08
197	Greg Brown (47)	.05
198	Ron Jaworski (48)	.08
199	Paul McFadden (49)	.05
200	Wes Hopkins (50)	.05
201	William Andrews	.10
202	Mike Pitts (52)	.05
203	Steve Bartkowski (53)	.08
204	Gerald Riggs (54)	.08
205	Alfred Jackson (55)	.05
206	Don Smith (56)	.05
207	Mike Kenn (57)	.05
208	Kenny Johnson (58)	.05
209	Stacey Bailey	.05
210	Joe Montana	1.25
211	Wendell Tyler (61)	.05
212	Keena Turner (62)	.08
213	Ray Wersching (63)	.05
214	Dwight Clark	.15
215	Dwaine Board (65)	.05
216	Roger Craig (66)	.15
217	Ronnie Lott (67)	.15
218	Freddie Solomon (68)	.08
219	Lawrence Taylor	.25
220	Zeke Mowatt (70)	.05
221	Harry Carson (71)	.06
222	Rob Carpenter (72)	.05
223	Bobby Johnson (73)	.05
224	Joe Morris (74)	.07
225	Mark Haynes (75)	.05
226	Lionel Manuel (76)	.05
227	Phil Simms	.15
228	Billy Simms	.12
229	Leonard Thompson (79)	.03
230	James Jones (80)	.05
231	Ed Murray (81)	.05
232	William Gay	.05
233	Gary Danielson (83)	.05
234	Curtis Green (84)	.05
235	Bobby Watkins (85)	.05
236	Doug English (86)	.05
237	James Lofton	.20
238	Eddie Lee Ivery (88)	.06
239	Mike Douglas (89)	.05
240	Gerry Ellis (90)	.05
241	Tim Lewis (91)	.08
242	Paul Coffman (92)	.05
243	Tom Flynn (93)	.05
244	Ezra Johnson (94)	.05
245	Lynn Dickey	.08
246	Eric Dickerson	.60
247	Jack Youngblood (97)	.08
248	Doug Smith (98)	.05
249	Jeff Kemp (99)	.05
250	Kent Hill	.05
251	Mike Lansford (101)	.05
252	Henry Ellard (102)	.35
253	LeRoy Irvin (103)	.06
254	Ron Brown (104)	.20
255	John Riggins	.06
256	Dexter Manley (106)	.10
257	Darrell Green (107)	.15

258	Joe Theismann (108)	.05
259	Mark Moseley (109)	.05
260	Clint Didier (110)	.05
261	Vernon Dean (111)	.05
262	Calvin Muhammad (112)	.05
263	Art Monk	.20
264	Bruce Clark	.08
265	Hoby Brenner (115)	.05
266	Dave Wilson (116)	.06
267	Hokie Gajan (117)	.05
268	George Rogers	.10
269	Rickey Jackson (119)	.08
270	Brian Hansen (120)	.04
271	Dave Waymer (121)	.05
272	Richard Todd (122)	.05
273	Jan Stenerud	.15
274	Ted Brown (124)	.05
275	Leo Lewis (125)	.05
276	Scott Studwell (126)	.05
277	Alfred Anderson (127)	.05
278	Rufus Bess (128)	.05
279	Darrin Nelson (129)	.05
280	Greg Coleman (130)	.05
281	Tommy Kramer	.05
282	Joe Montana (283)	1.25
283	Dan Marino (282)	1.00
284	Brian Hansen (285)	.05
285	Jim Arnold (284)	.05

1985 Topps USFL

This was the second and final year of Topps' production of United States Football League cards. The 132-card set was issued as a factory set. Cards were numbered alphabetically according to city and according to the player's last name. Printed on white cardboard stock, fronts show a bright red border with a white and blue stripe across the middle; the USFL logo appears in the upper right corner. The team name appears in heavy red type at the bottom of the card, and the player's name and position are in a yellow football above the team name. Card backs show a goalpost design in blue and red. The set includes rookies of Doug Flutie, Gary Clark and Gerald McNeil, plus Herschel Walker's second-year card.

		MT
Complete Set (132):		175.00
Common Player:		.35
1	Case DeBruijn	.35
2	Mike Katolin	.35
3	Bruce Laird	.35
4	Kit Lathrop	.35
5	Kevin Long	.35
6	Karl Lorch	.35
7	Dave Tipton	.35
8	Doug Williams	.40
9	Luis Zendejas	.35
10	Kelvin Bryant	.75
11	Willie Collier	.35
12	Irv Eatman	.50
13	Scott Fitzkee	.35
14	William Fuller	6.00
15	Chuck Fusina	.35
16	Pete Kugler	.35
17	Garcia Lane	.35
18	Mike Lush	.35
19	Sam Mills	8.00
20	Buddy Aydelette	.35
21	Joe Cribbs	.50
22	David Dumars	.35
23	Robin Earl	.35
24	Joey Jones	.35
25	Leon Perry	.35
26	Dave Pureifory	.35
27	Bill Roe	.35
28	Doug Smith	2.00
29	Cliff Stoudt	.35
30	Jeff Delaney	.35
31	Vince Evans	.50
32	Leonard Harris	2.00

33	Bill Johnson	.35
34	Marc Lewis	.35
35	David Martin	.35
36	Bruce Thornton	.35
37	Craig Walls	.35
38	Vincent White	.35
39	Luther Bradley	.35
40	Pete Catan	.35
41	Kiki DeAyala	.35
42	Tony Fritsch	.35
43	Sam Harrell	.35
44	Richard Johnson	1.50
45	Jim Kelly	40.00
46	Gerald McNeil	1.50
47	Clarence Verdin	2.00
48	Dale Walters	.35
49	Gary Clark	15.00
50	Tom Dinkel	.35
51	Mike Edwards	.35
52	Brian Franco	.35
53	Bob Gruber	.35
54	Robbie Mahfouz	.35
55	Mike Rozier	1.75
56	Brian Sipe	.50
57	J.T. Turner	.35
58	Howard Carson	.35
59	Wymon Henderson	.60
60	Kevin Nelson	.35
61	Jeff Partridge	.35
62	Ben Rudolph	.35
63	JoJo Townsell	.35
64	Eddie Weaver	.35
65	Steve Young	80.00
67	Tony Zendejas	.75
68	Mossy Cade	.35
69	Leonard Coleman	.35
69	John Corker	.35
70	Derrick Crawford	.35
71	Art Kuehn	.35
72	Walter Lewis	.35
73	Tyrone McGriff	.35
74	Tim Spencer	.35
75	Reggie White	30.00
76	Gizmo Williams	2.00
77	Sam Bowers	.35
78	Maurice Carthon	1.25
79	Clarence Collins	.35
80	Doug Flutie	70.00
81	Freddie Gilbert	.35
82	Kerry Justin	.35
83	Dave Lapham	.35
84	Rick Partridge	.35
85	Roger Ruzek	1.00
86	Herschel Walker	6.00
87	Gordon Banks	.35
88	Monte Bennett	.35
89	Albert Bentley	3.00
90	Novo Bojovic	.35
91	Dave Browning	.35
92	Anthony Carter	4.00
93	Bobby Hebert	3.00
94	Ray Pinney	.35
95	Stan Talley	.35
96	Ruben Vaughan	.35
97	Curtis Bledsoe	.35
98	Reggie Collier	.35
99	Jerry Doerger	.35
100	Jerry Golsteyn	.35
101	Bob Niziolek	.35
102	Joel Patten	.35
103	Ricky Simmons	.35
104	Joey Walters	.35
105	Marcus Dupree	.35
106	Jeff Gossett	.35
107	Frank Lockett	.35
108	Marcus Marek	.35
109	Kenny Neil	.35
110	Robert Pennywell	.35
111	Matt Robinson	.35
112	Dan Ross	.35
113	Doug Woodward	.35
114	Danny Buggs	.35
115	Putt Choate	.35
116	Greg Fields	.35
117	Ken Hartley	.35
118	Nick Mike-Mayer	.35
119	Rick Neuheisel	.35
120	Peter Raeford	.35
121	Gary Worthy	.35
122	Gary Anderson	3.00
123	Zenon Andrusyshyn	.35
124	Greg Boone	.35
125	Mike Butler	.35
126	Mike Clark	.35
127	Willie Gillespie	.35
128	James Harrell	.35
130	John Reaves	.35
131	Eric Truvillion	.35
132	Checklist 1-132	.50

1985 Topps USFL New Jersey Generals

This nine-card sheet features members of the USFL's New Jersey Generals. The panel is 7-1/2" x 10-1/2"; individual cards would be the standard size if they were cut out of the panel. The card front has an action photo of the player, along with his name, team name and team logo. The back is numbered and includes biographical and statistical information, plus a brief player profile. The card stock is gray; the print is yellow and red on the back.

		MT
Complete Set (9):		35.00
Common Player:		2.00
1	Walt Michaels	2.00
2	Sam Bowers	2.00
3	Clarence Collins	2.00
4	Doug Flutie	20.00
5	Gregory Johnson	2.00
6	Jim LeClair	3.00
7	Bobby Leopold	2.00
8	Herschel Walker	15.00
9	Membership card (schedule on back)	2.00

1986 Topps

Topps' 1986 offering was 396 cards for the fourth straight year. Cards showed a green background with diagonal white stripes; a photo of the player was enclosed in one of several colorful borders. The player's name is found at the bottom of the card; his team is at right. All-Pro cards show a small designation just above the player's name. Team cards show a yellow border. Cards were numbered according to the team's finish the previous season. Rookies in this set include William Perry, Al Toon, Jerry Rice, Keith Millard, Bernie Kosar, and Boomer Esiason. (Key: AP - All Pro)

		MT
Complete Set (396):		180.00
Common Player:		.05
Wax Box:		425.00
1	Marcus Allen	.65
2	Eric Dickerson	.30
3	Lionel James	.10
4	Steve Largent	.30
5	George Martin	.10
6	Stephone Paige	.10
7	Walter Payton	.75
8	Super Bowl XX	.20
9	Chicago Bears Team (Walter Payton)	.75
10	Jim McMahon	.30
11	Walter Payton (AP)	2.00
12	Matt Suhey	.05
13	Willie Gault	.10
14	Dennis McKinnon	.25
15	Emery Moorhead	.05
16	Jim Covert (AP)	.10
17	Jay Hilgenberg (AP)	.50
18	Kevin Butler	1.00
19	Richard Dent (AP)	1.00
20	William Perry	.80
21	Steve McMichael	.50
22	Dan Hampton	.25
23	Otis Wilson	.05
24	Mike Singletary	.60
25	Wilber Marshall	1.00
26	Leslie Frazier	.05
27	Dave Duerson	.35
28	Gary Fencik	.10
29	New England Patriots Team (Craig James)	.05
30	Tony Eason	.20
31	Steve Grogan	.15
32	Craig James	.10
33	Tony Collins	.05
34	Irving Fryar	1.50
35	Brian Holloway (AP)	.10
36	John Hannah (AP)	.35
37	Tony Franklin	.05
38	Garin Veris	.10
39	Andre Tippett (AP)	.35
40	Steve Nelson	.05
41	Raymond Clayborn	.05
42	Fred Marion	.10
43	Rich Camarillo	.05
44	Miami Dolphins Team (Dan Marino)	2.00
45	Dan Marino (AP)	15.00
46	Tony Nathan	.10
47	Ron Davenport	.10

48 Mark Duper .30
49 Mark Clayton .50
50 Nat Moore .05
51 Bruce Hardy .05
52 Roy Foster .05
53 Dwight Stephenson .05
54 *Fuad Reveiz* .20
55 Bob Baumhower .10
56 Mike Charles .05
57 Hugh Green .05
58 Glenn Blackwood .05
59 Reggie Roby .05
60 Los Angeles .25
Raiders Team
(Marcus Allen)
61 Marc Wilson .10
62 Marcus Allen (AP) 1.25
63 Dokie Williams .05
64 Todd Christensen .05
65 Chris Bahr .05
66 Fulton Walker .05
67 Howie Long .50
68 Bill Pickel .05
69 Ray Guy .15
70 *Greg Townsend* 1.00
71 Rod Martin .05
72 Matt Millen .05
73 Mike Haynes (AP) .10
74 Lester Hayes .05
75 Vann McElroy .05
76 Los Angeles Rams .15
Team
(Eric Dickerson)
77 Dieter Brock .10
78 Eric Dickerson 1.00
79 Henry Ellard 1.00
80 *Ron Brown* .30
81 Tony Hunter .10
82 Kent Hill (AP) .05
83 Doug Smith .05
84 Dennis Harrah .05
85 Jackie Slater .25
86 Mike Lansford .05
87 Gary Jeter .05
88 Mike Wilcher .05
89 Jim Collins .05
90 LeRoy Irvin .10
91 Gary Green .05
92 Nolan Cromwell .05
93 Dale Hatcher .05
94 New York Jets .10
Team
(Freeman McNeil)
95 Ken O'Brien .35
96 Freeman McNeil .20
97 *Tony Paige* .50
98 Johnny "Lam" .05
Jones
99 Wesley Walker .10
100 Kurt Sohn .05
101 *Al Toon* 1.00
102 Mickey Shuler .05
103 Marvin Powell .10
104 Pat Leahy .05
105 Mark Gastineau .25
106 Joe Klecko (AP) .10
107 Marty Lyons .05
108 Lance Mehl .05
109 Bobby Jackson .05
110 Dave Jennings .05
111 Denver Broncos .10
Team
(Sammy Winder)
112 John Elway 7.00
113 Sammy Winder .10
114 Gerald Wilhite .10
115 Steve Watson .10
116 *Vance Johnson* .50
117 Rick Karlis .05
118 Rulon Jones .05
119 *Karl Mecklenburg* 2.50
(AP)
120 Louis Wright .05
121 Mike Harden .05
122 *Dennis Smith* .50
123 Steve Foley .05
124 Dallas Cowboys .10
Team (Tony Hill)
125 Danny White .20
126 Tony Dorsett .50
127 Timmy Newsome .05
128 Mike Renfro .05
129 Tony Hill .10
130 Doug Cosbie (AP) .10
131 Rafael Septien .10
132 Ed "Too Tall" Jones .25
133 Randy White .20
134 Jim Jeffcoat .20
135 Everson Walls (AP) .05
136 Dennis Thurman .10
137 New York Giants .10
Team (Joe Morris)
138 Phil Simms .40
139 Joe Morris .20
140 *George Adams* .05
141 Lionel Manuel .05
142 Bobby Johnson .05
143 *Phil McConkey* .20
144 *Mark Bavaro* 1.00
145 Zeke Mowatt .05
146 Brad Benson .10
147 *Bart Oates* .60
148 *Leonard Marshall* .50
(AP)
149 Jim Burt .05
150 George Martin .05
151 Lawrence Taylor .75
(AP)

152 Harry Carson (AP) .15
153 Elvis Patterson .05
154 Sean Landeta .10
155 San Francisco .25
49ers Team
(Roger Craig)
156 Joe Montana 6.00
157 Roger Craig .75
158 Wendell Tyler .05
159 Carl Monroe .05
160 Dwight Clark .25
161 *Jerry Rice* 120.00
162 Randy Cross .05
163 Keith Fahnhorst .05
164 Jeff Stover .05
165 *Michael Carter* .50
166 Dwaine Board .05
167 Eric Wright .05
168 Ronnie Lott .75
169 Carlton Williamson .05
170 Washington .10
Redskins Team
(Dave Butz)
171 Joe Theismann .40
172 *Jay Schroeder* .50
173 George Rogers .15
174 Ken Jenkins .05
175 Art Monk (AP) .75
176 *Gary Clark* 2.00
177 Joe Jacoby .05
178 Russ Grimm .05
179 Mark Moseley .05
180 Dexter Manley .15
181 *Charles Mann* 1.00
182 Vernon Dean .05
183 *Raphel Cherry* .15
184 Curtis Jordan .05
185 Cleveland Browns .40
Team
(Bernie Kosar)
186 Gary Danielson .05
187 *Bernie Kosar* 2.00
188 Kevin Mack .50
189 *Earnest Byner* 1.00
190 Glen Young .05
191 Ozzie Newsome .30
192 Mike Baab .05
193 Cody Risien .05
194 Bob Golic .10
195 Reggie Camp .05
196 Chip Banks .10
197 Tom Cousineau .10
198 *Frank Minnifield* .30
199 Al Gross .05
200 Seattle Seahawks .10
Team (Curt Warner)
201 Dave Krieg .25
202 Curt Warner .15
203 Steve Largent (AP) .65
204 Norm Johnson .05
205 Daryl Turner .05
206 Jacob Green .05
207 Joe Nash .05
208 Jeff Bryant .05
209 Randy Edwards .05
210 Fredd Young .10
211 Kenny Easley .10
212 John Harris .05
213 Green Bay Packers .10
Team
(Paul Coffman)
214 Lynn Dickey .15
215 Gerry Ellis .05
216 Eddie Lee Ivery .05
217 Jessie Clark .05
218 James Lofton .60
219 Paul Coffman .05
220 Alphonso Carreker .05
221 Ezra Johnson .05
222 Mike Douglass .05
223 Tim Lewis .05
224 *Mark Murphy* .05
225 Passing Leaders 1.00
(Joe Montana,
Ken O'Brien)
226 Receiving Leaders .15
(Lionel James,
Roger Craig)
227 Rushing Leaders .25
(Marcus Allen,
Gerald Riggs)
228 Scoring Leaders .05
(Gary Anderson,
Kevin Butler)
229 Interception .05
Leaders
(Eugene Daniel,
Albert Lewis,
Everson Walls)
230 San Diego .20
Chargers Team
(Dan Fouts)
231 Dan Fouts .60
232 Lionel James .10
233 *Gary Anderson* 1.00
234 *Tim Spencer* .05
235 Wes Chandler .10
236 Charlie Joiner .25
237 Kellen Winslow .25
238 *Jim Lachey* .50
239 Bob Thomas .05
240 Jeffery Dale .05
241 Ralf Mojsiejenko .05
242 Detroit Lions Team .10
(Eric Hipple)
243 Eric Hipple .05
244 Billy Sims .15
245 James Jones .05

246 *Pete Mandley* .15
247 Leonard Thompson .05
248 *Lomas Brown* .50
249 Ed Murray .05
250 Curtis Green .05
251 William Gay .05
252 Jimmy Williams .05
253 Bobby Watkins .05
254 Cincinnati Bengals .75
Team
(Boomer Esiason)
255 *Boomer Esiason* 4.00
256 James Brooks .35
257 Larry Kinnebrew .10
258 Cris Collinsworth .05
259 Mike Martin .05
260 *Eddie Brown* .50
261 Anthony Munoz .25
262 Jim Breech .05
263 Ross Browner .10
264 Carl Zander .05
265 James Griffin .05
266 Robert Jackson .05
267 Pat McInally .10
268 Philadelphia Eagles .10
Team
(Ron Jaworski)
269 Ron Jaworski .15
270 Earnest Jackson .10
271 Mike Quick .10
272 John Spagnola .05
273 Mark Dennard .05
274 Paul McFadden .05
275 *Reggie White* 12.00
276 Greg Brown .05
277 Herman Edwards .05
278 Roynell Young .10
279 Wes Hopkins (AP) .05
280 Pittsburgh Steelers .10
Team (Walter
Abercrombie)
281 Mark Malone .05
282 Frank Pollard .05
283 Walter .10
Abercrombie
284 Louis Lipps .40
285 John Stallworth .15
286 Mike Webster .20
287 Gary Anderson (AP) .25
288 Keith Willis .05
289 Mike Merriweather .10
290 Dwayne Woodruff .05
291 Donnie Shell .10
292 Minnesota Vikings .10
Team
(Tommy Kramer)
293 Tommy Kramer .10
294 Darrin Nelson .05
295 Ted Brown .05
296 Buster Rhymes .15
297 *Anthony Carter* 2.00
298 *Steve Jordan* 1.00
299 *Keith Millard* .50
300 *Joey Browner* .75
301 John Turner .05
302 Greg Coleman .05
303 Kansas City Chiefs .10
Team
(Todd Blackledge)
304 Bill Kenney .05
305 Herman Heard .05
306 *Stephon Paige* .75
307 Carlos Carson .05
308 Nick Lowery .20
309 Mike Bell .05
310 Bill Maas .05
311 Art Still .05
312 *Albert Lewis* 1.25
313 Deron Cherry (AP) .20
314 Indianapolis Colts .10
Team (Rohn Stark)
315 Mike Pagel .05
316 Randy McMillan .05
317 *Albert Bentley* .40
318 George Wonsley .05
319 Robbie Martin .05
320 Pat Beach .05
321 Chris Hinton .05
322 *Duane Bickett* .50
323 Eugene Daniel .05
324 Cliff Odom .15
325 Rohn Stark (AP) .05
326 St. Louis Cardinals .10
Team (Stump
Mitchell)
327 Neil Lomax .15
328 Stump Mitchell .05
329 Ottis Anderson .20
330 J.T. Smith .05
331 Pat Tilley .05
332 Roy Green .05
333 Lance Smith .05
334 Curtis Greer .05
335 *Freddie Joe Nunn* .35
336 E.J. Junior .05
337 *Lonnie Young* .20
338 New Orleans Saints .10
Team
(Wayne Wilson)
339 *Bobby Hebert* .75
340 Dave Wilson .05
341 Wayne Wilson .05
342 Hoby Brenner .05
343 Stan Brock .05
344 Morten Andersen .35
345 Bruce Clark .05
346 Rickey Jackson .60
347 Dave Waymer .05
348 Brian Hansen .05

349 Houston Oilers .60
Team
(Warren Moon)
350 Warren Moon 4.00
351 *Mike Rozier* .30
352 Butch Woolfolk .05
353 Drew Hill .30
355 Tim Smith .05
356 Mike Munchak .30
357 *Ray Childress* 1.50
358 Frank Bush .05
359 Steve Brown .05
360 Atlanta Falcons .10
Team
(Gerald Riggs)
361 Dave Archer .05
362 Gerald Riggs .10
363 William Andrews .05
364 Billy Johnson .05
365 Arthur Cox .05
366 Mike Kenn .05
367 *Bill Fralic* .75
368 Mick Luckhurst .05
369 Rick Bryan .05
370 Bobby Butler .05
371 Rick Donnelly .05
372 Tampa Bay .10
Buccaneers Team
(James Wilder)
373 Steve DeBerg .25
374 *Steve Young* 35.00
375 James Wilder .05
376 Kevin House .05
377 Gerald Carter .05
378 Sean Farrell .05
379 Donald Igwebuike .05
380 David Logan .05
382 *Jeremiah Castille* .12
383 Buffalo Bills Team .10
(Greg Bell)
384 *Bruce Mathison* .15
385 Joe Cribbs .05
386 Greg Bell .15
387 Jerry Butler .05
388 *Andre Reed* 5.00
389 *Bruce Smith* 5.00
390 Fred Smerlas .05
391 Darryl Talley .50
392 Jim Haslett .05
393 Charles Romes .05
394 Checklist 1-132 .15
395 Checklist 133-264 .15
396 Checklist 265-396 .15

1986 Topps 1000 Yard Club

Issued one card per wax pack with the 1986 regular-issue cards, this 26-card set shows each player who gained 1,000 yards rushing or receiving the previous year. The card order was determined by the number of yards gained, with Marcus Allen, 1985's leading ground-gainer, ending up first. (San Francisco's Roger Craig gained 1,000 yards rushing and receiving the previous year, but only his rushing yardage is listed). Printed on heavy white cardboard stock, card fronts show an ornate arch design in light green. Backs are printed in red and orange.

	MT
Complete Set (26):	6.00
Common Player:	.10
1 Marcus Allen	.40
2 Gerald Riggs	.20
3 Walter Payton	1.00
4 Joe Morris	.30
5 Freeman McNeil	.20
6 Tony Dorsett	.50
7 James Wilder	.10
8 Steve Largent	1.00
9 Mike Quick	.10
10 Eric Dickerson	1.25
11 Craig James	.10
12 Art Monk	.20
13 Wes Chandler	.10
14 Drew Hill	.10
15 James Lofton	.20
16 Louis Lipps	.20
17 Cris Collinsworth	.10
18 Tony Hill	.10
19 Kevin Mack	.10
20 Curt Warner	.20
21 George Rogers	.10
22 Roger Craig	.40
23 Earnest Jackson	.10
24 Lionel James	.10
25 Stump Mitchell	.10
26 Earnest Byner	.10

1986 Topps Box Bottoms

These four cards were featured on the sides of 1986 Topps wax pack boxes, one per box. The cards, which are standard size, feature the top four teams in the NFL in 1985 - the two Super Bowl participants and their opponents in the conference championship games. The team is pictured on the front; the back identifies those in the picture.

	MT
Complete Set (4):	5.00
Common Player:	1.00
A Chicago Bears	2.50
B New England Patriots	1.00
C Los Angeles Rams	1.00
D Miami Dolphins	2.50

Values quoted in this guide reflect the retail price of a card — the price a collector can expect to pay when buying a card from a dealer. The wholesale price — that which a collector can expect to receive from a dealer when selling cards — will be significantly lower, depending on desirability and condition.

issued to hold the stickers; Walter Payton is on the front.

	MT
Complete Set (285):	20.00
Common Player:	.60
1 Walter Payton (left)	.60
2 Walter Payton (right)	.60
3 Richard Dent (left)	.10
4 Richard Dent (right)	.10
5 Richard Dent (Super Bowl MVP)	.40
6 Walter Payton	1.00
7 William Perry	.12
8 Jim McMahon (158)	.10
9 Richard Dent (159)	.10
10 Jim Covert (160)	.08
11 Dan Hampton (161)	.08
12 Mike Singletary (162)	
13 Jay Hilgenberg (163)	.06
14 Otis Wilson (164)	.04
15 Jimmie Giles	
16 Kevin House (166)	.03
17 Jeremiah Castille (167)	.03
18 James Wilder	.05
19 Donald Igwebuike (169)	.05
20 David Logan (170)	.05
21 Jeff Davis (171)	.05
22 Frank Garcia (172)	.05
23 Steve Young (173)	1.00
24 Stump Mitchell	.08
25 E.J. Junior	.05
26 J.T. Smith (176)	.05
27 Pat Tilley (177)	.05
28 Neil Lomax (178)	.06
29 Leonard Smith (179)	.05
30 Ottis Anderson (180)	.08
31 Curtis Greer (181)	.05
32 Roy Green (182)	.06
33 Tony Dorsett	.30
34 Tony Hill (184)	.05
35 Doug Cosbie (185)	.06
36 Everson Walls	.05
37 Randy White (187)	.10
38 Rafael Septien (188)	.05
39 Mike Renfro (189)	.05
40 Danny White (190)	.06
41 Ed "Too Tall" Jones (191)	.10
42 Earnest Jackson	.08
43 Mike Quick	.08
44 Wes Hopkins (194)	.05
45 Reggie White (195)	.75
46 Greg Brown (196)	.05
47 Paul McFadden (197)	.05
48 John Spagnola (198)	.05
49 Ran Jaworski (199)	.05
50 Herman Hunter (200)	.05
51 Gerald Riggs	.10
52 Mike Pitts (202)	.05
53 Buddy Curry (203)	.05
54 Billy Johnson	.12
55 Rick Donnelly (205)	.05
56 Rick Bryan (206)	.05
57 Bobby Butler (207)	.05
58 Mike Luckhurst (208)	.05
59 Mike Kenn (209)	.05
60 Roger Craig	.25
61 Joe Montana	1.75
62 Michael Carter (212)	.05
63 Eric Wright (213)	.05
64 Dwight Clark (214)	.05
65 Ronnie Lott (215)	.12
66 Carlton Williamson (216)	.05
67 Wendell Tyler (217)	.08
68 Dwaine Board (218)	.05
69 Joe Morris	.12
70 Leonard Marshall (220)	.05
71 Lionel Manuel (221)	.05
72 Harry Carson	.10
73 Phil Simms (223)	.10
74 Sean Landeta (224)	.05
75 Lawrence Taylor (225)	.15
76 Elvis Patterson (226)	.05
77 George Adams (227)	.05
78 James Jones	.08
79 Leonard Thompson	.05
80 William Graham (230)	.05
81 Mark Nichols (231)	.05
82 William Gay (232)	.05
83 Jimmy Williams (233)	.05
84 Billy Sims (234)	.12
85 Bobby Watkins (235)	.05
86 Ed Murray (236)	.05
87 James Lofton	.25
88 Jessie Clark (238)	.05
89 Tim Lewis (239)	.05
90 Eddie Lee Ivery	.08
91 Phillip Epps (241)	.05

1986 Topps Stickers

Topps included foil stickers in its sticker set again in 1986, and followed the format it used for previous issues. The stickers use a shadow box for the frame on the front, around a color photo. A card number appears on both sides. The back has its information printed in brown ink against a white background. Some stickers were issued in pairs, as indicated by the parenthesis after the player's name in the checklist. The All-Pro players are foil stickers (#s 132-143), as are #s 282-285. The Chicago Bears are featured on the covers of the corresponding album which was

No.	Player	Price
92	Ezra Johnson (242)	.05
93	Mike Douglass (243)	.05
94	Paul Coffman (244)	.05
95	Randy Scott (245)	.03
96	Eric Dickerson	.45
97	Dale Hatcher	.05
98	Ron Brown (248)	.06
99	LeRoy Irvin (249)	.05
100	Ken Hill (250)	.05
101	Dennis Harrah (251)	.05
102	Jackie Slater (252)	.08
103	Mike Wilcher (253)	.05
104	Doug Smith (254)	.05
105	Art Monk	.25
106	Joe Jacoby (256)	.05
107	Russ Grimm (257)	.05
108	George Rogers	.05
109	Dexter Manley (259)	.05
110	Jay Schroeder (260)	.12
111	Gary Calrk (261)	.50
112	Curtis Jordan (262)	.05
113	Charles Mann (263)	.05
114	Morten Andersen	.08
115	Rickey Jackson	.05
116	Glen Redd (266)	.05
117	Bobby Hebert (267)	.20
118	Hoby Brenner (268)	.05
119	Brian Hansen (269)	.05
120	Dave Waymer (270)	.05
121	Bruce Clark (271)	.05
122	Wayne Wilson (272)	.05
123	Joey Browner	.25
124	Darrin Nelson (274)	.08
125	Keith Millard (275)	.15
126	Anthony Carter	.35
127	Buster Rhymes (277)	.04
128	Steve Jordan (278)	.20
129	Greg Coleman (279)	.05
130	Ted Brown (280)	.05
131	John Turner (281)	.05
132	Harry Carson (144, All-Pro)	.20
133	Deron Cherry (145, All-Pro)	.10
134	Richard Dent (146, All-Pro)	.20
135	Mike Haynes (147, All-Pro)	.12
136	Wes Hopkins (148, All-Pro)	.10
137	Joe Klecko (149, All-Pro)	.10
138	Leonard Marshall (150, All-Pro)	.10
139	Karl Mecklenburg (151, All-Pro)	.05
140	Rohn Stark (152, All-Pro)	.10
141	Lawrence Taylor (153, All-Pro)	.25
142	Andre Tippett (154, All-Pro)	.12
143	Everson Walls (155, All-Pro)	.12
144	Marcus Allen (132, All-Pro)	.35
145	Gary Anderson (133, All-Pro)	.10
146	Doug Cosbie (134, All-Pro)	.15
147	Jim Covert (135, All-Pro)	.15
148	John Hannah (136, All-Pro)	.15
149	Jay Hilgenberg (137, All-Pro)	.12
150	Ken Hil (138, All-Pro)	.10
151	Brian Holloway (139, All-Pro)	.10
152	Steve Largent (140, All-Pro)	.75
153	Dan Marino (141, All-Pro)	1.50
154	Art Monk (142, All-Pro)	.25
155	Walter Payton (143, All-Pro)	.75
156	Anthony Munoz	.15
157	Boomer Esiason	.40
158	Cris Collinsworth (8)	.06
159	Eddie Edwards (9)	.05
160	James Griffin (10)	.05
161	Jim Breech (11)	.05
162	Eddie Brown (12)	.05
163	Ross Browner (13)	.05
164	James Brooks (14)	.07
165	Greg Bell	.08
166	Jerry Butler (16)	.05
167	Don Wilson (17)	.05
168	Andre Reed	.75
169	Jim Haslett (19)	.05
170	Bruce Mathison (20)	.05
171	Bruce Smith (21)	.40
172	Joe Cribbs (22)	.05
173	Charles Romes (23)	.05
174	Karl Mecklenburg	.08
175	Rulon Jones	.05
176	John Elway (26)	.40
177	Sammy Winder (27)	.10
178	Louis Wright (28)	.05
179	Steve Watson (29)	.05
180	Dennis Smith (30)	.05
181	Mike Harden (31)	.05
182	Vance Johnson (32)	.10
183	Kevin Mack	.10
184	Chip Banks (34)	.05
185	Bob Golic (35)	.05
186	Earnest Byner	.35
187	Ozzie Newsome (37)	.12
188	Bernie Kosar (38)	.60
189	Don Rogers (39)	.05
190	Al Gross (40)	.05
191	Clarence Weathers (41)	.08
192	Lionel James	.08
193	Dan Fouts	.40
194	Wes Chandler (44)	.06
195	Kellen Winslow (45)	.10
196	Gary Anderson (46)	.07
197	Charlie Joiner (47)	.08
198	Ralf Mojsiejenko (48)	.05
199	Bob Thomas (49)	.05
200	Tim Spencer (50)	.05
201	Deron Cherry	.10
202	Bill Maas (52)	.05
203	Herman Heard (53)	.05
204	Carlos Carson	.08
205	Nick Lowery (55)	.08
206	Bill Kenney (56)	.05
207	Albert Lewis (57)	.25
208	Art Still (58)	.05
209	Stephone Paige (59)	.25
210	Rohn Stark	.05
211	Chris Hinton	.10
212	Albert Bentley (62)	.05
213	Eugene Daniel (63)	.05
214	Pat Beach (64)	.05
215	Cliff Odom (65)	.05
216	Duane Bickett (66)	.20
217	George Wonsley (67)	
218	Randy McMillan (68)	.05
219	Dan Marino	1.50
220	Dwight Stephenson (70)	.08
221	Roy Foster (71)	.05
222	Mark Clayton	.20
223	Mark Duper (73)	.10
224	Fuad Reveiz (74)	.05
225	Reggie Roby (75)	.05
226	Tony Nathan (76)	.05
227	Ron Davenport (77)	.05
228	Freeman McNeil	.10
229	Joe Klecko	.08
230	Mark Gastineau (80)	.05
231	Ken O'Brien (81)	.06
232	Lance Mehl (82)	.05
233	Al Toon (83)	.20
234	Mickey Shuler (84)	.05
235	Pat Leahy (85)	.05
236	Wesley Walker (86)	.06
237	Drew Hill	.10
238	Warren Moon (88)	.40
239	Mike Rozier (89)	.10
240	Mike Munchak	.05
241	Tim Smith (91)	.05
242	Butch Woolfolk (92)	.05
243	Willie Drewrey (93)	.05
244	Keith Bostic (94)	.05
245	Jesse Baker (95)	.05
246	Craig James	.15
247	John Hannah	.12
248	Tony Eason (98)	.06
249	Andre Tippett (99)	.06
250	Tony Collins (100)	.05
251	Brian Holloway (101)	.05
252	Irving Fryar (102)	.10
253	Raymond Clayborn (103)	.05
254	Steve Nelson (104)	.05
255	Marcus Allen	.25
256	Mike Haynes (106)	.08
257	Todd Christensen (107)	.06
258	Howie Long	.12
259	Lester Hayes (109)	.05
260	Rod Martin (110)	.08
261	Dokie Williams (111)	.08
262	Chris Bahr (112)	.05
263	Bill Pickel (113)	.05
264	Curt Warner	.10
265	Steve Largent	.60
266	Fredd Young (116)	.06
267	Dave Krieg (117)	.08
268	Daryl Turner (118)	.05
269	John Harris (119)	.05
270	Randy Edwards (120)	.05
271	Kenny Easley (121)	.05
272	Jacob Green (122)	.05
273	Gary Anderson	.05
274	Mike Webster (124)	.07
275	Walter Abercrombie (125)	.08
276	Louis Lipps	.10
277	Frank Pollard (127)	.05
278	Mike Merriweather (128)	.05
279	Mark Malone (129)	.05
280	Donnie Shell (130)	.08
281	John Stallworth (131)	
282	Marcus Allen (284)	.50
283	Ken O'Brien (285)	.15
284	Kevin Butler (282)	.15
285	Roger Craig (283)	.35

1987 Topps

Topps' fifth straight 396-card set was bordered in white and carried two flags at the top of the card - one indicating the team, the other indicating the player name. His position was listed in the border above the name. Cards were numbered in order of the team's finish the previous year. This set, which seems to be one of the hottest sets since the '84 issue, includes such rookies as Randall Cunningham, Jim Everett, Reuben Mayes, John Offerdahl, Ernest Givins and Tim Harris. This set also features the last regular-issue card of all-time rushing leader Walter Payton. Three errors have been found in the set: On the back of card #274, Rueben Mayes, the statistical heading reads "Comp" for completions, when it should read "yards." The statistical heading was apparently intended for a quarterback instead of a running back. Also, the back of card #288, John Stallworth, is missing statistics from the years 1982-86. Finally, the reverse of Ross Browner's card (#263) contains a reference to the Bengals' 1982 Super Bowl win. The Bengals, however, lost to the 49ers that year. Not only that, the card also lists the Super Bowl date as 1-10-82 when it was actually played 1-24-82. (Key: AP - All Pro)

No.	Player	MT
	Complete Set (396):	45.00
	Common Player:	.05
	Wax Box:	60.00
1	Super Bowl XXI	.15
2	Todd Christensen	.05
3	Dave Jennings	.05
4	Charlie Joiner	.10
5	Steve Largent	.25
6	Dan Marino	2.00
7	Donnie Shell	.05
8	Phil Simms	.15
9	Giants team (Mark Bavaro)	.07
10	Phil Simms	.35
11	Joe Morris (AP)	.12
12	Maurice Carthon	.15
13	Lee Rouson	.05
14	Bobby Johnson	.05
15	Lionel Manuel	.05
16	Phil McConkey	.05
17	Mark Bavaro (AP)	.60
18	Zeke Mowatt	.05
19	Raul Allegre	.05
20	Sean Landeta	.05
21	Brad Benson	.05
22	Jim Burt	.05
23	Leonard Marshall	.40
24	Carl Banks	.50
25	Harry Carson	.12
26	Lawrence Taylor (AP)	.50
27	Terry Kinard	.20
28	Pepper Johnson	1.00
29	Erik Howard	.15
30	Broncos team (Gerald Wilhite)	.07
31	John Elway	4.00
32	Gerald Wilhite	.05
33	Sammy Winder	.05
34	Ken Bell	.05
35	Steve Watson	.05
36	Rick Karlis	.05
37	Keith Bishop	.05
38	Rulon Jones	.05
39	Karl Mecklenburg (AP)	.75
40	Louis Wright	.05
41	Mike Harden	.05
42	Dennis Smith	.40
43	Bears team (Walter Payton)	.50
44	Jim McMahon	.25
45	Doug Flutie	12.00
46	Walter Payton	1.25
47	Matt Suhey	.05
48	Willie Gault	.15
49	Dennis Gentry	.25
50	Kevin Butler	.25
51	Jim Covert (AP)	.05
52	Jay Hilgenberg	.25
53	Dan Hampton	.20
54	Steve McMichael	.15
55	William Perry	.35
56	Richard Dent	.50
57	Otis Wilson	.05
58	Mike Singletary	.50
59	Wilber Marshall	.50
60	Mike Richardson	.05
61	Dave Duerson	.15
62	Gary Fencik	.05
63	Redskins team (George Rogers)	.07
64	Jay Schroeder	.35
65	George Rogers	.05
66	Kelvin Bryant	.25
67	Ken Jenkins	.05
68	Gary Clark	.50
69	Art Monk	.50
70	Clint Didier	.15
71	Steve Cox	.05
72	Joe Jacoby	.05
73	Russ Grimm	.05
74	Charles Mann	.30
75	Dave Butz	.05
76	Dexter Manley (AP)	.05
77	Darrell Green (AP)	.30
78	Curtis Jordan	.05
79	Browns team	.07
80	Bernie Kosar	.50
81	Curtis Dickey	.05
82	Kevin Mack	.20
83	Herman Fontenot	.05
84	Brian Brennan	.20
85	Ozzie Newsome	.25
86	Jeff Gossett	.05
87	Cody Risien (AP)	.05
88	Reggie Camp	.05
89	Bob Golic	.05
90	Carl Hairston	.05
91	Chip Banks	.05
92	Frank Minnifield	.05
93	Hanford Dixon (AP)	.05
94	Gerald McNeil	.20
95	Dave Puzzuoli	.05
96	Patriots team (Andre Tippett)	.07
97	Tony Eason	.05
98	Craig James	.05
99	Tony Collins	.05
100	Mosi Tatupu	.05
101	Stanley Morgan	.15
102	Irving Fryar	.65
103	Stephen Starring	.05
104	Tony Franklin (AP)	.05
105	Rich Camarillo	.05
106	Garin Veris	.05
107	Andre Tippett (AP)	.12
108	Don Blackmon	.05
109	Ronnie Lippett	.30
110	Raymond Clayborn	.05
111	49ers team (Roger Craig)	.12
112	Joe Montana	4.00
113	Roger Craig	.30
114	Joe Cribbs	.05
115	Jerry Rice (AP)	10.00
116	Dwight Clark	.15
117	Ray Wersching	.05
118	Max Runager	.05
119	Jeff Stover	.05
120	Dwaine Board	.05
121	Tim McKyer	.30
122	Don Griffin	.40
123	Ronnie Lott (AP)	.30
124	Tom Holmoe	.05
125	Charles Haley	3.00
126	Jets team (Mark Gastineau)	.05
127	Ken O'Brien	.20
128	Pat Ryan	.05
129	Freeman McNeil	.15
130	Johnny Hector	.30
131	Al Toon (AP)	.50
132	Wesley Walker	.12
133	Mickey Shuler	.05
134	Pat Leahy	.05
135	Mark Gastineau	.05
136	Joe Klecko	.05
137	Marty Lyons	.05
138	Bob Crable	.05
139	Lance Mehl	.05
140	Dave Jennings	.05
141	Harry Hamilton	.15
142	Lester Lyles	.05
143	Bobby Humphery	.05
144	Rams team (Eric Dickerson)	.15
145	Jim Everett	3.00
146	Eric Dickerson (AP)	.50
147	Barry Redden	.05
148	Ron Brown	.15
149	Kevin House	.05
150	Henry Ellard	.60
151	Doug Smith	.05
152	Dennis Harrah (AP)	.05
153	Jackie Slater	.05
154	Gary Jeter	.05
155	Carl Ekern	.05
156	Mike Wilcher	.05
157	Jerry Gray	.25
158	LeRoy Irvin	.05
159	Nolan Cromwell	.05
160	Chiefs team (Todd Blackledge)	.07
161	Bill Kenney	.05
162	Stephone Paige	.25
163	Henry Marshall	.05
164	Carlos Carson	.05
165	Nick Lowery	.15
166	Irv Eatman	.10
167	Brad Budde	.05
168	Art Still	.05
169	Bill Maas (AP)	.05
170	Lloyd Burruss	.20
171	Deron Cherry (AP)	.15
172	Seahawks team (Curt Warner)	.07
173	Dave Krieg	.20
174	Curt Warner	.20
175	John L. Williams	1.00
176	Bobby Joe Edmonds	.20
177	Steve Largent	.60
178	Bruce Scholtz	.05
179	Norm Johnson	.05
180	Jacob Green	.05
181	Fredd Young	.05
182	Dave Brown	.05
183	Kenny Easley	.05
184	Bengals team (James Brooks)	.07
185	Boomer Esiason	.75
186	James Brooks	.12
187	Larry Kinnebrew	.05
188	Cris Collinsworth	.05
189	Eddie Brown	.35
190	Tim McGee	1.00
191	Jim Breech	.05
192	Anthony Munoz	.20
193	Max Montoya	.05
194	Eddie Edwards	.05
195	Ross Browner	.05
196	Emanuel King	.05
197	Louis Breeden	.05
198	Vikings team (Darrin Nelson)	.07
199	Tommy Kramer	.20
200	Darrin Nelson	.05
201	Allen Rice	.05
202	Anthony Carter	.30
203	Leo Lewis	.05
204	Steve Jordan	.40
205	Chuck Nelson	.05
206	Greg Coleman	.05
207	Gary Zimmerman	.30
208	Doug Martin	.05
209	Keith Millard	.05
210	Issiac Holt	.15
211	Joey Browner	.20
212	Rufus Bess	.05
213	Raiders team (Marcus Allen)	.15
214	Jim Plunkett	.15
215	Marcus Allen	.90
216	Napoleon McCallum	.12
217	Dokie Williams	.05
218	Todd Christensen	.05
219	Chris Bahr	.05
220	Howie Long	.25
221	Bill Pickel	.05
222	Sean Jones	1.50
223	Lester Hayes	.05
224	Mike Haynes	.05
225	Vann McElroy	.05
226	Fulton Walker	.05
227	Passing Leaders (Tommy Kramer, Dan Marino)	.50
228	Receiving Leaders (Jerry Rice, Todd Christensen)	.50
229	Rushing leaders (Eric Dickerson, Curt Warner)	.25
230	Scoring leaders (Kevin Butler, Tony Franklin)	.07
231	Interception leaders (Ronnie Lott, Deron Cherry)	.07
232	Dolphins team (Reggie Roby)	.07
233	Dan Marino	8.00
234	Lorenzo Hampton	.12
235	Tony Nathan	.05
236	Mark Duper	.12
237	Mark Clayton	.50
238	Nat Moore	.05
239	Bruce Hardy	.05
240	Reggie Roby	.05
241	Roy Foster	.05
242	Dwight Stephenson (AP)	.05
243	Hugh Green	.05
244	John Offerdahl	.50
245	Mark Brown	.05
246	Doug Betters	.05
247	Bob Baumhower	.05
248	Falcons team (Gerald Riggs)	.05
249	Dave Archer	.15
250	Gerald Riggs	.10
251	William Andrews	.05
252	Charlie Brown	.05
253	Arthur Cox	.05
254	Rick Donnelly	.05
255	Bill Fralic (AP)	.30
256	Mike Gann	.10
257	Rick Bryan	.05
258	Bret Clark	.05
259	Mike Pitts	.05
260	Cowboys team (Tony Dorsett)	.15
261	Danny White	.15
262	Steve Pelluer	.10
263	Tony Dorsett	.40
264	Herschel Walker	2.50
265	Timmy Newsome	.05
266	Tony Hill	.05
267	Mike Sherrard	.20
268	Jim Jeffcoat	.05
269	Ron Fellows	.05
270	Bill Bates	.20
271	Michael Downs	.05
272	Saints team (Bobby Hebert)	.12
273	Dave Wilson	.05
274	Rueben Mayes	.30
275	Hoby Brenner	.05
276	Eric Martin	.75
277	Morten Andersen	.35
278	Brian Hansen	.05
279	Rickey Jackson	.50
280	Dave Waymer	.05
281	Bruce Clark	.05
282	James Geathers	.20
283	Steelers team (Walter Abercrombie)	.07
284	Mark Malone	.05
285	Earnest Jackson	.05
286	Walter Abercrombie	.05
287	Louis Lipps	.15
288	John Stallworth	.15
289	Gary Anderson	.05
290	Keith Willis	.05
291	Mike Merriweather	.05
292	Lupe Sanchez	.05
293	Donnie Shell	.05
294	Eagles team (Keith Byars)	.30
295	Mike Reichenbach	.05
296	Randall Cunningham	18.00
297	Keith Byars	1.00
298	Mike Quick	.05
299	Kenny Jackson	.05
300	John Teltschik	.05
301	Reggie White (AP)	3.00
302	Ken Clarke	.05
303	Greg Brown	.05
304	Roynell Young	.05
305	Andre Waters	.50
306	Oilers team (Warren Moon)	.35
307	Warren Moon	2.25
308	Mike Rozier	.10
309	Drew Hill	.25
310	Ernest Givins	1.00
311	Lee Johnson	.10
312	Kent Hill	.05
313	Dean Steinkuhler	.30
314	Ray Childress	.60
315	John Grimsley	.25
316	Jesse Baker	.05
317	Lions team (Eric Hipple)	.07
318	Chuck Long	.12
319	James Jones	.05
320	Garry James	.05
321	Jeff Chadwick	.05
322	Leonard Thompson	.05
323	Pete Mandley	.05
324	Jimmie Giles	.05
325	Herman Hunter	.05
326	Keith Ferguson	.05
327	Devon Mitchell	.05
328	Cardinals team (Neil Lomax)	.07
329	Neil Lomax	.05
330	Stump Mitchell	.05
331	Earl Ferrell	.05
332	Vai Sikahema	.60
333	Ron Wolfley	.15
334	J.T. Smith	.05
335	Roy Green	.05
336	Al Baker	.05
337	Freddie Joe Nunn	.05
338	Cedrick Mack	.05
339	Chargers team (Gary Anderson)	.07
340	Dan Fouts	.50
341	Gary Anderson	.25
342	Wes Chandler	.20
343	Kellen Winslow	.20
344	Ralf Mojsiejenko	.05
345	Rolf Benirschke	.05
346	Lee Williams	.75
347	Leslie O'Neal	2.00
348	Billy Ray Smith	.05
349	Gill Byrd	.30
350	Packers team (Paul Ott Caruth)	.07
351	Randy Wright	.05
352	Kenneth Davis	.75
353	Gerry Ellis	.05
354	James Lofton	.50
355	Phillip Epps	.05
356	Walter Stanley	.25
357	Eddie Lee Ivery	.05
358	Tim Harris	.50
359	Mark Lee	.05
360	Mossy Cade	.05
361	Bills team (Jim Kelly)	1.25

362	*Jim Kelly*	6.00
363	Robb Riddick	.05
364	Greg Bell	.10
365	Andre Reed	1.00
366	*Pete Metzelaars*	.35
367	Sean McNanie	.05
368	Fred Smerlas	.05
369	Bruce Smith	1.00
370	Darryl Talley	.25
371	Charles Romes	.05
372	Colts team	.07
	(Rohn Stark)	
373	Jack Trudeau	.25
374	Gary Hogeboom	.05
375	Randy McMillan	.05
376	Albert Bentley	.10
377	Matt Bouza	.05
378	*Bill Brooks*	2.00
379	Rohn Stark (AP)	.05
380	Chris Hinton	.05
381	Ray Donaldson	.05
382	*Jon Hand*	.25
383	Buccaneers team	.07
	(James Wilder)	
384	Steve Young	5.00
385	James Wilder	.05
386	Frank Garcia	.05
387	Gerald Carter	.05
388	Phil Freeman	.05
389	Calvin Magee	.05
390	Donald Igwebuike	.05
391	David Logan	.05
392	Jeff Davis	.05
393	Chris Washington	.05
394	Checklist 1-132	.10
395	Checklist 133-264	.10
396	Checklist 265-396	.10

1987 Topps Box Bottoms

These cards can be distinguished from Topps' regular cards by the yellow borders around the photo on the front. Plus, the cards were on the bottom of 1987 Topps wax pack boxes, and would have to be cut out to measure the standard-size Topps cards. It's better to leave them intact. The cards also use a letter for numbering, instead of a number.

		MT
Complete Set (16):		10.00
Common Player:		.30
A	Mark Bavaro	.40
B	Todd Christensen	.50
C	Eric Dickerson	.65
D	John Elway	1.50
E	Rulon Jones	.30
F	Dan Marino	3.00
G	Karl Mecklenburg	.30
H	Joe Montana	3.00
I	Joe Morris	.50
J	Walter Payton	1.25
K	Jerry Rice	3.50
L	Phil Simms	.50
M	Lawrence Taylor	.60
N	Al Toon	.35
O	Curt Warner	.40
P	Reggie White	1.25

1987 Topps 1000 Yard Club

Printed on heavy white cardboard stock, 1,000 Yard Club cards were found inside wax packs of 1987 Topps football cards. Each card pictures a player who gained 1,000 or more yards rushing or receiving. Cards feature a parthenon design on the front in blue; backs are light blue and carry a game-by-game yardage summary for each player.

	MT
Complete Set (24):	4.50
Common Player:	.15

1	Eric Dickerson	.75
2	Jerry Rice	.75
3	Joe Morris	.30
4	Stanley Morgan	.15
5	Curt Warner	.20
6	Reuben Mayes	.15
7	Walter Payton	.90
8	Gerald Riggs	.20
9	Mark Duper	.15
10	Gary Clark	.15
11	George Rogers	.15
12	Al Toon	.25
13	Todd Christensen	.15
14	Mark Clayton	.15
15	Bill Brooks	.25
16	Drew Hill	.15
17	James Brooks	.15
18	Steve Largent	.60
19	Art Monk	.20
20	Ernest Givins	.20
21	Cris Collingsworth	.20
22	Wesley Walker	.15
23	J.T. Smith	.15
24	Mark Bavaro	.15

1987 Topps Stickers

Each of these stickers is 2-1/8" x 3" and features a new design element from previous years' issues - four footballs are included in the frame around the picture on the front, one for each corner. A sticker number appears on both sides. All-Pro foils were again produced, as were stickers in pairs; they are matched up as indicated by the number in parenthesis. The backs have red ink on a white background. The album cover this time features artwork devoted to the New York Giants.

		MT
Complete Set (285):		15.00
Common Player:		.05
1	Phil Simms (Super Bowl MVP)	.40
2	Super Bowl XXI (upper left)	.15
3	Super Bowl XXI (upper right)	.15
4	Super Bowl XXI (lower left)	.15
5	Super Bowl XXI (lower right)	.15
6	Mike Singletary	.12
7	Jim Covert (156)	.50
8	Willie Gault (157)	.06
9	Jim McMahon (158)	.08
10	Doug Flutie (159)	1.00
11	Richard Dent (160)	.08
12	Kevin Butler (161)	.05
13	Wilber Marshall (162)	.08
14	Walter Payton (163)	.60
15	Calvin Magee	.05
16	David Logan (165)	.05
17	Jeff Davis (166)	.05
18	Gerald Carter (167)	.05
19	James Wilder	.05
20	Chris Washington (168)	.05
21	Phil Freeman (169)	.05
22	Frank Garcia (170)	.05
23	Donald Igwebuike (171)	.05
24	Al (Bubba) Baker (175)	.08
25	Vai Sikhema (176)	.05
26	Leonard Smith (177)	.05
27	Ron Wolgley (178)	.05
28	J.T. Smith	.08
29	Roy Green (179)	.06
30	Cedric Mack (180)	.05
31	Neil Lomax (181)	.06
32	Stump Mitchell	.05
33	Herschel Walker	.50
34	Danny White (184)	.06
35	Michael Downs (185)	.05
36	Randy White (186)	.08
37	Eugene Lockhart (188)	.05

38	Mike Sherrard (189)	.20
39	Jim Jeffcoat (190)	.05
40	Tony Hill (191)	.06
41	Tony Dorsett	.35
42	Keith Byars (192)	.30
43	Andre Waters (193)	.06
44	Kenny Jackson (194)	.05
45	John Teltschik (195)	.05
46	Roynell Young (196)	.05
47	Randall Cunningham (197)	.60
48	Mike Reichenbach (198)	.05
49	Reggie White	.40
50	Mike Quick	.08
51	Bill Fralic (201)	.05
52	Sylvester Stamps (202)	.05
53	Bret Clark (203)	.05
54	William Andrews (204)	.05
55	Buddy Curry (205)	.05
56	Dave Archer (206)	.10
57	Rick Bryan (207)	.05
58	Gerald Riggs	.12
59	Charlie Brown	.05
60	Joe Montana	2.00
61	Jerry Rice	1.50
62	Carlton Williamson (212)	.05
63	Roger Craig (213)	.12
64	Ronnie Lott (214)	.15
65	Dwight Clark (215)	.15
66	Jeff Stover (216)	.05
67	Charles Haley (217)	.20
68	Ray Wersching (218)	.05
69	Lawrence Taylor	.30
70	Joe Morris	.12
71	Carl Banks (221)	.10
72	Mark Bavaro (222)	.06
73	Harry Carson (223)	.05
74	Phil Simms (224)	.10
75	Jim Burt (225)	.05
76	Brad Benson (226)	.05
77	Leonard Marshall (227)	.05
78	Jeff Chadwick	.05
79	Devon Mitchell (228)	.05
80	Chuck Long (229)	.06
81	Demetrious Johnson (230)	.05
82	Herman Hunter (231)	.05
83	Kieth Ferguson (232)	.05
84	Gary James (233)	.05
85	Leonard Thompson (234)	.05
86	James Jones	.08
87	Kenneth Davis	.35
88	Brian Noble (237)	.07
89	Al Del Greco (238)	.05
90	Mark Lee (239)	.05
91	Randy Wright	.05
92	Tim Harris (240)	.15
93	Phillip Epps (241)	.05
94	Walter Stanley (242)	.10
95	Eddie Lee Ivery (243)	.05
96	Doug Smith (247)	.05
97	Jerry Gray (248)	.05
98	Jim Everett (250)	.60
99	Jim Everett (250)	.60
100	Jackie Slater (251)	.06
101	Vince Newsome (252)	.10
102	LeRoy Irvin (253)	.10
103	Henry Ellard	.10
104	Eric Dickerson	.60
105	George Rogers (256)	.06
106	Darrell Green (257)	.07
107	Art Monk (258)	.10
108	Neal Olkewicz (260)	.05
109	Russ Grimm (261)	.05
110	Dexter Manley (262)	.05
111	Kelvin Bryant (263)	.08
112	Jay Schroeder	.15
113	Gary Clark	.15
114	Rickey Jackson	.08
115	Eric Martin (264)	.07
116	Dave Waymer (265)	.05
117	Morten Andersen (266)	.06
118	Bruce Clark (167)	.08
119	Hoby Brenner (269)	.07
120	Brian Hansen (270)	.05
121	Dave Wilson (271)	.05
122	Rueben Mayes	.08
123	Tommy Kramer	.08
124	Mark Malone (124)	.05
125	Anthony Carter (275)	.10
126	Keith Millard (276)	.08
127	Steve Jordan	.12
128	Chuck Nelson (277)	.06
129	Issiac Holt (278)	.05
130	Darrin Nelson (279)	.05
131	Gary Zimmerman (280)	.05
132	Mark Bavaro (146, All-Pro)	.10

133	Jim Covert (147, All-Pro)	.10
134	Eric Dickerson (148, All-Pro)	.35
135	Bill Fralic (149, All-Pro)	.10
136	Tony Franklin (150, All-Pro)	.10
137	Dennis Harrah (151, All-Pro)	.10
138	Dan Marino (152, All-Pro)	1.25
139	Joe Morris (153, All-Pro)	.25
140	Jerry Rice (154, All-Pro)	1.00
141	Cody Risien (155, All-Pro)	.10
142	Dwight Stephenson (282, All-Pro)	.12
143	Al Toon (283, All-Pro)	.20
144	Deron Cherry (284, All-Pro)	.12
145	Hanford Dixon (285, All-Pro)	.05
146	Darrell Green (132, All-Pro)	.15
147	Ronnie Lott (133, All-Pro)	.20
148	Bill Maas (134, All-Pro)	.10
149	Dexter Manley (135, All-Pro)	.10
150	Karl Mecklenburg (136, All-Pro)	.12
151	Mike Singletary (137, All-Pro)	.20
152	Rohn Stark (138, All-Pro)	.10
153	Lawrence Taylor (139, All-Pro)	.30
154	Andre Tippett (140, All-Pro)	.12
155	Reggie White (141, All-Pro)	.35
156	Boomer Esiason (7)	.15
157	Anthony Munoz (8)	.12
158	Tim McGee (9)	.20
159	Max Montoya (10)	.05
160	Jim Breech (11)	.05
161	Tim Krumrie (12)	.05
162	Eddie Brown (13)	.06
163	James Brooks	.10
164	Cris Collinsworth	.12
165	Charles Romes (16)	.05
166	Robb Riddick (17)	.05
167	Eugene Marve (18)	.05
168	Chris Burkett (20)	.10
169	Bruce Smith (21)	.12
170	Greg Bell (22)	.05
171	Pete Metzelaars (23)	.05
172	Jim Kelly	1.50
173	Andre Reed	.30
174	John Elway	.60
175	Mike Harden (24)	.05
176	Gerald Willhite (25)	.05
177	Rulon Jones (26)	.05
178	Ricky Hunley (27)	.05
179	Mark Jackson (29)	.05
180	Rich Karlis (30)	.05
181	Sammy Winder (31)	.08
182	Karl Mecklenburg	.08
183	Bernie Kosar	.35
184	Kevin Mack (34)	.05
185	Bob Golic (35)	.05
186	Ozzie Newsome (36)	.08
187	Brian Brennan	.05
188	Gerald McNeil (37)	.05
189	Hanford Dixon (38)	.05
190	Cody Risien (39)	.05
191	Chris Rockins (40)	.05
192	Gill Byrd (42)	.05
193	Kellen Winslow (43)	.08
194	Billy Ray Smith (44)	.05
195	Wes Chandler (45)	.05
196	Leslie O'Neal (46)	.25
197	Ralf Mojsiejenko (47)	.05
198	Lee Williams (48)	.20
199	Gary Anderson	.08
200	Dan Fouts	.25
201	Stephone Paige (51)	.08
202	Irv Eatman (52)	.05
203	Bill Kenney (53)	.05
204	Dino Hackett (54)	.05
205	Carlos Carson (55)	.05
206	Art Still (56)	.06
207	Lloyd Burruss (57)	.05
208	Deron Cherry	.08
209	Bill Maas	.08
210	Gary Hogeboom	.08
211	Rohn Stark	.05
212	Cliff Odom (62)	.05
213	Randy McMillan (63)	.05
214	Chris Hinton (64)	.05
215	Matt Bouza (65)	.05
216	Ray Donaldson (66)	.05
217	Bill Brooks (67)	.08
218	Jack Trudeau (68)	.06
219	Mark Duper	.15
220	Dan Marino	1.50
221	Dwight Stephenson (71)	.08
222	Mark Clayton (72)	.10
223	Roy Foster (73)	.05
224	John Offerdahl (74)	.20

225	Lorenzo Hampton (75)	.05
226	Reggie Roby (76)	.05
227	Tony Nathan (77)	.08
228	Johnny Hector (79)	.08
229	Wesley Walker (80)	.05
230	Mark Gastineau (81)	.10
231	Ken O'Brien (82)	.05
232	Dave Jennings (83)	.05
233	Mickey Shuler (84)	.05
234	Joe Klecko (85)	.05
235	Freeman McNeil	.10
236	Al Toon	.08
237	Warren Moon (88)	.35
238	Dean Steinkuhler (89)	.08
239	Mike Rozier (90)	.06
240	Ray Childress (92)	.08
241	Tony Zendejas (93)	.05
242	John Grimsley (94)	.05
243	Jesse Baker (95)	.05
244	Ernest Givins	.50
245	Drew Hill	.10
246	Tony Franklin	.05
247	Steve Grogan (96)	.06
248	Garin Veris (97)	.05
249	Stanley Morgan (98)	.05
250	Fred Morgan (98)	.06
251	Raymond Clayborn (100)	.07
252	Mosi Tatupu (101)	.05
253	Tony Eason (102)	.05
254	Andre Tippett (103)	.08
255	Todd Christensen (104)	.05
256	Howie Long (105)	.06
257	Marcus Allen (106)	.12
258	Vann McElroy (107)	.05
259	Dokie Williams	.05
260	Mike Haynes (108)	.08
261	Sean Jones	.10
262	Jim Plunkett (110)	.07
263	Chris Bahr (111)	.05
264	Dave Krieg (115)	.08
265	Jacob Green (116)	.05
266	Norm Johnson (117)	.05
267	Fredd Young (118)	.05
268	Steve Largent	.50
269	Dave Brown (119)	.05
270	Kenny Easley (120)	.05
271	Bobby Joe Edmonds (121)	.05
272	Curt Warner	.15
273	Mike Merriweather	.08
274	Mark Malone (124)	.05
275	Bryan Hinkle (125)	.05
276	Earnest Jackson (126)	.05
277	Keith Willis (128)	.05
278	Walter Abercrombie (129)	.06
279	Donnie Shell (130)	.08
280	John Stallworth (131)	.06
281	Louis Lipps	.10
282	Eric Dickerson (142)	.30
283	Dan Marino (143)	1.00
284	Tony Franklin (144)	.08
285	Todd Christensen	.12

1987 Topps American/ United Kingdom

These cards are smaller in size than their regular set counterparts, measuring 2-1/8" x 3". The cards, which were made available in the United Kingdom, also have different photos. However, the basic design remains similar to Topps' 1986 regular issue. The back has a football term explained inside a football (Talking Football), plus a card number. A special collector's box was also produced to house the set. The box had a set checklist on its side. Cards 76-87 form a team action puzzle on one side and William Perry on the other.

	MT
Complete Set (88):	40.00
Common Player:	.10
1	Phil Simms	.65
2	Joe Morris	.35
3	Mark Bavaro	.25
4	Sean Landeta	.10
5	Lawrence Taylor	2.00
6	John Elway	4.00
7	Sammy Winder	.10
8	Rulon Jones	.10
9	Karl Mecklenburg	.15
10	Walter Payton	4.00
11	Dennis Gentry	.10
12	Kevin Butler	.10
13	Jim Covert	.10
14	Richard Dent	.35
15	Mike Singletary	.50
16	Jay Schroeder	.50
17	George Rogers	.25
18	Gary Clark	.50
19	Art Monk	.50
20	Dexter Manley	.35
21	Darrell Green	.35
22	Bernie Kosar	1.00
23	Cody Risien	.10
24	Hanford Dixon	.25
25	Tony Eason	.25
26	Stanley Morgan	.25
27	Tony Franklin	.10
28	Andre Tippett	.25
29	Joe Montana	8.00
30	Jerry Rice	8.00
31	Ronnie Lott	.75
32	Ken O'Brien	.25
33	Freeman McNeil	.15
34	Al Toon	.25
35	Wesley Walker	.25
36	Eric Dickerson	1.50
37	Dennis Harrah	.10
38	Bill Maas	.25
39	Deron Cherry	.25
40	Curt Warner	.20
41	Bobby Joe Edmonds	.25
42	Steve Largent	2.00
43	Boomer Esiason	2.00
44	James Brooks	.25
45	Cris Collinsworth	.25
46	Tim McGee	.35
47	Tommy Kramer	.25
48	Marcus Allen	1.00
49	Todd Christensen	.35
50	Sean Jones	.35
51	Dan Marino	8.00
52	Mark Duper	.25
53	Mark Clayton	.30
54	Dwight Stephenson	.25
55	Gerald Riggs	.25
56	Bill Fralic	.25
57	Tony Dorsett	1.50
58	Herschel Walker	1.50
59	Rueben Mayes	.25
60	Lupe Sanchez	.10
61	Reggie White	2.50
62	Warren Moon	3.00
63	Ernest Givins	1.50
64	Drew Hill	.25
65	Jeff Chadwick	.25
66	Herman Hunter	.10
67	Vai Sikhema	.25
68	J.T. Smith	.25
69	Dan Fouts	1.00
70	Lee Williams	.50
71	Randy Wright	.25
72	Jim Kelly	7.00
73	Bruce Smith	.75
74	Bill Brooks	.35
75	Rohn Stark	.10
76	Team Action	.10
77	Team Action	.10
78	Team Action	.10
79	Team Action	.10
80	Team Action	.10
81	Team Action	.10
82	Team Action	.10
83	Team Action	.10
84	Team Action	.10
85	Team Action	.10
86	Team Action	.10
87	Team Action	.10
88	Checklist Card	.10

1988 Topps

This set, issued in August 1988, was issued by teams in order of finish. These standard-size cards again showed the team helmets on front and All-Pro and Super Rookie designations (this was Topps' first year using Super Rookie labels). This set is noteworthy for the inclusion of Bo Jackson's rookie football card. (Key: AP - All Pro, SP - Super Rookie)

		MT
Complete Set (396):		12.00
Common Player:		.05
Wax Box:		10.00
1	Super Bowl XXII	.10
2	Vencie Glenn	.05
3	Steve Largent	.15
4	Joe Montana	.80
5	Walter Payton	.30
6	Jerry Rice	.70
7	Redskins team (Kelvin Bryant)	.05
8	Doug Williams	.05
9	George Rogers	.05
10	Kelvin Bryant	.05
11	Timmy Smith, Kent Hill (SR)	.05
12	Art Monk, Ray Childress	.25
13	Gary Clark	.50
14	Ricky Sanders	.50
15	Steve Cox	.05
16	Joe Jacoby	.05
17	Charles Mann	.15
18	Dave Butz	.05
19	Darrell Green (AP)	.05
20	Dexter Manley	.05
21	Barry Wilburn	.05
22	Broncos team (Sammy Winder)	.05
23	John Elway (AP)	.75
24	Sammy Winder	.05
25	Vance Johnson	.20
26	Mark Jackson	.70
27	Ricky Nattiel (SR)	.12
28	Clarence Kay	.05
29	Rich Karlis	.05
30	Keith Bishop	.05
31	Mike Horan	.05
32	Rulon Jones	.05
33	Karl Mecklenburg	.12
34	Jim Ryan	.05
35	Mark Haynes	.05
36	Mike Harden	.05
37	49ers team (Roger Craig)	.05
38	Joe Montana	1.50
39	Steve Young	1.00
40	Roger Craig	.20
41	Tom Rathman	.50
42	Joe Cribbs	.05
43	Jerry Rice (AP)	2.00
44	Mike Wilson	.05
45	Ron Heller	.15
46	Ray Wersching	.05
47	Michael Carter	.05
48	Dwaine Board	.05
49	Michael Walter	.05
50	Don Griffin	.05
51	Ronnie Lott	.30
52	Charlie Haley	.30
53	Dana McLemore	.05
54	Saints Team (Bobby Hebert)	.05
55	Bobby Hebert	.30
56	Rueben Mayes	.05
57	Dalton Hilliard	.25
58	Eric Martin	.30
59	John Tice	.10
60	Brad Edelman	.05
61	Morten Andersen (AP)	.15
62	Brian Hansen	.05
63	Mel Gray	.60
64	Rickey Jackson	.30
65	Sam Mills	.50
66	Pat Swilling	.50
67	Dave Waymer	.05
68	Bears Team (Willie Gault)	.05
69	Jim McMahon	.15
70	Mike Tomczak	.25
71	Neal Anderson	.75
72	Willie Gault	.10
73	Dennis Gentry	.05
74	Dennis McKinnon	.05
75	Kevin Butler	.05
76	Jim Covert	.05
77	Jay Hilgenberg	.05
78	Steve McMichael	.05
79	William Perry	.05
80	Richard Dent	.20
81	Ron Rivera	.05
82	Mike Singletary (AP)	.20
83	Dan Hampton	.10
84	Dave Duerson	.05
85	Browns team (Bernie Kosar)	.05
86	Bernie Kosar	.05
87	Earnest Byner	.40
88	Kevin Mack	.10
89	Webster Slaughter	.75
90	Gerald McNeil	.05
91	Brian Brennan	.05
92	Ozzie Newsome	.20
93	Cody Risien	.05
94	Bob Golic	.05
95	Carl Hairston	.05
96	Mike Johnson	.20

97	Clay Matthews	.05
98	Frank Minnifield	.05
99	Hanford Dixon (AP)	.05
100	Dave Puzzuoli	.05
101	Felix Wright	.12
102	Oilers team (Warren Moon)	.20
103	Warren Moon	.75
104	Mike Rozier	.05
105	Alonzo Highsmith (SR)	.15
106	Drew Hill	.20
107	Ernest Givins	.40
108	Curtis Duncan	.50
109	Tony Zendejas	.12
110	Mike Munchak (AP)	.12
113	Al Smith	.35
114	Keith Bostic	.05
115	Jeff Donaldson	.05
116	Colts team (Eric Dickerson)	.15
117	Jack Trudeau	.05
118	Eric Dickerson (AP)	.30
119	Albert Bentley	.05
120	Matt Bouza	.05
121	Bill Brooks	.35
122	Dean Biasucci	.12
123	Chris Hinton	.05
124	Ray Donaldson	.05
125	Ron Solt	.10
126	Donnell Thompson	.05
127	Barry Krauss	.05
128	Duane Bickett	.10
129	Mike Prior	.15
130	Seahawks team (Curt Warner)	.05
131	Dave Krieg	.15
132	Curt Warner	.05
133	John L. Williams	.25
134	Bobby Joe Edmonds	.05
135	Steve Largent	.30
136	Raymond Butler	.05
137	Norm Johnson	.05
138	Ruben Rodriguez	.05
139	Blair Bush	.05
140	Jacob Green	.05
141	Joe Nash	.05
142	Jeff Bryant	.05
143	Fredd Young (AP)	.05
144	Brian Bosworth (SR)	.15
145	Kenny Easley (AP)	.05
146	Vikings team (Tommy Kramer)	.05
147	Wade Wilson	.50
148	Tommy Kramer	.05
149	Darrin Nelson	.05
150	D.J. Dozier (SR)	.12
151	Anthony Carter	.25
152	Leo Lewis	.05
153	Steve Jordan	.20
154	Gary Zimmerman	.05
155	Chuck Nelson	.05
156	Henry Thomas (SR)	.50
157	Chris Doleman	.60
158	Scott Studwell	.12
159	Jesse Solomon	.10
160	Joey Browner (AP)	.15
161	Neal Guggemos	.05
162	Steelers team (Louis Lipps)	.05
163	Mark Malone	.05
164	Walter Abercrombie	.05
165	Earnest Jackson	.05
166	Frank Pollard	.05
167	Dwight Stone	.30
168	Gary Anderson	.05
169	Harry Newsome	.10
170	Keith Willis	.05
171	Keith Gray	.05
172	David Little	.12
173	Mike Merriweather	.05
174	Dwayne Woodruff	.05
175	Patriots team (Irving Fryar)	.05
176	Steve Grogan	.10
177	Tony Eason	.05
178	Tony Collins	.05
179	Mosi Tatupu	.05
180	Stanley Morgan	.05
181	Irving Fryar	.30
182	Stephen Starring	.05
183	Tony Franklin	.05
184	Rich Camarillo	.05
185	Garin Veris	.05
186	Andre Tippett (AP)	.05
187	Ronnie Lippett	.05
188	Fred Marion	.05
189	Dolphins team (Dan Marino)	.50
190	Dan Marino	1.50
191	Troy Stradford (SR)	.10
192	Lorenzo Hampton	.05
193	Mark Duper	.10
194	Mark Clayton	.25
195	Reggie Roby	.05
196	Dwight Stephenson (AP)	.05
197	T.J. Turner	.05
198	John Bosa (SR)	.05
199	Jackie Shipp	.05
200	John Offerdahl	.05
201	Mark Brown	.05
202	Paul Lankford	.05
203	Chargers team (Kellen Winslow)	.05
204	Tim Spencer	.05

205	Gary Anderson	.10
206	Curtis Adams	.05
207	Lionel James	.05
208	Chip Banks	.05
209	Kellen Winslow	.15
210	Ralf Mojsiejenko	.05
211	Jim Lachey	.15
212	Lee Williams	.15
213	Billy Ray Smith	.05
214	Vencie Glenn	.25
215	NFL Passing Leaders (Bernie Kosar, Joe Montana)	.50
216	NFL Receiving Leaders (Al Toon, J.T. Smith)	.05
217	NFL Rushing Leaders (Charles White, Eric Dickerson)	.15
218	NFL Scoring Leaders (Jim Breech, Jerry Rice)	.30
219	NFL Interception Leaders (Keith Bostic, Mark Kelso, Mike Prior, Barry Wilburn)	.05
220	Bills team (Jim Kelly)	.30
221	Jim Kelly	1.00
222	Ronnie Harmon	.50
223	Robb Riddick	.05
224	Andre Reed	.50
225	Chris Burkett	.50
226	Pete Metzelaars	.05
227	Bruce Smith (AP)	.50
228	Darryl Talley	.12
229	Eugene Marve	.05
230	Cornelius Bennett	1.00
231	Mark Kelso	.20
232	Shane Conlan (SR)	.50
233	Eagles team (Randall Cunningham)	.25
234	Randall Cunningham	.50
235	Keith Byars	.50
236	Anthony Toney	.05
237	Mike Quick	.05
238	Kenny Jackson	.05
239	John Spagnola	.05
240	Paul McFadden	.05
241	Reggie White (AP)	.60
242	Ken Clarke	.05
243	Mike Pitts	.05
244	Clyde Simmons	.50
245	Seth Joyner	.85
246	Andre Waters	.12
247	Jerome Brown (SR)	.30
248	Cardinals team (Stump Mitchell)	.05
249	Neil Lomax	.05
250	Stump Mitchell	.05
251	Earl Ferrell	.05
252	Vai Sikahema	.05
253	J.T. Smith (AP)	.05
254	Roy Green	.10
255	Robert Awalt (AP)	.05
256	Freddie Joe Nunn	.05
257	Leonard Smith	.10
258	Travis Curtis	.05
259	Cowboys team (Herschel Walker)	.15
260	Danny White	.10
261	Herschel Walker	.25
262	Tony Dorsett	.20
263	Doug Cosbie	.05
264	Roger Ruzek	.12
265	Darryl Clack	.05
266	Ed "Too Tall" Jones	.15
267	Jim Jeffcoat	.05
268	Everson Walls	.05
269	Bill Bates	.05
270	Michael Downs	.05
271	Giants team (Mark Bavaro)	.05
272	Phil Simms	.30
273	Joe Morris	.05
274	Lee Rouson	.05
275	George Adams	.05
276	Lionel Manuel	.05
277	Mark Bavaro (AP)	.05
278	Raul Allegre	.05
279	Sean Landeta	.05
280	Erik Howard	.05
281	Leonard Marshall	.05
282	Carl Banks (AP)	.15
283	Pepper Johnson	.15
284	Harry Carson	.10
285	Lawrence Taylor	.50
286	Terry Kinard	.05
287	Rams team (Jim Everett)	.15
288	Jim Everett	.40
289	Charles White (AP)	.05
290	Ron Brown	.05
291	Henry Ellard	.05
292	Mike Lansford	.05
293	Dale Hatcher	.05
294	Doug Smith	.05
295	Jackie Slater (AP)	.05
296	Jim Collins	.05
297	Jerry Gray	.05
298	LeRoy Irvin	.05
299	Nolan Cromwell	.05
300	Kevin Greene	1.00

301	Jets team (Ken O'Brien)	.05
302	Ken O'Brien	.15
303	Freeman McNeil	.05
304	Johnny Hector	.05
305	Al Toon	.20
306	JoJo Townsell	.05
307	Mickey Shuler	.05
308	Pat Leahy	.05
309	Roger Vick	.05
310	Alex Gordon	.05
311	Troy Benson	.05
312	Bob Crable	.05
313	Harry Hamilton	.05
314	Packers team (Phil Epps)	.05
315	Randy Wright	.05
316	Kenneth Davis	.05
317	Phillip Epps	.05
318	Walter Stanley	.05
319	Frankie Neal	.05
320	Don Bracken	.05
321	Brian Noble	.15
322	Johnny Holland (SR)	.15
323	Tim Harris	.35
324	Mark Murphy	.05
325	Raiders team (Bo Jackson)	.50
326	Marc Wilson	.05
327	Bo Jackson (SR)	2.00
328	Marcus Allen	.20
329	James Lofton	.20
330	Todd Christensen	.05
331	Chris Bahr	.05
332	Stan Talley	.05
333	Howie Long	.10
334	Sean Jones	.05
335	Matt Millen	.05
336	Stacey Toran	.05
337	Vann McElroy	.05
338	Greg Townsend	.15
339	Bengals team (Boomer Esiason)	.15
340	Boomer Esiason	.50
341	Larry Kinnebrew	.05
342	Stanford Jennings	.05
343	Eddie Brown	.05
344	Jim Breech	.05
345	Anthony Munoz (AP)	.12
346	Scott Fulhage	.05
347	Tim Krumrie	.20
348	Reggie Williams	.05
349	David Fulcher	.30
350	Buccaneers team (James Wilder)	.05
351	Frank Garcia	.05
352	Vinny Testaverde (SR)	4.00
353	James Wilder	.05
354	Jeff Smith	.05
355	Gerald Carter	.05
356	Calvin Magee	.05
357	Donald Igwebuike	.05
358	Ron Holmes	.05
359	Chris Washington	.05
360	Ervin Randle	.05
361	Chiefs team (Bill Kenney)	.05
362	Bill Kenney	.05
363	Christian Okoye (SR)	.25
364	Paul Palmer	.05
365	Stephone Paige	.12
366	Carlos Carson	.05
367	Kelly Goodburn	.05
368	Bill Maas (AP)	.05
369	Mike Bell	.05
370	Dino Hackett	.15
371	Deron Cherry	.05
372	Lions team (James Jones)	.05
373	Chuck Long	.05
374	Garry James	.05
375	James Jones	.05
376	Pete Mandley	.05
377	Gary Lee (SR)	.05
378	Ed Murray	.05
379	Jim Arnold	.05
380	Dennis Gibson (SR)	.05
381	Mike Cofer	.05
382	James Griffin	.05
383	Falcons team (Gerald Riggs)	.05
384	Scott Campbell	.05
385	Gerald Riggs	.05
386	Floyd Dixon	.05
387	Rick Donnelly (AP)	.05
388	Bill Fralic (AP)	.05
389	Pepper Johnson	.15
390	Mike Gann	.05
391	Tony Casillas	.25
392	Rick Bryan	.05
393	John Rade	.05
394	Checklist 1-132	.05
395	Checklist 133-264	.05
396	Checklist 265-396	.05

Two players are featured on each card. The cards are numbered on the back using a letter and include a summary of the player's collegiate accomplishment. The cards are standard size.

		MT
Complete Set (16):		5.00
Common Player:		.20
A	Vinny Testaverde	.50
B	Dean Steinkuhler	.20
C	George Rogers	.20
D	Kenneth Sims	.20
E	Cornelius Bennett	.50
F	Bo Jackson	1.00
G	Ross Browner	.35
H	Doug Flutie	1.00
I	Herschel Walker	.50
J	Jim Plunkett	.50
K	Charles White	.25
L	Brad Budde	.20
M	Marcus Allen	.50
N	Mike Rozier	.25
O	Tony Dorsett	.75
P	Checklist	.20

1988 Topps 1000 Yard Club

One card from this 28-card set was again issued in a wax pack of Topps football cards. The standard-size glossy cards on thick white cardboard stock feature "1000" in bold green border around a full-color action photo. Backs feature a game-by-game recap of the runner or receiver's yardage.

		MT
Complete Set (28):		4.50
Common Player:		.10
1	Charles White	.10
2	Eric Dickerson	.75
3	J.T. Smith	.10
4	Jerry Rice	.75
5	Gary Clark	.25
6	Carlos Carson	.10
7	Drew Hill	.10
8	Curt Warner	.10
9	Al Toon	.10
10	Mike Rozier	.10
11	Ernest Givins	.10
12	Anthony Carter	.10
13	Reuben Mayes	.10
14	Steve Largent	.75
15	Herschel Walker	.75
16	James Lofton	.10
17	Gerald Riggs	.10
18	Mark Bavaro	.10
19	Roger Craig	.50
20	Webster Slaughter	.10
21	Henry Ellard	.10
22	Mike Quick	.10
23	Stump Mitchell	.10
24	Eric Martin	.10
25	Mark Clayton	.10
26	Chris Burkett	.10
27	Marcus Allen	.30
28	Andre Reed	.10

1988 Topps Stickers

These stickers can be distinguished from Topps' previous efforts by the two frames

1988 Topps Box Bottoms

The bottoms of 1988 Topps wax pack boxes had these cards, which honor award-winning achievements by professional players while they were in college.

used on the front to border the color photograph. An inner frame of yellow footballs is adjacent to an outer red frame of the picture. Each sticker measures 2-1/8" x 3" and is numbered on both sides. All-Pro stickers were produced as foil stickers again, and pairs of stickers were also made, as indicated by parentheses. Stickers 2-5 form a puzzle of Doug Williams featured in action during Super Bowl XXII. Williams is also featured on the back of the album cover which was produced to hold the stickers; the Redskins in action are featured on the front.

		MT
Complete Set (285):		15.00
Common Player:		.05
1	Doug Williams (Super Bowl XXII MVP)	.20
2	Super Bowl XXII	.08
3	Super Bowl XXII	.08
4	Super Bowl XXII	.08
5	Super Bowl XXII	.08
6	Neal Anderson (234)	.25
7	Willie Gault (224)	.05
8	Dennis Gentry (219)	.05
9	Dave Duerson (197)	.05
10	Steve McMichael (266)	.05
11	Dennis McKinnon (230)	.05
12	Mike Singletary (209)	.08
13	Jim McMahon (209)	.12
14	Richard Dent	.10
15	Vinny Testaverde (167)	.20
16	Gerald Carter (187)	.05
17	Jeff Smith (185)	.05
18	Chris Washington (212)	.05
19	Bobby Futrell (231)	.05
20	Calvin Magee (182)	.05
21	Ron Holmes (169)	.05
22	Ervin Randle	.05
23	James Wilder	.08
24	Neil Lomax	.08
25	Robert Awalt (161)	.05
26	Leonard Smith (177)	.05
27	Stump Mitchell (178)	.05
28	Vai Sikahema (280)	.06
29	Freddie Joe Nunn (222)	.05
30	Earl Ferrell (223)	.05
31	Roy Green (157)	.10
32	J.T. Smith	.10
33	Michael Downs	.05
34	Herschel Walker	.30
35	Roger Ruzek (269)	.05
36	Ed "Too Tall" Jones (245)	.07
37	Everson Walls (252)	.05
38	Bill Bates (213)	.05
39	Doug Cosbie (179)	.05
40	Eugene Lockhart (186)	.05
41	Danny White (205)	.07
42	Randall Cunningham	.40
43	Reggie White	.30
44	Anthony Toney (256)	.05
45	Mike Quick (248)	.08
46	John Spagnola (235)	.05
47	Clyde Simmons (275)	.20
48	Andre Waters (261)	.05
49	Keith Byars (265)	.08
50	Jerome Brown (240)	.15
51	John Rade	.05
52	Rick Donnelly	.05
53	Scott Campbell (160)	.05
54	Floyd Dixon (246)	.05
55	Gerald Riggs (236)	.06
56	Bill Fralic (267)	.08
57	Mike Gann (165)	.05
58	Tony Casillas (168)	.15
59	Rick Bryan (257)	.05
60	Jerry Rice	1.00
61	Ronnie Lott	.25
62	Ray Wersching (220)	.05
63	Charles Haley (281)	.06
64	Joe Montana (190)	.75
65	Joe Cribbs (221)	.05
66	Mike Wilson (203)	.05
67	Roger Craig (251)	.12
68	Michael Walter (162)	.05
69	Mark Bavaro	.08
70	Carl Banks	.05
71	George Adams (274)	.03
72	Phil Simms (216)	.15
73	Lawrence Taylor (181)	.12

74 Joe Morris (198) .06
75 Lionel Manuel (204) .05
76 Sean Landeta (210) .05
77 Harry Carson (159) .05
78 Chuck Long (166) .05
79 James Jones (159) .05
80 Gary James (158) .05
81 Gary Lee (176) .05
82 Jim Arnold (260) .05
83 Dennis Gibson (232) .05
84 Mike Cofer (242) .05
85 Pete Mandley .05
86 James Griffin .05
87 Randy Wright (206) .05
88 Phillip Epps (191) .05
89 Brian Noble (249) .05
90 Johnny Holland (258) .10
91 Dave Brown (156) .05
92 Brent Fullwood (207) .05
93 Kenneth Davis (194) .08
94 Tim Harris .15
95 Walter Stanley .15
96 Charles White .15
97 Jackie Slater .08
98 Jim Everett (271) .12
99 Mike Lansford (200) .05
100 Henry Ellard (199) .06
101 Dale Hatcher (170) .05
102 Jim Collins (268) .05
103 Jerry Gray (214) .05
104 LeRoy Irvin (276) .05
105 Darrell Green .12
106 Doug Williams .10
107 Gary Clark (247) .10
108 Charles Mann (171) .10
109 Art Monk (270) .12
110 Barry Wilburn (196) .05
111 Alvin Walton (188) .05
112 Dexter Manley (233) .05
113 Kelvin Bryant (180) .04
114 Morten Andersen .05
115 Rueben Mayes (244) .06
116 Brian Hansen (279) .05
117 Dalton Hilliard (241) .10
118 Rickey Jackson (195) .06
119 Eric Martin (189) .06
120 Mel Gray (278) .05
121 Bobby Hebert (215) .08
122 Pat Swilling .40
123 Anthony Carter .12
124 Wade Wilson (225) .20
125 Darrin Nelson (250) .05
126 D.J. Dozier (239) .06
127 Chris Doleman .30
128 Henry Thomas (255) .05
129 Jesse Solomon (211) .05
130 Neal Guggemos (243) .05
131 Joey Browner (208) .06
132 Carl Banks (152, All-Pro) .10
133 Joey Browner (145, All-Pro) .10
134 Hanford Dixon (149, All-Pro) .10
135 Rick Donnelly (147, All-Pro) .10
136 Kenny Easley (155, All-Pro) .15
137 Darrell Green (151, All-Pro) .15
138 Bill Maas (148, All-Pro) .10
139 Mike Singletary (153, All-Pro) .15
140 Bruce Smith (154, All-Pro) .20
141 Andre Tippett (146, All-Pro) .10
142 Reggie White (150, All-Pro) .20
143 Fredd Young (144, All-Pro) .10
144 Morten Andersen (143, All-Pro) .10
145 Mark Bavaro (133, All-Pro) .10
146 Eric Dickerson (141, All-Pro) .30
147 John Elway (134, All-Pro) .75
148 Bill Fralic (138, All-Pro) .10
149 Mike Munchak (135, All-Pro) .10
150 Anthony Munoz (142, All-Pro) .15
151 Jerry Rice (137, All-Pro) 1.00
152 Jackie Slater (132, All-Pro) .05
153 J.T. Smith (139, All-Pro) .10
154 Dwight Stephenson (140, All-Pro) .12
155 Charles White (136, All-Pro) .12

156 Larry Kinnebrew (91)
157 Stanford Jennings (31) .05
158 Eddie Brown (80) .05
159 Scott Fulhage (77) .05
160 Boomer Esiason (53) .12
161 Tim Krumrie (25) .05
162 Anthony Munoz (68) .08
163 Jim Breech .05
164 Reggie Williams .08
165 Andre Reed (57) .20
166 Cornelius Bennett (78) .30
167 Ronnie Harmon (15) .05
168 Shane Conlan (58) .15
169 Chris Burkett (21) .06
170 Mark Kelso (101) .08
171 Robb Riddick (108) .05
172 Bruce Smith .15
173 Jim Kelly .60
174 Jim Ryan .05
175 John Elway .60
176 Sammy Winder (81) .05
177 Karl Mecklenburg (26) .05
178 Mark Haynes (27) .05
179 Rulon Jones (39) .05
180 Ricky Nattiel (113) .05
181 Vance Johnson (73) .05
182 Mike Harden (20) .05
183 Frank Minnifield .05
184 Bernie Kosar .25
185 Earnest Byner (17) .12
186 Webster Slaughter (40) .15
187 Brian Brennan (16) .05
188 Carl Hairston (111) .05
189 Mike Johnson (119) .05
190 Clay Matthews (64) .06
191 Kevin Mack (88) .05
192 Kellen Winslow .12
193 Billy Ray Smith .05
194 Gary Anderson (93) .05
195 Dana Bible (118) .05
196 Elvis Patterson (110) .05
197 Lee Williams (9) .07
198 Curtis Adams (74) .05
199 Vencie Glenn (100) .05
200 Ralf Mojsiejenko (99) .05
201 Carlos Carson .05
202 Bill Maas .05
203 Christian Okoye (66) .15
204 Deron Cherry (75) .08
205 Dino Hackett (41) .05
206 Mike Bell (87) .05
207 Stephone Paige (92) .06
208 Bill Kenney (131) .05
209 Paul Palmer (12) .05
210 Jack Trudeau (76) .05
211 Albert Bentley (129) .06
212 Bill Brooks (18) .06
213 Dean Biasucci (38) .05
214 Cliff Odom (103) .05
215 Barry Krauss (121) .05
216 Mike Prior (72) .06
217 Eric Dickerson .35
218 Duane Bickett .08
219 Dwight Stephenson (8)
220 John Offerdahl (62) .10
221 Troy Stradford (65) .06
222 Jim Bosa (29) .04
223 Jackie Shipp (30) .05
224 Paul Lankford (7) .05
225 Mark Duper (124) .08
226 Dan Marino 1.50
227 Mark Clayton .15
228 Bob Crable .05
229 Al Toon .08
230 Freeman McNeil (11)
231 Johnny Hector (19) .05
232 Pat Leahy (83) .05
233 Ken O'Brien (112) .05
234 Alex Gordon (6) .05
235 Harry Hamilton (46) .05
236 Mickey Shuler (55) .05
237 Mike Rozier .08
238 Al Smith .05
239 Ernest Givins (126) .15
240 Warren Moon (50) .05
241 Drew Hill (117) .10
242 Alonzo Highsmith (84) .15
243 Mike Munchak (130) .06
244 Keith Bostic (115) .05
245 Sean Jones (36) .08
246 Stanley Morgan (54) .06
247 Garin Veris (107) .05
248 Stephen Starring (45) .05
249 Steve Grogan (89) .06
250 Irving Fryar (125) .10
251 Rich Camarillo (67) .05
252 Ronnie Lippett (37) .05
253 Fred Marion .05
254 Fred Marion .05
255 Howie Long (128) .12
256 James Lofton (44) .12
257 Vance Mueller (59) .05
258 Jerry Robinson (90) .05
259 Todd Christensen (79) .06

260 Vann McElroy (82) .05
261 Greg Townsend (48) .10
262 Bo Jackson .85
263 Marcus Allen .30
264 Curt Warner .08
265 Jacob Green (49) .06
266 Norm Johnson (10) .05
267 Brian Bosworth (56) .05
268 Bobby Joe Edmonds (102) .05
269 Dave Krieg (35) .07
270 Kenny Easley (109) .06
271 Steve Largent (98) .30
272 Fredd Young .05
273 David Little .05
274 Frank Pollard (71) .05
275 Dwight Stone (47) .08
276 Mike Merriweather (104) .06
277 Earnest Jackson .05
278 Delton Hall (120) .05
279 Gary Anderson (116) .05
280 Harry Newsome (28) .08
281 Dwayne Woodruff (63) .05
282 J.T. Smith (283) .05
283 Charles White (282) .05
284 Reggie White (285) .15
285 Morten Andersen (284) .10

1988 Topps Sticker Backs

These cards were left after collectors would remove the 1988 Topps stickers from their card. Each card measures 2-1/8" x 3" and features a prominent offensive player. The sticker has "Superstar" written at the top, above the color player photo. His name and card number appear at the bottom in a stat box, using 1 of 67, etc.

		MT
Complete Set (67):		5.00
Common Player:		.10

1 Doug Williams .10
2 Gary Clark .15
3 John Elway .50
4 Sammy Winder .05
5 Vance Johnson .07
6 Joe Montana 1.50
7 Roger Craig .15
8 Jerry Rice 1.00
9 Rueben Mayes .05
10 Eric Martin .10
11 Neal Anderson .30
12 Willie Gault .10
13 Bernie Kosar .25
14 Kevin Mack .05
15 Webster Slaughter .15
16 Warren Moon .40
17 Mike Rozier .10
18 Drew Hill .10
19 Eric Dickerson .30
20 Bill Brooks .05
21 Curt Warner .15
22 Steve Largent .40
23 Darrin Nelson .05
24 Anthony Carter .15
25 Earnest Jackson .05
26 Weegie Thompson .05
27 Stephen Starring .05
28 Stanley Morgan .10
29 Dan Marino 1.50
30 Troy Stadford .10
31 Mark Clayton .15
32 Curtis Adams .05
33 Kellen Winslow .15
34 Jim Kelly .60
35 Ronnie Harmon .25
36 Chris Burkett .35
37 Randall Cunningham .35
38 Anthony Toney .05
39 Mike Quick .10
40 Neil Lomax .05
41 Stump Mitchell .10
42 J.T. Smith .05
43 Herschel Walker .25
44 Herschel Walker .25
45 Joe Morris .12
46 Mark Bavaro .10
47 Charles White .15
48 Henry Ellard .10
49 Ken O'Brien .10
50 Freeman McNeil .05
51 Al Toon .12
52 Kenneth Davis .05
53 Walter Stanley .05
54 Marcus Allen .30
55 James Lofton .15
56 Boomer Esiason .20
57 Larry Kinnebrew .05
58 Eddie Brown .10
59 James Wilder .07
60 Gerald Carter .05
61 Christian Okoye .20
62 Carlos Carson .05
63 James Jones .05

64 Pete Mandley .05
65 Gerald Riggs .10
66 Floyd Dixon .05
67 Checklist Card .10

1989 Topps

DON MAJKOWSKI — GREEN BAY PACKERS • QB

Topps released its seventh straight 396-card set in late August 1989. Cards are standard size, with white borders and a multicolored stripe about three-quarters from the bottom. Player names and teams are at the bottom of the card in an opaque circle. Card backs feature a dark green on yellow design. There are a few errors in the set: Card #24, Eddie Brown, lists his birthday as 12/18 and it's actually 12/17; card #27, Boomer Esiason, has him a native of East Islip, when it should be West Islip; the front of card #56, Mark Kelso, reads "BILL" instead of "BILLS"; on Jay Hilgenberg's card, a "g" is missing from "Chicago" on the card front. The back of Mark Rypien's card (#253) lists 14 as his 1988 completion total, while it should read 114. Card #125, Robert Delpino, correctly shows his team designation as "Rams" on the front, but lists "Los Angeles Raiders" on the back; card #247, Karl Mecklenberg, lists him as being drafted in the second round when it should be the 12th. Rodney Holman's card also features a problem with the card front: there are six different variations of "BENGALS". One has a small space between the "B" and "E"; the second has the "B" a little above the rest of the line of type; the third has it just a little below; the fourth shows just the "B" with no other letters behind it; another shows the "B" partially superimposed over the "E"; another shows "CINCINNATI B" without the rest of "Bengals"; and the last one is the correct version. Rookies in this set include Sterling Sharpe, Don Majkowski, Ickey Woods, John Stephens, John Taylor, Erik McMillan, Keith Jackson and Tom Newberry. (Key: AP - All Pro, SR - Super Rookie)

		MT
Complete Set (396):		15.00
Common Player:		.05
Wax Box:		10.00

1 Super Bowl XXIII .50
2 Tim Brown .70
3 Eric Dickerson .12
4 Steve Largent .12
5 Dan Marino .60
6 49ers Team (Joe Montana) .30
7 Jerry Rice (AP) 1.25
8 Roger Craig (AP) .05
9 Ronnie Lott .15
10 Michael Carter .05
11 Charles Haley .05
12 Joe Montana 1.50
13 *John Taylor* 1.00
14 Michael Walter .05
15 *Mike Cofer* .10
16 Tom Rathman .12
17 *Danny Stubbs* .12
18 Tim McKyer .05

26 Tim Krumrie (AP) .05
27 Ickey Woods (SR) .15
28 Anthony Munoz .05
29 Tim McGee .05
30 Max Montoya .05
31 David Grant .05
32 *Rodney Holman* .25
33 David Fulcher .05
34 Jim Skow .05
35 James Brooks .05
36 Reggie Williams .05
37 Eric Thomas .10
38 Stanford Jennings .05
39 Jim Breech .05
40 Bills Team (Jim Kelly) .15
41 Shane Conlan (AP) .15
42 Scott Norwood (AP) .05
43 Cornelius Bennett .30
44 Bruce Smith (AP) .15
45 *Thurman Thomas* (SR) 2.00
46 Jim Kelly .50
47 John Kidd .05
48 Kent Hull .15
49 Art Still .05
50 Fred Smerlas .05
51 Derrick Burroughs .05
52 Andre Reed .30
53 Robb Riddick .05
54 Chris Burkett .05
55 Ronnie Harmon .20
56 Mark Kelso .05
57 Bears Team (Thomas Sanders) .05
58 Mike Singletary (AP) .10
59 Jay Hilgenberg (AP) .05
60 Richard Dent .05
61 Ron Rivera .05
62 Jim McMahon .05
63 Mike Tomczak .12
64 Neal Anderson .30
65 Dennis Gentry .05
66 Dan Hampton .05
67 David Tate .05
68 *Thomas Sanders* .10
69 Steve McMichael .05
70 Dennis McKinnon .05
71 *Brad Muster* .20
72 *Vestee Jackson* .10
73 Dave Duerson .05
74 Vikings Team (Keith Millard) .05
75 Joey Browner (AP) .05
76 Carl Lee (AP) .10
77 Gary Zimmerman (AP) .05
78 *Hassan Jones* .10
79 Anthony Carter .05
80 Ray Berry .05
81 Steve Jordan .05
82 Issiac Holt .05
83 Wade Wilson .05
84 Chris Doleman .20
85 Alfred Anderson .05
86 Keith Millard .05
87 Darrin Nelson .05
88 D.J. Dozier .05
89 Scott Studwell .05
90 Oilers Team (Tony Zendejas) .05
91 *Bruce Matthews* (AP) .30
92 Curtis Duncan .20
93 Warren Moon .40
94 *Johnny Meads* .10
95 Drew Hill .05
96 Alonzo Highsmith .05
97 Mike Munchak .05
98 Mike Rozier .05
99 Tony Zendejas .05
100 Jeff Donaldson .05
101 Ray Childress .05
102 Sean Jones .05
103 Ernest Givins .20
104 William Fuller .40
105 Allen Pinkett .15
106 Eagles Team (Randall Cunningham) .05
107 *Keith Jackson* (AP) .50
108 Reggie White (AP) .25
109 Clyde Simmons .25
110 John Teltschik .05
111 Wes Hopkins .05
112 Keith Byars .05
113 Jerome Brown .05
114 Mike Quick .05
115 Randall Cunningham .40
116 Anthony Toney .05
117 Ron Johnson .05
118 Terry Hoage .05
119 Seth Joyner .25
120 Eric Allen .40
121 *Cris Carter* 2.00
122 Rams Team (Greg Bell) .05
123 *Tom Newberry* (AP) .05
124 Pete Holohan .05
125 *Robert Delpino* .35
126 Carl Ekern .05
127 Greg Bell .05
128 Mike Lansford .05
129 Jim Everett .15
130 Mike Wilcher .05
131 Jerry Gray .05
132 Dale Hatcher .05

133 Doug Smith .05
134 Kevin Greene .15
135 Jackie Slater .05
136 *Aaron Cox* .12
137 Henry Ellard .05
138 Browns Team (Bernie Kosar) .05
139 Frank Minnifield (AP) .05
140 Webster Slaughter .25
141 Bernie Kosar .20
142 Charles Buchanan .05
143 Clay Matthews .05
144 *Reggie Langhorne* .30
145 Hanford Dixon .05
146 Brian Brennan .05
147 Earnest Byner .05
148 *Michael Dean Perry* 1.00
149 Kevin Mack .05
150 Matt Bahr .05
151 Ozzie Newsome .05
152 Saints Team (Craig Heyward) .05
153 Morten Andersen .05
154 Pat Swilling .25
155 Sam Mills .05
156 Lonzell Hill .05
157 Dalton Hilliard .05
158 *Craig Heyward* .50
159 *Vaughan Johnson* .30
160 Rueben Mayes .05
161 Gene Atkins .05
162 Bobby Hebert .20
163 Rickey Jackson .05
164 Eric Martin .05
165 Giants Team (Joe Morris) .05
166 Lawrence Taylor (AP) .15
167 Bart Oates .05
168 Carl Banks .05
169 Eric Moore .05
170 *Sheldon White* .12
171 *Mark Collins* .05
172 Phil Simms .15
173 Jim Burt .05
174 *Stephen Baker* .25
175 Mark Bavaro .05
176 Pepper Johnson .05
177 Lionel Manuel .05
178 Joe Morris .05
179 *John Elliott* .15
180 Gary Reasons .05
181 Seahawks Team (Dave Krieg) .05
182 *Brian Blades* (SR) .75
183 Steve Largent .25
184 Rufus Porter .15
185 Ruben Rodriguez .05
186 Curt Warner .05
187 Paul Moyer .05
188 Dave Krieg .05
189 Jacob Green .05
190 John L. Williams .05
191 *Eugene Robinson* .15
192 Brian Bosworth .05
193 Patriots Team (Tony Eason) .05
194 *John Stephens* (SR) .20
195 *Robert Perryman* .05
196 Andre Tippett .05
197 Fred Marion .05
198 Doug Flutie .75
199 Stanley Morgan .05
200 *Johnny Rembert* .10
201 Tony Eason .05
202 Marvin Allen .05
203 Raymond Clayborn .05
205 Colts Team (Chris Chandler) .05
206 Eric Dickerson (AP) .20
207 Chris Hinton (AP) .05
208 Duane Bickett .05
209 *Chris Chandler* 2.00
210 Jon Hand .05
211 Ray Donaldson .05
212 Dean Biasucci .05
213 Bill Brooks .05
214 *Chris Goode* .10
215 Clarence Verdin .20
216 Albert Bentley .05
217 Passing Leaders (Wade Wilson, Boomer Esiason) .05
218 Receiving Leaders (Henry Ellard, Al Toon) .05
219 Rushing Leaders (Herschel Walker, Eric Dickerson) .15
220 Scoring Leaders (Mike Cofer, Scott Norwood) .05
221 Interception Leaders (Scott Case, Erik McMillan) .05
222 Jets Team (Ken O'Brien) .10
223 *Erik McMillan* (SR) .10
224 *James Hasty* (SR) .12
225 Al Toon .05
226 *John Booty* .05
227 Johnny Hector .05
228 Ken O'Brien .05
229 Marty Lyons .05
230 Mickey Shuler .05

231	Robin Cole	.05
232	Freeman McNeil	.05
233	Marion Barber	.05
234	JoJo Townsell	.05
235	Wesley Walker	.05
236	Roger Vick	.05
237	Pat Leahy	.05
238	Broncos Team	.10
	(John Elway)	
239	Mike Horan (AP)	.05
240	Tony Dorsett	.25
241	John Elway	.50
242	Mark Jackson	.05
243	Sammy Winder	.05
244	Rich Karlis	.05
245	Vance Johnson	.05
246	Steve Sewell	.10
247	Karl Mecklenburg	.05
248	Rulon Jones	.05
249	Simon Fletcher	.30
250	Redskins Team	.05
	(Doug Williams)	
251	Chip Lohmiller (SR)	.30
252	Jamie Morris (SR)	.05
253	Mark Rypien (SR)	.40
254	Barry Wilburn	.05
255	Mark May	.10
256	Wilbur Marshall	.05
257	Charles Mann	.05
258	Gary Clark	.15
259	Doug Williams	.05
260	Art Monk	.15
261	Kelvin Bryant	.05
262	Dexter Manley	.05
263	Ricky Sanders	.05
264	Raiders Team	.05
	(Marcus Allen)	
265	Tim Brown (AP)	1.50
266	Jay Schroeder	.05
267	Marcus Allen	.12
268	Mike Haynes	.05
269	Bo Jackson	.75
270	Steve Beuerlein	1.00
271	Vann McElroy	.05
272	Willie Gault	.05
273	Howie Long	.05
274	Greg Townsend	.05
275	Mike Wise	.05
276	Cardinals Team	.05
	(Neil Lomax)	
277	Luis Sharpe	.05
278	Scott Dill	.05
279	Vai Sikahema	.05
280	Ron Wolfley	.05
281	David Galloway	.05
282	Jay Novacek	.75
283	Neil Lomax	.05
284	Robert Awalt	.05
285	Cedric Mack	.05
286	Freddie Joe Nunn	.05
287	J.T. Smith	.05
288	Stump Mitchell	.05
289	Roy Green	.05
290	Dolphins Team	.25
	(Dan Marino)	
291	Jarvis Williams	.10
	(SR)	
292	Troy Stradford	.05
293	Dan Marino	2.00
294	T.J. Turner	.05
295	John Offerdahl	.05
296	Ferrell Edmunds	.15
297	Scott Schwedes	.05
298	Lorenzo Hampton	.05
299	Jim Jensen	.05
300	Brian Sochia	.05
301	Reggie Roby	.05
302	Mark Clayton	.05
303	Chargers Team	.05
	(Tim Spencer)	
304	Lee Williams	.05
305	Gary Plummer	.15
306	Gary Anderson	.05
307	Gill Byrd	.05
308	Jamie Holland	.05
309	Billy Ray Smith	.05
310	Lionel James	.05
311	Mark Vlasic	.20
312	Curtis Adams	.05
313	Anthony Miller	1.00
314	Steelers Team	.05
	(Frank Pollard)	
315	Bubby Brister	.50
316	David Little	.05
317	Tunch Ilkin	.05
318	Louis Lipps	.05
319	Warren Williams	.10
320	Dwight Stone	.05
321	Merril Hoge	.20
322	Thomas Everett	.25
323	Rod Woodson	.75
324	Gary Anderson	.05
325	Buccaneer Team	.05
	(Ron Hall)	
326	Donnie Elder	.05
327	Vinny Testaverde	.15
328	Harry Hamilton	.05
329	James Wilder	.05
330	Lars Tate	.05
331	Mark Carrier	.65
332	Bruce Hill	.05
333	Paul Gruber	.12
334	Ricky Reynolds	.05
335	Eugene Marve	.05
336	Falcons Team	.05
	(J. Williams)	
337	Aundray Bruce	.10
	(SR)	
338	John Rade	.05
339	Scott Case	.05

340	Robert Moore	.05
341	Chris Miller	.60
342	Gerald Riggs	.05
343	Gene Lang	.05
344	Marcus Cotton	.05
345	Rick Donnelly	.05
346	John Settle	.10
347	Bill Fralic	.05
348	Chiefs Team	.05
	(Dino Hackett)	
349	Steve DeBerg	.05
350	Mike Stensrud	.05
351	Dino Hackett	.05
352	Deron Cherry	.05
353	Christian Okoye	.12
354	Bill Maas	.05
355	Carlos Carson	.05
356	Albert Lewis	.05
357	Paul Palmer	.05
358	Nick Lowery	.05
359	Stephone Paige	.05
360	Lions Team	.05
	(Chuck Long)	
361	Chris Spielman	.30
	(SR)	
362	Jim Arnold	.05
363	Devon Mitchell	.05
364	Mike Cofer	.05
365	Bennie Blades	.15
366	James Jones	.05
367	Garry James	.05
368	Pete Mandley	.05
369	Keith Ferguson	.05
370	Dennis Gibson	.05
371	Packers Team	.05
	(Johnny Holland)	
372	Brent Fullwood	.05
373	Don Majkowski	.20
374	Timothy Harris	.05
375	Keith Woodside	.10
376	Mark Murphy	.05
377	Dave Brown	.05
378	Perry Kemp	.10
379	Sterling Sharpe	1.50
380	Chuck Cecil	.25
381	Walter Stanley	.05
382	Cowboys Team	.05
	(Steve Pelluer)	
383	Michael Irvin (SR)	1.50
384	Bill Bates	.05
385	Herschel Walker	.15
386	Darryl Clack	.05
387	Danny Noonan	.05
388	Eugene Lockhart	.05
389	Ed "Too Tall" Jones	.05
390	Steve Pelluer	.05
391	Ray Alexander	.05
392	Nate Newton	.20
393	Garry Cobb	.05
394	Checklist 1-132	.05
395	Checklist 133-264	.05
396	Checklist 265-396	.05

1989 Topps Box Bottoms

The 16-card, standard-size set featured the weekly offensive and defensive award winners for the 1988 season. The cards were included four to the bottom of each box of 1989 football. Two players (offensive and defensive) are on each card.

		MT
Complete Set (16):		5.00
Common Player:		.25
A	Neal Anderson,	.25
	Terry Hoage	
B	Boomer Esiason,	.50
	Jacob Green	
C	Wesley Walker,	.25
	Gary Jeter	
D	Jim Everett,	.25
	Danny Noonan	
E	Neil Lomax,	.25
	Dexter Manley	
F	Kelvin Bryant,	.25
	Kevin Greene	
G	Roger Craig,	.50
	Tim Harris	
H	Dan Marino,	2.00
	Carl Banks	
I	Drew Hill,	.25
	Robin Cole	
J	Neil Lomax,	.50
	Lawrence Taylor	
K	Roy Green,	.25
	Tim Harris	
L	Bobby Hebert,	.25
	Aundray Bruce	
M	Ickey Woods,	.50
	Lawrence Taylor	
N	Louis Lipps,	.25
	Greg Townsend	
O	Curt Warner,	.25
	Tim Harris	
P	Dave Krieg,	.35
	Kevin Greene	

1989 Topps 1000 Yard Club

These standard-size cards, printed on heavy white card- board stock and featuring a full-color action shot of each NFL player who gained more tha 1,000 yards rushing or receiv- ing during the 1988 season, were included in wax packs of 1989 Topps football cards. Fronts feature a yellow-and- blue ribbon from the upper right corner, across the top and lead- ing to a "1000 Yard Club" medal at lower left. The photo and medal are bordered in red, with the player's name in white and his position in black also in the border. Card backs are in or- ange, with an ornate "1000 Yard Club" medal and ribbon reach- ing from the card number at up- per left to the bottom center of the card. Statistics mark the game-by-game progress of the runner-receiver's season.

		MT
Complete Set (24):		4.00
Common Player:		.10
1	Eric Dickerson	.60
2	Herschel Walker	.60
3	Roger Craig	.40
4	Henry Ellard	.10
5	Jerry Rice	.60
6	Eddie Brown	.10
7	Anthony Carter	.10
8	Greg Bell	.10
9	John Stephens	.10
10	Ricky Sanders	.10
11	Drew Hill	.10
12	Mark Clayton	.10
13	Gary Anderson	.10
14	Neal Anderson	.20
15	Roy Green	.10
16	Eric Martin	.10
17	Joe Morris	.10
18	Al Toon	.10
19	Ickey Woods	.20
20	Bruce Hill	.10
21	Lionel Manuel	.10
22	Curt Warner	.10
23	John Settle	.10
24	Mike Rozier	.10

1989 Topps Traded

This 132-card set was re- leased in March of 1990. It was a boxed set through only hobby dealers, similar to the baseball "Traded" sets that Topps had been issuing since 1981. The set includes 1989 rookies, play- ers not included in the regular '89 set and players that had been traded (now shown with their new team).

		MT
Complete Set (132):		18.00
Common Player:		.05
1	Eric Ball	.10
2	Tony Mandarich	.05
3	Shawn Collins	.10
4	Ray Bentley	.05
5	Tony Casillas	.10
6	Al Del Greco	.10
7	Dan Saleaumua	.10
8	Keith Bishop	.05
9	Rodney Peete	.40
10	Lorenzo White	.25
11	Steve Smith	.25
12	Pete Mandley	.05
13	Mervyn Fernandez	.05
14	Flipper Anderson	.30
15	Louis Oliver	.15
16	Rick Fenney	.05
17	Gary Jeter	.05
18	Greg Cox	.05
19	Bubba McDowell	.15
20	Ron Heller	.05
21	Tim McDonald	.25
22	Jerrol Williams	.10
23	Marion Butts	.40
24	Steve Young	1.00
25	Mike Merriweather	.05
26	Richard Johnson	.05
27	Gerald Riggs	.05
28	Dave Waymer	.05
29	Isaac Holt	.05
30	Deion Sanders	1.75
31	Todd Blackledge	.05
32	Jeff Cross	.30
33	Steve Wisniewski	.20
34	Ron Brown	.05
35	Ron Bernstine	.35
36	Jeff Uhlenhake	.08
37	Donnell Woolford	.12
38	Bob Gagliano	.12
39	Ezra Johnson	.05
40	Ron Jaworski	.05
41	Lawyer Tillman	.10
42	Lorenzo Lynch	.10
43	Mike Alexander	.05
44	Tim Worley	.15
45	Guy Bingham	.05

46	Cleveland Gary	.25
47	Danny Peebles	.05
48	Clarence Weathers	.05
49	Jeff Lageman	.10
50	Eric Metcalf	.65
51	Myron Guyton	.10
52	Steve Atwater	.20
53	John Fourcade	.05
54	Randall McDaniel	.12
55	Al Noga	.15
56	Sammie Smith	.10
57	Jesse Solomon	.05
58	Greg Kragen	.10
59	Don Beebe	.50
60	Hart Lee Dykes	.05
61	Trace Armstrong	.15
62	Steve Pelluer	.05
63	Barry Krauss	.05
64	Kevin Murphy	.05
65	Steve Tasker	.30
66	Jessie Small	.10
67	Dave Meggett	.25
68	Dean Hamel	.05
69	Jim Covert	.05
70	Troy Aikman	3.00
71	Raul Allegre	.05
72	Chris Jacke	.15
73	Leslie O'Neal	.25
74	Keith Taylor	.10
75	Steve Walsh	.50
76	Tracy Rocker	.05
77	Robert Massey	.12
78	Bryan Wagner	.05
79	Steve DeOssie	.05
80	Carnell Lake	.12
81	Frank Reich	.50
82	Tyrone Braxton	.10
83	Barry Sanders	12.00
84	Pete Stoyanovich	.20
85	Paul Palmer	.05
86	Billy Joe Tolliver	.10
87	Eric Hill	.08
88	Gerald McNeil	.05
89	Bill Hawkins	.05
90	Derrick Thomas	.75
91	Jim Harbaugh	1.00
92	Brian Williams	.05
93	Jack Trudeau	.05
94	Leonard Smith	.05
95	Gary Hogeboom	.05
96	A.J. Johnson	.10
97	Jim McMahon	.10
98	David Williams	.12
99	Rohn Stark	.05
100	Sean Landeta	.05
101	Tim Johnson	.08
102	Andre Rison	.50
103	Earnest Byner	.05
104	Don McPherson	.08
105	Zefross Moss	.08
106	Frank Stams	.10
107	Courtney Hall	.10
108	Marc Logan	.15
109	James Lofton	.15
110	Lewis Tillman	.50
111	Irv Pankey	.05
112	Ralf Mojsiejenko	.05
113	Bobby Humphrey	.08
114	Chris Burkett	.05
115	Greg Lloyd	.40
116	Matt Millen	.05
117	Carl Zander	.05
118	Wayne Martin	.25
119	Mike Saxon	.05
120	Herschel Walker	.12
121	Andy Heck	.08
122	Mark Robinson	.05
123	Keith Van Horne	.05
124	Ricky Hunley	.05
125	Timm Rosenbach	.25
126	Steve Grogan	.05
127	Stephen Braggs	.08
128	Terry Long	.05
129	Evan Cooper	.05
130	Robert Lyles	.05
131	Mike Webster	.05
132	Checklist	.05

1989 Topps American/ United Kingdom

This boxed set of 33 cards was distributed in the United Kingdom using a design similar to Topps' regular 1989 set. However, the card stock for the back is not grey, like it is for the regular cards; these ones have white backs. The set's checklist is included on the box; card numbers do not match those in the regular set.

		MT
Complete Set (33):		35.00
Common Player:		1.00
1	Anthony Carter	1.00
2	Jim Kelly	2.50
3	Bernie Kosar	1.50
4	John Elway	4.00
5	Andre Tippett	1.00
6	Henry Ellard	1.50
7	Eddie Brown	1.00
8	Gary Anderson	1.00

9	Eric Martin	1.00
10	Ickey Woods	1.00
11	Mike Singletary	1.00
12	Phil Simms	1.50
13	Brian Bosworth	1.00
14	Mark Clayton	1.00
15	Eric Dickerson	1.50
16	John Stephens	1.00
17	Neal Anderson	1.00
18	Al Toon	1.00
19	Lionel Manuel	.75
20	Joe Montana	7.00
21	Reggie White	2.00
22	Randall	1.75
	Cunningham	
23	Lawrence Taylor	1.50
24	Jim Everett	1.25
25	Neil Lomax	1.00
26	Herschel Walker	1.25
27	Roger Craig	1.25
28	Greg Bell	1.00
29	Ricky Sanders	1.00
30	Joe Morris	1.00
31	Curt Warner	1.00
32	Boomer Esiason	1.50
33	Dan Marino	7.00

1990 Topps

The 1990 Topps set, the largest since 1982, returned to 528 cards. A new addition to the Topps sets included 25 1990 draft pick cards; other subsets included four 1989 record break- ers, four league leader cards and a Super Bowl card. Each wax pack included one of 31 glossy 1,000 Yard Club insert cards fea- turing players who gained 1,000 yards or more during the 1989 NFL season. Because NFL Prop- erties denied Topps a license, cards have no free-standing team logos. A 196-card Bowman football set, also scheduled to be issued in 1990, was also scratched. Variations include cards #28, 193, 229 and 501- 528 - all the Topps horizontal is- sues - which originally appeared without the small black vertical "hashmarks" running below the red border and underneath the Topps logo. These were correct- ed very early; no premium value has been put on them, but they should fetch 35-50 cents over the regular card price. Also, Topps issued "corrected" cards, presumably both in wax and in factory sets, that do not have the "unauthorized" tagline. These are thought to be scarcer than the unauthorized cards. (Key: RB - Record Breaker).

		MT
Complete Set (528):		10.00
Common Player:		.04
Wax Box:		10.00
1	Joe Montana (RB)	.50
2	Flipper Anderson	.04
	(RB)	
3	Troy Aikman (RB)	.50
4	Kevin Butler (RB)	.04
5	Super Bowl XXIV	.04
6	Dexter Carter	.20
7	Matt Millen	.04
8	Jerry Rice	.75
9	Ronnie Lott	.10
10	John Taylor	.20
11	Guy McIntyre	.04
12	Roger Craig	.04
13	Joe Montana	1.00
14	Brent Jones	.75
15	Tom Rathman	.04
16	Harris Barton	.04
17	Charles Haley	.04
18	Pierce Holt	.04
19	Michael Carter	.04
20	Chet Brooks	.04
21	Eric Wright	.04
22	Mike Cofer	.04
23	Jim Fahnhorst	.04

24	Keena Turner	.04
25	Don Griffin	.04
26	Kevin Fagan	.08
27	Bubba Paris	.04
28	Rushing Leaders	.15
29	Steve Atwater	.04
30	Tyrone Braxton	.04
31	Ron Holmes	.04
32	Bobby Humphrey	.04
33	Greg Kragen	.04
34	David Treadwell	.04
35	Karl Mecklenburg	.04
36	Dennis Smith	.04
37	John Elway	.40
38	Vance Johnson	.04
39	Simon Fletcher	.04
40	Jim Juriga	.04
41	Mark Jackson	.04
42	Melvin Bratton	.04
43	Wymon	.10
	Henderson	
44	Ken Ball	.04
45	Sammy Winder	.04
46	Alphonso Carreker	.04
47	Orson Mobley	.04
48	Rodney Hampton	1.00
49	Dave Meggett	.12
50	Myron Guyton	.04
51	Phil Simms	.10
52	Lawrence Taylor	.10
53	Carl Banks	.04
54	Pepper Johnson	.04
55	Leonard Marshall	.04
56	Mark Collins	.04
57	Erik Howard	.04
58	Eric Dorsey	.10
59	Ottis Anderson	.04
60	Mark Bavaro	.04
61	Odessa Turner	.12
62	Gary Reasons	.04
63	Maurice Carthon	.04
64	Lionel Manuel	.04
65	Sean Landeta	.04
66	Perry Williams	.04
67	Pat Terrell	.12
68	Flipper Anderson	.15
69	Jackie Slater	.04
70	Tom Newberry	.04
71	Jerry Gray	.04
72	Henry Ellard	.04
73	Doug Smith	.04
74	Kevin Greene	.04
75	Jim Everett	.04
76	Mike Lansford	.04
77	Greg Bell	.04
78	Pete Holohan	.04
79	Robert Delpino	.04
80	Mike Wilcher	.04
81	Mike Piel	.04
82	Mel Owens	.04
83	Michael Stewart	.10
84	Ben Smith	.10
85	Keith Jackson	.25
86	Reggie White	.15
87	Eric Allen	.04
88	Jerome Brown	.04
89	Robert Drummond	.04
90	Anthony Toney	.04
91	Keith Byars	.04
92	Cris Carter	.30
93	Randall	.20
	Cunningham	
94	Ron Johnson	.04
95	Mike Quick	.04
96	Clyde Simmons	.04
97	Mike Pitts	.04
98	Izel Jenkins	.04
99	Seth Joyner	.04
100	Mike Schad	.04
101	Wes Hopkins	.04
102	Kirk Lowdermilk	.04
103	Rick Fenney	.04
104	Randall McDaniel	.04
105	Herschel Walker	.04
106	Al Noga	.04
107	Gary Zimmerman	.04
108	Chris Doleman	.04
109	Keith Millard	.04
110	Carl Lee	.04
111	Joey Browner	.04
112	Steve Jordan	.04
113	Reggie Rutland	.10
114	Wade Wilson	.04
115	Anthony Carter	.04
116	Rich Karlis	.04
117	Hassan Jones	.04
118	Henry Thomas	.04
119	Scott Studwell	.04
120	Ralf Mojsiejenko	.04
121	Earnest Byner	.04
122	Gerald Riggs	.04
123	Tracy Rocker	.04
124	A.J. Johnson	.04
125	Charles Mann	.04
126	Art Monk	.04
127	Ricky Sanders	.04
128	Gary Clark	.15
129	Jim Lachey	.04
130	Martin Mayhew	.15
131	Ravin Caldwell	.04
132	Don Warren	.04
133	Mark Rypien	.25
134	Ed Simmons	.10
135	Darryl Grant	.04
136	Darryl Green	.04
137	Chip Lohmiller	.04
138	Tony Bennett	.35
139	Tony Mandarich	.04

No.	Player	MT
140	Sterling Sharpe	.75
141	Tim Harris	.04
142	Don Majkowski	.04
143	Rich Moran	.04
144	Jeff Query	.04
145	Brent Fullwood	.04
146	Chris Jacke	.04
147	Keith Woodside	.04
148	Perry Kemp	.04
149	Herman Fontenot	.04
150	Dave Brown	.04
151	Brian Noble	.04
152	Johnny Holland	.04
153	Mark Murphy	.04
154	Bob Nelson	.04
155	*Darrell Thompson*	.25
156	Lawyer Tillman	.04
157	Eric Metcalf	.12
158	Webster Slaughter	.04
159	Frank Minnifield	.04
160	Brian Brennan	.04
161	Thane Gash	.04
162	Robert Banks	.04
163	Bernie Kosar	.04
164	David Grayson	.04
165	Kevin Mack	.04
166	Mike Johnson	.04
167	Tim Manoa	.04
168	Ozzie Newsome	.10
169	Felix Wright	.04
170	Al Baker	.04
171	Reggie Langhorne	.04
172	Clay Matthews	.04
173	Andrew Stewart	.04
174	*Barry Foster*	.10
175	Tim Worley	.04
176	Tim Johnson	.04
177	Carnell Lake	.04
178	Greg Lloyd	.04
179	Rod Woodson	.15
180	Tunch Ilkin	.04
181	Dermontti Dawson	.04
182	Gary Anderson	.04
183	Bubby Brister	.10
184	Louis Lipps	.04
185	Merril Hoge	.04
186	Mike Mularkey	.04
187	Derek Hill	.04
188	Rodney Carter	.04
189	Dwayne Carter	.04
190	Keith Willis	.04
191	Jerry Olsavsky	.04
192	Mark Stock	.04
193	Sacks Leaders	.04
194	Leonard Smith	.04
195	Darryl Talley	.04
196	Mark Kelso	.04
197	Kent Hull	.04
198	*Nate Odomes*	.30
199	Pete Metzelaars	.04
200	Don Beebe	.15
201	Ray Bentley	.04
202	Steve Tasker	.10
203	Scott Norwood	.04
204	Andre Reed	.20
205	Bruce Smith	.04
206	Thurman Thomas	.50
207	Jim Kelly	.35
208	Cornelius Bennett	.04
209	Shane Conlan	.04
210	Larry Kinnebrew	.04
211	*Jeff Alm*	.10
212	Robert Lyles	.04
213	Bubba McDowell	.04
214	Mike Munchak	.04
215	Bruce Matthews	.04
216	Warren Moon	.25
217	Drew Hill	.04
218	Ray Childress	.04
219	Steve Brown	.04
220	Alonzo Highsmith	.04
221	Allen Pinkett	.04
222	Sean Jones	.04
223	Johnny Meads	.04
224	John Grimsley	.04
225	*Haywood Jeffires*	.50
226	Curtis Duncan	.04
227	*Greg Montgomery*	.10
228	Ernest Givins	.04
229	Passing Leaders	.20
230	Robert Massey	.04
231	John Fourcade	.04
232	Dalton Hilliard	.04
233	Vaughan Johnson	.04
234	Hoby Brenner	.04
235	Pat Swilling	.04
236	Kevin Haverdink	.04
237	Bobby Hebert	.15
238	Sam Mills	.04
239	Eric Martin	.04
240	Lonzell Hill	.04
241	Steve Trapilo	.04
242	Rickey Jackson	.04
243	Craig Heyward	.04
244	Rueben Mayes	.04
245	Morten Anderson	.04
246	*Percy Snow*	.10
247	Pete Mandley	.04
248	Derrick Thomas	.30
249	Dan Saleaumua	.04
250	*Todd McNair*	.15
251	Leonard Griffin	.04
252	Jonathan Hayes	.04
253	Christian Okoye	.04
254	Albert Lewis	.04
255	Nick Lowery	.04
256	Kevin Ross	.04
257	Steve DeBerg	.04

No.	Player	MT
258	Stephone Paige	.04
259	*James Saxon*	.10
260	Herman Heard	.04
261	Deron Cherry	.04
262	Dino Hackett	.04
263	Neil Smith	.20
264	Steve Pelluer	.04
265	Eric Thomas	.04
266	Eric Ball	.04
267	Leon White	.04
268	Tim Krumrie	.04
269	Jason Buck	.04
270	Boomer Esiason	.20
271	Carl Zander	.04
272	Eddie Brown	.04
273	David Fulcher	.04
274	Tim McGee	.04
275	James Brooks	.04
276	*Rickey Dixon*	.10
277	Ickey Woods	.04
278	Anthony Munoz	.04
279	Rodney Holman	.04
280	Mike Alexander	.04
281	Mervyn Fernandez	.04
282	Steve Wisniewski	.04
283	Steve Smith	.04
284	Howie Long	.04
285	Bo Jackson	.45
286	Mike Dyal	.04
287	Thomas Benson	.04
288	Willie Gault	.04
289	Marcus Allen	.04
290	Greg Townsend	.04
291	Steve Beuerlein	.30
292	Scott Davis	.04
293	*Eddie Anderson*	.10
294	Terry McDaniel	.04
295	Tim Brown	.45
296	Bob Golic	.04
297	*Jeff Jaeger*	.12
298	*Jeff George*	1.00
299	Chip Banks	.04
300	Andre Rison	.25
301	Rohn Stark	.04
302	Keith Taylor	.04
303	Jack Trudeau	.04
304	Chris Hinton	.04
305	Ray Donaldson	.04
306	*Jeff Herrod*	.10
307	Clarence Verdin	.04
308	Jon Hand	.04
309	Bill Brooks	.04
310	Albert Bentley	.04
311	Mike Prior	.04
312	Pat Beach	.04
313	Eugene Daniel	.04
314	Duane Bickett	.04
315	Dean Biasucci	.04
316	*Richmond Webb*	.25
317	Jeff Cross	.04
318	Louis Oliver	.04
319	Sammie Smith	.04
320	Pete Stovanovich	.04
321	John Offerdahl	.04
322	Ferrell Edmunds	.04
323	Dan Marino	.75
324	Andre Brown	.04
325	Reggie Roby	.04
326	Jarvis Williams	.04
327	Roy Foster	.04
328	Mark Clayton	.04
329	Brian Sochia	.04
330	Mark Duper	.04
331	T.J. Turner	.04
332	Jeff Uhlenhake	.04
333	Jim Jensen	.04
334	*Cortez Kennedy*	.25
335	Andy Heck	.04
336	Rufus Porter	.04
337	Brian Blades	.15
338	Dave Krieg	.04
339	John L. Williams	.04
340	David Wyman	.04
341	*Paul Skansi*	.10
342	Eugene Robinson	.04
343	Joe Nash	.04
344	Jacob Green	.04
345	Jeff Bryant	.04
346	Ruben Rodriguez	.04
347	Norm Johnson	.04
348	Darren Comeaux	.04
349	*Andre Ware*	.20
350	Richard Johnson	.04
351	Rodney Peete	.10
352	Barry Sanders	1.25
353	Chris Spielman	.04
354	Eddie Murray	.04
355	Jerry Ball	.04
356	Mel Gray	.04
357	*Eric Williams*	.10
358	*Robert Clark*	.10
359	Jason Phillips	.04
360	*Terry Taylor*	.08
361	Bennie Blades	.25
362	Michael Cofer	.04
363	Jim Arnold	.04
364	*Marc Spindler*	.10
365	Jim Covert	.04
366	Jim Harbaugh	.20
367	Neal Anderson	.15
368	Mike Singletary	.04
369	John Roper	.04
370	Steve McMichael	.04
371	Dennis Gentry	.04
372	Brad Muster	.04
373	Ron Morris	.04
374	James Thornton	.04
375	Kevin Butler	.04

No.	Player	MT
376	Richard Dent	.04
377	Dan Hampton	.04
378	Jay Hilgenberg	.04
379	Donnell Woolford	.04
380	Trace Armstrong	.04
381	*Junior Seau*	1.00
382	Rod Bernstine	.15
383	Marion Butts	.15
384	Burt Grossman	.04
385	Darrin Nelson	.04
386	Leslie O'Neal	.04
387	Billy Joe Tolliver	.04
388	Courtney Hall	.04
389	Lee Williams	.04
390	Anthony Miller	.30
391	Gill Byrd	.04
392	Wayne Walker	.04
393	Billy Ray Smith	.04
394	Vencie Glenn	.04
395	Tim Spencer	.04
396	Gary Plummer	.04
397	Arthur Cox	.04
398	Jamie Holland	.04
399	*Keith McCants*	.10
400	Kevin Murphy	.04
401	Danny Peebles	.04
402	Mark Robinson	.04
403	Broderick Thomas	.04
404	Ron Hall	.04
405	Mark Carrier	.04
406	Paul Gruber	.04
407	Vinny Testaverde	.10
408	Bruce Hill	.04
409	Lars Tate	.04
410	Harry Hamilton	.04
411	Ricky Reynolds	.04
412	Donald Igwebuike	.04
413	Reuben Davis	.04
414	William Howard	.04
415	*Winston Moss*	.10
416	*Chris Singleton*	.10
417	Hart Lee Dykes	.04
418	Steve Grogan	.04
419	Bruce Armstrong	.04
420	Robert Perryman	.04
421	Andre Tippett	.04
422	Sammy Martin	.04
423	Stanley Morgan	.04
424	Cedric Jones	.04
425	Sean Farrell	.04
426	Marc Wilson	.04
427	John Stephens	.04
428	Eric Sievers	.04
429	*Maurice Hurst*	.10
430	Johnny Rembert	.04
431	Receiving Leaders	.25
432	Eric Hill	.04
433	Gary Hogeboom	.04
434	Timm Rosenbach	.04
435	Tim McDonald	.04
436	Rich Camarillo	.04
437	Luis Sharpe	.04
438	J.T. Smith	.04
439	Roy Green	.04
440	Ernie Jones	.15
441	Robert Awalt	.04
442	Vai Sikahema	.04
443	Joe Wolf	.04
444	Stump Mitchell	.04
445	David Galloway	.04
446	Ron Wolfley	.04
447	Freddie Joe Nunn	.04
448	*Blair Thomas*	.15
449	Jeff Lageman	.04
450	Tony Eason	.04
451	Eric McMillan	.04
452	Jim Sweeney	.04
453	Ken O'Brien	.04
454	Johnny Hector	.04
455	JoJo Townsell	.04
456	Roger Vick	.04
457	Dennis Hasty	.04
458	*Dennis Byrd*	.25
459	Ron Stallworth	.04
460	Mickey Shuler	.04
461	Bobby Humphery	.04
462	Kyle Clifton	.04
463	Al Toon	.04
464	Freeman McNeil	.04
465	Pat Leahy	.04
466	Scott Case	.04
467	Shawn Collins	.04
468	Floyd Dixon	.04
469	Deion Sanders	.35
470	Tony Casillas	.04
471	*Michael Haynes*	.50
472	Chris Miller	.25
473	John Settle	.04
474	Aundray Bruce	.04
475	Gene Lang	.04
476	*Tim Gordon*	.10
477	Scott Fulhage	.04
478	Bill Fralic	.04
479	*Jessie Tuggle*	.25
480	Marcus Cotton	.04
481	Steve Walsh	.04
482	Troy Aikman	1.25
483	Ray Horton	.04
484	*Tony Tolbert*	.20
485	Steve Folsom	.04
486	Ken Norton Jr.	.50
487	*Kelvin Martin*	.04
488	Jack Del Rio	.25
489	*Daryl Johnston*	1.00
490	Bill Bates	.04
491	Jim Jeffcoat	.04
492	Vince Albritton	.04
493	Eugene Lockhart	.04

No.	Player	MT
494	Mike Saxon	.04
495	James Dixon	.04
496	Willie Broughton	.04
497	Checklist 1-132	.04
498	Checklist 133-264	.04
499	Checklist 265-396	.04
500	Checklist 397-528	.04
501	Bears Team	.04
502	Bengals Team	.04
503	Bills Team	.04
504	Broncos Team	.04
505	Browns Team	.04
506	Buccaneers Team	.04
507	Cardinals Team	.04
508	Chargers Team	.04
509	Chiefs Team	.04
510	Colts Team	.04
511	Cowboys Team	.65
512	Dolphins Team	.04
513	Eagles Team	.04
514	Falcons Team	.04
515	49ers Team	.20
516	Giants Team	.04
517	Jets Team	.04
518	Lions Team	.04
519	Oilers Team	.10
520	Packers Team	.04
521	Patriots Team	.04
522	Raiders Team	.12
523	Rams Team	.04
524	Redskins Team	.04
525	Saints Team	.04
526	Seahawks Team	.04
527	Steelers Team	.04
528	Vikings Team	.04

ceiving during the 1989 NFL season are honored in this 30-card insert set. Cards were randomly included in 1990 Topps packs, one per pack. The front has a color picture, his and the set's name, plus the Topps' logo. Each back recaps each game from the 1989 season to show how the player reached the 1,000-yard milestone. The cards, numbered 1-30, are numbered according by yardage totals, with the leading yard gainer being #1, and so forth. The design for the card front is similar to the regular 1990 Topps football card design.

No.	Player	MT
	Complete Set (30):	3.50
	Common Player:	.05
1	Jerry Rice	.50
2	Christian Okoye	.15
3	Barry Sanders	1.00
4	Sterling Sharpe	.40
5	Mark Carrier	.15
6	Henry Ellard	.05
7	Andre Reed	.25
8	Neal Anderson	.25
9	Dalton Hilliard	.05
10	Anthony Miller	.20
11	Thurman Thomas	.25
12	James Brooks	.15
13	Webster Slaughter	.05
14	Gary Clark	.25
15	Tim McGee	.05
16	Art Monk	.15
17	Bobby Humphrey	.25
18	Flipper Anderson	.05
19	Ricky Sanders	.10
20	Greg Bell	.05
21	Vance Johnson	.05
22	Richard Johnson	.05
23	Eric Martin	.05
24	John Taylor	.25
25	Mervyn Fernandez	.05
26	Anthony Carter	.10
27	Brian Blades	.10
28	Roger Craig	.20
29	Ottis Anderson	.20
30	Mark Clayton	.07

1990 Topps Box Bottoms

These standard-size cards were included on the bottoms of 1990 Topps wax pack boxes. Each card has two photos on it; an offensive and defensive NFL Player of the Week from the 1989 season is featured. The back uses letters instead of card numbers and explains why the player was selected as the league's best performer for the week. The card design is similar to that which was used for Topps' regular 1990 set.

		MT
	Complete Set (16):	6.00
	Common Player:	.30
A	Jim Kelly, Dave Grayson	.50
B	Henry Ellard, Derrick Thomas	.50
C	Joe Montana, Vince Newsome	1.50
D	Bubby Brister, Tim Harris	.30
E	Christian Okoye, Keith Millard	.30
F	Warren Moon, Jerome Brown	.50
G	John Elway, Mike Merriweather	1.00
H	Webster Slaughter, Pat Swilling	.35
I	Rich Karlis, Lawrence Taylor	.35
J	Dan Marino, Greg Kragen	1.00
K	Boomer Esiason, Brent Williams	.35
L	Flipper Anderson, Pierce Holt	.30
M	Richard Johnson, David Fulcher	.30
N	John Taylor, Mike Prior	.50
O	Mark Rypien, Brett Faryniarz	.35
P	Greg Bell, Chris Doleman	.30

1990 Topps Traded

Like its predecessor, the Topps football update again pictured rookies and traded players on white cardboard stock. The issue was sold as a boxed set and was available only through hobby shops.

No.	Player	MT
	Complete Set (132):	15.00
	Common Player:	.03
1	Gerald McNeil	.03
2	Andre Rison	.15
3	Steve Walsh	.10
4	Lorenzo White	.10
5	Max Montoya	.05
6	William Roberts	.03
7	Alonzo Highsmith	.10
8	Chris Hinton	.10
9	Stanley Morgan	.10
10	Mickey Shuler	.03
11	Bobby Humphrey	.03
12	Gary Anderson	.03
13	Mike Tomczak	.03
14	Anthony Pleasant	.03
15	Walter Stanley	.03
16	Greg Bell	.10
17	*Tony Martin*	2.00
18	Terry Kinard	.03
19	Cris Carter	.50
20	James Wilder	.03
21	Jerry Kauric	.03
22	Irving Fryer	.03
23	Ken Harvey	.15
24	James Williams	.15
25	Ron Cox	.03
26	Andre Ware	.50
27	*Emmitt Smith*	6.00
28	Junior Seau	.50
29	Mark Carrier	.50
30	Rodney Hampton	.50
31	*Rob Moore*	1.25
32	Bern Brostek	.10
33	Dexter Carter	.40
34	Blair Thomas	.65
35	Harold Green	.30
36	Darrell Thompson	.20
37	Eric Green	.25
38	Renaldo Turnbull	.20
39	*Leroy Hoard*	.50
40	Anthony Thompson	.20
41	Jeff George	.50
42	Alexander Wright	.15
43	Richmond Webb	.25
44	Cortez Kennedy	.75
45	Ray Agnew	.10
46	Percy Snow	.15
47	Chris Singleton	.10
48	James Francis	.25
49	Tony Bennett	.25
50	*Reggie Cobb*	.20

No.	Player	MT
51	Barry Foster	.10
52	Ben Smith	.10
53	Anthony Smith	.10
54	Steve Christie	.10
55	Johnny Bailey	.20
56	Alan Grant	.03
57	Eric Floyd	.03
58	Robert Blackmon	.03
59	Brent Williams	.03
60	Raymond Clayborn	.03
61	Dave Duerson	.07
62	Derrick Fenner	.50
63	Ken Willis	.03
64	*Brad Baxter*	.25
65	Tony Paige	.03
66	Jay Schroeder	.15
67	Jim Breech	.03
68	Barry Word	.50
69	Anthony Dilweg	.10
70	*Rich Gannon*	2.00
71	*Stan Humphries*	.50
72	Jay Novacek	.50
73	Tommy Kane	.03
74	Everson Walls	.03
75	Mike Rozier	.10
76	Robb Thomas	.03
77	*Terance Mathis*	2.00
78	Leroy Irvin	.03
79	Jeff Donaldson	.03
80	Ethan Horton	.03
81	J.B. Brown	.03
82	Joe Kelly	.03
83	John Carney	.03
84	Dan Stryzinski	.03
85	John Kidd	.03
86	Al Smith	.03
87	Travis McNeal	.03
88	Reyna Thompson	.10
89	Rick Donnelly	.03
90	Marv Cook	.03
91	Mike Farr	.03
92	Daniel Stubbs	.03
93	Jeff Campbell	.20
94	Tim McKyer	.10
95	Ian Beckles	.03
96	Lemuel Stinson	.03
97	Frank Cornish	.03
98	Riki Ellison	.03
99	Jamie Mueller	.03
100	Brian Hansen	.03
101	Warren Powers	.03
102	Howard Cross	.03
103	Tim Grunhard	.03
104	Johnny Johnson	.20
105	*Calvin Williams*	.65
106	Keith McCants	.15
107	Lamar Lathon	.10
108	Steve Broussard	.35
109	Glenn Parker	.03
110	Alton Montgomery	.07
111	Jim McMahon	.07
112	Aaron Wallace	.25
113	Keith Sims	.07
114	Ervin Randle	.03
115	Walter Wilson	.03
116	Terry Wooden	.07
117	Bernard Cook	.03
118	Tony Stargell	.07
119	Jimmie Jones	.07
120	Andre Collins	.03
121	*Ricky Proehl*	.40
122	Darion Conner	.07
123	Jeff Rutledge	.03
124	Heath Sherman	.25
125	Tommie Agee	.03
126	Tory Epps	.03
127	Tom Hodson	.25
128	Jessie Hester	.03
129	Alfred Oglesby	.03
130	Chris Chandler	.03
131	*Fred Barnett*	.50
132	Checklist	.03

1990 Topps 1000 Yard Club

Players who gained more than 1,000 yards rushing or re-

1991 Topps

Topps' largest-ever football set was issued in August 1991. The style of the cards is the same as in 1991 Topps baseball and hockey. Subsets include highlights, all-pros, draft picks and super rookies. (Key: HL - highlight, LL - league leader)

	MT
Complete Set (660):	13.00
Complete Factory Set (660):	17.00

Common Player: .04
Wax Box: 10.00

1 Super Bowl XXV .08
2 Roger Craig (HL) .04
3 Derrick Thomas (HL) .12
4 Pete Stoyanovich (HL) .04
5 Ottis Anderson (HL) .04
6 Jerry Rice (HL) .30
7 Warren Moon (HL) .10
8 Warren Moon, Jim Everett (LL) .10
9 Thurman Thomas, Barry Sanders (LL) .50
10 Haywood Jeffries, Jerry Rice (LL) .25
11 Richard Johnson, Mark Carrier (LL) .04
12 Derrick Thomas, Charles Haley (LL) .10
13 Jumbo Elliott .04
14 Leonard Marshall .04
15 William Roberts .04
16 Lawrence Taylor .10
17 Mark Ingram .04
18 Rodney Hampton .75
19 Carl Banks .04
20 Ottis Anderson .04
21 Mark Collins .04
22 Pepper Johnson .04
23 Dave Meggett .04
24 Reyna Thompson .04
26 Mike Fox .04
27 Maurice Carthon .04
28 Jeff Hostetler .25
29 *Greg Jackson* .10
30 Sean Landeta .04
31 Bart Oates .04
32 Phil Simms .10
33 Erik Howard .04
34 Myron Guyton .04
35 Mark Bavaro .04
36 Jarrod Bunch .15
37 *Will Wolford* .04
38 Ray Bentley .04
39 Nate Odomes .04
40 Scott Norwood .04
41 Darryl Talley .04
42 Carwell Gardner .04
43 James Lofton .04
44 Shane Conlan .04
45 Steve Tasker .04
46 James Williams .04
47 Kent Hull .04
48 Al Edwards .04
49 Frank Reich .04
50 Leon Seals .04
51 Keith McKeller .04
52 Thurman Thomas .50
53 Leonard Smith .04
54 Andre Reed .15
55 Kenneth Davis .04
56 *Jeff Wright* .12
57 Jamie Mueller .04
58 Jim Ritcher .04
59 Bruce Smith .04
60 *Ted Washington* .10
61 Guy McIntyre .04
62 Michael Carter .04
63 Pierce Holt .04
64 Darryl Pollard .04
65 Mike Sherrard .04
66 Dexter Carter .04
67 Bubba Paris .04
68 Harry Sydney .04
69 Tom Rathman .04
70 Jesse Sapolu .04
71 Mike Cofer (S.F.) .04
72 Keith DeLong .04
73 Joe Montana 1.00
74 Bill Romanowski .04
75 John Taylor .15
76 Brent Jones .04
77 Harris Barton .04
78 Charles Haley .04
79 Eric Davis .04
80 Kevin Fagan .04
81 Jerry Rice 1.00
82 Dave Waymer .04
83 *Todd Marinovich* .25
84 Steve Smith .04
85 Tim Brown .12
86 Ethan Horton .04
87 Marcus Allen .04
88 Terry McDaniel .04
89 Thomas Benson .04
90 Roger Craig .04
91 Don Mosebar .04
92 Aaron Wallace .04
93 Eddie Anderson .04
94 Willie Gault .04
95 Howie Long .04
96 Jay Schroeder .04
97 Ronnie Lott .10
98 Bob Golic .04
99 Bo Jackson .35
100 Max Montoya .04
101 Scott Davis .04
102 Greg Townsend .04
103 Garry Lewis .04
104 Mervyn Fernandez .04
105 Steve Wisniewski .04
106 Jeff Jaeger .04
107 *Nick Bell* .20
108 *Mark Dennis* .08
109 Jarvis Williams .04
110 Mark Clayton .04

111 Harry Galbreah .04
112 Dan Marino 2.00
113 Louis Oliver .04
114 Pete Stoyanovich .04
115 Ferrell Edmunds .04
116 Jeff Cross .04
117 Richmond Webb .04
118 Jim Jensen .04
119 Keith Sims .04
120 Mark Duper .04
121 *Shawn Lee* .12
122 Reggie Roby .04
123 Jeff Uhlenhake .04
124 Sammie Smith .04
125 John Offerdahl .04
126 Hugh Green .04
127 Tony Paige .04
128 David Griggs .04
129 J.B. Brown .04
130 *Harvey Williams* .50
131 John Alt .04
132 Albert Lewis .04
133 Robb Thomas .04
134 Neil Smith .04
135 Stephone Paige .04
136 Nick Lowery .04
137 Steve DeBerg .04
138 *Rich Baldinger* .10
139 Percy Snow .04
140 Kevin Porter .04
141 Chris Martin .04
142 Deron Cherry .04
143 Derrick Thomas .30
144 Tim Grunhard .04
145 Todd McNair .04
146 David Szott .04
147 Dan Saleaumua .04
148 Jonathan Hayes .04
149 Christian Okoye .04
150 Dino Hackett .04
151 *Bryan Barker* .10
152 Kevin Ross .04
153 Barry Word .15
154 Stan Thomas .04
155 Brad Muster .04
156 Donnell Woolford .04
157 Neal Anderson .10
158 Jim Covert .04
159 Jim Harbaugh .10
160 Shaun Gayle .04
161 William Perry .04
162 Ron Morris .04
163 Mark Bortz .04
164 James Thornton .04
165 Ron Rivera .04
166 Kevin Butler .04
167 Jay Hilgenberg .04
168 Peter Tom Willis .04
169 Johnny Bailey .04
170 Ron Cox .04
171 Keith Van Horne .04
172 Mark Carrier .04
173 Richard Dent .04
174 Wendell Davis .10
175 Trace Armstrong .04
176 Mike Singletary .04
177 *Chris Zorich* .35
178 Gerald Riggs .04
179 Jeff Bostic .04
180 *Kurt Gouveia* .15
181 Stan Humphries .15
182 Chip Lohmiller .04
183 *Raleigh McKenzie* .10
184 Alvin Walton .04
185 Ernest Byner .04
186 Markus Koch .04
187 Art Monk .04
188 Ed Simmons .04
189 *Bobby Wilson* .10
190 Charles Mann .04
191 Darrell Green .04
192 Mark Rypien .15
193 Ricky Sanders .04
194 Jim Lachey .04
195 Martin Mayhew .04
196 Gary Clark .15
197 Wilber Marshall .04
198 Darryl Grant .04
199 Don Warren .04
200 *Ricky Ervins* .20
201 Eric Allen .04
202 Anthony Toney .04
203 Ben Smith .04
204 David Alexander .04
205 Jerome Brown .04
206 Mike Golic .04
207 Roger Ruzek .04
208 Andre Waters .04
209 Fred Barnett .15
210 Randall Cunningham .15
211 Mike Schad .04
212 Reggie White .15
213 Mike Bellamy .04
214 *Jeff Feagles* .08
215 Wes Hopkins .04
216 Clyde Simmons .04
217 Keith Byars .04
218 Seth Joyner .04
219 Byron Evans .04
220 Keith Jackson .04
221 Calvin Williams .15
222 Mike Dumas .04
223 Ray Childress .04
224 Ernest Givins .04
225 Lamar Lathon .04
226 Greg Montgomery .04
227 Mike Munchak .04

228 Al Smith .04
229 Bubba McDowell .04
230 Haywood Jeffries .15
231 Drew Hill .04
233 Warren Moon .25
234 *Doug Smith* .10
235 Cris Dishman .15
236 Teddy Garcia .04
237 Richard Johnson .04
238 Bruce Matthews .04
239 Gerald McNeil .04
240 Johnny Meads .04
241 Curtis Duncan .04
242 Sean Jones .04
243 Lorenzo White .10
244 *Rob Carpenter* .12
245 Bruce Reimers .04
246 Ickey Woods .04
247 Lewis Billups .04
248 Boomer Esiason .15
249 Tim Krumrie .04
250 David Fulcher .04
251 Jim Breech .04
252 Mitchell Price .04
253 Carl Zander .04
254 *Barney Bussey* .10
255 Leon White .04
256 Eddie Brown .04
257 James Francis .04
258 Harold Green .15
259 Anthony Munoz .04
260 James Brooks .04
261 *Kevin Walker* .12
262 Bruce Kozerski .04
263 David Grant .04
264 Tim McGee .04
265 Rodney Holman .04
266 *Dan McGwire* .15
267 Andy Heck .04
268 Dave Krieg .04
269 David Wyman .04
270 Robert Blackmon .04
271 Grant Feasel .04
272 *Patrick Hunter* .12
273 Travis McNeal .04
274 John L. Williams .04
275 Tony Woods .04
276 Derrick Fenner .10
277 Jacob Green .04
278 Brian Blades .04
279 Eugene Robinson .04
280 Terry Wooden .04
281 Jeff Bryant .04
282 Norm Johnson .04
283 Joe Nash .04
284 Rick Donnelly .04
285 Chris Warren .75
286 Tommy Kane .04
287 Cortez Kennedy .30
288 *Ernie Mills* .15
289 Dermontti Dawson .04
290 Tunch Ilkin .04
291 Tim Worley .04
293 Gary Anderson (Pit.) .04
294 Chris Calloway .04
295 Carnell Lake .04
296 Dan Stryzinski .04
297 Rod Woodson .04
298 *John Jackson* .10
299 Bubby Brister .04
300 Thomas Everett .04
301 Merril Hoge .04
302 Eric Green .10
303 Greg Lloyd .04
304 Gerald Williams .04
305 Bryan Hinkle .04
306 Keith Willis .04
307 Louis Lipps .04
308 Donald Evans .04
309 David Johnson .04
310 *Wesley Carroll* .10
311 Eric Martin .04
312 Brett Maxie .04
313 Rickey Jackson .04
314 Robert Massey .04
315 Pat Swilling .04
316 Morten Andersen .04
317 *Toi Cook* .10
318 Sam Mills .04
319 Steve Walsh .04
320 *Tommy Barnhardt* .10
321 Vince Buck .04
322 Joel Hilgenberg .04
323 Rueben Mayes .04
324 Renaldo Turnbull .04
325 Vaughan Johnson .04
326 Gill Fenerty .04
327 Stan Brock .04
328 Dalton Hilliard .04
329 Hoby Brenner .04
330 Craig Heyward .04
331 Jon Hand .04
332 Duane Bickett .04
333 Jessie Hester .04
334 Rohn Stark .04
335 Zefross Moss .04
336 Bill Brooks .04
337 Clarence Verdin .04
338 Mike Prior .04
339 Chip Banks .04
340 Dean Biasucci .04
341 Ray Donaldson .04
342 Jeff Herrod .04
343 Donnell Thompson .04
344 Chris Goode .04
345 Eugene Daniel .04
346 Pat Beach .04
347 Keith Taylor .04

349 Jeff George .30
350 Tony Siragusa .10
351 Randy Dixon .04
352 Albert Bentley .04
353 *Russell Maryland* .50
354 Mike Saxon .04
355 Godfrey Myles .08
356 *Mark Stepnoski* .12
357 *James Washington* .12
358 Jay Novacek .25
359 Kelvin Martin .04
360 Emmitt Smith 2.00
361 Jim Jeffcoat .04
362 Alexander Wright .10
363 James Dixon .04
364 Daniel Stubbs .04
365 Jack Del Rio .04
366 Jack Del Rio .10
367 *Mark Tuinei* .10
368 Michael Irvin .25
369 *John Gesek* .10
370 Ken Willis .04
371 Troy Aikman 1.00
372 Jimmie Jones .04
373 Nate Newton .04
374 Issiac Holt .04
375 *Alvin Harper* .30
376 Todd Kalis .04
377 Wade Wilson .04
378 Joey Browner .04
379 Chris Doleman .04
380 Hassan Jones .04
381 Henry Thomas .04
382 Darrell Fullington .04
383 Steve Jordan .04
384 Gary Zimmerman .04
385 Ray Berry .04
386 Cris Carter .04
387 Mike Merriweather .04
388 Carl Lee .04
389 Keith Millard .04
390 Reggie Rutland .04
391 Anthony Carter .04
392 Mark Dusbabek .04
393 Kirk Lowerdermilk .04
394 Al Noga .04
395 Herschel Walker .04
396 Randall McDaniel .04
397 *Herman Moore* 3.50
398 John Jackson, Eddie Murray .04
399 Lomas Brown .04
400 Marc Spindler .04
401 Bennie Blades .04
402 Kevin Glover .04
403 *Aubrey Matthews* .10
404 Michael Cofer (Det.) .04
405 Robert Clark .04
406 Eric Clark .04
407 William White .04
408 Rodney Peete .04
409 Mel Gray .04
410 Jim Arnold .04
411 Jeff Campbell .04
412 Chris Spielman .04
413 Jerry Ball .04
414 Dan Owens .04
415 Barry Sanders 1.25
416 Andre Ware .12
417 *Stanley Richard* .30
418 Gill Byrd .04
419 John Kidd .04
420 Sam Seale .04
421 Gary Plummer .04
422 Anthony Miller .04
423 Ronnie Harmon .04
424 Frank Cornish .04
425 Marion Butts .04
426 Leo Goeas .04
427 Junior Seau .30
428 Courtney Hall .04
429 Leslie O'Neal .04
430 Martin Bayless .04
431 John Carney .04
432 Lee Williams .04
433 Arthur Cox .04
434 Burt Grossman .04
435 *Nate Lewis* .25
436 Rod Bernstine .04
437 *Henry Rolling* .10
438 Billy Joe Tolliver .04
439 *Vince Clark* .10
440 Brian Noble .04
441 Charles Wilson .04
442 Don Majkowski .04
443 Tim Harris .04
444 Scott Stephen .04
445 Perry Kemp .04
446 Darrell Thompson .15
447 Chris Jacke .04
448 Mark Murphy .04
449 Ed West .04
450 LeRoy Butler .04
451 Keith Woodside .04
452 Tony Bennett .04
453 Mark Lee .04
454 *James Campen* .08
455 Robert Brown .04
456 Sterling Sharpe .25
457 Tony Mandarich .08
458 Johnny Holland .04
459 *Matt Brock* .12
460 Esera Tuaolo .08
461 Freeman McNeil .04
462 Terance Mathis .10
463 Rob Moore .20
464 Darrell Davis .04
465 Chris Burkett .04

466 Jeff Criswell .04
467 Tony Stargell .04
468 Ken O'Brien .04
469 Erik McMillan .04
470 Jeff Lageman .04
471 Pat Leahy .04
472 Dennis Byrd .04
473 Jim Sweeney .04
474 Brad Baxter .15
475 Joe Kelly .04
476 Al Toon .04
477 Joe Prokop .04
478 Mark Boyer .04
479 Kyle Clifton .04
480 James Hasty .04
481 *Browning Nagle* .25
482 Gary Anderson (T.B.) .04
483 Mark Carrier (T.B.) .04
484 Ricky Reynolds .04
485 Bruce Hill .04
486 Steve Christie .04
487 Paul Gruber .04
488 Jess Anderson .04
489 Reggie Cobb .30
490 Harry Hamilton .04
491 Vinny Testaverde .10
492 *Mark Royals* .08
493 Keith McCants .04
494 Ron Hall .04
495 Ian Beckles .04
496 Mark Robinson .04
497 Reuben Davis .04
498 Wayne Haddix .04
499 Kevin Murphy .04
500 Eugene Marve .04
501 Broderick Thomas .04
502 *Eric Swann* .20
503 Ernie Jones .04
504 Rich Camarillo .04
505 Tim McDonald .04
506 Freddie Joe Nunn .04
507 *Tim Jorden* .08
508 Johnny Johnson .30
509 Eric Hill .04
510 Derek Kennard .04
511 Ricky Proehl .12
512 Bill Lewis .04
513 Roy Green .04
514 Anthony Bell .04
515 Timm Rosenbach .04
516 *Jim Wahler* .10
517 Anthony Thompson .04
518 Ken Harvey .04
519 Luis Sharpe .04
520 Walter Reeves .04
521 Lonnie Young .04
522 Rod Saddler .04
523 *Todd Lyght* .15
524 Alvin Wright .04
525 Flipper Anderson .04
526 Jackie Slater .04
527 Damone Johnson .04
528 Cleveland Gary .04
529 Mike Piel .04
530 Buford McGee .04
531 Michael Stewart .04
532 Jim Everett .04
533 Mike Wilcher .04
534 Irv Pankey .04
535 Bern Brostek .04
536 Henry Ellard .04
537 Doug Smith .04
538 Larry Kelm .04
539 Pat Terrell .04
540 Jerry Gray .04
541 Kevin Greene .04
542 *Duval Love* .10
543 Frank Stams .04
544 *Mike Croel* .20
545 Mark Jackson .04
546 Greg Kragen .04
547 Karl Mecklenburg .04
548 Simon Fletcher .04
549 Bobby Humphrey .04
550 Ken Lanier .04
551 Vance Johnson .04
552 Ron Holmes .04
553 John Elway .40
554 Melvin Bratton .04
555 Dennis Smith .04
556 Ricky Nattiel .04
557 Clarence Kay .04
558 Michael Brooks .04
559 Mike Horan .04
560 Warren Powers .04
561 Keith Kartz .04
562 Shannon Sharpe .10
563 Wymon Henderson .04
564 Steve Atwater .04
565 David Treadwell .04
566 *Bruce Pickens* .10
567 Jessie Tuggle .04
568 Chris Hinton .04
569 Keith Jones .04
570 Bill Fralic .04
571 Mike Rozier .04
572 Scott Fulhage .04
573 Floyd Dixon .04
574 Andre Rison .25
575 Darion Conner .04
576 Brian Jordan .15
577 Michael Haynes .35
578 Oliver Barnett .04
579 Shawn Collins .04
580 Tim Green .04
581 Deion Sanders .35
582 Mike Kenn .04

583 Mike Kenn .04
584 Mike Gann .04
585 Chris Miller .04
586 Tory Epps .04
587 Steve Broussard .04
588 Gary Wilkins .04
589 *Eric Turner* .30
590 Thane Gash .04
591 Clay Matthews .04
592 Mike Johnson .04
593 Raymond Clayborn .04
594 Leroy Hoard .10
595 Reggie Langhorne .04
596 Mike Baab .04
597 Anthony Pleasant .04
598 David Grayson .04
599 *Rob Burnett* .12
600 Frank Minnifield .04
601 Gregg Rakoczy .04
602 Eric Metcalf .04
603 Paul Farren .04
604 Brian Brennan .04
605 Tony Jones .04
606 Stephen Braggs .04
607 Kevin Mack .04
608 *Pat Harlow* .10
609 Marv Cook .04
610 John Stephens .04
611 Ed Reynolds .04
612 Tim Goad .04
613 Chris Singleton .04
614 Bruce Armstrong .04
615 Tom Hodson .04
616 Sammy Martin .04
617 Andre Tippett .04
618 Johnny Rembert .04
619 Maurice Hurst .04
620 Vincent Brown .04
621 Ray Agnew .04
622 Ronnie Lippett .04
623 Greg McMurtry .04
624 Brent Williams .04
625 Jason Staurovsky .04
626 Marvin Allen .04
627 Hart Lee Dykes .04
628 Falcons Team .04
629 Bills Team .04
630 Bears Team .04
631 Bengals Team .04
632 Browns Team .04
633 Cowboys Team .04
634 Broncos Team .04
635 Lions Team .04
636 Packers Team .04
637 Oilers Team .10
638 Colts Team .15
639 Chiefs Team .04
640 Raiders Team (Tom Newberry) .04
641 Rams Team .04
642 Dolphins Team .04
643 Vikings Team .04
644 Patriots Team .04
645 Saints Team .04
646 Giants Team .04
647 Jets Team .04
648 Eagles Team .08
649 Cardinals Team .04
650 Steelers Team .04
651 Chargers Team .04
652 49ers Team .04
653 Seahawks Team .04
654 Buccaneers Team .04
655 Redskins Team .04
656 Checklist .04
657 Checklist .04
658 Checklist .04
659 Checklist .04
660 Checklist .04

1991 Topps 1000 Yard Club

HAYWOOD JEFFRIES

The 18 players featured in this insert set were receivers and running backs who gained more than 1,000 yards during the 1990 NFL season. Each card front has a color action photo, with the "1000 Yard Club" logo at the top. The photo has a red border at the top, while the player's name is at the bottom in an orange stripe. There is no border at the bottom or on the right, but the left side of the card has a red and purple border. The card back gives the player's game-by-game totals in blue and pink against a white background. A card number is in the upper right corner.

	MT
Complete Set (18):	6.00
Common Player:	.25

1	Jerry Rice	1.50
2	Barry Sanders	1.75
3	Thurman Thomas	.75
4	Henry Ellard	.25
5	Marion Butts	.75
6	Earnest Byner	.25
7	Andre Rison	.50
8	Bobby Humphrey	.25
9	Gary Clark	.35
10	Sterling Sharpe	1.25
11	Flipper Anderson	.25
12	Neal Anderson	.35
13	Haywood Jeffries	.45
14	Stephone Paige	.35
15	Drew Hill	.25
16	Barry Word	.35
17	Anthony Carter	.30
18	James Brooks	.25

1992 Topps

Topps issued its 759-card 1992 set in three series - 330, 330 and 99 cards. The fronts have action photos inside team color-coded frames bordered by white. The backs have a biography, statistics, a photo of the team's stadium and a player profile. Topps Gold cards were also produced for each card; these gold-foil versions were inserted one per foil pack.

	MT
Complete Set (759):	35.00
Complete Series 1 (330):	15.00
Complete Series 2 (330):	10.00
Complete Hi Series (99):	10.00
Common Player:	.05
Minor Stars:	.10
Series 1 or 2 Wax Box:	12.00
Series 3 Wax Box:	22.00

1	Tim McGee	.05
2	Rich Camarillo	.05
3	Anthony Johnson	.05
4	Lary Kelm	.05
5	Irving Fryar	.05
6	Joey Browner	.05
7	Michael Walter	.05
8	Cortez Kennedy	.15
9	Reyna Thompson	.05
10	John Friesz	.05
11	Leroy Hoard	.05
12	Steve McMichael	.05
13	Marvin Washington	.05
14	Clyde Simmons	.05
15	Stephone Paige	.05
16	Mike Utley	.20
17	Tunch Ilkin	.05
18	Lawrence Dawsey	.05
19	Vance Johnson	.05
20	Bryce Paup	.05
21	Jeff Wright	.05
22	Gill Fenerty	.05
23	Lamar Lathon	.05
24	Danny Copeland	.05
25	Marcus Allen	.05
26	Tim Green	.05
27	Pete Stoyanovich	.05
28	Alvin Harper	.10
29	Roy Foster	.05
30	Eugene Daniel	.05
31	Luis Sharpe	.05
32	Terry Wooden	.05
33	Jim Breech	.05
34	Randy Hilliard	.10
35	Roman Phifer	.05
36	Erik Howard	.05
37	Chris Singleton	.05
38	Matt Stover	.05
39	Tim Irwin	.05
40	Karl Mecklenburg	.05
41	Joe Phillips	.05
42	Bill Jones	.05
43	Mark Carrier	.05
44	George Jamison	.05
45	Rob Taylor	.05
46	Jeff Jaeger	.05
47	Don Majkowski	.05
48	Al Edwards	.05
49	Curtis Duncan	.05
50	Sam Mills	.05
51	Terance Mathis	.05
52	Brian Mitchell	.05
53	Mike Pritchard	.20
54	Calvin Williams	.12
55	Hardy Nickerson	.05
56	Nate Newton	.05
57	Steve Wallace	.05
58	John Offerdahl	.05
59	Aeneas Williams	.05
60	Lee Johnson	.05
61	Ricardo McDonald, Jeff Feagles	.12
62	David Richards	.05
63	Paul Gruber	.05
64	Greg McMurtry	.05
65	Jay Hilgenberg	.05
66	Tim Grunhard	.05
67	*Dwayne White*	.08
68	Don Beebe	.05
69	Simon Fletcher	.05
70	Warren Moon	.20
71	Chris Jacke	.05
72	Steve Wisniewski	.05
73	Mike Coffer	.05
74	Tim Johnson	.05
75	T.J. Turner	.05
76	Scott Case	.05
77	Michael Jackson	.10
78	Jon Hand	.05
79	Stan Brock	.05
80	Robert Blackmon	.05
81	David Johnson	.05
82	Damone Johnson	.05
83	Marc Spindler	.05
84	Larry Brown	.05
85	Ray Berry	.05
86	Andre Waters	.05
87	Carlos Huerta	.05
88	Brad Muster	.05
89	Chuck Cecil	.05
90	Nick Lowery	.05
91	Cornelius Bennett	.05
92	Jessie Tuggle	.05
93	*Mark Schlereth*	.10
94	Vestee Jackson	.05
95	Eric Bieniemy	.05
96	Jeff Hostetler	.15
97	Ken Lanier	.05
98	Wayne Haddix	.05
99	Lorenzo White	.05
100	Mervyn Fernandez	.05
101	Brent Williams	.05
102	Ian Beckles	.05
103	Harris Barton	.05
104	*Edgar Bennett*	.50
105	Mike Pitts	.05
106	Fuad Reveiz	.05
107	Vernon Turner	.05
108	*Tracy Hayworth*	.10
109	Checklist 1-110	.05
110	Tom Waddle	.15
111	Fred Stokes	.05
112	Howard Ballard	.05
113	David Szott	.05
114	Tim McKyer	.05
115	Kyle Clifton	.05
116	Tony Bennett	.05
117	Joel Hilgenberg	.05
118	Dwayne Harper	.05
119	Mike Baab	.05
120	Mark Clayton	.05
121	Eric Swann	.05
122	Neil O'Donnell	.10
123	Mike Munchak	.05
124	Howie Long	.05
125	John Elway	.50
126	Joe Prokop	.05
127	Pepper Johnson	.05
128	Richard Dent	.05
129	*Robert Porcher*	.15
130	Earnest Byner	.05
131	Kent Hull	.05
132	Mike Merriweather	.05
133	Scott Fulhage	.05
134	Kevin Porter	.05
135	Tony Casillas	.05
136	Dean Biasucci	.05
137	Ben Smith	.05
138	Bruce Kozerski	.05
139	Jeff Campbell	.05
140	Kevin Greene	.05
141	Gary Plummer	.05
142	Vincent Brown	.05
143	Ron Hall	.05
144	*Louis Aguiar*	.10
145	Mark Duper	.05
146	Jesse Sapolu	.05
147	Jeff Gossett	.05
148	Brian Noble	.05
149	Derek Russell	.15
150	*Carlton Bailey*	.15
151	Kelly Goodburn	.05
152	Audrey McMillian	.05
153	Neal Anderson	.05
154	Bill Maas	.05
155	Rickey Jackson	.05
156	Chris Miller	.05
157	Darren Comeaux	.05
158	David Williams	.05
159	Rich Gannon	.10
160	Kevin Mack	.05
161	Jim Arnold	.05
162	Reggie White	.15
163	Leonard Russell	.25
164	Doug Smith	.05
165	Tony Mandarich	.05
166	Greg Lloyd	.05
167	Jumbo Elliott	.05
168	Jonathan Hayes	.05
169	Jim Ritcher	.05
170	Mike Kenn	.05
171	James Washington	.05
172	Tim Harris	.05
173	James Thornton	.05
174	*John Brandes*	.10
175	*Fred McAfee*	.15
176	Henry Rolling	.05
177	Tony Paige	.05
178	Jay Schroeder	.05
179	Jeff Herrod	.05
180	Emmitt Smith	2.50
181	Wymon Henderson	.05
182	Rob Moore	.05
183	Robert Wilson	.05
184	*Michael Zordich*	.10
185	Jim Harbaugh	.05
186	Vince Workman	.05
187	Ernest Givins	.05
188	Herschel Walker	.05
189	Dan Fike	.05
190	Seth Joyner	.05
191	Steve Young	1.00
192	Dennis Gibson	.05
193	Darryl Talley	.05
194	Emile Harry	.05
195	Bill Fralic	.05
196	Michael Stewart	.05
197	James Francis	.05
198	Jerome Henderson	.05
199	John L. Williams	.05
200	Rod Woodson	.05
201	Mike Farr	.05
202	Greg Montgomery	.05
203	Andre Collins	.05
204	Scott Miller	.05
205	Clay Matthews	.05
206	Ethan Horton	.05
207	Rich Miano	.05
208	*Chris Mims*	.30
209	Anthony Morgan	.05
210	Rodney Hampton	.10
211	Chris Hinton	.05
212	Esera Tuaolo	.05
213	Shane Conlan	.05
214	John Carney	.05
215	Kenny Walker	.05
216	Scott Radecic	.05
217	Chris Martin	.05
218	Checklist 111-220	.05
219	Weseley Carroll	.05
220	Bill Romanowski	.05
221	Reggie Cobb	.15
222	Alfred Anderson	.05
223	Cleveland Gary	.05
224	*Eddie Blake*	.10
225	Chris Spielman	.05
226	John Roper	.05
227	*George Thomas*	.05
228	Jeff Faulkner	.05
229	Chip Lohmiller	.05
230	Hugh Millen	.05
231	Ray Horton	.05
232	James Campen	.05
233	Howard Cross	.05
234	Keith McKeller	.05
235	Dino Hackett	.05
236	Jerome Brown	.05
237	Andy Heck	.05
238	Jerome Brown	.05
239	Bruce Matthews	.05
240	Jeff Lageman	.05
241	Bobby Hebert	.05
242	Gary Anderson	.05
243	Mark Bortz	.05
244	Rich Moran	.05
245	Jeff Uhlenhake	.05
246	Ricky Sanders	.05
247	Clarence Kay	.05
248	Ed King	.05
249	Eddie Anderson	.05
250	*Amp Lee*	.35
251	Norm Johnson	.05
252	Michael Carter	.05
253	Felix Wright	.05
254	Leon Seals	.05
255	Nate Lewis	.05
256	Kevin Call	.05
257	Darryl Henley	.05
258	Jon Vaughn	.10
259	Matt Bahr, David Alexander	.05
260	Johnny Johnson	.15
261	Ken Norton	.05
262	Wendell Davis	.05
263	Eugene Robinson	.05
264	David Treadwell	.05
265	Michael Haynes	.25
266	Robb Thomas	.05
267	Nate Odomes	.05
268	Martin Mayhew	.05
269	Perry Kemp	.05
270	Jerry Ball	.05
271	*Tommy Vardell*	.20
272	Ernie Mills	.05
273	Mo Lewis	.05
274	Roger Ruzek	.05
275	Steve Smith	.05
276	*Bo Orlando*	.10
277	Louis Oliver	.05
278	Toi Cook	.05
279	Eddie Brown	.05
280	Keith McCants	.05
281	Rob Burnett	.05
282	Keith DeLong	.05
283	Stan Thomas	.05
284	Robert Brown	.05
285	John Alt	.05
286	Randy Dixon	.05
287	Siran Stubbs	.20
288	Ray Agnew	.05
289	Darion Conner	.05
290	Kirk Lowdermilk	.05
291	Greg Jackson	.05
292	Ken Harvey	.05
293	Jacob Green	.05
294	Mark Tuinei	.05
295	Mark Rypien	.15
296	*Gerald Robinson*	.08
297	*Broderick Thompson*	.05
298	Doug Widell	.05
299	Carwell Gardner	.05
300	Barry Sanders	1.25
301	Eric Metcalf	.05
302	Erick Thomas	.05
303	*Terrell Buckley*	.25
304	Byron Evans	.05
305	Johnny Hector	.05
306	Steve Broussard	.05
307	Gene Atkins	.05
308	Terry McDaniel	.05
309	Charles McRae	.05
310	Jim Lachey	.05
311	Pat Harlow	.05
312	Kevin Butler	.05
313	Scott Stephen	.05
314	Dermontti Dawson	.05
315	Johnny Meads	.05
316	Checklist 221-330	.05
317	Aaron Craver	.05
318	Michael Brooks	.05
319	Guy McIntyre	.05
320	Thurman Thomas	.25
321	Courtney Hall	.05
322	Dan Saleaumua	.05
323	*Vinson Smith*	.10
324	Steven Jordan	.05
325	Walter Reeves	.05
326	Erik Kramer	.05
327	Duane Bickett	.05
328	Tom Newberry	.05
329	John Kasay	.05
330	Dave Meggett	.05
331	Kevin Ross	.05
332	*Keith Hamilton*	.15
333	Dwight Stone	.05
334	Mel Gray	.05
335	Harry Galbreath	.05
336	William Perry	.05
337	Brian Blades	.05
338	Randall McDaniel	.05
339	*Pat Coleman*	.12
340	Michael Irvin	.25
341	Checklist 331-440	.05
342	Chris Mohr	.05
343	Greg Davis	.05
344	Dave Cadigan	.05
345	Art Monk	.05
346	Tim Goad	.05
347	Vinnie Clark	.05
348	David Fulcher	.05
349	Craig Heward	.05
350	Ronnie Lott	.05
351	Dexter Carter	.05
352	Mark Jackson	.05
353	Brian Jordan	.05
354	Ray Donaldson	.05
355	Jim Price	.05
356	Rod Bernstine	.05
357	*Tony Mayberry*	.10
358	*Richard Brown*	.10
360	Haywood Jeffires	.15
361	Henry Thomas	.05
362	Jeff Graham	.12
363	Don Warren	.05
364	Scott Davis	.05
365	Harlon Barnett	.05
366	Mark Collins	.05
367	Rick Tuten	.05
368	*Lonnie Marts*	.15
369	Dennis Smith	.05
370	Steve Tasker	.05
371	Robert Massey	.05
372	Ricky Reynolds	.05
373	Alvin Wright	.05
374	Kelvin Martin	.05
375	Vince Buck	.05
376	John Kidd	.05
378	Bryan Cox	.05
379	*Jamie Dukes*	.08
380	Anthony Munoz	.05
381	*Mark Gunn*	.10
382	Keith Henderson	.05
383	Charles Wilson	.05
384	*Shawn McCarthy*	.10
385	Ernie Jones	.05
386	Nick Bell	.05
387	Derrick Walker	.05
388	Mark Stepnoski	.05
389	Broderick Thomas	.05
390	Reggie Roby	.05
391	Bubba McDowell	.05
392	Eric Martin	.05
393	*Toby Cashton*	.10
394	Bern Brostek	.05
395	Christian Okoye	.05
396	Frank Minnifield	.05
397	Mike Golic	.05
398	Grant Feasel	.05
399	Michael Ball	.05
400	Mike Croel	.05
401	Maury Buford	.05
402	Jeff Bostic	.05
403	Sean Landeta	.05
404	Terry Allen	.35
405	Donald Evans	.05
406	Don Mosebar	.05
407	D.J. Dozier	.05
408	Bruce Pickens	.05
409	Jim Dombrowski	.05
410	Deron Cherry	.05
411	Richard Johnson	.05
412	Alexander Wright	.05
413	Tom Rathman	.05
414	Mark Dennis	.05
415	Phil Hansen	.05
416	Lonnie Young	.05
417	Burt Grossman	.05
418	Tony Covington	.05
419	John Stephens	.05
420	Jim Everett	.05
421	Johnny Holland	.05
422	*Mike Barber*	.12
423	Carl Lee	.05
424	*Craig Patterson*	.05
425	Greg Townsend	.05
426	Brett Perriman	.05
427	Morten Andersen	.05
428	John Gesek	.05
429	Bryan Barker	.05
430	John Taylor	.05
431	Donnell Woolford	.05
432	Ron Holmes	.05
433	Lee Williams	.05
434	Alfred Oglesby	.05
435	Jarrod Bunch	.05
436	*Carlton Haselrig*	.10
437	Rufus Porter	.05
438	Rohn Stark	.05
439	Tony Jones	.05
440	Andre Rison	.25
441	Eric Hill	.05
442	Jesse Solomon	.05
443	Jackie Slater	.05
444	Donnie Elder	.05
445	Brett Maxie	.05
446	Max Montoya	.05
447	Will Wolford	.05
448	Craig Taylor	.05
449	Jimmie Jones	.05
450	Anthony Carter	.05
451	*Brian Bollinger*	.08
452	Checklist 441-550	.05
453	Brad Edwards	.05
454	*Gene Chilton*	.05
455	Eric Allen	.05
456	William Roberts	.05
457	Eric Green	.05
458	Irvin Eatman	.05
459	Derrick Thomas	.15
460	Tommy Kane	.05
461	LeRoy Butler	.05
462	Oliver Barnett	.05
463	Anthony Smith	.05
464	Chris Dishman	.05
465	Pat Terrell	.05
466	Greg Kragen	.05
467	Rodney Peete	.05
468	Willie Drewrey	.05
469	Jim Wilks	.05
470	Vince Newsome	.05
471	Chris Gardocki	.05
472	Chris Chandler	.05
473	George Thornton	.05
474	Albert Lewis	.05
475	Kevin Glover	.05
476	*Joe Bowden*	.10
477	Harry Sydney	.05
478	Bob Golic	.05
479	Tony Zendejas	.05
480	Brad Baxter	.05
481	Steve Beuerlein	.15
482	Mark Higgs	.05
483	Drew Hill	.05
484	Bryan Millard	.05
485	Mark Kelso	.05
486	David Grant	.05
487	Gary Zimmerman	.05
488	Leonard Marshall	.05
489	Keith Jackson	.15
490	Sterling Sharpe	.10
491	Ferrell Edmunds	.05
492	Wilber Marshall	.05
493	Charles Haley	.05
494	Riki Ellison	.05
495	Bill Brooks	.05
496	Bill Hawkins	.05
497	Erik Williams	.05
498	*Leon Searcy*	.10
499	Mike Horan	.05
500	Pat Swilling	.05
501	Maurice Hurst	.05
502	William Fuller	.05
503	Tim Newton	.05
504	Lorenzo Lynch	.05
505	Tim Barnett	.05
506	Tom Thayer	.05
507	Chris Burkett	.05
508	Ronnie Harmon	.05
509	James Brooks	.05
510	Bennie Blades	.05
511	Roger Craig	.05
512	Tony Woods	.05
513	Greg Lewis	.05
514	Eric Pegram	.15
515	Elvis Patterson	.05
516	Jeff Cross	.05
517	Myron Guyton	.05
518	Jay Novacek	.15
519	*Leo Barker*	.10
520	Keith Byars	.05
521	Dalton Hilliard	.05
522	Ted Washington	.05
523	*Dexter McNabb*	.10
524	Frank Reich	.05
525	Henry Ellard	.05
526	Barry Foster	.05
527	Barry Word	.15
528	Gary Anderson	.05
529	Reggie Rutland	.05
530	Stephen Baker	.05
531	John Flannery	.05
532	Steve Wright	.05
533	Eric Sanders	.05
534	*Bob Whitfield*	.15
535	Gaston Green	.05
536	Anthony Pleasant	.05
537	Jeff Bryant	.05
538	Jarvis Williams	.05
539	Jim Morrissey	.05
540	Andre Tippett	.05
541	Gill Byrd	.05
542	Raleigh McKenzie	.05
543	Jim Sweeney	.05
544	David Lutz	.05
545	Wayne Martin	.05
546	Karl Wilson	.05
547	Pierce Holt	.05
548	Doug Smith	.05
549	*Nolan Harrison*	.10
550	Freddie Joe Nunn	.05
551	Eric Moore	.05
552	Cris Carter	.05
553	Kevin Gogan	.05
554	Harold Green	.05
555	Kenneth Davis	.05
556	Travis McNeal	.05
557	Jim Jensen	.05
558	Willie Green	.20
559	*Scott Galbraith*	.12
560	Louis Lipps	.05
561	Matt Brock	.05
562	Mike Prior	.05
563	Checklist 551-660	.05
564	Robert Delpino	.05
565	Vinny Testaverde	.05
566	Willie Gault	.05
567	Quinn Early	.05
568	Eric Moten	.05
569	Lance Smith	.05
570	Darrell Green	.05
571	Moe Gardner	.05
572	Steve Atwater	.05
573	Ray Childress	.05
574	Dave Krieg	.05
575	Bruce Armstrong	.05
576	Fred Barnett	.15
577	Don Griffin	.05
578	*David Brandon*	.10
579	Robert Young	.05
580	Keith Van Horne	.05
581	Jeff Criswell	.05
582	Lewis Tillman	.05
583	Bubby Brister	.05
584	Aaron Wallace	.05
585	Chris Doleman	.05
586	*Marty Carter*	.15
587	Chris Warren	.25
588	David Griggs	.05
589	Darrell Thompson	.05
590	Marion Butts	.05
591	Scott Norwood	.05
592	Lomas Brown	.05
593	Daryl Johnston	.05
594	*Alonzo Mitz*	.10
595	Tommy Barnhardt	.05
596	Tim Jorden	.05
597	Neil Smith	.05
598	Todd Marinovich	.12
599	Sean Jones	.05
600	Clarence Verdin	.05
601	Trace Armstrong	.05
602	*Steve Bono*	.50
603	Mark Ingram	.05
604	Flipper Anderson	.05
605	James Jones	.05
606	Al Noga	.05
607	Rick Bryan	.05
608	Eugene Lockhart	.05
609	Charles Mann	.05
610	James Hasty	.05
611	Tim Brown	.35
612	David Little	.05
613	Keith Sims	.05
614	Kevin Murphy	.05
615	Ray Crockett	.05
616	Jim Jeffcoat	.05
617	Patrick Hunter	.05
618	Keith Kartz	.05
619	Peter Tom Willis	.05
620	Vaughan Johnson	.05
621	Anthony Thompson	.05
622	Shawn Jefferson	.05
623	Anthony Thompson	.05
624	John Rienstra	.05
625	Don Maggs	.05
626	Todd Lyght	.05
627	Brent Jones	.05
628	Todd McNair	.05
629	Winston Moss	.05
630	Mark Carrier	.05
631	Dan Owens	.05
632	Sammie Smith	.05
633	James Lofton	.05

#	Player	Price
634	*Paul McJulien*	.10
635	Tony Tolbert	.05
636	Carnell Lake	.05
637	Gary Clark	.05
638	Brian Washington	.05
639	Jessie Hester	.05
640	Doug Riesenberg	.05
641	*Joe Walter*	.10
642	John Rade	.05
643	Wes Hopkins	.05
644	Kelly Stouffer	.05
645	Marv Cook	.05
646	Ken Clarke	.05
647	Bobby Humphrey	.05
648	Tim McDonald	.05
649	*Donald Frank*	.12
650	Richmond Webb	.05
651	Lemuel Stinson	.05
652	Merton Hanks	.05
653	Frank Warren	.05
654	Thomas Benson	.05
655	Al Smith	.05
656	Steve DeBerg	.05
657	*Jayice Pearson*	.10
658	Joe Morris	.05
659	Fred Strickland	.05
660	Kelvin Pritchett	.05
661	Lewis Billups	.05
662	Todd Collins	.05
663	Corey Miller	.05
664	Levon Kirkland	.05
665	Jerry Rice	1.00
666	Mike Lodish	.05
667	Chuck Smith	.05
668	Lance Olberding	.05
669	*Kevin Murphy*	.30
670	*Dale Carter*	.30
671	*Sean Gilbert*	.30
672	Ken O'Brien	.05
673	Ricky Proehl	.05
674	Junior Seau	.05
675	Courtney Hawkins	.05
676	Eddie Robinson	.05
677	Tom Jeter	.05
678	Jeff George	.05
679	Cary Conklin	.05
680	Rueben Mayes	.05
681	Sean Lumpkin	.05
682	Dan Marino	1.50
683	Ed McDaniel	.05
684	Greg Skrepenak	.05
685	Tracy Scroggins	.05
686	*Tommy Maddox*	.30
687	Mike Singletary	.05
688	Patrick Rowe	.05
689	Phillipi Sparks	.05
690	Joel Steed	.05
691	Kevin Fagan	.05
692	Deion Sanders	.05
693	Bruce Smith	.05
694	*David Klingler*	.10
695	Clayton Holmes	.05
696	Brett Favre	2.50
697	Marc Boutte	.05
698	Dwayne Sabb	.05
699	Ed McCaffrey	.05
700	Randall Cunningham	
701	*Quentin Coryatt*	.30
702	Bernie Kosar	.05
703	Vaughn Dunbar	.15
704	Browning Nagle	.05
705	Mark Wheeler	.05
706	Paul Siever	.05
707	Anthony Miller	.05
708	Corey Widmer	.05
709	Eric Dickerson	.05
710	Martin Bayless	.05
711	Jason Hanson	.05
712	Michael Dean Perry	.05
713	Billy Joe Toliver	.05
714	Chad Hennings	.05
715	*Bucky Richardson*	.30
716	Steve Israel	.05
717	Robert Harris	.05
718	Timm Rosenbach	.05
719	Joe Montana	1.00
720	*Derek Brown*	.15
721	*Robert Brooks*	1.50
722	Boomer Esiason	.05
723	Troy Auzenne	.05
724	John Fina	.05
725	Chris Crooms	.05
726	Eugene Chung	.05
727	Darren Woodson	.05
728	Leslie O'Neal	.05
729	Dan McGwire	.05
730	Al Toon	.05
731	Michael Brandon	.05
732	Steve DeOssie	.05
733	Jim Kelly	.30
734	Webster Slaughter	.05
735	Tony Smith	.05
736	Shane Collins	.05
737	Randal Hill	.05
738	Chris Holder	.05
739	Russell Maryland	.05
740	*Carl Pickens*	.75
741	Andre Reed	.05
742	*Steve Emtman*	.15
743	Carl Banks	.05
744	Troy Aikman	1.00
745	Mark Royals	.05
746	J.J. Birden	.05
747	Michael Cofer	.05
748	Darryl Ashmore	.05
749	Dion Lambert	.05
750	Phil Simms	.05
751	Reggie E. White	.05
752	Harvey Williams	.05
753	Ty Detmer	.05
754	Tony Brooks	.05
755	Steve Christie	.05
756	Lawrence Taylor	.05
757	Merril Hoge	.05
758	Robert Jones	.05
759	Checklist 661-792	.05

1992 Topps Gold

The 759-card, standard-sized set was a parallel to the base set and was inserted once every pack; three every rack pack, and 20 per 660-card factory set. The cards listed below replaced the seven checklist cards. Ten gold cards were also included with each 99-card Hi Series.

		MT
Complete Set (759):		130.00
Complete Series 1 (330):		60.00
Complete Series 2 (330):		50.00
Complete Hi Series (99):		20.00
Common Player:		.20
Veteran Stars:		1.5x-3x
Young Stars:		2x
RCs:		1.25x-2.5x
109	Freeman McNeil	.40
218	David Daniels	.40
316	Chris Hakel	.40
341	Ottis Anderson	.40
452	Shawn Moore	.40
563	Mike Mooney	.40
759	Curtis Whitley	.40

1992 Topps No. 1 Draft Picks

The four-card, standard-size set features No. 1 draft picks from 1990, 1991 and 1992, as well as Notre Dame standout Raghib "Rocket" Ismail. The cards were randomly inserted in 1992 Hi Series packs and the entire set was included with the 99-card Hi Series factory set.

		MT
Complete Set (4):		4.00
Common Player:		1.00
1	Jeff George	1.50
2	Russell Maryland	1.00
3	Steve Emtman	1.00
4	Rocket Ismail	1.25

1992 Topps 1000 Yard Club

Receivers and running backs who gained more than 1,000 yards during the 1991 NFL season are featured in this 20-card insert set. The white-bordered card front has a color action photo, along with the set's name at the top. The player's name is at the bottom in a green-and-white striped bar. The player's name and 1000 on the front are in red foil. The back has a game-by-game summary in a lime green panel against a background designed like a football field. Each card back is also numbered.

		MT
Complete Set (20):		15.00
Common Player:		.50
1	Emmitt Smith	6.00
2	Barry Sanders	4.00
3	Michael Irvin	2.00
4	Thurman Thomas	2.00
5	Gary Clark	.75
6	Haywood Jeffires	.75
7	Michael Haynes	1.50
8	Drew Hill	.50
9	Mark Duper	.75
10	James Lofton	1.00
11	Rodney Hampton	2.50
12	Mark Clayton	.75
13	Erric Pegram	1.00
14	Art Monk	1.00
15	Earnest Byner	.50
16	Gaston Green	.50
17	Christian Okoye	.50
18	Irving Fryar	.65
19	John Taylor	.75
20	Brian Blades	.50

1993 Topps

Topps issued its 1993 set in two 330-card series. Subsets include Franchise Players (9 cards), Team Leaders (28), Record Breakers (2), League Leaders (5), Draft Picks (30) and Field Generals (10). The card front has a color action photo surrounded by white borders. The player's name and team are at the bottom between team color-coded diagonal bars. The back has a mug shot, statistics, career summary and biography against a team color-coded background. Each pack contains one Topps Gold card. Topps Black Gold cards were also made and inserted one per every 48 packs.

		MT
Complete Set (660):		25.00
Comp. Factory Set (673):		35.00
Complete Series 1 (330):		15.00
Complete Series 2 (330):		10.00
Common Player:		.05
Minor Stars:		.10
Series 1 Wax Box:		20.00
Series 2 Wax Box:		12.00
1	Art Monk	.05
2	Jerry Rice	.50
3	Stanley Richard	.05
4	Ron Hall	.05
5	Daryl Johnston	.10
6	Wendell Davis	.05
7	Vaughn Dunbar	.10
8	Mike Jones	.05
9	Anthony Johnson	.05
10	Chris Miller	.05
11	Kyle Clifton	.05
12	*Curtis Conway*	1.00
13	Lionel Washington	.05
14	Reggie Johnson	.05
15	David Little	.05
16	Nick Lowery	.05
17	Darryl Williams	.05
18	Brent Jones	.05
19	Bruce Matthews	.05
20	Heath Sherman, John Kasay	.05
22	*Troy Drayton*	.35
23	Eric Metcalf	.05
24	Andre Tippett	.05
25	Rodney Hampton	.35
26	Henry Jones	.05
27	Jim Everett	.05
28	Steve Jordan	.05
29	LeRoy Butler	.05
30	Troy Vincent	.15
31	Nate Lewis	.05
32	Rickey Jackson	.05
33	Darion Conner	.05
34	*Tom Carter*	.25
35	Jeff George	.20
36	*Larry Centers*	.30
37	Reggie Cobb	.15
38	Mike Saxon	.05
39	Brad Baxter	.05
40	Reggie White	.12
41	Haywood Jeffires	.15
42	Alfred Williams	.05
43	Aaron Wallace	.05
44	Tracy Simien	.05
45	Pat Harlow	.05
46	D.J. Johnson	.05
47	Don Griffin	.05
48	Flipper Anderson	.05
49	Keith Kartz	.05
50	Bernie Kosar	.05
51	Kent Hull	.05
52	Erik Howard	.05
53	Pierce Holt	.05
54	Dwayne Harper	.05
55	Bennie Blades	.05
56	Mark Duper	.05
57	Brian Noble	.05
58	Jeff Feagles	.05
59	Michael Haynes	.20
60	Junior Seau	.15
61	Gary Anderson	.05
62	Jon Hand	.05
63	*Lin Elliott*	.10
64	*Dana Stubblefield*	.50
65	Vaughan Johnson	.05
66	Mo Lewis	.05
67	Aeneas Williams	.05
68	David Fulcher	.05
69	Chip Lohmiller	.05
70	Greg Townsend	.05
71	Simon Fletcher	.05
72	Sean Salisbury	.05
73	Christian Okoye	.05
74	Jim Arnold	.05
75	Bruce Smith	.05
76	Fred Barnett	.15
77	Bill Romanowski	.05
78	Dermontti Dawson	.05
79	Bern Brostek	.05
80	Warren Moon	.15
81	Bill Fralic	.05
82	Lomas Brown	.05
83	Duane Bickett	.05
84	Neil Smith	.05
85	Reggie White	.05
86	Tim McDonald	.05
87	Leslie O'Neal	.05
88	Steve Young	.50
89	Paul Gruber	.05
90	Wilber Marshall	.05
91	Trace Armstrong	.05
92	*Bobby Houston*	.10
93	George Thornton	.05
94	Keith McCants	.05
95	Ricky Sanders	.05
96	Jackie Harris	.20
97	Todd Marinovich	.12
98	Henry Thomas	.05
99	Jeff Wright	.05
100	John Elway	.50
101	*Garrison Hearst*	1.00
102	Roy Foster	.05
103	David Lang	.05
104	Matt Stover	.05
105	Lawrence Taylor	.10
106	Pete Stoyanovich	.05
107	Jessie Tuggle	.05
108	William White	.05
109	*Andy Harmon*	.12
110	John L. Williams	.05
111	Jon Vaughn	.05
112	John Alt	.05
113	Chris Jacke	.05
114	Jim Breech	.05
115	Eric Martin	.05
116	Derrick Walker	.05
117	Ricky Ervins	.12
118	Roger Craig	.05
119	Jeff Gossett	.05
120	Emmitt Smith	2.00
121	Bob Whitefield	.05
122	Alonzo Spellman	.05
123	David Klingler	.15
124	Tommy Maddox	.10
125	Robert Porcher	.05
126	Edgar Bennett	.15
127	Harvey Williams	.15
128	*Dave Brown*	1.00
129	Johnny Mitchell	.25
130	*Drew Bledsoe*	3.00
131	Zefross Moss	.05
132	Nate Odomes	.05
133	Rufus Porter	.05
134	Jackie Slater	.05
135	Steve Young	.50
136	Chris Calloway	.05
137	Steve Atwater	.05
138	Mark Carrier	.05
139	Marvin Washington	.05
140	Barry Foster	.05
141	Ricky Reynolds	.05
142	Bubba McDowell	.05
143	*Dan Footman*	.15
144	Richmond Webb	.05
145	Mike Pritchard	.12
146	Chris Spielman	.05
147	Dave Krieg	.05
148	Nick Bell	.15
149	Vincent Brown	.05
150	Seth Joyner	.05
151	Tommy Kane	.05
152	Carlton Gray	.25
153	Harry Newsome	.05
154	Rohn Stark	.05
155	Shannon Sharpe	.05
156	Charles Haley	.05
157	Cornelius Bennett	.05
158	Doug Riesenberg	.05
159	Amp Lee	.10
160	Sterling Sharpe	.40
161	Alonzo Mitz	.05
162	Pat Terrill	.05
163	Mark Schlereth	.05
164	Gary Anderson	.05
165	Quinn Early	.05
166	*Jerome Bettis*	1.25
167	Lawrence Dawsey	.05
168	Derrick Thomas	.15
169	Rodney Peete	.10
170	Jim Kelly	.05
171	Deion Sanders	.05
172	Richard Dent	.05
173	Emmitt Smith	.75
174	Barry Sanders	.50
175	Sterling Sharpe	.25
176	Cleveland Gary	.05
177	Terry Allen	.05
178	Vaughan Johnson	.05
179	Rodney Hampton	.05
180	Randall Cunningham	.05
181	Ricky Proehl	.05
182	Jerry Rice	.20
183	Reggie Cobb	.05
184	Earnest Byner	.05
185	Jeff Lageman	.05
186	Carlos Jenkins	.05
187	Cardinals Draft Picks	.50
188	Todd Lyght	.05
189	*Carl Simpson*	.12
190	Barry Sanders	1.25
191	Jim Harbaugh	.10
192	Roger Ruzek	.05
193	Brent Williams	.05
194	Chip Banks	.05
195	Mike Croel	.05
196	Marion Butts	.05
197	James Washington	.05
198	John Offerdahl	.05
199	Tom Rathman	.05
200	Joe Montana	1.25
201	Pepper Johnson	.05
202	Cris Dishman	.05
203	Adrian White	.10
204	*Reggie Brooks*	.25
205	Cortez Kennedy	.10
206	Robert Massey	.05
207	Toi Cook	.05
208	Harry Sydney	.05
209	*Lincoln Kennedy*	.15
210	Randall McDaniel	.05
211	Eugene Daniel	.05
212	Rob Burnett	.05
213	Steve Broussard	.05
214	Brian Washington	.05
215	*Leonard Renfro*	.12
216	Audray McMillian, Henry Jones	.05
217	Sterling Sharpe, Anthony Miller	.20
218	Clyde Simmons, Leslie O'Neal	.05
219	Emmitt Smith, Barry Foster	.50
220	Steve Young, Warren Moon	.12
221	Mel Gray	.05
222	Luis Sharpe	.05
223	Eric Moten	.05
224	Albert Lewis	.05
225	Alvin Harper	.30
226	Steve Wallace	.05
227	Mark Higgs	.15
228	Eugene Lockhart	.05
229	Sean Jones	.05
230	Buccaneers Draft Picks	.15
231	Jimmy Williams	.05
232	*Demetrius DuBose*	.15
233	John Roper	.05
234	Keith Hamilton	.05
235	Donald Evans	.05
236	Kenneth Davis	.05
237	*John Copeland*	.30
238	Leonard Russell	.12
239	Ken Harvey	.05
240	Dale Carter	.05
241	Anthony Pleasant	.05
242	Darrell Green	.05
243	*Natrone Means*	1.00
244	Rob Moore	.10
245	Chris Doleman	.05
246	J.B. Brown	.05
247	Ray Crockett	.05
248	John Taylor	.05
249	Russell Maryland	.05
250	Brett Favre	2.00
251	Carl Pickens	.50
252	Andy Heck	.05
253	Jerome Henderson	.05
254	Deion Sanders	.15
255	Steve Emtman	.05
256	Calvin Williams	.05
257	Sean Gilbert	.05
258	Don Beebe	.05
259	*Robert Smith*	1.00
260	Rogert Blackmon	.05
261	Jim Kelly	.10
262	Harold Green	.05
263	Clay Matthews	.05
264	John Elway	.10
265	Warren Moon	.10
266	Jeff George	.10
267	Derrick Thomas	.05
268	Howie Long	.05
269	Dan Marino	.60
270	Jon Vaughn	.05
271	Chris Burkett	.05
272	Barry Foster	.10
273	Marion Butts	.05
274	Chris Warren	.05
275	Giants Draft Picks	.15
276	Tony Casillas	.05
277	Jarrod Bunch	.05
278	Eric Green	.05
279	Stan Brock	.05
280	Chester McGlockton	.05
281	Ricky Watters	.40
282	Dan Saleaumua	.05
283	Rich Camarillo	.05
284	Cris Carter	.05
285	*Rick Mirer*	.25
286	Matt Brock	.05
287	Burt Grossman	.05
288	Andre Collins	.05
289	Mark Jackson	.05
290	Dan Marino	2.00
291	Cornelius Bennett	.05
292	Steve Atwater	.05
293	Bryan Cox	.05
294	Sam Mills	.05
295	Pepper Johnson	.05
296	Seth Joyner	.05
297	Chris Spielman	.05
298	Junior Seau	.05
299	Cortez Kennedy	.05
300	Broderick Thomas	.05
301	Todd McNair	.05
302	Nate Newton	.05
303	Mike Waltr	.05
304	Clyde Simmons	.05
305	Ernie Mills	.05
306	Steve Wisniewski	.05
307	*Coleman Rudolph*	.10
308	Thurman Thomas	.50
309	Reggie Roby	.05
310	Eric Swann	.05
311	Mark Wheeler	.05
312	Jeff Herrod	.05
313	Leroy Hoard	.05
314	*Patrick Bates*	.10
315	Earnest Byner	.05
316	Dave Meggett	.05
317	*George Teague*	.25
318	Ray Childress	.05
319	Mike Kenn	.05
320	Jason Hanson	.05
321	Gary Clark	.10
322	Chris Gardocki	.05
323	Ken Norton	.05
324	*Eric Curry*	.30
325	Byron Evans	.05
326	*O.J. McDuffie*	1.00
327	Dwight Stone	.05
328	Tommy Barnhardt	.05
329	Checklist 1-165	.05
330	Checklist 166-330	.05
331	Erik Williams	.05
332	Phil Hansen	.05
333	*Martin Harrison*	.15
334	Mark Ingram	.08
335	Mark Rypien	.08
336	Anthony Miller	.05
337	Antone Davis	.05
338	Mike Munchak	.05
339	Wayne Martin	.05
340	Joe Montana	1.50
341	*Deon Figures*	.15
342	Ed McDaniel	.05
343	Chris Burkett	.05
344	Tony Smith	.05
345	James Lofton	.05
346	Courtney Hawkins	.05
347	Dennis Smith	.05
348	Anthony Morgan	.05
349	Chris Goode	.05
350	Phil Simms	.10
351	Patrick Hunter	.05
352	Brett Perriman	.07
353	Corey Miller	.05
354	Harry Galbreath	.05
355	Mark Carrier	.05
356	Troy Drayton	.05
357	Greg Davis	.05
358	Tim Krumrie	.05
359	Tim McDonald	.05
360	Webster Slaughter	.05
361	Steve Christie	.05
362	Courtney Hall	.05
363	Charles Mann	.06
364	Vestee Jackson	.05
365	Robert Jones	.05
366	Rich Miano	.05
367	Morten Andersen	.06
368	Jeff Graham	.05
369	Martin Mayhew	.05
370	Anthony Carter	.05
371	Greg Kragen	.05
372	Ron Cox	.05
373	Perry Williams	.05
374	Willie Gault	.05
375	Chris Warren	.15
376	Reyna Thompson	.05
377	Bennie Thompson	.05
378	Kevin Mack	.05

379	Clarence Verdin	.05
380	Marc Boutte	.05
381	Marvin Jones	.15
382	Greg Jackson	.05
383	Steve Bono	.50
384	Terrell Buckley	.10
385	Garrison Hearst	.50
386	Mike Brim	.05
387	Jesse Sapolu	.05
388	Carl Lee	.05
389	Jeff Cross	.05
390	Karl Mecklenburg	.05
391	Chad Hennings	.05
392	Oliver Barnett	.05
393	Dalton Hilliard	.06
394	Broderick Thompson	.05
395	Raghib Ismail	.25
396	John Kidd	.05
397	Eddie Anderson	.05
398	Lamar Lathon	.05
399	Darren Perry	.05
400	Drew Bledsoe	2.00
401	Ferrell Edmunds	.05
402	Lomas Brown	.05
403	Drew Hill	.05
404	David Whitmore	.05
405	Mike Johnson	.05
406	Paul Gruber	.05
407	Kirk Lowdermilk	.05
408	Curtis Conway	.50
409	Bryce Paup	.05
410	Boomer Esiason	.08
411	Jay Schroeder	.05
412	Anthony Newman	.08
413	Ernie Jones	.05
414	Carlton Bailey	.05
415	Kenneth Gant	.05
416	Todd Scott	.05
417	Anthony Smith	.05
418	Erik McMillan	.05
419	Ronnie Harmon	.06
420	Andre Reed	.07
421	Wymon Henderson	.05
422	Carnell Lake	.05
423	Al Noga	.05
424	Curtis Duncan	.05
425	Mike Gann	.05
426	Eugene Robinson	.05
427	Scott Mersereau	.05
428	Chris Singleton	.05
429	Gerald Robinson	.05
430	Pat Swilling	.05
431	Ed McCaffrey	.05
432	Neal Anderson	.06
433	Joe Phillips	.05
434	Jerry Ball	.05
435	Tyrone Stowe	.05
436	Dana Stubblefield	.25
437	Eric Curry	.10
438	Derrick Fenner	.05
439	Mark Clayton	.06
440	Quentin Coryatt	.10
441	Willie Roaf	.10
442	Earnest Dye	.05
443	Jeff Jaeger	.05
444	Stan Humphries	.05
445	Johnny Johnson	.07
446	Larry Brown	.05
447	Kurt Gouveia	.05
448	Qadry Ismail	.25
449	Dan Footman	.05
450	Tom Waddle	.05
451	Kelvin Martin	.05
452	Kanavis McGhee	.05
453	Herman Moore	.50
454	Jesse Solomon	.05
455	Shane Conlan	.05
456	Joel Steed	.05
457	Charles Arbuckle	.05
458	Shane Dronett	.05
459	Steve Tasker	.05
460	Herschel Walker	.07
461	Willie Davis	.10
462	Al Smith	.05
463	O.J. McDuffie	.50
464	Kevin Fagan	.05
465	Hardy Nickerson	.05
466	Leonard Marshall	.05
467	John Baylor	.05
468	Jay Novacek	.06
469	Wayne Simmons	.10
470	Tommy Vardell	.06
471	Cleveland Gary	.05
472	Mark Collins	.05
473	Craig Heyward	.05
474	John Copeland	.08
475	Jeff Hostetler	.08
476	Brian Mitchell	.05
477	Natrone Means	.75
478	Brad Muster	.05
479	David Lutz	.05
480	Andre Rison	.30
481	Michael Zordich	.05
482	Jim McMahon	.06
483	Carlton Gray	.05
484	Chris Mohr	.05
485	Ernest Givins	.05
486	Tony Tolbert	.05
487	Vai Sikahema	.05
488	Larry Jackson	.05
489	James Hasty	.05
490	Reggie White	.10
491	Reggie Rivers	.25
492	Roman Phifer	.05
493	Levon Kirkland	.05
494	Demetrius DuBose	.10
495	William Perry	.05
496	Clay Matthews	.05
497	Aaron Jones	.05
498	Jack Trudeau	.05
499	Michael Brooks	.05
500	Jerry Rice	.60
501	Lonnie Marts	.05
502	Tim McGee	.05
503	Kelvin Pritchett	.05
504	Bobby Hebert	.06
505	Audray McMillian	.05
506	Chuck Cecil	.05
507	Leonard Renfro	.05
508	Ethan Horton	.05
509	Kevin Smith	.06
510	Louis Oliver	.05
511	John Stephens	.05
512	Browning Nagle	.07
513	Ricardo McDonald	.05
514	Leslie O'Neal	.05
515	Lorenzo White	.07
516	Thomas Smith	.10
517	Tony Woods	.05
518	Darryl Henley	.05
519	Robert Delpino	.05
520	Rod Woodson	.05
521	Phillippi Sparks	.05
522	Jessie Hester	.05
523	Shaun Gayle	.05
524	Brad Edwards	.05
525	Randall Cunningham	.10
526	Marv Cook	.05
527	Dennis Gibson	.05
528	Erric Pegram	.25
529	Terry McDaniel	.05
530	Troy Aikman	1.25
531	Irving Fryar	.05
532	Blair Thomas	.05
533	Jim Wilks	.05
534	Michael Jackson	.06
535	Eric Davis	.05
536	James Campen	.05
537	Steve Beuerlein	.10
538	Robert Smith	.15
539	J.J. Birden	.05
540	Broderick Thomas	.05
541	Darryl Talley	.05
542	Russell Freeman	.10
543	David Alexander	.05
544	Chris Mims	.07
545	Coleman Rudolph	.05
546	Steve McMichael	.05
547	David Williams	.05
548	Chris Hinton	.05
549	Jim Jeffcoat	.05
550	Howie Long	.05
551	Roosevelt Potts	.25
552	Bryan Cox	.05
553	David Richards	.05
554	Reggie Brooks	.40
555	Neil O'Donnell	.25
556	Irv Smith	.05
557	Henry Ellard	.05
558	Steve DeBerg	.05
559	Jim Sweeney	.05
560	Harold Green	.05
561	Darrell Thompson	.08
562	Vinny Testaverde	.08
563	Bubby Brister	.06
564	Sean Landeta	.05
565	Neil Smith	.05
566	Craig Erickson	.05
567	Jim Ritcher	.05
568	Don Mosebar	.05
569	John Gesek	.05
570	Gary Plummer	.05
571	Norm Johnson	.05
572	Ron Heller	.05
573	Carl Simpson	.05
574	Greg Montgomery	.05
575	Dana Hall	.05
576	Vencie Glenn	.05
577	Dean Biasucci	.05
578	Rod Bernstine	.07
579	Randall Hill	.07
580	Sam Mills	.05
581	Santana Dotson	.05
582	Greg Lloyd	.06
583	Eric Thomas	.05
584	Henry Rolling	.05
585	Tony Bennett	.05
586	Sheldon White	.05
587	Mark Kelso	.05
588	Marc Spindler	.05
589	Greg McMurtry	.07
590	Art Monk	.07
591	Marco Coleman	.05
592	Tony Jones	.05
593	Melvin Jenkins	.05
594	Kevin Ross	.05
595	William Fuller	.05
596	James Joseph	.05
597	Lamar McGriggs	.15
598	Gill Byrd	.05
599	Alexander Wright	.05
600	Rick Mirer	.10
601	Richard Dent	.05
602	Thomas Everett	.05
603	Jack Del Rio	.05
604	Jerome Bettis	.75
605	Ronnie Lott	.10
606	Marty Carter	.05
607	Arthur Marshall	.30
608	Lee Johnson	.05
609	Bruce Armstrong	.05
610	Ricky Proehl	.05
611	Will Wolford	.05
612	Mike Prior	.05
613	George Jamison	.05
614	Gene Atkins	.05
615	Merril Hoge	.05
616	Desmond Howard	.25
617	Jarvis Williams	.07
618	Marcus Allen	.07
619	Gary Brown	.05
620	Bill Brooks	.05
621	Eric Allen	.05
622	Todd Kelly	.10
623	Michael Dean Perry	.05
624	David Braxton	.05
625	Mike Sherrard	.05
626	Jeff Bryant	.05
627	Eric Bieniemy	.06
628	Tim Brown	.06
629	Troy Auzenne	.05
630	Michael Irvin	.35
631	Maurice Hurst	.05
632	Duane Bickett	.05
633	George Teague	.05
634	Vince Workman	.05
635	Renaldo Turnbull	.05
636	Johnny Bailey	.05
637	Dan Williams	.15
638	James Thornton	.05
639	Terry Allen	.06
640	Kevin Greene	.05
641	Tony Zendejas	.05
642	Scott Kowalkowski	.10
643	Jeff Query	.05
644	Brian Blades	.05
645	Keith Jackson	.08
646	Monte Coleman	.05
647	Guy McIntyre	.05
648	Barry Word	.05
649	Steve Everitt	.10
650	Patrick Bates	.10
651	Marcus Robertson	.05
652	John Carney	.05
653	Derek Brown	.06
654	Carwell Gardner	.05
655	Moe Gardner	.05
656	Andre Ware	.06
657	Keith Van Horne	.05
658	Hugh Millen	.05
659	Checklist 3 of 4	.05
660	Checklist 4 of 4	.05

1993 Topps Gold

The 660-card, standard-size set was inserted in each pack (Three per rack pack, five per jumbo) and was a parallel to the 1993 base Topps set. The four checklist cards were replaced by the player cards listed below.

		MT
Complete Set (660):		90.00
Complete Series 1 (330):		50.00
Complete Series 2 (330):		40.00
Common Player:		.15
Veteran Stars:		1.5x-3x
Young Stars:		1.25x-2.5x
RCs:		1.25x-2.5x
329	Terance Mathis	1.00
330	Alex Wojciechowicz	.50
659	Pat Chaffey	.50
660	Milton Mack	.50

1993 Topps Black Gold

These cards feature an action photo against a curved,

screened gold-foil background with white borders. The player's name is in a black stripe at the bottom; the set name is also on the card front. The numbered backs are in a horizontal format and include a player profile shot and a career summary against a blue-green background. Cards were randomly included in every 48th pack of 1993 Topps football; cards 1-22 were in Series I packs, while 23-44 were in Series II packs. "You Just Won" cards were also available in Series I packs, good for mail-in offers for cards 1-11, 12-22 and 1-22. Series II packs had offers for cards 23-33, 34-44, 23-44 and the entire set (1-44). Winners then became eligible to win one of 500 uncut sheets of the set.

		MT
Complete Set (44):		35.00
Complete Series 1 (22):		15.00
Complete Series 2 (22):		20.00
Common Player:		.50
Minor Stars:		1.00
1	Kelvin Martin	.50
2	Audray McMillian	.50
3	Terry Allen	.50
4	Vai Sikahema	.50
5	Clyde Simmons	.50
6	Lorenzo White	.50
7	Michael Irvin	2.00
8	Troy Aikman	5.00
9	Mark Kelso	.50
10	Cleveland Gary	.50
11	Greg Montgomery	.50
12	Jerry Rice	5.00
13	Rod Woodson	1.00
14	Leslie O'Neal	.50
15	Harold Green	.50
16	Randall Cunningham	1.00
17	Ricky Watters	2.00
18	Andre Rison	.50
19	Eugene Robinson	.50
20	Wayne Martin	.50
21	Chris Warren	1.00
22	Anthony Miller	.50
23	Steve Young	3.00
24	Tim Harris	.50
25	Emmitt Smith	8.00
26	Sterling Sharpe	1.00
27	Henry Jones	.50
28	Warren Moon	1.00
29	Barry Foster	.50
30	Dale Carter	.50
31	Mel Gray	.50
32	Barry Sanders	5.00
33	Dan Marino	8.00
34	Fred Barnett	.50
35	Deion Sanders	3.00
36	Simon Fletcher	.50
37	Donnell Woolford	.50
38	Reggie Cobb	.50
39	Brett Favre	8.00
40	Thurman Thomas	1.00
41	Rodney Hampton	.50
42	Eric Martin	.50
43	Pete Stoyanovich	.50
44	Herschel Walker	.50

1993 Topps FantaSports

The 200-card, 3" x 5" set is an interactive fantasy game in which the players are rated on a three-year basis. For $159, the collector could purchase the entire set which also included entry into the fantasy league, a stat book, worksheets and instructions. The collector who earned the best fantasy score over 18 games won four tickets to Super Bowl XXVIII. The game was test-marketed in four cities: Buffalo, Houston, Kansas City and Washington, D.C. "FantaSports" appears in gold foil on the top black border. The cards are arranged by position.

		MT
Complete Set (200):		120.00
Common Player:		.25
1	Chris Miller	.25
2	Jim Kelly	1.00
3	Jim Harbaugh	.75
4	David Klingler	.25
5	Bernie Kosar	.50
6	Troy Aikman	8.00
7	John Elway	5.00
8	Tommy Maddox	.25
9	Rodney Peete	.50
10	Andre Ware	.50
11	Brett Favre	20.00
12	Warren Moon	1.00
13	Jeff George	1.00
14	Dave Krieg	.50
15	Joe Montana	8.00
16	Todd Marinovich	.25
17	Jim Everett	.50
18	Dan Marino	20.00
19	Sean Salisbury	.25
20	Drew Bledsoe	8.00
21	Dave Brown	.75
22	Phil Simms	.50
23	Boomer Esiason	.50
24	Browning Nagle	.25
25	Randall Cunningham	.25
26	Neil O'Donnell	.50
27	Stan Humphries	1.00
28	Steve Young	5.00
29	Rick Mirer	3.00
30	Mark Rypien	.50
31	Kenneth Davis	.25
32	Thurman Thomas	1.50
33	Steve Broussard	.25
34	Neal Anderson	.50
35	Craig Heyward	.25
36	Derrick Fenner	.25
37	Harold Green	.25
38	Leroy Hoard	.25
39	Kevin Mack	.25
40	Eric Metcalf	1.00
41	Tommy Vardell	.25
42	Daryl Johnston	.75
43	Emmitt Smith	20.00
44	Barry Sanders	8.00
45	Edgar Bennett	.75
46	Lorenzo White	.50
47	Anthony Johnson	.25
48	Todd McNair	.25
49	Christian Okoye	.25
50	Harvey Williams	.75
51	Barry Word	.25
52	Nick Bell	.25
53	Eric Dickerson	.75
54	Jerome Bettis	5.00
55	Cleveland Gary	.25
56	Mark Higgs	.25
57	Tony Paige	.25
58	Terry Allen	.75
59	Roger Craig	.50
60	Robert Smith	1.25
61	Leonard Russell	.50
62	Jon Vaughn	.25
63	Vaughn Dunbar	.25
64	Dalton Hilliard	.25
65	Jarrod Bunch	.25
66	Rodney Hampton	.75
67	Dave Meggett	.25
68	Brad Baxter	.25
69	Heath Sherman	.25
70	Vai Sikahema	.25
71	Johnny Bailey	.25
72	Larry Centers	.25
73	Garrison Hearst	3.00
74	Barry Foster	.25
75	Eric Bieniemy	.25
76	Marion Butts	.25
77	Ronnie Harmon	.25
78	Natrone Means	4.00
79	Amp Lee	.25
80	Tom Rathman	.25
81	Ricky Watters	1.00
82	Chris Warren	1.00
83	John L. Williams	.25
84	Gary Anderson (RB)	.25
85	Reggie Cobb	.25
86	Vince Workman	.25
87	Reggie Brooks	.75
88	Earnest Byner	.25
89	Ricky Ervins	.25
90	Michael Haynes	.50
91	Mike Pritchard	.75
92	Andre Rison	.75
93	Don Beebe	.50
94	Andre Reed	.50
95	Curtis Conway	3.00
96	Wendell Davis	.25
97	Tom Waddle	.25
98	Carl Pickens	1.00
99	Michael Jackson	.50
100	Alvin Harper	.75
101	Michael Irvin	1.00
102	Vance Johnson	.25
103	Mel Gray	.50
104	Sterling Sharpe	1.00
105	Curtis Duncan	.25
106	Ernest Givins	.25
107	Haywood Jeffires	.50
108	Tim Brown	1.00
109	Willie Gault	.25
110	Flipper Anderson	.25
111	Henry Ellard	.75
112	Mark Duper	.50
113	O.J. McDuffie	2.00
114	Anthony Carter	.50
115	Cris Carter	1.00
116	Mike Farr	.25
117	Quinn Early	.50
118	Eric Martin	.25
119	Chris Calloway	.25
120	Mark Jackson	.25
121	Rob Moore	.50
122	Fred Barnett	.50
123	Calvin Williams	.50
124	Gary Clark	.50
125	Randal Hill	.50
126	Ricky Proehl	.50
127	Jeff Graham	.50
128	Ernie Mills	.50
129	Dwight Stone	.25
130	Nate Lewis	.25
131	Jerry Rice	8.00
132	John Taylor	.50
133	Tommy Kane	.25
134	Kelvin Martin	.25
135	Lawrence Dawsey	.50
136	Courtney Hawkins	.50
137	Art Monk	.50
138	Pete Metzelaars	.25
139	Jay Novacek	.50
140	Reggie Johnson	.25
141	Shannon Sharpe	.75
142	Jackie Harris	.25
143	Troy Drayton	.50
144	Keith Jackson	.25
145	Steve Jordan	.25
146	Johnny Mitchell	.50
147	Eric Green	.25
148	Derrick Walker	.25
149	Brent Jones	.50
150	Ron Hall	.25
151	Norm Johnson	.25
152	Jim Breech	.25
153	Matt Stover	.25
154	Lin Elliott	.25
155	Jason Hanson	.25
156	Chris Jacke	.25
157	Nick Lowery	.25
158	Pete Stoyanovich	.25
159	Roger Ruzek	.25
160	Gary Anderson (K)	.25
161	John Kasay	.25
162	Chip Lohmiller	.25
163	Chris Gardocki	.25
164	Mike Saxon	.25
165	Jim Arnold	.25
166	Rohn Stark	.25
167	Jeff Gossett	.25
168	Reggie Roby	.25
169	Harry Newsome	.25
170	Tommy Barnhardt	.25
171	Jeff Feagles	.25
172	Rick Camarillo	.25
173	Falcons Defense (Deion Sanders)	4.00
174	Bills Defense (Cornelius Bennett)	.50
175	Bears Defense (Mark Carrier) (DB)	.50
176	Bengals Defense (Darryl Williams)	.25
177	Browns Defense (Michael Dean Perry)	.50
178	Cowboys Defense (Russell Maryland)	.50
179	Broncos Defense (Steve Atwater)	.25
180	Lions Defense (Bennie Blades)	.25
181	Packers Defense (Reggie White)	1.00
182	Oilers Defense (Cris Dishman)	.25
183	Colts Defense (Steve Emtman)	.25
184	Chiefs Defense (Derrick Thomas)	1.00
185	Raiders Defense (Howie Long)	.50
186	Rams Defense (Sean Gilbert)	.25
187	Dolphins Defense (John Offerdahl)	.25
188	Vikings Defense (Chris Doleman)	.25
189	Patriots Defense (Andre Tippett)	.25
190	Saints Defense (Sam Mills)	.25
191	Giants Defense (Lawrence Taylor)	.75
192	Jets Defense (James Hasty)	.25
193	Eagles Defense (Clyde Simmons)	.50
194	Cardinals Defense (Eric Swann)	.50
195	Steelers Defense (Greg Lloyd)	.75
196	Chargers Defense (Junior Seau)	1.25
197	49ers Defense (Kevin Fagan)	.25
198	Seahawks Defense (Cortez Kennedy)	.75
199	Buccaneers Defense (Broderick Thomas)	.25
200	Redskins Defense (Darrell Green)	.50

1994 Topps

Topps issued its 1994 set in two 330-card series, along with its parallel Special Effects set. Two insert sets, Finest and Spectralight All-Pros, were also made. The regular cards have a front with a full-color action photo, bordered by a gold-foil border and white frame. The Topps logo appears on the front, too, along with the player's name, which is stamped in gold foil. The card back has a player photo, biographical and statistical information, a card number and a player profile. Subsets within the main set included Career Active Leaders, Draft Picks, Tools of the Game, and Measures of Greatness. Special Effects cards were issued one per pack.

	MT
Complete Set (660):	45.00
Complete Series 1 (330):	22.00
Complete Series 2 (330):	22.00
Common Player:	.05
Series 1 or 2 Wax Box:	30.00

1	Emmitt Smith	2.00
2	Russell Copeland	.08
3	Jesse Sapolu	.05
4	David Scott	.05
5	Rodney Hampton	.30
6	Bubba McDowell	.05
7	Bryce Paup	.05
8	Winston Moss	.05
9	Brett Perriman	.05
10	Rod Woodson	.10
11	John Randle	.05
12	David Wyman	.05
13	Jeff Cross	.05
14	Richard Cooper	.05
15	Johnny Mitchell	.10
16	David Alexander	.05
17	Ronnie Harmon	.07
18	Tyrone Stowe	.05
19	Chris Zorich	.05
20	Rob Burnett	.05
21	Harold Alexander	.05
22	Rod Stephens	.05
23	Mark Wheeler	.05
24	Dwayne Sabb	.05
25	Troy Drayton	.15
26	Kurt Gouveia	.05
27	Warren Moon	.15
28	Jeff Query	.05
29	Chuck Levy	.40
30	Bruce Smith	.10
31	Doug Riesenberg	.05
32	Willie Drewrey	.05
33	Nate Newton	.07
34	James Jett	.20
35	George Teague	.20
36	Marc Spindler	.05
37	Jack Del Rio	.05
38	Dale Carter	.05
39	Steve Atwater	.07
40	Herschel Walker	.05
41	James Hasty	.05
42	Seth Joyner	.10
43	Keith Jackson	.10
44	Tommy Vardell	.05
45	Antonio Langham	.05
46	Derek Brown	.25
47	John Wojciechowski	.05
48	Horace Copeland	.15
49	Luis Sharpe	.05
50	Pat Harlow	.05
51	David Palmer	.65
52	Tony Smith	.05
53	Tim Johnson	.05
54	Anthony Newman	.05
55	Terry Wooden	.05
56	Derrick Fenner	.05
57	Mike Fox	.05
58	Brad Hopkins	.05
59	Daryl Johnson	.08
60	Steve Young	.75
61	Scottie Graham	.35
62	Nolan Harrison	.05
63	David Richards	.05
64	Chris Mohr	.05
65	Hardy Nickerson	.05
66	Heath Sherman	.05
67	Irving Fryar	.10
68	Ray Buchanan	.05
69	Jay Taylor	.05
70	Shannon Sharpe	.15
71	Vinny Testaverde	.05
72	Renaldo Turnbull	.05
73	Dwight Stone	.05
74	Willie McGinnest	.25
75	Darrell Green	.07
76	Kyle Clifton	.05
77	Leo Goeas	.05
78	Ken Ruettgers	.05
79	Craig Heyward	.05
80	Andre Rison	.20
81	Chris Mims	.15
82	Gary Clark	.07
83	Ricardo McDonald	.05
84	Patrick Hunter	.05
85	Bruce Matthews	.05
86	Russell Maryland	.06
87	Gary Anderson	.05
88	Brad Edwards	.05
89	Carlton Bailey	.05
90	Qadry Ismail	.50
91	Terry McDaniel	.05
92	Willie Green	.05
93	Cornelius Bennett	.05
94	Paul Gruber	.05
95	Pete Stoyanovich	.08
96	Merton Hanks	.05
97	Tre' Johnson	.05
98	Jonathan Hayes	.05
99	Jason Elam	.15
100	Jerome Bettis	.50
101	Ronnie Lott	.08
102	Maurcie Hurst	.05
103	Kirk Lowdermilk	.05
104	Tony Jones	.05
105	Steve Beuerlein	.08
106	Isaac Davis	.05
107	Vaughan Johnson	.05
108	Terrell Buckley	.05
109	Pierce Holt	.05
110	Alonzo Spellman	.05
111	Patrick Robinson	.05
112	Cortez Kennedy	.10
113	Kevin Williams	.50
114	Brad Copeland	.05
115	Chris Doleman	.05
116	Jerry Rice	.45
117	Neil Smith	.08
118	Emmitt Smith	.75
119	Eugene Robinson, Nate Odomes	.05
120	Steve Young	.60
121	Carnell Lake	.05
122	Ernest Givins	.05
123	Henry Jones	.05
124	Michael Brooks	.05
125	Jason Hanson	.07
126	Andy Harmon	.05
127	Errict Rhett	.75
128	Harris Barton	.05
129	Greg Robinson	.05
130	Derrick Thomas	.10
131	Keith Kartz	.05
132	Lincoln Kennedy	.05
133	Leslie O'Neal	.05
134	Tim Goad	.05
135	Rohn Stark	.05
136	O.J. McDuffie	.40
137	Donnell Woolford	.05
138	Jamir Miller	.50
139	Eric Thomas	.05
140	Willie Roaf	.08
141	Wayne Gandy	.05
142	Mike Brim	.05
143	Kelvin Martin	.08
144	Edgar Bennett	.07
145	Michael Dean Perry	.05
146	Shante Carver	.05
147	Jesse Armstead	.05
148	Mo Elewonibi	.05
149	Dana Stubblefield	.35
150	Cody Carlson	.05
151	Vencie Glenn	.05
152	Levon Kirkland	.05
153	Derrick Moore	.15
154	John Fina	.05
155	Jeff Hostetler	.15
156	Courtney Hawkins	.20
157	Todd Collins	.05
158	Neil Smith	.05
159	Simon Fletcher	.08
160	Dan Marino	2.00
161	Sam Adams	.25
162	Marvin Washington	.05
163	John Copeland	.05
164	Eugene Robinson	.05
165	Mark Carrier	.05
166	Mike Kenn	.05
167	Tyrone Hughes	.05
168	Darren Carrington	.05
169	Shane Conlan	.05
170	Ricky Proehl	.05
171	Jeff Herrod	.05
172	Mark Carrier	.05
173	George Koonce	.05
174	Desmond Howard	.05
175	David Meggett	.05
176	Charles Haley	.06
177	Steve Wisniewski	.05
178	Dermontti Dawson	.05
179	Tim McDonald	.08
180	Broderick Thomas	.05
181	Bernard Dafney	.05
182	Bo Orlando	.10
183	Andre Reed	.10
184	Randall Cunningham	.15
185	Chris Spielman	.05
186	Keith Byars	.05
187	Ben Coates	.05
188	Tracy Simien	.05
189	Carl Pickens	.10
190	Reggie White	.15
191	Norm Johnson	.05
192	Brian Washington	.05
193	Stan Humphries	.05
194	Fred Stokes	.05
195	Dan Williams	.05
196	John Elway	.40
197	Eric Allen	.10
198	Hardy Nickerson	.05
199	Jerome Bettis	.25
200	Troy Aikman	1.00
201	Thurman Thomas	.40
202	Cornelius Bennett	.05
203	Michael Irvin	.20
204	Jim Kelly	.20
205	Junior Seau	.10
206	Heath Shuler	.25
207	Howard Cross	.05
208	Pat Swilling	.05
209	Pete Metzelaars	.05
210	Tony McGee	.05
211	Neil O'Donnell	.08
212	Eugene Chung	.05
213	J.B. Brown	.05
214	Marcus Allen	.15
215	Harry Newsome	.05
216	Greg Hill	.50
217	Ryan Yarborough	.30
218	Marty Carter	.05
219	Bern Brostek	.05
220	Boomer Esiason	.07
221	Vince Buck	.05
222	Jim Jeffcoat	.05
223	Bob Dahl	.05
224	Marion Butts	.06
225	Ron Moore	.50
226	Robert Blackmon	.05
227	Curtis Conway	.30
228	Jon Hand	.05
229	Shane Dronett	.05
230	Erik Williams	.05
231	Dennis Brown	.05
232	Ray Childress	.05
233	Johnnie Morton	.50
234	Kent Hull	.05
235	John Elliott	.05
236	Ron Heller	.05
237	J.J. Birden	.05
238	Thomas Randolph	.05
239	Chip Lohmiller	.07
240	Tim Brown	.10
241	Steve Tovar	.05
242	Moe Gardner	.05
243	Vincent Brown	.05
244	Tony Zendejas	.05
245	Eric Allen	.08
246	Joe King	.05
247	Mo Lewis	.05
248	Rod Bernstine	.07
249	Tom Waddle	.05
250	Junior Seau	.10
251	Eric Metcalf	.05
252	Cris Carter	.08
253	Bill Hitchcock	.05
254	Zefross Moss	.05
255	Morten Andersen	.07
256	Keith Rucker	.05
257	Chris Jacke	.05
258	Richmond Webb	.07
259	Herman Moore	.10
260	Phil Simms	.10
261	Mark Tuninei	.05
262	Don Beebe	.05
263	Marc Logan	.05
264	Willie Davis	.05
265	David Klingler	.15
266	Martin Mayhew	.05
267	Mark Bavaro	.05
268	Greg Lloyd	.05
269	Al Del Greco	.05
270	Reggie Brooks	.20
271	Greg Townsend	.05
272	Rohn Stark	.05
273	Marcus Allen	.05
274	Ronnie Lott	.05
275	Dan Marino	.65
276	Sean Gilbert	.07
277	LeRoy Butler	.05
278	Troy Auzenne	.05
279	Eric Swann	.05
280	Quentin Coryatt	.06
281	Anthony Pleasant	.05
282	Brad Baxter	.05
283	Carl Lee	.05
284	Courtney Hall	.05
285	Quinn Early	.05
286	Eddie Robinson	.05
287	Marco Coleman	.05
288	Harold Green	.05
289	Santana Dotson	.05
290	Robert Porcher	.05
291	Joe Phillips	.05
292	Mark McMillian	.05
293	Eric Davis	.05
294	Mark Jackson	.05
295	Darryl Talley	.05
296	Curtis Duncan	.05
297	Bruce Armstrong	.05
298	Eric Hill	.05
299	Andre Collins	.05
300	Jay Novacek	.08
301	Roosevelt Potts	.15
302	Eric Martin	.05
303	Chris Warren	.05
304	Deral Boykin	.05
305	Jessie Tuggle	.05
306	Glyn Milburn	.25
307	Terry Obee	.05
308	Eric Turner	.05
309	DeWayne Washington	.25
310	Sterling Sharpe	.35
311	Jeff Gossett	.05
312	John Carney	.05
313	Aaron Glenn	.20
314	Nick Lowery	.05
315	Thurman Thomas	.15
316	Troy Aikman	.65
317	Thurman Thomas	.10
318	Michael Irvin	.15
319	Steve Beuerlein	.07
320	Jerry Rice	.75
321	Alexander Wright	.05
322	Michael Bates	.05
323	Greg Davis	.05
324	Mark Bortz	.05
325	Kevin Greene	.05
326	Wayne Simmons	.05
327	Wayne Martin	.05
328	Michael Irvin	.30
329	Checklist 1	.05
330	Checklist 2	.05
331	Doug Pelfrey	.05
332	Myron Quyton	.05
333	Howard Ballard	.05
334	Ricky Ervins	.05
335	Steve Emtman	.05
336	Eric Curry	.05
337	Bert Emanuel	1.00
338	Darryl Ashmore	.05
339	Stevon Moore	.05
340	Garrison Hearst	.50
341	Vance Johnson	.05
342	Anthony Johnson	.05
343	Merril Hoge	.05
344	William Thomas	.05
345	Scott Mitchell	.15
346	Jim Everett	.05
347	Ray Crockett	.05
348	Bryan Cox	.07
349	Charles Johnson	.50
350	Randall McDaniel	.05
351	Michael Barrow	.05
352	Darrell Thompson	.05
353	Kevin Gogan	.05
354	Brad Daluiso	.05
355	Mark Collins	.05
356	Bryant Young	.30
357	Steve Christie	.05
358	Derek Kennard	.05
359	Jon Vaughn	.05
360	Drew Bledsoe	1.00
361	Randy Baldwin	.05
362	Kevin Ross	.05
363	Reuben Davis	.05
364	Chris Miller	.05
365	Tim McGee	.05
366	Tony Woods	.05
367	Dean Biasucci	.05
368	George Jamison	.05
369	Lorenzo Lynch	.05
370	Johnny Johnson	.05
371	Greg Kragen	.05
372	Vinson Smith	.05
373	Vince Workman	.05
374	Allen Aldridge	.20
375	Terry Kirby	.30
376	Mario Bates	.20
377	Dixon Edwards	.05
378	Leon Searcy	.05
379	Eric Guliford	.05
380	Gary Brown	.05
381	Phil Hansen	.05
382	Keith Hamilton	.05
383	John Alt	.05
384	John Taylor	.05
385	Reggie Cobb	.05
386	Rob Fredrickson	.30
387	Pepper Johnson	.05
388	Kevin Lee	.35
389	Stanley Richard	.05
390	Jackie Slater	.05
391	Darrick Brilz	.05
392	John Gesek	.05
393	Kelvin Pritchett	.05
394	Aeneas Williams	.05
395	Henry Ford	.25
396	Eric Mahlum	.20
397	Tom Rouen	.05
398	Vinnie Clark	.05
399	Jim Sweeney	.05
400	Troy Aikman	2.25
401	Tio Cook	.05
402	Dan Saleaumua	.05
403	Andy Heck	.05
404	Deon Figures	.10
405	Henry Thomas	.05
406	Glen Montgomery	.05
407	Trent Dilfer	2.00
408	Eddie Murray	.05
409	Gene Atkins	.05
410	Mike Sherrard	.05
411	Don Mosebar	.05
412	Thomas Smith	.05
413	Ken Norton	.05
414	Robert Brooks	.05
415	Jeff Lageman	.05
416	Tony Siragusa	.05
417	Brian Blades	.05
418	Matt Stover	.05
419	Jesse Solomon	.05
420	Reggie Roby	.05
421	Shawn Jefferson	.05
422	Marc Boutte	.05
423	William White	.05
424	Clyde Simmons	.05
425	Anthony Miller	.08
426	Brent Jones	.05
427	Tim Grunhard	.05
428	Alfred Williams	.05
429	Roy Barker	.05
430	Dante Jones	.05
431	Leroy Thompson	.05
432	Marcus Robertson	.05
433	Thomas Lewis	.50
434	Sean Jones	.05
435	Michael Haynes	.05
436	Albert Lewis	.05
437	Tim Bowens	.30
438	Marvcus Patton	.05
439	Rich Miano	.05
440	Craig Erickson	.05
441	Larry Allen	.20
442	Fernando Smith	.20
443	D.J. Johnson	.05
444	Leonard Russell	.05
445	Marshall Faulk	3.00
446	Najee Mustafaa	.05
447	Brian Hansen	.05
448	Isaac Bruce	4.00
449	Kevin Scott	.05
450	Natrone Means	.40
451	Tracy Rogers	.05
452	Mike Croel	.05
453	Anthony Edwards	.05
454	Brenston Buckner	.20
455	Tom Carter	.05
456	Burt Grossman	.05
457	Jimmy Spencer	.05
458	Raghib Ismail	.20
459	Fred Strickland	.05
460	Jeff Burris	.30
461	Adrian Hardy	.05
462	Lamar McGriggs	.05
463	Webster Slaughter	.05
464	Demetrius DuBose	.05
465	Dave Brown	.20
466	Kenneth Gant	.05
467	Erik Kramer	.05
468	Mark Ingram	.05
469	Roman Phifer	.05
470	Steve Young	.12
471	Nick Lowery	.08
472	Irving Fryar	.08
473	Art Monk	.08
474	Mel Gray	.08
475	Reggie White	.05
476	Eric Ball	.05
477	Dwayne Harper	.05
478	Will Shields	.05
479	Roger Harper	.05
480	Rick Mirer	.97
481	Vincent Brisby	.20
482	John Jurkovic	.05
483	Michael Jackson	.05
484	Ed Cunningham	.05
485	Brad Ottis	.15
486	Sterling Palmer	.05
487	Tony Bennett	.05
488	Mike Pritchard	.05
489	Bucky Brooks	.35
490	Troy Vincent	.05
491	Eric Green	.05
492	Van Malone	.25
493	Marcus Spears	.25
494	Brian Williams	.05
495	Robert Smith	.15
496	Haywood Jeffires	.07
497	Darrin Smith	.05
498	Tommy Barnhardt	.05
499	Anthony Smith	.05
500	Ricky Watters	.05
501	Antone Davis	.05
502	David Braxton	.05
503	Donnell Bennett	.50
504	Donald Evans	.05
505	Lewis Tillman	.05
506	Lance Smith	.05
507	Aaron Taylor	.20
508	Ricky Sanders	.05
509	Dennis Smith	.05
510	Barry Foster	.30
511	Stan Brock	.05
512	Henry Rolling	.05
513	Walter Reeves	.05
514	John Booty	.05
515	Kenneth Davis	.05
516	Cris Dishman	.05
517	Bill Lewis	.05
518	Jeff Bryant	.05
519	Brian Mitchell	.05
520	Joe Montana	1.00
521	Keith Sims	.05
522	Harry Colon	.05
523	Leon Lett	.05
524	Carlos Jenkins	.05
525	Victor Bailey	.15
526	Harvey Williams	.05
527	Irv Smith	.10
528	Alvin Harper	.20
529	John Thierry	.25
530	Brett Favre	2.00
531	Sean Dawkins	.30
532	Eric Pegram	.05
533	Jimmy Williams	.05
534	Michael Timpson	.05
535	Willie Anderson	.05
536	John Parrela	.05
537	Freddie Joe Nunn	.05
538	Doug Dawson	.05
539	Michael Stewart	.05
540	John Elway	.65
541	Ronnie Lott	.05
542	Barry Sanders	.50
543	Andre Reed	.08
544	Deion Sanders	.10
545	Dan Marino	.75
546	Carlton Bailey	.08
547	Emmitt Smith	1.00
548	Alvin Harper	.08
549	Eric Metcalf	.08
550	Jerry Rice	.50
551	Derrick Thomas	.08
552	Mark Collins	.05
553	Eric Turner	.08
554	Sterling Sharpe	.12
555	Steve Young	.25
556	Darnay Scott	1.00
557	Joel Steed	.05
558	Dennis Gibson	.05
559	Charles Mincy	.05
560	Rickey Jackson	.05
561	Dave Cadigan	.05
562	Rick Tuten	.05
563	Mike Caldwell	.05
564	Todd Steussie	.30
565	Kevin Smith	.05
566	Arthur Marshall	.05
567	Aaron Wallace	.05
568	Calvin Williams	.05
569	Todd Kelly	.05
570	Barry Sanders	1.25
571	Shaun Gayle	.05
572	Will Wolford	.05
573	Ethan Norton	.05
574	Chris Slade	.15
575	Jeff Wright	.05
576	Toby Wright	.20
577	Lamar Thomas	.05
578	Chris Singleton	.05
579	Ed West	.05
580	Jeff George	.08
581	Kevin Mitchell	.15
582	Chad Brown	.05
583	Rich Camarillo	.05
584	Gary Zimmerman	.05
585	Randal Hill	.05
586	Keith Cash	.05
587	Sam Mills	.05
588	Shawn Lee	.05
589	Kent Graham	.12
590	Steve Everitt	.05
591	Rob Moore	.05
592	Kevin Mawae	.20
593	Jerry Ball	.05
594	Larry Brown	.05
595	Tim Krumrie	.05
596	Aubrey Beavers	.30
597	Chris Hinton	.05
598	Greg Montgomery	.05
599	Jimmie Jones	.05
600	Jim Kelly	.20
601	Joe Johnson	.25
602	Tim Irwin	.05
603	Steve Jackson	.05
604	James Williams	.05
605	Blair Thomas	.05
606	Daman Hughes	.05
607	Russell Freeman	.05
608	Andre Hastings	.10
609	Ken Harvey	.05
610	Jim Harbaugh	.05
611	Emmitt Smith	.80
612	Andre Rison	.10
613	Steve Young	.20
614	Anthony Miller	.10
615	Barry Sanders	.50
616	Bernie Kosar	.05
617	Chris Gardocki	.05
618	William Floyd	.30
619	Matt Brock	.05
620	Dan Wilkinson	.45
621	Tony Meola	.05
622	Tony Tolbert	.05
623	Mike Zandofsky	.05
624	William Fuller	.05
625	Steve Jordan	.05
626	Mike Johnson	.05
627	Ferrell Edmunds	.05
628	Gene Williams	.05
629	Willie Beamon	.05
630	Gerald Perry	.05
631	John Baylor	.05
632	Carwell Gardner	.05
633	Thomas Everett	.08
634	Lamar Lathon	.05
635	Michael Bankston	.05
636	Ray Crittenden	.05
637	Kimble Anders	.05
638	Robert Delpino	.05
639	Darren Perry	.05
640	Byron Evans	.05
641	Mark Higgs	.05
642	Lorenzo Real	.05
643	Henry Ellard	.05
644	Trace Armstrong	.05
645	Greg McMurtry	.05
646	Steve McMichael	.05
647	Terance Mathis	.05
648	Eric Bieniemy	.05
649	Bobby Houston	.05
650	Alvin Harper	.05
651	James Folston	.15
652	Mel Gray	.05
653	Adrian Cooper	.05

654	Dexter Carter	.05
655	Don Griffin	.05
656	Corey Weimer	.05
657	Lee Johnson	.05
658	Nate Odomes	.05
659	Checklist 3	.05
660	Checklist 4	.05

1994 Topps Special Effects

The 660-card, regular-sized set was issued as a parallel to the 1994 base set. The cards were inserted every two packs (and rack packs) and feature a clear plastic prismatic coating with a holographic stripe.

	MT
Complete Set (660):	350.00
Complete Series 1 (330):	175.00
Complete Series 2 (330):	175.00
Common Player:	.30
Veteran Stars:	3.5x-7x
Young Stars:	2.5x-5x
RCs:	2x-4x

1994 Topps All-Pro

These 1994 Topps football inserts were included at a rate of one per every 36 Series II packs. Topps introduces its new Spectralight foil process for these cards, which feature 25 of the NFL's top stars. Each card is printed on a foil-stamped, foil-backed card.

	MT
Complete Set (25):	45.00
Common Player:	1.00
Minor Stars:	2.00
1 Michael Irvin	2.00
2 Erik Williams	1.00
3 Steve Wisniewski	1.00
4 Dermontti Dawson	1.00
5 Nate Newton	1.00
6 Harris Barton	1.00
7 Shannon Sharpe	2.00
8 Jerry Rice	10.00
9 Troy Aikman	10.00
10 Barry Sanders	12.00
11 Jerome Bettis	5.00
12 Jason Hanson	1.00
13 Eric Metcalf	1.00
14 Reggie White	2.00
15 Cortez Kennedy	1.00
16 Michael Dean Perry	1.00
17 Bruce Smith	1.00
18 Darryl Talley	1.00
19 Hardy Nickerson	1.00
20 Derrick Thomas	2.00
21 Mark Collins	1.00
22 Eric Allen	1.00
23 Tim McDonald	1.00
24 Marcus Robertson	1.00
25 Greg Montgomery	1.00

A card number in parentheses ( ) indicates the set is unnumbered.

1994 Topps 1000/3000

These cards were found one in every 32 packs of 1994 Topps football cards. They feature 20 receivers and running backs who gained 1,000 yards in 1993, plus 12 quarterbacks who threw for more than 3,000 yards. Each card front has the set name running along the left side of the card. The player's name and Topps' logo are in the bottom left corner. The back has an action photo and game-by-game recap of the player's 1993 season. Cards are numbered 1 of 32, etc.

	MT
Complete Set (32):	75.00
Common Player:	1.00
Minor Stars:	2.00
1 Jerry Rice	7.00
2 Chris Warren	2.00
3 Leonard Russell	1.00
4 Gary Brown	1.00
5 Tim Brown	2.00
6 Erric Pegram	1.00
7 Irving Fryar	1.00
8 Anthony Miller	1.00
9 Reggie Langhorne	1.00
10 Thurman Thomas	2.00
11 Reggie Brooks	1.00
12 Andre Rison	2.00
13 Ron Moore	1.00
14 Michael Irvin	2.00
15 Barry Sanders	8.00
16 Cris Carter	2.00
17 Rodney Hampton	2.00
18 Jerome Bettis	2.00
19 Sterling Sharpe	2.00
20 Emmitt Smith	14.00
21 John Elway	5.00
22 Brett Favre	14.00
23 Jim Kelly	2.00
24 Warren Moon	2.00
25 Phil Simms	1.00
26 Craig Erickson	1.00
27 Neil O'Donnell	1.00
28 Steve Young	5.00
29 Steve Beuerlein	1.00
30 Troy Aikman	7.00
31 Jeff Hostetler	1.00
32 Boomer Esiason	1.00

1994 Topps Archives 1956

The 120-card, standard-size set was a reprinted version of Topps' 1956 set (the checklist was not reprinted). The cards were sold in 12-card packs for $2 with whatever errors the originals had left in. The cards backs were printed in red and black on gray stock.

	MT
Complete Set (120):	20.00
Common Player:	.10
1 Johnny Carson	.10
2 Gordon Soltau	.10
3 Frank Varrichione	.10

4	Eddie Bell	.10
5	Alex Webster	.20
6	Norm Van Brocklin	2.00
7	Green Bay Packers Team Card	.30
8	Lou Creekmur	.20
9	Lou Groza	1.50
10	Tom Bienemann	.10
11	George Blanda	1.50
12	Alan Ameche	.40
13	Vic Janowicz	.40
14	Dick Moegle	.20
15	Fran Rogel	.10
16	Harold Giancanelli	.10
17	Emlen Tunnell	.60
18	Paul (Tank) Younger	.30
19	Bill Howton	.20
20	Jack Christiansen	.75
21	Darrell Brewster	.10
22	Chicago Cardinals Team Card	.30
23	Ed Brown	.20
24	Joe Campanella	.10
25	Leon Heath	.10
26	San Francisco 49ers Team Card	.30
27	Dick Flanagan	.10
28	Chuck Bednarik	1.00
29	Kyle Rote	.60
30	Les Richter	.20
31	Howard Ferguson	.10
32	Dorne Dibble	.10
33	Kenny Konz	.10
34	Dave Mann	.10
35	Rick Casares	.20
36	Art Donovan	1.00
37	Chuck Drazenovich	.10
38	Joe Arenas	.10
39	Lynn Chandnois	.10
40	Philadelphia Eagles Team Card	.30
41	Roosevelt Brown	.60
42	Tom Fears	.75
43	Gary Knafelc	.10
44	Joe Schmidt	1.00
45	Cleveland Browns Team Card (UER) (Card back does not credit the Browns with being Champs in 1955)	.60
46	Len Teeuws	.10
47	Bill George	.60
48	Baltimore Colts Team Card	.30
49	Eddie LeBaron	.40
50	Hugh McElhenny	1.25
51	Ted Marchibroda	.20
52	Adrian Burk	.10
53	Frank Gifford	3.50
54	Charley Toogood	.10
55	Tobin Rote	.20
56	Bill Stits	.10
57	Don Colo	.10
58	Ollie Matson	1.00
59	Harlon Hill	.10
60	Lenny Moore	2.00
61	Washington Redskins Team Card	.30
62	Billy Wilson	.20
63	Pittsburgh Steelers Team Card	.30
64	Bob Pellegrini	.10
65	Ken MacAfee	.20
66	Willard Sherman	.10
67	Roger Zatkoff	.10
68	Dave Middleton	.10
69	Ray Renfro	.20
70	Don Stonesifer	.10
71	Stan Jones	.60
72	Jim Mutscheller	.10
73	Volney Peters	.10
74	Leo Nomellini	.75
75	Ray Mathews	.10
76	Dick Bielski	.10
77	Charley Conerly	1.00
78	Elroy Hirsch	1.00
79	Bill Forester	.20
80	Jim Doran	.10
81	Fred Morrison	.10
82	Jack Simmons	.10
83	Bill McColl	.10
84	Bert Rechichar	.10
85	Joe Scudero	.10
86	Y.A. Tittle	3.00
87	Ernie Stautner	1.00
88	Norm Willey	.10
89	Bob Schnelker	.10
90	Dan Towler	.10
91	John Martinkovic	.10
92	Detroit Lions Team Card	.30
93	George Ratterman	.10
94	Chuck Ulrich	.10
95	Bobby Watkins	.10
96	Buddy Young	.30
97	Billy Wells	.10
98	Bob Toneff	.10
99	Bill McPeak	.10
100	Bobby Thomason	.10
101	Roosevelt Grier	.60
102	Ron Waller	.10
103	Bobby Dillon	.10
104	Leon Hart	.30
105	Mike McCormack	.60
106	John Olszewski	.10
107	Bill Wightkin	.10
108	George Shaw	.20
109	Dale Atkeson	.10
110	Joe Perry	1.00
111	Dale Dodrill	.10
112	Tom Scott	.10
113	New York Giants Team Card	.30
114	Los Angeles Rams Team Card (UER) (Back incorrect, Rams were not 1955 champs)	.30
115	Al Carmichael	.10
116	Bobby Layne	3.00
117	Ed Modzelewski	.20
118	Lamar McHan	.10
119	Chicago Bears Team Card	.30
120	Billy Vessels	.50

1994 Topps Archives 1956 Gold

The 120-card, standard-size set was issued as a gold parallel to the base 1956 reprint set and were randomly inserted into packs of 1956/57 packs.

	MT
Complete Set (120):	50.00
Common Player:	.25
Gold Cards:	1.25x-2.5x

1994 Topps Archives 1957

The 154-card, standard-size set was reprinted by Topps (except for the checklist) and was available in 12-card packs for $2. Any errors with the original 1957 set were not changed. The card backs were printed in red and black on gray card stock. Gold versions (3x) were also produced by Topps.

	MT
Complete Set (154):	20.00
Common Player:	.10
1 Eddie LeBaron	.30
2 Pete Retzlaff	.20
3 Mike McCormack	.50
4 Lou Baldacci	.10
5 Gino Marchetti	1.00
6 Leo Nomellini	.75
7 Bobby Watkins	.10
8 Dave Middleton	.10
9 Bobby Dillon	.10
10 Les Richter	.20
11 Roosevelt Brown	.50
12 Lavern Torgeson	.10
13 Dick Bielski	.10
14 Pat Summerall	1.00
15 Jack Butler	.10
16 John Henry Johnson	.75
17 Art Spinney	.10
18 Bob St. Clair	.50
19 Perry Jeter	.10
20 Lou Creekmur	.30
21 Dave Hanner	.10
22 Norm Van Brocklin	1.50
23 Don Chandler	.10

24	Al Dorow	.10
25	Tom Scott	.10
26	Ollie Matson	1.00
27	Fran Rogel	.10
28	Lou Groza	1.50
29	Billy Vessels	.20
30	Y.A. Tittle	2.00
31	George Blanda	1.50
32	Bobby Layne	2.00
33	Bill Howton	.10
34	Bill Wade	.20
35	Emlen Tunnell	.75
36	Leo Elter	.10
37	Clarence Peaks	.20
38	Don Stonesifer	.10
39	George Tarasovic	.10
40	Darrell Brewster	.10
41	Bert Rechichar	.10
42	Billy Wilson	.20
43	Ed Brown	.10
44	Gene Gedman	.10
45	Gary Knafelc	.10
46	Elroy Hirsch	1.00
47	Don Heinrich	.10
48	Gene Brito	.10
49	Chuck Bednarik	1.00
50	Dave Mann	.10
51	Bill McPeak	.10
52	Kenny Konz	.10
53	Alan Ameche	.40
54	Gordon Soltau	.10
55	Rick Casares	.30
56	Charlie Ane	.10
57	Al Carmichael	.10
58	Willard Sherman	.10
59	Kyle Rote	.50
60	Chuck Drazenovich	.10
61	Bobby Walston	.10
62	John Olszewski	.10
63	Ray Mathews	.10
64	Maurice Bassett	.10
65	Art Donovan	1.00
66	Joe Arenas	.10
67	Harlon Hill	.10
68	Yale Lary	.60
69	Bill Forester	.20
70	Bob Boyd	.10
71	Andy Robustelli	1.00
72	Sam Baker	.20
73	Bob Pellegrini	.10
74	Leo Sanford	.10
75	Sid Watson	.10
76	Ray Renfro	.20
77	Carl Taseff	.10
78	Clyde Conner	.10
79	J.C. Caroline	.10
80	Howard Cassady	.30
81	Tobin Rote	.20
82	Ron Waller	.10
83	Jim Patton	.20
84	Volney Peters	.10
85	Dick Lane	.60
86	Royce Womble	.10
87	Duane Putnam	.10
88	Frank Gifford	3.00
89	Steve Meilinger	.10
90	Buck Lansford	.10
91	Lindon Crow	.10
92	Ernie Stautner	.75
93	Preston Carpenter	.20
94	Raymond Berry	1.50
95	Hugh McElhenny	1.00
96	Stan Jones	.50
97	Dorne Dibble	.10
98	Joe Scudero	.10
99	Eddie Bell	.10
100	Joe Childress	.10
101	Elbert Nickel	.10
102	Walt Michaels	.20
103	Jim Mutscheller	.10
104	Earl Morrall	.40
105	Larry Strickland	.10
106	Jack Christiansen	.75
107	Fred Cone	.10
108	Bud McFadin	.10
109	Charley Conerly	1.00
110	Tom Runnels	.10
111	Ken Keller	.10
112	James Root	.10
113	Ted Marchibroda	.30
114	Don Paul	.10
115	George Shaw	.20
116	Dick Moegle	.20
117	Don Bingham	.10
118	Leon Hart	.20
119	Bart Starr	4.00
120	Paul Miller	.10
121	Alex Webster	.20
122	Ray Wietecha	.10
123	Johnny Carson	.10
124	Tommy McDonald	.30
125	Jerry Tubbs	.10
126	Jack Scarbath	.10
127	Ed Modzelewski	.20
128	Lenny Moore	1.00
129	Joe Perry	1.00
130	Bill Wightkin	.10
131	Jim Doran	.10
132	Howard Ferguson (UER) (Name misspelled Furgeson on front)	.10
133	Tom Wilson	.10
134	Dick James	.10
135	Jimmy Harris	.10
136	Chuck Ulrich	.10
137	Lynn Chandnois	.10
138	Johnny Unitas	5.00

139	Jim Ridlon	.10
140	Zeke Bratkowski	.20
141	Ray Krouse	.10
142	John Martinkovic	.10
143	Jim Cason	.10
144	Ken MacAfee	.10
145	Sid Youngelman	.10
146	Paul Larson	.10
147	Len Ford	1.00
148	Bob Toneff	.10
149	Ronnie Knox	.10
150	Jim David	.10
151	Paul Hornung	4.00
152	Paul (Tank) Younger	.30
153	Bill Svoboda	.10
154	Fred Morrison	.30

1994 Topps Archives 1957 Gold

The 154-card, standard-size set was issued as a gold parallel to the base 1957 reprint issue. The cards were randomly inserted into 1956/57 packs.

	MT
Complete Set (154):	50.00
Common Player:	.25
Gold Cards:	1.25x-2.5x

1995 Topps

Topps released its 1995 football set in two series - 248 cards in Series I and 220 in Series II. Each card is UV-coated and gold-foil stamped. Top free agents, hot draft picks, expansion team players, and Steve Young tribute cards are among the subsets in the set. 1,000 and 3,000 Yard Club theme cards are also part of the main set. A new addition to the regular cards is that Topps spotlights the player's achievements; if he led the conference in a statistical category, the stat is printed in red on the back (with a diamond added if he tied). Also on the horizontal card back, which is team color coordinated, are a closeup shot, stats, biographical information and a brief player profile. Inserts in Series I are Topps Finest, Finest Refractors, Hit List, Sensational Sophomores, Power Boosters and Yesteryear. An Instant Winner card was also randomly inserted at a rate of one per every 1,980 packs; the card entitles the finder to a complete 27-card Finest set with Finest Protectors. Series II inserts include: Air Raid, Finest Refractors, ProFiles, Power Boosters, Finest, and All-Pro.

	MT
Complete Set (468):	45.00
Comp. Series 1 (248):	25.00
Comp. Series 2 (220):	20.00

	Player	Price
	Common Player:	.05
	Minor Stars:	.10
	Hobby Wax Box:	40.00
	Retail Wax Box:	35.00
1	Barry Sanders (1,000 Yard Club)	.50
2	Chris Warren (1,000 Yard Club)	.05
3	Jerry Rice (1,000 Yard Club)	.50
4	Emmitt Smith (1,000 Yard Club)	1.00
5	Henry Ellard (1,000 Yard Club)	.05
6	Natrone Means (1,000 Yard Club)	.25
7	Terance Mathis (1,000 Yard Club)	.05
8	Tim Brown (1,000 Yard Club)	.05
9	Andre Reed (1,000 Yard Club)	.05
10	Marshall Faulk (1,000 Yard Club)	.20
11	Irving Fryar (1,000 Yard Club)	.05
12	Cris Carter (1,000 Yard Club)	.05
13	Michael Irvin (1,000 Yard Club)	.10
14	Jake Reed (1,000 Yard Club)	.05
15	Ben Coates (1,000 Yard Club)	.05
16	Herman Moore (1,000 Yard Club)	.05
17	Carl Pickens (1,000 Yard Club)	.05
18	Fred Barnett (1,000 Yard Club)	.05
19	Sterling Sharpe (1,000 Yard Club)	.05
20	Anthony Miller (1,000 Yard Club)	.05
21	Thurman Thomas (1,000 Yard Club)	.10
22	Andre Rison (1,000 Yard Club)	.10
23	Brian Blades (1,000 Yard Club)	.05
24	Rodney Hampton (1,000 Yard Club)	.05
25	Terry Allen (1,000 Yard Club)	.05
26	Jerome Bettis (1,000 Yard Club)	.25
27	Errict Rhett (1,000 Yard Club)	.40
28	Rob Moore (1,000 Yard Club)	.05
29	Shannon Sharpe	.05
30	Drew Bledsoe (3,000 Yard Club)	.50
31	Dan Marino (3,000 Yard Club)	1.00
32	Warren Moon (3,000 Yard Club)	.10
33	Steve Young (3,000 Yard Club)	.25
34	Brett Favre (3,000 Yard Club)	1.00
35	Jim Everett (3,000 Yard Club)	.05
36	Jeff George (3,000 Yard Club)	.05
37	John Elway (3,000 Yard Club)	.25
38	Jeff Hostetler (3,000 Yard Club)	.05
39	Randall Cunningham (3,000 Yard Club)	.10
40	Stan Humphries (3,000 Yard Club)	.05
41	Jim Kelly (3,000 Yard Club)	.10
42	Tommy Barnhardt	.05
43	Bob Whitfield	.05
44	William Thomas	.05
45	Glyn Milburn	.05
46	Steve Christie	.05
47	Kevin Mawae	.05
48	Vencie Glenn	.05
49	Eric Curry	.05
50	Jeff Hostetler	.05
51	Tyronne Stowe	.05
52	Steve Jackson	.05
53	Ben Coleman	.05
54	Brad Baxter	.05
55	Darryl Williams	.05
56	Troy Drayton	.05
57	George Teague	.05
58	Calvin Williams	.05
59	Jeff Cross	.05
60	Leroy Hoard	.05
61	John Carney	.05
62	Daryl Johnston	.05
63	Jim Jeffcoat	.05
64	Matt Stover	.05
65	Leroy Butler	.05
66	Curtis Conway	.05
67	O.J. McDuffie	.05
68	Robert Massey	.05
69	Ed McDaniel	.05
70	William Floyd	.25
71	Willie Davis	.05
72	William Roberts	.05
73	Chester McGlockton	.05
74	D.J. Johnson	.05
75	Rondell Jones	.05
76	Morten Andersen	.05
77	Glenn Parker	.05
78	William Fuller	.05
79	Ray Buchanan	.05
80	Maurice Hurst	.05
81	Wayne Gandy	.05
82	Marcus Turner	.05
83	Greg Davis	.05
84	Terry Wooden	.05
85	Thomas Everett	.05
86	Steve Broussard	.05
87	Tom Carter	.05
88	Glenn Montgomery	.05
89	Larry Allen	.05
90	Donnell Woolford	.05
91	John Alt	.05
92	Phil Hansen	.05
93	Seth Joyner	.05
94	Michael Brooks	.05
95	Randall McDaniel	.05
96	Tydus Winans	.05
97	Rob Fredrickson	.05
98	Ray Crockett	.05
99	Courtney Hall	.05
100	Merton Hanks	.05
101	Aaron Glenn	.05
102	Roosevelt Potts	.05
103	Leon Lett	.05
104	Jessie Tuggle	.05
105	Martin Mayhew	.05
106	William Roaf	.05
107	Todd Lyght	.05
108	Ernest Givins	.05
109	Tony McGee	.05
110	Barry Sanders	1.25
111	Dermontti Dawson	.05
112	Rick Tuten	.05
113	Vincent Brisby	.05
114	Charlie Garner	.05
115	Irving Fryar	.05
116	Stevon Moore	.05
117	Matt Darby	.05
118	Howard Cross	.05
119	John Gesek	.05
120	Jack Del Rio	.05
121	Marcus Allen	.10
122	Torrance Small	.05
123	Chris Mims	.05
124	Don Mosebar	.05
125	Carl Pickens	.05
126	Tom Rouen	.05
127	Garrison Hearst	.10
128	Charles Johnson	.25
129	Derek Brown	.05
130	Troy Aikman	.75
131	Troy Vincent	.05
132	Ken Ruettgers	.05
133	Michael Jackson	.05
134	Dennis Gibson	.05
135	Brett Perriman	.05
136	Jeff Graham	.05
137	Chad Brown	.05
138	Ken Norton	.05
139	Chris Slade	.05
140	Dave Brown	.05
141	Bert Emanuel	.25
142	Renaldo Turnbull	.05
143	Jim Harbaugh	.05
144	Michael Barrow	.05
145	Vincent Brown	.05
146	Bryant Young	.05
147	Boomer Esiason	.05
148	Sean Gilbert	.05
149	Greg Truitt	.05
150	Rod Woodson	.05
151	Robert Porcher	.05
152	Joe Phillips	.05
153	Gary Zimmerman	.05
154	Bruce Smith	.05
155	Randall Cunningham	.10
156	Fred Strickland	.05
157	Derrick Alexander	.25
158	James Williams	.05
159	Scott Dill	.05
160	Tim Bowens	.05
161	Floyd Turner	.05
162	Ronnie Harmon	.05
163	Wayne Martin	.05
164	John Randle	.05
165	Larry Centers	.05
166	Larry Brown	.05
167	Albert Lewis	.05
168	Michael Strahan	.05
169	Reggie Brooks	.05
170	Craig Heyward	.05
171	Pat Harlow	.05
172	Eugene Robinson	.05
173	Shane Conlan	.05
174	Bennie Blades	.05
175	Neil O'Donnell	.05
176	Steve Tovar	.05
177	Donald Evans	.05
178	Brent Jones	.05
179	Ray Childress	.05
180	Reggie White	.25
181	David Alexander	.05
182	Greg Hill	.25
183	Vinny Testaverde	.05
184	Jeff Burris	.05
185	Hardy Nickerson	.05
186	Terry Kirby	.05
187	Kirk Lowdermilk	.05
188	Eric Swann	.05
189	Chris Zorich	.05
190	Simon Fletcher	.05
191	Qadry Ismail	.05
192	Heath Shuler	.50
193	Michael Haynes	.05
194	Mike Sherrard	.05
195	Nolan Harrison	.05
196	Marcus Robertson	.05
197	Kevin Williams	.05
198	Moe Gardner	.05
199	Rick Mirer	.40
200	Junior Seau	.10
201	Byron Morris	.10
202	Willie McGinest	.05
203	Chris Spielman	.05
204	Darnay Scott	.40
205	Jesse Sapolu	.05
206	Marvin Washington	.05
207	Anthony Newman	.05
208	Cortez Kennedy	.10
209	Quentin Coryatt	.05
210	Neil Smith	.05
211	Keith Sims	.05
212	Sean Jones	.05
213	Tony Jones	.05
214	Lewis Tillman	.05
215	Darren Woodson	.05
216	Jason Hanson	.05
217	John Taylor	.05
218	Shawn Lee	.05
219	Kevin Greene	.05
220	Jerry Rice	.75
221	Ki-Jana Carter	.30
222	Tony Boselli	.10
223	Michael Westbrook	1.00
224	Kerry Collins	1.00
225	Kevin Carter	.05
226	Kyle Brady	.10
227	J.J. Stokes	1.00
228	Derrick Alexander	.05
229	Warren Sapp	.10
230	Ruben Brown	.10
231	Hugh Douglas	.10
232	Luther Elliss	.10
233	Rashaan Salaam	.30
234	Tyrone Poole	.10
235	Korey Stringer	.10
236	Devin Bush	.10
237	Cory Raymer	.10
238	Zach Wiegert	.10
239	Ron Davis	.10
240	Todd Collins	.10
241	Bobby Taylor	.10
242	Patrick Riley	.10
243	Scott Gragg	.10
244	Marcus Patton	.05
245	Alvin Harper	.05
246	Ricky Watters	.10
247	Checklist 1 of 2	.05
248	Checklist 2 of 2	.05
249	Terance Mathis	.05
250	Mark Carrier	.05
251	Elijah Alexander	.05
252	George Koonce	.05
253	Tony Bennett	.05
254	Steve Wisniewski	.05
255	Bernie Parmalee	.20
256	Dwayne Sabb	.05
257	Lorenzo Neal	.05
258	Corey Miller	.05
259	Fred Barnett	.05
260	Greg Lloyd	.05
261	Robert Blackmon	.05
262	Ken Harvey	.05
263	Eric Hill	.05
264	Russell Copeland	.05
265	Jeff Blake	.30
266	Carl Banks	.05
267	Jay Novacek	.05
268	Mel Gray	.05
269	Kimble Anders	.05
270	Cris Carter	.10
271	Johnny Mitchell	.05
272	Shawn Jefferson	.05
273	Doug Brien	.05
274	Sean Landeta	.05
275	Scott Mitchell	.10
276	Charles Wilson	.05
277	Anthony Smith	.05
278	Anthony Miller	.05
279	Steve Walsh	.05
280	Drew Bledsoe	.75
281	Jamir Miller	.05
282	Robert Brooks	.10
283	Sean Lumpkin	.05
284	Bryan Cox	.05
285	Byron Evans	.05
286	Chris Doleman	.05
287	Anthony Pleasant	.05
288	Steve Grant	.05
289	Doug Riesenberg	.05
290	Natrone Means	.40
291	Henry Thomas	.05
292	Mike Pritchard	.05
293	Courtney Hawkins	.05
294	Bill Bates	.05
295	Jerome Bettis	.20
296	Russell Maryland	.05
297	Stanley Richard	.05
298	William White	.05
299	Dan Wilkinson	.05
300	Steve Young	.75
301	Gary Brown	.05
302	Jake Reed	.05
303	Carlton Gray	.05
304	Levon Kirkland	.05
305	Shannon Sharpe	.05
306	Luis Sharpe	.05
307	Marshall Faulk	.50
308	Stan Humphries	.10
309	Chris Calloway	.05
310	Tim Brown	.10
311	Steve Everitt	.05
312	Raymont Harris	.05
313	Tim McDonald	.05
314	Trent Dilfer	.25
315	Kevin Williams	.05
316	Ray Crittenden	.05
317	Jim Kelly	.10
318	Andre Reed	.05
319	Chris Miller	.05
320	Bobby Houston	.05
321	Charles Haley	.05
322	Bernard Williams	.05
323	Bernard Williams	.05
324	Michael Bates	.05
325	Brian Mitchell	.05
326	Mike Johnson	.05
327	Eric Bieniemy	.05
328	Aubrey Beavers	.05
329	Dale Carter	.05
330	Emmitt Smith	2.00
331	Darren Perry	.05
332	Marquez Pope	.05
333	Clyde Simmons	.05
334	Corey Croom	.05
335	Thomas Randolph	.05
336	Harvey Williams	.05
337	Michael Timpson	.05
338	Eugene Daniel	.05
339	Shane Dronett	.05
340	Eric Turner	.05
341	Eric Metcalf	.05
342	Leslie O'Neal	.05
343	Mark Wheeler	.05
344	Mark Pike	.05
345	Brett Favre	2.00
346	Johnny Bailey	.05
347	Henry Ellard	.05
348	Chris Gardocki	.05
349	Henry Jones	.05
350	Dan Marino	2.00
351	Lake Dawson	.20
352	Mark McMillian	.05
353	Deion Sanders	.40
354	Antonio London	.05
355	Cris Dishman	.05
356	Ricardo McDonald	.05
357	Dexter Carter	.05
358	Kevin Smith	.05
359	Yancey Thigpen	.30
360	Chris Warren	.10
361	Quinn Early	.05
362	John Mangum	.05
363	Santana Dotson	.05
364	Raghib Ismail	.05
365	Aeneas Williams	.05
366	Dan Williams	.05
367	Sean Dawkins	.05
368	Pepper Johnson	.05
369	Roman Phifer	.05
370	Rodney Hampton	.05
371	Darrell Green	.05
372	Michael Zordich	.05
373	Andre Coleman	.05
374	Wayne Simmons	.05
375	Michael Irvin	.20
376	Clay Matthews	.05
377	Dewayne Washington	.05
378	Keith Byars	.05
379	Todd Collins	.25
380	Mark Collins	.05
381	Joel Steed	.05
382	Bart Oates	.05
383	Al Smith	.05
384	Rafael Robinson	.05
385	Mo Lewis	.05
386	Aubrey Matthews	.05
387	Corey Sawyer	.05
388	Bucky Brooks	.05
389	Erik Kramer	.05
390	Tyrone Hughes	.05
391	Terry McDaniel	.05
392	Craig Erickson	.05
393	Mike Flores	.05
394	Harry Swayne	.05
395	Irving Spikes	.05
396	Lorenzo Lynch	.05
397	Antonio Langham	.05
398	Edgar Bennett	.05
399	Thomas Lewis	.05
400	John Elway	.30
401	Jeff George	.10
402	Errict Rhett	.75
403	Bill Romanowski	.05
404	Alexander Wright	.05
405	Warren Moon	.10
406	Eddie Robinson	.05
407	John Copeland	.05
408	Robert Jones	.05
409	Steve Bono	.15
410	Cornelius Bennett	.05
411	Ben Coates	.05
412	Dana Stubblefield	.05
413	Darryl Talley	.05
414	Brian Blades	.05
415	Herman Moore	.20
416	Nick Lowery	.05
417	Donnell Bennett	.05
418	Van Malone	.05
419	Pete Stoyanovich	.05
420	Joe Montana	1.00
421	Steve Young (Steve Young Subset Cards)	.30
422	Steve Young (Steve Young Subset Cards)	.30
423	Steve Young (Steve Young Subset Cards)	.30
424	Steve Young (Steve Young Subset Cards)	.30
425	Steve Young (Steve Young Subset Cards)	.30
426	Rod Stephens	.05
427	Ellis Johnson (Draft Picks)	.10
428	Kordell Stewart (Draft Picks)	4.00
429	James Stewart (Draft Picks)	1.50
430	Steve McNair (Draft Picks)	3.00
431	Brian DeMarco (Draft Picks)	.10
432	Matt O'Dwyer (Draft Picks)	.10
433	Lorenzo Styles (Draft Picks)	.10
434	Anthony Cook (Draft Picks)	.20
435	Jesse James (Draft Picks)	.10
436	Darryl Pounds (Draft Picks)	.10
437	Derrick Graham (Carolina Panther Team)	.05
438	Vernon Turner (Carolina Panther Team)	.05
439	Carlton Bailey (Carolina Panther Team)	.05
440	Darion Conner (Carolina Panther Team)	.05
441	Randy Baldwin (Carolina Panther Team)	.05
442	Tim McKyer (Carolina Panther Team)	.05
443	Sam Mills (Carolina Panther Team)	.05
444	Bob Christian (Carolina Panther Team)	.05
445	Steve Lofton (Carolina Panther Team)	.05
446	Lamar Lathon (Carolina Panther Team)	.05
447	Tony Smith (Carolina Panther Team)	.05
448	Don Beebe (Carolina Panther Team)	.05
449	Barry Foster (Carolina Panther Team)	.05
450	Frank Reich (Carolina Panther Team)	.05
451	Pete Metzelaars (Carolina Panther Team)	.05
452	Reggie Cobb (Jacksonville Jaguar Expansion Team)	.05
453	Jeff Lageman (Jacksonville Jaguar Expansion Team)	.05
454	Derek Brown (Jacksonville Jaguar Expansion Team)	.05
455	Desmond Howard (Jacksonville Jaguar Expansion Team)	.05
456	Vinnie Clark (Jacksonville Jaguar Expansion Team)	.05
457	Keith Goganious (Jacksonville Jaguar Expansion Team)	.05
458	Shawn Bouwens (Jacksonville Jaguar Expansion Team)	.05
459	Rob Johnson (Jacksonville Jaguar Expansion Team)	2.00
460	Steve Beuerlein (Jacksonville Jaguar Expansion Team)	.05
461	Mark Brunell (Jacksonville Jaguar Expansion Team)	1.00
462	Harry Colon (Jacksonville Jaguar Expansion Team)	.05
463	Chris Hudson (Jacksonville Jaguar Expansion Team)	.05
464	Darren Carrington (Jacksonville Jaguar Expansion Team)	.05
465	Ernest Givins (Jacksonville Jaguar Expansion Team)	.05
466	Kelvin Pritchett (Jacksonville Jaguar Expansion Team)	.05
467	Checklist 3 of 4	.05
468	Checklist 4 of 4	.05

1995 Topps Air Raid

These 10 1995-96 Topps football inserts utilize the dynamic Power Matrix technology to highlight the best NFL wide receiver/quarterback tandems. The cards were random inserts in every 24th pack of Series II product, retail packs only.

		MT
	Complete Set (10):	60.00
	Common Player:	3.00
1	Steve Young, Jerry Rice	10.00
2	Warren Moon, Cris Carter	3.00
3	Jeff George, Terance Mathis	3.00
4	Dave Brown, Mike Sherrard	3.00
5	Drew Bledsoe, Ben Coates	10.00
6	John Elway, Shannon Sharpe	7.00
7	Jeff Blake, Carl Pickens	3.00
8	Dan Marino, Irving Fryar	20.00
9	Randall Cunningham, Fred Barnett	3.00
10	Troy Aikman, Michael Irvin	8.00

1995 Topps All-Pros

Twenty-two players who personify the best in the game are captured on these all-silver foil cards, exclusive inserts in 1995-96 Topps Seires II hobby packs. The cards are seeded one per every eight packs.

		MT
	Complete Set (22):	25.00
	Common Player:	1.00
1	Jerry Rice	4.00
2	Lomas Brown	1.00
3	Nate Newton	1.00
4	Dermontti Dawson	1.00
5	Keith Sims	1.00
6	Richmond Webb	1.00
7	Shannon Sharpe	1.00
8	Michael Irvin	1.00
9	Steve Young	4.00
10	Barry Sanders	6.00
11	Marshall Faulk	5.00
12	Bruce Smith	1.00
13	Dana Stubblefield	1.00
14	John Randle	1.00
15	Reggie White	1.00
16	Greg Lloyd	1.00
17	Junior Seau	1.00
18	Cornelius Bennett	1.00
19	Rod Woodson	1.00
20	Deion Sanders	3.00
21	Darren Woodson	1.00
22	Merton Hanks	1.00

1995 Topps Expansion Team Boosters

The 20-card, standard-size set was randomly inserted every 36 Series II packs and is a parallel version of the expansion subset in Series II. The cards are printed on 28-point stock with diffraction foil.

		MT
	Complete Set (30):	75.00
	Common Player:	2.50
437	Derrick Graham	2.50
438	Vernon Turner	2.50
439	Carlton Bailey	2.50
440	Darion Conner	2.50
441	Randy Baldwin	2.50

442	Tim McKyer	2.50
443	Sam Mills	3.50
444	Bob Christian	2.50
445	Steve Lofton	2.50
446	Lamar Lathon	2.50
447	Tony Smith (RB)	3.50
448	Don Beebe	3.50
449	Barry Foster	2.50
450	Frank Reich	3.50
451	Pete Metzelaars	2.50
452	Reggie Cobb	2.50
453	Jeff Lageman	2.50
454	Derek Brown (TE)	2.50
455	Desmond Howard	5.00
456	Vinnie Clark	2.50
457	Keith Goganious	2.50
458	Shawn Bowens	2.50
459	Rob Johnson	4.00
460	Steve Beuerlein	2.50
461	Mark Brunell	8.00
462	Harry Colon	2.50
463	Chris Hudson	2.50
464	Darren Carrington	2.50
465	Ernest Givins	3.50
466	Kelvin Pritchett	2.50

1995 Topps Finest Inserts

Topps added a little mystery to its 1995-96 football set when it created its Series I Finest insert cards. The cards, seeded one per every 36 packs, have black opaque protectors over them instead of the clear protectors. This means that collectors have to peel off the protector to see what card they have. They will, however, be able to determine what position the player plays; three different card backs, which are visible, were made - for quarterbacks, wide receivers and running backs. The card could even be a Refractor version; this is a parallel set which has cards seeded one per every 36 hobby packs or 432 retail packs. In addition, an Instant Winner card was inserted at a rate of one per every 1,980 packs. The card entitles the finder to a complete 27-card set with clear Finest protectors.

	MT
Complete Set (27):	90.00
Common Player:	1.50
Minor Stars:	3.00
Complete Refractor Set (27):	300.00
Refractors:	1x-2x
Troy Aikman	8.00
Stan Humphries	1.50
Dan Marino	16.00
Brett Favre	16.00
Steve Young	6.00
Jim Kelly	3.00
John Elway	6.00
Warren Moon	3.00
Drew Bledsoe	8.00
Barry Sanders	10.00
Natrone Means	3.00
Ricky Watters	3.00
Chris Warren	1.50
Marshall Faulk	3.00
Jerome Bettis	1.50
Rodney Hampton	1.50
Errict Rhett	3.00
Emmitt Smith	16.00
Jerry Rice	8.00
Andre Reed	1.50
Irving Fryar	1.50
Herman Moore	1.50
Tim Brown	1.50
Terance Mathis	1.50
Henry Ellard	1.50
Michael Irvin	3.00
Cris Carter	1.50

1995 Topps Finest Boosters

These cards were random inserts in 1995 Topps Series II packs. They are numbered B166-B187.

	MT
Complete Set (22):	100.00
Common Player:	2.00
Comp. Refractor Set (22):	200.00
Refractors:	1x-2x
166	Barry Sanders	12.00
167	Bryant Young	2.00
168	Boomer Esiason	2.00
169	Terance Mathis	2.00
170	Troy Aikman	10.00
171	Junior Seau	2.00
172	Rodney Hampton	2.00
173	Jim Everett	2.00
174	Dan Marino	18.00
175	Steve Young	10.00
176	Cris Carter	2.00
177	Eric Swann	2.00
178	Rick Mirer	4.00
179	Jerome Bettis	2.00
180	Emmitt Smith	18.00
181	Jim Kelly	2.00
182	John Elway	6.00
183	Dana Stubblefield	2.00
184	Drew Bledsoe	10.00
185	Jerry Rice	10.00
186	Michael Irvin	4.00
187	Bruce Smith	2.00

1995 Topps Florida Hot Bed

The 15-card standard-size set was inserted in each retail pack amd features top players who attended a Florida college. The card fronts depict a map outline of Florida with "Florida Hot Bed" printed in orange at the top. The player and team name are in gold foil near the card bottom. The card backs are numbered with the "FH" prefix and contain a player headshot with a commentary on his NFL career over a water background.

	MT
Complete Set (15):	25.00
Common Player:	1.00
1	Deion Sanders	4.00
2	Brian Blades	1.00
3	Errict Rhett	5.00
4	Kevin Williams	1.00
5	Cortez Kennedy	1.00
6	Corey Sawyer	1.00
7	Russell Maryland	1.00
8	Emmitt Smith	10.00
9	Vinny Testaverde	1.00
10	William Floyd	1.50
11	Brett Perriman	1.00
12	Nate Newton	1.00
13	Jim Kelly	1.50
14	LeRoy Butler	1.00
15	Michael Irvin	1.50

1995 Topps Hit List

Hit List features 20 of the hardest most feared defenders in the league. Topps uses a stone-crushing design for the cards, which were inserts in 1995-96 Topps football Series I packs. They were seeded one per every four packs, making them the most common of the inserts.

	MT
Complete Set (20):	10.00
Common Player:	.50
Minor Stars:	1.00
1	Pepper Johnson	.50
2	Elijah Alexander	.50
3	Joe Cain	.50
4	Andre Collins	.50
5	Chris Spielman	.50
6	Bryan Cox	.50
7	Ed McDaniel	.50
8	Jack Del Rio	.50
9	Jeff Herrod	.50
10	Greg Lloyd	1.00
11	Reggie White	1.50
12	Robert Jones	.50
13	Eric Turner	.50
14	Vincent Brown	.50
15	Kevin Greene	.50
16	Bruce Smith	1.00
17	Hardy Nickerson	.50
18	Seth Joyner	.50
19	Darryl Talley	.50
20	Junior Seau	1.50

1995 Topps 1000/3000 Boosters

This Power Boosters set is a parallel set of the 1,000- and 3,000-Yard Club subset cards found in Topps 1995 Series I. Each card is "boosted" up to 28-point stock on a dynamic full foil board stock. A Power Boosters card replaces two regular cards in every 36th pack.

	MT
Complete Set (41):	140.00
Common Player:	3.00
1	Barry Sanders	12.00
2	Chris Warren	3.00
3	Jerry Rice	10.00
4	Emmitt Smith	20.00
5	Henry Ellard	3.00
6	Natrone Means	3.00
7	Terance Mathis	3.00
8	Tim Brown	3.00
9	Andre Reed	3.00
10	Marshall Faulk	5.00
11	Irving Fryar	3.00
12	Cris Carter	3.00
13	Michael Irvin	3.00
14	Jake Reed	3.00
15	Ben Coates	3.00
16	Herman Moore	3.00
17	Carl Pickens	3.00
18	Fred Barnett	3.00
19	Sterling Sharpe	3.00
20	Anthony Miller	3.00
21	Thurman Thomas	3.00
22	Andre Rison	3.00
23	Brian Blades	3.00
24	Rodney Hampton	3.00
25	Terry Allen	3.00
26	Jerome Bettis	3.00
27	Errict Rhett	3.00
28	Rob Moore	3.00
29	Shannon Sharpe	3.00
30	Drew Bledsoe	10.00
31	Dan Marino	20.00
32	Warren Moon	3.00
33	Steve Young	7.00
34	Brett Favre	20.00
35	Jim Everett	3.00
36	Jeff George	3.00
37	John Elway	7.00
38	Jeff Hostetler	3.00
39	Randall Cunningham	3.00
40	Stan Humphries	3.00
41	Jim Kelly	3.00

1995 Topps Profiles

Topps' spokesman, San Francisco 49ers quarterback Steve Young, lends his insights and unique observations of 15 key players for this 1995-96 Topps Series II insert set. These all-silver foil cards are inserted at a rate of one per every 12th pack.

	MT
Complete Set (15):	35.00
Common Player:	1.00
1	Emmitt Smith	10.00
2	Chris Spielman	1.00
3	Rod Woodson	1.00
4	Deion Sanders	3.00
5	Junior Seau	1.00
6	Byron Evans	1.00
7	Jerome Bettis	1.00
8	Charles Haley	1.00
9	Jerry Rice	5.00
10	Barry Sanders	7.00
11	Hardy Nickerson	1.00
12	Natrone Means	1.00
13	Darren Woodson	1.00
14	Reggie White	1.00
15	Troy Aikman	4.00

1995 Topps Sensational Sophomores

Ten of the hottest 1994 rookies, including Rookie of the Year Marshall Faulk, comprise this 1995-96 Topps Series I insert set. The cards, printed with Dot Matrix technology, are inserted at a rate of one per every 24 packs and are found exclusively in retail packs.

	MT
Complete Set (10):	20.00
Common Player:	1.00
1	Marshall Faulk	4.00
2	Heath Shuler	2.00
3	Tim Bowens	1.00
4	Bryant Young	2.00
5	Dan Wilkinson	2.00
6	Errict Rhett	1.00
7	Andre Coleman	1.00
8	Aaron Glenn	1.00
9	Trent Dilfer	3.00
10	Byron Morris	2.00

1995 Topps Yesteryear

The 15 players who make up this 1995-96 Topps football Series I insert set have not only survived the test but have risen to the top. Each card, printed using Finest technology, features past and present photos and compares the player's rookie season to the previous one. Cards are random inserts, one per every 72 hobby packs.

	MT
Complete Set (15):	75.00
Common Player:	2.00
1	Stan Humphries	2.00
2	Dan Marino	20.00

3	Irving Fryar	2.00
4	Warren Moon	2.00
5	Steve Young	8.00
6	Kevin Greene	2.00
7	Jeff Hostetler	2.00
8	Jack Del Rio	2.00
9	Reggie White	2.00
10	Jerry Rice	10.00
11	Bruce Smith	2.00
12	Rod Woodson	2.00
13	Deion Sanders	7.00
14	Barry Sanders	10.00
15	Brett Favre	20.00

1995 Topps Factory Jaguars

The 473-card standard-size set was issued to honor the Jaguars debut season. The cards parallel the base set and each card has a foil Jaguars stamp. Reportedly, just 4,000 sets were produced.

	MT
Complete Set (473):	50.00
Common Player:	.10
Veteran Stars:	.75x-1.5x
Young Stars:	.6x-1.25x

1995 Topps Factory Panthers

The 473-card standard-size set was issued to commemorate the Panthers debut season. The set parallels the base set with card having a foil Carolina stamp. Reportedly, there were just 4,000 sets produced.

	MT
Complete Set (473):	50.00
Common Player:	.10
Veteran Stars:	.75x-1.5x
Young Stars:	.6x-1.25x

1996 Topps Promos

This six-card promo set was sent to dealers and media to provide a sneak peak at the designs for 1996 Topps Football. It arrived in a clear, cello pack containing all six cards.

	MT
Complete Set (6):	15.00
Common Player:	1.50
35	Quentin Coryatt	1.50
50	Kerry Collins	5.00
60	Mark Brunell	5.00
73	Mark Carrier	1.50
145	Mel Gray	1.50
405	Ben Coates	1.50

1996 Topps

Topps 1996 set marks the 40th year the company has been in football. To commemorate that milestone, Broadway Joe Namath, the New York Jets quarterback, who guaranteed a victory in the Super Bowl in 1969, guarantees this set is Topps best ever. As a tribute to Namath, Topps features him in a 10-card insert set which reprints his 10 Topps cards (1 in 18 packs). He also reviews 10 active NFL quarterbacks for his "Broadway's Reviews" insert set. A 40th Anniversary insert set features 40 of today's top stars pictured on original Topps card designs (one for every year). Other inserts include Turf Warriors, Hobby Masters, a Sweepstakes card (1 in 108 packs), which entitles the finder to one of the 40 sets made during the last 40 years, or all 40, if you're the grand prize winner). The regular 1996 Topps set has 440 cards in it. Each front has a color photo on it, with the player's name, position and team at the bottom between two parallel bars. Topps 40th Anniversary logo is also stamped on each card.

	MT
Complete Set (440):	35.00
Common Player:	.05
Minor Stars:	.10
Wax Box:	45.00
1	Troy Aikman	1.00
2	Kevin Greene	.05
3	Robert Brooks	.05
4	Eugene Daniel	.05
5	Rodney Peete	.05
6	James Hasty	.05
7	Tim McDonald	.05
8	Darick Holmes	.05
9	Morten Andersen	.05
10	Junior Seau	.05
11	Brett Perriman	.05
12	Eric Green	.05
13	Jim Flanigan	.05
14	Cortez Kennedy	.05
15	Orlando Thomas	.05
16	Anthony Miller	.05
17	Sean Gilbert	.05
18	Rob Fredrickson	.05
19	Willie Green	.05
20	Jeff Blake	.50
21	Trent Dilfer	.05
22	Chris Chandler	.05
23	Renaldo Turnbull	.05
24	David Meggett	.05
25	Heath Shuler	.40
26	Michael Jackson	.05
27	Thomas Randolph	.05
28	Keith Goganious	.05
29	Seth Joyner	.05
30	Wayne Chrebet	.05
31	Craig Newsome	.05
32	William Fuller	.05
33	Merton Hanks	.05
34	Dale Carter	.05
35	Quentin Coryatt	.05
36	Robert Jones	.05
37	Eric Metcalf	.05
38	Byron Morris	.05
39	Bill Brooks	.05
40	Barry Sanders	2.00
41	Michael Haynes	.05
42	Joey Galloway	.50
43	Robert Smith	.05
44	John Thierry	.05
45	Bryan Cox	.05
46	Anthony Parker	.05
47	Harvey Williams	.05
48	Terrell Davis	3.00
49	Darnay Scott	.10
50	Kerry Collins	.25
51	Cris Dishman	.05
52	Dwayne Harper	.05
53	Warren Sapp	.05
54	Will Moore	.05
55	Earnest Byner	.05
56	Aaron Glenn	.05
57	Michael Westbrook	.50
58	Vencie Glenn	.05
59	Rob Moore	.05
60	Mark Brunell	.75
61	Craig Heyward	.05
62	Eric Allen	.05
63	Bill Romanowski	.05
64	Dana Stubblefield	.05
65	Steve Bono	.05
66	George Koonce	.05
67	Larry Brown	.05
68	Warren Moon	.05
69	Erric Pegram	.05
70	Jim Kelly	.05
71	Jason Belser	.05
72	Henry Thomas	.05
73	Mark Carrier	.05
74	Terry Wooden	.05
75	Terry McDaniel	.05
76	O.J. McDuffie	.05
77	Dan Wilkinson	.05
78	Blake Brockermeyer	.05
79	Michael Barrow	.05
80	Dave Brown	.05

81	Todd Lyght	.05
82	Henry Ellard	.05
83	Jeff Lageman	.05
84	Anthony Pleasant	.05
85	Aeneas Williams	.05
86	Vincent Brisby	.05
87	Terrell Fletcher	.05
88	Brad Baxter	.05
89	Shannon Sharpe	.05
90	Errict Rhett	.20
91	Michael Zordich	.05
92	Dan Saleaumua	.05
93	Devin Bush	.05
94	Wayne Simmons	.05
95	Tyrone Hughes	.05
96	John Randle	.05
97	Tony Tolbert	.05
98	Yancey Thigpen	.40
99	J.J. Stokes	.50
100	Marshall Faulk	.40
101	Barry Minter	.05
102	Glenn Foley	.05
103	Chester McGlockton	.05
104	Carlton Gray	.05
105	Terry Kirby	.05
106	Darryll Lewis	.05
107	Thomas Smith	.05
108	Mike Fox	.05
109	Antonio Langham	.05
110	Drew Bledsoe	1.00
111	Troy Drayton	.05
112	Marvcus Patton	.05
113	Tyrone Wheatley	.05
114	Desmond Howard	.05
115	Johnny Mitchell	.05
116	Dave Krieg	.05
117	Natrone Means	.15
118	Herman Moore	.20
119	Darren Woodson	.05
120	Ricky Watters	.05
121	Emmitt Smith (1,000 Yard Club)	1.00
122	Barry Sanders (1,000 Yard Club)	.50
123	Curtis Martin (1,000 Yard Club)	.75
124	Chris Warren (1,000 Yard Club)	.05
125	Terry Allen (1,000 Yard Club)	.05
126	Ricky Watters (1,000 Yard Club)	.05
127	Errict Rhett (1,000 Yard Club)	.40
128	Rodney Hampton (1,000 Yard Club)	.05
129	Terrell Davis (1,000 Yard Club)	.50
130	Harvey Williams (1,000 Yard Club)	.05
131	Craig Heyward (1,000 Yard Club)	.05
132	Marshall Faulk (1,000 Yard Club)	.40
133	Rashaan Salaam (1,000 Yard Club)	.25
134	Garrison Hearst (1,000 Yard Club)	.05
135	Edgar Bennett (1,000 Yard Club)	.05
136	Thurman Thomas (1,000 Yard Club)	.05
137	Brian Washington	.05
138	Derek Loville	.05
139	Curtis Conway	.05
140	Isaac Bruce	.25
141	Ricardo McDonald	.05
142	Bruce Armstrong	.05
143	Will Wolford	.05
144	Thurman Thomas	.10
145	Mel Gray	.05
146	Napoleon Kaufman	.20
147	Terry Allen	.05
148	Chris Calloway	.05
149	Harry Colon	.05
150	Pepper Johnson	.05
151	Marco Coleman	.05
152	Shawn Jefferson	.05
153	Larry Centers	.05
154	Lamar Lathon	.05
155	Mark Chmura	.20
156	Dermontti Dawson	.05
157	Alvin Harper	.05
158	Randall McDaniel	.05
159	Allen Aldridge	.05
160	Chris Warren	.10
161	Jessie Tuggle	.05
162	Sean Lumpkin	.05
163	Bobby Houston	.05
164	Dexter Carter	.05
165	Erik Kramer	.05
166	Brock Marion	.05
167	Toby Wright	.05
168	John Copeland	.05
169	Sean Dawkins	.05
170	Tim Brown	.05
171	Darion Conner	.05
172	Aaron Hayden	.05
173	Charlie Garner	.05
174	Anthony Cook	.05
175	Derrick Thomas	.05
176	Willie McGinest	.05
177	Thomas Lewis	.05
178	Sherman Williams	.05
179	Cornelius Bennett	.05
180	Frank Sanders	.05
181	Leroy Hoard	.05
182	Bernie Parmalee	.05

183	Sterling Palmer	.05
184	Kelvin Pritchett	.05
185	Kordell Stewart	1.00
186	Brent Jones	.05
187	Robert Blackmon	.05
188	Adrian Murrell	.05
189	Edgar Bennett	.05
190	Rashaan Salaam	.50
191	Ellis Johnson	.05
192	Andre Coleman	.05
193	Will Shields	.05
194	Derrick Brooks	.05
195	Carl Pickens	.10
196	Carlton Bailey	.05
197	Terance Mathis	.05
198	Carlos Jenkins	.05
199	Derrick Alexander	.05
200	Deion Sanders	.40
201	Glyn Milburn	.05
202	Chris Sanders	.25
203	Raghib Ismail	.05
204	Fred Barnett	.05
205	Quinn Early	.05
206	Henry Jones	.05
207	Herschel Walker	.05
208	James Washington	.05
209	Lee Woodall	.05
210	Neil Smith	.05
211	Tony Bennett	.05
212	Ernie Mills	.05
213	Clyde Simmons	.05
214	Chris Slade	.05
215	Tony Boselli	.05
216	Ryan McNeil	.05
217	Rob Burnett	.05
218	Stan Humphries	.05
219	Rick Mirer	.05
220	Troy Vincent	.05
221	Sean Jones	.05
222	Marty Carter	.05
223	Boomer Esiason	.05
224	Charles Haley	.05
225	Sam Mills	.05
226	Greg Biekert	.05
227	Bryant Young	.05
228	Ken Dilger	.05
229	Levon Kirkland	.05
230	Brian Mitchell	.05
231	Hardy Nickerson	.05
232	Elvis Grbac	.05
233	Kurt Schulz	.05
234	Chris Doleman	.05
235	Tamarick Vanover	.50
236	Jesse Campbell	.05
237	William Thomas	.05
238	Shane Conlan	.05
239	Jason Elam	.05
240	Steve McNair	.50
241	Jerry Rice (1,000 Yard Club)	.50
242	Isaac Bruce (1,000 Yard Club)	.30
243	Herman Moore (1,000 Yard Club)	.05
244	Michael Irvin (1,000 Yard Club)	.05
245	Robert Brooks (1,000 Yard Club)	.05
246	Brett Perriman (1,000 Yard Club)	.05
247	Cris Carter (1,000 Yard Club)	.05
248	Tim Brown (1,000 Yard Club)	.05
249	Yancey Thigpen (1,000 Yard Club)	.20
250	Jeff Graham (1,000 Yard Club)	.05
251	Carl Pickens (1,000 Yard Club)	.05
252	Tony Martin (1,000 Yard Club)	.05
253	Eric Metcalf (1,000 Yard Club)	.05
254	Jake Reed (1,000 Yard Club)	.05
255	Quinn Early (1,000 Yard Club)	.05
256	Anthony Miller (1,000 Yard Club)	.05
257	Joey Galloway (1,000 Yard Club)	.25
258	Bert Emanuel (1,000 Yard Club)	.05
259	Terance Mathis (1,000 Yard Club)	.05
260	Curtis Conway (1,000 Yard Club)	.05
261	Henry Ellard (1,000 Yard Club)	.05
262	Mark Carrier (1,000 Yard Club)	.05
263	Brian Blades (1,000 Yard Club)	.05
264	William Roaf	.05
265	Ed McDaniel	.05
266	Nate Newton	.05
267	Bret Maxie	.05
268	Anthony Smith	.05
269	Mickey Washington	.05
270	Jerry Rice	1.00
271	Shaun Gayle	.05
272	Gilbert Brown	.05
273	Mark Bruener	.05
274	Eugene Robinson	.05
275	Marvin Washington	.05
276	Keith Sims	.05

277	Ashley Ambrose	.05
278	Garrison Hearst	.05
279	Donnell Woolford	.05
280	Cris Carter	.05
281	Curtis Martin	1.50
282	Scott Mitchell	.05
283	Stevon Moore	.05
284	Roman Phifer	.05
285	Ken Harvey	.05
286	Rodney Hampton	.05
287	Willie Davis	.05
288	Yonel Jourdain	.05
289	Brian DeMarco	.05
290	Reggie White	.05
291	Kevin Williams	.05
292	Gary Plummer	.05
293	Terrance Shaw	.05
294	Calvin Williams	.05
295	Eddie Robinson	.05
296	Tony McGee	.05
297	Clay Matthews	.05
298	Joe Cain	.05
299	Tim McKyer	.05
300	Greg Lloyd	.05
301	Steve Wisniewski	.05
302	Ray Buchanan	.05
303	Lake Dawson	.05
304	Kevin Carter	.05
305	Phillippi Sparks	.05
306	Emmitt Smith	2.00
307	Ruben Brown	.05
308	Tom Carter	.05
309	William Floyd	.05
310	Jim Everett	.05
311	Vincent Brown	.05
312	Dennis Gibson	.05
313	Lorenzo Lynch	.05
314	Corey Harris	.05
315	James Stewart	.05
316	Kyle Brady	.05
317	Irving Fryar	.05
318	Jake Reed	.05
319	Vinny Testaverde	.05
320	John Elway	.30
321	Tracy Scroggins	.05
322	Chris Spielman	.05
323	Horace Copeland	.05
324	Chris Zorich	.05
325	Mike Mamula	.05
326	Henry Ford	.05
327	Steve Walsh	.05
328	Stanley Richard	.05
329	Mike Jones	.05
330	Jim Harbaugh	.05
331	Darren Perry	.05
332	Ken Norton	.05
333	Kimble Anders	.05
334	Harold Green	.05
335	Tyrone Poole	.05
336	Mark Fields	.05
337	Darren Bennett	.05
338	Mike Sherrard	.05
339	Terry Ray	.05
340	Bruce Smith	.05
341	Daryl Johnston	.05
342	Vinnie Clark	.05
343	Mike Caldwell	.05
344	Vinson Smith	.05
345	Mo Lewis	.05
346	Brian Blades	.05
347	Rod Stephens	.05
348	David Palmer	.05
349	Blaine Bishop	.05
350	Jeff George	.05
351	George Teague	.05
352	Jeff Hostetler	.05
353	Michael Strahan	.05
354	Eric Davis	.05
355	Jerome Bettis	.05
356	Irv Smith	.05
357	Jeff Herrod	.05
358	Jay Novacek	.05
359	Bryce Paup	.05
360	Neil O'Donnell	.05
361	Eric Swann	.05
362	Corey Sawyer	.05
363	Ty Law	.05
364	Bo Orlando	.05
365	Marcus Allen	.05
366	Mark McMillian	.05
367	Mark Carrier	.05
368	Jackie Harris	.05
369	Steve Atwater	.05
370	Steve Young	1.00
371	Brett Favre (3,000 Yard Club)	.75
372	Scott Mitchell (3,000 Yard Club)	.05
373	Warren Moon (3,000 Yard Club)	.05
374	Jeff George (3,000 Yard Club)	.05
375	Jim Everett (3,000 Yard Club)	.05
376	John Elway (3,000 Yard Club)	.15
377	Erik Kramer (3,000 Yard Club)	.05
378	Jeff Blake (3,000 Yard Club)	.25
379	Dan Marino (3,000 Yard Club)	1.00
380	Dave Krieg (3,000 Yard Club)	.05
381	Drew Bledsoe (3,000 Yard Club)	.50
382	Stan Humphries (3,000 Yard Club)	.05

383	Troy Aikman (3,000 Yard Club)	.50
384	Steve Young (3,000 Yard Club)	.50
385	Jim Kelly (3,000 Yard Club)	.05
386	Steve Bono (3,000 Yard Club)	.05
387	David Sloan	.05
388	Jeff Graham	.05
389	Hugh Douglas	.05
390	Dan Marino	1.50
391	Winston Moss	.05
392	Darrell Green	.05
393	Mark Stepnoski	.05
394	Bert Emanuel	.05
395	Eric Zeier	.05
396	Willie Jackson	.05
397	Qadry Ismail	.05
398	Michael Brooks	.05
399	D'Marco Farr	.05
400	Brett Favre	2.00
401	Carnell Lake	.05
402	Pat Swilling	.05
403	Steve Grant	.05
404	Steve Tasker	.05
405	Ben Coates	.05
406	Steve Tovar	.05
407	Tony Martin	.05
408	Grant Hill	.05
409	Eric Guliford	.05
410	Michael Irvin	.05
411	Eric Hill	.05
412	Mario Bates	.05
413	Brian Stablein	.05
414	*Marcus Jones*	.05
415	*Reggie Brown*	.05
416	*Lawrence Phillips*	.50
417	*Alex Van Dyke*	.10
418	*Daryl Gardener*	.05
419	*Mike Alstott*	1.50
420	*Kevin Hardy*	.10
421	*Rickey Dudley*	.20
422	*Jerome Woods*	.05
423	*Eric Moulds*	1.50
424	*Cedric Jones*	.05
425	*Simeon Rice*	.40
426	*Marvin Harrison*	2.00
427	*Tim Biakabutuka*	.75
428	*Duane Clemons*	.05
429	*Alex Molden*	.05
430	*Keyshawn Johnson*	2.00
431	*Willie Anderson*	.05
432	*John Mobley*	.05
433	*Leeland McElroy*	.20
434	*Regan Upshaw*	.05
435	*Eddie George*	3.00
436	*Jonathan Ogden*	.10
437	*Eddie Kennison*	.05
438	*Jermain Mayberry*	.05
439	Checklist	.05
440	Checklist	.05

1996 Topps 40th Anniversary

EMMITT SMITH
DALLAS COWBOYS — RUNNING BACK

Forty of today's top NFL stars are featured on these 1996 Topps football cards, which utilize Topps original designs from its first 40 years of producing cards. Each player in the set represents a different year, using a classic pose from that set. The cards, seeded one per every six packs, have Topps 40th Anniversary logo stamped in gold foil on the front.

		MT
Complete Set (40):		70.00
Common Player:		1.00
Minor Stars:		2.00
1	Jim Harbaugh '56	1.00
2	Greg Lloyd '57	1.00
3	Barry Sanders '58	5.00
4	Merton Hanks '59	1.00
5	Herman Moore '60	1.00
6	Tim Brown '61	1.00
7	Brett Favre '62	10.00
8	Cris Carter '63	1.00
9	Curtis Martin '64	7.00
10	Bryce Paup '65	1.00
11	Stanley Richard '66	1.00
12	Blaine Bishop '67	1.00
13	Emmitt Smith '68	10.00
14	Carnell Lake '69	1.00
15	Marshall Faulk '70	4.00
16	Mike Morris '71	1.00
17	Shannon Sharpe '72	1.00
18	Steve Young '73	4.00
19	Jeff George '74	2.00
20	Junior Seau '75	1.00
21	Chris Warren '76	1.00
22	Heath Shuler '77	2.00
23	Jeff Blake '78	3.00
24	Reggie White '79	2.00
25	Jeff Hostetler '80	1.00
26	Errict Rhett '81	1.00
27	Rodney Hampton '82	1.00
28	Jerry Rice '83	5.00
29	Jim Everett '84	1.00
30	Isaac Bruce '85	3.00
31	Dan Marino '86	10.00
32	Marcus Allen '87	3.00
33	Erik Kramer '88	1.00
34	John Elway '89	5.00
35	Ricky Watters '90	1.00
36	Troy Aikman '91	5.00
37	Drew Bledsoe '92	5.00
38	Scott Mitchell '93	1.00
39	Rashaan Salaam '94	2.00
40	Kerry Collins '95	2.00

1996 Topps Broadway's Reviews

These 1996 Topps football inserts feature 10 of today's top quarterbacks pictured with an archive photo of Joe Namath. The horizontally-designed card front is designed like a filmstrip. The card back has Namath's review of the player, written by the Hall of Famer himself. Cards were seeded one per every 12 packs.

		MT
Complete Set (10):		30.00
Common Player:		1.50
1	Kerry Collins	.05
2	Drew Bledsoe	4.00
3	Jeff Blake	1.50
4	Brett Favre	7.00
5	Scott Mitchell	1.50
6	Troy Aikman	4.00
7	Steve Young	3.00
8	Jim Harbaugh	1.50
9	John Elway	2.50
10	Dan Marino	7.00

Post-1980 cards in Near Mint condition will generally sell for about 75% of the quoted Mint value. Excellent-condition cards bring no more than 40%.

1996 Topps Hobby Masters

These 20 cards, a hobby only insert, feature the game's top 10 superstars, as chosen by hobbyists. The cards, seeded one per every 36 packs of 1996 Topps football hobby, use 28-point foil board. The card front has a color action photo in the middle, with a closeup shot as the background. "Hobby Masters" is written towards the bottom of the card, along with the player's name, position and a team logo. Topps 40th Anniversary logo is also on the front.

		MT
Complete Set (20):		150.00
Common Player:		2.00
Minor Stars:		4.00
1	Brett Favre	25.00
2	Emmitt Smith	25.00
3	Drew Bledsoe	12.00
4	Marshall Faulk	10.00
5	Steve Young	12.00
6	Barry Sanders	18.00
7	Troy Aikman	12.00
8	Jerry Rice	12.00
9	Michael Irvin	4.00
10	Dan Marino	25.00
11	Chris Warren	4.00
12	Reggie White	2.00
13	Jeff Blake	4.00
14	Greg Lloyd	2.00
15	Curtis Martin	18.00
16	Junior Seau	2.00
17	Kerry Collins	4.00
18	Deion Sanders	7.00
19	Joey Galloway	10.00
20	John Elway	6.00

1996 Topps Namath Reprint

"Broadway Joe" Namath's 10 Topps cards are reprinted for this 1996 Topps football insert set, including his 1965 Topps rookie card, one of the most valuable modern-day football cards. The cards were seeded at a ratio of one per every 18 packs.

		MT
Complete Set (10):		50.00
Common Player:		5.00
1	1965	10.00
2	1966	5.00
3	1967	5.00
4	1968	5.00
5	1969	5.00
6	1970	5.00
7	1971	5.00
8	1972	5.00
9	1972	5.00
10	1973	5.00

1996 Topps Turf Warriors

This insert features 22 players on coated cards with an astroturf type surface. Turf Warriors are inserted every 36 packs of Topps Football.

		MT
Complete Set (22):		120.00
Common Player:		3.00
1	Bryce Paup	3.00
2	Ben Coates	3.00
3	Jim Harbaugh	3.00
4	Brian Mitchell	3.00
5	Brett Favre	20.00
6	Junior Seau	3.00
7	Michael Irvin	3.00
8	Steve Young	10.00
9	Terry McDaniel	3.00
10	Curtis Martin	16.00
11	Greg Lloyd	3.00
12	Cris Carter	3.00
13	Emmitt Smith	20.00
14	Reggie White	3.00
15	Marshall Faulk	6.00
16	Jerry Rice	14.00
17	Shannon Sharpe	3.00
18	Dan Marino	20.00
19	Ken Norton	3.00
20	Barry Sanders	3.00
21	Neil Smith	3.00
22	Troy Aikman	12.00

A player's name in *italic* type indicates a rookie card.

1996 Topps Chrome

Chrome Football includes 165 of the best cards from Topps Football and adds its chromium finish. Among the cards in Chrome are Draft Picks, 1000 Yard Club and 3000 Yard Club subsets. Four-card packs included Tide Turners and 40th Anniversary inserts, as well as Refractor versions of the entire set and all inserts.

		MT
Complete Set (165):		250.00
Common Player:		.25
Common Rookies (150-164):		1.00
Minor Stars:		.50
Wax Box:		230.00
1	Troy Aikman	3.00
2	Kevin Greene	.25
3	Robert Brooks	.25
4	Junior Seau	.50
5	Brett Perriman	.25
6	Cortez Kennedy	.25
7	Orlando Thomas	.25
8	Anthony Miller	.25
9	Jeff Blake	1.00
10	Trent Dilfer	1.00
11	Heath Shuler	.25
12	Michael Jackson	.25
13	Merton Hanks	.25
14	Dale Carter	.25
15	Eric Metcalf	.25
16	Barry Sanders	6.00
17	Joey Galloway	1.00
18	Bryan Cox	.25
19	Harvey Williams	.25
20	Terrell Davis	6.00
21	Darnay Scott	.25
22	Kerry Collins	.75
23	Warren Sapp	.25
24	Michael Westbrook	.25
25	Mark Brunell	3.00
26	Craig Heyward	.25
27	Eric Allen	.25
28	Dana Stubblefield	.25
29	Steve Bono	.25
30	Larry Brown	.25
31	Warren Moon	.50
32	Jim Kelly	.50
33	Terry McDaniel	.25
34	Dan Wilkinson	.25
35	Dave Brown	.25
36	Todd Lyght	.25
37	Aeneas Williams	.25
38	Shannon Sharpe	.50
39	Errict Rhett	.50
40	Yancey Thigpen	.50
41	J.J. Stokes	.25
42	Marshall Faulk	1.00
43	Chester McGlockton	.25
44	Darryll Lewis	.25
45	Drew Bledsoe	3.00
46	Tyrone Wheatley	.25
47	Herman Moore	1.00
48	Darren Woodson	.25
49	Ricky Watters	.50
50	Emmitt Smith TYC	2.50
51	Barry Sanders TYC	2.00
52	Curtis Martin TYC	1.50
53	Chris Warren TYC	.25
54	Errict Rhett TYC	.25
55	Rodney Hampton TYC	.25
56	Terrell Davis TYC	3.00
57	Marshall Faulk TYC	.50
58	Rashaan Salaam TYC	.25
59	Curtis Conway	.50
60	Isaac Bruce	1.00
61	Thurman Thomas	.50
62	Terry Allen	.25
63	Lamar Lathon	.25
64	Mark Chmura	.50
65	Chris Warren	.25
66	Jessie Tuggle	.25
67	Erik Kramer	.25
68	Tim Brown	.50
69	Derrick Thomas	.25
70	Willie McGinest	.25
71	Frank Sanders	.25
72	Bernie Parmalee	.25
73	Kordell Stewart	3.00
74	Brent Jones	.25
75	Edgar Bennett	.25
76	Rashaan Salaam	.50
77	Carl Pickens	.50
78	Terance Mathis	.25
79	Deion Sanders	1.50
80	Glyn Milburn	.25
81	Lee Woodall	.25
82	Neil Smith	.25
83	Stan Humphries	.25
84	Rick Mirer	.25
85	Troy Vincent	.25
86	Sam Mills	.25
87	Brian Mitchell	.25
88	Hardy Nickerson	.25
89	Tamarick Vanover	.50
90	Steve McNair	3.00
91	Jerry Rice TYC	1.50
92	Isaac Bruce TYC	.50
93	Herman Moore TYC	.50
94	Cris Carter TYC	.25
95	Tim Brown TYC	.25
96	Carl Pickens TYC	.25
97	Joey Galloway TYC	.50
98	Jerry Rice	3.00
99	Cris Carter	.50
100	Curtis Martin	3.00
101	Scott Mitchell	.25
102	Ken Harvey	.25
103	Rodney Hampton	.25
104	Reggie White	.50
105	Eddie Robinson	.25
106	Greg Lloyd	.25
107	Phillippi Sparks	.25
108	Emmitt Smith	5.00
109	Tom Carter	.25
110	Jim Everett	.25
111	James Stewart	.25
112	Kyle Brady	.25
113	Irving Fryar	.25
114	Vinny Testaverde	.25
115	John Elway	3.00
116	Chris Spielman	.25
117	Mike Mamula	.25
118	Jim Harbaugh	.50
119	Ken Norton	.25
120	Bruce Smith	.25
121	Daryl Johnston	.25
122	Blaine Bishop	.25
123	Jeff George	.50
124	Jeff Hostetler	.25
125	Jerome Bettis	.50
126	Jay Novacek	.25
127	Bryce Paup	.25
128	Neil O'Donnell	.25
129	Marcus Allen	1.00
130	Steve Young	2.00
131	Brett Favre TYC	3.00
132	Scott Mitchell TYC	.25
133	John Elway TYC	2.00
134	Jeff Blake TYC	.50
135	Dan Marino TYC	3.00
136	Drew Bledsoe TYC	1.50
137	Troy Aikman TYC	1.50
138	Steve Young TYC	1.00
139	Jim Kelly TYC	.25
140	Jeff Graham	.25
141	Hugh Douglas	.25
142	Dan Marino	6.00
143	Darrell Green	.25
144	Eric Zeier	.25
145	Brett Favre	6.00
146	Carnell Lake	.25
147	Ben Coates	.25
148	Tony Martin	.25
149	Michael Irvin	.50
150	*Lawrence Phillips*	15.00
151	*Alex Van Dyke*	1.00
152	*Kevin Hardy*	1.00
153	*Rickey Dudley*	6.00
154	*Eric Moulds*	40.00
155	*Simeon Rice*	1.00
156	*Marvin Harrison*	60.00
157	*Tim Biakabutuka*	20.00
158	*Duane Clemons*	1.00
159	*Keyshawn Johnson*	50.00
160	*John Mobley*	1.00
161	*Leeland McElroy*	2.00
162	*Eddie George*	65.00
163	*Jonathan Ogden*	1.00
164	*Eddie Kennison*	5.00
165	Checklist	.25

1996 Topps Chrome Refractors

Topps Chrome Refractors are a parallel of the Topps Chrome base set. Refractors were inserted one per 12 packs.

		MT
Complete Set (165):		1500.
Common Player:		3.00
Common Rookies (150-164):		6.00
Minor Stars:		6.00
1	Troy Aikman	45.00
2	Kevin Greene	3.00
3	Robert Brooks	3.00
4	Junior Seau	6.00
5	Brett Perriman	3.00
6	Cortez Kennedy	3.00
7	Orlando Thomas	3.00
8	Anthony Miller	3.00
9	Jeff Blake	10.00
10	Trent Dilfer	10.00
11	Heath Shuler	3.00
12	Michael Jackson	3.00
13	Merton Hanks	3.00
14	Dale Carter	3.00
15	Eric Metcalf	3.00
16	Barry Sanders	90.00
17	Joey Galloway	10.00
18	Bryan Cox	3.00
19	Harvey Williams	3.00
20	Terrell Davis	90.00
21	Darnay Scott	3.00
22	Kerry Collins	6.00
23	Warren Sapp	3.00
24	Michael Westbrook	3.00
25	Mark Brunell	40.00
26	Craig Heyward	3.00
27	Eric Allen	3.00
28	Dana Stubblefield	3.00
29	Steve Bono	3.00
30	Larry Brown	3.00
31	Warren Moon	6.00
32	Jim Kelly	6.00
33	Terry McDaniel	3.00
34	Dan Wilkinson	3.00
35	Dave Brown	3.00
36	Todd Lyght	3.00
37	Aeneas Williams	3.00
38	Shannon Sharpe	6.00
39	Errict Rhett	6.00
40	Yancey Thigpen	6.00
41	J.J. Stokes	3.00
42	Marshall Faulk	10.00
43	Chester McGlockton	3.00
44	Darryll Lewis	3.00
45	Drew Bledsoe	45.00
46	Tyrone Wheatley	3.00
47	Herman Moore	10.00
48	Darren Woodson	3.00
49	Ricky Watters	6.00
50	Emmitt Smith TYC	30.00
51	Barry Sanders TYC	30.00
52	Curtis Martin TYC	20.00
53	Chris Warren TYC	3.00
54	Errict Rhett TYC	3.00
55	Rodney Hampton TYC	3.00
56	Terrell Davis TYC	40.00
57	Marshall Faulk TYC	6.00
58	Rashaan Salaam TYC	3.00
59	Curtis Conway	6.00
60	Isaac Bruce	10.00
61	Thurman Thomas	6.00
62	Terry Allen	3.00
63	Lamar Lathon	3.00
64	Mark Chmura	6.00
65	Chris Warren	3.00
66	Jessie Tuggle	3.00
67	Erik Kramer	3.00
68	Tim Brown	6.00
69	Derrick Thomas	3.00
70	Willie McGinest	3.00
71	Frank Sanders	3.00
72	Bernie Parmalee	3.00
73	Kordell Stewart	60.00
74	Brent Jones	3.00
75	Edgar Bennett	3.00
76	Rashaan Salaam	6.00
77	Carl Pickens	6.00
78	Terance Mathis	3.00
79	Deion Sanders	20.00
80	Glyn Milburn	3.00
81	Lee Woodall	3.00
82	Neil Smith	3.00
83	Stan Humphries	3.00
84	Rick Mirer	3.00
85	Troy Vincent	3.00
86	Sam Mills	3.00
87	Brian Mitchell	3.00
88	Hardy Nickerson	3.00
89	Tamarick Vanover	6.00
90	Steve McNair	40.00
91	Jerry Rice TYC	18.00
92	Isaac Bruce TYC	6.00
93	Herman Moore TYC	6.00
94	Cris Carter TYC	3.00
95	Tim Brown TYC	3.00
96	Carl Pickens TYC	3.00
97	Joey Galloway TYC	6.00
98	Jerry Rice	3.00
99	Cris Carter	6.00
100	Curtis Martin	40.00
101	Scott Mitchell	3.00
102	Ken Harvey	3.00
103	Rodney Hampton	6.00
104	Reggie White	6.00
105	Eddie Robinson	3.00
106	Greg Lloyd	3.00
107	Phillippi Sparks	3.00
108	Emmitt Smith	75.00
109	Tom Carter	3.00
110	Jim Everett	3.00
111	James Stewart	3.00
112	Kyle Brady	3.00
113	Irving Fryar	3.00
114	Vinny Testaverde	3.00
115	John Elway	40.00
116	Chris Spielman	3.00
117	Mike Mamula	3.00
118	Jim Harbaugh	6.00
119	Ken Norton	3.00
120	Bruce Smith	3.00
121	Daryl Johnston	3.00
122	Blaine Bishop	3.00
123	Jeff George	6.00
124	Jeff Hostetler	3.00
125	Jerome Bettis	6.00
126	Jay Novacek	3.00
127	Bryce Paup	3.00
128	Neil O'Donnell	3.00
129	Marcus Allen	10.00
130	Steve Young	30.00
131	Brett Favre TYC	35.00
132	Scott Mitchell TYC	3.00
133	John Elway TYC	25.00
134	Jeff Blake TYC	6.00
135	Dan Marino TYC	35.00
136	Drew Bledsoe TYC	18.00
137	Troy Aikman TYC	18.00
138	Steve Young TYC	12.00
139	Jim Kelly TYC	3.00
140	Jeff Graham	3.00
141	Hugh Douglas	3.00
142	Dan Marino	80.00
143	Darrell Green	3.00
144	Eric Zeier	3.00
145	Brett Favre	90.00
146	Carnell Lake	3.00
147	Ben Coates	3.00
148	Tony Martin	3.00
149	Michael Irvin	6.00
150	Lawrence Phillips	75.00
151	Alex Van Dyke	6.00
152	Kevin Hardy	6.00
153	Rickey Dudley	20.00
154	Eric Moulds	125.00
155	Simeon Rice	6.00
156	Marvin Harrison	175.00
157	Tim Biakabutuka	40.00
158	Duane Clemons	6.00
159	Keyshawn Johnson	175.00
160	John Mobley	6.00
161	Leeland McElroy	10.00
162	Eddie George	200.00
163	Jonathan Ogden	6.00
164	Eddie Kennison	20.00
165	Checklist	3.00

1996 Topps Chrome 40th Anniversary

Originally found in Topps, this 40-card insert was printed with a Chrome finish and inserted every eight packs. 40th Anniversary insert celebrated 40 years of Topps football with today's players in classic poses and original card designs from 1955 to 1995.

		MT
Complete Set (40):		140.00
Common Player:		2.00
1	Jim Harbaugh (1956)	2.00
2	Greg Lloyd (1957)	2.00
3	Barry Sanders (1958)	20.00
4	Merton Hanks (1959)	2.00
5	Herman Moore (1960)	2.00
6	Tim Brown (1961)	2.00
7	Brett Favre (1962)	20.00
8	Cris Carter (1963)	2.00
9	Curtis Martin (1964)	10.00
10	Bryce Paup (1965)	2.00
11	Steve Bono (1966)	2.00
12	Blaine Bishop (1967)	2.00
13	Emmitt Smith (1968)	15.00
14	Carnell Lake (1969)	2.00
15	Marshall Faulk (1970)	4.00
16	Bam Morris (1971)	2.00
17	Shannon Sharpe (1972)	2.00
18	Steve Young (1973)	8.00
19	Jeff George (1974)	2.00
20	Junior Seau (1975)	2.00
21	Chris Warren (1976)	2.00
22	Heath Shuler (1977)	2.00
23	Jeff Blake (1978)	5.00
24	Reggie White (1979)	2.00
25	Jeff Hostetler (1980)	2.00
26	Errict Rhett (1981)	2.00
27	Rodney Hampton (1982)	2.00
28	Jerry Rice (1983)	10.00
29	Jim Everett (1984)	2.00
30	Isaac Bruce (1985)	5.00
31	Dan Marino (1986)	15.00
32	Marcus Allen (1987)	2.00
33	Erik Kramer (1988)	2.00
34	John Elway (1989)	12.00
35	Ricky Watters (1990)	2.00
36	Troy Aikman (1991)	10.00
37	Drew Bledsoe (1992)	10.00
38	Scott Mitchell (1993)	2.00
39	Rashaan Salaam (1994)	4.00
40	Kerry Collins (1995)	4.00

1996 Topps Chrome 40th Anniversary Refractors

Each card in Chrome's 40th Anniversary insert was also printed in a Refractor version. Refractors of this insert are found every 24 packs.

	MT
Complete Set (40):	375.00
Refractors:	2x-3x

1996 Topps Chrome Tide Turners

Tide Turners was a 10-card insert that was exclusively produced for Chrome. It featured top playmakers in the NFL and was inserted every 12 packs.

		MT
Complete Set (15):		70.00
Common Player:		1.50
1	Rashaan Salaam	3.00
2	Warren Moon	1.50
3	Marshall Faulk	4.00
4	Jeff Blake	3.00
5	Curtis Martin	10.00
6	Eric Metcalf	1.50
7	Errict Rhett	3.00
8	Scott Mitchell	1.50
9	Ricky Watters	3.00
10	Jerry Rice	8.00
11	Emmitt Smith	15.00
12	Erik Kramer	1.50
13	Jim Harbaugh	1.50
14	Barry Sanders	18.00
15	John Elway	6.00

1996 Topps Chrome Tide Turners Refractors

This 10-card set is a parallel to the regular Tide Turners inserts. It includes Topps' popular Refractor finish and was inserted every 48 packs.

	MT
Complete Set (15):	280.00
Refractors:	4x-6x

1996 Topps Gilt Edge

TERRELL DAVIS

As part of its sponsorship of the first-ever NFL Pro Bowl Experience card show held in conjunction with the Pro Bowl Game in February 1996, Topps issued this 90-card hobby exclusive set. The cards feature 84 members from the Pro Bowl rosters, plus five players who had Pro Bowl-caliber seasons and a checklist. Each card utilizes Topps gilt edge technology, which places gold gilt edging around every card. A gilt edge logo replaces the Topps logo on each card front too, which has a color action photo and one of the set's icons on it. The card back has biographical and statistical information at the top, with a set icon in the background. A recap of the player's 1995 accomplishments, a team logo and a close-up shot round out the back's design. In addition, a parallel version of the set was created using platinum gilt edging. These cards were seeded one per pack, as were Gilt Edge Pro Bowl Skills insert cards.

		MT
Complete Set (90):		25.00
Common Player:		.15
Minor Stars:		.30
Wax Box:		30.00
1	Brett Favre	4.00
2	Kevin Glover	.15
3	Nate Newton	.15
4	Randall McDaniel	.15
5	William Roaf	.15
6	Lomas Brown	.15
7	Jay Novacek	.15
8	Emmitt Smith	4.00
9	Barry Sanders	2.50
10	Jerry Rice	2.00
11	Herman Moore	.50
12	Larry Centers	.15
13	Chester McGlockton	.15
14	Dan Saleaumua	.15
15	Bruce Smith	.15
16	Neil Smith	.15
17	Junior Seau	.30
18	Bryce Paup	.15
19	Greg Lloyd	.30
20	Terry McDaniel	.15
21	Dale Carter	.15
22	Carnell Lake	.15
23	Steve Atwater	.15
24	Elbert Shelley	.15
25	Brian Mitchell	.15
26	Jeff Feagles	.15
27	Morten Andersen	.15
28	Dan Marino	4.00
29	Dermontti Dawson	.15
30	Steve Wisniewski	.15
31	Bruce Matthews	.15
32	Bruce Armstrong	.15
33	Richmond Webb	.15
34	Ben Coates	.15
35	Marshall Faulk	1.50
36	Chris Warren	.30
37	Carl Pickens	.30
38	Tim Brown	.15
39	Kimble Anders	.15
40	John Randle	.15
41	Eric Swann	.15
42	Reggie White	.30
43	Charles Haley	.15
44	Ken Norton	.15
45	Lee Woodall	.15
46	Ken Harvey	.15
47	Aeneas Williams	.15
48	Eric Davis	.15
49	Darren Woodson	.15
50	Merton Hanks	.15
51	Steve Tasker	.15
52	Glyn Milburn	.15
53	Jason Elam	.15
54	Darren Bennett	.15
55	Steve Young	2.00
56	Bart Oates	.15
57	Larry Allen	.15
58	Mark Tuinei	.15

59	Mark Chmura	.15
60	Michael Irvin	.30
61	Ricky Watters	.30
62	Cortez Kennedy	.15
63	Leslie O'Neal	.15
64	Bryan Cox	.15
65	Derrick Thomas	.15
66	Darryll Lewis	.15
67	Blaine Bishop	.15
68	Dana Stubblefield	.15
69	William Fuller	.15
70	Jessie Tuggle	.15
71	William Thomas	.15
72	Eric Allen	.15
73	Tim McDonald	.15
74	Jim Harbaugh	.30
75	Mark Stepnoski	.15
76	Keith Sims	.15
77	Gary Zimmerman	.15
78	Shannon Sharpe	.15
79	Anthony Miller	.15
80	Curtis Martin	3.00
81	Troy Aikman	2.00
82	Cris Carter	.30
83	Jeff Blake	1.00
84	Yancey Thigpen	1.00
85	Isaac Bruce	1.00
86	Sam Mills	.15
87	Terrell Davis	3.00
88	Larry Brown	.15
89	Joey Galloway	2.00
90	Checklist	.15

1996 Topps Gilt Edge Platinum

The 90-card, standard size parallel set was included in each pack. The card edges have a platinum "gilt edging" instead of gold.

	MT
Complete Set (90):	90.00
Common Player:	.40
Veteran Stars:	1.5x-3x
Young Stars:	1.25x-2.5x

1996 Topps Gilt Edge Definitive Edge

This 15-card skills insert set features top players on cards using five different designs; each design is used to cover three themes - Fire, Volcano and Fury; Warrior, Chieftan and Guardian; Strength, Courage and Endurance; Hurricane, Speed and Lightning; and Illusion, Mischief and Tricks. Nine of the players chosen for the set were also chosen to play in the Pro Bowl Game. One skills card was inserted in every pack.

		MT
	Complete Set (15):	30.00
	Common Player:	.25
1	Bruce Smith (Strength)	.25
2	Brett Favre (Courage)	8.00
3	Marcus Allen (Endurance)	.25
4	Junior Seau (Hurricane)	.25
5	Deion Sanders (Speed)	2.00
6	Jerry Rice (Lightning)	4.00
7	Steve Young (Fire)	4.00
8	Drew Bledsoe (Volcano)	3.00
9	Michael Irvin (Fury)	.50
10	Reggie White (Warrior)	.25
11	Dan Marino (Chieftan)	8.00
12	John Alt (Guardian)	.25
13	Barry Sanders (Illusion)	5.00
14	Orlando Thomas (Mischief)	.25
15	Kordell Stewart (Tricks)	4.00

Values quoted in this guide reflect the retail price of a card — the price a collector can expect to pay when buying a card from a dealer. The wholesale price — that which a collector can expect to receive when selling cards — will be significantly lower, depending on desirability and condition.

1996 Topps Laser

After its debut in baseball, Topps Laser Football arrived in four-card packs with 128 cards in the regular issue set. Laser featured surgically precise cutting across the entire card surface, with silver stamped AFC cards and gold stamped NFC cards. Laser was released in a single series and included three insert sets, called Bright Spots, 1996 Draft Picks and Stadium Stars.

		MT
	Complete Set (128):	70.00
	Common Player:	.25
	Minor Stars:	.50
	Wax Box:	100.00
1	Marshall Faulk	.50
2	Alonzo Spellman	.25
3	Frank Sanders	.25
4	Anthony Pleasant	.25
5	Scott Mitchell	.25
6	Robert Brooks	.50
7	Robert Jones	.25
8	Phillippi Sparks	.25
9	Rodney Peete	.25
10	Kordell Stewart	3.00
11	Ken Norton	.25
12	Brian Mitchell	.25
13	Ben Coates	.25
14	Quinn Early	.25
15	Emmitt Smith	6.00
16	Steve Bono	.25
17	Anthony Miller	.25
18	Mel Gray	.25
19	Neil O'Donnell	.25
20	Tim Brown	.50
21	Terrell Fletcher	.25
22	John Randle	.25
23	Fred Barnett	.25
24	Craig Heyward	.25
25	Ki-Jana Carter	.50
26	Eric Allen	.25
27	Warren Sapp	.25
28	Terry Wooden	.25
29	Darion Conner	.25
30	Mark Brunell	2.00
31	Vinny Testaverde	.25
32	Chris Calloway	.25
33	Steve Walsh	.25
34	Ken Dilger	.25
35	Bryan Cox	.25
36	Rob Moore	.25
37	Henry Thomas	.25
38	Henry Ellard	.25
39	Mark Chmura	.25
40	Jerry Rice	3.00
41	Michael Irvin	.50
42	Willie McGinest	.25
43	Steve McNair	3.00
44	Tamarick Vanover	2.00
45	Cris Carter	.25
46	Levon Kirkland	.25
47	Terry McDaniel	.25
48	Jessie Tuggle	.25
49	O.J. McDuffie	.25
50	Bruce Smith	.25
51	Tyrone Hughes	.25
52	Tony Martin	.25
53	Hardy Nickerson	.25
54	Garrison Hearst	.25
55	Sam Mills	.25
56	Mark Carrier	.25
57	Quentin Coryatt	.25
58	Neil Smith	.25
59	Michael Westbrook	2.00
60	Greg Lloyd	.25
61	Jeff Hostetler	.25
62	Wayne Chrebet	.25
63	Herschel Walker	.25
64	Pepper Johnson	.25
65	John Elway	3.00
66	Reggie White	.50
67	James Stewart	.25
68	Bernie Parmalee	.25
69	Robert Smith	.25
70	Drew Bledsoe	3.00
71	Marcus Patton	.25
72	Stan Humphries	.25
73	Darnay Scott	.25
74	Jim Kelly	.50
75	Terance Mathis	.25
76	Erik Kramer	.25
77	Marcus Allen	.50
78	Ernie Mills	.25
79	Harvey Williams	.25
80	Brett Favre	6.00
81	Seth Joyner	.25
82	Tyrone Poole	.25
83	Troy Aikman	3.00
84	Warren Moon	.50
85	Isaac Bruce	1.00
86	Errict Rhett	.50
87	Rick Mirer	.25
88	Anthony Smith	.25
89	Bert Emanuel	.25
90	Junior Seau	.50
91	Terry Allen	.25
92	Brent Jones	.25
93	Adrian Murrell	.25
94	Dave Brown	.25
95	Bryce Paup	.25
96	Jim Everett	.25
97	Brian Washington	.25
98	Jim Harbaugh	.25
99	Shannon Sharpe	.25
100	Dan Marino	6.00
101	Curtis Martin	4.00
102	Ricky Watters	.50
103	Yancey Thigpen	.50
104	Trent Dilfer	.50
105	Joey Galloway	3.00
106	Edgar Bennett	.25
107	Willie Jackson	.25
108	Mark Collins	.25
109	Rashaan Salaam	.50
110	Eric Metcalf	.25
111	Terrell Davis	4.00
112	Darryll Lewis	.25
113	Ken Harvey	.25
114	Rob Fredrickson	.25
115	Rodney Hampton	.25
116	Chris Slade	.25
117	Jeff George	.25
118	Lamar Lathon	.25
119	Curtis Conway	.50
120	Barry Sanders	3.00
121	Eric Zeier	.25
122	Jeff Blake	2.00
123	Derrick Thomas	.25
124	Tyrone Wheatley	.25
125	Steve Young	3.00
126	Napoleon Kaufman	.25
127	David Meggett	.25
128	Kerry Collins	.75

1996 Topps Laser Bright Spots

Bright Spots included 16 top young players on full-bleed, double-diffraction foil-stamped cards. Bright Spots were seeded every 24 packs of Laser.

		MT
	Complete Set (16):	175.00
	Common Player:	6.00
1	Curtis Martin	30.00
2	Tom Carter	6.00
3	Dave Brown	6.00
4	Wayne Chrebet	6.00
5	Rashaan Salaam	10.00
6	Mark Brunell	15.00
7	Elvis Grbac	6.00
8	Errict Rhett	6.00
9	Isaac Bruce	10.00
10	Kerry Collins	10.00
11	Mario Bates	6.00
12	Joey Galloway	20.00
13	Napoleon Kaufman	6.00
14	Tamarick Vanover	6.00
15	Marshall Faulk	8.00
16	Terrell Davis	30.00

1996 Topps Laser Draft Picks

Sixteen different 1996 draft picks can be found in this insert. Draft Picks inserts are laser cut with double-diffraction foil and inserted every 12 packs.

		MT
	Complete Set (16):	90.00
	Common Player:	5.00
1	Keyshawn Johnson	16.00
2	Lawrence Phillips	10.00
3	Bobby Hoying	5.00
4	Marco Battaglia	5.00
5	Kevin Hardy	5.00
6	Jerome Woods	5.00
7	Ray Mickens	5.00
8	John Mobley	5.00
9	Marvin Harrison	15.00
10	Walt Harris	5.00
11	Duane Clemons	5.00
12	Regan Upshaw	5.00
13	Brian Dawkins	5.00
14	Bobby Engram	10.00
15	Eddie Kennison	8.00
16	Jeff Lewis	5.00

1996 Topps Laser Stadium Stars

Stadium Stars included 16 of the top players in the NFL on cards that have a laser-sculpted cover that reveals a full-bleed card of the player underneath. These book-like inserts are seeded every 48 packs.

		MT
	Complete Set (16):	350.00
	Common Player:	10.00
1	Barry Sanders	50.00
2	Jim Harbaugh	10.00
3	Tim Brown	10.00
4	Jim Everett	10.00
5	Brett Favre	80.00
6	Junior Seau	10.00
7	Greg Lloyd	10.00
8	Cris Carter	10.00
9	Emmitt Smith	80.00
10	Dan Marino	80.00
11	Jeff Blake	20.00
12	Darrell Green	10.00
13	John Elway	30.00
14	Marcus Allen	10.00
15	Steve Young	35.00
16	Drew Bledsoe	50.00

1997 Topps

The 415-card set features a colored border on the left of the card front. In that border are the Topps' logo in gold foil in the lower left and the player's name in the upper left. The team's logo is in the upper right. A white border surrounds the three remaining sides. The backs have the player's name, team, position, bio, stats and highlights. A "Minted in Canton" parallel, which features a special gold foil stamp, was randomly seeded in packs.

		MT
	Complete Set (415):	40.00
	Common Player:	.05
	Minor Stars:	.10
	Minted Canton Cards:	5x-10x
	Wax Box:	40.00
1	Brett Favre	2.50
2	Lawyer Milloy	.05
3	Tim Biakabutuka	.10
4	Clyde Simmons	.05
5	Deion Sanders	.50
6	Anthony Miller	.05
7	Marquez Pope	.05
8	Mike Tomczak	.05
9	William Thomas	.05
10	Marshall Faulk	.20
11	John Randle	.05
12	Jim Kelly	.05
13	Steve Bono	.05
14	Rod Stephens	.05
15	Stan Humphries	.05
16	Terrell Buckley	.05
17	Ki-Jana Carter	.10
18	Marcus Robertson	.05
19	Corey Harris	.05
20	Rashaan Salaam	.10
21	Rickey Dudley	.05
22	Jamir Miller	.05
23	Martin Mayhew	.05
24	Jason Sehorn	.05
25	Isaac Bruce	.20
26	Johnnie Morton	.05
27	Antonio Langham	.05
28	Cornelius Bennett	.05
29	Joe Johnson	.05
30	Keyshawn Johnson	.40
31	Willie Green	.05
32	Craig Newsome	.05
33	Brock Marion	.05
34	Corey Fuller	.05
35	Ben Coates	.05
36	Ty Detmer	.05
37	Charles Johnson	.05
38	Willie Jackson	.05
39	Tyronne Drakeford	.05
40	Gus Frerotte	.05
41	Robert Blackmon	.05
42	Andre Coleman	.05
43	Mario Bates	.05
44	Chris Calloway	.05
45	Terry McDaniel	.05
46	Anthony Davis	.05
47	Stanley Pritchett	.05
48	Ray Buchanan	.05
49	Chris Chandler	.05
50	Ashley Ambrose	.05
51	Tyrone Braxton	.05
52	Pepper Johnson	.05
53	Frank Sanders	.05
54	Clay Matthews	.05
55	Bruce Smith	.05
56	Jermaine Lewis	.05
57	Mark Carrier	.05
58	Jeff Graham	.05
59	Keith Lyle	.05
60	Trent Dilfer	.10
61	Trace Armstrong	.05
62	Jeff Herrod	.05
63	Tyrone Wheatley	.05
64	Torrance Small	.05
65	Chris Warren	.05
66	Terry Kirby	.05
67	Erric Pegram	.05
68	Sean Gilbert	.05
69	Greg Biekert	.05
70	Ricky Watters	.10
71	Chris Hudson	.05
72	Tamarick Vanover	.10
73	Orlando Thomas	.05
74	Jimmy Spencer	.05
75	John Mobley	.05
76	Henry Thomas	.05
77	Santana Dotson	.05
78	Boomer Esiason	.05
79	Bobby Hebert	.05
80	Kerry Collins	.25
81	Bobby Engram	.05
82	Kevin Smith	.05
83	Rick Mirer	.10
84	Ted Johnson	.05
85	Derrick Alexander	.05
86	Hugh Douglas	.05
87	Rodney Harrison	.05
88	Roman Phifer	.05
89	Warren Moon	.20
90	Thurman Thomas	.10
91	Michael McCrary	.05
92	Dana Stubblefield	.05
93	Andre Hastings	.05
94	William Fuller	.05
95	Jeff Hostetler	.05
96	Danny Kanell	.05
97	Mark Fields	.05
98	Eddie Robinson	.05
99	Daryl Gardener	.05
100	Drew Bledsoe	1.00
101	Winslow Oliver	.05
102	Raymont Harris	.05
103	LeShon Johnson	.05
104	Byron Morris	.05
105	Herman Moore	.20
106	Keith Jackson	.05
107	Chris Penn	.05
108	Robert Griffith	.05
109	Jeff Burris	.05
110	Troy Aikman	1.00
111	Allen Aldridge	.05
112	Mel Gray	.05
113	Aaron Bailey	.05
114	Michael Strahan	.05
115	Adrian Murrell	.05
116	Chris Mims	.05
117	Robert Jones	.05
118	Derrick Brooks	.05
119	Tom Carter	.05
120	Carl Pickens	.05
121	Tony Brackens	.05
122	O.J. McDuffie	.05
123	Napoleon Kaufman	.05
124	Chris T. Jones	.05
125	Kordell Stewart	.75
126	Ray Zellars	.05
127	Jessie Tuggle	.05
128	Greg Kragen	.05
129	Brett Perriman	.05
130	Steve Young	.50
131	Willie Clay	.05
132	Kimble Anders	.05
133	Eugene Daniel	.05
134	Jevon Langford	.05
135	Shannon Sharpe	.05
136	Wayne Simmons	.05
137	Leeland McElroy	.05
138	Mike Caldwell	.05
139	Eric Moulds	.10
140	Eddie George	1.00
141	Jamal Anderson	.30
142	Michael Timpson	.05
143	Tony Tolbert	.05
144	Robert Smith	.10
145	Mike Alstott	.10
146	Gary Jones	.05
147	Terrance Shaw	.05
148	Carlton Gray	.05
149	Kevin Carter	.05
150	Darrell Green	.05
151	David Dunn	.05
152	Ken Norton	.05
153	Chad Brown	.05
154	Pat Swilling	.05
155	Irving Fryar	.05
156	Michael Haynes	.05
157	Shawn Jefferson	.05
158	Steve Grant	.05
159	James Stewart	.05
160	Derrick Thomas	.05
161	Tim Bowens	.05
162	Dixon Edwards	.05
163	Michael Barrow	.05
164	Antonio Freeman	.10
165	Terrell Davis	1.25
166	Henry Ellard	.05
167	Daryl Johnston	.05
168	Bryan Cox	.05
169	Chad Cota	.05
170	Vinny Testaverde	.05
171	Andre Reed	.05
172	Larry Centers	.05
173	Craig Heyward	.05
174	Glyn Milburn	.05
175	Hardy Nickerson	.05
176	Corey Miller	.05
177	Bobby Houston	.05
178	Marco Coleman	.05
179	Winston Moss	.05
180	Tony Banks	.30
181	Jeff Lageman	.05
182	Jason Belser	.05
183	James Jett	.05
184	Wayne Martin	.05
185	David Meggett	.05
186	Terrell Owens	.50
187	Willie Williams	.05
188	Eric Turner	.05
189	Chuck Smith	.05
190	Simeon Rice	.05
191	Kevin Greene	.05
192	Lance Johnston	.05
193	Marty Carter	.05
194	Ricardo McDonald	.05
195	Michael Irvin	.10
196	George Koonce	.05
197	Robert Porcher	.05
198	Mark Collins	.05
199	Louis Oliver	.05
200	John Elway	.50
201	Jake Reed	.05
202	Rodney Hampton	.05
203	Aaron Glenn	.05
204	Mike Mamula	.05
205	Terry Allen	.05
206	John Lynch	.05
207	Todd Lyght	.05
208	Dean Wells	.05
209	Aaron Hayden	.05
210	Blaine Bishop	.05
211	Bert Emanuel	.05
212	Mark Carrier	.05
213	Dale Carter	.05
214	Jimmy Smith	.05
215	Jim Harbaugh	.05
216	Jeff George	.05
217	Anthony Newman	.05
218	Ty Law	.05
219	Brent Jones	.05
220	Emmitt Smith	2.00
221	Bennie Blades	.05
222	Alfred Williams	.05
223	Eugene Robinson	.05
224	Fred Barnett	.05
225	Errict Rhett	.20
226	Leslie O'Neal	.05
227	Michael Sinclair	.05
228	Marvcus Patton	.05
229	Darrien Gordon	.05
230	Jerome Bettis	.10
231	Troy Vincent	.05
232	Ray Mickens	.05
233	Lonnie Johnson	.05
234	Charles Way	.05
235	Chris Sanders	.05
236	Bracey Walker	.05
237	Dave Krieg	.05
238	Kent Graham	.05
239	Ray Lewis	.05
240	Cris Carter	.05
241	Elvis Grbac	.05
242	Eric Davis	.05

243	Harvey Williams	.05
244	Eric Allen	.05
245	Bryant Young	.05
246	Terrell Fletcher	.05
247	Darren Perry	.05
248	Ken Harvey	.05
249	Marvin Washington	.05
250	Marcus Allen	.10
251	Darrin Smith	.05
252	James Francis	.05
253	Michael Jackson	.05
254	Ryan McNeil	.05
255	Mark Chmura	.10
256	Keenan McCardell	.05
257	Tony Bennett	.05
258	Irving Spikes	.05
259	Jason Dunn	.05
260	Joey Galloway	.25
261	Eddie Kennison	.40
262	Lonnie Marts	.05
263	Thomas Lewis	.05
264	Tedy Bruschi	.05
265	Steve Atwater	.05
266	Dorsey Levens	.20
267	Kurt Schulz	.05
268	Rob Moore	.05
269	Walt Harris	.05
270	Steve McNair	.75
271	Bill Romanowski	.05
272	Sean Dawkins	.05
273	Don Beebe	.05
274	Fernando Smith	.05
275	Willie McGinest	.05
276	Levon Kirkland	.05
277	Tony Martin	.05
278	Warren Sapp	.05
279	Lamar Smith	.05
280	Mark Brunell	1.00
281	Jim Everett	.05
282	Victor Green	.05
283	Mike Jones	.05
284	Charlie Garner	.05
285	Karim Abdul-Jabbar	.75
286	Michael Westbrook	.10
287	Lawrence Phillips	.10
288	Amani Toomer	.05
289	Neil Smith	.05
290	Barry Sanders	1.25
291	Willie Davis	.05
292	Bo Orlando	.05
293	Alonzo Spellman	.05
294	Eric Hill	.05
295	Wesley Walls	.05
296	Todd Collins	.05
297	Stevon Moore	.05
298	Eric Metcalf	.05
299	Darren Woodson	.05
300	Jerry Rice	1.00
301	Scott Mitchell	.05
302	Ray Crockett	.05
303	Jim Schwantz	.05
304	Steve Tovar	.05
305	Terance Mathis	.05
306	Earnest Byner	.05
307	Chris Spielman	.05
308	Curtis Conway	.10
309	Chris Dishman	.05
310	Marvin Harrison	.40
311	Sam Mills	.05
312	Brent Alexander	.05
313	Shawn Wooden	.05
314	DeWayne Washington	.05
315	Terry Glenn	.25
316	Winfred Tubbs	.05
317	Dave Brown	.05
318	Neil O'Donnell	.05
319	Anthony Parker	.05
320	Junior Seau	.10
321	Brian Mitchell	.05
322	Regan Upshaw	.05
323	Darryl Williams	.05
324	Chris Doleman	.05
325	Rod Woodson	.05
326	Derrick Witherspoon	.05
327	Chester McGlockton	.05
328	Mickey Washington	.05
329	Greg Hill	.05
330	Reggie White	.10
331	John Copeland	.05
332	Doug Evans	.05
333	Lamar Lathon	.05
334	Mark Maddox	.05
335	Natrone Means	.10
336	Corey Widmer	.05
337	Terry Wooden	.05
338	Merton Hanks	.05
339	Cortez Kennedy	.05
340	Tyrone Hughes	.05
341	Tim Brown	.05
342	John Jurkovic	.05
343	Carnell Lake	.05
344	Stanley Richard	.05
345	Darryll Lewis	.05
346	Dan Wilkinson	.05
347	Broderick Thomas	.05
348	Brian Williams	.05
349	Eric Swann	.05
350	Dan Marino	2.00
351	Anthony Johnson	.05
352	Joe Cain	.05
353	Quinn Early	.05
354	Seth Joyner	.05
355	Garrison Hearst	.05
356	Edgar Bennett	.05
357	Brian Washington	.05
358	Kevin Hardy	.05

359	Quentin Coryatt	.05
360	Tim McDonald	.05
361	Brian Blades	.05
362	Courtney Hawkins	.05
363	Ray Farmer	.05
364	Jesse Armstead	.05
365	Curtis Martin	1.25
366	Zach Thomas	.30
367	Frank Wycheck	.05
368	Darnay Scott	.05
369	Percy Ellsworth	.05
370	Desmond Howard	.05
371	Aeneas Williams	.05
372	Bryce Paup	.05
373	Michael Bates	.05
374	Brad Johnson	.05
375	Jeff Blake	.25
376	Donnell Woolford	.05
377	Mo Lewis	.05
378	Phillippi Sparks	.05
379	Michael Bankston	.05
380	LeRoy Butler	.05
381	Tyrone Poole	.05
382	Wayne Chrebet	.05
383	Chris Slade	.05
384	Checklist 1 of 2	.05
385	Checklist 2 of 2	.05
386	*Will Blackwell*	.75
387	*Tom Knight*	.10
388	*Darnell Autry*	.30
389	*Bryant Westbrook*	.50
390	*David LaFleur*	1.50
391	*Antowain Smith*	3.00
392	*Kevin Lockett*	.75
393	*Rae Carruth*	2.00
394	*Renaldo Wynn*	.10
395	*Jim Druckenmiller*	4.00
396	*Kenny Holmes*	.10
397	*Shawn Springs*	.75
398	*Troy Davis*	.40
399	*Dwayne Rudd*	.10
400	*Orlando Pace*	.75
401	*Byron Hanspard*	.50
402	*Corey Dillon*	4.00
403	*Walter Jones*	.10
404	*Reidel Anthony*	3.00
405	*Peter Boulware*	.10
406	*Reinard Wilson*	.10
407	*Pat Barnes*	.30
408	*Yatil Green*	.40
409	*Joey Kent*	.75
410	*Ike Hilliard*	2.50
411	*Jake Plummer*	10.00
412	*Darrell Russell*	.10
413	*James Farrior*	.10
414	*Tony Gonzalez*	1.50
415	*Warrick Dunn*	4.00

1997 Topps Career Best

This chase set includes Dan Marino, two cards of Marcus Allen, Reggie White and Jerry Rice.

		MT
Complete Set (5):		50.00
Common Player:		7.00
1	Dan Marino	25.00
2	Marcus Allen	7.00
3	Marcus Allen	7.00
4	Reggie White	7.00
5	Jerry Rice	12.00

1997 Topps Hall of Fame Autograph

This four-card insert featured autographs from the four current Hall of Fame inductees and carried an "HF" prefix on the card back. The Haynes and Webster cards were inserted one per 436 hobby packs (1:120 jumbo), Mara was inserted one per 872 hobby packs (1:240 jumbo) and the Shula card was seeded one per 290 hobby packs (1:80 jumbo).

	MT
Complete Set (4):	200.00
Common Player:	25.00

1	Don Shula	80.00
2	Wellington Mara	75.00
3	Mike Webster	25.00
4	Mike Haynes	30.00

1997 Topps Hall Bound

This 15-card set was inserted 1:36 hobby packs. The embossed cards were produced on die-cut mirror board. Card are numbered with a "HB" prefix.

		MT
Complete Set (15):		100.00
Common Player:		3.00
1	Jerry Rice	12.00
2	Rod Woodson	3.00
3	Marcus Allen	3.00
4	Reggie White	3.00
5	Emmitt Smith	20.00
6	Junior Seau	3.00
7	Troy Aikman	12.00
8	Bruce Smith	3.00
9	John Elway	8.00
10	Brett Favre	25.00
11	Thurman Thomas	3.00
12	Deion Sanders	6.00
13	Dan Marino	20.00
14	Steve Young	8.00
15	Barry Sanders	12.00

1997 Topps High Octane

Inserted 1:36 packs, the 15-card chase set includes "High Octane" at the top front of the cards, with the player's photo superimposed over a uniluster back. The team's logo is in the lower left, with the player's name in the lower right. The backs, which are numbered with an "HO" prefix, have the player's bio on the upper left, with his photo in the upper right. Four bar graphs are included in the center, with his highlights in the lower left.

		MT
Complete Set (15):		120.00
Common Player:		3.00
1	Brett Favre	25.00
2	Jerome Bettis	3.00
3	Jerry Rice	12.00
4	Junior Seau	3.00
5	Emmitt Smith	20.00
6	Herman Moore	3.00
7	Shannon Sharpe	3.00
8	Curtis Martin	12.00
9	Eddie George	12.00
10	Barry Sanders	12.00
11	John Elway	8.00
12	Steve Young	8.00
13	Drew Bledsoe	12.00
14	Troy Aikman	12.00
15	Dan Marino	20.00

A card number in
parentheses ( ) indicates
the set is unnumbered.

1997 Topps Mystery Finest

The Mystery Finest chase set features 20 Pro Bowl players pictured three different ways, in their team's away jersey (bronze card, 1:36 packs), the team's home uniform (silver card, 1:108) and their Pro Bowl jersey (gold card, 1:324). Bronze Refractor parallels are found 1:144, silver Refractors are located 1:432 and a Gold Refractor is seeded 1:1,296 packs. Cards are numbered with a "M" prefix.

		MT
Complete Set (20):		130.00
Common Player:		3.00
Bronze Refractors:		2x-3x
Silver Cards:		2x
Silver Refractors:		5x
Gold Cards:		8x
Gold Refractors:		12x-24x
1	Barry Sanders	12.00
2	Mark Brunell	12.00
3	Terrell Davis	12.00
4	Isaac Bruce	6.00
5	Jerry Rice	12.00
6	Drew Bledsoe	12.00
7	Carl Pickens	3.00
8	Steve Young	8.00
9	Cris Carter	3.00
10	John Elway	8.00
11	Junior Seau	3.00
12	Herman Moore	3.00
13	Vinny Testaverde	3.00
14	Jerome Bettis	3.00
15	Troy Aikman	12.00
16	Reggie White	3.00
17	Kerry Collins	5.00
18	Curtis Martin	12.00
19	Shannon Sharpe	3.00
20	Brett Favre	25.00

1997 Topps Season's Best

The 25-card chase set was seeded 1:16 packs. The set honors players in five different categories, rushing leaders (Thunder and Lightning), passing experts (Air Command), receiving specialists (Special Delivery), sack masters (Demolition Men) and all-purpose yardage gainers (Magicians).

		MT
Complete Set (25):		75.00
Common Player:		.75
Minor Stars:		1.50
1	Mark Brunell (Air Command)	8.00
2	Vinny Testaverde (Air Command)	.75
3	Drew Bledsoe (Air Command)	8.00
4	Brett Favre (Air Command)	16.00
5	Jeff Blake (Air Command)	1.50
6	Barry Sanders (Thunder & Lightning)	10.00
7	Terrell Davis (Thunder & Lightning)	8.00
8	Jerome Bettis (Thunder & Lightning)	1.50
9	Ricky Watters (Thunder & Lightning)	.75
10	Eddie George (Thunder & Lightning)	10.00
11	Brian Mitchell (Magicians)	.75
12	Tyrone Hughes (Magicians)	.75
13	Eric Metcalf (Magicians)	.75
14	Glyn Milburn (Magicians)	.75
15	Ricky Watters (Magicians)	.75
16	Kevin Greene (Demolition Men)	.75
17	Lamar Lathon (Demolition Men)	.75
18	Bruce Smith (Demolition Men)	.75
19	Michael Sinclair (Demolition Men)	.75
20	Derrick Thomas (Demolition Men)	.75
21	Jerry Rice (Special Delivery)	8.00
22	Herman Moore (Special Delivery)	.75
23	Carl Pickens (Special Delivery)	.75
24	Cris Carter (Special Delivery)	.75
25	Brett Perriman (Special Delivery)	.75

1997 Topps Underclassmen

Inserted 1:24 retail packs, the 10-card set is comprised of first and second year players. The "Underclassmen" logo is at the top center, with the player's photo superimposed over a multicolored holographic background. The player's name is printed in holographic foil at the bottom center. The backs, which are numbered with an "U" prefix, have the player's photo, name, bio, highlights and stats.

		MT
Complete Set (10):		75.00
Common Player:		2.50
Minor Stars:		5.00
1	Kerry Collins	5.00
2	Karim Abdul-Jabbar	10.00
3	Simeon Rice	2.50
4	Keyshawn Johnson	5.00
5	Eddie George	15.00
6	Eddie Kennison	5.00
7	Terry Glenn	12.00
8	Kevin Hardy	2.50
9	Steve McNair	8.00
10	Kordell Stewart	10.00

1997 Topps Chrome

Chrome Football is a 165-card set created with Topps chromium technology and a Topps Chrome logo added to regular Topps cards. Chrome arrived with a full parallel set of Refractors and four inserts also from Topps: Draft Year, Underclassmen, Season's Best and Career Best.

	MT
Complete Set (165):	200.00
Common Player:	.40
Common Player (143-163):	1.00

Minor Stars:		.75
Wax Box:		200.00
1	Brett Favre	6.00
2	Tim Biakabutuka	.40
3	Deion Sanders	1.50
4	Marshall Faulk	1.00
5	John Randle	.40
6	Stan Humphries	.40
7	Ki-Jana Carter	.75
8	Rashaan Salaam	.40
9	Rickey Dudley	.75
10	Isaac Bruce	1.00
11	Keyshawn Johnson	1.00
12	Ben Coates	.40
13	Ty Detmer	.40
14	Gus Frerotte	.40
15	Mario Bates	.40
16	Chris Calloway	.40
17	Frank Sanders	.40
18	Bruce Smith	.40
19	Jeff Graham	.40
20	Trent Dilfer	1.00
21	Tyrone Wheatley	.40
22	Chris Warren	.40
23	Terry Kirby	.40
24	*Tony Gonzalez*	15.00
25	Ricky Watters	.75
26	Tamarick Vanover	.40
27	Kerry Collins	2.00
28	Bobby Engram	.40
29	Derrick Alexander	.40
30	Hugh Douglas	.40
31	Thurman Thomas	.75
32	Drew Bledsoe	3.00
33	LeShon Johnson	.40
34	Byron Morris	.40
35	Herman Moore	1.00
36	Troy Aikman	3.00
37	Mel Gray	.40
38	Adrian Murrell	.75
39	Carl Pickens	.40
40	Tony Brackens	.40
41	O.J. McDuffie	.40
42	Napoleon Kaufman	1.00
43	Chris T. Jones	.40
44	Kordell Stewart	3.00
45	Steve Young	2.00
46	Shannon Sharpe	.40
47	Leeland McElroy	.40
48	Eric Moulds	.40
49	Eddie George	4.00
50	Jamal Anderson	.75
51	Robert Smith	.75
52	Mike Alstott	1.50
53	Darrell Green	.40
54	Irving Fryar	.40
55	Derrick Thomas	.40
56	Antonio Freeman	1.00
57	Terrell Davis	3.00
58	Henry Ellard	.40
59	Daryl Johnston	.40
60	Bryan Cox	.40
61	Vinny Testaverde	.40
62	Andre Reed	.40
63	Larry Centers	.40
64	Hardy Nickerson	.40
65	Tony Banks	1.50
66	David Meggett	.40
67	Simeon Rice	.40
68	*Warrick Dunn*	20.00
69	Michael Irvin	.75
70	John Elway	4.00
71	Jake Reed	.40
72	Rodney Hampton	.40
73	Aaron Glenn	.40
74	Terry Allen	.40
75	Blaine Bishop	.40
76	Bert Emanuel	.40
77	Mark Carrier	.40
78	Jimmy Smith	.40
79	Jim Harbaugh	.40
80	Brent Jones	.40
81	Emmitt Smith	5.00
82	Fred Barnett	.40
83	Errict Rhett	.40
84	Michael Sinclair	.40
85	Jerome Bettis	1.00
86	Chris Sanders	.40
87	Kent Graham	.40
88	Cris Carter	.40
89	Harvey Williams	.40
90	Eric Allen	.40
91	Bryant Young	.40
92	Marcus Allen	1.00
93	Michael Jackson	.40
94	Mark Chmura	.75
95	Keenan McCardell	.40
96	Joey Galloway	1.00
97	Eddie Kennison	1.00
98	Steve Atwater	.40
99	Dorsey Levens	1.00
100	Rob Moore	.40
101	Steve McNair	3.00
102	Sean Dawkins	.40
103	Don Beebe	.40
104	Willie McGinest	.40
105	Tony Martin	.40
106	Mark Brunell	3.00
107	Karim Abdul-Jabbar	1.00
108	Michael Westbrook	.40
109	Lawrence Phillips	.75
110	Barry Sanders	6.00
111	Willie Davis	.40
112	Wesley Walls	.40
113	Todd Collins	.40
114	Jerry Rice	3.00
115	Scott Mitchell	.40
116	Terance Mathis	.40

117	Chris Spielman	.40
118	Curtis Conway	.40
119	Marvin Harrison	1.00
120	Terry Glenn	2.00
121	Dave Brown	.40
122	Neil O'Donnell	.40
123	Junior Seau	.75
124	Reggie White	.75
125	Lamar Lathon	.40
126	Natrone Means	.75
127	Tim Brown	.40
128	Eric Swann	.40
129	Dan Marino	6.00
130	Anthony Johnson	.40
131	Edgar Bennett	.40
132	Kevin Hardy	.40
133	Brian Blades	.40
134	Curtis Martin	3.00
135	Zach Thomas	.75
136	Darnay Scott	.40
137	Desmond Howard	.40
138	Aeneas Williams	.40
139	Bryce Paup	.40
140	Brad Johnson	.75
141	Jeff Blake	1.00
142	Wayne Chrebet	.40
143	Will Blackwell	2.00
144	Tom Knight	1.00
145	Darnell Autry	2.00
146	Bryant Westbrook	2.00
147	David LaFleur	4.00
148	Antowain Smith	12.00
149	Rae Carruth	7.00
150	Jim Druckenmiller	8.00
151	Shawn Springs	3.00
152	Troy Davis	3.00
153	Orlando Pace	2.00
154	Byron Hanspard	7.00
155	Corey Dillon	20.00
156	Reidel Anthony	8.00
157	Peter Boulware	2.00
158	Reinard Wilson	1.00
159	Pat Barnes	1.25
160	Joey Kent	2.00
161	Ike Hilliard	8.00
162	Jake Plummer	70.00
163	Darrell Russell	1.00
164	Checklist 1	.40
165	Checklist 2	.40

1997 Topps Chrome Refractors

Refractors are a parallel of the Topps Chrome base set. They were inserted one per 12 packs.

		MT
Complete Set (165):		2400.
Common Player:		4.00
Common Player (143-163):		6.00
Minor Stars:		8.00
1	Brett Favre	90.00
2	Tim Biakabutuka	4.00
3	Deion Sanders	20.00
4	Marshall Faulk	8.00
5	John Randle	4.00
6	Stan Humphries	4.00
7	Ki-Jana Carter	8.00
8	Rashaan Salaam	8.00
9	Rickey Dudley	8.00
10	Isaac Bruce	8.00
11	Keyshawn Johnson	8.00
12	Ben Coates	4.00
13	Ty Detmer	4.00
14	Gus Frerotte	4.00
15	Mario Bates	4.00
16	Chris Calloway	4.00
17	Frank Sanders	4.00
18	Bruce Smith	4.00
19	Jeff Graham	4.00
20	Trent Dilfer	8.00
21	Tyrone Wheatley	4.00
22	Chris Warren	4.00
23	Terry Kirby	4.00
24	Tony Gonzalez	25.00
25	Ricky Watters	8.00
26	Tamarick Vanover	4.00
27	Kerry Collins	8.00
28	Bobby Engram	4.00
29	Derrick Alexander	4.00
30	Hugh Douglas	4.00
31	Thurman Thomas	8.00
32	Drew Bledsoe	45.00
33	LeShon Johnson	4.00
34	Byron Morris	4.00
35	Herman Moore	8.00
36	Troy Aikman	45.00
37	Mel Gray	4.00
38	Adrian Murrell	8.00
39	Carl Pickens	4.00
40	Tony Brackens	4.00
41	O.J. McDuffie	4.00
42	Napoleon Kaufman	15.00
43	Chris T. Jones	4.00
44	Kordell Stewart	40.00
45	Steve Young	30.00
46	Shannon Sharpe	4.00
47	Leeland McElroy	4.00
48	Eric Moulds	4.00
49	Eddie George	50.00
50	Jamal Anderson	8.00
51	Robert Smith	4.00
52	Mike Alstott	20.00
53	Darrell Green	4.00
54	Irving Fryar	4.00

55	Derrick Thomas	4.00
56	Antonio Freeman	20.00
57	Terrell Davis	50.00
58	Henry Ellard	4.00
59	Daryl Johnston	4.00
60	Bryan Cox	4.00
61	Vinny Testaverde	4.00
62	Andre Reed	4.00
63	Larry Centers	4.00
64	Hardy Nickerson	4.00
65	Tony Banks	8.00
66	David Meggett	4.00
67	Simeon Rice	4.00
68	Warrick Dunn	175.00
69	Michael Irvin	8.00
70	John Elway	45.00
71	Jake Reed	4.00
72	Rodney Hampton	4.00
73	Aaron Glenn	4.00
74	Terry Allen	4.00
75	Blaine Bishop	4.00
76	Bert Emanuel	4.00
77	Mark Carrier	4.00
78	Jimmy Smith	4.00
79	Jim Harbaugh	4.00
80	Brent Jones	4.00
81	Emmitt Smith	75.00
82	Fred Barnett	4.00
83	Errict Rhett	4.00
84	Michael Sinclair	4.00
85	Jerome Bettis	8.00
86	Chris Sanders	4.00
87	Kent Graham	4.00
88	Cris Carter	8.00
89	Harvey Williams	4.00
90	Eric Allen	4.00
91	Bryant Young	4.00
92	Marcus Allen	8.00
93	Michael Jackson	4.00
94	Mark Chmura	8.00
95	Keenan McCardell	4.00
96	Joey Galloway	8.00
97	Eddie Kennison	4.00
98	Steve Atwater	4.00
99	Dorsey Levens	8.00
100	Rob Moore	4.00
101	Steve McNair	25.00
102	Sean Dawkins	4.00
103	Don Beebe	4.00
104	Willie McGinest	4.00
105	Tony Martin	4.00
106	Mark Brunell	40.00
107	Karim Abdul-Jabbar	8.00
108	Michael Westbrook	4.00
109	Lawrence Phillips	4.00
110	Barry Sanders	90.00
111	Willie Davis	4.00
112	Wesley Walls	4.00
113	Todd Collins	4.00
114	Jerry Rice	45.00
115	Scott Mitchell	4.00
116	Terance Mathis	4.00
117	Chris Spielman	4.00
118	Curtis Conway	4.00
119	Marvin Harrison	8.00
120	Terry Glenn	10.00
121	Dave Brown	4.00
122	Neil O'Donnell	4.00
123	Junior Seau	8.00
124	Reggie White	8.00
125	Lamar Lathon	4.00
126	Natrone Means	8.00
127	Tim Brown	4.00
128	Eric Swann	4.00
129	Dan Marino	75.00
130	Anthony Johnson	4.00
131	Edgar Bennett	4.00
132	Kevin Hardy	4.00
133	Brian Blades	4.00
134	Curtis Martin	25.00
135	Zach Thomas	8.00
136	Darnay Scott	4.00
137	Desmond Howard	4.00
138	Aeneas Williams	4.00
139	Bryce Paup	4.00
140	Brad Johnson	8.00
141	Jeff Blake	8.00
142	Wayne Chrebet	8.00
143	Will Blackwell	8.00
144	Tom Knight	6.00
145	Darnell Autry	8.00
146	Bryant Westbrook	8.00
147	David LaFleur	20.00
148	Antowain Smith	100.00
149	Rae Carruth	35.00
150	Jim Druckenmiller	70.00
151	Shawn Springs	6.00
152	Troy Davis	12.00
153	Orlando Pace	10.00
154	Byron Hanspard	30.00
155	Corey Dillon	175.00
156	Reidel Anthony	50.00
157	Peter Boulware	6.00
158	Reinard Wilson	6.00
159	Pat Barnes	10.00
160	Joey Kent	6.00
161	Ike Hilliard	30.00
162	Jake Plummer	250.00
163	Darrell Russell	6.00
164	Checklist 1	4.00
165	Checklist 2	4.00

> Post-1980 cards in Near Mint condition will generally sell for about 75% of the quoted Mint value.
>
> Excellent-condition cards bring no more than 40%.

1997 Topps Chrome Draft Year

Draft Year is a 15-card insert highlighting two players from the last 15 draft classes. Each side features one of the best players to emerge from that particular draft. Draft Year was inserted 1:48. The Refractor versions were found once in every 144 packs.

		MT
Complete Set (15):		250.00
Common Player:		5.00
Minor Stars:		10.00
Refractors:		2x
DR1	Dan Marino, John Elway (1983)	40.00
DR2	Reggie White, Steve Young (1984)	15.00
DR3	Bruce Smith, Jerry Rice (1985)	20.00
DR4	Ronnie Harmon, Pat Swilling (1986)	5.00
DR5	Jim Harbaugh, Vinny Testaverde (1987)	5.00
DR6	Michael Irvin, Tim Brown (1988)	10.00
DR7	Troy Aikman, Barry Sanders (1989)	30.00
DR8	Emmitt Smith, Junior Seau (1990)	40.00
DR9	Brett Favre, Ricky Watters (1991)	45.00
DR10	Carl Pickens, Desmond Howard (1992)	5.00
DR11	Mark Brunell, Drew Bledsoe (1993)	30.00
DR12	Marshall Faulk, Isaac Bruce (1994)	10.00
DR13	Terrell Davis, Curtis Martin (1995)	30.00
DR14	Eddie George, Terry Glenn (1996)	35.00
DR15	Ike Hilliard, Shawn Springs (1997)	5.00

1997 Topps Chrome Season's Best

The 25-card Season's Best insert has five different subsets. Each of the five subsets consists of five cards featuring the season's top performers. Air Command features top quarterbacks, Thunder & Lightning has the top rushers, Magicians showcases the top total yardage gainers, Demolition Men highlights the top sack artists and Special Delivery has the top wide receivers. There are also five Career best cards for each category. Season's Best was inserted 1:12 with Refractors found 1:36.

		MT
Complete Set (25):		80.00
Common Player:		1.00
Minor Stars:		2.00
Refractors:		2x-3x
1	Mark Brunell (Air Command)	10.00
2	Vinny Testaverde (Air Command)	1.00

3	Drew Bledsoe (Air Command)	10.00
4	Brett Favre (Air Command)	20.00
5	Jeff Blake (Air Command)	2.00
6	Barry Sanders (Thunder & Lightning)	12.00
7	Terrell Davis (Thunder & Lightning)	10.00
8	Jerome Bettis (Thunder & Lightning)	2.00
9	Ricky Watters (Thunder & Lightning)	2.00
10	Eddie George (Thunder & Lightning)	15.00
11	Brian Mitchell (Magicians)	1.00
12	Tyrone Hughes (Magicians)	1.00
13	Eric Metcalf (Magicians)	1.00
14	Glyn Milburn (Magicians)	1.00
15	Ricky Watters (Magicians)	2.00
16	Kevin Greene (Demolition Men)	1.00
17	Lamar Lathon (Demolition Men)	1.00
18	Bruce Smith (Demolition Men)	1.00
19	Michael Sinclair (Demolition Men)	1.00
20	Derrick Thomas (Demolition Men)	1.00
21	Jerry Rice (Special Delivery)	10.00
22	Herman Moore (Special Delivery)	4.00
23	Carl Pickens (Special Delivery)	1.00
24	Cris Carter (Special Delivery)	1.00
25	Brett Perriman (Special Delivery)	1.00

1997 Topps Chrome Underclassmen

Underclassmen is a 10-card insert highlighting the top second and third year players. The set is inserted 1:8, with Refractor versions found 1:36. Cards are numbered with a "U" prefix.

		MT
Complete Set (10):		50.00
Common Player:		2.00
Refractors:		2x-3x
1	Kerry Collins	4.00
2	Karim Abdul-Jabbar	5.00
3	Simeon Rice	2.00
4	Keyshawn Johnson	3.00
5	Eddie George	14.00
6	Eddie Kennison	4.00
7	Terry Glenn	4.00
8	Kevin Hardy	2.00
9	Steve McNair	8.00
10	Kordell Stewart	10.00

1997 Topps Gallery

This 135-card base set features top player photos framed by a foil design. The Players Private Issue parallel set includes foil stamping and was inserted 1:12. Insert sets included Photo Gallery, Gallery of Heroes, Critics Choice and Peter Max Serigraphs.

		MT
Complete Set (135):		55.00
Common Player:		.20
Minor Stars:		.40
Private Issue Cards:		20x-40x
Private Issue Rookies:		10x-20x
Wax Box:		60.00
1	Orlando Pace	.50
2	Darrell Russell	.50
3	Shawn Springs	.50
4	Peter Boulware	.40
5	Bryant Westbrook	.40
6	Walter Jones	.20
7	Ike Hilliard	2.00
8	James Farrior	.20
9	Tom Knight	.20
10	Warrick Dunn	5.00
11	Tony Gonzalez	2.00
12	Reinard Wilson	.50
13	Yatil Green	.20
14	Reidel Anthony	3.00
15	Kenny Holmes	.20
16	Dwayne Rudd	.20
17	Renaldo Wynn	.20
18	David LaFleur	.75
19	Antowain Smith	3.00
20	Jim Druckenmiller	3.00
21	Rae Carruth	2.00
22	Byron Hanspard	.75
23	Jake Plummer	12.00
24	Corey Dillon	6.00
25	Darnell Autry	.50
26	Kevin Lockett	.20
27	Troy Davis	.75
28	Mike Alstott	.40
29	Napoleon Kaufman	.40
30	Terrell Davis	2.50
31	Byron Morris	.20
32	Dana Stubblefield	.20
33	Ki-Jana Carter	.40
34	Hugh Douglas	.20
35	Natrone Means	.40
36	Marshall Faulk	.40
37	Tyrone Wheatley	.40
38	Tony Banks	.50
39	Marvin Harrison	1.50
40	Eddie George	3.50
41	Eddie Kennison	.40
42	Ray Mickens	.20
43	Mike Mamula	.20
44	Tamarick Vanover	.20
45	Rashaan Salaam	.40
46	Trent Dilfer	.40
47	John Mobley	.20
48	Gus Frerotte	.20
49	Isaac Bruce	.50
50	Mark Brunell	2.50
51	Jamal Anderson	.40
52	Keyshawn Johnson	1.50
53	Curtis Conway	.20
54	Zach Thomas	.75
55	Simeon Rice	.20
56	Lawrence Phillips	.40
57	Ty Detmer	.20
58	Bobby Engram	.20
59	Joey Galloway	.75
60	Curtis Martin	2.50
61	Kevin Hardy	.20
62	Eric Moulds	.20
63	Michael Westbrook	.20
64	Robert Smith	.20
65	Karim Abdul-Jabbar	.50
66	Errict Rhett	.40
67	Ray Lewis	.20
68	Terry Glenn	.50
69	Leeland McElroy	.20
70	Kerry Collins	.50
71	Steve McNair	2.00
72	Kordell Stewart	2.00
73	Terry Allen	.20
74	Michael Irvin	.40
75	John Elway	1.50
76	Lamar Lathon	.20
77	Rob Moore	.20
78	Irving Fryar	.20
79	Jim Everett	.20
80	Steve Young	1.50
81	Bryan Cox	.20
82	Dale Carter	.20
83	Chris Warren	.20
84	Shannon Sharpe	.20
85	Reggie White	.40
86	Deion Sanders	1.00
87	Hardy Nickerson	.20
88	Edgar Bennett	.20
89	Kent Graham	.20
90	Dan Marino	4.00
91	Kevin Greene	.20
92	Derrick Thomas	.20
93	Carl Pickens	.20
94	Neil O'Donnell	.20
95	Drew Bledsoe	2.50
96	Michael Haynes	.20
97	Tony Martin	.20
98	Scott Mitchell	.20
99	Rodney Hampton	.20
100	Brett Favre	5.00
101	Darrell Green	.20
102	Rod Woodson	.20
103	Chris Spielman	.20
104	Jake Reed	.20

105	Jerry Rice	2.50
106	Jeff Hostetler	.20
107	Anthony Johnson	.20
108	Keenan McCardell	.20
109	Ben Coates	.20
110	Emmitt Smith	4.00
111	LeRoy Butler	.20
112	Steve Atwater	.20
113	Ricky Watters	.40
114	Jim Harbaugh	.40
115	Marcus Allen	.40
116	Levon Kirkland	.20
117	Jessie Tuggle	.20
118	Ken Norton	.20
119	Thurman Thomas	.40
120	Junior Seau	.40
121	Tim Brown	.20
122	Michael Jackson	.20
123	Eric Metcalf	.20
124	Herman Moore	.40
125	Bruce Smith	.20
126	Cris Carter	.20
127	Dave Brown	.20
128	Jeff Blake	.40
129	Robert Blackmon	.20
130	Barry Sanders	2.50
131	Blaine Bishop	.20
132	Jerome Bettis	.40
133	Stan Humphries	.20
134	Vinny Testaverde	.20
135	Troy Aikman	2.50

1997 Topps Gallery Critics Choice

Critics Choice is a 20-card insert featuring player action shots. The cards were inserted 1:24. Cards are numbered and carry a "CC" prefix.

		MT
Complete Set (20):		220.00
Common Player:		4.00
Minor Stars:		8.00
Inserted 1:24		
1	Barry Sanders	30.00
2	Jeff Blake	4.00
3	Vinny Testaverde	8.00
4	Ricky Watters	8.00
5	John Elway	20.00
6	Drew Bledsoe	15.00
7	Kordell Stewart	15.00
8	Mark Brunell	15.00
9	Troy Aikman	15.00
10	Brett Favre	30.00
11	Kevin Hardy	4.00
12	Shannon Sharpe	4.00
13	Emmitt Smith	20.00
14	Rob Moore	4.00
15	Eddie George	15.00
16	Herman Moore	8.00
17	Terry Glenn	8.00
18	Jim Harbaugh	4.00
19	Terrell Davis	25.00
20	Junior Seau	4.00

1997 Topps Gallery Gallery of Heroes

This 15-card insert features a player shot on a transparent, luminous card that looks like a stained glass window. They were inserted 1:36. Cards are numbered with a "GH" prefix.

		MT
Complete Set (15):		240.00
Common Player:		12.00
1	Desmond Howard	12.00
2	Marcus Allen	12.00
3	Kerry Collins	16.00
4	Troy Aikman	25.00
5	Jerry Rice	25.00
6	Drew Bledsoe	25.00
7	John Elway	18.00
8	Mark Brunell	25.00
9	Junior Seau	12.00
10	Brett Favre	45.00
11	Dan Marino	40.00
12	Barry Sanders	30.00
13	Reggie White	12.00
14	Emmitt Smith	40.00
15	Steve Young	18.00

1997 Topps Gallery Peter Max

This 10-card insert combines player pictures with colorful art. This insert can be found 1:24. A limited number of the cards were autographed by the artist, Peter max. Cards are numbered and carry a "PM" prefix.

		MT
Complete Set (10):		125.00
Common Player:		4.00
Autographs:		10x-20x
1	Brett Favre	25.00
2	Jerry Rice	15.00
3	Emmitt Smith	20.00
4	John Elway	10.00
5	Barry Sanders	18.00
6	Reggie White	4.00
7	Steve Young	10.00
8	Troy Aikman	15.00
9	Drew Bledsoe	15.00
10	Dan Marino	20.00

1997 Topps Gallery Photo Gallery

Photo Gallery features top players and double foil stamping. The 15-card set was inserted 1:24. Cards are numbered with a "PG" prefix.

		MT
Complete Set (15):		200.00
Common Player:		3.00
1	Eddie George	25.00
2	Drew Bledsoe	20.00
3	Brett Favre	35.00
4	Emmitt Smith	30.00
5	Dan Marino	30.00
6	Terrell Davis	20.00
7	Kevin Greene	3.00
8	Troy Aikman	20.00
9	Curtis Martin	20.00
10	Barry Sanders	20.00
11	Junior Seau	3.00
12	Deion Sanders	10.00
13	Steve Young	15.00
14	Reggie White	3.00
15	Jerry Rice	20.00

1997 Topps Stars

The 125-card set includes 100 NFL stars and 25 1997 NFL draft picks. Each card features diffraction and matte gold foil stamping. The Always Mint parallel set was seeded 1:18 packs. Topps Stars was offered exclusively to Topps Home Team Advantage members.

		MT
Complete Set (125):		50.00
Common Player:		.10
Minor Stars:		.20
Foil Stars:		15x-30x
Foil Rookies:		10x-20x
Wax Box:		80.00
1	Brett Favre	4.00
2	Michael Jackson	.10
3	Simeon Rice	.10
4	Thurman Thomas	.20
5	Karim Abdul-Jabbar	.50
6	Marvin Harrison	.20
7	John Elway	2.00
8	Carl Pickens	.20
9	Rod Woodson	.10
10	Kerry Collins	.30
11	Cortez Kennedy	.10
12	William Fuller	.10
13	Michael Irvin	.20
14	Tyrone Braxton	.10
15	Steve Young	1.25
16	Keith Lyle	.10
17	Blaine Bishop	.10
18	Jeff Hostetler	.10
19	Levon Kirkland	.10
20	Barry Sanders	3.00
21	Deion Sanders	1.00
22	Jamal Anderson	.20
23	Eric Davis	.10
24	Hardy Nickerson	.10
25	LeRoy Butler	.10
26	Mark Brunell	1.75
27	Aeneas Williams	.10
28	Curtis Martin	1.50
29	Wayne Chrebet	.10
30	Jerry Rice	1.75
31	Jake Reed	.10
32	Wayne Martin	.10
33	Derrick Alexander	.10
34	Isaac Bruce	.20
35	Terrell Davis	2.00
36	Jerome Bettis	.20
37	Keenan McCardell	.10
38	Derrick Thomas	.20
39	Jason Sehorn	.10
40	Keyshawn Johnson	.20
41	Jeff Blake	.20
42	Terry Allen	.10
43	Ben Coates	.10
44	William Thomas	.10
45	Bryce Paup	.10
46	Bryant Young	.10
47	Eric Swann	.10
48	Tim Brown	.20
49	Tony Martin	.10
50	Eddie George	2.00
51	Sam Mills	.10
52	Terry McDaniel	.10
53	Darren Woodson	.10
54	Ashley Ambrose	.10
55	Drew Bledsoe	1.75
56	Larry Centers	.10
57	Ty Detmer	.20
58	Merton Hanks	.10
59	Charles Johnson	.10
60	Dan Marino	3.50
61	Joey Galloway	.20
62	Junior Seau	.20
63	Brett Perriman	.10
64	Wesley Walls	.10
65	Chad Brown	.10
66	Henry Ellard	.10
67	Keith Jackson	.10
68	John Randle	.10
69	Chester McGlockton	.10
70	Emmitt Smith	3.50
71	Vinny Testaverde	.10
72	Steve Atwater	.10
73	Irving Fryar	.10
74	Gus Frerotte	.10
75	Terry Glenn	.30
76	Anthony Johnson	.10
77	Jimmy Smith	.10
78	Terrell Buckley	.10
79	Kimble Anders	.10

80	Cris Carter	.20
81	David Meggett	.10
82	Shannon Sharpe	.20
83	Adrian Murrell	.20
84	Herman Moore	.20
85	Bruce Smith	.20
86	Lamar Lathon	.10
87	Ken Harvey	.10
88	Curtis Conway	.20
89	Alfred Williams	.10
90	Troy Aikman	1.75
91	Carnell Lake	.10
92	Michael Sinclair	.10
93	Ricky Watters	.20
94	Kevin Greene	.20
95	Reggie White	.20
96	Tyrone Hughes	.10
97	Dale Carter	.10
98	Rob Moore	.10
99	Tony Tolbert	.10
100	Willie McGinest	.10
101	Orlando Pace	.20
102	Yatil Green	.75
103	Antowain Smith	5.00
104	David LaFleur	1.50
105	Jake Plummer	20.00
106	Will Blackwell	.50
107	Dwayne Rudd	.20
108	Corey Dillon	10.00
109	Pat Barnes	.50
110	Peter Boulware	.20
111	Tony Gonzalez	2.00
112	Renaldo Wynn	.20
113	Darrell Russell	.20
114	Bryant Westbrook	.20
115	James Farrior	.20
116	Joey Kent	.20
117	Rae Carruth	.20
118	Jim Druckenmiller	3.00
119	Byron Hanspard	.75
120	Ike Hilliard	1.25
121	Kevin Lockett	.20
122	Tom Knight	.20
123	Shawn Springs	.20
124	Troy Davis	.75
125	Darnell Autry	.30

1997 Topps Stars Future Pro Bowlers

Inserted 1:12 packs, the 15-card set features a player photo superimposed over a backdrop of Pro Bowl 1997 logos. The Topps Stars logo is in the upper left, while the Future Pro Bowlers logo is in the lower left. The player's name is to the right of the logo. The cards are numbered on the back with a prefix of "FPB".

		MT
Complete Set (15):		60.00
Common Player:		2.00
1	Ike Hilliard	3.00
2	Tom Knight	2.00
3	David LaFleur	3.00
4	Byron Hanspard	4.00
5	Kevin Lockett	2.00
6	Rae Carruth	3.00
7	Jim Druckenmiller	10.00
8	Darnell Autry	4.00
9	Joey Kent	2.00
10	Peter Boulware	2.00
11	Orlando Pace	4.00
12	Troy Davis	6.00
13	Antowain Smith	4.00
14	Bryant Westbrook	2.00
15	Yatil Green	3.00

Values quoted in this guide reflect the retail price of a card — the price a collector can expect to pay when buying a card from a dealer. The wholesale price — that which a collector can expect to receive when selling cards — will be significantly lower, depending on desirability and condition.

1997 Topps Stars Hall of Fame Rookie Reprints

The 10-card set was inserted 1:64 packs, while autographed versions were found 1:128 packs.

		MT
Complete Set (10):		60.00
Common Player:		5.00
Autographs:		3x-6x
1	George Blanda	5.00
2	Dick Butkus	10.00
3	Len Dawson	5.00
4	Jack Ham	5.00
5	Sam Huff	5.00
6	Deacon Jones	5.00
7	Ray Nitschke	5.00
8	Gale Sayers	10.00
9	Randy White	5.00
10	Kellen Winslow	5.00

1997 Topps Stars Pro Bowl Memories

The 10-card set was inserted 1:24 packs. The cards are laser cut through the middle with stars, which start small on the left and grow larger as the stars move to the right. The Pro Bowl logo is in the upper left, while "Pro Bowl Memories" and the player's name are printed vertically along the right border in the middle. The Topps Stars logo is in the lower right. The backs are numbered with a "PBM" prefix.

		MT
Complete Set (10):		100.00
Common Player:		3.00
1	Barry Sanders	25.00
2	Jeff Blake	6.00
3	Ken Harvey	3.00
4	Brett Favre	30.00
5	Jerry Rice	15.00
6	John Elway	15.00
7	Marshall Faulk	3.00
8	Steve Young	10.00
9	Mark Brunell	15.00
10	Troy Aikman	15.00

1997 Topps Stars Pro Bowl Stars

The 30-card set was inserted 1:24 packs. The card fronts

feature a player photo superimposed over a uniluster background of the Pro Bowl 1997 logo and the NFC or AFC logo. The Topps Stars logo is in the upper left, while the Pro Bowl logo is in the lower left, with the player's name and position to the right. The backs are numbered with a prefix of "PB".

		MT
Complete Set (30):		125.00
Common Player:		4.00
Minor Stars:		8.00
Inserted 1:24		
1	Brett Favre	30.00
2	Mark Brunell	15.00
3	Kerry Collins	8.00
4	Drew Bledsoe	15.00
5	Barry Sanders	30.00
6	Terrell Davis	25.00
7	Terry Allen	4.00
8	Jerome Bettis	8.00
9	Ricky Watters	4.00
10	Curtis Martin	10.00
11	Emmitt Smith	20.00
12	Kimble Anders	4.00
13	Jerry Rice	15.00
14	Carl Pickens	4.00
15	Herman Moore	8.00
16	Tony Martin	4.00
17	Isaac Bruce	8.00
18	Tim Brown	4.00
19	Wesley Walls	4.00
20	Shannon Sharpe	4.00
21	Dana Stubblefield	4.00
22	Reggie White	8.00
23	Bruce Smith	4.00
24	Bryant Young	4.00
25	Junior Seau	4.00
26	Kevin Greene	4.00
27	Derrick Thomas	4.00
28	Chad Brown	4.00
29	Deion Sanders	10.00
30	Rod Woodson	4.00

1998 Topps

Topps was issued in a single-series 360-card set in 1998. It contained a 30-card 1998 NFL Draft Picks subset that was seeded one per three packs. Cards utilize a gold border around the color shot of the player, with the Topps logo in the upper right, team logo in the lower left and the player's name and team printed up the right side. Backs are horizontal and add another shot of the player, along with statistics and bio information. Inserts in Topps include: Season's Best, Measures of Greatness, Myster Finest, Gridiron Gods (hobby), Hidden Gems (retail), Autographs (hobby) and Generation 2000.

		MT
Complete Set (360):		70.00
Common Player:		.10
Minor Stars:		.20
Wax Box:		50.00
1	Barry Sanders	2.00
2	Derrick Rodgers	.10
3	Chris Calloway	.10
4	Bruce Armstrong	.10
5	Horace Copeland	.10
6	Chad Brown	.10
7	Ken Harvey	.10
8	Levon Kirkland	.10
9	Glenn Foley	.20
10	Corey Dillon	.50
11	Sean Dawkins	.10
12	Curtis Conway	.20
13	Chris Chandler	.20
14	Kerry Collins	.20
15	Jonathan Ogden	.10
16	Sam Shade	.10
17	Vaughn Hebron	.10
18	Quentin Coryatt	.10
19	Jerris McPhail	.10
20	Warrick Dunn	1.00
21	Wayne Martin	.10

22	Chad Lewis	.10
23	Danny Kanell	.10
24	Shawn Springs	.10
25	Emmitt Smith	1.75
26	Todd Lyght	.10
27	Donnie Edwards	.10
28	Charlie Jones	.10
29	Willie McGinest	.10
30	Steve Young	.75
31	Darrell Russell	.10
32	Gary Anderson	.10
33	Stanley Richard	.10
34	Leslie O'Neal	.10
35	Dermontti Dawson	.10
36	Jeff Brady	.10
37	Kimble Anders	.10
38	Glyn Milburn	.10
39	Greg Hill	.10
40	Freddie Jones	.10
41	Bobby Engram	.10
42	Aeneas Williams	.10
43	Antowain Smith	.75
44	Reggie White	.20
45	Rae Carruth	.10
46	Leon Johnson	.10
47	Bryant Young	.10
48	Jamie Asher	.10
49	Hardy Nickerson	.10
50	Jerome Bettis	.20
51	Michael Strahan	.10
52	John Randle	.10
53	Kevin Hardy	.10
54	Eric Bjornson	.10
55	Morten Andersen	.10
56	Larry Centers	.10
57	Bryce Paup	.10
58	John Mobley	.10
59	Michael Bates	.10
60	Tim Brown	.20
61	Doug Evans	.10
62	Will Shields	.10
63	Jeff Graham	.10
64	Henry Jones	.10
65	Steve Broussard	.10
66	Blaine Bishop	.10
67	Ernie Conwell	.10
68	Heath Shuler	.10
69	Eric Metcalf	.10
70	Terry Glenn	.20
71	James Hasty	.10
72	Robert Porcher	.10
73	Keenan McCardell	.10
74	Tyrone Hughes	.10
75	Troy Aikman	1.00
76	Peter Boulware	.10
77	Rob Johnson	.20
78	Erik Kramer	.10
79	Kevin Smith	.10
80	Andre Rison	.10
81	Jim Harbaugh	.20
82	Chris Hudson	.10
83	Ray Zellars	.10
84	Jeff George	.20
85	Willie Davis	.10
86	Jason Gildon	.10
87	Robert Brooks	.10
88	Chad Cota	.10
89	Simeon Rice	.10
90	Mark Brunell	.75
91	Jay Graham	.10
92	Scott Greene	.10
93	Jeff Blake	.20
94	Jason Belser	.10
95	Derrick Alexander	.10
96	Ty Law	.10
97	Charles Johnson	.10
98	James Jett	.10
99	Darrell Green	.10
100	Brett Favre	2.00
101	George Jones	.10
102	Derrick Mason	.10
103	Sam Adams	.10
104	Lawrence Phillips	.10
105	Randal Hill	.10
106	John Mangum	.10
107	Natrone Means	.20
108	Bill Romanowski	.10
109	Terance Mathis	.10
110	Bruce Smith	.10
111	Pete Mitchell	.10
112	Duane Clemons	.10
113	Willie Clay	.10
114	Eric Allen	.10
115	Troy Drayton	.10
116	Derrick Thomas	.10
117	Charles Way	.10
118	Wayne Chrebet	.10
119	Bobby Hoying	.10
120	Michael Jackson	.10
121	Gary Zimmerman	.10
122	Yancey Thigpen	.10
123	Dana Stubblefield	.10
124	Keith Lyle	.10
125	Marco Coleman	.10
126	Karl Williams	.10
127	Stephen Davis	.10
128	Chris Sanders	.10
129	Cris Dishman	.10
130	Jake Plummer	1.00
131	Darryl Williams	.10
132	Merton Hanks	.10
133	Torrance Small	.10
134	Aaron Glenn	.10
135	Chester McGlockton	.10
136	William Thomas	.10
137	Kordell Stewart	1.00
138	Jason Taylor	.10
139	Lake Dawson	.10

140	Carl Pickens	.10
141	Eugene Robinson	.10
142	Ed McCaffrey	.10
143	Lamar Lathon	.10
144	Ray Buchanan	.10
145	Thurman Thomas	.20
146	Andre Reed	.10
147	Wesley Walls	.10
148	Rob Moore	.10
149	Darren Woodson	.10
150	Eddie George	1.00
151	Michael Irvin	.20
152	Johnnie Morton	.10
153	Ken Dilger	.10
154	Tony Boselli	.10
155	Randall McDaniel	.10
156	Mark Fields	.10
157	Phillippi Sparks	.10
158	William Roaf	.10
159	Troy Vincent	.10
160	Cris Carter	.10
161	Amp Lee	.10
162	Will Blackwell	.10
163	Chad Scott	.10
164	Henry Ellard	.10
165	Robert Jones	.10
166	Garrison Hearst	.10
167	James McKnight	.10
168	Rodney Harrison	.10
169	Adrian Murrell	.20
170	Rod Smith	.10
171	Desmond Howard	.10
172	Ben Coates	.10
173	David Palmer	.10
174	Zach Thomas	.10
175	Dale Carter	.10
176	Mark Chmura	.10
177	Elvis Grbac	.10
178	Jason Hanson	.10
179	Walt Harris	.10
180	Ricky Watters	.20
181	Ray Lewis	.10
182	Lonnie Johnson	.10
183	Marvin Harrison	.20
184	Dorsey Levens	.20
185	Tony Gonzalez	.10
186	Andre Hastings	.10
187	Kevin Turner	.10
188	Mo Lewis	.10
189	Jason Sehorn	.10
190	Drew Bledsoe	1.00
191	Michael Sinclair	.10
192	William Floyd	.10
193	Kenny Holmes	.10
194	Marvcus Patton	.10
195	Warren Sapp	.10
196	Junior Seau	.20
197	Ryan McNeil	.10
198	Tyrone Wheatley	.10
199	Robert Smith	.10
200	Terrell Davis	1.50
201	Brett Perriman	.10
202	Tamarick Vanover	.10
203	Stephen Boyd	.10
204	Zack Crockett	.10
205	Sherman Williams	.10
206	Neil Smith	.10
207	Jermaine Lewis	.10
208	Kevin Williams	.10
209	Byron Hanspard	.20
210	Warren Moon	.20
211	Tony McGee	.10
212	Raymont Harris	.10
213	Eric Davis	.10
214	Darrien Gordon	.10
215	James Stewart	.10
216	Derrick Mayes	.10
217	Brad Johnson	.10
218	Karim Abdul-Jabbar	.20
219	Hugh Douglas	.10
220	Terry Allen	.10
221	Rhett Hall	.10
222	Terrell Fletcher	.10
223	Carnell Lake	.10
224	Darryll Lewis	.10
225	Chris Slade	.10
226	Michael Westbrook	.10
227	Willie Williams	.10
228	Tony Banks	.20
229	Keyshawn Johnson	.20
230	Mike Alstott	.20
231	Tiki Barber	.20
232	Jake Reed	.10
233	Eric Swann	.10
234	Eric Moulds	.20
235	Vinny Testaverde	.10
236	Jessie Tuggle	.10
237	Ryan Wetnight	.10
238	Tyrone Poole	.10
239	Bryant Westbrook	.10
240	Steve McNair	.75
241	Jimmy Smith	.10
242	DeWayne Washington	.10
243	Robert Harris	.10
244	Rod Woodson	.20
245	Reidel Anthony	.20
246	Jessie Armstead	.10
247	O.J. McDuffie	.10
248	Carlton Gray	.10
249	LeRoy Butler	.10
250	Jerry Rice	1.00
251	Frank Sanders	.10
252	Todd Collins	.10
253	Fred Lane	.10
254	David Dunn	.10
255	Micheal Barrow	.10
256	Luther Ellis	.10

257	Scott Mitchell	.10
258	David Meggett	.10
259	Rickey Dudley	.10
260	Isaac Bruce	.20
261	Tony Martin	.10
262	Leslie Shepherd	.10
263	Derrick Thomas	.10
264	Greg Lloyd	.10
265	Terrell Buckley	.10
266	Antonio Freeman	.20
267	Tony Brackens	.10
268	Mark McMillian	.10
269	Dexter Coakley	.10
270	Dan Marino	1.75
271	Bryan Cox	.10
272	Leeland McElroy	.10
273	Jeff Burris	.10
274	Eric Green	.10
275	Darnay Scott	.10
276	Greg Clark	.10
277	Mario Bates	.10
278	Eric Turner	.10
279	Neil O'Donnell	.10
280	Herman Moore	.20
281	Gary Brown	.10
282	Terrell Owens	.20
283	Frank Wycheck	.10
284	Trent Dilfer	.20
285	Curtis Martin	.75
286	Ricky Proehl	.10
287	Steve Atwater	.10
288	Aaron Bailey	.10
289	William Henderson	.10
290	Marcus Allen	.20
291	Tom Knight	.10
292	Quinn Early	.10
293	Michael McCrary	.10
294	Bert Emanuel	.10
295	Tom Carter	.10
296	Kevin Glover	.10
297	Marshall Faulk	.20
298	Harvey Williams	.10
299	Chris Warren	.10
300	John Elway	.75
301	Eddie Kennison	.20
302	Gus Frerotte	.10
303	Regan Upshaw	.10
304	Kevin Gogan	.10
305	Napoleon Kaufman	.30
306	Charlie Garner	.10
307	Shawn Jefferson	.10
308	Tommy Vardell	.10
309	Mike Hollis	.10
310	Irving Fryar	.10
311	Shannon Sharpe	.10
312	Byron Morris	.10
313	Jamal Anderson	.10
314	Chris Gedney	.10
315	Chris Spielman	.10
316	Derrick Alexander	.10
317	O.J. Santiago	.10
318	Anthony Miller	.10
319	Ki-Jana Carter	.10
320	Deion Sanders	.40
321	Joey Galloway	.20
322	J.J. Stokes	.10
323	Rodney Thomas	.10
324	John Lynch	.10
325	Mike Pritchard	.10
326	Terrance Shaw	.10
327	Ted Johnson	.10
328	Ashley Ambrose	.10
329	Checklist	.10
330	Checklist	.10
331	*Jerome Pathon*	2.00
332	*Ryan Leaf*	6.00
333	*Duane Starks*	1.50
334	*Brian Simmons*	1.00
335	*Keith Brooking*	2.00
336	*Robert Edwards*	4.00
337	*Curtis Enis*	5.00
338	*John Avery*	3.00
339	*Fred Taylor*	10.00
340	*Germane Crowell*	3.00
341	*Hines Ward*	2.00
342	*Marcus Nash*	3.00
343	*Jacquez Green*	3.00
344	*Joe Jurevicius*	2.00
345	*Greg Ellis*	1.00
346	*Brian Griese*	6.00
347	*Tavian Banks*	2.00
348	*Robert Holcombe*	3.00
349	*Skip Hicks*	3.00
350	*Ahman Green*	3.00
351	*Takeo Spikes*	2.00
352	*Randy Moss*	20.00
353	*Andre Wadsworth*	2.00
354	*Jason Peter*	2.00
355	*Grant Wistrom*	2.00
356	*Charles Woodson*	5.00
357	*Kevin Dyson*	3.00
358	*Patrick Johnson*	2.00
359	*Tim Dwight*	4.00
360	*Peyton Manning*	12.00

Post-1980 cards in Near Mint condition will generally sell for about 75% of the quoted Mint value. Excellent-condition cards bring no more than 40%.

A player's name in *italic* type indicates a rookie card.

1998 Topps Autographs

This hobby-only insert featured autographs from 15 top players, with eight veterans, two rookies and the five 1997 NFL Hall of Fame inductees. Each card has a gold foil "Topps Certified Autograph Issue" stamp and was inserted one per 260 hobby packs. Cards are numbered with a "A" prefix.

		MT
Complete Set (15):		650.00
Common Player:		30.00
1	Randy Moss	220.00
2	Mike Alstott	40.00
3	Jake Plummer	70.00
4	Corey Dillon	50.00
5	Kordell Stewart	70.00
6	Eddie George	60.00
7	Jason Sehorn	30.00
8	Joey Galloway	30.00
9	Ryan Leaf	75.00
10	Peyton Manning	150.00
11	Dwight Stephenson	30.00
12	Anthony Munoz	30.00
13	Mike Singletary	30.00
14	Tommy McDonald	30.00
15	Paul Krause	30.00

1998 Topps Generation 2000

Generation 2000 showcases 15 of football's top young players who should lead the game into the year 2000. The inserts have the word "Generation" across the top and "2000" printed in silver, embossed foil across the bottom. These were numbered with a "GE" prefix and inserted one per 18 packs.

		MT
Complete Set (15):		60.00
Common Player:		2.00
Minor Stars:		4.00
1	Warrick Dunn	10.00
2	Tony Gonzalez	2.00
3	Corey Dillon	8.00
4	Antowain Smith	6.00
5	Mike Alstott	4.00
6	Kordell Stewart	8.00
7	Peter Boulware	2.00
8	Jake Plummer	10.00
9	Tiki Barber	4.00
10	Terrell Davis	12.00
11	Steve McNair	6.00
12	Curtis Martin	8.00
13	Napoleon Kaufman	6.00
14	Terrell Owens	2.00
15	Eddie George	8.00

A card number in parentheses ( ) indicates the set is unnumbered.

1998 Topps Gridiron Gods

This hobby exclusive insert captures 15 players on uniluster technology, which is a silver etched, holofoil looking background. Cards are numbered with a "G" prefix and inserted one per 36 packs.

		MT
Complete Set (15):		100.00
Common Player:		2.00
Minor Stars:		4.00
1	Barry Sanders	15.00
2	Jerry Rice	10.00
3	Herman Moore	4.00
4	Drew Bledsoe	10.00
5	Kordell Stewart	10.00
6	Tim Brown	2.00
7	Eddie George	8.00
8	Dorsey Levens	4.00
9	Warrick Dunn	8.00
10	Brett Favre	15.00
11	Terrell Davis	12.00
12	Steve Young	7.00
13	Jerome Bettis	4.00
14	Mark Brunell	8.00
15	John Elway	8.00

1998 Topps Hidden Gems

Hidden Gems were exclusive to retail packs and inserted one per 15. This 15-card set is printed on a plastic-like surface and numbered with a "HG" prefix.

		MT
Complete Set (15):		20.00
Common Player:		.50
1	Andre Reed	1.00
2	Kevin Greene	.50
3	Tony Martin	.50
4	Shannon Sharpe	1.00
5	Terry Allen	1.00
6	Brett Favre	8.00
7	Ben Coates	1.00
8	Michael Sinclair	.50
9	Keenan McCardell	.50
10	Brad Johnson	1.00
11	Mark Brunell	4.00
12	Dorsey Levens	1.00
13	Terrell Davis	8.00
14	Curtis Martin	2.00
15	Derrick Rodgers	.50

Values quoted in this guide reflect the retail price of a card — the price a collector can expect to pay when buying a card from a dealer. The wholesale price — that which a collector can expect to receive from a dealer when selling cards — will be significantly lower, depending on desirability and condition.

1998 Topps Measures Of Greatness

Fifteen different players that are bound for the Hall of Fame are featured in this insert printed on micro dyna-etch technology. The silver foil fronts that feature markings of a football field includes the insert name up the left side, with the player's name in a banner below it. Cards are numbered with a "MG" prefix and inserted one per 36 packs.

		MT
Complete Set (15):		70.00
Common Player:		2.00
Minor Stars:		4.00
1	John Elway	8.00
2	Marcus Allen	4.00
3	Jerry Rice	10.00
4	Tim Brown	2.00
5	Warren Moon	2.00
6	Bruce Smith	2.00
7	Troy Aikman	10.00
8	Reggie White	4.00
9	Irving Fryar	2.00
10	Barry Sanders	15.00
11	Cris Carter	2.00
12	Emmitt Smith	12.00
13	Dan Marino	12.00
14	Rod Woodson	2.00
15	Brett Favre	15.00

1998 Topps Mystery Finest

This 20-card insert arrives with black opaque protectors over the front and four different players on the back. Collectors needed to peel the fronts in order to determine which of the four players it was. Mystery Finest cards are numbered with a "M" prefix and inserted one per 36 packs. Refractor versions were also available and seeded one per 144 packs.

		MT
Complete Set (20):		125.00
Common Player:		2.00
Minor Stars:		4.00
Refractors:		3x
1	Steve Young	7.00
2	Dan Marino	17.00
3	Brett Favre	20.00
4	Drew Bledsoe	10.00
5	Mark Brunell	8.00
6	Troy Aikman	10.00
7	Kordell Stewart	10.00
8	John Elway	10.00
9	Barry Sanders	20.00
10	Jerome Bettis	4.00
11	Eddie George	10.00
12	Emmitt Smith	17.00
13	Curtis Martin	5.00
14	Warrick Dunn	10.00
15	Dorsey Levens	4.00
16	Terrell Davis	12.00
17	Herman Moore	4.00

18	Jerry Rice	10.00
19	Tim Brown	2.00
20	Yancey Thigpen	2.00

1998 Topps Season's Best

Season's Best includes 30 of the NFL's statistical leaders in six differerent categories on prismatic foilboard. Power & Speed are rushing leaders, Gunslingers are quarterbacks, Prime Targets are receiving leaders, Heavy Hitters are sack leaders, Quick Six are all-purpose yardage and Career Best are all-time leaders. These are numbered with a "SB" prefix and inserted one per 12 packs.

		MT
Complete Set (30):		90.00
Common Player:		1.00
Minor Stars:		2.00
1	Terrell Davis	8.00
2	Barry Sanders	10.00
3	Jerome Bettis	2.00
4	Dorsey Levens	2.00
5	Eddie George	5.00
6	Brett Favre	10.00
7	Mark Brunell	6.00
8	Jeff George	1.00
9	Steve Young	4.00
10	John Elway	6.00
11	Herman Moore	2.00
12	Rob Moore	1.00
13	Yancey Thigpen	1.00
14	Cris Carter	1.00
15	Tim Brown	1.00
16	Bruce Smith	1.00
17	Michael Sinclair	1.00
18	John Randle	1.00
19	Dana Stubblefield	1.00
20	Michael Strahan	1.00
21	Tamarick Vanover	1.00
22	Darrien Gordon	1.00
23	Michael Bates	1.00
24	David Meggett	1.00
25	Jermaine Lewis	1.00
26	Terrell Davis	8.00
27	Jerry Rice	8.00
28	Barry Sanders	10.00
29	John Randle	1.00
30	John Elway	6.00

1998 Topps Action Flats

This was the debut issue of Action Flats with a checklist of eight of the NFL's most celebrated star and rookie players in dynamic action poses. Each figure came with an exclusive special edition foil-stamped trading card that was different than their card in the Topps set. SRP was $2.99 for this product.

		MT
Complete Set (8):		25.00
Common Player:		3.00
	Troy Aikman	3.00
	John Elway	3.00
	Brett Favre	4.00
	Ryan Leaf	3.00
	Peyton Manning	5.00
	Dan Marino	3.00
	Jerry Rice	3.00
	Barry Sanders	4.00

Post-1980 cards in Near Mint condition will generally sell for about 75% of the quoted Mint value. Excellent-condition cards bring no more than 40%.

1998 Topps Chrome

Topps Chrome includes 165 cards from Topps reprinted with a chromium finish. The Topps logo is replaced on both the front and the back by a Topps Chrome logo. Cards are renumbered and reordered within the checklist for the mostpart. Each card was also available in a Refractor versions, while the three inserts - Hidden Gems, Measures of Greatness and Season's Best - are also reprinted from Topps and available in both regular and Refractor versions.

		MT
Complete Set (165):		300.00
Common Player:		.40
Common Rookie:		3.00
Minor Stars:		.75
Wax Box:		200.00
1	Barry Sanders	6.00
2	Duane Starks	3.00
3	J.J. Stokes	.40
4	Joey Galloway	.75
5	Deion Sanders	1.50
6	Anthony Miller	.40
7	Jamal Anderson	1.00
8	Shannon Sharpe	.40
9	Irving Fryar	.40
10	Curtis Martin	1.50
11	Shawn Jefferson	.40
12	Charlie Garner	.75
13	Robert Edwards	10.00
14	Napoleon Kaufman	1.50
15	Gus Frerotte	.40
16	John Elway	3.00
17	Jerome Pathon	3.00
18	Marshall Faulk	.75
19	Michael McCrary	.40
20	Marcus Allen	.75
21	Trent Dilfer	.75
22	Frank Wycheck	.40
23	Terrell Owens	.75
24	Herman Moore	.75
25	Neil O'Donnell	.40
26	Darnay Scott	.40
27	Keith Brooking	3.00
28	Eric Green	.40
29	Dan Marino	5.00
30	Antonio Freeman	.75
31	Tony Martin	.40
32	Isaac Bruce	.75
33	Rickey Dudley	.40
34	Scott Mitchell	.40
35	Randy Moss	85.00
36	Fred Lane	.75
37	Frank Sanders	.40
38	Jerry Rice	3.00
39	O.J. McDuffie	.40
40	Jessie Armstead	.40
41	Reidel Anthony	.40
42	Steve McNair	2.00
43	Jake Reed	.40
44	Charles Woodson	20.00
45	Tiki Barber	.40
46	Mike Alstott	.75
47	Keyshawn Johnson	.75
48	Tony Banks	.75
49	Michael Westbrook	.40
50	Chris Slade	.40
51	Terry Allen	.40
52	Karim Abdul-Jabbar	.75
53	Brad Johnson	.75
54	Tony McGee	.40
55	Kevin Dyson	15.00
56	Warren Moon	.75
57	Byron Hanspard	.40
58	Jermaine Lewis	.40
59	Neil Smith	.40
60	Tamarick Vanover	.40
61	Terrell Davis	3.00
62	Robert Smith	.75
63	Junior Seau	.40
64	Warren Sapp	.40
65	Michael Sinclair	.40
66	Ryan Leaf	20.00
67	Drew Bledsoe	3.00
68	Jason Sehorn	.40
69	Andre Hastings	.40
70	Tony Gonzalez	.75
71	Dorsey Levens	.75
72	Ray Lewis	.40
73	Grant Wistrom	3.00
74	Elvis Grbac	.40
75	Mark Chmura	.75
76	Zach Thomas	.40
77	Ben Coates	.40
78	Rod Smith	.40
79	Andre Wadsworth	6.00
80	Garrison Hearst	.40
81	Will Blackwell	.40
82	Cris Carter	.40
83	Mark Fields	.40
84	Ken Dilger	.40
85	Johnnie Morton	.40
86	Michael Irvin	.75
87	Eddie George	3.00
88	Rob Moore	.40
89	Takeo Spikes	3.00
90	Wesley Walls	.40
91	Andre Reed	.40
92	Thurman Thomas	.75
93	Ed McCaffrey	.40
94	Carl Pickens	.40
95	Jason Taylor	.40
96	Kordell Stewart	3.00
97	Greg Ellis	1.00
98	Aaron Glenn	.40
99	Jake Plummer	3.00
100	Checklist	.40
101	Chris Sanders	.40
102	Michael Jackson	.40
103	Bobby Hoying	.40
104	Wayne Chrebet	.40
105	Charles Way	.40
106	Derrick Thomas	.40
107	Troy Drayton	.40
108	Robert Holcombe	8.00
109	Pete Mitchell	.40
110	Bruce Smith	.40
111	Terance Mathis	.40
112	Lawrence Phillips	.40
113	Brett Favre	6.00
114	Darrell Green	.40
115	Charles Johnson	.40
116	Jeff Blake	.75
117	Mark Brunell	3.00
118	Simeon Rice	.40
119	Robert Brooks	.40
120	Jacquez Green	12.00
121	Willie Davis	.40
122	Jeff George	.75
123	Andre Rison	.40
124	Erik Kramer	.40
125	Peter Boulware	.40
126	Marcus Nash	10.00
127	Troy Aikman	3.00
128	Keenan McCardell	.40
129	Bryant Westbrook	.40
130	Terry Glenn	.75
131	Blaine Bishop	.40
132	Tim Brown	.75
133	Brian Griese	25.00
134	John Mobley	.40
135	Larry Centers	.40
136	Eric Bjornson	.40
137	Kevin Hardy	.40
138	John Randle	.40
139	Michael Strahan	.40
140	Jerome Bettis	.75
141	Rae Carruth	.40
142	Reggie White	.75
143	Antowain Smith	1.50
144	Aeneas Williams	.40
145	Bobby Engram	.40
146	Germane Crowell	15.00
147	Freddie Jones	.40
148	Kimble Anders	.40
149	Steve Young	2.00
150	Willie McGinest	.40
151	Emmitt Smith	5.00
152	Fred Taylor	35.00
153	Danny Kanell	.40
154	Warrick Dunn	3.00
155	Kerry Collins	.75
156	Chris Chandler	.75
157	Curtis Conway	.75
158	Curtis Enis	15.00
159	Corey Dillon	2.00
160	Glenn Foley	.75
161	Marvin Harrison	.75
162	Chad Brown	.40
163	Derrick Rodgers	.40
164	Levon Kirkland	.40
165	Peyton Manning	60.00

1998 Topps Chrome Refractors

All 165 cards in Topps Chrome were reprinted in Refractor versions and inserted one per 12 packs.

	MT
Refractor Cards:	6x-12x
Refractor Rookies:	2x-4x

A card number in parentheses ( ) indicates the set is unnumbered.

1998 Topps Chrome Hidden Gems

This 15-card set was reprinted from Topps in a chromium version and inserted one per 12 packs. Cards are numbered with "HG" prefix, while Refractors are seeded one per 24 packs.

		MT
Complete Set (15):		40.00
Common Player:		1.50
Minor Stars:		3.00
Refractors:		2x
1	Andre Reed	1.50
2	Kevin Greene	1.50
3	Tony Martin	1.50
4	Shannon Sharpe	1.50
5	Terry Allen	1.50
6	Brett Favre	15.00
7	Ben Coates	1.50
8	Michael Sinclair	1.50
9	Keenan McCardell	1.50
10	Brad Johnson	3.00
11	Mark Brunell	7.00
12	Dorsey Levens	3.00
13	Terrell Davis	10.00
14	Curtis Martin	4.00
15	Derrick Rodgers	1.50

1998 Topps Chrome Measures of Greatness

This 15-card set is reprinted from Topps in a chromium version and seeded one per 12 packs. The cards are numbered with a "HG" prefix, while Refractor versions are seeded one per 48 packs.

		MT
Complete Set (15):		80.00
Common Player:		1.50
Minor Stars:		3.00
Refractors:		3x
1	John Elway	7.00
2	Marcus Allen	3.00
3	Jerry Rice	8.00
4	Tim Brown	1.50
5	Warren Moon	1.50
6	Bruce Smith	1.50
7	Troy Aikman	8.00
8	Reggie White	3.00
9	Irving Fryar	1.50
10	Barry Sanders	15.00
11	Cris Carter	1.50
12	Emmitt Smith	12.00
13	Dan Marino	12.00
14	Rod Woodson	1.50
15	Brett Favre	15.00

Post-1980 cards in Near Mint condition will generally sell for about 75% of the quoted Mint value. Excellent-condition cards bring no more than 40%.

1998 Topps Chrome Season's Best

This 30-card insert was reprinted from Topps in a chromium version and inserted one per eight packs. The set is broken up with five cards in six different categories, including Power & Speed, Gunslingers, Prime Targets, Heavy Hitters, Quick Six and Career Best. Season's Best cards are numbered with a "SB" prefix and Refractor versions are seeded one per 24 packs.

		MT
Complete Set (30):		90.00
Common Player:		.50
Minor Stars:		1.00
Refractors:		2x
1	Terrell Davis	10.00
2	Barry Sanders	15.00
3	Jerome Bettis	1.00
4	Dorsey Levens	1.00
5	Eddie George	6.00
6	Brett Favre	15.00
7	Mark Brunell	5.00
8	Jeff George	1.00
9	Steve Young	4.00
10	John Elway	7.00
11	Herman Moore	1.00
12	Rob Moore	.50
13	Yancey Thigpen	.50
14	Cris Carter	1.00
15	Tim Brown	1.00
16	Bruce Smith	.50
17	Michael Smith	.50
18	John Randle	.50
19	Dana Stubblefield	.50
20	Michael Strahan	.50
21	Tamarick Vanover	.50
22	Darrien Gordon	.50
23	Michael Bates	.50
24	David Meggett	.50
25	Jermaine Lewis	.50
26	Terrell Davis	10.00
27	Jerry Rice	6.00
28	Barry Sanders	15.00
29	John Randle	.50
30	John Elway	7.00

1998 Topps Gold Label

Each card in this set was printed on 35 point spectra-reflective rainbow stock and was gold foiled-stamped with the player's name and the Gold Label logo. The backs of the cards reveal all relevant statistics, including career totals and career bests as well as insightful player commentary. Each card has a parallel Class 2 and a Class 3 card. The Class 2 cards have the name and logo in silver foil and were inserted 1:2 packs. The Class 3 singles were in prismatic gold foil and found 1:4 packs.

		MT
Complete Set (100):		125.00
Common Player:		.25
Minor Stars:		.50
Class 2 Cards:		2x
Class 2 Rookies:		1.5x
Name In Silver Foil		
Inserted 1:2		
Class 3 Cards:		3x
Class 3 Rookies:		2x
Name In Prismatic Gold Foil		
Inserted 1:4		
Wax Box:		110.00
1	John Elway	4.00
2	Rob Moore	.25
3	Jamal Anderson	1.50
4	Patrick Johnson	.25
5	Troy Aikman	4.00
6	Antowain Smith	1.50
7	Wesley Walls	.25
8	Curtis Enis	5.00
9	Jimmy Smith	.25
10	Terrell Davis	6.00
11	Marshall Faulk	1.00
12	Germane Crowell	4.00
13	Marcus Nash	4.00
14	Deion Sanders	.50
15	Dorsey Levens	.50
16	Corey Dillon	1.50
17	Fred Taylor	12.00
18	Derrick Thomas	.25
19	Kevin Dyson	4.00
20	Peyton Manning	15.00
21	Warren Sapp	.25
22	Robert Holcombe	3.00
23	Joey Galloway	1.00
24	Garrison Hearst	.50
25	Brett Favre	8.00
26	Aeneas Williams	.25
27	Danny Kanell	.25
28	Robert Smith	.50
29	Brad Johnson	1.00
30	Dan Marino	6.00
31	Elvis Grbac	.50
32	Terry Allen	.25
33	Frank Sanders	.25
34	Peter Boulware	.25
35	Tim Brown	.50
36	Thurman Thomas	.50
37	Rae Carruth	.25
38	Michael Irvin	.50
39	Brian Griese	8.00
40	Kordell Stewart	3.00
41	Johnnie Morton	.25
42	Robert Brooks	.25
43	Keenan McCardell	.25
44	Ben Coates	.25
45	Jerry Rice	4.00
46	Tony Simmons	2.50
47	Irving Fryar	.25
48	Jerome Pathon	2.00
49	Steve McNair	1.50
50	Warrick Dunn	4.00
51	Skip Hicks	4.00
52	Andre Wadsworth	2.00
53	Chris Chandler	.25
54	Curtis Conway	.50
55	Eddie George	3.00
56	Jeff Blake	.50
57	Greg Ellis	1.50
58	Scott Mitchell	.25
59	Antonio Freeman	1.00
60	Drew Bledsoe	4.00
61	Mark Brunell	3.00
62	Andre Rison	.50
63	Cris Carter	1.00
64	Jake Reed	.25
65	Napoleon Kaufman	1.50
66	Terry Glenn	.50
67	Jason Sehorn	.25
68	Rickey Dudley	.25
69	Junior Seau	.50
70	Jerome Bettis	1.00
71	J.J. Stokes	.50
72	Warren Moon	.50
73	Isaac Bruce	.50
74	Mike Alstott	1.00
75	Steve Young	2.50
76	Jacquez Green	4.00
77	Gus Frerotte	.25
78	Michael Jackson	.25
79	Carl Pickens	.50
80	Bruce Smith	.50
81	Shannon Sharpe	.50
82	Herman Moore	.50
83	Reggie White	1.00
84	Marvin Harrison	.75
85	Jake Plummer	3.00
86	Karim Abdul-Jabbar	.75
87	John Randle	.25
88	Robert Edwards	6.00
89	Jeff George	.50
90	Emmitt Smith	6.00
91	Terrell Owens	2.00
92	Trent Dilfer	1.00
93	Darrell Green	.25
94	Andre Reed	.25
95	Ryan Leaf	7.00
96	Rod Smith	.50
97	O.J. McDuffie	.25
98	John Avery	4.00
99	Charles Way	.25
100	Barry Sanders	8.00

A player's name in italic type indicates a rookie card.

1998 Topps Gold Label Black Label

Each of the three versions in this set are the same as in the base Gold Label set except for the logo is in black. Class 1 singles have the name in gold foil and are found 1:8 packs. Class 2 cards are in silver foil and inserted 1:16 packs. Class 3 singles are in prismatic gold foil and inserted 1:32 packs.

	MT
Class 1 Cards:	5x
Class 1 Rookies:	3x
Name In Gold Foil	
Inserted 1:8	
Class 2 Cards:	8x
Class 2 Rookies:	5x
Name In Silver Foil	
Inserted 1:16	
Class 3 Cards:	12x
Class 3 Rookies:	7x
Name In Prismatic Gold Foil	
Inserted 1:32	

1998 Topps Gold Label Red Label

Red Label cards are the same as the base Gold Label set except for the logo is in red foil and each card is sequentially numbered. Class 1 singles have the name in gold foil (1:94) and are numbered to 100. Class 2 singles are in silver foil (1:187) and numbered to 50. Class 3 cards are in prismatic gold foil (1:375) and numbered to 25.

	MT
Class 1 Cards:	20x-40x
Class 1 Rookies:	10x-20x
Name In Gold Foil	
Inserted 1:94	
Production 100 Sets	
Class 2 Cards:	25x-50x
Class 2 Rookies:	12x-25x
Name In Silver Foil	
Inserted 1:187	
Production 50 Sets	
Class 3 Cards:	50x-100x
Class 3 Rookies:	25x-50x
Name In Prismatic Gold Foil	
Inserted 1:375	
Production 25 Sets	

Values quoted in this guide reflect the retail price of a card — the price a collector can expect to pay when buying a card from a dealer. The wholesale price — that which a collector can expect to receive from a dealer when selling cards — will be significantly lower, depending on desirability and condition.

1998 Topps Season Opener

Topps Season Opener was a retail exclusive product comprised of 165 cards that paralleled Topps. While Topps cards were printed with a gold border, Season Opener cards used a silver border and a silver "Season Opener '98" stamp on a goal post to distinguish them. Packs contained seven cards and one Season Opener Sweepstakes card, with which collectors could win a trip to the Pro Bowl in Honolulu, Hawaii.

	MT
Complete Set (165):	180.00
Common Player:	.10
Minor Stars:	.20
Common Rookie:	2.50
Wax Box:	150.00
1 *Peyton Manning*	50.00
2 *Jerome Pathon*	5.00
3 *Duane Starks*	2.50
4 *Brian Simmons*	2.50
5 *Keith Brooking*	2.50
6 *Robert Edwards*	5.00
7 *Curtis Enis*	10.00
8 *John Avery*	5.00
9 *Fred Taylor*	30.00
10 *Germane Crowell*	10.00
11 *Hines Ward*	6.00
12 *Marcus Nash*	5.00
13 *Jacquez Green*	8.00
14 *Joe Jurevicius*	2.50
15 *Greg Ellis*	2.50
16 *Brian Griese*	25.00
17 *Tavian Banks*	5.00
18 *Robert Holcombe*	5.00
19 *Skip Hicks*	6.00
20 *Ahman Green*	5.00
21 *Takeo Spikes*	2.50
22 *Randy Moss*	60.00
23 *Andre Wadsworth*	5.00
24 *Jason Peter*	2.50
25 *Grant Wistrom*	2.50
26 *Charles Woodson*	10.00
27 *Kevin Dyson*	10.00
28 *Patrick Johnson*	5.00
29 *Tim Dwight*	10.00
30 *Ryan Leaf*	8.00
31 Chad Brown	.10
32 Levon Kirkland	.10
33 Corey Dillon	.50
34 Curtis Conway	.20
35 Chris Chandler	.10
36 Warrick Dunn	.75
37 Danny Kanell	.10
38 Emmitt Smith	1.50
39 Steve Young	.75
40 Kimble Anders	.10
41 Freddie Jones	.10
42 Bobby Engram	.10
43 Aeneas Williams	.10
44 Antowain Smith	.40
45 Reggie White	.20
46 Rae Carruth	.10
47 Jamie Asher	.10
48 Hardy Nickerson	.10
49 Jerome Bettis	.20
50 Michael Strahan	.10
51 John Randle	.10
52 Larry Centers	.10
53 Tim Brown	.20
54 Terry Glenn	.20
55 Keenan McCardell	.10
56 Troy Aikman	1.00
57 Peter Boulware	.10
58 Erik Kramer	.10
59 Andre Rison	.10
60 Jeff George	.20
61 Robert Brooks	.10
62 Simeon Rice	.10
63 Mark Brunell	1.00
64 Jeff Blake	.20
65 Brett Favre	2.00
66 Lawrence Phillips	.10
67 Randal Hill	.10
68 Terance Mathis	.10
69 Bruce Smith	.10
70 Troy Drayton	.10
71 Derrick Thomas	.10
72 Charles Way	.10
73 Bobby Hoying	.10

74	Michael Jackson	.10
75	Chris Sanders	.10
76	Cris Dishman	.10
77	Jake Plummer	1.00
78	Kordell Stewart	.75
79	Carl Pickens	.20
80	Ed McCaffrey	.30
81	Ray Buchanan	.10
82	Thurman Thomas	.20
83	Andre Reed	.10
84	Wesley Walls	.10
85	Rob Moore	.20
86	Eddie George	.75
87	Michael Irvin	.20
88	Johnnie Morton	.20
89	Cris Carter	.30
90	Garrison Hearst	.20
91	Rod Smith	.20
92	Ben Coates	.10
93	Zach Thomas	.20
94	Dale Carter	.10
95	Mark Chmura	.20
96	Elvis Grbac	.10
97	Ray Lewis	.10
98	Lonnie Johnson	.10
99	Darrell Green	.10
100	Marvin Harrison	.20
101	Dorsey Levens	.20
102	Tony Gonzalez	.20
103	Andre Hastings	.10
104	Jason Sehorn	.10
105	Drew Bledsoe	1.00
106	Junior Seau	.20
107	Robert Smith	.20
108	Terrell Davis	1.50
109	Neil Smith	.10
110	Jermaine Lewis	.10
111	Warren Moon	.20
112	Brad Johnson	.20
113	Karim Abdul-Jabbar	.20
114	Terry Allen	.20
115	Chris Slade	.10
116	Michael Westbrook	.10
117	Tony Banks	.20
118	Mike Alstott	.20
119	Jake Reed	.10
120	Bryant Westbrook	.10
121	Steve McNair	.75
122	Jimmy Smith	.20
123	Reidel Anthony	.10
124	Jessie Armstead	.10
125	O.J. McDuffie	.10
126	Jerry Rice	1.00
127	Frank Sanders	.10
128	Fred Lane	.20
129	Scott Mitchell	.10
130	Rickey Dudley	.10
131	Isaac Bruce	.20
132	Tony Martin	.10
133	Leslie Shepherd	.10
134	Derrick Thomas	.10
135	Antonio Freeman	.20
136	Dan Marino	1.50
137	Eric Green	.10
138	Darnay Scott	.10
139	Herman Moore	.20
140	Terrell Owens	.30
141	Trent Dilfer	.20
142	Marshall Faulk	.20
143	John Elway	1.00
144	Gus Frerotte	.10
145	Napoleon Kaufman	.40
146	Charlie Garner	.10
147	Irving Fryar	.10
148	Shannon Sharpe	.20
149	Jamal Anderson	.30
150	Chris Spielman	.10
151	Deion Sanders	.40
152	Joey Galloway	.20
153	J.J. Stokes	.10
154	Quinn Early	.10
155	Michael McCrary	.10
156	Willie McGinest	.10
157	Kevin Hardy	.10
158	Michael Barrow	.10
159	John Mobley	.10
160	Michael Sinclair	.10
161	Warren Sapp	.10
162	Michael Bates	.10
163	Pete Mitchell	.10
164	Barry Sanders	2.00
165	Checklist	.10

1998 Topps Stars

Each borderless card is printed on 20-point stock and uses luminous diffraction technology with matte gold-foil stamping.

Every card in this product is sequentially numbered. The Red and Bronze set are both considered base sets and are each numbered to 8,799. Three parallel sets include Silver, Gold and Gold Rainbow. The Silver singles were numbered to 3,999, the Gold cards are to 1,999 and inserted 1:2 packs, and the Gold Rainbow cards were numbered to 99 and found 1:41 packs.

	MT
Complete Set (150):	125.00
Common Red Player:	.20
Minor Red Stars:	.40
Common Red Rookie:	1.00
Production 8,799 Sets	
Bronze Cards:	1x
Production 8,799 Sets	
Silver Cards:	1.5x
Production 3,999 Sets	
Gold Cards:	3x
Gold Rookies:	2x
Production 1,999 Sets	
Inserted 1:2	
Gold Rainbow Cards:	15x-30x
Gold Rainbow Rookies:	5x-10x
Production 99 Sets	
Inserted 1:41	
Wax Box:	90.00
1 John Elway	2.50
2 *Duane Starks*	2.00
3 Bruce Smith	.20
4 Jeff Blake	.40
5 Carl Pickens	.40
6 Shannon Sharpe	.40
7 *Jerome Pathon*	3.00
8 Jimmy Smith	.40
9 Elvis Grbac	.20
10 Mark Brunell	2.00
11 Karim Abdul-Jabbar	.75
12 Terry Glenn	.75
13 Larry Centers	.20
14 Jeff George	.40
15 Terry Allen	.20
16 Charles Johnson	.20
17 Chris Spielman	.20
18 *Ahman Green*	4.00
19 *Kevin Dyson*	4.00
20 Dan Marino	4.00
21 *Andre Wadsworth*	2.00
22 Chris Chandler	.40
23 Kerry Collins	.40
24 Erik Kramer	.20
25 Warrick Dunn	2.00
26 Michael Irvin	.40
27 Herman Moore	.40
28 Dorsey Levens	.40
29 Cris Carter	.40
30 Drew Bledsoe	2.00
31 Kevin Greene	.20
32 Charles Way	.20
33 Bobby Hoying	.20
34 Tony Banks	.40
35 Steve Young	1.50
36 Trent Dilfer	.40
37 Warren Sapp	.20
38 Skip Hicks	2.50
39 Michael Jackson	.20
40 Curtis Martin	1.00
41 Thurman Thomas	.40
42 Corey Dillon	1.50
43 *Brian Griese*	8.00
44 Marshall Faulk	.75
45 Isaac Bruce	.40
46 *Fred Taylor*	12.00
47 Andre Rison	.20
48 O.J. McDuffie	.20
49 *John Avery*	3.00
50 Terrell Davis	4.00
51 *Robert Edwards*	6.00
52 Keyshawn Johnson	.40
53 Rickey Dudley	.20
54 *Hines Ward*	2.50
55 Irving Fryar	.20
56 Freddie Jones	.20
57 Michael Sinclair	.20
58 Darnay Scott	.20
59 *Tim Dwight*	2.50
60 Tim Brown	.40
61 Ray Lewis	.20
62 Curtis Enis	5.00
63 Emmitt Smith	4.00
64 Scott Mitchell	.20
65 Antonio Freeman	.75
66 Randy Moss	20.00
67 *Peyton Manning*	15.00
68 Danny Kanell	.20
69 Charlie Garner	.20
70 Mike Alstott	.75
71 *Grant Wistrom*	1.00
72 *Jacquez Green*	3.50
73 Gus Frerotte	.20
74 Peter Boulware	.20
75 Jerry Rice	2.50
76 Antowain Smith	1.00
77 *Brian Simmons*	1.00
78 Rod Smith	.40
79 Marvin Harrison	.40
80 *Ryan Leaf*	7.00
81 Keenan McCardell	.20
82 Derrick Thomas	.20
83 Zach Thomas	.40
84 Ben Coates	.20
85 Rob Moore	.40
86 Wayne Chrebet	.20
87 Napoleon Kaufman	.75
88 Levon Kirkland	.20
89 Junior Seau	.40
90 Eddie George	2.00
91 Warren Moon	.40
92 *Anthony Simmons*	1.00
93 Steve McNair	1.25
94 Frank Sanders	.20
95 Joey Galloway	.75
96 Jamal Anderson	.75
97 Rae Carruth	.20
98 Curtis Conway	.40
99 *Greg Ellis*	1.00
100 Kordell Stewart	2.00
101 *Germane Crowell*	3.50
102 Mark Chmura	.40
103 Robert Smith	.40
104 Andre Hastings	.40
105 Reggie White	.40
106 Jessie Armstead	.20
107 Kevin Hardy	.20
108 *Robert Holcombe*	3.50
109 Garrison Hearst	.40
110 Jerome Bettis	.40
111 Reidel Anthony	.40
112 Michael Westbrook	.40
113 *Patrick Johnson*	1.00
114 Andre Reed	.20
115 *Charles Woodson*	5.00
116 *Takeo Spikes*	2.00
117 *Marcus Nash*	3.00
118 *Tavian Banks*	3.00
119 Tony Gonzalez	.20
120 Jake Plummer	2.00
121 *Tony Simmons*	2.50
122 Aaron Glenn	.20
123 Ricky Watters	.40
124 Kimble Anders	.20
125 Barry Sanders	5.00
126 Terance Mathis	.20
127 Wesley Walls	.20
128 Bobby Engram	.20
129 Johnnie Morton	.20
130 Brett Favre	5.00
131 Brad Johnson	.40
132 John Randle	.20
133 Chris Sanders	.20
134 *Joe Jurevicius*	2.00
135 Deion Sanders	.40
136 Terrell Owens	1.00
137 Darrell Green	.20
138 Jermaine Lewis	.20
139 James Stewart	.20
140 Troy Aikman	2.50
141 Hardy Nickerson	.20
142 Blaine Bishop	.20
143 *Keith Brooking*	2.00
144 *Jason Peter*	1.00
145 Jake Reed	.20
146 Jason Sehorn	.20
147 Robert Brooks	.20
148 J.J. Stokes	.40
149 Michael Strahan	.20
150 Glenn Foley	.40

1998 Topps Stars Galaxy

Each single in this set has the bronze foil, was sequentially numbered to 100 and inserted 1:611 packs. Silver foil cards were numbered to 75 and found 1:814 packs. Gold foil cards were numbered to 50 and inserted 1:1,222. Gold Rainbow singles were the toughest to find with only five printed and inserted 1:12,215.

	MT
Complete Set (10):	750.00
Common Bronze Player:	25.00
Production 100 Sets	
Inserted 1:611	
Silver Cards:	1.5x
Production 75 Sets	
Inserted 1:814	
Gold Cards:	2x
Production 50 Sets	
Inserted 1:1,222	
G1 Brett Favre	200.00
G2 Barry Sanders	200.00
G3 Bruce Smith	25.00
G4 Herman Moore	50.00
G5 Tim Brown	50.00
G6 Steve Young	75.00
G7 Cris Carter	50.00
G8 John Elway	100.00

G9	Mark Brunell	100.00
G10	Terrell Davis	150.00

1998 Topps Stars Luminaries

Each card in this set has bronze foil stamping and is sequentially numbered to 100. Singles were tough to pull from packs at 1:407. The Silver parallel set has the foil stamping in silver and is numbered to 75 and was inserted 1:543 packs. The Gold parallel was numbered to 50 and inserted 1:814 packs. The last parallel set was the Gold Rainbow that was limited to five of each and found 1:8,144.

	MT
Complete Set (15):	850.00
Common Bronze Player:	25.00
Production 100 Sets	
Inserted 1:407	
Silver Cards:	1.5x
Production 75 Sets	
Inserted 1:543	
Gold Cards:	2x
Production 50 Sets	
Inserted 1:814	
L1 Brett Favre	120.00
L2 Steve Young	45.00
L3 John Elway	100.00
L4 Barry Sanders	120.00
L5 Terrell Davis	100.00
L6 Eddie George	50.00
L7 Herman Moore	25.00
L8 Tim Brown	25.00
L9 Jerry Rice	60.00
L10 Junior Seau	25.00
L11 Bruce Smith	25.00
L12 John Randle	25.00
L13 Peyton Manning	100.00
L14 Ryan Leaf	50.00
L15 Curtis Enis	35.00

1998 Topps Stars Rookie Reprints

Topps reprinted eight NFL Hall of Famers' rookie cards and inserted them 1:24 packs. Each card also has a parallel Autograph version with the odds at 1:153 packs.

	MT
Complete Set (8):	30.00
Common Player:	2.00
Inserted 1:24	
Autographs:	10x
Inserted 1:153	
1 Walter Payton	10.00
2 Don Maynard	4.00
3 Charlie Joiner	4.00
4 Fred Biletnikoff	4.00
5 Paul Hornung	4.00
6 Gale Sayers	6.00
7 John Hannah	2.00
8 Paul Warfield	4.00

1998 Topps Stars Supernova

Each single in this set has the bronze foil, was sequentially

numbered to 100 and inserted 1:611 packs. Silver foil cards were numbered to 75 and found 1:814 packs. Gold foil cards were numbered to 50 and inserted 1:1,222. Gold Rainbow singles were the toughest to find with only five printed and inserted 1:12,215.

	MT
Complete Set (10):	750.00
Common Bronze Player:	25.00
Production 100 Sets	
Inserted 1:611	
Silver Cards:	1.5x
Production 75 Sets	
Inserted 1:814	
Gold Cards:	2x
Production 50 Sets	
Inserted 1:1,222	
S1 Ryan Leaf	50.00
S2 Curtis Enis	60.00
S3 Kevin Dyson	45.00
S4 Randy Moss	200.00
S5 Peyton Manning	100.00
S6 Duane Starks	25.00
S7 Grant Wistrom	25.00
S8 Charles Woodson	60.00
S9 Fred Taylor	100.00
S10 Andre Wadsworth	45.00

1999 Topps

Each card in this 357-card set was printed on 16-pt. stock, with green borders and gold foil stamping. Included are 27 rookies that were seeded 1:5 packs. Other subsets include 10 Season Highlights and five Cleveland Browns Expansion Draft cards. Top inserts include: MVP Promotion, All Matrix, Autographs, Hall of Fame Autographs, Mystery Chrome, Picture Perfect, Record Numbers and Season's Best.

	MT
Complete Set (357):	75.00
Common Player:	.10
Minor Stars:	.20
Common Rookie:	1.00
Inserted 1:5	
Wax Box:	50.00
1 Terrell Davis	1.50
2 Adrian Murrell	.10
3 Ernie Mills	.10
4 Jimmy Hitchcock	.10
5 Charlie Garner	.10
6 Blaine Bishop	.10
7 Junior Seau	.20
8 Andre Rison	.10
9 Jake Reed	.10
10 Cris Carter	.40
11 Torrance Small	.10
12 Ronald McKinnon	.10
13 Tyrone Davis	.10
14 Warren Moon	.20
15 Joe Johnson	.10
16 Bert Emanuel	.10
17 Brad Culpepper	.10
18 Henry Jones	.10
19 Jonathan Ogden	.10
20 Terrell Owens	.40
21 Derrick Mason	.10
22 Jon Ritchie	.10
23 Eric Metcalf	.10
24 Kevin Carter	.10
25 Fred Taylor	1.00
26 DeWayne Washington	.10
27 William Thomas	.10
28 Raghib Ismail	.10
29 Jason Taylor	.10
30 Doug Flutie	.50
31 Michael Sinclair	.10
32 Yancey Thigpen	.10
33 Darnay Scott	.10
34 Amani Toomer	.10
35 Edgar Bennett	.10
36 LeRoy Butler	.10
37 Jessie Tuggle	.10
38 Andrew Glover	.10
39 Tim McDonald	.10
40 Marshall Faulk	.40

No.	Player	Price
41	Ray Mickens	.10
42	Kimble Anders	.10
43	Trent Green	.40
44	Dermontti Dawson	.10
45	Greg Ellis	.10
46	Hugh Douglas	.10
47	Amp Lee	.10
48	Lamar Thomas	.10
49	Curtis Conway	.20
50	Emmitt Smith	1.50
51	Elvis Grbac	.10
52	Tony Simmons	.20
53	Darrin Smith	.10
54	Donovin Darius	.10
55	Corey Chavous	.10
56	Phillippi Sparks	.10
57	Luther Elliss	.10
58	Tim Dwight	.40
59	Andre Hastings	.10
60	Dan Marino	1.50
61	Micheal Barrow	.10
62	Corey Fuller	.10
63	Bill Romanowski	.10
64	Derrick Rodgers	.10
65	Natrone Means	.30
66	Peter Boulware	.10
67	Brian Mitchell	.10
68	Cornelius Bennett	.10
69	Dedric Ward	.10
70	Drew Bledsoe	.75
71	Freddie Jones	.10
72	Derrick Thomas	.10
73	Willie Davis	.10
74	Larry Centers	.10
75	Mark Brunell	.75
76	Chuck Smith	.10
77	Desmond Howard	.10
78	Sedrick Shaw	.10
79	Tiki Barber	.10
80	Curtis Martin	.40
81	Barry Minter	.10
82	Skip Hicks	.20
83	O.J. Santiago	.10
84	Ed McCaffrey	.30
85	Terrell Buckley	.10
86	Charlie Jones	.10
87	Pete Mitchell	.10
88	La'Roi Glover	.10
89	Eric Davis	.10
90	John Elway	1.50
91	Kavika Pittman	.10
92	Fred Lane	.10
93	Warren Sapp	.10
94	Lorenzo Bromell	.10
95	Lawyer Milloy	.10
96	Aeneas Williams	.10
97	Michael McCrary	.10
98	Rickey Dudley	.10
99	Bryce Paup	.10
100	Jamal Anderson	.50
101	D'Marco Farr	.10
102	Johnnie Morton	.10
103	Jeff Graham	.10
104	Sam Cowart	.10
105	Bryant Young	.10
106	Jermaine Lewis	.10
107	Chad Bratzke	.10
108	Jeff Burris	.10
109	Roell Preston	.10
110	Vinny Testaverde	.20
111	Ruben Brown	.10
112	Darryll Lewis	.10
113	Billy Davis	.10
114	Bryant Westbrook	.10
115	Stephen Alexander	.10
116	Terrell Fletcher	.10
117	Terry Glenn	.30
118	Rod Smith	.20
119	Carl Pickens	.20
120	Tim Brown	.20
121	Mikhael Ricks	.10
122	Jason Gildon	.10
123	Charles Way	.10
124	Rob Moore	.20
125	Jerome Bettis	.30
126	Kerry Collins	.20
127	Bruce Smith	.10
128	James Hasty	.10
129	Ken Norton Jr.	.10
130	Charles Woodson	.40
131	Tony McGee	.10
132	Kevin Turner	.10
133	Jerome Pathon	.10
134	Garrison Hearst	.30
135	Craig Newsome	.10
136	Hardy Nickerson	.10
137	Ray Lewis	.10
138	Derrick Alexander	.10
139	Phil Hansen	.10
140	Joey Galloway	.50
141	Oronde Gadsden	.20
142	Herman Moore	.30
143	Bobby Taylor	.10
144	Mario Bates	.10
145	Kevin Dyson	.20
146	Aaron Glenn	.10
147	Ed McDaniel	.10
148	Terry Allen	.20
149	Ike Hilliard	.10
150	Steve Young	.50
151	Eugene Robinson	.10
152	John Mobley	.10
153	Kevin Hardy	.10
154	Lance Johnstone	.10
155	Willie McGinest	.10
156	Gary Anderson	.10
157	Dexter Coakley	.10
158	Mark Fields	.10
159	Steve McNair	.50
160	Corey Dillon	.50
161	Zach Thomas	.30
162	Kent Graham	.10
163	Tony Parrish	.10
164	Sam Gash	.10
165	Kyle Brady	.10
166	Donnell Bennett	.10
167	Tony Martin	.10
168	Michael Bates	.10
169	Bobby Engram	.10
170	Jimmy Smith	.20
171	Vonnie Holliday	.10
172	Simeon Rice	.10
173	Kevin Greene	.10
174	Mike Alstott	.40
175	Eddie George	.50
176	Michael Jackson	.10
177	Neil O'Donnell	.10
178	Sean Dawkins	.10
179	Courtney Hawkins	.10
180	Michael Irvin	.20
181	Thurman Thomas	.20
182	Cameron Cleeland	.20
183	Ellis Johnson	.10
184	Will Blackwell	.10
185	Ty Law	.10
186	Merton Hanks	.10
187	Dan Wilkinson	.10
188	Andre Wadsworth	.20
189	Troy Vincent	.10
190	Frank Sanders	.10
191	Stephen Boyd	.10
192	Jason Elam	.10
193	Kordell Stewart	.50
194	Ted Johnson	.10
195	Glyn Milburn	.10
196	Gary Brown	.10
197	Travis Hall	.10
198	John Randle	.10
199	Jay Riemersma	.10
200	Barry Sanders	2.00
201	Chris Spielman	.10
202	Rod Woodson	.10
203	Darrell Russell	.10
204	Tony Boselli	.10
205	Darren Woodson	.10
206	Muhsin Muhammad	.10
207	Jim Harbaugh	.20
208	Isaac Bruce	.30
209	Mo Lewis	.10
210	Dorsey Levens	.30
211	Frank Wycheck	.10
212	Napoleon Kaufman	.40
213	Walt Harris	.10
214	Leon Lett	.10
215	Karim Abdul	.20
216	Carnell Lake	.10
217	Byron Morris	.10
218	John Avery	.20
219	Chris Slade	.10
220	Robert Smith	.20
221	Mike Pritchard	.10
222	Ty Detmer	.10
223	Randall Cunningham	.40
224	Alonzo Mayes	.10
225	Jake Plummer	1.00
226	Derrick Mayes	.10
227	Jeff Brady	.10
228	John Lynch	.10
229	Steve Atwater	.10
230	Warrick Dunn	.50
231	Shawn Jefferson	.10
232	Erik Kramer	.10
233	Ken Dilger	.10
234	Ryan Leaf	.40
235	Ray Buchanan	.10
236	Kevin Williams	.10
237	Ricky Watters	.20
238	Dwayne Rudd	.10
239	Duce Staley	.20
240	Charlie Batch	.50
241	Tim Biakabutuka	.20
242	Tony Gonzalez	.20
243	Bryan Still	.10
244	Donnie Edwards	.10
245	Troy Aikman	1.00
246	Az-Zahir Hakim	.20
247	Curtis Enis	.40
248	Chris Chandler	.20
249	James Jett	.10
250	Brett Favre	2.00
251	Keith Poole	.10
252	Ricky Proel	.10
253	Shannon Sharpe	.20
254	Robert Jones	.10
255	Chad Brown	.10
256	Ben Coates	.20
257	Jacquez Green	.10
258	Jessie Armstead	.10
259	Dale Carter	.10
260	Antowain Smith	.40
261	Mark Chmura	.20
262	Michael Westbrook	.20
263	Marvin Harrison	.20
264	Darrien Gordon	.10
265	Rodney Harrison	.10
266	Charles Johnson	.10
267	Roman Phifer	.10
268	Reidel Anthony	.20
269	Jerry Rice	1.00
270	Eric Moulds	.50
271	Robert Porcher	.10
272	Deion Sanders	.40
273	Germane Crowell	.20
274	Randy Moss	2.00
275	Antonio Freeman	.40
276	Trent Dilfer	.30
277	Eric Turner	.10
278	Jeff George	.20
279	Levon Kirkland	.10
280	O.J. McDuffie	.10
281	Takeo Spikes	.10
282	Jim Flanigan	.10
283	Chris Warren	.10
284	J.J. Stokes	.20
285	Bryan Cox	.10
286	Sam Madison	.10
287	Priest Holmes	.40
288	Keenan McCardell	.10
289	Michael Strahan	.10
290	Robert Edwards	.30
291	Tommy Vardell	.10
292	Wayne Chrebet	.40
293	Chris Calloway	.10
294	Wesley Walls	.10
295	Derrick Brooks	.10
296	Trace Armstrong	.10
297	Brian Simmons	.10
298	Darrell Green	.10
299	Robert Brooks	.10
300	Peyton Manning	1.50
301	Dana Stubblefield	.10
302	Shawn Springs	.10
303	Leslie Shepherd	.10
304	Ken Harvey	.10
305	Jon Kitna	.50
306	Terance Mathis	.10
307	Andre Reed	.20
308	Jackie Harris	.10
309	Rich Gannon	.10
310	Keyshawn Johnson	.50
311	Victor Green	.10
312	Eric Allen	.10
313	Terry Fair	.10
314	Season Highlights (Jason Elam)	.10
315	Season Highlights (Garrison Hearst)	.10
316	Season Highlights (Jake Plummer)	.50
317	Season Highlights (Randall Cunningham)	.20
318	Season Highlights (Randy Moss)	1.00
319	Season Highlights (Jamal Anderson)	.20
320	Season Highlights (John Elway)	.75
321	Season Highlights (Doug Flutie)	.20
322	Season Highlights (Emmitt Smith)	.50
323	Season Highlights (Terrell Davis)	.75
324	Jerris McPhail	.10
325	Damon Gibson	.10
326	Jim Pyne	.10
327	Antonio Langham	.10
328	Freddie Solomon	.10
329	Ricky Williams	15.00
330	Daunte Culpepper	8.00
331	Chris Claiborne	1.75
332	Amos Zereoue	3.00
333	Chris McAlister	1.00
334	Kevin Faulk	4.00
335	James Johnson	2.50
336	Mike Cloud	1.75
337	Jevon Kearse	4.00
338	Akili Smith	8.00
339	Edgerrin James	15.00
340	Cecil Collins	8.00
341	Donovan McNabb	8.00
342	Kevin Johnson	5.00
343	Torry Holt	5.00
344	Rob Konrad	1.00
345	Tim Couch	15.00
346	David Boston	5.00
347	Karsten Bailey	1.75
348	Troy Edwards	5.00
349	Sedrick Irvin	1.75
350	Shaun King	6.00
351	Peerless Price	3.00
352	Brock Huard	2.50
353	Cade McNown	8.00
354	Champ Bailey	2.50
355	D'Wayne Bates	1.00
356	Checklist	.10
357	Checklist	.10

1999 Topps All Matrix

This 30-card insert is divided into three different subsets.

1200 Yard Club (10 running backs who rushed for 1200 yards or more), 3000 Yard Club (quarterbacks with rocket-arms) and '99 Rookie Rush (9 players from the 1999 NFL draft). Each is printed on dot matrix cards and were inserted 1:14 packs.

		MT
Complete Set (30):		120.00
Common Player:		1.00
Minor Stars:		2.00
Inserted 1:14		
1	1200 Yard Club (Fred Taylor)	6.00
2	1200 Yard Club (Ricky Watters)	2.00
3	1200 Yard Club (Curtis Martin)	3.00
4	1200 Yard Club (Eddie George)	4.00
5	1200 Yard Club (Marshall Faulk)	2.00
6	1200 Yard Club (Emmitt Smith)	8.00
7	1200 Yard Club (Barry Sanders)	12.00
8	1200 Yard Club (Garrison Hearst)	2.00
9	1200 Yard Club (Jamal Anderson)	2.00
10	1200 Yard Club (Terrell Davis)	10.00
11	3000 Yard Club (Chris Chandler)	1.00
12	3000 Yard Club (Steve McNair)	3.00
13	3000 Yard Club (Vinny Testaverde)	1.00
14	3000 Yard Club (Trent Green)	2.00
15	3000 Yard Club (Dan Marino)	8.00
16	3000 Yard Club (Drew Bledsoe)	5.00
17	3000 Yard Club (Randall Cunningham)	2.00
18	3000 Yard Club (Jake Plummer)	6.00
19	3000 Yard Club (Peyton Manning)	10.00
20	3000 Yard Club (Steve Young)	4.00
21	3000 Yard Club (Brett Favre)	12.00
22	99 Rookie Rush (Tim Couch)	15.00
23	99 Rookie Rush (Edgerrin James)	8.00
24	99 Rookie Rush (David Boston)	4.00
25	99 Rookie Rush (Akili Smith)	5.00
26	99 Rookie Rush (Troy Edwards)	2.00
27	99 Rookie Rush (Torry Holt)	3.00
28	99 Rookie Rush (Donovan McNabb)	5.00
29	99 Rookie Rush (Daunte Culpepper)	6.00
30	99 Rookie Rush (Ricky Williams)	15.00

1999 Topps Autographs

This 10-card set was a hobby exclusive that included 8 current stars and 2 top draft picks. Singles were found 1:509 packs except for the Ricky Williams single which was harder to find at 1:18,372.

		MT
Complete Set (10):		900.00
Common Player:		25.00
Inserted 1:509		
#A5 Inserted 1:18,372		
1	Randy Moss	200.00
2	Wayne Chrebet	35.00
3	Tim Couch	150.00
4	Joey Galloway	35.00
5	Ricky Williams	425.00
6	Doug Flutie	50.00
7	Terrell Owens	50.00
8	Marshall Faulk	35.00
9	Rod Smith	25.00
10	Dan Marino	150.00

1999 Topps Hall of Fame Autographs

The five inductees into the Hall of Fame for 1999 are included in this autographed set. Singles were inserted 1:1,832 packs.

		MT
Complete Set (5):		185.00
Common Player:		25.00
Inserted 1:1,832		
1	Eric Dickerson	50.00
2	Billy Shaw	25.00
3	Lawrence Taylor	80.00
4	Tom Mack	25.00
5	Ozzie Newsome	40.00

1999 Topps Mystery Chrome

Each card in this 20-card set is printed on chrome technology and inserted 1:36 packs. A parallel Refractor version was also made and inserted 1:144 packs.

		MT
Complete Set (20):		135.00
Common Player:		3.00
Inserted 1:36		
Mystery Chrome Refractor:		3x
Inserted 1:144		
1	Terrell Davis	15.00
2	Steve Young	6.00
3	Fred Taylor	10.00
4	Chris Claiborne	3.00
5	Terrell Davis	15.00
6	Randall Cunningham	5.00
7	Charlie Batch	7.00
8	Fred Taylor	10.00
9	Vinny Testaverde	3.00
10	Jamal Anderson	3.00
11	Randy Moss	20.00
12	Keyshawn Johnson	5.00
13	Vinny Testaverde	3.00
14	Chris Chandler	3.00
15	Fred Taylor	10.00
16	Ricky Williams	25.00
17	Chris Chandler	3.00
18	John Elway	15.00
19	Randy Moss	20.00
20	Troy Edwards	6.00

1999 Topps Picture Perfect

Each card in this 10-card set has an intentional error for collectors to find. A hint is printed on the back of each card and singles were inserted 1:14 packs.

		MT
Complete Set (10):		25.00
Common Player:		1.00
Inserted 1:14		
1	Steve Young	1.00
2	Brett Favre	6.00
3	Terrell Davis	4.00
4	Peyton Manning	4.00
5	Jake Plummer	3.00
6	Fred Taylor	3.00
7	Barry Sanders	6.00
8	Dan Marino	4.00
9	John Elway	4.00
10	Randy Moss	6.00

A card number in parentheses ( ) indicates the set is unnumbered.

1999 Topps Record Numbers

This set features 10 NFL Record Holders on a white stock card with silver foil. Singles were inserted 1:18 packs.

		MT
Complete Set (10):		35.00
Common Player:		1.00
Inserted 1:18		
1	Randy Moss	7.00
2	Terrell Davis	5.00
3	Emmitt Smith	5.00
4	Barry Sanders	7.00
5	Dan Marino	5.00
6	Brett Favre	7.00
7	Doug Flutie	2.00
8	Jerry Rice	3.50
9	Peyton Manning	4.00
10	Jason Elam	1.00

1999 Topps Season's Best

Thirty dominate players show their mettle in six categories printed on metallic foilboard. The following categories are: Bull Rushers (Running Backs), Rocket Launchers (Quarterbacks), Deep Threats (Wide Receivers), Power Packed (Defensive stars), Strike Force (Special Teams) and Career Best (top players). Singles were found 1:18 packs.

		MT
Complete Set (30):		100.00
Common Player:		1.00
Minor Stars:		2.00
Inserted 1:18		
1	Bull Rushers (Terrell Davis)	12.00
2	Bull Rushers (Jamal Anderson)	2.00
3	Bull Rushers (Garrison Hearst)	2.00
4	Bull Rushers (Barry Sanders)	15.00
5	Bull Rushers (Emmitt Smith)	10.00
6	Rocket Launchers (Randall Cunningham)	2.00
7	Rocket Launchers (Brett Favre)	15.00
8	Rocket Launchers (Steve Young)	5.00
9	Rocket Launchers (Jake Plummer)	8.00
10	Rocket Launchers (Peyton Manning)	12.00
11	Deep Threats (Antonio Freeman)	2.00
12	Deep Threats (Eric Moulds)	2.00
13	Deep Threats (Randy Moss)	15.00
14	Deep Threats (Rod Smith)	1.00
15	Deep Threats (Jimmy Smith)	1.00
16	Power Packed (Michael Sinclair)	1.00

17	Power Packed (Kevin Greene)	1.00
18	Power Packed (Michael Strahan)	1.00
19	Power Packed (Michael McCrary)	1.00
20	Power Packed (Hugh Douglas)	1.00
21	Strike Force (Deion Sanders)	3.00
22	Strike Force (Terry Fair)	1.00
23	Strike Force (Jacquez Green)	2.00
24	Strike Force (Corey Harris)	1.00
25	Strike Force (Tim Dwight)	3.00
26	Career Best (Dan Marino)	10.00
27	Career Best (Barry Sanders)	15.00
28	Career Best (Jerry Rice)	8.00
29	Career Best (Bruce Smith)	1.00
30	Career Best (Darrien Gordon)	1.00

1999 Topps Chrome

This 165-card set is the same as the regular Topps set except for each card is printed on a chromium card. For the first time in Topps Chrome the rookies were seeded 1:8 packs. Top inserts include: Refractors, All-Etch, Hall of Fame, Record Numbers and Season's Best. Each of the inserts also has a parallel Refractor version.

		MT
Complete Set (165):		700.00
Common Player:		.25
Minor Stars:		.50
Common Rookie:		6.00
Inserted 1:8		
Wax Box:		150.00
1	Randy Moss	5.00
2	Keyshawn Johnson	1.00
3	Priest Holmes	1.25
4	Warren Moon	.50
5	Joey Galloway	1.00
6	Zach Thomas	.50
7	Cameron Cleeland	.50
8	Jim Harbaugh	.50
9	Napoleon Kaufman	1.00
10	Fred Taylor	2.50
11	Mark Brunell	2.00
12	Shannon Sharpe	.50
13	Jacquez Green	.50
14	Adrian Murrell	.50
15	Cris Carter	1.00
16	Marshall Faulk	1.00
17	Drew Bledsoe	2.00
18	Curtis Martin	1.25
19	Johnnie Morton	.25
20	Doug Flutie	1.50
21	Carl Pickens	.50
22	Jerome Bettis	1.00
23	Derrick Alexander	.25
24	Antowain Smith	1.00
25	Barry Sanders	5.00
26	Reidel Anthony	.50
27	Wayne Chrebet	1.00
28	Terance Mathis	.25
29	Shawn Springs	.25
30	Emmitt Smith	3.50
31	Robert Smith	1.00
32	Charles Johnson	.50
33	Mike Alstott	1.00
34	Ike Hilliard	.25
35	Ricky Watters	.75
36	Charles Woodson	1.00
37	Rod Smith	.50
38	Pete Mitchell	.25
39	Derrick Thomas	.50
40	Dan Marino	3.50
41	Darnay Scott	.50
42	Jake Reed	.50
43	Chris Chandler	.50
44	Dorsey Levens	1.00
45	Kordell Stewart	1.25
46	Eddie George	1.25
47	Corey Dillon	1.00
48	Rich Gannon	.25
49	Chris Spielman	.25
50	Jerry Rice	2.50
51	Trent Dilfer	.75
52	Mark Chmura	.50
53	Jimmy Smith	.50
54	Isaac Bruce	.50
55	Karim Abdul	.75
56	Sedrick Shaw	.25
57	Jake Plummer	2.50
58	Tony Gonzalez	.50
59	Ben Coates	.50
60	John Elway	3.50
61	Bruce Smith	.50
62	Tim Brown	.50
63	Tim Dwight	1.00
64	Yancey Thigpen	.50
65	Terrell Owens	1.00
66	Kyle Brady	.25
67	Tony Martin	.25
68	Michael Strahan	.25
69	Deion Sanders	1.00
70	Steve Young	1.50
71	Dale Carter	.25
72	Ty Law	.25
73	Frank Wycheck	.25
74	Marshall Faulk	1.00
75	Vinny Testaverde	.50
76	Chad Brown	.25
77	Natrone Means	.75
78	Bert Emanuel	.25
79	Kerry Collins	.50
80	Randall Cunningham	1.00
81	Garrison Hearst	1.00
82	Curtis Enis	1.00
83	Steve Atwater	.25
84	Kevin Greene	.25
85	Steve McNair	1.25
86	Andre Reed	.50
87	J.J. Stokes	.50
88	Eric Moulds	1.00
89	Marvin Harrison	.75
90	Troy Aikman	2.50
91	Herman Moore	.75
92	Michael Irvin	.50
93	Frank Sanders	.50
94	Duce Staley	.50
95	James Jett	.25
96	Ricky Proehl	.25
97	Andre Rison	.50
98	Leslie Shepherd	.25
99	Trent Green	.75
100	Terrell Davis	3.50
101	Freddie Jones	.25
102	Skip Hicks	1.00
103	Jeff Graham	.25
104	Rob Moore	.50
105	Torrance Small	.25
106	Antonio Freeman	1.00
107	Robert Brooks	.25
108	Jon Kitna	1.25
109	Curtis Conway	.50
110	Brett Favre	5.00
111	Warrick Dunn	1.25
112	Elvis Grbac	.50
113	Corey Fuller	.25
114	Rickey Dudley	.25
115	Jamal Anderson	1.00
116	Terry Glenn	.75
117	Raghib Ismail	.25
118	John Randle	.25
119	Chris Calloway	.25
120	Peyton Manning	3.50
121	Keenan McCardell	.25
122	O.J. McDuffie	.50
123	Ed McCaffrey	.50
124	Charlie Batch	1.25
125	Jason Elam (Season Highlights)	.25
126	Randy Moss (Season Highlights)	2.50
127	John Elway (Season Highlights)	1.50
128	Emmitt Smith (Season Highlights)	1.50
129	Terrell Davis (Season Highlights)	1.50
130	Jerris McPhail	.25
131	Damon Gibson	.25
132	Jim Pyne	.25
133	Antonio Langham	.25
134	Freddie Solomon	.25
135	*Ricky Williams*	*100.00*
136	*Daunte Culpepper*	*40.00*
137	*Chris Claiborne*	*8.00*
138	*Amos Zereoue*	*20.00*
139	*Chris McAlister*	*6.00*
140	*Kevin Faulk*	*25.00*
141	*James Johnson*	*15.00*
142	*Mike Cloud*	*8.00*
143	*Jevon Kearse*	*25.00*
144	*Akili Smith*	*40.00*
145	*Edgerrin James*	*120.00*
146	*Cecil Collins*	*40.00*
147	*Donovan McNabb*	*40.00*
148	*Kevin Johnson*	*25.00*
149	*Torry Holt*	*25.00*
150	*Rob Konrad*	*8.00*
151	*Tim Couch*	*100.00*
152	*David Boston*	*25.00*
153	*Karsten Bailey*	*8.00*
154	*Troy Edwards*	*25.00*
155	*Sedrick Irvin*	*12.00*
156	*Shaun King*	*30.00*
157	*Peerless Price*	*15.00*
158	*Brock Huard*	*12.00*
159	*Cade McNown*	*40.00*
160	*Champ Bailey*	*15.00*
161	*D'Wayne Bates*	*6.00*
162	*Joe Germaine*	*12.00*
163	*Andy Katzenmoyer*	*8.00*
164	*Antoine Winfield*	*6.00*
165	Checklist	.25

1999 Topps Chrome Refractors

This is a parallel to the base with each single having a mirror shine to them. Singles were inserted 1:12 packs and rookies were found 1:32 packs.

	MT
Complete Set (165):	1800.
Refractor Cards:	6x-12x
Inserted 1:12	
Refractor Rookies:	2x
Inserted 1:32	

1999 Topps Chrome All Etch

This 30-card insert is divided into three tiers with 1,200 Yard Club, 3,000 Yard Club and '99 Rookie Rush. Singles were inserted 1:24 packs and a Refractor version was also produced and found 1:120 packs.

		MT
Complete Set (30):		170.00
Common Player:		3.00
Minor Stars:		6.00
Inserted 1:24		
Refractors:		2x
Inserted 1:120		
1	Fred Taylor (1200 Yard Club)	12.00
2	Ricky Watters (1200 Yard Club)	3.00
3	Curtis Martin (1200 Yard Club)	6.00
4	Eddie George (1200 Yard Club)	6.00
5	Marshall Faulk (1200 Yard Club)	3.00
6	Emmitt Smith (1200 Yard Club)	18.00
7	Barry Sanders (1200 Yard Club)	25.00
8	Garrison Hearst (1200 Yard Club)	3.00
9	Jamal Anderson (1200 Yard Club)	3.00
10	Terrell Davis (1200 Yard Club)	18.00
11	Chris Chandler (3000 Yard Club)	3.00
12	Steve McNair (3000 Yard Club)	6.00
13	Vinny Testaverde (3000 Yard Club)	3.00
14	Trent Green (3000 Yard Club)	3.00
15	Dan Marino (3000 Yard Club)	18.00
16	Drew Bledsoe (3000 Yard Club)	10.00
17	Randall Cunningham (3000 Yard Club)	6.00
18	Jake Plummer (3000 Yard Club)	12.00
19	Peyton Manning (3000 Yard Club)	18.00
20	Steve Young (3000 Yard Club)	8.00
21	Brett Favre (3000 Yard Club)	25.00
22	Tim Couch (99 Rookie Rushers)	30.00
23	Edgerrin James (99 Rookie Rushers)	15.00
24	David Boston (99 Rookie Rushers)	8.00
25	Akili Smith (99 Rookie Rushers)	10.00
26	Troy Edwards (99 Rookie Rushers)	8.00
27	Torry Holt (99 Rookie Rushers)	8.00
28	Donovan McNabb (99 Rookie Rushers)	10.00
29	Daunte Culpepper (99 Rookie Rushers)	10.00
30	Ricky Williams (99 Rookie Rushers)	30.00

1999 Topps Chrome Hall of Fame

This is a 30-card set of players that are gunning for a spot in Canton, Ohio. The set is divided into three categories (Hall Bound, Early Road to the Hall and Hall Hopefuls) each with a different card design. Hall Bound showcases veterans, Early Road to the Hall features young stars and Hall Hopefuls contains '99 draft picks. Singles were found 1:29 packs and Refractors were sequentially numbered to 100.

		MT
Complete Set (30):		200.00
Common Player:		3.00
Minor Stars:		6.00
Inserted 1:29		
Refractors:		4x
Inserted 1:485		
Production 100 Sets		
1	Akili Smith (Hall Hopefuls)	10.00
2	Troy Edwards (Hall Hopefuls)	8.00
3	Donovan McNabb (Hall Hopefuls)	10.00
4	Cade McNown (Hall Hopefuls)	10.00
5	Ricky Williams (Hall Hopefuls)	30.00
6	David Boston (Hall Hopefuls)	8.00
7	Daunte Culpepper (Hall Hopefuls)	10.00
8	Edgerrin James (Hall Hopefuls)	15.00
9	Torry Holt (Hall Hopefuls)	8.00
10	Tim Couch (Hall Hopefuls)	30.00
11	Terrell Davis (Early Road To)	18.00
12	Fred Taylor (Early Road To)	12.00
13	Antonio Freeman (Early Road To)	3.00
14	Jamal Anderson (Early Road To)	3.00
15	Randy Moss (Early Road To)	25.00
16	Joey Galloway (Early Road To)	3.00
17	Eddie George (Early Road To)	3.00
18	Jake Plummer (Early Road To)	12.00
19	Curtis Martin (Early Road To)	3.00
20	Peyton Manning (Early Road To)	18.00
21	Barry Sanders (Hall Bound)	25.00
22	Steve Young (Hall Bound)	8.00
23	Cris Carter (Hall Bound)	3.00
24	Emmitt Smith (Hall Bound)	18.00
25	John Elway (Hall Bound)	18.00
26	Drew Bledsoe (Hall Bound)	10.00
27	Troy Aikman (Hall Bound)	12.00
28	Brett Favre (Hall Bound)	25.00
29	Jerry Rice (Hall Bound)	12.00
30	Dan Marino (Hall Bound)	18.00

1999 Topps Chrome Record Numbers

This was a 10-card insert set that included the top players in the game. Singles were inserted 1:72 packs. A parallel Refractor version was also released and found 1:360 packs.

		MT
Complete Set (10):		120.00
Common Player:		4.00
Inserted 1:72		
Refractors:		2x
Inserted 1:360		
1	Randy Moss	25.00
2	Terrell Davis	18.00
3	Emmitt Smith	18.00
4	Barry Sanders	25.00
5	Dan Marino	18.00
6	Brett Favre	25.00
7	Doug Flutie	8.00
8	Jerry Rice	12.00
9	Peyton Manning	15.00
10	Jason Elam	4.00

1999 Topps Chrome Season's Best

The 30-card set is divided into six categories. Bull Rushers, Rocket Launchers, Deep Threats, Power Packed, Strike Force and Career Best. Each has a different design and was inserted 1:24 packs. A Refractor version was also produced and inserted 1:120 packs.

		MT
Complete Set (30):		125.00
Common Player:		3.00
Minor Stars:		6.00
Inserted 1:24		
Refractors:		2x
Inserted 1:120		
1	Terrell Davis (Bull Rushers)	18.00
2	Jamal Anderson (Bull Rushers)	6.00
3	Garrison Hearst (Bull Rushers)	6.00
4	Barry Sanders (Bull Rushers)	25.00
5	Emmitt Smith (Bull Rushers)	18.00
6	Randall Cunningham (Rocket Launchers)	6.00
7	Brett Favre (Rocket Launchers)	25.00
8	Steve Young (Rocket Launchers)	8.00
9	Jake Plummer (Rocket Launchers)	12.00
10	Peyton Manning (Rocket Launchers)	18.00
11	Antonio Freeman (Deep Threats)	6.00
12	Eric Moulds (Deep Threats)	6.00
13	Randy Moss (Deep Threats)	25.00
14	Rod Smith (Deep Threats)	3.00
15	Jimmy Smith (Deep Threats)	3.00
16	Michael Sinclair (Power Packed)	3.00
17	Kevin Greene (Power Packed)	3.00
18	Michael Strahan (Power Packed)	3.00
19	Michael McCrary (Power Packed)	3.00
20	Hugh Douglas (Power Packed)	3.00
21	Deion Sanders (Strike Force)	6.00
22	Terry Fair (Strike Force)	3.00
23	Jacquez Green (Strike Force)	3.00
24	Corey Harris (Strike Force)	3.00
25	Tim Dwight (Stike Force)	6.00
26	Dan Marino (Career Best)	18.00
27	Barry Sanders (Career Best)	25.00
28	Jerry Rice (Career Best)	12.00
29	Bruce Smith (Career Best)	3.00
30	Darrien Gordon (Career Best)	3.00

1999 Topps Collection

This was a 357-card set that paralleled the regular Topps issue. Each single in this set included the "Topps Collection" gold foil stamp on the fronts of the cards. They were issued in factory set form and SRP was $29.00.

		MT
Complete Set (357):		50.00
Common Player:		.10
Minor Stars:		.20
Common Rookie:		2.00
1	Terrell Davis	1.50
2	Adrian Murrell	.10
3	Ernie Mills	.10
4	Jimmy Hitchcock	.10
5	Charlie Garner	.20
6	Blaine Bishop	.10
7	Junior Seau	.20
8	Andre Rison	.20
9	Jake Reed	.20
10	Cris Carter	.50
11	Torrance Small	.10
12	Ronald McKinnon	.10
13	Tyrone Davis	.10
14	Warren Moon	.20
15	Joe Johnson	.10
16	Bert Emanuel	.20
17	Brad Culpepper	.10
18	Henry Jones	.10
19	Jonathan Ogden	.10
20	Terrell Owens	.50
21	Derrick Mason	.10
22	Jon Ritchie	.10
23	Eric Metcalf	.10
24	Kevin Carter	.10
25	Fred Taylor	1.00
26	DeWayne Washington	.10
27	William Thomas	.10
28	Raghib Ismail	.10
29	Jason Taylor	.10
30	Doug Flutie	.50
31	Michael Sinclair	.10
32	Yancey Thigpen	.20
33	Darnay Scott	.20
34	Amani Toomer	.10
35	Edgar Bennett	.10
36	LeRoy Butler	.10
37	Jessie Tuggle	.10
38	Andrew Glover	.10
39	Tim McDonald	.10
40	Marshall Faulk	.50
41	Ray Mickens	.10
42	Kimble Anders	.10
43	Trent Green	.20
44	Dermontti Dawson	.10
45	Greg Ellis	.10
46	Hugh Douglas	.10
47	Amp Lee	.10
48	Lamar Thomas	.10
49	Curtis Conway	.20

#	Player		#	Player		#	Player	
50	Emmitt Smith	1.50	168	Michael Bates	.10	285	Bryan Cox	.10
51	Elvis Grbac	.20	169	Bobby Engram	.10	286	Sam Madison	.10
52	Tony Simmons	.20	170	Jimmy Smith	.50	287	Priest Holmes	.50
53	Darrin Smith	.10	171	Vonnie Holliday	.10	288	Keenan McCardell	.10
54	Donovin Darius	.10	172	Simeon Rice	.10	289	Michael Strahan	.10
55	Corey Chavous	.10	173	Kevin Greene	.10	290	Robert Edwards	.30
56	Phillippi Sparks	.10	174	Mike Alstott	.50	291	Tommy Vardell	.10
57	Luther Elliss	.10	175	Eddie George	.75	292	Wayne Chrebet	.30
58	Tim Dwight	.50	176	Michael Jackson	.10	293	Chris Calloway	.10
59	Andre Hastings	.10	177	Neil O'Donnell	.20	294	Wesley Walls	.20
60	Dan Marino	1.50	178	Sean Dawkins	.10	295	Derrick Brooks	.10
61	Michael Barrow	.10	179	Courtney Hawkins	.10	296	Trace Armstrong	.10
62	Corey Fuller	.10	180	Michael Irvin	.20	297	Brian Simmons	.10
63	Bill Romanowski	.10	181	Thurman Thomas	.20	298	Darrell Green	.10
64	Derrick Rodgers	.10	182	Cameron Cleeland	.10	299	Robert Brooks	.10
65	Natrone Means	.20	183	Ellis Johnson	.10	300	Peyton Manning	1.75
66	Peter Boulware	.10	184	Will Blackwell	.10	301	Dana Stubblefield	.10
67	Brian Mitchell	.10	185	Ty Law	.10	302	Shawn Springs	.10
68	Cornelius Bennett	.10	186	Merton Hanks	.10	303	Leslie Shepherd	.10
69	Dedric Ward	.10	187	Dan Wilkinson	.10	304	Ken Harvey	.10
70	Drew Bledsoe	.75	188	Andre Wadsworth	.10	305	Jon Kitna	.50
71	Freddie Jones	.10	189	Troy Vincent	.10	306	Terance Mathis	.10
72	Derrick Thomas	.20	190	Frank Sanders	.20	307	Andre Reed	.20
73	Willie Davis	.10	191	Stephen Boyd	.10	308	Jackie Harris	.10
74	Larry Centers	.10	192	Jason Elam	.10	309	Rich Gannon	.10
75	Mark Brunell	.75	193	Kordell Stewart	.50	310	Keyshawn Johnson	.50
76	Chuck Smith	.10	194	Ted Johnson	.10	311	Victor Green	.10
77	Desmond Howard	.10	195	Glyn Milburn	.10	312	Eric Allen	.10
78	Sedrick Shaw	.10	196	Gary Brown	.10	313	Terry Fair	.10
79	Tiki Barber	.20	197	Travis Hall	.10	314	Jason Elam	.10
80	Curtis Martin	.50	198	John Randle	.10	315	Garrison Hearst	.10
81	Barry Minter	.10	199	Jay Riemersma	.10	316	Jake Plummer	.30
82	Skip Hicks	.20	200	Barry Sanders	2.00	317	Randall Cunningham	.20
83	O.J. Santiago	.10	201	Chris Spielman	.10	318	Randy Moss	1.00
84	Ed McCaffrey	.30	202	Rod Woodson	.10	319	Jamal Anderson	.25
85	Terrell Buckley	.10	203	Darrell Russell	.10	320	John Elway	.75
86	Charlie Jones	.10	204	Tony Boselli	.10	321	Doug Flutie	.30
87	Pete Mitchell	.10	205	Darren Woodson	.10	322	Emmitt Smith	.75
88	La'Roi Glover	.10	206	Muhsin Muhammed	.20	323	Terrell Davis	.75
89	Eric Davis	.10	207	Jim Harbaugh	.20	324	Jerris McPhail	.10
90	John Elway	1.50	208	Isaac Bruce	.50	325	Damon Gibson	.10
91	Kavika Pittman	.10	209	Mo Lewis	.10	326	Jim Pyne	.10
92	Fred Lane	.20	210	Dorsey Levens	.50	327	Antonio Langham	.10
93	Warren Sapp	.20	211	Frank Wycheck	.10	328	Freddie Solomon	.10
94	Lorenzo Bromell	.10	212	Napoleon Kaufman	.50	329	Ricky Williams	10.00
95	Lawyer Milloy	.10	213	Walt Harris	.10	330	Daunte Culpepper	7.00
96	Aeneas Williams	.10	214	Leon Lett	.10	331	Chris Claiborne	.10
97	Michael McCrary	.10	215	Karim Abdul	.20	332	Amos Zereoue	2.00
98	Rickey Dudley	.20	216	Carnell Lake	.10	333	Chris McAlister	2.00
99	Bryce Paup	.10	217	Byron Morris	.10	334	Kevin Faulk	3.00
100	Jamal Anderson	.50	218	John Avery	.20	335	James Johnson	3.00
101	D'Marco Farr	.10	219	Chris Slade	.10	336	Mike Cloud	2.00
102	Johnnie Morton	.10	220	Robert Smith	.50	337	Jevon Kearse	5.00
103	Jeff Graham	.10	221	Mike Pritchard	.10	338	Akili Smith	6.00
104	Sam Cowart	.10	222	Ty Detmer	.10	339	Edgerrin James	20.00
105	Bryant Young	.10	223	Randall Cunningham	.50	340	Cecil Collins	3.00
106	Jermaine Lewis	.10	224	Alonzo Mayes	.10	341	Donovan McNabb	8.00
107	Chad Bratzke	.10	225	Jake Plummer	.75	342	Kevin Johnson	6.00
108	Jeff Burris	.10	226	Derrick Mayes	.20	343	Torry Holt	6.00
109	Roell Preston	.10	227	Jeff Brady	.10	344	Rob Konrad	2.00
110	Vinny Testaverde	.30	228	John Lynch	.10	345	Tim Couch	12.00
111	Ruben Brown	.10	229	Steve Atwater	.10	346	David Boston	5.00
112	Darryll Lewis	.10	230	Warrick Dunn	.50	347	Karsten Bailey	3.00
113	Billy Davis	.10	231	Shawn Jefferson	.10	348	Troy Edwards	5.00
114	Bryant Westbrook	.10	232	Erik Kramer	.10	349	Sedrick Irvin	2.00
115	Stephen Alexander	.10	233	Ken Dilger	.10	350	Shaun King	8.00
116	Terrell Fletcher	.10	234	Ryan Leaf	.50	351	Peerless Price	4.00
117	Terry Glenn	.50	235	Ray Buchanan	.10	352	Brock Huard	3.00
118	Rod Smith	.30	236	Kevin Williams	.10	353	Cade McNown	8.00
119	Carl Pickens	.20	237	Ricky Watters	.30	354	Champ Bailey	3.00
120	Tim Brown	.30	238	Dwayne Rudd	.10	355	D'Wayne Bates	2.00
121	Mikhael Ricks	.10	239	Duce Staley	.50	356	Checklist	.10
122	Jason Gildon	.10	240	Charlie Batch	.75	357	Checklist	.10
123	Charles Way	.10	241	Tim Biakabutuka	.20			
124	Rob Moore	.20	242	Tony Gonzalez	.30			
125	Jerome Bettis	.50	243	Bryan Still	.10			
126	Kerry Collins	.20	244	Donnie Edwards	.10			
127	Bruce Smith	.20	245	Troy Aikman	1.00			
128	James Hasty	.10	246	Az-Zahir Hakim	.20			
129	Ken Norton Jr.	.10	247	Curtis Enis	.20			
130	Charles Woodson	.50	248	Chris Chandler	.20			
131	Tony McGee	.10	249	James Jett	.10			
132	Kevin Turner	.10	250	Brett Favre	2.00			
133	Jerome Pathon	.10	251	Keith Poole	.10			
134	Garrison Hearst	.30	252	Ricky Proehl	.10			
135	Craig Newsome	.10	253	Shannon Sharpe	.20			
136	Hardy Nickerson	.10	254	Robert Jones	.10			
137	Ray Lewis	.10	255	Chad Brown	.10			
138	Derrick Alexander	.10	256	Ben Coates	.20			
139	Phil Hansen	.10	257	Jacquez Green	.20			
140	Joey Galloway	.50	258	Jessie Armstead	.10			
141	Oronde Gadsden	.20	259	Dale Carter	.10			
142	Herman Moore	.30	260	Antowain Smith	.30			
143	Bobby Taylor	.10	261	Mark Chmura	.20			
144	Mario Bates	.10	262	Michael Westbrook	.20			
145	Kevin Dyson	.20	263	Marvin Harrison	.30			
146	Aaron Glenn	.10	264	Darrien Gordon	.10			
147	Ed McDaniel	.10	265	Rodney Harrison	.10			
148	Terry Allen	.20	266	Charles Johnson	.10			
149	Ike Hilliard	.20	267	Roman Pfifer	.10			
150	Steve Young	.75	268	Reidel Anthony	.20			
151	Eugene Robinson	.10	269	Jerry Rice	1.00			
152	John Mobley	.10	270	Eric Moulds	.50			
153	Kevin Hardy	.10	271	Robert Porcher	.10			
154	Lance Johnstone	.10	272	Deion Sanders	.30			
155	Willie McGinest	.10	273	Germane Crowell	.30			
156	Gary Anderson	.10	274	Randy Moss	2.00			
157	Dexter Coakley	.10	275	Antonio Freeman	.50			
158	Mark Fields	.10	276	Trent Dilfer	.20			
159	Steve McNair	.75	277	Eric Turner	.10			
160	Corey Dillon	.50	278	Jeff George	.30			
161	Zach Thomas	.20	279	Levon Kirkland	.10			
162	Kent Graham	.10	280	O.J. McDuffie	.20			
163	Tony Parrish	.10	281	Takeo Spikes	.10			
164	Sam Gash	.10	282	Jim Flanigan	.10			
165	Kyle Brady	.10	283	Chris Warren	.10			
166	Donnell Bennett	.10	284	J.J. Stokes	.20			
167	Tony Martin	.20						

1999 Topps Gold Label

This was a 100-card set that featured each single on prismatic 35-pt. spectral-reflective rainbow stock with the player's name and the Gold Label logo in gold foil. Each player had two other singles with a different photo on the foreground of each card. Each of those cards then had a parallel Black and Red Class issue. The Race to Gold insert also has a Black and Red Class parallels. SRP was $3.99 for four-card packs.

	MT
Complete Set (100):	100.00
Common Player:	.25

		MT
Minor Stars:		.50
Common Rookie:		1.00
Class 2 Cards:		2x
Class 2 Rookies:		1x
Inserted 1:2		
Class 3 Cards:		3x
Class 3 Rookies:		1.5x
Inserted 1:4		
Wax Box:		85.00
1	Terrell Davis	3.00
2	Jake Plummer	2.00
3	Michael Cloud	2.00
4	D'Wayne Bates	2.00
5	Jamal Anderson	1.00
6	Cecil Collins	6.00
7	Keyshawn Johnson	1.00
8	Jerome Bettis	1.00
9	Ricky Watters	.50
10	Brett Favre	4.00
11	Joe Germaine	3.00
12	Eddie George	1.00
13	Jevon Kearse	4.00
14	Skip Hicks	.50
15	James Johnson	3.00
16	Terry Glenn	1.00
17	Troy Edwards	4.00
18	Karsten Bailey	1.00
19	Trent Dilfer	.50
20	Barry Sanders	4.00
21	Vinny Testaverde	.50
22	Ed McCaffrey	.75
23	Shannon Sharpe	.50
24	Robert Smith	.50
25	Emmitt Smith	3.00
26	Rob Moore	.50
27	J.J. Stokes	.50
28	Champ Bailey	3.00
29	Napoleon Kaufman	.75
30	Fred Taylor	3.00
31	Corey Dillon	1.00
32	Sedrick Irvin	2.50
33	Chris McAlister	1.00
34	Warrick Dunn	1.00
35	Isaac Bruce	1.00
36	Peerless Price	3.00
37	Dorsey Levens	1.00
38	Wayne Chrebet	.75
39	Randall Cunningham	1.00
40	Dan Marino	3.00
41	Chris Chandler	.25
42	Mark Brunell	1.50
43	Kevin Johnson	4.00
44	Natrone Means	.50
45	Jerome Pathon	.25
46	Daunte Culpepper	6.00
47	Akili Smith	6.00
48	Keenan McCardell	.50
49	Steve McNair	1.00
50	Randy Moss	4.00
51	Terance Mathis	.25
52	Eric Moulds	1.00
53	Raghib Ismail	.25
54	Cade McNown	6.00
55	Kordell Stewart	1.25
56	Rob Konrad	2.00
57	Andre Rison	.50
58	Curtis Conway	.50
59	Chris Claiborne	2.00
60	Jerry Rice	2.00
61	Peyton Manning	3.00
62	Jimmy Smith	1.00
63	Doug Flutie	1.25
64	Frank Sanders	.50
65	Antowain Smith	1.00
66	Curtis Enis	1.00
67	Charlie Batch	1.50
68	Marvin Harrison	1.00
69	Garrison Hearst	.75
70	Ricky Williams	12.00
71	Torry Holt	4.00
72	Mike Alstott	1.00
73	Drew Bledsoe	3.00
74	O.J. McDuffie	.50
75	Donovan McNabb	6.00
76	Curtis Martin	1.00
77	Priest Holmes	1.00
78	Antonio Freeman	1.00
79	Herman Moore	1.00
80	Tim Couch	12.00
81	Troy Aikman	2.00
82	David Boston	4.00
83	Tim Brown	.50
84	Kevin Faulk	3.00
85	Cris Carter	1.00
86	Marshall Faulk	4.00
87	Shaun King	4.00
88	Terrell Owens	1.00
89	Carl Pickens	.50
90	Steve Young	1.25
91	Rod Smith	.75
92	Michael Irvin	.50
93	Ike Hilliard	.25
94	Jon Kitna	1.25
95	Brock Huard	3.00
96	Joey Galloway	1.00
97	Amos Zereoue	3.00
98	Duce Staley	.75
99	John Elway	3.00
100	Edgerrin James	15.00

Post-1980 cards in Near Mint condition will generally sell for about 75% of the quoted Mint value. Excellent-condition cards bring no more than 40%.

1999 Topps Gold Label Black Label

Each of the three Classes has a parallel Black Label card. The player's name and Topps Gold Label logo are in black foil. Class 1 singles were found 1:8 packs, Class 2 singles at 1:16 and Class 3 cards at 1:32.

	MT
Class 1 Cards:	4x
Class 1 Rookies:	1.5x
Inserted 1:8	
Class 2 Cards:	8x
Class 2 Rookies:	3x
Inserted 1:16	
Class 3 Cards:	12x
Class 3 Rookies:	5x
Inserted 1:32	

1999 Topps Gold Label Red Label

Each of the three Classes has a parallel Red Label card. The player's name and Topps Gold Label logo are in red foil. Class 1 singles were found 1:79 packs and were sequentially numbered to 100. Class 2 singles were inserted 1:157 and were numbered to 50. Class 3 singles were inserted 1:314 and numbered to 25.

	MT
Class 1 Cards:	10x-20x
Class 1 Rookies:	4x-8x
Inserted 1:79	
Production 100 Sets	
Class 2 Cards:	15x-30x
Class 2 Rookies:	6x-12x
Inserted 1:157	
Production 50 Sets	
Class 3 Cards:	25x-50x
Class 3 Rookies:	10x-20x
Inserted 1:314	
Production 25 Sets	

1999 Topps Gold Label Race to Gold

This 15-card insert set highlighted three players: Dan Marino, Walter Payton and Jerry Rice. Each player had five cards and was pictured with a current player who had the best chance of breaking a record that the original player owned. Singles were inserted 1:12 packs. Each single had a parallel Black Label version that was inserted 1:48 packs. Each also had a parallel Red Label version with #1-#5 inserted 1:11,867 and numbered to 13. Cards #6-#10 were found 1:4,638 and numbered to 34. Cards #11-#15 were found 1:1,968 and numbered to 80.

		MT
Complete Set (15):		65.00
Common Player:		1.50
Minor Stars:		3.00
Inserted 1:12		
Black Label Cards:		2x
Inserted 1:48		
Red Label Cards (1-5):		20x-40x
Inserted 1:11,867		
Red Label Cards (6-10):		12x-24x
Inserted 1:4,638		
Red Label Cards (11-15):		5x-10x
Inserted 1:1,968		
1	Brett Favre	12.00
2	Peyton Manning	10.00
3	Drew Bledsoe	5.00
4	Randall Cunningham	3.00
5	Jake Plummer	6.00
6	Emmitt Smith	8.00
7	Terrell Davis	8.00
8	Barry Sanders	12.00
9	Eddie George	4.00
10	Curtis Martin	3.00
11	Antonio Freeman	3.00
12	Eric Moulds	3.00
13	Joey Galloway	3.00
14	Rod Smith	1.50
15	Randy Moss	12.00

1999 Topps Season Opener

Topps Season Opener Football was a retail exclusive 165-card set that used the same photos as the regular Topps set but had blue borders and a Season Opener stamp in silver foil rather than green borders in the regular issue.

		MT
Complete Set (165):		60.00
Common Player:		.10
Minor Stars:		.20
Common Rookie:		1.50
Wax Box:		50.00
1	Jerry Rice	1.00
2	Emmitt Smith	1.50
3	Curtis Martin	.30
4	Ed McCaffrey	.20
5	Oronde Gadsden	.20
6	Byron Morris	.20
7	Michael Irvin	.20
8	Shannon Sharpe	.20
9	Levon Kirkland	.20
10	Fred Taylor	1.00
11	Andre Reed	.20
12	Chad Brown	.10
13	Skip Hicks	.20
14	Tim Dwight	.30
15	Michael Sinclair	.10
16	Carl Pickens	.20
17	Derrick Alexander	.10
18	Kevin Green	.10
19	Duce Staley	.20
20	Dan Marino	1.50
21	Frank Sanders	.20
22	Ricky Proehl	.10
23	Frank Wycheck	.10
24	Andre Rison	.20
25	Natrone Means	.20
26	Steve McNair	.30
27	Vonnie Holliday	.20
28	Charles Woodson	.30
29	Rob Moore	.20
30	John Elway	1.50
31	Derrick Thomas	.20
32	Jake Plummer	.75
33	Mike Alstott	.30
34	Keenan McCardell	.20
35	Mark Chmura	.20

36	Keyshawn Johnson	.30
37	Priest Holmes	.30
38	Antonio Freeman	.30
39	Ty Law	.10
40	Jamal Anderson	.30
41	Courtney Hawkins	.10
42	James Jett	.10
43	Aaron Glenn	.10
44	Jimmy Smith	.20
45	Michael McCrary	.10
46	Junior Seau	.20
47	Bill Romanowski	.10
48	Mark Brunell	.75
49	Yancey Thigpen	.20
50	Steve Young	.75
51	Cris Carter	.30
52	Vinny Testaverde	.20
53	Zach Thomas	.20
54	Kordell Stewart	.50
55	Tim Biakabutuka	.10
56	J.J. Stokes	.10
57	Jon Kitna	.30
58	Jacquez Green	.20
59	Marvin Harrison	.20
60	Barry Sanders	2.00
61	Darrell Green	.10
62	Terance Mathis	.10
63	Ricky Watters	.20
64	Chris Chandler	.20
65	Cameron Cleeland	.20
66	Rod Smith	.20
67	Freddie Jones	.10
68	Adrian Murrell	.20
69	Terrell Owens	.30
70	Troy Aikman	1.00
71	John Mobley	.10
72	Corey Dillon	.30
73	Rickey Dudley	.10
74	Randall Cunningham	.30
75	Muhsin Muhammed	.10
76	Stephen Boyd	.10
77	Tony Gonzalez	.30
78	Deion Sanders	.30
79	Ben Coates	.20
80	Brett Favre	2.00
81	Shawn Springs	.10
82	Dorsey Levens	.30
83	Ray Buchanan	.10
84	Charlie Batch	.50
85	John Randle	.10
86	Eddie George	.50
87	Ray Lewis	.10
88	Johnnie Morton	.10
89	Ray Hardy	.10
90	O.J. McDuffie	.20
91	Herman Moore	.30
92	Tim Brown	.30
93	Bert Emanuel	.10
94	Elvis Grbac	.20
95	Peter Boulware	.10
96	Curtis Conway	.20
97	Doug Flutie	.50
98	Jake Reed	.10
99	Ike Hilliard	.10
100	Randy Moss	2.00
101	Warren Sapp	.10
102	Bruce Smith	.10
103	Joey Galloway	.30
104	Napoleon Kaufman	.30
105	Warrick Dunn	.30
106	Wayne Chrebet	.30
107	Robert Brooks	.10
108	Antowain Smith	.30
109	Trent Dilfer	.20
110	Peyton Manning	1.50
111	Isaac Bruce	.20
112	John Lynch	.10
113	Terry Glenn	.30
114	Garrison Hearst	.30
115	Jerome Bettis	.30
116	Darnay Scott	.10
117	Lamar Thomas	.10
118	Chris Spielman	.10
119	Robert Smith	.20
120	Drew Bledsoe	.75
121	Reidel Anthony	.10
122	Wesley Walls	.10
123	Eric Moulds	.30
124	Terrell Davis	1.50
125	Dale Carter	.10
126	Charles Johnson	.10
127	Steve Atwater	.10
128	Jim Harbaugh	.20
129	Tony Martin	.10
130	Kerry Collins	.20
131	Trent Green	.30
132	Marshall Faulk	.30
133	Raghib Ismail	.10
134	Warren Moon	.30
135	Jerris McPhail	.10
136	Damon Gibson	.10
137	Jim Pyne	.10
138	Antonio Langham	.10
139	Freddie Solomon	.10
140	Randy Moss SH	1.00
141	John Elway SH	.75
142	Doug Flutie SH	.25
143	Emmitt Smith SH	.75
144	Terrell Davis SH	.75
145	*Troy Edwards*	3.00
146	*Torry Holt*	3.00
147	*Tim Couch*	12.00
148	*Sedrick Irvin*	2.00
149	*Ricky Williams*	12.00
150	*Peerless Price*	3.00
151	*Mike Cloud*	1.50
152	*Kevin Faulk*	3.00
153	*Kevin Johnson*	2.50
154	*James Johnson*	2.50
155	*Edgerrin James*	12.00
156	*D'Wayne Bates*	2.00
157	*Donovan McNabb*	5.00
158	*David Boston*	3.00
159	*Daunte Culpepper*	5.00
160	*Champ Bailey*	2.00
161	*Cecil Collins*	5.00
162	*Cade McNown*	5.00
163	*Brock Huard*	2.00
164	*Akili Smith*	4.00
165	Checklist	.10

1999 Topps Season Opener Autographs

Only two players signed in this insert and were inserted 1:7,126 packs.

		MT
Complete Set (2):		475.00
Common Player:		200.00
Inserted 1:7,126		
1	Tim Couch	275.00
2	Peyton Manning	200.00

1999 Topps Stars

Each card in this 140-card set was printed on 24-pt. stock with foil stamping, flood gloss and metallic ink. Each of the base cards had a star on the front. A parallel Two Star, Three Star and Four Star were released and each of the four issues had a parallel version. Insert sets include: Autographs, New Dawn, Pro Bowl Jersey Redemption, Rookie Relics, Rookie Reprints, Stars of the Game and Zone of Their Own. SRP was $3.00 for six-card pack.

		MT
Complete Set (140):		65.00
Common Player:		.20
Minor Stars:		.40
Common Rookie:		.75
Wax Box:		60.00
1	*Champ Bailey*	1.50
2	*Akili Smith*	3.00
3	*Randy Moss*	3.00
4	*Cade McNown*	4.00
5	*Torry Holt*	3.00
6	*Troy Edwards*	2.50
7	*David Boston*	2.50
8	*Edgerrin James*	10.00
9	*Daunte Culpepper*	4.00
10	*Tim Couch*	7.00
11	*Ricky Williams*	7.00
12	Fred Taylor	1.50
13	Barry Sanders	3.00
14	Emmitt Smith	2.00
15	Jerry Rice	1.50
16	Jake Plummer	1.25
17	Terrell Owens	.75
18	Eric Moulds	.75
19	Dan Marino	2.00
20	Steve McNair	.75
21	*Donovan McNabb*	4.00
22	Curtis Martin	.75
23	Peyton Manning	2.00
24	Garrison Hearst	.40
25	Eddie George	.75
26	Antonio Freeman	.75
27	Doug Flutie	1.00
28	*Kevin Faulk*	1.50
29	Brett Favre	3.00
30	Randall Cunningham	.75
31	Mark Brunell	1.25
32	Keyshawn Johnson	.75
33	Terrell Davis	2.00
34	Drew Bledsoe	1.25
35	Jerome Bettis	.75
36	Charlie Batch	1.00
37	Steve Young	.75
38	Jamal Anderson	.75
39	Troy Aikman	1.50
40	John Elway	2.00
41	*Amos Zereoue*	1.00
42	J.J. Stokes	.40
43	Antowain Smith	.75
44	Jimmy Smith	.75
45	*Shaun King*	4.00
46	*Jevon Kearse*	2.50
47	*Sedrick Irvin*	1.00
48	Rod Smith	.50
49	*Kevin Johnson*	2.50
50	Joey Galloway	.75
51	*Michael Cloud*	1.00
52	*D'Wayne Bates*	1.00
53	*Peerless Price*	2.00
54	Herman Moore	.50
55	*Rob Konrad*	1.00
56	*James Johnson*	1.50
57	*Cecil Collins*	1.50
58	Wayne Chrebet	.75
59	Cris Carter	.75
60	Tim Brown	.50
61	Frank Wycheck	.75
62	Charles Woodson	.75
63	*Antoine Winfield*	.75
64	Ryan Leaf	.50
65	Ricky Watters	.40
66	Yancey Thigpen	.20
67	Michael Westbrook	.40
68	Vinny Testaverde	.40
69	Kordell Stewart	.75
70	Duce Staley	.75
71	Shannon Sharpe	.40
72	Junior Seau	.40
73	Bruce Smith	.20
74	Frank Sanders	.40
75	Warren Sapp	.20
76	Robert Smith	.75
77	Andre Reed	.40
78	Darnay Scott	.20
79	Adrian Murrell	.40
80	Ricky Proehl	.20
81	Zach Thomas	.40
82	Deion Sanders	.75
83	Andre Rison	.40
84	Jake Reed	.40
85	Carl Pickens	.40
86	John Randle	.20
87	Jerome Pathon	.20
88	*Brock Huard*	1.50
89	Elvis Grbac	.20
90	Curtis Enis	.75
91	Rickey Dudley	.20
92	Amani Toomer	.20
93	Robert Brooks	.20
94	Derrick Alexander	.20
95	Reidel Anthony	.40
96	Mark Chmura	.40
97	Trent Dilfer	.40
98	*Ebenezer Ekuban*	.75
99	Tony Banks	.40
100	Terry Glenn	.75
101	Andre Hastings	.20
102	Ike Hilliard	.40
103	Michael Irvin	.40
104	Napoleon Kaufman	.75
105	Dorsey Levens	.75
106	Ed McCaffrey	.50
107	Natrone Means	.40
108	Skip Hicks	.40
109	James Jett	.20
110	Priest Holmes	.75
111	Tim Dwight	.75
112	Curtis Conway	.40
113	Jeff Blake	.40
114	Karim Abdul	.40
115	*Karsten Bailey*	1.25
116	Chris Chandler	.40
117	Germane Crowell	.40
118	Warrick Dunn	.75
119	Bert Emanuel	.20
120	*Jermaine Fazande*	1.25
121	*Joe Germaine*	1.25
122	Tony Gonzalez	.40
123	Jacquez Green	.40
124	Marvin Harrison	.75
125	Corey Dillon	.75
126	Ben Coates	.40
127	*Chris Claiborne*	1.00
128	Isaac Bruce	.75
129	Mike Alstott	.75
130	*Andy Katzenmoyer*	1.00
131	Jon Kitna	.75
132	Keenan McCardell	.40
133	Johnnie Morton	.20
134	O.J. McDuffie	.40
135	*Chris McAlister*	1.00
136	Terance Mathis	.20
137	Thurman Thomas	.40
138	Jermaine Lewis	.20
139	Rob Moore	.20
140	Brad Johnson	.75

1999 Topps Stars Parallel

This was a parallel to the base set. Each of the singles in this set were sequentially numbered to 299.

	MT
Parallel Cards:	5x-10x
Parallel Rookies:	2x-4x
Production 299 Sets	

1999 Topps Stars Two Star

This was a 60-card partial parallel to the base set. Each of the singles had two stars on the front and were inserted 1:1.5 packs.

	MT
Complete Set (60):	50.00
Two Star Cards:	1x

1999 Topps Stars Two Star Parallel

This was a parallel to the Two Star set. Singles from this insert were sequentially numbered to 249 and inserted 1:42 packs.

	MT
Complete Set (60):	500.00
Two Star Cards:	5x-10x
Two Star Rookies:	2x-4x
Production 249 Sets	

1999 Topps Stars Three Star

This was a 40-card partial parallel to the base set. Each single had three stars on the front and was inserted one-per-pack.

	MT
Complete Set (40):	35.00
Three Star Cards:	1x
Inserted 1:1	

1999 Topps Stars Three Star Parallel

This was a parallel to the Three Star insert. Each of the singles were sequentially numbered to 199 and inserted 1:79 packs.

	MT
Complete Set (40):	500.00
Three Star Cards:	6x-12x
Three Star Rookies:	3x-6x
Production 199 Sets	

Post-1980 cards in Near Mint condition will generally sell for about 75% of the quoted Mint value. Excellent-condition cards bring no more than 40%.

1999 Topps Stars Four Star

This was a 10-card partial parallel to the base set. Each single had four stars across the front. Singles were inserted 1:4 packs.

	MT
Complete Set (10):	25.00
Four Star Cards:	1x
Inserted 1:4	

1999 Topps Stars Four Star Parallel

This was a parallel to the Four Star insert set. Each single was sequentially numbered to 99 and inserted 1:634 packs.

	MT
Complete Set (10):	150.00
Four Star Cards:	6x-12x
Four Star Rookies:	3x-6x
Production 99 Sets	

1999 Topps Stars Autographs

This six-card insert set included autographs from the 1999 #1 overall draft pick Tim Couch and the 1998 Rookie of the Year Randy Moss. The first three cards in the set had a blue background and were inserted 1:419 packs. Cards #4 and #5 had a red background and were inserted 1:629. The last single had a gold background and was inserted 1:2,528 packs.

		MT
Complete Set (6):		375.00
Common Player:		25.00
Blue Inserted 1:419		
Gold Inserted 1:2,528		
Red Inserted 1:629		
1	Tim Couch B	125.00
2	Torry Holt B	35.00
3	David Boston B	25.00
4	Fred Taylor R	60.00
5	Marshall Faulk R	50.00
6	Randy Moss G	150.00

1999 Topps Stars New Dawn

This 20-card insert set included rookies from the 1999 season. Each was printed on 24-pt. stock, with super-premium select metallization treatment and foil stamping. The cards were sequentially numbered to 1,000 and inserted 1:31 packs.

		MT
Complete Set (20):		100.00
Common Player:		1.50
Minor Stars:		3.00
Inserted 1:31		
Production 1,000 Sets		
1	Tim Couch	12.00
2	Kevin Faulk	4.00
3	Troy Edwards	6.00
4	Champ Bailey	4.00
5	Peerless Price	4.00
6	Kevin Johnson	7.00
7	Edgerrin James	20.00
8	Daunte Culpepper	8.00
9	Torry Holt	6.00
10	Donovan McNabb	8.00
11	Shaun King	8.00
12	Michael Cloud	1.50
13	Cade McNown	8.00
14	David Boston	6.00
15	James Johnson	4.00
16	Karsten Bailey	1.50
17	Sedrick Irvin	3.00
18	Akili Smith	7.00
19	D'Wayne Bates	1.50
20	Ricky Williams	12.00

1999 Topps Stars Rookie Relics

This three-card insert set included rookie Torry Holt and rookies Kurt Warner and Donovan McNabb through redemption cards. Each single included a piece of a game-worn jersey and singles were inserted 1:209 packs.

		MT
Complete Set (3):		225.00
Common Player:		50.00
Inserted 1:209		
1	Kurt Warner	150.00
2	Torry Holt	50.00
3	Donovan McNabb	50.00

1999 Topps Stars Rookie Reprints

TERRY BRADSHAW
STEELERS
QUARTERBACK • A.F.C.

This two-card set included reprints of Terry Bradshaw and Roger Staubach's rookie cards. Singles were inserted 1:16 packs. Autographed version were also released at 1:629 packs.

	MT
Complete Set (2):	10.00
Common Player:	5.00
Inserted 1:16	
Terry Bradshaw	5.00
Roger Staubach	5.00

A card number in parentheses ( ) indicates the set is unnumbered.

A player's name in *italic type* indicates a rookie card.

1999 Topps Stars Stars of the Game

Each single in this 10-card insert set were printed on 24-pt. stock with foil stamping. Each was sequentially numbered to 1,999 and inserted 1:31 packs.

		MT
Complete Set (10):		100.00
Common Player:		2.50
Inserted 1:31		
Production 1,999 Sets		
1	Jamal Anderson	2.50
2	Dan Marino	10.00
3	Barry Sanders	12.00
4	Brett Favre	12.00
5	Emmitt Smith	10.00
6	Fred Taylor	6.00
7	John Elway	10.00
8	Randy Moss	12.00
9	Peyton Manning	10.00
10	Terrell Davis	8.00

1999 Topps Stars Zone of Their Own

This 10-card insert set included stars who have won individual awards and team titles. Each was printed on 24 pt. stock, foil stamped and sequentially numbered to 1,999. Singles were found 1:31 packs.

		MT
Complete Set (10):		60.00
Common Player:		2.50
Inserted 1:31		
Production 1,999 Sets		
1	Randy Moss	12.00
2	Eddie George	4.00
3	Tim Brown	2.50
4	Curtis Martin	2.50
5	Brett Favre	12.00
6	Barry Sanders	12.00
7	Warrick Dunn	2.50
8	Terrell Davis	8.00
9	Ricky Williams	10.00
10	Doug Flutie	5.00

1977 Touchdown Club

These 50 black-and-white cards were issued as a set in 1977 to honor several Hall-of-Fame caliber retired players. Each front has photo of the player in uniform, with his name below the photo. A black frame borders the photo and his name. The card back has the player's name and number at the top, with his position listed just below them. A brief career summary, listing the player's main honors and accomplishments, is also given. "Touchdown, 1977" is written at the bottom. All of the information on the back is contained within a black box. The set was designed for collectors who wanted the players' autographs; a list of their home addresses was included with the set.

	NM
Complete Set (50):	50.00

Common Player:		.75
1	Red Grange	5.00
2	George Halas	2.00
3	Benny Friedman	.75
4	Cliff Battles	1.00
5	Mike Michalske	.75
6	George McAfee	1.00
7	Beattie Feathers	1.25
8	Ernie Caddel	.75
9	George Musso	1.00
10	Sid Luckman	2.25
11	Cecil Isbell	.75
12	Bronko Nagurski	3.00
13	Hunk Anderson	.80
14	Dick Farman	.80
15	Aldo Forte	.90
16	Ki Aldrich	.80
17	Jim Lee Howell	.75
18	Ray Flaherty	.75
19	Hampton Pool	.80
20	Alex Wojchiechowicz	1.00
21	Bill Osmanski	.75
22	Hank Soar	.75
23	Dutch Clark	1.00
24	Joe Muha	.75
25	Don Hutson	1.50
26	Jim Poole	.85
27	Charley Malone	.75
28	Charlie Trippi	1.25
29	Andy Farkas	.75
30	Clarke Hinkle	1.00
31	Gary Famiglietti	.75
32	Bulldog Turner	1.25
33	Sammy Baugh	3.00
34	Pat Harder	.75
35	Tuffy Leemans	1.00
36	Ken Strong	1.00
37	Barney Poole	.75
38	Bruiser Kinard	1.00
39	Buford Ray	.75
40	Ace Parker	1.25
41	Buddy Parker	.75
42	Mel Hein	1.00
43	Ed Danowski	.75
44	Bill Dudley	1.25
45	Paul Stenn	.80
46	George Connor	1.00
47	George Connor	.75
48	Armand Niccolai	.75
49	Tony Canadeo	1.25
50	Bill Willis	1.50

1989 TV-4NFL Quarterbacks

The 20-card, 2-7/16" x 3-1/8" set features borderless portrait drawings by artist J.C. Ford. The card backs contain career highlights. The set was issued by a television station in Great Britain and were distributed to promote American football in the U.K.

		MT
Complete Set (20):		25.00
Common Player:		.75
1	Dutch Clark	.75
2	Sammy Baugh	1.50
3	Bob Waterfield	.75
4	Sid Luckman	.75
5	Otto Graham	1.00
6	Bobby Layne	.75
7	Norm Van Brocklin	.75
8	George Blanda	.75
9	Y.A. Tittle	1.00
10	Johnny Unitas	3.00
11	Bart Starr	1.25
12	Sonny Jurgensen	1.25
13	Joe Namath	2.50
14	Fran Tarkenton	1.50
15	Roger Staubach	2.50
16	Terry Bradshaw	3.00
17	Dan Fouts	1.25
18	Joe Montana	5.00
19	John Elway	2.00
20	Dan Marino	5.00

U

1992 Ultimate WLAF

The 200-card, WLAF set

features color photos with another color action photo on the card back, along with stats, bio information and a highlight. Each nine-pack of cards contained a game card in which the collector who spelled W-O-R-L-D won one million dollars. The final 20 cards are subsets which deal with playing the game (180-192) and collecting cards (193-200).

		MT
Complete Set (200):		5.00
Common Player:		.05
1	Barcelona Dragons '91 Team Statistics (Thomas Woods)	.10
2	Demetrius Davis	.15
3	Tim Egerton	.05
4	Scott Erney	.05
5	'91 Rushing Attempt Leader (Tony Baker)	.15
6	Anthony Greene	.05
7	Mike Hinnant (UER) (No position on front)	.05
8	Erik Naposki	.05
9	Paul Palmer	.15
10	Gene Taylor	.05
11	Thomas Woods	.05
12	Tony Rice	.25
13	Terry O'Shea	.05
14	Brett Wiese	.05
15	Kicking Leader (Phillip Alexander)	.05
16	Rushing/Scoring Leader (Eric Wilkerson)	.10
17	Barcelona Dragons Team Picture	.05
18	Barcelona Dragons Checklist	.05
19	Birmingham Fire '91 Team Statistics	.05
20	Eric Jones	.05
21	Steve Avery	.05
22	Willie Bouyer	.05
23	'91 Interception Leader (Anthony Parker)	.20
24	Elroy Harris	.05
25	James Henry	.05
26	Johnny Holland	.10
27	Mark Hopkins	.05
28	Arthur Hunter	.05
29	'91 Sacking Leader (Danny Lockett)	.10
30	Kirk Maggio	.05
31	John Miller	.05
32	Ricky Shaw	.05
33	Phil Ross	.05
34	Mike Norseth	.05
35	Birmingham Fire Team Picture	.05
36	Frankfurt Galaxy '91 Team Statistics	.05
37	Anthony Wallace	.05
38	Lew Barnes	.05
39	Richard Buchanan	.05
40	Yepi Pau'u	.05
41	Pat McGuirk (UER) (Played for Raleigh-Durham in 1991)	.05
42	Tony Baker	.15
43	1992 TV Schedule 1	.05
44	Tim Broady	.05
45	Lonnie Finch	.05
46	Chad Fortune	.05
47	Harry Jackson	.05
48	Jason Johnson	.05
49	Pat Moorer	.05
50	Mike Perez	.15
51	Mark Seals	.05
52	Cedric Stallworth	.05
53	Tom Whelihan	.05
54	Joe Johnson	.30
55	Frankfurt Galaxy Checklist	.05
56	London Monarchs '91 Team Statistics (Stan Gelbaugh)	.10
57	Stan Gelbaugh	.35
58	Jeff Alexander	.05
59	Dana Brinson	.05
60	Marlon Brown	.05
61	Dedrick Dodge	.05
62	Judd Garrett	.10
63	Greg Horne	.05
64	Jon Horton	.05
65	Danny Lockett	.10
66	Andre Riley	.05
67	Charlie Young	.10
68	David Smith	.05
69	Irvin Smith	.05
70	Rickey Williams	.05
71	Roland Smith	.05
72	William Kirksey	.05
73	Phillip Alexander	.05
74	London Monarchs Team Picture	.10
75	London Monarchs Checklist	.05

76	Montreal Machine '91 Team Statistics	.05
77	Rollin Putzier	.05
78	Adam Bob	.05
79	K.D. Dunn	.05
80	Darryl Holmes	.05
81	Ricky Johnson	.05
82	Michael Finn	.05
83	Chris Mohr	.15
84	Don Murray	.05
85	Bjorn Nittmo	.10
86	Michael Proctor	.10
87	Broderick Sargent	.05
88	Richard Shelton	.05
89	Emanuel King	.10
90	Pete Mandley	.15
91	Kris McCall	.05
92	1992 TV Schedule 2	.05
93	Montreal Machine Checklist	.05
94	NY/NJ Knights '91 Team Statistics	.05
95	Andre Alexander	.05
96	Pat Marlatt	.05
97	Cecil Fletcher	.05
98	Lonnie Turner	.05
99	Monty Gilbreath	.05
100	Tony Jones (UER) (Should be DB, not WR)	.05
101	Kip Lewis	.05
102	Bob Lilljedahl	.05
103	Mark Moore	.05
104	Falanda Newton	.05
105	Anthony Parker (UER) (Played for Chiefs in 1991, not Bears; was released by the Bears)	.20
106	Kendall Trainor	.10
107	Eric Wilkerson	.05
108	Tony Woods	.20
109	Reggie Slack	.10
110	Joey Banes	.05
111	Ron Sancho	.10
112	Mike Husar	.05
113	NY/NJ Knights Checklist	.05
114	Orlando Thunder '91 Team Statistics	.05
115	Byron Williams (UER) (Waived by Orlando and picked up by NY-NJ)	.05
116	Charlie Baumann	.15
117	Kevin Bell	.10
118	Rodney Lossow	.05
119	Myron Jones	.05
120	Bruce Lasane	.05
121	Eric Mitchel	.10
122	Billy Owens	.05
123	1992 TV Schedule 3	.05
124	Chris Roscoe	.05
125	Tommie Stowers	.05
126	Wayne Dickson (UER) (Not a rookie, he played for Orlando in 1991)	.05
127	Scott Mitchell	1.25
128	Karl Dunbar	.05
129	'91 Punt Return Leader (Dana Brinson)	.05
130	Orlando Thunder Checklist	.05
131	Sacramento Surge Team Statistics	.05
132	1992 TV Schedule 4	.05
133	Mike Adams	.05
134	Greg Couatte	.05
135	Mel Farr Jr. (Should be TE, not FB)	.10
136	Victor Floyd	.05
137	Paul Frazier	.05
138	Tom Gerhart	.05
139	Pete Najarian	.05
140	John Nies	.05
141	Carl Parker	.05
142	Saute Sapolu	.05
143	George Bethune	.05
144	David Archer	.35
145	John Buddenberg	.05
146	'91 Receiving Yardage Leader (Jon Horton) (UER) (Incorrect stats on back)	.05
147	Sacramento Surge Checklist	.05
148	San Antonio Riders '91 Team Statistics	.05
149	Ricky Blake	.05
150	Jim Gallery	.05
151	Jason Garrett	.75
152	John Garrett	.10
153	Broderick Graves	.05
154	Bill Hess	.05
155	Mike Johnson	.05
156	Lee Morris	.05
157	Dwight Pickens	.05
158	Kent Sullivan	.05
159	Ken Watson	.05

160	Ronnie Williams	.05
161	Titus Dixon	.05
162	Mike Kiselak	.05
163	Greg Lee	.05
164	'91 Receiving Leader (Judd Garrett) (Had 71 receptions in 1991, not 18; game high was 12, not 13)	.10
165	San Antonio Riders Checklist	.05
166	Tenth Week Summaries	.05
167	Randy Bethel	.05
168	Melvin Patterson	.05
169	Eric Harmon	.05
170	Patrick Jackson	.05
171	Tim James	.05
172	George Koonce	.15
173	Babe Laufenberg	.25
174	Amir Rasul	.05
175	'91 Passing Leader (Stan Gelbaugh)	.25
176	Jason Wallace	.05
177	Walter Wilson	.05
178	Power Meter Info	.15
179	Ohio Glory Checklist	.05
180	The Football Field (Jim Kelly)	.20
181	Moving the Ball (Jim Kelly)	.20
182	Defense/Back Field Cornerbacks and Safeties (Lawrence Taylor)	.20
183	Defense/Linebackers (Lawrence Taylor)	.20
184	Defense/Defensive Line - Defensive Tackles and Ends (Lawrence Taylor)	.20
185	Offensive/Offensive Line - Centers, Guards, Tackles and Tight Ends (Jim Kelly)	.05
186	Offense/Receivers (Lawrence Taylor)	.20
187	Offense/Running Backs (Jim Kelly)	.20
188	Offensive/Quarterback (Jim Kelly)	.05
189	Special Teams (Lawrence Taylor)	.10
190	Rules and Regulations - WL Rules that differ from NFL 1990 Rules	.05
191	Defensive Overview - Scoring Touchdowns and Extra Points	.05
192	Offensive Overview - Scoring, Field Goals and Safeties	.05
193	How to Collect - What is a Set (Lawrence Taylor)	.20
194	How to Collect - What is a Wax Pack (Lawrence Taylor)	.20
195	How to Collect - Premier Editions (Lawrence Taylor)	.20
196	How to Collect - What Creates Value (Lawrence Taylor)	.20
197	How to Collect - Rookie Cards (Jim Kelly)	.20
198	How to Collect - Grading Your Cards (Jim Kelly)	.20
199	How to Collect - Storing Your Cards (Jim Kelly)	.20
200	How to Collect - Trading Your Cards (Jim Kelly)	.20

1992 Ultimate WLAF Logo Holograms

The 10-card, standard-size set features holograms of each of the WLAF teams, which were randomly inserted in Ultimate packs.

		MT
Complete Set (10):		5.00
Common Player:		1.00
1	Barcelona Dragons	1.00
2	Birmingham Fire	1.00
3	Frankfurt Galaxy	1.00
4	London Monarchs	1.00
5	Montreal Machine	1.00
6	NY/NJ Knights	1.00
7	Ohio Glory	1.00
8	Orlando Thunder	1.00
9	Sacramento Surge	1.00
10	San Antonio Riders	1.00

1991 Ultra

This 300-card set features cards with color action photos with silver borders above and below the photo. The player's name, team and position is in white at the bottom. Backs have silver borders at the top and bottom, with a yellow-to-orange-to-green background. A mug shot is positioned between two smaller action photos on the back. A Rookie Prospect subset was also included; cards are numbered from 279-298. Two 10-card insert sets were also created - Ultra All-Stars and Ultra Performances. The All-Star cards were randomly inserted in 1991 packs which were sold in black boxes; the Performances cards were inserts in packs in green boxes.

		MT
Complete Set (300):		12.00
Common Player:		.05
Minor Stars:		.10
Wax Box:		10.00
1	Don Beebe	.05
2	Shane Conlan	.05
3	Pete Metzelaars	.05
4	Jamie Mueller	.05
5	Scott Norwood	.05
6	Andre Reed	.10
7	Leon Seals	.05
8	Bruce Smith	.05
9	Leonard Smith	.05
10	Thurman Thomas	.25
11	Lewis Billups	.05
12	Jim Breech	.05
13	James Brooks	.05
14	Eddie Brown	.05
15	Boomer Esiason	.10
16	David Fulcher	.05
17	Rodney Holman	.05
18	Bruce Kozerski	.05
19	Tim Krumrie	.05
20	Tim McGee	.05
21	Anthony Munoz	.05
22	Leon White	.05
23	Ickey Woods	.05
24	Carl Zander	.05
25	Brian Brennan	.05
26	Thane Gash	.05
27	Leroy Hoard	.05
28	Mike Johnson	.05
29	Reggie Langhorne	.05
30	Kevin Mack	.05
31	Clay Matthews	.05
32	Eric Metcalf	.05
33	Steve Atwater	.05
34	Melvin Bratton	.05
35	John Elway	.40
36	Bobby Humphrey	.05
37	Mark Jackson	.05
38	Vance Johnson	.05
39	Ricky Nattiel	.05
40	Steve Sewell	.05
41	Dennis Smith	.05
42	David Treadwell	.05
43	Mike Young	.05
44	Ray Childress	.05
45	Cris Dishman	.05
46	William Fuller	.05
47	Ernest Givins	.05
48	John Grimsley	.05
49	Drew Hill	.05
50	Haywood Jeffires	.05
51	Sean Jones	.05
52	Johnny Meads	.05
53	Warren Moon	.10
54	Al Smith	.05
55	Lorenzo White	.05
56	Albert Bentley	.05
57	Duane Bickett	.05
58	Bill Brooks	.05
59	Jeff George	.30
60	Mike Prior	.05
61	Rohn Stark	.05
62	Jack Trudeau	.05
63	Clarence Verdin	.05
64	Steve DeBerg	.05
65	Emile Harry	.05
66	Albert Lewis	.05
67	Nick Lowery	.05

68 Todd McNair .05
69 Christian Okoye .05
70 Stephone Paige .05
71 Kevin Porter .05
72 Derrick Thomas .10
73 Robb Thomas .05
74 Barry Word .05
75 Marcus Allen .10
76 Eddie Anderson .05
77 Tim Brown .10
78 Mervyn Fernandez .05
79 Willie Gault .05
80 Ethan Horton .05
81 Howie Long .05
82 Vance Mueller .05
83 Jay Schroeder .05
84 Steve Smith .05
85 Greg Townsend .05
86 Mark Clayton .05
87 Jim C. Jensen .05
88 Dan Marino 1.00
89 Tim McKyer .05
90 John Offerdahl .05
91 Louis Oliver .05
92 Reggie Roby .05
93 Sammie Smith .05
94 Hart Lee Dykes .05
95 Irving Fryar .05
96 Tommy Hodson .05
97 Maurice Hurst .05
98 John Stephens .15
99 Andre Tippett .05
100 Mark Boyer .05
101 Kyle Clifton .05
102 James Hasty .05
103 Erik McMillan .05
104 Rob Moore .05
105 Joe Mott .05
106 Ken O'Brien .05
107 Ron Stallworth .05
108 Al Toon .05
109 Gary Anderson .05
110 Bubby Brister .05
111 Thomas Everett .05
112 Merril Hoge .05
113 Louis Lipps .05
114 Greg Lloyd .05
115 Hardy Nickerson .05
116 Dwight Stone .05
117 Rod Woodson .10
118 Tim Worley .05
119 Rod Bernstine .05
120 Marion Butts .05
121 Gill Byrd .05
122 Arthur Cox .05
123 Burt Grossman .05
124 Ronnie Harmon .05
125 Anthony Miller .05
126 Leslie O'Neal .05
127 Gary Plummer .05
128 Sam Seale .05
129 Junior Seau .30
130 Broderick Thompson .05
131 Billy Joe Tolliver .05
132 Brian Blades .05
133 Jeff Bryant .05
134 Derrick Fenner .05
135 Jacob Green .05
136 Andy Heck .05
137 Patrick Hunter .05
138 Norm Johnson .05
139 Tommy Kane .05
140 Dave Krieg .05
141 John L. Williams .05
142 Terry Wooden .05
143 Steve Broussard .05
144 Keith Jones .05
145 Brian Jordan .05
146 Chris Miller .05
147 John Rade .05
148 Andre Rison .10
149 Mike Rozier .05
150 Deion Sanders .40
151 Neal Anderson .05
152 Trace Armstrong .05
153 Kevin Butler .05
154 Mark Carrier .05
155 Richard Dent .05
156 Dennis Gentry .05
157 Jim Harbaugh .10
158 Brad Muster .05
159 William Perry .05
160 Mike Singletary .05
161 Lemuel Stinson .05
162 Troy Aikman 1.00
163 Michael Irvin .30
164 Mike Saxon .05
165 Emmitt Smith 2.00
166 Jerry Ball .05
167 Michael Cofer .05
168 Rodney Peete .10
169 Barry Sanders 1.25
170 Robert Brown .05
171 Anthony Dilweg .05
172 Tim Harris .05
173 Johnny Holland .05
174 Perry Kemp .05
175 Don Majkowski .05
176 Brian Noble .05
177 Jeff Query .05
178 Sterling Sharpe .05
179 Charles Wilson .05
180 Keith Woodside .05
181 Flipper Anderson .05
182 Bern Brostek .05
183 Pat Carter .05
184 Aaron Cox .05

185 Henry Ellard .05
186 Jim Everett .05
187 Cleveland Gary .05
188 Jerry Gray .05
189 Kevin Greene .05
190 Mike Wilcher .05
191 Alfred Anderson .05
192 Joey Browner .05
193 Anthony Carter .05
194 Chris Doleman .05
195 Rick Fenney .05
196 Darrell Fullington .05
197 Rich Gannon .05
198 Hassan Jones .05
199 Steve Jordan .05
200 Mike Merriweather .05
201 Al Noga .05
202 Herschel Walker .05
203 Wade Wilson .05
204 Morten Andersen .05
205 Gene Atkins .05
206 Toi Cook .05
207 Craig Heyward .05
208 Dalton Hilliard .05
209 Vaughan Johnson .05
210 Eric Martin .05
211 Brett Perriman .10
212 Pat Swilling .05
213 Steve Walsh .05
214 Ottis Anderson .05
215 Carl Banks .05
216 Maurice Carthon .05
217 Mark Collins .05
218 Rodney Hampton .25
219 Erik Howard .05
220 Mark Ingram .05
221 Pepper Johnson .05
222 Dave Meggett .05
223 Phil Simms .05
224 Lawrence Taylor .10
225 Lewis Tillman .05
226 Everson Walls .05
227 Fred Barnett .05
228 Jerome Brown .05
229 Keith Byars .05
230 Randall Cunningham .10
231 Byron Evans .05
232 Wes Hopkins .05
233 Keith Jackson .05
234 Heath Sherman .05
235 Anthony Toney .05
236 Reggie White .10
237 Rich Camarillo .05
238 Ken Harvey .05
239 Eric Hill .05
240 Johnny Johnson .05
241 Ernie Jones .05
242 Tim McDonald .05
243 Timm Rosenbach .05
244 Jay Taylor .05
245 Dexter Carter .05
246 Mike Cofer .05
247 Kevin Fagan .05
248 Don Griffin .05
249 Charles Haley .05
250 Brent Jones .05
251 Joe Montana 1.00
252 Darryl Pollard .05
253 Tom Rathman .05
254 Jerry Rice 1.00
255 John Taylor .05
256 Steve Young 1.00
257 Gary Anderson .05
258 Mark Carrier .05
259 Chris Chandler .05
260 Reggie Cobb .05
261 Reuben Davis .05
262 Willie Drewrey .05
263 Ron Hall .05
264 Eugene Marve .05
265 Winston Moss .05
266 Vinny Testaverde .05
267 Broderick Thomas .05
268 Jeff Bostic .05
269 Earnest Byner .05
270 Gary Clark .05
271 Darrell Green .05
272 Jim Lachey .05
273 Wilber Marshall .05
274 Art Monk .05
275 Gerald Riggs .05
276 Mark Rypien .05
277 Ricky Sanders .05
278 Alvin Walton .05
279 Nick Bell .05
280 Eric Bieniemy .05
281 Jarrod Bunch .05
282 Mike Croel .10
283 Brett Favre 3.50
284 Moe Gardner .10
285 Pat Harlow .05
286 Randal Hill .25
287 Todd Marinovich .10
288 Russell Maryland .10
289 Dan McGwire .10
290 Ernie Mills .10
291 Herman Moore 3.50
292 Godfrey Myles .05
293 Browning Nagle .05
294 Mike Pritchard .30
295 Esera Tuaolo .05
296 Mark Vander Poel .05
297 Ricky Watters 2.00
298 Chris Zorich .20
299 Checklist Card .10
(Randall Cunningham, Emmitt Smith)

300 Checklist Card .10
(Randall Cunningham, Emmitt Smith)

1991 Ultra All-Stars

These cards, random inserts in 1991 Fleer Ultra packs, feature 10 top NFL players. Each card front has a shield with a head shot of the player, plus two smaller action photos against a gold background. A green stripe at the bottom contains the player's name, team and position. Each back has a career summary in a white box, bordered with a gold frame. Cards, which are numbered 1 of 10, etc., were randomly inserted in packs that were sold in black boxes.

MT
Complete Set (10): 12.00
Common Player: .50
Minor Stars: 1.00
1 Barry Sanders 5.00
2 Keith Jackson .50
3 Bruce Smith .50
4 Randall Cunningham 1.00
5 Dan Marino 6.00
6 Charles Haley .50
7 John L. Williams .50
8 Darrell Green .50
9 Stephone Paige .50
10 Kevin Greene 1.00

1991 Ultra Performances

Each card in this 10-card set features a color action photo on the front, with silver stripes as borders at the top and bottom. The player is pictured against a washed-out background with other players in it. The back has a player profile inside a black-and-silver border, plus a card number (1 of 10, etc.). These cards were random inserts in Fleer Ultra packs sold in green boxes.

MT
Complete Set (10): 25.00
Common Player: .50
Minor Stars: 1.00
1 Emmitt Smith 10.00
2 Andre Rison 1.00
3 Derrick Thomas 1.00
4 Joe Montana 6.00
5 Warren Moon 1.00
6 Mike Singletary .50
7 Thurman Thomas 1.00
8 Rod Woodson .50
9 Jerry Rice 6.00
10 Reggie White 1.00

A card number in parentheses ( ) indicates the set is unnumbered.

1991 Ultra Update

This 100-card set features top rookies and players who were traded during the 1991 season. Cards backs are numbered with a U prefix and have a mug shot of the player in a shield, surrounded by two smaller action shots. Fronts have an "Ultra Rookie" logo for the rookies.

MT
Complete Set (100): 35.00
Common Player: .10
Minor Stars: .20
1 Brett Favre 25.00
2 Moe Gardner .10
3 Tim McKyer .10
4 Bruce Pickens .10
5 Mike Pritchard .30
6 Cornelius Bennett .10
7 Phil Hansen .10
8 Henry Jones .10
9 Mark Kelso .10
10 James Lofton .10
11 Anthony Morgan .20
12 Stan Thomas .10
13 Chris Zorich .30
14 Reggie Rembert .10
15 Alfred Williams .10
16 Michael Jackson 1.00
17 Ed King .10
18 Joe Morris .10
19 Vince Newsome .10
20 Tony Casillas .10
21 Russell Maryland .20
22 Jay Novacek .20
23 Mike Croel .10
24 Gaston Green .10
25 Kenny Walker .10
26 Melvin Jenkins .10
27 Herman Moore 7.00
28 Kelvin Pritchett .10
29 Chris Spielman .10
30 Vinnie Clark .10
31 Allen Rice .10
32 Vai Sikahema .10
33 Esera Tuaolo .10
34 Mike Dumas .10
35 John Flannery .10
36 Allen Pinkett .10
37 Tim Barnett .20
38 Dan Saleaumua .10
39 Harvey Williams 1.00
40 Nick Bell .10
41 Roger Craig .10
42 Ronnie Lott .10
43 Todd Marinovich .10
44 Robert Delpino .10
45 Todd Lyght .20
46 Robert Young .10
47 Aaron Craver .20
48 Mark Higgs .20
49 Vestee Jackson .10
50 Carl Lee .10
51 Felix Wright .10
52 Darrell Fullington .10
53 Pat Harlow .10
54 Eugene Lockhart .10
55 Hugh Millen .20
56 Leonard Russell .25
57 Jon Vaughn .10
58 Quinn Early .10
59 Bobby Hebert .10
60 Rickey Jackson .10
61 Sam Mills .10
62 Jarrod Bunch .10
63 John Elliott .10
64 Jeff Hostetler .20
65 Ed McCaffrey 12.00
66 Kanavis McGhee .10
67 Mo Lewis .10
68 Browning Nagle .10
69 Blair Thomas .10
70 Antone Davis .10
71 Brad Goebel .10
72 Jim McMahon .10
73 Clyde Simmons .10
74 Randal Hill .25
75 Eric Swann .50
76 Tom Tupa .10
77 Jeff Graham 1.50
78 Eric Green .10
79 Neil O'Donnell 2.00
80 Huey Richardson .10
81 Eric Bieniemy .10

82 John Friesz .10
83 Eric Moten .10
84 Stanley Richard .20
85 Todd Bowles .10
86 Merton Hanks .75
87 Tim Harris .10
88 Pierce Holt .10
89 Ted Washington .10
90 John Kasay .10
91 Dan McGwire .10
92 Lawrence Dawsey .20
93 Charles McRae .10
94 Jesse Solomon .10
95 Robert Wilson .10
96 Ricky Ervins .20
97 Charles Mann .10
98 Bobby Wilson .10
99 Jerry Rice PV (PV) 2.00
100 Checklist .10

1992 Ultra

This 450-card set features full-bleed color action photos on the card fronts. The player's name is below a gold-foil stripe at the bottom, along with his team's name and position in bars color-coded according to his team's colors. The back is horizontal and shows a close-up and action shot of the player against a color-coded football field design. Statistics and the player's name are superimposed onto the card. A green marbleized area contains the player's team logo and biography. Subsets include Draft Picks (#s 417-446) and checklists (#s 447-450). Insert sets include Award Winners (10 cards, randomly in foil packs), and Signature Series sets for Chris Miller (10, in foil packs) and Reggie White (10, in foil packs).

MT
Complete Set (450): 20.00
Common Player: .05
Wax Box: 15.00
1 Steve Broussard .05
2 Rick Bryan .05
3 Scott Case .05
4 Darrion Conner .05
5 Bill Fralic .05
6 Moe Gardner .05
7 Tim Green .05
8 Michael Haynes .40
9 Chris Hinton .05
10 Mike Kenn .05
11 Tim McKver .05
12 Chris Miller .05
13 Erric Pegram .15
14 Mike Pritchard .20
15 Andre Rison .30
16 Jessie Tuggle .05
17 Carlton Bailey .25
18 Howard Ballard .05
19 Cornelius Bennett .05
20 Shane Conlan .05
21 Kenneth Davis .05
22 Kent Hull .05
23 Mark Kelso .05
24 James Lofton .05
25 Keith McKeller .05
26 Nate Odomes .05
27 Jim Ritcher .05
28 Leon Seals .05
29 Darryl Talley .05
30 Steve Tasker .05
31 Thurman Thomas .50
32 Will Wolford .05
33 Jeff Wright .05
34 Neal Anderson .20
35 Trace Armstrong .05
36 Mark Carrier .05
37 Wendell Davis .05
38 Richard Dent .05
39 Shaun Gayle .05
40 Jim Harbaugh .05
41 Jay Hilgenberg .05
42 Darren Lewis .05
43 Steve McMichael .05
44 Anthony Morgan .05
45 Brad Muster .05
46 William Perry .05

47 John Roper .05
48 Lemuel Stinson .05
49 Tom Waddle .15
50 Donnell Woolford .05
51 Leo Barker .10
52 Eddie Brown .05
53 James Francis .05
54 David Fulcher .05
55 David Grant .05
56 Harold Green .05
57 Rodney Holman .05
58 Lee Johnson .05
59 Tim Krumrie .05
60 Tim McGee .05
61 Alonzo Mitz .10
62 Anthony Munoz .05
63 Alfred Williams .05
64 Stephen Braggs .05
65 Richard Brown .10
66 Randy Hilliard .05
67 Leroy Hoard .05
68 Michael Jackson .15
69 Mike Johnson .05
70 James Jones .05
71 Tony Jones .05
72 Ed King .05
73 Kevin Mack .05
74 Clay Matthews .05
75 Eric Metcalf .05
76 Vince Newsome .05
77 Steve Beuerlein .20
78 Larry Brown .05
79 Tony Casillas .05
80 Alvin Harper .50
81 Issiac Holt .05
82 Ray Horton .05
83 Michael Irvin .40
84 Daryl Johnston .05
85 Kelvin Martin .05
86 Ken Norton .05
87 Jay Novacek .20
88 Emmitt Smith 5.00
89 Vinson Smith .15
90 Mark Stepnoski .05
91 Tony Tolbert .05
92 Alexander Wright .05
93 Steve Atwater .05
94 Tyrone Braxton .05
95 Michael Brooks .05
96 Mike Croel .05
97 John Elway .75
98 Simon Fletcher .05
99 Gaston Green .05
100 Mark Jackson .05
101 Keith Kartz .05
102 Greg Kragen .05
103 Greg Lewis .05
104 Karl Mecklenburg .05
105 Derek Russell .25
106 Steve Sewell .05
107 Dennis Smith .05
108 David Treadwell .05
109 Kenny Walker .05
110 Michael Young .05
111 Jerry Ball .05
112 Bennie Blades .05
113 Lomas Brown .05
114 Scott Conover .15
116 Mel Gray .05
117 Willie Green .15
118 Erik Kramer .05
119 Dan Owens .05
120 Rodney Peete .05
121 Brett Perriman .05
122 Barry Sanders 3.00
123 Chris Spielman .05
124 Marc Spindler .05
125 Willie White .05
126 Tony Bennett .05
127 Matt Brock .05
128 Leroy Butler .05
129 Chuck Cecil .05
130 Johnny Holland .05
131 Perry Kemp .05
132 Don Majkowski .05
133 Tony Mandarich .05
134 Brian Noble .05
135 Bryce Paup .05
136 Sterling Sharpe .30
137 Darrell Thompson .05
138 Mike Tomczak .05
139 Vince Workman .05
140 Ray Childress .05
141 Cris Dishman .05
142 Curtis Duncan .05
143 William Fuller .05
144 Ernest Givins .05
145 Haywood Jeffires .15
146 Sean Jones .05
147 Lamar Lathon .05
148 Bruce Matthews .05
149 Bubba McDowell .05
150 Johnny Meads .05
151 Warren Moon .40
152 Mike Munchak .05
153 Bo Orlando .30
154 Al Smith .05
155 Doug Smith .05
156 Lorenzo White .05
157 Chip Banks .05
158 Duane Bickett .05
159 Bill Brooks .05
160 Jon Hand .05
161 Jeff Herrod .05
162 Jessie Hester .05
163 Scott Radecic .05
164 Rohn Stark .05
165 Clarence Verdin .05

No.	Player	Price
166	Eugene Daniel	.05
167	John Alt	.05
168	Tim Barnett	.05
169	Tim Grunhard	.05
170	Dino Hackett	.05
171	Jonathan Hayes	.05
172	Bill Maas	.05
173	Chris Martin	.05
174	Christian Okoye	.05
175	Stephone Paige	.05
176	*Jayice Pearson*	.10
177	Kevin Porter	.05
178	Kevin Ross	.05
179	Dan Saleaumua	.05
180	Tracy Simien	.05
181	Neil Smith	.05
182	Derrick Thomas	.35
183	Robb Thomas	.05
184	Barry Word	.15
185	Marcus Allen	.08
186	Eddie Anderson	.05
187	Nick Bell	.15
188	Tim Brown	.30
189	Mervyn Fernandez	.05
190	Jeff Gossett	.05
191	Ethan Horton	.05
192	Jeff Jaeger	.05
193	Howie Long	.05
194	Ronnie Lott	.05
195	Todd Marinovich	.15
196	Don Mosebar	.05
197	Jay Schroeder	.05
198	Anthony Smith	.05
199	Greg Townsend	.05
200	Lionel Washington	.05
201	Steve Wisniewski	.05
202	Willie Anderson	.05
203	Robert Delpino	.05
204	Henry Ellard	.05
205	Jim Everett	.05
206	Kevin Greene	.05
207	Darryl Henley	.05
208	Damone Johnson	.05
209	Larry Kelm	.05
210	Todd Lyght	.05
211	Jackie Slater	.05
212	Michael Stewart	.05
213	Pat Terrell	.05
214	Robert Young	.05
215	Mark Clayton	.05
216	Bryan Cox	.05
217	Jeff Cross	.05
218	Mark Duper	.05
219	Mark Duper	.05
220	Harry Galbreath	.05
221	David Griggs	.05
222	Mark Higgs	.10
224	Jim Offerdahl	.05
225	Louis Oliver	.05
226	Tony Paige	.05
227	Reggie Roby	.05
228	Pete Stoyanovich	.05
229	Richmond Webb	.05
230	Terry Allen	.60
231	Ray Berry	.05
232	Anthony Carter	.05
233	Cris Carter	.05
234	Chris Doleman	.05
235	Rich Gannon	.10
236	Steve Jordan	.05
237	Carl Lee	.05
238	Randall McDaniel	.05
239	Mike Merriweather	.05
240	Harry Newsome	.05
241	John Randle	.05
242	Henry Thomas	.05
243	Bruce Armstrong	.05
244	Vincent Brown	.05
245	Marv Cook	.05
246	Irving Fryar	.05
247	Pat Harlow	.05
248	Maurice Hurst	.05
249	Eugene Lockhart	.05
250	Greg McMurtry	.05
251	Hugh Millen	.05
252	Leonard Russell	.35
253	Chris Singleton	.05
254	Andre Tippett	.05
255	Jon Vaughn	.10
256	Morten Andersen	.05
257	Gene Atkins	.05
258	Wesley Carroll	.05
259	Jim Dombrowski	.05
260	Quinn Early	.05
261	Bobby Hebert	.05
262	Joel Hilgenberg	.05
263	Rickey Jackson	.05
264	Vaughan Johnson	.05
265	Eric Martin	.05
266	Brett Maxie	.05
267	*Fred McAfee*	.20
268	Sam Mills	.05
269	Pat Swilling	.05
270	Floyd Turner	.05
271	Steve Walsh	.05
272	Stephen Baker	.05
273	Jarrod Bunch	.05
274	Mark Collins	.05
275	Jim Elliott	.05
276	Myron Guyton	.05
277	Rodney Hampton	.50
278	Jeff Hostetler	.25
279	Mark Ingram	.05
280	Pepper Johnson	.05
281	Sean Landeta	.05
282	Leonard Marshall	.05
283	Kanavis McGhee	.05
284	Dave Meggett	.05
285	Bart Oates	.05
286	Phil Simms	.10
287	Reyna Thompson	.05
288	Lewis Tillman	.05
289	Brad Baxter	.05
290	*Mike Brim*	.10
291	Chris Burkett	.05
292	Kyle Clifton	.05
293	James Hasty	.05
294	Joe Kelly	.05
295	Jeff Lageman	.05
296	Mo Lewis	.05
297	Erik McMillan	.05
298	Scott Mersereau	.05
299	Rob Moore	.05
300	Tony Stargell	.05
301	Jim Sweeney	.05
302	Marvin Washington	.05
303	Lonnie Young	.05
304	Eric Allen	.05
305	Fred Barnett	.15
306	Keith Byars	.05
307	Byron Evans	.05
308	Wes Hopkins	.05
309	Keith Jackson	.15
310	James Joseph	.05
311	Seth Joyner	.05
312	Roger Ruzek	.05
313	Clyde Simmons	.05
314	William Thomas	.05
315	Reggie White	.35
316	Calvin Williams	.15
317	Rich Camarillo	.05
318	Jeff Faulkner	.05
319	Ken Harvey	.05
320	Eric Hill	.05
321	Johnny Johnson	.10
322	Ernie Jones	.05
323	Tim McDonald	.05
324	Freddie Joe Nunn	.05
325	Luis Sharpe	.05
326	Eric Swann	.05
327	Aeneas Williams	.05
328	*Mike Zordich*	.15
329	Gary Anderson	.05
330	Bubby Brister	.05
331	Barry Foster	.50
332	Eric Green	.05
333	Bryan Hinkle	.05
334	Tunch Ilkin	.05
335	Carnell Lake	.05
336	Louis Lipps	.05
337	David Little	.05
338	Greg Lloyd	.05
339	Neil O'Donnell	.60
340	Rod Woodson	.08
341	Rod Bernstine	.05
342	Marion Butts	.08
343	Gill Byrd	.05
344	John Friesz	.05
345	Burt Grossman	.05
346	Courtney Hall	.05
347	Ronnie Harmon	.05
348	Shawn Jefferson	.05
349	Nate Lewis	.08
350	*Craig McEwen*	.10
351	Eric Moten	.05
352	Gary Plummer	.05
353	Henry Rolling	.05
354	Broderick Thompson	.05
355	Derrick Walker	.05
356	Harris Barton	.05
357	*Steve Bono*	.75
358	Todd Bowles	.05
359	Dexter Carter	.05
360	Michael Carter	.05
361	Keith DeLong	.05
362	Charles Haley	.05
363	Merton Hanks	.05
364	Tim Harris	.05
365	Brent Jones	.05
366	Guy McIntyre	.05
367	Tom Rathman	.05
368	Bill Romanowski	.05
369	Jesse Sapolu	.05
370	John Taylor	.05
371	Steve Young	2.00
372	Robert Blackmon	.05
373	Brian Blades	.05
374	Jacob Green	.05
375	Dwayne Harper	.05
376	Andy Heck	.05
377	Tommy Kane	.05
378	John Kassay	.05
379	Cortez Kennedy	.25
380	Bryan Millard	.05
381	Rufus Porter	.05
382	Eugene Robinson	.05
383	John L. Williams	.05
384	Terry Wooden	.05
385	Gary Anderson	.05
386	Ian Beckles	.05
387	Mark Carrier	.05
388	Reggie Cobb	.10
389	Tony Covington	.05
390	Lawrence Dawsey	.05
391	Ron Hall	.05
392	Keith McCants	.05
393	Charles McRae	.05
394	Tim Newton	.05
395	Jesse Solomon	.05
396	Vinny Testaverde	.05
397	Broderick Thomas	.05
398	Robert Wilson	.05
399	Earnest Byner	.05
400	Gary Clark	.05
401	Andre Collins	.05
402	Brad Edwards	.05
403	Kurt Gouveia	.05
404	Darrell Green	.05
405	Joe Jacoby	.05
407	Chip Lohmiller	.05
408	Charles Mann	.05
409	Wilber Marshall	.05
410	Brian Mitchell	.05
411	Art Monk	.05
412	Mark Rypien	.15
413	Ricky Sanders	.05
414	Mark Schlereth	.15
415	Fred Stokes	.05
416	Bobby Wilson	.05
417	*Corey Barlow*	.15
418	*Edgar Bennett*	.50
419	*Eddie Blake*	.15
420	*Terrell Buckley*	.30
421	*Willie Clay*	.15
422	*Rodney Culver*	.25
423	*Ed Cunningham*	.15
424	*Mark D'Onofrio*	.15
425	*Matt Darby*	.10
426	*Charles Davenport*	.10
427	*Will Furrer*	.20
428	*Keith Goganious*	.10
429	*Mario Bailey*	.05
430	*Chris Hakel*	.10
431	*Keith Hamilton*	.25
432	*Aaron Pierce*	.10
433	*Amp Lee*	.35
434	*Scott Lockwood*	.15
435	*Ricardo McDonald*	.15
436	*Dexter McNabb*	.15
437	*Chris Mims*	.40
438	*Mike Mooney*	.15
439	*Ray Roberts*	.15
440	*Patrick Rowe*	.15
441	*Leon Searcy*	.15
442	*Siran Stacy*	.20
443	*Kevin Turner*	.30
444	*Tommy Vardell*	.25
445	*Bob Whitfield*	.20
446	*Darryl Williams*	.25
447	Checklists	.05
448	Checklists	.05
449	Checklists	.05
450	Checklists	.05

1992 Ultra Award Winners

Each of the 10 players in this insert set had award-winning performances during the 1991 season. The front has a full-bleed photo of the player, along with a black marble-like strip at the bottom which contains the player's name and the award he won in gold foil. A black "Award Winner" logo is also superimposed in the lower right corner. The card back has a portrait of the player inside a shield, with his name in a banner above a career summary. Cards were randomly inserted in 1992 Fleer Ultra foil packs and are numbered 1 of 10, etc.

		MT
	Complete Set (10):	20.00
	Common Player:	1.50
1	Mark Rypien	1.75
2	Cornelius Bennett	1.50
3	Pat Swilling	1.50
4	Lawrence Dawsey	1.75
5	Thurman Thomas	4.00
6	Michael Irvin	5.00
7	Mike Croel	1.50
8	Barry Sanders	8.00
9	Anthony Munoz	1.50
10	Leonard Russell	2.00

> Post-1980 cards in Near Mint condition will generally sell for about 75% of the quoted Mint value. Excellent-condition cards bring no more than 40%.

1992 Ultra Chris Miller

These 10 cards were randomly inserted in 1992 Fleer Ultra foil packs as part of Fleer's signature series. Each card front has a player action photo inside an inner black and outer maroon marbleized border. Miller's name and "Performance Highlights" are in gold foil letters at the bottom. The back has a player portrait shot and career summary against a rose-colored background, plus a card number. Cards 11-12 were available only through a mail-in offer from Fleer; 10 1992 Fleer Ultra wrappers and $2 were required. In addition, Miller signed more than 2,000 cards.

	MT
Complete Set (10):	6.00
Common Miller:	.60
Autograph:	50.00

1992 Ultra Reggie White

These cards, part of Fleer's signature series, were random inserts in 1992 Fleer Ultra foil packs. Each card front has a color action photo bordered by green and gray marble frames. White's name and "Career Highlights" are in gold foil at the bottom. The back has a career summary and head shot against a gray marble-like background, plus a card number. Cards 11-12 were available only through a mail-in program to Fleer for 10 1992 Fleer Ultra wrappers and $2. These cards have rose-colored backs. White signed more than 2,000 randomly-inserted cards.

	MT
Complete Set (10):	10.00
Common White:	1.00
Autograph:	75.00

1993 Ultra

Fleer's 1993 Ultra set con-sists of 500 cards featuring UV coating and action photos. Insert sets include NFL Award Winners (10 cards), NFL League Leaders (10), All-Rookie Series (10), Stars (10), Touchdown Kings (10) and a Michael Irvin "Performance Highlights" set (10).

		MT
	Complete Set (500):	60.00
	Common Player:	.10
	Minor Stars:	.20
	Wax Box:	70.00
1	Vinnie Clark	.10
2	Darion Connor	.10
3	Eric Dickerson	.20
4	Moe Gardner	.10
5	Tim Green	.10
6	*Roger Harper*	.10
7	Michael Haynes	.10
8	Bobby Hebert	.10
9	Chris Hinton	.10
10	Pierce Holt	.10
11	Mike Kenn	.10
12	*Lincoln Kennedy*	.20
13	Chris Miller	.10
14	Mike Pritchard	.10
15	Andre Rison	.20
16	Deion Sanders	1.50
17	Tony Smith	.10
18	Jessie Tuggle	.10
19	Howard Ballard	.10
20	Don Beebe	.10
21	Cornelius Bennett	.10
22	Bill Brooks	.10
23	Kenneth Davis	.10
24	Phil Hansen	.10
25	Henry Jones	.10
26	Jim Kelly	.50
27	Nate Odomes	.10
28	*John Parrella*	.10
29	Andre Reed	.20
30	Frank Reich	.10
31	Jim Ritcher	.10
32	Bruce Smith	.10
33	*Thomas Smith*	.20
34	Darryl Talley	.10
35	Steve Tasker	.10
36	Thurman Thomas	.50
37	Jeff Wright	.10
38	Neal Anderson	.10
39	Trace Armstrong	.10
40	Mark Carrier	.10
41	*Curtis Conway*	2.50
42	Wendell Davis	.10
43	Richard Dent	.10
44	Shaun Gayle	.10
45	Jim Harbaugh	.10
46	Craig Heyward	.10
47	Darren Lewis	.10
48	Steve McMichael	.10
49	William Perry	.10
50	*Carl Simpson*	.10
51	Alonzo Spellman	.10
52	Keith Van Horne	.10
53	Tom Waddle	.10
54	Donnell Woolford	.10
55	*John Copeland*	.50
56	Derrick Fenner	.10
57	James Francis	.10
58	Harold Green	.10
59	David Klingler	.50
60	Tim Krumrie	.10
61	Ricardo McDonald	.10
62	*Tony McGee*	.75
63	Carl Pickens	1.50
64	Lamar Rogers	.10
65	Jay Schroeder	.10
66	Daniel Stubbs	.10
67	*Steve Tovar*	.10
68	Alfred Williams	.10
69	Darryl Williams	.10
70	Jerry Ball	.10
71	David Brandon	.10
72	Rob Burnett	.10
73	Mark Carrier	.10
74	*Steve Everett*	.20
75	*Dan Footman*	.10
76	Leroy Hoard	.10
77	Michael Jackson	.10
78	Mike Johnson	.10
79	Bernie Kosar	.20
80	Clay Mathews	.10
81	Eric Metcalf	.10
82	Michael Dean Perry	.10
83	Vinny Testaverde	.20
84	Tommy Vardell	.10
85	Troy Aikman	3.00
86	Larry Brown	.10
87	Tony Casillas	.10
88	Thomas Everett	.10
89	Charles Haley	.10
90	Alvin Harper	.20
91	Michael Irvin	.50
92	Jim Jeffcoat	.10
93	Daryl Johnston	.10
94	Robert Jones	.10
95	*Leon Lett*	.50
96	Russell Maryland	.10
97	Nate Newton	.10
98	Ken Norton	.10
99	Jay Novacek	.10
100	*Darrin Smith*	.50
101	Emmitt Smith	5.00
102	Kevin Smith	.10
103	Mark Stepnoski	.10
104	Tony Tolbert	.10
105	*Kevin Williams*	.30
106	Steve Atwater	.10
107	Rod Bernstine	.10
108	Mike Croel	.10
109	Robert Delpino	.10
110	Shane Dronett	.10
111	John Elway	1.50
112	Simon Fletcher	.10
113	Greg Kragen	.10
114	Tommy Maddox	.10
115	*Arthur Marshall*	.20
116	Karl Mecklenburg	.10
117	*Glyn Milburn*	1.00
118	*Reggie Rivers*	.10
119	Shannon Sharpe	.20
120	Dennis Smith	.10
121	Kenny Walker	.10
122	*Dan Williams*	.10
123	Bennie Blades	.10
124	Lomas Brown	.10
125	Bill Fralic	.10
126	Mel Gray	.10
127	Willie Green	.10
128	Jason Hanson	.10
129	*Antonio London*	.10
130	*Ryan McNeil*	.10
131	Herman Moore	2.00
132	Rodney Peete	.10
133	Brett Perriman	.10
134	Kelvin Pritchett	.10
135	Barry Sanders	3.00
136	Tracy Scroggins	.10
137	Chris Spielman	.10
138	Pat Swilling	.10
139	Andre Ware	.10
140	Edgar Bennett	1.00
141	Tony Bennett	.10
142	Matt Brock	.10
143	Terrell Buckley	.10
144	LeRoy Butler	.10
145	Mark Clayton	.10
146	Brett Favre	5.00
147	Jackie Harris	.20
148	Johnny Holland	.10
149	Bill Maas	.10
150	Brian Noble	.10
151	Bryce Paup	.10
152	Ken Ruettgers	.10
153	Sterling Sharpe	.20
154	*Wayne Simmons*	.10
155	John Stephens	.10
156	*George Teague*	.50
157	Reggie White	.20
158	*Michael Barrow*	.10
159	Cody Carlson	.10
160	Ray Childress	.10
161	Cris Duncan	.10
162	Curtis Duncan	.10
163	William Fuller	.10
164	Ernest Givins	.10
165	*Brad Hopkins*	.10
166	Haywood Jeffires	.10
167	Lamar Lathon	.10
168	Wilber Marshall	.10
169	Bruce Matthews	.10
170	Bubba McDowell	.10
171	Warren Moon	.20
172	Mike Munchak	.10
173	Eddie Robinson	.10
174	Al Smith	.10
175	Lorenzo White	.10
176	Lee Williams	.10
177	Chip Banks	.10
178	John Baylor	.10
179	Duane Bickett	.10
180	Kerry Cash	.10
181	Quentin Coryatt	.10
182	Rodney Culver	.10
183	Steve Emtman	.10
184	Jeff George	.50
185	Jeff Herrod	.10
186	Jessie Hester	.10
187	Anthony Johnson	.10
188	Reggie Langhorne	.10
189	*Roosevelt Potts*	.20
190	Rohn Stark	.10
191	Clarence Verdin	.10
192	Will Wolford	.10
193	Marcus Allen	.20
194	John Alt	.10
195	Tim Barnett	.10
196	J.J. Birden	.10
197	Dale Carter	.10
198	Willie Davis	.10
199	*Jamie Fields*	.10
200	Dave Krieg	.10
201	Nick Lowery	.10
202	*Charles Mincy*	.10
203	Joe Montana	3.00
204	Christian Okoye	.10
205	Dan Saleaumua	.10
206	*Will Shields*	.10
207	Tracy Simien	.10
208	Neil Smith	.10
209	Derrick Thomas	.20
210	Harvey Williams	.10
211	Barry Word	.10
212	Eddie Anderson	.10
213	*Patrick Bates*	.10
214	Nick Bell	.10
215	Tim Brown	.20
216	Willie Gault	.10
217	Gaston Green	.10
218	Ethan Horton	.10
219	*Billy Jo Hobert*	.75
220	Jeff Hostetler	.10
221	James Lofton	.10

#	Player	Price
222	Howie Long	.10
223	Todd Marinovich	.10
224	Terry McDaniel	.10
225	Winston Moss	.10
226	Anthony Smith	.10
227	Greg Townsend	.10
228	Aaron Wallace	.10
229	Lionel Washington	.10
230	Steve Wisniewski	.10
231	Willie Anderson	.10
232	*Jerome Bettis*	4.00
234	Shane Conlan	.10
235	*Troy Drayton*	1.00
236	Henry Ellard	.10
237	Jim Everett	.10
238	Cleveland Gary	.10
239	Sean Gilbert	.10
240	Darryl Henley	.10
241	David Lang	.10
242	Todd Lyght	.10
243	*Anthony Newman*	.10
244	Roman Phifer	.10
245	Gerald Robinson	.10
246	Henry Rolling	.10
247	Jackie Slater	.10
248	Keith Byars	.10
249	Marco Coleman	.10
250	Bryan Cox	.10
251	Jeff Cross	.10
252	Irving Fryar	.10
253	Mark Higgs	.10
254	*Dwight Hollier*	.10
255	Mark Ingram	.10
256	Keith Jackson	.10
257	*Terry Kirby*	1.00
258	Dan Marino	5.00
259	*O.J. McDuffie*	3.00
260	John Offerdahl	.10
261	Louis Oliver	.10
262	Pete Stoyanovich	.10
263	Troy Vincent	.10
264	Richmond Webb	.10
265	Jarvis Williams	.10
266	Terry Allen	.10
267	Anthony Carter	.10
268	Cris Carter	.20
269	Roger Craig	.10
270	Jack Del Rio	.10
271	Chris Doleman	.10
272	*Qadry Ismail*	.30
273	Steve Jordan	.10
274	Randall McDaniel	.10
275	Audray McMillian	.10
276	John Randle	.10
277	Sean Salisbury	.10
278	Todd Scott	.10
279	*Robert Smith*	4.00
280	Henry Thomas	.10
281	Ray Agnew	.10
282	Bruce Armstrong	.10
283	*Drew Bledsoe*	8.00
284	*Vincent Brisby*	1.00
285	Vincent Brown	.10
286	Eugene Chung	.10
287	Marv Cook	.10
288	Pat Harlow	.10
289	Jerome Henderson	.10
290	Greg McMurty	.10
291	Leonard Russell	.10
292	Chris Singleton	.10
293	Chris Slade	.20
294	Andre Tippett	.10
295	Brent Williams	.10
296	Scott Zolak	.10
297	Morten Andersen	.10
298	Gene Atkins	.10
299	Mike Buck	.10
300	Toi Cook	.10
301	Jim Dombrowski	.10
302	Vaughn Dunbar	.10
303	Quinn Early	.10
304	Joel Hilgenberg	.10
305	Dalton Hilliard	.10
306	Ricky Jackson	.10
307	Vaughan Johnson	.10
308	Reginald Jones	.10
309	Eric Martin	.10
310	Wayne Martin	.10
311	Sam Mills	.10
312	Brad Muster	.10
313	*Willie Roaf*	.20
314	*Irv Smith*	.20
315	Wade Wilson	.10
316	Carlton Bailey	.10
317	Michael Brooks	.10
318	Derek Brown	.10
319	*Marcus Buckley*	.10
320	Jarrod Bunch	.10
321	Mark Collins	.10
322	Eric Dorsey	.10
323	Rodney Hampton	.20
324	Mark Jackson	.10
325	Pepper Johnson	.10
326	Ed McCaffrey	.10
327	Dave Meggett	.10
328	Bart Oates	.10
329	Mike Sherrard	.10
330	Phil Simms	.10
331	*Michael Strahan*	.10
332	Lawrence Taylor	.20
333	Brad Baxter	.10
334	Chris Burkett	.10
335	Kyle Clifton	.10
336	Boomer Esiason	.10
337	James Hasty	.10
338	Johnny Johnson	.10
339	*Marvin Jones*	.20
340	Jeff Lageman	.10
341	Mo Lewis	.10
342	Ronnie Lott	.10
343	Leonard Marshall	.10

#	Player	Price
344	Johnny Mitchell	.10
345	Rob Moore	.10
346	Browning Nagle	.10
347	*Coleman Rudolph*	.10
348	Blair Thomas	.10
349	Eric Thomas	.10
350	Brian Washington	.10
351	Marvin Washington	.10
352	Eric Allen	.10
353	*Victor Bailey*	.20
354	Fred Barnett	.10
355	Mark Bavaro	.10
356	Randall Cunningham	.20
357	Byron Evans	.10
358	*Andy Harmon*	.10
359	Tim Harris	.10
360	*Lester Holmes*	.10
361	Seth Joyner	.10
362	Keith Millard	.10
363	*Leonard Renfro*	.10
364	Heath Sherman	.10
365	Vai Sikahema	.10
366	Clyde Simmons	.10
367	William Thomas	.10
368	Herschel Walker	.10
369	Andre Waters	.10
370	Calvin Williams	.10
371	Johnny Bailey	.10
372	Steve Beuerlein	.10
373	Rich Camarillo	.10
374	Chuck Cecil	.10
375	Chris Chandler	.10
376	Gary Clark	.10
377	*Ben Coleman*	.10
378	*Earnest Dye*	.10
379	Ken Harvey	.10
380	*Garrison Hearst*	3.00
381	Randal Hill	.10
382	Robert Massey	.10
383	Freddie Joe Nunn	.10
384	Ricky Proehl	.10
385	Luis Sharpe	.10
386	Tyronne Stowe	.10
387	Eric Swann	.10
388	Aeneas Williams	.10
389	*Chad Brown*	.50
390	Dermontti Dawson	.10
391	Donald Evans	.10
392	*Deon Figures*	.50
393	Barry Foster	.20
394	Jeff Graham	.10
395	Eric Green	.10
396	Kevin Greene	.10
397	Carlton Haselrig	.10
398	*Andre Hastings*	.75
399	D.J. Johnson	.10
400	Carnell Lake	.10
401	Greg Lloyd	.10
402	Neil O'Donnell	.40
403	Darren Perry	.10
404	Mike Tomczak	.10
405	Rod Woodson	.20
406	Eric Bieniemy	.10
407	Marion Butts	.10
408	Gill Byrd	.10
409	*Darren Carrington*	.20
410	*Darrien Gordon*	.75
411	Burt Grossman	.10
412	Courtney Hall	.10
413	Ronnie Harmon	.10
414	Stan Humphries	.20
415	Nate Lewis	.10
416	*Natrone Means*	3.00
417	Anthony Miller	.10
418	Chris Mims	.10
419	Leslie O'Neal	.10
420	Gary Plummer	.10
421	Stanley Richard	.10
422	Junior Seau	.20
423	Harry Swayne	.10
424	Jerrol Williams	.10
425	Harris Barton	.10
426	Steve Bono	1.00
427	Kevin Fagan	.10
428	Don Griffin	.10
429	Dana Hall	.10
430	*Adrian Hardy*	.10
431	Brent Jones	.10
432	*Todd Kelly*	.10
433	Amp Lee	.10
434	Tim McDonald	.10
435	Guy McIntyre	.10
436	Tom Rathman	.10
437	Jerry Rice	3.00
438	Bill Romanowski	.10
439	*Dana Stubblefield*	1.00
440	John Taylor	.10
441	Steve Wallace	.10
442	Mike Walter	.10
443	Ricky Watters	.50
444	Steve Young	3.00
445	Robert Blackmon	.10
446	Brian Blades	.10
447	Jeff Bryant	.10
448	Ferrell Edmunds	.10
449	*Carlton Gray*	.20
450	Dwayne Harper	.10
451	Andy Heck	.10
452	Tommy Kane	.10
453	Cortez Kennedy	.20
454	Kelvin Martin	.10
455	Dan McGwire	.10
456	*Rick Mirer*	.50
457	Rufus Porter	.10
458	Ray Roberts	.10
459	Eugene Robinson	.10
460	Chris Warren	1.00
461	John L. Williams	.10
462	Gary Anderson	.10

#	Player	Price
463	Tyji Armstrong	.10
464	Reggie Cobb	.10
465	*Eric Curry*	.50
466	Lawrence Dawsey	.10
467	Steve DeBerg	.10
468	Santana Dotson	.10
469	*Demetrius DuBose*	.20
470	Paul Gruber	.10
471	Ron Hall	.10
472	Courtney Hawkins	.10
473	Hardy Nickerson	.10
474	Ricky Reynolds	.10
475	Broderick Thomas	.10
476	Mark Wheeler	.10
477	Jimmy Williams	.10
478	Carl Banks	.10
479	*Reggie Brooks*	.75
480	Earnest Byner	.10
481	*Tom Carter*	.20
482	Andre Collins	.10
483	Brad Edwards	.10
484	Ricky Ervins	.10
485	Kurt Gouveia	.10
486	Darrell Green	.10
487	Desmond Howard	.20
488	Jim Lachey	.10
489	Chip Lohmiller	.10
490	Charles Mann	.10
491	Tim McGee	.10
492	Brian Mitchell	.10
493	Art Monk	.10
494	Mark Rypien	.10
495	Ricky Sanders	.10
496	Checklist	.10
497	Checklist	.10
498	Checklist	.10
499	Checklist	.10
500	Checklist	.10

1993 Ultra All-Rookies

Ten first-year players are featured on these cards, which were random inserts in 1993 Fleer Ultra 14- and 19-card packs. Each front has a color action photo against an orange background. The player's name and set title are stamped in gold foil at the bottom. The back, in a horizontal format, has a close-up shot of the player, plus career highlights, all against an orange-to-yellow background. Card backs are numbered 1 of 10, etc..

		MT
	Complete Set (10):	75.00
	Common Player:	2.00
	Minor Stars:	4.00
1	Patrick Bates	2.00
2	Jerome Bettis	15.00
3	Drew Bledsoe	30.00
4	Curtis Conway	7.00
5	Garrison Hearst	10.00
6	Qadry Ismail	4.00
7	Marvin Jones	2.00
8	Glyn Milburn	4.00
9	Rick Mirer	5.00
10	Kevin Williams	5.00

1993 Ultra Award Winners

These cards were randomly inserted in 1993 Fleer Ultra 14- and 19-card foil packs. The players who are featured delivered award-winning performances during the 1992 season, such as MVP and Rookie of the Year. Fronts have full-bleed photos on a borderless, gold metallic background. The set's name is at the top, while the player's name is at the bottom. The back has a gold metallic background, with sun rays radiating towards the sides. The player's name and award he won are stamped in silver foil on the back, which also includes his career highlights and another photo, plus a card number (1 of 10 etc.).

		MT
	Complete Set (10):	75.00
	Common Player:	3.00
	Minor Stars:	6.00
1	Troy Aikman	30.00
2	Dale Carter	3.00
3	Chris Doleman	3.00
4	Santana Dotson	3.00
5	Barry Foster	6.00
6	Jason Hanson	3.00
7	Cortez Kennedy	3.00
8	Carl Pickens	10.00
9	Steve Tasker	3.00
10	Steve Young	25.00

1993 Ultra Michael Irvin

This "Performance Highlights" set features 10 cards devoted to Dallas Cowboys wide receiver Michael Irvin. Each borderless card front features a color action photo and a black marble-like stripe which contains the set subtitle and logo in silver foil. Each back has a color photo, plus career highlights in silver foil letters on a blue-screeen panel with a silver foil frame. A black marble-like stripe creates a border at the card bottom. Cards are numbered 1 of 10, etc., and were random inserts in 1993 Fleer Ultra packs.

	MT
Complete Set (10):	10.00
Common Irvin:	1.00
Autograph Irvin:	80.00
Mail-In Irvin (11-12):	1.50

1993 Ultra League Leaders

Players who led the league in certain statistical categories are featured on these cards, which were random inserts in 1993 Fleer Ultra 14- and 19-card packs. The card fronts are borderless and have an action shot against a silver metallic background. The player's name is at the bottom; the set title is at the top. The back has a silver metallic background with rays radiating toward the sides. The player's name and set title are stamped in silver foil at the top. The category the player led the league in, and a career summary, follow. The cards are numbered 1 of 10, etc.

		MT
	Complete Set (10):	75.00
	Common Player:	3.00
	Minor Stars:	6.00
1	Troy Aikman	30.00
2	Dale Carter	3.00
3	Chris Doleman	3.00
4	Santana Dotson	3.00
5	Barry Foster	6.00
6	Jason Hanson	3.00
7	Cortez Kennedy	3.00
8	Carl Pickens	10.00
9	Steve Tasker	3.00
10	Steve Young	25.00

1993 Ultra Ultra Stars

Ten of the NFL's premiere players are featured on these cards, which were randomly inserted in 1993 Fleer Ultra 19-card foil packs only. Each front has an action shot of the player superimposed against a ghosted U.S. flag. A grey marble stripe appears at the bottom, along with the player's name, set title and spiraling football, which are stamped in gold foil. Each back has a close-up shot of the player on one side, plus career highlights on the other. The cards are numbered 1 of 10, etc..

		MT
	Complete Set (10):	110.00
	Common Player:	5.00
	Minor Stars:	10.00
1	Brett Favre	50.00
2	Barry Foster	5.00
3	Michael Irvin	10.00
4	Cortez Kennedy	5.00
5	Deion Sanders	15.00
6	Junior Seau	10.00
7	Derrick Thomas	5.00
8	Ricky Watters	10.00
9	Reggie White	10.00
10	Steve Young	30.00

1993 Ultra Touchdown Kings

Ten of the NFL's top offensive players are featured on these cards, which were random inserts in 1993 Fleer Ultra 14-card foil packs only. Each front has an action photo of the player superimposed against a ghosted football field and diagrammed plays. The player's name and set title are stamped in gold foil at the bottom, which has a green marble-like border. Each back is white with a player photo and stats against a background of play diagrams. The cards are numbered 1 of 10, etc..

		MT
	Complete Set (10):	85.00
	Common Player:	2.00
	Minor Stars:	4.00
1	Rodney Hampton	2.00
2	Dan Marino	15.00
3	Art Monk	2.00
4	Joe Montana	12.00
5	Jerry Rice	10.00
6	Andre Rison	4.00
7	Barry Sanders	20.00
8	Sterling Sharpe	4.00
9	Emmitt Smith	15.00
10	Thurman Thomas	4.00

1994 Ultra

Fleer Ultra Football contains 525 cards using a new design and includes loads of inserts. The first series had six new insert sets, plus a 10-card Rick Mirer highlight set. It also had new enhancements, like gold foil stamping on both sides and four different photos per card. The Series I inserts included: Award Winners (5); Second Year Standouts (15); First Rounders (20), with the cream of the 1994 Draft; Ultra Achievements (10), honoring veteran stars; Touchdown Kings (9) and Ultra Stars (9). Series II inserts included Hot Numbers (15), Scoring Power (6), and Wave of the Future (6).

		MT
	Complete Set (525):	50.00
	Complete Series 1 (325):	30.00
	Complete Series 2 (200):	20.00
	Common Player:	.10
	Minor Stars:	.20
	Series 1 Wax Box:	50.00
	Series 2 Wax Box:	50.00
1	Steve Beuerlein	.10
2	Gary Clark	.10
3	Randal Hill	.10
4	Seth Joyner	.10
5	*Jamir Miller*	.20
6	Ron Moore	.20
7	Luis Sharpe	.10
8	Clyde Simmons	.10
9	Eric Swann	.10
10	Aeneas Williams	.10
11	Chris Doleman	.10
12	*Bert Emanuel*	1.00
13	Moe Gardner	.10
14	Jeff George	.20
15	Roger Harper	.10
16	Pierce Holt	.10
17	Lincoln Kennedy	.10
18	Erric Pegram	.10
19	Andre Rison	.20
20	Deion Sanders	.75
21	Jessie Tuggle	.10
22	Cornelius Bennett	.10
23	Bill Brooks	.10
24	*Jeff Burris*	.20
25	Kent Hull	.10
26	Henry Jones	.10
27	Jim Kelly	.20
28	Marcus Patton	.10
29	Andre Reed	.15
30	Bruce Smith	.10
31	Thomas Smith	.10
32	Thurman Thomas	.20
33	Jeff Wright	.10
34	Trace Armstrong	.10
35	Mark Carrier	.10
36	Dante Jones	.10
37	Erik Kramer	.10
38	Terry Obee	.10
39	Alonzo Spellman	.10
40	*John Thierry*	.20
41	Tom Waddle	.10
42	Donnell Woolford	.10
43	Tim Worley	.10
44	Chris Zorich	.10
45	John Copeland	.10
46	Harold Green	.10
47	David Klingler	.10
48	Ricardo McDonald	.10
49	Tony McGee	.10
50	Louis Oliver	.10
51	Carl Pickens	.75
52	*Darnay Scott*	1.00
53	Steve Tovar	.10
54	*Dan Wilkinson*	.20
55	Darryl Williams	.10
56	*Derrick Alexander*	.50
57	Michael Jackson	.10
58	Tony Jones	.10
59	*Antonio Langham*	.20

#	Player	Price		#	Player	Price		#	Player	Price		#	Player	Price
60	Eric Metcalf	.10		178	Terry Kirby	.20		294	Eugene Robinson	.10		411	Kimble Anders	.10
61	Stevon Moore	.10		179	Dan Marino	3.00		295	Rod Stephens	.10		412	Donnell Bennett	.10
62	Michael Dean Perry	.10		180	Troy Vincent	.10		296	Chris Warren	.20		413	J.J. Birden	.10
63	Anthony Pleasant	.10		181	Richmond Webb	.10		297	Marty Carter	.10		414	Mark Collins	.10
64	Vinny Testaverde	.10		182	Terry Allen	.10		298	Horace Copeland	.10		415	Lake Dawson	.30
65	Eric Turner	.10		183	Cris Carter	.10		299	Eric Curry	.10		416	Greg Hill	.75
66	Tommy Vardell	.10		184	Jack Del Rio	.10		300	Santana Dotson	.10		417	Charles Mincy	.10
67	Troy Aikman	1.50		185	Vencie Glenn	.10		301	Craig Erickson	.20		418	Greg Biekert	.10
68	Larry Brown	.10		186	Randall McDaniel	.10		302	Paul Gruber	.10		419	Rob Fredrickson	.10
69	*Shante Carver*	.20		187	Warren Moon	.10		303	Courtney Hawkins	.10		420	Nolan Harrison	.10
70	Charles Haley	.10		188	*David Palmer*	.50		304	Martin Mayhew	.10		421	Jeff Jaeger	.10
71	Michael Irvin	.20		189	John Randle	.10		305	Hardy Nickerson	.10		422	Albert Lewis	.10
72	Leon Lett	.10		190	Todd Scott	.10		306	*Errict Rhett*	1.00		423	Chester McGlockton	.10
73	Nate Newton	.10		191	*Todd Steussie*	.20		307	Vince Workman	.10		424	Tom Rathman	.10
74	Jay Novacek	.10		192	Henry Thomas	.10		308	Reggie Brooks	.10		425	Harvey Williams	.10
75	Darrin Smith	.10		193	*DeWayne Washington*	.20		309	Tom Carter	.10		426	Isaac Bruce	2.00
76	Emmitt Smith	3.00						310	Andre Collins	.10		427	Troy Drayton	.10
77	Tony Tolbert	.10		194	Bruce Armstrong	.10		311	Brad Edwards	.10		428	Wayne Gandy	.10
78	Erik Williams	.10		195	Harlon Barnett	.10		312	Kurt Gouveia	.10		429	Fred Stokes	.10
79	Kevin Williams	.60		196	Drew Bledsoe	2.00		313	Darrell Green	.10		430	Robert Young	.10
80	Steve Atwater	.10		197	Vincent Brisby	.20		314	Ethan Horton	.10		431	Gene Atkins	.10
81	Rod Bernstine	.10		198	Vincent Brown	.10		315	Desmond Howard	.10		432	Aubrey Beavers	.10
82	Ray Crockett	.10		199	Marion Butts	.10		316	*Tre Johnson*	.20		433	Tim Bowens	.10
83	Mike Croel	.10		200	Ben Coates	.50		317	Sterling Palmer	.10		434	Keith Byars	.10
84	Shane Dronett	.10		201	Todd Collins	.10		318	*Heath Shuler*	.50		435	Jeff Cross	.10
85	Jason Elam	.10		202	Maurice Hurst	.10		319	Tyronne Stowe	.10		436	Mark Ingram	.10
86	John Elway	.50		203	*Willie McGinest*	.40		320	NFL 75th	.10		437	Keith Jackson	.10
87	Simon Fletcher	.10		204	Ricky Reynolds	.10			Anniversary			438	Michael Stewart	.10
88	Glyn Milburn	.10		205	Chris Slade	.10		321	Checklist	.10		439	Chris Hinton	.10
89	Anthony Miller	.10		206	*Mario Bates*	.30		322	Checklist	.10		440	Qadry Ismail	.15
90	Shannon Sharpe	.10		207	Derek Brown	.10		323	Checklist	.10		441	Carlos Jenkins	.10
91	Gary Zimmerman	.10		208	Vince Buck	.10		324	Checklist	.10		442	Warren Moon	.20
92	Bennie Blades	.10		209	Quinn Early	.10		325	Checklist	.10		443	David Palmer	.20
93	Lomas Brown	.10		210	Jim Everett	.10		326	Garrison Hearst	1.00		444	Jake Reed	.10
94	Mel Gray	.10		211	Michael Haynes	.10		327	Eric Hill	.10		445	Robert Smith	.40
95	Jason Hanson	.10		212	Tyrone Hughes	.10		328	Seth Joyner	.10		446	Todd Steussie	.10
96	Ryan McNeil	.10		213	*Joe Johnson*	.20		329	Jim McMahon	.10		447	DeWayne	.10
97	Scott Mitchell	.15		214	Vaughan Johnson	.10		330	Jamir Miller	.10			Washington	
98	Herman Moore	.75		215	William Roaf	.10		331	Ricky Proehl	.10		448	Marion Butts	.10
99	*Johnnie Morton*	.50		216	Renaldo Turnbull	.10		332	Clyde Simmons	.10		449	Tim Goad	.10
100	Robert Porcher	.10		217	Michael Brooks	.10		333	Chris Doleman	.10		450	Myron Guyton	.10
101	Barry Sanders	2.00		218	Dave Brown	.20		334	Bert Emanuel	.40		451	*Kevin Lee*	.20
102	Chris Spielman	.10		219	Howard Cross	.10		335	Jeff George	.20		452	Willie McGinest	.20
103	Pat Swilling	.10		220	Stacey Dillard	.10		336	D.J. Johnson	.10		453	Ricky Reynolds	.10
104	Edgar Bennett	.10		221	John Elliott	.10		337	Terance Mathis	.10		454	Michael Timpson	.10
105	Terrell Buckley	.10		222	Keith Hamilton	.10		338	Clay Matthews	.10		455	Morten Andersen	.10
106	Reggie Cobb	.10		223	Rodney Hampton	.20		339	Tony Smith	.10		456	Jim Everett	.10
107	Brett Favre	3.00		224	*Thomas Lewis*	.20		340	Don Beebe	.10		457	Michael Haynes	.10
108	Sean Jones	.10		225	David Meggett	.10		341	*Bucky Brooks*	.20		458	Joe Johnson	.10
109	Ken Ruettgers	.10		226	Corey Miller	.10		342	Jeff Burris	.20		459	Wayne Martin	.10
110	Sterling Sharpe	.20		227	*Thomas Randolph*	.10		343	Kenneth Davis	.10		460	Sam Mills	.10
111	Wayne Simmons	.10		228	Mike Sherrard	.10		344	Phil Hansen	.10		461	Irv Smith	.10
112	*Aaron Taylor*	.15		229	Kyle Clifton	.10		345	Pete Metzelaars	.10		462	Carlton Bailey	.10
113	George Teague	.10		230	Boomer Esiason	.15		346	Darryl Talley	.10		463	Chris Calloway	.10
114	Reggie White	.20		231	*Aaron Glenn*	.10		347	Joe Cain	.10		464	Mark Jackson	.10
115	Micheal Barrow	.10		232	James Hasty	.10		348	Curtis Conway	.60		465	Thomas Lewis	.20
116	Gary Brown	.10		233	Bobby Houston	.10		349	Shaun Gayle	.10		466	Thomas Randolph	.10
117	Cody Carlson	.10		234	Johnny Johnson	.10		350	Chris Gedney	.10		467	*Stevie Anderson*	.15
118	Ray Childress	.10		235	Mo Lewis	.10		351	Erik Kramer	.10		468	Brad Baxter	.10
119	Cris Dishman	.10		236	Ronnie Lott	.15		352	Vinson Smith	.10		469	Aaron Glenn	.10
120	Henry Ford	.15		237	Rob Moore	.10		353	John Thierry	.10		470	Jeff Lageman	.10
121	Haywood Jeffires	.10		238	Marvin Washington	.10		354	Lewis Tillman	.10		471	Johnny Mitchell	.10
122	Bruce Matthews	.10		239	*Ryan Yarborough*	.20		355	Mike Brim	.10		472	Art Monk	.15
123	Bubba McDowell	.10		240	Eric Allen	.10		356	Derrick Fenner	.10		473	William Fuller	.10
124	Marcus Robertson	.10		241	Victor Bailey	.10		357	James Francis	.10		474	*Charlie Garner*	2.00
125	Eddie Robinson	.10		242	Fred Barnett	.10		358	Louis Oliver	.10		475	Vaughn Hebron	.10
126	Webster Slaughter	.10		243	Mark Bavaro	.20		359	Darnay Scott	1.00		476	Bill Romanowski	.10
127	*Trev Alberts*	.20		244	Randall	.20		360	Dan Wilkinson	.20		477	William Thomas	.10
128	Tony Bennett	.10			Cunningham			361	Alfred Williams	.10		478	Greg Townsend	.10
129	Ray Buchanan	.10		245	Byron Evans	.10		362	Derrick Alexander	.20		479	Bernard Williams	.10
130	Quentin Coryatt	.10		246	William Fuller	.10		363	Rob Burnett	.10		480	Calvin Williams	.10
131	Eugene Daniel	.10		247	Andy Harmon	.10		364	Mark Carrier	.10		481	Eric Green	.10
132	Steve Emtman	.10		248	William Perry	.10		365	Steve Everitt	.10		482	Charles Johnson	.50
133	*Marshall Faulk*	6.00		249	Herschel Walker	.20		366	Leroy Hoard	.10		483	Carnell Lake	.10
134	Jim Harbaugh	.10		250	*Bernard Williams*	.20		367	Pepper Johnson	.10		484	*Bam Morris*	.50
135	Roosevelt Potts	.10		251	Dermontti Dawson	.10		368	Antonio Langham	.20		485	John L. Williams	.10
136	Rohn Stark	.10		252	Deon Figures	.10		369	Shante Carver	.10		486	Darren Carrington	.10
137	Marcus Allen	.20		253	Barry Foster	.20		370	Alvin Harper	.20		487	*Andre Coleman*	.20
138	*Donnell Bennett*	.20		254	Kevin Greene	.10		371	Daryl Johnston	.10		488	Isaac Davis	.10
139	Dale Carter	.10		255	*Charles Johnson*	1.00		372	Russell Maryland	.10		489	Dwane Harper	.10
140	Tony Casillas	.10		256	Levon Kirkland	.10		373	Kevin Smith	.10		490	Tony Martin	.10
141	Mark Collins	.10		257	Greg Lloyd	.10		374	Mark Stepnoski	.10		491	Mark Seay	.40
142	Willie Davis	.10		258	Neil O'Donnell	.20		375	Darren Woodson	.10		492	Richard Dent	.10
143	Tim Grunhard	.10		259	Darren Perry	.10		376	Allen Aldridge	.10		493	William Floyd	.75
144	*Greg Hill*	1.00		260	Dwight Stone	.10		377	Ray Crockett	.10		494	Rickey Jackson	.10
145	Joe Montana	2.50		261	Rod Woodson	.20		378	Karl Mecklenburg	.10		495	Brent Jones	.10
146	Tracy Simien	.10		262	John Carney	.10		379	Anthony Miller	.10		496	Ken Norton	.10
147	Neil Smith	.10		263	*Isaac Davis*	.20		380	Mike Pritchard	.10		497	Gary Plummer	.10
148	Derrick Thomas	.20		264	Courtney Hall	.10		381	Leonard Russell	.10		498	Deion Sanders	1.50
149	Tim Brown	.20		265	Ronnie Harmon	.10		382	Dennis Smith	.10		499	John Taylor	.20
150	*James Folston*	.15		266	Stan Humphries	.20		383	Anthony Carter	.10		500	*Lee Woodall*	.20
151	*Rob Fredrickson*	.20		267	Vance Johnson	.10		384	Van Malone	.10		501	Bryant Young	.30
152	Jeff Hostetler	.15		268	Natrone Means	.50		385	Robert Massey	.10		502	Sam Adams	.20
153	Raghib Ismail	.15		269	Chris Mims	.10		386	Scott Mitchell	.10		503	Howard Ballard	.10
154	James Jett	.15		270	Leslie O'Neal	.10		387	Johnnie Morton	.40		504	Michael Bates	.10
155	Terry McDaniel	.10		271	Stanley Richard	.10		388	Brett Perriman	.10		505	Trev Alberts,	.10
156	Winston Moss	.10		272	Junior Seau	.20		389	Tracy Scroggins	.10			Robert Blackmon	
157	Greg Robinson	.10		273	Harris Barton	.10		390	Robert Brooks	.30		506	John Kasay	.10
158	Anthony Smith	.10		274	Dennis Brown	.10		391	LeRoy Butler	.10		507	Kelvin Martin	.10
159	Steve Wisniewski	.10		275	Eric Davis	.10		392	Reggie Cobb	.10		508	Kevin Mawae	.10
160	Willie Anderson	.10		276	*William Floyd*	.50		393	Sean Jones	.10		509	Rufus Porter	.10
161	Jerome Bettis	.75		277	John Johnson	.10		394	George Koonce	.10		510	Lawrence Dawsey	.10
162	*Isaac Bruce*	4.00		278	Tim McDonald	.10		395	Steve McMichael	.10		511	*Trent Dilfer*	2.00
163	Shane Conlan	.10		279	Ken Norton	.10		396	Bryce Paup	.10		512	Thomas Everett	.10
164	*Wayne Gandy*	.10		280	Jerry Rice	1.50		397	Aaron Taylor	.10		513	Jackie Harris	.10
165	Sean Gilbert	.10		281	Jesse Sapolu	.10		398	Henry Ford	.10		514	Errict Rhett	1.50
166	Todd Lyght	.10		282	Dana Stubblefield	.10		399	Ernest Givins	.10		515	Henry Ellard	.10
167	Chris Miller	.10		283	Ricky Watters	.20		400	*Jeremy Nunley*	.15		516	John Friesz	.10
168	Anthony Newman	.10		284	*Bryant Young*	.75		401	Bo Orlando	.10		517	Ken Harvey	.10
169	Roman Phifer	.10		285	Steve Young	1.50		402	Al Smith	.10		518	Ethan Horton	.10
170	Jackie Slater	.10		286	*Sam Adams*	.20		403	Barron Wortham	.15		519	Tre Johnson	.10
171	Gene Atkins	.10		287	Brian Blades	.10		404	Trev Alberts	.20		520	Jim Lachey	.10
172	*Aubrey Beavers*	.20		288	Ferrell Edmunds	.10		405	Tony Bennett	.10		521	Heath Shuler	1.50
173	*Tim Bowens*	.20		289	Patrick Hunter	.10		406	Kerry Cash	.10		522	Tony Woods	.10
174	J.B. Brown	.10		290	Cortez Kennedy	.20		407	*Sean Dawkins*	.20		523	Checklist	.10
175	Marco Coleman	.10		291	Rick Mirer	.75		408	Marshall Faulk	3.00		524	Checklist	.10
176	Bryan Cox	.10		292	Nate Odomes	.10		409	Jim Harbaugh	.10		525	Checklist	.10
177	Irving Fryar	.10		293	Ray Roberts	.10		410	Jeff Herrod	.10				

1994 Ultra Achievement Awards

Ultra Achievement Awards featured NFL veteran stars with long records of significant accomplishments. Sterling Sharpe's record breaking reception record is an example of the achievements captured in this 10-card set.

		MT
Complete Set (10):		10.00
Common Player:		.50
1	Marcus Allen	.50
2	John Elway	1.00
3	Dan Marino	4.00
4	Joe Montana	3.00
5	Jerry Rice	2.00
6	Barry Sanders	2.00
7	Sterling Sharpe	.50
8	Emmitt Smith	4.00
9	Thurman Thomas	.50
10	Reggie White	.50

1994 Ultra Award Winners

Award Winners were found in random packs of 1994 Ultra Football. It showcases the AFC/NFC Offensive Rookies of the Year, Super Bowl MVP, Defensive Player of the Year, and the NFL Defensive Rookie of the Year. Each card shows the player on a three-photo background.

		MT
Complete Set (5):		10.00
Common Player:		1.00
1	Jerome Bettis	2.00
2	Rick Mirer	1.50
3	Emmitt Smith	5.00
4	Dana Stubblefield	1.00
5	Rod Woodson	1.00

1994 Ultra First Rounders

First Rounders could be found in 14, 17 and 20-card foil packs of Fleer Ultra Football. This 20-card set features the top selections in the '94 draft cast onto a cobweb-looking background, with a First Rounder stamp in the bottom left corner.

		MT
Complete Set (20):		15.00
Common Player:		.50
1	Sam Adams	.50
2	Trev Alberts	.50
3	Shante Carver	.50
4	Marshall Faulk	3.00
5	William Floyd	2.00
6	Rob Fredrickson	.50
7	Wayne Gandy	.50
8	Aaron Glenn	.50
9	Charles Johnson	.50
10	Joe Johnson	.50
11	Antonio Langham	.50
12	Willie McGinest	.50
13	Jamir Miller	.50
14	Johnnie Morton	.50
15	Heath Shuler	1.00
16	John Thierry	.50
17	DeWayne Washington	.50
18	Dan Wilkinson	.50
19	Bernard Williams	.50
20	Bryant Young	1.00

1994 Ultra Flair Hot Numbers

These cards feature the super premium quality of Fleer Flair, including double-thick card stock, polyester lamination and six-color printing. The Hot Number inserts, randomly included in Fleer Ultra Series II packs, showcase 15 running backs, quarterbacks and receivers who pile up yardage. Each card front has an action shot over a team-colored, swirling background. Different dates and numbers that are important to the pictured player appear within the background. Player names are written across the bottom in gold foil, with the Flair logo in the upper right corner. In the bottom right corner a large box, outlined in black, displays "Hot Numbers," with the player's uniform number inside the box. Card backs, numbered 1 of 15, etc., have another photo and career summary.

		MT
Complete Set (15):		25.00
Common Player:		.50
1	Troy Aikman	4.00
2	Jerome Bettis	1.00
3	Tim Brown	.50
4	John Elway	2.00
5	Rodney Hampton	.50
6	Michael Irvin	.75
7	Dan Marino	5.00
8	Joe Montana	4.00
9	Jerry Rice	3.00
10	Andre Rison	.50
11	Barry Sanders	3.00
12	Sterling Sharpe	.50
13	Emmitt Smith	5.00
14	Thurman Thomas	.75
15	Steve Young	3.00

Values quoted in this guide reflect the retail price of a card — the price a collector can expect to pay when buying a card from a dealer. The wholesale price — that which a collector can expect to receive from a dealer when selling cards — will be significantly lower, depending on desirability and condition.

1994 Ultra Flair Scoring Power

Each of these six insert cards contains a football background with the words "Scoring Power" running up and down opposite sides of the card. A black strip across the bottom of each card contains the player's name, and the words "Scoring Power." The inserts, randomly included in 1994 Fleer Ultra Series II packs, feature highly productive quarterbacks, running backs and wide receivers. The Fleer Flair logo is on each card front. Card backs have gold foil stamping, a photo, a career summary and a card number (1 of 6, etc.).

		MT
Complete Set (6):		20.00
Common Player:		3.00
1	Marcus Allen	3.00
2	Natrone Means	5.00
3	Jerry Rice	5.00
4	Andre Rison	3.00
5	Emmitt Smith	8.00
6	Ricky Watters	3.00

1994 Ultra Flair Wave of the Future

These 1994 Fleer Ultra Series II inserts, randomly included in packs, feature six top rookies from the 1994 season. Players are pictured in their NFL uniforms over an iridescent, swirling background. The player's name, Flair logo and set logo are stamped in gold foil on the card front. The card back has a photo, career summary and a number (1 of 6, etc.).

		MT
Complete Set (6):		10.00
Common Player:		1.00
1	Trent Dilfer	1.50
2	Marshall Faulk	3.00
3	Greg Hill	1.00
4	Charles Johnson	1.00
5	Heath Shuler	1.50
6	Dan Wilkinson	1.00

1994 Ultra Rick Mirer

Rick Mirer "Rookie of the Year" is a 10-card set inserted into Ultra packs. It highlights his rookie season and gives a brief history of Mirer.

	MT
Complete Set (10):	5.00
Common Mirer:	.50
Mirer Auto:	50.00

1994 Ultra Second Year Standouts

Second Year Standouts highlight high-profile 1993 rookies starting their second season. This 15-card set was inserted into foil packs of Ultra Football. Each card displays the second year standout with fireworks going off in the background.

		MT
Complete Set (15):		15.00
Common Player:		1.00
1	Jerome Bettis	1.50
2	Drew Bledsoe	5.00
3	Reggie Brooks	1.00
4	Tom Carter	1.00
5	Eric Curry	1.00
6	Jason Elam	1.00
7	Tyrone Hughes	1.00
8	James Jett	1.00
9	Terry Kirby	1.50
10	Natrone Means	1.00
11	Rick Mirer	1.00
12	Ron Moore	1.00
13	William Roaf	1.00
14	Chris Slade	1.00
15	Dana Stubblefield	1.00

1994 Ultra Ultra Stars

This nine-card set was found in only 17-card packs of Ultra Football. It includes some of the brightest stars in the NFL. Ultra Stars are also quite scarce and are printed on 100% etched-foil.

		MT
Complete Set (9):		125.00
Common Player:		5.00
1	Troy Aikman	25.00
2	Jerome Bettis	10.00
3	Tim Brown	5.00
4	Michael Irvin	10.00
5	Rick Mirer	5.00
6	Jerry Rice	25.00
7	Barry Sanders	25.00
8	Emmitt Smith	35.00
9	Rod Woodson	5.00

Post-1980 cards in Near Mint condition will generally sell for about 75% of the quoted Mint value. Excellent-condition cards bring no more than 40%.

1994 Ultra Touchdown Kings

Touchdown Kings are a 100% foil-etched shot of a nine players who have proven scoring ability. Since they were randomly inserted exclusively into 14 and 20-card packs of Ultra Football, they are the rarest insert set. Each card shows two shots of the featured player on a horizontal background

		MT
Complete Set (9):		85.00
Common Player:		3.00
Minor Stars:		6.00
1	Marcus Allen	6.00
2	Dan Marino	20.00
3	Joe Montana	15.00
4	Jerry Rice	15.00
5	Andre Rison	3.00
6	Sterling Sharpe	6.00
7	Emmitt Smith	20.00
8	Ricky Watters	6.00
9	Steve Young	10.00

1995 Ultra

Fleer released its 550-card 1995 Ultra set in two series - a 350-card Series I, plus a 200-card Ultra Extra set. Card fronts have a full-bleed color action photo, with the player name stamped in a square at the bottom, with a mountain range design. The card back has a number in the upper left corner and features two smaller color photos and a ghosted image on a horizontal background. The player's name and position are stamped in gold. A team helmet and 1994 and career statistic lines are also given. All regular and insert cards are on 40-percent thicker stock. A Gold Medallion parallel set, featuring 100-percent gold-foil embossed backgrounds, was also created for each regular and insert card. Cards were include one per pack. Ultra Extra is composed of subsets: 60 Rookies, 60 Player Updates, 60 Extra Stars, six Rollout cards and 12 Extra Effort cards. Series I insert sets include: Award Winners (1 in 5 packs), First Rounders (1 in 7), Touchdown Kings (1 in 7 12-card packs), Rising Stars (1 in 37), Ultra Stars (1 in 7 17-card packs), Ultra Achievement (1 in 7) and Second Year Standouts (1 in 5). Ultra Extra inserts include: 30 Ultrabilties cards (10 each for Guns, Bolts and Blasts; 1 in 5 packs), Big Finish (1 in 20, hobby exclusive packs), Ultra Magna Force (1 in 20, retail exclusive), and All-Rookie Team (1 in 55). Also found in Ultra Extra are Gold Medallion Hot Packs (1

in 72), which contain all Gold Medallion cards, and All-Rookie Team Hot Packs (1 per 360), which contain a complete set of All-Rookie Team inserts.

		MT
Complete Set (550):		70.00
Comp. Series 1 (350):		35.00
Comp. Series 2 (200):		35.00
Common Player:		.10
Minor Stars:		.20
Series 1 Wax Box:		55.00
Series 2 Wax Box:		75.00
1	Michael Bankston	.10
2	Larry Centers	.10
3	Garrison Hearst	.20
4	Eric Hill	.10
5	Seth Joyner	.10
6	Lorenzo Lynch	.10
7	Jamir Miller	.20
8	Clyde Simmons	.10
9	Eric Swann	.10
10	Aeneas Williams	.10
11	Devin Bush	.20
12	Ron Davis	.10
13	Chris Doleman	.10
14	Bert Emanuel	.40
15	Jeff George	.20
16	Roger Harper	.10
17	Craig Heyward	.10
18	Pierce Holt	.10
19	D.J. Johnson	.10
20	Terance Mathis	.10
21	Chuck Smith	.10
22	Jessie Tuggle	.10
23	Cornelius Bennett	.10
24	Reuben Brown	.10
25	Jeff Burris	.10
26	Matt Darby	.10
27	Phil Hansen	.10
28	Henry Jones	.10
29	Jim Kelly	.20
30	Mark Maddox	.10
31	Andre Reed	.20
32	Bruce Smith	.10
33	Don Beebe	.10
34	*Kerry Collins*	2.00
35	Darion Conner	.10
36	Pete Metzelaars	.10
37	Sam Mills	.10
38	Tyrone Poole	.20
39	Joe Cain	.10
40	Mark Carrier	.10
41	Curtis Conway	.10
42	Jeff Graham	.10
43	Raymont Harris	.10
44	Erik Kramer	.10
45	*Rashaan Salaam*	.50
46	Lewis Tillman	.10
47	Donnell Woolford	.10
48	Chris Zorich	.10
49	*Jeff Blake*	.50
50	Mike Brim	.10
51	*Ki-Jana Carter*	1.50
52	James Francis	.10
53	Carl Pickens	.20
54	Darnay Scott	.75
55	Steve Tovar	.10
56	Dan Wilkinson	.10
57	Alfred Williams	.10
58	Darryl Williams	.10
59	Derrick Alexander	.20
60	Rob Burnett	.10
61	Steve Everitt	.10
62	Leroy Hoard	.10
63	Michael Jackson	.10
64	Pepper Johnson	.10
65	Tony Jones	.10
66	Antonio Langham	.10
67	Anthony Pleasant	.10
68	Craig Powell	.20
69	Vinny Testaverde	.20
70	Eric Turner	.10
71	Troy Aikman	1.50
72	Charles Haley	.10
73	Michael Irvin	.20
74	Daryl Johnston	.10
75	Robert Jones	.10
76	Leon Lett	.10
77	Russell Maryland	.10
78	Jay Novacek	.10
79	Darrin Smith	.10
80	Emmitt Smith	3.00
81	Kevin Smith	.10
82	Erik Williams	.10
83	Kevin Williams	.10
84	*Sherman Williams*	.20
85	Darren Woodson	.10
86	Elijah Alexander	.20
87	Steve Atwater	.10
88	Ray Crockett	.10
89	Shane Dronett	.10
90	Jason Elam	.10
91	John Elway	.60
92	Simon Fletcher	.10
93	Glyn Milburn	.10
94	Anthony Miller	.10
95	Leonard Russell	.10
96	Shannon Sharpe	.20
97	Bennie Blades	.10
98	Lomas Brown	.10
99	Willie Clay	.10
100	Luther Elliss	.20
101	Mike Johnson	.10
102	Robert Massey	.10
103	Scott Mitchell	.10
104	Herman Moore	.50
105	Brett Perriman	.10
106	Robert Porcher	.10
107	Barry Sanders	2.50
108	Chris Spielman	.10
109	Edgar Bennett	.10
110	Robert Brooks	.10
111	LeRoy Butler	.10
112	Brett Favre	3.00
113	Sean Jones	.10
114	John Jurkovic	.10
115	George Koonce	.10
116	Wayne Simmons	.10
117	George Teague	.10
118	Reggie White	.20
119	Micheal Barrow	.10
120	Gary Brown	.10
121	Cody Carlson	.10
122	Ray Childress	.10
123	Cris Dishman	.10
124	Bruce Matthews	.10
125	*Steve McNair*	4.00
126	Marcus Robertson	.10
127	Webster Slaughter	.10
128	Al Smith	.10
129	Tony Bennett	.10
130	Ray Buchanan	.10
131	Quentin Coryatt	.10
132	Sean Dawkins	.10
133	Marshall Faulk	1.00
134	Stephen Grant	.10
135	Jim Harbaugh	.10
136	Jeff Herrod	.10
137	Ellis Johnson	.10
138	Tony Siragusa	.10
139	Steve Beuerlein	.10
140	*Tony Boselli*	.20
141	Darren Carrington	.10
142	Reggie Cobb	.10
143	Kelvin Martin	.10
144	Kelvin Pritchett	.10
145	Joel Smeenge	.10
146	*James Stewart*	2.50
147	Marcus Allen	.20
148	Kimble Anders	.10
149	Dale Carter	.10
150	Mark Collins	.10
151	Willie Davis	.10
152	Lake Dawson	.20
153	Greg Hill	.10
154	Trezelle Jenkins	.10
155	Darren Mickell	.10
156	Tracy Simien	.10
157	Neil Smith	.10
158	William White	.10
159	Joe Aska	.20
160	Greg Biekert	.10
161	Tim Brown	.20
162	Rob Fredrickson	.10
163	*Andrew Glover*	.20
164	Jeff Hostetler	.20
165	Raghib Ismail	.10
166	*Napoleon Kaufman*	3.00
167	Terry McDaniel	.10
168	Chester McGlockton	.10
169	Anthony Smith	.10
170	Harvey Williams	.10
171	Steve Wisniewski	.10
172	Gene Atkins	.10
173	Aubrey Beavers	.10
174	Tim Bowens	.10
175	Bryan Cox	.10
176	Jeff Cross	.10
177	Irving Fryar	.10
178	Dan Marino	3.00
179	O.J. McDuffie	.10
180	Billy Milner	.10
181	Bernie Parmalee	.20
182	Troy Vincent	.10
183	Richmond Webb	.10
184	Derrick Alexander	.20
185	Cris Carter	.20
186	Jack Del Rio	.10
187	Qadry Ismail	.10
188	Ed McDaniel	.10
189	Randall McDaniel	.10
190	Warren Moon	.20
191	John Randle	.10
192	Jake Reed	.10
193	Fuad Reveiz	.10
194	Korey Stringer	.10
195	DeWayne Washington	.10
196	Bruce Armstrong	.10
197	Drew Bledsoe	1.50
198	Vincent Brisby	.10
199	Vincent Brown	.10
200	Marion Butts	.10
201	Ben Coates	.10
202	Myron Guyton	.10
203	Maurice Hurst	.10
204	Mike Jones	.10
205	Ty Law	.20
206	Willie McGinest	.10
207	Chris Slade	.10
208	Mario Bates	.40
209	Quinn Early	.10
210	Jim Everett	.20
211	Mark Fields	.10
212	Michael Haynes	.10
213	Tyrone Hughes	.10
214	Joe Johnson	.10
215	Wayne Martin	.10
216	William Roaf	.10
217	Irv Smith	.10
218	Jimmy Spencer	.10
219	Winfred Tubbs	.10
220	Renaldo Turnbull	.10
221	Michael Brooks	.10
222	Dave Brown	.10
223	Chris Calloway	.10
224	Howard Cross	.10
225	John Elliott	.10
226	Keith Hamilton	.10
227	Rodney Hampton	.20
228	Thomas Lewis	.10
229	Thomas Randolph	.10
230	Mike Sherrard	.10
231	Michael Strahan	.10
232	*Tyrone Wheatley*	1.00
233	Brad Baxter	.10
234	*Kyle Brady*	.50
235	Kyle Clifton	.10
236	*Hugh Douglas*	.20
237	Boomer Esiason	.20
238	Aaron Glenn	.10
239	Bobby Houston	.10
240	Johnny Johnson	.10
241	Mo Lewis	.10
242	Johnny Mitchell	.10
243	Marvin Washington	.10
244	Fred Barnett	.10
245	Randall Cunningham	.20
246	William Fuller	.10
247	Charlie Garner	.10
248	Andy Harmon	.10
249	Greg Jackson	.10
250	*Mike Mamula*	.20
251	Bill Romanowski	.10
252	Bobby Taylor	.20
253	William Thomas	.10
254	Calvin Williams	.10
255	Michael Zordich	.10
256	Chad Brown	.10
257	*Mark Bruener*	.50
258	Dermontti Dawson	.10
259	Barry Foster	.10
260	Kevin Greene	.10
261	Charles Johnson	.40
262	Carnell Lake	.10
263	Greg Lloyd	.10
264	Bam Morris	.20
265	Neil O'Donnell	.20
266	Darren Perry	.10
267	Ray Seals	.10
268	*Kordell Stewart*	6.00
269	John L. Williams	.10
270	Rod Woodson	.20
271	Jerome Bettis	.20
272	Isaac Bruce	1.00
273	*Kevin Carter*	.20
274	Shane Conlan	.10
275	Troy Drayton	.10
276	Sean Gilbert	.10
277	Todd Lyght	.10
278	Chris Miller	.10
279	Anthony Newman	.10
280	Roman Phifer	.10
281	Robert Young	.10
282	John Carney	.10
283	Andre Coleman	.10
284	Courtney Hall	.10
285	Ronnie Harmon	.10
286	Dwayne Harper	.10
287	Stan Humphries	.20
288	Shawn Jefferson	.10
289	Tony Martin	.10
290	Natrone Means	.20
291	Chris Mims	.10
292	Leslie O'Neal	.20
293	Junior Seau	.20
294	Mark Seay	.10
295	Eric Davis	.10
296	William Floyd	.20
297	Merton Hanks	.10
298	Brent Jones	.10
299	Ken Norton	.10
300	Gary Plummer	.10
301	Jerry Rice	1.50
302	Deion Sanders	.75
303	Jesse Sapolu	.10
304	J.J. Stokes	2.00
305	Dana Stubblefield	.10
306	John Taylor	.10
307	Steve Wallace	.10
308	Lee Woodall	.10
309	Bryant Young	.10
310	Steve Young	1.50
311	Sam Adams	.10
312	Howard Ballard	.10
313	Robert Blackman	.10
314	Brian Blades	.10
315	*Joey Galloway*	3.00
316	Carlton Gray	.10
317	Cortez Kennedy	.20
318	Rick Mirer	.20
319	Eugene Robinson	.10
320	Chris Warren	.20
321	Terry Wooden	.10
322	Derrick Brooks	.20
323	Lawrence Dawsey	.10
324	Trent Dilfer	.75
325	Santana Dotson	.10
326	Thomas Everett	.10
327	Paul Gruber	.10
328	Jackie Harris	.10
329	Courtney Hawkins	.10
330	Martin Mayhew	.10
331	Hardy Nickerson	.10
332	Errict Rhett	1.50
333	*Warren Sapp*	.20
334	Charles Wilson	.10
335	Reggie Brooks	.10
336	Tom Carter	.10
337	Henry Ellard	.10
338	Ricky Ervins	.10
339	Darrell Green	.10
340	Ken Harvey	.10
341	Brian Mitchell	.10
342	Cory Raymer	.20
343	Heath Shuler	1.00
344	*Michael Westbrook*	1.50

345	Tony Woods	.10
346	Checklist	.10
347	Checklist	.10
348	Checklist	.10
349	Checklist	.10
350	Checklist	.10
351	Checklist	.10
352	Checklist	.10
353	Dave Krieg	.10
354	Rob Moore	.10
355	J.J. Birden	.10
356	Eric Metcalf	.10
357	Bryce Paup	.10
358	Willie Green	.10
359	Derrick Moore	.10
360	Michael Timpson	.10
361	Eric Bieniemy	.10
362	Keenan McCardell	.10
363	Andre Rison	.20
364	Lorenzo White	.10
365	Deion Sanders	1.00
366	Wade Wilson	.10
367	Aaron Craver	.10
368	Michael Dean Perry	.10
369	*Rod Smith*	10.00
370	Henry Thomas	.10
371	Mark Ingram	.10
372	Chris Chandler	.10
373	Mel Gray	.10
374	Flipper Anderson	.10
375	Craig Erickson	.10
376	Mark Brunell	1.50
377	Ernest Givens	.10
378	Randy Jordan	.10
379	Webster Slaughter	.10
380	*Tamarick Vanover*	1.50
381	Gary Clark	.10
382	Steve Emtman	.10
383	Eric Green	.10
384	Louis Oliver	.10
385	Robert Smith	.10
386	David Meggett	.10
387	Eric Allen	.10
388	Wesley Walls	.10
389	Herschel Walker	.10
390	Ronald Moore	.10
391	Adrian Murrell	.20
392	Charles Wilson	.10
393	Derrick Fenner	.10
394	Pat Swilling	.10
395	Kelvin Martin	.10
396	Rodney Peete	.10
397	Ricky Watters	.20
398	Erric Pegram	.10
399	Leonard Russell	.10
400	Alexander Wright	.10
401	Darrien Gordon	.10
402	Alfred Pupunu	.10
403	Elvis Grbac	.10
404	Derek Loville	.20
405	Steve Broussard	.10
406	Ricky Proehl	.10
407	Bobby Joe Edmonds	.10
408	Alvin Harper	.10
409	Dave Moore	.10
410	Terry Allen	.10
411	Gus Frerotte	.50
412	*Leslie Shepherd*	.20
413	*Stoney Case*	.20
414	*Frank Sanders*	1.50
415	*Roell Preston*	.20
416	*Lorenzo Styles*	.20
417	*Justin Armour*	.20
418	*Todd Collins*	.20
419	*Darick Holmes*	1.50
420	Kerry Collins	1.00
421	*Tyrone Poole*	.20
422	Rashaan Salaam	.30
423	*Todd Sauerbrun*	.20
424	Ki-Jana Carter	1.50
425	David Dunn	.20
426	*Earnest Hunter*	.20
427	Eric Zeier	1.00
428	*Eric Bjorson*	.20
429	*Sherman Williams*	.20
430	Terrell Davis	15.00
431	*Luther Elliss*	.20
432	*Kez McCorvey*	.20
433	*Antonio Freeman*	6.00
434	*Craig Newsome*	.20
435	*Chris Sanders*	2.00
436	*Chris Sanders*	1.50
437	*Zack Crockett*	.20
438	*Ellis Johnson*	.20
439	*Tony Boselli*	.20
440	James Stewart	.30
441	*J.J. Smith*	.20
442	*Tamarick Vanover*	1.50
443	*Derrick Alexander*	.20
444	*Chad May*	.20
445	*James Stewart*	.50
446	*Ty Law*	.20
447	*Curtis Martin*	4.00
448	Will Moore	.20
449	*Mark Fields*	.20
450	*Ray Zellars*	.20
451	*Charles Way*	.20
452	Tyrone Wheatley	1.00
453	*Kyle Brady*	.20
454	*Wayne Chrebet*	2.00
455	Hugh Douglas	.20
456	*Chris Jones*	1.00
457	*Mike Mamula*	.20
458	*Pat McCrary*	.20
459	*Bobby Taylor*	.20
460	Mark Bruener	.40
461	Kordell Stewart	2.00

462	*Kevin Carter*	.20
463	*Lovell Pinckney*	.20
464	*Johnny Thomas*	.20
465	*Terrell Fletcher*	.50
466	*Jimmy Oliver*	.20
467	J.J. Stokes	1.00
468	*Christian Fauria*	.20
469	Joey Galloway	2.00
470	*Derrick Brooks*	.20
471	*Warren Sapp*	.20
472	Michael Westbrook	.75
473	Garrison Hearst	.20
474	Jeff George	.20
475	Terance Mathis	.10
476	Andre Reed	.10
477	Bruce Smith	.10
478	Lamar Lathon	.10
479	Curtis Conway	.20
480	Jeff Blake	1.50
481	Carl Pickens	.20
482	Eric Turner	.10
483	Troy Aikman	.75
484	Michael Irvin	.20
485	Emmitt Smith	1.50
486	John Elway	.20
487	Shannon Sharpe	.10
488	Herman Moore	.20
489	Barry Sanders	1.00
490	Brett Favre	1.00
491	Reggie White	.20
492	Haywood Jeffires	.10
493	Sean Dawkins	.10
494	Marshall Faulk	1.00
495	Desmond Howard	.10
496	Steve Bono	.20
497	Derrick Thomas	.20
498	Irving Fryar	.10
499	Terry Kirby	.10
500	Dan Marino	1.75
501	O.J. McDuffie	.10
502	Cris Carter	.20
503	Warren Moon	.20
504	Jake Reed	.10
505	Drew Bledsoe	.75
506	Ben Coates	.10
507	Jim Everett	.10
508	Rodney Hampton	.10
509	Mo Lewis	.10
510	Tim Brown	.20
511	Jeff Hostetler	.20
512	Raghib Ismail	.20
513	Chester McGlockton	.10
514	Fred Barnett	.10
515	Greg Lloyd	.10
516	Bam Morris	.20
517	Rod Woodson	.10
518	Jerome Bettis	.20
519	Isaac Bruce	.75
520	Stan Humphries	.20
521	Natrone Means	.20
522	Junior Seau	.20
523	William Floyd	.20
524	Jerry Rice	.75
525	Steve Young	.75
526	Cortez Kennedy	.10
527	Rick Mirer	.20
528	Chris Warren	.20
529	Trent Dilfer	.20
530	Errict Rhett	.75
531	Darrell Green	.10
532	Heath Shuler	.50
533	Stoney Case	.10
534	Eric Zeier	.50
535	Kerry Collins	1.00
536	Steve McNair	1.50
537	Kordell Stewart	2.00
538	Rob Johnson	3.00
539	Eric Ball	.10
540	Darrick Brownlow	.10
541	Paul Butcher	.10
542	Carlester Crumpler	.10
543	Maurice Douglas	.10
544	Keith Elias	.10
545	Kenneth Gant	.10
546	Corey Harris	.10
547	Andre Hastings	.10
548	Thomas Holmco	.10
549	Lenny McGill	.10
550	Mark Pike	.10

foil background. Gold Medallions were found at a rate of one per pack.

	MT
Complete Set (550):	350.00
Complete Series 1 (350):	200.00
Complete Series 2 (200):	150.00
Gold Medallion Cards:	3x-6x

1995 Ultra Achievements

These 1995 Fleer Ultra Series I inserts feature 10 of the league's top performers. Cards were randomly included one per every seven packs. The card front has a color action photo, with the player's name and Ultra Achievement and Ultra logos stamped in gold. Running inside the card format are the player's achievements from the 1994 season. The card back, numbered 1 of 10, etc., has another color photo, with a box superimposed over the photo to provide a summary of the player's season recap. The achievements listed along the front borders repeat on the back.

		MT
Complete Set (10):		10.00
Common Player:		.50
Comp. Gold Set (10):		30.00
Gold Cards:		1x-2x
1	Drew Bledsoe	3.00
2	Cris Carter	.50
3	Ben Coates	.50
4	Mel Gray	.50
5	Jerry Rice	2.00
6	Barry Sanders	3.00
7	Deion Sanders	1.50
8	Herschel Walker	.50
9	DeWayne Washington	.50
10	Steve Young	2.00

1995 Ultra All-Rookie Team

These 1995 Fleer Ultra Extra inserts are the rarest of the series; they can be found one in every 55 packs. The cards are acetate and feature the top 10 rookies from the 1995 season. "Rookies" is written along one border of the card.

		MT
Complete Set (10):		160.00
Common Player:		10.00
Hot Pack Cards Half Price		
1	Michael Westbrook	15.00
2	Terrell Davis	40.00
3	Curtis Martin	30.00
4	Joey Galloway	20.00
5	Rashaan Salaam	10.00
6	J.J. Stokes	15.00
7	Napoleon Kaufman	20.00
8	Mike Mamula	10.00
9	Kyle Brady	10.00
10	Hugh Douglas	10.00

1995 Ultra Gold Medallion

Ultra Gold Medallions paralleled the regular-issue set with the same photo, but a gold

1995 Ultra Award Winners

These 1995 Fleer Ultra Series I inserts could be found one per every five packs. They feature six players who captured postseason awards after the 1994 season ended. The card front has a color photo of the player superimposed over a collage of the award he won. His name and the Ultra and Award Winner logos are stamped in gold. The player's name is also in gold on the back, which is numbered 1 of 6, etc. The back has a player photo on one half of the card, with a recap of why he won the specific award. The award trophy collage is again used for the background.

		MT
Complete Set (6):		10.00
Common Player:		.50
Comp. Gold Set (6):		20.00
Gold Cards:		1x-2x
1	Tim Bowens	.50
2	Marshall Faulk	1.25
3	Dan Marino	3.00
4	Barry Sanders	2.00
5	Deion Sanders	1.00
6	Steve Young	1.25

1995 Ultra First Rounders

These 1995 Fleer Ultra Series I inserts feature 20 of the top selections from the 1995 draft. The cards could be found one per every seven packs. The card front uses gold stamping for the Fleer Ultra and insert set logos, plus the player's name. A player photo is superimposed against a background collage of his team's logo. The back, numbered 1 of 20, etc., has the same collage as a background, plus a smaller player photo and a draft analysis of the player. His name also appears in gold at the top of the card.

		MT
Complete Set (20):		35.00
Common Player:		.50
Comp. Gold Set (20):		75.00
Gold Cards:		1x-2x
1	Derrick Alexander	.50
2	Tony Boselli	1.00
3	Kyle Brady	1.00
4	Mark Bruener	.50
5	Devin Bush	.50
6	Kevin Carter	.50
7	Ki-Jana Carter	3.00
8	Kerry Collins	2.00
9	Mark Fields	.50
10	Joe Galloway	5.00
11	Napoleon Kaufman	2.00
12	Ty Law	.50
13	Mike Mamula	.50
14	Steve McNair	6.00
15	Rashaan Salaam	3.00
16	Warren Sapp	1.00
17	James Stewart	1.00
18	J.J. Stokes	3.00
19	Michael Westbrook	2.00
20	Tyrone Wheatley	1.00

1995 Ultra Magna Force

These 1995 Fleer Ultra Extra inserts feature 20 top NFL stars and were random inserts in retail packs only, one every 20 packs.

		MT
Complete Set (20):		110.00
Common Player:		2.00
1	Emmitt Smith	20.00
2	Jerry Rice	10.00
3	Drew Bledsoe	10.00
4	Marshall Faulk	10.00
5	Heath Shuler	3.00
6	Carl Pickens	3.00
7	Ben Coates	2.00
8	Terry Allen	2.00
9	Terance Mathis	2.00
10	Fred Barnett	2.00
11	O.J. McDuffie	2.00
12	Garrison Hearst	3.00
13	Deion Sanders	6.00
14	Reggie White	3.00
15	Herman Moore	3.00
16	Brett Favre	20.00
17	William Floyd	3.00
18	Curtis Martin	20.00
19	Joey Galloway	12.00
20	Tyrone Wheatley	4.00

1995 Ultra Overdrive

These insert cards were exclusive to 1995 Fleer Ultra Extra hobby packs, one per every 20 packs. The card fronts have a metallic shine to them, with a color action photo in the center. Ultra Overdrive appears along the right border. The player's name and position are in the lower left corner. The card back, numbered of twenty, etc., features a ghosted image of an action photo, with a square around the player's head, which is in color. A brief player profile is also given.

		MT
Complete Set (20):		100.00
Common Player:		2.00
1	Barry Sanders	10.00
2	Troy Aikman	10.00
3	Natrone Means	10.00
4	Steve Young	10.00
5	Errict Rhett	2.00
6	Terrell Davis	14.00
7	Michael Westbrook	2.00
8	Michael Irvin	3.00
9	Chris Warren	3.00
10	Tim Brown	2.00
11	Jerome Bettis	2.00
12	Ricky Watters	2.00
13	Derrick Thomas	2.00
14	Bruce Smith	2.00
15	Rashaan Salaam	4.00
16	Jeff Blake	2.00
17	Alvin Harper	2.00
18	Shannon Sharpe	2.00
19	Eric Swann	2.00
20	Andre Rison	2.00

1995 Ultra Rising Stars

These inserts were randomly included one in every 37 packs, making them the scarcest of the 1995 Fleer Ultra Series I inserts. These nine cards, numbered 1 of 9, etc., are printed on acetate with an "ultra crystal" planetary design. The front has a color photo, with the player, set and insert set names in gold foil. The back, numbered 1 of 9, etc., also uses gold for the player name. He is pictured again as the background, with a brief career summary superimposed over it.

		MT
Complete Set (9):		60.00
Common Player:		3.00
Comp. Gold Set (9):		120.00
Gold Cards:		1x-2x
1	Jerome Bettis	3.00
2	Jeff Blake	7.00
3	Drew Bledsoe	15.00
4	Ben Coates	3.00
5	Marshall Faulk	8.00
6	Brett Favre	25.00
7	Natrone Means	6.00
8	Bam Morris	6.00
9	Eric Turner	3.00

1995 Ultra Second Year Standouts

This horizontally-designed insert set was featured in 1995 Fleer Ultra Series I packs, one per every five packs. The front uses gold stamping for the set and insert set logos, plus the name of the player, who is pictured twice. A team helmet collage is used for the background. The back, also horizontal, is numbered 1 of 15, etc., and features one of the players chosen as a top sophomore in the NFL. A color photo and brief recap of the player's rookie season accomplishments are also on the back. His name is in gold. The background says "2nd Year Standout" in a repeated pattern.

		MT
Complete Set (15):		15.00
Common Player:		.50
Comp. Gold Set (15):		30.00
Gold Cards:		1x-2x
1	Derrick Alexander	.50
2	Mario Bates	.50
3	Tim Bowens	.50
4	Bert Emanuel	1.25
5	Marshall Faulk	4.00
6	William Floyd	2.00
7	Rob Fredrickson	.50
8	Antonio Langham	.50
9	Bam Morris	2.00
10	Errict Rhett	3.00
11	Darnay Scott	.50

		MT
12	Heath Shuler	2.00
13	DeWayne Washington	.50
14	Dan Wilkinson	.50
15	Bryant Young	.50

1995 Ultra Ultra Stars

These 1995 Fleer Ultra Series I inserts were included one per every seven 17-card packs. They feature 10 of the NFL's top players. The horizontal card front has a larger photo of the player, against a collage of the same photo in different sizes and color patterns. Silver stamping is used for the player's name and set and insert set logos. The back, numbered 1 of 10, etc., uses silver foil and a horizontal format. A color photo is on one half of the card; a brief career summary comprises the other.

		MT
Complete Set (10):		15.00
Common Player:		.50
Comp. Gold Med. Set (10):		30.00
Gold Med. Cards:		1x-2x
1	Tim Brown	.50
2	Marshall Faulk	2.00
3	Irving Fryar	.50
4	Dan Marino	4.00
5	Natrone Means	.50
6	Jerry Rice	2.00
7	Barry Sanders	3.00
8	Deion Sanders	1.50
9	Emmitt Smith	4.00
10	Rod Woodson	.50

1995 Ultra Touchdown Kings

These 1995 Fleer Ultra Series I inserts feature 10 of the NFL's top touchdown scorers from 1994. The cards were random inserts, one every seventh 12-card packs. The front uses gold stamping for the player's name and insert and set logos. A TD with a crown on top of it appears in the lower right corner. A color player photo is superimposed against a crystal-like "TD"/football background. The card back, numbered 1 of 10, etc., has a color photo on one side; a recap of the player's scoring accomplishments from 1994 on the other. Gold foil stamping is used for the number and player's name.

		MT
Complete Set (10):		10.00
Common Player:		.50
Comp. Gold Set (10):		20.00
Gold Cards:		1x-2x
1	Marshall Faulk	2.00
2	Terance Mathis	.50
3	Natrone Means	.50

		MT
4	Herman Moore	.50
5	Carl Pickens	1.00
6	Jerry Rice	2.00
7	Andre Rison	.50
8	Emmitt Smith	3.00
9	Chris Warren	.50
10	Steve Young	2.00

1995 Ultra Ultrabilities

These 1995 Fleer Ultra Extra inserts could be found one per every five packs. The 30 cards are broken into three subsets of 10 cards each - Guns (quarterbacks), Bolts (receivers and running backs) and Blasts (hard-hitting defensive players and running backs). The respective subset name is on the card front in gold foil, along with the word Ultrabilities. The background is orange; the player's name is in white in a colored panel at the bottom. Each card back is numbered 1 of 30, etc., and includes a mug shot of the player, plus a ghosted image of him in action. A brief player profile is also provided. Near a team logo in the upper left corner is the player's name, in his team's primary uniform color. A word describing a key element of the player's skills is written along the right side of the card.

		MT
Complete Set (30):		65.00
Common Player:		1.00
1	Dan Marino (Guns)	10.00
2	Steve Young (Guns)	6.00
3	Drew Bledsoe (Guns)	6.00
4	Jeff Blake (Guns)	2.00
5	Troy Aikman (Guns)	6.00
6	John Elway (Guns)	4.00
7	Trent Dilfer (Guns)	3.00
8	Steve Bono (Guns)	2.00
9	Brett Favre (Guns)	10.00
10	Kerry Collins (Guns)	2.00
11	Barry Sanders (Bolts)	6.00
12	Errict Rhett (Bolts)	1.00
13	Emmitt Smith (Bolts)	10.00
14	Chris Warren (Bolts)	2.00
15	Irving Fryar (Bolts)	1.00
16	Charlie Garner (Bolts)	1.00
17	Joey Galloway (Bolts)	8.00
18	Eric Metcalf (Bolts)	1.00
19	Herman Moore (Bolts)	2.00
20	Robert Smith (Bolts)	1.00
21	Natrone Means (Blasts)	3.00
22	Derrick Thomas (Blasts)	1.00
23	Bruce Smith (Blasts)	1.00
24	Hugh Douglas (Blasts)	1.00
25	Mike Mamula (Blasts)	1.00
26	Jerome Bettis (Blasts)	2.00
27	Bam Morris (Blasts)	3.00
28	Tim Bowens (Blasts)	1.00
29	William Floyd (Blasts)	3.00
30	Daryl Johnston (Blasts)	1.00

Post-1980 cards in Near Mint condition will generally sell for about 75% of the quoted Mint value. Excellent-condition cards bring no more than 40%.

1996 Ultra

Fleer's 1996 Ultra football set is packed with rookies - 55 in all - featured as cards in a subset and two insert sets. The 15-card subset has the rookies in their college uniforms, with their new NFL team logos. Insert sets featuring rookies include a 30-card Ultra Rookies set and a 10-card All-Rookie Team set. Two other subsets were also produced for the 200-card set - First Impressions and Secret Weapons. The other insert card sets are Mr. Momentum, Sledgehammer, and Pulsating. Similar to last year's format, both NFC and AFC cards feature unique designs, with NFC players' last names printed against a blue background while a red background is used for AFC stars. 1995 Pro Bowl player cards have a special Pro Bowl designation. Each regular card has a full-bleed color action photo on the front. The back also has a color action photo, plus a ghosted image which has a recap of the player's 1995 season. Above the recap and along the top are 1995 and career totals; the player's name, team logo and biographical information are below. A card number is in the upper left corner of the horizontally-designed card back.

		MT
Complete Set (200):		35.00
Common Player:		.10
Minor Stars:		.20
Wax Box:		50.00
1	Larry Centers	.10
2	Garrison Hearst	.20
3	Rob Moore	.20
4	Eric Swann	.10
5	Aeneas Williams	.10
6	Bert Emanuel	.10
7	Jeff George	.20
8	Craig Heyward	.10
9	Terance Mathis	.10
10	Eric Metcalf	.10
11	Cornelius Bennett	.10
12	Darick Holmes	.20
13	Jim Kelly	.50
14	Bryce Paup	.10
15	Bruce Smith	.20
16	Mark Carrier	.10
17	Kerry Collins	.50
18	Lamar Lathon	.10
19	Derrick Moore	.10
20	Tyrone Poole	.10
21	Curtis Conway	.20
22	Jeff Graham	.10
23	Raymont Harris	.10
24	Erik Kramer	.10
25	Rashaan Salaam	.50
26	Jeff Blake	.50
27	Ki-Jana Carter	.20
28	Carl Pickens	.20
29	Darnay Scott	.20
30	Dan Wilkinson	.10
31	Leroy Hoard	.10
32	Michael Jackson	.10
33	Andre Rison	.20
34	Vinny Testaverde	.50
35	Eric Turner	.10
36	Troy Aikman	1.50
37	Charles Haley	.10
38	Michael Irvin	.20
39	Daryl Johnston	.10
40	Jay Novacek	.10
41	Deion Sanders	.75
42	Emmitt Smith	2.00
43	Steve Atwater	.10
44	Terrell Davis	4.00
45	John Elway	2.00
46	Anthony Miller	.10
47	Shannon Sharpe	.50
48	Scott Mitchell	.20
49	Herman Moore	.50
50	Johnnie Morton	.10

		MT
51	Brett Perriman	.10
52	Barry Sanders	3.00
53	Chris Spielman	.10
54	Edgar Bennett	.10
55	Robert Brooks	.20
56	Mark Chmura	.20
57	Brett Favre	3.00
58	Reggie White	.50
59	Mel Gray	.10
60	Haywood Jeffires	.10
61	Steve McNair	1.25
62	Chris Sanders	.20
63	Rodney Thomas	.20
64	Quentin Coryatt	.10
65	Sean Dawkins	.10
66	Ken Dilger	.10
67	Marshall Faulk	.50
68	Jim Harbaugh	.20
69	Tony Boselli	.10
70	Mark Brunell	1.50
71	Desmond Howard	.10
72	Jimmy Smith	.50
73	James Stewart	.10
74	Marcus Allen	.50
75	Steve Bono	.20
76	Lake Dawson	.10
77	Neil Smith	.10
78	Derrick Thomas	.20
79	Tamarick Vanover	.10
80	Bryan Cox	.10
81	Irving Fryar	.10
82	Eric Green	.10
83	Dan Marino	2.00
84	O.J. McDuffie	.20
85	Bernie Parmalee	.10
86	Cris Carter	.50
87	Qadry Ismail	.10
88	Warren Moon	.20
89	Jake Reed	.20
90	Robert Smith	.50
91	Drew Bledsoe	1.50
92	Vincent Brisby	.10
93	Ben Coates	.20
94	Curtis Martin	1.25
95	Willie McGinest	.10
96	David Meggett	.10
97	Mario Bates	.20
98	Quinn Early	.10
99	Jim Everett	.20
100	Michael Haynes	.10
101	Renaldo Turnbull	.10
102	Dave Brown	.10
103	Rodney Hampton	.20
104	Mike Sherrard	.10
105	Phillippi Sparks	.10
106	Tyrone Wheatley	.20
107	Hugh Douglas	.10
108	Boomer Esiason	.20
109	Aaron Glenn	.10
110	Mo Lewis	.10
111	Johnny Mitchell	.10
112	Tim Brown	.50
113	Jeff Hostetler	.10
114	Raghib Ismail	.10
115	Chester McGlockton	.10
116	Harvey Williams	.10
117	Fred Barnett	.10
118	William Fuller	.10
119	Charlie Garner	.20
120	Ricky Watters	.50
121	Calvin Williams	.10
122	Kevin Greene	.10
123	Greg Lloyd	.10
124	Bam Morris	.20
125	Neil O'Donnell	.20
126	Erric Pegram	.10
127	Kordell Stewart	2.00
128	Yancey Thigpen	.50
129	Rod Woodson	.20
130	Jerome Bettis	.50
131	Isaac Bruce	.50
132	Troy Drayton	.10
133	Sean Gilbert	.10
134	Chris Miller	.10
135	Andre Coleman	.10
136	Ronnie Harmon	.10
137	Aaron Hayden	.20
138	Stan Humphries	.20
139	Natrone Means	.50
140	Junior Seau	.20
141	William Floyd	.10
142	Merton Hanks	.10
143	Brent Jones	.10
144	Derek Loville	.10
145	Jerry Rice	1.50
146	J.J. Stokes	.50
147	Steve Young	1.25
148	Brian Blades	.10
149	Joey Galloway	1.00
150	Cortez Kennedy	.10
151	Rick Mirer	.20
152	Chris Warren	.20
153	Derrick Brooks	.10
154	Trent Dilfer	.50
155	Alvin Harper	.10
156	Jackie Harris	.10
157	Hardy Nickerson	.10
158	Errict Rhett	.20
159	Terry Allen	.20
160	Henry Ellard	.10
161	Brian Mitchell	.10
162	Heath Shuler	.20
163	Michael Westbrook	.20
164	*Tim Biakabutuka*	1.25
165	*Tony Brackens*	.20
166	*Rickey Dudley*	.75
167	*Bobby Engram*	.30
168	*Daryl Gardener*	.10

		MT
169	*Eddie George*	4.00
170	*Terry Glenn*	2.00
171	*Kevin Hardy*	.20
172	*Keyshawn Johnson*	2.50
173	*Cedric Jones*	.10
174	*Leeland McElroy*	.30
175	*Jonathan Ogden*	.10
176	*Lawrence Phillips*	.75
177	*Simeon Rice*	.20
178	*Regan Upshaw*	.10
179	Justin Armour (First Impressions)	.10
180	Kyle Brady (First Impressions)	.10
181	Devin Bush (First Impressions)	.10
182	Kevin Carter (First Impressions)	.10
183	Wayne Chrebet (First Impressions)	.50
184	Napoleon Kaufman (First Impressions)	.75
185	Frank Sanders (First Impressions)	.20
186	Warren Sapp (First Impressions)	.10
187	Eric Zeier (First Impressions)	.10
188	Ray Zellars (First Impressions)	.10
189	Bill Brooks (Secret Weapons)	.10
190	Chris Calloway (Secret Weapons)	.10
191	Zack Crockett (Secret Weapons)	.10
192	Antonio Freeman (Secret Weapons)	1.00
193	Tyrone Hughes (Secret Weapons)	.10
194	Daryl Johnston (Secret Weapons)	.10
195	Tony Martin (Secret Weapons)	.10
196	Keenan McCardell (Secret Weapons)	.10
197	Glyn Milburn (Secret Weapons)	.10
198	David Palmer (Secret Weapons)	.10
199	Checklist	.10
200	Checklist	.10

1996 Ultra All-Rookie Die Cuts

These 10 cards feature the top picks in the 1996 NFL Draft. The cards, which use a die-cut design, show the player in his college uniform. Red-foil stamping is used for "All Rookies," which is written along the left side of the card, below the player's name and foil-stamped Ultra logo. The card back has a ghosted player action photo on one side, with a smaller color action photo on the other. The player's name is at the top, next to a card number (1 of 10, etc.). Below the photo is a recap of the skills the player showed while he was in college. "All Rookies" is also stamped in red foil on the back. Cards were randomly inserted in 1996 Fleer Ultra packs, one every 180 packs.

		MT
Complete Set (10):		150.00
Common Player:		6.00
Minor Stars:		12.00
Inserted 1:180		
1	Bobby Engram	12.00
2	Daryl Gardener	6.00
3	Eddie George	50.00
4	Terry Glenn	20.00
5	Kevin Hardy	6.00
6	Keyshawn Johnson	30.00
7	Cedric Jones	6.00
8	Leeland McElroy	6.00
9	Jonathan Ogden	6.00
10	Simeon Rice	6.00

1996 Ultra Mr. Momentum

These 1996 Fleer Ultra inserts, seeded one per every 10 packs, use a holographic foil background to showcase players who jump start their teams. Gold foil stamping is used for the player's name, position, brand logo and "Mr. Momentum." The card back has a color photo in the background, with a card number (1 of 20, etc.) in the upper left corner. The player's name, team name and team logo are underneath. In the middle of the card is a recap of the player's 1995 season, and how he can sway the outcome of a game.

		MT
Complete Set (20):		45.00
Common Player:		1.00
Minor Stars:		2.00
Inserted 1:10		
1	Robert Brooks	1.00
2	Isaac Bruce	2.00
3	Terrell Davis	8.00
4	John Elway	6.00
5	Marshall Faulk	2.00
6	Brett Favre	8.00
7	Joey Galloway	2.00
8	Dan Marino	6.00
9	Curtis Martin	4.00
10	Herman Moore	2.00
11	Carl Pickens	1.00
12	Jerry Rice	4.00
13	Barry Sanders	8.00
14	Chris Sanders	1.00
15	Deion Sanders	2.00
16	Kordell Stewart	4.00
17	Tamarick Vanover	1.00
18	Chris Warren	1.00
19	Ricky Watters	2.00
20	Steve Young	3.00

1996 Ultra Pulsating

These 1996 Fleer Ultra inserts feature 10 of the NFL's most pulsating players. The special foil-enhanced cards were seeded one per every 20 packs. Gold foil stamping is used on the card front for the player's name, brand logo and a gold bar at the bottom, which has the word "Pulsating" etched into it. The back has a wavy pattern to it, similar to the foil design on the front. A color photo is in the card's center, with a wavy-lined recap of the player's 1995 season below. Gold foil is used for the player's name at the top, next to a card number (1 of 10, etc.).

		MT
Complete Set (10):		40.00
Common Player:		1.00
Minor Stars:		2.00
Inserted 1:20		
1	Isaac Bruce	2.00
2	Brett Favre	10.00

3	Joey Galloway	2.00
4	Curtis Martin	4.00
5	Rashaan Salaam	1.00
6	Barry Sanders	10.00
7	Deion Sanders	3.00
8	Emmitt Smith	8.00
9	Kordell Stewart	5.00
10	Chris Warren	1.00

1996 Ultra Rookies

Thirty of the NFL's top 1996 draft picks are featured on these 1996 Fleer Ultra inserts. The cards, seeded one per every three packs, have gold foil borders around a color action photo on the front. The Ultra logo and "Ultra Rookies" are incorporated into the border. A color stripe at the bottom has the player's name inside. The back has a square in the center containing another color photo, with biographical information below. Ultra Rookies is written at the top of the card, with the player's name and card number (1 of 30, etc.) in a color band below.

		MT
Complete Set (30):		45.00
Common Player:		1.00
Minor Stars:		2.00
Inserted 1:3		
1	Karim Abdul-Jabbar	4.00
2	Mike Alstott	4.00
3	Marco Battaglia	1.00
4	Tim Biakabutuka	2.00
5	Sean Boyd	1.00
6	Tony Brackens	1.00
7	Duane Clemons	1.00
8	Bobby Engram	2.00
9	Daryl Gardener	1.00
10	Eddie George	10.00
11	Terry Glenn	4.00
12	Kevin Hardy	1.00
13	Marvin Harrison	3.00
14	Dietrich Jells	1.00
15	Keyshawn Johnson	6.00
16	Lance Johnstone	1.00
17	Cedric Jones	1.00
18	Marcus Jones	1.00
19	Danny Kanell	1.00
20	Markco Maddox	1.00
21	Derrick Mayes	2.00
22	Leeland McElroy	1.00
23	Dell McGee	1.00
24	Alex Molden	1.00
25	Eric Moulds	5.00
26	Jonathan Ogden	1.00
27	Lawrence Phillips	2.00
28	Simeon Rice	1.00
29	Regan Upshaw	1.00
30	Jerome Woods	1.00

1996 Ultra Sledgehammer

These embossed cards, seeded one per every 15th 1996 Fleer Ultra hobby packs, feature the NFL's power players on both sides of the ball. The embossed front has a raised color action photo on it, with Sledgehammer written along the left side of the card. A logo appears in the lower left corner, framed in gold foil. The player's name is near the bottom in a white stripe; the brand logo is in the upper right corner. The card back has another color photo, with a colored square on it that summarizes the player's skills. The player's team name is written in his team's colors at the top, opposite a card number (1 of 10, etc.). The player's name appears toward the bottom of the card.

		MT
Complete Set (10):		45.00
Common Player:		2.00
Minor Stars:		4.00
Inserted 1:15 Hobby		
1	Jeff Blake	4.00
2	Terrell Davis	15.00
3	Hugh Douglas	2.00
4	Marshall Faulk	5.00
5	Michael Irvin	4.00
6	Steve McNair	7.00
7	Natrone Means	4.00
8	Errict Rhett	2.00
9	Emmitt Smith	10.00
10	Rodney Thomas	2.00

1996 Ultra Sensations

Ultra Sensations was a Series II product, but didn't resemble the Series I release. Instead it went a new direction with 100 cards that appeared in five different versions. Forty percent of the print run had gold borders, 30 percent blue, 20 percent marbleized gold, nine percent pewter and one percent holographic gold foil. The only differentiation between any of the versions was a thick border around the entire card. Ultra Sensations included two inserts: Creative Chaos and Random Rookies.

		MT
Complete Gold Set (100):		20.00
Common Player:		.10
Minor Stars:		.20
Blue Cards:		1.5x
Marbleized Gold Cards:		2x
Pewter Cards:		4x
Holographic Gold Cards:		15x
Wax Box:		30.00
1	Leeland McElroy	.30
2	Frank Sanders	.10
3	Eric Swann	.10
4	Jeff George	.10
5	Terrance Mathis	.10
6	Eric Metcalf	.10
7	Michael Jackson	.10
8	Eric Turner	.10
9	Jim Kelly	.10
10	Bryce Paup	.10
11	Bruce Smith	.10
12	Thurman Thomas	.20
13	Tim Biakabutuka	1.00
14	Kerry Collins	.30
15	Muhsin Muhammad	1.00
16	Winslow Oliver	.10
17	Curtis Conway	.10
18	Bryan Cox	.10
19	Bobby Engram	1.00
20	Erik Kramer	.10
21	Rashaan Salaam	.30
22	Jeff Blake	.30
23	Ki-Jana Carter	.20
24	Carl Pickens	.10
25	Troy Aikman	1.25
26	Michael Irvin	.20
27	Daryl Johnston	.10
28	Deion Sanders	.75
29	Emmitt Smith	2.50
30	Terrell Davis	1.75
31	John Elway	1.00
32	Anthony Miller	.10
33	John Mobley	.10
34	Scott Mitchell	.10
35	Herman Moore	.20
36	Barry Sanders	1.25
37	Edgar Bennett	.10
38	Robert Brooks	.10
39	Brett Favre	2.50
40	Reggie White	.20
41	Eddie George	3.00
42	Steve McNair	.75
43	Chris Sanders	.10
44	Quentin Coryatt	.10
45	Marshall Faulk	.30
46	Jim Harbaugh	.10
47	Marvin Harrison	2.00
48	Mark Brunell	1.00
49	Natrone Means	.10
50	Andre Rison	.10
51	Marcus Allen	.20
52	Steve Bono	.10
53	Greg Hill	.10
54	Tamarick Vanover	.30
55	Karim Abdul-Jabbar	.50
56	Dan Marino	2.50
57	O.J. McDuffie	.10
58	Zach Thomas	1.00
59	Cris Carter	.10
60	Warren Moon	.10
61	Jake Reed	.10
62	Drew Bledsoe	1.25
63	Ben Coates	.10
64	Terry Glenn	1.50
65	Curtis Martin	.75
66	Mario Bates	.10
67	Michael Haynes	.10
68	Dave Brown	.10
69	Rodney Hampton	.10
70	Amani Toomer	.10
71	Tyrone Wheatley	.10
72	Keyshawn Johnson	2.00
73	Neil O'Donnell	.10
74	Tim Brown	.10
75	Rickey Dudley	.30
76	Napoleon Kaufman	.10
77	Chester McGlockton	.10
78	Charlie Garner	.10
79	Chris T. Jones	.10
80	Ricky Watters	.20
81	Jerome Bettis	.10
82	Kordell Stewart	1.25
83	Rod Woodson	.10
84	Aaron Hayden	.10
85	Stan Humphries	.10
86	Junior Seau	.10
87	Tony Banks	1.00
88	Isaac Bruce	.50
89	Lawrence Phillips	.50
90	Derek Loville	.10
91	Jerry Rice	1.25
92	J.J. Stokes	.40
93	Steve Young	1.00
94	Joey Galloway	1.00
95	Rick Mirer	.10
96	Chris Warren	.10
97	Trent Dilfer	.10
98	Errict Rhett	.30
99	Terry Allen	.10
100	Michael Westbrook	.20

1996 Ultra Sensations Creative Chaos

Creative Chaos featured 10 players on double-sided cards that matched each player, resulting in 100 total cards. These inserts were included in every 12 packs.

		MT
Complete Set (100):		600.00
Common Player:		4.00
Minor Stars:		8.00
1	Emmitt Smith, Emmitt Smith	20.00
1	Emmitt Smith, Brett Favre	18.00
1	Emmitt Smith, Curtis Martin	16.00
1	Emmitt Smith, Chris Warren	12.00
1	Emmitt Smith, Deion Sanders	13.00
1	Emmitt Smith, Steve Young	14.00
1	Emmitt Smith, Jerry Rice	15.00
1	Emmitt Smith, Terrell Davis	15.00
1	Emmitt Smith, Carl Pickens	12.00
1	Emmitt Smith, Marshall Faulk	13.00
2	Brett Favre, Emmitt Smith	18.00
2	Brett Favre, Brett Favre	16.00
2	Brett Favre, Curtis Martin	14.00
2	Brett Favre, Chris Warren	10.00
2	Brett Favre, Deion Sanders	11.00
2	Brett Favre, Steve Young	12.00
2	Brett Favre, Jerry Rice	13.00
2	Brett Favre, Terrell Davis	13.00
2	Brett Favre, Carl Pickens	10.00
2	Brett Favre, Marshall Faulk	11.00
3	Curtis Martin, Emmitt Smith	16.00
3	Curtis Martin, Brett Favre	14.00
3	Curtis Martin, Curtis Martin	12.00
3	Curtis Martin, Chris Warren	8.00
3	Curtis Martin, Deion Sanders	9.00
3	Curtis Martin, Steve Young	10.00
3	Curtis Martin, Jerry Rice	11.00
3	Curtis Martin, Terrell Davis	11.00
3	Curtis Martin, Carl Pickens	8.00
3	Curtis Martin, Marshall Faulk	9.00
4	Chris Warren, Emmitt Smith	12.00
4	Chris Warren, Brett Favre	10.00
4	Chris Warren, Curtis Martin	8.00
4	Chris Warren, Chris Warren	4.00
4	Chris Warren, Deion Sanders	4.00
4	Chris Warren, Steve Young	4.00
4	Chris Warren, Jerry Rice	8.00
4	Chris Warren, Terrell Davis	4.00
4	Chris Warren, Carl Pickens	4.00
4	Chris Warren, Marshall Faulk	4.00
5	Deion Sanders, Emmitt Smith	13.00
5	Deion Sanders, Brett Favre	11.00
5	Deion Sanders, Curtis Martin	9.00
5	Deion Sanders, Chris Warren	4.00
5	Deion Sanders, Deion Sanders	8.00
5	Deion Sanders, Steve Young	8.00
5	Deion Sanders, Jerry Rice	8.00
5	Deion Sanders, Terrell Davis	8.00
5	Deion Sanders, Carl Pickens	4.00
5	Deion Sanders, Marshall Faulk	4.00
6	Steve Young, Emmitt Smith	14.00
6	Steve Young, Brett Favre	12.00
6	Steve Young, Curtis Martin	10.00
6	Steve Young, Chris Warren	4.00
6	Steve Young, Deion Sanders	4.00
6	Steve Young, Steve Young	4.00
6	Steve Young, Jerry Rice	8.00
6	Steve Young, Terrell Davis	9.00
6	Steve Young, Carl Pickens	4.00
6	Steve Young, Marshall Faulk	4.00
7	Jerry Rice, Emmitt Smith	15.00
7	Jerry Rice, Brett Favre	13.00
7	Jerry Rice, Curtis Martin	11.00
7	Jerry Rice, Chris Warren	8.00
7	Jerry Rice, Deion Sanders	13.00
7	Jerry Rice, Steve Young	8.00
7	Jerry Rice, Jerry Rice	10.00
7	Jerry Rice, Terrell Davis	10.00
7	Jerry Rice, Carl Pickens	8.00
7	Jerry Rice, Marshall Faulk	8.00
8	Terrell Davis, Emmitt Smith	15.00
8	Terrell Davis, Brett Favre	13.00
8	Terrell Davis, Curtis Martin	11.00
8	Terrell Davis, Chris Warren	8.00
8	Terrell Davis, Deion Sanders	8.00
8	Terrell Davis, Steve Young	9.00
8	Terrell Davis, Jerry Rice	10.00
8	Terrell Davis, Terrell Davis	10.00
8	Terrell Davis, Carl Pickens	8.00
8	Terrell Davis, Marshall Faulk	8.00
9	Carl Pickens, Emmitt Smith	12.00
9	Carl Pickens, Brett Favre	10.00
9	Carl Pickens, Curtis Martin	8.00
9	Carl Pickens, Chris Warren	4.00
9	Carl Pickens, Deion Sanders	4.00
9	Carl Pickens, Steve Young	8.00
9	Carl Pickens, Jerry Rice	4.00
9	Carl Pickens, Terrell Davis	4.00
9	Carl Pickens, Carl Pickens	4.00
9	Carl Pickens, Marshall Faulk	4.00
10	Marshall Faulk, Emmitt Smith	13.00
10	Marshall Faulk, Brett Favre	11.00
10	Marshall Faulk, Curtis Martin	9.00
10	Marshall Faulk, Chris Warren	4.00
10	Marshall Faulk, Deion Sanders	4.00
10	Marshall Faulk, Steve Young	4.00
10	Marshall Faulk, Jerry Rice	8.00
10	Marshall Faulk, Terrell Davis	8.00
10	Marshall Faulk, Carl Pickens	4.00
10	Marshall Faulk, Marshall Faulk	4.00

1996 Ultra Sensations Random Rookies

Random Rookies arrived with 80 percent of the print run in silver foil and 20 percent in gold foil. The set included 10 cards, with the first five in hobby and the second five in retail packs. Random Rookies were seeded one every 48 packs.

		MT
Complete Set (10):		60.00
Common Player:		2.00
Gold Cards:		2x-3x
1	Keyshawn Johnson	10.00
2	Eddie George	25.00
3	Leeland McElroy	4.00
4	Eric Moulds	2.00
5	Lawrence Phillips	4.00
6	Marvin Harrison	10.00
7	Tim Biakabutuka	8.00
8	Terry Glenn	20.00
9	Rickey Dudley	6.00
10	Tony Banks	8.00

1997 Ultra

The 350-card set featured 346 cards and four checklists. The fronts showcase a full-bleed photo with the Ultra logo in the upper left. The player's name is written in script at the bottom center, while the team and his position are printed beneath the name. The backs include two photos, with his name, bio and stats beginning in the center and continuing to the bottom. The Gold Medallion parallel cards were inserted one per pack, while the Platinum Medallion parallel cards were exclusive in hobby packs and found 1:100 packs. Inserts in Series I include Blitzkrieg, Play of the Game, Starring Role, Sunday School and Talent Show. Inserts in Series II include First Rounders, Rising Stars, Specialists, Comeback Kids, The Main Event, Ultra All-Rookie Team, Ultra Specialists, Ultra Stars, Million Dollar Moments, Memorabilia Offer Card, Lucky 13 Redemption Cards and REEBOK Chase Promotion.

		MT
Complete Set (350):		50.00
Complete Series 1 (200):		30.00
Complete Series 2 (150):		20.00
Common Player:		.10
Minor Stars:		.20
Series 1 Wax Box:		55.00
Series 2 Wax Box:		55.00
1	Brett Favre	2.50
2	Ricky Watters	.20
3	Dan Marino	2.00
4	Bryan Still	.10
5	Chester McGlockton	.10
6	Tim Biakabutuka	.20
7	Dave Brown	.10
8	Mike Alstott	.20
9	O.J. McDuffie	.10
10	Mark Brunell	1.25
11	Michael Bates	.10
12	Tyrone Wheatley	.10
13	Eddie George	1.50
14	Kevin Greene	.10
15	Jerris McPhail	.10
16	Harvey Williams	.10
17	Eric Swann	.10
18	Carl Pickens	.10
19	Darrell Davis	.10
20	Charles Way	.10
21	Jamie Asher	.10
22	Qadry Ismail	.10
23	Lawrence Phillips	.20
24	John Friesz	.10
25	Dorsey Levens	.20
26	Willie McGinest	.10
27	Chris T. Jones	.10
28	Cortez Kennedy	.10
29	Raymont Harris	.10
30	William Roaf	.10
31	Ted Johnson	.10
32	Tony Martin	.10
33	Jim Everett	.10
34	Ray Zellars	.10
35	Derrick Alexander	.10
36	Leonard Russell	.10
37	William Thomas	.10
38	Karim Abdul-Jabbar	.50
39	Kevin Turner	.10
40	Robert Brooks	.10
41	Kent Graham	.10
42	Tony Brackens	.10
43	Rodney Hampton	.10
44	Drew Bledsoe	1.25
45	Barry Sanders	1.50
46	Tim Brown	.10
47	Reggie White	.20
48	Terry Allen	.10
49	Jim Harbaugh	.10
50	John Elway	.75
51	William Floyd	.10
52	Michael Jackson	.10

53	Larry Centers	.10
54	Emmitt Smith	2.00
55	Bruce Smith	.10
56	Terrell Owens	.50
57	Deion Sanders	.50
58	Neil O'Donnell	.10
59	Kordell Stewart	1.00
60	Bobby Engram	.10
61	Keenan McCardell	.10
62	Ben Coates	.10
63	Curtis Martin	1.75
64	Hugh Douglas	.10
65	Eric Moulds	.10
66	Derrick Thomas	.20
67	Bam Morris	.10
68	Bryan Cox	.10
69	Rob Moore	.10
70	Michael Haynes	.10
71	Brian Mitchell	.10
72	Alex Molden	.10
73	Steve Young	.75
74	Andre Reed	.10
75	Michael Westbrook	.20
76	Eric Metcalf	.10
77	Tony Banks	.30
78	Ken Dilger	.10
79	John Henry Mills	.10
80	Ashley Ambrose	.10
81	Jason Dunn	.10
82	Trent Dilfer	.20
83	Wayne Chrebet	.10
84	Ty Detmer	.10
85	Aeneas Williams	.10
86	Frank Wycheck	.10
87	Jessie Tuggle	.10
88	Steve McNair	1.00
89	Chris Slade	.10
90	Anthony Johnson	.10
91	Simeon Rice	.10
92	Mike Tomczak	.10
93	Sean Jones	.10
94	Wesley Walls	.10
95	Thurman Thomas	.20
96	Scott Mitchell	.10
97	Desmond Howard	.10
98	Chris Warren	.10
99	Glyn Milburn (RB)	.10
100	Vinny Testaverde	.10
101	James Stewart	.10
102	Iheanyi Uwaezuoke	.10
103	Stan Humphries	.10
104	Terance Mathis	.10
105	Thomas Lewis	.10
106	Eddie Kennison	.40
107	Rashaan Salaam	.10
108	Curtis Conway	.10
109	Chris Sanders	.10
110	Marcus Allen	.20
111	Gilbert Brown	.10
112	Jason Sehorn	.10
113	Zach Thomas	.20
114	Bobby Hebert	.10
115	Herman Moore	.20
116	Ray Lewis	.10
117	Darnay Scott	.10
118	Jamal Anderson	.20
119	Keyshawn Johnson	.40
120	Adrian Murrell	.10
121	Sam Mills	.10
122	Irving Fryar	.10
123	Ki-Jana Carter	.10
124	Gus Frerotte	.10
125	Terry Glenn	.50
126	Quentin Coryatt	.10
127	Robert Smith	.10
128	Jeff Blake	.10
129	Natrone Means	.20
130	Isaac Bruce	.30
131	Lamar Lathon	.10
132	Johnnie Morton	.10
133	Jerry Rice	1.25
134	Errict Rhett	.20
135	Junior Seau	.20
136	Joey Galloway	.40
137	Napoleon Kaufman	.20
138	Troy Aikman	1.25
139	Kevin Hardy	.10
140	Jimmy Smith	.10
141	Edgar Bennett	.10
142	Hardy Nickerson	.10
143	Greg Lloyd	.10
144	Dale Carter (WR)	.10
145	Jake Reed	.10
146	Cris Carter	.10
147	Todd Collins	.10
148	Mel Gray	.10
149	Lawyer Milloy	.10
150	Kimble Anders	.10
151	Darick Holmes	.10
152	Bert Emanuel	.10
153	Marshall Faulk	.20
154	Frank Sanders	.10
155	Leeland McElroy	.20
156	Rickey Dudley	.10
157	Tamarick Vanover	.20
158	Kerry Collins	.40
159	Jeff Graham	.10
160	Jerome Bettis	.20
161	Greg Hill	.10
162	John Mobley	.10
163	Michael Irvin	.10
164	Marvin Harrison	.40
165	Jim Schwantz	.10
166	Jermaine Lewis	.10
167	Levon Kirkland	.10
168	Nilo Silvan	.10
169	Ken Norton	.10
170	Yancey Thigpen	.10

171	Antonio Freeman	.20
172	Terry Kirby	.10
173	Brad Johnson	.20
174	Reidel Anthony	1.50
175	Tiki Barber	1.50
176	Pat Barnes	.50
177	Michael Booker	.20
178	Peter Boulware	.50
179	Rae Carruth	1.00
180	Troy Davis	.50
181	Corey Dillon	3.00
182	Jim Druckenmiller	1.00
183	Warrick Dunn	2.50
184	James Farrior	.20
185	Yatil Green	.50
186	Walter Jones	.20
187	Tom Knight	.20
188	Sam Madison	.20
189	Tyrus McCloud	.10
190	Orlando Pace	.50
191	Jake Plummer	6.00
192	Dwayne Rudd	.20
193	Darrell Russell	.20
194	Sedrick Shaw	.50
195	Shawn Springs	.50
196	Bryant Westbrook	.50
197	Danny Wuerffel	.75
198	Reinard Wilson	.20
199	Checklist	.10
200	Checklist	.10
201	Rick Mirer	.10
202	Torrance Small	.10
203	Ricky Proehl	.10
204	Will Blackwell	.30
205	Warrick Dunn	2.50
206	Rob Johnson	.20
207	Jim Schwantz	.10
208	Ike Hilliard	1.00
209	Chris Canty	.10
210	Chris Boniol	.10
211	Jim Druckenmiller	.75
212	Tony Gonzalez	1.00
213	Scottie Graham	.10
214	Byron Hanspard	.50
215	Gary Brown	.10
216	Darrell Russell	.10
217	Sedrick Shaw	.20
218	Boomer Esiason	.10
219	Peter Boulware	.10
220	Willie Green	.10
221	Dietrich Jells	.10
222	Freddie Jones	.30
223	Eric Metcalf	.10
224	John Henry Mills	.10
225	Michael Timpson	.10
226	Danny Wuerffel	.50
227	Daimon Shelton	.10
228	Henry Ellard	.10
229	Flipper Anderson	.10
230	Hunter Goodwin	.10
231	Jay Graham	.50
232	Duce Staley	8.00
233	Lamar Thomas	.10
234	Rod Woodson	.10
235	Zack Crockett	.10
236	Ernie Mills	.10
237	Kyle Brady	.10
238	Jesse Campbell	.10
239	Anthony Miller	.10
240	Michael Haynes	.10
241	Qadry Ismail	.10
242	Tom Knight	.10
243	Brian Manning	.10
244	Derrick Mayes	.10
245	Jamie Sharper	.10
246	Sherman Williams	.10
247	Yatil Green	.30
248	Howard Griffith	.10
249	Brian Blades	.10
250	Mark Chmura	.20
251	Chris Darkins	.10
252	Willie Davis	.10
253	Quinn Early	.10
254	Marc Edwards	.10
255	Charlie Jones	.10
256	Jake Plummer	2.00
257	Heath Shuler	.10
258	Fred Barnett	.10
259	Koy Detmer	.20
260	Michael Booker	.10
261	Chad Brown	.10
262	Garrison Hearst	.20
263	Leon Johnson	.10
264	Antowain Smith	2.00
265	Darnell Autry	.40
266	Craig Heyward	.10
267	Walter Jones	.10
268	Dexter Coakley	.30
269	Mercury Hayes	.10
270	Brett Perriman	.10
271	Chris Spielman	.10
272	Kevin Greene	.10
273	Kevin Lockett	.10
274	Troy Davis	.30
275	Brent Jones	.10
276	Chris Chandler	.10
277	Bryant Westbrook	.20
278	Desmond Howard	.10
279	Tyrone Hughes	.10
280	Kez McCorvey	.10
281	Stephen Davis	.10
282	Steve Everitt	.10
283	Andre Hastings	.10
284	Marcus Robinson	30.00
285	Donnell Woolford	.10
286	Mario Bates	.10
287	Corey Dillon	1.25
288	Jackie Harris	.10

289	Lorenzo Neal	.10
290	Anthony Pleasant	.10
291	Andre Rison	.10
292	Amani Toomer	.10
293	Eric Turner	.10
294	Elvis Grbac	.10
295	Cris Dishman	.10
296	Tom Carter	.10
297	Mark Carrier	.10
298	Orlando Pace	.20
299	Jay Riemersma	.10
300	Daryl Johnston	.10
301	Joey Kent	.30
302	Ronnie Harmon	.10
303	Raghib Ismail	.10
304	Terrell Davis	1.25
305	Sean Dawkins	.10
306	Jeff George	.20
307	David Palmer	.10
308	Dwayne Rudd	.10
309	J.J. Stokes	.20
310	James Farrior	.10
311	William Fuller	.10
312	George Jones	.10
313	John Allred	.10
314	Tony Graziani	.10
315	Jeff Hostetler	.10
316	Keith Poole	.10
317	Neil Smith	.10
318	Steve Tasker	.10
319	Mike Vrabel	.10
320	Pat Barnes	.30
321	James Hundon	.10
322	O.J. Santiago	.10
323	Billy Davis	.10
324	Shawn Springs	.10
325	Reinard Wilson	.10
326	Charles Johnson	.10
327	Michael Barrow	.10
328	Derrick Mason	.10
329	Muhsin Muhammad	.10
330	David LaFleur	.50
331	Reidel Anthony	.75
332	Tiki Barber	1.00
333	Ray Buchanan	.10
334	John Elway	.75
335	Alvin Harper	.10
336	Damon Jones	.10
337	Dedric Ward	.10
338	Jim Everett	.10
339	Jon Harris	.10
340	Warren Moon	.10
341	Rae Carruth	.50
342	John Mobley	.10
343	Tyrone Poole	.10
344	Mike Cherry	.10
345	Horace Copeland	.10
346	Deon Figures	.10
347	Antowuan Wyatt	.10
348	Tommy Vardell	.10
349	Checklist	.10
350	Checklist	.10

ries II (the two checklist cards in each series were not issued in Platinum Medallion versions). A prismatic foil is used on the front of the card versus the silver foil used on regular-issue cards. In addition, the words "Platinum Medallion Edition" were printed across the front bottom right of the cards, while card backs carried a "P" prefix on the card number. Platinum Medallion parallels were issued at a rate of one per 100 hobby packs in both Series.

	MT
Platinum Stars:	40x-80x
Platinum Rookies:	20x-40x

1997 Ultra All-Rookie Team

This 12-card insert features the top rookies of 1997. An action shot of the players is set on a golden plaque. The cards were inserted once per 18 packs in Series II.

		MT
Complete Set (12):		70.00
Common Player:		3.00
Minor Stars:		6.00
1	Antowain Smith	10.00
2	Jay Graham	3.00
3	Ike Hilliard	6.00
4	Warrick Dunn	18.00
5	Tony Gonzalez	3.00
6	David LaFleur	3.00
7	Reidel Anthony	8.00
8	Rae Carruth	6.00
9	Byron Hanspard	3.00
10	Joey Kent	3.00
11	Kevin Lockett	3.00
12	Jake Plummer	8.00

1997 Ultra Gold

Gold Medallions ran parallel to the Ultra Football set, and included 198 cards from Series I and 148 cards from Series II (the two checklist cards in each series were not issued in Gold Medallion versions). The foil on the front of the card was printed in gold versus the silver foil used on regular-issue cards. In addition, the words "Gold Medallion Edition" were printed across the front bottom right of the cards, while card backs carried a "G" prefix on the card number. Gold Medallion parallels were issued at a rate of one per pack in both Series.

	MT
Gold Stars:	2x-4x
Gold Rookies:	2x

1997 Ultra Platinum

Platinum Medallions were a parallel set to the Ultra Football set and included 198 cards from Series I and 148 from Se-

1997 Ultra Comeback Kids

Comeback Kids contains 10 cards featuring the NFL's top go-to players. The cards are designed as die-cut wanted posters. They were inserted 1:8 in Series II.

		MT
Complete Set (10):		35.00
Common Player:		1.25
1	Dan Marino	10.00
2	Barry Sanders	7.00
3	Jerry Rice	5.00
4	John Elway	4.00
5	Steve Young	3.00
6	Deion Sanders	2.00
7	Mark Brunell	5.00
8	Tim Biakabutuka	1.25
9	Tony Banks	1.25
10	Terry Allen	1.25

1997 Ultra First Rounders

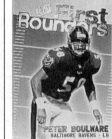

This 12-card insert features first-round draft picks who made an immediate impression in 1997. The card fronts feature an action shot of the player against a gridiron background. The insertion rate was 1:4 in Series II.

		MT
Complete Set (12):		18.00
Common Player:		.50
Minor Stars:		1.00
1	Antowain Smith	3.00
2	Rae Carruth	2.00
3	Peter Boulware	.50
4	Shawn Springs	1.00
5	Bryant Westbrook	.50
6	Orlando Pace	1.00
7	Jim Druckenmiller	5.00
8	Yatil Green	2.00
9	Reidel Anthony	2.00
10	Ike Hilliard	2.00
11	Darrell Russell	.50
12	Warrick Dunn	6.00

		MT
Common Player:		2.00
Die-Cut Cards:		2x-3x
1	Eddie George	8.00
2	Terry Glenn	4.00
3	Karim Abdul-Jabbar	5.00
4	Emmitt Smith	12.00
5	Dan Marino	12.00
6	Brett Favre	15.00
7	Keyshawn Johnson	2.00
8	Curtis Martin	8.00
9	Marvin Harrison	4.00
10	Barry Sanders	8.00
11	Jerry Rice	8.00
12	Terrell Davis	8.00
13	Troy Aikman	8.00
14	Drew Bledsoe	8.00
15	John Elway	6.00
16	Kordell Stewart	8.00
17	Kerry Collins	4.00
18	Steve Young	6.00

1997 Ultra Play of the Game

The 10-card set was inserted 1:8 packs in Series I. The front features three player photos. The back has information on a specific game that the player excelled in.

		MT
Complete Set (10):		30.00
Common Player:		1.00
1	Deion Sanders	3.00
2	Jerry Rice	7.00
3	Michael Westbrook	1.00
4	Steve McNair	5.00
5	Marshall Faulk	2.00
6	Terrell Davis	7.00
7	Mark Brunell	7.00
8	Isaac Bruce	2.00
9	Tony Banks	1.00
10	Jamal Anderson	2.00

1997 Ultra Reebok Bronze

The Reebok Chase Promotion consisted of parallel versions of 15 basic cards. The parallels featured a Reebok logo on the back and came in three tiers of scarcity (bronze, silver, and gold). The cards were inserted one per pack in Series II.

		MT
Complete Bronze Set (15):		3.00
Common Bronze Player:		.20
Gold Cards:		3x
Green Cards:		15x-30x
Red Cards:		8x-16x
Silver Cards:		1x
	Torrance Small	.20
	Jim Schwantz	.20
	Chris Boniol	.20
	Eric Metcalf	.20
	Jesse Campbell	.20
	Qadry Ismail	.20
	Brett Perriman	.20
	Chris Spielman	.20
	Desmond Howard	.20
	Steve Everitt	.20
	Lorenzo Neal	.20
	Neil Smith	.20
	Steve Tasker	.20
	John Elway	.75
	Tyrone Poole	.20

1997 Ultra Blitzkrieg

Inserted 1:6 packs, the 18-card set featured "Blitzkrieg" printed along the left border of the card. The player's photo is superimposed over a multiple-photo background. The player's name is printed vertically along the upper right border. The Ultra logo is in the lower right. The backs have the player's photo on the left, with his name in the upper right. His highlights appear to the right of the photo. The card number, which is labeled "of 18," is printed in the lower right. The Ultra Blitzkrieg die-cut parallel set was inserted 1:36 packs. The die-cut was featured on the left border. This insert was only available in Series I.

	MT
Complete Set (18):	90.00

1997 Ultra Rising Stars

Rising Stars were inserted 1:4 in Series II. The 10 cards feature a soon-to-be star player. The front has an action shot with a star-filled background.

		MT
Complete Set (10):		10.00
Common Player:		.50
Minor Stars:		1.00
1	Keyshawn Johnson	1.00
2	Terrell Davis	3.00
3	Kordell Stewart	3.00
4	Kerry Collins	1.00
5	Joey Galloway	1.00
6	Steve McNair	2.00
7	Jamal Anderson	.50
8	Michael Westbrook	.50
9	Marshall Faulk	.50
10	Isaac Bruce	1.00

1997 Ultra Rookies

The 12-card set was inserted 1:4 packs. The player is featured in his college photo on the front and superimposed over a purple and blue background. "Rookies" is printed in green at the bottom, with his name in silver foil in the lower right. The backs, which are numbered "of 12," features "Rookies" in the upper left and his highlights below. His photo and name are printed along the right side. The Ultra Rookies parallel version was seeded 1:18 packs. The parallel cards feature a sculpted-embossed player image over a matte finish background. Rookies were only available in Series I.

		MT
Complete Set (12):		20.00
Common Player:		.75
Gold Embossed:		2x-3x
1	Darnell Autry	2.00
2	Orlando Pace	1.50
3	Peter Boulware	.75
4	Shawn Springs	1.50
5	Bryant Westbrook	.75
6	Rae Carruth	2.00
7	Jim Druckenmiller	6.00
8	Yatil Green	1.00
9	James Farrior	.75
10	Dwayne Rudd	.75
11	Darrell Russell	.75
12	Warrick Dunn	8.00

Post-1980 cards in Near Mint condition will generally sell for about 75% of the quoted Mint value. Excellent-condition cards bring no more than 40%.

1997 Ultra Specialists

This 18-card insert features top players on a die-cut card that looks like a manilla file folder. The cards were inserted 1:6 in Series II. Ultra Specialists parallels the regular insert. Inserted 1:36, the die-cut folders open up to reveal an oversized photo. Ultra Specialists also appeared only in Series II.

		MT
Complete Set (18):		80.00
Common Player:		2.00
Ultra Specialists:		3x
1	Eddie George	8.00
2	Terry Glenn	6.00
3	Karim Abdul-Jabbar	3.00
4	Emmitt Smith	10.00
5	Brett Favre	12.00
6	Mark Brunell	6.00
7	Curtis Martin	6.00
8	Kerry Collins	2.00
9	Marvin Harrison	2.00
10	Jerry Rice	6.00
11	Tony Martin	2.00
12	Terrell Davis	6.00
13	Troy Aikman	6.00
14	Drew Bledsoe	6.00
15	John Elway	4.00
16	Kordell Stewart	6.00
17	Keyshawn Johnson	2.00
18	Steve Young	4.00

1997 Ultra Starring Role

The 10-card set was inserted 1:288 packs. The acrylic die-cut cards feature a silver-foil stamp on the front. The insert was featured in Series I.

		MT
Complete Set (10):		500.00
Common Player:		20.00
1	Emmitt Smith	90.00
2	Barry Sanders	70.00
3	Curtis Martin	50.00
4	Dan Marino	90.00
5	Keyshawn Johnson	20.00
6	Marvin Harrison	30.00
7	Terry Glenn	30.00
8	Eddie George	70.00
9	Brett Favre	100.00
10	Karim Abdul-Jabbar	30.00

1997 Ultra Ultra Stars

This 10-card set features

1997 Ultra Sunday School

Inserted 1:8 packs, the 10-card chase set features a player photo superimposed over a black background on the left side of the card. Also included in the background is a play diagramed in silver foil. The player's name is printed in silver foil in the lower left, while the Sunday School logo is printed vertically along the right border. The backs, numbered "of 10," have the player's photo on the left side, with his name, highlights and card number to the right of it. Only in Series I.

		MT
Complete Set (10):		40.00
Common Player:		1.00
1	Marvin Harrison	3.00
2	Barry Sanders	7.00
3	Troy Aikman	7.00
4	Drew Bledsoe	7.00
5	John Elway	5.00
6	Kordell Stewart	6.00
7	Kerry Collins	2.00
8	Steve Young	5.00
9	Deion Sanders	4.00
10	Joey Galloway	1.00

1997 Ultra Talent Show

Inserted 1:4 packs, this 10-card set features the player photo superimposed over a multi-colored background. The Talent Show logo appears in gold in the lower left, with the player's name in the lower right. The back, numbered "of 10," features a full-bleed photo of the player. Printed along the left border inside a box is the player's name, his highlights and card number. This insert appeared in Series I.

		MT
Complete Set (10):		12.00
Common Player:		.75

top players on a pattern holofoil background. Inserted 1:288 and found in Series II.

		MT
Complete Set (10):		425.00
Common Player:		30.00
1	Emmitt Smith	60.00
2	Barry Sanders	75.00
3	Curtis Martin	35.00
4	Dan Marino	60.00
5	Mark Brunell	35.00
6	Marvin Harrison	30.00
7	Terry Glenn	40.00
8	Eddie George	50.00
9	Brett Favre	75.00
10	Karim Abdul-Jabbar	30.00

1	Joey Galloway	2.00
2	Steve McNair	3.00
3	Marshall Faulk	1.00
4	Isaac Bruce	1.50
5	Michael Westbrook	.75
6	Zach Thomas	1.25
7	Jamal Anderson	.75
8	Mike Alstott	.75
9	Mark Brunell	4.00
10	Eddie Kennison	2.50

1997 Ultra The Main Event

This 10-card insert features headline making players. The cards are printed on canvas stock and resemble a top view of a boxing ring. The Main Event was inserted 1:8 in Series II.

		MT
Complete Set (10):		25.00
Common Player:		1.25
1	Dan Marino	8.00
2	Barry Sanders	7.00
3	Jerry Rice	4.00
4	Drew Bledsoe	4.00
5	John Elway	3.00
6	Troy Aikman	4.00
7	Deion Sanders	2.00
8	Joey Galloway	1.25
9	Steve McNair	3.00
10	Marshall Faulk	1.25

1998 Ultra

Ultra Football was released in two series in 1998 and contained a total of 425 cards. Series I had 197 veterans, three checklists and a 25-card 1998 Rookies subset seeded one per three packs. Series II had 132 player cards, 25 '98 Greats, three checklists and 40 rookies seeded one per three packs. Cards featured a full color shot of the player, with his name embossed foil writing in the lower right corner. Every card appears in three different parallels - Gold Medallion, Platinum Medallion and Masterpieces. Inserts in Series I include: Canton Classics, Flair Showcase Preview, Next Century, Sensational Sixty, Shots and Touchdown Kings. Inserts in Series II include: Rush Hour, Damage, Inc., Caught in the Draft, Indefensible and Exclamation Points.

		MT
Complete Set (425):		330.00
Complete Series 1 (225):		200.00
Complete Series 2 (200):		130.00
Common Player:		.15
Minor Stars:		.30
Common Rookie (201-225):		2.00
Common Rookie (386-425):		1.00
Inserted 1:3		
Wax Box Series 1:		125.00
Wax Box Series 2:		55.00
1	Barry Sanders	2.50
2	Brett Favre	2.50
3	Napoleon Kaufman	.50
4	Robert Smith	.30
5	Terry Allen	.15
6	Vinny Testaverde	.15
7	William Floyd	.15
8	Carl Pickens	.15
9	Antonio Freeman	.30
11	Elvis Grbac	.15
12	Kerry Collins	.30
13	Orlando Pace	.15
14	Steve Broussard	.15
15	Terance Mathis	.15
16	Tiki Barber	.30
17	Cris Carter	.15
18	Derrick Alexander	.15
19	Eric Metcalf	.15
20	Jeff George	.30
21	Leslie Shepherd	.15
22	Natrone Means	.30
23	Scott Mitchell	.15
24	Adrian Murrell	.15
25	Gilbert Brown	.15
26	Jimmy Smith	.15
27	Mark Bruener	.15
28	Troy Aikman	1.00
29	Warrick Dunn	1.50
30	Jay Graham	.15
31	Craig Whelihan	.15
32	Ed McCaffrey	.15
33	Jamie Asher	.15
34	John Randle	.15
35	Michael Jackson	.15
36	Rickey Dudley	.15
37	Sean Dawkins	.15
38	Andre Rison	.15
39	Bert Emanuel	.15
40	Jeff Blake	.30
41	Curtis Conway	.15
42	Eddie Kennison	.30
43	James McKnight	.15
44	Rae Carruth	.15
45	Tito Wooten	.15
46	Cris Dishman	.15
47	Ernie Conwell	.15
48	Fred Lane	.15
49	Jamal Anderson	.15
50	Lake Dawson	.15
51	Michael Strahan	.15
52	Reggie White	.30
53	Trent Dilfer	.30
54	Troy Brown	.15
55	Wesley Walls	.15
56	Chidi Ahanotu	.15
57	Dwayne Rudd	.15
58	Jerry Rice	1.25
59	Johnnie Morton	.15
60	Sherman Williams	.15
61	Steve McNair	.75
62	Yancey Thigpen	.15
63	Chris Chandler	.15
64	Dexter Coakley	.15
65	Horace Copeland	.15
66	Jerald Moore	.15
67	Leon Johnson	.15
68	Mark Chmura	.30
69	Michael Barrow	.15
70	Muhsin Muhammad	.15
71	Terry Glenn	.30
72	Tony Brackens	.15
73	Chad Scott	.15
74	Glenn Foley	.15
75	Keenan McCardell	.15
76	Peter Boulware	.15
77	Reidel Anthony	.30
78	William Henderson	.15
79	Tony Martin	.15
80	Tony Gonzalez	.15
81	Charlie Jones	.15
82	Chris Gedney	.15
83	Chris Calloway	.15
84	Dale Carter	.15
85	Ki-Jana Carter	.15
86	Shawn Springs	.15
87	Antowain Smith	.75
88	Eric Turner	.15
89	John Mobley	.15
90	Ken Dilger	.15
91	Bobby Hoying	.15
92	Curtis Martin	1.00
93	Drew Bledsoe	1.00
94	Gary Brown	.15
95	Marvin Harrison	.30
96	Todd Collins	.15
97	Chris Warren	.15
98	Danny Kanell	.15
99	Tony McGee	.15
100	Rod Smith	.15
101	Frank Sanders	.15
102	Irving Fryar	.15
103	Marcus Allen	.30
104	Marshall Faulk	.30
105	Bruce Smith	.15
106	Charlie Garner	.15
107	Jim Harbaugh	.30
108	Randal Hill	.15
109	Ricky Proehl	.15
110	Rob Moore	.15
111	Shannon Sharpe	.15
112	Warren Moon	.15
113	Zach Thomas	.15
114	Dan Marino	2.00
115	Duce Staley	.15
116	Eric Swann	.15
117	Kenny Holmes	.15
118	Merton Hanks	.15
119	Raymont Harris	.15
120	Terrell Davis	1.25
121	Thurman Thomas	.30
122	Wayne Martin	.15
123	Charles Way	.15
124	Chuck Smith	.15
125	Corey Dillon	1.00
126	Darnell Autry	.15
127	Isaac Bruce	.30
128	Joey Galloway	.30
129	Kimble Anders	.15
130	Aeneas Williams	.15
131	Andre Hastings	.15
132	Chad Lewis	.15
133	J.J. Stokes	.15
134	John Elway	1.00
135	Karim Abdul-Jabbar	.30
136	Ken Harvey	.15
137	Robert Brooks	.15
138	Rodney Thomas	.15
139	James Stewart	.15
140	Billy Joe Hobert	.15
141	Frank Wycheck	.15
142	Jake Plummer	1.50
143	Jerris McPhail	.15
144	Kordell Stewart	1.25
145	Terrell Owens	.30
146	Willie Green	.15
147	Anthony Miller	.15
148	Courtney Hawkins	.15
149	Larry Centers	.15
150	Gus Frerotte	.15
151	O.J. McDuffie	.15
152	Ray Zellars	.15
153	Terry Kirby	.15
154	Tommy Vardell	.15
155	Willie Davis	.15
156	Chris Canty	.15
157	Byron Hanspard	.15
158	Chris Penn	.15
159	Damon Jones	.15
160	Derrick Mayes	.15
161	Emmitt Smith	2.00
162	Keyshawn Johnson	.15
163	Mike Alstott	.50
164	Tom Carter	.15
165	Tony Banks	.15
166	Bryant Westbrook	.15
167	Chris Sanders	.15
168	Deion Sanders	.50
169	Garrison Hearst	.15
170	Jason Taylor	.15
171	Jerome Bettis	.30
172	John Lynch	.15
173	Troy Davis	.15
174	Freddie Jones	.15
175	Herman Moore	.30
176	Jake Reed	.15
177	Mark Brunell	1.00
178	Ray Lewis	.15
179	Stephen Davis	.15
180	Tim Brown	.15
181	Willie McGinest	.15
182	Andre Reed	.15
183	Darrien Gordon	.15
184	David Palmer	.15
185	James Jett	.15
186	Junior Seau	.15
187	Zack Crockett	.15
188	Brad Johnson	.30
189	Charles Johnson	.15
190	Eddie George	1.25
191	Jermaine Lewis	.15
192	Michael Irvin	.30
193	Reggie Brown	.15
194	Steve Young	.50
195	Warren Sapp	.15
196	Wayne Chrebet	.15
197	David Dunn	.15
198	(Dorsey Levens CL)	.15
199	(Troy Aikman CL)	.30
200	(John Elway CL)	.30
201	Peyton Manning	40.00
202	Ryan Leaf	20.00
203	Charles Woodson	15.00
204	Andre Wadsworth	5.00
205	Brian Simmons	3.00
206	Curtis Enis	15.00
207	Randy Moss	70.00
208	Germane Crowell	6.00
209	Greg Ellis	2.00
210	Kevin Dyson	8.00
211	Skip Hicks	6.00
212	Alonzo Mayes	2.00
213	Robert Edwards	12.00
214	Fred Taylor	25.00
215	Robert Holcombe	8.00
216	John Dutton	2.00
217	Vonnie Holliday	4.00
218	Tim Dwight	5.00
219	Tavian Banks	8.00
220	Marcus Nash	6.00
221	Jason Peter	2.00
222	Michael Myers	2.00
223	Takeo Spikes	4.00
224	Kivuusama Mays	2.00
225	Jacquez Green	7.00
226	Doug Flutie	2.50
227	Ike Hilliard	.15
228	Craig Heyward	.15
229	Kevin Hardy	.15
230	Jason Dunn	.15
231	Billy Davis	.15
232	Chester McGlockton	.15
233	Sean Gilbert	.15
234	Bert Emanuel	.15
235	Keith Byars	.15
236	Tyrone Wheatley	.15
237	Ricky Proehl	.15
238	Michael Bates	.15

239	Derrick Alexander	.15
240	Harvey Williams	.15
241	Mike Pritchard	.15
242	Paul Justin	.15
243	Jeff Hostetler	.15
244	Eric Moulds	.30
245	Jeff Burris	.15
246	Gary Brown	.15
247	Antwuan Wyatt	.15
248	Dan Wilkinson	.15
249	Chris Warren	.15
250	Lawrence Phillips	.15
251	Eric Metcalf	.15
252	Pat Swilling	.15
253	Lamar Smith	.15
254	Quinn Early	.15
255	Carlester Crumpler	.15
256	Eric Bieniemy	.15
257	Aaron Bailey	.15
258	Gabe Wilkins	.15
259	Rod Woodson	.15
260	Ricky Whittle	.15
261	Iheanyi Uwaezuoke	.15
262	Heath Shuler	.15
263	Darren Sharper	.15
264	John Henry Mills	.15
265	Marco Battaglia	.15
266	Yancey Thigpen	.15
267	Irv Smith	.15
268	Jamie Sharper	.15
269	Marcus Robinson	1.50
270	Dorsey Levens	.30
271	Qadry Ismail	.15
272	Desmond Howard	.15
273	Webster Slaughter	.15
274	Eugene Robinson	.15
275	Bill Romanowski	.15
276	Vincent Brisby	.15
277	Errict Rhett	.15
278	Albert Connell	.15
279	Thomas Lewis	.15
280	John Farquhar	.15
281	Marc Edwards	.15
282	Tyrone Davis	.50
283	Eric Allen	.15
284	Aaron Glenn	.15
285	Roosevelt Potts	.15
286	Kez McCorvey	.15
287	Joey Kent	.15
288	Jim Druckenmiller	.30
289	Sean Dawkins	.15
290	Edgar Bennett	.15
291	Vinny Testaverde	.30
292	Chris Slade	.15
293	Lamar Lathon	.15
294	Jackie Harris	.15
295	Jim Harbaugh	.30
296	Rob Fredrickson	.15
297	Ty Detmer	.15
298	Karl Williams	.15
299	Troy Drayton	.15
300	Curtis Martin	.75
301	Tamarick Vanover	.15
302	Lorenzo Neal	.15
303	John Hall	.15
304	Kevin Greene	.15
305	Bryan Still	.15
306	Neil Smith	.15
307	Mark Rypien	.15
308	Shawn Jefferson	.15
309	Aaron Taylor	.15
310	Sedrick Shaw	.15
311	O.J. Santiago	.15
312	Kevin Abrams	.15
313	Dana Stubblefield	.15
314	Daryl Johnston	.15
315	Yatil Green	.15
316	Jeff Graham	.15
317	Mario Bates	.15
318	Adrian Murrell	.30
319	Larry Brown	.15
320	Jahine Arnold	.15
321	Justin Armour	.15
322	Ricky Watters	.30
323	Lamont Warren	.15
324	Mack Strong	.15
325	Darnay Scott	.15
326	Brian Mitchell	.15
327	Rob Johnson	.30
328	Kent Graham	.15
329	Hugh Douglas	.15
330	Simeon Rice	.15
331	Corey Holliday	.15
332	Randall Cunningham	.75
333	Steve Atwater	.15
334	Latario Rachel	.15
335	Tony Martin	.15
336	Leroy Hoard	.15
337	Howard Griffith	.15
338	Kevin Lockett	.15
339	William Floyd	.15
340	Jerry Ellison	.15
341	Kyle Brady	.15
342	Michael Westbrook	.15
343	Kevin Turner	.15
344	David LaFleur	.15
345	Robert Jones	.15
346	Dave Brown	.15
347	Kevin Williams	.15
348	Amani Toomer	.15
349	Amp Lee	.15
350	Bryce Paup	.15
351	DeWayne Washington	.15
352	Mercury Hayes	.15
353	Scottie Graham	.15
354	Ray Crockett	.15

355	Ted Washington	.15
356	Pete Mitchell	.15
357	Billy Jenkins	.15
358	(Troy Aikman CL)	.50
359	(Drew Bledsoe CL)	.50
360	(Steve Young CL)	.40
361	Antonio Freeman	.30
362	Antowain Smith	.50
363	Barry Sanders	3.00
364	Bobby Hoying	.15
365	Brett Favre	3.00
366	Corey Dillon	.75
367	Dan Marino	2.00
368	Drew Bledsoe	1.50
369	Eddie George	1.25
370	Emmitt Smith	2.00
371	Herman Moore	.30
372	Jake Plummer	1.00
373	Jerome Bettis	.30
374	Jerry Rice	1.50
375	Joey Galloway	.30
376	John Elway	1.50
377	Kordell Stewart	1.00
378	Mark Brunell	1.00
379	Keyshawn Johnson	.15
380	Steve Young	1.00
381	Steve McNair	.75
382	Terrell Davis	2.00
383	Tim Brown	.15
384	Troy Aikman	1.50
385	Warrick Dunn	1.00
386	Ryan Leaf	10.00
387	Tony Simmons	4.00
388	Chris Howard	1.00
389	John Avery	5.00
390	Shaun Williams	2.00
391	Anthony Simmons	2.00
392	Rashaan Shehee	2.00
393	Robert Holcombe	3.00
394	Larry Shannon	1.00
395	Skip Hicks	3.00
396	Rod Rutledge	1.00
397	Donald Hayes	2.00
398	Curtis Enis	5.00
399	Mikhael Ricks	3.00
400	Brian Griese	25.00
401	Michael Pittman	2.00
402	Jacquez Green	4.00
403	Jerome Pathon	3.00
404	Ahman Green	8.00
405	Marcus Nash	4.00
406	Randy Moss	30.00
407	Terry Fair	3.00
408	Jammi German	2.00
409	Stephen Alexander	3.00
410	Grant Wistrom	2.00
411	Charlie Batch	25.00
412	Fred Taylor	15.00
413	Patrick Johnson	2.00
414	Robert Edwards	7.00
415	Keith Brooking	2.00
416	Peyton Manning	20.00
417	Duane Starks	2.00
418	Andre Wadsworth	2.00
419	Brian Alford	2.00
420	Brian Kelly	1.00
421	Joe Jurevicius	3.00
422	Tebucky Jones	1.00
423	R.W. McQuarters	2.00
424	Kevin Dyson	4.00
425	Charles Woodson	6.00

1998 Ultra Platinum Medallion

All 425 cards in Ultra Series I and II were also available in Platinum Medallion versions. These cards added a platinum tint to the background, showed the player image in black and white and added silver prismatic writing to the player's name. All cards were hobby-only with cards all regular cards sequentially numbered to 98, while the 25-card rookie subset in Series I and the 40-card rookie subset in Series II are numbered to only 66.

	MT
Platinum Medallion Cards:	50x-100x
Platinum Medallion Rookies:	4x-8x

1998 Ultra Canton Classics

Canton Classics features 10 future Hall of Famers on cards enhanced with 23 karat gold coating and embossing, with an etched border. Backs are numbered with a "CC" suffix and feature an off-color shot of the player along with some career highlights. These were inserted one per 288 packs.

		MT
Complete Set (10):		375.00
Common Player:		20.00
1	Terrell Davis	50.00
2	Brett Favre	70.00
3	John Elway	35.00
4	Barry Sanders	70.00
5	Eddie George	30.00
6	Jerry Rice	35.00
7	Emmitt Smith	50.00
8	Dan Marino	50.00
9	Troy Aikman	35.00
10	Marcus Allen	20.00

1998 Ultra Gold Medallion

All 425 cards in Ultra Series I and II were paralleled in Gold Medallion versions. The cards featured a gold tint to the front and were numbered with a "G" suffix. Throughout both series, they were inserted in hobby packs only at a rate of one per pack, except for the rookie subsets in both series which were seeded at one per 24 packs.

	MT
Gold Medallion Cards:	2x-4x
Gold Medallion Rookies:	1.5x

A card number in parentheses ( ) indicates the set is unnumbered.

and inserted 1:24. Only rookies who made an impact in '98 were included.

		MT
Complete Set (15):		100.00
Common Player:		3.00
Inserted 1:24		
1	Andre Wadsworth	3.00
2	Curtis Enis	7.00
3	Germane Crowell	5.00
4	Peyton Manning	20.00
5	Tavian Banks	5.00
6	Fred Taylor	15.00
7	John Avery	5.00
8	Randy Moss	30.00
9	Robert Edwards	6.00
10	Charles Woodson	8.00
11	Ryan Leaf	8.00
12	Ahman Green	5.00
13	Robert Holcombe	4.00
14	Jacquez Green	5.00
15	Skip Hicks	5.00

1998 Ultra Damage Inc.

Each single in this set has a business card look to it. Singles were found in Series II packs at 1:72.

		MT
Complete Set (15):		250.00
Common Player:		5.00
Inserted 1:72		
1	Terrell Davis	30.00
2	Joey Galloway	8.00
3	Kordell Stewart	15.00
4	Troy Aikman	20.00
5	Barry Sanders	40.00
6	Ryan Leaf	15.00
7	Antonio Freeman	8.00
8	Keyshawn Johnson	5.00
9	Eddie George	15.00
10	Warrick Dunn	15.00
11	Drew Bledsoe	20.00
12	Peyton Manning	40.00
13	Antowain Smith	8.00
14	Brett Favre	40.00
15	Emmitt Smith	30.00

1998 Ultra Exclamation Points

Exclamation Point cards can be found in Series II packs at 1:288. Each single in this 15-card set is printed on plastic and has a pattern holofoil front.

		MT
Complete Set (15):		550.00
Common Player:		15.00
Inserted 1:288		
1	Terrell Davis	50.00
2	Brett Favre	60.00
3	John Elway	50.00
4	Barry Sanders	60.00
5	Peyton Manning	60.00
6	Jerry Rice	30.00
7	Emmitt Smith	50.00
8	Dan Marino	50.00
9	Kordell Stewart	25.00
10	Mark Brunell	25.00
11	Ryan Leaf	30.00
12	Corey Dillon	20.00
13	Antowain Smith	15.00

14	Curtis Martin	15.00
15	Deion Sanders	15.00

1998 Ultra Flair Showcase Preview

This 10-card insert previewed the upcoming Flair Showcase set. Cards featured the designs of 1998 Flair Showcase and included the logo. They were inserted one per 144 packs of Series I.

		MT
Complete Set (10):		250.00
Common Player:		10.00
1	Kordell Stewart	30.00
2	Mark Brunell	20.00
3	Terrell Davis	30.00
4	Brett Favre	60.00
5	Steve McNair	10.00
6	Curtis Martin	10.00
7	Warrick Dunn	30.00
8	Emmitt Smith	45.00
9	Barry Sanders	45.00
10	Corey Dillon	20.00

1998 Ultra Indefensible

Each card in this 10-card set folds out from its original size and has embossed graphics on the front. Singles were inserted 1:144 packs.

		MT
Complete Set (10):		200.00
Common Player:		10.00
Inserted 1:144		
1	Jake Plummer	20.00
2	Mark Brunell	20.00
3	Terrell Davis	40.00
4	Jerry Rice	25.00
5	Barry Sanders	50.00
6	Curtis Martin	10.00
7	Warrick Dunn	20.00
8	Emmitt Smith	40.00
9	Dan Marino	40.00
10	Corey Dillon	15.00

1998 Ultra Next Century

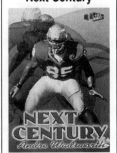

This 15-card insert featured top rookies from 1998 on

cards printed on 100 percent gold foil and sculpture embossing. Next Century inserts were numbered with a "NC" suffix and inserted one per 72 packs.

		MT
Complete Set (15):		200.00
Common Player:		5.00
1	Ryan Leaf	20.00
2	Peyton Manning	40.00
3	Charles Woodson	20.00
4	Randy Moss	50.00
5	Curtis Enis	20.00
6	Ahman Green	10.00
7	Peter Warrick	5.00
8	Andre Wadsworth	10.00
9	Germane Crowell	5.00
10	Robert Edwards	12.00
11	Tavian Banks	12.00
12	Takeo Spikes	5.00
13	Jacquez Green	12.00
14	Brian Simmons	6.00
15	Alonzo Mayes	5.00

1998 Ultra Rush Hour

Rush Hour singles were found in Series II packs at a rate of 1:6. Fleer included both veterans and rookies from '98 in this 20-card set.

		MT
Complete Set (20):		35.00
Common Player:		1.00
Minor Stars:		2.00
Inserted 1:6		
1	Robert Edwards	4.00
2	John Elway	4.00
3	Mike Alstott	3.00
4	Robert Holcombe	2.00
5	Mark Brunell	3.00
6	Deion Sanders	2.00
7	Curtis Martin	2.50
8	Curtis Enis	3.00
9	Dorsey Levens	1.00
10	Fred Taylor	6.00
11	John Avery	3.00
12	Eddie George	3.00
13	Jake Plummer	3.00
14	Andre Wadsworth	1.00
15	Fred Lane	1.00
16	Corey Dillon	2.50
17	Brett Favre	8.00
18	Kordell Stewart	3.00
19	Steve McNair	3.00
20	Warrick Dunn	3.00

1998 Ultra Sensational Sixty

This 60-card insert was available only in retail packs at a rate of one per pack. These were numbered with a "SS" suffix and found in Series I.

		MT
Complete Set (60):		45.00
Common Player:		.50
Minor Stars:		1.00
Inserted 1:1 Retail		
1	Karim Abdul-Jabbar	1.00
2	Troy Aikman	2.00
3	Terry Allen	.50
4	Mike Alstott	1.00
5	Tony Banks	1.00
6	Jerome Bettis	1.00
7	Drew Bledsoe	1.50
8	Peter Boulware	.50
9	Robert Brooks	.50
10	Tim Brown	.50
11	Isaac Bruce	1.00
12	Mark Brunell	1.50
13	Cris Carter	1.00
14	Kerry Collins	1.00
15	Curtis Conway	.50
16	Terrell Davis	3.00
17	Troy Davis	.50
18	Trent Dilfer	1.00
19	Corey Dillon	1.25
20	Warrick Dunn	1.50
21	John Elway	2.00

1998 Ultra Caught in the Draft

Caught in the Draft singles were found in Series II packs

Caught in the Draft caption: Charles Woodson

22	Bert Emanuel	.50
23	Brett Favre	4.00
24	Antonio Freeman	1.00
25	Gus Frerotte	.50
26	Joey Galloway	1.00
27	Eddie George	1.50
28	Jeff George	1.00
29	Elvis Grbac	.50
30	Marvin Harrison	1.00
31	Bobby Hoying	.50
32	Michael Irvin	1.00
33	Brad Johnson	1.00
34	Keyshawn Johnson	1.00
35	Dan Marino	3.00
36	Curtis Martin	1.00
37	Tony Martin	.50
38	Keenan McCardell	.50
39	Steve McNair	1.00
40	Warren Moon	1.00
41	Herman Moore	1.00
42	Johnnie Morton	.50
43	Terrell Owens	1.00
44	Carl Pickens	1.00
45	Jake Plummer	1.50
46	Jerry Rice	2.00
47	Andre Rison	.50
48	Barry Sanders	4.00
49	Deion Sanders	1.00
50	Junior Seau	.50
51	Shannon Sharpe	1.00
52	Antowain Smith	1.00
53	Emmitt Smith	3.00
54	Jimmy Smith	.50
55	Robert Smith	1.00
56	Kordell Stewart	1.50
57	Jeff Blake	.50
58	Charles Way	.50
59	Reggie White	1.00
60	Steve Young	1.25

1998 Ultra Shots

Shots was a 20-card insert that allowed photographers to discuss the shot that is captured on the card front. These were numbered with a "US" suffix and inserted one per six packs of Series I.

		MT
Complete Set (20):		45.00
Common Player:		1.50
Minor Stars:		3.00
1	Deion Sanders	3.00
2	Corey Dillon	4.00
3	Mike Alstott	3.00
4	Jake Plummer	4.00
5	Antowain Smith	3.00
6	Kordell Stewart	4.00
7	Curtis Martin	3.00
8	Bobby Hoying	1.50
9	Kerry Collins	3.00
10	Herman Moore	3.00
11	Terry Glenn	3.00
12	Eddie George	4.00
13	Drew Bledsoe	4.00
14	Steve McNair	3.00
15	Jerry Rice	4.00
16	Trent Dilfer	1.50
17	Joey Galloway	3.00
18	Dan Marino	8.00
19	Barry Sanders	10.00
20	Warrick Dunn	4.00

1998 Ultra Top 30 Parallel Set

This retail exclusive insert

could be found in Retail Series II packs at a rate of 1:1.

		MT
Complete Set (30):		30.00
Common Player:		.25
1	Warrick Dunn	.75
2	Troy Aikman	2.00
3	Trent Dilfer	.50
4	Tony Banks	.50
5	Tim Brown	.50
6	Terrell Davis	3.00
7	Steve McNair	.75
8	Steve Young	1.50
9	Mark Brunell	1.50
10	Kordell Stewart	1.00
11	Keyshawn Johnson	.75
12	John Elway	3.00
13	Joey Galloway	.50
14	Jerry Rice	2.00
15	Jerome Bettis	.50
16	Jake Plummer	1.50
17	Emmitt Smith	3.00
18	Eddie George	.75
19	Drew Bledsoe	1.50
20	Dan Marino	3.00
21	Curtis Martin	1.00
22	Curtis Conway	.25
23	Cris Carter	.50
24	Corey Dillon	.75
25	Carl Pickens	.25
26	Brett Favre	4.00
27	Bobby Hoying	.25
28	Barry Sanders	4.00
29	Antowain Smith	.50
30	Antonio Freeman	.50

1998 Ultra Touchdown Kings

This die-cut insert showcased 15 players on an embossed design. Cards were numbered on the back with a "TK" suffix and inserted one per 24 packs of Series I.

		MT
Complete Set (15):		100.00
Common Player:		3.00
Minor Stars:		6.00
1	Terrell Davis	12.00
2	Joey Galloway	6.00
3	Kordell Stewart	10.00
4	Corey Dillon	8.00
5	Barry Sanders	20.00
6	Cris Carter	3.00
7	Antonio Freeman	6.00
8	Mike Alstott	6.00
9	Eddie George	10.00
10	Warrick Dunn	10.00
11	Drew Bledsoe	10.00
12	Karim Abdul-Jabbar	10.00
13	Mark Brunell	10.00
14	Brett Favre	20.00
15	Emmitt Smith	15.00

1999 Ultra

Ultra Football is a 300-card set with 50 short-printed cards. The short prints are 40 Rookies (1:4) and 10 Super Bowl XXXIII (1:8). Ultra has two parallel sets with Gold and Platinum Medal-

lions. Other inserts include: As Good As It Gets, Caught in the Draft, Counterparts, Damage Inc. and Over the Top.

		MT
Complete Set (300):		200.00
Common Player:		.15
Minor Stars:		.30
Common Rookie (261-300):		2.00
Inserted 1:4		
Common Back 2 Back:		3.00
Inserted 1:8		
Wax Box:		75.00
1	Terrell Davis	2.50
2	Courtney Hawkins	.15
3	Cris Carter	.50
4	Darnay Scott	.15
5	Darrell Green	.15
6	Jimmy Smith	.30
7	Doug Flutie	.75
8	Michael Jackson	.15
9	Warren Sapp	.15
10	Greg Hill	.15
11	Karim Abdul	.50
12	Greg Ellis	.15
13	Dan Marino	2.00
14	Napoleon Kaufman	.50
15	Peyton Manning	2.50
16	Simeon Rice	.15
17	Tony Simmons	.30
18	Carlester Crumpler	.15
19	Charles Johnson	.15
20	Derrick Alexander	.15
21	Kent Graham	.15
22	Randall Cunningham	.50
23	Trent Green	.50
24	Chris Spielman	.15
25	Carl Pickens	.30
26	Bill Romanowski	.15
27	Jermaine Lewis	.15
28	Ahman Green	.30
29	Bryan Still	.15
30	Dorsey Levens	.50
31	Frank Wycheck	.15
32	Jerome Bettis	.50
33	Reidel Anthony	.30
34	Robert Jones	.15
35	Terry Glenn	.50
36	Tim Brown	.50
37	Eric Metcalf	.15
38	Kevin Greene	.15
39	Takeo Spikes	.15
40	Brian Mitchell	.15
41	Duane Starks	.15
42	Eddie George	1.00
43	Joe Jurevicius	.15
44	Kimble Anders	.15
45	Kordell Stewart	1.00
46	Leroy Hoard	.15
47	Rod Smith	.30
48	Terrell Owens	.75
49	Tony McGee	.15
50	Charles Woodson	.50
51	Andre Rison	.15
52	Chris Slade	.15
53	Frank Sanders	.30
54	Michael Irvin	.30
55	Jerome Pathon	.15
56	Desmond Howard	.15
57	Billy Davis	.15
58	Anthony Simmons	.15
59	James Jett	.15
60	Jake Plummer	1.50
61	John Avery	.30
62	Marvin Harrison	.50
63	Merton Hanks	.15
64	Ricky Proehl	.15
65	Steve Beuerlein	.15
66	Willie McGinest	.15
67	Bryce Paup	.15
68	Brett Favre	3.00
69	Brian Griese	1.00
70	Curtis Martin	.75
71	Drew Bledsoe	1.25
72	Jim Harbaugh	.30
73	Joey Galloway	.50
74	Natrone Means	.50
75	O.J. McDuffie	.15
76	Tiki Barber	.15
77	Wesley Walls	.15
78	Will Blackwell	.15
79	Bert Emanuel	.15
80	J.J. Stokes	.30
81	Steve McNair	1.00
82	Adrian Murrell	.15
83	Dexter Coakley	.15
84	Jeff George	.30
85	Marshall Faulk	.50
86	Tim Biakabutuka	.30
87	Troy Drayton	.15
88	Ty Law	.15
89	Brian Simmons	.15
90	Eric Allen	.15
91	Jon Kitna	.75
92	Junior Seau	.30
93	Kevin Turner	.15
94	Larry Centers	.15
95	Robert Edwards	.50
96	Rocket Ismail	.15
97	Sam Madison	.15
98	Stephen Alexander	.15
99	Trent Dilfer	.30
100	Vonnie Holliday	.30
101	Charlie Garner	.15
102	Deion Sanders	.75
103	Jamal Anderson	.75
104	Mike Vanderjagt	.15
105	Aeneas Williams	.15
106	Daryl Johnston	.15
107	Hugh Douglas	.15
108	Torrance Small	.15
109	Amani Toomer	.15
110	Amp Lee	.15
111	Germane Crowell	.30
112	Marco Battaglia	.15
113	Michael Westbrook	.15
114	Randy Moss	4.00
115	Ricky Watters	.50
116	Rob Johnson	.30
117	Tony Gonzalez	.30
118	Charles Way	.15
119	Chris Penn	.15
120	Eddie Kennison	.15
121	Elvis Grbac	.50
122	Eric Moulds	.50
123	Terry Fair	.15
124	Tony Banks	.30
125	Chris Chandler	.30
126	Emmitt Smith	2.00
127	Herman Moore	.50
128	Irv Smith	.15
129	Kyle Brady	.15
130	Lamont Warren	.15
131	Troy Davis	.15
132	Andre Reed	.30
133	Justin Armour	.15
134	James Hasty	.15
135	Johnnie Morton	.15
136	Reggie Barlow	.15
137	Robert Holcombe	.30
138	Sean Dawkins	.15
139	Steve Atwater	.15
140	Tim Dwight	.50
141	Wayne Chrebet	.30
142	Alonzo Mayes	.15
143	Mark Brunell	1.25
144	Antowain Smith	.50
145	Bam Morris	.15
146	Isaac Bruce	.50
147	Bryan Cox	.15
148	Bryant Westbrook	.15
149	Duce Staley	.15
150	Barry Sanders	3.00
151	La'Roi Glover	.15
152	Ray Crockett	.15
153	Tony Brackens	.15
154	Roy Barker	.15
155	Kerry Collins	.30
156	Andre Wadsworth	.30
157	Cameron Cleeland	.30
158	Koy Detmer	.15
159	Marcus Pollard	.15
160	*Patrick Jeffers*	7.00
161	Aaron Glenn	.15
162	Andre Hastings	.15
163	Bruce Smith	.15
164	David Palmer	.15
165	Erik Kramer	.15
166	Orlando Pace	.15
167	Robert Brooks	.30
168	Shawn Springs	.15
169	Terance Mathis	.15
170	Chris Calloway	.15
171	Gilbert Brown	.15
172	Charlie Jones	.15
173	Curtis Enis	.75
174	Eugene Robinson	.15
175	Garrison Hearst	.50
176	Jason Fain	.15
177	John Randle	.15
178	Keith Poole	.15
179	Kevin Hardy	.15
180	Keyshawn Johnson	.75
181	O.J. Santiago	.15
182	Jacquez Green	.30
183	Bobby Engram	.15
184	Damon Jones	.15
185	Freddie Jones	.15
186	Jake Reed	.15
187	Jerry Rice	1.50
188	Joey Kent	.15
189	Lamar Smith	.15
190	John Elway	2.00
191	Leon Johnson	.15
192	Mark Chmura	.30
193	Peter Boulware	.15
194	Zach Thomas	.30
195	Marc Edwards	.15
196	Mike Alstott	.75
197	Yancey Thigpen	.30
198	Oronde Gadsden	.30
199	Rae Carruth	.15
200	Troy Aikman	1.50
201	Shawn Jefferson	.15
202	Rob Moore	.30
203	Rickey Dudley	.15
204	Jason Taylor	.15
205	Curtis Conway	.30
206	Darrien Gordon	.15
207	Eric Green	.15
208	Jesse Armstead	.15
209	Keenan McCardell	.30
210	Robert Smith	.50
211	Mo Lewis	.15
212	Ryan Leaf	1.00
213	Steve Young	1.00
214	Tyrone Davis	.15
215	Chad Brown	.15
216	Ike Hilliard	.15
217	Jimmy Hitchcock	.15
218	Kevin Dyson	.30
219	Levon Kirkland	.15
220	Neil O'Donnell	.15
221	Ray Lewis	.15
222	Shannon Sharpe	.50
223	Skip Hicks	.50
224	Brad Johnson	.50
225	Charlie Batch	1.00
226	Corey Dillon	.75
227	Dale Carter	.15
228	John Mobley	.15
229	Hines Ward	.30
230	Leslie Shepherd	.15
231	Michael Strahan	.15
232	R.W. McQuarters	.15
233	Mike Pritchard	.15
234	Antonio Freeman	.75
235	Ben Coates	.30
236	Michael Bates	.15
237	Ed McCaffrey	.30
238	Gary Brown	.15
239	Mark Bruener	.15
240	Mikhael Ricks	.15
241	Muhsin Muhammad	.15
242	Priest Holmes	.15
243	Stephen Davis	.15
244	Vinny Testaverde	.30
245	Warrick Dunn	1.00
246	Derrick Mayes	.15
247	Fred Taylor	1.50
248	Drew Bledsoe CL	.50
249	Eddie George CL	.50
250	Steve Young CL	.50
251	Back-2-Back - Super Bowl XXXIII	3.00
252	Back-2-Back - Super Bowl XXXIII	3.00
253	Back-2-Back - Super Bowl XXXIII	3.00
254	Back-2-Back - Super Bowl XXXIII	3.00
255	Back-2-Back - Super Bowl XXXIII	3.00
256	Back-2-Back - Super Bowl XXXIII	3.00
257	Back-2-Back - Super Bowl XXXIII	3.00
258	Back-2-Back - Super Bowl XXXIII	3.00
259	Back-2-Back - Super Bowl XXXIII	3.00
260	Back-2-Back - Super Bowl XXXIII	3.00
261	*Ricky Williams*	40.00
262	*Tim Couch*	40.00
263	*Chris Claiborne*	4.00
264	*Champ Bailey*	5.00
265	*Torry Holt*	10.00
266	*Donovan McNabb*	20.00
267	*David Boston*	10.00
268	*Chris McAlister*	4.00
269	*Brock Huard*	5.00
270	*Daunte Culpepper*	20.00
271	*Matt Stinchcomb*	2.00
272	*Edgerrin James*	40.00
273	*Jevon Kearse*	10.00
274	*Ebenezer Ekuban*	2.00
275	*Kris Farris*	2.00
276	*Chris Terry*	2.00
277	*Jerame Tuman*	2.00
278	*Akili Smith*	20.00
279	*Aaron Gibson*	2.00
280	*Rahim Abdullah*	2.00
281	*Peerless Price*	8.00
282	*Antoine Winfield*	2.00
283	*Antwan Edwards*	2.00
284	*Rob Konrad*	4.00
285	*Troy Edwards*	10.00
286	*John Thornton*	2.00
287	*James Johnson*	6.00
288	*Gary Stills*	2.00
289	*Mike Peterson*	2.00
290	*Kevin Faulk*	8.00
291	*Jared DeVries*	2.00
292	*Martin Gramatica*	5.00
293	*Montae Reagor*	2.00
294	*Andy Katzenmoyer*	4.00
295	*Sedrick Irvin*	6.00
296	*D'Wayne Bates*	4.00
297	*Amos Zereoue*	8.00
298	*Dre' Bly*	2.00
299	*Kevin Johnson*	10.00
300	*Cade McNown*	20.00

1999 Ultra Gold Medallion

This is a 300-card parallel to the base and is the same except for each card is printed on gold

foil and stamped Gold Medallion Edition on the back. Veterans were inserted 1:1, Rookies 1:25 and Super Bowl singles at 1:50.

	MT
Complete Set (300):	600.00
Gold Cards:	2x-4x
Inserted 1:1	
Gold Rookies:	1.5x
Inserted 1:25	
Gold Back 2 Back:	5x-10x
Inserted 1:50	

1999 Ultra Platinum Medallion

This is a parallel to the base and is the same except for each card is printed on a silver stock and on the backs are sequentially numbered and have a Platinum Medallion stamp. Veterans are numbered to 99, Rookies to 65 and Super Bowl singles to 40.

	MT
Platinum Cards:	35x-70x
Production 99 Sets	
Platinum Rookies:	3x-6x
Production 65 Sets	
Platinum Back 2 Back:	25x-50x
Production 40 Sets	

1999 Ultra As Good As It Gets

Each of the 15 players in this set are the best in the NFL. Each is on a die-cut felt stock with silver and gold holofoil. Singles were inserted 1:288 packs.

		MT
Complete Set (15):		500.00
Common Player:		12.00
Inserted 1:288		
1	Warrick Dunn	12.00
2	Terrell Davis	50.00
3	Robert Edwards	12.00
4	Randy Moss	75.00
5	Peyton Manning	50.00
6	Mark Brunell	20.00
7	John Elway	50.00
8	Jerry Rice	30.00
9	Jake Plummer	25.00
10	Fred Taylor	30.00
11	Emmitt Smith	50.00
12	Dan Marino	50.00
13	Charlie Batch	20.00
14	Brett Favre	60.00
15	Barry Sanders	60.00

1999 Ultra Caught In The Draft

This 15-card set includes the top rookies from 1999 and captures them on a silver pattern holofoil card. They were inserted 1:18 packs.

	MT
Complete Set (15):	75.00
Common Player:	1.50

Minor Stars: 3.00
Inserted 1:18
1 Ricky Williams 20.00
2 Tim Couch 25.00
3 Chris Claiborne 3.00
4 Champ Bailey 4.00
5 Torry Holt 6.00
6 Donovan McNabb 10.00
7 David Boston 6.00
8 Andy Katzenmoyer 1.50
9 Daunte Culpepper 8.00
10 Edgerrin James 12.00
11 Cade McNown 10.00
12 Troy Edwards 6.00
13 Akili Smith 10.00
14 Peerless Price 6.00
15 Amos Zereoue 3.00

1999 Ultra Counterparts

Each card in this 15-card set highlights two players from the same team and puts them on an embossed silver holofoil card. Singles were found 1:36 packs.

MT
Complete Set (15): 100.00
Common Player: 4.00
Inserted 1:36
1 Troy Aikman, Michael Irvin 10.00
2 Drew Bledsoe, Ben Coates 8.00
3 Terrell Davis, Howard Griffith 15.00
4 Warrick Dunn, Mike Alstott 6.00
5 Brett Favre, Antonio Freeman 20.00
6 Jake Plummer, Frank Sanders 8.00
7 Randy Moss, Randall Cunningham 25.00
8 Eddie George, Steve McNair 8.00
9 Keyshawn Johnson, Wayne Chrebet 4.00
10 Ryan Leaf, Mikhael Ricks 6.00
11 Peyton Manning, Marshall Faulk 15.00
12 Barry Sanders, Tommy Vardell 20.00
13 Charlie Batch, Herman Moore 8.00
14 Emmitt Smith, Daryl Johnston 15.00
15 Kordell Stewart, Jerome Bettis 8.00

1999 Ultra Damage Inc.

This 15-card set includes the top players in the league and showcases them on a sculpted special silver foil card. Singles were found 1:72 packs.

MT
Complete Set (15): 180.00
Common Player: 6.00
Inserted 1:72
1 Brett Favre 30.00
2 Dan Marino 20.00
3 John Elway 20.00
4 Mark Brunell 12.00
5 Peyton Manning 20.00
6 Robert Edwards 6.00
7 Terrell Davis 20.00
8 Troy Aikman 15.00
9 Randy Moss 35.00
10 Kordell Stewart 10.00
11 Jerry Rice 15.00
12 Fred Taylor 15.00
13 Emmitt Smith 20.00
14 Charlie Batch 10.00
15 Barry Sanders 30.00

1999 Ultra Over The Top

This was a 20-card set that included gold foil stamping and was inserted 1:6 packs.

MT
Complete Set (20): 40.00
Common Player: 1.00
Minor Stars: 2.00
Inserted 1:6
1 Troy Aikman 5.00
2 Drew Bledsoe 4.00
3 Mark Brunell 4.00
4 Randall Cunningham 2.00
5 Jamal Anderson 2.00
6 Warrick Dunn 3.00
7 Robert Edwards 2.00
8 John Elway 8.00
9 Eddie George 4.00
10 Eric Moulds 1.00
11 Keyshawn Johnson 2.00
12 Ryan Leaf 1.00
13 Dan Marino 8.00
14 Steve McNair 3.00
15 Jake Plummer 4.00
16 Jerry Rice 5.00
17 Deion Sanders 2.00
18 Kordell Stewart 4.00
19 Fred Taylor 8.00
20 Steve Young 3.00

1991 Upper Deck Promos

These two promo card preview Upper Deck's 1991 debut football set. The design is similar to that which was used for the regular set, but the photos and card numbers for the two players' corresponding cards are different. Cards were also available through 900-number promotion by Upper Deck. The Montana card is $4; the Sanders card is $2.50.

MT
Complete Set (2): 12.00
Common Player: 7.00
1 Joe Montana 7.00
500 Barry Sanders 8.00

1991 Upper Deck

Issued in August, Upper Deck's premier football set was issued on foil packs. Upper Deck also randomly issued 2,500 autographed Joe Montana Heroes of Football cards. The set includes many of the elements from the baseball and hockey sets, including a "Star Rookies" subset. (Key: SR - star rookie, SL - season leader)

MT
Complete Set (700): 15.00
Complete Lo Series (500): 10.00
Complete Hi Series (200): 5.00
Complete Factory Set (700): 20.00
Common Player: .05
Low/High Wax Box: 10.00
1 Star Rookie Checklist .10
2 Eric Bieniemy (SR) .15
3 Mike Dumas (SR) .05
4 Mike Croel (SR) .15
5 Russell Maryland (SR) .50
6 Charles McRae (SR) .10
7 Dan McGwire (SR) .10
8 Mike Pritchard (SR) .35
9 Ricky Watters (SR) 1.75
10 Chris Zorich (SR) .30
11 Browning Nagle (SR) .20
12 Wesley Carroll (SR) .10
13 Brett Favre (SR) 5.00
14 Rob Carpenter (SR) .15
15 Eric Swann (SR) .25
16 Stanley Richard (SR) .35
17 Herman Moore (SR) 3.50
18 Todd Marinovich (SR) .10
19 Aaron Craver (SR) .10
20 Chuck Webb (SR) .05
21 Todd Lyght (SR) .10
22 Greg Lewis (SR) .10
23 Eric Turner (SR) .20
24 Alvin Harper (SR) .30
25 Jarrod Bunch (SR) .10
26 Bruce Pickens (SR) .10
27 Harvey Williams (SR) .50
28 Randal Hill (SR) .40
29 Nick Bell (SR) .15
30 Jim Everett, Henry Ellard .05
31 Randall Cunningham, Keith Jackson .15
32 Steve DeBerg, Stephone Paige .05
33 Warren Moon, Drew Hill .10
34 Dan Marino, Mark Clayton .20
35 Montana, Rice .40
36 Percy Snow .05
37 Kelvin Martin .05
38 Scott Case .05
39 John Gesek .10
40 Barry Word .15
41 Cornelius Bennett .05
42 Mike Kenn .05
43 Andre Reed .15
44 Bobby Hebert .05
45 William Perry .05
46 Dennis Byrd .05
47 Martin Mayhew .05
48 Issiac Holt .05
49 William White .05
50 JoJo Townsell .05
51 Jarvis Williams .05
52 Joey Browner .05
53 Pat Terrell .05
54 Joe Montana 1.00
55 Jeff Jerrod .05
56 Cris Carter .05
57 Jerry Rice .75
58 Brett Perriman .05
59 Kevin Fagen .05
60 Wayne Haddix .05
61 Tommy Kane .05
62 Pat Beach .05
63 Jeff Lageman .05
64 Hassan Jones .05
65 Bennie Blades .05
66 Tim McGee .05
67 Robert Blackmon .05
68 Fred Stokes .20
69 Barney Bussey .10
70 Eric Metcalf .05
71 Mark Kelso .05
72 Bears Checklist (Neal Anderson) .05
73 Bengals Checklist (Boomer Esiason) .05
74 Bills Checklist (Thurman Thomas) .25
75 Broncos Checklist (John Elway) .15
76 Browns Checklist (Eric Metcalf) .05
77 Buccaneers Checklist (Vinny Testaverde) .05
78 Cardinals Checklist (Johnny Johnson) .10
79 Chargers Checklist (Anthony Miller) .05
80 Chiefs Checklist (Derrick Thomas) .12
81 Colts Checklist (Jeff George) .12
82 Cowboys Checklist (Troy Aikman) .65
83 Dolphins Checklist (Dan Marino) .30
84 Eagles Checklist (Randall Cunningham) .10
85 Falcons Checklist (Deion Sanders) .12
86 49ers Checklist (Jerry Rice) .40
87 Giants Checklist (Lawrence Taylor) .08
88 Jets Checklist (Al Toon) .05
89 Lions Checklist (Barry Sanders) .50
90 Oilers Checklist (Warren Moon) .10
91 Packers Checklist (Sterling Sharpe) .20
92 Patriots Checklist (Andre Tippett) .05
93 Rams Checklist (Jim Everett) .05
94 Raiders Checklist (Bo Jackson) .25
95 Redskins Checklist (Art Monk) .05
96 Saints Checklist (Morten Andersen) .05
97 Seahawks Checklist (John L. Williams) .05
98 Steelers Checklist (Rod Woodson) .05
99 Vikings Checklist (Herschel Walker) .05
100 Checklist .05
101 Steve Young .75
102 Jim Lachey .05
103 Tom Rathman .05
104 Earnest Byner .05
105 Karl Mecklenburg .05
106 Wes Hopkins .05
107 Michael Irvin .20
108 Burt Grossman .05
109 Jay Novacek .25
110 Ben Smith .05
111 Rod Woodson .05
112 Ernie Jones .05
113 Bryan Hinkle .05
114 Vai Sikahema .05
115 Bubby Brister .05
116 Brian Blades .05
117 Don Majkowski .05
118 Rod Bernstine .05
119 Brian Noble .05
120 Eugene Robinson .05
121 John Taylor .12
122 Vance Johnson .05
123 Art Monk .05
124 John Elway .35
125 Dexter Carter .05
126 Anthony Miller .05
127 Keith Jackson .15
128 Albert Lewis .05
129 Bill Ray Smith .05
130 Clyde Simmons .05
131 Merril Hoge .05
132 Ricky Proehl .12
133 Tim McDonald .05
134 Louis Lipps .05
135 Ken Harvey .05
136 Sterling Sharpe .20
137 Gill Byrd .05
138 Tim Harris .05
139 Derrick Fenner .10
140 Johnny Holland .05
141 Ricky Sanders .05
142 Bobby Humphrey .05
143 Roger Craig .05
144 Steve Atwater .05
145 Ickey Woods .05
146 Randall Cunningham .15
147 Marion Butts .05
148 Reggie White .15
149 Ronnie Harmon .05
150 Mike Saxon .05
151 Greg Townsend .05
152 Troy Aikman 1.00
153 Shane Conlan .05
154 Deion Sanders .25
155 Bo Jackson .35
156 Jeff Hostetler .20
157 Albert Bentley .05
158 James Williams .05
159 Bill Brooks .05
160 Nick Lowery .05
161 Ottis Anderson .05
162 Kevin Greene .05
163 Neil Smith .05
164 Jim Everett .05
165 Derrick Thomas .25
166 John L. Williams .05
167 Timm Rosenbach .05
168 Leslie O'Neal .05
169 Clarence Verdin .05
170 Dave Krieg .05
171 Steve Broussard .05
172 Emmitt Smith 2.00
173 Andre Rison .25
174 Bruce Smith .05
175 Mark Clayton .05
176 Christian Okoye .05
177 Duane Bickett .05
178 Stephone Paige .05
179 Fredd Young .05
180 Mervyn Fernandez .05
181 Phil Simms .10
182 Pete Holohan .05
183 Pepper Johnson .05
184 Jackie Slater .05
185 Stephen Baker .05
186 Frank Cornish .05
187 Dave Waymer .05
188 Terance Mathis .10
189 Darryl Talley .05
190 James Hasty .05
191 Jay Schroeder .05
192 Kenneth Davis .05
193 Chris Miller .05
194 Scott Davis .05
195 Tim Green .05
196 Dan Saleaumua .05
197 Rohn Stark .05
198 John Alt .05
199 Steve Tasker .05
200 Checklist .05
201 Freddie Joe Nunn .05
202 Jim Breech .05
203 Roy Green .05
204 Gary Anderson (T.B.) .05
205 Rich Camarillo .05
206 Mark Bortz .05
207 Eddie Brown .05
208 Brad Muster .05
209 Anthony Munoz .05
210 Dalton Hilliard .05
211 Erik McMillan .05
212 Perry Kemp .05
213 Jim Thornton .05
214 Anthony Dilweg .05
215 Cleveland Gary .05
216 Leo Goeas .05
217 Mike Merriweather .05
218 Courtney Hall .05
219 Wade Wilson .05
220 Billy Joe Tolliver .05
221 Harold Green .10
222 Al Baker .05
223 Carl Zander .05
224 Thane Gash .05
225 Kevin Mack .05
226 Morten Andersen .05
227 Dennis Gentry .05
228 Vince Buck .05
229 Mike Singletary .05
230 Rueben Mayes .05
231 Mark Carrier (T.B.) .05
232 Tony Mandarich .05
233 Al Toon .05
234 Renaldo Turnbull .05
235 Broderick Thomas .05
236 Anthony Carter .05
237 Flipper Anderson .05
238 Jerry Robinson .05
239 Vince Newsome .05
240 Keith Millard .05
241 Reggie Langhorne .05
242 James Francis .05
243 Felix Wright .05
244 Neal Anderson .10
245 Boomer Esiason .15
246 Pat Swilling .05
247 Richard Dent .05
248 Craig Heyward .05
249 Ron Morris .05
250 Eric Moore .05
251 Jim Jensen .05
252 Anthony Toney .05
253 Sammie Smith .05
254 Calvin Williams .20
255 Dan Marino .75
256 Warren Moon .20
257 Tommie Agee .05
258 Haywood Jeffires .25
259 Eugene Lockhart .05
260 Drew Hill .05
261 Vinny Testaverde .10
262 Jim Arnold .05
263 Steve Christie .05
264 Chris Spielman .05
265 Reggie Cobb .25
266 John Stephens .05
267 Brent Williams .05
268 Jay Hilgenberg .05
269 Rodney Hampton .75
270 Irving Fryar .05
271 Terry McDaniel .05
272 Reggie Roby .05
273 Allen Pinkett .05
274 Tim McKyer .05
275 Bob Golic .05
276 Wilber Marshall .05
277 Ray Childress .05
278 Charles Mann .05
279 Cris Dishman .15
280 Mark Rypien .15
281 Michael Cofer (Det.) .05
282 Keith Byars .05
283 Mike Rozier .05
284 Seth Joyner .05
285 Jessie Tuggle .05
286 Mark Bavaro .05
287 Eddie Anderson .05
288 Sean Landeta .05
289 Howie Long .12
290 Reyna Thompson .05
291 Ferrell Edmunds .05
292 Willie Gault .05
293 John Offerdahl .05
294 Tim Brown .12
296 Kevin Ross .05
297 Lorenzo White .10
298 Dino Hackett .05
299 Curtis Duncan .05
300 Checklist .05
301 Andre Ware .12
302 David Little .05
303 Jerry Ball .05
304 Dwight Stone .05
305 Rodney Peete .05
306 Mike Baab .05
307 Tim Worley .05
308 Paul Farren .05
309 Carnell Lake .05
310 Clay Matthews .05
311 Alton Montgomery .05
312 Ernest Givins .05
313 Mike Horan .05
314 Sean Jones .05
315 Leonard Smith .05
316 Carl Banks .05
317 Jerome Brown .05
318 Everson Walls .05
319 Ron Heller .05
320 Mark Collins .05
321 Eddie Murray .05
322 Jim Harbaugh .10
323 Mel Gray .05
324 Keith Van Horne .05
325 Lomas Brown .05
326 Carl Lee .05
327 Ken O'Brien .05
328 Dermontti Dawson .05
329 Brad Baxter .15
330 Chris Doleman .05
331 Louis Oliver .05
332 Frank Stams .05
333 Mike Munchak .05
334 Fred Strickland .05
335 Mark Duper .05
336 Jacob Green .05
337 Tony Paige .05
338 Jeff Bryant .05
339 Lemuel Stinson .05
340 David Wyman .05
341 Lee Williams .05
342 Trace Armstrong .05
343 Junior Seau .30
344 John Roper .05
345 Jeff George .30
346 Herschel Walker .05
347 Sam Clancy .05
348 Steve Jordan .05
349 Nate Odomes .05
350 Martin Bayless .05
351 Brent Jones .05
352 Ray Agnew .05
353 Charles Haley .05
354 Andre Tippett .05
355 Ronnie Lott .10
356 Thurman Thomas .50
357 Fred Barnett .15
358 James Lofton .05
359 William Frizzell .10
360 Keith McKeller .05
361 Rodney Holman .05
362 Henry Ellard .05
363 David Fulcher .05
364 Jerry Gray .05
365 James Brooks .05
366 Tony Stargell .05
367 Keith McCants .05
368 Lewis Billups .05
369 Ervin Randle .05
370 Pat Leahy .05
371 Bruce Armstrong .05
372 Steve DeBerg .05
373 Guy McIntyre .05
374 Deron Cherry .05
375 Fred Marion .05
376 Michael Haddix .05
377 Kent Hull .05
378 Jerry Holmes .05
379 Jim Richter .05
380 Ed West .05
381 Richmond Webb .05
382 Mark Jackson .05
383 Tom Newberry .05
384 Ricky Nattiel .05
385 Keith Sims .05
386 Ron Hall .05
387 Ken Norton .05
388 Paul Gruber .05
389 Danny Stubbs .05
390 Ian Beckles .05
391 Hoby Brenner .05
392 Tory Epps .05
393 Sam Mills .05
394 Chris Hinton .05
395 Steve Walsh .05
396 Simon Fletcher .05
397 Tony Bennett .05
398 Aundray Bruce .05
399 Mark Murphy .05
400 Checklist .05
401 Barry Sanders (SL) .50
402 Jerry Rice (SL) .35
403 Warren Moon (SL) .10
404 Derrick Thomas (SL) .12
405 Nick Lowery (SL) .05
406 Mark Carrier (Chi., SL) .05

407	Michael Carter	.05
408	Chris Singleton	.05
409	Matt Millen	.05
410	Ronnie Lippett	.05
411	E.J. Junior	.05
412	Ray Donaldson	.05
413	Keith Willis	.05
414	Jessie Hester	.05
415	Jeff Cross	.05
416	Greg Jackson	.10
417	Alvin Walton	.05
418	Bart Oates	.05
419	Chip Lohmiller	.05
420	John Elliot	.05
421	Randall McDaniel	.05
422	Richard Johnson	.05
423	Al Noga	.05
424	Lamar Lathon	.05
425	Ricky Fenney	.05
426	Jack Del Rio	.05
427	Don Mosebar	.05
428	Luis Sharpe	.05
429	Steve Wisniewski	.05
430	Jimmie Jones	.05
431	Freeman McNeil	.05
432	Ron Rivera	.05
433	Hart Lee Dykes	.05
434	Mark Carrier (Chi.)	.05
435	Rob Moore	.15
436	Gary Clark	.12
437	Heath Sherman	.10
438	Darrell Greem	.05
439	Jessie Small	.05
440	Monte Coleman	.05
441	Leonard Marshall	.05
442	Richard Johnson	.05
443	Dave Meggett	.05
444	Barry Sanders	1.25
445	Lawrence Taylor	.10
446	Marcus Allen	.05
447	Johnny Johnson	.05
448	Aaron Wallace	.05
449	Anthony Thompson	.05
450	Garry Lewis	.05
451	Andre Rison (MVP)	.12
452	Thurman Thomas (MVP)	.25
453	Neal Anderson (MVP)	.05
454	Boomer Esiason (MVP)	.05
455	Eric Metcalf (MVP)	.05
456	Emmitt Smith (MVP)	1.00
457	Bobby Humphrey (MVP)	.05
458	Barry Sanders (MVP)	.50
459	Sterling Sharpe (MVP)	.20
460	Warren Moon (MVP)	.10
461	Albert Bentley (MVP)	.05
462	Steve DeBerg (MVP)	.05
463	Greg Townsend (MVP)	.05
464	Henry Ellard (MVP)	.05
465	Dan Marino (MVP)	.40
466	Anthony Carter (MVP)	.05
467	John Stephens (MVP)	.05
468	Pat Swilling (MVP)	.05
469	Ottis Anderson (MVP)	.05
470	Dennis Byrd (MVP)	.05
471	Randall Cunningham (MVP)	.10
472	Johnny Johnson (MVP)	.10
473	Rod Woodson (MVP)	.05
474	Anthony Miller (MVP)	.05
475	Jerry Rice (MVP)	.35
476	John L. Williams (MVP)	.05
477	Wayne Haddix (MVP)	.05
478	Earnest Byner (MVP)	.05
479	Doug Widell	.05
480	Tommy Hodson	.05
481	Shawn Collins	.05
482	Rickey Jackson	.05
483	Tony Casillas	.05
484	Vaughan Johnson	.05
485	Floyd Dixon	.05
486	Eric Green	.12
487	Harry Hamilton	.05
488	Gary Anderson (Pit.)	.05
489	Bruce Hill	.05
490	Gerald Williams	.05
491	Cortez Kennedy	.30
492	Chet Brooks	.05
493	Dwayne Harper	.05
494	Don Griffin	.05
495	Andy Heck	.05
496	David Treadwell	.05
497	Irv Pankey	.05
498	Dennis Smith	.05
499	Marcus Dupree	.05
500	Checklist	.05
501	Wendell Davis	.10
502	Matt Bahr	.05

503	Rob Burnett	.12
504	Maurice Carthon	.05
505	Donnell Woolford	.05
506	Howard Ballard	.05
507	Mark Boyer	.05
508	Eugene Marve	.05
509	Joe Kelly	.05
510	Will Wolford	.05
511	Robert Clark	.05
512	Matt Brock	.12
513	Chris Warren	.50
514	Ken Willis	.05
515	George Jamison	.12
516	Rufus Porter	.05
517	Mark Higgs	.25
518	Thomas Everett	.05
519	Robert Brown	.05
520	Gene Atkins	.05
521	Hardy Nickerson	.05
522	Johnny Bailey	.05
523	William Frizzell	.05
524	Steve McMichael	.05
525	Kevin Porter	.05
526	Carwell Gardner	.05
527	Eugene Daniel	.05
528	Vestee Jackson	.05
529	Chris Goode	.05
530	Leon Seals	.05
531	Darion Conner	.05
532	Stan Brock	.05
533	Kirby Jackson	.05
534	Marv Cook	.05
535	Bill Fralic	.05
536	Keith Woodside	.05
537	Hugh Green	.05
538	Grant Feasel	.05
539	Bubba McDowell	.05
540	Vai Sikahema	.05
541	Aaron Cox	.05
542	Roger Craig	.05
543	Robb Thomas	.05
544	Ronnie Lott	.10
545	Robert Delpino	.05
546	Greg McMurtry	.05
547	Jim Morrissey	.10
548	Johnny Rembert	.05
549	Markus Paul	.12
550	Karl Wilson	.12
551	Gaston Green	.05
552	Willie Drewrey	.05
553	Michael Young	.05
554	Tom Tupa	.05
555	John Friesz	.15
556	Cody Carlson	.35
557	Eric Allen	.05
558	Tom Bensen	.05
559	Scott Mersereau	.10
560	Lionel Washington	.05
561	Brian Brennan	.05
562	Jim Jeffcoat	.05
563	Jeff Jaeger	.05
564	David Johnson	.05
565	Danny Villa	.05
566	Don Beebe	.05
567	Michael Haynes	.30
568	Brett Faryniarz	.05
569	Mike Prior	.05
570	John Davis	.12
571	Vernon Turner	.12
572	Michael Brooks	.05
573	Mike Gann	.05
574	Ron Holmes	.05
575	Gary Plummer	.05
576	Bill Romanowski	.05
577	Chris Jacke	.05
578	Gary Reasons	.05
579	Tim Jorden	.08
580	Tim McKyer	.05
581	Johnny Jackson	.05
582	Ethan Horton	.05
583	Pete Stoyanovich	.05
584	Jeff Query	.05
585	Frank Reich	.05
586	Riki Ellison	.05
587	Eric Hill	.05
588	Anthony Shelton	.05
589	Steve Smith	.05
590	Garth Jax	.08
591	Greg Davis	.10
592	Bill Maas	.05
593	Henry Rolling	.10
594	Keith Jones	.05
595	Tootie Robbins	.25
596	Brian Jordan	.25
597	Derrick Walker	.12
598	Jonathan Hayes	.05
599	Nate Lewis	.25
600	Checklist 501-600	.05
601	AFC Checklist RF (Greg Lewis, Keith Traylor, Kenny Walker, Denver Broncos)	.15
602	James Jones	.15
603	Tim Barnett	.15
604	Ed King	.10
605	Shane Curry	.05
606	Mike Croel	.20
607	Bryan Cox	.50
608	Shawn Jefferson	.12
609	Kenny Walker	.25
610	Michael Jackson	.75
611	Jon Vaughn	.05
612	Greg Lewis	.05
613	Joe Valerio	.05
614	Pat Harlow	.10
615	Henry Jones	.20
616	Jeff Graham	.75

617	Darryll Lewis	.12
618	Keith Traylor	.10
619	Scott Miller	.05
620	Nick Bell	.10
621	John Flannery	.12
622	Leonard Russell	.50
623	Alfred Williams	.10
624	Browning Nagle	.15
625	Harvey Williams	.10
626	Dan McGwire	.10
627	Brett Favre, Moe Gardner, Erric Pegram, Bruce Pickens, Mike Pritchard (CL)	.50
628	William Thomas	.10
629	Lawrence Dawsey	.15
630	Aeneas Williams	.10
631	Stan Thomas	.05
632	Randal Hill	.15
633	Moe Gardner	.10
634	Alvin Harper	.25
635	Esera Tuaolo	.08
636	Russell Maryland	.20
637	Anthony Morgan	.15
638	Erric Pegram	1.00
639	Herman Moore	.75
640	Ricky Ervins	.20
641	Kelvin Pritchett	.10
642	Roman Phifer	.10
643	Antone Davis	.10
644	Mike Pritchard	.40
645	Vinnie Clark	.10
646	Jake Reed	1.00
647	Brett Favre	2.00
648	Todd Lyght	.10
649	Bruce Pickens	.05
650	Darren Lewis	.25
651	Wesley Carroll	.10
652	James Joseph	.25
653	Robert Delpino	.05
654	Vencie Glenn	.05
655	Jerry Rice	.20
656	Barry Sanders	.50
657	Ken Tippins	.05
658	Christian Okoye	.05
659	Rich Gannon	.05
660	Johnny Meads	.05
661	J.J. Birden	.10
662	Bruce Kozerski	.05
663	Felix Wright	.05
664	Al Smith	.05
665	Stan Humphries	.30
666	Alfred Anderson	.05
667	Nate Newton	.05
668	Vince Workman	.10
669	Ricky Reynolds	.05
670	Bryce Paup	.75
671	Gill Generty	.05
672	Darrell Thompson	.20
673	Anthony Smith	.05
674	Darryl Henley	.08
675	Brett Maxie	.05
676	Craig Taylor	.05
677	Steve Wallace	.05
678	Jeff Feagles	.08
679	James Washington	.10
680	Tim Harris	.05
681	Dennis Gibson	.05
682	Toi Cook	.10
683	Lorenzo Lynch	.05
684	Brad Edwards	.10
685	Ray Crockett	.10
686	Harris Barton	.05
687	Byron Evans	.05
688	Eric Thomas	.05
689	Jeff Criswell	.05
690	Eric Ball	.05
691	Brian Mitchell	.20
692	Quinn Early	.05
693	Aaron Jones	.05
694	Jim Dombrowski	.05
695	Jeff Bostic	.05
696	Tony Casillas	.05
697	Ken Lanier	.05
698	Henry Thomas	.05
699	Steve Beuerlein	.20
700	Checklist 601-700	.05
SP1	Darrell Green	.50

1991 Upper Deck Game Breaker Holograms

Nine top running backs are featured on these insert cards,

which were randomly included in 1991 Upper Deck packs. Series I packs contained cards 1-6; Series II packs had cards 7-9. Each card front has an action hologram against a background with a diagramed football play. "Gamebreakers" is in the bottom right corner, next to a stripe which has the player's name in it. The card backs are numbered with a "GB" prefix and contain the player's team logo and a career summary.

		MT
Complete Set (9):		8.00
Common Player:		.60
1	Barry Sanders	4.00
2	Thurman Thomas	1.25
3	Bobby Humphrey	.60
4	Earnest Byner	.60
5	Emmitt Smith	4.50
6	Neal Anderson	.60
7	Marion Butts	.60
8	James Brooks	.60
9	Marcus Allen	.75

1991 Upper Deck Joe Montana Heroes

This is the first set of Upper Deck's Football Heroes series. These 10 cards are devoted to 49er quarterback Joe Montana. Each card front has an oval framed with white and blue borders. A color photo is inside the oval. The card is two-toned - it shades from mustard to brown, and has the set logo in the bottom left corner. The card back is designed like a football field and includes a career summary and card number (1 of 9, etc.). Cards were random inserts in 1991 Upper Deck Series I packs. Montana autographed 2,500 of the cards. The tenth card is an unnumbered header card. A title appears on each card, too.

		MT
Complete Set (10):		15.00
Common Player:		1.50
Montana Header SP (NNO):		6.00
Montana Auto/2500:		200.00
1	1974-78 College Years (Joe Montana)	1.50
2	1981 A Star is Born (Joe Montana)	1.50
3	1984 Super Bowl MVP (Joe Montana)	1.50
4	1987 1st Passing Title (Joe Montana)	1.50
5	1988 Rematch (Joe Montana)	1.50
6	1989 NFL's MVP (Joe Montana)	1.50
7	1989 Back-to-Back (Joe Montana)	1.50
8	1990 Career Highs (Joe Montana)	1.50
9	Checklist Heroes 1-9 (Joe Montana) (Vernon Wells potrait of Montana)	1.50
----	Title/Header card SP (Joe Montana) (Unnumbered)	6.00

1991 Upper Deck Heroes Montana Box Bottoms

This eight-card set is identical to the Montana Heroes insert except they have blank backs and are oversized. Cards measure 5-1/4" x 7-1/4" and were

found on the bottom of 1991 Upper Deck low series wax boxes.

		MT
Complete Set (8):		5.00
Common Player:		1.00
1	1974-78 College Years	1.00
2	1981 A Star is Born	1.00
3	1984 Super Bowl MVP	1.00
4	1987 1st Passing Title	1.00
5	1988 Rematch	1.00
6	1989 NFL's MVP	1.00
7	1989 Back-to-Back	1.00
8	1990 Career Highs	1.00

1991 Upper Deck Joe Namath Heroes

Hall of Fame quarterback Joe Namath is featured in this Football Heroes set which starts where the similar Joe Montana set ended. Cards are numbered 10-18 and were randomly inserted in 1991 Upper Deck Series II packs. The front has an oval with a picture in it, bordered with a white and blue frame. The player's name is in the bottom right corner, along with a title. A "Football Heroes" logo is in the lower left corner. The back has a football field design and includes a career summary and card number. Namath autographed 2,500 cards; he autographed every 100th card "Broadway Joe."

		MT
Complete Set (10):		15.00
Common Player:		1.50
Namath Header SP (NNO):		6.00
Namath Auto/2500:		200.00
10	1962-65 Crimson Tide (Joe Namath)	1.50
11	1965 Broadway Joe (Joe Namath)	1.50
12	1967 4,000 Yards Passing (Joe Namath)	1.50
13	1968 AFL MVP (Joe Namath)	1.50
14	1969 Super Bowl III (Joe Namath)	1.50
15	1969 All-Pro (Joe Namath)	1.50
16	1972 400 Yards (Joe Namath)	1.50
17	1985 Hall of Fame (Joe Namath)	1.50
18	Checklist Heroes 10-18 (Joe Namath)	1.50
----	Title/Header Card SP (Joe Namath) (Unnumbered)	6.00

1991 Upper Deck Heroes Namath Box Bottoms

This eight-card set has identical photos to the Namath Heroes insert, but has blank backs and is printed on an over-sized format. The cards measure 5-1/4" x 7-1/4" and are found on the bottom of 1991 Upper Deck high series football wax boxes.

		MT
Complete Set (8):		5.00
Common Player:		1.00
10	1962-65 Crimson Tide	1.00
11	1965 Broadway Joe	1.00
12	1967 4,000 Yards Passing	1.00

13	1968 AFL MVP	1.00
14	1969 Super Bowl III	1.00
15	1969 All-Pro	1.00
16	1972 400 Yards	1.00
17	1985 Hall of Fame	1.00

1991 Upper Deck Sheets

Upper Deck offered two 8-1/2" x 11" sheets, with one commemorating the New York Giants Super Bowl XXV Champions and the second commemorating the 40th anniversary of the 1951 Rams championship team. The Giants sheet has the issue date, production run and issue number in the lower right hand corner. The Rams sheet was limited to 60,000.

		MT
Complete Set (2):		10.00
Common Player:		5.00
1	Los Angeles Rams Commemorative Sheet October 1991 (60,000)	5.00
2	New York Giants vs. Washington Redskins October 27, 1991 (Rodney Hampton, Lawrence Taylor, Dave Meggett, Jeff , (Ottis Anderson) (SB XXV Champions) (72,000)	5.00

1992 Upper Deck

Upper Deck's 1992 set was issued in two series - 440 and 220 each. The card front has an action photo with a shadowed border framed by a white border. The player's name is at the bottom left; his position and team logo are on the right. Both are encompassed by a granite bar with a team color-coded bar accent. The back has another photo, plus stats and a biography. Subsets include Star Rookies, All-Rookies, Team Checklists, Season Leaders, Team MVP, Rookie Force and NFL Scrapbook. Insert sets include a Gold set of 50 (each card has a gold hologram); Pro Bowlers; Game Breakers; Walter Payton; Football Heroes (Dan Marino); NFL Fanimation and Coach's Report, which features comments from former Pittsburgh Steelers coach Chuck Noll about top rookies and second-year players.

		MT
Complete Set (620):		17.00
Complete Series 1 (400):		10.00
Complete Series 2 (220):		7.00
Common Player:		.05
Series 1 or 2 Wax Box:		15.00
1	Star Rookie CL	.25
2	Edgar Bennett	.50
3	Eddie Blake	.08
4	Brian Bollinger	.08
5	Joe Bowden	.08
6	Terrell Buckley	.25
7	Willie Clay	.10
8	Ed Cunningham	.05
9	Matt Darby	.10
10	Will Furrer	.20
11	Chris Hakel	.10
12	Carlos Huerta	.10
13	Amp Lee	.30
14	Ricardo McDonald	.10
15	Dexter McNabb	.10
16	Chris Mims	.30

#	Player	
17	*Derrick Moore*	.50
18	*Robert Porcher*	.05
19	*Patrick Rowe*	.08
20	*Leon Searcy*	.08
21	*Torrance Small*	.08
22	*Jimmy Smith*	2.00
23	*Tony Smith*	.08
24	*Siran Stacy*	.08
25	*Kevin Turner*	.08
26	*Tommy Vardell*	.20
27	*Bob Whitfield*	.10
28	*Darryl Williams*	.10
29	*Jeff Sydner*	.10
30	All-Rookie Checklist	.10
31	Todd Marinovich	.10
33	Nick Bell	.10
34	Alvin Harper	.30
35	Mike Pritchard	.15
36	Lawrence Dawsey	.10
37	Tim Barnett	.05
38	John Flannery	.05
39	Stan Thomas	.05
40	Ed King	.05
41	Charles McRae	.08
42	Eric Moten	.08
43	Moe Gardner	.08
44	Kenny Walker	.08
45	Esera Tuaolo	.08
46	Alfred Williams	.10
47	Bryan Cox	.15
48	Mo Lewis	.05
49	Mike Croel	.08
50	Stanley Richard	.08
51	Tony Covington	.05
52	Larry Brown	.05
53	Aeneas Williams	.05
54	John Kasay	.05
55	Jon Vaughn	.05
56	David Fulcher	.05
57	Barry Foster	.40
58	Terry Wooden	.05
59	Gary Anderson	.05
60	Alfred Williams	.05
61	Robert Blackmon	.05
62	Brian Noble	.05
63	Terry Allen	.40
64	Darrell Green	.05
65	Darren Comeaux	.05
66	Rob Burnett	.05
67	Jerrod Bunch	.05
68	Michael Jackson	.15
69	Greg Lloyd	.05
70	Richard Brown	.05
71	Harold Green	.05
72	William Fuller	.05
73	Mark Carrier (TC)	.05
74	David Fulcher (TC)	.05
75	Cornelius Bennett (TC)	.05
76	Steve Atwater (TC)	.05
77	Kevin Mack (TC)	.05
78	Mark Carrier (TC)	.05
79	Tim McDonald (TC)	.05
80	Marion Butts (TC)	.05
81	Christian Okoye (TC)	.05
82	Jeff Herrod (TC)	.05
83	Emmitt Smith (TC)	1.00
84	Mark Duper (TC)	.05
85	Keith Jackson (TC)	.05
86	Andre Rison (TC)	.10
87	John Taylor (TC)	.05
88	Rodney Hampton (TC)	.10
89	Rob Moore (TC)	.05
90	Chris Spielman (TC)	.05
91	Haywood Jeffires (TC)	.05
92	Sterling Sharpe (TC)	.15
93	Irving Fryar (TC)	.05
94	Marcus Allen (TC)	.05
95	Henry Ellard (TC)	.05
96	Mark Rypien (TC)	.05
97	Pat Swilling (TC)	.05
98	Brian Blades (TC)	.05
99	Eric Green (TC)	.05
100	Anthony Carter (TC)	.05
101	Burt Grossman	.05
102	Gary Anderson	.05
103	Neil Smith	.05
104	Jeff Feagles	.05
105	Shane Conlan	.05
106	Jay Novacek	.05
107	Billy Brooks	.05
108	Mark Ingram	.05
109	Anthony Munoz	.05
110	Wendell Davis	.05
111	Jim Everett	.05
112	Bruce Matthews	.05
113	Mark Higgs	.20
114	Chris Warren	.10
115	Brad Baxter	.05
116	Greg Townsend	.05
117	Al Smith	.05
118	Jeff Cross	.05
119	Terry McDaniel	.05
120	Ernest Givins	.05
121	Fred Barnett	.05
122	Flipper Anderson	.05
123	Floyd Turner	.05
124	Stephen Baker	.05
125	Tim Johnson	.05
126	Brent Jones	.05
127	Leonard Marshall	.05
128	Jim Price	.05
129	Jessie Hester	.05
130	Mark Carrier	.05
131	Bubba McDowell	.05
132	Andre Tippett	.05
133	James Hasty	.05
134	Mel Gray	.05
135	Christian Okoye	.05
136	Earnest Byner	.05
137	Ferrell Edmunds	.05
138	Henry Ellard	.05
140	Brian Jordan	.05
141	Clarence Verdin	.05
142	Cornelius Bennett	.05
143	John Taylor	.05
144	Derrick Thomas	.05
145	Thurman Thomas	.25
146	Warren Moon	.25
147	Vinny Testaverde	.05
148	*Steve Bono*	.50
149	Robb Thomas	.05
150	John Friesz	.05
151	Eddie Anderson	.05
152	Eddie Anderson	.05
153	Kevin Greene	.05
154	Marion Butts	.05
155	Barry Sanders	1.25
156	Andre Rison	.25
157	Ronnie Lott	.10
158	Eric Allen	.05
159	Mark Clayton	.05
160	Terance Mathis	.05
161	Darryl Talley	.05
162	Eric Metcalf	.05
163	Reggie Cobb	.05
164	Ernie Jones	.05
165	David Griggs	.05
166	Tom Rathman	.05
167	Bubby Brister	.05
168	Broderick Thomas	.05
169	Chris Doleman	.05
170	Charles Haley	.05
171	Michael Haynes	.30
172	Rodney Hampton	.35
173	Nick Bell	.05
174	Gene Atkins	.05
175	Mike Merriweather	.05
176	Reggie Roby	.05
177	Bennie Blades	.05
178	John L. Williams	.05
179	Rodney Peete	.05
180	Greg Montgomery	.15
181	Vince Newsome	.05
182	Andre Collins	.05
183	Erik Kramer	.05
184	Bryan Hinkle	.05
185	Reggie White	.20
186	Bruce Armstrong	.05
187	Anthony Carter	.05
188	Pat Swilling	.05
189	Robert Delpino	.05
190	Brent Williams	.05
191	Johnny Johnson	.05
192	Aaron Craver	.05
193	Vincent Brown	.05
194	Herschel Walker	.10
195	Tim McDonald	.05
196	Gaston Green	.05
197	Brian Blades	.05
198	Rod Bernstine	.05
199	Brett Perriman	.05
200	John Elway	.40
201	Michael Carter	.05
202	Mark Carrier	.05
203	Cris Carter	.05
204	Kyle Clifton	.05
205	Alvin Wright	.10
206	Andre Ware	.05
207	Dave Waymer	.05
208	Darren Lewis	.05
209	Joey Browner	.05
210	Rich Miano	.05
211	Marcus Allen	.05
212	Steve Broussard	.05
213	Joel Hilgenberg	.05
214	*Bo Orlando*	.05
215	Clay Matthews	.05
216	Chris Hinton	.05
217	Al Edwards	.05
218	Tim Brown	.05
219	Sam Mills	.05
220	Don Majkowski	.05
221	James Francis	.05
222	Steve Hendrickson	.05
223	James Thornton	.05
224	Byron Evans	.05
225	Pepper Johnson	.05
226	Darryl Henley	.05
227	Simon Fletcher	.05
228	Hugh Millen	.05
229	Tim McGee	.05
230	Richmond Webb	.05
231	Tony Bennett	.05
232	Nate Odomes	.05
233	Scott Case	.05
234	Dalton Hilliard	.05
235	Paul Gruber	.05
236	Jeff Lageman	.05
237	Tony Mandarich	.05
238	Cris Dishman	.05
239	Steve Walsh	.05
240	Moe Gardner	.05
241	Bill Romanowski	.05
242	Chris Zorich	.05
243	Stephone Paige	.05
244	Mike Croel	.05
245	Leonard Russell	.30
246	Mark Rypien	.10
247	Aeneas Williams	.05
248	Steve Atwater	.05
249	Michael Stewart	.05
250	Pierce Holt	.05
251	Kevin Mack	.05
252	Sterling Sharpe	.10
253	Lawrence Dawsey	.05
254	Emmitt Smith	2.00
255	Todd Marinovich	.05
256	Neal Anderson	.05
257	Mo Lewis	.05
258	Vance Johnson	.05
259	Rickey Jackson	.05
260	Esera Tuaolo	.05
261	Wilber Marshall	.05
262	Keith Henderson	.05
263	William Thomas	.05
264	Rickey Dixon	.05
265	Dave Meggett	.05
266	Gerald Riggs	.05
267	Tim Harris	.05
268	Ken Harvey	.05
269	Clyde Simmons	.05
270	Irving Fryar	.05
271	Darion Conner	.05
272	Vince Workman	.05
273	Jim Harbaugh	.05
274	Lorenzo White	.05
275	Bobby Hebert	.05
276	Duane Bickett	.05
277	Jeff Bryant	.05
278	Scott Stephen	.05
279	Bob Golic	.05
280	Steve McMichael	.05
281	Jeff Graham	.05
282	Keith Jackson	.05
283	Howard Ballard	.05
284	Michael Brooks	.05
285	Freeman McNeil	.05
286	Rodney Holman	.05
287	Eric Bieniemy	.05
288	Seth Joyner	.05
289	Carwell Gardner	.05
290	Brian Mitchell	.05
291	Chris Miller	.05
292	Ray Berry	.05
293	Matt Brock	.05
294	Eric Thomas	.05
295	John Kasay	.05
296	Jay Hilgenberg	.05
297	Darrell Thompson	.05
298	Rich Gannon	.05
299	Steve Young	1.00
300	Mike Kenn	.05
301	Emmitt Smith (SL)	1.00
302	Haywood Jeffires (SL)	.05
303	Michael Irvin (SL)	.25
304	Warren Moon (SL)	.15
305	Chip Lohmiller (SL)	.05
306	Barry Sanders (SL)	.50
307	Ronnie Lott (SL)	.05
308	Pat Swilling (SL)	.05
309	Thurman Thomas (SL)	.25
310	Reggie Roby (SL)	.05
311	Season Leader Checklist	.05
312	Jacob Green	.05
313	Stephen Braggs	.05
314	Haywood Jeffires	.15
315	Freddie Joe Nunn	.05
316	Gary Clark	.05
317	Tim Barnett	.05
318	Mark Duper	.05
319	Eric Green	.05
320	Robert Wilson	.05
321	Michael Ball	.05
322	Eric Martin	.05
323	Alexander Wright	.05
324	Jessie Tuggle	.05
325	Ronnie Harmon	.05
326	Jeff Hostetler	.20
327	Eugene Daniel	.05
328	Ken Norton	.05
329	Reyna Thompson	.05
330	Jerry Ball	.05
331	Leroy Hoard	.05
332	Chris Martin	.05
333	Keith McKeller	.05
334	Brian Washington	.05
335	Eugene Robinson	.05
336	Maurice Hurst	.05
337	Dan Saleaumua	.05
338	Neil O'Donnell	.40
339	Dexter Davis	.05
340	Keith McCants	.05
341	Steve Beuerlein	.10
342	Roman Phifer	.05
343	Bryan Cox	.05
344	Art Monk	.05
345	Michael Irvin	.25
346	Vaughn Johnson	.05
347	Jeff Herrod	.05
348	Stanley Richard	.05
349	Michael Young	.05
350	Team MVP Checklist	.05
351	Jim Harbaugh (MVP)	.05
352	David Fulcher (MVP)	.05
353	Thurman Thomas (MVP)	.25
354	Gaston Green (MVP)	.05
355	Leroy Hoard (MVP)	.05
356	Reggie Cobb (MVP)	.05
357	Tim McDonald (MVP)	.05
358	Ronnie Harmon (MVP)	.05
359	Derrick Thomas (MVP)	.15
360	Jeff Herrod (MVP)	.05
361	Michael Irvin (MVP)	.25
362	Mark Higgs (MVP)	.10
363	Reggie White (MVP)	.10
364	Chris Miller (MVP)	.05
365	Steve Young (MVP)	.50
366	Rodney Hampton (MVP)	.10
367	Jeff Lageman (MVP)	.05
368	Barry Sanders (MVP)	.50
369	Haywood Jeffires (MVP)	.10
370	Tony Bennett	.05
371	Leonard Russell	.05
372	Jeff Jaeger	.05
373	Robert Delpino	.05
374	Mark Rypien	.05
375	Pat Swilling	.05
376	Cortez Kennedy	.05
377	Eric Green	.05
378	Cris Carter	.05
379	John Roper	.05
380	Barry Word	.05
381	Shawn Jefferson	.05
382	Tony Casillas	.05
383	*John Baylor*	.10
384	Al Noga	.05
385	Charles Mann	.05
386	Gil Byrd	.05
387	Chris Singleton	.05
388	James Joseph	.05
389	Larry Brown	.05
390	Chris Spielman	.05
391	Anthony Thompson	.05
392	Karl Mecklenburg	.05
393	Joe Kelly	.05
394	Kanavis McGhee	.05
395	Bill Maas	.05
396	Marv Cook	.05
397	Louis Lipps	.05
398	*Marty Carter*	.25
399	Louis Oliver	.05
400	Eric Swann	.05
401	*Troy Auzenne*	.10
402	Kurt Barber	.05
403	*Mark Boutte*	.10
404	*Dale Carter*	.10
405	*Marco Coleman*	.25
406	Quentin Coryatt	.40
407	*Shane Dronett*	.20
408	*Vaughn Dunbar*	.20
409	Steve Emtman	.15
410	*Dana Hall*	.10
411	*Jason Hansen*	.10
412	*Courtney Hawkins*	.30
413	*Terrell Buckley*	.10
414	*Robert Jones*	.10
415	David Klingler	.20
416	Tommy Maddox	.15
417	*Johnny Mitchell*	.50
418	Carl Pickens	1.00
419	Tracy Scroggins	.10
420	*Tony Sacca*	.15
421	Kevin Smith	.10
422	Alonzo Spellman	.10
423	Troy Vincent	.15
424	*Sean Gilbert*	.40
425	*Larry Webster*	.10
426	Rookie Force Checklist	.20
427	Bill Fralic	.05
428	Kevin Murphy	.05
429	Lemuel Stinson	.10
430	Harris Barton	.05
431	Dino Hackett	.10
432	John Stephens	.05
433	*Keith Jennings*	.10
434	Derrick Fenner	.05
435	*Kenneth Gant*	.25
436	Willie Gault	.05
437	Steve Jordan	.05
438	Charles Haley	.05
439	Keith Kartz	.05
440	Nate Lewis	.05
441	Doug Widell	.05
442	William White	.05
443	Eric Hill	.05
444	Melvin Jenkins	.05
445	David Wyman	.05
446	Ed West	.05
447	Brad Muster	.05
448	Ray Childress	.05
449	Kevin Ross	.05
450	Johnnie Jackson	.05
451	Tracy Simien	.05
452	Don Mosebar	.05
453	Jay Hilgenberg	.05
454	Wes Hopkins	.05
455	Jay Shcoreder	.05
456	Jeff Bostic	.05
457	Bryce Paup	.05
458	Dave Waymer	.05
459	Toi Cook	.05
460	Anthony Smith	.05
461	Don Griffin	.05
462	Bill Hawkins	.05
463	Courtney Hall	.05
464	Jeff Ulenhake	.05
465	Mike Sherrard	.05
466	James Jones	.05
467	Jerrol Williams	.05
468	Eric Ball	.05
469	Randall McDaniel	.05
470	Alvin Harper	.40
471	Tom Waddle	.10
472	Tony Woods	.05
473	Kelvin Martin	.05
474	Jon Vaughn	.10
475	Gil Fenerty	.05
476	Aundray Bruce	.05
477	Morton Anderson	.05
478	Lamar Lathon	.05
479	Steve DeOssie	.05
480	Marvin Washington	.05
481	Howie Long	.05
482	Calvin Williams	.05
483	Carl Carter	.05
484	Brett Favre	2.00
485	Johnny Bailey	.05
486	Jeff Gossett	.05
487	Carnell Lake	.05
488	*Michael Zordich*	.10
489	Henry Rolling	.05
490	Steve Smith	.05
491	Vestee Jackson	.05
492	Ray Crockett	.05
493	Dexter Carter	.05
494	Nick Lowery	.05
495	Cortez Kennedy	.15
496	Cleveland Gary	.05
497	Kelly Stouffer	.05
498	Carl Carter	.05
499	Shannon Sharpe	.30
500	Roger Craig	.05
501	Willie Drewrey	.05
502	Mark Schlereth	.05
503	Tony Martin	.05
504	Tom Newberry	.05
505	Ron Hall	.05
506	Scott Miller	.05
507	Donnell Woolford	.05
508	Dave Krieg	.05
509	Erric Pegram	.50
510	Checklist	.05
511	Barry Sanders	.50
512	Thurman Thomas (ScpBk)	.25
513	Warren Moon (ScpBk)	.10
514	John Elway (ScpBk)	.20
515	Ronnie Lott (ScpBk)	.10
516	Emmitt Smith (ScpBk)	1.00
517	Andre Rison (ScpBk)	.20
518	Steve Atwater (ScpBk)	.05
519	Steve Young (ScpBk)	.20
520	Mark Rypien (ScpBk)	.05
521	Rich Camarillo	.05
522	Mark Bavaro	.05
523	Brad Edwards	.05
524	*Chad Hennings*	.05
525	Tony Paige	.05
526	Shawn Moore	.05
527	*Sidney Johnson*	.05
528	*Sanjay Beach*	.05
529	Kelvin Pritchett	.05
530	Jerry Holmes	.05
531	Al Del Greco	.05
532	Bob Gagliano	.05
533	Drew Hill	.05
534	*Donald Frank*	.05
535	*Pio Sagapolutele*	.05
536	Donald Hollas	.05
537	Vernon Turner	.05
538	Bobby Humphrey	.05
539	Audray McMillen	.05
540	*Gary Brown*	.25
541	Wesley Carroll	.05
542	Nate Newton	.05
543	Vai Sikahema	.05
544	Chris Chandler	.05
545	*Nolan Harrison*	.10
546	Mark Green	.05
547	Ricky Watters	.50
548	J.J. Birden	.05
549	Cody Carlson	.05
550	Tim Green	.05
551	Mark Jackson	.05
552	Vince Buck	.05
553	George Jamison	.05
554	Anthony Pleasant	.05
555	Reggie Johnson	.05
556	John Jackson	.05
557	Ian Beckles	.05
558	Buford McGee	.05
559	Fuad Reveiz	.05
560	Joe Montana	1.00
561	Phil Simms	.05
562	Greg McMurtry	.05
563	Gerald Williams	.05
564	Dave Cadigan	.05
565	Rufus Porter	.05
566	Jim Kelly	.25
567	Deion Sanders	.50
568	Mike Singletary	.05
569	Boomer Esiason	.10
570	Andre Reed	.15
571	James Washington	.05
572	Jack Del Rio	.05
573	Gerald Perry	.05
574	Vinnie Clark	.05
575	Mike Piel	.05
576	Michael Dean Perry	.05
577	Rickey Proel	.05
578	Leslie O'Neal	.05
579	Russell Maryland	.15
580	Eric Dickerson	.05
581	Fred Strickland	.05
582	Nick Lowery	.05
583	*Joe Milinichik*	.06
584	Mark Vlasic	.05
585	James Lofton	.05
586	Bruce Smith	.15
587	Harvey Williams	.15
588	Bernie Kosar	.05
589	Carl Banks	.05
590	Jeff George	.05
591	*Fred Jones*	.10
592	Todd Scott	.05
593	Keith Jones	.05
594	Tootie Robbins	.05
595	*Todd Philcox*	.25
596	Browning Nagle	.05
597	Troy Aikman	1.25
598	Dan Marino	1.50
599	Lawrence Taylor	.15
600	Webster Slaughter	.05
601	Aaron Cox	.05
602	Matt Stover	.05
603	Keith Sims	.05
604	Dennis Smith	.05
605	Kevin Porter	.05
606	Anthony Miller	.10
607	Ken O'Brien	.05
608	Randall Cunningham	.20
609	Timm Rosenbach	.05
610	Junior Seau	.15
611	Johnny Rembert	.05
612	Rick Tuten	.05
613	Willie Green	.15
614	*Sean Salisbury*	.40
615	Martin Bayless	.05
616	Jerry Rice	.75
617	Randal Hill	.10
618	Dan McGwire	.05
619	Merril Hoge	.05
620	Checklist	.05

1992 Upper Deck Gold

Lawrence Taylor LB

These inserts, numbered with a G prefix, feature cards from three subsets - NFL Top Prospects (1-20), Quarterback Club (21-25) and veterans (26-50). Each 1992 Upper Deck Series I foil pack contained a 15-card foil pack of these cards. Jerry Rice and Andre Reed Game Breaker holograms were also randomly included in these packs. All players were licensed by NFL Properties. Each card front has a color action photo with a white border. The player's name and position are at the bottom for cards 1-20 and 26-50; Quarterback Club cards have the player's name printed along the left side in a black stripe. The backs have a closeup photo, statistics, biography or profile, except for the Prospects cards, which only have a summary of the player's career. The NFL Properties logo is on the back of the card, along with a gold Upper Deck hologram football, instead of the usual silver design.

		MT
Complete Set (50):		15.00
Common Player:		.10
1	*Steve Emtman*	.25
2	*Carl Pickens*	3.50
3	*Dale Carter*	.60
4	*Greg Skrepenak*	.10
5	*Kevin Smith*	.50
6	*Marco Coleman*	.50
7	*David Klingler*	.50
8	*Phillippi Sparks*	.10
9	*Tommy Maddox*	.50
10	*Quentin Coryatt*	.50
11	*Ty Detmer*	.25
12	*Vaughn Dunbar*	.40
13	*Ashley Ambrose*	.10
14	*Kurt Barber*	.10

15	Chester McGlockton	.10
16	*Todd Collins*	.35
17	*Steve Israel*	.10
18	*Marquez Pope*	.25
19	*Alonzo Spellman*	.50
20	*Tracy Scroggins*	.60
21	Jim Kelly	.50
22	Troy Aikman	1.00
23	Randall Cunningham	.50
24	Bernie Kosar	.10
25	Dan Marino	2.00
26	Andre Reed	.35
27	Deion Sanders	.50
28	Randall Hill	.40
29	Eric Dickerson	.10
30	Jim Kelly	.75
31	Bernie Kosar	.10
32	Mike Singletary	.10
33	Anthony Miller	.10
34	Harvey Williams	.10
35	Randall Cunningham	.50
36	Joe Montana	1.00
37	Dan McGwire	.10
38	Al Toon	.10
39	Carl Banks	.10
40	Troy Aikman	1.00
41	Junior Seau	.50
42	Jeff George	.50
43	Michael Dean Perry	.10
44	Lawrence Taylor	.30
45	Dan Marino	2.00
46	Jerry Rice	1.00
47	Boomer Esiason	.10
48	Bruce Smith	.10
49	Leslie O'Neal	.10
50	Form Checklist	.10

1992 Upper Deck Coach's Report

Top rookies and second-year players are analyzed by former Pittsburgh Steelers Coach Chuck Noll for this 20-card insert set. The set's logo is on the card front, along with a color full-bleed action photo and the player's name and position, which are printed on a pencil at the bottom of the card. The card back has a spiral notebook on top of a chalkboard and wooden desk. "From the desk of Chuck Noll" is written at the top; Noll's evaluation is on the notebook paper. The card number uses a "CR" prefix and appears at the top of the card in a white bar. Cards were randomly inserted in 1992 Upper Deck Series II hobby foil packs only.

		MT
Complete Set (20):		25.00
Common Player:		1.00
1	Mike Pritchard	1.00
2	Will Furrer	1.00
3	Alfred Williams	1.00
4	Tommy Vardell	1.00
5	Brett Favre	10.00
6	Alvin Harper	1.00
7	Mike Croel	1.00
8	Herman Moore	5.00
9	Edgar Bennett	3.00
10	Todd Marinovich	1.00
11	Aeneas Williams	1.00
12	Ricky Watters	4.00
13	Amp Lee	2.00
14	Terrell Buckley	1.00
15	Tim Barnett	1.00
16	Nick Bell	1.00
17	Leonard Russell	2.00
18	Lawrence Dawsey	1.00
19	Robert Porcher	1.00
20	Ricky Watters (CL)	2.00

> A card number in parentheses ( ) indicates the set is unnumbered.

1992 Upper Deck Fanimation

The artwork of artists Jim Lee and Rob Liefeld are featured on these 10 insert cards, available in 1992 Upper Deck Series II retail packs. Each card front features a color cartoon portraying the player, plus a "Fanimation" logo at the bottom. The back has a mug shot, biography and analysis of the player's strengths. The background has shades of red, orange and yellow. A card number, using an "F" for a prefix, also appears.

		MT
Complete Set (10):		30.00
Common Player:		2.00
1	Jim Kelly	2.00
2	Dan Marino	8.00
3	Lawrence Taylor	2.00
4	Deion Sanders	4.00
5	Troy Aikman	6.00
6	Junior Seau	2.00
7	Mike Singletary	2.00
8	Eric Dickerson	2.00
9	Jerry Rice	6.00
10	Checklist	2.00

1992 Upper Deck Game Breaker Holograms

Some of the NFL's top wide receivers are featured in this nine-card hologram set. The front has a hologram image against a football field background. The player's name is at the bottom, along with the Upper Deck logo. The back has a marble-like tablet which contains career highlights. The player's name and "Game Breakers" are at the top of the card. Each card back is also numbered, using a "GB" prefix. Cards 1, 3, 4, 6, 8 and 9 were random inserts in 1992 Upper Deck Series I packs; cards 2, 5, and 7 were in Series II packs.

		MT
Complete Set (9):		15.00
Common Player:		1.50
1	Art Monk	1.50
2	Drew Hill	1.50
3	Haywood Jeffires	1.50
4	Andre Rison	1.50
5	Mark Clayton	1.50
6	Jerry Rice	5.00
7	Michael Haynes	1.50
8	Andre Reed	1.50
9	Michael Irvin	2.00

> A player's name in *italic* type indicates a rookie card.

1992 Upper Deck Dan Marino Heroes

These 10 cards are a continuation of Upper Deck's Football Heroes set and starts with number 28, where the Walter Payton set left off. Cards, random inserts in 1992 Upper Deck Series II foil packs, have an oval picture on the front, featuring Dan Marino in a different stage in his career. The card's title is in the bottom right corner. The back has a marble-like background with career highlights, plus an Upper Deck hologram and card number. There is a checklist card in the set which is unnumbered.

		MT
Complete Set (10):		35.00
Common Marino:		3.50
Marino Header (NNO):		6.00
28	College Years (Dan Marino)	3.50
29	Rookie of the Year (Dan Marino)	3.50
30	5,000 Yards Passing (Dan Marino)	3.50
31	Super Bowl XIX (Dan Marino)	3.50
32	4,000 Yards Passing (Dan Marino)	3.50
33	200th Touchdown (Dan Marino)	3.50
34	30,000 Yards (Dan Marino)	3.50
35	Still Counting (Dan Marino)	3.50
36	Checklist (Dan Marino)	3.50

1992 Upper Deck Walter Payton Heroes

Some of the NFL's top wide receivers are featured in this nine-card hologram set. Hall of Fame running back Walter Payton and continue with card 19, where the Joe Namath Football Heroes series ended. Cards were random inserts in 1992 Upper Deck football Series II foil packs. Each card front has an oval with a picture of Payton in it during a different point in his career. The picture is bordered by a marble-like frame. The card title appears in the lower right corner. Each card back has a career summary on a marble background with dark gray borders. The back is numbered and includes an Upper Deck hologram football. An unnumbered header card was also made.

	MT
Complete Set (10):	30.00

1992 Upper Deck Heroes Payton Box Bottoms

Much like the Montana and Namath Heroes were printed on a 5-1/4" x 7-1/4" format in 1991, Walter Payton Heroes were printed on the bottoms of 1992 Upper Deck Series I boxes. All box bottoms are blank on the back and feature identical fronts to the Payton Heroes insert.

		MT
Complete Set (8):		5.00
Common Payton:		1.00
19	College Years 1971-74	1.00
20	Sweetness 1975	1.00
21	Career Year 1977	1.00
22	NFL Rushing Record 1984	1.00
23	2,000 Yard Seasons 1983-85	1.00
24	Super Bowl XX 1986	1.00
25	Walter Payton Day 1987	1.00
26	Hall of Fame Bound 1992	1.00

1992 Upper Deck Pro Bowl

Players from the 1992 Pro Bowl are featured on these insert cards randomly included in 1992 Upper Deck Series I foil packs. The front is horizontally designed and features pictures of two different players; the AFC player is on the left, while the NFC player appears on the right. "Pro Bowl" is written in silver foil on a rainbow colored panel which separates the two photos. The rainbow colored band creates a prism-like effect when held under a light. The players' names are at the bottom of the card in silver foil. Each back is in a horizontal format and includes a summary paragraph about each player. Cards are numbered with a PB prefix and include an Upper Deck hologram football.

		MT
Complete Set (16):		30.00
Common Player:		1.50
1	Jeffires, Irvin	4.00
2	Mark Clayton, Gary Clark	4.00
3	Anthony Munoz, Jim Lachey	1.50
4	Moon, Rypien	4.00
5	Thomas, Sanders	8.00
6	Butts, Smith	12.00
7	Townsend, White	4.00
8	Cornelius Bennett, Seth Joyner	1.50
9	Thomas, Swilling	1.50
10	Darryl Talley, Chris Spielman	1.50
11	Ronnie Lott, Mark Carrier	1.50
12	Steve Atwater, Shaun Gayle	1.50
13	Rod Woodson, Darrell Green	1.50
14	Jeff Gossett, Chip Lohmiller	1.50
15	Tim Brown, Mel Gray	1.50
16	Checklist	3.00

1992 Upper Deck NFL Sheets

Upper Deck produced four different NFL Sheets in 1992. They commemorated the AFC Championship, NFC Championship, Super Bowl XXVI and Comic Ball IV, with each having a blank back. The AFC and NFC Championship sheets were given away at Upper Deck's Super Bowl Card Show III and at the NFL Experience in Minneapolis. The Super Bowl XXVI sheet was given away at various locations in the Minneapolis area during the week of the Super Bowl.

		MT
Complete Set (4):		30.00
Common Player:		5.00
1	AFC Championship vs. Buffalo Bills Jan 12, 1992 (Thurman Thomas, Cornelius Bennett, Andre Reed, John Elway, (30,000)	5.00
2	NFC Championship vs. Washington Redskins Jan. 12, 1992 (Mark Rypien, Ricky Ervins, Charles Mann, Barry (30,000)	5.00
3	Super Bowl XXVII Jan. 26, 1992 (Mark Rypien, Ricky Ervins, Charles Mann, Gary Clark, Darrell Green,	10.00
4	Comic Ball IV Looney Tunes Characters (Lawrence Taylor, Jerry Rice, Thurman Thomas, Dan Marino) (15,000)	12.00

1992 Upper Deck SCD Sheets

This eight-card set of 8-1/2" x 11" sheets was produced by Upper Deck and included in the Sept. 18, 1992 issue of Sports Collector's Digest at a rate of one per issue. Each sheet contained six cards and sheets were numbered 1-8. Sheet backs were covered with the repeated phrase "Upper Deck Limited Edition Commemorative Sheet."

		MT
Complete Set (8):		75.00
Common Player:		8.00
1	Randall Cunningham, David Klingler, Dan Marino, Troy Aikman, Jim Kelly, Bernie Kosar	15.00

2	Phillippi Sparks, Dale Carter, Steve Emtman, Kevin Smith, Marco Coleman, Carl Pickens	8.00
3	Quentin Coryatt, Greg Skrepenak, Chester McGlockton, Kurt Barber, Vaughn Dunbar, Ashley Ambrose	8.00
4	Ty Detmer, Steve Israel, Tracy Scroggins, Todd Collins, Alonzo Spellman, Marquez Pope	8.00
5	Eric Dickerson, Randal Hill, Jim Kelly, Bernie Kosar, Deion Sanders, Andre Reed	10.00
6	Joe Montana, Mike Singletary, Randall Cunningham, Anthony Miller, Dan McGwire, Harvey Williams	10.00
7	Al Toon, Michael Dean Perry, Troy Aikman, Jeff George, Carl Banks, Junior Seau	10.00
8	Dan Marino, Tommy Maddox, Bruce Smith, Leslie O'Neal, Lawrence Taylor, Jerry Rice	15.00

1992-93 Upper Deck NFL Experience

This 50-card set was distributed during the NFL Experience/ Super Bowl Card Show held during the Super Bowl XXVII week Pasadena, Calif. Two designs are used for the card fronts. Cards 1-20 have color photos bordered by different colored stripes on the left and bottom sides. Cards 21-50 have the photos slanted to the left, edged by a ghosted background. Each card back has another photo of the player close up, plus a quote, profile or game summary. The cards, which have a Super Bowl theme, are numbered on the back and include the NFL Experience logo. Some cards were stamped with silver foil; others were stamped in gold. The gold foils are about five times more valuable.

		MT
Complete Set (50):		13.00
Common Player:		.20
1	Joe Montana	1.25
2	Roger Staubach	.25
3	Bart Starr	.25
4	Len Dawson	.20
5	Fred Biletnikoff	.20
6	Jim Plunkett	.20
7	Terry Bradshaw	.25
8	Jerry Rice	.75
9	Doug Williams	.20
10	Dan Marino	.85
11	David Klingler	.60
12	Steve Emtman	.20
13	Dale Carter	.20
14	Quentin Coryatt	.25
15	Tommy Maddox	.50
16	Vaughn Dunbar	.20
17	Marco Coleman	.30
18	Carl Pickens	.50
19	Sean Gilbert	.50
20	Tony Smith	.20

21	Jim Kelly	.80
22	Dan Marino	1.00
23	Boomer Esiason	.35
24	Bernie Kosar	.25
25	Ken O'Brien	.20
26	Deion Sanders	.30
27	Mike Singletary	.20
28	Andre Reed	.35
29	Michael Dean Perry	.20
30	Ricky Proehl	.30
31	Leslie O'Neal	.25
32	Jerry Rice	1.00
33	Eric Dickerson	.20
34	Troy Aikman	2.00
35	Bruce Smith	.45
36	Browning Nagle	.20
37	Carl Banks	.20
38	Harvey Williams	.20
39	Jeff George	.20
40	Lawrence Taylor	.25
41	Webster Slaughter	.20
42	Anthony Miller	.30
43	Randall Cunningham	.35
44	Timm Rosenbach	.20
45	Russell Maryland	.40
46	Randal Hill	.20
47	Dan McGwire	.20
48	Merril Hoge	.20
49	Kevin Fagan	.20
50	Junior Seau	.50

1993 Upper Deck

Upper Deck issued its 530-card 1993 set in one series. Each standard-size card has an action photo on the front, with two team color-coded stripes at the bottom with the player's name and position. His team name runs along the left side using team colors. The card back has a hologram, close-up photo, statistics and biographical information. Subsets include Star Rookies, All Rookie Team, NFL Hitmen, Team Checklist, Season Leaders and Berman's Best. Insert sets include America's Team, Future Heroes, Pro Bowlers and Team MVPs.

		MT
	Complete Set (530):	25.00
	Common Player:	.05
	Minor Stars:	.10
	Wax Box:	30.00
1	Star Rookie Checklist	.25
2	Eric Curry (SR)	.10
3	Rick Mirer (SR)	.30
4	Dan Williams (SR)	.10
5	Marvin Jones (SR)	.10
6	Willie Roaf (SR)	.10
7	Reggie Brooks (SR)	.10
8	Horace Copeland (SR)	.50
9	Lincoln Kennedy (SR)	.10
10	Curtis Conway (SR)	1.00
11	Drew Bledsoe (SR)	3.00
12	Patrick Bates (SR)	.10
13	Wayne Simmons (SR)	.10
14	Irv Smith (SR)	.10
15	Robert Smith (SR)	1.50
16	O.J. McDuffie (SR)	1.00
17	Darrien Gordon (SR)	.10
18	John Copeland (SR)	.10
19	Derek Brown (SR)	.10
20	Jerome Bettis (SR)	1.50
21	Deion Figures (SR)	.20
22	Glyn Milburn (SR)	.50
23	Garrison Hearst (SR)	1.00
24	Qadry Ismail (SR)	.50
25	Terry Kirby (SR)	.50
26	Lamar Thomas (SR)	.10
27	Tom Carter (SR)	.10
28	Andre Hastings (SR)	.25
29	George Teague (SR)	.20

30	All Rookie Checklist	.10
31	David Klingler (ART)	.05
32	Tommy Maddox (ART)	.05
33	Vaughn Dunbar (ART)	.05
34	Rodney Culver (ART)	.05
35	Carl Pickens (ART)	.05
36	Courtney Hawkins (ART)	.05
37	Tyji Armstrong (ART)	.05
38	Ray Roberts (ART)	.05
39	Troy Auzenne (ART)	.05
40	Shane Dronett (ART)	.05
41	Chris Mims (ART)	.05
42	Sean Gilbert (ART)	.05
43	Steve Emtman (ART)	.05
44	Robert Jones (ART)	.05
45	Marco Coleman (ART)	.05
46	Ricardo McDonald (ART)	.05
47	Quentin Coryatt (ART)	.05
48	Dana Hall (ART)	.05
49	Derren Perry (ART)	.05
50	Darryl Williams (ART)	.05
51	Kevin Smith (ART)	.05
52	Terrell Buckley (ART)	.05
53	Troy Vincent (ART)	.05
54	Lin Elliot (ART)	.05
55	Dale Carter (ART)	.05
56	Steve Atwater (NFL)	.05
57	Junior Seau (NFL)	.10
58	Ronnie Lott (NFL)	.05
59	Louis Oliver (NFL)	.05
60	Cortez Kennedy (NFL)	.05
61	Pat Swilling	.05
62	NFL Hitmen Checklist	.05
63	Curtis Conway (TC)	.05
64	Alfred Williams (TC)	.05
65	Jim Kelly (TC)	.10
66	Simon Fletcher (TC)	.05
67	Eric Metcalf (TC)	.05
68	Lawrence Dawsey (TC)	.05
69	Garrison Hearst (TC)	.40
70	Anthony Miller (TC)	.05
71	Neil Smith (TC)	.05
72	Jeff George (TC)	.05
73	Emmitt Smith (TC)	1.00
74	Dan Marino (TC)	1.00
75	Clyde Simmons (TC)	.05
76	Deion Sanders (TC)	.25
77	Ricky Watters (TC)	.10
78	Rodney Hampton (TC)	.05
79	Brad Baxter (TC)	.05
80	Barry Sanders (TC)	.50
81	Warren Moon (TC)	.10
82	Brett Favre (TC)	.50
83	Drew Bledsoe (TC)	1.00
84	Eric Dickerson (TC)	.05
85	Cleveland Gary (TC)	.05
86	Earnest Byner (TC)	.05
87	Wayne Martin (TC)	.05
88	Rick Mirer (TC)	.50
89	Barry Foster (TC)	.05
90	Terry Allen (TC)	.05
91	Vinnie Clark	.05
92	Howard Ballard	.05
93	Eric Ball	.05
94	Marc Boutte	.05
95	Larry Centers	.25
96	Gary Brown	.05
97	Hugh Millen	.05
98	Anthony Newman	.05
99	Darrell Thompson	.05
100	George Jamison	.05
101	James Francis	.05
102	Leonard Harris	.05
103	Lomas Brown	.05
104	James Lofton	.05
105	Jamie Dukes	.05
106	Quinn Early	.05
107	Ernie Jones	.05
108	Torrance Small	.05
109	Michael Carter	.05
110	Aeneas Williams	.05
111	Renaldo Turnbull	.05
112	Al Smith	.05
113	Troy Auzenne	.05
114	Stephen Baker	.05
115	Daniel Stubbs	.05
116	Dana Hall	.05
117	Lawrence Taylor	.10
118	Ron Hall	.05
119	Derrick Fenner	.05
120	Martin Mayhew	.05
121	Jay Schroeder	.05
122	Michael Zordich	.05
123	Ed McCaffery	.05
124	John Stephens	.05
125	Brad Edwards	.05

126	Don Griffin	.05
127	Broderick Thomas	.05
128	Ted Washington	.05
129	Haywood Jeffires	.05
130	Gary Plummer	.05
131	Mark Wheeler	.05
132	Ty Detmer	.50
133	Derrick Walker	.05
134	Henry Ellard	.05
135	Neal Anderson	.05
136	Bruce Smith	.05
137	Cris Carter	.10
138	Vaughn Dunbar	.05
139	Dan Marino	2.00
140	Troy Aikman	.75
141	Randall Cunningham	.10
142	Darryl Johnston	.05
143	Mark Clayton	.05
144	Rich Gannon	.05
145	Nate Newton	.05
146	Willie Gault	.05
147	Brian Washington	.05
148	Fred Barnett	.05
149	Gill Byrd	.05
150	Art Monk	.05
151	Stan Humphries	.10
152	Charles Mann	.05
153	Greg Lloyd	.05
154	Marvin Washington	.05
155	Bernie Kosar	.05
156	Pete Metzelaars	.05
157	Chris Hinton	.05
158	Jim Harbaugh	.05
159	Willie Davis	.05
160	Leroy Thompson	.05
161	Scott Miller	.05
162	Eugene Robinson	.05
163	David Little	.05
164	Pierce Holt	.05
165	James Hasty	.05
166	Dave Krieg	.05
167	Gerald Williams	.05
168	Kyle Clifton	.05
169	Bill Brooks	.05
170	Vance Johnson	.05
171	Greg Townsend	.05
172	Jason Belser	.05
173	Brett Perriman	.05
174	Steve Jordan	.05
175	Kelvin Martin	.05
176	Greg Kragen	.05
177	Kerry Cash	.05
178	Chester McGlockton	.05
179	Jim Kelly	.10
180	Todd McNair	.05
181	Leroy Hoard	.05
182	Seth Joyner	.05
183	Sam Gash	.05
184	Joe Nash	.05
185	Lin Elliott	.05
186	Robert Porcher	.05
187	Tom Hodson	.05
188	Greg Lewis	.05
189	Dan Saleaumua	.05
190	Chris Goode	.05
191	Henry Thomas	.05
192	Bobby Hebert	.05
193	Clay Matthews	.05
194	Mark Carrier	.05
195	Anthony Pleasant	.05
196	Eric Dorsey	.05
197	Clarence Verdin	.05
198	Marc Spindler	.05
199	Tommy Maddox	.05
200	Wendell Davis	.05
201	John Fina	.05
202	Alonzo Spellman	.05
203	Darryl Williams	.05
204	Mike Croel	.05
205	Ken Norton	.05
206	Mel Gray	.05
207	Chuck Cecil	.05
208	John Flannery	.05
209	Chip Banks	.05
210	Chris Martin	.05
211	Dennis Brown	.05
212	Vinny Testaverde	.05
213	Nick Bell	.05
214	Robert Delpino	.05
215	Mark Higgs	.05
216	Al Noga	.05
217	Andre Tippett	.05
218	Pat Swilling	.05
219	Phil Simms	.05
220	Ricky Proehl	.05
221	William Thomas	.05
222	Jeff Graham	.05
223	Darion Conner	.05
224	Mark Carrier	.05
225	Willie Green	.05
226	Reggie Rivers	.05
227	Andre Reed	.10
228	Deion Sanders	.40
229	Chris Doleman	.05
230	Jerry Ball	.05
231	Eric Dickerson	.05
232	Carlos Jenkins	.05
233	Mike Johnson	.05
234	Marco Coleman	.05
235	Leslie O'Neal	.05
236	Browning Nagle	.05
237	Carl Pickens	.05
238	Steve Emtman	.05
239	Alvin Harper	.05
240	Keith Jackson	.05
241	Jerry Rice	.75
242	Cortez Kennedy	.10

243	Tyji Armstrong	.05
244	Troy Vincent	.05
245	Randal Hill	.05
246	Robert Blackmon	.05
247	Junior Seau	.10
248	Sterling Sharpe	.05
249	Thurman Thomas	.10
250	David Klingler	.05
251	Jeff George	.20
252	Anthony Miller	.05
253	Earnest Byner	.05
254	Eric Swann	.05
255	Jeff Herrod	.05
256	Eddie Robinson	.05
257	Eric Allen	.05
258	John Taylor	.05
259	Sean Gilbert	.05
260	Ray Childress	.05
261	Michael Haynes	.05
262	Greg McMurtry	.05
263	Bill Romanowski	.05
264	Todd Lyght	.05
265	Clyde Simmons	.05
266	Webster Slaughter	.05
267	J.J. Birden	.05
268	Aaron Wallace	.05
269	Carl Banks	.05
270	Richardo McDonald	.05
271	Michael Brooks	.05
272	Dale Carter	.05
273	Mike Pritchard	.05
274	Derek Brown	.05
275	Burt Grossman	.05
276	Mark Schlereth	.05
277	Karl Mecklenburg	.05
278	Ricky Jackson	.05
279	Ricky Ervins	.05
280	Jeff Bryant	.05
281	Eric Martin	.05
282	Eric Martin	.05
283	Kevin Mack	.05
284	Brad Muster	.05
285	Kelvin Pritchett	.05
286	Courtney Hawkins	.05
287	Levon Kirkland	.05
288	Steve DeBerg	.05
289	Edgar Bennett	.10
290	Michael Dean Perry	.05
291	Richard Dent	.05
292	Howie Long	.05
293	Chris Mims	.05
294	Kurt Barber	.05
295	Wilber Marshall	.05
296	Ethan Horton	.05
297	Tony Bennett	.05
298	Johnny Johnson	.05
299	Craig Heyward	.05
300	Steve Isreal	.05
301	Kenneth Gant	.05
302	Eugene Chung	.05
303	Harvey Williams	.05
304	Jerrod Bunch	.05
305	Darren Perry	.05
306	Steve Christie	.05
307	John Randle	.05
308	Warren Moon	.10
309	Charles Haley	.05
310	Tony Smith	.05
311	Steve Broussard	.05
312	Alfred Williams	.05
313	Terrell Buckley	.05
314	Trace Armstrong	.05
315	Brian Mitchell	.05
316	Steve Atwater	.05
317	Nate Lewis	.05
318	Richard Brown	.05
319	Rufus Porter	.05
320	Pat Harlow	.05
321	Anthony Smith	.05
322	Jack Del Rio	.05
323	Darryl Talley	.05
324	Sam Mills	.05
325	Chris Miller	.05
326	Ken Harvey	.05
327	Rod Woodson	.10
328	Tony Tolbert	.05
329	Todd Kinchen	.05
330	Brian Noble	.05
331	David Meggett	.05
332	Chris Spielman	.05
333	Barry Word	.05
334	Jessie Hester	.05
335	Michael Jackson	.05
336	Mitchell Price	.05
337	Michael Irvin	.10
338	Simon Fletcher	.05
339	Keith Jennings	.05
340	Vai Sikahema	.05
341	Roger Craig	.05
342	Ricky Watters	.10
343	Reggie Cobb	.05
344	Kanavis McGhee	.05
345	Barry Foster	.10
346	Marion Butts	.05
347	Bryan Cox	.05
348	Wayne Martin	.05
349	Jim Everett	.10
350	Nate Odomes	.05
351	Anthony Johnson	.05
352	Rodney Hampton	.05
353	Terry Allen	.05
354	Derrick Thomas	.10
355	Calvin Williams	.05
356	Pepper Johnson	.05
357	John Elway	.30
358	Steve Young	.75
359	Emmitt Smith	2.00

360	Brett Favre	2.00
361	Cody Carlson	.05
362	Vincent Brown	.05
363	Gary Anderson	.05
364	Jon Vaughn	.05
365	Todd Marinovich	.05
366	Carnell Lake	.05
367	Kurt Gouveia	.05
368	Lawrence Dawsey	.05
369	Neil O'Donnell	.15
370	Duane Bickett	.05
371	Ronnie Harmon	.05
372	Rodney Peete	.05
373	Cornelius Bennett	.05
374	Brad Baxter	.05
375	Ernest Givins	.05
376	Keith Byars	.05
377	Eric Bieniemy	.05
378	Mike Brim	.05
379	Darren Lewis	.05
380	Heath Sherman	.05
381	Leonard Russell	.05
382	Brent Jones	.05
383	David Whitmore	.05
384	Ray Roberts	.05
385	John Offerdahl	.05
386	Keith McCants	.05
387	John Baylor	.05
388	Amp Lee	.05
389	Chris Warren	.20
390	Herman Moore	.50
391	Johnny Bailey	.05
392	Tim Johnson	.05
393	Eric Metcalf	.05
394	Chris Chandler	.05
395	Mark Rypien	.05
396	Christian Okoye	.05
397	Shannon Sharpe	.10
398	Eric Hill	.05
399	David Lang	.05
400	Bruce Matthews	.05
401	Harold Green	.05
402	Moe Lewis	.05
403	Terry McDaniel	.05
404	Wesley Carroll	.05
405	Richmond Webb	.05
406	Andre Rison	.10
407	Lonnie Young	.05
408	Tommy Vardell	.05
409	Gene Atkins	.05
410	Sean Salisbury	.05
411	Kenneth Davis	.05
412	John L. Williams	.05
413	Roman Phifer	.05
414	Bennie Blades	.05
415	Tim Brown	.10
416	Lorenzo White	.05
417	Tony Casillas	.05
418	Tom Waddle	.05
419	David Fulcher	.05
420	Jessie Tuggle	.05
421	Emmitt Smith (SL)	.75
422	Clyde Simmons (SL)	.05
423	Sterling Sharpe (SL)	.10
424	Sterling Sharpe (SL)	.10
425	Emmitt Smith (SL)	.75
426	Dan Marino (SL)	.75
427	Jones, McMillan (SL)	.05
428	Thurman Thomas (SL)	.10
429	Greg Montgomery (SL)	.05
430	Pete Stoyanovich (SL)	.05
431	Emmitt Smith (CL)	.50
432	Steve Young (BB)	.50
433	Jerry Rice (BB)	.40
434	Ricky Watters (BB)	.10
435	Barry Foster (BB)	.10
436	Cortez Kennedy (BB)	.10
437	Warren Moon (BB)	.10
438	Thurman Thomas (BB)	.10
439	Brett Favre (BB)	.50
440	Andre Rison (BB)	.05
441	Barry Sanders (BB)	.50
442	Chris Berman (CL)	.05
443	Moe Gardner	.05
444	Robert Jones	.05
445	Reggie Langhorne	.05
446	Willie Anderson	.05
447	James Washington	.05
448	Aaron Craver	.05
449	Jack Trudeau	.05
450	Neil Smith	.05
451	Chris Burkett	.05
452	Darren Woodson	.05
453	Drew Hill	.05
454	Barry Sanders	1.25
455	Jeff Cross	.05
456	Bennie Thompson	.05
457	Marcus Allen	.10
458	Tracy Scroggins	.05
459	Leroy Butler	.05
460	Joe Montana	1.25
461	Eddie Anderson	.05
462	Tim McDonald	.05
463	Ronnie Lott	.05
464	Gaston Green	.05
465	Shane Conlan	.05
466	Leonard Marshall	.05
467	Melvin Jenkins	.05
468	Don Beebe	.05
469	Johnny Mitchell	.05
470	Darryl Henley	.05
471	Boomer Esiason	.10
472	Mark Kelso	.05

473	John Booty	.05
474	Pete Stoyanovich	.05
475	Thomas Smith	.10
476	Carlton Gray	.10
477	Dana Stubblefield	.50
478	Ryan McNeil	.05
479	Natrone Means	1.00
480	Carl Simpson	.10
481	Robert O'Neal	.05
482	Demetrius Dubose	.10
483	Darrin Smith	.20
484	Michael Barrow	.10
485	Chris Slade	.40
486	Steve Tovar	.10
487	Ron George	.10
488	Steve Tasker	.05
489	Will Furrer	.10
490	Reggie White	.10
491	Sean Jones	.05
492	Gary Clark	.05
493	Donnell Woolford	.05
494	Steve Beuerlein	.05
495	Anthony Carter	.05
496	Louis Oliver	.05
497	Chris Zorich	.05
498	Bubba McDowell	.05
500	Adrian Cooper	.05
501	Bill Johnson	.05
502	Shawn Jefferson	.05
503	Siran Stacy	.05
504	James Jones	.05
505	Tom Rathman	.05
506	Vince Buck	.05
507	Kent Graham	.30
508	Darren Carrington	.10
509	Ricky Dixon	.05
510	Toi Cook	.05
511	Steve Smith	.05
512	Ostell Miles	.05
513	Phil Sparks	.05
514	Lee Williams	.05
515	Gary Reason	.05
516	Shane Dronett	.05
517	Jay Novacek	.05
518	Kevin Greene	.05
519	Derek Russell	.05
520	Quentin Coryatt	.10
521	Santana Dotson	.05
522	Donald Frank	.05
523	Mike Prior	.05
524	Dwight Hollier	.05
525	Eric Davis	.05
526	Dalton Hilliard	.05
527	Rodney Culver	.05
528	Jeff Hostetler	.10
529	Ernie Mills	.05
530	Craig Erickson	.05

1993 Upper Deck America's Team

This 15-card insert set is devoted to the players from Super Bowl Championship Dallas Cowboys teams. Cards 1-6 feature Cowboys from Super Bowl XII; players from Super Bowl XXVII are featured on cards 7-13. The front has a color action photo, plus the player's name and team stamped in silver foil along the left side of the card. An "America's Team" logo is also on the front. The back has this logo as a background, with a paragraph devoted to the player's accomplishments in the Super Bowl game. Cards are numbered with an "AT" prefix and were random inserts in 1993 Upper Deck hobby foil packs. There is also an unnumbered title card which features Emmitt Smith.

		MT
	Complete Set (15):	125.00
	Common Player:	5.00
	E. Smith Header:	15.00
1	Roger Staubach	12.00
2	Chuck Howley	5.00
3	Harvey Martin	5.00
4	Randy White	5.00
5	Bob Lilly	5.00
6	Drew Pearson	5.00

7	Emmitt Smith	45.00
8	Troy Aikman	25.00
9	Ken Norton	5.00
10	Robert Jones	5.00
11	Russell Maryland	5.00
12	Jay Novacek	5.00
13	Michael Irvin	7.00
14	Troy Aikman (CL)	10.00

1993 Upper Deck Future Heroes

These cards feature color action photos on the front, along with the team color-coded stripe on the left which contains the player's name. A 1993 "Future Heroes" logo is in gold foil in the bottom left corner, too. The back has another small color photo and player profile against a team color-coded background. The player's name and card number are at the top of the card. Numbering begins with #37, where the Upper Deck Football Series ended. These inserts, which were randomly included in all types of packs, also include an unnumbered title card which features Ricky Watters.

		MT
Complete Set (10):		15.00
Common Player:		1.00
37	Barry Foster	1.00
38	Junior Seau	1.00
39	Emmitt Smith	5.00
40	Troy Aikman	3.00
41	David Klingler	1.00
42	Ricky Watters	1.50
43	Barry Sanders	5.00
44	Brett Favre	5.00
45	Checklist	2.00

1993 Upper Deck Pro Bowl

These glossy cards feature two photos on the horizontally-designed front - a color photo on the left with holographic borders on the left and bottom, and a second photo on the right. Each player was a Pro Bowl selection; the Pro Bowl logo is on the front in the lower left corner. The card back has a blue- and white background with a career profile on it. A card number, using a "PB" prefix, also appears. Cards were random inserts in retail foil packs.

		MT
Complete Set (20):		160.00
Common Player:		5.00
1	Andre Reed	5.00
2	Dan Marino	30.00
3	Warren Moon	5.00
4	Anthony Miller	5.00
5	Barry Foster	5.00
6	Steve Atwater	5.00
7	Cortez Kennedy	5.00

8	Junior Seau	5.00
9	Jerry Rice	20.00
10	Michael Irvin	5.00
11	Sterling Sharpe	5.00
12	Steve Young	20.00
13	Troy Aikman	20.00
14	Brett Favre	30.00
15	Emmitt Smith	30.00
16	Rodney Hampton	5.00
17	Barry Sanders	25.00
18	Ricky Watters	5.00
19	Pat Swilling	5.00
20	Checklist	5.00

1993 Upper Deck Rookie Exchange

This set could be obtained by redeeming a "Trade Upper Deck" card, available randomly in every 72nd pack of Upper Deck football card packs. The card front uses Upper Deck's Electric printing, which gives it a metallic quality. A player photo is featured on the front, along with the player's name and position in a team color-coded bar at the bottom. His team name is also given, in silver letters. The back has another color photo on the left, plus a recap of the player's previous season. The player's name, position and card number, using an "RE" prefix, also appears on the card back.

		MT
Complete Set (7):		15.00
Common Player:		1.00
1	Rookie Trade Card	1.00
2	Drew Bledsoe	7.00
3	Rick Mirer	4.00
4	Garrison Hearst	2.00
5	Marvin Jones	1.00
6	Curtis Conway	1.50
7	Jerome Bettis	2.00

1993 Upper Deck Team MVPs

The Most Valuable Player on each of the 28 NFL teams is represented in this 29-card insert set. Each card front has a full-bleed color action photo, plus two team color-coded stripes at the bottom which contain the player's name and team. A Team MVP logo is also at the bottom of the card. Team color-coded stripes are also used on the back, which features another player photo and career highlights. A card number, using a "TM" prefix, is also given. Cards were random inserts in jumbo foil packs.

		MT
Complete Set (29):		20.00
Common Player:		.50

Minor Stars:

		1.00
1	Neal Anderson	.50
2	Harold Green	.50
3	Thurman Thomas	1.00
4	John Elway	2.00
5	Eric Metcalf	.50
6	Reggie Cobb	.50
7	Johnny Bailey	.50
8	Junior Seau	1.00
9	Derrick Thomas	1.00
10	Steve Emtman	.50
11	Troy Aikman	4.00
12	Dan Marino	7.00
13	Clyde Simmons	.50
14	Andre Rison	1.00
15	Steve Young	3.00
16	Rodney Hampton	1.00
17	Rob Moore	1.00
18	Barry Sanders	5.00
19	Warren Moon	1.00
20	Sterling Sharpe	1.00
21	Jon Vaughn	.50
22	Tim Brown	1.00
23	Jim Everett	.50
24	Gary Clark	.50
25	Wayne Martin	.50
26	Cortez Kennedy	1.00
27	Barry Foster	1.00
28	Terry Allen	.50
29	Checklist	.50

1993 Upper Deck Kansas City Chiefs

This 25-card team set is devoted to the Kansas City Chiefs. The cards use the same design format as Upper Deck's main 1993 issue. However, the cards, which are standard size, are numbered on the back using a "KC" prefix. The photos used on both sides are identical to those used for the regular set.

		MT
Complete Set (25):		8.00
Common Player:		.20
1	Nick Lowery	.25
2	Lonnie Marts	.20
3	Marcus Allen	1.00
4	Bennie Thompson	.20
5	Bryan Barker	.20
6	Christian Okoye	.25
7	Dale Carter	.25
8	Dan Saleaumua	.25
9	Dave Krieg	.25
10	Derrick Thomas	1.00
11	Doug Terry	.20
12	Fred Jones	.20
13	Harvey Williams	.60
14	J.J. Birden	.25
15	Joe Montana	3.00
16	John Alt	.25
17	Leonard Griffin	.20
18	Matt Blundin	.30
19	Neil Smith	.35
20	Tim Barnett	.25
21	Tim Grunhard	.20
22	Todd McNair	.25
23	Tracy Simien	.20
24	Willie Davis	.35
25	Joe Montana	2.00
	(Checklist back)	

1993 Upper Deck Dallas Cowboys

This 25-card team set is devoted to the Dallas Cowboys. The cards are standard size and use the same design as Upper Deck's regular 1993 set. These cards, however, are numbered on the back using a "D" prefix. But the photos on both sides are the same as those used for the regular set.

		MT
Complete Set (25):		10.00
Common Player:		.25
1	Alvin Harper	1.00
2	Charles Haley	.50
3	Jimmy Smith	.25
4	Darrin Smith	.25
5	Jim Jeffcoat	.25
6	Darryl Johnston	.75
7	Dixon Edwards	.25
8	Emmitt Smith	3.00
9	James Washington	.25
10	Jay Novacek	.40
11	Ken Norton	.40
12	Kenneth Gant	.25
13	Larry Brown	.25
14	Leon Lett	.35
15	Lin Elliott	.25
16	Mark Tuinei	.25
17	Michael Irvin	1.50
18	Nate Newton	.25
19	Robert Jones	.25
20	Thomas Everett	.25
21	Tony Casillas	.25

22	Tony Tolbert	.25
23	Troy Aikman	3.00
24	Russell Maryland	.50
25	Troy Aikman	2.00
	(Checklist back)	

1993 Upper Deck San Francisco 49ers

The San Francisco 49ers are represented in this 25-card team set from Upper Deck. The cards are standard size and follow the design format used in Upper Deck's regular 1993 issue. However, the card backs are numbered with an "SF" prefix. This set uses the same photos on each side as those which were used for the regular issue.

		MT
Complete Set (25):		8.00
Common Player:		.20
1	Amp Lee	.40
2	Bill Romanowski	.25
3	Brent Jones	.50
4	Dana Hall	.25
5	Dana Stubblefield	1.00
6	Dennis Brown	.20
7	Dexter Carter	.25
8	Don Griffin	.20
9	Eric Davis	.25
10	Guy McIntyre	.20
11	Jamie Williams	.20
12	Jerry Rice	2.00
13	John Taylor	.35
14	Keith DeLong	.25
15	Marc Logan	.25
16	Michael Walters	.20
17	Mike Cofer	.20
18	Odessa Turner	.20
19	Ricky Watters	.75
20	Steve Bono	.50
21	Steve Young	2.00
22	Ted Washington	.25
23	Tom Rathman	.35
24	Jesse Sapolu	.20
25	Steve Young	1.00
	(Checklist back)	

1993 Upper Deck Authenticated Classic Confrontations

The 3-1/2" x 5" card features Montana and Marino. "Classic Confrontations XIX" is printed on the right side of the card. The card back is sequentially numbered as "x of 20,000."

		MT
Complete Set (1):		20.00
Common Player:		20.00
1	Classic Confrontation (Joe Montana, Dan Marino)	20.00

1993-94 Upper Deck Miller Lite SB

The five-card, 5" x 3-1/2" set was sponsored by Miller and Tombstone Pizza. One card was issued in each 12-pack of Miller Lite. The set was available through mail-in UPC offers. All entries received were entered in a drawing for 1,000 Montana autographed sheets. The card fronts feature two quarterbacks from a past Super Bowl on a horizontal design. The backs include highlight info over a ghosted Super Bowl logo.

		MT
Complete Set (5):		20.00
Common Player:		2.50
1	Super Bowl XXVII (Troy Aikman, Jim Kelly)	5.00
2	Super Bowl XXVI (Jim Kelly, Mark Rypien)	2.50
3	Super Bowl XXIV (John Elway, Joe Montana)	7.00
4	Super Bowl XXI (John Elway, Phil Simms)	3.00
5	Super Bowl XIX (Joe Montana, Dan Marino)	8.00

1994 Upper Deck Pro Bowl Samples

The six-card, standard-size set was distributed at the National Convention in Houston. The cards are very similar to the basic insert issue, except that the card backs have "Sample Card" printed diagonally.

		MT
Complete Set (6):		25.00
Common Player:		2.50
1	Jerome Bettis	2.50
2	Brett Favre	10.00
3	John Elway	4.00
4	Thurman Thomas	2.50
5	Jerry Rice	6.00
6	Steve Young	4.00

1994 Upper Deck

The Upper Deck Co. kicked off its 1994 football campaign, with a 330-card, single series issue. Upper Deck also introduced an upgraded card design and an interactive 50-card insert set, called Predictor Series. Two parallel Electric Field sets were also available. All 330 regular-issue cards will also be printed using gold and silver foil. These sets-within-a-set are called Silver Electric and Gold Electric, respectively. There are two other insert sets, called Then and Now and Pro Bowl Holoview.

		MT
Complete Set (330):		35.00
Common Player:		.10
Minor Stars:		.20
Wax Box:		45.00
1	Dan Wilkinson	.20
2	Antonio Langham	.20
3	Derrick Alexander	.50
4	Charles Johnson	.50
5	Bucky Brooks	.20
6	Trev Alberts	.20
7	Marshall Faulk	6.00
8	Willie McGinest	.50
9	Aaron Glenn	.20
10	Ryan Yarborough	.20
11	Greg Hill	.50
12	Sam Adams	.20
13	John Thierry	.20
14	Johnnie Morton	.50
15	LeShon Johnson	.20
16	David Palmer	.20
17	Trent Dilfer	2.00
18	Jamir Miller	.20
19	Thomas Lewis	.20
20	Heath Shuler	.50
21	Wayne Gandy	.20
22	Isaac Bruce	4.00
23	Joe Johnson	.20
24	Mario Bates	.30
25	Bryant Young	.50
26	William Floyd	.50
27	Errict Rhett	1.00
28	Chuck Levy	.20
29	Darnay Scott	1.00
30	Rob Fredrickson	.20
31	Jamir Miller	.10
32	Thomas Lewis	.25
33	John Thierry	.10
34	Sam Adams	.25
35	Joe Johnson	.10
36	Bryant Young	.25
37	Wayne Gandy	.10
38	LaShon Johnson	.25
39	Mario Bates	.50
40	Greg Hill	.75
41	Andy Heck	.10
42	Warren Moon	.20
43	Jim Everett	.10
44	Bill Romanowski	.10
45	Michael Haynes	.10
46	Chris Doleman	.10
47	Merril Hoge	.10
48	Chris Miller	.10
49	Clyde Simmons	.10

50	Jeff George	.20
51	Jeff Burris	.20
52	Ethan Horton	.10
53	Scott Mitchell	.20
54	Howard Ballard	.10
55	Lawyer Tillman	.10
56	Marion Butts	.10
57	Erik Kramer	.10
58	Ken Norton	.20
59	Anthony Miller	.20
60	Chris Hinton	.10
61	Ricky Proehl	.10
62	Craig Heyward	.10
63	Darryl Talley	.10
64	Tim Worley	.10
65	Derrick Fenner	.10
66	Jerry Ball	.10
67	Darren Woodson	.10
68	Mike Croel	.10
69	Ray Crockett	.10
70	Tony Bennett	.10
71	Webster Slaughter	.10
72	Anthony Johnson	.10
73	Charles Mincy	.10
74	Calvin Jones	.40
75	Henry Ellard	.10
76	Troy Vincent	.10
77	Sean Salisbury	.10
78	Pat Harlow	.10
79	James Williams	.10
80	Derek Brown	.20
81	Marvin Jones	.10
82	Seth Joyner	.10
83	Deion Figures	.10
84	Stanley Richards	.10
85	Tom Rathman	.10
86	Rod Stephens	.10
87	Ray Seals	.10
88	Andre Collins	.10
89	Cornelius Bennett	.10
90	Richard Dent	.10
91	Louis Oliver	.10
92	Rodney Peete	.10
93	Jackie Harris	.10
94	Tracy Simien	.10
95	Greg Townsend	.10
96	Michael Stewart	.10
97	Irving Fryar	.10
98	Todd Collins	.10
99	Irv Smith	.10
100	Chris Calloway	.10
101	Kevin Greene	.10
102	John Friesz	.10
103	Steve Bono	.10
104	Brian Blades	.10
105	Reggie Cobb	.10
106	Eric Swann	.10
107	Mike Pritchard	.10
108	Bill Brooks	.10
109	Jim Harbaugh	.10
110	David Whitmore	.10
111	Eddie Anderson	.10
112	Ray Crittenden	.10
113	Mark Collins	.10
114	Brian Washington	.10
115	Barry Foster	.25
116	Gary Plummer	.10
117	Marc Logan	.10
118	John L. Williams	.20
119	Marty Carter	.10
120	Marvin Jones	.10
121	Ron Moore	.25
122	Pierce Holt	.10
123	Henry Jones	.10
124	Donnell Woolford	.10
125	Steve Tovar	.10
126	Anthony Pleasant	.10
127	Jay Novacek	.10
128	Dan Williams	.10
129	Barry Sanders	2.00
130	Robert Brooks	.10
131	Lorenzo White	.10
132	Kerry Cash	.10
133	Joe Montana	2.00
134	Jeff Hostetler	.10
135	Jerome Bettis	.75
136	Dan Marino	3.00
137	Vencie Glenn	.10
138	Vincent Brown	.10
139	Ricky Jackson	.10
140	Carlton Bailey	.10
141	Jeff Lageman	.10
142	William Thomas	.10
143	Neil O'Donnell	.20
144	Shawn Jefferson	.10
145	Steve Young	1.00
146	Chris Warren	.10
147	Courtney Hawkins	.10
148	Brad Edwards	.10
149	O.J. McDuffie	.25
150	David Lang	.10
151	Chuck Cecil	.10
152	Norm Johnson	.10
153	Pete Metzelaars	.10
154	Shaun Gayle	.10
155	Alfred Williams	.10
156	Eric Turner	.10
157	Emmitt Smith	3.00
158	Steve Atwater	.10
159	Robert Porcher	.10
160	Edgar Bennett	.10
161	Bubba McDowell	.10
162	Jeff Herrod	.10
163	Keith Cash	.10
164	Patrick Bates	.10
165	Todd Lyght	.10
166	Mark Higgs, Rob Burnett	.10

167	Carlos Jenkins	.10
168	Drew Bledsoe	2.00
169	Wayne Martin	.10
170	Mike Sherrard	.10
171	Ronnie Lott	.10
172	Fred Barnett	.10
173	Eric Green	.10
174	Leslie O'Neal	.10
175	Brent Jones	.10
176	John Vaughn	.10
177	Vince Workman	.10
178	Ron Middleton	.10
179	Terry McDaniel	.10
180	Willie Davis	.10
181	Gary Clark	.10
182	Bobby Hebert	.10
183	Russell Copeland	.10
184	Chris Gadney	.10
185	Tony McGhee	.10
187	Charles Haley	.10
188	Shannon Sharpe	.20
189	Mel Gray	.10
190	George Teague	.10
191	Ernest Givins	.10
192	Ray Buchannan	.10
193	J.J. Birden	.20
194	Tim Brown	.20
195	Tim Lester	.10
196	Marco Coleman	.10
197	Randall McDaniel	.10
198	Bruce Armstrong	.10
199	Willie Roaf	.10
200	Greg Jackson	.10
201	Johnny Mitchell	.10
202	Calvin Williams	.10
203	Jeff Graham	.10
204	Darren Carrington	.10
205	Jerry Rice	1.00
206	Cortez Kennedy	.20
207	Charles Wilson	.10
208	James Jenkins	.10
209	Ray Childress	.10
210	Leroy Butler	.10
211	Randal Hill	.10
212	Lincoln Kennedy	.10
213	Kenneth Davis	.10
214	Terry Obee	.10
215	Richardo McDonald	
216	Pepper Johnson	.10
217	Alvin Harper	.20
218	John Elway	.50
219	Derrick Moore	.10
220	Terrell Buckley	.10
221	Haywood Jeffires	.10
222	Jessie Hester	.10
223	Kimble Anders	.10
224	Raghib Ismail	.10
225	Roman Phifer	.10
226	Bryan Cox	.10
227	Cris Carter	.20
228	Sam Gash	.10
229	Renaldo Turnbull	.10
230	Rodney Hampton	.20
231	Johnny Johnson	.10
232	Tim Harris	.10
233	Leroy Thompson	.10
234	Junior Seau	.20
235	Tim McDonald	.10
236	Eugene Robinson	.10
237	Lawrence Dawsey	.10
238	Tim Johnson	.10
239	Jason Elam	.10
240	Willie Green	.10
241	Larry Centers	.10
242	Erric Pegram	.15
243	Bruce Smith	.10
244	Alonzo Spellman	.10
245	Carl Pickens	.30
246	Michael Jackson	.10
247	Kevin Williams	.25
248	Glyn Milburn	.15
249	Herman Moore	.50
250	Brett Favre	3.00
251	Al Smith	.10
252	Roosevelt Potts	.10
253	Marcus Allen	.20
254	Anthony Smith	.10
255	Sean Gilbert	.10
256	Keith Byars	.10
257	*Scottie Graham*	.50
258	Leonard Russell	.10
259	Eric Martin	.10
260	Jerrod Bunch	.10
261	Rob Moore	.10
262	Herschel Walker	.10
263	Levon Kirkland	.10
264	Chris Mims	.10
265	Ricky Watters	.25
266	Rick Mirer	.75
267	Santana Dotson	.10
268	Reggie Brooks	.15
269	Garrison Hearst	.50
270	Thurman Thomas	.25
271	Johnny Bailey	.10
272	Andre Rison	.20
273	Jim Kelly	.25
274	Mark Carrier	.10
275	David Klingler	.10
276	Eric Metcalf	.10
277	Troy Aikman	1.25
278	Simon Fletcher	.10
279	Pat Swilling	.10
280	Sterling Sharpe	.25
281	Cody Carlson	.10
282	Steve Emtman	.10
283	Neil Smith	.10
284	James Jett	.10
285	Shane Conlan	.10
286	Keith Jackson	.10
287	Qadry Ismail	.15
288	Chris Slade	.15
289	Derek Brown	.10
290	Phil Simms	.10
291	Boomer Esiason	.10
292	Eric Allen	.10
293	Rod Woodson	.20
294	Ronnie Harmon	.10
295	John Taylor	.20
296	Ferrell Edmunds	.10
297	Craig Erickson	.15
298	Brian Mitchell	.10
299	Dante Jones	.10
300	John Copeland	.10
301	Steve Beuerlein	.10
302	Deion Sanders	.75
303	Andre Reed	.20
304	Curtis Conway	.20
305	Harold Green	.10
306	Vinny Testaverde	.10
307	Michael Irvin	.50
308	Rod Bernstine	.10
309	Chris Spielman	.10
310	Reggie White	.20
311	Gary Brown	.10
312	Quentin Coryatt	.10
313	Derrick Thomas	.20
314	Greg Robinson	.10
315	Troy Drayton	.10
316	Terry Kirby	.15
317	John Randle	.10
318	Ben Coates	.50
319	Tyrone Hughes	.10
320	Corey Miller	.10
321	Brad Baxter	.10
322	Randall Cunningham	.25
323	Greg Lloyd	.10
324	Stan Humphries	.10
325	Dana Stubblefield	.20
326	Kelvin Martin	.10
327	Hardy Nickerson	.10
328	Desmond Howard	.10
329	Mark Carrier	.10
330	Darryl Johnston	.10

1994 Upper Deck Electric Silver

The 330-card, standard-size set was a parallel to the basic Upper Deck set. The cards differ from the gold versions by the logo that was produced with a foil finish instead of prismatic finish.

	MT
Complete Set (330):	120.00
Common Player:	.25
Veteran Stars:	2x-4x
Young Stars:	1.5x-3x
RCs:	1.25x-2.5x

1994 Upper Deck Electric Gold

The Upper Deck Co. kicked off its 1994 football campaign, with a 330-card, single series issue. Upper Deck also introduced an upgraded card design and an interactive 50-card insert set, called Predictor Series. Two parallel Electric Field sets were also available. All 330 regular-issue cards will also be printed using gold and silver foil. These sets-within-a-set are called Silver Electric and Gold Electric, respectively. There are two other insert sets, called Then and Now and Pro Bowl Holoview.

	MT
Complete Set (330):	1700.
Common Player:	3.00
Minor Stars:	6.00

1	*Dan Wilkinson*	6.00
2	*Antonio Langham*	15.00
3	*Derrick Alexander*	6.00
4	*Charles Johnson*	30.00
5	*Bucky Brooks*	10.00
6	*Trev Alberts*	8.00
7	*Marshall Faulk*	100.00
8	*Willie McGinest*	10.00
9	*Aaron Glenn*	6.00
10	*Ryan Yarborough*	6.00
11	*Greg Hill*	30.00
12	*Sam Adams*	10.00
13	*John Thierry*	10.00
14	*Johnnie Morton*	10.00
15	*LeShon Johnson*	10.00
16	*David Palmer*	15.00
17	*Trent Dilfer*	40.00
18	*Jamir Miller*	6.00
19	*Thomas Lewis*	15.00
20	*Heath Shuler*	15.00
21	*Wayne Gandy*	6.00
22	*Isaac Bruce*	80.00
23	*Joe Johnson*	6.00
24	*Mario Bates*	25.00
25	*Bryant Young*	20.00
26	*William Floyd*	30.00
27	*Errict Rhett*	80.00
28	*Chuck Levy*	6.00
29	*Darnay Scott*	55.00
30	*Rob Fredrickson*	10.00
31	Jamir Miller	3.00
32	Thomas Lewis	6.00
33	John Thierry	6.00
34	Sam Adams	6.00
35	Joe Johnson	3.00
36	Bryant Young	3.00
37	Wayne Gandy	3.00
38	LeShon Johnson	6.00
39	Mario Bates	6.00
40	Greg Hill	15.00
41	Andy Heck	3.00
42	Warren Moon	8.00
43	Jim Everett	3.00
44	Bill Romanowski	3.00
45	Michael Haynes	3.00
46	Chris Doleman	3.00
47	Merril Hoge	3.00
48	Chris Miller	3.00
49	Clyde Simmons	3.00
50	Jeff George	6.00
51	Jeff Burris	10.00
52	Ethan Horton	3.00
53	Scott Mitchell	6.00
54	Howard Ballard	3.00
55	Lawyer Tillman	3.00
56	Marion Butts	3.00
57	Erik Kramer	3.00
58	Ken Norton	3.00
59	Anthony Miller	6.00
60	Chris Hinton	3.00
61	Ricky Proehl	3.00
62	Craig Heyward	3.00
63	Darryl Talley	3.00
64	Tim Worley	3.00
65	Derrick Fenner	3.00
66	Jerry Ball	3.00
67	Darren Woodson	3.00
68	Mike Croel	3.00
69	Ray Crockett	3.00
70	Tony Bennett	3.00
71	Webster Slaughter	3.00
72	Anthony Johnson	3.00
73	Charles Mincy	3.00
74	Calvin Jones	10.00
75	Henry Ellard	3.00
76	Troy Vincent	3.00
77	Sean Salisbury	3.00
78	Pat Harlow	3.00
79	James Williams	3.00
80	Derek Brown	6.00
81	Marvin Jones	3.00
82	Seth Joyner	3.00
83	Deion Figures	3.00
84	Stanley Richards	3.00
85	Tom Rathman	3.00
86	Rod Stephens	3.00
87	Ray Seals	3.00
88	Andre Collins	3.00
89	Cornelius Bennett	3.00
90	Richard Dent	3.00
91	Louis Oliver	3.00
92	Rodney Peete	3.00
93	Jackie Harris	3.00
94	Tracy Simien	3.00
95	Greg Townsend	3.00
96	Michael Stewart	3.00
97	Irving Fryar	3.00
98	Todd Collins	3.00
99	Irv Smith	3.00
100	Chris Calloway	3.00
101	Kevin Greene	3.00
102	John Friesz	3.00
103	Steve Bono	3.00
104	Brian Blades	3.00
105	Reggie Cobb	3.00
106	Eric Swann	3.00
107	Mike Pritchard	3.00
108	Bill Brooks	3.00
109	Jim Harbaugh	3.00
110	David Whitmore	3.00
111	Eddie Anderson	3.00
112	Ray Crittenden	6.00
113	Mark Collins	3.00
114	Brian Washington	3.00
115	Barry Foster	6.00
116	Gary Plummer	3.00
117	Marc Logan	3.00
118	John L. Williams	6.00
119	Marty Carter	3.00
120	Marvin Jones	6.00
121	Ron Moore	6.00
122	Pierce Holt	3.00
123	Henry Jones	3.00
124	Donnell Woolford	3.00
125	Steve Tovar	3.00
126	Anthony Pleasant	3.00
127	Jay Novacek	3.00
128	Dan Williams	3.00
129	Barry Sanders	70.00
130	Robert Brooks	3.00
131	Lorenzo White	3.00
132	Kerry Cash	3.00
133	Joe Montana	80.00
134	Jeff Hostetler	3.00
135	Jerome Bettis	25.00
136	Dan Marino	125.00
137	Vencie Glenn	3.00
138	Vincent Brown	3.00
139	Ricky Jackson	3.00
140	Carlton Bailey	3.00
141	Jeff Lageman	3.00
142	William Thomas	3.00
143	Neil O'Donnell	6.00
144	Shawn Jefferson	3.00
145	Steve Young	60.00
146	Chris Warren	3.00
147	Courtney Hawkins	3.00
148	Brad Edwards	3.00
149	O.J. McDuffie	6.00
150	David Lang	3.00
151	Chuck Cecil	3.00
152	Norm Johnson	3.00
153	Pete Metzelaars	3.00
154	Shaun Gayle	3.00
155	Alfred Williams	3.00
156	Eric Turner	3.00
157	Emmitt Smith	125.00
158	Steve Atwater	3.00
159	Robert Porcher	3.00
160	Edgar Bennett	3.00
161	Bubba McDowell	3.00
162	Jeff Herrod	3.00
163	Keith Cash	3.00
164	Patrick Bates	3.00
165	Todd Lyght	3.00
166	Mark Higgs, Rob Burnett	3.00
167	Carlos Jenkins	3.00
168	Drew Bledsoe	75.00
169	Wayne Martin	3.00
170	Mike Sherrard	3.00
171	Ronnie Lott	3.00
172	Fred Barnett	3.00
173	Eric Green	3.00
174	Leslie O'Neal	3.00
175	Brent Jones	3.00
176	John Vaughn	3.00
177	Vince Workman	3.00
178	Ron Middleton	3.00
179	Terry McDaniel	3.00
180	Willie Davis	3.00
181	Gary Clark	3.00
182	Bobby Hebert	3.00
183	Russell Copeland	3.00
184	Chris Gadney	3.00
185	Tony McGhee	3.00
187	Charles Haley	3.00
188	Shannon Sharpe	6.00
189	Mel Gray	3.00
190	George Teague	3.00
191	Ernest Givins	3.00
192	Ray Buchannan	3.00
193	J.J. Birden	3.00
194	Tim Brown	6.00
195	Tim Lester	3.00
196	Marco Coleman	3.00
197	Randall McDaniel	3.00
198	Bruce Armstrong	3.00
199	Willie Roaf	3.00
200	Greg Jackson	3.00
201	Johnny Mitchell	3.00
202	Calvin Williams	3.00
203	Jeff Graham	3.00
204	Darren Carrington	3.00
205	Jerry Rice	60.00
206	Cortez Kennedy	6.00
207	Charles Wilson	3.00
208	James Jenkins	3.00
209	Ray Childress	3.00
210	Leroy Butler	3.00
211	Randal Hill	3.00
212	Lincoln Kennedy	3.00
213	Kenneth Davis	3.00
214	Terry Obee	3.00
215	Richardo McDonald	3.00
216	Pepper Johnson	3.00
217	Alvin Harper	6.00
218	John Elway	25.00
219	Derrick Moore	3.00
220	Terrell Buckley	3.00
221	Haywood Jeffires	3.00
222	Jessie Hester	3.00
223	Kimble Anders	3.00
224	Raghib Ismail	3.00
225	Roman Phifer	3.00
226	Bryan Cox	3.00
227	Cris Carter	6.00
228	Sam Gash	3.00
229	Renaldo Turnbull	3.00
230	Rodney Hampton	6.00
231	Johnny Johnson	3.00
232	Tim Harris	3.00
233	Leroy Thompson	3.00
234	Junior Seau	6.00
235	Tim McDonald	3.00
236	Eugene Robinson	3.00
237	Lawrence Dawsey	3.00
238	Tim Johnson	3.00
239	Jason Elam	3.00
240	Willie Green	3.00
241	Larry Centers	6.00
242	Erric Pegram	6.00
243	Bruce Smith	3.00
244	Alonzo Spellman	3.00
245	Carl Pickens	3.00
246	Michael Jackson	3.00
247	Kevin Williams	6.00
248	Glyn Milburn	6.00
249	Herman Moore	6.00
250	Brett Favre	125.00
251	Al Smith	3.00
252	Roosevelt Potts	3.00
253	Marcus Allen	6.00
254	Anthony Smith	3.00
255	Sean Gilbert	3.00
256	Keith Byars	3.00
257	*Scottie Graham*	10.00
258	Leonard Russell	3.00
259	Eric Martin	3.00
260	Jerrod Bunch	3.00
261	Rob Moore	3.00
262	Herschel Walker	3.00
263	Levon Kirkland	3.00
264	Chris Mims	3.00
265	Ricky Watters	6.00
266	Rick Mirer	30.00
267	Santana Dotson	3.00
268	Reggie Brooks	3.00
269	Garrison Hearst	25.00
270	Thurman Thomas	6.00
271	Johnny Bailey	3.00
272	Andre Rison	6.00
273	Jim Kelly	8.00
274	Mark Carrier	3.00
275	David Klingler	3.00
276	Eric Metcalf	3.00
277	Troy Aikman	60.00
278	Simon Fletcher	3.00
279	Pat Swilling	3.00
280	Sterling Sharpe	8.00
281	Cody Carlson	3.00
282	Steve Emtman	3.00
283	Neil Smith	3.00
284	James Jett	3.00
285	Shane Conlan	3.00
286	Keith Jackson	6.00
287	Qadry Ismail	6.00
288	Chris Slade	6.00
289	Derek Brown	6.00
290	Phil Simms	6.00
291	Boomer Esiason	3.00
292	Eric Allen	3.00
293	Rod Woodson	6.00
294	Ronnie Harmon	3.00
295	John Taylor	6.00
296	Ferrell Edmunds	6.00
297	Craig Erickson	6.00
298	Brian Mitchell	3.00
299	Dante Jones	3.00
300	John Copeland	3.00
301	Steve Beuerlein	3.00
302	Deion Sanders	45.00
303	Andre Reed	6.00
304	Curtis Conway	6.00
305	Harold Green	3.00
306	Vinny Testaverde	6.00
307	Michael Irvin	20.00
308	Rod Bernstine	3.00
309	Chris Spielman	3.00
310	Reggie White	6.00
311	Gary Brown	3.00
312	Quentin Coryatt	3.00
313	Derrick Thomas	6.00
314	Greg Robinson	3.00
315	Troy Drayton	3.00
316	Terry Kirby	6.00
317	John Randle	3.00
318	Ben Coates	10.00
319	Tyrone Hughes	3.00
320	Corey Miller	3.00
321	Brad Baxter	3.00
322	Randall Cunningham	6.00
323	Greg Lloyd	3.00
324	Stan Humphries	3.00
325	Dana Stubblefield	6.00
326	Kelvin Martin	3.00
327	Hardy Nickerson	3.00
328	Desmond Howard	3.00
329	Mark Carrier	3.00
330	Darryl Johnston	3.00

1994 Upper Deck Predictor Award Winners

Hobby Predictor cards predicted what player would win the 1994 Most Valuable Player and Rookie of the Year. Each category included nine players and a longshot card. If the player pictured won that category, the card was redeemable for a gold foil set of Hobby Predictors. If the pictured player finished second in his category, the card could be redeemed for a 10-card, gold foil set of his specific category.

	MT
Complete Set (20):	60.00
Common Player:	1.00
Minor Stars:	2.00
Inserted 1:20 Hobby	

1	Emmitt Smith	7.50
2	Barry Sanders	10.00
3	Jerome Bettis	2.00
4	Joe Montana	6.00
5	Dan Marino	7.50
6	Marshall Faulk	2.00
7	Dan Wilkinson	1.00
8	Sterling Sharpe	2.00
9	Thurman Thomas	2.00
10	The Longshot	2.00
11	Marshall Faulk	2.00
12	Trent Dilfer	2.00
13	Heath Shuler	1.00
14	David Palmer	1.00
15	Charles Johnson	1.00
16	Greg Hill	1.00
17	Johnnie Morton	1.00
18	Errict Rhett	1.00
19	Darney Scott	2.00
20	The Longshot	2.00

1994 Upper Deck Predictor League Leaders

The 30-card Retail Predictor insert set predicted the winner for 1994 rushing yardage, passing yardage and receiving yardage. As with the Hobby Predictors, a winner could be exchanged for the entire Retail Predictor set, while a second place finisher could be redeemed for his specific category 10-card set.

	MT
Complete Set (30):	80.00
Common Player:	1.00
Minor Stars:	2.00
Inserted 1:20 Retail	

1	Troy Aikman	5.00
2	Steve Young	4.00
3	John Elway	6.00
4	Joe Montana	6.00
5	Brett Favre	10.00
6	Heath Shuler	1.00
7	Dan Marino	7.50
8	Rick Mirer	2.00
9	Drew Bledsoe	5.00

A card number in parentheses ( ) indicates the set is unnumbered.

10	The Longshot	1.00
11	Emmitt Smith	7.50
12	Barry Sanders	10.00
13	Jerome Bettis	2.00
14	Rodney Hampton	1.00
15	Thurman Thomas	2.00
16	Marshall Faulk	2.00
17	Barry Foster	1.00
18	Reggie Brooks	1.00
19	Ricky Watters	2.00
20	The Longshot	1.00
21	Jerry Rice	5.00
22	Sterling Sharpe	2.00
23	Andre Rison	2.00
24	Michael Irvin	2.00
25	Tim Brown	2.00
26	Shannon Sharpe	2.00
27	Andre Reed	1.00
28	Irving Fryar	1.00
29	Charles Johnson	1.00
30	The Longshot	2.00

1994 Upper Deck Pro Bowl

The Upper Deck Pro Bowl insert set was randomly inserted into hobby and retail packs of 1994 Upper Deck football. It marked the debut of Holoview cards, which feature a three-dimensional image.

		MT
Complete Set (20):		100.00
Common Player:		2.00
Minor Stars:		4.00
Inserted 1:20		
1	Jerome Bettis	4.00
2	Jay Novacek	2.00
3	Shannon Sharpe	4.00
4	Brent Jones	2.00
5	Andre Rison	4.00
6	Tim Brown	4.00
7	Anthony Miller	2.00
8	Jerry Rice	12.00
9	Brett Favre	25.00
10	Emmitt Smith	18.00
11	Steve Young	10.00
12	John Elway	16.00
13	Warren Moon	4.00
14	Thurman Thomas	4.00
15	Ricky Watters	4.00
16	Rod Woodson	2.00
17	Reggie White	4.00
18	Tyrone Hughes	2.00
19	Derrick Thomas	4.00
20	Checklist	2.00

1994 Upper Deck 24K Gold

The eight-card, standard-size set has horizontal fronts with player facsimile autographs on the left and an etched portrait on the right. Even though the cards are numbered on the back out of 2,500, reportedly just 1,500 of each card was produced.

		MT
Complete Set (8):		550.00
Common Player:		40.00
1	Troy Aikman	75.00
2	Drew Bledsoe	75.00
3	Dan Marino	125.00
4	Rick Mirer	40.00
5	Joe Montana	80.00
6	Emmitt Smith	125.00
7	Thurman Thomas	40.00
8	Steve Young	60.00

1994-95 Upper Deck Sheets

The four-sheet, 8-1/2" x 11" set was issued at the Super Bowl Card Show VI in 1995.

	MT
Complete Set (4):	30.00

Common Sheet:		4.00
NNO	Rookie Class 1994	8.00
NNO	Super Bowl XXIX Autograph Sheet Jan. 26-29, 1995	4.00
NNO	Upper Deck Salutes / St. Louis Rams (Sean Gilbert, Kevin Carter, Isaac Bruce, Jerome Bettis, Chris	8.00
NNO	1995 Record Breaker (Dan Marino) (Numbered of 30,000)	12.00

1995 Upper Deck

This 300-card 1995 Upper Deck football set contains 270 regular cards and 30 Star Rookies. In addition, retail packs have each card featured in an Electric (one per pack) and Electric Gold (one per box) parallel sets. Each regular card front has a full-bleed color photo, with the Upper Deck logo in the upper left corner and the player's name at the bottom stamped in gold foil. The player's team name and his position are in white letters, below his name. The card back has an action photo, with statistics and a brief recap of his 1994 season underneath. A black panel along the left side of the card has a card number, with a team logo under it. The player's name and biographical information are also included in the panel. A set-within-a-set, Special Edition, was also created. These cards, featuring photos by Walter Iooss Jr., have a different design from the base brand and were found in hobby packs only, one per pack. Gold versions were also created for the Special Edition cards; they were available one per box. Continued from Collector's Choice are the Joe Montana Trilogy cards, numbers MT9-16, plus a header card. Pro Bowl and Hobby and Retail Predictors also return. In addition, one in 144 packs is a Predictor Pack, which contain certain types of insert cards, depending on if the pack is retail or hobby.

		MT
Complete Set (300):		30.00
Common Player:		.10
Minor Stars:		.20
Wax Box:		25.00
1	*Ki-Jana Carter*	.50
2	*Tony Boselli*	.20
3	*Steve McNair*	5.00
4	*Michael Westbrook*	1.50
5	*Kerry Collins*	2.00
6	*Kevin Carter*	.20
7	*James Stewart*	.20
8	*Joey Galloway*	4.00
9	*Kyle Brady*	.50
10	*J.J. Stokes*	1.50
11	*Derrick Alexander*	.20
12	*Warren Sapp*	.20
13	*Mark Fields*	.10
14	*Tyrone Wheatley*	1.00
15	*Napoleon Kaufman*	3.00
16	*James Stewart*	2.50
17	*Luther Elliss*	.10
18	*Rashaan Salaam*	.50
19	*Ty Law*	.20
20	*Mark Bruener*	.50
21	*Derrick Brooks*	.20
22	*Christian Fauria*	.20
23	*Ray Zellars*	.20
24	*Todd Collins*	.20
25	*Sherman Williams*	.20
26	*Frank Sanders*	.30
27	*Rodney Thomas*	.20
28	*Rob Johnson*	4.00
29	*Steve Stenstrom*	.20

30	*Curtis Martin*	5.00
31	Gary Clark	.10
32	Troy Aikman	1.00
33	Mike Sherrard	.10
34	Fred Barnett	.10
35	Henry Ellard	.10
36	Terry Allen	.10
37	Jeff Graham	.10
38	Herman Moore	.40
39	Brett Favre	3.00
40	Trent Dilfer	.20
41	Derek Brown	.10
42	Andre Rison	.10
43	Willie Anderson	.10
44	Jerry Rice	1.25
45	Andre Reed	.10
46	Sean Dawkins	.10
47	Irving Fryar	.10
48	Vincent Brisby	.10
49	Rob Moore	.10
50	Carl Pickens	.20
51	Vinny Testaverde	.10
52	Ray Childress	.10
53	Eric Green	.10
54	Anthony Miller	.10
55	Lake Dawson	.20
56	Tim Brown	.20
57	Stan Humphries	.10
58	Rick Mirer	.20
59	Randal Hill	.10
60	Charles Haley	.10
61	Chris Calloway	.10
62	Calvin Williams	.10
63	Ethan Horton	.10
64	Cris Carter	.20
65	Curtis Conway	.20
66	Scott Mitchell	.10
67	Edgar Bennett	.10
68	Craig Erickson	.10
69	Jim Everett	.10
70	Terance Mathis	.10
71	Robert Young	.10
72	Brent Jones	.10
73	Thurman Thomas	.20
74	Marshall Faulk	1.50
75	O.J. McDuffie	.10
76	Ben Coates	.10
77	Johnny Mitchell	.10
78	Darnay Scott	.50
79	Derrick Alexander	.10
80	Lorenzo White	.10
81	Charles Johnson	.20
82	John Elway	.40
83	Willie Davis	.10
84	James Jett	.10
85	Mark Seay	.10
86	Brian Blades	.10
87	Ronald Moore	.10
88	Alvin Harper	.10
89	Dave Brown	.10
90	Randall Cunningham	.10
91	Heath Shuler	.75
92	Jake Reed	.10
93	Donnell Woolford	.10
94	Barry Sanders	2.00
95	Reggie White	.20
96	Lawrence Dawsey	.10
97	Michael Haynes	.10
98	Bert Emanuel	.40
99	Troy Drayton	.10
100	Steve Young	1.25
101	Bruce Smith	.10
102	Roosevelt Potts	.10
103	Dan Marino	3.00
104	Michael Timpson	.10
105	Boomer Esiason	.10
106	David Klingler	.10
107	Eric Metcalf	.10
108	Gary Brown	.10
109	Neil O'Donnell	.20
110	Shannon Sharpe	.10
111	Joe Montana	1.25
112	Jeff Hostetler	.10
113	Ronnie Harmon	.10
114	Chris Warren	.20
115	Larry Centers	.10
116	Michael Irvin	.20
117	Rodney Hampton	.10
118	Herschel Walker	.10
119	Reggie Brooks	.10
120	Qadry Ismail	.10
121	Chris Zorich	.10
122	Chris Spielman	.10
123	Sean Jones	.10
124	Errict Rhett	.20
125	Tyrone Hughes	.10
126	Jeff George	.20
127	Chris Miller	.10
128	Ricky Watters	.20
129	Jim Kelly	.20
130	Tony Bennett	.10
131	Terry Kirby	.10
132	Drew Bledsoe	1.25
133	Johnny Johnson	.10
134	Dan Wilkinson	.10
135	Leroy Hoard	.10
136	Darryl Lewis	.10
137	Barry Foster	.10
138	Shane Dronett	.10
139	Marcus Allen	.20
140	Harvey Williams	.10
141	Tony Martin	.10
142	Rod Stephens	.10
143	Eric Swann	.10
144	Daryl Johnston	.10
145	Dave Meggett	.10
146	Charlie Garner	.10
147	Ken Harvey	.10
148	Warren Moon	.20

149	Steve Walsh	.10
150	Pat Swilling	.10
151	Terrell Buckley	.10
152	Courtney Hawkins	.10
153	Willie Roaf	.10
154	Chris Doleman	.10
155	Jerome Bettis	.20
156	Dana Stubblefield	.10
157	Cornelius Bennett	.10
158	Quentin Coryatt	.10
159	Bryan Cox	.10
160	Marion Butts	.10
161	Aaron Glenn	.10
162	Louis Oliver	.10
163	Eric Turner	.10
164	Cris Dishman	.10
165	John L. Williams	.10
166	Simon Fletcher	.10
167	Neil Smith	.10
168	Chester McGlockton	.10
169	Natrone Means	.20
170	Sam Adams	.10
171	Clyde Simmons	.10
172	Jay Novacek	.10
173	Keith Hamilton	.10
174	William Fuller	.10
175	Tom Carter	.10
176	John Randle	.10
177	Lewis Tillman	.10
178	Mel Gray	.10
179	George Teague	.10
180	Hardy Nickerson	.10
181	Mario Bates	.40
182	D.J. Johnson	.10
183	Sean Gilbert	.10
184	Bryant Young	.10
185	Jeff Burris	.10
186	Floyd Turner	.10
187	Troy Vincent	.10
188	Willie McGinest	.10
189	James Hasty	.10
190	*Jeff Blake*	.50
191	Stevon Moore	.10
192	Ernest Givins	.10
193	Bam Morris	.20
194	Ray Crockett	.10
195	Dale Carter	.10
196	Terry McDaniels	.10
197	Leslie O'Neal	.10
198	Cortez Kennedy	.10
199	Seth Joyner	.10
200	Emmitt Smith	3.00
201	Thomas Lewis	.10
202	Andy Harmon	.10
203	Ricky Ervins	.10
204	Fuad Reveiz	.10
205	John Thierry	.10
206	Johnnie Morton	.10
207	LeShon Johnson	.10
208	Charles Wilson	.10
209	Joe Johnson	.10
210	Charles Smith	.10
211	Roman Phifer	.10
212	Ken Norton	.10
213	Bucky Brooks	.10
214	Ray Buchanan	.10
215	Tim Bowens	.10
216	Vincent Brown	.10
217	Marcus Turner	.10
218	Derrick Fenner	.10
219	Antonio Langham	.10
220	Cody Carlson	.10
221	Greg Lloyd	.10
222	Steve Atwater	.10
223	Donnell Bennett	.10
224	Raghib Ismail	.10
225	John Carney	.10
226	Eugene Robinson	.10
227	Aeneas Williams	.10
228	Darrin Smith	.10
229	Phillipi Sparks	.10
230	Eric Allen	.10
231	Brian Mitchell	.10
232	David Palmer	.10
233	Mark Carrier	.10
234	Dave Krieg	.10
235	Robert Brooks	.10
236	Eric Curry	.10
237	Wayne Martin	.10
238	Craig Heyward	.10
239	Isaac Bruce	1.00
240	Deion Sanders	1.00
241	Steve Tasker	.10
242	Jim Harbaugh	.10
243	Aubrey Beavers	.10
244	Chris Slade	.10
245	Mo Lewis	.10
246	Alfred Williams	.10
247	Michael Dean Perry	.10
248	Marcus Robertson	.10
249	Kevin Greene	.10
250	Leonard Russell	.10
251	Greg Hill	.20
252	Rob Fredrickson	.10
253	Junior Seau	.20
254	Rick Tuten	.10
255	Garrison Hearst	.30
256	Russell Maryland	.10
257	Michael Brooks	.10
258	Bernard Williams	.10
259	Reggie Roby	.10
260	DeWayne Washington	.10
261	Raymont Harris	.10
262	Brett Perriman	.10
263	LeRoy Butler	.10
264	Santana Dotson	.10
265	Irv Smith	.10
266	Ron George	.10
267	Marquez Pope	.10

268	William Floyd	.20
269	Matt Darby	.10
270	Jeff Herrod	.10
271	Bernie Parmalee	.20
273	Leroy Thompson	.10
274	Marvin Jones	.10
275	Michael Jackson	.10
276	Al Smith	.10
277	Rod Woodson	.10
278	Glyn Milburn	.10
279	Kimble Anders	.10
280	Anthony Smith	.10
281	Andre Coleman	.10
282	Terry Wooden	.10
283	Ernest Givins	.10
284	Steve Beuerlein	.10
285	Mark Brunell	1.50
286	Keith Goganious	.10
287	Desmond Howard	.10
288	Darren Carrington	.10
289	Derek Brown	.10
290	Reggie Cobb	.10
291	Jeff Lageman	.10
292	Lamar Lathon	.10
293	Sam Mills	.10
294	Carlton Bailey	.10
295	Mark Carrier	.10
296	Willie Green	.10
297	Frank Reich	.10
298	Don Beebe	.10
299	Tim McKyer	.10
300	Pete Metzelaars	.10

1995 Upper Deck Electric Silver

The 300-card, standard-size parallel set was inserted every pack and features a silver-foil "Electric" stamp on the card front.

	MT
Complete Set (300):	125.00
Common Player:	.20
Veteran Stars:	2x-4x
Young Stars:	1.5x-3x
RCs:	1.25x-2.5x

1995 Upper Deck Electric Gold

The 300-card, standard-size set was a parallel to the base set and was inserted every 35 packs. The card fronts have a gold-foil "Electric" logo.

	MT
Complete Set (300):	1200.
Common Player:	1.50
Veteran Stars:	20x-35x
Young Stars:	15x-25x
RCs:	10x-18x

1995 Upper Deck Montana Trilogy

Continued from Upper Deck's 1995 Collector's Choice football are eight more Joe Montana Trilogy cards, seeded one per 12 packs. These cards, numbered 9-16 with an "MT" prefix, feature a metallic-like front background, with gold foil for the brand logo and a panel at

the bottom of the card which describes the card's title. The title is listed above in a black strip. The Montana Trilogy logo also appears on the front. The card back has a player photo and a recap of the play being depicted on the front.

		MT
Complete Set (9):		40.00
Common Player:		6.00
Header Card:		6.00
9	The Drive	6.00
10	Super Bowl XXII	6.00
11	1989 - Dream Season	6.00
12	NFL MVP Back-to-Back	6.00
13	Super Bowl XXIV	6.00
14	Super Bowl XXIV MVP	6.00
15	Back-to-Back Super Bowls	6.00
16	The Comeback	6.00
UDH	Trilogy Header	6.00

1995 Upper Deck Hobby Predictor

These 20 cards, random inserts in 1995 Upper Deck hobby packs, feature 18 players who were potential MVP and Rookie of the Year Award winners. Two longshot cards were also made. Cards were in one per every 30 packs. If the player featured won the category, or finished second in the voting, collectors could redeem the cards for prizes. Card backs, numbered using an "HP" prefix, explained the rules of the game.

		MT
Complete Set (20):		100.00
Common Player:		3.00
1	Dan Marino	15.00
2	Steve Young	7.00
3	Drew Bledsoe	7.00
4	Troy Aikman	7.00
5	Barry Sanders	7.00
6	Emmitt Smith	15.00
7	Jerry Rice	15.00
8	Ki-Jana Carter	5.00
9	John Elway	6.00
10	The Longshot	3.00
11	Ki-Jana Carter	5.00
12	Steve McNair	8.00
13	Michael Westbrook	4.00
14	Kerry Collins	3.00
15	Joey Galloway	7.00
16	Kyle Brady	3.00
17	Napoleon Kaufman	6.00
18	Tyrone Wheatley	5.00
19	Rashaan Salaam	5.00
20	The Longshot	3.00

1995 Upper Deck Retail Predictor

These 30 1995 Upper Deck football cards feature 28 players

with the potential to win either the rushing yardage, passing efficiency and receiving yardage categories. Cards were randomly inserted one per every 30 retail packs. The card back, numbered using an "RP" prefix, explained the rules for if a player finished first or second in a category, and what prizes collectors could receive if they redeemed a winning card.

		MT
Complete Set (30):		75.00
Common Player:		1.00
Minor Stars:		2.00
Inserted 1:30 Retail		
1	Dan Marino	7.50
2	Steve Young	4.00
3	Drew Bledsoe	5.00
4	Troy Aikman	5.00
5	John Elway	7.50
6	Brett Favre	10.00
7	Stan Humphries	1.00
8	Jeff George	2.00
9	Kerry Collins	2.00
10	Longshot	1.00
11	Barry Sanders	10.00
12	Chris Warren	1.00
13	Emmitt Smith	7.50
14	Natrone Means	2.00
15	Rodney Hampton	1.00
16	Marshall Faulk	3.00
17	Errict Rhett	2.00
18	Napoleon Kaufman	5.00
19	Ki-Jana Carter	1.00
20	Longshot	1.00
21	Jerry Rice	5.00
22	Ben Coates	1.00
23	Cris Carter	2.00
24	Andre Reed	1.00
25	Andre Rison	1.00
26	Tim Brown	2.00
27	Michael Irvin	2.00
28	Irving Fryar	1.00
29	Michael Westbrook	2.00
30	Longshot	1.00

1995 Upper Deck Pro Bowl

These 25 cards, random inserts one per every 35 packs of 1995 Upper Deck football, use the Holoview process. Top players from the 1995 Pro Bowl are included. In addition to the hologram front, which shows the player against a Hawaiian setting with palm trees, the Pro Bowl logo is in the upper right corner. The player's name, team, position and Upper Deck logo are along the bottom of the card, which uses a horizontal format for the front. The horizontal back has a photo of the player in his Pro Bowl uniform, against a ghosted action photo as a background. A recap of the player's 1994 season is also included, as is a card number, which uses a "PB" prefix.

		MT
Complete Set (25):		150.00
Common Player:		3.00
1	Barry Sanders	15.00
2	Brent Jones	3.00
3	Cris Carter	3.00
4	Emmitt Smith	30.00
5	Jay Novacek	3.00
6	Jerome Bettis	3.00
7	Jerry Rice	15.00
8	Michael Irvin	7.00
9	Ricky Watters	3.00
10	Steve Young	15.00
11	Troy Aikman	15.00
12	Warren Moon	3.00
13	Terance Mathis	3.00
14	Ben Coates	3.00
15	Chris Warren	3.00
16	Dan Marino	30.00
17	Drew Bledsoe	15.00
18	Irving Fryar	3.00
19	Jeff Hostetler	3.00
20	John Elway	10.00

21	Leroy Hoard	3.00
22	Marshall Faulk	8.00
23	Natrone Means	4.00
24	Tim Brown	3.00
25	Checklist	3.00

1995 Upper Deck Special Edition

SHANNON SHARPE

This set-within-a-set features the photography of Walter Iooss Jr. The cards, random inserts one per every 1995 Upper Deck hobby pack, use a different design from the base brand. Each card front has a full-bleed color action photo on it, with Special Edition written at the top of the card. The player's name is at the bottom of the card. Card backs are numbered using an "SE" prefix. Special Edition Gold versions were also created for each card in the set; these cards were seeded one per every box.

		MT
Complete Set (90):		45.00
Common Player:		.25
Minor Stars:		.50
Complete Gold Set (90):		600.00
Common Gold Player:		2.00
Minor Gold Stars:		4.00
Gold Stars:		5x-10x
1	Terry Kirby	.25
2	Marcus Allen	.50
3	Bernie Parmalee	.50
4	Vernon Turner	.25
5	Dolphins Defense	.25
6	Kevin Turner	.25
7	Henry Thomas	.25
8	Barry Sanders	3.00
9	Marshall Faulk	2.00
10	Bill Bates	.25
11	Stan Humphries	.50
12	Barry Foster	.25
13	Shannon Sharpe	.50
14	Joe Montana	2.00
15	Bryan Cox	.25
16	Dale Carter	.25
17	Drew Bledsoe	2.00
18	Dan Marino	4.00
19	Ricky Watters	.50
20	Alvin Harper	.50
21	49ers Offensive Line	.25
22	Dan Marino	4.00
23	Ronnie Harmon	.25
24	Michael Irvin	.50
25	Emmitt Smith	4.00
26	Jeff Christie	.25
27	Terry Allen	.25
28	Randall Cunningham	.50
29	Todd Steussie	.25
30	Warren Moon	.50
31	Vikings Defense	.25
32	Tony Tolbert	.25
33	William Fuller	.25
34	Bernard Williams	.25
35	Charlie Garner	.25
36	Troy Aikman	2.00
37	Alvin Harper	.50
38	Kenneth Gant	.25
39	Daryl Johnston	.25
40	Ben Coates	.25
41	Rickey Jackson	.25
42	O.J. McDuffie	.25
43	Marion Butts	.25
44	NFL Offenses	.25
45	Kimble Anders	.50
46	Natrone Means	.50
47	Richmond Webb	.25
48	Carlos Jenkins	.25
49	James Harris	.25
50	Dexter Carter	.25
51	Qadry Ismail	.25
52	Jeff Herrod	.25
53	Sean Jones	.25
54	Keith Sims	.25
55	William Floyd	.50
56	Don Majkowski	.25
57	Charger Defense	.25
58	Byron Evans	.25
59	Chad Hennings	.25
60	Eric Allen	.25
61	Curtis Martin	5.00
62	Napoleon Kaufman	1.00
63	Kevin Carter	.50

64	Luther Elliss	.25
65	Frank Sanders	2.00
66	Rob Johnson	1.00
67	Christian Fauria	.25
68	Kyle Brady	.50
69	Michael Westbrook	1.50
70	James A. Stewart	.50
71	Ty Law	.25
72	Rodney Thomas	.25
73	Jimmy Oliver	.25
74	James O. Stewart	.50
75	Dave Barr	.25
76	Kordell Stewart	4.00
77	Michael Westbrook	1.50
78	Bobby Taylor	.25
79	Mark Fields	.25
80	Kerry Collins	1.00
81	Natrone Means	.50
82	Chargers Offense	.25
83	Deion Sanders	1.50
84	Dana Stubblefield	.25
85	49ers Defense	.25
86	Alfred Pupunu	.25
87	Tim Harris	.25
88	Jerry Rice	2.00
89	Steve Young	2.00
90	Super Bowl XXIX Champs.	

1995 Upper Deck GTE Phone Cards AFC

The 15-card, 3-3/8" x 2-1/8" prepaid set has rounded corners and color action photos on the fronts. The card backs have instructions for usage on the five-unit cards.

		MT
Complete Set (15):		80.00
Common Player:		3.00
1	Marcus Allen	4.00
2	Drew Bledsoe	10.00
3	Gary Brown	3.00
4	Tim Brown	4.00
5	John Elway	7.00
6	Marshall Faulk	6.00
7	Barry Foster	3.00
8	Jim Kelly	4.00
9	Ronnie Lott	3.00
10	Dan Marino	20.00
11	Rick Mirer	4.00
12	Carl Pickens	3.00
13	Junior Seau	4.00
14	Vinny Testaverde	3.00
15	Title Card	3.00

1995 Upper Deck GTE Phone Cards NFC

The 15-card, 3-3/8" x 2-1/8" set is identical to the AFC set in design, but with NFC players. The card backs feature card usage instructions.

		MT
Complete Set (15):		60.00
Common Player:		3.00
1	Jerome Bettis	4.00
2	Gary Clark	3.00
3	Curtis Conway	4.00
4	Randall Cunningham	3.00
5	Rodney Hampton	4.00
6	Michael Haynes	3.00
7	Michael Irvin	4.00
8	Warren Moon	4.00
9	Hardy Nickerson	3.00
10	Jerry Rice	8.00
11	Andre Rison	4.00
12	Barry Sanders	8.00
13	Sterling Sharpe	4.00
14	Heath Shuler	6.00
15	Title Card	4.00

1995 Upper Deck Authenticated Joe Montana Jumbos

The four-card, 5" x 3-1/2" set was offered to collectors through UDA's catalog. Each card shows Montana playing in a different Super Bowl. The card backs feature regular and post season statistics.

		MT
Complete Set (4):		35.00
Common Player:		10.00
1	Super Bowl XVI (Joe Montana)	10.00
2	Super Bowl XIX (Joe Montana)	10.00
3	Super Bowl XXIII (Joe Montana)	10.00
4	Super Bowl XXIV (Joe Montana)	10.00

1995 Upper Deck Joe Montana Box Set

The 45-card, over-sized set highlights Montana's career

from childhood through the pros. The card fronts feature gold foil with commentary text on the backs. The set was limited to 38,000 sets.

		MT
Complete Set (45):		20.00
Common Player:		.60
1	A Star Is Born	.60
2	Quarterback State	.60
3	Making Of A Hero	.60
4	National Champion	.60
5	Never-Say-Die	.60
6	The Protege	.60
7	New Orleans - The First Victim	.60
8	The Catch	.60
9	Super Bowl Fever	.60
10	Super Bowl XVI	.60
11	Emergence Of A/Record-Breaker	.60
12	Career-Year	.60
13	Heroic Comeback	.60
14	Super Bowl XIX	.60
15	Repeat Performance	.60
16	First Passing Crown	.60
17	Super Bowl XXIII	.60
18	Super Leader	.60
19	Best Of The Best	.60
20	Super Bowl XXIV	.60
21	Four-Time Champs	.60
22	Team Of The 80's	.60
23	Back-To-Back MVP's	.60
24	Down, But Far From Out	.60
25	Farewell Performance	.60
26	The Trade	.60
27	First K.C. Comeback	.60
28	Playoff Magic	.60
29	Dueling Quaterbacks	.60
30	Another Milestone Falls	.60
31	39 300-Yard Games	.60
32	273 Touchdowns	.60
33	112.4 Pass Efficiency Rating	.60
34	92.3 Pass Efficiency Rating	.60
35	117 Wins	.60
36	31 Comeback Victories	.60
37	5,391 Attempts	.60
38	3 Super Bowl MVP's	.60
39	3,409 Completions	.60
40	40,551 Yards	.60
41	Bill Walsh	.60
42	Russ Francis	.60
43	Roger Craig	.60
44	Jerry Rice	.60
45	Dwight Clark	.60
NNO	Super Bowl XIX / Quarterbabck Duel (Numbered of 38,000)	5.00
JM16	Joe Montana (Promo)	2.00

Values quoted in this guide reflect the retail price of a card — the price a collector can expect to pay when buying a card from a dealer. The wholesale price — that which a collector can expect to receive when selling cards — will be significantly lower, depending on desirability and condition.

1996 Upper Deck

Upper Deck's Series I football has 300 cards in it, with more than 90 percent of them highlighting the actual game date of the photo on the card front. Silver foil stamping is used for an Upper Deck logo, team logo and the player's last name, which appears between two parallel foiled stripes. The back has a close-up shot of the player, statistics, a recap of the featured game and season highlights. Series I inserts include Game Jersey, Hobby and Retail Predictor cards, Team Trio, Hot Properties and Meet the Stars promotional scratch-off cards. These trivia cards give collectors a chance to meet Dan Marino and win Upper Deck merchandise. Cards were seeded one per every four packs.

		MT
Complete Set (300):		35.00
Common Player:		.10
Minor Stars:		.20
Wax Box:		50.00
1	Keyshawn Johnson	2.50
2	Kevin Hardy	.75
3	Simeon Rice	.20
4	Jonathan Ogden	.20
5	Cedric Jones	.10
6	Lawrence Phillips	.75
7	Tim Biakabutuka	1.00
8	Terry Glenn	2.00
9	Rickey Dudley	.75
10	Willie Anderson	.10
11	Alex Molden	.10
12	Regan Upshaw	.10
13	Walt Harris	.20
14	Eddie George	4.00
15	John Mobley	.10
16	Duane Clemons	.10
17	Eddie Kennison	.30
18	Marvin Harrison	3.00
19	Daryl Gardener	.10
20	Leeland McElroy	.30
21	Eric Moulds	2.00
22	Alex Van Dyke	.20
23	Mike Alstott	1.50
24	Jeff Lewis	.75
25	Bobby Engram	.30
26	Derrick Mayes	1.00
27	Karim Abdul-Jabbar	.75
28	Bobby Hoying	.75
29	Stepfret Williams	.10
30	Chris Darkins	.20
31	Stephen Davis	4.00
32	Danny Kanell	.75
33	Tony Brackens	.40
34	Leslie O'Neal	.10
35	Chris Doleman	.10
36	Larry Brown	.10
37	Ronnie Harmon	.10
38	Chris Spielman	.10
39	John Jurkovic	.10
40	Shawn Jefferson	.10
41	Tommy Vardell	.10
42	Eric Davis	.10
43	Willie Clay	.10
44	Marco Coleman	.10
45	Lorenzo White	.10
46	Neil O'Donnell	.20
47	Natrone Means	.20
48	Cornelius Bennett	.10
49	Steve Walsh	.10
50	Jerome Bettis	.20
51	Boomer Esiason	.10
52	Glyn Milburn	.10
53	Kevin Greene	.10
54	Seth Joyner	.10
55	Jeff Harrod	.10
56	Darren Woodson	.10
57	Dale Carter	.10
58	Lorenzo Lynch	.10
59	Tim Brown	.20
60	Jerry Rice	1.50
61	Garrison Hearst	.10
62	Eric Metcalf	.10
63	Leroy Hoard	.10
64	Thurman Thomas	.20
65	Sam Mills	.10
66	Curtis Conway	.20

67	Carl Pickens	.20
68	Deion Sanders	.75
69	Shannon Sharpe	.20
70	Herman Moore	.40
71	Robert Brooks	.20
72	Rodney Thomas	.20
73	Ken Dilger	.10
74	Mark Brunell	1.00
75	Marcus Allen	.20
76	Dan Marino	3.00
77	Robert Smith	.10
78	Drew Bledsoe	1.25
79	Jim Everett	.10
80	Rodney Hampton	.10
81	Adrien Murrell	.10
82	Daryl Hobbs	.10
83	Ricky Watters	.20
84	Yancey Thigpen	.50
85	Roman Phifer	.10
86	Tony Martin	.10
87	Dana Stubblefield	.10
88	Joey Galloway	1.00
89	Errict Rhett	.75
90	Terry Allen	.10
91	Aeneas Williams	.10
92	Craig Heyward	.10
93	Vinny Testaverde	.10
94	Bryce Paup	.10
95	Kerry Collins	.30
96	Rashaan Salaam	.30
97	Dan Wilkinson	.10
98	Jay Novacek	.10
99	John Elway	.30
100	Bennie Blades	.10
101	Edgar Bennett	.10
102	Darryll Lewis	.10
103	Marshall Faulk	.50
104	Bryan Schwartz	.10
105	Tamarick Vanover	.75
106	Terry Kirby	.10
107	John Randle	.10
108	Ted Johnson	.10
109	Mario Bates	.10
110	Philippi Sparks	.10
111	Marvin Washington	.10
112	Terry McDaniel	.10
113	Bobby Taylor	.10
114	Carnell Lake	.10
115	Troy Drayton	.10
116	Darren Bennett	.10
117	J.J. Stokes	.30
118	Rick Mirer	.20
119	Jackie Harris	.10
120	Ken Harvey	.10
121	Rob Moore	.10
122	Jeff George	.20
123	Andre Rison	.10
124	Darick Holmes	.20
125	Tim McKyer	.10
126	Alonzo Spellman	.10
127	Jeff Blake	.75
128	Kevin Williams	.10
129	Anthony Miller	.10
130	Barry Sanders	1.75
131	Brett Favre	3.00
132	Steve McNair	1.00
133	Jim Harbaugh	.20
134	Desmond Howard	.10
135	Steve Bono	.10
136	Bernie Parmalee	.10
137	Warren Moon	.10
138	Curtis Martin	2.00
139	Irv Smith	.10
140	Thomas Lewis	.10
141	Kyle Brady	.10
142	Napoleon Kaufman	.20
143	Mike Mamula	.10
144	Errict Pegram	.10
145	Isaac Bruce	1.00
146	Andre Coleman	.10
147	Merton Hanks	.10
148	Brian Blades	.10
149	Hardy Nickerson	.10
150	Michael Westbrook	.20
151	Larry Centers	.10
152	Morten Andersen	.10
153	Michael Jackson	.10
154	Bruce Smith	.10
155	Derrick Moore	.10
156	Mark Carrier	.10
157	John Copeland	.10
158	Emmitt Smith	3.00
159	Jason Elam	.10
160	Scott Mitchell	.10
161	Mark Chmura	.30
162	Blaine Bishop	.10
163	Tony Bennett	.10
164	Pete Mitchell	.10
165	Dan Saleaumua	.10
166	Pete Stoyanovich	.10
167	Cris Carter	.20
168	Vincent Brisby	.10
169	Wayne Martin	.10
170	Tyrone Wheatley	.20
171	Mo Lewis	.10
172	Harvey Williams	.10
173	Calvin Williams	.10
174	Norm Johnson	.10
175	Mark Rypien	.10
176	Stan Humphries	.20
177	Derek Loville	.10
178	Christian Fauria	.10
179	Warren Sapp	.20
180	Henry Ellard	.10
181	Jamir Miller	.10
182	Jessie Tuggle	.10
183	Stevon Moore	.10
184	Jim Kelly	.20

185	Mark Carrier	.10
186	Chris Zorich	.10
187	Harold Green	.10
188	Chris Boniol	.10
189	Allen Aldridge	.10
190	Brett Perriman	.10
191	Chris Jackie (Jacke)	.10
192	Todd McNair	.10
193	Floyd Turner	.10
194	Jeff Lageman	.10
195	Derrick Thomas	.10
196	Eric Green	.10
197	Orlanda Thomas	.10
198	Ben Coates	.10
199	Tyrone Hughes	.10
200	Dave Brown	.10
201	Brad Baxter	.10
202	Chester McGlockton	.10
203	Rodney Peete	.10
204	Willie Williams	.10
205	Kevin Carter	.10
206	Aaron Hayden	.20
207	Steve Young	1.00
208	Chris Warren	.20
209	Eric Curry	.10
210	Brian Mitchell	.10
211	Frank Sanders	.10
212	Terance Mathis	.10
213	Eric Turner	.10
214	Bill Brooks	.10
215	John Kasay	.10
216	Erik Kramer	.10
217	Darnay Scott	.20
218	Charles Haley	.10
219	Steve Atwater	.10
220	Jason Hanson	.10
221	LeRoy Butler	.10
222	Cris Dishman	.10
223	Sean Dawkins	.10
224	James O. Stewart	.10
225	Greg Hill	.10
226	Jeff Cross	.10
227	Qadry Ismail	.10
228	Dave Meggett	.10
229	Eric Allen	.10
230	Chris Calloway	.10
231	Wayne Chrebet	.10
232	Jeff Hostetler	.10
233	Andy Harmon	.10
234	Greg Lloyd	.10
235	Toby Wright	.10
236	Junior Seau	.10
237	Bryant Young	.10
238	Robert Blackmon	.10
239	Trent Dilfer	.10
240	Leslie Shepherd	.10
241	Eric Swann	.10
242	Bert Emanuel	.10
243	Antonio Langham	.10
244	Steve Christie	.10
245	Tyrone Poole	.10
246	Jim Flanigan	.10
247	Tony McGee	.10
248	Michael Irvin	.20
249	Bam Morris	.10
250	Terrell Davis	1.50
251	Johnnie Morton	.10
252	Sean Jones	.10
253	Chris Sanders	.30
254	Quentin Coryatt	.10
255	Willie Jackson	.10
256	Mark Collins	.10
257	Randal Hill	.10
258	David Palmer	.10
259	Will Moore	.10
260	Michael Haynes	.10
261	Mike Sherrard	.10
262	William Thomas	.10
263	Kordell Stewart	1.50
264	D'Marco Farr	.10
265	Terrell Fletcher	.10
266	Lee Woodall	.10
267	Eugene Robinson	.10
268	Alvin Harper	.10
269	Gus Frerotte	.10
270	Antonio Freeman	.10
271	Clyde Simmons	.10
272	Chuck Smith	.10
273	Steve Tasker	.10
274	Kevin Butler	.10
275	Steve Tovar	.10
276	Troy Aikman	1.00
277	Aaron Craver	.10
278	Henry Thomas	.10
279	Craig Newsome	.10
280	Brent Jones	.10
281	Michael Barrow	.10
282	Ray Buchanan	.10
283	Jimmy Smith	.10
284	Neil Smith	.10
285	O.J. McDuffie	.10
286	Jake Reed	.10
287	Ty Law	.10
288	Torrance Small	.10
289	Hugh Douglas	.10
290	Pat Swilling	.10
291	Charlie Garner	.10
292	Ernie Mills	.10
293	John Carney	.10
294	Ken Norton	.10
295	Cortez Kennedy	.10
296	Derrick Brooks	.10
297	Heath Shuler	.20
298	Reggie White	.10
299	Kimble Anders	.10
300	Willie McGinest	.10

1996 Upper Deck Game Jersey

Each of these 1996 Upper Deck insert cards features an actual piece of a player's game-worn uniform. Cards, seeded one per every 2,500 Series I packs, are numbered using a "GJ" prefix. There are two different cards of Jerry Rice and Dan Marino.

		MT
Complete Set (10):		4000.
Common Player:		150.00
1	Dan Marino	575.00
2	Jerry Rice	350.00
3	Joe Montana	550.00
4	Jerry Rice	350.00
5	Rashaan Salaam	150.00
6	Marshall Faulk	200.00
7	Dan Marino	575.00
8	Steve Young	300.00
9	Barry Sanders	650.00
10	Mark Brunell	325.00

1996 Upper Deck Predictor

All new die-cut F/X designs grace the fronts of these 1996 Upper Deck Series I inserts, which are now based on personal goals. For example, if Dan Marino passes for 450 or more yards in a game, a collector can mail in the Marino card for a special TV-CEL redemption card. The player's goal and the word "Predictor" are stamped in silver foil along the sides of the card. The back of the card explains the rules for the promotion. A maximum of 500 of each player's winning TV-CEL cards will be randomly inserted in packs. The same 20 players are represented in both retail and hobby versions, but the personal goals are different. The cards also use the corresponding "PH" or "PR" prefix for the card number.

		MT
Comp. Hobby Set (20):		200.00
Comp. Retail Set (20):		200.00
Common Player:		2.00
PH1	Dan Marino	10.00
PH2	Steve Young	5.00
PH3	Brett Favre	50.00
PH4	Drew Bledsoe	30.00
PH5	Jeff George	2.00
PH6	John Elway	20.00
PH7	Barry Sanders	50.00
PH8	Curtis Martin	8.00
PH9	Marshall Faulk	5.00
PH10	Emmitt Smith	10.00
PH11	Terrell Davis	30.00
PH12	Errict Rhett	4.00
PH13	Lawrence Phillips	4.00
PH14	Jerry Rice	5.00
PH15	Michael Irvin	10.00
PH16	Joey Galloway	5.00
PH17	Herman Moore	3.00
PH18	Isaac Bruce	3.00
PH19	Carl Pickens	3.00
PH20	Keyshawn Johnson	4.00
PR1	Dan Marino	10.00

PR2	Steve Young	25.00
PR3	Brett Favre	10.00
PR4	Drew Bledsoe	30.00
PR5	Jeff George	2.00
PR6	John Elway	20.00
PR7	Barry Sanders	6.00
PR8	Curtis Martin	30.00
PR9	Marshall Faulk	5.00
PR10	Emmitt Smith	10.00
PR11	Terrell Davis	30.00
PR12	Errict Rhett	2.00
PR13	Lawrence Phillips	2.00
PR14	Jerry Rice	6.00
PR15	Michael Irvin	10.00
PR16	Joey Galloway	5.00
PR17	Herman Moore	15.00
PR18	Isaac Bruce	15.00
PR19	Carl Pickens	5.00
PR20	Keyshawn Johnson	5.00

1996 Upper Deck Pro Bowl

The 20-card Pro Bowl set was inserted every 33 packs of Upper Deck's Series One football. Cards are numbered and carry a "PB" prefix.

		MT
Complete Set (20):		125.00
Common Player:		3.00
1	Warren Moon	3.00
2	Brett Favre	20.00
3	Steve Young	10.00
4	Barry Sanders	18.00
5	Emmitt Smith	20.00
6	Jerry Rice	12.00
7	Herman Moore	6.00
8	Michael Irvin	3.00
9	Mark Chmura	3.00
10	Reggie White	3.00
11	Jim Harbaugh	3.00
12	Jeff Blake	8.00
13	Curtis Martin	18.00
14	Marshall Faulk	7.00
15	Chris Warren	3.00
16	Bryan Cox	3.00
17	Junior Seau	3.00
18	Carl Pickens	3.00
19	Yancey Thigpen	3.00
20	Ben Coates	3.00

1996 Upper Deck Proview

One Proview card was inserted in each Upper Deck Tech retail pack. The cards feature a cel window with a player close up. The fronts include another photo and the backs have basic player information. Silver (1:35) and Gold (1:143) parallel versions were also created.

		MT
Complete Set (40):		120.00
Common Player:		1.00
Minor Stars:		2.00
1	Warren Moon	1.00
2	Jerry Rice	7.00
3	Brett Favre	16.00
4	Jim Harbaugh	1.00
5	Junior Seau	1.00
6	Jeff Blake	2.00
7	John Elway	5.00
8	Troy Aikman	7.00
9	Steve Young	5.00
10	Kordell Stewart	7.00
11	Drew Bledsoe	7.00
12	Jim Kelly	2.00
13	Dan Marino	14.00
14	Kerry Collins	2.00
15	Jeff Hostetler	1.00
16	Terry Allen	1.00
17	Carl Pickens	1.00
18	Mark Brunell	10.00
19	Keyshawn Johnson	4.00
20	Barry Sanders	10.00
21	Deion Sanders	4.00
22	Emmitt Smith	14.00
23	Curtis Conway	1.00
24	Herman Moore	2.00
25	Joey Galloway	2.00
26	Robert Smith	1.00
27	Eddie George	10.00
28	Curtis Martin	7.00
29	Marshall Faulk	2.00
30	Terrell Davis	7.00
31	Rashaan Salaam	1.00
32	Jamal Anderson	2.00
33	Karim Abdul-Jabbar	6.00
34	Edgar Bennett	1.00
35	Thurman Thomas	2.00
36	Jerome Bettis	2.00
37	Tim Brown	1.00
38	Chris Sanders	1.00
39	Eddie Kennison	4.00
40	Shannon Sharpe	1.00

1996 Upper Deck Hot Properties

Each of these 1996 Upper Deck Series I inserts features a different player on each side. The card design features a color action photo (outlined with a red glow) against a silver metallic background. Red foil is used for the Upper Deck logo and the word "Hot" in the set's logo. The card number, using an "HT" prefix, is on one side, above an Upper Deck football-shaped hologram. Cards were seeded one per every 11 Series I packs.

		MT
Complete Set (20):		125.00
Common Player:		2.00
1	Dan Marino, Drew Bledsoe	20.00
2	Jerry Rice, J.J. Stokes	10.00
3	Kordell Stewart, Deion Sanders	10.00
4	Brett Favre, Rick Mirer	20.00
5	Jeff Blake, Steve McNair	8.00
6	Emmitt Smith, Errict Rhett	20.00
7	John Elway, Warren Moon	6.00
8	Steve Young, Mark Brunell	10.00
9	Troy Aikman, Kerry Collins	12.00
10	Joey Galloway, Chris Sanders	8.00
11	Herman Moore, Cris Carter	2.00
12	Rodney Hampton, Terrell Davis	12.00
13	Carl Pickens, Isaac Bruce	5.00
14	Rashaan Salaam, Michael Westbrook	8.00
15	Marshall Faulk, Curtis Martin	12.00
16	Tamarick Vanover, Eric Metcalf	8.00
17	Keyshawn Johnson, Terry Glenn	12.00
18	Lawrence Phillips, Tim Biakabutuka	4.00
19	Kevin Hardy, Simeon Rice	2.00
20	Barry Sanders, Thurman Thomas	12.00

1996 Upper Deck Hot Properties Gold

This insert paralleled the

20-card Hot Properties insert, but the letters "Hot Properties" were printed in gold foil. Hot Properties Gold were seeded one per 71 packs.

	MT
Complete Set (20):	375.00
Gold Cards:	3x

1996 Upper Deck Game Face

Game Face inserts were only found in special retail packs, and were numbered GF1-GF10. They included a close-up shot of the player, who had his intense, "game face" on.

		MT
Complete Set (10):		10.00
Common Player:		1.00
1	Dan Marino	4.00
2	Barry Sanders	2.00
3	Jerry Rice	2.00
4	Stan Humphries	1.00
5	Drew Bledsoe	2.00
6	Greg Lloyd	1.00
7	Jim Harbaugh	1.00
8	Rashaan Salaam	1.00
9	Jeff Blake	1.00
10	Reggie White	1.00

1996 Upper Deck TV Cels

TV Cels were available by redeeming winner Predictor cards. They include a television-like frame with cel technology inside, which reveals the player's image when held to light. Cards are numbered and carry a "PH" prefix.

		MT
Complete Set (20):		500.00
Common Player:		10.00
1	Dan Marino	125.00
2	Steve Young	15.00
3	Brett Favre	35.00
4	Drew Bledsoe	20.00
5	Jeff George	10.00
6	John Elway	25.00
7	Barry Sanders	35.00
8	Curtis Martin	15.00
9	Marshall Faulk	10.00
10	Emmitt Smith	100.00
11	Terrell Davis	35.00
12	Errict Rhett	10.00
13	Lawrence Phillips	10.00
14	Jerry Rice	60.00
15	Michael Irvin	10.00
16	Joey Galloway	15.00
17	Herman Moore	10.00
18	Isaac Bruce	10.00
19	Carl Pickens	10.00
20	Keyshawn Johnson	45.00

1996 Upper Deck Silver

Denver Broncos - QB

Upper Deck's 1996 premium Silver Collection contains 210 regular cards of the top stars and rookies in the NFL, printed on silver paper stock. Silver foil is used for the player's name, team name, position and brand logo on the front, which has a full-bleed color action photo. The back has a black strip along the left side, with the player's name, position and biographical information in it, plus a team logo and card number toward the top. A color action photo is at the top of the card, with statistics underneath. Sub-

set cards are devoted to top players in certain offensive and defensive statistical leaders from the 1995 NFL season. Insert sets include All-NFL Team, All-Rookie Team, team helmet cards, Dan Marino Record Season, and a Rookie Draft Trade card, which is redeemable for 20-card Light F/X Rookie Redemption set from the 1996 NFL Draft. Cards were seeded one per every 103 packs.

		MT
Complete Set (225):		30.00
Common Player:		.10
Minor Stars:		.20
Wax Box:		20.00
1	Larry Centers	.10
2	Terance Mathis	.10
3	Justin Armour	.10
4	Kerry Collins	.30
5	Mike Flanagan	.10
6	Dan Wilkinson	.10
7	Eric Zeier	.75
8	Deion Sanders	.75
9	Steve Atwater	.10
10	Johnnie Morton	.10
11	Craig Newsome	.10
12	Denver Broncos Offensive Line	.10
13	Ken Dilger	.10
14	Mark Brunell	.50
15	Tamarick Vanover	.50
16	Bernie Parmalee	.10
17	Orlanda Thomas	.10
18	Will Moore	.10
19	Mark Fields	.10
20	Tyrone Wheatley	.20
21	Kyle Brady	.10
22	Napoleon Kaufman	.50
23	Mike Mamula	.10
24	Erric Pegram	.10
25	Brent Jones	.10
26	Aaron Hayden	.50
27	Christian Fauria	.10
28	Dallas Cowboys Offensive Lines	.10
29	Derrick Brooks	.10
30	Brian Mitchell	.10
31	Garrison Hearst	.20
32	Devin Bush	.10
33	Andre Reed	.10
34	Derrick Moore	.10
35	Erik Kramer	.10
36	Jeff Blake	.75
37	Andre Rison	.10
38	Troy Aikman	1.50
39	Anthony Miller	.10
40	Scott Mitchell	.10
41	Reggie White	.20
42	Chris Sanders	.40
43	Ellis Johnson	.10
44	Willie Jackson	.10
45	Steve Bono	.20
46	Terry Kirby	.10
47	Jake Reed	.10
48	Vincent Brisby	.10
49	Quinn Early	.10
50	Thomas Lewis	.10
51	Wayne Chrebet	.10
52	Pat Swilling	.10
53	Bobby Taylor	.10
54	Mark Bruener	.10
55	Jerry Rice	1.50
56	Natrone Means	.25
57	Rick Mirer	.10
58	Kevin Carter	.10
59	Hardy Nickerson	.10
60	Detroit Lions Offensive Lines	.10
61	Eric Swann	.10
62	Eric Metcalf	.10
63	Russell Copeland	.10
64	Pete Metzelaars	.10
65	Curtis Conway	.10
66	Darnay Scott	.20
67	Leroy Hoard	.10
68	Darren Woodson	.10
69	John Elway	.50
70	Brett Perriman	.10
71	Mark Chmura	.10
72	Chris Chandler	.10
73	Marshall Faulk	1.00
74	Pete Mitchell	.10
75	Willie Davis	.10
76	Irving Fryar	.10
77	Robert Smith	.10
78	Drew Bledsoe	1.00
79	Mario Bates	.30
80	Chris Calloway	.10
81	Boomer Esiason	.10
82	Harvey Williams	.10
83	Fred Barnett	.10
84	Neil O'Donnell	.10
85	Lee Woodall	.10
86	Junior Seau	.10
87	Brian Blades	.10
88	Chris Miller	.10
89	Warren Sapp	.10
90	Terry Allen	.10
91	Dave Krieg	.10
92	Bert Emanuel	.10
93	Jim Kelly	.20
94	Mark Carrier	.10
95	Jeff Graham	.10

96	Tony McGee	.10
97	Vinny Testaverde	.10
98	Michael Irvin	.30
99	Shannon Sharpe	.10
100	Chris Spielman	.10
101	Edgar Bennett	.10
102	Haywood Jeffires	.10
103	Quentin Coryatt	.10
104	Jeff Lageman	.10
105	Neil Smith	.10
106	O.J. McDuffie	.10
107	Warren Moon	.10
108	Ben Coates	.10
109	Michael Haynes	.10
110	Mike Sherrard	.10
111	Adrian Murrell	.10
112	Jeff Hostetler	.10
113	Charlie Garner	.10
114	Yancey Thigpen	.10
115	Steve Young	1.50
116	Tony Martin	.10
117	San Francisco Offensive Lines	.10
118	Jerome Bettis	.10
119	Alvin Harper	.10
120	Heath Shuler	.40
121	Rob Moore	.10
122	Chris Doleman	.10
123	Bruce Smith	.10
124	Sam Mills	.10
125	Donnell Woolford	.10
126	Harold Green	.10
127	Antonio Langham	.10
128	Charles Haley	.10
129	Aaron Craver	.10
130	Barry Sanders	1.50
131	Sean Jones	.10
132	Steve McNair	1.00
133	Tony Bennett	.10
134	Miami Dolphins Offensive Lines	.10
135	Greg Hill	.10
136	Eric Green	.10
137	John Randle	.10
138	Dave Meggett	.10
139	Irv Smith	.10
140	Dave Brown	.10
141	Oakland Raiders Offensive Lines	.10
142	Raghib Ismail	.10
143	Rodney Peete	.10
144	Kevin Greene	.10
145	Derek Loville	.10
146	Leslie O'Neal	.10
147	Cortez Kennedy	.10
148	Sean Gilbert	.10
149	Jackie Harris	.10
150	Henry Ellard	.10
151	Frank Sanders	.30
152	Jeff George	.20
153	Darick Holmes	.75
154	Tyrone Poole	.10
155	Rashaan Salaam	.75
156	Carl Pickens	.20
157	Eric Turner	.10
158	Jay Novacek	.10
159	Terrell Davis	1.50
160	Herman Moore	.40
161	Robert Brooks	.10
162	Rodney Thomas	.40
163	Sean Dawkins	.10
164	James O. Stewart	.10
165	Marcus Allen	.10
166	Dan Marino	3.00
167	Cris Carter	.20
168	Curtis Martin	3.00
169	Tyrone Hughes	.10
170	Rodney Hampton	.10
171	Hugh Douglas	.10
172	Tim Brown	.10
173	Ricky Watters	.10
174	Kordell Stewart	2.00
175	J.J. Stokes	.75
176	Stan Humphries	.10
177	Joey Galloway	.50
178	Isaac Bruce	.75
179	Errict Rhett	.50
180	Michael Westbrook	.75
181	Pittsburgh Steelers Offensive Lines	.10
182	Craig Heyward	.10
183	Bryce Paup	.10
184	Brett Maxie	.10
185	Kevin Butler	.10
186	John Copeland	.10
187	Keenan McCardell	.10
188	Emmitt Smith	3.00
189	Glyn Milburn	.10
190	Jason Hanson	.10
191	Brett Favre	3.00
192	Darryll Lewis	.10
193	Jim Harbaugh	.10
194	Desmond Howard	.10
195	Derrick Thomas	.10
196	Bryan Cox	.10
197	Amp Lee	.10
198	Ty Law	.10
199	Jim Everett	.10
200	Vencie Glenn	.10
201	Charles Wilson	.10
202	Terry McDaniel	.10
203	Calvin Williams	.10
204	Greg Lloyd	.10
205	Merton Hanks	.10
206	Andre Coleman	.10
207	Chris Warren	.10
208	D'Marco Farr	.10
209	Trent Dilfer	.20
210	Ken Harvey	.10
211	Jim Harbaugh	.10
212	Brett Favre SL	1.00
213	Curtis Martin SL	1.50
214	Carl Pickens	.10
215	Norm Johnson	.10
216	Bryce Paup	.10
217	Herman Moore	.10
218	Jerry Rice SL	.75
219	Orlanda Thomas	.10
220	Emmitt Smith SL	1.50
221	Tyrone Hughes	.10
222	Tamarick Vanover	.30
223	Rick Tuten	.10
224	San Francisco 49ers	.10
225	Detroit Lions	.10
NNO	Draft Trade Card	20.00

1996 Upper Deck Silver All-NFL

Top NFL stars have been selected for this 1996 Upper Deck Silver insert set. The 20 cards, seeded one per every five packs, are produced as a special Light F/X die-cut card. The front of the card has a gold foil border, with a photo in the center framed by a silver foil oval. The player's name is in a team color-coded bar below the photo. The Upper Deck logo and a team logo are stamped in silver foil on the front too, with All NFL Team written at the top. The back has a border which looks like a pigskin football. A square in the center has a color action photo in the top half, with the player's name and position given below. Then, a recap of the player's 1995 season and "All NFL Team" and a team logo follow. A card number, using an "AN" prefix, is in the upper left corner of the card.

		MT
	Complete Set (20):	45.00
	Common Player:	2.00
1	Herman Moore	3.00
2	Isaac Bruce	4.00
3	Jerry Rice	6.00
4	Michael Irvin	3.00
5	Eric Metcalf	2.00
6	Ben Coates	2.00
7	Brett Favre	10.00
8	Jim Harbaugh	2.00
9	Emmitt Smith	10.00
10	Barry Sanders	6.00
11	Chris Warren	3.00
12	Curtis Martin	8.00
13	Hugh Douglas	2.00
14	Neil Smith	2.00
15	Reggie White	3.00
16	Bryce Paup	2.00
17	Greg Lloyd	2.00
18	Carnell Lake	2.00
19	Merton Hanks	2.00
20	Tamarick Vanover	4.00

Values quoted in this guide reflect the retail price of a card — the price a collector can expect to pay when buying a card from a dealer. The wholesale price — that which a collector can expect to receive when selling cards — will be significantly lower, depending on desirability and condition.

A player's name in *italic type* indicates a rookie card.

1996 Upper Deck Silver All-Rookie Team

These 1996 Upper Deck Silver Collection insert cards, seeded one per every 18 packs, feature 20 of the top rookies selected to Upper Deck's "All-Rookie Team." The die-cut cards use Upper Deck's Light F/X technology. Cards are numbered and carry an "AR" prefix.

		MT
	Complete Set (20):	120.00
	Common Player:	3.00
1	Joey Galloway	12.00
2	Chris Sanders	6.00
3	J.J. Stokes	10.00
4	Ken Dilger	3.00
5	Pete Mitchell	3.00
6	Kordell Stewart	20.00
7	Kerry Collins	6.00
8	Tony Boselli	3.00
9	Terrell Davis	20.00
10	Rodney Thomas	6.00
11	Rashaan Salaam	6.00
12	Curtis Martin	24.00
13	Napoleon Kaufman	6.00
14	Hugh Douglas	3.00
15	Ellis Johnson	3.00
16	Kevin Carter	3.00
17	Derrick Brooks	3.00
18	Craig Newsome	3.00
19	Orlanda Thomas	3.00
20	Tamarick Vanover	3.00

1996 Upper Deck Silver Dan Marino

These four 1996 Upper Deck Silver Collection cards honor the record-setting 1995 season by future Hall of Famer Dan Marino. The cards, numbered with an "RS" prefix, were seeded one per every 81 packs.

		MT
	Complete Set (4):	60.00
	Common Player:	15.00
1	All-Time Completions 3,686	15.00
2	All-Time Passing Yards 47,003	15.00
3	All-Time Touchdown Pts. 342	15.00
4	300-Yards Passing Games 52	15.00

1996 Upper Deck Silver Helmet Cards

These 1996 Upper Deck Silver Collection insert cards were seeded one per every 23 packs. The cards, the first to use double-sided Light F/X technology, have a team helmet on one side, bordered on either side by a team color-coordinated panel which lists the team name or respective conference. A card number, using an "AC" or "NC" prefix, is also on this side. The opposite side has two action photos of teammates from that team, with their names below the photos in color-coded strips.

		MT
	Complete Set (30):	275.00
	Common Player:	3.00
NE1	Arizona Cardinals (Garrison Hearst, Frank Sanders)	3.00
NW1	Atlanta Falcons (Jeff George, Devin Bush)	3.00
NW2	Carolina Panthers (Sam Mills, Kerry Collins)	6.00
NC1	Chicago Bears (Erik Kramer, Rashaan Salaam)	6.00
AC1	Cincinnati Bengals (Jeff Blake, David Dunn)	8.00
AC2	Cleveland Browns (Vinny Testaverde, Eric Zeier)	3.00
NC2	Detroit Lions (Herman Moore, Luther Elliss)	6.00
AC3	Houston Oilers (Rodney Thomas, Chris Sanders)	6.00
AE1	Indianapolis Colts (Marshall Faulk, Ken Dilger)	8.00
AC4	Jacksonville Jaguars (Mark Brunell, James O. Stewart)	10.00
AW1	Kansas City Chiefs (Steve Bono, Tamarick Vanover)	3.00
NC3	Minnesota Vikings (Cris Carter, Orlanda Thomas)	3.00
NW3	New Orleans Saints (Mario Bates, Mark Fields)	3.00
NE2	New York Giants (Rodney Hampton, Tyrone Wheatley)	3.00
AE2	New York Jets (Wayne Chrebet, Hugh Douglas)	3.00
NE3	Philadelphia Eagles (Ricky Watters, Mike Mamula)	3.00
AW2	Seattle Seahawks (Chris Warren, Joey Galloway)	6.00
NW4	St. Louis Rams (Isaac Bruce, Kevin Carter)	8.00
NC4	Tampa Bay Buccaneers (Errict Rhett, Derrick Brooks)	6.00
NE4	Washington Redskins (Terry Allen, Michael Westbrook)	8.00
AC5	Pittsburgh Steelers (Greg Lloyd, Kordell Stewart)	18.00
AW4	San Diego Chargers (Natrone Means, Terrance Shaw)	6.00
NW5	San Francisco 49ers (Jerry Rice, J.J. Stokes)	20.00
AW4	Oakland Raiders (Tim Brown, Napoleon Kaufman)	6.00
AE3	Miami Dolphins (Dan Marino, Billy Milner)	40.00
NE5	Dallas Cowboys (Emmitt Smith, Sherman Williams)	40.00
AE4	Buffalo Bills (Jim Kelly, Darick Holmes)	6.00
NC5	Green Bay Packers (Robert Brooks, Craig Newsome)	6.00
AW5	Denver Broncos (John Elway, Terrell Davis)	20.00
AE5	New England Patriots (Drew Bledsoe, Curtis Martin)	25.00

1996 Upper Deck Silver Prime Choice Rookies

This 20-card set was available via redemption of a special trade card inserted in 1996 Upper Deck Silver. The card fronts feature a foil-accented photo and an inset photo of the player. The backs contain another player photo and biographical information.

		MT
	Complete Set (20):	45.00
	Common Player:	.50
	Minor Stars:	1.00
1	Keyshawn Johnson	6.00
2	Kevin Hardy	.50
3	Simeon Rice	.50
4	Tim Biakabutuka	1.50
5	Terry Glenn	4.00
6	Rickey Dudley	1.00
7	Alex Molden	.50
8	Regan Upshaw	.50
9	Eddie George	15.00
10	John Mobley	1.00
11	Eddie Kennison	1.00
12	Marvin Harrison	3.00
13	Leeland McElroy	1.00
14	Eric Moulds	6.00
15	Mike Alstott	5.00
16	Bobby Engram	1.00
17	Derrick Mayes	.50
18	Karim Abdul-Jabbar	4.00
19	Stepfret Williams	.50
20	Jeff Lewis	.50
NNO	Redemption Card Expired	1.00

1997 Upper Deck

The 300-card set includes subsets of Star Rookies (35 cards), Star Rookie Flashback (10 cards) and Game Dated Moments (30 cards). The base cards have the player's name printed vertically along the left border, with the Upper Deck logo and player's position in the lower left corner. The team's name is to the right of the Upper Deck logo on the card front.

		MT
	Complete Set (300):	40.00
	Common Player:	.10
	Minor Stars:	.20
	Game Dated Foils:	40x-80x
	Inserted 1:1,500	
	Wax Box:	45.00
1	Orlando Pace	.50
2	Darrell Russell	.10
3	Shawn Springs	.75
4	Bryant Westbrook	.30
5	Ike Hilliard	1.50
6	Peter Boulware	.10
7	Tom Knight	.10
8	Yatil Green	.50
9	Tony Gonzalez	1.00
10	Reidel Anthony	1.50
11	Warrick Dunn	2.50
12	Kenny Holmes	.10
13	Jim Druckenmiller	2.50
14	James Farrior	.10
15	David LaFleur	1.00
16	Antowain Smith	2.00
17	Rae Carruth	1.25
18	Dwayne Rudd	.10
19	Jake Plummer	6.00
20	Reinard Wilson	.10
21	Byron Hanspard	1.25
22	Will Blackwell	.50
23	Troy Davis	.50
24	Corey Dillon	2.50
25	Joey Kent	.75
26	Renaldo Wynn	1.00
27	Pat Barnes	1.00
28	Kevin Lockett	.10
29	Darnell Autry	1.00
30	Walter Jones	.10
31	(Trevor Pryce)	.10
32	(Dan Marino SRF)	2.00
33	(Steve Young SRF)	1.00
34	(John Elway SRF)	1.00
35	(Jerry Rice SRF)	1.00
36	Tim Brown SRF	.10
37	Deion Sanders SRF	.50
38	Troy Aikman SRF	1.00
39	Barry Sanders SRF	1.00
40	Emmitt Smith SRF	2.00
41	Junior Seau SRF	.10
42	Neil Smith	.10
43	Brett Perriman	.10
44	Jim Everett	.10
45	Qadry Ismail	.10
46	Dana Stubblefield	.10
47	Bryant Young	.10
48	Ken Norton Jr.	.10
49	Terrell Owens	.75
50	Jerry Rice	1.50
51	Steve Young	.75
52	Terry Kirby	.10
53	Chris Doleman	.10
54	Lee Woddall	.10
55	Merton Hanks	.10
56	Garrison Hearst	.10
57	Rashaan Salaam	.20
58	Raymont Harris	.10
59	Curtis Conway	.10
60	Bobby Engram	.10
61	Bryan Cox	.10
62	Walt Harris	.10
63	Tyrone Hughes	.10
64	Rick Mirer	.20
65	Jeff Blake	.20
66	Carl Pickens	.10
67	Tony McGee	.10
68	Ki-Jana Carter	.10
69	Ashley Ambrose	.10
70	Dan Wilkinson	.10
71	Chris Spielman	.10
72	Todd Collins	.10
73	Andre Reed	.10
74	Quinn Early	.10
75	Eric Moulds	.10
76	Darrick Holmes	.10
77	Thurman Thomas	.20
78	Bruce Smith	.10
79	Bryce Paup	.10
80	John Elway	2.00
81	Terrell Davis	2.00
82	Anthony Miller	.10
83	Shannon Sharpe	.10
84	Alfred Williams	.10
85	John Mobley	.10
86	Tory James	.10
87	Steve Atwater	.10
88	Darrien Gordon	.10
89	Mike Alstott	.10
90	Errict Rhett	.20
91	Trent Dilfer	.10
92	Courtney Hawkins	.10
93	Warren Sapp	.10
94	Regan Upshaw	.10
95	Hardy Nickerson	.10
96	Donnie Abraham	.10
97	Larry Centers	.10
98	Aeneas Williams	.10
99	Kent Graham	.10
100	Rob Moore	.10
101	Frank Sanders	.10
102	Leeland McElroy	.10
103	Eric Swann ERR.#103	.10
104	Simeon Rice	.10
105	Seth Joyner	.10
106	Stan Humphries	.10
107	Tony Martin	.10
108	Charlie Jones	.10
109	Andre Coleman	.10
110	Terrell Fletcher	.10
111	Junior Seau	.20
112	Eric Metcalf	.10
113	Chris Penn	.10
114	Marcus Allen	.20
115	Greg Hill	.10
116	Tamarick Vanover	.10
117	Lake Dawson	.10
118	Derrick Thomas	.10
119	Dale Carter	.10
120	Elvis Grbac	.10
121	Aaron Bailey	.10
122	Jim Harbaugh	.10
123	Marshall Faulk	.20
124	Sean Dawkins	.10
125	Marvin Harrison	.50
126	Ken Dilger	.10
127	Tony Bennett	.10
128	Jeff Herrod	.10
129	Chris Gardocki	.10
130	Cary Blanchard	.10
131	Troy Aikman	1.50
132	Emmitt Smith	2.00
133	Sherman Williams	.10
134	Michael Irvin	.20
135	Eric Bjornson	.10
136	Herschel Walker	.10
137	Tony Tolbert	.10
138	Deion Sanders	.50
139	Daryl Johnston	.10
140	Dan Marino	2.00
141	O.J. McDuffie	.10
142	Troy Drayton	.10
143	Karim Abdul-Jabbar	.75
144	Stanley Pritchett	.10
145	Fred Barnett	.10
146	Zach Thomas	.20
147	Sean Wooden	.10
148	Ty Detmer	.10
149	Derrick Witherspoon	
151	Ricky Watters	.20
152	Charlie Garner	.10
153	Chris T. Jones	.10
154	Irving Fryar	.10
155	Mike Mamula	.10
156	Troy Vincent	.10
157	Bobby Taylor	.10

158	Chris Boniol	.10
159	Devin Bush	.10
160	Bert Emanuel	.10
161	Jamal Anderson	.20
162	Terance Mathis	.10
163	Cornelius Bennett	.10
164	Ray Buchanan	.10
165	Chris Chandler	.10
166	Dave Brown	.10
167	Danny Kanell	.10
168	Rodney Hampton	.10
169	Tyrone Wheatley	.10
170	Amani Toomer	.10
171	Chris Calloway	.10
172	Thomas Lewis	.10
173	Phillip Sparks	.10
174	Mark Brunell	1.25
175	Keenan McCardell	.10
176	Willie Jackson	.10
177	Jimmy Smith	.10
178	Pete Mitchell	.10
179	Natrone Means	.20
180	Kevin Hardy	.10
181	Tony Brackens	.10
182	James O. Stewart	.10
183	Wayne Chrebet	.10
184	Keyshawn Johnson	.50
185	Adrian Murrell	.10
186	Neil O'Donnell	.10
187	Hugh Douglas	.10
188	Mo Lewis	.10
189	Marvin Washington	.10
190	Aaron Glenn	.10
191	Barry Sanders	3.00
192	Scott Mitchell	.10
193	Herman Moore	.20
194	Johnnie Morton	.10
195	Glyn Milburn	.10
196	Reggie Brown	.10
197	Jason Hanson	.10
198	Steve McNair	.75
199	Eddie George	1.25
200	Ronnie Harmon	.10
201	Chris Sanders	.10
202	Willie Davis	.10
203	Frank Wycheck	.10
204	Darryll Lewis	.10
205	Blaine Bishop	.10
206	Robert Brooks	.10
207	Brett Favre	3.00
208	Edgar Bennett	.10
209	Dorsey Levens	.20
210	Derrick Mayes	.10
211	Antonio Freeman	.30
212	Mark Chmura	.10
213	Reggie White	.20
214	Gilbert Brown	.10
215	LeRoy Butler	.10
216	Craig Newsome	.10
217	Kerry Collins	1.00
218	Wesley Walls	.10
219	Muhsin Muhammad	.10
220	Anthony Johnson	.10
221	Tshimanga Biakabutuka	.20
222	Kevin Greene	.10
223	Sam Mills	.10
224	John Kasay	.10
225	Michael Barrow	.10
226	Drew Bledsoe	1.25
227	Curtis Martin	.75
228	Terry Glenn	.50
229	Ben Coates	.10
230	Shawn Jefferson	.10
231	Willie McGinest	.10
232	Ted Johnson	.10
233	Lawyer Milloy	.10
234	Ty Law	.10
235	Willie Clay	.10
236	Tim Brown	.10
237	Rickey Dudley	.10
238	Napoleon Kaufman	.10
239	Chester McGlockton	.10
240	Rob Fredrickson	.10
241	Terry McDaniel	.10
242	Desmond Howard	.10
243	Jeff George	.10
244	Isaac Bruce	.20
245	Tony Banks	.50
246	Lawrence Phillips ERR.#247	.20
247	Kevin Carter	.10
248	Roman Phifer	.10
249	Keith Lyle	.10
250	Eddie Kennison	.50
251	Craig Heyward	.10
252	Vinny Testaverde	.10
253	Derrick Alexander	.10
254	Michael Jackson	.10
255	Bam Morris	.10
256	Eric Green	.10
257	Ray Lewis	.10
258	Antonio Langham	.10
259	Michael McCreary	.10
260	Gus Frerotte	.10
261	Terry Allen	.10
262	Brian Mitchell	.10
263	Michael Westbrook	.10
264	Sean Gilbert	.10
265	Rich Owens	.10
266	Ken Harvey	.10
267	Jeff Hostetler	.10
268	Michael Haynes	.10
269	Mario Bates	.10
270	Eric Allen ERR.#273	.10
271	Ray Zellars	.10
272	Joe Johnson	.10
273	Renaldo Turnbull	.10
274	Heath Shuler	.10
275	Daryl Hobbs	.10
276	John Friesz	.10
277	Brian Blades	.10
278	Joey Galloway	.30
279	Chris Warren	.10
280	Lamar Smith	.10
281	Cortez Kennedy	.10
282	Chad Brown	.10
283	Warren Moon	.10
284	Jerome Bettis	.20
285	Charles Johnson	.10
286	Kordell Stewart	1.00
287	Erric Pegram	.10
288	Norm Johnson	.10
289	Levon Kirkland	.10
290	Greg Lloyd	.10
291	Carnell Lake	.10
292	Brad Johnson	.10
293	Cris Carter	.10
294	Jake Reed	.10
295	Robert Smith	.10
296	Derrick Alexander	.10
297	John Randle	.10
298	Dixon Edwards	.10
299	Orlanda Thomas	.10
300	DeWayne Washington	.10

1997 Upper Deck Game Jersey

The 10-card set includes a piece of the player's jersey. The cards were inserted 1:2,500 packs. Cards are numbered with a "GM" prefix.

		MT
Complete Set (10):		3000.
Common Player:		150.00
1	Warren Moon	150.00
2	Joey Galloway	225.00
3	Terrell Davis	375.00
4	Brett Favre	650.00
5	Brett Favre	650.00
6	Reggie White	200.00
7	John Elway	425.00
8	Troy Aikman	350.00
9	Carl Pickens	150.00
10	Herman Moore	150.00

1997 Upper Deck MVP

The 20-card set featured the players on gold Light F/X Cel Chrome cards. Upper Deck produced 100 of each card. Cards are numbered with a "MP" prefix.

		MT
Complete Set (20):		2000.
Common Player:		40.00
Minor Stars:		80.00
1	Jerry Rice	200.00
2	Carl Pickens	40.00
3	Terrell Davis	200.00
4	Mike Alstott	80.00
5	Vinny Testaverde	40.00
6	Junior Seau	40.00
7	Marcus Allen	80.00
8	Troy Aikman	200.00
9	Dan Marino	300.00
10	Ricky Watters	40.00
11	Mark Brunell	200.00
12	Barry Sanders	300.00
13	Eddie George	200.00
14	Brett Favre	350.00
15	Kerry Collins	100.00
16	Drew Bledsoe	200.00
17	Napoleon Kaufman	100.00
18	Isaac Bruce	80.00
19	Terry Allen	40.00
20	Jerome Bettis	40.00

1997 Upper Deck Star Crossed

The 27-card set was inserted 1:27 packs. The player's photo is superimposed over an etched-foil starry background on the Light F/X cards. The cards are numbered on the back with an "SC" prefix.

		MT
Complete Set (30):		70.00
Common Player:		.75
Minor Stars:		1.50
1	Dan Marino	8.00
2	Mark Brunell	4.00
3	Kerry Collins	1.50
4	Jerry Rice	4.00
5	Kevin Greene	.75
6	Curtis Martin	3.00
7	Isaac Bruce	1.50
8	Eddie George	4.00
9	Deion Sanders	2.00
10	Troy Aikman	4.00
11	John Elway	4.00
12	Steve Young	3.00
13	Barry Sanders	6.00
14	Jerome Bettis	1.50
15	Herman Moore	1.50
16	Keyshawn Johnson	1.50
17	Simeon Rice	.75
18	Bruce Smith	.75
19	Drew Bledsoe	4.00
20	Kordell Stewart	4.00
21	Brett Favre	10.00
22	Emmitt Smith	8.00
23	Terrell Davis	4.00
24	Carl Pickens	.75
25	Terry Glenn	1.50
26	Reggie White	1.50
27	Rod Woodson	.75

1997 Upper Deck Team Mates

The 60-card set was inserted 1:4 packs. The die-cut cards feature the player's photo superimposed over a silver etched foil background. The die-cut cards fit together to show the two teammates from each team. The player's name, team, position and Upper Deck logo are printed in gold foil at the bottom. The cards are numbered on the back with a "TM" prefix.

		MT
Complete Set (60):		45.00
Common Player:		.25
Minor Stars:		.50
1	Simeon Rice	.25
2	Eric Swann	.25
3	Jamal Anderson	.50
4	Terance Mathis	.25
5	Vinny Testaverde	.25
6	Michael Jackson	.25
7	Thurman Thomas	.50
8	Bruce Smith	.25
9	Kerry Collins	.50
10	Anthony Johnson	.25
11	Bobby Engram	.25
12	Rashaan Salaam	.50
13	Carl Pickens	.25
14	Jeff Blake	.50
15	Troy Aikman	2.00
16	Emmitt Smith	4.00
17	John Elway	1.25
18	Terrell Davis	2.00
19	Herman Moore	.50
20	Barry Sanders	2.50
21	Brett Favre	5.00
22	Reggie White	.50
23	Eddie George	3.00
24	Steve McNair	1.00
25	Marshall Faulk	.50
26	Jim Harbaugh	.50
27	Mark Brunell	2.00
28	Keenan McCardell	.25
29	Marcus Allen	.50
30	Derrick Thomas	.25
31	Dan Marino	4.00
32	Karim Abdul-Jabbar	.75
33	Cris Carter	.75
34	Jake Reed	.25
35	Curtis Martin	2.00
36	Drew Bledsoe	2.00
37	Mario Bates	.25
38	Ray Zellars	.25
39	Keyshawn Johnson	.50
40	Adrian Murrell	.25
41	Tyrone Wheatley	.25
42	Rodney Hampton	.25
43	Napoleon Kaufman	.25
44	Tim Brown	.25
45	Ricky Watters	.50
46	Chris T. Jones	.25
47	Kordell Stewart	1.50
48	Jerome Bettis	.50
49	Junior Seau	.50
50	Tony Martin	.25
51	Steve Young	1.25
52	Jerry Rice	2.00
53	Joey Galloway	.50
54	Chris Warren	.25
55	Eddie Kennison	.75
56	Tony Banks	.75
57	Mike Alstott	.25
58	Errict Rhett	.50
59	Terry Allen	.25
60	Gus Frerotte	.25

1997 Upper Deck Crash the Game Super Bowl XXXI

Upper Deck produced this special You Crash the Game set for Super Bowl XXXI. The cards were inserted in issues of Sports Collectors Digest. If the player pictured on the card scored a touchdown in the Super Bowl, collectors could redeem the card for a complete parallel set printed on foil stock. The game cards feature a player photo on a purple background with the Super Bowl date printed in gold foil.

		MT
Complete Set (8):		15.00
Common Player:		.75
Comp. Foil Prize Set (9):		10.00
Common Foil Prize:		.75
A1	Drew Bledsoe	1.50
A2	Curtis Martin	1.50
A3	Ben Coates	.75
A4	Terry Glenn	1.50
N1	Brett Favre	3.00
N2	Edgar Bennett	.75
N3	Don Beebe	.75
N4	Antonio Freeman	1.00

1997 Upper Deck Black Diamond

The 180-card, regular-sized set was released in six-card packs. The set was tiered in three levels: 90 single diamond, 60 double diamonds (1:4) and 30 triple diamonds (1:30). A parallel gold version was issued for each card: single diamond (1:15), double diamonds (1:46) and triple diamonds (limited to a production of 50). One insert set was included, Title Quest.

		MT
Complete Set (180):		400.00
Comp. Single Diamond (90):		20.00
Comp. Double Diamond (60):		80.00
Comp. Triple Diamond (30):		320.00
Common Diamond (1-90):		.10
Common Double Diamond (91-150):		.75
Common Triple Diamond (151-180):		4.00
Wax Box:		100.00
1	Alfred Williams	.10
2	Alvin Harper	.10
3	Andre Hastings	.10
4	Andre Reed	.10
5	Anthony Johnson	.10
6	Anthony Miller	.10
7	Bam Morris	.10
8	Bobby Hebert	.10
9	Bobby Taylor	.10
10	Boomer Esiason	.10
11	Brett Perriman	.10
12	Brian Blades	.10
13	Bryan Cox	.10
14	Bryant Young	.10
15	Bryce Paup	.10
16	Carnell Lake	.10
17	Cedric Jones	.10
18	Chad Brown	.10
19	Charlie Garner	.10
20	Chris Chandler	.10
21	Cornelius Bennett	.10
22	Cortez Kennedy	.10
23	Cris Carter	.10
24	Dale Carter	.10
25	Daryl Gardner	.10
26	Derrick Alexander	.10
27	Derrick Mayes	.10
28	Don Beebe	.10
29	Eric Allen	.10
30	Eric Moulds	.10
31	Errict Rhett	.20
32	Frank Sanders	.10
33	Glyn Milburn	.10
34	Henry Ellard	.10
35	Jamal Anderson	.75
36	James O. Stewart	.10
37	Jason Dunn	.10
38	Jerry Rice	2.00
39	Jim Everett	.10
40	Jim Kelly	.10
41	Joey Galloway	1.00
42	John Carney	.10
43	John Elway	1.50
44	John Randle	.10
45	Karim Abdul-Jabbar	2.00
46	Keenan McCardell	.10
47	Ken Dilger	.10
48	Ken Norton	.10
49	Ki-Jana Carter	.10
50	Kordell Stewart	2.00
51	Lawrence Phillips	.10
52	Leslie O'Neal	.10
53	Mark Chmura	.10
54	Marshall Faulk	.25
55	Michael Haynes	.10
56	Michael Irvin	.20
57	Michael Jackson	.10
58	Michael Westbrook	.10
59	Mike Tomczak	.10
60	Napoleon Kaufman	1.00
61	Neil O'Donnell	.10
62	Neil Smith	.10
63	O.J. McDuffie	.10
64	Orlanda Thomas	.10
65	Rashaan Salaam	.20
66	Regan Upshaw	.10
67	Rick Mirer	.10
68	Rob Moore	.10
69	Ronnie Harmon	.10
70	Sam Mills	.10
71	Sean Dawkins	.10
72	Shawn Jefferson	.10
73	Stan Humphries	.10
74	Stepfret Williams	.10
75	Stephen Davis	.10
76	Steve Atwater	.10
77	Terance Mathis	.10
78	Terrell Fletcher	.10
79	Terry Glenn	2.50
80	Terry McDaniel	.10
81	Tony McGee	.10
82	Trent Dilfer	.10
83	Troy Drayton	.10
84	Ty Detmer	.10
85	Tyrone Hughes	.10
86	Walt Harris	.10
87	Wayne Chrebet	.10
88	Wesley Walls	.10
89	Willie Davis	.10
90	Willie McGinest	.10
91	Adrian Murrell	.75
92	Alex Molden	.75
93	Alex Van Dyke	.75
94	Andre Coleman	.75
95	Ben Coates	.75
96	Bobby Engram	.75
97	Bruce Smith	.75
98	Charles Johnson	.75
99	Chris Sanders	.75
100	Chris T. Jones	.75
101	Chris Warren	.75
102	Darnay Scott	.75
103	Dave Brown	.75
104	Derrick Thomas	.75
105	Drew Bledsoe	7.00
106	Edgar Bennett	.75
107	Emmitt Smith	14.00
108	Eric Bjornson	.75
109	Eric Metcalf	.75
110	Garrison Hearst	.75
111	Gus Frerotte	.75
112	Hardy Nickerson	.75
113	Herman Moore	1.50
114	Hugh Douglas	.75
115	Irving Fryar	.75
116	J.J. Stokes	.75
117	Jake Reed	.75
118	Jeff Hostetler	.75
119	Jeff Lewis	.75
120	Jim Harbaugh	.75
121	Johnnie Morton	.75
122	Jonathan Ogden	.75
123	Kevin Carter	.75
124	Kevin Greene	.75
125	Kevin Hardy	.75
126	Leeland McElroy	.75
127	Mike Alstott	1.50
128	Muhsin Muhammad	2.50
129	Natrone Means	.75
130	Quentin Coryatt	.75
131	Ray Lewis	.75
132	Ray Zellars	.75
133	Rickey Dudley	.75
134	Ricky Watters	.75
135	Robert Smith	.75
136	Scott Mitchell	.75
137	Sean Gilbert	.75
138	Shannon Sharpe	.75
139	Simeon Rice	.75
140	Stanley Pritchett	.75
141	Steve McNair	4.00
142	Steve Young	5.00
143	Tamarick Vanover	1.50
144	Terry Allen	.75
145	Thurman Thomas	.75
146	Tony Banks	3.00
147	Tony Martin	.75
148	Tyrone Wheatley	.75
149	Vinny Testaverde	.75
150	Zach Thomas	4.00
151	Amani Toomer	4.00
152	Barry Sanders	40.00
153	Bobby Hoying	4.00
154	Brett Favre	50.00
155	Carl Pickens	4.00
156	Curtis Conway	4.00
157	Curtis Martin	25.00
158	Dan Marino	50.00
159	Deion Sanders	10.00
160	Eddie George	40.00
161	Eddie Kennison	10.00
162	Elvis Grbac	4.00
163	Isaac Bruce	6.00
164	Jeff Blake	8.00
165	Jerome Bettis	4.00
166	Junior Seau	4.00
167	Kerry Collins	20.00
168	Keyshawn Johnson	10.00
169	Larry Centers	4.00
170	Marcus Allen	4.00
171	Mark Brunell	25.00
172	Marvin Harrison	10.00
173	Reggie White	4.00
174	Rodney Hampton	4.00
175	Terrell Davis	25.00
176	Tim Brown	4.00
177	Todd Collins	4.00
178	Troy Aikman	25.00
179	Tim Biakabutuka	4.00
180	Warren Moon	4.00

1997 Upper Deck Black Diamond Gold

Gold parallel cards were available for all 180 cards in the 1997 Black Diamond set. The only difference between regular and gold versions is that the silver foil that is used on regular-issue cards is replaced by gold foil. Gold version of Single Black Diamond cards (1-90) were seeded one per 15 packs, while gold versions of Double Black Diamond cards (91-150) were inserted every 46 packs and gold Triple Black Diamond cards (151-180) were limited to 50 each.

	MT
Complete Set (180):	2900.
Comp. Single Diamond (90):	150.00
Comp. Double Diamond (60):	250.00
Comp. Triple Diamond (30)	2500.
Gold Single Diamonds:	4x-8x
Gold Double Diamonds:	2x-4x
Gold Triple Diamonds:	5x-10x

1997 Upper Deck Black Diamond Title Quest

The 20-card, regular-sized, die-cut set was inserted in packs of 1997 Black Diamond football and was limited to a production of 100. The card fronts feature a square color action shot with a gold border.

		MT
Complete Set (20):		3000.
Common Player:		40.00
Minor Stars:		75.00
1	Dan Marino	350.00
2	Jerry Rice	200.00
3	Drew Bledsoe	200.00
4	Emmitt Smith	350.00
5	Troy Aikman	200.00
6	Steve Young	150.00
7	Brett Favre	350.00
8	John Elway	150.00
9	Barry Sanders	225.00
10	Jerome Bettis	75.00
11	Deion Sanders	100.00
12	Karim Abdul-Jabbar	125.00
13	Terrell Davis	225.00
14	Marshall Faulk	75.00
15	Curtis Martin	225.00
16	Eddie George	250.00
17	Steve McNair	125.00
18	Terry Glenn	75.00
19	Joey Galloway	75.00
20	Keyshawn Johnson	40.00

1997 Upper Deck Legends

Legends is a 208-card set featuring the greatest players from the NFL's past. Besides the 168 regular cards, a 30-card Super Bowl Memories by Walter Iooss, Jr. subset and a 10-card Legendary Leaders subset were added. A parallel of the 168 regular cards featuring player autographs was inserted 1:5. The insert sets are Sign of the Times, Big Game Hunters and Marquee Matchups.

		MT
Complete Set (208):		45.00
Common Player:		.10
Minor Stars:		.20
Wax Box:		125.00
1	Bart Starr	1.50
2	Jim Brown	2.50
3	Joe Namath	2.50
4	Walter Payton	2.50
5	Terry Bradshaw	2.50
6	Franco Harris	.50
7	Dan Fouts	.20
8	Steve Largent	.20
9	Johnny Unitas	1.50
10	Gale Sayers	1.00
11	Roger Staubach	2.50
12	Tony Dorsett	.50
13	Fran Tarkenton	1.00
14	Charley Taylor	.10
15	Ray Nitschke	.20
16	Jim Ringo	.10
17	Dick Butkus	1.00
18	Fred Biletnikoff	.20
19	Lenny Moore	.10
20	Len Dawson	.10
21	Lance Alworth	.10
22	Chuck Bednarik	.10
23	Raymond Berry	.10

24	Donnie Shell	.10
25	Mel Blount	.10
26	Willie Brown	.10
27	Ken Houston	.10
28	Larry Csonka	.50
29	Mike Ditka	.75
30	Art Donovan	.50
31	Sam Huff	.10
32	Lem Barney	.10
33	Hugh McElhenny	.10
34	Otto Graham	.75
35	Joe Greene	.50
36	Mike Rozier	.10
37	Lou Groza	.10
38	Ted Hendricks	.10
39	Elroy Hirsch	.10
40	Paul Hornung	.75
41	Charlie Joiner	.10
42	Deacon Jones	.20
43	Bill Bradley	.10
44	Floyd Little	.10
45	Willie Lanier	.10
46	Bob Lilly	.10
47	Sid Luckman	.10
48	John Mackey	.10
49	Don Maynard	.10
50	Mike McCormack	.10
51	Bobby Mitchell	.10
52	Ron Mix	.10
53	Marion Motley	.10
54	Leo Nomellini	.10
55	Mark Duper	.10
56	Mel Renfro	.10
57	Jim Otto	.10
58	Alan Page	.10
59	Joe Perry	.10
60	Andy Robustelli	.10
61	Lee Roy Selmon	.10
62	Jackie Smith	.10
63	Art Shell	.10
64	Jan Stenerud	.10
65	Gene Upshaw	.10
66	Y.A. Tittle	.10
67	Paul Warfield	.10
68	Kellen Winslow	.20
69	Randy White	.10
70	Larry Wilson	.10
71	Willie Wood	.10
72	Jack Ham	.10
73	Jack Youngblood	.10
74	Dan Abramowicz	.10
75	Dick Anderson	.10
76	Ken Anderson	.10
77	Steve Bartkowski	.10
78	Bill Bergey	.10
79	Rocky Bleier	.10
80	Cliff Branch	.10
81	John Brodie	.10
90	Bobby Bell	.10
82	Billy Cannon	.10
84	Gino Capelletti	.10
85	Harold Carmichael	.10
86	Dave Casper	.10
87	Wes Chandler	.10
88	Todd Christensen	.10
89	Dwight Clark	.10
90	Mark Clayton	.10
91	Cris Collinsworth	.10
92	Roger Craig	.10
93	Randy Cross	.10
94	Isaac Curtis	.10
95	Mike Curtis	.10
96	Ben Davidson	.10
97	Fred Dean	.10
98	Tom Dempsey	.10
99	Eric Dickerson	.10
100	Lynn Dickey	.10
101	John McKay	.10
102	Carl Eller	.10
103	Chuck Foreman	.10
104	Russ Francis	.10
105	Joe Gibbs	.10
106	Gary Garrison	.10
107	Randy Gradishar	.10
108	L.C. Greenwood	.10
109	Roosevelt Grier	.10
110	Steve Grogan	.10
111	Ray Guy	.10
112	John Hadl	.10
113	Jim Hart	.10
114	George Halas	.10
115	Mike Haynes	.10
116	Charlie Hennigan	.10
117	Chuck Howley	.10
118	Harold Jackson	.10
119	Tom Jackson	.10
120	Ron Jaworski	.10
121	John Jefferson	.10
122	Billy Johnson	.10
123	Ed "Too Tall" Jones	.10
124	Jack Kemp	1.50
125	Jim Kiick	.10
126	Billy Kilmer	.10
127	Jerry Kramer	.10
128	Paul Krause	.10
129	Daryle Lamonica	.10
130	Bill Walsh	.10
131	James Lofton	.10
132	Hank Stram	.10
133	Archie Manning	.10
134	Jim Marshall	.10
135	Harvey Martin	.10
136	Tommy McDonald	.10
137	Max McGee	.10
138	Reggie McKenzie	.10
139	Karl Mecklenberg	.10
140	Tom Landry	.20
141	Terry Metcalf	.10

142	Matt Millen	.10
143	Earl Morrall	.10
144	Mercury Morris	.10
145	Chuck Noll	.10
146	Joe Morris	.10
147	Mark Moseley	.10
148	Haven Moses	.10
149	Chuck Muncie	.10
150	Anthony Munoz	.10
151	Tommy Nobis	.10
152	Babe Parilli	.10
153	Drew Pearson	.10
154	Ozzie Newsome	.10
155	Jim Plunkett	.20
156	William Perry	.10
157	Johnny Robinson	.10
158	Ahmad Rashad	.30
159	George Rogers	.10
160	Sterling Sharpe	.10
161	Billy Sims	.10
162	Sid Gillman	.10
163	Mike Singletary	.10
164	Charlie Sanders	.10
165	Bubba Smith	.10
166	Ken Stabler	1.50
167	Freddie Soloman	.10
168	John Stallworth	.10
169	Dwight Stephenson	.10
170	Vince Lombardi	.30
171	Weeb Ewbank	.10
172	Lionel Taylor	.10
173	Otis Taylor	.10
174	Joe Theismann	.20
175	Bob Trumpy	.10
176	Mike Webster	.10
177	Jim Zorn	.10
178	Joe Montana	3.00
179	Packer Defense	.10
180	Bart Starr	.75
181	Max McGee	.10
182	Joe Namath	1.25
183	Johnny Unitas	.75
184	Len Dawson	.10
185	Chuck Howley	.10
186	Roger Staubach	.75
187	Paul Warfield	.10
188	Larry Csonka	.20
189	Fran Tarkenton	.20
190	Joe Green	.10
191	Ken Stabler	.10
192	Fred Biletnikoff	.10
193	Dick Anderson	.10
194	Harvey Martin	.10
195	Tony Dorsett	.20
196	Terry Bradshaw	1.00
197	John Stallworth	.10
198	Franco Harris	.20
199	Ken Anderson	.10
200	Joe Theismann	.10
201	Jim Plunkett	.10
202	Roger Craig	.10
203	William Perry	.10
204	Joe Morris	.10
205	Karl Mecklenberg	.10
206	Joe Montana	1.50
207	Joe Montana	1.50
208	Joe Montana	1.50

1997 Upper Deck Legends Big Game Hunters

This 20-card insert features the top 20 clutch QBs on a die-cut card. They were inserted 1:75. Cards are numbered with the "BG" prefix.

		MT
Complete Set (20):		800.00
Common Player:		20.00
Minor Stars:		40.00
1	Joe Montana	100.00
2	Bart Starr	50.00
3	Roger Staubach	75.00
4	Johnny Unitas	50.00
5	Terry Bradshaw	75.00
6	Ken Stabler	50.00
7	Jim Plunkett	40.00
8	Len Dawson	20.00
9	Fran Tarkenton	50.00
10	Dan Fouts	40.00
11	Daryle Lamonica	20.00
12	Y.A. Tittle	20.00
13	Joe Namath	80.00
14	Kenny Anderson	20.00

1997 Upper Deck Legends Sign of the Times

This 10-card insert features autographs from some of the greatest players ever. The set was limited to less than 1,000 total cards. Cards were numbered with a "ST" prefix.

1997 Upper Deck Legends Marquee Matchups

This 30-card insert features two of the NFL's greatest and creates a classic matchup. The cards use Light F/X technology and were inserted 1:17. Cards are numbered with a "MM" prefix.

		MT
Complete Set (30):		500.00
Common Player:		7.00
Minor Stars:		14.00
1	Joe Namath, Dan Fouts	30.00
2	Johnny Unitas, Joe Namath	40.00
3	Len Dawson, Bart Starr	25.00
4	Roger Staubach, Fran Tarkenton	30.00
5	Terry Bradshaw, Ken Stabler	30.00
6	Joe Montana, Kenny Anderson	45.00
7	Bart Starr, Johnny Unitas	30.00
8	Joe Greene, Jim Kiick	7.00
9	Franco Harris, Walter Payton	35.00
10	Ken Stabler, Dan Fouts	20.00
11	Charlie Joiner, Steve Largent	14.00
12	James Lofton, Drew Pearson	7.00
13	John Brodie, Deacon Jones	7.00
14	Fred Biletnikoff, Don Maynard	7.00
15	Jim Brown, Chuck Bednarik	30.00
16	Ray Nitschke, Gale Sayers	25.00
17	Paul Hornung, Dick Butkus	20.00
18	Joe Montana, Eric Dickerson	45.00
19	Tony Dorsett, Mike Singletary	14.00
20	Billy Sims, Chuck Foreman	7.00
21	Len Dawson, Willie Brown	7.00
22	Johnny Robinson, Larry Wilson	7.00
23	Marion Motley, Raymond Berry	7.00
24	Ron Mix, Jim Otto	7.00
25	Roger Staubach, Terry Bradshaw	35.00
26	Bob Lilly, Billy Kilmer	7.00
27	Ted Hendricks, Russ Francis	7.00
28	Babe Parilli, Jack Kemp	14.00
29	Deacon Jones, Alan Page	7.00
30	Dick Butkus, Ray Nitschke	25.00

1997 Upper Deck Legends Marquee Matchups

		MT
Complete Set (10):		2500.
Common Player:		125.00
1	Joe Montana	400.00
2	Fran Tarkenton	225.00
3	Johnny Unitas	275.00
4	Joe Namath	300.00
5	Terry Bradshaw	250.00
6	Jim Brown	200.00
7	Franco Harris	125.00
8	Walter Payton	300.00
9	Steve Largent	125.00
10	Bart Starr	275.00

1997 Upper Deck UD3

UD3 consists of a 90-card base set made up of three unique subsets. The first 30 cards are Prime Choice Rookies. The rookies are all featured with Light F/X technology. Cards 31-60 are Eye of a Champion. This subset features Cel-Chrome technology. The final subset is Pigskin Heroes. These cards feature two player shots on the front with an embossed, pigskin feel to the card. The inserts for UD3 are Generation eXcitement, Marquee Attraction and Signature Performers.

		MT
Complete Set (90):		75.00
Common Player:		.20
Minor Stars:		.40
Wax Box:		75.00
1	Orlando Pace	.50
2	Walter Jones	.20
3	Tony Gonzalez	1.00
4	David LaFleur	1.00
5	Jim Druckenmiller	4.00
6	Jake Plummer	10.00
7	Pat Barnes	1.00
8	Ike Hilliard	1.50
9	Reidel Anthony	2.00
10	Rae Carruth	1.50
11	Yatil Green	.50
12	Joey Kent	.50
13	Will Blackwell	.50
14	Kevin Lockett	.50
15	Warrick Dunn	4.00
16	Antowain Smith	3.00
17	Troy Davis	.50
18	Byron Hanspard	1.50
19	Corey Dillon	5.00
20	Darnell Autry	1.00
21	Peter Boulware	.20
22	Darrell Russell	.20
23	Kenny Holmes	.20
24	Reinard Wilson	.20
25	Renaldo Wynn	.20
26	Dwayne Rudd	.20
27	James Farrior	.20
28	Shawn Springs	.40
29	Bryant Westbrook	.20
30	Tom Knight	.20
31	Barry Sanders	6.00
32	Brett Favre	6.00
33	Brian Mitchell	.20
34	Curtis Martin	2.00
35	Dan Marino	5.00
36	Deion Sanders	1.50
37	Drew Bledsoe	3.00
38	Eddie George	4.00
39	Edgar Bennett	.20
40	Emmitt Smith	5.00
41	Isaac Bruce	.40
42	Jerome Bettis	.40
43	Jerry Rice	3.00
44	John Elway	3.00
45	Junior Seau	.20
46	Karim Abdul-Jabbar	.50
47	Kerry Collins	.50
48	Marshall Faulk	.50
49	Marvin Harrison	.50
50	Natrone Means	.40
51	Michael Irvin	.40
52	Reggie White	.40
53	Ricky Watters	.40
54	Stan Humphries	.20
55	Steve Young	2.00
56	Terry Glenn	.50
57	Thurman Thomas	.40
58	Tony Martin	.20
59	Troy Aikman	3.00
60	Vinny Testaverde	.20
61	Anthony Johnson	.20
62	Bobby Engram	.20
63	Carl Pickens	.20
64	Cris Carter	.20
65	Derrick Witherspoon	.20
66	Eddie Kennison	.50
67	Eric Swann	.20
68	Gus Frerotte	.20
69	Herman Moore	.40
70	Irving Fryar	.20
71	Jamal Anderson	.40
72	Jeff Blake	.40
73	Jim Harbaugh	.20
74	Joey Galloway	.40
75	Keenan McCardell	.20
76	Kevin Greene	.20
77	Keyshawn Johnson	.50
78	Kordell Stewart	3.00
79	Marcus Allen	.40
80	Mario Bates	.20
81	Mark Brunell	3.00
82	Michael Jackson	.20
83	Mike Alstott	.40
84	Scott Mitchell	.20
85	Shannon Sharpe	.20
86	Steve McNair	2.50
87	Terrell Davis	3.00
88	Tim Brown	.20
89	Ty Detmer	.20
90	Tyrone Wheatley	.20

1997 Upper Deck UD3 Generation Excitement

This 15-card insert features the NFL's most spectacular players. Each card has a die-cut, Light F/X design and features two action shots of the player on the front. The cards were inserted 1:11. Cards are numbered with a "GE" prefix.

		MT
Complete Set (15):		130.00
Common Player:		3.00
1	Jerry Rice	15.00
2	Carl Pickens	3.00
3	Curtis Conway	3.00
4	John Elway	15.00
5	Ike Hilliard	8.00
6	Marvin Harrison	5.00
7	Emmitt Smith	25.00
8	Barry Sanders	20.00
9	Deion Sanders	7.00
10	Rae Carruth	7.00
11	Curtis Martin	12.00
12	Terry Glenn	6.00
13	Napoleon Kaufman	5.00
14	Kordell Stewart	15.00
15	Jake Plummer	10.00

1997 Upper Deck UD3 Marquee Attraction

Marquee Attraction features the most collectible NFL players in a 15-card insert set. The cards are die-cut and feature Cel-Chrome technology. They were inserted 1:144 in UD3. Cards were numbered with a "MA" prefix.

		MT
Complete Set (15):		425.00
Common Player:		10.00
Minor Stars:		20.00
Inserted 1:144		
1	Steve Young	30.00
2	Troy Aikman	35.00
3	Keyshawn Johnson	20.00
4	Marcus Allen	10.00
5	Dan Marino	50.00
6	Mark Brunell	35.00
7	Eddie George	35.00
8	Brett Favre	70.00

9 Drew Bledsoe 35.00
10 Eddie Kennison 10.00
11 Terrell Davis 50.00
12 Warrick Dunn 35.00
13 Yatil Green 10.00
14 Troy Davis 10.00
15 Shawn Springs 10.00

1997 Upper Deck UD3 Signature Performers

Signature Performers is a four-card insert featuring special electric technology. The cards were autographed by the players in the set: Curtis Martin, Troy Aikman, Marcus Allen and Eddie George. The cards were inserted 1:1,500. Cards are numbered with a "PF" prefix.

		MT
Complete Set (4):		1100.
Common Player:		125.00
1	Curtis Martin	250.00
2	Troy Aikman	350.00
3	Marcus Allen	125.00
4	Eddie George	450.00

1998 UD3

UD Cubed Football consists of a 270-card base set built from three 30-card subsets. Each subset is printed on three different technologies. Future Shock features rookies, Next Wave has young stars and Upper Realm highlights the established stars. Future Shock Embossed cards are inserted 1:6, Light F/X is seeded 1:12 and Rainbow Foil cards are found 1:1.33. Next Wave Embossed cards are inserted 1:4, Light F/X are found 1:1.5 and Rainbow Foil cards are inserted 1:12. Upper Realm Embossed cards are seeded 1:1.25, Light F/X are found 1:6 and Rainbow Foil cards are inserted 1:24. Die-cut versions of each card were also produced.

	MT
Complete Set (270):	750.00
Common Player (1-30):	2.50
#1-30 Inserted 1:6	
Common Player (31-60):	1.25
#31-60 Inserted 1:4	
Common Player (61-90):	.50
#61-90 Inserted 1:1.25	
Common Player (91-120):	5.00
#91-120 Inserted 1:12	
Common Player (121-150):	.50
#121-150 Inserted 1:1.5	
Common Player (151-180):	2.50
#151-180 Inserted 1:6	
Common Player (181-210):	.75
#181-210 Inserted 1:1.33	
Common Player (211-240):	5.00
#211-240 Inserted 1:12	
Common Player (241-270):	7.00
#241-270 Inserted 1:24	
Wax Box:	75.00

1 Peyton Manning 25.00
2 Ryan Leaf 14.00
3 Andre Wadsworth 5.00
4 Charles Woodson 12.00
5 Curtis Enis 12.00
6 Grant Wistrom 2.50
7 Greg Ellis 2.50
8 Fred Taylor 12.00
9 Duane Starks 5.00
10 Keith Brooking 2.50
11 Takeo Spikes 5.00
12 Jason Peter 5.00
13 Anthony Simmons 5.00
14 Kevin Dyson 8.00
15 Brian Simmons 5.00
16 Robert Edwards 10.00
17 Randy Moss 40.00
18 John Avery 8.00
19 Marcus Nash 8.00
20 Jerome Pathon 5.00
21 Jacquez Green 8.00
22 Robert Holcombe 8.00
23 Patrick Johnson 5.00
24 Germane Crowell 8.00
25 Joe Jurevicius 5.00
26 Skip Hicks 8.00
27 Ahman Green 8.00
28 Brian Griese 8.00
29 Hines Ward 8.00
30 Tavian Banks 10.00
31 Warrick Dunn 8.00
32 Jake Plummer 8.00
33 Derrick Mayes 1.25
34 Napoleon Kaufman 2.50
35 Jamal Anderson 1.25
36 Marvin Harrison 1.25
37 Jermaine Lewis 1.25
38 Corey Dillon 6.00
39 Keyshawn Johnson 2.50
40 Mike Alstott 2.50
41 Bobby Hoying 2.50
42 Keenan McCardell 1.25
43 Will Blackwell 1.25
44 Peter Boulware 1.25
45 Tony Banks 2.50
46 Rod Smith 1.25
47 Tony Gonzalez 1.25
48 Antowain Smith 4.00
49 Rae Carruth 1.25
50 J.J. Stokes 1.25
51 Brad Johnson 2.50
52 Shawn Springs 1.25
53 Elvis Grbac 1.25
54 Jimmy Smith 2.50
55 Terry Glenn 2.50
56 Tiki Barber 1.25
57 Gus Frerotte 1.25
58 Danny Wuerffel 1.25
59 Fred Lane 2.50
60 Todd Collins 1.25
61 Barry Sanders 8.00
62 Troy Aikman 4.00
63 Dan Marino 6.00
64 Drew Bledsoe 4.00
65 Dorsey Levens 1.00
66 Jerome Bettis 1.00
67 John Elway 4.00
68 Steve Young 3.00
69 Terrell Davis 4.00
70 Kordell Stewart 3.00
71 Jeff George 1.00
72 Emmitt Smith 6.00
73 Irving Fryar .50
74 Brett Favre 8.00
75 Eddie George 3.00
76 Terry Allen .50
77 Warren Moon 1.00
78 Mark Brunell 3.00
79 Robert Smith 1.00
80 Jerry Rice 4.00
81 Tim Brown 1.00
82 Carl Pickens 1.00
83 Joey Galloway 1.00
84 Herman Moore 1.00
85 Adrian Murrell 1.00
86 Thurman Thomas 1.00
87 Robert Brooks .50
88 Michael Irvin 1.00
89 Andre Rison 1.00
90 Marshall Faulk 1.00
91 Peyton Manning 45.00
92 Ryan Leaf 25.00
93 Andre Wadsworth 8.00
94 Charles Woodson 20.00
95 Curtis Enis 20.00
96 Grant Wistrom 5.00
97 Greg Ellis 5.00
98 Fred Taylor 20.00
99 Duane Starks 8.00
100 Keith Brooking 8.00
101 Takeo Spikes 8.00
102 Jason Peter 8.00
103 Anthony Simmons 8.00
104 Kevin Dyson 12.00
105 Brian Simmons 5.00
106 Robert Edwards 15.00
107 Randy Moss 60.00
108 John Avery 12.00
109 Marcus Nash 12.00
110 Jerome Pathon 8.00
111 Jacquez Green 12.00
112 Robert Holcombe 12.00
113 Patrick Johnson 8.00
114 Germane Crowell 8.00
115 Joe Jurevicius 8.00
116 Skip Hicks 8.00
117 Ahman Green 12.00
118 Brian Griese 12.00
119 Hines Ward 12.00
120 Tavian Banks 15.00
121 Warrick Dunn 4.00
122 Jake Plummer 4.00
123 Derrick Mayes .50
124 Napoleon Kaufman 1.00
125 Jamal Anderson 1.00
126 Marvin Harrison 1.00
127 Jermaine Lewis .50
128 Corey Dillon 3.00
129 Keyshawn Johnson 1.00
130 Mike Alstott 1.00
131 Bobby Hoying 1.00
132 Keenan McCardell .50
133 Will Blackwell .50
134 Peter Boulware .50
135 Tony Banks 1.00
136 Rod Smith .50
137 Tony Gonzalez .50
138 Antowain Smith 2.00
139 Rae Carruth .50
140 J.J. Stokes .50
141 Brad Johnson 1.00
142 Shawn Springs .50
143 Elvis Grbac .50
144 Jimmy Smith 1.00
145 Terry Glenn 1.00
146 Tiki Barber 1.00
147 Gus Frerotte .50
148 Danny Wuerffel .50
149 Fred Lane 1.00
150 Todd Collins .50
151 Barry Sanders 20.00
152 Troy Aikman 10.00
153 Dan Marino 15.00
154 Drew Bledsoe 10.00
155 Dorsey Levens 5.00
156 Jerome Bettis 5.00
157 John Elway 10.00
158 Steve Young 8.00
159 Terrell Davis 10.00
160 Kordell Stewart 8.00
161 Jeff George 5.00
162 Emmitt Smith 15.00
163 Irving Fryar 2.50
164 Brett Favre 20.00
165 Eddie George 10.00
166 Terry Allen 2.50
167 Warren Moon 5.00
168 Mark Brunell 8.00
169 Robert Smith 5.00
170 Jerry Rice 10.00
171 Tim Brown 5.00
172 Carl Pickens 5.00
173 Joey Galloway 5.00
174 Herman Moore 5.00
175 Adrian Murrell 5.00
176 Thurman Thomas 5.00
177 Robert Brooks 2.50
178 Michael Irvin 5.00
179 Andre Rison 2.50
180 Marshall Faulk 5.00
181 *Peyton Manning* 10.00
182 *Ryan Leaf* 6.00
183 *Andre Wadsworth* 1.50
184 *Charles Woodson* 5.00
185 *Curtis Enis* 5.00
186 *Grant Wistrom* .75
187 *Greg Ellis* 1.50
188 *Fred Taylor* 5.00
189 *Duane Starks* 1.50
190 *Keith Brooking* 1.50
191 *Takeo Spikes* 1.50
192 *Jason Peter* 1.50
193 *Anthony Simmons* 1.50
194 *Kevin Dyson* 3.00
195 *Brian Simmons* 1.50
196 *Robert Edwards* 4.00
197 *Randy Moss* 15.00
198 *John Avery* 3.00
199 *Marcus Nash* 3.00
200 *Jerome Pathon* 1.50
201 *Jacquez Green* 3.00
202 *Robert Holcombe* 3.00
203 *Patrick Johnson* 1.50
204 *Germane Crowell* 1.50
205 *Joe Jurevicius* 1.50
206 *Skip Hicks* 1.50
207 *Ahman Green* 3.00
208 *Brian Griese* 3.00
209 *Hines Ward* 3.00
210 *Tavian Banks* 4.00
211 Warrick Dunn 18.00
212 Jake Plummer 18.00
213 Derrick Mayes 4.00
214 Napoleon Kaufman 6.00
215 Jamal Anderson 6.00
216 Marvin Harrison 4.00
217 Jermaine Lewis 4.00
218 Corey Dillon 12.00
219 Keyshawn Johnson 6.00
220 Mike Alstott 6.00
221 Bobby Hoying 6.00
222 Keenan McCardell 4.00
223 Will Blackwell 4.00
224 Peter Boulware 4.00
225 Tony Banks 6.00
226 Rod Smith 6.00
227 Tony Gonzalez 6.00
228 Antowain Smith 10.00
229 Rae Carruth 4.00
230 J.J. Stokes 6.00
231 Brad Johnson 6.00
232 Shawn Springs 4.00
233 Elvis Grbac 4.00
234 Jimmy Smith 6.00
235 Terry Glenn 6.00
236 Tiki Barber 6.00
237 Gus Frerotte 4.00
238 Danny Wuerffel 4.00
239 Fred Lane 6.00
240 Todd Collins 4.00
241 Barry Sanders 50.00
242 Troy Aikman 25.00
243 Dan Marino 40.00
244 Drew Bledsoe 25.00
245 Dorsey Levens 10.00
246 Jerome Bettis 10.00
247 John Elway 25.00
248 Steve Young 18.00
249 Terrell Davis 25.00
250 Kordell Stewart 20.00
251 Jeff George 10.00
252 Emmitt Smith 40.00
253 Irving Fryar 7.00
254 Brett Favre 50.00
255 Eddie George 20.00
256 Terry Allen 7.00
257 Warren Moon 10.00
258 Mark Brunell 20.00
259 Robert Smith 10.00
260 Jerry Rice 25.00
261 Tim Brown 7.00
262 Carl Pickens 7.00
263 Joey Galloway 10.00
264 Herman Moore 10.00
265 Adrian Murrell 7.00
266 Thurman Thomas 7.00
267 Robert Brooks 7.00
268 Michael Irvin 10.00
269 Andre Rison 7.00
270 Marshall Faulk 10.00

1998 UD3 Die Cuts

Die-cut versions were produced of each UD Cubed base card. The Embossed Die-Cut parallel is numbered to 2,000, Light F/X Die-Cut parallel cards are numbered to 1,000 and Rainbow Foil Die-Cuts are numbered to 100.

	MT
Common Player (1-90):	3.00
Production 2,000 Sets	
Common Player (91-180):	5.00
Production 1,000 Sets	
Common Player (181-270):	20.00
Production 100 Sets	

1 Peyton Manning 35.00
2 Ryan Leaf 12.00
3 Andre Wadsworth 5.00
4 Charles Woodson 15.00
5 Curtis Enis 15.00
6 Grant Wistrom 3.00
7 Greg Ellis 3.00
8 Fred Taylor 15.00
9 Duane Starks 6.00
10 Keith Brooking 3.00
11 Takeo Spikes 6.00
12 Jason Peter 6.00
13 Anthony Simmons 6.00
14 Kevin Dyson 10.00
15 Brian Simmons 6.00
16 Robert Edwards 10.00
17 Randy Moss 40.00
18 John Avery 10.00
19 Marcus Nash 10.00
20 Jerome Pathon 6.00
21 Jacquez Green 10.00
22 Robert Holcombe 10.00
23 Patrick Johnson 6.00
24 Germane Crowell 6.00
25 Joe Jurevicius 6.00
26 Skip Hicks 6.00
27 Ahman Green 10.00
28 Brian Griese 10.00
29 Hines Ward 10.00
30 Tavian Banks 12.00
31 Warrick Dunn 12.00
32 Jake Plummer 12.00
33 Derrick Mayes 3.00
34 Napoleon Kaufman 6.00
35 Jamal Anderson 6.00
36 Marvin Harrison 3.00
37 Jermaine Lewis 3.00
38 Corey Dillon 10.00
39 Keyshawn Johnson 6.00
40 Mike Alstott 6.00
41 Bobby Hoying 6.00
42 Keenan McCardell 3.00
43 Will Blackwell 3.00
44 Peter Boulware 3.00
45 Tony Banks 6.00
46 Rod Smith 3.00
47 Tony Gonzalez 3.00
48 Antowain Smith 6.00
49 Rae Carruth 3.00
50 J.J. Stokes 6.00
51 Brad Johnson 6.00
52 Shawn Springs 6.00
53 Elvis Grbac 6.00
54 Jimmy Smith 6.00
55 Terry Glenn 6.00
56 Tiki Barber 3.00
57 Gus Frerotte 3.00
58 Danny Wuerffel 3.00
59 Fred Lane 6.00
60 Todd Collins 3.00
61 Barry Sanders 25.00
62 Troy Aikman 12.00
63 Dan Marino 20.00
64 Drew Bledsoe 12.00
65 Dorsey Levens 6.00
66 Jerome Bettis 6.00
67 John Elway 12.00
68 Steve Young 12.00
69 Terrell Davis 12.00
70 Kordell Stewart 10.00
71 Jeff George 6.00
72 Emmitt Smith 20.00
73 Irving Fryar 3.00
74 Brett Favre 25.00
75 Eddie George 10.00
76 Terry Allen 3.00
77 Warren Moon 6.00
78 Mark Brunell 10.00
79 Robert Smith 6.00
80 Jerry Rice 12.00
81 Tim Brown 6.00
82 Carl Pickens 6.00
83 Joey Galloway 6.00
84 Herman Moore 6.00
85 Adrian Murrell 6.00
86 Thurman Thomas 6.00
87 Robert Brooks 3.00
88 Michael Irvin 6.00
89 Andre Rison 3.00
90 Marshall Faulk 6.00
91 Peyton Manning 50.00
92 Ryan Leaf 35.00
93 Andre Wadsworth 10.00
94 Charles Woodson 20.00
95 Curtis Enis 20.00
96 Grant Wistrom 5.00
97 Greg Ellis 10.00
98 Fred Taylor 20.00
99 Duane Starks 8.00
100 Keith Brooking 10.00
101 Takeo Spikes 10.00
102 Jason Peter 10.00
103 Anthony Simmons 10.00
104 Kevin Dyson 12.00
105 Brian Simmons 5.00
106 Robert Edwards 15.00
107 Randy Moss 55.00
108 John Avery 12.00
109 Marcus Nash 12.00
110 Jerome Pathon 10.00
111 Jacquez Green 15.00
112 Robert Holcombe 15.00
113 Patrick Johnson 10.00
114 Germane Crowell 10.00
115 Joe Jurevicius 10.00
116 Skip Hicks 10.00
117 Ahman Green 15.00
118 Brian Griese 15.00
119 Hines Ward 15.00
120 Tavian Banks 15.00
121 Warrick Dunn 20.00
122 Jake Plummer 20.00
123 Derrick Mayes 5.00
124 Napoleon Kaufman 10.00
125 Jamal Anderson 8.00
126 Marvin Harrison 8.00
127 Jermaine Lewis 5.00
128 Corey Dillon 15.00
129 Keyshawn Johnson 8.00
130 Mike Alstott 8.00
131 Bobby Hoying 8.00
132 Keenan McCardell 5.00
133 Will Blackwell 5.00
134 Peter Boulware 5.00
135 Tony Banks 8.00
136 Rod Smith 5.00
137 Tony Gonzalez 5.00
138 Antowain Smith 12.00
139 Rae Carruth 5.00
140 J.J. Stokes 5.00
141 Brad Johnson 8.00
142 Shawn Springs 5.00
143 Elvis Grbac 5.00
144 Jimmy Smith 8.00
145 Terry Glenn 8.00
146 Tiki Barber 8.00
147 Gus Frerotte 5.00
148 Danny Wuerffel 5.00
149 Fred Lane 8.00
150 Todd Collins 5.00
151 Barry Sanders 25.00
152 Troy Aikman 25.00
153 Dan Marino 40.00
154 Drew Bledsoe 25.00
155 Dorsey Levens 8.00
156 Jerome Bettis 8.00
157 John Elway 25.00
158 Steve Young 20.00
159 Terrell Davis 25.00
160 Kordell Stewart 20.00
161 Jeff George 8.00
162 Emmitt Smith 40.00
163 Irving Fryar 5.00
164 Brett Favre 50.00
165 Eddie George 20.00
166 Terry Allen 5.00
167 Warren Moon 8.00
168 Mark Brunell 8.00
169 Robert Smith 8.00
170 Jerry Rice 25.00
171 Tim Brown 8.00
172 Carl Pickens 8.00
173 Joey Galloway 8.00
174 Herman Moore 8.00
175 Adrian Murrell 8.00
176 Thurman Thomas 8.00
177 Robert Brooks 8.00
178 Michael Irvin 8.00
179 Andre Rison 5.00
180 Marshall Faulk 8.00
181 Peyton Manning 200.00
182 Ryan Leaf 100.00
183 Andre Wadsworth 40.00
184 Charles Woodson 60.00
185 Curtis Enis 75.00
186 Grant Wistrom 20.00
187 Greg Ellis 20.00
188 Fred Taylor 75.00
189 Duane Starks 20.00
190 Keith Brooking 20.00
191 Takeo Spikes 20.00
192 Jason Peter 20.00
193 Anthony Simmons 20.00
194 Kevin Dyson 50.00
195 Brian Simmons 20.00
196 Robert Edwards 50.00
197 Randy Moss 300.00
198 John Avery 50.00
199 Marcus Nash 50.00
200 Jerome Pathon 50.00
201 Jacquez Green 50.00
202 Robert Holcombe 60.00
203 Patrick Johnson 20.00
204 Germane Crowell 40.00
205 Joe Jurevicius 20.00
206 Skip Hicks 40.00
207 Ahman Green 50.00
208 Brian Griese 50.00
209 Hines Ward 50.00
210 Tavian Banks 50.00
211 Warrick Dunn 85.00
212 Jake Plummer 85.00
213 Derrick Mayes 20.00
214 Napoleon Kaufman 40.00
215 Jamal Anderson 30.00
216 Marvin Harrison 30.00
217 Jermaine Lewis 20.00
218 Corey Dillon 60.00
219 Keyshawn Johnson 30.00
220 Mike Alstott 30.00
221 Bobby Hoying 30.00
222 Keenan McCardell 20.00
223 Will Blackwell 20.00
224 Peter Boulware 20.00
225 Tony Banks 30.00
226 Rod Smith 20.00
227 Tony Gonzalez 20.00
228 Antowain Smith 50.00
229 Rae Carruth 20.00
230 J.J. Stokes 20.00
231 Brad Johnson 30.00
232 Shawn Springs 20.00
233 Elvis Grbac 30.00
234 Jimmy Smith 30.00
235 Terry Glenn 30.00
236 Tiki Barber 30.00
237 Gus Frerotte 20.00
238 Danny Wuerffel 30.00
239 Fred Lane 30.00
240 Todd Collins 20.00
241 Barry Sanders 200.00
242 Troy Aikman 100.00
243 Dan Marino 175.00
244 Drew Bledsoe 100.00
245 Dorsey Levens 30.00
246 Jerome Bettis 30.00
247 John Elway 100.00
248 Steve Young 85.00
249 Terrell Davis 100.00
250 Kordell Stewart 100.00
251 Jeff George 30.00
252 Emmitt Smith 175.00
253 Irving Fryar 30.00
254 Brett Favre 200.00
255 Eddie George 85.00
256 Terry Allen 30.00
257 Warren Moon 30.00
258 Mark Brunell 100.00
259 Robert Smith 30.00
260 Jerry Rice 100.00
261 Tim Brown 30.00
262 Carl Pickens 30.00
263 Joey Galloway 30.00
264 Herman Moore 30.00
265 Adrian Murrell 30.00
266 Thurman Thomas 30.00
267 Robert Brooks 20.00
268 Michael Irvin 30.00
269 Andre Rison 20.00
270 Marshall Faulk 30.00

1998 UD Choice Preview

Upper Deck released a 55-card UD Choice Preview set at retail outlets. The set consists of cards from the regular 1998 UD Choice set.

		MT
Complete Set (55):		10.00
Common Player:		.10
Minor Stars:		.20
Wax Box:		10.00
2	Rob Moore	.10
4	Larry Centers	.10
8	Jamal Anderson	.50
12	Byron Hanspard	.10
14	Jermaine Lewis	.10
20	Eric Moulds	.20
22	Bruce Smith	.10
24	Rae Carruth	.10
28	Winslow Oliver	.10
32	Bryan Cox	.10

#	Player	MT
35	Curtis Conway	.20
39	Jeff Blake	.10
40	Carl Pickens	.20
49	Deion Sanders	.30
53	Ed McCaffrey	.20
55	John Mobley	.10
58	Scott Mitchell	.10
62	Bryant Westbrook	.10
67	Reggie White	.20
70	LeRoy Butler	.10
72	Marshall Faulk	.50
76	Quentin Coryatt	.10
77	Keenan McCardell	.10
80	Jimmy Smith	.20
84	Andre Rison	.10
86	Tony Gonzalez	.10
92	Yatil Green	.10
96	Brad Johnson	.30
98	Jake Reed	.10
103	Troy Davis	.10
104	Andre Hastings	.10
110	Terry Glenn	.20
111	Ben Coates	.20
115	Danny Kanell	.10
119	Tiki Barber	.20
122	Glenn Foley	.20
124	Adrian Murrell	.20
129	Jeff George	.20
131	Darrell Russell	.10
136	Irving Fryar	.10
137	Mike Mamula	.10
143	Levon Kirkland	.10
147	Greg Lloyd	.10
150	Orlando Pace	.20
151	Isaac Bruce	.20
155	Eric Metcalf	.10
157	Tony Martin	.10
161	Merton Hanks	.10
165	J.J. Stokes	.20
168	Chad Brown	.10
173	Trent Dilfer	.30
175	Warren Sapp	.10
180	Steve McNair	.50
186	Gus Frerotte	.10
191	Chris Dishman	.10

1998 UD Choice

UD Choice was released in two series. Series One consists of a 255-card base set. The set has 165 regular cards featuring white borders and 27 full-bleed regular cards. Subsets include 30 Rookie Class cards and 30 Draw Your Own Trading Card contest winners. Three checklists round out the set. The base set is paralleled in Choice Reserve and Prime Choice Reserve. Inserts include StarQuest and Mini Bobbing Head cards. A Draw Your Own Trading Card entry was inserted in each pack. UD Choice Series Two consists of a 183-card base set, featuring the 30-card Domination Next subset (1:4). Series Two also has Choice Reserve and Prime Choice Reserve parallels. Inserts include NFL GameDay '99, StarQuest-RookQuest and Domination Next SE.

		MT
Complete Set (438):		70.00
Complete Series 1 (255):		35.00
Complete Series 2 (183):		35.00
Common Player:		.10
Minor Stars:		.20
Common Domination Next:		.75
Inserted 1:4		
Domination Next SE:		3x
Production 2,000 Sets		
Series 1 Wax Box:		40.00
Series 2 Wax Box:		40.00
1	Jake Plummer	.75
2	Rob Moore	.10
3	Simeon Rice	.10
4	Larry Centers	.10
5	Aeneas Williams	.10
6	Chris Gedney	.10
7	Jamal Anderson	.20
8	Michael Booker	.10
9	Ronnie Bradford	.10
10	Cornelius Bennett	.10
11	Terance Mathis	.10

#	Player	MT
12	Byron Hanspard	.20
13	Peter Boulware	.10
14	Jonathan Ogden	.10
15	Jermaine Lewis	.10
16	Tony Siragusa	.10
17	Brian Kinchen	.10
18	Michael Jackson	.10
19	Doug Flutie	.50
20	Eric Moulds	.10
21	Antowain Smith	.40
22	Bruce Smith	.10
23	Jay Riemersma	.10
24	Ruben Brown	.10
25	Fred Lane	.20
26	Rae Carruth	.10
27	Wesley Walls	.10
28	Winslow Oliver	.10
29	Tyrone Poole	.10
30	Lamar Lathon	.10
31	Anthony Johnson	.10
32	Erik Kramer	.10
33	Darnell Autry	.20
34	Bobby Engram	.10
35	Curtis Conway	.20
36	Jeff Jaeger	.10
37	Chris Penn	.10
38	Corey Dillon	.50
39	Jeff Blake	.20
40	Carl Pickens	.20
41	Ki-Jana Carter	.10
42	Reinard Wilson	.10
43	Tremain Mack	.10
44	Troy Aikman	1.00
45	Larry Allen	.10
46	Darren Woodson	.10
47	Anthony Miller	.10
48	Erik Williams	.10
49	Deion Sanders	.50
50	Rick Cunningham	.10
51	John Elway	1.00
52	Steve Atwater	.10
53	Ed McCaffrey	.10
54	Maa Tanuvasa	.10
55	John Mobley	.10
56	Bill Romanowski	.10
57	Shannon Sharpe	.20
58	Scott Mitchell	.10
59	Jason Hansen	.10
60	Herman Moore	.20
61	Luther Elliss	.10
62	Bryant Westbrook	.10
63	Kevin Abrams	.10
64	Brett Favre	2.00
65	Gilbert Brown	.10
66	Antonio Freeman	.20
67	Reggie White	.20
68	Mark Chmura	.10
69	Seth Joyner	.10
70	LeRoy Butler	.10
71	Marvin Harrison	.20
72	Marshall Faulk	.20
73	Ken Dilger	.10
74	Steve Morrison	.10
75	Zack Crockett	.10
76	Quentin Coryatt	.10
77	Keenan McCardell	.10
78	Mark Brunell	.75
79	Renaldo Wynn	.10
80	Jimmy Smith	.10
81	James O. Stewart	.10
82	Kevin Hardy	.10
83	Marcus Allen	.20
84	Andre Rison	.10
85	Pete Stoyanovich	.10
86	Tony Gonzalez	.10
87	Derrick Thomas	.10
88	Rich Gannon	.10
89	Elvis Grbac	.10
90	Dan Marino	1.50
91	Lawrence Phillips	.10
92	Yatil Green	.20
93	Zach Thomas	.10
94	Olindo Mare	.10
95	Charles Jordan	.10
96	Brad Johnson	.20
97	Cris Carter	.20
98	Jake Reed	.10
99	Ed McDaniel	.10
100	Dwayne Rudd	.10
101	Leroy Hoard	.10
102	Chris Wuerffel	.10
103	Troy Davis	.10
104	Andre Hastings	.10
105	Nicky Savoie	.10
106	Willie Roaf	.10
107	Ray Zellars	.10
108	Tedy Bruschi	.10
109	Drew Bledsoe	1.00
110	Terry Glenn	.20
111	Ben Coates	.20
112	Willie Clay	.10
113	Chris Slade	.10
114	Larry Whigham	.10
115	Danny Kanell	.10
116	Jessie Armstead	.10
117	Phillip Sparks	.10
118	Michael Strahan	.10
119	Tiki Barber	.20
120	Charles Way	.10
121	Chris Calloway	.10
122	Glenn Foley	.10
123	Wayne Chrebet	.20
124	Kyle Brady	.10
125	Keyshawn Johnson	.20
126	Aaron Glenn	.10
127	James Farrior	.10
128	Victor Green	.10
129	Jeff George	.20
130	Rickey Dudley	.10
131	Darrell Russell	.10

#	Player	MT
132	Tim Brown	.10
133	James Trapp	.10
134	Napoleon Kaufman	.40
135	Bobby Hoying	.10
136	Irving Fryar	.10
137	Mike Mamula	.10
138	Troy Vincent	.10
139	Bobby Taylor	.10
140	Chris Boniol	.10
141	Jerome Bettis	.20
142	Charles Johnson	.10
143	Levon Kirkland	.10
144	Carnell Lake	.10
145	Will Blackwell	.10
146	Tim Lester	.10
147	Greg Lloyd	.10
148	Tony Banks	.20
149	Ryan McNeil	.10
150	Orlando Pace	.10
151	Isaac Bruce	.20
152	Eddie Kennison	.20
153	Leslie O'Neal	.10
154	Darren Bennett	.10
155	Natrone Means	.20
156	Junior Seau	.20
157	Tony Martin	.10
158	Rodney Harrison	.10
159	Freddie Jones	.10
160	Terrell Owens	.20
161	Merton Hanks	.10
162	Chris Doleman	.10
163	Steve Young	.50
164	Chuck Levy	.10
165	J.J. Stokes	.20
166	Ken Norton	.10
167	Bennie Blades	.10
168	Chad Brown	.10
169	Warren Moon	.20
170	Cortez Kennedy	.10
171	Darryl Williams	.10
172	Michael Sinclair	.10
173	Trent Dilfer	.20
174	Mike Alstott	.40
175	Warren Sapp	.10
176	Reidel Anthony	.20
177	Derrick Brooks	.10
178	Horace Copeland	.10
179	Hardy Nickerson	.10
180	Steve McNair	.50
181	Anthony Dorsett	.10
182	Chris Sanders	.10
183	Derrick Mason	.10
184	Eddie George	1.00
185	Blaine Bishop	.10
186	Gus Frerotte	.10
187	Terry Allen	.10
188	Darrell Green	.10
189	Ken Harvey	.10
190	Matt Turk	.10
191	Chris Dishman	.10
192	Keith Thibodeaux	.10
193	Peyton Manning	5.00
194	Ryan Leaf	3.00
195	Charles Woodson	2.50
196	Andre Wadsworth	.30
197	Keith Brooking	.10
198	Jason Peter	.30
199	Curtis Enis	2.50
200	Randy Moss	10.00
201	Tre Thomas	.10
202	Robert Edwards	2.00
203	Kevin Dyson	1.00
204	Fred Taylor	2.50
205	Corey Chavous	.10
206	Grant Wistrom	.10
207	Vonnie Holliday	.40
208	Brian Simmons	.50
209	Jeremy Staat	.10
210	Alonzo Mayes	.10
211	Anthony Simmons	.10
212	Sam Cowart	.10
213	Flozell Adams	.10
214	Terry Fair	.10
215	Germane Crowell	.40
216	Robert Holcombe	2.00
217	Jacquez Green	2.00
218	Skip Hicks	.50
219	Takeo Spikes	.40
220	Az-Zahir Hakim	.10
221	Ahman Green	2.00
222	Chris Fuamatu-Ma'afal	.10

#	Player	MT
223	Darnell Autry	.10
224	John Randle	.10
225	Scott Mitchell	.10
226	Troy Aikman	.30
227	Terrell Davis	.30
228	Kordell Stewart	.30
229	Warrick Dunn	.20
230	Craig Newsome	.10
231	Brett Favre	.60
232	Kordell Stewart	.30
233	Barry Sanders	.50
234	Dan Marino	.50
235	Dan Marino	.50
236	Tamarick Vanover	.10
237	Warrick Dunn	.20
238	Andre Rison	.10
239	Dan Marino	.50
240	Reggie White	.10
241	Tim Brown	.10
242	Joe Montana	.30
243	Robert Brooks	.10
244	Danny Kanell	.10
245	Emmitt Smith	.50
246	Barry Sanders	.50
247	Brett Favre	.60
248	Brett Favre	.60
249	Jerome Bettis	.10
250	Kordell Stewart	.30

#	Player	MT
251	Terrell Davis	.30
252	Drew Bledsoe	.30
253	Troy Aikman	.30
254	Dan Marino	.50
255	Warrick Dunn	.30
256	Peyton Manning	6.00
257	Ryan Leaf	3.00
258	Andre Wadsworth	1.50
259	Charles Woodson	3.00
260	Curtis Enis	2.50
261	Grant Wistrom	.75
262	Greg Ellis	.75
263	Fred Taylor	3.00
264	Duane Starks	1.50
265	Keith Brooking	.75
266	Takeo Spikes	.75
267	Anthony Simmons	.75
268	Kevin Dyson	2.00
269	Robert Edwards	2.00
270	Randy Moss	10.00
271	John Avery	4.00
272	Marcus Nash	4.00
273	Jerome Pathon	2.00
274	Jacquez Green	2.00
275	Robert Holcombe	2.00
276	Patrick Johnson	.75
277	Germane Crowell	1.00
278	Tony Simmons	2.00
279	Joe Jurevicius	2.00
280	Skip Hicks	2.00
281	Sam Cowart	.75
282	Rashaan Shehee	1.50
283	Az-Zahir Hakim	1.00
284	Tim Dwight	4.00
285	Ahman Green	2.00
286	Adrian Murrell	.20
287	Corey Chavous	.10
288	Eric Swann	.10
289	Frank Sanders	.10
290	Eric Metcalf	.10
291	Jammi German	.50
292	Eugene Robinson	.10
293	Chris Chandler	.10
294	Tony Martin	.10
295	Jessie Tuggle	.10
296	Errict Rhett	.10
297	Jim Harbaugh	.10
298	Eric Green	.10
299	Ray Lewis	.10
301	Fred Coleman	.30
302	Rob Johnson	.20
303	Quinn Early	.10
304	Thurman Thomas	.20
305	Andre Reed	.10
306	Sean Gilbert	.10
307	Kerry Collins	.20
308	Jason Peter	.10
309	Michael Bates	.10
310	William Floyd	.10
311	Alonzo Mayes	.30
312	Tony Parrish	.30
313	Walt Harris	.10
314	Edgar Bennett	.10
315	Jeff Jaeger	.10
316	Brian Simmons	.20
317	David Dunn	.10
318	Ashley Ambrose	.10
319	Darnay Scott	.10
320	Neil O'Donnell	.10
321	Flozell Adams	.10
322	Stepfret Williams	.10
323	Emmitt Smith	1.50
324	Michael Irvin	.20
325	Chris Warren	.20
326	Eric Brown	.20
327	Rod Smith	.20
328	Terrell Davis	1.50
329	Neil Smith	.10
330	Darrien Gordon	.10
331	Curtis Alexander	.10
332	Barry Sanders	2.00
333	David Sloan	.10
334	Johnnie Morton	.10
335	Robert Porcher	.10
336	Tommy Vardell	.10
337	Vonnie Holliday	.20
338	Dorsey Levens	.20
339	Derrick Mayes	.10
340	Robert Brooks	.10
341	Raymont Harris	.10
342	E.G. Green	.75
343	Torrance Small	.10
344	Carlton Gray	.10
345	Aaron Bailey	.10
346	Jeff Burris	.10
347	Donovin Darius	.10
348	Tavian Banks	1.50
349	Aaron Beasley	.20
350	Tony Brackens	.10
351	Bryce Paup	.10
352	Chester McGlockton	.10
353	Leslie O'Neal	.10
354	Derrick Alexander	.10
355	Kimble Anders	.10
356	Tamarick Vanover	.10
357	Brock Marion	.10
358	Larry Shannon	.20
359	Karim Abdul-Jabbar	.30
360	Troy Drayton	.10
361	O.J. McDuffie	.10
362	John Randle	.10
363	David Palmer	.10
364	Robert Smith	.20
365	Kailee Wong	.20
366	Duane Clemons	.10
367	Kyle Turley	.20
368	Sean Dawkins	.10
369	Lamar Smith	.10
370	Cameron Cleeland	1.00

#	Player	MT
371	Keith Poole	.10
372	Tebucky Jones	.20
373	Willie McGinest	.10
374	Ty Law	.10
375	Lawyer Milloy	.10
376	Tony Carter	.10
377	Shaun Williams	.20
378	Brian Alford	.20
379	Tyrone Wheatley	.10
380	Jason Sehorn	.10
381	David Patten	.20
382	Scott Frost	.20
383	Mo Lewis	.10
384	Kevin Williams	.10
385	Curtis Martin	.30
386	Vinny Testaverde	.10
387	Mo Collins	.20
388	James Jett	.10
389	Eric Allen	.10
390	Jon Ritchie	.20
391	Harvey Williams	.10
392	Tre Thomas	.10
393	Rodney Peete	.10
394	Hugh Douglas	.10
395	Charlie Garner	.10
396	Karl Hankton	.10
397	Kordell Stewart	.75
398	George Jones	.10
399	Earl Holmes	.10
400	Hines Ward	1.00
401	Jason Gildon	.10
402	Ricky Proehl	.10
403	Az-Zahir Hakim	.20
404	Amp Lee	.10
405	Eric Hill	.10
406	Leonard Little	.10
407	Charlie Jones	.10
408	Craig Whelihan	.10
409	Terrell Fletcher	.10
410	Kenny Bynum	.10
411	Mikhael Ricks	.75
412	R.W. McQuarters	.50
413	Jerry Rice	1.00
414	Garrison Hearst	.20
415	Ty Detmer	.10
416	Gabe Wilkins	.10
417	Michael Black	.20
418	James McKnight	.10
419	Darrin Smith	.10
420	Joey Galloway	.20
421	Ricky Watters	.20
422	Warrick Dunn	.75
423	Brian Kelly	.10
424	Bert Emanuel	.10
425	John Lynch	.10
426	Regan Upshaw	.10
427	Yancey Thigpen	.10
428	Kenny Holmes	.10
429	Frank Wycheck	.10
430	Samari Rolle	.20
431	Brian Mitchell	.10
432	Stephen Alexander	.10
433	Jamie Asher	.10
434	Michael Westbrook	.10
435	Dana Stubblefield	.10
436	Dan Wilkinson	.10
437	Checklist (Dan Marino)	.75
438	Checklist (Jerry Rice)	.50

1998 UD Choice Mini Bobbing Head

Mini Bobbing Head cards were an insert in Series One. The 30-card set consists of cards that can be folded into a stand-up figure with a removable bobbing head. The cards were inserted one per four packs.

		MT
Complete Set (30):		15.00
Common Player:		.25
Minor Stars:		.50
M1	Jake Plummer	1.25
M2	Jamal Anderson	.25
M3	Michael Jackson	.25
M4	Bruce Smith	.25
M5	Rae Carruth	.25
M6	Curtis Conway	.50
M7	Jeff Blake	.50
M8	Troy Aikman	1.50
M9	Michael Irvin	.50
M10	Terrell Davis	1.50
M11	Barry Sanders	3.00
M12	Herman Moore	.50
M13	Reggie White	.50
M14	Dorsey Levens	.50
M15	Marvin Harrison	.25
M16	Keenan McCardell	.25
M17	Andre Rison	.25
M18	Dan Marino	3.00
M19	Curtis Martin	1.00
M20	Keyshawn Johnson	.25
M21	Tim Brown	.25
M22	Kordell Stewart	1.50
M23	Greg Lloyd	.25
M24	Junior Seau	.25
M25	Jerry Rice	1.50
M26	Merton Hanks	.25
M27	Joey Galloway	.50
M28	Warrick Dunn	1.25
M29	Warren Sapp	.25
M30	Darrell Green	.25

1998 UD Choice Choice Reserve

Choice Reserve is a parallel of the entire 438-card UD Choice set (255 cards from Series Two). The parallel was inserted one per six packs in each series.

	MT
Choice Reserve Cards:	5x-10x
Choice Reserve Rookies:	3x

1998 UD Choice Prime Choice Reserve

Prime Choice Reserve is a parallel of the complete 438-card UD Choice base set (255 cards from Series One and 183 from Series Two). This hobby-only set has "Prime Choice Reserve" foil-stamped on the card fronts and is numbered to 100.

	MT
PC Reserve Cards:	40x-80x
PC Reserve Rookies:	12x-25x

1998 UD Choice Starquest Blue

StarQuest is a 30-card, four-tiered insert in UD Choice Series One. Each tier has a different insertion rate and foil color. StarQuest 1-Star cards were seeded 1:1, 2-Star cards were found 1:7, 3-Stars were inserted 1:23 and 4-Stars are numbered to 100.

		MT
Complete Set (30):		15.00
Common Player:		.25
Minor Stars:		.50
Green Cards:		2x-4x
Red Cards:		5x-10x
Gold Cards:		40x-80x
W1	Warren Moon	.25
W2	Jerry Rice	1.00
W3	Jeff George	.25
W4	Brett Favre	2.00
W5	Junior Seau	.25
W6	Cris Carter	.25
W7	John Elway	1.00

#	Player	MT
W8	Troy Aikman	1.00
W9	Steve Young	.75
W10	Kordell Stewart	1.00
W11	Drew Bledsoe	1.00
W12	Dorsey Levens	.50
W13	Dan Marino	1.75
W14	Joey Galloway	.50
W15	Antonio Freeman	.50
W16	Jake Plummer	1.00
W17	Corey Dillon	.75
W18	Mark Brunell	.75
W19	Andre Rison	.25
W20	Barry Sanders	1.50
W21	Deion Sanders	.60
W22	Emmitt Smith	1.75
W23	Antowain Smith	.60
W24	Herman Moore	.50
W25	Napoleon Kaufman	.60
W26	Jerome Bettis	.50
W27	Eddie George	1.00
W28	Warrick Dunn	1.00
W29	Adrian Murrell	.25
W30	Terrell Davis	1.00

1998 Upper Deck

Upper Deck Series One Football consists of a 255-card base set. The base cards have a color photo bordered on three sides, with the player's name, team and position printed at the bottom. The set consists of 210 regular cards, 42 Star Rookie subset cards (1:4) and three checklists. The set is paralleled in UD Exclusives. Inserts include SuperPowers, Constant Threat, Define the Game (each with a tiered Quantum parallel), Game Jerseys and Hobby-Exclusive Game Jerseys.

		MT
Complete Set (255):		225.00
Common Player:		.15
Minor Stars:		.30
Common Rookie (1-42):		2.50
Wax Box:		120.00
1	Peyton Manning	45.00
2	Ryan Leaf	20.00
3	Andre Wadsworth	5.00
4	Charles Woodson	20.00
5	Curtis Enis	15.00
6	Grant Wistrom	2.50
7	Greg Ellis	2.50
8	Fred Taylor	25.00
9	Duane Starks	2.50
10	Keith Brooking	2.50
11	Takeo Spikes	4.00
12	Jason Peter	4.00
13	Anthony Simmons	2.50
14	Kevin Dyson	8.00
15	Brian Simmons	2.50
16	Robert Edwards	12.00
17	Randy Moss	70.00
18	John Avery	6.00
19	Marcus Nash	6.00
20	Jerome Pathon	4.00
21	Jacquez Green	8.00
22	Robert Holcombe	12.00
23	Patrick Johnson	2.50
24	Germane Crowell	7.00
25	Joe Jurevicius	4.00
26	Skip Hicks	6.00
27	Ahman Green	8.00
28	Brian Griese	20.00
29	Hines Ward	6.00
30	Tavian Banks	10.00
31	Tony Simmons	4.00
32	Victor Riley	2.50
33	Rashaan Shehee	4.00
34	R.W. McQuarters	2.50
35	Flozell Adams	2.50
36	Tre Thomas	2.50
37	Greg Favors	2.50
38	Jon Ritchie	2.50
39	Jessie Haynes	2.50
40	Ryan Sutter	2.50
41	Mo Collins	2.50
42	Tim Dwight	6.00
43	Chris Chandler	.15
44	Byron Hanspard	.15
45	Jessie Tuggle	.15
46	Jamal Anderson	.30
47	Terance Mathis	.15
48	Morten Andersen	.15
49	Jake Plummer	2.00
50	Mario Bates	.15

#	Player	MT
51	Frank Sanders	.15
52	Adrian Murrell	.30
53	Simeon Rice	.15
54	Aeneas Williams	.15
55	Eric Swann	.15
56	Jim Harbaugh	.15
57	Michael Jackson	.15
58	Peter Boulware	.15
59	Errict Rhett	.15
60	Jermaine Lewis	.15
61	Eric Zeier	.15
62	Rod Woodson	.15
63	Rob Johnson	.30
64	Antowain Smith	1.00
65	Bruce Smith	.15
66	Eric Moulds	.15
67	Andre Reed	.15
68	Thurman Thomas	.30
69	Lonnie Johnson	.15
70	Kerry Collins	.15
71	Kevin Greene	.15
72	Fred Lane	.30
73	Rae Carruth	.15
74	Michael Bates	.15
75	William Floyd	.15
76	Sean Gilbert	.15
77	Erik Kramer	.15
78	Edgar Bennett	.15
79	Curtis Conway	.15
80	Darnell Autry	.15
81	Ryan Wetnight	.15
82	Walt Harris	.15
83	Bobby Engram	.15
84	Jeff Blake	.30
85	Carl Pickens	.30
86	Darnay Scott	.15
87	Corey Dillon	1.25
88	Reinard Wilson	.15
89	Ashley Ambrose	.15
90	Troy Aikman	1.50
91	Michael Irvin	.30
92	Emmitt Smith	2.50
93	Deion Sanders	.50
94	David LaFleur	.15
95	Chris Warren	.15
96	Darren Woodson	.15
97	John Elway	1.50
98	Terrell Davis	1.50
99	Rod Smith	.30
100	Shannon Sharpe	.15
101	Ed McCaffrey	.15
102	Steve Atwater	.15
103	John Mobley	.15
104	Darrian Gordon	.15
105	Barry Sanders	3.00
106	Scott Mitchell	.15
107	Herman Moore	.30
108	Johnnie Morton	.15
109	Robert Porcher	.15
110	Bryant Westbrook	.15
111	Tommy Vardell	.15
112	Brett Favre	3.00
113	Dorsey Levens	.30
114	Reggie White	.30
115	Antonio Freeman	.30
116	Robert Brooks	.15
117	Mark Chmura	.30
118	Derrick Mayes	.15
119	Gilbert Brown	.15
120	Marshall Faulk	.30
121	Torrance Small	.15
122	Marvin Harrison	.30
123	Quentin Coryatt	.15
124	Ken Dilger	.15
125	Zack Crockett	.15
126	Mark Brunell	1.25
127	Bryce Paup	.15
128	Tony Brackens	.15
129	Renaldo Wynn	.15
130	Keenan McCardell	.15
131	Jimmy Smith	.30
132	Kevin Hardy	.15
133	Elvis Grbac	.15
134	Tamarick Vanover	.15
135	Chester McGlockton	.15
136	Andre Rison	.15
137	Derrick Alexander	.15
138	Tony Gonzalez	.15
139	Derrick Thomas	.15
140	Dan Marino	2.50
141	Karim Abdul-Jabbar	.30
142	O.J. McDuffie	.15
143	Yatil Green	.15
144	Charles Jordan	.15
145	Brock Marion	.15
146	Zach Thomas	.15
147	Brad Johnson	.30
148	Cris Carter	.30
149	Jake Reed	.15
150	Robert Smith	.15
151	John Randle	.15
152	Dwayne Rudd	.15
153	Randall Cunningham	.15
154	Drew Bledsoe	1.25
155	Terry Glenn	.30
156	Ben Coates	.15
157	Willie Clay	.15
158	Chris Slade	.15
159	Derrick Cullors	.15
160	Ty Law	.15
161	Danny Wuerffel	.30
162	Andre Hastings	.15
163	Troy Davis	.30
164	Billy Joe Hobert	.15
165	Eric Guliford	.15
166	Mark Fields	.15
167	Alex Molden	.15
168	Danny Kanell	.15
169	Tiki Barber	.30

#	Player	MT
170	Charles Way	.15
171	Amani Toomer	.15
172	Michael Strahan	.15
173	Jesse Armstead	.15
174	Jason Sehorn	.15
175	Glenn Foley	.30
176	Curtis Martin	1.00
177	Aaron Glenn	.15
178	Keyshawn Johnson	.30
179	James Farrior	.15
180	Wayne Chrebet	.15
181	Keith Byars	.15
182	Jeff George	.30
183	Napoleon Kaufman	.50
184	Tim Brown	.30
185	Darrell Russell	.15
186	Rickey Dudley	.15
187	James Jett	.15
188	Desmond Howard	.15
189	Bobby Hoying	.15
190	Charlie Garner	.15
191	Irving Fryar	.15
192	Chris T. Jones	.15
193	Mike Mamula	.15
194	Troy Vincent	.15
195	Kordell Stewart	1.50
196	Jerome Bettis	.30
197	Will Blackwell	.15
198	Levon Kirkland	.15
199	Carnell Lake	.15
200	Charles Johnson	.15
201	Greg Lloyd	.15
202	Donnell Woolford	.15
203	Tony Banks	.30
204	Amp Lee	.15
205	Isaac Bruce	.30
206	Eddie Kennison	.30
207	Ryan McNeil	.15
208	Craig Heyward	.15
209	Ernie Conwell	.15
210	Natrone Means	.30
211	Junior Seau	.30
212	Tony Martin	.15
213	Freddie Jones	.15
214	Bryan Still	.15
215	Rodney Harrison	.15
216	Steve Young	1.00
217	Jerry Rice	1.50
218	Garrison Hearst	.15
219	J.J. Stokes	.15
220	Ken Norton	.15
221	Greg Clark	.15
222	Bryant Young	.15
223	Gabe Wilkins	.15
224	Warren Moon	.30
225	Jon Kitna	.15
226	Ricky Watters	.30
227	Chad Brown	.15
228	Joey Galloway	.30
229	Shawn Springs	.15
230	Cortez Kennedy	.15
231	Trent Dilfer	.30
232	Warrick Dunn	2.00
233	Mike Alstott	.30
234	Warren Sapp	.15
235	Bert Emanuel	.15
236	Reidel Anthony	.15
237	Hardy Nickerson	.15
238	Derrick Brooks	.15
239	Steve McNair	.50
240	Yancey Thigpen	.15
241	Anthony Dorsett	.15
242	Blaine Bishop	.15
243	Kenny Holmes	.15
244	Eddie George	1.25
245	Chris Sanders	.15
246	Gus Frerotte	.15
247	Terry Allen	.15
248	Dana Stubblefield	.15
249	Michael Westbrook	.15
250	Darrell Green	.15
251	Brian Mitchell	.15
252	Ken Harvey	.15
253	Checklist A (Troy Aikman)	.75
254	Checklist B (Dan Marino)	1.25
255	Checklist C (Herman Moore)	.15

1998 Upper Deck Bronze

The UD Exclusives set parallels the Upper Deck Series One base set. One level is numbered to 100 and the other is a 1-of-1 set.

	MT
Bronze Cards:	40x-80x
Bronze Rookies:	2x-4x

1998 Upper Deck Constant Threat

Constant Threat is a 30-card insert seeded one per 12 packs. The cards have a horizontal layout and two player photos. The color player photo is on the left and a negative exposure is on the right. The cards also feature blue foil highlights. Cards are numbered with a "CT" prefix.

		MT
Complete Set (30):		150.00
Common Player:		1.50
Minor Stars:		3.00
1	Dan Marino	12.00
2	Peyton Manning	15.00
3	Randy Moss	20.00
4	Brett Favre	15.00
5	Mark Brunell	6.00
6	Keyshawn Johnson	1.50
7	John Elway	6.00
8	Troy Aikman	7.00
9	Steve Young	5.00
10	Kordell Stewart	6.00
11	Drew Bledsoe	7.00
12	Joey Galloway	3.00
13	Elvis Grbac	1.50
14	Marvin Harrison	3.00
15	Napoleon Kaufman	4.00
16	Ryan Leaf	8.00
17	Jake Plummer	7.00
18	Terrell Davis	10.00
19	Steve McNair	5.00
20	Barry Sanders	15.00
21	Deion Sanders	4.00
22	Emmitt Smith	12.00
23	Antowain Smith	4.00
24	Herman Moore	3.00
25	Curtis Martin	6.00
26	Jerry Rice	7.00
27	Eddie George	6.00
28	Warrick Dunn	7.00
29	Curtis Enis	8.00
30	Michael Irvin	3.00

1998 Upper Deck Constant Threat Bronze/Silver

The Constant Threat insert has a three-tiered Quantum parallel. The cards are die-cut and sequentially numbered. Tier One features silver foil and is numbered to 1,000, Tier Two has bronze foil and numbering to 25 and Tier Three has gold foil and is a 1-of-1 set.

	MT
Bronze Cards:	20x-40x
Silver Cards:	2x-4x

1998 Upper Deck Define the Game

Define the Game is a 30-card insert seeded one per eight packs. The cards feature a small color photo of the player with a larger black-and-white photo in the background. The front of each card has a word that describes the player and the definition. Cards are numbered with a "DG" prefix.

		MT
Complete Set (30):		100.00
Common Player:		1.00
Minor Stars:		2.00
1	Dan Marino	10.00
2	Curtis Enis	6.00
3	Dorsey Levens	2.00
4	Charles Woodson	4.00
5	Junior Seau	1.00
6	Tiki Barber	1.00
7	Randy Moss	12.00
8	Troy Aikman	6.00
9	Jake Plummer	6.00
10	Corey Dillon	4.00
11	Jerry Rice	6.00
12	Emmitt Smith	10.00
13	Herman Moore	2.00
14	Brad Johnson	2.00
15	Gus Frerotte	1.00
16	Ryan Leaf	7.00
17	Shannon Sharpe	1.00
18	Jermaine Lewis	1.00
19	Jerome Bettis	2.00
20	Barry Sanders	12.00
21	Terry Allen	1.00
22	Reidel Anthony	1.00
23	Isaac Bruce	2.00
24	Mike Alstott	3.00
25	Rae Carruth	1.00
26	Tamarick Vanover	1.00
27	Eddie George	5.00
28	Warrick Dunn	6.00
29	Tony Gonzalez	1.00
30	Keenan McCardell	1.00

1998 Upper Deck Define the Game Bronze/Silver

Define the Game has a three-tiered Quantum parallel. The cards are die-cut and sequentially numbered. Tier One is numbered to 1,500, Tier Two to 50 and Tier Three to 1.

	MT
Bronze Cards:	15x-30x
Silver Cards:	2x

1998 Upper Deck Game Jersey

The Game Jersey insert features 10 cards inserted 1:2,500. The set contains both veterans and rookies. The veteran cards feature a piece of game-used jersey and the rookie cards have a piece of jersey worn during the NFL rookie photo shoot. Dan Marino signed 13 of his cards. Cards are numbered with "GJ" prefix.

		MT
Complete Set (10):		3000.
Common Player:		150.00
1	Brett Favre	600.00
2	Reggie White	150.00
3	Barry Sanders	625.00
4	John Elway	425.00
5	Mark Brunell	300.00
6	Mike Alstott	200.00
7	Ryan Leaf	200.00
8	Andre Wadsworth	150.00
9	Robert Edwards	175.00
10	Kevin Dyson	150.00

Post-1980 cards in Near Mint condition will generally sell for about 75% of the quoted Mint value. Excellent-condition cards bring no more than 40%.

1998 Upper Deck Hobby Exclusive Game Jerseys

The Hobby-Exclusive Game Jersey insert features 10-cards inserted 1:288. The set features veterans and rookies. The veteran cards have a piece of game-worn jersey and the rookie cards have a piece of jersey from the NFL rookie photo shoot. Cards are numbered with "GJ" prefix.

		MT
Complete Set (10):		900.00
Common Player:		40.00
11	Dan Marino	250.00
12	Deion Sanders	100.00
13	Steve Young	110.00
14	Terrell Davis	140.00
15	Tim Brown	40.00
16	Peyton Manning	250.00
17	Takeo Spikes	40.00
18	Curtis Enis	100.00
19	Fred Taylor	125.00
20	John Avery	85.00

1998 Upper Deck SuperPowers

SuperPowers is a 30-card insert seeded one per four packs. The cards have a horizontal layout and feature a color photo on the left with a black-and-white photo on the right.

		MT
Complete Set (30):		45.00
Common Player:		.50
Minor Stars:		1.00
S1	Dan Marino	5.00
S2	Jerry Rice	3.00
S3	Napoleon Kaufman	1.50
S4	Brett Favre	6.00
S5	Andre Rison	.50
S6	Jerome Bettis	1.00
S7	John Elway	2.00
S8	Troy Aikman	3.00
S9	Steve Young	1.50
S10	Kordell Stewart	3.00
S11	Drew Bledsoe	3.00
S12	Antonio Freeman	1.00
S13	Mark Brunell	2.00
S14	Shannon Sharpe	.50
S15	Trent Dilfer	1.00
S16	Peyton Manning	6.00
S17	Cris Carter	.50
S18	Michael Irvin	1.00
S19	Terry Glenn	1.00
S20	Keyshawn Johnson	1.00
S21	Deion Sanders	1.50
S22	Emmitt Smith	5.00
S23	Marcus Allen	1.00
S24	Dorsey Levens	1.00
S25	Jake Plummer	3.00
S26	Eddie George	3.00
S27	Tim Brown	.50
S28	Warrick Dunn	3.00
S29	Reggie White	1.00
S30	Terrell Davis	3.00

1998 Upper Deck SuperPowers Bronze/Silver

The SuperPowers insert has a three-tiered Quantum parallel. The cards are die-cut and sequentially numbered. Tier One is numbered to 2,000, Tier Two to 100 and Tier Three is a 1-of-1 set.

	MT
Bronze Cards:	10x-20x
Silver Cards:	2x

1998 Upper Deck Black Diamond

The Black Diamond Football base set consists of 150 cards designated by the Black Diamond logo and a single Black Diamond in the lower right corner. Three parallel versions were produced. Double Black Diamond cards (inserted 1:1) have two diamonds and red Light F/X backgrounds. Triple Black Diamonds (1:5) have gold Light F/X backgrounds and Quadruple Black Diamonds (50 total sets) have black Light F/X backgrounds. The Premium Cuts insert (30 cards) features the same four diamond levels of scarcity and a special die-cut. Single Diamond (1:7), Double Diamond (1:15), Triple Diamond (1:30) and Quadruple Diamond (1:180) versions were created. Upper Deck also included a hobby-only "Mystery Premium Cut" insert in Black Diamond. The 30 cards feature Black Light F/X backgrounds, embossing and a horizontal die-cut design. The cards in the "Mystery" insert have different insertion rates.

	MT
Complete Set (150):	50.00
Common Player:	.25
Minor Stars:	.50
Doubles:	2x
Triples:	3x-6x
Quadruples:	40x-80x
Wax Box:	80.00
1 Kent Graham	.25
2 Darrell Russell	.25
3 Jim Harbaugh	.25
4 Cornelius Bennett	.25
5 Troy Vincent	.25
6 Natrone Means	.50
7 Michael Jackson	.25
8 Will Blackwell	.25
9 Greg Hill	.25
10 Andre Reed	.25
11 Darren Bennett	.25
12 Dan Marino	5.00
13 Tshimanga Biakabutuka	.25
14 Terrell Owens	.75
15 Cris Carter	.25
16 Darnell Autry	.50
17 Joey Galloway	.50
18 Terry Glenn	1.00
19 Ki-Jana Carter	.25
20 Isaac Bruce	.50
21 Shawn Jefferson	.25
22 Michael Irvin	.50
23 Warren Sapp	.25
24 Dave Brown	.25
25 Terrell Davis	2.50
26 Frank Wycheck	.25
27 Neil O'Donnell	.25
28 Scott Mitchell	.25
29 Michael Westbrook	.25
30 Tim Brown	.50
31 Antonio Freeman	.75
32 Jake Plummer	2.00
33 Irving Fryar	.25
34 Quentin Coryatt	.25
35 Jamal Anderson	.50

36 Jerome Bettis	.50
37 Keenan McCardell	.25
38 Derrick Alexander	.25
39 Stan Humphries	.25
40 Andre Rison	.25
41 Bruce Smith	.25
42 Garrison Hearst	.25
43 Zach Thomas	.50
44 Rae Carruth	.50
45 Kevin Greene	.25
46 Robert Smith	.25
47 Curtis Conway	.50
48 Christian Fauria	.25
49 Curtis Martin	2.00
50 Dan Wilkinson	.25
51 Eddie Kennison	.75
52 Mark Fields	.25
53 Anthony Miller	.25
54 Mike Alstott	1.00
55 Tiki Barber	.75
56 Neil Smith	.25
57 Gus Frerotte	.25
58 Adrian Murrell	.50
59 Johnnie Morton	.25
60 O.J. McDuffie	.25
61 Napoleon Kaufman	.50
62 Robert Brooks	.25
63 Byron Hanspard	.75
64 Ty Detmer	.25
65 Mark Brunell	2.00
66 Bam Morris	.25
67 Kordell Stewart	2.50
68 Elvis Grbac	.25
69 Antowain Smith	1.50
70 Junior Seau	.50
71 Tony Gonzalez	.50
72 Anthony Johnson	.25
73 Steve Young	1.50
74 Brian Manning	.25
75 Rick Mirer	.25
76 Warren Moon	.50
77 Torrian Gray	.25
78 Carl Pickens	.25
79 Tony Banks	1.00
80 Willie McGinest	.25
81 Deion Sanders	1.25
82 Warrick Dunn	3.00
83 Danny Wuerffel	.75
84 Rod Smith	.25
85 Steve McNair	1.75
86 Danny Kanell	.25
87 Herman Moore	.50
88 Brian Mitchell	.25
89 James Farrior	.25
90 Reggie White	.50
91 Simeon Rice	.25
92 James Jett	.25
93 Marshall Faulk	.50
94 Chris Chandler	.25
95 Mike Mamula	.25
96 Jimmy Smith	.25
97 Jamie Sharper	.25
98 Carnell Lake	.25
99 Marcus Allen	.50
100 Thurman Thomas	.50
101 Freddie Jones	.25
102 Karim Abdul-Jabbar	1.00
103 Kerry Collins	.50
104 Jerry Rice	2.50
105 Brad Johnson	.50
106 Raymont Harris	.25
107 Lamar Smith	.25
108 Drew Bledsoe	2.00
109 Corey Dillon	2.00
110 Lawrence Phillips	.25
111 Heath Shuler	.25
112 Emmitt Smith	4.00
113 Reidel Anthony	1.00
114 Ike Hilliard	.75
115 Shannon Sharpe	.25
116 Chris Sanders	.25
117 Keyshawn Johnson	.75
118 Barry Sanders	3.00
119 Cris Dishman	.25
120 Jeff George	.50
121 Dorsey Levens	.25
122 Rob Moore	.25
123 Ricky Watters	.50
124 Marvin Harrison	.75
125 Vinny Testaverde	.25
126 Charles Johnson	.25
127 Renaldo Wynn	.25
128 Todd Collins	.25
129 Tony Martin	.25
130 Derrick Thomas	.25
131 Wesley Walls	.25
132 Rod Woodson	.25
133 Troy Drayton	.25
134 Bryan Cox	.25
135 Shawn Springs	.25
136 Jake Reed	.25
137 Jeff Blake	.25
138 Craig Heyward	.25
139 Ben Coates	.25
140 Troy Aikman	2.50
141 Trent Dilfer	1.00
142 Troy Davis	.75
143 John Elway	2.00
144 Eddie George	2.50
145 Rodney Hampton	.25
146 Ed McCaffrey	.25
147 Terry Allen	.25
148 Wayne Chrebet	.50
149 Brett Favre	5.00
150 Daryl Johnston	.25

> A player's name in italic type indicates a rookie card.

1998 Upper Deck Black Diamond Premium Cut

Premium Cut is a 30-card insert with four diamond versions. The cards have a special die-cut and Light F/X technology. Single Diamond (inserted 1:7), Double Diamond (1:15), Triple Diamond (1:30) and Quadruple Diamond (1:180) versions were produced. Cards are numbered with a "PC" prefix.

	MT
Complete Set (30):	225.00
Common Player:	3.00
Minor Stars:	6.00
Doubles:	2x
Triples:	2x-4x
Quad Horizontals:	2x-4x
Quad Verticals:	5x-10x
1 Karim Abdul-Jabbar	6.00
2 Troy Aikman	12.00
3 Kerry Collins	6.00
4 Drew Bledsoe	12.00
5 Barry Sanders	20.00
6 Marcus Allen	6.00
7 John Elway	12.00
8 Adrian Murrell	3.00
9 Junior Seau	3.00
10 Eddie George	12.00
11 Antowain Smith	8.00
12 Reggie White	6.00
13 Dan Marino	24.00
14 Joey Galloway	6.00
15 Kordell Stewart	12.00
16 Terry Allen	3.00
17 Napoleon Kaufman	6.00
18 Curtis Martin	12.00
19 Steve Young	10.00
20 Rod Smith	3.00
21 Mark Brunell	12.00
22 Emmitt Smith	24.00
23 Rae Carruth	6.00
24 Brett Favre	30.00
25 Jeff George	6.00
26 Terry Glenn	6.00
27 Warrick Dunn	12.00
28 Herman Moore	6.00
29 Cris Carter	6.00
30 Terrell Davis	12.00

1998 Upper Deck Black Diamond Rookies

This 120-card set includes 90 regular player cards (all possessing Light F/X foil treatment) with each card sporting a Single Black Diamond, along with a 30-card, short-printed "Rookie Single Black Diamond" subset (1:4 packs). The parallel Double Black Diamond singles feature red Light F/X technology with veterans numbered to 3,000 and rookies to 2,500. The Triple Black Diamond parallel set has veterans numbered to 1,500 and rookies to 1,000. The Quadruple Black Diamond set has veterans numbered to 150 and rookies to 100.

	MT
Complete Set (120):	175.00
Common Player:	.15
Minor Stars:	.30
Common Rookie (91-120):	1.00
Inserted 1:4	
Double Cards:	2x-4x
Production 3,000 Sets	
Double Rookies:	1x
Production 2,500 Sets	
Triple Cards:	4x-8x
Production 1,500 Sets	
Triple Rookies:	2x
Production 1,000 Sets	
Quad. Cards:	20x-40x
Production 150 Sets	
Quad. Rookies:	3x-6x
Production 100 Sets	
Wax Box:	100.00
1 Jake Plummer	1.25
2 Adrian Murrell	.15
3 Frank Sanders	.15
4 Jamal Anderson	.75
5 Chris Chandler	.30
6 Tony Martin	.15
7 Jim Harbaugh	.30
8 Errict Rhett	.15
9 Michael Jackson	.30
10 Rob Johnson	.30
11 Antowain Smith	.50
12 Thurman Thomas	.30
13 Fred Lane	.15
14 Kerry Collins	.30
15 Rae Carruth	.15
16 Erik Kramer	.15
17 Edgar Bennett	.15
18 Curtis Conway	.30
19 Corey Dillon	.75
20 Neil O'Donnell	.15
21 Carl Pickens	.30
22 Troy Aikman	1.50
23 Emmitt Smith	2.00
24 Deion Sanders	.50
25 John Elway	1.50
26 Terrell Davis	2.50
27 Rod Smith	.30
28 Barry Sanders	3.00
29 Johnnie Morton	.15
30 Herman Moore	.30
31 Brett Favre	3.00
32 Antonio Freeman	.50
33 Dorsey Levens	.30
34 Marshall Faulk	.50
35 Marvin Harrison	.30
36 Zack Crockett	.15
37 Mark Brunell	1.25
38 Jimmy Smith	.30
39 Keenan McCardell	.30
40 Elvis Grbac	.30
41 Andre Rison	.30
42 Derrick Alexander	.15
43 Dan Marino	2.00
44 Karim Abdul-Jabbar	.30
45 Zach Thomas	.30
46 Brad Johnson	.30
47 Cris Carter	.50
48 Robert Smith	.50
49 Drew Bledsoe	1.25
50 Terry Glenn	.30
51 Ben Coates	.30
52 Danny Wuerffel	.30
53 Lamar Smith	.15
54 Sean Dawkins	.15
55 Danny Kanell	.30
56 Tiki Barber	.15
57 Ike Hilliard	.15
58 Curtis Martin	.50
59 Vinny Testaverde	.30
60 Keyshawn Johnson	.50
61 Napoleon Kaufman	.50
62 Jeff George	.30
63 Tim Brown	.30
64 Bobby Hoying	.30
65 Charlie Garner	.15
66 Duce Staley	.15
67 Kordell Stewart	1.25
68 Jerome Bettis	.50
69 Charles Johnson	.30
70 Tony Banks	.30
71 Isaac Bruce	.30
72 Eddie Kennison	.30
73 Natrone Means	.30
74 Bryan Still	.15
75 Junior Seau	.30
76 Steve Young	1.00
77 Jerry Rice	1.50
78 Garrison Hearst	.30
79 Ricky Watters	.30
80 Joey Galloway	.50
81 Warren Moon	.30
82 Warrick Dunn	1.00
83 Trent Dilfer	.30
84 Bert Emanuel	.15
85 Steve McNair	.75
86 Eddie George	.75
87 Yancey Thigpen	.15
88 Leslie Shepherd	.15
89 Terry Allen	.30
90 Michael Westbrook	.30
91 *Peyton Manning*	25.00
92 *Jacquez Green*	6.00
93 *Fred Taylor*	20.00
94 *Terry Fair*	3.00
95 *Patrick Johnson*	3.00

96 *Corey Chavous*	2.00
97 *Randy Moss*	50.00
98 *Curtis Enis*	10.00
99 *Rashaan Shehee*	3.00
100 *Kevin Dyson*	6.00
101 *Shaun Williams*	1.00
102 *Grant Wistrom*	2.00
103 *John Avery*	6.00
104 *Brian Griese*	12.00
105 *Ryan Leaf*	10.00
106 *Jerome Pathon*	2.00
107 *Sam Cowart*	1.00
108 *Germane Crowell*	6.00
109 *Ahman Green*	6.00
110 *Greg Ellis*	1.00
111 *Robert Holcombe*	6.00
112 *Marcus Nash*	6.00
113 *Duane Starks*	3.00
114 *Andre Wadsworth*	3.00
115 *Takeo Spikes*	3.00
116 *Eric Brown*	1.00
117 *Robert Edwards*	10.00
118 *Charlie Batch*	18.00
119 *Mikhael Ricks*	4.00
120 *Charles Woodson*	10.00

1998 Upper Deck Black Diamond Rookies Sheer Brilliance

Each of these hobby-only singles has the Quadruple Black Diamond stamp on the front and each is sequentially numbered to the player's uniform number multiplied by 100. Cards are numbered with a "B" prefix.

	MT
Complete Set (30):	325.00
Common Player:	4.00
Hobby Only	
1 Dan Marino (1300)	25.00
2 Troy Aikman (800)	20.00
3 Brett Favre (400)	50.00
4 Ryan Leaf (1600)	25.00
5 Peyton Manning (1800)	45.00
6 Barry Sanders (2000)	25.00
7 Emmitt Smith (2200)	15.00
8 John Elway (700)	30.00
9 Steve Young (800)	15.00
10 Steve McNair (900)	12.00
11 Antowain Smith (2300)	4.00
12 Corey Dillon (2800)	6.00
13 Terrell Davis (3000)	10.00
14 Mark Brunell (800)	15.00
15 Charles Woodson (2400)	12.00
16 Brian Griese (1400)	15.00
17 Curtis Martin (2800)	4.00
18 Keyshawn Johnson (1900)	6.00
19 Kordell Stewart (1000)	15.00
20 Eddie George (2700)	6.00
21 Drew Bledsoe (1500)	15.00
22 Jake Plummer (1600)	12.00
23 Warren Moon (100)	30.00
24 Curtis Enis (3900)	6.00
25 John Avery (2000)	6.00
26 Randy Moss (1800)	80.00
27 Rob Johnson (1100)	6.00
28 Warrick Dunn (2800)	6.00
29 Terry Allen (2100)	4.00
30 Robert Smith (2600)	4.00

> Post-1980 cards in Near Mint condition will generally sell for about 75% of the quoted Mint value. Excellent-condition cards bring no more than 40%.

1998 Upper Deck Black Diamond Rookies White Onyx

This insert incorporates a new design with Pearl Light F/X treatment and also has the Quadruple Black Diamond logo. Each is sequentially numbered to 2,250. Cards have an "ON" prefix.

	MT
Complete Set (30):	200.00
Common Player:	2.00
Minor Stars:	4.00
Production 2,250 Sets	
1 Peyton Manning	30.00
2 Corey Dillon	6.00
3 Jerome Bettis	4.00
4 Brett Favre	20.00
5 Napoleon Kaufman	4.00
6 Joey Galloway	4.00
7 John Elway	10.00
8 Troy Aikman	10.00
9 Robert Smith	2.00
10 Kordell Stewart	8.00
11 Garrison Hearst	4.00
12 Curtis Enis	8.00
13 Dan Marino	15.00
14 Jimmy Smith	2.00
15 Steve Young	6.00
16 Ryan Leaf	12.00
17 Steve McNair	6.00
18 Randy Moss	60.00
19 Curtis Martin	8.00
20 Barry Sanders	20.00
21 Rob Johnson	4.00
22 Emmitt Smith	15.00
23 Jake Plummer	8.00
24 Antonio Freeman	4.00
25 Mark Brunell	8.00
26 Warrick Dunn	8.00
27 Eddie George	8.00
28 Jerry Rice	10.00
29 Drew Bledsoe	8.00
30 Terrell Davis	15.00

1998 Upper Deck Encore

Encore was a fine-tuned version of Upper Deck's 1998 NFL Series I product that utilized a special rainbow-foil treatment on 150 of the earlier set's 255 cards (120 regular player cards and 30 Star Rookie subset cards). The rookies could be found 1:4 packs. The F/X set is a direct parallel of the entire Encore set. The differentiation comes in a color shift with a special "Encore F/X" callout featured on the card fronts and backs. Singles are sequentially numbered to 125.

	MT
Complete Set (150):	325.00
Common Player:	.20
Minor Stars:	.40
Common Rookie:	2.00
Inserted 1:4	
F/X Gold Cards:	25x-50x
F/X Gold Rookies:	2x-4x

Production 125 Sets

Wax Box:		135.00
1	*Peyton Manning*	50.00
2	*Ryan Leaf*	25.00
3	*Andre Wadsworth*	4.00
4	*Charles Woodson*	18.00
5	*Curtis Enis*	15.00
6	*Fred Taylor*	35.00
7	*Duane Starks*	4.00
8	*Keith Brooking*	4.00
9	*Takeo Spikes*	4.00
10	*Kevin Dyson*	10.00
11	*Robert Edwards*	10.00
12	*Randy Moss*	75.00
13	*John Avery*	8.00
14	*Marcus Nash*	10.00
15	*Jerome Pathon*	4.00
16	*Jacquez Green*	10.00
17	*Robert Holcombe*	8.00
18	*Pat Johnson*	4.00
19	*Skip Hicks*	10.00
20	*Ahman Green*	8.00
21	*Brian Griese*	20.00
22	*Hines Ward*	6.00
23	*Tavian Banks*	6.00
24	*Tony Simmons*	6.00
25	*Rashaan Shehee*	4.00
26	*R.W. McQuarters*	4.00
27	*Jon Ritchie*	2.00
28	*Ryan Sutter*	2.00
29	*Tim Dwight*	8.00
30	*Charlie Batch*	35.00
31	Chris Chandler	.40
32	Jamal Anderson	1.00
33	Terance Mathis	.20
34	Jake Plummer	2.00
35	Mario Bates	.20
36	Frank Sanders	.20
37	Adrian Murrell	.20
38	Jim Harbaugh	.40
39	Michael Jackson	.20
40	Jermaine Lewis	.20
41	Doug Flutie	1.50
42	Rob Johnson	.40
43	Antowain Smith	1.00
44	Eric Moulds	1.00
45	Thurman Thomas	.40
46	Kevin Greene	.20
47	Fred Lane	.40
48	Rae Carruth	.20
49	William Floyd	.20
50	Erik Kramer	.20
51	Edgar Bennett	.20
52	Curtis Conway	.40
53	Bobby Engram	.20
54	Jeff Blake	.40
55	Carl Pickens	.75
56	Darnay Scott	.20
57	Corey Dillon	1.50
58	Troy Aikman	2.50
59	Michael Irvin	.40
60	Emmitt Smith	3.50
61	Deion Sanders	1.00
62	John Elway	3.00
63	Terrell Davis	4.00
64	Rod Smith	.40
65	Shannon Sharpe	.40
66	Ed McCaffrey	.75
67	Barry Sanders	5.00
68	Scott Mitchell	.40
69	Herman Moore	.75
70	Johnnie Morton	.20
71	Brett Favre	5.00
72	Dorsey Levens	.40
73	Reggie White	1.00
74	Antonio Freeman	1.00
75	Robert Brooks	.20
76	Marshall Faulk	1.00
77	Marvin Harrison	.40
78	Mark Brunell	2.00
79	Keenan McCardell	.40
80	Jimmy Smith	.75
81	Elvis Grbac	.20
82	Andre Rison	.40
83	Tony Gonzalez	.20
84	Derrick Thomas	.20
85	Dan Marino	3.50
86	Karim Abdul	1.00
87	O.J. McDuffie	.40
88	Zach Thomas	.40
89	Brad Johnson	1.00
90	Cris Carter	1.00
91	Jake Reed	.20
92	Robert Smith	.40
93	John Randle	.20
94	Randall Cunningham	1.00
95	Drew Bledsoe	2.00
96	Terry Glenn	1.00
97	Ben Coates	.40
98	Danny Wuerffel	.20
99	Andre Hastings	.20
100	Troy Davis	.20
101	Danny Kanell	.20
102	Tiki Barber	.20
103	Amani Toomer	.20
104	Vinny Testaverde	.40
105	Glenn Foley	.40
106	Curtis Martin	1.00
107	Keyshawn Johnson	1.00
108	Wayne Chrebet	.75
109	Jeff George	.40
110	Napoleon Kaufman	1.00
111	Tim Brown	1.00
112	James Jett	.20
113	Bobby Hoying	.20
114	Charlie Garner	.20
115	Irving Fryar	.20

116	Kordell Stewart	2.00
117	Jerome Bettis	1.00
118	Will Blackwell	.20
119	Charles Johnson	.20
120	Tony Banks	.40
121	Amp Lee	.20
122	Isaac Bruce	.40
123	Eddie Kennison	.40
124	Natrone Means	.75
125	Junior Seau	.40
126	Bryan Still	.20
127	Steve Young	1.50
128	Jerry Rice	2.50
129	Garrison Hearst	.75
130	J.J. Stokes	.40
131	Terrell Owens	1.00
132	Warren Moon	.40
133	Jon Kitna	.40
134	Ricky Watters	.40
135	Joey Galloway	1.00
136	Trent Dilfer	.40
137	Warrick Dunn	2.00
138	Mike Alstott	1.00
139	Bert Emanuel	.20
140	Reidel Anthony	.20
141	Steve McNair	1.25
142	Yancey Thigpen	.20
143	Eddie George	2.00
144	Chris Sanders	.20
145	Gus Frerotte	.20
146	Terry Allen	.40
147	Michael Westbrook	.20
148	Troy Aikman CL	1.25
149	Dan Marino CL	1.50
150	Randy Moss CL	5.00

1998 Upper Deck Encore Constant Threat

This lineup showcases high-impact players who could affect the outcome of a game in the blink of an eye. Singles have the prefix "CT" before the card number and were inserted 1:11 packs.

		MT
Complete Set (15):		85.00
Common Player:		2.00
Inserted 1:11		
1	Dan Marino	10.00
2	Peyton Manning	15.00
3	Randy Moss	25.00
4	Brett Favre	12.00
5	Mark Brunell	4.00
6	John Elway	8.00
7	Ryan Leaf	7.00
8	Jake Plummer	5.00
9	Terrell Davis	10.00
10	Barry Sanders	12.00
11	Emmitt Smith	10.00
12	Curtis Martin	5.00
13	Eddie George	5.00
14	Warrick Dunn	5.00
15	Curtis Enis	4.00

1998 Upper Deck Encore Driving Forces

This insert consists of 14 NFL superstars, including top QB's, running backs and wide re-ceivers. Singles have the prefix "F" before the card number and were inserted 1:23. The parallel F/X Golds are in gold foil and were sequentially numbered to 1,500.

		MT
Complete Set (14):		85.00
Common Player:		3.00
Inserted 1:23		
F/X Golds:		2x
Production 1,500 Cards		
1	Terrell Davis	15.00
2	Barry Sanders	20.00
3	Doug Flutie	7.00
4	Mark Brunell	8.00
5	Garrison Hearst	3.00
6	Jamal Anderson	5.00
7	Jerry Rice	10.00
8	John Elway	12.00
9	Robert Smith	3.00
10	Kordell Stewart	8.00
11	Eddie George	8.00
12	Antonio Freeman	3.00
13	Dan Marino	15.00
14	Steve Young	7.00

1998 Upper Deck Encore Milestones

This collection includes cards that will boast special "UD Milestones" stamps. Designated sequential numbering for each gold-foil card signifies a remarkable milestone reached by that player for the '98 season. For example, Dan Marino (400th touchdown pass thrown on 11/28/98) will be crash-numbered to 400.

		MT
Complete Set (8):		1500.
Common Player:		50.00
1	Peyton Manning/26	325.00
12	Randy Moss/17	850.00
60	Emmitt Smith/124	75.00
62	John Elway/50	150.00
63	Terrell Davis/30	250.00
67	Barry Sanders/100	125.00
85	Dan Marino/400	50.00
128	Jerry Rice/184	50.00

1998 Upper Deck Encore Rookie Encore

The 1998 season produced a host of solid first-year players and this lineup captures the best of the best. Each card has the prefix "RE" before the number and were found 1:23 packs. The FX Gold parallel singles are in gold foil and are sequentially numbered to 500.

		MT
Complete Set (10):		80.00
Common Player:		2.00
Inserted 1:23		
F/X Golds:		2x-4x
Production 500 Sets		
1	Randy Moss	40.00
2	Peyton Manning	20.00
3	Charlie Batch	12.00
4	Fred Taylor	12.00
5	Robert Edwards	7.00
6	Curtis Enis	6.00
7	Robert Holcombe	2.00
8	Ryan Leaf	4.00
9	John Avery	4.00
10	Tim Dwight	4.00

Post-1980 cards in Near Mint condition will generally sell for about 75% of the quoted MT value. Excellent-condition cards bring no more than 40%.

1998 Upper Deck Encore Super Powers

These cards feature the hottest players who are in pursuit of a Super Bowl ring. Singles are on rainbow-foil stock and were inserted 1:11 packs. Cards are numbered with a "S" prefix.

		MT
Complete Set (15):		85.00
Common Player:		2.00
Inserted 1:11		
1	Dan Marino	10.00
2	Napoleon Kaufman	2.00
3	Brett Favre	12.00
4	John Elway	8.00
5	Randy Moss	25.00
6	Kordell Stewart	5.00
7	Mark Brunell	5.00
8	Peyton Manning	15.00
9	Emmitt Smith	10.00
10	Jake Plummer	5.00
11	Eddie George	5.00
12	Warrick Dunn	5.00
13	Jerome Bettis	2.00
14	Terrell Davis	10.00
15	Fred Taylor	10.00

1998 Upper Deck Encore Superstar Encore

This insert includes the top six players in the league including rookie Randy Moss. Each single has the prefix "RR" before the card number and were inserted 1:23 packs. The F/X Gold parallel singles were limited to only 25 of each.

		MT
Complete Set (6):		50.00
Common Player:		4.00
Inserted 1:23		
F/X Gold Cards:		20x-40x
F/X Gold Rookies:		10x-20x
Production 25 Sets		
1	Brett Favre	12.00
2	Barry Sanders	12.00
3	Mark Brunell	4.00
4	Emmitt Smith	8.00
5	Randy Moss	25.00
6	Terrell Davis	10.00

1998 Upper Deck Encore UD Authentics

This collection includes autographed cards of five NFL superstars: Mark Brunell, Dan Marino, Randy Moss, Terrell Davis and Joe Montana. Singles were inserted 1:288 packs.

		MT
Complete Set (5):		750.00
Common Player:		75.00
Inserted 1:288		
MB	Mark Brunell	75.00
DM	Dan Marino	200.00
RM	Randy Moss	275.00
TD	Terrell Davis	150.00
JM	Joe Montana	150.00

Values quoted in this guide reflect the retail price of a card — the price a collector can expect to pay when buying a card from a dealer. The wholesale price — that which a collector can expect to receive from a dealer when selling cards — will be significantly lower, depending on desirability and condition.

1999 UD Ionix

UD Ionix is a 90-card set with 30 seeded rookies found 1:4 packs. Each card is super thick, double laminated and metalized. Inserts include: Reciprocal, Astronomix, Electric Forces, HoloGrFX, Power F/X, UD Authentics and Warp Zone.

		MT
Complete Set (90):		160.00
Common Player:		.25
Minor Stars:		.50
Common Rookie:		2.50
Inserted 1:4		
Wax Box:		85.00
1	Jake Plummer	2.00
2	Adrian Murrell	.25
3	Jamal Anderson	1.00
4	Chris Chandler	.50
5	Priest Holmes	1.00
6	Michael Jackson	.50
7	Antowain Smith	1.00
8	Doug Flutie	1.50
9	Tshimanga Biakabutuka	.25
10	Muhsin Muhammad	.25
11	Erik Kramer	.25
12	Curtis Enis	1.00
13	Corey Dillon	1.00
14	Ty Detmer	.50
15	Justin Armour	.25
16	Troy Aikman	3.00
17	Emmitt Smith	3.00
18	John Elway	3.00
19	Terrell Davis	3.00
20	Barry Sanders	4.00
21	Charlie Batch	1.50
22	Brett Favre	4.00
23	Dorsey Levens	1.00
24	Marshall Faulk	1.00
25	Peyton Manning	3.00
26	Mark Brunell	1.50
27	Fred Taylor	2.00
28	Elvis Grbac	.50
29	Andre Rison	.50
30	Dan Marino	3.00
31	Karim Abdul	.75
32	Randall Cunningham	1.00
33	Randy Moss	5.00
34	Drew Bledsoe	1.50
35	Terry Glenn	.75
36	Danny Wuerffel	.25
37	Kent Graham	.25
38	Gary Brown	.25
39	Vinny Testaverde	.50
40	Keyshawn Johnson	1.00
41	Napoleon Kaufman	1.00
42	Tim Brown	.50
43	Koy Detmer	.25
44	Duce Staley	.50
45	Kordell Stewart	1.25
46	Jerome Bettis	1.00
47	Isaac Bruce	.75
48	Robert Holcombe	.25
49	Jim Harbaugh	.50
50	Natrone Means	.75
51	Steve Young	1.50
52	Jerry Rice	2.00
53	Jon Kitna	1.25
54	Joey Galloway	1.00
55	Warrick Dunn	1.25
56	Trent Dilfer	.75
57	Steve McNair	1.25
58	Eddie George	1.25
59	Skip Hicks	1.00
60	Michael Westbrook	.50
61	*Tim Couch*	25.00
62	*Ricky Williams*	25.00
63	*Daunte Culpepper*	10.00
64	*Akili Smith*	10.00
65	*Donovan McNabb*	10.00
66	*Michael Bishop*	7.00
67	*Brock Huard*	5.00
68	*Torry Holt*	8.00
69	*Cade McNown*	10.00
70	*Shaun King*	8.00
71	*Champ Bailey*	5.00
72	*Chris Claiborne*	4.00
73	*Jevon Kearse*	4.00
74	*D'Wayne Bates*	2.50
75	*David Boston*	8.00
76	*Edgerrin James*	25.00
77	*Sedrick Irvin*	4.00
78	*Dameane Douglas*	4.00
79	*Troy Edwards*	8.00
80	*Ebenezer Ekuban*	2.50
81	*Kevin Faulk*	8.00
82	*Joe Germaine*	5.00
83	*Kevin Johnson*	8.00
84	*Andy Katzenmoyer*	4.00
85	*Rob Konrad*	2.50
86	*Chris McAlister*	2.50
87	*Peerless Price*	5.00
88	*Tai Streets*	2.50
89	*Autry Denson*	4.00
90	*Amos Zereoue*	6.00

1999 UD Ionix Reciprocal

This is a parallel to the base and has the prefix R before the card number. Cards #1-60 were found 1:6 packs and the rookies #61-90 were inserted 1:19 packs. The word "Reciprocal" is printed on the fronts of each card.

		MT
Complete Set (90):		400.00
Reciprocal Cards:		2x-4x
Inserted 1:6		
Reciprocal Rookies:		2x
Inserted 1:19		

1999 UD Ionix Astronomix

Each card in this 25-card set highlights a statistical achievement by that particular player. Singles were inserted 1:23 packs.

		MT
Complete Set (25):		200.00
Common Player:		5.00
Inserted 1:23		
1	Keyshawn Johnson	5.00
2	Emmitt Smith	18.00
3	Eddie George	6.00
4	Fred Taylor	12.00
5	Peyton Manning	18.00
6	John Elway	18.00
7	Brett Favre	25.00
8	Terrell Davis	18.00
9	Mark Brunell	8.00
10	Dan Marino	18.00
11	Randall Cunningham	5.00
12	Steve McNair	5.00
13	Jamal Anderson	5.00
14	Barry Sanders	25.00
15	Jake Plummer	12.00
16	Drew Bledsoe	8.00
17	Jerome Bettis	5.00
18	Jerry Rice	12.00
19	Warrick Dunn	6.00
20	Steve Young	8.00
21	Terrell Owens	5.00
22	Ricky Williams	30.00
23	Akili Smith	12.00
24	Cade McNown	12.00
25	David Boston	10.00

A player's name in *italic type* indicates a rookie card.

1999 UD Ionix Electric Forces

This 20-card set includes the most collectible NFL stars of today. Singles were inserted 1:6 packs.

		MT
Complete Set (20):		60.00
Common Player:		2.00
Inserted 1:6		
1	Ricky Williams	15.00
2	Tim Couch	15.00
3	Daunte Culpepper	5.00
4	Akili Smith	5.00
5	Cade McNown	5.00
6	Donovan McNabb	5.00
7	Brock Huard	2.00
8	Michael Bishop	3.00
9	Torry Holt	4.00
10	Peerless Price	3.00
11	Peyton Manning	6.00
12	Jake Plummer	3.00
13	John Elway	6.00
14	Mark Brunell	3.00
15	Steve Young	2.50
16	Jamal Anderson	2.00
17	Kordell Stewart	2.50
18	Eddie George	2.50
19	Fred Taylor	4.00
20	Brett Favre	8.00

1999 UD Ionix HoloGrFX

The top NFL stars and rookies are included in this 10-card set. Singles were issued at 1:1,500 packs.

		MT
Complete Set (10):		1200.
Common Player:		75.00
Inserted 1:1,500		
1	Ricky Williams	250.00
2	Tim Couch	250.00
3	Cade McNown	100.00
4	Peyton Manning	150.00
5	Jake Plummer	125.00
6	Randy Moss	250.00
7	Barry Sanders	250.00
8	Jamal Anderson	75.00
9	Terrell Davis	175.00
10	Brett Favre	250.00

1999 UD Ionix Power F/X

The game's most impressive talents, with a mix of rookies and veterans are highlighted in this 9-card set. Singles were inserted 1:11 packs.

		MT
Complete Set (9):		40.00
Common Player:		2.00
Inserted 1:11		
1	Peyton Manning	7.00
2	Randy Moss	10.00
3	Terrell Davis	8.00
4	Steve Young	3.00
5	Dan Marino	8.00
6	Warrick Dunn	2.00

7	Keyshawn Johnson	2.00
8	Barry Sanders	10.00
9	Tim Couch	12.00

1999 UD Ionix UD Authentics

This 10-card set includes autographs from the top rookies from the 1999 draft. Each player signed 100 cards each except for Ricky Williams who signed only 50.

		MT
Complete Set (10):		1300.
Common Player:		60.00
Production 100 Sets		
Ricky Williams Only Signed 50		
MB	Michael Bishop	75.00
TC	Tim Couch	250.00
DC	Daunte Culpepper	125.00
TH	Torry Holt	85.00
BH	Brock Huard	60.00
SK	Shaun King	60.00
DM	Donovan McNabb	125.00
CM	Cade McNown	125.00
AS	Akili Smith	125.00
RW	Ricky Williams	500.00

1999 UD Ionix Warp Zone

A mix of stars and rookies from the NFL make up this 15-card set that was inserted 1:108 packs.

		MT
Complete Set (15):		375.00
Common Player:		10.00
Inserted 1:108		
1	Ricky Williams	75.00
2	Tim Couch	75.00
3	Cade McNown	25.00
4	Daunte Culpepper	25.00
5	Akili Smith	25.00
6	Brock Huard	10.00
7	Donovan McNabb	25.00
8	Jake Plummer	25.00
9	Jamal Anderson	10.00
10	John Elway	40.00
11	Randy Moss	50.00
12	Terrell Davis	40.00
13	Troy Aikman	25.00
14	Barry Sanders	50.00
15	Fred Taylor	25.00

1999 Upper Deck

Upper Deck is a 270-card set that includes 45 seeded rookies found 1:4 packs. Each base card has a parallel Exclusive Silver and Exclusive Gold. Other inserts include: 21 TD Salute, Game Jersey, Game Jersey Patch, Highlight Zone, Livewires, PowerDeck, Quarterback Class and Strike Force.

		MT
Complete Set (270):		250.00
Common Player:		.15
Minor Stars:		.30
Common Rookie:		2.00
Inserted 1:4		
Wax Box:		80.00
1	Jake Plummer	1.25
2	Adrian Murrell	.15
3	Rob Moore	.30
4	Larry Centers	.15
5	Simeon Rice	.15
6	Andre Wadsworth	.15
7	Frank Sanders	.30
8	Tim Dwight	.50
9	Ray Buchanan	.15
10	Chris Chandler	.30
11	Jamal Anderson	.50
12	O.J. Santiago	.15
13	Danny Kanell	.15
14	Terance Mathis	.15
15	Priest Holmes	.50

16	Tony Banks	.30
17	Ray Lewis	.15
18	Patrick Johnson	.15
19	Michael Jackson	.15
20	Michael McCrary	.15
21	Jermaine Lewis	.30
22	Eric Moulds	.50
23	Doug Flutie	.75
24	Antowain Smith	.50
25	Rob Johnson	.30
26	Bruce Smith	.15
27	Andre Reed	.15
28	Thurman Thomas	.30
29	Fred Lane	.15
30	Wesley Walls	.15
31	Tshimanga	.15
	Biakabutuka	
32	Kevin Greene	.15
33	Steve Beuerlein	.15
34	Muhsin Muhammad	.15
35	Rae Carruth	.15
36	Bobby Engram	.15
37	Curtis Enis	.30
38	Edgar Bennett	.15
39	Erik Kramer	.15
40	Steve Stenstrom	.15
41	Alonzo Mayes	.15
42	Curtis Conway	.30
43	Tony McGee	.15
44	Darnay Scott	.15
45	Jeff Blake	.30
46	Corey Dillon	.50
47	Ki-Jana Carter	.15
48	Takeo Spikes	.15
49	Carl Pickens	.30
50	Ty Detmer	.15
51	Leslie Shepherd	.15
52	Terry Kirby	.15
53	Marquez Pope	.15
54	Antonio Langham	.15
55	Jamir Miller	.15
56	Derrick Alexander	.15
57	Troy Aikman	1.25
58	Raghib Ismail	.15
59	Emmitt Smith	2.00
60	Michael Irvin	.30
61	David LaFleur	.15
62	Chris Warren	.15
63	Deion Sanders	.50
64	Greg Ellis	.15
65	John Elway	2.00
66	Bubby Brister	.30
67	Terrell Davis	2.00
68	Ed McCaffrey	.30
69	John Mobley	.15
70	Bill Romanowski	.15
71	Rod Smith	.30
72	Shannon Sharpe	.30
73	Charlie Batch	.75
74	Germane Crowell	.30
75	Johnnie Morton	.15
76	Barry Sanders	2.50
77	Robert Porcher	.15
78	Stephen Boyd	.15
79	Herman Moore	.50
80	Brett Favre	2.50
81	Mark Chmura	.30
82	Antonio Freeman	.50
83	Robert Brooks	.15
84	Vonnie Holliday	.15
85	Bill Schroeder	.15
86	Dorsey Levens	.50
87	Santana Dotson	.15
88	Peyton Manning	2.00
89	Jerome Pathon	.15
90	Marvin Harrison	.30
91	Ellis Johnson	.15
92	Ken Dilger	.15
93	E.G. Green	.15
94	Jeff Burris	.15
95	Mark Brunell	1.00
96	Fred Taylor	1.25
97	Jimmy Smith	.30
98	James Stewart	.15
99	Kyle Brady	.15
100	Dave Thomas	.15
101	Keenan McCardell	.15
102	Elvis Grbac	.30
103	Tony Gonzalez	.30
104	Andre Rison	.30
105	Donnell Bennett	.15
106	Derrick Thomas	.30
107	Warren Moon	.30
108	Derrick Alexander	.15
109	Dan Marino	2.00
110	O.J. McDuffie	.30
111	Karim Abdul	.30
112	John Avery	.30
113	Sam Madison	.15
114	Jason Taylor	.15
115	Zach Thomas	.30
116	Randall	.50
	Cunningham	
117	Randy Moss	3.00
118	Cris Carter	.50
119	Jake Reed	.15
120	Matthew Hatchette	.15
121	John Randle	.15
122	Robert Smith	.30
123	Drew Bledsoe	1.00
124	Ben Coates	.30
125	Terry Glenn	.30
126	Ty Law	.15
127	Tony Simmons	.15
128	Ted Johnson	.15
129	Tony Carter	.15
130	Willie McGinest	.15
131	Danny Wuerffel	.15

132	Cameron Cleeland	.15
133	Eddie Kennison	.15
134	Joe Johnson	.15
135	Andre Hastings	.15
136	La'Roi Glover	.15
137	Kent Graham	.15
138	Tiki Barber	.15
139	Gary Brown	.15
140	Ike Hilliard	.15
141	Jason Sehorn	.15
142	Michael Strahan	.15
143	Amani Toomer	.15
144	Kerry Collins	.30
145	Vinny Testaverde	.30
146	Wayne Chrebet	.30
147	Curtis Martin	.50
148	Mo Lewis	.15
149	Aaron Glenn	.15
150	Steve Atwater	.15
151	Keyshawn Johnson	.50
152	James Farrior	.15
153	Rich Gannon	.15
154	Tim Brown	.30
155	Darrell Russell	.15
156	Rickey Dudley	.15
157	Charles Woodson	.50
158	James Jett	.15
159	Napoleon Kaufman	.50
160	Duce Staley	.30
161	Doug Pederson	.15
162	Bobby Hoying	.15
163	Koy Detmer	.15
164	Kevin Turner	.15
165	Charles Johnson	.15
166	Mike Mamula	.15
167	Jerome Bettis	.50
168	Courtney Hawkins	.15
169	Will Blackwell	.15
170	Kordell Stewart	.75
171	Richard Huntley	.15
172	Levon Kirkland	.15
173	Hines Ward	.30
174	Trent Green	.30
175	Marshall Faulk	.15
176	Az-Zahir Hakim	.15
177	Amp Lee	.15
178	Robert Holcombe	.30
179	Isaac Bruce	.30
180	Kevin Carter	.15
181	Jim Harbaugh	.30
182	Junior Seau	.30
183	Natrone Means	.50
184	Ryan Leaf	.50
185	Charlie Jones	.15
186	Rodney Harrison	.15
187	Mikhael Ricks	.15
188	Steve Young	.75
189	Terrell Owens	.50
190	Jerry Rice	1.25
191	J.J. Stokes	.30
192	Irv Smith	.15
193	Bryant Young	.15
194	Garrison Hearst	.30
195	Jon Kitna	.75
196	Ahman Green	.30
197	Joey Galloway	.50
198	Ricky Watters	.30
199	Chad Brown	.15
200	Shawn Springs	.15
201	Mike Pritchard	.15
202	Trent Dilfer	.30
203	Reidel Anthony	.15
204	Bert Emanuel	.15
205	Warrick Dunn	.50
206	Jacquez Green	.30
207	Hardy Nickerson	.15
208	Mike Alstott	.50
209	Eddie George	.75
210	Steve McNair	.50
211	Kevin Dyson	.30
212	Frank Wycheck	.15
213	Jackie Harris	.15
214	Blaine Bishop	.15
215	Yancey Thigpen	.15
216	Brad Johnson	.50
217	Rodney Peete	.15
218	Michael Westbrook	.30
219	Skip Hicks	.50
220	Brian Mitchell	.15
221	Dan Wilkinson	.15
222	Dana Stubblefield	.15
223	Set Checklist #1	.15
224	Checklist #2	.15
225	Checklist #3	.15
226	*Champ Bailey*	6.00
227	*Chris McAlister*	4.00
228	*Jevon Kearse*	10.00
229	*Ebenezer Ekuban*	2.00
230	*Chris Claiborne*	5.00
231	*Andy Katzenmoyer*	5.00
232	*Tim Couch*	40.00
233	*Daunte Culpepper*	20.00
234	*Akili Smith*	20.00
235	*Donovan McNabb*	20.00
236	*Sean Bennett*	5.00
237	*Brock Huard*	6.00
238	*Cade McNown*	20.00
239	*Shaun King*	15.00
240	*Joe Germaine*	6.00
241	*Ricky Williams*	40.00
242	*Edgerrin James*	80.00
243	*Sedrick Irvin*	6.00
244	*Kevin Faulk*	8.00
245	*Rob Konrad*	4.00
246	*James Johnson*	6.00
247	*Amos Zereoue*	8.00
248	*Torry Holt*	10.00
249	*D'Wayne Bates*	4.00

250	*David Boston*	10.00
251	*Dameane Douglas*	2.00
252	*Troy Edwards*	10.00
253	*Kevin Johnson*	10.00
254	*Peerless Price*	6.00
255	*Antoine Winfield*	4.00
256	*Michael Cloud*	4.00
257	*Joe Montgomery*	5.00
258	*Jermaine Fazande*	2.00
259	*Scott Covington*	2.00
260	*Aaron Brooks*	4.00
261	*Patrick Kerney*	2.00
262	*Cecil Collins*	20.00
263	*Chris Greisen*	2.00
264	*Craig Yeast*	2.00
265	*Karsten Bailey*	2.00
266	*Reginald Kelly*	2.00
267	*Travis McGriff*	2.00
268	*Jeff Paulk*	2.00
269	*Jim Kleinsasser*	4.00
270	*Darrin Chiaverini*	2.00

1999 Upper Deck Exclusives Silver

This is a parallel to the base set and is the same card except for on the bottom of the card the words "UD Exclusives" are printed on it along with the sequential numbering to 100 on gold foil.

	MT
UDE Cards:	20x-40x
UDE Rookies:	3x
Production 100 Sets	

1999 Upper Deck Exclusives Gold

This is a parallel to the base set with each single sequentially numbered to only 1.

	MT
Production 1 Set	

1999 Upper Deck 21 TD Salute

This 10-card insert is a salute to Denver running back Terrell Davis for becoming the fourth NFL player in history to run for more than 2,000 yards in a single season. He also set a Broncos' franchise record with 21 rushing touchdowns. Singles were found 1:23 packs. A parallel Silver set was made and sequentially numbered to 100 and a Gold limited to only one.

		MT
Complete Set (10):		60.00
Common Player:		6.00
Inserted 1:23		
Quantum Silver:		8x-16x
Production 100 Sets		

Quantum Gold Production 1 Set

1	Terrell Davis	6.00
2	Terrell Davis	6.00
3	Terrell Davis	6.00
4	Terrell Davis	6.00
5	Terrell Davis	6.00
6	Terrell Davis	6.00
7	Terrell Davis	6.00
8	Terrell Davis	6.00
9	Terrell Davis	6.00
10	Terrell Davis	6.00

1999 Upper Deck Game Jersey

Singles from this 11-card set were inserted in both hobby and retail product at 1:2,500 packs. Each single has a piece of actual game-used (or rookie photo shoot-used) jersey on the fronts of the cards. Both Terrell Davis and Cade McNown signed cards to their jersey numbers of 30 and 8.

		MT
Complete Set (11):		2500.
Common Player:		100.00
Inserted 1:2,500		
JA	Jamal Anderson	100.00
DB	Drew Bledsoe	225.00
TC	Tim Couch	425.00
TC-A	Tim Couch Auto.	
TD	Terrell Davis	400.00
TD-A	Terrell Davis Auto.	
DF	Doug Flutie	175.00
EJ	Edgerrin James	350.00
KJ	Keyshawn Johnson	150.00
DM	Dan Marino	400.00
RM	Randy Moss	500.00
AS	Akili Smith	200.00
SY	Steve Young	175.00

1999 Upper Deck Game Jersey Hobby

This 12-card insert could only be found in hobby product at 1:288 packs. Each single includes a piece of game-used (or rookie photo shoot-used) jersey on the fronts of the cards. Both Tim Couch and Brock Huard signed cards to their jersey number of 2 and 5.

		MT
Complete Set (12):		1700.
Common Player:		60.00
Inserted 1:288		
TA	Troy Aikman	200.00
DV	David Boston	100.00
DC	Daunte Culpepper	150.00
JE	John Elway	250.00
BH	Brock Huard	60.00
BH-A	Brock Huard Auto.	
PM	Peyton Manning	250.00
MC	Donovan McNabb	150.00
CM	Cade McNown	150.00
CM-A	Cade McNown Auto.	
EM	Eric Moulds	60.00
JP	Jake Plummer	200.00
JR	Jerry Rice	200.00
BS	Barry Sanders	300.00

1999 Upper Deck Game Jersey Patch

Each single in this 20-card set has a piece of the team logo from the jersey on the card. Singles were inserted 1:7,500 packs.

		MT
Common Player:		150.00
Inserted 1:7,500		
TA	Troy Aikman	450.00
JA	Jamal Anderson	150.00
DB	Drew Bledsoe	400.00
DV	David Boston	200.00
TC	Tim Couch	700.00
DC	Daunte Culpepper	300.00
TD	Terrell Davis	600.00
JE	John Elway	700.00
DF	Doug Flutie	350.00
BH	Brock Huard	150.00
EJ	Edgerrin James	800.00
PM	Peyton Manning	600.00
DM	Dan Marino	600.00
DV	Donovan McNabb	300.00
CM	Cade McNown	300.00
RM	Randy Moss	800.00
JR	Jerry Rice	450.00
BS	Barry Sanders	800.00
AS	Akili Smith	300.00
SY	Steve Young	375.00

1999 Upper Deck Highlight Zone

This 20-card insert spotlights the top players in the NFL. Singles were printed on a foil board and found 1:23 packs. A Silver parallel was printed and sequentially numbered to 100, along with a Gold numbered to only 1.

		MT
Complete Set (20):		170.00
Common Player:		2.00
Minor Stars:		4.00
Inserted 1:23		
Quantum Silver:		5x-10x
Production 100 Sets		
Quantum Gold		
Production 1 Set		
1	Terrell Davis	15.00
2	Ricky Williams	20.00
3	Akili Smith	8.00
4	Charlie Batch	4.00
5	Jake Plummer	10.00
6	Emmitt Smith	15.00
7	Dan Marino	15.00
8	Tim Couch	20.00
9	Randy Moss	20.00
10	Troy Aikman	10.00
11	Barry Sanders	20.00
12	Jerry Rice	10.00
13	Mark Brunell	8.00
14	Jamal Anderson	2.00
15	Peyton Manning	12.00
16	Jerome Bettis	2.00
17	Donovan McNabb	8.00
18	Steve Young	6.00
19	Keyshawn Johnson	4.00
20	Brett Favre	20.00

1999 Upper Deck Livewires

Each card in this 15-card set has actual printed transcripts of statements made by big-name players during games. Singles were inserted 1:10 packs. A Silver parallel was produced and numbered to 100, along with a Gold that was limited to only one set.

		MT
Complete Set (15):		50.00
Common Player:		1.00
Minor Stars:		2.00
Inserted 1:10		
Quantum Silver:		10x-20x
Production 100 Sets		
Quantum Gold:		
Production 1 Set		
1	Jake Plummer	4.00
2	Jamal Anderson	1.00
3	Emmitt Smith	6.00
4	John Elway	6.00
5	Barry Sanders	8.00
6	Brett Favre	8.00
7	Mark Brunell	3.00
8	Fred Taylor	4.00
9	Randy Moss	8.00
10	Drew Bledsoe	3.00
11	Keyshawn Johnson	2.00
12	Jerome Bettis	2.00
13	Kordell Stewart	2.00
14	Terrell Owens	2.00
15	Eddie George	2.00

1999 Upper Deck PowerDeck I

Each of these singles are an interactive card that comes to life with game-action footage, sound, photos and career highlights of the featured player. Singles were found 1:288 packs.

		MT
Complete Set (8):		325.00
Common Player:		25.00
Inserted 1:288		
TC-PD	Tim Couch	60.00
DC-PD	Daunte Culpepper	25.00
JE-PD	John Elway	60.00
PM-PD	Peyton Manning	60.00
DM-PD	Dan Marino	60.00
CM-PD	Cade McNown	25.00
BS-PD	Barry Sanders	75.00
AS-PD	Akili Smith	25.00

1999 Upper Deck PowerDeck II

Each single in this set is a interactive card with game-action footage, sound, photos and career highlights of that featured player. Singles were found 1:24 packs.

		MT
Complete Set (8):		45.00
Common Player:		2.00
Inserted 1:24		
TA-PD	Troy Aikman	8.00
TD-PD	Terrell Davis	12.00
JG-PD	Joe Germaine	2.00
BH-PD	Brock Huard	2.00
SK-PD	Shaun King	4.00
Mc-PD	Donovan McNabb	8.00
JM-PD	Joe Montana	8.00
RM-PD	Randy Moss	16.00

1999 Upper Deck Quarterback Class

This 15-card insert includes the top QB's in the NFL along with rookies from 1999. Singles were found 1:10 packs. A parallel Silver was numbered to 100 and a parallel Gold was limited to only one set.

	MT
Complete Set (15):	50.00

		MT
Common Player:		1.00
Minor Stars:		2.00
Inserted 1:10		
Quantum Silver:		10x-20x
Production 100 Sets		
Quantum Gold		
Production 1 Set		
1	Tim Couch	10.00
2	Akili Smith	4.00
3	Daunte Culpepper	4.00
4	Cade McNown	4.00
5	Donovan McNabb	4.00
6	Brock Huard	1.00
7	John Elway	6.00
8	Dan Marino	6.00
9	Brett Favre	8.00
10	Charlie Batch	2.00
11	Steve Young	2.50
12	Jake Plummer	4.00
13	Peyton Manning	6.00
14	Mark Brunell	3.00
15	Troy Aikman	4.00

1999 Upper Deck Strike Force

This 30-card set includes the top scoring threats in the NFL and brings them to life on a silver-foil board card. Singles were inserted 1:4 packs. A parallel Silver was sequentially numbered to 100 and a Gold parallel was issued with only one set made.

		MT
Complete Set (30):		50.00
Common Player:		1.00
Minor Stars:		2.00
Inserted 1:4		
1	Jamal Anderson	1.00
2	Keyshawn Johnson	2.00
3	Eddie George	2.50
4	Steve Young	2.50
5	Emmitt Smith	4.00
6	Karim Abdul	1.00
7	Kordell Stewart	2.50
8	Cade McNown	3.50
9	Tim Couch	8.00
10	Corey Dillon	2.00
11	Peyton Manning	5.00
12	Curtis Martin	2.00
13	Jerome Bettis	2.00
14	Jon Kitna	2.00
15	Dan Marino	5.00
16	Eric Moulds	2.00
17	Charlie Batch	2.50
18	Ricky Williams	8.00
19	Terrell Owens	2.00
20	Ty Detmer	1.00
21	Curtis Enis	2.00
22	Doug Flutie	2.50
23	Randall Cunningham	2.00
24	Donovan McNabb	3.50
25	Steve McNair	2.50
26	Terrell Davis	5.00
27	Daunte Culpepper	3.50
28	Warrick Dunn	2.00
29	Akili Smith	3.50
30	Barry Sanders	6.00

1999 Upper Deck Black Diamond

This was a 150-card set that included 40 rookies that

		MT
Common Player:		1.00
Minor Stars:		2.00
Inserted 1:10		
Quantum Silver:		10x-20x
Production 100 Sets		
Quantum Gold		
Production 1 Set		
1	Tim Couch	10.00
2	Akili Smith	4.00
3	Daunte Culpepper	4.00
4	Cade McNown	4.00
5	Donovan McNabb	4.00
6	Brock Huard	1.00
7	John Elway	6.00
8	Dan Marino	6.00
9	Brett Favre	8.00
10	Charlie Batch	2.00
11	Steve Young	2.50
12	Jake Plummer	4.00
13	Peyton Manning	6.00
14	Mark Brunell	3.00
15	Troy Aikman	4.00

were inserted 1:4 packs. Each single has a parallel Diamond Cut card with veterans inserted 1:7 packs and rookies inserted 1:12. Each also has a parallel Final Cut single with veterans numbered to 100 and rookies numbered to 50. Other insert sets included: A Piece of History, Diamonation, Gallery, Might, Myriad, Skills and the Walter Payton Autograph Game Jersey card. SRP was $3.99 for six-card packs.

		MT
Complete Set (150):		140.00
Common Player:		.20
Minor Stars:		.40
Common Rookie:		1.50
Inserted 1:4		
Wax Box:		70.00
1	Adrian Murrell	.20
2	Jake Plummer	1.50
3	Rob Moore	.40
4	Frank Sanders	.40
5	Jamal Anderson	.75
6	Terance Mathis	.20
7	Chris Chandler	.40
8	Tim Dwight	.75
9	Jermaine Lewis	.20
10	Priest Holmes	.75
11	Peter Boulware	.20
12	Doug Flutie	1.25
13	Antowain Smith	.75
14	Eric Moulds	.75
15	Bruce Smith	.20
16	Rae Carruth	.20
17	Muhsin Muhammad	.40
18	Wesley Walls	.40
19	Tshimanga Biakabutuka	.40
20	Curtis Enis	.75
21	Curtis Conway	.40
22	Bobby Engram	.20
23	Darnay Scott	.40
24	Corey Dillon	.75
25	Jeff Blake	.40
26	Ty Detmer	.20
27	Terry Kirby	.20
28	Leslie Shepherd	.20
29	Emmitt Smith	3.00
30	Troy Aikman	2.00
31	Michael Irvin	.40
32	Raghib Ismail	.20
33	Brian Griese	1.50
34	Terrell Davis	3.00
35	Shannon Sharpe	.40
36	Rod Smith	.50
37	Barry Sanders	4.00
38	Herman Moore	.75
39	Charlie Batch	1.00
40	Johnnie Morton	.20
41	Brett Favre	4.00
42	Dorsey Levens	.75
43	Antonio Freeman	.75
44	Mark Chmura	.40
45	Peyton Manning	3.00
46	Jerome Pathon	.20
47	Marvin Harrison	.75
48	Fred Taylor	2.00
49	Mark Brunell	1.50
50	Jimmy Smith	.75
51	Keenan McCardell	.40
52	Andre Rison	.40
53	Elvis Grbac	.40
54	Derrick Alexander	.20
55	Tony Gonzalez	.40
56	Dan Marino	3.00
57	Oronde Gadsden	.40
58	O.J. McDuffie	.40
59	Randy Moss	4.00
60	Randall Cunningham	.75
61	Cris Carter	.75
62	Robert Smith	.75
63	Drew Bledsoe	1.50
64	Terry Glenn	.75
65	Ben Coates	.40
66	Billy Joe Hobert	.20
67	Eddie Kennison	.40
68	Cam Cleeland	.40
69	Gary Brown	.20
70	Ike Hilliard	.40
71	Amani Toomer	.40
72	Vinny Testaverde	.40
73	Keyshawn Johnson	.75
74	Curtis Martin	.75
75	Wayne Chrebet	.75
76	Tim Brown	.50
77	Rickey Dudley	.40
78	Napoleon Kaufman	.75
79	Charles Woodson	.75
80	Duce Staley	.75
81	Doug Pederson	.20
82	Charles Johnson	.20
83	Kordell Stewart	.75
84	Jerome Bettis	.75
85	Courtney Hawkins	.20
86	Isaac Bruce	.75
87	Marshall Faulk	.75
88	Trent Green	.40
89	Jim Harbaugh	.40
90	Junior Seau	.40
91	Natrone Means	.50
92	Lawrence Phillips	.40
93	Steve Young	1.25
94	Terrell Owens	.75
95	Jerry Rice	2.00
96	Jon Kitna	1.00
97	Ricky Watters	.50
98	Joey Galloway	.75
99	Shawn Springs	.20
100	Warrick Dunn	.75
101	Trent Dilfer	.40
102	Reidel Anthony	.40
103	Mike Alstott	.75
104	Steve McNair	1.00
105	Eddie George	1.00
106	Kevin Dyson	.40
107	Yancey Thigpen	.40
108	Michael Westbrook	.40
109	Brad Johnson	.75
110	Skip Hicks	.40
111	*Tim Couch*	20.00
112	*Akili Smith*	10.00
113	*Ricky Williams*	20.00
114	*Donovan McNabb*	12.00
115	*Edgerrin James*	30.00
116	*Cade McNown*	12.00
117	*Daunte Culpepper*	10.00
118	*Shaun King*	12.00
119	*Brock Huard*	4.00
120	*Joe Germaine*	3.00
121	*Troy Edwards*	7.00
122	*Champ Bailey*	5.00
123	*Kevin Faulk*	5.00
124	*David Boston*	7.00
125	*Kevin Johnson*	7.00
126	*Torry Holt*	7.00
127	*James Johnson*	5.00
128	*Peerless Price*	6.00
129	*D'Wayne Bates*	3.00
130	*Cecil Collins*	4.00
131	*Na Brown*	1.50
132	*Rob Konrad*	1.50
133	*Joel Makovicka*	1.50
134	*Dameane Douglas*	1.50
135	*Scott Covington*	1.50
136	*Daylon McCutcheon*	1.50
137	*Chris Claiborne*	3.00
138	*Karsten Bailey*	3.00
139	*Mike Cloud*	3.00
140	*Sean Bennett*	3.00
141	*Jermaine Fazande*	3.00
142	*Chris McAlister*	3.00
143	*Ebenezer Ekuban*	1.50
144	*Jeff Paulk*	1.50
145	*Jim Kleinsasser*	3.00
146	*Bobby Collins*	1.50
147	*Andy Katzenmoyer*	3.00
148	*Jevon Kearse*	7.00
149	*Amos Zereoue*	3.00
150	*Sedrick Irvin*	3.00

1999 Upper Deck Black Diamond Diamond Cut

This was a 150-card parallel to the base set. Each of these singles was printed on a die-cut card with a rainbow foil design. Veterans were inserted 1:7 packs and rookies were found 1:12.

		MT
Complete Set (150):		225.00
Diamond Cut Cards:		2x-4x
Inserted 1:7		
Diamond Cut Rookies:		1.5x
Inserted 1:12		

1999 Upper Deck Black Diamond Final Cut

This was a 150-card parallel to the base set. Each single was printed with gold foil and sequentially numbered. Veterans were numbered to 100 and rookies to 50.

		MT
Final Cut Cards:		15x-30x
Production 100 Sets		
Final Cut Rookies:		4x-8x
Production 50 Sets		

1999 Upper Deck Black Diamond A Piece of History

This was a 30-card insert set that displayed a single piece of a game-used football. Some singles were only found in hobby product and were inserted 1:179 packs. Others were inserted in both hobby and retail and they were found 1:359 packs. Each single had a parallel Double Diamond single that featured two pieces of a game-used football. Hobby singles were found 1:1,079 and hobby/retail singles were also inserted 1:1,079.

	MT
Complete Set (30):	1350.

1999 Upper Deck Black Diamond Diamonation

This was a 20-card insert set that included the most dominant players in the game. Singles were inserted 1:6 packs.

		MT
Complete Set (20):		50.00
Common Player:		1.50
Inserted 1:6		
1	Brett Favre	8.00
2	Eddie George	2.00
3	Terrell Davis	6.00
4	Jerome Bettis	1.50
5	Randall Cunningham	1.50
6	Jon Kitna	2.00
7	Troy Aikman	4.00
8	Marshall Faulk	2.00
9	Steve Young	3.00
10	Warrick Dunn	1.50
11	Jake Plummer	3.00
12	Fred Taylor	4.00
13	Antonio Freeman	1.50
14	Peyton Manning	6.00
15	Randy Moss	8.00
16	Steve McNair	2.00
17	Emmitt Smith	6.00
18	Terrell Owens	1.50
19	Kordell Stewart	1.50
20	Ricky Williams	8.00

Common Player:		25.00
H Inserted 1:179		
HR Inserted 1:359		
Double Diamond Cards:		2x
H Inserted 1:1,079		
HR Inserted 1:1,079		
TA	Troy Aikman	75.00
CB	Charlie Batch	35.00
DBl	Drew Bledsoe	45.00
DBo	David Boston	35.00
TB	Tim Brown	25.00
TC	Tim Couch	100.00
DC	Daunte Culpepper	65.00
TD	Terrell Davis	60.00
WD	Warrick Dunn	25.00
BF	Brett Favre	100.00
DF	Doug Flutie	60.00
BG	Brian Griese	45.00
TH	Torry Holt	50.00
BH	Brock Huard	35.00
EJ	Edgerrin James	125.00
KJ	Keyshawn Johnson	25.00
PM	Peyton Manning	100.00
DM	Dan Marino	100.00
CMa	Curtis Martin	25.00
DMc	Donovan McNabb	65.00
CM	Cade McNown	65.00
HM	Herman Moore	25.00
RM	Randy Moss	100.00
JP	Jake Plummer	50.00
JR	Jerry Rice	75.00
DS	Deion Sanders	25.00
AS	Akili Smith	60.00
ES	Emmitt Smith	75.00
RW	Ricky Williams	100.00
SY	Steve Young	60.00

1999 Upper Deck Black Diamond Gallery

This was a 10-card insert

set that featured candid gallery, portrait-style photography of the most collectible players in the NFL. Singles were inserted 1:14 packs.

		MT
Complete Set (10):		50.00
Common Player:		2.50
Inserted 1:14		
1	Akili Smith	6.00
2	Barry Sanders	12.00
3	Curtis Martin	2.50
4	Drew Bledsoe	5.00
5	Emmitt Smith	10.00
6	Keyshawn Johnson	2.50
7	Jerry Rice	8.00
8	Tim Couch	12.00
9	Terrell Owens	2.50
10	Troy Aikman	8.00

1999 Upper Deck Black Diamond Might

This was a 10-card insert set that included ten power-house players. Singles were inserted 1:12 packs.

		MT
Complete Set (10):		20.00
Common Player:		2.00
Inserted 1:12		
1	Antowain Smith	2.00
2	Steve McNair	3.00
3	Corey Dillon	3.00
4	Dan Marino	8.00
5	Eddie George	3.00
6	Jerome Bettis	2.00
7	Jerry Rice	6.00
8	Randall Cunningham	2.00
9	Brian Griese	3.50
10	Joey Galloway	2.00

1999 Upper Deck Black Diamond Myriad

This was a 10-card insert set that captured the electrifying exploits of NFL standouts in action. Singles were inserted 1:29 packs.

		MT
Complete Set (10):		65.00
Common Player:		3.00
Inserted 1:29		
1	Barry Sanders	12.00
2	Randy Moss	12.00
3	Terrell Davis	8.00
4	Brett Favre	12.00
5	Jamal Anderson	3.00
6	Mark Brunell	5.00
7	Edgerrin James	15.00
8	Steve Young	5.00
9	Ricky Williams	10.00
10	Warrick Dunn	3.00

A card number in parentheses ( ) indicates the set is unnumbered.

1999 Upper Deck Black Diamond Skills

This was a 10-card insert set that included the most versatile and skilled athletes in the game. Singles were found 1:29 packs.

		MT
Complete Set (10):		85.00
Common Player:		3.00
Inserted 1:29		
1	Drew Bledsoe	5.00
2	Fred Taylor	7.00
3	Dan Marino	10.00
4	Jake Plummer	6.00
5	Kurt Warner	30.00
6	Marshall Faulk	3.00
7	Randy Moss	12.00
8	Peyton Manning	12.00
9	Keyshawn Johnson	3.00
10	Tim Couch	12.00

1999 Upper Deck Black Diamond W. Payton Jersey Auto.

Walter Payton signed 34 of these singles that included a piece of a game-used jersey. Singles were randomly inserted.

		MT
WPA	Walter Payton 34	2000.

1999 Upper Deck Century Legends

This was a 173-card set that included both past and present NFL players. Cards #4,6,14, 26,31,38 and 43 were never produced. Each single has a parallel Century Collection die-cut that was numbered to 100. Other insert sets included: 20th Century Superstars, Epic Milestones, Epic Signatures, Jerseys of the Century, Tour de France and Walter Payton signed cards. SRP was $4.99 for 12-card packs.

		MT
Complete Set (173):		65.00
Common Player:		.15
Minor Stars:		.30
Common Rookie:		.50
#4,6,14,26,31,38 & 43 never produced		
Wax Box:		65.00
1	Jim Brown	2.00
2	Jerry Rice	1.00
3	Joe Montana	3.00
5	Johnny Unitas	1.00
7	Otto Graham	.30
8	Walter Payton	3.00
9	Dick Butkus	1.00
10	Bob Lilly	.15
11	Sammy Baugh	.30

12	Barry Sanders	2.00
13	Deacon Jones	.50
15	Gino Marchetti	.15
16	John Elway	1.50
17	Anthony Munoz	.15
18	Ray Nitschke	.30
19	Night Train Lane	.15
20	John Hannah	.15
21	Gale Sayers	1.00
22	Reggie White	.30
23	Ronnie Lott	.30
24	Jim Parker	.15
25	Merlin Olsen	.15
27	Dan Marino	1.50
28	Forrest Gregg	.15
29	Roger Staubach	1.50
30	Jack Lambert	.15
32	Marion Motley	.15
33	Earl Campbell	.50
34	Alan Page	.15
35	Bronko Nagurski	.30
36	Mel Blount	.15
37	Deion Sanders	.30
39	Sid Luckman	.15
40	Raymond Berry	.15
41	Bart Starr	1.00
42	Willie Lanier	.15
44	Terry Bradshaw	1.50
45	Herb Adderley	.30
46	Steve Largent	.30
47	Jack Ham	.15
48	John Mackey	.15
49	Bill George	.15
50	Willie Brown	.15
51	Jerry Rice	1.00
52	Barry Sanders	2.00
53	John Elway	1.50
54	Reggie White	.30
55	Dan Marino	1.50
56	Deion Sanders	.30
57	Bruce Smith	.15
58	Steve Young	.75
59	Emmitt Smith	1.50
60	Brett Favre	2.00
61	Rod Woodson	.15
62	Troy Aikman	1.00
63	Terrell Davis	1.50
64	Michael Irvin	.30
65	Andre Rison	.15
66	Warren Moon	.30
67	Thurman Thomas	.30
68	Randall Cunningham	.30
69	Jerome Bettis	.50
70	Junior Seau	.30
71	Drew Bledsoe	.75
72	Andre Reed	.15
73	Tim Brown	.30
74	Derrick Thomas	.15
75	Jake Plummer	.75
76	Kordell Stewart	.50
77	Herman Moore	.50
78	Shannon Sharpe	.30
79	Antonio Freeman	.50
80	Ricky Watters	.30
81	Warrick Dunn	.50
82	Mark Brunell	.75
83	Randy Moss	2.00
84	Fred Taylor	1.00
85	Curtis Martin	.50
86	Keyshawn Johnson	.50
87	Eddie George	.60
88	Marshall Faulk	.50
89	Joey Galloway	.50
90	Vinny Testaverde	.30
91	Garrison Hearst	.30
92	Jimmy Smith	.50
93	Doug Flutie	.75
94	Napoleon Kaufman	.50
95	Natrone Means	.30
96	Peyton Manning	1.50
97	Steve McNair	.60
98	Corey Dillon	.50
99	Terrell Owens	.50
100	Charlie Batch	.75
101	Brett Favre	2.00
102	Terrell Davis	1.50
103	Roger Staubach	1.00
104	Terry Bradshaw	1.00
105	Fran Tarkenton	.50
106	Walter Payton	3.00
107	Mark Brunell	.75
108	Jim Brown	1.50
109	Kordell Stewart	.50
110	Bart Starr	1.00
111	Steve Largent	.30
112	Raymond Berry	.15
113	Emmitt Smith	1.50
114	Forrest Gregg	.15
115	Drew Bledsoe	.75
116	Dick Butkus	.50
117	Johnny Unitas	.50
118	Joe Montana	3.00
119	Deacon Jones	.30
120	Steve Young	.75
121	Bob Lilly	.15
122	Troy Aikman	1.00
123	Alan Page	.15
124	Earl Campbell	.50
125	Deion Sanders	.30
126	Ronnie Lott	.50
127	Reggie White	.30
128	Marshall Faulk	.50
129	Gale Sayers	1.00
130	Night Train Lane	.15
131	*Ricky Williams*	6.00
132	*Tim Couch*	8.00
133	*Donovan McNabb*	4.00

134	*Daunte Culpepper*	4.00
135	*Edgerrin James*	12.00
136	*Cade McNown*	4.00
137	*Torry Holt*	2.50
138	David Boston	2.50
139	Champ Bailey	1.75
140	Peerless Price	2.00
141	*D'Wayne Bates*	.75
142	*Joe Germaine*	.75
143	Brock Huard	1.25
144	Chris Claiborne	.75
145	Jevon Kearse	2.00
146	Troy Edwards	2.50
147	Amos Zereoue	.75
148	Aaron Brooks	.75
149	Andy Katzenmoyer	.75
150	Kevin Faulk	1.50
151	*Shaun King*	4.00
152	Kevin Johnson	2.50
153	Dameane Douglas	.50
154	Mike Cloud	.50
155	Sedrick Irvin	1.50
156	*Akili Smith*	4.00
157	Rob Konrad	.50
158	Scott Covington	.50
159	*Jeff Paulk*	.50
160	Shawn Bryson	.50
161	Joe Montana	3.00
162	John Elway	1.50
163	Joe Namath	1.50
164	Jerry Rice	1.00
165	Terry Bradshaw	1.00
166	Jim Brown	2.00
167	Paul Warfield	.30
168	Herman Moore	.50
169	Walter Payton	3.00
170	Roger Staubach	1.00
171	Ken Stabler	1.00
172	Steve Young	.75
173	Troy Aikman	1.00
174	Fran Tarkenton	.50
175	Doug Williams	.15
176	Steve Largent	.30
177	Marcus Allen	.30
178	Mike Singletary	.30
179	Earl Campbell	.30
180	Dan Fouts	.30

1999 Upper Deck Century Legends Century Collection

This was a 173-card parallel to the base set. Each single was die-cut and sequentially numbered to 100.

		MT
Century Cards:		10x-20x
Century Rookies:		5x-10x
Production 100 Sets		

1999 Upper Deck Century Legends 20th Century Superstars

This 10-card insert set focused on the NFL's most-talked about players. Singles were inserted 1:11 packs.

		MT
Complete Set (10):		35.00
Common Player:		1.50
Inserted 1:11		
1	Tim Couch	8.00
2	Ricky Williams	6.00
3	Akili Smith	4.00
4	Donovan McNabb	4.00
5	Jake Plummer	3.00
6	Brett Favre	6.00
7	Steve Young	2.00
8	Randy Moss	6.00
9	Kordell Stewart	1.50
10	Peyton Manning	5.00

1999 Upper Deck Century Legends Epic Milestones

This was a 10-card insert set that pinpointed ten of the most impressive NFL milestones ever reached. Singles were inserted 1:11 packs.

		MT
Complete Set (10):		45.00
Common Player:		1.50
Inserted 1:11		
1	John Elway	5.00
2	Joe Montana	7.00
3	Randy Moss	7.00
4	Terrell Davis	5.00
5	Dan Marino	5.00
6	Jamal Anderson	1.50
7	Jerry Rice	4.00
8	Barry Sanders	7.00
9	Emmitt Smith	5.00
10	Walter Payton	7.00

1999 Upper Deck Century Legends Epic Signatures

This 30-card insert set included autographs of both past and present stars. Singles were inserted 1:23 packs. A parallel Gold version was also released for every player except for Johnny Unitas. Each of those singles were numbered to 100.

		MT
Complete Set (30):		1750.
Common Player:		10.00
Minor Stars:		20.00
Inserted 1:23		
Century Gold Cards:		2x
Unitas never produced		
Production 100 Sets		
TA	Troy Aikman	75.00
RB	Raymond Berry	10.00
TB	Terry Bradshaw	125.00
DB	Dick Butkus	75.00
EC	Earl Campbell	50.00
HC	Harold Carmichael	20.00
CC	Cris Carter	20.00
TD	Terrell Davis	85.00
LD	Len Dawson	20.00
DF	Dan Fouts	20.00
CJ	Charlie Joiner	20.00
SL	Steve Largent	25.00
FL	Floyd Little	10.00

DM	Dan Marino	180.00
MY	Don Maynard	20.00
AM	Art Monk	20.00
JM	Joe Montana	250.00
RM	Randy Moss	175.00
JN	Joe Namath	250.00
ON	Ozzie Newsome	10.00
DR	Dan Reeves	20.00
JR	Jerry Rice	250.00
GS	Gale Sayers	30.00
MS	Michael Singletary	10.00
RS	Roger Staubach	100.00
FT	Fran Tarkenton	65.00
JU	Johnny Unitas	125.00
PW	Paul Warfield	10.00
DW	Doug Williams	20.00
JY	Jack Youngblood	10.00

1999 Upper Deck Century Legends Jerseys of the Century

This nine-card insert set included swatches of game jerseys from both past and present NFL stars. Singles were inserted 1:418 packs.

		MT
Complete Set (9):		1600.
Common Player:		75.00
#9 never produced		
Inserted 1:418		
1	Jerry Rice	225.00
2	Roger Staubach	200.00
3	Warren Moon	75.00
4	Ken Stabler	125.00
5	Reggie White	75.00
6	Dan Marino	275.00
7	Doug Flutie	125.00
8	Bob Lilly	75.00
9	Jim Brown	250.00

1999 Upper Deck Century Legends Tour de Force

This was a 10-card insert set that highlighted the ten most important players in the NFL. Singles were inserted 1:23 packs.

		MT
Complete Set (10):		45.00
Common Player:		2.50
Inserted 1:23		
1	Tim Couch	12.00
2	Ricky Williams	10.00
3	Peyton Manning	8.00
4	Troy Aikman	6.00
5	Jake Plummer	5.00
6	Jamal Anderson	2.50
7	Terrell Davis	8.00
8	Barry Sanders	10.00
9	Fred Taylor	6.00
10	Keyshawn Johnson	2.50

1999 Upper Deck Century Legends Walter Payton

Walter Payton signed 50 UD Authentic cards and 34 Game-Used Jersey cards. Singles were randomly inserted.

		MT
WPACW.Payton AUTO/50		750.00
WPCLW.Payton Jersey AUTO/34		2500.

Post-1980 cards in Near Mint condition will generally sell for about 75% of the quoted Mint value. Excellent-condition cards bring no more than 40%.

1999 Upper Deck Encore

This was a 225-card set that included 45 rookies found 1:8 packs. Parallel sets included F/X and F/X Gold. Other insert sets included: Electric Currents, Game Used Helmets, Live Wires, Seize the Game, UD Authentics, Upper Realm and the Walter Payton Game Jersey card. SRP was $3.99 for six-card packs.

		MT
Complete Set (225):		275.00
Common Player:		.20
Minor Stars:		.40
Common Rookie:		3.00
Inserted 1:8		
Wax Box:		70.00
1	Jake Plummer	1.25
2	Adrian Murrell	.20
3	Rob Moore	.40
4	Simeon Rice	.20
5	Andre Wadsworth	.20
6	Frank Sanders	.20
7	Tim Dwight	.75
8	Chris Chandler	.40
9	Jamal Anderson	.75
10	O.J. Santiago	.20
11	Tony Graziani	.20
12	Terance Mathis	.20
13	Priest Holmes	.75
14	Stoney Case	.40
15	Ray Lewis	.20
16	Peter Boulware	.20
17	Scott Mitchell	.20
18	Jermaine Lewis	.20
19	Eric Moulds	.75
20	Doug Flutie	1.00
21	Antowain Smith	.75
22	Rob Johnson	.40
23	Bruce Smith	.20
24	Andre Reed	.40
25	Wesley Walls	.40
26	Tshimanga Biakabutuka	.40
27	Fred Lane	.20
28	Steve Beurlein	.20
29	Muhsin Muhammad	.40
30	Rae Carruth	.20
31	Bobby Engram	.20
32	Curtis Enis	.75
33	Edgar Bennett	.20
34	Curtis Conway	.40
35	Shane Matthews	.40
36	Tony McGee	.20
37	Darnay Scott	.40
38	Jeff Blake	.40
39	Corey Dillon	.75
40	Ki-Jana Carter	.20
41	Ty Detmer	.20
42	Leslie Shepherd	.20
43	Terry Kirby	.20
44	Antonio Langham	.20
45	Jamir Miller	.20
46	Marc Edwards	.20
47	Troy Aikman	1.50
48	Raghib Ismail	.20
49	Emmitt Smith	2.00
50	Michael Irvin	.40
51	Deion Sanders	.75
52	Greg Ellis	.20
53	Bubby Brister	.40
54	Terrell Davis	2.00
55	Ed McCaffrey	.75
56	Rod Smith	.75
57	Shannon Sharpe	.40
58	Brian Griese	1.50
59	Charlie Batch	1.00
60	Germane Crowell	.40
61	Johnnie Morton	.20
62	Robert Porcher	.20
63	Ron Rivers	.20
64	Herman Moore	.75
65	Brett Favre	3.00
66	Bill Schroeder	.40
67	Antonio Freeman	.75
68	Dorsey Levens	.75
69	Desmond Howard	.20
70	Vonnie Holliday	.20
71	Peyton Manning	2.00
72	Jerome Pathon	.20
73	Marvin Harrison	.75
74	Ken Dilger	.20
75	E.G. Green	.20

76	Cornelius Bennett	.20
77	Mark Brunell	1.25
78	Fred Taylor	1.50
79	Jimmy Smith	.75
80	James Stewart	.75
81	Keenan McCardell	.40
82	Carnell Lake	.40
83	Elvis Grbac	.40
84	Tony Gonzalez	.40
85	Andre Rison	.40
86	Derrick Thomas	.40
87	Warren Moon	.40
88	Derrick Alexander	.20
89	Dan Marino	2.00
90	O.J. McDuffie	.40
91	Karim Abdul	.40
92	Sam Madison	.20
93	Zach Thomas	.40
94	Tony Martin	.20
95	Randall Cunningham	.75
96	Randy Moss	3.00
97	Cris Carter	.75
98	Jake Reed	.40
99	John Randle	.40
100	Robert Smith	.75
101	Drew Bledsoe	1.25
102	Ben Coates	.40
103	Terry Glenn	.75
104	Tony Simmons	.40
105	Terry Allen	.40
106	Danny Wuerffel	.40
107	Cameron Cleeland	.40
108	Eddie Kennison	.20
109	Billy Joe Hobert	.20
110	Andre Hastings	.20
111	Kent Graham	.20
112	Tiki Barber	.40
113	Gary Brown	.20
114	Ike Hilliard	.40
115	Jason Sehorn	.20
116	Kerry Collins	.40
117	Vinny Testaverde	.40
118	Wayne Chrebet	.75
119	Curtis Martin	.75
120	Rick Mirer	.20
121	Aaron Glenn	.20
122	Keyshawn Johnson	.75
123	Rich Gannon	.40
124	Tim Brown	.40
125	Darrell Russell	.20
126	Tyrone Wheatley	.40
127	Charles Woodson	.75
128	Napoleon Kaufman	.75
129	Duce Staley	.75
130	Doug Pederson	.20
131	Kevin Turner	.20
132	Charles Johnson	.20
133	Jerome Bettis	.75
134	Courtney Hawkins	.20
135	Kordell Stewart	.75
136	Richard Huntley	.40
137	Levon Kirkland	.20
138	Hines Ward	.75
139	*Kurt Warner*	30.00
140	Marshall Faulk	.75
141	Az Hakim	.40
142	Amp Lee	.20
143	Isaac Bruce	.75
144	Kevin Carter	.20
145	Jim Harbaugh	.40
146	Junior Seau	.40
147	Natrone Means	.40
148	Rodney Harrison	.20
149	Mikhael Ricks	.20
150	Erik Kramer	.20
151	Steve Young	1.00
152	Terrell Owens	.75
153	Jerry Rice	1.50
154	J.J. Stokes	.40
155	*Jeff Garcia*	10.00
156	Lawrence Phillips	.40
157	Jon Kitna	1.00
158	Derrick Mayes	.40
159	Ricky Watters	.40
160	Chad Brown	.20
161	Shawn Springs	.20
162	Sean Dawkins	.20
163	Trent Dilfer	.40
164	Reidel Anthony	.20
165	Bert Emanuel	.20
166	Warrick Dunn	.75
167	Jacquez Green	.40
168	Mike Alstott	.75
169	Eddie George	1.00
170	Steve McNair	1.00
171	Kevin Dyson	.40
172	Frank Wycheck	.20
173	Blaine Bishop	.20
174	Yancey Thigpen	.20
175	Brad Johnson	.75
176	Michael Westbrook	.40
177	Skip Hicks	.20
178	Brian Mitchell	.20
179	Dana Stubblefield	.20
180	Stephen Davis	.75
181	*Champ Bailey*	5.00
182	*Chris McAlister*	4.00
183	*Jevon Kearse*	8.00
184	*Ebenezer Ekuban*	3.00
185	*Chris Claiborne*	3.00
186	*Andy Katzenmoyer*	5.00
187	*Tim Couch*	25.00
188	*Daunte Culpepper*	12.00
189	*Akili Smith*	12.00
190	*Donovan McNabb*	12.00
191	*Sean Bennett*	4.00
192	*Brock Huard*	5.00

193	*Cade McNown*	12.00
194	*Shaun King*	12.00
195	*Joe Germaine*	4.00
196	*Ricky Williams*	25.00
197	*Edgerrin James*	40.00
198	*Sedrick Irvin*	5.00
199	*Kevin Faulk*	5.00
200	*Rob Konrad*	4.00
201	*James Johnson*	5.00
202	*Amos Zereoue*	4.00
203	*Torry Holt*	8.00
204	*D'Wayne Bates*	3.00
205	*David Boston*	8.00
206	*Dameane Douglas*	3.00
207	*Troy Edwards*	8.00
208	*Kevin Johnson*	8.00
209	*Peerless Price*	6.00
210	*Antoine Winfield*	3.00
211	*Michael Cloud*	4.00
212	*Joe Montgomery*	4.00
213	*Jermaine Fazande*	4.00
214	*Scott Covington*	4.00
215	*Aaron Brooks*	4.00
216	*Terry Jackson*	4.00
217	*Cecil Collins*	6.00
218	*Olandis Gary*	15.00
219	*Craig Yeast*	3.00
220	*Karsten Bailey*	4.00
221	*Reginald Kelly*	3.00
222	*Travis McGriff*	3.00
223	*Jeff Paulk*	3.00
224	*Jim Kleinsasser*	4.00
225	*Jason Tucker*	8.00

1999 Upper Deck Encore F/X

This was a 225-card parallel to the base set. Each single from this set was numbered to 100.

		MT
F/X Cards:		15x-30x
F/X Rookies:		2x-4x
Production 100 Sets		
F/X Gold Cards:		
Production 1 Set		

1999 Upper Deck Encore F/X Gold

This was a 225-card parallel to the base set. Only one of each card was produced.

		MT
F/X Gold Cards:		
Production 1 Set		

1999 Upper Deck Encore Electric Currents

This was a 20-card insert set that featured the NFL's premier offensive stars. Singles were inserted 1:6 packs.

		MT
Complete Set (20):		25.00
Common Player:		.75
Minor Stars:		1.50
Inserted 1:6		
1	Steve Young	3.00
2	Doug Flutie	1.50
3	Jon Kitna	2.00
4	Randall Cunningham	1.50

1999 Upper Deck Encore Game-Used Helmets

This was a six-card insert set that included a piece of a game-used helmet of that respected player. Singles were inserted 1:575 packs.

		MT
Complete Set (6):		450.00
Common Player:		30.00
Inserted 1:575		
MB	Mark Brunell	60.00
TD	Terrell Davis	75.00
MF	Marshall Faulk	30.00
BF	Brett Favre	150.00
DM	Dan Marino	120.00
JR	Jerry Rice	100.00

1999 Upper Deck Encore Game-Used Rookie Helmets

This 15-card insert set included pieces of helmets used in NFL Rookie Shoot. Singles were inserted 1:575 packs.

		MT
Complete Set (15):		1000.
Common Player:		30.00
Inserted 1:575		
CB	Champ Bailey	70.00
DW	D'Wayne Bates	30.00
DB	David Boston	80.00
CC	Cecil Collins	80.00
TC	Tim Couch	150.00
DC	Daunte Culpepper	100.00
TE	Troy Edwards	80.00
KF	Kevin Faulk	60.00
TH	Torry Holt	80.00
BH	Brock Huard	60.00
EJ	Edgerrin James	200.00
KJ	Kevin Johnson	80.00
Mc	Donovan McNabb	100.00
CM	Cade McNown	100.00
AS	Akili Smith	100.00

1999 Upper Deck Encore Live Wires

This 15-card insert set included autographs of the top current NFL stars. Singles were inserted 1:144 packs.

		MT
Complete Set (15):		1200.
Common Player:		25.00
Inserted 1:144		
TA	Troy Aikman	85.00
DB	David Boston	40.00
MB	Mark Brunell	70.00
TC	Tim Couch	125.00
TE	Troy Edwards	40.00
KF	Kevin Faulk	25.00
TH	Torry Holt	40.00

5	Curtis Enis	1.50
6	Jerry Rice	5.00
7	Antonio Freeman	1.50
8	Keyshawn Johnson	1.50
9	Steve McNair	2.00
10	Kordell Stewart	1.50
11	Drew Bledsoe	3.00
12	Corey Dillon	1.50
13	Vinny Testaverde	.75
14	Tim Brown	.75
15	Antowain Smith	1.50
16	Charlie Batch	2.50
17	Stephen Davis	1.50
18	Isaac Bruce	1.50
19	Curtis Martin	1.50
20	Ricky Watters	.75

1999 Upper Deck Encore Seize the Game

This 30-card insert set included the game's biggest game-breakers. Cards #1-#20 were inserted 1:20 packs and cards #21-#30 were inserted 1:23 packs. Each single also has a parallel Gold version and each was numbered to 250.

		MT
Complete Set (30):		100.00
Common Player (1-20):		2.50
Inserted 1:20		
Common Player (21-30):		4.00
Inserted 1:23		
F/X Gold Cards:		3x
Production 250 Sets		
1	Donovan McNabb	5.00
2	Keyshawn Johnson	2.50
3	Eddie George	2.50
4	Randall Cunningham	2.50
5	Charlie Batch	4.00
6	Curtis Martin	2.50
7	Edgerrin James	15.00
8	Jake Plummer	5.00
9	Drew Bledsoe	5.00
10	Marshall Faulk	2.50
11	Fred Taylor	6.00
12	Terrell Owens	2.50
13	Jerome Bettis	2.50
14	Antonio Freeman	2.50
15	Corey Dillon	2.50
16	Jerry Rice	8.00
17	Curtis Enis	2.50
18	Warrick Dunn	2.50
19	Kordell Stewart	2.50
20	Jamal Anderson	2.50
21	Terrell Davis	8.00
22	Randy Moss	10.00
23	Troy Aikman	6.00
24	Dan Marino	8.00
25	Ricky Williams	10.00
26	Peyton Manning	8.00
27	Steve Young	4.00
28	Tim Couch	10.00
29	Emmitt Smith	8.00
30	Brett Favre	10.00

1999 Upper Deck Encore UD Authentics

This 15-card insert set included autographs of the top current NFL stars. Singles were inserted 1:144 packs.

		MT
Complete Set (15):		45.00
Common Player:		2.00
Inserted 1:11		
1	Jake Plummer	3.00
2	Jamal Anderson	2.00
3	Emmitt Smith	6.00
4	John Elway	6.00
5	Barry Sanders	8.00
6	Brett Favre	8.00
7	Mark Brunell	4.00
8	Fred Taylor	4.00
9	Randy Moss	8.00
10	Drew Bledsoe	3.00
11	Keyshawn Johnson	2.00
12	Jerome Bettis	2.00
13	Kordell Stewart	2.00
14	Terrell Owens	2.00
15	Eddie George	3.00

1999 Upper Deck Encore Upper Realm

This 10-card insert set pays tribute to ten of the NFL's current elite stars. Singles were inserted 1:12 packs.

		MT
Complete Set (10):		25.00
Common Player:		.75
Minor Stars:		1.50
Inserted 1:12		
1	Randy Moss	7.00
2	Warrick Dunn	1.50
3	Stephen Davis	1.50
4	Peyton Manning	5.00
5	Tim Biakabutuka	.75
6	Steve Young	2.50
7	Kurt Warner	12.00
8	Steve McNair	1.50
9	Dan Marino	5.00
10	Jake Plummer	2.50

1999 Upper Deck Encore Walter Payton

Walter Payton signed 34 Game Jersey cards. Each single included a swatch of a game-used jersey and his signature. Singles were randomly inserted into the product.

		MT
WPE	W.Payton Jersey AUTO/34	2500.

1999 Upper Deck HoloGrFX

This was a 90-card set that included 30 rookies found 1:2 packs. Each single had an Ausome parallel with veterans inserted 1:8 packs and rookies inserted 1:17. Other insert sets included: 24/7, Future Fame, Star View and UD Authentics. SRP was $1.99 for three-card packs.

		MT
Complete Set (90):		65.00
Common Player:		.20
Minor Stars:		.40
Common Rookies:		.75
Wax Box:		45.00
1	Jake Plummer	1.25
2	Jamal Anderson	.75
3	Priest Holmes	.75
4	Antowain Smith	.75

		MT
Complete Set (15):		45.00
Common Player:		2.00
Inserted 1:11		
BH	Brock Huard	25.00
EJ	Edgerrin James	150.00
SK	Shaun King	60.00
PM	Peyton Manning	150.00
CM	Cade McNown	60.00
RM	Randy Moss	125.00
JN	Joe Namath	125.00
KW	Kurt Warner	200.00

5	Doug Flutie	1.00
6	Tshimanga Biakabutuka	.40
7	Curtis Enis	.75
8	Corey Dillon	.75
9	Darnay Scott	.40
10	Leslie Shepherd	.20
11	Troy Aikman	1.50
12	Emmitt Smith	2.00
13	Michael Irvin	.40
14	Terrell Davis	2.00
15	Shannon Sharpe	.40
16	Rod Smith	.75
17	Barry Sanders	3.00
18	Charlie Batch	1.25
19	Herman Moore	.75
20	Brett Favre	3.00
21	Dorsey Levens	.75
22	Antonio Freeman	.75
23	Peyton Manning	2.00
24	Mark Brunell	1.25
25	Fred Taylor	1.50
26	Jimmy Smith	.75
27	Andre Rison	.40
28	Tony Gonzalez	.40
29	Dan Marino	2.00
30	Karim Abdul	.40
31	Randy Moss	3.00
32	Randall Cunningham	.75
33	Drew Bledsoe	1.25
34	Terry Glenn	.75
35	Cameron Cleeland	.40
36	Andre Hastings	.20
37	Amani Toomer	.20
38	Kent Graham	.20
39	Curtis Martin	.75
40	Keyshawn Johnson	.75
41	Vinny Testaverde	.40
42	Napoleon Kaufman	.75
43	Tim Brown	.40
44	Duce Staley	.75
45	Kordell Stewart	.75
46	Jerome Bettis	.75
47	Marshall Faulk	.75
48	Natrone Means	.50
49	Ryan Leaf	.75
50	Steve Young	1.00
51	Jerry Rice	1.50
52	Terrell Owens	.75
53	Joey Galloway	.75
54	Ricky Watters	.40
55	Jon Kitna	.75
56	Warrick Dunn	.75
57	Trent Dilfer	.40
58	Steve McNair	.75
59	Eddie George	.75
60	Brad Johnson	.75
61	*Tim Couch*	8.00
62	*Donovan McNabb*	4.00
63	*Akili Smith*	4.00
64	*Edgerrin James*	12.00
65	*Ricky Williams*	6.00
66	*Torry Holt*	2.50
67	*Champ Bailey*	1.50
68	*David Boston*	2.50
69	*Daunte Culpepper*	4.00
70	*Cade McNown*	4.00
71	*Troy Edwards*	2.50
72	*Kevin Johnson*	2.50
73	*James Johnson*	1.50
74	*Rob Konrad*	.75
75	*Kevin Faulk*	1.50
76	*Shaun King*	4.00
77	*Peerless Price*	2.00
78	*Michael Cloud*	.75
79	*Jermaine Fazande*	1.25
80	*D'Wayne Bates*	.75
81	*Brock Huard*	1.50
82	*Marty Booker*	.75
83	*Karsten Bailey*	.75
84	*Al Wilson*	.75
85	*Joe Germaine*	1.00
86	*Dameane Douglas*	.75
87	*Sedrick Irvin*	1.50
88	*Aaron Brooks*	1.00
89	*Cecil Collins*	1.75
90	*Michael Bishop*	1.50

1999 Upper Deck HoloGrFX Ausome

This was a 90-card parallel to the base set. Each single had gold foil added to the back-ground. Veterans were inserted

1:8 packs and rookies were found 1:17.

	MT
Complete Set (90):	150.00
Ausome Cards:	2x-4x
Inserted 1:8	
Ausome Rookies:	2x
Inserted 1:17	

1999 Upper Deck HoloGrFX 24/7

This was a 15-card insert set that captured the most exciting players in the NFL today. Singles were inserted 1:3 packs. A parallel Gold version was also made and singles were inserted 1:105 packs.

		MT
Complete Set (15):		35.00
Common Player:		1.00
Inserted 1:3		
1	Jake Plummer	2.00
2	Emmitt Smith	4.00
3	Terrell Davis	4.00
4	Peyton Manning	4.00
5	Drew Bledsoe	2.00
6	Troy Aikman	3.00
7	Ricky Williams	6.00
8	Keyshawn Johnson	1.00
9	Akili Smith	3.00
10	Eddie George	1.00
11	Edgerrin James	10.00
12	David Boston	1.50
13	Cade McNown	3.00
14	Jerome Bettis	1.00
15	Herman Moore	1.00

1999 Upper Deck HoloGrFX 24/7 Gold

This was a 15-card parallel to the 24/7 insert set. Singles were inserted 1:105 packs.

	MT
Gold Cards:	4x-8x
Inserted 1:105	

1999 Upper Deck HoloGrFX Future Fame

This was a six-card insert set that included the most impressive talents in the NFL. Singles were inserted 1:34 packs. A parallel Gold version was also released and inserted 1:431 packs.

		MT
Complete Set (6):		40.00
Common Player:		3.00
Inserted 1:34		
1	John Elway	10.00
2	Dan Marino	10.00
3	Emmitt Smith	10.00
4	Randy Moss	12.00
5	Tim Brown	3.00
6	Barry Sanders	12.00

1999 Upper Deck HoloGrFX Future Fame Gold

This was a six-card parallel to the Future Fame insert. Singles were inserted 1:431 packs.

	MT
Gold Cards:	3x
Inserted 1:431	

1999 Upper Deck HoloGrFX Star View

This was a nine-card insert set that focused on the NFL's marquee players. Singles were found 1:17 packs. A parallel Gold version was also released with singles inserted 1:210 packs.

		MT
Complete Set (9):		35.00
Common Player:		2.50
Inserted 1:17		
1	Dan Marino	5.00
2	Brett Favre	7.00
3	Barry Sanders	7.00
4	Terrell Davis	5.00
5	Mark Brunell	3.00
6	Eddie George	2.50
7	Fred Taylor	5.00
8	Tim Couch	7.00
9	Randy Moss	7.00

1999 Upper Deck HoloGrFX Star View Gold

This was a nine-card parallel to the Star View insert. Singles were inserted 1:210 packs.

	MT
Gold Cards:	3x
Inserted 1:210	

Post-1980 cards in Near Mint condition will generally sell for about 75% of the quoted Mint value. Excellent-condition cards bring no more than 40%.

1999 Upper Deck HoloGrFX UD Authentics

This was a 19-card insert set that included autographs of the top standouts in the league. Singles were inserted 1:144 packs.

		MT
Common Player:		25.00
Inserted 1:432		
TA	Troy Aikman	100.00
JA	Jamal Anderson	25.00
TC	Tim Couch	125.00
DC	Daunte Culpepper	70.00
TD	Terrell Davis	100.00
EG	Eddie George	60.00
TH	Torry Holt	50.00
BH	Brock Huard	25.00
EJ	Edgerrin James	200.00
SK	Shaun King	70.00
PM	Peyton Manning	175.00
DM	Donovan McNabb	70.00
CM	Cade McNown	70.00
EM	Eric Moulds	25.00
JP	Jake Plummer	100.00
JR	Jerry Rice	150.00
AS	Akili Smith	70.00
RW	Ricky Williams	125.00
SY	Steve Young	75.00

1999 Upper Deck MVP

MVP Football is a 220-card set that includes 20 unseeded rookie cards. Three different parallel sets were made with Gold Script, Silver Script and Super Script. Other inserts include: Draw Your Own Card, Drive Time, Dynamics, Game Used Souvenirs, Power Surge, Strictly Business and Theatre.

		MT
Complete Set (220):		40.00
Common Player:		.10
Minor Stars:		.20
Wax Box:		45.00
1	Jake Plummer	1.00
2	Adrian Murrell	.10
3	Larry Centers	.10
4	Frank Sanders	.10
5	Andre Wadsworth	.20
6	Rob Moore	.20
7	Simeon Rice	.10
8	Jamal Anderson	.50
9	Chris Chandler	.20
10	Chuck Smith	.10
11	Terance Mathis	.10
12	Tim Dwight	.50
13	Ray Buchanan	.10
14	O.J. Santiago	.10
15	Eric Zeier	.10
16	Priest Holmes	.50
17	Michael Jackson	.10
18	Jermaine Lewis	.20
19	Michael McCrary	.10
20	Rob Johnson	.20
21	Antowain Smith	.50
22	Thurman Thomas	.20
23	Doug Flutie	.75
24	Eric Moulds	.30
25	Bruce Smith	.10
26	Andre Reed	.20
27	Fred Lane	.10
28	Tshimanga Biakabutuka	.20
29	Rae Carruth	.10
30	Wesley Walls	.10
31	Steve Beuerlein	.10
32	Muhsin Muhammad	.10
33	Erik Kramer	.10
34	Edgar Bennett	.10
35	Curtis Conway	.20
36	Curtis Enis	.50
37	Bobby Engram	.10
38	Alonzo Mayes	.10
39	Corey Dillon	.50
40	Jeff Blake	.20
41	Carl Pickens	.20
42	Darnay Scott	.10
43	Tony McGee	.10
44	Ki-Jana Carter	.20
45	Ty Detmer	.10
46	Terry Kirby	.10
47	Justin Armour	.10
48	Freddie Solomon	.10
49	Marquez Pope	.10
50	Antonio Langham	.10
51	Troy Aikman	1.00
52	Emmitt Smith	1.50
53	Deion Sanders	.50
54	Raghib Ismail	.10
55	Michael Irvin	.20
56	Chris Warren	.20
57	Greg Ellis	.10
58	John Elway	1.50
59	Terrell Davis	1.50
60	Rod Smith	.20
61	Shannon Sharpe	.20
62	Ed McCaffrey	.20
63	John Mobley	.10
64	Bill Romanowski	.10
65	Barry Sanders	2.00
66	Johnnie Morton	.10
67	Herman Moore	.50
68	Charlie Batch	.75
69	Germane Crowell	.50
70	Robert Porcher	.10
71	Brett Favre	2.00
72	Antonio Freeman	.50
73	Dorsey Levens	.20
74	Mark Chmura	.20
75	Vonnie Holliday	.20
76	Bill Schroeder	.10
77	Marshall Faulk	.50
78	Marvin Harrison	.50
79	Peyton Manning	1.50
80	Jerome Pathon	.10
81	E.G. Green	.10
82	Ellis Johnson	.10
83	Mark Brunell	.75
84	Jimmy Smith	.20
85	Keenan McCardell	.10
86	Fred Taylor	1.00
87	James Stewart	.10
88	Kevin Hardy	.10
89	Elvis Grbac	.10
90	Andre Rison	.20
91	Derrick Alexander	.10
92	Tony Gonzalez	.20
93	Donnell Bennett	.10
94	Derrick Thomas	.20
95	Tamarick Vanover	.10
96	Dan Marino	1.50
97	Karim Abdul	.50
98	Zach Thomas	.20
99	O.J. McDuffie	.20
100	John Avery	.20
101	Sam Madison	.10
102	Randall Cunningham	.50
103	Cris Carter	.50
104	Robert Smith	.50
105	Randy Moss	2.00
106	Jake Reed	.10
107	Matthew Hatchette	.10
108	John Randle	.20
109	Drew Bledsoe	.75
110	Terry Glenn	.50
111	Ben Coates	.20
112	Ty Law	.10
113	Tony Simmons	.10
114	Ted Johnson	.10
115	Danny Wuerffel	.20
116	Lamar Smith	.10
117	Sean Dawkins	.10
118	Cameron Cleeland	.20
119	Joe Johnson	.10
120	Andre Hastings	.10
121	Kent Graham	.10
122	Gary Brown	.10
123	Amani Toomer	.20
124	Tiki Barber	.20
125	Ike Hilliard	.20
126	Jason Sehorn	.20
127	Vinny Testaverde	.10
128	Curtis Martin	.50
129	Keyshawn Johnson	.50
130	Wayne Chrebet	.50
131	Mo Lewis	.10
132	Steve Atwater	.10
133	Donald Hollas	.10
134	Napoleon Kaufman	.50
135	Tim Brown	.50
136	Darrell Russell	.10
137	Rickey Dudley	.20
138	Charles Woodson	.50
139	Koy Detmer	.10
140	Duce Staley	.50
141	Charlie Garner	.10
142	Doug Pederson	.10
143	Jeff Graham	.10
144	Charles Johnson	.10
145	Kordell Stewart	.75
146	Jerome Bettis	.50
147	Hines Ward	.20
148	Courtney Hawkins	.10
149	Will Blackwell	.10
150	Richard Huntley	.10
151	Levon Kirkland	.10
152	Trent Green	.30
153	Tony Banks	.20
154	Isaac Bruce	.30
155	Eddie Kennison	.20
156	Az-Zahir Hakim	.20
157	Amp Lee	.10
158	Robert Holcombe	.20
159	Ryan Leaf	.75
160	Natrone Means	.50
161	Jim Harbaugh	.20
162	Junior Seau	.20
163	Charlie Jones	.10
164	Rodney Harrison	.10
165	Steve Young	.75
166	Jerry Rice	1.00
167	Garrison Hearst	.30
168	Terrell Owens	.50
169	J.J. Stokes	.20
170	Bryant Young	.10
171	Ricky Watters	.30
172	Joey Galloway	.50
173	Jon Kitna	.50
174	Ahman Green	.20
175	Mike Pritchard	.10
176	Chad Brown	.10
177	Warrick Dunn	.75
178	Trent Dilfer	.20
179	Mike Alstott	.50
180	Reidel Anthony	.20
181	Bert Emanuel	.20
182	Jacquez Green	.20
183	Hardy Nickerson	.10
184	Steve McNair	.50
185	Eddie George	.75
186	Yancey Thigpen	.20
187	Frank Wycheck	.10
188	Kevin Dyson	.20
189	Jackie Harris	.10
190	Blaine Bishop	.10
191	Skip Hicks	.20
192	Michael Westbrook	.20
193	Stephen Alexander	.10
194	Leslie Shepherd	.10
195	Casey Weldon	.10
196	Brian Mitchell	.10
197	Dan Wilkinson	.10
198	Checklist Card #1 (Terrell Davis CL)	.50
199	Checklist Car #2 (Troy Aikman CL)	.30
200	Checklist Card #3 (Tim Couch CL)	3.00
201	*Ricky Williams*	8.00
202	*Tim Couch*	8.00
203	*Akili Smith*	4.00
204	*Daunte Culpepper*	4.00
205	*Torry Holt*	2.50
206	*Edgerrin James*	8.00
207	*David Boston*	2.50
208	*Peerless Price*	1.75
209	*Chris Claiborne*	1.00
210	*Champ Bailey*	1.25
211	*Cade McNown*	4.00
212	*Jevon Kearse*	2.00
213	*Joe Germaine*	1.50
214	*D'Wayne Bates*	.75
215	*Dameane Douglas*	.75
216	*Troy Edwards*	2.50
217	*Sedrick Irvin*	1.25
218	*Brock Huard*	1.25
219	*Amos Zereoue*	1.75
220	*Donovan McNabb*	4.00

1999 Upper Deck MVP Gold Script

This is a parallel to the base set and is the same except for the players facsimile signature on the front in gold foil along with all the other foil in gold too. On the back the hologram is in gold foil and each single is sequentially numbered to 100.

	MT
Gold Cards:	30x-60x
Gold Rookies:	10x-20x
Production 100 Sets	

1999 Upper Deck MVP Silver Script

This is a parallel to the base and is the same except for the players facsimile autograph on the front in silver foil and the words Silver Script on the back. Singles were inserted 1:2 packs.

	MT
Complete Set (220):	120.00
Silver Cards:	4x
Silver Rookies:	2x
Inserted 1:2	

1999 Upper Deck MVP Super Script

This is a parallel to the base set and each single has a holo foil facsimile signature of the player on the front and each is sequentially numbered to 25.

	MT
Super Cards:	75x-150x
Super Rookies:	20x-40x
Production 25 Sets	

1999 Upper Deck MVP Draw Your Own

Each single from this 30-card set is a drawing from a young collector from a previous contest winner. Singles were inserted 1:6 packs.

		MT
Complete Set (30):		18.00
Common Player:		.20
Minor Stars:		.40
Inserted 1:6		
1	Brett Favre	2.00
2	Emmitt Smith	1.50
3	John Elway	1.50
4	Emmitt Smith	1.50
5	Randy Moss	2.00
6	Terrell Davis	1.50
7	Steve Young	.75
8	Drew Bledsoe	.75
9	Troy Aikman	1.00
10	Terry Allen	.20
11	Warrick Dunn	.75
12	Kimble Anders	.20
13	Joey Galloway	.40
14	Barry Sanders	2.00
15	Mark Brunell	.75
16	Bruce Smith	.20
17	Randy Moss	2.00
18	Jerome Bettis	.40
19	John Elway	1.50
20	Jerome Bettis	.40
21	Brett Favre	2.00
22	Troy Aikman	1.00
23	Cris Carter	.75
24	Jason Gildon	.20
25	Randall Cunningham	.75
26	Thurman Thomas	.40
27	Jerry Rice	1.00
28	Jerome Bettis	.40
29	Steve Young	.75
30	Reggie White	.40

1999 Upper Deck MVP Drive Time

Each card in this 14-card set pays tribute to a star player who led the best offensive drive during the 1998 season. Singles were found 1:6 packs.

		MT
Complete Set (14):		10.00
Common Player:		.50
Minor Stars:		1.00
Inserted 1:6		
1	Steve Young	1.50
2	Kordell Stewart	1.25
3	Eric Moulds	1.00
4	Corey Dillon	1.00
5	Doug Flutie	1.50
6	Charlie Batch	1.50
7	Curtis Martin	1.00
8	Marshall Faulk	1.00
9	Terrell Owens	1.25
10	Antowain Smith	1.00
11	Troy Aikman	2.50
12	Drew Bledsoe	1.50
13	Keyshawn Johnson	1.00
14	Steve McNair	1.25

1999 Upper Deck MVP Dynamics

This 15-card set includes the top players in the NFL and puts them on a holo foil card. Singles were inserted 1:28 packs.

		MT
Complete Set (15):		65.00
Common Player:		2.00
Minor Stars:		4.00
Inserted 1:28		
1	John Elway	10.00
2	Steve Young	6.00
3	Jake Plummer	7.50
4	Fred Taylor	7.50
5	Mark Brunell	6.00
6	Joey Galloway	2.00
7	Terrell Davis	10.00
8	Randy Moss	15.00
9	Charlie Batch	5.00
10	Peyton Manning	10.00
11	Barry Sanders	15.00
12	Eddie George	5.00
13	Warrick Dunn	4.00
14	Jamal Anderson	2.00
15	Brett Favre	15.00

Values quoted in this guide reflect the retail price of a card — the price a collector can expect to pay when buying a card from a dealer. The wholesale price — that which a collector can expect to receive from a dealer when selling cards — will be significantly lower, depending on desirability and condition.

1999 Upper Deck MVP Game-Used Souvenirs

Each card in this 21-card set includes a piece of a game-used football by that player pictured on the card. Singles were inserted 1:130 packs.

		MT
Complete Set (21):		1400.
Common Player:		50.00
Inserted 1:130		
BS	Barry Sanders	160.00
ES	Emmitt Smith	120.00
DF	Doug Flutie	65.00
KJ	Keyshawn Johnson	60.00
JP	Jake Plummer	85.00
JE	John Elway	150.00
PM	Peyton Manning	125.00
RM	Randy Moss	175.00
TD	Terrell Davis	125.00
JA	Jamal Anderson	60.00
MC	Donovan McNabb	75.00
AS	Akili Smith	65.00
EJ	Edgerrin James	85.00
BH	Brock Huard	50.00
TH	Torry Holt	60.00
CB	Champ Bailey	50.00
DB	David Boston	60.00
DC	Daunte Culpepper	80.00
CM	Cade McNown	80.00
DM	Dan Marino	150.00

1999 Upper Deck MVP Power Surge

The game's most impressive talents are highlighted in this 15-card set. Each foil card was inserted 1:9 packs.

		MT
Complete Set (15):		20.00
Common Player		.75
Minor Stars:		1.50
Inserted 1:9		
1	Jerome Bettis	1.50
2	Eddie George	2.00
3	Karim Abdul	.75
4	Curtis Martin	1.50
5	Antowain Smith	1.75
6	Kordell Stewart	1.75
7	Curtis Enis	1.50
8	Joey Galloway	1.50
9	Mark Brunell	2.50
10	Peyton Manning	4.00
11	Antonio Freeman	1.50
12	Jerry Rice	3.50
13	Eric Moulds	1.50
14	Drew Bledsoe	2.00
15	Fred Taylor	3.50

Post-1980 cards in Near Mint condition will generally sell for about 75% of the quoted Mint value. Excellent-condition cards bring no more than 40%.

A player's name in *italic* type indicates a rookie card.

1999 Upper Deck MVP Strictly Business

Only the top players in the game were included in this 13-card insert. Singles were found 1:14 packs.

		MT
Complete Set (15):		45.00
Common Player:		2.00
Inserted 1:14		
1	Eddie George	3.00
2	Curtis Martin	2.00
3	Fred Taylor	5.00
4	Steve Young	3.00
5	Kordell Stewart	3.00
6	Corey Dillon	2.00
7	Dan Marino	7.50
8	Jake Plummer	4.00
9	Jerry Rice	5.00
10	Warrick Dunn	3.00
11	Jerome Bettis	2.00
12	John Elway	7.50
13	Randy Moss	10.00
14	Troy Aikman	5.00
15	Brett Favre	10.00

1999 Upper Deck MVP Theatre

Each card in this 15-card set pictures a star player in action. Singles were inserted 1:9 packs.

		MT
Complete Set (15):		20.00
Common Player:		.75
Minor Stars:		1.50
Inserted 1:9		
1	Terrell Davis	5.00
2	Corey Dillon	1.50
3	Brett Favre	6.00
4	Jerry Rice	3.00
5	Emmitt Smith	4.00
6	Dan Marino	4.00
7	Jerome Bettis	.75
8	Napoleon Kaufman	1.50
9	Keyshawn Johnson	1.50
10	Warrick Dunn	1.50
11	Barry Sanders	6.00
12	Troy Aikman	3.00
13	Jamal Anderson	1.50
14	Randall Cunningham	.75
15	Doug Flutie	1.75

1999 Upper Deck Ovation

This was a 90-card set that

included 30 rookies found 1:4 packs. Each single had a parallel Standing Ovation that was sequentially numbered to 50. Other insert sets included: A Piece of History, Center Stage, Curtain Calls, Spotlight, Star Performers, Super Signatures Silver and the Walter Payton Autographed Game Jersey. SRP was $3.99 for five-card packs.

		MT
Complete Set (90):		125.00
Common Player:		.25
Minor Stars:		.50
Common Rookie:		1.50
Inserted 1:4		
Wax Box:		100.00
1	Jake Plummer	1.25
2	Adrian Murrell	.25
3	Jamal Anderson	.75
4	Chris Chandler	.50
5	Tony Banks	.25
6	Antowain Smith	.50
7	Doug Flutie	1.00
8	Tshimanga Biakabutuka	.50
9	Steve Beuerlein	.25
10	Curtis Conway	.50
11	Curtis Enis	.75
12	Corey Dillon	.75
13	Jeff Blake	.50
14	Ty Detmer	.25
15	Troy Aikman	1.50
16	Emmitt Smith	2.00
17	Terrell Davis	2.00
18	Bubby Brister	.50
19	Barry Sanders	3.00
20	Charlie Batch	1.00
21	Brett Favre	3.00
22	Dorsey Levens	.50
23	Peyton Manning	2.00
24	Marvin Harrison	.75
25	Mark Brunell	1.25
26	Fred Taylor	1.50
27	Elvis Grbac	.25
28	Andre Rison	.25
29	Dan Marino	2.00
30	Karim Abdul	.50
31	Randall Cunningham	.75
32	Randy Moss	3.00
33	Drew Bledsoe	1.25
34	Terry Glenn	.75
35	Danny Wuerffel	.50
36	Cameron Cleeland	.50
37	Kerry Collins	.50
38	Amani Toomer	.25
39	Curtis Martin	.75
40	Keyshawn Johnson	.75
41	Napoleon Kaufman	.75
42	Tim Brown	.50
43	Doug Pederson	.25
44	Charles Johnson	.25
45	Kordell Stewart	1.00
46	Jerome Bettis	.75
47	Trent Green	.50
48	Marshall Faulk	.75
49	Natrone Means	.75
50	Jim Harbaugh	.50
51	Steve Young	1.00
52	Jerry Rice	1.50
53	Joey Galloway	.75
54	Jon Kitna	.75
55	Warrick Dunn	.75
56	Trent Dilfer	.50
57	Steve McNair	.75
58	Eddie George	.75
59	Brad Johnson	.50
60	Skip Hicks	.50
61	*Tim Couch*	20.00
62	*Donovan McNabb*	10.00
63	*Akili Smith*	10.00
64	*Edgerrin James*	20.00
65	*Ricky Williams*	20.00
66	*Torry Holt*	7.00
67	*Champ Bailey*	4.00
68	*David Boston*	7.00
69	*Daunte Culpepper*	10.00
70	*Cade McNown*	10.00
71	*Troy Edwards*	7.00
72	*Kevin Johnson*	7.00
73	*James Johnson*	4.00
74	*Rob Konrad*	3.00
75	*Kevin Faulk*	5.00
76	*Shaun King*	8.00
77	*Peerless Price*	5.00
78	*Michael Cloud*	3.00
79	*Jermaine Fazande*	1.50
80	*D'Wayne Bates*	3.00
81	*Brock Huard*	4.00
82	*Marty Booker*	1.50
83	*Karsten Bailey*	1.50
84	*Al Wilson*	3.00
85	*Joe Germaine*	4.00
86	*Dameane Douglas*	1.50
87	*Sedrick Irvin*	4.00
88	*Amos Zereoue*	5.00
89	*Cecil Collins*	10.00
90	*Ebenezer Ekuban*	1.50

A player's name in *italic* type indicates a rookie card.

1999 Upper Deck Ovation Standing Ovation

This was a 90-card parallel to the base set. Each single was sequentially numbered to 50.

	MT
Standing Ovation Cards:	35x-70x
Standing Ovation Rookies:	5x-10x
Production 50 Sets	

1999 Upper Deck Ovation A Piece of History

This 13-card insert set included pieces of game-used footballs. A total of 4,560 cards were produced and randomly inserted.

		MT
Complete Set (13):		1250.
Common Player:		50.00
Production 4,560 Total Cards		
DC	Daunte Culpepper	85.00
BF	Brett Favre	200.00
JG	Joe Germaine	50.00
TH	Torry Holt	65.00
BH	Brock Huard	50.00
EJ	Edgerrin James	180.00
DM	Dan Marino	180.00
MC	Donovan McNabb	85.00
CM	Cade McNown	85.00
JR	Jerry Rice	100.00
AS	Akili Smith	85.00
RW	Ricky Williams	200.00
SY	Steve Young	85.00

1999 Upper Deck Ovation Center Stage

This 24-card insert set was a three-tiered collection focusing on eight great running backs from the NFL's past to present. Cards #1–#8 were inserted 1:9, cards #9–#16 were found 1:25 and cards #17–#24 were pulled 1:99 packs.

		MT
Complete Set (24):		225.00
Common Player #1-8:		1.00
Inserted 1:9		
Common Player #9-16:		3.00
Inserted 1:25		
Common Player #17-24:		6.00
Inserted 1:99		
1	Walter Payton	3.00
2	Barry Sanders	5.00
3	Emmitt Smith	3.00
4	Terrell Davis	3.00
5	Jamal Anderson	1.00
6	Fred Taylor	2.00
7	Ricky Williams	8.00
8	Edgerrin James	6.00
9	Walter Payton	6.00
10	Barry Sanders	10.00
11	Emmitt Smith	6.00

12	Terrell Davis	6.00
13	Jamal Anderson	3.00
14	Fred Taylor	4.00
15	Ricky Williams	15.00
16	Edgerrin James	12.00
17	Walter Payton	18.00
18	Barry Sanders	30.00
19	Emmitt Smith	18.00
20	Terrell Davis	18.00
21	Jamal Anderson	6.00
22	Fred Taylor	12.00
23	Ricky Williams	45.00
24	Edgerrin James	35.00

3	Akili Smith	8.00
4	Edgerrin James	12.00
5	Ricky Williams	15.00
6	Torry Holt	5.00
7	Champ Bailey	4.00
8	David Boston	5.00
9	Daunte Culpepper	8.00
10	Cade McNown	8.00
11	Troy Edwards	5.00
12	Kevin Johnson	5.00
13	Joe Germaine	3.00
14	Brock Huard	3.00
15	Kevin Faulk	4.00

1999 Upper Deck Ovation Curtain Calls

This 30-card insert set focused on some of the most memorable accomplishments posted during the 1998 NFL season. Inserted 1:4 packs.

		MT
Complete Set (30):		85.00
Common Player:		1.00
Minor Stars:		2.00
Inserted 1:4		
1	Peyton Manning	7.00
2	Fred Taylor	5.00
3	Randy Moss	10.00
4	Cris Carter	2.00
5	Troy Aikman	5.00
6	Randall Cunningham	2.00
7	Mark Brunell	3.00
8	Jon Kitna	2.00
9	Steve McNair	2.00
10	Jake Plummer	5.00
11	Jerry Rice	5.00
12	Kordell Stewart	3.00
13	Warrick Dunn	2.00
14	Emmitt Smith	7.00
15	Jerome Bettis	2.00
16	Terrell Owens	2.00
17	Antonio Freeman	2.00
18	Joey Galloway	2.00
19	Curtis Martin	2.00
20	Tim Brown	1.00
21	Charlie Batch	2.00
22	Doug Flutie	3.00
23	Barry Sanders	10.00
24	Drew Bledsoe	3.00
25	Corey Dillon	2.00
26	Eddie George	2.00
27	Keyshawn Johnson	2.00
28	Steve Young	3.00
29	Brett Favre	10.00
30	Terrell Davis	7.00

1999 Upper Deck Ovation Spotlight

This was a 15-card insert set that featured the top players from the 1999 NFL Draft. Singles were inserted 1:9 packs.

		MT
Complete Set (15):		85.00
Common Player:		3.00
Inserted 1:9		
1	Tim Couch	15.00
2	Donovan McNabb	8.00

1999 Upper Deck Ovation Star Performers

This was a 15-card insert set that included some of the top names in the NFL. Singles were inserted 1:39 packs.

		MT
Complete Set (15):		135.00
Common Player:		5.00
Inserted 1:39		
1	Terrell Davis	15.00
2	Peyton Manning	15.00
3	Brett Favre	20.00
4	Dan Marino	15.00
5	Barry Sanders	20.00
6	Jamal Anderson	5.00
7	Mark Brunell	8.00
8	Jerome Bettis	5.00
9	Charlie Batch	6.00
10	Antowain Smith	5.00
11	Jake Plummer	8.00
12	Joey Galloway	5.00
13	Randy Moss	20.00
14	Steve Young	8.00
15	Warrick Dunn	5.00

1999 Upper Deck Ovation Super Signatures

This was a three-card insert set that included autographs from three retired NFL superstars. Each single was sequentially numbered to 300. A parallel Gold version was also released and each of those were numbered to 150. A parallel Rainbow version was made and each was sequentially numbered to 10.

		MT
Complete Set (3):		600.00
Common Player:		200.00
Production 300 Sets		
Gold Cards:		1.5x
Production 150 Sets		
Rainbow Cards:		
Production 10 Sets		
NA	Joe Namath	200.00
MN	Joe Montana	225.00
WP	Walter Payton	200.00

1999 Upper Deck Ovation Walter Payton Auto. Jersey

Walter Payton signed a total of 34 Game Jersey cards. Each came with a swatch of a game-used jersey and were sequentially numbered to 34. Singles were randomly inserted.

		MT
Complete Set (1):		2000.00
WPJ	Walter Payton	

1999 Upper Deck PowerDeck

This was a 30-card set that pictured each player on a digital trading card. Each card was to be used on a CD-Rom and contained complete stats, bios, 20 to 30 images, music, audio clips and game highlights. Each single also had a parallel Auxiliary single. The CD singles were issued one-per-pack and the Auxiliary cards were issued two-per-pack. Other insert sets included: Autographs, Most Valuable Performances, Powerful Moments, Time Capsule and Walter Payton Autograph Game Jersey. SRP was $4.99 for three-card packs.

		MT
Complete Set (30):		150.00
Common Player:		2.50
Inserted 1:1		
Wax Box:		90.00
1	Troy Aikman	6.00
2	Drew Bledsoe	5.00
3	Randy Moss	10.00
4	Barry Sanders	10.00
5	Brett Favre	10.00
6	Terrell Davis	8.00
7	Peyton Manning	8.00
8	Emmitt Smith	8.00
9	Dan Marino	8.00
10	Jake Plummer	5.00
11	Eddie George	4.00
12	Jerry Rice	6.00
13	Steve Young	4.00
14	Mark Brunell	5.00
15	Kordell Stewart	2.50
16	Keyshawn Johnson	2.50
17	Fred Taylor	6.00
18	Jamal Anderson	2.50
19	Cecil Collins	4.00
20	Ricky Williams	12.00
21	Tim Couch	12.00
22	Donovan McNabb	8.00
23	Akili Smith	7.00
24	Edgerrin James	20.00
25	Daunte Culpepper	8.00
26	Brock Huard	4.00
27	Torry Holt	6.00
28	David Boston	6.00
29	Cade McNown	8.00
30	Champ Bailey	3.50

1999 Upper Deck PowerDeck Auxiliary

Each card in this 30-card set was printed on regular cardboard stock. Singles were issued two-per-pack. Each single had a parallel one-of-one Gold card.

		MT
Complete Set (30):		30.00
Common Player:		.50
1	Troy Aikman	1.00
2	Drew Bledsoe	.75
3	Randy Moss	2.00
4	Barry Sanders	2.00
5	Brett Favre	2.00

1999 Upper Deck PowerDeck Autographed Cards

This was a 12-card insert set that included autographs from both veterans and prospects. Each single was sequentially numbered to 50.

		MT
Complete Set (12):		1250.
Common Player:		75.00
Production 50 Sets		
TA	Troy Aikman	175.00
CB	Champ Bailey	75.00
DB	David Boston	75.00
TC	Tim Couch	200.00
DC	Daunte Culpepper	125.00
TH	Torry Holt	75.00
BH	Brock Huard	75.00
EJ	Edgerrin James	300.00
DM	Dan Marino	250.00
CM	Cade McNown	125.00
JP	Jake Plummer	100.00
AS	Akili Smith	100.00

1999 Upper Deck PowerDeck Most Valuable Performances

This seven-card insert set highlighted historic performances in the Super Bowl and other notable games. Singles were inserted 1:287 packs. Each card also had a parallel Auxiliary single and they were also issued 1:287.

		MT
Complete Set (7):		300.00
Common Player:		15.00
Inserted 1:287		
Auxiliary Cards:		50%
Inserted 1:287		
1	Joe Montana	75.00
2	John Elway	45.00
3	Emmitt Smith	45.00
4	Jamal Anderson	15.00
5	Randy Moss	75.00
6	Brett Favre	75.00
7	Terrell Davis	45.00

1999 Upper Deck PowerDeck Powerful Moments

This six-card insert set showcased some of the most significant games in pro football history. Singles were inserted 1:23 packs. Each card had an

Auxiliary single that was also issued 1:23 packs.

		MT
Complete Set (6):		60.00
Common Player:		8.00
Inserted 1:23		
Auxiliary Cards:		50%
Inserted 1:23		
1	Joe Montana	15.00
2	Terrell Davis	8.00
3	John Elway	10.00
4	Randy Moss	15.00
5	Dan Marino	10.00
6	Emmitt Smith	10.00

1999 Upper Deck PowerDeck Time Capsule

This was a six-card insert set that included flashbacks of the greatest superstars' rookie seasons. Singles were found 1:7 packs. Each single had a parallel Auxiliary card that was also inserted 1:7 packs.

		MT
Complete Set (6):		40.00
Common Player:		7.00
Inserted 1:7		
Auxiliary Cards:		50%
Inserted 1:7		
1	Edgerrin James	15.00
2	Barry Sanders	12.00
3	Terrell Davis	7.00
4	Emmitt Smith	10.00
5	Dan Marino	10.00
6	Tim Couch	10.00

1999 Upper Deck Retro

This was a 165-card set that pictured both past and present NFL stars. Each card had a classic old-time look and feel. Each single had a parallel Gold card that was numbered to 175. Other insert sets included: Inkredible, Legends of the Fall, Old School/New School, Smashmouth and Throwback Attack. The packaging was unique in that each of the 24 packs were inserted into an actual lunch box. SRP was $4.99 for six-card packs.

		MT
Complete Set (165):		60.00
Common Player:		.15
Minor Stars:		.30
Common Rookie:		.75
Wax Box:		60.00
1	Jake Plummer	1.25
2	Adrian Murrell	.15
3	Rob Moore	.30
4	Frank Sanders	.15
5	David Boston	2.50
6	Tim Dwight	.75
7	Chris Chandler	.30
8	Jamal Anderson	.75
9	O.J. Santiago	.15
10	Terance Mathis	.15
11	Priest Holmes	.75
12	Tony Banks	.30
13	Patrick Johnson	.15
14	Scott Mitchell	.15
15	Jermaine Lewis	.15
16	Eric Moulds	.75
17	Doug Flutie	1.00
18	Antowain Smith	.50
19	Thurman Thomas	.30
20	Peerless Price	2.00
21	Fred Lane	.15
22	Tshimanga Biakabutuka	.30
23	Steve Beuerlein	.30
24	Muhsin Muhammad	.50
25	Rae Carruth	.15
26	Curtis Enis	.75
27	Walter Payton	5.00
28	Bobby Engram	.15
29	Cade McNown	4.00
30	Curtis Conway	.30
31	Darnay Scott	.30
32	Jeff Blake	.30
33	Corey Dillon	.75
34	Akili Smith	4.00
35	Carl Pickens	.30
36	Tim Couch	7.00
37	Ty Detmer	.15
38	Jim Brown	3.00
39	Kevin Johnson	2.50
40	Ozzie Newsome	.30
41	Troy Aikman	1.50
42	Raghib Ismail	.15
43	Emmitt Smith	2.00
44	Michael Irvin	.30
45	Deion Sanders	.50
46	Roger Staubach	2.00
47	John Elway	2.00
48	Bubby Brister	.30
49	Terrell Davis	2.00
50	Ed McCaffrey	.50
51	Rod Smith	.50
52	Shannon Sharpe	.30
53	Charlie Batch	1.00
54	Johnnie Morton	.15
55	Barry Sanders	3.00
56	Sedrick Irvin	1.50
57	Herman Moore	.50
58	Brett Favre	3.00
59	Mark Chmura	.30
60	Antonio Freeman	.75
61	Robert Brooks	.15
62	Dorsey Levens	.75
63	Peyton Manning	2.00
64	Jerome Pathon	.15
65	Marvin Harrison	.75
66	Edgerrin James	10.00
67	Ken Dilger	.15
68	Mark Brunell	1.25
69	Fred Taylor	1.50
70	Jimmy Smith	.75
71	James Stewart	.50
72	Keenan McCardell	.30
73	Elvis Grbac	.30
74	Michael Cloud	.75
75	Andre Rison	.30
76	Tony Gonzalez	.30
77	Warren Moon	.30
78	Derrick Alexander	.15
79	Dan Marino	2.00
80	O.J. McDuffie	.30
81	James Johnson	1.50
82	Paul Warfield	.30
83	Cecil Collins	2.50
84	Randall Cunningham	.75
85	Randy Moss	3.00
86	Cris Carter	.75
87	Fran Tarkenton	1.00
88	Daunte Culpepper	4.00
89	Robert Smith	.75
90	Drew Bledsoe	1.25
91	Terry Glenn	.75
92	Kevin Faulk	1.50
93	Tony Simmons	.30
94	Ben Coates	.30
95	Billy Joe Hobert	.15
96	Cameron Cleeland	.30
97	Eddie Kennison	.15
98	Andre Hastings	.15
99	Ricky Williams	6.00
100	Kerry Collins	.30
101	Joe Montgomery	.75
102	Gary Brown	.15
103	Ike Hilliard	.15
104	Amani Toomer	.15
105	Vinny Testaverde	.30
106	Wayne Chrebet	.75
107	Curtis Martin	.75
108	Joe Namath	2.50
109	Keyshawn Johnson	.75
110	Don Maynard	.50
111	Rich Gannon	.30
112	Tim Brown	.30
113	Charles Woodson	.75
114	Rickey Dudley	.15
115	Darrell Russell	.15
116	Napoleon Kaufman	.75
117	Donovan McNabb	4.00
118	Doug Pederson	.15
119	Duce Staley	.75
120	Torrance Small	.15
121	Charles Johnson	.15
122	Jerome Bettis	.75
123	Courtney Hawkins	.15
124	Kordell Stewart	.75
125	Troy Edwards	2.50

126	Amos Zereoue	.75
127	Trent Green	.50
128	Marshall Faulk	.75
129	Az Hakim	.30
130	Joe Germaine	.75
131	Torry Holt	2.50
132	Isaac Bruce	.75
133	Jim Harbaugh	.30
134	Junior Seau	.30
135	Natrone Means	.30
136	Ryan Leaf	.50
137	Dan Fouts	.50
138	Mikhael Ricks	.15
139	Steve Young	1.00
140	Terrell Owens	.75
141	Jerry Rice	1.50
142	J.J. Stokes	.30
143	Lawrence Phillips	.30
144	Joe Montana	3.50
145	Jon Kitna	.75
146	Ahman Green	.30
147	Joey Galloway	.75
148	Ricky Watters	.30
149	Brock Huard	1.50
150	Steve Largent	.75
151	Trent Dilfer	.50
152	Reidel Anthony	.30
153	Warrick Dunn	.75
154	Mike Alstott	.75
155	Shaun King	4.00
156	Eddie George	1.00
157	Steve McNair	1.00
158	Kevin Dyson	.30
159	Frank Wycheck	.15
160	Yancey Thigpen	.30
161	Brad Johnson	.75
162	Rodney Peete	.15
163	Michael Westbrook	.50
164	Skip Hicks	.30
165	Champ Bailey	1.50

1999 Upper Deck Retro Gold

This was a 165-card parallel to the base set. Each card included gold foil and was sequentially numbered to 175.

		MT
Gold Cards:		6x-12x
Gold Rookies:		3x-6x
Production 175 Sets		

1999 Upper Deck Retro Inkredible

This was a 30-card insert set that featured authentic autograph cards of past and present NFL stars. Singles were inserted 1:23 packs. Each single also had a parallel Gold version that was sequentially numbered to the player's jersey number.

		MT
Complete Set (30):		1500.
Common Player:		10.00
Minor Stars:		20.00
1:Box		
DB	David Boston	35.00
CC	Cris Carter	30.00
WC	Wayne Chrebet	20.00
TC	Tim Couch	100.00
DC	Daunte Culpepper	45.00

TD	Terrell Davis	75.00
DF	Dan Fouts	20.00
GH	Garrison Hearst	10.00
TH	Torry Holt	35.00
BH	Brock Huard	20.00
SK	Shaun King	45.00
JK	Jon Kitna	20.00
SL	Steve Largent	20.00
DL	Dorsey Levens	20.00
MC	Donovan McNabb	45.00
CM	Cade McNown	45.00
JM	Joe Montana	180.00
RM	Randy Moss	150.00
AM	Adrian Murrell	10.00
JN	Joe Namath	180.00
OZ	Ozzie Newsome	10.00
TO	Terrell Owens	20.00
WP	Walter Payton	275.00
AK	Akili Smith	45.00
AS	Antowain Smith	20.00
RS	Rod Smith	20.00
RG	Roger Staubach	100.00
FT	Fran Tarkenton	50.00
PW	Paul Warfield	10.00
RW	Ricky Williams	120.00

1999 Upper Deck Retro Legends of the Fall

This was a 30-card insert set that focused on both current and former NFL stars who transcended their eras. Singles were inserted 1:11 packs. Each card had a parallel Silver version that was sequentially numbered to 75.

		MT
Complete Set (30):		45.00
Common Player:		.75
Minor Stars:		1.50
Inserted 1:11		
Silver Cards:		10x-20x
Production 75 Sets		
1	Jake Plummer	2.50
2	Corey Dillon	1.50
3	Curtis Martin	1.50
4	Vinny Testaverde	.75
5	Brett Favre	6.00
6	Randy Moss	6.00
7	John Elway	4.50
8	Jerry Rice	3.00
9	Troy Aikman	3.00
10	Ricky Watters	.75
11	Keyshawn Johnson	1.50
12	Mark Brunell	2.00
13	Dorsey Levens	.75
14	Steve McNair	1.50
15	Emmitt Smith	4.50
16	Marshall Faulk	1.50
17	Priest Holmes	.75
18	Steve Young	2.00
19	Skip Hicks	.75
20	Eddie George	1.50
21	Garrison Hearst	.75
22	Drew Bledsoe	2.50
23	Warrick Dunn	1.50
24	Eric Moulds	1.50
25	Joey Galloway	1.50
26	Tim Brown	.75
27	Chris Chandler	.75
28	Peyton Manning	4.50
29	Antonio Freeman	1.50
30	Deion Sanders	1.50

1999 Upper Deck Retro Lunch Boxes

This was a 16-box set that was used for the packing of the packs. Each box was a usable lunch box that featured a player or players on both sides. Dual player boxes were inserted one-per-case.

		MT
Complete Set (16):		225.00
Common Player:		8.00
One dual box per case		
	Joe Montana	20.00
	Ricky Williams	15.00

	Randy Moss	15.00
	Barry Sanders	15.00
	John Elway	12.00
	Terrell Davis	8.00
	Dan Marino	12.00
	Joe Namath	15.00
	Joe Montana,	20.00
	John Elway	
	Joe Montana,	20.00
	Dan Marino	
	John Elway,	20.00
	Dan Marino	
	Joe Montana,	20.00
	Joe Namath	
	Ricky Williams,	20.00
	Tim Couch	
	Joe Namath,	20.00
	Dan Marino	
	Tim Couch,	20.00
	Joe Montana	
	Barry Sanders,	20.00
	Terrell Davis	

1999 Upper Deck Retro Old School/New School

This was a 30-card insert set that focused on the NFL's top stars of yesterday and today and paired one of each player on one card. Each of these singles were sequentially numbered to 1,000. A parallel Level 2 was issued and each was numbered to 50.

		MT
Complete Set (30):		200.00
Common Player:		2.00
Minor Stars:		4.00
Production 1,000 Sets		
Level 2 Cards:		5x-10x
Production 50 Sets		
1	Terrell Davis,	15.00
	Ricky Williams	
2	Joe Montana,	18.00
	Jake Plummer	
3	Cris Carter,	15.00
	Randy Moss	
4	Randall	7.00
	Cunningham,	
	Daunte Culpepper	
5	Brett Favre,	15.00
	Jon Kitna	
6	Emmitt Smith,	12.00
	Fred Taylor	
7	Mark Brunell,	6.00
	Brock Huard	
8	John Elway,	15.00
	Peyton Manning	
9	Steve Young,	8.00
	Cade McNown	
10	Don Maynard,	4.00
	Keyshawn Johnson	
11	Dan Marino,	15.00
	Tim Couch	
12	Jerry Rice,	10.00
	Terrell Owens	
13	Marshall Faulk,	20.00
	Edgerrin James	
14	Dan Fouts,	6.00
	Akili Smith	
15	Barry Sanders,	15.00
	Jamal Anderson	
16	Terry Glenn,	4.00
	David Boston	
17	Deion Sanders,	4.00
	Champ Bailey	
18	Andre Reed,	2.00
	Eric Moulds	
19	Junior Seau,	2.00
	Chris Claiborne	
20	Steve Largent,	4.00
	Joey Galloway	
21	Kordell Stewart,	6.00
	Shaun King	
22	Ricky Watters,	4.00
	Kevin Faulk	
23	Thurman Thomas,	2.00
	Warrick Dunn	
24	Tim Brown,	4.00
	Troy Edwards	
25	Jerome Bettis,	5.00
	Cecil Collins	
26	Isaac Bruce,	5.00
	Torry Holt	

27	Fran Tarkenton,	7.00
	Donovan McNabb	
28	Warren Moon,	5.00
	Charlie Batch	
29	Herman Moore,	2.00
	D'Wayne Bates	
30	Roger Staubach,	12.00
	Troy Aikman	

1999 Upper Deck Retro Smashmouth

This was a 15-card insert set that took a look at 15 of the game's most aggressive players. Singles were inserted 1:8 packs. A parallel Level 2 was also released and each was sequentially numbered to 100.

		MT
Complete Set (15):		20.00
Common Player:		.75
Minor Stars:		1.50
Inserted 1:8		
Level 2 Cards:		6x-12x
Production 100 Sets		
1	Fred Taylor	2.50
2	Jamal Anderson	1.50
3	John Elway	4.00
4	Brock Huard	1.50
5	Daunte Culpepper	3.00
6	Charlie Batch	1.50
7	Steve McNair	1.50
8	Corey Dillon	1.50
9	Natrone Means	.75
10	Randall	.75
	Cunningham	
11	Drew Bledsoe	2.00
12	Jerome Bettis	1.50
13	Antowain Smith	.75
14	Steve Young	2.00
15	Eddie George	1.50

1999 Upper Deck Retro Throwback Attack

This was a 15-card insert set that showcased collectible, modern players with playing styles of the bygone era of football. Singles were inserted 1:5 packs. Each card had a parallel Gold single that was sequentially numbered to 500.

		MT
Complete Set (15):		25.00
Common Player:		.75
Minor Stars:		1.50
Inserted 1:5		
Gold Cards:		3x-6x
Production 500 Sets		
1	Brett Favre	4.00
2	Herman Moore	.75
3	Troy Aikman	2.50
4	Eric Moulds	1.50
5	Tim Couch	4.00
6	Terrell Owens	1.50
7	Champ Bailey	1.50
8	Kordell Stewart	1.50
9	Mark Brunell	2.00
10	Curtis Martin	1.50
11	Torry Holt	1.75

12	David Boston	1.75
13	Doug Flutie	1.75
14	Edgerrin James	6.00
15	Akili Smith	3.00

1999 Upper Deck Retro Walter Payton

Walter Payton signed 200 UD Authentic cards and each was sequentially numbered.

		MT
WP1	W.Payton AUTO	300.00

1999 Victory

This was the premiere edition of Victory Football. The 440-card set included 60 rookie cards found one-per-pack. This was a retail-only release that didn't include any inserts. Subsets included: All-Victory, Season Leaders, Victory Parade, Rookie Flashback and '99 Rookie Class.

		MT
Complete Set (440):		70.00
Common Player:		.10
Minor Stars:		.20
Common Rookie:		.50
Inserted 1:1		
Wax Box:		35.00
1	Arizona Cardinals	.10
	visit	
2	Jake Plummer	.75
3	Adrian Murrell	.10
4	Michael Pittman	.10
5	Frank Sanders	.20
6	Andre Wadsworth	.10
7	Rob Moore	.20
8	Simeon Rice	.10
9	Kwamie Lassiter	.10
10	Mario Bates	.10
11	Atlanta Falcons	.10
	visit	
12	Jamal Anderson	.30
13	Chris Chandler	.20
14	Chuck Smith	.10
15	Terance Mathis	.10
16	Tim Dwight	.30
17	Ray Buchanan	.10
18	O.J. Santiago	.10
19	Lester Archambeau	.10
20	Baltimore Ravens	.10
	visit	
21	Tony Banks	.20
22	Priest Holmes	.30
23	Michael Jackson	.10
24	Jermaine Lewis	.20
25	Michael McCrary	.10
26	Rod Woodson	.20
27	Buffalo Bills visit	.10
28	Rob Johnson	.20
29	Antowain Smith	.30
30	Thurman Thomas	.20
31	Doug Flutie	.50
32	Eric Moulds	.30
33	Bruce Smith	.20
34	Andre Reed	.20
35	Phil Hansen	.10
36	Carolina Panthers	.10
	visit	
37	Fred Lane	.10
38	Tshimanga	.10
	Biakabutuka	
39	Rae Carruth	.10
40	Wesley Walls	.10
41	Steve Beuerlein	.10
42	Muhsin	.10
	Muhammad	
43	Kevin Greene	.10
44	Chicago Bears visit	.10
45	Erik Kramer	.10
46	Edgar Bennett	.10
47	Curtis Conway	.20
48	Curtis Enis	.30
49	Bobby Engram	.10
50	Alonzo Mayes	.10
51	Tony Parrish	.10
52	Glyn Milburn	.10
53	Cincinnati Bengals	.10
	visit	

54	Corey Dillon	.30
55	Jeff Blake	.20
56	Carl Pickens	.20
57	Darnay Scott	.10
58	Tony McGee	.10
59	Ki-Jana Carter	.10
60	Takeo Spikes	.10
61	Cleveland Browns	.10
	visit	
62	Ty Detmer	.10
63	Terry Kirby	.10
64	Derrick Alexander	.10
65	Leslie Shepherd	.10
66	Marquez Pope	.10
67	Antonio Langham	.10
68	Marc Edwards	.10
69	Dallas Cowboys	.10
	visit	
70	Troy Aikman	1.00
71	Emmitt Smith	1.50
72	Deion Sanders	.30
73	Raghib Ismail	.10
74	Michael Irvin	.20
75	Chris Warren	.10
76	Greg Ellis	.10
77	Kavika Pittman	.10
78	David LaFleur	.10
79	Denver Broncos	.10
	visit	
80	John Elway	1.50
81	Terrell Davis	1.50
82	Rod Smith	.20
83	Shannon Sharpe	.20
84	Ed McCaffrey	.20
85	John Mobley	.10
86	Bill Romanowski	.10
87	Jason Elam	.10
88	Howard Griffith	.10
89	Detroit Lions visit	.10
90	Barry Sanders	2.00
91	Johnnie Morton	.10
92	Herman Moore	.30
93	Charlie Batch	.50
94	Germane Crowell	.10
95	Robert Porcher	.10
96	Stephen Boyd	.10
97	Green Bay Packers	.10
	visit	
98	Brett Favre	2.00
99	Antonio Freeman	.30
100	Dorsey Levens	.30
101	Mark Chmura	.20
102	Vonnie Holliday	.20
103	Bill Schroeder	.10
104	LeRoy Butler	.10
105	William Henderson	.10
106	Indianapolis Colts	.10
	visit	
107	Peyton Manning	1.50
108	Marvin Harrison	.30
109	Ken Dilger	.10
110	Jerome Pathon	.10
111	E.G. Green	.10
112	Ellis Johnson	.10
113	Jeff Burris	.10
114	Jacksonville	.10
	Jaguars visit	
115	Mark Brunell	.75
116	Jimmy Smith	.20
117	Keenan McCardell	.20
118	Fred Taylor	1.00
119	James Stewart	.10
120	Dave Thomas	.10
121	Kyle Brady	.10
122	Bryce Paup	.10
123	Kansas City Chiefs	.10
	visit	
124	Elvis Grbac	.20
125	Andre Rison	.20
126	Derrick Alexander	.10
127	Tony Gonzalez	.20
128	Donnell Bennett	.10
129	Derrick Thomas	.20
130	Tamarick Vanover	.10
131	Donnie Edwards	.10
132	Miami Dolphins	.10
	visit	
133	Dan Marino	1.50
134	Karim Abdul	.30
135	Zach Thomas	.20
136	O.J. McDuffie	.20
137	John Avery	.20
138	Sam Madison	.10
139	Terrell Buckley	.10
140	Jason Taylor	.10
141	Oronde Gadsden	.20
142	Minnesota Vikings	.10
	visit	
143	Randall	.30
	Cunningham	
144	Cris Carter	.30
145	Robert Smith	.20
146	Randy Moss	2.00
147	Jake Reed	.10
148	Leroy Hoard	.10
149	Matthew Hatchette	.10
150	John Randle	.10
151	Gary Anderson	.10
152	New England	.10
	Patriots visit	
153	Drew Bledsoe	.75
154	Terry Glenn	.30
155	Ben Coates	.20
156	Ty Law	.10
157	Tony Simmons	.20
158	Ted Johnson	.10
159	Willie McGinest	.10
160	Tony Carter	.10

161	Shawn Jefferson	.10
162	New Orleans Saints visit	
163	Danny Wuerffel	.20
164	Lamar Smith	.10
165	Keith Poole	.10
166	Cameron Cleeland	.20
167	Joe Johnson	.10
168	Andre Hastings	.10
169	La'Roi Glover	.10
170	Aaron Craver	.10
171	New York Giants visit	
172	Kent Graham	.20
173	Gary Brown	.10
174	Amani Toomer	.10
175	Tiki Barber	.10
176	Ike Hilliard	.10
177	Jason Sehorn	.10
178	Michael Strahan	.10
179	Charles Way	.10
180	New York Jets visit	.10
181	Vinny Testaverde	.20
182	Curtis Martin	.30
183	Keyshawn Johnson	.30
184	Wayne Chrebet	.30
185	Mo Lewis	.10
186	Steve Atwater	.10
187	Leon Johnson	.10
188	Bryan Cox	.10
189	Oakland Raiders visit	
190	Rich Gannon	.10
191	Napoleon Kaufman	.30
192	Tim Brown	.30
193	Darrell Russell	.10
194	Rickey Dudley	.10
195	Charles Woodson	.30
196	Harvey Williams	.10
197	James Jett	.10
198	Philadelphia Eagles visit	.10
199	Koy Detmer	.10
200	Duce Staley	.10
201	Bobby Taylor	.10
202	Doug Pederson	.10
203	Karl Hankton	.10
204	Charles Johnson	.10
205	Kevin Turner	.10
206	Hugh Douglas	.10
207	Pittsburgh Steelers visit	.10
208	Kordell Stewart	.50
209	Jerome Bettis	.30
210	Hines Ward	.20
211	Courtney Hawkins	.10
212	Will Blackwell	.10
213	Richard Huntley	.10
214	Levon Kirkland	.10
215	Jason Gildon	.10
216	St. Louis Rams visit	.10
217	Trent Green	.30
218	Isaac Bruce	.20
219	Az Hakim	.20
220	Amp Lee	.10
221	Robert Holcombe	.20
222	Ricky Proehl	.10
223	Kevin Carter	.10
224	Marshall Faulk	.30
225	San Diego Chargers visit	.10
226	Ryan Leaf	.30
227	Natrone Means	.30
228	Jim Harbaugh	.20
229	Junior Seau	.20
230	Charlie Jones	.10
231	Rodney Harrison	.10
232	Terrell Fletcher	.10
233	Tremayne Stephens	.10
234	San Francisco 49ers visit	.10
235	Steve Young	.75
236	Jerry Rice	1.00
237	Garrison Hearst	.30
238	Terrell Owens	.30
239	J.J. Stokes	.20
240	Bryant Young	.10
241	Tim McDonald	.10
242	Merton Hanks	.10
243	Travis Jervey	.10
244	Seattle Seahawks visit	.10
245	Ricky Watters	.20
246	Joey Galloway	.30
247	Jon Kitna	.30
248	Ahman Green	.20
249	Mike Pritchard	.10
250	Chad Brown	.10
251	Christian Fauria	.10
252	Michael Sinclair	.10
253	Tampa Bay Bucs visit	
254	Warrick Dunn	.30
255	Trent Dilfer	.20
256	Mike Alstott	.30
257	Reidel Anthony	.20
258	Bert Emanuel	.10
259	Jacquez Green	.10
260	Hardy Nickerson	.10
261	Derrick Brooks	.10
262	Dave Moore	.10
263	Tennessee Titans visit	
264	Steve McNair	.30
265	Eddie George	.50
266	Yancey Thigpen	.20

267	Frank Wycheck	.10
268	Kevin Dyson	.20
269	Jackie Harris	.10
270	Blaine Bishop	.10
271	Willie Davis	.10
272	Washington 'Skins visit	.10
273	Skip Hicks	.20
274	Michael Westbrook	.20
275	Stephen Alexander	.10
276	Dana Stubblefield	.10
277	Brad Johnson	.30
278	Brian Mitchell	.10
279	Dan Wilkinson	.10
280	Stephen Davis	.20
281	John Elway (All-Victory Team)	.50
282	Dan Marino (All-Victory Team)	.50
283	Troy Aikman (All-Victory Team)	.30
284	Vinny Testaverde (All-Victory Team)	.10
285	Corey Dillon (All-Victory Team)	.10
286	Steve Young (All-Victory Team)	.20
287	Randy Moss (All-Victory Team)	.75
288	Drew Bledsoe (All-Victory Team)	.30
289	Jerome Bettis (All-Victory Team)	
290	Antonio Freeman (All-Victory Team)	.10
291	Fred Taylor (All-Victory Team)	.30
292	Doug Flutie (All-Victory Team)	.10
293	Jerry Rice (All-Victory Team)	.30
294	Peyton Manning (All-Victory Team)	.50
295	Brett Favre (All-Victory Team)	.50
296	Barry Sanders (All-Victory Team)	.50
297	Keyshawn Johnson (All-Victory Team)	.10
298	Mark Brunell (All-Victory Team)	.20
299	Jamal Anderson (All-Victory Team)	.10
300	Terrell Davis (All-Victory Team)	.50
301	Randall Cunningham (All-Victory Team)	.10
302	Kordell Stewart (All-Victory Team)	.10
303	Warrick Dunn (All-Victory Team)	.10
304	Jake Plummer (All-Victory Team)	.20
305	Junior Seau (All-Victory Team)	.10
306	Antowain Smith (All-Victory Team)	.10
307	Charlie Batch (All-Victory Team)	.20
308	Eddie George (All-Victory Team)	.20
309	Michael Irvin (All-Victory Team)	.10
310	Joey Galloway (All-Victory Team)	.10
311	Randall Cunningham (Season Leaders)	.10
312	Vinny Testaverde (Season Leaders)	.10
313	Steve Young (Season Leaders)	.20
314	Chris Chandler (Season Leaders)	.10
315	John Elway (Season Leaders)	.50
316	Steve Young (Season Leaders)	.20
317	Randall Cunningham (Season Leaders)	
318	Brett Favre (Season Leaders)	.50
319	Vinny Testaverde (Season Leaders)	.10
320	Peyton Manning (Season Leaders)	.50
321	Terrell Davis (Season Leaders)	.50
322	Jamal Anderson (Season Leaders)	.10
323	Garrison Hearst (Season Leaders)	.10
324	Barry Sanders (Season Leaders)	.50
325	Emmitt Smith (Season Leaders)	.30
326	Terrell Davis (Season Leaders)	.50
327	Fred Taylor (Season Leaders)	.30
328	Jamal Anderson (Season Leaders)	.10
329	Emmitt Smith (Season Leaders)	.30
330	Ricky Watters (Season Leaders)	.10

331	O.J. McDuffie (Season Leaders)	.10
332	Frank Sanders (Season Leaders)	.10
333	Rod Smith (Season Leaders)	.10
334	Marshall Faulk (Season Leaders)	.10
335	Antonio Freeman (Season Leaders)	.10
336	Randy Moss (Season Leaders)	.75
337	Antonio Freeman (Season Leaders)	
338	Terrell Owens (Season Leaders)	.10
339	Cris Carter (Season Leaders)	.10
340	Terance Mathis (Season Leaders)	.10
341	Jake Plummer (Victory Parade)	.20
342	Steve McNair (Victory Parade)	.10
343	Randy Moss (Victory Parade)	.75
344	Peyton Manning (Victory Parade)	.50
345	Mark Brunell (Victory Parade)	.20
346	Terrell Owens (Victory Parade)	.10
347	Antowain Smith (Victory Parade)	.10
348	Jerry Rice (Victory Parade)	.30
349	Troy Aikman (Victory Parade)	.30
350	Fred Taylor (Victory Parade)	.30
351	Charlie Batch (Victory Parade)	.10
352	Dan Marino (Victory Parade)	.50
353	Eddie George (Victory Parade)	.20
354	Drew Bledsoe (Victory Parade)	.10
355	Kordell Stewart (Victory Parade)	.10
356	Doug Flutie (Victory Parade)	.10
357	Deion Sanders (Victory Parade)	.10
358	Keyshawn Johnson (Victory Parade)	.10
359	Jerome Bettis (Victory Parade)	.10
360	Warrick Dunn (Victory Parade)	.10
361	John Elway (Rookie Flashback)	.50
362	Dan Marino (Rookie Flashback)	.50
363	Brett Favre (Rookie Flashback)	.50
364	Andre Rison (Rookie Flashback)	.10
365	Rod Woodson (Rookie Flashback)	.10
366	Jerry Rice (Rookie Flashback)	.30
367	Barry Sanders (Rookie Flashback)	.50
368	Thurman Thomas (Rookie Flashback)	.10
369	Troy Aikman (Rookie Flashback)	.30
370	Ricky Watters (Rookie Flashback)	.10
371	Jerome Bettis (Rookie Flashback)	.10
372	Reggie White (Rookie Flashback)	.10
373	Junior Seau (Rookie Flashback)	.10
374	Deion Sanders (Rookie Flashback)	.10
375	Chris Chandler (Rookie Flashback)	.10
376	Curtis Martin (Rookie Flashback)	.10
377	Kordell Stewart (Rookie Flashback)	.10
378	Mark Brunell (Rookie Flashback)	.10
379	Cris Carter (Rookie Flashback)	.10
380	Emmitt Smith (Rookie Flashback)	.30
381	Tim Couch	8.00
382	Donovan McNabb	5.00
383	Akili Smith	4.00
384	Edgerrin James	10.00
385	Ricky Williams	8.00
386	Torry Holt	3.00
387	Champ Bailey	2.00
388	David Boston	3.00
389	Chris Claiborne	1.00
390	Chris McAlister	1.00
391	Daunte Culpepper	5.00
392	Cade McNown	5.00
393	Troy Edwards	3.00
394	John Tait	.50
395	Anthony McFarland	1.00
396	Jevon Kearse	3.00
397	Damien Woody	.50

398	Matt Stinchcomb	.50
399	Luke Petitgout	.50
400	Ebenezer Ekuban	1.00
401	L.J. Shelton	.50
402	Marty Booker	.50
403	Antoine Winfield	1.00
404	Scott Covington	1.00
405	Antwan Edwards	1.00
406	Fernando Bryant	.50
407	Aaron Gibson	.50
408	Andy Katzenmoyer	1.00
409	Dimitrius Underwood	1.00
410	Patrick Kerney	.50
411	Al Wilson	1.00
412	Kevin Johnson	3.00
413	Joel Makovicka	1.00
414	Reginald Kelly	.50
415	Jeff Paulk	1.00
416	Brandon Stokley	1.00
417	Peerless Price	2.00
418	D'Wayne Bates	1.50
419	Travis McGriff	1.00
420	Sedrick Irvin	1.50
421	Aaron Brooks	1.50
422	Michael Cloud	1.00
423	Joe Montgomery	1.50
424	Shaun King	5.00
425	Dameane Douglas	1.00
426	Joe Germaine	1.50
427	James Johnson	2.00
428	Michael Bishop	2.00
429	Karsten Bailey	1.00
430	Craig Yeast	1.00
431	Jim Kleinsasser	1.00
432	Martin Gramatica	1.00
433	Jermaine Fazande	1.00
434	Dre' Bly	1.00
435	Brock Huard	1.50
436	Rob Konrad	1.00
437	Tony Bryant	1.00
438	Sean Bennett	1.50
439	Kevin Faulk	2.00
440	Amos Zereoue	1.00

1993 U.S. Playing Cards Ditka's Picks

The 56-card, standard-size set, with rounded corners, are actually playing cards. The fronts have a borderless action shot with each card having the same generic back. "Ditka's Picks," "NFL," and other logos appear on the backs.

		MT
Complete Set (56):		5.00
Common Player:		.05
1C	Steve Young	.30
1D	Joe Montana	.50
1H	Dan Marino	.05
1S	Troy Aikman	.50
2C	Jim Lachey	.05
2D	Richmond Webb	.05
2H	Wilber Marshall	.05
2S	Ronnie Lott	.10
3C	Sean Gilbert	.10
3D	Clay Matthews	.10
3H	Jeff Lageman	.05
3S	Audray McMillian	.05
4C	Morten Andersen	.05
4D	Pete Stoyanovich	.05
4H	Rohn Stark	.05
4S	Sean Landeta	.05
5C	Broderick Thomas	.05
5D	James Francis	.05
5H	Derrick Thomas	.20
5S	Tony Bennett	.05
6C	Seth Joyner	.10
6D	Percy Snow	.05
6H	Junior Seau	.20
6S	Chris Spielman	.10
7C	Pierce Holt	.05
7D	Rod Woodson	.20
7H	Ray Childress	.10
7S	Deion Sanders	.40
8C	Jay Novacek	.20
8D	Eric Green	.05
8H	Marv Cook	.05
8S	Brent Jones	.05
9C	Randall McDaniel	.05
9D	Mike Munchak	.05
9H	Bruce Matthews	.05
9S	Mark Stepnoski	.05
10C	Harris Barton	.05
10D	Steve Atwater	.05
10H	Henry Jones	.05
10S	Chuck Cecil	.05
11C	Sterling Sharpe	.20
11H	Anthony Miller	.10
11H	Haywood Jeffires	.10
11S	Jerry Rice	.50
12C	Reggie White	.20
12H	Cortez Kennedy	.10
12S	Chris Doleman	.05
13D	Emmitt Smith	.50
13D	Thurman Thomas	.20
13H	Barry Foster	.10
13S	Barry Sanders	1.00
WILD	Tom Waddle	.05
WILD	Steve Wisniewski	.05
NNO	Ditka's AFC Picks	.10
NNO	Ditka's NFC Picks	.10

1994 U.S. Playing Cards Ditka's Picks

The U.S. Playing Card Co. released a 56-card deck of playing cards, featuring a cast of NFL stars, as well as rookies expected to shine in the 1994 season. Each card in the four-color deck contains an action shot of the player with the denomination in the upper left and lower right hand corners.

		MT
Complete Set (56):		5.00
Common Player:		.05
1C	Sterling Sharpe	.20
1D	Rickey Jackson	.05
1H	Emmitt Smith	1.00
1S	Rod Woodson	.20
2C	Marcus Robertson	.05
2D	Rohn Stark	.05
2H	Dave Cadigan	.05
2S	Kevin Williams	.20
3C	John Kasay	.05
3D	Carlton Haselrig	.05
3H	Donnell Woolford	.05
3S	Dan Wilkinson	.20
4C	Marshall Faulk	1.00
4D	Greg Montgomery	.05
4H	Leslie O'Neal	.10
4S	Eric Curry	.10
5C	Eric Turner	.10
5D	Rick Mirer	.25
5H	Kevin Smith	.10
5S	Troy Vincent	.10
6C	Cornelius Bennett	.10
6D	Seth Joyner	.10
6H	Gary Zimmerman	.05
6S	LeRoy Butler	.05
7C	Tommy Vardell	.05
7D	Richmond Webb	.05
7H	Ben Coates	.20
7S	Steve Everitt	.05
8C	Tom Rathman	.05
8D	Ray Childress	.05
8H	Tim Brown	.20
8S	Mark Bavaro	.05
9C	Bennie Blades	.05
9D	John "Jumbo" Elliott	.05
9H	Jim Lachey	.05
9S	Neil Smith	.20
10C	Sean Gilbert	.10
10D	Steve Tasker	.10
10H	Chris Zorich	.10
10S	Haywood Jeffires	.10
11D	Jeff Hostetler	.10
11H	Junior Seau	.20
11S	Mark Stepnoski	.05
12C	Chris Spielman	.10
12D	Marcus Allen	.20
12H	Reggie White	.20
13C	Harris Barton	.05
13D	Andre Rison	.20
13D	Randall McDaniel	.05
13H	Cortez Kennedy	.10
13S	Norm Johnson	.05
WILD	Heath Shuler	.60
WILD	Shannon Sharpe	.10
NNO	Ditka's AFC Picks	.10
NNO	Ditka's NFC Picks	.10

1995 U.S. Playing Cards Ditka's Picks

The 56-card, standard-size set, with rounded edges, is similar in design to the 1994 set, with color photos on the card fronts and a generic card back.

		MT
Complete Set (56):		5.00
Common Player:		.05
1C	Randall McDaniel	.05
1D	Dan Marino	1.00
1H	Drew Bledsoe	.40
1S	Steve Young	.50
2C	Renaldo Turnbull	.05
2D	Tony Boselli	.10
2H	Ki-Jana Carter	.20
2S	Todd Sauerbrun	.05

3C	Aeneas Williams	.05
3D	Bruce Smith	.20
3S	Shawn Jefferson	.10
3S	Andy Harmon	.05
4C	Donnell Woolford	.05
4C	Ronnie Lott	.20
4H	Tim Brown	.20
4S	Charles Haley	.10
5C	Merton Hanks	.05
5D	Eric Turner	.10
5H	Ben Coates	.20
5S	Brian Williams	.05
6C	Eric Metcalf	.10
6D	Dave Meggett	.10
6H	Neil Smith	.05
6S	Ian Beckles	.05
7C	Herman Moore	.20
7D	Mel Gray	.05
7H	Ray Childress	.05
7S	Jim Lachey	.05
8C	Bennie Blades	.05
8D	Kevin Greene	.10
8H	Gary Zimmerman	.05
8S	Willie Roaf	.10
9C	Bryant Young	.05
9D	Bruce Matthews	.05
9H	Richmond Webb	.05
9S	Howard Cross	.05
10C	Seth Joyner	.05
10D	Marshall Faulk	.50
10H	Jeff Dellenbach	.05
10S	Cris Carter	.20
11C	Sean Gilbert	.10
11D	John Carney	.05
11H	Rohn Stark	.05
11S	Jerry Rice	.50
12C	Reggie White	.20
12D	Terry McDaniel	.05
12H	Rod Woodson	.20
12S	Daryl Johnston	.10
13C	Norm Johnson	.05
13D	Cortez Kennedy	.10
13H	Cornelius Bennett	.10
13S	Barry Sanders	1.00
WILD	Junior Seau	.20
WILD	Chris Spielman	.10
NNO	Ditka's NFC Picks	.10
NNO	Ditka's AFC Picks	.10

V

1967-68 Vikings

The 29-card, 8" x 10" set features black-and-white photos with blank backs.

		NM
Complete Set (29):		120.00
Common Player:		4.00
1	Grady Alderman (Tackle)	4.00
2	Grady Alderman (Offensive lineman)	4.00
3	John Beasley	4.00
4	Bob Berry	4.00
5	Larry Bowie	4.00
6	Gary Cuozzo	5.00
7	Doug Davis	4.00
8	Paul Dickinson	4.00
9	Paul Flatley	5.00
10	Bob Grim	5.00
11	Dale Hackbart	4.00
12	Don Hansen	4.00
13	Jim Hargrove	4.00
14	Clint Jones	5.00
15	Jeff Jordan	4.00
16	Joe Kapp	8.00
17	John Kirby	4.00
18	Gary Larsen	5.00
19	Earsell Mackbee	4.00
20	Marlin McKeever	5.00
21	Milt Sunde	5.00
22	David Tobey	4.00
23	Ron Vanderkelen	5.00
24	Jim Vellone	4.00
25	Bobby Walden	4.00
26	Lonnie Warwick	4.00
27	Gene Washington (Wide receiver)	5.00
28	Gene Washington (End)	5.00
29	Roy Winston	5.00

1969 Vikings Team Issue

The 27-card, 5" x 6-7/8" set features black-and-white borderless player portraits with blank backs.

		NM
Complete Set (27):		75.00
Common Player:		3.00
1	Bookie Bolin	3.00
2	Bobby Bryant	4.00
3	John Beasley	3.00

4	Gary Cuozzo	4.00
5	Doug Davis	3.00
6	Paul Dickson	3.00
7	Bob Grim	4.00
8	Dale Hackbart	3.00
9	Jim Hargrove	3.00
10	John Henderson	3.00
11	Wally Hilgenberg	4.00
12	Clinton Jones	4.00
13	Karl Kassulke	4.00
14	Kent Kramer	3.00
15	Gary Larsen	4.00
16	Bob Lee	3.00
17	Jim Lindsey	3.00
18	Earsell Mackbee	3.00
19	Mike McGill	3.00
20	Oscar Reed	3.00
21	Ed Sharockman	3.00
22	Steve Smith	3.00
23	Milt Sunde	3.00
24	Jim Vellone	3.00
25	Lonnie Warwick	3.00
26	Gene Washington	5.00
27	Charlie West	4.00

1971 Vikings Photos

The 52-card, 5" x 7-7/16" set consists of color close-up shots with blank backs. The player's name, position, and team name appear on the bottom border.

		NM
Complete Set (52):		125.00
Common Player:		2.00
1	Grady Alderman	2.00
2	Neil Armstrong (CO)	2.00
3	John Beasley	2.00
4	Bill Brown	4.00
5	Bob Brown	2.00
6	Bobby Bryant	3.00
7	Jerry Burns (CO)	3.00
8	Fred Cox	3.00
9	Gary Cuozzo	3.00
10	Doug Davis	2.00
11	Al Denson	2.00
12	Paul Dickson	2.00
13	Carl Eller	10.00
14	Bud Grant (CO)	12.00
15	Bob Grim	3.00
16	Leo Hayden	2.00
17	John Henderson	2.00
18	Wally Hilgenberg	3.00
19	Noel Jenke	2.00
20	Clint Jones	3.00
21	Karl Kassulke	3.00
22	Paul Krause	5.00
23	Gary Larsen	2.00
24	Bob Lee	2.00
25	Jim Lindsey	2.00
26	Jim Marshall	10.00
27	Bus Mertes (CO)	2.00
28	John Michels (CO)	2.00
29	Jocko Nelson (CO)	2.00
30	Dave Osborn	4.00
31	Alan Page	12.00
32	Jack Patera (CO)	3.00
33	Jerry Patton	2.00
34	Pete Perreault	2.00
35	Oscar Reed	2.00
36	Ed Sharockman	2.00
37	Norm Snead	6.00
38	Milt Sunde	3.00
39	Doug Sutherland	2.00
40	Mick Tingelhoff	4.00
41	Stu Voigt	3.00
42	John Ward	2.00
43	Lonnie Warwick	2.00
44	Gene Washington	6.00
45	Charlie West	2.00
46	Ed White	4.00
47	Carl Winfrey	2.00
48	Roy Winston	3.00
49	Jeff Wright	2.00
50	Nate Wright	2.00
51	Ron Yary	4.00
52	Godfrey Zaunbrecher	2.00

1971 Vikings Postcards

The 19-card, 5" x 7-7/16" set features color posed close-ups with the backs containing a typical postcard layout. Bio information appears in the upper left corner of the horizontal backs. The set was issued during the season.

		NM
Complete Set (19):		45.00
Common Player:		2.00
1	Grady Alderman	2.00
2	Neil Armstrong (CO)	2.00
3	John Beasley	2.00
4	Paul Dickson	2.00
5	Bud Grant (CO)	12.00
6	Wally Hilgenburg	2.00
7	Noel Jenke	
8	Paul Krause	5.00
9	Gary Larsen	2.00
10	Dave Osborn	4.00
11	Alan Page	12.00
12	Jerry Patton	2.00
13	Doug Sutherland	2.50
14	Mick Tingelhoff	4.00
15	Lonnie Warwick	2.00
16	Charlie West	2.00
17	Jeff Wright	2.00
18	Nate Wright	2.00
19	Godfrey Zaunbrecher	2.00

1978 Vikings Country Kitchen

The seven-card, 5" x 7" set features a black-and-white player headshot with bio and stat information on the backs. The card fronts have a white border with the player's name and "Minnesota Vikings" printed.

		NM
Complete Set (7):		35.00
Common Player:		4.00
1	Bobby Bryant	4.00
2	Tommy Kramer	6.00
3	Paul Krause	6.00
4	Ahmad Rashad	12.00
5	Jeff Siemon	4.00
6	Mick Tingelhoff	5.00
7	Sammie White	6.00

1983 Vikings Police

The 17-card, 2-5/8" x 4-1/8" set was sponsored by Green Giant, Burger King, Pillsbury and Minnesota Crime Prevention Officers Association. The fronts contain an action photo with the back including bio and stat information.

		MT
Complete Set (17):		10.00
Common Player:		.50
1	Checklist Card	.75
2	Tommy Kramer	1.00
3	Ted Brown	.50
4	Joe Senser	.50
5	Sammie White	.50
6	Doug Martin	.50
7	Matt Blair	1.00
8	Bud Grant (CO)	2.00
9	Scott Studwell	.75
10	Greg Coleman	.50
11	John Turner	.50
12	Jim Hough	.50
13	Joey Browner	1.00
14	Dennis Swilley	.50
15	Darrin Nelson	.75
16	Mark Mullaney	.50
17	Fran Tarkenton (All-Time Great)	3.00

1984 Vikings Police

The 18-card, 2-5/8" x 4-1/8" set, sponsored by Pillsbury, Burger King, the Minnesota Crime Prevention Officers Association and Green Giant, features an action shot on the card front with a crime prevention tip on the back.

		MT
Complete Set (18):		8.00
Common Player:		.40
1	Checklist Card	.50
2	Keith Nord	.40
3	Joe Senser	.40
4	Tommy Kramer	1.25
5	Darrin Nelson	.50
6	Tim Irwin	.40
7	Mark Mullaney	.40
8	Les Steckel (CO)	.40
9	Greg Coleman	.40
10	Tommy Hannon	.40
11	Curtis Rouse	.40
12	Scott Studwell	.50
13	Steve Jordan	1.00
14	Willie Teal	.40
15	Ted Brown	.40
16	Sammie White	1.00
17	Matt Blair	.40
18	Jim Marshall (All-Time Great)	2.50

1985 Vikings Police

The 16-card, 2-5/8" x 4-1/8" set was sponsored by Frito-Lay, Pepsi-Cola, KS95-FM and local law enforcement. The cards are similar in design to previous Police sets, with crime prevention tips on the backs.

		MT
Complete Set (16):		8.00
Common Player:		.40
1	Checklist Card	.50
2	Bud Grant (CO)	1.50
3	Matt Blair	.50
4	Alfred Anderson	.50
5	Fred McNeill	.40
6	Tommy Kramer	.75
7	Jan Stenerud	1.25
8	Sammie White	.75
9	Doug Martin	.40
10	Greg Coleman	.50
11	Steve Riley	.40
12	Walker Lee Ashley	.40
13	Tim Irwin	.40
14	Scott Studwell	.50
15	Darrin Nelson	.50
16	Mick Tingelhoff (All-Time Great)	.75

1986 Vikings Police

The 14-card, 2-5/8" x 4-1/8" set is similar to Police sets from previous years with a "Crime Prevention Tip" on the card back.

		MT
Complete Set (14):		8.00
Common Player:		.40
1	Jerry Burns (CO) (Checklist back)	.50
2	Darrin Nelson	.50
3	Tommy Kramer	.75
4	Anthony Carter	1.50
5	Scott Studwell	.50
6	Chris Doleman	1.50
7	Joey Browner	.75
8	Steve Jordan	.50
9	David Howard	.40
10	Tim Newton	.40
11	Leo Lewis	.40
12	Keith Millard	1.00
13	Doug Martin	.40
14	Bill Brown (All-Time Great)	.75

1987 Vikings Police

The 14-card, 2-5/8" x 4-1/8" set features a color action shot on the front with a "Crime Prevention Tip" on the back. Card No. 1, Purple Power '87, is a Vikings montage by artist Cliff Spohn. Over 2 million sets were distributed over a 14-week period by the Vikings, Campbell's Soup, Frito-Lay, KSTP-FM and the Minnesota Crime Prevention Association.

		MT
Complete Set (14):		8.00
Common Player:		.40
1	Purple Power '87 (checklist back)	.50
2	Jerry Burns (CO)	.50
3	Scott Studwell	.50
4	Tommy Kramer	.75
5	Gerald Robinson	.40
6	Wade Wilson	1.75
7	Anthony Carter	1.00
8	Terry Tausch	.40
9	Leo Lewis	.40
10	Keith Millard	.75
11	Carl Lee	.50
12	Steve Jordan	.50
13	D.J. Dozier	.75
14	Alan Page (ATG)	1.75

1988 Vikings Police

The 12-card, 2-5/8" x 4-1/8" set featured nine current players, one offense card, one defense card and one all-time great card (Paul Krause). The cards are similar in design to previous Police issues.

		MT
Complete Set (12):		5.00
Common Player:		.40
1	Vikings Offense (Checklist on back)	.50
2	Jesse Solomon	.50
3	Kirk Lowdermilk	.40
4	Darrin Nelson	.50
5	Chris Doleman	1.00
6	D.J. Dozier	.50
7	Gary Zimmerman	.75
8	Allen Rice	.40
9	Joey Browner	.75
10	Anthony Carter	1.00
11	Vikings Defense	.50
12	Paul Krause (All-Time Great)	1.00

1989 Vikings Police

The 10-card, standard-size set features color photos on the gray-border fronts. The card backs are horizontal and contain safety tips, bio information and career highlights. Production was limited to 175,000 for each card.

		MT
Complete Set (10):		5.00
Common Player:		.50
1	Team Card (schedule on back)	.75
2	Henry Thomas	1.00
3	Rick Fenney	.50
4	Chuck Nelson	.50
5	Jim Gustafson	.50
6	Wade Wilson	1.00
7	Randall McDaniel	.75
8	Jesse Solomon	.50
9	Anthony Carter	1.00
10	Joe Kapp (All-Time Great)	1.00

1989 Vikings Taystee Discs

The 12-disc, 2-3/4" in diameter set, features Minnesota players in closeups on the fronts with bio and stat information on the backs. Each disc was issued with a Taystee product in the Minnesota area.

		MT
Complete Set (12):		5.00
Common Player:		.50
1	Anthony Carter	1.00
2	Chris Doleman	1.00
3	Joey Browner	.75
4	Steve Jordan	.75
5	Scott Studwell	.50
6	Wade Wilson	1.00
7	Kirk Lowdermilk	.50
8	Tommy Kramer	.75
9	Keith Millard	.75
10	Rick Fenney	.50
11	Gary Zimmerman	.50
12	Darrin Nelson	.75

1990 Vikings Police

The 10-card, standard-size set was sponsored by Gatorade, WCCO Radio and local law enforcement and contained a crime prevention tip on the card backs.

		MT
Complete Set (10):		5.00
Common Player:		.50
1	Raymond Berry	.50
2	Anthony Carter	1.00
3	Chris Doleman	.75
4	Rick Fenney	.50
5	Hassan Jones	.75
6	Carl Lee	.50
7	Mike Merriweather	.50
8	Scott Studwell	.50
9	Herschel Walker	1.50
10	Wade Wilson	1.00

1991 Vikings Police

The 10-card, standard-size set was sponsored by KFAN Radio, Gatorade, K102 Radio and Super Bowl XXVI. The cards were distributed on a weekly basis by area police departments in the order listed below.

		MT
Complete Set (10):		5.00
Common Player:		.40
1	Rick Fenney	.40
2	Wade Wilson	.75
3	Mike Merriweather	.40
4	Hassan Jones	.40
5	Rich Gannon	1.00
6	Mark Dusbabek	.40
7	Sean Salisbury	.75
8	Reggie Rutland	.40
9	Tim Irwin	.40
10	Chris Doleman	.75

1992 Vikings Gatorade

Gatorade and the Minnesota Vikings teamed up to produce this 10-card team set.

		MT
Complete Set (10):		8.00
Common Player:		.50
1	Dennis Green	.75
2	John Randle	.75
3	Todd Scott	.50
4	Anthony Carter	.50
5	Steve Jordan	.50
6	Terry Allen	2.00
7	Brian Habib	.50
8	Fuad Reveiz	.50
9	Roger Craig	1.00
10	Cris Carter	2.00

1992 Vikings Police

The 10-card, standard-size set was sponsored by Gatorade, KFAN Radio, K102 Radio and local law enforcement. The card fronts have a color action shot framed by a purple border with the Gatorade logo centered on the card front bottom edge. The card backs have a black and white headshot and other sponsor logos.

		MT
Complete Set (10):		5.00
Common Player:		.40
1	Dennis Green (CO) (Schedule on back)	.75
2	John Randle	.75
3	Todd Scott	.40
4	Anthony Carter	1.00
5	Steve Jordan	.40
6	Terry Allen	2.00
7	Brian Habib	.40
8	Fuad Reveiz	.40
9	Roger Craig	1.00
10	Cris Carter	1.50

1993 Vikings Police

The 10-card, standard-size set is similar in design to the 1992 Police set, complete with the Gatorade logo on the card fronts and a black and white headshot on the horizontal card back.

		MT
Complete Set (10):		5.00
Common Player:		.40
1	Dennis Green (CO) (CL/Schedule on back)	.60
2	Henry Thomas	.60
3	Todd Scott	.40
4	Jack Del Rio	.60
5	Vencie Glenn	.40
6	Fuad Reveiz	.40
7	Cris Carter	1.25
8	Terry Allen	1.50
9	Roger Craig	.60
10	Carlos Jenkins	.40

1995 Vikings Police

The 10-card, standard-size set features a purple border on the card front with the Gatorade logo appearing in the left lower corner. The Vikings 35th anniversary logo is printed in the lower right corner of the card front, with the player's name and "Vikings" appearing centered along the top edge in a gray box. The card backs feature a black and white headshot with brief bio information.

		MT
Complete Set (10):		5.00
Common Player:		.40
1	Warren Moon (CL/Schedule on the back)	1.00
2	Randall McDaniel	.40
3	Jake Reed	.75
4	Jack Del Rio	.60
5	Cris Carter	.75
6	Fuad Reveiz	.40
7	Amp Lee	.40
8	John Randle	.60
9	Andrew Jordan	.40
10	DeWayne Washington	.60

1997 Vikings Police

The Minnesota Vikings were featured in this eight-card set, which was bordered in purple, with the Vikings logo in the upper right and the words "Minnesota Vikings" printed down the right side. Fronts also feature a color shot of the player with a General Security Services Corp. logo and a toll free number in the bottom left corner. Card backs feature a head shot of the player, stats and Vikadontis Rex and McGruff the Crime Dog logos along with The Minnesota Crime Prevention Association logo. Card No. 1 features a set checklist and 1997 team schedule.

		MT
Complete Set (8):		5.00
Common Player:		.40
1	Cris Carter, Jake Reed	1.00
2	Robert Smith	1.00
3	Jeff Brady	.40
4	Brad Johnson	1.50
5	Robert Griffith	.40
6	Randall McDaniel	.40
7	Leroy Hoard	.40
8	John Randle	.50

1986 Waddingtons Game

Produced in England, this NFL card game consists of 40 cards measuring 3-1/2" x 5-11/16". The card fronts feature color illustrations of NFL teams. Five different teams are portrayed on seven cards each. The other five cards in the set are interception cards, which have the NFL logo on the front. The backs of all the cards feature the NFL logo.

		MT
Complete Set (40):		60.00
Common Player:		.50

		MT
1	Bears 10 (Walter Payton)	3.00
2	Bears 20 (Walter Payton)	3.00
3	Bears 40 (Walter Payton)	3.00
4	Bears 50 (Walter Payton)	3.00
5	Bears First Down (Walter Payton)	3.00
6	Bears Punt (Walter Payton)	3.00
7	Bears Touchdown (Walter Payton)	3.00
8	Cowboys 10 (Danny White, Tony Dorsett)	1.00
9	Cowboys 20 (Danny White, Tony Dorsett)	1.00
10	Cowboys 40 (Danny White, Tony Dorsett)	1.00
11	Cowboys 50 (Danny White, Tony Dorsett)	1.00
12	Cowboys First Down (Danny White, Tony Dorsett)	1.00
13	Cowboys Punt (Danny White, Tony Dorsett)	1.00
14	Cowboys Touchdown (Danny White, Tony Dorsett)	1.00
15	Dolphins 10 (Lorenzo Hampton, Eric Laakso)	.50
16	Dolphins 20 (Lorenzo Hampton, Eric Laakso)	.50
17	Dolphins 40 (Lorenzo Hampton, Eric Laakso)	.50
18	Dolphins 50 (Lorenzo Hampton, Eric Laakso)	.50
19	Dolphins First Down (Lorenzo Hampton, Eric Laakso)	.50
20	Dolphins Punt (Lorenzo Hampton, Eric Laakso)	.50
21	Dolphins Touchdown (Lorenzo Hampton, Eric Laakso)	.50
22	Redskins 10 (John Riggins, Joe Theismann)	1.00
23	Redskins 20 (John Riggins, Joe Theismann)	1.00
24	Redskins 40 (John Riggins, Joe Theismann)	1.00
25	Redskins 50 (John Riggins, Joe Theismann)	1.00
26	Redskins First Down (John Riggins, Joe Theismann)	1.00
27	Redskins Punt (John Riggins, Joe Theismann)	1.00
28	Redskins Touchdown (John Riggins, Joe Theismann)	1.00
29	Steelers 10 (Terry Bradshaw, Lynn Swann)	2.00
30	Steelers 20 (Terry Bradshaw, Lynn Swann)	2.00
31	Steelers 40 (Terry Bradshaw, Lynn Swann)	2.00
32	Steelers 50 (Terry Bradshaw, Lynn Swann)	2.00
33	Steelers First Down (Terry Bradshaw, Lynn Swann)	2.00
34	Steelers Punt (Terry Bradshaw, Lynn Swann)	2.00
35	Steelers Touchdown (Terry Bradshaw, Lynn Swann)	2.00
36	Interception Card	.50
37	Interception Card	.50
38	Interception Card	.50
39	Interception Card	.50
40	Interception Card	.50

1988 Wagon Wheel

The eight-card, 6-5/16" x 4-5/16" set was issued in the United Kingdom by Burtons and each card was included in boxes of Chocolate Biscuits. Players are not specifically identified as the purpose of the set was to explain American football to the British by giving examples of positions.

		MT
	Complete Set (8):	60.00
	Common Player:	6.00
1	Defensive Back (Todd Bowles covering Mark Bavaro)	6.00
2	Defensive Lineman (Ed "Too Tall" Jones, Neil Lomax)	8.00
3	Kicker (Kevin Butler)	6.00
4	Linebacker (Bob Brudzinski)	6.00
5	Offensive Lineman (Keith Van Horne leading Walter Payton)	15.00
6	Quarterback (John Elway)	20.00
7	Receiver (Steve Largent between Vann McElroy and Mike Haynes)	10.00
8	Running Back (Rodney Carter of the Steelers)	6.00

1964 Wheaties Stamps

These unnumbered stamps, which measure 2-1/2" x 2-3/4", were created to be stored in an accompanying stamp album titled "Pro Bowl Football Player Stamp Album." Each stamp had a color photo of the player, plus his facsimile signature, bordered by a white frame. The stamps were in panels of 12 inside the album and were perforated so they could be put on the corresponding spot within the album. Two stickers were attached to the inside front cover. Four team logo stamps and 70 players are represented on the stamps, but there were no spots in the album for the logo stamps or those for Y.A. Tittle or Joe Schmidt.

		NM
	Complete Set (74):	250.00
	Common Player:	2.00
(1)	Herb Adderley	6.00
(2)	Grady Alderman	2.00
(3)	Doug Atkins	4.00
(4)	Sam Baker	2.00
(5)	Erich Barnes	2.00
(6)	Terry Barr	2.00
(7)	Dick Bass	2.00
(8)	Maxie Baughan	3.00
(9)	Raymond Berry	6.00
(10)	Charley Bradshaw	2.50
(11)	Jim Brown	35.00
(12)	Roger Brown	2.50
(13)	Timmy Brown	3.00
(14)	Gail Cogdill	2.00
(15)	Tommy Davis	2.00
(16)	Willie Davis	6.00
(17)	Bob DeMarco	2.00
(18)	Darrell Dess	2.00
(19)	Buddy Dial	3.00
(20)	Mike Ditka	18.00
(21)	Galen Fiss	2.00
(22)	Lee Folkins	2.00
(23)	Joe Fortunato	2.00
(24)	Bill Glass	3.00
(25)	John Gordy	2.00
(26)	Ken Gray	2.50
(27)	Forrest Gregg	5.00
(28)	Rip Hawkins	2.00
(29)	Charlie Johnson	3.00
(30)	John Henry Johnson	5.00
(31)	Henry Jordan	3.00
(32)	Jim Katcavage	2.00
(33)	Jerry Kramer	5.00
(34)	Joe Krupa	2.00
(35)	John LoVetere	2.00
(36)	Dick Lynch	3.00
(37)	Gino Marchetti	5.00
(38)	Joe Marconi	2.00
(39)	Tommy Mason	3.00
(40)	Dale Meinert	2.00
(41)	Lou Michaels	2.00
(42)	Minnesota Vikings Emblem	3.00
(43)	Bobby Mitchell	6.00
(44)	John Morrow	2.00
(45)	New York Giants Emblem	3.00
(46)	Merlin Olsen	10.00
(47)	Jack Pardee	4.00
(48)	Jim Parker	4.00
(49)	Bernie Parrish	2.00
(50)	Don Perkins	3.00
(51)	Richie Petitbon	2.00
(52)	Vince Promuto	2.00
(53)	Myron Pottios	2.00
(54)	Mike Pyle	2.00
(55)	Pete Retzlaff	3.00
(56)	Jim Ringo	5.00
(57)	Joe Rutgens	2.00
(58)	St. Louis Cardinals Emblem	3.00
(59)	San Francisco 49ers Emblem	3.00
(60)	Dick Schafrath	2.00
(61)	Joe Schmidt	6.00
(62)	Del Shofner	3.00
(63)	Norm Snead	3.00
(64)	Bart Starr	15.00
(65)	Jim Taylor	6.00
(66)	Roosevelt Taylor	2.00
(67)	Clendon Thomas	2.00
(68)	Y.A. Tittle	12.50
(69)	John Unitas	18.00
(70)	Bill Wade	3.00
(71)	Wayne Walker	2.00
(72)	Jesse Whittenton	2.00
(73)	Larry Wilson	5.00
(74)	Abe Woodson	2.00

1987 Wheaties

Specially-marked boxes of Wheaties cereal each contained one of these 5" x 7" posters. The posters, which were wrapped in cellophane, were produced by Starline Inc. with the cooperation of the NFLPA and organizational efforts of Michael Schechter Associates. Each front has a color action photo, with the player's name, team, position and uniform number listed in a white box at the bottom. "Wheaties" is written in a banner in the upper left corner. The poster back is numbered and includes biographical information and career summary notes. Bernie Kosar's card is not listed in the set on the checklist Wheaties provided on the box. It is assumed Kosar was pulled from the set at some point - his card is listed as a short print.

		MT
	Complete Set (26):	130.00
	Common Player:	2.50
1	Tony Dorsett	5.00
2	Herschel Walker	5.00
3	Marcus Allen	5.00
4	Eric Dickerson	6.00
5	Walter Payton	12.00
6	Phil Simms	4.00
7	Tommy Kramer	2.50
8	Joe Morris	2.50
9	Roger Craig	4.00
10	Curt Warner	3.50
11	Andre Tippett	2.50
12	Joe Montana	20.00
13	Jim McMahon	3.00
14	Bernie Kosar	25.00
15	Jay Schroeder	2.50
16	Al Toon	2.50
17	Mark Gastineau	2.50
18	Kenny Easley	2.50
19	Howie Long	2.50
20	Dan Marino	15.00
21	Karl Mecklenburg	3.25
22	John Elway	10.00
23	Boomer Esiason	5.00
24	Dan Fouts	4.00
25	Jim Kelly	10.00
26	Louis Lipps	3.00

1991 Wild Card National Promos

This three-card set was given away as a promo at the 12th Annual National Covention in Anaheim. The cards are numbered on the back, starting with the Dan McGwire card as "Prototype-2". Striped versions of the cards with a hologram in the upper left corner were also issued.

		MT
	Complete Set (3):	12.00
	Common Player:	2.50
2	Dan McGwire	6.00
3	Randal Hill	2.50
4	Todd Marinovich	6.00

1991 Wild Card College Draft Picks

Each of these cards features a glossy color action photo of a player in his college uniform. The card is black with an orange frame, which has different denominations running on top and down the right side. A circle with "1st Edition" appears in the lower left corner. The purple back has statistics, biographical information and a color photo. Striped, limited-edition Wild Card random inserts of each card were also produced (1 out of every 100 is wild). These cards had denominations of 5, 10, 20, 50, 100 and 1,000; the higher numbers were made in scarcer numbers. The finder was able to redeem the card for a like amount of the player's regular card.

		MT
	Complete Set (160):	15.00
	Common Player:	.05
1	Wild Card 1 (Todd Lyght)	.60
2	Kelvin Pritchett	.20
3	Robert Young	.05
4	Reggie Johnson	.05
5	Eric Turner	.50
6	Pat Tyrance	.10
7	Curvin Richards	.20
8	Calvin Stephens	.10
9	Corey Miller	.05
10	Michael Jackson	.30
11	Simmie Carter	.05
12	Roland Smith	.10
13	Pat O'Hara	.20
14	Scott Conover	.05
15	Wild Card 2 (Russell Maryland)	.75
16	Greg Amsler	.10
17	Moe Gardner	.30
18	Howard Griffith	.20
19	David Daniels	.10
20	Henry Jones	.10
21	Don Davey	.10
22	Wild Card 3 (Raghib (Rocket) Ismail)	1.00
23	Richie Andrews	.05
24	Shawn Moore	.25
25	Anthony Moss	.10
26	Vince Moore	.05
27	Leroy Thompson	.15
28	Darrick Brownlow	.20
29	Mel Agee	.10
30	Darryll Lewis	.25
31	Hyland Hickson	.05
32	Leonard Russell	1.00
33	Floyd Fields	.05
34	Esera Tuaolo	.15
35	Todd Marinovich	1.25
36	Gary Wellman	.10
37	Ricky Ervins	2.50
38	Pat Harlow	.20
39	Mo Lewis	.25
40	John Kasay	.30
41	Phil Hansen	.10
42	Kevin Donnalley	.10
43	Dexter Davis	.10
44	Vance Hammond	.05
45	Chris Gardocki	.10
46	Bruce Pickens	.20
47	Godfrey Myles	.15
48	Ernie Mills	.25
49	Derek Russell	.35
50	Chris Zorich	.25
51	Alfred Williams	.25
52	Jon Vaughn	.45
53	Adrian Cooper	.25
54	Eric Bieniemy	.25
55	Robert Bailey	.05
56	Ricky Watters	.25
57	Mark Vander Poel	.10
58	James Joseph	.50
59	Darren Lewis	.45
60	Wesley Carroll	.40
61	Dave Key	.10
62	Mike Pritchard	.75
63	Craig Erickson	.75
64	Browning Nagle	.75
65	Mike Dumas	.20
66	Andre Jones	.05
67	Herman Moore	.75
68	Greg Lewis	.60
69	James Goode	.05
70	Stan Thomas	.10
71	Jerome Henderson	.10
72	Doug Thomas	.10
73	Tony Covington	.10
74	Charles Mincy	.10
75	Kanavis McGhee	.20
76	Tom Backes	.05
77	Fernandus Vinson	.05
78	Marcus Robertson	.05
79	Eric Harmon	.05
80	Rob Selby	.05
81	Ed King	.20
82	William Thomas	.10
83	Mike Jones	.05
84	Paul Justin	.20
85	Robert Wilson	.05
86	Jesse Campbell	.10
87	Hayward Haynes	.05
88	Mike Croel	.75
89	Jeff Graham	.20
90	Vinnie Clark	.20
91	Keith Cash	.20
92	Tim Ryan	.10
93	Jarrod Bunch	.20
94	Stanley Richard	.30
95	Alvin Harper	.60
96	Bob Dahl	.10
97	Mark Gunn	.05
98	Frank Blevins	.05
99	Harvey Williams	1.00
100	Dixon Edwards	.20
101	Blake Miller	.05
102	Bobby Wilson	.25
103	Chuck Webb	.25
104	Randal Hill	.75
105	Shane Curry	.05
106	Barry Sanders	.75
107	Richard Fain	.15
108	Joe Garten	.05
109	Dean Dingham	.05
110	Mark Tucker	.05
111	Dan McGwire	1.00
112	Paul Glonek	.05
113	Tom Dohring	.05
114	Joe Sims	.05
115	Bryan Cox	.30
116	Bobby Olive	.05
117	Blaise Bryant	.15
118	Charles Johnson	.15
119	Brett Favre	2.00
120	Luis Cristobal	.05
121	Don Gibson	.05
122	Scott Ross	.05
123	Huey Richardson	.15
124	Chris Smith	.10
125	Duane Young	.05
126	Eric Swann	.30
127	Jeff Fite	.05
128	Eugene Williams	.05
129	Harlan Davis	.05
130	James Bradley	.05
131	Rob Carpenter	.20
132	Dennis Ransom	.05
133	Mike Arthur	.05
134	Chuck Weatherspoon	.30
135	Darrell Malone	.05
136	George Thornton	.05
137	Lamar McGriggs	.05
138	Alex Johnson	.05
139	Eric Moten	.10
140	Joe Valerio	.05
141	Jake Reed	.20
142	Ernie Thompson	.10
143	Roland Poles	.05
144	Randy Bethel	.05
145	Terry Bagsby	.05
146	Tim James	.05
147	Kenny Walker	.60
148	Nolan Harrison	.05
149	Keith Traylor	.20
150	Nick Subis	.05
151	Scott Zolak	.25
152	Pio Sagapolutele	.15
153	James Jones	.05
154	Mike Sullivan	.05
155	Joe Johnson	.05
156	Todd Scott	.10
157	Checklist 1	.05
158	Checklist 2	.05
159	Checklist 3	.05
160	Checklist 4	.05

1991 Wild Card NFL Prototypes

The six-card set promoted Wild Card's upcoming 1991 NFL set. The card fronts showcase an action photo bordered in black with different colored numbers around the top and right border. The Wild Card logo is in the upper left, with "NFL Premier Edition" printed inside a football in the lower left. The player's name and position are in the lower right. The card backs, numbered by a prefix of "prototype," have a photo of the player, his name, position and bio at the top. The player's stats are included inside a box at the bottom.

1991 Wild Card NFL

These cards, similar in design to Wild Cards' collegiate draft picks set, have a full-color glossy action photo on the front, with a black and yellow border. Multi-color numbers appear in the upper right corner and along the right side of the card. The player's name and position are in the lower right corner, opposite a football with the words "NFL Premier Edition" inside. The card back has a mug shot, statisitics, a card number and biographical information. Striped "Wild Cards," printed in limited editions, were also created for each card, in denominations of 10, 20, 50, 100 and 1,000. The card could be redeemed for a similar amount of the player's regular card, according to the denomination number in the stripe. A surprise Wild Card #126, was also created; finders could redeem it for a 10-card NFL Experience subset which featured players from the Buffalo Bills and Washington Redskins. Also created were three bonus cards, which enabled finders to redeem them for the item pictured - either a case of cards, a box of cards, or a Wild Card cap.

		MT
	Complete Set (160):	10.00
	Common Player:	.03
	Wax Box:	6.00
1	Jeff George	.35
2	Sean Jones	.03
3	Duane Bickett	.03
4	John Elway	.15
5	Christian Okoye	.08
6	Steve Atwater	.06
7	Anthony Munoz	.08
8	Dave Krieg	.08
9	Nick Lowery	.06
10	Albert Bentley	.06
11	Mark Jackson	.03
12	Jeff Bryant	.03
13	Johnny Hector	.03
14	John L. Williams	.08
15	Jim Everett	.15
16	Mark Duper	.08
17	Drew Hill	.08
18	Randal Hill	.60
19	Ernest Givins	.10
20	Ken O'Brien	.08
21	Blair Thomas	.40
22	Derrick Thomas	.15
23	Harvey Williams	.75
24	Simon Fletcher	.03
25	Stephone Paige	.06
26	Barry Wood	.25
27	Warren Moon	.20
28	Derrick Fenner	.12
29	Shane Conlan	.06
30	Karl Mecklenburg	.06
31	Gary Anderson	.08
32	Sammie Smith	.08
33	Steve DeBerg	.06
34	Dan McGwire	1.25
35	Roger Craig	.10
36	Tom Tupa	.08
37	Rod Woodson	.08
38	Junior Seau	.20
39	Bruce Pickens	.20
40	Greg Townsend	.03
41	Gary Clark	.12
42	Broderick Thomas	.06
43	Charles Mann	.06

1991 Wild Card NFL

		MT
	Complete Set (6):	40.00
	Common Player:	5.00
1	Troy Aikman	9.00
2	Barry Sanders	10.00
3	Thurman Thomas	9.00
4	Emmitt Smith	12.50
5	Jerry Rice	7.50
6	Lawrence Taylor	5.00

44	Browning Nagle	.75
45	James Joseph	.45
46	Emmitt Smith	2.00
47	Cornelius Bennett	.08
48	Maurice Hurst	.03
49	Art Monk	.10
50	Louis Lipps	.06
51	Mark Rypien	.20
52	Bubby Brister	.08
53	John Stephens	.06
54	Merril Hoge	.03
55	Kevin Mack	.06
56	Al Toon	.08
57	Ronnie Lott	.10
58	Eric Metcalf	.06
59	Vinny Testaverde	.08
60	Darrell Green	.10
61	Randall Cunningham	.15
62	Charles Haley	.06
63	Mark Carrier	.08
64	Jim Harbaugh	.10
65	Richard Dent	.08
66	Stan Thomas	.08
67	Neal Anderson	.15
68	Troy Aikman	1.25
69	*Mike Pritchard*	.40
70	Deion Sanders	.20
71	Andre Rison	.15
72	Keith Millard	.08
73	Jerry Rice	.85
74	Johnny Johnson	.25
75	Tim McDonald	.06
76	*Leonard Russell*	1.25
77	Keith Jackson	.08
78	Keith Byars	.06
79	Ricky Proehl	.10
80	Dexter Carter	.08
81	*Alvin Harper*	.75
82	Irving Fryar	.06
83	Marion Butts	.10
84	Alfred Williams	.15
85	Timm Rosenbach	.10
86	Steve Young	.60
87	Albert Lewis	.06
88	Rodney Peete	.08
89	Barry Sanders	.85
90	Bennie Blades	.06
91	Chris Spielman	.06
92	John Friesz	.35
93	Jerome Brown	.06
94	Reggie White	.08
95	Michael Irvin	.20
96	Keith McCants	.08
97	Vinnie Clark	.10
98	Louis Oliver	.03
99	Mark Clayton	.08
100	John Offerdahl	.03
101	Michael Carter	.06
102	John Taylor	.12
103	William Perry	.08
104	Gill Byrd	.06
105	Burt Grossman	.03
106	Herman Moore	1.50
107	Howie Long	.06
108	Bo Jackson	.35
109	Kelvin Pritchett	.12
110	Jacob Green	.06
111	Chris Doleman	.06
112	Herschel Walker	.12
113	Russell Maryland	.45
114	Anthony Carter	.08
115	Joey Browner	.06
116	Tony Mandarich	.06
117	Don Majkowski	.08
118	Ricky Ervins	1.50
119	Sterling Sharpe	.75
120	Tim Harris	.06
121	Hugh Millen	.75
122	Mike Rozier	.06
123	Chris Miller	.15
124	Morten Andersen	.06
125	*Neil O'Donnell*	1.50
126	Surprise Wild Card	.25
127	Eddie Brown	.06
128	James Francis	.08
129	James Brookss	.08
130	David Fulcher	.06
131	*Michael Jackson*	.75
132	Clay Matthews	.03
133	Scott Norwood	.03
134	Wesley Carroll	.40
135	Thurman Thomas	.40
136	Mark Ingram	.03
137	Bobby Hebert	.08
138	Bobby Wilson	.08
139	Craig Heyward	.06
140	Dalton Hilliard	.06
141	Jeff Hostetler	.20
142	Dave Meggett	.10
143	Cris Dishman	.20
144	Lawrence Taylor	.06
145	Leonard Marshall	.06
146	Pepper Johnson	.06
147	Todd Marinovich	1.25
148	Mike Croel	.75
149	Erik McMillan	.06
150	Flipper Anderson	.06
151	Cleveland Gary	.06
152	Henry Ellard	.08
153	Kevin Greene	.06
154	Michael Cofer	.03
155	Todd Lyght	.40
156	Bruce Smith	.08
157	Checklist 1	.06
158	Checklist 2	.06
159	Checklist 3	.06
160	Checklist 4	.06

1991 Wild Card NFL Redemption Cards

This surprise Wild Card, #126, inserted randomly in 1991 Wild Card NFL packs, could be redeemed for the 10-card NFL Experience subset which is listed below. The cards feature members of the Buffalo Bills and Washington Redskins.

		MT
Complete Set (10):		3.50
Common Player:		.12
126A	Mark Rypien	.60
126B	Ricky Ervins	1.50
126C	Darrell Green	.25
126D	Charles Mann	.12
126E	Art Monk	.30
126F	Thurman Thomas	.90
126G	Bruce Smith	.30
126H	Cornelius Bennett	.25
126I	Scott Norwood	.12
126J	Shane Conlan	.18

1991 Wild Card NFL Super Bowl Promos

Super Bowl XXVI is honored on this 10-card set, which spotlights five players from each team. The cards were handed out to attendees at the Super Bowl Card Show. The card fronts have an action photo borded in black, with different colored numbers on the top and right borders. The NFL Experience logo is in the lower left. The player's name and position are located in the lower right. The card backs showcase a player photo, his name, position and bio at the top of the card. A text box at the bottom of the card explains that Wild Card was a corporate sponsor of the Super Bowl Card Show III.

		MT
Complete Set (10):		30.00
Common Player:		1.00
1	Mark Rypien	5.00
2	Ricky Ervins	10.00
3	Darrell Green	2.00
4	Charles Mann	1.00
5	Art Monk	2.50
6	Thurman Thomas	7.50
7	Bruce Smith	2.50
8	Cornelius Bennett	1.00
9	Scott Norwood	1.00
10	Shane Conlan	1.50

1991-92 Wild Card Redemption Prototypes

The six-card, standard-size set was available to collectors via a redemption mail-in offer. In exchange for three Collegiate Football Surprise wild cards before April 30, 1992, collectors also received the set, which is similar to the 1992 Wild Card NFL set. The cards are numbered with the "P" prefix.

		MT
Complete Set (6):		2.00
Common Player:		.20
1	Edgar Bennett (Florida State)	1.00
2	Jimmy Smith (Jackson State)	.75
3	Will Furrer (Virginia Tech)	.20
4	Terrell Buckley (Florida State)	.30
5	Tommy Vardell (Stanford)	.30
6	Amp Lee (Florida State)	.30

Values quoted in this guide reflect the retail price of a card — the price a collector can expect to pay when buying a card from a dealer. The wholesale price — that which a collector can expect to receive when selling cards — will be significantly lower, depending on desirability and condition.

1992 Wild Card Prototypes

Picking up where the 1991 Wild Card Prototypes left off, this 12-card set begins with card No. P7. The card fronts include a color photo, bordered with colored numbers on the top and right border. The Wild Card logo is in the upper left, with the player's team name along the left side. His name and position are in the lower right. The team's helmet is printed in the lower left of the photo. The backs have the player's name, picture and bio on the right side of the card. The player's stats are located inside a box on the left side. The cards are numbered with the "P" prefix.

		MT
Complete Set (12):		25.00
Common Player:		1.00
7	Barry Sanders	4.00
8	John Taylor	2.00
9	John Elway	3.00
10	Erik Kramer	2.00
11	Christian Okoye	1.00
12	Leonard Russell	1.00
13	Barry Sanders	4.00
14	Earnest Byner	1.00
15	Warren Moon	2.50
16	Ronnie Lott	2.00
17	Michael Irvin	2.50
18	Haywood Jeffires	2.00

1992 Wild Card

This 460-card set showcased a color photo on the front, with the Wild Card logo in the upper left, the team name along the left border, team helmet in the lower left of the photo and player's name and position in the lower right. The border of the card front changes from white to gray to black. The card backs have the card number in the upper right, with the player's name, bio and photo along the right side. His stats are located in a box along the left border. Reportedly, Wild Card produced 30,000 10-box cases of the 250-card Series I product. Overall, 100 case cards and 1,000 box cards were seeded in foil packs. A numbered stripe on the front of the cards would carry denominations of 5, 10, 20, 50, 100 and 1,000. The Surprise Cards could be redeemed for a four-card set which included a P1 Barry Sanders (with Surprise Card No. 1) or P2 Emmitt Smith Stat Smasher card (with Series II Suprise Card No. 251), Red-Hot rookie card, Field Force card and a silver or gold Field Force card. In addition, a Barry Sanders promo card was handed out at the 1992 National Convention. It featured the National logo and had value stripes of 5, 10, 20, 50 and 100.

		MT
Complete Set (460):		15.00
Complete Series 1 (250):		7.50
Complete Series 2 (210):		7.50
Common Player:		.05
Minor Stars:		.10
Series 1/2 Wax Box:		8.00
1	Surprise Card	.10
2	Marcus Dupree	.05
3	Jackie Slater	.05
4	Robert Delpino	.05
5	Jerry Gray	.05
6	Jim Everett	.05
7	Roman Phifer	.05
8	Alvin Wright	.05
9	Todd Lyght	.05
10	Reggie White	.20
11	Randal Hill	.05
12	Keith Byars	.05
13	Clyde Simmons	.05
14	Keith Jackson	.05
15	Seth Joyner	.05
16	James Joseph	.05
17	Eric Allen	.05
18	Sammie Smith	.05
19	Mark Clayton	.05
20	Aaron Craver	.05
21	Hugh Green	.05
22	John Offerdahl	.05
23	Jeff Cross	.05
24	Ferrell Edmunds	.05
25	Mark Duper	.05
26	Ronnie Harmon	.05
27	Derrick Walker	.05
28	Gary Plummer	.05
29	Rod Bernstine	.05
30	Burt Grossman	.05
31	Donnie Elder	.05
32	John Friesz	.10
33	Bill Ray Smith	.05
34	Luis Sharpe	.05
35	Aeneas Williams	.10
36	Ken Harvey	.05
37	Johnny Johnson	.05
38	Eric Swann	.05
39	Tom Tupa	.05
40	Anthony Thompson	.05
41	Broderick Thomas	.05
42	Vinny Testaverde	.20
43	Mark Carrier	.05
44	Gary Anderson	.05
45	Keith McCants	.05
46	Reggie Cobb	.05
47	Lawrence Dawsey	.05
48	Kevin Murphy	.05
49	Keith Woodside	.05
50	Darrell Thompson	.05
51	Vinnie Clark	.05
52	Sterling Sharpe	.20
53	Mike Tomczak	.05
54A	Dan Majikowski (err)	.05
54B	Don Majikowski (cor)	.05
55	Tony Mandarich	.05
56	Mark Murphy	.05
57	Dexter McNabb	.05
58	Rick Fenney	.05
59	Cris Carter	.30
60	Wade Wilson	.05
61	Mike Merriweather	.05
62	Rich Gannon	.05
63	Herschel Walker	.05
64	Chris Doleman	.05
65	UER (Al Noga) (On front, he's a DE; on back, he's a DT)	.05
66	*Chris Mims*	.10
67	Ed Cunningham	.05
68	Marcus Allen	.20
69	*Kevin Turner*	.10
70	Howie Long	.05
71	Tim Brown	.20
72	Nick Bell	.05
73	Todd Marinovich	.05
74	Jay Schroeder	.05
75	Mervyn Fernandez	.05
76	Tony Smith	.05
77	John Alt	.05
78	Christian Okoye	.05
79	Nick Lowery	.05
80	Derrick Thomas	.10
81	Bill Maas	.05
82	Dino Hackett	.05
83	Deron Cherry	.05
84	Barry Word	.05
85	Mike Mooney	.05
86	Cris Dishman	.05
87	Bruce Matthews	.05
88	Tony Jones	.05
89	William Fuller	.05
90	Ray Childress	.05
91	Warren Moon	.10
92	Lorenzo White	.05
93	Joe Bowden	.05
94	Tom Rathman	.05
95	Keith Henderson	.05
96	Jesse Sapolu	.05
97	Charles Haley	.05
98	Steve Young	.50
99	John Taylor	.05
100	Tim Harris	.05
101	Scott Davis	.05
102	*Steve Bono*	.30
103	Mike Kenn	.05
104	Mike Farr	.05
105	Rodney Peete	.05
106	Jerry Ball	.05
107	Chris Spielman	.05
108	Barry Sanders	1.50
109	Bennie Blades	.05
110	Herman Moore	.50
111	Erik Kramer	.05
112	Vance Johnson	.05
113	Mike Croel	.05
114	Mark Jackson	.05
115	Steve Atwater	.05
116	Gaston Green	.05
117	John Elway	1.00
118	Simon Fletcher	.05
119	Karl Mecklenburg	.05
120	Hart Lee Dykes	.05
121	Jerome Henderson	.05
122	Chris Singleton	.05
123	Marv Cook	.05
124	Leonard Russell	.05
125	Hugh Millen	.05
126	Pat Harlow	.05
127	Andre Tippett	.05
128	Bruce Armstrong	.05
129	Gary Clark	.05
130	Art Monk	.10
131	Darrell Green	.05
132	Wilber Marshall	.05
133	Jim Lachey	.05
134	Earnest Byner	.05
135	Chip Lohmiller	.05
136	Mark Rypien	.10
137	Ricky Sanders	.05
138	Stan Thomas	.05
139	Neal Anderson	.05
140	Trace Armstrong	.05
141	Kevin Butler	.05
142	Mark Carrier	.05
143	Dennis Gentry	.05
144	Jim Harbaugh	.10
145	Richard Dent	.10
146	Andre Rison	.20
147	Bruce Pickens	.05
148	UER (Chris Hinton) (Dealt to Falcons in 1990, not 1989)	.05
149	Brian Jordan	.10
150	Chris Miller	.05
151	Moe Gardner	.05
152	Bill Fralic	.05
153	Michael Haynes	.10
154	Mike Pritchard	.10
155	Dean Biasucci	.05
156	Clarence Verdin	.05
157	Donnell Thompson	.05
158	Duane Bickett	.05
159	Jon Hand	.05
160	Sam Graddy	.05
161	Emmitt Smith	1.50
162	Michael Irvin	.20
163	Danny Noonan	.05
164	Jack Del Rio	.05
165	Jim Jeffcoat	.05
166	Alexander Wright	.05
167	Frank Minnifield	.05
168	Ed King	.05
169	Reggie Langhorne	.05
170	Mike Baab	.05
171	Eric Metcalf	.05
172	Clay Matthews	.05
173	Kevin Mack	.05
174	Mike Johnson	.05
175	Jeff Lageman	.05
176	Freeman McNeil	.05
177	Erik McMillan	.05
178	James Hasty	.05
179	Kyle Clifton	.05
180	Joe Kelly	.05
181	Phil Simms	.10
182	Everson Walls	.05
183	Jeff Hostetler	.10
184	Dave Meggett	.05
185	Matt Bahr	.05
186	Mark Ingram	.05
187	Rodney Hampton	.10
188	Kanavis McGhee	.05
189	Tim McGee	.05
190	Eddie Brown	.05
191	Rodney Holman	.05
192	Harold Green	.05
193	James Francis	.05
194	Anthony Munoz	.05
195	David Fulcher	.05
196	Tim Krumrie	.05
197	Bubby Brister	.05
198	Rod Woodson	.05
199	Louis Lipps	.05
200	Carnell Lake	.05
201	Don Beebe	.05
202	Thurman Thomas	.20
203	Cornelius Bennett	.05
204	Mark Kelso	.05
205	James Lofton	.10
206	Darryl Talley	.05
207	Morten Andersen	.05
208	Vince Buck	.05
209	Wesley Carroll	.05
210	Bobby Hebert	.05
211	Craig Heyward	.05
212	Dalton Hilliard	.05
213	Rickey Jackson	.05
214	Eric Martin	.05
215	Pat Swilling	.05
216	Steve Walsh	.05
217	Torrance Small	.05
218	Jacob Green	.05
219	Cortez Kennedy	.05
220	John L. Williams	.05
221	Terry Wooden	.05
222	Grant Feasel	.05
223	Siran Stacy	.05
224	Chris Hakel	.05
225	Todd Harrison	.05
226	Bob Whitfield	.05
227	Eddie Blake	.05
228	*Keith Hamilton*	.10
229	*Darryl Williams*	.10
230	Ricardo McDonald	.05
231	Alan Haller	.05
232	Leon Searcy	.05
233	Patrick Rowe	.05
234	*Edgar Bennett*	.30
235	*Terrell Buckley*	.30
236	Will Furrer	.05
237	*Amp Lee*	.20
238	*Jimmy Smith*	2.00
239	*Tommy Vardell*	.20
240	Leonard Russell	.05
241	Mike Croel	.05
242	Warren Moon	.10
243	Mark Rypien	.05
244	Thurman Thomas	.10
245	Emmitt Smith	.75
246	Checklist 1	.05
247	Checklist 2	.05
248	Checklist 3	.05
249	Checklist 4	.05
250	Checklist 5	.05
251	Surprise Card	.10
252	Erric Pegram	.10
253	Anthony Carter	.05
254	Roger Craig	.10
255	Hassan Jones	.05
256	Steve Jordan	.05
257	Randall McDaniel	.05
258	Henry Thomas	.05
259	Carl Lee	.05
260	Ray Agnew	.05
261	Irving Fryar	.05
262	Tom Waddle	.05
263	Greg McMurtry	.05
264	Stephen Baker	.05
265	Mark Collins	.05
266	Howard Cross	.05
267	Pepper Johnson	.05
268	Fred Barnett	.05
269	Heath Sherman	.05
270	William Thomas	.05
271	Bill Bates	.05
272	Issiac Holt	.05
273	Emmitt Smith	3.00
274	Eric Bieniemy	.05
275	Marion Butts	.05
276	Gill Byrd	.05
277	Robert Blackmon	.05
278	Brian Blades	.05
279	Joe Nash	.05
280	Bill Brooks	.05
281	Mel Gray	.05
282	Andre Ware	.05
283	Steve McMichael	.05
284	Brad Muster	.05
285	Ron Rivera	.05
286	Chris Zorich	.05
287	Chris Burkett	.05
288	Irv Eatman	.05
289	Rob Moore	.20
290	Joe Mott	.05
291	Brian Washington	.05
292	Michael Carter	.05
293	Dexter Carter	.05
294	Don Griffin	.05
295	John Taylor	.05
296	Ted Washington	.05
297	Monte Coleman	.05
298	Andre Collins	.05
299	Charles Mann	.05
300	Shane Conlan	.05
301	Keith McKeller	.05
302	Nate Odomes	.05
303	Riki Ellison	.05
304	Willie Gault	.05
305	Bob Golic	.05
306	Ethan Horton	.05
307	Ronnie Lott	.10
308	Don Mosebar	.05
309	Aaron Wallace	.05
310	Wymon Henderson	.05
311	Vance Johnson	.05
312	Ken Lanier	.05
313	Steve Sewell	.05
314	Dennis Smith	.05
315	Kenny Walker	.05
316	Chris Martin	.05
317	Albert Lewis	.05
318	Todd McNair	.05
319	*Tracy Simien*	.05
320	Percy Snow	.05
321	Mark Rypien	.05
322	Bryan Hinkle	.05
323	David Little	.05
324	Dwight Stone	.05
325	*Van Waiters*	.05
326	Pio Sagapolutele	.05
327	Michael Jackson	.10
328	Vestee Jackson	.05
329	Tony Paige	.05
330	Reggie Roby	.05
331	Haywood Jeffires	.10
332	Lamar Lathon	.05
333	Bubba McDowell	.05
334	Doug Smith	.05
335	Dean Steinkuhler	.05
336	Jessie Tuggle	.05
337	Freddie Joe Nunn	.05
338	Pat Terrell	.05
339	Tom McHale	.05
340	Sam Mills	.05
341	John Tice	.05
342	Brent Jones	.05
343	*Robert Porcher*	.20
344	*Mark D'Onofrio*	.05
345	David Tate	.05
346	*Courtney Hawkins*	.10
347	*Ricky Watters*	.50
348	Amp Lee	.10
349	Steve Young	.50
350	Natu Tuatagaloa	.05
351	Alfred Williams	.05
352	*Derek Brown*	.10
353	*Marco Coleman*	.10
354	*Tommy Maddox*	.10

355	Siran Stacy	.05
356	Greg Lewis	.05
357	Paul Gruber	.05
358	*Troy Vincent*	.10
359	Robert Wilson	.05
360	Jessie Hester	.05
361	Shaun Gayle	.05
362	Deron Cherry	.05
363	Wendell Davis	.05
364	*David Klingler*	.20
365	Jason Hanson	.05
366	*Marquez Pope*	.10
367	Robert Williams	.05
368	Kelvin Pritchett	.05
369	Dana Hall	.05
370	*David Brandon*	.05
371	Tim McKyer	.05
372	Darion Conner	.05
373	Derrick Fenner	.05
374	Hugh Millen	.05
375	Bill Jones	.05
376	J.J. Birden	.05
377	*Ty Detmer*	.10
378	*Alonzo Spellman*	.20
379	Sammie Smith	.05
380	Al Smith	.05
381	*Louis Clark*	.05
382	*Vernice Smith*	.05
383	Tony Martin	.20
384	Willie Green	.05
385	Sean Gilbert	.20
386	*Eugene Chung*	.05
387	Toi Cook	.05
388	Brett Maxie	.05
389	Steve Israel	.05
390	Mike Mularkey	.05
391	Barry Foster	.05
392	Hardy Nickerson	.05
393	*Johnny Mitchell*	.10
394	Thurman Thomas	.20
395	*Tony Smith*	.10
396	Keith Goganious	.05
397	*Matt Darby*	.05
398	*Nate Turner*	.05
399	Keith Jennings	.05
400	*Mitchell Benson*	.05
401	Kurt Barber	.05
402	Tony Sacca	.05
403	*Steve Hendrickson*	.05
404	Johnny Johnson	.05
405	Lorenzo Lynch	.05
406	Luis Sharpe	.05
407	Jim Everett	.05
408	Neal Anderson	.05
409	*Ashley Ambrose*	.10
410	*George Williams*	.05
411	Clarence Kay	.05
412	Dave Krieg	.05
413	Terrell Buckley	.10
414	Ricardo McDonald	.05
415	Kelly Stouffer	.05
416	Barney Bussey	.05
417	Ray Roberts	.05
418	*Fred McAfee*	.05
419	Fred Banks	.05
420	Tim McDonald	.05
421	*Darryl Williams*	.05
422	Bobby Abrams	.05
423	Tommy Vardell	.10
424	William White	.05
425	Billy Ray Smith	.05
426	Lemuel Stinson	.05
427	*Brad Johnson*	20.00
428	Herschel Walker	.20
429	Eric Thomas	.05
430	Anthony Thompson	.05
431	Ed West	.05
432	Edgar Bennett	.10
433	Warren Powers	.05
434	Byron Evans	.05
435	Rodney Culver	.05
436	Ray Horton	.05
437	Richmond Webb	.05
438	*Mark McMillian*	.05
439	Subset checklist	.05
440	*Lawrence Pete*	.05
441	*Rodney Smith*	.05
442	Mark Rodenhauser	.05
443	*Scott Lockwood*	.05
444	*Charles Davenport*	.05
445	Terry McDaniel	.05
446	Darren Perry	.10
447	*Darrick Owens*	.10
448	Alvin Wright	.05
449	Frank Stams	.05
450	*Santana Dotson*	.20
451	Mark Carrier	.05
452	Kevin Murphy	.05
453	Jeff Bryant	.05
454	Eric Allen	.05
455	*Brian Bollinger*	.05
456	Elston Ridgle	.05
457	Jim Riggs	.05
458	Series II, checklist #6	.05
459	Series II, checklist #7	.05
460	Series II, checklist #8	.05

1992 Wild Card Class Back Attack

Inserted in 1992 Wild Card WLAF foil packs, the five-card set showcases a color action photo on the front. A green and black border surrounds the photo, with different colored numbers running along the right side of the card. In a football in the lower left is printed "Class Back Attack" or "Red Hot Rookie." The player's name and team are listed in the lower right. The card backs, numbered with an "SP" prefix, feature the player's photo and bio at the top. A text box at the bottom invites collectors to collect all singles and then continue to collect sets of the different value denominations.

		MT
Complete Set (5):		16.00
Common Player:		1.25
1	Vaughn Dunbar	1.25
2	Barry Sanders	4.00
3	Emmitt Smith	7.50
4	Thurman Thomas	2.00
5	David Klingler (Red Hot Rookie; Surprise Card Redemption)	2.00

1992 Wild Card Field Force

Randomly seeded in 1992 Wild Card Series II foil packs, the 30-card set was also issued in both gold and silver foil versions. Each card front includes a photo which is bordered by a dark purple border on the left. It changes to purple and light purple as it runs to the right side of the card. The dark purple area on the left features gold or silver horizontal lines which run the length of the card. The Field Force logo is in the lower left, with the player's name and position in the lower right. The card back includes a photo on the left side and the player's stats on the right. The card number is located in the upper right.

		MT
Complete Set (30):		18.00
Common Player:		.25
1	Joe Montana	3.00
2	Quentin Coryatt	.75
3	Tommy Vardell	.50
4	Jim Kelly	1.00
5	John Elway	1.25
6	Ricky Watters	1.50
7	Vinny Testaverde	.25
8	Randal Hill	.25
9	Amp Lee	.50
10	Vaughn Dunbar	.25
11	Troy Aikman	3.50
12	Deion Sanders	.50
13	Rodney Hampton	1.50
14	Brett Favre	2.00
15	Warren Moon	.75
16	Browning Nagle	.25
17	Terrell Buckley	.30
18	Barry Sanders	3.00
19	Dan Marino	2.50
20	Carl Pickens	.60
21	Herschel Walker	.25
22	Ronnie Lott	.25
23	Steve Emtman	.30
24	Mark Rypien	.25
25	Bobby Hebert	.25
26	Dan McGwire	.25
27	Neil O'Donnell	1.00
28	Cris Carter	.25
29	Randall Cunningham	.60
30	Jerry Rice	2.00

1992 Wild Card Pro Picks

Randomly seeded in 1992 Wild Card Series II foil packs, the 30-card chase set includes a Red Hot Rookies' logo inside a football in the lower left corner. Different colored numbers border the top and right of the photo. The player's name and position are at the lower right. The backs, numbered "of 30," have the player's name, bio and photo on the right, with his highlights in a box on the left. Gold and silver editions were inserted one per jumbo pack.

		MT
Complete Set (8):		10.00
Common Player:		.30
1	Emmitt Smith	4.00
2	Mark Rypien	.30
3	Warren Moon	.50
4	Leonard Russell	.30

5	Thurman Thomas	.50
6	John Elway	1.00
7	Barry Sanders	2.00
8	Steve Young	1.50

1992 Wild Card Red Hot Rookies

This 30-card set is identified by a flaming football with the words "Red Hot Rookies" in the lower right corner. The set was inserted into Series II packs of Wild Card, with gold and silver versions also available one per jumbo pack. Red Hot Rookies were also available in 5, 10, 20, 50, 100 and 1,000 stripe varieties, with the stripe placed in the upper right hand corner of the photo.

		MT
Complete Set (30):		15.00
Complete Series 1 (10):		5.00
Complete Series 2 (20):		10.00
Common Player:		.50
1	Darryl Williams	.50
2	Amp Lee	.75
3	Will Furrer	.50
4	Edgar Bennett	1.50
5	Terrell Buckley	.50
6	Bob Whitfield	.50
7	Siran Stacy	.50
8	Jimmy Smith	1.00
9	Kevin Turner	.50
10	Tommy Vardell	.75
11	Surprise Card	1.00
12	Derek Brown	.50
13	Marco Coleman	1.00
14	Quentin Coryatt	1.00
15	Rodney Culver	.50
16	Ty Detmer	.50
17	Vaughn Dunbar	.50
18	Steve Emtman	.50
19	Sean Gilbert	1.00
20	Courtney Hawkins	1.25
21	David Klingler	1.00
22	Amp Lee	.90
23	Tommy Maddox	.50
24	Johnny Mitchell	1.25
25	Darren Perry	.50
26	Carl Pickens	1.00
27	Robert Porcher	.50
28	Tony Smith	.50
29	Alonzo Spellman	.50
30	Troy Vincent	.50

1992 Wild Card Running Wild Silver

Inserted one per 1992 Wild Card Series II jumbo pack, the 40-card set showcased the Running Wild logo inside an arrow which overlapped the photo. Arrows also ran the length of the card from the top to the Running Wild logo. The player's name and team are located in the lower right. The card backs have a player photo on the left side, with his stats in a box on the right.

		MT
Complete Set (40):		18.00
Common Player:		.30
1	Terry Allen	.75
2	Neal Anderson	.50
3	Eric Ball	.30
4	Nick Bell	.30
5	Edgar Bennett	.75
6	Rod Bernstine	.30
7	Marion Butts	.50
8	Keith Byars	.30
9	Earnest Byner	.30
10	Reggie Cobb	.30
11	Roger Craig	.30
12	Rodney Culver	.50
13	Barry Foster	.50
14	Cleveland Gary	.30
15	Harold Green	.50
16	Gaston Green	.30
17	Rodney Hampton	.75
18	Mark Higgs	.30
19	Dalton Hilliard	.30

20	Bobby Humphrey	.30
21	Amp Lee	.50
22	Kevin Mack	.30
23	Eric Metcalf	.75
24	Brad Muster	.30
25	Christian Okoye	.50
26	Tom Rathman	.30
27	Leonard Russell	.50
28	Barry Sanders	2.50
29	Heath Sherman	.30
30	Emmitt Smith	4.00
31	Blair Thomas	.30
32	Thurman Thomas	.75
33	Tommy Vardell	.50
34	Herschel Walker	.50
35	Chris Warren	.75
36	Ricky Watters	.75
37	Lorenzo White	.50
38	John L. Williams	.30
39	Barry Word	.30
40	Vince Workman	.50

1992 Wild Card Stat Smashers

Card Nos. 1-16 were randomly seeded in Series II foil packs, while card Nos. 17-52 were found one per pack in Series II jumbo packs. The card fronts have the Stat Smashers' logo in the upper right, while the player's name, team and position are in stripes near the bottom. A photo of the player is placed over a foil background. The card backs, numbered with a prefix of "SS," include the player's name, bio and photo on the left, while a highlights box appears on the right. A Barry Sanders card could be received in exchange for a Surprise Card in Series I. A Series I Surprise Card could be redeemed for an Emmitt Smith card.

		MT
Complete Set (52):		55.00
Complete Series 1 (16):		30.00
Complete Series 2 (36):		25.00
Common Player (1-16):		1.25
Common Player (17-52):		.45
1	Barry Sanders	6.00
2	Leonard Russell	2.00
3	Thurman Thomas	3.00
4	John Elway	4.00
5	Steve Young	4.00
6	Warren Moon	2.00
7	Terrell Buckley	1.25
8	Randall Cunningham	2.00
9	Steve Emtman	1.25
10	Dan Marino	10.00
11	Joe Montana	8.00
12	Carl Pickens	1.25
13	Jerry Rice	6.00
14	Deion Sanders	2.50
15	Tommy Vardell	2.00
16	Ricky Watters	3.00
17	Troy Aikman	6.00
18	Dale Carter	.60
19	Quentin Coryatt	.75
20	Vaughn Dunbar	.50
21	Mark Duper	.45
22	Eric Metcalf	.45
23	Brett Favre	10.00
24	Barry Foster	2.25
25	Jeff George	.75
26	Sean Gilbert	1.00
27	Jim Harbaugh	.45
28	Courtney Hawkins	1.25
29	Charles Haley	.45
30	Bobby Hebert	.50
31	Stan Humphries	.55
32	Michael Irvin	2.50
33	Jim Kelly	1.50
34	David Klingler	1.50
35	Ronnie Lott	.45
36	Tommy Maddox	1.00
37	Todd Marinovich	.45
38	Hugh Millen	.60
39	Art Monk	.60
40	Browning Nagle	.65
41	Neil O'Donnell	1.00
42	Tom Rathman	.50
43	Andre Rison	1.00
44	Mike Singletary	.50
45	Tony Smith	.45
46	Emmitt Smith	10.00
47	Pete Stoyanovich	.45
48	John Taylor	.60
49	Troy Vincent	.60
50	Herschel Walker	.60
51	Lorenzo White	.80
52	Rodney Culver	1.00

1992 Wild Card NASDAM

Produced for and handed out at the 1992 NASDAM trade show in Orlando, this five card set features a color action photo on a white-bordered card front. Different colored numbers surround the photo on the top and right borders. The NASDAM logo appears in the lower left of the photo, while the player's name and position are in the lower right. The player's team's nickname is printed along the left border. The backs feature a photo of the player, along with his name, bio and stats.

		MT
Complete Set (5):		3.00
Common Player:		.40
1	Edgar Bennett	1.50
2	Amp Lee	.60
3	Terrell Buckley	.60
4	Tony Smith	.40
5	Will Furrer (UER) (Misspelled Furer)	.40

1992 Wild Card NASDAM/SCAI Miami

Produced and handed out at the 1992 NASDAM/SCAI conference in Miami, the six-card set showcases only Miami Dolphins. The card fronts feature a color action photo, with the NASDAM/SCAI logo in the lower left of the photo. "Dolphins" is printed along the left side of the photo. The top and right borders of the photo include different colored numbers. The player's name and position are located in the lower right. The card backs feature the player's name, bio and photo inside a football shape on the right side of the card. His stats are listed inside a box on the left side.

		MT
Complete Set (6):		4.00
Common Player:		.75
1	Mark Clayton	1.50
2	Aaron Craver	.75
3	Tony Paige	.75
4	Mark Duper	1.25
5	Tony Martin	1.25
6	Reggie Roby	.75

1992 Wild Card Sacramento CardFest

This six-card San Francisco 49ers set was given out at Sacramento CardFest in 1992, and contains the logo for the event in the lower left hand corner. The design is consistent with other 1992 Wild Card designs, with a white framed background that includes multi-colored trim on the top and right edge.

		MT
Complete Set (6):		3.00
Common Player:		.40
1	Tom Rathman	.40
2	Steve Young	1.00
3	Steve Bono	1.00
4	Brett Jones	.40
5	Ricky Watters	.60
6	Amp Lee	.40

1992 Wild Card WLAF

With a reported press run of 6,000 10-box cases, this 150-card set featured players from the World League of American Football. Card fronts featured a color photo surrounded by black, gray and white. The city the player performed in is printed like a postmark on the right, while the team's logo is located in the lower left. The World League logo is included with the Wild Card logo inside a stamp in the upper right. The player's name and team are in the lower right. The card backs have the player's name printed under the photo, while his bio and card number are to the right of his photo. His highlights are listed in a box near the bottom of the card.

		MT
Complete Set (150):		9.00
Common Player:		.05
1	World Bowl Champs	.10
2	Pete Mandley	.10
3	Steve Williams	.05
4	Dee Thomas	.10
5	Emanuel King	.10
6	Anthony Dilweg	.25
7	Ben Brown	.05
8	Darryl Harris	.20
9	Aaron Emanuel	.20
10	Andre Brown	.10
11	Reggie McKenzie	.05
12	Darryl Holmes	.05
13	Michael Proctor	.05
14	Ricky Johnson	.05
15	Ray Savage	.05
16	George Searcy	.05
17	Titus Dixon	.05
18	Willie Fears	.10
19	Terrence Cooks	.05
20	Ivory Lee Brown	.20
21	Mike Johnson	.05
22	Doug Williams	.10
23	Brad Goebel	.20
24	Tony Boles	.15
25	Cisco Richard	.05
26	Robb White	.05
27	Darrell Colbert	.05
28	Wayne Walker	.10
29	Ronnie Williams	.05
30	Erik Norgard	.05
31	Darren Willis	.05
32	Kent Wells	.05
33	Phil Logan	.05
34	Pat O'Hara	.05
35	Melvin Patterson	.05
36	Amir Rasul	.05
37	Tom Rouen	.10
38	Chris Cochrane	.05
39	Randy Bethel	.05
40	Eric Harmon	.05
41	Archie Herring	.05
42	Tim James	.05
43	Babe Laufenberg	.15
44	Herb Welch	.05
45	Stefon Adams	.05
46	Tony Burse	.10
47	Carl Parker	.05
48	Mike Prugle	.05
49	Michael Jones	.05
50	David Archer	.25
51	Corian Freeman	.05
52	Eddie Brown	.15
53	Paul Green	.05
54	Basil Proctor	.05
55	Mike Sinclair	.05
56	Louis Riddick	.05
57	Roman Matuez	.05
58	Darryl Clack	.10
59	Willie Davis	.05
60	Glen Rodgers	.05
61	Grantis Bell	.05
62	Joe Howard-Johnson	.15
63	Rocen Keeton	.05
64	Dean Witkowski	.05
65	Stacey Simmons	.10
66	Roger Vick	.05
67	Scott Mitchell	.20
68	Todd Krumm	.05
69	Kerwin Bell	.15
70	Richard Carey	.05
71	Kip Lewis	.05
72	Andre Alexander	.05
73	Reggie Slack	.20
74	Falanda Newton	.10
75	Tony Woods	.10
76	Chris McLemore	.05
77	Eric Wilkerson	.10
78	Cornell Burbage	.05
79	Doug Pederson	.05
80	Brent Pease	.15
81	Monty Gilbreath	.05
82	Wes Pritchett	.05
83	Byron Williams	.05
84	Ron Sancho	.10
85	Tony Jones	.10
86	Anthony Wallace	.05
87	Mike Perez	.15
88	Steve Bartalo	.05
89	Teddy Garcia	.05
90	Joe Greenwood	.05
91	Tony Baker	.05
92	Glenn Cobb	.05
93	Mark Tucker	.05
94	Lyneil Mayo	.05

95	Alex Espinoza	.05
96	Mike Norseth	.15
97	Steve Avery	.05
98	John Brantley	.05
99	Eddie Britton	.05
100	Philip Doyle	.05
101	Elroy Harris	.05
102	John R. Holland	.10
103	Mark Hopkins	.05
104	Arthur Hunter	.05
105	Paul McGowan	.05
106	John Miller	.05
107	Shawn Moore	.05
108	Phil Ross	.05
109	Eugene Rowell	.05
110	Joe Valerio	.10
111	Harvey Wilson	.05
112	Irvin Smith	.05
113	Tony Sargent	.05
114	Ricky Shaw	.05
115	Curtis Moore	.05
116	Fred McNair	.05
117	Danny Lockett	.10
118	William Kirksey	.05
119	Stan Gelbaugh	.25
120	Judd Garrett	.15
121	Dedrick Dodge	.05
122	Dan Crossman	.05
123	Jeff Alexander	.05
124	Lew Barnes	.05
125	Willie Don Wright	.05
126	Johnny Thomas	.05
127	Richard Buchanan	.05
128	Chad Fortune	.05
129	Eric Lindstrom	.05
130	Ron Goetz	.05
131	Bruce Clark	.10
132	Anthony Greene	.10
133	Demetrius Davis	.10
134	Mike Roth	.05
135	Tony Moss	.05
136	Scott Erney	.10
137	Brad Henke	.05
138	Malcolm Frank	.05
139	Sean Foster	.05
140	Michael Titley	.05
141	Rickey Williams	.05
142	Karl Dunbar	.05
143	Carl Bax	.05
144	Willie Bouyer	.05
145	Howard Feggins	.05
146	David Smith	.05
147	Bernard Ford	.10
148	Checklist 1	.05
149	Checklist 2	.05
150	Checklist 3	.05

1992-93 Wild Card San Francisco

Originally produced for the Sports Collectors Card Expo in San Francisco in 1992, the six-card set focused solely on 49ers. The set was later reissued with a different logo for the 1993 Spring National Sports Collectors Convention in San Francisco. The 1993 set also had different card numbers and two different players. The card fronts have the show's logo in the lower left of the photo. The usual Wild Card denominations are printed along the top and right borders of the photo. The player's name and position are listed in the lower right. The card backs, numbered "of 6," have the player's name, bio and photo on the right, with stats listed in a box on the left. Cards listed below with an "A" are from the 1992 set, while those with a "B" are from the 1993 set.

		MT
	Complete Set (6):	4.00
	Common Player:	.30
1A	John Taylor	.30
1B	Tom Rathman	.30
2A	Amp Lee	.30
2B	Steve Young	.75
3A	Steve Bono	.60
3B	Steve Bono	.60
4A	Steve Young	.75
4B	Brent Jones	.30
5A	Tom Rathman	.30
5B	Ricky Watters	.50
6A	Don Griffin	.30
6B	Amp Lee	.30

Post-1980 cards in Near Mint condition will generally sell for about 75% of the quoted Mint value. Excellent-condition cards bring no more than 40%.

A card number in parentheses ( ) indicates the set is unnumbered.

1993 Wild Card Prototypes

Produced for the 1993 National Sports Collectors Convention, the six-card set showcases a full-bleed color photo. The Wild Card logo is printed in the upper left, with the player's name, team and position printed inside a gold 3-D band at the bottom. "NFL players" is printed on the right side of the band. The card backs have a photo of the player on the right side, with his name, bio and stats printed over a photo of the team's city skyline. The card numbers are prefixed by a "P." The numbers begin at P19, which is where the 1992 Wild Card promos ended.

		MT
	Complete Set (6):	5.00
	Common Player:	.50
19	Emmitt Smith	2.00
20	Ricky Watters	.50
21	Drew Bledsoe	1.50
22	Garrison Hearst	.50
23	Barry Foster	.50
24	Rick Mirer	.75

1993 Wild Card Superchrome Promos

The six-card foil set features the same design as the 1993 Wild Card Prototypes, except the card fronts are printed in chrome. The card backs are also designed the same as the 1993 Prototypes, except the card numbers carry an "SCP" prefix.

		MT
	Complete Set (6):	7.00
	Common Player:	.50
1	Emmitt Smith	3.00
2	Ricky Watters	.75
3	Drew Bledsoe	2.50
4	Garrison Hearst	.50
5	Barry Foster	.50
6	Rick Mirer	1.00

1993 Wild Card

The 260-card set features full-bleed photos, with the Wild Card logo in the upper left and the player's name, team and position printed in a gold 3-D band at the bottom. The card backs have a photo on the right side. The player's name, bio and stats are located to the left of the player photo and printed over a skyline of the team's city. Series I boasted Field Force, Red Hot Rookies and Stat Smashers chase cards. In 1994,

Wild Card changed its packages by adding Superchrome cards to packs. The Superchrome parallel cards were seeded in Superchrome 15-card low-series packs and 13-card high-series hobby packs. They are valued at four to nine times the value of the regular cards. In addition, denomination striped cards were randomly seeded into packs. Denominations fell between 5-1,000.

		MT
	Complete Set (260):	10.00
	Complete Series 1 (200):	6.00
	Complete Series 2 (60):	4.00
	Common Player:	.05
	Minor Stars:	.10
	Stripes 5/10/20:	2x-4x
	Stripes 50/100:	10x-20x
	Stripes 1000:	80x-160x
	Superchrome 1 Set (200):	20.00
	Superchrome 2 Set (60):	15.00
	Superchromes:	1.5x-3x
	Wax Box:	10.00
1	Surprise card	.05
2	Steve Young	.50
3	John Taylor	.05
4	Jerry Rice	.75
5	Brent Jones	.05
6	Ricky Watters	.20
7	Elvis Grbac	.30
8	Amp Lee	.05
9	Steve Bono	.20
10	Wendell Davis	.05
11	Mark Carrier	.05
12	Jim Harbaugh	.05
13	Curtis Conway	.40
14	Neal Anderson	.05
15	Tom Waddle	.05
16	Jeff Query	.05
17	David Klingler	.10
18	Eric Ball	.05
19	Derrick Fenner	.05
20	Steve Tovar	.05
21	Carl Pickens	.20
22	Ricardo McDonald	.05
23	Harold Green	.05
24	Keith McKeller	.05
25	Steve Christie	.05
26	Andre Reed	.10
27	Kenneth Davis	.05
28	Frank Reich	.05
29	Jim Kelly	.15
30	Bruce Smith	.05
31	Thurman Thomas	.20
32	Glyn Milburn	.30
33	John Elway	.40
34	Vance Johnson	.05
35	Greg Lewis	.05
36	Steve Atwater	.05
37	Shannon Sharpe	.05
38	Mike Croel	.05
39	Kevin Mack	.05
40	Lawyer Tillman	.05
41	Tommy Vardell	.05
42	Bernie Kosar	.05
43	Eric Metcalf	.05
44	Clay Matthews	.05
45	Keith McCants	.05
46	Broderick Thomas	.05
47	Lawrence Dawsey	.05
48	Reggie Cobb	.05
49	Lamar Thomas	.10
50	Courtney Hawkins	.05
51	Ivory Lee Brown	.05
52	Ernie Jones	.05
53	Freddie Joe Nunn	.05
54	Chris Chandler	.05
55	Randal Hill	.05
56	Lorenzo Lynch	.05
57	Garrison Hearst	1.00
58	Marion Butts	.05
59	Anthony Miller	.05
60	Eric Bieneimy	.05
61	Ronnie Harmon	.05
62	Junior Seau	.15
63	Gill Byrd	.05
64	Stan Humphries	.15
65	John Friesz	.05
66	J.J. Birden	.05
67	Joe Montana	1.00
68	Christian Okoye	.05
69	Dale Carter	.05
70	Barry Wood	.05
71	Derrick Thomas	.10
72	Todd McNair	.05
73	Harvey Williams	.05
74	Jack Trudeau	.05
75	Rodney Culver	.05
76	Anthony Johnson	.05
77	Steve Emtman	.05
78	Quentin Coryatt	.05
79	Keith Cash	.05
80	Jeff George	.10
81	Darrin Smith	.10
82	Jay Novacek	.05
83	Michael Irvin	.30
84	Alvin Harper	.20
85	Kevin Williams	.50
86	Troy Aikman	.60
87	Emmitt Smith	1.25
88	O.J. McDuffie	.50
89	Mike Williams	.05
90	Dan Marino	1.25
91	Aaron Craver	.05
92	Troy Vincent	.05
93	Keith Jackson	.05
94	Marco Coleman	.05
95	Mark Higgs	.05
96	Fred Barnett	.05
97	Wes Hopkins	.05
98	Randall Cunningham	.10
99	Heath Sherman	.05
100	Vai Sikahema	.05
101	Tony Smith	.05
102	Andre Rison	.10
103	Chris Miller	.05
104	Deion Sanders	.30
105	Mike Pritchard	.05
106	Steve Broussard	.05
107	Stephen Baker	.05
108	Carl Banks	.05
109	Jarrod Bunch	.05
110	Phil Simms	.10
111	Rodney Hampton	.15
112	Dave Meggett	.05
113	Pepper Johnson	.05
114	Coleman Rudolph	.05
115	Boomer Esiason	.10
116	Browning Nagle	.05
117	Rob Moore	.05
118	Marvin Jones	.10
119	Herman Moore	.25
120	Bennie Blades	.05
121	Erik Kramer	.05
122	Mel Gray	.05
123	Rodney Peete	.05
124	Barry Sanders	.75
125	Chris Spielman	.05
126	Lamar Lathon	.05
127	Ernest Givins	.05
128	Lorenzo White	.05
129	Michael Barrow	.05
130	Warren Moon	.10
131	Cody Carlson	.05
132	Reggie White	.10
133	Terrell Buckley	.05
134	Ed West	.05
135	Mark Brunell	2.00
136	Brett Favre	1.25
137	Edgar Bennett	.05
138	Sterling Sharpe	.10
139	George Teague	.10
140	Leonard Russell	.05
141	Drew Bledsoe	2.00
142	Eugene Chung	.05
143	Walter Stanley	.05
144	Scott Zolak	.05
145	Jon Vaughn	.05
146	Andre Tippet	.05
147	Alexander Wright	.05
148	Billy Joe Hobert	.20
149	Terry McDaniel	.05
150	Tim Brown	.10
151	Willie Gault	.05
152	Howie Long	.05
153	Todd Marinovich	.05
154	Jim Everett	.05
155	David Lang	.05
156	Henry Ellard	.05
157	Cleveland Gary	.05
158	Steve Israel	.05
159	Jerome Bettis	1.00
160	Jackie Slater	.05
161	Art Monk	.10
162	Ricky Sanders	.05
163	Brian Mitchell	.05
164	Reggie Brooks	.15
165	Mark Rypien	.05
166	Earnest Byner	.05
167	Andre Collins	.05
168	Quinn Early	.05
169	Fred McAfee	.05
170	Wesley Carroll	.05
171	Gene Atkins	.05
172	Derek Brown	.15
173	Vaughn Dunbar	.05
174	Ricky Jackson	.05
175	John L. Williams	.05
176	Carlton Gray	.10
177	Cortez Kennedy	.10
178	Kelly Stouffer	.05
179	Rick Mirer	.50
180	Dan McGwire	.05
181	Chris Warren	.15
182	Barry Foster	.05
183	Merril Hoge	.05
184	Darren Perry	.05
185	Deon Figures	.10
186	Jeff Graham	.15
187	Dwight Stone	.05
188	Neil O'Donnell	.10
189	Rod Woodson	.05
190	Alex Van Pelt	.05
191	Steve Jordan	.05
192	Roger Craig	.05
193	Qadry Ismail	.40
194	Robert Smith	.50
195	Gino Torretta	.10
196	Anthony Carter	.05
197	Terry Allen	.05
198	Rich Gannon	.05
199	Checklist #1	.05
200	Checklist #2	.05
201	Victor Bailey	.15
202	Michael Barrow	.05
203	Patrick Bates	.05
204	Jerome Bettis	.30
205	Drew Bledsoe	.75
206	Vincent Brisby	.75
207	Reggie Brooks	.10
208	Derek Brown	.10
209	Keith Byars	.05
210	Tom Carter	.15
211	Curtis Conway	.20
212	Russell Copeland	.10
213	John Copeland	.10
214	Eric Curry	.10
215	Troy Drayton	.30
216	Jason Elam	.10
217	Steve Everitt	.10
218	Deon Figures	.05
219	Irving Fryar	.05
220	Darrien Gordon	.20
221	Carlton Gray	.05
222	Kevin Greene	.05
223	Andre Hastings	.20
224	Michael Haynes	.05
225	Garrison Hearst	.40
226	Bobby Hebert	.05
227	Lester Holmes	.05
228	Jeff Hostetler	.10
229	Desmond Howard	.05
230	Tyrone Hughes	.20
231	Quadry Ismail	.20
232	Rocket Ismail	.10
233	James Jett	.05
234	Marvin Jones	.05
235	Todd Kelly	.05
236	Lincoln Kennedy	.10
237	Terry Kirby	.40
238	Bernie Kosar	.05
239	Derrick Lassic	.10
240	Wilber Marshall	.05
241	O.J. McDuffie	.30
242	Ryan McNeil	.05
243	Natrone Means	1.00
244	Glyn Milburn	.10
245	Rick Mirer	.40
246	Scott Mitchell	.10
247	Ron Moore	.30
248	Lorenzo Neal	.20
249	Erric Pegram	.20
250	Roosevelt Potts	.20
251	Leonard Renfro	.10
252	Greg Robinson	.10
253	Wayne Simmons	.10
254	Chris Slade	.10
255	Irv Smith	.20
256	Robert Smith	.20
257	Dana Stubblefield	.40
258	George Teague	.10
259	Kevin Williams	.10
260	Checklist	.05

1993 Wild Card Bomb Squad

According to reports, 10,000 of these 30-card sets were produced. They were seeded in high-number (201-260) packs. The chromium fronts feature an action shot of a wide receiver inside a football shape. "Bomb Squad" is printed on the left side of the football. The player's name, team and position are printed in a rectangle at the bottom of the card. The orange-colored backs showcase the player's name, team and position at the top. His stats are listed horizontally along the left side of the card, while a player photo is on the right.

		MT
	Complete Set (30):	12.00
	Common Player:	.30
1	Jerry Rice	2.00
2	John Taylor	.50
3	J.J. Birden	.50
4	Stephen Baker	.30
5	Victor Bailey	.50
6	O.J. McDuffie	.50
7	Haywood Jeffires	.50
8	Eric Green	.30
9	Johnny Mitchell	.50
10	Art Monk	.50
11	Quinn Early	.50
12	Troy Drayton	.50
13	Vincent Brisby	.50
14	Courtney Hawkins	.50
15	Tom Waddle	.30
16	Curtis Conway	.50
17	Andre Reed	.50
18	Carl Pickens	.50
19	Sterling Sharpe	.50
20	Shannon Sharpe	.50
21	Qadry Ismail	.50
22	Rocket Ismail	.50
23	Andre Rison	.50
24	Michael Haynes	.50
25	Alvin Harper	.50
26	Michael Irvin	.50
27	Michael Jackson	.50
28	Herman Moore	.75
29	Anthony Miller	.50
30	Gary Clark	.50

1993 Wild Card Bomb Squad B/B

This 15-card set is a double-front version of the Bomb Squad chase set. The same design is featured for each player on the front and back. Inserted one per 20-pack box of the 1993 Wild Card high-number jumbo packs, the cards were part of the 1,000 sets which were reportedly produced.

		MT
	Complete Set (15):	20.00
	Common Player:	1.25
1	Jerry Rice, John Taylor	4.00
2	Tom Waddle, Curtis Conway	1.25
3	Andre Reed, Carl Pickens	2.00
4	Sterling Sharpe, Shannon Sharpe	2.00
5	Qadry Ismail, Rocket Ismail	2.00
6	Andre Rison, Michael Haynes	2.00
7	Alvin Harper, Michael Irwin	2.00
8	Michael Jackson, Herman Moore	1.25
9	Anthony Miller, Gary Clark	1.25
10	J.J. Birden, Stephen Baker	1.25
11	Victor Bailey, O.J. McDuffie	1.25
12	Haywood Jeffires, Eric Green	1.25
13	Johnny Mitchell, Art Monk	1.25
14	Quinn Early, Troy Drayton	1.25
15	Vincent Brisby, Courtney Hawkins	2.00

1993 Wild Card Field Force

The 90-card chase set was randomly seeded into packs, however, it was released in three 30-card series based on Divisional alignment. The Field Force logo appears at the bottom left of the card fronts, while the player's name and position are located in the lower right. The Wild Card logo is in the upper left. The left border has black and blue jagged lines, while the rest of the card is blue and white. The card backs, numbered with either a "WFF," "EFF" or "CFF," depending on divisions, have a photo on the left and stats on the right. The card number is at the top right.

		MT
	Complete Set (90):	30.00
	Complete West Series (30):	10.00
	Complete East Series (30):	10.00
	Complete Cent. Series (30):	10.00
	Common Player:	.25
	Minor Stars:	.50
	Stripes 5/10/20:	1.5x-3x
	Stripes 50/100:	8x-16x
	Stripes 1000:	70x-140x
	Silver Cards:	1x-1.5x
	Gold Cards:	1x-2x
	Superchrome Set (10):	20.00
	Superchrome Cards:	1x-2x
31	Jerry Rice	2.00
32	Ricky Watters	.50
33	Steve Bono	1.00
34	Amp Lee	.25
35	Steve Young	2.00
36	Tommy Maddox	.25
37	Cleveland Gary	.25
38	John Elway	1.00
39	Glyn Milburn	.50
40	Stan Humphries	.75
41	Junior Seau	.75
42	Natrone Means	2.00
43	Dale Carter	.25
44	Joe Montana	2.00
45	Christian Okoye	.25

46	Deion Sanders	1.00
47	Roger Harper	.25
48	Steve Broussard	.25
49	Todd Marinovich	.25
50	BIlly Joe Hobert	.50
51	Patrick Bates	.25
52	Jerome Bettis	1.00
53	Willie Anderson	.25
54	Irv Smith	.25
55	Quinn Early	.25
56	Vaughn Dunbar	.25
57	Rick Mirer	2.00
58	Carlton Gary	.25
59	Chris Warren	.50
60	Dan McGwire	.25
61	Pete Metzelaars	.25
62	Kenneth Davis	.25
63	Thurman Thomas	.75
64	Chris Chandler	.50
65	Garrison Hearst	1.25
66	Ricky Proehl	.25
67	Steven Emtman	.25
68	Jeff George	.75
69	Clarence Verdin	.25
70	Troy Aikman	1.50
71	Emmitt Smith	2.50
72	Alvin Harper	.50
73	Michael Irvin	1.00
74	O.J. McDuffie	.50
75	Troy Vincent	.25
76	Keith Jackson	.25
77	Dan Marino	2.50
78	Leonard Renfro	.25
79	Heath Sherman	.25
80	Derek Brown	.25
81	Rodney Hampton	.50
82	James Hasty	.25
83	Johnny Mitchell	.25
84	Brad Baxter	.25
85	Leonard Russell	.25
86	Marv Cook	.25
87	Drew Bledsoe	5.00
88	Ricky Ervins	.25
89	Art Monk	.50
90	Earnest Byner	.25
91	Tom Waddle	.25
92	Neal Anderson	.25
93	Curtis Conway	.75
94	Harold Green	.25
95	Jeff Query	.25
96	Carl Pickens	1.00
97	David Klingler	.25
98	Michael Jackson	.25
99	Eric Metcalf	.25
100	Courtney Hawkins	.25
101	Eric Curry	.25
102	Reggie Cobb	.25
103	Mel Gray	.25
104	Barry Sanders	1.75
105	Rodney Peete	.25
106	Haywood Jeffires	.25
107	Cody Carlson	.25
108	Curtis Duncan	.25
109	Edgar Bennett	.50
110	George Teague	.25
111	Terrell Buckley	.25
112	Brett Favre	2.50
113	Deon Figures	.25
114	Rod Woodson	.25
115	Neil O'Donnell	.50
116	Barry Foster	.25
117	Cris Carter	.75
118	Gino Torretta	.25
119	Terry Allen	.25
120	Qadry Iamail	.25

1993 Wild Card Field Force Superchrome

A 10-card partial parallel set to the Field Force chase set, this featured the same design as the regular Field Force, except this set had chromium fronts. The card backs have a photo on the left, with stats on the right. The card number is printed in the upper right, prefixed by "SCF."

		MT
Complete Set (10):		12.00
Common Player:		.40
1	Jerry Rice	1.50
2	Glyn Milburn	.40
3	Joe Montana	1.50
4	Rick Mirer	.75
5	Troy Aikman	1.50
6	Emmitt Smith	3.00
7	Dan Marino	3.00
8	Drew Bledsoe	2.00
9	Barry Sanders	1.50
10	Brett Favre	3.00

Post-1980 cards in Near Mint condition will generally sell for about 75% of the quoted Mint value. Excellent-condition cards bring no more than 40%.

1993 Wild Card Red Hot Rookies

Randomly seeded into packs, the 30-card set was divided into three 10-card sets based on NFL divisions. The card fronts have the Red Hot Rookies logo in the lower left, with the Wild Card logo in the upper left. Various colored numbers border the photo on the top and right. The player's name and position are printed at the bottom. The backs -- numbered with a prefix of "WRHR," "ERHR" and "CRHR," depending on divisions -- have stats on the left. The player's name, bio and headshot are along the right side.

		MT
Complete Set (30):		18.00
Complete West Series (10):		8.00
Complete East Series (10):		5.00
Comp. Central Series (10):		5.00
Common Player (31-60):		.25
31	Dana Stubblefield	.60
32	Todd Kelly	.25
33	Dan Williams	.25
34	Glyn Milburn	.60
35	Natrone Means	1.00
36	Lincoln Kennedy	.25
37	Patrick Bates	.25
38	Jerome Bettis	1.00
39	Irv Smith	.60
40	Rick Mirer	1.00
41	Garrison Hearst	1.50
42	Kevin Williams	1.25
43	Terry Kirby	1.25
44	O.J. McDuffie	.60
45	Leonard Renfro	.25
46	Victor Bailey	.40
47	Marvin Jones	.40
48	Drew Bledsoe	3.00
49	Reggie Brooks	.40
	(UER) (Missing	
	career college stats)	
50	Tom Carter	.40
51	Curtis Conway	1.25
52	Dan Footman	.25
53	Lamar Thomas	.40
54	Eric Curry	.60
55	Ryan McNeil	.40
56	Michael Barrow	.40
57	Wayne Simmons	.40
58	George Teague	.40
59	Robert Smith	1.25
60	Qadry Ismail	.60

1993 Wild Card Red Hot Rookies Superchrome

This 10-card partial parallel set of Red Hot Rookies has the same design as the regular set, except it is done in chromium. The card backs are numbered with the "SCR" prefix. In addition, 20 high-number Superchrome Red Hot Rookies could be received by sending $29.95 to the company. Reportedly, 10,000 sets were produced.

		MT
Complete Set (10):		20.00
Common Player:		1.00
1	Dana Stubblefield	1.25
2	Glyn Milburn	1.00
3	Jerome Bettis	5.00
4	Rick Mirer	2.50
5	Garrison Hearst	3.00
6	Terry Kirby	1.50
7	Victor Bailey	1.00
8	Drew Bledsoe	6.00
9	Reggie Brooks	1.00
10	Qadry Ismail	1.25

1993 Wild Card Stat Smashers

This 20-card set features a silver foil front, with the Stat Smashers' logo in the upper right. The player's name, team and position are located in stripes at the bottom. The card backs, numbered with a "CSS" prefix, have the player's name, bio, headshot and highlights. The backs are black-bordered. In addition, a gold version was also randomly inserted. This set features players who play with teams in the AFC and NFC Central Divisions.

		MT
Complete Set (60):		60.00
Complete West Series (20):		20.00
Complete East Series (20):		20.00
Complete Central Series		
(20):		20.00
Common Player:		.50
Gold Cards:		.75x-1.25x
53	Ricky Watters	1.00
54	Jerry Rice	3.00
55	Steve Young	2.50
56	Shannon Sharpe	1.00
57	John Elway	1.50
58	Glyn Milburn	1.00
59	Marion Butts	.75
60	Junior Seau	1.00
61	Natrone Means	1.50
62	Joe Montana	4.00
63	J.J. Birden	.50
64	Michael Haynes	.75
65	Deion Sanders	2.00
66	Billy Joe Hobert	1.00
67	Nick Bell	.50
68	Jerome Bettis	1.50
69	Vaughn Dunbar	.50
70	Quinn Early	.75
71	Dan McGwire	.50
72	Rick Mirer	1.50
73	Kenneth Davis	.50
74	Thurman Thomas	1.00
75	Garrison Hearst	2.00
76	Ricky Proehl	.50
77	Jeff George	1.00
78	Rodney Culver	.50
79	Troy Aikman	3.00
80	Emmitt Smith	6.00
81	Michael Irvin	1.00
82	O.J. McDuffie	1.00
83	Keith Jackson	.75
84	Dan Marino	6.00
85	Heath Sherman	.50
86	Fred Barnett	.75
87	Rodney Hampton	1.00
88	Marvin Jones	.75
89	Brad Baxter	.50
90	Drew Bledsoe	5.00
91	Ricky Ervins	.50
92	Art Monk	.75
93	Neal Anderson	.75
94	Curtis Conway	1.75
95	John Copeland	1.00
96	Carl Pickens	1.00
97	David Klingler	.75
98	Michael Jackson	.75
99	Kevin Mack	.50
100	Eric Curry	1.00
101	Reggie Cobb	.50
102	Willie Green	.50
103	Barry Sanders	3.00
104	Haywood Jeffires	.75
105	Lorenzo White	.75
106	Sterling Sharpe	1.00
107	Brett Favre	3.00
108	Neil O'Donnell	1.00
109	Barry Foster	.75
110	Rich Gannon	.75
111	Robert Smith	1.75
112	Qadry Ismail	1.00

1993 Wild Card Stat Smashers Rookies

Produced in gold and silver foil versions, the 52-card set was randomly seeded one per jumbo pack. The designs of the card fronts and backs resemble the other Stat Smasher set.

		MT
Complete Set (52):		15.00
Common Player:		.25
Complete Gold Set (52):		25.00
Gold Cards:		.75x-1.5x
1	Todd Kelly	.25
2	Dana Stubblefield	.60
3	Curtis Conway	.60
4	John Copeland	.60
5	Russell Copeland	.40
6	Thomas Smith	.60
7	Glyn Milburn	.60
8	Jason Elam	.40
9	Steve Everitt	.40
10	Eric Curry	.60
11	Horace Copeland	.40
12	Ronald Moore	.60
13	Garrison Hearst	1.50
14	Natrone Means	1.00
15	Darrien Gordon	.40
16	Roosevelt Potts	.40
17	Kevin Williams	1.25
18	Derrick Lassic	.40
19	O.J. McDuffie	.60
20	Terry Kirby	.60
21	Scott Mitchell	.60
22	Victor Bailey	.40
23	Vaughn Hebron	.40
24	Lincoln Kennedy	.25
25	Michael Strahan	.25
26	Marvin Jones	.40
27	Tony McGee	.60
28	Ryan McNeil	.40
29	Micheal Barrow	.40
30	Wayne Simmons	.40
31	George Teague	.40
32	Vincent Brisby	.60
33	Drew Bledsoe	3.00
34	Rocket Ismail	.40
35	Patrick Bates	.25
36	James Jett	.40
37	Jerome Bettis	.60
38	Troy Drayton	.60
39	Tom Carter	.40
40	Reggie Brooks	.40
41	Lorenzo Neal	.40
42	Derek Brown (BB)	.60
43	Tyrone Hughes	.60
44	Rick Mirer	1.00
45	Carlton Gray	.25
46	Andre Hastings	.40
47	Deon Figures	.60
48	Qadry Ismail	.60
49	Robert Smith	.60
50	Irv Smith	.60
51	Chris Slade	.60
52	Willie Roaf	.60

1993 Wild Card Superchrome FF/RHR B/B

Wild Card doubled up card fronts from the Red Hot Rookies and Field Force on these back-to-back cards. The designs of both card fronts resemble the regular chase set design. This 10-card set was randomly seeded in Superchrome Series II packs. The cards are unnumbered.

		MT
Complete Set (10):		25.00
Common Player:		1.25
1	Troy Aikman,	2.50
	Dana Stubblefield	
2	Drew Bledsoe,	3.00
	Drew Bledsoe	
3	Brett Favre,	5.00
	Terry Kirby	
4	Dan Marino,	5.00
	Reggie Brooks	
5	Glyn Milburn,	1.25
	Rick Mirer	
6	Rick Mirer,	1.25
	Glyn Milburn	
7	Joe Montana,	3.00
	Jerome Bettis	
8	Jerry Rice,	2.50
	Garrison Hearst	
9	Barry Sanders,	2.50
	Victor Bailey	
10	Emmitt Smith,	5.00
	Qadry Ismail (UER)	
	(Misspelled	
	Quadry)	

1993 Wild Card Superchrome Rookies Promos

This five-card set featured purple chromium borders with the player photos inside a gold chrome oval. "Superchrome" is printed at the top, while "Rookies" is printed at the bottom. The player's name, team and position are printed within the gold oval at the top. In addition, "Wild Card sample" is printed on the card front. The card backs, numbered with a prefix of "P," are bordered in black and purple. The player's name, bio and highlights are included on the left, with a player photo on the right.

		MT
Complete Set (5):		6.00
Common Player:		.75
1	Rick Mirer	1.25
2	Reggie Brooks	.75
3	Glyn Milburn	.75
4	Drew Bledsoe	3.00
5	Jerome Bettis	1.25

1993 Wild Card Superchrome Rookies

This 50-card set, released in early 1994, was inserted six cards per Superchrome Rookies 15-card foil pack. The other nine cards were 1993 Wild Card cards. The chromium fronts showcase "Superchrome" at the top and "Rookies" at the bottom. A photo is located inside a gold oval, with the player's name, team and position printed inside. The card backs include a player photo on the right, while his name, bio and stats are listed on the left.

		MT
Complete Set (50):		20.00
Common Player:		.20
1	Dana Stubblefield	.50
2	Todd Kelly	.20
3	Curtis Conway	1.00
4	John Copeland	.50
5	Tony McGee	.50
6	Russell Copeland	.50
7	Thomas Smith	.30
8	Jason Elam	.30
9	Glyn Milburn	.50
10	Steve Everitt	.30
11	Demetrius DuBose	.20
12	Eric Curry	.50
13	Garrison Hearst	1.25
14	Ronald Moore	.50
15	Darrien Gordon	.30
16	Natrone Means	.75
17	Roosevelt Potts	.50
18	Derrick Lassic	.30
19	Kevin Williams	1.00
20	Scott Mitchell	.50
	(UER) (Text	
	indicates drafted in	
	'91; should be '90)	
21	O.J. McDuffie	.75
22	Terry Kirby	.50
23	Vaughn Hebron	.30
24	Victor Bailey	.30
25	Lincoln Kennedy	.20
26	Michael Strahan	.30
27	Marvin Jones	.30
28	Will Shields	.20
29	Ryan McNeil	.30
30	Micheal Barrow	.30
31	George Teague	.30
32	Wayne Simmons	.30
33	Vincent Brisby	.50
34	Drew Bledsoe	3.00
35	Patrick Bates	.20
36	James Jett	.30
37	Rocket Ismail	.50
38	Troy Drayton	.50
39	Jerome Bettis	.75
40	Tom Carter	.25
41	Reggie Brooks	.50
42	Tyrone Hughes	.50
43	Derek Brown	.50
44	Willie Roaf	.50
45	Carlton Gray	.20
46	Rick Mirer	.75
47	Andre Hastings	.50
48	Deon Figures	.50
49	Qadry Ismail	.50
50	Robert Smith	.50

1993 Wild Card Superchrome Rookies B/B

These 25 double-fronted back-to-back cards were randomly seeded in Superchrome Rookies foil packs. The unnumbered cards carry the same design as the regular Superchrome Rookies cards.

		MT
Complete Set (25):		30.00
Common Player:		.75
1	Victor Bailey,	.75
	Vaughn Hebron	
2	Micheal Barrow,	.75
	Ryan McNeil	
3	Patrick Bates,	.75
	Vincent Brisby	
4	Jerome Bettis,	2.00
	Natrone Means	
5	Drew Bledsoe,	5.00
	Rick Mirer	
6	Reggie Brooks,	.75
	Glyn Milburn	
7	Derek Brown RB,	1.25
	Tyrone Hughes	
8	Tom Carter,	.75
	Jason Elam	
9	Curtis Conway,	2.50
	Steve Everitt	
10	John Copeland,	1.25
	Tony McGee	
11	Russell Copeland,	.75
	Thomas Smith	
12	Eric Curry,	1.25
	Demetrius DuBose	
13	Troy Drayton,	1.25
	Darrien Gordon	
14	Deon Figures,	1.25
	Andre Hastings	
15	Carlton Gray,	.75
	Willie Roaf	
16	Garrison Hearst,	2.50
	Ronald Moore	
17	Qadry Ismail,	1.25
	Rocket Ismail	
18	James Jett,	2.00
	Robert Smith	
19	Marvin Jones,	.75
	Will Shields	
20	Todd Kelly,	1.25
	Dana Stubblefield	
21	Lincoln Kennedy,	.75
	Michael Strahan	
22	Terry Kirby,	2.00
	O.J. McDuffie	
23	Derrick Lassic,	2.00
	Kevin Williams	
24	Scott Mitchell,	2.00
	Roosevelt Potts	
25	Wayne Simmons,	.75
	George Teague	

1967 Williams Portraits

Measuring 8" x 10", these 512 charcoal portraits of NFL players were a Kraft Cheese promotion. Sold in eight-portrait sets for $1 and a proof of purchase from various Kraft Cheese products, the set was broken down into four eight-portrait groups for each of the 16 NFL teams. In addition, an album which held 32 portraits was available for $2. The unnumbered portraits featured the player's name and position under the player portrait. The backs of the portraits were blank. An 8" x 10" checklist sheet was also issued, but it is not considered a card.

		NM
Complete Set (512):		5000.
Common Player:		6.00
1	Taz Anderson	10.00
2	Gary Barnes	10.00
3	Lee Calland	10.00
4	Junior Coffey	12.00
5	Ed Cook	10.00
6	Perry Lee Dunn	10.00
7	Dan Grimm	10.00
8	Alex Hawkins	15.00
9	Randy Johnson	12.00
10	Lou Kirouac	10.00
11	Errol Linden	10.00
12	Billy Lothridge	10.00
13	Frank Marchlewski	10.00
14	Richard Marshall	10.00
15	Billy Martin	10.00
16	Tom Moore	12.00
17	Tommy Nobis	20.00
18	Jim Norton	10.00
19	Nick Rassas	10.00
20	Ken Reaves	10.00
21	Bobby Richards	10.00
22	Jerry Richardson	15.00
23	Bob Riggle	10.00

A player's name in *italic type* indicates a rookie card.

#	Player	Price
24	Karl Rubke	10.00
25	Marion Rushing	10.00
26	Chuck Sieminski	10.00
27	Steve Sloan	12.00
28	Ron Smith	10.00
29	Don Talbert	10.00
30	Ernie Wheelwright	12.00
31	Sam Williams	10.00
32	Jim Wilson	10.00
33	Sam Ball	10.00
34	Raymond Berry	30.00
35	Bob Boyd	12.00
36	Ordell Braase	10.00
37	Barry Brown	10.00
38	Bill Curry	12.00
39	Mike Curtis	15.00
40	Alvin Haymond	10.00
41	Jerry Hill	10.00
42	David Lee	10.00
43	Jerry Logan	10.00
44	Tony Lorick	10.00
45	Lenny Lyles	10.00
46	John Mackey	18.00
47	Tom Matte	15.00
48	Lou Michaels	12.00
49	Fred Miller	10.00
50	Lenny Moore	30.00
51	Jimmy Orr	12.00
52	Jim Parker	18.00
53	Glenn Ressler	10.00
54	Willie Richardson	12.00
55	Don Shinnick	10.00
56	Billy Ray Smith	12.00
57	Bubba Smith	20.00
58	Dan Sullivan	10.00
59	Dick Szymanski	10.00
60	Johnny Unitas	50.00
61	Bob Vogel	10.00
62	Rick Volk	10.00
63	Jim Welch	10.00
64	Butch Wilson	10.00
65	Charlie Bivins	10.00
66	Charlie Brown	10.00
67	Doug Buffone	12.00
68	Rudy Bukich	12.00
69	Ron Bull	12.00
70	Dick Butkus	50.00
71	Jim Cadile	10.00
72	Jack Concannon	10.00
73	Frank Cornish	10.00
74	Don Croftcheck	10.00
75	Dick Evey	10.00
76	Joe Fortunato	12.00
77	Curtis Gentry	10.00
78	Bobby Joe Green	10.00
79	John Henry Johnson	15.00
80	Bob Jones	10.00
81	Jimmy Jones	10.00
82	Ralph Kurek	10.00
83	Roger LeClerc	10.00
84	Andy Livingston	10.00
85	Bennie McRae	10.00
86	Johnny Morris	12.00
87	Richie Petitbon	12.00
88	Loyd Phillips	10.00
89	Brian Piccolo	45.00
90	Jim Purnell	10.00
91	Mike Pyle	10.00
92	Mike Reilly	10.00
93	Gale Sayers	50.00
94	George Seals	10.00
95	Roosevelt Taylor	12.00
96	Bob Wetoska	10.00
97	Erich Barnes	12.00
98	Johnny Brewer	10.00
99	Monte Clark	10.00
100	Gary Collins	15.00
101	Larry Conjar	10.00
102	Vince Costello	10.00
103	Ross Fichtner	10.00
104	Bill Glass	12.00
105	Ernie Green	15.00
106	Jack Gregory	10.00
107	Charlie Harraway	12.00
108	Gene Hickerson	10.00
109	Fred Hoaglin	10.00
110	Jim Houston	12.00
111	Mike Howell	10.00
112	Joe Bob Isbell	10.00
113	Walter Johnson	12.00
114	Jim Kanicki	10.00
115	Ernie Kellerman	10.00
116	Leroy Kelly	20.00
117	Dale Lindsey	10.00
118	Clifton McNeil	12.00
119	Milt Morin	12.00
120	Nick Pietrosante	10.00
121	Frank Ryan	15.00
122	Dick Schafrath	12.00
123	Randy Schultz	10.00
124	Ralph Smith	10.00
125	Carl Ward	10.00
126	Paul Warfield	20.00
127	Paul Wiggin	12.00
128	John Wooten	12.00
129	George Andrie	10.00
130	Jim Boeke	10.00
131	Frank Clarke	12.00
132	Mike Connelly	10.00
133	Buddy Dial	12.00
134	Leon Donohue	10.00
135	Dave Edwards	12.00
136	Mike Gaechter	10.00
137	Walt Garrison	15.00
138	Pete Gent	12.00
139	Cornell Green	15.00
140	Bob Hayes	20.00
141	Chuck Howley	15.00
142	Lee Roy Jordan	18.00
143	Bob Lilly	30.00
144	Tony Liscio	10.00
145	Warren Livingston	10.00
146	Dave Manders	10.00
147	Don Meredith	30.00
148	Ralph Neely	12.00
149	John Niland	10.00
150	Pettis Norman	12.00
151	Don Perkins	15.00
152	Jethro Pugh	12.00
153	Dan Reeves	30.00
154	Mel Renfro	18.00
155	Jerry Rhome	15.00
156	Les Shy	10.00
157	J.D. Smith	10.00
158	Willie Townes	10.00
159	Danny Villanueva	10.00
160	John Wilbur	10.00
161	Mike Alford	10.00
162	Lem Barney	18.00
163	Charley Bradshaw	10.00
164	Roger Brown	12.00
165	Ernie Clark	10.00
166	Gail Cogdill	12.00
167	Nick Eddy	12.00
168	Mel Farr	12.00
169	Bobby Felts	10.00
170	Ed Flanagan	10.00
171	Jim Gibbons	12.00
172	John Gordy	12.00
173	Larry Hand	10.00
174	Wally Hilgenberg	10.00
175	Alex Karras	20.00
176	Bob Kowalkowski	10.00
177	Ron Kramer	12.00
178	Mike Lucci	15.00
179	Bruce Maher	10.00
180	Amos Marsh	10.00
181	Darris McCord	10.00
182	Tom Nowatzke	10.00
183	Milt Plum	15.00
184	Wayne Rasmussen	10.00
185	Roger Shoals	10.00
186	Pat Studstill	12.00
187	Karl Sweetan	10.00
188	Bobby Thompson	10.00
189	Doug Van Horn	10.00
190	Wayne Walker	12.00
191	Tommy Watkins	10.00
192	Garo Yepremian	15.00
193	Herb Adderley	12.00
194	Lionel Aldridge	10.00
195	Donny Anderson	8.00
196	Ken Bowman	6.00
197	Zeke Bratkowski	8.00
198	Bob Brown (DT)	6.00
199	Tom Brown	6.00
200	Lee Roy Caffey	6.00
201	Don Chandler	7.00
202	Tommy Crutcher	6.00
203	Carroll Dale	8.00
204	Willie Davis	15.00
205	Boyd Dowler	8.00
206	Marv Fleming	7.00
207	Gale Gillingham	6.00
208	Jim Grabowski	6.00
209	Forrest Gregg	15.00
210	Doug Hart	6.00
211	Bob Jeter	6.00
212	Hank Jordan	12.00
213	Ron Kostelnik	6.00
214	Jerry Kramer	15.00
215	Bob Long	6.00
216	Max McGee	8.00
217	Ray Nitschke	18.00
218	Elijah Pitts	7.00
219	Dave Robinson	7.00
220	Bob Skoronski	7.00
221	Bart Starr	25.00
222	Fred Thurston	7.00
223	Willie Wood	18.00
224	Steve Wright	6.00
225	Dick Bass	15.00
226	Maxie Baughan	12.00
227	Joe Carollo	10.00
228	Bernie Casey	15.00
229	Don Chuy	10.00
230	Charlie Cowan	10.00
231	Irv Cross	12.00
232	Willie Ellison	12.00
233	Roman Gabriel	18.00
234	Bruce Gossett	10.00
235	Roosevelt Grier	18.00
236	Anthony Guillory	10.00
237	Ken Iman	10.00
238	Deacon Jones	20.00
239	Les Josephson	12.00
240	Jon Kilgore	10.00
241	Chuck Lamson	10.00
242	Lamar Lundy	12.00
243	Tom Mack	15.00
244	Tommy Mason	12.00
245	Tommy McDonald	15.00
246	Ed Meador	12.00
247	Bill Munson	15.00
248	Bob Nichols	10.00
249	Merlin Olsen	25.00
250	Jack Pardee	15.00
251	Bucky Pope	10.00
252	Joe Scibelli	10.00
253	Jack Snow	15.00
254	Billy Truax	12.00
255	Clancy Williams	10.00
256	Doug Woodlief	10.00
257	Grady Alderman	12.00
258	John Beasley	10.00
259	Bob Berry	12.00
260	Larry Bowie	10.00
261	Bill Brown	15.00
262	Fred Cox	12.00
263	Doug Davis	10.00
264	Paul Dickson	10.00
265	Carl Eller	18.00
266	Paul Flatley	10.00
267	Dale Hackbart	10.00
268	Don Hansen	10.00
269	Clint Jones	10.00
270	Jeff Jordan	10.00
271	Karl Kassulke	12.00
272	John Kirby	10.00
273	Gary Larsen	10.00
274	Jim Lindsey	10.00
275	Earsell Mackbee	10.00
276	Jim Marshall	18.00
277	Marlin McKeever	10.00
278	Dave Osborn	15.00
279	Jim Phillips	10.00
280	Ed Sharockman	10.00
281	Jerry Shay	10.00
282	Milt Sunde	12.00
283	Archie Sutton	10.00
284	Mick Tingelhoff	15.00
285	Ron Vanderkelen	10.00
286	Jim Vellone	10.00
287	Lonnie Warwick	10.00
288	Roy Winston	12.00
289	Doug Atkins	20.00
290	Vern Burke	10.00
291	Bruce Cortez	10.00
292	Gary Cuozzo	12.00
293	Ted Davis	10.00
294	John Douglas	10.00
295	Jim Garcia	10.00
296	Tom Hall	10.00
297	Jim Heidel	10.00
298	Leslie Kelley	10.00
299	Billy Kilmer	18.00
300	Kent Kramer	10.00
301	Jake Kupp	10.00
302	Earl Leggett	10.00
303	Obert Logan	10.00
304	Tom McNeill	10.00
305	John Morrow	10.00
306	Ray Ogden	10.00
307	Ray Rissmiller	10.00
308	George Rose	10.00
309	David Rowe	10.00
310	Brian Schweda	10.00
311	Dave Simmons	10.00
312	Jerry Simmons	10.00
313	Steve Stonebreaker	12.00
314	Jim Taylor	20.00
315	Mike Tilleman	10.00
316	Phil Vandersea	10.00
317	Joe Wendryhoski	10.00
318	Dave Whitsell	12.00
319	Fred Whittingham	10.00
320	Gary Wood	10.00
321	Ken Avery	10.00
322	Bookie Bolin	10.00
323	Henry Carr	12.00
324	Pete Case	10.00
325	Clarence Childs	10.00
326	Mike Ciccolella	10.00
327	Glen Condren	10.00
328	Bob Crespino	10.00
329	Don Davis	10.00
330	Tucker Frederickson	15.00
331	Charlie Harper	10.00
332	Phil Harris	10.00
333	Allen Jacobs	10.00
334	Homer Jones	12.00
335	Jim Katcavage	10.00
336	Tom Kennedy	10.00
337	Ernie Koy	10.00
338	Greg Larson	12.00
339	Spider Lockhart	10.00
340	Chuck Mercein	12.00
341	Jim Moran	10.00
342	Earl Morrall	15.00
343	Joe Morrison	12.00
344	Francis Peay	10.00
345	Del Shofner	12.00
346	Jeff Smith	10.00
347	Fran Tarkenton	40.00
348	Aaron Thomas	12.00
349	Larry Vargo	10.00
350	Freeman White	10.00
351	Sidney Williams	10.00
352	Willie Young	10.00
353	Sam Baker	10.00
354	Gary Ballman	10.00
355	Randy Beisler	10.00
356	Bob Brown (OT)	12.00
357	Timmy Brown	15.00
358	Mike Ditka	45.00
359	Dave Graham	10.00
360	Ben Hawkins	10.00
361	Fred Hill	10.00
362	King Hill	12.00
363	Lynn Hoyem	10.00
364	Don Hultz	10.00
365	Dwight Kelley	10.00
366	Israel Lang	10.00
367	Dave Lloyd	10.00
368	Aaron Martin	10.00
369	Ron Medved	10.00
370	John Meyers	10.00
371	Mike Morgan	10.00
372	Al Nelson	10.00
373	Jim Nettles	10.00
374	Floyd Peters	12.00
375	Gary Pettigrew	10.00
376	Ray Poage	10.00
377	Nate Ramsey	10.00
378	Dave Recher	10.00
379	Jim Ringo	15.00
380	Joe Scarpati	10.00
381	Jim Skaggs	10.00
382	Norm Snead	18.00
383	Harold Wells	10.00
384	Tom Woodeshick	12.00
385	Bill Asbury	10.00
386	John Baker	10.00
387	Jim Bradshaw	10.00
388	Rod Breedlove	10.00
389	John Brown	10.00
390	Amos Bullocks	10.00
391	Jim Butler	10.00
392	John Campbell	10.00
393	Mike Clark	10.00
394	Larry Gagner	10.00
395	Earl Gros	12.00
396	John Hilton	10.00
397	Dick Hoak	12.00
398	Roy Jefferson	12.00
399	Tony Jeter	10.00
400	Brady Keys	10.00
401	Ken Kortas	10.00
402	Ray Mansfield	10.00
403	Paul Martha	10.00
404	Ben McGee	10.00
405	Bill Nelsen	15.00
406	Kent Nix	10.00
407	Fran O'Brien	10.00
408	Andy Russell	15.00
409	Bill Saul	10.00
410	Don Shy	10.00
411	Clendon Thomas	12.00
412	Bruce Van Dyke	10.00
413	Lloyd Voss	10.00
414	Ralph Wenzel	10.00
415	J.R. Wilburn	10.00
416	Marv Woodson	10.00
417	Jim Bakken	12.00
418	Don Brumm	10.00
419	Vidal Carlin	10.00
420	Bobby Joe Conrad	12.00
421	Willis Crenshaw	10.00
422	Bob DeMarco	10.00
423	Pat Fischer	12.00
424	Billy Gambrell	10.00
425	Prentice Gault	12.00
426	Ken Gray	10.00
427	Jerry Hillebrand	10.00
428	Charlie Johnson	15.00
429	Bill Koman	10.00
430	Dave Long	10.00
431	Ernie McMillan	10.00
432	Dave Meggysey	10.00
433	Dale Meinert	10.00
434	Mike Melinkovich	10.00
435	Dave O'Brien	10.00
436	Sonny Randle	12.00
437	Bob Reynolds	10.00
438	Joe Robb	10.00
439	Johnny Roland	10.00
440	Roy Shivers	10.00
441	Sam Silas	10.00
442	Jackie Smith	18.00
443	Rick Sortun	10.00
444	Jerry Stovall	12.00
445	Chuck Walker	10.00
446	Bobby Williams	10.00
447	Dave Williams	12.00
448	Larry Wilson	18.00
449	Kermit Alexander	10.00
450	Cas Banaszek	10.00
451	Bruce Bosley	10.00
452	John Brodie	20.00
453	Joe Cerne	10.00
454	John David Crow	12.00
455	Tommy Davis	10.00
456	Bob Harrison	10.00
457	Matt Hazeltine	10.00
458	Stan Hindman	10.00
459	Charlie Johnson	10.00
460	Jim Johnson	18.00
461	Dave Kopay	10.00
462	Charlie Krueger	12.00
463	Roland Lakes	10.00
464	Gary Lewis	10.00
465	Dave McCormick	10.00
466	Kay McFarland	10.00
467	Clark Miller	10.00
468	George Mira	12.00
469	Howard Mudd	10.00
470	Frank Nunley	10.00
471	Dave Parks	12.00
472	Walt Rock	10.00
473	Len Rohde	10.00
474	Steve Spurrier	35.00
475	Monty Stickles	10.00
476	John Thomas	10.00
477	Bill Tucker	10.00
478	Dave Wilcox	12.00
479	Ken Willard	12.00
480	Dick Witcher	10.00
481	Willie Adams	6.00
482	Walt Barnes	6.00
483	Jim Carroll	6.00
484	Dave Crossan	6.00
485	Charlie Gogolak	7.00
486	Tom Goosby	6.00
487	Chris Hanburger	8.00
488	Rickie Harris	6.00
489	Len Hauss	7.00
490	Sam Huff	18.00
491	Steve Jackson	6.00
492	Mitch Johnson	6.00
493	Sonny Jurgensen	18.00
494	Carl Kammerer	6.00
495	Paul Krause	12.00
496	Joe Don Looney	12.00
497	Ray McDonald	6.00
498	Bobby Mitchell	15.00
499	Jim Ninowski	7.00
500	Brig Owens	6.00
501	Vince Promuto	6.00
502	Pat Richter	7.00
503	Joe Rutgens	6.00
504	Lonnie Sanders	6.00
505	Ray Schoenke	6.00
506	Jim Shorter	6.00
507	Jerry Smith	8.00
508	Ron Snidow	6.00
509	Jim Snowden	6.00
510	Charley Taylor	18.00
511	Steve Thurlow	6.00
512	A.D. Whitfield	6.00

1994 Ted Williams Card Co. NFL Football

The Ted Williams Card Co., associated with the famous baseball Hall of Famer, followed up its debut baseball set with a 90-card set devoted to NFL greats from the past. Football Hall of Famer Roger Staubach lends his name to the set - the "Roger Staubach's NFL Football '94" set. The cards are numbered and grouped by teams first, followed by the set's three subsets - Chalkboard Legends (famous coaches), Golden Arms (great quarterbacks) and Dawning of a Legacy (two active quarterbacks). Cards were sold in packs of 10, or jumbo packs of 18. The set is limited to 5,000 numbered cases, meaning perhaps 200,000 of each card was made. There were also random inserts from six different sets available - Path to Greatness; Etched in Stone; the Walter Payton Collection; the Auckland Collection; Instant Replays; and limited print cards for Charles Barkley, Fred Dryer and Ted Williams throwing a football. Roger Staubach and Terry Bradshaw promo cards were also issued to preview the 1994 set. Also produced for the set were 18 different POG cards, which were inserted one per pack. Each case of cards also included a "Trade For Roger" card, which enabled collectors to obtain a 9-card Roger Staubach set available only through the mail.

#	Player	MT
	Complete Set (90):	15.00
	Common Player:	.10
	Wax Box:	15.00
1	Roger Staubach	1.75
2	Tony Dorsett	.50
3	Bob Lilly	.35
4	Art Donovan	.25
5	Bert Jones	.30
6	Johnny Unitas	1.25
7	Jack Kemp	1.25
8	O.J. Simpson	1.75
9	Dick Butkus	.60
10	Gale Sayers	1.00
11	Mike Singletary	.25
12	Bronco Nagurski	.35
13	Ken Anderson	.25
14	Otto Graham	.35
15	Louis Groza	.25
16	Marion Motley	.30
17	Floyd Little	.15
18	Haven Moses	.10
19	Lem Barney	.25
20	Night Train Lane	.25
21	Bobby Layne	.40
22	Ray Nitschke	.25
23	Willie Wood	.25
24	White Shoes Johnson	.20
25	Mike Bell	.10
26	Buck Buchanan	.30
27	Len Dawson	.35
28	Roman Gabriel	.20
29	Leroy Irvin	.10
30	Deacon Jones	.30
31	Bob Waterfield	.35
32	Bob Griese	1.00
33	Carl Eller	.25
34	Fran Tarkenton	1.00
35	John Hannah	.25
36	Jim Plunkett	.20
37	Tom Dempsey	.15
38	Archie Manning	.25
39	Charlie Conerly	.25
40	Sam Huff	.25
41	Andy Robustelli	.25
42	Don Maynard	.25
43	Matt Snell	.15
44	Wesley Walker	.15
45	George Blanda	.40
46	Ben Davidson	.15
47	Jim Otto	.25
48	Norm Van Brocklin	.35
49	Harold Carmichael	.20
50	Joe Greene	.30
51	L.C. Greenwood	.15
52	Jack Lambert	.35
53	Lance Alworth	.35
54	Dan Fouts	.45
55	John Brodie	.30
56	Steve Largent	.35
57	Jim Zorn	.15
58	Jim Hart	.15
59	Mel Gray	.15
60	Lee Roy Selmon	.15
61	Sammy Baugh	.30
62	Sonny Jurgensen	.60
63	Checklist	.10
64	George Allen	.15
65	George Halas	.40
66	Tom Landry	.60
67	Vince Lombardi	.60
68	John Madden	.40
69	Chuck Noll	.20
70	Don Shula	.30
71	Hank Stram	.15
72	Checklist	.10
73	Terry Bradshaw	.85
74	Len Dawson	.35
75	Dan Fouts	.35
76	Bart Starr	.50
77	Roger Staubach	1.50
78	Fran Tarkenton	.75
79	Y.A. Tittle	.35
80	Johnny Unitas	1.25
81	Checklist	.10
82	Brett Favre	.50
83	Brett Favre	.65
84	Brett Favre	.65
85	Brett Favre	.65
86	Neil O'Donnell	.20
87	Neil O'Donnell	.20
88	Neil O'Donnell	.20
89	Neil O'Donnell	.20
90	Checklist	.10

1994 Ted Williams Card Co. Auckland Collection

The Auckland Collection of insert cards features artwork by sports artist Jim Auckland. The cards have a special paper stock. The color illustration on each front is framed by a white border. The card back, numbered using an "AC" prefix, has a collage of ghosted player illustrations, plus a player profile, all bordered with a red and white frame. Cards were random inserts.

#	Player	MT
	Complete Set (9):	30.00
	Common Player:	3.00
1	Brett Favre	6.00
2	Vince Lombardi	7.00
3	Walter Payton	8.00
4	Phil Simms	5.00
5	Bart Starr	7.00
6	Roger Staubach	8.00
7	Jim Thorpe	6.00
8	Johnny Unitas	7.00
9	Checklist	3.00

1994 Ted Williams Card Co. Charles Barkley

These limited-edition inserts, devoted to NBA star Charles Barkley, were randomly included in Roger Staubach's NFL Football '94 packs. The cards are numbered with a "CB" prefix.

		MT
Complete Set (1)		5.00
1	Charles Barkley (LP)	5.00

1994 Ted Williams Card Co. Etched in Stone

This 9-card insert set highlights the Hall of Fame career of quarterback Johnny Unitas. Each card front has either a color or action photo or sepia-toned photo against a full-bleed background. However, gold triangles are located in the upper left corner, with the set logo in it, and the lower right corner, where Unitas' name is located. Each card back is numbered with an "ES" prefix and presents text which traces Unitas' career. The brick red background of the cards form a puzzle which says "Etched in Stone" and shows a chisel and gold star.

		MT
Complete Set (9):		20.00
Common Unitas:		2.50
1	(Johnny Unitas) (1970 Championship Game)	2.50
2	Johnny Unitas (Super Bowl V)	2.50
3	Johnny Unitas (Memories)	2.50
4	Johnny Unitas (Injuries)	2.50
5	Johnny Unitas (1959 Rematch)	2.50
6	Johnny Unitas (College Days)	2.50
7	Johnny Unitas (1972)	2.50
8	Johnny Unitas (Greatest Game Ever)	2.50
9	Checklist	2.50

1994 Ted Williams Card Co. Instant Replays

Four great teams from the NFL's past are featured on these inserts, which were randomly included in Roger Staubach's NFL Football '94 packs. The cards, available in hobby stores on a regional basis, feature players from the New York Giants, Green

Bay Packers, Pittsburgh Steelers and Raiders. Each card front has either a sepia-toned or color photo, with gold filmstrip borders on the right and left side. The set logo is in the lower left corner, next to the player's name, which is in a filmstrip at the bottom. The orange back, numbered using an "IR" prefix, has the player's name at the top in a gold banner. A ghosted roll of film is in the background. Cards were random inserts in hobby packs only.

		MT
Complete Set (17):		40.00
Common Player:		1.50
1	Phil Simms	2.50
2	Y.A. Tittle	3.00
3	Sam Huff	2.00
4	Brad Van Pelt	1.50
5	Brett Favre	4.00
6	Bart Starr	6.00
7	Paul Hornung	4.00
8	Ray Nitschke	3.00
9	Neil O'Donnell	2.00
10	Terry Bradshaw	6.00
11	Joe Greene	3.00
12	Jack Lambert	3.00
13	Jeff Hostetler	2.00
14	Lyle Alzado	1.50
15	Dave Casper	1.50
16	Ken Stabler	3.00
17	Replays Checklist	1.50

1994 Ted Williams Card Co. Path to Greatness

This 9-card Roger Staubach NFL Football '94 insert set is devoted to collegiate coaches and players who went on to star in the NFL. Each card front has a gold framed border along the top and left side of the photo, which is either sepia toned or in color. The player's name is stamped in gold foil in a white banner at the bottom of the card, next to the set's logo. The backs, numbered using a "PG" prefix, have a summary of the player's collegiate accomplishments.

		MT
Complete Set (9):		35.00
Common Player:		1.25
1	Tony Dorsett	5.00
2	Red Grange	3.00
3	Bob Griese	4.00
4	Jeff Hostetler	2.00
5	Neil O'Donnell	1.75
6	Jim Plunkett	2.50
7	O.J. Simpson	12.00
8	Roger Staubach	8.00
9	Checklist	1.25

1994 Ted Williams Card Co. Sweetness - Walter Payton

These insert cards, devot-

ed to "Sweetness," Walter Payton, were random inserts in jumbo packs only. Each card front has a full-bleed color photo of Payton, with the set logos appearing in the corners on the right side of the card. The card back, numbered using a "WP" prefix, is blue. It includes an explanation about the card's title, which covers a specific point in the Hall of Famer's career.

		MT
Complete Set (9):		15.00
Common Player:		2.00
1	Ditka On Payton (Walter Payton)	2.00
2	Winning It All (Walter Payton)	2.00
3	Rookie (Walter Payton)	2.00
4	1977 (Walter Payton)	2.00
5	College (Walter Payton)	2.00
6	Payton vs. O.J. (Walter Payton)	4.00
7	Sweetness (Walter Payton)	2.00
8	The Records (Walter Payton)	2.00
9	Checklist Card	2.00

1994 Ted Williams Card Co. POG Cards

Each of these cards contains two POGs, measuring 1-5/8" in diameter. The POGs were intended to be punched out of the blue card, which is standard size. Each POG has a closeup shot of the player on the front, in either black-and-white or color, plus his name. A card number also appears on the front; the backs are blank. Each pack of 1994 Ted Williams Roger Staubach football cards contained one of these POG cards.

		MT
Complete Set (18):		5.00
Common Player:		.20
1	Roger Staubach, Brett Favre	.75
2	Roman Gabriel, Lee Roy Jordan	.25
3	Dan Fouts, John Brodie	.35
4	Terry Bradshaw, Bart Starr	.75
5	O.J. Simpson, Floyd Little	1.00
6	Pete Pihos, Larry Csonka	.25
7	Dick (Night Train) Lane, Carl Eller	.35
8	Sam Huff, Ben Davidson	.35
9	Jack Lambert, Jethro Pugh	.30
10	Mike Singletary, Harold Carmichael	.25
11	Chuck Noll, Bud Grant	.20
12	John Madden, Lyle Alzado	.20
13	Walter Payton, Gale Sayers	1.00
14	Fred Dryer, Ron Mix	.25
15	Bob Griese, Doug Williams	.30
16	Tony Dorsett, Red Grange	.50
17	Sonny Jurgensen, Jeff Hostetler	.30
18	Checklist Card	.20

A card number in parentheses ( ) indicates the set is unnumbered.

1994 Ted Williams Card Co. Trade for Staubach

A "Trade for Roger" redemption card was randomly seeded one per case in the 5,000 cases. The redemption card, along with $3, entitled the collector to receive a nine-card set. The redemption card was returned to collectors with a validation stamp on it. Card fronts include borderless color or black-and-white photos, with the Roger Staubach NFL Football logo at the top right and the Ted Williams Card Co. logo in the lower left. Staubach's name is printed in foil along the right border. The card backs include a write-up of various highlights of Staubach's life. Cards are numbered with a "TR" prefix.

		MT
Complete Set (10):		30.00
Common Player:		3.00
1	The Dodger (Roger Staubach)	3.00
2	College Years (Roger Staubach)	3.00
3	The Heisman Trophy (Roger Staubach)	3.00
4	The Draft (Roger Staubach)	3.00
5	Coach's Decision (Roger Staubach)	3.00
6	A Leader (Roger Staubach)	3.00
7	MVP Year (Roger Staubach)	3.00
8	Hall of Fame (Roger Staubach)	3.00
9	Checklist	3.00
10	Trade for Roger Redemption Card	

1974 Wonder Bread

Topps printed these 30 cards to be randomly included inside packages of Wonder Bread. Players from 18 NFL teams are represented on the cards, which have a closeup shot of the player and either a bright yellow or red border. The card back has biographical and statistical information about the player, plus a description and photograph illustrating a particular football play.

		NM
Complete Set (30):		25.00
Common Player:		.40
1	Jim Bakken	.45
2	Forrest Blue	.40
3	Bill Bradley	.40
4	Willie Brown	1.50
5	Larry Csonka	4.00
6	Ken Ellis	.40
7	Bruce Gossett	.40
8	Bob Griese	4.00
9	Chris Hanburger	.75
10	Winston Hill	.40
11	Jim Johnson	1.25
12	Paul Krause	1.00
13	Ted Kwalick	.85
14	Willie Lanier	1.50
15	Tom Mack	1.00
16	Jim Otto	1.50
17	Alan Page	1.75
18	Frank Pitts	.40
19	Jim Plunkett	1.50
20	Mike Reid	1.00
21	Paul Smith	.40
22	Bob Tucker	.75
23	Jim Tryer	.75
24	Eugene Upshaw	1.50
25	Phil Villapiano	1.00
26	Paul Warfield	2.00
27	Dwight White	.50
28	Steve Owens	.75
29	Jerrel Wilson	.40
30	Ron Yary	.75

1975 Wonder Bread

Once again, Topps produced this set for Wonder Bread to include the cards in specially-marked loaves of bread. The card front has a closeup shot of the player, with either a red or blue border surrounding it. The card back has statistics and biographical information about the player, plus questions and answers about the player and the game of football. The answers were written upside down.

		NM
Complete Set (24):		25.00
Common Player:		.35
1	Alan Page	1.50
2	Emmitt Thomas	.40
3	John Mendenhall	.35
4	Ken Houston	1.25
5	Jack Ham	1.25
6	L.C. Greenwood	.75
7	Tom Mack	.75
8	Winston Hill	.35
9	Isaac Curtis	.50
10	Terry Owens	.50
11	Drew Pearson	.60
12	Don Cockroft	.35
13	Bob Griese	2.50
14	Riley Odoms	.50
15	Chuck Foreman	.75
16	Forrest Blue	.35
17	Franco Harris	3.50
18	Larry Little	1.00
19	Bill Bergey	.60
20	Ray Guy	.90
21	Ted Hendricks	1.25
22	Levi Johnson	.35
23	Jack Mildren	.50
24	Mel Tom	.35

1976 Wonder Bread

FRANCO HARRIS
RUNNING BACK
STEELERS-A.F.C.

These 24 cards use two different frames for the card front; red frames are used for defensive players, while blue frames are used for the offensive players in the set. A close-up shot of the player is featured prominently on the front. Each back has biographical information about the player, plus a diagram of a favorite play of coach Hank Stram. The corresponding text indicates the offensive players' assignments for that particular play. Topps produced the cards for Wonder Bread to insert into loaves of bread.

		NM
Complete Set (24):		5.00
Common Player:		.20
1	Craig Morton	.35
2	Chuck Foreman	.35
3	Franco Harris	1.00
4	Mel Gray	.35
5	Charley Taylor	.60
6	Rich Caster	.20
7	George Kunz	.20
8	Rayfield Wright	.20
9	Gene Upshaw	.75
10	Tom Mack	.50
11	Len Hauss	.35
12	Garo Yepremian	.20
13	Cedrick Hardman	.20
14	Jack Youngblood	1.00
15	Wally Chambers	.20
16	Jerry Sherk	.20
17	Bill Bergey	.35
18	Jack Ham	.75
19	Fred Carr	.20
20	Jack Tatum	.35
21	Cliff Harris	.35
22	Emmitt Thomas	.20
23	Ken Riley	.20
24	Ray Guy	1.00

1984 Wranglers Carl's Jr.

The 10-card, 2-1/2" x 3-5/8" set was sponsored by Carl's Jr. restaurants and the Tempe Police Department in Arizona and featured top players from the USFL Arizona Wranglers football team. Included in the set is coach George Allen and former longtime NFL quarterback Greg Landry. The card fronts have a black and white posed photo with bio information appearing on the back.

		MT
Complete Set (10):		30.00
Common Player:		2.50
1	George Allen (CO)	8.00
2	Luther Bradley (27)	3.50
3	Trumaine Johnson (2)	3.50
4	Greg Landry (11)	6.00
5	Kit Lathrop (70)	2.50
6	John Lee (64)	2.50
7	Keith Long (33)	2.50
8	Alan Risher (7)	2.50
9	Tim Spencer (46)	3.50
10	Lenny Willis (89)	2.50

1984 Wranglers 8x10 Arizona

The eight-sheet, 8" x 10" set features two rows of four black and white cards, with the player's name printed below each card. The sheets are numbered.

		MT
Complete Set (8):		40.00
Common Panel:		5.00
1	Edward Dietrich PRES, Bill Harris VP, George Allen CO, G. Bruce Allen GM, Robert Barnes, Dennis Bishop, Mack	8.00
2	Clay Brown, Eddie Brown, Wamon Buggs, Bob Clasby, Frank Corral, Doug Cozen, Doug Dennison, Robert Dillon	6.00
3	Larry Douglas, Joe Ehrmann, Nick Eyre, Jim Fahnhorst, Doak Field, Bruce Gheesling, Frank Giddens, Alfondia	5.00
4	David Huffman, Hubert Hurst, Donnie Johnson, Randy Johnson, Trumaine Johnson, Jeff Kiewel, Bruce Laird, Greg	7.00
5	Kit Lathrop, John Lee, Alva Liles, Dan Lloyd, Kevin Long, Karl Lorch, Andy Melontree, Frank Minnifield	5.00
6	Tom Piette, Tom Porras, Paul Ricker, Alan Risher, Don Schwartz, Bobby Scott, Lance Shields, Ed Smith	5.00
7	Robert Smith, Tim Spencer, John Stadnik, Mark Stevenson, Dave Steif, Gerry Sullivan, Ted Sutton, Motrandy	5.00
8	Rob Taylor, Tom Thayer, Todd Thomas, Ted Walton, Stan White, Lenny Willis, Tim Wrightman, Wilbur Young	5.00

Z

1995 Zenith Promos

The four-card, standard-size set was issued to promote the 1995 Pinnacle Zenith set. "Promo" is printed across the card back but otherwise they are similar to the regular-issue cards.

		MT
Complete Set (4):		25.00
Common Player:		1.00
1	Emmitt Smith	10.00
94	Steve Young	5.00
97	Dan Marino	10.00
NNO	Title Card	1.00

1995 Zenith

This 1995 Pinnacle Football Series II-Zenith Edition is a super-premium set that was the most limited of all Pinnacle football releases. All 150 cards in the set are printed on gold foil and noticeably thicker card stock. Each card front has a player action photo, with the set logo in the upper right corner. The player's first name is stamped in gold along the right side, next to his last name in white letters. The card back is horizontal and includes another action photo and analysis/breakdown of where the player makes his yardage or other types of plays. The cards are numbered using a Z prefix. Three types of inserts were randomly included in packs - Second Season, Rookie Roll Call and Z-Team.

		MT
Complete Set (150):		50.00
Common Player:		.25
Minor Stars:		.50
Wax Box:		125.00
1	Emmitt Smith	10.00
2	Mark Carrier	.25
3	Johnny Mitchell	.25
4	Boomer Esiason	1.00
5	Jackie Harris	.25
6	Warren Moon	1.00
7	Harvey Williams	.25
8	Steve Walsh	.25
9	Cris Carter	1.00
10	Natrone Means	1.00
11	Art Monk	1.00
12	Johnny Johnson	.25
13	Adrian Murrell	.25
14	John Elway	4.00
15	Larry Centers	.25
16	Ricky Ervins	.25
17	Jeff Graham	.25
18	Ricky Watters	1.00
19	Eric Green	.25
20	Curtis Conway	.25
21	Jake Reed	.25
22	Michael Timpson	.25

23	Marcus Allen	1.00
24	Andre Rison	1.00
25	Terry Kirby	.25
26	Reggie White	1.00
27	Randall Cunningham	1.00
28	Jim Kelly	1.00
29	Robert Brooks	2.00
30	Terance Mathis	.25
31	Anthony Miller	1.00
32	Neil O'Donnell	1.00
33	Jeff Hostetler	.25
34	Drew Bledsoe	5.00
35	Irving Spikes	1.00
36	Keith Byars	.25
37	Rod Woodson	.25
38	Rob Moore	1.00
39	Scott Mitchell	.25
40	Cody Carlson	.25
41	Alvin Harper	.25
42	Chris Warren	1.00
43	Ben Coates	1.00
44	Jim Everett	.25
45	Vinny Testaverde	.25
46	Glyn Milburn	.25
47	Calvin Williams	.25
48	Fred Barnett	.25
49	Tim Brown	1.00
50	Lorenzo White	.25
51	Brent Jones	.25
52	Henry Ellard	.25
53	Rick Mirer	1.00
54	Junior Seau	1.00
55	Jeff Blake	1.00
56	Desmond Howard	.25
57	Jerry Rice	6.00
58	Lewis Tillman	.25
59	Roosevelt Potts	.25
60	Raghib Ismail	1.00
61	Eric Hill	.25
62	Brett Favre	10.00
63	Haywood Jeffires	.25
64	Barry Foster	1.00
65	Willie Anderson	.25
66	Troy Aikman	6.00
67	Herschel Walker	1.00
68	Sean Dawkins	1.00
69	Erric Pegram	.25
70	Irving Fryar	.25
71	Thurman Thomas	1.00
72	Eric Metcalf	.25
73	John Taylor	.25
74	Jeff George	1.00
75	Courtney Hawkins	.25
76	Carl Pickens	.25
77	Mike Sherrard	.25
78	Rodney Hampton	.25
79	Joe Montana	7.00
80	Willie Davis	.25
81	Chris Penn	.25
82	Dave Brown	.25
83	Gary Brown	.25
84	Andre Reed	1.00
85	Michael Irvin	1.00
86	Vincent Brisby	.25
87	Barry Sanders	7.00
88	Qadry Ismail	.25
89	Reggie Brooks	.25
90	Bruce Smith	.25
91	David Klingler	.25
92	Michael Haynes	.25
93	Derek Russell	.25
94	Steve Young	6.00
95	Terry Allen	.25
96	Mark Seay	.25
97	Dan Marino	10.00
98	All-Time TD Record (Jerry Rice)	6.00
99	Single-Season Recp. (Cris Carter)	1.00
100	Consecutive Games (Art Monk)	1.00
101	Cortez Kennedy	1.00
102	Stan Humphries	1.00
103	Herman Moore	1.00
104	Ron Moore	1.00
105	Chris Miller	.25
106	Jerome Bettis	1.00
107	Craig Erickson	.25
108	Keith Jackson	.25
109	Sterling Sharpe	1.00
110	Ronnie Harmon	.25
111	Deion Sanders	4.00
112	Steve Beuerlein	.25
113	Bernie Parmalee	.50
114	Leroy Hoard	.25
115	O.J. McDuffie	1.00
116	Garrison Hearst	2.00
117	Reggie Cobb	.25
118	Derek Brown	.25
119	David Palmer	.75
120	Gus Frerotte	1.00
121	Dan Wilkinson	.50
122	Chuck Levy	.25
123	Derrick Alexander	.50
124	Aaron Bailey	.25
125	Thomas Lewis	.25
126	Antonio Langham	.25
127	Bryan Reeves	.25
128	William Floyd	.75
129	Lake Dawson	.50
130	Bert Emanuel	1.00
131	Marshall Faulk	2.00
132	Heath Shuler	1.00
133	Mark Brunell	5.00
134	Willie McGinest	.50
135	Mario Bates	.50
136	Byron Morris	.75
137	Tim Bowens	.25
138	Errict Rhett	.50
139	Charlie Garner	1.00
140	Darnay Scott	.75
141	Greg Hill	.25
142	LeShon Johnson	.25
143	Charles Johnson	.50
144	Trent Dilfer	3.00
145	Gus Frerotte	1.00
146	Johnnie Morton	1.00
147	Glenn Foley	1.00
148	Perry Klein	.25
149	Ryan Yarborough	.25
150	Tydus Winans	.25

1995 Zenith Rookie Roll Call

These cards were randomly inserted in 1995 Pinnacle Series II-Zenith Edition packs, one per 72 packs. The 18-card set features some of the league's top rookies on an all-foil Dufex design. The front has an action photo, plus a second photo in a rectangle at the bottom with the insert set's starry logo in its upper left corner. Card backs are numbered using an "RC" prefix.

		MT
Complete Set (18):		250.00
Common Player:		7.50
Minor Stars:		15.00
Inserted 1:72		
1	Marshall Faulk	50.00
2	Charlie Garner	15.00
3	Derrick Alexander	7.50
4	Heath Shuler	15.00
5	Glenn Foley	15.00
6	Trent Dilfer	30.00
7	David Palmer	7.50
8	Gus Frerotte	15.00
9	Byron Morris	7.50
10	Mario Bates	7.50
11	Greg Hill	15.00
12	Errict Rhett	15.00
13	Darnay Scott	15.00
14	Lake Dawson	7.50
15	Bert Emanuel	15.00
16	LeShon Johnson	7.50
17	William Floyd	7.50
18	Charles Johnson	15.00

1995 Zenith Z-Team

Z-Team inserts in 1995 Pinnacle Series II-Zenith packs could be found one per every 24 packs. The cards feature 18 of today's legends, utilizing an all-new 3D Dufex printing technology. The card front has a photo of the player standing on the Z Team logo, with his name and position running down the left side of the card. A team helmet is in the lower left corner; the Zenith logo is in the upper right. The card back is numbered using a "ZT" prefix.

		MT
Complete Set (18):		450.00
Common Player:		10.00
1	Dan Marino	70.00
2	Troy Aikman	35.00

1995 Zenith Second Season

These Pinnacle Series II-Zenith Edition inserts pay tribute to the greatest moments from the 1994 post season, and the 25 players who made the plays happen. Included among the cards is one devoted to Joe Montana's final game. The front has the names of the teams and players involved in a game at the top; the insert set logo appears in the bottom left corner, opposite the Pinnacle logo. Card backs are numbered using an "SS" prefix. Cards were inserted one per six packs.

		MT
Complete Set (25):		140.00
Common Player:		3.00
Minor Stars:		6.00
1	Brett Favre	20.00
2	Dan Marino	20.00
3	Marcus Allen	6.00
4	Joe Montana	10.00
5	Vinny Testaverde	3.00
6	Emmitt Smith	20.00
7	Troy Aikman	10.00
8	Steve Young	10.00
9	William Floyd	3.00
10	Yancey Thigpen	6.00
11	Barry Foster	3.00
12	Natrone Means	6.00
13	Mark Seay	3.00
14	Stan Humphries	3.00
15	Tony Martin	3.00
16	Jerry Rice	10.00
17	Deion Sanders	7.00
18	Steve Young	10.00
19	Steve Young	10.00
20	Emmitt Smith	20.00
21	Troy Aikman	10.00
22	Jerry Rice (Super Bowl)	10.00
23	Ricky Watters (Super Bowl)	3.00
24	Steve Young (Super Bowl)	10.00
25	Jerry Rice, Steve Young (Super Bowl)	10.00

1996 Zenith Promos

The four-card, standard-size set was issued to promote

the 1996 Zenith release. The cards are basically identical to the regular-issue cards, except for "Promo" which is printed on the card backs.

		MT
Complete Set (4):		30.00
Common Player:		.50
4	Z-Team (Emmitt Smith)	25.00
32	Jerry Rice	4.00
36	John Elway	2.00
NNO	Title Card	.50

1996 Zenith

This 1996 Pinnacle Zenith set includes a 35-card Rookies subset, 15 Proof Positive cards, three checklists and one Triple Trouble card featuring Troy Aikman, Emmitt Smith and Michael Irvin. Each regular card has extra-thick card stock. The front has a color action photo of the player with a foil football with a silver glow around it. The player's name is in gold foil in the lower right corner; the brand logo is in gold foil in the upper left corner. The card back has a photo on the right side, with the player's name, position and team underneath. A card number, using a "Z" prefix, is in the upper left corner. A football field grid appears on the left, containing statistical achievement breakdowns by yardage increments. Each card in the regular set is also printed as part of an Artist's Proof parallel set. These cards use rainbow holographic gold foil stamping in the design and are seeded one per 23 packs. There were also three insert sets available: Noteworthy '95, Rookie Rising and Z-Team.

		MT
Complete Set (150):		40.00
Common Player:		.25
Minor Stars:		.50
Inserted 1:23		
Wax Box:		80.00
1	Dan Marino	4.00
2	Yancey Thigpen	.50
3	Marcus Allen	.50
4	Curtis Conway	.50
5	Troy Aikman	2.50
6	William Floyd	.25
7	Ricky Watters	.50
8	Herman Moore	.75
9	Jim Harbaugh	.25
10	Isaac Bruce	.50
11	Drew Bledsoe	2.50
12	Jeff Blake	.50
13	Tim Brown	.50
14	Deion Sanders	1.50
15	Greg Hill	.25
16	Ben Coates	.25
17	Errict Rhett	.25
18	Barry Sanders	5.00
19	Erik Kramer	.25
20	Emmitt Smith	4.00
21	Brett Favre	5.00
22	Jerome Bettis	.75
23	Garrison Hearst	.50
24	Michael Irvin	.50
25	Chris Warren	.25
26	Steve Young	2.00
27	Cris Carter	.75
28	Carl Pickens	.50
29	Lake Dawson	.25
30	Marshall Faulk	.75
31	Vincent Brisby	.25
32	Jerry Rice	2.50
33	Eric Metcalf	.25
34	Natrone Means	.50
35	Steve Bono	.25
36	John Elway	4.00
37	Jeff Hostetler	.25
38	Scott Mitchell	.25
39	Andre Rison	.50
40	Daryl Johnston	.25
41	Mark Brunell	2.50
42	Jeff George	.50

43	Mario Bates	.25
44	Erric Pegram	.25
45	Brent Jones	.25
46	Trent Dilfer	.75
47	Larry Centers	.25
48	Anthony Miller	.75
49	Reggie White	.75
50	Bill Brooks	.25
51	Chris Zorich	.25
52	Jim Kelly	.75
53	Junior Seau	.50
54	Chris Miller	.25
55	Gus Frerotte	.50
56	Andre Reed	.50
57	Darnay Scott	.50
58	Brett Perriman	.25
59	Edgar Bennett	.25
60	Warren Moon	.50
61	Neil O'Donnell	.50
62	Jay Novacek	.25
63	Bam Morris	.25
64	Jim Everett	.25
65	Ken Norton Jr.	.25
66	Tony Martin	.50
67	Steve Atwater	.25
68	Henry Ellard	.25
69	Rodney Hampton	.25
70	Derrick Thomas	.25
71	Stan Humphries	.25
72	Harvey Williams	.25
73	Greg Lloyd	.25
74	Jake Reed	.25
75	Charles Haley	.25
76	Quinn Early	.25
77	Rodney Peete	.25
78	Brian Blades	.25
79	Robert Brooks	.25
80	Terry Allen	.50
81	Dave Brown	.25
82	Derrick Alexander	.25
83	Terance Mathis	.25
84	Rick Mirer	.50
85	Herschel Walker	.25
86	Charlie Garner	.50
87	Jeff Graham	.25
88	Bruce Smith	.25
89	Terry Kirby	.25
90	Craig Heyward	.25
91	Bernie Parmalee	.25
92	Adrian Murrell	.50
93	Derek Loville	.25
94	Heath Shuler	.50
95	Shannon Sharpe	.50
96	Bert Emanuel	.50
97	Hugh Douglas	.25
98	Lovell Pinkney	.25
99	Sherman Williams	.25
100	Tony Boselli	.25
101	Wayne Chrebet	.75
102	Orlanda Thomas	.25
103	Darick Holmes	.50
104	Tyrone Wheatley	.25
105	Christian Fauria	.25
106	Frank Sanders	.50
107	Chad May	.25
108	James Stewart	.25
109	Ken Dilger	.25
110	Kyle Brady	.25
111	Todd Collins	.50
112	Terrell Fletcher	.50
113	Eric Bjornson	.25
114	Justin Armour	.25
115	Rob Johnson	.50
116	Terrell Davis	8.00
117	J.J. Stokes	.75
118	Rashaan Salaam	.50
119	Chris Sanders	.50
120	Kerry Collins	.75
121	Michael Westbrook	.50
122	Eric Zeier	.50
123	Curtis Martin	3.00
124	Rodney Thomas	.25
125	Kordell Stewart	4.00
126	Joey Galloway	1.00
127	Steve McNair	1.50
128	Napoleon Kaufman	1.50
129	Tamarick Vanover	.25
130	Stoney Case	.25
131	James Stewart	.25
132	Carl Pickens	.25
133	Jim Harbaugh	.25
134	Yancey Thigpen PP	.25
135	Ricky Watters	.25
136	Isaac Bruce PP	.25
137	Kordell Stewart PP	2.00
138	Jeff Blake PP	.25
139	Terrell Davis PP	4.00
140	Scott Mitchell	.25
141	Rodney Thomas	.25
142	Robert Brooks	.25
143	Joey Galloway PP	.50
144	Brett Favre PP	2.50
145	Kerry Collins PP	.25
146	Herman Moore	.25
147	Michael Irvin, Emmitt Smith, Troy Aikman	2.00
148	Dan Marino CL	1.00
149	Jerry Rice CL	.50
150	Emmitt Smith CL	.75

Post-1980 cards in Near Mint condition will generally sell for about 75% of the quoted Mint value. Excellent-condition cards bring no more than 40%.

1996 Zenith Artist's Proofs

Each card in Pinnacle's 1996 Zenith football has a parallel Artist's Proof version. The cards, seeded one per 23 packs, use a rainbow holographic gold foil stamping in the design.

	MT
Complete Set (150):	2000.
Common Player:	5.00
Minor Stars:	10.00
1 Dan Marino	125.00
2 Yancey Thigpen	15.00
3 Marcus Allen	10.00
4 Curtis Conway	10.00
5 Troy Aikman	80.00
6 William Floyd	10.00
7 Ricky Watters	10.00
8 Herman Moore	20.00
9 Jim Harbaugh	5.00
10 Isaac Bruce	15.00
11 Drew Bledsoe	80.00
12 Jeff Blake	15.00
13 Tim Brown	10.00
14 Deion Sanders	50.00
15 Greg Hill	5.00
16 Ben Coates	5.00
17 Errict Rhett	15.00
18 Barry Sanders	80.00
19 Erik Kramer	5.00
20 Emmitt Smith	125.00
21 Brett Favre	125.00
22 Jerome Bettis	10.00
23 Garrison Hearst	5.00
24 Michael Irvin	25.00
25 Chris Warren	10.00
26 Steve Young	80.00
27 Cris Carter	5.00
28 Carl Pickens	20.00
29 Lake Dawson	5.00
30 Marshall Faulk	70.00
31 Vincent Brisby	5.00
32 Jerry Rice	80.00
33 Eric Metcalf	5.00
34 Natrone Means	25.00
35 Steve Bono	10.00
36 John Elway	60.00
37 Jeff Hostetler	5.00
38 Scott Mitchell	5.00
39 Andre Rison	5.00
40 Daryl Johnston	5.00
41 Mark Brunell	60.00
42 Jeff George	10.00
43 Mario Bates	10.00
44 Erric Pegram	5.00
45 Brent Jones	5.00
46 Trent Dilfer	10.00
47 Larry Centers	5.00
48 Anthony Miller	5.00
49 Reggie White	10.00
50 Bill Brooks	5.00
51 Chris Zorich	5.00
52 Jim Kelly	10.00
53 Junior Seau	10.00
54 Chris Miller	5.00
55 Gus Frerotte	10.00
56 Andre Reed	5.00
57 Darnay Scott	20.00
58 Brett Perriman	5.00
59 Edgar Bennett	5.00
60 Warren Moon	10.00
61 Neil O'Donnell	10.00
62 Jay Novacek	5.00
63 Bam Morris	10.00
64 Jim Everett	5.00
65 Ken Norton Jr.	5.00
66 Tony Martin	5.00
67 Steve Atwater	5.00
68 Henry Ellard	5.00
69 Rodney Peete	5.00
70 Derrick Thomas	5.00
71 Stan Humphries	5.00
72 Harvey Williams	5.00
73 Greg Lloyd	5.00
74 Jake Reed	5.00
75 Charles Haley	5.00
76 Quinn Early	5.00
77 Rodney Peete	5.00
78 Brian Blades	5.00
79 Robert Brooks	20.00
80 Terry Allen	5.00
81 Dave Brown	5.00
82 Derrick Alexander	5.00
83 Terance Mathis	5.00
84 Rick Mirer	10.00
85 Herschel Walker	5.00
86 Charlie Garner	5.00
87 Jeff Graham	5.00
88 Bruce Smith	5.00
89 Terry Kirby	5.00
90 Craig Heyward	5.00
91 Bernie Parmalee	5.00
92 Adrian Murrell	5.00
93 Derek Loville	5.00
94 Heath Shuler	15.00
95 Shannon Sharpe	5.00
96 Bert Emanuel	20.00
97 Hugh Douglas	5.00
98 Lovell Pinkney	5.00
99 Sherman Williams	20.00
100 Tony Boselli	5.00
101 Wayne Chrebet	5.00
102 Orlanda Thomas	5.00
103 Darick Holmes	30.00
104 Tyrone Wheatley	20.00
105 Christian Fauria	5.00
106 Frank Sanders	20.00
107 Chad May	5.00
108 James Stewart	20.00
109 Ken Dilger	5.00
110 Kyle Brady	5.00
111 Todd Collins	10.00
112 Terrell Fletcher	5.00
113 Eric Bjornson	5.00
114 Justin Armour	5.00
115 Rob Johnson	5.00
116 Terrell Davis	75.00
117 J.J. Stokes	50.00
118 Rashaan Salaam	15.00
119 Chris Sanders	20.00
120 Kerry Collins	75.00
121 Michael Westbrook	40.00
122 Eric Zeier	15.00
123 Curtis Martin	90.00
124 Rodney Thomas	15.00
125 Kordell Stewart	75.00
126 Joey Galloway	60.00
127 Steve McNair	60.00
128 Napoleon Kaufman	30.00
129 Tamarick Vanover	15.00
130 Stoney Case	5.00
131 James Stewart	5.00
132 Carl Pickens	5.00
133 Jim Harbaugh	5.00
134 Yancey Thigpen PP	20.00
135 Ricky Watters	5.00
136 Isaac Bruce PP	12.00
137 Kordell Stewart PP	40.00
138 Jeff Blake PP	20.00
139 Terrell Davis PP	40.00
140 Scott Mitchell	5.00
141 Rodney Thomas	5.00
142 Robert Brooks	5.00
143 Joey Galloway PP	30.00
144 Brett Favre PP	60.00
145 Kerry Collins PP	35.00
146 Herman Moore	5.00
147 Michael Irvin, Emmitt Smith, Troy Aikman	125.00
148 Dan Marino CL	60.00
149 Jerry Rice CL	30.00
150 Emmitt Smith CL	60.00

1996 Zenith Noteworthy '95

This 18-card insert set recaps some of the top events from the 1995 season. Each card front has a closeup photo of the player on the top half, against a silver-foiled background which says Noteworthy '95. The brand logo is in the upper right corner. The bottom half of the card has gold foil to show an action photo. The player's name and accomplishment are in silver foil above it. The card back is horizontal and is numbered in the upper left corner. A player photo appears on the card's left side, between two parallel gold bars. A recap of the player's 1995 season is on the right side. The player's name and team name are in the top gold bar; his accomplishment is in the lower bar. Cards were random inserts, one per 12 packs of 1996 Pinnacle Zenith football.

	MT
Complete Set (18):	75.00
Common Player:	1.50
Minor Stars:	3.00
Inserted 1:12	
1 Dan Marino	8.00
2 Jerry Rice	6.00
3 Michael Irvin	3.00
4 Emmitt Smith	8.00
5 Michael Irvin, Emmitt Smith	6.00
6 Herman Moore	3.00
7 Brett Favre	12.00
8 Barry Sanders	12.00
9 Marcus Allen	3.00
10 Steve Young	5.00
11 John Elway	8.00
12 Warren Moon	3.00
13 Jim Kelly	3.00
14 Jim Everett	1.50
15 Charles Haley	1.50
16 Emmitt Smith	8.00
17 Troy Aikman	6.00
18 Larry Brown	1.50

1996 Zenith Rookie Rising

Pinnacle's 1996 version of Rookie Roll Call is its 18-card Rookie Rising set. The cards, randomly inserted one per 24 packs of 1996 Pinnacle Zenith football, feature players from the 1995 rookie class. The cards use a double-sided Dufex process, which gives each card a 3-D look. The front has an action photo of the player on top of a football. An official is on the horizon, signalling a touchdown. The player's name along the left side is stamped in gold foil, as are the brand logo in the upper left corner and the insert set name, in a colored panel at the bottom. The horizontal back has a closeup shot of the player, along with his team's helmet. A card number is in the upper right corner in a black rectangle.

	MT
Complete Set (18):	75.00
Common Player:	2.50
Minor Stars:	5.00
Inserted 1:24	
1 Sherman Williams	5.00
2 Curtis Martin	10.00
3 Michael Westbrook	7.00
4 Darick Holmes	5.00
5 James Stewart	5.00
6 Eric Zeier	5.00
7 Tamarick Vanover	5.00
8 J.J. Stokes	7.00
9 Kordell Stewart	15.00
10 Rodney Thomas	2.50
11 Kerry Collins	7.00
12 Terrell Davis	30.00
13 Steve McNair	12.00
14 Rashaan Salaam	7.00
15 Joey Galloway	7.00
16 Wayne Chrebet	7.00
17 Chris Sanders	5.00
18 Frank Sanders	7.00

1996 Zenith Z-Team

These 1996 Pinnacle inserts, using clear plastic for the card design, have a see-through design that includes gold foil-stamping and etched highlights. The card front has a black Z running through it, with an action player photo on it. See-through etched action photos appear on each side of the Z. Gold foil is used for the brand logo, which appears in the upper right corner, and the set icon, which is in the lower left corner, next to the gold foil-stamped player's name. The back repeats the photo design from the front, except the Z cuts through the main photo and has a brief career summary inside it. A card number is in the upper left corner.

	MT
Complete Set (18):	500.00
Common Player:	6.00
Minor Stars:	12.00
Inserted 1:72	
1 Troy Aikman	30.00
2 Drew Bledsoe	30.00
3 Errict Rhett	6.00
4 Emmitt Smith	45.00
5 Jerry Rice	30.00
6 Cris Carter	12.00
7 Curtis Martin	25.00
8 Deion Sanders	20.00
9 Brett Favre	60.00
10 Michael Irvin	12.00
11 Chris Warren	6.00
12 Dan Marino	45.00
13 Steve Young	25.00
14 Marshall Faulk	15.00
15 Barry Sanders	60.00
16 John Elway	45.00
17 Isaac Bruce	12.00
18 Carl Pickens	6.00

1997 Zenith

The 150-card, regular-sized set included Season Highlights (15), Awesome Foursome (1) and Rookies (35) subsets and was available in six-card packs. The base cards feature the player's image over a gold foil circle. The player's name is also printed in gold foil on the card face bottom. The card backs feature another photo with in-depth statistical information. Insert sets include Rookie Rising, V2, Z Team, Gold Mirror Mylar Z Team and the base-set parallel Artist's Proof.

	MT
Complete Set (150):	50.00
Common Player:	.15
Minor Stars:	.30
Wax Box:	90.00
1 Brett Favre	4.00
2 Jerry Rice	2.00
3 Shannon Sharpe	.15
4 Dan Marino	4.00
5 James Stewart	.15
6 Warren Moon	.15
7 Emmitt Smith	4.00
8 Kordell Stewart	2.00
9 Kerry Collins	.40
10 Ricky Watters	.15
11 Gus Frerotte	.15
12 Barry Sanders	3.00
13 Joey Galloway	.75
14 Marshall Faulk	.40
15 Todd Collins	.15
16 Steve McNair	.50
17 Tyrone Wheatley	.15
18 Isaac Bruce	.50
19 Troy Aikman	2.00
20 Larry Centers	.15
21 Alvin Harper	.15
22 Rashaan Salaam	.15
23 Eric Metcalf	.15
24 Jim Everett	.15
25 Ken Dilger	.15
26 Curtis Martin	3.00
27 Neil O'Donnell	.15
28 Thurman Thomas	.15
29 Andre Rison	.15
30 Steve Bono	.15
31 Garrison Hearst	.15
32 Junior Seau	.15
33 Napoleon Kaufman	.15
34 Jerome Bettis	.15
35 Frank Wycheck	.15
36 Lamar Smith	.15
37 Derrick Alexander	.15
38 Steve Young	1.50
39 Cris Carter	.15
40 O.J. McDuffie	.15
41 Deion Sanders	1.25
42 Robert Brooks	.15
43 Jeff Blake	.50
44 Marcus Allen	.15
45 Herman Moore	.15
46 Ray Zellars	.15
47 Tim Brown	.15
48 John Elway	1.50
49 Charles Johnson	.15
50 Rodney Peete	.15
51 Curtis Conway	.15
52 Kevin Greene	.15
53 Andre Reed	.15
54 Mark Brunell	2.00
55 Tony Martin	.15
56 Elvis Grbac	.15
57 Wayne Chrebet	.15
58 Vinny Testaverde	.15
59 Terry Allen	.15
60 Dave Brown	.15
61 LaShon Johnson	.15
62 Trent Dilfer	.15
63 Chris Warren	.15
64 Chris Sanders	.15
65 Kevin Carter	.15
66 Jim Harbaugh	.15
67 Terance Mathis	.15
68 Ben Coates	.15
69 Robert Smith	.15
70 Drew Bledsoe	2.00
71 Henry Ellard	.15
72 Scott Mitchell	.15
73 Andre Hastings	.15
74 Rodney Hampton	.15
75 Michael Jackson	.15
76 Jeff Hostetler	.15
77 Reggie White	.15
78 Kent Graham	.15
79 Adrian Murrell	.15
80 Carl Pickens	.15
81 Erik Kramer	.15
82 Terrell Davis	2.50
83 Sean Dawkins	.15
84 Jamal Anderson	.50
85 Stan Humphries	.15
86 Chris T. Jones	.15
87 Hardy Nickerson	.15
88 Anthony Johnson	.15
89 Michael Haynes	.15
90 Irving Spikes	.15
91 Bruce Smith	.15
92 Keenan McCardell	.15
93 Chris Chandler	.15
94 Tamarick Vanover	.15
95 Cortez Kennedy	.15
96 Roman Phifer	.15
97 Michael Irvin	.15
98 Tim Biakabutuka	.50
99 Stepfret Williams	.15
100 Eddie George	3.00
101 Karim Abdul-Jabbar	.50
102 Amani Toomer	.15
103 Tony Banks	.30
104 Regan Upshaw	.15
105 Leeland McElroy	.15
106 Jason Dunn	.15
107 Keyshawn Johnson	.40
108 Winslow Oliver	.15
109 Walt Harris	.15
110 Stanley Pritchett	.15
111 Eddie Kennison	.30
112 Terrell Owens	1.75
113 Duane Clemons	.15
114 John Mobley	.15
115 Simeon Rice	.15
116 Ernie Conwell	.15
117 Eric Moulds	.30
118 Marvin Harrison	.50
119 Rickey Dudley	.30
120 Mike Alstott	.30
121 Terry Glenn	.50
122 Brian Dawkins	.15
123 Kevin Hardy	.15
124 Bobby Engram	.30
125 Alex Van Dyke	.15
126 Zach Thomas	.75
127 Bryan Still	.15
128 Detron Smith	.15
129 Jerome Woods	.15
130 Muhsin Muhammad	.50
131 Lawrence Phillips	.30
132 Alex Molden	.15
133 Steve Young	.75
134 Troy Aikman	1.00
135 Junior Seau	.15
136 John Elway	.75
137 Dan Marino	2.00
138 Lawrence Phillips	.15
139 Brett Favre	2.00
140 Jerry Rice	1.00
141 Kerry Collins	.40
142 Barry Sanders	1.50
143 Mark Brunell	1.00
144 Drew Bledsoe	1.00
145 Eddie Kennison	.50
146 Marvin Harrison	.50
147 Emmitt Smith	2.00
148 Eddie George, Terry Glenn, Rickey Dudley, Bobby Hoying	2.00
149 Emmitt Smith	2.00
150 Dan Marino	2.00

1997 Zenith Artist's Proofs

Artist's Proofs paralled all 150 cards in the regular-issue set. The cards are distinguished by a holographic foil Artist's Proof stamp, and are inserted every 47 packs.

	MT
Complete Set (150):	1500.
Artist's Proof Cards:	15x-30x

1997 Zenith V2

The 18-card, regular-sized set features full-motion lenticular printing along with a conventional player photo. Inserted every 23 packs, the die-cut cards have "V2" printed underneath a motion picture with the player's name and team on the top and bottom of the horizontal card, respectively. The card backs are numbered with the "V" prefix and contain 1996 statistics and a brief highlight.

	MT
Complete Set (18):	350.00
Common Player:	6.00
1 Troy Aikman	25.00
2 John Elway	20.00
3 Jim Harbaugh	6.00
4 Barry Sanders	35.00
5 Deion Sanders	12.00
6 Drew Bledsoe	25.00
7 Dan Marino	45.00
8 Terrell Davis	30.00
9 Isaac Bruce	10.00
10 Jerome Bettis	6.00
11 Emmitt Smith	45.00

12	Brett Favre	50.00
13	Steve Young	15.00
14	Mark Brunell	25.00
15	Joey Galloway	6.00
16	Kordell Stewart	20.00
17	Jerry Rice	25.00
18	Curtis Martin	30.00

1997 Zenith Rookie Rising

The 24-card, regular-sized set was inserted every 23 packs of Pinnacle Zenith. The cards are individually numbered and feature the rookie on the card face in Dufex printing over a common stadium. The horizontal cards have "Rookie Rising" printed in gold script on the front with the player's name written in script in the upper left corner. The backs feature a player shot over a football.

		MT
Complete Set (24):		160.00
Common Player:		3.00
1	Eddie Kennison	5.00
2	Marvin Harrison	8.00
3	Keyshawn Johnson	8.00
4	Leeland McElroy	3.00
5	Terrell Owens	12.00
6	Terry Glenn	18.00
7	Bobby Engram	3.00
8	Karim Abdul-Jabbar	15.00
9	Lawrence Phillips	3.00
10	Amani Toomer	3.00
11	Eric Moulds	3.00
12	Jason Dunn	3.00

13	Stanley Pritchett	3.00
14	Eddie George	20.00
15	Muhsin Muhammad	5.00
16	Rickey Dudley	3.00
17	Tony Banks	5.00
18	Bryan Still	3.00
19	Tim Biakabutuka	3.00
20	Simeon Rice	3.00
21	Zach Thomas	8.00
22	Kevin Hardy	3.00
23	Jerris McPhail	3.00
24	Mike Alstott	6.00

1997 Zenith Z-Team

The 18-card, regular-sized set was inserted every 71 packs of Pinnacle Zenith while the parallel Gold Mirror Mylar Z Team set was found every 191 packs. The standard Z Team cards feature the player's image on a horizontal card with a "Z" printed on the left side over a large football backdrop. The card backs are numbered with the "Z" prefix and feature another player shot over a large football. A large black "Z" with a highlight text insert is on the left side. The Gold Mirror Mylar Z Team inserts are distinguishable by the reflective gold background on the card fronts. The card backs are essentially the same, with the exception of the words "Mirror Gold" printed along the left border.

		MT
Complete Set (18):		650.00
Common Player:		15.00
1	Emmitt Smith	80.00
2	Dan Marino	80.00
3	Jerry Rice	40.00
4	John Elway	30.00
5	Curtis Martin	50.00
6	Deion Sanders	25.00
7	Tony Banks	15.00
8	Jim Harbaugh	15.00
9	Joey Galloway	15.00
10	Troy Aikman	40.00
11	Brett Favre	80.00
12	Keyshawn Johnson	25.00
13	Eddie George	50.00
14	Barry Sanders	50.00
15	Kordell Stewart	40.00
16	Steve Young	30.00
17	Terrell Davis	50.00
18	Drew Bledsoe	40.00

1997 Zenith Z-Team Mirror Golds

Z-Team Mirror Golds feature all 18 cards in the regular Z-Team set, but these inserts feature a Mirror Gold finish, and are inserted every 191 packs.

	MT
Complete Set (18):	1600.
Mirror Golds:	2x-3x

MEMORABILIA/FIGURINES

1964 Coke Caps All-Stars AFL

The 44-cap, 1-1/8" in diameter set, found on bottles of Coca-Cola, was distributed in AFL cities. The cap outsides have a Coke logo with a football icon, while the inside of the cap features the player's face in black with surrounding text. A cap saver sheet was issued and could be redeemed for various prizes. Other Coke products, such as Fresca and Tab, also had the football caps.

		NM
Complete Set (44):		175.00
Common Player:		2.50
1	Tommy Addison	2.50
2	Dalva Allen	2.50
3	Lance Alworth	10.00
4	Houston Antwine	2.50
5	Fred Arbanas	2.50
6	Tony Banfield	2.50
7	Stew Barber	2.50
8	George Blair	2.50
9	Mel Branch	2.50
10	Nick Buoniconti	8.00
11	Doug Cline	2.50
12	Eldon Danehauer	2.50
13	Clem Daniels	5.00
14	Larry Eisenhauer	2.50
15	Earl Faison	2.50
16	Cookie Gilchrist	5.00
17	Freddy Glick	2.50
18	Larry Grantham	5.00
19	Ron Hall	2.50
20	Charlie Hennigan	5.00
21	E.J. Holub	2.50
22	Ed Husmann	2.50
23	Jack Kemp	25.00
24	Dave Kocourek	2.50
25	Keith Lincoln	5.00
26	Charlie Long	2.50
27	Paul Lowe	5.00
28	Archie Matsos	2.50
29	Jerry Mays	5.00
30	Ron Mix	5.00
31	Tom Morrow	2.50
32	Billy Neighbors	2.50
33	Jim Otto	5.00
34	Art Powell	5.00
35	Johnny Robinson	5.00
36	Tobin Rote	2.50
37	Bob Schmidt	2.50
38	Tom Sestak	2.50
39	Billy Shaw	2.50
40	Bob Talamini	2.50
41	Lionel Taylor	5.00
42	Jim Tyrer	2.50
43	Dick Westmoreland	2.50
44	Fred Williamson	5.00

1964 Coke Caps All-Stars NFL

The 44-cap, 1-1/8" in diameter set is virtually identical to the 44-cap AFL set of the same year. The outside of each cap has the Coke logo with a football, with the inside having the player's facial image. As with the AFL set, a Cap Saver sheet was issued with potential prizes for collectors. Other Coke products, such as Fresca and Tab, also had the football caps.

		NM
Complete Set (44):		160.00
Common Player:		2.50
1	Doug Atkins	2.50
2	Terry Barr	2.50
3	Jim Brown	25.00
4	Roger Brown	5.00
5	Roosevelt Brown	6.00
6	Timmy Brown	5.00
7	Bobby Joe Conrad	5.00
8	Willie Davis	6.00
9	Bob DeMarco	2.50
10	Darrell Dess	2.50
11	Mike Ditka	15.00
12	Bill Forester	2.50
13	Joe Fortunato	2.50
14	Bill George	5.00
15	Ken Gray	2.50
16	Forrest Gregg	8.00
17	Roosevelt Grier	6.00
18	Hank Jordan	5.00
19	Jim Katcavage	5.00
20	Jerry Kramer	7.00
21	Ron Kramer	5.00
22	Dick Lane	5.00
23	Dick Lynch	2.50
24	Gino Marchetti	6.00
25	Tommy Mason	2.50
26	Ed Meador	2.50
27	Bobby Mitchell	7.00
28	Larry Morris	2.50
29	Merlin Olsen	8.00
30	Jim Parker	5.00
31	Jim Patton	2.50
32	Myron Pottios	2.50
33	Jim Ringo	5.00
34	Dick Schafrath	2.50
35	Joe Schmidt	5.00
36	Del Shofner	5.00
37	Bob St. Clair	5.00
38	Jim Taylor	8.00
39	Roosevelt Taylor	2.50
40	Y.A. Tittle	10.00
41	Johnny Unitas	16.00
42	Larry Wilson	5.00
43	Willie Wood	5.00
44	Abe Woodson	5.00

1964 Coke Caps Browns

The 35-cap, 1-1/8" in diameter set was issued in Ohio and featured top Browns players, including a first-year cap of receiver Paul Warfield. The cap tops feature a football stamp while the inside depicts a Browns player. A Cap Saver sheet, featuring Frank Ryan, was also issued.

		NM
Complete Set (35):		125.00
Common Player:		2.50
1	Walter Beach	2.50
2	Larry Benz	2.50
3	Johnny Brewer	2.50
4	Jim Brown	30.00
5	John Brown	2.50
6	Monte Clark	5.00
7	Gary Collins	5.00
8	Vince Costello	2.50
9	Ross Fichtner	2.50
10	Galen Fiss	2.50
11	Bobby Franklin	2.50
12	Bob Gain	2.50
13	Bill Glass	2.50
14	Ernie Green	2.50
15	Lou Groza	8.00
16	Gene Hickerson	2.50
17	Jim Houston	2.50
18	Tom Hutchinson	2.50
19	Jim Kanicki	2.50
20	Mike Lucci	5.00
21	Dick Modzelewski	5.00
22	John Morrow	2.50
23	Jim Ninowski	2.50
24	Frank Parker	2.50
25	Bernie Parrish	5.00
26	Frank Ryan	5.00
27	Charlie Scales	2.50
28	Dick Schafrath	5.00
29	Roger Shoals	2.50
30	Jim Shorter	2.50
31	Billy Truax	5.00
32	Paul Warfield	16.00
33	Ken Webb	2.50
34	Paul Wiggin	2.50
35	John Wooten	5.00
NNO	Browns Saver Sheet Frank Ryan pictured	20.00

1964 Coke Caps Chargers

The 35-cap, 1-1/8" set was issued in Southern California and featured top players from the AFL Chargers. As with other cap sets, a Cap Saver sheet was also available and when completed, collectors could redeem it for various prizes.

		NM
Complete Set (35):		100.00
Common Player:		2.50
1	Chuck Allen	5.00
2	Lance Alworth	16.00
3	George Blair	2.50
4	Frank Buncom	2.50
5	Earl Faison	5.00
6	Kenny Graham	2.50
7	George Gross	2.50
8	Sam Gruneison	2.50
9	John Hadl	10.00
10	Dick Harris	2.50
11	Bob Jackson	2.50
12	Emil Karas	2.50
13	Dave Kocourek	2.50
14	Ernie Ladd	6.00
15	Bobby Lane	2.50
16	Keith Lincoln	5.00
17	Paul Lowe	5.00
18	Jacque MacKinnon	2.50
19	Gerry McDougall	2.50
20	Charlie McNeil	2.50
21	Bob Mitinger	2.50
22	Ron Mix	6.00
23	Don Norton	2.50
24	Ernie Park	2.50
25	Bob Petrich	2.50
26	Jerry Robinson	2.50
27	Don Rogers	2.50
28	Tobin Rote	5.00
29	Henry Schmidt	2.50
30	Pat Shea	2.50
31	Walt Sweeney	5.00
32	Jimmy Warren	2.50
33	Dick Westmoreland	2.50
34	Bud Whitehead	2.50
35	Ernie Wright	2.50
NNO	Chargers Saver Sheet	20.00

1964 Coke Caps Lions

The 35-cap, 1-1/8" set was distributed in Michigan and contains Detroit Lions players' images on the inside of each cap. A Cap Saver sheet was also issued and the caps could also be found on Coke products such as Fresca and Tab.

		NM
Complete Set (35):		100.00
Common Player:		2.50
1	Terry Barr	2.50
2	Carl Brettschneider	2.50
3	Roger Brown	5.00
4	Mike Bundra	2.50
5	Ernie Clark	2.50
6	Gail Cogdill	5.00
7	Larry Ferguson	2.50
8	Dennis Gaubatz	2.50
9	Jim Gibbons	5.00
10	John Gonzaga	2.50
11	John Gordy	2.50
12	Tom Hall	2.50
13	Alex Karras	10.00
14	Dick Lane	8.00
15	Dan LaRose	2.50
16	Yale Lary	8.00
17	Dick LeBeau	5.00
18	Dan Lewis	2.50
19	Gary Lowe	2.50
20	Bruce Maher	2.50
21	Darris McCord	2.50
22	Max Messner	2.50
23	Earl Morrall	7.00
24	Nick Pietrosante	2.50
25	Milt Plum	2.50
26	Daryl Sanders	2.50
27	Joe Schmidt	6.00
28	Bob Scholtz	2.50
29	J.D. Smith	5.00
30	Pat Studstill	5.00
31	Larry Vargo	2.50
32	Wayne Walker	5.00
33	Tom Watkins	2.50
34	Bob Whitlow	2.50
35	Sam Williams	2.50
NNO	Lions Saver Sheet	20.00

1964 Coke Caps Rams

The 35-cap, 1-1/8" set, issued in the Los Angeles area, had top Rams players and their image on the Coke bottle cap insides. The Cap Saver sheet could be redeemed for prizes and other Coke products also had the Rams bottle caps.

		NM
Complete Set (35):		85.00
Common Player:		2.50
1	Jon Arnett	5.00
2	Pervis Atkins	2.50
3	Terry Baker	5.00
4	Dick Bass	5.00
5	Charley Britt	2.50
6	Willie Brown	2.50
7	Joe Carollo	2.50
8	Don Chuy	2.50
9	Charlie Cowan	2.50
10	Lindon Crow	2.50
11	Carroll Dale	5.00
12	Roman Gabriel	6.00
13	Roosevelt Grier	6.00
14	Mike Henry	2.50
15	Art Hunter	2.50
16	Ken Iman	2.50
17	Deacon Jones	10.00
18	Cliff Livingston	2.50
19	Lamar Lundy	2.50
20	Marlin McKeever	2.50
21	Ed Meador	5.00
22	Bill Munson	5.00
23	Merlin Olsen	8.00
24	Jack Pardee	5.00
25	Art Perkins	2.50
26	Jim Phillips	2.50
27	Roger Pillath	2.50
28	Mel Profit	2.50
29	Joe Scibelli	2.50
30	Carver Shannon	2.50
31	Bobby Smith	2.50
32	Bill Swain	2.50
33	Frank Varrichione	2.50
34	Danny Villanueva	2.50
35	Nat Whitmyer	2.50
NNO	Rams Saver Sheet	20.00

1964 Coke Caps Redskins

The 32-cap, 1-1/8" in diameter set featured top players from the Redskins. Collectors who assembled the entire set before a specific expiration date could redeem it for prizes. The outside of the cap features the Coke logos with a stamp of a football, while the inside has the player's likeness. There may have been more of the 32 un-numbered caps issued than are listed below.

1964 Coke Caps Team Emblems NFL

The 14-cap, 1-1/8" in diameter set features a cap for each of the NFL teams. The Cap Saver sheet had a section for collecting the team emblem caps which were also available with other Coke products such as Fresca and Tab.

		NM
Complete Set (14):		50.00
Common Player:		5.00
1	Baltimore Colts	5.00
2	Chicago Bears	5.00
3	Cleveland Browns	5.00
4	Dallas Cowboys	7.00
5	Detroit Lions	5.00
6	Green Bay Packers	7.00
7	Los Angeles Rams	5.00
8	Minnesota Vikings	5.00
9	New York Giants	5.00
10	Philadelphia Eagles	5.00
11	Pittsburgh Steelers	5.00
12	San Francisco 49ers	6.00
13	St. Louis Cardinals	5.00
14	Washington Redskins	6.00

1965 Coke Caps All-Stars AFL

The 34-cap, 1-1/8" set features All-Stars from the AFL and was distributed in AFL cities along with local team caps. As with other caps, the outside features a Coke logo with a football icon and the inside depicts a facial image of an AFL All-Star. The caps are numbered with the "C" prefix.

		NM
Complete Set (34):		130.00
Common Player:		2.50
37	Jerry Mays	2.50
38	Cookie Gilchrist	4.00
39	Lionel Taylor	2.50
40	Goose Gonsoulin	4.00
41	Gino Cappelletti	4.00
42	Nick Buoniconti	6.00
43	Larry Eisenhauer	2.50
44	Babe Parilli	2.50
45	Jack Kemp	20.00
46	Billy Shaw	2.50
47	Scott Appleton	2.50
48	Matt Snell	2.50
49	Charlie Hennigan	2.50
50	Tom Flores	5.00
51	Clem Daniels	2.50
52	George Blanda	8.00
53	Art Powell	2.50
54	Jim Otto	5.00
55	Larry Grantham	2.50
56	Don Maynard	8.00
57	Gerry Philbin	2.50
58	E.J. Holub	2.50
59	Chris Burford	2.50
60	Ron Mix	5.00
61	Ernie Ladd	8.00
62	Fred Arbanas	2.50
63	Tom Sestak	2.50
64	Elbert Dubenion	2.50
65	Mike Stratton	2.50
66	Willie Brown	5.00
67	Sid Blanks	2.50
68	Len Dawson	8.00
69	Lance Alworth	8.00
70	Keith Lincoln	2.50

1965 Coke Caps All-Stars NFL

The 34-cap, 1-1/8" set featured NFL All-Stars and was distributed in NFL cities along with a Cap Saver sheet and local player caps. The completed sheet could be redeemed for various prizes. The caps are numbered with the "C" prefix.

		NM
Complete Set (34):		125.00
Common Player:		2.50
37	Sonny Jurgensen	8.00
38	Fran Tarkenton	12.00
39	Frank Ryan	2.50
40	Johnny Unitas	12.00
41	Tommy Mason	2.50
42	Mel Renfro	5.00
43	Ed Meador	2.50
44	Paul Krause	4.00
45	Irv Cross	4.00
46	Bill Brown	2.50
47	Joe Fortunato	2.50
48	Jim Taylor	6.00
49	John Henry Johnson	5.00
50	Pat Fischer	2.50
51	Bob Boyd	2.50
52	Terry Barr	2.50
53	Charley Taylor	5.00
54	Paul Warfield	8.00
55	Pete Retzlaff	2.50
56	Maxie Baughan	2.50
57	Matt Hazeltine	2.50
58	Ken Gray	2.50
59	Ray Nitschke	6.00
60	Myron Pottios	2.50
61	Charlie Krueger	2.50
62	Deacon Jones	7.00
63	Bob Lilly	7.00
64	Merlin Olsen	7.00
65	Jim Parker	5.00
66	Roosevelt Brown	2.50
67	Jim Gibbons	2.50
68	Mike Ditka	12.00
69	Willie Davis	5.00
70	Aaron Thomas	2.50

1965 Coke Caps Bills

The 35-cap, 1-1/8" set featuring the Bills was issued in western New York with a Cap Saver sheet, which could be redeemed for prizes such as an AFL leather football, a mini Bills megaphone, or a set of mini plastic AFL helmets. The cap tops have the Coke logo and a football stamp while the insides have the player's likeness. Hall of Fame quarterback Jack Kemp was the key player featured in the cap set. The caps are numbered with the "B" prefix.

		NM
Complete Set (35):		120.00
Common Player:		2.50
1	Ray Abbruzzese	2.50
2	Joe Auer	2.50
3	Stew Barber	2.50
4	Glenn Bass	2.50
5	Dave Behrman	2.50
6	Al Bemiller	2.50
7	George (Butch) Byrd	2.50
8	Wray Carlton	2.50
9	Hagood Clarke	2.50
10	Jack Kemp	25.00
11	Oliver Dobbins	2.50
12	Elbert Dubenion	2.50
13	Jim Dunaway	2.50
14	Booker Edgerson	2.50
15	George Flint	2.50
16	Pete Gogolak	5.00
17	Dick Hudson	5.00
18	Harry Jacobs	2.50
19	Tom Keating	2.50
20	Tom Day	2.50
21	Daryle Lamonica	10.00
22	Paul Maguire	8.00
23	Roland McDole	2.50
24	Dudley Meredith	2.50
25	Joe O'Donnell	2.50
26	Willie Ross	2.50
27	Ed Rutkowski	2.50
28	George Saimes	5.00
29	Tom Sestak	5.00
30	Billy Shaw	5.00
31	Bobby Smith	2.50
32	Mike Stratton	2.50
33	Gene Sykes	2.50
34	John Tracey	2.50
35	Ernie Warlick	2.50
NNO	Bills Saver Sheet	20.00

1965 Coke Caps Giants

The 35-cap, 1-1/8" set was distributed in the metropolitan New York area and featured key players from the Giants. The outside of the cap features a Coke logo and a football while the inside depicts one of the Giants players. A Cap Saver sheet was also available and completed sheets could be redeemed for prizes (NFL leather football, mini plastic NFL helmet set, mini Giants megaphone). The caps are numbered with the "G" prefix.

		NM
Complete Set (35):		100.00
Common Player:		2.50
1	Joe Morrison	2.50
2	Dick Lynch	2.50
3	Andy Stynchula	2.50
4	Clarence Childs	2.50
5	Aaron Thomas	2.50
6	Mickey Walker	2.50
7	Bill Winter	2.50
8	Bookie Bolin	2.50
9	Tom Scott	2.50
10	John Lovetere	2.50
11	Jim Patton	5.00
12	Darrell Dess	2.50
13	Dick James	2.50
14	Jerry Hillebrand	2.50
15	Dick Personen	2.50
16	Del Shofner	2.50
17	Erich Barnes	2.50
18	Roosevelt Brown	6.00
19	Greg Larson	2.50
20	Jim Katcavage	2.50
21	Frank Lasky	2.50
22	Lou Slaby	2.50
23	Jim Moran	2.50
24	Roger Anderson	2.50
25	Steve Thurlow	2.50
26	Ernie Wheelwright	2.50
27	Gary Wood	5.00
28	Tony Dimidio	2.50
29	John Contoulis	2.50
30	Tucker Fredrickson	5.00
31	Bob Timberlake	2.50
32	Chuck Mercein	2.50
33	Ernie Koy	2.50
34	Tom Costello	2.50
35	Homer Jones	5.00
NNO	Giants Saver Sheet	20.00

1965 Coke Caps Jets

The 35-cap, 1-1/8" in diameter set was issued in the New York City area and was highlighted by top players from the Jets. Collectors who redeemed the complete set were awarded either a leather AFL football, a mini plastic AFL helmet set, or a Jets mini megaphone. The caps were numbered with the "J" prefix. Joe Namath's cap is the key to the set.

		NM
Complete Set (35):		150.00
Common Player:		2.50
1	Don Maynard	10.00
2	George Sauer Jr.	5.00
3	Cosmo Iacavazzi	2.50
4	Jim O'Mahoney	2.50
5	Matt Snell	5.00
6	Clyde Washington	2.50
7	Jim Turner	2.50
8	Mike Taliaferro	2.50
9	Marshall Starks	2.50
10	Mark Smolinski	2.50
11	Bob Schweickert	2.50
12	Paul Rochester	2.50
13	Sherman Plunkett	2.50
14	Gerry Philbin	2.50
15	Pete Perreault	2.50
16	Dainard Paulson	2.50
17	Joe Namath	50.00
18	Winston Hill	2.50
19	Dee Mackey	2.50
20	Curley Johnson	2.50
21	Mike Hudock	2.50
22	John Huarte	5.00
23	Gordy Holz	2.50
24	Gene Heeter	2.50
25	Larry Grantham	5.00
26	Dan Ficca	2.50
27	Sam DeLuca	2.50
28	Bill Baird	2.50
29	Ralph Baker	2.50
30	Wahoo McDaniel	10.00
31	Jim Evans	2.50
32	Dave Herman	2.50
33	John Schmitt	2.50
34	Jim Harris	2.50
35	Bake Turner	5.00
NNO	Jets Saver Sheet	20.00

1965 Coke Caps Lions

		NM
Complete Set (36):		100.00
Common Player:		2.50
1	Pat Studstill	5.00
2	Bob Whitlow	2.50
3	Wayne Walker	5.00
4	Tom Watkins	2.50
5	Jim Simon	2.50
6	Sam Williams	2.50
7	Terry Barr	2.50
8	Jerry Rush	2.50
9	Roger Brown	2.50
10	Tom Nowatzke	5.00
11	Dick Lane	7.00
12	Dick Compton	2.50
13	Yale Lary	5.00
14	Dick LeBeau	5.00
15	Dan Lewis	5.00
16	Wally Hilgenburg	5.00
17	Bruce Maher	2.50
18	Darris McCord	2.50
19	Hugh McInnis	2.50
20	Ernie Clark	2.50
21	Gail Cogdill	2.50
22	Wayne Rasmussen	2.50
23	Joe Don Looney	8.00
24	Jim Gibbons	5.00
25	John Gonzaga	2.50
26	John Gordy	2.50
27	Bobby Thompson	2.50
28	J.D. Smith	5.00
29	Earl Morrall	6.00
30	Alex Karras	8.00
31	Nick Pietrosante	2.50
32	Milt Plum	2.50
33	Daryl Sanders	2.50
34	Joe Schmidt	8.00
35	Bob Scholtz	2.50
36	Team Logo	2.50
NNO	Lions Saver Sheet	20.00

1965 Coke Caps National NFL

The 70-cap, 1-1/8" set was issued in metropolitan areas that did not have (in 1965) an NFL team. The caps have red liners and depict a player's facial image on the inside. The top of the cap had a Coke logo and a football icon. The caps are numbered with the "C" prefix.

		NM
Complete Set (70):		200.00
Common Player:		2.50
1	Herb Adderley	5.00
2	Yale Lary	5.00
3	Dick LeBeau	2.50
4	Bill Brown	5.00
5	Jim Taylor	8.00
6	Joe Fortunato	2.50
7	Bill Boyd	2.50
8	Terry Barr	2.50
9	Dick Szymanski	2.50
10	Mick Tingelhoff	2.50
11	Wayne Walker	2.50
12	Matt Hazeltine	2.50
13	Ray Nitschke	7.00
14	Grady Alderman	2.50
15	Charlie Krueger	2.50
16	Tommy Mason	2.50
17	Willie Wood	5.00
18	Johnny Unitas	14.00
19	Lenny Moore	5.00
20	Fran Tarkenton	12.00
21	Deacon Jones	7.00
22	Bob Vogel	2.50
23	John Gordy	2.50
24	Jim Parker	2.50
25	Jim Gibbons	2.50
26	Merlin Olsen	7.00
27	Forrest Gregg	6.00
28	Roger Brown	2.50
29	Dave Parks	2.50
30	Raymond Berry	5.00
31	Mike Ditka	12.00
32	Gino Marchetti	5.00
33	Willie Davis	5.00
34	Ed Meador	2.50
35	Browns Logo	2.50
36	Colts Logo	2.50
37	Sam Baker	2.50
38	Irv Cross	5.00
39	Maxie Baughan	2.50
40	Vince Promuto	2.50
41	Paul Krause	2.50
42	Charley Taylor	5.00
43	John Paluck	2.50
44	Paul Warfield	8.00
45	Dick Modzelewski	2.50
46	Myron Pottios	2.50
47	Erich Barnes	2.50
48	Bill Koman	2.50
49	Art Thomas	2.50
50	Gary Ballman	2.50
51	Sam Huff	5.00
52	Ken Gray	2.50
53	Roosevelt Brown	6.00
54	Bobby Joe Conrad	2.50
55	Pat Fischer	2.50
56	Irv Goode	2.50
57	Floyd Peters	2.50
58	Charlie Johnson	5.00
59	John Henry Johnson	5.00
60	Charley Bradshaw	2.50
61	Jim Ringo	5.00
62	Pete Retzlaff	5.00
63	Sonny Jurgensen	8.00
64	Don Meredith	12.00
65	Bob Lilly	8.00
66	Bill Glass	2.50
67	Dick Schafrath	2.50
68	Mel Renfro	5.00
69	Jim Houston	2.50
70	Frank Ryan	2.50

1965 Coke Caps Packers

The 36-cap, 1-1/8" in diameter set featured Packers players and was issued in the greater metropolitan areas of Wisconsin, such as Milwaukee, Green Bay and Madison areas. Completed sets on a Cap Saver sheet could be redeemed for a variety of prizes before an expiration date. The caps are numbered with the "C" prefix.

		NM
Complete Set (36):		160.00
Common Player:		2.50
1	Herb Adderley	5.00
2	Lionel Aldridge	2.50
3	Hank Gremminger	2.50
4	Willie Davis	6.00
5	Boyd Dowler	5.00
6	Marv Fleming	2.50
7	Ken Bowman	2.50
8	Tom Brown	2.50
9	Doug Hart	2.50
10	Steve Wright	2.50
11	Dennis Claridge	2.50
12	Dave Hanner	2.50
13	Tommy Crutcher	2.50
14	Fred Thurston	5.00
15	Elijah Pitts	5.00
16	Lloyd Voss	2.50
17	Lee Roy Caffey	2.50
18	Dave Robinson	5.00
19	Bart Starr	14.00
20	Ray Nitschke	10.00
21	Max McGee	6.00
22	Don Chandler	2.50
23	Norm Masters	2.50
24	Ron Kostelnik	2.50
25	Carroll Dale	5.00
26	Hank Jordan	5.00
27	Bob Jeter	2.50
28	Bob Skoronski	2.50
29	Jerry Kramer	6.00
30	Willie Wood	6.00
31	Paul Hornung	14.00
32	Forrest Gregg	8.00
33	Zeke Bratkowski	5.00
34	Tom Moore	2.50
35	Jim Taylor	10.00
36	Team Logo	2.50
NNO	Packers Saver Sheet	20.00

1965 Coke Caps Patriots

The 36-cap, 1-1/8" set was issued in the New England area and a completed set on a Cap Saver sheet could be redeemed for a prize. The cap tops feature a Coke logo and an image of a football, while the inside has the facial image of a Patriots player. Other Coke products, such as Fresca and Tab, also had the player caps. The caps are numbered with a "C" prefix.

		NM
Complete Set (36):		100.00
Common Player:		2.50
1	Jon Morris	5.00
2	Don Webb	2.50
3	Charles Long	5.00
4	Tony Romeo	2.50
5	Bob Dee	2.50
6	Tommy Addison	2.50
7	Bob Yates	2.50
8	Ron Hall	2.50
9	Billy Neighbors	2.50
10	Jack Rudolph	2.50
11	Don Oakes	2.50
12	Tom Yewcic	2.50
13	Ron Burton	5.00
14	Jim Colclough	2.50
15	Larry Garron	5.00
16	Dave Watson	2.50
17	Art Graham	5.00
18	Babe Parilli	5.00
19	Jim Hunt	2.50
20	Don McKinnon	2.50
21	Houston Antwine	5.00
22	Nick Buoniconti	8.00
23	Ross O'Hanley	2.50
24	Gino Cappelletti	5.00
25	Chuck Shonta	2.50
26	Dick Felt	2.50
27	Mike Dukes	2.50
28	Larry Eisenhauer	2.50
29	Bob Schmidt	2.50
30	Len St. Jean	2.50
31	J.D. Garrett	2.50
32	Jim Whalen	2.50
33	Jim Nance	5.00
34	Eddie Wilson	2.50
35	Lonnie Farmer	2.50
36	Boston Patriots Logo	2.50
NNO	Patriots Saver Sheet	20.00

1965 Coke Caps Redskins

The 36-cap, 1-1/8" set was distributed in the Washington, D.C. area and featured top players from the Redskins. As with other Coke cap sets, the Redskins set could be collected on a Cap Saver sheet and redeemed for prizes. Other Coke products, such as Fresca and Tab, also had the player caps. The caps are numbered with a "C" prefix.

		NM
Complete Set (36):		100.00
Common Player:		2.50
1	Jimmy Carr	2.50
2	Fred Mazurek	2.50
3	Lonnie Sanders	2.50
4	Jim Steffen	2.50
5	John Nisby	2.50
6	George Izo	5.00
7	Vince Promuto	2.50
8	Johnny Sample	5.00
9	Pat Richter	5.00
10	Preston Carpenter	2.50
11	Sam Huff	8.00

12	Pervis Atkins	2.50
13	Fred Barnett	2.50
14	Len Hauss	5.00
15	Bill Anderson	2.50
16	John Reger	2.50
17	George Seals	2.50
18	J.W. Lockett	2.50
19	Tom Walters	2.50
20	Joe Rutgens	2.50
21	John Paluck	2.50
22	Fran O'Brien	2.50
23	Joe Rutgens	2.50
24	Rod Breedlove	2.50
25	Bob Pellegrini	2.50
26	Bob Jencks	2.50
27	Joe Hernandez	2.50
28	Sonny Jurgensen	10.00
29	Bob Toneff	2.50
30	Charley Taylor	8.00
31	Bob Shiner	2.50
32	Bobby Williams	2.50
33	Angelo Coia	2.50
34	Ron Snidow	2.50
35	Paul Krause	5.00
36	Team Logo	2.50
NNO	Redskins Saver Sheet	20.00

1966 Coke Caps All-Stars AFL

The 34-cap, 1-1/8" in diameter set was issued in AFL cities and could be collected on Cap Saver sheets, some of which had separate sections to place both the local and All-Star caps. The caps are virtually identical to previous Coke caps sets and were also found on Fresca and Tab products. The caps are numbered with a "C" prefix.

		NM
Complete Set (34):		120.00
Common Player:		2.00
37	Babe Parilli	4.00
38	Mike Stratton	2.00
39	Jack Kemp	18.00
40	Len Dawson	8.00
41	Fred Arbanas	2.00
42	Bobby Bell	4.00
43	Willie Brown	4.00
44	Buck Buchanan	4.00
45	Frank Buncom	2.00
46	Nick Buoniconti	4.00
47	Gino Cappelletti	4.00
48	Eldon Danenhauer	2.00
49	Clem Daniels	4.00
50	Les Duncan	4.00
51	Willie Frazier	2.00
52	Cookie Gilchrist	4.00
53	Dave Grayson	2.00
54	John Hadl	5.00
55	Wayne Hawkins	2.00
56	Sherrill Headrick	2.00
57	Charlie Hennigan	4.00
58	E.J. Holub	2.00
59	Curley Johnson	2.00
60	Keith Lincoln	4.00
61	Paul Lowe	4.00
62	Don Maynard	6.00
63	Jon Morris	2.00
64	Joe Namath	20.00
65	Jim Otto	4.00
66	Dainard Paulson	2.00
67	Art Powell	4.00
68	Walt Sweeney	4.00
69	Bob Talamini	2.00
70	Lance Alworth (UER, Name misspelled Alsworth)	8.00

1966 Coke Caps All-Stars NFL

The 34-cap, 1-1/8" set was issued in mostly NFL cities and some Cap Saver sheets had separate sections for both the local and All-Star caps. As with previous Coke Cap sheets, collectors could turn in a completed set for prizes. The caps are identical in design with other caps issues and could be found with Tab and Fresca products as well. The caps are numbered with a "C" prefix.

		NM
Complete Set (34):		120.00
Common Player:		2.00
37	Frank Ryan	4.00
38	Timmy Brown	4.00
39	Tucker Frederickson	2.00
40	Cornell Green	4.00
41	Bob Hayes	4.00
42	Charley Taylor	4.00
43	Pete Retzlaff	4.00
44	Jim Ringo	6.00
45	John Wooten	2.00
46	Dale Meinert	2.00
47	Bob Lilly	8.00
48	Sam Silas	2.00
49	Roosevelt Brown	6.00
50	Gary Ballman	2.00
51	Gary Collins	2.00
52	Sonny Randle	2.00
53	Charlie Johnson	2.00
54	Herb Adderley	4.00
55	Doug Atkins	4.00
56	Roger Brown	2.00
57	Dick Butkus	14.00
58	Willie Davis	4.00
59	Tommy McDonald	2.00
60	Alex Karras	6.00
61	John Mackey	4.00
62	Ed Meador	2.00
63	Merlin Olsen	4.00
64	Dave Parks	2.00
65	Gale Sayers	14.00
66	Fran Tarkenton	10.00
67	Mick Tingelhoff	2.00
68	Ken Willard	2.00
69	Willie Wood	4.00
70	Bill Brown	4.00

1966 Coke Caps Bills

The 36-cap, 1-1/8" in diameter set was distributed in western New York and was highlighted by Bills players. The caps are nearly identical in design as previous sets, except that the insides are numbered with a "B" prefix.

		NM
Complete Set (36):		120.00
Common Player:		2.00
1	Bill Laskey	2.00
2	Marty Schottenheimer	8.00
3	Stew Barber	2.00
4	Glenn Bass	2.00
5	Remi Prudhomme	2.00
6	Al Bemiller	2.00
7	George (Butch) Byrd	3.00
8	Wray Carlton	2.00
9	Hagood Clarke	2.00
10	Jack Kemp	25.00
11	Charlie Warner	2.00
12	Elbert Dubenion	3.00
13	Jim Dunaway	2.00
14	Booker Edgerson	2.00
15	Paul Costa	2.00
16	Henry Schmidt	2.00
17	Dick Hudson	2.00
18	Harry Jacobs	2.00
19	Tom Janik	2.00
20	Tom Day	2.00
21	Daryle Lamonica	5.00
22	Paul Maguire	6.00
23	Roland McDole	2.00
24	Dudley Meredith	2.00
25	Joe O'Donnell	2.00
26	Charlie Ferguson	2.00
27	Ed Rutkowski	2.00
28	George Saimes	2.00
29	Tom Sestak	3.00
30	Billy Shaw	2.00
31	Bobby Smith	2.00
32	Mike Stratton	3.00
33	Gene Sykes	2.00
34	John Tracey	2.00
35	Ernie Warlick	2.00
36	Bills Logo	2.00
NNO	Bills Saver Sheet	20.00

1966 Coke Caps Browns

The 36-cap, 1-1/8" set was part of Coke's 14-cap NFL set.

The caps have a Coke logo and football icon on the outside with a player's image on the inside. A Cap Saver sheet was also issued and, as with previous releases, a completed sheet could be redeemed for prizes. The caps are numbered with a "C" prefix.

		NM
Complete Set (36):		100.00
Common Player:		2.00
1	Jim Ninowski	3.00
2	Leroy Kelly	6.00
3	Lou Groza	6.00
4	Gary Collins	3.00
5	Bill Glass	3.00
6	Dale Lindsey	2.00
7	Galen Fiss	2.00
8	Ross Fichtner	2.00
9	John Wooten	2.00
10	Clifton McNeil	2.00
11	Paul Wiggin	2.00
12	Gene Hickerson	3.00
13	Ernie Green	2.00
14	Mike Howell	2.00
15	Dick Schafrath	2.00
16	Sidney Williams	2.00
17	Frank Ryan	3.00
18	Bernie Parrish	3.00
19	Vince Costello	2.00
20	John Brown (CO)	2.00
21	Monte Clark	2.00
22	Walter Roberts	2.00
23	Johnny Brewer	2.00
24	Walter Beach	2.00
25	Dick Modzelewski	2.00
26	Gary Lane	2.00
27	Jim Houston	2.00
28	Milt Morin	2.00
29	Erich Barnes	2.00
30	Tom Hutchinson	2.00
31	John Morrow	2.00
32	Jim Kanicki	2.00
33	Paul Warfield	8.00
34	Jim Garcia	2.00
35	Walter Johnson	2.00
36	Browns Logo	2.00
NNO	Browns Saver Sheet	20.00

1966 Coke Caps Cardinals

The 36-cap, 1-1/8" set was issued in conjunction with other NFL, AFL and All-Star sets. Cap Saver sheets were also issued and completed sheets could be redeemed for prizes. The caps are virtually identical in design to previous sets. The caps are numbered with a "C" prefix.

		NM
Complete Set (36):		80.00
Common Player:		2.00
1	Pat Fischer	3.00
2	Sonny Randle	2.00
3	Joe Childress	2.00
4	Dave Meggysey (UER, Name misspelled Meggyesy)	4.00
5	Joe Robb	2.00
6	Jerry Stovall	3.00
7	Ernie McMillan	3.00
8	Dale Meinert	2.00
9	Irv Goode	2.00
10	Bob DeMarco	2.00
11	Mal Hammack	2.00
12	Jim Bakken	3.00
13	Bill Thornton	2.00
14	Buddy Humphrey	2.00
15	Bill Koman	2.00
16	Larry Wilson	5.00
17	Charles Walker	2.00
18	Prentice Gautt	3.00
19	Charlie Johnson (UER, Name misspelled Charley)	3.00
20	Ken Gray	2.00
21	Dave Simmons	2.00
22	Sam Silas	2.00
23	Larry Stallings	2.00
24	Don Brumm	2.00
25	Bobby Joe Conrad	3.00
26	Bill Triplett	2.00
27	Luke Owens	2.00
28	Jackie Smith	5.00
29	Bob Reynolds	2.00
30	Abe Woodson	3.00
31	Jim Burson	2.00
32	Willis Crenshaw	2.00
33	Billy Gambrell	2.00
34	Ray Ogden	2.00
35	Herschel Turner	2.00
36	Cardinals Logo	2.00
NNO	Cardinals Saver Sheet	20.00

A player's name in *italic type* indicates a rookie card.

1966 Coke Caps Chiefs

The 36-cap, 1-1/8" set featured key players from the Chiefs and had the Coke logo with a football stamp on the top and a player's image on the inside. Player caps could also be found on Fresca and Tab bottles. The caps are numbered with a "C" prefix.

		NM
Complete Set (36):		100.00
Common Player:		2.00
1	E.J. Holub	3.00
2	Al Reynolds	2.00
3	Buck Buchanan	5.00
4	Curt Merz (SP)	8.00
5	Dave Hill	2.00
6	Bobby Hunt	2.00
7	Jerry Mays	3.00
8	Jon Gilliam	2.00
9	Walt Corey	2.00
10	Soloman Brannan	2.00
11	Aaron Brown	2.00
12	Bert Coan	2.00
13	Ed Budde	2.00
14	Tommy Brooker	2.00
15	Bobby Bell	5.00
16	Smokey Stover	2.00
17	Curtis McClinton	3.00
18	Jerrel Wilson	2.00
19	Ron Burton	3.00
20	Mike Garrett	5.00
21	Jim Tyrer	3.00
22	Johnny Robinson	3.00
23	Bobby Ply	2.00
24	Frank Pitts	2.00
25	Ed Lothamer	2.00
26	Sherrill Headrick	3.00
27	Fred Williamson	5.00
28	Chris Burford	2.00
29	Willie Mitchell	2.00
30	Otis Taylor	5.00
31	Fred Arbanas	2.00
32	Hatch Rosdahl	2.00
33	Reg Carolan	2.00
34	Len Dawson	8.00
35	Pete Beathard	3.00
36	Chiefs Logo	2.00
NNO	Chiefs Saver Sheet	20.00

1966 Coke Caps Colts

The 36-cap, 1-1/8" in diameter set was issued along with a Cap Saver sheet that, when completed, could be redeemed for various prizes. The caps are numbered with the "C" prefix.

		NM
Complete Set (36):		100.00
Common Player:		2.00
1	Ted Davis	2.00
2	Bob Boyd	2.00
3	Lenny Moore	8.00
4	Jackie Burkett	2.00
5	Jimmy Orr	3.00
6	Andy Stynchula	2.00
7	Mike Curtis	4.00
8	Jerry Logan	2.00
9	Steve Stonebreaker	2.00
10	John Mackey	6.00
11	Dennis Gaubatz	2.00
12	Don Shinnick	2.00
13	Dick Szymanski	2.00
14	Ordell Braase	2.00
15	Lenny Lyles	2.00
16	Rick Kestner	2.00
17	Dan Sullivan	2.00
18	Lou Michaels	3.00
19	Gary Cuozzo	3.00
20	Butch Wilson	2.00
21	Willie Richardson	3.00
22	Jim Welch	2.00
23	Tony Lorick	2.00
24	Billy Ray Smith	3.00
25	Fred Miller	2.00
26	Tom Matte	4.00
27	Johnny Unitas	12.00
28	Glenn Ressler	2.00
29	Alvin Haymond	2.00
30	Jim Parker	5.00
31	Butch Allison	2.00
32	Bob Vogel	2.00
33	Jerry Hill	2.00
34	Raymond Berry	8.00
35	Sam Ball	2.00
36	Colts Team Logo	2.00
NNO	Colts Saver Sheet	20.00

1966 Coke Caps Cowboys

The 36-cap, 1-1/8" set was issued to highlight the Cowboys. A Cap Saver sheet was also available, and when completed, could be redeemed for prizes. Fresca and Tab bottles also had the player caps. Key players in the set are Don Meredith, Dan Reeves and Bob Hayes. The caps are numbered with a "C" prefix.

		NM
Complete Set (36):		140.00
Common Player:		2.50
1	Mike Connelly	2.50
2	Tony Liscio	2.50
3	Jethro Pugh	2.50
4	Larry Stephens	2.50
5	Jim Colvin	2.50
6	Malcolm Walker	2.50
7	Danny Villanueva	2.50
8	Frank Clarke	4.00
9	Don Meredith	12.00
10	George Andrie	4.00
11	Mel Renfro	6.00
12	Pettis Norman	4.00
13	Buddy Dial	4.00
14	Pete Gent	4.00
15	Jerry Rhome	5.00
16	Bob Hayes	10.00
17	Mike Gaechter	2.50
18	Joe Bob Isbell	2.50
19	Harold Hays	2.50
20	Craig Morton	5.00
21	Jake Kupp	2.50
22	Cornell Green	4.00
23	Dan Reeves	12.00
24	Leon Donohue	2.50
25	Dave Manders	2.50
26	Warren Livingston	2.50
27	Bob Lilly	8.00
28	Chuck Howley	5.00
29	Don Bishop	2.50
30	Don Perkins	4.00
31	Jim Boeke	2.50
32	Dave Edwards	2.50
33	Lee Roy Jordan	5.00
34	Obert Logan	2.50
35	Ralph Neely	4.00
36	Cowboys Logo	2.50
NNO	Cowboys Saver Sheet	20.00

1966 Coke Caps Eagles

The 36-card, 1-1/8" set was issued with a Cap Saver sheet that could be redeemed for various prizes. The top of the caps had the Coke logo and a football icon while the inside had the player's image. The caps are numbered with the "C" prefix.

		NM
Complete Set (36):		75.00
Common Player:		2.00
1	Norm Snead	4.00
2	Al Nelson	2.00
3	Jim Skaggs	2.00
4	Glenn Glass	2.00
5	Pete Retzlaff	4.00
6	John Osmond	2.00
7	Ray Rissmiller	2.00
8	Lynn Hoyem	2.00
9	King Hill	4.00
10	Timmy Brown	4.00
11	Ollie Matson	6.00
12	Dave Lloyd	2.00
13	Jim Ringo	6.00
14	Floyd Peters	2.00
15	Gary Pettigrew	2.00
16	Frank Molden	2.00
17	Earl Gros	2.00
18	Fred Hill	2.00
19	Don Hultz	2.00
20	Ray Poage	2.00
21	Aaron Martin	2.00
22	Mike Morgan	2.00
23	Lane Howell	2.00
24	Ed Blaine	2.00
25	Jack Concannon	4.00
26	Sam Baker	2.00
27	Tom Woodeshick	2.00
28	Joe Scarpati	2.00
29	John Meyers	2.00
30	Nate Ramsey	2.00
31	Ben Hawkins	2.00
32	Bob Brown	4.00
33	Willie Brown	2.00
34	Ron Goodwin	2.00
35	Randy Beisler	2.00
36	Team Logo	2.00
NNO	Eagles Saver Sheet	20.00

1966 Coke Caps Falcons

The 36-cap, 1-1/8" in diameter set highlights top members of the Falcons. A Cap Saver sheet was also available which could be redeemed for prizes. Coke products, such as Fresca and Tab, also came with player caps. The final cap in the set, which is numbered with the "C" prefix, is the Falcons team cap.

		NM
Complete Set (36):		80.00
Common Player:		2.00
1	Tommy Nobis	7.00
2	Ernie Wheelwright	3.00
3	Lee Calland	2.00
4	Chuck Sieminski	2.00
5	Dennis Claridge	2.00
6	Ralph Heck	2.00
7	Alex Hawkins	3.00
8	Dan Grimm	2.00
9	Marion Rushing	2.00
10	Bobbie Johnson	2.00
11	Bobby Franklin	2.00
12	Bill McWatters	2.00
13	Billy Lothridge	3.00
14	Billy Martin	2.00
15	Tom Wilson	2.00
16	Dennis Murphy	2.00
17	Randy Johnson	3.00
18	Guy Reese	2.00
19	Frank Marchlewski	2.00
20	Don Talbert	2.00
21	Errol Linden	2.00
22	Dan Lewis	2.00
23	Ed Cook	2.00
24	Hugh McInnis	2.00
25	Frank Lasky	2.00
26	Bob Jencks	2.00
27	Bill Jobko	2.00
28	Nick Rassas	2.00
29	Bob Riggle	2.00
30	Ken Reaves	2.00
31	Bob Sanders	2.00
32	Steve Sloan	3.00
33	Ron Smith	2.00
34	Bob Whitlow	2.00
35	Roger Anderson	2.00
36	Falcons Logo	2.00
NNO	Falcons Saver Sheet	20.00

1966 Coke Caps 49ers

The 36-cap, 1-1/8" set was issued to highlight members of the 49ers. A Cap Saver sheet was also available and could be redeemed for prizes upon completion. Tab and Fresca also had player caps. The cap tops featured the Coke logo with a football icon while the bottom had the player's image. The caps are numbered with the "C" prefix.

		NM
Complete Set (36):		80.00
Common Player:		2.00
1	Bernie Casey	3.00
2	Bruce Bosley	2.00
3	Kermit Alexander	3.00
4	John Brodie	8.00
5	Dave Parks	3.00
6	Len Rohde	2.00
7	Walter Rock	2.00
8	George Mira	4.00
9	Karl Rubke	2.00
10	Ken Willard	4.00
11	John David Crow (UER, Name misspelled Crowe)	3.00
12	George Donnelly	2.00
13	Dave Wilcox	3.00
14	Vern Burke	2.00
15	Wayne Swinford	2.00
16	Elbert Kimbrough	2.00
17	Clark Miller	2.00
18	Dave Kopay	3.00
19	Joe Cerne	2.00
20	Roland Lakes	2.00
21	Charlie Krueger	2.00
22	Billy Kilmer	4.00
23	Jim Johnson	5.00
24	Matt Hazeltine	2.00
25	Mike Dowdle	2.00
26	Jim Wilson	2.00
27	Tommy Davis	2.00
28	Jim Norton	2.00
29	Jack Chapple	2.00
30	Ed Beard	2.00
31	John Thomas	2.00
32	Monty Stickles	2.00
33	Kay McFarland	2.00
34	Gary Lewis	2.00
35	Howard Mudd	2.00
36	49ers Logo	2.00
NNO	49ers Saver Sheet	20.00

1966 Coke Caps National NFL

The 70-cap, 1-1/8" set was available in mostly non-NFL cit-

1966 Coke Caps Giants

The 35-cap, 1-1/8" set highlights top Giants players and was issued with a Cap Saver sheet, which when completed, could be redeemed for various prizes. The cap is similar in design to previous cap issues, complete with the Coke logo. The caps are numbered with a "G" prefix.

		NM
Complete Set (35):		80.00
Common Player:		2.00
1	Joe Morrison	3.00
2	Dick Lynch	3.00
3	Pete Case	2.00
4	Clarence Childs	2.00
5	Aaron Thomas	2.00
6	Jim Carroll	2.00
7	Henry Carr	3.00
8	Bookie Bolin	2.00
9	Roosevelt Davis	2.00
10	John Lovetere	2.00
11	Jim Patton	3.00
12	Wendell Harris	2.00
13	Roger LaLonde	2.00
14	Jerry Hillebrand	2.00
15	Spider Lockhart	3.00
16	Del Shofner	3.00
17	Earl Morrall	5.00
18	Roosevelt Brown	5.00
19	Greg Larson	2.00
20	Jim Katcavage	3.00
21	Smith Reed	2.00
22	Lou Slaby	2.00
23	Jim Moran	2.00
24	Bill Swain	2.00
25	Steve Thurlow	2.00
26	Olen Underwood	2.00
27	Gary Wood	3.00
28	Larry Vargo	2.00
29	Jim Prestel (Cap saver sheet reads Ed Prestel)	2.00
30	Tucker Frederickson	3.00
31	Bob Timberlake	2.00
32	Chuck Mercein	3.00
33	Ernie Koy	3.00
34	Tom Costello	2.00
35	Homer Jones	3.00
NNO	Giants Saver Sheet	20.00

1966 Coke Caps Jets

The 35-cap, 1-1/8" in diameter set, distributed in western New York, featured key Jets players, including Joe Namath. A Cap Saver sheet was issued to help collectors complete the set and when completed, could be redeemed for prizes. The caps are numbered with a "J" prefix.

		NM
Complete Set (35):		120.00
Common Player:		2.00
1	Don Maynard	10.00
2	George Sauer Jr.	4.00
3	Paul Crane	2.00
4	Jim Colclough	2.00
5	Matt Snell	4.00
6	Sherman Lewis	2.00
7	Jim Turner	2.00
8	Mike Taliaferro	2.00
9	Cornell Gordon	2.00
10	Mark Smolinski	2.00
11	Al Atkinson	4.00
12	Paul Rochester	2.00
13	Sherman Plunkett	2.00
14	Gerry Philbin	4.00
15	Pete Lammons	4.00
16	Dainard Paulson	2.00
17	Joe Namath	45.00
18	Winston Hill	2.00
19	Dee Mackey	2.00
20	Curley Johnson	2.00
21	Verlon Biggs	2.00
22	Bill Mathis	4.00
23	Carl McAdams	2.00
24	Bert Wilder	2.00
25	Larry Grantham	4.00
26	Bill Yearby	2.00
27	Sam DeLuca	2.00
28	Bill Baird	2.00
29	Ralph Baker	2.00
30	Ray Abruzzese	2.00
31	Jim Hudson	2.00
32	Dave Herman	2.00
33	John Schmitt	2.00
34	Jim Harris	2.00
35	Bake Turner	4.00
NNO	Jets Saver Sheet	20.00

1966 Coke Caps Oilers

The 36-cap, 1-1/8" set featured the top players from the Oilers and was distributed in the Houston area. A Cap Saver sheet was also issued, and when redeemed, the collector could earn prizes. Fresca and Tab products also had the player caps. The caps are numbered with a "C" prefix.

		NM
Complete Set (36):		100.00
Common Player:		2.00
1	Scott Appleton	2.00
2	George Allen	4.00
3	Don Floyd	2.00
4	Ronnie Caveness	2.00
5	Jim Norton	2.00
6	Jacky Lee	4.00
7	George Blanda	10.00
8	Tony Banfield	2.00
9	George Rice	2.00
10	Charley Tolar	2.00
11	Bobby Jancik	2.00
12	Freddy Glick	2.00
13	Ode Burrell	2.00

The caps have the Coke logo and a football icon, while the bottoms have the player's image in black. The caps are numbered with a "C" prefix.

ies in addition to a Cap Saver sheet, which when redeemed, could earn collectors prizes. The cap tops have the Coke logo and a football icon, while the bottoms have the player's image in black. The caps are numbered with a "C" prefix.

		NM
Complete Set (70):		200.00
Common Player:		2.00
1	Larry Wilson	5.00
2	Frank Ryan	4.00
3	Norm Snead	4.00
4	Mel Renfro	4.00
5	Timmy Brown	4.00
6	Tucker Frederickson	2.00
7	Jim Bakken	2.00
8	Paul Krause	4.00
9	Irv Cross	4.00
10	Cornell Green	4.00
11	Pat Fischer	4.00
12	Bob Hayes	4.00
13	Charley Taylor	5.00
14	Pete Retzlaff	4.00
15	Jim Ringo	5.00
16	Maxie Baughan	4.00
17	Chuck Howley	4.00
18	John Wooten	2.00
19	Bob DeMarco	2.00
20	Dale Meinert	2.00
21	Gene Hickerson	2.00
22	George Andrie	2.00
23	Joe Rutgens	2.00
24	Bob Lilly	6.00
25	Sam Silas	2.00
26	Bob Brown (OT)	4.00
27	Dick Schafrath	2.00
28	Roosevelt Brown	6.00
29	Jim Houston	2.00
30	Paul Wiggin	2.00
31	Gary Ballman	2.00
32	Gary Collins	4.00
33	Sonny Randle	2.00
34	Charlie Johnson	4.00
35	Browns Logo	2.00
36	Packers Logo	2.00
37	Herb Adderley	6.00
38	Grady Alderman	2.00
39	Doug Atkins	4.00
40	Bruce Bosley	2.00
41	John Brodie	6.00
42	Roger Brown	2.00
43	Bill Brown	2.00
44	Dick Butkus	15.00
45	Lee Roy Caffey	4.00
46	John David Crow	4.00
47	Willie Davis	6.00
48	Mike Ditka	12.00
49	Joe Fortunato	2.00
50	John Gordy	2.00
51	Deacon Jones	6.00
52	Alex Karras	4.00
53	Dick LeBeau	2.00
54	Jerry Logan	2.00
55	John Mackey	4.00
56	Ed Meador	2.00
57	Tommy McDonald	2.00
58	Merlin Olsen	6.00
59	Jimmy Orr	2.00
60	Jim Parker	4.00
61	Dave Parks	2.00
62	Walter Rock	2.00
63	Gale Sayers	14.00
64	Pat Studstill	2.00
65	Fran Tarkenton	12.00
66	Mick Tinglehoff	2.00
67	Bob Vogel	2.00
68	Wayne Walker	2.00
69	Ken Willard	2.00
70	Willie Wood	5.00
NNO	National Saver Sheet	20.00

14	Walt Suggs	2.00
15	Bob McLeod	2.00
16	Johnny Baker	2.00
17	Danny Bradshaw	2.00
18	Gary Cutsinger	2.00
19	Doug Cline	2.00
20	Hoyle Granger	2.00
21	Bob Talamini	2.00
22	Don Trull	4.00
23	Charlie Hennigan	4.00
24	Sid Blanks	2.00
25	Pat Holmes	2.00
26	John Frongillo	2.00
27	John Whitehorn	2.00
28	George Kinney	2.00
29	Charles Frazier	2.00
30	Ernie Ladd	6.00
31	W.K. Hicks	2.00
32	Sonny Bishop	2.00
33	Larry Elkins	2.00
34	Glen Ray Hines	2.00
35	Bobby Maples	4.00
36	Oilers Logo	2.00
NNO	Oilers Saver Sheet	20.00

1966 Coke Caps Packers

The 36-cap, 1-1/8" set, issued in metropolitan areas in Wisconsin, was virtually identical in design to previous Coke player cap sets. A Cap Saver sheet was also available and a collector could redeem the completed sheet for various prizes. The caps are numbered with a "C" prefix.

		NM
Complete Set (36):		150.00
Common Player:		2.50
1	Herb Adderley	6.00
2	Lionel Aldridge	4.00
3	Bob Long	2.50
4	Willie Davis	6.00
5	Boyd Dowler	4.00
6	Marv Fleming	2.50
7	Ken Bowman	2.50
8	Tom Brown	2.50
9	Doug Hart	2.50
10	Steve Wright	2.50
11	Bill Anderson	2.50
12	Bill Curry	4.00
13	Tommy Crutcher	2.50
14	Fred Thurston	5.00
15	Elijah Pitts	5.00
17	Lloyd Voss	2.50
17	Lee Roy Caffey	4.00
18	Dave Robinson	2.50
19	Bart Starr	14.00
20	Ray Nitschke	8.00
21	Max McGee	5.00
22	Don Chandler	2.50
23	Richard Marshall	2.50
24	Ron Kostelnik	2.50
25	Carroll Dale	4.00
26	Hank Jordan	5.00
27	Bob Jeter	4.00
28	Bob Skoronski	2.50
29	Jerry Kramer	6.00
30	Willie Wood	6.00
31	Paul Hornung	14.00
32	Forrest Gregg	8.00
33	Zeke Bratkowski	4.00
34	Tom Moore	2.50
35	Jim Taylor	12.00
36	Packers Team Emblem	2.50
NNO	Packers Saver Sheet	20.00

1966 Coke Caps Patriots

The 36-cap, 1-1/8" in diameter set, distributed in the New England area, featured key players from the Patriots roster. A Cap Saver sheet was also issued to aid collectors in completing the set, which could then be redeemed for various prizes. The caps are numbered with a "C" prefix.

		NM
Complete Set (36):		75.00
Common Player:		2.00
1	Jon Morris	2.00
2	Don Webb	2.00
3	Charles Long	2.00
4	Tony Romeo	2.00
5	Bob Dee	2.00
6	Tommy Addison	4.00
7	Tom Neville	2.00
8	Ron Hall	2.00
9	White Graves	2.00
10	Ellis Johnson	2.00
11	Don Oakes	2.00
12	Tom Yewcic	2.00
13	Tom Hennessey	2.00
14	Jay Cunningham	2.00

15	Larry Garron	4.00
16	Justin Canale	2.00
17	Art Graham	4.00
18	Babe Parilli	4.00
19	Jim Hunt	2.00
20	Karl Singer	2.00
21	Houston Antwine	2.00
22	Nick Buoniconti	6.00
23	John Huarte	4.00
24	Gino Cappelletti	4.00
25	Chuck Shonta	2.00
26	Dick Felt	2.00
27	Mike Dukes	2.00
28	Larry Eisenhauer	2.00
29	Jim Fraser	2.00
30	Len St. Jean	2.00
31	J.D. Garrett	2.00
32	Jim Whalen	2.00
33	Jim Nance	4.00
34	Rick Arrington	2.00
35	Lonnie Farmer	2.00
36	Patriots Logo	2.00
NNO	Patriots Saver Sheet	20.00

1966 Coke Caps Rams

The 36-cap, 1-1/8" set features a Coke logo and a football icon on the cap top, as do the previous player cap sets. The cap insides depict a facial image of the player in black. Other Coke products, such as Fresca and Tab, also had the player caps. The caps are numbered with a "C" prefix.

		NM
Complete Set (36):		100.00
Common Player:		2.00
1	Tom Mack	5.00
2	Tom Moore	2.00
3	Bill Munson	3.00
4	Bill George	5.00
5	Joe Carollo	2.00
6	Dick Bass	3.00
7	Ken Iman	2.00
8	Charlie Cowan	2.00
9	Terry Baker	4.00
10	Don Chuy	2.00
11	Jack Pardee	5.00
12	Lamar Lundy	3.00
13	Bill Anderson	2.00
14	Roman Gabriel	6.00
15	Roosevelt Grier	6.00
16	Billy Truax	3.00
17	Merlin Olsen	8.00
18	Deacon Jones	7.00
19	Joe Scibelli	2.00
20	Marlin McKeever	2.00
21	Doug Woodlief	2.00
22	Chuck Lamson	2.00
23	Dan Currie	2.00
24	Maxie Baughan	3.00
25	Bruce Gossett	3.00
26	Les Josephson	3.00
27	Ed Meador	2.00
28	Anthony Guillory	2.00
29	Irv Cross	4.00
30	Tommy McDonald	3.00
31	Bucky Pope	2.00
32	Jack Snow	4.00
33	Joe Wendryhoski	2.00
34	Clancy Williams	2.00
35	Ben Wilson	2.00
36	Rams Logo	2.00
NNO	Rams Saver Sheet	20.00

1966 Coke Caps Steelers

The 36-cap, 1-1/8" set featured key players from the Steelers squad with the Coke logo and a football stamp on the cap top. The player's image was printed in black on the cap inside. A Cap Saver sheet was also issued and a completed sheet could be redeemed for various prizes. The caps are numbered with a "C" prefix.

		NM
Complete Set (36):		80.00
Common Player:		2.00
1	John Baker	2.00
2	Mike Lind	3.00
3	Ken Kortas	2.00
4	Willie Daniel	2.00
5	Roy Jefferson	3.00
6	Bob Hohn	2.00
7	Dan James	2.00
8	Gary Ballman	3.00
9	Brady Keys	2.00
10	Charley Bradshaw	2.00
11	Jim Bradshaw	2.00
12	Jim Butler	2.00
13	Paul Martha	4.00
14	Mike Clark	2.00
15	Ray Lemek	2.00

16	Clarence Peaks	3.00
17	Theron Sapp	2.00
18	Ray Mansfield	2.00
19	Chuck Hinton	2.00
20	Bill Nelsen	3.00
21	Rod Breedlove	2.00
22	Frank Lambert	2.00
23	Ben McGee	2.00
24	Myron Pottios	2.00
25	John Campbell	2.00
26	Andy Russell	4.00
27	Mike Sandusky	2.00
28	Bob Schmitz	2.00
29	Riley Gunnels	2.00
30	Clendon Thomas	3.00
31	Tommy Wade	2.00
32	Dick Hoak	3.00
33	Marv Woodson	2.00
34	Bob Nichols	2.00
35	John Henry Johnson	5.00
36	Steelers Logo	2.00
NNO	Steelers Saver Sheet	20.00

1971 Coke Caps Packers

The 22-cap, 1-1/8" set, issued in 1971, featured twist-off caps as well as the basic bottle opener cap. The twist-off cap is valued at twice the listings below. As with past Coke player sets, a Cap Saver sheet was issued to help collectors in completing the set.

		NM
Complete Set (22):		50.00
Common Player:		1.50
1	Ken Bowman	1.50
2	John Brockington	3.00
3	Bob Brown (DT)	1.50
4	Fred Carr	1.50
5	Jim Carter	1.50
6	Carroll Dale	1.50
7	Ken Ellis	1.50
8	Gale Gillingham	1.50
9	Dave Hampton	1.50
10	Doug Hart	1.50
11	Jim Hill	1.50
12	Dick Himes	1.50
13	Scott Hunter	1.50
14	MacArthur Lane	3.00
15	Bill Lueck	1.50
16	Al Matthews	1.50
17	Rich McGeorge	1.50
18	Ray Nitschke	5.00
19	Francis Peay	1.50
20	Dave Robinson	3.00
21	Alden Roche	1.50
22	Bart Starr	14.00

1981 Coke Caps

The 15-cap set was issued by Coke in conjunction with a collector contest, which distributed prizes to consumers who completed a column on the Cap Saver sheet. The prize for finding all seven caps from the middle row was $1,000, while the five caps in the third row earned the collector a "Mean" Joe Greene jersey. The first column required four caps and awarded a T-shirt. The most difficult caps to obtain were of Ed "Too Tall" Jones, Steve Fuller and Gene Upshaw. The caps were skip numbered.

		MT
Complete Set (15):		30.00
Common Player:		1.00
1	Joe Greene	3.00
3	Steve Grogan	1.50
6	Mike Siani	1.00
11	Dan Fouts	3.00
12	Wesley Walker	1.50
23	Harold Carmichael	1.50
30	Greg Pruitt	1.00
38	Gene Upshaw (SP)	
47	Steve Fuller (SP)	
49	Walter Payton (SP)	7.00
53	Ed "Too Tall" Jones (SP)	
107	Benny Barnes	1.00
108	Billy Sims	2.00
127	Robert Newhouse	1.00
146	Charlie Waters	1.00

> Post-1980 cards in Near Mint condition will generally sell for about 75% of the quoted Mint value. Excellent-condition cards bring no more than 40%.

1996 Corinthian Headliners Football

The 40-piece inaugural football set from Corinthian Marketing features top players such as Brett Favre, Emmitt Smith, Troy Aikman and Dan Marino and is available in single blister card packages.

		MT
Complete Set (40):		250.00
Common Player:		5.00
Special Pack Not Included In Set Price		
	Troy Aikman	10.00
	Marcus Allen	5.00
	Drew Bledsoe	10.00
	Tim Brown	5.00
	Cris Carter	5.00
	Kerry Collins	5.00
	John Elway	8.00
	Marshall Faulk	5.00
	Brett Favre	12.00
	Jeff George	5.00
	Kevin Greene	5.00
	Charles Haley	5.00
	Jim Harbaugh	5.00
	Jeff Hostetler	5.00
	Stan Humphries	5.00
	Daryl Johnston	5.00
	Jim Kelly	5.00
	Leon Lett	5.00
	Greg Lloyd	5.00
	Dan Marino	10.00
	Steve McNair	10.00
	Natrone Means	5.00
	Rick Mirer	5.00
	Nate Newton	5.00
	Jay Novacek	5.00
	Neil O'Donnell	5.00
	Jerry Rice	10.00
	Rashaan Salaam	5.00
	Barry Sanders	10.00
	Deion Sanders	6.00
	Junior Seau	5.00
	Heath Shuler	5.00
	Bruce Smith	5.00
	Emmitt Smith	10.00
	Kordell Stewart	15.00
	Ricky Watters	5.00
	Reggie White	5.00
	Kevin Williams	5.00
	Darren Woodson	5.00
	Steve Young	8.00
	QB's 4-Pack (Troy Aikman, Brett Favre, Dan Marino, Steve Young)	20.00

1997 Corinthian Headliners Football

		MT
Complete Set (40):		220.00
Common Player:		5.00
Special Packs Not Included In Set Price		
	Troy Aikman	6.00
	Marcus Allen	5.00
	Bill Bates	5.00
	Jerome Bettis	8.00
	Drew Bledsoe	6.00
	Robert Brooks	6.00
	Tim Brown	6.00
	Isaac Bruce	6.00
	Mark Brunell	8.00
	Cris Carter	5.00
	Mark Chmura	5.00
	Kerry Collins	5.00
	Brett Favre	8.00
	Gus Frerotte	5.00
	Eddie George	8.00
	Jeff George	5.00
	Kevin Greene	5.00
	Jim Harbaugh	5.00
	Jeff Hostetler	5.00
	Michael Irvin	6.00
	Keyshawn Johnson	6.00
	Greg Lloyd	5.00
	Dan Marino Away	7.00

	Dan Marino Home	7.00
	Curtis Martin	10.00
	Steve McNair	8.00
	Natrone Means	5.00
	Ken Norton Jr.	5.00
	Neil O'Donnell	5.00
	Jerry Rice	6.00
	Rashaan Salaam	5.00
	Deion Sanders	5.00
	Junior Seau	5.00
	Bruce Smith	5.00
	Emmitt Smith	7.00
	Kordell Stewart	10.00
	Vinny Testaverde	5.00
	Ricky Watters	5.00
	Reggie White	5.00
	Steve Young	5.00
	AFC QB 4-Pack (Drew Bledsoe, John Elway, Jim Harbaugh, Dan Marino)	20.00
	NFC QB 4-Pack (Troy Aikman, Kerry Collins, Brett Favre, Steve Young)	20.00
	RB's 4-Pack (Terry Allen, Marshall Faulk, Rashaan Salaam, Emmitt Smith)	20.00
	WR's 4-Pack (Cris Carter, Keyshawn Johnson, Jerry Rice, Deion Sanders)	20.00
	Heroes/Gridiron Set (Kerry Collins, Kevin Greene, Deion Sanders, Reggie White)	20.00

1993-95 Highland Mint Topps

The 19-card, standard-size set released over three years features Topps cards in bronze, silver and gold (cards that were minted in gold are listed as the first of three figures). Each card has a serial number along the bottom border and came with a certificate of authenticity.

		MT
Common Player (19):		50.00
Silver Cards:		3x-5x
Gold Cards:		5x-7x
1	Troy Aikman (1989 Topps Traded) (375/500/2500)	75.00
2	Marcus Allen (1983 Topps) (88/549)	60.00
3	Jerome Bettis (1993 Topps) (301/1566)	50.00
4	Drew Bledsoe (1993 Topps) (375/500/2500)	75.00
5	John Elway (1984 Topps) (500/2020)	60.00
6	Marshall Faulk (1994 Topps) (530/2500)	60.00
7	Brett Favre (1992 Topps) (110/714)	100.00
8	Michael Irvin (1989 Topps) (509/1633)	60.00
9	Jim Kelly (1987 Topps) (419/1165)	60.00
10	Dan Marino (1984 Topps) (375/500/2500)	100.00
11	Natrone Means (1993 Topps) (136/1026)	50.00
12	Rick Mirer (1993 Topps) (384/1982)	50.00
13	Jerry Rice (1986 Topps) (375/750/2500)	75.00
14	Barry Sanders (1989 Topps Traded) (375/750/2500)	75.00
15	Deion Sanders (1989 Topps Traded) (191/1033)	60.00
16	Sterling Sharpe (1989 Topps Traded) (171/901)	50.00
17	Emmitt Smith (1990 Topps) (375/500/2500)	100.00
18	Lawrence Taylor (1982 Topps) (585/1630)	50.00
19	Steve Young (1986 Topps) (375/500/2500)	60.00

1994-95 Highland Mint Legends Collection

The four-card, standard-size set was designed and produced by Highland Mint and came in both bronze and silver versions.

		MT
Common Player (4):		50.00
Silvers:		4x-5x
1	Joe Namath	50.00
2	Gale Sayers	50.00
3	Roger Staubach	50.00
4	Johnny Unitas	50.00

1994-96 Highland Mint Silver Medallions

The 27-medallion set features 12 Quarterback Club members, as well as six other top players. Each medallion weighs one troy ounce (.999 pure silver) and is individually numbered. The mintage was limited to 7,500, to commemorate the NFL's 75th anniversary. The medallions were delivered in plastic capsules within a velvet box. The medallion fronts feature a player likeness while the backs contain a team logo and player statistics.

		MT
Common Medallion (27):		20.00
1	Troy Aikman	30.00
2	Jerome Bettis	30.00
3	Drew Bledsoe	30.00
4	John Elway	25.00
5	Marshall Faulk	25.00
6	Michael Irvin	20.00
7	Jim Kelly	20.00
8	Dan Marino	40.00
9	Natrone Means	20.00
10	Rick Mirer	20.00
11	Jerry Rice	30.00
12	Barry Sanders	30.00
13	Deion Sanders (49ers)	22.00
14	Junior Seau	20.00
15	Emmitt Smith	40.00
16	Heath Shuler	25.00
17	Thurman Thomas	20.00
18	Steve Young	25.00
19	Brett Favre	40.00
20	Joe Montana	30.00
21	Heath Shuler	20.00
22	Trent Dilfer	20.00
23	Kerry Collins	30.00
24	Deion Sanders (Cowboys)	25.00
25	Rashaan Salaam	20.00
26	Joe Namath	20.00
27	Curtis Martin	30.00

1995 Highland Mint Gold Medallions

The solid-gold medallions retailed for $1,395 each and had the player's likeness on the front with league and team logos with statistics on the back. Limited to 100 each.

		MT
1	Dan Marino	1350.
2	Emmitt Smith	1350.

1995-96 Highland Mint Bronze Medallions

Each of the nine medallions retailed for $10 each with production at 25,000 each. As with other Highland Mint medallions, the pieces are packaged in a plastic capsule and within a velvet box and come with a certificate of authenticity.

		MT
Common Medallion (9):		10.00
1	Troy Aikman	10.00
2	Drew Bledsoe	10.00
3	Brett Favre	14.00
4	Dan Marino	14.00
5	Joe Montana	14.00
6	Jerry Rice	10.00
7	Deion Sanders	10.00
8	Emmitt Smith	14.00
9	Steve Young	10.00

1995-96 Highland Mint Pinnacle/ Upper Deck

The two-year set features Upper Deck and Pinnacle cards in bronze (4.25 ounces), silver (4.25) and gold (24kt.). Cards with just silver and bronze versions have two production numbers listed while cards with gold, silver and bronze versions have three production numbers noted.

	MT
Common Player (9):	50.00
Gold Cards:	9x-12x
Silver Cards:	3.5x-4.5x
1 Troy Aikman (1989 Score) (1,000/5,000)	50.00
2 Drew Bledsoe (1994 Score Sophomore Showcase) (1,000/5,000)	50.00
3 Dan Marino (1994 Pinnacle) (500/1,000/5,000)	75.00
4 Joe Montana (1992 Upper Deck) (500/1,000/5,000)	50.00
5 Errict Rhett (1994 Pinnacle) (500/2,500)	50.00
6 Jerry Rice (1995 Zenith Z-Team) (500/2,500)	50.00
7 Rashaan Salaam (1995 Pinnacle) (500/2,500)	50.00
8 Heath Shuler (1994 Pinnacle) (500/2,500)	50.00
9 Emmitt Smith (1990 Score) (1,000/5,000)	75.00

1996 Highland Mint Football Medallions

The two football-shaped medallions (1-7/8" x 1-1/8") retailed for $29.95 with a production total of 7,500.

	MT
Common Medallion (2):	30.00
1 Dan Marino	30.00
2 Emmitt Smith	30.00

1996 Highland Mint Gold Signature Series Medallions

The two-tone silver medallions have gold plating on the face and have a retail of $49.95 with a production total of 1,500.

	MT
Common Medallion (3):	50.00
1 Troy Aikman	50.00
2 Dan Marino	50.00
3 Emmitt Smith	50.00

1988 Starting Lineup Football

The 1988 set was Kenner's first issue in football, with 137 players released. The figures were sold in single blister packs which included a card of the player. Prices are for mint condition packages.

	MT
Complete Set (137):	8200.00
Common Piece:	35.00
Collector Stand:	30.00
Marcus Allen	85.00
Neal Anderson	35.00
Chip Banks	100.00

Mark Bavaro	55.00
Cornelius Bennett	175.00
Albert Bentley	75.00
Duane Bickett	100.00
Todd Blackledge	60.00
Brian Bosworth	40.00
Brian Brennan	60.00
Bill Brooks	70.00
James Brooks	60.00
Eddie Brown	60.00
Joey Browner	60.00
Aundray Bruce	60.00
Chris Burkett	125.00
Keith Byars	50.00
Scott Campbell	140.00
Carlos Carson	70.00
Harry Carson	50.00
Anthony Carter	75.00
Gerald Carter	40.00
Michael Carter	65.00
Tony Casillas	75.00
Jeff Chadwick	75.00
Deron Cherry	70.00
Ray Childress	100.00
Todd Christensen	100.00
Gary Clark	75.00
Mark Clayton	100.00
Cris Collinsworth	100.00
Doug Cosbie	125.00
Roger Craig	40.00
Randall Cunningham	
Jeff Davis	40.00
Ken Davis	120.00
Richard Dent	50.00
Eric Dickerson	75.00
Floyd Dixon	55.00
Tony Dorsett	275.00
Mark Duper	90.00
Tony Eason	175.00
Carl Ekern	80.00
Henry Ellard	55.00
John Elway	250.00
Phillip Epps	90.00
Boomer Esiason	80.00
Jim Everett	50.00
Brent Fullwood	80.00
Mark Gastineau	40.00
Willie Gault	110.00
Bob Golic	100.00
Jerry Gray	75.00
Darrell Green	240.00
Jacob Green	125.00
Roy Green	70.00
Steve Grogan	100.00
Ronnie Harmon	150.00
Bobby Hebert	150.00
Alonzo Highsmith	40.00
Drew Hill	40.00
Earnest Jackson	75.00
Rickey Jackson	80.00
Vance Johnson	50.00
Ed Jones	140.00
James Jones	50.00
Rod Jones	40.00
Rulon Jones	40.00
Steve Jordan	60.00
E.J. Junior	75.00
Jim Kelly	200.00
Bill Kenney	100.00
Bernie Kosar	40.00
Tommy Kramer	75.00
Dave Krieg	200.00
Tim Krumrie	100.00
Mark Lee	80.00
Ronnie Lippett	50.00
Louis Lipps	125.00
Neil Lomax	125.00
Chuck Long	60.00
Howie Long	125.00
Ronnie Lott	145.00
Kevin Mack	40.00
Mark Malone	175.00
Dexter Manley	40.00
Dan Marino	250.00
Eric Martin	50.00
Rueben Mayes	50.00
Jim McMahon	75.00
Freeman McNeil	40.00
Karl Mecklenburg	50.00
Mike Merriweather	80.00
Stump Mitchell	60.00
Art Monk	275.00
Joe Montana	240.00
Warren Moon	80.00
Stanley Morgan	50.00
Joe Morris	40.00
Darrin Nelson	60.00
Ozzie Newsome	100.00
Ken O'Brien	40.00
John Offerdahl	125.00
Christian Okoye	50.00
Mike Quick	40.00
Jerry Rice	375.00
Gerald Riggs	40.00
Reggie Rogers	50.00
Mike Rozier	40.00
Jay Schroeder	75.00
Mickey Shuler	40.00
Phil Simms	50.00
Mike Singletary	40.00
Bill Ray Smith	75.00
Bruce Smith	175.00
J.T. Smith	60.00
Troy Stradford	110.00
Lawrence Taylor	80.00
Vinnie Testaverde	75.00
Andre Tippett	40.00

Anthony Toney	40.00
Al Toon	40.00
Jack Trudeau	125.00
Herschel Walker	50.00
Curt Warner	40.00
Dave Waymer	75.00
Charles White	40.00
Danny White	100.00
Randy White	200.00
Reggie White	125.00
James Wilder	40.00
Doug Williams	50.00
Marc Wilson	225.00
Sammy Winder	40.00
Kellen Winslow	425.00
Rod Woodson	400.00
Randy Wright	150.00

1989 Starting Lineup Football

The 1989 set includes 123 players and is identifiable by the black-bordered cards. Included in the set is former New York Jets quarterback Ken O'Brien with his name misspelled.

	MT
Complete Set (122):	7000.00
Common Piece:	30.00
Set price does not include O'Brien Err.	

Marcus Allen	50.00
Neal Anderson	30.00
Carl Banks	125.00
Bill Bates	350.00
Mark Bavaro	40.00
Cornelius Bennett	75.00
Duane Bickett	175.00
Bennie Blades	125.00
Bubby Brister	60.00
Bill Brooks	80.00
James Brooks	40.00
Eddie Brown	50.00
Jerome Brown	300.00
Tim Brown	90.00
Joey Browner	75.00
Kelvin Bryant	50.00
Jim Burt	150.00
Keith Byars	50.00
Dave Cadigan	300.00
Anthony Carter	40.00
Michael Carter	40.00
Chris Chandler	80.00
Gary Clark	35.00
Shane Conlan	100.00
Jimbo Covert	300.00
Roger Craig	30.00
Randall Cunningham	60.00
Richard Dent	30.00
Hanford Dixon	125.00
Chris Doleman	125.00
Tony Dorsett	150.00
Dave Duerson	65.00
John Elway	200.00
Boomer Esiason	50.00
Jim Everett	30.00
Thomas Everett	175.00
Sean Farrell	225.00
Bill Fralic	250.00
Irving Fryar	175.00
David Fulcher	125.00
Ernest Givins	60.00
Alex Gordon	125.00
Charles Haley	200.00
Bobby Hebert	50.00
Johnny Hector	100.00
Drew Hill	30.00
Dalton Hilliard	40.00
Bryan Hinkle	350.00
Michael Irvin	125.00
Keith Jackson	50.00
Garry James	50.00
Sean Jones	90.00
Jim Kelly	250.00
Joe Kelly	75.00
Bernie Kosar	30.00
Tim Krumrie	150.00
Louis Lipps	150.00
Eugene Lockhart	150.00
James Lofton	100.00
Neil Lomax	40.00
Chuck Long	30.00
Howie Long	77.00
Ronnie Lott	100.00
Kevin Mack	30.00
Pete Mandley	30.00
Dexter Manley	30.00
Charles Mann	30.00
Lionel Manuel	30.00
Dan Marino	275.00

Leonard Marshall	100.00
Eric Martin	50.00
Rueben Mayes	50.00
Vann McElroy	60.00
Dennis McKinnon	100.00
Jim McMahon	30.00
Steve McMichael	300.00
Erik McMillan	60.00
Freeman McNeil	30.00
Keith Millard	100.00
Chris Miller	60.00
Frank Minnifield	100.00
Art Monk	80.00
Joe Montana	150.00
Warren Moon	75.00
Joe Morris	30.00
Anthony Munoz	225.00
Ricky Nattiel	40.00
Darrin Nelson	30.00
Danny Noonan	125.00
Ken O'Brien	30.00
Ken O'Brien error (Misspelled)	100.00
Steve Pelluer	100.00
Mike Quick	30.00
Andre Reed	125.00
Jerry Rice	60.00
Mike Rozier	40.00
Jay Schroeder	40.00
John Settle	60.00
Mickey Shuler	30.00
Phil Simms	30.00
Mike Singletary	30.00
Webster Slaughter	45.00
Bruce Smith	150.00
Chris Spielman	275.00
John Stephens	35.00
Kelly Stouffer	40.00
Pat Swilling	60.00
Lawrence Taylor	60.00
Vinny Testaverde	55.00
Thurman Thomas	180.00
Andre Tippett	40.00
Anthony Toney	30.00
Al Toon	30.00
Garin Veris	250.00
Herschel Walker	30.00
Curt Warner	40.00
Reggie White	60.00
Doug Williams	30.00
John Williams	100.00
Wade Wilson	100.00
Ickey Woods	30.00
Rod Woodson	350.00
Steve Young	375.00

1989 Starting Lineup Football Helmets

Kenner issued four different packages of NFL helmets: AFC Offensive, AFC Defensive, NFC Offensive and NFC Defensive. Every NFL team was included in the product, which was designed to provide SLU collectors with extra helmets. The offensive and defensive face masks differ.

	MT
Complete Set (4):	275.00

1990 Starting Lineup Football

The third release of Starting Lineup football includes 66 players and is highlighted by rookie pieces of Troy Aikman, Barry Sanders and Deion Sanders. The figures of Neal Anderson, Roger Craig, John Elway, Boomer Esiason, Bernie Kosar, Joe Montana, Mike Singletary and Reggie White each have different jersey versions (home and away).

	MT
Complete Set (66):	2000.00
Common Piece:	15.00
Set price does not include home uniforms	
Troy Aikman	80.00
Neal Anderson blue (Blue Uni.)	20.00
Neal Anderson white (White Uni.)	20.00
Mark Bavaro	75.00
Steve Beuerlein	45.00
Bubby Brister	75.00
James Brooks	30.00
Tim Brown	80.00
Cris Carter	275.00
Roger Craig red (Red Uni.)	25.00
Roger Craig white (White Uni.)	25.00
Randall Cunningham	30.00
Hart Lee Dykes	100.00
John Elway orange (Orange Uni.)	85.00
John Elway white (White Uni.)	85.00
Boomer Esiason black (Black Uni.)	20.00
Boomer Esiason white (White Uni.)	20.00
Jim Everett	15.00
Simon Fletcher	150.00
Doug Flutie	260.00
Dennis Gentry	50.00
Dan Hampton	100.00
Jim Harbaugh	75.00
Rodney Holman	60.00
Bobby Humphrey	25.00
Michael Irvin	60.00
Bo Jackson	16.00
Keith Jackson	25.00
Vance Johnson	30.00
Jim Kelly	35.00
Bernie Kosar brown (Brown Uni.)	20.00
Bernie Kosar white (White Uni.)	20.00
Louis Lipps	75.00
Don Majkowski	20.00
Charles Mann	50.00
Lionel Manuel	20.00
Dan Marino	250.00
Tim McGee	20.00
David Meggett	20.00
Mike Merriweather	75.00
Eric Metcalf	25.00
Keith Millard	35.00
Joe Montana red (Red Uni.)	75.00
Joe Montana white (White Uni.)	75.00
Warren Moon	35.00
Christian Okoye	20.00
Tom Rathman	75.00
Andre Reed	30.00
Gerald Riggs	15.00
Mark Rypien	20.00
Barry Sanders	180.00
Deion Sanders	50.00
Ricky Sanders	15.00
Clyde Simmons	100.00
Phil Simms	15.00
Mike Singletary blue (Blue Uni.)	30.00
Mike Singletary white (White Uni.)	30.00
Webster Slaughter	20.00
Bruce Smith	90.00
John Stephens	30.00
John Taylor	20.00
Thurman Thomas	40.00
Mike Tomczak	20.00
Greg Townsend	75.00
Odessa Turner	25.00
Herschel Walker	20.00
Steve Walsh	50.00
Reggie White green (Green Uni.)	40.00
Reggie White white (White Uni.)	30.00
Wade Wilson	50.00
Ickey Woods	50.00
Donnell Woolford	60.00
Tim Worley	75.00
Felix Wright	75.00

1991 Starting Lineup Football

The 1991 Starting Lineup set included just 26 figures and each blister card also contained a card and a coin of the featured player. The set is highlighted by Emmitt Smith's first appearance in Starting Lineup.

	MT
Complete Set (26):	550.00
Troy Aikman	80.00
Flipper Anderson	15.00
Neal Anderson	15.00
James Brooks	15.00
Eddie Brown	15.00
Mark Carrier	18.00
Boomer Esiason	15.00
James Francis	20.00
Jeff George	22.00
Rodney Hampton	25.00
Jim Harbaugh	50.00
Jeff Hostetler	25.00
Bobby Humphrey	14.00
Don Majkowski	18.00
Dan Marino	125.00
David Meggett	14.00
Joe Montana	30.00
Warren Moon	24.00
Christian Okoye	10.00
Jerry Rice	40.00
Andre Rison	25.00
Barry Sanders	80.00
Phil Simms	15.00
Emmitt Smith	175.00
Thurman Thomas	24.00
Herschel Walker	15.00

1991 Starting Lineup FB Headline Collection

The 1991 Headline series was the first for Kenner's football series. The six-figure set includes Joe Montana and Dan Marino.

	MT
Complete Set (6):	200.00
John Elway	100.00
Boomer Esiason	18.00
Dan Marino	110.00
Joe Montana	50.00
Jerry Rice	50.00
Barry Sanders	60.00

1992 Starting Lineup Football

Kenner's 1992 football set included 26 players and each blister card arrived with a card and a folded poster.

	MT
Complete Set (26):	425.00
Troy Aikman	45.00
Earnest Byner	12.00
Randall Cunningham	18.00
Rodney Hampton	15.00
Bobby Hebert	15.00
Jeff Hostetler	15.00
Michael Irvin	18.00
Bo Jackson	15.00
Haywood Jeffires	12.00
Seth Joyner	15.00
Jim Kelly	15.00
Ronnie Lott	25.00

Dan Marino	100.00
Joe Montana	40.00
Warren Moon	20.00
Rob Moore	12.00
Jerry Rice	35.00
Andre Rison	15.00
Mark Rypien	10.00
Barry Sanders	60.00
Deion Sanders	24.00
Emmitt Smith	80.00
Pat Swilling	12.00
Derrick Thomas	25.00
Thurman Thomas	15.00
Steve Young	65.00

1992 Starting Lineup FB Headline Collection

Kenner's second and last issue of the Headline series, the six-figure set includes Emmitt Smith and Barry Sanders.

	MT
Complete Set (6):	125.00
Joe Montana	25.00
Warren Moon	18.00
Mark Rypien	12.00
Barry Sanders	50.00
Emmitt Smith	60.00
Thurman Thomas	25.00

1993 Starting Lineup Football

Each blister card of the 1993 Starting Lineup release came with two cards. Notable first releases in the 27-player set include Ricky Watters and Junior Seau.

	MT
Complete Set (27):	325.00
Troy Aikman	30.00
Cornelius Bennett	10.00
Randall Cunningham	15.00
Chris Doleman	10.00
John Elway	90.00
Barry Foster	12.00
Michael Irvin	15.00
Rickey Jackson	8.00
Cortez Kennedy	15.00
David Klingler	12.00
Chip Lohmiller	12.00
Russell Maryland	12.00
Anthony Miller	12.00
Chris Miller	10.00
Joe Montana	50.00
Warren Moon blue (Blue Uni.)	20.00
Warren Moon white (White Uni.)	14.00
Andre Reed	12.00
Barry Sanders	40.00
Deion Sanders	15.00
Junior Seau	10.00
Sterling Sharpe	30.00
Emmitt Smith	25.00
Neil Smith	10.00
Pete Stoyanovich	15.00
Ricky Watters	18.00
Rod Woodson	20.00
Steve Young	25.00

1994 Starting Lineup Football

Kenner's 1994 Starting Lineup football set features 32 players, including first-year releases of Jerome Bettis, Drew Bledsoe, Brett Favre, Garrison Hearst and Rick Mirer.

	MT
Complete Set (32):	525.00
Troy Aikman	20.00
Jerome Bettis	30.00
Drew Bledsoe	60.00
Randall Cunningham	12.00
Boomer Esiason	10.00
Brett Favre	130.00
Barry Foster	8.00
Rodney Hampton	10.00
Ronnie Harmon	8.00
Garrison Hearst	15.00
Raghib Ismail	15.00
Brent Jones	10.00
Cortez Kennedy	10.00
Nick Lowery	10.00
Dan Marino	40.00
Eric Metcalf	10.00
Rick Mirer	12.00
Joe Montana	35.00
Ken Norton	12.00
Jerry Rice	20.00
Andre Rison	10.00
Barry Sanders	35.00
Deion Sanders	10.00
Junior Seau	10.00
Phil Simms	10.00
Emmitt Smith	35.00
Lawrence Taylor	15.00
Chris Warren	12.00
Lorenzo White	10.00
Reggie White	20.00
Rod Woodson	15.00
Steve Young	20.00

1995 Starting Lineup Football

The 1995 release includes 33 players and the rookie pieces of Marshall Faulk and Shannon Sharpe. Also included in the set is the final Joe Montana figure, depicted in a Kansas City Chiefs uniform.

	MT
Complete Set (33):	400.00
Troy Aikman	20.00
Jerome Bettis	18.00
Drew Bledsoe	25.00
Steve Christie	12.00
Ben Coates	20.00
Randall Cunningham	10.00
Willie Davis	10.00
Jim Everett	10.00
Marshall Faulk	35.00
Brett Favre	35.00
Irving Fryar	15.00
Jeff George	10.00
Stan Humphries	12.00
Michael Irvin	18.00
Johnny Johnson	10.00
Seth Joyner	12.00
Greg Lloyd	20.00
Dan Marino	30.00
Terry McDaniel	10.00
Natrone Means	18.00
Scott Mitchell	12.00
Joe Montana	50.00
Warren Moon	12.00
Hardy Nickerson	12.00
Michael Dean Perry	12.00
Jerry Rice	16.00
Barry Sanders	25.00

Deion Sanders	12.00
Shannon Sharpe	20.00
Emmitt Smith	30.00
Dan Wilkinson	17.00
Steve Young	15.00
Chris Zorich	10.00

1996 Starting Lineup Football

Kenner's 1996 football set includes 38 players and is highlighted by the regional Brett Favre and Troy Aikman releases. Favre's figure was available exclusively through the Wisconsin-based Shopko stores while an Aikman version was found at the Texas-based Albertson's chain. Rookie figures include Mark Brunell, Kerry Collins and Kordell Stewart.

	MT
Complete Set (38):	450.00
Troy Aikman	20.00
Troy Aikman Albertson	25.00
Troy Aikman Blue Star	300.00
Terry Allen	15.00
Steve Beuerlein	15.00
Jeff Blake	15.00
Drew Bledsoe	15.00
Steve Bono	12.00
Kyle Brady	12.00
Robert Brooks	15.00
Dave Brown	10.00
Isaac Bruce	25.00
Mark Brunell	35.00
Mark Carrier	10.00
Cris Carter	15.00
Kerry Collins	15.00
John Elway	30.00
Marshall Faulk	15.00
Brett Favre Shopko	35.00
Joey Galloway	24.00
Kevin Greene	15.00
Dan Marino	35.00
Steve McNair	30.00
Eric Metcalf	10.00
Jay Novacek	14.00
Bryce Paup	12.00
Carl Pickens	15.00
Frank Reich	12.00
Errict Rhett	12.00
Jerry Rice	15.00
Rashaan Salaam	8.00
Barry Sanders	30.00
Deion Sanders	10.00
Junior Seau	10.00
Emmitt Smith	35.00
Chris Spielman	15.00
Kordell Stewart	30.00
Ricky Watters	15.00
Reggie White	15.00
Harvey Williams	12.00
Steve Young	12.00

1997 Starting Lineup Football

1997 Kenner Starting Lineup Football featured 43 figures in the set, including the rookie pieces of Eddie George, Curtis Martin and Herman Moore. The cards for this set were produced by Kenner.

	MT
Complete Set (43):	550.00
Karim Abdul-Jabbar	15.00
Troy Aikman	12.00

Jamal Anderson	30.00
Jerome Bettis	12.00
Jeff Blake	10.00
Drew Bledsoe	15.00
Terry Bradshaw Hill's	16.00
Mark Brunell	12.00
Dale Carter	10.00
Larry Centers	10.00
Mark Chmura	10.00
Kerry Collins	10.00
Brian Cox	10.00
Terrell Davis	125.00
Quinn Early	10.00
John Elway	20.00
Brett Favre	20.00
Eddie George	30.00
Jeff George	10.00
Elvis Grbac	10.00
Kevin Greene	10.00
Marvin Harrison	25.00
Jim Harbaugh	10.00
Brad Johnson	23.00
Keyshawn Johnson	30.00
Daryl Johnston	12.00
Dan Marino	15.00
Curtis Martin	40.00
Tony Martin	10.00
Herman Moore	25.00
Jerry Rice	10.00
Willie Roaf	10.00
Deion Sanders	10.00
Bruce Smith	10.00
Emmitt Smith	15.00
Emmitt Smith Alb.	20.00
Phillipi Sparks	10.00
Kordell Stewart	15.00
Vinny Testaverde	10.00
Eric Turner	10.00
Chris Warren	10.00
Ricky Watters	10.00
Michael Westbrook	16.00
Reggie White	10.00
Steve Young	12.00

1997 Starting Lineup FB Classic Doubles

Classic Doubles consists of nine pairs of regular-size Starting Lineup figures. The packaged figures come with two trading cards, one for each player, produced by Kenner.

	MT
Complete Set (9):	225.00
F. Biletnikoff, T. Brown	35.00
T. Dorsett, E. Smith	30.00
B. Favre, B. Starr	25.00
B. Favre, B. Starr (SB Sticker)	25.00
D. Marino, B. Griese	25.00
J. Montana, D. Clark	25.00
J. Montana, J. Rice	25.00
W. Payton, B. Sanders	110.00
R. Staubach, T. Aikman	35.00

1997 Starting Lineup Football Gridiron Greats

Gridiron Greats is a nine figure set. These SLUs stand seven-inches tall. They do not come with a trading card.

	MT
Complete Set (9):	200.00
Brett Favre	30.00
Kevin Greene	15.00
Dan Marino	30.00
Joe Montana	25.00
Jerry Rice	25.00
Deion Sanders	20.00
Emmitt Smith	20.00
Thurman Thomas	15.00
Ricky Watters	18.00

1997 Starting Lineup FB Heisman Contenders

Heisman Contenders is a nine-figure set designed like the regular Starting Lineup series. The figures are painted wearing their college uniform. Each figure comes with a miniature replica of the Heisman Trophy.

	MT
Complete Set (9):	120.00
Tony Dorsett (1976)	12.00
Doug Flutie (1984)	16.00
Eddie George (1995)	20.00
Archie Griffin (1974-75)	10.00
Bo Jackson (1985)	12.00
Steve Owens (1969)	12.00
Johnny Rodgers (1972)	10.00
Barry Sanders (1988)	20.00
Danny Wuerffel (1996)	12.00

1998 Starting Lineup Football

1998 Kenner Starting Lineup Football featured 42 figures in the set, including the rookie pieces of Corey Dillon, Antonio Freeman and Antowain Smith.

	MT
Complete Set (42):	450.00
Troy Aikman	12.00
Terry Allen	10.00
Jerome Bettis	15.00
Drew Bledsoe	10.00
Tony Boselli	20.00
Derrick Brooks	20.00
Mark Brunell	12.00
Kerry Collins	10.00
Terrell Davis	25.00
Trent Dilfer	10.00
Corey Dillon	15.00
John Elway	16.00
Brett Favre	14.00
Antonio Freeman	18.00
Gus Frerotte	14.00
Joey Galloway	15.00
Eddie George	15.00
Terry Glenn	16.00
Elvis Grbac	10.00
Raymont Harris	10.00
Bobby Hoying	14.00
Carnell Lake	18.00
Lamar Lathon	10.00
Dan Marino	15.00
Randall McDaniel	20.00
Chester McGlockton	20.00
Scott Mitchell	7.00
Adrian Murrell	15.00
Nate Newton	20.00
Jonathan Ogden	20.00
Orlando Pace	22.00
Carl Pickens	12.00
Jerry Rice	12.00
Simeon Rice	10.00
Barry Sanders Special	25.00
Deion Sanders	12.00
Antowain Smith	15.00
Emmitt Smith	15.00
Kordell Stewart Special	18.00
Dana Stubblefield	15.00
Vinny Testaverde	12.00
Tyrone Wheatley	15.00
Reggie White	10.00
Steve Young	12.00

1998 Starting Lineup Football Extended

The 10-figure set includes the first figures of Mike Alstott, Ryan Leaf, Peyton Manning and Charles Woodson. The figures are packaged with a full-color collectable card.

	MT
Complete Set (10):	180.00
Common Player:	10.00
Mike Alstott	24.00
Terrell Davis	26.00
Jim Harbaugh	10.00
Ryan Leaf	10.00
Peyton Manning	65.00
Curtis Martin	16.00
Steve McNair	16.00
Deion Sanders	15.00
Shannon Sharpe	16.00
Charles Woodson	18.00

1998 Starting Lineup Football Classic Doubles

Classic Doubles consists of eight pairs of regular-size Starting Lineup figures. The packaged figures come with two trading cards, one for each player, produced by Kenner.

	MT
Complete Set (8):	170.00
Troy Aikman, Emmitt Smith	28.00
Marcus Allen, Mike Garrett	20.00
John Elway, Dan Marino	35.00
Joe Namath, Don Maynard	20.00
Jerry Rice, Steve Young	25.00
Deion Sanders, Herb Adderly	20.00
Junior Seau, Dick Butkus	25.00
Y.A. Tittle, Sam Huff	20.00

1998 Starting Lineup FB Classic Doubles QB Club

Each player in this six-figure set belongs to the QB Club.

	MT
Complete Set (6):	150.00
Drew Bledsoe	15.00
John Elway	25.00
Jim Harbaugh	15.00
Dan Marino	30.00
Emmitt Smith	25.00
Steve Young	25.00

1998 Starting Lineup Football Gridiron Greats

Gridiron Greats is a seven-figure set. They stand seven-inches tall and don't come with a trading card.

	MT
Complete Set (7):	150.00
Troy Aikman	20.00
Drew Bledsoe	25.00
Mark Brunell	25.00
John Elway	28.00
Barry Sanders	30.00
Junior Seau	20.00
Steve Young	20.00

1998 Starting Lineup Football Hall of Fame

The 11-figure set includes NFL players from the past, except for Vince Lombardi, and shows them in their old uniforms.

	MT
Complete Set (11):	100.00
Dick Butkus	12.00
Larry Csonka	12.00
Joe Greene	12.00
Deacon Jones	12.00
Bob Lilly	12.00
Vince Lombardi	18.00
Ray Nitschke	15.00
Gale Sayers	12.00
Bart Starr	12.00
Y.A. Tittle	10.00
Gene Upshaw	12.00

1998 Starting Lineup Football Heisman Contenders

Heisman Contenders is a 10-figure set designed like the

regular Starting Lineup series. The figures are painted wearing their college uniforms.

	MT
Complete Set (10):	100.00
Marcus Allen	10.00
Earl Campbell	10.00
John Cappelletti	10.00
Glenn Davis	8.00
Paul Hornung	12.00
Desmond Howard	8.00
Rashaan Salaam	8.00
Roger Staubach	12.00
Herschel Walker	12.00
Charles Woodson	15.00

1998 Starting Lineup Football 12" Figures

Each one of the five figures in this set measure 12-inches tall and come with complete gear. No cards were issued with these figures.

	MT
Complete Set (5):	100.00
Drew Bledsoe	25.00
John Elway	30.00
Brett Favre	30.00
Dan Marino	30.00
Jerry Rice	25.00

1999 Starting Lineup Football

This set was released in five different assortments and included the first figure of Randy Moss. Other players that had their first figures in the set included Warren Sapp, Jake Plummer, Dorsey Levens and Zach Thomas. Each figure came packaged with a regular sized trading card.

	MT
Complete Set (36):	450.00
Common Player:	10.00
Troy Aikman	10.00
Drew Bledsoe	10.00
Mark Brunell	12.00
Chris Chandler	12.00
Wayne Chrebet	12.00
Randall Cunningham	12.00

	MT
Terrell Davis	15.00
Dermontti Dawson	20.00
Corey Dillon	10.00
Warrick Dunn	15.00
John Elway	12.00
Curtis Enis	12.00
Brett Favre	10.00
Doug Flutie	14.00
Eddie George	15.00
Napoleon Kaufman	15.00
Ryan Leaf	10.00
Dorsey Levens	15.00
Peyton Manning	20.00
Dan Marino	12.00
Curtis Martin	12.00
Randy Moss	65.00
Jake Plummer	20.00
Jerry Rice	10.00
Andre Rison	10.00
Barry Sanders	12.00
Barry Sanders Meijer's	16.00
Warren Sapp	20.00
Emmitt Smith	10.00
Jimmy Smith	14.00
Neil Smith	10.00
Robert Smith	20.00
Kordell Stewart	10.00
Eric Swann	12.00
Zach Thomas	30.00
Ricky Watters	10.00
Steve Young	10.00

1999 Starting Lineup Football Extended

This release included eight figures, with seven of them being rookie figures. The top rookie figures included Ricky Williams, Tim Couch and Fred Taylor. There was only one assortment with 12 figures per case. There were three Williams figures per case. Each figure came packaged with a trading card of that player.

		MT
Complete Set (8):		120.00
Common Player:		12.00
1	Jamal Anderson	12.00
2	*Charlie Batch*	15.00
3	*Tim Couch*	30.00
4	*Ed McCaffery*	15.00
5	*Donovan McNabb*	18.00
6	*John Randle*	15.00

7	*Fred Taylor*	20.00
8	*Ricky Williams*	20.00

1999 Starting Lineup Football 12" Figures

Five of the top NFL stars were included in this set. These figures varied from the regular Starting Lineup figures and included such stars as Brett Favre and Terrell Davis.

	MT
Complete Set (5):	100.00
Terrell Davis	30.00
Brett Favre	25.00
Barry Sanders	30.00
Kordell Stewart	25.00
Steve Young	25.00

1999 Starting Lineup Football Classic Doubles

This set consisted of 10 pairs of figures. The pairs of players were stars from different NFL teams, including Randy Moss and Cris Carter of the Minnesota Vikings and John Elway and Terrell Davis of the Denver Broncos. The only variation from that theme was the pairing of Archie and Peyton Manning in one packaage.

	MT
Complete Set (10):	250.00
Cris Carter, Randy Moss	35.00
Jack Lambert, Jack Ham	18.00
Earl Campbell, Eddie George	15.00
Anthony Munoz, Boomer Esiason	15.00
John Elway, Terrell Davis	20.00
Mike Alstott, Warrick Dunn	15.00
Ken Stabler, Dave Casper	15.00
Archie Manning, Peyton Manning	30.00

Johnny Unitas, Rick Berry	15.00
Franco Harris, Jerome Bettis	15.00

1999 Starting Lineup Football Classic Doubles QB Club

The players in this 5-figure set all belong to the QB Club. Top players included Brett Favre and Troy Aikman.

	MT
Complete Set (5):	60.00
Troy Aikman	18.00
Terrell Davis	20.00
Brett Favre	18.00
Jake Plummer	18.00
Kordell Stewart	18.00

1999 Starting Lineup Football College Greats

This 9-figure set included top NFL players from the past and present in their college uniforms. The Heisman Trophy winners in the set had a small Heisman Trophy included in the packaging. The players in the set that did not win the Heisman Trophy had a small university pennant of the school they went to included in the packaging.

		MT
Complete Set (9):		100.00
1	Charlie Batch	20.00
2	Mark Brunell	15.00
3	Ernie Davis	10.00
4	Warrick Dunn	10.00
5	Curtis Martin	10.00
6	Randy Moss	35.00
7	Jim Plunkett	10.00
8	Charlie Ward	10.00
9	Ricky Williams	25.00

1999 Starting Lineup Football Gridiron Greats

This eight-figure set included mostly the top NFL players from the present. Dick Butkus was also included in the set.

	MT
Complete Set (8):	100.00
Dick Butkus	15.00
Terrell Davis	20.00
Warrick Dunn	16.00
Eddie George	20.00
Dan Marino	18.00
Curtis Martin	15.00
Barry Sanders	15.00
Kordell Stewart	15.00

COLLEGE

1993 Air Force Smokey

		MT
Complete Set (16):		15.00
Common Player:		.75
1	Fisher DeBerry (CO)	1.00
2	Dee Dowler	2.50
3	Chad Hennings	5.00
4	Carlton MacDonald	1.00
5	Terry Maki	1.00
6	Reggie Minton	1.00
7	Air Force Falcon	.75
8	Air Force Thunderbirds	.75
9	Cadet Field House	.75
10	Chapel	.75
11	Color Guard	.75
12	Commander-in-Chief's Trophy	.75
13	Drum and Bugle Corp	.75
14	Falcon Stadium	.75
15	Parachute Team	.75
16	Talon T-38	.75

1971 Alabama Team Sheets

		NM
Complete Set (6):		45.00
Common Player:		6.00
1	Mike Raines, Pat Raines, Terry Rowell, Gary Rutledge, Bubba Sawyer, Bill Sexton, Wayne Wheeler, Jack White, Steve	8.00
2	Johnny Musso, Lanny Norris, Robin Parkhouse, Jim Patterson, Steve Root, Jimmy Rosser, Jeff Rouzie, Robby Rowan, Steve Wade, David Watkins	10.00
3	Fred Marshall, Noah Miller, John Mitchell, Randy Moore, Gary Reynolds, Benny Rippetoe, Ronny Robertson, John, Steve Sprayberry, Rod Steakley	6.00
4	Richard Bryan, Chip Burke, Jerry Cash, Don Cokely, Greg Gantt, Jim Grammer, Wayne Hall, John Hannah, Rand Lambert, , David McMakin	8.00
5	Ellis Beck, Steve Bisceglia, Jeff Blitz, Buddy Brown, Steve Dean, Mike Denson, Joe Doughty, Mike Eckenrod, Pat, Joe LaBue	6.00
6	Wayne Adkinson, David Bailey, Marvin Barron, Jeff Beard, Andy Cross, John Croyle, Bill Davis, Terry Davis, Steve , Jimmy Horton, Wilbur Jackson	7.00

1972 Alabama

		NM
Complete Set (54):		95.00
Common Player:		1.50
1C	Skip Kubelius	1.50
1D	Terry Davis	2.50
1H	Robert Fraley	1.50
1S	Paul "Bear" Bryant (CO)	25.00
2C	David Watkins	1.50
2D	Bobby McKinney	1.50
2H	Dexter Wood	1.50
2S	Chuck Strickland	1.50
3C	John Hannah	15.00
3D	Tom Lusk	1.50
3H	Jim Krapf	1.50
3S	Warren Dyar	1.50
4C	Greg Gantt	2.50
4D	Johnny Sharpless	1.50
4H	Steve Wade	1.50
4S	John Rogers	1.50
5C	Doug Faust	1.50
5D	Jeff Rouzie	1.50
5H	Buddy Brown	1.50
5S	Randy Moore	1.50
6C	David Knapp	2.50
6D	Lanny Norris	1.50
6H	Paul Spivey	1.50
6S	Pat Raines	1.50
7C	Pete Pappas	1.50
7D	Ed Hines	1.50
7H	Mike Washington	1.50
7S	David McMakin	2.50
8C	Steve Dean	1.50
8D	Joe LaBue	1.50
8H	John Croyle	1.50
8S	Noah Miller	1.50
9C	Bobby Stanford	1.50
9D	Sylvester Croom	2.50
9H	Wilbur Jackson	6.00
9S	Ellis Beck	1.50
10C	Steve Bisceglia	1.50
10D	Andy Cross	1.50
10H	John Mitchell	2.50
10S	Bill Davis	1.50
11C	Gary Rutledge	2.50
11D	Randy Billingsley	1.50
11H	Randy Hall	1.50
11S	Ralph Stokes	1.50
12C	Jeff Blitz	1.50
12D	Robby Rowan	1.50
12H	Mike Raines	1.50
12S	Wayne Wheeler	1.50
13C	Steve Sprayberry	1.50
13D	Wayne Hall	2.50
13H	Morris Hunt	1.50
13S	Butch Norman	1.50
JK	Denny Stadium	1.50
JK	Memorial Coliseum	1.50

1973 Alabama

		NM
Complete Set (54):		80.00
Common Player:		1.50
1C	Skip Kubelius	1.50
1D	Mark Prudhomme	1.50
1H	Robert Fraley	1.50
1S	Paul "Bear" Bryant (CO)	20.00
2C	David Watkins	1.50
2D	Richard Todd	12.00
2H	Buddy Pope	1.50
2S	Chuck Strickland	1.50
3C	Bob Bryan	1.50
3D	Gary Hanrahan	1.50
3H	Greg Montgomery	1.50
3S	Warren Dyar	1.50
4C	Greg Gantt	2.50
4D	Johnny Sharpless	1.50
4H	Rick Watson	1.50
4S	John Rogers	1.50
5C	George Pugh	2.50
5D	Jeff Rouzie	1.50
5H	Buddy Brown	1.50
5S	Randy Moore	1.50
6C	Ray Maxwell	1.50
6D	Alan Pizzitola	1.50
6H	Paul Spivey	1.50
6S	Ron Robertson	1.50

1988 Alabama Winners

		MT
Complete Set (73):		10.00
Common Player:		.15
1	Title Card (Schedule on back)	.25
2	Charlie Abrams	.15
3	Sam Atkins	.15
4	Marco Battle	.15
5	George Bethune	.15
6	Scott Bolt	.15
7	Tommy Bowden	.15
8	Danny Cash	.15
9	John Cassimus	.15
10	David Casteal	.15
11	Terrill Chatman	.15
12	Andy Christoff	.15
13	Tommy Cole	.15
14	Tony Cox	.15
15	Howard Cross	.75
16	Bill Curry (CO)	.25
17	Johnny Davis	.25
18	Vantreise Davis	.15
19	Joe Demos	.15
20	Philip Doyle	.15
21	Jeff Dunn	.15
22	John Fruhmorgen	.15
23	Jim Fuller	.15
24	Greg Gilbert	.15
25	Pierce Goode	.25
26	John Guy	.15
27	Spencer Hammond	.15
28	Stacy Harrison	.15
29	Murry Hill	.15
30	Byron Holdbrooks	.15
31	Ben Holt	.15
32	Bobby Humphrey	.75
33	Gene Jelks	.50
34	Kermit Kendrick	.15
35	William Kent	.15
36	David Lenoir	.15
37	Butch Lewis	.15
38	Don Lindsey	.15
39	John Mangum	.50
40	Tim Matheny	.15
41	Mac McWhorter	.25
42	Chris Mohr	.25
43	Larry New	.15
44	Gene Newberry	.15
45	Lee Ozmint	.15
46	Trent Patterson	.15
47	Greg Payne	.15
48	Thomas Rayam	.15
49	Chris Robinette	.15
50	Larry Rose	.15
51	Derrick Rushton	.15
52	Lamonde Russell	.15
53	Craig Sanderson	.15
54	Wayne Shaw	.15
55	Willie Shepherd	.15
56	Roger Shultz	.15
57	David Smith	.15
58	Homer Smith	.15
59	Mike Smith	.15
60	Byron Sneed	.15
61	Robert Stewart	.15
62	Vince Strickland	.15
63	Brian Stutson	.15
64	Vince Sutton	.15
65	Derrick Thomas	5.00
66	Steve Turner	.15
67	Alan Ward	.15
68	Lorenzo Ward	.15
69	Steve Webb	.15
70	Woody Wilson	.15
71	Chip Wisdom	.15
72	Willie Wyatt	.15
73	Mike Zuga	.15

1989 Alabama Coke 20

		MT
Complete Set (20):		10.00
Common Player:		.35
C1	Paul "Bear" Bryant (CO)	1.50
C2	John Hannah	.75
C3	Fred Sington	.35
C4	Derrick Thomas	1.50
C5	Dwight Stephenson	.75
C6	Cornelius Bennett	1.00
C7	Ozzie Newsome	1.00
C8	Joe Namath (Art)	2.00
C9	Steve Sloan	.60
C10	Bill Curry (CO)	.35
C11	Paul "Bear" Bryant (CO)	1.50
C12	Big Al (Mascot)	.35
C13	Scott Hunter	.50
C14	Lee Roy Jordan	.75
C15	Walter Lewis	.35
C16	Bobby Humphrey	.35
C17	John Mitchell	.35
C18	Johnny Musso	.75
C19	Pat Trammell	.35
C20	Ray Perkins (CO)	.60

1989 Alabama Coke 580

ALABAMA'S FINEST

		MT
Complete Set (580):		35.00
Common Player:		.08
1	Paul "Bear" Bryant (CO)	.75
2	W.T. Van De Graff	.08
3	A.T.S. Hubert	.08
4	Bill Buckler	.08
5	Hoyt (Wu) Winslett	.08
6	Tony Holm	.08
7	Fred Sington Sr.	.15
8	John Suther	.08
9	Johnny Cain	.08
10	Tom Hupke	.15
11	Millard Howell	.25
12	Steve Wright	.08
13	Bill Searcy	.08
14	Riley Smith	.08
15	Arthur "Tarzan" White	.08
16	Joe Kilgrow	.08
17	Leroy Monsky	.08
18	James Ryba	.08
19	Carey Cox	.08
20	Holt Rast	.08
21	Joe Domnanovich	.08
22	Don Whitmire	.15
23	Harry Gilmer	.25
24	Vaughn Mancha	.08
25	Ed Salem	.08
26	Bobby Marlow	.30
27	George Mason	.08
28	Billy Neighbors	.25
29	Lee Roy Jordan	.50
30	Wayne Freeman	.08
31	Dan Kearley	.08
32	Joe Namath	1.00
33	David Ray	.15
34	Paul Crane	.08
35	Steve Sloan	.25
36	Richard Cole	.08
37	Cecil Dowdy	.15
38	Bobby Johns	.08
39	Ray Perkins	.30
40	Dennis Homan	.25
41	Ken Stabler	.60
42	Robert W. Boylston	.08
43	Mike Hall	.08
44	Alvin Samples	.08
45	Johnny Musso	.25
46	Bryant-Denny Stadium	.08
47	Tom Surlas	.08
48	John Hannah	.30
49	Jim Krapf	.08
50	John Mitchell	.15
51	Buddy Brown	.08
52	Woodrow Lowe	.15
53	Wayne Wheeler	.08
54	Leroy Cook	.08
55	Sylvester Croom	.15
56	Mike Washington	.08
57	Ozzie Newsome	.50
58	Barry Krauss	.15
59	Marty Lyons	.25
60	Jim Bunch	.08
61	Don McNeal	.15
62	Dwight Stephenson	.30
63	Bill Davis	.08
64	E.J. Junior	.15
65	Tommy Wilcox	.15
66	Jeremiah Castille	.15
67	Bobby Swafford	.08
68	Cornelius Bennett	.50
69	David Knapp	.15
70	Bobby Humphrey	.30
71	Van Tiffin	.08
72	Sid Smith	.08
73	Pat Trammell	.25
74	Mickey Andrews	.08
75	Steve Bowman	.08
76	Bob Baumhower	.25
77	Bob Cryder	.08
78	Bryon Braggs	.15
79	Warren Lyles	.08
80	Steve Mott	.08
81	Walter Lewis	.15
82	Ricky Moore	.08
83	Wes Neighbors	.08
84	Derrick Thomas	.75
85	Kermit Kendrick	.08
86	Larry Rose	.08
87	Charlie Marr	.08
88	James Whatley	.08
89	Erin Warren	.08
90	Charlie Holm	.08
91	Fred Davis	.08
92	John Wyhonic	.08
93	Jimmy Nelson	.08
94	Roy Steiner	.08
95	Tom Whitley	.08
96	John Wozniak	.08
97	Ed Holdnak	.08
98	Al Lary	.08
99	Mike Mizerany	.08
100	Pat O'Sullivan	.08
101	Jerry Watford	.08
102	Cecil Ingram	.08
103	Mike Fracchia	.08
104	Benny Nelson	.08
105	Tommy Tolleson	.08
106	Creed Gilmer	.08
107	John Calvert	.08
108	Derrick Slaughter	.08
109	Mike Ford	.08
110	Bruce Stephens	.08
111	Danny Ford	.25
112	Jimmy Grammer	.08
113	Steve Higginbotham	.08
114	David Bailey	.08
115	Greg Gantt	.25
116	Terry Davis	.15
117	Chuck Strickland	.08
118	Bobby McKinney	.08
119	Wilbur Jackson	.25
120	Mike Raines	.08
121	Steve Sprayberry	.08
122	David McMakin	.15
123	Ben Smith	.08
124	Steadman Shealy	.25
125	John Rogers	.08
126	Ricky Davis	.15
127	Conley Duncan	.08
128	Wayne Rhodes	.08
129	Buddy Seay	.08
130	Alan Pizzitola	.08
131	Richard Todd	.25
132	Charlie Ferguson	.08
133	Charley Hannah	.15
134	Wiley Barnes	.08
135	Mike Brock	.08
136	Murray Legg	.08
137	Wayne Hamilton	.08
138	David Hannah	.08
139	Jim Bob Harris	.08
140	Bart Krout	.08
141	Bob Cayavec	.08
142	Joe Beazley	.08
143	Mike Adcock	.08
144	Albert Bell	.08
145	Mike Shula	.40
146	Curt Jarvis	.08
147	Freddie Robinson	.08
148	Bill Condon	.08
149	Howard Cross	.30
150	Joe Demyanovich	.08
151	Major Ogilvie	.25
152	Perron Shoemaker	.08
153	Ralph Jones	.08
154	Vic Bradford	.08
155	Ed Hickerson	.08
156	Mitchell Olenski	.08
157	George Hecht	.08
158	Russ Craft	.08
159	Joey Jones	.25
160	Jack Green	.08
161	Lowell Tew	.15
162	Lamar Moye	.08
163	Jesse Richardson	.15
164	Harold Lutz	.08
165	Travis Hunt	.08
166	Ed Culpepper	.08
167	Nick Germanos	.08
168	Billy Rains	.08
169	Don Cochran	.08
170	Cotton Clark	.08
171	Gaylon McCollogh	.08
172	Tim Bates	.08
173	Wayne Cook	.08
174	Jerry Duncan	.08
175	Steve Davis	.08
176	Donnie Sutton	.08
177	Randy Barron	.08
178	Frank Mann	.08
179	Jeff Rouzie	.08
180	John Croyle	.08
181	Skip Kubelius	.08
182	Steve Bisceglia	.08
183	Gary Rutledge	.15
184	Mike Dubose	.08
185	Johnny Davis	.25
186	K.J. Lazenby	.08
187	Jeff Rutledge	.25
188	Mike Tucker	.08
189	Tony Nathan	.25
190	Buddy Aydelette	.08
191	Steve Whitman	.08
192	Ricky Tucker	.08
193	Randy Scott	.08
194	Warren Averitte	.08
195	Doug Vickers	.08
196	Jackie Cline	.08
197	Wayne Davis	.08
198	Hardy Walker	.08
199	Paul Ott Carruth	.15
200	Paul "Bear" Bryant (CO)	.75

No.	Player	Price
201	Randy Rockwell	.08
202	Chris Mohr	.15
203	Walter Merrill	.08
204	Johnny Sullivan	.08
205	Harold Newman	.08
206	Erskine Walker	.08
207	Ted Cook	.08
208	Charles Compton	.08
209	Bill Cadenhead	.08
210	Butch Avinger	.08
211	Bobby Wilson	.08
212	Sid Youngelman	.25
213	Leon Fuller	.08
214	Tommy Brooker	.15
215	Richard Williamson	.25
216	Riggs Stephenson	.25
217	Al Clemens	.08
218	Grant Gillis	.08
219	Johnny Mack Brown	.40
220	Major Ogilvie	.25
221	Fred Pickhard	.08
222	Herschel Caldwell	.08
223	Emile Barnes	.08
224	Mike McQueen	.08
225	Ray Abruzzese	.15
226	Jesse Bendross	.25
227	Lew Bostick	.08
228	Jimmy Bowdoin	.08
229	Dave Brown	.08
230	Tom Calvin	.08
231	Ken Emerson	.08
232	Calvin Frey	.08
233	Thornton Chandler	.15
234	George Weeks	.08
235	Randy Edwards	.08
236	Phillip Brown	.08
237	Clay Whitehurst	.08
238	Chris Goode	.08
239	Preston Gothard	.08
240	Herb Hannah	.08
241	John M. Snoderly	.08
242	Scott Hunter	.25
243	Bobby Jackson	.08
244	Bruce Jones	.08
245	Robbie Jones	.08
246	Terry Jones	.08
247	Leslie Kelley	.08
248	Larry Lauer	.08
249	'61 National Champs (Tommy Brooker, Pat Trammell, Lee Roy Jordan, Paul "Bear" Bryant, Mike Fracchia,	.25
250	Bobby Luna	.08
251	Keith Pugh	.08
252	Alan McElroy	.08
253	'25 National Champs (Team Photo)	.15
254	Curtis McGriff	.25
255	Norman Mosley	.08
256	Herky Mosley	.08
257	Ray Ogden	.15
258	Pete Jilleba	.08
259	Benny Perrin	.08
260	Claude Perry	.08
261	Tommy Cole	.08
262	Ed Versprille	.08
263	'30 National Champs (Team Photo)	.15
264	Don Jacobs	.08
265	Robert Skelton	.08
266	Joe Curtis	.08
267	Bart Starr	.75
268	Young Boozer	.08
269	Tommy Lewis	.15
270	Woody Umphrey	.08
271	Carney Laslie	.08
272	Russ Wood	.08
273	David Smith	.08
274	Paul Spivey	.08
275	Linnie Patrick	.08
276	Ron Durby	.08
277	'26 National Champs (Team Photo)	.15
278	Robert Higginbotham	.08
279	William Oliver	.08
280	Stan Moss	.08
281	Eddie Propst	.08
282	Laurien Stapp	.08
283	Clem Gryska	.08
284	Clark Pearce	.08
285	Pete Cavan	.08
286	Tom Newton	.08
287	Rich Wingo	.15
288	Rickey Gilliland	.08
289	Conrad Fowler	.08
290	Rick Neal	.08
291	James Blevins	.08
292	Dick Flowers	.08
293	Marshall Brown	.08
294	Jeff Beard	.08
295	Pete Moore	.08
296	Vince Boothe	.08
297	Charley Boswell	.08
298	Van Marcus	.08
299	Randy Billingsley	.08
300	Paul "Bear" Bryant (CO)	.75
301	Gene Blackwell	.08
302	Johnny Mosley	.08
303	Ray Perkins (CO)	.25
304	Harold Drew (CO)	.08
305	Frank Thomas (CO) (Not the Frank Thomas that went to Auburn)	.25
306	Wallace Wade	.15
307	Newton Godfree	.08
308	Steve Williams	.08
309	Al Lewis	.08
310	Fred Grant	.08
311	Jerry Brown	.08
312	Mal Moore	.15
313	Tilden Campbell	.08
314	Jack Smalley	.08
315	Paul "Bear" Bryant (CO)	.75
316	C.B. Clements	.08
317	Billy Piper	.08
318	Robert Lee Hamner	.08
319	Donnie Faust	.08
320	Gary Bramblett	.08
321	Pete Kim	.08
322	Fred Berrey	.08
323	Paul "Bear" Bryant (CO)	.75
324	John Fruhmorgen	.08
325	Jim Fuller	.08
326	Doug Allen	.08
327	Russ Mosley	.08
328	Ricky Thomas	.08
329	Vince Sutton	.08
330	Larry Roberts	.15
331	Rick McLain	.08
332	Charles Eckerly	.08
333	'34 National Champs (Team Photo)	.15
334	Eddie McCombs	.08
335	Scott Allison	.08
336	Vince Cowell	.08
337	David Watkins	.08
338	Jim Duke	.08
339	Don Harris	.08
340	Lanny Norris	.08
341	Thad Flanagan	.08
342	Albert Elmore	.08
343	Alan Gray	.08
344	David Gilmer	.08
345	Hal Self	.08
346	Ben McLeod	.08
347	Clell (Butch) Hobson	.50
348	Jimmy Carroll	.08
349	Frank Canterbury	.08
350	John Byrd Williams	.08
351	Marvin Barron	.08
352	William Stone	.08
353	Barry Smith	.15
354	Jerrill Sprinkle	.08
355	Hank Crisp (CO)	.08
356	Bobby Smith	.08
357	Charles Gray	.08
358	Marlin Dyess	.08
359	'41 National Champs (Team Photo)	.15
360	Robert Moore	.08
361	1961 National Champs (Billy Neighbors, Pat Trammell, Darwin Holt) (Team Photo)	.15
362	Tommy White	.08
363	Earl Wesley	.08
364	John O'Linger	.08
365	Bill Battle	.08
366	Butch Wilson	.08
367	Tim Davis	.08
368	Larry Wall	.08
369	Hudson Harris	.08
370	Mike Hopper	.08
371	Jackie Sherrill	.40
372	Tom Somerville	.08
373	David Chatwood	.08
374	George Ranager	.08
375	Tommy Wade	.25
376	'64 National Champs (Joe Namath)	.60
377	Reid Drinkard	.08
378	Mike Hand	.08
379	Ed White	.25
380	Angelo Stafford	.08
381	Ellis Beck	.08
382	Wayne Hall	.15
383	Randy Lee Hall	.08
384	Jack O'Rear	.08
385	Colenzo Hubbard	.08
386	Gus White	.08
387	Rich Watson	.08
388	Steve Allen	.08
389	John David Crow Jr.	.15
390	Britton Cooper	.08
391	Mike Rodriguez	.08
392	Steve Wade	.08
393	William J. Rice	.08
394	Greg Richardson	.08
395	Joe Jones	.15
396	Todd Richardson	.08
397	Antonio Smiley	.08
398	Duff Morrison	.08
399	Jay Grogan	.08
400	Steve Booker	.08
401	Larry Abney	.08
402	Bill Abston	.08
403	Wayne Adkinson	.08
404	Charles Allen	.08
405	Phil Allman	.08
406	1965 National Champs (1965 Seniors)	.25
407	James Angelich	.08
408	Troy Barker	.08
409	George Bethune	.08
410	Bill Blair	.08
411	Clark Boler	.08
412	Duffy Boles	.08
413	Ray Bolden	.08
414	Bruce Bolton	.08
415	Alvin Davis	.08
416	Baxter Booth	.08
417	Paul Boschung	.08
418	1979 National Champs (Team Photo)	.25
419	Richard Brewer	.08
420	Jack Brown	.08
421	Larry Brown	.08
422	David Brungard	.08
423	Jim Burkett	.08
424	Auxford Burks	.08
425	Jim Cain	.08
426	Dick Turpin	.08
427	Neil Callaway	.08
428	David Casteal	.08
429	Phil Chaffin	.08
430	Howard Chappell	.08
431	Bob Childs	.08
432	Knute Rockne Christian	.08
433	Richard Ciemny	.08
434	J.B. Whitworth	.08
435	Mike Clements	.08
436	1973 National Champs (Coaching Staff)	.08
437	Rocky Colburn	.08
438	Danny Collins	.08
439	James Taylor	.08
440	Joe Compton	.08
441	Bob Conway	.08
442	Charlie Stephens	.08
443	Kerry Goode	.15
444	Joe LaBue	.08
445	Allen Crumbley	.08
446	Bill Curry (CO)	.15
447	David Bedwell	.08
448	Jim Davis	.08
449	Mike Dean	.08
450	Steve Dean	.08
451	Vince DeLaurentis	.08
452	Gary Deniro	.08
453	Jim Dildy	.08
454	Joe Dildy	.08
455	Jimmy Dill	.08
456	Jamie Dismuke	.08
457	Junior Davis	.08
458	Warren Dyar	.08
459	Hugh Morrow	.08
460	Grady Elmore	.08
461	1978 National Champs (Jeff Rutledge, Tony Nathan, Barry Krauss, Marty Lyons, Rich Wingo)	.25
462	Ed Hines	.08
463	D. Joe Gambrell	.08
464	Kavanaugh (Kay) Francis	.08
465	Robert Fraley	.08
466	Milton Frank	.08
467	Jim Franko	.08
468	Buddy French	.08
469	Wayne Rhoads	.08
470	Ralph Gandy	.08
471	Danny Gilbert	.08
472	Greg Gilbert	.08
473	Joe Godwin	.08
474	Richard Grammer	.08
475	Louis Green	.08
476	Gary Martin	.08
477	Bill Hannah	.08
478	Allen Harpole	.08
479	Neb Hayden	.08
480	Butch Henry	.08
481	Norwood Hodges	.08
482	Earl Smith	.08
483	Darwin Holt	.08
484	Scott Homan	.08
485	Nathan Rustin	.08
486	Gene Raburn	.08
487	Ellis Houston	.08
488	Frank Howard	.08
489	Larry Hughes	.08
490	Joe Kelley	.08
491	Charlie Harris	.08
492	Legion Field	.08
493	Tim Hurst	.08
494	Hunter Husband	.08
495	Lou Ikner	.08
496	Craig Epps	.08
497	Jug Jenkins	.08
498	Billy Johnson	.08
499	David Johnson	.08
500	Jon Hand	.25
501	Max Kelley	.08
502	Terry Killgore	.08
503	Eddie Lowe	.08
504	Noah Langdale	.08
505	Ed Lary	.08
506	Foy Leach	.08
507	Harry Lee	.08
508	Jim Loftin	.08
509	Curtis Lynch	.08
510	John Mauro	.08
511	Ray Maxwell	.08
512	Frank McClendon	.08
513	Tom McCrary	.08
514	Sonny McGahey	.08
515	John McIntosh	.08
516	David McIntyre	.08
517	Wes Thompson	.08
518	James Melton	.08
519	John Miller	.08
520	Fred Mims	.08
521	Dewey Mitchell	.08
522	Lydell Mitchell (Linebacker)	.08
523	Greg Montgomery	.15
524	Jimmie Moore	.08
525	Randy Moore	.08
526	Ed Morgan	.08
527	Norris Hamer	.08
528	Frank Mosely	.08
529	Sidney Neighbors	.08
530	Rod Nelson	.08
531	James Nisbet	.08
532	Mark Nix	.08
533	L.W. Noonan	.08
534	Louis Thompson	.08
535	William Oliver	.08
536	Gary Otten	.08
537	Wayne Owen	.08
538	Steve Patterson	.08
539	Charley Pell	.25
540	Bob Pettee	.08
541	Gordon Pettus	.08
542	Gary Phillips	.08
543	Clay Walls	.08
544	Douglas Potts	.08
545	Mike Stock	.08
546	John Mark Prudhomme	.08
547	George Pugh	.15
548	Pat Raines	.08
549	Joe Riley	.08
550	Wayne Trimble	.08
551	Darryl White	.08
552	Bill Richardson	.08
553	Ray Richeson	.08
554	Danny Ridgeway	.08
555	Terry Sanders	.08
556	Kenneth Roberts	.08
557	Jimmy Watts	.08
558	Ronald Robertson	.08
559	Norbie Ronsonet	.08
560	Jimmy Lynn Rosser	.08
561	Terry Rowell	.08
562	Larry Joe Ruffin	.08
563	Jack Rutledge	.08
564	Al Sabo	.08
565	David Sadler	.08
566	Donald Sanford	.08
567	Hayward Sanford	.08
568	Paul Tripoli	.08
569	Lou Scales	.08
570	Kurt Schmissrauter	.08
571	Willard Scissum	.08
572	Joe Sewell	.15
573	Jimmy Sharpe	.08
574	Willie Shepherd	.08
575	Jack Smalley Jr.	.08
576	Jim Simmons (Tight End)	.08
577	Jim Simmons (Tackle)	.08
578	Malcolm Simmons	.08
579	Dave Sington	.08
580	Fred Sington Jr.	.15

1992 Alabama Greats Hoby

		MT
	Complete Set (42):	12.00
	Common Player:	.25
1	Bob Baumhower	.50
2	Cornelius Bennett	.75
3	Buddy Brown	.25
4	Paul "Bear" Bryant (CO)	.75
5	Johnny Cain	.25
6	Jeremiah Castille	.35
7	Leroy Cook	.25
8	Paul Crane	.35
9	Philip Doyle	.25
10	Harry Gilmer	.35
11	Jon Hand	.50
12	Herb Hannah	.25
13	John Hannah	.75
14	Dennis Homan	.35
15	Dixie Howell	.35
16	Bobby Humphrey	.35
17	Don Hutson	.75
18	Curt Jarvis	.35
19	Lee Roy Jordan	.75
20	Barry Krauss	.35
21	Woodrow Lowe	.35
22	Marty Lyons	.35
23	Vaughn Mancha	.25
24	John Mangum	.35
25	Bobby Marlow	.35
26	Don McNeal	.35
27	Chris Mohr	.35
28	Johnny Musso	.50
29	Billy Neighbors	.35
30	Ozzie Newsome	.75
31	Ray Perkins	.50
32	Fred Sington	.25
33	Ken Stabler	.75
34	Siran Stacy	.35
35	Dwight Stephenson	.50
36	Robert Stewart	.25
37	Derrick Thomas	1.00
38	Van Tiffin	.25
39	Mike Washington	.25
40	Arthur "Tarzan" White	.25
41	Tommy Wilcox	.35
42	Willie Wyatt	.25

1980 Arizona Police

		NM
	Complete Set (24):	90.00
	Common Player:	3.00
1	Brian Clifford	3.00
2	Mark Fulcher	3.00
3	Bob Gareeb	3.00
4	Marcellus Green	4.00
5	Drew Hardville	3.00
6	Neal Harris	3.00
7	Richard Hersey	3.00
8	Alfondia Hill	3.00
9	Tim Holmes	3.00
10	Jack Housley	3.00
11	Glenn Hutchinson	3.00
12	Bill Jensen	3.00
13	Frank Kalil	3.00
14	Dave Liggins	3.00
15	Tom Manno	3.00
16	Bill Nettling	3.00
17	Hubert Oliver	6.00
18	Glenn Perkins	3.00
19	John Ramseyer	3.00
20	Mike Robinson	3.00
21	Chris Schultz	4.00
22	Larry Smith (CO)	4.00
23	Reggie Ware (SP)	30.00
24	Bill Zivic	3.00

1981 Arizona Police

		MT
	Complete Set (27):	40.00
	Common Player:	2.00
1	Moe Ankney (ACO)	3.00
2	Van Brandon	2.00
3	Bob Carter	2.00
4	Brian Christiansen	2.00
5	Mark Fulcher	2.00
6	Bob Gareeb	2.00
7	Gary Gibson	2.00
8	Mark Gobel	2.00
9	Alfred Gross	2.00
10	Kevin Hardcastle	2.00
11	Neal Harris	2.00
12	Brian Holland	2.00
13	Ricky Hunley	4.00
14	Frank Kalil	2.00
15	Jeff Kiewel	2.00
16	Chris Knudsen	2.00
17	Ivan Lesnik	2.00
18	Tony Neely	2.00
19	Glenn Perkins	2.00
20	Randy Robbins	2.00
21	Gerald Roper	2.00
22	Chris Schultz	3.00
23	Gary Shaw	2.00
24	Larry Smith (CO)	2.00
25	Tom Tunnicliffe	3.00
26	Sergio Vega	3.00
27	Brett Weber	3.00

1982 Arizona Police

		MT
	Complete Set (26):	35.00
	Common Player:	1.50
1	Brad Anderson	1.50
2	Steve Boadway	1.50
3	Bruce Bush	1.50
4	Mike Freeman	1.50
5	Marsharne Graves	1.50
6	Courtney Griffin	1.50
7	Al Gross	2.00
8	Julius Holt	1.50
9	Lamonte Hunley	2.00
10	Ricky Hunley	2.50
11	Vance Johnson	5.00
12	Chris Kaesman	1.50
13	John Kaiser	1.50
14	Mark Keel	1.50
15	Jeff Kiewell	1.50
16	Ivan Lesnik	1.50
17	Glenn McCormick	1.50
18	Ray Moret	1.50
19	Tony Neely	1.50
20	Byron Nelson	1.50
21	Glenn Perkins	1.50
22	Randy Robbins	1.50
23	Larry Smith (CO)	2.00
24	Tom Tunnicliffe	1.50
25	Kevin Ward	1.50
26	David Wood	1.50

1983 Arizona Police

		MT
	Complete Set (24):	35.00
	Common Player:	1.50
1	John Barthalt	1.50
2	Steve Boadway	1.50
3	Chris Brewer	1.50
4	Lynnden Brown	1.50
5	Charlie Dickey	1.50
6	Jay Dobins	1.50
7	Joe Drake	1.50
8	Allan Durden	2.00
9	Byron Evans	5.00
10	Nils Fox	1.50
11	Mike Freeman	1.50
12	Marsharne Graves	1.50
13	Lamonte Hunley	2.00
14	Vance Johnson	4.00
15	John Kaiser	1.50
16	Ivan Lesnik	1.50
17	Byron Nelson	2.00
18	Randy Robbins	1.50
19	Craig Schiller	1.50
20	Larry Smith (CO)	2.00
21	Tom Tunnicliffe	2.00
22	Mark Walczak	1.50
23	David Wood	1.50
24	Max Zendejas	2.00

1984 Arizona Police

		MT
	Complete Set (25):	15.00
	Common Player:	.75
1	Alfred Jenkins	2.00
8	John Connor	1.00
13	Max Zendejas	1.00
15	Gordon Bunch	.75
19	Allen Durden	1.00
23	Lynnden Brown	.75
25	Vance Johnson	2.00
28	Tom Bayse	.75
35	Brent Wood	.75
40	Greg Turner	.75
47	Steve Boadway	.75
52	Nils Fox	.75
54	Craig Vesling	.75
62	David Connor	.75
67	Charlie Dickey	.75
78	Brian Denton	.75
79	John DuBose	.75
82	Joe Drake	.75
85	Joy Dobyns	.75
86	Mark Walczak	.75
92	David Wood	.75
98	Lamonte Hunley	1.00
99	John Barthalt	.75
NNO	Larry Smith (CO)	1.00

1985 Arizona Police

		MT
	Complete Set (23):	15.00
	Common Player:	.75
1	Alfred Jenkins	1.50
2	David Adams	.75
6	Chuck Cecil	2.00
13	Max Zendejas	1.00
15	Gordon Bunch	.75
18	Jeff Fairholm	1.00
19	Allen Durden	1.00
29	Don Be'ans	.75
32	Joe Prior	.75
42	Blake Custer	.75
44	Boomer Gibson	.75
48	Byron Evans	3.00
50	Val Bichekas	.75
52	Joe Tofflemire	1.00
54	Craig Vesling	.75
59	Jim Birmingham	.75
72	Curt DiGiacomo	.75
73	Lee Brunelli	.75
78	John DuBose	.75
83	Gary Parrish	.75
95	Cliff Thorpe	.75
96	Glenn Howell	.75
NNO	Larry Smith (CO)	1.00

1986 Arizona Police

		MT
	Complete Set (24):	15.00
	Common Player:	.75
1	David Adams	.75
2	Frank Arriola	.75
3	Val Biehekas	.75
4	Jim Birmingham	.75
5	Chuck Cecil	1.50
6	James Debow	.75
7	Brian Denton	.75
8	Byron Evans	2.00
9	Jeff Fairholm	1.00
10	Boomer Gibson	.75
11	Eugene Hardy	.75
12	Derek Hill	1.50
13	Jon Horton	.75
14	Alfred Jenkins	1.25
15	Danny Lockett	.75
16	Stan Mataele	.75
17	Chris McLemore	.75
18	Jeff Rinehart	.75
19	Ruben Rodriguez	1.00
20	Martin Rudolph	.75
21	Larry Smith (CO)	1.00
22	Joe Tofflemire	.75
23	Dana Wells	.75
24	Brent Wood	.75

1987 Arizona Police

Complete Set (23): MT 15.00
Common Player: .75

2	Bobby Watters	1.00
3	Doug Pfaff	.75
6	Chuck Cecil	1.50
11	Gary Coston	.75
18	Jeff Fairholm	1.00
22	Eugene Hardy	.75
26	Troy Cephers	.75
34	Charles Webb	.75
38	James Debow	.75
40	Art Greathouse	.75
43	Jerry Beasley	.75
44	Boomer Gibson	.75
47	Gallen Allen	.75
52	Joe Tofflemire	1.00
60	Jeff Rinehart	.75
64	Kevin McKinney	.75
68	Tom Lynch	.75
82	Derek Hill	1.25
84	Kevin Singleton	1.00
87	Chris Singleton	3.00
97	George Hinkle	.75
99	Dana Wells	.75
NNO	Dick Tomey (CO)	1.25

1988 Arizona Police

Complete Set (25): MT 15.00
Common Player: .75

2	Bobby Watters	1.00
4	Darryl Lewis	2.00
5	Durrell Jones	.75
8	Reggie McGill	.75
10	Ronald Veal	1.00
15	Jeff Hammerschmidt	.75
22	Scott Geyer	.75
24	R. Groppenbacher	.75
25	David Eldridge	.75
35	Mario Hampton	.75
38	James Debow	.75
40	Art Greathouse	.75
50	Darren Case	.75
51	Doug Penner	.75
52	Joe Tofflemire	1.00
63	John Brandom	.75
65	Ken Hakes	.75
74	Glenn Parker	1.25
78	Rob Woods	.75
82	Derek Hill	1.25
84	Kevin Singleton	1.00
87	Chris Singleton	2.00
96	Brad Henke	.75
99	Dana Wells	.75
NNO	Dick Tomey (CO)	1.00

1989 Arizona Police

Complete Set (26): MT 12.00
Common Player: .60

1	Zeno Alexander	.60
2	John Brandom	.60
3	Todd Burden	.60
4	Darren Case	.60
5	David Eldridge	.60
6	Nick Fineanganofo	.60
7	Scott Geyer	.60
8	Art Greathouse	.60
9	Richard Griffith	.60
10	Ken Hakes	.60
11	Jeff Hammerschmidt	.60
12	Mario Hampton	.60
13	Darryl Lewis	1.50
14	Kip Lewis	.60
15	George Malauulu	.75
16	Reggie McGill	.60
17	John Nies	.60
18	Glenn Parker	1.00
19	Mike Parker	.60
20	Doug Pfaff	.60
21	David Roney	.60
22	Pete Russell	.60
23	Chris Singleton	1.50
24	Paul Tofflemire	.60
25	Dick Tomey (CO)	.75
26	Ronald Veal	.75

1992 Arizona Police

Complete Set (21): MT 10.00
Common Player: .50

1	Tony Bouie	1.00
2	Heath Bray	.50
3	Charlie Camp	.50
4	Ontiwaun Carter	.60
5	Richard Griffith	.50
6	Sean Harris	.75
7	Mike Heemsbergen	.50
8	Jimmy Hopkins	.50
9	Billy Johnson	.50
10	Keshon Johnson	.50
11	Chuck Levy	1.25
12	Richard Maddox	.60
13	George Malauulu	.60
14	Darryl Morrison	.75
15	Mani Ott	.50
16	Ty Parten	.50
17	Mike Scurlock	.60
18	Warner Smith	.50
19	Dick Tomey (CO)	.60
20	Terry Vaughn	.50
21	Rob Waldrop	.75

1993 Army Smokey

Complete Set (15): MT 12.00
Common Player: .75

1	Paul Andrzejewski	.75
2	Kevin Czarnecki	.75
3	Chad Davis	.75
4	Glenn Davis	3.00
5	Mark Escobedo	.75
6	Gary Graves	.75
7	Leamon Hall	1.00
8	Jason Miller	1.00
9	Mike Plaia	.75
10	Rick Roper	1.00
11	Jim Slomka	.75
12	Bob Sutton (CO)	.75
13	Jason Sutton	.75
14	Pat Zelley	.75
15	Army Mule (Mascot)	.75

1972 Auburn Tigers

Complete Set (54): NM 70.00
Common Player: 1.50

1C	Ken Calleja	1.50
1D	James Owens	1.50
1H	Mac Lorendo	1.50
1S	Ralph (Shug) Jordan (CO)	6.00
2C	Rick Neel	1.50
2D	Ted Smith	1.50
2H	Eddie Welch	1.50
2S	Mike Neel	1.50
3C	Larry Taylor	1.50
3D	Rett Davis	1.50
3H	Rusty Fuller	1.50
3S	Lee Gross	1.50
4C	Bruce Evans	1.50
4D	Rusty Deen	1.50
4H	Johnny Simmons	1.50
4S	Bill Newton	1.50
5C	David Beverly	2.00
5D	Dave Lyon	1.50
5H	Mike Fuller	3.00
5S	Bill Luka	1.50
6C	Ken Bernich	1.50
6D	Andy Steele	1.50
6H	Wade Whatley	1.50
6S	Bob Newton	2.00
7C	Benny Sivley	2.00
7D	Gardner Jett	2.00
7H	Rob Spivey	2.00
7S	Jay Casey	1.50
8C	David Langner	1.50
8D	Terry Henley	1.50
8H	Thomas Gossom	1.50
8S	Joe Tanory	1.50
9C	Chris Linderman	1.50
9D	Harry Unger	1.50
9H	Kenny Burks	1.50
9S	Sandy Cannon	1.50
10C	Roger Mitchell	1.50
10D	Jim McKinney	1.50
10H	Gaines Lanier	1.50
10S	Dave Beck	1.50
11C	Bob Farrior	1.50
11D	Miles Jones	1.50
11H	Tres Rogers	1.50
11S	David Hughes	1.50
12C	Sherman Moon	1.50
12D	Danny Sanspree	1.50
12H	Steve Taylor	1.50
12S	Randy Walls	1.50
13C	Steve Wilson	1.50
13D	Bobby Davis	1.50
13H	Hamlin Caldwell	1.50
13S	Dan Nugent	1.50
JK	Joker - Auburn Memorial Coliseum	1.50
JK	Joker - Cliff Hare Stadium	1.50

1973 Auburn Tigers

Complete Set (54): NM 60.00
Common Player: 1.50

1C	Ken Calleja	1.50
1D	Chris Wilson	1.50
1H	Lee Hayley	1.50
1S	Ralph (Shug) Jordan (CO)	5.00
2C	Rick Neel	1.50
2D	Johnny Sumner	1.50
2H	Mitzi Jackson	1.50
2S	Jim Pitts	1.50
3C	Steve Stanaland	1.50
3D	Rett Davis	1.50
3H	Rusty Fuller	1.50
3S	Lee Gross	1.50
4C	Bruce Evans	1.50
4D	Rusty Deen	1.50
4H	Liston Eddins	1.50
4S	Bill Newton	1.50
5C	Jimmy Sirmans	1.50
5D	Harry Ward	1.50
5H	Mike Fuller	2.50
5S	Bill Luka	1.50
6C	Ken Bernich	1.50
6D	Andy Steele	1.50
6H	Wade Whatley	1.50
6S	Bob Newton	2.00
7C	Benny Sivley	2.00
7D	Rick Telhiard	2.00
7H	Rob Spivey	2.00
7S	David Williams	1.50
8C	David Langner	1.50
8D	Chuck Fletcher	1.50
8H	Thomas Gossom	1.50
8S	Holley Caldwell	1.50
9C	Chris Linderman	1.50
9D	Ed Butler	1.50
9H	Kenny Burks	1.50
9S	Mike Flynn	1.50
10C	Roger Mitchell	1.50
10D	Jim McKinney	1.50
10H	Gaines Lanier	1.50
10S	Carl Hubbard	1.50
11C	Bob Farrior	1.50
11D	Ronnie Jones	1.50
11H	Billy Woods	1.50
11S	David Hughes	1.50
12C	Sherman Moon	1.50
12D	Mike Gates	1.50
12H	Steve Taylor	1.50
12S	Randy Walls	1.50
13C	Roger Pruett	1.50
13D	Bobby Davis	1.50
13H	Hamlin Caldwell	1.50
13S	Dan Nugent	1.50
JK	Joker - Auburn Memorial Coliseum	1.50
JK	Joker - Cliff Hare Stadium	1.50

1989 Auburn Coke 20

Complete Set (20): MT 8.00
Common Player: .35

C1	Pat Dye (CO)	.50
C2	Zane Smith	.35
C3	War Eagle (Mascot)	.50
C4	Tucker Frederickson	.50
C5	John Heisman	.50
C6	Ralph (Shug) Jordan (CO)	.50
C7	Pat Sullivan	.50
C8	Terry Beasley	.35
C9	Punt Bama Punt (Ralph (Shug) Jordan, Paul "Bear" Bryant)	.50
C10	Retired Jerseys (Pat Sullivan, Terry Beasley)	.50
C11	Bo Jackson	2.00
C12	Lawyer Tillman	.75
C13	Gregg Carr	.35
C14	Lionel James	.50
C15	Joe Cribbs	.60
C16	Heisman Winners (Pat Sullivan, Bo Jackson, Pat Dye CO)	1.00
C17	Aundray Bruce	.50
C18	Aubie (Mascot)	.35
C19	Tracy Rocker	.35
C20	James Brooks	1.00

1989 Auburn Coke 580

Complete Set (580): MT 30.00
Common Player: .07

1	Pat Dye (CO) (His First Game)	.25
2	Auburn's First Team (1892 Team Photo)	.15
3	Pat Sullivan	.25
4	Over The Top (Bo Jackson)	.75
5	Jimmy Hitchcock	.07
6	Walter Gilbert	.07
7	Monk Gafford	.07
8	Frank D'Agostino	.07
9	Joe Childress	.15
10	Jim Pyburn	.15
11	Tex Warrington	.07
12	Travis Tidwell	.15
13	Fob James	.07
14	Jim Phillips	.15
15	Zeke Smith	.07
16	Mike Fuller	.15
17	Ed Dyas	.07
18	Jack Thornton	.07
19	Ken Rice	.07
20	Freddie Hyatt	.07
21	Jackie Burkett	.15
22	Jimmy Sidle	.15
23	Buddy McClinton	.07
24	Larry Willingham	.15
25	Bob Harris	.07
26	Bill Cody	.07
27	Lewis Colbert	.07
28	Brent Fullwood	.25
29	Tracy Rocker	.15
30	Kurt Grain	.07
31	Walter Reeves	.15
32	Jordan-Hare Stadium	.07
33	Ben Tamburello	.07
34	Benji Roland	.07
35	Chris Knapp	.07
36	Dowe Aughtman	.07
37	Auburn Tigers Logo	.07
38	Tommie Agee	.15
39	Bo Jackson	.75
40	Freddy Weygand	.15
41	Rodney Garner	.07
42	Brian Shulman	.07
43	Jim Thompson	.07
44	Shan Morris	.07
45	Ralph (Shug) Jordan	.15
46	Stacy Searels	.07
47	1957 Champs (Team Photo)	.07
48	Mike Kolen	.15
49	A Challenge Met (Pat Dye)	.15
50	Mark Dorminey	.07
51	Greg Staples	.07
52	Randy Campbell	.07
53	Duke Donaldson	.07
54	Yann Cowart	.07
55	Second Blocked Punt (vs. Alabama 1972)	.15
56	Keith Uecker	.15
57	David Jordan	.07
58	Tim Drinkard	.07
59	Connie Frederick	.15
60	Pat Arrington	.07
61	Willie Howell	.07
62	Terry Page	.07
63	Ben Thomas	.07
64	Ron Stallworth	.15
65	Charlie Trotman	.07
66	Ed West	.15
67	James Brooks	.50
68	Changing of the Guard (Doug Barfield, Ralph (Shug) Jordan)	.15
69	Ken Bernich	.07
70	Chris Woods	.07
71	Ralph (Shug) Jordan (CO)	.15
72	Steve Dennis (CO)	.07
73	Reggie Herring (CO)	.07
74	Al Del Greco	.15
75	Wayne Hall (CO)	.07
76	Langdon Hall	.07
77	Donnie Humphrey	.07
78	Jeff Burger	.15
79	Vernon Blackard	.07
80	Larry Blakeney (CO)	.07
81	Doug Smith	.07
82	Two Eras Meet (Ralph (Shug) Jordan, Vince Dooley)	.15
83	Kyle Collins	.07
84	Bobby Freeman	.07
85	Pat Sullivan (CO)	.25
86	Neil Callaway (CO)	.07
87	William Andrews	.25
88	Curtis Kuykendall	.07
89	David Campbell	.07
90	Seniors of '83	.25
91	Bud Casey (CO)	.07
92	Jay Jacobs (CO)	.07
93	Al Del Greco	.15
94	Pate Mote	.07
95	Rob Shuler	.07
96	Jerry Beasley	.07
97	Pat Washington	.07
98	Ed Graham	.07
99	Leon Myers	.07
100	Paul Davis (CO)	.07
101	Tom Banks Jr.	.15
102	Mike Simmons	.07
103	Alex Bowden	.07
104	Jim Bone	.07
105	Wincent Harris	.07
106	James Daniel	.07
107	Jimmy Carter	.07
108	Leading Passers (Pat Sullivan)	.25
109	Alvin Mitchell	.07
110	Mark Clement	.07
111	Bob Brown	.07
112	Shot Senn	.07
113	Loran Carter	.07
114	Pat Dye's First Team (Team Photo)	.15
115	Bob Hix	.07
116	Bo Russell	.07
117	Mike Mann	.07
118	Mike Shirey	.07
119	Pat Dye (CO)	.15
120	Kevin Greene	.25
121	Auburn Creed	.07
122	Jordan's All-Americans (Ralph (Shug) Jordan, Tucker Frederickson, Jimmy Sidle)	.15
123	Dave Blanks	.07
124	Scott Bolton	.07
125	Vince Dooley	.15
126	Tim Jessie	.07
127	Joe Davis	.07
128	Clayton Beauford	.07
129	Wilbur Hutsell (AD)	.07
130	Joe Whit	.07
131	Gary Kelley	.07
132	Bo Jackson	.75
133	Aundray Bruce	.25
134	Ronny Bellew	.07
135	Hindman Wall	.07
136	Frank Warren	.07
137	Abb Chrietzberg	.07
138	Collis Campbell	.07
139	Randy Stokes	.07
140	Teedy Faulk	.07
141	Reese McCall	.15
142	Jeff Jackson	.07
143	Bill Burgess	.07
144	Willie Huntley	.07
145	Doug Huntley	.07
146	Bacardi Bowl (Walter Gilbert)	.07
147	Russ Carreker	.07
148	Joe Moon	.07
149	A Look Ahead (Pat Dye)	.15
150	Joe Sullivan	.07
151	Scott Riley	.07
152	Larry Ellis	.07
153	Jeff Parks	.07
154	Gerald Williams	.07
155	Mike Griffith	.07
156	First Blocked Punt (vs. Alabama 1972)	.15
157	Bill Beckwith (ADMIN)	.07
158	Celebration (1957 Action Photo)	.15
159	Tommy Carroll	.15
160	John Dailey	.07
161	George Stephenson	.07
162	Danny Arnold	.07
163	Mike Edwards	.07
164	1894 Auburn-Alabama Trophy	.15
165	Don Anderson	.07
166	Alvin Briggs	.07
167	Herb Waldrop (CO)	.07
168	Jim Skuthan	.07
169	Alan Hardin	.07
170	Coaching Generations (Pat Sullivan, Bobby Freeman)	.25
171	Georgia Celebration (1971 Locker Room)	.07
172	Auburn 17, Alabama 16 (1972)	.15
173	Nat Ceasar	.07
174	Billy Hitchcock	.15
175	SEC Championship Trophy	.15
176	Dr. James E. Martin (PRES)	.07
177	Ricky Westbrook	.15
178	Fob James	.15
179	Stacy Dunn	.07
180	Tracy Turner	.07
181	Pat Dye (CO)	.15
182	In the Record Book (Terry Beasley)	.07
183	Ed "Foots" Bauer	.07
184	1984 Sugar Bowl Scoreboard	.07
185	Mark Robbins	.07
186	Paul White (CO)	.07
187	Hindman Wall (AD)	.07
188	David Beverly	.15
189	Sugar Bowl Trophy	.07
190	Edmund Nelson	.07
191	Edmund Nelson	.07
192	Cliff Hare	.07
193	Byron Franklin	.15
194	Richard Manry	.07
195	Malcolm McCary	.07
196	Patrick Waters (ADMIN)	.07
197	Chester Willis	.07
198	Alex Dudchock	.07
199	In the Record Book (Pat Sullivan)	.25
200	Victory Ride (Pat Dye) (CO)	.15
201	Dr. George Petrie (CO)	.07
202	D.M. Balliet (CO)	.07
203	G.H. Harvey (CO)	.07
204	F.M. Hall (CO)	.07
205	John Heisman (CO)	.25
206	Billy Watkins (CO)	.07
207	J.R. Kent (CO)	.07
208	Mike Harvey (CO)	.07
209	Billy Bates (CO)	.07
210	Mike Donahue (CO)	.07
211	W.S. Kienholz (CO)	.07
212	Mike Donahue (CO)	.07
213	Boozer Pitts (CO)	.07
214	David Morey (CO)	.07
215	George Bohler (CO)	.07
216	John Floyd (CO)	.07
217	Chet Wynne (CO)	.07
218	Jack Meagher (CO)	.07
219	Carl Voyles (CO)	.07
220	Earl Brown (CO)	.07
221	Ralph (Shug) Jordan (CO)	.07
222	Doug Barfield (CO)	.15
223	Most Career Points (Bo Jackson)	.35
224	Sonny Ferguson (CO)	.07
225	Ronnie Ross	.07
226	Gardner Jett	.15
227	Jerry Wilson	.07
228	Dick Schmatz	.07
229	Morris Savage	.07
230	James Owens	.07
231	Eddie Welch	.07
232	Lee Hayley	.07
233	Dick Hayley	.07
234	Jeff McCollum	.07
235	Rick Freeman	.07
236	Bobby Freeman (CO)	.07
237	Auburn 32, Alabama 22 (Trophy)	.15
238	Chip Powell	.07
239	Nick Ardillo	.07
240	Don Bristow	.07
241	Bucky Waid	.07
242	Greg Robert	.07
243	Ray Rollins	.07
244	Tommy Hicks	.07
245	Steve Wallace	.15
246	David Hughes	.07
247	Chuck Hurston	.07
248	Jimmy Long	.07
249	John Cochran (AD)	.07
250	Bobby Davis	.07
251	G.W. Clapp	.07
252	Jere Colley	.07
253	Tim James	.07
254	Joe Dolan	.07
255	Jerry Gordon	.07
256	Billy Edge	.07
257	Lawyer Tillman	.25
258	John McAfee	.07
259	Scotty Long	.07
260	Billy Austin	.07
261	Tracy Rocker	.15
262	Mickey Sutton	.07
263	Tommy Traylor	.07
264	Billy Van Dyke	.07
265	Sam McClurkin	.07
266	Mike Flynn	.07
267	Jim Sirmans	.07
268	Reggie Ware	.15
269	Bill Luke	.07
270	Don Machen	.07
271	Bill Grisham	.07
272	Bruce Evans	.07
273	Hank Hall	.07
274	Tommy Lunceford	.07
275	Pat Thomas	.07
276	Marvin Trott	.07
277	Brad Everett	.07
278	Frank Reeves	.07
279	Bishop Reeves	.07
280	Carver Reeves	.07
281	Billy Haas	.07
282	Dye's First AU Bowl (Pat Dye) (CO)	.15
283	Nate Hill	.07
284	Bucky Howard	.07
285	Tim Christian	.07
286	Tim Christian (CO)	.07
287	Tom Nettleman	.07
288	Carl Hubbard	.07
289	Auburn's Biggest Wins (Chart)	.07
290	Jay Jacobs	.07
291	Jimmy Pettus	.07
292	Cliff Hare Stadium	.07
293	Richard Wood	.15
294	Sandy Cannon	.07
295	Bill Braswell	.07
296	Foy Thompson	.07
297	Robert Margeson	.07
298	Pipeline to the Pros (Seven Pro Players)	.25
299	Bill Evans	.07
300	Marvin Tucker	.07
301	Jack Locklear	.07
302	Mike Locklear	.07
303	Harry Unger	.07
304	Lee Markle Sellers	.07
305	Ted Foret	.07
306	Bobby Foret	.07
307	Mike Neel	.07
308	Rick Neel	.07
309	Mike Alford	.07
310	Mac Crawford	.07
311	Bill Cunningham	.07

312 Legends (Pat Sullivan, Jeff Burger) .25
313 Frank LaRussa .07
314 Chris Vacarella .07
315 Gerald Robinson .15
316 Ronnie Baynes .07
317 Dave Edwards .07
318 Steve Taylor .07
319 Phillip Gilchrist .07
320 Ben McCurdy .07
321 Dave Hill .15
322 Jimmy Reynolds .07
323 Chuck Fletcher .07
324 Bogue Miller .07
325 Dave Beck .07
326 Johnny Simmons .07
327 Howard Simpson .07
328 Benny Sivley .15
329 1987 SEC Champions (Team Photo) .15
330 Frank Cox .07
331 Phil Gargis .07
332 Don Webb .07
333 Dan Presley .07
334 Al Giffin .07
335 Don Lewis .07
336 Eric Floyd .15
337 Stadium (Ralph (Shug) Jordan) .15
338 Terry Hendly .07
339 Billy Atkins .07
340 Tony Long .07
341 Jimmy Clemmer .07
342 John Valentine .07
343 Bruce Bylsma .07
344 Merrill Shirley .07
345 Kenny Howard (CO) .07
346 Hal Hamrick .07
347 Greg Zipp .07
348 Mac Champion .07
349 Most Tackles in One Game (Kurt Crain) .07
350 Leading Career Rushers (Bo Jackson) .35
351 Homer Williams .07
352 Mike Gates .07
353 Rusty Fuller .07
354 Rusty Deen .07
355 Stalwart Defenders (Bob Harris, Mark Dorminey) .07
356 Heroes of '56 (Ralph (Shug) Jordan, Jerry Elliott, Frank Reeves) .15
357 Road to the Top (Cartoon) .15
358 Cleve Wester .07
359 Line Stars (Jackie Burkett, Zeke Smith) .15
360 Bob Scarbrough .07
361 Jimmy Speiner .07
362 Danny Speiner .07
363 Alvin Bresler .07
364 Wade Whatley .07
365 Lance Hill .07
366 Andy Steele .07
367 John Whatley .07
368 Alton Shell .07
369 Larry Blakeney .07
370 Mickey Zofko .07
371 Gene Lorendo (CO) .07
372 Mac Lorendo .07
373 Buddy Davidson (CO) .07
374 Dave Woodward .07
375 Richard Guthrie .07
376 George Rose .07
377 Alan Bollinger .07
378 Danny Sanspree .07
379 Winky Giddens .07
380 Franklin Fuller .07
381 Charles Collins .07
382 Auburn, 23-22 (Scoreboard) .07
383 Jeff Weekley .07
384 Larry Haynie .07
385 Miles Jones .07
386 Bobby Wilson .15
387 Bobby Lauder .07
388 Charlie Glenn .07
389 Claude Saia .07
390 Tom Bryan .07
391 Lee Gross .07
392 Jerry Popwell .07
393 Tommy Groat .07
394 Neal Dettmering .07
395 Dr. W.S. Bailey (ADMIN) .07
396 Jim Pitts .07
397 College Football History (Cliff Hare Stadium) .07
398 Doc Griffith .07
399 Liston Eddins .07
400 Woody Woodall .07
401 Auburn Helmet .07
402 Skip Johnston .07
403 Trey Gainous .07
404 Randy Walls .07
405 Jimmy Partin .07
406 Dick Ingwerson .07

407 David Shelby .07
408 Harry Ward .07
409 Thomas Gossom .07
410 Sanford T. Gower .07
411 Architects of the Future (Jeff Beard, Ralph (Shug) Jordan) .15
412 Ed Butler .07
413 Bob Butler .07
414 Ben Strickland .07
415 Jeff Lott .07
416 Harris Rabren .07
417 Mike McQuaig .07
418 Steve Wilson .07
419 Jorge Portela .07
420 Dave Middleton .15
421 Tommy Yearout .07
422 Gusty Yearout .07
423 The Auburn Stadium .07
424 Cliff Hare Stadium .07
425 Oscar Burford .07
426 Cliff Hare Stadium .07
427 Cliff Hare Stadium .07
428 Jordan-Hare Stadium .07
429 Jack Meagher (CO) .07
430 Jeff Beard (AD) .07
431 Frank Young (ADMIN) .07
432 Frank Riley .07
433 Ernie Warren .07
434 Brian Atkins .07
435 George Atkins .07
436 Ricky Sanders .35
437 George Kenmore .07
438 Don Heller .07
439 Pat Meagher .07
440 Tim Davis .07
441 Tiger Meat (Cooks) .07
442 Joe Connally (CO) .07
443 Bob Newton .15
444 Bill Newton .07
445 David Langner .07
446 Charlie Langner .07
447 Brownie Flournoy (ADMIN) .07
448 Mike Hicks .07
449 Larry Hill .07
450 Tim Baker .07
451 Danny Bentley .07
452 Tommy Lowry .07
453 Jim Price .07
454 Lloyd Nix .07
455 Kenny Burks .07
456 Rusty Deen, Sallie Deen (ADMIN) .07
457 Johnny Sumner .07
458 Scott Blackmon .07
459 Chuck Maxime .07
460 Big SEC Wins (Chart) .07
461 Bo Davis .07
462 George Rose .07
463 Bob Bradley .07
464 Steve Osburne .07
465 George Gross .07
466 Andy Gross .07
467 M.L. Brackett .07
468 Herman Wilkes .07
469 Roger Mitchell .07
470 Bobby Beaird .07
471 Sammy Oates .07
472 Jimmy Ricketts .07
473 Bucky Ayters .07
474 Bill James .07
475 Johnny Wallis .07
476 Chris Jornson .07
477 Joe Overton .07
478 Tommy Lorino .07
479 James Warren .07
480 Lynn Johnson .07
481 Sam Mitchell .07
482 Sedrick McIntyre .07
483 Mike Holtzclaw .07
484 Dave Ostrowski .07
485 Jim Walsh .07
486 Mike Henley .07
487 Roy Tatum .07
488 Al Parks .07
489 Billy Wilson .15
490 Ken Luke .07
491 Phillip Hall .07
492 Bruce Yates .07
493 Dan Hataway .07
494 Joe Leichtnam .07
495 Danny Fulford .07
496 Ken Hardy .07
497 Rob Spivey .07
498 Rick Telhiard .07
499 Ron Yarbrough .07
500 Leo Sexton .07
501 Dick McGowen (CO) .07
502 Lee Kidd .07
503 Rex McKissick .07
504 Fagen Canzoneri, Zach Jenkins .07
505 Jim Bouchillon .07
506 Forrest Blue .25
507 Mike Helms .07
508 Bobby Hunt .15
509 John Liptak .07
510 James McKinney .07
511 Ed Baker .07
512 Heisman Trophies .25
513 Eddy Jackson .07
514 Jimmy Powell .07

515 Jerry Elliott .07
516 Jimmy Jones .07
517 Jimmy Laster .07
518 Larry Laster .07
519 Jerry Sansom .07
520 Don Downs .07
521 Danny Skutack .07
522 Keith Green .07
523 Spence McCracken .07
524 Lloyd Cheatham .07
525 Mike Shows .07
526 Spec Kelley .07
527 Dick McGowen .07
528 Jon Kilgore .07
529 Frank Gatski .25
530 Joel Eaves .07
531 John Adcock .07
532 Jimmy Fenton .07
533 Mike McCartney .07
534 Harrison McCraw .07
535 Mailon Kent .07
536 Dickie Flournoy .07
537 Coker Barton .07
538 Scotty Elam .07
539 Tim Wood .07
540 Terry Fuller .07
541 Johnny Kern .07
542 Mike Currier .07
543 Richard Cheek .07
544 Dan Dickerson .07
545 Arnold Fagen .07
546 John "Rat" Riley .07
547 Jimmy Burson .15
548 Bob Fleming .07
549 Mike Fitzhugh .07
550 Jim Patton .25
551 Bryant Harvard .07
552 Leon Cochran .07
553 Wayne Frazier .07
554 Phillip Dembowski .07
555 Alex Spurlin, Ed Spurlin .07
556 Bill Kilpatrick .07
557 Gaines Lanier .07
558 Johnny McDonald .07
559 Ray Powell .07
560 Jimmy Putman .07
561 Bobby Wasden .07
562 Roger Pruett .07
563 Don Braswell .07
564 Jim Jeffery .07
565 Auburn - A TV Favorite (Pat Dye) (CO) .15
566 Lamar Rawson .07
567 Larry Rawson .07
568 David Rawson .07
569 Hal Herring (CO) .07
570 Pat Sullivan .25
571 John Cochran .07
572 Jerry Gulledge .07
573 Steve Stanaland .15
574 Greg Zipp .07
575 John Trotman .07
576 Clyde Baumgartner .07
577 Jay Casey .07
578 Ralph O'Gwynne .07
579 Sid Scarborough .07
580 Tom Banks Sr. .15

1991 Auburn Hoby

Complete Set (42): 9.00
Common Player: .25
523 Thomas Bailey .25
524 Corey Barlow .35
525 Reggie Barlow .35
526 Fred Baxter .35
527 Eddie Blake .35
528 Herbert Casey .25
529 Pedro Cherry .25
530 Darrel Crawford .35
531 Tim Cromartie .25
532 Juan Crum .25
533 Karekin Cunningham .25
534 Alonzo Etheridge .25
535 Joe Frazier .25
536 Pat Dye (AD/CO) .35
537 Thery George .25
538 Chris Gray .25
539 Victor Hall .25
540 Randy Hart .25
541 Chris Holland .25
542 Chuckie Johnson .25
543 Anthony Judge .25
544 Corey Lewis .25
545 Reid McMillion .25
546 Bob Meeks .25
547 Dale Overton .35
548 Mike Pelton .35
549 Bennie Pierce .25
550 Mike Pina .25
551 Anthony Redmon .25
552 Tony Richardson .25
553 Richard Shea .35
554 Fred Smith .25
555 Otis Mounds .25
556 Ricky Sutton .25
557 Alex Thomas .25
558 Greg Thompson .25
559 Tim Tillman .25
560 Jim Von Wyl .25
561 Stan White .50
562 Darrell Williams .25

563 James Willis .25
564 Jon Wilson .25

1993 Baylor

Complete Set (21): 15.00
Common Player: .75
1 Lamone Alexander .75
2 Joseph Asbell .75
3 Marvin Callies .75
4 Todd Crawford .75
5 Earnest Crownover .75
6 Will Davidson 1.00
7 Chris Dull .75
8 Raynor Finley .75
9 J.J. Joe 2.00
10 Phillip Kent .75
11 David Leaks .75
12 Scotty Lewis 1.00
13 Fred Miller 1.00
14 Bruce Nowak .75
15 Mike Oatis .75
16 Chuck Pope .75
17 Adrian Robinson 2.00
18 Tyrone Smith .75
19 Andrew Swasey .75
20 Byron Thompson .75
21 Tony Tubbs .75

1984 BYU All-Time Greats

Complete Set (15): 18.00
Common Player: .50
1 Steve Young 10.00
2 Eldon Fortie .50
3 Bart Oates 1.50
4 Pete Van Valkenburg .60
5 Mike Mees .50
6 Wayne Baker .50
7 Gordon Gravelle .60
8 Gordon Hudson .60
9 Kurt Gunther .50
10 Todd Shell .60
11 Chris Farasopoulos 1.00
12 Paul Howard .50
13 Dave Atkinson .50
14 Paul Linford .50
15 Phil Odle .60

1984-85 BYU National Champions

Complete Set (15): 25.00
Common Player: 1.50
1 Mark Allen 1.50
2 Adam Hysbert 1.50
3 Larry Hamilton 1.50
4 Jim Hermann 1.50
5 Kyle Morrell 2.00
6 Lee Johnson 1.50
7 David Mills 1.50
8 Garrick Wright, Matich Wright, Anae Wright, Louis Wong 3.00
9 Jim Hermann, Larry Hamilton 2.00
10 Louis Wong 1.50
11 Bosco in Holiday Bowl (Robbie Bosco) 5.00
12 BYU Cougar Stadium 1.50
13 UPI Final Top 20 1.50
14 BYU National Championship Roster 1.50
15 Schedule and Scores For 1984 1.50

1990 BYU Safety

Complete Set (12): 15.00
Common Player: 1.00
1 Rocky Beigel 1.00
2 Matt Bellini 1.50
3 Tony Crutchfield 1.00
4 Ty Detmer 6.00
5 Norm Dixon 1.00
6 Earl Kauffman 1.00
7 Rich Kaufusi 1.50
8 Bryan May 1.00
9 Brent Nyberg 1.00
10 Chris Smith 1.50
11 Mark Smith 1.00
12 Robert Stephens 1.00

1991 BYU Safety

Complete Set (16): 10.00
Common Player: .75
1 Josh Arnold .75
2 Rocky Biegel .75

3 Scott Charlton .75
4 Tony Crutchfield .75
5 Ty Detmer 3.00
6 LaVell Edwards (CO) 1.50
7 Scott Giles .75
8 Derwin Gray 1.00
9 Shad Hansen .75
10 Brad Hunter .75
11 Earl Kauffman .75
12 Jared Leavitt .75
13 Micah Matsuzaki .75
14 Bryan May .75
15 Peter Tuipulotu .75
16 Matt Zundel .75

1992 BYU Safety

Complete Set (16): 10.00
Common Player: .60
1 Tyler Anderson .60
2 Randy Brock .60
3 Brad Clark .60
4 Eric Drage 1.00
5 LaVell Edwards (CO) 1.00
6 Mike Empey .60
7 Lenny Gomes .60
8 Derwin Gray 1.00
9 Shad Hansen .60
10 Eli Herring .60
11 Micah Matsuzaki .60
12 Patrick Mitchell .75
13 Garry Pay .60
14 Greg Pitts .60
15 Byron Rex .75
16 Jamal Willis 1.00

1993 BYU

Complete Set (20): 12.00
Common Player: .60
1 Tyler Anderson .60
2 Randy Brock .75
3 Frank Christianson .60
4 Eric Drage 1.00
5 LaVell Edwards .60
6 Mike Empey .60
7 Lenny Gomes .75
8 Kalin Hall .60
9 Nathan Hall .60
10 Hema Heimuli .75
11 Todd Herget .60
12 Eli Herring .60
13 Micah Matsuzaki .60
14 Casey Mazzotta .60
15 Patrick Mitchell .60
16 Evan Pilgrim 1.00
17 Greg Pitts .60
18 Vic Tarleton .60
19 John Walsh 3.00
20 Jamal Willis 1.00

1988 California Smokey

Complete Set (12): 12.00
Common Player: 1.25
1 Rob Bimson 1.25
2 Joel Dickson 1.25
3 Robert DosRemedios 1.25
4 Mike Ford 1.25
5 Darryl Ingram 1.25
6 David Ortega 1.25
7 Chris Richards 1.25
8 Bruce Snyder (CO) 1.50
9 Troy Taylor 2.00
10 Natu Tuatagaloa 2.00
11 Majett Whiteside 1.25
12 Dave Zawatson 1.25

1989 California Smokey

Complete Set (16): 12.00
Common Player: 1.00
1 John Hardy 1.00
2 Mike Ford 1.00
10 Robbie Keen 1.00
11 Troy Taylor 1.25
20 Dwayne Jones 1.00
21 Travis Oliver 1.00
34 Darrin Greer 1.00
40 David Ortega 1.00
41 Dan Slevin 1.00
52 Troy Auzenne 3.00
69 Tony Smith 1.00
80 Junior Tagaloa 1.00
83 Michael Smith 1.00
95 DeWayne Odom 1.00
99 Joel Dickson 1.00
NNO Bruce Snyder (CO) 1.25

1990 California Smokey

Complete Set (16): 10.00
Common Player: .75
1 Troy Auzenne (52) 2.00

2 John Belli (61) .75
3 Joel Dickson (99) .75
4 Ron English (42) .75
5 Rhett Hall (57) 2.00
6 John Hardy (1) .75
7 Robbie Keen (10) .75
8 DeWayne Odom (95) .75
9 Mike Pawlawski (9) 1.50
10 Castle Redmond (37) .75
11 James Richards (64) .75
12 Ernie Rogers (68) .75
13 Bruce Snyder (CO) .75
14 Brian Treggs (3) 1.00
15 Anthony Wallace (6) .75
16 Greg Zomalt (28) .75

1991 California Smokey

Complete Set (16): 14.00
Common Player: .75
1 Troy Auzenne 1.50
2 Chris Cannon .75
3 Cornell Collier .75
4 Sean Dawkins 3.00
5 Steve Gordon .75
6 Mike Pawlawski 1.25
7 Bruce Snyder (CO) .75
8 Todd Steussie 2.00
9 Mack Travis .75
10 Brian Treggs 1.00
11 Russell White 2.00
12 Jason Wilborn .75
13 David Wilson .75
14 Brent Woodall .75
15 Eric Zomalt 1.25
16 Greg Zomalt .75

1992 California Smokey

Complete Set (16): 10.00
Common Player: .60
1 Chidi Ahanotu .60
2 Wolf Barber .60
3 Mick Barsala .60
4 Doug Brien 1.50
5 Al Casner .60
6 Lindsey Chapman .60
7 Sean Dawkins 2.50
8 Keith Gilbertson (CO) .75
9 Eric Mahlum 1.00
10 Chris Noonan .60
11 Todd Steussie 1.50
12 Mack Travis .60
13 Russell White 1.50
14 Jerrott Willard 1.00
15 Eric Zomalt 1.00
16 Greg Zomalt .60

1993 California Smokey

Complete Set (16): 10.00
Common Player: .60
1 Dave Barr 2.00
2 Doug Brien 1.25
3 Mike Caldwell .60
4 Lindsey Chapman .60
5 Jerod Cherry .60
6 Michael Davis .60
7 Tyrone Edwards .60
8 Keith Gilbertson (CO) .60
9 Jody Graham .60
10 Marty Holly .60
11 Paul Joiner .60
12 Eric Mahlum .75
13 Damien Semien .60
14 Todd Steussie 1.25
15 Jerrott Willard .75
16 Eric Zomalt .75

1995 California Smokey

Complete Set (16): 8.00
Common Player: .50
1 Pat Barnes .50
2 Nai'il Benjamin .60
3 Sean Bullard .50
4 Je'Rod Cherry .50
5 Duane Clemons 1.00
6 Dante Depaola .50
7 Kevin Devine .50
8 Keith Gilbertson (CO) .60
9 Andy Jacobs .50
10 Ryan Longwell .50
11 Ben Lynch .50
12 Reynard Rutherford .50

13	James Stallworth	.50
14	Regan Upshaw	2.00
15	Iheanyi Uwaezuoke	.75
16	Brandon Whiting	.50

1989 Clemson

		MT
	Complete Set (32):	20.00
	Common Player:	.75
1	Wally Ake (CO)	.75
2	Larry Beckman (CO)	.75
3	Mitch Belton (32)	.75
4	Scott Beville (61)	.75
5	Doug Brewster (92)	.75
6	Larry Brinson (CO)	1.00
7	Reggie Demps (30)	.75
8	Robin Eaves (44)	.75
9	Barney Farrar (CO)	.75
10	Stacy Fields (46)	.75
11	Vance Hammond (90)	.75
12	Eric Harmon (76)	.75
13	Ken Hatfield (CO)	1.50
14	Jerome Henderson (36)	1.50
15	Les Herrin (75)	.75
16	Roger Hinshaw (CO)	.75
17	John Johnson (12)	1.50
18	Reggie Lawrence (34)	.75
19	Stacy Long (67)	.75
20	Eric Mader (82)	.75
21	Arlington Nunn (39)	.75
22	David Puckett (68)	.75
23	Danny Sizer (54)	.75
24	Robbie Spector (2)	.75
25	Rick Stockstill (CO)	1.00
26	Bruce Taylor (6)	.75
27	Doug Thomas (41)	.75
28	The Tiger (Mascot)	.75
29	Tiger Paw Title Card	.75
30	Bob Trott (CO)	.75
31	Larry Van Der Heyden (CO)	.75
32	Richard Wilson (CO)	.75

1950 C.O.P. Betsy Ross

		NM
	Complete Set (6):	75.00
	Common Player:	8.00
1	Don Campora	8.00
2	Don Hardey	8.00
3	Robert Klein	8.00
4	Eddie LeBaron	35.00
5	Eddie Macon	15.00
6	John Rohde	8.00

1990 Colorado Smokey

		MT
	Complete Set (16):	16.00
	Common Player:	.75
1	Eric Bieniemy	2.50
2	Joe Garten	1.00
3	Darian Hagan	2.00
4	George Hemingway	.75
5	Garry Howe	.75
6	Tim James	.75
7	Charles Johnson	2.50
8	Bill McCartney (CO)	1.00
9	Dave McCloughan	1.00
10	Kanavis McGhee	1.00
11	Mike Pritchard	5.00
12	Tom Rouen	1.00
13	Michael Simmons	.75
14	Mark Vander Poel	1.00
15	Alfred Williams	2.50
16	Ralphie (Mascot)	.75

1992 Colorado Pepsi

		MT
	Complete Set (12):	15.00
	Common Player:	1.00
1	Greg Biekert	2.00
2	Pat Blottiaux	1.00
3	Ronnie Bradford	1.50
4	Chad Brown	2.50
5	Marcellous Elder	1.50
6	Deon Figures	2.50
7	Jim Hansen	1.00
8	Jack Keys	1.00
9	Bill McCartney (CO)	2.00
10	Clint Moles	1.00
11	Jason Perkins	1.00
12	Scott Starr	1.00

1993 Colorado Smokey

		MT
	Complete Set (16):	15.00
	Common Player:	1.00
1	Craig Anderson	1.00
2	Mitch Berger	1.50
3	Jeff Brunner	1.00
4	Dennis Collier	1.00
5	Dwayne Davis	1.00
6	Brian Dyet	1.00

7	Sean Embree	1.00
8	Garrett Ford	1.00
9	James Hill	1.00
10	Charles Johnson	3.00
11	Greg Lindsey	1.00
12	Sam Rogers	1.00
13	Mark Smith	1.00
14	Duke Tobin	1.00
15	Ron Woolfork	1.50
16	Derek Agnew	1.00

1994 Colorado Smokey

		MT
	Complete Set (16):	18.00
	Common Player:	.75
1	Blake Anderson	.75
2	Norm Barnett	.75
3	Tony Berti	1.00
4	Ken Browne	.75
5	Christian Fauria	2.00
6	Darius Holland	1.50
7	Chris Hudson	1.50
8	Ted Johnson	1.50
9	Vance Joseph	.75
10	Jon Knutson	.75
11	Bill McCartney (CO)	1.50
12	Erik Mitchell	.75
13	Kordell Stewart	8.00
14	Derek West	.75
15	Michael Westbrook	4.00
16	Team Logo	.75

1973 Colorado State

JIM KENNEDY
Tight End

		NM
	Complete Set (8):	75.00
	Common Player:	6.00
1	Wes Cerveny	6.00
2	Mark Driscoll	6.00
3	Jim Kennedy	6.00
4	Greg Kuhn	6.00
5	Willie Miller	20.00
6	Al Simpson (SP)	12.00
7	Jan Stuebbe (SP)	12.00
8	Tom Wallace	6.00

1987 Duke Police

		MT
	Complete Set (16):	25.00
	Common Player:	1.50
1	Andy Andreasik (60)	1.50
2	Brian Bernard (93)	1.50
3	Bob Calamari (31)	1.50
4	Jason Cooper (22)	1.50
5	Dave Demore (92)	1.50
6	Mike Dimitrio (21)	1.50
7	Jim Godfrey (56)	1.50
8	Doug Green (5)	1.50
9	Stanley Monk (24)	1.50
10	Chris Port (73)	1.50
11	Steve Ryan (63)	1.50
12	Steve Slayden (7)	2.00
13	Steve Spurrier (CO)	9.00
14	Dewayne Terry (27)	1.50
15	Fonda Williams (19)	1.50
16	Blue Devil (Mascot)	2.00

1988 Florida Burger King

ERNIE MILLS -14-
WIDE RECEIVER

	MT
Complete Set (16):	60.00

	Common Player:	.75
1	Florida Gators Team	5.00
2	Emmitt Smith (22)	45.00
3	David Williams (73)	1.25
4	Jeff Roth (96)	.75
5	Rhondy Weston (68)	1.00
6	Stacey Simmons (25)	1.00
7	Huey Richardson (90)	1.25
8	Wayne Williams (23)	1.00
9	Charlie Wright (79)	.75
10	Tracy Daniels (63)	.75
11	Ernie Mills (14)	3.00
12	Willie McGrady (38)	.75
13	Chris Bromley (52)	.75
14	Louis Oliver (18)	2.00
15	Galen Hall (CO)	1.25
16	Albert the Alligator (Mascot)	.75

1989 Florida

		MT
	Complete Set (22):	16.00
	Common Player:	.50
1	Dale Van Sickle	.50
2	Cris Collinsworth	1.00
3	Wilber Marshall	1.50
4	Jack Youngblood	1.00
5	Steve Spurrier	4.00
6	David Little	.75
7	Bruce Bennett	.50
8	Charlie LaPradd	.50
9	John L. Williams	1.50
10	Steve Tannen	.75
11	Neal Anderson	1.50
12	Larry Dupree	.50
13	Guy Dennis	.50
14	Jarvis Williams	.75
15	Bill Carr	.50
16	Clifford Charlton	.50
17	Wes Chandler	.75
18	David Galloway	.50
19	Carlos Alvarez	.50
20	Lomas Brown	1.00
21	Larry Smith	.50
22	Ricky Nattiel	.75

1989 Florida Smokey

		MT
	Complete Set (16):	35.00
	Common Player:	.75
1	Chris Bromley (52)	1.00
2	Richard Fain (28)	1.25
3	John David Francis (7)	1.00
4	Galen Hall (CO) (SP)	7.00
5	Tony Lomack (20)	1.00
6	Willie McClendon (5)	1.00
7	Pat Moorer (45)	1.00
8	Kyle Morris (1)	1.00
9	Huey Richardson (90)	1.25
10	Stacey Simmons (25)	1.00
11	Emmitt Smith (22)	25.00
12	Richard Starowesky (75)	1.00
13	Kerry Watkins (4)	1.00
14	Albert (Mascot)	1.00
15	Cheerleaders	1.25
16	Gator Helmet	1.00

1990 Florida Smokey

		MT
	Complete Set (12):	15.00
	Common Player:	1.00
1	Terence Barber (3)	1.00
2	Chris Bromley (52)	1.00
3	Richard Fain (28)	1.25
4	Willie McClendon (5)	1.25
5	Dexter McNabb (21)	1.25
6	Ernie Mills (14)	2.50
7	Mark Murray (54)	1.00
8	Jerry Odom	1.00
9	Huey Richardson (90)	1.25
10	Steve Spurrier (CO)	4.00
11	Albert and Alberta (Mascots)	1.00
12	Mr. Two-Birts (Fan)	1.00

1991 Florida Smokey

	MT
Complete Set (12):	12.00

	Common Player:	1.00
1	Ephesians Bartley	1.25
2	Mike Brandon	1.00
3	Brad Culpepper	1.50
4	Arden Czyzewski	1.00
5	Cal Dixon	1.25
6	Tre Everett	1.00
7	Hesham Ismail	1.00
8	Shane Matthews	2.50
9	Steve Spurrier (CO)	4.00
10	Mark White	1.00
11	Will White	1.00
12	Albert and Alberta (Mascots)	1.00

1993 Florida State

		MT
	Complete Set (6):	85.00
	Common Player:	6.00
1	Bobby Bowden (CO)	15.00
2	Derrick Brooks	15.00
3	Corey Sawyer	10.00
4	Tamarick Vanover	30.00
5	Charlie Ward	25.00
6	Chief Osceola (Mascot)	6.00

1996 Florida State

		MT
	Complete Set (12):	10.00
	Common Player:	.50
1	Chad Bates, Todd Fordham	.50
2	Scott Bentley	1.00
3	Byron Capers	.75
4	James Colzie	1.00
5	Andre Cooper	1.00
6	Henri Crockett	1.00
7	Warrick Dunn	5.00
8	Sean Hamlet	.75
9	Sean Liss	.75
10	Wayne Messam	1.00
11	Connell Spain	1.00
12	Reinard Wilson	2.00

1986 Fort Hayes State

		MT
	Complete Set (27):	30.00
	Common Player:	1.25
1	Kelly Barnard	1.25
2	James Bess	1.25
3	Eric Busenbark	1.25
4	Sylvester Butler	1.25
5	Channing Day	1.25
6	Edward Faagai	1.25
7	Randy Fayette	1.25
8	Gerald Hall	1.25
9	Mike Hipp	1.25
10	Sam Holloway	1.25
11	Howard Hood	1.25
12	James Jermon	1.25
13	Randy Jordan	1.25
14	John Kelsh	1.25
15	Randy Knox	1.25
16	Robert Long	1.25
17	Les Miller	1.25
18	Frankie Neal	1.25
19	Paul Nelson	1.25
20	Darryl Pittman	1.25
21	Mike Shoff	1.25
22	Kip Stewart	1.25
23	Rod Timmons	1.25
24	Rob Ukleya	1.25
25	John Vincent (CO)	1.25
26	Rick Wheeler	1.25
27	Mike Worth	1.25

1987 Fresno State Burger King

		MT
	Complete Set (16):	25.00
	Common Player:	1.50
1	Gene Taylor	1.50
5	Michael Stewart	3.00
9	Kevin Sweeney	3.00
12	Eric Buechele	1.50
19	Rod Webster	1.50
26	Kelly Skipper	1.50
28	Barry Belli	1.50
32	Kelly Brooks	1.50
45	David Grayson	2.00
67	Jethro Franklin	1.50
71	Jeff Truschel	1.50
80	John O'Leary	1.50
81	Stephen Baker	3.00
83	Henry Ellard	6.00
86	Stephone Paige	4.00
NNO	Jim Sweeney (CO)	2.00

1989 Fresno State Smokey

	MT
Complete Set (16):	15.00

	Common Player:	1.00
1	Mark Barsotti	1.00
2	Rich Bartlewski	1.00
3	Ron Cox	2.50
4	Myron Jones	1.00
5	Steve Loop	1.00
6	Fil Lujan	1.00
7	Darrel Martin	1.00
8	Lance Oberparleiter	1.00
9	Dwight Pickens	1.00
10	Marquez Pope	3.00
11	Nick Ruggeroli	1.00
12	Jim Sweeney CO	1.50
13	Jeff Thiesen	1.00
14	Paul Vial	1.00
15	James Williams	1.00
16	Bulldog Stadium	1.00

1990 Fresno State Smokey

		MT
	Complete Set (16):	15.00
	Common Player:	1.00
1	Mark Barsotti	1.25
2	Ron Cox	1.50
3	Aaron Craver	1.50
4	DeVonne Edwards	1.00
5	Courtney Griffin	1.00
6	Jesse Hardwick	1.00
7	Melvin Johnson	1.00
8	Brian Lasho	1.00
9	Kelvin Means	1.00
10	Marquez Pope	2.50
11	Zack Rix	1.00
12	Nick Ruggeroli	1.00
13	Jim Sweeney (CO)	1.25
14	Erick Tanuvasa	1.00
15	Jeff Thiesen	1.00
16	James Williams	1.50

1988 Georgia McDag

TIM WORLEY
Tailback

		MT
	Complete Set (16):	20.00
	Common Player:	1.00
1	UGA IV (Mascot)	1.00
2	Vince Dooley (AD/CO)	3.00
3	Steve Crumley	1.00
4	Aaron Chubb	1.00
5	Keith Henderson	2.00
6	Steve Harmon	1.00
7	Terrie Webster	1.00
8	John Kasay	2.50
9	Wayne Johnson	1.00
10	Tim Worley	2.00
11	Wycliffe Lovelace	1.00
12	Brent Collins	1.00
13	Vince Guthrie	1.00
14	Todd Wheeler	1.00
15	Bill Goldberg	1.00
16	Rodney Hampton	10.00

1989 Georgia 200

KEVIN BUTLER

		MT
	Complete Set (200):	18.00
	Common Player:	.10
1	Vince Dooley (AD)	.20
2	Ivy M. Shiver	.10
3	Vince Dooley (CO)	.20
4	Vince Dooley (CO)	.20
5	Ray Goff (CO)	.20
6	Ray Goff (CO)	.20
7	Wally Butts (CO)	.20
8	Wally Butts (CO)	.20

9	Herschel Walker	.75
10	Frank Sinkwich	.20
11	Bob McWhorter	.10
12	Joe Bennett	.10
13	Dan Edwards	.10
14	Tom A. Nash	.10
15	Herb Maffett	.10
16	Ralph Maddox	.10
17	Vernon Smith	.10
18	Bill Hartman Jr.	.10
19	Frank Sinkwich	.20
20	Joe O'Malley	.10
21	Mike Castronis	.10
22	Aschel M. Day	.10
23	Herb St. John	.10
24	Craig Hertwig	.10
25	Johnny Rauch	.10
26	Harry Babcock	.10
27	Bruce Kemp	.10
28	Pat Dye	.20
29	Fran Tarkenton	1.00
30	Larry Kohn	.10
31	Ray Rissmiller	.10
32	George Patton	.10
33	Mixon Robinson	.10
34	Lynn Hughes	.10
35	Bill Stanfill	.20
36	Robert Dicks	.10
37	Lynn Hunnicutt	.10
38	Tommy Lyons	.10
39	Royce Smith	.10
40	Steve Greer	.10
41	Randy Johnson	.20
42	Mike Wilson	.10
43	Joel Parrish	.10
44	Ben Zambiasi	.10
45	Allan Leavitt	.10
46	George Collins	.10
47	Rex Robinson	.10
48	Scott Woerner	.10
49	Herschel Walker	.75
50	Bob Burns	.10
51	Jimmy Payne	.10
52	Fred Brown	.10
53	Kevin Butler	.20
54	Don Porterfield	.10
55	Mac McWhorter	.10
56	John Little	.10
57	Marion Campbell	.20
58	Zeke Bratkowski	.30
59	Buck Belue	.20
60	Duward Pennington	.10
61	Lamar Davis	.10
62	Steve Wilson	.10
63	Leman L. Rosenberg	.10
64	Dennis Hughes	.10
65	Wayne Radloff	.10
66	Lindsay Scott	.20
67	Wayne Swinford	.10
68	Kim Stephens	.10
69	Willie McClendon	.20
70	Ron Jenkins	.10
71	Jeff Lewis	.10
72	Larry Rakestraw	.20
73	Spike Jones	.10
74	Tom Nash Jr.	.10
75	Vassa Cate	.10
76	Theron Sapp	.20
77	Claude Hipps	.20
78	Charley Trippi	.30
79	Mike Weaver	.10
80	Anderson Johnson	.10
81	Matt Robinson	.20
82	Bill Krug	.10
83	Todd Wheeler	.10
84	Mack Guest	.10
85	Frank Ros	.10
86	Jeff Hipp	.10
87	Milton Leathers	.10
88	George Morton	.10
89	Jim Broadway	.10
90	Tim Morrison	.10
91	Homer Key	.10
92	Richard Tardits	.20
93	Tommy Thurson	.10
94	Bob Kelley	.10
95	Bob McWhorter	.10
96	Vernon Smith	.10
97	Eddie Weaver	.10
98	Bill Stanfill	.20
99	Scott Williams	.10
100	Checklist Card	.10
101	Len Hauss	.20
102	Jim Griffith	.10
103	Nat Dye	.10
104	Quinton Lumpkin	.10
105	Mike Garrett	.10
106	Glynn Harrison	.10
107	Aaron Chubb	.10
108	John Brantley	.10
109	Pat Hodgson	.10
110	Guy McIntyre	.30
111	Keith Harris	.10
112	Mike Cavan	.10
113	Kevin Jackson	.10
114	Jim Cagle	.10
115	Charles Whittemore	.10
116	Graham Batchelor	.10
117	Art DeCarlo	.20
118	Kendall Keith	.10
119	Jeff Pyburn	.20
120	James Ray	.10
121	Mack Burroughs	.10
122	Jimmy Vickers	.10
123	Charley Britt	.10

124	Matt Braswell	.10
125	Jake Richardson	.10
126	Ronnie Stewart	.10
127	Tim Crowe	.10
128	Troy Sadowski	.10
129	Robert Honeycutt	.10
130	Warren Gray	.10
131	David Guthrie	.10
132	John Lastinger	.20
133	Chip Wisdom	.10
134	Butch Box	.10
135	Tony Cushenberry	.10
136	Vince Guthrie	.10
137	Floyd Reid	.20
138	Mark Hodge	.10
139	Joe Happe	.10
140	Al Bodine	.10
141	Gene Chandler	.10
142	Tommy Lawhorne	.10
143	Bobby Walden	.20
144	Douglas McFalls	.10
145	Jim Milo	.10
146	Billy Payne	.75
147	Paul Holmes	.10
148	Bob Clemens	.10
149	Kenneth Sims	.10
150	Reid Moseley Jr.	.10
151	Tim Callaway	.10
152	Rusty Russell	.10
153	Jim McCollough	.10
154	Wally Williamson	.10
155	John Bond	.10
156	Charley Trippi	.30
157	The Play (Lindsay Scott)	.20
158	Joe Boland	.10
159	Michael Babb	.10
160	Jimmy Poulos	.10
161	Chris McCarthy	.10
162	Billy Mixon	.10
163	Dicky Clark	.10
164	David Rholetter	.10
165	Chuck Heard	.10
166	Pat Field	.10
167	Preston Ridlehuber	.10
168	Heyward Allen	.10
169	Kirby Moore	.10
170	Chris Welton	.10
171	Bill McKenny	.10
172	Steve Boswell	.10
173	Bob Towns	.10
174	Anthony Towns	.10
175	Porter Payne	.10
176	Bobby Garrard	.10
177	Jack Griffith	.10
178	Herschel Walker	.75
179	Andy Perhach	.10
180	Dr. Charles Herty (CO)	.10
181	Kent Lawrence	.20
182	David McKnight	.10
183	Joe Tereshinski	.20
184	Cicero Lucas	.10
185	Glenn "Pop" Warner (CO)	.20
186	Tony Flack	.10
187	Kevin Butler	.20
188	Bill Mitchell	.10
189	Poulos vs. Tech (Jimmy Poulos)	.10
190	Pete Case	.20
191	Pete Tinsley	.10
192	Joe Tereshinski	.20
193	Jimmy Harper	.10
194	Don Leebern	.10
195	Harry Mehre (CO)	.10
196	Retired Jerseys (Herschel Walker, Theron Sapp, Charley Trippi, Frank Sinkwich)	.30
197	Terrie Webster	.10
198	George Woodruff (CO)	.10
199	First Georgia Team (1892 Team Photo)	.10
200	Checklist Card	.10

1989 Georgia Police

		MT
Complete Set (16):		15.00
Common Player:		.75
1	Hiawatha Berry (58)	.75
2	Brian Cleveland (37)	.75
3	Demetrius Douglas (53)	.75
4	Alphonso Ellis (33)	.75
5	Ray Goff (CO)	1.00
6	Bill Goldberg (95)	.75
7	Rodney Hampton (7)	8.00
8	David Hargett (25)	.75
9	Joey Hester (1)	.75
10	John Kasay (3)	2.00
11	Mo Lewis	3.00
12	Arthur Marshall (12)	1.50
13	Curt Mull (50)	.75
14	Ben Smith (26)	1.50
15	Greg Talley (11)	.75
16	Kirk Warner (83)	.75

1990 Georgia Police

		MT
Complete Set (14):		10.00
Common Player:		.75
1	John Allen (44)	.75
2	Brian Cleveland (37)	.75
3	Norman Cowins (59)	.75
4	Alphonso Ellis (33)	.75
5	Ray Goff (CO)	1.00
6	David Hargett (25)	.75
7	Sean Hunnings (6)	.75
8	Preston Jones (14)	1.00
9	John Kasay (3)	1.50
10	Arthur Marshall (12)	1.50
11	Jack Swan (76)	.75
12	Greg Talley (11)	.75
13	Lemonte Tellis (77)	.75
14	Chris Wilson (16)	.75

1991 Georgia Police

		MT
Complete Set (16):		15.00
Common Player:		.75
1	John Allen	.75
2	Chuck Carswell	.75
3	Russell DeFoor	.75
4	Ray Goff (CO)	1.00
5	David Hargett	.75
6	Andre Hastings	2.50
7	Garrison Hearst	6.00
8	Arthur Marshall	1.25
9	Kevin Maxwell	.75
10	DeWayne Simmons	.75
11	Jack Swan	.75
12	Greg Talley	.75
13	Lemonte Tellis	.75
14	Chris Wilson	.75
15	George Wynn	.75
16	UGA V (Mascot)	.75

1992 Georgia Police

		MT
Complete Set (15):		12.00
Common Player:		.50
1	Mitch Davis	.60
2	Damon Evans	.50
3	Torrey Evans	.50
4	Ray Goff (CO)	.60
5	Andre Hastings	2.00
6	Garrison Hearst	5.00
7	Donnie Maib	.50
8	Alec Millen	.50
9	Shannon Mitchell	.50
10	Mack Strong	1.00
11	Jack Swan	.50
12	UGA (Mascot)	.50
13	Bernard Williams	.60
14	Chris Wilson	.50
15	Eric Zeier	6.00

1993 Georgia Police

		MT
Complete Set (16):		18.00
Common Player:		.50
1	Scott Armstrong	.50
2	Brian Bohannon	.50
3	Carlo Butler	.50
4	Charlie Clemons	.50
5	Mitch Davis	.60
6	Terrell Davis	12.00
7	Randall Godfrey	.75
8	Ray Goff (CO)	.60
9	Frank Harvey	.50
10	Travis Jones	.50
11	Shannon Mitchell	.50
12	Greg Tremble	.50
13	Bernard Williams	.60
14	Chad Wilson	.50
15	Eric Zeier	3.00
16	UGA (Mascot)	.50

1991 Georgia Southern

		MT
Complete Set (45):		30.00
Common Player:		.60
1	Tracy Ham	4.00
2	Tim Foley	1.50
3	Vance Pike	.60
4	Dennis Franklin	.60
5	Ernest Thompson	.60
6	Giff Smith	.60
7	Flint Matthews	.60
8	Joe Ross	.60
9	Gerald Harris	.60
10	Monty Sharpe	.60
11	The Beginning (Erskine "Erk" Russell) (CO)	1.00
12	Mike West	.60
13	Jessie Jenkins	.60
14	'85 Championship (Ring)	.60
15	Erskine "Erk" Russell (CO)	1.00
16	Tim Brown	.75
17	Taz Dixon	.60
18	'86 Championship	.60
19	Sean Gainey	.60
20	James "Peanut" Carter	.75
21	Ricky Harris	.75
22	Fred Stokes	2.00
23	Randell Boone	.60
24	Ronald Warnock	.60
25	Raymond Gross	.60
26	Robert Underwood	.60
27	Frank Johnson	.60
28	Darren Alford	.60
29	Darrell Hendrix	.60
30	Raymond Gross	.60
31	Hugo Rossignol	.60
32	Charles Carper	.60
33	Melvin Bell	.60
34	The Catch (Tracy Ham to Frank Johnson)	1.50
35	Karl Miller	.60
36	Our House - Allen E. Paulson Stadium	.60
37	Danny Durham	.60
38	'89 Championship	.60
39	Tony Belser	.60
40	Nay Young	.60
41	Steve Bussoletti	.60
42	Tim Stowers (CO)	.60
43	Rodney Oglesby	.60
44	'90 Championship	.60
45	Tracy Ham	4.00

1989 Hawaii

		MT
Complete Set (25):		10.00
Common Player:		.50
3	Michael Coulson	.50
4	Walter Briggs	.50
5	Gavin Robertson	.50
7	Jason Elam	3.00
16	Clayton Mahuka	.50
18	Garrett Gabriel	.60
19	Kim McCloud	.50
27	Kyle Ah Loo	.50
28	Dane McArthur	.50
30	Travis Sims	.50
31	David Maeva	.50
37	Mike Tresler	.50
56	Jamal Farmer	.60
56	Mark Odom	.50
61	Allen Smith	.50
66	Manly Williams	.50
67	Larry Jones	.50
71	Sean Robinson	.50
72	Shawn Alivado	.50
81	Leo Goeas	1.00
86	Larry Khan-Smith	.50
89	Chris Roscoe	.50
91	Augie Apelu	.50
97	Dana Directo	.50
NNO	Bob Wagner (CO)	.60

1990 Hawaii 7-Eleven

		MT
Complete Set (50):		15.00
Common Player:		.35
1	Sean Abreu (40)	.35
2	Joaquin Barnett (53)	.35
3	Darrick Branch (87)	.35
4	David Brantley (9)	.35
5	Akili Calhoun (98)	.35
6	Michael Carter (3)	.35
7	Shawn Ching (72)	.35
8	Jason Elam (7)	2.00
9	Jamal Farmer (43)	.50
10	Garrett Gabriel (18)	.50
11	Brian Gordon (15)	.35
12	Kenny Harper (6)	.35
13	Mitchell Kaaialii (57)	.35
14	Larry Khan-Smith (86)	.35
15	Haku Kahoano (94)	.35
16	Nuuanu Kaulia (94)	.35
17	Eddie Kealoha (38)	.35
18	Zerin Khan (14)	.35
19	David Maeva (31)	.35
20	Dane McArthur (28)	.35
21	Kim McCloud (19)	.35
22	Jeff Newman (1)	.35
23	Mark Odom (56)	.35
24	Louis Randall (51)	.35
25	Gavin Robertson (5)	.35
26	Sean Robinson (71)	.35
27	Tavita Sagapolu (77)	.35
28	Lyno Samana (45)	.35
29	Walter Santiago (12)	.35
30	Joe Sardo (21)	.35
31	Travis Sims (30)	.35
32	Allen Smith (61)	.35
33	Jeff Snyder (26)	1.50
34	Richard Stevenson (33)	.35
35	David Tanuvasa (44)	.35
36	Mike Tresler (37)	.35
37	Lemoe Tua (60)	.35
38	Peter Viliamu (69)	.35
39	Bob Wagner (50)	.50
40	Terry Whitaker (2)	.35
41	Manly Williams (66)	.35
42	Jerry Winfrey (90)	.35
43	Aloha Stadium	.35
44	Assistant Coaches	.35
45	Defense (Nuuanu Kaulia)	.35
46	Offense (Jamal Farmer)	.50
47	Special Teams (Jason Elam)	.75
48	BYU Victory (Jamal Farmer)	.50
49	UH Logo	.35
50	WAC Logo	.35

1991 Hoby SEC Stars

HERSCHEL WALKER

		MT
Complete Set (396):		50.00
Common Player:		.15
1	Paul "Bear" Bryant (CO)	2.00
2	Johnny Musso	.50
3	Keith McCants	.25
4	Cecil Dowdy	.15
5	Thomas Rayam	.15
6	Van Tiffin	.15
7	Efrum Thomas	.15
8	Jon Hand	.25
9	David Smith	.15
10	Larry Rose	.15
11	Lamonde Russell	.15
12	Mike Washington	.15
13	Tommy Cole	.15
14	Roger Shultz	.15
15	Spencer Hammond	.15
16	John Fruhmorgen	.15
17	Gene Jelks	.25
18	John Mangum	.25
19	George Thornton	.25
20	Billy Neighbors	.25
21	Howard Cross	.40
22	Jeremiah Castille	.25
23	Derrick Thomas	1.00
24	Terrill Chatman	.15
25	Ken Stabler	1.25
26	Lee Ozmint	.15
27	Philip Doyle	.15
28	Kermit Kendrick	.15
29	Chris Mohr	.15
30	Tommy Wilcox	.15
31	Gary Hollingsworth	.15
32	Sylvester Croom	.25
33	Willie Wyatt	.15
34	Pooley Hubert	.15
35	Bobby Humphrey	.25
36	Vaughn Mancha	.15
37	Reggie Slack	.40
38	Vince Dooley (CO)	.40
39	Ed King	.25
40	Connie Frederick	.15
41	Jeff Burger	.25
42	Monk Gafford	.15
43	David Rocker	.25
44	Jim Pyburn	.15
45	Bob Harris	.15
46	Travis Tidwell	.15
47	Ralph (Shug) Jordan (CO)	.40
48	Zeke Smith	.25
49	Terry Beasley	.25
50	Pat Sullivan	.40
51	Stacy Danley	.25
52	Jimmy Hitchcock	.15
53	John Wiley	.15
54	Greg Taylor	.15
55	Lamar Rogers	.25
56	Rob Selby	.15
57	James Joseph	.25
58	Mike Kolen	.15
59	Kevin Greene	.50
60	Ben Thomas	.15
61	Shayne Wasden	.15
62	Tex Warrington	.15
63	Tommie Agee	.25
64	Jim Phillips	.25
65	Lawyer Tillman	.40
66	Mark Dorminey	.15
67	Steve Wallace	.25
68	Ed Dyas	.15
69	Alexander Wright	.25
70	Lionel James	.25
71	Aundray Bruce	.25
72	Edmund Nelson	.15
73	Jack Youngblood	.50
74	Carlos Alvarez	.25
75	Ricky Nattiel	.25
76	Bill Carr	.15
77	Guy Dennis	.15
78	Charles Casey	.15
79	Louis Oliver	.40
80	John Reaves	.25
81	Wayne Peace	.15
82	Charlie LaPradd	.15
83	Wes Chandler	.40
84	Richard Trapp	.15
85	Ralph Ortega	.15
86	Tommy Durrance	.15
87	Burton Lawless	.25
88	Bruce Bennett	.15
89	Huey Richardson	.25
90	Larry Smith	.15
91	Trace Armstrong	.40
92	Nat Moore	.40
93	James Jones	.40
94	Kay Stephenson	.25
95	Scot Brantley	.15
96	Ray Criswell	.15
97	Steve Tannen	.15
98	Ernie Mills	.40
99	Bruce Vaughn	.15
100	Steve Spurrier	2.50
101	Crawford Ker	.25
102	David Galloway	.25
103	David Williams	.25
104	Lomas Brown	.40
105	Fernando Jackson	.15
106	Jeff Roth	.15
107	Mark Murray	.15
108	Kirk Kirkpatrick	.15
109	Ray Goff (CO)	.15
110	Quinton Lumpkin	.15
111	Royce Smith	.15
112	Larry Rakestraw	.25
113	Kevin Butler	.15
114	Aschel M. Day	.15
115	Scott Woerner	.25
116	Herb St. John	.15
117	Ray Rissmiller	.15
118	Buck Belue	.15
119	George Collins	.15
120	Joel Parrish	.15
121	Terry Hoage	.25
122	Frank Sinkwich	.25
123	Billy Payne	.50
124	Zeke Bratkowski	.25
125	Herschel Walker	1.00
126	Pat Dye (CO)	.40
127	Vernon Smith	.15
128	Rex Robinson	.15
129	Mike Castronis	.15
130	Pop Warner (CO)	.40
131	George Patton	.25
132	Harry Babcock	.15
133	Lindsay Scott	.25
134	Bill Stanfill	.15
135	Bill Hartman Jr.	.15
136	Eddie Weaver	.15
137	Tim Worley	.40
138	Ben Zambiasi	.40
139	Bob McWhorter	.15
140	Rodney Hampton	1.00
141	Len Hauss	.25
142	Wallace Butts	.25
143	Andy Johnson	.25
144	I.M. Shiver Jr.	.15
145	Clyde Johnson	.15
146	Steve Meilinger	.15
147	Howard Schnellenberger (CO)	.50
148	Irv Goode	.25
149	Sam Ball	.15
150	Babe Parilli	.40
151	Rick Norton	.25
152	Warren Bryant	.25
153	Mike Pfeifer	.15
154	Sonny Collins	.15
155	Mark Higgs	.40
156	Randy Holleran	.15
157	Bill Ransdell	.15
158	Joey Worley	.15
159	Jim Kovach	.25
160	Joe Federspiel	.25
161	Larry Seiple	.25
162	Darryl Bishop	.15
163	George Blanda	1.00
164	Oliver Barnett	.25
165	Paul Calhoun	.15
166	Dicky Lyons	.25
167	Tom Hutchinson	.25
168	George Adams	.25
169	Derrick Ramsey	.25
170	Rick Kestner	.15
171	Art Still	.40
172	Rick Nuzum	.15
173	Richard Jaffe	.15
174	Rodger Bird	.15
175	Jeff Van Note	.40
176	Herschel Turner	.15
177	Lou Michaels	.25
178	Ray Correll	.15
179	Doug Moseley	.15
180	Bob Gain	.25
181	Tommy Casanova	.40
182	Mike Anderson	.15
183	Craig Burns	.15
184	A.J. Duhe	.25
185	Lyman White	.15
186	Paul Dietzel (CO)	.15
187	Paul Lyons	.15
188	Eddie Ray	.15
189	Roy Winston	.25
190	Brad Davis	.15
191	Mike Williams	.15
192	Karl Wilson	.25
193	Ronnie Estay	.15
194	Malcolm Scott	.15
195	Greg Jackson	.15
196	Willie Teal	.25
197	Eddie Fuller	.15
198	Ralph Norwood	.15
199	Bert Jones	.40
200	Y.A. Tittle	.50
201	Jerry Stovall	.40
202	Henry Thomas	.40
203	Lance Smith	.15
204	Doug Moreau	.25
205	Tyler LaFauci	.15
206	George Bevan	.15
207	Robert Dugas	.25
208	Carlos Carson	.25
209	Andy Hamilton	.15
210	James Britt	.15
211	Wendell Davis	.40
212	Ron Sancho	.15
213	Johnny Robinson	.40
214	Eric Martin	.40
215	Michael Brooks	.25
216	Toby Caston	.25
217	Jesse Anderson	.15
218	Jimmy Webb	.15
219	Mardye McDole	.15
220	David Smith	.15
221	Dana Moore	.15
222	Cedric Corse	.15
223	Louis Clark	.15
224	Walter Packer	.15
225	George Wonsley	.25
226	Billy Jackson	.25
227	Bruce Plummer	.15
228	Aaron Pearson	.15
229	Glen Collins	.15
230	Paul Davis (CO)	.15
231	Wayne Jones	.15
232	John Bond	.15
233	Johnnie Cooks	.25
234	Robert Young	.15
235	Don Smith	.15
236	Kent Hull	.40
237	Tony Shell	.15
238	Steve Freeman	.25
239	James Williams	.15
240	Tom Goode	.15
241	Stan Black	.15
242	Bo Russell	.15
243	Ricky Byrd	.15
244	Frank Dowsing	.15
245	Wayne Harris	.40
246	Richard Keys	.15
247	Artie Cosby	.15
248	Dave Marler	.15
249	Michael Haddix	.25
250	Jerry Clower	.25
251	Bill Bell	.15
252	Jerry Bouldin	.15
253	Parker Hall	.15
254	Allen Brown	.15
255	Bill Smith	.15
256	Freddie Joe Nunn	.25
257	John Vaught (CO)	.25
258	Buford McGee	.15
259	Kenny Dill	.15
260	Jim Miller	.15
261	Doug Jacobs	.15
262	John Dottley	.15
263	Willie Green	.40
264	Tony Bennett	.40
265	Stan Hindman	.15
266	Charles Childers	.15
267	Harry Harrison	.15
268	Todd Sandroni	.15
269	Glynn Griffing	.15
270	Chris Mitchell	.15
271	Shawn Cobb	.15
272	Doug Elmore	.15
273	Dawson Pruett	.15
274	Warner Alford	.15
275	Archie Manning	1.00
276	Kelvin Pritchett	.25
277	Pat Coleman	.15
278	Stevon Moore	.25
279	John Darnell	.15
280	Wesley Walls	.25
281	Billy Brewer	.25
282	Mark Young	.15
283	Aaron Townsend	.15
284	Billy Ray Adams	.15
285	Jim Dunaway	.25
286	Paige Cothren	.15
287	Jake Gibbs	.40
288	Jim Urbanek	.15
289	Tony Thompson	.15
300	Johnny Majors (CO)	.40
301	Roland Poles	.15
302	Alvin Harper	.50
303	Doug Baird	.15
304	Greg Burke	.15
305	Sterling Henton	.15
306	Preston Warren	.15
307	Stanley Morgan	.50
308	Bobby Scott	.15
309	Doug Atkins	.40
310	Bill Young	.15
311	Bob Garmon	.15
312	Herman Weaver	.15
313	Dewey Warren	.15
314	John Boynton	.15
315	Bob Davis	.15
316	Pat Ryan	.25
317	Keith DeLong	.25
318	Bobby Dodd (CO)	.25
319	Ricky Townsend	.15

320	Eddie Brown	.25
321	Herman Hickman (CO)	.25
322	Nathan Dougherty	.15
323	Mickey Marvin	.15
324	Reggie Cobb	.40
325A	Condredge Holloway	.50
325B	Josh Cody	.15
326A	Anthony Hancock	.40
326B	Jack Jenkins	.15
327A	Steve Kiner	.15
327B	Bob Goodridge	.15
328A	Mike Mauck	.15
328B	Chris Gaines	.15
329A	Bill Bates	.40
329B	Willie Geny	.15
330A	Austin Denney	.25
330B	Bob Laws	.15
331A	Robert Nevland (CO)	.40
331B	Rob Monaco	.15
332A	Bob Suffridge	.15
332B	Chuck Scott	.15
333A	Abe Shires	.15
333B	Hek Wakefield	.15
334A	Robert Shaw	.40
334B	Ken Stone	.15
335	Mark Adams	.15
336	Ed Smith	.15
337	Dan McGugin (CO)	.15
338	Doug Mathews	.15
339	Whit Taylor	.40
340	Gene Moshier	.15
341	Christine Hauck	.15
342	Lee Nalley	.15
343	Wamon Buggs	.15
344	Jim Arnold	.25
345	Buford Ray	.25
346	Will Wolford	.25
347	Steve Bearden	.15
348	Frank Mordica	.15
349	Barry Burton	.15
350	Bill Wade	.40
351	Tommy Woodroof	.15
352	Steve Wade	.15
353	Preston Brown	.15
354	Ben Roderick	.15
355	Charles Horton	.15
356	DeMond Winston	.15
357	John North	.15
358	Don Orr	.15
359	Art Demmas	.15
360	Mark Johnson	.15
361	Hootie Ingram (AD)	.25
362	Gene Stallings (CO)	.50
363	Alabama Checklist	.15
364	Pat Dye (CO)	.25
365	Auburn Checklist	.15
366	Vince Dooley (AD)	.25
367	Ray Goff (CO)	.25
368	Georgia Checklist	.15
369	C.M. Newton (AD)	.25
370	Bill Curry (CO)	.25
371	Kentucky Checklist	.15
372	Joe Dean (AD)	.15
373	Curley Hallman (CO)	.25
374	LSU Checklist	.15
375	Warner Alford (CO)	.25
376	Billy Brewer (CO)	.25
377	Ole Miss Checklist	.15
378	Larry Templeton (AD)	.15
379	Jackie Sherrill (CO)	.40
380	Mississippi State Checklist	.15
381	Bill Arnsparger (AD)	.25
382	Steve Spurrier (CO)	1.25
383	Florida Checklist	.15
384	Doug Dickey (AD)	.15
385	Johnny Majors (CO)	.25
386	Tennessee Checklist	.15
387	Paul Hoolahan (AD)	.15
388	Gerry DiNardo (CO)	.25
389	Vanderbilt Checklist	.15
390	The Iron Bowl - Alabama vs. Auburn	.40
391	Largest Outdoor Cocktail Party Florida vs. Georgia	.15
392	The Egg Bowl Mississippi State vs. Ole Miss	.15
393	The Beer Barrel - Kentucky vs. Tennessee	.15
394	Drama on Halloween - LSU vs. Ole Miss	.15
395	Tennessee Hoedown Tennessee vs. Vanderbilt	.15
396	Roy Kramer (COMM)	.15

1991 Hoby SEC Stars Signature

		MT
Complete Set (10):		375.00
Common Player:		15.00
1	Carlos Alvarez	15.00
2	Zeke Bratkowski	25.00
3	Jerry Clower	15.00
4	Condredge Holloway	25.00
5	Bert Jones	50.00
6	Archie Manning	75.00
7	Ken Stabler	100.00
8	Pat Sullivan	50.00
9	Jeff Van Note	20.00
10	Bill Wade	25.00

1992 Houston Motion Sports

		MT
Complete Set (66):		30.00
Common Player:		.50
1	Freddie Gilbert	.60
2	Lorenzo Dickson	.50
3	Sherman Smith	1.00
4	Brad Whigham	.50
5	Allen Aldridge	1.00
6	Truett Akin	.50
7	Nahala Johnson	.50
8	1980 Garden State Bowl (Terald Clark)	.50
9	1977 Cotton Bowl	.60
10	Tyrone Davis	.50
11	Kevin Bleier	.50
12	Nigel Ventress	.50
13	Darren Woods	.50
14	Linton Weatherspoon	.50
15	John R. Morris	.50
16	Kevin Batiste	.60
17	Kelvin McKnight	.50
18	Stewart Carpenter	.50
19	Ron Peters	.50
20	Stephen Dixon	.60
21	Chandler Evans	.50
22	Tyler Mucho	.50
23	Kevin Labay	.50
24	Steve Clarke	.50
25	Keith Jack	.50
26	Steve Matejka	.50
27	The Astrodome	.50
28	Roman Anderson	.50
29	Quarterback U (Andre Ware, David Klingler)	1.50
30	Cougar Pride (Andre Ware, David Klingler)	1.50
31	Bayou Bucket (Annual Houston vs. Rice game)	.50
32	Jeff Tait	.50
33	Donald Douglas	.50
34	Victor Mamich	.50
35	John W. Brown	.50
36	Zach Chatman	.50
37	Jason Youngblood	.50
38	David Klingler	2.00
39	John H. Brown	.50
40	Tommy Guy	.50
41	1980 Cotton Bowl (Game action)	.60
42	1973 Bluebonnet Bowl (Game action)	.60
43	Chris Pezman	.50
44	Tracy Good	.50
45	Stephen Harris	.50
46	Ryan McCoy	.60
47	Michael Newhouse	.50
48	Jimmy Klingler	1.50
49	Joe Wheeler	.50
50	Eric Harrison	.50
51	Craig Hall	.50
52	Shasta (Mascot)	.50
53	NCAA Records (Passing and Receiving)	.60
54	Darrell Clapp	.50
55	Eric Blount	.50
56	Tiandre Sanders	.50
57	Kyle Allen	.50
58	Brisket Howard	.50
59	Greg Thornburgh	.50
60	Wilson Whitley	1.00
61	Andre Ware	2.00
62	John Jenkins (CO)	.60
NNO	Ad Card Motion Sports	.50
NNO	Front Card	.50
NNO	Back Card	.50
NNO	Checklist	.50

1988 Humboldt State Smokey

		MT
Complete Set (11):		12.00
Common Player:		1.25
1	Richard Ashe (1)	1.25
2	Darin Bradbury (64)	1.25
3	Rodney Dorsett (7)	1.25
4	Dave Harper (55)	1.25
5	Earl Jackson (6)	1.25
6	Derek Mallard (82)	1.25
7	Scott Reagan (60)	1.25
8	Wesley White (1)	1.25
9	Paul Wienecke (40)	1.25
10	William Williams (14)	1.25
11	Kelvin Windham (30)	1.25

1989 Idaho

		MT
Complete Set (12):		12.00
Common Player:		.75
3	Brian Smith	.75
13	Tim S. Johnson	.75
16	Lee Allen	.75
17	John Friesz	5.00
20	Todd Hoiness	.75
25	David Jackson	.75
53	Steve Unger	.75
58	John Rust	.75
63	Troy Wright	.75
67	Todd Neu	.75
83	Michael Davis	.75
93	Mike Zeller	.75

1990 Illinois Centennial

		MT
Complete Set (45):		25.00
Common Player:		.35
1	Harold "Red" Grange	3.00
2	Dick Butkus	2.50
3	Ray Nitschke	1.50
4	Jim Grabowski	.50
5	Alex Agase	.50
6	Claude Young	.50
7	Scott Studwell	.50
8	Tony Eason	.50
9	John Mackovic	.75
10	Jack Trudeau	.75
11	Jeff George	2.00
12	Rose Bowl Coaches (Ray Eliot, Pete Elliott, Mike White)	.35
13	George Huff	.35
14	David Williams	.35
15	Bob Zuppke	.50
16	George Halas	2.00
17	Dike Eddleman	.35
18	Dave Wilson	.35
19	Tab Bennett	.35
20	Jim Juriga	.35
21	John Karras	.35
22	Bobby Mitchell	1.00
23	Dan Beaver	.35
24	Joe Rutgens	.50
25	Bill Burrell	.35
26	J.C. Caroline	.50
27	Al Brosky	.35
28	Don Thorp	.35
29	First Football Team	.35
30	Harold "Red" Grange (Retired)	1.00
31	Memorial Stadium	.35
32	Chris White	.35
33	Early Stars (Ralph Chapman, Perry Graves, Bart Macomber)	.35
34	Early Stars (John Depler, Jim McMillen)	.35
35	Early Stars (Burt Ingwerson, Butch Nowack, Bernie Shively)	.35
36	Great Quarterbacks (Fred Custardo, Mike Wells, Tom O'Connell)	.35
37	Great Running Backs (Thomas Rooks, Abe Woodson, Keith Jones)	.50
38	Great Receivers (Mike Bellamy, Doug Dieken, John Wright)	.50
39	Great Offensive (Forrest Van Hook, Larry McCarren, Chris Babyar)	.35
40	Great Defensive Backs (Craig Swope, George Donnelly, Mike Gower)	.35
41	Great Linebackers (Charles Boerlo, Don Hansen, John Sullivan)	.35
42	Defensive Linemen (Archie Sutton, Chuck Studley, Scott Davis)	.35
43	Great Kickers (Mike Bass K, Bill Brown, Frosty Peters)	.35
44	Retired Numbers (Dick Butkus)	1.50
45	Football Centennial Logo	.35

1992 Illinois

		MT
Complete Set (48):		18.00
Common Player:		.35
1	Derek Allen	.35
2	Jeff Arneson	.35
3	Randy Bierman	.35
4	Darren Boyer	.35
5	Rod Boykin	.35
6	Mike Cole	.35
7	Chad Copher	.35
8	Fred Cox	.50
9	Robert Crumpton	.50
10	Ken Dilger	2.00
11	Jason Edwards	.35
12	Greg Engel	.35
13	Steve Feagin	.35
14	Erik Foggey	.35
15	Kevin Hardy	3.00
16	Jeff Hasenstab	.35
17	John Holecek	.50
18	Brad Hopkins	.75
19	John Horn	.35
20	Dana Howard	1.00
21	Jon Kerr	.35
22	Jeff Kinney	.50
23	Jim Klein	.35
24	Todd Leach	.35
25	Wagner Lester	.35
26	Lashon Ludington	.35
27	Clinton Lynch	.35
28	Tim McCloud	.35
29	David Olson	.35
30	Antwoine Patton	.50
31	Jim Pesek	.35
32	Alfred Pierce	.35
33	Mark Qualls	.35
34	Phil Rathke	.35
35	Chris Richardson	.50
36	Derrick Rucker	.35
37	Aaron Shelby	.35
38	John Sidari	.35
39	J.J. Strong	.35
40	Mike Suarez	.35
41	Lou Tepper (CO)	.50
42	Scott Turner	.35
43	Jason Verduzco	1.00
44	Tyrone Washington	.35
45	Forry Wells	.35
46	Pat Wendt	.35
47	John Wright	.35

1982 Indiana State Police

		MT
Complete Set (64):		175.00
Common Player:		3.00
1	David Allen	3.00
2	Doug Arnold	3.00
3	James Banks	3.00
4	Scott Bartel	3.00
5	Kurt Bell	3.00
6	Terry Bell	3.00
7	Steve Bidwell	3.00
8	Keith Bonney	3.00
9	Mark Boster	3.00
10	Bobby Boyce	3.00
11	Steve Brickey (CO)	3.00
12	Mark Bryson	3.00
13	Steve Buxton	3.00
14	Ed Campbell	3.00
15	Jeff Campbell	5.00
16	Tom Chapman	3.00
17	Cheerleaders (Ruth Ann Medworth DIR)	4.00
18	Darrold Clardy	3.00
19	Wayne Davis	3.00
20	Herbert Dawson	3.00
21	Richard Dawson	4.00
22	Chris Delaplaine	3.00
23	Max Dillon	3.00
24	Rick Dwenger	3.00
25	Ed Foggs	3.00
26	Allen Hartwig	3.00
27	Pat Henderson (CO)	3.00
28	Don Hitz	3.00
29	Pete Hoener (CO)	3.00
30	Bob Hopkins	3.00
31	Kris Huber (Baton Twirler)	4.00
32	Leroy Irvin	20.00
33	Mike Johannes	3.00
34	Anthony Kimball	3.00
35	Gregg Kimbrough	3.00
36	Bob Koehne	3.00
37	Jerry Lasko (CO)	3.00
38	Kevin Lynch	3.00
39	Dan Maher	3.00
40	Ed Martin	3.00
41	Regis Mason	3.00
42	Rob McIntyre	3.00
43	Quintin Mikell	3.00
44	Jeff Miller	3.00
45	Mark Miller	3.00
46	Mike Osborne	3.00
47	Max Payne (CO)	3.00
48	Scott Piercy	3.00
49	Dennis Raetz (CO)	3.00
50	Kevin Ramsey	3.00
51	Dean Reader	3.00
52	Eric Robinson	3.00
53	Walter Seaphus	3.00
54	Sparkettes (Marthann Markler DIR)	4.00
55	John Spradley	3.00
56	Manual Studway	3.00
57	Sam Suggs	3.00
58	Larry Swart	3.00
59	Bob Tyree	3.00
60	Bob Turner (CO)	3.00
61	Brad Verdun	3.00
62	Keith Ward	3.00
63	Sean Whiten	3.00
64	Perry Willett	3.00

1971 Iowa Team Photos

		NM
Complete Set (4):		25.00
Common Sheet:		6.00
1	Geoff Mickelson, Craig Clemons, Frank Holmes, Levi Mitchell, Charles Podolak, Lorin Lynch, Steve Penney, Larry	8.00
2	Alan Schaefer, Dave Triplett, John Muller, Jim Kaiser, Wendell Bell, Clark Malmer, Rich Solomon, Kelly	6.00
3	Bill Schoonover, Frank Sunderman, Craig Darling, Tom Cabalka, Dave Simms, Bill Rose, Buster Hoinkes, Charles	6.00
4	Kyle Skogman, Jerry Reardon, Dave Harris, Rob Fick, Mike Dillner, Ike White, Mark Nelson, Harry Kokolus	6.00

1984 Iowa

		MT
Complete Set (60):		50.00
Common Player:		.75
1	Kevin Angel	.75
2	Kerry Burt	.75
3	Fred Bush	.75
4	Craig Clark	.75
5	Zane Corbin	.75
6	Nate Creer	.75
7	Dave Croston	.75
8	George Davis	.75
9	Jeff Drost	.75
10	Quinn Early	4.00
11	Mike Flagg	.75
12	Hayden Fry (CO)	2.50
13	Bruce Gear	.75
14	Owen Gill	2.00
15	Bill Glass	1.00
16	Mike Haight	1.50
17	Bill Happel	.75
18	Kevin Harmon	1.00
19	Ronnie Harmon	4.00
20	Craig Hartman	.75
21	Jon Hayes	2.00
22	Erric Hedgeman	.75
23	Scott Helverson	.75
24	Mike Hooks	.75
25	Paul Hufford	.75
26	Keith Hunter	.75
27	George Little	.75
28	Chuck Long	2.00
29	J.C. Love-Jordan	.75
30	George Millett	.75
31	Devon Mitchell	1.00
32	Tom Nichol	.75
33	Kelly O'Brien	.75
34	Hap Peterson	.75
35	Joe Schuster	1.00
36	Tim Sennott	.75
37	Ken Sims	.75
38	Mark Sindlinger	.75
39	Robert Smith	.75
40	Kevin Spitzig	.75
41	Larry Station	.75
42	Mike Stoops	.75
43	Dave Strobel	.75
44	Mark Vlasic	2.00
45	Jon Vrieze	.75
46	Tony Wancket	.75
47	Herb Webster	.75
48	Coaching Staff	1.00
49	Captains	1.50
50	Bowl Players	1.00
51	Harmon Brothers (Kevin Harmon, Ronnie Harmon)	1.50
52	Cheerleaders	1.00
53	Pompons	1.00
54	Kinnick Stadium	.75
55	Herky the Hawk (Mascot)	.75
56	Rose Bowl Ring	.75
57	Peach Bowl Trophy	.75
58	Gator Bowl Stadium	.75
59	Floyd of Rosedale (Trophy)	.75
60	Checklist Card	.75

1987 Iowa

		MT
Complete Set (63):		40.00
Common Player:		.60
1	Mark Adams	.60
2	Dave Alexander	1.00
3	Bill Anderson	.60
4	Tim Anderson	.60
5	Rick Bayless	.60
6	Jeff Beard	.60
7	Mike Burke	.60
8	Kerry Burt	.60
9	Malcolm Christie	.60
10	Craig Clark	.60
11	Marv Cook	2.00
12	Jeff Croston	.60
13	Greg Divis	.60
14	Quinn Early	2.50
15	Greg Fedders	.60
16	Mike Flagg	.60
17	Melvin Foster	.60
18	Hayden Fry (CO)	2.00
19	Grant Goodman	.60
20	Dave Haight	1.00
21	Merton Hanks	3.00
22	Deven Harberts	.60
23	Kevin Harmon	.75
24	Chuck Hartlieb	1.25
25	Tork Hook	.60
26	Rob Houghtlin	.60
27	David Hudson	.60
28	Myron Keppy	.60
29	Jeff Koeppel	.60
30	Bob Kratch	1.50
31	Peter Marciano	.60
32	Jim Mauro	.60
33	Marc Mazzeri	.60
34	Dan McGwire	2.00
35	Mike Miller	.60
36	Joe Mott	1.00
37	James Pipkins	.60
38	Tom Poholsky	.75
39	Jim Poynton	.60
40	J.J. Puk	.75
41	Brad Quast	.60
42	Jim Reilly	.60
43	Matt Ruhland	.60
44	Bob Schmitt	.60
45	Joe Schuster	.75
46	Dwight Sistrunk	.75
47	Mark Stoops	.60
48	Steve Thomas	.60
49	Kent Thompson	.60
50	Travis Watkins	.60
51	Herb Wester	.60
52	Anthony Wright	.60
53	Big 10 Championship Ring and Rose Bowl Ring	
54	Cheerleaders	.75
55	Floyd of Rosedale (Trophy)	.60
56	Freedom Bowl (Game Action Photo)	.75
57	Herky the Hawk (Mascot)	.60
58	Holiday Bowl (Game Action Photo)	.75
59	Indoor Practice Facility	.60
60	Iowa Team Captains (Quinn Early and five others)	1.50
61	Kinnick Stadium	.60
62	Peach Bowl (Game Action Photo)	.60
63	Pom Pons (Cheerleaders)	1.00

1988 Iowa

		MT
Complete Set (64):		30.00
Common Player:		.50
2	Travis Watkins	.60

4 James Pipkins .50
5 Mike Burke .50
8 Chuck Hartlieb 1.00
10 Anthony Wright .50
14 Tom Poholsky .60
16 Deven Harberts .50
18 Leroy Smith .50
20 David Hudson .50
21 Tony Stewart .50
22 Sean Smith .50
23 Richard Bass .50
26 Peter Marciano .50
29 Greg Brown .50
30 Grant Goodman .50
31 John Derby .50
32 Mike Saunders 1.00
35 Brad Quast .50
38 Chet Davis .50
40 Marc Mazzeri .50
41 Mark Stoops .50
42 Tork Hook .50
44 Keaton Smiley .50
45 Merton Hanks 2.00
48 Tyrone Berrie .50
50 Bill Anderson .50
51 Jeff Koeppel .50
53 Greg Fedders .50
57 Matt Ruhland .50
58 Greg Davis .50
60 Bob Schmitt .50
61 Dave Turner .50
64 Dave Haight .75
66 Melvin Foster .50
67 Jim Poynton .50
68 Tim Anderson .50
70 Bob Kratch 1.00
71 Jim Johnson .50
74 George Hawthorne .50
75 Greg Aegerter .50
77 Paul Glonek .50
80 Steve Green .50
81 Brian Wise .50
82 Jon Filloon .50
84 Marv Cook 1.50
85 John Palmer .60
87 Jeff Skillett .50
88 Tom Ward .50
95 Jim Reilly .50
96 Ron Geater .50
97 Joe Mott .75
99 Moses Santos .50
NNO Team Captains 1.00
(Marv Crook and four others)
NNO Hayden Fry (CO) 1.00
NNO Holiday Bowl 1987 .75
(Hayden Fry) (CO)
NNO Peach Bowl (Game .60
Action Photo)
NNO Holiday Bowl 1986 .60
(Game Action Photo)
NNO Herky the Hawk .50
(Mascot)
NNO Cheerleaders .60
NNO Kinnick Stadium .50
NNO Pom Pons .60
(Cheerleaders)
NNO Championship .50
Rings
NNO Indoor Practice .50
Facility
NNO Symbolic Tiger .50
Hawk (Helmet)

1989 Iowa

Complete Set (90): 30.00 MT
Common Player: .40
1 Greg Aegerter .40
2 Kevin Allendorf .40
3 Bill Anderson .40
4 Richard Bass .40
5 Rob Baxley .40
6 Nick Bell 1.50
7 Phil Bradley .40
8 Greg Brown .40
9 Doug Buch .40
10 Gary Clark .40
11 Roderick Davis .40
12 Scott Davis 1.00
13 John Derby .50
14 Mike Devlin .40
15 Jason Dumont .40
16 Mike Ertz .40
17 Ted Faley .40
18 Greg Fedders .40
19 Mike Ferroni .50
20 Jon Filloon .40
21 Melvin Foster .40
22 Hayden Fry (CO) 1.00
23 Ron Geater .40
24 Ed Gochenour .40
25 Merton Hanks 2.00
26 Jim Hartlieb .50
27 George Hawthorne .40
28 Tork Hook .40
29 Danan Hughes 1.00
30 Jim Johnson .40
31 Jeff Koeppel .40
32 Marvin Lampkin .40
33 Peter Marciano .40
34 Ed Marshall .40
35 Kirk McGowan .40
36 Mike Miller .40
37 Lew Montgomery .40
38 George Murphy .40

39 John Palmer .50
40 James Pipkins .40
41 Tom Poholsky .50
42 Eddie Polly .40
43 Jim Poynton .40
44 Brad Quast .40
45 Matt Rodgers .75
46 Matt Ruhland .40
47 Ron Ryan .40
48 Moses Santos .40
49 Mike Saunders .75
50 Doug Scott .40
51 Jeff Skillett .40
52 Leroy Smith .40
53 Sean Smith .40
54 Sean Snyder .40
55 Tony Stewart .40
56 Mark Stoops .40
57 Dave Turner .40
58 Darin Vande Zande .40
59 Ted Velicer .40
60 Travis Watkins .40
61 Dusty Weiland .40
62 Ladd Wessles .40
63 Matt Whitaker .40
64 Brian Wise .40
65 Anthony Wright .40
66 100 Years of Iowa .40
Football (Logo)
67 The Tigerhawk .40
(School Logo)
68 Herky the Hawk .40
(Mascot)
69 Kinnick Stadium .40
70 Hawkeye Fans .40
71 NFL Tradition .40
(Logo)
72 1982 Beach Bowl .40
(Logo)
73 1982 Rose Bowl .40
(Logo)
74 1983 Gator Bowl .40
(Logo)
75 1984 Freedom .40
Bowl (Logo)
76 1986 Holiday Bowl .40
(Logo)
77 1986 Rose Bowl .40
(Logo)
78 1987 Holiday Bowl .40
(Logo)
79 1988 Beach Bowl .40
(Logo)
80 Big Ten Conference .40
(Logo)
81 Iowa Marching .40
Band
82 Indoor Practice .40
Facility
83 Iowa Locker .40
Rooms
84 Iowa Weight Room .40
85 Iowa Class Rooms .40
86 Players' Lounge .40
87 Floyd of Rosedale .40
(Trophy)
88 Medical Facilities .40
89 Media Coverage .40
90 Television .40
Coverage (Camera)

1993 Iowa

Complete Set (64): 25.00 MT
Common Player: .40
1 Ryan Abraham .50
2 Greg Allen .40
3 Jeff Andrews .40
4 Jeff Anttila .40
5 Jefferson Bates .40
6 George Bennett .40
7 Lloyd Bickham .40
8 Larry Blue .40
9 Pat Boone .40
10 Tyrone Boudreaux .40
11 Paul Burmeister .75
12 Tyler Casey .40
13 Billy Coats .40
14 Maurea Crain .40
15 Ernest Crank .50
16 Mike Dailey .40
17 Anthony Dean .50
18 Bobby Diaco .40
19 Mike Duprey .40
20 Billy Ennis-Inge .40
21 Matt Eyde .40
22 Fritz Fequiere .75
23 Hayden Fry (CO) 1.00
24 Willie Guy .40
25 John Hartlieb .50
26 Jason Henlon .40
27 Matt Hilliard .50
28 Mike Hornaday .40
29 Rob Huber .40
30 Chris Jackson .40
31 Harold Jasper .75
32 Jamar Jones .40
33 Kent Kahl .40
34 Cliff King .40
35 John Kline .40
36 Tom Knight .50
37 Aaron Kooiker .40
38 Andy Kreider .40
39 Bill Lange .40
40 Doug Laufenberg .40
41 Hal Mady .50

42 Brian McCullouch .40
43 Jason Olejniczak .40
44 Chris Palmer .40
45 Scott Plate .50
46 Marquis Porter .40
47 Matt Purdy .40
48 Matt Quest .40
49 Damien Robinson .40
50 Todd Romano .40
51 Mark Roussell .40
52 Ted Serama .40
53 Scott Sether .40
54 Sedrick Shaw .50
55 Scott Slutzker .50
56 Ryan Terry .50
57 Mike Wells .40
58 Casey Wiegmann .40
59 Parker Wildeman .40
60 Big Ten Conference .40
(Logo card)
61 Hawkeyes .40
Schedule
62 Herky (Mascot) .40
63 Indoor Practice .40
Facility
64 Kinnick Stadium .40

1997 Iowa

Complete Set (19): 30.00 MT
Common Player: 1.50
1 Brett Chambers 1.50
2 Billy Coats 1.50
3 Ryan Driscoll 2.00
4 Bill Ennis-Inge 2.50
5 Rodney Flier 1.50
6 Hayden Fry 2.50
7 Nick Gallery 1.50
8 Aaron Granquist 1.50
9 Brion Hurley 1.50
10 Tom Knight 3.00
11 Mark Mitchell 1.50
12 Demo Odems 1.50
13 Jon Ortlieb 1.50
14 Bill Reardon 1.50
15 Damien Robinson 2.00
16 Ted Serama 1.50
17 Ross Verba 3.00
18 Hawk Watch (1996 2.00
Seniors Iowa
Hawkeyes Football)
19 Hawkeyes Logo 1.50

1989 Kansas

MAURICE DOUGLAS

Complete Set (40): 12.00 MT
Common Player: .35
1 Kelly Donohoe .75
2 Roger Robben .35
3 Tony Sands .35
4 Paul Zaffaroni .35
5 Lance Flachsbarth .35
6 Brad Fleeman .35
7 Chip Budde .50
8 Bill Hundelt .35
9 Dan Newbrough .35
10 Gary Oatis .35
11 B.J. Lohsen .35
12 John Fritch .35
13 Russ Bowen .35
14 Smith Holland .35
15 Jason Priest .35
16 Scott McCabe .35
17 Jason Tyrer .35
18 Mongo Allen .35
19 Glen Mason (CO) 1.00
20 Deral Boykin .35
21 Quintin Smith .35
22 Mark Koncz .35
23 John Baker .50
24 Football Staff .50
(schedule on back)
25 Maurice Hooks .35
26 Frank Hatchett .35
27 Paul Friday .35
28 Doug Terry .35
29 Kenny Drayton .35
30 Jim New .35
31 Chris Perez .35
32 Maurice Douglas 1.25
33 Curtis Moore .35
34 David Gordon .35
35 Matt Nolen .35
36 Dave Walton .35

37 King Dixon .50
38 Memorial Stadium .35
39 Jayhawks in Action .50
(Kelly Donohoe)
40 Jayhawks in Action .50
(John Baker) (OL)
NNO Title Card .75

1992 Kansas

Complete Set (52): 20.00 MT
Common Player: .40
1 Mark Allison .40
2 Hassan Bailey .50
3 Greg Ballard .40
4 Martin Blakeney .40
5 Kristopher Booth .40
6 Charley Bowen .40
7 Gilbert Brown 1.00
8 Dwayne Chandler .40
9 Brian Christian .40
10 David Converse .40
11 Monte Cozzens .40
12 Don Davis .40
13 Maurice Douglas 1.00
14 Dan Eichloff .50
15 Chad Fette .40
16 Matt Gay .40
17 Harold Harris .40
18 Rodney Harris .40
19 Steve Harvey .40
20 Hessley .40
Hempstead
21 Chip Hilleary 1.00
22 Dick Holt .40
23 Guy Howard .40
24 Chaka Johnson .40
25 John Jones .40
26 Rod Jones .40
27 Kwamie Lassiter .50
28 Trace Liggett .40
29 Keith Loneker .40
30 Dave Marcum .40
31 Glen Mason (CO) .75
32 Chris Maumalanga 1.00
33 Gerald McBurrows .40
35 Robert Mitchell .40
36 Ty Moeder .40
37 Kyle Moore .40
38 Ron Page .40
39 Chris Powell .40
40 Dan Schmidt .40
41 Ashaundai Smith .40
42 Mike Steele .40
43 Dana Stubblefield 4.00
44 Wes Swinford .40
45 Larry Thiel .40
46 Frederick Thomas .50
47 Pete Vang .40
48 Robert Vaughn .40
49 George White .50
50 Sylvester Wright .40
NNO Schedule Card .40
NNO Coaching Staff .40

1982 Kentucky Schedules

Complete Set (19): 45.00 MT
Common Player: 3.00
1 Richard Abraham 3.00
2 Glenn Amerson 3.00
3 Effley Brooks 3.00
4 Shawn Donigan 3.00
5 Rod Francis 3.00
6 Terry Henry 3.00
7 Ben Johnson 3.00
8 Dave Lyons 3.00
9 John Maddox 3.00
10 Rob Mangas 4.00
11 David "Buzz" 3.00
Meers
12 Andy Molls 3.00
13 Tom Petty 3.00
14 Don Roe 3.00
15 Todd Shadowen 3.00
16 Gerald Smyth 3.00
17 Pete Venable 3.00
18 Allan Watson 3.00
19 Steve Williams 3.00

1986 Kentucky Schedules

Complete Set (4): 15.00 MT
Common Player: 4.00
1 Jerry Claiborne (CO) 4.00
2 Mark Higgs 7.50
3 Marc Logan 6.00
4 Bill Ransdell 4.00

1981 Louisville Police

Complete Set (64): 125.00 MT
Common Player: 1.00
1 Title Card SP 50.00
(Catch That
Cardinal Spirit)
2 Bob Weber (CO) 1.00
3 Assistant Coaches 1.00
4 Jay Trautwein 1.00
5 Darrell Wimberly 1.00
6 Jeff Van Camp 1.00
7 Joe Welch 1.00
8 Fred Blackmon 1.00
9 Lamar "Toot" 1.00
Evans
10 Tom Blair 1.00
11 Joe Kader 1.00
12 Mike Trainor 1.00
13 Richard Tharpe 1.00
14 Gene Hagan 1.00
15 Greg Jones 1.00
16 Leon Williams 1.00
17 Ellsworth Larkins 1.00
18 Sebastian Curry 1.00
19 Frank Minnifield 6.00
20 Roger Clay 1.00
21 Mark Blasinsky 1.00
22 Mike Cruz 1.00
23 David Arthur 1.00
24 Johnny Unitas (In 15.00
front background,
list of Cardinals who
played pro ball)
25 John DeMarco 1.00
26 Eric Rollins 1.00
27 Jack Pok 1.00
28 Pete McCartney 1.00
29 Mark Clayton 15.00
30 Jeff Hortert 1.00
31 Pete Bowen 1.00
32 Robert Niece 1.00
33 Todd McMahan 1.00
34 John Wall 1.00
35 Kelly Stickrod 1.00
36 Jim Miller 1.00
37 Tom Moore 1.00
38 Kurt Knop 1.00
39 Mark Musgrave 1.00
40 Tony Campbell 1.00
41 Mark Wilson 1.00
42 Robert Mitchell 1.00
43 Courtney Jeter 1.00
44 Wayne Taylor 1.00
45 Jeff Speedy 1.00
46 Donald Craft 1.00
47 Glenn Hunter 1.00
48 1981 Louisville 1.00
Schedule
49 Greg Hickman 1.00
50 Nate Dozier 1.00
51 Pat Patterson 1.00
52 Scott Gannon 1.00
53 Dean May 1.00
54 David Hatfield 1.00
55 Mike Nuzzolese 1.00
56 John Ayers 1.00
57 Lamar Cummins 1.00
58 Bill Olsen (AD) 1.00
59 Tailgating 1.00
60 Football Complex 1.00
61 Marching Band 1.00
62 Cheerleaders 1.00
63 Administration 1.00
Bldg.
64 Cardinal Bird 1.00

1990 Louisville Smokey

Complete Set (16): 25.00 MT
Common Player: 1.25
1 Greg Brohm 1.25
2 Jeff Brohm 1.50
3 Pete Burkey 1.25
4 Mike Flores 1.25
5 Dan Gangwer 1.25
6 Reggie Johnson 1.50
7 Scott McAllister 1.25
8 Ken McKay 1.25
9 Browning Nagle 4.00
10 Ed Reynolds 1.25
11 Mark Sander 1.25
12 Howard 5.00
Schnellenberger
(CO)
13 Ted Washington 2.50
14 Klaus Wilmsmeyer 2.00
15 Cardinal Bird 1.25
(Mascot)
16 Cardinal Stadium 1.25

1992 Louisville Kraft

Complete Set (30): 15.00 MT
Common Player: .60
1 Jamie Asher 1.50
2 Xzavia Atkins .60
3 Kevin Blumeier .60
4 Greg Brohm .60
5 Jeff Brohm .75
6 Brandon Brookfield .60
7 Ray Buchanan 2.00
8 Rawle Bynoe .60
9 Tom Cavallo .60
10 Kevin Cook .60

11 Andy Culley .60
12 Ralph Dawkins .75
13 Dave Debold .60
14 Chris Fitzpatrick .60
15 Kevin Gaines .60
16 Jose Gonzalez .60
17 Jim Hanna .60
18 Ken Harnden .60
19 Ivey Henderson .60
20 Joe Johnson 1.50
21 Robert Knuutila .60
22 Marty Lowe 1.00
23 Roman Oben 1.25
24 Garin Patrick .60
25 Leonard Ray .60
26 Shawn Rodriguez .60
27 Anthony Shelman 1.00
28 Brevin Smith .60
29 Jason Stinson .75
30 Ben Sumpter .75

1993 Louisville Kraft

Complete Set (30): 15.00 MT
Common Player: .60
1 Jamie Asher 1.25
2 Aaron Bailey .60
3 Zoe Barney .60
4 Anthony Bridges .60
5 Jeff Brohm .75
6 Brandon Brookfield .60
7 Kendall Brown .60
8 Tom Carrol .60
9 Tom Cavallo .60
10 Kevin Cook .60
11 Ralph Dawkins .75
12 Dave Debold .60
13 Reggie Ferguson .60
14 Chris Fitzpatrick .60
15 Johnny Frost .60
16 Jim Hanna .60
17 Ivey Henderson .60
18 Marcus Hill .60
19 Shawn Jackson .60
20 Joe Johnson 1.25
21 Marty Lowe .75
22 Vertis McKinney .60
23 Greg Minnis .60
24 Roman Oben 1.00
25 Garin Patrick .60
26 Terry Quinn .60
27 Leonard Ray .60
28 Anthony Shelman .75
29 Jason Stinson .60
30 Ben Sumpter .60

1983 LSU Sunbeam

Complete Set (100): 12.00 MT
Common Player: .10
1 1958 LSU National .20
Championship
Team
2 Abe Mickal .10
3 Carlos Carson .10
4 Charles Alexander .10
5 Steve Ensminger .10
6 Ken Kavanaugh Sr. .20
7 Bert Jones .50
8 David Woodley .20
9 Jerry Marchand .10
10 Clyde Lindsey .10
11 James Britt .20
12 Warren Rabb .10
13 Mike Hillman .10
14 Nelson Stokley .10
15 Abner Wimberly .10
16 Terry Robiskie .20
17 Steve Van Buren .30
18 Doug Moreau .20
19 George Tarasovic .10
20 Billy Cannon .30
21 Jerry Stovall .20
22 Joe Labruzzo .10
23 Mickey Mangham .10
24 Craig Burns .10
25 Y.A. Tittle .75
26 Wendell Harris .20
27 Leroy Labat .10
28 Hokie Gajan .20
29 Mike Williams .10
30 Sammy Grezaffi .10
31 Clinton Burrell .10
32 Orlando McDaniel .10
33 George Bevan .10
34 Johnny Robinson .20
35 Billy Masters .10
36 J.W. Brodnax .10
37 Tommy Casanova .20
38 Fred Miller .10
39 George Rice .10
40 Earl Gros .20
41 Lynn LeBlanc .10
42 Jim Taylor .40
43 Joe Tumenello .10
44 Tommy Davis .10
45 Alvin Dark .30
46 Richard Picou .10
47 Chaille Percy .10
48 John Garlington .20
49 Mike Morgan .10
50 Charles "Bo" .10
Strange
51 Max Fugler .30

52	Don Schwab	.10
53	Dennis Gaubatz	.20
54	Jimmy Field	.10
55	Warren Capone	.10
56	Albert Richardson	.10
57	Charley Cusiman	.10
58	Brad Davis	.10
59	Gaynell "Gus" Kinchen	.10
60	Roy "Moonie" Winston	.20
61	Mike Anderson	.10
62	Jesse Fatherree	.10
63	Gene "Red" Knight	.10
64	Tyler LaFauci	.10
65	Emile Fournet	.10
66	Gaynell "Gus" Tinsley	.20
67	Remi Prudhomme	.20
68	Marvin "Moose" Stewart	.10
69	Jerry Guillot	.10
70	Steve Cassidy	.10
71	Bo Harris	.20
72	Robert Dugas	.10
73	Malcolm Scott	.10
74	Charles "Pinky" Rohm	.10
75	Gerald Keigley	.10
76	Don Alexander	.10
77	A.J. Duhe	.20
78	Ronnie Estay	.10
79	John Wood	.10
80	Andy Hamilton	.20
81	Jay Michaelson	.10
82	Kenny Konz	.20
83	Tracy Porter	.10
84	Billy Truax	.20
85	Alan Risher	.10
86	John Adams	.10
87	Tommy Neck	.10
88	Brad Boyd	.10
89	Greg LaFluer	.10
90	Bill Elko	.10
91	Binks Miciotto	.10
92	Lew Sibley	.10
93	Willie Teal	.10
94	Lyman White	.10
95	Chris Williams	.10
96	Sid Fournet	.10
97	Leonard Marshall	.20
98	Ramsey Dardar	.10
99	Kenny Bordelon	.10
100	Fred "Skinny" Hall	.10

1985 LSU Police

		MT
Complete Set (16):		8.00
Common Player:		.50
1	Mitch Andrews	.50
2	Bill Arnsparger (CO)	.75
3	Roland Barbay	.50
4	Michael Brooks	1.00
5	Shawn Burks	.50
6	Tommy Clapp	.50
7	Matt DeFrank	.50
8	Kevin Guidry	.50
9	Dalton Hilliard	1.50
10	Garry James	.75
11	Norman Jefferson	.50
12	Rogie Magee	.50
13	Mike the Tiger (Mascot)	
14	Craig Rathjen	.50
15	Jeff Wickersham	.75
16	Karl Wilson	.75

1986 LSU Police

		MT
Complete Set (16):		8.00
Common Player:		.50
1	Nacho Albergamo	.50
2	Eric Andolsek	1.00
3	Bill Arnsparger (CO)	.75
4	Roland Barbay	.50
5	Michael Brooks	1.00
6	Chris Carrier	.50
7	Toby Caston	1.00
8	Wendell Davis	1.50
9	Kevin Guidry	.50
10	John Hazard	.50
11	Oliver Lawrence	.50
12	Rogie Magee	.50
13	Sam Martin	.75
14	Darrell Phillips	.50
15	Steve Rehage	.50
16	Ron Sancho	.75

1987 LSU Police

		MT
Complete Set (16):		10.00
Common Player:		.50
1	Nacho Albergamo	.50
2	Eric Andolsek	.75
3	Mike Archer (CO)	.75
4	David Browndyke	.50
5	Chris Carrier	.50
6	Wendell Davis	1.00
7	Matt DeFrank	.50
8	Nicky Hazard	.50
9	Eric Hill	1.00
10	Tommy Hodson	1.50
11	Greg Jackson	1.00
12	Brian Kinchen	1.00
13	Darren Malbrough	.50
14	Sam Martin	.50
15	Ron Sancho	.50
16	Harvey Williams	3.50

1988 LSU Police

		MT
Complete Set (16):		8.00
Common Player:		.50
1	Mike the Tiger (Mascot)	.50
2	Mike Archer (CO)	.75
3	Tommy Hodson	1.50
4	Harvey Williams	2.50
5	David Browndyke	.50
6	Karl Dunbar	.50
7	Eddie Fuller	.50
8	Mickey Guidry	.50
9	Greg Jackson	.75
10	Clint James	.50
11	Victor Jones	.50
12	Tony Moss	.50
13	Ralph Norwood	.50
14	Darrell Phillips	.50
15	Ruffin Rodrigue	.50
16	Ron Sancho	.50

1989 LSU Police

EDDIE FULLER · 33 · SENIOR · TAILBACK ·

		MT
Complete Set (16):		8.00
Common Player:		.50
1	Mike the Tiger (Mascot)	.50
2	David Browndyke	.50
3	Mike Archer (CO)	.75
4	Ruffin Rodrigue (68)	.50
5	Marc Boutte (95)	1.00
6	Clint James (70)	.50
7	Jimmy Young (5)	.50
8	Alvin Lee (26)	.50
9	Eddie Fuller (33)	.50
10	Tiger Stadium	.50
11	Harvey Williams (22)	2.00
12	Verge Ausberry (98)	.50
13	Karl Dunbar (63)	.50
14	Tommy Hodson (13)	1.25
15	Tony Moss (6)	.50
16	The Golden Girls (Cheerleaders)	.75

1992 LSU McDag

RAY ADAMS ~ CORNERBACK

	MT
Complete Set (16):	6.00

Common Player:

1	Curley Hallman (CO)	.50
2	Ray Adams	.50
3	Chad Loup	.75
4	Odell Beckham	.50
5	Wesley Jacob	.50
6	Kevin Mawae	1.00
7	Clayton Mouton	.50
8	Roovelroe Swan	.50
9	Ricardo Washington	.50
10	David Walkup	.50
11	Jessie Daigle	.50
12	Carlton Buckles	.50
13	Anthony Williams	.50
14	Darron Landry	.50
15	Frank Godfrey	.50
16	Pedro Suarez	.50

1969 Maryland Team Sheets

		NM
Complete Set (6):		25.00
Common Panel:		6.00
1	Bill Backus, Lou Bracken, Sonny Demczuk, Roland Merritt, Rich Slaninka, Ralph Sonntag, Mike Stubljar,Jim	6.00
2	Bill Bell CO, George Boutselis CO, Albert Ferguson CO, James Kehoe CO, Roy Lester CO, Dim Montero CO, Lee Royer	6.00
3	Pat Burke, John Dyer, Craig Gienger, Tony Greene, Bob MacBride, Bill Meister, Russ Nolan, Ray Soporowski	6.00
4	Steve Ciambor, Kenny Dutton, Dan Kecman, Bob Mahnic, Len Santacroce, David Seifert, Len Spicer, Rick Stoll	6.00
5	Bob Colbert, John Dill, Henry Gareis, Bill Grant, Glenn Kubany, Bill Reilly, Wally Stalnaker, Gary	6.00
6	Paul Fitzpatrick, Larry Marshall, Tom Miller, Will Morris, Dennis O'Hara, Scott Shank, Jeff Shugars, Al	6.00

1991 Maryland HS Big 33

		MT
Complete Set (34):		18.00
Common Player:		.75
1	Asim Penny	1.00
2	Louis Jason	1.00
3	Mark McCain	1.00
4	Matthew Byrne	.75
5	Mike Gillespie	.75
6	Ricky Rowe	.75
7	David DeArmas	1.00
8	Duane Ashman	.75
9	James Cunningham	.75
10	Keith Kormanik	.75
11	Leonard Green	.75
12	Larry Washington	.75
13	Raphael Wall	.75
14	Kai Hebron	.75
15	Coy Gibbs	1.00
16	Lenard Marcus	.75
17	John Taliaferro	1.00
18	J.C. Price	.75
19	Jamal Cox	1.00
20	Rick Budd	.75
21	Shaun Marshall	.75
22	Allan Jenkins	.75
23	Bryon Turner	.75
24	Ryan Foran	.75
25	John Summerday	.75
26	Joshua Austin	.75
27	Emile Palmer	.75
28	John Teter	.75
29	John Kennedy	.75
30	Clarence Collins	.75
31	Daryl Smith	.75
32	David Wilkins	.75
33	David Thomas	.75
34	Russell Thomas	1.00

1988 McNeese State McDag/Police

Tony Citizen Tailback 1988

	MT
Complete Set (16):	6.00
Common Player:	.50
1	Sonny Jackson (CO)	.50
2	Lance Wiley	.50
3	Brian McZeal	.50
4	Berwick Davenport	.50
5	Gary Irvin	.50
6	Glenn Koch	.50
7	Chad Habetz	.50
8	Pete Sinclair	.50
9	Tony Citizen	.50
10	Scott Dieterich	.50
11	Hud Jackson	.50
12	Darrin Andrus	.50
13	Jeff Mathews	.50
14	Devin Babineaux	.50
15	Jeff Delhomme	.50
16	Eric LeBlanc, Mike Pierce	.50

1989 McNeese State McDag/Police

		MT
Complete Set (16):		6.00
Common Player:		.50
1	Marc Stampley	.50
2	Mark LeBlanc	.50
3	Kip Texada	.50
4	Brian Champagne	.50
5	Ronald Scott	.50
6	Jimmy Poirier	.50
7	Cliff Buckner	.50
8	Jericho Loupe	.50
9	Vaughn Calbert	.50
10	Rodney Burks	.50
11	Troy Jones	.50
12	Chris Andrus	.50
13	Robbie Vizier	.50
14	Kenneth Pierce	.50
15	Bobby Smith	.50
16	Trent Lee	.50

1990 McNeese State McDag/Police

Kip Texada Cornerback 1990

		MT
Complete Set (16):		6.00
Common Player:		.50
1	Hud Jackson	.50
2	Wes Watts	.50
3	Mark LeBlanc	.50
4	Jeff Delhomme	.50
5	Mike Reed	.50
6	Chuck Esponge	.50
7	Ronald Scott	.50
8	Ken Naquin	.50
9	Steve Aultman	.50
10	Sean Judge	.50
11	Greg Rayson	.50
12	Kip Texada	.50
13	Mike Pierce	.50
14	Jimmy Poirier	.50
15	Ronald Solomon	.50
16	Eric Foster	.50

A card number in parentheses ( ) indicates the set is unnumbered.

1991 Miami Police

	MT
Complete Set (16):	15.00

1991 McNeese State McDag/Police

Erwin Brown Running Back/Wide Receiver 1991 cNeese Cowboys

		MT
Complete Set (16):		6.00
Common Player:		.50
1	Jessie Armstead	1.50
2	Irwin Brown	.50
3	Marcus Bowie	.50
4	Wes Watts	.50
5	Brian Brumfield	.50
6	Marc Stampley	.50
7	Sean Judge	.50
8	Joey Bernard	.50
9	Ken Naquin	.50
10	Bobby Smith	.50
11	Sam Breaux	.50
12	Ronald Scott	.50
13	Edward Dyer	.50
14	Blayne Rush	.50
15	Ronald Solomon	.50
16	Steve Aultman	.50

1992 McNeese State McDag/Police

McNeese Cowboys '92 ERIC ACHESON QUARTERBACK

		MT
Complete Set (16):		6.00
Common Player:		.50
1	Eric Acheson	.50
2	Pat Neck	.50
3	Marcus Bowie	.50
4	Marty Posey	.50
5	Brian Brumfield	.50
6	Terry Irving	.75
7	Eric Fleming	.50
8	Lance Guidry	.50
9	Ken Naquin	.50
10	Chris Fontenette	.50
11	Sam Breaux	.50
12	Dana Scott	.50
13	Edward Dyer	.50
14	Blayne Rush	.50
15	Ronald Solomon	.50
16	Steve Aultman	.50

1990 Miami Smokey

		MT
Complete Set (16):		18.00
Common Player:		.75
1	Randy Bethel (93)	.75
2	Wesley Carroll (81)	2.00
3	Rob Chudzinski (84)	.75
4	Leonard Conley (28)	1.50
5	Luis Cristobal (59)	.75
6	Maurice Crum (49)	.75
7	Shane Curry (44)	1.50
8	Craig Erickson (7)	4.00
9	Dennis Erickson (CO)	2.00
10	Darren Handy (66)	.75
11	Randal Hill (3)	4.00
12	Carlos Huerta (27)	1.50
13	Russell Maryland (67)	3.00
14	Stephen McGuire (30)	1.50
15	Roland Smith (16)	.75
16	Mike Sullivan (79)	.75

Common Player:

1	Jessie Armstead	1.00
2	Micheal Barrow	1.50
3	Hurlie Brown	1.00
4	Dennis Erickson (CO)	2.00
5	Anthony Hamlet	1.00
6	Carlos Huerta	1.50
7	Herbert James	1.00
8	Claude Jones	1.00
9	Stephen McGuire	1.50
10	Eric Miller	1.00
11	Joe Moore	1.00
12	Charles Pharms	1.00
13	Leon Searcy	2.00
14	Darrin Smith	2.00
15	Lamar Thomas	1.50
16	Gino Torretta	2.00

1992 Miami Police

HURRICANE FOOTBALL LAMAR THOMAS #36 - SR Wide Receiver

		MT
Complete Set (16):		15.00
Common Player:		.75
1	Jessie Armstead	1.00
2	Micheal Barrow	1.50
3	Coleman Bell	.75
4	Mark Caesar	.75
5	Horace Copeland (UER) (Name misspelled Horrace on front)	2.00
6	Mario Cristobal	.75
7	Dennis Erickson (CO)	1.50
8	Casey Greer	.75
9	Stephen McGuire	1.00
10	Ryan McNeil	1.50
11	Rusty Medearis	.75
12	Darrin Smith	1.50
13	Darryl Spencer	.75
14	Lamar Thomas	2.00
15	Gino Torretta	2.00
16	Kevin Williams (WR)	3.00

1993 Miami Bumble Bee

		MT
Complete Set (16):		12.00
Common Player:		.60
1	Rudy Barber	.60
2	Robert Bass	.60
3	Donnell Bennett	2.00
4	Jason Budroni	.60
5	Marcus Carey	.60
6	Ryan Collins	1.00
7	Frank Costa	1.00
8	Dennis Erickson (CO)	.60
9	Terris Harris	.60
10	Chris T. Jones	2.00
11	Larry Jones	1.50
12	Darren Krein	.60
13	Kenny Lopez	.60
14	Kevin Patrick	.60
15	Dexter Seigler	.60
16	Paul White	.60

1907 Michigan Postcards

		NM
Complete Set (15):		600.00
Common Player:		30.00
1	Dave Allerdice	40.00
2	William Casey	30.00
3	William Embs	30.00
4	Keene Fitzpatrick (TR)	30.00
5	Flanagan	30.00
6	Walter Graham	30.00
7	H.S. Hammond	30.00
8	John Loell	30.00
9	Paul Magoffin	40.00
10	James Miller	30.00
11	Walter Rheinschild	30.00
12	Mason Rumney	30.00
13	Adolph "Germany" Schultz	125.00
14	William Wasmund	30.00
15	Fielding Yost (CO)	125.00

1977 Michigan

		NM
Complete Set (21):		25.00
Common Player:		.75
1	John Anderson	1.25
2	Russell Davis	1.25
3	Mark Donahue	.75
4	Walt Downing	.75
5	Bill Dufek	1.25
6	Jon Giesler (SP)	2.00
7	Steve Graves	.75
8	Curtis Greer	2.00
9	Dwight Hicks	2.50
10	Derek Howard	.75
11	Harlan Huckleby	2.50
12	Gene Johnson	.75
13	Dale Keitz	.75
14	Mike Kenn	2.50
15	Rick Leach	2.50
16	Mark Schmerge	.75
17	Ron Simpkins	1.25
18	Curt Stephenson (SP)	2.00
19	Gerry Szara (SP)	2.00
20	Rick White	.75
21	Gregg Willner	.75

1989 Michigan

		MT
Complete Set (22):		12.00
Common Player:		.50
1	H.O. "Fritz" Crisler (CO)	.60
2	Anthony Carter	1.50
3	Willie Heston	.50
4	Reggie McKenzie	.50
5	Bo Schembechler (CO)	1.50
6	Dan Dierdorf	1.50
7	Jim Harbaugh	1.50
8	Bennie Oosterbaan	.50
9	Jamie Morris	.60
10	Gerald R. Ford	1.50
11	Curtis Greer	.60
12	Ron Kramer	.60
13	Calvin O'Neal	.50
14	Bob Chappuis	.50
15	Fielding Yost (CO)	.60
16	Dennis Franklin	.50
17	Benny Friedman	.60
18	Jim Mandich	.60
19	Rob Lytle	.60
20	Bump Elliott	.60
21	Harry Kipke	.50
22	Dave Brown	.60

1988 Mississippi McDag

		MT
Complete Set (2):		4.00
Common Player:		2.00
15	Mark Young	2.00
16	Bryan Owen	2.00

1991 Mississippi Hoby

		MT
Complete Set (42):		9.00
Common Player:		.25
439	Gary Abide	.25
440	Dwayne Amos	.25
441	Tyji Armstrong	1.00
442	Tyrone Ashley	.25
443	Darron Billings	.25
444	Danny Boyd	.25
445	Billy Brewer (CO)	.35
446	Chad Brown	.35
447	Tony Brown	.25
448	Vincent Brownlee	.25
449	Jeff Carter	.35
450	Richard Chisolm	.25
451	Clint Conlee	.25
452	Marvin Courtney	.25
453	Cliff Dew	.25
454	Johnny Dixon	.25
455	Artis Ford	.25
456	Chauncey Godwin	.25
457	Brian Harper	.25
458	David Harris	.25
459	Pete Harris	.25
460	David Herring	.25
461	James Holcombe	.25
462	Kevin Ingram	.25
463	Phillip Kent	.35
464	Derrick King	.25
465	Brian Lee	.25
466	Jim Lentz	.25
467	Everett Lindsay	.25
468	Tom Luke	.25
469	Thomas McLeish	.25
470	Wesley Melton	.25
471	Tyrone Montgomery	.75
472	Deano Orr	.25
473	Darrick Owens	.35
474	Lynn Ross	.25
475	Russ Shows	.25
476	Eddie Small	.35

477	Trea Southerland	.25
478	Gerald Vaughn	.25
479	Abner White	.25
480	Sebastian Williams	.25

1991 Mississippi State Hoby

		MT
Complete Set (42):		9.00
Common Player:		.25
481	Lance Aldridge	.25
482	Treddis Anderson	.25
483	Shea Bell	.25
484	Chris Bosarge	.25
485	Daniel Boyd	.25
486	Jerome Brown	.25
487	Torrance Brown	.25
488	Keith Carr	.25
489	Herman Carroll	.25
490	Keo Coleman	.35
491	Michael Davis	.25
492	Trenell Edwards	.25
493	Chris Firle	.25
494	Lee Ford	.25
495	Tay Galloway	.25
496	Chris Gardner	.25
497	Arleye Gibson	.25
498	Tony Harris	.25
499	Willie Harris	.25
500	Kevin Henry	.35
501	Jackie Sherrill (CO)	.50
502	John James	.25
503	Tony James	.25
504	Todd Jordan	.25
505	Keith Joseph	.25
506	Kelvin Knight	.25
507	Lee Lipscomb	.25
508	Juan Long	.25
509	Kyle McCoy	.25
510	Tommy Morrell	.25
511	Kelly Ray	.25
512	Mike Riley	.25
513	Kenny Roberts	.25
514	William Robinson	.25
515	Bill Sartin	.25
516	Kenny Stewart	.25
517	Rodney Stowers	.50
518	Anthony Thames	.25
519	Edward Williams	.25
520	Nate Williams	.25
521	Karl Williamson	.25
522	Marc Woodard	.25

1992 Mobil Cotton Bowl

		MT
Complete Set (24):		35.00
Common Player:		1.00
1	The Cotton Bowl	1.00
2	Sammy Baugh	2.50
3	Doak Walker	2.00
4	Dicky Moegle	1.00
5	Bobby Layne	2.50
6	Curtis Sanford (Founder)	1.00
7	John Kimbrough	1.00
8	Ernie Davis	5.00
9	Lance Alworth	2.00
10	James Street, Darrell Royal CO	1.50
11	Mike Singletary	1.50
12	Roger Staubach	4.00
13	Earl Campbell	3.50
14	Wilson Whitley	1.00
15	Jim Swink	1.00
16	Martin Ruby	1.00
17	Davey O'Brien	1.50
18	Gene Stallings, Paul "Bear" Bryant (CO)	2.50
19	Bo Jackson	2.00
20	Joe Theismann	1.50
21	Mr. Cotton Bowl (Field Scovell)	1.00
22	Ken Hatfield	1.00
23	Joe Montana	5.00
24	Mobil Cotton Bowl Classic CL	1.00

1974 Nebraska

		NM
Complete Set (54):		65.00
Common Player:		1.00
1	Tom Osborne (CO)	20.00
2	Terry Rogers	1.00
3	Tom Ruud	1.50
4	Jeff Schneider	1.00
5	Mark Heydorff	1.00
6	Dean Gissler	1.00
7	Jim Burrow	1.00
8	Al Eveland	1.00
9	Chuck Jones	1.00
10	Brad Jenkins	1.00
11	Dave Butterfield	1.00
12	Rich Duda	1.50
13	Steve Hoins	1.00
14	Ron Pruitt	1.00
15	Tony Davis	1.50
16	Mike Fultz	1.00
17	Chad Leonardi	1.00

18	John Starkebaum	1.00
19	Marvin Crenshaw	1.50
20	Larry Mushinskie	1.00
21	Tom Pate	1.00
22	David Humm	4.00
23	Willie Thornton	1.50
24	Dave Redding	1.00
25	Dave Shamblin	1.00
26	Earl Everett	1.00
27	Rik Bonness	1.50
28	Mark Doak	1.00
29	John Lee	1.00
30	Mike Coyle	1.00
31	George Kyros	1.00
32	Gary Higgs	1.00
33	Dennis Pavelka	1.00
34	Jeff Moran	1.00
35	John O'Leary	1.00
36	Percy Eichelberger	1.00
37	Greg Jorgensen	1.00
38	George Mills	1.00
39	Terry Luck	1.00
40	Don Westbrook	1.00
41	Mike Offner	1.00
42	Stan Waldemore	1.00
43	Stan Hegener	1.00
44	Bobby Thomas	1.00
45	Bob Martin	1.00
46	Ritch Bahe	1.00
47	Tom Heiser	1.00
48	Steve Wieser	1.00
49	Ardell Johnson	1.00
50	Chuck Malito	1.00
51	Bob Lingenfelter	1.00
52	Wonder Monds	1.50
53	Bob Nelson	1.50
54	Memorial Stadium	1.50

1977 Nebraska

		NM
Complete Set (54):		65.00
Common Player:		1.00
1	Tom Osborne (CO)	15.00
2	Tom Alward	1.00
3	Dan Anderson	1.00
4	Frosty Anderson	1.00
5	Al Austin	1.00
6	Ritch Bahe	1.00
7	John Bell	1.00
8	Rik Bonness	1.50
9	Randy Borg	1.00
10	Rich Costanzo	1.00
11	Maury Damkroger	1.50
12	Tony Davis	1.50
13	Mark Doak	1.00
14	Richard Duda	1.50
15	John Dutton	3.00
16	Pat Fischer	3.00
17	Marvin Crenshaw	1.50
18	Dean Gissler	1.00
19	Dave Goeller	1.00
20	Percy Eichelberger	1.00
21	Stan Hegener	1.00
22	Dave Humm	2.50
23	Ardell Johnson	1.00
24	Doug Johnson	1.00
25	Chuck Jones	1.00
26	Wonder Monds	1.50
27	Terry Rogers	1.00
28	Bob Revelle	1.00
29	Tom Pate	1.00
30	Mike O'Holleran	1.00
31	Ron Pruitt	1.00
32	Bob Nelson	1.50
33	Larry Mushinskie	1.00
34	Jeff Moran	1.00
35	Bob Martin	1.00
36	Ralph Powell	1.00
37	Steve Manstedt	1.00
38	Brent Longwell	1.00
39	George Kyros	1.00
40	Zaven Yaralian	1.00
41	Bob Wolfe	1.00
42	Steve Wieser	1.00
43	Daryl White	1.00
44	Bob Thornton	1.00
45	John Starkebaum	1.00
46	Dave Shamblin	1.00
47	Don Westbrook	1.50
48	Bob Schmit	1.50
49	Rich Sanger	1.50
50	Willie Thornton	1.50
51	Tom Ruud	1.50
52	Steve Runty	1.00
53	Stadium (Red)	1.50
54	Stadium (Black)	1.50

1989 Nebraska 100

		MT
Complete Set (100):		40.00
Common Player:		.35
1	Tony Davis	.50
2	Keith Jones	.35
3	Turner Gill	1.25
4	Dave Butterfield	.35
5	Wonder Monds	.50
6	Dave Rimington	.75
7	John Dutton	.75
8	Irving Fryar	3.00
9	Dean Steinkuhler	.75
10	Mike Rozier	1.25
11	Jarvis Redwine	.75
12	Randy Schleusener	.35

13	Junior Miller	.50
14	Broderick Thomas	1.25
15	Steve Taylor	.50
16	Neil Smith	2.00
17	John McCormick	.35
18	Danny Noonan	.50
19	Mike Fultz	.35
20	Vince Ferragamo	1.00
21	Jerry Tagge	.75
22	Jeff Kinney	.50
23	Rich Glover	.50
24	Johnny Rodgers	1.25
25	Rik Bonness	.50
26	Dave Humm	.50
27	Mark Traynowicz	.35
28	Harry Grimminger	.35
29	Bill Lewis	.50
30	Jim Skow	.50
31	Larry Kramer	.35
32	Tony Jeter	.35
33	Robert Brown	.35
34	Larry Wachholtz	.35
35	Wayne Meylan	.50
36	Bob Newton	.50
37	Willie Harper	.50
38	Bob Martin	.35
39	Jerry Murtaugh	.50
40	Daryl White	.35
41	Larry Jacobson	.35
42	Joe Armstrong	.35
43	Laverne Allers	.35
44	Freeman White	.35
45	Marvin Crenshaw	.50
46	Forrest Behm	.35
47	Jerry Minnick	.35
48	Tom Davis	.35
49	Kelvin Clark	.50
50	Tom Rathman	1.25
51	Sam Francis	.35
52	Joe Orduna	.50
53	Ed Weir	.35
54	Bill Thornton	.35
55	Bob Devaney (CO)	.75
56	Bret Clark	.35
57	Frank Solich	.35
58	Tim Smith	.35
59	George Andrews	.35
60	Rick Berns	.50
61	Monte Johnson	.50
62	Walt Barnes	.35
63	Jim McFarland	.35
64	Jimmy Williams	.35
65	Vic Halligan	.35
66	Guy Chamberlin	.35
67	Hugh Rhea	.35
68	George Sauer	.50
69	E.O. Stiehm (CO)	.35
70	Walter G. Booth (CO)	.35
71	First Night Game (Memorial Stadium)	.35
72	Memorial Stadium	.35
73	M-Stadium Expansions	.35
74	Andra Franklin	.75
75	Ron McDole	.50
76	Pat Fischer	.50
77	Dan McMullen	.35
78	Charles Brock	.35
79	Verne Lewellen	.35
80	Bob Nelson	.50
81	Roger Craig	3.00
82	Fred Shirey	.35
83	Tom Novak	.35
84	Ray Richards	.35
85	Warren Alfson	.35
86	Lawrence Ely	.35
87	Mike Rozier	1.25
88	Dean Steinkuhler	.75
89	John Dutton	.75
90	Dave Rimington	.75
91	Johnny Rodgers	1.25
92	Herbie Husker (Mascot)	.35
93	Tom Osborne (CO)	1.25
94	Broderick Thomas	1.25
95	Bob Reynolds	.50
96	Mike Tingelhoff (UER) (Name misspelled Tinglehoff)	.75
97	Lloyd Cardwell	.35
98	Johnny Rodgers	1.25
99	'70 National Champs (Team Photo)	.50
100	'71 National Champs (Team Photo)	.50
NNO	Title Card (Contest on back)	.50

1993 Nebraska

		MT
Complete Set (25):		15.00
Common Player:		.50
1	Trev Alberts	2.00
2	Mike Anderson	.75
3	Ernie Beler	.75
4	Byron Bennett	.75
5	Troy Bromawn (Men's baseball)	.50
6	NaFeesah Brown (Women's basketball)	.50

7	Jed Dalton (Men's baseball)	.50
8	Sumner Darling (Men's gymnastics)	.50
9	Corey Dixon	.75
10	Troy Dumas	.75
11	Nicole Duval (Women's gymnastics)	.50
12	Mike Eierman (Wrestling)	.50
13	Amy Erlenbusch (Women's softball)	.50
14	Dennis Harrison (Men's gymnastics)	.50
15	Jamar Johnson (Men's basketball)	1.00
16	Calvin Jones	1.50
17	Laura Luther (Women's volleyball)	.50
18	Denise McMillen (Women's softball)	.50
19	Bruce Moore	.75
20	David Noonan	1.00
21	Lori Phillips (Women's gymnastics)	.50
22	Eric Piatkowski (Men's basketball)	2.00
23	Nikki Stricker (Women's volleyball)	.50
24	Frank Velazquez (Wrestling)	.50
25	Meggan Yedsena (Women's basketball)	.50

1994 Nebraska

		MT
Complete Set (21):		12.00
Common Player:		.50
1	Kelly Aspergren (Women's volleyball)	.50
2	Jaron Boone (Men's basketball)	1.00
3	Terry Connealy	.75
4	Jed Dalton (Men's basketball)	.50
5	Troy Dumas	.75
6	Cody Dusenberry (Women's softball)	.50
7	Nicole Duval (Women's gymnastics)	.50
8	Richard Grace (Men's gymnastics)	.50
9	Donta Jones	.50
10	Rick Kieffer (Men's gymnastics)	.50
11	Barron Miles	1.00
12	Darin Petersen	.50
13	Cory Schlesinger	2.00
14	Ed Stewart	.75
15	Erick Strickland (Men's basketball)	.75
16	Joy Taylor (Women's gymnastics)	.50
17	Emily Thompson (Women's basketball)	.50
18	Tanya Upthegrove (Women's basketball)	.50
19	Zach Wiegert	1.50
20	Billie Winsett (Women's volleyball)	.50
21	Rob Zatechka	1.50

1996 Nebraska

1988 Mississippi McDag (continued, right column)

8	Mark Gilman	1.00
9	Aaron Graham	1.50
10	Luther Hardin	1.00
11	Jason Jenkins	1.00
12	Chester Johnson	1.00
13	Jeff Makovicka	1.50
14	Brian Nunns	1.00
15	Steve Ott	1.00
16	Aaron Penland	1.00
17	Christian Peter	1.50
18	Darren Schmadeke	1.50
19	Tony Veland	1.00
20	Steve Volin	1.00
21	Tyrone Williams	1.00
22	Checklist Card	1.00
	Team Logo	

1979 North Carolina Schedules

		NM
Complete Set (4):		12.00
Common Player:		3.00
1	Ricky Barden	3.00
2	Steve Junkman	3.00
3	Matt Kupec	5.00
4	Doug Paschal	3.00

1982 North Carolina Schedules

		MT
Complete Set (8):		25.00
Common Player:		3.00
1	Kelvin Bryant	7.50
2	Alan Burrus	3.00
3	David Drechsler	3.00
4	Rod Elkins	4.00
5	Jack Parry	3.00
6	Greg Poole	3.00
7	Ron Spruill	3.00
8	Mike Wilcher	4.00

1986 North Carolina Schedules

		MT
Complete Set (4):		15.00
Common Player:		3.00
1	Walter Bailey	3.00
2	Harris Barton	6.00
3	C.A. Brooks	3.00
4	Eric Streater	4.00

1988 North Carolina

		MT
Complete Set (16):		15.00
Common Player:		1.00
1	Mack Brown (CO)	1.50
2	Pat Crowley	1.00
3	Torin Dorn	2.00
4	Jeff Garnica	1.25
5	Antonio Goss	1.25
6	Jonathan Hall	1.25
7	Darrell Hamilton	1.00
8	Creighton Incorminias	1.00
9	John Keller	1.00
10	Randy Marriott	1.00
11	Deems May	1.00
12	John Reed	1.00
13	James Thompson	1.25
14	Steve Steinbacher	1.00
15	Dan Vooletich	1.00
16	Mitch Wike	1.00

1991 North Carolina Schedules

		MT
Complete Set (3):		7.00
Common Player:		2.00
1	Eric Gash	2.00
2	Dwight Hollier	4.00
3	Tommy Thigpen	2.00

1993 North Carolina State

		MT
Complete Set (56):		25.00
Common Player:		.50
1	John Akins	.75
2	Darryl Beard	.50
3	Ricky Bell	.50
4	Geoff Bender	.50
5	Chuck Browning	.50
6	Chuck Cole	.50
7	Chris Colton	.50
8	Eric Counts	.50
9	Damien Covington	1.00
10	Dallas Dickerson	.50
11	Gary Downs	.50
12	Brian Fitzgerald	.50
13	Ed Gallon	.50
14	Ledel George	.50

1996 Nebraska (Tommie Frazier card)

#	Player	Price
15	Walt Gerard	.50
16	Gregg Giannamore	.50
17	Eddie Goines	1.00
18	Ray Griffis	.50
19	Mike Harrison	.50
20	Terry Harvey	.50
21	George Hegamin	1.00
22	Chris Hennie-Roed	.50
23	Adrian Hill	.50
24	Robert Hinton	.50
25	David Inman	.50
26	Dave Janik	.50
27	Shawn Johnson	.50
28	Tyler Lawrence	.50
29	Miller Lawson	.50
30	Sean Maguire	.50
31	Drea Major	.50
32	Mike Moore	.50
33	James Newsome	.50
34	Mike O'Cain (CO)	.50
35	Loren Pinkney	.50
36	Carlos Pruitt	.50
37	Carl Reeves	1.00
38	Jon Rissler	.50
39	Chad Robinson	.50
40	Ryan Schultz	.75
41	William Strong	.75
42	Jimmy Sziksai	.50
43	Eric Taylor	.50
44	Pat Threatt	.50
45	Steve Videtich	.75
46	James Walker	.75
47	Todd Ward	.75
48	DeWayne Washington	2.00
49	Heath Woods	.50
50	Scott Woods	.50
51	Defensive Coaches (Buddy Green, Kent Briggs, Ken Pettus, Jeff Snipes, Henry Trevathan)	.50
52	Offensive Coaches (Ted Cain, Robbie Caldwell, Jimmy Kiser, Brette Simmons, Dick Portee)	.50
53	Tri-Captains (John Akins, Todd Ward, DeWayne Washington)	.50
54	Carter-Finley Stadium	.50
55	Checklist	.50
56	Title Card	.75

1989 North Texas McDag

		MT
Complete Set (16):		7.00
Common Player:		.50
1	Clay Bode	.50
2	Scott Bowles	.50
3	Keith Chapman	.50
4	Darrin Collins	.50
5	Tony Cook	.50
6	Scott Davis	1.00
7	Byron Gross	.50
8	Larry Green	.50
9	Major Greene	1.00
10	Carl Brewer	.50
11	J.D. Martinez	.50
12	Charles Monroe	.50
13	Kregg Sanders	.50
14	Lou Smith	.50
15	Jeff Tutson	.50
16	Trent Touchstone	.50

1990 North Texas McDag

		MT
Complete Set (16):		9.00
Common Player:		.50
1	Scott Davis	.75
2	Byron Gross	.50
3	Tony Cook	.50
4	Walter Casey	.50
5	Erric Pegram	4.00
6	Clay Bode	.50
7	Scott Bowles	.50
8	Shawn Wash	.50
9	Isaac Barnett	.50
10	Paul Gallamore	.50
11	J.D. Martinez	.50
12	Velton Morgan	.50
13	Major Greene	.75
14	Bart Helsley	.50
15	Jeff Tutson	.50
16	Tony Walker	.50

1992 Northwestern Louisiana State

		MT
Complete Set (16):		7.00
Common Player:		.50
1	Darius Adams	.50
2	Paul Arevalo	.50
3	Brad Brown	.50
4	Steve Brown	.60
5	J.J. Eldridge	.50
6	Sam Goodwin (CO)	.60
7	Adrian Hardy	.50
8	Guy Hedrick	.50
9	Brad Laird	.60
10	Lawann Latson	.50
11	Deon Ridgell	.50
12	Bryan Roussell	.50
13	Brannon Rowlett	.50
14	Marcus Spears	.60
15	Carlos Treadway	.60
16	Vic (Team Mascot)	.50

1930 Notre Dame Postcards

		NM
Complete Set (25):		800.00
Common Player:		30.00
1	Marty Brill	35.00
2	Frank Carideo	35.00
3	Tom Conley	30.00
4	Al Culver (October 25)	30.00
5	Dick Donaghue (October 18)	30.00
6	Nordy Hoffmann	30.00
7	Al Howard (November 15)	30.00
8	Chuck Jaskwich (November 22)	30.00
9	Clarence Kaplan (October 18)	30.00
10	Tom Kassis	30.00
11	Ed Koska (November 22)	30.00
12	Joe Kurth	35.00
13	Bernie Leahy	50.00
14	Bernie Leahy	125.00
15	Dick Mahoney (November 8)	30.00
16	Art McManmon (November 1)	30.00
17	Bert Metzger	30.00
18	Larry "Moon" Mullins	50.00
19	John O'Brien	30.00
20	Bucky O'Connor	30.00
21	Joe Savoldi	35.00
22	Marchmont Schwartz	35.00
23	Robert Terlaak (November 8)	30.00
24	George Vik (October 25)	30.00
25	Tom Yarr	35.00

1988 Notre Dame

		MT
Complete Set (60):		20.00
Common Player:		.25
1	Golden Dome	.50
2	Lou Holtz (CO)	2.00
3	Mark Green	.50
4	Andy Heck	.75
5	Ned Bolcar	.50
6	Anthony Johnson	.50
7	Flash Gordon	.50
8	Pat Ellers	.25
9	Raghib Ismail	5.00
10	Ted FitzGerald	.25
11	Ted Healy	.25
12	Braxston Banks	.50
13	Steve Belles	.25
14	Steve Alaniz	.25
15	Chris Zorich	2.00
16	Kent Graham	1.00
17	Mike Brennan	.25
18	Marty Lippincott	.25
19	Rod West	.25
20	Dean Brown	.25
21	Tom Gorman	.25
22	Tony Rice	1.50
23	Steve Roddy	.25
24	Reggie Ho	.50
25	Pat Terrell	.75
26	Joe Jarosz	.25
27	Mike Stonebreaker	1.00
28	David Jandric	.25
29	Jeff Alm	.75
30	Pete Graham	.25
31	Corny Southall	.25
32	Joe Allen	.25
33	Jim Sexton	.25
34	Michael Crounse	.25
35	Kurt Zackrison	.25
36	Stan Smagala	.50
37	Mike Heidt	.25
38	Frank Stams	.75
39	D'Juan Francisco	.50
40	Tim Ryan	.50
41	Arnold Ale	.25
42	Andre Jones	.25
43	Wes Pritchett	.25
44	Tim Grunhard	.75
45	Chuck Killian	.25
46	Scott Kowalkowski	.50
47	George Streeter	.25
48	Donn Grimm	.25
49	Ricky Watters	6.00
50	Ryan Mihalko	.25
51	Tony Brooks	.75
52	Todd Lyght	1.00
53	Winston Sandri	.25
54	Aaron Robb	.25
55	Derek Brown (TE)	1.00
56	Bryan Flannery	.25
57	Kevin McShane	.25
58	Billy Hackett	.25
59	George Williams	.25
60	Frank Jacobs	.25

1988 Notre Dame Smokey

		MT
Complete Set (14):		30.00
Common Player (1-10):		1.50
Common Sport (11-14):		1.50
1	Braxston Banks (39)	2.00
2	Ned Bolcar (47)	1.50
3	Tom Gorman (87)	1.50
4	Mark Green (24)	2.00
5	Andy Heck (66)	2.00
6	Lou Holtz (CO)	3.50
7	Anthony Johnson (22)	2.00
8	Wes Pritchett (34)	1.50
9	George Streeter (27)	1.50
10	Ricky Watters (12)	9.00
11	Men's Soccer	1.50
12	Volleyball	1.50
13	Women's Basketball	1.50
14	Women's Tennis	1.50

1989 Notre Dame 1903-32

		MT
Complete Set (22):		7.00
Common Player:		.35
1	Hunk Anderson	.50
2	Bert Metzger	.35
3	Roger Kiley	.35
4	Nordy Hoffman	.35
5	Knute Rockne (CO)	2.00
6	Elmer Layden	.75
7	Gus Dorais	.50
8	Ray Eichenlaub	.35
9	Don Miller	.50
10	Moose Krause	.75
11	Jesse Harper	.35
12	Jack Cannon	.35
13	Eddie Anderson	.35
14	Louis Salmon	.35
15	John Smith	.35
16	Harry Stuhldreher	.75
17	Joe Kurth	.35
18	Frank Carideo	.35
19	Marchy Schwartz	.35
20	Adam Walsh	.35
21	George Gipp	2.00
22	Jim Crowley	.75

1989 Notre Dame 1935-59

		MT
Complete Set (22):		7.00
Common Player:		.35
1	Frank Leahy (CO)	.75
2	John Lattner	.75
3	Jim Martin	.50
4	Joe Heap	.35
5	Paul Hornung	1.25
6	Bill Shakespeare	.75
7	Bob Dove	.35
8	Bob Williams	.35
9	Al Ecuyer	.35
10	George Connor	.75
11	Leon Hart	.75
12	Joe Beinor	.35
13	Bill Fischer	.35
14	Angelo Bertelli	.75
15	Ralph Guglielmi	.75
16	Pat Filley	.35
17	Emil (Red) Sitko	.50
18	Don Schaefer	.35
19	Monty Stickles	.50
20	Creighton Miller	.35
21	Chuck Sweeney	.35
22	John Lujack	1.00

1989 Notre Dame 1964-87

		MT
Complete Set (22):		7.00
Common Player:		.35
1	Dan Devine (CO)	.50
2	Joe Theismann	1.00
3	Tom Gatewood	.50
4	Timmy Brown	1.25
5	Ara Parseghian (CO)	.75
6	Jim Lynch	.50
7	Luther Bradley	.35
8	Ross Browner	.50
9	John Huarte	1.00
10	Bob Crable	.50
11	Ken McAfee	.50
12	Alan Page	.75
13	Vagas Ferguson	.50
14	Dick Arrington	.35
15	Bob Golic	.50
16	Mike Townsend	.35
17	Walt Patulski	.50
18	Allen Pinkett	.50
19	Terry Hanratty	.75
20	Dave Casper	.75
21	Jack Snow	.75
22	Nick Eddy	.50

1990 Notre Dame Promos

		MT
Complete Set (10):		7.00
Common Player:		.50
1	Knute Rockne (CO)	1.00
2	Joe Theismann	1.00
3	Joe Montana	4.00
4	George Gipp	1.00
5	Notre Dame Stadium	.50
6	Ara Parseghian (CO)	.75
7	Frank Leahy (CO)	.50
8	Lou Holtz (CO)	.75
9	Tony Rice	.50
10	Rocky Bleier	.75

1990 Notre Dame 200

		MT
Complete Set (200):		18.00
Common Player:		.10
1	Joe Montana	1.25
2	Tim Brown	.50
3	Reggie Barnett	.20
4	Joe Theismann	.50
5	Bob Clasby	.10
6	Dave Casper	.20
7	George Kunz	.20
8	Vince Phelan	.10
9	Tom Gibbons	.10
10	Tom Thayer	.20
11	Notre Dame Helmet	.10
12	John Scully	.10
13	Lou Holtz (CO)	.30
14	Larry Dinardo	.20
15	Greg Marx	.10
16	Greg Dingens	.10
17	Jim Seymour	.20
18	1979 Cotton Bowl (Program)	.10
19	Mike Kadish	.20
20	Bob Crable	.20
21	Tony Rice	.20
22	Phil Carter	.10
23	Ken McAfee	.20
24	Nick Eddy	.20
25	1988 National Champs (Trophies)	.20
26	Clarence Ellis	.20
27	Joe Restic	.10
28	Dan Devine (CO)	.20
29	John K. Carney	.10
30	Stacey Toran	.20
31	47th Sugar Bowl (Program)	.10
32	J. Heavens	.10
33	Mike Fanning	.10
34	Dave Vinson	.10
35	Ralph Gugliemi	.10
36	Reggie Ho	.10
37	Allen Pinkett	.20
38	Jim Browner	.20
39	Blair Kiel	.20
40	Joe Montana	1.25
41	Rocky Bleier	.30
42	Terry Hanratty	.20
43	Tom Regner	.20
44	Pete Holohan	.20
45	Greg Bell	.20
46	Dave Duerson	.20
47	Frank Varrichione	.20
48	1988 Championship (Team Photo)	.20
49	Ted Burgmeier	.10
50	Ara Parseghian (CO)	.30
51	Mike Townsend	.10
52	Liberty Bowl 1983 (Program)	.10
53	Tony Furjanic	.10
54	Luther Bradley	.20
55	Steve Niehaus	.20
56	56th Orange Bowl (Program)	.10
57	32nd Gator Bowl (Program)	.10
58	40th Sugar Bowl (Program)	.10
59	52nd Cotton Bowl (Program)	.10
60	1975 Orange Bowl (Program)	.10
61	Wayne Bullock	.10
62	Larry Moriarty	.10
63	Jim Lynch	.20
64	Mike McCoy	.20
65	Tony Hunter	.20
66	1984 Aloha Bowl (Program)	.10
67	Dave Huffman	.10
68	John Lattner	.20
69	Tom Gatewood	.20
70	Knute Rockne (CO)	.35
71	Phil Pozderac	.10
72	Ross Browner	.20
73	Pete Demmerle	.10
74	Sunkist Fiesta Bowl (Program)	.10
75	Walt Patulski	.20
76	George Gipp	.50
77	LeRoy Leopold	.10
78	John Huarte	.30
79	Tony Yelovich (CO)	.10
80	John Lujack	.30
81	Cotton Bowl Classic (Program)	.10
82	Tim Huffman	.10
83	Bob Golic	.20
84	Tom Clements	.20
85	39th Orange Bowl (Program)	.10
86	James J. White (ADMIN)	.10
87	Frank Carideo	.10
88	Vinny Cerrato	.10
89	Louis Salmon	.10
90	Bob Burger	.10
91	Gerry Dinardo	.20
92	Mike Creaney	.10
93	John Krimm	.10
94	Vagas Ferguson	.10
95	Kris Haines	.10
96	Gus Dorais	.20
97	Tom Schoen	.10
98	Jack Robinson	.10
99	Joe Heap	.10
100	Checklist 1-99	.10
101	Gary Darnell (CO)	.10
102	Peter Vaas (CO)	.10
103	1924 National Champs (Team Photo)	.20
104	Wayne Millner	.20
105	Moose Krause	.20
106	Jack Cannon	.10
107	Christy Flanagan	.10
108	Bob Lehmann	.10
109	1947 Champions (Team Photo)	.20
110	Joe Kurth	.10
111	Tommy Yarr	.10
112	Nick Buoniconti	.30
113	Jim Smithberger	.10
114	Joe Beinor	.10
115	Pete Cordelli (CO)	.10
116	Daryle Lamonica	.30
117	Kevin Hardy	.10
118	Creighton Miller	.20
119	Bob Gladieux	.20
120	Fred Miller (Later Miller Brewing)	.20
121	Gary Potempa	.10
122	Bob Kuechenberg	.20
123	Jesse Harper (CO)	.10
124	1929 National Champs (Team Photo)	.20
125	Alan Page	.30
126	Don Miller	.20
127	1943 National Champs (Team Photo)	.20
128	Bob Wetoska	.10
129	Skip Holtz (CO)	.10
130	Hunk Anderson (CO)	.10
131	Bob Williams	.10
132	1966 National Champs (Team Photo)	.10
133	Jim Reilly	.10
134	Earl "Curly" Lambeau	.20
135	Ernie Hughes	.10
136	Dick Bumpas (CO)	.10
137	Jay Haynes (CO)	.10
138	Harry Stuhldreher	.20
139	1971 Cotton Bowl (Game Photo)	.20
140	1930 National Champs (Team Photo)	.20
141	Larry Conjar	.20
142	1977 National Champs (Team Photo)	.20
143	Pete Duranko	.20
144	Heisman Winners (Seven Trophy Winners)	.30
145	Bill Fisher	.10
146	Marchy Schwartz	.10
147	Chuck Heater (CO)	.10
148	Bert Metzger	.10
149	Bill Shakespeare	.20
150	Adam Walsh	.10
151	Nordy Hoffman	.10
152	Ted Gradel	.10
153	Monty Stickles	.20
154	Neil Worden	.10
155	Pat Filley	.10
156	Angelo Bertelli	.20
157	Nick Pietrosante	.10
158	Art Hunter	.10
159	Ziggy Czarobski	.10
160	1925 Rose Bowl (Program)	.10
161	Al Ecuyer	.10
162	1949 Notre Dame Champs (Team Photo)	.10
163	Elmer Layden	.20
164	Joe Moore (CO)	.10
165	1946 National Champs (Team Photo)	.10
166	Frank Rydzewski	.10
167	Bud Boeringer	.10
168	Jerry Groom	.10
169	Jack Snow	.20
170	Joe Montana	1.25
171	John Smith	.10
172	Frank Leahy (CO)	.30
173	Emil "Red" Sitko	.20
174	Dick Arrington	.10
175	Eddie Anderson	.10
176	1928 Army (Logo and score)	.10
177	1913 Army (Logo and score)	.10
178	1935 Ohio State (Logo and game score)	.10
179	1946 Army (Logo and game score)	.10
180	1953 Georgia Tech (Logo and game score)	.10
181	Don Schaefer	.10
182	1973 Football Team (Team Photo)	.20
183	Bob Dove	.10
184	Dick Szymanski	.10
185	Jim Martin	.20
186	1957 Oklahoma (Logo and score)	.10
187	1966 Michigan State (Logo and game score)	.10
188	1973 USC (Logo and game score)	.10
189	1980 Michigan (Logo and game score)	.10
190	1982 Michigan (Logo and game score)	.10
191	Chuck Sweeney	.10
192	Notre Dame Stadium	.10
193	Roger Kiley	.10
194	Ray Eichenlaub	.10
195	George Connor	.20
196	1982 Pittsburgh (Logo and game score)	.10
197	1986 USC (Logo and game score)	.10
198	1988 Miami (Logo and game score)	.10
199	1988 USC (Logo and game score)	.10
200	Checklist 101-199	.10

1990 Notre Dame 60

		MT
Complete Set (60):		25.00
Common Player:		.35
1	Joe Allen	.35
2	William Pollard	.35
3	Tony Smith	.35
4	Tony Brooks	.75
5	Kenny Spears	.35
6	Mike Heldt	.35
7	Derek Brown (TE)	.75
8	Rodney Culver	.75
9	Ricky Watters	3.00
10	Raghib Ismail	2.50
11	Lou Holtz (CO)	.75
12	Chris Zorich	1.00
13	Erik Simien	.35
14	Shawn Davis	.35
15	Greg Davis	.35
16	Walter Boyd	.35
17	Tim Ryan	.50
18	Lindsay Knapp	.35
19	Junior Bryant	.35
20	Mike Stonebreaker	.50
21	Randy Scianna	.35
22	Rick Mirer	6.00
23	Ryan Mihalko	.35
24	Todd Lyght	.75
25	Andre Jones	.35
26	Rod Smith (DB)	.50

27	Winston Sandri	.35
28	Bob Dahl	.50
29	Stuart Tyner	.35
30	Brian Shannon	.35
31	Shawn Smith	.35
32	Jim Sexton	.35
33	Dorsey Levens	1.00
34	Lance Johnson	.35
35	George Poorman	.35
36	Irv Smith	1.00
37	George Williams	.35
38	George Marshall	.50
39	Reggie Brooks	2.00
40	Scott Kowalkowski	.50
41	Jerry Bodine	.35
42	Karmeeleyah McGill	.35
43	Donn Grimm	.35
44	Billy Hackett	.35
45	Jordan Halter	.35
46	Mirko Jurkovic	.75
47	Mike Callan	.35
48	Justin Hall	.35
49	Nick Smith	.35
50	Brian Ratigan	.35
51	Eric Jones	.35
52	Todd Norman	.35
53	Devon McDonald	.50
54	Marc deManigold	.35
55	Bret Hankins	.35
56	Adrian Jarrell	.35
57	Craig Hentrich	.50
58	Demetrius DuBose	.75
59	Gene McGuire	.75
60	Ray Griggs	.35

1990 Notre Dame Greats

		MT
Complete Set (22):		8.00
Common Player:		.35
1	Clarence Ellis	.50
2	Rocky Bleier	.75
3	Tom Regner	.50
4	Jim Seymour	.35
5	Joe Montana	3.00
6	Art Hunter	.50
7	Mike McCoy	.50
8	Bud Boeringer	.35
9	Greg Marx	.35
10	Nick Buoniconti	.75
11	Pete Demmerle	.35
12	Fred Miller	.35
13	Tommy Yarr	.35
14	Frank Rydzewski	.35
15	Dave Duerson	.50
16	Ziggy Czarobski	.35
17	Jim White	.50
18	Larry DiNardo	.50
19	George Kunz	.50
20	Jack Robinson	.35
21	Steve Niehaus	.50
22	John Scully	.50

1992 Notre Dame

		MT
Complete Set (59):		25.00
Common Player:		.35
1	Lou Holtz (CO)	1.00
2	Rick Mirer	4.00
3	Demetrius DuBose	.75
4	Lee Becton	1.25
5	Pete Bercich	.50
6	Jerome Bettis	4.00
7	Reggie Brooks	1.50
8	Junior Bryant	.35
9	Jeff Burris	1.25
10	Tom Carter	1.00
11	Willie Clark	.35
12	John Covington	.50
13	Travis Davis	.35
14	Lake Dawson	1.50
15	Mark Zataveski	.35
16	Paul Failla	.75
17	Jim Flanigan	.75
18	Oliver Gibson	.35
19	Justin Goheen	.50
20	Tracy Graham	.35
21	Ray Griggs	.35
22	Justin Hall	.35
23	Jordan Halter	.35
24	Brian Hamilton	.50
25	Craig Hentrich	.50
26	Germaine Holden	.35
27	Adrian Jarrell	.50
28	Clint Johnson	.50
29	Lance Johnson	.35
30	Lindsay Knapp	.50
31	Ryan Leahy (Not alphabetical order)	.50
32	Greg Lane	.50
33	Dean Lytle	.35
34	Bernard Mannelly	.35
35	Oscar McBride	.35
36	Devon McDonald	.50
37	Kevin McDougal	1.00
38	Karl McGill	.35
39	Mike McGlinn	.35
40	Mike Miller	.75
41	Jeremy Nau	.35
42	Todd Norman	.50
43	Tim Ruddy (Not alphabetical order)	.50

44	William Pollard	.35
45	Brian Ratigan	.35
46	Leshane Saddler	.35
47	Jeremy Sample	.35
48	Irv Smith	1.00
49	Laron Moore (Not alphabetical order)	.35
50	Anthony Peterson (No alphabetical order)	.50
51	Charles Stafford	.35
52	Nick Smith	.35
53	Greg Stec	.35
54	John Taliaferro	.35
55	Aaron Taylor	1.00
56	Stuart Tyner	.35
57	Ray Zellars (Not alphabetical order)	1.50
58	Tyler Young (Not alphabetical order)	.35
59	Bryant Young	1.50

1993 Notre Dame

		MT
Complete Set (72):		20.00
Common Player:		.25
1	Jeremy Akers	.35
2	Joe Babey	.25
3	Huntley Bakich	.25
4	Jason Beckwith	.25
5	Lee Becton	.75
6	Pete Bercich	.25
7	Jeff Burris	1.25
8	Pete Chryplewicz	.25
9	Willie Clark	.25
10	John Covington	.35
11	Travis Davis	.25
12	Lake Dawson	1.25
13	Paul Failla	.50
14	Jim Flanigan	.50
15	Reggie Fleurima	.25
16	Ben Foos	.25
17	Herbert Gibson	.25
18	Oliver Gibson	.50
19	Justin Goheen	.35
20	Tracy Graham	.25
21	Paul Grasmanis	.35
22	Jordan Halter	.25
23	Brian Hamilton	.35
24	Germaine Holden	.25
25	Lou Holtz (CO)	1.00
26	Robert Hughes	.25
27	Adrian Jarrell	.35
28	Clint Johnson	.35
29	Lance Johnson	.35
30	Thomas Knight	.35
31	Jim Kordas	.35
32	Greg Lane	.35
33	Ryan Leahy	.35
34	Will Lyell	.35
35	Dean Lytle	.25
36	Brian Magee	.25
37	Alton Malden	.25
38	Derrick Mayes	1.50
39	Oscar McBride	.35
40	Mike McCullough	.50
41	Kevin McDougal	.50
42	Mike McGlinn	.25
43	Brian Meter	.25
44	Mike Miller	.50
45	Steve Misetic	.25
46	Jeremy Nau	.25
47	Todd Norman	.35
48	Kevin Pendergast	.35
49	Anthony Peterson	.25
50	David Quist	.25
51	Jeff Riney	.25
52	Tim Ruddy	.35
53	Leshane Saddler	.25
54	Jeremy Sample	.25
55	Charles Stafford	.25
56	Greg Stec	.25
57	Cliff Stroud	.25
58	John Taliaferro	.25
59	Aaron Taylor	1.00
60	Bobby Taylor	1.25
61	Bill Wagasy	.25
62	Leon Wallace	.25
63	Shawn Wooden	.35
64	Renaldo Wynn	.35
65	Bryant Young	1.25
66	Mark Zataveski	.35
67	Dusty Zeigler	.35
68	Ray Zellars	1.25
69	Blue Roster Checklist	.25
70	Gold Roster Checklist	.25
71	Green Roster Checklist	.25
72	White Roster Checklist	.25

1961 Nu-Card

		NM
Complete Set (80):		175.00
Common Player:		2.00
101	Bob Ferguson	5.00
102	Ron Snidow	3.00
103	Steve Barnett	2.00
104	Greg Mather	2.00
105	Vern Von Sydow	2.00
106	John Hewitt	2.00
107	Eddie Johns	2.00
108	Walt Rappold	2.00
109	Roy Winston	4.00
110	Bob Boyda	2.00
111	Bill Neighbors	5.00
112	Don Purcell	2.00
113	Ken Byers	2.00
114	Ed Pine	2.00
115	Fred Oblak	2.00
116	Bobby Iles	2.00
117	John Hadl	18.00
118	Charlie Mitchell	2.00
119	Bill Swinford	2.00
120	Bill King	2.00
121	Mike Lucci	5.00
122	Dave Sarette	2.00
123	Alex Kroll	3.00
124	Steve Bauwens	2.00
125	Jimmy Saxton	3.00
126	Steve Simms	2.00
127	Andy Timura	2.00
128	Gary Collins	6.00
129	Ron Taylor	2.00
130	Bobby Dodd	8.00
131	Curtis McClinton	6.00
132	Ray Poage	3.00
133	Gus Gonzales	2.00
134	Dick Locke	2.00
135	Larry Libertore	2.00
136	Stan Sczurek	2.00
137	Pete Case	3.00
138	Jesse Bradford	2.00
139	Coolidge Hunt	2.00
140	Walter Doleschal	2.00
141	Bill Williamson	2.00
142	Pat Trammell	6.00
143	Ernie Davis	65.00
144	Chuck Lamson	2.00
145	Bobby Plummer	3.00
146	Sonny Gibbs	3.00
147	Joe Ellers	2.00
148	Roger Kochman	2.00
149	Norman Beal	2.00
150	Sherwyn Torson	2.00
151	Russ Hepner	2.00
152	Joe Romig	2.00
153	Larry Thompson	2.00
154	Tom Perdue	2.00
155	Ken Bolin	2.00
156	Art Perkins	2.00
157	Jim Sanderson	2.00
158	Bob Asack	2.00
159	Dan Celoni	2.00
160	Bill McGuirt	2.00
161	Dave Hoppmann	2.00
162	Gary Barnes	2.00
163	Don Lisbon	3.00
164	Jerry Cross	2.00
165	George Pierovich	2.00
166	Roman Gabriel	25.00
167	Billy White	2.00
168	Gale Weidner	2.00
169	Charles Rieves	2.00
170	Jim Furlong	2.00
171	Tom Hutchinson	3.00
172	Galen Hall	8.00
173	Wilburn Hollis	2.00
174	Don Kasso	2.00
175	Bill Miller	3.00
176	Ron Miller	2.00
177	Joe Williams	2.00
178	Mel Mellin	2.00
179	Tom Vassell	2.00
180	Mike Cotton	3.00

1961 Nu-Card Pennant Inserts

		NM
Complete Set (264):		800.00
Common Player:		3.00
1	Air Force/Georgetown	3.00
2	Air Force/Queens	3.00
3	Air Force/Upsala	3.00
4	Alabama/Boston U	4.00
5	Alabama/Cornell	3.00
6	Alabama/Detroit	4.00
7	Alabama/Harvard	4.00
8	Alabama/Wisconsin	4.00
9	Allegheny/Colorado St.	3.00
10	Allegheny/Oregon	3.00
11	Allegheny/Piedmont	3.00
12	Allegheny/Wm. and Mary	3.00
13	Arizona/Kansas	3.00
14	Arizona/Mississippi	3.00
15	Arizona/Pennsylvania	3.00
16	Arizona/S.M.U.	3.00
17	Army/Ga. Tech	3.00
18	Army/Iowa	3.00
19	Army/Johns Hopkins	3.00
20	Army/Maryland	3.00
21	Army/Missouri	3.00
22	Army/Pratt	3.00
23	Army/Purdue	3.00
24	Auburn/Florida	4.00
25	Auburn/Gettysburg	3.00
26	Auburn/Illinois	4.00
27	Auburn/Syracuse	4.00
28	Auburn/Virginia	4.00

29	Barnard/Colombia	3.00
30	Barnard/Maine	3.00
31	Barnard/N. Carolina	3.00
32	Baylor/Colorado St.	3.00
33	Baylor/Drew	3.00
34	Baylor/Oregon	3.00
35	Baylor/Piedmont	3.00
36	Boston Coll./Minnesota	3.00
37	Boston Coll./Norwich	3.00
38	Boston Coll./Winthrop	3.00
39	Boston U./Cornell	3.00
40	Boston U./Rensselaer	3.00
41	Boston U./Stanford	3.00
42	Boston U./Temple	3.00
43	Boston U./Utah State	3.00
44	Bridgeport/Holy Cross	3.00
45	Bridgeport/N.Y.U.	3.00
46	Bridgeport/Northwestern	3.00
47	Bucknell/Illinois	3.00
48	Bucknell/Syracuse	3.00
49	Bucknell/Virginia	3.00
50	California/Delaware	3.00
51	California/Hofstra	3.00
52	California/Kentucky	3.00
53	California/Marquette	3.00
54	California/Michigan	4.00
55	California/Notre Dame	7.50
56	California/Wingate	3.00
57	Charleston/Dickinson	3.00
58	Charleston/Lafayette	3.00
59	Charleston/U. of Mass.	3.00
60	Cincinnati/Maine	3.00
61	Cincinnati/Ohio West	3.00
62	Citadel/Columbia	3.00
63	Citadel/Maine	3.00
64	Citadel/N. Carolina	3.00
65	Coast Guard/Drake	3.00
66	Coast Guard/Penn St.	3.00
67	Coast Guard/Yale	3.00
68	Coker/UCLA	3.00
69	Coker/Wingate	3.00
70	Colby/Kings Point	3.00
71	Colby/Queens	3.00
72	Colby/Rice	3.00
73	Colby/Upsala	3.00
74	Colgate/Dickinson	3.00
75	Colgate/Lafayette	3.00
76	Colgate/U. of Mass.	3.00
77	Colgate/Springfield	3.00
78	Colgate/Texas AM	3.00
79	C.O.P./Princeton	3.00
80	C.O.P./Oklahoma St.	3.00
81	C.O.P./Oregon St.	3.00
82	Colorado St./Drew	3.00
83	Colorado St./Oregon	3.00
84	Colorado St./Piedmont	3.00
85	Colorado St./Wm. and Mary	3.00
86	Columbia/Dominican	3.00
87	Columbia/Maine	3.00
88	Columbia/N. Carolina	3.00
89	Cornell/Harvard	3.00
90	Cornell/Rensselaer	3.00
91	Cornell/Stanford	3.00
92	Cornell/Wisconsin	3.00
93	Dartmouth/Michigan St.	3.00
94	Dartmouth/Ohio U.	3.00
95	Dartmouth/Wagner	3.00
96	Davidson/Ohio Wesl.	3.00
97	Davidson/S. Carolina	3.00
98	Davidson/Texas Tech	3.00
99	Delaware/Marquette	3.00
100	Delaware/Michigan	3.00
101	Delaware/Notre Dame	5.00
102	Delaware/UCLA	3.00
103	Denver/Florida State	4.00
104	Denver/Indiana	3.00
105	Denver/Iowa State	3.00
106	Denver/USC	3.00
107	Denver/VMI	3.00
108	Detroit/Harvard	3.00
109	Detroit/Rensselaer	3.00
110	Detroit/Stanford	3.00
111	Detroit/Utah State	3.00
112	Dickinson/U. of Mass.	3.00
113	Dickinson/Regis	3.00
114	Dickinson/Springfield	3.00
115	Dickinson/Texas AM	3.00

116	Dominican/North Carolina	3.00
117	Drake/Duke	3.00
118	Drake/Kentucky	3.00
119	Drake/Middlebury	3.00
120	Drake/Penn St.	3.00
121	Drake/St. Peters	3.00
122	Drake/Yale	3.00
123	Drew/Middlebury	3.00
124	Drew/Oregon	3.00
125	Drew/Piedmont	3.00
126	Drew/Wm. and Mary	3.00
127	Duke/Middlebury	3.00
128	Duke/Rhode Island	3.00
129	Duke/Seton Hall	3.00
130	Duke/Yale	3.00
131	Finch/Long Island AT	3.00
132	Finch/Michigan St.	3.00
133	Finch/Ohio U.	3.00
134	Finch/Wagner	3.00
135	Florida/Gettysburg	3.00
136	Florida/Illinois	4.00
137	Florida/Syracuse	4.00
138	Florida/Virginia	4.00
139	Florida St./Indiana	4.00
140	Florida St./Iowa St.	4.00
141	Florida St./So. Cal.	4.00
142	Florida St./VMI	4.00
143	Georgetown/Kings Point	3.00
144	Georgetown/Rice	3.00
145	Georgia/Missouri	3.00
146	Georgia/Ohio Wesleyan	3.00
147	Georgia/Rutgers	3.00
148	Georgia/So. Carolina	4.00
149	Ga. Tech/Johns Hopkins	3.00
150	Ga. Tech/Maryland	3.00
151	Ga. Tech/Missouri	3.00
152	Gettysburg/Syracuse	3.00
153	Harvard/Miami	4.00
154	Harvard/NC State	3.00
155	Harvard/Stanford	3.00
156	Harvard/Utah State	3.00
157	Harvard/Wisconsin	3.00
158	Hofstra/Marquette	3.00
159	Hofstra/Michigan	4.00
160	Hofstra/Navy	3.00
161	Hofstra/UCLA	3.00
162	Holy Cross/Navy	3.00
163	Holy Cross/New York	3.00
164	Holy Cross/Northwestern	3.00
165	Holy Cross/Nyack	3.00
166	Howard/Kentucky	3.00
167	Howard/Villanova	3.00
168	Illinois/Syracuse	3.00
169	Indiana/Iowa State	3.00
170	Indiana/VMI	3.00
171	Iowa/Maryland	3.00
172	Iowa/Missouri	3.00
173	Iowa/Pratt	3.00
174	Iowa State/So. Cal.	4.00
175	Johns Hopkins/Pratt	3.00
176	Johns Hopkins/Purdue	3.00
177	Kansas/St. Francis	3.00
178	Kansas/S.M.U.	3.00
179	Kansas State/N.Y.U.	3.00
180	Kansas State/T.C.U.	3.00
181	Kentucky/Maryland	3.00
182	Kentucky/Middlebury	3.00
183	Kentucky/New Hampshire	3.00
184	Kentucky/Penn State	5.00
185	Kentucky/St. Peter's	3.00
186	Kentucky/Seton Hall	3.00
187	Kentucky/Villanova	3.00
188	Kings Point/Queens	3.00
189	Kings Point/Rice	3.00
190	Kings Point/Upsala	3.00
191	Lafayette/U. of Mass.	3.00
192	Lafayette/Regis	3.00
193	Long Isl. AT/Michigan St.	3.00
194	Long Isl. AT/Ohio U.	3.00
195	Long Isl. AT/Wagner	3.00
196	Loyola/Minnesota	3.00
197	Loyola/Norwich	3.00
198	Loyola/Winthrop	3.00
199	Marquette/Michigan	4.00
200	Marquette/Navy	3.00
201	Marquette/New Paltz	3.00
202	Marquette/Notre Dame	5.00
203	Marquette/UCLA	3.00
204	Maryland/Missouri	3.00
205	Mass./Regis	3.00
206	Mass./Springfield	3.00
207	Mass./Texas AM	3.00
208	Michigan/Navy	4.00

209	Michigan/New Paltz	3.00
210	Michigan/UCLA	4.00
211	Michigan St./Ohio U.	3.00
212	Michigan St./Wagner	3.00
213	Middlebury/Penn St.	3.00
214	Middlebury/Yale	3.00
215	Minnesota/Norwich	3.00
216	Minnesota/Winthrop	3.00
217	Mississippi/Penn	3.00
218	Mississippi/St. Francis	3.00
219	Missouri/Purdue	3.00
220	Navy/Notre Dame	7.50
221	Navy/UCLA	4.00
222	Navy/Wingate	3.00
223	New Hampshire/Villanova	3.00
224	N.Y.U./Northwestern	3.00
225	NCE/Temple	3.00
226	NCE/Wisconsin	3.00
227	NC State/Temple	3.00
228	Northwestern/TCU	3.00
229	Norwich/Winthrop	3.00
230	Notre Dame/UCLA	7.50
231	Notre Dame/Wingate	5.00
232	Ohio U./Wagner	3.00
233	Ohio Wesl./Roberts	3.00
234	Ohio Wesl./S. Carolina	3.00
235	Oklahoma St./Oregon St.	3.00
236	Oklahoma St./Princeton	3.00
237	Oregon/Piedmont	3.00
238	Oregon/Wm. and Mary	3.00
239	Oregon St./Princeton	3.00
240	Penn State/St. Peter's	3.00
241	Penn State/Seton Hall	3.00
242	Penn State/Yale	3.00
243	Penn/S.M.U.	3.00
244	Penn/St. Francis	3.00
245	Queens/Rice	3.00
246	Queens/Upsala	3.00
247	Rensselaer/Stanford	3.00
248	Rensselaer/Temple	3.00
249	Rensselaer/Utah State	3.00
250	Rhode Island/Yale	3.00
251	Rice/Upsala	3.00
252	Roberts/So. Carolina	3.00
253	Roberts/Texas Tech	3.00
254	Rutgers/So. Carolina	3.00
255	St. Francis/S.M.U.	3.00
256	St. Peter's/Villanova	3.00
257	St. Peter's/Yale	3.00
258	So. California/VMI	4.00
259	So. Carolina/Texas Tech	3.00
260	Syracuse/Virginia	3.00
261	Temple/Wisconsin	3.00
262	UCLA/Wingate	4.00
263	Utah State/Wisconsin	3.00
264	Villanova/Yale	3.00

1991 Oberlin College Heisman Club

		MT
Complete Set (5):		5.00
Common Player:		1.00
1	50 Years, Two Careers (C.W. "Doc" Savage, J.H. Nichols) (Athletic Directors)	1.00
2	John W. Heisman (CO)	2.00
3	Oberline's 1892 Team	1.00
4	Oberlin's Fauver Twins (Doc Edgar Fauver, Doc Edwin Fauver)	1.00
5	Oberlin's Four Horsemen (Carl Semple, Carl Williams, H.K. Regal, C.W. "Doc" Savage)	1.00

1979 Ohio State Greats

		NM
Complete Set (53):		35.00
Common Player:		.75
1C	Chris Ward	.75
1D	Jan White	1.00
1H	Ernest R. Godfrey (ACO)	.75

1S	Ray Pryor	.75
2C	Ray Griffin	1.00
2D	Tom Deleone	1.00
2H	Francis A. Schmidt (CO)	.75
2S	Dave Foley	1.00
3C	Tom Cousineau	1.25
3D	Randy Gradishar	2.00
3H	Jim Parker	2.00
3S	Rufus Mayes	1.00
4C	Aaron Brown	1.00
4D	John Hicks	1.25
4H	Vic Janowicz	1.50
4S	Rex Kern	1.50
5C	Chris Ward	.75
5D	Van Decree	.75
5H	Les Horvath	1.50
5S	Jim Otis	1.50
6C	Tom Skladany	1.25
6D	Randy Gradishar	2.00
6H	Bill Willis	1.25
6S	Ted Provost	.75
7C	Bob Brudzinski	1.00
7D	Archie Griffin	2.50
7H	James Daniell	.75
7S	Jim Stillwagon	1.25
8C	Ted Smith	.75
8D	John Hicks	1.25
8H	Gust Zarnas	.75
8S	Jack Tatum	1.50
9C	Tom Skladany	1.25
9D	Neal Colzie	1.00
9H	Gomer Jones	.75
9S	Tim Anderson	.75
10C	Archie Griffin	2.50
10D	Pete Cusick	.75
10H	Wes Fesler	1.00
10S	John Brockington	1.50
11C	Tim Fox	1.00
11D	Van Decree	.75
11H	Gaylord Stinchcomb	.75
11S	Mike Sensibaugh	1.00
12C	Tom Skladany	1.25
12D	Archie Griffin	2.50
12H	Chic Harley	.75
12S	Jim Stillwagon	1.25
13C	Kurt Schumacher	1.00
13D	Steve Meyers	1.00
13H	Tom Cousineau	1.25
13S	Jack Tatum	1.50
JK	Howard Jones (CO)	

1988 Ohio State

WOODY HAYES
HEAD COACH

		MT
Complete Set (22):		40.00
Common Player:		.40
1	Bob Brudzinski	.50
2	Keith Byars	1.50
3	Hopalong Cassady	1.00
4	Arnold Chonko	.50
5	Wes Fesler	.40
6	Randy Gradishar	1.00
7	Archie Griffin	1.50
8	Chic Harley	.40
9	Woody Hayes (CO)	1.00
10	John Hicks	.50
11	Les Horvath	1.00
12	Jim Houston	.75
13	Vic Janowicz	1.00
14	Pepper Johnson	.75
15	Ike Kelley	.40
16	Rex Kern	.75
17	Jim Lachey	.75
18	Jim Parker	1.00
19	Tom Skladany	.40
20	Chris Spielman	1.00
21	Jim Stillwagon	.75
22	Jack Tatum	1.00

1989 Ohio State

		MT
Complete Set (22):		8.00
Common Player:		.40
1	Mike Tomczak	1.00
2	Paul Warfield	1.50
3	Kirk Lowdermilk	.50
4	Bob Ferguson	.50
5	Jack Graf	.40
6	Tim Fox	.50
7	Eric Kumerow	.50
8	Neal Colzie	.50
9	Jim Otis	.75
10	John Brockington	1.00

11	Cornelius Greene	.40
12	Jim Marshall	1.00
13	Tim Spencer	.50
14	Don Scott	.40
15	Chris Ward	.50
16	Marcus Marek	.50
17	Dave Foley	.50
18	Bill Willis	.75
19	John Frank	.75
20	Rufus Mayes	.50
21	Tom Tupa	.75
22	Jan White	.50

1990 Ohio State

		MT
Complete Set (22):		8.00
Common Player:		.35
1	Jeff Uhlenhake	.50
2	Ray Ellis	.35
3	Todd Bell	.50
4	Jeff Logan	.35
5	Pete Johnson	.75
6	Van DeCree	.35
7	Ted Provost	.35
8	Mike Lanese	.35
9	Aaron Brown	.50
10	Pete Cusick	.35
11	Vlade Janakievski	.35
12	Steve Myers	.35
13	Ted Smith	.35
14	Doug Donley	.50
15	Ron Springs	.50
16	Ken Fritz	.35
17	Jeff Davidson	.35
18	Art Schlichter	.75
19	Tom Cousineau	.75
20	Call Murray	.35
21	Brian Baschnagel	.50
22	Joe Staysniak	.35

1992 Ohio State

		MT
Complete Set (59):		20.00
Common Player:		.25
1	John Cooper (CO)	.75
2	Kirk Herbstreit	.50
3	Steve Tovar	1.00
4	Chico Nelson	.25
5	Tim Patillo	.25
6	Tito Paul	.50
7	Jim Borchers	.25
8	Craig Powell	.75
9	Deron Brown	.25
10	Alex Rodriguez	.25
11	Chris Sanders	1.50
12	Cedric Saunders	.25
13	Walter Taylor	.40
14	Jack Thrush	.25
15	Brian Stablein	.50
16	Tim Walton	.25
17	Rod Smith	.50
18	Brad Pope	.25
19	William Houston	.25
20	Dan Wilkinson	1.50
21	Jason Winrow	.40
22	Mark Williams	.25
23	Jason Simmons	.50
24	Luke Fickell	.50
25	Tim Williams	.25
26	Raymont Harris	1.50
27	Preston Harrison	.25
28	Len Hartman	.25
29	Eddie George	3.00
30	Jayson Gwinn	.50
31	Korey Stringer	1.00
32	Tom Lease	.25
33	Randall Brown	.25
34	DeWayne Carter	.25
35	Bryan Cook	.25
36	Allen DeGraffenreid	.50
37	Brian Stoughton	.25
38	Derrick Foster	.25
39	Butler By'not'e	.75
40	Jeff Cothran	.75
41	Robert Davis	.25
42	Joey Galloway	5.00
43	Roger Harper	.75
44	Bobby Hoying	1.50
45	C.J. Kelly	.25
46	Brent Johnson	.25
47	Paul Long	.25
48	Joe Metzger	.25
49	Jason Louis	.25
50	Dave Monnot	.25
51	Greg Beatty	.25
52	Pete Beckman	.25
53	Matt Bonhaus	.25
54	Marlon Kerner	.50
55	Alan Kline	.25
56	Greg Kuszmaul	.25
57	Buckeye Flashback - October 12, 1968 (Jim Otis)	.40
58	Buckeye Flashback - September 30, 1972	.40
NNO	Title Card (CL)	.40

A card number in parentheses ( ) indicates the set is unnumbered.

1997 Ohio State

		MT
Complete Set (24):		25.00
Common Player:		1.00
1	Greg Bellisari	1.50
2	Matt Calhoun	1.00
3	Shane Clark	1.00
4	Dan Colson	1.00
5	John Cooper CO	1.50
6	LeShun Daniels	1.00
7	Luke Fickell	1.00
8	Matt Finkes	2.00
9	Anthony Gwinn	1.50
10	Bob Houser	1.00
11	Ty Howard	1.50
12	Josh Jackson	1.00
13	D.J. Jones	1.00
14	Rob Kelly	1.50
15	Heath Knisely	1.00
16	Ryan Miller	1.00
17	Juan Porter	1.00
18	Chad Pulliam	1.00
19	Dimitrious Stanley	1.50
20	Buster Tillman	1.50
21	Mike Vrabel	2.00
22	American Marketing Associates	1.00
23	1997 Senior Rose Bowl Champions	1.50
24	Team Logo	1.00
25	Sponsor card	1.00

1982 Oklahoma Playing Cards

		MT
Complete Set (56):		40.00
Common Player:		.50
C1	Action Shot (Joe Washington)	1.00
C2	Coaches 1895-1934	.50
C3	All-Americans 1946-48 (Buddy Burris)	1.00
C4	All-Americans 1953-54 (Buck McPhail, J.D. Roberts, Max Boydston, Kurt Burris)	1.00
C5	All-Americans 1963-69 (Ralph Neely, Carl McAdams, Bob Kalsu, Steve Owens)	1.00
C6	All-Americans 1974-75 (Kyle Davis, Tinker Owens, Dewey Selmon, Lee Roy Selmon)	1.00
C7	1951 (Jim Weatherall)	1.00
C8	1952 (Billy Vessels)	1.00
C9	NCAA Champions 1955	1.00
C10	Action Shot (Uwe Von Schamann)	.50
C11	Action Shot (Tony DiRienzo)	.50
C12	Action Shot (Joe Washington)	1.00
C13	Action Shot (Tinker Owens)	.50
D1	Action Shot (Joe Washington)	1.00
D2	Coaches 1935-1982	.50
D3	All-Americans 1949 (Jimmy Owens, Darrell Royal)	1.00
D4	All-Americans 1955-56 (Bo Bolinger, Ed Gray, Jerry Tubbs, Terry McDonald)	1.00
D5	All-Americans 1966-71 (Granville Liggins, Steve Zabel, Ken Mendenhall, Jack Mildren)	
D6	All-Americans 1975-76 (Terry Webb, Billy Brooks, Jimbo Elrod, Mike Vaughan)	1.00
D7	1953 (J.D. Roberts)	1.00
D8	1969 (Steve Owens)	1.50
D9	NCAA Champions 1956	1.00
D10	Barry Switzer (CO)	.50
D11	Action Shot (Lucius Selmon)	.50
D12	Action Shot (Elvis Peacock)	.50
D13	Action Shot (Billy Sims)	1.00
H1	Action Shot (Jimbo Elrod)	.50
H2	All-Americans 1913-37	1.00
H3	All-Americans 1949-51 (Jim Weatherall)	1.00
H4	All-Americans 1957-59 (Bill Krisher, Clendon Thomas, Bob Harrison, Jerry Thompson)	1.00
H5	All-Americans 1971-74 (Greg Pruitt, Tom Brahaney, Derland Moore, Rod Shoate)	1.00
H6	All-Americans 1976-78 (Zac Henderson, Greg Roberts, Daryl Hunt, George Cumby)	1.00
H7	1975 (Lee Roy Selmon)	1.50
H8	1978 (Billy Sims)	1.50
H9	NCAA Champions 1974	1.00
H10	Action Shot (Lee Roy Selmon)	1.00
H11	Action Shot (Tinker Owens)	.50
H12	Action Shot	.50
H13	Action Shot (Lee Roy Selmon)	1.00
S1	Action Shot (Horace Ivory)	.50
S2	All-Americans 1938-46	1.00
S3	All-Americans 1951-52 (Tom Catlin, Billy Vessels, Eddie Crowder)	1.00
S4	All-Americans 1962-63 (Leon Cross, Wayne Lee, Jim Grisham, Joe Don Looney)	1.00
S5	All-Americans 1973-75 (Lucius Selmon, Eddie Foster, John Roush, Joe Washington)	1.00
S6	All-Americans 1978-81 (Reggie Kinlaw, Billy Sims, Louis Oubre, Terry Crouch)	1.00
S7	1978 (Greg Roberts)	1.00
S8	NCAA Champions 1950	1.00
S9	NCAA Champions 1975	1.00
S10	Action Shot (Bobby Proctor) (CO)	.50
S11	Action Shot (Steve Davis)	.50
S12	Action Shot (Greg Pruitt)	1.00
S13	Action Shot (Elvis Peacock)	.50
JK1	Sooner Schooner	.50
JK2	Sooner Schooner	.50
NNO	Mail Order Card	.50
NNO	Mail Order Card	.50

1986 Oklahoma

		MT
Complete Set (16):		8.00
Common Player:		.35
1	Championship Ring - 1985 National Champs	.50
2	Orange Bowl (In Bowl Day)	.35
3	On The Road To Record	.35
4	Graduation Record	.35
5	President of Exxon (Lawrence G. Rawl)	.35
6	Barry Switzer (Winners)	1.50
7	Win Streaks Hold Records	.35
8	Brian Bosworth	1.00
9	Heisman Trophy (Billy Vessels 1952, Steve Owens 1969, Billy Sims 1978)	.75
10	All-America Sooners (Tony Casillas)	.75
11	Jamelle Holieway	.50
12	Sooner Strength	.35
13	Sooner Support	.35
14	Go Sonners (Crimson and Cream)	.35
15	Border Battle (Oklahoma vs. Texas)	.50
16	Barry Switzer (CO) (SP) (Caricature; "I Want You...; '86 OU football schedule on back)	2.50

1986 Oklahoma McDag

		MT
Complete Set (16):		20.00
Common Player:		1.00
1	Brian Bosworth	3.00
2	Sonny Brown	1.00
3	Steve Bryan	1.00
4	Lydell Carr	1.50
5	Patrick Collins	1.50
6	Jamelle Holieway	2.00
7	Mark Hutson	1.00
8	Keith Jackson	6.00
9	Troy Johnson	1.00
10	Dante Jones	3.00
11	Tim Lashar	1.00
12	Paul Migliazzo	1.00
13	Anthony Phillips	1.00
14	Darrell Reed	1.00
15	Derrick Shepard	1.50
16	Spencer Tillman	1.50

1987 Oklahoma Police

		MT
Complete Set (16):		18.00
Common Player:		.75
1	Eric Mitchel	1.25
4	Jamelle Holieway	2.00
10	David Vickers	.75
25	Anthony Stafford	1.25
29	Rickey Dixon	2.00
33	Patrick Collins	1.25
40	Darrell Reed	.75
45	Lydell Carr	1.25
50	Dante Jones	2.00
66	Jon Phillips	.75
68	Anthony Phillips	.75
75	Greg Johnson	.75
79	Mark Hutson	.75
80	Troy Johnson	.75
88	Keith Jackson	6.00
98	Dante Williams	.75
NNO	Barry Switzer (CO)	3.00

1988 Oklahoma Greats

		MT
Complete Set (30):		7.00
Common Player:		.20
1	Jerry Anderson	.20
2	Dee Andros	.30
3	Dean Blevins	.20
4	Rick Bryan	.50
5	Paul (Buddy) Burris	.20
6	Eddie Crowder	.30
7	Jack Ging	.20
8	Jim Grisham	.30
9	Jimmy Harris	.30
10	Scott Hill	.20
11	Eddie Hinton	.30
12	Earl Johnson	.20
13	Don Key	.20
14	Tim Lashar	.20
15	Granville Liggins	.50
16	Thomas Lott	.30
17	Carl McAdams	.30
18	Jack Mitchell	.20
19	Billy Pricer	.20
20	John Roush	.20
21	Darrell Royal	.50
22	Lucius Selmon	.20
23	Ron Shotts	.20
24	Jerry Tubbs	.30
25	Bob Warmack	.30
26	Joe Washington	.50
27	Jim Weatherall	.30
28	'86 Sooner Great Game	.20
29	'75 Sooners	.20
30	Checklist Card	.30

1988 Oklahoma Police

		MT
Complete Set (16):		18.00
Common Player:		1.00
1	Rotnei Anderson	2.00
2	Eric Bross	1.00
3	Mike Gaddis	2.50
4	Scott Garl	1.00
5	James Goode	1.00
6	Jamelle Holieway	2.00
7	Bob Latham	1.00
8	Ken McMichel	1.00
9	Eric Mitchel	1.50
10	Leon Perry	1.50
11	Anthony Phillips	1.00
12	Anthony Stafford	1.50
13	Barry Switzer (CO)	4.00
14	Mark Vankeirsbilck	1.00
15	Curtice Williams	1.00
16	Dante Williams	1.00

1989 Oklahoma Police

		MT
Complete Set (16):		15.00
Common Player:		1.00
1	Tom Backes	1.00
2	Frank Blevins	1.00
3	Eric Bross	1.00
4	Adrian Cooper	3.00
5	Scott Evans	1.00
6	Mike Gaddis	2.00
7	Gary Gibbs (CO)	1.50
8	James Goode	1.00
9	Ken McMichel	1.00
10	Leon Perry	1.50
11	Mike Sawatzky	1.00
12	Don Smitherman	1.00
13	Kevin Thompson	1.00
14	Mark VanKeirsbilck	1.00
15	Mike Wise	1.00
16	Dante Williams	1.00

1991 Oklahoma Police

		MT
Complete Set (16):		15.00
Common Player:		1.00
1	Gary Gibbs (CO)	1.50
2	Cale Gundy	2.00
3	Charles Franks	1.00
4	Mike Gaddis	1.50
5	Brad Reddell	1.00
6	Brandon Houston	1.00
7	Chris Wilson	1.00
8	Darnell Walker	1.00
9	Mike McKinley	1.00
10	Kenyon Rasheed	2.00
11	Joe Bowden	2.00
12	Jason Belser	2.00
13	Steve Collins	1.00
14	Reggie Barnes	1.00
15	Randy Wallace	1.00
16	Proctor Land	1.00

1953 Oregon

		NM
Complete Set (20):		340.00
Common Player:		15.00
1	Farrell Albright	20.00
2	Ted Anderson	15.00
3	Len Berrie	15.00
4	Tom Elliott	15.00
5	Tim Flaherty	15.00
6	Cecil Hodges	15.00
7	Barney Holland	15.00
8	Dick James	25.00
9	Harry Johnson	15.00
10	Dave Lowe	15.00
11	Jack Patera	35.00
12	Ron Pheister	20.00
13	John Reed	15.00
14	Hal Reeve	20.00
15	Larry Rose	15.00
16	George Shaw	25.00
17	Lon Stiner Jr.	15.00
18	Ken Sweitzer	15.00
19	Keith Tucker	15.00
20	Dean Van Leuven	15.00

1956 Oregon

		NM
Complete Set (19):		285.00
Common Player:		15.00
1	Bruce Brenn	15.00
2	Jack Brown	15.00
3	Reanous Cochran	15.00
4	Jack Crabtree	20.00

5	Tom Crabtree	15.00
6	Tom Hale	15.00
7	Spike Hillstrom	15.00
8	Jim Linden	15.00
9	Hank Loumena	15.00
10	Nick Markulis	15.00
11	Phil McHugh	15.00
13	Harry Mondale	15.00
14	Leroy Phelps	15.00
15	Jack Pocock	15.00
16	John Roventos	15.00
17	Jim Shanley	15.00
18	Ron Stover	20.00
19	J.C. Wheeler	15.00

1958 Oregon

		NM
	Complete Set (20):	260.00
	Common Player:	15.00
1	Greg Altenhofen	15.00
2	Darrel Aschbacher	20.00
3	Dave Fish	15.00
4	Sandy Fraser	15.00
5	Dave Grosz	20.00
6	Bob Grottkau	20.00
7	Marlan Holland	15.00
8	Tom Keele	15.00
9	Alden Kimbrough	15.00
10	Don Laudenslager	15.00
11	Riley Mattson	25.00
12	Bob Peterson	15.00
13	Dave Powell	15.00
14	Len Read	15.00
15	Will Reeve	15.00
16	Joe Schaffeld	15.00
17	Charlie Tourville	15.00
18	Dave Urell	15.00
19	Pete Welch	15.00
20	Willie West	25.00

1991 Oregon Smokey

		MT
	Complete Set (12):	12.00
	Common Player:	1.00
1	Bud Bowie	1.00
2	Rich Brooks (CO)	3.00
3	Sean Burwell	1.00
4	Eric Castle	1.50
5	Andy Conner	1.00
6	Joe Farwell	1.00
7	Matt LaBounty	1.50
8	Gregg McCallum	1.00
9	Daryle Smith	1.00
10	Jeff Thomason	1.50
11	Tommy Thompson	1.00
12	Marcus Woods	1.50

1988 Oregon State Smokey

		MT
	Complete Set (12):	12.00
	Common Player:	1.25
1	Troy Bussanich	1.25
2	Andre Harris	1.25
3	Teddy Johnson	1.25
4	Jason Kent	1.25
5	Dave Kragthorpe (CO)	1.25
6	Mike Matthews	1.25
7	Phil Ross	1.25
8	Brian Taylor	1.25
9	Robb Thomas	2.50
10	Esera Tuaolo	2.50
11	Erik Wilhelm	2.50
12	Dowell Williams	1.25

1990 Oregon State Smokey

		MT
	Complete Set (16):	10.00
	Common Player:	1.00
1	Brian Beck	1.00
2	Martin Billings	1.00
3	Matt Booher	1.00
4	George Breland	1.00
5	Brad D'Ancona	1.00
6	Dennis Edwards	1.00
7	Brent Huff	1.00
8	James Jones	1.00
9	Dave Kragthorpe (CO)	1.00
10	Todd McKinney	1.00
11	Torey Overstreet	1.00
12	Reggie Pitchford	1.00
13	Todd Sahlfeld	1.00
14	Scott Thompson	1.00
15	Esera Tuaolo	2.00
16	Maurice Wilson	1.00

1991 Oregon State Smokey

		MT
	Complete Set (12):	10.00
	Common Player:	1.00
1	Adam Albaugh	1.00
2	Jamie Burke	1.00
3	Chad de Sully	1.00
4	Dennis Edwards	1.00
5	James Jones	1.00
6	Fletcher Keister	1.00
7	Tom Nordquist	1.00
8	Tony O'Billovich	1.00
9	Jerry Pettibone (CO)	1.25
10	Mark Price	1.00
11	Todd Sahlfeld	1.00
12	Earl Zackery	1.00

1992 Oregon State Smokey

		MT
	Complete Set (12):	9.00
	Common Player:	.75
1	Zechariah Davis	.75
2	Chad De Sully	.75
3	Michael Hale	.75
4	Fletcher Keister	.75
5	Chad Paulson	.75
6	Rico Petrini	.75
7	Jerry Pettibone (CO)	1.00
8	Sailusi Poulivaati	.75
9	Tony O'Billovich	.75
10	Dwayne Owens	.75
11	J.J. Young	1.50
12	Maurice Wilson	.75

1994 Oregon State Smokey

		MT
	Complete Set (12):	8.00
	Common Player:	.75
1	William Ephraim	.75
2	Johnny Feinga	.75
3	John Garrett	.75
4	Michael Hale	.75
5	Tom Holmes	.75
6	Cory Huot	.75
7	Rico Petrini	.75
8	Cameron Reynolds	.75
9	Kane Rogers	.75
10	Don Shanklin	1.00
11	Reggie Tongue	.75
12	J.J. Young	1.00

1988 Penn State Police

JOE PATERNO
Head Football Coach

		MT
	Complete Set (12):	25.00
	Common Player:	1.25
5	Michael Timpson	4.00
20	Jim Greene	1.25
28	Brian Chizmar	1.25
31	Andre Collins	4.00
32	Blair Thomas	4.00
39	Eddie Johnson	1.25
66	Steve Wisniewski	4.00
75	Rich Schonewolf	1.25
78	Roger Duffy	1.25
84	Keith Karpinski	1.25
NNO	Joe Paterno (CO)	5.00
NNO	Penn State Mascot - The Nittany Lion	1.50

1989 Penn State Police

		MT
	Complete Set (15):	20.00
	Common Player:	1.00
1	Brian Chizmar	1.00
2	Andre Collins	2.50
3	David Daniels	2.50
4	Roger Duffy	1.00
5	Tim Freeman	1.00
6	Scott Gob	1.00
7	David Jakob	1.00
8	Geoff Japchen	1.00
9	Joe Paterno (CO)	4.00
10	Sherrod Rainge	1.00
11	Rich Schonewolf	1.00
12	Dave Szott	2.50
13	Blair Thomas	2.50
14	Leroy Thompson	4.00
15	Nittany Lion (Mascot)	1.00

1990 Penn State Police

		MT
	Complete Set (16):	15.00
	Common Player:	.75
1	Gerry Collins	.75
2	David Daniels	1.25
3	Jim Deter	.75
4	Mark D'Onofrio	1.25
5	Sam Gash	2.00
6	Frank Giannetti	.75
7	Keith Goganious	1.25
8	Doug Helkowski	.75
9	Hernon Henderson	.75
10	Matt McCartin	.75
11	Joe Paterno (CO)	3.00
12	Darren Perry	2.00
13	Tony Sacca	2.00
14	Terry Smith	.75
15	Willie Thomas	.75
16	Leroy Thompson	2.50

1991-92 Penn State Legends

		MT
	Complete Set (51):	15.00
	Common Player:	.35
1	Joe Paterno (CO)	2.00
2	Kurt Allerman	.35
3	Chris Bahr	.50
4	Matt Bahr	.50
5	Bruce Bannon	.35
6	Greg Buttle	.50
7	John Capelletti	.75
8	Bruce Clark	.35
9	Andre Collins	.75
10	Shane Conlan	.75
11	Chris Conlin	.35
12	Randy Crowder	.35
13	Keith Dorney	.50
14	D.J. Dozier	.75
15	Bill Dugan	.35
16	Chuck Fusina	.50
17	Leon Gajecki	.35
18	Jack Ham	1.25
19	Bob Higgins	.35
20	John Hufnagel	.75
21	Kenny Jackson	.50
22	Tim Johnson	.35
23	Dave Joyner	.35
24	Roger Kochman	.35
25	Ted Kwalick	.50
26	Richie Lucas	.75
27	Matt Millen	.75
28	Lydell Mitchell	.75
29	Bob Mitinger	.35
30	John Nessel	.35
31	Ed O'Neil	.50
32	Dennis Onkotz	.35
33	Darren Perry	.50
34	Charlie Pittman	.50
35A	Tom Rafferty (ERR) (Photo actually T. Quinn)	5.00
35B	Tom Rafferty (COR)	1.25
36	Mike Reid (UER) (Reversed negative)	1.25
37	Glenn Ressler	.50
38	Dave Robinson	.50
39	Mark Robinson	.35
40	Randy Sidler	.35
41	John Skorupan	.50
42	Neal Smith	.35
43	Steve Suhey	.50
44	Sam Tamburo	.35
45	Blair Thomas	1.25
46	Curt Warner	1.50
47	Steve Wisniewski	.75
48	Charlie Zapiec	.35
49	Michael Zordich	.50
50	Harry Wilson, Joe Bedenk	.35
P1	Joe Paterno (CO) (Promo)	4.00
P10	Shane Conlan (Promo)	2.00
P18	Jack Ham (Promo)	2.50
NNO	Checklist Card	.35

1992 Penn State Police

		MT
	Complete Set (16):	20.00
	Common Player:	.60
1	Richie Anderson	1.00
2	Lou Benfatti	1.00
3	Derek Bochna	.60
4	Kyle Brady	4.00
5	Kerry Collins	8.00
6	Troy Drayton	2.00
7	John Gerak	1.00
8	Reggie Givens	1.00
9	Shelly Hammonds	.60
10	Greg Huntington	.60
11	Tyoka Jackson	1.00
12	O.J. McDuffie	4.00
13	Lee Rubin	.60
14	E.J. Sandusky	.60
15	Tisen Thomas	.60
16	Brett Wright	.60

1993 Penn State

		MT
	Complete Set (25):	18.00
	Common Player:	.50
1	Mike Archie, Ki-Jana Carter, Stephen Pitts	5.00
2	Lou Benfatti	.75
3	Derek Bochna	.50
4	Kyle Brady	3.00
5	Kerry Collins	5.00
6	Criag Fayak	.50
7	Marlon Forbes	.50
8	Brian Gelzheiser	1.00
9	Bucky Greeley	.50
10	Ryan Grube	.75
11	Shelly Hammonds	.75
12	Jeff Hartings	.75
13	Rob Holmberg	.75
14	Tyoka Jackson	.75
15	Mike Malinoski	.75
16	Brian Monaghan	.75
17	Brian O'Neal	.75
18	Jeff Perry	.75
19	Derick Pickett	.50
20	Tony Pittman	.50
21	Eric Ravotti	.75
22	Lee Rubin	.50
23	Vin Stewart	.50
24	Tisen Thomas	.50
25	Phil Yeboah-Kodie	.75

1989 Pittsburgh

		MT
	Complete Set (22):	10.00
	Common Player:	.30
1	Tony Dorsett	2.00
2	Pop Warner (CO)	.40
3	Hugh Green	.60
4	Matt Cavanaugh	.50
5	Mike Gottfried	.40
6	Jimbo Covert	.50
7	Bob Peck	.30
8	Gibby Welch	.30
9	Bill Daddio	.40
10	Jock Sutherland (CO)	.40
11	Joe Walton	.40
12	Dan Marino	4.00
13	Russ Grimm	.40
14	Mike Ditka	2.00
15	Marshall Goldberg	.50
16	Bill Fralic	.40
17	Paul Martha	.40
18	Joe Schmidt	.75
19	Rickey Jackson	.60
20	Ave Daniell	.30
21	Bill Maas	.40
22	Mark May	.40

1990 Pitt Foodland

		MT
	Complete Set (12):	8.00
	Common Player:	.50
1	Curtis Bray	.50
2	Craig Gob	.50
3	Paul Hackett (CO)	.50
4	Keith Hamilton	1.50
5	Ricardo McDonald	1.50
6	Ronald Redmon	.50
7	Curvin Richards	.50
8	Louis Riddick	.50
9	Chris Sestili	.50
10	Olanda Truitt	1.50
11	Alex Van Pelt	1.50
12	Nelson Walker	.50

1991 Pitt Foodland

		MT
	Complete Set (12):	7.00
	Common Player:	.75
1	Richard Allen	.75
2	Curtis Bray	.75
3	Jeff Christy	.75
4	Steve Israel	1.00
5	Scott Kaplan	.75
6	Ricardo McDonald	.75
7	Dave Moore	.75
8	Eric Seaman	.75
9	Chris Sestili	.75
10	Alex Van Pelt	1.50
11	Nelson Walker	.75
12	Kevin Williams (HB)	.75

1991 Pitt State

		MT
	Complete Set (18):	12.00
	Common Player:	.60
1	Chuck Broyles (CO)	.60
2	Darren Dawson	.60
3	Kendall Gammon	.60
4	Jamie Goodson	.60
5	Brian Hoover	.60
6	James Jenkins	.60
7	Ky Kiger	.60
8	Phil McCoy	.60
9	Kline Minniefield	.60
10	Ron Moore	4.00
11	Jeff Mundhenke	.60
12	Brian Pinamonti	.60
13	Michael Rose	.60
14	Shane Tafoya	.60
15	Ronnie West	1.25
16	Michael Wilber	.60
17	Troy Wilson	1.50
18	Team Photo	1.25
		.60

1992 Pitt State

		MT
	Complete Set (18):	10.00
	Common Player:	.60
1	Ron Moore	2.00
2	Craig Jordan	.60
3	Joel Thornton	.60
4	Don Tolar	.60
5	Andy Kesinger	.60
6	Mike Brockel	.60
7	Troy Wilson	1.25
8	Brian Hutchins	.60
9	Chris Hanna	.60
10	Coaching Staff	.60
11	Gus Gorilla (Mascot)	.60
12	Lance Gosch	.60
13	Jerry Boone, Chad Watskey	.60
15	Jeff Moreland, Scott Lutz	.60
15	Ronnie Fuller, Mickey Beagle	.60
16	Todd Hafner, Kevin Duncan	.60
17	Duke Palmer, Eric Perks	.60
18	Kris Mengarelli	.60

1989 Purdue Legends Smokey

		MT
	Complete Set (16):	25.00
	Common Player:	1.25
1	Fred Akers (CO)	1.50
2	Jim Everett (LEG)	4.00
3	Bob Griese (LEG)	6.00
4	Mark Herrmann (LEG)	2.00
5	Bill Hitchcock	1.25
6	Steve Jackson	1.50
7	Derrick Kelson	1.25
8	Leroy Keyes (LEG)	2.00
9	Shawn McCarthy	1.25
10	Dwayne O'Connor	1.25
11	Mike Phipps (LEG)	2.00
12	Darren Trieb	1.25
13	Tony Vinson	1.25
14	Calvin Williams	3.00
15	Rod Woodson (LEG)	5.00
16	Dave Young (LEG)	1.25

1990 Rice Aetna

		MT
	Complete Set (12):	12.00
	Common Player:	1.00
1	O.J. Brigance	1.50
2	Trevor Cobb	2.50
3	Tim Fitzpatrick	1.00
4	Fred Goldsmith (CO)	2.00
5	David Griffin	1.00
6	Eric Henley	1.50
7	Donald Hollas	2.50
8	Richard Segina	1.00
9	Matt Sign	1.00
10	Bill Stone	1.00
11	Trey Teichelman (UER) (Misspelled Tichelman on front and back)	1.00
12	Alonzo Williams	1.00

1991 Rice Aetna

		MT
	Complete Set (12):	12.00
	Common Player:	1.00
1	Mike Appelbaum	1.00
2	Louis Balady	1.00
3	Nathan Bennett	1.00
4	Trevor Cobb	2.00
5	Herschel Crowe	1.00
6	David Griffin	1.00
7	Eric Henley	1.50
8	Matt Sign	1.00
9	Larry Stuppy	1.00
10	Trey Teichelman	1.00
11	Alonzo Williams	1.00
12	Greg Willig	1.00

1992 Rice Taco Cabana

		MT
	Complete Set (12):	12.00
	Common Player:	1.00
1	Shawn Alberding	1.00
2	Mike Appelbaum	1.00
3	Louis Balady	1.00
4	Nathan Bennett	1.00
5	Trevor Cobb	2.00
6	Josh LaRocca	1.00
7	Jimmy Lee	1.50
8	Corey Seymour	1.00
9	Matt Sign	1.00
10	Emmett Waldron	1.50
11	Alonzo Williams	1.00
12	Taco Cabana (Advertisement)	1.00

1993 Rice Taco Cabana

		MT
	Complete Set (12):	12.00
	Common Player:	1.00
1	Nathan Bennett	1.00
2	Cris Cooley	1.50
3	Bert Emanuel	5.00
4	Jimmy Golden	1.00
5	Tom Hetherington	1.00
6	Ed Howard	1.00
7	Jimmy Lee	1.50
8	Corey Seymour	1.00
9	Clemente Torres	1.00
10	Emmett Waldron	1.50
11	Sean Washington	1.50
12	Taco Cabana Ad Card	1.00

1990 San Jose State Smokey

		MT
	Complete Set (15):	10.00
	Common Player:	.75
1	Bob Bleisch (90)	.75
2	Sheldon Canley (20)	.75
3	Paul Franklin (37)	.75
4	Anthony Gallegos (72)	.75
5	Steve Hieber (48)	.75
6	Everett Lampkins (43)	.75
7	Kelly Liebengood (21)	.75
8	Ralph Martini (9)	.75
9	Lyneil Mayo (62)	.75
10	Mike Powers (57)	.75
11	Mike Scialabba (46)	.75
12	Terry Shea (CO)	.75
13	Freddie Smith (4)	.75
14	Eddie Thomas (26)	.75
15	Brian Woods (64)	.75

1992 San Jose State

		MT
	Complete Set (20):	10.00
	Common Player:	.60
1	Maceo Barbosa	.60
2	Bobby Blackmon	.60
3	David Blakes	.60
4	Walter Brooks Jr.	.60
5	Greg Bruggeman	.60
6	Bryce Burnett	.60
7	Doug Calcagno	.60
8	Gary Charlton	.60
9	Chris Clarke	.60
10	Hesh Colar	.60
11	Jeff Greeney	.60
12	Leon Hawthorne	.60
13	Peni Iosefa	.60
14	Byron Jackson	.60
15	Robbie Miller	.60
16	Freddie Smith	.60
17	Spencer Smith	.60
18	Simon Vaofi	.60
19	Matt Veatch	.60
20	Blair Zerr	.60

1969 South Carolina Team Sheets

		NM
Complete Set (6):		45.00
Common Player:		6.00
1	Tim Bice, Candler Boyd, Don Buckner, Ronald Bunch, Bob Cole, Carl Cowart, Don Dunning, Mike Fair, Tony Fusaro,	6.00
2	Allen Brown, Don Somma, Billy Tharp, Scott Townsend, Pat Watson, Bob Wehmeyer, Bob White, C urtis Williams, Tom	6.00
3	Andy Chavous, Wally Orrel, Ronnie Palmer, Hyrum Pierce, Jimmy Poole, Roy Don Reeves, Larry Royal, Gene Schwarting,	6.00
4	Paul Dietzel CO Larry Jones CO, Johnny Menger CO, Pride Ratterree CO, Bill Rowe CO, Bill Shalosky CO, Lou Holtz, Dick Weldon CO	15.00
5	Ben Garnto, Gordon Gibson, Johnny Glass, Jimmy Gobble, Dave Grant, Johnny Gregory, Bob Harris, Rudy Holloman, Earl	6.00
6	Jimmy Killen, Joe Komoroski, Dave Lucas, Bob Mauro, George McCarthy, Toy McCord, Wally Medlin, Bob Morris, Warren	6.00

1974 Southern Cal Discs

		NM
Complete Set (30):		75.00
Common Player:		2.00
1	Bill Bain	2.50
2	Otha Bradley	2.50
3	Kevin Bruce	2.00
4	Mario Celotto	2.00
5	Marvin Cobb	4.00
6	Anthony Davis	8.00
7	Joe Davis	2.00
8	Shelton Diggs	2.50
9	Dave Farmer	2.00
10	Pat Haden	10.00
11	Donnie Hickman	2.00
12	Doug Hogan	2.00
13	Mike Howell	2.00
14	Gary Jeter	4.00
15	Steve Knutson	2.00
16	Chris Limahelu	2.50
17	Bob McCaffrey	2.00
18	J.K. McKay	4.00
19	John McKay (CO)	5.00
20	Jim O'Bradovich	4.00
21	Charles Phillips	2.50
22	Ed Powell	2.00
23	Marvin Powell	4.00
24	Danny Reece	2.50
25	Art Riley	2.00
26	Traveller II (Richard Sako)	2.50
27	Trojan Statue (Tommy Trojan)	2.50
28	USC Song Girls	2.50
29	USC Song Girls	2.50
30	Richard Wood	4.00

1988 Southern Cal Smokey

		MT
Complete Set (17):		12.00
Common Player:		.75
1	Erik Affholter	1.25
2	Gene Arrington	.75
3	Scott Brennan	.75
4	Jeff Brown	.75
5	Tracy Butts	.75
6	Martin Chesley	.75
7	Paul Green	.75
8	John Guerrero	.75
9	Chris Hale	.75
10	Rodney Peete	4.00
11	Dave Powroznik	.75
12	Mark Sager	.75
13	Mike Serpa	.75
14	Larry Smith (CO)	1.25
15	Chris Sperle	.75
16	Joe Walshe	.75
17	Steven Webster	.75

1988 Southern Cal Winners

		MT
Complete Set (73):		15.00
Common Player:		.15
1	Title Card (schedule on back)	.25
2	George Achica	.25
3	Marcus Allen	2.00
4	Jon Arnett	.35
5	Johnny Baker	.15
6	Damon Bame	.15
7	Chip Banks	.35
8	Mike Battle	.25
9	Hal Bedsole	.25
10	Ricky Bell	.35
11	Jeff Bregel	.15
12	Tay Brown	.15
13	Brad Budde	.25
14	Dave Cadigan	.25
15	Pat Cannamela	.15
16	Paul Cleary	.15
17	Sam Cunningham	.35
18	Anthony Davis	.50
19	Clarence Davis	.25
20	Morley Drury	.15
21	John Ferraro	.15
22	Bill Fisk	.15
23	Roy Foster	.25
24	Mike Garrett	.35
25	Frank Gifford	1.25
26	Ralph Heywood	.15
27	Pat Howell	.15
28	Gary Jeter	.25
29	Dennis Johnson	.15
30	Mort Kaer	.15
31	Grenny Lansdell	.15
32	Ronnie Lott	1.25
33	Paul McDonald	.25
34	Tim McDonald	.35
35	Ron Mix	.35
36	Don Mosebar	.35
37	Artimus Parker	.25
38	Charles Phillips	.15
39	Erny Pinckert	.15
40	Marvin Powell	.15
41	Aaron Rosenberg	.15
42	Tim Rossovich	.25
43	Jim Sears	.15
44	Gus Shaver	.15
45	Nate Shaw	.15
46	O.J. Simpson	5.00
47	Ernie Smith	.15
48	Harry Smith	.15
49	Larry Stevens	.15
50	Lynn Swann	1.00
51	Brice Taylor	.15
52	Dennis Thurman	.25
53	Keith Van Horne	.25
54	Cotton Warburton	.15
55	Charles White	.50
56	Elmer Willhoite	.15
57	Richard Wood	.25
58	Ron Yary	.35
59	Adrian Young	.15
60	Charles Young (UER) (listed as Adrian Young on card front)	.25
61	Pete Adams, John Grant	.15
62	Bill Bain, Jim O'Bradovich	.25
63	Nate Barrager, Francis Tappan	.15
64	Booker Brown, Steve Riley	.15
65	Al Cowlings, Jimmy Gunn, Charles Weaver	1.00
66	Jack Del Rio, Duane Bickett	.50
67	Clay Matthews, Bruce Matthews	.50
68	Marlin McKeever, Mike McKeever	.35
69	Orv Mohler, Garrett Arbelbide	.15
70	Sid Smith, Marv Montgomery	.15
71	John Vella, Willie Hall	.25
72	Don Williams, Jesse Hibbs	.15
73	Stan Williamson, Tony Slaton	.15

1989 Southern Cal Smokey

		MT
Complete Set (23):		10.00
Common Player:		.60
1	Dan Barnes	.60
2	Dwight Carner	.60
3	Delmar Chesley	.60
4	Cleveland Colter	.60
5	Aaron Emanuel	1.25
6	Scott Galbraith	1.25
7	Leroy Holt	.75
8	Randy Hord	.60
9	John Jackson	1.50
10	Brad Leggett	.60
11	Marching Band	.60
12	Dan Owens	1.50
13	Brent Parkinson	.60
14	Tim Ryan	1.50
15	Bill Schultz	.60
16	Larry Smith (CO)	.75
17	Ernest Spears	.60
18	J.P. Sullivan	.60
19	Cordell Sweeney	.60
20	Traveler (Horse Mascot)	.60
21	Marlon Washington	.60
22	Michael Williams	.60
23	Yell Leaders and Song Girls	.75

1991 Southern Cal College Classics

		MT
Complete Set (100):		30.00
Common Player:		.25
1	Charles White	.75
2	Anthony Davis	.75
3	Clay Matthews	.75
4	Hoby Brenner	.35
5	Mike Garrett	.50
6	Bill Sharman (Basketball)	1.25
7	Bob Seagren (Track)	.35
8	Mike McKeever	.35
9	Celso Kalache (Volleyball)	.25
10	John Williams (CO) (Water Polo)	.25
11	John Naber (Swimming)	.50
12	Brad Budde	.35
13	Tim Ryan	.35
14	Mark Tucker	.25
15	Rodney Peete	1.00
16	Art Mazmanian (Baseball)	.25
17	Red Badgro (Baseball)	.35
18	Sue Habernigg (Women's Swimming)	.25
19	Craig Fertig	.25
20	John Block (Basketball)	.50
21	Jen-Kai Liu (Volleyball)	.25
22	Kim Ruddins (Women's Volleyball)	.25
23	Al Cowlings	1.00
24	Ronnie Lott	1.00
25	Adam Johnson (Volleyball)	1.50
26	Fred Lynn (Baseball)	.50
27	Rick Leach (Tennis)	.35
28	Tim Rossovich	.50
29	Marvin Powell	.35
30	Ron Yary	.50
31	Ken Ruettgers	.50
32	Bob Yoder (CO) (Men's Volleyball)	.25
33	Megan McCallister (Women's Volleyball)	.25
34	Dave Cadigan	.35
35	Jeff Bregel	.25
36	Michael Wayman (Tennis)	.25
37	Sippy Woodhead-Kantzer (Women's Swimming)	.50
38	Tim Hovland (Volleyball)	1.00
39	Steve Busby (Baseball)	.50
40	Tom Seaver (Baseball)	2.00
41	Anthony Colorito	.25
42	Wayne Carlander (Basketball)	.35
43	Erik Affholter	.35
44	Jim Obradovich	.35
45	Duane Bickett	.50
46	Leslie Daland (Women's Swimming)	.25
47	Ole Oleson (Track)	.25
48	Ed Putnam (Baseball)	.25
49	Stan Smith (Tennis)	.75
50	Jeff Hart (Golf)	.25
51	Jack Del Rio	.50
52	Bob Boyd (CO) (Basketball)	.35
53	Pat Haden	1.00
54	John Lambert (Basketball)	.35
55	Pete Beathard	.75
56	Anna-Maria Fernandez (Women's Tennis)	.50
57	Marta Figueras-Dotti (Women's Golf)	.35
58	Don Mosebar	.35
59	Don Doll	.35
60	Dave Stockton (Golf)	.75
61	Trisha Laux (Women's Tennis)	.25
62	Roy Foster	.35
63	Bruce Matthews	.35
64	Steve Sogge	.35
65	Tracy Nakamura (Women's Golf)	.35
66	Marv Montgomery	.25
67	Jack Tingley (Swimming)	.25
68	Larry Stevens	.25
69	Harry Smith	.25
70	Bill Bain	.25
71	Mark McGwire (Baseball)	3.00
72	Brad Brink (Baseball)	.25
73	Richard Wood	.35
74	Rod Dedeaux (CO) (Baseball)	.50
75	Paul Westphal (Basketball)	1.25
76	Al Krueger	.25
77	James McConica (Swimming)	.25
78	Rod Martin	.35
79	Bill Yardley (Volleyball)	.25
80	Bill Stetson (Volleyball)	.25
81	Ray Looze (Swimming)	.25
82	Dan Jorgensen (Swimming)	.25
83	Anna-Lucia Fernandez (Women's Tennis)	.35
84	Terri O'Loughlin (Women's Swimming)	.25
85	John Grant	.25
86	Chris Lewis (Tennis)	.25
87	Steve Timmons (Volleyball)	2.00
88	Dr. Dallas Long (Track)	.35
89	John McKay (CO)	.50
90	Joe Bottom (Swimming)	.25
91	John Jackson	.35
92	Paul McDonald	.25
93	Jimmy Gunn	.25
94	Rod Sherman	.25
95	Cecilia Fernandez (Women's Tennis)	.25
96	Doug Adler (Tennis)	.25
97	Ron Orr (Swimming)	.25
98	Debbie Landreth Brown (Women's Volleyball)	.25
99	Debbie Green (Women's Volleyball)	.25
100	Pat Harrison (Baseball)	.25

1991 Southern Cal Smokey

		MT
Complete Set (16):		8.00
Common Player:		.60
1	Kurt Barber	1.25
2	Ron Dale	.60
3	Derrick Deese	1.00
4	Michael Gaytan	.60
5	Matt Gee	.60
6	Calvin Holmes	1.00
7	Scott Lockwood	1.00
8	Michael Moody	.60
9	Marvin Pollard	.60
10	Mark Raab	.60
11	Larry Smith (CO)	.75
12	Raoul Spears	.60
13	Matt Willig	.60
14	Alan Wilson	.60
15	James Wilson	.60
16	Traveler (The Trojan Horse)	.60

1992 Southern Cal Smokey

		MT
Complete Set (16):		8.00
Common Player:		.60
1	Wes Bender	.60
2	Estrus Crayton	.60
3	Eric Dixon	.60
4	Travis Hannah	1.50
5	Zuri Hector	.60
6	Lamont Hollinquest	.60
7	Yonnie Jackson	.60
8	Bruce Luizzi	.60
9	Mike Mooney	.60
10	Stephon Pace	.60
11	Joel Scott	.60
12	DeNail Sparks	.60
13	Titus Tuiasosopo	.60
14	Larry Wallace	.60
15	David Webb	.60
16	Title Card ART	.60

1988 Southwestern Louisiana McDag

BRIAN MITCHELL
Quarterback

		MT
Complete Set (12):		6.00
Common Player:		.50
1	Brian Mitchell (QB rolling out)	2.00
2	Brian Mitchell (QB over center)	2.00
3	Chris Gannon (DE signalling sideline)	.50
4	Chris Gannon (DE awaiting snap)	.50
5	Willie Culpepper	.75
6	Greg Eagles	.50
7	Steve McKinney	.50
8	Pat Decuir	.50
9	Leslie Luquette	.50
10	Robert Johnson	.50
11	Lisa McCoy (Cheerleader)	.50
12	Michelle Aubert (Cheerleader)	.50

1991 Stanford All-Century

JIM PLUNKETT   QB

		MT
Complete Set (100):		100.00
Common Player:		.75
1	Frankie Albert	1.25
2	Lester Archambeau	1.00
3	Bruno Banducci	.75
4	Benny Barnes	1.00
5	Guy Benjamin	2.00
6	Mike Boryla	1.25
7	Marty Brill	.75
8	John Brodie	6.00
9	Jackie Brown	.75
10	George Buehler	1.00
11	Don Bunce	1.25
12	Chris Burford	1.25
13	Walter Camp (CO)	2.50
14	Gordy Ceresino	.75
15	Jack Chapple	.75
16	Toi Cook	2.00
17	Bill Corbus	.75
18	Steve Dils	2.50
19	Pat Donovan	1.25
20	John Elway	20.00
21	Chuck Evans	.75
22	Skip Face	.75
23	Hugh Gallarneau	.75
24	Rod Garcia	.75
25	Bob Garrett	.75
26	Rick Gervais	.75
27	John Gillory	.75
28	Bobby Grayson	1.00
29	Bones Hamilton	1.00
30	Ray Handley	2.00
31	Mark Harmon	.75
32	Marv Harris	.75
33	Emile Harry	1.25
34	Tony Hill	2.50
35	Brian Holloway	1.25
36	John Hopkins	.75
37	Dick Horn	.75
38	Jeff James	1.00
39	Gary Kerkorian	.75
40	Gordon King	1.00
41	Younger Klippert	.75
42	Pete Kmetovic	.75
43	Jim Lawson	.75
44	Pete Lazetich	.75
45	Dave Lewis	1.00
46	Vic Lindskog	.75
47	James Lofton	6.00
48	Ken Margerum	1.25
49	Ed McCaffrey	2.00
50	Charles McCloud	.75
51	Bill McColl	1.00
52	Duncan McColl	.75
53	Milt McColl	.75
54	Jim Merlo	1.00
55	Phil Moffatt	.75
56	Bob Moore	1.00
57	Sam Morley	.75
58	Monk Moscrip	.75
59	Brad Muster	2.50
60	Ken Naber	.75
61	Darrin Nelson	2.00
62	Ernie Nevers	3.00
63	Dick Norman	.75
64	Blaine Nye	1.25
65	Don Parish	.75
66	John Paye	2.00
67	Gary Pettigrew	1.00
68	Jim Plunkett	6.00
69	Randy Poltl	.75
70	Seraphim Post	.75
71	John Ralston (CO)	1.25
72	Bob Reynolds	.75
73	Don Robesky	.75
74	Doug Robison	.75
75	Greg Sampson	.75
76	John Sande	.75
77	Turk Schonert	2.00
78	Jack Schulz	.75
79	Clark Shaughnessy (CO)	1.25
80	Ted Shipkey	.75
81	Jeff Siemon	2.00
82	Andy Sinclair	.75
83	Malcolm Snider	1.00
84	Norm Standlee	1.00
85	Roger Stillwell	.75
86	Chuck Taylor (CO)	.75
87	Dink Templeton	.75
88	Tiny Thornhill (CO)	.75
89	Dave Tipton	.75
90	Keith Topping	.75
91	Randy Vataha	.75
92	Garin Veris	1.25
93	Jon Volpe	2.50
94	Bill Walsh (CO)	5.00
95	Pop Warner (CO)	2.00
96	Gene Washington	2.00
97	Vincent White	.75
98	Paul Wiggin	1.25
99	John Wilbur	1.00
100	Dave Wyman	1.25

1992 Stanford

		MT
Complete Set (35):		15.00
Common Player:		.35
1	Seyon Albert	.35
2	Estevan Avila	.50
3	Tyler Batson	.35
4	Guy Benjamin (ACO)	.60
5	David Calomese	.35
6	Mike Cook	.50
7	Chris Dalman	.50
8	Dave Garnett	.35
9	Ron George	1.00
10	Darrien Gordon	2.00
11	Tom Holmoe (ACO)	.60
12	Derron Klafter	.35
13	J.J. Lasley	.50
14	John Lynch	.60
15	Glyn Milburn	4.00
16	Fernando Montes (ACO)	.50
17	Vince Otoupal	.35
18	Rick Pallow	.35
19	Ron Redell	.35
20	Aaron Rembisz	.35
21	Bill Ring (ACO)	.50
22	Ellery Roberts	.60
23	Scott Schumann (ACO)	.35
24	Terry Shea (ACO)	.35
25	Bill Singler (ACO)	.35
26	Paul Stonehouse	.35
27	Dave Tipton (ACO)	.35
28	Keena Turner (ACO)	.75
29	Fred von Appen (ACO)	.35
30	Bill Walsh (CO)	3.00
31	Ryan Wetnight	2.00
32	Tom Williams	.35
33	Mike Wilson (ACO)	.50
34	Billy Wittman	.35
35	Checklist Card (J.J. Lasley)	.50

1993 Stanford

		MT
Complete Set (18):		10.00
Common Player:		.50
1	Jeff Bailey	.50
2	Parker Bailey	.50
3	Roger Boden	.50
4	Hartwell Brown	.50
5	Vaughn Bryant	.60
6	Brian Cassidy	.50
7	Glen Cavanaugh	.50
8	Kevin Garnett	.50
9	Mark Hatzenbuhler	.50
10	Steve Hoyem	.60
11	Mike Jerich	.50
12	Paul Nickel	.50
13	Toby Norwood	.60
14	Tyrone Parker	.60
15	Ellery Roberts	.60
16	David Shaw	.50
17	Bill Walsh (CO)	2.50
18	Josh Wright	.50

1989 Syracuse Burger King

		MT
Complete Set (15):		15.00
Common Player:		1.00
1	David Bavaro	1.50
2	Blake Bednars	1.00
3	Alban Brown	1.00
4	Dan Burey	1.00
5	Rob Burnett	2.50
6	Fred DeRiggi	1.00
7	John Flannery	2.00
8	Duane Kinnon	1.00
9	Dick MacPherson (CO)	2.00
10	Rob Moore	5.00
11	Michael Owens	1.50
12	Bill Scharr	1.00
13	Turnell Sims	1.00
14	Sean Whiteman	1.00
15	Terry Wooden	2.50

1991 Syracuse Program Cards

		MT
Complete Set (36):		30.00
Common Player:		.75
1	George Rooks	.75
2	Marvin Graves	4.00
3	Andrew Dees	.75
4	Glen Young	1.00
5	Chris Gedney	2.00
6	Paul Pasqualoni	1.00
7	Terrence Wisdom	.75
8	John Biskup	.75
9	Mark McDonald	.75
10	Dan Conley	1.00
11	Kevin Mitchell	.75
12	Qadry Ismail	6.00
13	John Lusardi	.75
14	David Walker	.75
15	John Capachione	.75
16	Shelby Hill	1.25
17	Dwayne Joseph	.75
18	Greg Walker	.75
19	Jerry Sharp	.75
20	Tim Sandquist	.75
21	Chuck Bull	.75
22	Jo Jo Wooden	.75
23	Terry Richardson	.75
24	Doug Womack	.75
25	Reggie Terry	.75
26	Garland Hawkins	.75
27	Tony Montemorra	.75
28	Chip Todd	.75
29	Pat O'Neill	1.00
30	Kevin Barker	.75
31	John Reagan	.75
32	Pat O'Rourke	.75
33	Jim Wentworth	.75
34	Ernie Brown	.75
35	John Nilsen	.75
36	Al Wooten	.75

1980 Tennessee Police

		NM
Complete Set (19):		37.00
Common Player:		1.50
1	Bill Bates	1.50
2	James Berry	1.50
3	Chris Bolton	1.50
4	Mike L. Cofer	1.50
5	Glenn Ford	1.50
6	Anthony Hancock	1.50
7	Brian Ingram	1.50
8	Tim Irwin	1.50
9	Kenny Jones	1.50
10	Wilbert Jones	1.50
11	Johnny Majors (CO)	1.50
12	Bill Marren	1.50
13	Danny Martin	1.50
14	Jim Noonan	1.50
15	Lee North	1.50
16	Hubert Simpson	1.50
17	Danny Spradlin	1.50
18	John Warren	1.50
19	Brad White	1.50

1990 Tennessee Centennial

		MT
Complete Set (294):		30.00
Common Player:		.10
1	Vince Moore	.20
2	Steve Matthews	.10
3	Joey Chapman	.10
4	Terence Cleveland	.10
5	Thomas Wood	.10
6	J.J. McCleskey	.10
7	Jason Julian	.10
8	Andy Kelly	.20
9	Derrick Folsom	.10
10	Chip McCallum	.10
11	Lloyd Kerr	.10
12	Cory Fleming	.30
13	Kevin Zurcher	.10
14	Lee England	.10
15	Carl Pickens	2.00
16	Sterling Henton	.10
17	Lee Wood	.10
18	Kent Elmore	.10
19	Craig Faulkner	.10
20	Keith Denson	.10
21	Preston Warren	.10
22	Floyd Miley	.10
23	Earnest Fields	.10
24	Tony Thompson	.10
25	Jeremy Lincoln	.30
26	David Bennett	.10
27	Greg Burke	.10
28	Tavio Henson	.10
29	Kevin Wendelboe	.10
30	Cedric Kline	.10
31	Keith Jeter	.10
32	Chris Russ	.10
33	DeWayne Dotson	.10
34	Mike Rapien	.10
35	Clemons McCroskey	.10
36	Mark Fletcher	.10
37	Chuck Smith	.20
38	Jeff Tullis	.10
39	Kelly Days	.10
40	Shazzon Bradley	.10
41	Reggie Ingram	.10
42	Roland Poles	.10
43	Tracy Smith	.10
44	Chuck Webb	.30
45	Shon Walker	.20
46	Eric Riffer	.10
47	Greg Amsler	.10
48	J.J. Surlas	.10
49	Brian Bradley	.10
50	Tom Myslinski	.20
51	John Fisher	.10
52	Craig Martin	.10
53	Carey Bailey	.10
54	Houston Thomas	.10
55	Ryan Patterson	.10
56	Chad Goodin	.10
57	Brian Spivey	.10
58	Todd Kelly	.10
59	Mike Stowell	.10
60	Jim Fenwick	.10
61	Marc Jones	.10
62	Chris Ragan	.10
63	Rodney Gordon	.10
64	Mark Needham	.10
65	Patrick Lenoir	.10
66	Martin Williams	.10
67	Brad Seiber	.10
68	Larry Smith	.10
69	Jerry Teel	.10
70	Charles McRae	.30
71	Rex Hargrove	.10
72	James Wilson	.10
73	Doug Baird	.10
74	Mark Moore	.10
75	Lance Nelson	.10
76	Robert Todd	.10
77	Greg Gerardi	.10
78	Antone Davis	.30
79	Eric Still	.10
80	Anthony Morgan	.75
81	Alvin Harper	1.00
82	Charles Longmire	.10
83	Mark Adams	.10
84	Chris Benson	.10
85	Horace Morris	.10
86	Harlan Davis	.10
87	Darryl Hardy	.10
88	Tracy Hayworth	.20
89	Von Reeves	.10
90	Marion Hobby	.10
91	John Ward (ANN)	.10
92	Roderick Lewis	.10
93	Orion McCants	.10
94	James Warren	.10
95	Mario Brunson	.10
96	Joe Davis	.10
97	Shawn Truss	.10
98	Keith Steed	.10
99	Kacy Rodgers	.10
100	Johnny Majors (CO)	.10
101	Phillip Fulmer (CO)	.30
102	Larry Lacewell (CO)	.20
103	Charlie Coe (CO)	.10
104	Tommy West (CO)	.10
105	David Cutcliffe (CO)	.10
106	Jack Sells (CO)	.10
107	Rex Norris (CO)	.10
108	John Chavis (CO)	.10
109	Tim Keane (CO)	.10
110	Recruiter (Tim Mingey)	.10
111	Sr. Admin. Asst. (Bill Higdon)	.10
112	Tim Kerin (TR)	.10
113	Bruno Pauletto (CO)	.10
114	Vols 17, Co. State 14 (Chuck Webb)	.20
115	Vols 24, UCLA 6 (Chuck Webb)	.20
116	Vols 28, Duke 6 (Game Action Photo)	.10
117	Vols 21, Auburn 14 (Game Action Photo)	.10
118	Vols 17, Georgia 14 (Jason Julian)	.10
119	Vols 30, Alabama 47 (Roland Poles)	.10
120	Vols 45, LSU 39 (Charles McRae)	.20
121	Vols 52, Akron 9 (Brian Spivey)	.10
122	Vols 33, Ole Miss 21 (Alvin Harper)	.30
123	Vols 31, Kentucky 10 (Kelly Days)	.10
124	Vols 17, Vanderbilt 10 (Game Action Photo)	.10
125	'90 Mobil Cotton Bowl 1 (Jason Julian)	.10
126	'90 Mobil Cotton Bowl 2 (Andy Kelly)	.10
127	'90 Mobil Cotton Bowl 3 (Chuck Webb)	.20
128	'90 Mobil Cotton Bowl 4 (Scoreboard)	.10
129	Eric Still	.10
130	Chris Benson	.10
131	Preston Warren	.10
132	Lee England	.10
133	Kent Elmore	.10
134	Eric Still	.10
135	Chuck Webb	.30
136	Marion Hobby	.10
137	Kent Elmore	.10
138	Antone Davis	.30
139	Thomas Woods	.10
140	Charles McRae	.30
141	Preston Warren	.10
142	Darryl Hardy	.10
143	Offense or Defense (Carl Pickens)	1.00
144	Carl Pickens	2.00
145	Chuck Webb	.30
146	Thomas Woods	.10
147	Total Offense Game (Andy Kelly)	.10
148	The TVA (Offensive Line)	.10
149	Smokey (Mascot)	.10
150	Director of Athletics (Doug Dickey)	.10
151	Neyland Stadium	.10
152	Neyland-Thompson Ctr	.10
153	Gibbs Hall (Dormitory)	.10
154	Asst. AD (Carmen Tegano) (Academics and Athletics)	.10
155	Gene McEver (HOF)	.10
156	Beattie Feathers (HOF)	.30
157	Robert Neyland (HOF) (CO)	.50
158	Herman Hickman (HOF)	.20
159	Bowden Wyatt (HOF)	.20
160	Hank Lauricella (HOF)	.20
161	Doug Atkins (HOF)	.30
162	Johnny Majors (HOF)	.30
163	Bobby Dodd (HOF)	.30
164	Bob Suffridge (HOF)	.20
165	Nathan Dougherty (HOF)	.10
166	George Cafego (HOF)	.10
167	Bob Johnson (HOF)	.20
168	Ed Molinski (HOF)	.10
169	Reggie White	2.00
170	Willie Gault	.60
171	Doug Atkins	.30
172	Keith DeLong	.20
173	Ron Widby	.20
174	Bill Johnson	.20
175	Jack Reynolds	.30
176	Tim McGee	.50
177	Harry Galbreath	.20
178	Roland James	.20
179	Abe Shires	.10
180	Ted Daffer	.10
181	Bob Foxx	.10
182	Richmond Flowers	.30
183	Beattie Feathers	.30
184	Condredge Holloway	.50
185	Larry Sievers	.20
186	Johnnie Jones	.10
187	Carl Zander	.20
188	Dale Jones	.10
189	Bruce Wilkerson	.20
190	Terry McDaniel	.30
191	Craig Colquitt	.10
192	Stanley Morgan	.75
193	Curt Watson	.10
194	Bobby Majors	.10
195	Steve Kiner	.20
196	Paul Naumoff	.20
197	Bud Sherrod	.10
198	Murray Warmath	.20
199	Steve DeLong	.20
200	Bill Pearman	.10
201	Bobby Gordon	.10
202	John Michels	.10
203	Bill Mayo	.10
204	Andy Kozar	.10
205	1892 Volunteers (Team Photo)	.10
206	1900 Volunteers (Team Photo)	.10
207	1905 Volunteers (Team Photo)	.10
208	1907 Volunteers (Individual player photos)	.10
209	1916 Volunteers (Team Photo)	.10
210	1914 Volunteers (Team Photo)	.10
211	1896 Volunteers (Team Photo)	.10
212	1908 Volunteers (Team Photo)	.10
213	1926 Volunteers (Team Photo)	.10
214	1930 Volunteers (Team Photo)	.10
215	1934 Volunteers (Team Photo)	.10
216	1938 Volunteers (Team Photo)	.10
217	1940 Volunteers (Team Photo)	.10
218	1944 Volunteers (Team Photo)	.10
219	1945 Volunteers (Team Photo)	.10
220	1954 Volunteers (Team Photo)	.10
221	1969 Volunteers (Team Photo)	.10
222	1962 Volunteers (Team Photo)	.10
223	1976 Volunteers (Team Photo)	.10
224	1985 Volunteers (Team Photo)	.10
225	1978 Volunteers (Team Photo)	.10
226	1980 Volunteers (Team Photo)	.10
227	1984 Volunteers (Team Photo)	.10
228	1988 Volunteers (Team Photo)	.10
229	James Baird	.10
230	Condredge Holloway	.50
231	J.G. Lowe	.10
232	E.A. McLean	.10
233	Lemont Holt Jeffers	.10
234	Howard Johnson	.10
235	Malcolm Aiken	.10
236	Toby Palmer	.10
237	Sam Bartholomew	.10
238	Ray Graves	.10
239	Billy Bevis	.10
240	Bert Rechichar	.20
241	Jim Beutel	.10
242	Mike Lucci	.30
243	Hal Wantland	.10
244	Jackie Walker	.10
245	Ron McCartney	.10
246	Robert Shaw	.30
247	Lee North	.10
248	James Berry	.10
249	Carl Zander	.20
250	Chris White	.10
251	Timmy Sims	.10
252	Tim McGee	.50
253	Keith DeLong	.20
254	1931 NY Charity Game (Program)	.10
255	1941 Super Bowl (Program)	.10
256	1945 Rose Bowl (Program)	.10
257	1957 Gator Bowl (Program)	.10
258	1968 Orange Bowl (Program)	.10
259	1972 Bluebonnet Bowl (Program)	.10
260	1981 Graden State Bowl (Program)	.10
261	1968 Sugar Bowl (Program)	.10
262	Checklist 1-76	.10
263	Checklist 77-152	.10
264	Checklist 153-228	.10
265	Checklist 229-294	.10
266	Chris White	.10
267	Kelsey Finch	.10
268	Johnnie Jones	.10
269	Johnnie Jones	.10
270	Curt Watson	.10
271	William Howard	.10
272	Bubba Wyche	.10
273	Tony Robinson	.30
274	Daryl Dickey	.10
275	Alan Cockrell, Willie Gault	.30
276	Alan Cockrell	.10
277	Bobby Scott	.30
278	Tony Robinson	.30
279	Jeff Francis	.10
280	Alvin Harper	1.00
281	Johnny Mills	.10
282	Thomas Woods	.10
283	Bob Lund	.10
284	Gene McEver	.10
285	Stanley Morgan	.75
286	Fuad Reveiz	.30
287	Kent Elmore	.10
288	Jimmy Colquitt	.10
289	Willie Gault	.60
290	100 Years Celebration (Reggie White)	.75
291	The 100 Years Kickoff (Group Photo)	.10
292	Like Father, Like Son (Keith DeLong, Steve DeLong)	.30
293	Offense and Defense (Raleigh McKenzie, Reggie McKenzie)	.20
294	It's Football Time (1990 schedule on back)	.20

1991 Tennessee Hoby

		MT
Complete Set (42):		25.00
Common Player:		.25
397	Mark Adams	.25
398	Carey Bailey	.25
399	David Bennett	.25
400	Shazzon Bradley	.25
401	Kenneth Campbell	.25
402	Dale Carter	1.50
403	Joey Chapman	.25
404	Jerry Colquitt	.50
405	Bernard Daffney	.50
406	Craig Faulkner	.25
407	Earnest Fields	.25
408	John Fisher	.25
409	Cory Fleming	.75
410	Mark Fletcher	.25
411	Tom Fuhler	.25
412	Johnny Majors (CO)	.50
413	Darryl Hardy	.25
414	Aaron Hayden	3.00
415	Tavio Henson	.25
416	Reggie Ingram	.25
417	Andy Kelly	.50
418	Todd Kelly	.75
419	Patrick Lenoir	.25
420	Roderick Lewis	.25
421	Jeremy Lincoln	.50
422	J.J. McCleskey	.25
423	Floyd Miley	.25
424	Chris Mims	1.50
425	Tom Myslinski	.35
426	Carl Pickens	5.00
427	Roc Powe	.25
428	Von Reeves	.25
429	Eric Riffer	.25
430	Kacy Rodgers	.25
431	Steve Session	.25
432	Heath Shuler	6.00
433	Chuck Smith	.35
434	James O. Stewart	3.00
435	Mike Stowell	.25
436	J.J. Surlas	.35
437	Shon Walker	.35
438	James Wilson	.25

1991 Texas HS Legends

		MT
Complete Set (25):		18.00
Common Player:		.60
1	Marty Akins	.60
2	Gil Bartosh	.60
3	Bill Bradley	1.00
4	Chris Gilbert	1.25
5	Glynn Gregory	.75
6	Charlie Haas	.60
7	Craig James	2.00
8	Boody Johnson	.60
9	Ernie Koy Jr.	.75
10	Glenn Lippman	.60
11	Jack Pardee	.60
12	Billy Patterson	.60
13	Billy Sims	3.00
14	Byron Townsend	.60
15	Doyle Traylor	.60
16	Joe Washington Jr.	1.00
17	Allie White	.60
18	Wilson Whitley	.75
19	Gordon Wood	.75
20	Willie Zapalac	.60
21	Cover Card 1	.60
22	Cover Card 2	.60
23	Cover Card 3	.60
24	Cover Card 4	.60
25	Cover Card 5	.60

1993 Texas Taco Bell

		MT
Complete Set (50):		25.00
Common Player:		.50
1	Mike Adams	2.00
2	Thomas Baskin	.50
3	Tony Brackens	2.00
4	Steve Bradley	.50
5	Blake Brockermeyer (Wearing home jersey)	1.50
6	Blake Brockermeyer (Wearing away jersey)	1.50
7	Phil Brown	.50
8	Chris Carter	.50
9	Stonie Clark	.75
10	Gerald Crawford	.50
11	Trent Elliot	.50
13	Joey Ellis	.75
14	John Elmore	.75
15	Jon Feick	.50
16	Victor Frazier	.50
17	Jimmy Hakes	.50
18	Anthony Holmes	.50
19	Brian Howard	.50
20	Jon Hunter	.50
21	Curtis Jackson	.75
22	Eric Jackson	.50
23	Bryan Johnson	.75
24	James Lane	.50
25	Doug Livingston	.50
26	Chad Lucas	.50
27	John Mackovic (CO)	1.00
28	Van Malone	1.25
29	Justin McLemore	.75
30	Shea Morenz	2.50
31	Dan Neil	.75
32	Cosmo Palmieri	.50
33	Joe Phillips	.50
34	Lovell Pinkney	2.50
35	Chris Rapp	.50
36	Robert Reed	.50
37	Jason Reeves	.50
38	Troy Riemer	.50
39	Scott Szeredy	.50
40	Tre Thomas	.75
41	Winfred Tubbs	1.50
42	Duane Vacek	.75
43	Brian Vasek	.75
44	Rodrick Walker	1.00
45	Norman Watkins	.50
46	Kevin Watler	.50
47	Pascal Watty	.50
48	Bryant Westbrook	.75
49	Longhorns Band	.50
50	Taco Bell Logo Card - 1993 Texas schedule	.50

1992 Texas A and M

RODNEY THOMAS 20
TEXAS A&M
TEXAS A&M UNIVERSITY

		MT
Complete Set (65):		25.00
Common Player:		.35
1	Matt Miller	.50
2	Steve Emerson	.35
3	Brad Cooper	.50
4	Mike Hendricks	.50
5	Dexter Wesley	.35
6	Darrell Red	.35
7	Antonio Shorter	1.00
8	Larry Wallace	.35
9	Kefa Chatham	.35
10	Billy Mitchell	.35
11	Patrick Bates	2.00
12	Greg Hill	5.00
13	Tommy Preston	.35
14	Ryan Mathews	.35
15	Steve Kenney	.35
16	John Richard	.35
17	John Ellisor	.35
18	Ryan Kern	.35

19	Jeff Jones	.35
20	Chris Sanders	.35
21	Reggie Graham	.35
22	David Davis	.35
23	Tony Harrison	.50
24	Jason Mathews	.50
25	Otis Nealy	.35
26	Kent Petty	.35
27	Rodney Thomas	5.00
28	Sam Adams	2.00
29	Clif Groce	.35
30	Tyler Harrison	.35
31	Eric England	.35
32	Jason Atkinson	.50
33	Lance Teichelman	.35
34	Marcus Buckley	2.00
35	Steve Solari	.35
36	Aggie Coaches	.50
37	Derrick Frazier	.50
38	James McKeehan	.50
39	Doug Carter	.35
40	Larry Jackson	.35
41	Brian Mitchell	.75
42	Greg Schorp	.50
43	Greg Cook	.35
44	Kyle Maxfield	.35
45	Todd Mathison	.35
46	Chris Dausin	.35
47	Junior White	.35
48	Wilbert Biggens	.35
49	Terry Venetoulias	.35
50	Jessie Cox	.35
51	R.C. Slocum (CO)	1.00
52	Defensive Coaches (Bob Davie, Kirk Doll, Bill Johnson, Trent Walters)	.35
53	Offensive Coaches (Mike Sherman, Shawn Slocum, Bob Toledo, Gary Kubiak, David Culley)	.50
54	Recruiting Coordinator (Tim Cassidy)	.35
55	Yell Leaders (Steve Scanlon, Adin Pfeuffer, Tim Isgitt, Ronnie McDonald, Mark Rollins)	.35
56	A and M Band	.35
57	Reveille V Mascot	.35
58	Twelfth Man Statue	.50
59	Bonfire	.35
60	Training Facility	.35
61	Kyle Field	.35
62	Texas A and M Campus	.35
NNO	Front Card (Texas A and M Logo)	.35
NNO	Back Card	.35
NNO	Checklist Card	.35

1995 Tony's Pizza College Mascots

		MT
Complete Set (20):		7.00
Common Player:		.25
1	Alabama Crimson Tide	.50
2	Auburn Tigers	.40
3	Arizona Wildcats	.25
4	Boston College Eagles	.25
5	Colorado Buffaloes	.40
6	Florida State Seminoles	.50
7	Florida Gators	.50
8	Kansas State Wildcats	.25
9	Miami Hurricanes	.50
10	Michigan Wolverines	.50
11	Nebraska Cornhuskers	.50
12	Notre Dame Fightin' Irish	.50
13	Penn State Nittany Lions	.50
14	Tennessee Volunteers	.50
15	Texas Longhorns	.40
16	Texas A M Aggies	.40
17	UCLA Bruins	.50
18	USC Trojans	.50
19	Washington Huskies	.40
20	Wisconsin Badgers	.25

1991 UNLV

		MT
Complete Set (12):		8.00
Common Player:		.75
1	Cheerleaders and Songleaders	.75
2	Gang Tackle	.75
3	Instant Offense (Hernandez Cooper)	.75
4	No Escape	.75

5	On The Move	.75
6	Punching It In	.75
7	Ready To Fire (Derek Stott)	.75
8	Rebel Fever	.75
9	Rebel Sack	.75
10	Silver Bowl (Sam Boyd)	.75
11	Jim Strong (CO)	.75
12	Team Photo	1.00

1990 Virginia

		MT
Complete Set (16):		25.00
Common Player:		1.25
1	Chris Borsari	1.25
2	Ron Carey	1.25
3	Paul Collins	1.25
4	Tony Covington	3.00
5	Derek Dooley	1.25
6	Joe Hall	1.25
7	Myron Martin	1.25
8	Bruce McGonnigal	1.50
9	Jake McInerney	1.25
10	Keith McMeans	1.25
11	Herman Moore	12.00
12	Shawn Moore	4.00
13	Trevor Ryals	1.25
14	Chris Stearns	1.25
15	Jason Wallace	1.25
16	George Welsh (CO)	1.50

1992 Virginia Coca-Cola

		MT
Complete Set (16):		15.00
Common Player:		1.00
1	Bobby Goodman	1.25
2	Michael Husted	2.00
3	Greg Jeffries	2.00
4	Charles Keiningham	1.00
5	Terry Kirby	5.00
6	Kenneth Miles	1.00
7	Tim Samec	1.00
8	Chris Slade	3.50
9	Alvin Snead	1.00
10	Gary Steele	1.00
11	Jeff Tomlin	1.00
12	Terrence Tomlin	1.00
13	David Ware	1.00
14	George Welsh (CO)	1.25
15	Virginia 20, Clemson 7; Sept. 8, 1990	1.00
16	Virginia 20, N.Carolina 17; Nov 14, 1987	1.00

1993 Virginia Coca-Cola

		MT
Complet Set (16):		15.00
Common Player:		1.00
1	Tom Burns	1.00
2	Peter Collins	1.00
3	Bill Curry	1.00
4	Mark Dixon	1.00
5	Bill Edwards	1.00
6	P.J. Killian	1.00
7	Keith Lyle	1.00
8	Greg McClellan	1.00
9	Matt Mikeska	1.00
10	Aaron Mundy	1.00
11	Jim Reid	1.00
12	Josh Schrader	1.00
13	Jerrod Washington	1.00
14	George Welsh (CO)	1.00
15	Cavalier Spirit (Cheerleaders)	1.00
16	Cavalier Mascot	1.00

1973 Washington KFC

		NM
Complete Set (30):		350.00
Common Player:		12.00
1	Jim Anderson	12.00
2	Jim Andrilenas	12.00
3	Glen Bonner	18.00
4	Bob Boustead	12.00
5	Skip Boyd	18.00
6	Gordie Bronson	12.00
7	Reggie Brown	12.00
8	Dan Celoni	12.00
9	Brian Daheny	12.00
10	Fred Dean	12.00
11	Pete Elswick	12.00
12	Dennis Fitzpatrick	12.00
13	Bob Graves	12.00
14	Pedro Hawkins	12.00
15	Rick Hayes	12.00
16	Barry Houlihan	12.00
17	Roberto Jourdan	12.00
18	Washington Keenan	12.00
19	Eddie King	12.00

20	Jim Kristoff	12.00
21	Murphy McFarland	12.00
22	Walter Oldes	12.00
23	Louis Quinn	12.00
24	Frank Reed	18.00
25	Dain Rodwell	12.00
26	Ron Stanley	12.00
27	Joe Tabor	12.00
28	Pete Taggares	12.00
29	John Whitacre	12.00
30	Hans Woldseth	12.00
NNO	Color Team Photo (Large 8x10)	18.00
NNO	Coaches Photo (Large 8x10)	25.00

1988 Washington Smokey

		MT
Complete Set (16):		15.00
Common Player:		1.00
1	Ricky Andrews	1.00
2	Bern Brostek	2.00
3	Dennis Brown	2.00
4	Cary Conklin	2.00
5	Tony Covington	1.00
6	Darryl Hall	1.00
7	Martin Harrison	2.00
8	Don James (CO)	2.00
9	Aaron Jenkins	1.00
10	Le-Lo Lang	2.00
11	Art Malone	1.00
12	Andre Riley	1.00
13	Brian Slater	1.00
14	Vince Weathersby	1.00
15	Brett Wiese	1.00
16	Mike Zandofsky	1.50

1990 Washington Smokey

		MT
Complete Set (16):		15.00
Common Player (1-12):		.75
Common Player (13-16):		.75
1	Eric Briscoe (28)	.75
2	Mark Brunell (11)	6.00
3	James Clifford (53)	.75
4	John Cook (93)	.75
5	Ed Cunningham (79)	2.00
6	Dana Hall (5)	2.50
7	Don James (CO)	1.50
8	Donald Jones (48)	.75
9	Dean Kirkland (51)	.75
10	Greg Lewis (20)	2.00
11	Orlando McKay (4)	.75
12	Travis Richardson (58)	.75
13	Kelley Larsen (Women's Volleyball)	.75
14	Michelle Reid (Women's Volleyball)	.75
15	Ashleigh Robertson (Women's Volleyball)	.75
16	Gail Thorpe (Women's Volleyball)	.75

1991 Washington Smokey

		MT
Complete Set (16):		15.00
Common Player (1-12):		.75
Common Player (13-16):		.75
1	Mario Bailey	1.50
2	Beno Bryant	1.50
3	Brett Collins	.75
4	Ed Cunningham	1.50
5	Steve Emtman	2.00
6	Dana Hall	2.00
7	Billy Joe Hobert	4.00
8	Dave Hoffmann	.75
9	Don James (CO)	1.25
10	Donald Jones	.75
11	Siupeli Malamala	1.50
12	Orlando McKay	.75

13	Diane Flick (Women's Volleyball)	.75
14	Kelley Larsen (Women's Volleyball)	.75
15	Ashleigh Robertson (Women's Volleyball)	.75
16	Dana Thompson (Women's Volleyball)	.75

1992 Washington Greats/Pacific

		MT
Complete Set (110):		15.00
Common Player:		.15
1	Don James (CO)	.50
2	Cary Conklin	.50
3	Tom Cowan	.15
4	Thane Cleland	.15
5	Steve Pelluer	.50
6	Sonny Sixkiller	.50
7	Koll Hagen	.15
8	Danny Greene	.15
9	George Black	.15
10	Mike Baldassin	.15
11	Bill Douglas	.15
12	Tom Flick	.25
13	Brian Slater	.15
14	Dick Sprague	.15
15	Bob Schloredt	.35
16	Bill Smith	.15
17	Marv Bergmann	.15
18	Sam Mitchell	.25
19	Bill Earley	.15
20	Clarence Dirks	.15
21	Jimmie Cain	.15
22	Don Heinrich	.35
23	Paul (Socko) Sulkosky	.15
24	By Haines	.15
25	Joe Steele	.15
26	Bob Monroe	.15
27	Roy McKasson	.15
28	Charlie Mitchell	.25
29	Ernie Steele	.15
30	Kyle Heinrich	.25
31	Travis Richardson	.15
32	Hugh McElhenny	1.00
33	George Wildcat Wilson	.15
34	Merle Hufford	.15
35	Steve Thompson	.15
36	Jim Krieg	.15
37	Chuck Olson	.15
38	Charley Russell	.15
39	Duane Wardlow	.15
40	Jay MacDowell	.15
41	Alf Hemstad	.15
42	Max Starcevich	.15
43	Ray Mansfield	.25
44	Brooks Biddle	.15
45	Toussaint Tyler	.35
46	Randy Van Diver	.15
47	John Cook	.15
48	Paul Skansi	.25
49	Tim Meamber	.15
50	Milt Bohart	.15
51	Curt Marsh	.25
52	Antowaine Richardson	.15
53	Jim Rodgers	.15
54	Mike Rohrbach	.15
55	Dan Agen	.15
56	Tom Turnure	.15
57	Ron Medved	.25
58	Vick Markov	.15
59	Carl (Bud) Ericksen	.15
60	Bill Kinnune	.15
61	Karsten (Corky) Lewis	.15
62	Sam Robinson	.25
63	Dave Nisbet	.15
64	Barry Bullard	.15
65	Norm Dicks	.25
66	Rick Redman	.35
67	Mark Jerue	.25
68	Jeff Toews	.15
69	Fletcher Jenkins	.15
70	Ray Horton	.25
71	Tom Erlandson	.15
72	Steve Alvord	.15
73	Dean Browning	.15

74	Scott Greenwood	.15
75	Bo Yates	.15
76	Jake Kupp	.25
77	Jim Owens (CO)	.15
78	Don McKeta	.15
79	Ben Davidson	.50
80	Tim Bullard	.15
81	Bill Albrecht	.15
82	Jim Cope	.15
83	Earl Monlux	.15
84	Paul Schwegler	.15
85	Steve Bramwell	.15
86	Ted Holzknecht	.15
87	Larry Hatch	.15
88	John Brady	.15
89	Bob Hivner	.15
90	Chuck Nelson	.25
91	Jeff Jaeger	.25
92	Rich Camarillo	.25
93	Jim Houston	.25
94	Jim Skaggs	.15
95	John Cherberg (CO)	.15
96	Bo Cornell	.25
97	Bill Cahill	.15
98	Dean McAdams	.15
99	Gil Dobie (CO)	.25
100	Walter Shiel	.15
101	Enoch Bagshaw (CO)	.15
102	Ray Eckmann	.15
103	Luther Carr	.15
104	Jimmy Bryan	.15
105	Darrell Royal	.35
106	Ray Frankowski	.15
107	Ray Pinney	.25
108	Skip Boyd	.15
109	Al Burleson	.15
110	Dennis Fitzpatrick	.25
NNO	Checklist Card	3.00
AU32	Hugh McElhenny (Certified Autograph, serially numbered of 1000)	50.00

1992 Washington Pay Less

		MT
Complete Set (16):		15.00
Common Player:		.75
1	Walter Bailey	.75
2	Jay Barry	.75
3	Mark Brunell	5.00
4	Beno Bryant	1.00
5	James Clifford	.75
6	Jaime Fields	.75
7	Travis Hanson	.75
8	Billy Joe Hobert (SP)	4.00
9	Dave Hoffmann	.75
10	Matt Jones	.75
11	Lincoln Kennedy	2.00
12	Andy Mason	.75
13	Shane Pahukoa	.75
14	Tommie Smith	.75
15	Darius Turner	.75
16	Team Photo (Schedule)	.75

1993 Washington Safeway

		MT
Complete Set (16):		10.00
Common Player:		.75
1	Beno Bryant	1.00
2	Hillary Butler	.75
3	D'Marco Farr	1.50
4	Jamal Fountaine	.75
5	Tom Gallagher	.75
6	Travis Hanson	.75
7	Damon Huard	1.50
8	Matt Jones	.75
9	Pete Kaligis	.75
10	Napoleon Kaufman	5.00
11	Joe Kralik	.75
12	Andy Mason	.75
13	Jim Nevelle	.75
14	Pete Pierson	.75
15	Steve Springstead	.75
16	John Werdel	.75

1994 Washington

		MT
Complete Set (12):		12.00
Common Player:		.60
1	Eric Bjornson	.75
2	Mark Bruener	3.00
3	Richie Chambers	1.00
4	Frank Garcia	1.00
5	Russell Hairston	.60
6	Damon Huard	1.25
7	Napoleon Kaufman	3.50
8	David Killpatrick	.60
9	Lamar Lyons	.60
10	Andrew Peterson	1.00
11	Donovan Schmidt	.60
12	Richard Thomas	.60

1995 Washington

		MT
Complete Set (16):		8.00

Common Player:		.50
1	Ink Aleaga	.75
2	Eric Battle	.75
3	Ernie Conwell	.50
4	Deke Devers	.50
5	Mike Ewaliko	.50
6	Scott Greenlaw	.50
7	Trevor Highfield	.50
8	Stephen Hoffmann	.50
9	Damon Huard	1.00
10	Dave Janoski	.50
11	Patrick Kesi	.50
12	Jim Lambright (CO)	.75
13	Lawyer Milloy	1.50
14	Leon Neal	.50
15	Reggie Reser	.50
16	Richard Thomas	.50

1988 Washington State Smokey

		MT
Complete Set (12):		12.00
Common Player:		1.00
3	Timm Rosenbach	2.00
18	Shawn Landrum	1.00
19	Artie Holmes	1.00
31	Steve Broussard	2.00
42	Ron Lee	1.00
55	Tuineau Alipate	1.00
60	Mike Utley	4.00
65	Chris Dyko	1.00
74	Jim Michalczik	1.00
75	Tony Savage	1.00
76	Ivan Cook	1.00
82	Doug Wellsandt	1.00

1990 Washington State Smokey

		MT
Complete Set (16):		8.00
Common Player:		.75
1	Lewis Bush (48)	.75
2	Carrie Couturier (Women's Volleyball)	.75
3	Steve Cromer (70)	.75
4	C.J. Davis (1)	.75
5	John Diggs (22)	.75
6	Alvin Dunn (27)	.75
7	Aaron Garcia (9)	.75
8	Bob Garman (74)	.75
9	Brad Gossen (12)	1.00
10	Calvin Griggs (5)	.75
11	Kelly Hankins (Women's Volleyball)	.75
12	Jason Hanson (4)	2.50
13	Kristen Hovde (Women's Volleyball)	.75
14	Keri Killebrew (Women's Volleyball)	.75
15	Chris Moton (6)	.75
16	Ron Ricard (26)	.75

1991 Washington State Smokey

		MT
Complete Set (16):		9.00
Common Player (1-12):		.75
Common Player (13-16):		.75
1	Lewis Bush	.75
2	Chad Cushing	.75
3	C.J. Davis	.75
4	Bob Garman	.75
5	Jason Hanson	2.00
6	Gabriel Oladipo	.75
7	Anthony Prior	1.50
8	Jay Reyna	.75
9	Lee Tilleman	.75
10	Kirk Westerfield	.75
11	Butch Williams	.75
12	Michael Wright	.75
13	Carrie Couturier (Women's Volleyball)	.75
14	Kelly Hankins (Women's Volleyball)	.75
15	Kristen Hovde (Women's Volleyball)	.75
16	Keri Killebrew (Women's Volleyball)	.75

1992 Washington State Smokey

		MT
Complete Set (20):		20.00
Common Player (1-12):		.50
Common Player (13-20):		.50
1	Drew Bledsoe	12.00
2	Phillip Bobo	.75
3	Lewis Bush	.50

4	C.J. Davis	.50
5	Shaumbe Wright-Fair	.75
6	Bob Garman	.50
7	Ray Hall	.50
8	Torey Hunter	.75
9	Kurt Loertscher	.50
10	Anthony McClanahan	.50
11	John Rushing	.50
12	Clarence Williams	.75
13	Betty Bartram (Women's Volleyball)	.50
14	Krista Beightol (Women's Volleyball)	.50
15	Carrie Gilley (Women's Volleyball)	.50
16	Shannan Griffin (Women's Volleyball)	.50
17	Becky Howlett (Women's Volleyball)	.50
18	Kristen Hovde (Women's Volleyball)	.50
19	Keri Killebrew (Women's Volleyball)	.50
20	Cindy Fredrick CO, M. Farokhmanesh ACO, Gweyn Leabo ACO (Women's Volleyball)	.50

1974 West Virginia

		NM
Complete Set (53):		80.00
Common Player:		1.00
1C	Stu Wolpert	1.00
1D	Mountaineer Coaches	4.00
1H	Leland Byrd (AD)	1.00
1S	Bobby Bowden (CO)	25.00
2C	Jay Sheehan	1.00
2D	Tom Brandner	1.00
2H	Tom Bowden	1.00
2S	Chuck Smith	1.00
3C	Ray Marshall	1.00
3D	Randy Swinson	1.00
3H	Tom Loadman	1.00
3S	Bob Kaminski	1.00
4C	Ron Lee	3.00
4D	Kirk Lewis	1.00
4H	Greg Dorn	1.00
4S	Emil Ros	1.00
5C	Mark Burke	1.00
5D	Rory Fields	1.00
5H	Gary Lombard	1.00
5S	Brian Gates	1.00
6C	John Schell	1.00
6D	Paul Jordan	1.00
6H	Mike Hubbard	1.00
6S	Chuck Kelly	1.00
7C	Rick Pennypacker	2.00
7D	Heywood Smith	1.00
7H	Jack Eastwood	1.00
7S	Andy Peters	1.00
8C	Steve Dunlap	1.00
8D	Dave Wilcher	2.00
8H	Greg Anderson	1.00
8S	Ken Culbertson	1.00
9C	David Van Halanger	1.00
9D	Rick Shaffer	1.00
9H	Rich Lukowski	1.00
9S	Al Gluchoski	1.00
10C	Dwayne Woods	1.00
10D	Ben Williams	2.00
10H	John Adams	1.00
10S	Tom Florence	1.00
11C	Marcus Mauney	1.00
11D	John Spraggins	1.00
11H	Bruce Huffman	1.00
11S	Bernie Kirchner	1.00
12C	Artie Owens	2.00
12D	Charlie Miller	1.00
12H	1974 Cheerleaders	1.00
12S	Eddie Russell	1.00
13C	Danny Buggs	4.00
13D	Marshall Mills	1.00
13H	John Everly	4.00
13S	Jeff Merrow	4.00
JK	Student Foundation	1.00

1988 West Virginia

		MT
Complete Set (16):		20.00
Common Player:		1.00
1	Charlie Baumann	1.50
2	Anthony Brown	1.00
3	Willie Edwards	1.00
4	Theron Ellis	1.50
5	Chris Haering	1.00
6	Major Harris	3.00
7	Undra Johnson	1.50
8	Kevin Koken	1.00
9	Pat Marlatt	1.00
10	Eugene Napoleon	1.00
11	Don Nehlen (CO)	2.00
12	Bo Orlando	3.00
13	Chris Parker	1.00
14	Robert Pickett	1.00
15	Brian Smider	1.00
16	John Stroia	1.00

1990 West Virigina Program Cards

		MT
Complete Set (49):		35.00
Common Player:		.75
1	Tarris Alexander	.75
2	Leroy Axem	.75
3	Michael Beasley	.75
4	Calvin Bell	.75
5	Matt Bland	.75
6	John Brown	1.25
7	Brad Carroll	.75
8	Mike Collins	.75
9	Mike Compton	1.25
10	Cecil Doggette	.75
11	Rick Dolly	.75
12	Theron Ellis	1.25
13	Charlie Fedorco	.75
14	Garrett Ford	.75
15	Scott Gaskins	.75
16	Boris Graham	.75
17	Keith Graley	.75
18	Chris Gray	.75
19	Greg Hertzog	.75
20	Ed Hill	.75
21	Verne Howard	.75
22	James Jett	4.00
23	Greg Jones	.75
24	Jon James	.75
25	Ted Kester	.75
26	Darroll Mitchell	.75
27	John Murphy	.75
28	Don Nehlen (CO)	2.50
29	Tim Newsom	.75
30	Joe Pabian	.75
31	John Ray	.75
32	Steve Redd	.75
33	Joe Ruth	.75
34	Alex Shook	.75
35	Jeff Sniffen	.75
36	Ray Staten	.75
37	Rick Stead	.75
38	Darren Studstill	2.00
39	Lorenzo Styles	2.00
40	Gary Tillis	.75
41	Rico Tyler	.75
42	Darrell Whitmore	2.00
43	E.J. Wheeler	.75
44	Darrick Wiley	.75
45	Tim Williams	.75
46	Sam Wilson	.75
47	Dale Wolfley	.75
48	Rob Yachini	.75
49	Mountaineer Field	.75

1991 West Virginia ATG

		MT
Complete Set (50):		15.00
Common Player:		.35
1	Jeff Hostetler	2.50
2	Tom Allman	.35
3	Russ Bailey	.35
4	Paul Bischoff	.35
5	Bruce Bosley	.50
6	Jim Braxton	.50
7	Danny Buggs	.50
8	Harry Clarke	.35
9	Ken Culbertson	.35
10	Willie Drewrey	.50
11	Steve Dunlap	.35
12	Garrett Ford	.35
13	Dennis Fowlkes	.35
14	Bob Gresham	.50
15	Chris Haering	.50
16	Major Harris	1.00
17	Steve Hathaway	.35
18	Rick Hollins	.35
19	Chuck Howley	1.00
20	Sam Huff	1.25
21	Brian Jozwiak	.50
22	Gene Lamone	.35
23	Oliver Luck	.75
24	Kerry Marbury	.35
25	Joe Marconi	.50
26	Jeff Merrow	.50
27	Steve Newberry	.35
28	Bob Orders	.35
29	Artie Owens	.50
30	Tom Pridemore	.50
31	Mark Raugh	.35
32	Reggie Rembert	.50
33	Ira Rodgers	.35
34	Mike Sherwood	.35
35	Joe Stydahar	.50
36	Renaldo Turnbull	1.25
37	Paul Woodside	.35
38	Fred Wyant	.35
39	Carl Leatherwood	.35
40	Darryl Talley	1.00
41	David Grant	.50
42	Bobby Bowden (CO)	1.00
43	Jim Carlen (CO)	.35
44	Frank Cignetti (CO)	.35
45	Gene Corum (CO)	.35
46	Art Lewis (CO)	.35
47	Don Nehlen (CO)	.50
48	New Mountaineer Field	.35
49	Old Mountaineer Field	.35
50	Lambert Trophy	.50

1991 West Virginia Program Cards

		MT
Complete Set (42):		25.00
Common Player:		.75
1	Tarris Alexander	.75
2	Johnathan Allen	.75
3	Leroy Axem	.75
4	Joe Ayuso	.75
5	Michael Beasley	.75
6	Rich Braham	1.00
7	Tom Briggs	.75
8	John Cappa	.75
9	Mike Collins	1.00
10	Mike Compton	1.00
11	Doug Cooley	.75
12	Cecil Doggette	.75
13	Rick Dolly	.75
14	Garrett Ford	.75
15	Scott Gaskins	1.00
16	Boris Graham	.75
17	Keith Graley	.75
18	Chris Gray	.75
19	Barry Hawkins	.75
20	Ed Hill	1.00
21	James Jett	3.00
22	Jon Jones	.75
23	Jim LeBlanc	1.00
24	David Mayfield	1.00
25	Adrian Murrell	3.00
26	Sam Mustipher	.75
27	Tim Newsom	.75
28	Tommy Orr	.75
29	Joe Pabian	.75
30	John Ray	.75
31	Wes Richardson	1.00
32	Nate Rine	.75
33	Joe Ruth	.75
34	Alex Shook	.75
35	Kwame Smith	.75
36	Darren Studstill	2.00
37	Lorenzo Styles	1.50
38	Gary Tillis	.75
39	Ron Weaver	.75
40	Darrell Whitmore	2.50
41	Darrick Wiley	.75
42	Rodney Woodard	.75

1992 West Virginia Program Cards

		MT
Complete Set (49):		25.00
Common Player:		.75
1	Tarris Alexander	.75
2	Joe Avila	.75
3	Leroy Axem	.75
4	Mike Baker	.75
5	Sean Biser	.75
6	Mike Booth	.75
7	Rich Braham	1.00
8	Tom Briggs	.75
9	Tim Brown	.75
10	Darius Burwell	.75
11	John Cappa	.75
12	Matt Ceglie	.75
13	Mike Collins	.75
14	Mike Compton	1.00
15	Rick Dolly	.75
16	Garrett Ford	.75
17	Scott Gaskins	1.00
18	Boris Graham	.75
19	Dan Harless	.75
20	Barry Hawkins	.75
21	Ed Hill	1.00
22	James Jett	3.00
23	Mark Johnson	.75
24	Jon Jones	.75
25	Jake Kelchner	2.50
26	Harold Kidd	.75
27	Jim LeBlanc	1.00
28	David Mayfield	1.00
29	Brian Moore	.75
30	Adrian Murrell	2.50
31	Robert Nelson	.75
32	Tommy Orr	.75
33	Joe Pabian	.75
34	Brett Parise	.75
35	Steve Perkins	.75
36	Steve Redd	.75
37	Wes Richardson	1.00
38	Nate Rine	.75
39	Tom Robsock	.75
40	Kwame Smith	.75
41	Darren Studstill	1.50
42	Lorenzo Styles	1.50
43	Matt Taffoni	.75
44	Mark Ulmer	.75
45	Mike Vanderjagt	.75
46	Darrick Wiley	.75
47	Dale Williams	.75
48	Rodney Woodard	.75
49	James Wright	.75

1993 West Virginia

		MT
Complete Set (49):		20.00
Common Player:		.50
1	Zach Abraham	.50
2	Tarris Alexander	.50
3	Mike Baker	.50
4	Aaron Beasley	.50
5	Derrick Bell	.50
6	Mike Booth	.50
7	Rich Braham	.75
8	Tim Brown	.50
9	Mike Collins	.75
10	Doug Costin	.50
11	Calvin Edwards	.50
12	Jim Freeman	.50
13A	Big East Trophy	1.50
13B	Daymeian Gallimore	1.50
14	Jimmy Gary	.50
15	Scott Gaskins	.75
16	Buddy Hager	.50
17	Dan Harless	.50
18	John Harper	.50
19	Barry Hawkins	.75
20	Ed Hill	.75
21	Jon Jones	.50
22	Jay Kearney	.50
23	Jake Kelchner	2.00
24	Harold Kidd	.50
25	Chris Klick	.50
26	Jim LeBlanc	.75
27	Chris Ling	.50
28	David Mayfield	.75
29	Keith Morris	.50
30	Tommy Orr	.50
31	Joe Pabian	.50
32	Ken Painter	.50
33	Steve Perkins	.50
34	Maurice Richards	.50
35	Wes Richardson	.50
36	Nate Rine	.50
37	Tom Robsock	.50
38	Todd Sauerbrun	1.50
39	Darren Studstill	1.50
40	Matt Taffoni	.50
41	Keith Taparausky	.50
42	Mark Ulmer	.50
43	Robert Walker	1.25
44	Charles Washington	.50
45	Darrick Wiley	.50
46	Dale Williams	.50
47	James (Puppy) Wright	.50
48	Don Nehlen (CO)	1.00
49	Mountaineer Field	.50

1992 Wisconsin Program Cards

		MT
Complete Set (27):		20.00
Common Player:		.75
1	Troy Vincent	2.50
2	Tim Krumrie	1.25
3	Barry Alvarez (CO)	1.50
4	Pat Richter	1.25
5	Nate Odomes	1.25
6	Ron Vander Kelen	1.50
7	Don Davey	1.25
8	Alan Ameche	2.00
9	Randy Wright	1.25
10	Ken Bowman	1.00
11	Chuck Belin	.75
12	Elroy Hirsch	2.00
13	Paul Gruber	1.25
14	Al Toon	1.50
15	Richard Johnson	1.00
16	Pat Harder	1.00
17	Gary Casper	.75
18	Rufus Ferguson	.75
19	Pat O'Donahue	.75
20	Dennis Lick	.75
21	Jeff Dellenbach	1.00
22	Jim Bakken	1.00
23	Milt Bruhn (CO)	.75
24	Mike Webster	1.50
25	Dave McClain (CO)	.75
26	Bill Marek	.75
27	Rick Graf	.75

1990 Wyoming Smokey

		MT
Complete Set (16):		20.00
Common Player:		1.50
1	Tom Corontzos (18)	1.50
2	Jay Daffer (34)	1.50
3	Mitch Donahue (49)	2.00
4	Sean Fleming (42)	1.50
5	Pete Gosar (53)	1.50
6	Robert Midgett (57)	1.50
7	Bryan Mooney (9)	1.50
8	Doug Rigby (77)	1.50
9	Mark Timmer (48)	1.50
10	Paul Wallace (25)	1.50
11	Shawn Wiggins (15)	1.50
12	Gordy Wood (95)	1.50
13	Willie Wright (96)	1.50
14	Cowboy Joe Mascot	
16	Title Card Cowboy logo	1.50

1993 Wyoming Smokey

		MT
Complete Set (16):		12.00
Common Player:		.75
1	John Burrough	.75
2	Wade Constance	.75
3	Mike Fitzgerald	.75
4	Jarrod Heidmann	.75
5	Joe Hughes	.75
6	Kenny Johnson	1.00
7	Mike Jones	.75
8	Cody Kelly	.75
9	Rob Levin	.75
10	Prentice Rhone	.75
11	Greg Scanlan	1.00
12	Cory Talich	.75
13	Kurt Whitehead	.75
14	Thomas Williams	.75
15	Tyrone Williams	.75
16	Ryan Yarborough	3.00

1992 Youngstown State

		MT
Complete Set (54):		20.00
Common Player:		.40
1	Ramon Amill	.40
2	Dan Black	.40
3	Trent Boykin	.40
4	Reginald Brown	.40
5	Mark Brungard	1.00
6	Larry Bucciarelli	.40
7	David Burch	.40
8	Nick Cochran	.40
9	Brian Coman	.40
10	Ken Conatser (ACO)	.40
11	Darnell Clark	1.00
12	Dave DelBoccio	.40
13	Tom Dillingham	.40
14	John Englehardt	.40
15	Marcus Evans	.40
16	Malcolm Everette	.40
17	Drew Gerber	.40
18	Michael Ghent	.40
19	Aaron Green	.40
20	Jon Heacock (ACO)	.40
21	Alfred Hill (ACO)	.40
22	Terica Jones	.40
23	Craig Kertesz	.40
24	Paul Kokos Jr	.40
25	Reginald Lee	.40
26	Raymond Miller	.50
27	Brian Moore (ACO)	.40
28	Mike Nezbeth	.40
29	William Norris	.40
30	James Panozzo	.40
31	Derek Pixley	.40
32	Jeff Powers	.40
33	David Quick	.40
34	John Quintana	.40
35	Mike Rekstis	.40
36	Demario Ridgeway	.40
37	Dave Roberts	.40
38	Chris Sammarone	.50
39	Randy Smith	.40
40	Tamron Smith	.50
41	John Steele	.40
42	Jim Tressel (CO)	1.00
43	Chris Vecchione	.40
44	Lester Weaver	.40
45	Jeffrey Wilkins	.50
46	Herb Williams	.40
47	Ryan Wood	.40
48	Don Zwisler	.40
49	Penguin Pros Card 1	.50
50	Penguin Pros Card 2	.50
51	First-Team All-American	.50
52	Did You Know 1	.40
53	Did You Know 2	.40
54	Did You Know 3	.40

1991 Pennsylvania HS Big 33

		MT
Complete Set (36):		35.00
Common Player:		.50
PA1	Dietrich Jells	2.00
PA2	Mike Archie	3.00
PA3	Tony Miller	.50
PA4	Edmund Robinson	.50
PA5	Brian Miller	.75
PA6	Marvin Harrison	5.00
PA7	Mike Cawley	.50
PA8	Thomas Marchese	.50
PA9	Scott Milanovich	2.00
PA10	Shawn Wooden	1.00
PA11	Curtis Martin	12.00
PA12	William Khayat	.50
PA13	Jermell Fleming	.50
PA14	Ray Zellars	4.00
PA15	Jon Witman	.75
PA16	Chris McCartney	.50
PA17	David Rebar	.50
PA18	Mark Zatavesk	.75
PA19	Todd Atkins	.50
PA20	Shannon Stevens	.50
PA21	Keith Conlin	.75
PA22	John Bowman	.50
PA23	Maurice Lawrence	.50
PA24	Mike Halapin	.50
PA25	Steve Keim	.50
PA26	Dennis Martin	.50
PA27	Keith Morris	.50
PA28	Chris Villarrial	.50
PA29	Thomas Tumulty	.50
PA30	Jason Augustino	.50
PA31	Gregory Delong	.50
PA32	James Moore	.50
PA33	Eric Clair	.75
PA34	Tyler Young	.50
PA35	Jeffrey Sauve	.50
PA36	Terry Hammons	.50

1995 Roox HS

		MT
Complete Set (39):		18.00
Common Player:		.50
1	Wesley Crane	.50
2	Nili Hammond	.50
3	Daniel Anglin	.50
4	Ronnie Williams	.50
5	Harold Blackmon	.50
6	Tim Lavery	.50
7	Babatunde Ridley	.50
8	Fred Wakefield	.50
9	Bobie Singleton	.50
10	Chris Janek	.50
11	Steffan Nicholson	.50
12	Scott Mullen	.50
13	Jason Scherer	.50
14	Kevin Beard Jr.	.50
15	Michael Sergeant	.50
16	Marcus Smith	.50
17	Eric Garrett	.50
18	Chris Pickett	.50
19	Michael Burden	.50
20	Nick Abruzzo	.50
21	Stanley Williams	.50
22	Joey Goodspeed	.50
23	Stephen Olien	.50
24	R.J. Luke	.50
25	Matt Kelly	.50
26	Ricardo King	.50
27	Tamaine Hills	.50
28	Michael Yarborough	.50
29	Brian Schmitz	.50
30	Joe Carroll	.50
31	Roy Sessions	.50
32	Marcus Hood	.50
33	Lorenzo Smith	.50
34	Karlton Thomas	.50
40	Carlos Polk	.50
41	Montinez Williams	.50
42	Neil Carroll	.50
43	Shaka Jones	.50
---	Cover Card - blankbacked	.10

1996 Roox Prep Star AT/EA/SE

		MT
Complete Set (142):		70.00
Common Player:		.50
AT1	David Garrard	.50
AT2	Erik Lipton	.50
AT3	Tim Olmstead	.50
AT4	Craig Powers	.50
AT5	Jason Thompson	.50
AT6	William Combs	.50
AT7	Gil Harris	.50
AT8	Golden Myers	.50
AT9	Chris Willetts	.50
AT10	Chris Ramseur	.50
AT11	Anthony Sanders	.50
AT12	Ali Culpepper	.50
AT13	Dominique Stevenson	.50
AT14	Rondell White	.50
AT15	David Foster	.50
AT16	Luis Moreno	.50
AT17	Sherman Scott	.50
AT18	Doug Bost	.50
AT19	Terry Denoon	.50
AT20	Dave Johnson	.50
AT21	Dain Lewis	.50
AT22	Chris McDaniel	.50
AT23	Chadwick Scott	.50
AT24	Brian Scott	.50
AT25	Bobby Graham	.50
AT26	Steve Shipp	.50
AT27	Jimmy Caldwell	.50
AT28	Rico Gladden	.50
AT29	Evan Kay	.50
AT30	Rashad Slade	.50
AT31	Nate Krill	.50
AT32	Chris Luzar	.50
AT33	Graham Manley	.50
AT34	Neely Page	.50
AT35	David Pugh	.50
AT36	Jason Cox	.50
AT37	Jason McFeasters	.50
AT38	John Miller	.50
AT39	Bobby Dameron	.50
AT40	Keith Esteppe	.50
AT41	Tim Falls	.50
AT42	Jeman Jacobs	.50
AT43	Scott McLain	.50
AT44	Ty Hunt	.50
AT45	Jeff Chambers	.50
AT46	Nick Gilliland	.50

AT47 Buddy Young .50
AT48 DeAngelo Lloyd .50
AT49 Ben Bacot .50
AT50 Corey Nelson .50
AT51 Jimi Massey .50
AT52 Sam Scott .50
AT53 Mike Winfield .50
AT54 Jayvon McKinney .50
EA1 Luke Richmond .50
EA2 Mike Gaydosz .50
EA3 Eddie Campbell .50
EA4 Dan Ellis .50
EA5 Darin Miller .50
EA6 Ravon Anderson .50
EA7 Jason Murray .50
EA8 Brett Aurilla .50
EA9 Tremayne Bendross .50
EA10 Sean Fisher .50
EA11 J.R. Johnson .50
EA12 Victor Strader .50
EA13 Dennis Thomas .50
EA14 Quentin Harris .50
EA15 Reggie Garrett .50
EA16 Patrick O'Brien .50
EA17 Guenter Kryszon .50
EA18 Kareem McKenzie .50
EA19 Martin Bibla .50
EA20 Joe Collins .50
EA21 John Kuchmek .50
EA22 Greg Ransom .50
EA23 Tim Sample .50
EA24 Marty Wensel .50
EA25 Jack Bloom .50
EA26 Nate Ritzenhaler .50
EA27 Charley Powell .50
EA28 Ron Graham .50
EA29 Joe McKinney .50
EA30 Jeremiah Clarke .50
EA31 Frank Fodera .50
EA32 John Yura .50
EA33 Jonathon Harris .50
EA34 Ben Martin .50
EA35 Cory Wire .50
EA36 Sean Bell .50
EA37 Brad Eissler .50
EA38 Lavar Arrington .50
SE1 Kenny Kelly .50
SE2 Daniel Cobb .50
SE3 Phillip Deas .50
SE4 Adam Cox .50
SE5 Ron Johnson .50
SE6 Tommy Banks .50
SE7 Sherrod Dickson .50
SE8 Davey Ford Jr. .50
SE9 Travis Henry .50
SE10 William McCray .50
SE11 Dan Morgan .50
SE12 Adrian Peterson .50
SE13 Darrell Jackson .50
SE14 Orlando Iglesias .50
SE15 Eddie Williams .50
SE16 Matt Wright .50
SE17 Fred Weary .50
SE18 Braxton Anderson .50
SE19 Romaro Miller .50
SE20 Ronald Boldin .50
SE21 Otis Duhart .50
SE22 Jabari Ellison .50
SE23 Tom Hillard .50
SE24 Ryan Smith .50
SE25 Erik Strange .50
SE26 Sam Matthews .50
SE27 Thomas Pittman .50
SE28 Andrew Zow .50
SE29 Gerard Warren .50
SE30 Adrian Wilson .50
SE31 Char-Ron Dorsey .50
SE32 Kennard Ellis .50
SE33 Jabari Holloway .50
SE34 Melvin Richey .50
SE35 Willie Sams .50
SE36 Josh Weldon .50
SE37 Travis Carroll .50
SE38 Cortez Allen .50
SE39 Andra Davis .50
SE40 Matt Miller .50
SE41 Whit Smith .50
SE42 Stanford Simmons .50
SE43 Tony Dixon .50
SE44 Clifton Robinson .50
SE45 Hugh Holmes .50
SE46 Abdul Howard .50
SE47 Rob Pate .50
SE48 Matt Howard .50
SE49 Terrence Trammell .50
SE50 Earl Williams .50
--- Jesse Palmer .50

1996 Roox Prep Star C/W

MT
Complete Set (145): 70.00
Common Player: .50
C1 B.J. Tiger .50
C2 Ryan Lown .50
C3 Sherard Poteete .50
C4 Eric Gooden .50
C5 Ken Alsop .50
C6 Levi Mehl .50
C7 Justin Galimore .50
C8 Dallas Davis .50
C9 Ahmed Kabba .50
C10 Aaron Lockett .50
C11 Kevin Wendling .50
C12 Ryan Humphrey .50
C13 Brandon Stephens .50
C14 Dan Engel .50
C15 Jared Holland .50
C16 Tango McCauley .50
C17 Kyle Jenson .50
C18 Kody Hergert .50
C19 Jon Rutherford .50
C20 John Teasdale .50
C21 Steve Wiedower .50
C22 Joshua Graham .50
C23 John Robertson .50
C24 Austin Lee .50
C25 Brandon Washington .50
C26 Andy Wisne .50
C27 Bary Holleyman .50
C28 Darren Palladino .50
C29 Mike Burke .50
C30 Thomas Fortune .50
C31 Pete Battisti .50
C32 Monty Beisel .50
C33 John Paul Keserich .50
C34 Garrett Masters .50
C35 Bubba Babb .50
C36 Marlon Guess .50
C37 Stanley Peters .50
C38 Harold Burgess .50
C39 Courtney Hysaw .50
C40 Darcey Levy .50
C41 Zach Magalei .50
C42 Drew Smith .50
C43 Jeff Ferguson .50
C44 Eric Rosel .50
C45 Jeremy Toles .50
C46 Jason Krause .50
C47 Jeff Gloy .50
C48 Brandan Kramer .50
C49 Marques Spivey .50
W1 Randy Fasani .50
W2 Todd Mortensen .50
W3 Spencer Brinton .50
W4 Greg Cicero .50
W5 Scott McEwan .50
W6 Drew Miller .50
W7 Austin Moherman .50
W8 David Priestley .50
W9 David Carr .50
W10 Chris Czernek .50
W11 Jared Flint .50
W12 Josh Rogers .50
W13 Damion Barton .50
W14 Eddie Gayles .50
W15 Mike Rhodes .50
W16 Donovan Calhoun .50
W17 Dante Clay .50
W18 James Creason .50
W19 Tony Elam .50
W20 Brian Palmer .50
W21 Roderick Walker .50
W22 Terrynce White .50
W23 Michael Yancy .50
W24 Ken-Yon Rambo .50
W25 Eddie Gorton .50
W26 Ja'Warren Hooker .50
W27 Jeff Johnson .50
W28 Cody Joyce .50
W29 Rossi Martin .50
W30 Rashawn Owens .50
W31 Joey Getherall .50
W32 Jamien McCullum .50
W33 Brandon Nash .50
W34 Tafiti Uso .50
W35 Lonnie Ford .50
W36 Antoine Harris .50
W37 Corey Lee Smith .50
W38 Donnell Burch .50
W39 Lee Turner .50
W40 Brian Polak .50
W41 Mike Souza .50
W42 Kurt Vollers .50
W43 Craig Brooks .50
W44 Ron Price .50
W45 Mike Wambolt .50
W46 Ralph Zarate .50
W47 Jim Adams .50
W48 Ed Anderson .50
W49 Justin David .50
W50 Brian Hart .50
W51 Nic Hawkins .50
W52 Brandon Hoopes .50
W53 Kris Keene .50
W54 Travis Pfeifer .50
W55 Langston Walker .50
W56 Andre Carter .50
W57 John Jackson .50
W58 Welton Kage .50
W59 Anthony Thomas .50
W60 Justin Bannan .50
W61 Ryan Nielsen .50
W62 Brandon Manumaleuna .50
W63 Kyle Roselle .50
W64 Darrell Daniels .50
W65 Bobby Demars .50
W66 Tracy Hunt .50
W67 Zeke Moreno .50
W68 Tim Shear .50
W69 Kori Dickerson .50
W70 Ty Gregorak .50
W71 Malachi Keddington .50
W72 Don Meyers .50
W73 Tony Thompson .50
W74 Ife Ohalete .50
W75 Antuan Simmons .50
W76 Albus Brooks .50
W77 Dewey Hale .50
W78 Kameron Jones .50
W79 Lamont Thompson .50
W80 Fred Washington .50
W81 Shanga Wilson .50
W82 Marques Anderson .50
W83 DeMario Franklin .50
W84 Melvin Justice .50
W85 Kris Richard .50
W86 Julius Thompson .50
W87 Wes Tufaga .50
W88 Zak Haselmo .50
W89 Jeremy Kelly .50
W90 John Gonzalez .50
W91 Robert Jackson .50
W92 Rod Perry Jr. .50
W93 Charles Tharp .50
W94 Marcus Brady .50
W95 Merle Sango .50

1996 Roox Prep Star MW/SW

MT
Complete Set (115): 80.00
Common Player: .75
MW1 Zack Kustock .75
MW2 Tyler Evans .75
MW3 Bob Johnson .75
MW4 Chris Ludban .75
MW5 Ken Stopka .75
MW6 Kyle Van Sluys .75
MW7 Sean Penny .75
MW8 Bill Andrews .75
MW9 James Harrison .75
MW10 DeWayne Hogan .75
MW11 Carlos Honare .75
MW12 Ray Jackson .75
MW13 Greg Simpson .75
MW14 Israel Thompson .75
MW15 Ernest Brown .75
MW16 Sam Crenshaw .75
MW17 Adrian Duncan .75
MW18 Kahill Hill .75
MW19 Teddy Johnson .75
MW20 Omari Jordan .75
MW21 Jason Kemble .75
MW22 Jace Sayler .75
MW23 Tim Stratton .75
MW24 Adam Fay .75
MW25 Josh Jakubowski .75
MW26 Ben Mast .75
MW27 Mike Collins .75
MW28 Oliver King .75
MW29 Rocky Nease .75
MW30 Josh Parrish .75
MW31 Clifton Reta .75
MW32 Brian Wise .75
MW33 Maurice Williams .75
MW34 Kevin Bell .75
MW35 Derek Burns .75
MW36 Andre Cooper .75
MW37 Jason Dox .75
MW38 Raesche Hill .75
MW39 Javon Ptak .75
MW40 Ben Pulfer .75
MW41 Heath Queen .75
MW42 Bill Seymour .75
MW43 Demetrius Smith .75
MW44 Ben Sobieski .75
MW45 Hubert Thompson .75
MW46 Jake Frysinger .75
MW47 Jason Ott .75
MW48 Kyle Vanden Bosch .75
MW49 Kurt Anderson .75
MW50 Napoleon Harris .75
MW51 Jason Manson .75
MW52 Joel Mesman .75
MW53 Jeff Skibitsky .75
MW54 T.J. Turner .75
MW55 Mike Clinkscale .75
MW56 Jamie Grant .75
MW57 Kyle Moffatt .75
MW58 Abdullah Muhammad .75
MW59 Eric Parker .75
MW60 Mike Young .75
MW61 Pat Gibson .75
MW62 Brendan Rauh .75
MW63 Antwan Randle El .75
MW64 Levron Williams .75
SW1 Edmond Stansbury .75
SW2 Grant Elam .75
SW3 Regan George .75
SW4 Matt Schobel .75
SW5 Hodges Mitchell .75
SW6 Twone Simmons .75
SW7 Donald Williams .75
SW8 Jason Coffey .75
SW9 Corey Harris .75
SW10 Shon Jones .75
SW11 Burnest Rhodes .75
SW12 Adrian Thomas .75
SW13 Robert Williams .75
SW14 Daniel Belcha .75
SW15 Damon Daniels .75
SW16 Raymond Turner .75
SW17 Chad Irwin .75
SW18 Ed Kelly .75
SW19 Miles Koon .75
SW20 Luke Nichols .75
SW21 Dennis Jones .75
SW22 Rodney Endsley .75
SW23 Norman McKinney .75
SW24 Terry Williams .75
SW25 David Warren .75
SW26 Lonnie Madison .75
SW27 Shaun Rogers .75
SW28 Mike Minott .75
SW29 Evan Perroni .75
SW30 Grant Irons .75
SW31 Josh Spoerl .75
SW32 Tommy Tull .75
SW33 Chad Chester .75
SW34 Devon Lemons .75
SW35 Antowan Alexander .75
SW36 Jay Brooks .75
SW37 Quenton Jammer .75
SW38 Derrick Yates .75
SW39 Gary Baxter .75
SW40 Danny Black .75
SW41 Brandon Couts .75
SW42 Derek Dorris .75
SW43 Mitchell Jameson .75
SW44 Mickey Jones .75
SW45 Kevon Morton .75
SW46 Rod Sheppard .75
SW47 J.R. Pouncey .75
SW48 Sterlin Gilbert .75
SW49 Terry Burrell .75
SW50 Jason Stevenson .75

1996 Roox Shrine Bowl HS

MT
Complete Set (74): 35.00
Common Player (NC1-NC36): .50
Common Player (SC1-SC36): .50
NC1 Rocky Hunt .50
NC2 Cam Holland .50
NC3 Derrick Chambers .50
NC4 Ramondo North .50
NC5 Bo Manis .50
NC6 Antonio Graham .50
NC7 Clayton White .50
NC8 Billy Young .50
NC9 Joshua Tucker .50
NC10 Rod Emery .50
NC11 Matt Burdick .50
NC12 Chad Gathings .50
NC13 Brian Ray .50
NC14 Brandon Spoon .50
NC15 Dauntae Finger .50
NC16 Raymond Massey .50
NC17 Damien Bennett .50
NC18 Bennie Griffin .50
NC19 Randolph Galloway .50
NC20 Titus Pettigrew .50
NC21 Chris McCoy .50
NC22 Virgil Johnson .50
NC23 Marcus Reaves .50
NC24 Scottie Stepp .50
NC25 Julius Bell .50
NC26 Robert Williams .50
NC27 Rashad Burke .50
NC28 Michael Cox .50
NC29 Kwabena Greene .50
NC30 Tim Burgess .50
NC31 Scott Smith .50
NC32 Steven Lindsey .50
NC33 Charles Berry .50
NC34 Chris Satterfield .50
NC35 Eric Leak .50
NC36 Nick Means MG .50
SC1 Ikie Curry .50
SC2 Shaun Ellis .50
SC3 Zabeion McRoy .50
SC4 Will McLaurin .50
SC5 Jarvis Davis .50
SC6 Justin Hill .50
SC7 Antwon Black .50
SC8 Justin Watts .50
SC9 Ray Mazyck .50
SC10 Chris McGee .50
SC11 Stan Manning .50
SC12 Micale Chandler .50
SC13 Deveron Harper .50
SC14 Brian Wolford .50
SC15 Tim Winfield .50
SC16 Donovan Norman .50
SC17 Chip Brogden .50
SC18 Seth Stoddard .50
SC19 Nakia Adderson .50
SC20 Adam Varnadore .50
SC21 Lance Legree .50
SC22 Scott Greer .50
SC23 B.J. Little .50
SC24 Kinte Wilson .50
SC25 Rod Joseph .50
SC26 Benji Wallace .50
SC27 Don Moore .50
SC28 Cecil Caldwell .50
SC29 Thomas Washington .50
SC30 Rory Gallman .50
SC31 Courtney Brown .50
SC32 Jermale Kelly .50
SC33 Walsh Dingle .50
SC34 Mal Lawyer .50
SC35 Will Gainey .50
SC36 Bird Bourne MG .50
--- South Carolina Title Card .10
--- North Carolina Title Card .10

1991 Texas HS Legends

MT
Complete Set (25): 18.00
Common Player: .60
1 Marty Akins .60
2 Bill Bradley 1.00
3 Chris Gilbert 1.25
4 Glynn Gregory .75
5 Charlie Haas .60
6 Craig James 2.00
7 Boody Johnson .60
8 Ernie Koy Jr. .75
9 Glenn Lippman .60
10 Jack Pardee 1.00
11 Billy Patterson .60
12 Billy Sims 3.00
13 Byron Townsend .60
14 Joe Washington Jr. 1.00
15 Allie White .60
16 Wilson Whitley .75
17 Gordon Wood .75
18 Willie Zapalac .60
19 Cover Card 1 .60
20 Cover Card 2 .60
21 Cover Card 3 .60
22 Cover Card 4 .60
23 Cover Card 5 .60

1990 Versailles HS

MT
Complete Set (20): 8.00
Common Player: .50
1 Kevin Bergman .50
2 A.J. Bey .50
3 Brad Bey .75
4 Ed Dingman .50
5 Brian Griesdorn .50
6 Al Hetrick (CO) .75
7 Garth Hoellrich .50
8 Trent Huff .50
9 Brian Keiser .50
10 Lane Knore .50
11 Brian Kunk .50
12 Keenan Leichty .50
13 Marc Litten .50
14 Craig Oliver .50
15 Jon Pothast .50
16 Joe Rush .50
17 Shane Schultz .50
18 Mark Siekman .50
19 Matt Stall .50
20 Nathan Subler .50

CANADIAN

1991 All-World CFL

		MT
Complete Set (110):		3.00
Common Player:		.04
1	Raghib (Rocket) Ismail	.25
2	Bruce McNall (owner)	.04
3	Ray Alexander	.08
4	Matt Clark	.08
5	Bobby Jurasin	.08
6	Dieter Brock (LEG)	.08
7	Doug Flutie	.75
8	Stewart Hill	.04
9	James Mills	.08
10	Raghib (Rocket) Ismail, With Bruce McNall	.25
11	Tom Clements (LEG)	.15
12	Lui Passaglia	.20
13	Ian Sinclair	.08
14	Chris Skinner	.08
15	Joe Theismann (LEG)	.15
16	Jon Volpe	.30
17	Deatrich Wise	.04
18	Danny Barrett	.08
19	Warren Moon (LEG)	.25
20	Leo Blanchard	.04
21	Derrick Crawford	.08
22	Lloyd Fairbanks	.08
23	David Beckman (CO)	.04
24	Matt Finlay	.04
25	Darryl Hall	.04
26	Ron Hopkins	.08
27	Wally Buono (CO)	.04
28	Kenton Leonard	.08
29	Brent Matich	.04
30	Greg Peterson	.04
31	Steve Goldman (CO)	.04
32	Allen Pitts	.25
33	Raghib (Rocket) Ismail	.25
34	Danny Bass	.08
35	John Gregory (CO)	.04
36	Rod Connop	.04
37	Craig Ellis	.08
38	Raghib (Rocket) Ismail (Rookie)	.25
39	Ron Lancaster (CO)	.08
40	Tracy Ham	.25
41	Ray Macoritti	.08
42	Willie Pless	.08
43	Bob O'Billovich (CO)	.04
44	Michael Soles	.08
45	Reggie Taylor	.15
46	Henry Williams	.20
47	Adam Rita (CO)	.04
48	Larry Wruck	.08
49	Grover Covington	.08
50	Rocky DePietro	.08
51	Darryl Rogers (CO)	.04
52	Pete Giftopoulos	.08
53	Herman Heard	.08
54	Mike Kerrigan	.08
55	Reggie Barnes (AS)	.08
56	Derrick McAdoo	.08
57	Paul Osbaldiston	.08
58	Earl Winfield	.08
59	Greg Battle (AS)	.08
60	Damon Allen	.08
61	Reggie Barnes	.15
62	Bob Molle	.04
63	Raghib (Rocket) Ismail	.25
64	Irv Daymond	.04
65	Andre Francis	.04
66	Bart Hull	.15
67	Stephen Jones	.08
68	Raghib (Rocket) Ismail	.25
69	Glenn Kulka	.08
70	Loyd Lewis	.04
71	Rob Smith	.04
72	Roger Aldag	.08
73	Kent Austin	.25
74	Ray Elgaard	.08
75	Mike Clemons (AS)	.25
76	Jeff Fairholm	.08
77	Richie Hall	.04
78	Willis Jacox	.08
79	Eddie Lowe	.04
80	Ray Elgaard (AS)	.08
81	Donald Narcisse	.15
82	James Mills (AS)	.08
83	Dave Ridgway	.08
84	Ted Wahl	.08
85	Carl Brazley	.08
86	Mike Clemons	.35
87	Matt Dunigan	.35
88	Grey Cup (Checklist 1)	.04
89	Harold Hallman	.08
90	Rodney Harding	.08
91	Don Moen	.08
92	Raghib (Rocket) Ismail	.25
93	Reggie Pleasant	.08
94	Darrell Smith (UER) (One L on front, two on back)	.15
95	Group Shot (Checklist 2)	.04
96	Chris Schultz	.08
97	Don Wilson	.04
98	Greg Battle	.08
99	Lyle Bauer	.04
100	Less Browne	.08
101	Raghib (Rocket) Ismail	.25
102	Tom Burgess	.15
103	Mike Gray	.04
104	Rod Hill	.08
105	Warren Hudson	.08
106	Tyrone Jones	.15
107	Stan Mikawos	.04
108	Robert Mimbs	.15
109	James West	.08
110	Raghib (Rocket) Ismail	.25
P1	Rocket Ismail Promo# (numbered P)	1.00
NNO	Raghib (Rocket) Ismail (Autographed card/1600)	50.00

1992 All-World CFL

		MT
Complete Set (180):		10.00
Common Player:		.05
1	Checklist 1-90	.05
2	Draft Picks Checklist	.05
4	Western Final	.05
5	Eastern Final	.05
6	79th Grey Cup	.05
	Grey Cup Most Outstanding Player (Rocket Ismail)	.20
7	Memorable Grey Cups 1909	.05
8	Memorable Grey Cups 1969	.05
9	Memorable Grey Cups 1982	.05
10	Memorable Grey Cups 1989	.05
11	Jeff Braswell	.05
12	Glenn Kulka	.05
13	Will Johnson	.20
14	Lance Chomyc	.10
15	Stan Mikawos	.05
16	Bobby Jurasin	.20
17	Terry Baker	.05
18	Tracy Ham	.50
19	Todd Wiseman	.05
20	Rob Crifo	.05
21	Chris Morris	.20
22	Jon Volpe	.50
23	Donald Narcisse	.20
24	David Williams	.20
25	Paul Clatney	.05
26	Willie Pless	.20
27	Rickey Foggie	.20
28	Denny Chronopoulos	.05
29	Darryl Sampson	.05
30	Patrick Wayne	.05
31	Terrence Jones	.20
32	Larry Wruck	.10
33	Angelo Snipes	.50
34	Tony Champion	.20
35	Steve Taylor	.20
36	Lorne King	.05
37	Roger Aldag	.10
38	Damon Allen	.30
39	Chris Walby	.10
40	Doug Davies	.05
41	Dan Rashovich	.05
42	Mark Scott	.05
43	Reggie Pleasant	.10
44	Bob Cameron	.05
45	Danny McManus	.20
46	Matt Clark	.10
47	Bart Hull	.10
48	Hank Llesic	.05
49	Pee Wee Smith	.30
50	Irv Daymond	.05
51	Greg Battle (J.P. McCaffrey Trophy)	.10
52	Will Johnson (Norm Fieldgate Trophy)	.10
53	Lance Chomyc (Lew Hayman Trophy)	.10
54	Jim Mills (DeMarco-Becket Memorial Trophy)	.10
55	Jon Volpe (Jackie Parker Trophy)	.20
56	Raghib (Rocket) Ismail (Frank M. Gibson Trophy)	.30
57	Dave Ridgway (David Dryburgh Memorial Trophy)	.10
58	Chris Walby (Leo Dandurand Trophy)	.10
59	Doug Flutie (Jeff Nicklin Memorial Trophy)	.75
60	Robert Mimbs (Jeff Russell Memorial Trophy)	.20
61	Jon Volpe (Eddie James Memorial Trophy)	.20
62	Blake Marshall (Dr. Beattie Martin Trophy)	.10
63	Eric Streater	.10
64	Carl Brazley	.05
65	Kent Warnock	.05
66	Brian Bonner	.05
67	Tom Burgess	.20
68	Bob Gordon	.05
69	Milson Jones	.10
70	Todd Dillon	.05
71	Keyvan Jenkins	.20
72	Ken Evraire	.20
73	Willis Jacox	.20
74	Carl Bland	.05
75	Daniel Hunter	.20
76	Chris Schultz	.05
77	Earl Winfield	.20
78	Henry Williams	.30
79	Matt Dunigan	.75
80	Mark McLoughlin	.05
81	Craig Ellis	.10
82	Rodney Harding	.20
83	Scott Douglas	.05
84	Ray Elgaard	.20
85	Doug Flutie	1.00
86	Gary Lewis	.05
87	Rod Hill	.10
88	Greg Stumon	.10
89	Ray Alexander	.20
90	Blake Dermott	.05
91	Checklist 91-180	.05
92	Trophy Winners CL	.10
93	British Columbia CL	.05
94	Calgary CL	.05
95	Edmonton CL	.05
96	Saskatchewan CL	.05
97	Hamilton CL	.05
98	Ottawa CL	.05
99	Toronto CL	.05
100	Winnipeg CL	.05
101	James West	.20
102	Jeff Fairholm	.20
103	Mike Campbell	.05
104	Darren Flutie	.40
105	Blake Marshall	.25
106	Loyd Lewis	.05
107	Enis Jackson	.05
108	John Motton	.20
109	Ken Walcott	.05
110	Richie Hall	.05
111	Greg Peterson	.05
112	Wally Zatylny	.05
113	Lui Passaglia	.25
114	Darryl Hall	.05
115	Michael Soles	.10
116	Doug Brewster	.05
117	Mike Gray	.05
118	Mike Trevathan	.05
119	Don Moen	.05
120	Chris Armstrong	.05
121	Lucius Floyd	.05
122	Ken Pettway	.05
123	Anthony Drawhorn	.20
124	Brian Walling	.05
125	Troy Westwood	.20
126	Reggie Barnes	.20
127	Raghib (Rocket) Ismail	.50
128	Rod Connop	.10
129	Chris Major	.20
130	David Bovell	.05
131	Quency Williams	.05
132	Michel Bourgeau	.05
133	Harold Hallman	.10
134	Junior Thurman	.20
135	Stewart Hill	.05
136	Brent Matich	.05
137	Leroy Blugh	.05
138	Nick Mazzoli	.05
139	Dave Ridgway	.20
140	Matt Finlay	.05
141	Mike Clemons	1.00
142	Jason Riley	.05
143	Stacey Hairston	.05
144	Jim Mills	.10
145	Paul Randolph	.05
146	David Sapunjis	.25
147	Charles Gordon	.05
148	Chris Tsangaris	.05
149	Darrell Smith	.20
150	Leo Groenewegen	.05
151	Greg Battle	.20
152	Bruce Covernton	.10
153	Paul Osbaldiston	.10
154	Don Wilson	.05
155	Kent Austin	.30
156	Jamie Morris	.05
157	Andre Francis	.05
158	O.J. Brigance	.20
159	Less Browne	.10
160	Alondra Johnson	.05
161	Dexter Manley	.20
162	Bob Poley	.05
163	Ed Berry	.05
164	Pete Giftopoulos	.05
165	Glen Suitor	.05
166	Eddie Thomas	.05
167	Danny Barrett	.20
168	Robert Mimbs	.20
169	Jim Sandusky	.20
170	Maurice Smith	.05
171	David Conrad	.05
172	Larry Willis	.05
173	Ian Sinclair	.05
174	Allen Pitts	.50
175	Don McPherson	.05
176	Ray Bernard	.05
177	Dale Sanderson	.05
178	Dan Ferrone	.10
179	Vic Stevenson	.05
180	Rob Smith	.05
P1	Doug Fluti Promo# (Numbered P)	1.50
P2	Rocket Ismail Promo# (Numbered P)	1.00

1982 Bantam/FBI CFL Discs

		MT
Complete Set (31):		300.00
Common Player:		5.00
1	Junior Ah You	10.00
2	Zenon Andrusyshyn	10.00
3	Leon Bright	10.00
4	Bob Cameron	5.00
5	Tom Clements	35.00
6	Jim Corrigall	10.00
7	Tom Cousineau	15.00
8	Carl Crennell	10.00
9	Dave Cutler	10.00
10	Peter Dalla Riva	15.00
11	Dave Fennell	5.00
12	Vince Ferragamo	25.00
13	Tom Forzani	10.00
14	Tony Gabriel	25.00
15	Gabriel Gregoire	5.00
16	Billy Hardee	5.00
17	Larry Highbaugh	10.00
18	Condredge Holloway	25.00
19	Mark Jackson	5.00
20	Billy Johnson (White Shoes)	25.00
21	Larry Key	5.00
22	Marc Lacelle	5.00
23	Ian Mofford	5.00
24	Gerry Organ	10.00
25	Tony Petruccio	5.00
26	Tony Proudfoot	10.00
27	Randy Rhino	15.00
28	Ian Santer	5.00
29	Jerry Tagge	15.00
30	Jim Washington	10.00
31	Tom Wilkinson	15.00

1954 Blue Ribbon Tea CFL

		NM
Complete Set (80):		9000.
Common Player:		100.00
1	Jack Jacobs	250.00
2	Neil Armstrong	150.00
3	Lorne Benson	100.00
4	Tom Casey	125.00
5	Vincent Drake	100.00
6	Tommy Ford	100.00
7	Bud Grant	500.00
8	Dick Huffman	125.00
9	Gerry James	150.00
10	Bud Korchak	100.00
11	Tom Lumsden	100.00
12	Steve Patrick	100.00
13	Keith Pearce	100.00
14	Jesse Thomas	100.00
15	Buddy Tinsley	125.00
16	Alan Scott Wiley	100.00
17	Winty Young	100.00
18	Joseph Zaleski	100.00
19	Ron Vaccher	100.00
20	John Gramling	100.00
21	Bob Simpson	150.00
22	Bruno Bitkowski	125.00
23	Kaye Vaughan	125.00
24	Don Carter	100.00
25	Gene Roberts	100.00
26	Howie Turner	100.00
27	Avatus Stone	100.00
28	Tom McHugh	100.00
29	Clyde Bennett	100.00
30	Bill Berezowski	100.00
31	Eddie Bevan	100.00
32	Dick Brown	100.00
33	Bernie Custis	125.00
34	Merle Hapes	125.00
35	Tip Logan	100.00
36	Vince Mazza	125.00
37	Pete Neumann	125.00
38	Vince Scott	125.00
39	Ralph Toohy	100.00
40	Frank Anderson	100.00
41	Bob Dean	100.00
42	Leon Manley	100.00
43	Bill Zock	125.00
44	Frank Morris	150.00
45	Jim Quondamatteo	100.00
46	Eagle Keys	150.00
47	Bernie Faloney	400.00
48	Jackie Parker	500.00
49	Ray Willsey	100.00
50	Mike King	100.00
51	Johnny Bright	300.00
52	Gene Brito	125.00
53	Stan Heath	125.00
54	Roy Jenson	100.00
55	Don Loney	100.00
56	Eddie Macon	100.00
57	Peter Maxwell-Muir	100.00
58	Tom Miner	100.00
59	Jim Prewett	100.00
60	Lowell Wagner	100.00
61	Red O'Quinn	125.00
62	Ray Poole	125.00
63	Jim Staton	100.00
64	Alex Webster	200.00
65	Al Dekdebruin	100.00
66	Ed Bradley	100.00
67	Tex Coulter	150.00
68	Sam Etcheverry	500.00
69	Larry Grigg	100.00
70	Tom Hugo	100.00
71	Chuck Hunsinger	100.00
72	Herb Trawick	125.00
73	Virgil Wagner	125.00
74	Phil Adrian	100.00
75	Bruce Coulter	100.00
76	Jim Miller	100.00
77	Jim Mitchener	100.00
78	Tom Moran	100.00
79	Doug McNichol	100.00
80	Joey Pal	100.00

1988 Bootlegger B.C. Lions

		MT
Complete Set (13):		15.00
Common Player:		1.00
1	Jamie Buis	1.00
2	Jan Carinci	1.00
3	Dwayne Derban	1.00
4	Roy Dewalt	3.00
5	Andre Francis	1.25
6	Rick Klassen	2.00
7	Kevin Konar	1.25
8	Scott Lecky	1.00
9	James Parker	3.00
10	John Ulmer	1.00
11	Peter VandenBos	1.00
12	Todd Wiseman	1.00
13	NNO Title Card (Corporate Sponsors)	1.25

1971 Chevron B.C. Lions

		NM
Complete Set (50):		225.00
Common Player:		3.00
Common SP:		12.00
1	George Anderson	3.00
2	Josh Ashton	4.00
3	Ross Boice (SP)	12.00
4	Paul Brothers	3.00
5	Tom Cassese	3.00
6	Roy Cavallin	3.00
7	Rusty Clark (SP)	12.00
8	Owen Dejanovich (CO)	3.00
9	Dave Denny	3.00
10	Brian Donnelly	3.00
11	Steve Duich (SP)	12.00
12	Jim Duke	3.00
13	Dave Easley	3.00
14	Trevor Ekdahl	4.00

15	Jim Evenson	4.00
16	Greg Findlay	3.00
17	Ted Gerela	3.00
18	Dave Golinsky	3.00
19	Lefty Hendrickson	3.00
20	Lach Heron	3.00
21	Gerry Herron	3.00
22	Larry Highbaugh (SP)	12.00
23	Wayne Holm	3.00
24	Bob Howes	3.00
25	Max Huber	3.00
26	Garrett Hunsperger	3.00
27	Lawrence James (SP)	12.00
28	Brian Kelsey (SP)	12.00
29	Eagle Keys (CO)	4.00
30	Mike Leveille	3.00
31	John Love	3.00
32	Ray Lychak	3.00
33	Dick Lyons (SP)	12.00
34	Wayne Matherne	3.00
35	Ken McCullough (CO)	3.00
36	Don Moorhead	3.00
37	Peter Palmer	3.00
38	Jackie Parker (GM)	12.00
39	Ken Phillips	3.00
40	Cliff Powell	3.00
41	Gary Robinson	3.00
42	Ken Sugarman	4.00
43	Bruce Taupier	3.00
44	Jim Tomlin (SP)	12.00
45	Bud Tynes (CO)	3.00
46	Carl Weathers (SP)	12.00
47	Jim White	3.00
48	Mike Wilson	3.00
49	Jim Young	8.00
50	Contest Card (For Chevron)	3.00

1971 Chiquita CFL All-Stars

		NM
Complete Set (13):		200.00
Common Pair:		15.00
1	Bill Baker, 2 Ken Sugarman	20.00
3	Wayne Giardino, 4 Peter Dalla Riva	20.00
5	Leon McQuay, 6 Jim Thorpe	25.00
7	George Reed, 8 Jerry Campbell	20.00
9	Tommy Joe Coffey, 10 Terry Evanshen	25.00
11	Jim Young, 12 Mark Kosmos	20.00
13	Ron Forwick, 14 Jack Abendschan	15.00
15	Don Jonas, 16 Al Marcellin	20.00
17	Joe Theismann, 18 Jim Corrigall (Toronto Argonauts)	50.00
19	Ed George, 20 Dick Dupuis	15.00
21	Ted Dushinski, 22 Bob Swift	15.00
23	John Lagrone, 24 Bill Danychuk	15.00
25	Garney Henley, 26 John Williams	20.00
NNO	Yellow Viewer	40.00

1961 CKNW B.C. Lions

		NM
Complete Set (30):		200.00
Common Player:		6.00
1	By Bailey	15.00
2	Nub Beamer	6.00
3	Bob Belak (Kings Drive-In)	6.00
4	Neil Beaumont	6.00
5	Bill Britton (Nestle's Quik)	6.00
6	Tom Brown (Kings Drive-In)	8.00
7	Mike Cacic	6.00
8	Jim Carphin	6.00
9	Bruce Claridge	6.00
10	Pat Claridge	6.00
11	Steve Cotter	6.00
12	Lonnie Dennis (Nestle's Quik)	6.00
13	Norm Fieldgate	8.00
14	Willie Fleming	18.00
15	George Grant	6.00
16	Sonny Homer (Nestle's Quik)	8.00
17	Bob Jeter	10.00
18	Dick Johnson	6.00
19	Earl Keeley	6.00
20	Vic Kristopatis	6.00
21	Gordie Mitchell	6.00
22	Rae Ross (Nestle's Quik)	6.00
23	Bob Schloredt	8.00
24	Gary Schwertfeger	6.00
25	Mel Semenko (Kings Drive-In)	6.00

26	Ed Sullivan	8.00
27	Barney Therrien (Nestle's Quik)	6.00
28	Ed Vereb	6.00
29	Don Vicic	6.00
30	Ron Watton	6.00

1962 CKNW B.C. Lions

		NM
Complete Set (32):		200.00
Common Player:		5.00
1	By Bailey	15.00
2	Nub Beamer	5.00
3	Neil Beaumont	5.00
4	Bob Belak	5.00
5	Walt Bilicki	5.00
6	Tom Brown (Shop-Easy)	8.00
7	Mark Burton (Shop-Easy)	8.00
8	Mike Cacic	5.00
9	Jim Carphin	5.00
10	Pat Claridge	5.00
11	Steve Cotter	5.00
12	Lonnie Dennis	5.00
13	Norm Fieldgate	8.00
14	Willie Fleming (Shop-Easy)	18.00
15	Dick Fouts	8.00
16	George Grant	5.00
17	Ian Hagemoen	5.00
18	Tommy Hinton	8.00
19	Sonny Homer	8.00
20	Joe Kapp	25.00
21	Earl Keeley	5.00
22	Vic Kristopatis (Shop-Easy)	5.00
23	Tom Larscheid	5.00
24	Mike Martin	5.00
25	Gordie Mitchell	5.00
26	Baz Nagle	5.00
27	Bob Schloredt	8.00
28	Gary Schwertfeger	5.00
29	Willie Taylor	8.00
30	Barney Therrien	5.00
31	Don Vicic	5.00
32	Tom Walker	5.00

1965 Coke Caps CFL

		NM
Complete Set (230):		600.00
Common Player:		3.00
1	Neal Beaumont	3.00
2	Tom Brown	6.00
3	Mack Burton	3.00
4	Mike Cacic	3.00
5	Pat Claridge	3.00
6	Steve Cotter	3.00
7	Norm Fieldgate	6.00
8	Greg Findlay	3.00
9	Willie Fleming	7.50
10	Dick Fouts	3.00
11	Tom Hinton	6.00
12	Sonny Homer	3.00
13	Joe Kapp	15.00
14	G. Kasapis	3.00
15	Peter Kempf	3.00
16	Bill Lasseter	3.00
17	Mike Martin	3.00
18	Ron Morris	3.00
19	Bill Munsey	3.00
20	Paul Seale	3.00
21	Steve Shafer	3.00
22	Ken Sugarman	3.00
23	Bob Swift	3.00
24	J. Williams	3.00
25	Ron Albright (UER) (misspelled Albright)	3.00
26	Lu Bain	3.00
27	Frank Budd	3.00
28	Lovell Coleman	4.00
29	Eagle Day	3.00
30	P. Dudley	3.00
31	Jim Furlong	3.00
32	George Hansen	3.00
33	Wayne Harris	9.00
34	Herman Harrison	6.00
35	Pat Holmes	3.00
36	Art Johnson	3.00
37	Jerry Keeling	6.00
38	Roger Kramer	4.00
39	Hal Krebs	3.00
40	Don Luzzi	6.00
41	Pete Manning	3.00
42	Dale Parsons	3.00
43	R. Payne	3.00
44	Larry Robinson	3.00
45	Gerry Shaw	3.00
46	Don Stephenson	3.00
47	Bob Taylor	3.00
48	Ted Woods	3.00
49	Jon Anabo	3.00
50	R. Ash	3.00
51	Jim Battle	3.00
52	Charlie Brown	3.00
53	Tommy Joe Coffey	6.00
54	Marcel Deleeuw	3.00
55	Al Ecuyer	3.00
56	Ron Forwick	3.00
57	Jim Higgins	3.00
58	H. Huth	3.00

59	R. Kerbow	3.00
60	Oscar Kruger	3.00
61	T. Machan	3.00
62	G. McKee	3.00
63	Bill Mitchell	3.00
64	Barry Mitchelson	3.00
65	Roger Nelson	6.00
66	Bill Redell	3.00
67	M. Rohliser	3.00
68	Howie Schumm	3.00
69	E.A. Sims	3.00
70	John Sklopan	3.00
71	Jim Stinnette	3.00
72	Barney Therrien	3.00
73	Jim Thomas	3.00
74	Neil Thomas	3.00
75	B. Tobin	3.00
76	Terry Wilson	3.00
77	Art Baker	3.00
78	John Barrow	6.00
79	Gene Ceppetelli	3.00
80	J. Cimba	3.00
81	Dick Cohee	3.00
82	Frank Cosentino	4.00
83	Johnny Counts	3.00
84	Stan Crisson	3.00
85	Tommy Grant	7.50
86	Garney Henley	7.50
87	H. Hoerster	3.00
88	Zeno Karcz	3.00
89	Ellison Kelly	7.50
90	Bob Krouse	3.00
91	Billy Ray Locklin	3.00
92	Chet Miksza	3.00
93	Angelo Mosca	15.00
94	Bronko Nagurski	7.50
95	Ted Page	3.00
96	Don Sutherin	6.00
97	Dave Viti	3.00
98	Dick Walton	3.00
99	Billy Wayte	3.00
100	Joe Zuger	3.00
101	Jim Andreotti	3.00
102	John Baker	4.00
103	G. Beretta	3.00
104	Bill Bewley	3.00
105	Garland Boyette	4.00
106	Doug Daigneault	3.00
107	George Dixon	7.50
108	D. Dolatri	3.00
109	Ted Elsby	3.00
110	Don Estes	3.00
111	Terry Evenshen	9.00
112	Clare Exelby	3.00
113	Larry Fairholm	4.00
114	Bernie Faloney	15.00
115	Don Fuell	3.00
116	M. Gibbons	3.00
117	Ralph Goldston	3.00
118	Al Irwin	3.00
119	John Kenerson	3.00
120	Ed Learn	3.00
121	Moe Levesque	3.00
122	Bob Minihane	3.00
123	Jim Reynolds	3.00
124	Billy Roy	3.00
125	L. Tominson	3.00
126	Ernie White	3.00
127	Rick Black	3.00
128	Mike Blum	3.00
129	Billy Joe Booth	3.00
130	Jim Cain	3.00
131	Bill Cline	3.00
132	Merv Collins	3.00
133	Jim Conroy	3.00
134	Larry DeGraw	3.00
135	Jim Dillard	3.00
136	Gene Gaines	6.00
137	Don Gilbert	3.00
138	Russ Jackson	15.00
139	Ken Lehmann	3.00
140	Bob O'Billovich	3.00
141	John Pentecost	3.00
142	Joe Poirier	3.00
143	Moe Racine	3.00
144	Sam Scoccia	3.00
145	Bo Scott	7.50
146	Jerry Selinger	3.00
147	Marshall Shirk	3.00
148	Bill Siekierski	3.00
149	Ron Stewart	7.50
150	Whit Tucker	6.00
151	Ron Atchison	6.00
152	Al Benecick	3.00
153	Clyde Brock	3.00
154	Ed Buchanan	3.00
155	R. Cameron	3.00
156	Hugh Campbell	7.50
157	Henry Dorsch	3.00
158	Larry Dumelie	3.00
159	Garner Ekstran	3.00
160	Martin Fabi	3.00
161	Bob Good	3.00
162	Bob Kosid	3.00
163	Ron Lancaster	9.00
164	Hal Ledyard	3.00
165	Len Legault	3.00
166	Ron Meadmore	3.00
167	Bob Ptacek	3.00
168	George Reed	9.00
169	Dick Schnell	3.00
170	Wayne Shaw	3.00
171	Ted Urness	6.00
172	Dale West	3.00
173	Reg Whitehouse	3.00
174	Gene Wlasiuk	3.00
175	Jim Worden	3.00
176	Dick Aldridge	3.00

177	Walt Balasiuk	3.00
178	Ron Brewer	3.00
179	W. Dickey	3.00
180	B. Dugan	3.00
181	L. Ferguson	3.00
182	Don Fuell	3.00
183	Ed Harrington	3.00
184	Ron Howell	3.00
185	F. Laroue	3.00
186	Sherman Lewis	7.50
187	Marv Luster	3.00
188	Dave Mann	4.00
189	Pete Martin	3.00
190	Marty Martinello	3.00
191	Lamar McHan	6.00
192	Danny Nykoluk	3.00
193	Jackie Parker	20.00
194	Dave Pivec	3.00
195	Jim Rountree	3.00
196	Dick Shatto	7.50
197	Billy Shipp	3.00
198	Len Sparks	3.00
199	D. Still	3.00
200	Norm Stoneburgh	3.00
201	Dave Thelan	6.00
202	J. Vilanus	3.00
203	J. Walter	3.00
204	P. Watson	3.00
205	John Wydareny	3.00
206	Billy Cooper	3.00
207	Wayne Dennis	3.00
208	Paul Desjardins	3.00
209	N. Dunford	3.00
210	Farrell Funston	3.00
211	Herb Gray	7.50
212	Roger Hamelin	3.00
213	Barrie Hansen	3.00
214	Henry Janzen	3.00
215	Hal Ledyard	3.00
216	Leo Lewis	7.50
217	Brian Palmer	3.00
218	Art Perkins	3.00
219	Cornel Piper	3.00
220	Ernie Pitts	3.00
221	Kenny Ploen	7.50
222	Dave Raimey	4.00
223	Norm Rauhaus	3.00
224	Frank Rigney	6.00
225	Roger Savoie	3.00
226	Jackie Simpson	3.00
227	Dick Thornton	4.00
228	Sherwyn Thorson	3.00
229	Ed Elmer	3.00
230	Bill Whisler	3.00

1952 Crown Brand

		NM
Complete Set (48):		2000.
Common Player:		50.00
1	John Brown	50.00
2	Tom Casey	75.00
3	Tommy Ford	50.00
4	Ian Gibb	50.00
5	Dick Huffman	75.00
6	Jack Jacobs	100.00
7	Thomas Lumsden	50.00
8	George McPhail	50.00
9	Jim McPherson	50.00
10	Buddy Tinsley	75.00
11	Ron Vaccher	50.00
12	Al Wiley	50.00
13	Ken Charlton	75.00
14	Glenn Dobbs	75.00
15	Sully Glasser	50.00
16	Nelson Greene	50.00
17	Bert Iannone	50.00
18	Art McEwan	50.00
19	Jimmy McFaul	50.00
20	Bob Pelling	50.00
21	Chuck Radley	50.00
22	Martin Ruby	100.00
23	Jack Russell	50.00
24	Roy Wright	50.00
25	Paul Alford	50.00
26	Sugarfoot Anderson	50.00
27	Dick Bradley	50.00
28	Bob Bryant	50.00
29	Cliff Cyr	50.00
30	Cal Green	50.00
31	Stan Heath	50.00
32	Stan Kaluzniak	50.00
33	Guss Knickerhm	50.00
34	Paul Salata	50.00
35	Murry Sullivan	50.00
36	Dave West	50.00
37	Joe Aquirre	50.00
38	Claude Arnold	50.00
39	Bill Briggs	50.00
40	Mario DeMarco	50.00
41	Mike King	50.00
42	Donald Lord	50.00
43	Frank Morris	75.00
44	Gayle Pace	50.00
45	Rod Pantages	50.00
46	Rollin Prather	50.00
47	Chuck Quilter	50.00
48	Jim Quondamatteo	50.00

1993 Dream Cards Winnipeg Bombers

		MT
Complete Set (12):		6.00

Common Player:		.50
1	Matt Dunigan	2.00
2	Greg Battle	1.00
3	Nathaniel Bolton	.50
4	Stan Mikawos	.50
5	Miles Gorrell	.50
6	Troy Westwood	1.00
7	Michael Richardson	1.00
8	David Black	.50
9	Chris Walby	.75
10	David Williams	.75
11	Blaise Bryant	.75
12	Bob Cameron	.50

1981 Edmonton Journal Eskimos

		MT
Complete Set (16):		175.00
Common Player:		5.00
1	Dave Fennell	7.50
2	Brian Fryer	5.00
3	Jim Germany	6.00
4	Gary Hayes	5.00
5	Larry Highbaugh	10.00
6	Joe Hollimon	5.00
7	Ed Jones	5.00
8	Dan Kearns	5.00
9	Brian Kelly	15.00
10	Dan Kepley	10.00
11	Neil Lumsden	6.00
12	Warren Moon	75.00
13	James Parker	15.00
14	Tom Scott	10.00
15	Waddell Smith	5.00
16	Bill Stevenson	5.00

1984 Edmonton Journal Eskimos

		MT
Complete Set (13):		40.00
Common Player:		3.50
1	Leo Blanchard	3.50
2	Marco Cyncar	5.00
3	Blake Dermott	3.50
4	Brian Fryer	3.50
5	Joe Hollimon	3.50
6	James Hunter	3.50
7	Greg Marshall	5.00
8	Mike Nelson (CO)	3.50
9	Hector Pothier	3.50
10	Paul Rudzinski (ACO)	3.50
11	Bill Stevenson	5.00
12	Tom Towns	3.50
13	Eric Upton	3.50

1981 JOGO CFL B/W

		MT
Complete Set (51):		200.00
Common Player:		.50
1	Richard Crump	2.00
2	Tony Gabriel	7.50
3	Gerry Organ	1.00
4A	Greg Marshall	2.50
4B	J.C. Watts (SP)	40.00
5	Mike Raines	1.00
6	Larry Brune	1.00
7	Randy Rhino	2.50
8	Bruce Clark	4.00
9	Condredge Holloway	7.50
10	Dave Newman	1.00
11	Cedric Minter	1.00
12	Peter Muller	1.00
13	Vince Ferragamo	8.00
14	James Scott	2.00
15	Billy Johnson (White Shoes)	6.00
16	David Overstreet	6.00
17	Keith Gary	1.50
18	Tom Clements	15.00
19	Keith Baker	1.00
20	David Shaw	1.00
21	Ben Zambiasi	3.00
22	John Priestner	1.00
23	Warren Moon	100.00
24	Tom Wilkinson	3.00
25	Brian Kelly	3.00
26	Dan Kepley	2.00
27	Larry Highbaugh	2.50
28	David Boone	1.00
29	John Henry White	1.00
30	Joe Paopao	1.00
31	Larry Key	1.00
32	Glen Jackson	1.00
33	Joe Hollimon	1.00
34	Dieter Brock	6.00
35	Mike Holmes	1.00
36	William Miller	1.00
37	John Helton	3.00
38	Joe Poplawski	1.50
39	Joe Barnes	3.00
40	John Hufnagel	6.00
41	Bobby Thompson	1.00
42	Steve Stapler	1.00
43	Tom Cousineau	6.00
44	Bruce Threadgill	1.00
45	Ed McAleney	1.00
46	Leif Petterson	1.50

47	Paul Bennett	1.00
48	James Reed	1.00
49	Gerry Dattilio	1.50
50	Checklist Card	1.50

1982 JOGO Ottawa

		MT
Complete Set (24):		8.00
Common Player:		.40
1	Jordan Case	.50
2	Larry Brune	.50
3	Val Belcher	.40
4	Greg Marshall	.75
5	Mike Raines	.40
6	Rick Sowieta	.40
7	John Glassford	.40
8	Bruce Walker	.40
9	Jim Reid	.50
10	Kevin Powell	.40
11	Jim Piaskoski	.40
12	Kelvin Kirk	.40
13	Gerry Organ	.50
14	Carl Brazley	.75
15	William Mitchell	.40
16	Billy Hardee	.40
17	Jonathan Sutton	.40
18	Doug Seymour	.40
19	Pat Staub	.40
20	Larry Tittley	.40
21	Pat Stoqua	.40
22	Sam Platt	.40
23	Gary Dulin	.40
24	John Holland	.50

1982 JOGO Ottawa Past

		MT
Complete Set (16):		25.00
Common Player (1-12):		1.25
Common Player (13-16):		2.00
Common DP:		.75
1	Tony Gabriel	3.00
2	Whit Tucker (DP)	1.50
3	Dave Thelen	2.00
4	Ron Stewart (DP)	1.50
5	Russ Jackson	3.50
6	Kaye Vaughan	2.00
7	Bob Simpson	2.00
8	Ken Lehmann	1.50
9	Lou Bruce	1.25
10	Wayne Giardino (DP)	.75
11	Moe Racine	1.25
12	Gary Schreider	2.00
13	Don Sutherin	4.00
14	Mark Kosmos (DP)	1.25
15	Jim Foley (DP)	2.00
16	Jim Conroy	.75

1983 JOGO CFL Limited

		MT
Complete Set (110):		900.00
Common Player:		.50
1	Steve Ackroyd	4.00
2	Joe Barnes	12.00
3	Bob Bronk	4.00
4	Jan Carinci	4.00
5	Gordon Elser	4.00
6	Dan Ferrone	5.00
7	Terry Greer	12.00
8	Mike Hameluck	4.00
9	Condredge Holloway	15.00
10	Greg Holmes	4.00
11	Hank Llesic	10.00
12	John Malinosky	4.00
13	Cedric Minter	4.00
14	Don Moen	4.00
15	Rick Mohr	4.00
16	Darrell Nicholson	4.00
17	Paul Pearson	5.00
18	Matthew Teague	4.00
19	Geoff Townsend	4.00
20	Tom Trifaux	4.00
21	Darrell Wilson	4.00
22	Earl Wilson	4.00
23	Ricky Barden	4.00
24	Roger Cattelan	4.00
25	Michael Collymore	4.00
26	Charles Cornelius	4.00
27	Mariet Ford	4.00
28	Tyron Gray	5.00
29	Steve Harrison	4.00
30	Tim Hook	4.00
31	Greg Marshall	4.00
32	Ken Miller	4.00
33	Dave Newman	4.00
34	Rudy Phillips	4.00
35	Jim Reid	4.00
36	Junior Robinson	4.00
37	Mark Seale	4.00
38	Rick Sowieta	4.00
39	Pat Stoqua	4.00
40	Skip Walker	10.00
41	Al Washington	4.00
42	J.C. Watts	50.00
43	Keith Baker	4.00
44	Dieter Brock	35.00
45	Rocky DiPietro	20.00

No.	Player	Price
46	Howard Fields	4.00
47	Ron Johnson	6.00
48	John Priestner	4.00
49	Johnny Shepherd	4.00
50	Mike Walker	6.00
51	Ben Zambiasi	12.00
52	Nick Arakgi	5.00
53	Brian DeRoo	4.00
54	Denny Ferdinand	4.00
55	Willie Hampton	4.00
56	Kevin Starkey	4.00
57	Glen Weir	4.00
58	Larry Crawford	4.00
59	Tyrone Crews	4.00
60	James Curry	10.00
61	Roy DeWalt	12.00
62	Mervyn Fernandez	50.00
63	Sammy Green	4.00
64	Glen Jackson	4.00
65	Glenn Leonhard	4.00
66	Nelson Martin	4.00
67	Joe Paopao	8.00
68	Lui Passaglia	10.00
69	Al Wilson	4.00
70	Nick Bastaja	4.00
71	Paul Bennett	4.00
72	John Bonk	4.00
73	Aaron Brown	4.00
74	Bob Cameron	4.00
75	Tom Clements	60.00
76	Rick House	5.00
77	John Hufnagel	15.00
78	Sean Kehoe	4.00
79	James Murphy	12.00
80	Tony Norman	4.00
81	Joe Poplawski	4.00
82	Willard Reaves	15.00
83	Bobby Thompson	4.00
84	Wylie Turner	4.00
85	Dave Fennell	6.00
86	Jim Germany	4.00
87	Larry Highbaugh	6.00
88	Joe Hollimon	4.00
89	Dan Kepley	10.00
90	Neil Lumsden	4.00
91	Warren Moon	500.00
92	James Parker	12.00
93	Dale Potter	4.00
94	Angelo Santucci	4.00
95	Tom Towns	4.00
96	Tom Tuinei	5.00
97	Danny Bass	12.00
98	Ray Crouse	4.00
99	Gerry Dattilio	7.50
100	Tom Forzani	4.00
101	Mike Levenseller	4.00
102	Mike McTague	5.00
103	Bernie Morrison	4.00
104	Darrell Toussaint	4.00
105	Chris DeFrance	4.00
106	Dwight Edwards	5.00
107	Vince Goldsmith	10.00
108	Homer Jordan	4.00
109	Mike Washington	4.00
110A	Darrell Moir (Set number on back)	12.00
110B	Darrell Moir (Without set number)	50.00

1983 JOGO Quarterbacks

		MT
Complete Set (9):		75.00
Common Player:		1.50
1	Dieter Brock	5.00
2	Tom Clements	7.50
3	Gerry Dattilio	1.50
4	Roy DeWalt	3.00
5	Johnny Evans	1.50
6	Condredge Holloway	4.00
7	John Hufnagel	4.00
8	Warren Moon	40.00
9	J.C. Watts	25.00

1984 JOGO CFL

		MT
Complete Set (160):		275.00
Complete Series 1 (110):		150.00
Complete Series 2 (50):		125.00
Common Player (1-110):		1.00
Common PLayer (111-160):		2.50
1	Mike Hameluck	1.50
2	Bob Bronk	1.00
3	Paul Pearson	1.00
4	Dan Ferrone	1.50
5	Paul Bennett	1.00
6	Joe Barnes	4.00
7	Condredge Holloway	6.00
8	Terry Greer	5.00
9	Vince Goldsmith	3.00
10	Darrell Wilson	1.00
11	Tom Trifaux	1.00
12	Kelvin Pruenster	1.00
13	Earl Wilson	1.00
14	Hank Llesic	2.50
15	Stephen Del Col	1.00
16	Lamont Meacham	1.00
17	Lester Brown	1.00
18	Rob Forbes	1.00
19	Darrell Nicholson	1.00
20	James Curry	2.50
21	Skip Walker	2.50
22	J.C. Watts	25.00
23	Kevin Powell	1.00
24	Dean Dorsey	2.00
25	Tyron Gray	2.50
26	Mike Hudson	1.50
27	Dan Rashovich	1.00
28	Rudy Phillips	1.50
29	Larry Tittley	1.00
30	Ricky Barden (UER) (Number missing)	1.00
31	Mark Seale	1.00
32	Prince McJunkins	1.50
33	Kevin Dalliday	1.00
34	Rick Sowieta	1.00
35	Roger Cattelan	1.00
36	Damir Dupin	1.00
37	Jack Williams	1.00
38	Dave Newman	1.00
39	Maurice Doyle	1.00
40	Tim Hook	1.00
41	Dieter Brock	12.00
42	Rufus Crawford	5.00
43	Steve Kearns	1.00
44	Ross Francis	1.00
45	Henry Waszczuk	1.00
46	Mark Streeter	1.00
47	Mike McIntyre	1.00
48	John Priestner	1.00
49	Paul Palma	1.00
50	Mike Walker	1.50
51	Mike Barker	1.00
52	Todd Brown	1.00
53	Andre Francis	2.00
54	Glenn Keeble	1.00
55	Turner Gill	10.00
56	Eugene Belliveau	1.00
57	Willie Hampton	1.00
58	Ken Ciancone	1.00
59	Preston Young	1.00
60	Stanley Washington	1.00
61	Denny Ferdinand	1.00
62	Steve Smith	1.00
63	Rick Klassen	1.50
64	Larry Crawford	1.50
65	John Henry White	1.00
66	Bernie Glier	1.00
67	Don Taylor	1.00
68	Roy DeWalt	3.00
69	Mervyn Fernandez	25.00
70	John Blain	1.00
71	James Parker	4.00
72	Henry Vereen	1.00
73	Gerald Roper	1.00
74	Jim Sandusky	12.00
75	John Pankratz	1.00
76	Tom Clements	10.00
77	Vernon Pahl	1.00
78	Trevor Kennerd	2.50
79	Stan Mikawos	1.00
80	Ken Hailey	1.00
81	James Murphy	4.00
82	Jeff Boyd	2.00
83	Bob Cameron	1.00
84	Jerome Erdman	1.00
85	Tyrone Jones	2.50
86	John Bonk	1.00
87	John Sturdivant	1.00
88	Dan Huclack	1.00
89	Tony Norman	1.00
90	Kevin Neiles	1.00
91	Dave Kirzinger	1.00
92	Kevin Molle	1.00
93	Jerry DeBrouolny	1.00
94	Larry Hogue	1.00
95	Ken Moore	1.00
96	Jerry Friesen	1.00
97	Mike McTague	1.50
98	Jason Riley	1.00
99	Roger Aldag	1.00
100	Dave Ridgway	4.00
101	Eric Upton	1.00
102	Laurent DesLauriers	1.00
103	Brian Fryer	1.00
104	Brian DeRoo	1.00
105	Neil Lumsden	1.00
106	Hector Pothier	1.00
107	Brian Kelly	12.00
108	Dan Kepley	3.00
109	Danny Bass	5.00
110	Nick Arakgi	1.50
111	Lyle Bauer	2.50
112	Al Washington	2.50
113	Michel Bourgeau	3.00
114	Keith Gooch	2.50
115	Sean Kehoe	2.50
116	Ken Clark	3.00
117	Orlando Flanagan	2.50
118	Greg Vavra	2.50
119	Mark Bragagnolo	2.50
120	Dave Cutler	7.50
121	Nick Hebeler	2.50
122	Harry Skipper	5.00
123	Frank Robinson	3.00
124	DeWayne Jett	3.00
125	Mark Young	2.50
126	Felix Wright	25.00
127	Bob Poley	2.50
128	Leo Ezerins	2.50
129	Johnny Shepherd	3.00
130	Jeff Inglis	2.50
131	Dwaine Wilson	2.50
132	Aaron Hill	2.50
133	Brian Dudley	2.50
134	Ned Armour	2.50
135	Darryl Hall	2.50
136	Vince Phason	2.50
137	Terry Lymon	2.50
138	Jerry Dobrovolny	2.50
139	Richard Nemeth	2.50
140	Matt Dunigan	60.00
141	Rick Mohr	2.50
142	Lawrie Skolrood	2.50
143	Craig Ellis	6.00
144	Steve Johnson	2.50
145	Glen Suitor	3.00
146	Jeff Roberts	2.50
147	Greg Fieger	2.50
148	Sterling Hinds	2.50
149	Willard Reaves	9.00
150	John Pitts	2.50
151	Delbert Fowler	3.00
152	Mark Hopkins	2.50
153	Pat Cantner	2.50
154	Scott Flagel	3.00
155	Don Rose	2.50
156	David Shaw	2.50
157	Mark Moors	2.50
158	Chris Walby	5.00
159	Eugene Belliveau	2.50
160	Trevor Kennerd	10.00

1984 JOGO Ottawa Yesterday's Heroes

		MT
Complete Set (22):		75.00
Common Player:		3.50
1	Tony Gabriel	5.00
2	Whit Tucker	3.50
3	Dave Thelen	3.50
4	Ron Stewart	3.50
5	Russ Jackson	10.00
6	Kaye Vaughan	3.50
7	Bob Simpson	3.50
8	Ken Lehmann	3.50
9	Lou Bruce	3.50
10	Wayne Giardino	3.50
11	Moe Racine	3.50
12	Gary Schreider	3.50
13	Don Sutherin	5.00
14	Mark Kosmos	3.50
15	Jim Foley	3.50
16	Jim Conroy	3.50
17	George Brancato	5.00
18	Art Green	5.00
19	Rudy Sims	5.00
20	Jim Coode	5.00
21	Jerry Campbell	5.00
22	Jim Piaskoski	5.00

1985 JOGO CFL

		MT
Complete Set (110):		150.00
Common Player:		1.00
1	Mike Hameluck	1.50
2	Michel Bourgeau	1.50
3	Waymon Alridge	1.00
4	Daric Zeno	1.50
5	J.C. Watts	20.00
6	Kevin Gray	1.00
7	Steve Harrison	1.00
8	Ralph Dixon	1.00
9	Jo Jo Heath	1.00
10	Rick Sowieta	1.00
11	Brad Fawcett	1.00
12	Lamont Meacham	1.00
13	Dean Dorsey	1.50
14	Bernard Quarles	1.00
15	Mike Caterbone	1.00
16	Bob Stephen	1.00
17	Nick Benjamin	1.50
18	Tim McCray	1.50
19	Chris Sigler	1.00
20	Tony Johns	1.00
21	Jason Riley	1.00
22	Ralph Scholz	1.00
23	Ken Hobart	2.50
24	Paul Bennett	1.00
25	Dan Ferrone	1.50
26	Jim Kalafat	1.00
27	William Mitchell	1.00
28	Denny Ferdinand	1.00
29	James Curry	2.50
30	Jeff Inglis	1.00
31	Bob Bronk	1.00
32	Dan Petschenig	1.00
33	Terry Greer	4.00
34	Condredge Holloway	5.00
35	Ian Beckstead	1.00
36	James Parker	3.00
37	Tim Cowan	1.50
38	Roy DeWalt	2.50
39	Mervyn Fernandez	15.00
40	Bernie Glier	1.00
41	Keyvan Jenkins	3.00
42	Melvin Byrd	2.00
43	Ron Robinson	2.00
44	Andre Jones	1.00
45	Jim Sandusky	6.00
46	Darnell Clash	2.50
47	Rick Klassen	1.00
48	Brian Kelly	6.00
49	Rick House	1.50
50	Stewart Hill	3.00
51	Chris Woods	3.00
52	Darryl Hall	1.50
53	Laurent DesLauriers	1.00
54	Larry Cowan	1.00
55	Matt Dunigan	15.00
56	Andre Francis	1.50
57	Roy Kurtz	1.00
58	Steve Raquet	1.00
59	Turner Gill	5.00
60	Sandy Armstrong	1.00
61	Nick Arakgi	1.50
62	Mike McTague	1.50
63	Aaron Hill	1.00
64	Brett Williams	2.00
65	Trevor Bowles	1.50
66	Mark Hopkins	1.00
67	Frank Kosec	1.00
68	Ken Ciancone	1.00
69	Dwaine Wilson	1.00
70	Mark Stevens	1.00
71	George Voelk	1.00
72	Doug Scott	1.00
73	Rob Smith	1.00
74	Alan Reid	1.00
75	Rick Mohr	1.00
76	Dave Ridgway	3.50
77	Homer Jordan	1.00
78	Terry Leschuk	1.00
79	Rick Goltz	1.00
80	Neil Quilter	1.00
81	Joe Paopao	2.50
82	Stephen Jones	2.50
83	Scott Redl	2.50
84	Tony Dennis	1.00
85	Glen Suitor	1.50
86	Mike Anderson	1.00
87	Stewart Fraser	1.00
88	Fran McDermott	1.00
89	Craig Ellis	3.00
90	Eddie Ray Walker	2.00
91	Trevor Kennerd	3.00
92	Pat Cantner	1.00
93	Tom Clements	10.00
94	Glen Steele	1.00
95	Willard Reaves	4.00
96	Tony Norman	1.00
97	Tyrone Jones	2.50
98	Jerome Erdman	1.00
99	Sean Kehoe	1.00
100	Kevin Neiles	1.00
101	Ken Hailey	1.00
102	Scott Flagel	1.50
103	Mark Moors	1.00
104	Gerry McGrath	1.00
105	James Hood	1.00
106	Randy Ambrosie	1.00
107	Terry Irvin	1.00
108	Joe Barnes	3.00
109	Richard Nemeth	1.00
110	Darrell Patterson	1.00

1985 JOGO Ottawa Program Inserts

		MT
Complete Set (9):		50.00
Common Player:		5.00
1	1960 Grey Cup Team	5.00
2	Russ Jackson	12.00
3	Angelo Mosca	10.00
4	Joe Poirier	5.00
5	Sam Scoccia	5.00
6	Gilles Archambeault	5.00
7	Ron Lancaster	5.00
8	Tom Jones	5.00
9	Gerry Nesbitt	5.00

1986 JOGO CFL

		MT
Complete Set (169):		135.00
Common Series 1 (110):		75.00
Common Series 2 (59):		60.00
Common Player (1-110):		.75
Common Player (111-169):		.75
1	Ken Hobart	2.00
2	Tom Porras	1.25
3	Jason Riley	.75
4	Ron Ingram	.75
5	Steve Stapler	1.25
6	Mike Derks	.75
7	Grover Covington	5.00
8	Lance Shields	1.25
9	Mike Robinson	.75
10	Mark Napiorkowski	.75
11	Romel Andrews	.75
12	Ed Gatoveckas	.75
13	Tony Champion	5.00
14	Dale Sanderson	.75
15	Mark Barousse	.75
16	Nick Benjamin	1.25
17	Reginal Butts	.75
18	Tom Burgess	6.00
19	Todd Dillon	3.00
20	Jim Reid	1.25
21	Robert Reid	.75
22	Roger Cattelan	.75
23	Kevin Powell	.75
24	Randy Fabi	.75
25	Gerry Hornett	.75
26	Rick Sowieta	.75
27	Warren Hudson	1.25
28	Steven Cox	.75
29	Dean Dorsey	1.25
30	Michel Bourgeau	1.25
31	Ken Joiner	.75
32	Mark Seale	.75
33	Condredge Holloway	4.00
34	Bob Bronk	.75
35	Jeff Inglis	.75
36	Lance Chomyc	1.50
37	Craig Ellis	2.00
38	Marcellus Greene	.75
39	David Marshall	.75
40	Kerry Parker	.75
41	Darrell Wilson	.75
42	Walter Lewis	3.50
43	Sandy Armstrong	.75
44	Ken Ciancone	.75
45	Steve Raquet	.75
46	Lemont Jeffers	.75
47	Paul Gray	.75
48	Jacques Chapdelaine	.75
49	Rick Ryan	.75
50	Mark Hopkins	.75
51	Glenn Keeble	.75
52	Roy Kurtz	.75
53	Brian Dudley	.75
54	Mike Gray	.75
55	Tyrone Crews	.75
56	Roy DeWalt	2.50
57	Mervyn Fernandez	6.00
58	Bernie Glier	.75
59	James Parker	3.00
60	Bruce Barnett	.75
61	Keyvan Jenkins	1.50
62	Alan Wilson	.75
63	Delbert Fowler	1.25
64	James Jefferson	5.00
65	James West	7.50
66	Laurent DesLauriers	.75
67	Damon Allen	10.00
68	Roy Bennett	3.00
69	Hasson Arbubakrr	.75
70	Tom Clements	7.50
71	Trevor Kennerd	1.50
72	Perry Tuttle	3.50
73	Pat Cantner	.75
74	Mike Hameluck	.75
75	Rob Prodanovic	.75
76	James Bell	1.25
77	Hector Pothier	.75
78	Milson Jones	2.00
79	Craig Shaffer	.75
80	Chris Skinner	1.25
81	Matt Dunigan	7.50
82	Tom Dixon	.75
83	Brian Pillman	1.25
84	Randy Ambrosie	.75
85	Rick Johnson	3.50
86	Larry Hogue	.75
87	Garrett Doll	.75
88	Stu Laird	1.25
89	Greg Fieger	.75
90	Sean McKeown	.75
91	Rob Bresciani	.75
92	Harold Hallman	2.50
93	Jamie Harris	.75
94	Dan Rashovich	.75
95	David Conrad	.75
96	Glen Suitor	1.25
97	Mike Siroishka	.75
98	Michael McGruder	3.00
99	Brad Calip	.75
100	Mike Anderson	.75
101	Trent Bryant	.75
102	Gary Lewis	.75
103	Tony Dennis	.75
104	Paul Tripoli	.75
105	Daric Zeno	.75
106	Michael Elarms	.75
107	Donohue Grant	.75
108	Ray Elgaard	15.00
109	Joe Paopao	2.00
110	Dave Ridgway	2.50
111	Rudy Phillips	1.25
112	Carl Brazley	1.25
113	Andre Francis	.75
114	Mitchell Price	1.50
115	Wayne Lee	.75
116	Tim McCray	1.50
117	Scott Virkus	.75
118	Nick Hebeler	.75
119	Eddie Ray Walker	1.25
120	Bobby Johnson	.75
121	Mike McTague	.75
122	Jeff Inglis	.75
123	Joe Fuller	.75
124	Steve Crane	.75
125	Bill Henry	.75
126	Ron Brown	.75
127	Henry Taylor	.75
128	Greg Holmes	.75
129	Steve Harrison	.75
130	Paul Osbaldiston	3.00
131	Craig Walls	.75
132	Clorindo Grilli	.75
133	Marty Palazeti	.75
134	Darryl Hall	.75
135	David Black	.75
136	Bennie Thompson	2.50
137	Darryl Sampson	.75
138	James Murphy	2.50
139	Scott Flagel	.75
140	Trevor Kennerd	2.00
141	Bob Molle	.75
142	Darrell Patterson	.75
143	Stan Mikawos	.75
144	John Sturdivant	.75
145	Tyrone Jones	2.00
146	Jim Zorn	15.00
147	Steve Howlett	.75
148	Jeff Volpe	.75
149	Jerome Erdman	.75
150	Ned Armour	.75
151	Rick Klassen	1.25
152	Brett Williams	2.00
153	Richie Hall	.75
154	Ray Alexander	2.50
155	Willie Pless	5.00
156	Marion Jones	.75
157	Danny Bass	3.50
158	Frank Balkovec	.75
159	Less Browne	4.00
160	Paul Osbaldiston	1.50
161	Trevor Bowles	.75
162	David Daniels	.75
163	Kevin Konar	1.50
164	Gary Allen	2.00
165	Karlton Watson	.75
166	Ron Hopkins	1.25
167	Rob Smith	.75
168	Garrett Doll	.75
169	Rod Skillman	2.00

1987 JOGO CFL

		MT
Complete Set (110):		90.00
Common Player:		.60
1	Jim Reid	2.00
2	Nick Benjamin	1.00
3	Dean Dorsey	1.00
4	Hasson Arbubakrr	.60
5	Gerald Alphin	6.00
6	Larry Willis	3.00
7	Rick Wolkensperg	.60
8	Roy DeWalt	2.00
9	Michel Bourgeau	1.00
10	Anthony Woodson	.60
11	Marv Allemang	.60
12	Jerry Dobrovolny	.60
13	Larry Mohr	.60
14	Kyle Hall	.60
15	Irv Daymond	.60
16	Ken Ford	.60
17	Leo Groenewegen	.60
18	Michael Cline	.60
19	Gilbert Renfroe	3.00
20	Danny Barrett	6.00
21	Dan Petschenig	.60
22	Gill Fenerty (UER) (Misspelled Gil on card front)	10.00
23	Lance Chomyc	1.00
24	Jake Vaughan	.60
25	John Congemi	2.00
26	Kelvin Pruenster	.60
27	Mike Siroishka	.60
28	Dwight Edwards	1.00
29	Darnell Clash	1.50
30	Glenn Kulka	1.50
31	Jim Kardash	.60
32	Selwyn Drain	.60
33	Ian Sinclair	.60
34	Pat Cantner	.60
35	Trevor Kennerd	2.50
36	Bob Cameron	.60
37	Willard Reaves	3.00
38	Jeff Treftlin	.60
39	David Black	.60
40	Chris Walby	.60
41	Tom Clements	4.00
42	Mike Gray	.60
43	Bennie Thompson	1.50
44	Tyrone Jones	2.00
45	Ken Winey	.60
46	Nick Arakgi	1.00
47	James West	.60
48	Ken Pettway	.60
49	James Murphy	2.50
50	Carl Fodor	.60
51	Tom Muecke	2.00
52	Alvis Satele	.60
53	Grover Covington	2.00
54	Tom Porras	.60
55	Jason Riley	.60
56	Jed Tommy	.60
57	Bernie Ruoff	1.00
58	Ed Gatoveckas	.60
59	Wayne Lee	.60
60	Ken Hobart	1.50
61	Frank Robinson	.60
62	Mike Robinson	.60
63	Ben Zambiasi (UER) (No team listed on front of card)	2.00
64	Byron Williams	.60
65	Lance Shields	.60
66	Ralph Scholz	.60
67	Earl Winfield	5.00
68	Terry Lehne	.60
69	Alvin Bailey	.60
70	David Sauve	.60
71	Bernie Glier	.60
72	Nelson Martin	.60
73	Kevin Konar	.60
74	Greg Peterson	.60
75	Harold Hallman	1.50
76	Sandy Armstrong	.60
77	Glenn Harper	.60
78	Rick Worman	1.50
79	Darrell Toussaint	.60
80	Larry Hogue	.60
81	Rick Johnson	2.50

82	Richie Hall	.60
83	Stu Laird	1.00
84	Mike Emery	.60
85	Cliff Toney	.60
86	Matt Dunigan	6.00
87	Hector Pothier	.60
88	Stewart Hill	1.50
89	Stephen Jones	1.50
90	Dan Huclack	.60
91	Mark Napiorkowski	.60
92	Mike Derks	.60
93	Mike Walker	1.50
94	Michael McGruder	2.00
95	Terry Baker	3.00
96	Bobby Jurasin	4.00
97	James Curry	2.50
98	Tracey Mack	.60
99	Tom Burgess	3.50
100	Steve Crane	.60
101	Glen Suitor	1.00
102	Walter Bender	.60
103	Jeff Bentrim	2.00
104	Eric Florence	.60
105	Terry Cochrane	.60
106	Tony Dennis	.60
107	Dave Albright	.60
108	David Sidoo	.60
109	Harry Skipper	1.00
110	Dave Ridgway	2.00

1988 JOGO CFL

Complete Set (110): MT 110.00
Common Player: .60

1	Roy DeWalt	2.00
2	Jim Reid	1.25
3	Patrick Wayne	.60
4	Jerome Erdman	.60
5	Tom Dixon	.60
6	Brad Fawcett	.60
7	Tom Muecke	1.25
8	Mike Hudson	.60
9	Orville Lee	1.50
10	Michel Bourgeau	1.00
11	Dan Sellers	.60
12	Rob Pavan	.60
13	Rae Robirtis	.60
14	Rod Brown	.60
15	Ken Evraire	1.00
16	Irv Daymond	.60
17	Tim Jessie	1.00
18	Jim Sandusky	4.00
19	Blake Dermott	1.00
20	Brian Warren	.60
21	Mike Walker	3.00
22	Tom Porras	1.00
23	Less Browne	1.25
24	Paul Osbaldiston	1.00
25	Vernell Quinn	.60
26	Mike Derks	.60
27	Arnold Grevious	.60
28	Jim Lorenz	.60
29	Mike Robinson	.60
30	Doug Davies	.60
31	Earl Winfield	3.00
32	Wally Zatylny	2.00
33	Martin Sartin	.60
34	Lee Knight	.60
35	Jason Riley	.60
36	Darrell Gorbin	.60
37	Tony Champion	2.50
38	Steve Stapler	1.00
39	Scott Flagel	1.00
40	Grover Covington	1.50
41	Mark Napiorkowski	.60
42	Jacques Chapdelaine	.60
43	Lance Shields	1.00
44	Donohue Grant	.60
45	Henry Williams	25.00
46	Trevor Bowles	1.00
47	Don Wilson	.60
48	Tracy Ham	15.00
49	Richie Hall	1.00
50	Rob Bresciani	.60
51	James Curry	1.25
52	Kent Austin	15.00
53	Jeff Bentrim	1.00
54	Dave Ridgway	1.25
55	Terry Baker	.60
56	Lance Chomyc	1.00
57	Paul Sandor	.60
58	Kevin Cummings	.60
59	John Congemi	1.25
60	Gilbert Renfroe	1.50
61	Jake Vaughan	.60
62	Doran Major	.60
63	Dwight Edwards	1.00
64	Bruce Elliott	.60
65	Lorenzo Graham	.60
66	Jim Kardash	.60
67	Reggie Pleasant	1.50
68	Carl Brazley	1.00
69	Gill Fenerty	5.00
70	Selwyn Drain	.60
71	Warren Hudson	1.00
72	Willie Fears	.60
73	Randy Ambrosie	.60
74	George Ganas	.60
75	Glenn Kulka	1.00
76	Kelvin Pruenster	.60
77	Darrell Smith	1.50
78	Jearld Baylis	1.50
79	Blaine Schmidt	.60
80	Tony Visco	1.00
81	Carl Fodor	.60
82	Rudy Phillips	1.00
83	Craig Watson	1.00
84	Kent Warnock	1.00
85	Ken Ford	.60
86	Blake Marshall	2.00
87	Terry Cochrane	.60
88	Shawn Faulkner	.60
89	Marshall Toner	.60
90	Darren Yewshyn	.60
91	Eugene Belliveau	.60
92	Jay Christensen	.60
93	Anthony Parker	1.25
94	Walter Ballard	.60
95	Matt Dunigan	6.00
96	Andre Francis	1.00
97	Rickey Foggie	6.00
98	Delbert Fowler	.60
99	Michael Allen	.60
100	Greg Battle	6.00
101	Mike Gray	.60
102	Dan Wicklum	.60
103	Paul Shorten	.60
104	Paul Clatney	.60
105	Rod Hill	2.00
106	Steve Rodehutskors	.60
107	Sean Salisbury	4.00
108	Vernon Pahl	.60
109	Trevor Kennerd	1.00
110	David Williams	2.50

1988 JOGO CFL League

James Jefferson #20

Complete Set (106): MT 250.00
Common Player: 1.25

1	Walter Ballard	1.25
2	Jan Carinci	1.25
3	Larry Crawford	1.25
4	Tyrone Crews	1.25
5	Andre Francis	2.00
6	Bernie Glier	1.25
7	Keith Gooch	1.25
8	Kevin Konar	1.25
9	Scott Lecky	1.25
10	James Parker	3.00
11	Jim Sandusky (Traded)	10.00
12	Greg Stumon	1.25
13	Todd Wiseman (Not listed on checklist card)	1.25
14	Gary Allen	2.00
15	Scott Flagel (Traded)	3.00
16	Harold Hallman	1.25
17	Larry Hogue (UER) (Misspelled Hogue)	1.25
18	Ron Hopkins	1.25
19	Stu Laird	2.00
20	Andy McVey	1.25
21	Bernie Morrison	1.25
22	Tim Petros	1.25
23	Bob Poley	1.25
24	Tom Spoletini	1.25
25	Emmanuel Tolbert	4.00
26	Larry Willis	1.25
27	Damon Allen	4.00
28	Danny Bass	4.00
29	Stanley Blair	1.25
30	Marco Cyncar	1.25
31	Tracy Ham	25.00
32	Milson Jones	4.00
33	Stephen Jones	3.00
34	Jerry Kauric	3.00
35	Hector Pothier	1.25
36	Tom Richards	3.00
37	Chris Skinner	2.00
38	Henry Williams	40.00
39	Larry Wruck	1.25
40	Pat Brady	1.25
41	Grover Covington	3.00
42	Rocky DiPietro	4.00
43	Howard Fields	1.25
44	Miles Gorrell	1.25
45	Johnnie Jones	1.25
46	Tom Porras	2.00
47	Jason Riley	1.25
48	Dale Sanderson	1.25
49	Ralph Scholz	1.25
50	Lance Shields	2.00
51	Steve Stapler	1.25
52	Mike Walker	3.00
53	Gerald Alphin	4.00
54	Nick Arakgi (SP) (Retired before season)	20.00
55	Nick Benjamin	2.00
56	Tom Dixon	1.25
57	Leo Groenewegen	1.25
58	Will Lewis	2.00
59	Greg Marshall (Injured and retired)	5.00
60	Larry Mohr	1.25
61	Kevin Powell (Traded)	3.00
62	Jim Reid	2.00
63	Art Schlichter	8.00
64	Rick Wolkensperg	1.25
65	Anthony Woodson	1.25
66	Dave Albright	1.25
67	Roger Aldag	1.25
68	Mike Anderson	1.25
69	Kent Austin	25.00
70	Tom Burgess	6.00
71	James Curry	3.00
72	Ray Elgaard	4.00
73	Denny Ferdinand	1.25
74	Bobby Jurasin	6.00
75	Gary Lewis	1.25
76	Dave Ridgway	3.00
77	Harry Skipper	2.00
78	Glen Suitor	2.00
79	Ian Beckstead	1.25
80	Lance Chomyc	1.25
81	John Congemi	3.00
82	Gill Fenerty	8.00
83	Dan Ferrone	2.00
84	Warren Hudson	2.00
85	Hank Llesic	3.50
86	Jim Kardash	1.25
87	Glenn Kulka	2.00
88	Don Moen	1.25
89	Gilbert Renfroe	3.00
90	Chris Schultz	1.25
91	Darrell Smith	3.00
92	Lyle Bauer	1.25
93	Nick Bastaja	1.25
94	David Black	1.25
95	Bob Cameron	1.25
96	Randy Fabi	1.25
97	James Jefferson	6.00
98	Stan Mikawos	1.25
99	James Murphy	3.00
100	Ken Pettway	1.25
101	Willard Reaves (Signed with Redskins)	12.00
102	Darryl Sampson	1.25
103	Chris Walby	4.00
104	James West	5.00
105	Tom Clements (SP) (Retired before season)	20.00
106	Checklist Card SP	6.00

1989 JOGO CFL

Complete Set (160): MT 95.00
Complete Series 1 (110): 60.00
Complete Series 2 (50): 35.00
Common Player (1-160): .50

1	Mike Kerrigan	2.50
2	Ian Beckstead	.50
3	Lance Chomyc	.75
4	Gill Fenerty	3.50
5	Lee Morris	.50
6	Todd Wiseman	.50
7	John Congemi	.75
8	Harold Hallman	.75
9	Jim Kardash	.50
10	Kelvin Pruenster	.50
11	Blaine Schmidt	.50
12	Bruce Holmes	.50
13	Ed Berry	.50
14	Bobby McAllister	2.50
15	Frank Robinson	.75
16	Darrell Corbin	.50
17	Jason Riley	.50
18	Darrell Patterson	.50
19	Darrell Harle	.50
20	Mark Napiorkowski	.50
21	Derrick McAdoo	2.00
22	Sam Loucks	.50
23	Ronnie Glanton	.50
24	Lance Shields	.75
25	Tony Champion	2.00
26	Floyd Salazar	.50
27	Tony Visco	.75
28	Glenn Kulka	.75
29	Reggie Pleasant	.75
30	Rod Skillman	.50
31	Grover Covington	1.50
32	Gerald Alphin	2.00
33	Gerald Wilcox	.75
34	Daniel Hunter	.50
35	Tony Kimbrough	.75
36	Willie Fears	.75
37	Tyrone Thurman	4.00
38	Dean Dorsey	.75
39	Tom Schimmer	.50
40	Ken Evraire	.75
41	Steve Wiggins	.50
42	Donovan Wright	.50
43	Tuineau Alipate	.50
44	Richie Hall	.50
45	Rob Bresciani	.50
46	Tom Burgess	1.50
47	Jeff Fairholm	4.00
48	John Hoffman	.50
49	Dave Ridgway	1.25
50	Terry Baker	.75
51	Mike Hildebrand	.50
52	Danny Bass	2.50
53	Jeff Braswell	.50
54	Michel Bourgeau	.75
55	Ken Ford	.50
56	Enis Jackson	.50
57	Tony Hunter	1.25
58	Andre Francis	.75
59	Larry Wruck	.75
60	Pierre Vercheval	1.00
61	Keith Wright	.50
62	Andrew McConnell	.50
63	Gregg Stumon	.75
64	Steve Taylor	3.00
65	Brett Williams	.75
66	Tracy Ham	5.00
67	Stewart Hill	.75
68	Eugene Belliveau	.50
69	Tom Porras	.75
70	Jay Christensen	.50
71	Michael Soles	1.00
72	John Mandarich	1.25
73	Dan Wicklum	.50
74	Shawn Daniels	.50
75	Marshall Toner	.50
76	Kent Warnock	.75
77	Terrence Jones	4.00
78	Damon Allen	2.00
79	Kevin Konar	.75
80	Phillip Smith	.50
81	Marcus Thomas	.50
82	Jamie Taras	.50
83	Rob Moretto	.50
84	Eugene Mingo	.50
85	Matt Dunigan	5.00
86	Jan Carinci	.50
87	Anthony Parker	2.00
88	Keith Gooch	.50
89	Ron Howard	.50
90	David Williams	1.50
91	Less Browne	.75
92	Quency Williams	.50
93	Tim McCray	.75
94	Jeff Croonen	.50
95	Greg Battle	2.00
96	Moustafa Ali	.50
97	Michael Allen	.50
98	David Black	.50
99	Paul Randolph	.50
100	Trevor Kennerd	.75
101	Ken Pettway	.50
102	Sean Salisbury	2.50
103	Bob Cameron	.50
104	Tim Jessie	.75
105	Leon Hatzilioannou	.50
106	Matt Pearce	.50
107	Paul Clatney	.50
108	Randy Fabi	.50
109	Mike Gray	.50
110	James Murphy	2.00
111	Danny Barrett	1.50
112	Wally Zatylny	.75
113	Tony Truelove	.50
114	Leroy Blugh	.50
115	Reggie Taylor	1.50
116	Mark Zeno	2.50
117	Paul Wetmore	.50
118	Mark McLoughlin	.50
119	Randy Ambrosie	.50
120	Will Johnson	.75
121	Brock Smith	.50
122	Willie Gillus	.50
123	Andy McVey	.50
124	Wes Cooper	.50
125	Tyrone Pope	.50
126	Craig Ellis	1.50
127	Darrel Hopper	.50
128	Brad Fawcett	.50
129	Pat Miller	.50
130	Irv Daymond	.50
131	Bob Molle	.50
132	James Mills	3.00
133	Darrell Wallace	.75
134	Jerry Beasley	.50
135	Loyd Lewis	.50
136	Bernie Glier	.50
137	Eric Streater	2.00
138	Gerald Roper	.50
139	Brad Tierney	.50
140	Patrick Wayne	.50
141	Craig Watson	.50
142	Doug Landry	3.50
143	Orville Lee	1.50
144	Rocco Romano	.50
145	Todd Dillon	1.00
146	Michel Lamy	.50
147	Tony Cherry	3.50
148	Flint Fleming	.50
149	Kennard Martin	.50
150	Lorenzo Graham	.50
151	Junior Thurman	1.50
152	Darnell Graham	.50
153	Dan Ferrone	.75
154	Matt Finlay	.50
155	Brent Matich	.50
156	Kent Austin	5.00
157	Will Lewis	.50
158	Mike Walker	1.50
159	Tim Petros	.75
160	Stu Laird	1.50

1990 JOGO CFL

RICKEY FOOGIE

Complete Set (220): MT 60.00
Complete Series 1 (110): 30.00
Complete Series 2 (110): 30.00
Common Player: .25

1	1989 Grey Cup Champs (Saskatchewan)	1.00
2	Kent Austin	2.50
3	James Ellingson	.40
4	Vince Goldsmith	.40
5	Gary Lewis	.25
6	Bobby Jurasin	1.00
7	Tim McCray	.40
8	Chuck Klingbeil	1.50
9	Albert Brown	.25
10	Dave Ridgway	.75
11	Tony Rice	3.00
12	Richie Hall	.25
13	Jeff Fairholm	1.00
14	Ray Elgaard	1.25
15	Sonny Gordon	.25
16	Peter Giftopoulos	.75
17	Mike Kerrigan	1.00
18	Jason Riley	.25
19	Wally Zatylny	.40
20	Derrick McAdoo	.40
21	Dale Sanderson	.25
22	Paul Osbaldiston	.40
23	Todd Dillon	.40
24	Miles Gorrell	.25
25	Earl Winfield	.75
26	Bill Henry	.25
27	Darrell Harle	.25
28	Ernie Schramayr	.25
29	Greg Peterson	.25
30	Marshall Toner	.25
31	Danny Barrett	1.50
32	Mike Palumbo	.25
33	Ken Ford	.25
34	Brock Smith	.25
35	Tom Spoletini	.25
36	Will Johnson	.40
37	Terrence Jones	1.50
38	Darcy Kopp	.25
39	Tim Petros	.40
40	Mitchell Price	.40
41	Junior Thurman	1.00
42	Kent Warnock	.40
43	Darrell Smith	1.00
44	Chris Schultz (UER) (No team on back)	.25
45	Kelvin Pruenster	.25
46	Matt Dunigan	3.00
47	Lance Chomyc	.40
48	John Congemi	.75
49	Mike Clemons	10.00
50	Glenn Harper	.25
51	Branko Vincic	.25
52	Tom Porras	.40
53	Reggie Pleasant	.40
54	Randy Marriott	.25
55	James Parker	.75
56	Don Moen	.40
57	James West	1.00
58	Trevor Kennerd	.75
59	Warren Hudson	.40
60	Tom Burgess	1.50
61	David Black	.25
62	Matt Pearce	.25
63	Steve Rodehutskors	.25
64	Rod Hill	.40
65	Nick Benjamin	.40
66	Bob Cameron	.25
67	Leon Hatziioannou	.25
68	Robert Mimbs	2.50
69	Mike Gray	.25
70	Ken Winey	.25
71	Mike Hildebrand	.25
72	Brett Williams	.40
73	Tracy Ham	2.50
74	Danny Bass	.75
75	Mark Norman	.25
76	Andre Francis	.40
77	Todd Storme	.25
78	Henry Williams	5.00
79	Kevin Clark	.75
80	Enis Jackson	.25
81	Leroy Blugh	.25
82	Jeff Braswell	.40
83	Larry Wruck	.40
84A	Mike McLean (ERR) (Photo actually 24 Mike Hildebrand)	3.00
84B	Mike McLean (COR) (Two players shown)	5.00
85	Leo Groenewegen (UER) (Misspelled Groenewegan on card back)	.25
86	Mark Gastineau	1.50
87	Larry Clarkson	.25
88	Major Harris	2.50
89	Ray Alexander	.40
90	Joe Paopao	.40
91	Ian Sinclair	.40
92	Tony Visco (UER) (British Columbia on front, correct ly has team as Toronto on front)	.25
93	Lui Passaglia	.75
94	Doug Flutie	20.00
95	Glenn Kulka	.40
96	Bruce Holmes	.25
97	Stacey Dawsey	.25
98	Damon Allen	.75
99	Ken Evraire	.40
100	David Williams	.60
101	Gregg Stumon	.40
102	Scott Flagel	.40
103	Gerald Roper	.25
104	Tony Cherry	1.00
105	Jim Mills	.25
106	Dean Dorsey	.40
107	Patrick Wayne	.25
108	Reggie Barnes	2.00
109	Kari Yli-Renko	.25
110	Ken Hobart	.75
111	Doug Flutie	15.00
112	Grover Covington	.75
113	Michael Allen	.25
114	Mike Walker	.75
115	Danny McManus	4.00
116	Greg Battle	1.25
117	Quency Williams	.25
118	Jeff Croonen	.25
119	Paul Randolph	.25
120	Rick House	.40
121	Rob Smith	.40
122	Mark Napiorkowski	.25
123	Ed Berry	.25
124	Rob Crifo	.25
125	Gord Weber	.25
126	Jeff Boyd	.40
127	Paul McGowan	.40
128	Reggie Taylor	.75
129	Warren Jones	.25
130	Blake Marshall	.40
131	Darrell Corbin	.25
132	Jim Rockford	.25
133	Richard Nurse	.25
134	Bryan Illerbrun	.25
135	Mark Waterman	.25
136	Doug Landry	1.25
137	Ronnie Glanton	.25
138	Mark Guy	.40
139	Mike Anderson	.25
140	Remi Trudel	.25
141	Stephen Jones	1.00
142	Mike Derks	.25
143	Michel Bourgeau (Edmonton Oilers)	.40
144	Jeff Bentrim	.40
145	Roger Aldag	.40
146	Donald Narcisse	2.50
147	Troy Wilson	.25
148	Glen Suitor	.40
149	Stewart Hill	1.00
150	Chris Johnstone	.25
151	Mark Mathis	.25
152	Blaine Schmidt	.25
153	Craig Ellis	.75
154	John Mandarich	.25
155	Steve Zatylny	.25
156	Michel Lamy	.25
157	Irv Daymond	.40
158	Tom Porras	.40
159	Rick Worman	.40
160	Major Harris	1.50
161	Darryl Hall	.40
162	Terry Andrysiak	.40
163	Harold Hallman	.40
164	Carl Brazley	.25
165	Kevin Smellie	.40
166	Mark Campbell	.25
167	Andy McVey	.25
168	Derrick Crawford	.25
169	Howard Dell	.25
170	Dave Van Belleghem	.25
171	Don Wilson	.25
172	Robert Smith	.40
173	Keith Browner	.40
174	Chris Munford	.25
175	Gary Wilkerson	.25

176	Rickey Foggie (UER) (Misspelled Foogie on card front)	1.25
177	Robin Belanger	.25
178	Andrew Murray	.25
179	Paul Masotti	.40
180	Chris Gaines	.25
181	Joe Clausi	.25
182	Greg Harris	.25
183	David Bovell	.25
184	Eric Streater	.40
185	Larry Hogue	.25
186	Jan Carinci	.25
187	Floyd Salazar	.25
188	Alondra Johnson	.40
189	Jay Christensen (UER) (Misspelled Christenson on card fro nt)	.40
190	Rick Ryan	.25
191	Willie Pless	1.50
192	Walter Ballard	.25
193	Lee Knight	.25
194	Ray Macoritti	.40
195	Dan Payne	.25
196	Dan Sellers	.25
197	Rae Robirtis	.25
198	Dave Mossman	.25
199	Sam Loucks	.25
200	Derek MacCready	.25
201	Tony Cherry	.75
202	Ali Moustafa	.40
203	Terry Baker	.25
204	Matt Finlay	.25
205	Daniel Hunter	.25
206	Chris Major	2.00
207	Henry Smith	.25
208	David Sapunjis	4.00
209	Darrell Wallace	.40
210	Mark Singer	.25
211	Tuineau Alipate	.25
212	Tony Champion	1.25
213	Mike Lazecki	.25
214	Larry Clarkson	.25
215	Lorenzo Graham	.25
216	Tony Martino	.25
217	Ken Watson	.25
218	Paul Clatney	.25
219	Ken Pettway	.25
220	Tyrone Jones	1.00

1991 JOGO CFL

		MT
Complete Set (220):		6.00
Complete Series 1 (110):		3.00
Complete Series 2 (110):		3.00
Common Player:		.04
1	Tracy Ham	.35
2	Larry Wruck	.08
3	Pierre Vercheval	.04
4	Rod Connop	.04
5	Michel Bourgeau	.04
6	Leroy Blugh	.04
7	Mike Walker	.04
8	Ray Macoritti	.04
9	Michael Soles	.04
10	Brett Williams	.15
11	Blake Marshall	.15
12	David Williams	.08
13	Enis Jackson	.04
14	Craig Ellis	.15
15	Reggie Taylor	.15
16	Mike McLean	.04
17	Blake Dermott	.04
18	Henry Williams	.50
19	Jordan Gaertner	.04
20	Willie Pless	.15
21	Danny Bass	.15
22	Trevor Bowles	.04
23	Rob Davidson	.04
24	Mark Norman	.04
25	Ron Lancaster (CO)	.10
26	Chris Johnstone	.04
27	Randy Ambrosie	.04
28	Glenn Kulka	.04
29	Gerald Wilcox	.15
30	Kari Yli-Renko	.04
31	Daniel Hunter	.04
32	Bryan Illerbrun	.04
33	Terry Baker	.04
34	Jeff Braswell	.04
35	Andre Francis	.04
36	Irv Daymond	.04
37	Sean Foudy	.04
38	Brad Tierney	.04
39	Gregg Stumon	.04
40	Scott Flagel	.04
41	Gerald Roper	.04
42	Charles Wright	.04
43	Rob Smith	.04
44	James Ellingson	.04
45	Damon Allen	.08
46	John Congemi	.04
47	Reggie Barnes	.20
48	Stephen Jones	.15
49	Rob Prodanovic	.04
50	Steve Goldman	.04
51	Patrick Wayne	.04
52	David Conrad	.04
53	John Krupke	.04
54	Loyd Lewis	.04
55	Tony Cherry	.20
56	Terrence Jones	.25
57	Dan Wicklum	.04
58	Allen Pitts	.50
59	Junior Thurman	.04

60	Ron Hopkins	.04
61	Andy McVey	.04
62	Leo Blanchard	.04
63	Mark Singer	.04
64	Darryl Hall	.04
65	David McCrary	.04
66	Mark Guy	.04
67	Marshall Toner	.04
68	Derrick Crawford	.04
69	Danny Barrett	.20
70	Kent Warnock	.08
71	Brent Matich	.04
72	Mark McLoughlin	.04
73	Joe Clausi	.04
74	Wally Buono (CO)	.04
75	Will Johnson	.04
76	Walter Ballard	.04
77	Matt Finlay	.04
78	David Sapunjis	.35
79	Greg Peterson	.04
80	Paul Clatney	.04
81	Lloyd Fairbanks	.04
82	Herman Heard	.15
83	Richard Nurse	.04
84	Dave Richardson	.04
85	Ernie Schramayr	.04
86	Todd Dillon	.04
87	Tuineau Alipate	.04
88	Peter Giftopoulos	.04
89	Miles Gorrell	.04
90	Earl Winfield	.20
91	Paul Osbaldiston	.04
92	Dale Sanderson	.04
93	Jason Riley	.04
94	Ken Evraire	.04
95	Lee Knight	.04
96	Tim Lorenz	.04
97	Derrick McAdoo	.15
98	Bobby Dawson	.04
99	Rickey Royal	.04
100	Ronald Veal	.20
101	Grover Covington	.20
102	Mike Kerrigan	.20
103	Rocky DiPietro	.20
104	Mark Dennis	.04
105	Tony Champion	.20
106	Tony Visco	.04
107	Darrell Harle	.04
108	Wally Zatylny	.04
109	David Beckman (CO)	.04
110	Checklist 1-110	.04
111	Jeff Fairholm	.04
112	Roger Aldag	.04
113	Dave Albright	.04
114	Gary Lewis	.04
115	Dan Rashovich	.04
116	Lucius Floyd	.04
117	Bob Poley	.04
118	Donald Narcisse	.20
119	Bobby Jurasin	.15
120	Orville Lee	.15
121	Stacey Hairston	.04
122	Richie Hall	.04
123	John Gregory (CO)	.04
124	Rick Worman	.04
125	Dave Ridgway	.15
126	Wayne Drinkwater	.04
127	Eddie Lowe	.04
128	Mike Hogue	.04
129	Larry Hogue	.15
130	Milson Jones	.15
131	Ray Elgaard	.20
132	Dave Pitcher	.04
133	Vic Stevenson	.04
134	Albert Brown	.04
135	Mike Anderson	.04
136	Glen Suitor	.04
137	Kent Austin	.30
138	Mike Gray	.04
139	Steve Rodehutskors	.04
140	Eric Streater	.04
141	David Black	.15
142	James West	.15
143	Danny McManus	.30
144	Darryl Sampson	.04
145	Bob Cameron	.04
146	Tom Burgess	.35
147	Rick House	.04
148	Chris Walby	.15
149	Michael Allen	.04
150	Warren Hudson	.04
151	David Bovell	.04
152	Rob Crifo	.04
153	Lyle Bauer	.04
154	Trevor Kennerd	.20
155	Troy Johnson	.04
156	Less Browne	.04
157	Nick Benjamin	.04
158	Matt Pearce	.04
159	Tyrone Jones	.04
160	Rod Hill	.04
161	Bob Molle	.04
162	Lee Hull	.04
163	Greg Battle	.20
164	Robert Mimbs	.30
165	Giulio Caravatta	.04
166	James Mills	.15
167	Ian Sinclair	.04
168	Robin Belanger	.04
169	Deatrich Wise	.04
170	Chris Skinner	.04
171	Norman Jefferson	.04
172	Larry Clarkson	.04
173	Chris Major	.35
174	Stewart Hill	.04
175	Tony Hunter	.04
176	Stacey Dawsey	.04

177	Doug Flutie	1.00
178	Mike Trevathan	.04
179	Jearld Baylis	.04
180	Matt Clark	.25
181	Ken Pettway	.04
182	Lloyd Joseph	.04
183	Jon Volpe	1.00
184	Leo Groenewegen	.04
185	Carl Coulter	.04
186	O.J. Brigance	.35
187	Ryan Hanson	.04
188	Rocco Romano	.04
189	Ray Alexander	.04
190	Bob O'Billovich (CO)	.04
191	Paul Wetmore	.04
192	Harold Hallman	.04
193	Ed Berry	.04
194	Brian Warren	.04
195	Matt Dunigan	.40
196	Kelvin Pruenster	.04
197	Ian Beckstead	.04
198	Carl Brazley	.04
199	Trevor Kennerd	.15
200	Reggie Pleasant	.04
201	Kevin Smellie	.04
202	Don Moen	.04
203	Blaine Schmidt	.04
204	Chris Schultz	.04
205	Lance Chomyc	.04
206	Darrell Smith	.20
207	Dan Ferrone	.04
208	Chris Gaines	.04
209	Keith Castello	.04
210	Chris Munford	.04
211	Rodney Harding	.20
212	Darryl Ford	.04
213	Rickey Foggie	.20
214	Don Wilson	.04
215	Andrew Murray	.04
216	Jim Sandusky	.04
217	Mike Clemons	1.25
218	Bruce Elliott	.04
219	Mike McCarthy	.04
220	Checklist	.04

1991 JOGO CFL Stamp Card Inserts

		MT
Complete Set (3):		30.00
Common Player:		10.00
1	Albert H.G. Grey	10.00
2	Trevor Kennerd	10.00
NNO	Grey Cup Trophy (Grey Cup Winners listed on card back)	10.00

1992 JOGO CFL Promos

		MT
Complete Set (7):		12.00
Common Player:		.75
A1	Mike Clemons	2.00
A2	Jon Volpe	2.00
A3	Rocket Rat (Cartoon character)	.75
P1	Mike Clemons	3.00
P2	Jon Volpe	3.00
CC1	Ken Danby Art Coll. Classic Library	.75
CC2	Ken Danby Art Coll. Classic Library	.75

1992 JOGO CFL

	MT
Complete Set (220):	20.00

Common Player:		.05
1	David Bovell	.05
2	Don Moen	.10
3	Ian Beckstead	.05
4	David Williams	.05
5	Hank Ilesic	.05
6	Brian Warren	.05
7	Paul Massotti	.10
8	Kelvin Pruenster	.05
9	Mike Clemons	1.00
10	Chris Schultz	.10
11	Andrew Murray	.05
12	Lance Chomyc	.10
13	Ed Berry	.05
14	Harold Hallman	.10
15	Dave Van Bellegehem	.05
16	Rodney Harding	.10
17	Rickey Foggie	.20
18	Darrell Smith	.25
19	Bob Skemp	.05
20	Carl Brazley	.10
21	J.P. Izquierdo	.05
22	Mike Campbell	.10
23	Reggie Pleasant	.10
24	Dan Ferrone	.10
25	Kevin Smellie	.05
26	Don Wilson	.05
27	Adam Rita (CO)	.05
28	Greg Peterson	.05
29	David Sapunjis	.50
30	Srecko Zizakovic	.05
31	Carl Bland	.05
32	Errol Tucker	.05
33	Allen Pitts	.30
34	Pee Wee Smith	.30
35	Will Johnson	.30
36	Kent Warnock	.10
37	Brent Matich	.05
38	Stu Laird	.10
39	Shawn Beals	.05
40	Darcy Kopp	.05
41	Ken Moore	.05
42	Alondra Johnson	.10
43	Matt Finlay	.05
44	Andy McVey	.05
45	Paul Clatney	.05
46	Karl Anthony	.05
47	Bruce Covernton	.35
48	Mark McLoughlin (UER) (Name misspelled several times on t he card back)	.10
49	Pat Hinds	.05
50	Eric Mitchel (UER) (Misspelled Mitchell on both sides)	.20
51	Dan Wicklum	.05
52	Tim Cofield	.25
53	Steve Taylor	.35
54	Darryl Hall	.10
55	Angelo Snipes	.60
56	Shawn Daniels	.05
57	Terrence Jones	.25
58	Brian Bonner	.05
59	Kari Yli-Renko	.05
60	Denny Chronopoulos	.05
61	Damon Allen	.10
62	Reggie Barnes	.30
63	Andre Francis (UER) (Misspelled Frances on card front)	.05
64	Rob Smith	.25
65	Anthony Drawhorn	.20
66	David Conrad (UER) (Back text says team is Green Rider s)	.05
67	Irv Daymond	.05
68	Terry Baker	.10
69	Daniel Hunter	.05
70	Gord Weber	.05
71	Tom Burgess	.30
72	Charles Gordon	.05
73	Bobby Gordon	.05
74	Jock Climie	.25
75	Patrick Wayne	.05
76	Sean Foudy	.05
77	James Ellingson	.10
78	Gregg Stumon	.10
79	John Kropke	.10
80	Stephen Jones	.25
81	Ron Smeltzer	.05
82	Scott Campbell	.50
83	Henry Williams	1.00
84	Willie Pless	.25
85	Dan Murphy	.05
86	Chris Armstrong	.05
87	Tracy Ham	.50
88	Larry Wruck	.10
89	Rod Connop	.05
90	Jim Sandusky	.25
91	Randy Ambrosie	.05
92	Michel Bourgeau	.05
93	Bennie Goods (UER) (Misspelled Benny)	.10
94	Rob Davidson	.05
95	Leroy Blugh	.05
96	Brian Walling	.05
97	Michael Soles	.10
98	Craig Ellis	.25
99	Pierre Vercheval	.10
100	Matt Dunigan	.40

101	Enis Jackson	.05
102	Tom Muecke	.20
103	Jed Roberts	.05
104	Steve Krupey	.05
105	Blake Marshall	.35
106	Trevor Bowles	.10
107	Eddie Thomas	.05
108	Rocket Rat (Jogo Mascot)	.10
109	Checklist 1-110 (UER) (50 Eric Mitchell 93 Benny Goods)	.10
110	Tom Burgess	.35
111	Bob Cameron	.05
112	James West	.20
113	Chris Walby	.15
114	David Black	.10
115	Nick Benjamin	.10
116	Matt Pearce	.05
117	Bob Molle	.05
118	Rod Hill	.10
119	Kyle Hall	.05
120	Danny McManus	.35
121	Calvin Murphy	.15
122	Stan Mikawos	.05
123	Bobby Evans	.05
124	Larry Willis	.10
125	Eric Streater	.20
126	Perry Tuttle	.20
127	Leon Hatziioannou	.05
128	Sammy Garza	.05
129	Greg Battle	.25
130	Elfrid Payton	.25
131	Troy Westwood	.20
132	Mike Gray	.05
133	Dave Vankoughnett	.05
134	Paul Randolph	.05
135	Darryl Sampson	.05
136	Less Browne	.10
137	Quency Williams	.05
138	Robert Mimbs	.35
139	Matt Dunigan	1.50
140	Dan Rashovich	.05
141	Dan Farthing	.05
142	Bruce Boyko	.05
143	Kim McCloud	.05
144	Richie Hall	.05
145	Paul Vajda	.05
146	Willis Jacox	.25
147	Glen Scrivner	.05
148	Dave Ridgway	.15
149	Lucius Floyd	.10
150	James King	.05
151	Kent Austin	.50
152	Jeff Fairholm	.10
153	Roger Aldag	.05
154	Albert Brown	.05
155	Chris Gioskos	.05
156	Stacey Hairston	.05
157	Glen Suitor	.10
158	Milson Jones	.10
159	Vic Stevenson	.05
160	Bob Poley	.05
161	Bobby Jurasin	.20
162	Gary Lewis	.05
163	Donald Narcisse	.25
164	Mike Anderson	.05
165	Nick Mazzoli	.05
166	Lance Trumble	.05
167	Dale Sanderson	.05
168	Todd Wiseman	.05
169	Mark Dennis	.05
170	Peter Giftopoulos	.10
171	Ken Evraire	.05
172	Darrell Harle	.05
173	Terry Wright	.05
174	Jamie Morris	.20
175	Corris Ervin	.05
176	Don McPherson	.30
177	Jason Riley	.05
178	Tim Jackson	.05
179	Todd Dillon	.10
180	Lee Knight	.05
181	Scott Douglas	.05
182	Dave Richardson	.05
183	Wally Zatylny	.10
184	Rickey Martin	.05
185	John Motton	.30
186	Mark Waterman	.05
187	Ernie Schramayr	.05
188	Miles Gorrell	.05
189	Tony Champion	.25
190	Earl Winfield	.25
191	John Zajdel	.05
192	Danny Barrett	.30
193	Ian Sinclair	.10
194	Norman Jefferson	.10
195	Ryan Hanson	.05
196	Matt Clark	.15
197	Leo Groenewegen	.05
198	Ray Alexander	.10
199	James Mills	.20
200	Jon Volpe	.60
201	Doug Hocking	.05
202	Tony Kimbrough	.05
203	Lui Passaglia	.25
204	Bruce Holmes	.05
205	Jamie Taras	.05
206	Derek MacCready	.05
207	Jay Christensen	.05
208	O.J. Brigance	.30
209	Robin Belanger	.05
210	Stewart Hill	.05
211	Mike Marasco	.05
212	Mike Trevathan	.05
213	Chris Major	.25
214	Steve Rodehutskors	.10

215	Paul Wetmore	.05
216	Ken Pettway	.05
217	Darren Flutie	1.25
218	Giulio Caravatta	.05
219	Murray Pezim	.10
220	Checklist 111-220	.10

1992 JOGO CFL Missing Years

		MT
Complete Set (22):		20.00
Common Player:		1.00
1	Larry Smith	1.50
2	Mike Nelms	1.50
3	John Sciarra	2.00
4	Ed Chalupka	1.00
5	Mike Rae	1.50
6	Terry Metcalf (UER) (His CFL years were 78-80, not 78-9 0)	2.50
7	Chuck Ealey	5.00
8	Junior Ah-You	1.50
9	Mike Samples	1.00
10	Ray Nettles	1.00
11	Dickie Harris	3.00
12	Willie Burden	3.00
13	Johnny Rodgers	5.00
14	Anthony Davis	3.00
15	Joe Pisarcik (UER) (His CFL years were 74-76, not 74-7 5)	1.50
16	Jim Washington	1.00
17	Tom Scott (UER) (11 years in CFL, not 10)	1.50
18	Butch Norman	1.00
19	Steve Molnar	1.00
20	Jerry Tagge	2.50
21	Leon Bright (UER) (His CFL years were 77-80, not 77-9 9)	2.50
22	Waddell Smith	2.00

1992 JOGO CFL Stamp Cards

		MT
Complete Set (5):		30.00
Common Player:		6.00
1	CFL Hall of Fame Museum and Statue	6.00
2	Toronto Argonauts 1991 Grey Cup Champs	6.00
3	Tom Pate Memorial Trophy	6.00
4	Russ Jackson (MVP)	6.00
5	Oldest Trophy in The Hall of Fame (Montreal Football Challenge Cup)	6.00

Post-1980 cards in Near Mint condition will generally sell for about 75% of the quoted Mint value. Excellent-condition cards bring no more than 40%.

1993 JOGO CFL

Dong Flutie '93

	MT
Complete Set (220):	60.00
Complete Series 1 (110):	35.00
Complete Series 2 (110):	25.00
Common Player:	.20

1	Stephen Jones	.50
2	Chris Gioskos	.20
3	Treamelle Taylor	.20
4	Irv Daymond	.20
5	Gord Weber	.20
6	James Ellingson	.35
7	Lybrant Robinson	.20
8	Michael Allen	.75
9	Greg Stumon	.35
10	Darren Joseph	.35
11	Terry Baker	.35
12	Denis Chronopoulos	.20
13	Tom Burgess	1.00
14	Wayne Walker	.50
15	Brendan Rogers	.20
16	Matt Pearce	.20
17	Chris Tsangaras	.20
18	Leon Hatziioannou	.20
19	Bob Cameron	1.00
20	Don Smith	.20
21	Michael Richardson	1.00
22	Jayson Dzikowicz	.20
23	Matt Dunigan	2.00
24	Steve Grant	.20
25	Rob Crifo	.20
26	Dave Vankoughnett	.20
27	Paul Massotti	.35
28	Blaine Schmidt	.20
29	Dave Van Belleghem	.20
30	Hank Ilesic	.20
31	Reggie Pleasant	.35
32	Tracy Ham	1.00
33	Mike Clemons	2.00
34	Lance Chomyc	.35
35	Ken Benson	.20
36	Chris Green	.20
37	Mike Campbell	.35
38	Chris Schultz	.35
39	Reggie Rogers	.35
40	John Hood	.35
41	Dave Richardson	.20
42	Mike Jovanovich	.20
43	Joey Jauch	.35
44	Lubo Zizakovich	.20
45	Don McPherson	.35
46	Brett Williams	.50
47	Tod Wiseman	.20
48	Jim Jauch	.20
49	Erus Sanchez	.35
50	Scott Walker	.20
51	Roger Hennig	.20
52	Glen Suitor	.35
53	Bobby Jurasin	.35
54	Scott Hendrickson	.20
55	Venson Donelson	.20
56	Dan Rashovich	.20
57	Kent Austin	.75
58	Ray Elgaard	.35
59	Dave Ridgway	.50
60	Byron Williams	.20
61	Larry Ryckman (PRES)	.20
62	Karl Anthony	.20
63	Greg Knox	.20
64	Ken Moore	.20
65	Allen Pitts	.50
66	Matt Finlay	.35
67	Tony Martino	.20
68	Harold Hasselbach	1.00
69	David Sapunjis	1.00
70	Andy McVey	.20
71	Stu Laird	.35
72	Derrick Crawford	.20
73	Mark McLoughlin	.20
74A	Will Johnson (ERR) (Eskimo logo)	2.00
74B	Will Johnson (COR) (Stampeder logo)	.75
75	Don Wilson	.20
76	J.P. Izquierdo	.20
77	Henry Williams	1.25
78	Larry Wruck	.35
79	David Shelton	.35
80	Damion Lyons	.20
81	Jed Roberts	.20
82	Trent Brown	.20
83	Michel Bourgeau	.35
84	Blake Dermott	.35
85	Willie Pless	.50
86	Leroy Blugh	.20
87	Steve Krupey	.20
88	Jim Sandusky	.35
89	Danny Barrett	.50
90	James West	.50
91	Glen Scrivner	.20
92	Tyrone Jones	.35
93A	Jon Volpe (Photo has poor color)	2.00
93B	John Volpe (corrected)	.75
94	Less Browne	.35
95	Matt Clark	.35
96	Andre Francis	.35
97	Darren Flutie	1.25
98	Ray Alexander	.35
99	Rob Smith	1.00
100	Fred Anderson (Managing General Partner)	.35
101	Rob White	.20
102	Bobby Humphrey	.35
103	Willie Bouyer	.20
104	Titus Dixon	.35
105	John Wiley	.20
106	Kerwin Bell	1.00
107	Carl Parker	.20
108	Mike Oliphant	.75
109	David Archer	2.50
110	Freeman Baysinger	.35
111	Gerlad Alphin	.35
112	Gerald Wilcox	.35
113	Reggie Barnes	.50
114	Michel Raby	.20
115	Charles Wright	.20
116	Brett Young	.35
117	Charles Gordon	.20
118	Anthony Drawhorn	.35
119	Daved Benefield	.35
120	Patrick Burke	.20
121	Joe Sardo	.20
122	Dexter Manley	.35
123	Bruce Beaton	.20
124	Joe Fuller	.20
125	Michel Lamy	.20
126	Terrence Jones	.50
127	Jeff Croonen	.20
128	Leonard Johnson	.20
129	Dan Payne	.20
130	Carlton Lance	.20
131	Errol Brown	.20
132	Wayne Drinkwater	.20
133	Malvin Hunter	.20
134	Maurice Crum	.20
135	Brooks Findlay	.20
136	Ray Bernard	.20
137	Paul Osbaldiston	.35
138	Mark Dennis	.35
139	Glenn Kulka	.35
140	Lee Knight	.20
141	Mike O'Shea	1.00
142	Paul Bushey	.20
143	Nick Mazzoli	.20
144	Earl Winfield	.50
145	Gary Wilkerson	.20
146	Jason Riley	.20
147	Bob MacDonald	.35
148	Dale Sanderson	.20
149	Bobby Dawson	.20
150	Rod Connop	.20
151	Tony Woods	.35
152	Dan Murphy	.20
153	Mike DuMaresq	.20
154	Alan Boyko	.20
155	Vaughn Booker	.75
156	Elfrid Payton	.35
157	Mike Kerrigan	.50
158	Charles Anthony	.20
159	Brent Matich	.20
160	Craig Hendrickson	.20
161	Dave Pitcher	.20
162	Stewart Hill	.35
163	Terryl Ulmer	.20
164	Paul Cranmer	.20
165	Mike Saunders	1.50
166	Doug Flutie	2.00
167	Kelian Matthews	.20
168	Kip Texada	.20
169	Jonathan Wilson	.20
170	Bruce Dickson	.20
171	Mike Trevathan	.35
172	Vic Stevenson	.20
173	Keith Powe	.20
174	Eddie Taylor	.20
175	Tim Lorenz	.20
176	Sesan Millington	.35
177	Ryan Hanson	.20
178	Ed Berry	.20
179	Kent Warnock	.35
180	Spencer McLennan	.20
181	Brian Walling	.35
182	Danny McManus	.35
183	Donovan Wright	.20
184	Giulio Caravatta	.20
185	Derek MacCready	.20
186	Greg Eaglin	.20
187	Jim Mills	.20
188	Tom Europe	.20
189	Zock Allen	.20
190	Ian Sinclair	.35
191	O.J. Brigance	1.00
192	Steve Rodehutskors	.35
193	Lou Cafazzo	.20
194	Mark Dube	.20
195	Srecko Zizakovich	.20
196	Alondra Johnson	.35
197	Rocco Romano	.20
198	Raymond Biggs	.20
199	Frank Marof	.20
200	Brian Wiggins	.35
201	Marvin Pope	.20
202	Gerald Vaughn	.20
203	Todd Storme	.20
204	Blair Zerr	.20
205	Eric Johnson	.35
206	Mark Pearce	.20
207	Will Moore	2.00
208	Bruce Plummer	.20
209	Kari Yli-Renko	.20
210	Doug Parrish	.20
211	Warren Hudson	.20
212	Kevin Whitley	.20
213	Enis Jackson	.20
214	Wally Zatylny	.35
215	Bruce Elliott	.20
216	Harold Hallman	.35
217	Glenn Rogers	.20
218	Manny Hazard	.50
219	Robert Clark	.35
220	Doug Flutie (UER) (Three misspelled Tree on back)	2.00

1993 JOGO CFL Missing Years

	MT
Complete Set (22):	15.00
Common Player:	.60

1B	Jim Edwards	1.00
2B	Lou Harris	.75
3B	George Mira	1.25
4B	Fred Biletnikoff	3.50
5B	Randy Halsall	.60
6B	Don Sweet	.60
7B	Jim Coode	.60
8B	Steve Mazurak	.75
9B	Wayne Allison	.60
10B	Paul Williams	.60
11B	Eric Allen	1.25
12B	M.L. Harris	.75
13B	James Sykes	1.50
14B	Chuck Zapiec	.75
15B	George McGowan	.60
16B	Bob Macoritti	.75
17B	Chuck Walton	.60
18B	Willie Armstead	.75
19B	Rocky Long	.60
20B	Gene Mack	.60
21B	David Green	1.25
22B	Don Warrington	.75

1994 JOGO CFL Caravan

	MT
Complete Set (22):	40.00
Common Player:	1.00

1	Glenn Kulka	1.00
2	Jock Climie	2.00
3	Danny Barrett	3.00
4	Stephen Jones	2.00
5	Mike Clemons	4.00
6	Pierre Vercheval	1.50
7	Ken Evraire	1.50
8	Brett Williams (UER) (Misspelled Willians on card front)	1.50
9	Wally Zatylny	1.50
10	Mike O'Shea	2.50
11	Earl Winfield	2.00
12	Mike Oliphant	2.00
13	Matt Dunigan	4.00
14	Chris Walby	2.00
15	Tracy Ham	3.00
16	Darrell Smith	2.00
17	Glen Suitor	1.50
18	Mark McLoughlin	1.00
19	Bruce Covernton	1.50
20	Willie Pless	2.00
21	Henry Williams	4.00
22	Lui Passaglia	1.50

1994 JOGO CFL

	MT
Complete Set (310):	75.00
Complete Series 1 (110):	20.00
Complete Series 2 (110):	20.00
Complete Series 3 (90):	35.00
Common Player (1-110):	.15
Common Player (111-220):	.15
Common Player (221-310):	.30

1	Danny Barrett	.50
2	Remi Trudel	.15
3	Terry Baker	.15
4	Paul Clatney	.15
5	Michael Richardson	.75
6	John Kropke	.30
7	Glenn Kulka	.15
8	Daved Benefield	.30
9	Derek MacCready	.15
10	Jessie Small	.30
11	Chris Gioskos	.15
12	Gregg Stumon	.30
13	Lee Johnson	.30
14	Michael Jefferson Jr.	.15
15	Mario Perry	.15
16	Joe Mero	.15
17	Reggie Barnes	.30
18	Mike Stowell	.15
19	Tony Moss	.15
20	Antoine Worthman	.15
21	Joe Fuller	.15
22	Daniel Hunter	.15
23	Doug Flutie	2.50
24	Douglas Craft	.50
25	Lubo Zizakovic	.15
26	Srecko Zizakovic	.15
27	Stu Laird	.30
28	Brian Wiggins	.30
29	Will Johnson	.50
30	David Sapunjis	1.00
31	Rocco Romano	.15
32	Raymond Biggs	.15
33	Ken Moore	.15
34	Matt Finlay	.30
35	Ian Sinclair	.30
36	Glen Scrivner	.15
37	Less Browne	.30
38	Darren Flutie	1.00
39	Freeman Baysinger	.15
40	Kent Austin	.50
41	Donovan Wright	.15
42	Cory Philpot	1.50
43	Tom Europe	.15
44	Giulio Caravatta	.15
45	Mike Clemons	1.50
46	Leon Hatziioannou	.15
47	Blaine Schmidt	.15
48	Reggie Pleasant	.30
49	Paul Masotti	.30
50	Pierre Vercheval	.30
51	Duane Forde	.15
52	Jeff Fairholm	.30
53	Carl Coulter	.15
54	Bobby Gordon	.15
55	Mike Jovanovich	.15
56	Chris Johnstone	.15
57	Matt Pearce	.15
58	Bob Cameron	.75
59	Brett MacNeil	.15
60	Blaise Bryant	.40
61	Chris Tsangaris	.15
62	Dave Vankoughnett	.15
63	Gerald Alphin	.30
64	Alfred Jackson	.30
65	Jayson Dzikowicz	.15
66	Bobby Evans	.15
67	Dave Ridgway	.30
68	Bobby Jurasin	.30
69	Dan Payne	.15
70	Ray Elgaard	.50
71	Dan Farthing	.15
72	Glen Suitor	.30
73	Mike Saunders	1.00
74	Brent Matich	.15
75	Scott Hendrickson	.15
76	Dan Rashovich	.15
77	Wayne Drinkwater	.15
78	Larry Wruck	.30
79	J.P. Izquierdo	.15
80	Jed Roberts	.15
81	Michel Bourgeau	.30
82	Malvin Hunter	.15
83	Bruce Dickson	.15
84	Jim Sandusky	.50
85	Mike DuMaresq	.15
86	Tracy Gravely	.30
87	Tracy Ham	1.00
88	John Congemi	.30
89	Darrell Corbin	.15
90	Maurice Kelly	.30
91	Doug Flutie (MVP)	2.50
92	Alfred Jordan	.30
93	Curtis Mayfield	.40
94	David Hollis	.15
95	James Blake	.15
96	Anthony Blue	.30
97	Jeffrey Sawyer	.15
98	Al Whiting	.15
99	Brad LaCombe	.15
100	Wally Zatylny	.30
101	Bob Torrance	.15
102	Jeffery Fields	.15
103	John G. Motton Jr.	.30
104	Todd Wiseman	.15
105	Mike O'Shea	.75
106	Scott Douglas	.15
107	Dale Sanderson	.15
108	David Diaz-Infante	.30
109	Mike Kiselak	.15
110	Chris Thieneman	.15
111	Horace Brooks	.30
112	Andre Francis	.30
113	Nick Mazzoli	.15
114	Irv Daymond	.15
115	Alfred Smith	.30
116	Stephen Jones	.40
117	Bruce Beaton	.15
118	Corey Dowden	.15
119	Gerald Collins	.30
120	Joe Washington	.30
121	Irvin Smith	.15
122	Harold Nash Jr.	.30
123	Ray Savage Jr.	.15
124	Billy Scott	.15
125	Aaron Kanner	.15
126	Ben Williams	.40
127	Keith Browner	.30
128	Eros Sanchez	.30
129	Don Caparotti	.15
130	Earnest Fields	.15
131	O.J. Brigance	.75
132	Walter Wilson	.30
133	Allen Pitts	.50
134	Tony Stewart	.30
135	Marvin Pope	.15
136	Tony Martino	.15
137	Vince Danielsen	.15
138	Pee Wee Smith	.50
139	Bruce Covernton	.40
140	Greg Knox	.15
141	Gerald Vaughn	.15
142	Jay McNeil	.15
143	Larry Ryckman (OWN)	.15
144	Blair Zerr	.15
145	Danny McManus	.75
146	Jamie Taras	.15
147	Kelly Sims	.30
148	Denny Chronopoulos	.15
149	Enis Jackson	.15
150	Virgil Robertson	.15
151	Tyrone Chatman	.15
152	Brian Forde	.15
153	Andrew Stewart	.15
154	Ryan Hanson	.15
155	Francois Belanger	.15
156	Tony O'Billovich	.15
157	Erik White	.30
158	Kevin Whitley	.15
159	Chris Schultz	.30
160	Mike Campbell	.15
161	Wayne Lammie	.15
162	Keith Ballard	.15
163	Neil Fort	.15
164	Charles Anthony	.15
165	John Buddenberg	.15
166	Allan Boyko	.15
167	Paul Randolph	.15
168	Gerald Wilcox	.40
169	Brendan Rogers	.15
170	Kim Phillips	.15
171	David Williams	.30
172	James Pruitt	.30
173	Kevin O'Brien	.15
174	Tre Everett	.30
175	Hurlie Brown	.15
176	Malcolm Frank	.15
177	Sean Brantley	.15
178	Aaron Ruffin	.15
179	Anthony Drawhorn	.30
180	Larry Thompson	.75
181	Brooks Findlay	.15
182	Dallas Rysavy	.15
183	Ray Bernard	.15
184	Donald Narcisse	.75
185	Warren Jones	.30
186	Tom Gerhart	.15
187	David Robinson Jr.	.30
188	Damon Allen	.30
189	Henry Williams	1.00
190	Jay Christensen	.30
191	Trent Brown	.15
192	Rod Connop	.15
193	Michael Soles	.30
194	Vance Hammond	.15
195	Maurice Miller	.15
196	Shar Pourdanesh	.50
197	Elfrid Payton	.30
198	Ken Benson	.15
199	David Maeva	.15
200	Carlos Huerta	.30
201	Prince Wimbley III	.30
202	Anthony Calvillo	2.00
203	Kenny Wilhite	.30
204	Peter Shorts	.15
205	Willie Fears	.30
206	Rod Harris	.75
207	Terry Wright	.15
208	Stephen Bates	.30
209	John Hood	.30
210	Steven McKee	.15
211	Richard Nurse	.30
212	Lee Knight	.15
213	Joey Jauch	.30
214	Dave Richardson	.15
215	Paul Bushey	.15
216	Lou Cafazzo	.15
217	Don Odegard	.15
218	Mark Ledbetter	.15
219	Curtis Moore	.15
220	CFL Team Helmets (Set number card)	.30
221	Patrick Burke	.30
222	Dean Noel	.60
223	Leonard Johnson	.30
224	Darren Joseph	.60
225	Adam Rita (CO)	.30
226	Fred Ward	.60
227	Tony Bailey	.30
228	Frank Marof	.30
229	Andrew Thomas	.60
230	Peter Tuipulotu	.60
231	Shawn Beals	.30
232	Ken Watson	.30
233	Robert Holland	.30
234	John Terry	.30
235	Michael Philbrick	.30
236	Reggie Slack	1.25
237	Gary Wilkerson (UER) (First name misspelled Garry on bac k)	.30
238	Brett Young	.30
239	Eric Carter	.60
240	Sheldon Canley	.60
241	Lester Smith	.30
242	Donald Igwebuike	.60
243	Keith Ballard	.30
244	Roger Reinson	.30
245	Dwayne Dmytryshyn	.30
246	Marvin Coleman	.30
247	Ken Burress	.30
248	Jearld Baylis	.75
249	Rickey Foggie	.75
250	Dave Dinnall	.60
251	Darrell Harle	.30
252	Peter Martin	.60
253	Val St. Germain	.30
254	Tim Cofield	.75
255	Charles Gordon	.30
256	Keilly Rush	.30
257	James Pruitt	.60
258	Brian McCurdy	.60
259	Joe Johnson (UER) (Front says last name is Jackson)	.60
260	Joe Burgos	.30
261	Tim Jackson	.30
262	George Nimako	.60
263	Hency Charles	.30
264	Eric Drage	.60
265	Joe Sardo	.30
266	Norm Casola	.30
267	Dave Irwin	.60
268	Tommy Henry	.30
269	Taly Williams	.30
270	Swift Burch III	.30
271	Keita Crespina	.30
272	Michael Brooks	.60
273	Chris Armstrong	.30
274	Karl Anthony	.30
275	David Archer	3.00
276	Kevin Robson	.30
277	Jamie Holland	.60
278	Don Smith	.30
279	Norris Thomas	.60
280	Matt Dunigan	1.50
281	Greg Clarke	.30
282	Del Lyles	.30
283	Alan Wetmore	.30
284	Errol Brown	.30
285	Ryan Carey	.30
286	Rob Davidson	.30
287	Ed Kucy	.30
288	Tom Burgess	1.00
289	Peter Miller	.30
290	Dale Joseph	.30
291	Chris Burns	.30
292	Nathaniel Bolton	.60
293	Byron Williams	.15
294	David Harper	.30
295	Jason Wallace	.30
296	Greg Joelson	.15
297	Doug Parrish	.30
298	Sean Fleming	.30
299	Mike Lee	.60
300	Chris Morris	.60
301	Eddie Brown	.60
302	Blake Dermott	.30
303	Brian Walling	.60
304	Charles Miles	.60
305	Rob Crifo	.60
306	Nick Benjamin	.60
307	Jim Speros (PR/OWN)	.60
308	Robert Presbury	.30
309	Mike Pringle	2.50
310	Jon Volpe	1.00

1994 JOGO CFL Hall of Fame C

	MT
Complete Set (25):	18.00
Common Player:	.75

C1	Leo Lewis	2.00
C2	Tom Brown	.75
C3	Samuel Berger	.75
C4	David Fennell	1.25
C5	Arthur Chipman	.75
C6	Tony Gabriel	1.25
C7	Frank Clair	.75
C8	Dean Griffing	.75
C9	Hec Crighton	.75
C10	Eddie James	.75
C11	Andrew Currie	.75
C12	Ab Box	.75
C13	Gord Perry	.75
C14	Terry Evanshen	2.00
C15	Syd Halter	.75
C16	Don Luzzi	1.25
C17	Norm Kimball	.75
C18	Percival Molson	.75
C19	Bob Kramer	.75
C20	Angelo Mosca	2.50
C21	Ralph Cooper	.75
C22	Ken Charlton	.75
C23	Jim Young	1.25
C24	Joe Tubman	.75
C25	Virgil Wagner	1.25

1994 JOGO CFL Hall of Fame D

	MT
Complete Set (25):	18.00
Common Player:	.75

D1	Teddy Morris	.75
D2	John Ferraro	.75
D3	Len Back	.75
D4	Harold Ballard	1.25

D5	Seppi DuMoulin	.75
D6	Herman Harrison	1.25
D7	William Foulds	.75
D8	Peter Dalla Riva	1.25
D9	John Metras	.75
D10	Don Sutherin	1.25
D11	Ken Preston	.75
D12	Ellison Kelly	1.25
D13	Annis Stukus	.75
D14	Brian Timmis	.75
D15	Ralph Sazio	.75
D16	Hugh Stirling	.75
D17	Jimmie Simpson	.75
D18	Russ Rebholz	.75
D19	Seymour Wilson	.75
D20	Paul Rowe	.75
D21	Jeff Russel	.75
D22	Art Stevenson	.75
D23	Whit Tucker	1.25
D24	Dave Thelen	1.25
D25	Tom Wilkinson	2.00

1994 JOGO CFL Hall of Fame Inductees

		MT
Complete Set (5):		5.00
Common Player:		.75
1	Bill Baker	1.00
2	Tom Clements	2.50
3	Gene Gaines	1.00
4	Don McNaughton	.75
5	Title Card	.75

1994 JOGO CFL Missing Years

		MT
Complete Set (20):		12.00
Common Player:		.50
C1	Steve Ferrughelli (UER) (Photo actually John O'Leary)	1.50
C2	Rhome Nixon	.75
C3	Don Moorhead	.75
C4	Mike Widger	.75
C5	Pete Catan	.75
C6	Ron Meeks	.50
C7	Ezzret Anderson	1.25
C8	Bill Hatanaka	.50
C9	Joe Jackson	.75
C10	Tom Campana	.75
C11	Vernon Perry	1.00
C12	Ian Mofford	.75
C13	Walter Highsmith	.75
C14	Jake Dunlop	.75
C15	Bill Stevenson	.50
C16	Pete Lavorato	.50
C17	Cyril McFall	.50
C18	Maurice Butler	.50
C19	Tom Pate	1.25
C20	Eugene Clark	1.25

1995 JOGO CFL

		MT
Complete Set (399):		145.00
Complete Series 1 (110):		40.00
Complete Series 2 (110):		40.00
Complete Series 3 (110):		40.00
Complete Update Set (69):		25.00
Common Player:		.20
1	Doug Flutie	3.00
2	Lubo Zizakovic	.20
3	Srecko Zizakovic	.20
4	Greg Knox	.20
5	Kenny Walker	.35
6	Raymond Biggs	.20
7	Stu Laird	.35
8	Jeff Garcia	10.00
9	Alfred Jordan	.35
10	Tracy Gravely	.35
11	Tracy Ham	.75
12	O.J. Brigance	.75
13	Mike Pringle	1.50
14	Nick Subis	.20
15	Irvin Smith	.20
16	Shar Pourdanesh	.35
17	Lester Smith	.20
18	Josh Miller	.20
19	Jamie Taras	.20
20	Darren Flutie	1.00
21	Danny McManus	.75
22	Spencer McLennan	.20
23	Tony Collier	.20
24	Cory Philpot	1.00
25	Ian Sinclair	.35
26	Dave Chaytors	.20
27	Dave Ritchie (UER) (Richie on front)	.20
28	Rob Wallow	.20
29	Brad Breedlove	.50
30	Adrian Smith	.20
31	Stephen Bates	.20
32	Don Odegard	.20
33	Eric Nelson	.20
34	Danton Barto	.20
35	Donald Smith	.20
36	Gary Morris	.20
37	Mike Jovanovich	.20
38	Danny Barrett	.35
39	Ray Alexander	.35
40	John Kropke	.35
41	Remi Trudel	.20
42	Ray Bernard	.20
43	Pat Mahon	.20
44	Dan Murphy	.20
45	Stefen Reid	.20
46	Marcus Gates	.20
47	Tom Gerhard	.20
48	Mike Kiselak	.20
49	David Archer	2.00
50	Tommie Smith	.20
51	Roman Anderson	.20
52	Tony Burse	.20
53	Todd Jordan	.20
54	Peter Shorts	.20
55	Jimmy Klingler	.75
56	Mark Ledbetter	.20
57	Thomas Rayam	.20
58	Andre Strode	.20
59	Eddie Davis	.20
60	Jimmie Reed	.20
61	Fernando Thomas	.20
62	Craig Gibson	.20
63	Akaba Delaney	.20
64	Mike Clemons	1.25
65	Kent Austin	.75
66	Joe Burgos	.20
67	John Terry	.20
68	Don Wilson	.20
69	Eric Blount (DE)	.20
70	Reggie Barnes	.35
71	Darrick Branch	.20
72	P.J. Gleason	.20
73	Rod Connop	.20
74	J.P. Izquierdo	.20
75	Jed Roberts	.20
76	Jim Sandusky	.35
77	Chris Vargas	.20
78	Henry Williams	.75
79	Michael Soles	.35
80	Robert Holland	.20
81	Larry Wruck	.35
82	Dale Sanderson	.20
83	Anthony Calvillo	.75
84	Kalin Hall	.20
85	Sam Rogers	.20
86	Lee Knight	.20
87	Wally Zatylny	.35
88	Earl Winfield	.35
89	Dave Richardson	.20
90	Mike O'Shea	.75
91	Bruce Boyko	.20
92	Dave Ridgway	.35
93	Dave Van Belleghem	.20
94	Mike Anderson	.20
95	Ray Elgaard	.35
96	Dan Rashovich	.20
97	Wayne Drinkwalter	.20
98	Brent Match	.20
99	Joe Fuller	.20
100	Freeman Baysinger	.20
101	Billy Joe Tolliver	.75
102	Martin Patton	.20
103	Wayne Walker	.35
104	Bjorn Nittmo	.75
105	Alan Wetmore	.20
106	K.D. Williams	.20
107	Bob Cameron	.75
108	Ken Burress	.20
109	Chris Johnstone	.20
110	Allan Boyko	.20
111	David Sapunjis	1.25
112	Matt Finlay	.35
113	Jamie Crysdale	.20
114	Marvin Pope	.20
115	Craig Brenner	.20
116	Vince Danielsen	.20
117	Will Johnson	.35
118	Tony Stewart	.20
119	Chris Wright	.50
120	Grant Carter	.20
121	Karl Anthony	.20
122	Elfrid Payton	.35
123	Ken Watson	.20
124	Cory Mantyka	.20
125	Todd Furdyk	.20
126	Keithen McCant	.20
127	Ryan Hanson	.20
128	Glen Scrivner	.20
129	Mike Trevathan	.35
130	Tom Europe	.20
131	Giulio Caravatta	.20
132	Eddie Thomas	.20
133	Shelton Quarles	.20
134	Robert E. Davis II	.20
135	Damon Allen	.35
136	Derek Brown	.20
137	Joe Horn	.50
138	John Tweet Martin	.20
139	Greg Battle	.35
140	Ed Berry	.20
141	Irv Daymond	.20
142	Jay Christensen	.35
143	Michael Richardson	.50
144	James Ellingson	.35
145	Brett Young	.35
146	Kai Bjorn	.20
147	James Monroe	.20
148	Eric Geter	.20
149	Emanuel Martin	.20
150	DeWayne Knight	.20
151	Mike Saunders	1.00
152	David Harper	.20
153	Bobby Humphrey	.35
154	Charles Franks	.20
155	Jeffrey Sawyer	.20
156	John Buddenberg	.20
157	Willie Fears	.35
158	Jason Wallace	.20
159	Robert Gordon	.20
160	Scott Player	.35
161	York Kurinsky	.20
162	Stephen Anderson	.20
163	Shonte Peoples	.20
164	Angelo Snipes	.50
165	Ted Long	.20
166	Anthony Drawhorn	.35
167	Marvin Graves	.20
168	Joe Sardo	.20
169	Duane Forde	.20
170	P.J. Martin	.20
171	Jock Climie	.20
172	Jeff Fairholm	.35
173	Tommy Henry	.20
174	Paul Masotti	.35
175	Chris Green	.20
176	Bruce Dickson	.20
177	Darian Hagan	.20
178	Malvin Hunter	.20
179	Steve Krupey	.20
180	Sean Fleming	.20
181	Blake Dermott	.35
182	Leroy Blugh	.20
183	Steve Taylor	.50
184	Eric Carter	.35
185	Jessie Small	.35
186	Blaine Schmidt	.20
187	Lou Cafazzo	.20
188	Doug Davies	.20
189	Kelvin Means	.20
190	Derek R. Grier	.20
191	Darren Joseph	.35
192	Aaron Ruffin	.20
193	Dan Farthing	.20
194	Dan Payne	.20
195	Brooks Findlay	.20
196	Paul Vajda	.20
197	Ron Goetz	.20
198	Tim Broady	.20
199	Terryl Ulmer	.20
200	Harold Nash Jr.	.20
201	Mike Stowell	.20
202	Ben Williams	.20
203	Curtis Mayfield	.35
204	Reggie Rogers	.35
205	Donnell Johnson	.20
206	Jon Heidenreich	.20
207	Ronald Perry	.20
208	Robbie Keen	.20
209	Alex Mash Jr.	.20
210	Jason Mallett	.20
211	Miles Gorrell	.20
212	Juran Bolden	.75
213	Greg Clark	.20
214	Ryan Carey	.20
215	Del Lyles	.20
216	Brendan Rogers	.20
217	Kevin Robson	.20
218	Paul Randolph	.20
219	Shannon Garrett	.20
220	Charlie Clemons	.20
221	Matt Dunigan	1.50
222	Jay McNeil	.20
223	Denny Chronopoulos	.20
224	Bobby Pandelidis	.20
225	Bruce Beaton	.20
226	Mark Pearce	.20
227	Rocco Romano	.20
228	Alondra Johnson	.35
229	Tony Martino	.20
230	John James	.20
231	Courtney Griffin	.20
232	Robert Davis	.20
233	Manny Hazard	.35
234	Joe Mero	.20
235	Maurice Kelly	.35
236	Michael Morreale	.20
237	Reggie Slack	.50
238	Greg Eaglin	.20
239	Noah Cantor	.20
240	Shawn Daniels	.20
241	Charles Gordon	.20
242	Enis Jackson	.20
243	Matt Clark	.35
244	Dave Lucas	.20
245	Roger Hennig	.20
246	Leonard Nelson	.20
247	George Bethune	.20
248	Maurice Miller	.20
249	Kenny Walker	.35
250	Andre Ware	1.00
251	Jay Macias	.20
252	Mark Ricks	.20
253	Chris Tsangaris	.20
254	Wayne Lammie	.20
255	Derek MacCready	.20
256	Paul Yatkowski	.20
257	Horace Brooks	.35
258	Kerry Brown	.20
259	Jude St. John	.20
260	Mike Schad	1.00
261	Malcolm Frank	.20
262	Kenny Wilhite	.35
263	Bill Hess	.20
264	Grady Cavness	.35
265	Roosevelt Collins Jr.	.20
266	Darren Muilenberg	.20
267	Kitrick Taylor	.75
268	Chuck Esty	.20
269	Myron M. Wise	.20
270	James King	.20
271	Jim Kemp	1.00
272	Oscar Giles	.35
273	Dave Ritchie (CO)	.20
274	Joe Kralik	.20
275	Troy Mills	.20
276	Mark Stock	.20
277	Pierre Vercheval	.35
278	Terry Baker	.35
279	Scott Douglas	.20
280	Leon Hatziioannou	.20
281	Jeff Cummins	.20
282	Allen Pitts	.50
283	Ken Walcott	.20
284	Swift Burch III	.20
285	Charles Davis	.20
286	Leo Groenewegen	.20
287	Bennie Goods	.35
288	Craig Hendrickson	.20
289	John Kalin	.20
290	Trent Brown	.20
291	Marc Tobert	.20
292	Nick Mazzoli	.20
293	Singor Mobley	.20
294	Dondre Owens	.20
295	Kerwin Bell	.75
296	Mike Kerrigan	.50
297	Hassan Bailey	.20
298	Frank Marof	.20
299	Derrick McAdoo	.35
300	Brian McCurdy	.35
301	Larry Thompson	.50
302	Errol Brown	.20
303	Troy Alexander	.20
304	Dave Pitcher	.20
305	Joey Jauch	.35
306	Gene Makowsky	.20
307	Ventson Donelson	.20
308	Gary Rogers	.20
309	Carl Coulter	.20
310	Chris Gioskos	.20
311	Mike DuMaresq	.20
312	Rob Crifo	.20
313	Terry Smith	.20
314	Don Robinson	.20
315	Uzooma Okeke	.20
316	Eldonta Osborne	.20
317	Rob Hitchcock	.20
318	Ray Savage Jr.	.20
319	Terry Beauford	.20
320	Cliff Baskerville	.20
321	David Gamble	.20
322	Darrius Watson	.20
323	Tim Daniel	.20
324	Len Johnson	.20
325	Blaise Bryant	.35
326	Doug Hocking	.20
327	Sean Graham	.20
328	Jamie Holland	.35
329	Matt Pearce	.20
330	Doug Flutie (C.F.L. MVP)	2.00
331	Donald Narcisse	.50
332	Chuck Reed	.20
333	Sheldon Benoit	.20
334	John Motton	.35
335	Franco Grilla	.20
336	Brett MacNeil	.20
337	Wade Miller	.20
338	Steven McKee	.20
339	Brad Elberg	.20
340	Greg Patrick	.20
341	Andrew Grigg	.20
342	Kevin McDougal	.20
343	Prince Wimbley III	.35
344	Sam Hairston	.20
345	Curtis Gordon	.20
346	Chris Keneally	.20
347	Michael Philbrick	.20
348	Keith Embray	.20
349	Steve Grant	.20
350	Taly Williams	.20
351	Garry Sawatzky	.20
352	Dean Noel	.35
353	Mike Armstrong	.20
354	David Pool	.20
355	Tyrone Edwards	.20
356	Tim Cofield	1.00
357	Gerald Vaughn	.20
358	Mark McLoughlin	.20
359	Robert Dougherty	.20
360	Norm Casola	.20
361	Shawn Knight	.20
362	Kelvin Means	.20
363	Reggie Pleasant	.35
364	Jim Smyrl	.20
365	Fred Montgomery	.20
366	Ron Perry	.20
367	Jami Anderson	.20
368	Jeff Reinebold	.20
369	Steve Brannon	.20
370	Jimmy Cunningham	.50
371	Damion Lyons	.20
372	John Tweet Martin	.20
373	Mike Campbell	.20
374	Jonathan Wilson	.20
375	Sandy Annunziata	.20
376	Brian Walling	.20
377	Eric Blount (RB)	.50
378	Tom Gerhart	.20
379	Milt Stegall	.20
380	Bob Kronenberg	.20
381	Barry Rose	.20
382	Tim Walton	.20
383	Kelvin Harris	.20
384	Dwayne Provo	.20
385	Jayson Dzikowicz	.20
386	Melendez Byrd	.20
387	Val St. Germain	.20
388	Dave Vankoughnett	.20
389	Aaron Kanner	.20
390	Nicky Richards	.20
391	Rohan Marley	.50
392	Chris Burns	.20
393	Joe Fuller	.20
394	Donovan Gans	.20
395	Jermaine Chaney	.20
396	Jackie Kellogg	.20
397	Ray Savage Jr.	.20
398	Oscar Giles	.35
399	Jeff Neal	.20

1995 JOGO CFL Athletes in Action

		MT
Complete Set (21):		10.00
Common Player:		.40
1	Kelly Sims	.60
2	Craig Hendrickson	.40
3	Kerwin Bell	1.50
4	Glenn Harper	.40
5	Jim Sandusky	.40
6	Eldonta Osborne	.40
7	Guy Earle	.40
8	Charles Anthony	.40
9	O.J. Brigance	1.50
10	Junior Thurman	.60
11	Erik White	.60
12	Henry Newby	.40
13	Darryl Sampson	.40
14	Tony Woods	.40
15	Sean Brantley	.40
16	Shalon Baker	.40
17	Greg Frers	.40
18	Danny Barrett	.60
19	John Earle	.40
20	Tracy Ham	2.00
21	Jimmy Klingler	1.00

1995 JOGO CFL Missing Years

		MT
Complete Set (20):		12.00
Common Player:		.50
1D	Jimmy Jones	.75
2D	Charlie Brandon	.50
3D	Erik Kramer (UER) (name spelled Krammer)	3.00
4D	Jeff Avery	.50
5D	Wally Buono	.50
6D	Mike Strickland	.75
7D	Bob Toogood	.75
8D	Joe Hernandez	.50
9D	Doug Battershill	.50
10D	Al Brenner	.50
11D	Tim Anderson	.50
12D	Ted Provost	.50
13D	Eugene Goodlow	.75
14D	Rudy Florio	.50
15D	Joey Walters	.75
16D	Bob Viccars	.50
17D	Tyrone Walls	.50
18D	John Harvey	.75
19D	Dick Aldridge	.50
20D	Grady Cavness	.75

1996 JOGO CFL

This 220-card set features players from the Canadian Football League.

		MT
Complete Set (220):		50.00
Common Player:		.20
1	Jeff Garcia	.50
2	Jeff Cummins	.50
3	Terry Baker	.35
4	James Taras	.20
5	Eric Blount RB	.50
6	Dan Rashovich	.20
7	Dale Sanderson	.20
8	Paul Masotti	.35
9	Giulio Caravatta	.20
10	Stefen Reid	.20
11	Lee Knight	.20
12	Dave Vankoughnett	.20
13	Stu Laird	.35
14	Todd Storme	.20
15	Glenn Rogers Jr.	.20
16	Miles Gorrell	.20
17	Mike Kiselak	.20
18	Mike Trevathan	.50
19	Troy Westwood	.20
20	Michael Jovanovich	.20
21	Alan Wetmore	.20
22	Bruce Covernton	.35
23	Ryan Carey	.20
24	Larry Wruck	.20
25	Lou Cafazzo	.20
26	Mac Cody	1.00
27	Todd Furdyk	.20
28	Shannon Garrett	.20
29	Kenny Wilhite	.35
30	Bruce Beaton	.20
31	Tony Martino	.20
32	Brooks Findlay	.20
33	Matt Dunigan	1.00
34	Ed Kucy	.20
35	Mike Clemons	1.00
36	Cory Philpot	1.00
37	Steve Taylor	.50
38	Jackie Kellogg	.20
39	Spencer McLennan	.20
40	Jason Mallett	.20
41	Robert Mimbs	.75
42	Doug Davies	.20
43	Malvin Hunter	.20
44	Wayne Lammle	.20
45	David Maeva	.20
46	Jay McNeil	.20
47	Ed Berry	.20
48	Irvin Smith	.20
49	Wade Miller	.20
50	Dan Farthing	.20
51	Tom Gerhart	.20
52	Ray Bernard	.20
53	Jude St. John	.20
54	Terry Vaughn	.20
55	Shelton Quarles	.20
56	Kelvin Anderson	1.50
57	Mike Withycombe	.20
58	Sean Graham	.20
59	Errol Brown	.20
60	Swift Burch III	.20
61	Jed Roberts	.20
62	Ted Long	.20
63	Mike Morreale	.20
64	Tyrone Chatman	.20
65	Anthony McClanahan	.20
66	David Pitcher	.20
67	Shannon Baker	.20
68	Fred Childress	.20
69	John Terry	.20
70	Chris Morris	.50
71	Andrew Grigg	.20
72	Reggie Givens	.50
73	Cory Mantyka	.20
74	Alfred Jordan	.35
75	Harold Nash Jr.	.20
76	Brett MacNeil	.20
77	Brent Matich	.20
78	Gerry Collins	.20
79	Johnson Joseph	.20
80	Jimmy Cunningham	.50
81	Eddie Davis	.20
82	Tom Europe	.20
83	Darryl Hall	.35
84	Tracy Gravely	.20
85	Bob Cameron	.50
86	Paul McCallum	.20
87	Tyrone Williams	.20
88	Maurice Kelly	.35
89	Sammie Brennan	.20
90	Ken Benson	.20
91	Sean Millington	.20
92	Greg Knox	.20
93	Kevin Robson	.20
94	Rod Harris	.50
95	Charles Gordon	.20
96	Donald Smith	.20
97	Joe Mero	.20
98	Reggie Slack	.50
99	Garry Sawatzky	.20
100	Adrion Smith	.20
101	Allan Boyko	.20
102	Scott Hendrickson	.20
103	Eddie Britton	.20
104	Will Johnson	.50
105	John Raposo	.20
106	Chris Tsangaris	.20
107	Cooper Harris	.20
108	Quinn Magnuson	.20
109	Blaine Schmidt	.20
110	David Archer	2.00
111	David Sapunjis	.75
112	Stephen Anderson	.20
113	Raymond Biggs	.20
114	Jean-Agnes Charles	.20
115	Vince Danielsen	.20
116	Wayne Drinkwalter	.35
117	Farell Duclair	.20
118	Duane Forde	.20
119	Rohn Meyer	.20
120	Travis Moore	.20
121	Kevin Reid	.20
122	Roger Reinson	.20
123	Gonzalo Floyd	.20
124	Dwayne Provo	.20
125	Peter Tuipulotu	.20
126	Curtis Mayfield	.20
127	Ray Elgaard	.50
128	John James	.20
129	Dave Van Belleghem	.20
130	J.P. Izquierdo	.20
131	Darren Joseph	.35
132	Frank Jagas	.20
133	Heath Rylance	.20
134	Rick Walters	.20
135	Michael Philbrick	.20
136	Val St. Germain	.20
137	Justin Ring	.20
138	Mike Campbell	.20
139	Burt Thornton	.20
140	Jason Kaiser	.20
141	Tim Brown	.20
142	Ken Watson	.20
143	Tommie Frasier	2.50
144	Tyrone Rodgers	.20
145	Craig Hendrickson	.20
146	Johnny R. Scott	.20

147	Mark Pimiskern	.20
148	Frank Pimiskern	.20
149	Carl Coulter	.20
150	Reggie Carthon	.20
151	Ronald Williams	.20
152	Ted Alford	.20
153	Dave Chaytors	.20
154	Robert Gordon	.20
155	Jayson Dzikowicz	.20
156	Lubo Zizakovic	.20
157	Mike Hendricks	.20
158	Obie Spanic	.20
159	Andre Bolduc	.20
160	Robert Drummond	.50
161	Chuck Esty	.20
162	Tommy Henry	.20
163	Nick Richards	.20
164	Profail Grier	.20
165	Melvin Aldridge	.20
166	Uzooma Okeke	.20
167	Courtney Griffin	.20
168	Leonard Humphries	.20
169	Jason Wallace	.20
170	Derek MacCready	.20
171	Franky West	.20
172	Kelvin Means	.20
173	David Harper	.20
174	Rob Stevenson	.20
175	John Kalin	.20
176	Nigel Williams	.20
177	Chris Armstrong	.50
178	Douglas Craft	.50
179	Michael Soles	.35
180	Mike Saunders	1.00
181	Michel Lamy	.20
182	Jock Climie	.50
183	Grant Carter	.20
184	Hency Charles	.20
185	Jason Bryant	.20
186	Dexter Dawson	.20
187	Glen Scrivener	.20
188	K.D. Williams	.20
189	Dean Lytle	.20
190	Donovan Wright	.20
191	Andrew Henry	.20
192	Doug Flutie	3.50
193	Brendan Rogers	.20
194	Darian Hagan	.20
195	Jeff Fairholm	.35
196	Marcello Simmons	.35
197	Oscar Giles	.35
198	Chris Gioskos	.20
199	Dan Murphy	.20
200	Norm Casola	.20
201	Vic Stevenson	.20
202	Duane Dmytryshyn	.20
203	Christopher Perez	.20
204	Noah Cantor	.20
205	Mike Vanderjagt	.20
206	George Nimako	.35
207	Andrew Stewart	.20
208	Pierre Vercheval	.35
209	Chris Green	.20
210	Maurice Miller	.20
211	Leroy Blugh	.35
212	Jim Sandusky	.35
213	Thomas Rayam	.20
214	Cody Ledbetter	.20
215	Michael Sellers	.20
216	Reggie Pleasant	.50
217	Errol Martin	.20
218	Trent Brown	.20
219	Bruce Dickson	.20
220	Dan Payne	.20

1989 KFC Calgary

		MT
Complete Set (24):		10.00
Common Player:		.40
3	David McCrary	.40
4	Brent Matich	.40
8	Danny Barrett	1.50
9	Terrence Jones	1.25
12	Tim Petros	.60
13	Mark McLoughlin	.40
15	Ron Hopkins	.60
20	Chris Major	1.25
24	Greg Peterson	.40
25	Shawn Faulkner	.40
32	Darcy Kopp	.40
34	Andy McVey	.40
39	Doug (Tank) Landry	1.00
59	Leo Blanchard	.40
61	Tom Spoletini	.40
65	Mike Palumbo	.40
66	Dan Ferrone	.40
74	Mitchell Price	.60
76	Marshall Toner	.40
84	Eugene Belliveau	.60
85	Brock Smith	.40
89	Larry Willis	.75
93	Kent Warnock	.75
97	Ken Ford	.40

1990 KFC Calgary

		MT
Complete Set (24):		10.00
Common Player:		.50
1	Walter Ballard	.50
2	Danny Barrett	1.50
3	Eddie Brown	.75
4	Joe Clausi	.50
5	Lloyd Fairbanks	.75
6	Matt Finlay	.75
7	Ken Ford	.50
8	Ron Hopkins	.75
9	Keyvan Jenkins	1.25
10	Will Johnson	.75
11	Terrence Jones	1.25
12	David McCrary	.50
13	Mark McLoughlin	.50
14	Andy McVey	.50
15	Brent Matich	.50
16	Mike Palumbo	.50
17	Greg Peterson	.50
18	Tim Petros	.75
19	Mitchell Price	.75
20	Brock Smith	.50
21	Tom Spoletini	.50
22	Junior Thurman	1.25
23	Marshall Toner	.50
24	Kent Warnock	.75

1984 McDonald's Ottawa

		MT
Complete Set (4):		10.00
Common Player:		2.00
1	Ken Miller, Rudy Phillips, Jim Reid	2.00
2	Gary Dulin, Greg Marshall, Junior Robinson	2.00
3	Kevin Powell, Tyron Gray, Skip Walker	2.00
4	Rick Sowieta, Bruce Walker, J.C. Watts	5.00

1983 Mohawk B.C. Lions

		MT
Complete Set (24):		18.00
Common Player:		.60
1	John Blain	.60
2	Tim Cowan	.60
3	Larry Crawford	1.00
4	Tyrone Crews	.60
5	James Curry	1.00
6	Roy Dewalt	1.50
7	Mervyn Fernandez	3.00
8	Sammy Greene	.60
9	Jo Jo Heath	.60
10	Nick Hebeler	.60
11	Glen Jackson	.60
12	Tim Kearse	.60
13	Rick Klassen	1.00
14	Kevin Konar	1.00
15	Glenn Leonhard	.60
16	Nelson Martin	.60
17	Mack Moore	.60
18	John Pankratz	.60
19	Joe Paopao	1.25
20	Lui Passaglia	2.00
21	Don Taylor	.60
22	Mike Washburn	.60
23	John Henry White	.60
24	Al Wilson	.60

1984 Mohawk B.C. Lions

		MT
Complete Set (32):		18.00
Common Player:		.50
1	Ned Armour	.50
2	John Blain	.50
3	Melvin Byrd	.75
4	Darnell Clash	1.00
5	Tim Cowan	.50
6	Larry Crawford	.75
7	Tyrone Crews	.50
8	Roy DeWalt	1.50
9	Mervyn Fernandez	3.00
10	Bernie Glier	.50
11	Dennis Guevin	.50
12	Nick Hebeler	.50
13	Bryan Illerbrun	.50
14	Glen Jackson	.50
15	Andre Jones	.50
16	Rick Klassen	.75
17	Kevin Konar	.75
18	Glenn Leonhard	.50
19	Nelson Martin	.50
20	Billy McBride	.50
21	Mack Moore	.50
22	John Pankratz	.50
23	James Parker	1.25
24	Lui Passaglia	1.50
25	Ryan Potter	.50
26	Gerald Roper	.50
27	Jim Sandusky	2.00
28	Don Taylor	.50
29	John Henry White	.50
30	Al Wilson	.50
31	Team Card	.75
32	Checklist	.75

1985 Mohawk B.C. Lions

		MT
Complete Set (32):		18.00
Common Player:		.50
1	John Blain	.50
2	Jamie Buis	.50
3	Melvin Byrd	.75
4	Darnell Clash	1.00
5	Tim Cowan	.75
6	Tyrone Crews	.50
7	Mark DeBrueys	.50
8	Roy Dewalt	1.50
9	Mervyn Fernandez	3.00
10	Bernie Glier	.50
11	Keith Gooch	.50
12	Dennis Guevin	.50
13	Nick Hebeler	.50
14	Bryan Illerbrun	.50
15	Glen Jackson	.50
16	Keyvan Jenkins	1.00
17	Andre Jones	.50
18	Rick Klassen	.75
19	Kevin Konar	.75
20	Glenn Leonhard	.50
21	Nelson Martin	.50
22	John Pankratz	.50
23	James Parker	1.25
24	Lui Passaglia	1.50
25	Ryan Potter	.75
26	Ron Robinson	.75
27	Gerald Roper	.50
28	Jim Sandusky	2.00
29	John Henry White	.50
30	Al Wilson	.50
31	Team Photo	.75
32	Checklist	.75

1963 Nalley's Coins

		NM
Complete Set (160):		2750.
Common Player:		4.00
1	Jackie Parker	20.00
2	Dick Shatto	8.00
3	Dave Mann	5.00
4	Danny Nykoluk	4.00
5	Billy Shipp	4.00
6	Doug McNichol	4.00
7	Jim Rountree	4.00
8	Art Johnson	4.00
9	Walt Radzick	4.00
10	Jim Andreotti	4.00
11	Gerry Philip	20.00
12	Lynn Bottoms	20.00
13	Ron Morris (SP)	100.00
14	Nobby Wirkowski (CO)	20.00
15	John Wydareny	20.00
16	Gerry Wilson	20.00
17	Gerry Patrick (SP)	50.00
18	Aubrey Linne	20.00
19	Norm Stoneburgh	20.00
20	Ken Beck	20.00
21	Russ Jackson	15.00
22	Kaye Vaughan	8.00
23	Dave Thelen	8.00
24	Ron Stewart	8.00
25	Moe Racine	4.00
26	Jim Conroy	4.00
27	Joe Poirier	4.00
28	Mel Seminko	4.00
29	Whit Tucker	8.00
30	Ernie White	4.00
31	Frank Clair (CO)	20.00
32	Marv Bevan	20.00
33	Jerry Selinger	20.00
34	Jim Cain	20.00
35	Mike Snodgrass	20.00
36	Ted Smale	20.00
37	Billy Joe Booth	20.00
38	Len Chandler	20.00
39	Rick Black	20.00
40	Allen Schau	20.00
41	Bernie Faloney	15.00
42	Bobby Kuntz	4.00
43	Joe Zuger	4.00
44	Hal Patterson	12.00
45	Bronko Nagurski	10.00
46	Zeno Karcz	4.00
47	Hardiman Cureton	4.00
48	John Barrow	8.00
49	Tommy Grant	8.00
50	Garney Henley	8.00
51	Dick Easterly	20.00
52	Frank Cosentino	20.00
53	Geno DeNobile	20.00
54	Ralph Goldston	20.00
55	Chet Miksza	20.00
56	Bob Minihane	20.00
57	Don Sutherin	40.00
58	Ralph Sazio (CO)	20.00
59	Dave Viti (SP)	35.00
60	Angelo Mosca (SP)	100.00
61	Sandy Stephens	8.00
62	George Dixon	8.00
63	Don Clark	4.00
64	Don Paquette	4.00
65	Billy Wayte	4.00
66	Ed Nickla	4.00
67	Marv Luster	8.00
68	Joe Stracina	4.00
69	Bobby Jack Oliver	4.00
70	Ted Elsby	4.00
71	Jim Trimble (CO)	20.00
72	Bob Leblanc	20.00
73	Dick Schnell	20.00
74	Milt Crain	20.00
75	Dick Dalatri	20.00
76	Billy Roy	20.00
77	Dave Hoppmann	20.00
78	Billy Ray Locklin	20.00
79	Ed Learn (SP)	125.00
80	Meco Poliziani (SP)	40.00
81	Leo Lewis	8.00
82	Kenny Ploen	8.00
83	Steve Patrick	4.00
84	Farrell Funston	4.00
85	Charlie Shepard	4.00
86	Ronnie Latourelle	4.00
87	Gord Rowland	4.00
88	Frank Rigney	5.00
89	Cornel Piper	4.00
90	Ernie Pitts	4.00
91	Roger Hagberg	30.00
92	Herb Gray	50.00
93	Jack Delveaux	20.00
94	Roger Savoie	20.00
95	Nick Miller	20.00
96	Norm Rauhaus	20.00
97	Cec Luining	20.00
98	Hal Ledyard	20.00
99	Neil Thomas	20.00
100	Bud Grant (CO)	75.00
101	Eagle Keys (CO)	20.00
102	Mike Wicklum	8.00
103	Bill Mitchell	4.00
104	Mike Lashuk	4.00
105	Tommy Joe Coffey	8.00
106	Zeke Smith	4.00
107	Joe Hernandez	4.00
108	Johnny Bright	8.00
109	Don Getty	8.00
110	Nat Dye	4.00
111	James Earl Wright	20.00
112	Mike Volcan (SP)	35.00
113	Jon Rechner	20.00
114	Len Vella	20.00
115	Ted Frechette	20.00
116	Larry Fleisher	20.00
117	Oscar Kruger	20.00
118	Ken Peterson	20.00
119	Bobby Walden	30.00
120	Mickey Ording	20.00
121	Pete Manning	4.00
122	Harvey Wylie	8.00
123	Tony Pajaczkowski	8.00
124	Wayne Harris	10.00
125	Earl Lunsford	8.00
126	Don Luzzi	4.00
127	Ed Buckanan	4.00
128	Lovell Coleman	5.00
129	Hal Krebs	4.00
130	Eagle Day	8.00
131	Bobby Dobbs (CO)	20.00
132	George Hansen	20.00
133	Roy Jokanovich (SP)	75.00
134	Jerry Keeling	30.00
135	Larry Anderson	20.00
136	Bill Crawford	20.00
137	Ron Albright	20.00
138	Bill Britton	20.00
139	Jim Dillard	20.00
140	Jim Furlong	20.00
141	Dave Skrien (CO)	5.00
142	Willie Fleming	10.00
143	Nub Beamer	4.00
144	Norm Fieldgate	8.00
145	Joe Kapp	35.00
146	Tom Hinton	8.00
147	Pat Claridge	4.00
148	Bill Munsey	4.00
149	Mike Martin	4.00
150	Tom Brown	8.00
151	Ian Hagemoen	20.00
152	Jim Carphin	20.00
153	By Bailey	40.00
154	Steve Cotter	20.00
155	Mike Cacic	20.00
156	Neil Beaumont	20.00
157	Lonnie Dennis	20.00
158	Barney Therrien	20.00
159	Sonny Homer	20.00
160	Walt Bilicki	20.00
S1	Toronto Shield	50.00
S2	Ottawa Shield	50.00
S3	Hamilton Shield	50.00
S4	Montreal Shield	50.00
S5	Winnipeg Shield	50.00
S6	Edmonton Shield	50.00
S7	Calgary Shield	50.00
S8	British Columbia Shield	50.00

1964 Nalley's Coins

		NM
Complete Set (100):		720.00
Common Player:		4.00
1	Joe Kapp	30.00
2	Willie Fleming	10.00
3	Norm Fieldgate	4.00
4	Bill Murray	4.00
5	Tom Brown	10.00
6	Neil Beaumont	4.00
7	Sonny Homer	4.00
8	Lonnie Dennis	4.00
9	Dave Skrien	4.00
10	Dick Fouts (CO)	4.00
11	Paul Seale	4.00
12	Peter Kempf	4.00
13	Steve Shafer	4.00
14	Tom Hinton	8.00
15	Pat Claridge	4.00
16	By Bailey	8.00
17	Nub Beamer	5.00
18	Steve Cotter	4.00
19	Mike Cacic	4.00
20	Mike Martin	4.00
21	Eagle Day	12.00
22	Jim Dillard	4.00
23	Pete Murray	4.00
24	Tony Pajaczkowski	8.00
25	Don Luzzi	4.00
26	Wayne Harris	10.00
27	Harvey Wylie	4.00
28	Bill Crawford	4.00
29	Jim Furlong	4.00
30	Lovell Coleman	5.00
31	Pat Haines	4.00
32	Bob Taylor	4.00
33	Ernie Danjean	4.00
34	Jerry Keeling	8.00
35	Larry Robinson	4.00
36	George Hansen	4.00
37	Ron Albright	4.00
38	Larry Anderson	4.00
39	Bill Miller	4.00
40	Bill Britton	4.00
41	Lynn Amadee	8.00
42	Mike Lashuk	4.00
43	Tommy Joe Coffey	8.00
44	Junior Hawthorne	4.00
45	Nat Dye	4.00
46	Al Ecuyer	4.00
47	Howie Schumm	4.00
48	Zeke Smith	4.00
49	Mike Wicklum	4.00
50	Mike Volcan	4.00
51	E.A. Sims	4.00
52	Bill Mitchell	4.00
53	Ken Reed	4.00
54	Len Vella	4.00
55	Johnny Bright	8.00
56	Don Getty	8.00
57	Oscar Kruger	4.00
58	Ted Frechette	4.00
59	James Earl Wright	4.00
60	Roger Nelson	4.00
61	Ron Lancaster	10.00
62	Bill Clarke	4.00
63	Bob Shaw	4.00
64	Ray Purdin	4.00
65	Ron Atchison	8.00
66	Ted Urness	4.00
67	Bob Ptacek	4.00
68	Neil Habig	4.00
69	Garner Ekstran	4.00
70	Gene Wlasiuk	4.00
71	Jack Gotta	4.00
72	Dick Cohee	4.00
73	Ron Meadmore	4.00
74	Martin Fabi	4.00
75	Bob Good	4.00
76	Len Legault	4.00
77	Al Benecick	4.00
78	Dale West	4.00
79	Reg Whitehouse	4.00
80	George Reed	10.00
81	Kenny Ploen	8.00
82	Leo Lewis	10.00
83	Dick Thornton	5.00
84	Steve Patrick	4.00
85	Frank Rigney	5.00
86	Cornel Piper	4.00
87	Sherwyn Thorson	4.00
88	Ernie Pitts	4.00
89	Roger Hagberg	5.00
90	Bud Grant (CO)	50.00
91	Jack Delveaux	4.00
92	Farrell Funston	4.00
93	Ronnie Latourelle	4.00
94	Roger Hamelin	4.00
95	Gord Rowland	4.00
96	Herb Gray	10.00
97	Nick Miller	4.00
98	Norm Rauhaus	4.00
99	Bill Whisler	4.00
100	Hal Ledyard	4.00
S1	British Columbia Shield	45.00
S2	Calgary Shield	45.00
S3	Edmonton Shield	45.00
S4	Saskatchewan Shield	45.00
S5	Winnipeg Shield	45.00

1976 Nalley's Chips CFL

		NM
Complete Set (30):		300.00
Common Player:		8.00
1	Bill Baker	20.00
2	Eric Guthrie	8.00
3	Lou Harris	10.00
4	Layne McDowell	8.00
5	Ray Nettles	8.00
6	Lui Passaglia	25.00
7	John Sciarra	15.00
8	Wayne Smith	8.00
9	Michael Strickland	8.00
10	Jim Young	20.00
11	Dave Cutler	8.00
12	Larry Highbaugh	12.00
13	John Koniszewski	8.00
14	Bruce Lemmerman	8.00
15	George McGowan	12.00
16	Dale Potter	8.00
17	Charlie Turner	8.00
18	Tyrone Walls	8.00
19	Don Warrington	8.00
20	Tom Wilkinson	25.00
21	Willie Burden	35.00
22	Larry Cates	8.00
23	Lloyd Fairbanks	12.00
24	Joe Forzani	8.00
25	Tom Forzani	8.00
26	Rick Galbos	8.00
27	John Helton	15.00
28	Harold Holton	8.00
29	Rudy Linterman	12.00
30	Joe Pisarcik	15.00

1968 O-Pee-Chee CFL

		NM
Complete Set (132):		1100.
Common Player:		6.00
1	Roger Murphy	15.00
2	Charlie Parker	6.00
3	Mike Webster	6.00
4	Carroll Williams	6.00
5	Phil Brady	6.00
6	Dave Lewis	6.00
7	John Baker	6.00
8	Basil Bark	6.00
9	Donnie Davis	6.00
10	Pierre Desjardins	6.00
11	Larry Fairholm	6.00
12	Peter Paquette	6.00
13	Ray Lychak	6.00
14	Ted Collins	6.00
15	Margene Adkins	15.00
16	Ron Stewart	20.00
17	Russ Jackson	35.00
18	Bo Scott	15.00
19	Joe Poirier	6.00
20	Wayne Giardino	6.00
21	Gene Gaines	15.00
22	Billy Joe Booth	6.00
23	Whit Tucker	15.00
24	Rick Black	6.00
25	Ken Lehmann	12.00
26	Bob Brown	6.00
27	Moe Racine	6.00
28	Dick Thornton	6.00
29	Bob Taylor	6.00
30	Mel Profit	12.00
31	Dave Mann	8.00
32	Marv Luster	12.00
33	Ed Buchanan	6.00
34	Ed Harrington	8.00
35	Jim Dillard	6.00
36	Bob Taylor	6.00
37	Ron Arends	6.00
38	Mike Wadsworth	6.00
39	Wally Gabler	12.00
40	Pete Martin	6.00
41	Danny Nykoluk	6.00
42	Bill Frank	6.00
43	Gordon Christian	6.00
44	Tommy Joe Coffey	20.00
45	Ellison Kelly	6.00
46	Angelo Mosca	30.00
47	John Barrow	6.00
48	Bill Danychuk	12.00
49	Jon Hohman	6.00
50	Bill Redell	6.00
51	Joe Zuger	6.00
52	Willie Bethea	12.00
53	Dick Cohee	6.00
54	Tommy Grant	15.00
55	Garney Henley	20.00
56	Ted Page	6.00
57	Bob Krouse	6.00
58	Phil Minnick	6.00
59	Butch Pressley	6.00
60	Dave Raimey	8.00
61	Sherwyn Thorson	6.00
62	Bill Whisler	6.00
63	Roger Hamelin	6.00
64	Chuck Harrison	6.00
65	Ken Nielsen	12.00
66	Ernie Pitts	6.00
67	Mitch Zainasky	6.00
68	John Schneider	6.00
69	Ron Kirkland	6.00
70	Paul Desjardins	6.00
71	Luther Selbo	6.00
72	Don Gilbert	6.00
73	Bob Lueck	6.00
74	Gerry Shaw	6.00
75	Chuck Zickefoose	6.00
76	Frank Andruski	6.00
77	Lanny Boleski	6.00
78	Terry Evanshen	20.00
79	Jim Furlong	6.00
80	Wayne Harris	20.00
81	Jerry Keeling	15.00
82	Roger Kramer	8.00
83	Pete Liske	20.00
84	Dick Suderman	8.00
85	Granville Liggins	20.00
86	George Reed	30.00
87	Ron Lancaster	30.00
88	Alan Ford	6.00
89	Gordon Barwell	6.00
90	Wayne Shaw	6.00
91	Bruce Bennett	15.00
92	Henry Dorsch	6.00
93	Ken Reed	6.00

94	Ron Atchison	15.00
95	Clyde Brock	6.00
96	Alex Benecick	6.00
97	Ted Urness	12.00
98	Wally Dempsey	6.00
99	Don Gerhardt	6.00
100	Ted Dushinski	6.00
101	Ed McQuarters	12.00
102	Bob Kosid	6.00
103	Gary Brandt	6.00
104	John Wydareny	6.00
105	Jim Thomas	6.00
106	Art Perkins	6.00
107	Frank Cosentino	12.00
108	Earl Edwards	8.00
109	Garry Lefebvre	6.00
110	Greg Pipes	8.00
111	Ian MacLeod	6.00
112	Dick Dupuis	6.00
113	Ron Forwick	6.00
114	Jerry Griffin	6.00
115	John LaGrone	12.00
116	E.A. Sims	6.00
117	Greenard Poles	6.00
118	Leroy Sledge	6.00
119	Ken Sugarman	6.00
120	Jim Young	30.00
121	Garner Ekstran	12.00
122	Jim Evenson	12.00
123	Greg Findlay	6.00
124	Ted Gerela	8.00
125	Lach Heron	8.00
126	Mike Martin	6.00
127	Craig Murray	6.00
128	Pete Ohler	6.00
129	Sonny Homer	6.00
130	Bill Lasseter	6.00
131	John McDowell	6.00
132	Checklist Card	60.00

1968 O-Pee-Chee CFL Poster Inserts

		NM
Complete Set (16):		325.00
Common Player:		15.00
1	Margene Adkins	20.00
2	Tommy Joe Coffey	25.00
3	Frank Cosentino	18.00
4	Terry Evanshen	25.00
5	Larry Fairholm	15.00
6	Wally Gabler	15.00
7	Russ Jackson	35.00
8	Ron Lancaster	30.00
9	Pete Liske	25.00
10	Dave Mann	18.00
11	Ken Nielsen	18.00
12	Dave Raimey	18.00
13	George Reed	30.00
14	Carroll Williams	15.00
15	Jim Young	30.00
16	Joe Zuger	15.00

1970 O-Pee-Chee CFL

		NM
Complete Set (115):		300.00
Common Player:		2.00
1	Ed Harrington	5.00
2	Danny Nykoluk	2.00
3	Marv Luster	4.00
4	Dave Raimey	3.00
5	Bill Symons	3.00
6	Tom Wilkinson	20.00
7	Mike Wadsworth	2.00
8	Dick Thornton	3.00
9	Jim Tomlin	2.00
10	Mel Profit	2.00
11	Bob Taylor	4.00
12	Dave Mann	3.00
13	Tommy Joe Coffey	5.00
14	Angelo Mosca	15.00
15	Joe Zuger	3.00
16	Garney Henley	10.00
17	Mike Strofolino	2.00
18	Billy Ray Locklin	2.00
19	Ted Page	2.00
20	Bill Danychuk	3.00
21	Bob Krouse	2.00
22	John Reid	2.00
23	Dick Wesolowski	2.00
24	Willie Bethea	3.00
25	Ken Sugarman	3.00
26	Rich Robinson	2.00
27	Dave Tobey	2.00
28	Paul Brothers	2.00
29	Charlie Brown	2.00
30	Jerry Bradley	2.00
31	Ted Gerela	3.00
32	Jim Young	8.00
33	Gary Robinson	2.00
34	Bob Howes	2.00
35	Greg Findlay	2.00
36	Trevor Ekdahl	3.00
37	Ron Stewart	6.00
38	Joe Poirier	2.00
39	Wayne Giardino	2.00
40	Tom Schuette	2.00
41	Roger Perdrix	2.00
42	Jim Mankins	2.00
43	Jay Roberts	2.00
44	Ken Lehmann	3.00
45	Jerry Campbell	3.00
46	Billy Joe Booth	3.00
47	Whit Tucker	5.00
48	Moe Racine	3.00
49	Corey Colehour	3.00
50	Dave Gasser	2.00
51	Jerry Griffin	3.00
52	Greg Pipes	3.00
53	Roy Shatzko	2.00
54	Ron Forwick	2.00
55	Ed Molstad	2.00
56	Ken Ferguson	2.00
57	Terry Swarn	5.00
58	Tom Nettles	2.00
59	John Wydareny	2.00
60	Bayne Norrie	2.00
61	Wally Gabler	3.00
62	Paul Desjardins	2.00
63	Peter Francis	2.00
64	Bill Frank	2.00
65	Chuck Harrison	2.00
66	Gene Lakusiak	2.00
67	Phil Minnick	2.00
68	Doug Strong	2.00
69	Glen Schapansky	2.00
70	Ed Ulmer	2.00
71	Bill Whisler	2.00
72	Ted Collins	2.00
73	Larry DeGraw	2.00
74	Henry Dorsch	2.00
75	Alan Ford	2.00
76	Ron Lancaster	20.00
77	Bob Kosid	2.00
78	Bobby Thompson	2.00
79	Ted Dushinski	2.00
80	Bruce Bennett	4.00
81	George Reed	15.00
82	Wayne Shaw	2.00
83	Cliff Shaw	2.00
84	Jack Abendschan	2.00
85	Ed McQuarters	5.00
86	Jerry Keeling	2.00
87	Gerry Shaw	2.00
88	Basil Bark (UER) (Misspelled Back)	2.00
89	Wayne Harris	6.00
90	Jim Furlong	2.00
91	Larry Robinson	2.00
92	John Helton	10.00
93	Dave Cranmer	2.00
94	Lanny Boleski (UER) (Misspelled Larry)	2.00
95	Herman Harrison	5.00
96	Granville Liggins	5.00
97	Joe Forzani	2.00
98	Terry Evanshen	8.00
99	Sonny Wade	6.00
100	Dennis Duncan	2.00
101	Al Phaneuf	2.00
102	Larry Fairholm	2.00
103	Moses Denson	4.00
104	Gino Baretta	2.00
105	Gene Ceppetelli	2.00
106	Dick Smith	2.00
107	Gordon Judges	2.00
108	Harry Olszewski	2.00
109	Mike Webster	2.00
110	Checklist 1-115	30.00
111	Outstanding Player (list from 1953-1969)	8.00
112	Player of the Year (list from 1954-1969)	8.00
113	Lineman of the Year (list from 1955-1969)	6.00
114	CFL Coaches (listed on card front)	6.00
115	Identifying Player (explanation of uniform numbering system)	15.00

1970 O-Pee-Chee CFL Push-Out Inserts

		NM
Complete Set (16):		200.00
Common Player:		10.00
1	Ed Harrington	10.00
2	Danny Nykoluk	10.00
3	Tommy Joe Coffey	10.00
4	Angelo Mosca	30.00
5	Ken Sugarman	12.00
6	Jay Roberts	10.00
7	Joe Poirier	12.00
8	Corey Colehour	10.00
9	Dave Gasser	10.00
10	Wally Gabler	15.00
11	Paul Desjardins	10.00
12	Larry DeGraw	10.00
13	Jerry Keeling	20.00
14	Gerry Shaw	10.00
15	Terry Evanshen	25.00
16	Sonny Wade	12.00

1971 O-Pee-Chee CFL

		NM
Complete Set (132):		250.00
Common Player:		1.00
1	Bill Symons	5.00
2	Mel Profit	1.50
3	Jim Tomlin	1.00
4	Ed Harrington	1.50
5	Jim Corrigall	4.00
6	Chip Barrett	1.00
7	Marv Luster	3.00
8	Ellison Kelly	4.00
9	Charlie Bray	1.00
10	Pete Martin	1.00
11	Tony Moro	1.00
12	Dave Raimey	1.50
13	Joe Theismann	100.00
14	Greg Barton	6.00
15	Leon McQuay	6.00
16	Don Jonas	6.00
17	Doug Strong	1.00
18	Paul Brule	1.00
19	Bill Frank	1.00
20	Joe Critchlow	1.00
21	Chuck Liebrock	1.00
22	Rob McLaren	1.00
23	Bob Swift	1.00
24	Rick Shaw	1.00
25	Ross Richardson	1.00
26	Benji Dial	1.00
27	Jim Heighton	1.00
28	Ed Ulmer	1.00
29	Glen Schapansky	1.00
30	Larry Slagle	1.00
31	Tom Cassese	1.00
32	Ted Gerela	1.00
33	Bob Howes	1.00
34	Ken Sugarman	1.50
35	A.D. Whitfield	1.50
36	Jim Young	6.00
37	Tom Wilkinson	10.00
38	Lefty Hendrickson	1.00
39	Dave Golinsky	1.00
40	Gerry Herron	1.00
41	Jim Evenson	1.00
42	Greg Findlay	1.00
43	Garrett Hunsperger	1.00
44	Jerry Bradley	1.00
45	Trevor Ekdahl	1.50
46	Bayne Norrie	1.00
47	Henry King	1.00
48	Terry Swarn	1.50
49	Jim Thomas	1.50
50	Bob Houmard	1.50
51	Don Trull	3.00
52	Dave Cutler	8.00
53	Mike Law	1.00
54	Dick Dupuis	1.50
55	Dave Gasser	1.00
56	Ron Forwick	1.00
57	John LaGrone	1.50
58	Greg Pipes	1.50
59	Ted Page	1.00
60	John Wydareny	1.50
61	Joe Zuger	1.50
62	Tommy Joe Coffey	6.00
63	Rensi Perdoni	1.00
64	Bob Taylor	2.50
65	Garney Henley	6.00
66	Dick Wesolowski	1.00
67	Dave Fleming	1.00
68	Bill Danychuk	1.50
69	Angelo Mosca	15.00
70	Bob Krouse	1.00
71	Tony Gabriel	18.00
72	Wally Gabler	1.50
73	Bob Steiner	1.00
74	John Reid	1.00
75	Jon Hohman	1.00
76	Barry Ardern	1.00
77	Jerry Campbell	1.50
78	Billy Cooper	1.00
79	Dave Braggins	1.00
80	Tom Schuette	1.00
81	Dennis Duncan	1.00
82	Moe Racine	1.00
83	Rod Woodward	1.00
84	Al Marcelin	1.50
85	Garry Wood	5.00
86	Wayne Giardino	1.00
87	Roger Perdrix	1.00
88	Hugh Oldham	1.00
89	Rick Cassatta	2.50
90	Jack Abendschan	1.50
91	Don Bahnuik	1.00
92	Bill Baker	10.00
93	Gordon Barwell	1.00
94	Gary Brandt	1.00
95	Henry Dorsch	1.00
96	Ted Dushinski	1.00
97	Alan Ford	1.00
98	Ken Frith	1.00
99	Ralph Galloway	1.00
100	Bob Kosid	1.00
101	Ron Lancaster	15.00
102	Silas McKinnie	1.00
103	George Reed	8.00
104	Gene Ceppetelli	1.00
105	Merl Code	1.00
106	Peter Dalla Riva	8.00
107	Moses Denson	2.50
108	Pierre Desjardins	1.00
109	Terry Evanshen	6.00
110	Larry Fairholm	1.00
111	Gene Gaines	5.00
112	Ed George	1.50
113	Gordon Judges	1.00
114	Garry Lefebvre	1.00
115	Al Phaneuf	1.50
116	Steve Smear	5.00
117	Sonny Wade	3.00
118	Frank Andruski	1.00
119	Basil Bark	1.00
120	Lanny Boleski	1.00
121	Joe Forzani	1.50
122	Jim Furlong	1.00
123	Wayne Harris	6.00
124	Herman Harrison	4.00
125	John Helton	4.00
126	Wayne Holm	1.00
127	Fred James	1.00
128	Jerry Keeling	4.00
129	Rudy Linterman	1.50
130	Larry Robinson	1.50
131	Gerry Shaw	1.00
132	Checklist Card	25.00

1971 O-Pee-Chee CFL Poster Inserts

		NM
Complete Set (16):		150.00
Common Player:		6.00
1	Tommy Joe Coffey	15.00
2	Herman Harrison	15.00
3	Bill Frank	6.00
4	Ellison Kelly	10.00
5	Charlie Bray	6.00
6	Bill Danychuk	7.50
7	Saskatchewan Roughriders (Ron Lancaster)	20.00
8	Bill Symons	7.50
9	Steve Smear	10.00
10	Angelo Mosca	20.00
11	Wayne Harris	15.00
12	Greg Findlay	6.00
13	John Wydareny	7.50
14	Garney Henley	15.00
15	Al Phaneuf	7.50
16	Ed Harrington	6.00

1972 O-Pee-Chee CFL

		NM
Complete Set (132):		175.00
Common Player:		1.00
1	Bob Krouse	2.50
2	John Williams	1.00
3	Garney Henley	6.00
4	Dick Wesolowski	1.00
5	Paul McKay	1.00
6	Bill Danychuk	1.50
7	Angelo Mosca	10.00
8	Tommy Joe Coffey	5.00
9	Tony Gabriel	10.00
10	Mike Blum	1.00
11	Doug Mitchell	1.00
12	Emery Hicks	1.00
13	Max Anderson	1.00
14	Ed George	1.50
15	Mark Kosmos	1.50
16	Ted Collins	1.00
17	Peter Dalla Riva	5.00
18	Pierre Desjardins	1.00
19	Terry Evanshen	6.00
20	Larry Fairholm	1.50
21	Jim Foley	1.50
22	Gordon Judges	1.00
23	Barry Randall	1.00
24	Brad Upshaw	1.00
25	Jorma Kuisma	1.00
26	Mike Widger	1.00
27	Joe Theismann	50.00
28	Greg Barton	4.00
29	Bill Symons	3.00
30	Leon McQuay	4.00
31	Jim Corrigall	4.00
32	Jim Stillwagon	4.00
33	Dick Thornton	1.50
34	Marv Luster	4.00
35	Paul Desjardins	1.00
36	Mike Eben	1.00
37	Eric Allen	5.00
38	Chip Barrett	1.00
39	Noah Jackson	3.00
40	Jim Young	6.00
41	Trevor Ekdahl	1.50
42	Garrett Hunsperger	1.00
43	Willie Postler	1.00
44	George Anderson	1.00
45	Ron Estay	4.00
46	Johnny Musso	15.00
47	Eric Guthrie	1.00
48	Monroe Eley	1.00
49	Don Bunce	5.00
50	Jim Evenson	1.50
51	Ken Sugarman	1.50
52	Dave Golinsky	1.00
53	Wayne Harris	5.00
54	Jerry Keeling	4.00
55	Herman Harrison	4.00
56	Larry Robinson	1.50
57	John Helton	4.00
58	Gerry Shaw	1.00
59	Frank Andruski	1.00
60	Basil Bark	1.00
61	Joe Forzani	1.50
62	Jim Furlong	1.00
63	Rudy Linterman	1.50
64	Granville Liggins	4.00
65	Lanny Boleski	1.00
66	Hugh Oldham	1.00
67	Dave Braggins	1.00
68	Jerry Campbell	1.50
69	Al Marcelin	1.50
70	Tom Pullen	1.00
71	Rudy Sims	1.00
72	Marshall Shirk	1.00
73	Tom Laputka	1.00
74	Barry Ardern	1.00
75	Billy Cooper	1.00
76	Dan Deever	1.00
77	Wayne Giardino	1.00
78	Terry Wellesley	1.00
79	Ron Lancaster	12.00
80	George Reed	10.00
81	Bobby Thompson	1.00
82	Jack Abendschan	1.00
83	Ed McQuarters	3.00
84	Bruce Bennett	3.00
85	Bill Baker	5.00
86	Don Bahnuik	1.00
87	Gary Brandt	1.00
88	Henry Dorach	1.00
89	Ted Dushinski	1.00
90	Alan Ford	1.00
91	Bob Kosid	1.00
92	Greg Pipes	1.50
93	John LaGrone	1.00
94	Dave Gasser	1.00
95	Bob Taylor	1.50
96	Dave Cutler	5.00
97	Dick Dupuis	1.00
98	Ron Forwick	1.00
99	Bayne Norrie	1.00
100	Jim Henshall	1.00
101	Charlie Turner	1.00
102	Fred Dunn	1.00
103	Sam Scarber	1.00
104	Bruce Lemmerman	5.00
105	Don Jonas	6.00
106	Doug Strong	1.00
107	Ed Williams	1.00
108	Paul Markle	1.00
109	Gene Lakusiak	1.00
110	Bob LaRose	1.00
111	Rob McLaren	1.00
112	Pete Ribbins	1.00
113	Bill Frank	1.00
114	Bob Swift	1.00
115	Chuck Liebrock	1.00
116	Joe Critchlow	1.00
117	Paul Williams	1.00
118	Pro Action	1.00
119	Pro Action	1.00
120	Pro Action	1.00
121	Pro Action	1.00
122	Pro Action	1.00
123	Pro Action	1.00
124	Pro Action	1.00
125	Pro Action	1.00
126	Pro Action	1.00
127	Pro Action	1.00
128	Pro Action	1.00
129	Pro Action	1.00
130	Pro Action	1.00
131	Pro Action	1.00
132	Checklist Card	30.00

1972 O-Pee-Chee CFL Trio Sticker Insert

		NM
Complete Set (24):		250.00
Common Player:		4.00
1	Johnny Musso, 2 Ron Lancaster, 3 Don Jonas	4.00
4	Jerry Campbell, 5 Bill Symons, 6 Ted Collins	4.00
7	Dave Cutler, 8 Paul McKay, 9 Rudy Sims	4.00
10	Wayne Harris, 11 Greg Pipes, 12 Chuck Ealey	4.00
13	Ron Estay, 14 Jack Abendschan, 15 Paul Markle	4.00
16	Jim Stillwagon, 17 Terry Evanshen, 18 Willie Postler	4.00
19	Hugh Oldham, 20 Joe Theismann, 21 Ed George	4.00
22	Larry Robinson, 23 Bruce Lemmerman, 24 Garney Henley	4.00
25	Bill Baker, 26 Bob LaRose, 27 Frank Andruski	4.00
28	Don Bunce, 29 George Reed, 30 Doug Strong	4.00
31	Al Marcelin, 32 Leon McQuay, 33 Peter Dalla Riva	4.00
34	Dick Dupuis, 35 Bill Danychuk, 36 Marshall Shirk	4.00
37	Jerry Keeling, 38 John LaGrone, 39 Bob Krouse	4.00
40	Jim Young, 41 Ed McQuarters, 42	4.00
43	Dick Thornton, 44 Larry Fairholm, 45 Garrett Hunsperger	4.00
46	Dave Braggins, 47 Greg Barton, 48 Mark Kosmos	4.00
49	John Helton, 50 Bobby Taylor, 51 Dick Wesolowski	4.00
52	Don Bahnuik, 53 Rob McLaren, 54 Granville Liggins	4.00
55	Monroe Eley, 56 Bob Thompson, 57 Ed Williams	4.00
58	Tom Pullen, 59 Jim Corrigall, 60 Pierre Desjardins	4.00
61	Ron Forwick, 62 Angelo Mosca, 63 Tom Laputka	4.00
64	Herman Harrison, 65 Dave Gasser, 66 John Williams	4.00
67	Trevor Ekdahl, 68 Bruce Bennett, 69 Gerry Shaw	4.00
70	Jim Foley, 71 Pete Ribbins, 72 Marv Luster	4.00

1952 Parkhurst CFL

		NM
Complete Set (100):		3000.
Common Player (1-19):		20.00
Common Player (20-100):		30.00
1	Watch The Games	50.00
2	Teamwork	20.00
3	Football Equipment	20.00
4	Hang Onto The Ball	20.00
5	The Head On Tackle	20.00
6	The Football Field	20.00
7	The Lineman's Stance	20.00
8	Centre's Spiral Pass	20.00
9	The Lineman	20.00
10	The Place Kick	20.00
11	The Cross-Body Block	20.00
12	T Formation	20.00
13	Falling On The Ball	20.00
14	The Throw	20.00
15	Breaking From Tackle	20.00
16	How To Catch A Pass	20.00
17	The Punt	20.00
18	Shifting The Ball	20.00
19	Penalty Signals	20.00
20	Leslie Ascott	30.00
21	Robert Marshall	30.00
22	Tom Harpley	30.00
23	Robert McClelland	30.00
24	Rod Smylie	30.00
25	Bill Bass	30.00
26	Fred Black	30.00
27	Jack Carpenter	30.00
28	Bob Hack	30.00
29	Ulysses Curtis	50.00
30	Nobby Wirkowski	50.00
31	George Arnett	30.00
32	Lorne Parkin	30.00
33	Alex Toogood	30.00
34	Marshall Haymes	30.00
35	Shanty McKenzie	30.00
36	Byron Karrys	30.00
37	George Rooks	30.00
38	Red Ettinger	40.00
39	Al Bruno	40.00
40	Stephen Karrys	30.00
41	Herb Trawick	50.00
42	Sam Etcheverry	350.00
43	Marv Melrowitz	30.00
44	John Red O'Quinn	50.00
45	Jim Ostendarp	30.00
46	Tom Tofaute	30.00
47	Joey Pal	30.00
48	Ray Cicia	30.00
49	Bruce Coulter	35.00
50	Jim Mitchener	30.00
51	Lally Lalonde	30.00
52	Jim Staton	30.00
53	Glenn Douglas	30.00
54	Dave Tomlinson	30.00
55	Ed Salem	30.00
56	Virgil Wagner	50.00
57	Dawson Tilley	30.00
58A	Cec Findlay	40.00
58B	Tommy Manastersky	40.00
59	Frank Nable	30.00
60	Chuck Anderson	30.00
61	Charlie Hubbard	30.00
63	Benny MacDonnell	30.00
64	Peter Karpuk	30.00
65	Tom O'Malley	30.00
66	Bill Stanton	30.00
67	Matt Anthony	30.00
68	John Morneau	30.00
69	Howie Turner	30.00
70	Alton Baldwin	30.00
71	John Bovey	30.00
72	Bruno Bitkowski	35.00
73	Gene Roberts	30.00
74	John Wagoner	30.00
75	Ted MacLarty	30.00
76	Jerry Lefebvre	30.00

77	Buck Rogers	30.00
78	Bruce Cummings	30.00
79	Hal Wagner	40.00
80	Joe Shinn	30.00
81	Eddie Bevan	30.00
82	Ralph Sazio	50.00
83	Bob McDonald	30.00
84	Vince Scott	40.00
85	Jack Stewart	30.00
86	Ralph Bartolini	30.00
87	Blake Taylor	30.00
88	Richard Brown	30.00
89	Douglas Gray	30.00
90	Alex Muzyka	30.00
91	Pete Neumann	50.00
92	Jack Rogers	30.00
93	Bernie Custis	40.00
94	Cam Fraser	30.00
95	Vince Mazza	40.00
96	Peter Wooley	30.00
97	Earl Valiquette	30.00
98	Floyd Cooper	30.00
99	Louis DiFrancisco	30.00
100	Robert Simpson	125.00

1956 Parkhurst CFL

NM
Complete Set (50): 3500.
Common Player: 40.00

1	Art Walker	80.00
2	Frank Anderson	40.00
3	Normie Kwong	150.00
4	Johnny Bright	150.00
5	Jackie Parker	500.00
6	Bob Dean	40.00
7	Don Getty	125.00
8	Rollie Miles	100.00
9	Ted Tully	40.00
10	Frank Morris	90.00
11	Martin Ruby	80.00
12	Mel Beckett	80.00
13	Bill Clarke	40.00
14	John Wozniak	40.00
15	Larry Isbell	40.00
16	Ken Carpenter	80.00
17	Sully Glasser	40.00
18	Bobby Marlow	90.00
19	Paul Anderson	40.00
20	Gord Sturtridge	80.00
21	Alex Macklin	40.00
22	Duke Cook	40.00
23	Bill Stevenson	40.00
24	Lynn Bottoms	80.00
25	Aramis Dandoy	40.00
26	Peter Muir	40.00
27	Harvey Wylie	80.00
28	Joe Yamauchi	40.00
29	John Alderton	40.00
30	Bill McKenna	40.00
31	Edward Kotowich	40.00
32	Herb Gray	100.00
33	Calvin Jones	100.00
34	Herman Day	40.00
35	Buddy Leake	40.00
36	Robert McNamara	40.00
37	Bud Grant	300.00
38	Gord Rowland	80.00
39	Glen McWhinney	40.00
40	Lorne Benson	40.00
41	Sam Etcheverry	300.00
42	Joey Pal	40.00
43	Tom Hugo	40.00
44	Tex Coulter	80.00
45	Doug McNichol	40.00
46	Tom Moran	40.00
47	Red O'Quinn	80.00
48	Hal Patterson	200.00
49	Jacques Belec	40.00
50	Pat Abruzzi	100.00

1981 Police Saskatchewan

MT
Complete Set (10): 15.00
Common Player: 1.25

1	Roger Aldag (44)	2.00
2	Joe Barnes (7)	1.25
3	Lester Brown (22)	1.25
4	Dwight Edwards (33)	1.25
5	Vince Goldsmith (78)	2.00
6	John Hufnagel (12)	5.00
7	Ken McEachern (20)	1.25
8	Mike Samples (66)	1.25
9	Joey Walters (17)	1.25
10	Lyall Woznesensky (76)	1.25

1982 Police Hamilton

MT
Complete Set (35): 20.00
Common Player: .50

1	Marv Allemang	.50
2	Jeff Arp	.50
3	Keith Baker	.50
4	Gerald Bess	.75
5	Mark Bragagnolo	.50
6	Carmelo Carteri	.50
7	Tom Clements	7.50
8	Grover Covington	3.00
9	Rocky DiPietro	4.00
10	Howard Fields	.50
11	Ross Francis	.50
12	Ed Fulton	.50
13	Peter Gales	.50
14	Ed Gataveckas	.50
15	Dave Graffi	.50
16	Obie Graves	.50
17	Hazen Henderson	.50
18	Ron Johnson	1.25
19	Dave Marler	.75
20	Jim Muller	.50
21	Leroy Paul	.50
22	John Priestner	.75
23	Dave Purves	.50
24	James Ramey	.50
25	Doug Redl	.50
26	Bernie Ruoff	.75
27	David Sauve	.50
28	David Shaw	.50
29	Kerry Smith	.50
30	Steve Stapler	.75
31	Kyle Stevens	.50
32	Mike Walker	2.00
33	Henry Waszczuk	.50
34	Harold Woods	.50
35	Ben Zambiasi	2.50

1982 Police Saskatchewan

MT
Complete Set (16): 12.00
Common Player: .75

2	Greg Fieger	.75
7	Joe Adams	.75
12	John Hufnagel	4.00
17	Joey Walters	.75
20	Ken McEachern	.75
21	Marcellus Greene	.75
25	Steve Dennis	.75
29	Fran McDermott	.75
37	Frank Robinson	1.00
44	Roger Aldag	1.25
57	Bob Poley	.75
66	Mike Samples	.75
69	Don Swafford	.75
74	Chris DeFrance	.75
76	Lyall Woznesensky	.75
78	Vince Goldsmith	1.50

1982 Police Winnipeg

MT
Complete Set (24): 10.00
Common Player: .40

1	Nick Bastaja	.40
2	Paul Bennett	.40
3	John Bonk	.40
4	Dieter Brock	2.50
5	Peter Catan	.40
6	Leo Ezerins	.40
7	Eugene Goodlow	1.50
8	John Helton	1.50
9	Rick House	.60
10	Mark Jackson	.60
11	Ray Jauch (CO)	.40
12	Milson Jones	.40
13	Trevor Kennerd	1.25
14	Stan Mikawos	.40
15	William Miller	.60
16	Tony Norman	.40
17	Vince Phason	.40
18	Reggie Pierson	.40
19	Joe Poplawski	.60
20	James Reed	.40
21	Franky Smith	.40
22	Bobby Thompson	.40
23	Chris Walby	1.00
24	Charles Williams	.40

1983 Police Hamilton

MT
Complete Set (37): 20.00
Common Player: .50

1	Marv Allemang	.50
2	Jeff Arp	.50
3	Keith Baker	.50
4	Harold E. Ballard (PRES)	2.00
5	Mike Barker	.50
6	Gerald Bess	.75
7	Pat Brady	.50
8	Mark Bragagnolo	.50
9	Tom Clements	7.50
10	Grover Covington	3.00
11	Rufus Crawford	.50
12	Rocky DiPietro	4.00
13	Leo Ezerins	.50
14	Howard Fields	.50
15	Ross Francis	.50
16	Ed Gataveckas	.50
17	Peter Gales	.50
18	Paul Gohier	.50
19	Dave Graffi	.50
20	Ron Johnson	1.25
21	Steve Kearns	.50
22	Wayne Lee	.50
23	Mike McIntyre	.50
24	Paul Palma	.50
25	George Piva	.50
26	Mitchell Price	.75
27	John Priestner	.75
28	Bernie Ruoff	.75
29	David Sauve	.50
30	Johnny Shepherd	.50
31	Steve Stapler	1.00
32	Mark Streeter	.50
33	Jeff Tedford	.50
34	Mike Walker	2.00
35	Henry Waszczuk	.50
36	Felix Wright	2.50
37	Ben Zambiasi	2.50

1983 Police Saskatchewan

MT
Complete Set (16): 12.00
Common Player: .75

9	Ron Robinson	1.00
12	John Hufnagel	3.00
13	Ken Clark	1.00
18	Mike Washington	1.00
24	Marshall Hamilton	.75
25	Mike Emery	.75
30	Duane Galloway	.75
33	Dwight Edwards	1.00
36	Dave Ridgway	2.00
42	Eddie Lowe	.75
58	J.C. Pelusi	.75
60	Karl Morgan	.75
61	Bryan Illerbrun	.75
65	Neil Quilter	.75
72	Ray Elgaard	3.00
74	Chris DeFrance	.75

1984 Police Ottawa

MT
Complete Set (10): 30.00
Common Player: .75

1	Greg Marshall	1.25
2	Dave Newman	.75
3	Rudy Phillips	1.25
4	Jim Reid	1.25
5	Mark Seale (SP)	20.00
6	Rick Sowieta	1.25
7	Pat Stoqua	1.25
8	Skip Walker	2.50
9	Al Washington	.75
10	J.C. Watts	8.00

1985 Police Ottawa

MT
Complete Set (10): 6.00
Common Player: .50

1	Ricky Barden	.50
2	Michel Bourgeau	.75
3	Roger Cattelan	.50
4	Ken Clark	.75
5	Dean Dorsey	.75
6	Greg Marshall	.75
7	Kevin Powell	.50
8	Jim Reid	.75
9	Rick Sowieta	.75
10	J.C. Watts	3.00

1962 Post Cereal CFL

NM
Complete Set (137): 1600.
Common Player: 7.50

1A	Don Clark (Brown Back)	20.00
1B	Don Clark (SP) (White Back)	60.00
2	Ed Meadows	7.50
3	Meco Poliziani	7.50
4	George Dixon	20.00
5	Bobby Jack Oliver	10.00
6	Ross Buckle	7.50
7	Jack Espenship	7.50
8	Howard Cissell	7.50
9	Ed Nickla	7.50
10	Ed Learn	7.50
11	Billy Ray Locklin	7.50
12	Don Paquette	7.50
13	Milt Crain	7.50
14	Dick Schnell	7.50
15	Dick Cohee	7.50
16	Joe Francis	7.50
17	Gilles Archambeault	7.50
18	Angelo Mosca	25.00
19	Ernie White	7.50
20	George Brancato	7.50
21	Ron Lancaster	35.00
22	Jim Cain	7.50
23	Gerry Nesbitt	7.50
24	Russ Jackson	30.00
25	Bob Simpson	18.00
26	Sam Scoccia	7.50
27	Tom Jones	7.50
28	Kaye Vaughan	15.00
29	Chuck Stanley	7.50
30	Dave Thelen	15.00
31	Gary Schreider	7.50
32	Jim Reynolds	7.50
33	Doug Daigneault	7.50
34	Joe Poirier	10.00
35	Clare Exelby	7.50
36	Art Johnson	7.50
37	Menan Schriewer	7.50
38	Art Darch	7.50
39	Cookie Gilchrist	25.00
40	Brian Aston	7.50
41	Bobby Kuntz (SP)	50.00
42	Gerry Patrick	7.50
43	Norm Stoneburgh	7.50
44	Billy Shipp	7.50
45	Jim Andreotti	15.00
46	Tobin Rote	20.00
47	Dick Shatto	15.00
48	Dave Mann	10.00
49	Ron Morris	5.00
50	Lynn Bottoms	10.00
51	Jim Rountree	7.50
52	Bill Mitchell	7.50
53	Wes Gideon (SP)	50.00
54	Boyd Carter	7.50
55	Ron Howell	10.00
56	John Barrow	15.00
57	Bernie Faloney	20.00
58	Ron Ray	7.50
59	Don Sutherin	15.00
60	Frank Cosentino	10.00
61	Hardiman Cureton	10.00
62	Hal Patterson	20.00
63	Ralph Goldston	7.50
64	Tommy Grant	15.00
65	Larry Hickman	7.50
66	Zeno Karcz	10.00
67	Garney Henley	20.00
68	Gerry McDougall	10.00
69	Vince Scott	7.50
70	Gerry James	15.00
71	Roger Hagberg	10.00
72	Gord Rowland	10.00
73	Ernie Pitts	7.50
74	Frank Rigney	12.00
75	Norm Rauhaus	7.50
76	Leo Lewis	20.00
77	Mike Wright	7.50
78	Jack Delveaux	7.50
79	Steve Patrick	7.50
80	Dave Burkholder	7.50
81	Charlie Shepard	7.50
82	Kenny Ploen	20.00
83	Ronnie Latourelle	7.50
84	Herb Gray	15.00
85	Hal Ledyard	7.50
86	Cornel Piper (SP)	50.00
87	Farrell Funston	7.50
88	Ray Smith	7.50
89	Clair Branch	7.50
90	Fred Burket	7.50
91	Dave Grosz	7.50
92	Bob Golic	10.00
93	Billy Gray	7.50
94	Neil Habig	7.50
95	Reg Whitehouse	7.50
96	Jack Gotta	10.00
97	Bob Ptacek	7.50
98	Jerry Keeling	15.00
99	Ernie Danjean	7.50
100	Don Luzzi	12.00
101	Wayne Harris	20.00
102	Tony Pajaczkowski	15.00
103	Earl Lunsford	15.00
104	Ernie Warlick	15.00
105	Gene Filipski	12.00
106	Eagle Day	15.00
107	Bill Crawford	7.50
108	Oscar Kruger	7.50
109	Gino Fracas	10.00
110	Don Stephenson	7.50
111	Jim Letcavits	7.50
112	Howie Schumm	7.50
113	Jackie Parker	45.00
114	Rollie Miles	15.00
115	Johnny Bright	20.00
116	Don Getty	15.00
117	Bobby Walden	10.00
118	Roger Nelson	15.00
119	Al Ecuyer	7.50
120	Ed Gray	7.50
121	Vic Chapman (SP)	50.00
122	Earl Keeley	7.50
123	Sonny Homer	7.50
124	Bob Jetter	20.00
125	Jim Carphin	7.50
126	By Bailey	15.00
127	Norm Fieldgate	15.00
128	Vic Kristopaitis	7.50
129	Willie Fleming	20.00
130	Don Vicic	7.50
131	Tom Brown (SP)	50.00
132	Tom Hinton (SP)	50.00
133	Pat Claridge	7.50
134	Bill Britton	7.50
135	Neal Beaumont	10.00
136	Nub Beamer (SP)	50.00
137	Joe Kapp	60.00
NNO	Post Album	75.00

1963 Post Cereal CFL

NM
Complete Set (160): 900.00
Common Player: 5.00

1	Larry Hickman	7.50
2	Dick Schnell	5.00
3	Don Clark	7.50
4	Ted Page	5.00
5	Milt Crain	7.50
6	George Dixon	10.00
7	Ed Nickla	5.00
8	Barrie Hansen	5.00
9	Ed Learn	5.00
10	Billy Ray Locklin	5.00
11	Bobby Jack Oliver	7.50
12	Don Paquette	5.00
13	Sandy Stephens	12.00
14	Billy Wayte	5.00
15	Jim Reynolds	5.00
16	Ross Buckle	5.00
17	Bob Geary	5.00
18	Bobby Lee Thompson	5.00
19	Mike Snodgrass	5.00
20	Billy Joe Booth	7.50
21	Jim Cain	5.00
22	Kaye Vaughan	10.00
23	Doug Daigneault	5.00
24	Millard Flemming	5.00
25	Russ Jackson	25.00
26	Joe Poirier	7.50
27	Moe Racine	5.00
28	Norb Roy	5.00
29	Ted Smale	5.00
30	Ernie White	7.50
31	Whit Tucker	10.00
32	Dave Thelen	10.00
33	Len Chandler	5.00
34	Jim Conroy	7.50
35	Jerry Selinger	5.00
36	Ron Stewart	12.00
37	Jim Andreotti	7.50
38	Jackie Parker	25.00
39	Lynn Bottoms	7.50
40	Gerry Patrick	5.00
41	Gerry Philip	5.00
42	Art Johnson	5.00
43	Aubrey Linne	5.00
44	Dave Mann	7.50
45	Marty Martinello	5.00
46	Doug McNichol	5.00
47	Ron Morris	5.00
48	Walt Radzick	5.00
49	Jim Rountree	5.00
50	Dick Shatto	10.00
51	Billy Shipp	5.00
52	Norm Stoneburgh	5.00
53	Gerry Wilson	5.00
54	Danny Nykoluk	5.00
55	John Barrow	10.00
56	Frank Cosentino	7.50
57	Hardiman Cureton	7.50
58	Bobby Kuntz	7.50
59	Bernie Faloney	20.00
60	Garney Henley	12.00
61	Zeno Karcz	7.50
62	Dick Easterly	5.00
63	Bronko Nagurski	12.00
64	Hal Patterson	15.00
65	Ron Ray	5.00
66	Don Sutherin	8.00
67	Dave Viti	5.00
68	Joe Zuger	7.50
69	Angelo Mosca	20.00
70	Ralph Goldston	5.00
71	Tommy Grant	10.00
72	Geno DeNobile	5.00
73	Dave Burkholder	5.00
74	Jack Delveaux	5.00
75	Farrell Funston	5.00
76	Herb Gray	10.00
77	Roger Hagberg	7.50
78	Henry Janzen	7.50
79	Ronnie Latourelle	5.00
80	Leo Lewis	10.00
81	Cornel Piper	5.00
82	Ernie Pitts	5.00
83	Kenny Ploen	10.00
84	Norm Rauhaus	7.50
85	Charlie Shepard	5.00
86	Gar Warren	5.00
87	Dick Thornton	7.50
88	Hal Ledyard	5.00
89	Frank Rigney	7.50
90	Gord Rowland	5.00
91	Don Walsh	5.00
92	Bill Burrell	5.00
93	Ron Atchison	9.00
94	Billy Gray	5.00
95	Neil Habig	5.00
96	Bob Ptacek	7.50
97	Ray Purdin	5.00
98	Ted Urness	8.00
99	Dale West	7.50
100	Reg Whitehouse	5.00
101	Clair Branch	5.00
102	Bill Clarke	5.00
103	Garner Ekstran	7.50
104	Jack Gotta	7.50
105	Len Legault	5.00
106	Larry Dumelie	5.00
107	Bill Britton	5.00
108	Ed Buchanan	5.00
109	Lovell Coleman	7.50
110	Bill Crawford	5.00
111	Ernie Danjean	5.00
112	Eagle Day	9.00
113	Jim Furlong	5.00
114	Wayne Harris	15.00
115	Roy Jakanovich	5.00
116	Phil Lohmann	5.00
117	Earl Lunsford	8.00
118	Don Luzzi	8.00
119	Tony Pajaczkowski	8.00
120	Pete Manning	7.50
121	Harvey Wylie	8.00
122	George Hansen	5.00
123	Pat Holmes	5.00
124	Larry Robinson	7.50
125	Johnny Bright	15.00
126	Jon Rechner	5.00
127	Al Ecuyer	5.00
128	Don Getty	12.00
129	Ed Gray	5.00
130	Oscar Kruger	5.00
131	Jim Letcavits	5.00
132	Mike Lashuk	7.50
133	Don Duncalfe	5.00
134	Bobby Walden	7.50
135	Tommy Joe Coffey	12.00
136	Nat Dye	5.00
137	Roy Stevenson	5.00
138	Howie Schumm	5.00
139	Roger Nelson	8.00
140	Larry Fleisher	7.50
141	Dunc Harvey	5.00
142	James Earl Wright	7.50
143	By Bailey	8.00
144	Nub Beamer	5.00
145	Neal Beaumont	7.50
146	Tom Brown	8.00
147	Pat Claridge	5.00
148	Lonnie Dennis	7.50
149	Norm Fieldgate	5.00
150	Willie Fleming	12.00
151	Dick Fouts	7.50
152	Tom Hinton	8.00
153	Sonny Homer	7.50
154	Joe Kapp	30.00
155	Tom Larscheid	5.00
156	Mike Martin	5.00
157	Mel Mein	5.00
158	Mike Cacic	5.00
159	Walt Bilicki	5.00
160	Earl Keeley	7.50
NNO	Post Album	75.00

1991 Queen's University

MT
Complete Set (52): 12.00
Common Card (1-51): .30
Common Card (P1-P5): 3.00

1	First Rugby Team (Team Photo)	.75
2	Grey Cup Years (Harry Batstone, Frank R. Leadlay)	.75
3	1978 Vanier Cup Champs	.30
4	1978 Vanier Cup Champs	.30
5	Tim Pendergast	.30
6	Brad Elberg	.30
7	Ken Kirkwood	.30
8	Kyle Wanzel	.30
9	Brian Alford	.30
10	Paul Kozan	.30
11	Paul Beresford	.30
12	Ron Herman	.30
13	Mike Ross	.30
14	Tom Black	.30
15	Steve Yovetich	.30
16	Mark Robinson	.30
17	Don Rorwick	.30
18	Ed Kidd	.30
19	Jamie Galloway	.30
20	Dan Wright	.30
21	Scott Gray	.30
22	Dan McCullough	.30
23	Steve Othen	.30
24	Doug Hargreaves (CO)	.30
25	Sue Bolton (CO)	.30
26	Coaching Staff	.50
27	Joel Dagnone	.30
28	Mark Morrison	.30
29	Rob Krog	.30
30	Dan Pawliw	.30
31	Greg Bryk	.30
32	Eric Dell	.30
33	Mike Boone	.30
34	James Paterson	.30
35	Jeff Yach	.30
36	Peter Pain	.30
37	Aron Campbell	.30
38	Chris McCormick	.30
39	Jason Moller	.30
40	Terry Huhtala	.30
41	Matt Zarowny	.30
42	David St. Amour	.30
43	Frank Tindall	.30
44	Ron Stewart	1.00
45	Jim Young	1.00
46	Bob Howes	.30
47	Stu Lang	.30
48	Mike Schad (In College Uniform)	.75
49	Mike Schad (In Philadelphia Eagles Uniform)	.75
50	Jock Climie	1.00
51	Checklist	.30
P1	Jock Climie	3.00
P1AU	Jock Climie (AU/100)	30.00
P2	Ron Stewart	4.00
P2AU	Ron Stewart (AU/300)	30.00

P3	Jim Young	4.00
P4	Stu Lang	3.00
P5	Mike Schad	3.00
P5AU	Mike Schad (AU/100)	30.00
NNO	Title Card	.75

1981 Red Rooster Calgary Stampeders

		MT
	Complete Set (40):	25.00
	Common Player:	.60
1	Willie Armstead	.60
2	Doug Battershill	.60
3	Willie Burden (From waist up)	3.00
4	Willie Burden (Head and shoulders)	3.00
5	Scott Burk (UER) (Misspelled Burke 4th line of bio)	.60
6	Al Burleson	.60
7	Ken Dombrowski	.60
8	Lloyd Fairbanks	1.25
9	Rob Forbes	.60
10	Tom Forzani	1.00
11	Miles Gorrell	.60
12	J.T. Hay	.60
13	John Holland	1.00
14	Norm Hopely	.60
15	Jeff Inglis	.60
16	Lepoleon Ingram	.60
17	Terry Irvin	.60
18	Ken Johnson	1.00
19	Franklin King	.60
20	Dave Kirzinger	.60
21	Frank Kosec	.60
22	Tom Krebs	.60
23	Reggie Lewis	.60
24	Robert Lubig	.60
25	Scott MacArthur	.60
26	Ed McAleney	.60
27	Mike McTague	1.00
28	Mark Moors	.60
29	Bernie Morrison	.60
30	Mark Nelson	.60
31	Ray Odums	.60
32	Ronnie Paggett	.60
33	John Palazeti	.60
34	John Prassas	.60
35	Tom Reimer	.60
36	James Sykes (Close-up)	3.00
37	James Sykes (From waist up)	3.00
38	Bruce Threadgill	.60
39	Bob Viccars	.60
40	Merv Walker	.60

1981 Red Rooster Edmonton Eskimos

		MT
	Complete Set (40):	50.00
	Common Player:	.60
1	Leo Blanchard	.60
2	David Boone	.60
3	Brian Broomell	.60
4	Hugh Campbell (CO)	1.25
5	Dave Cutler	2.50
6	Marco Cyncar	1.00
7	Ron Estay	.60
8	Dave Fennell	1.00
9	Emilio Fraietta	.60
10	Brian Fryer	.60
11	Jim Germany	1.00
12	Gary Hayes	.60
13	Larry Highbaugh	1.25
14	Joe Hollimon	.60
15	Hank Ilesic	1.25
16	Ed Jones	.60
17	Dan Kearns	.60
18	Sean Kehoe	.60
19	Brian Kelly	2.50
20	Dan Kepley	1.25
21	Stu Lang	.60
22	Pete Lavorato	.60
23	Neil Lumsden	1.00
24	Bill Manchuk	.60
25	Mike McLeod	.60
26	Ted Milian	.60
27	Warren Moon	25.00
28	James Parker	2.00
29	John Pointer	.60
30	Hector Pothier	.60
31	Dale Potter	.60
32	Angelo Santucci	.60
33	Tom Scott	1.00
34	Waddell Smith	1.00
35	Bill Stevenson	.60
36	Tom Towns	.60
37	Eric Upton	.60
38	Mark Wald	.60
39	Ken Walter	.60
40	Tom Wilkinson	3.00

1995 R.E.L. CFL

		MT
	Complete Set (250):	35.00
	Common Player:	.10
1	Doug Flutie	1.25
2	Bruce Covernton	.20
3	Jamie Crysdale	.10
4	Matt Finlay	.10
5	Alondra Johnson	.20
6	Will Johnson	.20
7	Greg Knox	.10
8	Stu Laird	.20
9	Kenton Leonard	.10
10	Tony Martino	.10
11	Mark McLoughlin	.10
12	Allen Pitts	.25
13	Marvin Pope	.10
14	Rocco Romano	.10
15	David Sapunjis	.50
16	Pee Wee Smith	.20
17	Tony Stewart	.10
18	Srecko Zizakovic	.10
19	Kerwin Bell	.35
20	Leroy Blugh	.10
21	Rod Connop	.20
22	Blake Dermott	.20
23	Lucius Floyd	.10
24	Bennie Goods	.10
25	Glenn Harper	.10
26	Craig Hendrickson	.10
27	Robert Holland	.10
28	Malvin Hunter	.10
29	John Kalin	.10
30	Nick Mazzoli	.10
31	Willie Pless	.25
32	Jim Sandusky	.20
33	Michael Soles	.10
34	Marc Tobert	.10
35	Henry Williams	.35
36	Larry Wruck	.10
37	Lee Knight	.10
38	Shawn Prendergast	.10
39	Richard Nurse	.10
40	Eric Carter	.20
41	Frank Marof	.10
42	Roger Hennig	.10
43	Derek Grier	.10
44	Kelvin Means	.10
45	Michael Philbrick	.20
46	Jessie Small	.20
47	Mike O'Shea	.35
48	Marcus Cotton	.10
49	Hassan Bailey	.10
50	Anthony Calvillo	.50
51	Mike Kerrigan	.25
52	Hank Ilesic	.10
53	Paul Osbaldiston	.20
54	Earl Winfield	.20
55	Danton Barto	.10
56	Tim Cofield	.25
57	Bruce Perkins	.10
58	Damion Lyons	.10
59	Joe Horn	.20
60	Rickey Foggie	.25
61	Bobby Dawson	.10
62	Eddie Brown	.20
63	Vance Hammond	.10
64	Ed Berry	.10
65	Stephen Bates	.10
66	Greg Battle	.10
67	Gary Anderson	.10
68	Donald Smith	.10
69	Adrion Smith	.10
70	Rodney Harding	.50
71	Damon Allen	.20
72	Junior Robinson	.10
73	Ken Watson	.10
74	Nick Subis	.10
75	Mike Pringle	1.00
76	Shar Pourdanesh	.20
77	Elfrid Payton	.20
78	Josh Miller	.10
79	Carlos Huerta	.20
80	Tracy Ham	.50
81	Tracey Gravely	.10
82	Matt Goodwin	.10
83	Neil Fort	.10
84	O.J. Brigance	.35
85	Jearld Baylis	.10
86	Mike Alexander	.10
87	Shannon Culver	.10
88	Robert Clark	.20
89	Courtney Griffin	.10
90	Demetrious Maxie	.10
91	Terryl Ulmer	.10
92	Lybrant Robinson	.10
93	Troy Alexander	.10
94	Darren Joseph	.20
95	Warren Jones	.20
96	Dan Rashovich	.20
97	Glenn Kulka	.10
98	Dale Joseph	.10
99	Scott Hendrickson	.10
100	Ron Goetz	.10
101	Ventson Donelson	.10
102	Mike Anderson	.10
103	Brent Matich	.10
104	Donald Narcisse	.25
105	Tom Burgess	.20
106	Bobby Jurasin	.20
107	Ray Elgaard	.25
108	Brian Bonner	.25
109	Robbie Keen	.10
110	Bjorn Nittmo	.35
111	Rod Harris	.25
112	Martin Patton	.10
113	Mike Johnson	.10
114	Billy Joe Tolliver	.35
115	Curtis Mayfield	.20
116	Ben Jefferson	.10
117	Jon Heidenreich	.10
118	Mike Stowell	.10
119	Alex Mash	.10
120	Alex Mash	.10
121	Ray Savage	.10
122	Mario Perry	.10
123	Ron Perry	.10
124	Joe Fuller	.10
125	Jonathan Wilson	.10
126	Anthony Shelton	.10
127	Emanuel Martin	.10
128	Ray Alexander	.20
129	Michael Richardson	.25
130	Irv Daymond	.10
131	Terry Baker	.20
132	Danny Barrett	.20
133	James Ellingson	.20
134	John Kropke	.10
135	Garry Lewis	.10
136	James Monroe	.10
137	Brett Young	.10
138	Remi Trudel	.10
139	Jed Tommy	.10
140	Odessa Turner	.20
141	David Black	.20
142	Eric Geter	.10
143	Sammy Garza	.10
144	Loyd Lewis	.10
145	Enis Jackson	.10
146	Danny McManus	.35
147	Cory Philpot	.75
148	Glen Scrivner	.10
149	Ian Sinclair	.20
150	Ian Sinclair	.20
151	Vic Stevenson	.10
152	Andrew Stewart	.10
153	Jamie Taras	.10
154	Rob Gordon	.10
155	Tom Europe	.10
156	Spencer McLennan	.10
157	Mike Trevathan	.20
158	Matt Clark	.20
159	Daved Benefield	.20
160	Darren Flutie	.50
161	Charles Gordon	.10
162	Ryan Hanson	.10
163	Kent Austin	.25
164	Reggie Barnes	.20
165	Mike Clemons	.75
166	Jock Climie	.10
167	Duane Forde	.10
168	Leon Hatziioannou	.10
169	Wayne Lammle	.10
170	Paul Masotti	.20
171	George Nimako	.10
172	Calvin Tiggle	.10
173	Don Wilson	.10
174	Lui Passaglia	.20
174	Chris Tsangaris	.10
175	Darrick Branch	.10
176	Carl Coulter	.10
177	P.J. Martin	.10
178	Eric Blount (DE)	.10
179	Norm Casola	.10
180	Joe Burgos	.10
181	John Buddenberg	.10
182	George Bethune	.10
183	Oscar Giles	.20
184	Myron Wise	.10
185	Roman Anderson	.10
186	Dave Harper	.10
187	Mike Saunders	.50
188	Roosevelt Collins	.10
189	Peter Shorts	.10
190	Willie Fears	.10
191	Mike Kiselak	.10
192	Malcolm Frank	.10
193	Joe Kralik	.10
194	David Archer	1.25
195	Billy Hess	.10
196	Mark Stock	.10
197	James King	.10
198	Tony Burse	.10
199	Donovan Gans	.10
200	Keith Woodside	.10
201	Anthony Drawhorn	.20
202	Jimmy Klingler	.35
203	Matt Dunigan	.75
204	John Motton	.10
205	Scott Player	.10
206	Franco Grilla	.10
207	Shonte Peoples	.10
208	Derrick Crawford	.10
209	Fernando Thomas	.10
210	Delius Morris	.10
211	Roosevelt Patterson	.10
212	Willie McClendon	.10
213	Jason Phillips	.10
214	Mike James	.10
215	Andre Strode	.10
216	Chris Dyko	.10
217	Chris Walby	.10
218	Miles Gorrell	.10
219	Dave Vankoughnett	.10
220	Del Lyles	.10
221	Bob Cameron	.35
222	Troy Westwood	.10
223	Reggie Slack	.25
224	Blaise Bryant	.20
225	Gerald Wilcox	.20
226	David Williams	.25
227	Keilly Rush	.10
228	Stan Mikawos	.10
229	Paul Randolph	.10
230	Greg Clark	.10
231	Jason Mallett	.10
232	Juran Bolden	.35
233	Brett MacNeil	.10
234	Chris Johnstone	.10
235	Toronto Argonauts Logo	.10
236	Ottawa Rough Riders Logo	.10
237	Hamilton Tiger-Cats Logo	.10
238	Winnipeg Blue Bombers Logo	.10
239	Saskatchewan Roughriders/Logo	.10
240	Calgary Stampeders Logo	.10
241	Edmonton Eskimos Logo	.10
242	B.C. Lions Logo	.10
243	Memphis Mad Dogs Logo	.10
244	Birmingham Barracudas Logo	.10
245	San Antonio Texans Logo	.10
246	Shreveport Pirates Logo	.10
247	Baltimore Stallions Logo	.10
248	Grey Cup Logo	.10
249	Checklist #1	.20
250	Checklist #2	.20
P1	(Doug Flutie) (Promo numbered one of 2500)	2.00
AU1	(Doug Flutie) (AUTO) (signed card)	50.00

1971 Royal Bank B.C. Lions

		NM
	Complete Set (16):	50.00
	Common Player:	2.50
1	George Anderson	2.50
2	Paul Brothers	2.50
3	Brian Donnelly	2.50
4	Dave Easley	2.50
5	Trevor Ekdahl	3.50
6	Jim Evenson	3.50
7	Greg Findlay	2.50
8	Lefty Hendrickson	2.50
9	Bob Howes	2.50
10	Garrett Hunsperger	2.50
11	Wayne Matherne	2.50
12	Don Moorhead	2.50
13	Ken Phillips	2.50
14	Ken Sugarman	3.50
15	Tom Wilkinson	10.00
16	Jim Young	10.00

1973 Royal Bank B.C. Lions

		NM
	Complete Set (16):	50.00
	Common Player:	2.50
1	Barry Ardern	2.50
2	Monroe Eley	3.50
3	Bob Friend	2.50
4	Eric Guthrie	2.50
5	Garrett Hunsperger	2.50
6	Wayne Matherne	2.50
7A	Don Moorhead (Black border)	2.50
7B	Don Moorhead (Silver border)	2.50
8	Johnny Musso	7.50
9	Ray Nettles	2.50
10	Pete Palmer	2.50
11	Gary Robinson (SP)	20.00
12	Al Wilson	2.50
13	Mike Wilson	2.50
14	Jim Young	7.50
15	Coaches (Bud Tynes, Ken McCullough, Owen Dejanovich, Eagle Keys)	2.50

1974 Royal Bank B.C. Lions

		NM
	Complete Set (14):	40.00
	Common Player:	2.50
1	Bill Baker	6.00
2	Karl Douglas	2.50
3	Layne McDowell	2.50
4	Ivan MacMillan	2.50
5	Bud Magrum	2.50
6	Don Moorhead	2.50
7	Johnny Musso	7.50
8	Ray Nettles	2.50
9	Brian Sopatyk	2.50
10	Curtis Wester	3.50
11	Slade Willis	2.50
12	Al Wilson	2.50
13	Jim Young	7.50
14	Coaching Staff	3.50

1975 Royal Bank B.C. Lions

		NM
	Complete Set (14):	40.00
	Common Player:	2.50
1	Brock Ansley	2.50
2	Terry Bailey	2.50
3	Bill Baker	6.00
4	Elton Brown	2.50
5	Grady Cavness	3.50
6	Ross Clarkson	2.50
7	Joe Fourqurean	2.50
8	Lou Harris	3.50
9	Layne McDowell	2.50
10	Don Moorhead	2.50
11	Tony Moro	2.50
12	Ray Nettles	2.50
13	Curtis Wester	3.50
14	Jim Young	7.50

1976 Royal Bank B.C. Lions

		NM
	Complete Set (15):	40.00
	Common Player:	2.50
1	Terry Bailey	2.50
2	Bill Baker	6.00
3	Ted Dushinski	2.50
4	Eric Guthrie	2.50
5	Lou Harris	3.50
6	Glen Jackson	2.50
7	Rocky Long	2.50
8	Layne McDowell	2.50
9	Ray Nettles	2.50
10	Gary Robinson	6.00
11	John Sciarra	6.00
12	Wayne Smith	2.50
13	Michael Strickland	2.50
14	Al Wilson	2.50
15	Jim Young	7.50

1977 Royal Bank B.C. Lions

		NM
	Complete Set (12):	40.00
	Common Player:	2.50
1	Doug Carlson	2.50
2	Sam Cvijanovich	2.50
3	Ted Dushinski	2.50
4	Paul Giroday	2.50
5	Glen Jackson	2.50
6	Frank Landy	2.50
7	Lui Passaglia	7.50
8	John Sciarra	6.00
9	Michael Strickland	2.50
10	Jerry Tagge	7.50
11	Al Wilson	2.50
12	Jim Young	7.50

1978 Royal Bank B.C. Lions

		NM
	Complete Set (12):	40.00
	Common Player:	2.50
1	Terry Bailey	2.50
2	Leon Bright	5.00
3	Doug Carlson	2.50
4	Grady Cavness	3.50
5	Al Charuk	2.50
6	Paul Giroday	2.50
7	Larry Key	2.50
8	Frank Landy	2.50
9	Lui Passaglia	7.50
10	Jerry Tagge	7.50
11	Al Wilson	2.50
12	Jim Young	7.50

1987 Royal Studios Saskatchewan Roughriders

		MT
	Complete Set (40):	35.00
	Common Player:	.75
1	Dave Albright	.75
2	Roger Aldag	1.00
3	Mike Anderson	.75
4	Tron Armstrong	.75
5	Terry Baker	1.00
6	Walter Bender	1.25
7	Jeff Bentrim	1.25
8	Todd Brown	.75
9	Tom Burgess	3.00
10	Coaching Staff (John Hufnagel, Dick Adams, John Gregory, Ted Heath, Gary Hoffman, M. Samples)	1.00
11	Terry Cochrane	.75
12	David Conrad	.75
13	Steve Crane	.75
14	James Curry	2.00
15	Tony Dennis	.75
16	Ray Elgaard	3.00
17	Denny Ferdinand	1.00
18	Roderick Fisher	.75
19	Joe Fuller	.75
20	Gainer The Gopher (Team Mascot)	.75
21	Norris Gibbs	.75
22	Nick Hebeler	.75
23	Bryan Illerbrun	1.00
24	Alan Johns	.75
25	Bobby Jurasin	3.00
26	Eddie Lowe	1.00
27	Tracey Mack	.75
28	Tim McCray	1.50
29	Mike McGruder	1.00
30	Ken Moore	.75
31	Dan Rashovich	.75
32	Scott Redl	.75
33	Dave Ridgway	1.25
34	Dave Sidoo	.75
35	Harry Skipper	1.00
36	Lawrie Skolrood	.75
37	Vic Stevenson	.75
38	Glen Suitor	1.00
39	Brendan Taman Asst. EQ MG, Ivan Gutfriend Athletic Therapist, Norm Fong EQ MG	.75
40	Mark Urness	.75

1988 Royal Studios Saskatchewan Roughriders

		MT
	Complete Set (54):	40.00
	Common Player:	.50
1	Dave Albright	.50
2	Roger Aldag (DP)	.75
3	Mike Anderson	.50
4	Kent Austin (DP)	4.00
5	Terry Baker	.75
6	Jeff Bentrim	.75
7	Rob Bresciani	.50
8	Albert Brown	.50
9	Tom Burgess (DP)	2.50
10	Coaching Staff (Gary Hoffman, Dick Adams, Dan Daniel, Ted Heath, John Gregory, Steve Goldman)	.75
11	Dick Cohee and The Store (and The Store)	.50
12	David Conrad	.50
13	Steve Crane	.50
14	James Curry (DP)	1.25
15	Dream Team (Cheerleaders)	1.25
16	Ray Elgaard	2.50
17	James Ellingson	.50
18	Jeff Fairholm	1.25
19	Denny Ferdinand	.75
20	The Flame (Team Mascot)	.50
21	Norm Fong, Ivan Gutfriend (Equipment/Trainer)	.50
22	Joe Fuller	.50
23	Gainer The Gopher (Team Mascot)	.50
24	Vince Goldsmith	1.00
25	John Gregory (CO)	.50
26	Richie Hall	.50
27	Bill Henry	.50
28	James Hood	.50
29	Bryan Illerbrun (UER) (Name misspelled Brian on front and back)	.75
30	Milson Jones	1.25
31	Bobby Jurasin (DP)	2.50
32	Tim Kearse	.50
33	Rick Klassen	.75
34	Gary Lewis	.75
35	Eddie Lowe	.75
36	Greg McCormack	.75
37	Tim McCray	1.00
38	Ray McDonald	.75
39	Mike McGruder	.75
40	Ken Moore	.50
41	Donald Narcisse	2.00
42	Dan Rambo, Brendan Taman (Rider Scouting)	.50
43	Dan Rashovich	.75
44	Dameon Reilly	.75
45	Dave Ridgway (DP)	1.00
46	Rocco Romano	.75
47	Harry Skipper	.75
48	Vic Stevenson	.75
49	Glen Suitor	.75
50	Jeff Treftlin	.50
51	Mark Urness	.50
52	Eddie Ray Walker	.50
53	John Walker	.50
54	Jeff Watson	.50

1989 Royal Studios Saskatchewan Roughriders

		MT
	Complete Set (54):	35.00
	Common Player:	.50
1	Dave Albright	.50
2	Roger Aldag (DP)	.75

3	Tuineau Alipate	.75
4	Mike Anderson	.50
5	Kent Austin	3.00
6	Terry Baker	.75
7	Jeff Bentrim	.75
8	Rob Bresciani	.50
9	Albert Brown	.50
10	Tom Burgess (DP)	2.50
11	Coaching Staff	.75
12	Steve Crane	.50
13	James Curry	1.25
14	Kevin Dixon	.50
15	Dream Team (Cheerleaders sponsored by CKRM)	1.00
16	Wayne Drinkwalter	.75
17	Ray Elgaard	2.00
18	James Ellingson	.50
19	Jeff Fairholm	.50
20	The Flame	.50
21	Norm Fong, Ivan Gutfriend (Equipment/Trainer)	.50
22	Gainer The Gopher (DP) (Team Mascot)	.50
23	John Gregory (CO)	.75
24	Vince Goldsmith	.75
25	Mark Guy	.75
26	Richie Hall (DP)	.50
27	John Hoffman	.75
28	Bryan Illerbrun (UER) (Name misspelled Brian on front and back)	.75
29	Milson Jones	.75
30	Bobby Jurasin (DP)	2.00
31	Chuck Klingbeil	.75
32	Gary Lewis	.75
33	Eddie Lowe	.50
34	Greg McCormack	.50
35	Tim McCray	1.00
36	Ray McDonald	.50
37	Ken Moore	.50
38	Cedric Moses	.50
39	Donald Narcisse	1.50
40	Dan Payne	.50
41	Bob Poley	.50
42	Dan Rashovich	.50
43	Dave Ridgway (DP)	1.00
44	Junior Robinson	.75
45	Harry Skipper	.50
46	Vic Stevenson	.50
47	Glen Suitor	.50
48	Jeff Treftlin	.50
49	Kelly Trithart	.50
50	Mark Urness	.50
51	Lionel Vital	.50
52	Eddie Ray Walker	.75
53	Steve Wiggins	.50
54	Donovan Wright	.50

1990 Royal Studios Saskatchewan Roughriders

		MT
Complete Set (60):		35.00
Common Player:		.50
1	Dick Adams (CO)	.50
2	Dave Albright	.50
3	Roger Aldag	.75
4	Tuineau Alipate	.50
5	Mike Anderson	.50
6	Kent Austin	3.00
7	Tony Belser	.50
8	Jeff Bentrim	.75
9	Bruce Boyko	.75
10	Albert Brown	.75
11	Paul Bushey	.50
12	Larry Donovan (CO)	.50
13	Dream Team (Cheerleaders sponsored by CKRM)	.75
14	Wayne Drinkwalter	.75
15	Sean Dykes	.50
16	Ray Elgaard	2.00
17	Jeff Fairholm	1.00
18	Norman Fong MG, Ivan Gutfriend MG	.50
19	Alan Ford (GM)	.50
20	Lucius Floyd	.75
21	Gainer The Gopher (Team Mascot)	.50
22	Chris Gioskos	.50
23	Vince Goldsmith	1.00
24	John Gregory (CO)	.75
25	Mark Guy	.75
26	Stacey Hairston	.75
27	Richie Hall	.50
28	Greg Harris	.50
29	Ted Heath (CO)	.50
30	Gary Hoffman (CO)	.50
31	John Hoffman	.50
32	Larry Hogue	.50
33	Bobby Jurasin	2.00
34	Milson Jones	1.00
35	James King	.50
36	Chuck Klingbeil	1.00
37	Mike Lazecki	.50
38	Orville Lee	1.50
39	Gary Lewis	.75
40	Eddie Lowe	.75
41	Greg McCormack	.50
42	Tim McCray	1.00

43	Ken Moore	.50
44	Donald Narcisse	1.50
45	Dave Pitcher	.50
46	Bob Poley	.50
47	Brent Pollack	.50
48	Dan Rashovich	.50
49	Tony Rice	1.50
50	Dave Ridgway	1.00
51	Pal Sartori	.50
52	Saskatchewan Roughriders	1.00
53	Glen Scrivner	.50
54	Tony Simmons	.50
55	Vic Stevenson	.50
56	Glen Suitor	1.00
57	Jeff Treftlin	.75
58	Kelly Trithart (UER) (Name misspelled Trihart on front and back)	.75
59	Lionel Vital	.50
60	Slater Zaleski	.50

1991 Royal Studios Saskatchewan Roughriders

		MT
Complete Set (66):		35.00
Common Player:		.40
1	Dick Adams (CO)	.40
2	Dave Albright	.40
3	Roger Aldag	.60
4	Mike Anderson	.40
5	Kent Austin	3.00
6	John Bankhead	.60
7	1990 Miss Grey Cup (Kerry Beutler)	.60
8	Allan Boyko	.60
9	Bruce Boyko	.60
10	Doug Brewster	.40
11	Albert Brown	.60
12	Paul Bushey	.40
13	Coaching Staff	.40
14	Larry Donovan (CO)	.40
15	Wayne Drinkwalter	.60
16	Sean Dykes	.40
17	Ray Elgaard	2.00
18	Jeff Fairholm	1.00
19	Dan Farthing	.40
20	Lucius Ford	.60
21	Gainer The Gopher (Team Mascot)	.40
22	Chris Gioskos (UER) (Name misspelled Gioskas on front)	.60
23	Sonny Gordon	.40
24	John Gregory (CO)	.60
25	Stacey Hairston	.60
26	Richie Hall	.60
27	Greg Harris	.40
28	Major Harris	1.50
29	Ted Heath (CO)	.40
30	Gary Hoffman (CO)	.40
31	John Hoffman	.40
32	Larry Hogue	.60
33	Willis Jacox	1.50
34	Ray Jauch (CO)	.60
35	Gene Jelks	1.50
36	Milson Jones	1.00
37	Bobby Jurasin	2.00
38	James King	.40
39	Mike Lazecki	.40
40	Orville Lee	1.50
41	Gary Lewis	.60
42	Eddie Lowe	.60
43	Paul Maines	.40
44	Don Matthews (CO)	.40
45	Dane McArthur	.40
46	David McCrary	.40
47	Don Narcisse	1.50
48	Offensive Line	.40
49	David Pitcher	.40
50	Bob Poley	.40
51	Brent Pollack	.40
52	Basil Proctor	.40
53	Dan Rashovich	.40
54	Dave Ridgway (UER) (Name misspelled Ridgeway on back)	1.00
55	Roughriders vs The Rocket	1.00
56	Roughriders Team	.60
57	Glen Scrivner	.40
58	Keith Stephens	.40
59	Vic Stevenson	.40
60	Glen Suitor	1.00
61	Chris Thieneman	.40
62	Jeff Treftlin	.60
63	Kelly Trithart	.60
64	Paul Vaida	.40
65	Ted Wahl	.40
66	Rick Worman	1.00

1971 Sargent Promotions Stamps

		NM
Complete Set (225):		240.00
Common Player:		.75
1	Jim Young	7.50
2	Trevor Ekdahl	1.25

3	Ted Gerela	1.25
4	Jim Evenson	1.25
5	Ray Lychak	.75
6	Dave Golinsky	.75
7	Ted Warkentin	1.25
8	A.D. Whitfield	1.25
9	Lach Heron	1.25
10	Ken Phillips	.75
11	Lefty Hendrickson	.75
12	Paul Brothers	.75
13	Eagle Keys (CO)	1.50
14	Garrett Hunsperger	.75
15	Greg Findlay	.75
16	Dave Easley	.75
17	Barrie Hansen	.75
18	Wayne Dennis	.75
19	Jerry Bradley	.75
20	Gerry Herron	.75
21	Gary Robinson	.75
22	Bill Whisler	.75
23	Bob Howes	.75
24	Tom Wilkinson	6.00
25	Tom Cassese	.75
26	Dick Suderman	1.25
27	Jerry Keeling	4.00
28	John Helton	4.00
29	Jim Furlong	.75
30	Fred James	.75
31	Howard Starks	.75
32	Craig Koinzan	.75
33	Frank Andruski	.75
34	Joe Forzani	1.25
35	Herb Schumn	.75
36	Gerry Shaw	.75
37	Lanny Boleski	.75
38	Jim Duncan (CO)	.75
39	Hugh McKinnis	.75
40	Basil Bark	.75
41	Herman Harrison	4.00
42	Larry Robinson	1.25
43	Larry Lawrence	.75
44	Granville Liggins	2.00
45	Wayne Harris	4.00
46	John Atamian	.75
47	Wayne Holm	.75
48	Rudy Linterman	1.25
49	Jim Sillye	.75
50	Terry Wilson	.75
51	Don Trull	2.00
52	Rusty Clark	.75
53	Ted Page	.75
54	Ken Ferguson	.75
55	Alan Pitcaithley	.75
56	Bayne Norrie	.75
57	Dave Gasser	.75
58	Jim Thomas	.75
59	Terry Swarn	1.25
60	Ron Forwick	.75
61	Henry King	.75
62	John Wydareny	1.25
63	Ray Jauch (CO)	1.25
64	Jim Henshall	.75
65	Dave Cutler	4.00
66	Fred Dunn	.75
67	Dick Dupuis	1.25
68	Fritz Greenlee	.75
69	Jerry Griffin	1.25
70	Allen Ische	.75
71	John LaGrone	1.25
72	Mike Law	.75
73	Ed Molstad	.75
74	Greg Pipes	1.25
75	Roy Shatzko	.75
76	Joe Zuger	1.25
77	Wally Gabler	1.25
78	Tony Gabriel	6.00
79	John Reid	.75
80	Dave Fleming	.75
81	Jon Hohman	.75
82	Tommy Joe Coffey	5.00
83	Dick Wesolowski	.75
84	Gordon Christian	.75
85	Steve Worster	6.00
86	Bob Taylor	1.50
87	Doug Mitchell	.75
88	Al Dorow (CO)	1.25
89	Angelo Mosca	7.50
90	Bill Danychuk	1.25
91	Mike Blum	.75
92	Garney Henley	6.00
93	Bob Steiner	.75
94	John Manel	..75
95	Bob Krouse	.75
96	John Williams	.75
97	Scott Henderson	.75
98	Ed Chalupka	.75
99	Paul McKay	.75
100	Rensi Perdoni	.75
101	Ed George	1.25
102	Al Phaneuf	.75
103	Sonny Wade	2.00
104	Moses Denson	2.00
105	Terry Evanshen	6.00
106	Pierre Desjardins	.75
107	Larry Fairholm	.75
108	Gene Gaines	4.00
109	Bobby Lee Thompson	.75
110	Mike Widger	.75
111	Gene Ceppetelli	.75
112	Barry Randall	.75
113	Sam Etcheverry (CO)	2.50
114	Mark Kosmos	1.25
115	Ted Collins	.75
116	Peter Dalla Riva	4.00
117	John Couture	.75
118	Tony Passander	.75

119	Garry Lefebvre	.75
120	George Springate	.75
121	Gordon Judges	.75
122	Steve Smear	2.50
123	Tom Pullen	.75
124	Merl Code	.75
125	Steve Booras	.75
126	Hugh Oldham	.75
127	Moe Racine	.75
128	John Kruspe	.75
129	Ken Lehmann	1.25
130	Billy Cooper	.75
131	Marshall Shirk	.75
132	Tom Schuette	.75
133	Doug Specht	.75
134	Dennis Duncan	.75
135	Jerry Campbell	1.25
136	Wayne Giardino	.75
137	Roger Perdrix	.75
138	Jack Gotta (CO)	.75
139	Terry Wellesley	.75
140	Dave Braggins	.75
141	Dave Pivec	.75
142	Rod Woodward	.75
143	Garry Wood	2.00
144	Al Marcelin	1.25
145	Dan Dever	.75
146	Ivan MacMillan	.75
147	Wayne Smith	.75
148	Barry Ardern	.75
149	Rick Cassatta	1.25
150	Bill Van Burkleo	.75
151	Ron Lancaster	5.00
152	Wayne Shaw	.75
153	Bob Kosid	.75
154	George Reed	7.50
155	Don Bahnuik	.75
156	Gordon Barwell	.75
157	Clyde Brock	.75
158	Alan Ford	.75
159	Jack Abendschan	.75
160	Steve Molnar	.75
161	Al Rankin	.75
162	Bobby Thompson	.75
163	Dave Skrien (CO)	.75
164	Nolan Bailey	.75
165	Bill Baker	5.00
166	Bruce Bennett	1.50
167	Gary Brandt	.75
168	Charlie Collins	.75
169	Henry Dorsch	.75
170	Ted Dushinski	.75
171	Bruce Gainer	.75
172	Ralph Galloway	.75
173	Ken Frith	.75
174	Cliff Shaw	.75
175	Silas McKinnie	.75
176	Mike Eben	.75
177	Greg Barton	2.00
178	Joe Theismann	20.00
179	Charlie Bray	.75
180	Roger Scales	.75
181	Bob Hudspeth	.75
182	Bill Symons	1.50
183	Dave Raimey	1.25
184	Dave Cranmer	1.25
185	Mel Profit	1.25
186	Paul Desjardins	.75
187	Tony Moro	.75
188	Leo Cahill (CO)	.75
189	Chip Barrett	.75
190	Pete Martin	.75
191	Walt Balasiuk	.75
192	Jim Corrigall	1.50
193	Ellison Kelly	5.00
194	Jim Tomlin	.75
195	Marv Luster	2.00
196	Jim Thorpe	2.00
197	Jim Stillwagon	4.00
198	Ed Harrington	.75
199	Jim Dye	.75
200	Leon McQuay	2.50
201	Rob McLaren	.75
202	Benji Dial	.75
203	Chuck Liebrock	.75
204	Glen Schapansky	.75
205	Ed Ulmer	.75
206	Ross Richardson	.75
207	Lou Andrus	.75
208	Paul Robson	.75
209	Paul Brule	.75
210	Doug Strong	.75
211	Dick Smith	.75
212	Bill Frank	.75
213	Jim Spavital (CO)	.75
214	Rick Shaw	.75
215	Joe Critchlow	.75
216	Don Jonas	3.00
217	Bob Swift	.75
218	Larry Kerychuk	.75
219	Bob McCarthy	.75
220	Gene Lakusiak	.75
221	Jim Heighton	.75
222	Chuck Harrison	.75
223	Lance Fletcher	.75
224	Larry Slagle	.75
225	Wayne Giesbrecht	.75

1956 Shredded Wheat CFL

		NM
Complete Set (105):		9000.
Common Player:		80.00
A1	Peter Muir	80.00
A2	Harry Langford	80.00
A3	Tony Pajaczkowski	150.00

A4	Bob Morgan	80.00
A5	Baz Nagle	80.00
A6	Alex Macklin	80.00
A7	Bob Geary	80.00
A8	Don Klosterman	125.00
A9	Bill McKenna	80.00
A10	Bill Stevenson	80.00
A11	Charles Baillie	80.00
A12	Berdett Hess	80.00
A13	Lynn Bottoms	80.00
A14	Doug Brown	80.00
A15	Jack Hennemier	80.00
B1	Frank Anderson	80.00
B2	Don Barry	80.00
B3	Johnny Bright	200.00
B4	Kurt Burris	80.00
B5	Bob Dean	80.00
B6	Don Getty	150.00
B7	Normie Kwong	200.00
B8	Earl Lindley	80.00
B9	Art Walker	100.00
B10	Rollie Miles	125.00
B11	Frank Morris	125.00
B12	Jackie Parker	300.00
B13	Ted Tully	80.00
B14	Frank Ivy	90.00
B15	Bill Rowekamp	80.00
C1	Al Sherman	80.00
C2	Larry Cabrelli	80.00
C3	Ron Kelly	80.00
C4	Edward Kotowich	80.00
C5	Buddy Leake	100.00
C6	Thomas Lumsden	80.00
C7	Bill Smitiuk	80.00
C8	Buddy Tinsley	125.00
C9	Ron Vaccher	80.00
C10	Eagle Day	125.00
C11	Buddy Allison	80.00
C12	Bob Haas	90.00
C13	Steve Patrick	80.00
C14	Keith Pearce (UER) (Misspelled Pierce on front)	80.00
C15	Lorne Benson	80.00
D1	George Arnett	80.00
D2	Eddie Bevan	80.00
D3	Art Darch	80.00
D4	John Fedosoff	80.00
D6	Ron Howell	90.00
D7	Alex Muzyka	80.00
D8	Chet Miksza	80.00
D9	Walt Nikorak	80.00
D10	Pete Neumann	125.00
D11	Steve Oneschuk	80.00
D12	Vince Scott	125.00
D13	Ralph Toohy	80.00
D14	Ray Truant	80.00
D15	Nobby Wirkowski	100.00
E1	Pete Bennett	80.00
E2	Fred Black	80.00
E3	Jim Copeland	80.00
E4	Al Pfeifer	80.00
E5	Ron Albright	80.00
E6	Tom Dublinski	80.00
E7	Billy Shipp	80.00
E8	Baz Mackie	80.00
E9	Bill McFarlane	80.00
E10	John Sopinka	100.00
E11	Dick Brown	80.00
E12	Gerry Doucette	80.00
E13	Dan Shaw	80.00
E14	Dick Shatto	175.00
E15	Bill Swiacki	100.00
F1	Ray Syrnyk	80.00
F2	Martin Ruby	125.00
F3	Bobby Marlow	125.00
F4	Doug Kiloh	80.00
F5	Gord Sturtridge	90.00
F6	Stan Williams	80.00
F7	Larry Isbell	80.00
F8	Ken Casner	80.00
F9	Mel Becket	100.00
F10	Reg Whitehouse	80.00
F11	Harry Lampman	80.00
F12	Mario DeMarco	90.00
F13	Ken Carpenter	80.00
F14	Frank Filchock	100.00
F15	Frank Tripucka	125.00
G1	Tom Tracy	150.00
G2	Pete Ladygo	80.00
G3	Sam Scoccia	80.00
G4	Joe Upton	80.00
G5	Bob Simpson	80.00
G6	Bruno Bitkowski	90.00
G7	Joe Stracini (UER) (Misspelled Straccini on card front)	80.00
G8	Hal Ledyard	80.00
G9	Milt Graham	80.00
G10	Bill Sowalski	80.00
G11	Avatus Stone	80.00
G12	John Boich	100.00
G13	Don Pinhey (UER) (Misspelled Bob Pinkney on card front)	80.00
G14	Peter Karpuk	80.00
G15	Frank Clair	125.00

1994 Smokey Sacramento

		MT
Complete Set (18):		30.00

Common Player:		1.25
1	Fred Anderson (GEO)	1.25
2	David Archer	5.00
3	George Bethune	1.25
4	David Diaz-Infante	1.25
5	Willie Fears	1.50
6	Corian Freeman	1.25
7	Pete Gardere	1.50
8	Tom Gerhart	1.25
9	Rod Harris	1.25
10	Bobby Humphery	2.50
11	Mike Kiselak	1.25
12	Mark Ledbetter	1.25
13	Maurice Miller	1.25
14	Troy Mills	1.25
15	Mike Oliphant	2.50
16	James Pruitt	1.25
17	Junior Robinson	1.25
18	Kay Stephenson (CO)	1.25

1993 Sport Chek Calgary Stampeders

		MT
Complete Set (24):		15.00
Common Player:		.60
1	Karl Anthony	.60
2	Raymond Biggs	.60
3	Douglas Craft	.60
4	Doug Davies	.60
5	Mark Dube	.60
6	Matt Finlay	.60
7	Doug Flutie	4.00
8	Fred Gatlin	.60
9	Keyvan Jenkins	1.00
10	Alondra Johnson	.60
11	Pat Mahon	.60
12	Tony Martino	.60
13	Mark McLoughlin	.60
14	Andy McVey	.60
15	Will Moore	2.50
16	Mark Pearce	.60
17	Allen Pitts	1.25
18	David Sapunjis	1.25
19	Junior Thurman	1.25
20	Gerald Vaughn	.60
21	Ken Watson	.60
22	Brian Wiggins	1.00
23	Blair Zerr	.60
24	Srecko Zizakovic	1.00

1958 Topps CFL

		NM
Complete Set (88):		500.00
Common Player:		5.00
1	Paul Anderson	12.00
2	Leigh McMillan	5.00
3	Vic Chapman	5.00
4	Bobby Marlow	12.00
5	Mike Cacic	5.00
6	Ron Pawlowski	5.00
7	Frank Morris	9.00
8	Earl Keeley	6.00
9	Don Walsh	5.00
10	Bryan Engram	5.00
11	Bobby Kuntz	6.00
12	Jerry Janes	5.00
13	Don Bingham	5.00
14	Paul Fedor	5.00
15	Tommy Grant	12.00
16	Don Getty	20.00
17	George Brancato	6.00
18	Jackie Parker	40.00
19	Alan Valdes	5.00
20	Paul Dekker	5.00
21	Frank Tripucka	12.00
22	Gerry McDougall	9.00
23	Duke Dewveall	6.00
24	Ted Smale	5.00
25	Tony Pajaczkowski	12.00
26	Don Pinhey	5.00
27	Buddy Tinsley	12.00
28	Cookie Gilchrist	35.00
29	Larry Isbell	5.00
30	Bob Kelley	5.00
31	Tom "Corky" Tharp	6.00
32	Steve Patrick	5.00
33	Hardiman Cureton	5.00
34	Joe Mobra	5.00
35	Harry Lunn	5.00
36	Gord Rowland	6.00
37	Herb Gray	15.00
38	Bob Simpson	15.00
39	Cam Fraser	5.00
40	Kenny Ploen	18.00
41	Lynn Bottoms	5.00
42	Bill Stevenson	5.00
43	Jerry Selinger	5.00
44	Oscar Kruger	9.00
45	Gerry James	15.00
46	Dave Mann	12.00
47	Tom Dimitroff	5.00
48	Vince Scott	12.00
49	Fran Rogel	6.00
50	Henry Hair	5.00
51	Bob Bagby	5.00
52	Gerry Doucette	5.00
53	Ken Carpenter	6.00
54	Bernie Faloney	25.00
55	John Barrow	20.00
56	George Druxman	5.00
57	Rollie Miles	12.00

#	Player	Price
58	Jerry Cornelison	5.00
59	Harry Langford	5.00
60	Johnny Bright	20.00
61	Ron Clinkscale	5.00
62	Jack Hill	5.00
63	Ron Quillian	5.00
64	Ted Tully	5.00
65	Pete Neft	5.00
66	Arvyd Buntins	5.00
67	Normie Kwong	20.00
68	Matt Phillips	5.00
69	Pete Bennett	5.00
70	Vern Lofstrom	5.00
71	Norm Stoneburgh	5.00
72	Danny Nykoluk	5.00
73	Chuck Dubuque	5.00
74	John Varone	5.00
75	Bob Kimoff	5.00
76	John Pyeatt	5.00
77	Pete Neumann	12.00
78	Ernie Pitts	9.00
79	Steve Oneschuk	5.00
80	Kaye Vaughan	12.00
81	Joe Yamauchi	5.00
82	Harvey Wylie	9.00
83	Berdett Hess	5.00
84	Dick Shatto	20.00
85	Floyd Harrawood	5.00
86	Ron Atchison	12.00
87	Bobby Judd	5.00
88	Keith Pearce	9.00

1959 Topps CFL

		NM
Complete Set (88):		400.00
Common Player:		4.00
1	Norm Rauhaus	10.00
2	Cornel Piper (UER) (Misspelled Cornell on both sides)	4.00
3	Leo Lewis	20.00
4	Roger Savoie	4.00
5	Jim Van Pelt	10.00
6	Herb Gray	10.00
7	Gerry James	10.00
8	By Bailey	12.00
9	Tom Hinton	8.00
10	Chuck Quilter	4.00
11	Mel Gillett	4.00
12	Ted Hunt	4.00
13	Sonny Homer	5.00
14	Bill Jessup	4.00
15	Al Dorow (Checklist 1-44 back)	20.00
16	Norm Fieldgate	12.00
17	Urban Henry	5.00
18	Paul Cameron	4.00
19	Bruce Claridge	4.00
20	Jim Bakhtiar	4.00
21	Earl Lunsford	12.00
22	Walt Radzick	4.00
23	Ron Albright	4.00
24	Art Scullion	4.00
25	Ernie Warlick	6.00
26	Nobby Wirkowski	5.00
27	Harvey Wylie	4.00
28	Gordon Brown	4.00
29	Don Luzzi	10.00
30	Hal Patterson	20.00
31	Jackie Simpson	15.00
32	Doug McNichol	4.00
33	Bob MacLellan	4.00
34	Ted Elsby	4.00
35	Mike Kovac	4.00
36	Bob Leary	4.00
37	Hal Krebs	4.00
38	Steve Jennings	4.00
39	Don Getty	12.00
40	Normie Kwong	12.00
41	Johnny Bright	15.00
42	Art Walker	5.00
43	Jackie Parker (UER) (Incorrectly listed as Tackle on card front)	35.00
44	Don Barry (Checklist 45-88 back)	20.00
45	Tommy Joe Coffey	25.00
46	Mike Volcan	4.00
47	Stan Renning	4.00
48	Gino Fracas	9.00
49	Ted Smale	4.00
50	Mack Yoho	5.00
51	Bobby Gravens	4.00
52	Milt Graham	4.00
53	Lou Bruce	4.00
54	Bob Simpson	12.00
55	Bill Sowalski	4.00
56	Russ Jackson	40.00
57	Don Clark	4.00
58	Dave Thelen	10.00
59	Larry Cowart	4.00
60	Dave Mann	5.00
61	Norm Stoneburgh (UER) (Misspelled Stoneburg)	4.00
62	Ronnie Knox	9.00
63	Dick Shatto	12.00
64	Bobby Kuntz	4.00
65	Phil Muntz	4.00
66	Gerry Doucette	4.00
67	Sam DeLuca	5.00
68	Boyd Carter	4.00
69	Vic Kristopaitis	9.00
70	Gerry McDougall (UER) (Misspelled Jerry)	5.00
71	Vince Scott	10.00
72	Angelo Mosca	35.00
73	Chet Miksza	4.00
74	Eddie Macon	5.00
75	Harry Lampman	4.00
76	Bill Graham	4.00
77	Ralph Goldston	5.00
78	Cam Fraser	4.00
79	Ron Dundas	4.00
80	Bill Clarke	4.00
81	Len Legault	4.00
82	Reg Whitehouse	4.00
83	Dale Parsons	4.00
84	Doug Kiloh	4.00
85	Tom Whitehouse	4.00
86	Mike Hagler	4.00
87	Paul Anderson	4.00
88	Danny Banda	5.00

1960 Topps CFL

		NM
Complete Set (88):		500.00
Common Player:		4.00
1	By Bailey	12.00
2	Paul Cameron	4.00
3	Bruce Claridge	4.00
4	Chuck Dubuque	4.00
5	Randy Duncan	12.00
6	Norm Fieldgate	10.00
7	Urban Henry	5.00
8	Ted Hunt	4.00
9	Bill Jessup	4.00
10	Ted Tully	4.00
11	Vic Chapman	4.00
12	Gino Fracas	5.00
13	Don Getty	10.00
14	Ed Gray	4.00
15	Oscar Kruger (Checklist 1-44 back)	20.00
16	Rollie Miles	10.00
17	Jackie Parker	30.00
18	Joe-Bob Smith (UER) (Misspelled Bob-Joe on both sides)	4.00
19	Mike Volcan	4.00
20	Art Walker	5.00
21	Ron Albright	4.00
22	Jim Bakhtiar	4.00
23	Lynn Bottoms	5.00
24	Jack Gotta	8.00
25	Joe Kapp	50.00
26	Earl Lunsford	9.00
27	Don Luzzi	9.00
28	Art Scullion	4.00
29	Hugh Simpson	4.00
30	Ernie Warlick	8.00
31	John Barrow	12.00
32	Paul Dekker	4.00
33	Bernie Faloney	20.00
34	Cam Fraser	4.00
35	Ralph Goldston	5.00
36	Ron Howell	5.00
37	Gerry McDougall (UER) (Misspelled Jerry)	4.00
38	Angelo Mosca	20.00
39	Pete Neumann	8.00
40	Vince Scott	8.00
41	Ted Elsby	4.00
42	Sam Etcheverry	25.00
43	Mike Kovac	4.00
44	Ed Learn	4.00
45	Ivan Livingstone (Checklist 45-88 back)	20.00
46	Hal Patterson	18.00
47	Jackie Simpson	12.00
48	Veryl Switzer	4.00
49	Bill Bewley	9.00
50	Joel Wells	4.00
51	Ron Atchison	9.00
52	Ken Carpenter	5.00
53	Bill Clarke	4.00
54	Ron Dundas	4.00
55	Mike Hagler	4.00
56	Jack Hill	4.00
57	Doug Kiloh	4.00
58	Bobby Marlow	10.00
59	Bob Mulgado	4.00
60	George Brancato	4.00
61	Lou Bruce	4.00
62	Hardiman Cureton	4.00
63	Russ Jackson	25.00
64	Gerry Nesbitt	4.00
65	Bob Simpson	10.00
66	Ted Smale	4.00
67	Dave Thelen	9.00
68	Kaye Vaughan	8.00
69	Pete Bennett	4.00
70	Boyd Carter	4.00
71	Gerry Doucette	4.00
72	Bobby Kuntz	5.00
73	Alex Panton	4.00
74	Tobin Rote	18.00
75	Jim Rountree	5.00
76	Dick Shatto	10.00
77	Norm Stoneburgh	4.00
78	Tom "Corky" Tharp	5.00
79	George Druxman	4.00
80	Herb Gray	10.00
81	Gerry James	10.00
82	Leo Lewis	10.00
83	Ernie Pitts	4.00
84	Kenny Ploen	15.00
85	Norm Rauhaus	4.00
86	Gord Rowland	4.00
87	Charlie Shepard	5.00
88	Don Clark	10.00

1961 Topps CFL

		NM
Complete Set (132):		900.00
Common Player:		6.00
1	By Bailey	15.00
2	Bruce Claridge	6.00
3	Norm Fieldgate	12.00
4	Willie Fleming	20.00
5	Urban Henry	7.50
6	Bill Herron	6.00
7	Tom Hinton	10.00
8	Sonny Homer	6.00
9	Bob Jeter	15.00
10	Vic Kristopaitis	6.00
11	Baz Nagle	6.00
12	Ron Watton	6.00
13	Joe Yamauchi	6.00
14	Bob Schloredt	15.00
15	B.C. Lions Team	12.00
16	Ron Albright	6.00
17	Gordon Brown	6.00
18	Gerry Doucette	6.00
19	Gene Filipski	6.00
20	Joe Kapp	30.00
21	Earl Lunsford	12.00
22	Don Luzzi	12.00
23	Bill McKenna	6.00
24	Ron Morris	6.00
25	Tony Pajaczkowski	12.00
26	Lorne Reid	6.00
27	Art Scullion	6.00
28	Ernie Warlick	10.00
29	Stampeders Team	12.00
30	Johnny Bright	15.00
31	Vic Chapman	6.00
32	Gino Fracas	7.50
33	Tommy Joe Coffey	18.00
34	Don Getty	15.00
35	Ed Gray	6.00
36	Oscar Kruger	7.50
37	Rollie Miles	12.00
38	Roger Nelson	6.00
39	Jackie Parker	35.00
40	Howie Schumm	6.00
41	Joe-Bob Smith (UER) (Misspelled Bob-Joe on both sides)	6.00
42	Art Walker	7.50
43	Eskimos Team	12.00
44	John Barrow	15.00
45	Paul Dekker	6.00
46	Tom Dublinski	6.00
47	Bernie Faloney	25.00
48	Cam Fraser	6.00
49	Ralph Goldston	7.50
50	Ron Howell	6.00
51	Gerry McDougall	7.50
52	Pete Neumann	12.00
53	Bronko Nagurski	15.00
54	Vince Scott	10.00
55	Steve Oneschuk	7.50
56	Hal Patterson	20.00
57	Jim Taylor	7.50
58	Tiger-Cats Team	12.00
59	Ted Elsby	6.00
60	Don Clark	7.50
61	Dick Cohee	10.00
62	George Dixon	20.00
63	Wes Gideon	6.00
64	Harry Lampman	6.00
65	Meco Poliziani	6.00
66	Charles Baillie	6.00
67	Howard Cissell	6.00
68	Ed Learn	6.00
69	Tom Moran	6.00
70	Jack Simpson	12.00
71	Bill Bewley	7.50
72	Tom Hugo	6.00
73	Alouettes Team	15.00
74	Gilles Archambeault	6.00
75	Lou Bruce	6.00
76	Russ Jackson	30.00
77	Tom Jones	6.00
78	Gerry Nesbitt	6.00
79	Ron Lancaster	40.00
80	Joe Kelly	6.00
81	Joe Poirier	7.50
82	Doug Daigneault	6.00
83	Kaye Vaughan	10.00
84	Dave Thelen	15.00
85	Ron Stewart	25.00
86	Ted Smale	6.00
87	Bob Simpson	15.00
88	Ottawa Rough Riders Team	12.00
89	Don Allard	6.00
90	Ron Atchison	12.00
91	Bill Clarke	6.00
92	Ron Dundas	6.00
93	Jack Gotta	10.00
94	Bob Golic	7.50
95	Jack Hill	6.00
96	Doug Kiloh	7.50
97	Len Legault	6.00
98	Doug McKenzie	6.00
99	Bob Ptacek	6.00
100	Roy Smith	6.00
101	Saskatchewan Roughriders Team	12.00
102	Checklist 1-132	90.00
103	Jim Andreotti	7.50
104	Boyd Carter	6.00
105	Dick Fouts	7.50
106	Cookie Gilchrist	25.00
107	Bobby Kuntz	7.50
108	Jim Rountree	7.50
109	Dick Shatto	15.00
110	Norm Stoneburgh	6.00
111	Dave Mann	10.00
112	Ed Ochiena	6.00
113	Bill Stribling	6.00
114	Tobin Rote	20.00
115	Stan Wallace	6.00
116	Billy Shipp	7.50
117	Argonauts Team	15.00
118	Dave Burkholder	6.00
119	Jack Delveaux	6.00
120	George Druxman	6.00
121	Farrell Funston	7.50
122	Herb Gray	12.00
123	Gerry James	12.00
124	Ronnie Latourelle	6.00
125	Leo Lewis	15.00
126	Steve Patrick	6.00
127	Ernie Pitts	6.00
128	Kenny Ploen	15.00
129	Norm Rauhaus	7.50
130	Gord Rowland	7.50
131	Charlie Shepard	7.50
132	Winnipeg Blue Bombers Team Card	20.00

1961 Topps CFL Transfers

		NM
Complete Set (24):		700.00
Common Player (1-15):		25.00
Common Team (19-27):		20.00
1	Don Clark	30.00
2	Gene Filipski	30.00
3	Willie Fleming	40.00
4	Cookie Gilchrist	45.00
5	Jack Hill	25.00
6	Bob Jeter	30.00
7	Joe Kapp	65.00
8	Leo Lewis	40.00
9	Gerry McDougall	25.00
10	Jackie Parker	50.00
11	Hal Patterson	40.00
12	Kenny Ploen	40.00
13	Bob Ptacek	25.00
14	Ron Stewart	40.00
15	Dave Thelen	40.00
16	British Columbia Lions Logo/Pennant	20.00
20	Calgary Stampeders Logo/Pennant	20.00
21	Edmonton Eskimos Logo/Pennant	20.00
22	Hamilton Tiger-Cats Logo/Pennant	20.00
23	Montreal Alouettes Logo/Pennant	20.00
24	Ottawa Rough Riders Logo/Pennant	20.00
25	Saskatchewan Roughriders Logo/Pennant	20.00
26	Toronto Argonauts Logo/Pennant	20.00
27	Winnipeg Blue Bombers Logo/Pennant	20.00

1962 Topps CFL

		NM
Complete Set (169):		500.00
Common Player (1-169):		2.00
1	By Bailey	6.00
2	Nub Beamer	2.00
3	Tom Brown	8.00
4	Mack Burton	2.00
5	Mike Cacic	2.00
6	Pat Claridge	2.00
7	Steve Cotter	2.00
8	Lonnie Dennis	2.00
9	Norm Fieldgate	5.00
10	Willie Fleming	10.00
11	Tom Hinton	4.00
12	Sonny Homer	3.00
13	Joe Kapp	14.00
14	Tom Larscheid	2.00
15	Gordie Mitchell	2.00
16	Baz Nagle	2.00
17	Norris Stevenson	2.00
18	Barney Therrien (UER) (Misspelled Therien on card front)	2.00
19	Don Vicic	2.00
20	B.C. Lions Team	8.00
21	Ed Buchanan	2.00
22	Joe Carruthers	2.00
23	Lovell Coleman	4.00
24	Barrie Cyr	2.00
25	Ernie Danjean	3.00
26	Gene Filipski	4.00
27	George Hansen	2.00
28	Earl Lunsford	5.00
29	Don Luzzi	4.00
30	Bill McKenna	2.00
31	Tony Pajaczkowski	4.00
32	Chuck Quilter	2.00
33	Lorne Reid	2.00
34	Art Scullion	2.00
35	Jim Walden	2.00
36	Harvey Wylie	2.00
37	Calgary Stampeders Team Card	8.00
38	Johnny Bright	10.00
39	Vic Chapman	2.00
40	Marion Drew Deese	2.00
41	Al Ecuyer	2.00
42	Gino Fracas	3.00
43	Don Getty	6.00
44	Ed Gray	2.00
45	Urban Henry	3.00
46	Bill Hill	2.00
47	Mike Kmeche	2.00
48	Oscar Kruger	3.00
49	Mike Lashuk	2.00
50	Jim Letcavits	2.00
51	Roger Nelson	4.00
52	Jackie Parker	15.00
53	Howie Schumm	2.00
54	Jim Shipka	2.00
55	Bill Smith	2.00
56	Jo Bob Smith	2.00
57	Art Walker	2.00
58	Edmonton Eskimos Team Card	8.00
59	John Barrow	8.00
60	Hardiman Cureton	2.00
61	Geno DeNobile	2.00
62	Tom Dublinski	2.00
63	Bernie Faloney	12.00
64	Cam Fraser	2.00
65	Ralph Goldston	3.00
66	Tommy Grant	7.00
67	Garney Henley	15.00
68	Ron Howell	2.00
69	Zeno Karcz	3.00
70	Gerry McDougall (UER) (Misspelled Jerry)	3.00
71	Chet Miksza	2.00
72	Bronko Nagurski	6.00
73	Hal Patterson	10.00
74	George Scott	2.00
75	Vince Scott	4.00
76	Hamilton Tiger-Cats Team Card	8.00
77	Ron Brewer	3.00
78	Ron Brooks	2.00
79	Howard Cissell	2.00
80	Don Clark	3.00
81	Dick Cohee	2.00
82	John Conroy	2.00
83	Milt Crain	2.00
84	Ted Elsby	2.00
85	Joe Francis	3.00
86	Gene Gaines	8.00
87	Barrie Hansen	2.00
88	Mike Kovac	2.00
89	Ed Learn	2.00
90	Billy Ray Locklin	2.00
91	Marv Luster	6.00
92	Bobby Jack Oliver	3.00
93	Sandy Stephens	8.00
94	Montreal Alouettes Team Card	10.00
95	Gilles Archambeault	2.00
96	Bruno Bitkowski	3.00
97	Jim Conroy	3.00
98	Doug Daigneault	2.00
99	Dick Desmarais	2.00
100	Russ Jackson	15.00
101	Tom Jones	2.00
102	Ron Lancaster	20.00
103	Angelo Mosca	15.00
104	Gerry Nesbitt	2.00
105	Joe Poirier	3.00
106	Moe Racine	2.00
107	Gary Schreider	2.00
108	Bob Simpson	6.00
109	Ted Smale	2.00
110	Ron Stewart	7.00
111	Dave Thelen	6.00
112	Kaye Vaughan	4.00
113	Ottawa Rough Ridgers Team Card	8.00
114	Ron Atchison (UER) (Misspelled Atcheson on card front)	4.00
115	Danny Banda	2.00
116	Al Benecick	2.00
117	Clair Branch	2.00
118	Fred Burket	2.00
119	Bill Clarke	2.00
120	Jim Copeland	2.00
121	Ron Dundas	2.00
122	Bob Golic	2.00
123	Jack Gotta	4.00
124	Dave Grosz	2.00
125	Neil Habig	3.00
126	Jack Hill	2.00
127	Len Legault	2.00
128	Bob Ptacek	2.00
129	Roy Smith	2.00
130	Saskatchewan Roughriders Team Card	8.00
131	Lynn Bottoms	3.00
132	Dick Fouts	3.00
133	Wes Gideon	2.00
134	Cookie Gilchrist	15.00
135	Art Johnson	2.00
136	Bobby Kuntz	2.00
137	Dave Mann	4.00
138	Marty Martinello	2.00
139	Doug McNichol	2.00
140	Bill Mitchell	2.00
141	Danny Nykoluk	2.00
142	Walt Radzick	2.00
143	Tobin Rote	10.00
144	Jim Rountree	3.00
145	Dick Shatto	8.00
146	Billy Shipp	3.00
147	Norm Stoneburgh	2.00
148	Toronto Argonauts Team Card	10.00
149	Dave Burkholder	2.00
150	Jack Delveaux	2.00
151	George Druxman	2.00
152	Farrell Funston	3.00
153	Herb Gray	5.00
154	Roger Hagberg	2.00
155	Gerry James	6.00
156	Henry Janzen	2.00
157	Ronnie Latourelle	2.00
158	Hal Ledyard	2.00
159	Leo Lewis	6.00
160	Steve Patrick	2.00
161	Cornel Piper	2.00
162	Ernie Pitts	2.00
163	Kenny Ploen	6.00
164	Norm Rauhaus	3.00
165	Frank Rigney	6.00
166	Gord Rowland	3.00
167	Roger Savoie	2.00
168	Charlie Shepard	3.00
169	Winnipeg Blue Bombers Team Card	20.00

1963 Topps CFL

		NM
Complete Set (88):		300.00
Common Player (1-88):		2.50
1	Willie Fleming	12.00
2	Dick Fouts	3.50
3	Joe Kapp	15.00
4	Nub Beamer	2.50
5	By Bailey	6.00
6	Tom Walker	2.50
7	Sonny Homer	3.50
8	Tom Hinton	5.00
9	Lonnie Dennis	2.50
10	British Columbia Lions Team Card	7.50
11	Ed Buchanan	2.50
12	Ernie Danjean	2.50
13	Eagle Day	6.00
14	Earl Lunsford	5.00
15	Don Luzzi	5.00
16	Tony Pajaczkowski	5.00
17	Jerry Keeling	15.00
18	Pat Holmes	2.50
19	Wayne Harris	15.00
20	Calgary Stampeders Team Card	7.50
21	Tommy Joe Coffey	7.50
22	Mike Lashuk	2.50
23	Bobby Walden	5.00
24	Don Getty	8.00
25	Len Vella	2.50
26	Ted Frechette	2.50
27	E.A. Sims	2.50
28	Nat Dye	2.50
29	Edmonton Eskimos Team Card	7.50
30	Bernie Faloney	10.00
31	Hal Patterson	8.00
32	John Barrow	6.00
33	Sam Fernandez	2.50
34	Garney Henley	12.00
35	Joe Zuger	5.00
36	Hardiman Cureton	2.50
37	Zeno Karcz	2.50
38	Bobby Kuntz	3.50
39	Hamilton Tiger-Cats Team Card	7.50
40	George Dixon	6.00
41	Don Clark	3.50
42	Marv Luster	5.00
43	Bobby Jack Oliver	3.50
44	Billy Ray Locklin	2.50
45	Sandy Stephens	6.00
46	Milt Crain	3.50
47	Meco Poliziani	2.50
48	Ted Elsby	2.50
49	Montreal Alouettes Team Card	9.00
50	Russ Jackson	15.00
51	Ron Stewart	8.00
52	Dave Thelen	6.00
53	Kaye Vaughan	5.00
54	Joe Poirier	3.50
55	Moe Racine	2.50
56	Whit Tucker	10.00
57	Ernie White	2.50
58	Ottawa Rough Ridgers Team Card	7.50
59	Bob Ptacek	2.50
60	Ray Purdin	2.50
61	Dale West	3.50
62	Neil Habig	2.50

No.	Player	Price
63	Jack Gotta	3.50
64	Billy Gray	2.50
65	Don Walsh	2.50
66	Bill Clarke	2.50
67	Saskatchewan Roughriders Team Card	7.50
68	Jackie Parker	15.00
69	Dave Mann	5.00
70	Dick Shatto	6.00
71	Norm Stoneburgh (UER) (Misspelled Stoneburg front)	2.50
72	Clare Exelby	2.50
73	Art Johnson	2.50
74	Doug McNichol	2.50
75	Danny Nykoluk	2.50
76	Walt Radzick	2.50
77	Toronto Argonauts Team Card	9.00
78	Leo Lewis	6.00
79	Kenny Ploen	7.00
80	Henry Janzen	3.50
81	Charlie Shepard	3.50
82	Roger Hagberg	3.50
83	Herb Gray	6.00
84	Frank Rigney	5.00
85	Jack Delveaux	2.50
86	Ronnie Latourelle	2.50
87	Winnipeg Blue Bombers Team Card	7.50
88	Checklist Card	50.00

1964 Topps CFL

NM

Complete Set (88): 300.00
Common Player (1-88): 2.50

No.	Player	Price
1	Willie Fleming	12.00
2	Dick Fouts	3.50
3	Joe Kapp	15.00
4	Nub Beamer	2.50
5	Tom Brown	5.00
6	Tom Walker	2.50
7	Sonny Homer	3.50
8	Tom Hinton	5.00
9	Lonnie Dennis	2.50
10	B.C. Lions Team	7.50
11	Lovell Coleman	4.00
12	Ernie Danjean	2.50
13	Eagle Day	5.00
14	Jim Furlong	2.50
15	Don Luzzi	5.00
16	Tony Pajaczkowski	5.00
17	Jerry Keeling	6.00
18	Pat Holmes	2.50
19	Wayne Harris	7.50
20	Calgary Stampeders Team Card	7.50
21	Tommy Joe Coffey	7.50
22	Al Ecuyer	2.50
23	Checklist Card	35.00
24	Don Getty	6.00
25	Len Vella	2.50
26	Ted Frechette	2.50
27	E.A. Sims	2.50
28	Nat Dye	2.50
29	Edmonton Eskimos Team Card	7.50
30	Bernie Faloney	15.00
31	Hal Patterson	8.00
32	John Barrow	6.00
33	Tommy Grant	6.00
34	Garney Henley	9.00
35	Joe Zuger	3.50
36	Hardiman Cureton	2.50
37	Zeno Karcz	3.50
38	Bobby Kuntz	3.50
39	Hamilton Tiger-Cats Team Card	7.50
40	George Dixon	7.50
41	Dave Hoppmann	2.50
42	Dick Walton	2.50
43	Jim Andreotti	3.50
44	Billy Ray Locklin	2.50
45	Fred Burket	2.50
46	Milt Crane	3.50
47	Meco Poliziani	2.50
48	Ted Elsby	2.50
49	Montreal Alouettes Team Card	9.00
50	Russ Jackson	15.00
51	Ron Stewart	8.00
52	Dave Thelen	5.00
53	Kaye Vaughan	5.00
54	Joe Poirier	3.50
55	Moe Racine	2.50
56	Whit Tucker	6.00
57	Ernie White	2.50
58	Ottawa Roughriders Team Card	7.50
59	Bob Ptacek	2.50
60	Ray Purdin	2.50
61	Dale West	3.50
62	Neil Habig	2.50
63	Jack Gotta	3.50
64	Billy Gray	2.50
65	Don Walsh	2.50
66	Bill Clarke	2.50
67	Saskatchewan Roughriders Team Card	7.50
68	Jackie Parker	15.00
69	Dave Mann	4.00
70	Dick Shatto	6.00
71	Norm Stoneburgh	2.50
72	Clare Exelby	2.50
73	Jim Christopherson	2.50
74	Sherman Lewis	6.00
75	Danny Nykoluk	2.50
76	Walt Radzick	2.50
77	Toronto Argonauts Team Card	9.00
78	Leo Lewis	6.00
79	Kenny Ploen	6.00
80	Henry Janzen	3.50
81	Charlie Shepard	3.50
82	Roger Hagberg	3.50
83	Herb Gray	6.00
84	Frank Rigney	5.00
85	Jack Delveaux	2.50
86	Ronnie Latourelle	2.50
87	Winnipeg Blue Bombers Team Card	7.50
88	Checklist Card	50.00

1965 Topps CFL

NM

Complete Set (132): 325.00
Common Player (1-132): 2.00

No.	Player	Price
1	Neal Beaumont	6.00
2	Tom Brown	6.00
3	Mike Cacic	2.00
4	Pat Claridge	2.00
5	Steve Cotter	2.00
6	Lonnie Dennis	2.00
7	Norm Fieldgate	4.00
8	Willie Fleming	10.00
9	Dick Fouts	3.00
10	Tom Hinton	4.00
11	Sonny Homer	3.00
12	Joe Kapp	12.00
13	Paul Seale	2.00
14	Steve Shafer	2.00
15	Bob Swift	2.00
16	Larry Anderson	2.00
17	Lu Bain	2.00
18	Lovell Coleman	3.00
19	Eagle Day	4.00
20	Jim Furlong	2.00
21	Wayne Harris	6.00
22	Herman Harrison	12.00
23	Jerry Keeling	5.00
24	Hal Krebs	2.00
25	Don Luzzi	4.00
26	Tony Pajaczkowski	4.00
27	Larry Robinson	4.00
28	Bob Taylor	3.00
29	Ted Woods	2.00
30	Jon Anabo	2.00
31	Jim Battle	2.00
32	Charlie Brown	2.00
33	Tommy Joe Coffey	7.50
34	Marcel Deleeuw	2.00
35	Al Ecuyer	2.00
36	Jim Higgins	2.00
37	Oscar Kruger	3.00
38	Barry Mitchelson	2.00
39	Roger Nelson	4.00
40	Bill Redell	2.00
41	E.A. Sims	2.00
42	Jim Stinnette	2.00
43	Jim Thomas	2.00
44	Terry Wilson	2.00
45	Art Baker	2.00
46	John Barrow	6.00
47	Dick Cohee	3.00
48	Frank Cosentino	4.00
49	Johnny Counts	2.00
50	Tommy Grant	5.00
51	Garney Henley (See also number 57)	9.00
52	Zeno Karcz	3.00
53	Ellison Kelly	12.00
54	Bobby Kuntz	3.00
55	Angelo Mosca	12.00
56	Bronko Nagurski	6.00
57	Don Sutherin (UER) (number 51 on back)	12.00
58	Dave Viti	2.00
59	Joe Zuger	3.00
60	Checklist 1-60	25.00
61	Jim Andreotti	3.00
62	Harold Cooley	2.00
63	Nat Craddock	2.00
64	George Dixon	6.00
65	Ted Elsby	2.00
66	Clare Exelby	2.00
67	Bernie Faloney	12.00
68	Al Irwin	2.00
69	Ed Learn	2.00
70	Moe Levesque	2.00
71	Bob Minihane	2.00
72	Jim Reynolds	2.00
73	Billy Roy	2.00
74	Billy Joe Booth	3.00
75	Jim Cain	2.00
76	Larry DeGraw	2.00
77	Don Estes	2.00
78	Gene Gaines	5.00
79	John Kennerson	2.00
80	Roger Kramer	3.00
81	Ken Lehmann	3.00
82	Bill O'Billovich	3.00
83	Joe Poirier	3.00
84	Bill Quinter	2.00
85	Jerry Selinger	2.00
86	Bill Siekierski	2.00
87	Len Sparks	2.00
88	Whit Tucker	4.00
89	Ron Atchison	4.00
90	Ed Buchanan	2.00
91	Hugh Campbell	10.00
92	Henry Dorsch	2.00
93	Garner Ekstran	3.00
94	Martin Fabi	2.00
95	Bob Good	2.00
96	Ron Lancaster	12.00
97	Bob Ptacek	2.00
98	George Reed	25.00
99	Wayne Shaw	2.00
100	Dale West	3.00
101	Reg Whitehouse	2.00
102	Jim Worden	2.00
103	Ron Brewer	3.00
104	Don Fuell	2.00
105	Ed Harrington	3.00
106	George Hughley	2.00
107	Dave Mann	2.00
108	Marty Martinello	2.00
109	Danny Nykoluk	2.00
110	Jackie Parker	15.00
111	Dave Pivec	2.00
112	Walt Radzick	2.00
113	Lee Sampson	2.00
114	Dick Shatto	5.00
115	Norm Stoneburgh	2.00
116	Jim Vollenweider	2.00
117	John Wydareny	3.00
118	Billy Cooper	2.00
119	Farrell Funston	3.00
120	Herb Gray	5.00
121	Henry Janzen	3.00
122	Leo Lewis	6.00
123	Brian Palmer	2.00
124	Cornel Piper	2.00
125	Ernie Pitts	3.00
126	Kenny Ploen	6.00
127	Norm Rauhaus	3.00
128	Frank Rigney	4.00
129	Roger Savoie	2.00
130	Dick Thornton	4.00
131	Bill Whisler	2.00
132	Checklist 61-132	40.00

1965 Topps CFL Transfers

NM

Complete Set (27): 500.00
Common Player (1-27): 20.00

No.	Player	Price
1	British Columbia Lions Crest	20.00
2	British Columbia Lions Pennant	20.00
3	Calgary Stampeders Crest	20.00
4	Calgary Stampeders Pennant	20.00
5	Edmonton Eskimos Crest	20.00
6	Edmonton Eskimos Pennant	20.00
7	Hamilton Tiger-Cats Crest	20.00
8	Hamilton Tiger-Cats Pennant	20.00
9	Montreal Alouettes Crest	20.00
10	Montreal Alouettes Pennant	20.00
11	Ottawa Rough Riders Crest	20.00
12	Ottawa Rough Riders Pennant	20.00
13	Saskatchewan Roughriders Crest	20.00
14	Saskatchewan Roughriders Pennant	20.00
15	Toronto Argonauts Crest	20.00
16	Toronto Argonauts Pennant	20.00
17	Winnipeg Blue Bombers Crest	20.00
18	Winnipeg Blue Bombers Pennant	20.00
19	Quebec Provincial Crest	20.00
20	Ontario Provincial Crest	20.00
21	Manitoba Provincial Crest	20.00
22	Saskatchewan Provincial Crest	20.00
23	Alberta Provincial Crest	20.00
24	British Columbia Provincial Crest	20.00
25	Northwest Territories Crest	20.00
26	Yukon Territory Territorial Crest	20.00
27	Canada	30.00

1988 Vachon CFL

MT

Complete Set: (160) 135.00
Common Player (1-160): .75

No.	Player	Price
1	Dave Albright	1.00
2	Roger Aldag	1.00
3	Marv Allemang	.75
4	Damon Allen	2.50
5	Gary Allen	1.00
6	Randy Ambrosie	.75
7	Mike Anderson	.75
8	Kent Austin	4.00
9	Terry Baker	1.00
10	Danny Bass	3.00
11	Nick Bastaja	.75
12	Greg Battle	2.50
13	Lyle Bauer	.75
14	Jearld Baylis	2.00
15	Ian Beckstead	.75
16	Walter Bender	1.50
17	Nick Benjamin	1.00
18	David Black	.75
19	Leo Blanchard	.75
20	Trevor Bowles	.75
21	Ken Braden	.75
22	Rod Brown	.75
23	Less Browne	1.00
24	Jamie Buis	.75
25	Tom Burgess	3.50
26	Bob Cameron	1.00
27	Jan Carinci	.75
28	Tony Champion	2.50
29	Jacques Chapdelaine	.75
30	Tony Cherry	2.50
31	Lance Chomyc	1.00
32	John Congemi	.75
33	Rod Connop	.75
34	David Conrad	.75
35	Grover Covington	2.00
36	Larry Crawford	1.25
37	James Curry	.75
38	Marco Cyncar	1.00
39	Gabriel DeLaGarza	.75
40	Mike Derks	.75
41	Blake Dermott	1.00
42	Roy DeWalt (SP)	4.00
43	Todd Dillon	1.25
44	Rocky DiPietro	2.00
45	Kevin Dixon (SP)	2.00
46	Tom Dixon	.75
47	Selwyn Drain	.75
48	Matt Dunigan	7.50
49	Ray Elgaard	3.00
50	Jerome Erdman	.75
51	Randy Fabi	.75
52	Gill Fenerty	2.00
53	Denny Ferdinand	1.00
54	Dan Ferrone	1.00
55	Howard Fields	.75
56	Matt Finlay	.75
57	Rickey Foggie	2.00
58	Delbert Fowler	1.00
59	Ed Gataveckas	.75
60	Keith Gooch	.75
61	Miles Gorrell	.75
62	Mike Gray	.75
63	Leo Groenewegen	.75
64	Ken Hailey	.75
65	Harold Hallman	1.00
66	Tracy Ham	5.00
67	Rodney Harding	2.00
68	Glenn Harper	.75
69	J.T. Hay	.75
70	Larry Hogue	.75
71	Ron Hopkins (SP)	2.00
72	Hank Ilesic	.75
73	Bryan Illerbrun	.75
74	Lemont Jeffers	.75
75	James Jefferson	2.00
76	Rick Johnson	.75
77	Chris Johnstone	.75
78	Johnnie Jones	.75
79	Milson Jones	1.50
80	Stephen Jones	2.00
81	Bobby Jurasin	2.50
82	Jerry Kauric	1.00
83	Dan Kearns	.75
84	Trevor Kennerd	2.00
85	Mike Kerrigan	4.00
86	Rick Klassen	2.00
87	Lee Knight	.75
88	Kevin Konar	1.00
89	Glenn Kulka	1.25
90	Doug (Tank) Landry	2.00
91	Scott Lewis	.75
92	Orville Lee	1.50
93	Marc Lewis	1.00
94	Eddie Lowe	.75
95	Lynn Madsen	.75
96	Chris Major	3.00
97	Doran Major	.75
98	Tony Martino	.75
99	Tim McCray	1.25
100	Michael McGruder	1.25
101	Sean McKeown (SP)	4.00
102	Andy McVey	.75
103	Stan Mikawos	.75
104	James Mills	2.00
105	Larry Mohr	.75
106	Bernie Morrison	.75
107	James Murphy	1.50
108	Paul Osbaldiston	1.00
109	Anthony Parker	1.50
110	James Parker	2.00
111	Greg Peterson	.75
112	Tim Petros	1.25
113	Reggie Pleasant	1.25
114	Willie Pless	.75
115	Bob Poley	.75
116	Tom Porras	1.50
117	Hector Pothier	.75
118	Jim Reid	1.50
119	Robert Reid	.75
120	Gilbert Renfroe	2.00
121	Tom Richards	1.25
122	Dave Ridgway	2.00
123	Rae Robirtis	.75
124	Gerald Roper	.75
125	Darryl Sampson	.75
126	Jim Sandusky	2.50
127	David Sauve	.75
128	Art Schlichter	2.00
129	Ralph Scholz	.75
130	Mark Seale	1.00
131	Dan Sellers	.75
132	Lance Shields	1.00
133	Ian Sinclair	1.50
134	Mike Siroishka	.75
135	Chris Skinner	.75
136	Harry Skipper	1.00
137	Darrell Smith	3.00
138	Tom Spoletini	.75
139	Steve Stapler	1.00
140	Bill Stevenson	.75
141	Gregg Stumon	1.25
142	Glen Suitor	.75
143	Emmanuel Tolbert	2.50
144	Perry Tuttle (SP)	4.00
145	Peter VandenBos	.75
146	Jake Vaughan	.75
147	Chris Walby	1.50
148	Mike Walker	1.50
149	Patrick Wayne	.75
150	James West	1.00
151	Brett Williams	1.50
152	David Williams	2.50
153	Henry Williams	8.00
154	Tommy Williams	.75
155	Larry Willis	1.00
156	Don Wilson	.75
157	Earl Winfield	2.50
158	Rick Worman	2.00
159	Larry Wruck	.75
160	Kari Yli-Renko	.75

1989 Vachon CFL

MT

Complete Set (160): 125.00
Common Player (1-160): .75

No.	Player	Price
1	Tony Williams	1.00
2	Sean Foudy	.75
3	Tom Schimmer	.75
4	Ken Evraire	1.00
5	Gerald Wilcox	1.00
6	Damon Allen	2.00
7	Tony Kimbrough	.75
8	Dean Dorsey	1.00
9	Rocco Romano	.75
10	Ken Braden	.75
11	Kari Yli-Renko	.75
12	Darrel Hopper	.75
13	Irv Daymond	.75
14	Orville Lee	1.00
15	Steve Howlett	.75
16	Kyle Hall	.75
17	Reggie Ward	.75
18	Gerald Alphin	2.00
19	Troy Wilson	.75
20	Patrick Wayne	.75
21	Harold Hallman	1.25
22	John Congemi	1.50
23	Doran Major	.75
24	Hank Ilesic	1.50
25	Gilbert Renfroe	2.00
26	Rodney Harding	1.00
27	Todd Wiseman	.75
28	Chris Schultz	.75
29	Carl Brazley	1.00
30	Darrell Smith	2.50
31	Glenn Kulka	1.00
32	Bob Skemp	.75
33	Don Moen	1.00
34	Jearld Baylis	2.00
35	Lorenzo Graham	.75
36	Warren Hudson	.75
37	Gill Fenerty	2.00
38	Paul Masotti	1.00
39	Reggie Pleasant	1.25
40	Scott Flagel	.75
41	Mike Kerrigan	2.50
42	Frank Robinson	1.00
43	Jacques Chapdelaine	.75
44	Jacques Chapdelaine	.75
45	Miles Gorrell	.75
46	Mike Walker	.75
47	Jason Riley	.75
48	Grover Covington	1.50
49	Ralph Scholz	.75
50	Mike Derks	.75
51	Derrick McAdoo	1.50
52	Rocky DiPietro	2.00
53	Lance Shields	1.00
54	Dale Sanderson	.75
55	Tim Lorenz	.75
56	Rod Skillman	.75
57	Jed Tommy	.75
58	Paul Osbaldiston	1.00
59	Darrell Corbin	.75
60	Tony Champion	1.50
61	Romel Andrews	.75
62	Bob Cameron	.75
63	Greg Battle	2.00
64	Rod Hill	1.00
65	Steve Rodehutskors	1.00
66	Trevor Kennerd	1.50
67	Moustafa Ali	1.00
68	Mike Gray	.75
69	Bob Molle	.75
70	Tim Jessie	1.00
71	Matt Pearce	.75
72	Will Lewis	.75
73	Sean Salisbury	2.50
74	Chris Walby	1.00
75	Jeff Croonen	.75
76	David Black	.75
77	Buster Rhymes	2.00
78	James Murphy	1.50
79	Stan Mikawos	.75
80	Lee Saltz	2.00
81	Bryan Illerbrun	.75
82	Donald Narcisse	3.00
83	Milson Jones	1.00
84	Dave Ridgway	1.50
85	Glen Suitor	.75
86	Terry Baker	1.00
87	James Curry	1.50
88	Harry Skipper	.75
89	Bobby Jurasin	2.00
90	Gary Lewis	.75
91	Roger Aldag	1.00
92	Jeff Fairholm	2.00
93	Dave Albright	.75
94	Ray Elgaard	2.50
95	Kent Austin	3.50
96	Tom Burgess	3.00
97	Richie Hall	.75
98	Eddie Lowe	.75
99	Vince Goldsmith	1.00
100	Tim McCray	1.00
101	Leo Blanchard	.75
102	Tom Spoletini	.75
103	Dan Ferrone	1.00
104	Doug (Tank) Landry	1.50
105	Chris Major	1.50
106	Mike Palumbo	.75
107	Terrence Jones	2.00
108	Larry Willis	1.25
109	Kent Warnock	.75
110	Tim Petros	1.00
111	Marshall Toner	.75
112	Ken Ford	.75
113	Ron Hopkins	.75
114	Eric Kramer	7.50
115	Stu Laird	.75
116	Vernell Quinn	.75
117	Lemont Jeffers	.75
118	Derrick Taylor	.75
119	Jay Christensen	1.00
120	Mitchell Price	.75
121	Rod Connop	.75
122	Mark Norman	.75
123	Andre Francis	1.00
124	Reggie Taylor	1.50
125	Rick Worman	1.00
126	Marco Cyncar	.75
127	Blake Dermott	.75
128	Jerry Kauric	1.00
129	Steve Taylor	2.00
130	Dave Richardson	.75
131	John Mandarich	1.00
132	Gregg Stumon	1.00
133	Tracy Ham	4.00
134	Danny Bass	2.50
135	Blake Marshall	1.50
136	Jeff Braswell	.75
137	Larry Wruck	1.00
138	Warren Jones	.75
139	Stephen Jones	1.50
140	Tom Richards	1.50
141	Tony Cherry	1.50
142	Anthony Parker	.75
143	Gerald Roper	.75
145	Lui Passaglia	2.00
146	Mack Moore	.75
147	Jamie Taras	.75
148	Rickey Foggie	1.50
149	Matt Dunigan	6.00
150	Anthony Drawhorn	1.00
151	Eric Streater	1.25
152	Marcus Thomas	.75
153	Wes Cooper	.75
154	James Mills	1.00
155	Peter VandenBos	.75
156	James Barker	1.50
157	Andrew Murray	.75
158	Larry Crawford	1.25
159	Kevin Konar	1.00
160	David Williams	1.50

1959 Wheaties CFL

NM

Complete Set (48): 4000.
Common Player (1-48): 60.00

No.	Player	Price
1	Ron Adam	60.00
2	Bill Bewley	75.00
3	Lynn Bottoms	60.00
4	Johnny Bright	150.00
5	Ken Carpenter	75.00
6	Tony Curcillo	60.00
7	Sam Etcheverry	200.00
8	Bernie Faloney	200.00
9	Cam Fraser	75.00
10	Don Getty	125.00
11	Jack Gotta	75.00
12	Milt Graham	60.00
13	Jack Hill	60.00
14	Ron Howell	75.00
15	Russ Jackson	200.00

16	Gerry James	125.00
17	Doug Kiloh	60.00
18	Ronnie Knox	75.00
19	Vic Kristopaitis	60.00
20	Oscar Kruger	60.00
21	Bobby Kuntz	75.00
22	Normie Kwong	175.00
23	Leo Lewis	150.00
24	Harry Lunn	60.00
25	Don Luzzi	100.00
26	Dave Mann	75.00
27	Bobby Marlow	90.00
28	Gerry McDougall	75.00
29	Doug McNichol	60.00
30	Rollie Miles	100.00
31	Red O'Quinn	90.00
32	Jackie Parker	250.00
33	Hal Patterson	150.00

34	Don Pinhey	60.00
35	Kenny Ploen	125.00
36	Gord Rowland	75.00
37	Vince Scott	90.00
38	Art Scullion	60.00
39	Dick Shatto	125.00
40	Bob Simpson	125.00
41	Jackie Simpson (UER) (Misspelled Jacki)	100.00
42	Bill Sowalski	60.00
43	Norm Stoneburgh	60.00
44	Buddy Tinsley	90.00
45	Frank Tripucka	100.00
46	Jim Van Pelt	60.00
47	Ernie Warlick	75.00
48	Nobby Wirkowski	100.00

CERTIFIED PRICE GUIDE

1894 Mayo Cut Plug (N302)

CARD	MINT	NM/M+	NM/M	NM+	NM
Common Player:					
Frank Hinkey			4500	2550	2025
Poe	5500	4625		7500	6000

1933 Sport Kings

CARD	MINT	NM/M+	NM/M	NM+	NM
4 Red Grange	5000	3700	3600	1250	1000
6 Jim Thorpe	5000	3750	3000	1650	1350
35 Knute Rockne	5750	4250	3500	1225	1000

1935 National Chicle

CARD	MINT	NM/M+	NM/M	NM+	NM
Common Player, 1-24:	1850	850	700	275	225
Common Player, 25-36:		1200	995	400	325
(All listed cards are Rookie cards)					
1 Dutch Clark				1100	900
7 Ken Strong		4775	3995	375	300
9 Knute Rockne		12000	10000	3000	2450
10 Cliff Battles	4600	2400	1895	375	300
34 Bronko Nagurski				6750	5500
36 Bernie Masterson				1450	1100

1948 Bowman

CARD	MINT	NM/M+	NM/M	NM+	NM
Common Player:	350	180	145	32.50	25
Short-Prints:	450	345	275	95	75
(All listed cards are Rookie cards)					
1 Joe Tereshinski		800	650	125	100
3 Johnny Lujack		1050	875	445	340
7 Steve Van Buren		625	500	215	170
8 Kenny Washington		195	155	75	60
12 Charley Conerly		1075	875	445	340
17 Charlie Trippi		445	355	175	140
22 Sammy Baugh		1550	1250	625	495
26 Bob Waterfield	900	700	575	225	185
36 Bulldog Turner		850	700	350	275
60 Elbert Nickel		445	355	165	135
61 Alex Wojciechowicz		375	290	145	110
63 Pete Pihos		650	525	265	215
80 Bill Dudley		365	290	145	115
95 George McAfee		315	260	140	110
99 Harry Gilmer	1400	515	425	210	170
107 Sid Luckman		800	650	275	225
108 Buford Ray		1225	995	500	400

1948 Leaf

CARD	MINT	NM/M+	NM/M	NM+	NM
Common Player, 1-49:	350	275	225	75	60
Common Player, 50-98:	800	435	350	185	150
(All listed cards are Rookie cards)					
1 Sid Luckman		1825	1500	450	375
3 Bulldog Turner		550	450	110	90
4 Doak Walker		750	600	155	125
6 Bobby Layne		1850	1500	375	300
13 Johnny Lujack		750	600	200	175
15 Charlie Justice		550	450	125	100
16 Pete Pihos		600	475	115	95
17 Kenny Washington		375	300	65	50
19 George McAfee		750	600	145	125
22 Steve Van Buren		850	700	325	275
26 Bob Waterfield		1175	950	325	300
29 Charlie Trippi		750	600	125	100
34 Sammy Baugh		3000	2750	800	650
36 Bill Dudley		525	425	135	110
37 George Connor		500	400	135	110
52 Leo Nomellini		1800	1450	325	250
53 Charley Conerly		1500	1200	325	250
54 Chuck Bednarik		2250	1800	500	400
73 Jackie Jensen		2650	2250	375	300
91 Leon Hart		1000	800	210	165
98 Al DiMarco		1050	850	220	175

1949 Leaf

CARD	MINT	NM/M+	NM/M	NM+	NM
Common Player:		225	175	45	35
1 Bob Hendren(R)		295	235	115	95
15 Sid Luckman		375	310	155	125
16 Charlie Trippi		165	135	70	55
22 Bill Dudley		165	135	70	55
26 Sammy Baugh		1050	850	380	315
28 Pete Pihos	950	165	135	65	50
40 George Connor		165	135	70	55
41 George McAfee		165	135	70	55
49 Charley Conerly		310	245	125	100
56 John Lujack		300	245	125	100
67 Bobby Layne		550	450	220	175
79 Steve Van Buren	950	300	245	125	100
89 Bob Waterfield	950	350	275	145	115
134 Chuck Bednarik		600	475	155	125
150 Bulldog Turner		475	380	190	155

1950 Bowman

CARD	MINT	NM/M+	NM/M	NM+	NM
Common Player:	180	125	100	32.50	25
1 Doak Walker	1450	1000	800	450	350
5 Y.A. Tittle(R)	2100	1175	950	325	275
6 Lou Groza(R)	1050	715	575	225	175
9 Tony Canadeo(R)	365	210	170	80	65
15 Tank Younger(R)	380	235	185	65	50
16 Glenn Davis(R)	1000	500	400	155	125
17 Bob Waterfield	800	410	325	105	85
23 Steve Van Buren	600	345	275	70	55
26 John Lujack	700	410	325	105	85
27 Sid Luckman	875	575	450	100	75
28 Bulldog Turner	325	185	150	55	45
29 Bill Dudley	325	240	195	70	55
35 Joe Perry(R)	1100	650	525	225	175
36 Frankie Albert(R)	325	175	145	45	35
37 Bobby Layne	1000	615	495	190	155
43 Marion Motley(R)	1250	600	475	185	150
45 Otto Graham(R)	2400	1250	1000	440	350
51 Tom Fears(R)	600	345	275	95	75
52 Elroy Hirsch(R)	1000	620	495	220	175
78 Dante Lavelli(R)	555	325	255	95	75
100 Sammy Baugh	1250	950	750	200	160
103 Charley Conerly	650	325	250	95	75
107 Leo Nomellini	625	315	250	90	70
123 Buddy Young(R)	400	220	180	65	50
128 Jim Finks(R)	325	220	175	60	45
129 Charlie Trippi	375	250	200	70	55
132 Chuck Bednarik	550	360	290	90	70
134 Pete Pihos	500	175	145	60	45
144 Knox Ramsey(R)	875	575	450	100	75

1951 Bowman

CARD	MINT	NM/M+	NM/M	NM+	NM
Common Player:	225	105	80	35	27
1 Weldon Humble(R)	875	450	350	95	75
2 Otto Graham	950	750	600	240	185
4 Norm Van Brocklin	2750	1500	1200	375	300
6 Tom Fears	265	175	145	65	50
10 Steve Van Buren	425	250	200	80	65
12 Chuck Bednarik	425	350	275	105	85
13 Bulldog Turner	235	210	170	65	50
15 John Lujack	475	275	225	80	65
20 Tom Landry(R)	2500	1250	1150	625	500
21 Arnie Weinmeister(R)	350	215	175	65	50
25 Doak Walker	400	250	200	80	65
32 Y.A. Tittle	1100	715	575	165	135
34 Sammy Baugh	1400	650	525	225	180
40 Bob Waterfield	425	250	200	95	75
42 Glenn Davis	375	210	170	80	65
46 Pete Pihos	475	250	200	95	75
56 Charley Conerly	440	295	235	90	70
73 Dante Lavelli	235	160	130	65	50
75 Lou Groza	475	355	285	105	85
76 Elroy Hirsch	425	250	200	95	75
90 Tony Canadeo	450	250	200	95	75
91 Emlen Tunnell(R)	700	435	340	155	125
96 Ernie Stautner	495	300	240	105	85
102 Bobby Layne	850	475	375	160	125
105 Joe Perry	475	295	235	95	75
109 Marion Motley	400	250	200	80	65
130 Jim Finks	235	165	135	65	50
137 Charlie Trippi	235	185	150	65	50
140 Leo Nomellini	475	300	245	80	65
144 Bill Dudley	750	500	450	120	90

1952 Bowman (Large)

CARD	MINT	NM/M+	NM/M	NM+	NM
Common Player:	425	250	200	85	65
1 Norm Van Brocklin	4500	2000	1495	800	600
2 Otto Graham	3450	1300	1050	515	410
4 Steve Owen(R)	650	325	250	115	95
9 Joe Spencer(SP)	950	450	350	125	100
10 Chuck Bednarik(SP)	2400	1435	1150	275	225
12 Charlie Trippi	750	365	295	115	95
13 Tom Fears	900	400	325	115	95
14 Paul Brown	2000	850	700	345	275
16 Frank Gifford(R)	6250	2750	2500	800	650
17 Y.A. Tittle	2000	1150	1000	325	255
18 Charlie Justice(SP)	1600	750	600	275	225
19 George Connor(SP)	1200	500	415	150	125
23 Gino Marchetti(R)	1750	750	600	250	200
27 Bob Miller(SP)(R)	2250	1350	1100	500	400
28 Kyle Rote(SP)(R)	1100	610	485	240	195
29 Hugh McElhenny(R)	1950	875	700	365	295
30 Sammy Baugh	3250	1600	1300	550	450
36 John Lee Hancock(SP)(R)	3000	1500	1200	610	490
37 Elroy Hirsch(SP)	1000	600	475	215	175
39 Emlen Tunnell	850	375	300	110	90
45 Steve Van Buren(SP)	2000	1000	800	475	375
46 Art Donovan(SP)(R)	2500	1300	1050	650	525
48 George Halas	2400	1150	950	370	295
54 Glen Christian(SP)	650	315	250	125	100
55 Andy Davis(SP)	600	315	250	125	100
57 Wayne Millner(R)	700	410	320	145	115
63 Charley Conerly(SP)	3600	2000	1625	950	750
64 Howard Hartley(SP)	650	320	250	125	100
72 John Schweder(SP)(R)	3750	2200	1750	900	700
73 Vitamin Smith(SP)	1550	750	600	300	230
78 Bobby Layne	2000	1000	800	350	275
81 John Kastan(SP)	900	450	360	185	150
82 Harry Minarik(SP)(R)	1150	650	495	245	195
83 Joe Perry	1400	685	550	270	225
85 Andy Robustelli(R)	1550	700	600	300	245
90 Thomas Johnson(SP)	1000	525	425	180	145
91 Leon Heath(SP)	1000	500	400	175	145
92 Pete Pihos	750	400	325	135	110
99 Joe Stydahar(SP)(R)	4500	2475	1995	900	700
100 Dick Alban(SP)	900	440	360	220	175
105 Lou Groza	1050	550	450	220	175
108 Hubert Johnston(SP)(R)	3600	1250	1000	430	350
109 Volney Quinlan(SP)	850	450	360	210	165
117 Jim OODonahue(SP)	1000	600	475	210	170
118 Darrell Hogan(SP)	2000	1000	800	400	325
125 Leo Nomellini	1350	675	550	240	195
126 Steve Romanik(SP)(R)	2250	1350	1100	615	490
127 Ollie Matson(SP)(R)	2800	1350	1100	510	410
128 Dante Lavelli	1850	1000	800	345	275
129 Jack Christiansen(R)	1500	750	600	295	230
135 Gene Ronzani(SP)(R)	5250	3000	2400	1150	950
136 Bert Rechichar(SP)	1600	800	650	265	210
137 Bob Waterfield	1300	625	500	200	165
140 Yale Lary(R)	1350	700	560	250	200
142 Tom Landry	4750	2500	2000	1000	800
144 Jim Lansford(SP)(R)	15000	8500	6500	2750	2250

1952 Bowman (Small)

CARD	MINT	NM/M+	NM/M	NM+	NM
Common Player:	325	185	150	50	40
1 Norm Van Brocklin	2500	1000	815	265	265
2 Otto Graham	1200	625	510	330	265
3 Doak Walker	325	175	140	60	45
4 Steve Owen(R)	325	175	140	60	45
10 Chuck Bednarik	595	315	250	100	80
13 Tom Fears	650	365	295	105	85
14 Paul Brown	1200	750	600	250	200
16 Frank Gifford(R)	2995	1850	1500	515	420
17 Y.A. Tittle	900	625	500	130	105
23 Gino Marchetti(R)	995	620	495	165	135
28 Kyle Rote(R)	475	250	200	80	65
29 Hugh McElhenny(R)	1200	550	450	225	180
30 Sammy Baugh	1850	1000	800	315	250
37 Elroy Hirsch	475	250	200	95	75
39 Emlen Tunnell	325	175	140	60	45
45 Steve Van Buren	475	300	250	75	60
46 Art Donovan(R)	1395	750	600	245	195
48 George Halas	1400	755	610	250	200
63 Charley Conerly	475	260	210	80	65
78 Bobby Layne	900	550	450	150	120
83 Joe Perry	575	300	245	100	80
85 Andy Robustelli(R)	995	525	425	155	125
92 Pete Pihos	900	500	325	125	85
105 Lou Groza	475	300	235	80	65
125 Leo Nomellini	475	250	200	80	65
127 Ollie Matson(R)	1500	950	750	185	150
129 Jack Christiansen(R)	700	375	310	125	100
137 Bob Waterfield	550	305	245	100	80
140 Yale Lary(R)	715	395	315	130	105
142 Tom Landry	2750	1550	1250	500	400

1953 Bowman

CARD	MINT	NM/M+	NM/M	NM+	NM
Common Player:		245	190	60	45
Common Short-Print:		315	250	75	60
1 Eddie LeBaron(R)	4500	1450	1100	155	125
6 Doak Walker		410	325	80	65
9 Marion Motley		410	325	125	100
11 Norm Van Brocklin	3500	1200	700	185	150
15 Dante Lavelli		425	335	75	75
17 Charlie Trippi		475	375	75	60
20 Charley Conerly		400	325	80	65
21 Bobby Layne		750	600	155	125
22 Elroy Hirsch	1200	750	500	125	100
23 Jim Finks		265	220	60	45
24 Chuck Bednarik		600	480	95	75
25 Kyle Rote		375	300	65	50
26 Otto Graham		1100	875	210	170
32 Hugh McElhenny		500	400	95	75
36 Tom Fears		375	295	75	60
37 George Connor		350	275	75	55
38 Bill Walsh		300	245	65	50
43 Frank Gifford(SP)		1450	1250	500	400
53 Emlen Tunnell(SP)		725	575	125	100
56 Y.A. Tittle		750	600	155	125
62 Ray Renfro(SP)(R)		375	315	80	65
73 Pete Pihos		800	650	160	125
88 Leo Nomellini		325	270	70	55
93 Ted Marchibroda(R)		305	245	65	50
95 Lou Groza		750	600	155	125

1954 Bowman

CARD	MINT	NM/M+	NM/M	NM+	NM
Common Player, 1-64, 97-128:	85	40	30		
Common Player, 65-96:	120	75	60		
1 Ray Matthews	375	235	190	40	30
4 Doug Atkins(R)	295	105	85	70	55
6 Joe Perry	205	80	65	50	40
8 Norm Van Brocklin	275	115	95	70	55
9 Pete Pihos	175	80	65	25	20
11 Zeke Bratkowski(R)	185	70	55	25	20
12 Ollie Matson	200	75	60	25	20
20 Tom Fears	175	90	70	40	30
23 George Blanda(R)	1150	450	370	275	225
32 Elroy Hirsch	250	95	75	50	40
40 Otto Graham	500	185	150	110	90
41 Doak Walker	185	70	55	40	30
42 Y.A. Tittle	425	150	120	80	65
52 Lou Groza	200	105	85	32.50	25
53 Bobby Layne	425	150	120	80	65
54 Hugh McElhenny	195	100	80	50	40

CARD	MINT	NM/M+	NM/M	NM+	NM
55 Frank Gifford	700	250	200	100	80
57 Chuck Bednarik	220	95	75	50	40
60 Charlie Trippi	175	65	50	32.50	25
76 Leo Nomellini	325	155	125	80	65
85 Lou Creekmur	235	110	90	65	50
111 Dante Lavelli	175	90	70	25	20
113 Charley Conerly	195	95	75	50	40
128 John Lattner(R)	850	650	400	115	95
1955 Bowman					
Common Player, 1-64:	70	35	25		
Common Player, 65-160:	90	45	35		
1 Doak Walker	525	155	125	80	65
2 Mike McCormack(R)	285	90	70	50	40
7 Frank Gifford	600	185	150	120	95
8 Alan Ameche(R)	325	125	100	60	45
14 Len Ford(R)	285	90	70	50	40
16 Charlie Conerly	245	76	60	45	35
25 Ollie Matson	245	75	60	32.50	25
32 Norm Van Brocklin	325	100	80	55	45
37 Lou Groza	205	75	60	32.50	25
42 John Henry Johnson(R)	300	90	70	55	45
44 Joe Perry	245	75	60	37.50	45
52 Pat Summerall(R)	450	120	95	80	65
62 George Blanda	500	155	125	110	90
70 Jim Ringo(R)	325	100	80	60	45
71 Bobby Layne	525	190	150	95	75
72 Y.A. Tittle	525	175	145	95	75
75 Hugh McElhenny	175	100	80	32.50	25
87 Rick Casares(R)	205	65	50	37.50	30
101 Bob St. Clair(R)	325	100	80	55	45
104 Leo Nomellini	250	75	60	45	35
119 Frank Gatski(R)	245	75	60	45	35
121 Andy Robustelli	185	60	45	32.50	25
133 Vic Janowicz	185	60	45	32.50	25
134 Ernie Stautner	185	60	45	32.50	25
136 Emlen Tunnell	185	60	45	32.50	25
139 Charlie Trippi	205	65	50	32.50	25
152 Tom Landry	1495	500	400	250	200
158 Chuck Bednarik	245	75	60	45	35
160 L.G. Dupre(R)	300	135	110	50	40
1955 Topps All-American					
Common Player:	240	100	80	35	25
Common Short-Print:	300	125	100	40	30
1 Herman Hickman	950	400	325	125	100
12 Otto Graham	1475	400	335	225	175
16 Knute Rockne	1425	600	500	315	250
20 Sammy Baugh	1350	400	325	185	150
27 Red Grange	1650	650	495	345	275
29 Leo Nomellini(SP)	400	170	135	90	70
37 Jim Thorpe	3500	950	785	450	350
38 Amos Alonzo Stagg	425	180	145	90	70
52 Johnny Lujack	400	185	150	50	40
56 Ernie Nevers	445	190	155	75	60
59 Doc Blanchard	435	185	150	60	45
68 Four Horsemen(SP)	4500	1350	1100	525	425
85 Sid Luckman	850	310	245	110	90
97 Don Hutson(SP)	1025	455	400	245	195
98 Beattie Feathers(SP)	725	225	190	75	60
100 Fats Henry	1450	625	500	175	140
1956 Topps					
Common Player:	80	35	25		
Team Card:	110	75	60	35	25
1 Jack Carson	775	550	450	275	225
6 Norm Van Brocklin	180	120	95	37.50	30
9 Lou Groza	165	100	80	37.50	30
11 George Blanda	360	155	125	70	55
13 Vic Janowicz	220	115	95	50	40
22 Chicago Cardinals(SP)	525	270	215	120	95
28 Chuck Bednarik	175	90	70	37.50	30
36 Art Donovan	165	90	70	37.50	30
41 Roosevelt Brown(R)	255	100	80	37.50	30
44 Joe Schmidt(R)	290	100	80	50	40
47 Bill George(R)	255	75	60	32.50	25
49 Eddie LeBaron	165	90	70	37.50	30
50 Hugh McElhenny	185	80	65	37.50	30
53 Frank Gifford	525	200	175	95	75
58 Ollie Matson	360	190	155	80	65
60 Lenny Moore	550	280	225	110	90
61 Washington Redskins(SP)	515	275	220	110	90
71 Stan Jones(R)	220	120	95	50	40
77 Charley Conerly	165	95	75	35	27.50
78 Elroy Hirsch	175	95	75	37.50	30
86 Y.A. Tittle	450	125	100	65	50
101 Roosevelt Grier(R)	215	115	90	50	40
110 Joe Perry	140	90	70	32.50	25
116 Bobby Layne	265	125	100	50	40
120 Billy Vessels(R)	300	160	130	60	45
Checklist	1650	1350	1100	375	295
1957 Topps					
Common Player, 1-88:	90	35	25	16	12.50
Common Player, 89-154:	140	60	45	20	15
1 Eddie LeBaron	450	175	140	50	40
6 Leo Nomellini	205	60	45	25	20
22 Norm Van Brocklin	250	95	75	37.50	30
28 Lou Groza	205	80	65	32.50	25
30 Y.A. Tittle	410	145	115	50	40
31 George Blanda	375	125	100	50	40
32 Bobby Layne	300	120	95	60	45
46 Elroy Hirsch	205	70	55	32.50	25

CARD	MINT	NM/M+	NM/M	NM+	NM
49 Chuck Bednarik	155	80	65	25	20
58 Willard Sherman(no RAMS)	1395	675	550	240	190
65 Art Donovan	185	70	55	40	30
85 Dick Lane(R)	325	110	90	65	50
88 Frank Gifford	550	215	175	130	105
94 Raymond Berry(R)	750	450	350	190	155
95 Hugh McElhenny	275	100	80	37.50	30
104 Earl Morrall(R)	425	155	125	75	60
109 Charlie Conerly	255	115	90	45	35
119 Bart Starr(R)	3995	1500	1200	450	400
128 Lenny Moore	395	135	110	70	55
129 Joe Perry	255	90	70	45	35
138 Johnny Unitas(R)	5750	1550	1200	450	400
151 Paul Hornung(R)	3950	1400	1125	600	450
154 Fred Morrison	425	155	125	80	60
Checklist	3995	1400	1150	950	750
1958 Topps					
Common Player:	75	35	25	12.50	
2 Bobby Layne	235	105	85	45	35
22 Johnny Unitas	1195	625	500	120	95
62 Jim Brown(R)	13500	2100	1800	625	500
66 Bart Starr	775	245	200	125	100
73 Frank Gifford	365	165	135	70	55
86 Y.A. Tittle	265	120	95	50	40
90 Sonny Jurgensen(R)	875	250	200	125	100
120 Raymond Berry	265	125	100	50	40
129 George Blanda	300	135	110	60	45
1959 Topps					
Common Player:	40				
1 Johnny Unitas	550	325	275	125	100
4 Max McGee(R)	125	65	50	25	20
10 Jim Brown	2200	1000	800	160	125
20 Frank Gifford	235	95	80	70	55
23 Bart Starr	280	175	145	80	65
40 Bobby Layne	200	80	65	32.50	25
51 Sam Huff(R)	205	120	95	70	55
55 Ray Berry	125	65	50	25	20
82 Paul Hornung	275	145	115	75	60
103 Alex Karras(R)	225	80	65	45	35
116 Jerry Kramer(R)	145	80	65	32.50	25
130 Y.A. Tittle	210	95	80	32.50	25
132 Jim Parker(R)	110	70	55	25	20
140 Bobby Mitchell(R)	160	95	75	45	35
155 Jim Taylor(R)	125	65	50	25	20
1960 Fleer					
1 Harvey White(R)	95	50	40	25	20
20 Sammy Baugh	200	100	80	65	50
58 George Blanda	160	100	80	65	50
116 Hank Stram	170	95	75	65	55
118 Ron Mix(R)	140	70	55	50	45
124 Jack Kemp(R)	2000	600	500	315	250
1960 Topps					
1 Johnny Unitas	525	350	300	100	80
23 Jim Brown	525	200	165	125	100
51 Bart Starr	275	95	75	55	45
54 Paul Hornung	220	100	80	55	45
56 Forrest Gregg(R)	185	70	55	45	35
74 Frank Gifford	275	80	65	50	40
80 Sam Huff	140	50	40	30	25
93 Bobby Layne	185	75	60	32.50	25
113 Y.A. Tittle	140	60	45	32.50	25
132 Washington Redskins	195	75	60	37.50	30
1961 Fleer					
11 Jim Brown	950	235	190	155	125
30 Johnny Unitas	275	160	130	90	70
41 Don Meredith(R)	535	315	250	155	125
59 John Brodie(R)	200	115	90	65	50
88 Bart Starr	215	125	100	65	50
89 Jim Taylor	125	70	55	37.50	30
90 Paul Hornung	180	100	80	55	45
117 Bobby Layne	145	75	65	32.50	25
155 Jack Kemp(SP)	900	440	350	235	185
166 George Blanda	150	100	80	55	45
188 Tom Flores(SP)(R)	145	90	70	45	35
197 Jim Otto(R)	195	135	110	75	60
215 Don Maynard(R)	295	160	130	90	75
1961 Topps					
1 Johnny Unitas	575	285	225	140	115
35 Alex Karras	125	70	55	32.50	25
39 Bart Starr	275	80	65	50	40
40 Paul Hornung	170	90	75	45	35
41 Jim Taylor	150	65	50	37.50	30
58 Y.A. Tittle	190	75	60	37.50	30
59 John Brodie(R)	215	95	75	45	35
67 Checklist	250	115	90	65	50
71 Jim Brown	600	200	160	100	80
77 Jim Brown(1,257 yards)	195	115	95	45	35
95 Sonny Jurgensen	170	75	60	32.50	25
104 Bobby Layne	150	75	60	32.50	25
122 Checklist	195	90	70	55	45
145 George Blanda	125	70	55	40	30
150 Don Maynard(R)	150	105	85	50	40
166 Jack Kemp	850	295	235	160	130
182 Jim Otto(R)	200	80	65	45	35
186 Tom Flores(R)	120	70	55	45	35
198 Checklist	510	185	145	75	60
1962 Fleer					
46 George Blanda	275	150	120	90	70

CARD	MINT	NM/M+	NM/M	NM+	NM
59 Don Maynard	180	100	80	55	45
72 Jim Otto	175	75	60	45	35
74 Fred Williamson(R)	100	60	45	32.50	25
79 Jack Kemp	1100	550	450	375	300
86 Ernie Ladd(R)	155	90	70	50	40
1962 Topps					
Common Player:	65	35	27.50	16	12.50
Common Short-Print:	100	65	50	25	17.50
1 Johnny Unitas	900	700	575	155	125
5 Raymond Berry(SP)	175	95	75	25	20
17 Mike Ditka(R)	900	750	650	240	190
28 Jim Brown	900	750	700	155	125
36 Ernie Davis(SP)(R)	600	375	300	165	130
39 Don Meredith(SP)	525	350	275	125	100
62 Dallas Cowboys	125	90	70	25	20
63 Bart Starr(SP)	375	250	200	95	75
64 Paul Hornung(SP)	275	180	145	65	50
66 Jim Taylor(SP)	160	105	85	37.50	30
69 Fuzzy Thurston(R)(SP)	125	90	70	25	20
75 Green Bay Packers(SP)	115	75	60	25	20
76 Checklist(SP)	375	250	200	95	75
79 Ollie Matson(SP)	150	100	80	25	20
88 Roman Gabriel(SP)(R)	300	250	200	70	55
90 Fran Tarkenton(SP)(R)	4000	1550	1250	250	200
92 Hugh McElhenny(SP)	105	70	55	37.50	30
101 Minnesota Vikings(SP)	115	75	60	25	20
102 Y.A. Tittle	160	125	100	37.50	30
104 Frank Gifford	325	250	200	50	40
110 Sam Huff(SP)	105	75	60	25	20
115 Sonny Jurgensen	200	155	125	25	20
127 Bobby Layne	175	125	100	37.50	30
151 Billy Kilmer(R)	200	150	120	45	35
164 Norm Snead(SP)(R)	160	105	85	37.50	30
176 Checklist	650	450	350	155	125
1963 Fleer					
Common Player:	55	25	20		
1 Larry Garron(R)		50	35		
6 Charles Long(SP)(R)	500	315	250	225	180
10 Nick Buoniconti(R)	300	130	105	95	75
15 Don Maynard	200	115	90	60	45
23 Cookie Gilchrist(R)	125	70	55	45	40
24 Jack Kemp	900	475	375	210	175
36 George Blanda	170	105	85	65	50
47 Len Dawson(R)	775	500	400	250	200
63 Jim Otto	100	60	45	35	30
64 Bob Dougherty(SP)	675	275	250	165	135
72 Lance Alworth(R)	750	460	365	315	250
Checklist	1100	625	500	450	350
1963 Topps					
Common Player:	25				
Common Short-Print:	40	30	25		
1 Johnny Unitas	750	440	340	155	125
14 Jim Brown(SP)	1550	840	675	250	200
19 Lou Groza(SP)	140	65	50	32.50	25
44 Deacon Jones(R)	400	185	150	50	40
49 Y.A. Tittle(SP)	310	165	135	50	40
59 Sam Huff(SP)	140	65	50	32.50	25
62 Mike Ditka	475	170	135	75	60
74 Don Meredith(SP)	390	215	170	65	50
82 Bob Lilly(R)	975	525	425	155	125
85 Checklist	195	105	85	32.50	25
86 Bart Starr	310	165	135	50	40
95 Willie Wood(R)	210	115	90	35	27.50
96 Ray Nitschke(R)	615	350	275	100	80
98 Fran Tarkenton	385	215	170	50	40
107 Jim Marshall(R)	195	95	75	37.50	30
110 Sonny Jurgensen(SP)	170	95	75	32.50	25
155 Larry Wilson(R)	195	105	85	32.50	25
170 Checklist	475	225	175	75	60
1964 Philadelphia					
1 Raymond Berry	110	65	50	25	20
3 John Mackey(R)	125	70	55	32.50	25
12 Johnny Unitas	250	95	75	50	40
14 Don Shula(Colts Play Card)	135	65	50	32.50	25
17 Mike Ditka	200	80	65	40	32.50
30 Jim Brown	400	165	135	100	80
48 Bob Lilly	200	90	70	45	35
51 Don Meredith	180	90	70	45	35
71 Herb Adderley(R)	155	60	45	32.50	25
72 Willie Davis(R)	145	80	65	37.50	30
74 Paul Hornung	145	80	60	35	27.50
79 Bart Starr	200	105	85	65	50
84 Vince Lombardi (Packers Play Card)	145	75	60	37.50	30
91 Merlin Olsen(R)	235	100	75	60	50
109 Fran Tarkenton	190	100	80	50	40
117 Frank Gifford	190	90	70	50	40
124 Y.A. Tittle	110	50	40	25	20
197 Checklist 1	180	95	75	45	35
198 Checklist 2	265	135	110	65	50
1964 Topps					
1 Tommy Addison(SP)	150	80	65	45	35
30 Jack Kemp(SP)	895	425	335	250	200
31 Daryle Lamonica(R)	265	130	105	75	60
68 George Blanda(SP)	265	130	105	65	50
82 Checklist	220	130	105	65	50
90 Bobby Bell(R)	185	75	60	45	35
91 Buck Buchanan(R)	175	75	60	45	35
96 Len Dawson(SP)	335	175	145	95	75

CARD	MINT	NM/M+	NM/M	NM+	NM
121 Don Maynard	140	80	65	37.50	30
125 Matt Snell(R)	95	60	45	25	20
148 Jim Otto(SP)	115	75	60	32.50	25
155 Lance Alworth	185	100	80	50	40
159 John Hadl(R)	195	105	85	55	42.50
176 Checklist	675	375	295	185	150
1965 Philadelphia					
12 Johnny Unitas	200	95	75	45	35
19 Mike Ditka	135	65	50	25	20
31 Jim Brown	325	150	120	80	65
41 Paul Warfield(R)	425	185	150	95	75
47 Bob Lilly	105	75	60	25	20
50 Don Meredith	135	75	60	32.50	25
53 Mel Renfro(R)	160	75	60	37.50	30
76 Paul Hornung	145	90	75	32.50	25
81 Bart Starr	150	70	55	35	27.50
105 Carl Eller(R)	150	65	50	25	20
110 Fran Tarkenton	160	75	60	37.50	30
195 Charley Taylor(R)	305	150	120	75	60
197 Checklist 1	105	50	40	25	20
198 Checklist 2	185	90	70	45	35
1965 Topps					
Common Short-Print:	75	35	30	16	12.50
1 Tommy Addison(SP)	210	105	85	45	35
3 Nick Buoniconti(SP)	145	75	60	32.50	25
5 Gino Cappelletti(SP)	115	60	47.50	25	20
35 Jack Kemp(SP)	1150	600	475	250	200
36 Daryle Lamonica(SP)	235	120	95	50	40
46 Willie Brown(SP)(R)	375	210	165	80	65
51 Cookie Gilchrist(SP)	145	75	60	32.50	25
69 George Blanda(SP)	525	265	215	115	90
87 Checklist 1-88(SP)	800	435	345	185	145
91 Bobby Bell(SP)	145	90	70	32.50	25
94 Buck Buchanan(SP)	145	75	60	32.50	25
99 Len Dawson(SP)	475	245	190	100	80
116 Winston Hill(R)	115	60	47.50	25	20
117 John Huarte(SP)(R)	170	90	70	37.50	30
121 Don Maynard	210	105	85	45	35
122 Joe Namath(SP)(R)		4000	3500	2750	1600
127 Matt Snell(SP)	145	75	60	32.50	25
133 Fred Biletnikoff(SP)(R)	1150	600	475	250	200
137 Ben Davidson(SP)(R)	295	150	120	65	50
139 Tom Flores(SP)	160	80	65	35	27.50
145 Jim Otto(SP)	145	75	60	32.50	25
155 Lance Alworth(SP)	375	215	165	80	65
161 John Hadl(SP)	170	90	70	35	27.50
176 Checklist 89-176(SP)	1200	625	500	250	200
1966 Philadelphia					
24 Johnny Unitas	180	90	70	37.50	30
31 Dick Butkus(R)	1100	625	500	185	150
32 Mike Ditka	140	80	65	32.50	25
38 Gale Sayers(R)	2750	850	600	250	200
39 Gale Sayers(play card)	150	75	60	32.50	25
41 Jim Brown	330	160	130	70	55
58 Bob Hayes(R)	300	185	150	32.50	25
61 Don Meredith	150	75	60	32.50	25
88 Bart Starr	250	155	125	95	75
114 Fran Tarkenton	115	60	45	25	20
198 Checklist 2	250	125	100	50	40
1966 Topps					
Funny Rings	125	65	50	35	25
1 Tommy Addison	125	65	50	25	20
15 Funny Ring Checklist	1500	950	750	345	275
26 Jack Kemp	1050	475	375	210	170
48 George Blanda	255	130	105	50	40
61 Checklist	255	135	110	50	40
67 Len Dawson	230	125	100	45	35
75 Otis Taylor(R)	120	60	47.50	25	20
95 Don Maynard	160	75	60	25	20
96 Joe Namath	950	525	425	250	200
104 Fred Biletnikoff	320	165	135	65	50
119 Lance Alworth	195	105	85	37.50	30
132 Checklist	575	325	250	115	90
1967 Philadelphia					
7 Tommy Nobis(R)	110	50	40	25	20
23 Johnny Unitas	165	90	70	37.50	30
28 Dick Butkus	325	150	120	75	60
29 Mike Ditka	135	65	50	32.50	25
35 Gale Sayers	410	155	125	90	70
43 Leroy Kelly(R)	165	75	60	37.50	30
46 Paul Warfield	110	50	40	25	20
54 Lee Roy Jordan(R)	135	75	60	32.50	25
57 Don Meredith	110	50	40	25	20
58 Dan Reeves(R)	165	75	60	45	35
82 Bart Starr	125	65	50	32.50	25
106 Fran Tarkenton	110	50	40	25	20
123 Paul Hornung	110	50	40	25	20
197 Checklist 1	160	65	50	32.50	25
198 Checklist 2	190	90	70	45	35
1967 Topps					
24 Jack Kemp	550	250	200	90	70
59 Checklist	225	115	90	50	40
61 Len Dawson	100	60	45	25	20
82 Wahoo McDaniel(R)	180	115	95	37.50	30
97 Don Maynard	110	50	40	25	20
98 Joe Namath	4000	315	250	170	135
106 Fred Biletnikoff	165	90	70	37.50	30
123 Lance Alworth	250	75	60	32.50	25

CARD	MINT	NM/M+	NM/M	NM+	NM
132 Checklist	335	165	135	75	60
1968 Topps					
1 Bart Starr	155	105	85	45	35
25 Don Meredith	90	60	45	25	20
65 Joe Namath	340	185	150	95	75
75 Gale Sayers	205	100	80	55	45
100 Johnny Unitas	150	85	70	32.50	25
127 Dick Butkus	155	90	70	45	35
142 George Blanda	100	65	50	32.50	25
149 Jack Kemp	255	130	105	70	55
161 Fran Tarkenton	100	50	40	25	20
162 Mike Ditka	105	60	45	25	20
173 Floyd Little(R)	80	50	40	25	20
196 Bob Griese(R)	400	225	175	105	85
219 Checklist	90	60	45	25	20
1969 Topps					
Common Player, 1-132:	35				
Common Player, 133-263:	40				
1 Leroy Kelly	275	40	30	25	20
25 Johnny Unitas	195	90	70	40	35
26 Brian Piccolo(R)	400	155	125	95	75
51 Gale Sayers	285	125	100	65	50
75 Don Meredith	125	50	40	25	20
100 Joe Namath	400	155	125	95	75
120 Larry Csonka(R)	650	160	130	75	60
139 Dick Butkus	125	60	45	32.50	25
150 Fran Tarkenton	105	50	37.50	25	20
161 Bob Griese	155	70	55	37.50	30
215 Bart Starr	125	70	55	45	35
1970 Topps					
1 Len Dawson	175	45	35	20	15
10 Bob Griese	85	37.50	30	20	15
30 Bart Starr	120	37.50	30	25	20
59 Alan Page(R)	150	75	60	37.50	30
70 Gale Sayers	175	65	50	45	35
75 Lem Barney(R)	85	32.50	25	20	15
80 Fran Tarkenton	120	45	35	20	15
90 O.J. Simpson(R)	375	155	125	75	60
114 Bubba Smith(R)	145	65	50	32.50	25
150 Joe Namath	255	105	85	70	55
162 Larry Csonka	135	65	50	32.50	25
180 Johnny Unitas	120	60	45	25	20
190 Dick Butkus	150	60	45	25	20
1971 Topps					
1 Johnny Unitas	250	90	70	37.50	30
2 Marty Schottenheimer(R)	105	37.50	30	25	20
25 Dick Butkus	110	60	45	25	20
45 Larry Csonka	75	37.50	30	20	15
71 Alan Page(R)	80	45	35	25	20
113 Ken Houston(R)	85	37.50	30	25	20
114 Willie Lanier(R)	90	37.50	30	25	20
120 Fran Tarkenton	105	40	35	25	20
150 Gale Sayers	170	65	50	37.50	30
156 Terry Bradshaw(R)	975	300	235	200	165
160 Bob Griese	85	37.50	30	25	20
200 Bart Starr	135	65	50	32.50	25
245 Joe Greene(R)	300	100	80	65	50
250 Joe Namath	300	150	120	65	50
260 O.J. Simpson	145	50	40	25	20
1972 Topps					
Common High-Number, 264-351:	60	40	30	25	20
13 John Riggins(R)	135	60	45	32.50	25
55 Archie Manning(R)	80	45	35	25	20
65 Jim Plunkett(R)	65	45	35	25	20
93 Ted Hendricks(R)	65	37.50	30	25	20
100 Joe Namath	150	95	75	32.50	25
101 L.C. Greenwood(R)	65	37.50	30	25	20
106 Lyle Alzado(R)	60	37.50	30	20	15
110 Gale Sayers	75	50	40	25	20
120 Terry Bradshaw(IA)	75	45	35	20	15
122 Roger Staubach(IA)	85	37.50	30	25	20
150 Terry Bradshaw	105	65	50	37.50	30
160 O.J. Simpson	65	37.50	30	25	20
165 Johnny Unitas	90	50	40	25	20
186 Gene Upshaw(R)	55	32.50	25	20	15
200 Roger Staubach(R)	500	315	275	200	160
225 Fran Tarkenton	55	32.50	25	20	15
230 Joe Greene	50	32.50	25	20	15
240 Larry Little(R)	55	32.50	25	20	15
244 Charlie Joiner(R)	85	60	45	32.50	25
271 Paul Warfield(AP)	180	100	80	65	50
272 Bob Griese(AP)	140	95	80	65	55
279 Alan Page(AP)	110	65	50	32.50	25
280 Bob Lily(AP)	175	75	65	45	40
281 Ted Hendricks(AP)	125	75	60	35	27.50
291 Steve Spurrier(R)	285	155	125	100	80
294 Checklist 264-351	240	155	125	100	80
300 Alan Page	155	115	90	65	50
338 Steve Spurrier(IA)	190	100	80	50	40
341 Dick Butkus(IA)	175	110	90	75	60
343 Joe Namath(IA)	475	250	200	175	150
1973 Topps					
15 Terry Bradshaw	85	70	55	32.50	25
34 Ken Anderson(R)	65	55	45	25	20
60 Fran Tarkenton	55	45	35	20	15
77 Art Shell(R)	70	55	45	25	20
89 Franco Harris(R)	175	95	75	50	40
115 Jack Ham(R)	100	75	60	32.50	25

CARD	MINT	NM/M+	NM/M	NM+	NM
322 Dan Dierdorf(R)	70	55	45	25	20
343 Jack Youngblood(R)	65	45	35	20	15
400 Joe Namath	140	80	65	37.50	30
455 Johnny Unitas	75	55	40	25	20
475 Roger Staubach	130	80	65	40	30
487 Ken Stabler(R)	295	155	125	75	60
500 O.J. Simpson	60	45	35	20	15
1974 Topps					
1 O.J. Simpson	70	55	45	25	20
105 Ahmad Rashad(R)	55	45	35	20	15
130 O.J. Simpson(AP)	47.50	37.50	30	20	15
150 Johnny Unitas	55	45	35	25	20
220 Franco Harris	60	50	40	20	15
451 Ken Stabler	70	55	45	25	20
470 Terry Bradshaw	70	45	35	20	15
500 Roger Staubach	95	70	55	25	20
1975 Topps					
12 Mel Blount(R)	80	50	40	32.50	25
39 Rocky Bleier(R)	50	32.50	25	20	15
65 Drew Pearson(R)	55	32.50	25	20	15
100 Joe Namath	80	55	45	32.50	25
145 Roger Staubach	90	50	40	32.50	25
282 Lynn Swann(R)	175	90	70	55	45
367 Dan Fouts(R)	400	75	60	45	35
380 Ken Stabler	60	32.50	25	20	15
416 Joe Theismann(R)	160	60	45	32.50	25
1976 Topps					
148 Walter Payton(R)	700	225	180	140	115
158 Randy White(R)	85	50	40	30	25
220 Jack Lambert(R)	85	70	55	40.50	30
395 Roger Staubach	50	32.50	25	20	15
427 Ed 'Too Tall' Jones(R)	70	45	35	25	20
1977 Topps					
177 Steve Largent(R)	150	95	75	60	50
360 Walter Payton	100	55	45	32.50	25
1978 Topps					
200 Walter Payton	75	60	45	32.50	25
315 Tony Dorsett(R)	100	70	55	45	35
320 John Stallworth(R)	50	35	25	20	15
1979 Topps					
160 Tony Dorsett	50	32.50	25	20	15
308 Ozzie Newsome(R)	45	32.50	25	20	15
310 James Lofton(R)	45	25	20	16	12.50
390 Earl Campbell(R)	100	65	50	37.50	30
480 Walter Payton	45	32.50	25	20	15
1980 Topps					
160 Walter Payton	45	32.50	25	20	15
225 Phil Simms(R)	45	35	27.50	20	15

CARD	GEM	MINT	NM/M+	NM/M	NM+
1981 Topps					
150 Kellen Winslow(R)			30		15
194 Art Monk(R)			45		20
216 Joe Montana(R)	7900		450		150
1982 Topps					
434 Lawrence Taylor(R)			105		25
486 Ronnie Lott(R)			60		25
488 Joe Montana			75		30
489 Joe Montana (IA)	275				
1983 Topps					
294 Marcus Allen(R)			75		35
1984 Topps					
63 John Elway(R)	4000		300		110
111 Howie Long(R)			35		15
123 Dan Marino(R)	1800		250		90
124 Dan Marino (IR)	250		35		15
280 Eric Dickerson(R)			50		
353 Roger Craig	125				
358 Joe Montana			40		
1984 Topps USFL					
36 Jim Kelly(R)			190		65
52 Steve Young(R)			275		215
58 Reggie White(R)			190		65
74 Herschel Walker(R)			50		30
1985 Topps					
4 Dan Marino(RB)			40		20
157 Joe Montana	450		50		15
192 Dan Marino, Joe Montana (Passing Leaders)	400		40		15
238 John Elway			65		25
251 Warren Moon(R)	450		60		30
314 Dan Marino			75		20
1985 Topps USFL					
45 Jim Kelly	145		55		30
65 Steve Young	400		100		60
75 Reggie White	125		55		25
80 Doug Flutie	525		125		55
86 Herschel Walker	125		45		15
1986 Topps					
11 Walter Payton	400				
45 Dan Marino	800		85		25
112 John Elway			65		15
156 Joe Montana			100		20
161 Jerry Rice(R)	7000		650		85
374 Steve Young			150		40

CARD	GEM	MINT	NM/M+	NM/M	NM+
1987 Topps					
45 Doug Flutie (R)			35		22.50
115 Jerry Rice	300		40		20
233 Dan Marino	100				
296 Randall Cunningham (R)			45		20
1989 Pro Set					
32 Thurman Thomas(R)			20		
89 Michael Irvin(R)			20		
314 Cris Carter(R)	35				
381 Joe Montana	120				
486 Deion Sanders(R)	60		20		
490 Troy Aikman(R)	90		15		
494 Barry Sanders(R)	175		35		20
1989 Score					
13 Dan Marino	100				
18 Michael Irvin(R)	125		25		12.50
27 Chris Chandler(R)	75		20		
72 Cris Carter(R)	250		35		20
86 Tim Brown(R)	150		30		
211 Thurman Thomas(R)	100		25		15
243 Doug Flutie	65		20		
246 Deion Sanders(R)	150		30		15
257 Barry Sanders(R)	1000		200		115
258 Derrick Thomas(R)	125		35		15
270 Troy Aikman(R)	500		65		35
272 Andre Rison(R)	60		20		12.50
1989 Topps					
121 Cris Carter (R)	100				
293 Dan Marino	45				
1989 Topps Traded					
30T Deion Sanders(R)	50		25		15
70T Troy Aikman(R)	125		20		12
83T Barry Sanders	200		35		20
1990 Fleer					
284 Barry Sanders	60		20		
1990 Fleer Update					
U4 Jeff George	30				
U40 Emmitt Smith(R)	275		30		20
1990 Pro Set					
685 Emmitt Smith(R)			40		
1990 Score Supplemental					
101T Emmitt Smith(R)	1750		80		45
1990 Topps Tiffany					
8 Jerry Rice	150		30		
37 John Elway	175		40		
323 Dan Marino	175		40		
352 Barry Sanders	275		55		
482 Troy Aikman	125		25		
1990 Topps Traded					
27T Emmitt Smith(R)	175				
1991 Pacific					
551 Brett Favre(R)	125				
1991 Score					
611 Brett Favre(R)	80		20		
1991 Stadium Club					
94 Brett Favre(R)	500		70		40
1991 Ultra					
283 Brett Favre(R)	150		20		
291 Herman Moore(R)			15		
1991 Ultra Update					
U1 Brett Favre	200		35		12
U65 Ed McCaffrey(R)	100		25		12
1991 Upper Deck					
13 Brett Favre (R)	100				
1992 Bowman					
100 Emmitt Smith	85		40		16
170 Barry Sanders	85		40		16
180 Emmitt Smith(Foil SP)	135		70		45
221 Barry Sanders(Foil)	110		55		20
1992 Stadium Club					
602 Troy Aikman	60		25		12.50
606 Barry Sanders	60		25		12.50
608 Jerry Rice	60		25		12.50
637 Barry Sanders	45		15		12.50
645 Jerry Rice	75		30		15
650 Joe Montana	60		25		12.50
653 Robert Brooks(R)	85		32		15
660 Dan Marino	85		25		12.50
683 Brett Favre	1000		175		75
1992 Topps					
696 Brett Favre (Gold)			40		
1992 Wild Card					
427 Brad Johnson (R)	275				
1993 Bowman					
20 Garrison Hearst(R)	75		35		15
166 Mark Brunell(R)	90		25		12.50
200 Joe Montana	75		35		15
280 Drew Bledsoe(R)	200		45		15
300 Emmitt Smith	75		30		15
335 Brett Favre	75		40		15
1993 Pinnacle Rookies					
1 Drew Bledsoe			190		

CARD	GEM	MINT	NM/M+	NM/M	NM+
1993 Select					
166 Drew Bledsoe(R)	150		45		25
1993 SP					
6 Jerome Bettis(R)	195		50		25
8 Robert Smith(R)	250		45		20
9 Drew Bledsoe	1250		225		45
91 Mark Brunell(R)	500		90		35
1993 Wild Card					
141 Drew Bledsoe(R)			25		
1994 Bowman					
2 Marshall Faulk(R)	250		50		
68 Isaac Bruce (R)	200		50		
372 Dorsey Levens(R)	150		35		
1994 SP					
3 Marshall Faulk(R)	800		100		20
3 Marshall Faulk(Die-cut Foil)			125	25	
1995 Bowman					
3 Steve McNair(R)	100		25		12.50
8 Joey Galloway(R)	125		35		15
18 Napoleon Kaufman(R)	75		25		12.50
105 Kordell Stewart(R)	125		55		25
217 Antonio Freeman(R)	125		30		12.50
301 Curtis Martin(R)	75		25		12.50
1995 BowmanÖs Best					
R3 Steve McNair(R)	150		40		15
R3 Steve McNair(Refractor)			125		
R4 Michael Westbrook(R)	90				
R8 Joey Galloway(R)	125		35		12.50
R18 Napoleon Kaufman(R)	90		35		12.50
R47 Frank Sanders(R)	50		20		
R60 Kordell Stewart(R)	100		30		15
R74 Curtis Martin(R)	100		30		
R90 Antonio Freeman(R)	100		30		15
1995 Finest					
166 Joey Galloway(R)	60		20		
216 Frank Sanders(R)	60		20		
264 Curtis Martin(R)	70		25		
1995 Iowa Barnstormers					
Kurt Warner	800		200		
1995 Pacific Crown Royale					
73 Antonio Freeman(R)	75		20		
78 Curtis Martin(R)	75		20		
78 Curtis Martin(copper)			55		
126 Steve McNair(R)	100				
135 Kordell Stewart(R)	85		30		
136 Terrell Davis(R)	300		90		
1995 Playoff Contenders					
126 Terrell Davis(R)			25		
1995 Select Certified					
26 Drew Bledsoe (Mirror Gold)	75		35		15
30 Dan Marino(Mirror Gold)	115		45		20
46 John Elway(Mirror Gold)	80		32		15
50 Brett Favre(Mirror Gold)	75		30		15
106 Michael Westbrook(R)	100		30		
107 Frank Sanders(R)	65		25		
117 Curtis Martin(R)	100		30		
117 Curtis Martin(Mirror Gold)	165		65		30
125 Napoleon Kaufman(R)	60		25		
125 Napoleon Kaufman (Mirror Gold)	200		90		40
126 Terrell Davis(R)	300		140		90
126 Terrell Davis(Mirror Gold)	900		325		125
129 Kordell Stewart(R)	85		30		
129 Kordell Stewart(Mirror Gold)	180		75		30
133 J.J. Stokes(R)			16		
135 Joey Galloway(R)	85		30		
1995 Select Certified Future					
5 Joey Galloway	65		16		
6 J.J. Stokes	40				
1995 SP					
3 Steve McNair(R)	400		70		20
6 Joey Galloway(R)	300		60		15
18 Curtis Martin(R)	150		35		15
130 Terrell Davis(R)	1000		100		45
130 Terrell Davis(die-cut)	1000		100		35
179 Wayne Chrebet(R)	150		25		
1995 SP Championship					
14 Terrell Davis(R)	250		65		
36 Kordell Stewart(R)	50		15		
1995 Ultra					
268 Kordell Stewart(R)			30		
315 Joey Galloway(R)			20		
369 Rod Smith(R)			30		
430 Terrell Davis(R)			80		
433 Antonio Freeman(R)			30		
447 Curtis Martin(R)			22.50		
1996 BowmanÖs Best					
147 Terrell Owens(R)	120		50		
165 Marvin Harrison (R)	125		30		
168 Eric Moulds(R)	65		20		12
170 Eddie George(R)	125		40		17
180 Keyshawn Johnson(R)	85		25		
1996 Finest					
40 Dan Marino(Refractor)	50				

CARD	GEM	MINT	NM/M+	NM/M	NM+
40 Dan Marino(Gold Refractor)	150				
140 Barry Sanders(Refractor)	165				
225 Keyshawn Johnson(R)	125		20		
243 Marvin Harrison(R)	100		30		
338 Terrell Owens(R)	80		25		
1996 Pacific Crown Royale					
39 Terrell Owens(R)	250				
124 Eddie George(R)	100		40		
1996 Select Certified					
41 Terrell Davis	55		25		12
91 Marvin Harrison(R)	100		35		
92 Stephen Davis (R)	100				
100 Eddie George(R)	100		35		15
102 Eric Moulds(R)	60		20		
105 Keyshawn Johnson(R)	90		25		12
1996 SP					
1 Keyshawn Johnson(R)	350		60		12
5 Eddie George(R)	600		100		15
6 Terry Glenn (R)	160				
7 Terrell Owens(R)	350		60		12
17 Eric Moulds(R)	250		40		
18 Marvin Harrison (R)	400		75		
20 Stephen Davis (R)	350		60		
59 Jamal Anderson(R)	325		60		15
126 Mike Alstott(R)	150		40		
1996 Topps					
435 Eddie George(R)	60				
1996 Topps Chrome					
154 Eric Moulds(R)	150		50		15
156 Marvin Harrison(R)	400		100		
157 Tim Biakabutuka(R)	70				
159 Keyshawn Johnson(R)	350		85		20
162 Eddie George(R)	400		00		20
1997 Bowman's Best					
1 Brett Favre	35		10		
90 Dan Marino	35		10		
96 Jake Plummer(R)	80		25		
96 Jake Plummer(Refractor)	100		30		15
96 Jake Plummer (Atomic Refractor)	125		35		15
108 Corey Dillon(R)	35				
125 Warrick Dunn(Refractor)	40		12.50		
1997 Finest					
176 Corey Dillon(Refractor)	45		20		12
234 Jake Plummer(R)	80		40		15
234 Jake Plummer(Refractor)	125		75		30
270 Warrick Dunn(Refractor)	40		15		
270 Warrick Dunn(Refractor)	75		30		15
1997 Pacific					
115 Terrell Davis(Platinum Blue)			135		
1997 Pacific Revolution					
135 Jon Kitna(R)					30
1997 Pinnacle Totally Certified					
88 Terrell Davis(Platinum Gold)			400		
144 Warrick Dunn(R)(Platinum Blue)			40		
1997 SkyBox E-X2000					
1 Jake Plummer(R)	500		140		90
30 Warrick Dunn(R)	225				
1997 SP Authentic					
10 Warrick Dunn(R)	150		40		
19 Antowain Smith(R)	100				
23 Jake Plummer(R)	500		175		
25 Corey Dillon(R)	350				
1997 Topps					
402 Corey Dillon(R)			30		
1997 Topps Chrome					
44 Kordell Stewart(Refractor)	75		30		15
68 Warrick Dunn(R)	100		30		15
68 Warrick Dunn(Refractor)	200		100		50
148 Antowain Smith(R)	75		30		12.50
155 Corey Dillon(R)	100		25		12.50
155 Corey Dillon(Refractor)	125		90		30
162 Jake Plummer(R)	250		85		40
162 Jake Plummer(Refractor)	500		200		75
1997 Topps Stars					
103 Antowian Smith(R)	45		20		12.50
105 Jake Plummer(R)	150		50		15
105 Jake Plummer - foil	400		175		85
108 Corey Dillon(R)	35		12.50		
1997 Upper Deck					
19 Jake Plummer(R)	60		25		
1998 Bowman					
1 Peyton Manning(R)	100		45		12
7 Brian Griese(R)	50		15		
10 Ryan Leaf(R)	30		15		
11 Fred Taylor(R)	75		15		
182 Randy Moss(R)	85		30		15
206 Charlie Batch(R)	35		20		
1998 Bowman Chrome					
1 Peyton Manning(R)	400		100		20
7 Brian Griese(R)	100		35		15
10 Ryan Leaf(R)	60		30		15
11 Fred Taylor(R)	135		45		20

CARD	GEM	MINT	NM/M+	NM/M	NM+
15 Tim Dwight(R)			42		
26 Skip Hicks(R)			30		
182 Randy Moss(R)	240		95		55
206 Charlie Batch	75		35		
1998 Bowman's Best					
109 Randy Moss(R)	100		45		25
109 Randy Moss(Refractor)	165		80		35
112 Peyton Manning(R)	125		40		12
112 Peyton Manning(Refractor)	70		35		15
119 Ryan Leaf(R)	30				
125 Fred Taylor(R)	50		15		
1998 Finest					
121 Peyton Manning(R)	125		40		12.50
121 Peyton Manning(Refractor)	200				
121 Peyton Manning (No-Protector Refractor)	300		30		15
122 Brian Griese(R)	60		20		
131 Curtis Enis(R)	30		15		
135 Randy Moss(R)	120		50		15
135 Randy Moss(Refractor)	350		140		85
135 Randy Moss (No-Protector Refractor)	225		130		60
141 Fred Taylor(R)	75		20		12.50
141 Fred Taylor(Refractor)	135		45		20
141 Fred Taylor (No-Protector Refractor)	110		45		20
142 Charles Woodson(R)	45		25		12.50
144 Robert Edwards(R)	25				
145 Kevin Dyson(R)	30				
150 Ryan Leaf(R)	45		20		12.50
160 Emmitt Smith(Refractor)	65		35		17.50
1998 Flair Showcase					
3 Peyton Manning(Row 0)	185				
3 Peyton Manning(Row 2)			20		
5 Randy Moss(Row 2)			20		
5 Randy Moss(Row 3)	65		17.50		
5 Randy Moss(Row 0)	350				
18 Ryan Leaf(Row 0)			45		
1998 Fleer					
237 Randy Moss(R)			25		
1998 Fleer Brilliants					
139 Fred Taylor(R)	50				
140 Randy Moss(R)	200		85		37
1998 Leaf Rookies & Stars					
199 Randy Moss(R)	300		110		37
218 Fred Taylor(R)	175		50		15
233 Peyton Manning(R)	400		100		12
235 Brian Griese(R)	150		40		
237 Charlie Batch(R)	75				
1998 Playoff Momentum					
106 Fred Taylor (R)	150				
131 Randy Moss(R)	325				
1998 Score					
233 Peyton Manning(R)	85		25		12.50
235 Randy Moss(R)	80		25		12.50
242 Fred Taylor(R)	50		16		
245 Brian Griese(R)	50		22.50		
251 Ryan Leaf(R)	30		16		
1998 SkyBox E-X2001					
49 Brian Griese(R)	50		25		12
50 Charlie Batch(R)	50		25		12
54 Peyton Manning(R)	350		60		15
60 Fred Taylor(R)	125		30		15
240 Randy Moss(R)	250		85		35
1998 SkyBox Premium					
224 Ryan Leaf(R)			25		
227 Fred Taylor(R)	80		25		
231 Peyton Manning(R)	400		60		
240 Randy Moss(R)	250		60		
243 Brian Griese(R)	60		20		
1998 SkyBox Thunder					
238 Ryan Leaf(R)	60		25		12.50
239 Peyton Manning(R)	75		35		15
242 Randy Moss	140		50		30
1998 Stadium Club					
15 Terrell Davis (Chrome Refractor)	50		25		12.50
166 Ryan Leaf(R)	35		15		
178 Brian Griese(R)	45		16		
189 Randy Moss(R)	90		40		20
189 Randy Moss(1st Day)			75		
190 Charles Woodson(R)	30		15		
191 Fred Taylor(R)	50		15		
195 Peyton Manning(R)	100		40		12
1998 SP Authentic					
11 Brian Griese(R)	950		250		50
14 Peyton Manning(R)	2500		600		150
16 Fred Taylor(R)	2000		250		40
18 Randy Moss(R)	2500		600		150
23 Charles Woodson(R)			75		
26 Ryan Leaf(R)	250		110		50
29 Kevin Dyson(R)			60		
1998 SPx Finite					
187 Fred Taylor(R)	7000				

CARD	GEM	MINT	NM/M+	NM/M	NM+
1998 Topps					
332 Ryan Leaf(R)	40			20	12.50
337 Curtis Enis(R)	40			20	
339 Fred Taylor(R)	60			20	
346 Brian Griese(R)	45			16	
352 Randy Moss(R)	100			40	15
360 Peyton Manning(R)	125			40	15
1998 Topps Chrome					
13 Robert Edwards(R)	30			16	
16 John Elway(Refractor)	70			30	15
35 Randy Moss(R)	200			75	35
35 Randy Moss(Refractor)	450			250	110
44 Charles Woodson(R)	35			15	
66 Ryan Leaf(R)	75			25	12.50
99 Jake Plummer(Refractor)	100				
113 Brett Favre(Refractor)	50				
120 Jacquez Green(R)	30			15	
133 Brian Griese(R)	125			50	12.50
133 Brian Griese(Refractor)	145			55	20
152 Fred Taylor(R)	175			60	15
152 Fred Taylor(Refractor)	190			80	45
158 Curtis Enis	75			30	12.50
165 Peyton Manning(R)	400			100	45
165 Peyton Manning(Refractor)	400			85	40
1998 Topps Gold Label					
10 Terrell Davis	25				
25 Brett Favre	45				
95 Ryan Leaf(R)	50				
100 Barry Sanders	35				
1998 Topps Season Opener					
1 Peyton Manning(R)	300			75	15
9 Fred Taylor(R)	135			30	10
16 Brian Griese(R)	125			25	
22 Randy Moss(R)	200			60	15
1998 Ultra					
201 Peyton Manning(R)	300			60	30
202 Ryan Leaf(R)	80			30	20
203 Charles Woodson(R)	60			20	
206 Curtis Enis(R)	40			15	
207 Randy Moss(R)	275			60	30
207 Randy Moss (Gold Medallion)	250			135	70
213 Robert Edwards(R)	60			15	
214 Fred Taylor(R)	300			30	15
214 Fred Taylor(Gold Medallion)	150			55	25
400 Brian Griese(R)	100			30	
1998 Upper Deck					
1 Peyton Manning(R)	300			80	25
2 Ryan Leaf(R)	65			20	12.50
4 Charles Woodson(R)	45			20	2.50
5 Curtis Enis(R)	50			20	12.50
8 Fred Taylor(R)	150			40	20
16 Robert Edwards(R)	60			30	15
17 Randy Moss(R)	300			80	25
28 Brian Griese(R)	125			35	20
1998 Upper Deck Black Diamond Rookies					
91 Peyton Manning(R)				60	
93 Fred Taylor(R)	150				
97 Randy Moss(R)	200			60	
1998 Upper Deck Encore					
1 Peyton Manning(R)	325				
5 Curtis Enis(R)	35				
12 Randy Moss(R)	275				
21 Brian Griese(R)	75				
1999 Bowman Chrome					
155 Cade McNown(R)	100				
157 Kevin Johnson(R)	55				
158 Tim Couch(R)	125				
161 Edgerrin James(R)	275				
168 Donovan McNabb(R)	100				
174 Torry Holt(R)	45				
175 Shaun King(R)	80				
182 Ricky Williams(R)	125				
1999 Bowman's Best					
110 Kurt Warner(R)	125				
115 Edgerrin James(R)	125				
132 Tim Couch(R)	75				
1999 Donruss Elite					
170 Tim Couch(R)	200			75	
180 Edgerrin James(R)	300			75	
190 Donovan McNabb(R)	75				
191 Cade McNown(R)	75				
197 Akili Smith(R)	75				
199 Ricky Williams(R)	175			60	
1999 E-X Century					
69 Edgerrin James (R)	250				
1999 Finest					
147 Jevon Kearse(R)	40				
152 Edgerrin James(R)	150				
158 Ricky Williams(R)	75				
164 Tim Couch(R)	100				
165 Cade McNown(R)	40				
166 Donovan McNabb(R)	40				
168 Shaun King(R)	40				
175 Torry Holt(R)	30				

CARD	GEM	MINT	NM/M+	NM/M	NM+
1999 Flair Showcase					
176 Edgerrin James(R)	950				
192 Ricky Williams(R)	500				
1999 Fleer Focus					
40 Kurt Warner (R)	80				
1999 Fleer Mystique					
101 Tim Couch(R)	250				
102 Donovan McNabb(R)	150				
103 Akili Smith(R)	125				
106 Ricky Williams(R)	200				
107 Edgerrin James(R)	400				
138 Shaun King(R)	125				
1999 Leaf Certified					
189 Tim Couch(R)	200				
192 Olandis Gary(R)	250				
198 Edgerrin James (R)	350			100	
208 Ricky Williams (R)	175				
1999 Pacific					
343 Kurt Warner(R)	500			150	40
1999 Playoff Momentum					
144 Kurt Warner(R)	250				
151 Tim Couch(R)	100				
154 Edgerrin James(R)	150				
155 Ricky Williams(R)	100				
172 Shaun King(R)	80				
1999 Score					
221 Tim Couch(R)	400				
1999 SkyBox Molten Metal					
127 Ricky Williams(R)	45				
132 Cade McNown(R)	40				
133 Donovan McNabb(R)	30				
134 Shaun King(R)	30				
137 Edgerrin James(R)	75				
147 Tim Couch(R)	45				
151 Olandis Gary(R)	40				
1999 Stadium Club Chrome					
123 Edgerrin James(R)	100				
131 Shaun King(R)	50				
137 Cade McNown(R)	50				
138 Ricky Williams(R)	75				
143 Tim Couch(R)	75				
1999 SP Authentic					
91 Ricky Williams(R)	1500				
92 Tim Couch (R)	2000				
94 Edgerrin James(R)	2500				
1999 SP Signature					
171 Ricky Williams(R)	250			100	
172 Cade McNown(R)	150				
173 Tim Couch(R)	275			110	
174 Daunte Culpepper(R)	150			30	
177 Donovan McNabb(R)	150			30	
179 Shaun King(R)	150				
180 Torry Holt(R)	125				
1999 Topps					
329 Ricky Williams(R)	90			25	
339 Edgerrin James(R)	125			35	
345 Tim Couch(R)	90			25	
353 Cade McNown(R)	30			12	
1999 Topps Chrome					
135 Ricky Williams(R)	225				
136 Daunte Culpepper(R)	150				
145 Edgerrin James(R)	325			175	
151 Tim Couch(R)	275			125	
156 Shaun King(R)	150				
159 Cade McNown(R)	175				
1999 Ultra					
261 Ricky Williams(R)	175			45	
262 Tim Couch(R)	175			45	
266 Donovan McNabb(R)	100				
272 Edgerrin James(R)	275			75	
278 Akili Smith(R)	100				
300 Cade McNown(R)	100				
1999 Upper Deck					
232 Tim Couch(R)	200				
235 Donovan McNabb(R)	120				
238 Cade McNown(R)	120				
242 Edgerrin James(R)	225				
1999 Upper Deck Encore					
139 Kurt Warner(R)	175				
1999 Upper Deck MVP					
201 Ricky Williams(R)	35			15	
202 Tim Couch(R)	40			15	
203 Akili Smith(R)	30				
206 Edgerrin James(R)	75			25	
211 Cade McNown(R)	30				
220 Donovan McNabb(R)	30				
2000 Upper Deck Pros and Prospects					
85 Peter Warrick(R)	800				

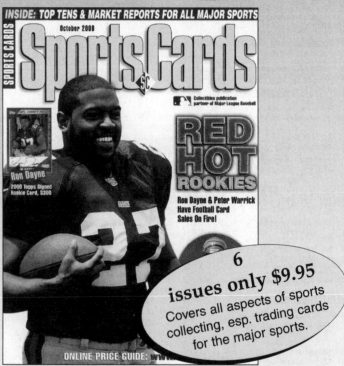

VITAL SPORTS REFERENCE BOOKS

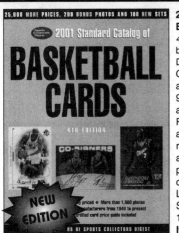

2001 Standard Catalog™ of Basketball Cards
4th Edition
by Price Guide Editors of Sports Collectors Digest
Over 125,000 cards from 1948 - 2000 are checklisted and priced. More than 900 sets from all the top manufacturers are listed including Topps, Fleer, Score, Pacific, Upper Deck, SkyBox, Hoops and more. NBA, WNBA, CBA, college, regional, Olympic, food sets and more are covered. Includes a certified card price guide, autograph price guide and complete pricing for Kenner Starting Lineup and other figurines.
Softcover • 8-1/2 x 11 • 368 pages
1,500+ b&w photos
Item# SCBC4 • $21.95

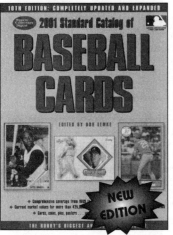

2001 Standard Catalog™ of Baseball Cards
10th Edition
edited by Bob Lemke
Over 425,000 cards from 1869 - early 2000 releases. More than 600,000 accurate, real-world prices for making crucial buying and selling decisions (each individually reviewed, updated and reverified for accuracy). Over 12,000 large clear photos of card fronts and backs to help you identify and grade your own cards.
Softcover • 8-1/2 x 11 • 1,664 pages
12,000+ b&w photos
Item# SB10 • $39.95

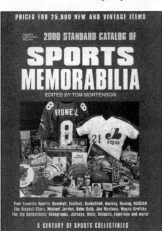

2000 Standard Catalog™ of Sports Memorabilia
by Tom Mortenson
This is the largest, most comprehensive catalog of football, baseball, basketball, hockey and other sport memorabilia ever compiled. Accurate market pricing for thousands of items including autographs, uniforms, equipment, ticket stubs, press pins, publications, pennants, books, figurines and much more.
Softcover • 8-1/2 x 11 • 496 pages
2,000 b&w photos
Item# SMEM1 • $21.95

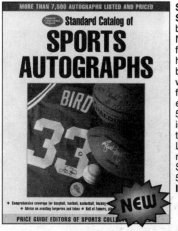

Standard Catalog™ of Sports Autographs
by Tom Mortenson
Now you can buy and sell autographs from current and retired stars, plus hall-of-famers from football, basketball, baseball, hockey, racing, boxing, golf, wrestling and more with complete confidence. More than 7,500 autographs, each individually priced with more than 500 large, clear photos will aid you in identification and determining authenticity. Includes listings for Official Major League, World Series and commemorative baseballs.
Softcover • 8-1/2 x 11 • 160 pages
500+ b&w photos
Item# SPAU1 • $21.95

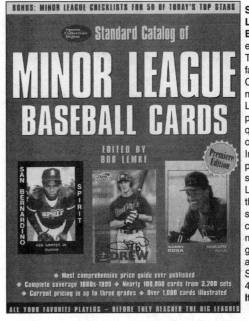

Standard Catalog™ of Minor League Baseball Cards
edited by Bob Lemke
Trace the careers of your favorite stars from before Ty Cobb to today's starters in the most complete source for Minor League baseball cards ever published. Information on card quantities and rare issues are only found in this volume. Included are more than 40,000 players and 3,200 team sets, some going back to the 1880s. Listings are priced in up to three different grades. Special sections list all minor league cards for 50 of today's top major league stars. A great guide for baseball fans of all ages.
Softcover • 8-1/2 x 11
480 pages • 400 bw photos
Item# SG02 • $24.95

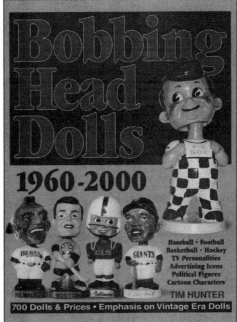

Bobbing Head Dolls
1960-2000
by Tim Hunter
This first-ever price and identification guide features hundreds of dolls, including: baseball, football, basketball, hockey, TV stars, advertising icons, political figures and cartoon characters. Learn how to identify which series a doll is from, if it's a rare variation, and how much it's worth. Do you have the common Houston Astros doll worth $80 or the scarce Astros version with the shooting star decal priced at $700? With over 250 photos and 700 individual listings, you're sure to find values for the dolls in your collection.
Softcover • 8-1/2 x 11
160 pages • 250+ bw photos
30+ color photos
Item# BOBHD • $19.95